Stanley Gibbo
SIMPLIFIED
CATALOGUE

Stamps of the World 1995

An illustrated and priced three-volume guide to the postage stamps of the whole world, excluding changes of paper, perforation, shade and watermark

VOLUME 2

FOREIGN COUNTRIES K–Z

STANLEY GIBBONS LTD
London and Ringwood

**By Appointment to
Her Majesty the Queen
Stanley Gibbons Limited
London
Philatelists**

61st Edition

**Published in Great Britain by
Stanley Gibbons Ltd
Publications Editorial, Sales Office and Distribution Centre
5, Parkside, Christchurch Road,
Ringwood, Hampshire BH24 3SH
Telephone 01425 472363**

ISBN: 085259-397-X

**Published as Stanley Gibbons Simplified Stamp Catalogue from 1934 to 1970, renamed Stamps of the World in 1971, and produced in two (1982–88) or three (from 1989) volumes as Stanley Gibbons Simplified Catalogue of Stamps of the World.
This volume published October 1995**

S.G. ITEM No. 2882 (95)

Printed in Great Britain by Bemrose Security Printing, London & Derby

Stanley Gibbons SIMPLIFIED CATALOGUE

Stamps of the World

This popular catalogue is a straightforward three-volume listing of the stamps that have been issued everywhere in the world since the very first–Great Britain's famous Penny Black in 1840.

This edition continues the three-volume format. Volume 1 (Foreign countries A-J) appears in September, Volume 2 (Foreign countries K–Z) in October, and Volume 3 covering Commonwealth countries in December.

Readers are reminded that the Catalogue Supplements, published in each issue of **Gibbons Stamp Monthly,** can be used to update the listings in **Stamps of the World** as well as our twenty-two part standard catalogue. To make the supplement even more useful the Type numbers given to the illustrations are now the same in the Stamps of the World as in the standard catalogues. The first Catalogue Supplement to this Volume appeared in the August 1995 issue of **Gibbons Stamp Monthly.**

Gibbons Stamp Monthly can be obtained through newsagents or on postal subscription from Stanley Gibbons Publications, 5, Parkside, Christchurch Road, Ringwood, Hants BH24 3SH.

The catalogue has many important features:

- As an indication of current values virtually every stamp is priced. Thousands of alterations have been made since the last edition
- By being set out on a simplified basis that excludes changes of paper, perforation, shade, watermark, gum or printer's and date imprints it is particularly easy to use. (For its exact scope see "Information for users" pages following.)
- The thousands of illustrations and helpful descriptions of stamp designs make it of maximum appeal to collectors with thematic interests.
- Its catalogue numbers are the world-recognised Stanley Gibbons numbers throughout.
- Helpful introductory notes for the collector are included, backed by much historical, geographical and currency information.
- A very detailed index gives instant location of countries in this volume, and a cross-reference to those included in other volumes.

Over 2,290 stamps and 944 new illustrations have been added to the listings in this volume. Last year's three-volume edition contained over 312,400 stamps and 747,750 illustrations.

The listings in this edition are based on the standard catalogues: Part 1 (British Commonwealth) (1995 edition), Part 2 (Austria & Hungary) (5th edition), Part 3 (Balkans) (3rd edition), Part 4 (Benelux) (4th edition), Part 5 (Czechoslovakia & Poland) (5th edition), Part 6 (France) (4th edition), Part 7 (Germany) (4th edition), Part 8 (Italy & Switzerland) (4th edition), Part 9 (Portugal & Spain) (3rd edition), Part 10 (Russia) (4th edition), Part 11 (Scandinavia) (4th edition), Part 12 (Africa since Independence A-E) (2nd edition), Part 13 (Africa since Independence F-M) (1st edition), Part 14 (Africa since Independence N-Z) (1st edition), Part 15 (Central America) (2nd edition), Part 16 (Central Asia) (3rd edition), Part 17 (China) (5th edition), Part 18 (Japan & Korea) (3rd edition), Part 19 (Middle East) (4th edition), Part 20 (South America) (3rd edition), Part 21 (South-East Asia) (3rd edition), and Part 22 (United States) (4th edition).

Important price revisions made specially for this edition include Korea (South Korea), Liberia, Rumania to 1945 and Russia from 1945.

Stanley Gibbons Stamp Catalogue
Complete List of Parts

1 British Commonwealth
(Annual in two volumes)

Foreign Countries

2 Austria & Hungary (5th edition, 1994)
Austria • Bosnia & Herzegovina • U.N. (Vienna) • Hungary

3 Balkans (3rd edition, 1987)
Albania • Bulgaria • Greece & Islands • Rumania • Yugoslavia

4 Benelux (4th edition, 1993)
Belgium & Colonies • Netherlands & Colonies • Luxembourg

5 Czechoslovakia & Poland (5th edition, 1994)
Czechoslovakia • Bohemia & Moravia • Slovakia • Poland

6 France (4th edition, 1993)
France • Colonies • Andorra • Monaco

7 Germany (4th edition, 1992)
Germany • States • Colonies • Post Offices

8 Italy & Switzerland (4th edition, 1993)
Italy & Colonies • Fiume • San Marino • Vatican City • Trieste • Liechtenstein • Switzerland • U.N. (Geneva)

9 Portugal & Spain (3rd edition, 1991)
Andorra • Portugal & Colonies • Spain & Colonies

10 Russia (4th edition, 1991)
Russia • Baltic States • Mongolia • Tuva

11 Scandinavia (4th edition, 1994)
Aland Islands • Denmark • Faroe Islands • Finland • Greenland • Iceland • Norway • Sweden

12 Africa since Independence A-E (2nd edition, 1983)
Algeria • Angola • Benin • Bophuthatswana • Burundi • Cameroun • Cape Verde • Central African Republic • Chad • Comoro Islands • Congo • Djibouti • Equatorial Guinea • Ethiopia

13 Africa since Independence F-M (1st edition, 1981)
Gabon • Guinea • Guinea-Bissau • Ivory Coast • Liberia • Libya • Malagasy Republic • Mali • Mauritania • Morocco • Mozambique

14 Africa since Independence N-Z (1st edition, 1981)
Niger Republic • Rwanda • St. Thomas & Prince • Senegal • Somalia • Sudan • Togo • Transkei • Tunisia • Upper Volta • Venda • Zaire

15 Central America (2nd edition, 1984)
Costa Rica • Cuba • Dominican Republic • El Salvador • Guatemala • Haiti • Honduras • Mexico • Nicaragua • Panama

16 Central Asia (3rd edition, 1992)
Afghanistan • Iran • Turkey

17 China (5th edition, 1995)
China • Taiwan • Tibet • Foreign P.O.s

18 Japan & Korea (3rd edition, 1992)
Japan • Ryukyus • Korean Empire • South Korea • North Korea

19 Middle East (4th edition, 1990)
Bahrain • Egypt • Iraq • Israel • Jordan • Kuwait • Lebanon • Oman • Qatar • Saudi Arabia • Syria • U.A.E. • Yemen A.R. • Yemen P.D.R

20 South America (3rd edition, 1989)
Argentina • Bolivia • Brazil • Chile • Colombia • Ecuador • Paraguay • Peru • Surinam • Uruguay • Venezuela

21 South-East Asia (3rd edition, 1995)
Bhutan • Burma • Indonesia • Kampuchea • Laos •Nepal • Philippines • Thailand • Vietnam

22 United States (4th edition, 1994)
U.S. & Possessions • Canal Zone • Marshall Islands • Micronesia • U.N. (New York, Geneva, Vienna)

Thematic Catalogues

Stanley Gibbons Catalogues for use with **Stamps of the World**

Collect Aircraft on Stamps (1st edition, 1994)

Collect Birds on Stamps (3rd edition, 1992)

Collect Butterflies and Other Insects on Stamps (1st edition, 1991)

Collect Chess on Stamps (1st edition, 1992)

Collect Fungi on Stamps (out of print)

Collect Mammals on Stamps (out of print)

Collect Railways on Stamps (2nd edition, 1990)

Collect Shells on Stamps (forthcoming)

Collect Ships on Stamps (2nd edition, 1993)

Information for users

Aim

The aim of this catalogue is to provide a straightforward illustrated and priced guide to the postage stamps of the whole world to help to enjoy the greatest hobby of the present day.

Arrangement

The catalogue lists countries in alphabetical order and there is a complete index at the end of each volume. For ease of reference country names are also printed at the head of each page.

Within each country, postage stamps are listed first. They are followed by separate sections for such other categories as postage due stamps, parcel post stamps, express stamps, official stamps, etc.

All catalogue lists are set out according to dates of issue of the stamps, starting from the earliest and working through to the most recent. New issues received too late for inclusion in the main lists will be found as "Addenda" at the end of each volume.

Scope of the Catalogue

The *Simplified Catalogue of Stamps of the World* contains listings of postage stamps only. Apart from the ordinary definitive, commemorative and airmail stamps of each country – which appear first in each list – there are sections for the following where appropriate:

postage due stamps
parcel post stamps
official stamps
express and special delivery stamps
charity and compulsory tax stamps
newspaper and journal stamps
printed matter stamps
registration stamps
acknowledgement of receipt stamps
late fee and too late stamps
military post stamps
recorded message stamps
personal delivery stamps

We receive numerous enquiries from collectors about other items which do not fall within the categories set out above and which consequently do not appear in the catalogue lists. It may be helpful, therefore, to summarise the other kinds of stamp that exist but which we deliberately exclude from this postage stamp catalogue.

We do *not* list the following:

Fiscal or revenue stamps: stamps used solely in collecting taxes or fees for non-postal purposes. Examples would be stamps which pay a tax on a receipt, represent the stamp duty on a contract or frank a customs document. Common inscriptions found include: Documentary, Proprietary, Inter. Revenue, Contract Note.

Local stamps: postage stamps whose validity and use are limited in area, say to a single town or city, though in some cases they provided, with official sanction, services in parts of countries not covered by the respective government.

Local carriage labels and Private local issues: many labels exist ostensibly to cover the cost of ferrying mail from one of Great Britain's offshore islands to the nearest mainland post office. They are not recognised as valid for national or international mail. Examples: Calf of Man, Davaar, Herm, Lundy, Pabay, Stroma. Items from some other places have only the status of tourist souvenir labels.

Telegraph stamps: stamps intended solely for the prepayment of telegraphic communication.

Bogus or "phantom" stamps: labels from mythical places or non-existent administrations. Examples in the classical period were Sedang, Counani, Clipperton Island and in modern times Thomond and Monte Bello Islands. Numerous labels have also appeared since the War from dissident groups as propaganda for their claims without authority from the home governments. Common examples are labels for "Free Albania", "Free Rumania", and "Free Croatia" and numerous issues for Nagaland, Indonesia and the South Moluccas ("Republik Maluku Selatan").

Railway letter fee stamps: special stamps issued by railway companies for the conveyance of letters by rail. Example: Talyllyn Railway. Similar services are now offered by some bus companies and the labels they issue likewise do not qualify for inclusion in the catalogue.

Perfins ("perforated initials"): numerous postage stamps may be found with initial letters or designs punctured through them by tiny holes. These are applied by private and public concerns as a precaution against theft and do not qualify for separate mention.

Information for users

Labels: innumerable items exist resembling stamps but – as they do not prepay postage – they are classified as labels. The commonest categories are:

– propaganda and publicity labels: designed to further a cause or campaign;

– exhibition labels: particularly souvenirs from philatelic events;

– testing labels: stamp- size labels used in testing stamp-vending machines;

– Post Office training school stamps: British stamps overprinted with two thick vertical bars or SCHOOL SPECIMEN are produced by the Post Office for training purposes;

– seals and stickers: numerous charities produce stamp-like labels, particularly at Christmas and Easter, as a means of raising funds and these have no postal validity.

Cut-outs: items of postal stationery, such as envelopes, cards and wrappers, often have stamps impressed or imprinted on them. They may usually be cut out and affixed to envelopes, etc., for postal use if desired, but such items are not listed in this catalogue.

Collectors wanting further information about exact definitions are referred to *Philatelic Terms Illustrated,* published by Stanley Gibbons and containing many illustrations in colour (third edition price £7.50 plus £3 postage and packing).

There is also a priced listing of the postal fiscals of Great Britain in our Part 1 *(British Commonwealth)* Catalogue and in Volume 1 of the *Great Britain Specialised* Catalogue (5th and later editions)

Although, as stated, none of the above qualify for inclusion in this postage stamp catalogue, this does not imply that they are of no interest to certain collectors. Indeed, in the 1950s a group was formed in Great Britain called the 'Cinderella Stamp Club', whose object is the study of all those stamps which Stanley Gibbons do *not* list in their catalogues.

Catalogue Numbers

Stanley Gibbons catalogue numbers are recognised universally and any individual stamp can be identified by quoting a catalogue number (the one at the left of the column) prefixed by the name of the country and the letters "S.G.". Do not confuse the catalogue number with the type numbers which refer to illustrations.

Prices

Prices in the left-hand column are for unused stamps and those in the right-hand column for used. Prices are given in pence and pounds:

100 pence (p) = 1 pound (£1).

Prices are shown as follows:

10 means 10p (10 pence);
1.75 means £1.75 (1 pound and 75 pence);
For £100 and above, prices are in whole pounds.

Our prices are for stamps in fine average condition, and in issues where condition varies we may ask more for the superb and less for the sub-standard.

The minimum price quote is 10p which represents a handling charge rather than basis for valuing common stamps.

The prices quoted are generally for the cheapest variety of stamps but it is worth noting that differences of watermark, perforation, or other details, outside the scope of this catalogue, may often increase the value of the stamp.

Where prices are not given in either column it is either because the stamps are not known to exist in that particular condition, or, more usually, because there is no reliable information as to value.

All prices are subject to change without prior notice and we give no guarantee to supply all stamps priced. Prices quoted for albums, publications, etc. advertised in this catalogue are also subject to change without prior notice.

Due to different production methods it is sometimes possible for new editions of Parts 2 to 22 to appear showing revised prices which are not included in that year's Stamps of the World.

Unused Stamps

In the case of stamps from *Great Britain* and the *Commonwealth,* prices for unused stamps of Queen Victoria to King George V are for lightly hinged examples; unused prices of King Edward VIII to Queen Elizabeth II issues are for unmounted mint. The prices of unused *Foreign* stamps are for lightly hinged examples for those issued before 1946, thereafter for examples unmounted mint.

Used Stamps

Prices for used stamps generally refer to postally used examples, though for certain issues it is for

Information for users

Guarantee

All stamps supplied by us are guaranteed originals in the following terms:

If not as described, and returned by the purchaser, we undertake to refund the price paid to us in the original transaction. If any stamp is certified as genuine by the Expert Committee of the Royal Philatelic Society, London, or by B.P.A. Expertising Ltd., the purchaser shall not be entitled to make any claim against us for any error, omission or mistake in such certificate.

Consumers' statutory rights are not affected by the above guarantee.

Currency

At the beginning of each country brief details give the currencies in which the values of the stamps are expressed. The dates, where given, are those of earliest stamp issues in the particular currency. Where the currency is obvious, e.g. where the colony has the same currency as the mother country, no details are given.

Illustrations

Illustrations of surcharges and overprints, which are shown and not described, are actual size; stamp illustrations are reduced to $\frac{3}{4}$ linear, *unless otherwise stated.*

"Key-Types"

A number of standard designs occur so frequently in the stamps of the French, German, Portuguese and Spanish colonies that it would be a waste of space to repeat them. Instead these are all illustrated on page xii together with the descriptive names and letters by which they are referred to in the lists.

Type Numbers

These are bold figures found below each illustration. References to "Type **6**", for example, in the lists of a country should therefore be understood to refer to the illustration below which the number **"6"** appears. These type numbers are also given in the second column of figures alongside each list of stamps, thus indicating clearly the design of each stamp. In the case of Key-Types – see above – letters take the place of the type numbers.

Where an issue comprises stamps of similar design, represented in this catalogue by one illustration, the corresponding type numbers should be taken as indicating this general design.

Where there are blanks in the type number column it means that the type of the corresponding stamps is that shown by the last number above in the type column of the same issue.

A dash (–) in the type column means that no illustration of the stamp is shown.

Where type numbers refer to stamps of another country, e.g. where stamps of one country are overprinted for use in another, this is always made clear in the text.

Stamp Designs

Brief descriptions of the subjects of the stamp designs are given either below or beside the illustrations, at the foot of the list of the issue concerned, or in the actual lists. Where a particular subject, e.g. the portrait of a well-known monarch, recurs frequently the description is not repeated, nor are obvious designs described.

Generally, the unillustrated designs are in the same shape and size as the one illustrated, except where otherwise indicated.

Surcharges and Overprints

Surcharges and overprints are usually described in the headings to the issues concerned. Where the actual wording of a surcharge or overprint is given it is shown in bold type.

Some stamps are described as being "Surcharged in words", e.g. **TWO CENTS,** and others "Surcharged in figures and words", e.g. **20 CENTS,** although of course many surcharges are in foreign languages and combinations of words and figures are numerous. There are often bars, etc., obliterating old values or inscriptions but in general these are only mentioned where it is necessary to avoid confusion.

No attention is paid in this catalogue to colours of overprints and surcharges so that stamps with the same overprint in different colours are not listed separately.

Numbers in brackets after the descriptions of an overprinted or surcharged stamps are the catalogue numbers of the overprinted stamps.

Note – the words "inscribed" or "inscription" always refer to wording incorporated in the design of a stamp and not surcharges or overprints.

Coloured Papers

Where stamps are printed on coloured paper the description is given as e.g. '3'4c. black on blue" – a stamp printed in black on blue paper. No attention is paid in this catalogue to differences in the texture of paper, e.g. laid, wove.

Information for users

Watermarks

Stamps having different watermarks, but otherwise the same, are not listed separately. No reference is therefore made to watermarks in this volume.

Stamp Colours

Colour names are only required for the identification of stamps, therefore they have been made as simple as possible. Thus "scarlet", "vermilion", "carmine" are all usually called red. Qualifying colour names have been introduced only where necessary for the sake of clearness.

Where stamps are printed in two or more colours the central portion of the design is in the first colour given, unless otherwise stated.

Perforations

All stamps are perforated unless otherwise stated. No distinction is made between the various gauges of perforation but early stamp issues which exist both imperforated and perforated are usually listed separately.

Where a heading states "Imperf or perf" or "Perf or rouletted" this does not necessarily mean that all values of the issue are found in both conditions.

Dates of Issue

The date given at the head of each issue is that of the appearance of the earliest stamp in the series. As stamps of the same design or issue are usually grouped together a list of King George VI stamps, for example, headed "1938" may include stamps issued from 1938 to the end of the reign.

Miniature Sheets

These are outside the scope of this catalogue but are listed in all other Stanley Gibbons catalogues.

"Appendix" Countries

We regret that since 1968, it has been necessary to establish an Appendix (at the end of each country as appropriate) to which numerous stamps have had to be consigned. Several countries imagine that by issuing huge quantities of unnecessary stamps they will have a ready source of income from stamp collectors – and particulary from the less-experienced ones. Stanley Gibbons refuse to encourage this exploitation of the hobby and we do not stock the stamps concerned.

Two kinds of stamp are therefore given the briefest of mentions in the Appendix, purely for the sake of record. Administrations issuing stamps greatly in excess of true postal needs have the offending issues placed there. Likewise it contains stamps which have not fulfilled all the normal conditions for full catalogue listing.

These conditions are that the stamps must be issued by a legitimate postal authority, recognised by the government concerned, and are adhesives, valid for proper postal use in the class of service for which they are inscribed. Stamps, with the exception of such categories as postage dues and officials, must be available to the general public at face value with no artificial restrictions being imposed on their distribution.

The publishers of this catalogue have observed, with concern, the proliferation of "artificial" stamp-issuing territories. On several occasions this has resulted in separately inscribed issues for various component parts of otherwise united states or territories.

Stanley Gibbons Publications have decided that where such circumstances occur, they will not, in the future, list these items in the SG catalogue without first satisfying themselves that the stamps represent a genuine political, historical or postal division within the country concerned. Any such issues which do not fulfil this stipulation will be recorded in the Catalogue Appendix only.

Stamps in the Appendix are kept under review in the light of any newly acquired information about them. If we are satisfied that a stamp qualifies for proper listing in the body of the catalogue it is moved there.

"Undesirable Issues"

The rules governing many competitive exhibitions - including the Melville Competition - are set by the Fédération Internationale de Philatelie and stipulate a downgrading of marks for stamps classed as "undesirable issues".

This catalogue can be taken as a guide to status. All stamps in the main listings and Addenda are acceptable. Stamps in the Appendix should not be entered for competition as these are the "undesirable issues".

Particular care is advised with Aden Protectorate States, Ajman, Bhutan, Chad, Fujeira, Khor Fakkan, Manama, Ras al Khaima, Sharjah, Umm al Qiwain and Yemen. Totally bogus stamps exist (as explained in Appendix notes) and these are to be avoided also for competition. As distinct from "undesirable stamps" certain categories are not covered in this catalogue purely by reason of its scope (see page v). Consult the particular competition rules to see if such are admissible even though not listed by us.

Where to Look for More Detailed Listings

The present work deliberately omits details of paper, perforation, shade and watermark. But as you become more absorbed in stamp collecting and wish to get greater enjoyment from the hobby you may well want to study these matters.

All the information you require about any particular postage stamp will be found in the main Stanley Gibbons Catalogues

Commonwealth countries in Volume 3 are covered by the Part 1 (British Commonwealth) Catalogue published annually in two volumes.

For foreign countries you can easily find which catalogue to consult by looking at the country headings in the present book.

To the right of each country name are code letters specifying which volume of our main catalogues contains that country's listing.

The code letters are as follows:

Pt. 2 Part 2
Pt. 3 Part 3 etc.

(See page iv for complete list of Parts.)

So, for example, if you want to know more about Chinese stamps than is contained in the *Simplified Catalogue of Stamps of the World* the reference to

CHINA Pt.17

guides you to the Gibbons Part 17 *(China)* Catalogue listing for the details you require.

New editions of Part 2 to 22 appear at irregular intervals.

Correspondence

Whilst we welcome information and suggestions we must ask correspondents to include the cost of postage for the return of any stamps submitted plus registration where appropriate. Letters should be addressed to The Catalogue Editor at Ringwood.

Where information is solicited purely for the benefit of the enquirer we regret we cannot undertake to reply unless stamps or reply coupons are sent to cover postage.

Identification of Stamps

We regret we do not give opinions as to the genuineness of stamps, nor do we identify stamps or number them by our Catalogue.

Users of this catalogue are referred to our companion booklet entitled *Stamp Collecting – How to Identify Stamps*. It explains how to look up stamps in this catalogue, contains a full checklist of stamp inscriptions and gives help in dealing with unfamiliar scripts. It is available from Stanley Gibbons at £2.95, postage extra.

Stanley Gibbons would like to complement your collection

At Stanley Gibbons we offer a range of services which are designed to complement your collection.

Our modern stamp shop, the largest in Europe, together with our rare stamp department has one of the most comprehensive stocks of Great Britain in the world, so whether you are a beginner or an experienced philatelist you are certain to find something to suit your special requirements.

Alternatively through our Mail Order services you can control the growth of your collection from the comfort of your own home. Our Postal Sales Department regularly sends out mailings of Special Offers. We can also help with your wants lists–so why not ask us for those elusive items?

And don't forget Stanley Gibbons Auctions which holds regular sales each year. Come along in person or send in a written bid for the items you require. For details of current subscription rates for Auction catalogues write to Stanley Gibbons Auctions, 399 Strand, London WC2R 0LX.

Why not take advantage of the many services we have to offer? Visit our premises in the Strand or, for more information, write to the appropriate address on page x.

Stanley Gibbons Holdings Plc Addresses

Stanley Gibbons Limited, Stanley Gibbons Auctions

399 Strand, London WC2R 0LX
Telephone 0171 8368444 Fax 0171 8367342 for all departments.

Auction Room and Specialist Stamp Departments. Open Monday-Friday 9.30 a.m. to 5 p.m.
Shop. Open Monday–Friday 8.30 a.m. to 6 p.m. and (Saturday 10 a.m. to 4 p.m.)

Stanley Gibbons Publications

5 Parkside, Christchurch Road, Ringwood, Hants BH24 3SH
Telephone 01425 472363 (24 hour answerphone service)
Fax 01425 470247.

Publications Showroom (at above address). Open Monday–Friday 9.00 a.m. to 3 p.m.

Publications Mail Order. FREEPHONE 0800 611622. Monday–Friday 8.30 a.m. to 5 p.m.

Urch Harris & Co. (a division of Stanley Gibbons Ltd),
U.H. New Issue Service,
1 Denmark Avenue, Bristol BS1 5HD.
Telephone 0117 934 9333 Fax 0117 9273037
Monday–Friday 8.30 a.m. to 5 p.m.

Stanley Gibbons Publications Overseas Representation

Stanley Gibbons Publications are represented overseas by the following sole distributors (*), main distributors (**) or licensees (***).

Australia*
Lighthouse Philatelics (Aust) Pty. Ltd., P.O. Box 763, Strawberry Hills, New South Wales, 2012 Australia.

Stanley Gibbons (Australia) Pty. Ltd.***
P.O. Box 863J, Melbourne 3001, Australia.

Belgium and Luxembourg **
Davo c/o Philac, Rue du Midi 48, Bruxelles, 1000 Belgium.

Canada*
Lighthouse Publications (Canada) Ltd., 255 Duke Street, Montreal, Quebec, Canada H3C 2M2.

Denmark**
Davo c/o Lindner Falzlos, Gl Randers vej 28, 8450 Hammel, Denmark.

Finland**
Davo c/o Suomen Postimerkkeily Ludvingkatu 5 SF-00130 Helsinki, Finland.

France*
Davo France (Casteilla), 10 Rue Leon Foucault
78184 St. Quentin Yvelines, Cesex, France

Germany and Austria*
Leuchtturm Albenverlag, Paul Koch KG AM Spakenberg 45, Postfach 1340, D-2054 Geesthacht, Germany.

Hong Kong**
Po-on Stamp Service, G.P.O. Box 2498, Hong Kong.

Israel**
Capital Stamps, P.O. Box 3769, Jerusalem 91036, Israel.

Italy*
Secrian Srl, Via Pantelleria 2, 1-20156, Milan, Italy.

Japan**
Japan Philatelic Co. Ltd., P.O. Box 2, Suginami-Minami, Tokyo, Japan.

Netherlands*
Davo Publications, P.O. Box 411, 7400 AK Deventer, Netherlands.

New Zealand***
Stanley Gibbons (New Zealand) Ltd., P.O. Box 80 Wellington, New Zealand.

Norway**
Davo Norge A/S, P.O. Box 738 Sentrum, N-0105, Oslo, Norway.

Singapore***
Stanley Gibbons (Singapore) Pte Ltd., Raffles City P.O. Box 1689, Singapore 9117.

South Africa***
Philatelics Holdings (Pty) Ltd., P.O. Box 930, Parklands, RSA 2121.

Republic Coin and Stamp Accessories (Pty) Ltd.,** P.O. Box 11199, Johannesburg, RSA 2000.

Sweden*
Chr Winther Soerensen AB, Box 43, S-310 Knaered, Sweden.

Switzerland**
Phila Service, Burgstrasse 160, CH 4125, Riehen, Switzerland.

USA*
Lighthouse Publications Inc., P.O. Box 705, 274 Washington Avenue, Hackensack, New Jersey 07602-0705, U.S.A.

West Indies/Caribbean**
Hugh Dunphy, P.O. Box 413, Kingston 10, Jamaica, West Indies.

Abbreviations

Anniv.	denotes	Anniversary
Assn.	"	Association
Bis.	"	Bistre
Bl.	"	Blue
Bldg.	"	Building
Blk.	"	Black
Br.	"	British *or* Bridge
Brn.	"	Brown
B.W.I.	"	British West Indies
C.A.R.I.F.T.A.	"	Caribbean Free Trade Area
Cent.	"	Centenary
Chest.	"	Chestnut
Choc.	"	Chocolate
Clar.	"	Claret
Coll.	"	College
Commem.	"	Commemoration
Conf.	"	Conference
Diag.	"	Diagonally
E.C.A.F.E.	"	Economic Commission for Asia and Far East
Emer.	"	Emerald
E.P.T. Conference	"	European Postal and Telecommunications Conference
Exn.	"	Exhibition
F.A.O.	"	Food and Agriculture Organization
Fig.	"	Figure
G.A.T.T.	"	General Agreement on Tariffs and Trade
G.B.	"	Great Britain
Gen.	"	General
Govt.	"	Government
Grn.	"	Green
Horiz.	"	Horizontal
H.Q.	"	Headquarters
Imperf.	"	Imperforate
Inaug.	"	Inauguration
Ind.	"	Indigo
Inscr.	"	Inscribed *or* inscription
Int.	"	International
I.A.T.A.	"	International Air Transport Association
I.C.A.O.	"	International Civil Aviation Organization
I.C.Y.	"	International Co-operation Year
I.G.Y.	"	International Geophysical Year
I.L.O.	"	International Labour Office (or later, Organization)
I.M.C.O.	"	Inter-Governmental Maritime Consultative Organization
I.T.U.	"	International Telecommunication Union
Is.	"	Islands
Lav.	"	Lavender
Mar.	"	Maroon
mm.	"	Millimetres
Mult.	"	Multicoloured
Mve.	denotes	Mauve
Nat.	"	National
N.A.T.O.	"	North Atlantic Treaty Organization
O.D.E.C.A	"	Organization of Central American States
Ol.	"	Olive
Optd.	"	Overprinted
Orge *or* oran.	"	Orange
P.A.T.A.	"	Pacific Area Travel Association
Perf.	"	Perforated
Post.	"	Postage
Pres.	"	President
P.U.	"	Postal Union
Pur.	"	Purple
R.	"	River
R.S.A.	"	Republic of South Africa
Roul.	"	Rouletted
Sep.	"	Sepia
S.E.A.T.O.	"	South East Asia Treaty Organization
Surch.	"	Surcharged
T.	"	Type
T.U.C.	"	Trades Union Congress
Turq.	"	Turquoise
Ultram.	"	Ultramarine
U.N.E.S.C.O.	"	United Nations Educational, Scientific & Cultural Organization
U.N.I.C.E.F.	"	United Nations Children's Fund
U.N.O.	"	United Nations Organization
U.N.R.W.A.	"	United Nations Relief and Works Agency for Palestine Refugees in the Near East
U.N.T.E.A.	"	United Nations Temporary Executive Authority
U.N.R.R.A.	"	United Nations Relief and Rehabilitation Administration
U.P.U.	"	Universal Postal Union
Verm.	"	Vermilion
Vert.	"	Vertical
Vio.	"	Violet
W.F.T.U.	"	World Federation of Trade Unions
W.H.O.	"	World Health Organization
Yell.	"	Yellow

Arabic Numerals

As in the case of European figures, the details of the Arabic numerals vary in different stamp designs, but they should be readily recognised with the aid of this illustration:

٠	١	٢	٣	٤
0	1	2	3	4
٥	٦	٧	٨	٩
5	6	7	8	9

Key-types

(see note on page vii)

French Group

A. "Blanc."

B. "Mouchon."

C. "Merson."

D. "Tablet."

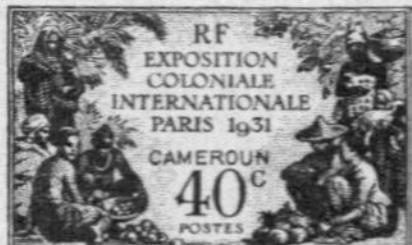

E.

F.

G.

H

"International Colonial Exhibition"

H.

I. "Faidherbe."

J. "Palms."

K. "Balay."

L. "Natives."

German Group

M. "Figure."

N. "Yacht."

Spanish Group

O. "Yacht."

X. "Alfonso

XII."

Portuguese Group

Y. "Baby."

Z. "Curly Head"

P. "Crown."

Q. "Em-

bossed."

R. "Figures."

S. "Carlos."

W. "Due."

STANLEY GIBBONS SIMPLIFIED CATALOGUE OF STAMPS OF THE WORLD—VOLUME 2 COUNTRIES K–Z

KAMPUCHEA — Pt. 21

Following the fall of the Khmer Rouge government, which had terminated the Khmer Republic, the People's Republic of Kampuchea was proclaimed on 10 January 1979.
Kampuchea was renamed Cambodia in 1989.

100 cents = 1 riel

105 Soldiers with Flag and Independence Monument, Phnom Penh

106 Moscow Kremlin and Globe

1980. Multicoloured. Without gum.
402 0.1 r. Type **105** . . . . 1·90 1·90
403 0.2 r. Khmer people and flag 3·75 3·75
404 0.5 r. Fisherman pulling in nets 5·00 5·00
405 1 r. Armed forces and Kampuchean flag . . . . . 8·25 8·25

1982. 60th Anniv of U.S.S.R. Multicoloured.
406 50 c. Type **106** 15 10
407 1 r. Industrial complex and map of U.S.S.R. 30 10

107 Arms of Kampuchea

1983. 4th Anniv of People's Republic of Kampuchea. Multicoloured.
408 50 c. Type **107** 25 10
409 1 r. Open book illustrating national flag and arms (horiz) 50 15
410 3 r. Stylized figures and map 1·40 40

108 Runner with Olympic Torch

109 "Salatura genutia"

1983. Olympic Games, Los Angeles (1984) (1st issue). Multicoloured.
412 20 c. Type **108** 10 10
413 50 c. Javelin throwing 15 10
414 80 c. Pole vaulting 20 10
415 1 r. Discus throwing 35 15
416 1 r. 50 Relay (horiz) 50 20
417 2 r. Swimming (horiz) 85 30
418 3 r. Basketball . . . . 1·25 45
See also Nos. 526/32.

1983. Butterflies. Multicoloured.
420 20 c. Type **109** 15 10
421 50 c. "Euploea althaea juvia" 20 15
422 80 c. "Byasa polyeuctes termessus" (horiz) 40 20
423 1 r. "Stichophthalma howqua" (horiz) 70 25
424 1 r. 50 "Kallima inachus formosana" . . . . 1·25 45
425 2 r. "Precis orithya orithya" 1·75 60
426 3 r. "Catopsilia pomona pomona" . . . . 2·75 80

110 Srah Srang

1983. Khmer Culture. Multicoloured.
427 20 c. Type **110** 10 10
428 50 c. Bakong 15 10
429 80 c. Ta Som (vert) 25 10
430 1 r. North gate, Angkor Thom (vert) 40 15
431 1 r. 50 Kennora (winged figures) (vert) 70 25
432 2 r. Apsara (carved figures), Angkor (vert) 75 25
433 3 r. Banteai Srei (goddess), Tevoda (vert) . . . . . . 1·25 40

111 Dancers with Castanets

112 Detail of Fresco

1983. Folklore. Multicoloured.
434 50 c. Type **111** 25 10
435 1 r. Dancers with grass headdresses 55 20
436 3 r. Dancers with scarves . . 1·25 40

1983. 500th Birth Anniv of Raphael (artist).
438 **112** 20 c. multicoloured . . . 10 10
439 – 50 c. multicoloured . . . 20 10
440 – 80 c. multicoloured . . . 25 15
441 – 1 r. multicoloured 45 20
442 – 1 r. 50 multicoloured . . 80 25
443 – 2 r. multicoloured 95 35
444 – 3 r. multicoloured . . . . 1·50 45
DESIGNS: Nos. 439/44, different details of frescoes by Raphael.

113 Montgolfier Balloon

114 Cobra

1983. Bicentenary of Manned Flight. Mult.
446 20 c. Type **113** 10 15
447 30 c. "La Ville d'Orleans", 1870 20 10
448 50 c. Charles's hydrogen balloon 30 15
449 1 r. Blanchard and Jeffries crossing Channel, 1785 . . 50 20
450 1 r. 50 Salomon Andree's balloon flight over Arctic 85 35
451 2 r. Auguste Piccard's stratosphere balloon "F.N.R.S." 90 40
452 3 r. Hot-air balloon race . . 1·50 50

1983. Reptiles. Multicoloured.
454 20 c. Crested lizard (horiz) . . 15 10
455 30 c. Type **114** 20 10
456 80 c. Trionyx turtle (horiz) . . 25 10
457 1 r. Chameleon 45 15
458 1 r. 50 Boa constrictor . . . 75 25
459 2 r. Crocodile (horiz) 90 25
460 3 r. Turtle (horiz) . . . . . . 1·40 40

115 Rainbow Lory

116 Sunflower

1983. Birds. Multicoloured.
461 20 c. Type **115** 20 10
462 50 c. Barn swallow 30 15
463 80 c. Golden eagle (horiz) . . 50 25
464 1 r. Griffon vulture (horiz) . . 85 40
465 1 r. 50 Javanese collared dove (horiz) . . . . 1·25 55
466 2 r. Magpie . . . . 1·60 70
467 3 r. Great Indian hornbill . . 2·50 1·10

1983. Flowers. Multicoloured.
468 20 c. Type **116** 10 10
469 50 c. "Caprifoliaceae" 15 10
470 80 c. "Bougainvillea" 25 10
471 1 r. "Ranunculaceae" 40 15
472 1 r. 50 "Nyctagynaeceae" . . . 75 25
473 2 r. Cockscomb 90 25
474 3 r. Roses . . . . 1·40 40

117 Luge

1983. Winter Olympic Games, Sarajevo (1984) (1st issue). Multicoloured.
475 1 r. Type **117** 40 15
476 2 r. Biathlon 90 25
477 4 r. Ski-jumping . . . . . . 1·75 50
478 5 r. Two-man bobsleigh . . . 1·90 60
479 7 r. Ice hockey . . . . 2·75 85
See also Nos. 496/502.

118 "Cyprinidae"

1983. Fishes. Multicoloured.
481 20 c. Type **118** 15 10
482 50 c. Trout 20 10
483 80 c. Catfish 25 10
484 1 r. Moray eel 50 15
485 1 r. 50 "Cyprinidae" (different) 90 25
486 2 r. "Cyprinidae" (different) . 1·00 25
487 3 r. "Cyprinidae" (different) . 1·40 40

119 Factory and Gearwheel

1983. Festival of Rebirth. Multicoloured.
488 50 c. Type **119** 20 10
489 1 r. Tractor and cow (horiz) 35 15
490 3 r. Bulk carrier, train, car and bridge . . . . 2·50 60

120 Red Cross and Sailing Ship

1984. 5th Anniv of National Liberation. Mult.
492 50 c. Type **120** 20 10
493 1 r. Three soldiers, flags and temple 35 15
494 3 r. Crowd surrounding temple 1·00 35

MINIMUM PRICE

The minimum price quoted is 10p which represents a handling charge rather than a basis for valuing common stamps. For further notes about prices, see introductory pages.

121 Speed Skating

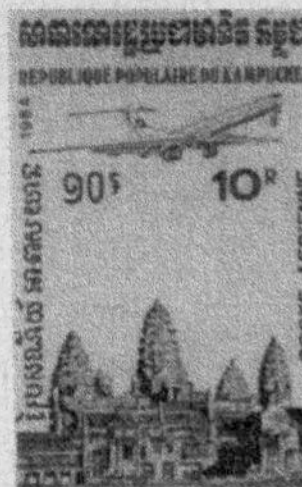

122 Ilyushin Il-62M Jet over Angkor Vat

1984. Winter Olympic Games, Sarajevo (2nd issue). Multicoloured.
496 20 c. Type **121** 10 10
497 50 c. Ice hockey 15 10
498 80 c. Skiing 20 10
499 1 r. Ski jumping 50 15
500 1 r. 50 Skiing (different) . . . 75 25
501 2 r. Cross-country skiing . . . 90 25
502 3 r. Ice skating (pairs) . . . . 1·25 40

1984. Air.
504 **122** 5 r. multicoloured . . . . 2·50 75
505 10 r. multicoloured . . . 4·75 1·50
506 15 r. multicoloured . . . 7·25 2·25
507 25 r. multicoloured . . . 12·25 3·75
For design as Type **122** but inscribed "R.P. DU KAMPUCHEA", see Nos. 695/8.

123 Cattle Egret

124 Doves and Globe

1984. Birds. Multicoloured.
508 10 c. Type **123** 15 10
509 40 c. Black-headed shrike . . 40 25
510 80 c. Slaty-headed parakeet . 75 35
511 1 r. Golden-fronted leafbird . 1·10 35
512 1 r. 20 Red-winged crested cuckoo . . . . 1·25 40
513 2 r. Grey wagtail . . . . . . 2·10 85
514 2 r. 50 Forest wagtail . . . . 2·50 95

1984. International Peace in South-East Asia Forum, Phnom Penh. Mult, background colour given.
515 **124** 50 c. green 20 10
516 1 r. blue 40 15
517 3 r. violet . . . . 1·25 35

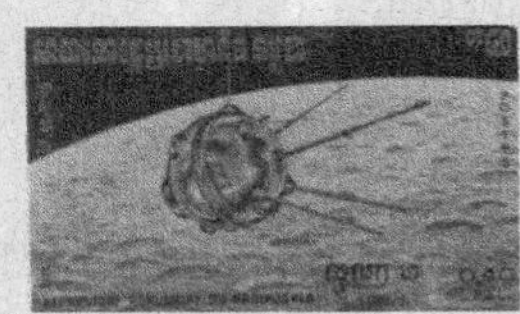

125 "Luna 2"

1984. Space Research. Multicoloured.
518 10 c. "Luna 1" 10 10
519 40 c. Type **125** 15 10
520 80 c. "Luna 3" 25 10
521 1 r. "Soyuz 6" and cosmonauts (vert) 40 15
522 1 r. 20 "Soyuz 7" and cosmonauts (vert) 65 20
523 2 r. "Soyuz 8" and cosmonauts (vert) 75 25
524 2 r. 50 Book, rocket and S. P. Korolev (Russian spaceship designer) (vert) . . . . . 1·25 40

126 Throwing the Discus

1984. Olympic Games, Los Angeles (2nd issue). Multicoloured.
526 20 c. Type **126** 10 10
527 50 c. Long jumping 15 10
528 80 c. Hurdling 25 10
529 1 r. Relay 50 15
530 1 r. 50 Pole vaulting 75 25
531 2 r. Throwing the javelin . . . 90 25
532 3 r. High jumping . . . . . . 1·25 40

128 Coyote

1984. Dog Family. Multicoloured.

535 10 c. Type **128** 10 10
536 40 c. Dingo 15 10
537 80 c. Hunting dog 25 10
538 1 r. Golden jackal 45 15
539 1 r. 20 Red fox 75 20
540 2 r. Maned wolf (vert) 1·25 25
541 2 r. 50 Wolf 1·75 40

129 "BB-1002" Type Diesel Locomotive (1966)

1984. Locomotives. Multicoloured.

542 10 c. Type **129** 10 10
543 40 c. "BB-1052" type diesel locomotive (1966) 15 10
544 80 c. Franco-Belgian steam locomotive (1945) 25 15
545 1 r. "231-505" type steam locomotive (1929) 45 20
546 1 r. 20 "803" type railcar (1968) 75 25
547 2 r. "BDE-405" type diesel locomotive (1957) 1·10 35
548 2 r. 50 "DS-01" type diesel railcar (1929) 1·60 50

130 Magnolia

1984. Flowers. Multicoloured.

549 10 c. Type **130** 10 10
550 40 c. "Plumeria" sp. 15 10
551 80 c. "Himenoballis" sp. 25 10
552 1 r. "Peltophorum roxburghii" 45 15
553 1 r. 20 "Couroupita guianensis" 70 20
554 2 r. "Lagerstroemia" sp. 1·10 25
555 2 r. 50 "Thevetia perubiana" 1·75 40

131 Mercedes Benz

1984. Cars. Multicoloured.

556 20 c. Type **131** 10 10
557 50 c. Bugatti 15 10
558 80 c. Alfa Romeo 35 10
559 1 r. Franklin 50 15
560 1 r. 50 Hispano-Suiza 85 20
561 2 r. Rolls Royce 1·25 25
562 3 r. Tatra 1·50 35

132 Sra Lai (Rattle) **133** Gazelle

1984. Musical Instruments. Multicoloured.

564 10 c. Type **132** 10 10
565 40 c. Skor drum (horiz) 15 10
566 80 c. Skor drums (different) 35 15
567 1 r. Thro khmer (stringed instrument) (horiz) 50 20
568 1 r. 20 Raneat ek (xylophone) (horiz) 85 25
569 2 r. Raneat kong (bells) (horiz) 1·25 30
570 2 r. 50 Thro khe (stringed instrument) (horiz) 1·25 50

1984. Mammals. Multicoloured.

571 10 c. Type **133** 10 10
572 40 c. Roe deer 15 10
573 80 c. Hare (horiz) 25 15
574 1 r. Red deer 50 20
575 1 r. 20 Indian elephant 75 30
576 2 r. Genet (horiz) 90 40
577 2 r. 50 Kouprey (horiz) 1·25 60

134 "Madonna and Child" **136** Footballers

135 Bullock Cart

1984. 450th Death Anniv of Correggio (artist). Multicoloured.

578 20 c. Type **134** 10 10
579 50 c. Detail showing man striking monk 15 10
580 80 c. "Madonna and Child" (different) 25 15
581 1 r. "Madonna and Child" (different) 40 20
582 1 r. 50 "Mystical Marriage of St. Catherine" 70 30
583 2 r. "Pieta" 75 40
584 3 r. Detail showing man descending ladder 1·25 60

1985. 6th Anniv of People's Republic National Festival. Multicoloured.

586 50 c. Type **135** 40 10
587 1 r. Horse-drawn passenger cart 65 25
588 3 r. Elephants 1·60 50

1985. World Cup Football Championship, Mexico. Designs showing footballers.

590 **136** 20 c. multicoloured 10 10
591 – 50 c. multicoloured 25 10
592 – 80 c. multicoloured 45 15
593 – 1 r. multicoloured 55 25
594 – 1 r. 50 multicoloured 80 35
595 – 2 r. multicoloured 1·00 45
596 – 3 r. multicoloured 1·60 70

137 Eska-Mofa Motor Cycle, 1939

1985. Centenary of Motor Cycle. Multicoloured.

598 20 c. Type **137** 10 10
599 50 c. Wanderer, 1939 25 10
600 80 c. Premier, 1929 45 15
601 1 r. Ardie, 1939 55 25
602 1 r. 50 Jawa, 1932 80 35
603 2 r. Simson, 1983 1·00 45
604 3 r. "CZ 125", 1984 1·60 70

138 "Gymnopilus spectabilis"

1985. Fungi. Multicoloured.

606 20 c. Type **138** 10 10
607 50 c. "Coprinus micaceus" 25 10
608 80 c. "Amanita pantherina" 45 15
609 1 r. "Hebeloma crustuliniforme" 60 25
610 1 r. 50 "Amanita muscaria" 90 35
611 2 r. "Coprinus comatus" 1·10 45
612 3 r. "Amanita caesarea" 1·75 70

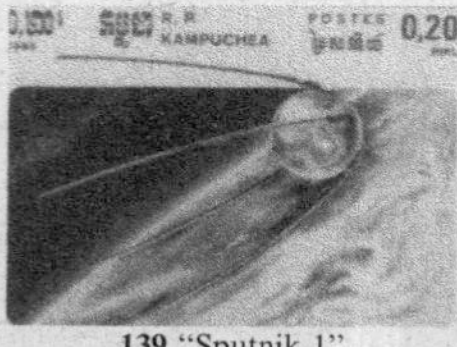
139 "Sputnik 1"

1985. Space Exploration. Multicoloured.

613 20 c. Type **139** 10 10
614 50 c. Rocket on transporter and Yuri Gagarin (first man in space) 25 10
615 80 c. "Vostok 6" and Valentina Tereshkova (first woman in space) 45 15
616 1 r. Space walker 55 25
617 1 r. 50 "Salyut"–"Soyuz" link 80 35
618 2 r. "Lunokhod 1" (lunar vehicle) 1·00 45
619 3 r. "Venera" (Venus probe) 1·60 70

140 Absara Group

1985. Traditional Dances. Multicoloured.

621 50 c. Type **140** 35 10
622 1 r. Tepmonorom dance 70 25
623 3 r. Absara solo dancer (vert) 1·75 75

140a Captured Nazi Standards, Red Square, Moscow

1985. 40th Anniv of End of Second World War. Multicoloured.

623a 50 c. Rejoicing soldiers in Berlin 30 10
623b 1 r. Type **140a** 55 25
623c 3 r. Tank battle 1·75 75

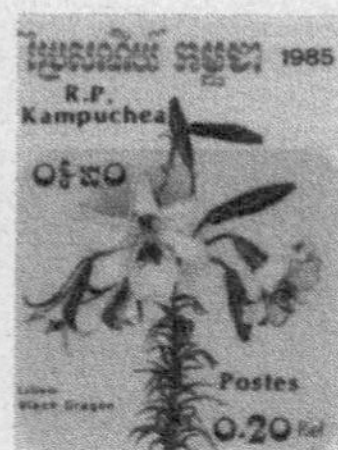

141 Tortoiseshell Cat **142** "Black Dragon" Lily

1985. Domestic Cats. Multicoloured.

624 20 c. Type **141** 10 10
625 50 c. Tortoiseshell (different) 25 10
626 80 c. Tabby 45 15
627 1 r. Long-haired Siamese 60 25
628 1 t. 50 Sealpoint Siamese 1·00 35
629 2 r. Grey cat 1·25 45
630 3 r. Black cat 2·00 70

1985. Flowers. Multicoloured.

631 20 c. Type **142** 10 10
632 50 c. "Iris delavayi" 25 10
633 80 c. "Crocus aureus" 45 15
634 1 r. "Cyclamen persicum" 60 25
635 1 r. 50 "Primula malacoides" 90 35
636 2 r. "Viola tricolor Ullswater" 1·10 45
637 3 r. "Crocus purpureus grandiflorus" 1·75 70

143 "Per Italiani" (Antoine Watteau) **144** Lenin and Arms

1987. International Music Year. Multicoloured.

638 20 c. Type **143** 10 10
639 50 c. "St. Cecilia" (Carlos Saraceni) 25 10
640 80 c. "Still Life with Violin" (Jean Baptiste Oudry) (horiz) 45 15
641 1 r. "Three Musicians" (Fernand Leger) 55 25
642 1 r. 50 Orchestra 80 35
643 2 r. "St. Cecilia" (Bartholomeo Schedoni) 1·00 45
644 3 r. "Harlequin with Violin" (Christian Caillard) 1·60 70

1985. 115th Birth Anniv of Lenin. Multicoloured.

646 1 r. Type **144** 60 25
647 3 r. Lenin on balcony and map 1·60 70

145 Saffron-cowled Blackbird

1985. "Argentina '85" International Stamp Exhibition, Buenos Aires. Birds. Multicoloured.

648 20 c. Type **145** 15 10
649 50 c. Saffron finch (vert) 30 15
650 80 c. Blue and yellow tanager (vert) 50 20
651 1 r. Scarlet-headed blackbird 70 25
652 1 r. 50 Amazon kingfisher (vert) 1·40 35
653 2 r. Toco toucan (vert) 1·90 45
654 3 r. Rufous-bellied thrush 2·50 70

146 River Launch, 1942

1985. Water Craft. Multicoloured.

655 10 c. Type **146** 15 10
656 40 c. River launch, Cambodia, 1948 25 15
657 80 c. Tug, Japan, 1913 45 20
658 1 r. Dredger, Holland 65 25
659 1 r. 20 Tug, U.S.A. 1·10 35
660 2 r. River freighter 1·50 45
661 2 r. 50 River tanker, Panama 2·00 70

147 "The Flood" (Michelangelo) **148** Son Ngoe Minh

1985. "Italia '85" International Stamp Exhibition, Rome. Paintings. Multicoloured.

662 20 r. Type **147** 10 10
663 50 r. "The Virgin of St. Marguerite" (Mazzola) 25 10
664 80 r. "The Martyrdom of St. Peter" (Zampieri Domenichino) 45 15
665 1 r. "Allegory of Spring" (detail) (Sandro Botticelli) 55 25
666 1 r. 50 "The Sacrifice of Abraham" (Caliari) 80 35
667 2 r. "The Meeting of Joachim and Anne" (Giotto) 1·00 45
668 3 r. "Bacchus" (Michel Angelo Carravaggio) 1·60 70

1985. Festival of Rebirth.

670 **148** 50 c. multicoloured 15 10
671 1 r. multicoloured 40 15
672 3 r. multicoloured 1·10 45

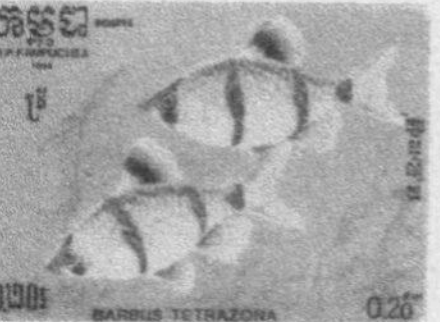
149 Five-banded Barb

1985. Fishes. Multicoloured.

673 20 c. Type **149** 10 10
674 50 c. "Ophiocephalus micropeltes" 25 10
675 80 c. Goldfish 45 15
676 1 r. "Trichogaster leeri" 55 25
677 1 r. 50 "Puntius hexazona" 80 35
678 2 r. "Betta splendens" 1·00 45
679 3 r. "Datnioides microlepis" 1·60 70

150 Footballers

152 "Mir" Space Station and Spacecraft

151 Cob

1986. World Cup Football Championship, Mexico.
680 150 20 c. multicoloured . . . 10 10
681 – 50 c. multicoloured . . . 25 10
682 – 80 c. multicoloured . . . 45 15
683 – 1 r. multicoloured . . . 55 25
684 – 1 r. 50 multicoloured . . . 80 35
685 – 2 r. multicoloured . . . 1·00 45
686 – 3 r. multicoloured . . . 1·60 70
DESIGNS: 50 c. to 3 r. show Various footballing scenes.

1986. Horses. Multicoloured.
688 20 c. Type **151** . . . 10 10
689 50 c. Arab . . . 25 10
690 80 c. Australian pony . . . 45 15
691 1 r. Appaloosa . . . 55 25
692 1 r. 50 Quarter horse . . . 80 35
693 2 r. Vladimir heavy draught horse . . . 1·00 45
694 3 r. Andalusian . . . 1·60 70

1986. 27th Russian Communist Party Congress. Multicoloured.
694a 50 c. Type **152** . . . 25 10
694b 1 r. Lenin . . . 55 25
694c 5 r. Statue and launch of space rocket . . . 2·50 1·00

1986. Air. As Nos. 504/7 but inscr "R.P. DU KAMPUCHEA".
695 **122** 5 r. multicoloured . . . 2·75 95
696 10 r. multicoloured . . . 5·75 1·60
697 15 r. multicoloured . . . 8·50 2·50
698 25 r. multicoloured . . . 15·00 4·25

153 Edaphosaurus

1986. Prehistoric Animals. Multicoloured.
699 20 c. Type **153** . . . 10 10
700 50 c. Sauroctonus . . . 25 10
701 80 c. Mastodonsaurus . . . 45 15
702 1 r. Rhamphorhynchus (vert) . . . 60 25
703 1 r. 50 Brachiosaurus brancai (vert) . . . 90 35
704 2 r. Tarbosaurus bataar (vert) . . . 1·10 45
705 3 r. Indricotherium (vert) . . . 1·75 70

154 "Luna 3"

1986. 25th Anniv of First Man in Space. Multicoloured.
706 10 c. Type **154** . . . 10 10
707 40 c. "Vostok" . . . 25 10
708 80 c. "Vostok" with rocket . . . 45 15
709 1 r. Cosmonaut Leonov on space walk . . . 55 25
710 1 r. 20 "Salyut" and "Soyuz" preparing to dock . . . 80 35
711 2 r. Soviet space station . . . 1·00 45
712 2 r. 50 Cosmonaut Leonov and spacecraft . . . 1·60 75

155 Baksei Chmkrong Temple, 920

1986. Khmer Culture. Multicoloured.
713 20 c. Type **155** . . . 10 10
714 50 c. Buddha's head . . . 25 10
715 80 c. Prea Vihear monastery, Dangrek . . . 45 15
716 1 r. Fan with design of man and woman . . . 55 25
717 1 r. 50 Fan with design of men fighting . . . 80 35
718 2 r. Fan with design of dancer . . . 1·00 45
719 3 r. Fan with design of dragon-drawn chariot . . . 1·60 70

156 Tricar, 1885

1986. Centenary (1985) of Motor Car. Mercedes Benz Models. Multicoloured.
720 20 c. Type **156** . . . 10 10
721 50 c. Limousine, 1935 . . . 25 10
722 80 c. Open tourer, 1907 . . . 45 15
723 1 r. Light touring car, 1920 . . . 55 25
724 1 r. 50 Cabriolet, 1932 . . . 80 35
725 2 r. "SKK" tourer, 1938 . . . 1·00 45
726 3 r. "190", 1985 . . . 1·60 70

157 "Danaus genutia"

159 Solar System, Copernicus, Galileo and Tycho Brahe (astronomers)

158 English Kogge of Richard II's Reign

1986. Butterflies. Multicoloured.
727 20 c. Type **157** . . . 15 10
728 50 c. "Graphium amtiphates" . . . 35 15
729 80 c. "Papilio demoleus" . . . 65 20
730 1 r. "Danaus sita" . . . 75 35
731 1 r. 50 "Idea blanchardi" . . . 1·10 45
732 2 r. "Papilio polytes" . . . 1·40 60
733 3 r. "Dabasa payeni" . . . 2·25 95

1986. Medieval Ships.
734 20 c. Type **158** . . . 10 10
735 50 c. Kogge . . . 25 10
736 80 c. Knarr . . . 45 15
737 1 r. Galley . . . 55 25
738 1 r. 50 Norman ship . . . 80 35
739 2 r. Mediterranean usciere . . . 1·10 45
740 3 r. French kogge . . . 1·75 70

1986. Appearance of Halley's Comet. Multicoloured.
741 10 c. Type **159** . . . 10 10
742 20 c. "Nativity" (Giotto) and comet from Bayeux Tapestry . . . 10 10
743 50 c. Comet, 1910, and Mt. Palomar observatory, U.S.A. . . . 25 10
744 80 c. Edmond Halley and "Planet A" space probe . . . 45 15
745 1 r. 20 Diagram of comet's trajectory and "Giotto" space probe . . . 60 25
746 1 r. 50 "Vega" space probe and camera . . . 80 35
747 2 r. Thermal pictures of comet . . . 1·00 45

160 Ruy Lopez Segura

1986. "Stockholmia 86" International Stamp Exhibition. Chess. Multicoloured.
749 20 c. Type **160** . . . 10 10
750 50 c. Francois-Andre Philidor . . . 25 10
751 80 c. Karl Anderssen and Houses of Parliament, London . . . 45 15
752 1 r. Wilhelm Steinitz and Charles Bridge, Prague . . . 60 25
753 1 r. 50 Emmanuel Lasker and medieval knight . . . 90 35
754 2 r. Jose Capablanca and Morro Castle, Cuba . . . 1·10 45
755 3 r. Aleksandr Alekhine . . . 1·75 70

161 "Parodia maassii"

162 Bananas

1986. Cacti. Multicoloured.
757 20 c. Type **161** . . . 10 10
758 50 c. "Rebutia marsoneri" . . . 25 10
759 80 c. "Melocactus evae" . . . 45 15
760 1 r. "Gymnocalycium valnicekianum" . . . 55 25
761 1 r. 50 "Discocactus silichromus" . . . 80 35
762 2 r. "Neochilenia simulans" . . . 1·00 45
763 3 r. "Weingartia chiquichuquensis" . . . 1·60 70

1986. Fruit. Multicoloured.
764 10 c. Type **162** . . . 10 10
765 40 c. Papaya . . . 20 10
766 80 c. Mangoes . . . 45 15
767 1 r. Breadfruit . . . 55 35
768 1 r. 20 Lychees . . . 60 25
769 2 r. Pineapple . . . 1·00 45
770 2 r. 50 Grapefruit (horiz) . . . 1·40 55

163 Concorde

1986. Aircraft. Multicoloured.
771 20 c. Type **163** . . . 10 10
772 50 c. Douglas DC-10 . . . 25 10
773 80 c. Boeing 747SP . . . 45 15
774 1 r. Ilyushin Il-62M . . . 55 25
775 1 r. 50 Ilyushin Il-86 . . . 80 35
776 2 r. Antonov An-24 . . . 1·10 45
777 3 r. Airbus Industrie A-300 . . . 1·75 70

164 Elephant and Silver Containers on Tray

1986. Festival of Rebirth. Silverware. Mult.
778 50 c. Type **164** . . . 25 10
779 1 r. Tureen . . . 55 20
780 3 r. Dish on stand . . . 1·60 45

165 Kouprey

1986. Endangered Animals. Cattle. Mult.
781 20 c. Type **165** . . . 10 10
782 20 c. Gaur . . . 10 10
783 80 c. Bateng cow and calf . . . 45 15
784 1 r. 50 Asiatic water buffalo . . . 1·40 50

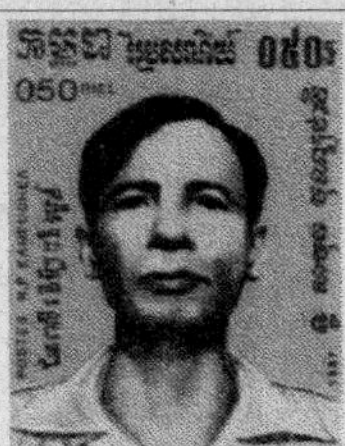
166 Tou Samuth (revolutionary)

1987. National Festival. 8th Anniv of People's Republic.
785 **166** 50 c. multicoloured . . . 20 10
786 1 r. multicoloured . . . 40 15
787 3 r. multicoloured . . . 1·10 35

167 Biathlon

1987. Winter Olympic Games, Calgary (1988) (1st issue). Multicoloured.
788 20 c. Type **167** . . . 10 10
789 50 c. Figure skating . . . 25 10
790 80 c. Speed skating . . . 45 15
791 1 r. Ice hockey . . . 55 25
792 1 r. 50 Two-man luge . . . 80 35
793 2 r. Two-man bobsleigh . . . 1·00 45
794 3 r. Cross-country skiing . . . 1·60 70
See also Nos. 864/70.

168 Weightlifting

1987. Olympic Games, Seoul (1988) (1st issue). Multicoloured.
796 20 c. Type **168** . . . 10 10
797 50 c. Archery (horiz) . . . 25 10
798 80 c. Fencing (horiz) . . . 45 15
799 1 r. Gymnastics . . . 55 25
800 1 r. 50 Discus throwing (horiz) . . . 80 35
801 2 r. Javelin throwing . . . 1·00 45
802 3 r. Hurdling . . . 1·60 70
See also Nos. 875/81.

169 Papillon

1987. Dogs. Multicoloured.
804 20 c. Type **169** . . . 10 10
805 50 c. Greyhound . . . 25 10
806 80 c. Great dane . . . 45 15
807 1 r. Doberman . . . 55 25
808 1 r. 50 Samoyed . . . 80 35
809 2 r. Borzoi . . . 1·00 45
810 3 r. Rough collie . . . 1·60 70

170 "Sputnik 1"

171 Flask

1987. Space Exploration. Multicoloured.
811 20 c. Type **170** . . . 10 10
812 50 c. "Soyuz 10" . . . 25 10
813 80 c. "Proton" . . . 45 15
814 1 r. "Vostok 1" . . . 55 25
815 1 r. 50 "Salyut" . . . 80 35
816 2 r. "Kosmos" . . . 1·00 45
817 3 r. "Luna 2" . . . 1·60 70

1987. Metalwork. Multicoloured.

819	50 c. Type **171**	20	10
820	1 r. Repousse box	50	25
821	1 r. 50 Teapot and cups on tray	75	35
822	3 r. Ornamental sword	1·50	70

172 Carmine Bee Eater

1987. "Capex '87" International Stamp Exhibition, Toronto. Birds. Multicoloured.

823	20 c. Type **172**	10	10
824	50 c. Hoopoe (vert)	25	10
825	80 c. South African crowned crane (vert)	45	15
826	1 r. Barn owl (vert)	55	25
827	1 r. 50 Grey-headed kingfisher (vert)	80	35
828	2 r. Red-whiskered bulbul	1·00	45
829	3 r. Purple heron (vert)	1·60	70

173 Horatio F. Phillip's Machine, 1893

1987. Experimental Aircraft Designs. Mult.

831	20 c. Type **173**	10	10
832	50 c. John Stringfellow, 1848	25	10
833	80 c. Thomas Moy, 1875	45	15
834	1 r. Leonardo da Vinci, 1490	55	25
835	1 r. 50 Sir George Cayley, 1840	80	35
836	2 r. Sir Hiram Maxim, 1894	1·00	45
837	3 r. William Samuel Henson, 1842	1·60	70

174 Giant Tortoise

1987. Reptiles. Multicoloured.

839	20 c. Type **174**	10	10
840	50 c. "Uromastix acanthinuros"	25	10
841	80 c. "Cyclura macleayi"	45	15
842	1 r. "Phrynosoma coronatum"	55	25
843	1 r. 50 "Sauromalus obesus"	80	35
844	2 r. "Ophisaurus apodus"	1·00	45
845	3 r. "Thamnophis sirtalis tetrataenia"	1·60	70

175 Kamov Ka-15

1987. "Hafnia 87" International Stamp Exhibition, Copenhagen. Helicopters. Multicoloured.

846	20 c. Type **175**	10	10
847	50 c. Kamov Ka-18	25	10
848	80 c. Westland WG-13 Lynx	45	15
849	1 r. Sud Aviation SA 341 Gazelle	55	25
850	1 r. 50 Sud Aviation SA 330E Puma	80	35
851	2 r. Boeing-Vertol CH-47 Chinook	1·00	45
852	3 r. Boeing UTTAS	1·60	70

176 Revolutionaries

178 Earth Station Dish Aerial

177 Magirus-Deutz No. 21

1987. 70th Anniv of Russian October Revolution. Multicoloured.

853a	2 r. Revolutionaries on street corner (horiz)	95	40
853b	3 r. Type **176**	1·25	50
853c	5 r. Lenin receiving ticker-tape message (horiz)	2·50	1·00

1987. Fire Engines. Multicoloured.

854	20 c. Type **177**	10	10
855	50 c. "SIL-131" rescue vehicle	25	10
856	80 c. "Cas-25" fire pump	45	15
857	1 r. Sirmac Saab "424"	60	25
858	1 r. 50 Rosenbaum-Falcon	85	35
859	2 r. Tatra "815-PRZ"	1·10	45
860	3 r. Chubbfire "C-44-20"	1·60	70

1987. Telecommunications. Multicoloured.

861	50 c. Type **178**	10	10
862	1 r. Technological building with radio microwave aerial	55	25
863	3 r. Intersputnik programme earth station (horiz)	1·60	70

179 Speed Skating

1988. Winter Olympic Games, Calgary (2nd issue). Multicoloured.

864	20 c. Type **179**	10	10
865	50 c. Ice hockey	25	10
866	80 c. Slalom	45	15
867	1 r. Ski jumping	55	25
868	1 r. 50 Biathlon	80	35
869	2 r. Ice dancing	1·00	45
870	3 r. Cross-country skiing	1·60	70

180 Irrigation Canal Bed

1988. Irrigation Projects. Multicoloured.

872	50 c. Type **180**	10	10
873	1 r. Dam construction	50	20
874	3 r. Dam and bridge	1·50	65

181 Beam Exercise

1988. Olympic Games, Seoul (2nd issue). Women's Gymnastics. Multicoloured.

875	20 c. Type **181**	10	10
876	50 c. Bar exercise (horiz)	25	10
877	80 c. Ribbon exercise	45	15
878	1 r. Hoop exercise	55	25
879	1 r. 50 Baton exercise	80	35
880	2 r. Ball exercise (horiz)	1·00	45
881	3 r. Floor exercise (horiz)	1·60	70

182 White Long-haired Cat

1988. "Juvalux 88" 9th Youth Philately Exhibition, Luxembourg. Cats. Multicoloured.

883	20 c. Type **182**	10	10
884	50 c. Abyssinian (vert)	25	10
885	80 c. Ginger and white long-haired cat (vert)	45	15
886	1 r. Tortoiseshell queen and kitten	55	25
887	1 r. 50 Brown cat (vert)	80	35
888	2 r. Black long-haired cat (vert)	1·00	45
889	3 r. Grey cat (vert)	1·60	70

183 "Emerald Seas" (liner)

1988. "Essen 88" International Stamp Fair. Ships. Multicoloured.

891	20 c. Type **183**	10	10
892	50 c. Car ferry	20	10
893	80 c. Freighter	35	10
894	1 r. "Kosmonavt Yury Gagarin" (research ship)	50	15
895	1 r. 50 Tanker	55	20
896	2 r. Hydrofoil	75	30
897	3 r. Hovercraft	1·25	35

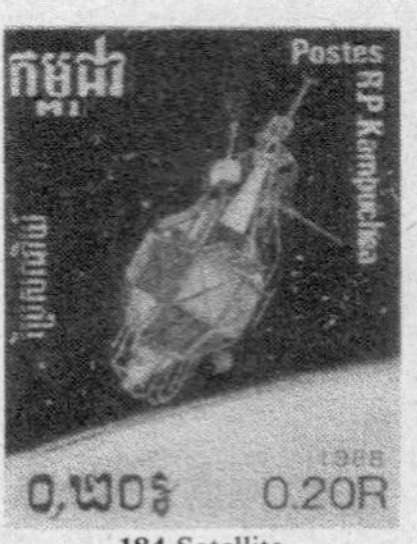

184 Satellite

186 "Helicostyla florida"

185 "Xiphophorus helleri"

1988. Space Exploration. Designs showing different satellites.

899	**184**	20 c. multicoloured	10	10
900	–	50 c. multicoloured	20	10
901	–	80 c. multicoloured	35	10
902	–	1 r. multicoloured (horiz)	50	15
903	–	1 r. 50 multicoloured (horiz)	55	20
904	–	2 r. multicoloured (horiz)	75	30
905	–	3 r. multicoloured (horiz)	1·25	35

1988. "Finlandia 88" International Stamp Exhibition, Helsinki. Tropical Fish. Multicoloured.

907	20 c. Type **185**	10	10
908	50 c. "Hemigrammus ocellifer ocellifer"	20	10
909	80 c. "Macropodus opercularis"	35	10
910	1 r. "Carassius auratus auratus"	50	15
911	1 r. 50 "Hyphessobrycon ineai"	55	20
912	2 r. "Corynopoma riisei"	75	30
913	3 r. "Mollienisia latipinna"	1·25	35

1988. Sea Shells. Multicoloured.

915	20 c. Type **186**	10	10
916	50 c. "Helicostyla marinduquensis"	20	10
917	80 c. "Helicostyla fulgens"	35	10
918	1 r. "Helicostyla woodiana"	50	15
919	1 r. 50 "Chloraea sirena"	55	20
920	2 r. "Helicostyla mirabilis"	75	30
921	3 r. "Helicostyla limansauensis"	1·25	35

187 "Coccinella septempunctata"

1988. Insects. Multicoloured.

922	20 c. Type **187**	10	10
923	50 c. "Zonabride geminata"	20	10
924	80 c. "Carabus auronitens"	35	10
925	1 r. "Apis mellifera"	50	15
926	1 r. 50 "Mantis sp."	55	20
927	2 r. "Aeshna sp."	75	30
928	3 r. "Malachius aeneus"	1·25	35

188 "Cattleya aclandiae"

1988. Orchids. Multicoloured.

929	20 c. Type **188**	10	10
930	50 c. "Odontoglossum" "Royal Sovereign"	20	10
931	80 c. "Cattleya labiata"	35	10
932	1 r. "Ophrys apifera"	50	15
933	1 r. 50 "Laelia anceps"	55	20
934	2 r. "Laelia pumila"	75	30
935	3 r. "Stanhopea tigrina" (horiz)	1·25	35

189 Egyptian Banded Cobra

190 Walking Dance

1988. Reptiles. Multicoloured.

936	20 c. Type **189**	10	10
937	50 c. Common iguana	20	10
938	80 c. Long-nosed vine snake (horiz)	35	10
939	1 r. Common box turtle (horiz)	50	15
940	1 r. 50 Iguana (horiz)	55	20
941	2 r. Viper (horiz)	75	30
942	3 r. Common cobra	1·25	35

1988. Festival of Rebirth. Khmer Culture. Multicoloured.

943	50 c. Type **190**	20	10
944	1 r. Peacock dance	50	15
945	3 r. Kantere dance	1·25	35

191 Bridge

1989. Multicoloured.

946	50 c. Type **191**	25	10
947	1 r. More distant view of bridge	50	20
948	3 r. Closer view of bridge	1·60	65

192 Cement Works

1989. National Festival. 10th Anniv of People's Republic of Kampuchea. Multicoloured.

949	3 r. Bayon Earth Station (horiz)	20	10
950	12 r. Electricity generating station 4 (horiz)	75	30
951	30 r. Type **192**	2·10	85

193 Footballers

1989. World Cup Football Championship, Italy.
952 **193** 2 r. multicoloured 10 10
953 – 3 r. multicoloured 20 10
954 – 5 r. multicoloured 30 10
955 – 10 r. multicoloured . . . 65 25
956 – 15 r. multicoloured . . . 1·00 40
957 – 20 r. multicoloured . . . 1·25 50
958 – 35 r. multicoloured . . . 2·40 95
DESIGNS: 3 r. to 35 r. Various footballing scenes.

194 Train

1989. Trains.
960 **194** 2 r. multicoloured 10 10
961 – 3 r. multicoloured 20 10
962 – 5 r. multicoloured 30 10
963 – 10 r. multicoloured . . . 65 25
964 – 15 r. multicoloured . . . 1·00 40
965 – 20 r. multicoloured . . . 1·25 50
966 – 35 r. multicoloured . . . 2·40 95
DESIGNS: 3 r. to 35 r. Various trains.

195 Fidel Castro 196 Scarlet Macaw

1989. 30th Anniv of Cuban Revolution.
968 **195** 12 r. multicoloured . . . 90 40

1989. Parrots. Multicoloured.
969 20 c. Type **196** 10 10
970 80 c. Sulphur-crested cockatoo 10 10
971 3 r. Rose-ringed parakeet . . 25 10
972 6 r. Blue and yellow macaw . . 50 15
973 10 r. Cape parrot 90 30
974 15 r. Blue-fronted amazon . . 1·40 45
975 25 r. White-capped parrot (horiz) 2·10 70

197 Skiing

1989. Winter Olympic Games, Albertville. Multicoloured.
977 2 r. Type **197** 10 10
978 3 r. Biathlon 20 10
979 5 r. Cross-country skiing . . . 30 10
980 10 r. Ski jumping 65 25
981 15 r. Speed skating . . . . . 1·00 40
982 20 r. Ice hockey . . . . 1·25 50
983 35 r. Two-man bobsleighing . 2·40 95

198 "Nymphaea capensis" (pink)

1989. Water Lilies. Multicoloured.
985 20 c. Type **198** 10 10
986 80 c. "Nymphaea capensis" (mauve) 10 10
987 3 r. "Nymphaea lotus dentata" 25 10
988 6 r. "Dir. Geo. T. Moore" . . 50 15
989 10 r. "Sunrise" 90 30
990 15 r. "Escarbonce" . . . . . 1·40 45
991 25 r. "Cladstoniana" . . . . . 2·10 70

199 Wrestling

1989. Olympic Games, Barcelona. Multicoloured.
993 2 r. Type **199** 10 10
994 3 r. Gymnastics (vert) 20 10
995 5 r. Putting the shot 30 10
996 10 r. Running (vert) 65 25
997 15 r. Fencing . . . . 1·00 40
998 20 r. Canoeing (vert) . . . . 1·40 50
999 35 r. Hurdling (vert) . . . . 2·40 95

200 Downy Boletus

1989. Fungi. Multicoloured.
1001 20 c. Type **200** 10 10
1002 80 c. Red-staining inocybe . 10 10
1003 3 r. Honey fungus 25 10
1004 6 r. Field mushroom 50 15
1005 10 r. Brown roll-rim 90 30
1006 15 r. Shaggy ink cap . . . . 1·40 45
1007 25 r. Parasol mushroom . . 2·10 70

201 Shire Horse

1989. Horses. Multicoloured.
1008 2 r. Type **201** 10 10
1009 3 r. Brabant 20 10
1010 5 r. Bolounais 30 10
1011 10 r. Breton 65 25
1012 15 r. Vladimir heavy draught horse . . . . 1·00 40
1013 20 r. Italian heavy draught horse . . . . 1·25 50
1014 35 r. Freiberger . . . . . . 2·40 95

KATANGA Pt. 14

The following stamps were issued by Mr. Tshombe's Government for independent Katanga. In 1963 Katanga was reunited with the Central Government of Congo.

1960. Various stamps of Belgian Congo optd **KATANGA** and bar or surch also. (a) Masks issue of 1948.
1 1 f. 50 on 1 f. 25 mauve and blue 50 20
2 3 f. 50 on 2 f. 50 green & brown 50 25
3 20 f. purple and red . . . . . 1·75 90
4 50 f. black and brown . . . . 4·00 3·25
5 100 f. black and red . . . . 30·00 22·00

(b) Flowers issue of 1952. Flowers in natural colours; colours given are of backgrounds and inscriptions.
6 10 c. yellow and purple . . . 10 10
7 15 c. green and red 10 10
8 20 c. grey and green 15 15
9 25 c. orange and green . . . 15 15
10 40 c. salmon and green . . . 15 15
11 50 c. turquoise and red . . . 20 20
12 60 c. purple and green . . . 15 15
13 75 c. grey and lake 20 20
14 1 f. lemon and red 25 25
15 2 f. buff and olive 30 30
16 3 f. pink and green 40 35
17 4 f. lavender and sepia . . . 60 50
18 5 f. green and purple 60 50
19 6 f. 50 lilac and red 60 45
20 7 f. brown and green 80 70
21 8 f. yellow and green 80 70
22 10 f. olive and purple . . . 11·50 9·00

(c) Wild animals issue of 1959.
23 10 c. brown, sepia and blue . . 15 10
24 20 c. blue and red 15 10
25 40 c. brown and blue 15 10
26 50 c. multicoloured 15 10
27 1 f. black, green and brown . . 5·25 3·25
28 1 f. 50 black and yellow . . . 8·75 6·00
29 2 f. black, brown and red . . . 40 10
30 3 f. black, purple and slate . . 3·25 2·50
31 5 f. brown, green and sepia . . 60 25
32 6 f. 50 brown, yellow and blue 75 25
33 8 f. bistre, violet and brown . 1·10 35
34 10 f. multicoloured . . . . . 1·60 50

(d) Madonna.
35 **102** 50 c. brown, ochre & chest 15 15
36 1 f. brown, violet and blue 15 15
37 2 f. brown, blue and slate 20 20

(e) African Technical Co-operation Commission. Inscr in French or Flemish.
38 **103** 3 f. salmon and slate . . . 7·00 7·00
39 3 f. 50 on 3 f. sal & slate . 2·10 2·10

1960. Independence. Independence issue of Congo optd **11 JUILLET DE L'ETAT DU KATANGA**.
40 **106** 20 c. bistre 10 10
41 50 c. red 10 10
42 1 f. green 10 10
43 1 f. 50 brown 10 10
44 2 f. mauve 10 10
45 3 f. 50 violet 15 10
46 5 f. blue 15 10
47 6 f. 50 black 15 10
48 10 f. orange 25 20
49 20 f. blue 45 30

5 6 Pres. Tshombe

1961. Katanga Art.
50 **5** 10 c. green 10 10
51 20 c. violet 10 10
52 50 c. blue 10 10
53 1 f. 50 green 10 10
54 2 f. brown 10 10
55 – 3 f. 50 blue 10 10
56 – 5 f. turquoise 10 10
57 – 6 f. brown 10 10
58 – 6 f. 50 blue 10 10
59 – 8 f. purple 15 10
60 – 10 f. brown 15 10
61 – 20 f. myrtle 25 20
62 – 50 f. brown 50 40
63 – 100 f. turquoise 85 70
DESIGNS: 3 f. 50 to 8 f. "Preparing food". 10 f. to 100 f. "Family circle".

1961. 1st Anniv of Independence. Portrait in brown.
64 **6** 6 f. 50 + 5 f. red, green & gold 1·25 1·00
65 8 f. + 5 f. red, green and gold 1·25 1·00
66 10 f. + 5 f. red, green and gold 1·25 1·00

7 "Tree" 8 Early Aircraft, Train and Safari

1961. Katanga International Fair. Vert symbolic designs as T **7**.
67 **7** 50 c. red, green and black . . 10 10
68 – 1 f. black and blue 10 10
69 – 2 f. 50 black and yellow . . . 15 15
70 **7** 3 f. 50 red, brown and black . 15 15
71 – 5 f. black and violet 25 25
72 – 6 f. 50 black and yellow . . . 30 30

1961. Air.
73 **8** 3 f. 50 multicoloured . . . . 3·00 3·00
74 – 6 f. 50 multicoloured . . . . 1·10 1·10
75 **8** 8 f. multicoloured . . . . . 3·25 3·00
76 – 10 f. multicoloured . . . . . 2·10 1·10
DESIGNS: 6 f. 50, 10 f. Tail of Boeing 707.

9 Gendarme in armoured Vehicle

1962. Katanga Gendarmerie.
77 **9** 6 f. multicoloured . . . . . 2·25 2·25
78 8 f. multicoloured 35 35
79 10 f. multicoloured 45 45

POSTAGE DUE STAMPS

1960. Postage Due stamps of Belgian Congo handstamped **KATANGA**. (a) On Nos. D 270/4.
D50 **D 86** 10 c. olive 80 80
D51 20 c. blue 80 80
D52 50 c. green . . . . . 1·00 1·00
D53 1 f. brown
D54 2 f. orange

(b) On Nos. D 330/6.
D55 **D 99** 10 c. brown . . . . . . 3·25 3·25
D56 20 c. purple . . . . . . 3·25 3·25
D57 50 c. green . . . . . . 3·25 3·25
D58 1 f. blue . . . . 1·00 1·00
D59 2 f. red . . . . 2·00 2·00
D60 4 f. violet . . . . . . 2·75 2·75
D61 6 f. blue . . . . 3·25 3·25

KHMER REPUBLIC Pt. 21

Cambodia was renamed Khmer Republic on 9th October 1970.

100 cents = 1 riel

78 "Attack"

1971. Defence of Khmer Territory.
285 **78** 1 r. multicoloured 10 10
286 3 r. multicoloured 20 10
287 10 r. multicoloured 50 20

79 "World Races" and U.N. Emblem

1971. Racial Equality Year.
288 **79** 3 r. multicoloured 10 10
289 7 r. multicoloured 35 15
290 8 r. multicoloured 55 25

80 General Post Office, Phnom Penh

1971.
291 **80** 3 r. multicoloured 20 15
292 9 r. multicoloured 40 20
293 10 r. multicoloured 50 30

81 Global Emblem

1971. World Telecommunications Day. Multicoloured.
294 3 r. Type **81** 10 10
295 4 r. Type **81** 20 10
296 7 r. I.T.U. emblem 30 15
297 8 r. I.T.U. emblem 40 20

82 "Erythrina indica"

1971. Wild Flowers. Multicoloured.
298 2 r. Type **82** 25 20
299 3 r. "Bauhinia variegata" . . 35 25
300 6 r. "Butea frondosa" 70 30
301 10 r. "Lagerstroemia floribunda" (vert) 90 50

83 Arms of the Republic 84 Monument and Flag

1971. 1st Anniv of Republic.
302 **83** 3 r. bistre and green 15 10
303 **84** 3 r. multicoloured 10 10
304 4 r. multicoloured 20 10
305 **83** 8 r. bistre and orange . . . 25 15
306 10 r. bistre and brown . . 50 20
307 **84** 10 r. multicoloured 50 25

85 U.N.I.C.E.F. Emblem 86 Book Year Emblem

1971. 25th Anniv of U.N.I.C.E.F.
309 **85** 3 r. purple 20 10
310 5 r. blue 25 15
311 9 r. red and violet 45 30

1972. Int Book Year.
312 **86** 3 r. green, purple & blue . 15 10
313 8 r. blue, green and purple 25 15
314 9 r. bistre and green . . . 45 20

87 Lion of St. Mark's

1972. U.N.E.S.C.O. "Save Venice" Campaign.
316 87 3 r. brown, buff and purple 20 10
317 – 5 r. brown, buff and green 35 20
318 – 10 r. brown, blue & green 65 20
DESIGNS—HORIZ. 5 r. St. Mark's Basilica. VERT. 10 r. Bridge of Sighs.

88 U.N. Emblem

89 Dancing Apsaras (relief), Angkor

1972. 25th Anniv of Economic Commission for Asia and the Far East (C.E.A.E.O.)
320 88 3 r. red 15 10
321 6 r. blue 20 15
322 9 r. red 35 20

1972.
324 89 1 r. brown 10 10
325 3 r. violet 15 10
326 7 r. red 25 15
327 8 r. brown 30 15
328 9 r. green 40 20
329 10 r. blue 55 20
330 12 r. purple 70 25
331 14 r. blue 85 40

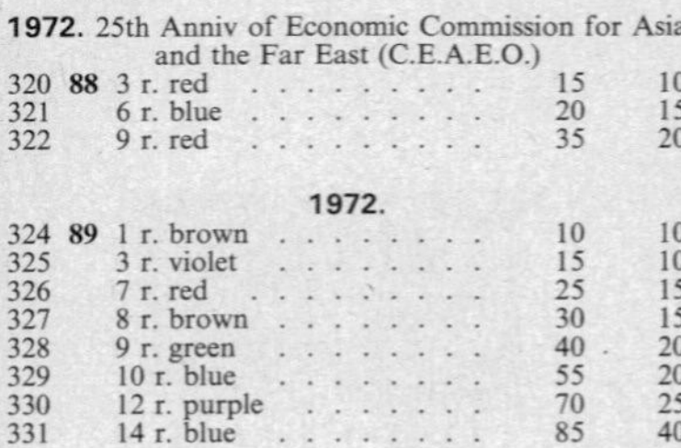
90 "UIT" on TV Screen

91 Conference Emblem

1972. World Telecommunications Day.
332 90 3 r. black, green and yellow 15 10
333 9 r. black, blue and red 35 15
334 14 r. black, blue and brown 55 25

1972. U.N. Environmental Conservation Conference, Stockholm.
335 91 3 r. green, brown and violet 15 10
336 12 r. violet and green 40 20
337 15 r. green and violet 55 35

92 Javan Rhinoceros

94 Hoisting Flag

1972. Wild Animals.
339 92 3 r. black, red and violet 25 10
340 – 4 r. violet, brown and purple 35 10
341 – 6 r. brown, green and blue 60 20
342 – 7 r. brown, green and bistre 60 20
343 – 8 r. black, green and blue 85 20
344 – 10 r. black, blue and green 1·25 30
DESIGNS: 4 r. Mainland serow; 6 r. Thamin; 7 r. Banteng; 8 r. Water buffalo; 10 r. Gaur.

1972. Olympic Games, Munich. Nos. 164 of Cambodia and 302, 306 and 336/7 of Khmer Republic optd **XXe JEUX OLYMPIQUES MUNICH 1972**, Olympic rings and emblem.
345 83 3 r. brown and green 25 20
346 10 r. bistre and brown 60 50
347 – 12 r. green and brown 1·50 50
348 91 12 r. violet and green 70 50
349 15 r. green and violet 75 50

1972. 2nd Anniv of Republic.
350 94 3 r. multicoloured 10 10
351 5 r. multicoloured 15 10
352 9 r. multicoloured 35 20

1972. Red Cross Aid for War Victims. No. 164 of Cambodia and 302, 306 and 336/7 of Khmer Republic surch **SECOURS AUX VICTIMES DE GUERRE**, red cross and value.
353 83 3 r. + 2 r. brown & green 20 20
354 10 r. + 6 r. bistre & brown 45 45
355 – 12 r. + 7 r. green & brown 1·75 55
356 91 12 r. + 7 r. violet & green 55 55
357 15 r. + 8 r. green & violet 1·00 1·00

96 Garuda

97 Crest and Temple

1973. Air.
358 96 3 r. red 10 15
359 30 r. blue 1·40 70
360 50 r. lilac 2·50 1·40
361 100 r. green 4·00 2·25

1973. New Constitution.
362 97 3 r. multicoloured 10 10
363 12 r. multicoloured 15 15
364 14 r. multicoloured 35 20

98 Apsara

99 Interpol Emblem

1972. Angkor Sculptures.
366 98 3 r. black 10 10
367 – 8 r. blue 15 10
368 – 10 r. brown 35 20
DESIGNS: 8 r. Devata (12th century). 10 f. Devata (10th century).

1973. 50th Anniv of International Criminal Police Organization (Interpol).
370 99 3 r. green and turquoise 10 10
371 7 r. green and brown 20 15
372 10 r. green and brown 30 15

100 Marshal Lon Nol

1973. Honouring Marshal Lon Nol, 1st President of Republic.
374 100 3 r. black, brown & green 10 10
375 8 r. brown, black and green 20 15
376 14 r. brown and black 20 15

102 Copernicus and Space Rocket

1974. 500th Birth Anniv of Nicolas Copernicus (astronomer). Multicoloured.
382 1 r. Type 102 (postage) 10 10
383 5 r. Copernicus and "Mariner II" 10 10
384 10 r. Copernicus and "Apollo" 25 15
385 25 r. Copernicus and "Telstar" 70 35
386 50 r. Copernicus and spacewalker 1·25 70
387 100 r. Copernicus and spaceship landing on Moon 3·00 1·50
388 150 r. Copernicus, and Moon-landing craft leaving "Apollo" 4·25 2·75
389 200 r. Copernicus and "Skylab III" (air) 5·25 2·75
390 250 r. Copernicus and Concorde 7·50 3·75

1974. 4th Anniv of Republic. Various stamps optd **4E ANNIVERSAIRE DE LA REPUBLIQUE.**
391 78 10 r. multicoloured 70 50
392 77 50 r. on 3 r. multicoloured 1·75 1·40
393 94 100 r. on 5 r. multicoloured 3·75 3·25
No. 392 is additionally optd **REPUBLIQUE KHMERE** in French and Cambodian.

104 Xylophone

1975. Unissued stamps of Cambodia showing musical instruments, surch **REPUBLIQUE KHMERE** in French and Cambodian and new value. Multicoloured.
394 5 r. on 8 r. Type **104**
395 20 r. on 1 r. So (two string violin)
396 160 r. on 7 r. Khoung vong (bronze gongs)
397 180 r. on 14 r. Two drums
398 235 r. on 12 r. Barrel-shaped drum
399 500 r. on 9 r. Xylophone (different)
400 1000 r. on 10 r. Boat-shaped xylophone
401 2000 r. on 3 r. Twenty-stringed guitar on legs
Set of 8 £130

POSTAGE DUE STAMPS

D 101 Frieze, Angkor Vat

1974.
D378 D 101 2 r. brown 15 15
D379 6 r. green 25 25
D380 8 r. mauve 30 30
D381 10 r. blue 35 35

APPENDIX

The following stamps have either been issued in excess of postal needs or have not been available to the public in reasonable quantities at face value. Such stamps may later be given full listing if there is evidence of regular postal use.

1972.

Moon Landing of "Apollo 16". Embossed on gold foil. Air 900 r. x 2.

Visit of Pres. Nixon to China. Embossed on gold foil. Air 900 r. x 2.

Olympic Games, Munich. Embossed on gold foil. Air 900 r. x 2.

1973.

Gold Medal Winners, Munich Olympics. Embossed on gold foil. Air 900 r. x 2.

World Cup Football Championships, West Germany (1974). Embossed on gold foil. Air 900 r. x 4.

1974.

Pres. Kennedy and "Apollo 11". Embossed on gold foil. Air 1100 r. x 2.

500th Birth Anniv of Nicolas Copernicus (astronomer). Embossed on gold foil. Air 1200 r.

Centenary of U.P.U. (1st issue). Postage 10, 60 r.; Air 700 r., 1200 r. Embossed on gold foil.

1975.

Olympic Games, Montreal (1976). Postage 5, 10, 15, 25 r.; Air 50, 100, 150, 200, 250 r., 1200 r. embossed on gold foil.

World Cup Football Championships, West Germany (1974). Postage 1, 5, 10, 25 r.; Air 50, 100, 150, 200, 250 r., 1200 r. embossed on gold foil.

Centenary of U.P.U. (2nd issue). Postage 15, 20, 70, 160, 180, 235 r.; Air 500, 1000, 2000 r., 2000 r. embossed on gold foil.

KHOR FAKKAN

From 1965 various issues were produced for this dependency, some being overprinted on, or in the same designs as, issues for Sharjah.

APPENDIX

The following stamps have either been issued in excess of postal needs or have not been available to the public in reasonable quantities at face value. Such stamps may later be given full listing if there is evidence of regular postal use.

1965.

Views. Nos. 75/80 of Sharjah optd. Air 10, 20, 30, 40, 75, 100 n.p.

Boy and Girl Scouts. Nos. 74 and 89 of Sharjah optd. 2, 2 r.

Birds. Nos. 101/6 of Sharjah optd. Air 30, 40, 75, 150 n.p., 2, 3 r.

Olympic Games, Tokyo 1964. Nos. 95/7 of Sharjah optd. 40, 50 n.p. 2 r.

New York World's Fair. Nos. 81/3 of Sharjah optd. Air 20, 40 n.p. 1 r.

Pres. Kennedy Commem. Nos. 98/100 of Sharjah optd. Air 40, 60, 100 n.p.

Centenary of I.T.U. Postage 1, 2, 3, 4, 5, 50 n.p., 1 r., 120 n.p.

Pan-Arab Games, Cairo. 50 p. × 5.

1966.

International Co-operation Year. 50 n.p. × 8.

Churchill Commemoration. 2, 3, 4, 5 r.

Roses. 20, 35, 60, 80 n.p. 1 r., 125 n.p.

Fish. 1, 2, 3, 4, 5, 15, 20, 30, 40, 50, 75 n.p., 1, 2, 3, 4, 5, 10 r.

Int. Stamp Exhibition, Washington D.C. (SIPEX). 80, 120 n.p., 2 r.

New Currency Surcharges in Rials and Piastres.

(a) 1965 I.T.U. Cent., issue. 10 p. on 50 n.p., 16 p. on 120 n.p., 1 r. on 1 r.

(b) Churchill issue. 1 r. on 2 r., 2 r. on 3 r., 3 r. on 4 r., 4 r. on 5 r.

(c) Roses issue. 1 p. on 20 n.p., 2 p. on 35 n.p., 4 p. on 60 n.p., 6 p. on 80 n.p., 10 p. on 125 n.p., 12 p. on 1 r.

New Currency Surcharges in Dirhams and Riyals.

(a) 1965 Pan-Arab Games issue. 20 d. on 50 p. × 5.

(b) Fish issue. 1 d. on 1 n.p., 2 d. on 2 n.p., 3 d. on 3 n.p., 4 d. on 4 n.p., 5 d. on 5 n.p., 15 d. on 15 n.p., 20 d. on 20 n.p., 30 d. on 30 n.p., 40 d. on 40 n.p., 50 d. on 50 n.p., 75 d. on 75 n.p., 1 r. on 1 r., 2 r. on 2 r., 3 r. on 3 r., 4 r. on 4 r., 5 r. on 5 r., 10 r. on 10 r.

3rd Death Anniv of Pres. J. Kennedy. Optd on 1966 Int. Stamp Exhibition issue. 80 d. on 80 n.p., 120 d. on 120 n.p., 2 r. on 2 r.

World Football Cup Championship, England. ½ r. × 7.

1967.

4th Death Anniv of Pres. J. Kennedy. Optd on 1966 Int. Stamp Exhibition issue. 80 d. on 80 n.p., 120 d. on 120 n.p., 2 r. on 2 r.

1968.

Famous Paintings. Optd on Sharjah. Postage 1, 2, 3, 4, 5, 30, 40, 60, 75 d.; Air 1, 2, 3, 4, 5 r.

Winter Olympic Games, Grenoble. Optd on Sharjah. Postage 1, 2, 3, 4, 5 d.; Air 1, 2, 3 r.

Previous Olympic Games. Optd on Sharjah. Air 25, 50, 75 d., 1 r. 50, 3, 4 r.

Olympic Games, Mexico. Optd on Sharjah. 10, 20, 30 d., 2, 2 r. 40, 5 r.

1969.

12th World Jamboree. Optd on 1968 issue of Sharjah. Postage 1, 2, 3, 4, 5, 10 d.; Air 30, 50, 60 d., 1 r. 50.

Martyrs of Liberty. Optd on 1968 issue of Sharjah. Air 35 d. × 4, 60 d. × 4, 1 r. × 4.

Sportsmen and women. Optd on 1968 issue of Sharjah. Postage 20, 30, 40, 60 d., 1 r. 50, 2 r. 50; Air 35, 50 d., 1, 2, 3 r. 25, 4, 4 r.

A number of issues on gold or silver foil also exist, but it is understood that these were mainly for presentation purposes, although valid for postage.

In common with the other states of the United Arab Emirates the Khor Fakkan stamp contract was terminated on 1 August 1972, and any further new issues released after that date were unauthorised.

KIAUTSCHOU (KIAOCHOW) Pt. 7

A port in Shantung, China, leased by Germany from China in 1898. It was occupied by Japan in 1914, but reverted to China in 1922.

1900. 100 pfennige = 1 mark
1905. 100 cents = 1 dollar (Chinese)

1900. No. 9 of German Post Offices in China surch **5 Pfg.**
3 9 5 pf. on 10 pf. red 48·00 50·00

1901. "Yacht" key-types inscr "KIAUTSCHOU".
11 N 3 pf. brown 2·00 2·00
12 5 pf. green 2·40 80
13 10 pf. red 4·25 1·60
14 20 pf. blue 10·00 8·75
15 25 pf. black & red on yell 22·00 32·00
16 30 pf. black & orge on buff 22·00 27·00
17 40 pf. black and red 24·00 29·00
18 50 pf. black & pur on buff 25·00 29·00
19 80 pf. black & red on pink 48·00 70·00
20 O 1 m. red 85·00 £140
21 2 m. blue £130 £150
22 3 m. black £110 £275
23 5 m. red and black £400 £800

1905. "Yacht" key-types inscr "KIAUTSCHOU".
34 N 1 c. brown 85 1·25
35 2 c. green 1·00 1·00
36 4 c. red 1·25 75
37 10 c. blue 1·00 1·10
38 20 c. black and red 1·50 18·00
39 40 c. black and red on pink 2·50 55·00
40 O ½ d. red 6·00 75·00
41 1 d. blue 7·50 65·00
42 1½ d. black 8·50 £150
43 2½ d. red and black 40·00 £450

KIONGA — Pt. 9

Part of German E. Africa, occupied by the Portuguese during the 1914/18 war, and now incorporated in Mozambique.

1916. "King Carlos" key-type of Lourenco Marques optd **REPUBLICA** and surch **KIONGA** and new value.

1	S	½ c. on 100 r. blue on blue . .	3·50	3·25
2		1 c. on 100 r. blue on blue	3·50	3·25
3		2½c. on 100 r. blue on blue	3·50	3·25
4		5 c. on 100 r. blue on blue	3·50	3·25

KOREA — Pt. 18

A peninsula to the S. of Manchuria in E. Asia. Formerly an empire under Chinese suzerainty, it was annexed by Japan in 1910 and used Japanese stamps. After the defeat of Japan in 1945, Russian and United States Military administrations were set up in Korea to the north and south of the 38th Parallel respectively; in 1948 South Korea and North Korea became independent republics.

1884. 100 mon = 1 tempo
1895. 5 poon = 1 cheun
1900. 10 re (or rin) = 1 cheun.
100 cheun = 1 weun

EMPIRE OF KOREA

1

3 Korean Flag

(4)

1894.

1	**1**	5 m. red	32·00	£1600
2		10 m. blue	7·50	£1500

1895.

7	**3**	5 p. green	10·00	9·00
8		10 p. blue	16·00	7·00
9		25 p. lake	10·00	12·00
10a		50 p. violet	10·00	6·50

1897. Optd with T **4**.

12	**3**	5 p. green	12·00	10·00
13		10 p. blue	20·00	18·00
14		25 p. lake	24·00	22·00
15		50 p. violet	30·00	20·00

1899. Surch in Korean characters.

17	**3**	1 (p.) on 5 p. green (No. 7)	£800	£450
20		1 (p.) on 5 p. green (No. 12)	£250	£200
18		1 (p.) on 25 p. red (No. 9) . .	£110	75·00
21		1 (p.) on 25 p. red (No. 14)	50·00	32·00

6

7 National Emblems

8

1900. T **6**, 7 (2 ch.), 8 (2 ch.) and similar designs.

22a	2 r. grey	75	1·50
23	1 ch. green	5·50	4·00
24	2 ch. blue (T **7**)	35·00	38·00
25	2 ch. blue (T **8**)	8·00	7·00
26	3 ch. orange	7·50	7·50
27	4 ch. red	10·00	9·00
28	5 ch. pink	10·00	10·00
29	6 ch. blue	12·00	11·00
30	10 ch. purple	18·00	16·00
31a	15 ch. purple	30·00	25·00
32	20 ch. red	50·00	38·00
33	50 ch. green and pink	£180	£120
34	1 wn. multicoloured	£225	£180
35	2 wn. green and purple	£325	£225

9 Imperial Crown

17 Falcon, Sceptre and Orb

1902. 40th Anniv of Emperor's Accession as King.

36	**9**	3 ch. orange	32·00	25·00

INDEX

Countries can be quickly located by referring to the index at the end of this volume.

(10) (11) (12) (16)

Types **10** to **12** are in two parts, the horizontal strokes (one, two or three) representing the value figures and the bottom part being the character for "cheun".

Some variation can be found in these woodblock overprints.

1902.

(a) Surch as Types **10** to **12**.

37	**3**	1 ch. on 25 p. red (No. 9) .	8·50	6·50
38		1 ch. on 25 p. red (No. 14) .	45·00	45·00
39		2 ch. on 25 p. red (No. 9) .	8·50	7·00
40		1 ch. on 25 p. red (No. 14) .	42·00	40·00
42		2 ch. on 50 p. violet (No 10a)	—	£350
43		3 ch. on 25 p. red (No. 9) .	42·00	90·00
44		3 ch. on 25 p. red (No. 14) .		
46		3 ch. on 50 p. violet (No. 10a)	8·00	10·00
47		3 ch. on 50 p. violet (No. 16)	12·00	12·00

(b) Surch as T **16** (Japanese "sen" character) and strokes.

49	**3**	3 ch. on 50 p. violet	£650	£500

1903.

50	**17**	2 r. grey	50	75
51		1 ch. purple	4·50	4·50
52		2 ch. green	4·50	4·50
53		3 ch. orange	5·50	5·50
54		4 ch. red	6·50	6·00
55		5 ch. brown	9·00	8·00
56		6 ch. lilac	9·00	8·50
57		10 ch. blue	12·00	10·00
58		15 ch. red on yellow	22·00	22·00
59		20 ch. purple on yellow	30·00	32·00
60		50 ch. red on green	90·00	95·00
61		1 wn. lilac on lilac	£150	£160
62		2 wn. purple on orange	£250	£250

SOUTH KOREA

1946. 100 cheun = 1 weun
1953. 100 weun = 1 hwan
1962. 100 chon = 1 won

A. UNITED STATES MILITARY GOVERNMENT

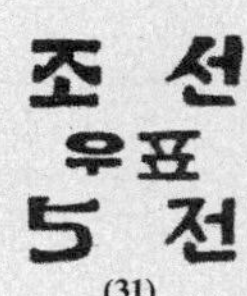

(31)

33 National Emblem

1946. Stamps of Japan surch as T **31**.

69	5 ch. on 5 s. purple (No. 396)	9·25	12·50
70	5 ch. on 14 s. red and brown (No. 324)	1·50	2·10
71	10 ch. on 40 s. purple (No. 406)	1·50	2·10
72	20 ch. on 6 s. blue (No. 397) .	1·50	2·10
73	30 ch. on 27 s. red (No. 4040)	1·50	1·60
74	5 wn. on 17 s. violet (No. 402)	9·25	10·00

1946. Liberation from Japanese Rule.

75	–	3 ch. yellow	85	65
76	–	5 ch. green	85	55
77	–	10 ch. red	85	45
78	–	20 ch. blue	85	45
79	**33**	50 ch. purple	2·10	50
80		1 wn. brown	2·10	70

DESIGN: 3 ch. to 20 ch. Family and flag.

34 Dove of Peace and Map of Korea

1946. 1st Anniv of Liberation.

81	**34**	50 ch. violet	5·75	3·00

35 U.S. and Korean Flags

36 Kyongju Observatory

39 Golden Crown of Silla

40 Admiral Li Sun Sin

1946. Resumption of Postal Service between Korea and U.S.A.

82	**35**	10 wn. red	10·00	5·00

1946.

83	**36**	50 ch. blue	1·60	1·60
84	–	1 wn. brown	2·10	1·60
85	–	2 wn. blue	2·10	2·10
86	**39**	5 wn. mauve	17·00	12·50
87	**40**	10 wn. green	17·00	12·50

DESIGNS—As Type **36**: 1 wn. Hibiscus. 2 wn. Map of Korea.

41 Korean Alphabet

42 Li Jun, patriot

44 16th-century "Turtle" Ship

45 Letters Surrounding Globe

1946. 500th Anniv of Creation of Korean Alphabet.

88	**41**	50 ch. blue	5·00	2·50

1947.

89	**42**	5 w. green	11·00	8·25
90	–	10 w. blue	10·00	8·25
91	–	20 w. red	4·25	3·25
92	**44**	50 w. brown	65·00	38·00

DESIGNS: 10 w. Admiral Li Sun Sin. 20 w. Independence Arch, Seoul.

1947. Resumption of Int Postal Service.

93	**45**	10 w. blue	15·00	7·50

46 Douglas DC-4 and Globe

1947. Air. Inauguration of Air Mail Service.

94	**46**	50 w. red	6·50	3·25
126		150 w. blue	1·25	90
127		150 w. green	7·50	

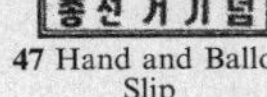

47 Hand and Ballot Slip

48 Casting Votes

1948. South Korea Election.

95	**47**	2 w. orange	12·50	5·75
96		5 w. mauve	22·00	10·00
97		10 w. violet	35·00	17·00
98	**48**	20 w. red	60·00	25·00
99		50 w. blue	45·00	21·00

49 Korean Flag and Laurel Wreath

1948. Olympic Games.

100	**49**	5 w. green	£140	60·00
101	–	10 w. violet	60·00	21·00

DESIGN—VERT: 10 w. Runner with torch.

50 Capitol and Ears of Rice

51 Korean Family

1948. Meeting of First National Assembly.

102	**50**	4 w. brown	21·00	11·00

1948. Promulgation of Constitution.

103	**51**	4 w. green	65·00	29·00
104	–	10 w. brown	42·00	18·00

DESIGN—HORIZ: 10 w. Flag of Korea.

52 Dr. Syngman Rhee (First President)

53 Hibiscus

1948. Election of First President.

105	**52**	5 w. blue	£180	85·00

B. REPUBLIC OF KOREA

1948. Proclamation of Republic.

106	–	4 w. blue	38·00	21·00
107	**53**	5 w. mauve	55·00	25·00

DESIGN: 4 w. Dove and olive branch.

54 Li Jun

55 Kyongju Observatory

1948.

108	**54**	4 w. red	65	50
109	**55**	14 w. blue	65	50

56 Doves and U.N. Emblem

57 Citizen and Date

1949. Arrival of U.N. Commission.

110	**56**	10 w. blue	38·00	18·00

1949. National Census.

111	**57**	15 w. violet	42·00	21·00

58 Children and Plant

1949. 20th Anniv of Children's Day.

112	**58**	15 w. violet	22·00	11·00

59 Hibiscus

60 Map of Korea and Magpies

61 Dove and Globe

62 Admiral Li Sun Sin

1949.

113	–	1 w. red	5·00	2·50
114	–	2 w. grey	2·50	1·60
115	–	5 w. green	16·00	6·75
116	–	10 w. green	2·00	50
117	**59**	15 w. red	45	50
118	–	20 w. brown	45	50
119	–	30 w. green	50	50
120	–	50 w. blue	45	20
121	**60**	65 w. blue	1·50	50

122 – 100 w. olive 50 50
123 61 200 w. green 60 35
124 – 400 w. brown 60 40
125 62 500 w. blue 60 45
DESIGNS—VERT: As Type **59**: 1 w. Postman; 2 w. Worker and factory; 5 w. Harvesting rice; 10 w. Manchurian cranes; 20 w. Diamond Mountains; 30 w. Ginseng plant; 50 w. South Gate, Seoul; 100 w. Tabo Pogoda, Kyongju. HORIZ: As Type **61**: 400 w. Diamond Mountains.

63 Symbol and Phoenix   **64** Steam Train

1949. 1st Anniv of Independence.
128 **63** 15 w. blue . . . . 26·00 12·50

1949. 50th Anniv of Korean Railways.
129 **64** 15 w. blue . . . . 65·00 29·00

65 Korean Flag   **66** Post-horse Warrant

1949. 75th Anniv of U.P.U.
130 **65** 15 w. multicoloured . . . . 22·00 13·50

1950. 50th Anniv of Membership of U.P.U.
131 **66** 15 w. green . . . . 27·00 12·50
132 65 w. brown . . . . 17·00 7·50

67 Douglas DC-2 and Globe   **68** Demonstrators   **69** Capitol, Seoul

1950. Air. Opening of Internal Air Mail Service.
133 **67** 60 w. blue . . . . 10·00 3·25

1950. 31st Anniv of Abortive Proclamation of Independence.
134 **68** 15 w. olive . . . . 29·00 11·00
135 65 w. violet . . . . 12·50 5·75

1950. 2nd South Korean Election.
136 **69** 30 w. multicoloured . . . . 11·50 5·75

70 Dr. Syngman Rhee   **71** Flag and Mountains

1950. Unification of Korea.
137 **70** 100 w. blue . . . . 3·75 1·90
138 **71** 100 w. green . . . . 4·50 2·10
139 – 200 w. green . . . . 3·00 1·40
DESIGN—HORIZ: 200 w. Map of Korea and flags of U.N. and Korea (35×24 mm).

73 Manchurian Crane   **76** Post-horse Warrant   **77** Fairy (8th Cent painting)

1951. Perf. or roul.
140 **73** 5 w. brown . . . . 2·25 50
181 – 20 w. violet 70 65
187 – 50 w. green . . . . 2·50 1·60
183 **76** 100 w. blue . . . . 2·10 1·25
193 **77** 1,000 w. green . . . . . . 2·50 85
DESIGNS—HORIZ: 20 w. Astrological Tiger (ancient painting); 50 w. Dove and Korean flag.

1951. Surch with new value.
145 **54** 100 w. on 4 w. red . . . . 4·25 2·50
146 **59** 200 w. on 15 w. red . . . . 11·00 5·75
147 **54** 300 w. on 4 w. red . . . . 4·25 1·60
156 – 300 w. on 10 w. (116) . . . 10·00 1·60
149 **55** 300 w. on 14 w. blue . . . 4·25 1·60
150 **59** 300 w. on 15 w. red . . . . 4·25 1·60
151 – 300 w. on 20 w. (118) . . . 4·25 1·60
152 – 300 w. on 30 w. (119) . . . 4·25 1·60
153 – 300 w. on 50 w. (120) . . . 4·25 1·60
154 **60** 300 w. on 65 w. blue . . . 4·50 1·60
155 – 300 w. on 100 w. (122) . . 4·25 1·60

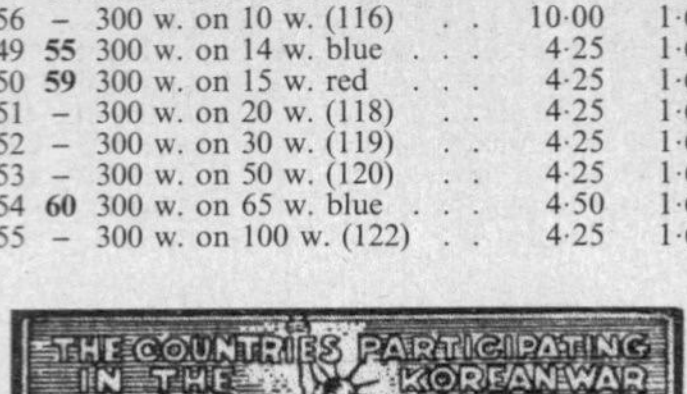

80 Statue of Liberty and Flags

1951. Participation in Korean War. Flags in national colours. A. As Type **80** in green. B. As Type **80** but showing U.N. Emblem and doves in blue.

		A	B
158	500 w. Australia	8·25	8·25
159	500 w. Belgium	8·25	8·25
160	500 w. Britain	8·25	8·25
161	500 w. Canada	8·25	8·25
162	500 w. Colombia	8·25	8·25
163	500 w. Denmark	30·00	30·00
164	500 w. Ethiopia	8·25	8·25
165	500 w. France	8·25	8·25
166	500 w. Greece	8·25	8·25
167	500 w. India	27·00	27·00
168	500 w. Italy (with crown)	27·00	27·00
169	500 w. Italy (without crown)	12·50	12·50
170	500 w. Luxembourg	27·00	27·00
171	500 w. Netherlands	10·00	10·00
172	500 w. New Zealand	10·00	10·00
173	500 w. Norway	27·00	27·00
174	500 w. Philippines	8·25	8·25
175	500 w. Sweden	8·25	8·25
176	500 w. Thailand	8·25	8·25
177	500 w. Turkey	8·25	8·25
178	500 w. Union of S. Africa	8·25	8·25
179	500 w. U.S.A.	8·25	8·25

The prices are the same for unused or used.

1951. Air. No. 126 surch **500 WON**.
180 **46** 500 w. on 150 w. blue . . 1·00 50

82 Buddha of Sokkuram   **83** Pulguksa Temple, Kyongju

84 Monument to King Muryol, Kyongju   **85** Shrine of Admiral Li Sun Sin, Tongyong

1952. Inscr "KOREA".
184 **82** 200 w. red . . . . 1·60 1·25
185 **83** 300 w. green 60 65
191 **84** 500 w. red . . . . 3·00 85
192 500 w. blue . . . . 11·50 9·00
194 **85** 2,000 w. blue . . . . . . 2·50 85

86 President Syngman Rhee

1952. President's Election to 2nd Term of Office.
195 **86** 1,000 w. green . . . . . . 5·00 2·50

87 Douglas DC-3 over Freighter

1952. Air.
196 **87** 1,200 w. brown . . . . . 1·10 40
197 1,800 w. blue . . . . . 1·10 40
198 4,200 w. violet . . . . . 1·60 60
For stamps in new currency, see Nos. 210/12.

MINIMUM PRICE

The minimum price quoted is 10p which represents a handling charge rather than a basis for valuing common stamps. For further notes about prices, see introductory pages.

88 Tree-planting   **89** Monument to King Muryol. Kyongju

91 Pagoda Park, Seoul   **92** Sika Deer   **93** Sika Deer

1953. New currency. With character "hwan" after figure of value.
244 **88** 1 h. blue 85 10
200 **84** 2 h. blue 85 35
201 5 h. green 85 10
203 **88** 10 h. green . . . . 3·25 50
204 – 10 h. brown . . . . 3·25 50
205 **85** 20 h. brown . . . . 4·25 65
206 **91** 30 h. blue . . . . 2·10 60
242 **92** 100 h. brown . . . . 17·00 1·60
243 **91** 200 h. violet . . . . 6·75 85
208 **93** 500 h. orange . . . . 50·00 4·25
209 1000 h. brown . . . . . . £140 5·75
DESIGN: No. 204, "Metopta rectifasciata" (moth) and Korean flag.
For designs without character after figure of value, see Nos. 273 etc.

1953. Air. New Currency.
210 **87** 12 h. blue . . . . 1·25 40
211 18 h. violet . . . . 1·25 40
212 42 h. green . . . . 2·40 85

94 Field Hospital

1953. Red Cross Fund. Crosses in red.
213 **94** 10 h. + 5 h. green . . . . 8·25 3·75
214 – 10 h. + 5 h. blue . . . . 8·25 3·75
DESIGN—VERT: No. 214, Nurses supporting wounded soldier.

95 Y.M.C.A. Badge and Map   **96** Douglas DC-6 over East Gate, Seoul

1953. 50th Anniv of Korean Y.M.C.A.
215 **95** 10 h. red and black . . . . 5·00 2·50

1954. Air.
216 **96** 25 h. brown . . . . 3·00 1·25
217 35 h. bright purple . . . . 3·25 1·60
218 38 h. green . . . . 3·75 1·60
219 58 h. blue . . . . 4·00 2·00
296 70 h. turquoise . . . . . . 6·50 3·25
220 71 h. deep blue . . . . . . 5·00 2·50
297 110 h. brown . . . . 5·75 3·25
298 205 h. mauve . . . . 6·50 3·25

98 Tokto Island   **99** Erosion Control

1954.
221 – 2 h. purple . . . . 1·40 40
222 – 5 h. blue . . . . 1·40 40
223 **98** 10 h. green . . . . 1·90 40
DESIGN: 2 h., 5 h. Rocks off Tokto Is.

1954. 4th World Forestry Congress, Dehru Dun.
224 **99** 10 h. green . . . . 1·75 85
225 19 h. green . . . . 1·75 85

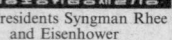

100 Presidents Syngman Rhee and Eisenhower   **101** "Rebirth of Industry"

1954. Korea–United States Mutual Defence Treaty.
226 **100** 10 h. blue . . . . 3·00 1·40
227 19 h. brown . . . . 2·10 1·10
228 71 h. green . . . . 4·50 2·10

1955. Reconstruction.
229 **101** 10 h. brown . . . . 5·00 85
230 15 h. violet . . . . 5·00 85
231 20 h. blue . . . . 5·00 85
232 50 h. mauve . . . . 8·25 85
269 50 h. red . . . . 7·50 85

102 Rotary Emblem   **103** Pres. Syngman Rhee

1955. 50th Anniv of Rotary International.
236 **102** 20 h. violet . . . . 4·75 2·25
237 25 h. green . . . . 2·10 1·10
238 71 h. purple . . . . 2·50 1·25

1955. 80th Birthday of President.
239 **103** 20 h. blue . . . . 9·25 4·25

104 Independence Arch, Seoul

1955. 10th Anniv of Liberation.
240 **104** 40 h. green . . . . 3·00 1·50
241 100 h. brown . . . . 3·50 1·60

105 Hibiscus   **106** King Sejong   **107** Kyongju Observatory

1955. Without character after figure of value.
273 **88** 2 h. blue 25 10
309 **89** 4 h. blue 85 10
310 5 h. green 85 10
247 **105** 10 h. mauve . . . . 1·25 50
311 – 10 h. green 85 10
248 **106** 20 h. purple . . . . 3·00 50
312 **105** 20 h. mauve 85 10
280 – 30 h. violet . . . . 1·60 15
281 **106** 40 h. purple . . . . 1·60 15
282 **107** 50 h. violet . . . . 3·25 15
315 – 55 h. purple . . . . 3·00 40
250 **92** 100 h. purple . . . . 17·00 1·60
316 **107** 100 h. violet . . . . 4·25 40
285 **92** 200 h. purple . . . . 4·25 50
318 **91** 400 h. violet . . . . 55·00 2·50
251 **93** 500 h. brown . . . . 50·00 4·25
320 1000 h. brown . . . . . . 85·00 8·25
DESIGNS—HORIZ: No. 311, South Gate, Seoul; 280, Tiger. VERT: No. 315, Haegumgang.

108 Runners and Torch   **109** U.N. Emblem

1955. 36th National Athletic Meeting.
252 **108** 20 h. purple . . . . 3·75 1·90
253 55 h. green . . . . 3·75 1·90

1955. 10th Anniv of U.N.
254 **109** 20 h. green . . . . 3·00 1·50
255 55 h. blue . . . . 2·75 1·40

110 Admiral Li Sun Sin and 16th-century "Turtle" Ship

1955. 10th Anniv of Korean Navy.
256 **110** 20 h. blue . . . . 4·25 2·10

111 Admiration Pagoda — 112 Pres. Syngman Rhee

1956. 81st Birthday of President.
257 **111** 20 h. green . . . . 3·50 1·60

1956. President's Election to Third Term of Office.
261 **112** 20 h. brown . . . . 45·00 21·00
262 55 h. blue . . . . 18·00 9·25

113 Torch and Olympic Rings — 114 Central P.O., Seoul

1956. Olympic Games.
263 **113** 20 h. brown . . . . 4·25 2·10
264 55 h. green . . . . 4·25 2·10

1956. Stamp Day. Inscr "4289.12.4".
265 **114** 20 h. turquoise . . . . . 5·00 2·50
266 – 50 h. red . . . . 9·25 4·25
267 – 55 h. green . . . . 3·25 1·60
DESIGNS—VERT: 50 h. Stamp of 1884. HORIZ: 55 h. Man leading post-pony.

119 I.T.U. Emblem and Radio Mast — 120 Korean Scout and Badge

1957. 5th Anniversary of Korea's Admission to International Telecommunications Union.
290 **119** 40 h. blue . . . . 2·50 1·25
291 55 h. green . . . . 2·50 1·25

1957. 50th Anniversary of Boy Scout Movement.
293 **120** 40 h. purple . . . . 2·40 1·10
294 55 h. purple . . . . 2·40 1·10

1957. Flood Relief Fund. As No. 281 but Korean inscr and premium added and colour changed.
299 40 h. + 10 h. green . . . . . 3·25 1·40

123 Mercury, Flags and Freighters — 124 Star of Bethlehem and Pine Cone

1957. Korean-American Friendship Treaty.
301 **123** 40 h. orange . . . . . . 1·60 85
302 205 h. green . . . . 3·50 1·60

1957. Christmas and New Year Issue.
304 **124** 15 h. brown, green & orange 3·75 1·60
305 – 25 h. green, red & yellow 3·25 1·60
306 – 30 h. blue, green & yellow 5·75 2·50
DESIGNS: 25 h. Christmas tree and tassels; 30 h. Christmas tree and dog by window.

125 Winged Letter — 126 Korean Children regarding future

1958. Postal Week.
321 **125** 40 h. blue and red . . . . 1·50 75

1958. 10th Anniv of Republic of Korea.
323 **126** 20 h. grey . . . . 1·25 60
324 – 40 h. red . . . . 1·75 85
DESIGN—HORIZ: 40 h. Hibiscus flowers forming figure "10".

127 U.N.E.S.C.O. Headquarters, Paris — 128 Children flying Kites

1958. Inaug of U.N.E.S.C.O. Building, Paris.
326 **127** 40 h. orange and green . 1·10 60

1958. Christmas and New Year.
330 **128** 15 h. green . . . . 2·50 85
331 – 25 h. red, yellow and blue 2·50 85
332 – 30 h. red, blue and yellow 3·25 1·25
DESIGNS—VERT: 25 h. Christmas tree, tassels and wicker basket (cooking sieve); 30 h. Children in traditional festive costume.

129 Rejoicing Crowds in Pagoda Park, Flag and Torch

1959. 40th Anniv of Abortive Proclamation of Independence.
334 **129** 40 h. purple and brown . 1·10 60

130 Marines going Ashore from Landing-craft

1959. 10th Anniv of Korean Marine Corps.
336 **130** 40 h. green . . . . 1·10 60

131

1959. 10th Anniv of Korea's Admission to W.H.O.
339 **131** 40 h. purple and pink . . 1·10 60

132 Diesel Train

1959. 60th Anniv of Korean Railways.
341 **132** 40 h. sepia and brown . . 1·40 75

133 Runners in Relay Race

1959. 40th Korean National Games.
343 **133** 40 h. brown and blue . . 1·40 65

134 Red Cross and Korea

1959. Red Cross. Inscr "1959 4292".
345 **134** 40 h. red and green . . . 1·10 60
346 – 55 h. red and mauve . . 1·10 60
DESIGN: 55 h. Red Cross on Globe.

135 Korean Postal Flags Old and New — 136 Mice in Korean Costume and New Year Emblem

1959. 75th Anniv of Korean Postal Service.
348 **135** 40 h. red and blue . . . . 1·10 60

1959. Christmas and New Year.
350 **136** 15 h. pink, blue and grey 1·40 35
351 – 25 h. red, green and blue 1·40 40
352 – 30 h. red, black & mauve 2·25 60
DESIGNS: 25 h. Carol singers; 30 h. Crane.

137 U.P.U. Monument — 138 Honey Bee and Clover

1960. 60th Anniv of Admission of Korea to U.P.U.
354 **137** 40 h. brown and turquoise 1·00 50

1960. Children's Savings Campaign.
356 **138** 10 h. yellow, sepia & green 1·25 10
357 – 20 h. brown, blue & pink 1·25 10
DESIGN: 20 h. Snail and Korean money-bag.
For these stamps in new currency, see Nos. 452 etc.

139 "Uprooted Tree" — 140 Pres. Eisenhower

1960. World Refugee Year.
358 **139** 40 h. red, blue and green 1·10 60

1960. Visit of President Eisenhower of United States.
360 **140** 40 h. blue, red and green 3·50 1·75

141 Schoolchildren

1960. 75th Anniv of Educational System.
362 **141** 40 h. purple, brown & olive 1·10 60

142 Assembly — 143 "Liberation"

1960. Inauguration of House of Councillors.
364 **142** 40 h. blue . . . . 1·10 60

1960. 15th Anniv of Liberation.
366 **143** 40 h. lake, blue and ochre 1·10 60

144 Weightlifting — 145 Barn Swallow and Insulators

1960. Olympic Games.
368 **144** 20 h. brown, flesh & turq 1·50 85
369 – 40 h. brown, blue & turq 1·50 85
DESIGN: 40 h. South Gate, Seoul.

1960. 75th Anniv of Korean Telegraph Service.
371 **145** 40 h. violet, grey and blue 1·10 60

146 "Rebirth of Republic" — 147 "Torch of Culture"

1960. Establishment of New Government.
373 **146** 40 h. green, blue & orange 1·10 60

1960. Cultural Month.
376 **147** 40 h. yellow, lt blue & bl 1·10 60

148 U.N. Flag — 149 U.N. Emblem and Gravestones

1960. 15th Anniv of U.N.
378 **148** 40 h. blue, green & mauve 1·10 60

1960. Establishment of U.N. Memorial Cemetery.
380 **149** 40 h. brown and orange 1·10 60

150 "National Stocktaking" — 151 Festival Stocking

1960 Census of Population and Resources.
382 **150** 40 h. red, drab and blue 1·00 50

1960. Christmas and New Year Issue.
384 – 15 h. brown, yellow & grey 75 15
385 **151** 25 h. red, green and blue 65 10
386 – 30 h. red, yellow and blue 55 40
DESIGNS: 15 h. Ox's head; 30 h. Girl bowing in New Year's greeting.

152 Wind-sock and Ancient Rain-gauge

1961. World Meteorological Day.
388 **152** 40 h. ultramarine and blue 1·00 50

153 Family, Sun and Globe

1961. World Health Day.
390 **153** 40 h. brown and salmon 1·00 50

154 Students' Demonstration — 155 Workers and Conference Emblem

1961. 1st Anniv of April Revolution (Overthrow of Pres. Syngman Rhee).
392 **154** 40 h. green, red and blue 1·50 75

1961. Int Community Development Conf, Seoul.
394 **155** 40 h. turquoise . . . . . 1·10 60

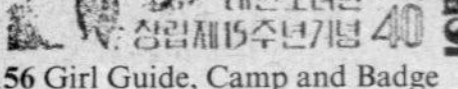
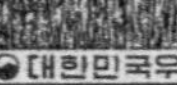

156 Girl Guide, Camp and Badge
157 Soldier's Grave

1961. 15th Anniv of Korean Girl Guide Movement.
396 **156** 40 h. turquoise . . . . . 1·10 60

1961. Memorial Day.
398 **157** 40 h. black and drab . . . 2·75 1·25

158 Soldier with Torch
159 "Three Liberations"

1961. Revolution of 16 May (Seizure of Power by Gen. Pak Chung Hi).
400 **158** 40 h. brown and yellow . 2·75 1·25

1961. Liberation Day.
402 **159** 40 h. multicoloured . . . 2·75 1·25

160 Korean Forces, Flag and Destroyer
161 "Korean Art" (Kyongbok Palace Art Gallery)

1961. Armed Forces Day.
404 **160** 40 h. multicoloured . . . 2·50 1·25

1961. 10th Korean Art Exhibition.
406 **161** 40 h. chocolate & brown 1·10 60

162 Birthday Candle

1961. 15th Anniv of U.N.E.S.C.O.
408 **162** 40 h. blue and green . . . 1·10 60

163 Mobile X-Ray Unit

1961. T.B. Vaccination Week.
410 **163** 40 h. brown, black & lt brn 1·10 60

164 Ginseng
165 King Sejong

166 White-bellied Black Woodpecker
167 Rice Harvester

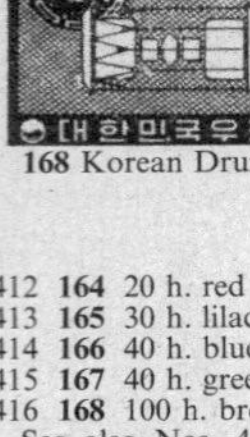

168 Korean Drum
169 Douglas DC-8 over Pagoda

1961.
412 **164** 20 h. red . . . . 1·60 40
413 **165** 30 h. lilac . . . . 1·60 40
414 **166** 40 h. blue and red . . . 3·25 50
415 **167** 40 h. green . . . . 3·00 60
416 **168** 100 h. brown . . . . . . 5·00 65
See also Nos. 467 etc., and for stamps inscribed "REPUBLIC OF KOREA", see Nos. 641, etc. and 785/95.

1961. Air.
417 **169** 50 h. violet and blue . . 12·50 5·75
418 – 100 h. brown and blue . 16·00 8·25
419 – 200 h. brown and blue . 25·00 12·50
420 – 400 h. green and blue . 25·00 12·50
DESIGNS: Plane over: 100 h. West Gate, Suwon; 200 h. Gateway and wall of Toksu Palace, Seoul; 400 h. Pavilion, Kyongbok Palace, Seoul.
See also Nos. 454 etc.

170 I.T.U. Emblem as Satellite

1962. 10th Anniv of Admission into I.T.U.
421 **170** 40 h. red and blue . . . 2·10 1·00

171 Triga Mark II Reactor

1962. 1st Korean Atomic Reactor.
423 **171** 40 h. green, drab and blue 1·10 60

172 Mosquito and Emblem

1962. Malaria Eradication.
424 **172** 40 h. red and green . . . 1·50 75

173 Girl and Y.W.C.A. Emblem

1962. 40th Anniv of Korean Y.W.C.A.
426 **173** 40 h. blue and orange . . 1·60 75

174 Emblem of Asian Film Producers' Federation
175 Soldiers crossing Han River Bridge

1962. 9th Asian Film Festival, Seoul.
427 **174** 40 h. violet, red & turquoise 1·25 60

1962. 1st Anniv of 16th May Revolution.
428 – 30 h. green and brown . 1·60 75
429 **175** 40 h. brown, green & turq 1·60 75
430 – 200 h. yellow, red & blue 14·00 8·75
DESIGNS—HORIZ: 30 h. "Industrial Progress" (men moving cogwheel up slope); 200 h. "Egg" containing Korean badge and industrial skyline.

176 20-oared "Turtle" Ship

1962. 370th Anniv of Hansan Naval Victory over Japanese.
433 **176** 2 w. blue and light blue . . 3·00 1·50
434 – 4 w. black, violet & turq 4·25 2·10
DESIGN: 4 w. 16-oared "turtle" ship.

177 Chindo Dog
178 "Hanabusaya asiatica"

179 Statue of Goddess Mikuk Besal
213 Longhorn Beetle

180 Farmers' Dance
181 12th-century Wine-jug

214 Factory, Fishes and Corn
182 Mison

183 13th-century Printing-block and Impression used for "Tripitaka Koreana"
191 Sika Deer

192 Bell of King Kyongbok
215 Boddhisatva Sokkuram Shrine

216 Tile, Silla Dynasty
217 "Azure Dragon", Koguryo period

1962. New Currency.
537 **177** 20 ch. brown 25 10
468 **178** 40 ch. blue 25 10
469 **179** 50 ch. brown 25 10
540 **213** 60 ch. brown 40 10
541 **180** 1 w. blue . . . . 1·60 10
542 **179** 1 w. 50 grey 30 10
543 **164** 2 w. red . . . . 3·25 10
472 **165** 3 w. purple . . . . . . 4·25 40
545 **167** 2 w. green 30 10
422 **181** 5 w. blue . . . . 5·00 85
547 **214** 7 w. mauve . . . . . . 2·50 40
548 **168** 10 w. brown . . . . . . 3·75 40
549 **182** 20 w. mauve . . . . . . 5·00 10

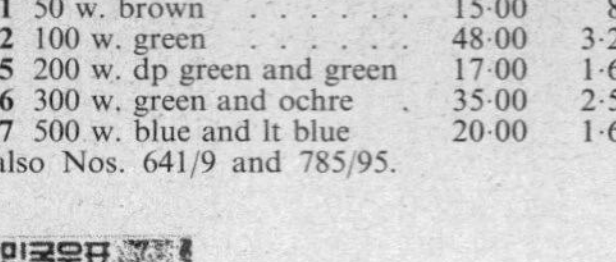

550 **183** 40 w. purple . . . . . . 6·75 85
551 **191** 50 w. brown . . . . . . 15·00 85
552 **192** 100 w. green . . . . . . 48·00 3·25
553 **215** 200 w. dp green and green 17·00 1·60
554 **216** 300 w. green and ochre . 35·00 2·50
555 **217** 500 w. blue and lt blue 20·00 1·60
See also Nos. 641/9 and 785/95.

184 Scout Badge and Korean Flag
185 Mackerel, Trawler and Nets

1962. 40th Anniv of Korean Scout Movement.
446 **184** 4 w. brown, red and blue 1·60 75
447 4 w. green, red and blue 1·60 75

1962. 10th Indo-Pacific Fishery Council Meeting, Seoul.
449 **185** 4 w. blue and turquoise . 1·50 75

186 I.C.A.O. Emblem

1962. 10th Anniv of Korea's Entry into International Civil Aviation Organization.
450 **186** 4 w. blue and brown . . . 1·60 85

1962. Children's Savings Campaign. As Nos. 356/7 but new currency.
452 1 w. yellow, brown and green 5·75 50
570 2 w. brown, blue and pink . . 8·25 65

1962. Air. New Currency.
454 **169** 5 w. blue and violet . . . 41·00 16·00
512 – 10 w. brown and turquoise (As No. 418) . . . . . 6·00 3·25
513 – 20 w. brown and green (As No. 419) . . . . . 13·00 5·75
563 **169** 39 w. drab and blue . . 4·00 2·00
514 – 40 w. green and blue (As No. 420) . . . . . 12·50 5·75
564 – 64 w. green and blue (As No. 418) . . . . . 5·00 2·00
565 78 w. blue and green (As No. 419) . . . . . 7·50 2·00
566 – 112 w. green and blue (As No. 420) . . . . . 4·00 2·00

187 Electric Power Plant

1962. Inauguration of 1st Korean Economic Five Year Plan.
458 **187** 4 w. violet and orange . . 4·25 1·60
459 – 4 w. ultramarine and blue 4·25 1·60
DESIGN: No. 459, Irrigation Dam.
See also Nos. 482/3, 528/9, 593/4 and 634/5.

188 Campaign Emblem

1963. Freedom from Hunger.
460 **188** 4 w. green, buff and blue 1·00 50

189 Globe and Letters

1963. 1st Anniv of Asian-Oceanic Postal Union.
462 **189** 4 w. mauve, olive & blue 1·10 60

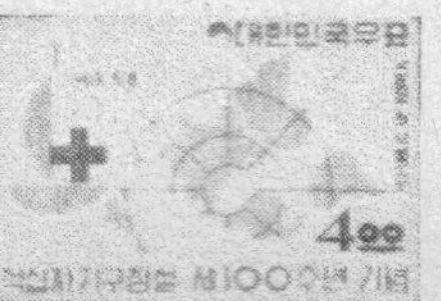

190 Centenary Emblem and Map

1963. Centenary of Red Cross.
464 **190** 4 w. red, grey and blue . . 1·10 60
465 4 w. red, grey and salmon 1·10 60

1963. Flood Relief. As No. 545, but new colour and inscr with premium.
479 4 w. + 1 w. blue . . . . . . 2·50 1·25

193 "15" and Hibiscus

1963. 15th Anniv of Republic.
480 **193** 4 w. red, violet and blue 2·10 1·10

194 Nurse and Emblem

1963. 15th Anniv of Korean Army Nursing Corps.
481 **194** 4 w. black, turquoise & grn 1·90 85

1963. Five Year Plan. Dated "1963". As T **187**.
482 4 w. violet and blue . . . . . 3·25 85
483 4 w. chocolate and brown . . 3·25 85
DESIGNS: No. 482, Cement Factory, Mun'gyong, and bag of cement, No. 483, Miner and coal train, Samch'ok region.

195 Rock Temples of Abu Simbel **196**

1963. Nubian Monuments Preservation.
484 **195** 3 w. green and drab . . . 4·50 2·10
485 **196** 4 w. green and drab . . . 4·50 2·10
Nos. 484/5 were issued together, se-tenant, forming a composite design.

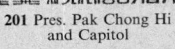

197 Rugby Football and Athlete

198 Nurse and Motor Clinic

1963. 44th National Games.
487 **197** 4 w. green, brown & blue 2·75 1·25

1963. 10th Anniv of Korean T.B. Prevention Society.
488 **198** 4 w. blue and red . . . . 1·50 75

199 Eleanor Roosevelt

200 U.N. Headquarters

1963. 15th Anniv of Declaration of Human Rights.
489 **199** 3 w. brown and blue . . . 1·10 60
490 – 4 w. blue, olive and buff 1·10 60
DESIGN: 4 w. Freedom torch and globe.

1963. 15th Anniv of U.N. Recognition of Korea.
492 **200** 4 w. olive, blue and black 1·10 60

201 Pres. Pak Chong Hi and Capitol

202 "Tai-Keum" (Bamboo Flute)

1963. Inaug. of President Pak Chong Hi.
494 **201** 4 w. blue, turquoise & blk 30·00 12·50

1963. Musical Instruments and Players. As T **202**.
495 4 w. olive, brown and drab . 2·75 1·40
496 4 w. black, blue and light blue 2·75 1·40
497 4 w. olive, mauve and pink . 2·75 1·40
498 4 w. sepia, violet and grey . . 2·75 1·40
499 4 w. blue, brown and pink . . 2·75 1·40
500 4 w. turquoise, black and blue 2·75 1·40
501 4 w. violet, bistre and yellow 2·75 1·40
502 4 w. blue, brown and mauve 2·75 1·40
503 4 w. black, blue and purple . 2·75 1·40
504 4 w. black, brown and pink . 2·75 1·40
MUSICAL INSTRUMENTS (and players): VERT: No. 495, Type **202**. No. 496, "Wul-keum" (banjo); No. 497, "Tang-piri" (flageolet); No. 498, "Na-bal" (trumpet); No. 499, "Hyang-pipa" (lute); No. 500, "Pyenkyeng" jade chimer; No. 501, "Taipyeng-so" (clarinet); No. 502, "Chang-ko" (double-ended drum). HORIZ: No. 503, "Wa-kong-hu" (harp); No. 504, "Kaya-ko" (zither).

203 Symbols of Metric System

204 "U.N.E.S.C.O."

1964. Introduction of Metric System in Korea.
505 **203** 4 w. multicoloured . . . 1·10 60

1964. 10th Anniv of Korean U.N.E.S.C.O. Committee.
506 **204** 4 w. ultramarine, red & bl 1·40 65

205 Symbols of Industry and Census

1964. National Industrial Census (1963).
507 **205** 4 w. brown, black & grey 1·10 60

206 Y.M.C.A. Emblem and Profile of Young Man

1964. 50th Anniv of Korean Y.M.C.A.
508 **206** 4 w. red, blue and green 1·10 60

207 Fair Emblem, Ginseng Root and Freighter

1964. New York World's Fair.
509 **207** 40 w. brown, green & buff 2·50 1·40
510 – 100 w. blue, brown & lt blue 16·00 6·75
DESIGN: 100 w. Korean pavilion at Fair.

208 Secret Garden

1964. Background in pale blue.
517 **208** 1 w. green 85 20
518 – 2 w. olive 65 50
519 – 3 w. turquoise 70 50
520 – 4 w. green . . . . . . 1·60 85
521 – 5 w. violet . . . . . . 3·25 1·60
522 – 6 w. blue . . . . 3·25 1·60
523 – 7 w. brown . . . . . . 5·00 2·50
524 – 8 w. brown . . . . . . 4·25 1·60
525 – 9 w. violet . . . . . . 3·25 1·60
526 – 10 w. green . . . . . . 5·75 2·50
DESIGNS: 2 w. Whahong Gate; 3 w. Uisang Pavilion; 4 w. Mt. Songni; 5 w. Paekma River; 6 w. Anab Pond; 7 w. Choksok Pavilion; 8 w. Kwanghan Pavilion; 9 w. Whaom Temple; 10 w. Chonjeyon Falls.

1964. Five Year Plan. Dated "1964". As T **187**.
528 4 w. black and turquoise . . 2·50 85
529 4 w. blue and yellow . . . . 2·50 85
DESIGNS: No. 528, Trawlers and fish, No. 529, Oil refinery and barrels.

209 Wheel and Globe

1964. Colombo Plan Day.
530 **209** 4 w. lt brown, brn & grn 1·10 60

210 "Helping Hand"

1964. 15th Anniv of Korea's Admission to W.H.O.
532 **210** 4 w. black, olive and green 1·10 60

211 Running

218 Federation Emblem

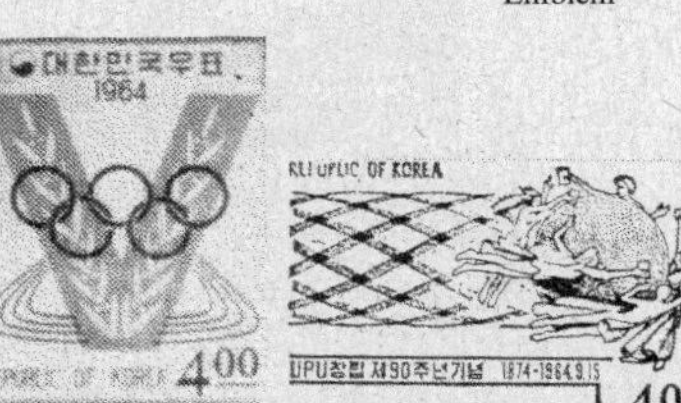
219 Olympic "V" Emblem

212 U.P.U. Monument, Berne, and Ribbons

1964. 45th National Games, Inchon.
534 **211** 4 w. pink, green & purple 2·75 1·25

1964. 90th Anniv of U.P.U.
535 **212** 4 w. brown, blue and pink 1·10 60

1964. 5th Meeting of Int. Federation of Asian and Western Pacific Contractors' Assns.
556 **218** 4 w. green, light green and brown . . . . 1·10 60

1964. Olympic Games, Tokyo.
557 **219** 4 w. blue, turquoise & brn 1·60 85
558 – 4 w. mauve, blue & green 1·60 85
559 – 4 w. brown, ultram & blue 1·60 85
560 – 4 w. mauve, brown & blue 1·60 85
561 – 4 w. brown, purple and blue 1·60 85
DESIGNS—HORIZ: No. 558, Running; No. 559, Rowing; No. 560, Horse-jumping; No. 561, Gymnastics.

220 Unissued 1884 100 m. Stamp

221 Pine Cone

1964. 80th Anniv of Korean Postal Services.
567 **220** 3 w. blue, violet & mauve 1·60 85
568 – 4 w. black, violet & olive 2·10 1·10
DESIGNS: 4 w. Hong Yong Sik, 1st Korean Postmaster-general.

1965. Korean Plants. Plants multicoloured, background colours given.
571 **221** 4 w. turquoise . . . . . . 1·25 65
572 – 4 w. grey (Plum blossom) 1·25 65
573 – 4 w. blue (Forsythia) . . . 1·25 65
574 – 4 w. green (Azalea) . . . . 1·25 65
575 – 4 w. pink (Lilac) . . . . . 1·25 65
576 – 4 w. grey (Wild rose) . . . 1·25 65
577 – 4 w. green (Balsam) . . . 1·25 65
578 – 4 w. grey (Hibiscus) . . . 1·25 65
579 – 4 w. flesh (Crepe myrtle) 1·25 65
580 – 4 w. turquoise-blue (Ullung chrysanthemum) . . . . 1·25 65
581 – 4 w. buff (Paulownia, tree) 1·25 65
582 – 4 w. blue (Bamboo) . . . 1·25 65

222 Folk Dancing

1965. Pacific Area Travel Assn Conf, Seoul.
584 **222** 4 w. violet, brown & turq 85 25

223 Flag and Doves

1965. Military Aid for Vietnam.
586 **223** 4 w. brown, blue & yellow 85 20

224 "Food Production" **225** "Family Scales"

1965. Agricultural Seven Year Plan.
588 **224** 4 w. brown, green & black 85 25

1965. Family-Planning Month.
589 **225** 4 w. green, drab & lt green 85 25

226 I.T.U. Emblem and Symbols

1965. Centenary of I.T.U.
591 **226** 4 w. black, red and blue 65 20

1965. Five Year Plan. Dated "1965". As T **187**.
593 4 w. blue and pink . . . . . 1·25 65
594 4 w. sepia and brown . . . . 1·25 65
DESIGNS: No. 593, "Korea" (freighter) at quayside and crates; No. 594, Fertiliser plant and wheat.

227 Flags of Australia, Belgium, Great Britain, Canada and Colombia

1965. 15th Anniv of Outbreak of Korean War.
595 **227** 4 w. multicoloured . . . 80 50
596 – 4 w. multicoloured . . . 80 50
597 – 4 w. multicoloured . . . 80 50
598 – 4 w. multicoloured . . . 80 50
599 – 10 w. multicoloured . . . 3·50 1·60
DESIGNS: (U.N. Emblem and flags of): No. 596, Denmark, Ethiopia, France, Greece and India; No. 597, Italy, Luxembourg, Netherlands, New Zealand and Norway; No. 598, Philippines, Sweden, Thailand, Turkey and South Africa; No. 599, General MacArthur and flags of Korea, U.N. and U.S.A.

228 Flag and Sky-writing ("20")

229 Ants and Leaf

1965. 20th Anniv of Liberation.
601 **228** 4 w. red, violet and blue 1·10 60
602 – 10 w. red, blue and violet 1·60 85
DESIGN: 10 w. South Gate and fireworks.

1965. Savings Campaign.
603 **229** 4 w. sepia, ochre & green 85 25

230 Hoisting Flag **231** Radio Aerial

1965. 15th Anniv of Recapture of Seoul.
604 **230** 3 w. olive, blue & salmon . . 2·40 1·25

1965. 80th Anniv of Korean Telecommunications.
605 **231** 3 w. green, black and blue . . 90 50
606 – 10 w. black, blue & yellow . . 1·50 75
DESIGN: 10 w. Telegraphist of 1885.

1965. Flood Relief. As No. 545, but colour changed and inscr with premium.
607 4 w. + 2 w. blue . . . . . . 2·10 1·25

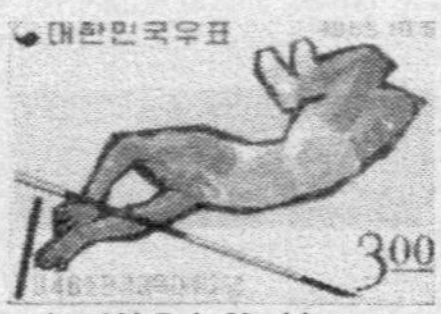

232 Pole Vaulting

1965. National Athletic Meeting, Kwangju.
608 **232** 3 w. multicoloured . . . . 1·75 85

1965. Aid for Children. As No. 545, but colour changed and inscr with premium.
609 4 w. + 2 w. purple . . . . . 2·10 1·25

233 I.C.Y. Emblem

1965. International Co-operation Year and 20th Anniv of United Nations.
610 **233** 3 w. red, green & dp green . . 85 25
611 – 10 w. ultramarine, grn & bl . . 1·50 75
DESIGN—VERT: 10 w. U.N. flag and headquarters, New York.

234 Child posting Letter **235** Children with Toboggan

1965. 10th Communications Day.
613 **234** 3 w. multicoloured . . . . 1·90 85
614 – 10 w. red, blue and green . . 3·50 1·60
DESIGN: 10 w. Airmail envelope and telephone receiver.

1965. Christmas and New Year.
615 **235** 3 w. blue, red and green . . 1·60 25
616 – 4 w. blue, red & turquoise . . 1·60 25
DESIGN: 4 w. Boy and girl in traditional costume.

236 Freedom House **237** Mandarin

1966. Opening of Freedom House, Panmunjom.
618 **236** 7 w. black, emererald & green . . 1·40 75
619 39 w. black, lilac & green . . 7·50 2·50

1966. Korean Birds. Multicoloured.
621 3 w. Type **237** . . . . 1·50 85
622 5 w. Manchurian Crane . . . 1·50 85
623 7 w. Ring-necked Pheasant . . 2·00 1·00

238 Pine Forest **239** Printing Press and Pen

1966. Reafforestation Campaign.
625 **238** 7 w. brown and green . . 1·00 50

1966. 10th Newspaper Day.
626 **239** 7 w. purple, yellow & turq . . 1·00 50

240 Curfew Bell and Young Koreans **241** W.H.O. Building

1966. Youth Guidance Month.
627 **240** 7 w. orange, green & blue . . 1·00 50

1966. Inauguration of W.H.O. Headquarters, Geneva.
628 **241** 7 w. black, blue & yellow . . 1·10 60
629 39 w. red, grey and yellow . . 7·75 3·25

242 Pres. Pak, Handclasp and Flags

1966. Pres. Pak Chung-Hi's State Tour of South-East Asia.
631 **242** 7 w. multicoloured . . . 5·00 2·50

243 Girl Scout and Flag

1966. 20th Anniv of Korean Girl Scouts.
632 **243** 7 w. black, green & yellow . . 1·75 85

244 Student and Ewha Women's University **246** Alaska Pollack

1966. 80th Anniv of Korean Women's Education.
633 **244** 7 w. multicoloured . . . 1·25 50

1966. 5-Year Plan. Dated "1966". As T **187**.
634 7 w. ultramarine and blue . . 1·10 50
635 7 w. black and yellow . . . . 2·50 1·10
DESIGNS: No. 634, Map and transport; No. 635, Radar aerials and telephone.

1966. Korean Fishes. Multicoloured.
637 3 w. Type **246** . . . . 1·60 85
638 5 w. Manchurian trout . . . 1·60 85
639 7 w. Yellow corvina . . . . 1·90 1·00

247 Incense-burner **249** Buddha, Kwanchok Temple

1966. Inscr "REPUBLIC OF KOREA".
641 **213** 60 ch. green 20 10
642 **180** 1 w. green . . . . 3·25 10
643 **164** 2 w. green 15 10
644 **165** 3 w. brown 15 10
645 **181** 5 w. blue . . . . 4·25 40
646 **214** 7 w. blue . . . . 4·50 35
647 **247** 13 w. blue . . . . . . 4·25 50
709 **182** 20 w. green and light green 17·00 85
710 **183** 40 w. green and olive . . 12·50 85
711 **191** 50 w. brown and bistre . . 6·75 60
648 – 60 w. green . . . . 9·25 50
649 **249** 80 w. green . . . . 3·25 40
DESIGN—As Type **247**. 60 w. 12th-century porcelain vessel.

250 Children and Hemispheres

1966. 15th Assembly of World Conf. of Teaching Profession (WCOTP), Seoul.
650 **250** 7 w. violet, brown & blue . . 1·00 50

251 Factory within Pouch

1966. Savings Campaign.
652 **251** 7 w. multicoloured . . . . 1·10 50

252 People on Map of Korea

1966. National Census.
653 **252** 7 w. multicoloured . . . . 1·10 50

253 "Lucida lateralis"

1966. Insects. Multicoloured.
654 3 w. Type **253** . . . . 1·60 85
655 5 w. "Hexacentrus japonicus" (grasshopper) . . . . 1·60 85
656 7 w. "Sericinus montela" (butterfly) . . . . 1·60 85

254 C.I.S.M. Emblem and "Round Table" Meeting **255** Soldiers and Flags

1966. 21st General Assembly of International Military Sports Council (C.I.S.M.), Seoul.
658 **254** 7 w. multicoloured . . . . 1·10 50

1966. 1st Anniv of Korean Troops in Vietnam.
660 **255** 7 w. multicoloured . . . . 4·25 2·10

256 Wrestling **257** Lions Emblem and Map

1966. 47th Athletic Meeting, Seoul.
661 **256** 7 w. multicoloured . . . . 1·90 1·00

1966. 5th Orient and South-East Asian Lions Convention, Seoul.
662 **257** 7 w. multicoloured . . . . 1·00 50

258 University Emblem "20" and Shields

1966. 20th Anniv of Seoul University.
664 **258** 7 w. multicoloured . . . . 1·00 50

259 A.P.A.C.L. Emblem

1966. 12th Conference of Asian People's Anti-Communist League (A.P.A.C.L.), Seoul.
665 **259** 7 w. multicoloured . . . . 1·00 50

260 Presidents Pak and Johnson **261** U.N.E.S.C.O. Symbols and Emblem

1966. President Johnson's Visit to Korea.
667 **260** 7 w. multicoloured . . . 1·50 75
668 83 w. multicoloured . . . 8·25 4·25

1966. 20th Anniv of U.N.E.S.C.O.
670 **261** 7 w. multicoloured . . . 1·00 50

1966. Hurricane Relief. As No. 646 but colour changed and premium added.
672 7 w. + 2 w. red . . . . . . 2·75 1·25

262 "Lucky Bag" **263** Eurasian Badger

1966. Christmas and New Year. Multicoloured.
673 5 w. Type **262** . . . . 1·60 40
674 7 w. Sheep (vert) . . . . . . 1·60 40

1966. Korean Fauna. Multicoloured.
676 3 w. Type **263** . . . . 1·60 85
677 5 w. Asiatic black bear . . . 1·60 85
678 7 w. Tiger . . . . 1·90 1·00

264 "Syncom" Satellite **265** Presidents Pak and Lubke

1967. 15th Anniv of Korea's Admission to I.T.U.
680 **264** 7 w. multicoloured . . . 1·40 65

1967. Visit of Pres. Lubke of West Germany to Korea.
682 **265** 7 w. multicoloured . . . 1·90 70

266 Coin, Factories and Houses **267** Okwangdae Mask

1967. 1st Anniv of Korean Revenue Office.
684 **266** 7 w. sepia and green . . . 1·00 50

1967. Folklore. Multicoloured.
685 4 w. Type **267** . . . . 1·25 60
686 5 w. Sandi mask . . . . . . 1·50 75
687 7 w. Mafoe mask . . . . . . 2·00 1·00
The 5 w. is horiz.

268 J.C.I. Emblem and Pavilion **269** Map Emblem

1967. International Junior Chamber of Commerce Conference, Seoul.
689 **268** 7 w. multicoloured . . . 85 25

1967. 5th Asian Pacific Dental Congress, Seoul.
691 **269** 7 w. multicoloured . . . 85 25

270 Korean Pavilion **271** Worker and Soldier

1967. World Fair, Montreal.
693 **270** 7 w. black, red and yellow . . 1·50 75
694 83 w. black, red and blue . . 11·00 5·00

1967. Veterans' Day.
696 **271** 7 w. multicoloured . . . 85 25

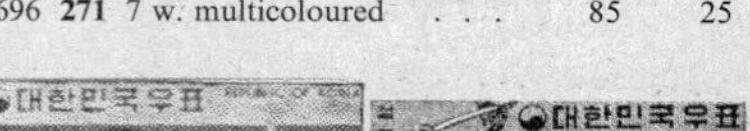

272 Railway Wheel and Rail **273** Sword Dance

1967. 2nd Five Year Plan.
697 272 7 w. black, yellow & brn . . . 2·40 1·10
698 – 7 w. orange, brown & blk . . . 2·40 1·10
DESIGN: No. 698, Nut and bolt.
See also 773/4, 833/4, 895/6 and 981/2.

1967. Folklore. Multicoloured.
699 4 w. Type 273 . . . . 1·25 60
700 5 w. Peace dance (vert) . . . . 1·50 75
701 7 w. Buddhist dance (vert) . . 2·00 1·00

274 Soldier and Family
275 President Pak and Phoenix 

1967. Fund for Korean Troops Serving in Vietnam.
703 274 7 w. + 3 w. black & purple 2·25 1·25

1967. Inaug of President Pak for 2nd Term.
704 275 7 w. multicoloured . . . . 7·00 3·25

276 Scout, Badge and Camp

1967. 3rd Korean Scout Jamboree. Multicoloured.
706 7 w. Type 276 . . . . 1·40 65
707 20 w. Scout badge, bridge and tent . . . . 4·50 2·10

280 Girls on Swing

1967. Folklore. Multicoloured.
712 4 w. Type 280 . . . . 1·50 75
713 5 w. Girls on seesaw (vert) . . 1·90 85
714 7 w. Girls dancing (vert) . . . 2·25 1·10

281 Freedom Centre
282 Boxing 

1967. 1st World Anti-Communist League Conf, Taipei. Multicoloured.
716 5 w. Type 281 . . . . 90 50
717 7 w. Hand grasping chain (vert) 90 50

1967. National Athletic Meeting, Seoul. Mult.
719 5 w. Type 282 . . . . 1·50 75
720 7 w. Basketball . . . . 1·50 75

283 Students' Memorial, Kwangjoo
284 Decade Emblem 

1967. Students' Day.
721 283 7 w. multicoloured 90 50

1967. International Hydrological Decade.
722 284 7 w. multicoloured 90 50

285 Children spinning Top
286 Playing Shuttlecock 

1967. Christmas and New Year.
723 285 5 w. blue, red and pink . . 1·60 40
724 – 7 w. brown, blue & bistre . 1·60 40
DESIGN: 7 w. Monkey and Signs of the Zodiac.

1967. Folklore. Multicoloured.
726 4 w. Type 286 . . . . 1·60 85
727 5 w. "Dalmaji" (horiz) . . . 2·10 1·00
728 7 w. Archery . . . . 2·00 1·00

287 Microwave Transmitter

1967. Inauguration of Microwave Telecommunications Service.
730 287 7 w. black, green and blue 1·40 65

288 Carving, King Songdok's Bell
289 5th–6th century Earrings 
290 Korean Flag 

1968.
732 288 1 w. brown and yellow . 15 10
733 289 5 w. yellow and green . . 2·50 10
734 290 7 w. red and blue 65 10
For designs similar to Type 290 see Nos. 771, 780, 787/8, 790 and 827.

291 W.H.O. Emblem
292 E.A.T.A. Emblem and Korean Motif 

1968. 20th Anniv of W.H.O.
735 291 7 w. multicoloured . . . 90 50

1968. 2nd East Asia Travel Association Conference, Seoul.
737 292 7 w. multicoloured . . . 90 50

293 C.A.C.C.I. Emblem, Korean Doorknocker and factories
294 Pres. Pak and Emperor Haile Selassie 

1968. 2nd Conference of Confederation of Asian Chambers of Commerce and Industry (C.A.C.C.I.), Seoul.
739 293 7 w. multicoloured . . . 90 50

1968. Visit of Emperor of Ethiopia.
741 294 7 w. multicoloured . . . 2·50 1·25

295 Post-bag
296 Atomic and Development Symbols 

1968. Postman's Day. Multicoloured.
743 5 w. Type 295 . . . . 90 50
744 7 w. Postman 90 50

1968. Promotion of Science and Technology.
745 296 7 w. blue, green and red 40 25

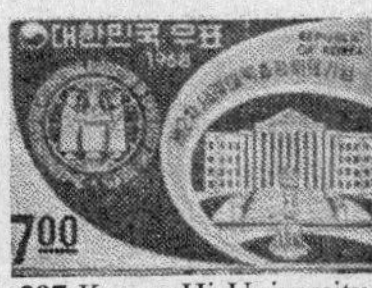

297 Kyung Hi University and Conference Emblem
298 "Liberation" 

1968. 2nd Conf of Int Assn of University Presidents.
746 297 7 w. multicoloured . . . 85 25

1968. Liberation of Suppressed Peoples' Campaign.
748 298 7 w. multicoloured . . . 90 50

299 Reservist
300 Stylised Peacock 

1968. Army Reservists' Fund.
749 299 7 w. + 3 w. black & green 3·25 1·25

1968. 20th Anniv of Republic.
750 300 7 w. multicoloured 90 50

301 Fair Entrance
302 Assembly Emblem 

1968. 1st Korean Trade Fair, Seoul.
751 301 7 w. multicoloured 90 50

1968. 3rd General Assembly of Asian Pharmaceutical Association Federation.
752 302 7 w. multicoloured 90 50

303 Scout Badge
304 Soldier and Battle Scene 

1968. 6th Far East Scout Conference, Seoul.
753 303 7 w. multicoloured . . . . 1·60 85

1968. 20th Anniv of Korean Armed Forces.
754 304 7 w. orange and green . . 4·25 1·60
755 – 7 w. blue and light blue . . 4·25 1·60
756 – 7 w. blue and orange . . . 4·25 1·60
757 – 7 w. light blue and blue . . 4·25 1·60
758 – 7 w. green and orange . . 4·25 1·60
DESIGNS: No. 755, Sailor and naval guns. 756, Servicemen and flags. 757, Airman and jet fighters. 758, Marine and landings.

305 Colombo Plan Emblem and Globe

1968. 19th Meeting of Colombo Plan Consultative Committee, Seoul.
759 305 7 w. multicoloured 85 40

306 (I) Olympic Emblems 307 (II)

1968. Olympic Games, Mexico. Multicoloured.
760 7 w. Type 306 . . . . 8·25 4·25
761 7 w. Type 307 . . . . 8·25 4·25
762 7 w. Cycling (I) . . . . 8·25 4·25
763 7 w. Cycling (II) . . . . . . 8·25 4·25
764 7 w. Boxing (I) . . . . 8·25 4·25
765 7 w. Boxing (II) . . . . 8·25 4·25
766 7 w. Wrestling (I) . . . . . . 8·25 4·25
767 7 w. Wrestling (II) . . . . . 8·25 4·25
The two types of each design may be identified by the position of the country name at the foot of the design–ranged right in types I, and left in types II. On three of the designs (excluding "Cycling") the figures of value are on left and right respectively. Types I and II of each design were issued together horizontally se-tenant within the sheets of 50 stamps.

308 Statue of Woman
309 Coin and Symbols 

1968. 60th Anniv of Women's Secondary Education.
769 308 7 w. multicoloured . . . 75 20

1968. National Wealth Survey.
770 309 7 w. multicoloured . . . 75 20

1968. Disaster Relief Fund. As No. 734, but with additional inscr and premium added.
771 290 7 w. + 3 w. red and blue 14·00 5·75

310 Shin Eui Ju Memorial
311 Demonstrators 

1968. Anniv of Student Uprising, Shin Eui Ju (1945).
772 310 7 w. multicoloured . . . 1·00 50

1968. 2nd Five Year Plan. As T 272. Dated "1968". Multicoloured.
773 7 w. Express motorway . . . 1·90 90
774 7 w. "Clover-leaf" road junction 1·90 90

1968. Human Rights Year.
775 311 7 w. multicoloured . . . 85 20

312 Christmas Lanterns
314 Korean House and UN Emblems 

1968. Christmas and New Year. Multicoloured.
776 5 w. Type 312 . . . . 2·10 60
777 7 w. Cockerel . . . . 2·10 60

1968. 20th Anniv of South Korea's Admission to U.N.
779 314 7 w. multicoloured . . . 85 20

1969. Military Helicopter Fund. As No. 734 but colours changed and inscr with premium added.
780 290 7 w. + 3 w. red, bl & grn 2·75 1·25

315 Torch and Monument, Pagoda Park, Seoul
316 Hyun Choong Sa and "Turtle" Ships 

1969. 50th Anniv of Samil (Independence) Movement.
781 315 7 w. multicoloured . . . 90 25

1969. Dedication of Rebuilt Hyun Choong Sa (Shrine of Admiral Li Sun Sin).
782 316 7 w. multicoloured . . . 75 25

317 President Pak and Yang di-Pertuan Agong
318 Stone Temple Lamp 

1969. Visit of Yang di-Pertuan Agong (Malaysian Head-of-State).
783 317 7 w. multicoloured . . . 2·40 1·10

1969.
785 178 40 ch. green (18 × 22 mm) 50 10
786 318 5 w. purple 45 10
787 290 7 w. blue . . . . 2·75 10
788 7 w. blue* 85 10
789 168 10 w. blue (22 × 18 mm) 11·00 75

790 **290** 10 w. blue 1·10 10
791 – 20 w. green 85 10
792 – 30 w. green 3·00 10
793 **183** 40 w. blue and pink (18 × 22 mm) 20·00 1·60
794 – 40 w. mauve and blue 90 10
795 – 100 w. brown and purple 70·00 2·50

DESIGNS—As Type **318**. VERT: 20 w. Wine jug. 40 w; (No. 794), Porcelain Jar, Yi Dynasty; 100 w. Seated Buddha (bronze). HORIZ: 30 w. "Duck" Vase.

*No. 788 has the face value shown as "7" only, omitting the noughts shown on No. 787.

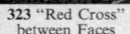

323 "Red Cross" between Faces — **324** "Building the Nation's Economy"

1969. 50th Anniv of League of Red Cross Societies.
796 **323** 7 w. multicoloured 85 20

1969. "Second Economy Drive".
798 **324** 7 w. multicoloured 85 15

325 Presidents Pak and Nguyen van Thieu

1969. Visit of President Nguyen van Thieu of South Vietnam.
799 **325** 7 w. multicoloured 2·40 1·10

326 Reafforestation and Flooded Fields — **327** Ignition of Second-stage Rocket

1969. Flood and Drought Damage Prevention Campaign. Multicoloured.
801 7 w. Type **326** 75 25
802 7 w. Withered and flourishing plants 75 25

1969. First Man on the Moon.
803 **327** 10 w. blue, black and red 1·90 90
804 – 10 w. blue, black and red 1·90 90
805 – 20 w. multicoloured 1·90 90
806 – 20 w. multicoloured 1·90 90
807 – 40 w. blue, red and black 1·90 90

DESIGNS: No. 804, Separation of modules from rocket; No. 805, Diagram of lunar orbit; No. 806, Astronauts on Moon; No. 807, Splashdown of "Apollo 11".

328 Stepmother admonishing Kongji — **332** Steam Locomotive of 1899

1969. Korean Fairy Tales (1st series). "Kongji and Patji". Multicoloured.
809 5 w. Type **328** 1·60 85
810 7 w. Kongji and Sparrows 1·60 85
811 10 w. Kongji and Ox 2·50 1·25
812 20 w. Kongji in Sedan-chair 2·75 1·25

See also Nos. 828/31, 839/42, 844/7 and 853/6.

1969. 70th Anniv of Korean Railways. Multicoloured.
814 7 w. Type **332** 1·00 40
815 7 w. Early steam and modern diesel locomotives 90 40

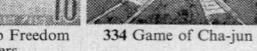

333 Northrop Freedom Fighters — **334** Game of Cha-jun

1969. 20th Anniv of Korean Air Force. Multicoloured.
816 10 w. Type **333** 90 25
817 10 w. McDonnell-Douglas F-4D Phantom II fighter 1·10 25

1969. 10th Korean Traditional Arts Contest, Taegu.
818 **334** 7 w. multicoloured 85 40

335 Molecule and Institute Building — **336** Presidents Pak and Hamani

1969. Completion of Korean Institute of Science and Technology.
819 **335** 7 w. multicoloured 85 40

1969. Visit of President Hamani of Niger Republic.
820 **336** 7 w. multicoloured 1·75 85

337 Football — **342** Students ringing "Education"

1969. 50th Anniv of National Athletic Meeting. Multicoloured.
822 10 w. Type **337** 1·50 75
823 10 w. Volleyball 1·50 75
824 10 w. Korean wrestling 1·50 75
825 10 w. Fencing 1·50 75
826 10 w. Korean karate 1·50 75

Nos. 824/6 are horiz.

1969. Searchlight Fund. As T **290**, but inscr "7 + 3" only.
827 7 w. + 3 w. blue and red 3·00 1·25

1969. Korean Fairy Tales. (2nd series). "The Hare's Liver". As T **328**. Multicoloured.
828 5 w. Princess and Doctors 1·25 50
829 7 w. Hare arriving at Palace 1·25 50
830 10 w. Preparing to remove the Hare's liver 1·60 75
831 20 w. Escape of the Hare 1·90 85

1969. Second Five-year Plan. As T **272**. Dated "1969". Multicoloured.
833 7 w. "Agriculture and Fisheries" 75 40
834 7 w. Emblems of Industry 75 40

1969. 1st Anniv of National Education Charter.
835 **342** 7 w. multicoloured 75 15

343 Toy Dogs — **344** Woman with Letter and U.P.U. Monument, Berne

1969. Lunar New Year ("Year of the Dog"). Multicoloured.
836 5 w. Type **343** 1·00 25
837 7 w. Candle and lattice doorway 1·00 25

1970. 70th Anniv of Korea's Admission to U.P.U.
838 **344** 10 w. multicoloured 7·50 3·25

1970. Korean Fairy Tales (3rd series). "The Sun and the Moon". As T **328**. Multicoloured.
839 5 w. Mother meets the tiger 1·25 50
840 7 w. Tiger in disguise 1·25 50
841 10 w. Children chased up a tree 1·60 75
842 20 w. Children escape to Heaven 2·50 1·25

1970. Korean Fairy Tales (4th series). "The Woodcutter and the Fairy". As T **328**. Mult.
844 10 w. Woodcutter hiding Fairy's dress 2·00 1·00
845 10 w. Fairy as Woodcutter's Wife 2·00 1·00
846 10 w. Fairy and children fly to Heaven 2·00 1·00
847 10 w. Happy reunion 2·00 1·00

353 I.E.Y. Emblem and Open Book — **354** Seated Buddha and Korean Pavilion

1970. International Education Year.
849 **353** 10 w. multicoloured 4·50 2·10

1970. "EXPO 70" World Fair, Osaka, Japan.
850 **354** 10 w. multicoloured 3·25 1·60

355 "4-11" Club Emblem — **356** Bank Emblem and Cash

1970. 15th "4-11" Club (young farmers' organization) Central Contest, Suwon.
851 **355** 10 w. multicoloured 1·40 65

1970. 3rd General Meeting of Asian Development Bank, Seoul.
852 **356** 10 w. multicoloured 1·40 65

1970. Korean Fairy Tales (5th series). "Heungbu and Nolbu". As T **328**. Multicoloured.
853 10 w. Heungbu tending swallow 2·10 1·00
854 10 w. Heungbu finds treasure in pumpkin 2·10 1·00
855 10 w. Nolbu with pumpkin 2·10 1·00
856 10 w. Nolbu chased by devil 2·10 1·00

361 Royal Palanquin (Yi dynasty) — **362** New Headquarters Building

1970. Early Korean Transport.
858 **361** 10 w. multicoloured 1·90 85
859 – 10 w. multicoloured 1·90 85
860 – 10 w. multicoloured 1·90 85
861 – 10 w. black, ochre and blue 1·25 25

DESIGN—HORIZ: No. 859, Tramcar, 1899; 860, Emperor Sunjong's cadillac, 1903; 861, An Chang Nam's Nieuport 28 biplane, 1922.

1970. Opening of New U.P.U. Headquarters Building, Berne.
862 **362** 10 w. multicoloured 60 30

363 Dish Aerial and Hemispheres

1970. Inauguration of Satellite Communications Station, Kum San.
863 **363** 10 w. multicoloured 1·60 65

364 "PEN" and Quill Pen — **366** Postal Code Symbol

365 Section of Motorway

1970. 37th International P.E.N. (literary organization) Congress, Seoul.
864 **364** 10 w. multicoloured 60 25

1970. Opening of Seoul–Pusan Motorway.
865 **365** 10 w. multicoloured 1·60 85

1970. Introduction of Postal Codes.
866 **366** 10 w. multicoloured 60 25

INDEX

Countries can be quickly located by referring to the index at the end of this volume.

367 Parcel Sorting Area — **368** Children's Hall and Boy

1970. Inauguration of Postal Mechanization.
867 **367** 10 w. multicoloured 60 25

1970. Opening of Children's Hall, Seoul.
869 **368** 10 w. multicoloured 60 30

369 "Mountain and River" (Yi In Moon)

1970. Korean Paintings of Yi Dynasty (1st series). Multicoloured.
870 10 w. Type **369** 1·25 65
871 10 w. "Jongyangsa Temple" (Chong Son) 1·25 65
872 10 w. "Mountain and River by Moonlight" (Kim Doo Ryang) (vert) 1·25 65

See also Nos. 887/89, 897/899, 947/52, 956/8 and 961/5.

370 P.T.T.I. Emblem — **371** WAC and Corps Badge

1970. Councillors' Meeting, Asian Chapter of Postal, Telegraph and Telephone International (Post Office Trade Union Federation).
874 **370** 10 w. multicoloured 90 50

1970. 20th Anniv of Korean Women's Army Corps.
875 **371** 10 w. multicoloured 90 50

372 Pres. Pak and Flag

1970.
876 **372** 10 w. multicoloured 3·00 55
877 – 10 w. black, green & blue 3·25 1·25

DESIGN—VERT: No. 877, Pres. Pak and industrial complex.

373 Presidents Pak and Sanchez Hernandez

1970. Visit of Pres. Hernandez of El Salvador.
878 **373** 10 w. multicoloured 2·10 1·00

374 "People and Houses"

1970. National Census.
880 **374** 10 w. multicoloured 85 25

375 Diving

1970. 51st National Athletic Games, Seoul.
881 10 w. Type **375** . . . . 2·50 1·25
882 10 w. Hockey . . . . 2·50 1·25
883 10 w. Baseball . . . . 2·50 1·25

376 Police Badge and Activities **377** Bell and Globe

1970. National Police Day.
885 **376** 10 w. multicoloured . . . 1·00 30

1970. 25th Anniv of United Nations.
886 **377** 10 w. multicoloured . . . 65 30

1970. Korean Paintings of the Yi Dynasty (2nd series). Vert designs at T **369**, showing animals. Multicoloured.
887 30 w. "Fierce Tiger" (Shim Sa Yung) . . . . 3·75 1·60
888 30 w. "Cats and Sparrows" (Pyun Sang Byuk) . . . . . 3·75 1·60
889 30 w. "Dog with Puppies" (Yi Am) . . . . 3·75 1·60

378 Kite and Reel **380** Fields ("Food Production")

379 Quotation and Emblems on Globe

1970. Lunar New Year ("Year of the Pig"). Multicoloured.
891 10 w. Type **378** 65 20
892 10 w. Toy pig 65 20

1970. 15th Communications Day.
894 **379** 10 w. multicoloured . . . 65 30

1970. 2nd Five Year Plan. At T **272**. Dated "1970". Multicoloured.
895 10 w. "Port Development" . . 75 20
896 10 w. "House Construction" 75 20

1970. Korean Paintings of the Yi Dynasty (3rd series). Vert designs as T **369**. Multicoloured.
897 10 w. "Chokpyokdo" (river cliff) (Kim Hong Do) . . . . . . 1·40 65
898 10 w. "Hen and Chicks" ("Hwajae"–Pyn Sang Byuk) 1·40 65
899 10 w. "The Flute-player" (Shin Yun Bok) . . . . 1·40 65

1971. Economic Development (1st series). Mult.
901 10 w. Type **380** . . . . 1·00 30
902 10 w. Dam ("Electric Power") (horiz) . . . . 1·00 30
903 10 w. Map on crate ("Exports") (horiz) . . . . 1·00 30
See also Nos. 905/7 and 910/12.

381 Coal-mining **382** Globe, Torch and Spider

1971. Economic Development (2nd series). Mult.
905 10 w. Type **381** 75 20
906 10 w. Cement works (vert) . . 75 20
907 10 w. Fertilizer plant 75 20

1971. Anti-Espionage Month.
909 **382** 10 w. multicoloured . . . 90 50

383 Motorway Junction **384** Reservist and Badge

1971. Economic Develepment (3rd series). Mult.
910 10 w. Type **383** 75 20
911 10 w. Scales ("Gross National Income") (horiz) 75 20
912 10 w. Bee and coins ("Increased Savings") (horiz) 75 20

1971. Home Reserve Forces Day.
914 **384** 10 w. multicoloured . . . 80 30

385 W.H.O. Emblem, Stethoscope and Microscope **386** Underground Train

1971. 20th World Health Day.
915 **385** 10 w. multicoloured . . . 70 30

1971. Construction of Seoul Underground Railway System.
916 **386** 10 w. multicoloured . . . 1·00 20

387 Footballer **388** Veteran and Association Flag

1971. First Asian Soccer Games, Seoul.
917 **387** 10 w. multicoloured . . . 1·50 75

1971. 20th Korean Veterans' Day.
918 **388** 10 w. multicoloured . . . 70 20

389 Girl Scouts **390** Torch and Economic Symbols

1971. 25th Anniv of Korean Girl Scouts Federation.
919 **389** 10 w. multicoloured . . . 55 20

1971. 10th Anniv of May 16th Revolution.
920 **390** 10 w. multicoloured . . . 70 20

391 "Telecommunications" **392** I.L.O. Emblem

1971. 3rd World Telecommunications Day.
921 **391** 10 w. multicoloured . . . 85 20

1971. "The Work of the United Nations Organization".
922 **392** 10 w. mauve, black & grn 2·50 1·25
923 – 10 w. blue, black & mauve 2·50 1·25
924 – 10 w. multicoloured . . . 2·50 1·25
925 – 10 w. blue, black & mauve 2·50 1·25
926 – 10 w. mauve, black & grn 2·50 1·25
927 – 10 w. blue, black & mauve 2·50 1·25
928 – 10 w. mauve, black & blue 2·50 1·25
929 – 10 w. black, green & mauve 2·50 1·25
930 – 10 w. mauve, black & blue 2·50 1·25
931 – 10 w. blue, black & mauve 2·50 1·25
932 – 10 w. mauve, black & blue 2·50 1·25
933 – 10 w. black, mauve & grn 2·50 1·25
934 – 10 w. mauve, blue & black 2·50 1·25
935 – 10 w. black, mauve & grn 2·50 1·25
936 – 10 w. mauve, black & blue 2·50 1·25
937 – 10 w. blue, black & mauve 2·50 1·25
938 – 10 w. mauve, black & blue 2·50 1·25
939 – 10 w. black, mauve & grn 2·50 1·25
940 – 10 w. mauve, black & blue 2·50 1·25
941 – 10 w. blue, black & mauve 2·50 1·25
942 – 10 w. mauve, black & grn 2·50 1·25
943 – 10 w. black, blue & mauve 2·50 1·25
944 – 10 w. multicoloured . . . 2·50 1·25
945 – 10 w. black, blue & mauve 2·50 1·25
946 – 10 w. black, mauve & grn 2·50 1·25
EMBLEMS: No. 923, Food and Agriculture Organization; No. 924, General Assembly and New York Headquarters; No. 925, U.N.E.S.C.O.; No. 926, W.H.O.; No. 927, World Bank; No. 928, International Development Association; No 929, Security Council; No. 930, International Finance Corporation; No. 931, International Monetary Fund; No. 932, International Civil Aviation Organization; No. 933, Economic and Social Council; No. 934, South Korean Flag; No. 935, Trusteeship Council; No. 936, U.P.U.; No. 937, I.T.U.; No. 938, World Meteorological Organization; No. 939, Int Court of Justice; No. 940, I.M.C.O.; No. 941, U.N.I.C.E.F.; No. 942, International Atomic Energy Agency; No. 943, United Nations Industrial Development Organization; No. 944, United Nations Commission for the Unification and Rehabilitation of Korea; No. 945, United Nations Development Programme; No. 946, United Nations Conference on Trade and Development.

393 "Boating" (Shin Yun Bok)

1971. Korean Paintings of the Yi Dynasty (4th series). Multicoloured.
947 10 w. Type **393** . . . . 3·75 1·60
948 10 w. "Greeting Travellers" . . 3·75 1·60
949 10 w. "Tea Ceremony" . . . . 3·75 1·60
950 10 w. "Lady and Servants on Country Road" . . . . . . 3·75 1·60
951 10 w. "Couple Walking" . . . 3·75 1·60
952 10 w. "Fairy and Boy beneath Pine Tree" (Li Chae Kwan) (vert) . . . . 3·25 1·60
Nos. 947/51 show "Folk Customs" paintings by Shin Yun Bok.

394 Pres. Pak, Emblem and Motorway **395** Camp Fire and Badge

1971. Re-election of Pres. Pak for 3rd Term.
954 **394** 10 w. multicoloured . . . 2·50 1·25

1971. Korean Paintings of the Yi Dynasty (5th series). As T **393**. Multicoloured.
956 10 w. "Chasing the Cat" (Kim Deuk Shin) . . . . 2·10 1·10
957 10 w. "Valley Family" (Li Chae Kwan) (vert) . . . . 2·10 1·10
958 10 w. "Man Reading" (Li Chae Kwan) (vert) . . . . 2·10 1·10

1971. 13th World Scout Jamboree, Asagiri, Japan.
960 **395** 10 w. multicoloured . . . 55 20

1971. Korean Paintings of the Yi Dynasty (6th series). As T **393**. Multicoloured.
961 10 w. "Classroom" . . . . . . 3·75 1·60
962 10 w. "Wrestling Match" . . . 3·75 1·60
963 10 w. "Danser with Musicians" 3·75 1·60
964 10 w. "Weavers" . . . . 3·75 1·60
965 10 w. "Drawing Water at the Well" . . . . 3·75 1·60
Nos. 961/5 depict genre paintings by Kim Hong Do.

396 Cogwheel and Asian Map

1971. 3rd Asian Labour Minister's Conference, Seoul.
967 **396** 10 w. multicoloured . . . 75 20

397 Judo

1971. 52nd National Athletic Meeting, Seoul. Multicoloured.
969 10 w. Type **397** . . . . 1·25 60
970 10 w. Archery . . . . 1·25 60

398 Korean symbol on Palette

1971. 20th National Fine Art Exhibition.
972 **398** 10 w. multicoloured . . . 70 20

399 Doctor and Globe **400** Emblems and "Vocational Skills"

1971. 7th Congress of Medical Associations from Asia and Oceania.
973 **399** 10 w. multicoloured . . . 55 20

1971. 2nd National Vocational Skill Contest for High School Students.
974 **400** 10 w. multicoloured . . . 70 20

401 Callipers and "K" Emblem

1971. 10th Anniv of Industrial Standardisation.
976 **401** 10 w. multicoloured . . . 70 20

402 Fairy Tale Rats **403** Emblem and Hangul Alphabet

1971. Lunar New Year ("Year of the Rat"). Multicoloured.
977 10 w. Type **402** 85 20
978 10 w. Flying Crane 85 20

1971. 50th Anniv of Hangul Hakhoe (Korean Language Research Society).
980 **403** 10 w. multicoloured . . . 70 20

1971. 2nd Five-Year Plan. As T **272**. Dated "1971". Multicoloured.
981 10 w. Atomic power plant . . 60 20
982 10 w. Hydro-electric power project 65 20

404 Korean Red Cross Building on Map **405** Globe and Open Book

1971. South–North Korean Red Cross Conference, Panmunjom.
983 **404** 10 w. multicoloured . . . 80 30

1971. International Book Year.
985 **405** 10 w. multicoloured . . . 55 20

406 "Intelsat 4" and Korean Earth Station **407** Speed-skating

1971. 20th Anniv of Korea's Membership of I.T.U.
987 **406** 10 w. multicoloured . . . 85 20

1972. Winter Olympic Games, Sapporo, Japan. Multicoloured.
988 10 w. Type **407** . . . . . . 1·25 60
989 10 w. Figure-skating . . . . . 1·25 60

408 Forestry Map **410** E.C.A.F.E. Emblem and Industrial Symbols

409 Scarab Beetles and Emblem

1972. "Trees for Unity" Campaign.
991 **408** 10 w. multicoloured . . . 70 20

1972. 20th Anniv of Korean Junior Chamber of Commerce.
992 **409** 10 w. multicoloured . . . 60 20

1972. 25th Anniv of U.N. Economic Commission for Asia and the Far East.
993 **410** 10 w. multicoloured . . . 70 20

411 Flags of Member Countries **412** Reserve Forces' Flag

1972. 10th Anniv of Asian and Oceanic Postal Union.
994 **411** 10 w. multicoloured . . . 70 20

1972. Home Reserve Forces Day.
995 **412** 10 w. multicoloured . . . 80 30

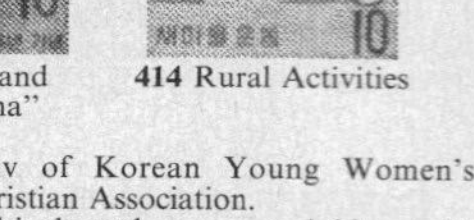

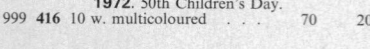

413 Emblem and "Terias harina" **414** Rural Activities

1972. 50th Anniv of Korean Young Women's Christian Association.
996 **413** 10 w. multicoloured . . . 1·00 30

1972. "New Community" (rural development) Movement.
997 **414** 10 w. multicoloured . . . 70 20

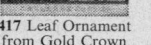

415 "Anti-Espionage" and Korean Flag **416** Children with Balloons

1972. Anti-Espionage Month.
998 **415** 10 w. multicoloured . . . 70 20

1972. 50th Children's Day.
999 **416** 10 w. multicoloured . . . 70 20

417 Leaf Ornament from Gold Crown

419 Kalkot, Koje Island, Hanryo Straits Park

418 Lake Paengnokdam, Mt. Halla Park

1972. Treasures from King Munyong's Tomb. Multicoloured.
1000 10 w. Type **417** 60 20
1001 10 w. Gold earrings (horiz) 65 20

1972. National Parks (1st series).
1002 **418** 10 w. multicoloured . . 80 20
1003 **419** 10 w. multicoloured . . 80 20
See also Nos. 1018/19 and 1026/7.

420 Marguerite and Conference Emblem **421** Gwanghwa Gate and National Flags

1972. U.N. Environmental Conservation Conference, Stockholm.
1004 **420** 10 w. multicoloured . . 70 20

1972. 7th Asian and Pacific Council (ASPAC) Ministerial Meeting, Seoul.
1006 **421** 10 w. multicoloured . . 60 25

422 Pasture ("Development of Rural Economy") **423** "Love Pin"

1972. 3rd Five-Year Plan. Dated "1972". Multicoloured.
1007 10 w. Type **422** . . . . . . 1·10 50
1008 10 w. Foundry ladle ("Heavy Industries") . . . . . . 1·10 50
1009 10 w. Crate and Globe ("Increased Exports") . . . 1·10 50

1972. Disaster Relief Fund.
1010 **423** 10 w. + 5 w. red & blue 90 50

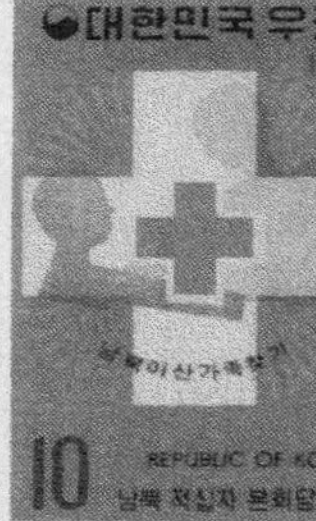

424 Judo **425** Family Reunion through Red Cross

1972. Olympic Games, Munich. Multicoloured.
1011 20 w. Type **424** . . . . . 1·00 50
1012 20 w. Weightlifting . . . . . 1·00 50
1013 20 w. Wrestling . . . . . 1·00 50
1014 20 w. Boxing . . . . . 1·00 50

1972. 1st Plenary Meeting of South-North Korean Red Cross Conference, Pyongyang.
1016 **425** 10 w. multicoloured . . 80 30

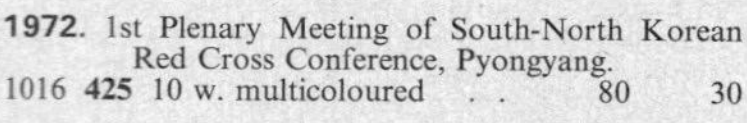

426 Bulkuk Temple, Kyongju Park **428** Conference Emblem within "5"

427 Statue and Bopju Temple, Mt. Sokri Park

1972. National Parks (2nd series).
1018 **426** 10 w. multicoloured . . 55 20
1019 **427** 10 w. multicoloured . . 55 20

1972. 5th Asian Judicial Conference, Seoul.
1020 **428** 10 w. multicoloured . . 70 20

429 Lions Badge between Korean Emblems

1972. 11th Orient and South-East Asian Lions Convention, Seoul.
1021 **429** 10 w. multicoloured . . . 50 20

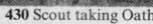

430 Scout taking Oath **431** Dolls and Ox's Head

1972. 50th Anniv of Korean Boy Scouts Movement.
1022 **430** 10 w. multicoloured . . . 85 50

1972. Lunar New Year ("Year of the Ox"). Multicoloured.
1023 10 w. Type **431** 85 20
1024 10 w. Revellers in balloon . . 85 20

432 Temple, Mt. Naejang Park **433** Madeungryong Pass, Mt. Sorak Park

1972. National Parks. (3rd series).
1026 **432** 10 w. multicoloured . . . 80 20
1027 **433** 10 w. multicoloured . . . 80 20

434 President Pak, Flag and "Development"

1972. Re-election of President Pak.
1028 **434** 10 w. multicoloured . . . 2·10 1·10

435 National Central Museum, Kyongbok Palace **437** Korean Family

436 Temple, Mt. Sorak

1973. Korean Tourist Attractions (1st series).
1030 **435** 10 w. multicoloured . . . 70 15
1031 **436** 10 w. multicoloured . . . 70 15
See also Nos. 1042/3, 1048/9, 1057/8 and 1075/6.

1973. Korean Unification Campaign.
1032 **437** 10 w. multicoloured . . . 40 15

438 "V" Sign and Flags **439** Construction Workers and Cogwheel

1973. Return of Korean Forces from South Vietnam.
1033 **438** 10 w. multicoloured . . 45 20

1973. 10th Workers' Day.
1034 **439** 10 w. multicoloured . . 40 15

440 W.M.O. Emblem and Satellite **442** Wonsam Costume (woman's ceremonial)

1973. Centenary of World Meteorological Organization.
1035 **440** 10 w. multicoloured . . 40 15

1973. Korean Court Costumes of the Yi Dynasty (1st series). Multicoloured. Background colours given.
1037 – 10 w. orange . . . . . . 1·25 60
1038 **442** 10 w. orange . . . . . . 1·25 60
DESIGN: No. 1037, Kujangbok (king's ceremonial costume);
See also Nos. 1045/6, 1053/4, 1060/1 and 1078/9.

443 Nurse with Lamp **444** Reservists and Flag

1973. 50th Anniv of Korean Nurses' Association.
1040 **443** 10 w. multicoloured . . 55 15

1973. Home Reserve Forces Day.
1041 **444** 10 w. multicoloured . . 75 25

445 Palmi Island **446** Sain-am Rock, Mt. Dokjol

1973. Korean Tourist Attractions (2nd series).
1042 **445** 10 w. multicoloured . . 70 15
1043 **446** 10 w. multicoloured . . 70 15

447 Table Tennis Player

1973. Victory of South Korean Women's Team in World Table Tennis Championships, Sarajevo.
1044 **447** 10 w. multicoloured . . 1·25 60

1973. Korean Court Costumes of the Yi Dynasty (2nd series). As T **442**. Mult. Background colours given.
1045 10 w. purple . . . . 1·25 60
1046 10 w. green . . . . 1·25 60
DESIGNS: No. 1045, Konryongpo (king's costume). No. 1046, Jokui (queen's ceremonial costume).

450 Admiral Li Sun Sin's Shrine, Asan **451** Limestone Cavern, Kusan-ni

1973. Korean Tourist Attractions (3rd series).
1048 **450** 10 w. multicoloured . . 70 35
1049 **451** 10 w. multicoloured . . 70 35

452 Children's Choir

1973. 20th Anniv of World Vision Int.
1050 **452** 10 w. multicoloured . . . 70 20

453 Love Pin and "Disasters"

1973. Disaster Relief Fund.
1051 **453** 10 w. + 5 w. mult . . . 65 15

454 Steel Converter **457** Table Tennis Bat and Ball

1973. Inauguration of Pohang Steel Works.
1052 **454** 10 w. multicoloured . . . 50 15

1973. Korean Court Costumes of the Yi Dynasty. (3rd series). As T **442**. Mult. Background colours given.
1053 10 w. blue . . . . 1·25 60
1054 10 w. pink . . . . 1·25 60
DESIGNS: No. 1053, Kangsapo (crown prince's) costume, No. 1054, Tangui (princess's) costume.

1973. Table Tennis Gymnasium Construction Fund.
1056 **457** 10 w. + 5 w. mve & grn 45 20

458 Namhae Suspension Bridge **459** Hongdo Island

1973. Korean Tourist Attractions (4th series).
1057 **458** 10 w. multicoloured . . . 40 10
1058 **459** 10 w. multicoloured . . . 40 10

460 Interpol and Korean Police Emblems

1973. 50th Anniv of International Criminal Police Organization (Interpol).
1059 **460** 10 w. multicoloured . . . 40 10

1973. Korean Court Costumes of the Yi Dynasty (4th series). As T **442**. Mult. Background colours given.
1060 10 w. yellow . . . . 1·25 60
1061 10 w. blue . . . . 1·25 60
DESIGNS: No. 1060, Kumkwanchobok (court official's) costume. No. 1061, Hwalot (queen's wedding) costume.

465 Manchurian Cranes **466** Sommal Lily **467** Motorway and Farm

1973.
1063 – 1 w. brown 15 10
1063a – 3 w. black and blue . . 25 10
1064 – 5 w. brown 10 10
1064a – 6 w. turquoise and green 20 10
1065 **465** 10 w. ultramarine & blue 40 10
1066 **466** 10 w. red, black & green 85 10
1067 **467** 10 w. green and red . . 25 10
1068 – 30 w. brown and yellow 35 10
1068a – 50 w. green and brown 30 10
1068b – 60 w. brown and yellow 35 10
1068c – 80 w. black and brown 45 10
1069 – 100 w. yellow & brown 22·00 1·60
1069a – 100 w. red 55 10
1069b – 200 w. brown and pink 85 10
1069c – 300 w. red and lilac . . 1·75 10
1069d – 500 w. multicoloured . . 11·00 85
1069e – 500 w. purple & brown 2·10 60
1069f – 1,000 w. green . . . . 5·50 85

DESIGNS—VERT: 1 w. Mask of old man; 5 w. Siberian chipmunk; 6 w. Lily; 30 w. Honey Bee; 50 w. Pot with Lid; 60 w. Jar; 100 w. (No. 1069) Gold Crown, Silla dynasty; 100 w. (No. 1069a) Admiral Yi Soon Shin; 300 w. Pobjusa Temple; 500 w. (No. 1069d) Gold Crown; 500 w. (No. 1069e) Carved dragon (tile Backje Dynasty). LARGER 24×33 mm: 100 w. Flying deities (relief from bronze bell, Sangwe on Temple). HORIZ: 3 w. Magpie; 80 w. Ceramic horseman; 200 w. Muryangsujeon Hall, Busok Temple.
For designs similar to Type **465** but with frame, see Type **703**.

470 Tennis

1973. 54th National Athletic Meeting, Pusan. Multicoloured.
1070 10 w. Type **470** 40 10
1071 10 w. Hurdling 40 10

471 Children with Stamp Albums

1973. Philatelic Week.
1072 **471** 10 w. multicoloured . . 35 10

472 Soyang River Dam

1973. Inauguration of Soyang River Dam.
1074 **472** 10 w. multicoloured . . 30 10

473 Mt. Mai, Chinan **474** Tangerine Grove, Cheju Island

1973. Korean Tourist Attractions (5th series).
1075 **473** 10 w. multicoloured . . 40 10
1076 **474** 10 w. multicoloured . . 40 10

475 Match, Cigarette and Flames **478** Tiger and Candles

1973. 10th Fire Prevention Day.
1077 **476** 10 w. multicoloured . . 25 10

1973. Korean Court Costumes of the Yi Dynasty (5th series). As T **442**. Mult. Back-ground colours given.
1078 10 w. orange 75 35
1079 10 w. pink 75 35
DESIGNS: No. 1078, Pyongsangbok (official's wife) costume, No. 1079, Kokunbok (military officer's) costume.

1973. Lunar New Year ("Year of the Tiger"). Multicoloured.
1081 10 w. Type **478** 40 10
1082 10 w. Decorated top 45 10

479 Korean Girl and Flame Emblem

1973. 25th Anniv of Declaration of Human Rights.
1084 **479** 10 w. multicoloured . . 25 10

480 Boeing 747-200 Jetliner and Polar Zone

1973. Air.
1085 **480** 110 w. blue and pink . . 7·50 3·25
1086 – 135 w. red and green . . 7·50 3·25
1087 – 145 w. red and blue . . . 7·50 3·25
1088 – 180 w. yellow and lilac . 10·00 3·25
DESIGNS—Jetliner and Postal Zones on Map. 135 w. South-east Asia; 145 w. India, Australasia and North America; 180 w. Europe, Africa and South America.

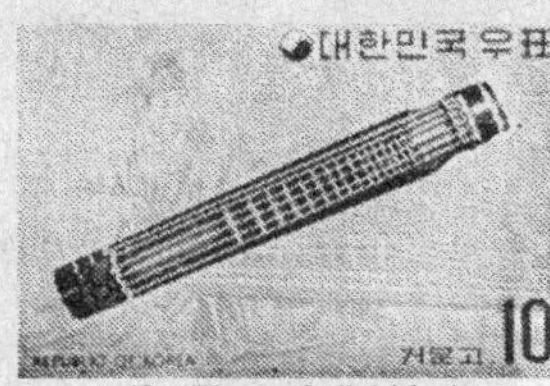

481 "Komunko" (zither)

1974. Traditional Musical Instruments (1st series). Multicoloured. Background colours given.
1089 **481** 10 w. blue 50 10
1090 – 30 w. orange 85 40
DESIGN: 30 w. "Nagak" (conch trumpet).
See also Nos. 1098/9, 1108/9, 1117/18 and 1132/3.

483 Apricots **485** Reservist and Factory

1974. Fruits (1st series). Multicoloured.
1092 10 w. Type **483** 25 10
1093 30 w. Strawberries . . . . 1·00 50
See also Nos. 1104/5, 111/2, 1120/1 and 1143/4.

1974. Home Reserve Forces Day.
1095 **485** 10 w. multicoloured . . . 30 10

486 W.P.Y. Emblem **489** Mail Train and Communications Emblem

1974. World Population Year.
1096 **486** 10 w. multicoloured . . . 25 10

1974. Traditional Musical Instruments (2nd series). As T **481**. Multicoloured. Background colours given.
1098 10 w. blue 60 10
1099 30 w. green . . . . 1·25 60
DESIGNS: 10 w. "Tchouk"; 30 w. "Eu".

1974. Communications Day.
1101 **489** 10 w. multicoloured . . . 60 15

490 C.A.F.E.A.-I.C.C. Emblem on Globe **491** Port Installations

1974. 22nd Session of International Chamber of Commerce's Commission on Asian and Far Eastern Affairs, Seoul.
1102 **490** 10 w. multicoloured . . . 25 10

1974. Inaug. of New Port Facilities, Inchon.
1103 **491** 10 w. multicoloured . . . 40 10

1974. Fruits (2nd series). As T **483**. Mult.
1104 10 w. Peaches 40 10
1105 30 w. Grapes . . . . 1·00 50

494 U.N.E.S.C.O. Emblem and Extended Fan **499** Cross and Emblems

1974. 20th Anniv of South Korean U.N.E.S.C.O. Commission.
1107 **494** 10 w. multicoloured . . . 25 10

1974. Traditional Musical Instruments (3rd series). As T **481**. Multicoloured. Background colours given.
1108 10 w. orange 40 10
1109 30 w. pink . . . . 1·00 50
DESIGNS: 10 w. "A-chaing" (stringed instrument); 30 w. "Kyobang-ko" (drum).

1974. Fruits (3rd series). As T **483**. Multicoloured.
1111 10 w. Pears 40 10
1112 30 w. Apples 85 40

1974. "Explo 74"–2nd International Training Congress on Evangelism. Multicoloured.
1114 10 w. Type **499** 20 10
1115 10 w. Emblem and Korean map on Globe 20 10

501 Underground Train

1974. Opening of Seoul Underground Railway.
1116 501 10 w. multicoloured . . 85 10

1974. Traditional Musical Instruments (4th series). As T **481**. Multicoloured. Background colours given.
1117 10 w. blue 40 10
1118 30 w. pink . . . . 1·10 40
DESIGNS: No. 1117, So ("Pan pipes"); No. 1118, Haikem (Two-stringed fiddle).

1974. Fruits (4th series). As T **483**. Multicoloured.
1120 10 w. Cherries 40 10
1121 30 w. Persimmons 60 35

506 Rifle Shooting

1974. 55th National Athletic Meeting, Seoul. Multicoloured.
1123 10 w. Type **506** 25 10
1124 30 w. Rowing 65 40

508 U.P.U. Emblem **509** Symbols of Member Countries

1974. Centenary of U.P.U.
1125 **508** 10 w. multicoloured (postage) 20 10
1126 110 w. multicoloured (air) 2·00 1·00

1974. First World Conference of People-to-People International.
1128 **509** 10 w. multicoloured . . 20 10

510 Korean Stamps of 1884

1974. Philatelic Week and 90th Anniv of First Korean Stamps.
1129 **510** 10 w. multicoloured . . 30 10

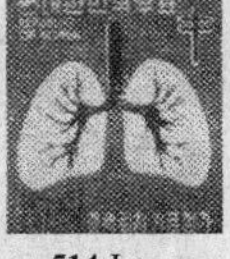

511 Taekwondo Contestants **514** Lungs

1974. First Asian Taekwondo Championships, Seoul.
1131 **511** 10 w. multicoloured . . 30 10

1974. Traditional Musical Instruments (5th series). As T **481**. Multicoloured. Background colours given.
1132 10 w. pink 40 10
1133 30 w. ochre 90 40
DESIGNS: 10 w. Pak (clappers); 30 w. Pyenchong (chimes).

1974. Tuberculosis Control Fund.
1135 **514** 10 w. + 5 w. red & green 25 10

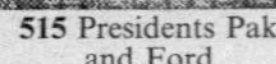

515 Presidents Pak and Ford **516** Yook Young Soo (wife of Pres. Pak)

1974. State Visit of President Ford of United States.
1136 **515** 10 w. multicoloured . . . 40 20

1974. Yook Young Soo Memorial Issue.
1138 **516** 10 w. green 40 15
1139 10 w. orange 40 15
1140 10 w. violet 40 15
1141 10 w. blue 40 15

1974. Fruits (5th series). As T **483**. Multicoloured.
1143 10 w. Tangerines 40 10
1144 30 w. Chestnuts 75 15

519 "Good Luck" Purse **521** U.P.U. Emblem and "75"

1974. Lunar New Year ("Year of the Rabbit"). Multicoloured.
1146 10 w. Type **519** 35 10
1147 10 w. Toy rabbits 35 10

1975. 75th Anniv of Korea's Membership of U.P.U. Multicoloured.
1149 10 w. Type **521** 25 10
1150 10 w. U.P.U. emblem and paper dart 25 10

523 Dove with "Good Luck" Card

1975. Inauguration of National Welfare Insurance System.
1151 **523** 10 w. multicoloured . . . 20 10

524 Dr. Schweitzer, Map and Syringe **525** Salpuli Dancer

1975. Birth Centenary of Dr. Albert Schweitzer.
1152 **524** 10 w. bistre 40 15
1153 10 w. mauve 40 15
1154 10 w. orange 40 15
1155 10 w. green 40 15

1975. Korean Folk Dances (1st series). Multicoloured, background colour given.
1156 **525** 10 w. green 40 10
1157 – 10 w. blue 40 10
DESIGN: No. 1157, Exorcism in dance.
See also Nos. 1168/9, 1175/6, 1193/4 and 1208/9.

527 Globe and Rotary Emblem

1975. 70th Anniv of Rotary International.
1159 **527** 10 w. multicoloured . . . 25 10

528 Women and I.W.Y. Emblem

1975. International Women's Year.
1160 **528** 10 w. multicoloured . . . 20 10

529 Violets **531** Saemaeul Township

1975. Flowers (1st series). Multicoloured.
1161 10 w. Type **529** 35 10
1162 10 w. Anemones 35 10
See also Nos. 1171/2, 1184/5, 1199/1200 and 1213/4.

1975. National Afforestation Campaign. Multicoloured.
1163 10 w. Type **531** 50 10
1164 10 w. Lake and trees 50 10
1165 10 w. "Green" forest 50 10
1166 10 w. Felling timber 50 10
Nos. 1163/6 were issued together se-tenant in horizontal strips of four within the sheet, forming a composite design.

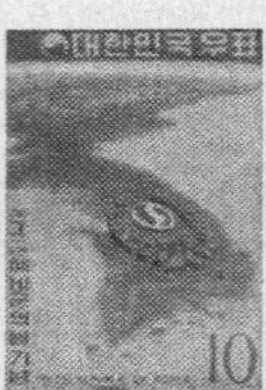

535 H.R.F. Emblem on Map of Korea **536** Butterfly Dance

1975. Homeland Reserve Forces Day.
1167 **535** 10 w. multicoloured . . . 30 10

1975. Folk Dances (2nd series). Multicoloured, background colour given.
1168 **536** 10 w. green 45 10
1169 – 10 w. yellow 45 10
DESIGN: No. 1169, Victory dance.

538 Rhododendron **540** Metric Symbols

1975. Flowers (2nd series). Multicoloured.
1171 10 w. Type **538** 40 10
1172 10 w. Clematis 40 10

1975. Centenary of Metric Convention.
1173 **540** 10 w. multicoloured . . 25 10

541 Soldier and Incense Pot **542** Mokjoong Dance

1975. 20th Memorial Day.
1174 **541** 10 w. multicoloured . . 20 10

1975. Folk Dances (3rd series). Multicoloured.
1175 **542** 10 w. blue 45 10
1176 – 10 w. pink 45 10
DESIGN: No. 1176, Malttungi dancer.

544 Flags of South Korea, U.N. and U.S

1975. 25th Anniv of Korean War. Multicoloured.
1178 10 w. Type **544** 35 10
1179 10 w. Flags of Ethiopia, France, Greece, Canada and South Africa 35 10
1180 10 w. Flags of Luxembourg, Australia, U.K., Colombia and Turkey 35 10
1181 10 w. Flags of Netherlands, Belgium, Philippines, New Zealand and Thailand . . . 35 10

548 Presidents Pak and Bongo **549** Iris

1975. State Visit of President Bongo of Gabon.
1182 **548** 10 w. multicoloured . . . 30 10

1975. Flowers (3rd series). Multicoloured.
1184 10 w. Type **549** 40 10
1185 10 w. Thistle 40 10

551 Scout Scarf **552** Freedom Flame

1975. "Nordjamb 75" World Scout Jamboree, Norway. Multicoloured.
1186 10 w. Type **551** 30 10
1187 10 w. Scout oath 30 10
1188 10 w. Scout camp 30 10
1189 10 w. Axe and rope 30 10
1190 10 w. Camp fire 30 10

1975. 30th Anniv of Liberation. Multicoloured.
1191 20 w. Type **552** 35 10
1192 20 w. Balloon emblems . . . 35 10

554 Drum Dance **556** Taekwondo Contestant

1975. Folk Dances (4th series). Multicoloured, background colour given.
1193 **554** 20 w. yellow 90 40
1194 – 20 w. orange 90 40
DESIGN: No. 1194, Bara dance.

1975. Second World Taekwondo Championships, Seoul.
1196 **556** 20 w. multicoloured . . . 25 10

557 Assembly Hall

1975. Completion of National Assembly Hall.
1197 **557** 20 w. multicoloured . . . 25 10

558 Dumper Truck and Emblem **559** Broad-bell Flower

1975. Contractors' Association Convention, Seoul.
1198 **558** 20 w. multicoloured . . . 20 10

1975. Flowers (4th series). Multicoloured.
1199 20 w. Type **559** 85 40
1200 20 w. Bush clover 85 40

561 Morse Key and Dish Aerial

1975. 90th Anniv of Korean Telecommunications.
1201 **561** 20 w. black, orge & pur 35 10

562 Yeongweol Caves **564** Flag and Missiles

1975. International Tourism Day. Multicoloured.
1202 20 w. Type **562** 25 10
1203 20 w. Mount Sorak 25 10

1975. Korean Armed Forces Day.
1204 **564** 20 w. multicoloured . . 25 10

565 "Gymnastics" **567** "Kangaroo" Collector

1975. 56th National Athletic Meeting. Multicoloured.
1205 20 w. Type **565** 20 10
1206 20 w. "Handball" 20 10

1975. Philatelic Week.
1207 **567** 20 w. multicoloured . . 25 10

568 Sogo Dance **570** U.N. Emblem and Handclasps

1975. Folk Dances (5th series). Multicoloured, background colour given.
1208 **568** 20 w. blue 90 40
1209 – 20 w. yellow 90 40
DESIGN: No. 1209, Bupo Nori dance.

1975. 30th Anniv of United Nations.
1211 **570** 20 w. multicoloured . . 20 10

571 Red Cross and Emblems **572** Camellia

1975. 70th Anniv of Korean Red Cross.
1212 **571** 20 w. multicoloured . . 35 10

1975. Flowers (5th series). Multicoloured.
1213 20 w. Type **572** . . . . . . 1·10 60
1214 20 w. Gentian . . . . 1·10 60

574 Union Emblem **575** Children Playing

1975. 10th Anniv of Asian Parliamentary Union.
1215 **574** 20 w. multicoloured . . 20 10

1975. Lunar New Year. Multicoloured.
1216 20 w. Type **575** 30 10
1217 20 w. Dragon ("Year of the Dragon") 30 10

577 Electric Train

1975. Opening of Cross-country Electric Railway.
1219 **577** 20 w. multicoloured . . . 30 10

578 "Dilipa fenestra"

1976. Butterflies (1st series). Multicoloured, background colour given.
1220 **578** 20 w. red 65 10
1221 – 20 w. blue 65 10
DESIGN: No. 1221 "Luehdorfia puziloi".
See also Nos. 1226/7, 1246/7, 1254/5 and 1264/5.

580 Institute Emblem and Science Emblems

581 Japanese White-necked Crane

1976. 10th Anniv of Korean Institute of Science and Technology.
1222 **580** 20 w. multicoloured . . . 25 10

1976. Birds (1st series). Multicoloured.
1223 20 w. Type **581** 55 15
1224 20 w. Great Bustard 55 15
See also Nos. 1243/4, 1251/2, 1257/8 and 1266/7.

583 Globe and Telephones

1976. Telephone Centenary.
1225 **583** 20 w. multicoloured . . . 20 10

584 "Papilio xuthus"

1976. Butterflies (2nd series). Multicoloured, background colour given.
1226 **584** 20 w. yellow 65 10
1227 – 20 w. green 65 10
DESIGN: No. 1227, "Parnassius bremeri".

586 "National Development"

587 Eye and People

1976. Homeland Reserve Forces Day.
1228 **586** 20 w. multicoloured . . . 30 10

1976. World Health Day. Prevention of Blindness.
1229 **587** 20 w. multicoloured . . . 30 10

588 Pres. Pak and Flag

589 Ruins of Moenjodaro

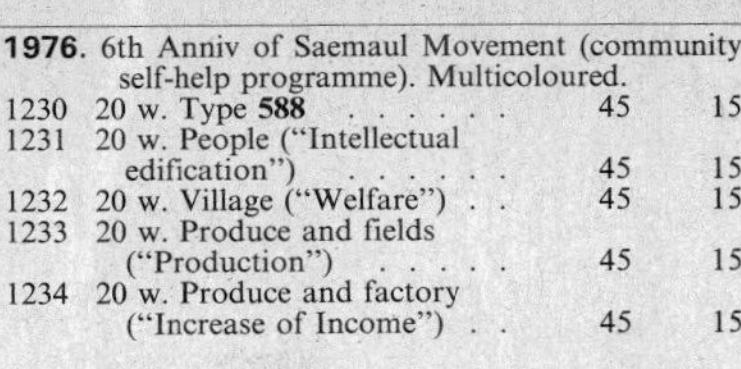

1976. 6th Anniv of Saemaul Movement (community self-help programme). Multicoloured.
1230 20 w. Type **588** 45 15
1231 20 w. People ("Intellectual edification") 45 15
1232 20 w. Village ("Welfare") . . 45 15
1233 20 w. Produce and fields ("Production") 45 15
1234 20 w. Produce and factory ("Increase of Income") . . 45 15

1976. Moenjodaro (Pakistan) Preservation Campaign.
1235 **589** 20 w. multicoloured . . 40 10

590 U.S. Flags of 1776 and 1976

591 Camp Scene on Emblem

1976. Bicentenary of American Revolution.
1236 **590** 100 w. red, blue & black 2·40 1·10
1237 – 100 w. red, blue & black 2·40 1·10
1238 – 100 w. red, blue & black 2·40 1·10
1239 – 100 w. red, blue & black 2·40 1·10
1240 – 100 w. red, blue & black 2·40 1·10
DESIGNS: No. 1237, Statue of Liberty; No. 1238, Map of United States; No. 1239, Liberty Bell; No. 1240, American astronaut.

1976. 30th Anniv of Korean Girl Scouts Federation.
1242 **591** 20 w. multicoloured . . 40 10

592 Blue-winged Pitta

594 Buddha and Temple

1976. Birds (2nd series). Multicoloured.
1243 20 w. Type **592** 55 10
1244 20 w. White-bellied Black Woodpecker 55 10

1976. U.N.E.S.C.O. Campaign for Preservation of Borobudur Temple (in Indonesia).
1245 **594** 20 w. multicoloured . . . 25 10

595 Eastern Pale Clouded Yellow

1976. Butterflies (3rd series). Multicoloured, background colour given.
1246 **595** 20 w. olive 55 10
1247 – 20 w. violet 55 10
DESIGN: No. 1247, Chinese windmill.

597 Protected Family

598 Volleyball

1976. National Life Insurance.
1248 **597** 20 w. multicoloured . . . 30 10

1976. Olympic Games, Montreal. Multicoloured.
1249 20 w. Type **598** 35 10
1250 20 w. Boxing 35 10

600 Black Wood Pigeon

602 Children and Books

1976. Birds (3rd series). Multicoloured.
1251 20 w. Type **600** 55 10
1252 20 w. Oystercatcher 55 10

1976. Books for Children.
1253 **602** 20 w. multicoloured . . 25 10

603 "Hestina assimilis"

1976. Butterflies (4th series). Multicoloured, background colour given.
1254 **603** 20 w. brown . . . . . . 1·60 85
1255 – 20 w. drab . . . . 1·60 85
DESIGN: No. 1255, Blue triangle.

604a Corps Members and Flag

605 Black-faced Spoonbill

1976. 1st Anniv of Korean Civil Defence Corps.
1256 **604a** 20 w. multicoloured . . . 30 10

1976. Birds (4th series). Multicoloured.
1257 20 w. Type **605** 55 10
1258 20 w. Black stork 55 10

607 Chamsungdan, Mani Mountain

1976. International Tourism Day. Multicoloured.
1259 20 w. Type **607** 25 10
1260 20 w. Ilchumun Gate, Tongdosa 25 10

609 Cadet and Parade

610 "Musa basjoo" (flower arrangement, Cheong Jo the Great)

1976. 30th Anniv of Korean Military Academy.
1261 **609** 20 w. multicoloured . . . 25 10

1976. Philatelic Week.
1262 **610** 20 w. black, red and drab 25 10

611 Yellow-legged Tortoiseshell

613 European Black Vulture

1976. Butterflies (5th series). Multicoloured, background colour given.
1264 **611** 20 w. light green . . . . 1·90 85
1265 – 20 w. purple . . . . . 1·90 85
DESIGN: No. 1265, "Fabriciana nerippe".

1976. Birds (5th series). Multicoloured.
1266 20 w. Type **613** . . . . 2·10 1·00
1267 20 w. Whistling Swan . . . . 2·10 1·00

615 Snake (bas-relief, Kim Yu Shin's tomb)

619 Dish Aerial

617 "Training Technicians"

1976. Lunar New Year (Year of the Snake). Multicoloured.
1268 20 w. Type **615** 30 10
1269 20 w. Door knocker with Manchurian cranes 30 10

1977. 4th Five Year Economic Development Plan. Multicoloured.
1271 20 w. Type **617** 40 10
1272 20 w. Tanker ("Heavy Industries") 40 10

1977. 5th Anniv of Korea's I.T.U. Membership.
1273 **619** 20 w. multicoloured . . 30 10

620 Korean Broadcasting Centre

621 Jar with Grape Design

1977. 50th Anniv of Broadcasting in Korea.
1274 **620** 20 w. multicoloured . . 35 10

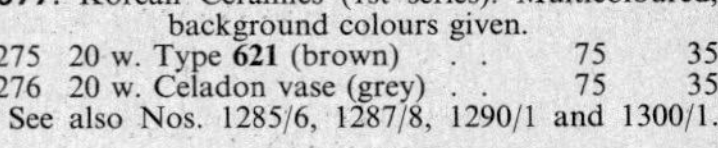

1977. Korean Ceramics (1st series). Multicoloured, background colours given.
1275 20 w. Type **621** (brown) . . 75 35
1276 20 w. Celadon vase (grey) . . 75 35
See also Nos. 1285/6, 1287/8, 1290/1 and 1300/1.

623 "Two-children" Family

624 Reserve Soldier

1977. Family Planning.
1277 **623** 20 w. green, turq & orge 85 10

1977. Ninth Homeland Reserve Forces Day.
1278 **624** 20 w. multicoloured . . 30 10

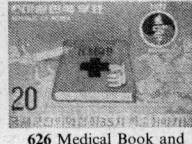

625 Diagram of Brain

626 Medical Book and Equipment

1977. 10th Anniv of Science Day.
1279 **625** 20 w. multicoloured . . 20 10

1977. 35th International Military Medicine Meeting.
1280 **626** 20 w. multicoloured . . 45 10

627 Child with Flowers

628 Veterans' Flag and Emblem

1977. 20th Anniv of Children's Charter.
1281 **627** 20 w. multicoloured . . 20 10

1977. 25th Anniv of Korean Veterans' Day.
1282 **628** 20 w. multicoloured . . 40 10

629 Statue of Buddha, Sokkulam Grotto

630 Celadon Jar

1977. 2600th Birth Anniv of Buddha.
1283 **629** 20 w. olive 30 10

1977. Korean Ceramics (2nd series). Multicoloured, background colours given.
1285 20 w. Type **630** (pink) 45 10
1286 20 w. Porcelain vase (blue) (vert) 45 10

632 "Buddha" Celadon Wine Jar

1977. Korean Ceramics (3rd series). Multicoloured, background colours given.

1287 20 w. Type 632 (mauve) . . . 45 10
1288 20 w. Celadon vase (pale blue) 45 10

수해구제
+10
(634)

635 Celadon Vase, Black Koryo Ware

1977. Flood Relief. No. 791 surch with T 634.

1289 20 w. + 10 w. green . . . . 2·40 1·25

1977. Korean Ceramics (4th series). Multicoloured, background colours given.

1290 20 w. Type 635 (stone) . . . 45 10
1291 20 w. White porcelain bowl (green) (horiz) 45 10

637 Ulleung-do Island 639 Servicemen

1977. World Tourism Day. Multicoloured.

1292 20 w. Type 637 . . . . 30 10
1293 20 w. Haeundae Beach . . . 30 10

1977. Armed Forces Day.

1294 639 20 w. multicoloured . . . 20 10

640 641

"Mount Inwang Clearing-up after the Rain" (detail from drawing by Chung Seon)

1977. Philatelic Week.

1295 640 20 w. multicoloured . . . 40 10
1296 641 20 w. multicoloured . . . 40 10

Nos. 1294/5 were issued in se-tenant pairs throughout the sheet, forming a composite design.

642 Rotary Emblem and Koryo Dynasty Bronze Bell

643 South Korean Flag over Everest

1977. 50th Anniv of Korean Rotary Club.

1298 642 20 w. multicoloured . . . 25 10

1977. South Korean Conquest of Mount Everest.

1299 643 20 w. multicoloured . . . 50 10

644 Punch'ong Bottle 646 Hands preserving Nature

1977. Korean Ceramics (5th series). Multicoloured, background colours given.

1300 20 w. Type 644 (brown) . . 50 10
1301 20 w. Celadon cylindrical bottle (pale brown) 50 10

1977. Nature Conservation.

1302 646 20 w. blue, green & brn 15 10

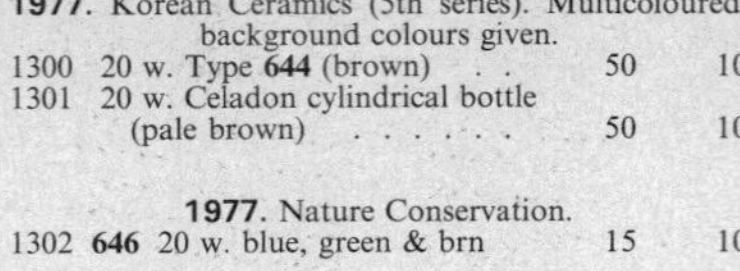

647 Children with Kites 649 Clay Pigeon Shooting

1977. Lunar New Year ("Year of the Horse"). Multicoloured.

1303 20 w. Type 647 . . . . 25 10
1304 20 w. Horse (bas-relief, Kim Yu Shin's tomb) 25 10

1977. 42nd World Shooting Championships, Seoul. Multicoloured.

1306 20 w. Type 649 . . . . . . 20 10
1307 20 w. Air pistol shooting . . 20 10
1308 20 w. Air rifle shooting . . . 20 10

652 Korean Airlines Boeing 747-200

1977. 25th Anniv of Korean Membership of I.C.A.O.

1310 652 20 w. multicoloured . . 45 10

653 "Exports"

1977. Korean Exports.

1311 653 20 w. multicoloured . . 35 10

654 Ships and World Map

1978. National Maritime Day.

1312 654 20 w. multicoloured . . 30 10

655 Three-storey Pagoda, Hwaom Temple

656 Seven-storey Pagoda, T'app'yong-ri

1978. Stone Pagodas (1st series).

1313 655 20 w. multicoloured . . 35 10
1314 656 20 w. multicoloured . . 35 10

See also Nos. 1319/20, 1322/5 and 1340/1.

657 Ants with Coins

658 Seoul Sejong Cultural Centre, Hahoe Mask and Violin

1978. Savings Encouragement.

1315 657 20 w. multicoloured . . 30 10

1978. Opening of Seoul Sejong Cultural Centre.

1316 658 20 w. multicoloured . . 25 10

659 Standard Bearer 660 Pigeon and Young

1978. Tenth Homeland Reserve Forces Day.

1317 659 20 w. multicoloured . . . 25 10

1978. Family Planning.

1318 660 20 w. black and green . . 20 10

661 Pagoda, Punhwang Temple

662 Pagoda, Miruk Temple

1978. Stone Pagodas (2nd series).

1319 661 20 w. multicoloured . . . 65 35
1320 662 20 w. multicoloured . . . 65 35

663 National Assembly

1978. 30th Anniv of National Assembly.

1321 663 20 w. multicoloured . . . 20 10

664 Tabo Pagoda, Pulguk Temple

665 Three-storey Pagoda, Pulguk Temple

1978. Stone Pagodas (3rd series).

1322 664 20 w. multicoloured . . . 35 10
1323 665 20 w. multicoloured . . . 35 10

666 Ten-storey Pagoda, Kyongch'on Temple

667 Nine-storey Octagonal Pagoda, Wolchong Temple

1978. Stone Pagodas (4th series).

1324 666 20 w. multicoloured . . . 45 10
1325 667 20 w. multicoloured . . . 45 10

668 Emblem and Hands with Tools

669 Crater Lake, Mt. Baeguda and Bell of Joy

1978. 24th International Youth Skill Olympics, Pusan.

1326 668 20 w. multicoloured . . . 20 10

1978. 30th Anniv of Republic of Korea.

1328 669 20 w. multicoloured . . . 20 10

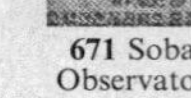

670 Army Nursing Officer

671 Sobaeksan Observatory and Telescope

1978. 30th Anniv of Army Nursing Corps.

1329 670 20 w. multicoloured . . 20 10

1978. Opening of Sobaeksan Observatory.

1330 671 20 w. multicoloured . . 40 10

672 Kyonghoeru Pavilion, Kyonbok Palace

673 Baeg-do Island

1978. World Tourism Day.

1331 672 20 w. multicoloured . . 20 10
1332 673 20 w. multicoloured . . 20 10

674 Customs Officers and Flag

1978. Centenary of Custom House.

1333 674 20 w. multicoloured . . 25 10

675 Armed Forces

676 Earthenware Figures, Silla Dynasty

1978. 30th Anniv of Korean Armed Forces.

1334 675 20 w. multicoloured . . 30 10

1978. Culture Month.

1335 676 20 w. black and green . 20 10

677 Painting of a Lady. (Shin Yoo n-bok)

678 Young Men and Y.M.C.A. Emblem

1978. Philatelic Week.

1336 677 20 w. multicoloured . . 30 10

1978. 75th Anniv of Korean Y.M.C.A.

1338 678 20 w. multicoloured . . 20 10

679 Hand smothering Fire

1978. Fire Prevention Campaign.

1339 679 20 w. multicoloured . . 20 10

680 Thirteen-storey Pagoda, Jeonghye Temple
681 Three-storey Pagoda, Jinjeon Temple

1978. Stone Pagodas (5th series).

1340	**680**	20 w. multicoloured . . .	30	10
1341	**681**	20 w. multicoloured . . .	30	10

682 Snow Scene
684 People within Hibiscus

1978. Lunar New Year ("Year of the Sheep"). Multicoloured.

1342	20 w. Type **682**	25	10
1343	20 w. Sheep (bas-relief, Kim Yu Shin's tomb)	25	10

1978. 10th Anniv of National Education Charter.

1345	**684**	20 w. multicoloured . . .	20	10

685 President Pak

1978. Re-election of President Pak.

1346	**685**	20 w. multicoloured . . .	30	10

686 Golden Mandarinfish
687 Lace Bark Pine

1979. Nature Conservation.

1348	**686**	20 w. multicoloured . . .	25	10
1349	**687**	20 w. multicoloured . . .	25	10

688 Samil Monument
689 Worker and Bulldozer

1979. 60th Anniv of Samil Independence Movement.

1350	**688**	20 w. multicoloured . . .	20	10

1979. Labour Day.

1351	**689**	20 w. multicoloured . . .	20	10

690 Tabo Pagoda, Pulgak Temple
695 Hand holding Symbols of Security

1979. Korean Art. Multicoloured.

1352	20 w. Type **690**	25	10
1353	20 w. Gilt-bronze Maitreya	25	10
1354	20 w. Gold crown of Silla . .	25	10
1355	20 w. Celadon vase	25	10
1356	60 w. "Tano Day Activities" (silk screen) (50×33 mm)	45	10

1979. Strengthening National Security.

1358	**695**	20 w. multicoloured . . .	20	10

696 Pulguk Temple and P.A.T.A. Emblem

1979. 28th Pacific Area Travel Association Conference, Seoul.

1359	**696**	20 w. multicoloured . .	25	10

697 Presidents Pak and Senghor

1979. Visit of President Senghor of Senegal.

1360	**697**	20 w. multicoloured . .	20	10

698 Basketball
699 Children playing

1979. 8th World Women's Basketball Championships, Seoul.

1362	**698**	20 w. multicoloured . .	40	10

1979. International Year of the Child.

1363	**699**	20 w. multicoloured . .	25	10

700 Children on Swing

1979. Family Planning.

1364	**700**	20 w. multicoloured . .	20	10

701 Mandarins
702 "Neofinettia falcata" (orchid)

1979. Nature Conservation.

1365	**701**	20 w. multicoloured . .	40	10
1366	**702**	20 w. multicoloured . .	40	10

703 Manchurian Cranes

1979.

1367	**703**	10 w. black and green	30	10
1368	–	15 w. dp green & green	15	10
1369	–	20 w. bistre, black & blue	10	10
1370	–	30 w. multicoloured . .	20	10
1371	–	40 w. multicoloured . .	20	10
1372	–	50 w. brown, red & orge	15	10
1373	–	60 w. grey, purple & mve	25	10
1374	–	70 w. multicoloured . .	35	10
1375	–	80 w. yellow, blk & red	25	10
1376	–	90 w. buff, green and orange	25	10
1377	–	100 w. purple & mauve	40	10
1377a	–	100 w. black	45	10
1378	–	150 w. black, bistre and blue	45	10
1379	–	200 w. brown and green	35	10
1380	–	300 w. blue	65	10
1381	–	400 w. green, brown and deep green	2·25	10
1381a	–	400 w. blue, ochre, brown and grey	65	10
1382	–	450 w. brown	1·60	10
1383	–	500 w. dp green & green	85	15
1383a	–	550 w. black	1·75	20
1384	–	600 w. multicoloured .	1·00	20
1385	–	700 w. multicoloured .	1·25	20
1386	–	800 w. multicoloured .	1·60	20
1387	–	1000 w. lt brown & brn	1·60	30
1388	–	1000 w. lt brown & brn	1·60	30
1389	–	5000 w. multicoloured .	11·00	1·50

DESIGNS:—As T **703**: HORIZ: 15 w. Mt. Sorak; 50 w. Earthenware model of wagon; 90 w. Paikryung Island; 1000 w. Duck earthenware vessels (1387 facing right; 1388 facing left). VERT: 20 w. Tolharubang (stone grandfather); 30 w. National flag; 40 w. "Hibiscus syriacus"; 60 w. Porcelain jar, Yi Dynasty; 70 w. Kyongju Observatory; 80 w. Mounted warrior (pottery vessel); 100 w. (1377) Ryu Kwan Soon; 100 w. (1377a) Chung Yak Yong (writer); 150 w. Porcelain jar, Chosun Dynasty; 200 w. Ahn Joong Geun; 300 w. Ahn Chang Ho; 400 w. Koryo celadon incense burner; 450, 550 w. Kim Ku (organizer of Korean Independence Party); 500 w. Brick with mountain landscape; 600 w. Hong Yung Sik (postal reformer); 700 w. Duck (lid of incense burner). 29×41 mm: 800 w. Dragon's head flagpole finial; 5000 w. Tiger.

See also No. 1065.

725 People suffering from Traffic Pollution

1979. Environmental Protection.

1390	**725**	20 w. brown and green	20	10

726 Common Goral
727 "Convallaria leiskei" Miquel

1979. Nature Conservation.

1391	**726**	20 w. multicoloured . . .	35	10
1392	**727**	20 w. multicoloured . . .	35	10

728 Presidents Pak and Carter

1979. Visit of President Carter of United States.

1393	**728**	20 w. multicoloured . . .	20	10

729 Exhibition Building and Emblem

1979. Opening of Korea Exhibition Centre.

1395	**729**	20 w. multicoloured . . .	20	10

730 Boeing 747-200 and Globe

1979. 10th Anniv of Korean Air Lines.

1396	**730**	20 w. multicoloured . . .	30	10

731 "The Courtesans' Sword Dance" (Shin Yun-bok)

1979. United States "5000 Years of Korean Art" Exhibition (1st issue).

1397	**731**	60 w. multicoloured . . .	65	35

See also Nos. 1402/3, 1406/7, 1420/1, 1426/7, 1433/4, 1441/2 and 1457/8.

732 Mount Mai, North Cholla Province
733 Dragon's Head Rock, Cheju Island

1979. World Tourism Day.

1399	**732**	20 w. multicoloured . .	20	10
1400	**733**	20 w. multicoloured . .	20	10

734 Heart, Donors and Blood Drop

1979. Blood Donors.

1401	**734**	20 w. red and green . .	30	10

735 White Porcelain Jar with Grape Design
736 Mounted Warrior (pottery vessel)

1979. "5000 Years of Korean Art" Exhibition (2nd issue).

1402	**735**	20 w. multicoloured . .	40	10
1403	**736**	20 w. multicoloured . .	40	10

737 "Moon Travel" (Park Chung Jae)

1979. Philatelic Week.

1404	**737**	20 w. multicoloured . .	20	10

738 Hahoe Mask
739 Golden Amitabha with Halo

1979. "5000 Years of Korean Art" Exhibition (3rd issue).

1406	**738**	20 w. multicoloured . .	40	10
1407	**739**	20 w. multicoloured . .	40	10

740 Rain Frog
741 Asian Polypody

1979. Nature Conservation.

1408	**740**	20 w. multicoloured . .	20	10
1409	**741**	20 w. multicoloured . .	20	10

742 Monkey (bas-relief, Kim Yun Shin's tomb)
743 Children playing Yut

1979. Lunar New Year ("Year of the Monkey").

1410	**742**	20 w. multicoloured . .	15	10
1411	**743**	20 w. multicoloured . .	15	10

744 President Choi Kyu Hah

1979. Presidential Inauguration.

1413	**744**	20 w. multicoloured . .	20	10

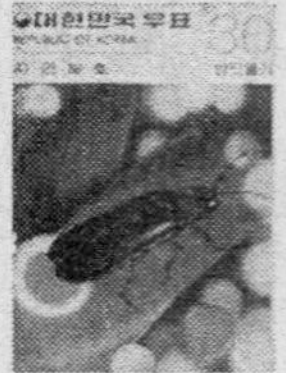

745 Firefly

746 Meesun Tree

1980. Nature Conservation (5th series).

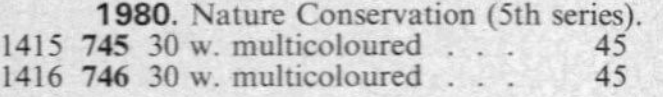

1415 **745** 30 w. multicoloured . . . 45 10
1416 **746** 30 w. multicoloured . . . 45 10

747 President Pak

748 Earthenware Kettle

749 "Landscape" (Kim Hong Do)

1980. President Pak Commemoration.
1417 **747** 30 w. red 20 10
1418 30 w. purple 20 10

1980. Exhibition "5000 Years of Korean Art" (4th issue).
1420 **748** 30 w. multicoloured . . . 40 10
1421 **749** 60 w. multicoloured . . . 50 10

750 "Lotus"

751 "Magpie and Tiger"

1980. Folk Paintings (1st series).
1423 **750** 30 w. multicoloured . . . 30 15
1424 **751** 60 w. multicoloured . . . 50 25
See also Nos. 1429/31, 1437/40 and 1453/6.

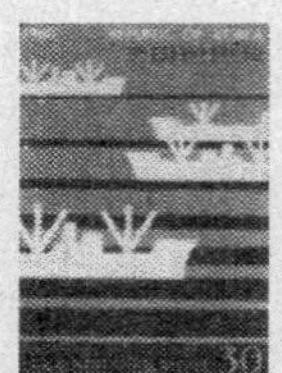

752 Merchant Ships

1980. Korean Merchant Navy.
1425 **752** 30 w. multicoloured . . . 30 10

753 "Heavenly Horse" (tomb painting)

754 Banner Staff with Dragonhead Finial

1980. Exhibition "5000 Years of Korean Art" (5th series).
1426 **753** 30 w. multicoloured . . . 40 10
1427 **754** 30 w. multicoloured . . . 40 10

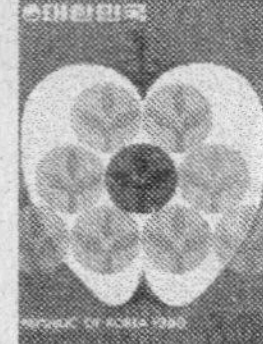

755 "Fruition"

1980. 10th Anniv of Saemaul Movement (community self-help programme).
1428 **755** 30 w. multicoloured . . 20 10

756 "Red Phoenix"

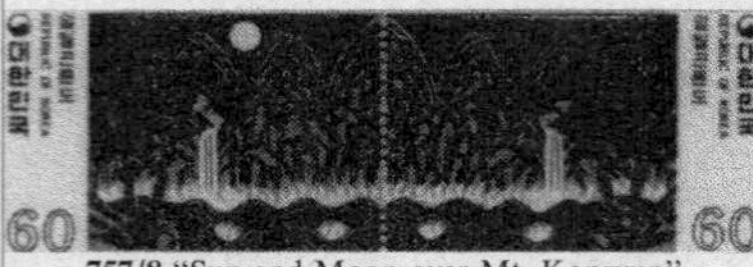

757/8 "Sun and Moon over Mt. Konryun". (½-size illustration)

1980. Folk Paintings (2nd series).
1429 **756** 30 w. multicoloured . . 20 10
1430 **757** 60 w. multicoloured . . 85 40
1431 **758** 60 w. multicoloured . . 85 40
Nos. 1430/1 were issued together in se-tenant pairs within the sheet, forming a composite design.

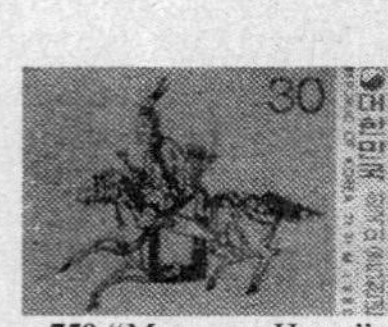

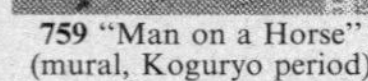

759 "Man on a Horse" (mural, Koguryo period)

760 "Tiger" (granite sculpture)

1980. Exhibition "5000 Years of Korean Art" (6th issue).
1433 **759** 30 w. multicoloured . . 40 10
1434 **760** 30 w. multicoloured . . 40 10

761 U.N. Flag and Rifle

762 "Venus de Milo" and Contestants

1980. 30th Anniv of Intervention of U.N. Forces in Korean War.
1435 **761** 30 w. multicoloured . . 30 10

1980. "Miss Universe" Beauty Contest, Seoul.
1436 **762** 30 w. multicoloured . . 30 10

763 "Rabbits Pounding Grain in a Mortar"

764 "Dragon in Cloud"

1980. Folk Paintings (3rd series).
1437 **763** 30 w. multicoloured . . 40 10
1438 **764** 30 w. multicoloured . . 40 10

765 "Pine Tree"

766 "Flowers and Manchurian Cranes" (detail, folding screen)

1980. Folk Paintings (4th series).
1439 **765** 30 w. multicoloured . . . 40 10
1440 **766** 30 w. multicoloured . . . 50 15

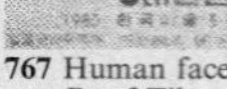

767 Human faced Roof Tile

768 "White Tiger" (mural)

1980. Exhibition "5000 Years of Korean Art" (7th issue).
1441 **767** 30 w. multicoloured . . . 30 10
1442 **768** 30 w. multicoloured . . . 30 10

769 Football

770 President Chun Doo Hwan

1980. 10th President's Cup Football Tournament.
1443 **769** 30 w. multicoloured . . . 25 10

1980. Presidential Inauguration.
1444 **770** 30 w. multicoloured . . . 25 10

771 Woman Soldier and Emblem

1980. 30th Anniv of Women's Army Corps.
1446 **771** 30 w. multicoloured . . . 20 10

772 River Baegma

773 Three Peaks of Dodam

1980. World Tourism Day.
1447 **772** 30 w. pink and purple . . 25 10
1448 **773** 30 w. yellow, green & bl 25 10

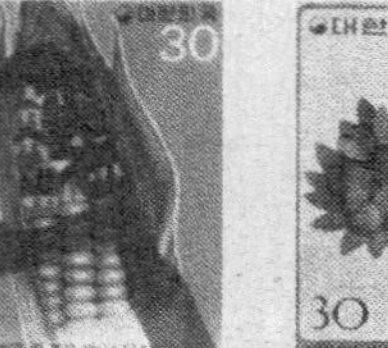

774 Corn-cob and Micrometer

775 Tree

1980. Population and Housing Census.
1449 **774** 30 w. multicoloured . . . 25 10

1980. 75th Anniv of Korean Red Cross.
1450 **775** 30 w. multicoloured . . . 35 10

776 "Angels delivering Mail" (Kim Ki Chul)

1980. Philatelic Week.
1451 **776** 30 w. multicoloured . . 25 10

777 "Ten Long-life Symbols"

781 Deva King (sculpture)

1980. Folk Paintings (5th series). Multicoloured.
1453 30 w. Type **777** 30 10
1454 30 w. "Herb of eternal youth" and deer 30 10
1455 30 w. Pine and deer eating herb 30 10
1456 30 w. Pine, water and rock . 30 10
Nos. 1453/6 were issued together in horiz setenant strips of four within the sheet, each strip forming a composite design.

1980. Exhibition "5000 Years of Korean Art" (8th series).
1457 **781** 30 w. black 40 10
1458 30 w. red 40 10

782 Cable Ship and Cross-section of Cable

1980. Inauguration of Korea-Japan Submarine Cable.
1459 **782** 30 w. multicoloured . . 30 10

783 Cock (bas-relief Kim Yu Shin's tomb)

784 Cranes

1980. Lunar New Year ("Year of the Cock").
1460 **783** 30 w. multicoloured . . 30 10
1461 **784** 30 w. multicoloured . . 30 10

785 President Chun Doo Hwan and Factory within "Hibiscus syriacus"

1981. Presidential Inauguration.
1463 **785** 30 w. multicoloured . . 20 10

786 "Korea Sun" (tanker)

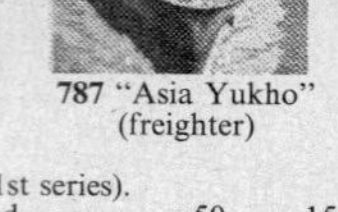

787 "Asia Yukho" (freighter)

1981. Ships (1st series).
1465 **786** 30 w. multicoloured . . 50 15
1466 **787** 90 w. multicoloured . . 75 15
See also Nos. 1470/1, 1482/5 and 1501/2.

788 National Assembly Building

1981. Inaugural Session of 11th National Assembly.
1467 **788** 30 w. brown and gold . . 20 10

789 Symbols of Disability and I.Y.D.P. Emblem **790** Disabled Person in Wheelchair at Foot of Steps

1981. International Year of Disabled Persons.
1468 **789** 30 w. multicoloured . . . 20 10
1469 **790** 90 w. multicoloured . . . 45 15

791 "Saturn" (bulk-carrier)

792 "Hanjin Seoul" (container ship)

1981. Ships (2nd series).
1470 **791** 30 w. deep purple, purple and blue 45 15
1471 **792** 90 w. grey, blue and red 80 15

793 Council Emblem on Ribbon

1981. Advisory Council on Peaceful Unification Policy.
1472 **793** 40 w. multicoloured . . . 20 10

794 "Clean Rivers and Air" **795** Birds visiting Breeding Grounds

1981. World Environment Day.
1473 **794** 30 w. multicoloured . . . 20 10
1474 **795** 90 w. multicoloured . . . 35 10

796 Presidents Chun and Suharto of Indonesia

1981. Presidential Visit to A.S.E.A.N. Countries. Multicoloured.
1475 40 w. Type **796** 20 10
1476 40 w. Pres. Chun and Sultan of Malaysia 20 10
1477 40 w. Handshake and flags of South Korea and Singapore 20 10
1478 40 w. Pres. Chun and King of Thailand 20 10
1479 40 w. Presidents Chun and Marcos of Philippines . . . 20 10
1480 40 w. Pres. Chun and flags of Korea, Singapore, Malaysia and Philippines (39 × 43 mm) 20 10

802 "Chung Ryong No. 3" (tug)

803 "Soo Gong No. 71" (trawler)

1981. Ships (3rd series).
1482 **802** 40 w. multicoloured . . 55 15
1483 **803** 100 w. multicoloured . . 85 15

804 "Aldebaran" (log carrier)

805 "Hyundai No. 1" (car carrier)

1981. Ships (4th series).
1484 **804** 40 w. multicoloured . . 55 15
1485 **805** 100 w. multicoloured . . 85 15

806 Korean with Flag and Dates on Graph **812** W.H.O. Emblem and Citizens

807 Glider

1981. 36th Anniv of Liberation.
1486 **806** 40 w. multicoloured . . 25 20

1981. 3rd Model Aeronautic Competition. Multicoloured.
1487 10 w. Type **807** 35 15
1488 20 w. Elastic-powered airplane 35 15
1489 40 w. Line-controlled airplane 35 15
1490 50 w. Radio-controlled airplane 35 15
1491 80 w. Radio-controlled helicopter 35 15

1981. 32nd Session of W.H.O. Regional Committee for the Western Pacific, Seoul.
1492 **812** 40 w. multicoloured . . 20 10

813 Seoul Communications Tower **814** Ulreung Island

1981. World Tourism Day.
1493 **813** 40 w. multicoloured . . 25 10
1494 **814** 40 w. multicoloured . . 25 10

815 Cycling

816 Swimming

1981. 62nd National Sports Meeting, Seoul.
1495 **815** 40 w. multicoloured . . 30 10
1496 **816** 40 w. multicoloured . . 30 10

817 Presidents Chun and Carazo Odio **818** Hand holding Plate with F.A.O. Emblem

1981. Visit of President Carazo Odio of Costa Rica.
1497 **817** 40 w. multicoloured . . . 20 10

1981. World Food Day.
1498 **818** 40 w. multicoloured . . . 25 10

819 Airliner and Clouds **820** South Gate of Seoul and Olympic Rings

1981. National Aviation Day.
1499 **819** 40 w. orange, brown and silver 40 10

1981. Choice of Seoul as 1988 Olympic Host City.
1500 **820** 40 w. multicoloured . . . 30 10

821 "Stolt Hawk" (chemical carrier)

822 Passenger Ferry

1981. Ships (5th series).
1501 **821** 40 w. black 55 15
1502 **822** 100 w. blue 85 15

823 "Hang gliding" (Kim Kyung Jun)

1981. Philatelic Week.
1503 **823** 40 w. multicoloured . . . 25 10

824 Camellia and Dog **825** Children flying Kite

1981. Lunar New Year ("Year of the Dog").
1505 **824** 40 w. multicoloured . . . 25 10
1506 **825** 40 w. multicoloured . . . 25 10

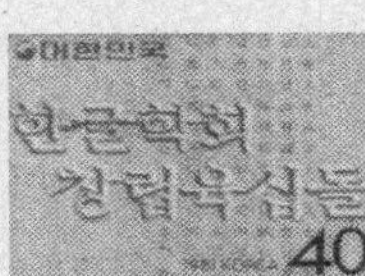
826 "Hangul Hakhoe"

1981. 60th Anniv of Hangul Hakhoe (Korean Language Society).
1508 **826** 40 w. multicoloured . . . 30 10

827 Telephone and Dish Aerial **828** Scout Emblem and Logs forming "75"

1982. Inauguration of Korea Telecommunication Authority.
1509 **827** 60 w. multicoloured . . 35 10

1982. 75th Anniv of Boy Scout Movement.
1510 **828** 60 w. multicoloured . . 25 10

829 Young Woman **830** Dividers and World Map

1982. 60th Anniv of Korean Young Women's Christian Association.
1511 **829** 60 w. multicoloured . . 25 10

1982. Centenary of International Polar Year.
1512 **830** 60 w. multicoloured . . 25 10

831 Music and "Hibiscus syriacus"

1982. Children's Day.
1513 **831** 60 w. multicoloured . . 35 10

832 President Chun and Samuel Doe

1982. Visit of Samuel Doe (Liberian Head of State).
1514 **832** 60 w. multicoloured . . 20 10

833 Centenary Emblem

1982. Centenary of Korea–United States Friendship Treaty.
1516 **833** 60 w. multicoloured . . 20 10
1517 – 60 w. multicoloured . . 20 10
DESIGN: No. 1517, Statue of Liberty and Seoul South Gate.

835 Presidents Chun and Mobutu

1982. Visit of President Mobutu of Zaire.
1519 **835** 60 w. multicoloured . . 20 10

836 "Territorial Expansion by Kwanggaeto the Great" (Lee Chong Sang)

837 "General Euljimunduck's Great Victory at Salsoo" (Park Kak Soon)

1982. Documentary Paintings (1st series).
1521 **836** 60 w. multicoloured . . . 30 10
1522 **837** 60 w. multicoloured . . . 1·40 65
See also Nos. 1523/4, 1537/8 and 1548/9.

838 "Shilla's Repulse of Invading Tang Army" (Oh Seung Woo)

839 "General Kang Kam Chan's Great Victory at Kyiju" (Lee Yong Hwan)

1982. Documentary Paintings (2nd series).
1523 **838** 60 w. multicoloured . . . 30 10
1524 **839** 60 w. multicoloured . . . 30 10

840 Convention Emblem and Globe

841 Presidents Chun and Moi of Kenya

1982. 55th International Y's Men's Club Convention, Seoul.
1525 **840** 60 w. multicoloured . . . 20 10

1982. Presidential Visits to Africa and Canada. Multicoloured.
1526 60 w. Type **841** 25 10
1527 60 w. Presidents Chun and Shagari of Nigeria 25 10
1528 60 w. Presidents Chun and Bongo of Gabon 25 10
1529 60 w. Presidents Chun and Diouf of Senegal 25 10
1530 60 w. Flags of South Korea and Canada 25 10

846 National Flag

1982. Centenary of National Flag.
1532 **846** 60 w. multicoloured . . . 30 10

847 Emblem and Player

1982. Second Seoul Table Tennis Championships.
1534 **847** 60 w. multicoloured . . . 40 10

848 Baseball Player

1982. 27th World Baseball Championship Series, Seoul.
1535 **848** 60 w. brown 25 10

849 Exhibition Centre

1982. Seoul International Trade Fair.
1536 **849** 60 w. multicoloured . . 20 10

850 "Admiral Yi Sun Sin's Great Victory at Hansan" (Kim Hyung Ku)

851 "General Kim Chwa Jin's Chungsanri Battle" (Sohn Soo Kwang)

1982. Documentary Paintings (3rd series).
1537 **850** 60 w. multicoloured . . 50 10
1538 **851** 60 w. multicoloured . . 60 10

852 "Miners reading Consolatory Letters" (Um Soon Keun)

1982. Philatelic Week.
1539 **852** 60 w. multicoloured . . 20 10

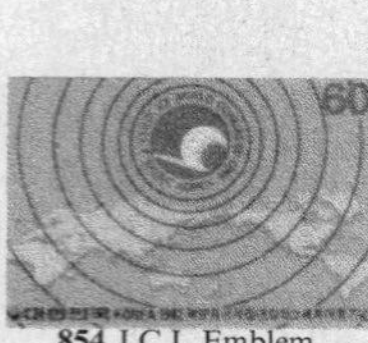

853 Presidents Chung and Suharto

1982. Visit of President Suharto of Indonesia.
1541 **853** 60 w. multicoloured . . 20 10

854 J.C.I. Emblem over World Map

855 "Intelsat 5" and "4-A" orbiting globe

1982. 37th Junior Chamber International World Congress, Seoul.
1543 **854** 60 w. multicoloured . . 20 10

1982. Second U.N. Conference on the Exploration and Peaceful Uses of Outer Space, Vienna.
1544 **855** 60 w. multicoloured . . . 30 10

856 Pig (bas-relief, Kim Yu Shin's tomb)

1982. Lunar New Year ("Year of the Pig").
1545 60 w. Type **856** 30 10
1546 60 w. Magpies and Korean moneybag 30 10

858 "General Kwon Yul's Great Victory at Haengju" (Oh Seung Woo)

859 "Kim Chong Suh's Exploitation of Yukin" (Kim Tae)

1982. Documentary Paintings (4th series).
1548 **858** 60 w. multicoloured . . . 60 10
1549 **859** 60 w. multicoloured . . . 60 10

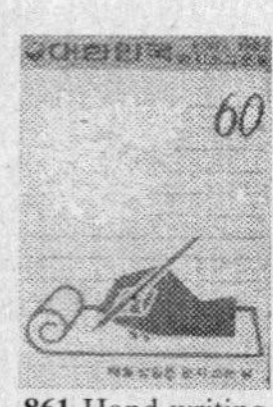

860 Flags of South Korea and Turkey

861 Hand writing Letter

1982. Visit of President Evran of Turkey.
1550 **860** 60 w. multicoloured . . . 25 10

1982. Letter Writing Campaign.
1552 **861** 60 w. multicoloured . . . 20 10

862 Emblem, Airliner, Container Ship and Cranes

863 Hyundai "Pony 2"

1983. International Customs Day.
1553 **862** 60 w. multicoloured . . . 50 15

1983. Korean-made Vehicles (1st series). Multicoloured.
1554 60 w. Type **863** 45 10
1555 60 w. Keohwa Jeep 45 10
See also Nos. 1558/9, 1564/5, 1572/3 and 1576/7.

865 President Chun and Sultan of Malaysia

1983. Visit of Sultan of Malaysia.
1556 **865** 60 w. multicoloured . . . 20 10

866 Daewoo "Maepsy" **867** Kia "Bongo" Minibus

1983. Korean-made Vehicles (2nd series).
1558 **866** 60 w. multicoloured . . . 45 10
1559 **867** 60 w. multicoloured . . . 45 10

868 Former General Bureau of Postal Administration

869 Central Post Office, Seoul

1983. "Philakorea 84" International Stamp Exhibition, Seoul. Centenary of Korean Postal Service (1st series).
1560 **868** 60 w. multicoloured . . 25 10
1561 **869** 60 w. multicoloured . . 25 10
See also Nos. 1566/7, 1574/5 and 1603/6.

870 Old Village Schoolroom

1983. Teachers' Day.
1562 **870** 60 w. multicoloured . . 20 10

871 Asia Motor Co. Bus **872** Kia "Super Titan" Truck

1983. Korean-made Vehicles (3rd series).
1564 **871** 60 w. multicoloured . . 45 10
1565 **872** 60 w. multicoloured . . 45 10

873 Early Postman

1983. "Philakorea 84" International Stamp Exhibition, Seoul. Centenary of Korean Postal Service (2nd series).
1566 **873** 70 w. multicoloured . . 30 10
1567 – 70 w. multicoloured . . 30 10
DESIGN: No. 1567, Modern postman on motor-cycle.

875 "Communications in Outer Space" (Chun Ja Eun)

1983. World Communications Year.
1568 **875** 70 w. multicoloured . . 20 10

876 Whooper Swans at Sunrise **877** Emblems of Science and Engineering

1983. Inaug of Communications Insurance.
1570 **876** 70 w. multicoloured . . 45 10

1983. Korean Symposium on Science and Technology, Seoul.
1571 **877** 70 w. multicoloured . . 20 10

878 Daewoo Dump Truck **879** Hyundai Cargo Lorry

1983. Korean-made Vehicles (4th series).
1572 **878** 70 w. multicoloured . . . 45 10
1573 **879** 70 w. multicoloured . . . 45 10

880 Mail carried by Horse

1983. "Philakorea 84" International Stamp Exhibition, Seoul. Centenary of Korean Postal Service (3rd series). Multicoloured.
1574 70 w. Type **880** 30 10
1575 70 w. Mail truck and Douglas DC-8-60 Super Sixty airliner 30 10

882 Dong-A Concrete Mixer Truck **883** Dong-A Tanker

1983. Korean-made Vehicles (5th series).
1576 **882** 70 w. multicoloured . . . 45 10
1577 **883** 70 w. multicoloured . . . 45 10

884 President Chun and King Hussein **885** Woman with Fan

1983. Visit of King Hussein of Jordan.
1578 **884** 70 w. multicoloured . . . 20 10

1983. 53rd American Society of Travel Agents World Congress, Seoul.
1580 **885** 70 w. multicoloured . . . 25 10

886 I.P.U. Emblem and Flags

1983. 70th Inter-Parliamentary Union Conference, Seoul.
1581 **886** 70 w. multicoloured . . . 30 10

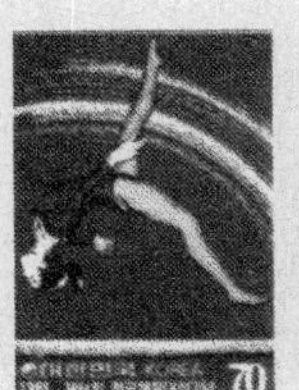

887 Gymnastics **888** Football

1983. 64th National Sports Meeting, Inchon.
1583 **887** 70 w. multicoloured . . . 25 10
1584 **888** 70 w. multicoloured . . . 25 10

889 Presidents Chun and U San Yu of Burma **894** Rain Drops containing Symbols of Industry, Light and Food

1983. Presidential Visits. Multicoloured.
1585 70 w. Type **889** 50 20
1586 70 w. Presidents Chun and Giani Zail Singh of India 50 20
1587 70 w. Presidents Chun and Jayewardene of Sri Lanka 50 20
1588 70 w. Flags of South Korea and Australia 50 20
1589 70 w. Flags of South Korea and New Zealand 50 20

1983. Development of Water Resources and 10th Anniv of Soyang-gang Dam.
1591 **894** 70 w. multicoloured . . 25 10

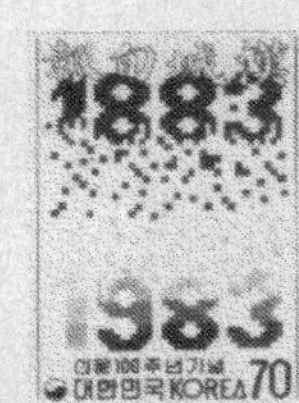

895 Centenary Dates **896** Tree with Lungs and Cross of Lorraine

1983. Centenary of 1st Korean Newspaper "Hansong Sunbo".
1592 **895** 70 w. multicoloured . . 25 10

1983. 30th Anniv of Korean National Tuberculosis Association.
1593 **896** 70 w. multicoloured . . 25 10

897 Presidents Chun and Reagan **898** Child collecting Stamps

1983. Visit of President Reagan of United States of America.
1594 **897** 70 w. multicoloured . . 25 10

1983. Philatelic Week.
1596 **898** 70 w. multicoloured . . 20 10

899 Rat (bas-relief, Kim Yu Shin's tomb)

1983. Lunar New Year ("Year of the Rat"). Multicoloured.
1598 70 w. Type **899** 30 10
1599 70 w. Manchurian cranes and pine 30 10

901 Bicentenary Emblem **902** 5 m. and 10 m. Stamps, 1884

1984. Bicentenary of Catholic Church in Korea.
1601 **901** 70 w. red, violet & silver 25 10

1984. "Philakorea 84" International Stamp Exhibition, Seoul. Centenary of Korean Postal Service (4th series). Multicoloured.
1603 70 w. Type **902** 25 10
1604 70 w. 5000 w. stamp, 1983 . . 25 10

904 Old Postal Emblem and Post Box

1984. "Philakorea 84" International Stamp Exhibition, Seoul. Centenary of Korean Postal Service (5th series). Multicoloured.
1605 70 w. Type **904** 30 10
1606 70 w. Modern postal emblem and post box 30 10

906 President Chun and Sultan

1984. Visit of Sultan of Brunei.
1607 **906** 70 w. multicoloured . . . 25 10

907 President Chun and Sheikh Khalifa

1984. Visit of Sheikh Khalifa of Qatar.
1609 **907** 70 w. multicoloured . . . 25 10

908 Child posting Letter

1984. Centenary of Korean Postal Administration. Multicoloured.
1611 70 w. Type **908** 25 10
1612 70 w. Postman in city 25 10

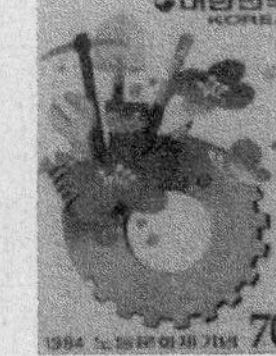

910 Pope John Paul II **911** Cogwheel, Worker's Tools and Flowers

1984. Visit of Pope John Paul II.
1614 **910** 70 w. black 35 10
1615 70 w. multicoloured . . . 35 10

1984. Labour Festival.
1617 **911** 70 w. multicoloured . . 20 10

912 Globe, Airliner, Container Ship and Emblem **913** Map and Flags of S. Korea and Sri Lanka

1984. 63rd/64th Sessions of Customs Co-operation Council, Seoul.
1618 **912** 70 w. multicoloured . . . 65 15

1984. Visit of President Jayewardene of Sri Lanka.
1619 **913** 70 w. multicoloured . . . 30 10

914 Symbols and Punctuation Marks **915** Expressway

1984. 14th Asian Advertising Congress, Seoul.
1621 **914** 70 w. multicoloured . . 25 10

1984. Opening of 88 Olympic Expressway.
1622 **915** 70 w. multicoloured . . 30 10

916 Laurel, "Victory" and Olympic Rings **917** A.B.U. Emblem and Microphone

1984. 90th Anniv of International Olympic Committee.
1623 **916** 70 w. multicoloured . . 30 10

1984. 20th Anniv of Asia-Pacific Broadcasting Union.
1624 **917** 70 w. multicoloured . . 25 10

918 Flags of S. Korea and Senegal

1984. Visit of President Abdou Diouf of Senegal.
1625 **918** 70 w. multicoloured . . 20 10

919 Archery **921** Crucifixion

1984. Olympic Games, Los Angeles. Multicoloured.
1627 70 w. Type **919** 40 10
1628 440 w. Fencing . . . . . . 1·60 65

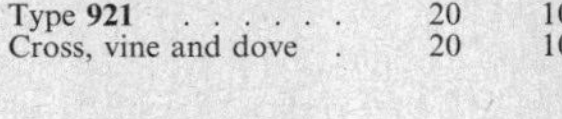

1984. Centenary of Korean Protestant Church. Multicoloured.
1629 70 w. Type **921** 20 10
1630 70 w. Cross, vine and dove . 20 10

923 Man carrying Silk-covered Lantern

1984. Folk Customs (1st series). "Wedding" (Kim Kyo Man). Multicoloured.
1632 70 w. Type **923** 20 10
1633 70 w. Bridegroom on horse 20 10
1634 70 w. Man playing clarinet . 20 10
1635 70 w. Bride in sedan chair (51 × 35 mm) 20 10

See also Nos. 1657/8, 1683/4, 1734/8, 1808/11, 1840/3, 1858/61 and 1915/18.

927 Pres. Chun and Mt. Fuji

1984. Pres. Chun's Visit to Japan.
1637 **927** 70 w. multicoloured . . 35 10

928 Flags of S. Korea and Gambia

1984. Visit of President Sir Dawada Kairaba Jawara of Gambia.
1639 **928** 70 w. multicoloured . . . 30 10

929 Symbols of International Trade

930 Namsan Tower and National Flags

1984. "Sitra '84" International Trade Fair, Seoul.
1641 **929** 70 w. multicoloured . . . 30 10

1984. Visit of President El Hadj Omar Bongo of Gabon.
1642 **930** 70 w. multicoloured . . . 30 10

931 Badminton

932 Magnifying Glass and Exhibition Emblem

1984. 65th National Sports Meeting, Taegu. Multicoloured.
1644 70 w. Type **931** 30 10
1645 70 w. Wrestling 30 10

1984. "Philakorea 1984" International Stamp Exhibition, Seoul. Multicoloured.
1646 70 w. Type **932** 30 10
1647 70 w. South Gate, Seoul, and stamps (horiz) 30 10

934 Presidents Chun and Gayoom

1984. Visit of President Maumoon Abdul Gayoom of the Maldives.
1650 **934** 70 w. multicoloured . . . 30 10

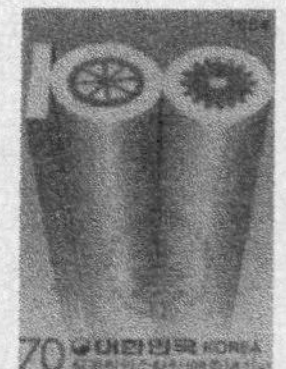
935 "100" and Industrial Symbols

1984. Centenary of Korean Chamber of Commerce and Industry.
1652 **935** 70 w. multicoloured . . . 30 10

936 Children playing Jaegi-chagi

937 Ox (bas-relief, Kim Yu Shin's tomb)

1984. Lunar New Year ("Year of the Ox").
1653 **936** 70 w. multicoloured . . . 30 10
1654 **937** 70 w. multicoloured . . . 30 10

INDEX

Countries can be quickly located by referring to the index at the end of this volume.

938 I.Y.Y. Emblem

1985. International Youth Year.
1656 **938** 70 w. multicoloured . . 15 10

939 Pounding Rice for New Year Rice Cake

940 Welcoming Year's First Full Moon

1985. Folk Customs (2nd series).
1657 **939** 70 w. multicoloured . . 30 10
1658 **940** 70 w. multicoloured . . 30 10

941 Seoul Olympic Emblem

1985. Olympic Games, Seoul (1988) (1st issue). Multicoloured.
1659 70 w. + 30 w. Type **941** . . 40 20
1660 70 w. + 30 w. Hodori (mascot) 40 20
See also Nos. 1673/4, 1678/8, 1694/5, 1703/10, 1747/50, 1752/5, 1784/7, 1814/17, 1826/7, 1835/6 and 1844/7.

943 "Still Life with Doll" (Lee Chong Woo)

944 "Rocky Mountain in Early Spring Morning" (Ahn Jung Shik)

1985. Modern Art (1st series).
1662 **943** 70 w. multicoloured . . 30 10
1663 **944** 70 w. multicoloured . . 30 10
See also Nos. 1680/1, 1757/60, 1791/4 and 1875/8.

945 Flags, Statue of Liberty and President Chun

946 Flags, Seoul South Gate and National Flower

1985. Presidential Visit to United States.
1664 **945** 70 w. multicoloured . . 30 10

1985. Visit of President Mohammed Zia-ul-Haq of Pakistan.
1666 **946** 70 w. multicoloured . . 30 10

947 Underwood Hall

1985. Centenary of Yonsei University.
1668 **947** 70 w. black, buff & green 30 10

948 Flags and Map

1985. Visit of President Luis Alberto Monge of Costa Rica.
1669 **948** 70 w. multicoloured . . . 30 10

949 Silver Carp

950 Sailfish

1985. Fishes (1st series).
1671 **949** 70 w. multicoloured . . . 40 10
1672 **950** 70 w. multicoloured . . . 40 10
See also Nos. 1730/3, 1797/1800, 1881/4, 1903/6 and 1951/4.

951 Rowing

952 National Flags

1985. Olympic Games, Seoul (1988) (2nd issue). Multicoloured.
1673 70 w. + 30 w. Type **951** . . . 40 20
1674 70 w. + 30 w. Hurdling . . . 40 20

1985. Visit of President Hussain Muhammed Ershad of Bangladesh.
1676 **952** 70 w. multicoloured . . . 35 10

953 National Flags

1985. Visit of President Joao Bernardo Vieira of Guinea-Bissau.
1678 **953** 70 w. multicoloured . . . 30 10

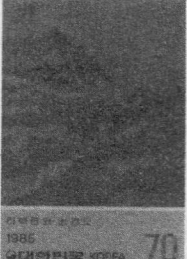
954 "Spring Day on the Farm" (Huh Paik Ryun)

955 "The Exorcist" (Kim Chung Hyun)

1985. Modern Art (2nd issue).
1680 **954** 70 w. multicoloured . . 35 10
1681 **955** 70 w. multicoloured . . 35 10

956 Heavenly Lake, Paekdu and National Flower

1985. 40th Anniv of Liberation.
1682 **956** 70 w. multicoloured . . 35 10

957 Wrestling

958 Janggi

1985. Folk Customs (3rd series).
1683 **957** 70 w. multicoloured . . 35 10
1684 **958** 70 w. multicoloured . . 35 10

959 "The Spring of My Home" (Lee Won Su and Hong Nan Pa)

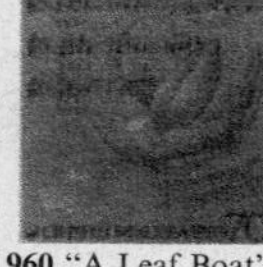
960 "A Leaf Boat" (Park Hong Keun and Yun Yong Ha)

1985. Korean Music (1st series).
1685 **959** 70 w. multicoloured . . 35 15
1686 **960** 70 w. multicoloured . . 35 15
See also Nos. 1728/9, 1776/7, 1854/5, 1862/3, 1893/4, 1935/6, 1996/7 and 2064/5.

1985. Olympic Games, Seoul (1988) (3rd issue). As T **951**. Multicoloured.
1687 70 w. + 30 w. Basketball . . 40 20
1688 70 w. + 30 w. Boxing . . . 40 10

961 Satellite, "100" and Dish Aerial

962 Meetings Emblem

1985. Centenary of First Korean Telegraph Service.
1690 **961** 70 w. multicoloured . . 35 10

1985. World Bank and International Monetary Fund Meetings, Seoul.
1691 **962** 70 w. multicoloured . . 35 10

963 U.N. Emblem and Doves

964 Red Cross and Hands (detail "Creation of Adam", Michelangelo)

1985. 40th Anniv of U.N.O.
1692 **963** 70 w. multicoloured . . 35 10

1985. 80th Anniv of Korea Red Cross.
1693 **964** 70 w. black, red and blue 45 10

1985. Olympic Games, Seoul (1988) (4th issue). As T **951**. Multicoloured.
1694 70 w. + 30 w. Cycling . . . 40 20
1695 70 w. + 30 w. Canoeing . . 40 20

965 Cancelled Stamp on Envelope

966 Tiger (bas-relief, Kim Yu Shin's tomb)

1985. Philatelic Week.
1697 **965** 70 w. multicoloured . . . 35 10

1985. Lunar New Year ("Year of the Tiger").
1698 **966** 70 w. multicoloured . . . 35 10

967 Mount Fuji and Boeing 747 Airliner

1985. 20th Anniv of Korea-Japan Treaty on Basic Relations.
1699 **967** 70 w. mult (postage) . . 60 10
1700 370 w. multicoloured (air) 1·40 25

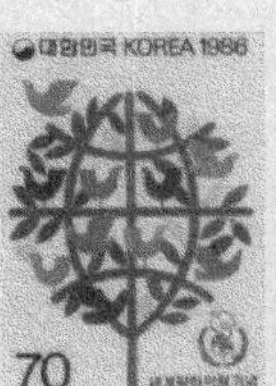

968 Doves and Globe

970 Pres. Chun, Big Ben and Korean and British Flags

1986. International Peace Year.
1701 **968** 70 w. multicoloured . . . 35 10
1702 400 w. multicoloured . . 1·40 85

1986. Olympic Games, Seoul (1988) (5th series). As T **951**. Multicoloured.
1703 70 w. + 30 w. Show jumping (postage) 40 20
1704 70 w. + 30 w. Fencing . . . 40 20
1705 70 w. + 30 w. Football . . . 40 20
1706 70 w. + 30 w. Gymnastics . 40 20
1707 370 w. + 100 w. As No. 1703 (air) . . . . 1·25 1·25
1708 400 w. + 100 w. As No. 1704 1·25 1·25
1709 440 w. + 100 w. As No. 1705 1·25 1·25
1710 470 w. + 100 w. As No. 1706 1·25 1·25

1986. Presidential Visit to Europe. Multicoloured.
1711 70 w. Type **970** 40 10
1712 70 w. Pres. Chun, Eiffel Tower and Korean and French flags 40 10
1713 70 w. Pres. Chun, Belgian Parliament and Korean and Belgian flags 40 10
1714 70 w. Pres. Chun, Cologne Cathedral and Korean and West German flags 40 10

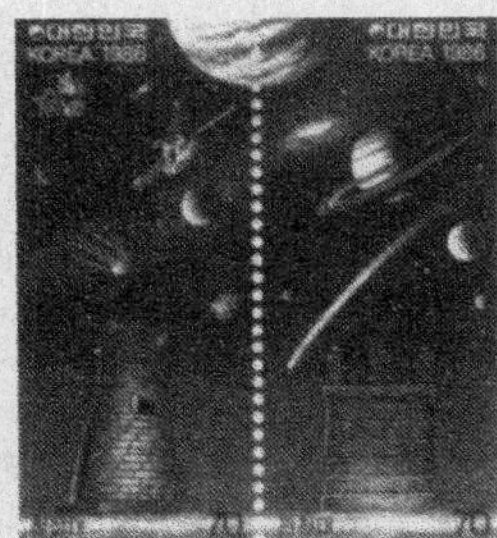

974 Kyongju Observatory **975** Kwanchon Observatory

1986. Science (1st series). Appearance of Halley's Comet.
1716 **974** 70 w. multicoloured . . . 1·60 85
1717 **975** 70 w. multicoloured . . . 1·60 85
See also Nos. 1781/2, 1833/4, 1864/5 and 1898/9.

976 General Assembly Emblem **977** Swallowtail and Flowers

1986. 5th Association of National Olympic Committees General Assembly, Seoul.
1718 **976** 70 w. multicoloured . . . 40 10

1986. "Ameripex '86" International Stamp Exhibition, Chicago. Multicoloured.
1719 70 w. Type **977** . . . . 1·75 50
1720 370 w. "Papilio bianor" . . . 1·75 85
1721 400 w. Swallowtails . . . . . 1·75 85
1722 440 w. Swallowtail and frog 1·75 85
1723 450 w. Swallowtail . . . . . 1·75 85
1724 470 w. "Papilio bianor" . . . 1·75 85
Nos. 1719/24 were printed together, se-tenant, forming a composite design.

983 Male and Female Symbols in Balance

1986. Centenary of Korean Women's Education.
1725 **983** 70 w. multicoloured . . 35 10

984 National Flags

1986. Visit of President Andre Kolingba of Central African Republic.
1726 **984** 70 w. multicoloured . . 35 10

985 "Half Moon" (Yun Keuk Young)

986 "Let's Go and Pick the Moon" (Yun Seok Juna and Park Tae Hyun)

1986. Korean Music (2nd series).
1728 **985** 70 w. multicoloured . . 65 35
1729 **986** 70 w. multicoloured . . 1·00 50

987 Eoreumchi

988 Sweetfish

989 Sardine

990 Hammerhead Sharks

1986. Fishes (2nd series).
1730 **987** 70 w. multicoloured . . 70 35
1731 **988** 70 w. multicoloured . . 70 35
1732 **989** 70 w. multicoloured . . 70 35
1733 **990** 70 w. multicoloured . . 70 35

991 Flag Carrier and Gong Player **996** Child

1986. Folk Customs (4th series). Farm Music. Multicoloured.
1734 70 w. Type **991** 30 10
1735 70 w. Drummer and piper . 30 10
1736 70 w. Drummer and gong player 30 10
1737 70 w. Men with ribbons . . 30 10
1738 70 w. Man and woman with child 30 10
Nos. 1734/8 were printed together, se-tenant, forming a composite design.

1986. Family Planning.
1739 **996** 80 w. multicoloured . . 40 10

997 Bridge and "63" Building

1986. Completion of Han River Development. Multicoloured.
1740 30 w. Type **997** 40 10
1741 60 w. Buildings and excursion boat 40 10
1742 80 w. Rowing boat and Seoul Tower 40 10
Nos. 1740/2 were printed together, se-tenant, forming a composite design.

1000 Emblem **1004** Boy fishing for Stamp

1002 "5", Delegates and Juan Antonio Samaranch (President of International Olympic Committee)

1986. 10th Asian Games, Seoul. Multicoloured.
1743 80 w. Type **1000** 40 10
1744 80 w. Firework display . . . 40 10

1986. 5th Anniv of Choice of Seoul as 1988 Olympic Games Host City.
1746 **1002** 80 w. multicoloured . . 85 40

1986. Olympic Games, Seoul (1988) (6th issue). As T **951**. Multicoloured.
1747 80 w. + 50 w. Weightlifting (postage) 40 20
1748 80 w. + 50 w. Handball . . . 40 20
1749 370 w. + 100 w. As No. 1747 (air) . . . . 1·25 1·25
1750 400 w. + 100 w. As No. 1748 1·25 1·25

1986. Olympic Games, Seoul (1988) (7th issue). As T **951**. Multicoloured.
1752 80 w. + 50 w. Judo (postage) 40 20
1753 80 w. + 50 w. Hockey . . . 40 20
1754 440 w. + 100 w. As No. 1752 (air) . . . . 1·25 1·25
1755 470 w. + 100 w. As No. 1753 1·25 1·25

1986. Philatelic Week.
1756 **1004** 80 w. multicoloured . . 40 10

1005 "Chunhyang-do" (Kim Un Ho)

1006 "Flowers" (Lee Sang Bum)

1007 "Portrait of a Friend" (Ku Bon Wung)

MINIMUM PRICE

The minimum price quoted is 10p which represents a handling charge rather than a basis for valuing common stamps. For further notes about prices, see introductory pages.

1008 "Woman in a Ski Suit" (Son Ung Seng)

1986. Modern Art (3rd series).
1757 **1005** 80 w. multicoloured . . 65 35
1758 **1006** 80 w. multicoloured . . 65 35
1759 **1007** 80 w. multicoloured . . 60 35
1760 **1008** 80 w. multicoloured . . 60 35

1009 Rabbit **1010** Eastern Broad-billed Roller

1986. Lunar New Year ("Year of the Rabbit").
1761 **1009** 80 w. multicoloured . . 35 10

1986. Birds. Multicoloured.
1762 80 w. Type **1010** 50 10
1763 80 w. Japanese waxwing . . 50 10
1764 80 w. Black-naped oriole . . 50 10
1765 80 w. Black-capped kingfisher 50 10
1766 80 w. Hoopoe 50 10

1011 Siberian Tiger **1012** Bleeding Heart

1987. Endangered Animals. Multicoloured.
1767 80 w. Type **1011** . . . . . . 1·25 60
1768 80 w. Leopard cat . . . . . 1·25 60
1769 80 w. Red fox . . . . 1·25 60
1770 80 w. Wild boar . . . . . . 1·25 60

1987. Flowers. Multicoloured.
1771 550 w. Type **1012** . . . . . 1·90 25
1772 550 w. Diamond bluebell . . 1·90 25
1773 550 w. "Erythronium japonicum" . . . . 1·90 25
1774 550 w. Pinks . . . . 1·90 25
1775 550 w. "Chrysanthemum zawadskii" . . . . 1·90 25

1013 "Barley field" (Park Wha Mok and Yun Yong Ha)

1014 "Magnolia" (Cho Young Shik and Kim Dong Jin)

1987. Korean Music (3rd series).
1776 **1013** 80 w. multicoloured . . 1·60 85
1777 **1014** 80 w. multicoloured . . 1·60 85

1015 National Flags and Korean National Flower

1987. Visit of President Ahmed Abdallah Abderemane of Comoros.
1778 **1015** 80 w. multicoloured . . 30 10

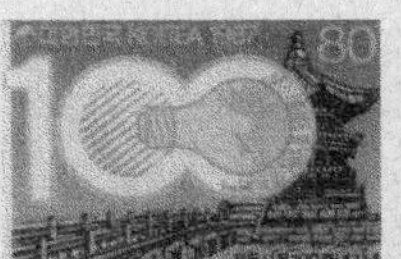

1016 "100", Light Bulb and Hyang Woen Jeong

1987. Centenary of Electric Light in Korea.
1780 **1016** 80 w. multicoloured . . 35 10

1017 Punggi Wind Observatory **1019** Globes, Crane and Ship

1987. Science (2nd series).
1781 **1017** 80 w. dp brown & brown 1·60 85
1782 – 80 w. brown & dp brown 1·60 85
DESIGN: Rain gauge.

1987. 15th International Association of Ports and Harbours General Session, Seoul.
1783 **1019** 80 w. multicoloured . . 40 10

1987. Olympic Games, Seoul (1988) (8th issue). As T **951**. Multicoloured.
1784 80 w. + 50 w. Wrestling . . 40 25
1785 80 w. + 50 w. Tennis 40 25
1786 80 w. + 50 w. Diving 40 25
1787 80 w. + 50 w. Show jumping 40 25

1020 Flags and Doves

1987. Visit of President U San Yu of Burma.
1789 **1020** 80 w. multicoloured . . 40 10

1021 "Valley of Peach Blossoms" (Pyen Kwan Sik)

1022 "Rural Landscape" (Lee Yong Wu)

1023 "Man" (Lee Ma Dong)

1024 "Woman with Water Jar on Head", (sculpture Yun Hyo Chung)

1987. Modern Art (4th series).
1791 **1021** 80 w. multicoloured . . 1·60 85
1792 **1022** 80 w. multicoloured . . 1·60 85
1793 **1023** 80 w. multicoloured . . 1·60 85
1794 **1024** 80 w. multicoloured . . 1·60 85

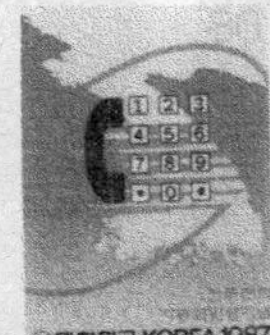

1025 Map and Digital Key Pad

1987. Completion of Automatic Telephone Network (1795) and Communications for Information Year (1796).
1795 80 w. Type **1025** 35 10
1796 80 w. Emblem 35 10

1027 Pilchards

1028 Eel

1029 Barbel

1030 Ray

1987. Fishes (3rd series).
1797 **1027** 80 w. multicoloured . . 1·60 85
1798 **1028** 80 w. multicoloured . . 1·60 85
1799 **1029** 80 w. multicoloured . . 1·60 85
1800 **1030** 80 w. multicoloured . . 1·60 85

1031 Statue of Indomitable Koreans (detail) and Flags **1033** Map and Pen within Profile

1987. Opening of Independence Hall. Mult.
1801 80 w. Type **1031** 60 10
1802 80 w. Monument of the Nation and aerial view of Hall . . 60 10

1987. 16th Pacific Science Congress, Seoul.
1804 **1033** 80 w. multicoloured . . 35 10

1034 Flags and Seoul South Gate

1987. Visit of President Virgilio Barco of Colombia.
1806 **1034** 80 w. multicoloured . . 40 10

1035/1038 Festivities (½-size illustration)

1987. Folk Customs (5th series). Harvest Moon Day.
1808 **1035** 80 w. multicoloured . . 1·60 85
1809 **1036** 80 w. multicoloured . . 1·60 85
1810 **1037** 80 w. multicoloured . . 1·60 85
1811 **1038** 80 w. multicoloured . . 1·60 85
Nos. 1808/11 were issued together, se-tenant, forming a composite design.

1039 Telephone Dials forming Number **1040** Service Flags and Servicemen

1987. Installation of over 10,000,000 Telephone Lines.
1812 **1039** 80 w. multicoloured . . 40 10

1987. Armed Forces Day.
1813 **1040** 80 w. multicoloured . . 40 10

1987. Olympic Games, Seoul (1988) (9th issue). As T **951**. Multicoloured.
1814 80 w. + 50 w. Table tennis 40 20
1815 80 w. + 50 w. Shooting . . . 40 20
1816 80 w. + 50 w. Archery . . . 40 20
1817 80 w. + 50 w. Volleyball . . 40 20

1041 Stamps around Child playing Trumpet **1042** Korean Scientist and Map

1987. Philatelic Week.
1819 **1041** 80 w. multicoloured . . 35 10

1987. 1st Anniv of South Korea's Signing of Antarctic Treaty.
1820 **1042** 80 w. multicoloured . . 35 10

1043 Dragon **1044** Scattered Sections of Apple

1987. Lunar New Year ("Year of the Dragon").
1821 **1043** 80 w. multicoloured . . 35 10

1988. Compulsory Pension Programme.
1822 **1044** 80 w. multicoloured . . 30 10

1045 Base and Gentoo Penguins **1046** Flag, Olympic Stadium and President Roh Tae Woo

1988. Completion of Antarctic Base.
1823 **1045** 80 w. multicoloured . . 30 10

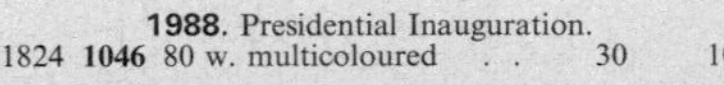

1988. Presidential Inauguration.
1824 **1046** 80 w. multicoloured . . 30 10

1047 Yachting **1048** Crane

1988. Olympic Games, Seoul (1988) (10th issue). Multicoloured.
1826 80 w. + 20 w. Type **1047** . . 35 20
1827 80 w. + 20 w. Taekwondo . 35 20

1988. Japanese White-necked Crane. Mult.
1829 80 w. Type **1049** 65 35
1830 80 w. Crane taking off . . . 65 35
1831 80 w. Crane with wings spread 65 35
1832 80 w. Two cranes in flight . 65 35

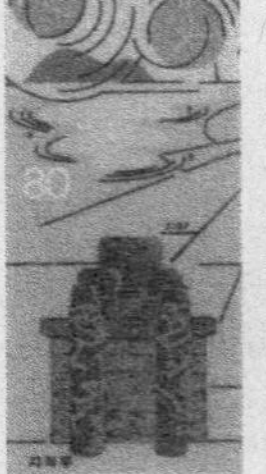

1053 Water Clock **1055** Torch Carrier

1988. Science (3rd series). Multicoloured.
1833 80 w. Type **1053** 30 10
1834 80 w. Sundial 30 10
Nos. 1833/4 were issued together, se-tenant, forming a composite design.

1988. Olympic Games, Seoul (1988) (11th issue). Multicoloured.
1835 80 w. + 20 w. Type **1055** . . 35 20
1836 80 w. + 20 w. Stadium . . . 35 20

1057 Globe and Red Cross as Candle **1058** Computer Terminal

1988. 125th Anniv of International Red Cross.
1838 **1057** 80 w. multicoloured . . 30 10

1988. 1st Anniv of National Use of Telepress.
1839 **1058** 80 w. multicoloured . . 30 10

1059 Woman sitting by Pool and Woman on Swing **1063** Olympic Flag and Pierre de Coubertin (founder of modern Games)

1988. Folk Customs (6th series). Tano Day. Multicoloured.
1840 80 w. Type **1059** 65 35
1841 80 w. Women dressing their hair 65 35
1842 80 w. Woman on swing and boy smelling flowers 65 35
1843 80 w. Boys wrestling 65 35
Nos. 1840/3 were issued together, se-tenant, forming a composite design.

1988. Olympic Games, Seoul (1988) (12th issue). Multicoloured.
1844 80 w. Type **1063** 30 10
1845 80 w. Olympic monument . . 30 10
1846 80 w. View of Seoul (vert) 30 10
1847 80 w. Women in Korean costume (vert) 30 10

1067 Stamps forming Torch Flame **1068** Pouring Molten Metal from Crucible

1988. "Olymphilex '88" Olympic Stamps Exhibition, Seoul.
1849 **1067** 80 w. multicoloured . . 30 10

1988. 22nd International Iron and Steel Institute Conference, Seoul.
1851 **1068** 80 w. multicoloured . . 30 10

1069 Gomdoori (mascot)

1988. Paralympic Games, Seoul.
1852 80 w. Type **1069** . . . . 1·25 60
1853 80 w. Archery 30 10

1071 "Homesick" (Lee Eun Sang and Kim Dong Jin)

1072 "The Pioneer" (Yoon Hae Young and Cho Doo Nam)

1988. Korean Music (4th series).
1854 **1071** 80 w. multicoloured . . 30 10
1855 **1072** 80 w. multicoloured . . 30 10

1073 Girls on See-saw

1074 Dancers

1988. Lunar New Year ("Year of the Snake").
1856 **1073** 80 w. multicoloured . . 30 10

1989. Folk Customs (7th series). Mask Dance. Multicoloured.
1858 80 w. Type **1074** 65 35
1859 80 w. Dancer with fans . . . 65 35
1860 80 w. Dancer holding branch 65 35
1861 80 w. Dancer with "Lion" . . 65 35
Nos. 1858/61 were issued together, se-tenant, forming a composite design.

1079 "Arirang"

1080 "Doraji-taryong"

1989. Korean Music (5th series).
1862 **1079** 80 w. multicoloured . . 25 10
1863 **1080** 80 w. multicoloured . . 25 10

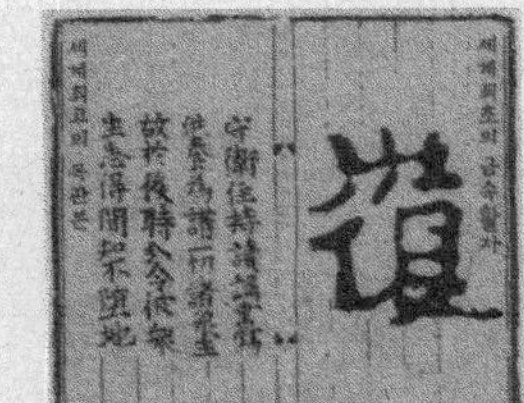
1081 Wooden Type Printing

1082 Metal Type Printing

1989. Science (4th series).
1864 **1081** 80 w. brn, bis & stone 60 10
1865 **1082** 80 w. brn, bis & stone 60 10
Nos. 1864/5 were issued together, se-tenant, forming a composite design.

1083 Teeth, Globe, Pencil and Book

1084 Hand with Stick in Heart

1989. 14th Asian–Pacific Dental Congress.
1866 **1083** 80 w. multicoloured . . 25 10

1989. Respect for the Elderly.
1867 **1084** 80 w. multicoloured . . 25 10

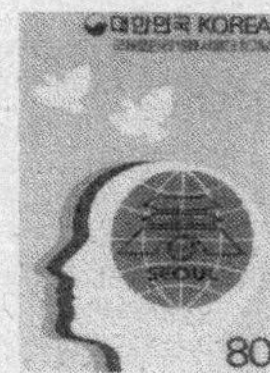
1085 Emblem

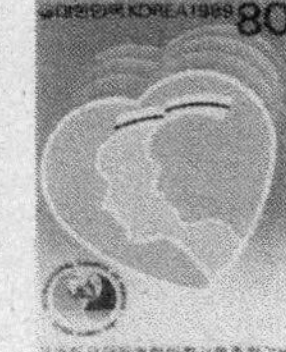
1086 Profiles within Heart

1989. Rotary Int. Convention, Seoul.
1868 **1085** 80 w. multicoloured . . 25 10

1989. 19th International Council of Nurses Congress, Seoul.
1869 **1086** 80 w. multicoloured . . 25 10

1087 "Communication"

1088 "Longevity"

1989. National Information Technology Month.
1870 **1087** 80 w. multicoloured . . 25 10

1989. World Environment Day.
1871 **1088** 80 w. multicoloured . . 25 10

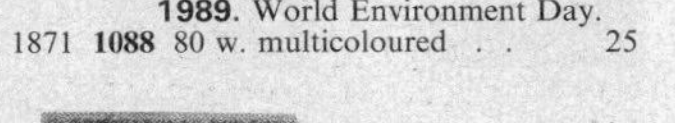

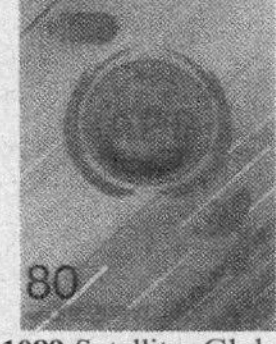
1089 Satellite, Globe and Dish Aerial

1090 "Liberty guiding the People" (detail, Eugene Delacroix)

1989. 10th Anniv of Asia–Pacific Telecommunity.
1872 **1089** 80 w. multicoloured . . 25 10

1989. Bicentenary of French Revolution.
1873 **1090** 80 w. multicoloured . . 25 10

1091 Apple and Flask

1989. 5th Asian and Oceanic Biochemists Federation Congress, Seoul.
1874 **1091** 80 w. multicoloured . . 25 10

1092 "White Ox" (Lee Joong Sub)

1093 "Street Stall" (Park Lae Hyun)

1094 "Little Girl" (Lee Bong Sang)

1095 "Autumn Scene" (Oh Ji Ho)

1989. Modern Art (5th series).
1875 **1092** 80 w. multicoloured . . 25 10
1876 **1093** 80 w. multicoloured . . 25 10
1877 **1094** 80 w. multicoloured . . 25 10
1878 **1095** 80 w. multicoloured . . 25 10

1096 Hunting Scene

1097 Goddess of Law and Ancient Law Code

1989. Seoul Olympics Commemorative Festival and World Sports Festival for Ethnic Koreans.
1879 **1096** 80 w. multicoloured . . 25 10

1989. 1st Anniv of Constitutional Court.
1880 **1097** 80 w. multicoloured . . 25 10

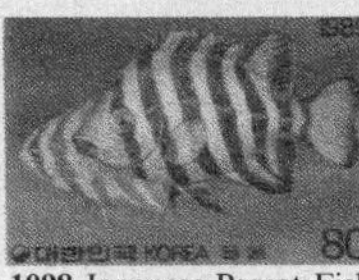
1098 Japanese Parrot Fish

1099 Spined Loach

1100 Torrent Catfish

1101 Pinecone Fish

1989. Fishes (4th series).
1881 **1098** 80 w. multicoloured . . 25 10
1881 **1099** 80 w. multicoloured . . 25 10
1882 **1100** 80 w. multicoloured . . 25 10
1883 **1101** 80 w. multicoloured . . 25 10

1102 Emblem

1989. 44th International Eucharistic Congress, Seoul.
1885 **1102** 80 w. multicoloured . . 25 10

1103 Control Tower and Boeing 747

1989. 29th International Civil Airports Association World Congress, Seoul.
1886 **1103** 80 w. multicoloured . . 35 10

1104 Scissors cutting Burning Banner

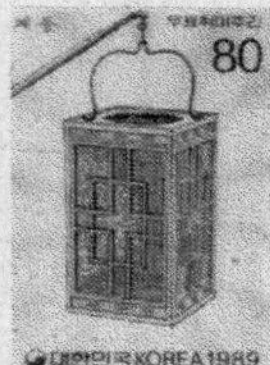
1105 Lantern

1989. Fire Precautions Month.
1887 **1104** 80 w. multicoloured . . 25 10

1989. Philatelic Week.
1888 **1105** 80 w. multicoloured . . 25 10

1106 Cranes

1107 New Year Custom

1989. Lunar New Year ("Year of the Horse").
1890 **1106** 80 w. multicoloured . . 25 10
1891 **1107** 80 w. multicoloured . . 25 10

1108 "Pakyon Fall"

1109 "Chonan Samgori"

1990. Korean Music (6th series).
1893 **1108** 80 w. multicoloured . . 25 10
1894 **1109** 80 w. multicoloured . . 25 10

1110 Clouds, Umbrella and Satellite

1111 Child with Rose

1990. World Meteorological Day.
1895 **1110** 80 w. multicoloured . . 25 10

1990. 40th Anniv of U.N.I.C.E.F. Work in Korea.
1896 **1111** 80 w. multicoloured . . 25 10

1112 Cable, Fish and Route Map

1990. Completion of Cheju Island–Kohung Optical Submarine Cable.
1897 **1112** 80 w. multicoloured . . 25 10

1113 Gilt-bronze Maitreya — 1114 Spear and Dagger Moulds

1990. Science (5th series). Metallurgy.
1898 **1113** 100 w. multicoloured . . 25 10
1899 **1114** 100 w. multicoloured . . 25 10

1115 Housing and "20"

1990. 20th Anniv of Saemaul Movement (community self-help programme).
1900 **1115** 100 w. multicoloured . . 25 10

1116 Youths

1117 Butterfly Net catching Pollution

1990. Youth Month.
1901 **1116** 100 w. multicoloured . . 25 10

1990. World Environmental Day.
1902 **1117** 100 w. multicoloured . . 25 10

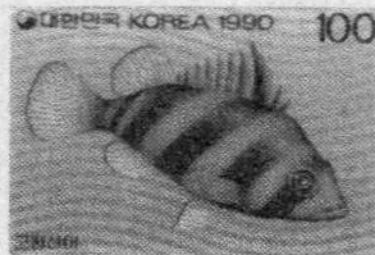

1118 Belted Beard Grunt

1119 Puffer

1120 Salmon Trout

1121 Butterling

1990. Fishes (5th series).
1903 **1118** 100 w. multicoloured . . 25 10
1904 **1119** 100 w. multicoloured . . 25 10
1905 **1120** 100 w. multicoloured . . 25 10
1906 **1121** 100 w. multicoloured . . 25 10

1122 Automatic Sorting Machines — **1123** Bandaged Teddy Bear in Hospital Bed

1990. Opening of Seoul Mail Centre.
1907 **1122** 100 w. multicoloured . . 25 10

1990. Road Safety Campaign.
1909 **1123** 100 w. multicoloured . . 25 10

1124 Campfire

1125 Lily

1990. 8th Korean Boy Scouts Jamboree, Kosong.
1910 **1124** 100 w. multicoloured . . 25 10

1990. Wild Flowers (1st series). Multicoloured.
1911 370 w. Type **1125** 75 30
1912 400 w. Asters . . . . 1·25 60
1913 440 w. Pheasant's eye . . . 85 30
1914 470 w. Scabious 90 30
See also Nos. 1956/9, 1992/5, 2082/5 and 2133/6.

1129 Washing Wool

1133 Church

1990. Folk Customs (8th series). Hand Weaving.
1915 **1129** 100 w. red, yellow & blk 50 10
1916 – 100 w. multicoloured . 50 10
1917 – 100 w. multicoloured . 50 10
1918 – 100 w. multicoloured . 50 10
DESIGNS: No. 1916, Spinning; 1917, Dyeing spun yarn; 1918, Weaving.

1990. Centenary of Anglican Church in Korea.
1919 **1133** 100 w. multicoloured . 25 10

1134 Top of Tower

1135 Peas in Pod

1990. 10th Anniv of Seoul Communications Tower.
1920 **1134** 100 w. black, blue & red 25 10

1990. Census.
1921 **1135** 100 w. multicoloured . 25 10

1136 "40" and U.N. Emblem

1137 Inlaid Case with Mirror

1990. 40th Anniv of U.N. Development Programme.
1922 **1136** 100 w. multicoloured . 25 10

1990. Philatelic Week.
1923 **1137** 100 w. multicoloured . 25 10

1138 Children feeding Ram

1140 Mascot

1990. Lunar New Year ("Year of the Sheep"). Multicoloured.
1925 100 w. Type **1138** 25 10
1926 100 w. Crane flying above mountains 25 10

1990. "Expo '93" World's Fair, Taejon (1st issue). Multicoloured.
1928 100 w. Type **1140** 25 10
1929 440 w. Yin and Yang (exhibition emblem) . . . 1·25 60
See also Nos. 1932/3, 2000/1 and 2058/61.

1142 Books and Emblem

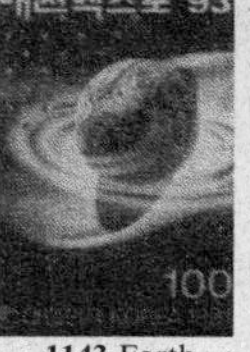

1143 Earth

1991. 30th Anniv of Saemaul Minlibrary.
1931 **1142** 100 w. multicoloured . . 25 10

1991. "Expo '93" World's Fair, Taejon (2nd issue). Multicoloured.
1932 100 w. Type **1143** 25 10
1933 100 w. Expo Tower 25 10

1145 "In a Flower Garden" (Uh Hyo Sun and Kwon Kil Sang)

1146 "Way to the Orchard" (Park Hwa Mok and Kim Kong Sun)

1991. Korean Music (7th series).
1935 **1145** 100 w. multicoloured . . 25 10
1936 **1146** 100 w. multicoloured . . 25 10

1147 Moth

1148 Beetle

1149 Butterfly

1150 Beetle

1151 Cicada

1152 Water Beetle

1153 Hornet

1154 Ladybirds

1155 Dragonfly

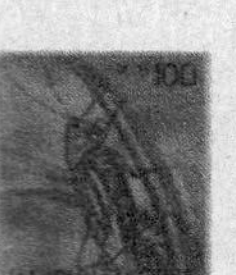

1156 Grasshopper

1991. Insects.
1937 **1147** 100 w. multicoloured . . 25 10
1938 **1148** 100 w. multicoloured . . 25 10
1939 **1149** 100 w. multicoloured . . 25 10
1940 **1150** 100 w. multicoloured . . 25 10
1941 **1151** 100 w. multicoloured . . 25 10
1942 **1152** 100 w. multicoloured . . 25 10
1943 **1153** 100 w. multicoloured . . 25 10
1944 **1154** 100 w. multicoloured . . 25 10
1945 **1155** 100 w. multicoloured . . 25 10
1946 **1156** 100 w. multicoloured . . 25 10

1157 Flautist and Centre — **1158** Flag and Provisional Government Building

1991. 40th Anniv of Korean Traditional Performing Arts Centre.
1947 **1157** 100 w. multicoloured . . 25 10

1991. 72nd Anniv of Establishment of Korean Provisional Government in Shanghai.
1948 **1158** 100 w. multicoloured . 25 10

1159 Urban Landscape and Emblem

1991. Employment for Disabled People.
1949 **1159** 100 w. multicoloured . 25 10

1160 Bouquet

1991. Teachers' Day.
1950 **1160** 100 w. multicoloured . 25 10

1161 "Microphysogobio longidorsalis"

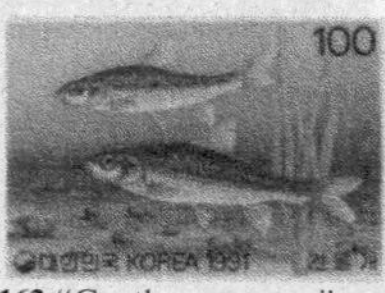

1162 "Gnathopogon majimae"

1163 "Therapon oxyrhynchus"

1164 "Psettina ijimae"

1991. Fishes (6th series).
1951 **1161** 100 w. multicoloured . 25 10
1952 **1162** 100 w. multicoloured . 25 10
1953 **1163** 100 w. multicoloured . 25 10
1954 **1164** 100 w. multicoloured . 25 10

1165 Animals waiting to Board Bus

1166 "Aerides japonicum"

1991. "Waiting One's Turn" Campaign.
1955 **1165** 100 w. multicoloured . 25 10

1991. Wild Flowers (2nd series). Mult.
1956 100 w. Type **1166** 25 10
1957 100 w. "Heloniopsis orientalis" 25 10
1958 370 w. "Aquilegia buergeriana" 75 30
1959 440 w. "Gentiana zollingeri" 90 30

1167 Scout with Semaphore Flags

1168 "Y.M.C.A."

1991. 17th World Scout Jamboree.
1960 **1167** 100 w. multicoloured . 25 10

1991. Young Men's Christian Association World Assembly, Seoul.
1962 **1168** 100 w. multicoloured . 25 10

1169 Rusted Train and Family Members Reunited

1170 Globe, Rainbow, Dove and U.N. Emblem

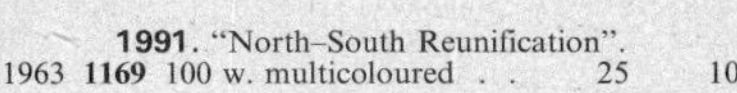

1991. "North–South Reunification".
1963 **1169** 100 w. multicoloured . . 25 10

1991. Admission of South Korea to United Nations Organization.
1964 **1170** 100 w. multicoloured . . 25 10

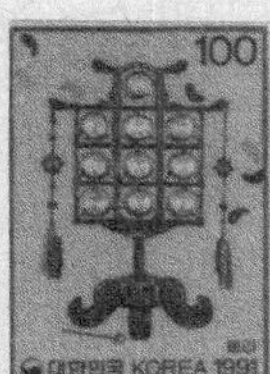

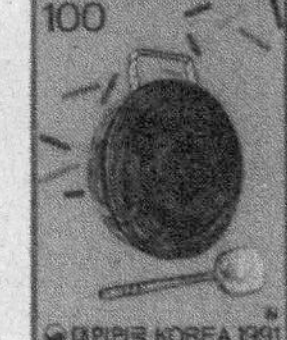

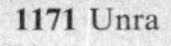

1171 Unra **1172** Jing

1173 Galgo **1174** Saeng-hwang

1991. Traditional Musical Instruments (1st series).
1965 **1171** 100 w. multicoloured . . 25 10
1966 **1172** 100 w. multicoloured . . 25 10
1967 **1173** 100 w. multicoloured . . 25 10
1968 **1174** 100 w. multicoloured . . 25 10
See also Nos. 1981/4.

1175 Film and Theatrical Masks **1176** Globe and Satellite

1991. Culture Month.
1969 **1175** 100 w. multicoloured . . 25 10

1991. "Telecom 91" International Telecommunications Exhibition, Geneva.
1970 **1176** 100 w. multicoloured . . 25 10

1177 Hexagonals **1178** Bamboo

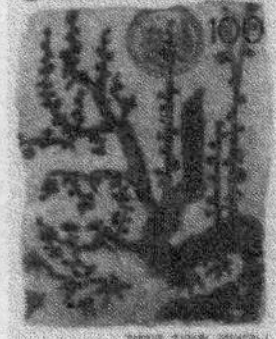

1179 Geometric **1180** Tree

1991. Korean Beauty (1st series). Kottams (patterns on walls).
1971 **1177** 100 w. multicoloured . . 25 10
1972 **1178** 100 w. multicoloured . . 25 10
1973 **1179** 100 w. multicoloured . . 25 10
1974 **1180** 100 w. multicoloured . . 25 10
See also Nos. 2006/9, 2068/71 and 2103/6.

1181 Light Bulb turning off Switch **1182** Stamps

1991. Energy Saving Campaign.
1975 **1181** 100 w. multicoloured . 25 10

1991. Philatelic Week.
1976 **1182** 100 w. multicoloured . 25 10

1183 Landscape

1991. Lunar New Year ("Year of the Monkey"). Multicoloured.
1978 100 w. Type **1183** 25 10
1979 100 w. Flying kites 25 10

1185 Yonggo **1186** Chwago

1187 Kkwaenggwari **1188** T'ukchong

1992. Traditional Musical Instruments (2nd series).
1981 **1185** 100 w. multicoloured . 25 10
1982 **1186** 100 w. multicoloured . 25 10
1983 **1187** 100 w. multicoloured . 25 10
1984 **1188** 100 w. multicoloured . 25 10

1189 White Hibiscus **1190** Satellite

1992. "Hibiscus syriacus" (national flower). Multicoloured.
1985 100 w. Type **1189** 15 10
1986 100 w. Pink hibiscus 15 10

1992. Science Day.
1987 **1191** 100 w. multicoloured . 15 10

1192 Pong-Gil Yoon **1193** Children and Heart

1992. 60th Death Anniv of Pong-Gil Yoon (Independence fighter).
1988 **1192** 100 w. multicoloured . 15 10

1992. Child Protection.
1989 **1193** 100 w. multicoloured . 15 10

1194 Warship attacking Settlement **1195** Farmer

1992. 400th Anniv of Start of Im-Jin War.
1990 **1194** 100 w. multicoloured . . 15 10

1992. 60th International Fertilizer Industry Association Conference, Seoul.
1991 **1195** 100 w. multicoloured . . 15 10

1992. Wild Flowers (3rd series). As T **1166**. Multicoloured.
1992 100 w. "Lychnis wilfordii" . . 15 10
1993 100 w. "Lycoris radiata" . . 15 10
1994 370 w. "Commelina communis" 85 20
1995 440 w. "Calanthe striata" . . 70 20

1196 "Longing for Mt. Keumkang" (Han Sang Ok and Choi Young Shurp) **1197** "The Swing" (Kim Mal Bong and Geum Su Hyeon)

1992. Korean Music (8th series).
1996 **1196** 100 w. multicoloured . . 15 10
1997 **1197** 100 w. multicoloured . . 15 10

1198 Gymnastics **1199** Stylized View of Exhibition

1992. Olympic Games, Barcelona. Multicoloured.
1998 100 w. Type **1198** 15 10
1999 100 w. Pole vaulting 15 10

1992. "Expo '93" World's Fair, Taejon (3rd issue). Multicoloured.
2000 100 w. Type **1199** 15 10
2001 100 w. "Expo 93" 15 10

1201 Korea Exhibition Centre and South Gate, Seoul

1992. 21st Universal Postal Union Congress, Seoul (1st issue). Multicoloured.
2003 100 w. Type **1201** 15 10
2004 100 w. Tolharubang (stone grandfather), Cheju 15 10
See also Nos. 2075/6, 2088 and 2112/15.

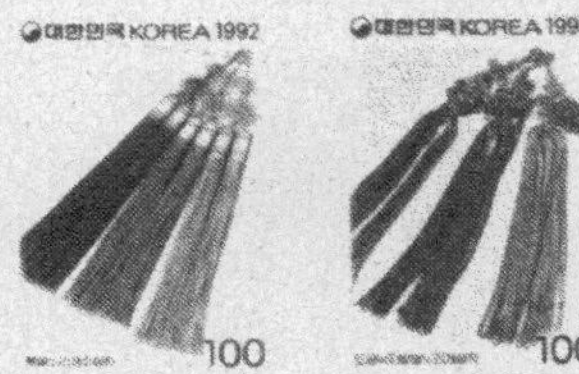

1203 Woven Pattern **1204** Fruit and Flower Decorations

1205 Carved Decorations **1206** Coral, Butterfly and Pine Resin Decorations

1992. Korean Beauty (2nd series). Maedeups (tassels).
2006 **1203** 100 w. multicoloured . . 15 10
2007 **1204** 100 w. multicoloured . . 15 10
2008 **1205** 100 w. multicoloured . . 15 10
2009 **1206** 100 w. multicoloured . . 15 10

1207 Pong Chang Yi **1208** Hwang Young Jo (Barcelona, 1992)

1992. 60th Death Anniv of Pong Chang Yi (independence fighter).
2010 **1207** 100 w. brown & orange 15 10

1992. Korean Winners of Olympic Marathon. Multicoloured.
2011 100 w. Type **1208** 15 10
2012 100 w. Shon Kee Chung (Berlin, 1936) 15 10

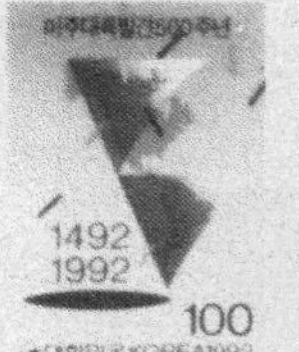

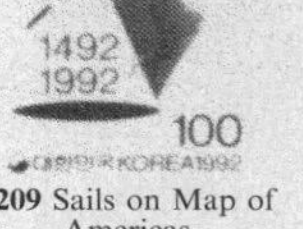

1209 Sails on Map of Americas **1210** Heads and Speech Balloon

1992. 500th Anniv of Discovery of America by Columbus.
2014 **1209** 100 w. multicoloured . 15 10

1992. Campaign for Purification of Language.
2015 **1210** 100 w. multicoloured . 15 10

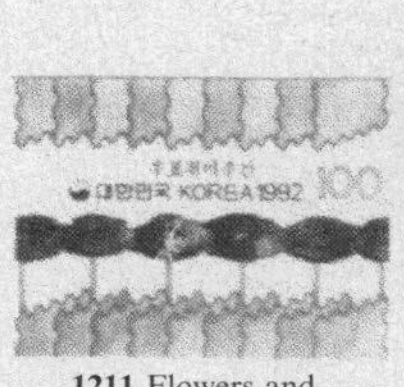

1211 Flowers and Stamps **1212** Cockerels in Snow-covered Yard

1992. Philatelic Week.
2016 **1211** 100 w. multicoloured . 15 10

1992. Lunar New Year ("Year of the Cock"). Mult.
2018 100 w. Type **1212** 15 10
2019 100 w. Flying kites 15 10

1214 Emblem, Globe and Woman holding Bowl

1992. International Nutrition Conference, Rome.
2021 **1214** 100 w. multicoloured . 15 10

1215 View of Centre and Logo

1993. Inauguration of Seoul Arts Centre's Opera House.
2022 **1215** 110 w. multicoloured . 20 10

1216 Pres. Kim Young Sam, Flag and Mt. Paektu Lake **1217** National Flag

1993. Inauguration of 14th President.
2023 **1216** 110 w. multicoloured . 20 10

1993. Multicoloured.
2025 10 w. Type **1217** 10 10
2026 20 w. White stork 10 10
2027 30 w. Magnolia (horiz) . . . 10 10
2028 40 w. Korean white pine . . 10 10
2032 90 w. Scops owl 15 10
2034 110 w. "Hibiscus syriacus" . 20 10
2035 130 w. Narcissi 20 10
2036 160 w. Pine tree (horiz) . . 25 10
2037 180 w. Little tern (horiz) . . 30 10
2038 370 w. Drum dance (horiz) . 60 20
2040 440 w. Hahoi mask and Ssirum wrestlers (horiz) 75 25

2044 710 w. King Sejong 1·00 15
2046 900 w. Statuette of Buddha 1·50 50
2047 910 w. As 710 w. 1·50 50
2048 930 w. Celadon pitcher 1·60 55

1243 Student and Computer
1244 Emblem and Map

1993. Korean Student Inventions Exhibition.
2051 **1243** 110 w. mauve and silver 20 10

1993. International Human Rights Conference, Vienna, Austria.
2052 **1244** 110 w. multicoloured 20 10

1245 Hand scooping Globe from Water
1246 Matsu-take Mushroom ("Tricholoma matsutake")

1993. "Water is Life".
2053 **1245** 110 w. multicoloured 20 10

1993. Fungi. (1st series). Multicoloured.
2054 110 w. Type **1246** 20 10
2055 110 w. "Ganoderma lucidum" 20 10
2056 110 w. "Lentinula edodes" 20 10
2057 110 w. Oyster fungus ("Pleurotus ostreatus") 20 10
See also Nos 2095/8.

1247 Government Pavilion
1248 International Pavilion and Mascot

1249 Recycling Art Pavilion
1250 Telecom Pavilion

1993. "Expo '93" World's Fair, Taejon (4th issue).
2058 **1247** 110 w. multicoloured 20 10
2059 **1248** 110 w. multicoloured 20 10
2060 **1249** 110 w. multicoloured 20 10
2061 **1250** 110 w. multicoloured 20 10

1251 Emblems

1993. 19th Congress of International Society of Orthopaedic and Trauma Surgery.
2063 **1251** 110 w. multicoloured 20 10

1252 "O Dol Ddo Gi" (Cheju Island folk song)
1253 "Ong He Ya" (barley threshing song)

1993. Korean Music (9th series).
2064 **1252** 110 w. multicoloured 20 10
2065 **1253** 110 w. multicoloured 20 10

1254 Janggu Drum Dance
1255 Emblem

1993. "Visit Korea" Year (1994) (1st issue).
2066 **1254** 110 w. multicoloured 20 10
2067 **1255** 110 w. multicoloured 20 10
See also Nos. 2086/7.

1256 "Twin Tigers" (military officials, 1st to 3rd rank)
1260 Campaign Emblem

1993. Korean Beauty (3rd series). Hyoongbae (embroidered insignia of the Chosun dynasty). Multicoloured.
2068 110 w. Type **1256** 20 10
2069 110 w. "Single Crane" (civil officials, 4th to 9th rank) 20 10
2070 110 w. "Twin Cranes" (civil officials, 1st to 3rd rank) 20 10
2071 110 w. "Dragon" (King) 20 10

1993. Anti-litter Campaign.
2072 **1260** 110 w. multicoloured 20 10

1261 "Eggplant and Oriental Long-nosed Locust" (Shin Sa-im Dang)
1262 "Weaving"

1993. Philatelic Week.
2073 **1261** 110 w. multicoloured 20 10

1993. 21st Universal Postal Union Congress, Seoul (2nd issue). Paintings by Kim Hong Do. Multicoloured.
2075 110 w. Type **1262** 20 10
2076 110 w. "Musicians and a Dancer" (vert) 20 10

1263 Ribbon and Globe as "30", Freighter and Ilyushin Il-86 Airliner

1993. 30th Trade Day.
2078 **1263** 110 w. multicoloured 20 10

1264 Sapsaree and Kite

1993. Lunar New Year. ("Year of the Dog"). Multicoloured.
2079 110 w. Type **1264** 20 10
2080 110 w. Puppy with New Year's Greetings bow 20 10

1993. Wild Flowers (4th series). As T **1166**.
2082 110 w. "Weigela hortensis" 20 10
2083 110 w. "Iris ruthenica" 20 10
2084 110 w. "Aceriphyllum rossii" 20 10
2085 110 w. Marsh marigold ("Caltha palustris") 20 10

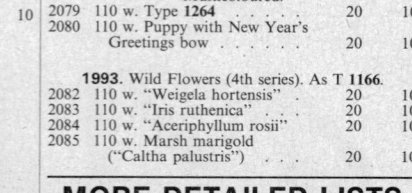

1266 Flautist on Cloud
1267 T'alch'um Mask Dance

1994. "Visit Korea" Year (2nd issue).
2086 **1266** 110 w. multicoloured 20 10
2087 **1267** 110 w. multicoloured 20 10

1268 Medal, Horse, Envelope and Emblem
1269 Monument

1994. 21st Universal Postal Union Congress, Seoul (3rd issue).
2088 **1268** 300 w. multicoloured 50 15

1994. 75th Anniv of Samil (Independence) Movement.
2090 **1269** 110 w. multicoloured 20 10

1270 Great Purple

1994. Protection of Wildlife and Plants. Multicoloured.
2091 110 w. Type **1270** (butterfly) 20 10
2092 110 w. "Allomyrina dichotoma" (beetle) 20 10

1271 Family of Mandarins

1994. International Year of the Family.
2094 **1271** 110 w. multicoloured 20 10

1994. Fungi (2nd series). As T **1246**. Multicoloured.
2095 110 w. Common morel ("Morchella esculenta") 20 10
2096 110 w. "Gomphus floccosus" 20 10
2097 110 w. "Cortinarius purpurascens" 20 10
2098 110 w. "Oudemansiella platyphylla" 20 10

1272 Museum

1994. War Memorial Museum, Yongsan (Seoul).
2100 **1272** 110 w. multicoloured 20 10

1273 Text and Dove

1994. "Philakorea 1994" International Stamp Exhibition, Seoul (1st issue).
2101 **1273** 910 w. multicoloured 1·50 50
See also Nos. 2107/9.

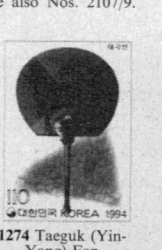

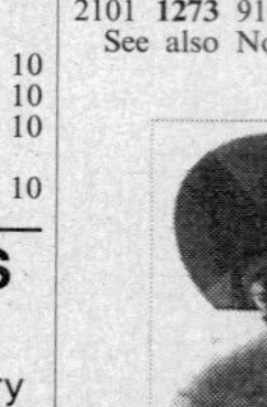

1274 Taeguk (Yin-Yang) Fan
1275 Crane Fan

1276 Pearl Fan
1277 Wheel Fan

1994. Korean Beauty (4th series). Fans.
2103 **1274** 110 w. multicoloured 20 10
2104 **1275** 110 w. multicoloured 20 10
2105 **1276** 110 w. multicoloured 20 10
2106 **1277** 110 w. multicoloured 20 10

1278 "Wintry Days" (Kim Chong Hui)
1282 "Sword Dance" (Sin Yun Bok)

1994. "Philakorea 1994" International Stamp Exhibition, Seoul (2nd issue). Multicoloured.
2107 130 w. Type **1278** 20 10
2108 130 w. "Grape" (Choe Sok Hwan) 20 10
2109 130 w. "Riverside Scene" (Kim Duk Sin) 20 10

1994. 21st Universal Postal Union Congress, Seoul (4th issue). Multicoloured.
2112 130 w. Type **1282** 20 10
2113 130 w. "Book Shelves" (detail of folk painting showing stamps) 20 10
2114 130 w. Congress emblem 20 10
2115 130 w. Hong Yung Sik (postal reformer) and Heinrich von Stephan (founder of U.P.U) 20 10

1283 Old Map
1284 Mail Van

1994. 600th Anniv of Adoption of Seoul as Capital of Korea.
2118 **1283** 130 w. multicoloured 20 10

1994. Transport. Multicoloured.
2122 300 w. Type **1284** 50 15
2123 390 w. Airplane 60 20
2126 540 w. Train 90 30
2131 1190 w. River cruiser 1·90 65

1994. Wild Flowers (5th series). As T **1166**. Multicoloured.
2133 130 w. "Gentiana jamesii" 20 10
2134 130 w. "Geranium eriostemon var. megalanthum" 20 10
2135 130 w. "Leontopodium japonicum" 20 10
2136 130 w. "Lycoris aurea" 20 10

1285 "Water Melon and Field Mice" (detail of folding screen, Shin Saimdang)

1994. Philatelic Week.
2137 **1285** 130 w. multicoloured 20 10

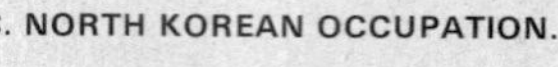

C. NORTH KOREAN OCCUPATION.

(**1** "Democratic People's Republic of Korea")

1950. Nos. 116 and 118/19, optd with Type **1**.
1 10 w. green 30·00
2 20 w. brown 8·50
3 30 w. green 9·50

NORTH KOREA

100 cheun = 1 won.

GUM. All stamps of North Korea up to No. N1506 are without gum, except where otherwise stated.

A. RUSSIAN OCCUPATION

1 Hibiscus **2** Diamond Mountains

1946. Perf, roul or imperf.

N1 **1** 20 ch. red . . . . 45·00 32·00
N2 **2** 50 ch. green . . . . 15·00 15·00
N4b 50 ch. red . . . . 8·50 8·50
N5b 50 ch. violet . . . . 10·00 12·00

4 Gen. Kim Il Sung and Flag **5** Peasants

1946. 1st Anniv of Liberation from Japan.

N6 **4** 50 ch. brown £150 £110

1947. Perf, roul or imperf.

N 7 **5** 1 wn. green . . . . 5·00 4·00
N 8 1 wn. violet . . . . 15·00 10·00
N 9 1 wn. blue on buff . . . . 5·50 4·50
N10 1 wn. blue . . . . 3·25 2·50

6 **7** **8**

1948. 2nd Anniv of Labour Law.

N11 **6** 50 ch. blue £225 £180

1948. 3rd Anniv of Liberation from Japan.

N12 **7** 50 ch. red £175

1948. Promulgation of Constitution.

N13 **8** 50 ch. blue and red . . . . £160 40·00

B. KOREAN PEOPLE'S DEMOCRATIC REPUBLIC

9 North Korean Flag **10**

1948. Establishment of People's Republic. Roul.

N16 **9** 25 ch. violet . . . . 3·50 3·50
N17 50 ch. blue . . . . 6·00 6·00

1949. Roul or perf.

N18 **10** 6 wn. red and blue . . . . 2·00 2·00

11 Kim Il Sung University, Pyongyang **12** North Korean Flags

11a Kim Il Sung University, Pyongyang

1949. Roul.

N19 **11** 1 wn. violet . . . . . . 45·00 20·00
N20 **11a** 1 wn. blue . . . . 45·00 20·00

1949. 4th Anniv of Liberation from Japan. Roul or perf.

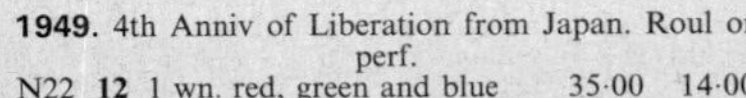

N22 **12** 1 wn. red, green and blue 35·00 14·00

13 Order of the National Flag **14** Liberation Monument, Pyongyang

15 Soldier and Flags **16** Peasant and Worker

17 Tractor **18** Capitol, Seoul

1950. Perf, roul or imperf. Various sizes.

N24 **13** 1 wn. green (A) . . . . . 2·00 1·00
N25 1 wn. orange (A) . . . . . — 25·00
N26 1 wn. orange (B) . . . . 12·00 12·00
N27 1 wn. green (C) . . . . . 1·75 1·25
N28 1 wn. olive (D) . . . . . 5·50 4·50

SIZES: (A) $23\frac{3}{4}\times37\frac{1}{2}$ mm. (B) $20\times32\frac{1}{2}$ mm. (C) $22\times35\frac{1}{2}$ mm. (D) $22\frac{1}{2}\times36\frac{1}{2}$ mm.

1950. 5th Anniv of Liberation from Japan. Roul, perf or imperf. Various sizes.

N29 **14** 1 wn. red, indigo and blue 90 90
N30 1 wn. orange . . . . . . 6·00 5·00
N31 **15** 2 wn. black, blue red 90 90
N32 **16** 6 wn. green (A) . . . . . 1·25 1·25
N36 6 wn. red (B) . . . . . . 12·50 11·00
N33 **17** 10 wn. brown (C) . . . . 2·00 2·00
N37 10 wn. brown (D) . . . . 18·00 13·50

SIZES: (A) 20×30 mm. (B) 22×33 mm. (C) 20×28 mm. (D) 22×30 mm.

1950. Capture of Seoul by North Korean Forces. Roul.

N38 **18** 1 wn. red, blue and green 35·00 32·00

19 **20** Kim Gi Ok and Aeroplane

1951. Order of Admiral Li Sun Sin. Imperf or perf.

N39 **19** 6 wn. orange . . . . . . 6·50 5·00

1951. Air Force Hero Kim Gi Ok. Imperf.

N40 **20** 1 wn. blue . . . . 5·00 2·00

21 Russian and North Korean Flags **22** Kim Ki U (hero) **23** N. Korean and Chinese Soldiers

1951. 6th Anniv of Liberation from Japan. Roul or perf.

N41 **21** 1 wn. blue . . . . 3·50 2·50
N42 1 wn. red . . . . 3·50 2·50
N43 **22** 1 wn. blue . . . . 3·50 2·50
N44 1 wn. red . . . . 3·75 2·50
N45 **23** 2 wn. blue . . . . 6·50 5·00
N46 2 wn. red . . . . 8·50 7·50

All values exist on buff and on white paper.

24 Order of Soldier's Honour **25** **26** Woman Partisan, Li Su Dok

1951. Imperf or perf.

N47 **24** 40 wn. red . . . . 7·50 4·50

1951. Co-operation of Chinese People's Volunteers. Imperf or perf.

N49 **25** 10 wn. blue . . . . 5·00 3·25

1952. Partisan Heroes. Imperf or perf.

N50 **26** 70 wn. brown . . . . . . 3·00 1·00

27 **28** Gen. P'eng Teh-huai **29** Munition Worker

1952. Peace Propaganda. Imperf or perf.

N51 **27** 20 wn. blue, green & red 4·00 2·00

1952. Honouring Commander of Chinese People's Volunteers. Imperf.

N52 **28** 10 wn. purple . . . . . . 6·00 3·00

1952. Labour Day. Imperf or perf.

N53 **29** 10 wn. red . . . . 13·00 13·00

30 **31** **32**

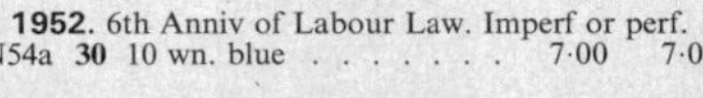

1952. 6th Anniv of Labour Law. Imperf or perf.

N54a **30** 10 wn. blue . . . . 7·00 7·00

1952. Anti-U.S. Imperialism Day. Imperf or perf.

N55 **31** 10 wn. red . . . . 13·00 13·00

1952. North Korean and Chinese Friendship. Imperf or perf.

N56b **32** 20 wn. deep blue . . . . 9·00 9·00

33 **34**

1952. 7th Anniv of Liberation from Japan. Imperf or perf.

N57 **33** 10 wn. red . . . . 10·00 10·00
N58 **34** 10 wn. red . . . . 12·00 12·00

35 **36** **37**

1952. Int. Youth Day. With gum. Imperf or perf.

N59 **35** 10 wn. green . . . . 6·00 6·00

1953. 5th Anniv of People's Army. Imperf or perf.

N60 **36** 10 wn. red . . . . 12·50 12·50
N61 **37** 40 wn. purple . . . . . . 12·50 12·50

38 **39**

1953. Int. Women's Day. With gum. Imperf or perf.

N62 **38** 10 wn. red . . . . 8·00 8·00
N63 **39** 40 wn. green . . . . 8·00 8·00

40 **41**

1953. Labour Day. Imperf or perf.

N64 **40** 10 wn. green . . . . 7·50 7·50
N65 **41** 40 wn. orange . . . . . . 7·50 7·50

42 **43**

1953. Anti-U.S. Imperialism Day. With gum. Imperf or perf.

N66 **42** 10 wn. turquoise . . . . 13·00 13·00
N67 **43** 40 wn. red . . . . 13·00 13·00

44 **45**

1953. 4th World Youth Festival, Bucharest. With gum. Imperf or perf.

N68 **44** 10 wn. blue and green . . 3·25 2·75
N69 **45** 20 wn. green and pink . . 3·25 2·75

46 **47**

1953. Armistice and Victory Issue. With gum. Imperf or perf.

N70a **46** 10 wn. brown & yellow 38·00 32·00

1953. 8th Anniv of Liberation from Japan. Imperf.

N71 **47** 10 wn. red . . . . £120 90·00

48 **49** Liberation Monument, Pyongyang

1953. 5th Anniv of People's Republic. Imperf or perf.

N72 **48** 10 wn. blue and red . . . 11·00 11·00

1953. With gum. Imperf or perf.

N73 **49** 10 wn. slate . . . . 3·75 3·50

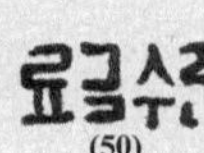

(50) **(51)**

1954. No. N18 optd "Fee Collected" in Korean characters, T **50**.

N74 **10** 6 wn. red and blue . . . £120 £120

1954. Nos. N18 and N39 surch with T **51**.

N75 **10** 5 wn. on 6 wn. red & blue 8·00 8·00
N76 **19** 5 wn. on 6 wn. orange . . 45·00 40·00

52 **53**

1954. Post-war Economic Reconstruction. With gum. Imperf or perf.

N77 **52** 10 wn. blue . . . . 6·00 6·00

1954. 6th Anniv of People's Army. With gum. Imperf or perf.

N78 **53** 10 wn. red . . . . 10·00 10·00

54

55

1954. Int. Women's Day. With gum. Imperf or perf.
N79 **54** 10 wn. red . . . . 5·50 5·50

1954. Labour Day. With gum. Imperf or perf.
N80 **55** 10 wn. red . . . . 6·00 6·00

56

57 Taedong Gate, Pyongyang

1954. Anti-U.S. Imperialism Day. With gum. Imperf or perf.
N81 **56** 10 wn. red . . . . 15·00 15·00

1954. Imperf or perf.
N82 **57** 5 wn. lake . . . . 2·00 75
N83 5 wn. brown . . . . . . 2·00 75

58

59 Soldier

1954. National Young Activists' Conf. With gum. Imperf or perf.
N84 **58** 10 wn. red, blue and slate 3·00 3·00

1954. 9th Anniv of Liberation from Japan. With gum. Imperf or perf.
N85 **59** 10 wn. red . . . . 6·00 6·00

60 North Korean Flag

61 Hwanghae Iron Works

62 Hwanghae Iron Works and Workers

194. 6th Anniv of People's Republic. With gum. Imperf or perf.
N86 **60** 10 wn. blue and red . . . 5·00 5·00

1954. Economic Reconstruction. Imperf or perf.
N87 **61** 10 wn. blue . . . . 2·00 50
N88 **62** 10 wn. brown . . . . . . 2·00 50

63

64

1955. 7th Anniv of People's Army. With gum. Imperf or perf.
N89 **63** 10 wn. red . . . . 3·50 3·50

1955. Int. Women's Day. With gum. Imperf or perf.
N90 **64** 10 wn. deep blue . . . . . 3·50 3·50

65

66

1955. Labour Day. With gum. Imperf or perf.
N91 **65** 10 wn. green . . . . . . 3·25 3·25
N92 **66** 10 wn. red . . . . 3·25 3·25

67 Admiral Li Sun Sin

68

1955. Imperf or perf.
N93 **67** 1 wn. blue on green . . . 1·25 20
N94 2 wn. red on buff . . . . 1·75 25
N95 2 wn. red . . . . 3·00 50

1955. 9th Anniv of Labour Law. With gum. Imperf or perf.
N96 **68** 10 wn. red . . . . 3·50 2·50

69 Liberation Monument and Flags

1955. 10th Anniv of Liberation from Japan. Imperf or perf.
N97 **69** 10 wn. green . . . . . . 2·00 1·50
N98 10 wn. red, blue and brown ($29\frac{1}{2} \times 42\frac{1}{2}$ mm) . . . . 1·25 1·00

70

71

1955. Soviet Union Friendship Month. Imperf or perf.
N 99 **70** 10 wn. red . . . . 1·50 1·00
N100 10 wn. red and blue . . 2·25 1·50
N101 **71** 20 wn. red and slate . . 3·25 2·50
N102 20 wn. red and blue . . 1·50 1·25
SIZES: No. N99, $22 \times 32\frac{1}{2}$ mm; No. N100, $29\frac{1}{2} \times 43$ mm; No. N101, $18\frac{1}{2} \times 32$ mm; No. N102, 25×43 mm.

72 Son Rock

73

74

1956. Haegumgang Maritime Park. Imperf or perf.
N103 **72** 10 wn. blue on blue . . 3·00 1·75

1956. 8th Anniv of People's Army. Imperf or perf.
N104 **73** 10 wn. red on green . . 5·50 5·50

1956. Labour Day. Imperf or perf.
N105 **74** 10 wn. blue . . . . . . 3·50 2·75

75 Machinist

76 Taedong Gate, Pyongyang

77 Woman Harvester

78 Moranbong Theatre, Pyongyang

1956. Imperf or perf.
N106 **75** 1 wn. brown 90 60
N107 **76** 2 wn. blue 90 60
N108 **77** 10 wn. red 90 60
N109 **78** 40 wn. green . . . . . . 5·00 3·50

79 Miner

80 Boy Bugler and Girl Drummer

1956. 10th Anniv of Labour Law. Imperf or perf.
N110 **79** 10 wn. brown . . . . . 1·75 1·00

1956. 10th Anniv of Children's Union. Imperf or perf.
N111 **80** 10 wn. brown . . . . . . 4·00 2·75

81 Workers

82 Industrial Plant

1956. 10th Anniv of Sex Equality Law. Imperf or perf.
N112 **81** 10 wn. brown . . . . . . 2·00 1·40

1956. 10th Anniv of Nationalization of Industry. Imperf or perf.
N113 **82** 10 wn. brown . . . . . . 27·00 11·50

83 Liberation Tower

84 Kim Il Sung University

1956. 11th Anniv of Liberation from Japan. Imperf or perf.
N114 **83** 10 wn. red . . . . 1·50 80

1956. 10th Anniv of Kim Il Sung University. Imperf or perf.
N115 **84** 10 wn. brown . . . . . . 2·50 1·75

85 Boy and Girl

86 Pak Ji Won

1956. 4th Democratic Youth League Congress. Imperf or perf.
N116 **85** 10 wn. brown . . . . . . 2·50 1·50

1957. 220th Birth Anniv of Pak Ji Won ("Yonam"), statesman. Imperf or perf.
N117 **86** 10 wn. blue . . . . 1·50 90

87 Tabo Pagoda, Pulguksa

88 Ulmil Pavilion, Pyongyang

89 Furnaceman

1957. Imperf, perf or roul.
N118 **87** 5 wn. blue . . . . 1·00 75
N119 **88** 40 wn. green . . . . . . 2·00 1·25

1957. Production and Economy Campaign. With or without gum. Imperf or perf.
N121 **89** 10 wn. blue . . . . . . 2·50 1·25

90 Furnaceman

91 Voters and Polling Booth

1957. 2nd General Election. Imperf or perf.
N122 **90** 1 wn. orange 45 30
N123 2 wn. brown 45 30
N124 **91** 10 wn. red . . . . 2·50 1·25

92 Ryongwangjong, Pyongyang

93 Lenin and Flags

94 Kim Il Sung at Pochonbo

95 Lenin

96 Pouring Steel

1957. 1530th Anniv of Pyongyang. Imperf or perf.
N125 **92** 10 wn. green 60 25

1957. 40th Anniv of Russian Revolution. Imperf or perf.
N126 **93** 10 wn. green 75 40
N127 **94** 10 wn. red 75 40
N128 **95** 10 wn. blue 75 40
N129 **96** 10 wn. orange . . . . . . 1·25 40
No. N126 exists with gum.

97 Congress Emblem

98 Liberation Monument, Spassky Tower and Flags

1957. 4th World Trade Unions Federation Congress. Leipzig. Imperf (with or without gum) or perf.
N130 **97** 10 wn. blue and green . 80 50

1957. Russian Friendship Month. Imperf or perf.
N131 **98** 10 wn. green . . . . . . 1·75 50

99 Weighing a Baby

100 Bandaging a Hand

1957. Red Cross. Imperf, perf or roul.
N132 **99** 1 wn. red . . . . 3·50 2·00
N133 2 wn. red . . . . 3·50 2·00
N134 **100** 10 wn. red . . . . . . 10·00 4·50
No. N133 exists with or without gum.

101 Koryo Celadon Jug (12th century)

102 Koryo Incense-burner (12th century)

1958. Korean Antiquities. Imperf (with or without gum) or perf.
N135 **101** 10 wn. blue . . . . . 3·00 50
N136 **102** 10 wn. green . . . . . 3·00 50

103 Woljong Temple Pagoda

104 Soldier

1958. With gum (5 wn.), without gum (10 wn.). Imperf or perf.
N137 **103** 5 wn. green . . . . . . 1·00 50
N138 10 wn. blue . . . . . . 1·50 75

1958. 10th Anniv of People's Army. No gum (No. N139) with or without gum (No. N140). Imperf or perf.
N139 **104** 10 wn. blue . . . . . . 1·25 50
N140 – 10 wn. red . . . . . . 1·75 65
DESIGN—HORIZ: ($37\frac{1}{2} \times 26$ mm.): No. N140, Soldier, flag and Hwanghae Iron Works.

106 Lisunov Li-2 over Pyongyang

1958. Air. Imperf or perf.
N141 **106** 20 wn. blue . . . . . . 4·25 1·00

107 Sputniks

108 Sputnik encircling Globe

1958. I.G.Y. Inscr "1957-1958". Imperf or perf.
N142 **107** 10 wn. slate 45 10
N143 **108** 20 wn. slate 45 10
N144 – 40 wn. slate . . . . . . 3·00 30
N145 **107** 70 wn. slate 50 20
DESIGN—HORIZ: 40 wn. Sputnik over Pyongyang Observatory.
Nos. N142/4 exist with or without gum.

109 Furnaceman

110 Hwanghae Iron Works

1958. Young Socialist Constructors' Congress, Pyongyang. Imperf or perf.
N146 **109** 10 wn. blue . . . . . . 1·75 50

1958. Opening of Hwanghae Iron Works. Imperf or perf.
N147 **110** 10 wn. blue . . . . . . 2·50 65

111 Commemorative Badge

112 Federation Emblem

1958. Farewell to Chinese People's Volunteers (1st issue). Imperf or perf.
N148 **111** 10 wn. purple and blue 1·00 40
See also No. N158.

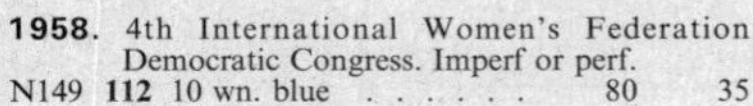

1958. 4th International Women's Federation Democratic Congress. Imperf or perf.
N149 **112** 10 wn. blue 80 35

113 Conference Emblem

1958. 1st World Young Workers' Trade Union Federation Conference, Prague. Imperf or perf.
N150 **113** 10 wn. brown & green 1·25 35

114 Flats, East Ward, Pyongyang

115 Workers' Flats, Pyongyang

1958. Rehousing Progress. Imperf or perf.
N151 **114** 10 wn. blue . . . . . . 2·00 50
N152 **115** 10 wn. green . . . . . . 2·00 50

117 Pyongyang Railway Station

119 Textile Worker

1958. 10th Anniv of Korean People's Republic. Imperf or perf.
N153 – 10 wn. green . . . . . . 3·00 50
N154 **117** 10 wn. green . . . . . . 7·50 1·50
N155 – 10 wn. brown and buff 1·50 50
N156 **119** 10 wn. brown . . . . . . 5·25 1·75
N157 – 10 wn. brown . . . . . . 4·00 1·00
DESIGNS—HORIZ: No. N153, Hungnam Fertiliser Plant; No. N157, Yongp'ung Dam, Pyongyang. VERT: No. N155, Arms of People's Republic.

121 Volunteer and Troop Train

122 Transplanting Rice

1958. Farewell to Chinese People's Volunteers (2nd issue). Imperf or perf.
N158 **121** 10 wn. sepia . . . . . . 20·00 6·50

1958. Imperf or perf.
N159 **122** 10 wn. sepia 40 15

123 Winged Horse of Chollima

124 N. Korean and Chinese Flags

1958. National Production Executives' Meeting, Pyongyang. With or without gum. Imperf or perf.
N160 **123** 10 wn. red . . . . . . 1·60 30

1958. N. Korean-Chinese Friendship Month. With or without gum. Imperf or perf.
N161 **124** 10 wn. red, blue & green 75 30

125 Farm Workers

126 Gen. Ulji Mun Dok

1959. National Co-operative Farming Congress, Pyongyang. With or without gum. Imperf or perf.
N162 **125** 10 wn. blue 65 25

1959. With gum. Imperf or perf.
N163 **126** 10 wn. red and yellow . 1·50 50
See also Nos. N165/7 and N216/19.

127 Women with Banner

128 Rocket and Moon

1959. National Conference of Women Socialist Constructors, Pyongyang. With or without gum.
N164 **127** 10 ch. brown and red . 75 30

1959. Revalued currency. Portraits as T **126**. Imperf (with or without gum) or perf (with gum).
N165 – 2 ch. blue on green . . 60 10
N166 – 5 ch. purple on buff . . 70 10
N167 **126** 10 ch. red on cream . . 85 10
PORTRAITS: 2 ch. General Kang Gam Chan; 5 ch. General Chon Bong Jun.

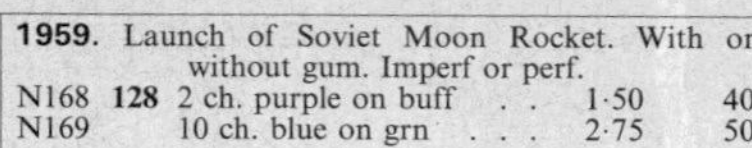

1959. Launch of Soviet Moon Rocket. With or without gum. Imperf or perf.
N168 **128** 2 ch. purple on buff . . 1·50 40
N169 10 ch. blue on grn . . . 2·75 50

129 "Irrigation"

130 Inscribed Tree at Partisan H.Q., Chongbong

131 Kim Il Sung Statue

132 Mt. Paekdu

1959. Land Irrigation Project. Imperf or perf.
N170 **129** 10 ch. multicoloured . . 2·00 45

1959. Partisan Successes against Japanese 1937–39. With gum (No. N172) or no gum (others). Perf (N172) or imperf or perf (others).
N171 **130** 5 ch. multicoloured . . . 1·50 35
N172 **131** 10 ch. blue & turquoise 1·00 10
N173 **132** 10 ch. violet . . . . . . 1·75 40

133 "Flying Horse" Tractor

1959. "Great Perspectives" (1st issue: Development of Industrial Mechanisation). With or without gum. Perf, roul or imperf.
N174 **133** 1 ch. red, olive and green 45 10
N175 – 2 ch. multicoloured . . 2·50 40
N176 – 2 ch. red, pink and violet 60 10
N177 – 5 ch. orange, brown & ochre 60 15
N178 – 10 ch. blue, green & brown 70 15
N179 – 10 ch. green, lt green & brn . . . . . . 1·00 20
DESIGNS: No. N175, Electric shunting locomotive; N176, "Red Star 58" bulldozer; N177, "Flying Horse" excavator; N178, "SU-50" universal lathe; N179, "Victory 58" lorry.
See also Nos. N189a/200 and N275/79.

134 Armistice Building, Panmunjom

135 Protest Meeting

136 "Hoisting link between N. and S. Korea"

137 Emigration "Pickets"

1959. Campaign for Withdrawal of U.S. Forces from S. Korea. With gum. Perf (20 ch.) or imperf or perf (others).
N180 **134** 10 ch. blue & ultramarine 55 20
N181 **135** 20 ch. deep blue & blue 75 30
N182 **136** 70 ch. brown, cream and purple . . . . . . 4·00 1·60

1959. Campaign Against Emigration of South Koreans. With gum.
N183 **137** 20 ch. brown and sepia . 90 30

138 Korean Type of "1234"

139 Books breaking Chains

140 Emblems of Peace, Labour and Letters

141 Korean Alphabet of 1443

1959. International Book Exibition, Leipzig. With gum (No. N184, N186) or no gum (others).
N184 **138** 5 ch. sepia . . . . . . 4·00 40
N185 **139** 5 ch. red and green . . 1·50 30
N186 **140** 10 ch. blue . . . . . . 2·50 75
N187 **141** 10 ch. violet and blue . 2·50 50

142 Pig Farm

143 Rotary Cement Kiln

1959. Animal Husbandry. With gum (5 ch.) or no gum (2 ch.).
N188 – 2 ch. brown, grn & buff 40 15
N189 **142** 5 ch. cream, blue & brn 60 20
DESIGN—HORIZ: 2 ch. Cow-girl with Cattle.

1959. "Great Perspectives" (2nd issue: Production Targets). With gum (Nos. N190 and N192) or no gum (others). Perf (N197/8 and N200), perf or imperf (others).
N189a **143** 1 ch. brown, choc & blue 25 10
N190 – 2 ch. multicoloured . . 50 10
N191 – 5 ch. multicoloured . . 90 25
N192 – 10 ch. multicoloured . 1·10 35
N193 – 10 ch. purple, yell & bl 50 10
N194 – 10 ch. yellow, grn & red 75 10
N195 – 10 ch. multicoloured . 50 10
N196 – 10 ch. blue, light blue and green 60 10
N197 – 10 ch. multicoloured . 50 10
N198 – 10 ch. green, buff and brown 75 10
N199 – 10 ch. brown & orange 50 10
N200 – 10 ch. multicoloured 95 15
DESIGNS–VERT: No. N190, Electric power lines and dam; No. N191, Loading fertilizers into truck. HORIZ: No. N192, Factory, electric power lines and dam; No. N193, Harvesting; No. N194, Sugar-beet, factory and pieces of sugar; No. N195, Steel furnace; No. N196, Trawlers; No. N197, Pig-iron workers; No. N198, Coal miners; No. N199, Girl picking apples; No. N200, Textile worker.

144 Sika Deer

145 Congress Emblem

1959. Game Preservation. No gum (5 ch.), with gum (10 ch.).
N201 – 5 ch. multicoloured . . 90 20
N202 – 5 ch. yellow, brown & bl 90 10
N203 – 5 ch. sepia, green & brn 90 10
N204 – 5 ch. brown, black & blue 90 35
N205 **144** 10 ch. multicoloured . . 1·50 25
N206 – 10 ch. red, brown and green on cream . . . 2·75 50
DESIGNS—HORIZ: No. N201, Chinese water deer; No. N202, Siberian weasel; No. N203, Steppe polecat; No. N204, European otter; No. N206, Ring-necked Pheasant.

1960. 3rd Korean Trade Unions Federation Congress. With gum.
N207 **145** 5 ch. multicoloured . . 35 10

146 "Chungnyon-ho" (freighter)

1959. Transport. With gum.
N208 – 5 ch. purple . . . . . . 7·50 1·00
N209 146 10 ch. green . . . . . . 2·25 60
DESIGN: 5 ch. Electric train.

147 Soldier, Tractor and Plough
148 Knife Dance

1960. 12th Anniv of Korean People's Army. With gum.
N210 147 5 ch. violet and blue . . 32·00 28·00

1960. Korean National Dances. Multicoloured.
N211 5 ch. Type 148 . . . . . . 1·60 10
N212 5 ch. Drum dance . . . . . 1·60 10
N213 10 ch. Farmers' dance . . . 1·60 20

149 Women of Three Races
150 Kim Jong Ho (geographer)

1960. 50th Anniv of Int Women's Day. With gum.
N214 149 5 ch. mauve and blue . 40 15
N215 – 10 ch. green and orange 50 25
DESIGN—VERT: 10 ch. Woman operating lathe.

1960. Korean Celebrities. With gum.
N216 150 1 ch. grey and green . . 50 10
N217 – 2 ch. blue and yellow . . 70 10
N218 – 5 ch. blue and yellow . . 2·75 20
N219 – 10 ch. brown and ochre 70 10
PORTRAITS: 2 ch. Kim Hong Do (painter); 5 ch. Pak Yon (musician); 10 ch. Chong Da San (scholar).

151 Grapes
152 Lenin

1960. Wild Fruits. Fruits in natural colours. With or without gum (N221/2), with gum (others).
N220 5 ch. olive and turquoise . . 55 15
N221 5 ch. drab and blue 55 15
N222 5 ch. olive and blue 55 15
N223 10 ch. olive and orange . . 70 20
N224 10 ch. green and pink . . . 70 20
FRUITS: No. N220, T 151; No. N221, Fruit of "Actinidia arguta planch"; No. N222, Pine-cone; No. N223, Hawthorn berries; No. N224, Horse-chestnut.

1960. 90th Birth Anniv of Lenin. With gum.
N225 152 10 ch. purple 40 15

153 Koreans and American Soldier (caricature)
154 Arch of Triumph Square, Pyongyang

1960. Campaign Day for Withdrawal of U.S. Forces from South Korea. With gum.
N226 153 10 ch. blue 90 20

1960. Views of Pyongyang.
N227 154 10 ch. green 60 10
N228 – 20 ch. slate 90 20
N229 – 40 ch. green . . . . . 2·00 35
N230 – 70 ch. green . . . . . 2·75 45
N231 – 1 wn. blue . . . . . . 4·00 70
VIEWS OF PYONGYANG: 20 ch. River Taedong promenade; 40 ch. Youth Street; 70 ch. People's Army Street; 1 wn. Sungri Street.

155 Russian Flag on Moon (14.9.59)
156 "Mirror Rock"

1960. Russian Cosmic Rocket Flights. With gum (5 ch.) or no gum (10 ch.).
N232 – 5 ch. turquoise . . . . 2·25 1·60
N233 155 10 ch. multicoloured . . 2·50 75
DESIGN: 5 ch. "Lunik 3" approaching Moon (4.10.59).

1960. Diamond Mountains Scenery (1st issue). Multicoloured.
N234 5 ch. Type 156 . . . . . . 60 10
N235 5 ch. Devil-faced Rock . . 60 10
N236 10 ch. Dancing Dragon Bridge (horiz) . . . . 2·50 2·00
N237 10 ch. Nine Dragon Falls . 2·75 1·50
N238 10 ch. Mt. Diamond on the Sea (horiz) 90 10
See also Nos. N569/72, N599/601 and N1180/4.

157 Lily
158 Guerrillas in the Snow

1960. Flowers. Multicoloured. With gum (N242), with or without gum (others).
N239 5 ch. Type 157 . . . . . . 15 25
N240 5 ch. Rhododendron . . . 75 15
N241 10 ch. Hibiscus . . . . . . 1·25 20
N242 10 ch. Blue campanula . . 1·25 20
N243 10 ch. Mauve campanula . 1·25 20

1960. Revolutionary Leadership of Kim Il Sung.
N244 158 5 ch. red 20 10
N245 – 10 ch. blue 45 10
N246 – 10 ch. red 45 10
N247 – 10 ch. blue 45 10
N248 – 10 ch. red 45 10
DESIGNS: No. N245, Kim Il Sung talks to guerrillas; No. N246, Kim Il Sung at Pochonbo; No. N247, Kim Il Sung on bank of Amnok River; No. N248, Kim Il Sung returns to Pyongyang.

159 Korean and Soviet Flags
160 "North Korean–Soviet Friendship"

1960. 15th Anniv of Liberation from Japan.
N249 159 10 ch. red, blue & brown 60 15

1960. North Korean–Soviet Friendship Month.
N250 160 10 ch. lake on cream . 35 15

161 Okryu Bridge, Pyongyang

1960. Pyongyang Buildings.
N251 161 10 ch. blue . . . . . 1·50 20
N252 – 10 ch. violet . . . . . 1·10 15
N253 – 10 ch. green 50 10
DESIGNS: No. N252, Grand Theatre, Pyongyang; No. N253, Okryu Restaurant.

162 Tokro River Dam

1960. Inauguration of Tokro River Hydro-electric Power Station. With gum.
N254 162 5 ch. blue 70 10

163
164 Quayside Welcome

1960. 15th Anniv of World Federation of Trade Unions.
N255 163 10 ch. light blue, ultram and blue 25 10

1960. Repatriation of Korean Nationals from Japan.
N256 164 10 ch. purple . . . . . 2·50 20

165 Lenin and Workers
166 Football

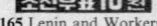

1960. Korea–Soviet Friendship. With gum.
N257 165 10 ch. brown and flesh 25 10

1960. Liberation Day Sports Meeting, Pyongyang. Multicoloured.
N258 5 ch. Running (vert) 60 10
N259 5 ch. Weightlifting (vert) . . 60 10
N260 5 ch. Cycling (vert) . . . . 2·25 15
N261 5 ch. Gymnastics (vert) . . . 60 10
N262 5 ch. Type 166 . . . . . . 1·10 15
N263 10 ch. Swimming 60 10
N264 10 ch. Moranbong Stadium, Pyongyang 60 10

167 Friendship Monument, Pyongyang
168 Federation Emblem

1960. 10th Anniv of Entry of Chinese Volunteers into Korean War. With gum.
N265 – 5 ch. mauve 20 10
N266 167 10 ch. blue 20 10
DESIGN—HORIZ: 5 ch. Chinese and Korean soldiers celebrating.

1960. 15th Anniv of World Democratic Youth Federation.
N267 168 10 ch. multicoloured . . 30 10

169 White-backed Woodpecker
170 Korean Wrestling

1960. Birds.
N268 169 2 ch. multicoloured . . 2·25 15
N268a – 5 ch. multicoloured . . 2·50 15
N269 – 5 ch. brown, yell & bl 3·75 35
N270 – 10 ch. yellow, brn & grn 2·75 20
DESIGNS—HORIZ: 5 ch. (N268a), Mandarin ducks; 10 ch. Black-naped oriole. VERT: 5 ch. (N269), Scops owl.

1960. Sports and Games. Multicoloured.
N271 5 ch. Type 170 . . . . . . 45 10
N272 5 ch. Riding on swing (vert) 45 10
N273 5 ch. Archery . . . . . . 1·40 20
N274 10 ch. Jumping on see-saw (vert) 45 10

171 Cogwheel and Corn ("Mechanization of Rural Economy")
172 Cultivated Ginseng

1961. "Great Perspectives" (3rd issue: Targets of Seven-Year Plan, 1961–67. Inscr "1961"). Mult.
N275 5 ch. Type 171 . . . . . . 60 10
N276 5 ch. Cogwheel and textiles 1·10 10

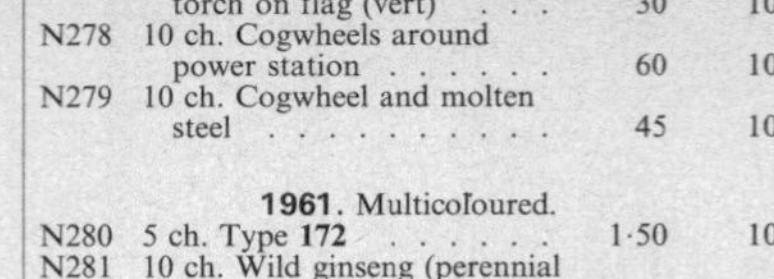
N277 10 ch. Hammer, sickle and torch on flag (vert) . . . 30 10
N278 10 ch. Cogwheels around power station 60 10
N279 10 ch. Cogwheel and molten steel 45 10

1961. Multicoloured.
N280 5 ch. Type 172 . . . . . . 1·50 10
N281 10 ch. Wild ginseng (perennial herb) . . . . 1·50 10

173 Aldehyde Shop

1961. Construction of Vinalon Factory. With gum.
N282 173 5 ch. red and yellow . . 60 10
N283 – 10 ch. green and yellow 1·10 10
N284 – 10 ch. blue and yellow 1·10 10
N285 – 20 ch. purple and yellow 1·25 15
DESIGNS: No. N283, Glacial acetic acid shop; No. N284, Polymerization and saponification shop; No. N285, Spinning shop.
See also Nos. N338/41.

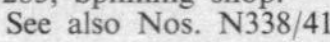

174 Construction Work
175 Museum Building

1961. Construction of Children's Palace, Pyongyang. With gum.
N286 174 2 ch. red on yellow . . 35 12

1961. Completion of Museum of Revolution, Pyongyang. With gum.
N287 175 10 ch. red 25 8

176 Cosmic Rocket
177 Wheat Harvester

1961. Launching of Soviet Venus Rocket.
N288 176 10 ch. red, yellow & blue 60 15

1961. Agricultural Mechanisation. With gum.
N289 – 5 ch. violet 50 10
N290 – 5 ch. green 50 10
N291 177 5 ch. green 50 10
N292 – 10 ch. blue 60 10
N293 – 10 ch. purple 60 10
DESIGNS: No. N289, Tractor-plough; No. N290, Disc-harrow; No. N292, Maize-harvester; No. N293, Tractors.

178
179 Agriculture

1961. Opening of Training Institute.
N294 178 10 ch. brown on buff . 25 10

1961. 15th Anniv of Land Reform Law. With gum.
N295 179 10 ch. green on yellow 45 15

180
181 Mackerel

1961. 15th Anniv of National Programme. With gum.
N296 180 10 ch. purple & yellow 20 10

1961. Marine Life.
N297 181 5 ch. multicoloured . . 90 10
N298 – 5 ch. black and blue . . 2·00 25
N299 – 10 ch. blue, black & lt bl 2·50 25
N300 – 10 ch. multicoloured . . 90 10
N301 – 10 ch. brown, yell & grn 90 10
DESIGNS: No. N298, Common dolphin; No. N299, Whale sp; No. N300, Tunny; No. N301, Pollack.

182 Tractor-crane 183 Tree-planting

1961. With gum.
N302 **182** 1 ch. brown 40 10
N303 – 2 ch. brown 45 10
N304 – 5 ch. green 60 10
N305 – 10 ch. violet 75 20
DESIGNS—HORIZ: 2 ch. Heavy-duty lorry; 5 ch. Eight-metres turning lathe. VERT: 10 ch. 3000-ton press.
See also Nos. N378/9c.

1961. Re-afforestation Campaign. With gum.
N306 **183** 10 ch. green 75 15

184 "Peaceful Unification" Banner

1961. Propaganda for Peaceful Reunification of Korea.
N307 **184** 10 ch. multicoloured . . 5·50 1·50

185 Pioneers visiting Battlefield

1961. 15th Anniv of Children's Union. Mult.
N308 5 ch. Pioneers bathing . . . 40 10
N309 10 ch. Pioneer bugler . . . 1·25 20
N310 10 ch. Type **185** 40 10

186 "Labour Law" 187 Apples

1961. 15th Anniv of Labour Law. With gum.
N311 **186** 10 ch. blue on yellow . . . 20 10

1961. Fruit. Multicoloured.
N312 5 ch. Peaches 60 10
N313 5 ch. Plums 60 10
N314 5 ch. Type **187** 60 10
N315 10 ch. Persimmons 60 10
N316 10 ch. Pears 60 10

188 Yuri Gagarin and "Vostok-1"

1961. World's First Manned Space Flight.
N317 **188** 10 ch. ultramarine & bl 35 10
N318 10 ch. violet and blue . . 35 10

189 Power Station

1961. 15th Anniv of Nationalization of Industries Law. With gum.
N319 **189** 10 ch. brown . . . . . 2·75 60

190 Women at Work 191 Children planting Tree

1961. 15th Anniv of Sex Equality Law. With gum.
N320 **190** 10 ch. red 35 10

1961. Children. Multicoloured.
N321 5 ch. Type **191** 60 10
N322 5 ch. Reading book 30 10
N323 10 ch. Playing with ball . . 30 10
N324 10 ch. Building a house . . 30 10
N325 10 ch. Waving flag 30 10

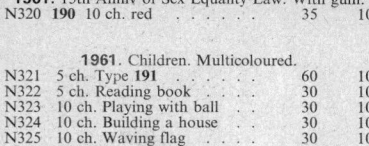

192 Poultry and Stock-breeding 193 Soldiers on March (statue)

1961. Improvement in Living Standards. Mult.
N326 5 ch. Type **192** 60 10
N327 10 ch. Fabrics and textile factory . . . . 1·10 10
N328 10 ch. Trawler and fish (horiz) 1·00 20
N329 10 ch. Grain-harvesting (horiz) 50 10

1961. 25th Anniv of Fatherland Restoration Association. With gum.
N330 – 10 ch. violet 40 10
N331 – 10 ch. violet 25 10
N332 **193** 10 ch. blue and buff . . 25 10
DESIGNS—Marshal Kim Il Sung; No. N330, Seated under tree; No. N331, Working at desk.

194 Party Emblem and Members 195 Miner

1961. Fourth Korean Workers' Party Congress, Pyongyang. With gum.
N333 **194** 10 ch. green 20 10
N334 – 10 ch. purple 20 10
N335 – 10 ch. red 20 10
DESIGNS—VERT: No. N334, "Chollima" statue, Pyongyang. HORIZ: No. N335, Marshal Kim Il Sung.

1961. Miners' Day. With gum.
N336 **195** 10 ch. brown . . . . . 1·75 60

196 Pak in Ro 197 Aldehyde Shop

1961. 400th Birth Anniv of Pak in Ro (poet).
N337 **196** 10 ch. indigo on blue . 45 15

1961. Completion of Vinalon Factory. With gum.
N338 **197** 5 ch. red and yellow . . 60 10
N339 – 10 ch. brown & yellow 90 10
N340 – 10 ch. blue and yellow 90 10
N341 – 20 ch. purple & yellow 1·40 20
DESIGNS: No. N339, Glacial-acetic shop; No. N340, Polymerization and saponification shop; No. N341, Spinning shop.

198 Korean and Chinese Flags 199 Basketball

1961. North Korean Friendship Treaties with China and the U.S.S.R.
N342 – 10 ch. multicoloured . 40 10
N343 **198** 10 ch. red, blue & yellow 40 10
DESIGN: No. N342, Korean and Soviet flags.

1961. Physical Culture Day. With gum.
N344 – 2 ch. grey 50 10
N345 – 5 ch. blue 75 10
N346 **199** 10 ch. blue 75 10
N347 – 10 ch. blue 75 10
N348 – 10 ch. purple 75 10
N349 – 20 ch. red 50 10
DESIGNS: 2 ch. Table tennis; 5 ch. Flying model glider; 10 ch. (No. N347) Rowing; 10 ch. (No. N348) High jumping; 20 ch. Sports emblem.

(200) 201 General Rock

1961. Centenary of Publication of Map "Taidong Yu Jido" by Kim Jung Ho. No. N216 surch with T **200**.
N350 **150** 5 ch. on 1 ch. grey and green . . . . 35·00 24·00

1961. Mt. Chilbo Scenery. With gum.
N351 **201** 5 ch. blue 45 10
N352 – 5 ch. brown 45 10
N353 – 10 ch. violet 90 20
N354 – 10 ch. blue 90 20
N355 – 10 ch. blue 90 20
DESIGNS—HORIZ: No. N352, Chonbul Peak; No. N354, Tiled House Rock; No. N355, Rainbow Rock. VERT: No. N353, Mansa Peak.

202 "Agriculture and Industry" 203 Winged Horse and Congress Emblem

1961. With gum.
N356 **202** 10 ch. green 35 10

1961. Fifth World Federation of Trade Unions Congress, Moscow. With gum.
N357 **203** 10 ch. blue, purple & vio 25 10

204 "Red Banner" Class Electric Locomotive 205 Ice Hockey

1961. Railway Electrification. With gum.
N359 – 10 ch. brown and grey 45 10
N360 – 10 ch. brown and green 45 10
N361 **205** 10 ch. brown and blue 45 10
N362 – 10 ch. brown and blue 45 10
DESIGNS: No. N359, Figure skating; No. N360, Speed skating; No. N362, Skiing.

206 Grain Harvest 207 Tiger

1962. "Six Heights" of Production Targets (1st series). Inscr "1962". With gum.
N363 – 5 ch. red, violet and grey 30 10
N364 – 5 ch. brown and grey . . 1·75 30
N365 **206** 10 ch. yellow, black & bl 30 10
N366 – 10 ch. red, yellow & blue 90 10
N367 – 10 ch. black and blue . . 75 15
N368 – 10 ch. yellow, brn & blue 30 10
DESIGNS: No. N363, Ladle and molten steel; No. N364, Coal trucks; No. N366, Fabrics and mill; No. N367, Trawler and catch; No. N368, Construction of flats.
See also Nos. N440/5.

1962. Animals.
N369 **207** 2 ch. multicoloured . . . 1·75 15
N370 – 2 ch. brown and green 1·25 10
N371 – 5 ch. yellow and green 1·25 10
N372 – 10 ch. brown and green 1·50 15
ANIMALS—HORIZ: 2 ch. (No. N370), Racoon-dog; 5 ch. Chinese ferret-badger; 10 ch. Asiatic black bear.

208 Kayagum Player 209 "Leuhdorfia puziloi"

1962. Musical Instruments and Players (1st series). Multicoloured.
N373 10 ch. Type **208** . . . . . . 1·75 20
N374 10 ch. Man playing haegum (two-stringed bowed instrument) . . . . 1·75 20
N375 10 ch. Woman playing wolgum (banjo) . . . . 1·75 20
N376 10 ch. Man playing chotdae (flute) . . . . 1·75 20
N377 10 ch. Woman playing wagonghu (harp) . . . . . 1·75 20
See also Nos. N473/7.

1962. As T **182**. Inscr "1962". With gum (Nos. N379 and 379b), no gum (others).
N378 5 ch. green 50 10
N379 10 ch. blue 75 15
N379a 10 ch. brown . . . . - 3·75
N379b 5 wn. brown . . . . 9·50 3·00
N379c 10 wn. purple . . . . . . 11·50 6·00
DESIGNS—VERT: 5 ch. Hydraulic press; 10 ch. (2), Three-ton hammer; 10 wn. Tunnel drill. HORIZ: 5 wn. Hobbing machine.
See also Nos. N415/22, N513/15 and 573.

1962. Butterflies. Multicoloured.
N380 5 ch. Type **209** . . . . . . 2·25 15
N381 10 ch. "Sericinus telamon" (purple background) . . . 2·25 15
N382 10 ch. Keeled apollo (lilac background) . . . . . . 2·25 15
N383 10 ch. Peacock (green background) . . . . . . 2·25 15

210 G. S. Titov and "Vostok-2"

1962. Second Soviet Manned Space Flight.
N384 **210** 10 ch. multicoloured . . 45 15

211 Marshal Kim Il Sung and (inset) addressing Workers 212 Kim Chaek

1962. Marshal Kim Il Sung's 50th Birthday. With gum.
N385 **211** 10 ch. red 45 15
N386 – 10 ch. green 45 15
N387 – 10 ch. blue 45 10
DESIGN: No. 387, Kim Il Sung in fur hat and (inset) inspecting battle-front.

1962. Korean Revolutionaries (1st series). With gum.
N388 **212** 10 ch. sepia 35 10
N389 – 10 ch. blue 35 10
N390 – 10 ch. red 35 10
N391 – 10 ch. purple 35 10
N392 – 10 ch. green 35 10
N393 – 10 ch. blue 35 10
N394 – 10 ch. brown 35 10
PORTRAITS: No. N389, Kang Gon; N390, An Gil; N391, Ryu Gyong Su; N392/3, Kim Jong Suk; N394, Choe Chun Guk.
See also Nos. N478/82 and N733/5.

213 Mother with Children 214 Black-faced Spoonbill

1962. National Mothers' Meeting, Pyongyang.
N395 **213** 10 ch. multicoloured . . 30 10

1962. Birds. Inscr "1962". Multicoloured.
N396 5 ch. Type **214** . . . . . . 1·00 15
N397 5 ch. Brown hawk owl . . . . 3·50 20
N398 10 ch. Eastern broad-billed roller . . . . 2·00 20
N399 10 ch. Black paradise flycatcher . . . . 2·00 20
N400 20 ch. Whistling swan . . . 2·00 20

215 Victory Flame **216** Gilthead

1962. 25th Anniv of Battle of Pochonbo.
N401 **215** 10 ch. multicoloured . . 55 10

1962. Fish. Inscr "1962". Multicoloured.
N402 5 ch. Type **216** 90 10
N403 5 ch. Hairtail 90 10
N404 10 ch. Shad . . . . 1·25 15
N405 10 ch. Sea bass . . . . . . 1·25 15
N406 10 ch. Stonehead . . . . . . 1·25 15

217 Waterdropper **218** Radial Drill **219** Chong Da San

1962. Antiques. With gum.
N407 – 4 ch. black and blue . . 60 10
N408 **217** 5 ch. black and ochre . 60 10
N409 A 10 ch. black and green . 75 10
N410 B 10 ch. black and orange 75 10
N411 C 10 ch. black and purple 75 10
N412 D 10 ch. black and brown 75 10
N413 E 10 ch. black and yellow 75 10
N414 – 40 ch. black and grey . 2·50 35
DESIGNS—VERT: 4 ch. Brush pot; 40 ch. Porcelain decanter. HORIZ: A, Inkstand; B, Brushstand; C, Turtle paperweight; D, Inkstone; E, Document case.

1962. Double frame-line. With gum.
N415 – 2 ch. green 25 10
N415a – 2 ch. brown . . . . . . - 3·75
N416 – 4 ch. blue 75 10
N417 **218** 5 ch. blue 35 10
N418 – 5 ch. purple 35 10
N419 – 10 ch. purple 40 10
N420 – 40 ch. blue . . . . . . 2·75 20
N421 – 90 ch. blue . . . . . . 1·40 30
N422 – 1 wn. brown . . . . . 4·50 50
DESIGNS—VERT: 2 ch. Vertical milling machine; 5 ch. (No. N418), Hydraulic hammer; 1 wn. Spindle drill. HORIZ: 4 ch. "Victory April 15" motor-car; 10 ch. All-purpose excavator; 40 ch. Trolley-bus; 90 ch. Planning machine.
See also Nos. N513/15 and N573.

1962. Birth Bicentenary of Chong Da San (philosopher).
N423 **219** 10 ch. purple 35 10

220 Voter **222** Globe and "Vostok 3" and "4"

221 Pyongyang

1962. Election of Deputies to National Assembly. Multicoloured.
N424 10 ch. Type **220** 60 10
N425 10 ch. Family going to poll 60 10

1962. 1535th Anniv of Pyongyang. With gum.
N426 **221** 10 ch. black and blue . . 65 10

1962. 1st "Team" Manned Space Flight.
N427 **222** 10 ch. indigo, blue & red 75 30

223 Spiraea **224** "Uibang Ryuchui"

1962. Korean Plants. Plants in natural colours; frame and inscr colours given.
N428 **223** 5 ch. lt green and green 70 10
N429 – 10 ch. green and red . . 70 10
N430 – 10 ch. blue and purple 70 10
N431 – 10 ch. green and olive . 70 10
PLANTS: No. N429, Ginseng; No. N430, Campanula; No. N431, "Rheumcoreanum makai (Polyonaceae)".

1962. 485th Anniv of Publication of "Uibang Ryuchui" (medical encyclopaedia).
N432 **224** 10 ch. multicoloured . 1·75 30

225 Science Academy **226** Fisherwomen

1962. 10th Anniv of Korean Science Academy.
N433 **225** 10 ch. blue & turquoise 1·00 10

1962.
N434 **226** 10 ch. blue 70 10

227 European Mink

1962. Animals.
N435 **227** 4 ch. brown and green 45 10
N436 – 5 ch. blue, drab & green 45 10
N437 – 10 ch. blue and yellow 60 10
N438 – 10 ch. sepia & turquoise 60 10
N439 – 20 ch. brown and blue 1·25 15
ANIMALS—HORIZ: No. N436, Chinese hare. VERT: No. N437, Eurasian red squirrel; No. N438, Common goral; No. N439, Siberian Chipmunk.

228 Harvesting

1963. "Six Heights" of Production Targets (2nd issue). Inscr "1963". Multicoloured.
N440 5 ch. Miner 70 20
N441 10 ch. Type **228** 40 10
N442 10 ch. Furnaceman 30 10
N443 10 ch. Construction worker 30 10
N444 10 ch. Textiles loom operator 65 10
N445 40 ch. Fisherman and trawler 1·75 40

229 Soldier **230** Peony

1963. 15th Anniv of Korean People's Army. With gum.
N446 – 5 ch. brown 50 10
N447 **229** 10 ch. red 60 10
N448 – 10 ch. blue 85 10
DESIGNS: 5 ch. Airman; 10 ch. Sailor.

1963. Korean Flowers. Multicoloured.
N449 5 ch. Type **230** 45 10
N450 10 ch. Rugosa rose 75 10
N451 10 ch. Azalea 75 10
N452 20 ch. Campion 75 10
N453 40 ch. Orchid . . . . . . 2·25 35

231 "Sadangch'um" (Korean folk dance) **232** Revolutionaries

1963. International Music and Dancing Contest, Pyongyang. Multicoloured.
N454 10 ch. Type **231** . . . . . . 1·25 15
N455 10 ch. Dancer with fan . . . 1·25 15

1963. 3rd Anniv of South Korean Rising of April, 1960.
N456 **232** 10 ch. multicoloured . . 25 10

233 Karl Marx **234** Children in Chemistry Class

1963. 145th Birth Anniv of Karl Marx. With gum.
N457 **233** 10 ch. blue 30 10

1963. Child Care and Amenities. Multicoloured.
N458 2 ch. Type **234** 65 10
N459 5 ch. Children running . . . 50 10
N460 10 ch. Boy conducting choir 1·50 10
N461 10 ch. Girl chasing butterfly 2·75 20

235 Armed Koreans and American Soldier (caricature)

1963. Campaign Month for Withdrawal of U.S. Forces from South Korea.
N462 **235** 10 ch. multicoloured . . 45 10

236 "Cyrtoclytus capra"

1963. Korean Beetles. Multicoloured designs. Colours of beetles given.
N463 5 ch. Type **236** 65 10
N464 10 ch. multicoloured 95 10
N465 10 ch. red and blue 95 10
N466 10 ch. indigo, blue & purple 95 10
BEETLES: No. N464, "Cicindela chinensis". No. N465, "Purpuricenus lituratus". No. N466, "Agapanthia pilicornis".

237 Soldier with Flag **238** North Korean Flag

1963. 10th Anniv of Victory in Korean War.
N467 **237** 10 ch. multicoloured . . 30 10

1963. 15th Anniv of People's Republic. Mult.
N468 10 ch. Type **238** 30 10
N469 10 ch. N. Korean Badge . . 30 10

239 Namdae Gate, Kaesong **240** Ajaeng (bowed zither)

1963. Ancient Korean Buildings (1st series). With gum.
N470 **239** 5 ch. black 20 10
N471 – 10 ch. blue 40 10
N472 – 10 ch. brown 40 10
BUILDINGS: No. N471, Taedong Gate, Pyongyang; No. N472, Potong Gate, Pyongyang.
See also Nos. N537/8.

1963. Musical Instruments and Players (2nd series). Multicoloured. Nos. N473 and N476 with gum.
N473 3 ch. Type **240** 75 10
N474 5 ch. Pyongyon (jade chimes) 75 10
N475 10 ch. Saenap (brass bowl) 1·40 10
N476 10 ch. Rogo (drums in frame) 1·40 10
N477 10 ch. Piri ("wooden pipe") 1·40 10

1963. Korean Revolutionaries (2nd issue). As T **212**. With gum.
N478 5 ch. brown 25 10
N479 5 ch. purple 25 10
N480 10 ch. rose 30 10
N481 10 ch. slate 30 10
N482 10 ch. dull purple 30 10
PORTRAITS: No. N478, Kwon Yong Byok. No. N479, Ma Dong Hui. No. N480, Li Je Sun. No. N481, Pak Dal. No. N482, Kim Yong Bom.

241 Nurse with Children **242** Hwajang Hall

1963. Child Welfare. Multicoloured.
N483 10 ch. Type **241** 30 10
N484 10 ch. Children in playground 30 10

1963. Mount Myohyang Resort. Multicoloured.
N485 5 ch. Type **242** 35 10
N486 10 c. Mountain stream and chalet 75 10
N487 10 ch. Kwanum Pavilion and stone pagoda 65 10
N488 10 ch. Rope bridge across river 1·75 15
Nos. N487/8 are horiz.

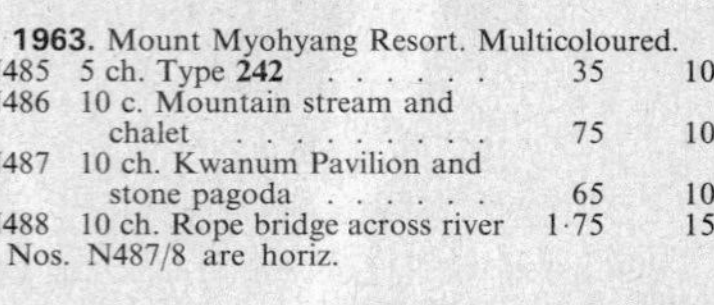

243 Furnaceman **244** Children hoeing

1963. Seven Year Plan. With gum.
N489 **243** 5 ch. red 20 10
N490 – 10 ch. grey . . . . . . 1·50 20
N491 – 10 ch. red . . . . . . 1·50 10
N492 – 10 ch. lilac 85 10
DESIGNS—VERT: No. N490, Construction workers. HORIZ: No. N491, Power technicians; No. N492, Miners.

1963. "Hung Bo" (fairytale). Multicoloured.
N493 5 ch. Type **244** 30 10
N494 10 ch. Tying up broken leg of swallow 90 10
N495 10 ch. Barn swallow dropping gourd seed 90 10
N496 10 ch. Sawing through giant gourd 50 10
N497 10 ch. Treasure inside gourd 50 10

245 Marksman

1963. Marksmanship. Multicoloured.
N498 5 ch. Type **245** 30 10
N499 10 ch. Marksman with small-bore rifle 55 10
N500 10 ch. Marksman with standard rifle 55 10

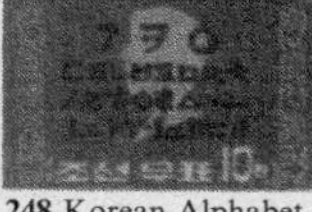

246 Sinuiju Chemical Fibre Factory **248** Korean Alphabet

247 Strikers

1964. Chemical Fibres Factories. With gum.
N501 **246** 10 ch. slate 75 10
N052 – 10 ch. purple 75 10
DESIGN: No. N502, Chongjin Chemical Fibre Factory.

1964. 35th Anniv of Wonsan General Strike. With gum.
N503 **247** 10 ch. brown 60 10

1964. 520th Anniv of Korean Alphabet.
N504 **248** 10 ch. green, buff & brn 20 10

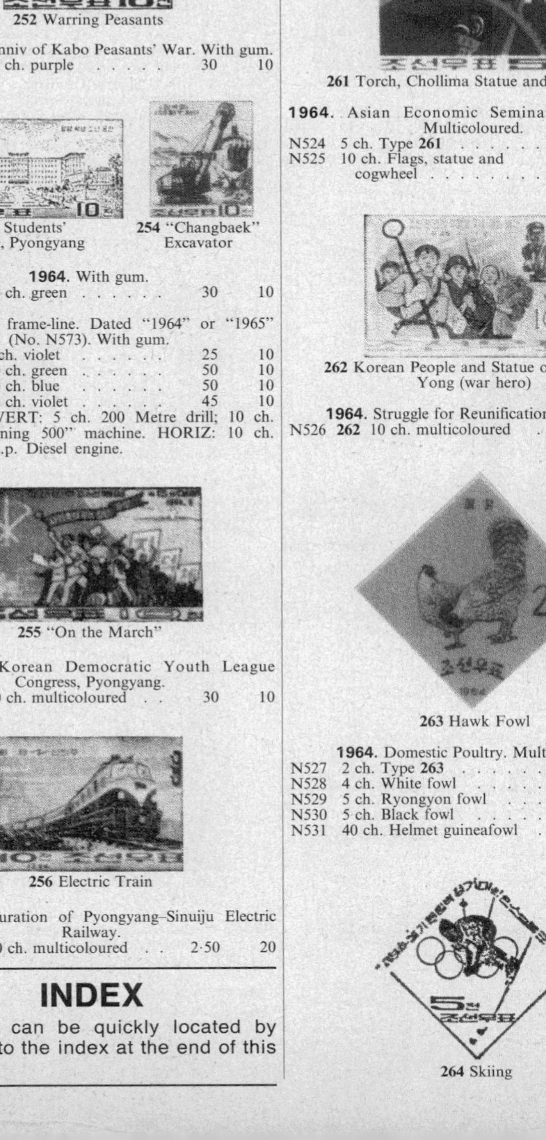

249 Lenin **250** Whale-catcher

1964. 40th Death Anniv of Lenin. With gum.
N505 **249** 10 ch. red 30 10

1964. Fishing Industry. Multicoloured.
N506 5 ch. Type **250** 40 10
N507 5 ch. Trawler No. 051 . . . 40 10
N508 10 ch. Trawler No. 397 . . . 85 20
N509 10 ch. Trawler No. 738 . . . 85 20

251 Insurgents

1964. 45th Anniv of Rising of 1st March. With gum.
N510 **251** 10 ch. purple 30 10

252 Warring Peasants

1964. 70th Anniv of Kabo Peasants' War. With gum.
N511 **252** 10 ch. purple 30 10

253 Students' Palace, Pyongyang **254** "Changbaek" Excavator

1964. With gum.
N512 **253** 10 ch. green 30 10

1964. Single frame-line. Dated "1964" or "1965" (No. N573). With gum.
N513 – 5 ch. violet 25 10
N514 **254** 10 ch. green 50 10
N515 – 10 ch. blue 50 10
N573 – 10 ch. violet 45 10
DESIGNS—VERT: 5 ch. 200 Metre drill; 10 ch. (N573) "Horning 500" machine. HORIZ: 10 ch. (N515) 400 h.p. Diesel engine.

255 "On the March"

1964. 5th Korean Democratic Youth League Congress, Pyongyang.
N516 **255** 10 ch. multicoloured . . 30 10

256 Electric Train

1964. Inauguration of Pyongyang–Sinuiju Electric Railway.
N517 **256** 10 ch. multicoloured . . 2·50 20

INDEX

Countries can be quickly located by referring to the index at the end of this volume.

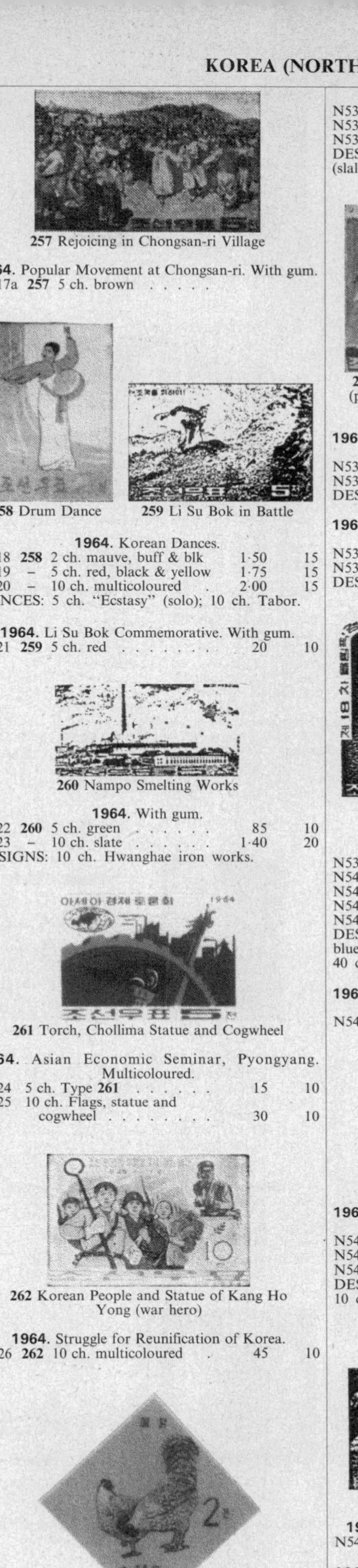

257 Rejoicing in Chongsan-ri Village

1964. Popular Movement at Chongsan-ri. With gum.
N517a **257** 5 ch. brown . . . . .

258 Drum Dance **259** Li Su Bok in Battle

1964. Korean Dances.
N518 **258** 2 ch. mauve, buff & blk 1·50 15
N519 – 5 ch. red, black & yellow 1·75 15
N520 – 10 ch. multicoloured . 2·00 15
DANCES: 5 ch. "Ecstasy" (solo); 10 ch. Tabor.

1964. Li Su Bok Commemorative. With gum.
N521 **259** 5 ch. red 20 10

260 Nampo Smelting Works

1964. With gum.
N522 **260** 5 ch. green 85 10
N523 – 10 ch. slate . . . . . . 1·40 20
DESIGNS: 10 ch. Hwanghae iron works.

261 Torch, Chollima Statue and Cogwheel

1964. Asian Economic Seminar, Pyongyang. Multicoloured.
N524 5 ch. Type **261** 15 10
N525 10 ch. Flags, statue and cogwheel 30 10

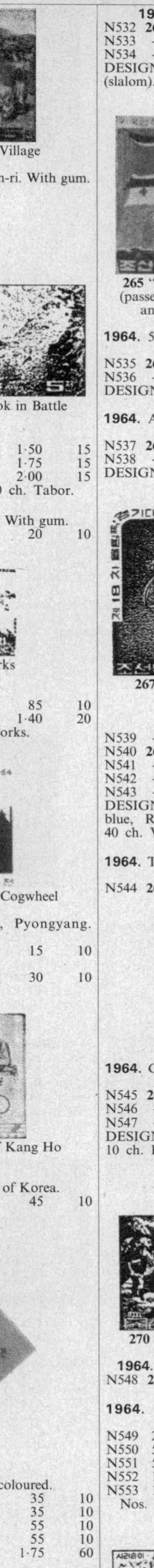

262 Korean People and Statue of Kang Ho Yong (war hero)

1964. Struggle for Reunification of Korea.
N526 **262** 10 ch. multicoloured . 45 10

263 Hawk Fowl

1964. Domestic Poultry. Multicoloured.
N527 2 ch. Type **263** 35 10
N528 4 ch. White fowl 35 10
N529 5 ch. Ryongyon fowl . . . 55 10
N530 5 ch. Black fowl 55 10
N531 40 ch. Helmet guineafowl . 1·75 60

264 Skiing

1964. Winter Olympic Games, Innsbruck.
N532 **264** 5 ch. red, blue and buff 50 10
N533 – 10 ch. blue, green & buff 75 10
N534 – 10 ch. blue, red & buff 75 10
DESIGNS: No. N533, Ice skating; N534, Skiing (slalom).

265 "Tobolsk" (passenger ship) and Flags **266** Tonggun Pavilion Uiju

1964. 5th Anniv of Agreement for Repatriation of Koreans in Japan.
N535 **265** 10 ch. red, blue & lt blue 1·00 20
N536 – 30 ch. multicoloured . . 80 15
DESIGN: 30 ch. Return of repatriates.

1964. Ancient Korean Buildings (2nd series). With gum.
N537 **266** 5 ch. purple 10 10
N538 – 10 ch. green 30 10
DESIGN: 10 ch. Inpang Pavilion, Kanggye City.

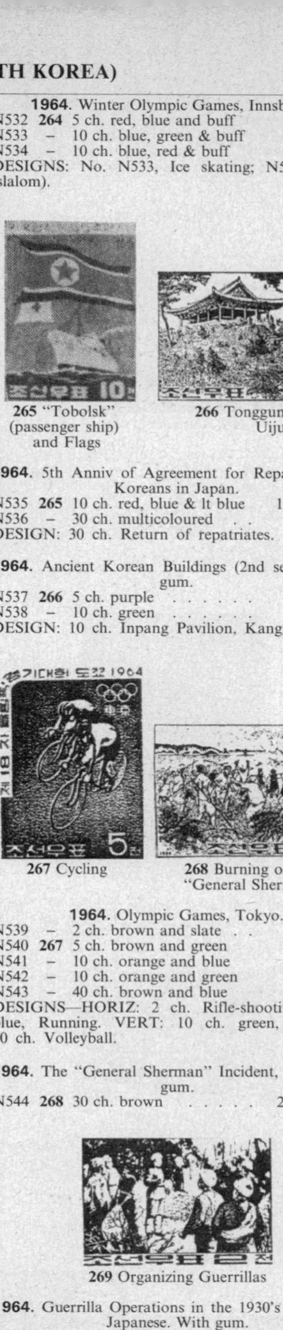

267 Cycling **268** Burning of the "General Sherman"

1964. Olympic Games, Tokyo.
N539 – 2 ch. brown and slate . . 25 10
N540 **267** 5 ch. brown and green 75 10
N541 – 10 ch. orange and blue 35 10
N542 – 10 ch. orange and green 35 10
N543 – 40 ch. brown and blue 60 35
DESIGNS—HORIZ: 2 ch. Rifle-shooting; 10 ch. blue, Running. VERT: 10 ch. green, Wrestling; 40 ch. Volleyball.

1964. The "General Sherman" Incident, 1866. With gum.
N544 **268** 30 ch. brown . . . . . 2·00 30

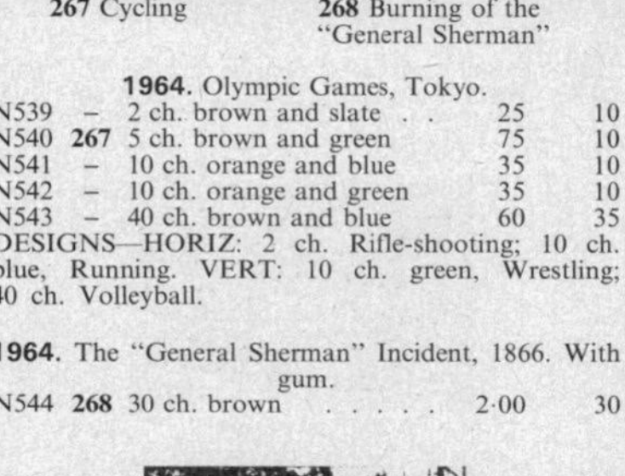

269 Organizing Guerrillas

1964. Guerrilla Operations in the 1930's against the Japanese. With gum.
N545 **269** 2 ch. violet 15 10
N546 – 5 ch. blue 20 10
N547 – 10 ch. black 30 10
DESIGNS: 5 ch. Kim Il Sung addressing guerrillas; 10 ch. Battle scene at Xiaowangqing.

270 Students attacking **271** Weightlifting

1964. Kwangju Students Rising, 1929. With gum.
N548 **270** 10 ch. violet . . . . . . 1·60 15

1964. "GANEFO" Athletic Games, Djakarta, Indonesia (1963). Multicoloured.
N549 2 ch. Type **271** 25 10
N550 5 ch. Athlete breasting tape 30 10
N551 5 ch. Boxing 30 10
N552 10 ch. Football 75 15
N553 10 ch. Globe Emblem . . . 30 15
Nos. N551/3 are horiz.

272 Lynx **273** Vietnamese Attack

1964. Animals. With gum.
N554 2 ch. sepia (Type **272**) . . 60 10
N555 5 ch. sepia (Leopard cat) . . 1·50 10
N556 10 ch. brown (Leopard) . . 2·00 10
N557 10 ch. sepia (Yellow-throated marten) . . . . . . 2·00 10

1964. Support for People of Vietnam.
N558 **273** 10 ch. multicoloured . . 30 10

274 Prof. Kim Bong Han and Emblems

1964. Kyongrak Biological Systems.
N559 **274** 2 ch. purple and olive 50 10
N560 – 5 ch. green, orange & bl 75 10
N561 – 10 ch. red, yellow & blue 1·10 10
DESIGNS: ($33\times23\frac{1}{2}$ mm): 5 ch. "Bonghan" duct; 10 ch. "Bonghan" corpuscle; Each include emblems as in Type **274**.

275 Farmers, Tractor and Lorry

1964. Agrarian Programme. Multicoloured.
N562 5 ch. Type **275** 10 10
N563 10 ch. Peasants with scroll and book 30 10
N564 10 ch. Peasants, one writing in book 30 10

276 Chung Jin gets a Pistol **277** Girl with Korean Products

1964. The Struggle to capture Japanese Arms. With gum.
N565 **276** 4 ch. brown 25 10

1964. Economic 7 Year Plan. Multicoloured. With gum (5 ch.) or no gum (others).
N566 5 ch. Type **277** 20 10
N567 10 ch. Farm girl 30 10
N568 10 ch. Couple on winged horse ($23\frac{1}{2}\times23\frac{1}{2}$ mm) 30 10

278 Three Fairies Rock **280** Soldiers Advancing, Fusong

1964. Diamond Mountains Scenery (2nd issue). Inscr "1964". Multicoloured. Without gum (2, 4 ch.) or with gum (others).
N569 2 ch. Type **278** 60 10
N570 4 ch. Ryonju Falls . . . . 2·00 10
N571 10 ch. The Ten Thousand Rocks, Manmulsang . . . 70 10
N572 10 ch. Chinju Falls . . . . 2·00 10

1965. Guerrilla Operations against the Japanese, 1934–40. With gum.
N574 **280** 10 ch. violet 30 10
N575 – 10 ch. violet 30 10
N576 – 10 ch. green 30 10
DESIGNS: No. N575, Soldiers descending hill, Hongqihe; No. N576, Soldiers attacking hill post, Luozigou.

281 Tuman River **282** Union Badge

1965. Korean Rivers. Multicoloured.
N577 2 ch. Type **281** 35 5
N578 5 ch. Taedong (vert) . . . . 1·25 15
N579 10 ch. Amnok 50 10

1965. First Congress of Landworkers' Union, Pyongyang. With gum.
N580 **282** 10 ch. multicoloured . . 30 10

283 Furnacemen and Workers

1965. 10 Major Tasks of 7 Year Plan. With gum.
N581 **283** 10 ch. multicoloured . . 30 10

284 Miners' Strike, Sinhung Colliery

1965. 35th Anniv of Strikes and Peasants' Revolt. With gum.
N582 **284** 10 ch. olive . . . . . 1·00 10
N583 – 10 ch. brown . . . . . 1·00 10
N584 – 40 ch. purple . . . . . 1·00 20
DESIGNS: 10 ch. Strikers at Pyongyang Rubber Factory; 40ch. Revolt of Tanchon peasants.

285 Embankment Construction **286** Hand holding Torch

1965. Sunhwa River Works. With gum.
N585 **285** 10 ch. multicoloured . . 30 10

1965. 5th Anniv of South Korean Rising of April 19th. Multicoloured. With gum.
N586 10 ch. Type **286** 20 10
N587 40 ch. Student-hero, Kim Chio 45 20

287 Power Station under Construction

1965. Construction of Thermal Power Station, Pyongyang. With gum.
N588 **287** 5 ch. brown and blue . . 25 10

288 African and Asian

1965. 10th Anniv of 1st Afro-Asian Conf. Bandung. With gum.
N589 **288** 10 ch. multicoloured . . 30 10

289 Rejoicing of Koreans

1965. 10th Anniv of General Assn of Koreans in Japan. With gum.
N590 **289** 10 ch. blue and red . . 25 10
N591 – 40 ch. indigo, blue & red 45 15
DESIGN: 40 ch. Patriot and flag.

290 Workers in Battle **291** "Victory 64" 10-ton Lorry

1965. 2nd Afro-Asian Conf, Algiers. With gum.
N592 **290** 10 ch. black, yellow & red 55 10
N593 – 40 ch. black, yellow & red 1·10 25
DESIGN: 40 ch. Korean and African soldiers.
The Algiers Conference did not take place.

1965. With gum.
N594 **291** 10 ch. green 75 10

292 Kim Chang Gol

1965. War Heroes (1st series). With gum.
N595 **292** 10 ch. green 30 10
N596 – 10 ch. brown 30 10
N597 – 40 ch. purple 75 20
PORTRAITS: No. N596, Cho Gun Sil and machine-gun; No. N597, An Hak Ryong and machine-gun.
See also Nos. N781/3 and N850/1.

293 Marx and Lenin

1965. Postal Ministers' Congress, Peking. With gum.
N598 **293** 10 ch. black, yell & red 1·50 15

294 Lake Samil

1965. Diamond Mountains Scenery (3rd issue). Multicoloured. With gum.
N599 2 ch. Type **294** 60 10
N600 5 ch. Chipson Peak . . . . 1·00 10
N601 10 ch. Kwanum Falls . . . 2·75 25

295 Amnok River, Kusimuldong **296** Footballer and Games' Emblem

1965. Scenes of Japanese War. With gum.
N602 **295** 5 ch. green and blue . . 35 10
N603 – 10 ch. turquoise & blue 60 10
DESIGN: 10 ch. Lake Samji.

1965. "GANEFO" Football Games, Pyongyang. Multicoloured. With gum.
N604 10 ch. Type **296** 90 10
N605 10 ch. Games emblem and Moranbong Stadium . . 90 10

297 Workers and Map **298** Engels

1965. 20th Anniv of Liberation from Japan. With gum.
N606 **297** 10 ch. multicoloured . 30 10

1965. 145th Birth Anniv of Engels. With gum.
N607 **298** 10 ch. brown 30 10

299 Pole Vaulting **302** Kim Chaek Iron Works

301 Korean Fighters

1965. Sports. Multicoloured. With gum.
N608 2 ch. Type **299** 25 10
N609 4 ch. Throwing the javelin 1·50 20
N610 10 ch. Throwing the discus 35 10
N611 10 ch. High jumping (horiz) 35 10
N612 10 ch. Putting the shot (horiz) 35 10

1965. 20th Anniv of Korean Workers' Party. Each black, yellow and red. With gum.
N613 10 ch. Type **301** 45 10
N614 10 ch. Party emblem . . . 45 10
N615 10 ch. Lenin and Marx . . . 45 10
N616 10 ch. Workers marching . . 45 10
N617 10 ch. Fighters 45 10
N618 40 ch. Workers 45 10
Nos. N613/8 each have a red banner in the background and were issued together in blocks of 6 (3 × 2), forming a composite design, within the sheet.

1965. With gum.
N620 **302** 10 ch. purple 95 10
N621 – 10 ch. brown 95 10
DESIGN: 10 ch. Chongjin Steel Works.

303 Grass carp **304** Building House

1965. Freshwater Fish. Multicoloured. With gum.
N622 2 ch. Rainbow trout 50 10
N623 4 ch. Dolly Varden trout . . 65 10
N624 10 ch. Brown trout (surfacing water) . . . . 1·40 15
N625 10 ch. Carp diving (date at left) 1·40 15
N626 10 ch. Type **303** . . . . . 1·40 15
N627 40 ch. Crucian carp . . . . 2·25 30

1965. Kim Hong Do's Drawings. With gum.
N628 2 ch. green (Type **304**) . . 20 10
N629 4 ch. purple (Weaving) . . 55 10
N630 10 ch. brown (Wrestling) . . 35 10
N631 10 ch. blue (School class) . . 35 10
N632 10 ch. red (Dancing) 85 10
N633 10 ch. violet (Blacksmiths) 75 10

305 Children in Workshop **306** Whale-catcher

1965. Life at Pyongyang Children's and Students' Palace. Multicoloured. With gum.
N634 2 ch. Type **305** 20 10
N635 4 ch. Boxing 20 10
N636 10 ch. Chemistry 75 10
N637 10 ch. Playing violin and accordion 75 10

1965. Korean Fishing Boats. With gum.
N638 **306** 10 ch. blue . . . . . . 1·10 15
N639 – 10 ch. green . . . . . 1·10 15
DESIGN: 10 ch. Fishing Fleet Service Vessel.

307 Great Tit **308** Silkworm Moth ("Bombyx mori") and Cocoon

1965. Korean Birds. Inscr "1965". Multicoloured. With gum.
N640 4 ch. Black-capped kingfisher (vert) . . . . 1·25 10
N641 10 ch. Type **307** . . . . . 1·75 15
N642 10 ch. Pied wagtail (facing left) 1·75 15
N643 10 ch. Azure-winged magpie (facing right) . . . . . . 1·75 15
N644 40 ch. Black-tailed hawfinch 4·00 45

1965. Korean Sericulture. With gum.
N645 **308** 2 ch. green . . . . . . 3·75 20
N646 – 10 ch. brown . . . . . 3·75 30
N647 – 10 ch. purple . . . . . 3·75 30
MOTHS AND COCOONS: No. N646, Ailathus silk moth ("Samia cynthia"); No. N647, Chinese oak silk moth ("Antheraea pernyi").

309 Hooded Crane **310** Squid

1965. Wading Birds. With gum.
N648 **309** 2 ch. brown . . . . . . 2·25 10
N649 – 10 ch. blue . . . . . . 2·25 20
N650 – 10 ch. purple . . . . . 2·25 20
N651 – 40 ch. green . . . . . 4·75 45
BIRDS: No. N649, Japanese white-necked crane; No. N650, Manchurian crane; No. N651, Grey heron.

1965. Korean Molluscs. Multicoloured. With gum.
N652 5 ch. Type **310** . . . . . . 1·50 15
N653 10 ch. Octopus . . . . . . 1·50 20

311 Spotbill Duck **312** Circus Theatre, Pyongyang

1965. Korean Ducks. Multicoloured. With gum.
N654 2 ch. Type **311** . . . . . . 1·75 10
N655 4 ch. Ruddy shelduck . . . 1·75 15
N656 10 ch. Mallard . . . . . . 2·50 20
N657 40 ch. Baikal teal . . . . . 3·75 60

1965. Korean Circus. With gum except No. N661.
N658 **312** 2 ch. blue, black & brn 50 10
N659 – 10 ch. blue, red & black 1·25 10
N660 – 10 ch. red, black & green 1·25 10
N661 – 10 ch. orange, sepia & grn 1·25 10
N662 – 10 ch. red, yellow & turq 1·25 10
DESIGNS—VERT: No. N659, Trapeze artistes; No. N660, Performer with hoops on seesaw; No. N661, Tightrope dancers; No. N662, Performer with revolving cap on stick.

313 "Marvel of Peru" ("Mirabilis jalapa") **314** "Finn" Class Yacht

1965. Korean Flowers. Multicoloured. With gum except No. N663.
N663 4 ch. Type **313** 70 10
N664 10 ch. Peony . . . . 1·10 10
N665 10 ch. Moss rose . . . . . 1·10 10
N666 10 ch. Magnolia . . . . . . 1·10 10

1965. Yachts. Multicoloured. With gum.
N667 2 ch. Type **314** 50 15
N668 10 ch. "5.5" 85 30
N669 10 ch. "Dragon" 85 30
N670 40 ch. "Star" . . . . 1·60 60

315 Cuban, Korean and African **316** Hosta

1966. African-Asian and Latin American Friendship Conference, Havana. With gum.
N671 **315** 10 ch. multicoloured . . 30 10

1966. Wild Flowers. Mult. With gum. (a) 1st series.
N672 2 ch. Type **316** 40 10
N673 4 ch. Dandelion 40 10
N674 10 ch. Pink convolvulus . . 60 10
N675 10 ch. Lily-of-the-valley . . 60 10
N676 40 ch. Catalpa blossom . . 1·75 20

(b) 2nd series.

N677 2 ch. Polyanthus 40 10
N678 4 ch. Lychnis 40 10
N679 10 ch. Adonis 60 10
N680 10 ch. Orange lily 60 10
N681 90 ch. Rhododendron . . . 2·75 30

317 Farmer and Wife

1966. 20th Anniv of Land Reform Law. With gum.
N682 **317** 10 ch. multicoloured . . 20 10

318 Troops advancing, Dashahe
319 Silla Bowl

1966. Paintings of Guerrilla Battles, 1937–39. With gum, except No. N684.
N683 **318** 10 ch. red 30 10
N684 – 10 ch. turquoise 30 10
N685 – 10 ch. purple 30 10
DESIGNS AND BATTLES: No. N684, Troops firing from trees, Taehongdan; No. N685, Troops on hillside, Jiansanfeng.

1966. Art Treasures of Silla Dynasty. With gum.
N686 **319** 2 ch. ochre 65 10
N687 – 5 ch. black 65 10
N688 – 10 ch. violet 90 10
DESIGNS: 5 ch. Earthenware jug. 10 ch. Censer.

320 Hands holding Torch, Rifle and Hammer
321 Torch and Patriots

1966. 80th Anniv of Labour Day. With gum.
N689 **320** 10 ch. multicoloured . . . 30 10

1966. 30th Anniv of Association for Restoration of Fatherland.
N690 **321** 10 ch. red and yellow . 30 10

322 Harvester

1966. Aid for Agriculture. Multicoloured.
N691 5 ch. Type **322** 25 10
N692 10 ch. Labourer 35 10

323 Young Pioneers

1966. 20th Anniv of Korean Children's Union. Without gum.
N693 **323** 10 ch. multicoloured . . 30 10

324 Kangson Steel Works

1966. Korean Industries. With gum.
N694 **324** 10 ch. grey . . . . . . 1·10 15
N695 – 10 ch. red (Pongung Chemical Works) . . 1·10 15

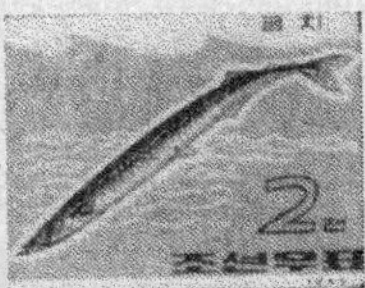
325 Saury

1966. Korean Fishes. With gum except Nos. 699/700.
N696 **325** 2 ch. blue, green & pur 50 10
N697 – 5 ch. purple, green & brn 65 10
N698 – 10 ch. blue, buff & green 1·00 20
N699 – 10 ch. purple and green 1·00 20
N700 – 40 ch. green, buff & blue 2·50 35
FISHES: 5 ch. Cod; 10 ch. (No. N698), Salmon, (No. N699), "Pleurogrammus azonus"; 40 ch. "Pink" salmon.

326 Professor Kim Bong Han

1966. Kyungrak Biological System. With gum.
N701 **326** 2 ch. blue, green & yell 45 10
N702 – 4 ch. multicoloured . . 45 10
N703 – 5 ch. multicoloured . . 45 10
N704 – 10 ch. multicoloured . 45 10
N705 – 10 ch. multicoloured . 45 10
N706 – 10 ch. multicoloured . 45 10
N707 – 15 ch. multicoloured . 45 10
N708 – 40 ch. multicoloured . 45 10
DESIGNS: No. N704, Kyongrak Institute; No. 708, Figure of Man; N702/3, 705/7, Diagram of system.
Nos. N701/8 were issued together, se-tenant, forming a composite design.

327 Leonov in Space ("Voskhod 2")

1966. Cosmonauts Day. Multicoloured.
N710 5 ch. Type **327** 20 10
N711 10 ch. "Luna 9" 55 10
N712 40 ch. "Luna 10" . . . . 1·10 20

328 Footballers

1966. World Cup Football Championship. Mult.
N713 10 ch. Type **328** . . . . . 1·25 25
N714 10 ch. Jules Rimet Cup, football and boots . . . 1·25 25
N715 10 ch. Goalkeeper saving goal (vert) . . . . 1·25 25

329 Defence of Seoul

1966. Korean War of 1950–53. With gum.
N716 **329** 10 ch. green 35 10
N717 – 10 ch. purple 35 10
N718 – 10 ch. purple 35 10
DESIGNS: No. N717, Battle on Mt. Napal; No. N718, Battle for Height 1211.

330 Women in Industry

1966. 20th Anniv of Sex Equality Law.
N719 **330** 10 ch. multicoloured . 30 10

331 Industrial Workers
332 Water-jar Dance

1966. 20th Anniv of Industrial Nationalization.
N720 **331** 10 ch. multicoloured . 60 10

1966. Korean Dances. Multicoloured. 5 ch., 40 ch. with or without gum; others without.
N721 5 ch. Type **332** 60 10
N722 10 ch. Bell dance . . . . . 1·25 15
N723 10 ch. "Dancer in a Mural Painting" . . . . . . 1·25 15
N724 15 ch. Sword dance . . . . 1·50 20
N725 40 ch. Gold Cymbal dance 2·40 30

333 Korean attacking U.S. Soldier
334 Yakovlev Yak-12M Crop-spraying

1966. Korean Reunification Campaign. With gum.
N726 **333** 10 ch. green 40 10
N727 – 10 ch. purple 40 10
N728 – 10 ch. lilac . . . . . . 2·25 45
DESIGNS: No. N727, Korean with young child; No. N728, Korean with shovel, industrial scene and electric train.

1966. Industrial Uses of Aircraft. With gum except 2 ch. and 5 ch.
N729 **334** 2 ch. green and purple 40 10
N730 – 5 ch. brown and green 3·25 15
N731 – 10 ch. sepia and blue 1·25 10
N732 – 40 ch. brown and blue 1·25 10
DESIGNS: 5 ch. Yakovlev Yak-18U (forest-fire observation); 10 ch. Lisunov Li-2 (geological survey); 40 ch. Lisunov Li-2 (detection of fish shoals).

1966. Korean Revolutionaries (3rd issue). As T **212**. With gum.
N733 10 ch. violet (O Jung Hub)
N734 10 ch. green (Kim Gyong Sok)
N735 10 ch. blue (Li Dong Gol)

335 Kim Il Sung University

1966. 20th Anniv of Kim Il Sung University. With gum.
N736 **335** 10 ch. violet 50 10

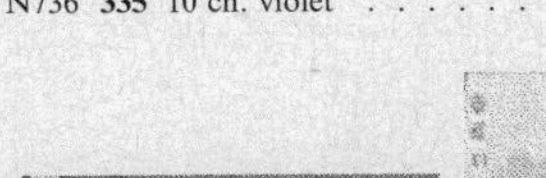

336 Judo
337 Hoopoe

1966. Ganefo Games, Phnom-Penh.
N737 **336** 5 ch. black, green & bl 45 10
N738 – 10 ch. black, myrtle and green 45 10
N739 – 10 ch. black and red . . 45 10
DESIGNS: No. N738, Basketball; No. N739, Table tennis.

1966. Korean Birds. Multicoloured. Inscr "1966".
N740 2 ch. Common rosefinch . . 70 10
N741 5 ch. Type **337** 90 10
N742 10 ch. Black-breasted thrush (blue background) . . . . 1·10 15
N743 10 ch. Crested lark (green background) . . . . 1·10 15
N744 40 ch. White-bellied black woodpecker . . . . 2·50 40
The 2 ch. and 10 ch. (both) are horiz.

338 Building Construction

1966. "Increased Production with Economy". Multicoloured. Without gum (40 ch.) or with gum (others).
N745 5 ch. Type **338** 25 10
N746 10 ch. Furnaceman and graph 45 10
N747 10 ch. Machine-tool production 45 10
N748 40 ch. Miners and pithead 1·40 15

339 Parachuting

1966. National Defence Sports. With gum.
N749 **339** 2 ch. brown 65 10
N750 – 5 ch. red 55 10
N751 – 10 ch. blue . . . . . . 2·00 10
N752 – 40 ch. green . . . . . . 1·60 20
DESIGNS: 5 ch. Show jumping; 10 ch. Motor cycle racing; 40 ch. Radio receiving and transmitting competition.

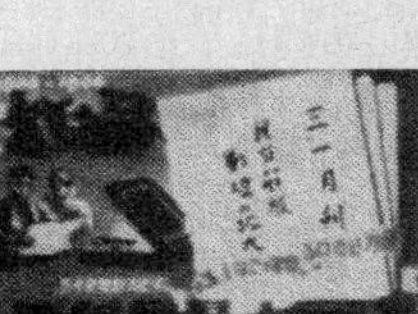
340 "Samil Wolgan" (Association Magazine)
341 Red Deer

1966. 30th Anniv of "Samil Wolgan" Magazine.
N753 **340** 10 ch. multicoloured . . 50 10

1966. Korean Deer. Multicoloured.
N754 2 ch. Type **341** 20 5
N755 5 ch. Sika deer 35 10
N756 10 ch. Indian muntjac (erect) 70 10
N757 10 ch. Reindeer (grazing) . 70 10
N758 70 ch. Fallow deer . . . . 2·50 25

342 Blueberries
343 Onpo Rest Home

1966. Wild Fruit. Multicoloured.
N759 2 ch. Type **342** 25 10
N760 5 ch. Wild pears 35 10
N761 10 ch. Wild raspberries . . 50 10
N762 10 ch. Schizandra 50 10
N763 10 ch. Wild plums 50 10
N764 40 ch. Jujube . . . . 1·40 15

1966. Korean Rest Homes. With gum.
N765 **343** 2 ch. violet 25 10
N766 – 5 ch. turquoise 35 10
N767 – 10 ch. green 50 10
N768 – 40 ch. black 80 20
REST HOMES: 5 ch. Mt. Myohyang; 10 ch. Songdowon; 40 ch. Hongwon.

344 Soldier

1967. 19th Anniv of Army Day. Without gum.
N769 **344** 10 ch. green, yell & red 25 10

345 Sow

1967. Domestic Animals. Multicoloured. Without gum. 40 ch. also with gum.
N770 5 ch. Type **345** 25 10
N771 10 ch. Goat 35 10
N772 40 ch. Ox 85 25

346 Battle Scene

1967. 30th Anniv of Battle of Pochonbo. With gum.
N773 **346** 10 ch. orange, red & grn 50 10

347 Students

1967. Compulsory Technical Education for Nine Years.
N774 **347** 10 ch. multicoloured . . 25 10

348 Table Tennis Player

1967. 29th International Table Tennis Championships, Pyongyang. Designs showing players in action. 5 ch. with or without gum.
N775 **348** 5 ch. multicoloured . . 25 5
N776 – 10 ch. multicoloured . . 50 10
N777 – 40 ch. multicoloured . . 95 15

349 Anti-aircraft Defences

1967. Paintings of Guerrilla War against the Japanese. With gum.
N778 **349** 10 ch. blue 35 10
N779 – 10 ch. purple . . . . . 1·40 25
N780 – 10 ch. violet 35 10
PAINTINGS: No. N779, Blowing-up railway bridge; No. N780, People helping guerrillas in Wangyugou.

1967. War Heroes (2nd series). As T **292**. Designs showing portraits and combat scenes. With gum.
N781 10 ch. slate 40 10
N782 10 ch. violet 40 10
N783 10 ch. blue 75 10
PORTRAITS: No. N781, Li Dae Hun and grenade-throwing; No. N782, Choe Jong Un and soldiers charging; No. N783, Kim Hwa Ryong and air dog-fighter aircraft.

350 Workers

1967. Labour Day.
N784 **350** 10 ch. multicoloured . . 25 10

351 Card Game

1967. Korean Children. Multicoloured.
N785 5 ch. Type **351** 55 10
N786 10 ch. Children modelling tractor 45 10
N787 40 ch. Children playing with ball 90 20

352 Victory Monument

1967. Unveiling of Battle of Ponchonbo Monument.
N788 **352** 10 ch. multicoloured . . 30 10

353 Attacking Tank

354 "Polygonatum japonicum"

1967. Monuments to War of 1950–53. 2 ch. with or without gum.
N789 **353** 2 ch. green & turquoise 20 10
N790 – 5 ch. sepia and green . 85 10
N791 – 10 ch. brown and buff 30 10
N792 – 40 ch. brown and blue 60 15
MONUMENTS: 5 ch. Soldier-musicians; 10 ch. Soldier; 40 ch. Soldier with children.

1967. Medicinal Plants. Multicoloured; background colour of 10 ch. values given to aid identification. Nos. 793/5 and 797 with or without gum.
N793 2 ch. Type **354** 35 10
N794 5 ch. "Hibiscus manihot" . 40 10
N795 10 ch. "Scutellaria baicalensis" (turquoise) 55 10
N796 10 ch. "Pulsatilla koreana" (blue) 55 10
N797 10 ch. "Rehmannian glutinosa" (yellow) . . . 55 10
N798 40 ch. "Tanacetum boreale" 1·75 35

355 Servicemen

1967. People's Army. Multicoloured. 5 ch. with or without gum.
N799 5 ch. Type **355** 20 10
N800 10 ch. Soldier and farmer . 25 10
N801 10 ch. Officer decorating soldier 25 10

356 Freighter "Chollima"

1967. With gum.
N802 **356** 10 ch. green 60 10

357 "Reclamation of Tideland"

1967. "Heroic Struggle of the Chollima Riders". Paintings. Without gum (5 ch.) or with gum (others).
N803 – 5 ch. agate 40 10
N804 **357** 10 ch. slate 55 10
N805 – 10 ch. green 55 10
DESIGNS—VERT: 5 ch. "Drilling Rock Precipice"; 10 ch. (N805), "Felling Trees".

358 "Erimaculus isenbeckii"

1967. Crabs. Multicoloured.
N806 2 ch. Type **358** 75 15
N807 5 ch. "Neptunus trituberculatus" 95 15
N808 10 ch. "Paralithodes camtschatica" . . . . . 1·40 15
N809 40 ch. "Chionoecetes opilio" 2·25 40

359 Electric Train and Hand switching points

1967. Propaganda for Reunification of Korea.
N810 **359** 10 ch. multicoloured . 2·25 40

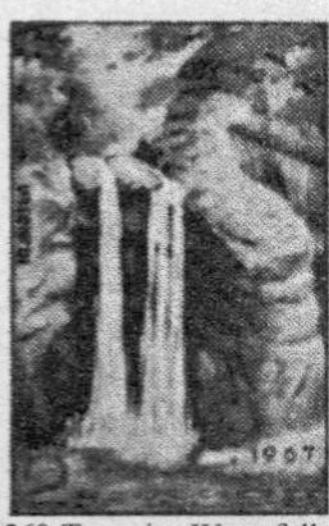
360 Tongrim Waterfall

361 Chollima Flying Horse and Banners

1967. Korean Waterfalls. 2 ch. with or without gum. Multicoloured.
N811 2 ch. Type **360** . . . . . . 1·75 15
N812 10 ch. Sanju waterfall, Mt. Myohyang . . . . 2·50 20
N813 40 ch. Sambang waterfall, Mt. Chonak . . . . 4·50 45

1967. "The Revolutionary Surge Upwards". Various designs incorporating the Chollima Flying Horse.
N814 – 5 ch. blue 75 20
N815 – 10 ch. red 25 10
N816 – 10 ch. green 25 10
N817 – 10 ch. lilac 25 10
N817 **361** 10 ch. red 20 10
DESIGNS—HORIZ: 5 ch. Ship, train and lorry (Transport); No. N815, Bulldozers (Building construction); No. N816, Tractors (Rural development); No. N817, Heavy presses (Machine-building industry).

362 Lenin

1967. 50th Anniv of Russian October Revolution.
N819 **362** 10 ch. brown, yell & red 25 10

363 Voters and Banner

1967. Korean Elections. Multicoloured.
N820 10 ch. Type **363** 35 10
N821 10 ch. Woman casting vote (vert) 35 10

364 European Black Vulture

1967. Birds of Prey. Multicoloured. With gum.
N822 2 ch. Type **364** . . . . 1·50 25
N823 10 ch. Booted eagle (horiz) 2·75 35
N824 40 ch. White-bellied sea eagle 3·50 55

365 Chongjin

1967. North Korean Cities. With gum.
N825 **365** 5 ch. green 45 10
N826 – 10 ch. lilac 45 10
N827 – 10 ch. violet 45 10
DESIGNS: No. N826, Humhung; No. N827, Sinuiju.

366 Kim Il Sung at Head of Columns

1967. Battle of Pochonbo Monument. Detail of Monument. Multicoloured.
N828 10 ch. Type **366** 25 10
N829 10 ch. Head of right-hand column 25 10
N830 10 ch. Tail of right-hand column 25 10
N831 10 ch. Head of left-hand column 25 10
N832 10 ch. Tail of left-hand column 25 10
N833 10 ch. Centre of right-hand column 25 10
N834 10 ch. Centre of left-hand column 25 10
SIZES—HORIZ: Nos. N829/32, 43 × 28 mm. Nos. 833/34, 56 × 28 mm.
The centrepiece of the Monument is flanked by two columns of soldiers, headed by Kim Il Sung.

367 Soldier brandishing Red Book

1967. "Let us carry out the Decisions of the Workers' Party Conference!". Multicoloured.
N835 10 ch. Type **367** 25 10
N836 10 ch. Militiaman holding bayonet 25 10
N837 10 ch. Foundryman and bayonet 25 10

368 Whaler firing Harpoon

1967. With gum.
N838 **368** 10 ch. blue . . . . . . 1·25 25

369 Airman, Soldier and Sailor

1968. 20th Anniv of People's Army. Mult. With gum.
N839 10 ch. Type **369** 30 10
N840 10 ch. Soldier below attack in snow 30 10
N841 10 ch. Soldier below massed ranks 30 10
N842 10 ch. Soldier holding flag 30 10
N843 10 ch. Soldier holding book 30 10
N844 10 ch. Soldiers and armed workers with flag 30 10
N845 10 ch. Furnaceman and soldier 30 10
N846 10 ch. Soldier saluting . . . 30 10
N847 10 ch. Charging soldiers . . 30 10
N848 10 ch. Soldier, sailor and airman below flag 30 10

1968. War Heroes (3rd series). As T **292**. With gum.
N850 10 ch. violet 25 10
N851 10 ch. purple 25 10
PORTRAITS: No. N850, Han Gye Ryol firing Bren gun; No. N851, Li Su Bok charging up hill.

370 Dredger "September 2"

371 Ten-storey Flats, East Pyongyang

372 Palace of Students and Children, Kaesong

1968. With gum.
N852 **370** 5 ch. green 30 10
N853 **371** 10 ch. blue 30 10
N854 **372** 10 ch. blue 30 10

373 Marshal Kim Il Sung

1968. Marshal Kim Il Sung's 56th Birthday. With gum.

N855 **373** 40 ch. multicoloured . . 65 40

374 Kim Il Sung with Mother

1968. Childhood of Kim Il Sung. Multicoloured.

N856 10 ch. Type **374** 35 10
N857 10 ch. Kim Il Sung with his father . . . 35 10
N858 10 ch. Setting out from home, aged 13 . . . . 35 10
N859 10 ch. Birthplace at Mangyongdae 35 10
N860 10 ch. Mangyong Hill . . . 35 10

375 Matsu-take Mushroom

1968. Mushrooms. With gum.

N861 **375** 5 ch. brown and green . 2·00 25
N862 – 10 ch. ochre, brn & grn . 3·25 35
N863 – 10 ch. brown and green 3·25 35

DESIGNS: No. N862, Black mushroom. No. N863, Cultivated mushroom.

376 Leaping Horseman

1968. 20th Anniv of Korean People's Democratic Republic. Multicoloured. With gum.

N864 10 ch. Type **376** 70 10
N865 10 ch. Four servicemen . . . 70 10
N866 10 ch. Soldier with bayonet . 70 10
N867 10 ch. Advancing with banners 70 10
N868 10 ch. Statue 70 10
N869 10 ch. Korean flag 70 10
N870 10 ch. Soldier and peasant with flag 70 10
N871 10 ch. Machine-gunner with flag 70 10

377 Domestic Products

378 Proclaiming the Ten Points

1968. Development of Light Industries. Multicoloured. With gum.

N872 2 ch. Type **377** 25 10
N873 5 ch. Textiles . . . . 1·00 10
N874 10 ch. Tinned produce . . . 40 40

1968. Kim Il Sung's Ten Point Political Programme. Multicoloured.

N875 2 ch. Type **378** 15 10
N876 5 ch. Soldier and artisan (horiz) 20 10

379 Livestock

1968. Development of Agriculture. Mult. With gum.

N877 5 ch. Type **379** 25 10
N878 10 ch. Fruit-growing . . . 25 10
N879 10 ch. Wheat-harvesting . . 25 10

380 Scallop

1968. Shellfish. Multicoloured. With gum.

N880 5 ch. Type **380** 90 10
N881 5 ch. Venus clam 90 10
N882 10 ch. Mussel . . . . . . 1·50 20

381 Museum of the Revolution, Pochonbo

382 Grand Theatre, Pyongyang

1968.

N883 **381** 2 ch. green 20 10
N884 **382** 10 ch. brown 65 10

383 Irrigation

1969. Rural Development. Multicoloured.

N885 3 ch. Type **383** 20 10
N886 5 ch. Agricultural mechanisation 20 10
N887 10 ch. Electrification 40 10
N888 40 ch. Applying fertilisers and spraying trees 60 10

384 Grey Rabbits

1969. Rabbits. Mult. With or without gum.

N889 2 ch. Type **384** 35 10
N890 10 ch. Black rabbits 35 10
N891 10 ch. Brown rabbits . . . 35 10
N892 10 ch. White rabbits . . . 35 10
N893 40 ch. Doe and young . . . 1·10 15

385 "Age and Youth"

1969. Public Health Service.

N894 **385** 2 ch. brown and blue . 35 10
N895 – 10 ch. blue and red . . 65 10
N896 – 40 ch. green and yellow 1·40 20

DESIGNS: 10 ch. Nurse with syringe; 40 ch. Auscultation by woman doctor.

386 Sowing Rice Seed

1969. Agricultural Mechanisation.

N897 **386** 10 ch. green 45 10
N898 – 10 ch. pink 45 10
N899 – 10 ch. black 45 10
N900 – 10 ch. brown 45 10

DESIGNS: No. N898, Rice harvester; No. N899, Weed-spraying machine; Nos. N900, Threshing machine.

387 Ponghwa

1969. Revolutionary Historical Sites. Multicoloured.

N901 10 ch. Type **387** 25 10
N902 10 ch. Mangyongdae, birthplace of Kim Il Sung 25 10

388 Kim crosses into Manchuria, 1926, aged 13

1969. Kim Il Sung in Manchuria. Multicoloured. No. N907 with gum.

N903 10 ch. Type **388** 40 10
N904 10 ch. Leading strike of Yuwen Middle School boys, 1927 40 10
N905 10 ch. Leading anti-Japanese demonstration in Kirin, 1928 40 10
N906 10 ch. Presiding at meeting of Young Communist League, 1930 . . . . 40 10
N907 10 ch. Meeting of young revolutionaries 40 10

389 Birthplace at Chilgol

1969. Commemoration of Mrs. Kang Ban Sok, mother of Kim Il Sung. Multicoloured.

N908 10 ch. Type **389** 30 10
N909 10 ch. With members of Women's Association . . . 30 10
N910 10 ch. Resisting Japanese police . . . . 2·50 40

390 Pegaebong Bivouac

1969. Bivouac Sites in the Guerrilla War against the Japanese. Multicoloured.

N911 5 ch. Type **390** 20 10
N912 10 ch. Mupo site (horiz) . . 30 10
N913 10 ch. Chongbong site . . . 30 10
N914 40 ch. Konchang site (horiz) 1·00 20

391 Chollima Statue

392 Museum of the Revolution, Pyongyang

1969.

N915 **391** 10 ch. blue 25 10
N916 **392** 10 ch. green 25 10

393 Mangyong Chickens

395 Statue of Marshal Kim Il Sung

394 Marshal Kim Il Sung and Children

1969. Korean Poultry.

N917 **393** 10 ch. blue 45 10
N918 – 10 ch. violet . . . . . 1·25 15

DESIGN: No. N918, Kwangpo ducks.

1969. Kim Il Sung's Educational System. Mult.

N919 2 ch. Type **394** 25 10
N920 10 ch. Worker with books . 25 10
N921 40 ch. Students with books 50 20

1969. Memorials on Pochonbo Battlefield. Inscr "1937.6.4". Multicoloured.

N922 5 ch. Machine-gun post . . 25 10
N923 10 ch. Type **395** 25 10
N924 10 ch. "Aspen-tree" monument 25 10
N925 10 ch. Glade Konjang Hill 25 10

396 Teaching at Myongsin School

1969. Commemoration of Kim Hyong Jik, father of Kim Il Sung. Multicoloured.

N926 10 ch. Type **396** 30 10
N927 10 ch. Secret meeting with Korean National Association members . . 30 10

397 Relay Runner

1969. 20th Anniv of Sports Day.

N928 **397** 10 ch. multicoloured . . 35 10

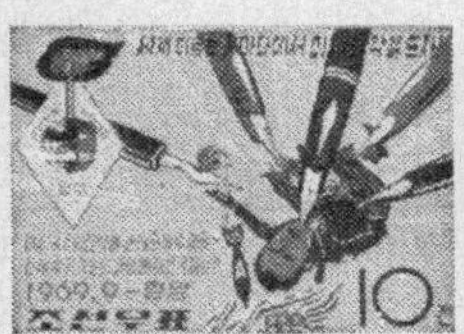
398 President Nixon attacked by Pens

1969. Anti-U.S. Imperialism Journalists' Conference, Pyongyang.

N929 **398** 10 ch. multicoloured . . 35 10

399 Fighters and Battle

1969. Implementation of Ten-Point Programme of Kim Il Sung. Multicoloured.

N930 5 ch. Type **399** (Reunification of Korea) 20 10
N931 10 ch. Workers upholding slogan (vert) 20 10

400 Bayonet Attack over U.S. Flag

1969. Anti-American Campaign.

N932	**400**	10 ch. multicoloured . .	35	10

401 Armed Workers

1969. Struggle for the Reunification of Korea. Multicoloured.

N933	10 ch. Workers stabbing U.S. soldier	20	10
N934	10 ch. Kim Il Sung and crowd with flags	20	10
N935	50 ch. Type **401**	50	20

Nos. N933/5 are vert.

402 Yellowtail

1969. Korean Fishes. Multicoloured.

N936	5 ch. Type **402**	60	10
N937	10 ch. Dace	90	10
N938	40 ch. Mullet	1·75	25

403 Freighter "Taesungsan"

1969.

N939	**403**	10 ch. purple	60	10

405 Dahwangwai (1935)

1970. Guerrilla Conference Places.

N940	**405**	2 ch. blue and green . .	25	10
N941	–	5 ch. brown and green	25	10
N942	–	10 ch. lt green and green	25	10

DESIGNS: 5 ch. Yaoyinggou (barn) (1935); 10 ch. Xiaohaerbaling (tent) (1940).

406 Lake Chon

407 Vietnamese Soldier and Furnaceman

1970. Mt. Paekdu, Home of Revolution (1st issue). Inscr "1970".

N943	**406**	10 ch. black, brn & grn	40	10
N944	–	10 ch. black, grn & yell	40	10
N945	–	10 ch. purple, bl & yell	40	10
N946	–	10 ch. black, blue and pink	40	10

DESIGNS: No. N944, Piryu Peak; No. N945, Pyongsa (Soldier) Peak; No. N946, Changgun (General) Peak.

See also Nos. 979/81.

1970. Help for the Vietnamese People.

N947	**407**	10 ch. green, brn & red	20	10

408 Receiving his Father's Revolvers from his Mother

1970. Revolutionary Career of Kim Il Sung. Multicoloured.

N948	10 ch. Type **408**	65	20
N949	10 ch. Receiving smuggled weapons from his mother	65	20
N950	10 ch. Talking to farm workers	65	20
N951	10 ch. At Kalun meeting, 1930	65	20

409 Lenin

410 March of Koreans

1970. Birth Centenary of Lenin.

N952	**409**	10 ch. brn & cinnamon	30	10
N953	–	10 ch. brown and green	30	10

DESIGN: No. N953, Lenin making a speech.

1970. 15th Anniv of Association of Koreans in Japan.

N954	**410**	10 ch. red	20	10
N955	–	10 ch. purple	20	10

411 Uniformed Factory Worker

412 Students and Newspapers

1970. Workers' Militia.

N956	**411**	10 ch. green, brn & mve	20	10
N957	–	10 ch. green, brown & bl	20	10

DESIGN—HORIZ: No. N957, Militiaman saluting.

1970. Peasant Education. Multicoloured.

N958	2 ch. Type **412**	35	10
N959	5 ch. Peasant with book . .	20	10
N960	10 ch. Students in class . .	20	10

413 "Electricity Flows"

1970. Commemoration of Army Electrical Engineers.

N961	**413**	10 ch. brown	40	10

414 Soldier with Rifle

1970. Campaign Month for Withdrawal of U.S. Troops from South Korea.

N962	**414**	5 ch. violet	15	10
N963	–	10 ch. purple	30	10

DESIGN: 10 ch. Soldier and partisan.

415 Rebel wielding Weapons

1970. Struggle in South Korea against U.S. Imperialism.

N964	**415**	10 ch. violet	20	10

416 Labourer ("Fertilisers")

417 Railway Guard

1970. Encouragement of Increased Productivity.

N965	**416**	10 ch. green, pink & brn	30	10
N966	–	10 ch. green, red & brn	50	10
N967	–	10 ch. blue, green & brn	30	10
N968	–	10 ch. bistre, brn & grn	30	10
N969	–	10 ch. violet, grn & brn	30	10

DESIGNS: No. N966, Furnaceman ("Steel"); No. N967, Operative ("Machines"); No. N968, Labourer ("Building Construction"); No. N969, Miner ("Mining").

1970. "Speed the Transport System".

N970	**417**	10 ch. blue, orge & grn	65	15

418 Agriculture

1970. Executive Decisions of the Workers' Party Congress. Designs embodying book.

N971	**418**	5 ch. red	20	10
N972	–	10 ch. green	70	15
N973	–	40 ch. green	70	15

DESIGNS: 10 ch. Industry; 40 ch. The Armed Forces.

419 Chollima Statue and Workers' Party Banner

421 Emblem of League

1970. 25th Anniv of Korean Workers' Party.

N974	**419**	10 ch. red, brown & buff	20	10

1971. 25th Anniv of League of Socialist Working Youth.

N976	**421**	10 ch. red, brown & blue	15	10

422 Log Cabin, Nanhutou

1971. 35th Anniv of Nanhutou Guerrilla Conference.

N977	**422**	10 ch. multicoloured . .	20	10

423 Tractor Driver

1971. 25th Anniv of Land Reform Law.

N978	**423**	2 ch. red, green & black	20	10

1971. Mt. Paekdu, Home of Revolution (2nd issue). As T **406** but inscr "1971".

N979	2 ch. black, olive and green	35	10
N980	5 ch. pink, black and slate	1·50	15
N981	10 ch. black, red and grey	60	10

DESIGNS—HORIZ: 2 ch. General view; 10 ch. Western peak. VERT: 5 ch. Waterfall.

424 Popyong Museum

1971. Museum of the Revolution.

N982	**424**	10 ch. brown and yellow	20	10
N983	–	10 ch. blue and orange	20	10
N984	–	10 ch. green and orange	20	10

DESIGNS: No. N983, Mangyongdae Museum; No. N984, Chunggang Museum.

425 Miner

1971. Six Year Plan for Coal Industry.

N985	**425**	10 ch. multicoloured . .	40	10

426 Kim Il Sung

1971. Founding of Anti-Japanese Guerrilla Army. Multicoloured.

N986	10 ch. Type **426**	35	10
N987	10 ch. Kim Il Sung founding Anti-Japanese Guerrilla Army	35	10
N988	10 ch. Kim Il Sung addressing the people	35	10
N989	10 ch. Kim Il Sung and members of Children's Corps	35	10

Nos. N987/9 are horiz.

428 Hands holding Hammer and Rifle

1971. 85th Anniv of Labour Day.

N990	**428**	1 w. red, brown & buff	1·75	40

429 Soldiers and Map

430 Monument

1971. 35th Anniv of Association for Restoration of Fatherland.

N991	**429**	10 ch. red, buff & black	35	10

1971. Battlefields in Musan Area, May 1939. Multicoloured.

N992	5 ch. Type **430**	15	10
N993	10 ch. Machine guns in perspex cases (horiz)	20	10
N994	40 ch. Huts among birch trees (horiz)	55	15

431 Koreans Marching

432 Flame Emblem

1971. Solidarity of Koreans in Japan.

N995	**431**	10 ch. brown	20	10

1971. 25th Anniv of Korean Childrens' Union.

N996	**432**	10 ch. red, yellow and blue	20	10

433 Marchers and Banners

434 Foundryman

1971. 6th Congress of League of Socialist Working Youth.

N997	433	5 ch. red, buff and black	10	10
N998	–	10 ch. red, green & black	20	10

DESIGN: 10 c. Marchers and banner under globe.

1971. 25th Anniv of Labour Law.

N999	434	5 ch. black, purple & buff	20	10

435 Young Women

1971. 25th Anniv of Sex Equality Law.

N1000	435	5 ch. multicoloured	20	10

436 Schoolchildren

1971. 15th Anniv of Compulsory Primary Education.

N1001	436	10 ch. multicoloured	35	10

437 Choe Yong Do and Combat Scene

1971. Heroes of the Revolutionary Struggle in South Korea.

N1002	437	5 ch. black and green	25	10
N1003	–	10 ch. red and brown	25	10
N1004	–	10 ch. black and red	25	10

DESIGNS: No. N1003, Revolutionary with book; No. N1004, Kim Jong Tae and scene of triumph.

438 Two Foundrymen

1971. 25th Anniv of Nationalization of Industry Law.

N1005	438	5 ch. black, grn & brn	65	10

439 Struggle in Korea

1971. The Anti-Imperialist and Anti-U.S. Imperialist Struggles.

N1006	439	10 ch. red, black and brown	15	10
N1007	–	10 ch. brown, black and blue	25	10
N1008	–	10 ch. red, black and pink	35	10
N1009	–	10 ch. black, olive and green	15	10
N1010	–	10 ch. orange, black and red	15	10
N1011	–	40 ch. green, black and pink	35	15

DESIGNS: No. N1007, Struggle in Vietnam; N1008, Soldier with rifle and airplane marked "EC"; N1009, Struggle in Africa; N1010, Cuban soldier and Central America; N1011, Bayonetting U.S. soldier.

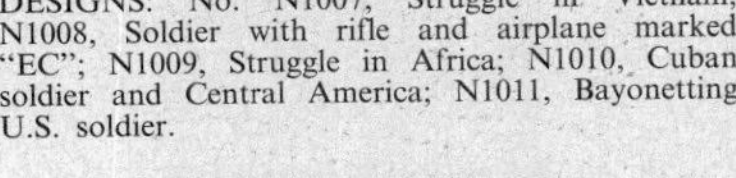

440 Kim Il Sung University

1971. 25th Anniv of Kim Il Sung University.

N1012	440	10 ch. grey, red & yellow	20	10

441 Iron-ore Ladle (Mining)

1971. Tasks of Six Year Plan. Multicoloured.

N1013		10 ch. Type **441**	1·00	15
N1014		10 ch. Workers and text	20	10
N1015		10 ch. Railway track (Transport)	1·00	15
N1016		10 ch. Hand and wrench (Industry)	25	10
N1017		10 ch. Mechanical scoop (Construction)	1·00	15
N1018		10 ch. Manufactured goods (Trade)	25	10
N1019		10 ch. Crate on hoists (Exports)	20	10
N1020		10 ch. Lathe (Heavy Industries)	1·00	15
N1021		10 ch. Freighter (Shipping)	55	10
N1022		10 ch. Household equipment (Light Industries)	20	10
N1023		10 ch. Corncob and wheat (Agriculture)	30	10

442 Technicians

1971. Cultural Revolution. Multicoloured.

N1024		2 ch. Type **442**	20	10
N1025		5 ch. Mechanic	25	10
N1026		10 ch. Schoolchildren	30	10
N1027		10 ch. Chemist	50	10
N1028		10 ch. Composer at piano	85	15

443 Workers with Red Books

1971. Ideological Revolution. Multicoloured.

N1029		10 ch. Type **443**	20	10
N1030		10 ch. Workers reading book	20	10
N1031		10 ch. Workers' lecture	20	10
N1032		10 ch. Worker and pneumatic drill	20	10

444 Korean Family

1971. Improvement in Living Standards.

N1033	444	10 ch. multicoloured	15	10

445 Furnaceman

1971. Implementation of Decisions of Fifth Workers' Party Conference.

N1034	445	10 ch. multicoloured	60	10

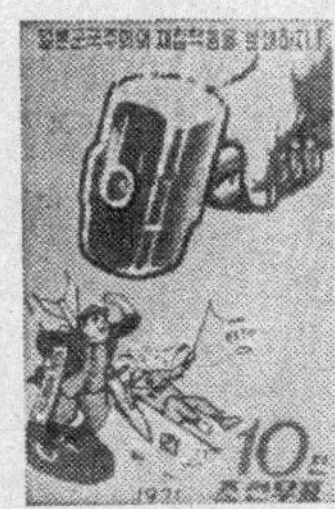

446

447 6000-ton Press

1971. Solidarity with South Korean Revolutionaries.

N1036	446	10 ch. brown, blue and black	30	10
N1037	–	10 ch. brown, flesh and red	30	10
N1038	–	10 ch. multicoloured	30	10
N1039	–	10 ch. multicoloured	30	10

DESIGNS—VERT: No. N1037, U.S. soldier attacked by poster boards; No. N1038, Hands holding rifles aloft. HORIZ: No. N1039, Men advancing with rifles.

1971.

N1040	447	2 ch. brown	50	10
N1041	–	5 ch. blue	90	15
N1042	–	10 ch. green	90	10
N1043	–	10 ch. green	90	10

DESIGNS: No. N1041, Refrigerated freighter "Ponghwasan"; No. N1042, 300 h.p. bulldozer; No. N1043, "Sungrisan" lorry.

448 Title-page and Militants

1971. 35th Anniv of "Samil Wolgan" Magazine.

N1044	448	10 ch. red, green & blk	45	10

452 Poultry Chicks

1972. Poultry Breeding.

N1051	452	5 ch. yellow, black & brown	25	10
N1052	–	10 ch. orange, bistre and brown	35	10
N1053	–	40 ch. blue, orange and deep blue	55	15

DESIGNS: 10 ch. Chickens and battery egg house; 40 ch. Eggs and fowls suspended from hooks.

453 Scene from "Village Shrine"

1972. Films of Guerrilla War.

N1054	453	10 ch. grey and green	60	10
N1055	–	10 ch. blue, pur & orge	60	10
N1056	–	10 ch. purple, bl & yell	60	10

DESIGNS: No. N1055, Patriot with pistol ("A Sea of Blood"); No. N1056, Guerrilla using bayonet ("The Lot of a Self-Defence Corps Member").

454 Kim Il Sung acknowledging Greetings

1972. Kim Il Sung's 60th Birthday. Scenes in the life of Kim Il Sung, dated "1912–1972". Mult.

N1057		5 ch. Type **454**	20	10
N1058		5 ch. In campaign H.Q.	20	10
N1059		5 ch. Military conference (horiz)	20	10
N1060		10 ch. In wheatfield (horiz)	30	10
N1061		10 ch. Directing construction (horiz)	1·50	40
N1062		10 ch. Talking to foundry workers (horiz)	20	10
N1063		10 ch. Aboard whaler (horiz)	45	10
N1064		10 ch. Visiting a hospital (horiz)	40	10
N1065		10 ch. Viewing orchard (horiz)	20	10
N1066		10 ch. With survey party on Haeju–Hasong railway line (horiz)	1·50	40
N1067		10 ch. Meeting female workers at silk factory (horiz)	50	15
N1068		10 ch. Village conference (horiz)	20	10
N1069		10 ch. Touring chicken factory (horiz)	20	10
N1070		40 ch. Relaxing with children	45	20
N1071		1 wn. Giant portrait and marchers	70	40

INDEX

Countries can be quickly located by referring to the index at the end of this volume.

455 Bugler sounding "Charge".

1972. 40th Anniv of Guerrilla Army.

N1073	455	10 ch. multicoloured	45	10

456 Pavilion of Ryongpo

1972. Historic Sites of the 1950–53 War. Mult.

N1074		2 ch. Type **456**	15	10
N1075		5 ch. Houses at Onjong	15	10
N1076		10 ch. Headquarters, Kosanjin	15	10
N1077		40 ch. Victory Museum, Chonsung-dong	30	10

457 Volleyball

1972. Olympic Games, Munich. Multicoloured.

N1078		2 ch. Type **457**	25	10
N1079		5 ch. Boxing (horiz)	35	10
N1080		10 ch. Judo	40	10
N1081		10 ch. Wrestling (horiz)	40	10
N1082		40 ch. Rifle-shooting	95	10

458 Chollima Street, Pyongyang

1971. Chollima Street, Pyongyang. Multicoloured.

N1083		5 ch. Bridge and skyscraper blocks	1·60	35
N1084		10 ch. Type **458**	60	15
N1085		10 ch. Another view of street	60	15

459 Dredger

1972. Development of Natural Resources. Multicoloured.

N1086		5 ch. Type **459**	35	10
N1087		10 ch. Forestry	50	10
N1088		40 ch. Reclaiming land from the sea	60	15

460 Ferrous Industry

1972. Tasks of the Six-Year Plan. The Metallurgical Industry. Inscr "1971–1976". Multicoloured.

N1089		10 ch. Type **460**	80	10
N1090		10 ch. Non-ferrous Industry	40	10

461 Iron Ore Industry

1972. Tasks of the Six-Year Plan. The Mining Industry. Inscr "1971–1976". Multicoloured.
N1091 10 ch. Type **461** 40 10
N1092 10 ch. Coal mining industry 1·10 15

462 Electronic and Automation Industry

1972. Tasks of the Six-Year Plan. The Engineering Industry. Inscr "1971–1976". Multicoloured.
N1093 10 ch. Type **462** 40 10
N1094 10 ch. Single-purpose machines 40 10
N1095 10 ch. Machine tools . . . 40 10

463 Clearing Virgin Soil

1972. Tasks of the Six-Year Plan. Rural Economy. Multicoloured.
N1096 10 ch. Type **463** 45 10
N1097 10 ch. Irrigation 45 10
N1098 10 ch. Harvesting 45 10

464 Automation

1972. Tasks of the Six-Year Plan. Inscr "1971–1976". Multicoloured.
N1099 10 ch. Type **464** 60 10
N1100 10 ch. Agricultural mechanisation 45 10
N1101 10 ch. Lightening of household chores 45 10

465 Chemical Fibres and Materials

1972. Tasks of the Six-Year Plan. The Chemical Industry. Inscr "1971–1976". Multicoloured.
N1102 10 ch. Type **465** 45 10
N1103 10 ch. Fertilisers, insecticides and weed killers 45 10

466 Textiles

1972. Tasks of the Six-Year Plan. Consumer Goods. Inscr "1971–1976". Multicoloured.
N1104 10 ch. Type **466** 45 10
N1105 10 ch. Kitchen ware and overalls 45 10
N1106 10 ch. Household goods . . 45 10

467 Fish, Fruit and Vegetables

1972. Tasks of the Six-Year Plan. The Food Industry. Multicoloured.
N1107 10 ch. Type **467** 45 10
N1108 10 ch. Tinned foods 45 10
N1109 10 ch. Food packaging . . 45 10

468 Electrifying Railway Lines

1972. Tasks of the Six-Year Plan. Transport. Inscr "1971–1976". Multicoloured.
N1110 10 ch. Type **468** 35 10
N1111 10 ch. Laying new railway track 35 10
N1112 10 ch. Freighters 40 10

469 Soldier with Shell

1972. North Korean Armed Forces. Multicoloured.
N1113 10 ch. Type **469** 35 10
N1114 10 ch. Marine 35 10
N1115 10 ch. Air Force pilot . . 35 10

470 "Revolution of 19 April 1960"

1972. The Struggle for Reunification of Korea. Multicoloured.
N1116 10 ch. Type **470** 15 10
N1117 10 ch. Marchers with banner 15 10
N1118 10 ch. Insurgents with red banner 15 10
N1119 10 ch. Attacking U.S. and South Korean soldiers . 15 10
N1120 10 ch. Workers with posters 15 10
N1121 10 ch. Workers acclaiming revolution . . . . 1·75 45
N1122 10 ch. Workers and manifesto 15 10

471 Single-spindle Automatic Lathe

1972. Machine Tools.
N1123 **471** 5 ch. green and purple 25 10
N1124 – 10 ch. blue and green 35 10
N1125 – 40 ch. green & brown 80 15
DESIGNS—HORIZ: 10 ch. "Kusong-3" lathe; VERT: 40 ch. 2,000 ton crank press.

472 Casting Vote

1972. National Elections. Multicoloured.
N1126 10 ch. Type **472** 25 10
N1127 10 ch. Election campaigner 25 10

475 Soldier

1973. 25th Anniv of Founding of Korean People's Army. Multicoloured.
N1130 5 ch. Type **475** 20 10
N1131 10 ch. Sailor 30 10
N1132 40 ch. Airman 70 25

476 Wrestling Site

1973. Scenes of Kim Il Sung's Childhood, Mangyongdae. Multicoloured.
N1133 2 ch. Type **476** 15 10
N1134 5 ch. Warship rock 15 10
N1135 10 ch. Swinging site (vert) 20 10
N1136 10 ch. Sliding rock 20 10
N1137 40 ch. Fishing site 60 15

477 Monument to Socialist Revolution and Construction, Mansu Hill

1973. Museum of the Korean Revolution.
N1138 **477** 10 ch. multicoloured . . 25 10
N1139 – 10 ch. multicoloured . . 25 10
N1140 – 40 ch. multicoloured . . 50 15
N1141 – 3 wn. green and yellow 2·50 60
DESIGNS—As Type **477**: 10 ch. (No. 1139) Similar monument but men in military clothes; 40 ch. Statue of Kim Il Sung. HORIZ—60 × 29 mm: 3 wn. Museum building.

478 Karajibong Camp

1973. Secret Camps by Tuman-Gang in Guerrilla War, 1932. Multicoloured.
N1142 10 ch. Type **478** 15 10
N1143 10 ch. Soksaegol Camp . . 15 10

479

1973. Menace of Japanese Influence in South Korea.
N1144 **479** 10 ch. multicoloured . . 20 10

480 Wrecked U.S. Tanks

1973. Five-point Programme for Reunification of Korea. Multicoloured.
N1145 2 ch. Type **480** 25 10
N1146 5 ch. Train and crane lifting tractor . . . . 1·40 15
N1147 10 ch. Leaflets falling on crowd 15 10
N1148 10 ch. Hand holding leaflet and map of Korea . . . 25 10
N1149 40 ch. Banner and globe . . 40 20

481 Lorries

482 Volleyball

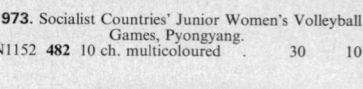

1973. Lorries and Tractors. Multicoloured.
N1150 10 ch. Type **481** 35 10
N1151 10 ch. Tractors and earth-moving machine 35 10

1973. Socialist Countries' Junior Women's Volleyball Games, Pyongyang.
N1152 **482** 10 ch. multicoloured . 30 10

483 Battlefield

1973. 20th Anniv of Victory in Korean War.
N1153 **483** 10 ch. green, red and black 20 10
N1154 – 10 ch. brown, blue and black 20 10
DESIGNS: 10 ch. Urban fighting.

484 "The Snow Falls"

1973. Mansudae Art Troupe. Dances. Multicoloured.
N1155 10 ch. Type **481** 50 10
N1156 25 ch. "A Bumper Harvest of Apples" . . . . 1·10 25
N1157 40 ch. "Azalea of the Fatherland" . . . . . . 1·40 30

485 Schoolchildren

1973. Ten Years Compulsory Secondary Education.
N1158 **485** 10 ch. multicoloured . 25 10

486 "Fervour in the Revolution"

1973. The Works of Kim Il Sung (1st series).
N1159 **486** 10 ch. brown, red and yellow 15 10
N1160 – 10 ch. brown, green and yellow 15 10
N1161 – 10 ch. lake, brown and yellow 15 10
DESIGNS: No. N1160, Selected works; No. N1161, "Strengthen the Socialist System".
See also Nos. N1217/8.

487 Celebrating Republic

1973. 25th Anniv of People's Republic. Multicoloured.
N1162 5 ch. Type **487** 10 10
N1163 10 ch. Fighting in Korean War 10 10
N1164 40 ch. Peace and reconstruction . . . . . 1·60 40

488 Pobwang Peak

1973. Mt. Myohyang. Multicoloured.

N1165 2 ch. Type **488** 25 10
N1166 5 ch. Inhodae Pavilion . . 35 10
N1167 10 ch. Taeha Falls (vert) . 1·25 30
N1168 40 ch. Rongyon Falls (vert) 1·75 30

489 Party Memorial Building

1973. Party Memorial Building.

N1169 **489** 1 wn. brown, grey and buff 95 30

490 Football and Handball

1973. National People's Sports Meeting. Mult.

N1170 2 ch. Type **490** 50 10
N1171 5 ch. High jumper and woman sprinter 25 10
N1172 10 ch. Skaters and skiers . 40 10
N1173 10 ch. Wrestling and swinging 30 10
N1174 40 ch. Parachutist and motor cyclists . . . . 1·60 25

491 Weightlifting **492** Chongryu Cliff

1973. Junior Weightlifting Championships of Socialist Countries.

N1175 **491** 10 ch. blue, brown and green 25 10

1973. Scenery of Moran Hill, Pyongyang. Multicoloured.

N1176 2 ch. Type **492** 40 15
N1177 5 ch. Moran Waterfall . . 1·75 40
N1178 10 ch. Pubyok Pavilion . . 50 10
N1179 40 ch. Ulmil Pavilion . . . 65 15

493 Rainbow Bridge **494** Magnolia Flower

1973. Diamond Mountains Scenery (4th issue). Multicoloured.

N1180 2 ch. Type **493** 85 15
N1181 5 ch. Suspension footbridge, Okryudong (horiz) . . . 85 15
N1182 10 ch. Chonnyo Peak . . . 50 10
N1183 10 ch. Chilchung Rock and Sonji Peak (horiz) . . . 50 10
N1184 40 ch. Sujong and Pari Peaks (horiz) 60 15

1973.

N1185 **494** 10 ch. multicoloured . 40 10

495 S. Korean Revolutionaries

1973. South Korean Revolution. Multicoloured

N1186 10 ch. Type **495** 15 10
N1187 10 ch. Marching revolutionaries 15 10

496 Cock sees Butterflies

1973. Scenes from "Cock Chasing Butterflies". Fairy Tale. Multicoloured.

N1188 2 ch. Type **496** 75 10
N1189 5 ch. Butterflies discuss how to repel cock 90 10
N1190 10 ch. Cock chasing butterflies with basket . 1·40 15
N1191 10 ch. Cock chasing butterfly up cliff . . . . 1·60 20
N1192 40 ch. Cock chasing butterflies over cliff . . 1·90 25
N1193 90 ch. Cock falls into sea and butterflies escape . . . 2·40 30

497 Yonpung

1973. Historical Sites of War and Revolution (40 ch.). Multicoloured.

N1196 2 ch. Type **497** 10 10
N1197 5 ch. Hyangha 10 10
N1198 10 ch. Changgol 15 10
N1199 40 ch. Paeksong 55 10

498 Science Library, Kim Il Sung University

1973. New Buildings in Pyongyang.

N1200 **498** 2 ch. violet 50 10
N1201 – 5 ch. green 15 10
N1202 – 10 ch. brown 25 10
N1203 – 40 ch. brown and buff 55 10
N1204 – 90 ch. buff 95 15

DESIGNS—HORIZ: 10 ch. Victory Museum; 40 ch. People's Palace of Culture; 90 ch. Indoor stadium. VERT: 5 ch. Building No. 2, Kim Il Sung University.

499 Red Book

1973. Socialist Constitution of North Korea. Multicoloured.

N1205 10 ch. Type **499** 15 10
N1206 10 ch. Marchers with red book & banners 15 10
N1207 10 ch. Marchers with red book & emblem 15 10

500 Oriental Great Reed Warbler

1973. Korean Songbirds. Multicoloured.

N1208 5 ch. Type **500** . . . . . 1·25 15
N1209 10 ch. Grey starling (facing right) . . . . 1·75 20
N1210 10 ch. Daurian starling (facing left) . . . . . . 1·75 20

503 Chollima Statue

1974. The Works of Kim Il Sung (2nd series). Multicoloured.

N1217 10 ch. Type **503** 65 10
N1218 10 ch. Bayonets threatening U.S. soldier 15 10

504 Train in Station

1974. Opening of Pyongyang Metro. Multicoloured.

N1219 10 ch. Type **504** 45 10
N1220 10 ch. Escalators 45 10
N1221 10 ch. Station Hall 45 10

505 Capital Construction Front

1974. Five Fronts of Socialist Construction. Multicoloured.

N1222 10 ch. Type **505** 15 10
N1223 10 ch. Agricultural front . . 25 10
N1224 10 ch. Transport front . . . 75 15
N1225 10 ch. Fisheries front . . . 50 10
N1226 10 ch. Industrial front (vert) 25 10

506 Marchers with Banners

1974. 10th Anniv of Publication of "Theses on the Socialist Rural Question in Our Country". Multicoloured.

N1227 10 ch. Type **506** 15 10
N1228 10 ch. Book and rejoicing crowd 15 10
N1229 10 ch. Tractor & banners . 15 10

Nos. 1227/9 were issued together se-tenant forming a composite design.

507 Manure Spreader

1974. Farm Machinery.

N1230 **507** 2 ch. green, black & red 40 10
N1231 – 5 ch. red, black & blue 40 10
N1232 – 10 ch. red, black & grn 40 10

DESIGNS: 5 ch. "Progress" tractor; 10 ch. "Mount Taedoksan" tractor.

508 Archery (Grenoble)

1974. North Korean Victories at International Sports Meetings. Multicoloured.

N1233 2 ch. Type **508** 65 15
N1234 5 ch. Gymnastics (Varna) . 15 10
N1235 10 ch. Boxing (Bucharest) . 25 10
N1236 20 ch. Volleyball (Pyongyang) 15 10
N1237 30 ch. Rifle shooting (Sofia) 45 10
N1238 40 ch. Judo (Tbilisi) 65 15
N1239 60 ch. Model aircraft flying (Vienna) (horiz) 95 20
N1240 1 wn. 50 Table tennis (Peking) (horiz) . . . . 1·75 30

509 Book and Rejoicing Crowd

1974. First Country with No Taxes.

N1241 **509** 10 ch. multicoloured . 20 10

510 Drawing up Programme in Woods

1974. Kim Il Sung during the Anti-Japanese Struggle. Multicoloured.

N1242 10 ch. Type **510** 25 10
N1243 10 ch. Giving directions to Pak Dal 25 10
N1244 10 ch. Presiding over Nanhutou Conference . . . 25 10
N1245 10 ch. Supervising creation of strongpoint 25 10

511 Sun Hui loses her Sight

1974. Scenes from "The Flower Girl" (revolutionary opera). Multicoloured.

N1246 2 ch. Type **511** 40 10
N1247 5 ch. Death of Ggot Bun's mother 40 10
N1248 10 ch. Ggot Bun throws boiling water at landlord 75 10
N1249 40 ch. Ggot Bun joins revolutionaries . . . . 1·25 15

512 Leopard Cat

1974. 15th Anniv of Pyongyang Zoo. Multicoloured.

N1251 2 ch. Type **512** 50 10
N1252 5 ch. Lynx 50 10
N1253 10 ch. Red fox 50 10
N1254 10 ch. Wild boar 50 10
N1255 20 ch. Dhole 50 15
N1256 40 ch. Brown bear 60 25
N1257 60 ch. Leopard . . . . . . 1·00 25
N1258 70 ch. Tiger . . . . 1·40 30
N1259 90 ch. Lion . . . . 1·75 35

513 "Rosa acucularis lindly"

1974. Roses. Multicoloured.

N1261 2 ch. Type **513** 40 10
N1262 5 ch. Yellow sweet briar . 45 10
N1263 10 ch. Pink aromatic rose 55 10
N1264 10 ch. Aronia sweet briar (yellow centres) 55 10
N1265 40 ch. Multi-petal sweet briar 1·40 10

INDEX

Countries can be quickly located by referring to the index at the end of this volume.

515 Weigela

1974. Flowering Plants of Mt. Paekdu. Mult.

N1267 2 ch. Type **515** 30 10
N1268 5 ch. Amaryllis 30 10
N1269 10 ch. Red lily 30 10
N1270 20 ch. Orange lily 40 10
N1271 40 ch. Azalea 65 10
N1272 60 ch. Yellow lily . . . . . 1·10 10

516 Postwoman and Construction Site

1974. Cent of U.P.U. and Admission of North Korea to Union. Multicoloured.

N1273 10 ch. Type **516** . . . . . 1·25 15
N1274 25 ch. Chollima monument 10 10
N1275 40 ch. Globe and Antonov An-12 aircraft 90 15

517 "Rana nigromaculata"

1974. Frogs and Toad. Multicoloured.

N1276 2 ch. Type **517** 50 10
N1277 5 ch. "Bombina orientalis" 60 10
N1278 10 ch. "Rana catesbiana" 75 15
N1279 40 ch. "Bufo bufo" . . . . 1·60 25

518 "Women of Namgang Village"

1974. Korean Paintings. Multicoloured.

N1281 2 ch. Type **518** 50 10
N1282 5 ch. "An Old Man on the Rakdong River" (60 × 49 mm) 60 10
N1283 10 ch. "Morning in the Nae-kumgang" (bridge) . . . 75 10
N1284 20 ch. "Mt. Kumgang" (60 × 49 mm) . . . . . . 1·00 15

519 "Elektron 1" and "Elektron 2", 1964

1974. Cosmonauts Day. Multicoloured.

N1286 10 ch. Type **519** 15 10
N1287 20 ch. "Proton 1", 1965 . . 25 10
N1288 30 ch. "Venera 3", 1966 . . 40 10
N1289 40 ch. "Venera 5" and "Venera 6", 1969 . . . . 50 10

521 Antonov An-2 Biplane

1974. Civil Aviation. Multicoloured

N1292 2 ch. Type **521** 30 10
N1293 5 ch. Lisunov Li-2 . . . . 30 10
N1294 10 ch. Ilyushin Il-14P . . 40 10
N1295 40 ch. Antonov An-24 . . 75 25
N1296 60 ch. Ilyushin Il-18 . . . 1·25 50

522 "Rhododendron redowskianum"

1974. Plants of Mt. Paekdu. Multicoloured.

N1298 2 ch. Type **522** 35 10
N1299 5 ch. "Dryas octopetala" . . 35 10
N1300 10 ch. "Potentilla fruticosa" 40 10
N1301 20 ch. "Papaver somniferum" 50 10
N1302 40 ch. "Phyllodoce caerulea" 70 20
N1303 60 ch. "Oxytropis anertii" 1·25 40

523 "Sobaek River in the Morning"

1974. Modern Korean Paintings. (1st series). Multicoloured.

N1304 10 ch. Type **523** 60 10
N1305 20 ch. "Combatants of Mt. Laohei" (60 × 40 mm) . 65 10
N1306 30 ch. "Spring in the Fields" 75 15
N1307 40 ch. "Tideland Night" . 2·50 20
N1308 60 ch. "Daughter" (60 × 54 mm) 90 40

See also Nos. N1361/5, N1386/96 and N1485/9.

525 Log cabin, Unha Village

1974. Historic Sites of the Revolution.

N1310 – 5 ch. multicoloured . . 10 10
N1311 **525** 10 ch. multicoloured . 10 10

DESIGN: 5 ch. Munmyong.

526 Sesame

1974. Oil-producing Plants. Multicoloured.

N1312 2 ch. Type **526** 40 10
N1313 5 ch. "Perilla frutescens" . 45 10
N1314 10 ch. Sunflower 50 10
N1315 40 ch. Castor bean 85 40

527 Kim Il Sung as Guerrilla Leader

1974. Kim Il Sung. Multicoloured.

N1316 10 ch. Type **527** 20 10
N1317 10 ch. Commander of the People's Army (52 × 35 mm) 20 10
N1318 10 ch. "The commander is also a son of the people" (52 × 35 mm) 20 10
N1319 10 ch. Negotiating with the Chinese anti-Japanese unit (52 × 35 mm) 20 10

528

1974. Grand Monument on Mansu Hill. Mult.

N1320 10 ch. Type **528** 15 10
N1321 10 ch. As T **528** but men in civilian clothes 15 10
N1322 10 ch. As T **528** but men facing left 15 10
N1323 10 ch. As No. N1322 but men in civilian clothes 15 10

529 Factory Ship "Chilbosan"

1974. Deep-sea Fishing. Multicoloured.

N1324 2 ch. Type **529** 70 25
N1325 5 ch. Trawler support ship "Paekdusan" 70 25
N1326 10 ch. Freighter "Moranbong" 70 25
N1327 20 ch. Whale-catcher . . . 70 25
N1328 30 ch. Trawler 70 25
N1329 40 ch. Stern trawler 70 25

539 Kim Il Sung crosses River Agrok

1975. 50th Anniv of Kim Il Sung's crossing of River Agrok.

N1349 **539** 10 ch. multicoloured . . 25 10

540 Pak Yong Sun "World Table Tennis Queen"

1975. Pak Yong Sun, Winner of 33rd World Table Tennis Championships, Calcutta.

N1350 **540** 10 ch. multicoloured . . 50 10

541 Common Zebra

1975. Pyongyang Zoo. Multicoloured.

N1352 10 ch. Type **541** 30 10
N1353 10 ch. African buffalo . . . 30 10
N1354 20 ch. Giant panda (horiz) 80 10
N1355 25 ch. Bactrian camel . . . 70 15
N1356 30 ch. Indian elephant . . . 1·25 20

542 "Blue Dragon"

1975. 7th-century Mural Paintings from Koguryo Tombs, Kangso.

N1357 10 ch. Type **542** 65 10
N1358 15 ch. "White Tiger" . . . 85 10
N1359 25 ch. "Red Phoenix" (vert) 1·00 10
N1360 40 ch. "Snake-turtle" . . . 1·40 25

543 "Spring in the Guerrilla Base" (1968)

1975. Modern Korean Paintings (2nd series). Anti-Japanese struggle. Multicoloured.

N1361 10 ch. Type **543** 35 10
N1362 10 ch. "Revolutionary Army landing at Unggi" (1969) 35 10
N1363 15 ch. "Sewing Team Members" (1961) 55 10
N1364 20 ch. "Girl Watering Horse" (1969) . . . . 1·00 15
N1365 30 ch. "Kim Jong Suk giving Guidance to Children's Corps" (1970) 80 20

544 Cosmonaut

1975. Cosmonauts' Day. Multicoloured.

N1366 10 ch. Type **544** 15 10
N1367 30 ch. "Lunokhod" moon vehicle (horiz) 40 10
N1368 40 ch. "Soyuz" spacecraft and "Salyut" space laboratory (horiz) 55 15

546 The Beacon lit at Pochonbo, 1937

1975. Kim Il Sung during the Guerrilla War against the Japanese. Multicoloured.

N1370 10 ch. Type **546** 25 10
N1371 10 ch. "A Bowl of Parched-rice Powder", 1938 . . . 25 10
N1372 10 ch. Guiding the Nanpaizi meeting, November, 1938 25 10
N1373 10 ch. Welcoming helper . 25 10
N1374 10 ch. Lecturing the guerrillas 25 10
N1375 15 ch. Advancing into the homeland, May 1939 . . 35 10
N1376 25 ch. By Lake Samji, May 1939 . . . . 45 10
N1377 30 ch. At Sinsadong, May 1939 . . . . 55 10
N1378 40 ch. Xiaohaerbaling meeting, 1940 . . . . . 65 15

547 Vase of Flowers and Kim Il Sung's Birthplace

1975. Kim Il Sung's 63rd Birthday. Multicoloured.

N1379 10 ch. Type **547** 10 10
N1379a 40 ch. Kim Il Sung's birthplace, Mangyongdae 35 10

548 South Korean Insurgent

1975. 15th Anniv of April 19th Rising.

N1380 **548** 10 ch. multicoloured . 15 10

549 "Kingfisher at a Lotus Pond"

1975. Paintings of Li Dynasty. Multicoloured.

N1381 5 ch. Type **549** . . . . . . 1·10 10
N1382 10 ch. "Crabs" 75 10
N1383 15 ch. "Rose of Sharon" . 1·10 15
N1384 25 ch. "Lotus and Water Cock" . . . . 1·50 30
N1385 30 ch. "Tree Peony and Red Junglefowl" . . . . . . 2·25 30

1975. Modern Korean Paintings (3rd series). Fatherland Liberation War. Dated designs as T **543**. Multicoloured.

N1386 5 ch. "On the Advance Southward" (1966) (vert) 20 10
N1387 10 ch. "The Assigned Post" (girl sentry) (1968) (vert) 25 10
N1388 15 ch. "The Heroism of Li Su Bok" (1965) 30 10
N1389 25 ch. "Retaliation" (woman machine-gunner) (1970) . 50 20
N1390 30 ch. "The awaited Troops" (1970) 60 20

1975. Modern Korean Paintings (4th series). Socialist Construction. As T **543**. Multicoloured.

N1391 10 ch. "Pine Tree" (1966) (vert) 45 10
N1392 10 ch. "The Blue Signal Lamp" (1960) (vert) . . 1·40 10
N1393 15 ch. "A Night of Snowfall" (1963) 50 10
N1394 20 ch. "Smelters" (1968) . . 60 15
N1395 25 ch. "Tideland Reclamation" (1961) . . 60 15
N1396 30 ch. "Mount Paekdusan" (1966) 60 20

550 Flag and Building

553

1975. 20th Anniv of "Chongryon" Association of Koreans in Japan.

N1397 **550** 10 ch. multicoloured . 15 10
N1398 3 wn. multicoloured . 2·50 55

1975. Diving. Multicoloured.

N1400 10 ch. Type **552** 15 10
N1401 25 ch. Piked somersault (man) 40 10
N1402 40 ch. "Head first" entry (woman) 85 15

1975. Campaign against U.S. Imperialism.

N1403 **553** 10 ch. multicoloured . 15 10

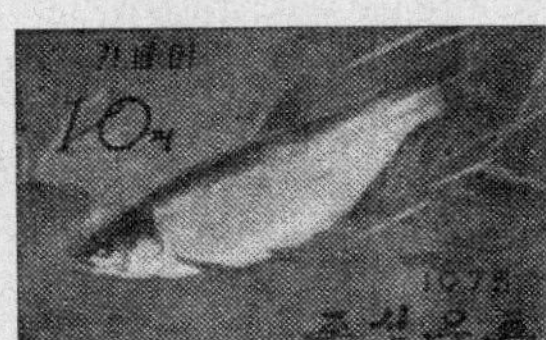

554 Memorial Fish

1975. Fresh-water Fish. Multicoloured.

N1404 10 ch. Type **554** 40 10
N1405 10 ch. Whitefish (fish swimming to right) . . . 40 10
N1406 15 ch. "Opsanichthys bidens" 60 10
N1407 25 ch. Naere . . . . . . 1·00 15
N1408 30 ch. Catfish (fish swimming to right) . . . . 1·25 20
N1409 30 ch. Snakehead (fish swimming to left) . . . 1·25 20

555

1975. 10th Socialist Countries' Football Tournament, Pyongyang.

N1410 **555** 5 ch. multicoloured . . 25 10
N1411 – 10 ch. multicoloured . 25 10
N1412 – 15 ch. multicoloured . 30 10
N1413 – 20 ch. multicoloured . 40 15
N1414 – 50 ch. multicoloured . 75 35

DESIGNS: 10 ch. to 50 ch. Various footballers.

556 Blue and Yellow Macaw

557 Flats

1975. Birds. Multicoloured.

N1416 10 ch. Type **556** 90 10
N1417 15 ch. Sulphur-crested cockatoo . . . . 1·10 10
N1418 20 ch. Blyth's parakeet . . 1·40 20
N1419 25 ch. Rainbow lory . . . 1·60 30
N1420 30 ch. Budgerigar . . . . 1·90 30

1975. New Buildings in Pyongyang. Multicoloured.

N1421 90 ch. Saesallim (formerly Sangwon) St. . . . . . 1·50 40
N1422 1 wn. Type **557** . . . . . 1·75 45
N1423 2 wn. Potonggang Hotel . 2·75 60

552 "Feet first" entry (man)

558 White Peach Blossom

559 Sejongbong

1975. Blossoms of Flowering Trees. Multicoloured.

N1424 10 ch. Type **558** 30 10
N1425 15 ch. Red peach blossom 30 10
N1426 20 ch. Red plum blossom 45 15
N1427 25 ch. Apricot blossom . . 60 15
N1428 30 ch. Cherry blossom . . . 85 20

1975. Landscapes in the Diamond Mountains. Multicoloured.

N1429 5 ch. Type **559** 40 10
N1430 10 ch. Chonsondae 65 10
N1431 15 ch. Pisamun 85 10
N1432 25 ch. Manmulsang . . . . 1·10 20
N1433 30 ch. Chaehabong . . . . 1·25 20

560 Azalea

1975. Flowers of the Azalea Family. Multicoloured.

N1434 5 ch. Type **560** 35 10
N1435 10 ch. White azalea 35 10
N1436 15 ch. Wild rhododendron 50 10
N1437 20 ch. White rhododendron 50 15
N1438 25 ch. Rhododendron . . . 65 15
N1439 30 ch. Yellow rhododendron 90 20

561 Gliders

1975. Training for National Defence. Mult.

N1440 5 ch. Type **561** 30 10
N1441 5 ch. Radio-controlled model airplane 30 10
N1442 10 ch. "Free fall parachutist" (vert) 45 10
N1443 10 ch. Parachutist landing on target (vert) 45 10
N1444 20 ch. Parachutist with bouquet of flowers (vert) 55 15

562 Wild Apple

1975. Fruit Tree Blossom. Multicoloured.

N1446 10 ch. Type **562** 30 10
N1447 15 ch. Wild pear 30 10
N1448 20 ch. Hawthorn 40 15
N1449 25 ch. Chinese quince . . . 55 15
N1450 30 ch. Flowering quince . . 65 60

563 Torch of Juche

1975. 30th Anniv of Korean Workers' Party. Multicoloured.

N1451 2 ch. "Victory" and American graves 10 10
N1452 2 ch. Sunrise over Mt. Paekdu-san 10 10
N1453 5 ch. Type **563** 10 10
N1454 5 ch. Chollima Statue and sunset over Pyongyang 10 10
N1455 10 ch. Korean with Red Book 10 10
N1456 10 ch. Chollima Statue . . 10 10
N1457 25 ch. Crowds and burning building 35 10
N1458 70 ch. Flowers and map of Korea 95 15

564 Welcoming Crowd

1975. 30th Anniv of Kim Il Sung's Return to Pyongyang.

N1460 **564** 20 ch. multicoloured . 25 15

565 Workers holding "Juche" Torch

1975. 30th Anniv of "Rodong Simmun" (Journal of the Central Committee of the Worker's Party.)

N1461 **565** 10 ch. multicoloured . 50 10

566 Hyonmu Gate

1975. Ancient Wall-Gates of Pyongyang. Multicoloured.

N1463 10 ch. Type **566** 10 10
N1464 10 ch. Taedong Gate . . . 10 10
N1465 15 ch. Potong Gate 20 10
N1466 20 ch. Chongum Gate . . 35 15
N1467 30 ch. Chilsong Gate (vert) 45 25

567

1975. Views of Mt. Chilbo.

N1468 **567** 10 ch. multicoloured . 40 10
N1469 – 10 ch. multicoloured . 40 10
N1470 – 15 ch. multicoloured . 65 10
N1471 – 20 ch. multicoloured . 75 15
N1472 – 30 ch. multicoloured . 85 20

DESIGNS: Nos. N1468/72, various views.

568 Right-hand Section of Monument

1975. Historic Site of Revolution in Wangjaesan. Multicoloured.

N1473 10 ch. Type **568** 10 10
N1474 15 ch. Left-hand section of monument 20 10
N1475 25 ch. Centre section of monument 30 15
N1476 30 ch. Centre section, close up 40 20

No. N1475 is 38 × 60 mm and No. N1476, 60 × 38 mm.

569 Marchers with Flags

1976. 30th Anniv of Korean League of Socialist Working Youth. Multicoloured.

N1477 2 ch. Flags and Emblem . . 15 10
N1478 70 ch. Type **569** 90 40

570 Geese

1976. Ducks and Geese. Multicoloured.
N1479 10 ch. Type **570** 40 10
N1480 20 ch. "Perennial" duck . . 90 10
N1481 40 ch. Kwangpo duck . . . 1·60 20

571 "Oath"

1976. Korean Peoples Army (sculptural works). Multicoloured.
N1482 5 ch. Type **571** 10 10
N1483 10 ch. "Union of Officers with Men" (horiz) 15 10
N1484 10 ch. "This Flag to the Height" 15 10

572 "Rural Road at Evening"

1976. Modern Korean Paintings (5th series). Social Welfare. Multicoloured.
N1485 10 ch. Type **572** 35 10
N1486 15 ch. "Passing on Technique" (1970) . . . 45 10
N1487 25 ch. "Mother (and Child)" (1965) 55 15
N1488 30 ch. "Medical Examination at School" (1970) (horiz) 75 15
N1489 40 ch. "Lady Doctor of Village" (1970) (horiz) . 90 20

573 Worker holding Text of Law

1976. 30th Anniv of Agrarian Reform Law.
N1490 **573** 10 ch. multicoloured . 20 10

574 Telephones and Satellite

1976. Centenary of First Telephone Call. Multicoloured. With or without gum.
N1491 2 ch. Type **574** 40 10
N1492 5 ch. Satellite and antenna 40 10
N1493 10 ch. Satellite and telecommunications systems 40 10
N1494 15 ch. Telephone and linesman . . . . 1·10 10
N1495 25 ch. Satellite and map of receiving stations . . . . 1·50 15
N1496 40 ch. Satellite and cable-laying barge . . . . . . 1·75 20

575 Cosmos

1976. Flowers. Multicoloured.
N1498 5 ch. Type **575** 25 10
N1499 10 ch. Dahlia 25 10
N1500 20 ch. Zinnia 45 15
N1501 40 ch. China aster 70 25

576 Fruit and Products

1976. Pukchong Meeting of Korean Workers' Party Presidium. Multicoloured.
N1502 5 ch. Type **576** 45 10
N1503 10 ch. Fruit and orchard scene 45 10

577 "Pulgunji" Type Electric Locomotive

1976. Railway Locomotives. Multicoloured.
N1504 5 ch. Type **577** 25 10
N1505 10 ch. "Chaju" type underground train . . . 55 10
N1506 15 ch. "Saebyol" type diesel locomotive 70 15

GUM. All the following stamps were issued with gum, except where otherwise stated.

578 Satellite

1976. Space Flight. With or without gum.
N1507 **578** 2 ch. multicoloured . . 15 10
N1508 – 5 ch. multicoloured . . 15 10
N1509 – 10 ch. multicoloured . 20 10
N1510 – 15 ch. multicoloured . 30 10
N1511 – 25 ch. multicoloured . 45 15
N1512 – 40 ch. multicoloured . 70 20
DESIGNS: 5 ch. to 40 ch. Various satellites and space craft.

579 Kim Il Sung beside Car

1976. Kim Il Sung's 64th Birthday.
N1514 **579** 10 ch. multicoloured . 40 10

580 Bat and Ribbon

1976. 3rd Asian Table Tennis Championships. Multicoloured. Without gum.
N1516 5 ch. Type **580** 25 10
N1517 10 ch. Three women players with flowers 25 10
N1518 20 ch. Player defending . . 45 10
N1519 25 ch. Player making attacking shot 75 15

581 Kim Il Sung announcing Establishment of Association

1976. 40th Anniv of Association for the Restoration of the Fatherland. Without gum.
N1521 **581** 10 ch. multicoloured . . 10 10

582 Golden Pheasant

1976. Pheasants. Multicoloured. With or without gum.
N1522 2 ch. Type **582** 60 10
N1523 5 ch. Lady Amherst's pheasant 60 15
N1524 10 ch. Silver pheasant . . . 70 20
N1525 15 ch. Reeve's pheasant . . 80 20
N1526 25 ch. Temminck's tragopan 1·00 25
N1527 40 ch. Ringed-necked pheasant (albino) . . . . 1·25 35

583 Monument and Map of River

585 Bronze Medal (Hockey, Pakistan)

584 Running

1976. Potong River Monument. Without gum.
N1529 **583** 10 ch. brown & green 20 10

1976. Olympic Games, Montreal. Multicoloured.
N1530 2 ch. Type **584** 20 10
N1531 5 ch. Diving 20 10
N1532 10 ch. Judo 20 10
N1533 15 ch. Gymnastics 30 10
N1534 25 ch. Gymnastics 80 15
N1535 40 ch. Fencing . . . . . . 1·25 20

1976. Olympic Medal Winners (1st issue). Multicoloured.
N1537 2 ch. Type **585** 25 10
N1538 5 ch. Bronze medal (shooting, Rudolf Dollinger) 25 10
N1539 10 ch. Silver medal (boxing, Li Byong Uk) 25 15

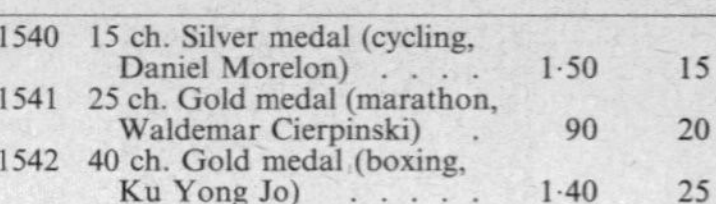
N1540 15 ch. Silver medal (cycling, Daniel Morelon) . . . . 1·50 15
N1541 25 ch. Gold medal (marathon, Waldemar Cierpinski) . 90 20
N1542 40 ch. Gold medal (boxing, Ku Yong Jo) . . . . . 1·40 25

586 Boxing (Ku Yong Jo)

1976. Olympic Medal Winners (2nd issue). Multicoloured.
N1544 2 ch. Type **586** 25 10
N1545 5 ch. Gymnastics (Nadia Comaneci) 25 10
N1546 10 ch. Pole vaulting (Tadeusz Slusarki) 25 10
N1547 15 ch. Hurdling (Guy Drut) 30 10
N1548 20 ch. Cycling (Bernt Johansson) . . . . . . 2·50 15
N1549 40 ch. Football (East Germany) . . . . 1·50 20

587 U.P.U. Headquarters, Berne

1976. International Festivities. Multicoloured.
N1551 2 ch. Type **587** 40 10
N1552 5 ch. Footballers (World Cup) 40 10
N1553 10 ch. Olympic Stadium . 40 10
N1554 15 ch. Olympic Village . . 40 10
N1555 25 ch. Junk and satellite . 70 20
N1556 40 ch. Satellites 75 20

588 Azure-winged Magpies

1976. Embroidery. Multicoloured. With or without gum.
N1558 2 ch. Type **588** . . . . . . 1·25 15
N1559 5 ch. White magpie 90 15
N1560 10 ch. Roe deer 30 10
N1561 15 ch. Black-naped oriole and magnolias . . . . 1·40 15
N1562 25 ch. Fairy with flute (horiz) 70 15
N1563 40 ch. Tiger . . . . 1·60 40

589 Roman "5" and Flame

1976. 5th Non-aligned States' Summit Conference, Colombo. Without gum.
N1565 **589** 10 ch. multicoloured 10 10

590 Trophy and Certificate

1976. World Model Plane Championships (1975). Multicoloured. Without gum.

N1566	5 ch. Type **590**	20	10
N1567	10 ch. Trophy and medals	30	10
N1568	20 ch. Model airplane and emblem	45	10
N1569	40 ch. Model glider and medals	75	15

591 "Pulgungi" Type Diesel Shunting Locomotive

1976. Locomotives. Multicoloured.

N1570	2 ch. Type **591**	40	10
N1571	5 ch. "Saebyol" type diesel locomotive	55	10
N1572	10 ch. "Saebyol" type diesel shunting locomotive	65	10
N1573	15 ch. Electric locomotive	75	10
N1574	25 ch. "Kumsung" type diesel locomotive	95	15
N1575	40 ch. "Pulgungi" type electric locomotive	1·10	20

592 House of Culture

1976. House of Culture. Without gum.

N1577	**592**	10 ch. brown and black	15	10

593 Kim Il Sung visiting Tosongrang

1976. Revolutionary Activities of Kim Il Sung. Multicoloured.

N1578	2 ch. Type **593**	20	10
N1579	5 ch. Kim Il Sung visits pheasants	20	10
N1580	10 ch. Kim Il Sung on hilltop	25	10
N1581	15 ch. Kim Il Sung giving house to farmhand	30	10
N1582	25 ch. Kim Il Sung near front line	70	10
N1583	40 ch. Kim Il Sung walking in rain	70	15

594 Kim Il Sung with Union Members

1976. 50th Anniv of Down-with-Imperialism Union. Without gum.

N1585	**594**	20 ch. multicoloured	35	15

604 Searchlights and Kim Il Sung's Birthplace

605 Spring Costume

1977. New Year. Without gum.

N1589	**604**	10 ch. multicoloured	10	10

1977. National Costumes of Li Dynasty. Mult.

N1590	10 ch. Type **605** (postage)	45	10
N1591	15 ch. Summer costume	60	10
N1592	20 ch. Autumn costume	70	15
N1593	40 ch. Winter costume (air)	1·10	20

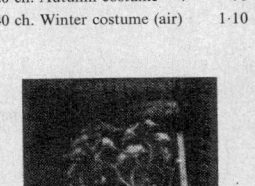

606 Two Deva Kings (Koguryo Dynasty)

1977. Korean Cultural Relics. Multicoloured.

N1594	2 ch. Type **606** (post)	25	10
N1595	5 ch. Gold-copper decoration, Koguryo Dynasty	25	10
N1596	10 ch. Copper Buddha, Koryo Dynasty	35	10
N1597	15 ch. Gold-copper Buddha, Paekje Dynasty	45	10
N1598	25 ch. Gold crown, Koguryo Dynasty	55	15
N1599	40 ch. Gold-copper sun decoration, Koguryo Dynasty (horiz)	70	20
N1600	50 ch. Gold crown, Silla Dynasty (air)	90	35

607 Worker with Five-point Programme

1977. Five-point Programme for Remaking Nature. Without gum.

N1601	**607**	10 ch. multicoloured	20	10

608 Pine Branch and Map of Korea

1977. 60th Anniv of Korean National Association. Without gum.

N1602	**608**	10 ch. multicoloured	35	10

609 Championship Emblem and Trophy

1977. 34th World Table Tennis Championships. Multicoloured. Without gum.

N1603	10 ch. Type **609** (postage)	20	10
N1604	15 ch. Pak Yong Sun	30	10
N1605	20 ch. Pak Yong Sun with trophy	50	15
N1606	40 ch. Pak Yong Ok and Yang Ying (air)	95	20

610 Kim Il Sung founds Guerrilla Army at Mingyuegou

1977. Kim Il Sung's 65th Birthday. Multicoloured.

N1607	2 ch. Type **610**	10	10
N1608	5 ch. In command of army	10	10
N1609	10 ch. Visiting steel workers in Kangson	25	10
N1610	15 ch. Before battle	20	10
N1611	25 ch. In schoolroom	25	10
N1612	40 ch. Viewing bumper harvest	35	10

611 "Chollima 72" Trolleybus

1977. Trolleybuses. Without gum.

N1614	**611**	5 ch. blue, lilac & black	75	10
N1615	–	10 ch. red, green & blk	75	10

DESIGN: 10 ch. "Chollima 74" trolleybus.

612 Red Flag and Hand holding Rifle

1977. 45th Anniv of Korean People's Revolutionary Army. Without gum.

N1616	**612**	40 ch. red, yellow & blk	50	20

613 Proclamation and Watchtower

1977. 40th Anniv of Pochonbo Battle. Without gum.

N1617	**613**	10 ch. multicoloured	10	10

614 Koryo White Ware Teapot

1977. Korean Porcelain. Multicoloured.

N1618	10 ch. Type **614** (postage)	30	10
N1619	15 ch. White vase, Li Dynasty	40	10
N1620	20 ch. Celadon vase, Koryo Dynasty	65	10
N1621	40 ch. Celadon vase with lotus decoration, Koryo Dynasty (air)	1·10	15

615 Postal Transport

1977. Postal Services. Multicoloured. Without gum.

N1623	2 ch. Type **615**	60	15
N1624	10 ch. Postwoman delivering letter	25	10
N1625	30 ch. Mil Mi-8 helicopter	90	30
N1626	40 ch. Ilyushin Il-18 airliner and world map	90	30

616 "Rapala arata"

1977. Butterflies and Dragonflies. Multicoloured.

N1627	2 ch. Type **616** (postage)	35	10
N1628	5 ch. "Colias aurora"	55	10
N1629	10 ch. Poplar admiral	75	10
N1630	15 ch. "Anax partherope"	1·00	10
N1631	25 ch. "Sympetrum pedemontanum elatum"	1·25	10
N1632	50 ch. "Papilio maackii" (air)	1·50	20

617 Grey Cat

618

1977. Cats. Multicoloured.

N1634	2 ch. Type **617**	90	10
N1635	10 ch. Black and white cat	1·25	15
N1636	25 ch. Ginger cat	1·90	20

1977. Dogs. Multicoloured.

N1638	5 ch. Type **618** (postage)	75	10
N1639	15 ch. Chow	1·00	10
N1640	50 ch. Pungsang dog (air)	1·60	15

619 Kim Il Sung and President Tito

1977. Visit of President Tito.

N1642	**619**	10 ch. multicoloured	10	10
N1643		15 ch. multicoloured	15	10
N1644		20 ch. multicoloured	25	10
N1645		40 vh. multicoloured	35	10

620 Girl and Symbols of Education

1977. 5th Anniv of 11-year Compulsory Education. Without gum.

N1646	**620**	10 ch. multicoloured	10	10

621 "Mactra sulcataria"

622 Students and "Theses"

1977. Shellfish and Fish. Multicoloured.

N1647	2 ch. Type **621** (postage)	35	10
N1648	5 ch. "Natica fortunei"	50	15
N1649	10 ch. "Ara inflata"	70	15
N1650	25 ch. "Rapana thomasiana"	1·00	20
N1651	50 ch. "Sphoeroides porphyreus" (air)	1·60	30

1977. Kim Il Sung's "Theses on Socialist Education". Multicoloured. Without gum.
N1653 10 ch. Type **622** 10 10
N1654 20 ch. Students, crowd and text 15 10

623 "Juche" Torch **624** Jubilant Crowd

1977. Seminar on the Juche Idea. Multicoloured. Without gum.
N1655 2 ch. Type **623** 10 10
N1656 5 ch. Crowd and red book 10 10
N1657 10 ch. Chollima Statue and flags 10 10
N1658 15 ch. Handclasp and red flag on world map 10 10
N1659 25 ch. Map of Korea and anti-U.S. slogans 15 10
N1660 40 ch. Crowd and Mt. Paekdu-san 20 10

1977. Election of Deputies to Supreme People's Assembly. Without gum.
N1662 **624** 10 ch. multicoloured . 10 10

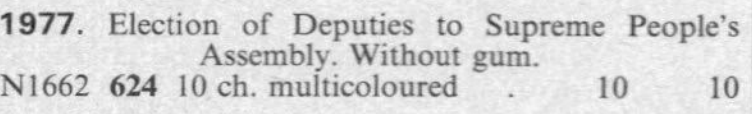

625 Footballers

1977. World Cup Football Championship, Argentina. Without gum.
N1663 **625** 10 ch. multicoloured . 50 15
N1664 15 ch. multicoloured . 90 20
N1665 – 40 ch. multicoloured . 1·60 25
DESIGNS: 15, 40 ch. Different football scenes.

626 Kim Il Sung with Rejoicing Crowds

1977. Re-election of Kim Il Sung. Without gum.
N1667 **626** 10 ch. multicoloured . 10 10

627 Chollima Statue and Symbols of Communication

1977. 20th Anniv of Socialist Countries' Communication Organization. Without gum.
N1668 **627** 10 ch. multicoloured . 20 10

638 Chollima Statue and City Skyline

1978. New Year. Without gum.
N1687 **638** 10 ch. multicoloured . 10 10

639 Skater in 19th-century Costume **640** Post-rider and "Horse-ticket"

1978. Winter Olympic Games, Sapporo and Innsbruck. Multicoloured.
N1688 2 ch. Type **639** (postage) . 40 10
N1699 5 ch. Skier 40 10
N1690 10 ch. Woman skater . . . 40 10
N1691 15 ch. Hunter on skis . . . 50 10
N1692 20 ch. Woman (in 19th-century costume) on skis 50 10
N1693 25 ch. Viking with long-bow 1·25 15
N1694 40 ch. Skier (air) . . . . . 1·40 15

1978. Postal Progress. Multicoloured.
N1696 2 ch. Type **640** (postage) . 25 10
N1697 5 ch. Postman on motorcycle 1·50 10
N1698 10 ch. Electric train and postvan . . . . 1·50 15
N1699 15 ch. Mail steamer and Mil Mi-8 helicopter 65 15
N1700 25 ch. Tupolev Tu-154 airliner and satellite 75 15
N1701 40 ch. Dove and U.P.U. Headquarters (air) . . . 50 15

641 "Self-portrait" **643** Show Jumping

642 "Chungsong" Tractor

1978. 400th Birth Anniv of Rubens.
N1703 **641** 2 ch. multicoloured . . 25 10
N1704 5 ch. multicoloured . . 25 10
N1705 40 ch. multicoloured . 1·50 20

1978. Farm Machines. Without gum.
N1707 **642** 10 ch. red and black . 35 10
N1708 – 10 ch. brown and black 35 10
DESIGN: No. N1708, Sprayer.

1978. Olympic Games, Moscow (1980). Equestrian Events. Multicoloured.
N1709 2 ch. Type **643** 25 10
N1710 5 ch. Jumping bar 35 10
N1711 10 ch. Cross-country . . . 45 10
N1712 15 ch. Dressage 50 10
N1713 25 ch. Water splash . . . 75 15
N1714 40 ch. Dressage (different) 1·25 15

644 Soldier

1978. Korean People's Army Day. Multicoloured. Without gum.
N1716 5 ch. Type **644** 10 10
N1717 10 ch. Servicemen saluting 10 10

645 "Mangyongbong" (Freighter)

1978. Korean Ships. Multicoloured.
N1718 2 ch. Type **645** (postage) . . 1·75 45
N1719 5 ch. "Hyoksin" (freighter) 35 15
N1720 10 ch. "Chongchongang" (gas carrier) 35 15
N1721 30 ch. "Sonbong" (tanker) 60 20
N1722 50 ch. "Taedonggang" (freighter) (air) . . . . . 1·10 40

646 Uruguayan Footballer

1978. World Cup Football Championship Winners. Multicoloured.
N1724 5 ch. Type **646** (postage) . . 40 10
N1725 10 ch. Italian player 40 10
N1726 15 ch. West German player 40 10
N1727 25 ch. Brazilian player . . . 40 10
N1728 40 ch. English player . . . 75 10
N1729 50 ch. Hands holding World Cup (vert) (air) 65 35

647 Footballers (1930 Winners, Uruguay)

1978. History of World Cup Football Championship. Multicoloured.
N1731 20 ch. Type **647** (postage) 75 15
N1732 20 ch. Italy, 1934 . . . . . 75 15
N1733 20 ch. France, 1938 . . . . 75 15
N1734 20 ch. Brazil, 1950 . . . . 75 15
N1735 20 ch. Switzerland, 1954 . . 75 15
N1736 20 ch. Sweden, 1958 . . . . 75 15
N1737 20 ch. Chile, 1962 . . . . . 75 15
N1738 20 ch. England, 1966 . . . 75 15
N1739 20 ch. Mexico, 1970 . . . . 75 15
N1740 20 ch. West Germany, 1974 75 15
N1741 20 ch. Argentina, 1978 . . . 75 15
N1742 50 ch. Footballers and emblem (air) 75 15

648 "Sea of Blood" (opera)

1978. Art from the Period of Anti-Japanese Struggle. Multicoloured.
N1744 10 ch. Type **648** 25 10
N1745 15 ch. Floral kerchief embroidered with map of Korea 35 10
N1746 20 ch. "Tansimjul" (maypole dance) 50 15

649 Red Flag and "7", Electricity and Coal

1978. Second 7 Year Plan. Multicoloured. Without gum.
N1748 5 ch. Type **649** 25 10
N1749 10 ch. Steel and non-ferrous metal 30 10
N1750 15 ch. Engineering and chemical fertilizer . . . 35 10
N1751 30 ch. Cement and fishing 55 10
N1752 50 ch. Grain and tideland reclamation 75 10

650 Gymnastics (Alfred Flatow)

1978. Olympic Games History and Medal-winners. Multicoloured.
N1753 20 ch. Type **650** 60 15
N1754 20 ch. Runners (Michel Theato) 60 15
N1755 20 ch. Runners (Wyndham Halswelle) 60 15
N1756 20 ch. Rowing (William Kinnear) 60 15
N1757 20 ch. Fencing (Paul Anspach) . . . . 1·25 25
N1758 20 ch. Runners (Ugo Frigerio) 60 15
N1759 20 ch. Runners (Ahmed El Quafi) 60 15
N1760 20 ch. Cycling (Robert Charpentier) . . . . . . 1·50 35
N1761 20 ch. Gymnastics (Josep Stalder) 60 15
N1762 20 ch. Boxing (Lazio Papp) 85 20
N1763 20 ch. Runners (Ronald Delany) 60 15
N1764 20 ch. High jump (Jolanda Balas) 60 15
N1765 20 ch. High jump (Valery Brumel) 60 15
N1766 20 ch. Gymnastics (Vera Caslavska) 60 15
N1767 20 ch. Rifle shooting (Li Ho Jun) 60 15

651 Douglas DC-8-63 and Comte Gentleman

1978. Airplanes. Multicoloured.
N1769 2 ch. Type **651** 40 10
N1770 10 ch. Ilyushin Il-62M and Avia BH-25 . . . . . . 50 10
N1771 15 ch. Douglas DC-8-63 and Savoia Marchetti S-71 65 10
N1772 20 ch. Tupolev Tu-144 and Kalinin K-5 . . . . . . 75 10
N1773 25 ch. Tupolev Tu-154 and Antonov An-2 biplane . 75 10
N1774 30 ch. Ilyushin Il-18 . . . 75 10
N1775 40 ch. Concorde and Wibault 283 trimotor . . . . . . 1·75 40

652 White-bellied Black Woodpecker and Map **653** Demonstrators and Korean Map

1978. White-bellied Black Woodpecker Preservation. Multicoloured.
N1777 5 ch. Type **652** 55 15
N1778 10 ch. Woodpecker and eggs 65 20
N1779 15 ch. Woodpecker feeding young 85 25
N1780 25 ch. Woodpecker feeding young (different) . . . . 1·00 35
N1781 50 ch. Adult woodpecker on tree trunk . . . . 1·60 40

1978. 30th Anniv of Democratic People's Republic of Korea. Multicoloured. Without gum.
N1783 10 ch. Type **653** 10 10
N1784 10 ch. Flag and soldiers . . 10 10
N1785 10 ch. Flag and "Juche" . 10 10
N1786 10 ch. Red Flag 10 10
N1787 10 ch. Chollima Statue and city skyline 10 10
N1788 10 ch. "Juche" torch and men of three races 10 10

654 Cat and Pup — **668** Red Flag and Pine Branch

655 Footballers

1978. Animal Paintings by Li Am. Multicoloured.

N1789	10 ch. Type **654**	1·75	30
N1790	15 ch. Cat up a tree	1·75	30
N1791	40 ch. Wild geese	1·75	30

1978. Argentina's Victory in World Cup Football Championship. Without gum.

N1792	**655** 10 ch. multicoloured.	65	10
N1793	– 15 ch. multicoloured	75	15
N1794	– 25 ch. multicoloured	90	20

DESIGNS: 15, 25 ch. Different football scenes.

1979. New Year. Without gum.

N1812	**668** 10 ch. multicoloured	15	10

669 Kim Il Sung with Children's Corps Members, Maanshan

1979. International Year of the Child (1st issue). Multicoloured.

(a) Paintings of Kim Il Sung and children.

N1813	5 ch. Type **669**	15	10
N1814	10 ch. Kim Il Sung and Children's Corps members in classroom	25	10
N1815	15 ch. New Year gathering	30	10
N1816	20 ch. Kim Il Sung and children in snow	45	10
N1817	30 ch. Kim Il Sung examines children's schoolbooks (vert)	50	10

(b) Designs showing children

N1818	10 ch. Tug-of-war	15	10
N1819	15 ch. Dance "Growing up Fast"	40	15
N1820	20 ch. Children of many races and globe	40	10
N1821	25 ch. Children singing	65	15
N1822	30 ch. Children in toy spaceships	40	10

See also Nos. N1907/17.

670 Rose

1979. Roses. Multicoloured.

N1824	1 wn. Red rose		
N1825	3 wn. White rose		
N1826	5 wn. Type **670**		
N1827	10 wn. Deep pink rose		

See also Nos. N1837/42.

MINIMUM PRICE

The minimum price quoted is 10p which represents a handling charge rather than a basis for valuing common stamps. For further notes about prices, see introductory pages.

671 Warriors on Horseback — **672** Red Guard and Industrial Skyline

1979. "The Story of Two Generals". Multicoloured. Without gum.

N1828	5 ch. Type **671**	20	10
N1829	10 ch. Farm labourer blowing feather	30	10
N1830	10 ch. Generals fighting on foot	30	10
N1831	10 ch. Generals on horseback	30	10

1979. 20th Anniv of Worker-Peasant Red Guards. Without gum.

N1832	**672** 10 ch. multicoloured	15	10

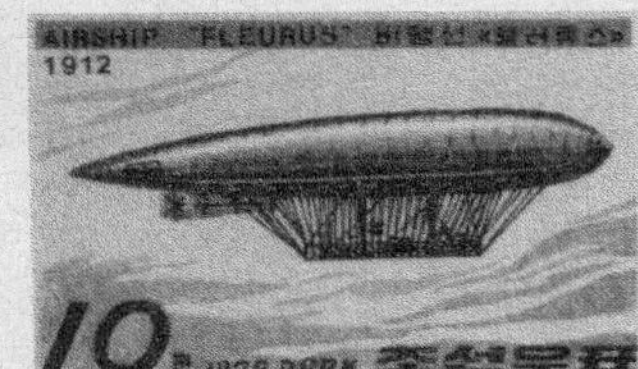

673 Clement-Bayard Airship "Fleurus"

1979. Airships. Multicoloured. Without gum.

N1833	10 ch. Type **673**	75	15
N1834	20 ch. N.1 "Norge"	75	15

674 Crowd of Demonstrators

1979. 60th Anniv of 1st March Popular Uprising. Without gum.

N1836	**674** 10 ch. blue and red	15	10

1979. Roses. As Nos. N1824/7. Multicoloured.

N1837	5 ch. Type **670** (postage)	25	10
N1838	10 ch. As No. N1827	30	10
N1839	15 ch. As No. N1824	35	10
N1840	20 ch. Yellow rose	45	10
N1841	30 ch. As No. 1825	60	10
N1842	50 ch. Deep pink rose (different) (air)	80	15

675 Table Tennis Trophy — **676** Marchers with Red Flag

1979. 35th World Table Tennis Championship, Pyongyang. Multicoloured. With or without gum.

N1843	5 ch. Type **675**	15	10
N1844	10 ch. Women's doubles	15	10
N1845	15 ch. Women's singles	25	10
N1846	20 ch. Men's doubles	40	10
N1847	30 ch. Men's singles	60	10

1979. Socialist Construction under Banner of Juche Idea. Multicoloured. Without gum.

N1849	5 ch. Type **676**	10	10
N1850	10 ch. Map of Korea	10	10
N1851	10 ch. Juche torch	10	10

677 Badge — **678** Emblem, Satellite orbiting Globe and Aerials

1979. Order of Honour of the Three Revolutions. Without gum.

N1852	**677** 10 ch. blue	10	10

1979. World Telecommunications Day. Without gum.

N1853	**678** 10 ch. multicoloured	25	10

679 Advancing Soldiers and Monument

1979. 40th Anniv of Battle in Musan Area. Without gum.

N1854	**679** 10 ch. mauve, light blue and blue	20	10

680 Exhibition Entrance

1979. International Friendship Exhibition. Without gum.

N1855	**680** 10 ch. multicoloured	10	10

681 "Peonies"

1979. 450th Death Anniv of Albrecht Durer (artist). Multicoloured.

N1856	15 ch. Type **681**	45	20
N1857	20 ch. "Columbines"	90	20
N1858	25 ch. "A Great Tuft of Grass"	90	20
N1859	30 ch. "Wing of a Bird"	1·25	40

682 Fencing

1979. Olympic Games, Moscow (2nd issue). Multicoloured. With gum (10, 40 ch. only).

N1861	5 ch. Type **682**	30	10
N1862	10 ch. Gymnastics	45	10
N1863	20 ch. Yachting	60	15
N1864	30 ch. Athletics	75	15
N1865	40 ch. Weightlifting	85	15

683 Hunting

1979. Horse-riding (people of Koguryo Dynasty). Multicoloured.

N1867	5 ch. Type **683**	15	10
N1868	10 ch. Archery contest	40	10
N1869	15 ch. Man beating drum on horseback	40	10
N1870	20 ch. Man blowing horn	60	10
N1871	30 ch. Man and horse, armoured with chainmail	45	10
N1872	50 ch. Hawking (air)	2·00	15

684 Judo — **685** Warrior's Costume

1979. Olympic Games, Moscow (3rd issue). Multicoloured. With gum (5, 15, 20, 30 ch. only).

N1873	5 ch. Type **684**	30	10
N1874	10 ch. Volleyball	30	10
N1875	15 ch. Cycling	1·25	25
N1876	20 ch. Basketball	50	15
N1877	25 ch. Canoeing	50	15
N1878	30 ch. Boxing	75	25
N1879	40 ch. Shooting	70	20

1979. Warrior Costumes of Li Dynasty.

N1881	**685** 5 ch. multicoloured	20	10
N1882	– 10 ch. multicoloured	20	10
N1883	– 15 ch. multicoloured	30	10
N1884	– 20 ch. multicoloured	45	10
N1885	– 30 ch. multicoloured	60	10
N1886	– 50 ch. multicoloured (air)	90	15

DESIGNS: 10 ch. to 50 ch. Different costumes.

686 Wrestling — **687** Monument

1979. Olympic Games, Moscow (4th issue). Multicoloured.

N1887	10 ch. Type **686**	25	10
N1888	15 ch. Handball	30	10
N1889	20 ch. Archery	90	25
N1890	25 ch. Hockey	2·00	45
N1891	30 ch. Rowing	1·00	15
N1892	40 ch. Football	1·50	25

1979. Chongbong Monument. Without gum.

N1894	**687** 10 ch. multicoloured	20	10

688 Bottle-feeding Fawn

1979. Sika Deer. Multicoloured.

N1895	5 ch. Type **688** (post.)	25	10
N1896	10 ch. Doe and fawn	25	10
N1897	15 ch. Stag drinking from stream	25	15
N1898	20 ch. Stag	35	15
N1899	30 ch. Stag and doe	50	25
N1900	50 ch. Antlers and deer (air)	85	35

689 Moscovy Ducks

1979. Central Zoo, Pyongyang. Multicoloured.

N1901	5 ch. Type **689** (postage)	40	10
N1902	10 ch. Ostrich	40	10
N1903	15 ch. Common turkey	40	10
N1904	20 ch. Dalmatian pelican	65	15
N1905	30 ch. Vulturine guinea-fowl	80	15
N1906	50 ch. Mandarin ducks (air)	1·25	35

690 Girl with Model Viking Ship

1979. International Year of the Child (2nd issue). Multicoloured.

N1907	20 ch. Type **690**	1·00	20
N1908	20 ch. Boys with model train	2·50	85
N1909	20 ch. Boy with model biplane	1·25	20
N1910	20 ch. Boy with model spaceman	80	20

N1911 30 ch. Boy with model speedboat . . . . 1·50 30
N1912 30 ch. Boy sitting astride toy train . . . . 2·50 85
N1913 30 ch. Boy and model airplane 1·60 30
N1914 30 ch. Boy and flying spaceman . . . . 1·00 30

691 Footballers

1979. International Year of the Child (3rd issue). Multicoloured.
N1916 20 ch. Type **691** . . . . . 1·00 20
N1917 30 ch. Footballers (different) 1·50 30

692 "Inimicus japonicus"

1979. Marine Life. Multicoloured.
N1919 20 ch. Type **692** 75 10
N1920 30 ch. "Sebastes schlegeli" (fish) . . . . 1·00 20
N1921 50 ch. Northern sealion . . 1·60 30

693 Cross-country Skiing (Sergei Saveliev)

1979. Winter Olympic Games, Lake Placid. Multicoloured.
N1922 10 ch. Figure skating (Irina Rodnina and Aleksandr Zaitsev) (horiz) 50 15
N1923 20 ch. Ice hockey (Russian team) (horiz) 75 20
N1924 30 ch. Ladies 5 km relay (horiz) . . . . 1·25 25
N1925 40 ch. Type **693** . . . . . 1·50 30
N1926 50 ch. Ladies' speed skating (Tatiana Averina) . . . . 1·90 35

694 Bee collecting Nectar

1979. Bees. Multicoloured.
N1928 20 ch. Type **694** 90 10
N1929 30 ch. Bee and flowers . . 1·10 15
N1930 50 ch. Bee hovering over flower . . . . 1·25 25

695 Kim Jong Suk's Birthplace, Heoryong

1979. Historic Revolutionary Sites.
N1931 **695** 10 ch. multicoloured . 15 10
N1932 – 10 ch. brown, blue & blk 15 10
DESIGN: No. N1932, Sinpa Revolutionary Museum.

696 Mt. Paekdu

1980. New Year.
N1933 **696** 10 ch. multicoloured . 55 10

697 Student and Books

1980. Studying.
N1934 **697** 10 ch. multicoloured . 25 10

698 Conveyor Belt

1980. Unryul Mine Conveyor Belt.
N1935 **698** 10 ch. multicoloured . 55 10

699 Children of Three Races

1980. International Day of the Child. Multicoloured.
N1936 10 ch. Type **699** 30 10
N1937 10 ch. Girl dancing to accordion 50 10
N1938 10 ch. Children in fairground aeroplane 40 10
N1939 10 ch. Children as astronauts 30 10
N1940 10 ch. Children on tricycles 1·00 30
N1941 10 ch. Children with toy train 1·40 45
N1942 10 ch. "His loving care for the children, future of the fatherland" (59½ × 38 mm) 30 10

700 Monument

1980. Chongsan-ri Historic Site. Multicoloured.
N1944 5 ch. Type **700** 10 10
N1945 10 ch. Meeting place of the General Membership . . 15 10

701 Monument

1980. Monument marking Kim Jong Suk's Return.
N1946 **701** 10 ch. multicoloured . 15 10

702 Vasco Nunez de Balboa

1980. Conquerors of the Earth. Multicoloured.
N1947 10 ch. Type **702** 50 10
N1948 20 ch. Francisco de Orellana 75 20
N1949 30 ch. Haroun Tazieff . . . 1·00 35
N1950 40 ch. Edmund Hillary and Sherpa Tenzing . . . . . 1·50 45

703 Museum

1980. Ryongpo Revolutionary Museum.
N1952 **703** 10 ch. blue and black 20 10

704 Rowland Hill and Stamps

1980. Death Centenary (1979) of Sir Rowland Hill. Multicoloured.
N1953 30 ch. Type **704** . . . . . . 3·25 75
N1954 50 ch. Rowland Hill and stamps (different) . . . . 3·25 75

705 North Korean Red Cross Flag

1980. World Red Cross Day. Multicoloured.
N1955 10 ch. Type **705** 70 20
N1956 10 ch. Henri Dunant (founder) 70 20
N1957 10 ch. Nurse and child . . 70 20
N1958 10 ch. Red Cross biplane and ship . . . . 1·00 25
N1959 10 ch. Red Cross helicopter 1·00 25
N1960 10 ch. Children playing at nurses 70 20
N1961 10 ch. Red Cross Map over Korea and forms of transport . . . . 2·50 60

706 Fernando Magellan

1980. Conquerors of the Sea. Multicoloured.
N1963 10 ch. Type **706** . . . . . . 1·50 25
N1964 20 ch. Fridtjof Nansen . . 1·50 25
N1965 30 ch. Auguste and Jacques Piccard . . . . 2·00 25
N1966 40 ch. Jacques-Yves Cousteau 2·25 55

707 Korean Stamps and Penny Black

1980. "London 1980" International Stamp Exhibition. Multicoloured.
N1968 10 ch. Type **707** (postage) 1·50 40
N1969 20 ch. Korean cover and British Guiana 1 c. black and red . . . . 1·50 30
N1970 30 ch. Early Korean stamp and modern cover . . . . 1·25 25
N1971 50 ch. Korean stamps . . . 2·00 35
N1972 40 ch. Korean stamp and miniature sheet (air) . . . 1·50 35

708 Wright Brothers

1980. Conquerors of Sky and Space. Multicoloured.
N1974 10 ch. Type **708** 60 15
N1975 20 ch. Louis Bleriot . . . 90 25
N1976 30 ch. Anthony Fokker . . 1·25 40
N1977 40 ch. Secondo Campini and Frank Whittle . . . . . 1·75 45

709 Space Station and Planet

710 Flag and Banners

1980. Conquerors of the Universe. Multicoloured.
N1979 10 ch. Orbiting space station 30 10
N1980 20 ch. Type **709** 40 20
N1981 30 ch. Prehistoric animals and spaceships . . . . . . 1·00 35
N1982 40 ch. Prehistoric animals and birds and spaceship . . . 1·40 45

1980. 25th Anniv of General Association of Korean Residents in Japan (Chongryon).
N1984 **710** 10 ch. multicoloured . 20 10

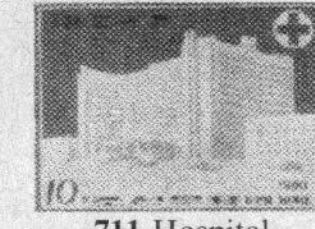
711 Hospital

1980. Pyongyang Maternity Hospital.
N1985 **711** 10 ch. blue, pur & blk 45 15

712 Health Centre

1980. Changgangwon Health Centre, Pyongyang.
N1986 **712** 2 ch. black and blue . 15 10

713 Hand holding Rifle

714 Workers' Hostel, Samjiyon

1980. 50th Anniv of Revolutionary Army.
N1987 **713** 10 ch. multicoloured . 25 10

1980.
N1988 **714** 10 ch. brown, bl & blk 30 10
N1989 – 10 ch. black and green 50 20
N1990 – 10 ch. black and red . 50 20
N1991 – 10 ch. black and yellow 50 20
N1992 – 10 ch. multicoloured . 30 10
N1993 – 10 ch. multicoloured . 30 10
N1994 – 10 ch. multicoloured . 1·00 35
N1995 – 10 ch. green and black 75 25
N1996 – 10 ch. grey, blue & blk 3·50 60
N1997 – 10 ch. multicoloured 3·50 60
DESIGNS: No. N1989, "Taedonggang" rice transplanter; N1990, "Chongsan-ri" rice harvester; N1991, Maize harvester; N1992, Revolutionary building, Songmun-ri; N1993, Revolutionary building, Samhwa; N1994, Sundial of 1438; N1995, 16th-century "turtle" ship; N1996, Pungsan dog; N1997, Japanese quail.

715 Party Emblem

1980. Sixth Korean Workers' Party Congress. Multicoloured.

N1998 10 ch. Type **715** 15 10
N1999 10 ch. Students and Laurel leaf on globe 15 10
N2000 10 ch. Group with accordion 45 15
N2001 10 ch. Group with banner, microscope, book and trophy 25 10
N2002 10 ch. Worker with book and flag 75 25
N2003 10 ch. Worker with spanner and flag 75 25
N2004 10 ch. Marchers with torch and flags 15 10
N2005 10 ch. Emblem, marchers and map 20 10

716 Dribbling Ball

1980. World Cup Football Championship, 1978–1982. Multicoloured.

N2007 20 ch. Type **716** . . . . . 3·00 90
N2008 30 ch. Tackle . . . . 4·50 1·10

717 Irina Rodnina and Aleksandr Zaitsev

1980. Winter Olympic Gold Medal Winners.

N2010 **717** 20 ch. multicoloured . 5·50 1·75

718 "Soldier with Horse" 719 Kepler, Astrolabe and Satellites

1980. 450th Death Anniv (1978) of Albrecht Durer (artist).

N2012 **718** 20 ch. multicoloured . 5·00 1·50

1980. 350th Death Anniv of Johannes Kepler (astronomer).

N2014 **719** 20 ch. multicoloured . 3·00 1·25

720 German 1 m. and Russian 30 k. "Graf Zeppelin" Stamps

1980. 3rd International Stamp Fair, Essen. Mult.

N2016 10 ch. Type **720** 90 25
N2017 20 ch. As 10 ch. but 2 m. and 35 k. stamps . . . . . 1·90 45
N2018 30 ch. As 10 ch. but 4 m. and 1 r. stamps . . . . . . 2·50 65

721 Shooting (Aleksandr Melentev)

1980. Olympic Medal Winners. Multicoloured.

N2020 10 ch. Type **721** 50 15
N2021 20 ch. Cycling (Robert Dill-Bundi) . . . . 2·75 75
N2022 25 ch. Gymnastics (Stoyan Deltchev) . . . . 1·00 25
N2023 30 ch. Wrestling (Chang Se Hong and Li Ho Pyong) 1·00 25
N2024 35 ch. Weightlifting (Ho Bong Chol) . . . . 1·00 25
N2025 40 ch. Running (Marita Koch) . . . . 1·50 30
N2026 50 ch. Modern Pentathlon (Anatoli Starostin) . . . 1·60 35

722 Tito 723 Convair CV 340

1980. President Tito of Yugoslavia Commemoration.

N2028 **722** 20 ch. multicoloured .

1980. 25th Anniv of First Post-War Flight of Lufthansa.

N2029 **723** 20 ch. multicoloured . 4·00 1·75

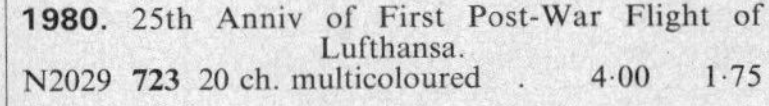

724 "The Rocket"

1980. 150th Anniv of Liverpool–Manchester Railway.

N2031 **724** 20 ch. multicoloured . 5·00 1·75

725 Steam and Electric Locomotives

1980. Centenary of First Electric Train.

N2033 **725** 20 ch. multicoloured . 5·00 1·75

726 Hammarskjold 727 Fischer and Spassky

1980. 75th Birth Anniv of Dag Hammarskjold (Former Secretary General of United Nations).

N2035 **726** 20 ch. multicoloured . 2·50 1·25

1980. World Chess Championship, Merano.

N2037 **727** 20 ch. multicoloured . 5·50 1·75

728 Stolz 729 Chollima Statue

1980. Birth Centenary of Robert Stolz (composer).

N2039 **728** 20 ch. multicoloured . . 3·75 1·50

1981. New Year. Without gum.

N2043 **729** 10 ch. multicoloured . . 1·50 40

730 Russian Fairy Tale

1981. International Year of the Child (1979) (4th issue). Fairy Tales. Multicoloured.

N2042 10 ch. Type **730** . . . . . . 1·50 40
N2043 10 ch. Icelandic tale . . . . 1·50 40
N2044 10 ch. Swedish tale . . . . 1·50 40
N2045 10 ch. Irish tale . . . . . . 1·50 40
N2046 10 ch. Italian tale . . . . . 1·50 40
N2047 10 ch. Japanese tale . . . . 1·50 40
N2048 10 ch. German tale . . . . 1·50 40

731 Changgwang Street

1981. Changgwang Street, Pyongyang.

N2050 **731** 10 ch. multicoloured . . 35 10

732 Footballers

1981. World Cup Football Championship, Spain (1982) (1st issue). Multicoloured.

N2051 10 ch. Type **732** . . . . . . 2·75 65
N2052 20 ch. Hitting ball past defender . . . . 2·75 65
N2053 30 ch. Disputing possession of ball . . . . 2·75 65

See also Nos. N2055/9 and N2201/6.

733 Map, Emblem and World Cup

1981. World Cup Football Championship, Spain (1982) (2nd issue). Multicoloured.

N2055 10 ch. Type **733** . . . . . . 1·75 45
N2056 15 ch. Footballers . . . . . 1·75 45
N2057 20 ch. Heading ball . . . . 1·75 45
N2058 25 ch. Footballers (different) 1·75 45
N2059 30 ch. Footballers (different) 1·75 45

734 Workers with Book and Marchers with Banner

1981. Implementation of Decision of the 6th Koreans' Party Congress. Multicoloured.

N2061 2 ch. Type **734** 10 10
N2062 10 ch. Worker with book 10 10
N2063 10 ch. Workers and industrial plant 25 10
N2064 10 ch. Electricity and coal (horiz) 70 25
N2065 10 ch. Steel and non-ferrous metals (horiz) 25 10
N2066 10 ch. Cement and fertilizers (horiz) 25 10
N2067 30 ch. Fishing and fabrics (horiz) 25 10
N2068 40 ch. Grain and harbour (horiz) 25 10
N2069 70 ch. Clasped hands . . . 20 10
N2070 1 w. Hand holding torch . 30 15

735 Footballers

1981. Gold Cup Football Championship, Uruguay.

N2071 **735** 20 ch. multicoloured . 3·00 1·00

736 Dornier Do-X Flying Boat

1981. "Naposta '81" International Stamp Exhibition, Stuttgart. Multicoloured.

N2073 10 ch. Type **736** . . . . . 2·50 50
N2074 20 ch. Airship "Bodensee" 2·50 50
N2075 30 ch. "Gotz von Berlichingen" . . . . . 1·25 40

737 Telecommunications Equipment

1981. World Telecommunications Day.

N2077 **737** 10 ch. multicoloured . 1·75 20

738 "Iris pseudacorus"

1981. Flowers. Multicoloured.

N2078 10 ch. Type **738** 75 15
N2079 20 ch. "Iris pallasii" . . . 1·00 20
N2080 30 ch. "Gladiolus gandavensis" . . . . . 1·40 30

739 Austrian "WIPA 1981" and Rudolf Kirchschlager Stamps

1981. "WIPA 1981" International Stamp Exhibition, Vienna. Multicoloured.

N2081 20 ch. Type **739** . . . . . 1·90 60
N2082 30 ch. Austrian Maria Theresa and Franz Joseph stamps . . . . 2·50 80

740 Rings Exercise

1981. Centenary of International Gymnastic Federation. Multicoloured.

N2084 10 ch. Type **740** 55 20
N2085 15 ch. Horse exercise . . . 75 25
N2086 20 ch. Backwards somersault 1·10 35
N2087 25 ch. Floor exercise . . . 1·25 40
N2088 30 ch. Exercise with hoop 1·40 45

741 Armed Workers

1981. 50th Anniv of Mingyuehgou Meeting.

N2090 **741** 10 ch. multicoloured . 20 10

742 Farm Building, Sukchon

1981. 20th Anniv of Agricultural Guidance System and Taean Work System.

N2091 **742** 10 ch. green, black and gold 20 10
N2092 – 10 ch. blue, black and gold 20 10

DESIGN: No. N2092, Taean Revolutionary Museum.

743 Woman and Banner

1981. 55th Anniv of Formation of Women's Anti-Japanese Association.

N2093 **743** 5 wn. multicoloured . . 2·75 1·10

743a Scene from Opera

1981. 10th Anniv of "Sea of Blood" (opera).

N2094 **743a** 10 wn. multicoloured

744 Joan of Arc

1981. 550th Death Anniv of Joan of Arc. Multicoloured.

N2095 10 ch. Type **744** . . . . . 2·50 60
N2096 10 ch. Archangel Michael 2·75 75
N2097 70 ch. Joan of Arc in armour 2·75 75

745 Torch, Mountains and Flag

1981. 55th Anniv of Down with Imperialism Union.

N2099 **745** 1 wn. 50 multicoloured 40 20

746 "Young Girl by the Window"

1981. 375th Birth Anniv of Rembrandt (artist). Multicoloured.

N2100 10 ch. Type **746** 55 25
N2101 20 ch. "Rembrandt's Mother" 1·25 45
N2102 30 ch. "Saskia van Uylenburgh" . . . . . 1·75 70
N2103 40 ch. "Pallas Athene" . . 2·25 90

747 Emblem and Banners over Pyongyang

1981. Symposium of Non-Aligned Countries on Food Self-Sufficiency, Pyongyang. Multicoloured.

N2105 10 ch. Type **747** 20 10
N2106 50 ch. Harvesting 50 10
N2107 90 ch. Factories, tractors and marchers with banner . 70 15

748 St. Paul's Cathedral

1981. Wedding of Prince of Wales (1st issue). Multicoloured.

N2108 10 ch. Type **748** . . . . . 2·00 45
N2109 20 ch. Great Britain Prince of Wales Investiture Stamp 2·00 45
N2110 30 ch. Lady Diana Spencer 2·00 45
N2111 40 ch. Prince Charles in military uniform . . . . 2·00 45

See also Nos. N2120/3.

749 "Four Philosophers" (detail)

1981. Paintings by Rubens. Multicoloured.

N2113 10 ch. Type **749** 55 25
N2114 15 ch. "Portrait of Helena Fourment" 85 35
N2115 20 ch. "Portrait of Isabella Brandt" . . . . 1·25 45
N2116 25 ch. "Education of Maria de Medici" . . . . . . 1·50 60
N2117 30 ch. "Helena Fourment and her Child" . . . . . . 1·75 70
N2118 40 ch. "Helena Fourment in her Wedding Dress" . . . 2·25 90

750 Royal Couple

1981. Wedding of Prince of Wales (2nd issue). Multicoloured.

N2120 10 ch. Type **750** . . . . . . 3·00 90
N2121 20 ch. Couple on balcony after wedding . . . . . . 3·00 90
N2122 30 ch. Couple outside St. Paul's Cathedral . . . . 3·00 90
N2123 70 ch. Full-length wedding portrait of couple . . . . 3·00 90

751 Rowland Hill and Stamps

1981. "Philatokyo '81" International Stamp Exhibition. Multicoloured.

N2125 10 ch. Korean 2 ch. Seminar on Juche Idea stamp (41 × 29 mm) 75 20
N2126 10 ch. Korean 10 and 70 ch. stamps (41 × 29 mm) . . 2·00 75
N2127 10 ch. Type **751** . . . . . . 2·00 75
N2128 20 ch. Korean Fairy Tale stamps . . . . 1·75 40
N2129 30 ch. Japanese stamps . . 3·00 90

752 League Members and Flag

1981. Seventh League of Socialist Working Youth Congress, Pyongyang.

N2131 **752** 10 ch. multicoloured . . 20 10
N2132 80 ch. multicoloured . . 60 10

753 Government Palace, Sofia, Bulgarian Arms and Khan Asparuch

1981. 1300th Anniv of Bulgarian State.

N2133 **753** 10 ch. multicoloured . 15 10

754 Dimitrov

1981. Birth Centenary of Georgi Dimitrov (Bulgarian statesman).

N2134 **754** 10 ch. multicoloured . . 15 10

755 Emblem, Boeing 747-200, City Hall and Mercedes "500"

1981. "Philatelia '81" International Stamp Fair, Frankfurt-am-Main.

N2135 **755** 20 ch. multicoloured . 2·25 35

756 Concorde, Airship "Graf Zeppelin" and Count Zeppelin

1981. "Philexfrance 82" International Stamp Exhibition, Paris. Multicoloured. (a) As T **756**.

N2136 10 ch. Type **756** . . . . . 2·75 40
N2137 20 ch. Concorde, Breguet Provence and Santos-Dumont's biplane "14 bis" 3·25 75
N2138 30 ch. "Mona Lisa" and stamps . . . . 1·75 30

(b) Size 32 × 53 mm.

N2140 10 ch. Hotel des Invalides, Paris . . . . 1·50 45
N2141 20 ch. President Mitterand of France . . . . 1·50 45
N2142 30 ch. International Friendship Exhibition building . . . . 1·50 45
N2143 70 ch. Kim Il Sung . . . . 1·50 45

757 Rising Sun

758 Emblem and Flags

1982. New Year.

N2144 **757** 10 ch. multicoloured . 30 10

1982. "Prospering Korea". Multicoloured.

N2145 2 ch. Type **758** 15 10
N2146 10 ch. Industry 25 10
N2147 10 ch. Agriculture 25 10
N2148 10 ch. Mining 45 10
N2149 10 ch. Arts 25 10
N2150 10 ch. Al Islet lighthouse, Uam-ri 75 15
N2151 40 ch. Buildings 50 15

759 "The Hair-do"

1982. Birth Centenary of Pablo Picasso (artist). Multicoloured.

N2152 10 ch. Type **759** 75 20

N2153 10 ch. "Paulo on a donkey" 1·75 35

N2154 20 ch. "Woman Leaning on Arm" 90 25

N2155 20 ch. "Harlequin" . . . . 1·75 35

N2156 25 ch. "Child with Pigeon" 1·90 50

N2157 25 ch. "Reading a Letter" 1·75 35

N2158 35 ch. "Portrait of Gertrude Stein" . . . . 1·50 30

N2159 35 ch. "Harlequin" (different) 1·75 35

N2160 80 ch. "Minotaur" . . . . 1·75 35

N2161 90 ch. "Mother with Child" 1·75 35

760 Fireworks over Pyongyang

1982. Kim Il Sung's 70th Birthday. Multicoloured.

N2163 10 ch. Kim Il Sung's birthplace, Mangyongdae 20 10

N2164 10 ch. Type **760** 20 10

N2165 10 ch. "The Day will dawn on downtrodden Korea" . . 20 10

N2166 10 ch. Signalling start of Pochonbo Battle 20 10

N2167 10 ch. Kim Il Sung starting Potong River project . . 20 10

N2168 10 ch. Embracing bereaved children 20 10

N2169 10 ch. Kim Il Sung as Supreme Commander . . 20 10

N2170 10 ch. "On the Road of Advance" 20 10

N2171 10 ch. Kim Il Sung kindling flame of Chollima Movement, Kansong Steel Plant 75 25

N2172 10 ch. Kim Il Sung talking to peasants 20 10

N2173 10 ch. Kim Il Sung fixing site of reservoir 30 10

N2174 20 ch. Kim Il Sung visiting Komdok Valley 75 25

N2175 20 ch. Kim Il Sung visiting Red Flag Company . . . 20 10

N2176 20 ch. Kim Il Sung teaching Juche farming methods 20 10

N2177 20 ch. Kim Il Sung visiting iron works 35 10

N2178 20 ch. Kim Il Sung talking with smelters 35 10

N2179 20 ch. Kim Il Sung at chemical plant 45 10

N2180 20 ch. Kim Il Sung with fishermen 40 10

Nos. 2165/80 are horiz designs.

761 Soldier saluting

1982. 50th Anniv of People's Army.

N2182 **761** 10 ch. multicoloured . 25 10

762 "The Bagpiper" (Durer) 763 Surveyors

1982. Fourth Essen International Stamp Fair.

N2183 **762** 30 ch. multicoloured . 3·75 40

1982. Implementation of Four Nature-remaking Tasks.

N2184 **763** 10 ch. multicoloured . 25 10

764 Princess as Baby 765 Tower of the Juche Idea Pyongyang

1982. 21st Birthday of Princess of Wales.

N2185 **764** 10 ch. multicoloured . 60 20

N2186 – 20 ch. multicoloured . 1·25 35

N2187 – 30 ch. multicoloured . 1·50 45

N2188 – 50 ch. multicoloured . 2·00 60

N2189 – 60 ch. multicoloured . 2·00 60

N2190 – 70 ch. multicoloured . 2·00 60

N2191 – 80 ch. multicoloured . 2·00 60

DESIGNS: 20 to 80 ch. Princess at various ages.

1982.

2193 **765** 2 wn. multicoloured . . 1·25 30

2194 – 3 wn. orange and black 1·75 40

DESIGN: (26 × 38 mm) 3 wn. Arch of Triumph.

766 Tiger

1982. Tigers.

N2195 **766** 20 ch. multicoloured . 1·25 35

N2196 – 30 ch. multicoloured . 1·90 35

N2197 – 30 ch. mult (horiz) . . 2·75 45

N2198 – 40 ch. mult (horiz) . . 2·75 45

N2199 – 80 ch. mult (horiz) . . 2·75 45

DESIGNS: 30 to 80 ch. Tigers.

767 Group 1 Countries

1982. World Cup Football Championship, Spain (3rd issue). Multicoloured.

N2201 10 ch. Type **767** 60 20

N2202 20 ch. Group 2 countries . 1·25 25

N2203 30 ch. Group 3 countries . 1·75 30

N2204 40 ch. Group 4 countries . 2·10 40

N2205 50 ch. Group 5 countries . 2·50 50

N2206 60 ch. Group 6 countries . 3·00 50

768 Rocket Launch 769 Charlotte von Stein

1982. The Universe. Multicoloured.

N2208 10 ch. Type **768** . . . . . . 1·50 60

N2209 20 ch. Spaceship over globe 1·50 60

N2210 80 ch. Spaceship between globe and moon . . . . 1·50 60

1982. 150th Death Anniv of Johann von Goethe (writer). Multicoloured.

N2212 10 ch. Type **769** 50 25

N2213 10 ch. Goethe's mother . . 1·50 45

N2214 20 ch. Goethe's sister . . . 75 30

N2215 20 ch. Angelika Kauffmann 1·50 45

N2216 25 ch. Charlotte Buff . . . 90 35

N2217 25 ch. Anna Amalia . . . . 1·50 45

N2218 35 ch. Lili Schonemann . . 1·25 40

N2219 35 ch. Charlotte von Lengefeld . . . . 1·50 45

N2220 80 ch. Goethe . . . . . . 1·60 45

770 Player holding aloft World Cup

1982. World Cup Football Championship Results. Multicoloured.

N2222 20 ch. Type **770** . . . . . . 1·25 30

N2223 30 ch. Group of players with World Cup . . . . 1·75 50

N2224 30 ch. Type **770** . . . . . 2·50 65

N2225 40 ch. As No. N2203 . . . 2·50 65

N2226 80 ch. King Juan Carlos of Spain and two players with World Cup . . . . . . 2·50 65

771 Princess and Prince William of Wales

1982. 1st Wedding Anniv of Prince and Princess of Wales.

N2228 **771** 30 ch. multicoloured . . 4·50 1·75

772 Royal Couple with Prince William

1982. Birth of Prince William of Wales. Multicoloured.

N2230 10 ch. Couple with Prince William (different) . . . 1·50 50

N2231 10 ch. Princess of Wales holding bouquet . . . . 3·00 1·50

N2232 20 ch. Couple with Prince William (different) . . . 1·75 60

N2233 20 ch. Prince Charles carrying baby, and Princess of Wales 3·00 1·50

N2234 30 ch. Type **772** . . . . . . 2·00 75

N2235 30 ch. Prince Charles carrying baby, and Princess of Wales (different) . . . . 3·00 1·50

N2236 40 ch. Princess with baby 2·75 90

N2237 40 ch. Prince and Princess of Wales (horiz) . . . . . 4·75 1·90

N2238 50 ch. Princess with baby (different) . . . . 3·50 1·00

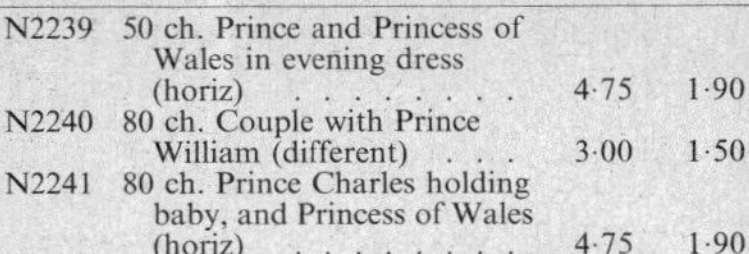

N2239 50 ch. Prince and Princess of Wales in evening dress (horiz) . . . . 4·75 1·90

N2240 80 ch. Couple with Prince William (different) . . . 3·00 1·50

N2241 80 ch. Prince Charles holding baby, and Princess of Wales (horiz) . . . . 4·75 1·90

773 Airship "Nulli Secundus II", 1908

1982. Bicentenary of Manned Flight (1st issue). Multicoloured.

N2243 10 ch. Type **773** . . . . . 1·25 40

N2244 10 ch. Pauley and Egg's dirigible balloon "The Dolphin", 1818 . . . . . 2·50 60

N2245 20 ch. Tissandier Brothers' airship, 1883 . . . . . . 1·50 50

N2246 20 ch. Guyton de Morveau's balloon, 1784 . . . . . 2·50 60

N2247 30 ch. Parseval airship PL-VII, 1912 . . . . 2·00 60

N2248 30 ch. Sir George Cayley's airship, 1837 . . . . . . 2·50 60

N2249 40 ch. Comte de Lennox's balloon "Eagle", 1834 . 2·25 60

N2250 40 ch. Camille Vert's balloon "Poisson Volant", 1859 . 2·50 60

N2251 80 ch. Dupuy de Lome's airship, 1872 . . . . . . 2·50 60

774 "Utopic Post Balloon" (Balthasar Antoine Dunker)

1982. Bicentenary of Manned Flight (2nd issue). Multicoloured.

N2253 10 ch. Type **774** . . . . . 1·50 40

N2254 10 ch. Montgolfier balloon at Versailles, 1783 . . . . 3·00 60

N2255 20 ch. "... and they fly into heaven and have no wings ..." . . . . 2·00 50

N2256 20 ch. Montgolfier Brothers' balloon, 1783 . . . . . 3·00 60

N2257 30 ch. Pierre Testu-Brissy's test flight, 1798 . . . . 2·50 60

N2258 30 ch. Charles's hydrogen balloon landing at Nesle, 1783 . . . . 3·00 60

N2259 40 ch. Gaston Tissandier's test flight of "Zenith", 1875 . 3·00 60

N2260 40 ch. Blanchard and Jeffries' balloon flight over English Channel, 1785 . . . . . 3·00 60

N2261 80 ch. Henri Giffard's balloon "Le Grand Ballon Captif" at World Fair, 1878 . . 3·00 60

775 Turtle with Scroll

1982. Tale of the Hare. Multicoloured.

N2263 10 ch. Type **775** 90 15

N2264 20 ch. Hare riding on turtle 1·25 20

N2265 30 ch. Hare and turtle before Dragon King . . . . . 1·50 30

N2266 40 ch. Hare back on land 2·00 40

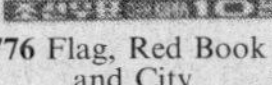

776 Flag, Red Book and City 777 Tower of Juche Idea

1982. 10th Anniv of Socialist Constitution.
N2267 **776** 10 ch. multicoloured . 25 10

1983. New Year.
N2268 **777** 10 ch. multicoloured . 15 10

778 Children reading "Saenal"

1983. 55th Anniv of "Saenal" Newspaper.
N2269 **778** 10 ch. multicoloured . 50 10

779 "Man in Oriental Costume"

1983. Paintings by Rembrandt. Multicoloured.
N2270 10 ch. Type **779** 75 30
N2271 10 ch. "Child with dead Peacocks" (detail) . . . 2·50 60
N2272 20 ch. "The Noble Slav" . 1·50 40
N2273 20 ch. "Old Man in Fur Hat" 2·50 60
N2274 30 ch. "Dr. Tulp's Anatomy Lesson" (detail) . . . . 2·75 75
N2275 30 ch. "Portrait of a fashionable Couple" . . 2·50 60
N2276 40 ch. "Two Scholars disputing" . . . . 2·00 50
N2277 40 ch. "Woman with Child" 2·50 60
N2278 80 ch. "Woman holding an Ostrich Feather Fan" . . 2·50 60

780 "Gross Basenach II" and "Graf Zeppelin" over Cologne

1983. "Luposta" International Air Mail Exhibition, Cologne. Multicoloured.
N2280 30 ch. Type **780** . . . . . 3·00 90
N2281 40 ch. Parsevel airship PL-II over Cologne . . . . . . 3·00 90

781 Banner and Monument

1983. 50th Anniv of Wangjaesan Meeting.
N2283 **781** 10 ch. multicoloured . 20 10

782 Karl Marx

1983. Death Centenary of Karl Marx.
N2284 **782** 10 ch. multicoloured . 50 25

783 Scholar, Marchers and Map of Journey

1983. 60th Anniv of Thousand-ri Journey for Learning.
N2285 **783** 10 ch. multicoloured . 50 10

784 "Madonna of the Goldfinch"

1983. 500th Birth Anniv of Raphael. Multicoloured.
N2286 10 ch. Type **784** . . . . . 1·50 40
N2287 20 ch. "The School of Athens" (detail) . . . . 2·25 60
N2288 30 ch. "Madonna of the Grand Duke" . . . . . 2·50 55
N2289 50 ch. "Madonna of the Chair" . . . . 2·75 55
N2290 50 ch. "Madonna of the Lamb" . . . . 2·25 60
N2291 80 ch. "The Beautiful Gardener" . . . . . . 2·25 60

785 Department Store No. 1

1983. Pyongyang Buildings. Multicoloured.
N2293 2 ch. Chongryu Restaurant 20 10
N2294 10 ch. Part of Munsu Street 30 10
N2295 10 ch. Ice Rink 40 10
N2296 40 ch. Type **785** 60 15
N2297 70 ch. Grand People's Study House 75 25

786 Emblem and Crowd

1983. 5th Anniv of International Institute of Juche Idea.
N2298 **786** 10 ch. multicoloured . 15 10

787 Judo

1983. Olympic Games, Los Angeles (1st issue). Multicoloured.
N2299 20 ch. Type **787** . . . . . 1·00 50
N2300 20 ch. Wrestling . . . . . 1·90 50
N2301 30 ch. Judo (different) (value in gold) . . . . . . 1·00 50
N2302 30 ch. Judo (different) (value in black) . . . . . . 1·90 50
N2303 40 ch. Boxing . . . . . . 1·00 50
N2304 40 ch. Li Ho Jun (1972 shooting gold medalist) 1·90 50
N2305 50 ch. Weightlifting . . .
N2306 50 ch. Wrestling (different) 1·90 50
N2307 80 ch. Boxing (different) . 1·90 50
See also Nos. N2359/64.

788 Satellite, Masts and Dish Aerial

1983. World Communications Year (1st issue).
N2309 **788** 10 ch. multicoloured . . 1·50 20
See also Nos. N2349/53.

789 Emblem, Giant Panda and Stamp

1983. "Tembal 83" International Thematic Stamp Exhibition, Basel. Multicoloured.
N2310 20 ch. Type **789** . . . . . 1·75 35
N2311 30 ch. Emblem, flag and Basel Town Post stamp . . . . 1·90 35

790 "Colourful Cow" (kogge), 1402

1983. Old Ships. Multicoloured.
N2312 20 ch. Type **790** . . . . . . 1·10 45
N2313 20 ch. "Turtle" ship, 1592 2·40 75
N2314 35 ch. "Great Harry" (warship), 1555 . . . . . 1·50 55
N2315 35 ch. Admiral Li Sun Sin and "turtle" ship . . . . . 2·40 75
N2316 50 ch. "Eagle of Lubeck" (galleon), 1567 . . . . . 2·10 70
N2317 50 ch. "Merkur" (full-rigged sailing ship), 1847 . . . 2·40 75
N2318 80 ch. "Herzogin Elisabeth" (cadet ship) . . . . . 2·40 75

791 "Locomotion", 1825

1983. Railway Locomotives. Multicoloured.
N2320 20 ch. Type **791** . . . . . . 1·25 60
N2321 20 ch. "Drache", 1848 . . . 3·50 1·00
N2322 35 ch. "Der Adler", 1835 . 1·75 80
N2323 35 ch. Korean steam locomotive, 1853 . . . . 3·50 1·00
N2324 50 ch. "Austria", 1837 . . . 2·75 80
N2325 50 ch. Bristol and Exeter Railway steam locomotive, 1853 . . . . 3·50 1·00
N2326 80 ch. Caledonian Railway locomotive, 1859 . . . . 3·50 1·00

792 Map, Hand and Weapons

1983. 10th Anniv of Publication of Five-point Policy for Korea's Reunification.
N2328 **792** 10 ch. multicoloured . . 25 10

793 Emblem, Tower of Juche Idea and Fireworks

1983. World Conference on Journalists against Imperialism and for Friendship and Peace, Pyongyang. Multicoloured.
N2329 10 ch. Type **793** 30 10
N2330 40 ch. Emblem and rainbow and clasped hands . . . 50 15
N2331 70 ch. Emblem, map and hand with raised forefinger 75 20

794 Worker and Banners

1983. "Let's Create the Speed of the 80s".
N2332 **794** 10 ch. multicoloured . 25 10

795 Soldier and Rejoicing Crowd

1983. 30th Anniv of Victory in Liberation War.
N2333 **795** 10 ch. multicoloured . 25 10

796 "Gorch Foch" (cadet barque) and Korean 1978 2 ch. Stamp

1983. "Bangkok 1983" International Stamp Exhibition.
N2334 **796** 40 ch. multicoloured . 3·00 1·25

797 Skiing

1983. Winter Olympic Games, Sarajevo (1984). Multicoloured.
N2336 10 ch. Type **797** 75 35
N2337 20 ch. Figure skating (vert) 2·50 60
N2338 30 ch. Skating (pair) . . . 2·00 90
N2339 50 ch. Ski jumping . . . . 2·00 90
N2340 50 ch. Ice hockey (vert) . . 2·50 60
N2341 80 ch. Speed skating (vert) 2·50 60

798 Workers and Soldier with Books

1983. 35th Anniv of Korean People's Democratic Republic.
N2343 **798** 10 ch. multicoloured . 35 10

799 Archery **800** Girls holding Hands

1983. Folk Games. Multicoloured.
N2344 10 ch. Type **799** . . . . . 1·75 40
N2345 10 ch. Flying kites 90 20
N2346 40 ch. See-sawing 75 20
N2347 40 ch. Swinging 90 20

1983. Korean–Chinese Friendship.
N2348 **800** 10 ch. multicoloured . . 15 10

801 Envelopes and Forms of Transport **802** Portrait

1983. World Communications Year (2nd issue). Multicoloured.
N2349 30 ch. Mail van, motorcyclist and hand holding magazines . . . . 3·75 1·10
N2350 30 ch. Satellite, globe and dish aerial . . . . 1·75 70
N2351 40 ch. Type **801** . . . . . 3·75 1·10
N2352 40 ch. Television cameraman 1·75 70
N2353 80 ch. Telephone and aerial 1·75 70

1983. Paintings by Rubens. Multicoloured.
N2355 40 ch. Type **802** . . . . . 2·00 90
N2356 40 ch. Portrait (different) (horiz) . . . . 2·50 1·00
N2357 80 ch. "The Sentencing of Midas" (horiz) . . . . . 2·50 1·00

803 Sprinting

1983. Olympic Games, Los Angeles (2nd issue). Multicoloured.
N2359 10 ch. Type **803** 75 20
N2360 20 ch. Show jumping . . . 1·75 45
N2361 30 ch. Cycling . . . . . . 3·00 55
N2362 50 ch. Handball . . . . . 2·00 60
N2363 50 ch. Fencing . . . . . . 1·75 45
N2364 80 ch. Gymnastics . . . . 1·75 45

804 "St. Catherine" **805** Kimilsungflower

804a Cat

1983. 450th Death Anniv of Antonio Correggio (artist) (1984). Multicoloured.
N2366 20 ch. Type **804** . . . . . 1·75 60
N2367 20 ch. "Morning" (detail) 2·50 75
N2368 35 ch. "Madonna" . . . . 1·75 60
N2369 35 ch. "Morning" (different) 2·50 75
N2370 50 ch. "Madonna with St. John" . . . . 1·75 60
N2371 50 ch. "St. Catherine" (different) . . . . . . 2·50 75
N2372 80 ch. "Madonna and Child" 2·50 75

1983. Cats. Multicoloured, frame colour given.
N2373a **804a** 10 ch. green 50 10
N2373b – 10 ch. gold 50 10
N2373c – 10 ch. blue 50 10
N2373d – 10 ch. red 50 10
N2373e – 10 ch. silver 50 10
DESIGNS: Different cats' heads.

1983. New Year.
N2374 **805** 10 ch. multicoloured . 65 10

806 Worker and Workers' Party Flag

1984. "Under the Leadership of the Workers' Party". Multicoloured.
N2375 10 ch. Type **806** 25 10
N2376 10 ch. Ore-dressing plant No. 3, Komdok General Mining Enterprise, and Party Flag 40 10

807 Farm Worker, Rice and Maize

1984. 20th Anniv of Publication of "Theses of the Socialist Rural Question in Our Country".
N2377 **807** 10 ch. multicoloured . 25 10

808 Changdok School, Chilgol

1984. Kim Il Sung's 72nd Birthday.
N2378 **808** 5 ch. green, black & bl 25 10
N2379 – 10 ch. multicoloured . 25 10
DESIGN: 10 ch. Birthplace, Mangyongdae, and rejoicing crowd.

809 "Spanish Riding School" (Julius von Blaas)

1984. "Espana 84" International Stamp Exhibition, Madrid. Multicoloured.
N2380 10 ch. Type **809** . . . . . 1·75 50
N2381 20 ch. "Ferdinand of Austria" (Rubens) . . . . 1·75 50

MORE DETAILED LISTS
are given in the Stanley Gibbons Catalogues referred to in the country headings. For lists of current volumes see introduction

810 "La Donna Velata" **812** Construction Site

811 Map and Second Stage Pumping Station

1984. 500th Birth Anniv (1983) of Raphael (artist). Multicoloured.
N2383 10 ch. "Portrait of Agnolo Doni" . . . . 1·50 50
N2384 20 ch. Type **810** . . . . . 1·50 50
N2385 30 ch. "Portrait of Jeanne d'Aragon" . . . . 1·50 50

1984. 25th Anniv of Kiyang Irrigation System.
N2387 **811** 10 ch. multicoloured . . 50 10

1984. Construction on Five District Fronts.
N2388 **812** 10 ch. red, black & yell 50 10

813 Bobsleighing (East Germany)

1984. Winter Olympic Games Medal Winners. Multicoloured.
N2389 10 ch. Ski jumping (Matti Nykaenen) . . . . 1·75 50
N2390 20 ch. Speed skating (Karin Enke) . . . . 1·50 40
N2391 20 ch. Slalom (Max Julen) 1·75 50
N2392 30 ch. Type **813** . . . . . 1·50 40
N2393 30 ch. Downhill skiing (Maria Walliser) . . . . 1·75 50
N2394 40 ch. Cross-country skiing (Thomas Wassberg) . . . 2·75 60
N2395 80 ch. Cross-country skiing (Marja-Liisa Hamalainen) 2·75 60

814 Type "E" Goods Locomotive

1984. Essen International Stamp Fair. Mult.
N2397 20 ch. Type "202" express locomotive . . . . 3·25 65
N2398 30 ch. Type **814** . . . . . . 3·25 65

815 "Mlle. Fiocre in the Ballet 'La Source'"

1984. 150th Birth Anniv of Edgar Degas (artist). Multicoloured.
N2400 10 ch. Type **815** . . . . . . 1·50 25
N2401 20 ch. "The Dance Foyer at the Rue le Peletier Opera" 2·50 25
N2402 30 ch. "Race Meeting" . . 3·75 40

816 Map of Pyongnam Irrigation System and Reservoir

1984. Irrigation Experts Meeting, Pyongyang.
N2404 **816** 2 ch. multicoloured . . 40 10

817 Korean Stamp and Building **818** Crowd and Banners

1984. U.P.U. Congress Stamp Exn, Hamburg.
N2405 **817** 20 ch. multicoloured . 3·00 40

1984. Proposal for Tripartite Talks.
N2407 **818** 10 ch. multicoloured . 40 10

819 Nobel experimenting

1984. 150th Birth Anniv (1983) of Alfred Bernhard Nobel (inventor). Multicoloured.
N2408 20 ch. Type **819** . . . . . 3·00 45
N2409 30 ch. Portrait of Nobel . 3·00 45

820 Drinks, Tinned Food, Clothes and Flats

1984. Improvements of Living Standards.
N2411 **820** 10 ch. multicoloured . 40 10

821 Sunhwa School, Mangyongdae

1984. School of Kim Hyong Jik (Kim Il Sung's Father).
N2412 **821** 10 ch. multicoloured . 40 10

822 Armed Crowd with Banners

1984. 65th Anniv of Kuandian Conference.
N2413 **822** 10 ch. multicoloured . 40 10

823 "Thunia bracteata"

1984. Flowers. Multicoloured.
N2414 10 ch. "Cattleya loddigesii" 60 10
N2415 20 ch. Type **823** 90 25
N2416 30 ch. "Phalaenopsis amabilis" . . . . 1·25 40

824 Swordfish and Trawler

1984. Fishing Industry. Multicoloured.
N2418 5 ch. Type **824** 50 15
N2419 10 ch. Marlin and trawler 70 25
N2420 40 ch. "Histiophorus orientalis" and game fishing launch 2·25 95

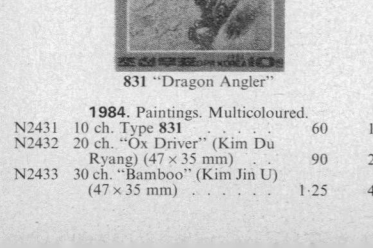

825 Revolutionary Museum, Chilgol

1984.
N2421 **825** 10 ch. multicoloured 40 10

826 Kim Hyok, Cha Gwang Su and Youth

828 Clock Face

827 Inauguration of a French Railway Line, 1860

1984. "Let's All become the Kim Hyoks and Cha Gwang Sus of the '80s".
N2422 **826** 10 ch. multicoloured 40 10

1984. Centenary (1983) of "Orient Express". Multicoloured.
N2423 10 ch. Type **827** 90 25
N2424 20 ch. Opening of a British railway line, 1821 2·00 55
N2425 30 ch. Inauguration of Paris-Rouen line, 1843 2·75 85

1984. Centenary of Greenwich Meridian.
N2427 **828** 10 ch. multicoloured. 2·50 1·00

829 Grand Theatre, Hamburg

830 Turning on Machinery

1984.
N2429 **829** 10 ch. blue 40 10

1984. Automation of Industry.
N2430 **830** 40 ch. multicoloured 60 30

831 "Dragon Angler"

1984. Paintings. Multicoloured.
N2431 10 ch. Type **831** 60 10
N2432 20 ch. "Ox Driver" (Kim Du Ryang) (47 × 35 mm) 90 25
N2433 30 ch. "Bamboo" (Kim Jin U) (47 × 35 mm) 1·25 40

832 Tsiolkovsky

1984. K. E. Tsiolkovsky (space scientist). Mult.
N2435 20 ch. Type **832** 90 25
N2436 30 ch. "Sputnik" orbiting Earth 1·25 40

833 "Pongdaesan"

1984. Container Ships. Multicoloured.
N2438 10 ch. Type **833** 80 15
N2439 20 ch. "Ryongnamsan" 1·10 35
N2440 30 ch. "Rungrado" 1·60 50

834 Caracal

1984. Animals. Multicoloured.
N2442 10 ch. Spotted hyenas 60 10
N2443 20 ch. Type **834** 90 25
N2444 30 ch. Black-backed jackals 1·25 40
N2445 40 ch. Foxes 1·60 60

835 Marie Curie

836 Chestnut-eared Aracari

1984. 50th Anniv of Marie Curie (physicist).
N2447 **835** 10 ch. multicoloured 60 10

1984. Birds. Multicoloured.
N2449 10 ch. Hoopoe 70 10
N2450 20 ch. South African crowned cranes 1·10 25
N2451 30 ch. Saddle-bill stork 1·50 40
N2452 40 ch. Type **836** 1·90 60

837 Cosmonaut

1984. Space Exploration. Multicoloured.
N2454 10 ch. Type **837** 60 10
N2455 20 ch. Cosmonaut on space-walk 90 25
N2456 30 ch. Cosmonaut (different) 1·25 40

838 "Arktika"

1984. Russian Ice-breakers. Multicoloured.
N2458 20 ch. Type **838** 1·25 35
N2459 30 ch. "Ermak" 1·75 50

839 Mendeleev

1984. 150th Birth Anniv of Dmitri Mendeleev (chemist).
N2461 **839** 10 ch. multicoloured 60 10

840 Kim Il Sung in U.S.S.R

1984. Kim Il Sung's Visits to Eastern Europe. Multicoloured.
N2463 10 ch. Type **840** 60 10
N2464 10 ch. In Poland 60 10
N2465 10 ch. In German Democratic Republic 60 10
N2466 10 ch. In Czechoslovakia 60 10
N2467 10 ch. In Hungary 60 10
N2468 10 ch. In Bulgaria 60 10
N2469 10 ch. In Rumania 60 10

841 Freesia

1985. New Year.
N2471 **841** 10 ch. multicoloured 40 10

842 Journey Route, Steam Locomotive and Memorials

1985. 60th Anniv of 1000 ri Journey by Kim Il Sung. Multicoloured.
N2472 5 ch. Type **842** 40 10
N2473 10 ch. Boy trumpeter and schoolchildren following route 40 10

Nos. N2472/3 were issued together, se-tenant, forming a composite design.

843 Cugnot's Steam Car, 1769

844 Camp, Mt. Paekdu

1985. History of the Motor Car (1st series). Multicoloured.
N2474 10 ch. Type **843** 60 10
N2475 15 ch. Goldsworthy Gurney steam omnibus, 1825 75 15
N2476 20 ch. Gottlieb Daimler diesel car, 1885 90 25
N2477 25 ch. Benz three-wheeled diesel car, 1886 1·10 35
N2478 30 ch. Peugeot diesel car, 1891 1·25 40
See also Nos. N2562/6.

1985. Korean Revolution Headquarters.
N2480 **844** 10 ch. multicoloured 40 20

845 Taechodo Lighthouse

846 Hedgehog challenges Tiger

1985. Lighthouses. Multicoloured.
N2481 10 ch. Type **845** 75 10
N2482 20 ch. Sodo 1·10 30
N2483 30 ch. Pido 1·60 45
N2484 40 ch. Suundo 2·00 70

1985. "The Hedgehog defeats the Tiger" (fable). Multicoloured.
N2485 10 ch. Type **846** 60 10
N2486 20 ch. Tiger goes to stamp on rolled-up hedgehog 90 25
N2487 30 ch. Hedgehog clings to tiger's nose 1·25 40
N2488 35 ch. Tiger flees 1·40 50
N2489 40 ch. Tiger crawls before hedgehog 1·60 60

847 "Pleurotus cornucopiae"

848 West Germany v. Hungary, 1954

1985. Fungi. Multicoloured.
N2490 10 ch. Type **847** 60 10
N2491 20 ch. Oyster fungus 90 25
N2492 30 ch. "Catathelasma ventricosum" 1·25 40

1985. World Cup Football Championship Finals.
N2493 **848** 10 ch. black, buff & brn 60 10
N2494 – 10 ch. multicoloured 60 10
N2495 – 20 ch. black, buff & brn 90 25
N2496 – 20 ch. multicoloured 90 25
N2497 – 30 ch. black, buff & brn 1·25 40
N2498 – 30 ch. multicoloured 1·25 40
N2499 – 40 ch. black, buff & brn 1·60 60
N2500 – 40 ch. multicoloured 1·60 60

DESIGNS—VERT: N2496 West Germany v. Netherlands, 1974; N2499, England v. West Germany, 1966. HORIZ: N2494, Brazil v. Italy, 1970; N2495, Brazil v. Sweden, 1958; N2497, Brazil v. Czechoslovakia, 1962; N2498, Argentina v. Netherlands, 1968; N2500, Italy v. West Germany, 1982.

849 Date and Kim Il Sung's Birthplace

850 Horn Player

1985. 73rd Birthday of Kim Il Sung.
N2502 **849** 10 ch. multicoloured 40 10

1985. 4th-century Musical Instruments. Mult.
N2503 10 ch. Type **850** 60 10
N2504 20 ch. So (pipes) player 90 25

851 Chongryon Hall, Tokyo

852 Common Marmoset

1985. 30th Anniv of Chongryon (General Association of Korean Residents in Japan).
N2505 **851** 10 ch. brown 40 10

1985. Mammals. Multicoloured.
N2506 5 ch. Type **852** 45 10
N2507 10 ch. Ring-tailed lemur 45 10

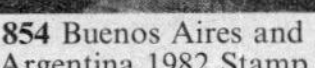

854 Buenos Aires and Argentina 1982 Stamp

855 Dancer and Gymnast

1985. "Argentina '85" International Stamp Exhibition, Buenos Aires. Multicoloured.

N2509 10 ch. Type **854** 60 10
N2510 20 ch. Iguacu Falls and Argentina 1984 and North Korea 1978 stamps (horiz) 90 25

1985. 12th World Youth and Students' Festival, Moscow. Multicoloured.

N2512 10 ch. Type **855** 60 10
N2513 20 ch. Spassky Tower, Moscow, and Festival emblem 90 25
N2514 40 ch. Youths of different races 1·60 60

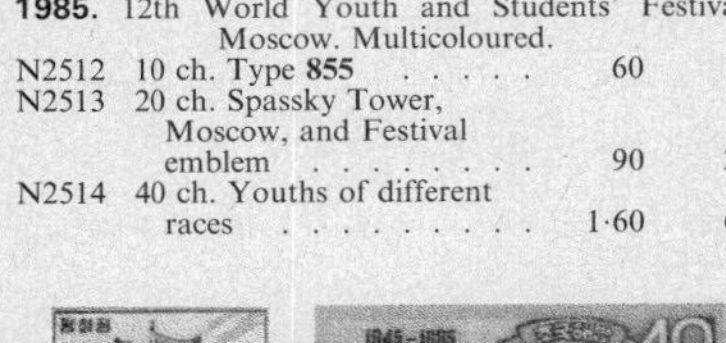

856 Peace Pavilion, Youth Park

857 Liberation Celebrations

1985. Pyongyang Buildings.

N2515 **856** 2 ch. black and green 20 10
N2516 – 40 ch. brown and lt brn 45 20
DESIGN: 40 ch. Multi-storey flats, Chollima Street.

1985. 40th Anniv of Liberation.

N2517 – 5 ch. red, black & blue 20 10
N2518 – 10 ch. multicoloured 40 10
N2519 – 10 ch. brown, blk & grn 40 10
N2520 – 10 ch. multicoloured 40 10
N2521 **857** 10 ch. yellow, blk & red 40 10
N2522 – 10 ch. red, orange & blk 40 10
N2523 – 40 ch. multicoloured 60 20
DESIGNS—HORIZ: No. N2517, Soldiers with rifles and flag; N2518, Crowd with banners and Flame of Juche; N2519, Korean and Soviet soldiers raising arms; N2520, Japanese soldiers laying down weapons; N2523, Students bearing banners. VERT: N2522, Liberation Tower, Moran Hill, Pyongyang.

858 Halley and Comet

1985. Appearance of Halley's Comet. Multicoloured.

N2525 10 ch. Type **858** 60 10
N2526 20 ch. Diagram of comet's flight and space probe 90 25

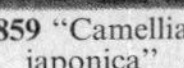

859 "Camellia japonica"

861 Party Founding Museum

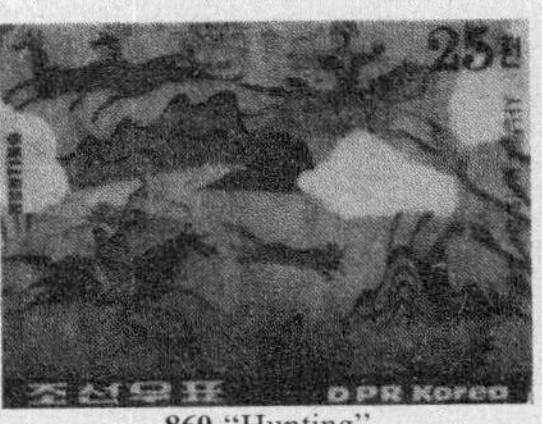

860 "Hunting"

1985. Flowers. Multicoloured.

N2528 10 ch. "Hippeastrum hybridum" 60 10
N2529 20 ch. Type **859** 90 25
N2530 30 ch. "Cyclamen persicum" 1·25 40

1985. Koguryo Culture.

N2531 10 ch. "Hero" (vert) 60 10
N2532 15 ch. "Heroine" (vert) 75 15
N2533 20 ch. "Flying Fairy" 90 25
N2534 25 ch. Type **860** 1·10 35

1985. 40th Anniv of Korean Workers' Party. Multicoloured.

N2536 5 ch. Type **861** 20 10
N2537 10 ch. Soldier with gun and workers 40 10
N2538 10 ch. Soldiers and flag 40 10
N2539 40 ch. Statue of worker, peasant and intellectual holding aloft party emblem 60 20

862 Arch of Triumph, Pyongyang

863 Colosseum, Rome, and N. Korea 1975 10 ch. Stamp

1985. 40th Anniv of Kim Il Sung's Return.

N2541 **862** 10 ch. brown and green 40 10

1985. "Italia '85" International Stamp Exhibition, Rome. Multicoloured.

N2542 10 ch. Type **863** 60 10
N2543 20 ch. "The Holy Family" (Raphael) (vert) 90 25
N2544 30 ch. Head of "David" (statue, Michelangelo) (vert) 1·25 40

864 Mercedes Benz Type "300"

1985. South-West German Stamp Fair, Sindelfingen. Multicoloured.

N2546 10 ch. Type **864** 60 10
N2547 15 ch. Mercedes Benz Type "770" 75 15
N2548 20 ch. Mercedes Benz "W 150" 90 25
N2549 30 ch. Mercedes Type "600" 1·25 40

865 Tackle

1985. World Cup Football Championship, Mexico (1st issue). Multicoloured.

N2551 20 ch. Type **865** 90 25
N2552 30 ch. Three players 1·25 40
See also Nos. N2558/9 and N2577/82.

866 Dancers

1985. International Youth Year. Multicoloured.

N2554 10 ch. Type **866** 60 10
N2555 20 ch. Sports activities 90 25
N2556 30 ch. Technology 1·25 40

867 Players

1985. World Cup Football Championship, Mexico (2nd issue). Multicoloured.

N2558 20 ch. Type **867** 90 25
N2559 30 ch. Goalkeeper and players 1·25 40

868 Juche Torch

869 Amedee Bollee and Limousine, 1901

1986. New Year.

N2561 **868** 10 ch. multicoloured 40 10

1986. History of the Motor Car (2nd series). Multicoloured.

N2562 10 ch. Type **869** 60 10
N2563 20 ch. Stewart Rolls, Henry Royce and "Silver Ghost", 1906 90 25
N2564 25 ch. Giovanni Agnelli and Fiat car, 1912 1·10 35
N2565 30 ch. Ettore Bugatti and "Royal" coupe, 1928 1·25 40
N2566 40 ch. Louis Renault and fiacre, 1906 1·60 60

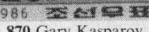

870 Gary Kasparov

872 Tongdu Rock, Songgan

871 Cemetery Gate

1986. World Chess Championship, Moscow.

N2568 **870** 20 ch. multicoloured 90 25

1986. Revolutionary Martyrs' Cemetery, Pyongyang. Multicoloured.

N2570 5 ch. Type **871** 20 10
N2571 10 ch. Bronze sculpture (detail) 40 10

1986. 37th Anniv of Pres. Kim Il Sung's Visit to Songgan Revolutionary Site.

N2572 **872** 10 ch. multicoloured 40 10

873 Buddhist Scriptures Museum

1986. Mt. Myohyang Buildings.

N2573 **873** 10 ch. brown and green 40 10
N2574 – 20 ch. violet and red 50 10
DESIGN: 20 ch. Taeung Hall.

874 "Amphiprion frenatus"

1986. Fishes. Multicoloured.

N2575 10 ch. Pennant coralfish 60 10
N2576 20 ch. Type **874** 90 25

875 Footballers and Flags of Italy, Bulgaria and Argentina

1986. World Cup Football Championship, Mexico (3rd issue). Designs showing footballers and flags of participating countries. Multicoloured.

N2577 10 ch. Type **875** 60 10
N2578 20 ch. Mexico, Belgium, Paraguay and Iraq 90 25
N2579 25 ch. France, Canada, U.S.S.R. and Hungary 1·10 35
N2580 30 ch. Brazil, Spain, Algeria and Northern Ireland 1·25 40
N2581 35 ch. West Germany, Uruguay, Scotland and Denmark 1·40 50
N2582 40 ch. Poland, Portugal, Morocco and England 1·60 60

876 Singer, Pianist and Emblem

1986. 4th Spring Friendship Art Festival, Pyongyang.

N2584 **876** 1 wn. multicoloured 1·25 55

877 Daimler "Motorwagen", 1886

878 Mangyong Hill

1986. 60th Anniv of Mercedes-Benz (car manufacturers). Multicoloured.

N2585 10 ch. Type **877** 60 10
N2586 10 ch. Benz "velo", 1894 60 10
N2587 20 ch. Mercedes car, 1901 90 25
N2588 20 ch. Benz limousine, 1909 90 25
N2589 30 ch. Mercedes "tourenwagen", 1914 1·25 40
N2590 30 ch. Mercedes-Benz "170" 6-cylinder, 1931 1·25 40
N2591 40 ch. Mercedes-Benz "380", 1933 1·60 60
N2592 40 ch. Mercedes-Benz "540 K", 1936 1·60 60

1986. 74th Birthday of Kim Il Sung.

N2594 **878** 10 ch. multicoloured 30 10

879 Crowd

1968. 50th Anniv of Association for the Restoration of the Fatherland.

N2595 **879** 10 ch. multicoloured 30 10

880 Dove carrying Letter

881 "Mona Lisa" (Leonardo da Vinci)

1986. International Peace Year. Multicoloured.

N2596 10 ch. Type **880** 60 10
N2597 20 ch. U.N. Headquarters, New York 90 25
N2598 30 ch. Dove, globe and broken missiles 1·25 40

1986.

N2600 **881** 20 ch. multicoloured 90 25

882 Pink Iris

883 Kim Un Suk

1986. Irises. Multicoloured.

N2601 20 ch. Type **882** 90 25
N2602 30 ch. Violet iris 1·25 40

1986. Tennis Players. Multicoloured.

N2604 10 ch. Type **883** (postage) 60 10
N2605 20 ch. Ivan Lendl 90 25
N2606 30 ch. Steffi Graf . . . . . 1·25 40
N2607 50 ch. Boris Becker (air) . . 1·75 75

884 Sulphur-crested Cockatoo

1986. "Stampex '86" Stamp Exhibition, Adelaide, Australia.

N2608 **884** 10 ch. multicoloured . 60 10

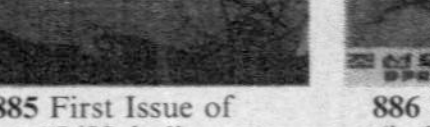

885 First Issue of "L'Unita"

886 "Express II" (icebreaker) and Sweden 1872 20 ore Stamp

1986. National "L'Unita" (Italian Communist Party newspaper) Festival, Milan. Multicoloured.

N2610 10 ch. Type **885** 60 10
N2611 20 ch. Milan Cathedral . . 90 25
N2612 30 ch. "Pieta" (Michelangelo) (vert) . . . . 1·25 40

1986. "Stockholmia 86" International Stamp Exhibition, Stockholm.

N2614 **886** 10 ch. multicoloured . 90 20

887 Reprint of First Stamp

1986. 40th Anniv of First North Korean Stamps (1st issue). Multicoloured.

N2616 10 ch. Type **887** (postage) 60 10
N2617 15 ch. Imperforate reprint of first stamp 75 15
N2618 50 ch. 1946 50 ch. violet stamp (air) . . . . 1·75 75

See also Nos. N2619/21.

888 Postal Emblems and 1962 and 1985 Stamps

1986. 40th Anniv of First North Korean Stamps (2nd issue). Multicoloured.

N2619 10 ch. Type **888** (postage) 60 10
N2620 15 ch. General Post Office and 1976 and 1978 stamps 75 15
N2621 50 ch. Kim Il Sung, first stamp and reprint (vert) (air) . . . . 1·75 75

1986. World Cup Football Championship Results. Nos. N2577/82 optd **1st: ARG 2nd: FRG 3rd: FRA 4th: BEL.**

N2622 10 ch. multicoloured . . . 60 10
N2623 20 ch. multicoloured . . . 90 25
N2624 25 ch. multicoloured . . . 1·10 35
N2625 30 ch. multicoloured . . . 1·25 40
N2626 35 ch. multicoloured . . . 1·40 50
N2627 40 ch. multicoloured . . . 1·60 60

890 Flag and Man with raised Fist

892 Schoolchildren

891 Gift Animals House

1986. 60th Anniv of Down-with-Imperialism Union.

N2629 **890** 10 ch. multicoloured . 30 10

1986. 1st Anniv of Gift Animals House, Central Zoo, Pyongyang.

N2630 **891** 2 wn. multicoloured . 3·00 1·10

1986. 40th Anniv of U.N.E.S.C.O. Multicoloured.

N2631 10 ch. Type **892** 60 10
N2632 50 ch. Anniversary emblem, Grand People's Study House and tele-communications (horiz) 1·75 75

893 Communications Satellite

1986. 15th Anniv of Intersputnik.

N2633 **893** 5 wn. multicoloured . 7·00 3·00

894 Oil tanker leaving Lock

1986. West Sea Barrage.

N2634 **894** 10 ch. multicoloured . 30 10
N2635 – 40 ch. green, black and gold 90 20
N2636 – 1 wn. 20 multicoloured 2·25 60

DESIGNS: 20 ch. Aerial view of dam; 1 wn. 20, Aerial view of lock.

895 Common Morel

896 Machu Picchu, Peru, and N. Korea Taedong Gate Stamp

1986. Minerals and Fungi. Multicoloured.

N2637 10 ch. Lengenbachite (postage) 60 10
N2638 10 ch. Common funnel cap 60 10
N2639 15 ch. Rhodochrosite . . . 75 15
N2640 15 ch. Type **895** 75 15
N2641 50 ch. Annabergite (air) 1·75 75
N2642 50 ch. Blue russula . . . . 1·75 75

1986. North Korean Three-dimensional Photographs and Stamps Exhibition, Lima, Peru.

N2643 **896** 10 ch. multicoloured . 60 10

897 Pine Tree

898 "Pholiota adiposa"

1987. New Year. Multicoloured.

N2645 10 ch. Type **897** 30 10
N2646 40 ch. Hare 75 25

1987. Fungi. Multicoloured.

N2647 10 ch. Type **898** 40 10
N2648 20 ch. Chanterelle 70 20
N2649 30 ch. "Boletus impolitus" 1·00 30

899 Kim Ok Song (composer)

901 East Pyongyang Grand Theatre

1987. Musicians' Death Anniversaries. Mult.

N2651 10 ch. Maurice Ravel (composer, 50th anniv) 40 10
N2652 10 ch. Type **899** (22nd anniv) 40 10
N2653 20 ch. Giovanni Lully (composer, 300th anniv) 70 20
N2654 30 ch. Franz Liszt (composer, centenary (1986)) . . . . 1·00 30
N2655 40 ch. Violins (250th anniv of Antonio Stradivari (violin maker) . . . . 1·25 40
N2656 40 ch. Christoph Gluck (composer, bicent) . . . 1·25 40

1987. Buildings.

N2658 **901** 5 ch. green 15 10
N2659 – 10 ch. brown 25 10
N2660 – 3 wn. blue . . . . . . 4·00 1·25

DESIGNS—VERT: 10 ch. Pyongyang Koryo Hotel; HORIZ: 3 wn. Rungnado Stadium.

902 "Gorch Foch" (German cadet barque)

1987. Sailing Ships. Multicoloured.

N2661 20 ch. Type **902** (postage) 70 20
N2662 30 ch. "Tovarishch" (Russian cadet barque) (vert) . . . 1·00 30
N2663 50 ch. "Belle Poule" (cadet schooner) (vert) (air) . . 1·50 45
N2664 50 ch. "Sagres II" (Portuguese cadet barque) (vert) . . . 1·50 45
N2665 1 wn. Koryo period merchantman . . . . . . 3·00 95
N2666 1 wn. "Dar Mlodziezy" (Polish cadet full-rigged ship) (vert) . . . . 3·00 95

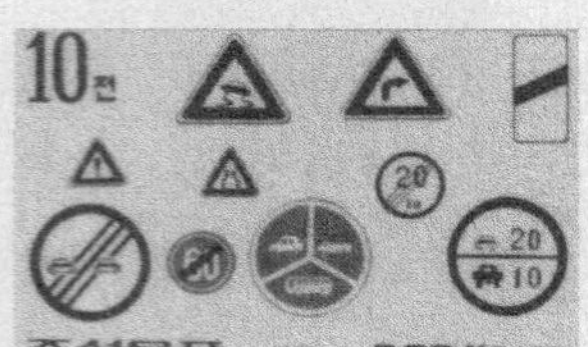

903 Road Signs

1987. Road Safety.

N2667 **903** 10 ch. blue, red and black (postage) 40 10
N2668 – 10 ch. red and black . . 40 10
N2669 – 20 ch. blue, red & blk 70 20
N2670 – 50 ch. red and black (air) 1·50 50

DESIGNS: Nos. N2668/70, Different road signs.

904 Fire Engine

1987. Fire Engines.

N2671 **904** 10 ch. multicoloured (postage) 40 10
N2672 – 20 ch. multicoloured . . 70 20
N2673 – 30 ch. multicoloured . . 1·00 30
N2674 – 50 ch. multicoloured (air) 1·50 50

DESIGNS: N2672/4, Different machines.

905 "Apatura ilia" and Spiraea

1987. Butterflies and Flowers. Multicoloured.

N2675 10 ch. Type **905** 40 10
N2676 10 ch. "Ypthima argus" and fuchsia 40 10
N2677 20 ch. "Neptis philyra" and aquilegia 70 20
N2678 20 ch. "Papilio protenor" and chrysanthemum 70 20
N2679 40 ch. "Parantica sita" and celosia . . . . 1·25 40
N2680 40 ch. "Vanessa indica" and hibiscus . . . . 1·25 40

906 Association Monument, Pyongyang

907 Doves, Emblem and Tree

1987. 70th Anniv of Korean National Association (independence movement).

N2681 **906** 10 ch. red, silver & blk 25 10

1987. 5th Spring Friendship Art Festival, Pyongyang.

N2682 **907** 10 ch. multicoloured . 25 10

908 Mangyong Hill

909 Bay

1987. 75th Birthday of Kim Il Sung. Mult.

N2683 10 ch. Type **908** 25 10
N2684 10 ch. Kim Il Sung's birthplace, Mangyongdae (horiz) 25 10
N2685 10 ch. "A Bumper Crop of Pumpkins" (62 × 41 mm) 25 10
N2686 10 ch. "Profound Affection for the Working Class" 25 10

1987. Horses. Multicoloured.

N2687 10 ch. Type **909** 40 10
N2688 10 ch. Bay (different) . . . 40 10
N2689 40 ch. Grey rearing . . . . 1·25 40
N2690 40 ch. Grey on beach . . . 1·25 40

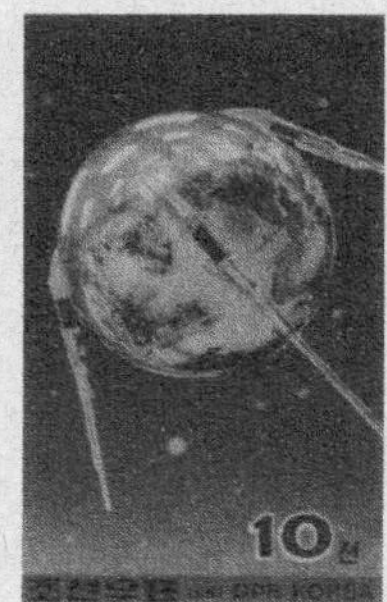

910 "Sputnik 1" (first artificial satellite)

1987. Transport. Multicoloured.

N2691 10 ch. Type **910** (30th anniv of flight) 40 10
N2692 10 ch. Electric train "Juche" (horiz) 40 10
N2693 10 ch. Electric locomotive "Mangyongdae" (horiz) 40 10
N2694 20 ch. Laika (30th anniv of first animal in space) . . 70 20
N2695 20 ch. Tupolev Tu-144 supersonic airliner (horiz) 70 20
N2696 20 ch. Concorde (11th anniv of first commercial flight) (horiz) 70 20
N2697 30 ch. Count Ferdinand von Zeppelin (70th death anniv) and airship LZ-4 (horiz) 1·00 30
N2698 80 ch. Zeppelin and diagrams and drawings of airships (horiz) . . . . 3·00 1·00

911 Musk Ox

1987. "Capex '87" International Stamp Exhibition, Toronto. Multicoloured.

N2699 10 ch. Type **911** 40 10
N2700 40 ch. Jacques Cartier, his ship "Grande Hermine" and ice-breaker (horiz) . 1·25 40
N2701 60 ch. Ice hockey (Winter Olympics, Calgary, 1988) (horiz) . . . . 1·75 60

912 Trapeze Artistes

1987. International Circus Festival, Monaco. Multicoloured.

N2702 10 ch. Type **912** 40 10
N2703 10 ch. "Brave Sailors" (North Korean acrobatic act) (vert) 40 10
N2704 20 ch. Clown and elephant (vert) 70 20
N2705 20 ch. North Korean artiste receiving "Golden Clown" award 70 20
N2706 40 ch. Performing horses and cat act . . . . 1·25 40
N2707 50 ch. Prince Rainier and his children applauding . . . 1·50 50

913 Attack on Watch Tower

1987. 50th Anniv of Battle of Pochonbo.

N2708 **913** 10 ch. brown, black and ochre 25 10

914 Sports

1987. Angol Sports Village.

N2709 **914** 5 ch. brown and gold 15 10
N2710 – 10 ch. blue and gold . 25 10
N2711 – 40 ch. brown and gold 75 25
N2712 – 70 ch. blue and gold . 1·25 40
N2713 – 1 wn. red and gold . . 1·90 60
N2714 – 1 wn. 20 violet . . . . 2·25 70

DESIGNS: Exteriors of—10 ch. Indoor swimming pool; 40 ch. Weightlifting gymnasium; 70 ch. Table tennis gymnasium; 1 wn. Football stadium; 1 wn. 20, Handball gymnasium.

915 Mandarins

1987. Mandarins. Multicoloured.

N2715 20 ch. Type **915** 70 15
N2716 20 ch. Mandarins on shore 70 15
N2717 20 ch. Mandarins on branch 70 15
N2718 40 ch. Mandarins in water 1·25 40

916 Exhibition Site and 1987 3 wn. Stamp

1987. "Olymphilex '87" Olympic Stamps Exhibition, Rome.

N2719 **916** 10 ch. multicoloured . 40 10

917 Underground Station and Guard

1987. Railway Uniforms. Multicoloured.

N2721 10 ch. Type **917** 25 10
N2722 10 ch. Underground train and station supervisor . . . 25 10
N2723 20 ch. Guard and train . . 40 10
N2724 30 ch. Guard and train . . 55 20
N2725 40 ch. "Orient Express" guard 75 25
N2726 40 ch. German ticket controller and steam train 75 25

918 White Stork

920 Victory Column

919 Ice Skating

1987. "Hafnia 87" International Stamp Exhibition, Copenhagen. Multicoloured.

N2727 40 ch. Type **918** . . . . . 1·00 30
N2728 60 ch. "Danmark" (cadet ship) and "Little Mermaid", Copenhagen 1·25 40

1987. Winter Olympic Games, Calgary (1988). Multicoloured.

N2729 40 ch. Type **919** . . . . . 1·00 30
N2730 40 ch. Ski jumping . . . . 1·00 30
N2731 40 ch. Skiing (value on left) (horiz) . . . . 1·00 30
N2732 40 ch. Skiing (value on right) (horiz) . . . . 1·00 30

1987. 750th Anniv of Berlin and "Philatelia '87" International Stamp Exhibition, Cologne. Mult.

N2734 10 ch. Type **920** 40 10
N2735 20 ch. Reichstag (horiz) . 70 20
N2736 30 ch. Pfaueninsel Castle . 1·00 30
N2737 40ch. Charlottenburg Castle (horiz) . . . . 1·25 40

921 Garros and Bleriot XI

1987. Birth Centenary of Roland Garros (aviator) and Tennis as an Olympic Sport. Multicoloured.

N2739 20 ch. Type **921** 70 20
N2740 20 ch. Ivan Lendl (tennis player) 70 20
N2741 40 ch. Steffi Graf (tennis player) . . . . 1·25 40

923 Pyongyang Buildings

1988. New Year. Multicoloured.

N2744 10 ch. Type **923** 20 10
N2745 40 ch. Dragon 75 25

924 Banner and Newspaper

925 Birthplace, Mt. Paekdu

1988. 60th Anniv of "Saenal" Newspaper.

N2746 **924** 10 ch. multicoloured . . 20 10

1988. Kim Jong Il's Birthday.

N2747 **925** 10 ch. multicoloured . . 20 10

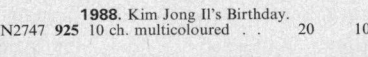

926 Henry Dunant (founder)

1988. 125th Anniv of International Red Cross. Multicoloured.

N2749 10 ch. Type **926** 20 10
N2750 20 ch. North Korean Red Cross emblem and map 40 15
N2751 20 ch. International Committee headquarters, Geneva 40 15
N2752 40 ch. Pyongyang Maternity Hospital, doctor and baby 75 25

927 "Santa Maria"

1988. 500th Anniv (1992) of Discovery of America by Christopher Columbus. Multicoloured.

N2754 10 ch. Type **927** 25 15
N2755 20 ch. "Pinta" 55 20
N2756 30 ch. "Nina" 75 25

Nos. N2754/6 were issued together, se-tenant, forming a composite design of Columbus's ships leaving Palos.

928 Hot-air Balloons

929 Dancers

1988. "Juvalux '88" International Youth Stamp Exhibition, Luxembourg. Multicoloured.

N2758 40 ch. Type **928** 75 25
N2759 60 ch. Early railway locomotive and railway map of Luxembourg, 1900 1·10 35

1988. 6th Spring Friendship Art Festival, Pyongyang. Multicoloured.

N2760 10 ch. Singer (poster) . . . 20 10
N2761 1 wn. 20 Type **929** . . . . 2·25 75

930 Inaugural Congress Emblem

931 Birthplace, Mangyongdae

1988. 10th Anniv of International Institute of the Juche Idea.

N2762 **930** 10 ch. multicoloured . 20 10

1988. 76th Birthday of Kim Il Sung.

N2763 **931** 10 ch. multicoloured . 20 10

932 "Urho" (ice-breaker)

1988. "Finlandia 88" International Stamp Exhibition, Helsinki. Multicoloured.

N2765 40 ch. Type **932** . . . . . 1·00 25
N2766 60 ch. Matti Nykaenen (Olympic Games ski-jumping medallist) . . . 1·10 35

933 Postcard for 1934 Championship

934 Emblem

1988. World Cup Football Championship, Italy (1st issue). Multicoloured.

N2767 10 ch. Football match . . 20 10
N2768 20 ch. Type **933** 40 15
N2769 30 ch. Player tackling (horiz) 55 20

See also Nos. N2924/7.

1988. 13th World Youth and Students' Festival, Pyongyang (1st issue). Multicoloured.

N2771 5 ch. Type **934** 10 10
N2772 10 ch. Dancer 20 10
N2773 10 ch. Gymnast and gymnasium, Angol Sports Village 20 10
N2774 10 ch. Map of Korea, globe and doves 20 10
N2775 10 ch. Finger pointing at shattered nuclear rockets 20 10
N2776 1 wn. 20 Three differently coloured hands and dove 2·25 75

See also Nos. N2860/3 and N2879/80.

935 Fairy

936 Mallards

1988. "Eight Fairies of Mt. Kumgang" (tale). Multicoloured.

N2777 10 ch. Type **935** 20 10
N2778 15 ch. Fairy at pool and fairies on rainbow . . . 30 10
N2779 20 ch. Fairy and woodman husband 40 15
N2780 25 ch. Couple with baby . 50 15
N2781 30 ch. Couple with son and daughter 55 20
N2782 35 ch. Family on rainbow 65 20

1988. "Praga '88" International Stamp Exhibition, Prague. Multicoloured.

N2783 20 ch. Type **936** 40 15
N2784 40 ch. Vladimir Remek (Czechoslovak cosmonaut) 75 25

937 Red Crossbill

1988. Birds. Multicoloured.

N2785 10 ch. Type **937** 30 15
N2786 15 ch. Stonechat 60 15
N2787 20 ch. European nuthatch 75 25
N2788 25 ch. Great spotted woodpecker 95 25
N2789 30 ch. Common kingfisher 1·10 30
N2790 35 ch. Bohemian waxwing 1·25 30

938 Fair Emblem

1988. 40th International Stamp Fair, Riccione.

N2791 **938** 20 ch. multicoloured . 40 15

939 Emu

1988. Bicentenary of Australian Settlement. Mult.

N2793 10 ch. Type **939** 45 20
N2794 15 ch. Satin bowerbirds . . 65 20
N2795 25 ch. Laughing kookaburra (vert) . . . . 1·10 30

940 Floating Crane "5-28"

1988. Ships. Multicoloured.

N2797 10 ch. Type **940** 25 10
N2798 20 ch. Freighter "Hwanggumsan" 50 20
N2799 30 ch. Freighter "Changjasan Chongnyon-ho" 70 25
N2800 40 ch. Liner "Samjiyon" . . 1·00 30

941 "Hansa"

1988. 150th Birth Anniv of Count Ferdinand von Zeppelin (airship pioneer). Multicoloured.

N2801 10 ch. Type **941** 20 10
N2802 20 ch. "Schwaben" 40 15
N2803 30 ch. "Viktoria Luise" . . 55 20
N2804 40 ch. LZ-3 . . . . 75 25

942 Kim Il Sung and Jambyn Batmunkh

944 Tower of Juche Idea

943 Hero and Labour Hero of the D.P.R.K. Medals

1988. Kim Il Sung's Visit to Mongolia.

N2806 **942** 10 ch. multicoloured . 20 10

1988. National Heroes Congress.

N2807 **943** 10 ch. multicoloured . 20 10

1988. 40th Anniv of Democratic Republic. Multicoloured.

N2808 5 ch. Type **944** 10 10
N2809 10 ch. Smelter and industrial buildings 20 10
N2810 10 ch. Soldier and Mt. Paekdu 20 10
N2811 10 ch. Map of Korea and globe 20 10
N2812 10 ch. Hand holding banner, globe and doves 20 10

945 "Sunflowers" (Vincent van Gogh)

946 Emblem

1988. "Filacept 88" Stamp Exhibition, The Hague. Multicoloured.

N2814 40 ch. Type **945** 75 25
N2815 60 ch. "The Chess Game" (Lucas van Leyden) (horiz) 1·10 35

1988. 16th Session of Socialist Countries' Post and Telecommunications Conference, Pyongyang.

N2816 **946** 10 ch. multicoloured . 20 10

947 Chaju "82" 10-ton Truck

948 "Owl"

1988. Tipper Trucks. Multicoloured.

N2817 20 ch. Type **947** 40 15
N2818 40 ch. Kumsusan-ho 40-ton truck 75 25

1988. Paintings by O Un Byol. Multicoloured.

N2819 10 ch. Type **948** 20 10
N2820 15 ch. "Dawn" (cockerel) 30 10
N2821 20 ch. "Beautiful Rose received by Kim Il Sung" 40 15
N2822 25 ch. "Sun and Bamboo" 50 15
N2823 30 ch. "Autumn" (fruit tree) 55 20

949 "Chunggi" Type Steam Locomotive No. 35

1988. Railway Locomotives. Multicoloured.

N2824 10 ch. Type **949** 20 10
N2825 20 ch. "Chunggi" type steam locomotive No. 22 . . . 40 15
N2826 30 ch. "Chongiha" type electric locomotive No. 3 55 20
N2827 40 ch. "Chunggi" type steam locomotive No. 307 . . . 75 25

950 Pirmen Zurbriggen (downhill skiing)

1988. Winter Olympic Games, Calgary, Medal Winners. Multicoloured.

N2828 10 ch. Type **950** 20 10
N2829 20 ch. Yvonne van Gennip (speed skating) 40 15
N2830 30 ch. Marjo Matikainen (cross-country skiing) . . 55 20
N2831 40 ch. U.S.S.R. (ice hockey) (horiz) 75 25

951 Yuri Gagarin

1988. 1st Man and Woman in Space. Mult.

N2833 20 ch. Type **951** 40 15
N2834 40 ch. Valentina Tereshkova 75 25

952 Nehru

953 Chollima Statue

1988. Birth Centenary of Jawaharlal Nehru (Indian statesman) and "India 89" International Stamp Exhibition, New Delhi.

N2835 **952** 20 ch. purple, black and gold 40 15

1989. New Year. Multicoloured.

N2837 10 ch. Type **953** 20 10
N2838 20 ch. "The Dragon Angler" (17th-century painting) 40 15
N2839 40 ch. "Tortoise and Serpent" (Kangso tomb painting) (horiz) 75 25

954 Archery

1989. National Defence Training. Multicoloured.

N2840 10 ch. Type **954** 20 10
N2841 15 ch. Rifle shooting . . . 30 10
N2842 20 ch. Pistol shooting . . . 40 15
N2843 25 ch. Parachuting 50 15
N2844 30 ch. Launching model glider 55 20

955 Dobermann Pinscher

957 Agriculture

1989. Animals presented to Kim Il Sung. Mult.

N2845 10 ch. Type **955** 20 10
N2846 20 ch. Labrador 40 15
N2847 25 ch. German shepherd . 50 15
N2848 30 ch. Rough collies (horiz) 55 20
N2849 35 ch. Serval (horiz) . . . 65 20

1989. 25th Anniv of Publication of "Theses on the Socialist Rural Question in our Country" by Kim Il Sung.

N2852 **957** 10 ch. multicoloured . 20 10

958 The Gypsy and Grapes

959 Korean Girl

1989. Fungi and Fruits. Multicoloured.

N2853 10 ch. Type **958** 20 10
N2854 20 ch. Caesar's mushroom and magnolia vine . . . 40 15
N2855 25 ch. "Lactarius hygrophoides" and "Eleagnus crispa" . . . 50 15
N2856 30 ch. "Agaricus placomyces" and Chinese gooseberries 55 20
N2857 35 ch. Horse mushroom and "Lycium chinense" . . . 65 20
N2858 40 ch. Elegant boletus and "Juglans cordiformis" . 75 25

1989. 13th World Youth and Students' Festival, Pyongyang (2nd issue). Multicoloured.

N2860 10 ch. Type **959** 20 10
N2861 20 ch. Children of different races 40 15
N2862 30 ch. Fairy and rainbow 55 20
N2863 40 ch. Young peoples and Tower of Juche Idea . . 75 25

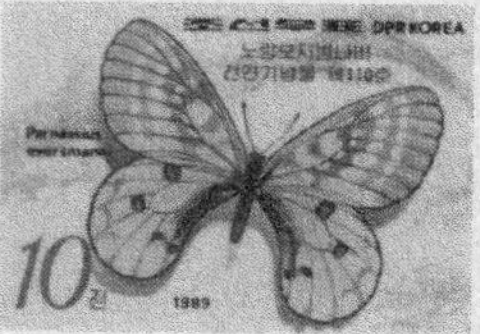

960 "Parnassius eversmanni"

1969. Insects. Multicoloured.

N2864 10 ch. Type **960** 20 10
N2865 15 ch. "Colias heos" . . . 30 10
N2866 20 ch. "Dilipa fenestra" . . 40 15
N2867 25 ch. "Buthus martensis" . 50 15
N2868 30 ch. "Trichogramma ostriniae" 55 20
N2869 40 ch. "Damaster constricticollis" 75 25

961 Dancers (poster)

962 Birthplace, Mangyongdae

1989. Spring Friendship Art Festival, Pyongyang.

N2871 **961** 10 ch. multicoloured . 20 10

1989. 77th Birthday of Kim Il Sung.

N2872 **962** 10 ch. multicoloured . 20 10

963 Battle Plan and Monument to the Victory

1989. 50th Anniv of Battle of the Musan Area.
N2873 **963** 10 ch. blue, flesh & red . . . 20 10

964 Modern Dance

1989. Chamo System of Dance Notation. Multicoloured.
N2874 10 ch. Type **964** 20 10
N2875 20 ch. Ballet 40 15
N2876 25 ch. Modern dance (different) 50 15
N2877 30 ch. Traditional dance . . 55 20

965 Hands supporting Torch **966** Victorious Badger

1989. 13th World Youth and Students' Festival, Pyongyang (3rd issue).
N2879 **965** 5 ch. blue 10 10
N2880 – 10 ch. brown 20 10
DESIGN: 10 ch. Youth making speech.

1989. "Badger measures the Height" (cartoon film). Multicoloured.
N2881 10 ch. Cat, bear and badger race to flag pole 20 10
N2882 40 ch. Cat and bear climb pole while badger measures shadow 75 25
N2883 50 ch. Type **966** 95 30

967 Kyongju Observatory and Star Chart **969** Pele (footballer) and 1978 25 ch. Stamp

1989. Astronomy.
N2884 **967** 20 ch. multicoloured . . 40 15

1989. "Brasiliana 89" International Stamp Exhibition, Rio de Janeiro.
N2887 **969** 40 ch. multicoloured . . 75 25

970 Nurse and Ambulance

1989. Emergency Services. Multicoloured.
N2888 10 ch. Type **970** 20 10
N2889 20 ch. Surgeon and ambulance 40 15
N2890 30 ch. Fireman and fire engine 55 20
N2891 40 ch. Fireman and engine (different) 75 25

971 Kaffir Lily **972** Air Mail Letter and Postal Transport

1989. Plants presented to Kim Il Sung. Mult.
N2892 10 ch. Type **971** 20 10
N2893 15 ch. Tulips 30 10
N2894 20 ch. Flamingo lily . . . 40 15
N2895 25 ch. "Rhododendron obtusum" 50 15
N2896 30 ch. Daffodils 55 20

1989. 150th Anniv of the Penny Black and "Stamp World London 90" International Stamp Exhibition (1st issue). Multicoloured.
N2898 5 ch. Type **972** 10 10
N2899 10 ch. Post box and letters 20 10
N2900 20 ch. Stamps, tweezers and magnifying glass 40 15
N2901 30 ch. First North Korean stamps 55 20
N2902 40 ch. Universal Postal Union emblem and headquarters, Berne 75 25
N2903 50 ch. Sir Rowland Hill and Penny Black 95 30
See also No. N2956.

973 "Bistorta incana"

1989. Alpine Flowers. Multicoloured.
N2904 10 ch. "Iris setosa" . . . 20 10
N2905 15 ch. "Aquilegia japonica" 30 10
N2906 20 ch. Type **973** 40 15
N2907 25 ch. "Rodiola elongata" 50 15
N2908 30 ch. "Sanguisorba sitchensis" 55 20

974 Tree, Mt. Paekdu **975** Skipping

1989. Slogan-bearing Trees (1st series). Mult.
N2910 10 ch. Type **974** 20 10
N2911 3 wn. Tree, Oun-dong, Pyongyang . . . . . . 5·50 1·75
N2912 5 wn. Tree, Mt. Kanbaek 9·50 3·25
See also No. N2931.

1989. Children's Games. Multicoloured.
N2913 10 ch. Type **975** 20 10
N2914 20 ch. Windmill 40 15
N2915 30 ch. Kite 55 20
N2916 40 ch. Whip and top . . . 75 25

977 Diesel Train and Sinpa Youth Station

1989. Railway Locomotives. Multicoloured.
N2918 10 ch. Type **977** 20 10
N2919 20 ch. "Pulgungi" type electric locomotive . . . 40 15
N2920 25 ch. Diesel locomotive . 50 15
N2921 30 ch. Diesel locomotive (different) 55 20
N2922 40 ch. Steam locomotive . 75 25
N2923 50 ch. Steam locomotive (different) 95 30

978 Players and Map of Italy

1989. World Cup Football Championship, Italy (2nd issue). Multicoloured.
N2924 10 ch. Type **978** 20 10
N2925 20 ch. Free kick 40 15
N2926 30 ch. Goal mouth scrimmage 55 20
N2927 40 ch. Goalkeeper diving for ball 75 25

979 Megellan (navigator)

1989. "Descobrex '89" International Stamp Exhibition, Portugal.
N2928 **979** 30 ch. multicoloured . . 75 20

980 Mangyong Hill and Pine Branches **981** Ryukwoli

1990. New Year. Multicoloured.
N2929 10 ch. Type **980** 20 10
N2930 20 ch. Koguryo mounted archers 40 15

1990. Slogan-bearing Trees (2nd series). As T **974**. Multicoloured.
N2931 5 ch. Tree, Mt. Paekdu . . 10 10

1990. Dogs. Multicoloured.
N2932 20 ch. Type **981** 40 15
N2933 30 ch. Palryuki 55 20
N2934 40 ch. Komdungi 75 25
N2935 50 ch. Oulruki 95 30

982 Birthplace, Mt. Paekdu **983** Stone Instruments and Primitive Man

1990. Birthday of Kim Jong Il.
N2936 **982** 10 ch. brown 20 10

1990. Evolution of Man. Multicoloured.
N2937 10 ch. Type **983** 20 10
N2938 40 ch. Palaeolithic and Neolithic man 75 25

984 Rungna Bridge, Pyongyang

1990. Bridges. Multicoloured.
N2939 10 ch. Type **984** 20 10
N2940 20 ch. Potong bridge, Pyongyang 40 15
N2941 30 ch. Sinuiji-Ryucho Island Bridge 55 20
N2942 40 ch. Chungsongui Bridge, Pyongyang 75 25

985 Infantryman **987** Dancers (poster)

986 "Atergatis subdentatus"

1990. Warriors' Costumes. Multicoloured.
N2943 20 ch. Type **985** 40 15
N2944 30 ch. Archer 55 20
N2945 50 ch. Military commander in armour 95 30
N2946 70 ch. Officer's costume, 10th–14th centuries . . . 1·25 40
Nos. N2943/5 depict costumes from the 3rd century B.C. to the 7th century A.D.

1990. Crabs. Multicoloured.
N2947 20 ch. Type **986** 40 15
N2948 30 ch. "Platylambrus validus" 55 20
N2949 50 ch. "Uca arcuata" . . . 95 30

1990. Spring Friendship Art Festival, Pyongyang.
N2950 **987** 10 ch. multicoloured . . 20 10

988 Monument at Road Folk, Mangyongdae **989** "Gymnocalycium sp."

1990. 78th Birthday of Kim Il Sung.
N2951 **988** 10 ch. green and gold . 20 10

1990. Cacti. Multicoloured.
N2953 10 ch. Type **989** 20 10
N2954 30 ch. "Pyllocactus hybridus" 55 20
N2955 50 ch. "Epiphyllum truncatum" 95 30

990 Exhibition Emblem **991** Congo Peafowl

1990. "Stamp World London 90" International Stamp Exhibition (2nd issue).
N2956 **990** 20 ch. red and black . . 40 15

1990. Peafowl. Multicoloured.
N2958 10 ch. Type **991** 30 10
N2959 20 ch. Common peafowl . . 70 20

992 Dolphin and Submarine

1990. Bio-engineering. Multicoloured.
N2961 10 ch. Type **992** 20 10
N2962 20 ch. Bat and dish aerial 40 15
N2963 30 ch. Eagle and Tupolev Tu-154 jet airliner . . . 70 20
N2964 40 ch. Octopus and rockets 90 25

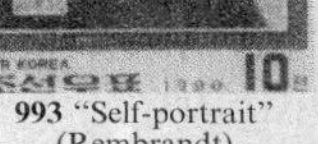

993 "Self-portrait" (Rembrandt) **994** K. H. Rummenigge (footballer)

1990. "Belgica 90" International Stamp Exhibition, Brussels. Multicoloured.
N2965 10 ch. Type **993** 20 10
N2966 20 ch. "Self-portrait" (Raphael) 40 15
N2967 30 ch. "Self-portrait" (Rubens) 55 20

1990. "Dusseldorf '90" International Youth Stamp Exhibition. Multicoloured.
N2968 20 ch. Steffi Graf (tennis player) 40 15
N2969 30 ch. Exhibition emblem . 55 20
N2970 70 ch. Type **994** . . . . . 1·25 40

995 Workers' Stadium, Peking, and Games Mascot

1990. 11th Asian Games, Peking (Nos. N2971/2) and 3rd Asian Winter Games, Samjiyon (N2973). Multicoloured.

N2971 10 ch. Type **995** 20 10
N2972 30 ch. Chollima Statue and sportsmen 55 20
N2973 40 ch. Sportsmen and Games emblem 75 25

996 Ball

1990. West Germany, Winners of World Cup Football Championship. Multicoloured.

N2974 15 ch. Emblem of F.I.F.A. (International Federation of Football Associations) 30 10
N2975 20 ch. Jules Rimet 40 15
N2976 25 ch. Type **996** 50 15
N2977 30 ch. Olympic Stadium, Rome (venue of final) . . 55 20
N2978 35 ch. Goalkeeper 65 20
N2979 40 ch. Emblem of West German Football Association 75 25

997 Kakapo and Map of New Zealand

1990. "New Zealand 1990" International Stamp Exhibition, Auckland.

N2981 **997** 30 ch. multicoloured . 70 20

999 Head of Procession

1990. Koguryo Wedding Procession. Mult.

N2983 10 ch. Type **999** 20 10
N2984 30 ch. Bridegroom 55 20
N2985 50 ch. Bride in carriage . . 95 30
N2986 1 wn. Drummer on horse 1·90 65

Nos. N2983/6 were issued together, se-tenant, forming a composite design.

1000 Marchers descending Mt. Paekdu

1990. Rally for Peace and Reunification of Korea.

N2987 **1000** 10 ch. multicoloured 20 10

1001 Praying Mantis

1990. Insects. Multicoloured.

N2989 20 ch. Type **1001** 40 15
N2990 30 ch. Ladybird 55 20
N2991 40 ch. "Pheropsophus jessoensis" 75 25
N2992 70 ch. "Phyllium siccifolium" 1·25 40

1002 Footballers

1990. North–South Reunification Football Match, Pyongyang. Multicoloured.

N2993 10 ch. Type **1002** 20 10
N2994 20 ch. Footballers (different) 40 15

1003 Concert Emblem **1004** Ox

1990. National Reunification Concert.

N2996 **1003** 10 ch. multicoloured 20 10

1990. Farm Animals.

N2997 **1004** 10 ch. brown & green 20 10
N2998 – 20 ch. lilac & yellow . 40 15
N2999 – 30 ch. grey and red . 55 20
N3000 – 40 ch. green and yellow 75 25
N3001 – 50 ch. brown and blue 95 30

DESIGNS: 20 ch. Pig; 30 ch. Goat; 40 ch. Sheep; 50 ch. Horse.

1005 Chinese and North Korean Soldiers **1006** Anniversary Emblem

1990. 40th Anniv of Participation of Chinese Volunteers in Korean War. Multicoloured.

N3002 10 ch. Type **1005** 20 10
N3003 20 ch. Populace welcoming volunteers (horiz) . . . 40 15
N3004 30 ch. Rejoicing soldiers and battle scene (horiz) . . . 55 20
N3005 40 ch. Post-war reconstruction (horiz) . 75 25

1990. 40th Anniv of United Nations Development Programme.

N3007 **1006** 1 wn. blue, silver & blk 1·90 65

1007 Sturgeon **1008** Sheep

1990. Fishes.

N3008 **1007** 10 ch. brown & green 20 10
N3009 – 20 ch. green and blue 40 15
N3010 – 30 ch. blue and puple 55 20
N3011 – 40 ch. brown and blue 75 25
N3012 – 50 ch. violet and green 95 30

DESIGNS: 20 ch. Sea bream; 30 ch. Flying fish; 40 ch. Fat greenling; 50 ch. Ray.

1990. New Year.

N3013 **1008** 40 ch. multicoloured 75 25

1009 Moorhen **1010** Giant Panda

1990. Birds.

N3014 **1009** 10 ch. blue, grn & blk 25 10
N3015 – 20 ch. brown, bistre and black 50 15
N3016 – 30 ch. green, grey and black 65 20
N3017 – 40 ch. brown, orange and black 90 30
N3018 – 50 ch. ochre, brown and black . . . . 1·10 35

DESIGNS: 20 ch. Jay; 30 ch. Three-toed woodpecker; 40 ch. Whimbrel; 50 ch. Water rail.

1991. "Phila Nippon '91" International Stamp Exhibition, Tokyo. Multicoloured.

N3019 10 ch. Type **1010** 20 10
N3020 20 ch. Two giant pandas feeding 40 15
N3021 30 ch. Giant panda clambering onto branch 55 20
N3022 40 ch. Giant panda on rock 75 25
N3023 50 ch. Two giant pandas . . 95 30
N3024 60 ch. Giant panda in tree fork . . . . 1·10 35

1011 Changsan

1991. Revolutionary Sites.

N3026 5 ch. Type **1011** 10 10
N3027 10 ch. Oun 20 10

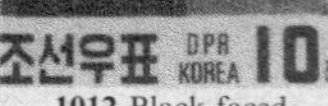

1012 Black-faced Spoonbills **1014** Hedgehog Fungus

1013 "Clossiana angarensis"

1991. Endangered Birds. Multicoloured.

N3028 10 ch. Type **1012** 20 10
N3029 20 ch. Grey herons 35 10
N3030 30 ch. Great egrets 50 15
N3031 40 ch. Manchurian cranes 75 20
N3032 50 ch. Japanese white-necked cranes 90 25
N3033 70 ch. White storks . . . . 1·10 30

1991. Alpine Butterflies. Multicoloured.

N3034 10 ch. Type **1013** 10 10
N3035 20 ch. "Erebia embla" . . . 25 10
N3036 30 ch. Camberwell beauty 35 10
N3037 40 ch. Comma 50 15
N3038 50 ch. Eastern pale clouded yellow 60 20
N3039 60 ch. "Theela betulae" . . 70 25

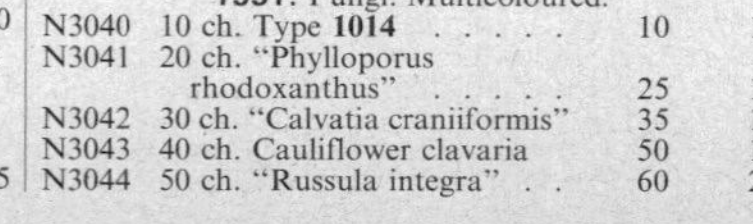

1991. Fungi. Multicoloured.

N3040 10 ch. Type **1014** 10 10
N3041 20 ch. "Phylloporus rhodoxanthus" 25 10
N3042 30 ch. "Calvatia craniiformis" 35 10
N3043 40 ch. Cauliflower clavaria 50 15
N3044 50 ch. "Russula integra" . . 60 20

1015 Kumchon

1991. Revolutionary Sites. Multicoloured.

N3045 10 ch. Type **1015** 10 10
N3046 40 ch. Samdung 50 15

1016 Dr. Kye Ung Sang (researcher) **1017** Emblem and Venue

1991. Silkworm Research. Multicoloured.

N3047 10 ch. Type **1016** 10 10
N3048 20 ch. Chinese oak silk moth 25 10
N3049 30 ch. "Attacus ricini" . . 35 10
N3050 40 ch. "Antheraea yamamai" 50 15
N3051 50 ch. Silkworm moth . . 60 20
N3052 60 ch. "Aetias artemis" . . 70 25

1991. 9th Spring Friendship Art Festival, Pyongyang.

N3053 **1017** 10 ch. multicoloured 10 10

1018 Emperor Penguins **1020** Map and Kim Jong Ho

1019 People's Palace of Culture (venue)

1991. Antarctic Exploration. Multicoloured.

N3054 10 ch. Type **1018** 10 10
N3055 20 ch. Research station . . 25 10
N3056 30 ch. Elephant seals . . . 35 10
N3057 40 ch. Research ship . . . 75 25
N3058 50 ch. Southern black-backed gulls 60 20

1991. 85th International Union Conference, Pyongyang.

N3060 **1019** 10 ch. dp green, grn & sil 10 10
N3061 – 1 wn. 50 multicoloured 1·75 60

DESIGN: 1 wn. 50, Conference emblem and azalea.

1991. 130th Anniv of Publication of Kim Jong Ho's Map of Korea.

N3062 **1020** 90 ch. black, stone & sil 1·10 35

1021 Cynognathus

1991. Dinosaurs. Multicoloured.

N3063 10 ch. Type **1021** 10 10
N3064 20 ch. Brontosaurus . . . 25 10
N3065 30 ch. Stegosaurus and allosaurus 35 10
N3066 40 ch. Pterosauria 50 15
N3067 50 ch. Ichthyosaurus . . . 60 20

1022 Sprinting

1991. Olympic Games, Barcelona (1992). Mult.

N3068	10 ch. Type **1022**	10	10
N3069	10 ch. Hurdling	10	10
N3070	20 ch. Long jumping	25	10
N3071	20 ch. Throwing the discus	25	10
N3072	30 ch. Putting the shot	35	10
N3073	30 ch. Pole vaulting	35	10
N3074	40 ch. High jumping	50	15
N3075	40 ch. Throwing the javelin	50	15

1023 Cats and Birds

1991. Cats. Multicoloured.

N3077	10 ch. Type **1023**	10	10
N3078	20 ch. Cat and rat	15	10
N3079	30 ch. Cat and butterfly	20	10
N3080	40 ch. Cats with ball	25	10
N3081	50 ch. Cat and frog	30	10

1025 Wild Horse

1991. Horses. Multicoloured.

N3083	10 ch. Type **1025**	10	10
N3084	20 ch. Hybrid of wild ass and wild horse	15	10
N3085	30 ch. Przewalski's horse	20	10
N3086	40 ch. Wild ass	25	10
N3087	50 ch. Wild horse (different)	30	10

1026 Pennant Coralfish

1991. Fishes. Multicoloured.

N3088	10 ch. Type **1026**	10	10
N3089	20 ch. Big-spotted triggerfish	15	10
N3090	30 ch. Anemone fish	20	10
N3091	40 ch. Blue surgeon fish	25	10
N3092	50 ch. Angelfish	30	10

1027 Rhododendrons

1991. Flowers. Multicoloured.

N3094	10 ch. Begonia	10	10
N3095	20 ch. Gerbera	15	10
N3096	30 ch. Type **1027**	20	10
N3097	40 ch. Phalaenopsis	25	10
N3098	50 ch. "Impatiens sultanii"	30	10
N3099	60 ch. Streptocarpus	35	10

Nos. N3097/9 commemorate "CANADA '92" International Youth Stamp Exhibition, Montreal.

1028 Panmunjom 1029 Magnolia

1991.

N3100	**1028** 10 ch. multicoloured	10	10

1991. National Flower.

N3101	**1029** 10 ch. multicoloured	10	10

1030 Players

1991. Women's World Football Championship, China. Multicoloured.

N3102	10 ch. Type **1030**	10	10
N3103	20 ch. Dribbling the ball	15	10
N3104	30 ch. Heading the ball	20	10
N3105	40 ch. Overhead kick	25	10
N3106	50 ch. Tackling	30	10
N3107	60 ch. Goalkeeper	35	10

1031 Squirrel Monkeys

1992. Monkeys. Multicoloured.

N3108	10 ch. Type **1031**	10	10
N3109	20 ch. Pygmy marmosets	15	10
N3110	30 ch. Red-handed tamarins	20	10

1032 Eagle Owl

1992. Birds of Prey. Multicoloured.

N3112	10 ch. Type **1032**	10	10
N3113	20 ch. Common buzzard	15	10
N3114	30 ch. African fish eagle	20	10
N3115	40 ch. Steller's sea eagle	25	10
N3116	50 ch. Golden eagle	30	10

1033 Birthplace, Mt. Paekdu

1992. Birthday of Kim Jong Il. Mt. Paekdu. Multicoloured.

N3118	10 ch. Type **1033**	10	10
N3119	20 ch. Mountain summit	15	10
N3120	30 ch. Mountain lake	20	10
N3121	40 ch. Mountain lake (different)	25	10

1034 Service Bus

1992. Transport.

N3123	**1034** 10 ch. multicoloured	10	10
N3124	– 20 ch. multicoloured	15	10
N3125	– 30 ch. multicoloured	20	10
N3126	– 40 ch. multicoloured	25	10
N3127	– 50 ch. multicoloured	30	10
N3128	– 60 ch. multicoloured	35	10

DESIGNS: 20 ch. to 60 ch. Different buses and trams.

1035 Dancers and Emblem

1992. Spring Friendship Art Festival, Pyongyang.

N3129	**1035** 10 ch. multicoloured	10	10

1036 Birthplace, Mangyongdae

1992. 80th Birthday of Kim Il Sung. Revolutionary Sites. Multicoloured.

N3130	10 ch. Type **1036** (post)	10	10
N3131	10 ch. Party emblem and monument	10	10
N3132	10 ch. Map and house on stilts	10	10
N3133	10 ch. Statue of soldier and house	10	10
N3134	40 ch. Cogwheels and building	25	10
N3135	40 ch. Chollima Statue and building	25	10
N3136	1 wn. 20 Monument and West Sea Barrage (air)	70	25

1038 Soldiers on Parade

1992. 60th Anniv of People's Army. Multicoloured.

N3139	10 ch. Type **1038**	10	10
N3140	10 ch. Couple greeting soldier	10	10
N3141	10 ch. Army, air force and navy personnel	10	10

1039 Hurdling

1992. Olympic Games, Barcelona. Multicoloured.

N3142	10 ch. Type **1039**	10	10
N3143	20 ch. High jumping	15	10
N3144	30 ch. Putting the shot	20	10
N3145	40 ch. Sprinting	25	10
N3146	50 ch. Long jumping	30	10
N3147	60 ch. Throwing the javelin	35	10

1040 Planting Crops

1992. Evolution of Man. Designs showing life in the New Stone Age (10, 20 ch.) and the Bronze Age (others). Multicoloured.

N3149	10 ch. Type **1040** (post)	10	10
N3150	20 ch. Family around cooking pot	15	10
N3151	30 ch. Ploughing fields	20	10
N3152	40 ch. Performing domestic chores	25	10
N3153	50 ch. Building a dolmen (air)	30	10

1041 White-bellied Black Woodpecker 1042 Map and Hands holding Text

1992. Birds. Multicoloured.

N3154	10 ch. Type **1041**	10	10
N3155	20 ch. Ring-necked pheasant	15	10

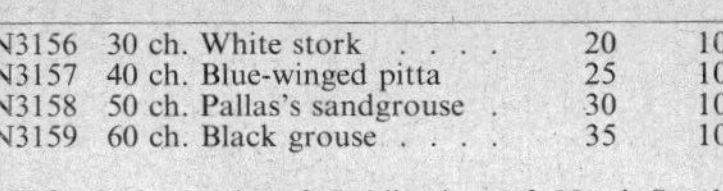

N3156	30 ch. White stork	20	10
N3157	40 ch. Blue-winged pitta	25	10
N3158	50 ch. Pallas's sandgrouse	30	10
N3159	60 ch. Black grouse	35	10

1992. 20th Anniv of Publication of North-South Korea Joint Agreement.

N3161	**1042** 1 wn. 50 multicoloured	90	30

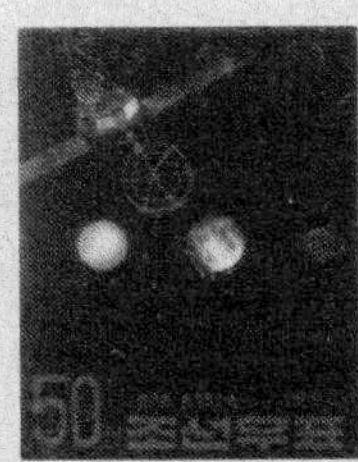

1043 "Bougainvillea spectabilis" 1044 Venus, Earth, Mars and Satellite

1992. Flowers. Multicoloured.

N3163	10 ch. Type **1043**	10	10
N3164	20 ch. "Ixora chinensis"	15	10
N3165	30 ch. "Dendrobium taysuwie"	20	10
N3166	40 ch. "Columnea gloriosa"	25	10
N3167	50 ch. Crinum	30	10
N3168	60 ch. "Ranunculus asiaticus"	35	10

1992. The Solar System. Multicoloured.

N3169	50 ch. Type **1044**	30	10
N3170	50 ch. Jupiter	30	10
N3171	50 ch. Saturn	30	10
N3172	50 ch. Uranus	30	10
N3173	50 ch. Neptune and Pluto	30	10

Nos. N3169/73 were issued together, se-tenant, forming a composite design.

1045 Yacht 1046 Moreno Mannini (defender)

1992. "Riccione '92" Stamp Fair. Multicoloured.

N3175	10 ch. Type **1045**	10	10
N3176	20 ch. Sailboard	15	10
N3177	30 ch. Sailing dinghy	20	10
N3178	40 ch. Sailing dinghy (different)	25	10
N3179	50 ch. Yacht (different)	30	10
N3180	60 ch. Emblem	45	15

1992. Sampdoria, Italian Football Champion, 1991. Multicoloured.

N3181	20 ch. Type **1046**	15	10
N3182	30 ch. Gianluca Vialli (forward)	20	10
N3183	40 ch. Pietro Vierchowod (defender)	25	10
N3184	50 ch. Fausto Pari (defender)	30	10
N3185	60 ch. Roberto Mancini (forward)	35	10
N3186	1 wn. Paolo Mantovani (club president)	60	20

1047 Black-belts warming up

1992. 8th World Taekwondo Championship, Pyongyang. Multicoloured.

N3188	10 ch. Type **1047**	10	10
N3189	30 ch. "Roundhouse" kick	20	10
N3190	50 ch. High kick	30	10
N3191	70 ch. Flying kick	40	15
N3192	90 ch. Black-belt breaking tiles with fist	55	20

1048 Common Toad ("Bufo bufo")

1992. Frogs and Toads. Multicoloured.

N3194	40 ch. Type **1048** (post)	25	10
N3195	40 ch. Moor frog ("Rana arvalis")	25	10
N3196	40 ch. "Rana chosenica"	25	10
N3197	70 ch. Common pond frog ("Rana nigromaculata")	40	15
N3198	70 ch. Japanese tree toad ("Hyla japonica")	40	15
N3199	70 ch. "Rana coreana" (air)	40	15

1049 "Rhododendron mucronulatum"

1992. World Environment Day. Multicoloured.

N3200 10 ch. Type **1049** (post) . . . 10 10
N3201 30 ch. Barn swallow . . . 20 10
N3202 40 ch. "Stewartia koreana" (flower) 25 10
N3203 50 ch. "Dictyoptera aurora" (insect) 30 10
N3204 70 ch. "Metasequoia glyptostroboides" (tree) 40 15
N3205 90 ch. Chinese salamander 55 20
N3206 1 wn. 20 "Ginkgo biloba" (plant) (air) 70 25
N3207 1 wn. 40 Spotted sculpin 80 25

1050 Fin Whale ("Balaenoptera physalis")

1992. Whales and Dolphins. Multicoloured.

N3208 50 ch. Type **1050** (post) . . 30 10
N3209 50 ch. Common dolphin ("Delphinus delphis") . . 30 10
N3210 50 ch. Killer Whale ("Orcinus orca") 30 10
N3211 50 ch. Hump-backed whale ("Megaptera nodosa") . 30 10
N3212 50 ch. Bottle-nosed whale ("Berardius bairdii") . . 30 10
N3213 50 ch. Sperm whale ("Physeter catadon") (air) 30 10

1051 Mother and Chicks

1992. New Year. Roosters in various costumes. Multicoloured.

N3214 10 ch. Type **1051** 10 10
N3215 20 ch. Lady 15 10
N3216 30 ch. Warrior 20 10
N3217 40 ch. Courtier 25 10
N3218 50 ch. Queen 30 10
N3219 60 ch. King 35 10

1052 Choe Chol Su (boxing)

1992. Gold Medal Winners at Barcelona Olympics. Multicoloured.

N3221 10 ch. Type **1052** 10 10
N3222 20 ch. Pae Kil Su (gymnastics) 15 10
N3223 30 ch. Flags of Spain and North Korea, flame, gold medal and archer 20 10
N3224 40 ch. Church of the Holy Family (Barcelona) and games mascot and emblem 25 10
N3225 50 ch. Ri Hak Son (freestyle wrestling) 30 10
N3226 60 ch. Kim Il (freestyle wrestling) 35 10

1053 Golden Mushroom

1055 League Members and Flag

1054 "Keumkangsania asiatica"

1993. Fungi. Multicoloured.

N3227 10 ch. Type **1053** 10 10
N3228 20 ch. Shaggy caps 15 10
N3229 30 ch. "Ganoderma lucidum" 20 10
N3230 40 ch. Brown mushroom 25 10
N3231 50 ch. "Volvaria bombycina" 30 10
N3232 60 ch. "Sarcodon aspratus" 35 10

1993. Plants. Multicoloured.

N3234 10 ch. Type **1054** 10 10
N3235 20 ch. "Echinosophora koreensis" 15 10
N3236 30 ch. "Abies koreana" . 20 10
N3237 40 ch. "Benzoin angustifolium" 25 10
N3238 50 ch. "Abeliophyllum distichum" 30 10
N3239 60 ch. "Abelia mosanensis" 35 10

1993. 8th League of Socialist Working Youth Congress. Multicoloured.

N3241 10 ch. Type **1055** 10 10
N3242 40 ch. Flame, League emblem and text 25 10

1056 Phophyong Revolutionary Site Tower and March Corps Emblem

1057 Tower of Juche Idea and Grand Monument, Mt. Wangjae

1993. 70th Anniv of Thousand-ri Journey for Learning.

N3243 **1056** 10 ch. multicoloured 10 10

1993. 60th Anniv of Wangjaesan Meeting.

N3244 **1057** 5 ch. multicoloured . 10 10

1058 "Kimjomgil" (begonia)

1059 Pilot Fish

1993. 51st Birthday of Kim Jong Il.

N3245 **1058** 10 ch. multicoloured 10 10

1993. Fishes. Multicoloured.

N3247 10 ch. Type **1059** 10 10
N3248 20 ch. Japanese stingray . 15 10
N3249 30 ch. Moonfish 20 10
N3250 40 ch. Coelacanth 25 10
N3251 50 ch. Grouper 30 10

1060/1064 "Spring on the Hill" (½-size illustration)

1993. 18th-century Korean Painting.

N3253 **1060** 40 ch. multicoloured 25 10
N3254 **1061** 40 ch. multicoloured 25 10
N3255 **1062** 40 ch. multicoloured 25 10
N3256 **1063** 40 ch. multicoloured 25 10
N3257 **1064** 40 ch. multicoloured 25 10

Nos. N3253/7 were issued together, se-tenant, forming the composite design illustrated.

1065 Violinist, Dancers and Emblem

1993. Spring Friendship Art Festival, Pyongyang.

N3258 **1065** 10 ch. multicoloured 10 10

MINIMUM PRICE

The minimum price quoted is 10p which represents a handling charge rather than a basis for valuing common stamps. For further notes about prices, see introductory pages.

1066 Books

1993. 80th Birthday of Kim Il Sung and Publication of his "Reminiscences With the Century".

N3259 **1066** 10 ch. multicoloured 10 10

1067 Kwangbok Street

1993. Pyongyang. Multicoloured.

N3261 10 ch. Type **1067** 10 10
N3262 20 ch. Chollima Street . . . 15 10
N3263 30 ch. Munsu Street 20 10
N3264 40 ch. Moranbong Street . 25 10
N3265 50 ch. Thongil Street . . . 30 10

1068 "Trichogramma dendrolimi" (fly)

1069 Ri In Mo

1993. Insects. Multicoloured.

N3267 10 ch. Type **1068** 10 10
N3268 20 ch. "Brachymeria obscurata" (fly) 15 10
N3269 30 ch. "Metrioptera brachyptera (cricket) . . 20 10
N3270 50 ch. European field cricket 30 10
N3271 70 ch. "Geocoris pallidipennis" (beetle) . . 45 15
N3272 90 ch. "Cyphonony x dorsalis" (wasp) fighting spider 55 20

1993. Return from Imprisonment of Ri In Mo (war correspondent).

N3273 **1069** 10 ch. multicoloured 10 10

1070 Footballers

1071 Grey-headed Green Woodpecker

1993. World Cup Football Championship, U.S.A.

N3275 **1070** 10 ch. multicoloured 10 10
N3276 – 20 ch. multicoloured 15 10
N3277 – 30 ch. multicoloured 20 10
N3278 – 50 ch. multicoloured 30 10
N3279 – 70 ch. multicoloured 45 15
N3280 – 90 ch. multicoloured 55 20

DESIGNS: 20 ch. to 90 ch. Various footballing scenes.

1993. Birds. Multicoloured.

N3281 10 ch. Type **1071** 10 10
N3282 20 ch. King bird of paradise 15 10
N3283 30 ch. Lesser bird of paradise 20 10
N3284 40 ch. "Steganura paradisea" 25 10
N3285 50 ch. Magnificent bird of paradise 30 10
N3286 60 ch. Greater bird of paradise 40 15

Nos. N3283/4 also commemorate "Indopex '93" International Stamp Exhibition, Surabaya.

1072 Korean Peninsula and Flag (½-size illustration)

1993. Self-adhesive. Roul.

N3287 **1072** 1 w. 50 multicoloured 90 30

No. N3287 is for any one of the six stamps which together make up the design illustrated. They are peeled from a card backing.

1073 Kim Myong Nam (weightlifting, 1990)

1993. World Champions. Multicoloured.

N3293 10 ch. Type **1073** 10 10
N3294 20 ch. Kim Kwang Suk (gymnastics, 1991) . . . 15 10
N3295 30 ch. Pak Yong Sun (table tennis, 1975, 1977) . . . 20 10
N3296 50 ch. Kim Yong Ok (radio direction-finding, 1990) 30 10
N3297 70 ch. Han Yun Ok (taekwondo, 1987, 1988, 1990) 45 15
N3298 90 ch. Kim Yong Sik (free-style wrestling, 1986, 1989) 55 20

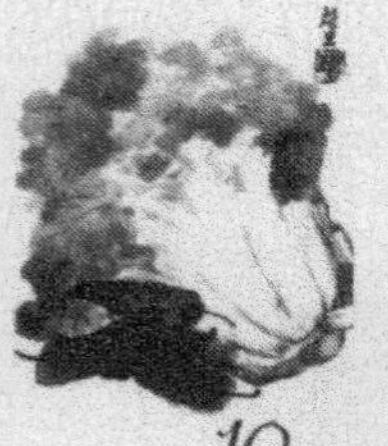

1074 Cabbage and Chilli Peppers

1075 State Arms

1993. Fruits and Vegetables. Multicoloured.

N3299 10 ch. Type **1074** 10 10
N3300 20 ch. Squirrels and horse chestnuts 15 10
N3301 30 ch. Grapes and peach 20 10
N3302 40 ch. Birds and persimmon 25 10
N3303 50 ch. Tomatoes, aubergine and cherries 30 10
N3304 60 ch. Radish, onion and garlic 40 15

1993.

N3305 **1075** 10 ch. orange 10 10

1076 Soldiers and Civilians

1993. 40th Anniv of Victory in Liberation War. Multicoloured.

N3306 10 ch. Type **1076** 10 10
N3307 10 ch. Officer and soldier 10 10
N3308 10 ch. Guided missiles on low-loaders on parade . . . 10 10
N3309 10 ch. Anti-aircraft missiles on lorries on parade . . 10 10
N3310 10 ch. Self-propelled missile launchers (tracked vehicles) on parade 10 10
N3311 10 ch. Machine gun placement (30 × 48 mm) 10 10
N3312 10 ch. Soldier with flag (30 × 48 mm) 10 10
N3313 10 ch. Soldier and flags (30 × 48 mm) 10 10
N3314 10 ch. Kim Il Sung at strategic policy meeting 10 10
N3315 10 ch. Kim Il Sung directing battle for Height 1211 10 10
N3316 10 ch. Kim Il Sung at munitions factory . . . 10 10
N3317 10 ch. Kim Il Sung with tank commanders 10 10
N3318 10 ch. Kim Il Sung with triumphant soldiers . . . 10 10
N3319 20 ch. Kim Il Sung with artillery unit 15 10
N3320 20 ch. Kim Il Sung encouraging machine gun crew 15 10
N3321 20 ch. Kim Il Sung studying map of Second Front . . 15 10
N3322 20 ch. Kim Il Sung with airmen 15 10
N3323 20 ch. Musicians ("Alive is art of Korea") 15 10

1077 Choe Yong Do

1078 "Robinia sp."

1993. National Reunification Prize Winners. Multicoloured.

N3325 10 ch. Type **1077** 10 10
N3326 20 ch. Kim Ku 15 10
N3327 30 ch. Hong Myong Hui . 20 10
N3328 40 ch. Ryo Un Hyong . . 25 10
N3329 50 ch. Kim Jong Thae . . 30 10
N3330 60 ch. Kim Chaek 40 15

1993. "Taipei '93" International Stamp Exhibition, Taipeh. Multicoloured.

N3331 20 ch. Type **1078** 15 10
N3332 30 ch. Hippeastrum 20 10

1079 Newton

1080 King Tongmyong shooting Bow

1993. 350th Birth Anniv (1992) of Sir Isaac Newton (mathematician and scientist). Multicoloured.

N3334 10 ch. Type **1079** 10 10
N3335 20 ch. Apple tree and formula of law of gravitation . . 15 10
N3336 30 ch. Satellite, reflecting telescope, dish aerial, globe and rocket 20 10
N3337 50 ch. Formula of binomial theorem 30 10
N3338 70 ch. Newton's works and statue 45 15

1993. Restoration of King Tongmyong of Koguryo's Tomb. Multicoloured.

N3339 10 ch. Type **1080** 10 10
N3340 20 ch. King Tongmyong saluting crowd 15 10
N3341 30 ch. Restoration monument 20 10
N3342 40 ch. Temple of the Tomb of King Tongmyong (horiz) 25 10
N3343 50 ch. Tomb (horiz) . . . 30 10

1082 "Cyrtopodium andresoni"

1084 Mao Tse-tung at Yanan, 1944

1993. Orchids. Multicoloured.

N3346 10 ch. Type **1082** 10 10
N3347 20 ch. "Cattleya CV" . . . 15 10
N3348 30 ch. "Cattleya intermedia" "Oculata" 20 10
N3349 40 ch. Potinaria "Maysedo godensia" 25 10
N3350 50 ch. Kimilsungia 30 10

1993. Birth Centenary of Mao Tse-tung. Multicoloured.

N3352 10 ch. Type **1084** 10 10
N3353 20 ch. Seated portrait (Peking, 1960) 15 10
N3354 30 ch. Casting a vote, 1953 20 10
N3355 40 ch. With pupils at Shaoshan Secondary School, 1959 . . . . . . 25 10

1085 Phungsan

1086 Purple Hyosong Flower

1994. New Year. Dogs. Multicoloured.

N3358 10 ch. Type **1085** 10 10
N3359 20 ch. Yorkshire terriers . 15 10
N3360 30 ch. Gordon setter . . . 20 10
N3361 40 ch. Pomeranian 25 10
N3362 50 ch. Spaniel with pups . 30 10

1994. 52nd Birthday of Kim Jong Il. Multicoloured.

N3364 10 ch. Type **1086** 10 10
N3365 40 ch. Yellow hyosong flower 25 10

1087 Red and Black Dragon-eye

1994. Goldfishes. Multicoloured.

N3367 10 ch. Type **1087** 10 10
N3368 30 ch. Red and white bubble-eye 20 10
N3369 50 ch. Red and white long-finned wenyu 30 10
N3370 70 ch. Red and white fringetail 40 15

1088 Crowd with Banners

1089 Wheat, Banner and Woman writing

1994. 20th Anniv of Publication of "Programme for Modelling the Whole Society on the Juche Idea" by Kim Jong Il.

N3371 **1088** 20 ch. multicoloured 15 10

1994. 30th Anniv of Publication of "Theses on the Socialist Rural Question in Our Country" by Kim Il Sung. Multicoloured.

N3373 10 ch. Type **1089** 10 10
N3374 10 ch. Electricity generating systems and pylon . . . 10 10
N3375 10 ch. Lush fields, grain and tractor 10 10
N3376 40 ch. Modern housing, books, food crops and laboratory technician . . 25 10
N3377 40 ch. Revellers 25 10

1090 "Mangyongbong-92"(passenger ship)

1091 National Flag

1994. Ships. Multicoloured.

N3379 20 ch. Type **1090** 15 10
N3380 30 ch. "Osandok" (cargo ship) 20 10
N3381 40 ch. "Ryongaksan" (factory stern trawler) 25 10
N3382 50 ch. Stern trawler . . . 30 10

1994.

N3384 **1091** 10 ch. red and blue 10 10

1092 Birthplace and Magnolia (national flower)

1093 "Chrysosplenium sphaerospermum"

1994. 81st Birthday of Kim Il Sung. Multicoloured.

N3385 10 ch. Type **1092** 10 10
N3386 40 ch. Birthplace, Manyongdae, and Kim Il Sung flower 25 10

1994. Alpine Plants on Mt. Paekdu. Multicoloured.

N3388 10 ch. Type **1093** 10 10
N3389 20 ch. "Campanula cephalotes" 15 10
N3390 40 ch. "Trollius macropetalus" 25 10
N3391 40 ch. "Gentiana algida" 25 10
N3392 50 ch. "Sedum kamtschaticum" 30 10

1094 National Olympic Committee Emblem

1095 Red Cross Launch ("Relief on the Sea")

1994. Centenary of International Olympic Committee. Multicoloured.

N3394 10 ch. Type **1094** 10 10
N3395 20 ch. Pierre de Coubertin (founder) 15 10
N3396 30 ch. Olympic flag and flame 20 10
N3397 50 ch. Emblem of Centennial Olympic Congress, Paris . 30 15

1994. 75th Anniv of International Red Cross and Red Crescent Federation. Multicoloured.

N3399 10 ch. Tram, pedestrians on footbridge and traffic lights ("Prevention of Traffic Accident") 10 10
N3400 20 ch. Type **1095** 15 10
N3401 30 ch. Planting tree ("Protection of Environment") 20 10
N3402 40 ch. Dam ("Prevention of Drought Damage") 25 10

1994. No. N3287 surch **160** in circle.

N3403 **1072** 1 wn. 60 on 1 wn. 50 multicoloured . . . 95 30

1097 Northern Fur Seal

1994. Marine Mammals. Multicoloured.

N3404 10 ch. Type **1097** 10 10
N3405 40 ch. Southern elephant seal 25 10
N3406 60 ch. Southern sealion . . 35 10

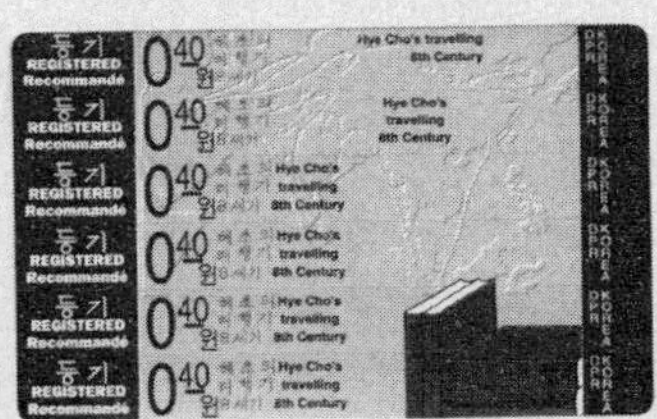
1098 Map of Asia and Books (½-size illustration)

1994. 8th-century Travels of Hye Cho. Self-adhesive. Roul.

N3408 **1098** 40 ch. multicoloured . 25 10

No. N3408 is for any one of the six stamps which together make up the design illustrated. They are peeled from a card backing.

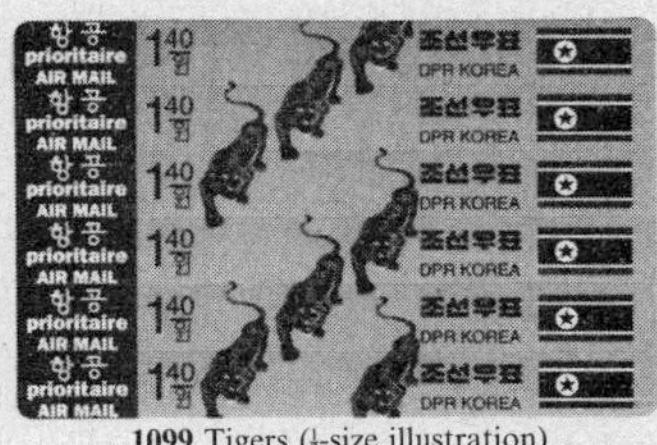
1099 Tigers (½-size illustration)

1994. Self-adhesive. Roul.

N3409 **1099** 1 wn. 40 multicoloured 85 30

No. N3409 is for any one of the six stamps which together make up the design illustrated. They are peeled from a card backing.

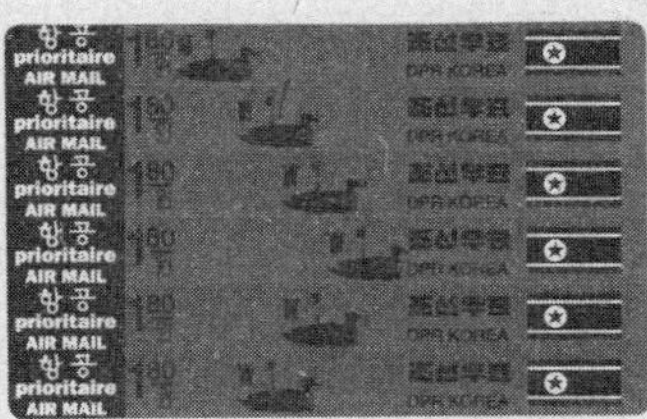
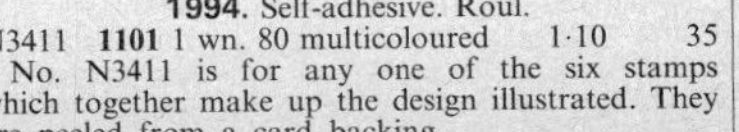
1101 "Turtle" Ships (½-size illustration)

1994. Self-adhesive. Roul.

N3411 **1101** 1 wn. 80 multicoloured 1·10 35

No. N3411 is for any one of the six stamps which together make up the design illustrated. They are peeled from a card backing.

1102 "Phalium strigatum"

1104 Korean Script and "100"

1103 Trapeze

1994. Crustacea. Multicoloured.

N3412 30 ch. Type **1102** 20 10
N3413 40 ch. "Gomphina veneriformis" 25 10

1994. Circus Acrobatics. Multicoloured.

N3416 10 ch. Type **1103** 10 10
N3417 20 ch. Reino (Swedish acrobat) performing rope dance 15 10
N3418 30 ch. Seesaw performer . . 20 10
N3419 40 ch. Unicycle juggler . . 25 10

1994. Birth Centenary of Kim Hyong Jik (father of Kim Il Sung). Multicoloured.

N3420 **1104** 10 ch. multicoloured . 10 10

1105 Jon Pong Jun and Battle Scene

1994. Centenary of Kabo Peasant War.

N3422 **1105** 10 ch. multicoloured . 10 10

1107 Crowd and Banner

1109 "Acorus calamus"

1108 Onsong Fish

1994. Revolutionary Economic Strategy.

N3424 **1107** 10 ch. multicoloured . 10 10

1994. Fossils. Multicoloured.

N3425 40 ch. Type **1108** 25 10
N3426 40 ch. Metasequoia 25 10
N3427 40 ch. Mammoth teeth . . 25 10
N3428 80 ch. Archaeopteryx . . . 45 15

1994. Medicinal Plants. Multicoloured.

N3429 20 ch. Type **1109** 10 10
N3430 30 ch. "Arctium lappa" . . 20 10

APPENDIX

The following stamps have either been issued in excess of postal needs or have not been available to the public in reasonable quantities at face value. Such stamps may later be given full listing if there is evidence of regular postal use.

1976.

Olympic Games, Montreal. Three-dimensional stamps showing Olympic events. 5, 10, 15, 20, 25, 40 ch.

1977.

Olympic Games, Montreal. Three-dimensional stamps showing medals. 5, 10, 15, 20, 25, 40 ch.
Olympic Games, Montreal. 1976 Olympic Games issue optd with winners' names. 5, 10, 15, 20, 25, 40 ch.

1979.

XIII Winter Olympic Games, 1980. Nos. N1688/94 optd 2, 5, 10, 15, 20, 25, 40 ch.

1981.
Nobel Prizes for Medicine. Nos. N1955/61 optd 7×10 ch.
World Cup Football Championship, Spain (1982). Nos. N1731/41 optd 12×20 ch.
World Cup Football Championship, Spain (1982). Three-dimensional stamps. Air 20, 30 ch.

1982.
21st Birthday of Princess of Wales. Nos. N2108/11 and N2120/3 optd 10, 20, 30, 40 ch. 10, 20, 30, 70 ch.
Birth of Prince William of Wales. Nos. N2185/91 optd 10, 20, 30, 50, 60, 70, 80 ch.
Birth of Prince William of Wales. Three-dimensional stamps. 3×30 ch.

1983.
XXIII Olympic Games, Los Angeles, 1984. Nos. N2084/8 optd 10, 15, 20, 25, 30 ch.

1984.
European Royal History. 81×10 ch.

KOUANG TCHEOU (KWANGCHOW) — Pt. 17

An area and port of S. China, leased by France from China in April 1898. It was returned to China in February 1943.

1906. 100 centimes = 1 franc
1919. 100 cents = 1 piastre

Unless otherwise stated the following are optd or surch on stamps of Indo-China.

1906. Surch **Kouang Tcheou-Wan** and value in Chinese.

No.	Type	Description	Unused	Used
1	8	1 c. olive	1·50	1·50
2		2 c. red on yellow	1·50	1·40
3		4 c. purple on grey	2·00	1·90
4		5 c. green	2·00	2·00
5		10 c. red	2·00	2·00
6		15 c. brown on blue	5·00	4·75
7		20 c. red on green	2·00	2·00
8		25 c. blue	2·00	2·00
9		30 c. brown on cream	2·50	2·50
10		35 c. black on yellow	3·50	3·25
11		40 c. black on grey	2·50	2·50
12		50 c. brown on cream	10·00	10·00
13	D	75 c. brown on orange	15·00	15·00
14	8	1 f. green	18·00	18·00
15		2 f. brown on yellow	18·00	18·00
16	D	5 f. mauve on lilac	£120	£120
17	8	10 f. red on green	£150	£150

1908. Native types surch **KOUANG-TCHEOU** and value in Chinese.

No.	Type	Description	Unused	Used
18	10	1 c. black and brown	40	45
19		2 c. black and brown	40	50
20		4 c. black and blue	45	50
21		5 c. black and green	45	45
22		10 c. black and red	45	45
23		15 c. black and violet	1·10	1·10
24	11	20 c. black and violet	2·00	2·00
25		25 c. black and blue	2·50	2·50
26		30 c. black and brown	4·25	4·50
27		35 c. black and green	5·75	6·00
28		40 c. black and brown	6·00	6·00
29		50 c. black and red	6·50	6·50
30	12	75 c. black and orange	6·50	6·50
31	–	1 f. black and red	7·50	7·50
32	–	2 f. black and green	20·00	20·00
33	–	5 f. black and blue	40·00	40·00
34	–	10 f. black and violet	60·00	60·00

1919. Nos. 18/34 surch in figures and words.

No.	Type	Description	Unused	Used
35	10	⅖ on 1 c. black and brown	40	45
36		⅘ c. on 2 c. black and brown	35	45
37		1⅗ c. on 4 c. black and blue	50	55
38		2 c. on 5 c. black and green	55	55
39		4 c. on 10 c. black and red	1·40	85
40		6 c. on 15 c. black & violet	55	45
41	11	8 c. on 20 c. black & violet	2·00	1·90
42		10 c. on 25 c. black and blue	5·50	5·00
43		12 c. on 30 c. black & brown	1·10	85
44		14 c. on 35 c. black & green	1·25	1·10
45		16 c. on 40 c. black & brown	90	70
46		20 c. on 50 c. black and red	90	65
47	12	30 c. on 75 c. black & orange	3·50	3·50
48	–	40 c. on 1 f. black and red	4·25	4·25
49	–	80 c. on 2 f. black and green	5·00	4·25
50	–	2 p. on 5 f. black and blue	95·00	90·00
51	–	4 p. on 10 f. black & violet	12·00	11·50

1923. Native types optd **KOUANG-TCHEOU** only. (Value in cents and piastres).

No.	Type	Description	Unused	Used
52	10	⅒ c. red and grey	15	30
53		⅕ c. black and blue	15	30
54		⅖ c. black and brown	20	30
55		⅘ c. black and red	25	35
56		1 c. black and brown	35	35
57		2 c. black and green	55	55
58		3 c. black and violet	55	55
59		4 c. black and orange	55	55
60		5 c. black and red	55	55
61	11	6 c. black and red	70	55
62		7 c. black and green	55	70
63		8 c. black on lilac	90	55
64		9 c. black & yellow on green	90	85
65		10 c. black and blue	85	85
66		11 c. black and violet	85	85
67		12 c. black and brown	85	85
68		15 c. black and orange	1·40	1·40
69		20 c. black and blue on buff	90	85
70		40 c. black and red	1·75	1·75
71		1 p. black & green on green	4·75	4·75
72		2 p. black & purple on pink	7·50	7·75

1927. Pictorial types optd **KOUANG-TCHEOU**.

No.	Type	Description	Unused	Used
73	22	⅒ c. olive	15	30
74		⅕ c. yellow	20	30
75		⅖ c. blue	25	35
76		⅘ c. brown	30	35
77		1 c. orange	40	45
78		2 c. green	55	55
79		3 c. blue	55	55
80		4 c. mauve	55	55
81		5 c. violet	55	55
82	23	6 c. red	50	55
83		7 c. brown	50	55
84		8 c. olive	55	55
85		9 c. purple	65	65
86		10 c. blue	65	65
87		11 c. orange	65	70
88		12 c. green	65	65
89	24	15 c. brown and red	1·10	1·10
90		20 c. grey and violet	1·40	1·40
91	–	25 c. mauve and brown	1·40	1·40
92	–	30 c. olive and blue	95	95
93	–	40 c. blue and red	90	85
94	–	50 c. grey and green	1·00	1·00
95	–	1 p. black, yellow and blue	2·50	2·50
96	–	2 p. blue, orange and red	2·75	2·75

1937. 1931 issue optd **KOUANG-TCHEOU**.

No.	Type	Description	Unused	Used
98	33	⅒ c. blue	15	30
99		⅕ c. lake	20	30
100		⅖ c. red	15	30
101		½ c. brown	15	25
102		⅘ c. violet	30	30
103	33	1 c. brown	20	30
104		2 c. green	20	30
126	–	3 c. brown	30	30
105	–	3 c. green	50	45
106	–	4 c. blue	55	55
127	–	4 c. green	30	30
128	–	4 c. yellow	1·00	1·00
107	–	5 c. purple	55	55
129	–	5 c. green	35	35
108	–	6 c. red	35	45
130	–	7 c. black	35	45
131	–	8 c. lake	35	45
132	–	9 c. black on yellow	40	45
109	–	10 c. blue	65	65
133	–	10 c. blue on pink	50	55
110	–	15 c. blue	40	45
134	–	18 c. blue	20	30
111	–	20 c. red	40	45
112	–	21 c. green	40	45
135	–	22 c. green	35	35
113	–	25 c. purple	1·60	1·60
136	–	25 c. blue	45	45
114	–	30 c. brown	35	45
115	36	50 c. brown	55	60
116		60 c. purple	60	60
137		70 c. blue	45	45
117		1 p. green	85	90
118		2 p. red	1·00	1·00

1939. New York World's Fair. As T **28** of Mauritania.

No.	Type	Description	Unused	Used
119		13 c. red	50	55
120		23 c. deep blue and blue	50	55

1939. 150th Anniv of French Revolution. As T **29** of Mauritania.

No.	Type	Description	Unused	Used
121		6 c. + 2 c. green	3·75	3·75
122		7 c. + 3 c. brown	3·75	3·75
123		9 c. + 4 c. orange	3·75	3·75
124		13 c. + 10 c. red	3·75	3·75
125		23 c. + 20 c. blue	3·75	3·75

KUWAIT — Pt. 19

An independent Arab Shaikhdom on the N.W. coast of the Persian Gulf with Indian and later British postal administration. On 1st February, 1959, the Kuwait Government assumed responsibility for running its own postal service. In special treaty relations with Great Britain until 19 June 1961 when Kuwait became completely independent.

For stamps issued by Indian and British postal administrations, see Vol. 3.

1958. 100 naye paise = 1 rupee.
1961. 1,000 fils = 1 dinar.

20 Shaikh Abdullah

21 Dhow

1958.

No.	Type	Description	Unused	Used
131	20	5 n.p. green	15	10
132		10 n.p. red	20	10
133		15 n.p. brown	20	10
134		20 n.p. violet	20	10
135		25 n.p. salmon	35	10
136		40 n.p. purple	75	20
137	21	40 n.p. blue	45	10
138	–	50 n.p. red	40	10
139	–	75 n.p. green	45	15
140	–	1 r. purple	50	10
141	–	2 r. blue and brown	2·50	25
142	–	5 r. turquoise	4·00	1·25
143	–	10 r. lilac	13·00	3·75

DESIGNS—HORIZ: As Type **21**: 50 n.p. Oil pipelines; 75 n.p. Power Station. (36×20 mm): 1 r. Oil rig; 2 r. Single-masted dhow; 5 r. Kuwait Mosque; 10 r. Main Square, Kuwait Town.

22 Shaikh Abdullah and Flag

1960. 10th Anniv of Shaikh's Accession.

No.	Type	Description	Unused	Used
144	22	40 n.p. red and olive	25	10
145		60 n.p. red and blue	35	15

1961. As 1958 issue but currency changed and new designs.

No.	Type	Description	Unused	Used
146	20	1 f. green	15	10
147		2 f. red	15	10
148		4 f. brown	15	10
149		5 f. violet	15	10
150		8 f. red	20	10
151		15 f. purple	25	10
152	–	20 f. green (as 5 f.)	50	10
153	–	25 f. blue	90	10
154	–	30 f. blue & brown (as 2 r.)	1·25	10
155	–	35 f. black and red	75	40
156	21	40 f. blue (32×22 mm)	1·25	15
157	–	45 f. brown	50	10
158	–	75 f. brown & grn (as 2 r.)	2·50	60
159	–	90 f. brown and blue	1·75	35
160	–	100 f. red	3·25	10
161	21	250 f. green (32×22 mm)	1·00	1·50
162	–	1 d. orange	10·00	1·50
163	–	3 d. red (as 5 r.)	25·00	18·00

NEW DESIGNS—37×20 mm: 25, 100 f. Vickers Viscount 700 airliner over South Pier, Mina al Ahmadi; 35 f., 90 f. Shuwaikh Secondary School; 45 f., 1 d. Wara Hill.

23 Telegraph Pole

1962. 4th Arab Telecommunications Union Conference.

No.	Type	Description	Unused	Used
164	23	8 f. blue and black	15	10
165		20 f. red and black	30	20

1962. Arab League Week. As T **76** of Libya.

No.	Type	Description	Unused	Used
166		20 f. purple	10	10
167		45 f. brown	30	20

25 Mubarakiya School, Shaikh Abdullah and Shaikh Mubarak

1962. Golden Jubilee of Mubarakiya School.

No.	Type	Description	Unused	Used
168	25	8 f. multicoloured	15	10
169		20 f. multicoloured	40	15

26 National Flag and Crest

1962. National Day.

No.	Type	Description	Unused	Used
170	26	8 f. multicoloured	10	10
171		20 f. multicoloured	35	20
172		45 f. multicoloured	80	30
173		90 f. multicoloured	1·25	1·00

1962. Malaria Eradication. As T **26a** of Yemen.

No.	Type	Description	Unused	Used
174		4 f. green and turquoise	10	10
175		25 f. grey and green	30	25

28 "Industry and Progress"

1962. Bicentenary of Sabah Dynasty.

No.	Type	Description	Unused	Used
176	28	8 f. multicoloured	10	10
177		20 f. multicoloured	25	15
178		45 f. multicoloured	55	15
179		75 f. multicoloured	95	50

29 Mother and Child

31 "Education from Oil"

30 Campaign Emblem, Palm and Domestic Animals

1963. Mothers' Day. Centres black and green; value black; country name red.

No.	Type	Description	Unused	Used
180	29	8 f. yellow	10	10
181		20 f. blue	20	15
182		45 f. olive	45	25
183		75 f. grey	70	40

1963. Freedom from Hunger. Design in brown and green. Background colours given.

No.	Type	Description	Unused	Used
184	30	4 f. blue	10	10
185		8 f. yellow	25	15
186		20 f. lilac	50	25
187		45 f. pink	1·25	90

1963. Education Day.
188 31 4 f. brown, blue and yellow 10 10
189 20 f. green, blue and yellow 30 10
190 45 f. purple, blue and yellow 60 25

32 Shaikh Abdullah and Flags

1963. 2nd Anniv of National Day. Flags in green, black and red; values in black.
191 32 4 f. blue 40 30
192 5 f. ochre 60 55
193 20 f. violet 3·00 2·25
194 50 f. olive 6·00 3·75

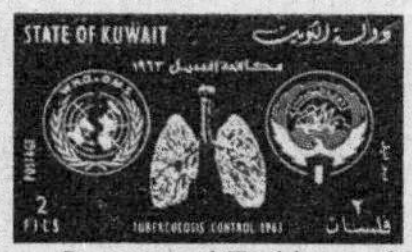

33 Human Lungs, and Emblems of W.H.O. and Kuwait

1963. W.H.O. "Tuberculosis Control" Campaign. Emblem yellow: Arms black, green and red.
195 33 2 f. black and ochre 10 10
196 4 f. black and green 10 10
197 8 f. black and blue 20 10
198 20 f. black and lake 80 35

34 Municipal Hall and Scroll

1963. New Constitution. Centres dull purple; Amir red.
199 34 4 f. red 10 20
200 8 f. green 15 25
201 20 f. purple 25 30
202 45 f. brown 45 35
203 75 f. violet 65 65
204 90 f. blue 1·40 2·00

35 Football
36 Scales of Justice and Globe 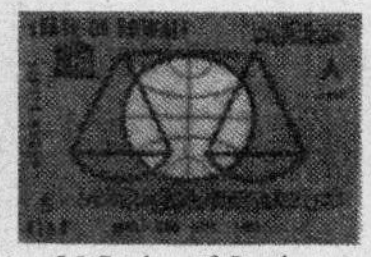

1963. Arab Schools Games. Multicoloured.
205 1 f. Type 35 10 10
206 4 f. Basketball 10 10
207 5 f. Swimming 10 10
208 8 f. Running 15 10
209 15 f. Throwing the javelin 30 15
210 20 f. Pole vaulting 40 20
211 35 f. Gymnastics 90 35
212 45 f. Gymnastics 1·25 75
Nos. 207, 209/11 are horiz.

1963. 15th Anniv of Declaration of Human Rights.
213 36 8 f. black, turquoise & vio 10 10
214 20 f. black, yellow & grey 40 20
215 25 f. black, buff and blue 60 30

37 Shaikh Abdullah
38 Rameses II in War Chariot 

1964.
216 37 1 f. multicoloured. 10 10
217 2 f. multicoloured. 10 10
218 4 f. multicoloured. 15 10
219 5 f. multicoloured. 15 10
220 8 f. multicoloured. 25 10
221 10 f. multicoloured. 25 10
222 15 f. multicoloured. 35 10
223 20 f. multicoloured. 35 10
224 25 f. multicoloured. 40 10
225 30 f. multicoloured. 55 10
226 40 f. multicoloured. 75 10
227 45 f. multicoloured. 90 10
228 50 f. multicoloured. 95 10
229 70 f. Multicoloured. 1·00 20
230 75 f. Multicoloured. 1·50 30
231 90 f. Multicoloured. 1·50 30
232 100 f. Multicoloured. 1·75 20
233 – 250 f. Multicoloured. 5·50 50
234 – 1 d. Multicoloured. 15·00 2·50
Nos. 233/4 are larger (25 × 30 mm).

1964. Nubian Monuments Preservation.
235 38 8 f. purple, blue and buff 15 10
236 20 f. violet, blue & lt blue 35 15
237 30 f. violet, blue & turquoise 45 25

39 Mother and Child

1964. Mother's Day.
238 39 8 f. blue, green and grey 10 10
239 20 f. blue, green and red 25 10
240 30 f. blue, green and bistre 35 20
241 45 f. blue, green and blue 50 20

40 Nurse giving B.C.G. Vaccine to Patient, and Bones of Chest
41 Dhow and Microscope 

1964. World Health Day.
242 40 8 f. green and brown 35 10
243 20 f. red and green 90 20

1964. Education Day.
244 41 8 f. multicoloured 15 10
245 15 f. multicoloured 30 10
246 20 f. multicoloured 35 15
247 30 f. multicoloured 60 25

42 Dhow and Doves

1964. 3rd Anniv of National Day. Badge in blue, brown, black, red and green.
248 42 8 f. black and bistre 15 10
249 20 f. black and green 25 10
250 30 f. black and grey 40 15
251 45 f. black and blue 55 25

43 A.P.U. Emblem
44 Hawker Siddeley Comet 4C and Douglas DC-3 Airliners 

1964. 10th Anniv of Arab Postal Union's Permanent Office, Cairo.
252 43 8 f. brown and blue 35 10
253 20 f. blue and yellow 50 10
254 45 f. brown and olive 90 35

1964. Air. 10th Anniv of Kuwait Airways. Sky in blue; aircraft blue, red and black.
255 44 20 f. black and bistre 45 15
256 25 f. black and brown 55 15
257 30 f. black and olive 65 20
258 45 f. black and brown 85 35

45 Conference Emblem
46 Dhow, Doves and Oil-drilling Rig 

1965. 1st Arab Journalists' Conference, Kuwait.
259 45 8 f. multicoloured 15 10
260 20 f. multicoloured 35 15

1965. 4th Anniv of National Day.
261 46 10 f. multicoloured 15 10
262 15 f. multicoloured 30 15
263 20 f. multicoloured 45 20

47 I.C.Y. Emblem
48 Mother and Children 

1965. International Co-operation Year.
264 47 8 f. black and red 30 10
265 20 f. black and blue 75 30
266 30 f. black and green 1·10 50
The stamps are inscribed "CO-OPERATIVE".

1965. Mothers' Day.
267 48 8 f. multicoloured 20 10
268 15 f. multicoloured 30 20
269 20 f. multicoloured 50 25

49 Weather Kite

1965. World Meteorological Day.
270 49 4 f. blue and yellow 30 10
271 5 f. blue and orange 30 10
272 20 f. blue and green 1·40 50

50 Census Graph

1965. Population Census.
273 50 8 f. black, brown & turquoise 20 10
274 20 f. black, pink and green 60 20
275 50 f. black, green and red 1·40 60

1965. Deir Yassin Massacre. As T 52a of Yemen.
276 4 f. red and blue 25 10
277 45 f. red and green 1·75 60

51 Atomic Symbol and Tower of Shuwaikh Secondary School

1965. Education Day.
278 51 4 f. multicoloured 15 10
279 20 f. multicoloured 40 15
280 45 f. multicoloured 75 35

52 I.T.U. Emblem and Symbols
53 Saker Falcon 

1965. I.T.U. Centenary.
281 52 8 f. red and blue 30 10
282 20 f. red and green 75 20
283 45 f. blue and red 1·75 55

1965. Reconstitution of Burnt Algiers Library. As T 53a of Yemen.
284 8 f. green, red and black 30 10
285 15 f. red, green and black 80 15

1965. Centre in sepia.
286 53 8 f. purple 75 10
287 15 f. olive 1·10 10
288 20 f. blue 1·25 10
289 25 f. red 1·25 15
290 30 f. green 1·75 20
291 45 f. blue 2·75 30
292 50 f. purple 3·25 40
293 90 f. red 5·00 1·25

54 Open Book
55 Shaikh Sabah 

1966. Education Day.
294 54 8 f. multicoloured 20 10
295 20 f. multicoloured 45 10
296 30 f. multicoloured 70 25

1966.
297 55 4 f. multicoloured 15 10
298 5 f. multicoloured 15 10
299 20 f. multicoloured 40 10
300 30 f. multicoloured 55 10
301 40 f. multicoloured 70 15
302 45 f. multicoloured 75 20
303 70 f. multicoloured 1·75 50
304 90 f. multicoloured 2·00 75

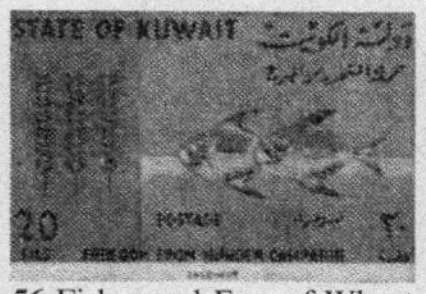

56 Fishes and Ears of Wheat

1966. Freedom from Hunger.
305 56 20 f. multicoloured 1·50 25
306 45 f. multicoloured 2·00 55

57 Eagle and Scales of Justice

1966. 5th Anniv of National Day.
307 57 20 f. multicoloured 85 20
308 25 f. multicoloured 95 25
309 45 f. multicoloured 1·75 65

58 Cogwheel and Map of Arab States
59 Mother and Children 

1966. Arab Countries Industrial Development Conference, Kuwait.
310 58 20 f. green black and blue 60 10
311 50 f. green, black & brown 1·00 35

1966. Mothers' Day.
312 59 20 f. multicoloured 30 12
313 45 f. multicoloured 70 35

60 Red Crescent Emblem of Medicine
61 "Man and his Cities" 

1966. 5th Arab Medical Conference, Kuwait.
314 60 15 f. red and blue 35 10
315 30 f. red, blue and pink 75 20

1966. World Health Day.
316 61 8 f. multicoloured 25 10
317 10 f. multicoloured 35 10

62 W.H.O. Building
63 Symbol of Blood Donation 

1966. Inaug of W.H.O. Headquarters, Geneva.
318 62 5 f. green, blue and red 45 10
319 10 f. green, blue & turq 80 10

1966. Traffic Day. As T 66 of Yemen.
320 10 f. red, emerald and green 50 10
321 20 f. emerald, red and green 75 20

1966. Blood Bank Day.
322 63 4 f. multicoloured 40 10
323 8 f. multicoloured 85 25

64 Shaikh Ahmad and "British Fusilier" (tanker)

1966. 20th Anniv of 1st Crude Oil Shipment.
324 **64** 20 f. multicoloured 60 20
325 45 f. multicoloured . . . . 1·40 60

65 Ministry Building

1966. Inauguration of Ministry of Guidance and Information. Building.
326 **65** 4 f. red and brown 15 10
327 5 f. brown and green . . . 15 10
328 8 f. green and violet 20 10
329 20 f. orange and blue . . . 60 15

66 Dhow, Lobster, Fish and Crab 67 U.N. Flag

1966. F.A.O. Near East Countries Fisheries Conference, Kuwait.
330 **66** 4 f. multicoloured 35 20
331 20 f. multicoloured . . . . 1·40 55

1966. U.N. Day.
332 **67** 20 f. multicoloured 75 20
333 45 f. multicoloured . . . . 1·50 65

68 U.N.E.S.C.O. Emblem 69 Ruler and University Shield

1966. 20th Anniv of U.N.E.S.C.O.
334 **68** 20 f. multicoloured 75 20
335 45 f. multicoloured . . . . 1·50 65

1966. Opening of Kuwait University.
336 **69** 8 f. multicoloured 25 10
337 10 f. multicoloured 25 10
338 20 f. multicoloured 75 20
339 45 f. multicoloured . . . . 1·50 70

70 Ruler and Heir-Apparent

1966. Appointment of Heir-Apparent.
340 **70** 8 f. multicoloured 25 10
341 20 f. multicoloured 60 15
342 45 f. multicoloured . . . . 1·25 55

71 Scout Badge 72 Symbol of Learning

1966. 30th Anniv of Kuwait Scouts.
343 **71** 4 f. brown and green . . . 75 15
344 20 f. green and brown . . . 2·50 70

1967. Education Day.
345 **72** 10 f. multicoloured 25 10
346 45 f. multicoloured 70 25

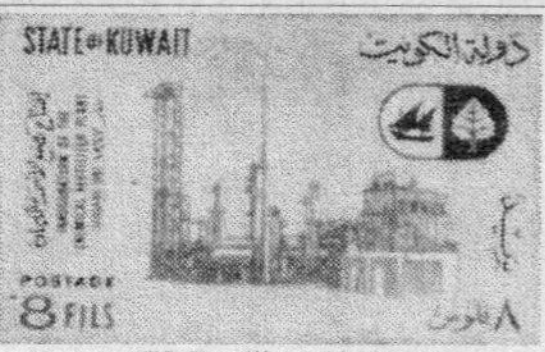

73 Fertiliser Plant

1967. Inauguration of Chemical Fertiliser Plant.
347 **73** 8 f. purple, green and blue 40 10
348 20 f. blue, green and buff 1·00 20

74 Ruler, Dove and Olive-branch

1967. 6th Anniv of National Day.
349 **74** 8 f. multicoloured 25 10
350 20 f. multicoloured 65 20

75 Map and Municipality Building 76 Arab Family

1967. 1st Arab Cities Organization Conf, Kuwait.
351 **75** 20 f. multicoloured . . . . 1·00 25
352 30 f. multicoloured . . . . 1·50 1·75

1967. Family's Day.
353 **76** 20 f. multicoloured . . . . 1·00 25
354 45 f. multicoloured . . . . 1·50 60

77 Arab League Emblem 78 Sabah Hospital

1967. Arab Cause Week.
355 **77** 8 f. blue and grey 15 10
356 10 f. green and yellow . . 15 10

1967. World Health Day.
357 **78** 8 f. multicoloured 45 10
358 20 f. multicoloured . . . . 1·40 15

79 Nubian Statues

1967. Arab Week for Nubian Monuments Preservation.
359 **79** 15 f. green, brown & yellow 60 15
360 20 f. green, purple and blue 90 25

80 Traffic Policeman

1967. Traffic Day.
361 **80** 8 f. multicoloured 75 15
362 20 f. multicoloured . . . . 1·75 45

MINIMUM PRICE

The minimum price quoted is 10p which represents a handling charge rather than a basis for valuing common stamps. For further notes about prices, see introductory pages.

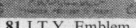

81 I.T.Y. Emblem 82 "Reaching for Knowledge"

1967. International Tourist Year.
363 **81** 20 f. black, blue & turq . . 55 15
364 45 f. black, blue and mauve 1·25 50

1967. "Eliminate Illiteracy" Campaign.
365 **82** 8 f. multicoloured 75 10
366 20 f. multicoloured . . . . 1·50 40

83 Map of Palestine 84 Factory and Cogwheels

1967. U.N. Day.
367 **83** 20 f. red and blue 60 15
368 45 f. red and orange . . . . 1·40 75

1967. 3rd Arab Labour Ministers' Conference.
369 **84** 20 f. yellow and red 60 15
370 45 f. yellow and slate . . . 1·40 70

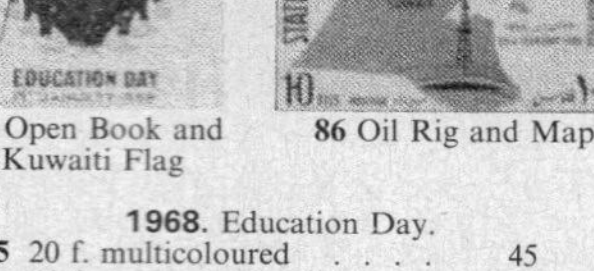

85 Open Book and Kuwaiti Flag 86 Oil Rig and Map

1968. Education Day.
371 **85** 20 f. multicoloured 45 10
372 45 f. multicoloured . . . . 1·25 55

1968. 30th Anniv of Oil Discovery in Greater Burgan Field.
373 **86** 10 f. multicoloured 65 15
374 20 f. multicoloured . . . . 1·25 55

87 Ruler and Sun Rays 88 Book, Eagle and Sun

1968. 7th Anniv of National Day.
375 **87** 8 f. multicoloured 20 10
376 10 f. multicoloured 20 10
377 15 f. multicoloured 30 10
378 20 f. multicoloured 45 15

1968. Teachers' Day.
379 **88** 8 f. multicoloured 25 10
380 20 f. multicoloured 55 15
381 45 f. multicoloured . . . . 1·25 55

89 Family Picnicking

1968. Family Day.
382 **89** 8 f. multicoloured 20 10
383 10 f. multicoloured 20 10
384 15 f. multicoloured 30 10
385 20 f. multicoloured 45 20

90 Ruler, W.H.O. and State Emblems

1968. World Health Day and 20th Anniv of W.H.O.
386 **90** 20 f. multicoloured 60 20
387 45 f. multicoloured . . . . 1·40 60

91 Dagger on Deir Yassin, and Scroll

1968. 20th Anniv of Deir Yassin Massacre.
388 **91** 20 f. red and blue 80 25
389 45 f. red and violet . . . . 2·75 70

92 Pedestrians on Road Crossing 93 Torch and Map

1968. Traffic Day.
390 **92** 10 f. multicoloured 75 20
391 15 f. multicoloured . . . . 1·25 25
392 20 f. multicoloured . . . . 1·75 50

1968. Palestine Day.
393 **93** 10 f. multicoloured 80 25
394 20 f. multicoloured . . . . 1·40 30
395 45 f. multicoloured . . . . 2·75 1·00

94 Palestine Refugees

1968. Human Rights Year.
396 **94** 20 f. multicoloured 25 15
397 30 f. multicoloured 35 25
398 45 f. multicoloured 65 30
399 90 f. multicoloured . . . . 1·25 1·00

95 National Museum 96 Man reading Book

1968.
400 **95** 1 f. green and sepia 10 10
401 2 f. green and plum . . . 10 10
402 5 f. red and black 15 10
403 8 f. green and brown . . . 20 10
404 10 f. purple and blue . . . 20 10
405 20 f. blue and brown . . . 40 10
406 25 f. orange and blue . . . 50 10
407 30 f. green and blue . . . 65 20
408 45 f. slate and purple . . . 95 20
409 50 f. red and green . . . 1·40 40

1968. International Literacy Day.
410 **96** 15 f. multicoloured 25 10
411 20 f. multicoloured 60 15

97 Refugee Children and U.N. Headquarters

1968. United Nations Day.
412 **97** 20 f. multicoloured 25 10
413 30 f. multicoloured 40 20
414 45 f. multicoloured 60 25

98 Chamber of Commerce Building

1968. Inauguration of Kuwait Chamber of Commerce and Industry Building.

415 **98** 10 f. purple and orange . . . 25 10
416 15 f. blue and mauve . . . 25 10
417 20 f. green and brown . . . 35 15

99 Conference Emblem

1968. 14th Arab Chambers of Commerce, Industry and Agriculture Conference.

418 **99** 10 f. multicoloured 25 10
419 15 f. multicoloured 30 10
420 20 f. multicoloured 40 20
421 30 f. multicoloured 60 35

100 Refinery Plant **101** Holy Koran, Scales and People

1968. Inauguration of Shuaiba Refinery.

422 **100** 10 f. multicoloured . . . 30 15
423 20 f. multicoloured . . . 55 15
424 30 f. multicoloured . . . 80 35
425 45 f. multicoloured . . . 1·40 60

1968. 1,400th Anniv of the Holy Koran.

426 **101** 8 f. multicoloured 30 10
427 20 f. multicoloured . . . 75 15
428 30 f. multicoloured . . . 1·10 40
429 45 f. multicoloured . . . 1·40 60

102 Boeing 707

1969. Inauguration of Boeing 707 Aircraft by Kuwait Airways.

430 **102** 10 f. multicoloured . . . 40 15
431 20 f. multicoloured . . . 80 25
432 25 f. multicoloured . . . 1·00 45
433 45 f. multicoloured . . . 2·00 80

103 Globe and Symbols of Engineering and Science

1969. Education Day.

434 **103** 15 f. multicoloured . . . 30 15
435 20 f. multicoloured . . . 50 25

104 Hilton Hotel **105** Family and Teachers' Society Emblem

1969. Inauguration of Kuwait Hilton Hotel.

436 **104** 10 f. multicoloured . . . 25 15
437 20 f. multicoloured . . . 50 15

1969. Education Week.

438 **105** 10 f. multicoloured . . . 25 15
439 20 f. multicoloured . . . 50 15

INDEX

Countries can be quickly located by referring to the index at the end of this volume.

106 Flags and Laurel **107** Emblem, Teacher and Class

1969. 8th Anniv of National Day.

440 **106** 15 f. multicoloured . . . 25 15
441 20 f. multicoloured . . . 30 15
442 30 f. multicoloured . . . 50 30

1969. Teachers' Day.

443 **107** 10 f. multicoloured . . . 20 15
444 20 f. multicoloured . . . 40 15

108 Kuwaiti Family

1969. Family Day.

445 **108** 10 f. multicoloured . . . 25 15
446 20 f. multicoloured . . . 45 15

109 Ibn Sina, Nurse with Patient and W.H.O. Emblem **110** Motor-cycle Police

1969. World Health Day.

447 **109** 15 f. multicoloured . . . 50 15
448 20 f. multicoloured . . . 60 15

1969. Traffic Day.

449 **110** 10 f. multicoloured . . . 1·00 20
450 20 f. multicoloured . . . 2·00 30

111 I.L.O. Emblem

1969. 50th Anniv of I.L.O.

451 **111** 10 f. gold, black and red 20 10
452 20 f. gold, black and green 35 15

112 Tanker "Al Sabahiah"

1969. 4th Anniv of Kuwait Shipping Company.

453 **112** 20 f. multicoloured . . . 90 30
454 45 f. multicoloured . . . 1·90 95

113 Woman writing Letter **114** Amir Shaikh Sabah

1969. International Literacy Day.

455 **113** 10 f. multicoloured . . . 20 10
456 20 f. multicoloured . . . 40 20

1969. Portraits multicoloured; background colours given.

457 **114** 8 f. blue 25 10
458 10 f. red 25 10
459 15 f. grey 35 10
460 20 f. yellow 40 10
461 25 f. lilac 50 10
462 30 f. orange 70 10
463 45 f. drab 95 10
464 **114** 50 f. green . . . . 1·25 10
465 70 f. blue . . . . 1·50 25
466 75 f. blue . . . . 1·75 30
467 90 f. brown . . . . 2·25 35
468 250 f. purple . . . . . . 1·00 60
469 500 f. green . . . . . . 11·00 1·75
470 1 d. purple . . . . . . 18·00 2·50

115 "Appeal to World Conscience" **116** Earth Station

1969. United Nations Day.

471 **115** 10 f. blue, black and green 25 15
472 20 f. blue, black and ochre 50 15
473 45 f. blue, black and red 1·00 45

1969. Inauguration of Kuwait Satellite Communications Station. Multicoloured.

474 20 Type **116** 90 20
475 45 f. Dish aerial on Globe (vert) 1·90 70

117 Refugee Family **118** Globe, Symbols and I.E.Y. Emblem

1969. Palestinian Refugee Week.

476 **117** 20 f. multicoloured. . . . 1·25 25
477 45 f. multicoloured . . . . 2·75 75

1970. International Education Year.

478 **118** 20 f. multicoloured 40 20
479 45 f. multicoloured . . . . 1·00 60

119 Shoue

1970. Kuwait Sailing Dhows. Multicoloured.

480 8 f. Type **119** 40 10
481 10 f. Sambuk 40 10
482 15 f. Baggala 60 20
483 20 f. Battela 75 15
484 25 f. Bum 90 35
485 45 f. Baggala . . . . 1·75 40
486 50 f. Dhow-building . . . . . 2·00 60

120 Kuwaiti Flag

1970. 9th Anniv of National Day.

487 **120** 15 f. multicoloured 40 15
488 20 f. multicoloured 50 15

121 Young Commando and Dome of the Rock, Jerusalem

1970. Support for Palestine Commandos. Multicoloured.

489 10 f. Type **121** 60 20
490 20 f. Commando in battle-dress 1·25 20
491 45 f. Woman commando . . . 2·75 90

122 Parents with "Children"

1970. Family Day.

492 **122** 20 f. multicoloured . . . 30 15
493 30 f. multicoloured . . . 50 25

123 Arab League Flag, Emblem and Map

1970. 25th Anniv of Arab League.

494 **123** 20 f. ochre, green and blue 25 10
495 45 f. violet, green and pink 50 20

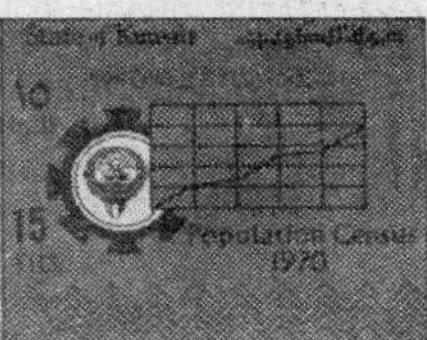

124 Census Emblem and Graph

1970. Population Census.

496 **124** 15 f. multicoloured . . . 25 10
497 20 f. multicoloured . . . 35 15
498 30 f. multicoloured . . . 60 30

125 Cancer the Crab in "Pincers" **126** Traffic Lights and Road Signs

1970. World Health Day.

499 **125** 20 f. multicoloured . . . 35 10
500 30 f. multicoloured . . . 55 25

1970. Traffic Day.

501 **126** 20 f. multicoloured . . . 1·25 25
502 30 f. multicoloured . . . 1·75 60

127 Red Crescent

1970. International Red Cross and Crescent Day.

503 **127** 10 f. multicoloured . . . 40 15
504 15 f. multicoloured . . . 60 15
505 30 f. multicoloured . . . 1·50 55

128 New Headquarters Building

1970. Opening of New U.P.U. Headquarters Building, Berne.

506 **128** 20 f. multicoloured . . . 50 10
507 30 f. multicoloured . . . 75 40

129 Amir Shaikh Sabah **130** U.N. Symbols

1970.

508 **129** 20 f. multicoloured . . . 50 20
509 45 f. multicoloured . . . 1·50 65

1970. 25th Anniv of United Nations.

511 **130** 20 f. multicoloured . . . 30 15
512 45 f. multicoloured . . . 60 25

131 "Medora" (tanker) at Sea Island Jetty

1970. Oil Shipment Facilities, Kuwait.

513	131	20 f. multicoloured . . .	1·00	25
514		45 f. multicoloured . . .	2·00	70

132 Kuwaiti and U.N. Emblems and Hand writing

1970. International Literacy Day.

515	132	10 f. multicoloured . . .	60	20
516		15 f. multicoloured . . .	80	20

133 Guards and Badge

1970. First Graduation of National Guards.

517	133	10 f. multicoloured . . .	50	20
518		20 f. multicoloured . . .	1·00	20

134 Symbols and Flag
136 Map of Palestine on Globe

135 Dr. C. Best, Sir F. Banting (discoverers of insulin) and syringe

1971. 10th Anniv of National Day.

519	134	20 f. multicoloured . . .	65	15
520		30 f. multicoloured . . .	90	30

1971. World Health Day, and 50th Anniv of Discovery of Insulin.

521	135	20 f. multicoloured . . .	75	15
522		45 f. multicoloured . . .	1·75	45

1971. Palestine Week.

523	136	20 f. multicoloured . . .	1·00	20
524		45 f. multicoloured . . .	2·25	55

137 I.T.U. Emblem
138 "Three Races"

1971. World Telecommunications Day.

525	137	20 f. black, brown & silver	1·00	20
526		45 f. black, brown & gold	2·25	55

1971. Racial Equality Year.

527	138	15 f. multicoloured . . .	30	10
528		30 f. multicoloured . . .	60	35

139 A.P.U. Emblem

1971. 25th Anniv of Founding of Arab Postal Union at Sofar Conference.

529	139	20 f. multicoloured . . .	50	15
530		45 f. multicoloured . . .	1·25	40

140 Book, Pupils, Globes and Pen

1971. International Literacy Day.

531	140	25 f. multicoloured . . .	55	15
532		60 f. multicoloured . . .	1·40	70

141 Footballers

1971. Regional Sports Tournament, Kuwait. Multicoloured.

533	20 f. Type **141**	60	15
534	30 f. Footballer blocking attack	1·25	45

142 Emblems of U.N.I.C.E.F. and Kuwait

1971. 25th Anniv of U.N.I.C.E.F.

535	142	25 f. multicoloured . . .	50	20
536		60 f. multicoloured . . .	1·10	75

143 Book Year Emblem

1972. International Book Year.

537	143	20 f. black and brown . .	50	10
538		45 f. black and green . .	1·10	55

144 Crest and Laurel

1972. 11th Anniv of National Day.

539	144	20 f. multicoloured . . .	60	10
540		45 f. multicoloured . . .	1·50	55

145 Telecommunications Centre

1972. Inauguration of Telecommunications Centre, Kuwait.

541	145	20 f. multicoloured	1·25	20
542		45 f. multicoloured	2·75	80

146 Human Heart
147 Nurse and Child

1972. World Health Day and World Heart Month.

543	146	20 f. multicoloured	1·25	20
544		45 f. multicoloured	2·75	80

1972. International Red Cross and Crescent Day.

545	147	8 f. multicoloured	50	10
546		40 f. multicoloured	2·50	70

148 Football

1972. Olympic Games, Munich. Multicoloured.

547	2 f. Type **148**	10	10
548	4 f. Running	10	10
549	5 f. Swimming	15	10
550	8 f. Gymnastics	25	10
551	10 f. Throwing the discus . . .	30	10
552	15 f. Show jumping	40	10
553	20 f. Basketball	45	15
554	25 f. Volleyball	50	40

149 Produce and Fishing Boat
151 Ancient Capitals

150 Bank Emblem

1972. 11th F.A.O. Near East Regional Conference, Kuwait.

555	149	5 f. multicoloured	30	10
556		10 f. multicoloured	55	10
557		20 f. multicoloured	1·10	30

1972. 20th Anniv of National Bank of Kuwait.

558	150	10 f. multicoloured	25	10
559		35 f. multicoloured	1·00	50

1972. Archaeological Excavations on Failaka Island. Multicoloured.

560	2 f. Type **151**	10	15
561	5 f. View of excavations . . .	25	10
562	10 f. "Leaf" capital	40	10
563	15 f. Excavated building . . .	60	20

152 Floral Emblem
153 Interpol Emblem

1973. 12th Anniv of National Day.

564	152	10 f. multicoloured	25	10
565		20 f. multicoloured	55	15
566		30 f. multicoloured	1·40	60

1973. 50th Anniv of International Criminal Police Organization (Interpol).

567	153	10 f. multicoloured	50	15
568		15 f. multicoloured	90	25
569		20 f. multicoloured	1·40	60

154 C.I.S.M. Emblem and Flags
155 Airways Building

1973. 25th Anniv of International Military Sports Council (C.I.S.M.).

570	154	30 f. multicoloured . . .	75	30
571		40 f. multicoloured . . .	85	40

1973. Opening of Kuwait Airways H.Q. Building.

572	155	10 f. multicoloured . . .	30	10
573		15 f. multicoloured . . .	50	20
574		20 f. multicoloured . . .	60	25

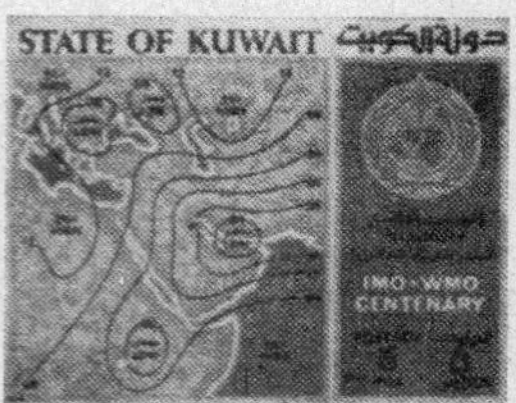

156 Weather Map of Middle East

1973. Centenary of World Meteorological Organization.

575	156	5 f. multicoloured	30	20
576		10 f. multicoloured . . .	50	20
577		15 f. multicoloured . . .	80	45

157 Shaikhs Ahmed and Sabah

1973. 50th Anniv of 1st Kuwait Stamp Issue (overprints on India of 1923).

578	157	10 f. multicoloured . . .	40	10
579		20 f. multicoloured . . .	75	15
580		70 f. multicoloured . . .	2·50	1·25

158 Mourning Dove

1973. Birds and Hunting Equipment. Multicoloured.

581	5 f. Type **158**	40	15
582	5 f. Hoopoe	40	15
583	5 f. Rock dove	40	15
584	5 f. Stone-curlew	40	15
585	8 f. Great grey shrike	40	15
586	8 f. Red-backed shrike	40	15
587	8 f. Black-headed shrike . . .	40	15
588	8 f. Golden oriole	40	15
589	10 f. Willow warbler	40	15
590	10 f. Great reed warbler . . .	40	15
591	10 f. Blackcap	40	15
592	10 f. Barn swallow	40	15
593	15 f. Rock thrush	65	15
594	15 f. Redstart	65	15
595	15 f. Common wheatear	65	15
596	15 f. Bluethroat	65	15
597	20 f. Houbara bustard	85	20
598	20 f. Pin-tailed sandgrouse . .	85	20
599	20 f. Giant wood rail	85	20
600	20 f. Spotted crake	85	20
601	25 f. American kestrel	1·00	30
602	25 f. Great black-backed gull .	1·00	30
603	25 f. Purple heron	1·00	30
604	25 f. Wryneck	1·00	30
605	30 f. European bee eater . . .	1·40	40
606	30 f. Saker falcon	1·40	40
607	30 f. Grey wagtail	1·40	40
608	30 f. Pied wagtail	1·40	40
609	45 f. Bird snares	1·75	75
610	45 f. Driving great grey shrike into net	1·75	75
611	45 f. Stalking rock dove with hand net	1·75	75
612	45 f. Great grey shrike and disguised lure	1·75	75

Nos. 602/12 are size 38 × 38 mm.

159 Flame Emblem

160 Congress Emblem

1973. 25th Anniv of Declaration of Human Rights.

613 159 10 f. multicoloured . . . 30 10
614 40 f. multicoloured . . . 1·00 30
615 75 f. multicoloured . . . 1·75 90

1974. 4th Congress of Arab Veterinary Union, Kuwait.

616 160 30 f. multicoloured . . . 55 25
617 40 f. multicoloured . . . 70 60

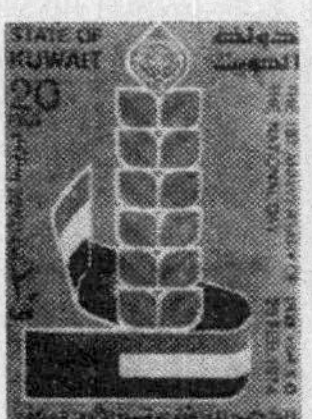

161 Flag and Wheat Ear Symbol

163 Tournament Emblem

162 A.M.U. Emblem

1974. 13th Anniv of National Day.

618 161 20 f. multicoloured . . . 30 10
619 30 f. multicoloured . . . 50 25
620 70 f. multicoloured . . . 1·25 1·00

1974. 12th Conference of Arab Medical Union and 1st Conference of Kuwait Medical Society.

621 162 30 f. multicoloured . . . 1·25 30
622 40 f. multicoloured . . . 1·75 70

1974. 3rd Arabian Gulf Trophy Football Tournament, Kuwait.

623 163 25 f. multicoloured . . . 70 15
624 45 f. multicoloured . . . 1·50 80

164 Institute Buildings

1974. Inauguration of Kuwait Institute for Scientific Research.

625 164 15 f. multicoloured . . . 70 25
626 20 f. multicoloured . . . 1·10 30

165 Emblems of Kuwait, Arab Postal Union and U.P.U.

167 Council Emblem and Flags of Member States

166 Symbolic Telephone Dial

1974. Centenary of U.P.U.

627 165 20 f. multicoloured . . . 20 15
628 30 f. multicoloured . . . 25 30
629 60 f. multicoloured . . . 45 50

1974. World Telecommunications Day.

630 166 10 f. multicoloured . . . 40 15
631 30 f. multicoloured . . . 80 30
632 40 f. multicoloured . . . 1·00 40

1974. 17th Anniv of Signing Arab Economic Unity Agreement.

633 167 20 f. green, black and red 45 10
634 30 f. red, black and green 80 30

168 "Population Growth"

1974. World Population Year.

635 168 30 f. multicoloured . . . 75 20
636 70 f. multicoloured . . . 1·75 90

169 Fund Building

1974. Kuwait Fund for Arab Economic Development.

637 169 10 f. multicoloured . . . 30 15
638 20 f. multicoloured . . . 70 50

170 Shuaiba Emblem

1974. 10th Anniv of Shuaiba Industrial Area.

639 170 10 f. multicoloured . . . 30 10
640 20 f. multicoloured . . . 70 15
641 30 f. multicoloured . . . 1·10 60

171 Arms of Kuwait and "14"

1975. 14th Anniv of National Day.

642 171 20 f. multicoloured . . . 40 10
643 70 f. multicoloured . . . 1·25 80
644 75 f. multicoloured . . . 1·50 95

172 Census Symbols

1975. Population Census.

645 172 8 f. multicoloured 15 10
646 20 f. multicoloured . . . 35 10
647 30 f. multicoloured . . . 55 25
648 70 f. multicoloured . . . 1·60 75
649 100 f. multicoloured . . . 2·00 90

173 I.W.Y. and Kuwait Women's Union Emblems

1975. International Women's Year.

650 173 15 f. multicoloured . . . 50 15
651 20 f. multicoloured . . . 50 15
652 30 f. multicoloured . . . 80 45

174 Classroom within Open Book

1975. International Literacy Day.

653 174 20 f. multicoloured 50 15
654 30 f. multicoloured 75 40

175 I.S.O. Emblem

176 U.N. Flag, Rifle and Olive-branch

1975. World Standards Day.

655 175 10 f. multicoloured 25 15
656 20 f. multicoloured 55 15

1975. 30th Anniv of U.N.O.

657 176 20 f. multicoloured 35 10
658 45 f. multicoloured 75 45

177 Shaikh Sabah

1975.

659 177 8 f. multicoloured 35 10
660 20 f. multicoloured 70 10
661 30 f. multicoloured . . . . 1·00 10
662 50 f. multicoloured . . . . 1·50 10
663 90 f. multicoloured . . . . 3·50 40
664 100 f. multicoloured . . . 4·00 40

178 Kuwait "Skyline"

1976. 15th Anniv of National Day.

665 178 10 f. multicoloured 30 15
666 20 f. multicoloured 60 15

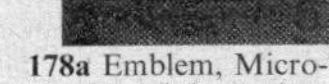

178a Emblem, Microscope and Operation

179 Early and Modern Telephones

1976. 2nd Annual Conference of Kuwait Medical Association.

667 178a 5 f. multicoloured 30 15
668 10 f. multicoloured . . . 60 15
669 30 f. multicoloured . . . 1·75 55

1976. Telephone Centenary.

670 179 5 f. black and orange . . . 20 15
671 15 f. black and blue . . . 55 15

180 Eye

1976. World Health Day.

672 180 10 f. multicoloured 40 15
673 20 f. multicoloured 75 15
674 30 f. multicoloured . . . . 1·25 55

181 Red Crescent Emblem

1976. 10th Anniv of Kuwait Red Crescent Society.

675 181 20 f. multicoloured . . . 40 15
676 30 f. multicoloured . . . 70 30
677 45 f. multicoloured . . . 1·25 55
678 75 f. multicoloured . . . 2·00 1·40

182 Suburb of Manama

183 Basketball

1976. U.N. Human Settlements Conference.

679 182 10 f. multicoloured . . . 30 15
680 20 f. multicoloured . . . 60 15

1976. Olympic Games, Montreal. Multicoloured.

681 4 f. Type **183** 10 10
682 8 f. Running 15 10
683 10 f. Judo 15 10
684 15 f. Handball 20 10
685 20 f. Figure-skating 25 10
686 30 f. Volleyball 40 25
687 45 f. Football 55 35
688 70 f. Swimming 75 85

184 Ethnic Heads and Map of Sri Lanka

185 Torch, U.N.E.S.C.O. Emblem and Kuwaiti Arms

1976. Non-Aligned Countries' Congress, Colombo.

689 184 20 f. multicoloured . . . 30 10
690 30 f. multicoloured . . . 55 15
691 45 f. multicoloured . . . 75 45

1976. 30th Anniv of U.N.E.S.C.O.

692 185 20 f. multicoloured . . . 40 10
693 45 f. multicoloured . . . 1·00 40

186 Pot-throwing

187 Diseased Knee

1977. Popular Games. Multicoloured.

694 5 f. Type **186** 15 10
695 5 f. Kite-flying 15 10
696 5 f. Balancing sticks 15 10
697 5 f. Spinning tops 15 10
698 10 f. Blind-man's-buff (horiz) . . 15 10
699 10 f. Rowing (horiz) 15 10
700 10 f. Rolling hoops (horiz) . . . 15 10
701 10 f. Rope game (horiz) . . . 15 10
702 15 f. Skipping 20 10
703 15 f. Marbles 20 10
704 15 f. Carting 20 10
705 15 f. Teetotum (tops) 20 10
706 20 f. Halma (horiz) 30 15
707 20 f. Model boating (horiz) . . 30 15
708 20 f. Pot and candle (horiz) . . 30 15
709 20 f. Hide-and-seek (horiz) . . 30 15
710 30 f. Knuckle bones 30 15
711 30 f. Hiding the stone 30 15
712 30 f. Hopscotch 30 15
713 30 f. Catch-as-catch-can . . . 30 15
714 40 f. Bowls (horiz) 60 30
715 40 f. Hockey (horiz) 60 30
716 40 f. Guessing game (horiz) . . 60 30
717 40 f. Jacks (horiz) 60 30
718 60 f. Hiding the cake (horiz) . . 70 45
719 60 f. Chess (horiz) 70 45
720 60 f. Story-telling (horiz) . . . 70 45
721 60 f. Treasure hunt (horiz) . . 70 45
722 70 f. Hobby horses (horiz) . . 85 60
723 70 f. Hide-and-seek (horiz) . . 85 60
724 70 f. Catch shadow (horiz) . . 85 60
725 70 f. Throwing game (horiz) . . 85 60

1977. World Rheumatism Year.

726 187 20 f. multicoloured . . . 40 15
727 30 f. multicoloured . . . 60 15
728 45 f. multicoloured . . . 90 35
729 75 f. multicoloured . . . 1·25 1·00

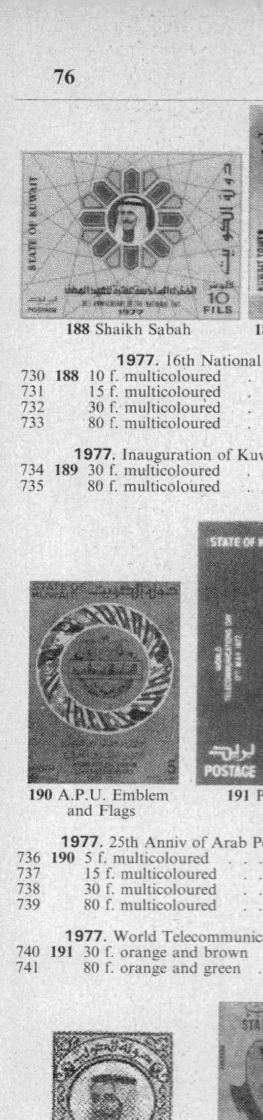

188 Shaikh Sabah 189 Kuwait Tower

1977. 16th National Day.
730 **188** 10 f. multicoloured 15 10
731 15 f. multicoloured . . . 20 10
732 30 f. multicoloured . . . 45 15
733 80 f. multicoloured . . . 1·00 70

1977. Inauguration of Kuwait Tower.
734 **189** 30 f. multicoloured . . . 75 15
735 80 f. multicoloured . . . 2·25 70

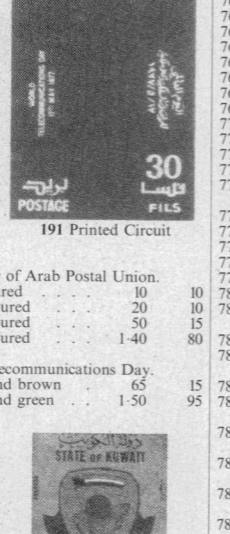

190 A.P.U. Emblem and Flags 191 Printed Circuit

1977. 25th Anniv of Arab Postal Union.
736 **190** 5 f. multicoloured . . . 10 10
737 15 f. multicoloured . . . 20 10
738 30 f. multicoloured . . . 50 15
739 80 f. multicoloured . . . 1·40 80

1977. World Telecommunications Day.
740 **191** 30 f. orange and brown . 65 15
741 80 f. orange and green . . 1·50 95

192 Shaikh Sabah 193 Championship Emblem

1977.
742 **192** 15 f. brown, black & blue 40 10
743 25 f. brown, black & yell 70 10
744 30 f. brown, black & red 90 10
745 80 f. brown, black & vio 2·00 15
746 100 f. brown, black & orge 2·75 20
747 150 f. brown, black & blue 4·50 45
748 200 f. brown, black & olive 5·50 70

1977. 4th Asian Youth Basketball Championships.
749 **193** 30 f. multicoloured . . . 50 15
750 80 f. multicoloured . . . 1·25 70

194 "Popular Dancing" (O. Al-Nakeeb)

1977. Children's Paintings. Multicoloured.
751 15 f. Type **194** 25 10
752 15 f. "Al Deirah" (A. M. al-Onizi) 25 10
753 30 f. "Fishing" (M. al-Jasem) 55 20
754 30 f. "Dug al-Harees" (B. al-Sa'adooni) (vert) 55 20
755 80 f. "Fraisa Dancing" (M al-Mojaibel) (vert) . . . . . 1·40 75
756 80 f. "Kuwaiti Girl" (K. Ghazi) (vert) . . . . 1·40 75

195 Dome of the Rock and Palestinian Freedom Fighters

1978. Palestinian Freedom Fighters.
757 **195** 30 f. multicoloured . . . 90 25
758 80 f. multicoloured . . . 2·25 1·25

196 Dentist treating Patient

1978. 10th Arab Dental Union Congress.
759 **196** 30 f. multicoloured . . . 70 15
760 80 f. multicoloured . . . 1·60 85

197 Carrying Water from Dhows

1978. Water Resources. Multicoloured.
761 5 f. Type **197** 15 10
762 5 f. Camel 10 10
763 5 f. Water carrier 10 10
764 5 f. Pushing water in cart . . 15 10
765 10 f. Irrigation with donkey . 10 10
766 10 f. Water troughs 10 10
767 10 f. Water pool 10 10
768 10 f. Watering crops 10 10
769 15 f. Bedouin watering sheep 10 10
770 15 f. Women at pool 10 10
771 15 f. Animals drinking . . . 10 10
772 15 f. Camp site 10 10
773 20 f. Oasis 15 10
774 20 f. Washing and drinking at home 15 10
775 20 f. Water urn 15 10
776 20 f. Piped water 15 10
777 25 f. Desalination plant . . . 20 15
778 25 f. Water tanker 20 15
779 25 f. Filling water tankers . . 20 15
780 25 f. Modern water tanks . . 20 15
781 30 f. Catching water during storm (vert) 25 15
782 30 f. Water tank (vert) . . . 25 15
783 30 f. "Umbrella" catching water (vert) 25 15
784 30 f. Two water tanks (vert) . 25 15
785 80 f. Carrying water on donkey (vert) 85 50
786 80 f. Woman carrying water can (vert) 85 50
787 80 f. Woman with waterskins (vert) 85 50
788 80 f. Tanker delivering water (vert) 85 50
789 100 f. Piping water into tank (vert) . . . . 1·00 70
790 100 f. Water cistern (vert) . . 1·00 70
791 100 f. Filling cistern (vert) . . 1·00 70
792 100 f. Drawing water from well (vert) . . . . 1·00 70

198 Symbols of Development

1978. 17th National Day.
793 **198** 30 f. multicoloured . . . 35 10
794 80 f. multicoloured . . . 90 50

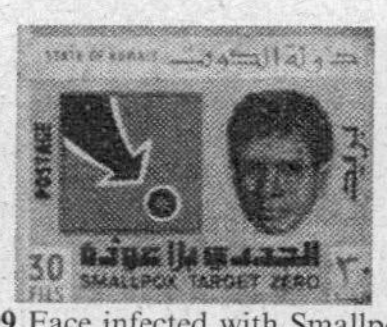

199 Face infected with Smallpox

1978. Global Eradication of Smallpox.
795 **199** 30 f. multicoloured . . . 45 10
796 80 f. multicoloured . . . 1·10 60

200 Microwave Antenna 201 Shaikh Jabir

1978. 10th World Telecommunications Day.
797 **200** 30 f. multicoloured . . . 35 10
798 80 f. multicoloured . . . 1·10 60

1978. Portrait in brown; background colour given.
799 **201** 15 f. green 35 10
800 30 f. orange 70 10
801 80 f. purple . . . . . . 1·50 15
802 100 f. green . . . . . . 1·75 15
803 130 f. brown . . . . . . 2·75 45
804 180 f. violet . . . . . . 4·00 55
805 1 d. red . . . . 11·00 75
806 4 d. blue . . . . 40·00 4·75
Nos. 805/6 are larger, 24 × 29 mm.

202 Mount Arafat, Pilgrims and Kaaba

1978. Pilgrimage to Mecca.
807 **202** 30 f. multicoloured 50 15
808 80 f. multicoloured . . . . 1·25 70

203 U.N. and Anti-Apartheid Emblems

1978. International Anti-Apartheid Year.
809 **203** 30 f. multicoloured 40 15
810 80 f. multicoloured 95 55
811 180 f. multicoloured . . . 1·75 1·25

204 Refugees

1978. 30th Anniv of Declaration of Human Rights.
812 **204** 30 f. multicoloured 40 15
813 80 f. multicoloured 80 50
814 100 f. multicoloured . . . 1·40 1·25

205 Information Centre

1978. Kuwait Information Centre.
815 **205** 5 f. multicoloured 10 10
816 15 f. multicoloured 20 10
817 30 f. multicoloured 50 20
818 80 f. multicoloured . . . . 1·10 65

206 Kindergarten 207 Kuwaiti Flag and Doves

1979. International Year of the Child.
819 **206** 30 f. multicoloured 40 15
820 80 f. multicoloured . . . . 1·00 75

1979. 18th National Day.
821 **207** 30 f. multicoloured 30 10
822 80 f. multicoloured 70 55

208 Crops and Greenhouse

1979. 4th Arab Agriculture Ministers Congress.
823 **208** 30 f. multicoloured 35 15
824 80 f. multicoloured 90 70

209 World Map, Koran and symbols of Arab Achievements 210 Children flying Kites

1979. The Arabs.
825 **209** 30 f. multicoloured . . . 35 15
826 80 f. multicoloured . . . 90 70

1979. Children's Paintings. Multicoloured.
827 30 f. Type **210** 35 15
828 30 f. Girl and doves 35 15
829 30 f. Crowd and balloons . . 35 15
830 80 f. Boys smiling (horiz) . . 95 70
831 80 f. Children in landscape (horiz) 95 70
832 80 f. Tug-of-war (horiz) . . . 95 70

211 Wave Pattern and Television Screen 212 International Military Sports Council Emblem

1979. World Telecommunications Day.
833 **211** 30 f. multicoloured . . . 35 15
834 80 f. multicoloured . . . 90 65

1979. 29th International Military Football Championship.
835 **212** 30 f. multicoloured . . . 35 15
836 80 f. multicoloured . . . 90 65

213 Child and Industrial Landscape

1979. World Environment Day.
837 **213** 30 f. multicoloured . . . 45 15
838 80 f. multicoloured . . . 1·40 75

214 Children supporting Globe 215 Children with Television

1979. 50th Anniv of International Bureau of Education.
839 **214** 30 f. multicoloured . . . 35 15
840 80 f. multicoloured . . . 90 60
841 130 f. multicoloured . . . 1·40 90

1979. 25th Anniv of Kuwaiti Kindergartens. Children's Drawings. Multicoloured.
842 30 f. Type **215** 40 15
843 80 f. Children with flags . . 1·00 65

216 The Kaaba, Mecca 217 Figure, with Dove and Torch, clothed in Palestinian Flag

1979. Pilgrimage to Mecca.
844 **216** 30 f. multicoloured . . . 50 15
845 80 f. multicoloured . . . 1·25 65

1979. International Day of Solidarity with Palestinians.
846 **217** 30 f. multicoloured . . . 1·50 20
847 80 f. multicoloured . . . 2·50 1·25

218 Boeing 747 and Douglas DC-3

1979. 25th Anniv of Kuwait Airways.
848 **218** 30 f. multicoloured . . . 50 15
849 80 f. multicoloured . . . 1·40 90

219 Oyster Shell with Pearl bearing Map of Kuwait

1980. 19th National Day.

850 **219** 30 f. multicoloured . . . 40 15
851 80 f. multicoloured . . . 1·10 60

220 Graph with Human Figures

1980. Population Census.

852 **220** 30 f. black, silver and blue 40 15
853 80 f. black, gold & orange 1·00 60

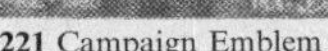

221 Campaign Emblem **222** Municipality Building

1980. World Health Day. Anti-Smoking Campaign.

854 **221** 30 f. multicoloured . . . 65 15
855 80 f. multicoloured . . . 1·60 80

1980. 50th Anniv of Kuwait Municipality.

856 **222** 15 f. multicoloured . . . 25 10
857 30 f. multicoloured . . . 45 20
858 80 f. multicoloured . . . 1·10 80

223 "The Future"

1980. Children's Imagination of Future Kuwait. Multicoloured.

859 30 f. Type **223** 50 15
860 80 f. Motorways . . . . 1·40 75

224 Hand blotting out Factory

1980. World Environment Day.

861 **224** 30 f. multicoloured . . . 55 20
862 80 f. multicoloured . . . 1·50 80

225 Volleyball **226** O.P.E.C. Emblem and Globe

1980. Olympic Games, Moscow. Multicoloured.

863 15 f. Type **225** 20 15
864 15 f. Tennis 20 15
865 30 f. Swimming 30 20
866 30 f. Weightlifting 30 20
867 30 f. Basketball 30 20
868 30 f. Judo 30 20
869 80 f. Gymnastics 75 50
870 80 f. Badminton 75 50
871 80 f. Fencing 75 50
872 80 f. Football 75 50

1980. 20th Anniv of Organization of Petroleum Exporting Countries.

873 **226** 30 f. multicoloured . . . 60 15
874 80 f. multicoloured . . . 1·40 80

227 Mosque and Kaaba, Mecca

1980. 1400th Anniv of Hegira.

875 **227** 15 f. multicoloured . . . 25 10
876 30 f. multicoloured . . . 50 20
877 80 f. multicoloured . . . 1·25 80

228 Dome of the Rock **229** Ibn Sina (Avicenna)

1980. International Day of Solidarity with Palestinian People.

878 **228** 30 f. multicoloured . . . 1·25 25
879 80 f. multicoloured . . . 2·75 1·50

1980. Birth Millenary of Ibn Sina (philosopher and physician).

880 **229** 30 f. multicoloured . . . 50 15
881 80 f. multicoloured . . . 1·25 80

230 Islamic Symbols **231** Person in Wheelchair playing Snooker

1981. First Islamic Medicine Conference, Kuwait.

882 **230** 30 f. multicoloured . . . 65 15
883 80 f. multicoloured . . . 1·60 90

1981. International Year of Disabled People. Multicoloured.

884 30 f. Type **231** 65 15
885 80 f. Girl in wheelchair . . . 1·60 90

232 Symbols of Development and Progress

1981. 20th National Day.

886 **232** 30 f. multicoloured . . . 70 15
887 80 f. multicoloured . . . 1·60 90

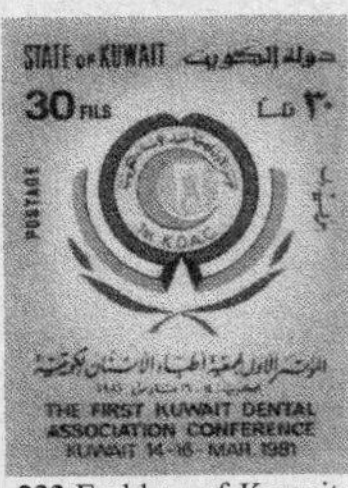

233 Emblem of Kuwait Dental Association **234** "Lamp"

1981. First Kuwait Dental Association Conference.

888 **233** 30 f. multicoloured . . . 1·00 20
889 80 f. multicoloured . . . 2·50 1·25

1981. World Red Cross and Red Crescent Day.

890 **234** 30 f. multicoloured . . . 90 20
891 80 f. multicoloured . . . 2·25 1·25

235 Emblems of I.T.U. and W.H.O. and Ribbons forming Caduceus **236** Tanker polluting Sea and Car polluting Atmosphere

1981. World Telecommunications Day.

892 **235** 30 f. multicoloured 90 20
893 70 f. multicoloured . . . . 2·00 1·25

1981. World Environment Day.

894 **236** 30 f. multicoloured 85 30
895 80 f. multicoloured . . . . 2·10 1·25

237 Sief Palace

1981.

896 **237** 5 f. multicoloured 10 10
897 10 f. multicoloured 10 10
898 15 f. multicoloured 10 10
899 25 f. multicoloured 15 10
900 30 f. multicoloured 15 10
901 40 f. multicoloured 20 10
902 60 f. multicoloured 30 10
903 80 f. multicoloured 40 10
904 100 f. multicoloured . . . 50 10
905 115 f. multicoloured . . . 55 15
906 130 f. multicoloured . . . 60 10
907 150 f. multicoloured . . . 70 15
908 180 f. multicoloured . . . 85 20
909 250 f. multicoloured . . . 1·10 25
910 500 f. multicoloured . . . 2·50 35
911 1 d. multicoloured . . . . 4·75 55
912 2 d. multicoloured . . . . 9·50 1·50
913 3 d. multicoloured . . . . 14·00 3·00
914 4 d. multicoloured . . . . 19·00 8·00

Nos. 911/14 are larger, 33 × 28 mm and have a different border.

238 Pilgrims

1981. Pilgrimage to Mecca.

915 **238** 30 f. multicoloured . . . . 1·00 20
916 80 f. multicoloured . . . . 2·50 90

239 Palm Trees, Sheep, Camel, Goat and F.A.O. Emblem

1981. World Food Day.

917 **239** 30 f. multicoloured 90 20
918 80 f. multicoloured . . . . 2·25 90

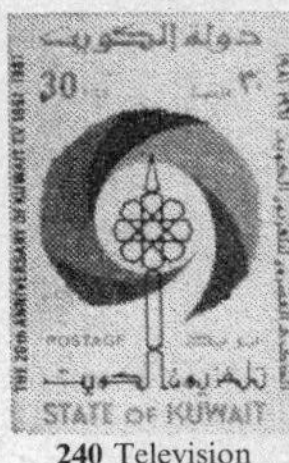

240 Television Emblem **241** Blood Circulation Diagram

1981. 20th Anniv of Kuwait Television.

919 **240** 30 f. multicoloured 80 20
920 80 f. multicoloured . . . . 1·75 80

1982. 1st International Symposium on Pharmacology of Human Blood Vessels.

921 **241** 30 f. multicoloured . . . . 1·00 25
922 80 f. multicoloured . . . . 2·50 1·00

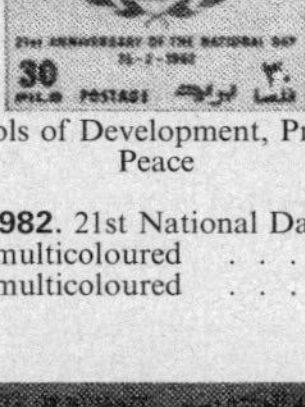

242 Symbols of Development, Progress and Peace

1982. 21st National Day.

923 **242** 30 f. multicoloured . . . 45 20
924 80 f. multicoloured . . . 1·10 80

243 Emblem of Kuwait Boy Scouts Association on Globe

1982. 75th Anniv of Boy Scout Movement.

925 **243** 30 f. multicoloured . . . 70 20
926 80 f. multicoloured . . . 1·60 90

244 Emblem of Arab Pharmacists Union

1982. Arab Pharmacists Day.

927 **244** 30 f. multicoloured . . . 1·00 25
928 80 f. multicoloured . . . 2·50 1·00

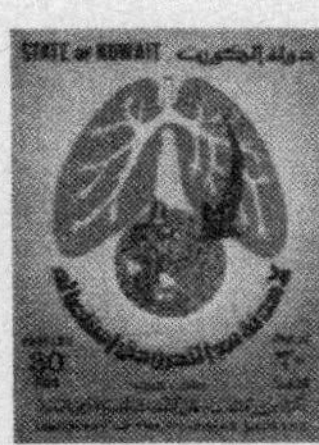

245 Red Crescent, Arab and W.H.O. Emblem **246** A.P.U. Emblem

1982. World Health Day.

929 **245** 30 f. multicoloured . . . 75 25
930 80 f. multicoloured . . . 2·00 1·00

1982. 30th Anniv of Arab Postal Union.

931 **246** 30 f. black, pink and green 1·00 25
932 80 f. black, green and pink 2·50 1·00

247 Lungs and Microscope **249** Museum Exhibits

248 Crest and Emblems of Kuwait Football Association and Olympic Committee

1982. Centenary of Discovery of Tubercle Bacillus.

933 **247** 30 f. multicoloured . . . 1·25 25
934 80 f. multicoloured . . . 2·75 1·25

1982. World Cup Football Championship, Spain.

935 **248** 30 f. multicoloured . . . 75 25
936 80 f. multicoloured . . . 2·00 1·00

1982. 10th Anniv of Science and Natural History Museum.

937 **249** 30 f. multicoloured . . . 1·00 30
938 80 f. multicoloured . . . 2·50 1·40

250 Container Ship

1982. 6th Anniv of United Arab Shipping Company. Multicoloured.
939 30 f. Type **250** 65 30
940 80 f. Freighter . . . . 1·90 95

251 Palm Trees

1982. Arab Palm Tree Day.
941 **251** 30 f. multicoloured . . . 40 25
942 80 f. multicoloured . . . 1·00 85

252 Pilgrims

1982. Pilgrimage to Mecca.
943 **252** 15 f. multicoloured . . . 35 10
944 30 f. multicoloured . . . 75 25
945 80 f. multicoloured . . . 1·75 90

253 Desert Flower

1983. Desert Plants. Multicoloured; background colours given.
946 10 f. green (vert) 10 10
947 10 f. violet 10 10
948 10 f. pink 10 10
949 10 f. red 10 10
950 10 f. brown 10 10
951 10 f. green 10 10
952 10 f. orange 10 10
953 10 f. red 10 10
954 10 f. brown 10 10
955 10 f. blue 10 10
956 15 f. green 15 15
957 15 f. purple 15 15
958 15 f. blue 15 15
959 15 f. blue 15 15
960 15 f. green 15 15
961 15 f. red 15 15
962 15 f. brown 15 15
963 15 f. blue 15 15
964 15 f. mauve 15 15
965 15 f. red 15 15
966 30 f. brown 30 30
967 30 f. red 30 30
968 30 f. blue 30 30
969 30 f. green 30 30
970 30 f. red 30 30
971 30 f. blue 30 30
972 30 f. green 30 30
973 30 f. mauve 30 30
974 30 f. brown 30 30
975 30 f. yellow 30 30
976 40 f. red (horiz) 40 30
977 40 f. green 40 30
978 40 f. violet 40 30
979 40 f. blue 40 30
980 40 f. violet 40 30
981 40 f. green 40 30
982 40 f. mauve 40 30
983 40 f. brown 40 30
984 40 f. blue 40 30
985 40 f. green 40 30
986 80 f. violet 80 60
987 80 f. green 80 60
988 80 f. yellow 80 60
989 80 f. brown 80 60
990 80 f. blue 80 60
991 80 f. yellow 80 60
992 80 f. green 80 60
993 80 f. violet 80 60
994 80 f. brown 80 60
995 80 f. yellow 80 60
DESIGNS: Various plants.

254 Peace Dove on Map of Kuwait

1983. 22nd National Day.
996 **254** 30 f. multicoloured . . . 60 20
997 80 f. multicoloured . . . 1·40 85

255 I.M.O. Emblem

1983. 25th Anniv of International Maritime Organization.
998 **255** 30 f. multicoloured . . . 60 20
999 80 f. multicoloured . . . 1·40 85

256 Virus and Map of Africa

1983. Third International Conference on Impact of Viral Diseases on Development of Middle East and African Countries.
1000 **256** 15 f. multicoloured . . . 30 15
1001 30 f. multicoloured . . . 60 25
1002 80 f. multicoloured . . . 1·50 90

257 Stylized Figures exercising

1983. World Health Day.
1003 **257** 15 f. multicoloured . . . 35 15
1004 30 f. multicoloured . . . 70 25
1005 80 f. multicoloured . . . 1·60 95

258 U.P.U., W.C.Y. and I.T.U. Emblems

1983. World Communications Year.
1006 **258** 15 f. multicoloured . . . 35 15
1007 30 f. multicoloured . . . 70 25
1008 80 f. multicoloured . . . 1·60 95

259 Map of Kuwait and Dhow

1983. World Environment Day.
1009 **259** 15 f. multicoloured . . . 45 15
1010 30 f. multicoloured . . . 90 25
1011 80 f. multicoloured . . . 2·00 95

260 Walls of Jerusalem

1983. World Heritage Convention.
1012 **260** 15 f. multicoloured . . . 40 15
1013 30 f. multicoloured . . . 80 25
1014 80 f. multicoloured . . . 1·75 90

261 Pilgrims in Mozdalipha

1983. Pilgrimage to Mecca.
1015 **261** 15 f. multicoloured . . . 40 15
1016 30 f. multicoloured . . . 80 25
1017 80 f. multicoloured . . . 1·75 90

262 Arab within Dove

1983. International Day of Solidarity with Palestinian People.
1018 **262** 15 f. multicoloured . . . 45 15
1019 30 f. multicoloured . . . 90 25
1020 80 f. multicoloured . . . 2·00 90

263 Kuwait Medical Association and Congress Emblems

1984. 21st Pan-Arab Medical Congress.
1021 **263** 15 f. multicoloured . . . 40 15
1022 30 f. multicoloured . . . 80 25
1023 80 f. multicoloured . . . 1·75 90

264 State Arms within Key

1984. Inauguration of New Health Establishments.
1024 **264** 15 f. multicoloured . . . 40 15
1025 30 f. multicoloured . . . 80 25
1026 80 f. multicoloured . . . 1·75 90

265 Dove and Globe

266 Symbols of Medicine within Head

1984. 23rd National Day.
1027 **265** 15 f. multicoloured . . . 40 15
1028 30 f. multicoloured . . . 80 25
1029 80 f. multicoloured . . . 1·75 90

1984. 2nd International Medical Science Conference.
1030 **266** 15 f. multicoloured . . . 40 15
1031 30 f. multicoloured . . . 80 25
1032 80 f. multicoloured . . . 1·75 90

267 Douglas DC-3

1984. 30th Anniv of Kuwait Airways Corporation.
1033 **267** 30 f. lt blue, blue & yell 75 20
1034 80 f. lt blue, bl and mve 2·00 90

268 Magazine Covers **269** Family and Emblems

1984. 25th Anniv of "Al-Arabi" Magazine.
1035 **268** 15 f. multicoloured . . . 25 15
1036 30 f. multicoloured . . . 60 25
1037 80 f. multicoloured . . . 1·50 90

1984. World Health Day.
1038 **269** 15 f. multicoloured . . . 40 15
1039 30 f. multicoloured . . . 80 25
1040 80 f. multicoloured . . . 1·75 90

270 Sudanese Orphan and Village

1984. Hanan Kuwaiti Village, Sudan.
1041 **270** 15 f. multicoloured . . . 35 15
1042 30 f. multicoloured . . . 70 25
1043 80 f. multicoloured . . . 1·50 90

271 I.C.A.O., Kuwait Airport and Kuwait Airways Emblems

1984. 40th Anniv of I.C.A.O.
1044 **271** 15 f. multicoloured . . . 40 15
1045 30 f. multicoloured . . . 80 25
1046 80 f. multicoloured . . . 1·75 90

272 Map of Arab Countries and Youths

1984. Arab Youth Day.
1047 **272** 30 f. multicoloured . . . 80 25
1048 80 f. multicoloured . . . 1·60 90

273 Swimming

1984. Olympic Games, Los Angeles. Multicoloured.
1049 30 f. Type **273** 40 40
1050 30 f. Hurdling 40 40
1051 80 f. Judo 40 40
1052 80 f. Equestrian 40 40

274 Anniversary Emblem, Camera, Airplane, Al-Aujairy Observatory and Wind Tower

1984. 10th Anniv of Science Club.
1053 **274** 15 f. multicoloured . . . 50 15
1054 30 f. multicoloured . . . 95 25
1055 80 f. multicoloured . . . 1·90 90

275 Stoning the Devil

1984. Pilgrimage to Mecca.

1056 **275** 30 f. multicoloured . . . 80 25
1057 80 f. multicoloured . . . 1·75 90

276 Anniversary Emblem

1984. 20th Anniv of International Telecommunications Satellite Consortium (Intelsat).

1058 **276** 30 f. multicoloured . . . 80 25
1059 80 f. multicoloured . . . 1·75 90

277 Council Emblem

278 Hands breaking Star

1984. 5th Supreme Council Session of Gulf Co-operation Council.

1060 **277** 30 f. multicoloured . . . 70 25
1061 80 f. multicoloured . . . 1·40 85

1984. International Day of Solidarity with Palestinian People.

1062 **278** 30 f. multicoloured . . . 80 25
1063 80 f. multicoloured . . . 1·75 90

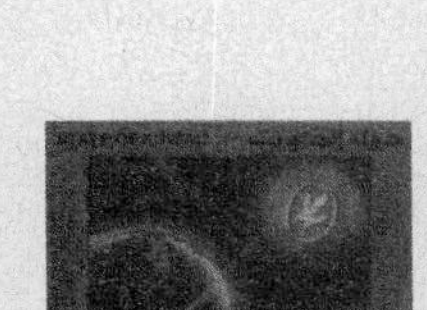
279 Company Emblem as Satellite

280 I.Y.Y. Emblem

1984. 50th Anniv of Kuwait Oil Company.

1064 **279** 30 f. multicoloured . . . 80 25
1965 80 f. multicoloured . . . 1·75 90

1985. International Youth Year.

1066 **280** 30 f. multicoloured . . . 40 20
1067 80 f. multicoloured . . . 1·00 60

281 "24", Hand holding Flame and Dove

282 Programme Emblem

1985. 24th National Day.

1068 **281** 30 f. multicoloured . . . 70 25
1069 80 f. multicoloured . . . 1·60 80

1985. International Programme for Communications Development.

1070 **282** 30 f. multicoloured . . . 80 25
1071 80 f. multicoloured . . . 1·75 90

283 Emblem

284 Molar

1985. 1st Arab Gulf Social Work Week.

1072 **283** 30 f. multicoloured . . . 80 25
1073 80 f. multicoloured . . . 1·75 90

1985. 3rd Kuwait Dental Association Conference.

1074 **284** 30 f. multicoloured . . . 1·00 25
1075 80 f. multicoloured . . . 2·25 1·00

285 Emblem

286 Globe and Figures

1985. Population Census.

1076 **285** 30 f. multicoloured . . . 80 25
1077 80 f. multicoloured . . . 1·75 90

1985. World Health Day.

1078 **286** 30 f. multicoloured . . . 90 25
1079 80 f. multicoloured . . . 2·00 95

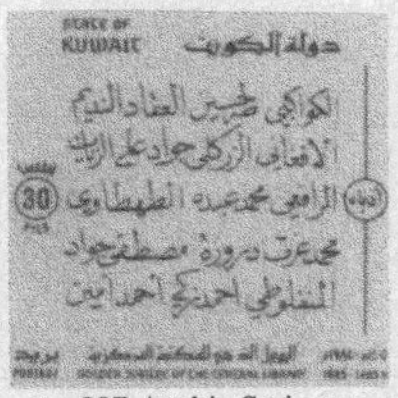

287 Arabic Script

No. 1080

No. 1081

No. 1082

No. 1083

No. 1084

No. 1085

No. 1086

No. 1087

1985. 50th Anniv of Central Library. Square designs showing titles of books and names of authors in Arabic script (first line of text illustrated above).

1080 30 f. gold 65 55
1081 30 f. gold 65 55
1082 30 f. gold 65 55
1083 30 f. gold 65 55
1084 80 f. black and gold . . . . 1·50 1·25
1085 80 f. black and gold . . . . 1·50 1·25
1086 80 f. black and gold . . . . 1·50 1·25
1087 80 f. black and gold . . . . 1·50 1·25

288 Seascape

1985. World Environment Day.

1088 **288** 30 f. multicoloured . . . 1·40 30
1089 80 f. multicoloured . . . 3·00 1·10

289 Anniversary Emblem

1985. 25th Anniv of Organization of Petroleum Exporting Countries.

1090 **289** 30 f. dp blue, bl & mve 1·00 25
1091 80 f. dp blue, bl & brn 2·25 1·25

290 Emblem and Heads

1985. Introduction of Civilian Identity Cards.

1092 **290** 30 f. multicoloured . . . 80 20
1093 80 f. multicoloured . . . 1·75 1·00

291 Flag on Globe within Symbolic Design

1985. International Day of Solidarity with Palestinian People.

1094 **291** 15 f. multicoloured . . . 65 20
1095 30 f. multicoloured . . . 1·25 40
1096 80 f. multicoloured . . . 2·75 1·25

292 Birds

1986. 25th National Day.

1097 **292** 15 f. multicoloured . . . 50 20
1098 30 f. multicoloured . . . 1·00 40
1099 80 f. multicoloured . . . 2·50 1·40

293 Emblem

294 W.H.O. Emblem as Flower

1986. 20th Anniv of Kuwait Red Crescent.

1100 **293** 20 f. multicoloured . . . 70 20
1101 25 f. multicoloured . . . 80 30
1102 70 f. multicoloured . . . 2·25 1·25

1986. World Health Day.

1103 **294** 20 f. multicoloured . . . 70 20
1104 25 f. multicoloured . . . 80 30
1105 70 f. multicoloured . . . 2·25 1·25

295 I.P.Y. Emblem

1986. International Peace Year.

1106 **295** 20 f. green, blue & black 65 20
1107 25 f. blue, yellow & black 75 30
1108 70 f. blue, mauve & black 2·00 1·25

HAVE YOU READ THE NOTES AT THE BEGINNING OF THIS CATALOGUE?

These often provide the answers to the enquiries we receive.

296 "Al Mirqab" (container ship)

1986. 10th Anniv of United Arab Shipping Company. Multicoloured.

1109 20 f. Type **296** . . . . 1·00 20
1110 70 f. "Al Mubarakiah" (container ship) . . . . . 2·75 1·50

297 Bank Emblem on Map

1986. 25th Anniv of Gulf Bank.

1111 **297** 20 f. multicoloured . . . 65 20
1112 25 f. multicoloured . . . 75 30
1113 70 f. multicoloured . . . 2·00 1·40

298 Zig-zags and Diamonds

1986. Sadu Art. Multicoloured.

1114 20 f. Type **298** 60 20
1115 70 f. Triangles and symbols 1·75 90
1116 200 f. Stripes and triangles . 4·50 2·50

299 Dove on Manacled Hand pointing to Map

1986. International Day of Solidarity with Palestinian People.

1117 **299** 20 f. multicoloured . . . 90 20
1118 25 f. multicoloured . . . 1·25 40
1119 70 f. multicoloured . . . 2·75 1·50

300 Conference Emblem

1987. 5th Islamic Summit Conference.

1120 **300** 25 f. multicoloured . . . 60 20
1121 50 f. multicoloured . . . 1·25 40
1122 150 f. multicoloured . . 2·75 1·50

301 Map in National Colours and Symbols of Development

1987. 26th National Day.

1123 **301** 50 f. multicoloured . . . 80 25
1124 150 f. multicoloured . . 2·00 1·25

302 Health Science Centre

1987. 3rd Kuwait International Medical Sciences Conference: Infectious Diseases in Developing Countries.

1125 **302** 25 f. multicoloured . . . 40 20
1126 150 f. multicoloured . . 2·00 1·25

303 Campaign Emblem

1987. World Health Day. Child Immunization Campaign.

1127 **303** 25 f. multicoloured . . . 40 20
1128 50 f. multicoloured . . . 80 30
1129 150 f. multicoloured . . 2·00 1·40

304 Jerusalem

1987. "Jerusalem is an Arab City".

1130 **304** 25 f. multicoloured . . . 30 15
1131 50 f. multicoloured . . . 60 30
1132 150 f. multicoloured . . 1·75 1·00

305 Pilgrims in Miqat Wadi Mihrim

1987. Pilgrimage to Mecca.

1133 **305** 25 f. multicoloured . . . 25 15
1134 50 f. multicoloured . . . 50 25
1135 150 f. multicoloured . . 1·40 75

306 Emblem

308 Project Monument and Site Plan

307 Buoy and Container Ship

1987. Arab Telecommunications Day.

1136 **306** 25 f. multicoloured . . . 25 15
1137 50 f. multicoloured . . . 50 20
1138 150 f. multicoloured . . 1·40 75

1987. World Maritime Day.

1139 **307** 25 f. multicoloured . . . 30 20
1140 50 f. multicoloured . . . 65 30
1141 150 f. multicoloured . . 1·75 90

1987. Al-Qurain Housing Project.

1142 **308** 25 f. multicoloured . . . 25 15
1143 50 f. multicoloured . . . 50 20
1144 150 f. multicoloured . . 1·40 75

309 Unloading Container Ship

1987. 10th Anniv of Ports Public Authority.

1145 **309** 25 f. multicoloured . . . 20 10
1146 50 f. multicoloured . . . 40 20
1147 150 f. multicoloured . . 1·10 60

310 Symbolic Design

311 Emblem

1987. International Day of Solidarity with Palestinian People.

1148 **310** 25 f. multicoloured . . . 20 10
1149 50 f. multicoloured . . . 40 20
1150 150 f. multicoloured . . 1·10 60

1988. 25th Anniv of Women's Cultural and Social Society.

1151 **311** 25 f. multicoloured . . . 20 10
1152 50 f. multicoloured . . . 40 20
1153 150 f. multicoloured . . 1·10 60

312 Emblem

313 Hands holding W.H.O. Emblem

1988. 27th National Day.

1154 **312** 25 f. multicoloured . . . 20 10
1155 50 f. multicoloured . . . 40 20
1156 150 f. multicoloured . . 1·10 60

1988. World Health Day. 40th Anniv of W.H.O.

1157 **313** 25 f. multicoloured . . . 15 10
1158 50 f. multicoloured . . . 35 20
1159 150 f. multicoloured . . 1·00 50

314 Regional Maritime Protection Organization Symbol

315 Society Emblem

1988. 10th Anniv of Kuwait Regional Convention for Protection of Marine Environment.

1160 **314** 35 f. dp blue, bl & brn 25 15
1161 50 f. dp blue, bl & grn 35 20
1162 150 f. dp blue, bl & lilac 1·00 50

1988. 25th Anniv of Kuwait Teachers' Society.

1163 **315** 25 f. multicoloured . . . 15 10
1164 50 f. multicoloured . . . 35 20
1165 150 f. multicoloured . . 1·00 50

316 Pilgrims at al-Sail al-Kabir Miqat

1988. Pilgrimage to Mecca.

1166 **316** 25 f. multicoloured . . . 15 10
1167 50 f. multicoloured . . . 35 20
1168 150 f. multicoloured . . 1·00 50

317 Gang of Youths lying in wait for Soldiers

318 Ring of Dwellings around Key

1988. Palestinian "Intifida" Movement.

1169 **317** 50 f. multicoloured . . . 35 20
1170 150 f. multicoloured . . 1·00 50

1988. Arab Housing Day.

1171 **318** 50 f. multicoloured . . . 35 20
1172 100 f. multicoloured . . . 70 35
1173 150 f. multicoloured . . . 1·00 50

319 Map of Palestine highlighted on Globe

320 Volunteers embracing Globe

1988. International Day of Solidarity with Palestinian People.

1174 **319** 50 f. multicoloured . . . 35 20
1175 100 f. multicoloured . . . 70 35
1176 150 f. multicoloured . . . 1·00 50

1988. International Volunteer Day.

1177 **320** 50 f. multicoloured . . . 35 20
1178 100 f. multicoloured . . . 70 35
1179 150 f. multicoloured . . . 1·00 50

321 Conference, Kuwait Society of Engineers and Arab Engineers Union Emblems

1989. 18th Arab Engineering Conference.

1180 **321** 50 f. multicoloured . . . 35 20
1181 100 f. multicoloured . . . 70 35
1182 150 f. multicoloured . . . 1·00 50

322 Flags as Figures supporting Map

323 Conference Emblem

1989. 28th National Day.

1183 **322** 50 f. multicoloured . . . 35 20
1184 100 f. multicoloured . . . 70 35
1185 150 f. multicoloured . . . 1·00 50

1989. 5th Kuwait Dental Association Conference.

1186 **323** 50 f. multicoloured . . . 35 20
1187 150 f. multicoloured . . . 70 35
1188 250 f. multicoloured . . . 1·00 50

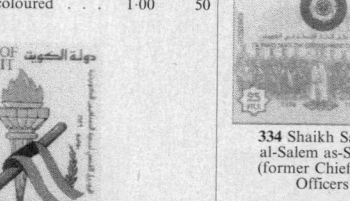

324 Emblems

325 Anniversary Emblem

1989. World Health Day.

1189 **324** 50 f. multicoloured . . . 35 20
1190 150 f. multicoloured . . . 70 35
1191 250 f. multicoloured . . . 1·00 50

1989. 10th Anniv of Arab Board for Medical Specializations.

1192 **325** 50 f. multicoloured . . . 35 20
1193 150 f. multicoloured . . . 70 35
1194 250 f. multicoloured . . . 1·00 50

326 Torch, Pen and Flag

1989. 25th Anniv of Kuwait Journalists' Association.

1195 **326** 50 f. multicoloured . . . 35 20
1196 200 f. multicoloured . . . 85 45
1197 250 f. multicoloured . . . 1·00 50

327 Attan'eem Migat, Mecca

1989. Pilgrimage to Mecca.

1198 **327** 50 f. multicoloured . . . 30 15
1199 150 f. multicoloured . . 60 30
1200 200 f. multicoloured . . 85 45

328 Al-Qurain Housing Project

329 Tree

1989. Arab Housing Day.

1201 **328** 25 f. multicoloured . . . 10 10
1202 50 f. multicoloured . . . 30 15
1203 150 f. multicoloured . . 60 30

1989. Greenery Week.

1204 **329** 25 f. multicoloured . . . 10 10
1205 50 f. multicoloured . . . 25 15
1206 150 f. multicoloured . . 60 30

330 Dhow

331 Emblem and Map

1989. Coil Stamps.

1207 **330** 50 f. gold and green . . 45 20
1208 100 f. gold and blue . . 80 25
1209 200 f. gold and red . . . 1·50 55

1989. 5th Anniv of Gulf Investment Corporation.

1210 **331** 25 f. multicoloured . . . 10 10
1211 50 f. multicoloured . . . 25 15
1212 150 f. multicoloured . . 60 30

332 Emblem

333 Zakat House

1989. 1st Anniv of "Declaration of Palestine State".

1213 **332** 50 f. multicoloured . . . 25 10
1214 150 f. multicoloured . . 60 30
1215 200 f. multicoloured . . 85 45

1989. Orphanage Sponsorship Project.

1216 **333** 25 f. multicoloured . . . 10 10
1217 50 f. multicoloured . . . 25 10
1218 150 f. multicoloured . . 60 30

334 Shaikh Sabah al-Salem as-Sabah (former Chief) and Officers

335 Globe and Dove

1989. 50th Anniv (1988) of Kuwait Police.

1219 **334** 25 f. multicoloured . . . 10 10
1220 50 f. multicoloured . . . 20 10
1221 150 f. multicoloured . . 60 30

1990. 29th National Day.

1222 **335** 25 f. multicoloured . . . 10 10
1223 50 f. multicoloured . . . 20 10
1224 150 f. multicoloured . . 60 30

336 Earth, Clouds and Weather Balloon

1990. World Meteorological Day.

1225 **336** 50 f. multicoloured . . . 20 10
1226 100 f. multicoloured . . 40 20
1227 150 f. multicoloured . . 60 30

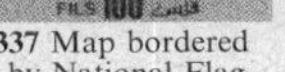

337 Map bordered by National Flag **338** Lanner Falcon

1990. World Health Day.

1228 **337** 50 f. multicoloured . . . 20 10
1229 100 f. multicoloured . . 40 20
1230 150 f. multicoloured . . 60 30

1990.

1231 **338** 50 f. gold and blue . . . 25 15
1232 100 f. gold and red . . . 45 25
1233 150 f. gold and green . . . 70 35

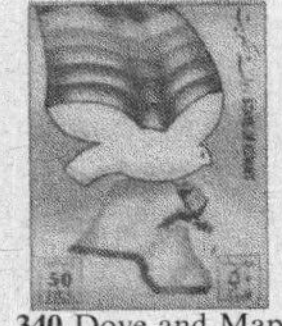

339 Soldiers carrying Kuwait Flag **340** Dove and Map

1991. Liberation (1st issue).

1234 **339** 25 f. multicoloured . . . 10 10
1235 50 f. multicoloured . . . 20 10
1236 150 f. multicoloured . . 60 30

See also Nos. 1243/84.

1991. Peace.

1237 **340** 50 f. multicoloured . . . 20 10
1238 100 f. multicoloured . . 40 20
1239 150 f. multicoloured . . 60 30

341 Flag, Map and Globe **342** Sweden

1991. Reconstruction.

1240 **341** 50 f. multicoloured . . . 20 10
1241 150 f. multicoloured . . 60 30
1242 200 f. multicoloured . . 80 40

1991. Liberation (2nd issue). Each showing a dove coloured with the flag of one of the assisting nations. Multicoloured.

1243 50 f. Type **342** 20 10
1244 50 f. Soviet Union 20 10
1245 50 f. United States of America 20 10
1246 50 f. Kuwait 20 10
1247 50 f. Saudi Arabia 20 10
1248 50 f. United Nations 20 10
1249 50 f. Singapore 20 10
1250 50 f. France 20 10
1251 50 f. Italy 20 10
1252 50 f. Egypt 20 10
1253 50 f. Morocco 20 10
1254 50 f. United Kingdom 20 10
1255 50 f. Philippines 20 10
1256 50 f. United Arab Emirates . . 20 10
1257 50 f. Syria 20 10
1258 50 f. Poland 20 10
1259 50 f. Australia 20 10
1260 50 f. Japan 20 10
1261 50 f. Hungary 20 10
1262 50 f. Netherlands 20 10
1263 50 f. Denmark 20 10
1264 50 f. New Zealand 20 10
1265 50 f. Czechoslovakia 20 10
1266 50 f. Bahrain 20 10
1267 50 f. Honduras 20 10
1268 50 f. Turkey 20 10
1269 50 f. Greece 20 10
1270 50 f. Oman 20 10
1271 50 f. Qatar 20 10
1272 50 f. Belgium 20 10
1273 50 f. Sierra Leone 20 10
1274 50 f. Argentina 20 10
1275 50 f. Norway 20 10
1276 50 f. Canada 20 10
1277 50 f. Germany 20 10
1278 50 f. South Korea 20 10
1279 50 f. Bangladesh 20 10
1280 50 f. Bulgaria 20 10
1281 50 f. Senegal 20 10
1282 50 f. Spain 20 10
1283 50 f. Niger 20 10
1284 50 f. Pakistan 20 10

343 "Human Terror" **344** Emblem

1991. 1st Anniv of Iraqi Invasion. Multicoloured.

1286 50 f. Type **343** 20 10
1287 100 f. "Invasion of Kuwait" 40 20
1288 150 f. "Environmental Terrorism" (horiz) 60 30

1991. 30th Anniv of Organization of Petroleum Exporting Countries.

1290 **344** 25 f. multicoloured . . . 10 10
1291 50 f. multicoloured . . . 20 10
1292 150 f. multicoloured . . 65 35

345 National Flag, Arabic Script and Broken Chains

1991. Campaign to Free Kuwaiti Prisoners of War. Each black and yellow.

1293 50 f. Type **345** 20 10
1294 150 f. Prison bars, "Don't Forget Our P.O.W.'s" and broken chains 65 35

346 Names of Member Countries forming Tree

1991. 12th Gulf Co-operation Council Summit Conference, Kuwait. Multicoloured.

1296 25 f. Type **346** 10 10
1297 150 f. National flags as leaves of plant 65 35

347 I.L.Y. Emblem

1992. International Literacy Year.

1299 **347** 50 f. blue and buff . . . 20 10
1300 100 f. blue and yellow . 45 25
1301 150 f. blue and mauve . 65 35

348 Doves and National Flag

1992. 31st National Day (1302) and 1st Anniv of Liberation (1303).

1302 **348** 50 f. black, green and red 20 10
1303 – 150 f. multicoloured . . 65 35

DESIGN: 150 f. Assisting nations' flags.

349 Dromedaries

1992.

1305 **349** 25 f. multicoloured . . . 10 10
1306 50 f. multicoloured . . . 20 10
1307 150 f. multicoloured . . . 65 35
1308 200 f. multicoloured . . . 85 45
1309 350 f. multicoloured . . . 1·59 75

350 Paddle, La Giralda Tower and Kuwaiti Pavilion

1992. "Expo '92" World's Fair, Seville. Multicoloured.

1310 50 f. Type **350** 20 10
1311 50 f. Dhows 20 10
1312 50 f. Dhow 20 10
1313 50 f. Kuwaiti Pavilion and dhow 20 10
1314 150 f. Kuwaiti Pavilion on hoist of Spanish flag 65 35
1315 150 f. Paddle and La Giralda Tower on hoist of Kuwaiti flag 65 35
1316 150 f. Paddle, La Giralda Tower and dhow on fly of Spanish flag 65 35
1317 150 f. Kuwaiti Pavilion and dhow on fly of Kuwaiti flag 60 35

351 Snake around Top of Palm Tree

1992. 2nd U.N. Conference on Environment and Development, Rio de Janeiro, Brazil. Multicoloured.

1319 150 f. Type **351** 65 35
1320 150 f. Snakes, Kuwait colours on map and palm tree . . . 65 35
1321 150 f. Skull, snake around tree trunk and dead fish . . . 65 35
1322 150 f. Snake around camel's neck and bird 65 35

Nos. 1319/22 were issued together, se-tenant, forming a composite design of the painting "Environmental Terrorism".

352 Palace of Justice

1992.

1324 **352** 25 f. multicoloured . . . 10 10
1325 50 f. multicoloured . . . 20 10
1326 100 f. multicoloured . . . 45 35
1327 150 f. multicoloured . . . 65 35
1328 250 f. multicoloured . . . 1·10 55

353 Running and Handball

1992. Olympic Games, Barcelona. Multicoloured.

1329 50 f. Swimming and football 20 10
1330 100 f. Type **353** 45 25
1331 150 f. Judo and show jumping 65 35

Each value also portrays the Olympic flag and Prince Fahed al-Ahmad al-Sabah, President of several sports organizations, who was killed in the Iraqi invasion.

354 Tanks, Demonstrators with Placards and Executed Civilians

1992. 2nd Anniv of Iraqi Invasion. Children's drawings. Multicoloured.

1332 50 f. Type **354** 20 10
1333 50 f. Soldiers rounding up civilians 20 10
1334 50 f. Military vehicles and Kuwait Towers 20 10
1335 50 f. Battle scene 20 10
1336 150 f. Tanks, bleeding eye and soldiers 65 35
1337 150 f. Battle scene around fortifications 65 35
1338 150 f. Liberation 65 35
1339 150 f. Soldiers and military vehicles 65 35

355 Burning Well

1992. 1st Anniv of Extinguishing of Oil Well Fires. Multicoloured.

1341 25 f. Type **355** 10 10
1342 50 f. Spraying dampener on fire 20 10
1343 150 f. Close-up of spraying . 65 35
1344 250 f. Extinguished well (horiz) 1·10 55

356 Kuwait Towers **357** Laying Bricks to form "32"

1993.

1345 **356** 25 f. multicoloured . . . 10 10
1346 100 f. multicoloured . . 45 25
1347 150 f. multicoloured . . 65 35

1993. 32nd National Day.

1348 **357** 25 f. multicoloured . . . 10 10
1349 50 f. multicoloured . . . 20 10
1350 150 f. multicoloured . . 65 35

358 Symbols of Oppression and Freedom **359** Hands Signing

1993. 2nd Anniv of Liberation.

1351 **358** 25 f. multicoloured . . . 10 10
1352 50 f. multicoloured . . . 20 10
1353 150 f. multicoloured . . 65 35

1993. Deaf Child Week.

1354 **359** 25 f. multicoloured . . . 10 10
1355 50 f. multicoloured . . . 20 10
1356 150 f. multicoloured . . 65 35
1357 350 f. multicoloured . . 1·50 75

360 Chained Prisoner **361** Hand scratching Map

1993. Campaign to Free Kuwaiti Prisoners of War. Multicoloured.

1358	50 f. Type **360**	20	10
1359	150 f. Chained hand, hoopoe and barred window (horiz)	65	35
1360	200 f. Screaming face on wall of empty cell	85	45

1993. 3rd Anniv of Iraqi Invasion.

1361	**361**	50 f. multicoloured	20	10
1362		150 f. multicoloured	65	35

362 Emblem

1993. 40th Anniv of Kuwait Air Force.

1363	**362**	50 f. multicoloured	20	10
1364		150 f. multicoloured	65	35

363 Flower and Dove **364** Anniversary Emblem

1994. 33rd National Day.

1365	**363**	25 f. multicoloured	10	10
1366		50 f. multicoloured	20	10
1367		150 f. multicoloured	65	35

1994. 3rd Anniv of Liberation.

1368	**364**	25 f. multicoloured	10	10
1369		50 f. multicoloured	20	10
1370		150 f. multicoloured	65	35

365 Anniversary Emblem **366** Stylized Emblems

1994. 25th Anniv of Central Bank of Kuwait.

1371	**365**	25 f. multicoloured	10	10
1372		50 f. multicoloured	20	10
1373		150 f. multicoloured	65	35

1994. International Year of the Family. Multicoloured.

1374	50 f. Type **366**	20	10
1375	150 f. Three I.Y.F. emblems	65	35
1376	200 f. Globe, emblem and spheres (horiz)	85	45

367 Emblem on Sky **368** Fingerprint in Water

1994. 20th Anniv of Industrial Bank of Kuwait.

1377	**367**	50 f. multicoloured	20	10
1378		100 f. gold, blue and black	45	25
1379		150 f. multicoloured	65	35

1994. Martyrs' Day. Multicoloured.

1380	50 f. Type **368**	20	10
1381	100 f. Fingerprint in sand	45	25
1382	150 f. Fingerprint in national colours	65	35
1383	250 f. Fingerprint in clouds over Kuwait Towers	1·10	55

369 Anniversary Emblem **370** Free and Imprisoned Doves

1994. 75th Anniv of I.L.O.

1385	**369**	50 f. multicoloured	20	10
1386		150 f. multicoloured	65	35
1387		350 f. multicoloured	1·50	75

1994. 4th Anniv of Iraqi Invasion.

1388	**370**	50 f. multicoloured	20	10
1389		150 f. multicoloured	65	35
1390		350 f. multicoloured	1·50	75

371 Emblem **372** Anniversary Emblem

1994. Kuwait Ports Authority.

1391	**371**	50 f. multicoloured	20	10
1392		150 f. multicoloured	65	35
1393		350 f. multicoloured	1·50	75

1994. 20th Anniv of Kuwait Science Club.

1394	**372**	50 f. multicoloured	20	10
1395		100 f. multicoloured	45	25
1396		150 f. multicoloured	65	35

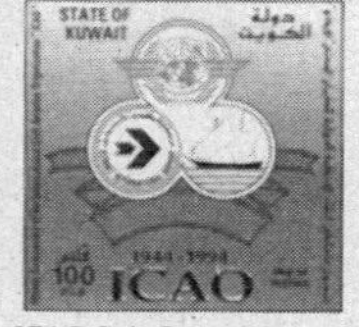

373 Map and Building **374** I.C.A.O. and Kuwait International Airport Emblems

1994. Inauguration of Arab Towns Organization Permanent Headquarters. Multicoloured.

1397	50 f. Type **373**	20	10
1398	100 f. Close-up of arched facade	45	25
1399	150 f. Door	65	35

1994. 50th Anniv of International Civil Aviation Organization. Multicoloured.

1400	100 f. Type **374**	45	25
1401	150 f. Emblems and Tower	65	35
1402	350 f. Airplane and "50 years"	1·50	75

POSTAGE DUE STAMPS

D 34 D 51

1963.

D199	D **34**	1 f. brown and black	10	20
D200		2 f. violet and black	15	25
D201		5 f. blue and black	25	20
D202		8 f. green and black	45	35
D203		10 f. yellow and black	65	65
D204		25 f. red and black	1·40	2·00

The above stamps were not sold to the public unused until 1st July, 1964.

1965.

D276	D **51**	4 f. red and yellow	15	30
D277		15 f. red and blue	45	50
D278		40 f. blue and green	95	1·25
D279		50 f. green and mauve	1·25	1·50
D280		100 f. blue and yellow	2·25	3·00

KYRGYZSTAN Pt. 10

Formerly Kirghizia, a constituent republic of the Soviet Union, Kyrgyzstan became independent in 1991. Its capital Frunze reverted to its previous name of Bishkek.

1992. 100 kopeks = 1 rouble
1993. 100 tyin = 1 som

1 Sary-Chelek Nature Reserve **2** Eagle

1992.

1	**1**	15 k. multicoloured	50	50

1992.

2	**2**	50 k. multicoloured	20	20

3 "Cattle at Issyk-kule" (G. A. Aitiev)

1992.

3	**3**	1 r. multicoloured	50	50

4 Carpet and Samovar

1992.

4	**4**	1 r. 50 multicoloured	70	70

5 Cave Paintings

1993. National Monuments. Multicoloured.

5	10 k. Type **5**	10	10
6	50 k. 11th-century tower, Burana (vert)	10	10
7	1 r. + 25 k. Tomb, Talas (vert)	10	10
8	2 r. + 50 k. Mausoleum, Uzgen	15	15
9	3 r. Yurt	25	25
10	5 r. + 50 k. Statue of Manas, Bishkek	45	45
11	9 r. Cultural complex, Bishkek	85	85

10оо КЫРГЫЗСТАН (6) 20 т. КЫРГЫЗСТАН (7)

1993. Nos. 5940, 6073 and 4671 of Russia surch as T **6**.

13	10 k. on 1 k. brown	60	60
14	20 k. on 2 k. brown	1·25	1·25
15	30 k. on 3 k. red	1·75	1·75

1993. Nos. 4672/3 of Russia surch as T **7**.

16	20 t. on 4 k. red	40	40
17	30 t. on 6 k. blue	60	60

8 Map

1993. 2nd Anniv of Independence (18) and 1st Anniv of Admission to United Nations (19). Multicoloured.

18	50 t. Type **8**	1·00	1·00
19	60 t. U.N. emblem, national flag and Government Palace, Bishkek (vert)	1·40	1·40

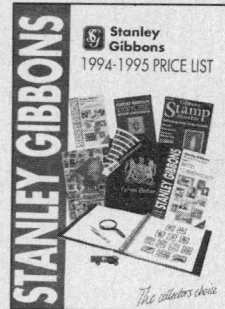

9 Komuz

1993. Music.

20	**9**	30 t. multicoloured	25	25

10 Dog

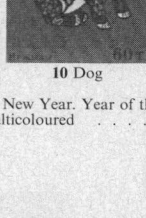

1994. New Year. Year of the Dog.

22	**10**	60 t. multicoloured	55	55

LA AGUERA Pt. 9

An administrative district of Spanish Sahara whose stamps it later used.

1920. Rio de Oro stamps optd **LA AGUERA.**
1 **15** 1 c. green . . . . 1·40 1·40
2 2 c. brown . . . . 1·40 1·40
3 5 c. green . . . . 1·40 1·40
4 10 c. red . . . . 1·40 1·40
5 15 c. yellow . . . . 1·40 1·40
6 20 c. violet . . . . 1·40 1·40
7 25 c. blue . . . . 1·40 1·40
8 30 c. brown . . . . 1·40 1·40
9 40 c. pink . . . . 1·40 1·40
10 50 c. blue . . . . 3·75 3·50
11 1 p. red . . . . 8·50 6·50
12 4 p. purple . . . . 25·00 22·00
13 10 p. orange . . . . 45·00 45·00

2

1923.
14 **2** 1 c. blue 70 70
15 2 c. green 70 70
16 5 c. green 70 70
17 10 c. red 70 70
18 15 c. brown 70 70
19 20 c. yellow 70 70
20 25 c. blue 70 70
21 30 c. brown 70 70
22 40 c. red 85 85
23 50 c. purple . . . . 3·00 2·75
24 1 p. mauve . . . . 7·50 5·75
25 4 p. violet . . . . 17·00 16·00
26 10 p. orange . . . . 20·00 19·00

LAOS Pt. 21

Laos (previously part of Fr. Indo-China) became independent in 1951.

1951. 100 cents = 1 piastre.
1955. 100 cents = 1 kip.

1 River Mekong **2** King Sisavang Vong

1951.
1 **1** 10 c. green and turquoise . . 20 20
2 20 c. red and claret 20 30
3 30 c. blue and indigo . . . . 1·00 85
4 – 50 c. brown 50 35
5 – 60 c. orange and red 45 50
6 – 70 c. turquoise and blue . . . 45 50
7 – 1 p. violet and purple 45 50
8 **2** 1 p. 50 purple and brown . . 90 65
9 – 2 p. green and grey . . . . . 16·00 4·00
10 – 3 p. red and claret 90 75
11 – 5 p. blue and indigo 1.25 80
12 – 10 p. purple and brown . . . 2·75 1·25
DESIGNS—HORIZ: As Type **1**: 50 c. to 70 c. Luang Prabang; 1 p. and 2 p. to 10 p. Vientiane.

3 Laotian Woman

4 Laotian Woman Weaving

1952.
13 **3** 30 c. violet and blue (post) . 40 35
14 80 c. turquoise and green . . 40 35
15 1 p. 10 red 90 35
16 1 p. 90 blue and deep blue . . 1·40 80
17 3 p. sepia and purple . . . . 1·40 80

18 – 3 p. 30 purple and violet (air) 85 60
19 **4** 10 p. green and blue . . . . 1·90 1·25
20 20 p. red . . . . 3·25 2·00
21 30 p. purple and sepia . . . . 4·75 3·50
DESIGN: As Type **4**: 3 p. 30, Vat Pra Keo shrine.

5 King Sisavang Vong and U.P.U. Monument

1952. 1st Anniv of Admission to U.P.U.
22 **5** 80 c. violet, bl & ind (postage) 75 85
23 1 p. brown, red and lake . . 75 75
24 1 p. 20 blue and violet . . . 75 85
25 1 p. 50 brown, emerald & grn 75 85
26 1 p. 90 turquoise and sepia . 1·10 1·25

27 25 p. indigo and blue (air) . 4·25 4·75
28 50 p. sepia, purple and brown 5·00 5·50

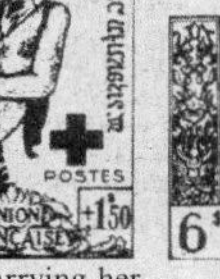

6 Girl carrying her Brother **7** Native Musicians

1953. Red Cross Fund. Cross in red.
29 **6** 1 p. 50 + 1 p. brown & blue 2·75 2·75
30 3 p. + 1 p. 50 red and green 2·75 2·75
31 3 p. 90 + 2 p. 50 brown & sep 2·50 2·75

1953.
32 **7** 4 p. 50 turquoise and blue . 1·00 85
33 6 p. brown and slate . . . . 1·10 85

8 Buddha

1953. Air. Statues of Buddha.
34 – 4 p. green 95 85
35 – 6 p. 50 green . . . . 1·40 1·10
36 – 9 p. green . . . . 2·00 1·50
37 **8** 11 p. 50 orange, brown & red 2·75 2·50
38 – 40 p. purple . . . . 6·50 2·50
39 – 100 p. bistre . . . . 13·50 10·50
Nos. 34 and 37 are horiz and the rest vert.

9 Vientiane

1954. Jubilee of King Sisavang Vong.
40 **9** 2 p. violet and blue (postage) 50·00 35·00
41 3 p. red and brown . . . . 45·00 38·00

42 50 p. turquoise & blue (air) £140 £160

10 Ravana

1955. Air. "Ramayana" (dramatic poem).
43 **10** 2 k. blue and green . . . . 1·00 90
44 – 4 k. red and brown . . . . 1·25 1·25
45 – 5 k. olive, brown and red . . 2·50 1·75
46 – 10 k. black, orange & brown 4·50 3·00
47 – 20 k. olive, green and violet 5·50 4·25
48 – 30 k. black, brown and blue 7·50 5·50
DESIGNS—HORIZ: 4 k. Hanuman, the white monkey; 5 k. Ninh Laphath, the black monkey. VERT: 10 k. Sita and Rama; 20 k. Luci and Ravana's friend; 30 k. Rama.

11 Buddha and Worshippers

1956. 2500th Anniv of Buddhist Era.
49 **11** 2 k. brown (postage) . . . . 3·50 2·25
50 3 k. black . . . . 3·50 2·25
51 5 k. sepia . . . . 5·50 3·50

52 20 k. red (air) . . . . . . 35·50 30·00
53 30 k. olive and green . . . . 35·00 32·00
Nos. 49/53 were wrongly inscribed as commemorating the birth anniversary of Buddha.

12 U.N. Emblem **13**

1956. 1st Anniv of Admission to U.N.
54 **12** 1 k. black (postage) 50 45
55 2 k. blue 65 50
56 4 k. red 90 70
57 6 k. violet . . . . 1·10 90

58 **13** 15 k. blue (air) . . . . . . 4·00 4·00
59 30 k. lake . . . . 5·50 5·50

14 Flute-player

1957. Native Musical Instruments.
60 **14** 2 k. multicoloured (postage) 1·25 80
61 – 4 k. multicoloured . . . . . 1·25 80
62 – 8 k. blue, brown and orange 2·10 95

63 – 12 k. green, violet & red (air) 1·90 1·90
64 – 14 k. brown, blue and red . 2·25 2·25
65 – 20 k. turquoise, green and violet . . . . 2·50 2·50
DESIGNS: Natives playing instruments—VERT: 4 k. Pipes; 14 k. Violin; 20 k. Drum. HORIZ: 8 k. Xylophone; 12 k. Bells.

15 Harvesting Rice

1957. Rice Cultivation.
66 **15** 3 k. multicoloured 70 40
67 – 5 k. brown, red and green . 70 50
68 – 16 k. violet, olive and blue 1·50 90
69 – 26 k. chocolate, brown & grn 1·90 1·50
DESIGNS—VERT: 5 k. Drying rice; 16 k. Winnowing rice. HORIZ: 26 k. Polishing rice.

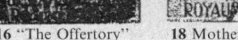

16 "The Offertory" **18** Mother and Child

17 Carrier Elephants

1957. Air. Buddhism Commem.
70 **16** 10 k. blue, brown and& violet 60 60
71 – 15 k. brown, yellow & choc 90 90
72 – 18 k. bistre and green . . . 1·25 1·25
73 – 24 k. lake, black and yellow 2·40 2·40
DESIGNS—HORIZ: 15 k. "Meditation" (children on river craft); 24 k. (48 × 36½ mm) "The Great Renunciation" (natives with horse). VERT: 18 k. "Serenity" (head of Buddhist).

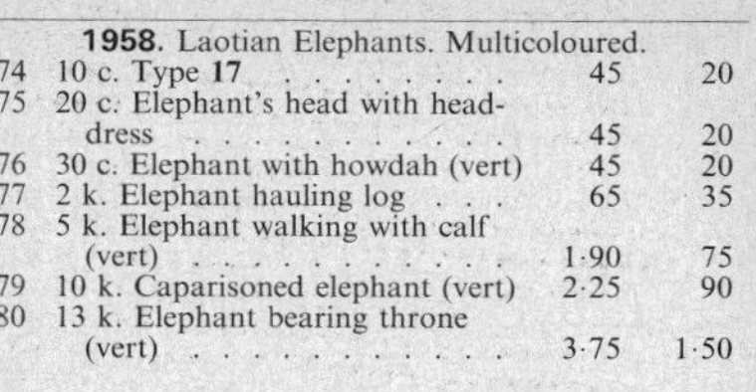

1958. Laotian Elephants. Multicoloured.
74 10 c. Type **17** 45 20
75 20 c. Elephant's head with head-dress 45 20
76 30 c. Elephant with howdah (vert) 45 20
77 2 k. Elephant hauling log . . . 65 35
78 5 k. Elephant walking with calf (vert) . . . . 1·90 75
79 10 k. Caparisoned elephant (vert) 2·25 90
80 13 k. Elephant bearing throne (vert) . . . . 3·75 1·50

1958. Air. 3rd Anniv of Laotian Red Cross. Cross in red.
81 **18** 8 k. black and violet 90 90
82 12 k. olive and brown . . . 90 90
83 15 k. turquoise and green . . 1·10 1·10
84 20 k. violet and bistre . . . 1·25 1·25

19

1958. Inauguration of U.N.E.S.C.O. Headquarters Building, Paris.
85 **19** 50 c. multicoloured 25 20
86 – 60 c. multicoloured 25 20
87 – 70 c. multicoloured 25 20
88 – 1 k. multicoloured 45 25
DESIGNS—VERT: 60 c. Woman, children and part of exterior of U.N.E.S.C.O. building; 70 c. Woman and children hailing U.N.E.S.C.O. building superimposed on globe. HORIZ: 1 k. General view of U.N.E.S.C.O. building and Eiffel Tower.

20 King Sisavang Vong

1959.
89 **20** 4 k. lake 30 30
90 6 k. 50 brown 30 30
91 9 k. mauve 30 30
92 13 k. green 30 30

21 Stage Performance **22** Portal of Vat Phou Temple, Pakse

1959. Education and Fine Arts.
93 **21** 1 k. multicoloured 20 15
94 – 2 k. lake, violet and black . 25 15
95 – 3 k. black, green and purple 30 20
96 – 5 k. green, yellow and violet 45 35
DESIGNS—VERT: 2 k. Student and "Lamp of Learning"; 5 k. Stage performers and Buddhist temple. HORIZ: 3 k. Teacher and children with "Key to Education".

1959. Laotian Monuments. Multicoloured.
97 50 c. Type **22** 15 15
98 1 k. 50 That Ing Hang, Savannakhet 15 15
99 2 k. 50 Vat Phou Temple, Pakse 20 20
100 7 k. That Luang, Vientiane . 30 30
101 11 k. As 7k., different view . 30 30
102 12 k. 50 Phou-si Temple, Luang Prabang 45 45
The 1 k. 50, 2 k. 50 and 11 k. are horiz and the rest vert.

1960. World Refugee Year. Nos. 89 and 79 surch **ANNEE MONDIALE DU REFUGIE 1959–1960** and premium.
103 4 k. + 1 k. lake 50 70
104 10 k. + 1 k. multicoloured . . 50 70

24 Plain of Jars, Xieng Khouang **25** Funeral Urn

1960. Air. Tourist Propaganda. Multicoloured.

105 9 k. 50 Type **24** 25 25
106 12 k. Papheng Falls, Champassak 35 30
107 15 k. Pair of bullocks with cart 50 45
108 19 k. Buddhist monk and village 60 50

The 12 k. and 15 k. are horiz and the rest vert.

1961. Funeral of King Sisavang Vong.

109 **25** 4 k. bistre, black and red 30 30
110 – 6 k. 50 brown and black 30 30
111 – 9 k. brown and black . . . 30 30
112 – 25 k. black 70 70

DESIGNS: 6 k. 50, Urn under canopy; 9 k. Catafalque on dragon carriage; 25 k. King Sisavang Vong.

26 Temples and Statues ("Pou Gneu Nha Gneu")

27 King Savang Vatthana

1962. Air. Festival of Makha Bousa.

113 **26** 11 k. green, red and yellow 30 30
114 – 14 k. blue and orange 30 30
115 – 20 k. multicoloured . . . 50 50
116 – 25 k. multicoloured . . . 60 60

DESIGNS: 14 k. Bird ("Garuda"). 20 k. Flying deities ("Hanuman"). LARGER (36×48 mm): 25 k. Warriors ("Nang Teng One").

1962.

117 **27** 1 k. purple, red and blue . 10 10
118 2 k. purple, red and mauve 15 15
119 5 k. purple, red & turq . . 25 15
120 10 k. purple, red and bistre 40 25

28 Laotian Boy

29 Royal Courier

1962. Malaria Eradication.

121 **28** 4 k. olive, black & green . 20 10
122 – 9 k. brown, black & turq . 20 20
123 – 10 k. red, yellow & olive . 40 25

DESIGNS: 9 k. Laotian girl. 10 k. Campaign emblem.

1962. Philatelic Exn, Vientiane and Stamp Day. Multicoloured.

124 50 c. Modern mail transport (horiz) 60 80
125 70 c. Dancer and globe (horiz) 20 20
126 1 k. Royal courier on elephant 35 35
127 1 k. 50 Type **29** 35 35

30 Fisherman

1963. Freedom from Hunger. Multicoloured.

128 1 k. Type **30** 20 15
129 4 k. Threshing rice (vert) . . 20 20
130 5 k. Planting rice and oxen in paddy field 25 25
131 9 k. Harvesting rice (vert) . . 40 40

31 Queen of Laos

32 Laotian supporting U.N. Emblem

1963. Red Cross Centenary.

132 **31** 4 k. multicoloured 20 20
133 6 k. multicoloured 25 25
134 10 k. multicoloured . . . 30 30

1963. 15th Anniv of Declaration of Human Rights. Imperf or perf.

135 **32** 4 k. purple, blue and red . 50 30

33 Temple, Map and Rameses II

1964. Nubian Monuments Preservation.

136 **33** 4 k. multicoloured 20 20
137 6 k. multicoloured 30 30
138 10 k. multicoloured 35 35

34 Offertory Vase and Horn

1964. "Constitutional Monarchy". Multicoloured.

139 10 k. Type **34** 20 15
140 15 k. Seated Buddha of Vat Pra Keo 30 20
141 20 k. Laotians walking across map 35 30
142 40 k. Royal Palace, Luang Prabang 70 55

35 Phra Vet and wife

36 Meo Warrior

1964. Folklore. Phra Vet Legend. Multicoloured.

143 10 k. Type **35** 25 25
144 32 k. "Benediction" 35 35
145 45 k. Phame and wife 40 40
146 55 k. Arrest of Phame 70 70

1964. "People of Laos".

147 – 25 k. black, brown and green (postage) 60 60
148 **36** 5 k. multicoloured (air) . . 25 15
149 – 10 k. flesh, slate and purple 35 20
150 – 50 k. brown, drab and lilac 1·40 85

DESIGNS: 10 k. Kha hunter; 25 k. Girls of three races; 50 k. Thai woman.

37 "Cethoeia biblis"

1965. Laotian Butterflies.

151 **37** 10 k. multicoloured (postage) 75 40
152 – 25 k. violet, black & yellow 1·10 60
153 – 40 k. yellow, brn and grn 1·90 90
154 – 20 k. brown & ochre (air) 1·10 60

BUTTERFLIES—As Type **37**: 25 k. "Precis cebrene". HORIZ: (48×27 mm): 20 k. "Attacus atlas"; 40 k. "Dysphania militaris".

38 Wattay Airport ("French Aid")

1965. Foreign Aid.

155 **38** 25 k. mauve, brown & turq 30 20
156 – 45 k. brown and green . . . 35 30
157 – 55 k. brown and blue . . . 50 40
158 – 75 k. multicoloured 60 50

DESIGNS—VERT: 45 k. Mother bathing child (water resources: "Japanese Aid"); 75 k. School and plants (education and cultivation: "American Aid"). HORIZ: 55 k. Studio of radio station ("British Aid").

39 Hophabang

1965.

159 **39** 10 k. multicoloured 20 15

40 Teleprinter operator, Globe and Map

1965. I.T.U. Centenary.

160 **40** 5 k. brown, violet & purple 20 15
161 – 30 k. brown, blue & green 30 30
162 – 50 k. multicoloured 50 35

DESIGNS: 30 k. Globe, map, telephonist and radio operator; 50 k. Globe, radio receiver and mast.

1965. Surch.

163 **20** 1 k. on 4 k. lake 20 15
164 5 k. on 6 k. brown 25 20

42 Mother and Baby

43 Leopard Cat

1965. 6th Anniv of U.N. "Protection of Mother and Child".

165 **42** 35 k. blue and red 70 30

1965. Air. Laotian Fauna.

166 **43** 22 k. yellow, brown & grn 30 25
167 – 55 k. brown, sepia & blue 40 30
168 – 75 k. brown and green . . . 65 40
169 – 100 k. brown, black & yell 90 60
170 – 200 k. black and red . . 1·90 1·40

DESIGNS: 55 k. Phayre's flying squirrel. 75 k. Javan mongoose. 100 k. Chinese porcupine. 200 k. Binturong.

44 U.N. Emblem on Map

45 Bulls in Combat

1965. 20th Anniv of U.N.

171 **44** 5 k. blue, drab and green 20 15
172 25 k. blue, drab & purple 25 20
173 40 k. blue, drab and blue 35 35

1965. Laotian Folklore. Multicoloured.

174 10 k. Type **45** 25 20
175 20 k. Tikhy (form of hockey) 30 20
176 25 k. Pirogue race 45 30
177 50 k. Rocket festival 50 40

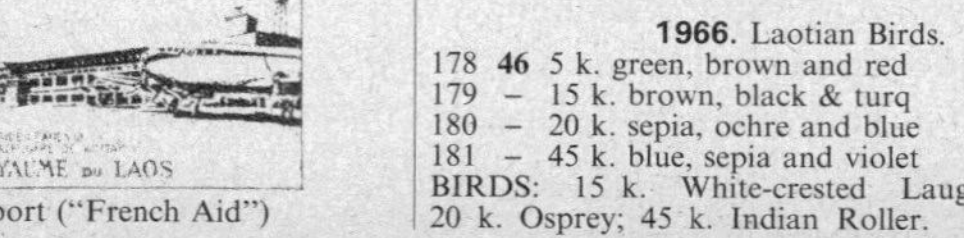

46 Slaty-headed Parakeet

1966. Laotian Birds.

178 **46** 5 k. green, brown and red 60 20
179 – 15 k. brown, black & turq 70 40
180 – 20 k. sepia, ochre and blue 95 60
181 – 45 k. blue, sepia and violet 3·00 2·10

BIRDS: 15 k. White-crested Laughing Thrush; 20 k. Osprey; 45 k. Indian Roller.

47 W.H.O. Building

1966. Inaug. of W.H.O. Headquarters, Geneva.

182 **47** 10 k. blue and turquoise . 20 20
183 25 k. green and red 25 20
184 50 k. black and blue . . . 45 45

48 Ordination of Priests

1966. Laotian Folklore. Multicoloured.

186 10 k. Type **48** 25 15
187 25 k. Sand-hills ceremony . . 25 20
188 30 k. "Wax pagoda" procession (vert) 35 30
189 40 k. "Sou-Khouan" ceremony (vert) 40 35

49 U.N.E.S.C.O. Emblem

1966. 20th Anniv of U.N.E.S.C.O.

190 **49** 20 k. orange and black . . 15 15
191 30 k. blue and black . . . 25 20
192 40 k. green and black . . . 30 25
193 60 k. red and black 45 40

50 Letter, Carrier Pigeon and Emblem

1966. International Correspondence Week.

195 **50** 5 k. blue, brown and red . 20 15
196 20 k. purple, black & green 30 20
197 40 k. brown, red and blue 40 25
198 45 k. black, green & purple 45 30

51 Flooded Village

52 Carving, Siprapouthbat Pagoda

1967. Mekong Delta Flood Relief. Multicoloured.

200 20 k. + 5 k. Type **51** 25 25
201 40 k. + 10 k. Flooded market-place 40 40
202 60 k. + 15 k. Flooded airport 1·10 1·10

1967. Buddhist Art.

204 **52** 5 k. green and brown . . . 15 15
205 – 20 k. blue and sepia . . . 25 20
206 – 50 k. purple and sepia . . 35 35
207 – 70 k. drab and purple . . 45 35

DESIGNS: (carvings in temple pagodas, Luang Prabang): 30 k. Visoun; 50 k. Xiengthong; 70 k. Visoun (different).

53 General Post Office

1967. Opening of New G.P.O. Building, Vientiane.

208 **53** 25 k. brown, green and pur 20 20
209 50 k. blue, green and slate 30 25
210 70 k. red, green and brown 50 35

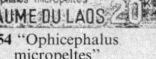

54 "Ophicephalus micropeltes"　**55** "Cassia fistula"

1967. Fishes.

211 **54** 20 k. black, bistre and blue 25 25
212 – 35 k. slate, bistre and turq 30 25
213 – 45 k. sepia, ochre and green 50 30
214 – 60 k. black, bistre and green 65 40

DESIGNS: 35 k. "Pangasianodon gigas"; 45 k. "Mastocembelus armatus"; 60 k. "Notopterus".

1967. Flowers. Multicoloured.

215 30 k. Type **55** 25 25
216 55 k. "Curcuma singularia" 35 30
217 75 k. "Poinciana regia" 50 40
218 80 k. "Plumeria acutifolia" 60 45

56 Harvesting

1967. 10th Anniv of Laotian Red Cross.

219 **56** 20 k. + 5 k. multicoloured 25 25
220 50 k. + 10 k. multicoloured 85 35
221 60 k. + 15 k. multicoloured 55 55

57 Banded Krait

1967. Reptiles. Multicoloured.

223 5 k. Type **57** 20 15
224 40 k. Marsh crocodile 25 20
225 100 k. Pit viper 75 50
226 200 k. Water monitor (lizard) 1·60 1·25

58 Human Rights Emblem

1968. Human Rights Year. Emblem in red and green.

227 **58** 20 k. green 20 20
228 30 k. brown 25 20
229 50 k. blue 50 35

59 Military Parade　**60** W.H.O. Emblem

1968. Army Day. Multicoloured.

231 15 k. Type **59** (postage) 20 15
232 20 k. Soldiers and tank in battle 30 15
233 60 k. Soldiers and Laotian flag 50 25
234 200 k. Parade of colours before National Assembly building (air) 75 55
235 300 k. As 200 k. 1·25 70

1968. 20th Anniv of W.H.O.

237 **60** 15 k. brown, red & purple 25 20
238 30 k. brown, green & blue 30 20
239 70 k. brown, purple & red 50 30
240 110 k. brown and purple 70 45
241 250 k. brown, blue & green 1·75 1·00

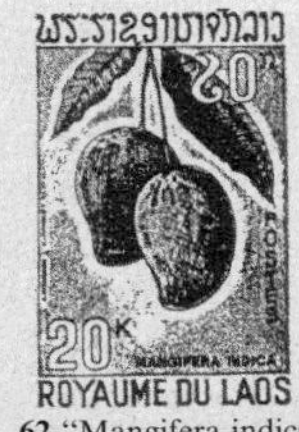

61 "Chrysochroa mnizechi"　**62** "Mangifera indica"

1968. Insects.

243 **61** 30 k. blue, yellow and green (postage) 40 25
244 – 50 k. black, orange & pur 55 35
245 – 90 k. blue, orange & ochre 1·10 55
246 – 120 k. black & orange (air) 1·10 55
247 – 160 k. multicoloured 1·40 75

INSECTS—VERT: 50 k. "Aristobia approximator"; 90 k. "Eutaenia corbetti". HORIZ: 120 k. "Dorysthenes walkeri"; 160 k. "Megaloxantha bicolor".

1968. Laotian Fruits.

248 **62** 20 k. green, blue & black 15 15
249 – 50 k. green, red and blue 30 25
250 – 180 k. green, brown & orge 80 70
251 – 250 k. green, brown & yell 1·25 90

DESIGNS—VERT: 50 k. "Tamarindus indica". HORIZ: 180 k. "Artocarpus intregrifolia"; 250 k. "Citrullus vulgaris".

63 Hurdling

1968. Olympic Games, Mexico.

252 **63** 15 k. green, blue & brown 20 15
253 – 80 k. brown, turq & blue 40 30
254 – 100 k. blue, brown & green 55 30
255 – 110 k. brown, red and blue 65 40

DESIGNS: 80 k. Tennis. 100 k. Football. 110 k. High-jumping.

64 Oriental Door, Wat Ongtu (detail)

1969. Wat Ongtu Temple.

256 **64** 150 k. gold, black and red 1·10 60
257 – 200 k. gold, black and red 1·75 90

DESIGN: 200 k. Central door, Wat Ongtu.

65 "Pharak praying to the Gods"

1969. Laotian "Ballet Royal". Designs showing dance characters. Multicoloured.

258 10 k. Type **65** (postage) 25 15
259 15 k. "Soukhib ordered to attack" 35 20
260 20 k. "Thotsakan reviewing troops" 40 30
261 30 k. "Nang Sida awaiting punishment" 60 35
262 40 k. "Pharam inspecting his troops" 75 35
263 60 k. "Hanuman about to rescue Nang Sida" 1·25 50
264 110 k. "Soudagnou battling with Thotsakan" (air) 1·75 1·25
265 300 k. "Pharam dancing with Thotsakkan" 3·75 2·25

66 Handicrafts Workshop, Vientiane

1969. 10th Anniv of I.L.O.

267 **66** 30 k. violet & red (postage) 25 20
268 60 k. purple and green 60 30
269 – 300 k. black & brown (air) 2·25 1·40

DESIGN: 300 k. Elephants moving logs.

67 Chinese Pangolin

1969. "Wild Animals" (1st series). Multicoloured.

270 15 k. Type **67** (postage) 30 20
271 30 k. Type **67** 30 25
272 70 k. Sun bear (air) 35 30
273 120 k. Common gibbon (vert) 75 50
274 150 k. Tiger 80 60

See also Nos. 300/3 and 331/5.

68 Royal Mausoleum, Luang Prabang

1969. 10th Death Anniv of King Sisavang Vong.

275 **68** 50 k. ochre, blue and green 60 40
276 – 70 k. ochre and lake 70 40

DESIGN: 70 k. King Sisavang Vong (medallion).

69 "Lao Woman being Groomed" (Leguay)

1969. Air. Paintings by Marc Leguay (1st series). Multicoloured.

277 10 k. Type **69** 1·25 70
278 150 k. "Village Market" (horiz) 1·75 90

See also Nos. 285, 307/9 and 357/61.

70 Carved Capital, Wat Xiengthong

1970. Laotian Pagodas. Multicoloured.

279 70 k. Type **70** (postage) 60 50
280 100 k. Library, Wat Sisaket (air) 90 40
281 120 k. Wat Xiengthong (horiz) 1·50 70

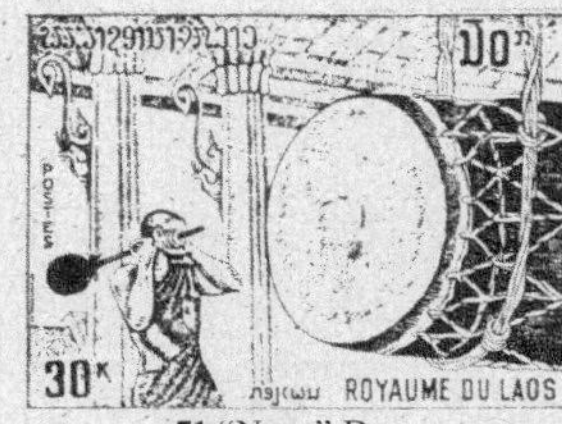

71 "Noon" Drum

1970. Laotian Drums.

282 **71** 30 k. mult (postage) 65 50
283 – 55 k. black, green & brown 1·00 65
284 – 125 k. brown, yellow and flesh (air) 1·75 1·00

DESIGNS—HORIZ: 55 k. Bronze drum. VERT: 125 k. Wooden drum.

1970. Air. Paintings by Marc Leguay (2nd series). As T **69**. Multicoloured.

285 150 k. "Banks of the Mekong" 1·75 90

72 Franklin D. Roosevelt

1970. Air. 25th Death Anniv of Franklin D. Roosevelt (American statesman).

286 **72** 120 k. slate and green 1·00 70

73 "Lenin explaining Electrification Plan" (L. Shmatko)

1970. Birth Centenary of Lenin.

287 **73** 30 k. multicoloured 35 25
288 70 k. multicoloured 45 40

1970. "Support for War Victims". Nos. 258/65 ("Ballet Royal") surch **Soutien aux Victimes de la Guerre** and value.

289 10 k. + 5 k. mult (postage) 40 40
290 15 k. + 5 k. multicoloured 40 40
291 20 k. + 5 k. multicoloured 40 40
292 30 k. + 5 k. multicoloured 40 40
293 40 k. + 5 k. multicoloured 70 70
294 60 k. + 5 k. multicoloured 90 90
295 110 k. + 5 k. mult (air) 1·75 1·75
296 300 k. + 5 k. multicoloured 2·75 2·75

75 Weaving Silk

1970. "EXPO 70" World Fair, Osaka, Japan. Laotian Silk Industry.

297 **75** 30 k. bl, brn & red (postage) 40 25
298 – 70 k. multicoloured 70 45
299 – 125 k. multicoloured (air) 85 70

DESIGNS: 70 k. Silk-spinning; 125 k. Winding skeins.

76 Wild Boar　**77** Buddha, U.N. Emblem and New York H.Q.

1970. Wild Animals (2nd series).

300 **76** 20 k. brown & grn (postage) 45 25
301 – 60 k. brown and olive 75 40
302 – 210 k. black, red and yellow (air) 2·00 1·25
303 – 500 k. green, brown & orge 4·00 2·40

ANIMALS: 210 k. Leopard. 500 k. Gaur.

1970. 25th Anniv of U.N.O. Multicoloured.

304 30 k. Type **77** (postage) 40 30
305 70 k. Type **77** 60 50
306 125 k. Nang Thorani ("Goddess of the Earth") and New York H.Q. (air) 1·25 85

1970. Air. Paintings by Marc Leguay (3rd series). As T **69**. Multicoloured.

307 100 k. "Village Track" 50 40
308 120 k. "Paddy-field in Rainy Season" (horiz) 70 50
309 150 k. "Village Elder" 80 60

MINIMUM PRICE

The minimum price quoted is 10p which represents a handling charge rather than a basis for valuing common stamps. For further notes about prices, see introductory pages.

78 "Nakhanet"

1971. Laotian Mythology (1st series). Frescoes from Triumphal Arch, Vientiane. Multicoloured.

310 **78** 70 k. orange, brown & red (postage) 50 35
311 – 85 k. green, yellow & blue 60 45
312 – 125 k. multicoloured (air) 1·25 65

DESIGNS: DIAMOND. 85 k. "Rahu". HORIZ: 49×36 mm: 125 k. "Underwater duel between Nang Matsa and Hanuman".

See also Nos. 352/4 and 385/7.

79 Silversmiths

1971. Laotian Traditional Crafts. Multicoloured.

313 30 k. Type **79** 20 20
314 50 k. Potters 40 20
315 70 k. Pirogue-builder (horiz 49×36 mm) 50 30

80 Laotian and African Children

1971. Racial Equality Year.

316 **80** 30 k. blue, red and green . 25 15
317 – 60 k. violet, red and yellow 45 30

DESIGN: 60 k. Laotian dancers and musicians.

81 Buddhist Monk at That Luang

1971. 50th Anniv of Vientiane Rotary Club.

318 **81** 30 k. violet, brown & blue 35 20
319 – 70 k. grey, red and blue . . 50 35

DESIGN—VERT: 70 k. Laotian girl on "Dragon" staircase.

82 "Dendrobium agregatum" **83** Dancers from France and Laos

1971. Laotian Orchids. Multicoloured.

320 30 k. Type **82** (postage) . . . 45 25
321 40 k. "Rynchostylis giganterum" 65 40
322 50 k. "Ascocentrum miniatur" (horiz) 70 40
323 60 k. "Paphiopedilum exul" 90 50
324 70 k. "Trichoglottis fasciata" (horiz) 95 65
325 80 k. Cattleya (horiz) . . . . 1·10 65
326 125 k. Brasilian cattleya (horiz) (air) . . . . 1·75 80
327 150 k. "Vanda teres" (horiz) 1·90 1·10

Nos. 321, 323 and 325 are smaller 22×36 or 36×22 mm. Nos. 326/7 are larger, 48×27 mm.

The orchid on No. 320 is depicted in its normal (inverted) position.

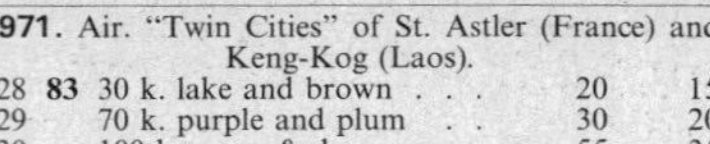
1971. Air. "Twin Cities" of St. Astler (France) and Keng-Kog (Laos).

328 **83** 30 k. lake and brown . . . 20 15
329 70 k. purple and plum . . 30 20
330 100 k. green & deep green 55 35

1971. Wild Animals (3rd series). As T **76** but with square format (36×36 mm.).

331 25 k. black, vio & blue (postage) 20 20
332 40 k. black, green and olive 30 30
333 50 k. orange and green . . . 45 40
334 85 k. brown, green & emerald 70 60
335 300 k. brown and green (air) 1·40 1·00

DESIGNS: 25 k., 40 k. Common palm civet; 50 k. Lesser Malay chevrotain; 85 k. Sambar; 300 k. Javan rhinoceros.

85 Laotian Woman (design from 1952 issue)

1971. 20th Anniv Laotian Stamps.

336 **85** 30 k. chocolate, brown and violet (postage) 20 20
337 – 40 k. multicoloured . . . 20 20
338 – 50 k. black, flesh and blue 35 25
339 – 125 k. violet, brn & grn (air) 70 50

DESIGNS—VERT: (36×48 mm): 40 k. Violinist (As No. 64); 50 k. Rama (As No. 48); 125 k. "The Offertory" (As Type **16**).

86 "Sunset on the Mekong" (Prisayane)

1971. Air. Paintings by Chamnane Prisayane. Mult.

341 125 k. Type **86** 55 45
342 150 k. "Quiet Morning at Ban Tane Pieo" 75 65

87 Children reading Book

1972. International Book Year.

343 **87** 30 k. green (postage) . . . 20 15
344 – 70 k. brown 30 25
345 – 125 k. violet (air) 70 45

DESIGNS: 70 k. Laotian illustrating manuscript. (48×27 mm): 125 k. Father showing manuscripts to children.

88 Nam Ngum Dam and Obelisk

1972. 25th Anniv of E.C.A.F.E. (Economic Commission for Asia and the Far East). Multicoloured.

346 40 k. Type **88** (postage) . . . 20 20
347 80 k. Type **88** 30 25
348 145 k. Lake and Spill-way, Nam Ngum Dam (air) 80 50

89 "The Water-carrier"

1972. 25th Anniv of U.N.I.C.E.F. Drawings by Lao Schoolchildren. Multicoloured.

349 50 k. Type **89** 25 20
350 80 k. "Teaching Bamboo-weaving" 30 25
351 120 k. "Riding a Water-buffalo" 70 45

90 "Nakharath"

1972. Laotian Mythology (2nd series).

352 **90** 100 k. green 40 30
353 – 120 k. lilac 70 45
354 – 150 k. brown 80 55

DESIGNS: 120 k. "Nang Kinnali". 150 k. "Norasing".

91 Festival Offerings

1972. Air. That Luang Religious Festival.

355 **91** 110 k. brown 45 35
356 – 125 k. purple 65 50

DESIGN: 125 k. Festival procession.

1972. Air. Paintings by Marc Leguay (4th series). As T **69**. Multicoloured.

357 50 k. "In the Paddy Field" (detail) 25 20
358 50 k. "In the Paddy Field" (different detail) 25 20
359 70 k. "Village in the Rainy Season" (detail) 35 25
360 70 k. "Village in the Rainy Season" (different detail) . . 35 25
361 120 k. "Laotian Mother" . . . 70 45

Nos. 357/8 and 359/60 when placed together form the complete painting in each case.

92 Attopeu Religious Costume **93** "Lion" Guardian, That Luang

1973. Regional Costumes.

362 **92** 40 k. yellow, mauve & brown (postage) 40 20
363 – 90 k. black, lake & brown 70 30
364 – 120 k. brown, sepia & mve (air) 70 35
365 – 150 k. ochre, lake & brown 90 45

DESIGNS: 90 k. Phongsaly festival costume; 120 k. Luang Prabang wedding costume; 150 k. Vientiane evening dress.

1973. 55th Anniv of Lions International.

366 **93** 40 k. red, purple and blue 35 20
367 – 80 k. red, yellow and blue 55 35
368 – 150 k. multicoloured (air) 1·00 70

DESIGN: 150 k. Lions emblem and statue of King Saysetthathirath, Vientiane.

94 Satellite passing Rahu

1973. Space in Retrospect. Multicoloured.

369 80 k. Type **94** 35 20
370 150 k. Landing module and Laotian festival rocket. . . . 80 40

95 Dr. Gerhard Hansen and Map of Laos

1973. Centenary of Identification of Leprosy Bacillus by Hansen.

371 **95** 40 k. purple, dp pur & orge 45 30
372 80 k. red, brown & yellow 70 40

96 "Benediction" **97** "Nang Mekhala". (Goddess of the Sea)

1973. 25th Anniv of Laotian Boy Scouts Association.

373 **96** 70 k. yellow & brn (postage) 55 35
374 – 110 k. violet & orange (air) 55 20
375 – 150 k. blue, drab & brown 75 35

DESIGNS—HORIZ: 110 k. Camp-fire entertainment. 150 k. Scouts helping flood victims, Vientiane, 1966.

1973. Air. I.M.O. Cent.

376 **97** 90 k. brown, red & mauve 55 30
377 – 150 k. brown, red & lt brn 1·00 50

DESIGN: 150 k. "Chariot of the Sun".

99 Interpol H.Q., Paris

1973. 50th Anniv of Int. Criminal Police Organization (Interpol).

382 **99** 40 k. blue (postage) . . . 30 20
383 80 k. brown and bistre . . 35 20
384 – 150 k. violet, red and green (air) 80 35

DESIGN—48×27 mm: 150 k. Woman in opium-poppy field.

100 "Phra Sratsvady"

1974. Air. Laotian Mythology (3rd series).

385 **100** 100 k. red, brown & lilac 70 30
386 – 110 k. brown, lilac & red 85 40
387 – 150 k. violet, brn & orge 1·25 60

DESIGNS: 110 k. "Phra Indra"; 150 k. "Phra Phrom".

101 Boy and Postbox **102** "Eranthemum nervosum"

1974. Centenary of U.P.U.

388 **101** 70 k. brown, green & blue (postage) 40 25
389 80 k. brown, blue & green 50 30
390 – 200 k. brown & red (air) 1·75 1·00

DESIGN—HORIZ: (48×36 mm): 200 k. Laotian girls with letters, and U.P.U. Monument, Berne (Type **105**).

1974. Laotian Flora.

391 **102** 30 k. violet & grn (postage) 35 25
392 – 50 k. multicoloured . . . 50 30
393 – 80 k. red, green & brown 80 40
394 – 500 k. green & brown (air) 3·50 1·90

DESIGNS—HORIZ: (36×26 mm): 50 k. "Nenuphar nymphea lotus"; 80 k. "Kapokier des falaises Schefflera". SQUARE: (36×36 mm): 500 k. "Nepenthes phillamphora".

103 Mekong Ferry carrying Bus

1974. Laotian Transport.

395 **103** 25 k. brown & orge (postage) 45 20
396 – 90 k. brown and bistre . . 1·10 70
397 – 250 k. brown & green (air) 2·00 1·25
DESIGNS—VERT: 90 k. Bicycle rickshaw. HORIZ: 250 k. Mekong house boat.

104 Marconi, and Laotians with Transistor Radio

1974. Birth Centenary of Guglielmo Marconi (radio pioneer).

398 **104** 60 k. grey, green & brown (postage) 30 20
399 90 k. grey, brown & green 45 30
400 – 200 k. blue & brown (air) 1·50 60
DESIGN: 200 k. Communications methods.

105 U.P.U. Monument and Laotian Girls

1974. Air. Centenary of U.P.U.

401 **105** 500 k. lilac and red . . . 2·25 1·75

106 "Diastocera wallichi"

1974. Insects. Beetles.

403 **106** 50 k. brown, black & green (postage) 55 45
404 – 90 k. black, turq & grn . . 1·10 60
405 – 100 k. black, orange & brn 1·25 85
406 – 110 k. violet, brn & grn (air) 1·25 55
DESIGNS: 90 k. "Macrochenus isabellunis"; 100 k. "Purpuricenus malaccensis"; 110 k. "Sternocera multipunctata".

107 Pagoda and Sapphire

1974. "Mineral Riches".

407 **107** 100 k. brown, green & blue 40 30
408 – 110 k. brown, blue & yellow 50 30
DESIGN: 110 k. Gold-panning and necklace.

108 King Savang Vatthana, Prince Souvanna Phouma, and Prince Souvanouvong

1975. 1st Anniv (1974) of Laotian Peace Treaty.

409 **108** 80 k. brown, ochre & grn 30 25
410 300 k. brown, ochre & pur 70 50
411 420 k. brown, ochre & turquoise 80 60

109 Fortune-teller's Chart

1975. Chinese New Year "Year of the Rabbit". Multicoloured.

413 40 k. Type **109** 35 20
414 200 k. Fortune-teller . . . . 1·10 50
415 350 k. Lao woman riding rabbit (vert) . . . . 2·00 90

110 U.N. Emblem and Frieze

113 Buddha and Stupas

1975. International Women's Year.

416 **110** 100 k. blue and green . . 40 25
417 – 200 k. orange and blue . 70 35
DESIGN: 200 k. I.W.Y. Emblem.

1975. "Pravet Sandone" Religious Festival.

420 **112** 80 k. multicoloured . . . 35 20
421 – 110 k. multicoloured . . 45 25
422 – 120 k. multicoloured . . 55 45
423 – 130 k. multicoloured . . 90 50
DESIGNS: 110 k. to 130 k. various legends.

112

1975. U.N.E.S.C.O. Campaign to Save the Temple of Borobudur.

424 **113** 100 k. green, blue & brn 30 25
425 – 200 k. brown, green & bis 55 30
DESIGN: 200 k. Temple sculptures.

114 Laotian Arms

115 Thatiang, Vien-Tran

1976.

427 **114** 1 k. multicoloured . . . 10 10
428 2 k. multicoloured . . . 10 10
429 5 k. multicoloured . . . 15 10
430 10 k. multicoloured . . . 20 20
431 200 k. multicoloured . . 1·00 1·00

1976. Pagodas. Multicoloured.

433 1 k. Type **115** 10 10
434 2 k. Phonsi, Luang Prabang . 10 10
435 30 k. Type **115** 10 10
436 80 k. As 2 k. 40 30
437 100 k. As 2 k. 50 45
438 300 k. Type **115** . . . . . 1·50 90

116 Silversmith

1977. Laotian Crafts. Multicoloured.

440 1 k. Type **116** 10 10
441 2 k. Weaver 10 10
442 20 k. Potter 25 25
443 50 k. Basket-weaver 30 25

117 Gubarev, Grechko and "Salyut" Space Station

1977. 60th Anniv of Russian Revolution. Multicoloured.

445 5 k. Type **117** 10 10
446 20 k. Lenin 10 10
447 50 k. As 20 k. 20 20
448 60 k. Type **117** 35 25
449 100 k. Kremlin and Government Palace, Vientiane 70 50
450 250 k. As 100 k. . . . . . . 1·60 1·25

118 Laotian Arms

119 Soldiers with Flag

1978.

452 **118** 5 k. yellow and black . . . 10 10
453 10 k. sepia and black . . . 10 10
454 50 k. purple and black . . 15 10
455 100 k. green and black . . 50 25
456 250 k. violet and black . . 1·25 70

1978. Army Day. Multicoloured.

457 20 k. Type **119** 10 10
458 40 k. Soldiers attacking village (horiz) 15 15
459 300 k. Anti-aircraft guns . . . 1·60 75

120 Printed Circuit and Map of Laos

121 Marchers with Banner

1978. World Telecommunications Day.

460 **120** 30 k. orange, brown & sil 10 10
461 – 250 k. multicoloured . . . 70 50
DESIGN: 250 k. Printed circuit, map and transmitter tower.

1979. National Day. Multicoloured.

462 20 k. Type **121** 10 10
463 50 k. Women with flag 25 15
464 400 k. Dancer . . . . 1·75 75

122 Woman posting Letter

123 Children playing Ball

1978. 15th Anniv of Asian-Oceanic Postal Union. Multicoloured.

466 5 k. Type **122** 10 10
467 10 k. Post Office counter . . . 10 10
468 80 k. As 10 k. 40 25
469 100 k. Type **122** 50 30

1979. International Year of the Child (1st series). Multicoloured. Without gum.

470 20 k. Type **123** 10 10
471 50 k. Children at school (horiz) 25 15
472 200 k. Mother feeding child . 1·50 45
473 500 k. Nurse inoculating child 4·25 1·10

124 Elephant, Buffalo and Pirogues

1979. Transport. Multicoloured.

475 5 k. Type **124** 15 10
476 10 k. Buffalo carts 15 10
477 70 k. As No. 476 . . . . . . 50 15
478 500 k. Type **124** . . . . 2·25 1·25

125 Dancing Child

1979. International Year of the Child (2nd series). Multicoloured. Without gum.

479 100 k. Children playing musical instruments (horiz) 40 25
480 200 k. Child releasing dove . 65 40
481 600 k. Type **125** . . . . 2·25 1·25

126 Forest and Paddy Field

1980. 5th Anniv of Republic (1st issue) and 25th Anniv of People's Front. Multicoloured. Without gum.

483 30 c. Type **126** 15 10
484 50 c. Classroom and doctor examining baby (horiz) . . 20 10
485 1 k. Three women 50 20
486 2 k. Dam and electricity pylons (horiz) . . . . 1·10 65

127 Lenin Reading

1980. 110th Birth Anniv of Lenin. Multicoloured.

488 1 k. Type **127** 15 10
489 2 k. Lenin writing 35 15
490 3 k. Lenin and red flag (vert) . 55 20
491 4 k. Lenin making speech (vert) 90 30

128 Workers in Field

1980. 5th Anniv of Republic (2nd issue). Multicoloured. Without gum.

493 50 c. Type **128** 10 10
494 1 k. 60 Loading logs on lorry and elephant hauling logs . . . 30 15
495 4 k. 60 Veterinary workers tending animals 70 35
496 5 k. 40 Workers in paddy field 1·00 45

129 Emblems of Industry, Technology, Transport, Sport and Art

1981. 26th P.C.U.S. (Communist Party) Congress. Multicoloured.

498 60 c. Type **129** 15 10
499 4 k. 60 Communist star breaking manacles and globe 80 30
500 5 k. Laurel branch and broken bomb . . . . 1·00 35

131 Player heading Ball — **132** Disabled person on Telephone

1981. World Cup Football Championship, Spain (1982) (1st issue). Multicoloured.

503 1 k. Type **131** 20 10
504 2 k. Receiving ball 35 10
505 3 k. Passing ball 55 20
506 4 k. Goalkeeper diving for ball (horiz) 80 25
507 5 k. Dribbling . . . . 1·10 40
508 6 k. Kicking ball . . . . . . 1·50 50
See also Nos. 545/50.

1981. International Year of Disabled Persons. Multicoloured.

509 3 k. Type **132** 50 20
510 5 k. Disabled teacher . . . . 1·10 40
511 12 k. Person in wheelchair mending net . . . . 3·00 60

133 Wild Cat

1981. Wild Cats. Multicoloured.

512 10 c. Type **133** 10 10
513 20 c. Fishing cat 10 10
514 30 c. Caracal 10 10
515 40 c. Clouded leopard 15 10
516 50 c. Flat-headed cat 15 10
517 9 k. Jungle cat . . . . 3·00 70

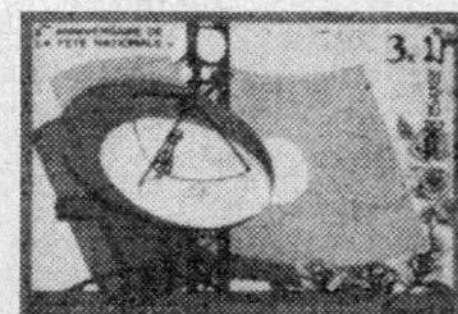

134 Dish Aerial and Flag

1981. 6th National Day Festival. Multicoloured.

518 3 k. Type **134** 50 30
519 4 k. Soldier and flag 65 40
520 5 k. Girls presenting flowers to soldier, flag and map of Laos 95 50

135 Indian Elephant

1982. Indian Elephant. Multicoloured.

521 1 k. Type **135** 20 10
522 2 k. Elephant carrying log . . 45 15
523 3 k. Elephant with passengers 70 25
524 4 k. Elephant in trap 90 35
525 5 k. Elephant and young . . 1·25 35
526 5 k. Herd of elephants . . . 1·60 50

136 Laotian Wrestling

1982. Laotian Wrestling.

527 **136** 50 c. multicoloured . . . 10 10
528 – 1 k. 20 multicoloured . . 20 10
529 – 2 k. multicoloured . . . 35 20
530 – 2 k. 50 multicoloured . . 55 30
531 – 4 k. multicoloured . . . 80 35
532 – 5 k. multicoloured . . . 1·40 45
DESIGNS: 1 k. 20 to 5 k. Various wrestling scenes.

137 "Nymphaea zanzibariensis"

1982. Water Lilies. Multicoloured.

533 30 c. Type **137** 10 10
534 40 c. "Nelumbo nucifera" "Great Rose" 10 10
535 60 c. "Nymphaea rosea" . . . 10 10
536 3 k. "Nymphaea nouchali" . . 60 35
537 4 k. "Nymphaea White" . . . 95 40
538 7 k. "Nelumbo nucifera" "Gaertn White" . . . . . 1·90 50

138 Barn Swallow

1982. Birds. Multicoloured.

539 50 c. Type **138** 20 15
540 1 k. Hoopoe 40 35
541 2 k. Common kingfisher . . . 85 55
542 3 k. Black-naped blue monarch 1·25 70
543 4 k. Grey wagtail (horiz) . . 1·40 1·10
544 10 k. Long-tailed tailor bird (horiz) . . . . 4·75 2·10

139 Football

1982. World Cup Football Championship, Spain (2nd issue).

545 **139** 1 k. multicoloured . . . 20 10
546 – 2 k. multicoloured . . . 40 10
547 – 3 k. multicoloured . . . 55 20
548 – 4 k. multicoloured . . . 70 25
549 **139** 5 k. multicoloured . . . 1·10 40
550 – 6 k. multicoloured . . . 1·40 45
DESIGNS: 2 k. to 6 k. Various designs showing football scenes.

140 "Herona marathus"

1982. Butterflies. Multicoloured.

552 1 k. Type **140** 20 10
553 2 k. "Neptis paraka" 40 20
554 3 k. "Euripus halitherses" . . 70 30
555 4 k. "Lebadea martha" . . . . 1·10 40
556 5 k. "Iton semamora" (42 × 26 mm) . . . . 1·75 75
557 6 k. "Elymnias hypermnestra" (59 × 41 mm) . . . . 2·00 1·00

142 Raft

1982. River Craft. Multicoloured.

559 50 c. Type **142** 10 10
560 60 c. Sampan 15 10
561 1 k. House boat 25 10
562 2 k. Passenger steamer . . . 50 25
563 3 k. Ferry 70 30
564 8 k. Self-propelled barge . . . 1·90 70

143 Vat Chanh

1982. Pagodas. Multicoloured.

565 50 c. Type **143** 10 10
566 60 c. Vat Inpeng 15 10
567 1 k. Vat Dong Mieng 25 10
568 2 k. Ho Tay 50 20
569 3 k. Vat Ho Pha Keo 70 25
570 8 k. Vat Sisaket . . . . 1·90 60

145 Poodle

1982. Dogs. Multicoloured.

591 50 c. Type **145** 10 10
592 60 c. Samoyed 10 10
593 1 k. Boston terrier 25 10
594 2 k. Cairn terrier 65 20
595 3 k. Chihuahua 90 25
596 8 k. Bulldog . . . . 2·50 60

146 Woman watering Crops

1982. World Food Day. Multicoloured.

597 7 k. Type **146** . . . . 1·40 45
598 8 k. Woman transplanting rice 1·75 55

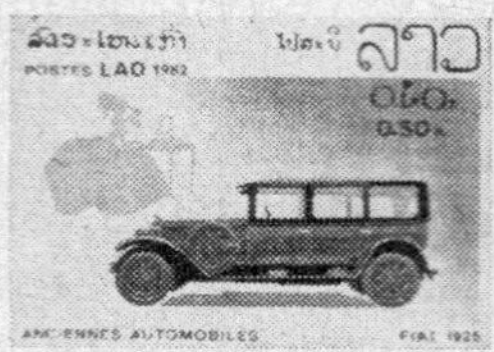

147 Fiat, 1925

1982. Cars. Multicoloured.

599 50 c. Type **147** 10 10
600 60 c. Peugeot, 1925 . . . . . . 10 10
601 1 k. Berliet, 1925 . . . . 25 10
602 2 k. Ballot, 1925 . . . . 65 20
603 3 k. Renault, 1926 . . . . . . 90 25
604 8 k. Ford, 1925 . . . . 2·50 60

148 President Souphanouvong

1982. 7th Anniv of Republic. Multicoloured.

605 50 c. Type **148** 10 10
606 1 k. Tractors (horiz) 25 10
607 2 k. Cow (horiz) 35 20
608 3 k. Lorry passing dish aerial (horiz) 50 35
609 4 k. Nurse examining child . . 75 35
610 5 k. Classroom (horiz) 95 45
611 6 k. Dancer . . . . 1·40 50

149 Dimitrov, Flag and Arms of Bulgaria

1982. Birth Centenary of Georgi Dimitrov (Bulgarian statesman).

612 **149** 10 k. multicoloured . . . 1·90 1·25

150 Kremlin and Arms of U.S.S.R. — **151** Hurdling

1982. 60th Anniv of U.S.S.R. Multicoloured.

613 3 k. Type **150** 60 40
614 4 k. Doves and maps of U.S.S.R. and Laos 90 70

1983. Olympic Games, Los Angeles. Multicoloured.

616 50 c. Type **151** 10 10
617 1 k. Javelin 20 10
618 2 k. Basketball 40 15
619 3 k. Diving 60 25
620 4 k. Gymnastics 80 40
621 10 k. Weightlifting . . . . . 2·25 60

152 Bucking Horse

1983. Horses. Multicoloured.

623 50 c. Type **152** 10 10
624 1 k. Rearing black horse . . . 20 10
625 2 k. Trotting brown horse . . 40 15
626 3 k. Dappled horse 65 25
627 4 k. Wild horse crossing snow 90 40
628 10 k. Horse in paddock . . . 2·50 60

153 "St. Catherine of Alexandria" — **154** Soviet and Czech Cosmonauts

1983. 500th Birth Anniv of Raphael (artist). Multicoloured.

629 50 c. Type **153** 10 10
630 1 k. "Adoration of the Kings" 20 10
631 2 k. "Madonna of the Grand Duke" 40 15
632 3 k. "St. George and the Dragon" 65 25
633 4 k. "The Vision of Ezekiel" 90 35
634 10 k. "Adoration of the Kings" (different) . . . . 2·50 60

1983. Cosmonauts. Multicoloured.

636 50 c. Type **154** 10 10
637 50 c. Soviet cosmonaut and Miroslaw Hermaszewski (Polish) 10 10
638 1 k. Soviet cosmonaut and Sigmund Jahn (East German) 20 10
639 1 k. Nikolai Rukavishnikov (Soviet) and Georgi Ivanov (Bulgarian) 20 10
640 2 k. V. Kubasov (Soviet) and Bertalan Farkas (Hungarian) 40 15
641 3 k. V. Dzhanibekov (Soviet) and Gurragchaa (Mongolian) . . 65 25
642 4 k. Soviet and Rumanian cosmonauts 80 35
643 6 k. Soviet cosmonaut and Arnaldo Tamayo (Cuban) 1·25 40
644 10 k. Soviet and French cosmonauts . . . . 2·40 60

155 Jacques Charles's Hydrogen Balloon, 1783

1983. Bicentenary of Manned Flight. Mult.

646 50 c. Type **155** 10 10
647 1 k. Blanchard and Jeffries' balloon, 1785 . . . . . . 20 10
648 2 k. Vincenzo Lunardi's balloon (London–Ware flight), 1784 40 15
649 3 k. Modern hot-air balloon over city 75 25
650 4 k. Massed balloon ascent, 1890 80 30
651 10 k. Auguste Piccard's stratosphere balloon "F.N.R.S.", 1931 . . . . . 2·50 60

157 "Dendrobium sp."

1983. Flowers. Multicoloured.

654 1 k. Type **157** 20 10
655 2 k. "Aerides odoratum" . . . 40 15
656 3 k. "Dendrobium aggregatum" 70 25
657 4 k. "Dendrobium" 80 30
658 5 k. "Moschatum" . . . . . 1·00 40
659 6 k. "Dendrobium sp." (different) . . . . 1·25 45

158 Downhill Skiing

1983. Winter Olympic Games, Sarajevo (1984) (1st issue). Multicoloured.

660 50 c. Type **158** 10 10
661 1 k. Slalom 25 10
662 2 k. Ice hockey 50 15
663 3 k. Speed skating 75 25
664 4 k. Ski-jumping . . . . . 1·00 30
665 10 k. Luge . . . . 2·40 80

See also Nos. 696/702.

160 "Notopterus chitala"

1983. Fishes of Mekong River. Multicoloured.

668 1 k. Type **160** 20 10
669 2 k. "Cyprinus carpio" 40 15
670 3 k. "Pangasius sp." 65 25
671 4 k. "Catlocarpio siamensis" 75 30
672 5 k. "Morulius sp." . . . . . 1·00 40
673 6 k. "Tilapia nilotica" . . . . 1·25 45

161 Magellan and "Vitoria"

1983. Explorers and their Ships. Multicoloured.

674 1 k. Type **161** 35 20
675 2 k. Jacques Cartier and "Grande Hermine" 75 30
676 3 k. Columbus and "Santa Maria" . . . . 1·25 50
677 4 k. Pedro Alvares Cabral and "El Ray" . . . . 1·40 60
678 5 k. Cook and H.M.S. "Resolution" . . . . 1·90 80
679 6 k. Charcot and "Pourquoi-pas?" . . . . 2·25 90

No. 679 is inscribed "Cabot".

162 Tabby Cat

1983. Domestic Cats. Multicoloured.

680 1 k. Type **162** 20 10
681 2 k. Long-haired Persian . . 40 15
682 3 k. Siamese 65 25
683 4 k. Burmese 75 30
684 5 k. Persian . . . . 1·00 40
685 6 k. Tortoiseshell . . . . . . 1·25 45

163 Marx, Book, Sun and Signature

1983. Death Centenary of Karl Marx. Mult.

686 1 k. Marx, dove, globe and flags 30 10
687 4 k. Type **163** 90 35
688 6 k. Marx and flags . . . . . 1·60 65

164 Elephant dragging Log

1983. 8th Anniv of Republic. Multicoloured.

689 1 k. Type **164** 30 10
690 4 k. Cattle and pig (horiz) . . 90 35
691 6 k. Crops . . . . 1·60 65

165 Carrier Pigeon and Telex Machine

1983. World Communications Year. Multicoloured.

692 50 c. Type **165** 10 10
693 1 k. Early telephone, hand-set and receiver 25 10
694 4 k. Television tube and aerial 80 35
695 6 k. Satellite and dish aerial . 1·50 55

166 Ice Skating **167** Tiger

1984. Winter Olympic Games, Sarajevo (2nd issue). Multicoloured.

696 50 c. Type **166** 10 10
697 1 k. Speed skating 30 10
698 2 k. Biathlon 40 15
699 3 k. Luge (horiz) 80 30
700 4 k. Downhill skiing (horiz) . . 95 35
701 5 k. Ski-jumping . . . . . . 1·40 45
702 6 k. Slalom . . . . 1·60 55

1984. Endangered Animals. The Tiger. Mult.

704 25 c. Type **167** 10 10
705 25 c. Tigers (horiz) 10 10
706 3 k. Tiger and cubs (horiz) . . 90 30
707 4 k. Tiger cubs . . . . 1·10 40

168 Diving

1984. Olympic Games, Los Angeles (2nd issue). Multicoloured.

708 50 c. Type **168** 10 10
709 1 k. Volleyball 25 10
710 2 k. Running 40 15
711 4 k. Basketball 85 25
712 5 k. Judo . . . . 1·10 35
713 6 k. Football . . . . 1·50 40
714 7 k. Gymnastics . . . . 1·75 50

169 Tuned Drums

1984. Musical Instruments. Multicoloured.

716 1 k. Type **169** 20 10
717 2 k. Xylophone 35 15
718 3 k. Pair of drums 70 25
719 4 k. Hand drum 90 25
720 5 k. Barrel drum . . . . . . 1·10 35
721 6 k. Pipes and string instrument 1·75 55

170 National Flag **171** "Great Chess"

1984. National Day. Multicoloured.

722 60 c. Type **170** 15 10
723 1 k. National arms 35 10
724 2 k. As No. 723 . . . . 50 20

1984. 60th Anniv of International Chess Federation. Multicoloured.

725 50 c. Type **171** 10 10
726 1 k. Renaissance game ("The Three Ages of Man" (15th-century miniature attr. to Estienne Porchier)) 25 10
727 2 k. Teaching chess 40 15
728 2 k. Margrave Otto IV of Brandenburg playing chess with his wife (German early 14th-century drawing) . . . 40 15
729 3 k. Four men at chess-board 75 30
730 4 k. Two women playing . . . 1·00 35
731 8 k. Two men playing . . . . 2·25 55

Nos. 725, 727 and 729/31 show illustrations from King Alfonso X's "Book of Chess, Dice and Tablings".

172 "Cardinal Nino de Guevara" (El Greco) **173** "Adonis aestivalis"

1984. "Espana 84" International Stamp Exhibition, Madrid. Multicoloured.

733 50 c. Type **172** 10 10
734 1 k. "Gaspar de Guzman, Duke of Olivares, on Horseback" (Velazquez) 25 10
735 2 k. "The Annunciation" (Murillo) 40 15
736 2 k. "Portrait of a Lady" (Zurbaran) 40 15
737 3 k. "The Family of Charles IV" (Goya) 75 30
738 4 k. "Two Harlequins" (Picasso) 1·00 35
739 8 k. "Abstract" (Miro) . . . 2·25 55

1984. Woodland Flowers. Multicoloured.

741 50 c. Type **173** 10 10
742 1 k. "Alpinia speciosa" . . . 25 10
743 2 k. "Cassia lechenaultiana" 40 15
744 2 k. "Aeschynanthus speciosus" 40 15
745 3 k. "Datura meteloides" . . 75 30
746 4 k. "Quamoclit pennata" . . 95 35
747 8 k. "Commelina benghalensis" 2·25 55

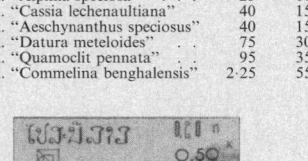

174 Nazzaro

1984. 19th Universal Postal Union Congress Philatelic Salon, Hamburg. Cars. Multicoloured.

748 50 c. Type **174** 10 10
749 1 k. Daimler 25 10
750 2 k. Delage 40 15
751 2 k. Fiat "S 57/14B" 40 15
752 3 k. Bugatti 75 30
753 4 k. Itala . . . . 1·10 35
754 8 k. Blitzen Benz . . . . . . 2·25 55

175 "Madonna and Child"

1984. 450th Death Anniv of Correggio (artist). Multicoloured.

756 50 c. Type **175** 10 10
757 1 k. Detail showing horsemen resting 25 10
758 2 k. "Madonna and Child" (different) 40 15
759 2 k. "Mystical Marriage of St. Catherine" 40 15
760 3 k. "Four Saints" 75 30
761 4 k. "Noli me Tangere" . . . 95 35
762 8 k. "Christ bids Farewell to the Virgin May" . . . . 1·90 55

176 "Luna 1"

1984. Space Exploration. Multicoloured.

764 50 c. Type **176** 10 10
765 1 k. "Luna 2" 25 10
766 2 k. "Luna 3" 40 15
767 2 k. Kepler and "Sputnik 2" . . 40 15
768 3 k. Newton & Lunokhod 2 . . 75 30
769 4 k. Jules Verne and "Luna 13" 1·00 35
770 8 k. Copernicus and space station 2·10 60

177 Malaclemys Terrapin

1984. Reptiles. Multicoloured.

771 50 c. Type **177** 10 10
772 1 k. Banded krait 25 10
773 2 k. Indian python (vert) . . . 40 15
774 2 k. Reticulated python . . . 40 15
775 3 k. Tokay gecko 80 30
776 4 k. "Natrix subminiata" . . . 1·10 40
777 8 k. Dappled ground gecko . . 2·40 65

178 Greater Glider

1984. "Ausipex 84" International Stamp Exhibition, Melbourne. Marsupials. Multicoloured.

778 50 c. Type **178** 10 10
779 1 k. Platypus 25 10
780 2 k. Southern hairy-nosed wombat 40 15
781 2 k. Tasmanian devil 40 15
782 3 k. Thylacine 75 30
783 4 k. Tiger cat . . . . 1·00 35
784 8 k. Wallaby . . . . 2·10 60

179 Nurse with Mother and Child

1984. Anti-poliomyelitis Campaign. Multicoloured.

786 5 k. Type **179** . . . . 1·10 50
787 6 k. Doctor inoculating child 1·40 55

180 Dragon Stair-rail

1984. Laotian Art. Multicoloured.

788 50 c. Type **180** 10 10
789 1 k. Capital of column 25 10
790 2 k. Decorative panel depicting god 40 15
791 2 k. Decorative panel depicting leaves 40 15
792 3 k. Stylized leaves (horiz) . . 70 30
793 4 k. Triangular flower decoration (horiz) . . . . 1·00 35
794 8 k. Circular lotus flower decoration . . . . 1·90 60

181 River House Boat

1984. 9th Anniv of Republic. Multicoloured.

795 1 k. Type **181** 45 15
796 2 k. Passengers boarding Fokker Friendship airplane 50 20
797 4 k. Building a bridge . . . . 1·10 45
798 10 k. Building a road . . . . 2·50 1·00

182 Players with Ball

1985. World Cup, Mexico (1986) (1st issue). Multicoloured.

799 50 c. Type **182** 10 10
800 1 k. Heading the ball 25 10
801 2 k. Defending the ball . . . 45 15
802 3 k. Running with ball . . . 70 20
803 4 k. Taking possession of ball 1·10 35
804 5 k. Heading the ball (different) 1·40 45
805 6 k. Saving a goal . . . . . 1·75 55

See also Nos. 868/74.

183 Motor Cycle

1985. Centenary of Motor Cycle. Multicoloured.

807 50 c. Type **183** 10 10
808 1 k. Gnome Rhone, 1920 . . 25 10
809 2 k. F.N. "M67C", 1928 . . 45 15
810 3 k. Indian "Chief", 1930 . . 70 20
811 4 k. Rudge Multi, 1914 . . . 1·10 35
812 5 k. Honda "Benly J", 1953 . 1·40 45
813 6 k. CZ, 1938 . . . . 1·75 55

184 "Amanita muscaria"

1985. Fungi. Multicoloured.

814 50 c. Type **184** 10 10
815 1 k. "Boletus edulis" 20 10
816 2 k. "Coprinus comatus" . . . 45 15
817 2 k. "Amanita rubescens" . . 45 15
818 3 k. "Xerocomus subtomentosus" 85 25
819 4 k. "Lepiota procera" . . . 1·40 35
820 8 k. "Paxillus involutus" . . 2·25 70

184a Battle Plan and Scene

1985. 40th Anniv of End of World War II. Multicoloured.

820a 1 k. Type **184a** 30 15
820b 2 k. Monument and military parade, Red Square, Moscow 60 25
820c 4 k. Street battle and battle plan, Stalingrad . . . . . 1·25 40
820d 5 k. Battle plan and Reichstag, Berlin . . . . 1·50 50
820e 6 k. Soviet Memorial, Berlin-Treptow, and military parade at Brandenburg Gate . . 1·75 60

185 Lenin reading "Pravda"

1985. 115th Birth Anniv of Lenin. Multicoloured.

821 1 k. Type **185** 25 10
822 2 k. Lenin 45 30
823 10 k. Lenin addressing meeting 2·40 1·50

186 "Cattleya percivaliana"

1985. "Argentina '85" International Stamp Exhibition, Buenos Aires. Orchids. Multicoloured.

824 50 c. Type **186** 10 10
825 1 k. "Odontoglossum luteo-purpureum" 25 10
826 2 k. "Cattleya lueddemanniana" 45 15
827 2 k. "Maxillaria sanderiana" 45 15
828 3 k. "Miltonia vexillaria" . . . 70 25
829 4 k. "Oncidium varicosum" . . 1·10 35
830 8 k. "Cattleya dowiana" . . . 2·50 70

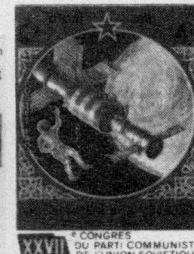

187 Rhesus Macaque

188 "Apollo" Rocket on Launch Pad

1985. Mammals. Multicoloured.

832 2 k. Type **187** 45 15
833 3 k. Kouprey 70 25
834 4 k. Porcupine (horiz) . . . . 1·10 35
835 5 k. Asiatic black bear (horiz) 1·40 45
836 10 k. Chinese pangolin . . . . 2·75 90

1985. 10th Anniv of "Soyuz"–"Apollo" Flight. Multicoloured.

837 50 c. Type **188** 10 10
838 1 k. "Soyuz" rocket on launch pad 25 10
839 2 k. "Apollo" approaching "Soyuz" (horiz) 50 15
840 2 k. "Soyuz" approaching "Apollo" (horiz) 50 15
841 3 k. "Apollo" and crew (horiz) 80 25
842 4 k. "Soyuz" and crew (horiz) 1·10 35
843 8 k. "Apollo" and "Soyuz" docked (horiz) . . . . 2·25 70

189 Fiat Biplane

1985. "Italia '85" International Stamp Exhibition, Rome. Multicoloured. (a) Aircraft.

844 50 c. Type **189** 15 10
845 1 k. Cant Z.501 Gabbiano flying boat 30 10
846 2 k. Marina Fiat MF.5 flying boat 60 15
847 3 k. Macchi Castoldi MC-100 flying boat 90 25
848 4 k. Anzani biplane . . . . . 1·25 35
849 5 k. Ambrosini biplane . . . . 1·50 45
850 6 k. Piaggio P-148 . . . . . . 1·90 55

(b) Columbus and his ships.

852 1 k. "Pinta" 30 10
853 2 k. "Nina" 60 10
854 3 k. "Santa Maria" 90 25
855 4 k. Christopher Columbus . . 1·25 35
856 5 k. Map of Columbus's first voyage . . . . 1·50 45

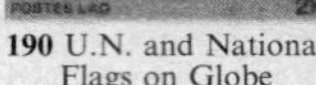
190 U.N. and National Flags on Globe

191 Woman feeding Child

1985. 40th Anniv of U.N.O. Multicoloured.

857 2 k. Type **190** 65 40
858 3 k. U.N. emblem and Laotian arms on globe 95 55
859 10 k. Map on globe . . . . . 3·25 1·75

1985. Lao Health Services. Multicoloured.

860 1 k. Type **191** 25 15
861 3 k. Red Cross nurse tending child (horiz) 90 40
862 4 k. Red Cross nurse tending patient (horiz) . . . . . . 1·10 70
863 10 k. Mother breast-feeding baby 2·50 1·50

192 Soldier, Workers and Symbols of Industry and Agriculture

1985. 10th Anniv of Republic. Multicoloured.

864 3 k. Type **192** 80 50
865 10 k. Soldier, workers and symbols of transport and communications . . . . . . 2·75 1·75

193 Soldier with Flag and Workers

1985. 30th Anniv of People's Revolutionary Party. Multicoloured.

866 2 k. Type **193** 70 40
867 8 k. Soldier with flag and workers (different) . . . . 2·40 1·40

194 Footballers

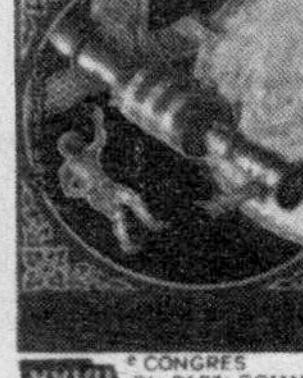
194a Cosmonaut, "Mir" Space Complex and Earth

1986. World Cup Football Championship, Mexico (2nd issue).

868 **194** 50 c. multicoloured . . . 10 10
869 – 1 k. multicoloured 25 10
870 – 2 k. multicoloured 50 15
871 – 3 k. multicoloured 75 25
872 – 4 k. multicoloured 90 30
873 – 5 k. multicoloured . . . . 1·10 40
874 – 6 k. multicoloured . . . . 1·40 55

DESIGNS: 1 k. to 6 k. Various football scenes.

1986. 17th Soviet Communist Party Congress. Multicoloured.

875a 4 k. Type **194a** 90 35
875b 20 k. Lenin and Red flag . . 4·50 95

195 "Pelargonium grandiflorum"

196 "Aporia hippia"

1986. Flowers. Multicoloured.

876 50 c. Type **195** 10 10
877 1 k. "Aquilegia vulgaris" . . 25 10
878 2 k. "Fuchsia globosa" . . . 50 15
879 3 k. "Crocus aureus" 75 25
880 4 k. "Althaca rosea" 90 30
881 5 k. "Gladiolus purpureo" . . 1·10 45
882 6 k. "Hyacinthus orientalis" 1·75 65

1986. Butterflies. Multicoloured.

883 50 c. Type **196** 10 10
884 1 k. "Euthalia irrubescens" . 25 10
885 2 k. "Japonica lutea" 50 15
886 3 k. "Pratapa ctesia" 75 25
887 4 k. "Kallina inachus" 90 30
888 5 k. "Ixias pyrene" . . . . . 1·10 45
889 6 k. "Parantica sita" . . . . 1·75 65

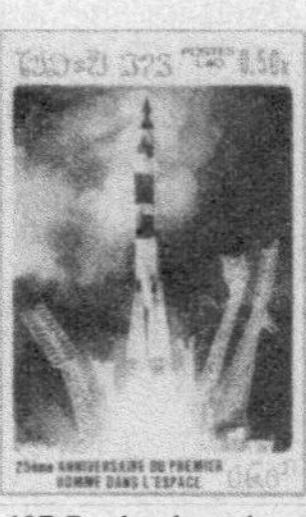
197 Rocket launch at Baikanur Space Centre

198 Giraffe

1986. 25th Anniv of First Man in Space. Multicoloured.

890 50 k. Type **197** 10 10
891 1 k. "Molniya" communications satellite 20 10
892 2 k. "Salyut" space station (horiz) 50 20
893 3 k. Yuri Gargarin, "Sputnik 1" and rocket debris (horiz) . . 70 30
894 4 k. "Luna 3" and moon . . . 95 40
895 5 k. Komarov on first space walk 1·40 50
896 6 k. "Luna 16" lifting off from moon . . . . 1·60 90

1986. Animals. Multicoloured.

898	50 c. Type **198**	10	10
899	1 k. Lion	20	10
900	2 k. African elephant	40	20
901	3 k. Red kangaroo	60	30
902	4 k. Koala	80	40
903	5 k. Greater flamingo	1·00	50
904	6 k. Giant panda	1·75	90

199 Boeing 747-100

1986. Air. Airplanes. Multicoloured.

906	20 k. Type **199**	2·50	1·90
907	50 k. Ilyushin Il-86	7·00	5·25

200 Great Argus Pheasant. (half-size illustration)

1986. Pheasants. Multicoloured.

908	50 c. Type **200**	10	10
909	1 k. Silver pheasant	25	10
910	2 k. Ring-necked pheasant	50	20
911	3 k. Lady Amherst's pheasant	75	30
912	4 k. Reeve's pheasant	90	40
913	5 k. Golden pheasant	1·10	50
914	6 k. Copper pheasant	1·75	90

201 "Elaphe guttata"

1986. Snakes. Multicoloured.

915	50 c. Type **201**	10	10
916	1 k. "Lampropeltis doliata annulata" (horiz)	25	10
917	2 k. "Thalerophis richardi"	25	10
918	2 k. "Diadophis amabilis" (horiz)	50	25
919	4 k. "Boiga dendrophila" (horiz)	90	40
920	5 k. Python (horiz)	1·10	50
921	6 k. Cobra	1·75	90

202 Bayeux Tapestry (detail) and Comet Head

1986. Appearance of Halley's Comet. Multicoloured.

922	50 c. Comet over Athens (65×21 mm)	10	10
923	1 k. Type **202** (44×21 mm)	30	10
924	2 k. Edmond Halley and comet tail (20×21 mm)	60	20
925	3 k. "Vega" space probe and comet head (44×21 mm)	90	30
926	4 k. Galileo and comet tail (20×21 mm)	1·10	40
927	5 k. Comet head (20×21 mm)	1·40	50
928	6 k. "Giotto" space probe and comet tail (44×21 mm)	1·75	90

Nos. 923/4 were printed together, se-tenant, forming a composite design. Nos. 925/6 and 927/8 were similarly arranged.

203 Keeshond

204 "Mammillaria matudae"

1986. "Stockholmia 86" International Stamp Exhibition. Dogs. Multicoloured.

930	50 c. Type **203**	10	10
931	1 k. Elkhound	20	10
932	2 k. Bernese	45	25
933	3 k. Pointing griffon	70	35
934	4 k. Sheepdog	90	45
935	5 k. Irish terrier	1·10	55
936	6 k. Briard	1·60	80

1986. Cacti. Multicoloured.

938	50 c. Type **204**	10	10
939	1 k. "Mammillaria theresae"	25	10
940	2 k. "Ariocarpus trigonus"	45	20
941	3 k. "Notocactus crassigibbus"	65	30
942	4 k. "Astrophytum asterias hybridum"	80	40
943	5 k. "Melocactus manzanus"	1·00	50
944	6 k. "Astrophytum ornatum hybridum"	1·25	60

205 Arms and Dove on Globe

206 Vat Phu Champasak

1986. International Peace Year. Multicoloured.

945	3 k. Type **205**	85	40
946	5 k. Dove on smashed bomb	1·25	60
947	10 k. People supporting emblem	2·50	1·25

1984. 40th Anniv of U.N.E.S.C.O. Multicoloured.

948	3 k. Type **206**	75	30
949	4 k. Dish aerial and map on globe	1·00	40
950	9 k. People reading books (horiz)	2·00	80

207 Speed Skating

1987. Winter Olympic Games, Calgary (1988). Multicoloured.

951	50 c. Type **207**	10	10
952	1 k. Biathlon	25	10
953	2 k. Figure skating (pairs)	50	25
954	3 k. Luge (horiz)	70	35
955	4 k. Four-man bobsleigh (horiz)	90	45
956	5 k. Ice hockey (horiz)	1·10	55
957	6 k. Ski-jumping (horiz)	1·40	70

208 Gymnast and Urn

1987. Olympic Games, Seoul (1988) (1st issue). Sports and Greek Pottery. Multicoloured.

959	50 c. Type **208**	10	10
960	1 k. Discus-thrower and vase (horiz)	25	10
961	2 k. Runner and urn	50	25
962	3 k. Show-jumper and bowl (horiz)	70	35
963	4 k. Javelin-thrower and plate	90	45
964	5 k. High-jumper and bowl with handles (horiz)	1·10	55
965	6 k. Wrestlers and urn	1·40	70

See also Nos. 1053/9.

209 Great Dane

1987. Dogs. Multicoloured.

967	50 c. Type **209**	10	10
968	1 k. Black labrador	25	10
969	2 k. St. Bernard	50	15
970	3 k. Black German shepherd	70	25
971	4 k. German shepherd	90	30
972	5 k. Beagle	1·10	45
973	6 k. Golden retriever	1·50	50

210 "Sputnik 1"

1987. 30th Anniv of Launch of First Artificial Satellite. Multicoloured.

974	50 c. Type **210**	10	10
975	1 k. "Sputnik 2"	20	10
976	2 k. "Cosmos 97"	40	20
977	3 k. "Cosmos"	60	30
978	4 k. "Mars"	75	35
979	5 k. "Luna 1"	95	45
980	9 k. "Luna 3" (vert)	1·50	75

211 "MONTREAL" Handstamp on Letter to Quebec and Schooner

1987. "Capex 87" International Stamp Exhibition, Toronto. Ships and Covers. Multicoloured.

981	50 c. Type **211**	10	10
982	1 k. "PAID MONTREAL" on letter and schooner	20	10
983	2 k. Letter from Montreal to London and full-rigged ship	40	20
984	3 k. 1840 letter to Williamsburgh and early screw-steamer	60	30
985	4 k. 1844 letter to London and early screw-steamer	80	40
986	5 k. 1848 letter and early paddle-steamer	1·00	50
987	6 k. 1861 letter and river paddle-steamer	1·25	60

212 Horse

1987. Horses. Multicoloured.

989	50 c. Type **212**	10	10
990	1 k. Chestnut horse	25	15
991	2 k. Black horse with sheepskin noseband	50	30
992	3 k. Dark chestnut horse	75	45
993	4 k. Black horse	1·00	60
994	5 k. Chestnut horse with plaited mane	1·40	85
995	6 k. White horse	1·75	1·00

213 Volvo "480"

1987. Motor Cars. Multicoloured.

996	50 c. Type **213**	10	10
997	1 k. Alfa Romeo "33"	20	10
998	2 k. Ford "Fiesta"	40	20
999	3 k. Ford "Fiesta" (different)	65	30
1000	4 k. Ford "Granada"	80	40
1001	5 k. Citroen "AX"	1·25	60
1002	6 k. Renault "21"	1·40	70

214 "Vanda teres"

1987. Orchids. Multicoloured.

1004	3 k. Type **214**	10	10
1005	7 k. "Laeliocattleya" sp.	15	10
1006	10 k. "Paphiopedilum" hybrid	25	10
1007	39 k. "Sobralia" sp.	85	40
1008	44 k. "Paphiopedilum" hybrid (different)	95	45
1009	47 k. "Paphiopedilum" hybrid (different)	1·10	50
1010	50 k. "Cattleya trianaei"	1·25	60

215 Elephants

1987. "Hafnia 87" International Stamp Exhibition, Copenhagen. Elephants. Multicoloured.

1012	50 c. Type **215**	10	10
1013	1 k. Three elephants	20	10
1014	2 k. Elephant feeding	40	20
1015	3 k. Elephant grazing on grass	60	30
1016	4 k. Baby elephant with adult elephant feeding from tree	80	40
1017	5 k. Elephant walking	1·10	60
1018	6 k. Elephant (vert)	1·40	70

216 Building Bamboo House

1987. International Year of Shelter for the Homeless. Multicoloured.

1020	1 k. Type **216**	10	10
1021	27 k. Building wooden house	60	30
1022	46 k. House on stilts	1·25	60
1023	70 k. Street of houses on stilts	1·75	90

217 "Botia macracantha"

1987. Fishes. Multicoloured.

1024	3 k. Type **217**	10	10
1025	7 k. "Oxymocanthus longirostris"	15	10
1026	10 k. "Adioryx caudimaculatus"	25	10
1027	39 k. "Synchiropus splendidus"	85	40
1028	44 k. "Cephalopolis miniatus"	95	45
1029	47 k. "Dendrochirus zebra"	1·10	50
1030	50 k. "Pomacantus semicirculatus"	1·25	60

218 Watering Seedlings

1987. World Food Day. Multicoloured.

1031	1 k. Type **218**	10	10
1032	3 k. Harvesting maize (vert)	10	10
1033	5 k. Harvesting rice	15	10
1034	63 k. Children with fish (vert)	1·50	70
1035	142 k. Tending pigs and poultry	3·50	1·50

219 Wounded Soldiers on Battlefield

1987. 70th Anniv of Russian Revolution. Multicoloured.

1036	1 k. Type **219**	20	10
1037	2 k. Mother and baby	40	20
1038	4 k. Storming the Winter Palace	80	40
1039	8 k. Lenin amongst soldiers and sailors	1·50	70
1040	10 k. Lenin labouring in Red Square	1·90	90

HAVE YOU READ THE NOTES AT THE BEGINNING OF THIS CATALOGUE?

These often provide the answers to the enquiries we receive.

220 Hoeing

1987. Rice Culture in Mountain Regions. Mult.

1041 64 k. Type **220** . . . . 1·40 70
1042 100 k. Working in paddy fields 2·25 1·10

221 Laotheung Costume

1987. Ethnic Costumes. Multicoloured.

1043 7 k. Type **221** 25 10
1044 38 k. Laoloum costume . . . 90 40
1045 144 k. Laosoun costume . . 3·00 1·40

222 Two-man Bobsleigh

1988. Winter Olympic Games, Calgary (2nd issue). Multicoloured.

1046 1 k. Type **222** 10 10
1047 4 k. Biathlon (shooting) . . . 15 10
1048 20 k. Cross-country skiing . . 50 25
1049 42 k. Ice hockey . . . . 1·00 50
1050 63 k. Speed skating . . . . . 1·50 75
1051 70 k. Slalom . . . . 1·75 90

223 Throwing the Javelin

1988. Olympic Games, Seoul (2nd issue). Mult.

1053 2 k. Type **223** 10 10
1054 5 k. Triple-jumping 15 10
1055 10 k. Men's gymnastics . . . 25 15
1056 12 k. Pirogue racing 30 15
1057 38 k. Women's gymnastics . 90 45
1058 46 k. Fencing . . . . 1·10 50
1059 100 k. Wrestling . . . . . . 2·50 1·25

224 Trachodon

1988. "Juvalux 88" Youth Philately Exhibition, Luxembourg. Prehistoric Animals. Multicoloured.

1061 3 k. Type **224** 10 10
1062 7 k. Tyrannosaurus (vert) . . 15 10
1063 39 k. "Iguanodon bernissartensis" (vert) . . . 80 35
1064 44 k. Scolosaurus (vert) . . . 1·25 60
1065 47 k. Phororhacus (vert) . . . 1·25 60
1066 50 k. "Ceratosaurus nasicornis" 1·40 65

The inscriptions on the 7 and 50 k. values have been transposed.

225 Adults in Hygiene Class

1988. 40th Anniv of W.H.O. Multicoloured.

1068 5 k. Type **225** 10 10
1069 27 k. Fumigating houses . . 55 25
1070 164 k. Woman pumping fresh water (vert) . . . . . . 3·50 1·40

226 "Sans Pareil"

227 "Plumieria rubra"

1988. "Essen 88" International Stamp Fair. Early Steam Locomotives. Multicoloured.

1071 6 k. Type **226** 10 10
1072 15 k. "Rocket" 30 15
1073 20 k. "Royal George" (horiz) 40 20
1074 25 k. "Trevithick" (horiz) . . 50 25
1075 30 k. "Novelty" (horiz) . . 65 30
1076 100 k. "Tom Thumb" (horiz) 2·25 1·10

1988. "Finlandia 88" International Stamp Exhibition, Helsinki. Flowers. Multicoloured.

1078 8 k. Type **227** 20 10
1079 9 k. "Althaea rosea" 25 10
1080 15 k. "Ixora coccinea" . . . 35 15
1081 33 k. "Cassia fistula" . . . 75 35
1082 64 k. "Dahlia coccinea" (red) 1·50 70
1083 69 k. "Dahlia coccinea" (yellow) . . . . 1·75 90

228 Sash Pattern

1988. Decorative Stencil Patterns.

1085 **228** 1 k. multicoloured . . . 10 10
1086 – 2 k. yellow, red and black 10 10
1087 – 3 k. multicoloured . . . 10 10
1088 – 25 k. multicoloured . . . 50 25
1089 – 163 k. multicoloured . . 3·50 1·25

DESIGNS: (stencils for): VERT: 2 k. Pagoda doors; 3 k. Pagoda walls. HORIZ: 25 k. Pagoda pillars; 163 k. Skirts.

229 Dove and Figures

230 Stork-billed Kingfisher

1988. 125th Anniv of Red Cross Movement. Multicoloured.

1090 4 k. Type **229** 10 10
1091 52 k. Red Cross workers with handicapped people . . . 1·00 50
1092 144 k. Red Cross worker vaccinating baby (horiz) . 3·50 1·10

1988. Birds. Multicoloured.

1093 6 k. Type **230** 20 10
1094 10 k. Japanese quail 25 10
1095 13 k. Blossom-headed parakeet 35 15
1096 44 k. Orange-breasted green pigeon 80 40
1097 63 k. Black-crested bulbul . 1·40 70
1098 64 k. Mountain imperial pigeon 1·60 80

231 Red Cross Workers loading Supplies into Pirogue

1988. Completion of First Five-Year Plan. Multicoloured.

1099 20 k. Type **231** 50 10
1100 40 k. Library 90 45
1101 50 k. Irrigating fields . . . . 1·25 60
1102 100 k. Improvement in communications . . . . . 2·50 1·40

232 Ruy Lopez Segura

1988. Chess Players. Multicoloured.

1103 1 k. Type **232** 10 10
1104 2 k. A. Anderssen 10 10
1105 3 k. P. Murphy 15 10
1106 6 k. Wilhelm Steinitz 25 10
1107 7 k. Emanuel Lasker 30 15
1108 12 k. Jose Raul Capablanca . 50 20
1109 172 k. Aleksandr Alekhine . . 4·25 1·75

233 Tortoiseshell Cat

1989. "India 89" International Stamp Exhibition, New Delhi. Cats. Multicoloured.

1110 5 k. Type **233** 10 10
1111 6 k. Brown cat 15 10
1112 10 k. Black and white cat . . 25 10
1113 20 k. Ginger cat 50 15
1114 50 k. Black cat . . . . 1·00 35
1115 172 k. Grey and white cat . . 3·50 1·25

234 Gunboat, Tank, Soldiers and Flags

1989. 40th Anniv of People's Army. Multicoloured.

1117 1 k. Type **234** 10 10
1118 2 k. Soldier teaching mathematics (vert) 10 10
1119 3 k. Army medics vaccinating civilians 15 10
1120 250 k. Peasant, revolutionary, worker and soldiers . . . . 5·50 1·00

235 Footballers

1989. World Cup Football Championship, Italy (1990) (1st issue). Multicoloured.

1121 10 k. Type **235** 15 10
1122 15 k. Footballer looking to pass ball 25 10
1123 20 k. Ball hitting player on chest 40 15
1124 25 k. Tackle 55 20
1125 45 k. Dribbling ball 90 35
1126 105 k. Kicking ball . . . . . 2·25 90

See also Nos. 1168/73.

236 Couple planting Sapling

1989. Preserve Forests Campaign. Multicoloured

1128 4 k. Type **236** 10 10
1129 10 k. Burning and fallen trees 20 10
1130 12 k. Man felling tree (vert) 25 15
1131 200 k. Trees on map (vert) 4·00 2·50

MINIMUM PRICE

The minimum price quoted is 10p which represents a handling charge rather than a basis for valuing common stamps. For further notes about prices, see introductory pages.

237 Camilo Cienfuegos, Fidel Castro and Flag

238 Skaters

1989. 30th Anniv of Cuban Revolution. Multicoloured.

1132 45 k. Type **237** . . . . . . 1·25 35
1133 50 d. Cuban and Laotian flags 1·25 35

1989. Winter Olympic Games, Albertville (1992) (1st issue). Ice Skating. Multicoloured.

1134 9 k. Type **238** 20 10
1135 10 k. Pair figure skating (horiz) 20 10
1136 15 k. Ice dancing 35 15
1137 24 k. Female skater 50 25
1138 29 k. Pair 55 25
1139 114 k. Male skater . . . . . . 2·50 1·00

See also Nos. 1196/1201, 1237/41 and 1276/80.

239 High jumping

241 Sapodillas

240 "Poor on Seashore"

1989. Olympic Games, Barcelona (1992) (1st issue). Multicoloured.

1141 5 k. Type **239** 15 10
1142 15 k. Gymnastics 45 25
1143 20 k. Cycling (horiz) 60 30
1144 25 k. Boxing (horiz) 75 40
1145 70 k. Archery . . . . 1·90 1·00
1146 120 k. Swimming . . . . . . 3·95 2·10

See also Nos. 1179/84, 1231/5 and 1282/6.

1989. "Philexfrance '89" International Stamp Exhibition, Paris. Paintings by Picasso. Mult.

1148 5 k. Type **240** 10 10
1149 7 k. "Motherhood" 15 10
1150 8 k. "Portrait of Jaime S. le Bock" 20 15
1151 9 k. "Harlequins" 25 15
1152 105 k. "Boy with Dog" . . . 2·25 1·00
1153 114 k. "Girl on Ball" . . . . 2·25 1·00

1989. Fruits. Multicoloured.

1155 5 k. Type **241** 10 10
1156 20 k. Sugar-apples 45 20
1157 20 k. Guavas 45 20
1158 30 k. Durians 70 30
1159 50 k. Pomegranates . . . . 1·10 50
1160 172 k. "Moridica charautia" 3·75 1·75

242 Sikhotabong Temple, Khammouane

243 Nehru and Woman

1989. Temples. Multicoloured.

1161 5 k. Type **242** 10 10
1162 15 k. Dam Temple, Vientiane 35 20
1163 61 k. Ing Hang Temple, Savannakhet . . . . 1·10 65
1164 161 k. Ho Vay Phra Luang Temple, Vientiane . . . . 3·75 2·10

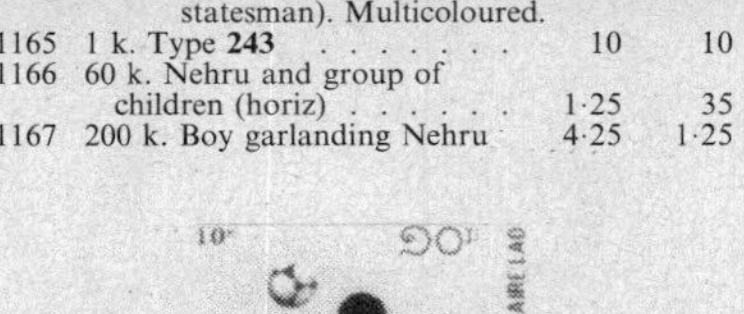

1989. Birth Centenary of Jawaharlal Nehru (Indian statesman). Multicoloured.

1165 1 k. Type **243** 10 10
1166 60 k. Nehru and group of children (horiz) . . . . . . 1·25 35
1167 200 k. Boy garlanding Nehru 4·25 1·25

244 Footballer

1990. World Cup Football Championship, Italy (2nd issue).

1168 **244** 10 k. multicoloured . . . 25 10
1169 – 15 k. multicoloured . . . 35 15
1170 – 20 k. multicoloured . . . 50 25
1171 – 25 k. multicoloured . . . 60 30
1172 – 45 k. multicoloured . . . 1·10 55
1173 – 105 k. multicoloured . . . 2·75 1·25

DESIGNS: 15 to 105 k. Different footballing scenes.

245 Teacher and Adult Class

1990. International Literacy Year. Multicoloured.

1175 10 k. Type **245** 25 10
1176 50 k. Woman teaching child (vert) . . . . 1·40 70
1177 60 k. Monk teaching adults 1·50 75
1178 150 k. Group reading and writing under tree . . . . 3·75 1·75

246 Basketball

1990. Olympic Games, Barcelona (1992) (2nd issue). Multicoloured.

1179 10 k. Type **246** 20 10
1180 30 k. Hurdling 60 25
1181 45 k. High jumping 95 40
1182 50 k. Cycling . . . . 1·10 45
1183 60 k. Throwing the javelin . . 1·25 50
1184 90 k. Tennis . . . . 2·00 80

247 Great Britain 1840 Penny Black and Mail Coach

1990. "Stamp World London 90" International Stamp Exhibition. Multicoloured.

1186 15 k. Type **247** 35 15
1187 20 k. U.S. 1847 5 c. stamp and early steam locomotive . . 45 20
1188 40 k. France 1849 20 c. stamp and mail balloons 90 35
1189 50 k. Sardinia 1851 5 c. stamp and post rider . . . . . . 1·10 45
1190 60 k. Indo-China 1892 1 c. stamp and elephant . . . . 1·40 50
1191 100 k. Spain 1850 6 c. stamp and galleon . . . . 2·25 90

248 Ho Chi Minh addressing Crowd

1990. Birth Centenary of Ho Chi Minh. Mult.

1193 40 k. Type **248** 85 35
1194 60 k. Ho Chi Minh and Laotian President . . . . 1·25 50
1195 160 k. Ho Chi Minh and Vietnamese flag (vert) . . 3·50 1·40

249 Speed Skating

1990. Winter Olympic Games, Albertville (1992) (2nd issue). Multicoloured.

1196 10 k. Type **249** 20 10
1197 25 k. Cross-country skiing (vert) 55 20
1198 30 k. Downhill skiing . . . 65 25
1199 35 k. Tobogganing 75 30
1200 80 k. Figure skating (pairs) (vert) . . . . 1·75 70
1201 90 k. Biathlon . . . . 2·00 80

250 That Luang, 1867

1990. 430th Anniv of That Luang. Multicoloured.

1203 60 k. Type **250** . . . . . . 1·40 55
1204 70 k. That Luang, 1930 . . 1·50 60
1205 130 k. That Luang, 1990 (vert) 2·75 1·10

251 Tui

1990. "New Zealand '90" International Stamp Exhibition, Auckland. Multicoloured.

1206 10 k. Type **251** 20 10
1207 15 k. Sky lark 30 10
1208 20 k. New Zealand sooty oystercatcher 40 15
1209 50 k. Common cormorant . . 1·00 40
1210 60 k. "Demigretta sacra" . . 1·25 50
1211 100 k. Brown kiwi . . . . . 2·50 1·00

252 Brown-antlered Deer

1990. Mammals. Multicoloured.

1213 10 k. Type **252** 25 10
1214 20 k. Gaur 50 20
1215 40 k. Wild water buffalo . . 1·00 40
1216 45 k. Kouprey . . . . 1·00 40
1217 120 k. Javan rhinoceros . . 3·00 1·25

253 Surgeons Operating

1990. 40th Anniv of U.N. Development Programme. Multicoloured.

1218 30 k. Type **253** 60 25
1219 45 k. Fishermen . . . . . . 1·00 40
1220 80 k. Air-traffic controller (vert) 1·60 65
1221 90 k. Electricity plant workers 1·75 70

254 Rice Ceremony

1990. New Year. Multicoloured.

1222 5 k. Type **254** 10 10
1223 10 k. Elephant in carnival parade 25 10
1224 50 k. Making offerings at temple . . . . 1·25 50
1225 150 k. Family ceremony . . . 3·75 1·50

255 Memorial, Wreath and Eternal Flame

1990. 15th National Day Festival. Multicoloured.

1226 15 k. Type **255** 40 15
1227 20 k. Celebration parade . . 50 20
1228 80 k. Hospital visit . . . . 2·00 80
1229 120 k. Girls parading with banner . . . . 2·75 1·10

257 Two-man Kayak

1991. Olympic Games, Barcelona (1992) (3rd issue). Multicoloured.

1231 22 k. Type **257** 10 10
1232 32 k. Canoeing 10 10
1233 285 k. Diving (vert) 95 40
1234 330 k. Yachting (vert) . . . . 1·10 45
1235 1000 k. Swimming . . . . . 3·25 1·25

258 Bobsleighing

1991. Winter Olympic Games, Albertville (1992) (3rd issue). Multicoloured.

1237 32 k. Type **258** 10 10
1238 135 k. Cross-country skiing (horiz) 45 20
1239 250 k. Ski jumping (horiz) . . 85 35
1240 275 k. Biathlon (horiz) . . . 95 40
1241 900 k. Speed skating (horiz) 3·00 1·25

259 Pha Pheng Falls, Champassak

1991. Tourism. Multicoloured.

1243 155 k. Type **259** 45 15
1244 220 k. Pha Tang mountains, Vanvieng 65 25
1255 235 k. Tat Set waterfall, Saravane (vert) 75 30
1256 1000 k. Plain of Jars, Xieng Khouang (vert) . . . . . . 2·75 1·10

260 Match Scene

1991. World Cup Football Championship, U.S.A. (1994) (1st issue). Multicoloured.

1247 32 k. Type **260** 10 10
1248 330 k. Goalkeeper catching ball 1·10 45
1249 340 k. Player controlling ball (vert) . . . . 1·25 50
1250 400 k. Player dribbling ball 1·50 60
1251 500 k. Tackle . . . . 1·90 75

See also Nos. 1292/6.

261 Planting Saplings

1991. National Tree Planting Day. Multicoloured.

1253 350 k. Type **261** 70 25
1254 700 k. Planting saplings (different) . . . . 2·00 80
1255 800 k. Removing saplings from store . . . . 2·40 95

262 "Mallard"

1991. "Espamer '91" Spain-Latin American Stamp Exhibition, Buenos Aires. Railway Locomotives. Multicoloured.

1256 25 k. Type **262** 10 10
1257 32 k. Pacific "231" steam locomotive 15 10
1258 285 k. American locomotive 1·10 45
1259 650 k. "Canadian Pacific" steam locomotive . . . . 2·40 95
1260 750 k. "Beyer-Garratt" (wrongly inscr "Garrant") locomotive . . . . 3·00 1·25

263 Spindle Festival

1991. Traditional Music. Multicoloured.

1262 20 k. Type **263** 10 10
1263 220 k. Mong player (vert) . . 60 25
1264 275 k. Siphandone singer (vert) 70 25
1265 545 k. Khap ngum singer . . 1·60 60
1266 690 k. Phouthaydam dance 2·00 80

264 Great Purple

1991. "Phila Nippon '91" International Stamp Exhibition, Tokyo. Butterflies. Multicoloured.

1267 55 k. Type **264** 20 10
1268 90 k. "Luehdorfia puziloi" (wrongly inscr "Luendorfia") 30 10
1269 255 k. "Papilio bianor" . . . 75 30
1270 285 k. Swallowtail 85 35
1271 900 k. Mikado swallowtail . 2·75 1·10

265 Emblem and Pattern

266 Bobsleigh

1991. International Decade for Cultural Development (1988–97). Multicoloured.

1273 285 k. Type **265** 45 20
1274 330 k. Emblem and drum . . 55 20
1275 1000 k. Emblem and pipes . 1·60 65

1992. Winter Olympic Games, Albertville (4th issue). Multicoloured.

1276 200 k. Type **266** 60 25
1277 220 k. Slalom skiing 65 25
1278 250 k. Downhill skiing (horiz) 75 30
1279 500 k. One-man luge . . . . 1·50 60
1280 600 k. Figure skating . . . . 1·75 70

267 Running 269 Argentinian and Italian Players and Flags

268 Pest Control

1992. Olympic Games, Barcelona (4th issue). Multicoloured.

1282	32 k. Type **267**	10	10
1283	245 k. Baseball	75	30
1284	275 k. Tennis	80	30
1285	285 k. Basketball	85	35
1286	900 k. Boxing (horiz)	2·75	1·10

1992. World Health Day. Multicoloured.

1288	200 k. Type **268**	60	25
1289	255 k. Anti-smoking campaign	75	30
1290	330 k. Donating blood	1·00	40
1291	1000 k. Vaccinating child (vert)	3·25	1·25

1992. World Cup Football Championship, U.S.A. (1994) (2nd issue). Multicoloured.

1292	260 k. Type **269**	60	25
1293	305 k. German and English players and flags	85	35
1294	310 k. American flag, ball and trophy	90	35
1295	350 k. Italian and English players and flags	1·10	45
1296	800 k. German and Argentinian players and flags	2·50	1·00

270 Boy Drumming 272 Doorway and Ruins

271 Common Cobra

1992. International Children's Day. Children at Play. Multicoloured.

1298	220 k. Type **270**	75	30
1299	285 k. Girls skipping (horiz)	1·00	40
1300	330 k. Boys racing on stilts	1·10	45
1301	400 k. Girls playing "escape" game (horiz)	1·40	55

1992. Snakes. Multicoloured.

1302	280 k. Type **271**	75	30
1303	295 k. Common cobra	80	30
1304	420 k. "Trimeresurus wagleri"	1·10	45
1305	700 k. King cobra (vert)	2·25	90

1992. Restoration of Wat Phou. Multicoloured.

1306	185 k. Type **272**	50	20
1307	220 k. Doorway (different)	60	25
1308	1200 k. Doorway with collapsed porch (horiz)	3·50	1·40

273 "Pinta" and Juan Martinez's Map

1992. "Genova '92" International Thematic Stamp Exhibition. Multicoloured.

1309	100 k. Type **273**	30	10
1310	300 k. Piri Reis's letter and caravelle (vert)	90	35
1311	350 k. Magellan's ship and Paolo del Pozo Toscanelli's world map	1·10	45
1312	400 k. Gabriel de Vallesca's map and Vasco da Gama's ship	1·25	50
1313	455 k. Juan Martinez's map and Portuguese four-masted caravel	1·40	55

274 Woman in Traditional Costume

1992. Traditional Costumes of Laotian Mountain Villages.

1315	274	25 k. multicoloured	10	10
1316	–	55 k. multicoloured	15	10
1317	–	400 k. multicoloured	1·10	45
1318	–	1200 k. multicoloured	3·75	1·25

DESIGNS: 55 to 1200 k. Different costumes.

275 Crested Gibbon 276 Praying before Buddha

1992. Climbing Mammals. Multicoloured.

1319	10 k. Type **275**	10	10
1320	100 k. Variegated langur	30	10
1321	250 k. Pileated gibbon	70	30
1322	430 k. Francois's monkey	1·25	50
1323	800 k. Lesser slow loris	2·25	90

1994. National Customs. Multicoloured.

1324	100 k. Type **276**	30	10
1325	140 k. Wedding (horiz)	40	15
1326	160 k. Religious procession (horiz)	50	20
1327	1500 k. Monks receiving alms (horiz)	4·75	1·90

277 New York

1994. 130th Anniv of Underground Railway Systems. Multicoloured.

1328	15 k. Type **277**	10	10
1329	50 k. Berlin	20	10
1330	100 k. Paris	40	15
1331	200 k. London	80	30
1332	900 k. Moscow	3·50	1·40

278 Malayan Bullfrog

1994. Amphibians. Multicoloured.

1334	55 k. Type **278**	20	10
1335	90 k. Muller's clawed frog	30	10
1336	100 k. Glass frog (vert)	35	15
1337	185 k. Giant toad	70	30
1338	1200 k. Common tree frog (vert)	4·25	1·75

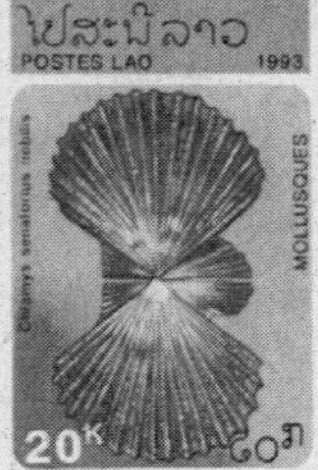

279 Common Tree-shrew 280 Noble Scallop

1994. Mammals. Multicoloured.

1339	45 k. Type **279**	15	10
1340	60 k. Philippine flying lemur	20	10
1341	120 k. Loris	35	15
1342	500 k. Eastern tarsier	1·50	60
1343	600 k. Giant gibbon	1·75	70

1994. Molluscs. Multicoloured.

1344	20 k. Type **280**	10	10
1345	30 k. Precious wentletrap	10	10
1346	70 k. Spider conch	25	10
1347	500 k. Aulicus cone	1·75	70
1348	1000 k. Milleped spider conch	3·50	1·40

281 Drugs and Skull smoking

1994. Anti-drugs Campaign. Multicoloured.

1349	200 k. Type **281**	70	30
1350	430 k. Burning seized drugs	1·50	60
1351	900 k. Instructing on dangers of drugs	3·00	1·25

282 House 283 Greater Spotted Eagle

1994. Traditional Houses. Multicoloured.

1352	32 k. Type **282**	10	10
1353	200 k. Thatched house with gable end (horiz)	70	30
1354	650 k. Thatched house (horiz)	2·25	90
1355	750 k. House with tiled roof (horiz)	2·50	1·00

1994. Birds of Prey. Multicoloured.

1356	10 k. Type **283**	10	10
1357	100 k. Spotted little owl	35	15
1358	330 k. Pied harrier (horiz)	1·10	45
1359	1000 k. Short-toed eagle	3·50	1·40

284 Fighting Forest Fire

1994. Environmental Protection. Multicoloured.

1360	32 k. Type **284**	10	10
1361	40 k. Wildlife on banks of River Mekong	15	10
1362	260 k. Paddy fields	85	35
1363	1100 k. Oxen in river	1·40	55

285 "Narathura atosia"

1994. "Bangkok 1993" International Stamp Exhibition. Butterflies. Multicoloured.

1364	35 k. Type **285**	10	10
1365	80 k. "Parides philoxenus"	25	10
1366	150 k. "Euploea harrisi"	50	20
1367	220 k. Yellow orange-tip	75	30
1368	500 k. Female common palm fly	1·75	70

286 Footballer 287 Hesperornis

1994. World Cup Football Championship, U.S.A. Multicoloured.

1370	10 k. Type **286**	10	10
1371	20 k. Brazil player	10	10
1372	285 k. Uruguay player	90	35
1373	400 k. Germany player	1·25	50
1374	800 k. Forward challenging goalkeeper	2·50	1·00

1994. Prehistoric Birds. Multicoloured.

1376	10 k. Type **287**	10	10
1377	20 k. Dronte	10	10
1378	150 k. Archaeopteryx	50	20
1379	600 k. Phororhachos	2·00	80
1380	700 k. "Dinornis maximus"	2·25	90

288 Olympic Flag and Flame

1994. Centenary of International Olympic Committee. Multicoloured.

1382	100 k. Type **288**	35	10
1383	250 k. Ancient Greek athletes (horiz)	90	30
1384	1000 k. Pierre de Coubertin (founder) and modern athlete	3·50	1·10

POSTAGE DUE STAMPS

D 5 Vat Sisaket Shrine D 6 Sampans D 98 Serpent

1952.

D22	D 5	10 c. brown	20	35
D23		20 c. violet	20	35
D24		50 c. red	20	30
D25		1 p. green	25	35
D26		2 p. blue	25	35
D27		5 p. purple	70	80
D28	D 6	10 p. blue	1·10	1·25

1973.

D378	D 98	10 k. black, brn & yell	10	10
D379		15 k. black, yell & grn	10	10
D380		20 k. black, green & bl	15	15
D381		50 k. black, blue & red	30	30

APPENDIX

The following stamps have either been issued in excess of postal needs or have not been available to the public in reasonable quantities at face value. Such stamps may later be given full listing if there is evidence of regular postal use.

1975.

Centenary of U.P.U. Postage 10, 15, 30, 40 k; Air 1000, 1500 k. On gold foil 2500, 3000 k.

"Apollo-Soyuz" Space Link. Postage 125, 150, 200, 300 k.; Air 450, 700 k.

Bicentenary of American Revolution. Postage 10, 15, 40, 50, 100, 125, 150, 200 k.: Air 1000, 1500 k.

LATAKIA Pt. 19

The former state of the Alaouites which changed its name to Latakia in 1930.
Latakia was merged with Syria in 1936.

100 centimes = 1 piastre.

1931. As 1930 stamps of Syria (T **26/7**) optd **LATTAQUIE** and in Arabic.
64 0 p. 10 purple . . . 20 15
66 0 p. 20 blue . . . 20 20
67 0 p. 20 red . . . 30 30
68 0 p. 25 green . . . 30 30
69 0 p. 25 violet . . . 50 50
70 0 p. 50 violet . . . 50 50
71 0 p. 75 red . . . 50 50
72 1 p. green . . . 50 50
73 1 p. 50 brown . . . 80 80
74 1 p. 50 green . . . 90 90
75 2 p. violet . . . 90 90
76 3 p. green . . . 1·60 1·60
77 4 p. orange . . . 1·50 1·50
78 4 p. 50 red . . . 1·50 1·50
79 6 p. green . . . 1·60 1·60
80 7 p. 50 blue . . . 1·60 1·60
81 10 p. brown . . . 2·25 2·25
82 15 p. green . . . 3·00 3·00
83 25 p. purple . . . 7·00 7·00
84 50 p. brown . . . 6·00 6·00
85 100 p. red . . . 16·00 16·00

1931. Air. As 1931 air stamps of Syria optd **LATTAQUIE** and in Arabic.
86 0 p. 50 yellow . . . 25 25
87 0 p. 50 brown . . . 40 40
88 1 p. brown . . . 70 70
89 2 p. blue . . . 90 90
90 3 p. green . . . 1·10 1·10
91 5 p. purple . . . 2·50 2·50
92 10 p. blue . . . 3·50 3·50
93 15 p. red . . . 4·50 4·50
94 25 p. orange . . . 8·00 8·00
95 50 p. black . . . 12·00 12·00
96 100 p. mauve . . . 12·00 12·00

POSTAGE DUE STAMPS

1931. Nos. D197/8 of Syria optd **LATTAQUIE** and in Arabic.
D86 8 p. black on blue . . . 8·50 8·50
D87 15 p. black on red . . . 6·50 6·50

LATVIA Pt. 10

A country on the Baltic Sea. Previously part of the Russian Empire, Latvia was independent from 1918 to 1940 when it became part of the U.S.S.R. Following the dissolution of the U.S.S.R. in 1991, Latvia once again became an independent republic.

1918. 100 kapeikas = 1 rublis.
1923. 100 santimu = 1 lats.
1991. 100 kopeks = 1 (Russian) rouble.
1992. 100 kopeks = 1 Latvian rouble.
1993. 100 santimu = 1 lats.

1 4 5 Rising Sun

1918. Printed on back of German war maps. Imperf or perf.
15 **1** 3 k. lilac . . . 10 10
16 5 k. red . . . 10 10
17 10 k. blue . . . 10 10
18 15 k. green . . . 10 10
41 20 k. orange . . . 10 10
20 25 k. grey . . . 50 35
21 35 k. brown . . . 20 20
42 40 k. purple . . . 30 10
22 50 k. violet . . . 20 20
44 75 k. green . . . 25 15
29 3 r. red and blue . . . 1·25 75
30 5 r. red and brown . . . 1·00 85

1919. Liberation of Riga. Imperf.
24 **4** 5 k. red . . . 20 15
25 15 k. green . . . 20 15
26 35 k. brown . . . 35 10

For stamps of Type **1** and **4** optd with a cross, with or without Russian letters "Z A", see under North-West Russia Nos. 21/42.

1919. Imperf or perf.
27 **5** 10 k. blue . . . 45 35

6 7

1919. 1st Anniv of Independence. (a) Size 33 × 45 mm.
32 **6** 10 k. red and brown . . . 35 35

(b) Size 28 × 38 mm.
33 **6** 10 k. red and brown . . . 20 20
34 35 k. green and blue . . . 20 20
35 1 r. red and green . . . 50 50

1919. Liberation of Courland.
36 **7** 10 k. red and brown . . . 10 10
37 25 k. green and blue . . . 20 20
38 35 k. blue and black . . . 30 30
39 1 r. brown and green . . . 85 85

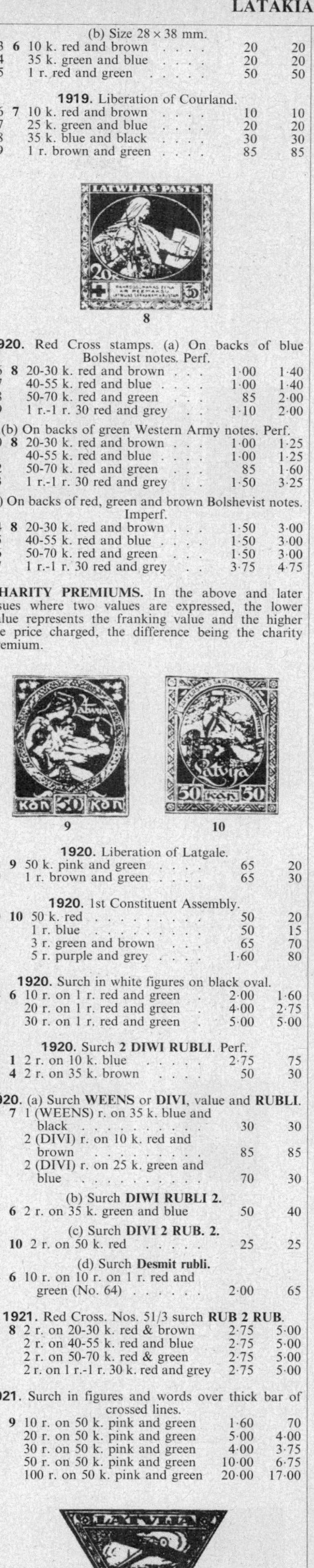

8

1920. Red Cross stamps. (a) On backs of blue Bolshevist notes. Perf.
46 **8** 20-30 k. red and brown . . . 1·00 1·40
47 40-55 k. red and blue . . . 1·00 1·40
48 50-70 k. red and green . . . 85 2·00
49 1 r.-1 r. 30 red and grey . . . 1·10 2·00

(b) On backs of green Western Army notes. Perf.
50 **8** 20-30 k. red and brown . . . 1·00 1·25
51 40-55 k. red and blue . . . 1·00 1·25
52 50-70 k. red and green . . . 85 1·60
53 1 r.-1 r. 30 red and grey . . . 1·50 3·25

(c) On backs of red, green and brown Bolshevist notes. Imperf.
54 **8** 20-30 k. red and brown . . . 1·50 3·00
55 40-55 k. red and blue . . . 1·50 3·00
56 50-70 k. red and green . . . 1·50 3·00
57 1 r.-1 r. 30 red and grey . . . 3·75 4·75

CHARITY PREMIUMS. In the above and later issues where two values are expressed, the lower value represents the franking value and the higher the price charged, the difference being the charity premium.

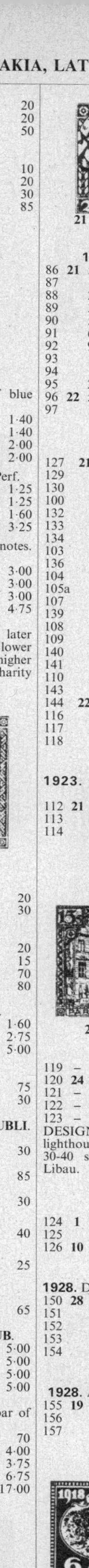

9 10

1920. Liberation of Latgale.
58 **9** 50 k. pink and green . . . 65 20
59 1 r. brown and green . . . 65 30

1920. 1st Constituent Assembly.
60 **10** 50 k. red . . . 50 20
61 1 r. blue . . . 50 15
62 3 r. green and brown . . . 65 70
63 5 r. purple and grey . . . 1·60 80

1920. Surch in white figures on black oval.
64 **6** 10 r. on 1 r. red and green . . . 2·00 1·60
65 20 r. on 1 r. red and green . . . 4·00 2·75
66 30 r. on 1 r. red and green . . . 5·00 5·00

1920. Surch **2 DIWI RUBLI**. Perf.
67 **1** 2 r. on 10 k. blue . . . 2·75 75
68 **4** 2 r. on 35 k. brown . . . 50 30

1920. (a) Surch **WEENS** or **DIVI**, value and **RUBLI**.
69 **7** 1 (WEENS) r. on 35 k. blue and black . . . 30 30
70 2 (DIVI) r. on 10 k. red and brown . . . 85 85
71 2 (DIVI) r. on 25 k. green and blue . . . 70 30

(b) Surch **DIWI RUBLI 2.**
72 **6** 2 r. on 35 k. green and blue . . . 50 40

(c) Surch **DIVI 2 RUB. 2.**
73 **10** 2 r. on 50 k. red . . . 25 25

(d) Surch **Desmit rubli.**
74 **6** 10 r. on 10 r. on 1 r. red and green (No. 64) . . . 2·00 65

1921. Red Cross. Nos. 51/3 surch **RUB 2 RUB.**
75 **8** 2 r. on 20-30 k. red & brown . . . 2·75 5·00
76 2 r. on 40-55 k. red and blue . . . 2·75 5·00
77 2 r. on 50-70 k. red & green . . . 2·75 5·00
78 2 r. on 1 r.-1 r. 30 k. red and grey . . . 2·75 5·00

1921. Surch in figures and words over thick bar of crossed lines.
79 **9** 10 r. on 50 k. pink and green . . . 1·60 70
80 20 r. on 50 k. pink and green . . . 5·00 4·00
81 30 r. on 50 k. pink and green . . . 4·00 3·75
82 50 r. on 50 k. pink and green . . . 10·00 6·75
83 100 r. on 50 k. pink and green . . . 20·00 17·00

19

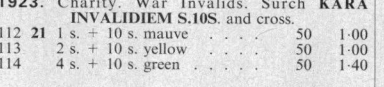

1921. Air. Value in "RUBLU". Imperf or perf.
84 **19** 10 r. green . . . 5·00 1·50
85 20 r. blue . . . 5·00 1·60
See also Nos. 155/7.

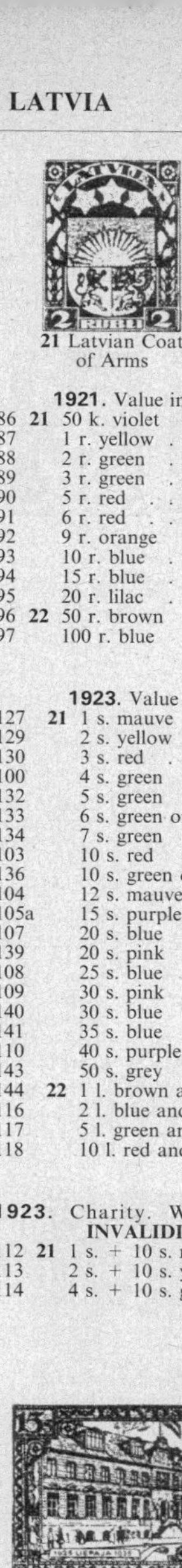

21 Latvian Coat of Arms 22 Great Seal of Latvia

1921. Value in "Kopeks" or "Roubles".
86 **21** 50 k. violet . . . 25 10
87 1 r. yellow . . . 25 25
88 2 r. green . . . 20 10
89 3 r. green . . . 30 25
90 5 r. red . . . 80 10
91 6 r. red . . . 1·25 1·00
92 9 r. orange . . . 90 50
93 10 r. blue . . . 85 10
94 15 r. blue . . . 2·50 60
95 20 r. lilac . . . 13·50 1·40
96 **22** 50 r. brown . . . 17·00 4·25
97 100 r. blue . . . 18·00 3·75

1923. Value in "Santimi" or "Lats".
127 **21** 1 s. mauve . . . 15 10
129 2 s. yellow . . . 15 10
130 3 s. red . . . 15 10
100 4 s. green . . . 45 10
132 5 s. green . . . 30 10
133 6 s. green on yellow . . . 10 10
134 7 s. green . . . 30 15
103 10 s. red . . . 85 10
136 10 s. green on yellow . . . 10·00 10
104 12 s. mauve . . . 25 20
105a 15 s. purple on red . . . 3·25 10
107 20 s. blue . . . 2·00 10
139 20 s. pink . . . 5·75 10
108 25 s. blue . . . 50 10
109 30 s. pink . . . 4·75 15
140 30 s. blue . . . 1·60 10
141 35 s. blue . . . 1·50 10
110 40 s. purple . . . 1·90 15
143 50 s. grey . . . 3·00 15
144 **22** 1 l. brown and bistre . . . 5·75 15
116 2 l. blue and light blue . . . 18·00 1·60
117 5 l. green and light green . . . 55·00 4·75
118 10 l. red and light red . . . 5·00 6·00

1923. Charity. War Invalids. Surch **KARA INVALIDIEM S.10S.** and cross.
112 **21** 1 s. + 10 s. mauve . . . 50 1·00
113 2 s. + 10 s. yellow . . . 50 1·00
114 4 s. + 10 s. green . . . 50 1·40

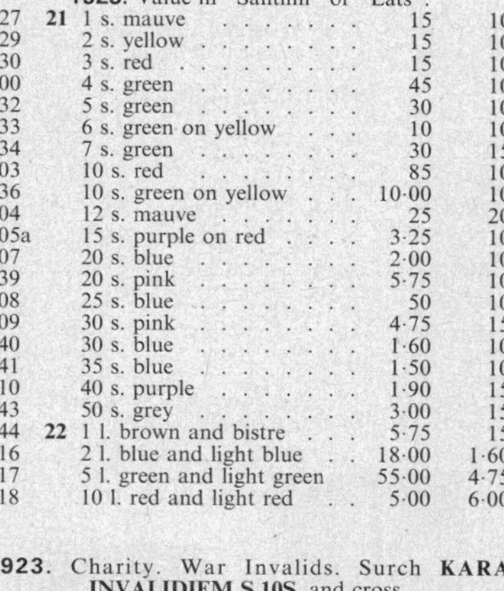

24 Town Hall 28 Pres. J. Cakste

1925. 300th Anniv of City of Libau.
119 – 6-12 s. blue and red . . . 1·75 4·00
120 **24** 15-25 s. brown and blue . . . 1·00 2·75
121 – 25-35 s. green and violet . . . 3·25 2·75
122 – 30-40 s. lake and blue . . . 5·75 11·50
123 – 50-60 s. violet and green . . . 7·75 15·00
DESIGNS—HORIZ: 6-12 s. Harbour and lighthouse; 25-35 s. Spa health pavilion. VERT: 30-40 s. St. Anna's Church; 50-60 s. Arms of Libau.

1927. Surch.
124 **1** 15 s. on 40 k. purple . . . 50 40
125 15 s. on 50 k. violet . . . 1·50 1·60
126 **10** 1 l. on 3 r. green & brown . . . 6·75 13·50

1928. Death of President Cakste and Memorial Fund.
150 **28** 2-12 s. orange . . . 4·00 3·25
151 6-16 s. green . . . 4·00 3·25
152 15-25 s. lake . . . 4·00 3·25
153 25-35 s. blue . . . 4·00 3·25
154 30-40 s. red . . . 4·00 3·25

1928. Air. Value in "SANTIMU" or "SANTIMI".
155 **19** 10 s. green . . . 1·60 1·00
156 15 s. red . . . 2·40 80
157 25 s. blue . . . 3·25 90

29 Ruins at Rezekne 30 Venta

1928. 10th Anniv of Independence. Views.
158 **29** 6 s. purple and green . . . 1·00 15
159 – 15 s. green and brown . . . 1·00 15
160 – 20 s. green and red . . . 1·40 50
161 – 30 s. brown and blue . . . 1·60 20
162 – 50 s. pink and grey . . . 2·00 2·00
163 – 1 l. sepia and brown . . . 4·00 1·75
DESIGNS: 15 s. Jelgava (Mitau); 20 s. Cesis (Wenden); 30 s. Liepaja (Libau); 50 s. Riga; 1 l. National Theatre, Riga.

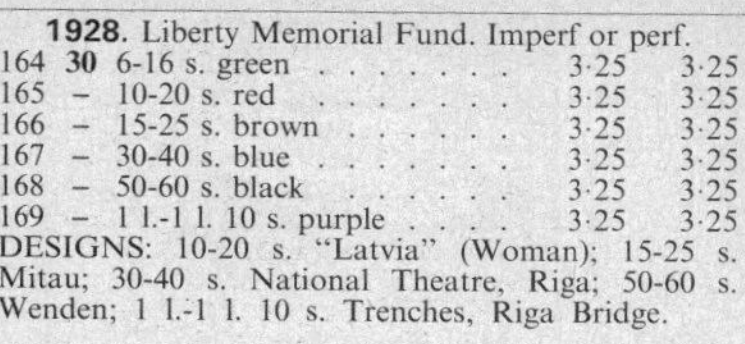

1928. Liberty Memorial Fund. Imperf or perf.
164 **30** 6-16 s. green . . . 3·25 3·25
165 – 10-20 s. red . . . 3·25 3·25
166 – 15-25 s. brown . . . 3·25 3·25
167 – 30-40 s. blue . . . 3·25 3·25
168 – 50-60 s. black . . . 3·25 3·25
169 – 1 l.-1 l. 10 s. purple . . . 3·25 3·25
DESIGNS: 10-20 s. "Latvia" (Woman); 15-25 s. Mitau; 30-40 s. National Theatre, Riga; 50-60 s. Wenden; 1 l.-1 l. 10 s. Trenches, Riga Bridge.

32 Z. A. Meierovics 33 J. Rainis

1929. 3rd Death Anniv of Meierovics (Foreign Minister). Imperf or perf.
170 **32** 2-4 s. yellow . . . 4·00 4·00
171 6-12 s. green . . . 4·00 4·00
172 15-25 s. purple . . . 4·00 4·00
173 25-35 s. blue . . . 4·00 4·00
174 30-40 s. blue . . . 4·00 4·00

1930. Memorial Fund for J. Rainis (writer and politician). Imperf or perf.
175 **33** 1-2 s. purple . . . 1·00 1·50
176 2-4 s. orange . . . 1·00 1·50
177 4-8 s. green . . . 1·00 1·50
178 6-12 s. brown and green . . . 1·00 1·50
179 10-20 s. red . . . 17·00 30·00
180 15-30 s. green and brown . . . 17·00 30·00

34 Durbe Castle

1930. Air. J. Rainis Memorial Fund. Imperf or perf.
181 **34** 10-20 s. green and red . . . 10·00 11·50
182 15-30 s. red and green . . . 10·00 11·50

35 36

1930. Anti-T.B. Fund.
183 – 1-2 s. red and purple . . . 50 50
184 – 2-4 s. red and orange . . . 50 50
185 **35** 4-8 s. red and green . . . 1·00 80
186 – 5-10 s. brown and green . . . 1·40 1·10
187 – 6-12 s. yellow and green . . . 1·40 1·10
188 – 10-20 s. black and red . . . 2·00 1·60
189 – 15-30 s. green and brown . . . 1·50 1·50
190 – 20-40 s. blue and red . . . 2·00 2·00
191 – 25-50 s. lilac, blue and red . . . 3·00 2·50
192 **36** 30-60 s. lilac, green & blue . . . 3·25 4·25
DESIGNS—VERT: As Type **35**: 1-2 s., 2-4 s. The Crusaders' Cross; 5-10 s. G. Zemgalis; 6-12 s. Tower; 10-20 s. J. Cakste; 15-30 s. Floral design; 20-40 s. A. Kviesis. HORIZ: As Type **36**: 25-50 s. Sanatorium.

1931. Nos. 183/92 surch.
196 9 on 6-12 s. yellow and green . . . 65 1·60
197 16 on 1-2 s. red and purple . . . 13·50 20·00
198 17 s. 2-4 s. red and orange . . . 1·25 1·60
199 19 on 4-8 s. red and green . . . 4·75 7·50
200 20 on 5-10 s. brown and green . . . 2·50 7·50
201 23 on 15-30 s. green & brown . . . 1·00 1·00
202 25 on 10-20 s. black and red . . . 2·75 4·25
203 35 on 20-40 s blue and red . . . 4·00 6·00
204 45 on 25-50 s. lilac, blue and red . . . 11·50 18·00
205 55 on 30-60 s. lilac, green & bl . . . 13·50 28·00

1931. Air. Charity. Nos. 155/7 surch **LATVIJAS AIZSARGI** and value. Imperf or perf.
206 **19** 50 on 10 s. green . . . 13·50 18·00
207 1 l. on 15 s. red . . . 13·50 18·00
208 1 l. 50 on 2 s. blue . . . 13·50 18·00

38 Foreign Invasion

1932. Militia Maintenance Fund. Imperf or perf.
209 – 1-11 s. blue and purple . . . 3·25 3·75
210 **38** 2-17 s. orange and olive . . . 3·25 3·75
211 – 3-23 s. red and brown . . . 3·25 3·75
212 – 4-34 s. green . . . 3·25 3·75
213 – 5-45 s. green . . . 3·25 3·75
DESIGNS: 1-11 s. The Holy Oak and Kriva telling stories; 3-23 s. Lacplesis, the deliverer; 4-34 s. The Black Knight (enemy) slaughtered; 5-45 s. Laimdota, the spirit of Latvia, freed.

39 Infantry Manoeuvres

1932. Militia Maintenance Fund. Imperf or perf.
214 – 6-25 s. purple and brown 5·75 6·75
215 **39** 7-35 s. blue and green 5·75 6·75
216 – 10-45 s. sepia and green 5·75 6·75
217 – 12-55 s. green and red 5·75 6·75
218 – 15-75 s. violet and red 5·75 6·75
DESIGNS—HORIZ: 6-25 s. Troops on march. VERT: 10-45 s. First aid to soldier; 12-55 s. Army kitchen; 15-75 s. Gen. J. Balodis.

41

1932. Air. Charity. Imperf or perf.
219 **41** 10-20 s. black and green 13·50 18·00
220 15-30 s. red and grey 13·50 18·00
221 25-50 s. blue and grey 13·50 18·00

1932. Riga Exn. of Lettish Products. Optd **Latvijas razojumu izstade Riga. 1932.g.10.-18.IX.**
222 **21** 3 s. red 50 40
223 10 s. green on yellow 1·50 80
224 20 s. pink 2·00 70
225 35 s. blue 3·25 85

43 Leonardo da Vinci 44 "Mourning Mother" Memorial, Riga

1932. Air. Charity. Pioneers of Aviation. Imperf or perf.
226 – 5-25 s. green and brown 13·50 17·00
227 **43** 10-50 s. green and brown 13·50 17·00
228 – 15-75 s. green and red 13·50 17·00
229 – 20-100 s. mauve and green 13·50 17·00
230 – 25-125 s. blue and brown 13·50 17·00
DESIGNS—VERT: 5 s. Icarus; 15 s. Charles's hydrogen balloon. HORIZ: 20 s. Wright Type A; 25 s. Bleriot XI.

1933. Air. Wounded Latvian Airmen Fund. Imperf or perf.
231 – 2-52 s. brown and black 9·25 12·50
232 **44** 3-53 s. red and black 9·25 12·50
233 – 10-60 s. green and black 9·25 12·50
234 – 20-70 s. red and black 9·25 12·50
DESIGNS: 2 s. Fall of Icarus; 10 s., 20 s. Proposed tombs for airmen.

1933. Air. Charity. Riga–Bathurst Flight. Nos. 155/7 optd **LATVIJA-AFRIKA 1933** or surch also.
235 10 s. green 20·00 27·00
236 15 s. red 20·00 27·00
237 25 s. blue 20·00 32·00
238 50 s. on 15 s. red £110 £325
239 100 s. on 25 s. blue £110 £325
In the event the aircraft crashed at Neustettin, Germany, and the mail was forwarded by ordinary post.

46 Biplane under Fire at Riga

1933. Air Charity. Wounded Latvian Airmen Fund. Imperf or perf.
240 – 3-53 s. blue and orange 20·00 23·00
241 **46** 7-57 s. brown and blue 20·00 23·00
242 – 35-135 s. black and blue 20·00 23·00
DESIGNS: 3 s. Monoplane taking off; 35 s. Map and aircraft.

47 Glanville Brothers' Gee-Bee Super Sportster

1933. Air. Charity. Wounded Latvian Airmen Fund. Imperf or perf.
243 **47** 8-68 s. grey and brown 27·00 50·00
244 – 12-112 s. green and purple 27·00 50·00
245 – 30-130 s. grey and blue 38·00 50·00
246 – 40-190 s. blue and purple 27·00 50·00
DESIGNS: 12 s. Supermarine S6B seaplane; 30 s. Airship "Graf Zeppelin" over Riga; 40 s. Dornier Do-X flying boat.

48 President's Palace 50 A. Kronvalds 51

1934. 15th Anniv of New Constitution.
247 **48** 3 s. red 10 15
248 – 5 s. green 15 10
249 – 10 s. green 2·00 10
250 – 20 s. red 2·00 10
251 – 35 s. blue 10 15
252 **48** 40 s. brown 10 15
DESIGNS: 5, 10 s. Arms and shield; 20 s. Allegory of Latvia; 35 s. Government Building.

1936. Lettish Intellectuals.
253 **50** 3 s. red 1·60 4·25
254 – 10 s. green 1·60 4·25
255 – 20 s. mauve 1·60 5·00
256 – 35 s. blue 1·60 5·00
PORTRAITS: 10 s. A. Pumpurs; 20 s. J. Maters; 35 s. Auseklis.

1936. White Cross Fund. Designs incorporating Cross and Stars device as in T **51**.
257 **51** 3 s. red 1·50 3·25
258 – 10 s. green 1·50 3·25
259 – 20 s. mauve 1·50 4·00
260 – 35 s. blue 1·50 4·00
DESIGNS: 10 s. Oak leaves; 20 s. Doctors and patient; 35 s. Woman holding shield.

53 Independence Monument, Rauna (Ronneburg) 54 President Ulmanis

1937. Monuments.
261 **53** 3 s. red 35 1·40
262 – 5 s. green 35 60
263 – 10 s. green 35 35
264 – 20 s. red 85 1·00
265 – 30 s. blue 1·40 1·25
266 – 35 s. blue 1·40 1·50
267 – 40 s. brown 2·25 2·50
DESIGNS—VERT: 10 s. Independence Monument, Jelgava (Mitau); 20 s. War Memorial, Valka (Walk); 30 s. Independence Monument, Iecava (Eckau); 35 s. Independence Monument, Riga; 40 s. Col. Kalpak's Grave, Visagalas Cemetery. HORIZ: 5 s. Cemetery Gate, Riga.

1937. President Ulmanis's 60th Birthday.
268 **54** 3 s. red and orange 15 10
269 5 s. light green and green 15 15
270 10 s. deep green and green 25 35
271 20 s. purple and red 55 35
272 25 s. grey and blue 1·10 65
273 30 s. deep blue and blue 1·10 60
274 35 s. indigo and blue 1·00 50
275 40 s. lt brown and brown 85 75
276 50 s. green and black 90 80

56 Gaizinkalns, Livonia 57 General J. Balodis

1938. 20th Anniv of Independence.
278 **56** 3 s. red 10 10
279 – 5 s. green 10 10
280 **57** 10 s. green 20 10
281 – 20 s. mauve 20 10
282 – 30 s. blue 60 20
283 – 35 s. slate 65 10
284 – 40 s. mauve 80 15
DESIGNS: As Type **56**: 5 s. Latgale landscape; 30 s; City of Riga; 35 s. Rumba waterfall, Courland; 40 s. Zemgale landscape. As Type **57**: 20 s. President Ulmanis.

MINIMUM PRICE

The minimum price quoted is 10p which represents a handling charge rather than a basis for valuing common stamps. For further notes about prices, see introductory pages.

58 Elementary School, Riga

1939. 5th Anniv of Authoritarian Government.
285 **58** 3 s. brown 50 85
286 – 5 s. green 50 85
287 – 10 s. green 1·40 1·00
288 – 20 s. red 1·60 1·40
289 – 30 s. blue 1·25 1·00
290 – 35 s. blue 1·60 1·50
291 – 40 s. purple 2·75 1·00
292 – 50 s. black 3·25 1·00
DESIGNS: 5 s. Jelgava Castle; 10 s. Riga Castle; 2 s. Independence Memorial; 30 s. Eagle and National Flag; 35 s. Town Hall, Daugavpils; 40 s. War Museum and Powder-magazine, Riga; 50 s. Pres. Ulmanis.

59 Reaping 60 Arms of Courland, Livonia and Latgale 61 Arms of Latvian Soviet Socialist Republic

1939. Harvest Festival. Dated "8 X 1939".
294 **59** 10 s. green 65 20
295 – 20 s. red (Apples) 1·00 15

1940.
296 **60** 1 s. violet 15 20
297 2 s. yellow 15 20
298 3 s. red 10 15
299 5 s. brown 10 10
300 7 s. green 10 40
301 10 s. green 60 10
302 20 s. red 60 10
303 30 s. brown 75 25
304 35 s. blue 10 70
305 50 s. green 85 30
306 1 l. olive 1·60 35

1940. Incorporation of Latvia in U.S.S.R.
307 **61** 1 s. violet 15 20
308 2 s. yellow 15 15
309 3 s. red 10 10
310 5 s. olive 10 10
311 7 s. green 10 45
312 10 s. green 30 10
313 20 s. red 65 10
314 30 s. blue 1·40 30
315 35 s. blue 10 55
316 40 s. brown 60 65
317 50 s. grey 1·40 65
318 1 l. brown 1·60 1·10
319 5 l. green 11·50 7·50

63 Latvian Arms 64

1991.
320 **63** 5 k. silver, brown & lt brn 10 10
321 10 k. silver, brown & drab 10 10
322 15 k. silver, sepia & brown 10 10
323 20 k. silver, blue & lt blue 35 35
324 40 k. silver, green and light green 65 65
325 50 k. silver, brown and lilac 85 85
326 **64** 100 k. multicoloured 1·60 1·60
327 200 k. multicoloured 3·25 3·25

1991. Nos. 4672, 6073 and 6077 of Russia surch **LATVIJA** and new value.
328 100 k. on 7 k. blue 20 20
329 300 k. on 2 k. brown 65 65
330 500 k. on 2 k. brown 1·10 1·10
331 1000 k. on 2 k. brown 2·25 2·25
358 25 r. on 4 k. red 2·40 2·40

67 Main Statue, Liberty Monument, Riga 68 Olympic Committee Symbol

1991.
336 **67** 10 k. multicoloured 10 10
337 15 k. multicoloured 10 10
338 20 k. multicoloured 10 10
339 30 k. multicoloured 10 10
340 50 k. multicoloured 55 55
341 100 k. multicoloured 1·10 1·10

1992. Recognition of Latvian Olympic Committee.
342 **68** 50 k. + 25 k. red, silver and drab 65 65
343 – 50 k. + 25 k. red, silver and grey 65 65
344 **68** 100 k. + 50 k. red, gold and bistre 1·40 1·40
DESIGN: No. 343. As T **68** but symbols smaller and inscribed "BERLIN 18.09.91." at left.

69 Vaidelotis 72 Children in Fancy Dress around Christmas Tree

1992. Statues from the base of the Liberty Monument, Riga.
345 – 10 k. black and brown 10 10
346 **69** 20 k. brown and grey 10 10
347 – 30 k. deep lilac and lilac 10 10
348 **69** 30 k. deep brown & brown 10 10
349 – 40 k. blue and grey 35 35
350 **69** 50 k. green and grey 40 40
351 – 50 k. black and grey 40 40
352 – 100 k. purple and mauve 85 85
353 – 200 k. deep blue and blue 1·60 1·60
DESIGNS: Nos. 345, 347 and 353, Kurzeme (warrior with shield): Nos. 349 and 351/2, Lachplesis (two figures).

1992. Birds of the Baltic. As Nos. 506/9 of Lithuania.
359 5 r. black and red 15 15
360 5 r. brown, black and red 15 15
361 5 r. sepia, brown and red 15 15
362 5 r. brown, black and red 15 15
DESIGNS: Nos 359, Osprey ("Pandion haliaetus"); 360, Black-tailed godwit ("Limosa limosa"); 361. Goosander ("Mergus merganser"); 362, Common shelducks ("Tadorna tadorna").

1992. Christmas. Multicoloured.
363 2 r. Type **72** 20 20
364 3 r. Angel choir 50 50
365 10 r. Type **72** 1·75 1·75
366 15 r. Adoration of the Kings 2·50 2·50

1993. Nos. 4855, 5296 and 5295 of Russia surch **LATVIJA** and new value.
367 50 r. on 6 k. multicoloured 25 25
368 100 r. on 6 k. multicoloured 50 50
369 300 r. on 6 k. multicoloured 1·75 1·75

74 Kuldiga Couple 75 Emblem

1993. Costumes. Multicoloured.
370 5 s. Type **74** 10 10
371 10 s. Alsunga 25 25
372 20 s. Lielvarde 45 45
373 50 s. Rucava 1·25 1·25
374 100 s. Zemgale 2·40 2·40
375 500 s. Ziemellatgale 12·00 12·00

1993. National Song Festival.
377 **75** 3 s. black, gold and brown 10 10
378 5 s. black, gold and lilac 10 10
379 – 15 s. multicoloured 35 35
DESIGN: 15 s. Abstract.

76 Pope John Paul II 77 Flags

1993. Papal Visit.
380 **76** 15 s. multicoloured 35 35

1993. 75th Anniv of First Republic.
381 **77** 5 s. multicoloured 10 10
382 15 s. multicoloured 35 35

78 Valters

79 Biathlon

1994. 100th Birthday of Evalds Valters (actor).
383 **78** 15 s. brown, light brown and gold 35 35

1994. Winter Olympic Games, Lillehammer, Norway. Multicoloured.
384 5 s. Type **79** 10 10
385 10 s. Two-man bobsleigh . . . 20 20
386 15 s. One-man luge 35 35
387 100 s. Figure skating . . . . . 2·25 2·25

80 Reed Hut

1994. 70th Anniv of Latvian Ethnological Open-air Museum, Bergi.
389 **80** 5 s. multicoloured 10 10

81 Streetball

82 Kurzeme

1994. Basketball Festival, Riga.
390 **81** 15 s. black, grey and orange 35 35

1994. Regional Arms.
391 **82** 1 s. red, black and silver . 10 10
392 – 3 s. silver, black and blue . 10 10
393 – 5 s. silver, black and red . 10 10
394 – 10 s. silver, black and blue . 20 20
DESIGNS: 3 s. Zemgale; 5 s. Vidzeme; 10 s. Latgale.

LEBANON Pt. 19

A territory N. of the Holy Land, formerly part of the Turkish Empire, Greater Lebanon was given a separate status under French Mandate in 1920. Until September 1923, the French occupation stamps of Syria were used and these were followed by the joint issue of 1923, Nos. 97 etc., of Syria. Independence was proclaimed in 1941, but the country was not evacuated by French troops until 1946.

100 centimes = 1 piastre
100 piastres = 1 Lebanese pound

1924. Stamps of France surch **GRAND LIBAN** and value.
1 **11** 10 c. on 2 c. red 40 40
2 **18** 25 c. on 5 c. orange 40 30
3 50 c. on 10 c. green 35 30
4 **15** 75 c. on 15 c. green . . . . 1·10 85
5 **18** 1 p. on 20 c. brown 40 30
6 1 p. 25 on 25 c. blue . . . 2·40 1·10
7 1 p. 50 on 30 c. orange . . 1·00 45
8 1 p. 50 on 30 c. red 85 45
9 **15** 2 p. 50 on 50 c. blue . . . 85 45
10 **13** 2 p. on 40 c. red and blue . 2·50 1·90
11 3 p. on 60 c. violet and blue 4·50 3·25
12 5 p. on 1 f. red and green . 4·50 4·25
13 10 p. on 2 f. orange and green 6·75 4·75
14 25 p. on 5 f. blue and yellow 12·00 10·00

1924. Air. Nos. 10/13 optd **Poste par Avion**.
22 **13** 2 p. on 40 c. red and blue . 5·50 5·50
23 3 p. on 60 c. violet and blue 5·50 5·50
24 5 p. on 1 f. red and green . 5·50 5·50
25 10 p. on 2 f. orange and green 5·50 5·50

1924. "Pasteur" issue of France surch **GRAND LIBAN** and value.
15 **30** 50 c. on 10 c. green 40 30
16 1 p. 50 on 30 c. red . . . . 1·00 90
17 2 p. 50 on 50 c. blue . . . 90 35

1924. "Olympic Games" issue of France surch **GRAND LIBAN** and value.
18 **31** 50 c. on 10 c. green . . . . 25·00 25·00
19 – 1 p. 25 on 25 c. red . . . . 25·00 25·00
20 – 1 p. 50 on 30 c. red & black 25·00 25·00
21 – 2 p. 50 on 50 c. blue . . . 25·00 25·00

1924. Stamps of France surch **Gd Liban** and value in English and Arabic.
26 **11** 10 c. on 2 c. red 15 20
27 **18** 25 c. on 5 c. orange 30 30
28 50 c. on 10 c. green 40 40
39 **15** 75 c. on 15 c. green 55 55
30 **18** 1 p. on 20 c. brown 30 30
31 1 p. 25 on 25 c. blue . . . 85 85
32 1 p. 50 on 30 c. red 40 40
33 1 p. 50 on 30 c. orange . . 32·00 32·00
34 2 p. on 35 c. violet 85 85
35 **13** 2 p. on 40 c. red and blue . 30 30
36 2 p. on 45 c. green and blue 9·50 9·50
37 3 p. on 60 c. violet and blue 85 85
38 **15** 3 p. on 60 c. violet . . . . 1·10 1·10
39 4 p. on 85 c. red . . . . . 1·10 1·10
40 **13** 5 p. on 1 f. red and green . 1·60 1·60
41 10 p. on 2 f. orange & turq 4·25 4·25
42 25 p. on 5 f. blue and yellow 6·00 6·00

1924. "Pasteur" issue of France surch **Gd Liban** and value in English and Arabic.
43 **30** 50 c. on 10 c. green 30 20
44 75 c. on 15 c. green 40 60
45 1 p. 50 on 30 c. red 75 60
46 2 p. on 45 c. red . . . . . 1·40 1·10
47 2 p. 50 on 50 c. blue . . . 60 20
48 4 p. on 75 c. blue . . . . . 1·40 1·10

1924. Nos. 401/4 (Olympic Games) and Ronsard stamps of France surch **Gd Liban** and value in English and Arabic.
49 **31** 50 c. on 10 c. green . . . . 28·00 28·00
50 – 1 p. 25 on 25 c. red . . . . 28·00 28·00
51 – 1 p. 50 on 30 c. red & black 28·00 28·00
52 – 2 p. 50 on 50 c. blue . . . 28·00 28·00
53 **35** 4 p. on 75 c. blue . . . . . 1·25 1·25

1924. Air. Stamps of France surch **Gd Liban Avion** and value in English and Arabic.
54 **13** 2 p. on 40 c. red and blue . 5·50 5·50
55 3 p. on 60 c. violet and blue 5·50 5·50
56 5 p. on 1 f. red and green . 5·50 5·50
57 10 p. on 2 f. red and green . 5·50 5·50

5 Cedar of Lebanon

7 Tripoli

6 Beirut

1925. Views.
58 **5** 10 c. violet 20 10
59 **6** 25 c. black 30 20
60 – 50 c. green (Tripoli) 20 10
61 – 75 c. red (Beit ed-Din) . . . 35 20
62 – 1 p. red (Baalbek) 80 40
63 – 1 p. 25 green (Mouktara) . . 75 85
64 – 1 p. 50 red (Tyre) 35 15
65 – 2 p. sepia (Zahle) 55 20
66 – 2 p. 50 blue (Baalbek) 85 65
67 – 3 p. brown (Deir el-Kamar) . . 90 75
68 – 5 p. violet (Sidon) . . . . . 1·25 1·10
69 **7** 10 p. plum . . . . 2·25 1·60
70 – 25 p. blue (Beirut) . . . . . 6·75 6·25

1925. Air. Stamps as last optd **AVION** in English and Arabic.
71 – 2 p. sepia . . . . 2·25 2·25
72 – 3 p. brown . . . . 2·25 2·25
73 – 5 p. violet . . . . 2·25 2·25
74 **7** 10 p. plum . . . . 2·25 2·25

1926. Air. Same stamps but optd with Bleriot XI airplane instead.
75 – 2 p. sepia . . . . 2·25 2·25
76 – 3 p. brown . . . . 2·25 2·25
77 – 5 p. violet . . . . 2·25 2·25
78 **7** 10 p. plum . . . . 2·25 2·25

1926. War Refugee Charity. As 1925 but surch **Secours aux Refugies Afft.** and premium in English and Arabic.
79 **6** 25 c. + 25 c. black . . . . 2·25 2·25
80 – 50 c. + 25 c. green . . . . 2·25 2·25
81 – 75 c. + 25 c. red . . . . . 2·25 2·25
82 – 1 p. + 50 c. red . . . . . 2·25 2·25
83 – 1 p. 25 + 50 c. green . . . 3·00 3·00
84 – 1 p. 50 + 50 c. red . . . . 3·00 3·00
85 – 2 p. + 75 c. sepia . . . . 2·50 2·50
86 – 2 p. 50 + 75 c. blue . . . . 3·00 3·00
87 – 3 p. + 1 p. brown . . . . 3·00 3·00
88 – 5 p. + 1 p. violet . . . . 3·00 3·00
89 **7** 10 p. + 2 p. plum . . . . 3·25 3·25
90 – 25 p. + 5 p. blue . . . . . 3·25 3·25

1926. Air. Nos. 75/78 surch **Secours aux Refugies Afft.** and premium in English and Arabic.
91 – 2 p. + 1 p. sepia . . . . . 5·50 5·50
92 – 3 p. + 2 p. brown . . . . . 5·50 5·50
93 – 5 p. + 3 p. violet . . . . . 5·50 5·50
94 **7** 10 p. + 5 p. plum . . . . . 5·50 5·50

1926. As 1925 surch in English and Arabic figures and bars.
95 – 3 p. 50 on 75 c. red 40 40
96b **6** 4 p. on 25 c. black 85 85
98 – 4 p. 50 on 75 c. red . . . . 1·10 1·10
99 – 6 p. on 2 p. 50 blue 75 75
100 – 7 p. 50 on 2 p. 50 blue . . 1·10 1·10
101 – 12 p. on 1 p. 25 green . . . 80 80
102 – 15 p. on 25 p. blue . . . . 1·10 1·10
103 – 20 p. on 1 p. 25 green . . . 3·00 3·00

1927. Pictorial and provisional stamps of Lebanon optd **Republique Libanaise.**
104 **5** 10 c. violet 10 10
105 – 50 c. green 10 10
106 – 1 p. red 10 10
107 – 1 p. 50 red 20 20
108 – 2 p. sepia 40 30
109 – 3 p. brown 30 15
110 **6** 4 p. on 25 c. black (No. 96) . 20 10
111 – 4 p. 50 on 75 c. red 20 15
112 – 5 p. violet . . . . 1·10 35
113 – 7 p. 50 on 2 p. 50 blue (No. 100) 30 15
114 **7** 10 p. plum . . . . 1·25 60
115 – 15 p. on 25 p. blue (No. 102) 3·50 2·50
117 – 25 p. blue . . . . 5·25 4·25

1927. Air. Nos. 75/78 optd **Republique Libanaise** in one or two lines and bar.
118 – 2 p. sepia . . . . 2·25 2·25
119 – 3 p. brown . . . . 2·25 2·25
120 – 5 p. violet . . . . 2·25 2·25
121 **7** 10 p. plum . . . . 2·25 2·25

الجمهورية اللبنانية
(10.)

1928. Nos. 104/117 optd with T **10** or surch also.
145 **5** 5 c. on 10 c. violet 10 10
124 10 c. violet 15 15
125 – 50 c. green . . . . 1·00 1·00
146 – 50 c. on 75 c. red 30 30
126 – 1 p. red 30 30
127 – 1 p. 50 red . . . . 1·00 1·00
128 – 2 p. sepia 60 60
147 – 2 p. on 1 p. 25 green 30 30
129 – 3 p. brown 80 80
148 **6** 4 p. on 25 c. black 30 30
131 – 4 p. 50 on 75 c. red . . . . 1·00 1·00
132 – 5 p. violet . . . . 1·90 1·90
149 – 7 p. 50 on 2 p. 50 blue . . . 90 90
134 **7** 10 p. plum . . . . 2·75 2·75
135 – 15 p. on 25 p. blue . . . . . 4·75 4·75
136 – 25 p. blue . . . . 5·50 5·50

1928. Air. Optd **Republique Libanaise** in English and Arabic (latter as T **10**) and aeroplane.
151 – 50 c. green 25 25
152 – 50 c. on 75 c. red (No. 146) 25 25
153 – 1 p. red 30 30
141 – 2 p. sepia . . . . 1·60 1·60
154 – 2 p. on 1 p. 25 grn (No. 147) 70 70
142 – 3 p. brown . . . . 1·10 1·10
143 – 5 p. violet . . . . 1·60 1·60
144 **7** 10 p. plum . . . . 1·60 1·60
155 – 15 p. on 25 p. blue (No. 135) £170 £170
156 – 25 p. blue £110 £110

14 "Bombyx mori" Larva, Cocoon and Moth

1930. Silk Congress.
157 **14** 4 p. sepia . . . . 8·75 8·75
158 $4\frac{1}{2}$ p. red . . . . 8·75 8·75
159 $7\frac{1}{2}$ p. blue . . . . 8·75 8·75
160 10 p. violet . . . . 8·75 8·75
161 15 p. green . . . . 8·75 8·75
162 25 p. red . . . . 8·75 8·75

15 Cedars of Lebanon

16a Baalbek

1930. Views.
163 – 10 c. orange (Beirut) . . 10 10
164 **15** 20 c. brown 10 10
165 – 25 c. blue (Baalbek) . . . 15 15
166 – 50 c. brown (Bickfaya) . . 70 35
166b – 75 c. brown (Baalbek) . . 35 25
167 – 1 p. green (Saida) . . . 50 25
167a – 1 p. plum (Saida) 50 25
168 – 1 p. 50 plum (Beit ed-Din) 80 80
168a – 1 p. 50 green (Beit ed-Din) 50 25
169 – 2 p. blue (Tripoli) . . . 1·00 40
170 – 3 p. sepia (Baalbek) . . . 1·00 40
171 – 4 p. brown (Nahr-el-Kelb) 1·25 15
172 – 4 p. 50 red (Beaufort) . . 1·25 50
173 – 5 p. black (Beit ed-Din) 65 25
251 – 5 p. blue (Nahr el-Kalb) 80 15
174 – 6 p. purple (Tyre) . . . 1·10 95
175 **16a** 7 p. 50 blue . . . . . . 1·25 30
176 – 10 p. green (Hasbaya) . 2·50 30
177 – 15 p. purple (Afka Falls) 3·75 90
178 – 25 p. green (Beirut) . . . 4·75 1·10
179 – 50 p. grn (Deir el-Kamar) 18·00 5·00
180 – 100 p. black (Baalbek) . 18·00 7·25

17 Jebeil (Byblos)

1930. Air. Potez 29-4 biplane and views as T **17**.
181 50 c. purple (Rachaya) . . . 25 20
182 1 p. green (Broumana) 25 20
183 2 p. orange (Baalbek) 55 60
184 3 p. red (Hasroun) 55 40
185 5 p. green (Byblos) 55 40
186 10 p. red (Kadisha) . . . . . 1·10 1·10
187 15 p. brown (Beirut) 80 95
188 25 p. violet (Tripoli) . . . . 1·50 1·40
189 50 p. lake (Kabelais) . . . . 4·75 4·50
190 100 p. brown (Zahle) . . . . 6·50 6·00

18 Skiing

1936. Air. Tourist Propaganda.
191 **18** 50 c. green . . . . 1·25 1·50
192 – 1 p. orange . . . . 1·90 1·75
193 **18** 2 p. violet . . . . 1·90 1·75
194 – 3 p. green . . . . 1·90 1·75
195 **18** 5 p. red . . . . 1·90 1·75
196 – 10 p. brown . . . . . . 1·50 1·75
197 – 15 p. red . . . . 27·00 27·00
198 **18** 25 p. green . . . . 75·00 75·00
DESIGN: 1, 3, 10, 15 p. Jounieh Bay.

20 Cedar of Lebanon

21 President Edde

22 Lebanese Landscape

1937.
199 **20** 10 c. red 15 10
200 20 c. blue 15 10
201 25 c. lilac 20 10
202 50 c. red 20 10
203 75 c. brown 25 15
207 **21** 3 p. violet 80 40
208 4 p. brown 40 10
209 4 p. 50 red 50 20
211 **22** 10 p. red 90 30
212 $12\frac{1}{2}$ p. blue 45 15
213 15 p. green 75 35
214 20 p. brown 60 15
215 25 p. red 65 20
216 50 p. violet . . . . 1·50 45
217 100 p. sepia . . . . 2·25 1·00

23 Exhibition Pavilion, Paris

1937. Air. Paris International Exhibition.
218 **23** 50 c. black 85 85
219 1 p. green 85 85
220 2 p. brown 85 85
221 3 p. green 85 85
222 5 p. green 1·10 1·10
223 10 p. red 5·00 5·00
224 15 p. red 5·00 5·00
225 25 p. brown 10·00 10·00

25 Ruins of Baalbek

1937. Air.
226 – 50 c. blue 10 10
227 – 1 p. brown 15 10
228 – 2 p. sepia 25 15
229 – 3 p. red 60 50
230 – 5 p. green 30 40
231 **25** 10 p. violet 30 20
232 – 15 p. blue 90 95
233 – 25 p. violet 2·75 2·75
234 – 50 p. green 5·50 4·25
235 – 100 p. brown 2·75 2·25
DESIGN: 50 c. to 5 p. Beit ed-Din.

1938. Surch in English and Arabic figures.
236 **21** 2 p. on 3 p. violet 40 35
237 2½ p. on 4 p. brown 40 35

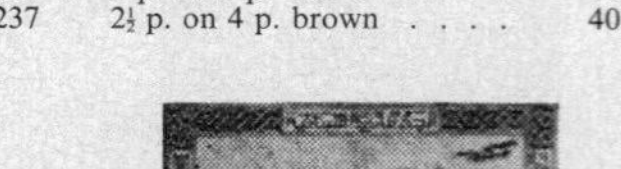

27 Medical College, Beirut

1938. Air. Medical Congress.
238 **27** 2 p. green 1·60 1·60
239 3 p. orange 1·60 1·60
240 5 p. violet 3·00 3·00
241 10 p. red 7·25 7·25

28 Maurice Nogues and Liore et Olivier LeO H.24-3 Flying Boat over Beirut

32 Emir Bechir Chehab

1938. Air. 10th Anniv of 1st France-Lebanese Air Service.
242 **28** 10 p. purple 2·40 2·40

1938. Surch.
243 – 6 p. on 7 p. 50 blue (No. 175) 90 90
244 – 7 p. 50 on 50 p. grn (No. 179) 90 90
245 – 7 p. 50 on 100 p. blk (No. 180) 90 90
246 **22** 12 p. 50 on 7 p. 50 blue 2·10 2·10
247 12½ on 7 p. 50 blue 25 25

1939. As T **16a**. but with differing figures and Arabic inscriptions in side panels, and imprint at foot "IMP. CATHOLIQUE-BEYROUTH-LIBAN" instead of "HELIO VAUGIRARD".
248 1 p. green 75 10
249 1 p. 50 purple 85 40
250 7 p. 50 red 1·10 50
DESIGN: Beit ed-Din.

1942. 1st Anniv of Proclamation of Independence.
252 **32** 50 c. green (postage) 1·75 1·75
253 1 p. 50 purple 1·75 1·75
254 6 p. red 1·75 1·75
255 15 p. blue 1·75 1·75
256 – 10 p. purple (air) 3·00 3·00
257 – 50 p. green 3·00 3·00
DESIGN: 10, 50 p. Airplane over mountains.

1943. Surch in English and Arabic and with old values cancelled with ornaments.
258 2 p. on 4 p. brown (No. 208) 3·50 3·00
259 6 p. on 7 p. 50 red (No. 250) 65 35
260 10 p. on 12½ p. blue (No. 212) 65 40

37 Parliament House

38 Bechamoun

1944. 2nd Anniv of Proclamation of Independence.
265 **37** 25 p. red (postage) 6·75 6·75
266 – 50 p. blue 6·75 6·75
267 **37** 150 p. blue 6·75 6·75
268 – 200 p. purple 6·75 6·75
DESIGN: 50 p., 200 p. Government House.
269 **38** 25 p. green (air) 2·00 1·90
270 50 p. orange 3·00 2·25
271 – 100 p. brown 3·00 1·75
272 – 200 p. violet 4·25 3·25
273 – 300 p. green 13·50 10·50
274 – 500 p. brown 30·00 22·00
DESIGNS: 100 p., 200 p. Rachaya Citadel; 300 p., 500 p. Beirut.

38a Beirut Isolation Hospital

المؤتمر الطبي العربي السادس
١٩٤٤
(39)

1944. 10th Medical Congress. Horiz designs optd with T **39**.
275 **38a** 10 p. red (postage) 4·25 4·25
276 20 p. blue 4·25 4·25
277 – 20 p. orange (air) 1·90 1·90
278 – 50 p. blue 1·90 1·90
279 – 100 p. purple 3·00 3·00
DESIGN: Nos. 277/9, Bhannes Sanatorium.

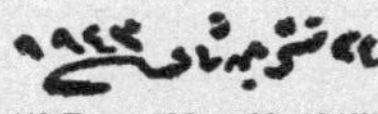
(40 Trans "Nov. 23, 1943")

1944. President's Return to Office. 1st Anniv. Nos. 265/74 optd with T **40**.
280 **37** 25 p. red (postage) 9·00 9·00
281 – 50 p. blue 9·00 9·00
282 **37** 150 p. blue 9·00 9·00
283 – 200 p. purple 9·00 9·00
284 **38** 25 p. green (air) 3·25 3·25
285 – 50 p. orange 5·50 5·50
286 – 100 p. brown 7·25 7·25
287 – 200 p. violet 14·00 14·00
288 – 300 p. green 18·00 18·00
289 – 500 p. brown 32·00 32·00

1945. Surch in English and Arabic figures and ornaments.
261 – 2 p. on 5 p. blue (No. 251) 40 20
262 – 3 p. on 5 p. blue (No. 251) 40 20
263 **22** 6 p. on 12½ p. blue 55 35
264 7½ p. on 12½ p. blue 75 95

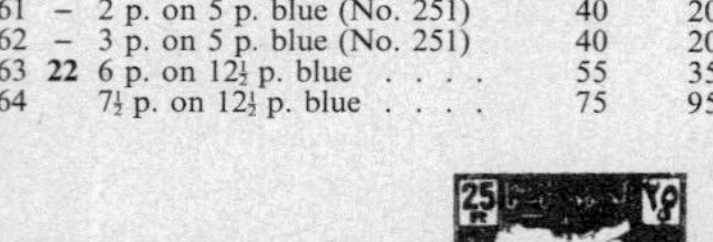

41 Crusader Castle, Byblos

42 Falls of R. Litani

1945.
397 **41** 7 p. 50 red (postage) 2·50 10
398 10 p. purple 4·50 10
399 12 p. 50 blue 11·00 30
290 15 p. brown 2·00 1·75
291 20 p. green 2·00 1·75
292 – 25 p. blue 2·00 1·75
400 **41** 25 p. violet 17·00 45
293 – 50 p. red 4·00 2·25
401 **41** 50 p. green 35·00 2·75
294 **42** 25 p. brown (air) 1·25 1·00
295 50 p. purple 1·75 1·40
296 – 200 p. violet 7·25 2·50
297 – 300 p. black 15·00 5·25
DESIGNS—HORIZ: Nos. 292, 293, Crusader Castle, Tripoli; Nos. 296/7, Cedar of Lebanon and skier.

43 V(ictory) and National Flag

44 V(ictory) and Lebanese Soldiers at Bir-Hakeim

1946. Victory, "V" in design. (a) Postage.
298 **43** 7 p. 50 brown, red & pink 80 10
299 10 p. mauve, pink and red 1·00 10
300 12 p. 50 lake, red & mauve 1·00 15
301 15 p. green, emerald & red 1·90 15
302 20 p. myrtle, green and red 1·60 10
303 25 p. dp. blue, lt blue & red 2·75 45
304 50 p. blue, pink and red 5·00 1·25
305 100 p. black, grey and red 8·25 3·00

(b) Air.
306 **44** 15 p. green, yellow and red 45 15
307 20 p. red and blue 45 30
308 25 p. blue, yellow and red 50 30
309 50 p. grey, violet and red 85 30
310 100 p. violet and red 2·75 95
311 150 p. brown and red 3·25 1·50

1946. As T **43** but without "V" sign.
312 7 p. 50 lake, red and mauve 60 10
313 10 p. dp. blue, mauve and red 90 10
314 12 p. 50 brown, green and red 1·00 10
315 15 p. brown, pink and red 1·90 20
316 20 p. blue, orange and red 1·60 20
317 25 p. myrtle, green and red 2·75 30
318 50 p. dp blue, lt blue and red 5·00 1·25
319 100 p. dp grey, lt grey & red 8·25 3·00

45 Grey Herons

1946.
320 **45** 12 p. 50 red (postage) 11·00 25
321 10 p. orange (air) 4·25 65
322 25 p. blue 5·25 35
323 50 p. green 10·50 1·00
324 100 p. purple 18·00 4·50

46 Cedar of Lebanon

47

1946.
325 **46** 50 c. brown 10 10
326 1 p. purple 10 10
327 2 p. 50 violet 20 10
328 5 p. red 45 10
329 6 p. grey 50 10

1946. Air. Arab Postal Congress.
330 **47** 25 p. blue 70 35
331 50 p. green 85 55
332 75 p. red 1·40 95
333 150 p. violet 2·75 2·00

48 Cedar of Lebanon

49 President, Bridge and Tablet

1947.
333a **48** 50 c. brown 45 10
333b 2 p. 50 green 95 10
333c 5 p. red 1·40 10

1947. Air. Evacuation of Foreign Troops from Lebanon.
334 **49** 25 p. blue 80 50
335 50 p. red 90 90
336 75 p. black 1·50 1·25
337 150 p. green 3·00 2·25

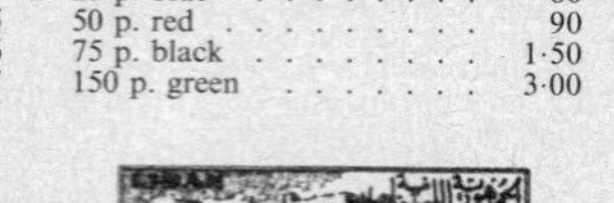

50 Crusader Castle, Tripoli

51 Jounieh Bay

1947.
338 **50** 12 p. 50 red (postage) 4·25 20
339 25 p. blue 5·25 25
340 50 p. green 16·00 45
341 100 p. violet 22·00 4·00
342 **51** 5 p. green (air) 25 10
343 10 p. mauve 20 10
344 15 p. red 40 10
344a 15 p. green 5·00 80
345 20 p. orange 60 10
345a 20 p. red 60 10
346 25 p. blue 90 10
347 50 p. red 1·90 20
348 **51** 100 p. purple 4·25 35
349 – 150 p. purple 9·00 70
350 – 200 p. slate 14·00 3·50
351 – 300 p. black 19·00 8·25
DESIGN: 150 p. to 300 p. Grand Serail Palace.

54 Phoenician Galley

1947. Air. 12th Congress of U.P.U., Paris.
352 – 10 p. blue 60 25
353 – 15 p. red 75 35
354 – 25 p. blue 1·00 60
355 **54** 50 p. green 2·75 75
356 – 75 p. violet 3·50 1·25
357 – 100 p. brown 5·00 2·50
DESIGN—VERT: 10 p. to 25 p. Posthorn.

55 Faraya Bridge and Statue

1947. Air. Red Cross Fund. Cross in red.
358 **55** 12 p. 50 + 25 p. green 5·50 4·50
359 25 p. + 50 p. blue 6·00 5·00
360 – 50 p. + 100 p. brown 8·25 6·00
361 – 75 p. + 150 p. violet 17·00 12·00
362 – 100 p. + 200 p. grey 27·00 17·00
DESIGN: 50 p. to 100 p. Djounie Bay and statue.

56 Cedar of Lebanon

58 Lebanese Landscape

1948.
363 **56** 50 c. blue (postage) 15 10
407 50 c. red 10 10
364 1 p. brown 35 10
408 1 p. orange 30 10
365 2 p. 50 mauve 65 10
409 2 p. 50 violet 1·25 10
366 3 p. green 90 10
367 5 p. red 1·00 10
410 5 p. purple 1·00 10
368 – 7 p. 50 red 2·00 10
369 – 10 p. purple 2·75 10
370 – 12 p. 50 blue 6·75 20
371 – 25 p. blue 8·25 70
372 – 50 p. green 17·00 4·75
DESIGN—HORIZ: 7 p. 50, to 50 p. Zebaide Aqueduct.
373 **58** 5 p. red (air) 30 10
374 10 p. mauve 65 10
375 15 p. brown 1·60 10
376 20 p. slate 2·75 15
377 25 p. blue 6·75 65
378 50 p. black 11·00 1·25

59 Europa on Bull

61 Apollo on Sun Chariot

1948. 3rd Meeting of U.N.E.S.C.O., Beirut.
379 **59** 10 p. red (postage) 1·60 1·00
380 12 p. 50 violet 2·25 1·50
381 25 p. olive 2·75 1·50
382 – 30 p. brown 2·75 1·60
383 – 40 p. green 4·50 1·75
DESIGN—VERT: 30, 40 p. Avicenna (philosopher and scientist).
384 **61** 7 p. 50 blue (air) 1·10 85
385 15 p. black 1·40 85
386 20 p. brown 2·50 1·75
387 – 35 p. red 4·00 2·25
388 – 75 p. green 7·75 4·50
DESIGN—HORIZ: 35, 75 p. Symbolical figure.

63 Camel

64 Sikorsky S-51 Helicopter

1949. 75th Anniv of U.P.U.

389	**63**	5 p. violet (postage)	75	50
390		7 p. 50 red	1·40	80
391		12 p. 50 blue	1·60	1·10
392	**64**	25 p. blue (air)	4·25	1·75
393		50 p. green	7·50	2·50

66 Nahr el-Kalb Bridge

1950.

411	**66**	7 p. 50 red	1·90	15
412		10 p. lilac	2·75	10
413		12 p. 50 pale blue	5·50	20
414		25 p. deep blue	8·25	65
415		50 p. green	17·00	4·75

See also Nos. 433/7.

67 Congressional Flags

1950. Lebanese Emigrants' Congress. Inscr "MOIS DES EMIGRES–ETE 1950".

416	**67**	7 p. 50 green (postage)	40	10
417		12 p. mauve	40	10
418	–	5 p. blue (air)	1·40	25
419	–	15 p. violet	2·25	45
420	–	25 p. brown	80	35
421	–	35 p. green	1·50	75

DESIGNS—HORIZ: 5, 15 p. House Martins; 25, 35 p. Pres. Bishara al-Khoury and bldg.

70 Crusader Castle, Sidon

1950. Air.

422	**70**	10 p. brown	60	10
423		15 p. green	80	10
424		20 p. red	1·60	30
425		25 p. blue	3·50	1·00
426		50 p. grey	5·00	2·00

1950. Surch with figures and bars.

427	**56**	1 p. on 3 p. green	45	10
428	**46**	2 p. 50 on 6 p. grey	55	10

73 Cedar of Lebanon

74 Nahr el-Kalb Bridge

75 Crusader Castle, Sidon

1951.

429	**73**	50 c. red (postage)	35	10
430		1 p. brown	35	10
431		2 p. 50 grey	1·60	10
432		5 p. red	1·50	10
433	**74**	7 p. 50 red	1·90	20
434		10 p. purple	2·75	10
435		12 p. 50 turquoise	5·50	30
436		25 p. blue	8·25	60
437		50 p. green	17·00	4·75
438	**75**	10 p. turquoise (air)	80	10
439		15 p. brown	1·75	10
440		20 p. red	1·75	10
441		25 p. blue	2·00	15
442		35 p. mauve	5·00	1·60
443		50 p. violet	9·00	1·10

Type **74** is similar to Type **66** but left value tablets differ.

For other values as Type **74** see Nos. 561/3.

76 Cedar

77 Baalbek

1952.

444	**76**	50 c. green (postage)	40	10
445		1 p. brown	45	10
446		2 p. 50 blue	65	10
447		5 p. red	1·00	15
448	**77**	7 p. 50 red	1·40	30
449		10 p. violet	3·00	40
450		12 p. 50 blue	3·00	40
451		25 p. blue	4·00	1·00
452	–	50 p. green	12·00	1·75
453	–	100 p. brown	22·00	4·75
454	–	5 p. red (air)	30	10
455	–	10 p. grey	45	10
456	–	15 p. mauve	80	10
457	–	20 p. orange	1·25	25
458	–	25 p. blue	1·25	25
459	–	35 p. blue	2·00	25
460	–	50 p. green	7·00	35
461	–	100 p. blue	48·00	1·50
462	–	200 p. green	28·00	2·75
463	–	300 p. sepia	38·00	6·50

DESIGNS—HORIZ: As Type **77**: Postage: 50, 100 p. Beaufort Castle. Air: 5 p. to 35 p. Beirut Airport; 50 p. to 300 p. Amphitheatre, Byblos.

78 Cedar of Lebanon **79** General Post Office **80** Douglas DC-4

1953.

464	**78**	50 c. blue (postage)	40	10
465		1 p. red	40	10
466		2 p. 50 lilac	50	10
560		2 p. 50 red	35	10
467		5 p. green	1·00	12
468	**79**	7 p. 50 red	1·75	25
469		10 p. green	2·10	40
470		12 p. 50 turquoise	3·00	50
471		25 p. blue	4·75	65
472		50 p. brown	8·25	1·75
473	**80**	5 p. green (air)	30	10
474		10 p. red	55	10
475		15 p. red	80	10
476		20 p. turquoise	1·25	10
477		25 p. blue	3·25	10
478		35 p. brown	4·50	15
479		50 p. blue	6·50	30
480		100 p. sepia	10·00	2·75

For 20 p. green as Type **79** see No. 636.

81 Cedar of Lebanon **82** Beit ed-Din Palace

83 Baalbek

1954.

481	**81**	50 c. blue (postage)	15	10
482		1 p. orange	15	10
483		2½ p. violet	55	10
484		5 p. green	60	10
485	**82**	7 p. 50 red	1·40	30
486		10 p. green	2·00	30
487		12 p. 50 blue	3·00	40
488		25 p. deep blue	4·50	1·25
489		50 p. turquoise	7·75	2·75
490		100 p. sepia	16·00	5·00
491	**83**	5 p. green (air)	40	10
492		10 p. violet	70	10
493		15 p. red	80	10
494		20 p. brown	1·10	10
495		25 p. blue	1·25	10
496		35 p. sepia	1·75	20
497	–	50 p. green	5·50	25
498	–	100 p. red	9·00	35
499	–	200 p. sepia	20·00	1·10
500	–	300 p. blue	32·00	2·25

DESIGN—HORIZ: 50 p. to 300 p. Litani Irrigation Canal.

For other values in this design see Nos. 564/7.

84 Khalde Airport, Beirut

1954. Air. Opening of Beirut International Airport.

501	**84**	10 p. red and pink	60	25
502		25 p. blue and ultramarine	1·50	40
503		35 p. brown and sepia	1·60	55
504		65 p. green and grey	4·25	1·90

1955. Arab Postal Union. As T **96a** of Syria but smaller, 27×37 mm. Inscr "LIBAN" at top.

505		12 p. 50 green (postage)	25	15
506		25 p. violet	35	15
507		2 p. 50 brown (air)	20	15

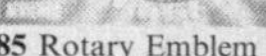

85 Rotary Emblem **86** Cedar of Lebanon

87 Jeita Grotto **88** Skiers

1955. Air. 50th Anniv of Rotary International.

508	**85**	35 p. green	70	50
509		65 p. blue	1·25	75

1955.

510	**86**	50 c. blue (postage)	15	10
511		1 p. red	15	10
512		2 p. 50 violet	25	10
552		2 p. 50 blue	2·25	10
513		5 p. green	45	10
514	**87**	7 p. 50 red	55	10
515		10 p. green	95	10
516		12 p. 50 blue	1·10	10
517		25 p. blue	2·75	10
518		50 p. green	3·50	30
519	**88**	5 p. turquoise (air)	40	20
520		15 p. red	55	15
521		20 p. violet	1·00	15
522		25 p. blue	1·90	20
523		35 p. brown	3·00	35
524		50 p. brown	6·75	60
525		65 p. blue	9·50	1·40

For other colours and new values as Type **88** see Nos. 568/70 and for redrawn Type **86** see Nos. 582/5, 686 and 695/7.

89 Visitor from Abroad **90** Cedar of Lebanon **91** Globe and Columns

92 Oranges

1955. Air. Tourist Propaganda.

526	**89**	2 p. 50 slate and purple	10	10
527		12 p. 50 blue & ultramarine	30	15
528		25 p. blue and indigo	75	20
529		35 p. blue and green	1·00	30

1955.

530	**90**	50 c. blue (postage)	15	10
531		1 p. orange	30	10
532		2 p. 50 violet	15	10
533		5 p. green	20	10
534	**91**	7 p. 50 red and yellow	35	10
535		10 p. green and brown	40	10
536		12 p. 50 blue and green	60	10
537		25 p. blue and mauve	1·40	10
538		50 p. myrtle and blue	1·60	15
539		100 p. sepia and pink	2·75	60
540	**92**	5 p. yellow and green (air)	15	10
541		10 p. orange and green	35	10
542		15 p. red and green	40	10
543		20 p. orange and brown	60	10
544	–	25 p. violet and blue	85	10
545	–	35 p. lake and green	1·40	15
546	–	50 p. yellow and black	1·40	15
547	–	65 p. yellow and green	3·00	20
548	–	100 p. orange and green	4·75	60
549	–	200 p. red and green	6·75	3·00

DESIGNS—VERT: 25 p. to 50 p. Grapes. HORIZ: 4 p. to 200 p. Quinces.

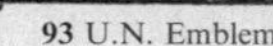

93 U.N. Emblem **94** Masks, Columns and Gargoyle

1956. Air. 10th Anniv of U.N.

550	**93**	35 p. blue	3·00	2·25
551		65 p. green	3·50	2·75

1956. Air. Baalbek International Drama Festival. Inscr "FESTIVAL INTERNATIONAL DE BAALBECK".

553	**94**	2 p. 50 sepia	40	15
554		10 p. green	55	25
555	–	12 p. 50 blue	55	30
556	–	25 p. violet	80	40
557	–	35 p. purple	1·60	50
558	–	65 p. slate	1·90	1·25

DESIGNS—HORIZ: 12 p. 50, 25 p. Temple ruins at Baalbek. VERT: 35 p., 65 p. Double bass, masks and columns.

1957. As T **74** but inscr "LIBAN".

561		7 p. 50 red	70	10
562		10 p. brown	1·10	10
563		12 p. 50 blue	1·25	10

1957. Air. Arabic inscription changed. New values and colours.

564	–	10 p. violet	20	10
565	–	15 p. orange	35	10
566	–	20 p. green	40	10
567	–	25 p. blue	50	10
568	**88**	35 p. green	1·25	20
569		65 p. purple	2·75	50
570		100 p. brown	4·50	90

DESIGN: 10 p. to 25 p. As Nos. 497/500.

95 Pres. Chamoun and King Faisal II of Iraq

1957. Air. Arab Leaders' Conference, Beirut.

571	**95**	15 p. orange	50	25
572	–	15 p. blue	50	25
573	–	15 p. purple	50	25
574	–	15 p. mauve	50	25
575	–	15 p. green	50	25
576	–	25 p. turquoise	50	25
577	–	100 p. brown	3·25	1·60

DESIGNS—HORIZ: 15 p. values as Type **95** show Pres. Chamoun and King Hussein of Jordan (No. 572), Abdallah Khalil of Sudan (No. 573), Pres. Shukri Bey al-Quwatli of Syria (No. 574) and King Saud of Saudi Arabia (No. 575). 25 p. Map and Pres. Chamoun. 100 p. (44×44 mm Diamond shape), The six Arab Leaders.

97 Runners **98** Miners

1957. 2nd Pan-Arabian Games, Beirut.

578	**97**	2 p. 50 c. sepia (postage)	40	15
579	–	12½ p. blue	60	20
580	–	35 p. purple (air)	1·50	60
581	–	50 p. green	2·00	95

DESIGNS—VERT: 12½ p. Footballers. HORIZ: 35 p. Fencers; 50 p. Stadium.

1957.

582	**86**	50 c. blue (16½×20½ mm) (postage)	15	10
582a		50 c. violet (17×21½ mm)	25	10
583		1 p. brown (16½×20½ mm)	20	10
583a		1 p. red (17×21½ mm)	25	10
584		2 p. 50 violet (16½×20½ mm)	25	10
584a		2 p. 50 blue (17×21¼ mm)	45	10
584b		2 p. 50 green (17×21¼ mm)	30	10
585		5 p. green (16½×20½ mm)	45	10
586	**98**	7½ p. pink	70	10
587		10 p. brown	65	10
588		12½ p. blue	85	10
589	–	25 p. blue	1·00	10
590	–	50 p. green	1·50	15
591	–	100 p. brown	3·25	45
592	–	5 p. green (air)	25	10
593	–	10 p. orange	15	10
594	–	15 p. brown	20	10
595	–	20 p. red	35	10
596	–	25 p. blue	60	10
597	–	35 p. purple	85	15
598	–	50 p. green	1·25	20
599	–	65 p. brown	1·75	25
600	–	100 p. grey	2·25	75

DESIGNS: POSTAGE—As Type **86**: 50 c., 2 p. 50 Figures in uniform size. 1 p., 5 p. Short dash under "P". As Type **98**: VERT: 25 p. to 100 p. Potter. AIR—As Type **98**: HORIZ: 5 p. to 25 p. Cedar of Lebanon with signs of the Zodiac, bird and ship. 35 to 100 p. Chamoun Electric Power Station.

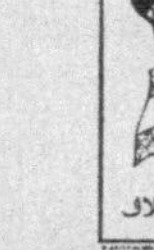

99 Cedar of Lebanon **100** Soldier and Flag

101 Douglas DC-6B at Khalde Airport

1959.

601 99 50 c. blue (postage) . . . 15 10
602 1 p. orange . . . 35 10
603 2 p. 50 violet . . . 35 10
604 5 p. green . . . 30 10
605 100 12 p. 50 blue . . . 55 10
606 25 p. blue . . . 60 10
607 50 p. brown . . . 1·10 15
608 100 p. sepia . . . 2·25 30
609 101 5 p. green (air) . . . 55 10
610 10 p. purple . . . 55 10
611 15 p. violet . . . 80 10
612 20 p. red . . . 1·10 10
613 25 p. violet . . . 1·50 20
614 – 35 p. myrtle . . . 80 20
615 – 50 p. turquoise . . . 1·00 20
616 – 65 p. sepia . . . 1·60 30
617 – 100 p. blue . . . 2·25 45

DESIGN—HORIZ: Nos. 614/17, Factory cogwheel and telegraph pylons.

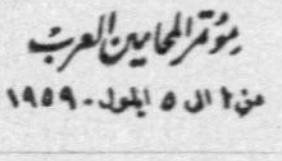

(102)

1959. Lawyers' Conference. Nos. 538 and 546 (air) surch as T **102**.

618 30 p. on 50 p. myrtle and blue (postage) . . . 60 45
619 40 p. on 50 p. yellow and black (air) . . . 55 40

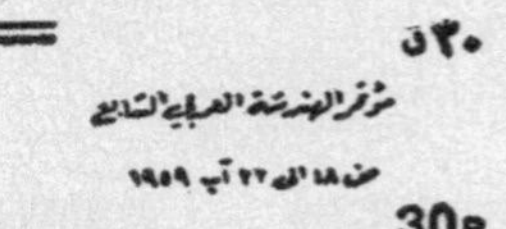

(103)

1959. Air. Engineers' Conference Nos. 614 and 616 surch as T **103**.

620 30 p. on 35 p. myrtle . . . 50 30
621 40 p. on 65 p. sepia . . . 75 40

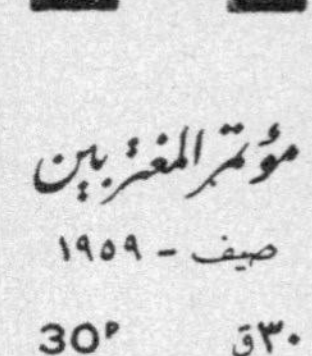

(104) 105 Discus Thrower

1959. Emigrants' Conference No. 590 surch as T **104**.

622 30 p. on 50 p. green . . . 50 15
623 40 p. on 50 p. green . . . 75 35

1959. Air. 3rd Mediterranean Games, Beirut.

624 105 15 p. green . . . 40 15
625 – 30 p. brown . . . 60 25
626 – 40 p. blue . . . 1·25 35

DESIGNS—VERT: 30 p. Weightlifting. HORIZ: 40 p. Games emblem.

106 Soldiers with Standard 108 Planting Tree

1959. Air. 16th Anniv of Independence.

627 106 40 p. red and black . . . 65 35
628 60 p. red and green . . . 95 55

1959. Surch.

629 100 7 p. 50 on 12 p. 50 blue . . . 15 10
630 10 p. on 12 p. 50 blue . . . 20 10
631 15 p. on 25 p. blue . . . 30 10
632 – 40 p. on 50 p. green (No. 590) . . . 65 30
633 88 40 p. on 65 p. purple (air) . . . 1·40 45

1960. Air. 25th Anniv of Friends of the Tree Society.

634 108 20 p. purple and green . . . 45 20
635 40 p. sepia and green . . . 65 40

1960. Air. As T **79** but colours of name and value tablets reversed.

636 20 p. green . . . 40 20

109 Pres. Chehab

1960. Air.

637 109 5 p. green . . . 10 10
638 10 p. blue . . . 15 10
639 15 p. brown . . . 15 10
640 20 p. sepia . . . 20 10
641 30 p. olive . . . 35 10
642 40 p. red . . . 35 10
643 50 p. blue . . . 60 15
644 70 p. purple . . . 65 25
645 100 p. green . . . 1·40 60

110 Arab League Centre 111 "Uprooted Tree"

1960. Inaug. of Arab League Centre, Cairo.

646 110 15 p. turquoise . . . 25 20

1960. Air. World Refugee Year. (a) Size $20\frac{1}{2} \times 36\frac{1}{2}$ mm.

647 111 25 p. brown . . . 30 35
648 40 p. green . . . 50 45

(b) Size $19\frac{1}{2} \times 35\frac{1}{2}$ mm.

648b 111 25 p. brown . . . 50 50
648c 40 p. green . . . 90 1·10

112 Martyrs' Monument

1960. Air. Martyrs' Commemoration.

649 112 20 p. purple and green . . . 45 15
650 40 p. blue and green . . . 40 20
651 – 70 p. olive and black . . . 1·00 55

DESIGN—VERT: 70 p. Detail of statues on monument.

113 Pres. Chehab and King Mohammed V 114 Pres. Chehab

1960. Air. Visit of King Mohammed V of Morocco.

652 113 30 p. brown & dp brown . . . 50 20
653 70 p. brown and black . . . 1·00 55

1960.

654 114 50 c. green . . . 10 10
655 2 p. 50 olive . . . 10 10
656 5 p. green . . . 15 10
657 7 p. 50 brown . . . 30 10
658 15 p. blue . . . 45 10
659 50 p. purple . . . 90 15
660 100 p. brown . . . 1·40 35

115 Child 116 Dove, Map and Flags

1960. Air. Mother and Child Days.

661 115 20 p. red and yellow . . . 45 10
662 20 p. + 10 p. red & yellow . . . 55 30
663 – 60 p. blue & light blue . . . 1·00 40
664 – 60 p. + 15 p. blue & lt bl . . . 1·25 65

DESIGN: Nos. 663/4, Mother and child.

1960. Air. World Lebanese Union Meeting. Beirut. Multicoloured.

665 20 p. Type **116** . . . 20 10
666 40 p. Cedar of Lebanon and homing pigeons . . . 40 15
667 70 p. Globes and Cedar of Lebanon (horiz) . . . 65 30

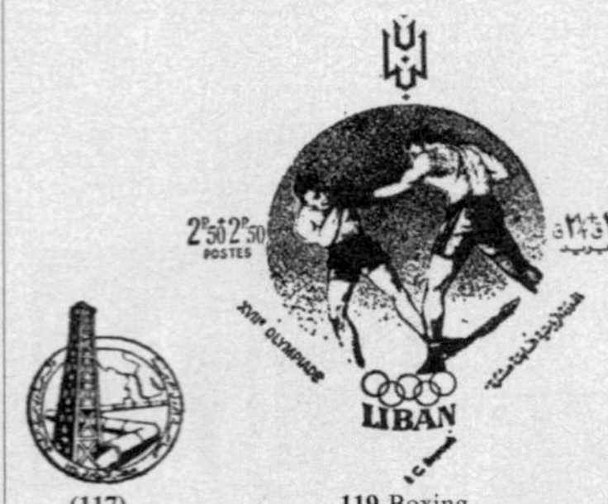

(117) 119 Boxing

1960. Arabian Oil Congress, Beirut. Optd with T **117**.

668 86 5 p. green (No. 585) . . . 10 10
669 110 15 p. turquoise . . . 35 15

1960. Air. World Refugee Year. Nos. 647/8 surch in English and Arabic.

669a 111 20 p. + 10 p. on 40 p. grn . . . 5·00 5·00
669b 30 p. + 15 p. on 25 p. brn . . . 7·75 7·75

1961. Olympic Games.

670 119 2 p. 50 + 2 p. 50 brown and blue (postage) . . . 10 10
671 – 5 p. + 5 p. brown and orge . . . 15 15
672 – 7 p. 50 + 7 p. 50 brn & vio . . . 25 20
673 – 15 p. + 15 p. brown & red (air) . . . 1·75 1·50
674 – 25 p. + 25 p. brown & grn . . . 1·75 1·50
675 – 35 p. + 35 p. brown & bl . . . 1·75 1·50

DESIGNS: 5 p. Wrestling; 7 p. 50, Putting the shot; 15 p. Fencing; 25 p. Cyclying; 35 p. Swimming.

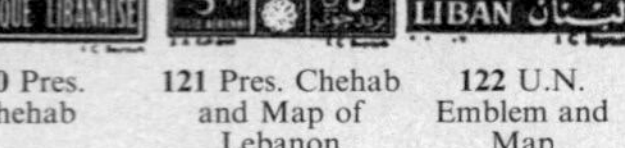
120 Pres. Chehab 121 Pres. Chehab and Map of Lebanon 122 U.N. Emblem and Map

1961.

676 120 2 p. 50 ultramarine and blue (postage) . . . 15 10
677 7 p. 50 purple and blue . . . 25 10
678 10 p. brown and yellow . . . 35 10
679 121 5 p. green & lt green (air) . . . 15 10
680 10 p. brown and ochre . . . 35 10
681 70 p. violet and mauve . . . 1·10 45
682 – 200 p. blue and bistre . . . 2·50 1·50

DESIGN—HORIZ: 200 p. Casino, Maameltein.

1961. Air. 15th Anniv of U.N.O.

683 122 20 p. purple and blue . . . 30 10
684 – 30 p. green and brown . . . 45 15
685 – 50 p. light blue & ultram . . . 75 35

DESIGNS—VERT: 30 p. U.N. emblem and Baalbek ruins. HORIZ: 50 p. View of U.N. Headquarters and Manhattan.

123 Cedar 124 Bay of Maameltein

1961. Redrawn version of T **86** (different arrangement at foot). (a) Shaded background.

686 123 2 p. 50 myrtle . . . 45 10

(b) As T **123** but plain background.

695 2 p. 50 yellow . . . 15 10
696 5 p. lake . . . 25 10
697 10 p. black . . . 35 10

1961. Air.

687 124 15 p. lake . . . 20 10
688 30 p. blue . . . 35 15
689 40 p. sepia . . . 45 20

125 Weaving

1961. Air. Labour Day.

690 – 30 p. red . . . 85 25
691 125 70 p. blue . . . 1·25 70

DESIGN: 30 p. Pottery.

126 Water-skiers

1961. Air. Tourist Month.

692 – 15 p. violet and blue . . . 45 15
693 126 40 p. blue and flesh . . . 65 45
694 – 70 p. olive and flesh . . . 1·00 70

DESIGNS—VERT: 15 p. Firework display. HORIZ: 70 p. Tourists in punt.

127 G.P.O., Beirut

1961.

698 127 2 p. 50 mauve (postage) . . . 35 10
699 5 p. green . . . 50 10
700 15 p. blue . . . 45 10
701 – 35 p. green (air) . . . 35 20
702 – 50 p. brown . . . 55 30
703 – 100 p. black . . . 80 60

DESIGN: 35 p. to 100 p. Motor highway, Dora.

128 Cedars of Lebanon 129 Tyre Waterfront

1961.

704 128 50 c. green (postage) . . . 10 10
705 1 p. brown . . . 15 10
706 2 p. 50 blue . . . 20 10
707 5 p. red . . . 25 10
708 7 p. 50 violet . . . 40 10
709 – 10 p. purple . . . 55 10
710 – 15 p. blue . . . 65 10
711 – 50 p. green . . . 8·50 45
712 – 100 p. black . . . 1·90 70
713 129 5 p. red (air) . . . 20 10
714 10 p. violet . . . 20 10
715 15 p. blue . . . 30 10
716 20 p. orange . . . 30 10
717 30 p. green . . . 40 10
718 – 40 p. purple . . . 50 20
719 – 50 p. blue . . . 60 20
720 – 70 p. green . . . 85 45
721 – 100 p. sepia . . . 1·50 60

DESIGNS—HORIZ: Nos. 709/12, Zahle. VERT: Nos. 718/21, Afka Falls.

See also Nos. 729/34.

130 U.N.E.S.C.O. Building, Beirut

1961. Air. 15th Anniv of U.N.E.S.C.O. Mult.

722 20 p.Type **130** . . . 35 10
723 30 p. U.N.E.S.C.O. emblem and cedar (vert) . . . 45 20
724 50 p. U.N.E.S.C.O. Building, Paris . . . 85 40

131 Tomb of Unknown Soldier 132 Scout Bugler

1961. Independence and Evacuation of Foreign Troops Commem. Multicoloured.

725 10 p. Type **131** (postage) . . . 25 10
726 15 p. Soldier and flag . . . 35 10
727 25 p. Cedar emblem (air) . . . 30 20
728 50 p. Emirs Bashir and Fakhreddine . . . 55 45

The 25 p. and 50 p. are horiz.

1962. As Nos. 704/21 but with larger figures of value.

729 128 50 c. green (postage) . . . 15 10
730 1 p. brown . . . 15 10
731 2 p. 50 blue . . . 20 10
732 – 15 p. blue . . . 1·90 15
733 129 5 p. red (air) . . . 35 10
734 – 40 p. purple . . . 4·00 50

1962. Lebanese Scout Movement Commemorative.
735 ½ p. black, yell & grn (postage) . . 10 10
736 1 p. multicoloured 10 10
737 2½ p. green, black and red . . 10 10
738 6 p. multicoloured 20 10
739 10 p. yellow, black and blue . . 35 10
740 15 p. multicoloured (air) . . . 35 20
741 20 p. yellow, black and violet . 50 30
742 25 p. multicoloured 85 40
DESIGNS—VERT: ½ p. Type **132**; 6 p. Lord Baden-Powell; 20 p. Saluting hand. HORIZ: 1 p. Scout with flag, cedar and badge; 2½ p. Stretcher party, badge and laurel; 10 p. Scouts and camp fire; 15 p. Cedar and Guide badge; 25 p. Cedar and Scout badge.

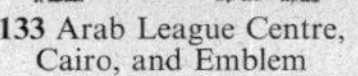
133 Arab League Centre, Cairo, and Emblem
134 Blacksmith

1962. Air. Arab League Week.
743 **133** 20 p. blue and turquoise . . 40 20
744 30 p. lake and pink . . . 45 30
745 50 p. geeen and turquoise . . 75 45
See also Nos. 792/5.

1962. Air. Labour Day.
746 **134** 5 p. green and blue . . . 25 10
747 10 p. blue and pink . . . 30 10
748 – 25 p. violet and pink . . . 35 15
749 – 35 p. mauve and blue . . . 45 25
DESIGN—HORIZ: 25 p., 35 p. Tractor.

1962. European Shooting Championships Nos. 670/5 optd **CHAMPIONNAT D'EUROPE DE** TIR/2 JUIN 1962 in English and Arabic.
750 **119** 2 p. 50 + 2 p. 50 (postage) 30 30
751 – 5 p. + 5 p. 55 40
752 – 7 p. 50 + 7 p. 50 . . . . 70 40
753 – 15 p. + 15 p. (air) 65 65
754 – 25 p. + 25 p. . . . . . . 1·40 1·40
755 – 35 p. + 35 p. . . . . . . 1·90 1·90

136 Hand grasping Emblem
137 Rock Temples of Abu Simbel

1962. Air. Malaria Eradication.
756 **136** 30 p. brown & lt brown . . 40 30
757 – 70 p. violet and lilac . . . 60 55
DESIGN: 70 p. Campaign emblem.

1962. Nubian Monuments.
758 **137** 5 p. bl & ultram (postage) . 30 10
759 15 p. lake and brown . . . 40 15
760 – 30 p. yellow and grn (air) . . 85 45
761 – 50 p. olive and grey . . . 1·40 90
DESIGNS: 30 p., 50 p. Bas-relief.

138 Playing-card Symbols
139 Schoolboy

1962. Air. European Bridge Championships.
762 **138** 25 p. multicoloured . . . 1·60 1·10
763 40 p. multicoloured . . . 1·90 1·10

1962. Schoolchildren's Day.
764 **139** 30 p. mult (postage) . . . 35 15
765 – 45 p. multicoloured (air) . . 55 25
DESIGN: 45 p. Teacher.

140
141 Cherries

1962. Air. 19th Anniv of Independence.
766 **140** 25 p. green, red & turq . . 55 35
767 25 p. violet, red & turq . . 55 35
768 25 p. blue, red & turquoise . 55 35

1962. Fruits. Multicoloured.
769 50 c. Type **141** (postage) . . 15 10
770 1 p. Figs 15 10
771 2 p. 50 Type **141** 20 10
772 5 p. Figs 30 10
773 7 p. 50 Type **141** 30 10
774 10 p. Grapes 40 10
775 17 p. 50 Grapes 50 10
776 30 p. Grapes 80 15
777 50 p. Oranges . . . . . . 1·25 40
778 100 p. Pomegranates . . . . 3·00 90
779 5 p. Apricots (air) 30 10
780 10 p. Plums 40 10
781 20 p. Apples 50 10
782 30 p. Plums 65 20
783 40 p. Apples 80 20
784 50 p. Pears . . . . 1·00 25
785 70 p. Medlars . . . . . . 1·40 40
786 100 p. Lemons . . . . . . 1·90 70

142 Reaping
143 Nurse tending Baby

1963. Air. Freedom from Hunger.
787 **142** 2 p. 50 yellow and blue . . 15 10
788 5 p. yellow and green . . 15 10
789 7 p. 50 yellow & purple . 30 10
790 – 15 p. green and red . . . 30 15
791 – 20 p. green and red . . . 40 20
DESIGN—HORIZ: 15 p., 20 p. Three ears of wheat within hand.

1963. Air. Arab League Week. As T **133** but inscr "1963".
792 5 p. violet and blue 15 10
793 10 p. green and blue 30 15
794 15 p. brown and blue 20 25
795 20 p. grey and blue 40 40

1963. Air. Red Cross Centenary.
796 – 5 p. green and red . . . 15 10
797 – 20 p. blue and red . . . 40 10
798 **143** 35 p. red and black . . . 45 25
799 40 p. violet and red . . . 55 35
DESIGN—HORIZ: 5, 20 p. Blood transfusion.

144 Allegory of Music
145 Flag and rising Sun

1963. Air. Baalbek Festival.
800 **144** 35 p. orange and blue . . 55 35

1963. Air. 20th Anniv of Independence. Flag and sun in red and yellow.
801 **145** 5 p. turquoise 20 10
802 10 p. green 30 15
803 25 p. blue 35 40
804 40 p. drab 55 65

146 Cycling
147 Hyacinth

1964. 4th Mediterranean Games, Naples (1963).
805 **146** 2 p. 50 brown and purple (postage) 10 10
806 – 5 p. orange and blue . . 25 10
807 – 10 p. brown and violet . . 35 10
808 – 15 p. orange & green (air) . 35 10
809 – 17 p. 50 brown & blue . . 55 15
810 – 30 p. brown & turq . . . 55 30
DESIGNS—VERT: 5 p. Basketball; 10 p. Running; 15 p. Tennis. HORIZ: 17 p. 50 Swimming; 30 p. Skiing.

1964. Flowers. Multicoloured.
811 50 c. Type **147** (postage) . . 20 10
812 1 p. Type **147** 20 10
813 2 p. 50 Type **147** 20 10
814 5 p. Cyclamen 20 10
815 7 p. 50 Cyclamen 20 10
816 10 p. Poinsettia 30 10
817 17 p. 50 Anemone 55 10
818 30 p. Iris . . . . 1·00 20
819 50 p. Poppy . . . . 1·60 45
820 5 p. Lily (air) 20 10
821 10 p. Ranunculus 50 10
822 20 p. Anemone 40 10
823 40 p. Tuberose 70 25
824 45 p. Rhododendron . . . . 1·00 25
825 50 p. Jasmine 95 25
826 70 p. Yellow broom . . . . 1·40 55
Nos. 816/26 are vert, size 26½ × 37 mm.

148 Cedar of Lebanon **149**

1964.
827 **148** 50 c. green 20 10
828 **149** 50 c. green 15 10
829 2 p. 50 blue 20 10
830 5 p. mauve 30 10
831 7 p. 50 orange 30 10
832 17 p. purple 50 10

150 Child on Rocking-horse
152 "Flame of Freedom"

151 League Session

1964. Air. Children's Day.
833 – 5 p. multicoloured 20 10
834 – 10 p. multicoloured . . . 25 10
835 **150** 20 p. multicoloured . . . 40 20
836 40 p. multicoloured . . . 45 55
DESIGN—HORIZ: 5 p., 10 p. Girls skipping.

1964. Air. Arab League Meeting.
837 **151** 5 p. buff, brown and black 35 15
838 10 p. black 20 20
839 15 p. turquoise 45 30
840 20 p. mauve, brn & sepia 95 40

1964. Air. 15th Anniv of Declaration of Human Rights.
841 **152** 20 p. red, salmon & brown 25 10
842 – 40 p. orange, grey & blue 45 25
DESIGN: 40 p. Flame on pedestal bearing U.N. emblem.

153 Sick Child
154 Clasped Wrists

1964. Air. "Bal des Petits Lits Blancs" (Ball for children's charity).
843 **153** 2 p. 50 multicoloured . . . 15 10
844 5 p. multicoloured . . . 15 10
845 15 p. multicoloured . . . 20 10
846 – 17 p. 50 multicoloured . . 30 15
847 – 20 p. multicoloured . . 35 15
848 – 40 p. multicoloured . . 40 25
DESIGN—HORIZ: (55 × 25½ mm): 17 p. 50 to 40 p. Children in front of palace (venue of ball).

1964. Air. World Lebanese Union Congress, Beirut.
849 **154** 20 p. black, yellow & grn 35 20
850 40 p. black, yellow & pur 55 40

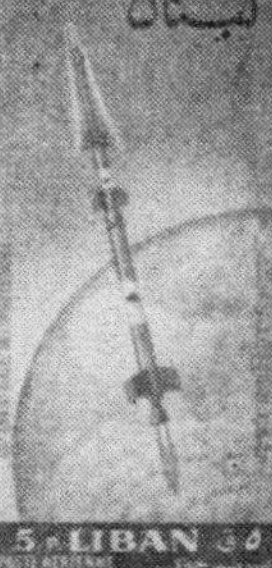

155 Rocket in Flight
156 Temple Columns

1964. Air. 21st Anniv of Independence.
851 **155** 5 p. multicoloured 20 15
852 10 p. multicoloured . . . 20 15
853 – 40 p. blue and black . . . 55 40
854 – 70 p. purple and black . . 1·00 75
DESIGNS—HORIZ: 40 p. to 70 p. "Struggle for Independence" (battle scene).

1965. Baalbek Festival.
855 **156** 2 p. 50 black and orange (postage) 15 10
856 – 7 p.50 black and blue . . 50 20
857 – 10 p. multicoloured (air) . 15 10
858 – 15 p. multicoloured . . . 30 10
859 – 25 p. multicoloured . . . 30 25
860 – 40 p. multicoloured . . . 55 35
DESIGNS—VERT: (28 × 55 mm): 10 p., 15 p. Man in costume; 25 p., 40 p. Woman in costume.

157 Swimming

1965. Olympic Games, Tokyo.
861 **157** 2 p. 50 black, blue and mauve (postage) 10 10
862 – 7 p. 50 purple, green & brn 40 25
863 – 10 p. grey, brown & green 50 35
864 – 15 p. black and green (air) 20 10
865 – 25 p. green and purple . . 35 15
866 – 40 p. brown and blue . . 50 25
DESIGNS—HORIZ: 7 p. 50 Fencing; 15 p. Horse-jumping; 40 p. Gymnastics. VERT: 10 p. Basketball; 25 p. Rifle-shooting.

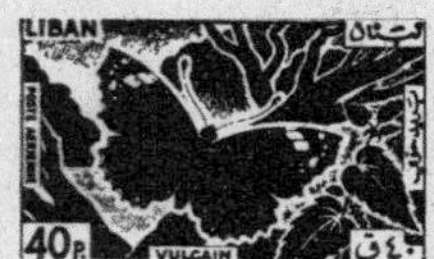
158 "Vanessa atalanta"

1965. (a) Postage. Birds.
867 – 5 p. multicoloured 30 10
868 – 10 p. multicoloured 45 10
869 – 15 p. chocolate, orge & brn 85 10
870 – 17 p. 50 purple, red & blue 1·25 10
871 – 20 p. black, yellow & green 1·40 15
872 – 32 p. 50 yellow, brn & grn . 2·50 40

(b) Air. Butterflies.
873 – 30 p. yellow, brown & red 15 10
874 – 35 p. blue, red & bistre . 30 15
875 **158** 40 p. brown, red & green 35 15
876 – 45 p. brown, yellow & blue 45 20
877 – 70 p. multicoloured . . . 50 35
878 – 85 p. black, orange & green 80 35
879 – 100 p. blue and plum . . 1·10 35
880 – 200 p. brown, blue & pur 2·50 55
881 – 300 p. sepia, yellow & green 3·25 1·10
882 – 500 p. brown and blue . . 7·25 2·75
DESIGNS—BIRDS: 5 p. Bullfinch; 10 p. Goldfinch. 15 p. Hoopoe; 17 p. 50 Red-legged partridge. 20 p. Golden oriole; 32 p. 50 European bee eater. BUTTERFLIES: 30 p. "Pericallia matronula"; 35 p. "Heliconius cyrbia"; 45 p. "Satyrus semele"; 70 p. "Papilio machaon"; 85 p. "Anthocharis cardamines"; 100 p. "Morpho cypris"; 200 p. "Erasmia sanguiflua"; 300 p. "Papilio crassus". LARGER (35½ × 25 mm): 500 p. "Charaxes ameliae".

159 Pope Paul and Pres. Helou

1965. Air. Pope Paul's Visit to Lebanon.
883 **159** 45 p. violet and gold . . . 1·90 1·10

160 Sheep

1965.

884 – 50 c. multicoloured 15 10
885 – 1 p. grey, black and mauve 50 10
886 160 2 p. 50 yellow, sepia & grn 35 10
DESIGNS: 50 c. Cow and calf. 1 p. Rabbit.

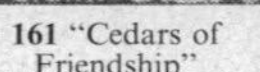
161 "Cedars of Friendship"  162 "Silk Manufacture"

1965. Air.

887 161 40 p. multicoloured 45 15

1965. Air. World Silk Congress, Beirut. Multicoloured.

888 2 p. 50 Type **162** 10 10
889 5 p. Type **162** 10 10
890 7 p. 50 Type **162** 15 10
891 15 p. Weaver and loom 20 10
892 30 p. As 15 p. 35 15
893 40 p. As 15 p. 50 20
894 50 p. As 15 p. 65 35

163 Parliament Building

1965. Air. Centenary of Lebanese Parliament.

895 163 35 p. brown, ochre & red 50 15
896 40 p. brown, ochre & green 60 20

164 U.N. Emblem and Headquarters  165 Playing-card "King"

1965. Air. 20th Anniv of U.N.

897 164 2 p. 50 blue 10 10
898 10 p. red 15 10
899 17 p. 50 violet 20 10
900 30 p. green 35 15
901 40 p. brown 50 30

1965. Air. World Bridge Chamipionships, Beirut.

902 165 2 p. 50 multicoloured 20 10
903 15 p. multicoloured 30 10
904 17 p. 50 multicoloured 35 20
905 40 p. multicoloured 65 30

166 Dagger on Deir Yassin, Palestine 167 I.T.U. Emblem and Symbols

1965. Air. Deir Yassin Massacre.

906 166 50 p. multicoloured 45 35

1966. Air. Centenary (1965) of I.T.U.

907 167 2 p. 50 multicoloured 15 10
908 15 p. multicoloured 35 10
909 17 p. 50 multicoloured 50 15
910 25 p. multicoloured 50 25
911 40 p. multicoloured 60 45

168 Stage Performance

1966. Air. Baalbek Festival. Multicoloured.

912 2 p. 50 Type **168** 15 10
913 5 p. Type **168** 15 10
914 7 p. 50 Ballet performance 15 10
915 15 p. Ballet performance 35 10
916 30 p. Concert 20 20
917 40 p. Concert 40 30
The 7 p. 50 and 15 p. are vert.

169 Tabaria 170 W.H.O. Building

1966. Tourism. Multicoloured.

918 50 c. Hippodrome, Beirut (postage) 10 10
919 1 p. Pigeon Grotto, Beirut 10 10
920 2 p. 50 Type **169** 10 10
921 5 p. Ruins, Beit-Mery 15 10
922 7 p. 50 Ruins, Anfar 15 10
923 10 p. Djezzine Falls (air) 20 10
924 15 p. Sidon Castle 25 10
925 20 p. Amphitheatre, Byblos 30 10
926 30 p. Sun Temple, Baalbek 45 10
927 50 p. Palace, Beit ed-Din 50 10
928 60 p. Nahr-el Kalb 65 30
929 70 p. Tripoli 90 45

1966. Air. Inauguration of W.H.O. Headquarters, Geneva.

930 170 7 p. 50 green 25 10
931 17 p. 50 red 15 10
932 25 p. blue 20 20

171 Skiing

1966. Air. International Cedars Festival.

933 171 2 p. 50 brown, red & green 25 10
934 – 5 p. multicoloured 25 10
935 – 17 p. 50 multicoloured 40 15
936 – 25 p. red, brown & green 45 30
DESIGNS: 5 p. Toboganning; 17 p. 50, Cedar in snow; 25 p. Ski-lift.

172 Inscribed Sarcophagus

1966. Air. Phoenician Invention of the Alphabet.

937 172 10 p. brown, black & grn 15 10
938 – 15 p. brown, ochre & mve 25 10
939 – 20 p. sepia, blue & ochre 35 20
940 – 30 p. brown, orange & yell 40 30
DESIGNS: 15 p. Phoenician sailing ship; 20 p. Mediterranean route map showing spread of Phoenician alphabet; 30 p. Kadmus with alphabet tablet.

173 Child in Bath  174 Decade Emblem

1966. Air. Int Children's Day. Multicoloured.

941 2 p. Type **173** 10 10
942 5 p. Boy and doll in rowing boat 15 10
943 7 p. 50 Girl skiing 30 10
944 15 p. Girl giving food to bird 20 15
945 20 p. Boy doing homework 30 25

1966. Air. International Hydrological Decade.

947 174 5 p. ultramarine, bl & orge 15 10
948 10 p. red, blue and orange 15 10
949 – 15 p. sepia, green & orange 25 15
950 – 20 p. blue, green & orange 20 20
DESIGN: 15 p., 20 p. Similar "wave" pattern.

175 Rev. Daniel Bliss (founder) 176 I.T.Y. Emblem

177 Beit ed-Din Palace

1966. Air. Centenary of American University, Beirut.

951 175 20 p. brown, yell & grn 35 10
952 – 30 p. green, brn & blue 40 15
DESIGN: 30 p. University Chapel.

1967. International Tourist Year (1st issue). (a) Postage.

954 176 50 c. multicoloured 10 10
955 1 p. multicoloured 10 10
956 2 p. 50 multicoloured 10 10
957 5 p. multicoloured 15 10
958 7 p. 50 multicoloured 25 10

(b) Air. Multicoloured.

959 10 p. Tabaria 25 10
960 15 p. Pigeon Rock, Beirut 30 10
961 17 p. 50 Type **177** 30 10
962 20 p. Sidon 30 10
963 25 p. Tripoli 35 10
964 30 p. Byblos 20 10
965 35 p. Ruins, Tyre 30 10
966 40 p. Temple, Baalbek 45 10
See also Nos. 977/80.

178 Signing Pact, and Flags

1967. Air. 22nd Anniv of Arab League Pact.

967 178 5 p. multicoloured 10 10
968 10 p. multicoloured 15 10
969 15 p. multicoloured 30 15
970 20 p. multicoloured 20 30

179 Veterans War Memorial Building, San Francisco

1967. Air. San Francisco Pact of 1945. Mult.

971 2 p. 50 Type **179** 15 20
972 5 p. Type **179** 15 20
973 7 p. 50 Type **179** 15 20
974 10 p. Scroll and flags of U.N. and Lebanon 15 10
975 20 p. As 10 p. 20 10
976 30 p. As 10 p. 30 20

180 Temple Ruins, Baalbek

1967. Air. International Tourist Year (2nd issue). Multicoloured.

977 5 p. Type **180** 15 10
978 10 p. Ruins, Anjar 20 10
979 15 p. Ancient bridge, Nahr-Ibrahim 30 10
980 20 p. Grotto, Jeita 35 15

181

1967. Air. India Day.

981 181 2 p. 50 red 10 10
982 5 p. red 15 10
983 7 p. 50 brown 15 10
984 10 p. blue 15 10
985 15 p. green 40 15

182

1967. Air. 22nd Anniv of Lebanon's Admission to U.N.

986 182 2 p. 50 red 10 10
987 5 p. blue 10 10
988 7 p. 50 green 10 10
989 – 10 p. red 10 10
990 – 20 p. blue 25 10
991 – 30 p. green 45 15
DESIGN: 10, 20, 30 p. U.N. Emblem.

183 Goat and Kid

1967. Animals and Fishes. Multicoloured.

992 50 c. Type **183** (postage) 10 10
993 1 p. Cattle 10 10
994 2 p. 50 Sheep 10 10
995 5 p. Dromedaries 15 10
996 10 p. Donkey 20 10
997 15 p. Horses 40 10
998 20 p. Shark (air) 40 10
999 30 p. Needle-fish 40 10
1000 40 p. Pollack 60 10
1001 50 p. Wrasse 70 15
1002 70 p. Red mullet 1·25 25
1003 100 p. Salmon 1·40 35

184 Ski Jumping

1968. Air. International Ski Congress. Beirut.

1004 184 2 p. 50 multicoloured 15 10
1005 – 5 p. multicoloured 25 10
1006 – 7 p. 50 multicoloured 25 10
1007 – 10 p. multicoloured 30 10
1008 – 25 p. multicoloured 25 25
DESIGNS: 5 p. to 10 p. Skiing (all different); 25 p. Congress emblem of Cedar and skis.

185 Princess Khaskiah

1968. Air. Emir Fakhreddine II Commem. Mult.

1009 2 p. 50 Type **185** 15 10
1010 5 p. Emir Fakhreddine II 15 10
1011 10 p. Sidon Citadel 20 5
1012 15 p. Chekif Citadel 30 10
1013 17 p. 50 Beirut Citadel 15 15
The 10 p., 15 p. and 17 p. 50, are horiz designs.

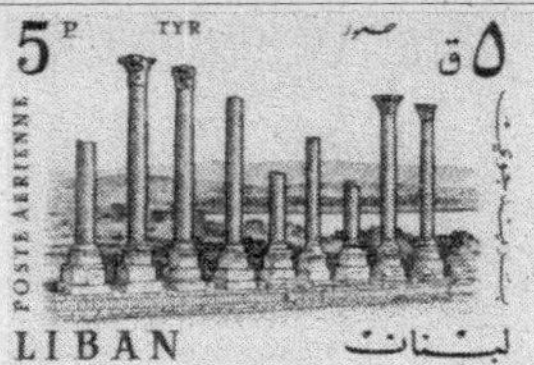

186 Colonnade

1968. Air. Tyre Antiquities.

1014 – 2 p. 50 brn, cream & pink 15 10
1015 **186** 5 p. brown, blue & yellow 25 10
1016 – 7 p. 50 brown, buff & grn 30 10
1017 – 10 p. brown, blue & orange 15 15

DESIGNS—VERT: 2 p. 50, Roman bust; 10 p. Bas-relief. HORIZ: 7 p. 50, Arch.

187 Justinian and Mediterranean Map

1968. Air. 1st Anniv of Faculty of Law, Beirut.

1019 5 p. Justinian (vert) 10 10
1020 10 p. Justinian (vert) 15 10
1021 15 p. Type **187** 20 10
1022 20 p. Type **187** 30 15

188 Arab League Emblem

190 Jupiter's Temple Ruins, Baalbek

189 Cedar on Globe

1968. Air. Arab Appeal Week.

1023 **188** 5 p. multicoloured 10 10
1024 10 p. multicoloured 15 10
1025 15 p. multicoloured 25 10
1026 20 p. multicoloured 30 15

1968. Air. 3rd World Lebanese Union Congress, Beirut.

1027 **189** 2 p. 50 multicoloured 10 10
1028 5 p. multicoloured 15 10
1029 7 p. 50 multicoloured 20 10
1030 10 p. multicoloured 30 15

1968. Air. Baalbek Festival. Multicoloured.

1031 5 p. Type **190** 10 10
1032 10 p. Bacchus's Temple 10 10
1033 15 p. Corniche, Jupiter's Temple 25 15
1034 20 p. Portal, Bacchus's Temple 35 20
1035 25 p. Columns, Bacchus's Temple 55 25

191 Long Jumping and Atlantes

1968. Air. Olympic Games, Mexico.

1036 **191** 5 p. black, yellow & blue 15 10
1037 – 10 p. black, blue & purple 20 10
1038 – 15 p. multicoloured 20 10
1039 – 20 p. multicoloured 25 15
1040 – 25 p. brown 45 25

DESIGNS: (each incorporating Aztec relic): 10 p. High-jumping; 15 p. Fencing; 20 p. Weightlifting; 25 p. "Sailing boat" with oars.

192 Lebanese driving Tractor ("Work protection")

193 Minshiya Stairs

1968. Air. Human Rights Year. Multicoloured.

1041 10 p. Type **192** 15 10
1042 15 p. Citizens ("Social Security") 20 10
1043 25 p. Young men of three races ("Unity") 25 15

1968. Air. Centenary of 1st Municipal Council (Deir el-Kamar). Multicoloured.

1044 10 p. Type **193** 15 10
1045 15 p. Serai kiosk 20 10
1046 25 p. Ancient highway 25 15

194 Nurse and Child

1969. Air. U.N.I.C.E.F. Commem. Multicoloured.

1047 **194** 5 p. black, brown & blue 10 10
1048 – 10 p. black, green & yell 15 10
1049 – 15 p. black, red & purple 25 10
1050 – 20 p. black, blue & yellow 30 10
1051 – 25 p. black, ochre & mve 35 15

DESIGNS: 10 p. Produce. 15 p. Mother and child. 20 p. Child with book. 25 p. Children with flowers.

195 Ancient Coin

1969. Air. 20th Anniv of International Museums Council (I.C.O.M.). Exhibits in National Museum Beirut. Multicoloured.

1052 2 p. 50 Type **195** 15 10
1053 5 p. Gold dagger, Byblos 20 10
1054 7 p. 50 Detail of Ahiram's Sarcophagus 20 10
1055 30 p. Jewelled pectoral 15 30
1056 40 p. Khalde "bird" vase 30 45

196 Water-skiing

1969. Air. Water-Sports. Multicoloured.

1057 2 p. 50 Type **196** 15 10
1058 5 p. Water-skiing (group) 20 10
1059 7 p. 50 Paraskiing (vert) 35 10
1060 30 p. Sailing (vert) 30 30
1061 40 p. Yacht-racing 50 50

197 Frontier Guard

1969. Air. 25th Anniv of Independence. The Lebanese Army.

1062 2 p. Type **197** 15 10
1063 5 p. Unknown Soldier's Tomb 25 10
1064 7 p. 50 Army Foresters 30 10
1065 15 p. Road-making 10 15
1066 30 p. Military ambulance and Sud Aviation Alouette III helicopter 20 25
1067 40 p. Skiing patrol 25 45

198 Concentric Red Crosses

1971. Air. 25th Anniv of Lebanese Red Cross.

1068 **198** 15 p. red and black 15 10
1069 – 85 p. red and black 80 80

DESIGN: 85 p. Red Cross in shape of cedar of Lebanon.

199 Foil and Flags of Arab States

1971. Air. 10th International Fencing Championships. Multicoloured.

1070 10 p. Type **199** 20 10
1071 15 p. Foil and flags of foreign nations 25 10
1072 35 p. Contest with foils 30 35
1073 40 p. Epee contest 40 35
1074 50 p. Contest with sabres 50 40

200 "Farmers at Work" (12th-century Arab painting)

1971. Air. 50th Anniv (1969) of I.L.O.

1075 **200** 10 p. multicoloured 15 10
1076 40 p. multicoloured 55 30

201 U.P.U. Monument and New H.Q. Building, Berne

1971. Air. New U.P.U. Headquarters Building, Berne.

1077 **201** 15 p. red, black & yellow 15 10
1078 35 p. yell, black and pink 30 25

202 "Ravens setting fire to Owls" (14th-century painting)

1971. Air. Children's Day. Multicoloured.

1079 15 p. Type **202** 30 10
1080 85 p. "The Lion and the Jackal" (13th-century painting), (horiz 39 × 29 mm) 90 45

203 Arab League Flag and Map

1971. Air. 25th Anniv of Arab League.

1081 **203** 30 p. multicoloured 40 15
1082 70 p. multicoloured 55 45

204 Jamhour Electricity Sub-station

1971. Air. Multicoloured.

1083 5 p. Type **204** 15 10
1084 10 p. Maameltein Bridge 20 10
1085 15 p. Hoteliers' School 20 10
1086 20 p. Litani Dam 40 10
1087 25 p. Interior of T.V. set 15 10
1088 35 p. Bziza Temple 30 10
1089 40 p. Jounieh Harbour 30 15
1090 45 p. Radar scanner, Beirut Airport 35 15
1091 50 p. Hibiscus 50 20
1092 70 p. School of Sciences Building 65 20
1093 85 p. Oranges 95 35
1094 100 p. Satellite Communications Station, Arbanieh 1·10 60

205 Insignia of Imam al Ouzai (theologian)

1971. Air. Lebanese Celebrities.

1095 **205** 25 p. brown, gold & grn 15 15
1096 – 25 p. brown, gold & yell 15 15
1097 – 25 p. brown, gold & yell 15 15
1098 – 25 p. brown, gold & grn 15 15

PORTRAITS: No. 1096, Bechara el Khoury (poet and writer). No. 1097, Hassan Kamel el Sabbah (scientist). No. 1098, Gibran Khalil Gibran (writer).

206 I.E.Y. Emblem and Computer Card

1971. Air. International Education Year.

1099 **206** 10 p. multicoloured 15 10
1100 40 p. multicoloured 25 25

207 Dahr-el-Basheq Sanatorium

208 "Solar Wheel" Emblem

1971. Air. Tuberculosis Relief Campaign.

1101 **207** 50 p. multicoloured 45 30
1102 – 100 p. multicoloured 65 45

DESIGN: 100 p. Different view of Sanatorium.

1971. Air. 16th Baalbek Festival.

1103 **208** 15 p. orange and blue 25 10
1104 – 85 p. black, blue & orge 65 55

DESIGN: 85 p. Corinthian capital.

209 Field-gun

1971. Air. Army Day. Multicoloured.

1105 15 p. Type **209** 15 10
1106 25 p. Dassault Mirage IIICJ jet fighters 80 20
1107 40 p. Army Command H.Q. 35 25
1108 70 p. "Tarablous" (naval patrol-boat) 1·25 45

210 Interior Decoration

212 U.N. Emblem

211 Lenin

1971. Air. 2nd Anniv of Burning of Al-Aqsa Mosque, Jerusalem.
1109 **210** 15 p. bistre and brown 20 10
1110 35 p. bistre and brown 45 20

1971. Air. Birth Centenary of Lenin. Mult.
1111 30 p. Type **211** 30 20
1112 70 p. Lenin in profile 55 60

1971. Air. 25th Anniv of United Nations.
1113 **212** 15 p. multicoloured 20 10
1114 85 p. multicoloured 65 35

213 "Europa" Mosaic, Byblos

1971. Air. World Lebanese Union.
1115 **213** 10 p. multicoloured 25 10
1116 40 p. multicoloured 65 20

1972. Various stamps surch.
1117 5 p. on 7 p. 50 (No. 922) (postage) 15 10
1118 5 p. on 7 p. 50 (No. 958) 15 10
1119 25 p. on 32 p. 50 (No. 872) 65 10
1120 5 p. on 7 p. 50 (No. 1016) (air) 15 10
1121 100 p. on 300 p. (No. 881) 1·00 55
1122 100 p. on 500 p. (No. 882) 1·00 55
1123 200 p. on 300 p. (No. 881) 2·10 1·10

217 Morning Glory

218 Ornate Arches

1973. Air. Multicoloured.
1124 2 p. 50 Type **217** 15 10
1125 5 p. Roses 30 10
1126 15 p. Tulips 20 10
1127 25 p. Lilies 35 10
1128 40 p. Carnations 45 15
1129 50 p. Iris 65 10
1130 70 p. Apples 1·00 15
1131 75 p. Grapes 1·10 25
1132 100 p. Peaches 1·40 35
1133 200 p. Pears 2·75 35
1134 300 p. Cherries 4·00 70
1135 500 p. Oranges 5·50 1·25

1973. Air. Lebanese Domestic Architecture.
1136 – 35 p. multicoloured 35 25
1137 **218** 50 p. multicoloured 45 40
1138 – 85 p. multicoloured 80 50
1139 – 100 p. multicoloured 95 70
DESIGNS: Nos. 1136 and 1138/39, Various Lebanese dwellings.

219 Girl with Lute

1973. Air. Ancient Costumes. Multicoloured.
1140 5 p. Woman with rose 25 10
1141 10 p. Shepherd 30 10
1142 20 p. Horseman 15 15
1143 25 p. Type **219** 20 20

220 Swimming

1973. Air. 5th Pan-Arab Schools' Games, Beirut. Multicoloured.
1144 5 p. Type **220** 20 10
1145 10 p. Running 20 10
1146 15 p. Gymnastics 30 10
1147 20 p. Volleyball 40 10
1148 25 p. Basketball 30 15
1149 50 p. Table-tennis 80 30
1150 75 p. Handball 65 50
1151 100 p. Football 1·25 75

221 Brasilia

1973. Air. 150th Anniv of Brazil's Independence. Multicoloured.
1153 5 p. Type **221** 15 10
1154 20 p. Salvador (Bahia) in 1823 15 20
1155 25 p. Map and Phoenician galley 15 20
1156 50 p. Emperor Pedro I and Emir Fakhreddine II 40 20

222 Marquetry

223 Cedar of Lebanon

1973. Air. Lebanese Handicrafts. Multicoloured.
1157 10 p. Type **222** 15 10
1158 20 p. Weaving 25 10
1159 35 p. Glass-blowing 45 10
1160 40 p. Pottery 60 15
1161 50 p. Metal-working 70 15
1162 70 p. Cutlery-making 70 30
1163 85 p. Lace-making 1·00 40
1164 100 p. Handicrafts Museum 1·60 45

1974.
1165 **223** 50 c. green, brn & orge 15 10

224 Camp Site and Emblems

1974. Air. 11th Arab Scout Jamboree, Smar-Jubeil, Lebanon. Multicoloured.
1166 2 p. 50 Type **224** 20 10
1167 5 p. Scout badge and map 20 10
1168 7 p. 50 Map of Arab countries 20 10
1169 10 p. Lord Baden-Powell and Baalbek 25 10
1170 15 p. Guide and camp 35 10
1171 20 p. Lebanese Guide and Scout badge 20 15
1172 25 p. Scouts around camp-fire 30 15
1173 30 p. Globe and Scout badge 35 20
1174 35 p. Flags of participating countries 45 30
1175 50 p. Scout chopping wood for old man 50 20

225 Mail Train

1974. Centenary of U.P.U. Multicoloured.
1176 5 p 50 Type **225** 10 10
1177 20 p. Container ship 40 10
1178 25 p. Congress building, Lausanne, and U.P.U. H.Q., Berne 40 10
1179 50 p. Airliner 50 45

226 Congress Building, Sofar

227 "Mountain Road" (O. Onsi)

1974. Air. 25th Anniv of Arab Postal Union. Multicoloured.
1180 5 p. Type **226** 10 10
1181 20 p. View of Sofar 30 10
1182 25 p. A.P.U. H.Q., Cairo 40 15
1183 50 p. Ministry of Posts, Beirut 80 45

1974. Air. Lebanese Paintings. Multicoloured.
1184 50 p. Type **227** 75 35
1185 50 p. "Clouds" (M. Farroukh) 75 35
1186 50 p. "Woman" (G. K. Gebran) 75 35
1187 50 p. "Embrace" (C. Gemayel) 75 35
1188 50 p. "Self-portrait" (H. Serour) 75 35
1189 50 p. "Portrait" (D. Corm) 75 35

228 Hunter killing Lion

1974. Air. Hermel Excavations. Multicoloured.
1190 5 p. Type **228** 15 10
1191 10 p. Astarte 20 10
1192 25 p. Dogs hunting boar 60 25
1193 35 p. Greco-Roman tomb 95 55

229 Book Year Emblem

1974. Air. International Book Year (1972).
1194 **229** 5 p. multicoloured 10 10
1195 10 p. multicoloured 15 10
1196 25 p. multicoloured 50 25
1197 35 p. multicoloured 75 50

230 Magnifying Glass

231 Georgina Rizk in Lebanese Costume

1974. Air. Stamp Day. Multicoloured.
1198 5 p. Type **230** 10 10
1199 10 p. Linked posthorns 10 10
1200 15 p. Stamp-printing 25 10
1201 20 p. "Stamp" in mount 35 15

1974. Air. Miss Universe 1971 (Georgina Rizk). Multicoloured.
1202 5 p. Type **231** 10 10
1203 20 p. Head-and-shoulders portrait 30 10
1204 25 p. Type **231** 35 15
1205 50 p. As 20 p. 40 45

232 Winds

234 Discus-throwing

233 U.N.I.C.E.F. Emblem and Sikorsky S-55 Helicopter

1974. Air. U.N. Conference on Human Environment, Stockholm, 1972. Multicoloured.
1207 5 p. Type **232** 10 10
1208 25 p. Mountains and plain 20 15
1209 30 p. Trees and flowers 20 15
1210 10 p. Sea 35 40

1974. Air. 25th Anniv of U.N.I.C.E.F. Multicoloured.
1212 20 p. Type **233** 45 10
1213 25 p. Emblem and child welfare clinic 35 15
1214 35 p. Emblem and kindergarten class 50 20
1215 70 p. Emblem and schoolgirls in laboratory 55 35

1974. Air. Olympic Games, Munich, 1972. Multicoloured.
1217 5 p. Type **234** 15 10
1218 10 p. Putting the shot 20 10
1219 15 p. Weight-lifting 25 10
1220 35 p. Running 45 20
1221 50 p. Wrestling 45 25
1222 85 p. Javelin-throwing 90 35

235 Symbols of Archaeology

1975. Air. "Beirut–University City". Multicoloured.
1224 20 p. Type **235** 25 30
1225 25 p. Science and medicine 30 25
1226 35 p. Justice and commerce 45 35
1227 70 p. Industry and commerce 75 35

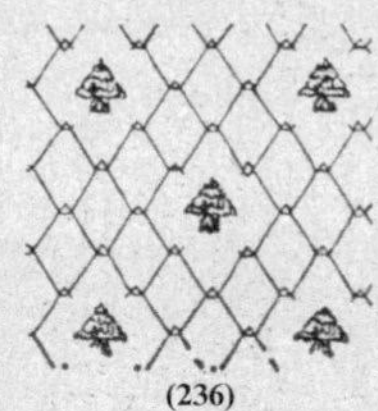

(236)

1978. Air. Various stamps optd with different patterns as T **236**. (a) Tourist Views. Nos. 1090, 1092/3.
1228 45 p. Radar scanner, Beirut Airport 40 10
1229 70 p. School of Sciences Building 80 20
1230 85 p. Oranges 80 25

(b) Flowers and Fruits. Nos. 1124/35.
1231 2 p. 50 Morning glory 10 10
1232 5 p. Type **217** 10 10
1233 15 p. Tulips 20 10
1234 25 p. Lilies 45 10
1235 40 p. Carnations 40 15
1236 50 p. Iris 55 15
1237 70 p. Apples 1·00 20
1238 75 p. Grapes 1·25 20
1239 100 p. Peaches 1·10 30
1240 200 p. Pears 2·25 1·25
1241 300 p. Cherries 3·25 2·25
1242 500 p. Oranges 6·75 3·25

(c) Lebanese Domestic Architecture. Nos. 1136/9.
1243 – 35 p. multicoloured 55 10
1244 **218** 50 p. multicoloured 75 15
1245 – 85 p. multicoloured 90 25
1246 – 100 p. multicoloured 1·10 30

(d) Ancient Costumes. Nos. 1140/3.
1247 5 p. Woman with rose 10 10
1248 10 p. Shepherd 15 10
1249 20 p. Horseman 35 10
1250 25 p. Type **219** 20 10

(e) Lebanese Handicrafts. Nos. 1157/8, 1160/4.
1251 10 p. Type **222** 15 10
1252 20 p. Weaving 30 10
1253 40 p. Pottery 40 15
1254 50 p. Metal-working 55 15
1255 70 p. Cutlery-making 90 20
1256 85 p. Lace-making 1·10 25
1257 100 p. Handicraft Museum 1·10 30

237 Mikhail Naimy (poet) and View of al-Chakroub Baskinta

1978. Air. Mikhail Naimy Festival Week. Mult.
1258 25 p. Mikhail Naimy and Sannine mountains 40 15
1259 50 p. Type **237** 60 30
1260 75 p. Mikhail Naimy (vert) 70 45

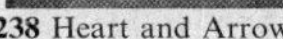
238 Heart and Arrow **239** Army Badge

1978. Air. World Health Day.
1261 **238** 50 p. blue, red and black 45 35

1980. Army Day. Multicoloured.
1262 25 p. Type **239** (postage) . . 40 15
1263 50 p. Statue of Emir Fakhr el Dine on horseback (air) . . 55 35
1264 75 p. Soldiers with flag (horiz) 85 40

240 13th-century European King

1980. Air. 50th Anniv (1974) of International Chess Federation. Multicoloured.
1265 50 p. Rook, knight and anniv emblem (horiz) . . . . . . 1·50 50
1266 75 p. Type **240** . . . . 2·00 90
1267 100 p. Rook and Lebanese Chess Federation emblem 2·00 1·00
1268 150 p. 18th-century French rook, king and knight . . . 2·75 1·50
1269 200 p. Painted faience rook, queen and bishop . . . . . 3·50 2·00

241 Congress, U.P.U. and Lebanon Postal Emblems

1981. Air. 18th U.P.U. Congress, Rio de Janeiro (1979).
1270 **241** 25 p. blue, gold and black 20 20
1271 50 p. pink, gold & black 45 35
1272 75 p. green, gold & black 70 30

242 Children on Raft **243** President Sarkis

1981. Air. International Year of the Child (1979).
1273 **242** 100 p. multicoloured . . 95 45

1981. 5th Anniv of Election of President Sarkis.
1274 **243** 125 p. multicoloured . . 1·00 40
1275 300 p. multicoloured . . 2·50 95
1276 500 p. multicoloured . . 4·00 1·25

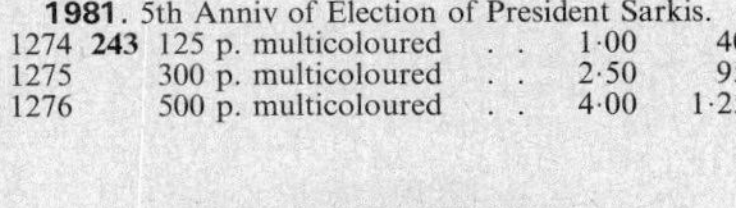

244 Society Emblem and Children

1981. Air. Cent. (1978) of Al-Makassed Islamic Welfare Society. Multicoloured.
1277 50 p. Type **244** 50 25
1278 75 p. Institute building . . . 75 35
1279 100 p. Al-Makassed (founder) 90 30

245 Stork carrying Food

1982. World Food Day (1981). Multicoloured.
1280 50 p. Type **245** 50 25
1281 75 p. Ear of wheat and globe 50 35
1282 100 p. Fruit, fish and grain 65 60

246 W.C.Y. Emblem **247** Phoenician Galley flying Scout Flag

1983. World Communications Year.
1283 **246** 300 p. multicoloured . . 1·60 95

1983. 75th Anniv of Boy Scout Movement. Multicoloured.
1284 200 p. Type **247** . . . . . . 1·40 65
1285 300 p. Scouts lowering flag and signalling by semaphore . 1·90 95
1286 500 p. Camp . . . . 3·25 1·40

248 "The Soul is Back"

1983. Birth Centenary of Gibran (poet and painter). Multicoloured.
1287 200 p. Type **248** . . . . . 1·50 65
1288 300 p. "The Family" . . . . 2·00 95
1288 500 p. "Gibran" . . . . . . 3·25 1·40
1289 1000 p. "The Prophet" . . . 6·75 3·25

249 Cedar of Lebanon **250** Iris

1984.
1292 **249** 5 p. multicoloured . . . 10 10

1984. Flowers. Multicoloured.
1293 10 p. Type **250** 15 10
1294 25 p. Periwinkle 30 15
1295 50 p. Barberry 40 30

251 Dove with Laurel over Buildings

1984. Lebanese Army. Multicoloured.
1296 75 p. Type **251** 50 40
1297 150 p. Cedar and soldier holding rifle . . . . 1·00 75
1298 300 p. Broken chain, hand holding laurel wreath and cedar . . . . 2·10 1·10

252 Temple Ruins, Fakra

1984. Multicoloured.
1299 100 p. Type **252** 85 45
1300 200 p. Temple ruins, Bziza . . 1·40 55
1301 500 p. Roman arches and relief, Tyre . . . . 3·25 1·40

253 President taking Oath

1988. Installation of President Amin Gemayel.
1302 **253** L£25 multicoloured . . . 50 40

254 Map of South America and Cedar of Lebanon

1989. 1st World Festival of Lebanese Youth in Uruguay.
1303 **254** L£5 multicoloured . . . 20 10

255 Satellite, Flags and Earth **256** Children

1988. "Arabsat" Telecommunications Satellite.
1304 **255** L£10 multicoloured . . . 25 15

1988. U.N.I.C.E.F. Child Survival Campaign.
1305 **256** L£15 multicoloured . . . 40 30

257 Arabic "75" and Scout Emblems **258** President, Map and Dove

1988. 75th Anniv (1987) of Arab Scouts Movement.
1306 **257** L£20 multicoloured . . . 60 15

1988. International Peace Year (1986).
1307 **158** L£50 multicoloured . . . 1·00 40

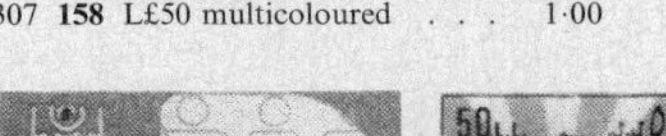

259 Red Cross and Figures **260** Cedar of Lebanon

1988. Red Cross.
1308 **259** L£10 + L£1 red, silver and black 25 25
1309 – L£20 + L£2 multicoloured 50 20
1310 – L£30 + L£3 silver, green and red 75 35
DESIGNS: L£20, Helmeted heads; L£30, Globe, flame, and dove holding map of Lebanon.

1989.
1314 **260** L£50 green and mauve . 10 10
1315 L£70 green and brown . . 35 10
1316 L£100 green and yellow 55 10
1317 L£200 green and blue . . 1·10 55
1318 L£500 dp green and green 2·75 1·40

POSTAGE DUE STAMPS

1924. Postage Due stamps of France surch **GRAND LIBAN** and value in "CENTIEMES" or "PIASTRES".
D26 **D 11** 50 c. on 10 c. brown . . 2·50 2·50
D27 1 p. on 20 c. olive . . . 2·50 2·50
D28 2 p. on 30 c. red . . . 2·50 2·50
D29 3 p. on 50 c. purple . . 2·50 2·50
D30 5 p. on 1 f. red on yellow 2·50 2·50

1924. Postage Due stamps of France Surch **GD Liban** and value in English and Arabic.
D58 **D 11** 50 c. on 10 c. brown . 2·75 2·50
D59 1 p. on 20 c. olive . . . 2·75 2·50
D60 2 p. on 30 c. red . . . 2·75 2·50
D61 3 p. on 50 c. purple . . 2·75 2·50
D62 5 p. on 1 f. red on yell 2·75 2·50

D 7 Nahr el-Kelb

1925.
D75 **D 7** 50 c. brown on yellow . 30 30
D76 – 1 p. black on red . . . 45 45
D77 – 2 p. black on blue . . . 70 70
D78 – 3 p. brown on orange 1·50 1·50
D79 – 5 p. black on green . . 2·00 2·00
DESIGNS—HORIZ: 1 p. Pine Forest, Beirut; 2 p. Pigeon Grotto, Beirut; 3 p. Beaufort Castle; 5 p. Baalbeck.

1927. Optd **Republique Libanaise** and bars.
D122 **D 7** 50 c. brown on yellow 30 30
D123 – 1 p. black on red . . . 50 50
D124 – 2 p. black on blue . . 75 75
D125 – 3 p. brown on orange 2·00 2·00
D126 – 5 p. black on green . . 2·75 2·75

1928. Nos. D122/6 optd with T **10**.
D145 **D 7** 50 c. brown on yellow 70 70
D146 – 1 p. black on red . . . 70 70
D147 – 2 p. black on blue . . 1·40 1·40
D148 – 3 p. brown on orange 3·00 2·75
D149 – 5 p. black on green . . 3·25 3·00

D 18

D 19 Bas-relief from Sarcophagus of King Ahiram at Byblos

D 32

1931.
D191 **D 18** 50 c. black on red . . 25 25
D192 – 1 p. black on blue . . 50 50
D193 – 2 p. black on yellow . 60 60
D194 – 3 p. black on green . 60 60
D195 **D 32** 5 p. black on orange 3·75 3·75
D196 **D 19** 8 p. black on red . . 2·25 2·25
D252 **D 32** 10 p. green . . . . . 3·50 3·50
D197 – 15 p. black . . . . . 2·00 2·00
DESIGNS: 1 p. Bas-relief of Phoenician galley; 2 p. Arabesque; 3 p. Garland; 15 p. Statuettes.

D 43 National Museum

1945.
D298 **D 43** 2 p. black on lemon . 2·50 2·40
D299 5 p. blue on red . . . 3·00 3·00
D300 25 p. blue on green . 4·00 4·00
D301 50 p. purple on blue . 4·50 4·50

D 53

1947.
D352 **D 53** 5 p. black on green . 2·75 70
D353 25 p. black on yellow 24·00 1·60
D354 50 p. black on blue . 14·50 3·25

D 59 Monument at Hermel

1948.

D379	D 59	2 p. black on yellow	1·60	45
D380		3 p. black on red	4·00	1·50
D381		10 p. black on blue	10·00	3·00

D 67

1950.

D416	D 67	1 p. red	70	10
D417		5 p. blue	1·60	50
D418		10 p. green	3·50	90

D 78

1952.

D464	D 78	1 p. mauve	20	10
D465		2 p. violet	15	10
D466		3 p. green	50	20
D467		5 p. blue	40	20
D468		10 p. brown	90	40
D469		25 p. black	6·50	85

D 81

D 93

1953.

D481	D 81	1 p. red	15	10
D482		2 p. green	15	10
D483		3 p. orange	20	10
D484		5 p. purple	30	15
D485		10 p. brown	40	20
D486		15 p. blue	1·00	50

1955.

D550	D 93	1 p. brown	10	10
D551		2 p. green	10	10
D552		3 p. turquoise	10	10
D553		5 p. red	15	10
D554		10 p. myrtle	25	10
D555		15 p. blue	30	15
D556		25 p. purple	45	35

D 178

D 184 Emir Kakhreddine II

1967.

D967	D 178	1 p. green	10	20
D968		5 p. mauve	15	20
D969		15 p. blue	15	15

1968.

D1004	D 184	1 p. slate and grey	10	20
D1005		2 p. turquoise & green	10	20
D1006		3 p. orange & yellow	10	20
D1007		5 p. purple and red	15	15
D1008		10 p. olive & yellow	25	5
D1009		15 p. blue and violet	15	15
D1010		25 p. blue & lt blue	40	40

POSTAL TAX STAMPS

These were issued between 1946 and 1962 for compulsory use on inland mail (and sometimes on mail to Arab countries) to provide funds for various purposes.

(T 41)

(T 42)

1946. Lebanese Army. Fiscal stamp as Type T **41** surch with Type T **42**.

T289	T **41**	5 p. on 30 c. brown	17·00	1·25

(T 50) (T 56)

1947. Aid to War in Palestine. Surch as Type T **42** but with top lines as Type T **50**.

T338	T **41**	5 p. on 25 c. green	12·00	1·50
T339		5 p. on 30 c. brown	17·00	1·50
T340		5 p. on 60 c. blue	25·00	1·50
T341		5 p. on 3 p. pink	12·00	1·50
T343		5 p. on 10 p. red	55·00	2·75
T342		5 p. on 15 p. blue	12·00	1·50

The top line of the overprint on No. T 343 differs from Type T **50**, and No. T 341 comes either as Type T **50** or with a similar inscription.

1947. Aid to War in Palestine. As No. T 341 but with figure "5" at left instead of "0" and without inscr between figures.

T345	T **41**	5 p. on 3 p. pink	£225	16·00

1948. Lebanese Army. No. T 289 optd with T **56**.

T363	T **41**	5 p. on 30 c. brown	17·00	1·75

T 95 Family and Ruined House

1956. Earthquake Victims.

T559	T **95**	2 p. 50 brown	2·25	10

T 99 Rebuilding

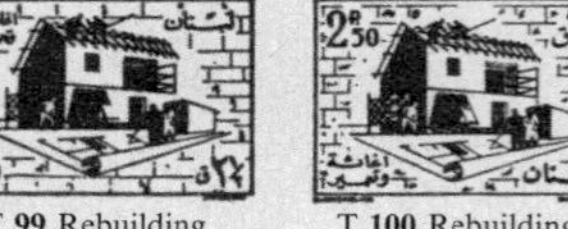
T 100 Rebuilding

1957. Earthquake Victims.

T601	T **99**	2 p. 50 brown	2·50	15
T602		2 p. 50 green	1·00	15
T603	T **100**	2 p. 50 brown	2·00	10

T 132 Rebuilding

T 133 Rebuilding

1961. Earthquake Victims.

T729	T **132**	2 p. 50 brown	1·25	10
T730	T **133**	2 p. 50 blue	1·00	10

LIBERIA Pt. 13

A republic on the W. coast of Africa, founded as a home for freed slaves.

100 cents = 1 dollar

1

2

1860.

7	**1**	6 c. red	23·00	32·00
2		12 c. blue	22·00	27·00
3		24 c. green	22·00	27·00

1880.

13	**1**	1 c. blue	3·25	4·75
14		2 c. red	2·25	3·25
15		6 c. mauve	4·25	5·50
16		12 c. yellow	4·25	6·00
17		24 c. red	5·00	6·75

1881.

18	**2**	3 c. black	4·25	3·25

3

4

5 "Alligator" (first settlers' ship)

1882.

47	**3**	8 c. blue	2·50	2·50
20		16 c. red	3·75	3·00

1886.

49	**3**	1 c. red	60	65
50		2 c. green	60	75
23		3 c. mauve	70	75
52		4 c. brown	80	75
27		6 c. grey	1·75	1·75
54	**4**	8 c. grey	2·75	2·75
55		16 c. yellow	3·75	3·75
29	**5**	32 c. blue	12·00	12·00

7 Liberian Star

8 African Elephant

9 Oil Palm

10 Pres. H. R. W. Johnson

11 Vai Woman

12 Seal

13 Star

15 Hippopotamus

17 President Johnson

1892.

75	**7**	1 c. red	30	30
76		2 c. blue	30	30
77	**8**	4 c. black and green	2·10	1·60
78	**9**	6 c. green	85	75
79	**10**	8 c. black and brown	60	75
80	**11**	12 c. red	60	85
81	**12**	16 c. lilac	2·10	1·60
82	**13**	24 c. green on yellow	1·50	1·25
83	**12**	32 c. blue	3·00	3·25
84	**15**	$1 black and blue	8·75	7·75
85	**13**	$2 brown on buff	4·25	3·75
86	**17**	$5 black and red	5·50	5·50

1893. Surch **5 5 Five Cents**.

103	**9**	5 c. on 6 c. green	5·50	5·50

24

1894. Imperf or roul.

117	**24**	5 c. black and red	3·25	3·25

35

36

1897.

144	**9**	1 c. purple	45	35
145		1 c. green	85	50
146	**15**	2 c. black and bistre	1·50	1·10
147		2 c. black and red	1·60	1·40
148	**8**	5 c. black and lake	1·60	1·10
149		5 c. black and blue	3·00	2·00
150	**10**	10 c. blue and yellow	1·00	50
151	**11**	15 c. black	85	65
152	**12**	20 c. red	1·90	1·60
153	**13**	25 c. green	1·50	1·50
154	**12**	30 c. blue	4·25	4·00
155	**35**	50 c. black and brown	2·75	2·75

The prices in the "used" column of sets marked with a dagger (†) against the date of issue are for stamps "cancelled to order" from remainder stocks. Postally used specimens are worth appreciably more.

†1897.

156	**36**	3 c. red and green	25	10

1901. Official stamps of 1892–98 optd **ORDINARY**

175	**9**	1 c. purple (No. O157)	50·00	35·00
176		1 c. green (O158)	18·00	18·00
177	**7**	2 c. blue (O120)	50·00	50·00
178	**15**	2 c. black and brn (O159)	£100	45·00
179		2 c. black & red (O160)	25·00	30·00
180	**24**	5 c. green and lilac (O130)	£130	£130
181	**8**	5 c. black and red (O161)	£100	£100
182		5 c. black and bl (O162)	20·00	25·00
183	**10**	8 c. black and brn (O122)	75·00	
184		10 c. blue and yell (O163)	25·00	30·00
169	**11**	12 c. red (O92)	£100	£100
185		15 c. black (O164)	18·00	25·00
170	**12**	16 c. lilac (O93)		
186		16 c. lilac (O124)	£140	£140
187		20 c. red (O165)	22·00	28·00
171	**13**	24 c. green and yell (O94)	£225	£250
188		24 c. green on yell (O125)	25·00	30·00
189		25 c. green (O166)	28·00	38·00
190	**12**	30 c. blue (O167)	20·00	27·00
191	**13**	32 c. blue (O126)	£150	£150
192	**35**	50 c. black & brn (O168)	25·00	30·00
172	**15**	$1 black and bl (O96)	£1000	£1000
193		$1 black and bl (O127)	£170	£250
194	**13**	$2 brown on buff (O128)	£1300	£1300
174	**17**	$5 black and red (O98)	£2500	£2500
196		$5 black and red (O129)	£1400	£1400

1902. Surch **75 c.** and bar.

206	**15**	75 c. on $1 black & blue	7·50	10·00

40 Liberty

1903.

209	**40**	3 c. black	25	15

1903. Surch in words.

216	**12**	10 c. on 16 c. lilac	2·50	4·50
217	**13**	15 c. on 24 c. green on yell	2·50	5·00
218	**12**	20 c. on 32 c. blue	3·75	4·75

1904. Surch

219	**9**	1 c. on 5 c. on 6 c. green (No. 103)	60	80
220	**8**	2 c. on 4 c. black and green (No. O89)	3·75	4·50
221	**12**	2 c. on 30 c. blue (No. 154)	5·25	7·75

50 African Elephant

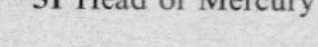
51 Head of Mercury

52 Mandingo Tribesmen

53 Pres. Barclay and Executive Mansion

†1906.

224 **50** 1 c. black and green . . . 1·00 50
225 **51** 2 c. black and red 15 15
226 – 5 c. black and blue . . . . 2·00 75
227 – 10 c. black and red . . . . 6·50 90
228 – 15 c. green and violet . . . 7·00 2·75
229 – 20 c. black & orange . . . 7·00 2·10
230 – 25 c. grey and blue 75 20
231 – 30 c. violet 70 15
232 – 50 c. black and green . . . 75 20
233 – 75 c. black & brown . . . 7·00 2·10
234 – $1 black and pink . . . . 1·90 25
235 **52** $2 black and green . . . . 3·00 35
236 **53** $5 grey and red . . . . . . 5·75 50

DESIGNS—As Type **50**: 5 c. Chimpanzee; 15 c. Agama lizard; 75 c. Pygmy hippopotamus. As Type **51**: 10 c. Great blue turaco; 20 c. Great egret; 25 c. Head of Liberty on coin; 30 c. Figures "30"; 50 c. Liberian flag. As Type **53**: $1 Head of Liberty.

55 Coffee Plantation

56 Gunboat "Lark"

57 Commerce

†1909. The 10 c. is perf or roul.

250 **55** 1 c. black and green . . . 25 15
251 – 2 c. black and red 25 15
252 **56** 5 c. black and blue . . . . 1·75 35
254 **57** 10 c. black and purple . . 25 20
255 – 15 c. black and blue . . . 1·25 35
256 – 20 c. green and red . . . . 2·50 50
257 – 25 c. black and brown . . 1·75 35
258 – 30 c. brown . . . . 1·75 35
259 – 50 c. black and green . . . 2·75 60
260 – 75 c. black and brown . . 2·25 45

DESIGNS—As Type **55**: 2 c. Pres. Barclay; 15 c. Vai woman spinning cotton; 20 c. Pepper plant; 25 c. Village hut; 30 c. Pres. Barclay (in picture frame). As Type **56**: 50 c. Canoeing; 75 c. Village (design shaped like a book).

1909. No. 227 surch **Inland 3 Cents.**

261 – 3 c. on 10 c. black & red . . 3·50 5·00

†1910. Surcharged **3 CENTS INLAND POSTAGE.** Perf or rouletted.

274 **57** 3 c. on 10 c. black & purple 35 25

1913. Various types surch with new value and bars or ornaments.

322 – 1 c. on 2 c. black and red (No. 251) . . . . 2·25 3·00
290 **57** + 2 c. on 3 c. on 10 c. blk and purple . . . . 60 1·25
323 **56** 2 c. on 5 c. black & blue . 2·25 3·50
292 – 2 c. on 15 c. black and blue (No. 255) . . . . 1·25 1·25
279 – 2 c. on 25 c. grey & blue (A) (No. 230) . . . . 7·50 5·00
281 – 2 c. on 25 c. black and brown (A) (No. 257) . . . . . 7·50 5·00
295 – 2 c. on 25 c. black and brown (B) (No. 257) . . . . . . 4·50 4·50
296 – 5 c. on 20 c. green & red (No. 256) . . . . 85 3·25
280 – 5 c. on 30 c. violet (C) (No. 231) . . . . 7·50 5·00
282 – 5 c. on 30 c. brown (C) (No. 258) . . . . 7·50 5·00
297 – 5 c. on 30 c. brown (D) (No. 258) . . . . 3·75 3·75
278 **36** 8 c. on 3 c. red and green 60 30
283 – 10 c. on 50 c. black and green (E) (No. 259) . . . . . . 9·25 9·25
301 – 10 c. on 50 c. black and green (F) (No. 259) . . . . . . 8·25 8·25
303 – 20 c. on 75 c. black and brown (No. 260) . . . . 3·25 6·25
304 **53** 25 c. on $1 black & pink . 23·00 23·00
305 – 50 c. on $2 black and green (No. 235) . . . . 7·50 7·50
308 – $1 on $5 grey and red (No. 236) . . . . 28·00 28·00

Descriptions of surcharges. (A) **1914 2 CENTS.** (B) **2** over ornaments. (C) **1914 5 CENTS.** (D) **5** over ornaments. (E) **1914 10 CENTS.** (F) **10** and ornaments.

INDEX

Countries can be quickly located by referring to the index at the end of this volume.

64 House on Providence Is
65 Monrovia Harbour, Providence Is

†1915.

288 **64** 2 c. red 20 10
289 **65** 3 c. violet 20 10

1916. Liberian Frontier Force. Surch **LFF 1 C.**

332 **9** 1 c. on 1 c. green . . . . 75·00 75·00
333 **50** 1 c. on 1 c. black and grn £275 £275
334 **55** 1 c. on 1 c. black and grn 1·75 3·75
335 – 1 c. on 2 c. black and red (No. 251) . . . . 1·75 3·75

1916. Surch **1916** over new value.

339 **1** 3 c. on 6 c. mauve . . . . 23·00 23·00
340 5 c. on 12 c. yellow . . . . 4·00 5·00
341 10 c. on 24 c. red . . . . . 4·00 4·50

1917. Surch **1917** and value in words.

342 **13** 4 c. on 25 c. green . . . . 6·00 7·50
343 **52** 5 c. on 30 c. violet (No. 231) 30·00 38·00

1918. Surch **3 CENTS.**

345 **57** 3 c. on 10 c. black & purple 2·40 5·00

91 Bongo

93

92 African Palm Civet

94 Traveller's Tree

†1918.

349 **91** 1 c. black and green . . . 65 25
350 **92** 2 c. black and red 65 25
351 – 5 c. black and blue 15 10
352 **93** 10 c. green 20 10
353 – 15 c. green and black . . . 2·50 20
354 – 20 c. black and red 50 15
355 **94** 25 c. green . . . . 3·25 25
356 – 30 c. black and mauve . . 11·00 70
357 – 50 c. black and blue . . . 11·50 1·10
358 – 75 c. black and olive . . . 1·00 25
359 – $1 blue and brown . . . . 4·00 25
360 – $2 black and violet . . . . 6·00 30
361 – $5 brown . . . . 6·00 40

DESIGNS—As Type **91**: 5 c. Coat of Arms; 15 c. Oil palm; 20 c. Statue of Mercury; 75 c. Heads of Mandingos; $5 "Liberia" seated. As Type **92**: 50 c. Lungfish (or Mudskipper); $1 Coast view; $2 Liberia College. As Type **93**: 30 c. Palm-nut Vulture.

1918. Geneva Red Cross Fund. Surch **TWO CENTS** and red cross.

375 **91** 1 c. + 2 c. black and green 75 75
376 **92** 2 c. + 2 c. black and red 75 75
377 – 5 c. + 2 c. black and blue 25 1·00
378 **93** 10 c. + 2 c. green . . . . 50 1·00
379 – 15 c. + 2 c. green & black 2·40 1·75
380 – 20 c. + 2 c. black and red 1·50 3·00
381 **94** 25 c. + 2 c. green . . . . 3·25 3·25
382 – 30 c. + 2 c. black & mve 8·75 4·75
383 – 50 c. + 2 c. black & blue 7·00 5·75
384 – 75 c. + 2 c. black & olive 2·10 5·25
385 – $1 + 2 c. blue and brown 4·25 7·00
386 – $2 + 2 c. black and violet 5·75 11·50
387 – $5 + 2 c. brown . . . . . 14·00 23·00

1920. Surch **1920** and value and two bars.

393 **91** 3 c. on 1 c. black & grn 1·50 2·75
394 **92** 4 c. on 2 c. black & red 1·50 3·00
395 **R 42** 5 c. on 10 c. black & bl 3·75 4·25
396 5 c. on 10 c. black & red 3·75 4·25
397 5 c. on 10 c. black & grn 3·75 4·25
398 5 c. on 10 c. black & vio 3·75 4·25
399 5 c. on 10 c. black & red 3·75 4·25

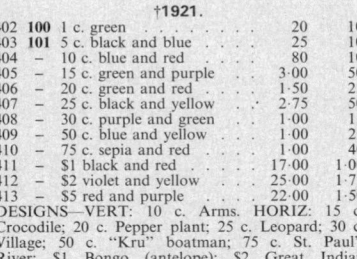

100 Cape Mesurado

101 Pres. D. E. Howard

†1921.

402 **100** 1 c. green 20 10
403 **101** 5 c. black and blue 25 10
404 – 10 c. blue and red 80 10
405 – 15 c. green and purple . . 3·00 50
406 – 20 c. green and red . . . . 1·50 25
407 – 25 c. black and yellow . . 2·75 50
408 – 30 c. purple and green . . 1·00 15
409 – 50 c. blue and yellow . . . 1·00 25
410 – 75 c. sepia and red . . . . 1·00 40
411 – $1 black and red . . . . . 17·00 1·00
412 – $2 violet and yellow . . . 25·00 1·75
413 – $5 red and purple . . . . 22·00 1·50

DESIGNS—VERT: 10 c. Arms. HORIZ: 15 c. Crocodile; 20 c. Pepper plant; 25 c. Leopard; 30 c. Village; 50 c. "Kru" boatman; 75 c. St. Paul's River; $1 Bongo (antelope); $2 Great Indian hornbill; $5 African elephant.

†1921. Optd **1921.**

414 **100** 1 c. green . . . . 2·75 50
415 **64** 2 c. red . . . . 2·75 50
416 **65** 3 c. violet . . . . 3·50 50
417 **101** 5 c. black and blue . . . . 2·25 50
418 – 10 c. blue and red . . . . 5·25 50
419 – 15 c. green and purple . . 7·00 1·00
420 – 20 c. green and red . . . . 3·25 60
421 – 25 c. black and yellow . . 7·00 1·00
422 – 30 c. purple and green . . 3·75 50
423 – 50 c. blue and yellow . . . 3·00 70
424 – 75 c. sepia and red . . . . 3·00 50
425 – $1 black and red . . . . . 18·00 1·50
426 – $2 violet and yellow . . . 28·00 2·50
427 – $5 red and purple . . . . 23·00 3·25

107 Arrival of First Settlers in "Alligator"

†1923. Centennial issue.

466 **107** 1 c. black and blue . . . . 16·00 70
467 2 c. brown and red . . . . 16·00 70
468 5 c. blue and olive . . . . 12·50 70
469 10 c. mauve and green . . 4·75 70
470 $1 brown and red . . . . 7·00 70

108 J. J. Roberts Memorial

109 House of Representatives, Monrovia

116 Palm Trees

117 Map of Africa

118 President King

†1923.

471 **108** 1 c. green . . . . 3·25 10
472 **109** 2 c. brown and red . . . . 3·25 10
473 – 3 c. black and lilac 25 10
474 – 5 c. black and blue . . . . 28·00 15
475 – 10 c. brown and grey . . . 25 10
476 – 15 c. blue and bistre . . . 17·00 50
477 – 20 c. mauve and green . . 2·00 50
478 – 25 c. brown and red . . . 38·00 50
479 – 30 c. mauve and brown . . 50 20
480 – 50 c. orange and purple . . 1·00 40
481 – 75 c. blue and grey . . . . 1·50 65
482 **110** $1 violet and red . . . . . 3·25 1·00
483 – $2 blue and orange . . . . 3·75 65
484 – $5 brown and green . . . 10·00 65

DESIGNS—As Type **108**: 3 c. Star; 5, 10 c. Pres. King; 50 c. Pineapple. As Type **109**: 15 c. Hippopotamus; 20 c. Kob (antelope); 25 c. African buffalo; 30 c. Natives making palm oil; 75 c. Carrying elephant tusk. As Type **110**: $2 Stockton lagoon; $5 Styles of huts.

1926. Surch **Two Cents** and thick bar or wavy lines or ornamental scroll.

504 **91** 2 c. on 1 c. black & green 2·75 4·25

1928.

511 **116** 1 c. green 15 15
512 2 c. violet 20 20
513 3 c. brown 35 20
514 **117** 5 c. blue 55 35
515 **118** 10 c. grey 70 35
516 **117** 15 c. purple . . . . 3·25 1·40
517 $1 brown . . . . 28·00 13·50

1936. Nos. O518 and 512/13 surch **AIR MAIL SIX CENTS.**

525 **116** 6 c. on 1 c. green . . . . £140 85·00
526 6 c. on 2 c. violet . . . . £140 85·00
527 6 c. on 3 c. brown . . . . £140 85·00

122 Ford "Tin Goose"

1936. Air. 1st Air Mail Service of 28th February.

530 **122** 1 c. black and green . . . 25 10
531 2 c. black and red 25 10
532 3 c. black and violet . . . 40 10
533 4 c. black and orange . . 40 15
534 5 c. black and blue . . . 45 15
535 6 c. black and green . . . 45 20

1936. Nos. 350/61 surch **1936** and new values in figures.

536 1 c. on 2 c. black and red . . 30 50
537 3 c. on 5 c. black and blue . . 30 45
538 4 c. on 10 c. green 25 40
539 6 c. on 15 c. green and black 30 55
540 8 c. on 20 c. black and red . . 20 60
541 12 c. on 30 c. black and mauve 2·75 2·25
542 14 c. on 50 c. black and blue 1·50 1·75
543 16 c. on 75 c. black and olive 50 1·00
544 18 c. on $1 blue and brown . 60 1·40
545 22 c. on $2 black and violet . 60 1·50
546 24 c. on $5 brown . . . . . . 75 1·60

1936. Nos. O363/74 optd with Star and **1936** or surch also in figures and words.

547 1 c. on 2 c. black and red . . 30 50
548 3 c. on 5 c. black and blue . . 25 50
549 4 c. on 10 c. green 20 45
550 6 c. on 15 c. green & brown . 25 60
551 8 c. on 20 c. black and lilac . 30 60
552 12 c. on 30 c. black & violet 2·50 2·00
553 14 c. on 50 c. black & brown 1·00 1·50
554 16 c. on 75 c. black & brown 45 90
555 18 c. on $1 blue and olive . . 50 1·00
556 22 c. on $2 black and olive . . 60 1·25
557 24 c. on $5 green . . . . . . 75 1·50
558 25 c. green and brown . . . . 1·00 2·00

126 Hippopotamus

1937.

559 – 1 c. black and green . . . 1·00 35
560 – 2 c. black and red . . . . 1·00 30
561 – 3 c. black and purple . . 1·00 35
562 **126** 4 c. black and orange . . 1·50 60
563 – 5 c. black and blue . . . 2·25 50
564 – 6 c. black and green . . . 45 20

DESIGNS: 1 c. Black and white casqued hornbill; 2 c. Bushbuck; 3 c. African buffalo; 5 c. Western reef heron; 6 c. Pres. Barclay.

127 Tawny Eagle in Flight

128 Three-engine Flying Boat

129 Little Egrets

1938. Air.

565 **127** 1 c. green 40 10
566 **128** 2 c. red 15 10
567 – 3 c. olive 30 10
568 **129** 4 c. orange 35 10
569 – 5 c. green 50 10
570 **128** 10 c. violet 25 10
571 – 20 c. mauve 30 15
572 – 30 c. grey 1·10 15
573 **127** 50 c. brown 2·25 25
574 – $1 blue 1·40 25

DESIGNS—VERT: 20 c., $1 Sikorsky S-43 amphibian. HORIZ: 3, 30 c. Lesser black-backed gull in flight.

130 Immigrant Ships nearing Liberian Coast

1940. Centenary of Founding of Liberian Commonwealth.

575 **130** 3 c. blue 50 15
576 – 5 c. brown 20 10
577 – 10 c. green 25 15

DESIGNS: 5 c. Seal of Liberia and Flags of original Settlements; 10 c. Thos. Buchanan's house and portrait.

1941. Centenary of First Postage Stamps. Nos. 575/7 optd **POSTAGE STAMP CENTENNIAL 1840-1940** and portrait of Rowland Hill.

578 **130** 3 c. blue (postage) 1·75 1·75
579 – 5 c. brown 1·75 1·75
580 – 10 c. green 1·75 1·75
581 **130** 3 c. blue (air) 1·40 1·40
582 – 5 c. brown 1·40 1·40
583 – 10 c. green 1·40 1·40

Nos. 581/3 are additionally optd with airplane and **AIR MAIL**.

1941. Red Cross Fund. Nos. 575/7 surch **RED CROSS** plus Red Cross and **TWO CENTS**.

584 **130** + 2 c. on 3 c. blue (post) 1·40 1·40
585 – + 2 c. on 5 c. brown 1·40 1·40
586 – + 2 c. on 10 c. green 1·40 1·40
587 **130** + 2 c. on 3 c. blue (air) 1·40 1·40
588 – + 2 c. on 5 c. brown 1·40 1·40
589 – + 2 c. on 10 c. green 1·40 1·40

Nos. 587/9 are additionally optd with airplane and **AIR MAIL**.

1941. Air. 1st Flight to U.S.A. Nos. 565/74 surch **First Flight LIBERIA-U.S. 1941, 50 c.** and bar.

594 **127** 50 c. on 1 c. £2000 £250
595 **128** 50 c. on 2 c. £150 75·00
596 – 50 c. on 3 c. £225 75·00
597 **129** 50 c. on 4 c. 70·00 35·00
598 50 c. on 5 c. 70·00 35·00
599 **128** 50 c. on 10 c. 48·00 38·00
600 – 50 c. on 20 c. £1500 £150
601 – 50 c. on 30 c. 80·00 30·00
602 **127** 50 c. brown 80·00 35·00
603 – $1 blue 48·00 30·00

The first flight was cancelled and covers were sent by ordinary mail. The flight took place in 1942 and the stamps were reissued but with the date obliterated.

1942. As Nos. 594/601 but with date "1941" obliterated by two bars.

604 **127** 50 c. on 1 c. green 8·50 8·50
605 **128** 50 c. on 2 c. red 6·00 6·75
606 – 50 c. on 3 c. green 7·50 7·50
607 **129** 50 c. on 4 c. orange 7·00 7·00
608 50 c. on 5 c. green 7·00 7·00
609 **128** 50 c. on 10 c. violet 5·25 6·25
610 – 50 c. on 20 c. mauve 5·25 6·25
611 – 50 c. on 30 c. grey 7·50 7·50
612 **127** 50 c. brown 7·50 7·50
613 – $1 blue 6·25 7·50

138 Miami–Monrovia Air Route

139 Bushbuck

1942. Air.

614 **138** 10 c. red 20 10
615 – 12 c. blue 30 10
616 – 24 c. green 35 10
617 **138** 30 c. green 35 10
618 35 c. lilac 40 15
619 50 c. purple 50 15
620 70 c. olive 55 30
621 $1.40 red 75 50

DESIGN: 12, 24 c. Boeing 247 airliner over Liberian Agricultural and Industrial Fair.

1942.

622 – 1 c. brown and violet 80 20
623 – 2 c. brown and blue 80 20
624 – 3 c. brown and green 1·25 45
625 **139** 4 c. red and black 2·00 70
626 – 5 c. brown and olive 1·75 70
627 – 10 c. black and red 3·75 1·10

DESIGNS—HORIZ: 1 c. Royal antelope; 2 c. Water chevrotain; 3 c. Jentink's duiker; 5 c. Banded duiker. VERT: 10 c. Diana monkey.

1944. Stamps of 1928 and 1937 surch.

628 **116** 1 c. on 2 c. violet 7·50 7·50
634 **126** 1 c. on 4 c. black & orge 48·00 40·00
629 **118** 1 c. on 10 c. grey 9·25 5·50
635 – 2 c. on 3 c. black and purple (No. 561) 48·00 40·00
630 **117** 2 c. on 5 c. blue 3·25 3·25
632 **116** 3 c. on 2 c. violet 27·00 30·00
636 – 4 c. on 5 c. black and blue (No. 563) 28·00 28·00
633 **118** 4 c. on 10 c. grey 3·25 3·25
637 – 5 c. on 1 c. black and green (No. 559) 85·00 55·00
638 – 6 c. on 2 c. black and red (No. 560) 12·50 16·00
639 – 10 c. on 6 c. black and green (No. 564) 14·00 16·00

1944. Air stamps of 1936 and 1938 surch.

643 **128** 10 c. on 2 c. red 27·00 30·00
644 **129** 10 c. on 5 c. green 11·50 11·50
640 **122** 30 c. on 1 c. black & grn 70·00 50·00
645 30 c. on 3 c. olive (No. 567) £100 85·00
646 **129** 30 c. on 4 c. orange 11·50 11·50
641 **122** 50 c. on 3 c. black & vio 20·00 23·00
642 70 c. on 2 c. black & red 50·00 50·00
647 – $1 on 3 c. olive (No. 567) 42·00 42·00
648 **127** $1 on 50 c. brown 27·00 22·00

150 Pres. Roosevelt reviewing Troops

1945. Pres. Roosevelt Memorial.

650 **150** 3 c. black & pur (postage) 15 15
651 5 c. black and blue 30 25
652 70 c. black & brown (air) 1·00 1·00

151 Opening Monrovia Harbour Project

1946. Opening of Monrovia Harbour Project by Pres. Tubman.

653 **151** 5 c. blue (postage) 25 15
654 24 c. green (air) 2·40 2·75

1947. As T **151**, but without inscr at top.

655 5 c. violet (postage) 15 15
656 25 c. red (air) 1·00 1·75

152 1st Postage Stamps of United States and Liberia

1947. U.S. Postage Stamps Centenary and 87th Anniv of Liberian Postal Issues.

657 **152** 5 c. red (postage) 20 15
658 12 c. green (air) 30 15
659 22 c. violet 40 20
660 50 c. blue 50 25

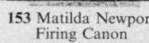

153 Matilda Newport Firing Canon

154 Liberty

1947. 125th Anniv of Defence of Monrovia.

662 **153** 1 c. black & green (post) 15 10
663 3 c. black and violet 20 10
664 5 c. black and blue 20 15
665 10 c. black and yellow 1·25 45
666 25 c. black and red (air) 95 35

1947. Centenary of National Independence.

667 – 1 c. green (postage) 20 10
668 **154** 2 c. purple 20 10
669 – 3 c. purple 30 15
670 – 5 c. blue 40 15
671 – 12 c. orange (air) 60 20
672 – 25 c. red 75 35
673 – 50 c. brown 90 70

DESIGNS—VERT: 1 c. Liberian star; 3 c. Arms of Liberia; 4 c. Map of Liberia; 12 c. J. J. Roberts Monument; 25 c. Liberian Flag; 50 c. (26½ × 33 mm) Centenary Monument.

156 Douglas DC-3

1948. Air. First Liberian International Airways Flight (Monrovia-Dakar).

674 **156** 25 c. red 1·50 1·00
675 50 c. blue 2·40 1·50

157 Joseph J. Roberts

1949. Liberian Presidents. Portrait and name in black.

(a) Postage.

676 – 1 c. green (Roberts) 1·60 3·25
677 **157** 1 c. green 15 10
678 – 1 c. pink (Roberts) 25 15
679 – 2 c. pink (Benson) 35 35
680 – 2 c. yellow (Benson) 35 15
681 – 3 c. mauve (Warner) 35 35
682 – 4 c. olive (Payne) 35 55
683 – 5 c. blue (Mansion) 45 55
684 – 6 c. orange (Roye) 55 95
685 – 7 c. green (Gardner and Russell) 70 1·25
686 – 8 c. red (Johnson) 70 1·40
687 – 9 c. purple (Cheeseman) 1·10 1·10
688 – 10 c. yellow (Coleman) 75 35
689 – 10 c. grey (Coleman) 40 20
690 – 15 c. orange (Gibson) 85 40
691 – 15 c. blue (Gibson) 25 15
692 – 20 c. grey (A. Barclay) 1·25 70
693 – 20 c. red (A. Barclay) 50 45
694 – 25 c. red (Howard) 1·60 1·10
695 – 25 c. blue (Howard) 50 45
696 – 50 c. turquoise (King) 3·25 95
697 – 50 c. purple (King) 70 60
698 – $1 mauve (E. Barclay) 5·75 70
699 – $1 brown (E. Barclay) 4·00 55

(b) Air.

700 – 25 c. blue (Tubman) 1·00 55
701 – 25 c. green (Tubman) 75 35

Nos. 676 and 678 have a different portrait of Roberts wearing a moustache.

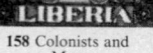

158 Colonists and Map

159 Hand holding Book

1949. Multicoloured.

702 1 c. Settlers approaching village (postage) 50 75
703 2 c. Rubber tapping and planting 50 75
704 3 c. Landing of first colonists in 1822 1·00 1·50
705 5 c. Jehudi Ashmun and Matilda Newport defending stockade 50 75
706 25 c. Type **158** (air) 1·25 1·50
707 50 c. Africans and coat of arms 2·75 3·25

1950. National Literacy Campaign.

708 **159** 5 c. blue (postage) 20 15
709 – 25 c. red (air) 70 70

DESIGN—VERT: 25 c. Open book and rising sun.

160 U.P.U. Monument, Berne

1950. 75th Anniv of U.P.U.

711 **160** 5 c. black and grn (post) 20 15
712 – 10 c. black and mauve 30 30
713 – 25 c. purple & orge (air) 3·25 3·25

DESIGNS—HORIZ: 10 c. Standehaus, Berne. VERT: 25 c. U.P.U. Monument, Berne.

161 Carey, Ashmun and Careysburg

162 U.N. Headquarters

163 Flags and U.N. Emblem

1952. Designs all show portrait of Ashmun.

715 – 1 c. green (postage) 10 10
716 **161** 2 c. blue and red 10 10
717 – 3 c. green and purple 10 10
718 – 4 c. green and brown 15 10
719 – 5 c. red and blue 20 15
720 – 10 c. blue and red 25 20
721 – 25 c. black & pur (air) 35 35
722 – 50 c. red and blue 1·00 45

DESIGNS—VERT: 1 c. Seal of Liberia; 3 c. Harper and Harper City; 5 c. Buchanan and Upper Buchanan. HORIZ: 4 c. Marshall and Marshall City; 10 c. Roberts and Robertsport; 25 c. Monroe and Monrovia; 50 c. Tubman and map.

1952. U.N. Commem.

724 **162** 1 c. blue (postage) 10 10
725 – 4 c. blue and pink 15 10
726 – 10 c. brown and yellow 25 20
727 **163** 25 c. red and blue (air) 55 45

DESIGNS—HORIZ: 4 c. Liberian and U.N. flags and scroll; 10 c. Liberian and U.N. emblems.

164 Modern Road-building

1953. Air. Transport.

729 **164** 12 c. brown 15 15
730 – 25 c. purple 75 30
731 – 35 c. violet 1·00 35
732 – 50 c. orange 65 25
733 – 70 c. green 1·25 40
734 – $1 blue 1·40 55

DESIGNS: 25 c. "African Glen" (freighter) in Monrovia Harbour; 35 c. Diesel locomotive; 50 c. Free Port of Monrovia; 70 c. Roberts Field Airport; $1 Tubman Bridge.

165 Common Bulbul

166 Blue-throated Roller

1953. Imperf or perf.
735 **165** 1 c. red and blue 60 15
736 **166** 3 c. blue and salmon . . . 60 15
737 – 4 c. brown and yellow . . 85 20
738 – 5 c. turquoise & mauve . . 1·00 20
739 – 10 c. mauve and green . . 1·00 20
740 – 12 c. orange and brown . 1·60 30
BIRDS: As Type **165**: 4 c. Yellow-casqued hornbill; 5 c. Giant kingfisher. As Type **166**: 10 c. African jacana; 12 c. Broad-tailed paradise whydah.

167 Hospital

1954. Liberian Govt. Hospital Fund.
741 – 5 c. + 5 c. black and purple (postage) 20 15
742 – 10 c. + 5 c. black and red (air) 15 20
743 **167** 20 c. + 5 c. black & grn 25 25
744 – 25 c. + 5 c. black, red and blue 30 20
DESIGNS—As Type **167**: 5 c. Medical research workers; 10 c. Nurses. 46×35 mm: 25 c. Doctor examining patient.

168 Children of the World

1954. Air. U.N.I.C.E.F.
745 **168** $5 ultramarine, red & blue 27·00 23·00

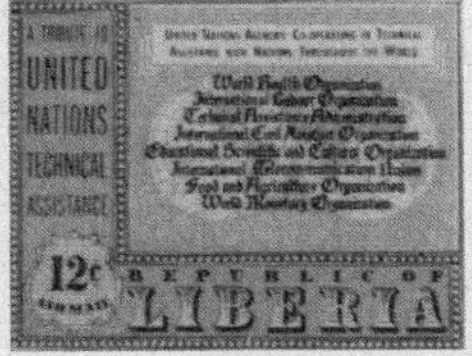

169 U.N. Organizations

1954. Air. U.N. Technical Assistance.
746 **169** 12 c. black and blue . . . 25 15
746 – 15 c. brown and yellow . 25 15
747 – 20 c. black and green . . 30 20
749 – 25 c. blue and red 35 25
DESIGNS: 15 c. Printers; 20 c. Mechanic; 25 c. Teacher and students.

1954. Air. Visit of President Tubman to U.S.A. As Nos. 729/34 but colours changed and inscr "COMMEMORATING PRESIDENTIAL VISIT TO U.S.A."
750 12 c. orange 20 20
751 25 c. blue 80 25
752 35 c. red . . . . 3·25 1·40
753 50 c. mauve 80 30
754 70 c. brown . . . . 1·10 50
755 $1 green . . . . 1·60 3·25

170 Football

171 "Callichilia stenosepala"

1955. Sports.
756 – 3 c. red & grn (post) . . . 15 10
757 **170** 5 c. black and orange . . 15 10
758 – 25 c. violet and yellow . . 25 20
759 – 10 c. blue & mve (air) . . 20 15
760 – 12 c. brown and blue . . 15 15
761 – 25 c. red and green . . 20 20
DESIGNS—VERT: 3 c. Tennis; 25 c. Boxing (No. 758). HORIZ: 10 c. Baseball; 12 c. Swimming; 25 c. Running (No. 761).

1955. Flowers.
763 **171** 6 c. yellow, salmon & green (postage) 15 10
764 – 7 c. red, yellow & green . 15 10
765 – 8 c. buff, blue and green 20 10
766 – 9 c. green and orange . . 25 15
767 – 20 c. yellow, green and violet (air) 15 15
768 – 25 c. yellow, green & red 20 20
FLOWERS—VERT: 7 c. "Gomphia subcordata"; 8 c. "Listrostachys chudata"; 9 c. "Mussaenda isertiana". HORIZ: 20 s. "Costus"; 25 c. "Barteria nigritiana".

172 U.N. General Assembly

173 Tapping Rubber and Rotary Emblem

1955. Air. 10th Anniv of U.N.
769 – 10 c. blue and red 20 10
770 **172** 15 c. black and violet . . 25 15
771 – 25 c. brown and green . . 35 15
772 – 50 c. green and red . . . 1·00 20
DESIGNS—VERT: 10 c. U.N. emblem; 25 c. Liberian Secretary of State signing U.N. Charter. HORIZ: 50 c. Page from U.N. Charter.

1955. 50th Anniv of Rotary International.
773 **173** 5 c. green & yell (postage) 25 15
774 – 10 c. blue and red (air) . 15 50
775 – 15 c. brown, yellow & red 20 65
DESIGNS: 10 c. Rotary International H.Q., Evanston; 15 c. View of Monrovia.

174 Coliseum, New York

1956. 5th International Philatelic Exhibition, New York.
777 – 3 c. brown and green (postage) 15 10
778 **174** 4 c. brown and green . . 10 25
779 – 6 c. purple and black . . 20 10
780 **174** 10 c. blue and red (air) . 25 15
781 – 12 c. violet and orange . 20 15
782 – 15 c. purple & turquoise 25 20
DESIGNS—VERT: 3 c., 15 c. Statue of Liberty. HORIZ: 6 c., 12 c. The Globe.

175 Chariot Race

1956. Olympic Games.
784 – 4 c. brown & olive (post) 15 15
785 – 6 c. black and green . . . 15 10
786 – 8 c. brown and blue . . . 20 10
787 **175** 10 c. black and red . . . 25 10
788 – 12 c. purple and grn (air) 20 15
789 – 20 c. multicoloured . . . 30 20
DESIGNS—HORIZ: 4 c. Olympic rings, eastern grey kangaroo and emu; 8 c. Goddess of Victory; 12 c., 20 c. Olympic torch superimposed on map of Austrialia. VERT: 6 c. Discus thrower.

176 Douglas DC-6B "John Alden" at Idelwild Airport

1957. 1st Anniv of Inauguration of Liberia–U.S. Direct Air Service.
791 **176** 3 c. blue & orge (postage) 15 15
792 – 5 c. black and mauve . . 20 20
793 **176** 12 c. blue & green (air) . 30 25
794 – 15 c. black and brown . . 30 25
795 **176** 25 c. blue and red 45 25
796 – 50 c. black and blue . . . 85 30
DESIGN: 5, 15, 50 c. President Tubman and "John Alden" at Roberts Field, Liberia.

MINIMUM PRICE

The minimum price quoted is 10p which represents a handling charge rather than a basis for valuing common stamps. For further notes about prices, see introductory pages.

177 Children's Playground

1957. Inaug of Antoinette Tubman Child Welfare Foundation. Inscr as in T **177**.
797 **177** 4 c. green & red (postage) 10 10
798 – 5 c. brown & turquoise . . 15 10
799 – 6 c. violet and bistre . . 15 10
800 – 10 c. blue and red 20 15
801 – 15 c. brown & blue (air) 20 15
802 – 35 c. purple and grey . . . 35 25
DESIGNS: 5 c. Teacher with pupil; 6 c. National anthem with choristers; 10 c. Children viewing welfare home; 15 c. Nurse inoculating youth; 35 c. Kamara triplets.

178 German Flag and Brandenburg Gate

1958. Pres. Tubman's European Tour. Flags in national colours.
804 **178** 5 c. blue (postage) 15 10
805 – 5 c. brown 15 10
806 – 5 c. red 15 10
807 – 10 c. black (air) 25 15
808 – 15 c. green 25 20
809 – 15 c. blue 25 20
810 – 15 c. violet 25 20
DESIGNS: Flags of: Netherlands and windmill (No. 805); Sweden and Royal Palace, Stockholm (No. 806); Italy and Colosseum (No. 807); France and Arc de Triomphe (No. 808); Switzerland and Alpine chalet (No. 809); Vatican City and St. Peter's Basilica (No. 810).

179 Map of the World

180 Africans and Map

1958. 10th Anniv of Declaration of Human Rights.
811 **179** 3 c. blue and black 25 15
812 – 5 c. brown and blue . . . 20 20
813 – 10 c. orange and black . . 30 75
814 – 12 c. black and red 40 35
DESIGNS: 5 c. U.N. Emblem and H.Q. building. 10 c. U.N. Emblem. 12 c. U.N. Emblem and initials of U.N. Agencies.

1959. Africa Freedom Day.
816 **180** 20 c. orge & brn (postage) 30 30
817 – 25 c. brown & blue (air) 35 20
DESIGN: 25 c. Two Africans looking at Pres. Tubman's declaration of Africa Freedom Day.

181

182 Abraham Lincoln

1959. Inaug of U.N.E.S.C.O. Building, Paris.
818 **181** 25 c. pur & grn (postage) 35 40
819 – 25 c. red and blue (air) . 35 30
DESIGN—HORIZ: No. 819 U.N.E.S.C.O. Headquarters, Paris.

1959. 150th Birth Anniv of Abraham Lincoln.
821 **182** 10 c. blk & blue (postage) 25 30
822 15 c. black and orange . . 30 30
823 25 c. black & grn (air) . . 55 50

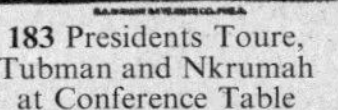
183 Presidents Toure, Tubman and Nkrumah at Conference Table

184 "Care of Refugees"

1960. "Big Three" Conf, Saniquellie, Liberia.
825 **183** 25 c. black & red (postage) 35 25
826 – 25 c. black, bl & buff (air) 35 25
DESIGN: No. 826, Medallion portraits of Presidents Toure (Guinea), Tubman (Liberia) and Nkrumah (Ghana).

1960. World Refugee Year.
827 **184** 25 c. green & blk (postage) 35 30
828 25 c. blue & black (air) . 55 40

185

186 Weightlifting

1960. 10th Anniv of African Technical Co-operation (C.C.T.A.).
830 **185** 25 c. green & blk (postage) 35 50
831 – 25 c. brown and blue (air) 45 35
DESIGN: No. 831, Map of Africa with symbols showing fields of assistance.

1960. Olympic Games, Rome.
832 **186** 5 c. brn and grn (postage) 20 15
833 – 10 c. brown and purple . 40 75
834 – 15 c. brown and orange . 35 30
835 – 25 c. brown & blue (air) 70 80
DESIGNS—HORIZ: 10 c. Rowing; 25 c. Javelin-throwing. VERT: 15 c. Walking.

187 Stamps of 1860 and Map

188 "Guardians of Peace"

1960. Liberian Stamp Centenary. Stamps, etc., in green, red and blue. Colours of map and inscriptions given.
837 **187** 5 c. black (postage) . . . 25 15
838 20 c. brown 40 40
839 25 c. blue (air) 50 40

1961. Membership of U.N. Security Council.
841 **188** 25 c. blue & red (postage) 45 35
842 – 25 c. blue and red (air) . 45 25
DESIGN—HORIZ: No. 842, Dove of Peace, Globe and U.N. Emblem.

189 Anatomy Class, University of Liberia

190 President Roberts

1961. 15th Anniv of U.N.E.S.C.O.
845 **189** 25 c. brn & grn (postage) 35 35
846 – 25 c. brown & violet (air) 35 25
DESIGN: No. 846, Science class, University of Liberia.

1961. 150th Birth Anniv of Joseph J. Roberts (first President of Liberia).
848 **190** 5 c. sepia & orge (postage) 20 15
849 – 10 c. sepia and blue . . . 35 15
850 – 25 c. sepia & green (air) . 45 35
DESIGNS—HORIZ: 10 c. Pres. Roberts and old and new presidential mansions; 25 c. Pres. Roberts and Providence Is.

191 Scout and Sports

1961. Liberian Boy Scout Movement.
852 **191** 5 c. sepia & vio (postage) 25 20
853 – 10 c. ochre and blue . . . 30 20
854 – 25 c. sepia & green (air) . 40 30
DESIGNS—HORIZ: 10 c. Scout badge and scouts in camp. VERT: 25 c. Scout and badge.

192 Hammarskjold and U.N. Emblem **193** Campaign Emblem

1962. Dag Hammarskjold Commem.
856 **192** 20 c. blk & blue (postage) . . 30 20
857 25 c. black & pur (air) . . 35 25

1962. Malaria Eradication.
859 **193** 25 c. green & red (postage) 35 25
860 – 25 c. orange & violet (air) 35 25
DESIGN—HORIZ: No. 860, Campaign emblem and slogan.

194 Pres. Tubman and New York Skyline **195** U.N. Emblem

1962. Air. President's Visit to U.S.A.
862 **194** 12 c. multicoloured . . . 25 15
863 25 c. multicoloured . . . 35 30
864 50 c. multicoloured . . . 70 55

1962. U.N. Day.
865 **195** 20 c. bistre & grn (postage) 35 30
866 – 25 c. blue & dp blue (air) 45 30
DESIGN: 25 c. U.N. emblem and flags.

196 Treasury Building **197** F.A.O. Emblem, Bowl and Spoon

1962. Liberian Government Buildings.
868 – 1 c. orge & blue (postage) 10 15
869 **196** 5 c. violet and blue . . . 15 10
870 – 10 c. brown and buff . . . 20 15
871 – 15 c. blue and salmon . . 25 20
872 – 80 c. yellow and brown . 1·60 1·00
873 – 12 c. lake & green (air) . . 25 15
874 – 50 c. blue and orange . . 1·00 90
875 – 70 c. blue and mauve . . 1·40 1·00
876 **196** $1 black and orange . . . 2·00 1·10
BUILDINGS: 1 c., 80 c. Executive; 10 c., 50 c. Information; 12 c., 15 c., 70 c. Capitol.

1963. Freedom from Hunger.
877 **197** 5 c. pur & turq (postage) 15 10
878 – 25 c. yellow & green (air) 35 20
DESIGN: 25 c. F.A.O. emblem and Globe.

198 Rocket

1963. Space Exploration.
880 **198** 10 c. yell & blue (postage) 20 15
881 – 15 c. brown and blue . . 35 40
882 – 25 c. green & orge (air) . 45 30
DESIGNS—HORIZ: 15 c. Space capsule. VERT: 25 c. "Telstar" TV satellite.

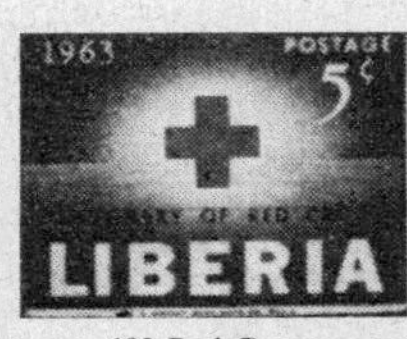

199 Red Cross **200** "Unity" Scroll

1963. Red Cross Centenary.
884 **199** 5 c. green & red (postage) 15 15
885 – 10 c. grey and red 20 20
886 – 25 c. violet & red (air) . . 35 30
887 – 50 c. blue and red . . . . 1·00 85
DESIGNS—VERT: 10 c. Emblem and torch. HORIZ: 25 c. Red Cross and Globe; 50 c. Emblem and Globe.

1963. Conference of African Heads of State, Addis Ababa.
888 **200** 20 c. brn & grn (postage) 40 35
889 – 25 c. red and green (air) 45 30
DESIGN: 25 c. Map of Africa (inscr "AFRICAN SUMMIT CONFERENCE").

201 Ski-jumping **202** President Kennedy

1963. Winter Olympic Games, Innsbruck. (1964).
890 **201** 5 c. blue and red (postage) 20 20
891 – 10 c. red and blue (air) . 25 25
892 – 25 c. orange and green . 35 35
DESIGNS—VERT: 10 c. Olympic flame. HORIZ: 25 c. Olympic rings. All have mountain scenery as backgrounds.

1964. President Kennedy Memorial Issue.
894 **202** 20 c. blk & blue (postage) 35 20
895 – 25 c. black & pur (air) . . 45 25
DESIGN—VERT: 25 c. Pres. Kennedy, full face portrait.

203 "Relay I" Satellite **204** Mt. Fuji

1964. Space Communications.
897 – 10 c. orange and green . 20 15
898 **203** 15 c. blue and mauve . . 25 20
899 – 25 c. yellow, black & blue 45 25
SATELLITES—HORIZ: 10 c. "Syncom"; 25 c. "Mariner II".

1964. Olympic Games, Tokyo.
901 **204** 10 c. green and yellow . . 15 10
902 – 15 c. purple and red . . . 20 15
903 – 25 c. red and buff 45 20
DESIGNS: 15 c. Japanese arch and Olympic Flame; 25 c. Cherry blossom and stadium.

205 Scout Bugle **206** "The Great Emancipator" (statue)

1965. Liberian Boy Scouts.
905 – 5 c. brown and blue (postage) 25 15
906 **205** 10 c. ochre and green . . 40 25
907 – 25 c. blue and red (air) . 50 35
DESIGNS—VERT: 5 c. Scout badge and saluting hand; 25 c. Liberian flag within scout badge.

1965. Death Centenary of Abraham Lincoln.
909 **206** 5 c. brown and sepia . . 20 25
910 – 20 c. green & lt brown . 35 30
911 – 25 c. blue and purple . . 40 40
DESIGNS—HORIZ: 20 c. Bust of Lincoln, and Pres. Kennedy. VERT: 25 c. Lincoln statue, Chicago (after St. Gaudens).

207 I.C.Y. Emblem

1965. International Co-operation Year.
913 **207** 12 c. brown and orange . 70 25
914 25 c. brown and blue . . 40 25
915 50 c. brown and green . . 80 70

208 I.T.U. Emblem and Symbols

1965. Cent. of I.T.U.
917 **208** 25 c. brn & grn (post) . . 40 50
918 35 c. mauve and black . . 60 50
919 50 blue and red (air) . . . 80 45

209 Pres. Tubman and Flag **210** Sir Winston Churchill

1965. Pres. Tubman's 70th Birthday. Multicoloured.
921 25 c. Type **209** (postage) . . . 35 30
922 25 c. President and Liberian arms (air) 35 25

1966. Churchill Commemoration.
924 **210** 15 c. black & orge (postage) 30 30
925 – 20 c. black and green . . . 35 25
926 – 25 c. black and blue (air) 40 30
DESIGNS—HORIZ: 20 c. Churchill in uniform of Trinity House Elder Brother; 25 c. Churchill and Houses of Parliament.

211 Pres. Roberts **212** Footballers and Hemispheres

1966. Liberian Presidents.
928 **211** 1 c. black & pink (postage) 10 10
929 – 2 c. black and yellow . . . 10 10
930 – 3 c. black and violet . . . 10 10
931 – 4 c. black and yellow . . . 75 50
932 – 5 c. black and orange . . . 10 10
933 – 10 c. black and green . . . 15 10
934 – 25 c. black and blue . . . 35 20
935 – 50 c. black and mauve . . 70 65
936 – 80 c. black and red . . . 1·25 95
937 – $1 black and brown . . . 1·40 15
938 – $2 black and purple . . . 3·25 2·75
939 – 25 c. black and green (air) 35 25
PRESIDENTS: 2 c. Benson; 3 c. Warner; 4 c. Payne; 5 c. Roye; 10 c. Coleman; 25 c. (postage) Howard; 25 c. (air) Tubman; 50 c. King; 80 c. Johnson; $1 Barclay; $2 Cheesman.

1966. World Cup Football Championships.
940 **212** 10 c. brown & turquoise . 15 15
941 – 25 c. brown and mauve . . 35 30
942 – 35 c. brown and orange . . 50 45
DESIGNS—VERT: 25 c. Presentation cup, football and boots; 35 c. Footballer.

213 Pres. Kennedy taking Oath **214** Children on See-saw

1966. 3rd Death Anniv (Nov. 22nd) of Pres. Kennedy.
944 **213** 15 c. black & red (postage) 25 15
945 – 20 c. purple and blue . . . 35 20
946 – 25 c. blue, black and ochre (air) 45 30
947 – 35 c. blue and pink 85 45
DESIGNS: 20 c. Kennedy stamps of 1964; 25 c. U.N. General Assembly and Pres. Kennedy; 35 c. Pres. Kennedy and rocket on launching pad.

1966. 20th Anniv of U.N.I.C.E.F.
949 **214** 5 c. blue and red 20 20
950 – 80 c. brown and green . . 1·50 1·50
DESIGN: 80 c. Child playing "Doctors".

215 Giraffe **216** Scout Emblem and Various Sports

1966. Wild Animals. Multicoloured.
951 2 c. Type **215** 10 10
952 3 c. Lion 20 15
953 5 c. Crocodile (horiz) 15 10
954 10 c. Chimpanzees 40 20
955 15 c. Leopard (horiz) 50 25
956 20 c. Black rhinoceros (horiz) . 60 40
957 25 c. African elephant 70 50

1967. World Scout Jamboree, Idaho.
958 – 10 c. purple and green . . 20 15
959 **216** 25 c. red and blue 35 50
960 – 40 c. brown and green . . 85 60
DESIGNS—VERT: 10 c. Jamboree emblem. HORIZ: 40 c. Scout by campfire, and Moon landing.

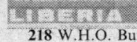

217 Pre-Hispanic Sculpture **218** W.H.O. Building, Brazzaville

1967. Publicity for Olympic Games, Mexico (1968).
962 **217** 10 c. violet and orange . . 75 85
963 – 25 c. orange, black & blue 35 40
964 – 40 c. red and green . . . 60 65
DESIGNS—VERT: 25 c. Aztec calendar. HORIZ: 40 c. Mexican sombrero, guitar and ceramics.

1967. Inauguration of W.H.O.'s Regional Office, Brazzaville.
966 **218** 5 c. yellow and blue . . . 20 20
967 – 80 c. green and yellow . . 1·25 1·25
DESIGN—VERT: 80 c. As Type **218** but in vertical format.

219 Boy with Rattle **220** Ice-hockey

1967. Musicians and Instruments. Multicoloured.
968 2 c. Type **219** 15 15
969 3 c. Tomtom and soko violin 20 20
970 5 c. Mang harp 25 25
971 10 c. Alimilim 30 30
972 15 c. Xylophone drums . . . 35 35
973 25 c. Tomtoms 50 40
974 35 c. Oral harp 75 60
The 3 c. and 5 c. are horiz designs.

1967. Publicity for Winter Olympic Games, Grenoble (1968).
975 **220** 10 c. blue and green . . . 15 20
976 – 25 c. violet and blue . . . 35 30
977 – 40 c. brown and orange . . 85 50
DESIGNS: 25 c. Ski-jumping; 40 c. Tobogganing.

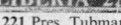

221 Pres. Tubman **222** Human Rights Emblem

1967. Re-election of Pres. Tubman for 6th Term.
979 **221** 25 c. brown and blue . . 35 25

1968. Human Rights Year.
981 **222** 3 c. blue and red 10 10
982 80 c. green and brown . . 1·60 1·60

223 Dr. King and Hearse **224** Throwing the Javelin and Statue of Diana

1968. Martin Luther King Commem.
984 **223** 15 c. brown and blue . . 25 20
985 – 25 c. brown and blue . . 40 30
986 – 35 c. black and olive . . 60 65
DESIGNS—VERT: 25 c. Dr. Martin Luther King. HORIZ: Dr. King and Lincoln Monument.

1968. Olympic Games, Mexico.
988 **224** 15 c. violet and brown . . 25 15
989 – 25 c. blue and red 35 15
990 – 35 c. brown and green . . 50 30
DESIGNS: 25 c. Throwing the discus and Quetzalcoatl sculpture; 35 c. High-diving and Xochilcalco bas-relief.

225 President Tubman **226** I.L.O. Symbol

1968. 25th Anniv of Pres. Tubman's Administration.
992 **225** 25 c. black, brown & silver 45 50

1969. 50th Anniv of I.L.O.
994 **226** 25 c. blue & gold (postage) 35 35
995 – 80 c. green & gold (air) . 1·50 1·40
DESIGN: 80 c. As Type **226** but vertical.

227 "Prince Balthasar Carlos" (Velasquez) **228** Bank Emblem on "Tree"

1969. Paintings (1st series). Multicoloured.
996 3 c. Type **227** 10 10
997 5 c. "Red Roofs" (Pissarro) 20 10
998 10 c. "David and Goliath" (Caravaggio) 30 15
999 12 c. "Still Life" (Chardin) . 30 15
1000 15 c. "The Last Supper" (Leonardo da Vinci) . . . 35 15
1001 20 c. "Regatta at Argenteuil" (Monet) 50 20
1002 25 c. "Judgement of Solomon" (Giorgione) 45 25
1003 35 c. "The Sistine Madonna" (Raphael) 60 30
Nos. 997/1001 are horiz.
See also Nos. 1010/1017.

1969. 5th Anniv of African Development Bank.
1004 **228** 25 c. brown and blue . . 45 40
1005 80 c. red and green . . . 1·50 1·10

229 Memorial Plaque **230** Peace Dove and Emblems

1969. 1st Man on the Moon.
1006 **229** 15 c. blue and ochre . . 25 15
1007 – 25 c. blue and orange . . 35 20
1008 – 35 c. red and slate . . . 50 25
DESIGNS—VERT: 25 c. Moon landing and Liberian; 35 c. "Kennedy" stamp of 1966; 35 c. Module lifting off from Moon.

1969. Paintings (2nd series). As T **227**. Multicoloured.
1010 3 c. "The Gleaners" (Millet) 15 10
1011 5 c. "View of Toledo" (El Greco) 20 15
1012 10 c. "Heads of Negroes" (Rubens) 30 15
1013 12 c. "The Last Supper" (El Greco) 30 20
1014 15 c. "Peasants Dancing" (Brueghel) 35 20
1015 20 c. "Hunters in the Snow" (Brueghel) 40 25
1016 25 c. "Descent from the Cross" (detail, Weyden) 45 30
1017 35 c. "The Conception" (Murillo) 60 40
Nos. 1010, 1012/15 are horiz.

1970. 25th Anniv of United Nations.
1018 **230** 5 c. grn & silver (postage) 15 25

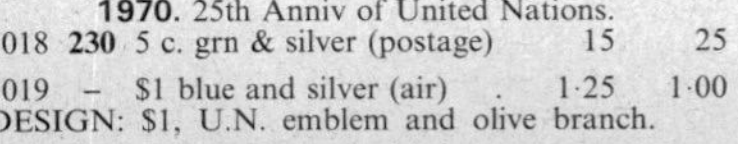

1019 – $1 blue and silver (air) . 1·25 1·00
DESIGN: $1, U.N. emblem and olive branch.

231 World Cup "Football" Emblem

1970. World Cup Football Championships, Mexico.
1020 **231** 5 c. brown and blue . . 20 15
1021 – 10 c. brown and green . . 25 20
1022 – 25 c. gold and purple . . 45 30
1023 – 35 c. red and blue . . . 60 45
DESIGN—VERT: 10 c. Tialoc, Mexican Rain God; 25 c. Jules Rimet Cup. HORIZ: 35 c. Football in sombrero.

232 Japanese Singer and Festival Plaza

1970. Expo 70. Multicoloured.
1025 2 c. Type **232** 10 10
1026 3 c. Japanese singer and Expo hall 15 10
1027 5 c. Aerial view of "EXPO 70" 15 10
1028 7 c. "Tanabata" Festival . . 30 10
1029 8 c. "Awa" Dance Festival . . 30 15
1030 25 c. "Sado-Okesa" Dance Festival 45 25

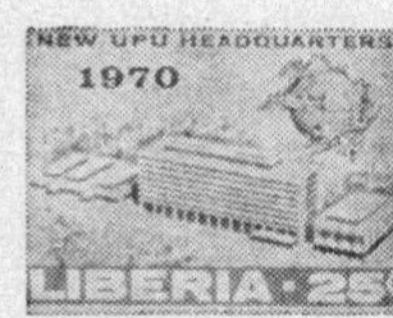

233 New H.Q. Building

1970. Inauguration of New U.P.U. Headquarters Building, Berne.
1032 **233** 25 c. brown and blue . . 35 35
1033 – 80 c. brown & chestnut 1·50 1·50
DESIGN—VERT: 80 c. Similar to Type **233** but with larger U.P.U. monument.

234 "The First Consul" (Vien)

1970. Birth Bicentenary of Napoleon Bonaparte. Multicoloured.
1034 3 c. Type **234** 20 10
1035 5 c. "Napoleon visiting school" (unknown artist) 30 15
1036 10 c. "Napoleon Bonaparte" (detail, Isabey) 35 15
1037 12 c. "The French Campaign" (Meissonier) 40 20
1038 20 c. "The Abdication" (Bouchot) 50 30
1039 25 c. "Meeting of Napoleon and Pope Pius VII" (Demarne) 60 35
Design of 10 c. is incorrectly attributed to Gerard on the stamp.

235 Pres. Tubman

1970. Pres. Tubman's 75th Birthday.
1041 **235** 25 c. multicoloured . . 35 25

236 "Adoration of the Magi" (Van der Weyden)

1970. Christmas. "The Adoration of the Magi" by artists as below. Multicoloured.
1043 3 c. Type **236** 10 10
1044 5 c. H. Memling 15 10
1045 10 c. S. Lochner 25 15
1046 12 c. A. Altdorfer (vert) . . . 30 15
1047 20 c. H. van der Goes 35 15
1048 25 c. H. Bosch (vert) 40 30

237 Bapende Mask **239** Pres. Tubman and Women at Ballot Box

238 Astronauts on Moon

1971. African Ceremonial Masks. Mask from different tribes. Multicoloured.
1050 2 c. Type **237** 10 10
1051 3 c. Dogon 15 10
1052 5 c. Baoule 15 15
1053 6 c. Dedougou 20 15
1054 9 c. Dan 25 15
1055 15 c. Bamileke 30 20
1056 20 c. Bapende (different) . . . 40 30
1057 25 c. Bamileke costume . . . 60 30

1971. "Apollo 14". Moon Mission. Multicoloured.
1058 3 c. Type **238** 15 10
1059 5 c. Astronaut and Moon vehicle 15 10
1060 10 c. Erecting U.S. flag on Moon 20 10
1061 12 c. Splashdown 40 15
1062 20 c. Astronauts leaving capsule 45 15
1063 25 c. "Apollo 14" crew . . . 60 20

1971. 25th Anniv of Liberian Women's Suffrage.
1065 **239** 3 c. blue and brown . . . 15 30
1066 – 80 c. brown and green . . 1·50 1·50
DESIGN—HORIZ: 80 c. Pres. Tubman, women and map.

240 Hall of Honour, Munich

1971. Olympic Games, Munich (1972) (1st issue). Views of Munich. Multicoloured.
1067 3 c. Type **240** 15 10
1068 5 c. View of central Munich 15 10
1069 10 c. National Museum 20 10
1070 12 c. Max Joseph's Square . . 25 10
1071 20 c. Propylaen, King's Square 40 15
1072 25 c. Liesel-Karistadt Fountain 60 20

241 American Scout **242** Pres. William Tubman

1971. World Scout Jamboree, Asagiri, Japan. Scouts in national uniforms. Multicoloured.
1074 3 c. Type **241** 15 10
1075 5 c. West Germany 15 10
1076 10 c. Australia 20 15
1077 12 c. Great Britain 25 15
1078 20 c. Japan 40 20
1079 25 c. Liberia 60 30

1971. Pres. Tubman Memorial Issue.
1081 **242** 3 c. brown, blue & black 10 10
1082 25 c. brown, pur & blk 35 35

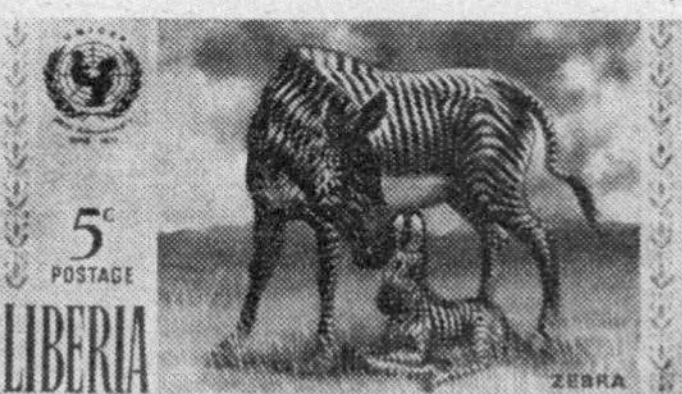

243 Common Zebra and Foal

1971. 25th Anniv of U.N.I.C.E.F. Animals with young. Multicoloured.
1083 5 c. Type **243** 20 10
1084 7 c. Koalas 30 15
1085 8 c. Guanaco 35 15
1086 10 c. Red fox and cubs . . . 45 15
1087 20 c. Savanna monkeys . . . 65 25
1088 25 c. Brown bears 90 35

244 Cross-country Skiing and Sika Deer

1971. Winter Olympic Games, Sapporo, Japan. Sports and Hokkaido Animals. Multicoloured.
1090 2 c. Type **244** 10 10
1091 3 c. Tobogganing and black woodpecker 40 15
1092 5 c. Ski-jumping and Brown bear 15 10
1093 10 c. Bob-sleighing and common guillemots . . . 75 15
1094 15 c. Figure-skating and Northern pika 30 20
1095 25 c. Slalom-skiing and Manchurian cranes . . . . 1·50 45

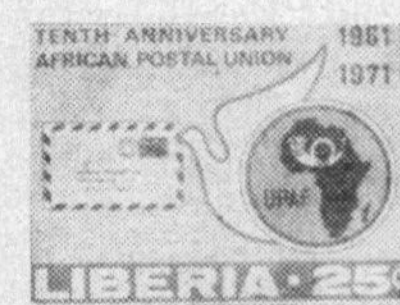

245 A.P.U. Emblem, Dove and Letter

1971. 10th Anniv of African Postal Union.
1097 **245** 25 c. orange and blue . . 35 50
1098 80 c. brown and grey . . 1·60 1·50

246 "Elizabeth" (emigrant ship) at Providence Island

1972. 150th Anniv of Liberia.
1099 **246** 3 c. green and blue . . . 50 50
1100 – 20 c. blue and orange . . 35 20
1101 **246** 25 c. purple & orange . . 1·50 55
1102 – 35 c. purple and green . . 60 40
DESIGNS—VERT: 20 c., 35 c. Arms and Founding Fathers Monument, Monrovia.

247 Pres. Tolbert and Map

1972. Inaug. of Pres. Wm. R. Tolbert Jnr.

1104 **247** 25 c. brown and green . . 35 25
1105 – 80 c. brown and blue . . 1·60 80

DESIGN—VERT: 80 c. Pres. Tolbert standing by desk.

248 Football

1972. Olympic Games, Munich (2nd issue). Multicoloured.

1106 3 c. Type **248** 10 10
1107 5 c. Swimming 15 10
1108 10 c. Show-jumping 25 10
1109 12 c. Cycling 30 15
1110 20 c. Long-jumping 45 20
1111 25 c. Running 60 25

249 Globe and Emblem

251 Emperor Haile Selassie

250 Astronaut and Moon Rover

1972. 50th Anniv of Int Y's Men's Clubs.

1113 **249** 15 c. violet and gold . . 40 15
1114 – 90 c. green and blue . . 1·75 1·75

DESIGN: 90 c. Club emblem on World Map.

1972. Moon Mission of "Apollo 16". Mult.

1115 3 c. Type **250** 10 10
1116 5 c. Reflection on visor . . . 10 10
1117 10 c. Astronauts with cameras . . 15 10
1118 12 c. Setting up equipment . . 20 15
1119 20 c. "Apollo 16" emblem . . 40 20
1120 25 c. Astronauts in Moon Rover 50 50

1972. Emperor Haile Selassie of Ethiopia's 80th Birthday.

1122 **251** 20 c. green and yellow . 40 30
1123 25 c. purple & yellow . . 45 40
1124 35 c. brown & yellow . . 60 60

252 H.M.S. "Ajax" (ship of the line), 1809

1972. Famous Ships of the British Royal Navy. Multicoloured.

1125 3 c. Type **252** 35 25
1126 5 c. H.M.S. "Hogue" (screw ship of the line), 1848 . . . 65 25
1127 7 c. H.M.S. "Ariadne" (frigate), 1816 . . . . 85 30
1128 15 c. H.M.S. "Royal Adelaide" (ship of the line), 1828 . . 1·00 55
1129 20 c. H.M.S. "Rinaldo" (screw sloop), 1860 . . . . . . 1·40 70
1130 25 c. H.M.S. "Nymphe" (screw sloop), 1888 . . . . . . 1·90 1·00

253 Pres. Tolbert taking Oath

1972. First Year President Tolbert Presidency.

1132 **253** 15 c. multicoloured . . 35 15
1133 25 c. multicoloured . . 70 70

254 Klaus Dibiasi and Italian Flag

1973. Olympic Games, Munich. Gold-medal Winners. Multicoloured.

1135 5 c. Type **254** 10 10
1136 8 c. Borzov and Soviet flag . 15 10
1137 10 c. Yanagida and Japanese flag 15 10
1138 12 c. Spitz and U.S. flag . . 20 15
1139 15 c. Keino and Kenyan flag . 25 15
1140 25 c. Meade and Union Jack . 35 25

255 Astronaut on Moon

1973. Moon Flight of "Apollo 17". Multicoloured.

1142 2 c. Type **255** 10 10
1143 3 c. Testing lunar rover at Cape Kennedy 10 10
1144 10 c. Collecting Moon rocks . . 15 10
1145 15 c. Lunar rover on Moon . . 20 15
1146 20 c. "Apollo 17" crew at Cape Kennedy 30 20
1147 25 c. Astronauts on Moon . . 35 25

256 British G.W.R. Locomotive

1973. Historical Railways. Steam locomotives of 1895-1905. Multicoloured.

1149 2 c. Type **256** 20 10
1150 3 c. Holland 30 10
1151 10 c. France 55 15
1152 15 c. U.S.A. 75 20
1153 20 c. Japan . . . . 1·60 25
1154 25 c. Germany . . . . . . 2·50 30

257 O.A.U. Emblem

1973. 10th Anniv of Organization of African Unity.

1156 **257** 3 c. multicoloured . . . 10 10
1157 5 c. multicoloured . . . 10 10
1158 10 c. multicoloured . . 15 10
1159 15 c. multicoloured . . 20 15
1160 25 c. multicoloured . . 35 25
1161 50 c. multicoloured . . 70 70

258 Edward Jenner and Roses

1973. 25th Anniv of W.H.O. Multicoloured.

1162 1 c. Type **258** 15 10
1163 4 c. Sigmund Freud and violets 15 10
1164 10 c. Jonas Salk and chrysanthemums 25 10
1165 15 c. Louis Pasteur and scabious 40 15
1166 20 c. Emil von Behring and mallow 45 20
1167 25 c. Sir Alexander Fleming and rhododendrons 75 25

259 Stanley Steamer, 1910

1973. Vintage Cars. Multicoloured.

1169 2 c. Type **259** 10 10
1170 3 c. Cadillac Model A, 1903 . 10 10
1171 10 c. Clement-Baynard, 1904 . 15 10
1172 15 c. Rolls-Royce Silver Ghost tourer, 1907 . . . . . . 25 15
1173 20 c. Maxwell gentleman's speedster, 1905 . . . . . 35 20
1174 25 c. Chadwick, 1907 . . . . 50 25

260 Copernicus, Armillary Sphere and Satellite Communications System

1973. 500th Birth Anniv of Copernicus. Mult.

1176 1 c. Type **260** 10 10
1177 4 c. Eudoxus solar system . . 10 10
1178 10 c. Aristotle, Ptolemy and Copernicus 15 10
1179 15 c. "Saturn" and "Apollo" spacecraft 25 15
1180 20 c. Astronomical observatory satellite 35 20
1181 25 c. Satellite tracking-station 50 25

261 Radio Mast and Map of Africa

1974. 20th Anniv of "Eternal Love Winning Africa". Radio Station. Multicoloured.

1183 13 c. Type **261** 25 25
1184 15 c. Radio Mast and map of Liberia 35 25
1185 17 c. Type **261** 35 50
1186 25 c. As 15 c. 50 40

262 "Thomas Coutts" (full-rigged sailing ship) and "Aureol" (liner)

1974. Cent of U.P.U. Multicoloured.

1187 2 c. Type **262** 20 10
1188 3 c. Boeing 707 airliner and liner, satellite and Monrovia Post Office 30 10
1189 10 c. U.S. and Soviet Telecommunications satellites 15 10
1190 15 c. Postal runner and Boeing 707 airliner 25 20
1191 20 c. British Rail High-speed Train and Liberian mail-van 55 25
1192 25 c. American Pony Express rider 50 35

263 Fox Terrier

1974. Dogs. Multicoloured.

1194 5 c. Type **263** 15 10
1195 10 c. Boxer 20 10
1196 16 c. Chihuahua 30 15
1197 19 c. Beagle 35 20
1198 25 c. Golden retriever . . . 40 25
1199 50 c. Collie 75 50

264 West Germany v. Chile Match

1974. World Cup Football Championships, West Germany. Scenes from semi-final matches. Multicoloured.

1201 1 c. Type **264** 10 10
1202 2 c. Australia v. East Germany 10 10
1203 5 c. Brazil v. Yugoslavia . . 15 10
1204 10 c. Zaire v. Scotland . . . 20 10
1205 12 c. Netherlands v. Uruguay 25 15
1206 15 c. Sweden v. Bulgaria . . 30 15
1207 20 c. Italy v. Haiti 40 20
1208 25 c. Poland v. Argentina . . 60 25

265 "Chrysiridia madagascariensis"

1974. Tropical Butterflies. Multicoloured.

1210 1 c. Type **265** 10 10
1211 2 c. "Catagramma sorana" . . 10 10
1212 5 c. "Erasmia pulchella" . . 20 10
1213 17 c. "Morpho cypris" . . . 50 25
1214 25 c. "Agrias amydon" . . . 70 35
1215 40 c. "Vanessa cardui" . . . 1·40 45

266 Pres. Tolbert and Gold Medallion

1974. "Family of Man" Award to President Tolbert. Multicoloured.

1217 3 c. Type **266** 10 25
1218 $1 Pres. Tolbert, medallion and flag . . . . 1·40 1·40

267 Churchill with Troops

1974. Birth Centenary of Sir Winston Churchill. Multicoloured.

1219 3 c. Type **267** 10 10
1220 10 c. Churchill and aerial combat 30 10
1221 15 c. Churchill aboard "Liberty" ship in Channel 55 15
1222 17 c. Churchill reviewing troops in desert 30 15
1223 20 c. Churchill crossing Rhine 40 20
1224 25 c. Churchill with Roosevelt 50 25

268 Marie Curie

1978. International Women's Year. Multicoloured.

1226 2 c. Type **268** 10 10
1227 3 c. Mahalia Jackson 10 10
1228 5 c. Joan of Arc 10 10
1229 10 c. Eleanor Roosevelt . . . 15 10
1230 25 c. Matilda Newport . . . 50 25
1231 50 c. Valentina Tereshkova . 70 55

269 Old State House, Boston, and U.S. 2 c. "Liberty Bell" Stamp of 1926

1975. Bicentenary of American Independence.

1233 5 c. Type **269** 15 10
1234 10 c. George Washington and 1928 "Valley Forge" stamp 30 10
1235 15 c. Philadelphia and 1937 "Constitution" stamp . . . 45 15
1236 20 c. Benjamin Franklin and 1938 "Ratification" stamp . 50 15
1237 25 c. Paul Revere's Ride and 1925 "Lexington-Concord" stamp 70 20
1238 50 c. "Santa Maria" and 1893 "Columbus' Landing" stamp 2·00 55

270 Dr. Schweitzer, Yellow Baboon and Lambarene Hospital

1975. Birth Centenary of Dr Albert Schweitzer. Multicoloured.

1240 1 c. Type **270** 10 10
1241 3 c. Schweitzer, African elephant and canoe 15 10
1242 5 c. Schweitzer, African buffalo and canoe 75 20
1243 6 c. Schweitzer, kob and dancer 30 10
1244 25 c. Schweitzer, lioness and village woman 75 25
1245 50 c. Schweitzer, common zebras and clinic scene . . 1·40 65

271 "Apollo" Spacecraft

1975. "Apollo-Soyuz" Space Link. Multicoloured.

1247 5 c. Type **271** 10 10
1248 10 c. "Soyuz" spacecraft . . 15 10
1249 15 c. American-Russian hand-clasp 20 15
1250 20 c. Flags and maps of America and Russia . . . 25 15
1251 25 c. Leonov and Kubasov 35 20
1252 50 c. Slayton, Brand and Stafford 95 50

272 Presidents Tolbert and Stevens, and Signing Ceremony

1975. Liberia–Sierra Leone Mano River Union Agreement.

1254 **272** 2 c. multicoloured . . . 10 10
1255 3 c. multicoloured . . . 10 10
1256 5 c. multicoloured . . . 10 10
1257 10 c. multicoloured . . . 15 10
1258 25 c. multicoloured . . . 35 25
1259 50 c. multicoloured . . . 70 70

273 Figure-skating

1976. Winter Olympic Games, Innsbruck. Multicoloured.

1260 1 c. Type **273** 10 10
1261 4 c. Ski-jumping 20 20
1262 10 c. Skiing (slalom) 30 20
1263 25 c. Ice-hockey 60 30
1264 35 c. Speed-skating 90 40
1265 50 c. Two-man bobsledding 1·25 65

274 Pres. Tolbert taking Oath

1976. Inauguration of President William R. Tolbert, Jr. Multicoloured.

1267 3 c. Type **274** 10 10
1268 25 c. Pres. Tolbert in Presidential Chair (vert) 35 25
1269 $1 Liberian crest, flat and commemorative gold coin 1·90 1·40

275 Weightlifting

1976. Olympic Games, Montreal. Multicoloured.

1270 2 c. Type **275** 10 10
1271 3 c. Pole-vaulting 10 10
1272 10 c. Hammer and shot-put 30 15
1273 25 c. Sailing 65 35
1274 35 c. Gymnastics 90 60
1275 50 c. Hurdling . . . . 1·25 65

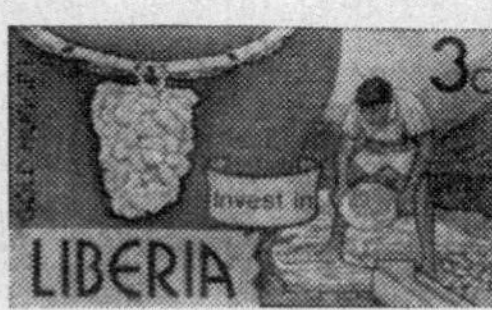

276 Bell's Telephone and Receiver

1976. Telephone Centenary. Multicoloured.

1277 1 c. Type **276** 10 10
1278 4 c. Mail-coach 10 10
1279 5 c. "Intelsat 4" satellite . . 15 10
1280 25 c. Cable-ship "Dominia", 1926 . . . . 1·00 30
1281 40 c. Futuristic train . . . 1·00 50
1282 50 c. Wright Flyer I, airship "Graf Zeppelin" and Concorde . . . . 1·75 60

277 Gold Nugget Pendant

1976. Liberian Products (1st series). Multicoloured.

1284 1 c. Mano River Bridge . . 10 10
1285 3 c. Type **277** 10 10
1286 5 c. "V" ring 10 10
1286a 7 c. As No. 1286 . . . . . 15 25
1287 10 c. Rubber tree and tyre 15 10
1287a 15 c. Combine harvester . . 20 10
1287b 17 c. As No. 1289 . . . . 35 10
1287c 20 c. Hydro-electric plant . 30 15
1288 25 c. Mesurado shrimp . . 35 25
1288a 27 c. Dress and woman tie-dying cloth 40 25
1289 55 c. Barracuda . . . . . 1·10 35
1289a $1 Train carrying iron ore 1·10 25

For designs as Type **277** but in a smaller size, see Nos. 1505/8.

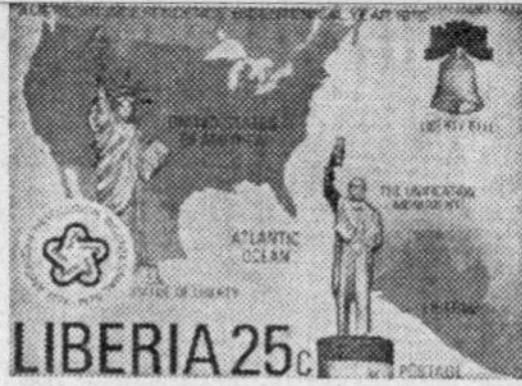

278 Black Rhinoceros

1976. Animals. Multicoloured.

1290 2 c. Type **278** 10 10
1291 3 c. Bongo 10 10
1292 5 c. Chimpanzee (vert) . . . 15 10
1293 15 c. Pygmy hippopotamus 40 15
1294 25 c. Leopard 80 40
1295 $1 Gorilla . . . . 3·00 90

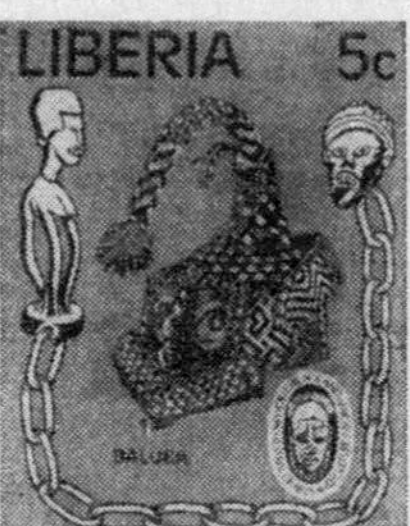

279 Statue of Liberty and Unification Monument on Maps of U.S.A. and Liberia

1976. Bicentenary of American Revolution. Multicoloured.

1297 25 c. Type **279** 35 25
1298 $1 Presidents Washington and Ford (U.S.A.), Roberts and Tolbert (Liberia) . . . . . 1·40 1·25

280 Baluba Masks

1977. Second World Black and African Festival of Arts and Culture, Lagos (Nigeria). Tribal Masks. Multicoloured.

1300 5 c. Type **280** 10 10
1301 10 c. Bateke 15 10
1302 15 c. Basshilele 20 15
1303 20 c. Igungun 30 15
1304 25 c. Maisi 35 20
1305 50 c. Kifwebe 70 45

281 Latham's Francolin

1977. Liberian Wild Birds. Multicoloured.

1307 5 c. Type **281** 40 10
1308 10 c. Narina trogon 60 15
1309 15 c. Rufous-crowned roller . 60 20
1310 20 c. Brown-cheeked hornbill 65 25
1311 25 c. Common bulbul 75 30
1312 50 c. African fish eagle . . . 1·50 80

282 Alwin Schockemohle (individual jumping)

1977. Olympic Games, Montreal. Equestrian Gold-medal Winners. Multicoloured.

1314 5 c. Edmund Coffin (military dressage) (postage) 15 10
1315 15 c. Type **282** 40 20
1316 20 c. Christine Stuckelberger (dressage) 50 30
1317 25 c. "Nations Prize" (French team) 70 35
1318 55 c. Military dressage (U.S.A. team) (air) . . . . 1·25 70

283 Queen Elizabeth II

1977. Silver Jubilee of Queen Elizabeth II. Multicoloured.

1320 15 c. Type **283** 35 15
1321 25 c. Queen Elizabeth and Prince Philip with President and Mrs. Tubman of Liberia.
1322 80 c. Queen Elizabeth, Prince Philip and Royal Arms . . 2·40 70

284 "Blessing the Children"

1977. Christmas. Multicoloured.

1324 20 c. Type **284** 50 25
1325 25 c. "The Good Shepherd" 70 35
1326 $1 "Jesus and the Woman of Samaria at the Well" . . . 2·00 1·00

285 Dornier Do-X Flying Boat

1978. "Progress in Aviation". Multicoloured.

1327 2 c. Type **285** 10 10
1328 3 c. Space shuttle "Enterprise" on Boeing 747 . . . . 10 10
1329 5 c. Edward Rickenbacker and Douglas DC-3 . . . . . . 10 10
1330 25 c. Charles Lindbergh and "Spirit of St. Louis" . . . 45 20
1331 35 c. Louis Bleriot and Bleriot XI monoplane 65 35
1332 50 c. Wright Brothers and Flyer I 90 55

286 Santos-Dumont's Airship "Ballon No. 9 La Badaleuse", 1903

1978. 75th Anniv of First Zeppelin Flight. Multicoloured.

1334 2 c. Type **286** 10 10
1335 3 c. Thomas Baldwin's airship "U.S. Military No. 1", 1908 10 10
1336 5 c. Tissandier brothers' airship, 1883 . . . . 10 10
1337 25 c. Parseval airship PL-VII, 1912 . . . . 40 20
1338 40 c. Airship "Nulli Secundus II", 1908 . . . . 75 35
1339 50 c. Beardmore airship R-34, 1919 . . . . 85 55

WORLD CUP ARGENTINA 1978
LIBERIA 2c
5c
LIBERIA

287 Tackling **288** Coronation Chair

1978. World Cup Football Championship, Argentina.

1341 **287** 2 c. multicoloured . . . 10 10
1342 – 3 c. mult (horiz) 10 10
1343 – 10 c. mult (horiz) 15 10
1344 – 25 c. mult (horiz) 35 20
1345 – 35 c. multicoloured . . . 50 25
1346 – 50 c. mult (horiz) . . . . 1·00 50

DESIGNS: Nos. 1342/6 Different match scenes.

1978. 25th Anniv of Coronation. Multicoloured.

1348 5 c. Type **288** 10 25
1349 25 c. Imperial State Crown . 35 25
1350 $1 Buckingham Palace (horiz) 1·40 1·00

289 Mohammed Ali Jinnah and Flags

1978. Birth Centenary of Mohammed Ali Jinnah (first Governor-General of Pakistan).
1352 **289** 30 c. multicoloured 1·50 1·50

290 Carter and Tolbert Families

1978. Visit of President Carter of U.S.A. Mult.
1353 5 c. Type **290** 10 10
1354 25 c. Presidents Carter and Tolbert with Mrs. Carter at microphones 25 20
1355 $1 Presidents Carter and Tolbert in open car 1·40 1·40

291 Italy v. France **292** Timber Truck

1978. Argentina's Victory in World Cup Football Championship. Multicoloured.
1356 1 c. Brazil v. Spain (horiz) 10 10
1357 2 c. Type **291** 10 10
1358 10 c. Poland v. West Germany (horiz) 15 10
1359 27 c. Peru v. Scotland 40 25
1360 35 c. Austria v. West Germany 50 25
1361 50 c. Argentinian players with Cup 1·00 50

1978. 8th World Forestry Congress, Djakarta. Multicoloured.
1363 5 c. Chopping up log (horiz) 10 10
1364 10 c. Type **292** 15 10
1365 25 c. Felling trees (horiz) 25 20
1366 50 c. Loggers (horiz) 70 70

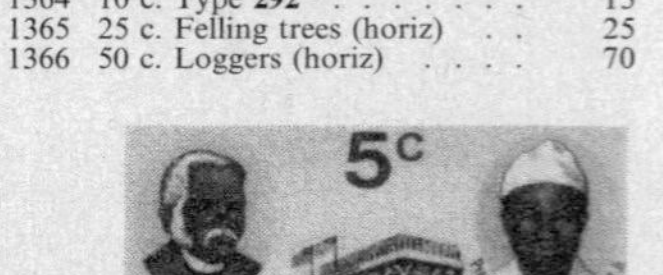

293 Presidents Gardner and Tolbert with Monrovia Post Office

1979. Centenary of U.P.U. Membership. Mult.
1367 5 c. Type **293** 10 10
1368 35 c. Presidents Gardner and Tolbert with U.P.U. emblem 50 65

294 "25" and Radio Waves

1979. 25th Anniv of Radio ELWA. Multicoloured.
1369 35 c. Type **294** 50 25
1370 $1 Radio tower 1·40 1·40

295 I.Y.C., Decade of the African Child and S.O.S. Villages Emblems

1979. International Year of the Child. Multicoloured.
1371 5 c. Type **295** 10 10
1372 25 c. As Type **295** but with UNICEF instead of S.O.S. Villages emblem 25 20
1373 35 c. Type **295** 50 25
1374 $1 As No. 1372 1·40 1·40

296 Clasped Arms and Torches

1979. Organization for African Unity Summit Conference, Monrovia. Multicoloured.
1375 5 c. Type **296** 10 10
1376 27 c. Masks 40 25
1377 35 c. African animals 50 50
1378 50 c. Thatched huts and Common Bulbuls 1·25 70

297 Sir Rowland Hill and Liberian 15 c. Stamp, 1974

1979. Death Centenary of Sir Rowland Hill. Multicoloured.
1379 3 c. Type **297** 10 10
1380 10 c. Pony Express rider 15 10
1381 15 c. British mail coach 20 35
1382 25 c. "John Penn" (paddle-steamer) 75 55
1383 27 c. Stanier Pacific locomotive 75 60
1384 50 c. Concorde 1·50 90

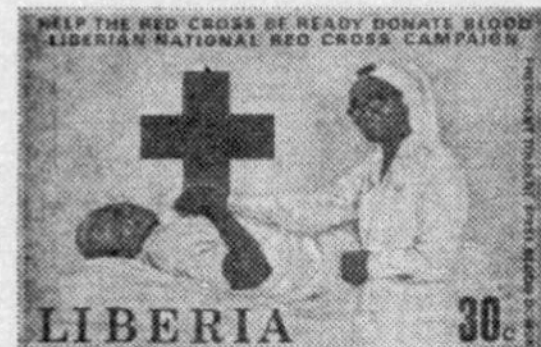

298 President Tolbert giving Blood

1979. National Red Cross Blood Donation Campaign. Multicoloured.
1386 30 c. Type **298** 45 25
1387 50 c. President Tolbert and Red Cross 70 70

299 "World Peace" (tanker)

1979. 2nd World Maritime Day and 30th Anniv of Liberia Maritime Programme. Multicoloured.
1388 5 c. Type **299** 30 15
1389 $1 "World Peace" (different) 2·25 2·00

300 "A Good Turn"

1979. Scout Paintings by Norman Rockwell. Multicoloured.
1390 5 c. Scout giving first aid to pup ("A Good Scout") 20 15
1391 5 c. Type **300** 20 15
1392 5 c. "Good Friends" 20 15
1393 5 c. "Spirit of America" 20 15
1394 5 c. "Scout Memories" 20 15
1395 5 c. "The Adventure Trail" 20 15
1396 5 c. "On My Honour" 20 15
1397 5 c. "A Scout is Reverent" 20 15
1398 5 c. "The Right Way" 20 15
1399 5 c. "The Scoutmaster" 20 15
1400 10 c. "A Scout is Loyal" 35 20
1401 10 c. "An Army of Friendship" 35 20
1402 10 c. "Carry on" 35 20
1403 10 c. "A Good Scout" 35 20
1404 10 c. "The Campfire Story" 35 20
1405 10 c. "High Adventure" 35 20
1406 10 c. "Mighty Proud" 35 20
1407 10 c. "Tomorrow's Leader" 35 20
1408 10 c. "Ever Onward" 35 20
1409 10 c. "Homecoming" 35 20
1410 15 c. "Scouts of Many Trails" 40 25
1411 15 c. "America builds for Tomorrow" 40 25
1412 15 c. "The Scouting Trail" 40 25
1413 15 c. "A Scout is Reverent" 40 25
1414 15 c. "A Scout is Helpful" 40 25
1415 15 c. "Pointing the Way" 40 25
1416 15 c. "A Good Sign All Over the World" 40 25
1417 15 c. "To Keep Myself Physically Strong" 40 25
1418 15 c. "A Great Moment" 40 25
1419 15 c. "Growth of a Leader" 40 25
1420 25 c. "A Scout is Loyal" 60 35
1421 25 c. "A Scout is Friendly" 60 35
1422 25 c. "We Too, Have a Job to Do" 60 35
1423 25 c. "I Will do my Best" 60 35
1424 25 c. "A Guiding Hand" 60 35
1425 25 c. "Breakthrough for Freedom" 60 35
1426 25 c. "Scouting is Outing" 60 35
1427 25 c. "Beyond the Easel" 60 35
1428 25 c. "Come and Get It" 60 35
1429 25 c. "America's Manpower begins with Boypower" 60 35
1430 35 c. "All Together" 80 45
1431 35 c. "Men of Tomorrow" 80 45
1432 35 c. "Friend in Need" 80 45
1433 35 c. "Our Heritage" 80 45
1434 35 c. "Forward America" 80 45
1435 35 c. "Can't Wait" 80 45
1436 35 c. "From Concord to Tranquility" 80 45
1437 35 c. "We Thank Thee" 80 45
1438 35 c. "So Much Concern" 80 45
1439 35 c. "Spirit of '76" 80 45

301 Mrs. Tolbert and Children

1979. S.O.S. Children's Village, Monrovia. Multicoloured.
1440 25 c. Mrs. Tolbert and children (different) (horiz) 35 50
1441 40 c. Type **301** 60 50

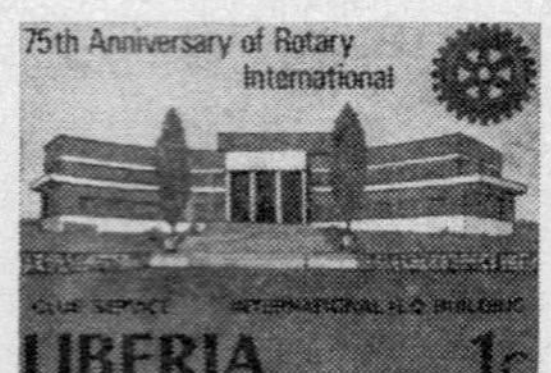

302 International Headquarters, Evanston, Illinois

1979. 75th Anniv of Rotary International. Multicoloured.
1442 1 c. Type **302** 10 10
1443 5 c. Vocational services 10 10
1444 17 c. Wheelchair patient and nurse (community service) (vert) 20 35
1445 27 c. Flags (international service) 40 50
1446 35 c. Different races holding hands around globe (health, hunger and humanity) 50 50
1447 50 c. President Tolbert and map of Africa (17th anniv of Monrovia Rotary Club) (vert) 1·00 1·00

303 Ski-jumping

1980. Winter Olympic Games, Lake Placid. Multicoloured.
1449 1 c. Type **303** 10 10
1450 5 c. Pairs figure skating 10 10
1451 17 c. Bobsleigh 20 35
1452 27 c. Cross-country skiing 50 50
1453 35 c. Speed skating 50 50
1454 50 c. Ice hockey 1·00 1·00

304 Presidents Tolbert of Liberia and Stevens of Sierra Leone and View of Mano River

1980. 5th Anniv of Mano River Union and 1st Anniv (1979) of Postal Union.
1456 **304** 8 c. multicoloured 10 10
1457 27 c. multicoloured 40 50
1458 35 c. multicoloured 50 50
1459 80 c. multicoloured 1·50 1·50

305 Redemption Horn

1981. People's Redemption Council (1st series). Multicoloured.
1460 1 c. Type **305** 10 10
1461 10 c. M/Sgt. Doe and allegory of redemption (horiz) 10 10
1462 14 c. Map, soldier and citizens (horiz) 15 15
1463 $2 M/Sgt. Samuel Doe (chairman of Council) 3·75 3·75
See also Nos. 1475/8.

306 Players and Flags of Argentine, Uruguay, Italy and Czechoslovakia

1981. World Cup Football Championships, Spain (1982). Multicoloured.
1464 3 c. Type **306** 10 10
1465 5 c. Players and flags of Hungary, Italy, Germany, Brazil and Sweden 10 10
1466 20 c. Players and flags of Italy, Germany, Brazil and Sweden 20 20
1467 27 c. Players and flags of Czechoslovakia, Brazil, Great Britain and Germany 25 25
1468 40 c. Players and flags of Italy, Brazil, Germany and Netherlands 60 60
1469 55 c. Players and flags of Netherlands and Uruguay 80 80

307 M/Sgt. Doe and Crowd

1981. 1st Anniv of People's Redemption Council. Multicoloured.
1471 22 c. Type **307** 20 20
1472 27 c. M/Sgt. Doe and national flag 25 25
1473 30 c. Hands clasping arms, sunrise and map 45 45
1474 $1 M/Sgt. Doe, "Justice" and soldiers 1·40 1·40

1981. People's Redemption Council (2nd series).
1475 6 c. Type **305** 10 10
1476 23 c. As No. 1461 20 20
1477 31 c. As No. 1462 45 45
1478 41 c. As No. 1463 60 60

MINIMUM PRICE

The minimum price quoted is 10p which represents a handling charge rather than a basis for valuing common stamps. For further notes about prices, see introductory pages.

308 John Adams

309 Prince Charles and Lady Diana Spencer

1981. Presidents of the United States (1st series). Multicoloured.

1479 4 c. Type **308** 10 10
1480 5 c. William Henry Harrison 10 10
1481 10 c. Martin Van Buren . . . 15 15
1482 17 c. James Monroe 20 20
1483 20 c. John Quincy Adams . . 25 25
1484 22 c. James Madison 25 25
1485 27 c. Thomas Jefferson . . . 35 30
1486 30 c. Andrew Jackson 55 50
1487 40 c. John Tyler 80 70
1488 80 c. George Washington . . 1·50 1·50
See also Nos. 1494/1503, 1519/27 and 1533/42.

1981. British Royal Wedding. Multicoloured.

1490 31 c. Type **309** 30 30
1491 41 c. Intertwined initials . . . 40 40
1492 62 c. St. Paul's Cathedral . . 60 60

1981. Presidents of the United States (2nd series). As T **308**. Multicoloured.

1494 6 c. Rutherford B. Hayes . . 10 10
1495 12 c. Ulysses S. Grant . . . 15 15
1496 14 c. Millard Fillmore . . . 20 15
1497 15 c. Zachary Taylor 20 15
1498 20 c. Abraham Lincoln . . . 25 20
1499 27 c. Andrew Johnson . . . 30 25
1500 31 c. James Buchanan . . . 50 45
1501 41 c. James A. Garfield . . . 70 60
1502 50 c. James K. Polk 80 70
1503 55 c. Franklin Pierce . . . . 1·00 85

1981. Liberian Products (2nd series). As T **277**, but smaller, 33 × 20 mm. Multicoloured.

1504a 1 c. Mano River Bridge . . 10 10
1505 3 c. Type **277** 10 10
1506 6 c. Rubber tree and tyre . . 10 10
1506a 15 c. Combine harvester . . 20 15
1507 25 c. Mesurado shrimp . . . 35 35
1508 31 c. Hydro-electric plant . . 45 45
1509 41 c. Dress and woman tie-dying cloth 60 55
1509a 80 c. Barracuda . . . . . . 1·90 1·50
1510 $1 Diesel train carrying iron ore . . . . 2·50 1·50

310 Disabled Children

312 Lady Diana Spencer

311 Examination Room

1982. International Year of Disabled People (1981). Multicoloured.

1515 23 c. Type **310** 35 35
1516 62 c. Child leading blind woman 1·25 95

1982. 30th Anniv of West African Examination Council.

1517 **311** 6 c. multicoloured . . . 10 10
1518 31 c. multicoloured . . . 45 45

1982. Presidents of the United States (3rd series). As T **308**. Multicoloured.

1519 4 c. William Taft 10 25
1520 5 c. Calvin Coolidge 10 10
1521 6 c. Benjamin Harrison . . . 15 15
1522 10 c. Warren Harding 20 25
1523 22 c. Grover Cleveland . . . 45 45
1524 27 c. Chester Arthur 50 70
1525 31 c. Woodrow Wilson . . . 60 60
1526 41 c. William McKinley . . . 70 80
1527 80 c. Theodore Roosevelt . . 1·50 1·60

1982. Princess of Wales. 21st Birthday. Mult.

1529 31 c. Type **312** 45 45
1530 41 c. Lady Diana Spencer (different) 60 60
1531 62 c. Lady Diana accepting flower . . . . 1·25 1·25

1982. Presidents of the United States (4th series). As T **308**. Multicoloured.

1533 4 c. Jimmy Carter 10 10
1534 6 c. Gerald Ford 15 15
1535 14 c. Harry Truman 25 25
1536 17 c. Franklin D. Roosevelt 30 30
1537 23 c. Lyndon B. Johnson . . 40 40
1538 27 c. Richard Nixon 45 50
1539 31 c. John F. Kennedy . . . 50 60
1540 35 c. Ronald Reagan 60 80
1541 50 c. Herbert Hoover . . . 80 90
1542 55 c. Dwight D. Eisenhower 1·00 1·00

1982. Birth of Prince William of Wales. Nos. 1529/31 optd **ROYAL BABY 21-6-82 PRINCE WILLIAM.**

1544 31 c. Type **312** 45 45
1545 41 c. Lady Diana Spencer (different) 60 60
1546 62 c. Lady Diana accepting flower 95 95

314 Lt. Col. Fallah nGaida Varney

1983. 3rd Anniv of National Redemption Day. Multicoloured.

1548 3 c. Type **314** 10 10
1549 6 c. Commander-in-Chief Samuel Doe 10 10
1550 10 c. Major-General Jlatoh Nicholas Podier 15 15
1551 15 c. Brigadier-General Jeffery Sei Gbatu 20 15
1552 31 c. Brigadier-General Thomas Gunkama Quiwonkpa . . 50 45
1553 41 c. Colonel Abraham Doward Kollie 60 80

315 National Archives Centre

1983. Opening of National Archives Centre. Multicoloured.

1555 6 c. Type **315** 10 10
1556 31 c. National Archives Centre 50 45

316 "Circumcision of Christ"

1983. Christmas. 500th Birth Anniv of Raphael. Multicoloured.

1557 6 c. Type **316** 10 10
1558 15 c. "Adoration of the Magi" (detail) 20 15
1559 25 c. "The Annunciation" (detail) 40 35
1560 31 c. "Madonna of the Baldachino" 50 45
1561 41 c. "Holy Family" (detail) 60 55
1562 62 c. "Madonna and Child with Five Saints" (detail) . . . 90 85

317 Graduates of M.U.R. Training Programmes

1984. 10th Anniv (1983) of Mano River Union. Multicoloured.

1564 6 c. Type **317** 10 10
1565 25 c. Map of Africa 40 35
1566 31 c. Presidents and map of member states 50 45
1567 41 c. President of Guinea signing Accession Agreement 70 85

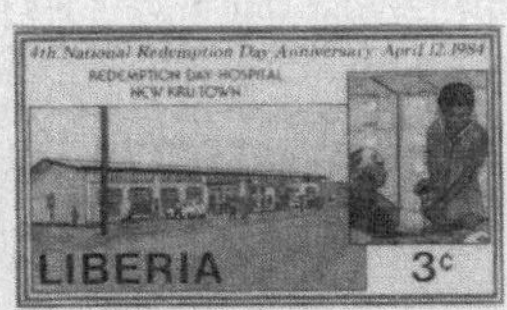

318 Redemption Day Hospital, New Kru Town

1984. 4th Anniv of National Redemption Day. Multicoloured.

1569 3 c. Type **318** 10 10
1570 10 c. Ganta-Harpa Highway project 15 15
1571 20 c. Opening of Constitution Assembly 35 30
1572 31 c. Commander-in-Chief Doe launching Ganta-Harper Highway project 50 45
1573 41 c. Presentation of Draft Constitution 70 85

319 "Adoration of the Magi"

1984. Rubens Paintings (1st series). Multicoloured.

1574 6 c. Type **319** 10 10
1575 15 c. "Coronation of Catherine" 25 20
1576 25 c. "Adoration of the Magi" 70 70
1577 31 c. "Madonna and Child with Halo" 85 85
1578 41 c. "Adoration of the Shepherds" . . . . 1·10 1·10
1579 62 c. "Madonna and Child with Saints" . . . . 1·75 1·75
See also Nos. 1612/17.

320 Jesse Owens

1984. Olympic Games, Los Angeles. Multicoloured.

1581 3 c. Type **320** 10 10
1582 4 c. Rafer Johnson 10 10
1583 25 c. Miruts Yifter 65 65
1584 41 c. Kipchoge Keino . . . . 1·10 1·10
1585 62 c. Muhammad Ali . . . . 1·75 1·75

321 Liberian Ducks and Water Birds

1984. Louisiana World Exposition. Multicoloured.

1587 6 c. Type **321** 60 20
1588 31 c. Bulk carrier loading ore at Buchanan Harbour . . . . 1·25 75
1589 41 c. Liberian fishes . . . . . 1·10 1·10
1590 62 c. Diesel train carrying iron ore . . . . 1·75 1·75

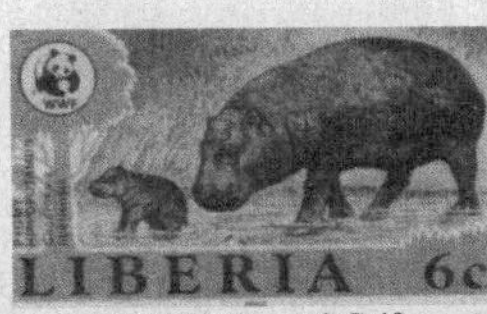

322 Mother and Calf

1984. Pygmy Hippopotami. Multicoloured.

1591 6 c. Type **322** 20 10
1592 10 c. Pair of hippopotami . . 30 15
1593 20 c. Close-up of hippopotamus 70 35
1594 31 c. Hippopotamus and map 1·00 50

323 Mrs. Doe and Children

1984. Indigent Children's Home, Bensonville. Multicoloured.

1595 6 c. Type **323** 10 10
1596 31 c. Mrs. Doe and children (different) 85 85

324 New Soldiers' Barracks

1985. 5th Anniv of National Redemption Day. Multicoloured.

1597 6 c. Type **324** 10 10
1598 31 c. Pan-African Plaza . . . 85 85

325 Bohemian Waxwing

1985. Birth Bicentenary of John J. Audubon (ornithologist). Multicoloured.

1599 1 c. Type **325** 10 10
1600 3 c. Bay-breasted warbler . . 20 10
1601 6 c. White-winged crossbill . 25 15
1602 31 c. Grey phalarope . . . . 1·25 85
1603 41 c. Eastern bluebird . . . 1·75 1·25
1604 62 c. Common cardinal . . . 2·50 1·90

326 Germany v. Morocco, 1970

1985. World Cup Football Championship, Mexico (1986). Multicoloured.

1605 6 c. Type **326** 10 10
1606 15 c. Zaire v. Brazil, 1974 . . 20 15
1607 25 c. Tunisia v. Germany, 1978 60 60
1608 31 c. Cameroun v. Peru, 1982 (vert) 75 75
1609 41 c. Algeria v. Germany, 1982 95 95
1610 62 c. Senegal team . . . . . 1·40 1·40

327 "Mirror of Venus" (detail)

328 Women transplanting rice

1985. Rubens Paintings (2nd series). Mult.

1612 6 c. Type **327** 10 10
1613 15 c. "Adam and Eve in Paradise" (detail) 20 15
1614 25 c. "Andromeda" (detail) . 60 60
1615 31 c. "The Three Graces" (detail) 75 75
1616 41 c. "Venus and Adonis" (detail) 95 95
1617 62 c. "The Daughters of Leucippus" (detail) . . . . 1·40 1·40

1985. World Food Day.

1619 **328** 25 c. multicoloured . . . 50 60
1620 31 c. multicoloured . . . 60 75

329 Queen Mother in Garter Robes

330 Alamo, San Antonio, Texas

1985. 85th Birthday of Queen Elizabeth the Queen Mother. Multicoloured.

1621	31 c. Type **329**	35	30
1622	41 c. At the races	55	50
1623	62 c. Waving to the crowds	80	70

1986. "Ameripex '86" International Stamp Exhibition, Chicago. Multicoloured.

1625	25 c. Type **330**	60	60
1626	31 c. Liberty Bell, Philadelphia	75	75
1627	80 c. Magnifying glass, emblem and Liberian stamps	1·90	1·90

331 Unveiling Ceremony, 1886 (after E. Moran)

333 Royal Theatre. Gendarmenmarkt

332 Max Julen (Men's Giant Slalom)

1986. Centenary of Statue of Liberty. Multicoloured.

1628	20 c. Type **331**	30	50
1629	31 c. Frederic-Auguste Bartholdi (sculptor) and statue	75	75
1630	$1 Head of statue	2·40	2·40

1987. Winter Olympic Games, Calgary (1988). 1984 Games Gold Medallists. Multicoloured.

1631	3 c. Type **332**	10	10
1632	6 c. Debbi Armstrong (women's giant slalom)	10	10
1633	31 c. Peter Angerer (biathlon)	35	55
1634	60 c. Bill Johnson (men's downhill)	1·10	1·10
1635	80 c. East German team (four-man bobsleigh)	1·40	1·40

1987. Liberian–German Friendship. 750th Anniv of Berlin. Multicoloured.

1637	6 c. Type **333**	10	10
1638	31 c. Kaiser Friedrich Museum, River Spree	35	55
1639	60 c. Charlottenburg Palace	1·10	1·10
1640	80 c. Kaiser Wilhelm Memorial Church	1·40	1·40

334 Othello and Desdemona ("Othello")

1987. William Shakespeare. Multicoloured.

1642	3 c. Type **334**	10	10
1643	6 c. Romeo and Juliet ("Romeo and Juliet")	10	10
1644	10 c. Falstaff ("The Merry Wives of Windsor")	15	10
1645	15 c. Falstaff, Doll Tearsheet and Prince Hal ("Henry IV", Part 2)	20	15
1646	31 c. Hamlet holding Yorick's skull ("Hamlet")	35	50
1647	60 c. Macbeth and the three witches ("Macbeth")	1·00	1·00
1648	80 c. Lear and companions in the storm ("King Lear")	1·40	1·40
1649	$2 William Shakespeare and Globe Theatre, Southwark	3·25	3·25

335 Emblem

1987. Amateur Radio Week. 25th Anniv of Liberia Radio Amateur Association. Multicoloured.

1650	10 c. Type **335**	15	10
1651	10 c. Amateur radio enthusiasts	15	10
1652	35 c. Certificate awarded to participants in anniversary "On the Air" activity	40	30
1653	35 c. Globe, flags and banner	40	30

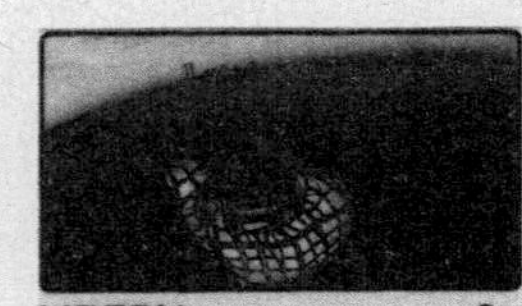

336 Illuminated Torch Flame

1987. Centenary of Statue of Liberty. Multicoloured.

1654	6 c. Type **336**	10	10
1655	6 c. Scaffolding around statue's head	10	10
1656	6 c. Men working on head	10	10
1657	6 c. Men working on crown	10	10
1658	6 c. Statue's toes	10	10
1659	15 c. Statue behind "Sir Winston Churchill" (cadet schooner)	35	20
1660	15 c. "Bay Queen" (harbour ferry)	35	20
1661	15 c. Posters on buildings and crowd	20	15
1662	15 c. Tug and schooner in bay	35	20
1663	15 c. Decorated statues around building	20	15
1664	31 c. Fireworks display around statue	35	25
1665	31 c. Statue floodlit	35	25
1666	31 c. Statue's head	35	25
1667	31 c. Fireworks display around statue (different)	35	25
1668	31 c. Statue (half-length)	35	25
1669	60 c. Wall poster on building (vert)	70	85
1670	60 c. Yachts and cabin cruisers on river (vert)	1·25	75
1671	60 c. Measuring statue's nose (vert)	70	85
1672	60 c. Plastering nose (vert)	70	85
1673	60 c. Finishing off repaired nose (vert)	70	85

337 Dr. Doe (President), Dr. Moniba (Vice-President), Flags and Hands

1988. 2nd Anniv of Second Republic.

1674	**337**	10 c. multicoloured	15	10
1675		35 c. multicoloured	40	30

338 Breast-feeding

1988. U.N.I.C.E.F. Child Survival and Development Campaign. Multicoloured.

1676	3 c. Type **338**	10	10
1677	6 c. Oral rehydration therapy (vert)	10	10
1678	31 c. Immunization	35	25
1679	$1 Growth monitoring (vert)	1·50	1·50

339 Chief Justice Emmanuel N. Gbalazeh swearing-in Dr. Samuel Kanyon Doe

1988. Inauguration of Second Republic.

1680	**339**	6 c. multicoloured	10	10

340 Footballer and Stadium

1988. 2nd Anniv of Opening of Samuel Kanyon Doe Sports Complex.

1681	**340**	31 c. multicoloured	35	25

341 Child and Volunteer reading

1988. 25th Anniv of U.S. Peace Corps in Liberia.

1682	**341**	10 c. multicoloured	10	10
1683		35 c. multicoloured	40	30

342 Pres. Doe, Farm Workers and Produce

1988. Green Revolution.

1684	**342**	10 c. multicoloured	10	10
1685		35 c. multicoloured	40	30

344 Emblem

345 "GP 10" Locomotive, Nimba

1988. 25th Anniv of Organization of African Unity.

1687	**344**	10 c. multicoloured	10	10
1688		35 c. multicoloured	40	60
1689		$1 multicoloured	1·60	1·60

1988. Locomotives. Multicoloured.

1690	10 c. Type **345**	10	10
1691	35 c. Triple engined iron ore train	80	80

346 Helping Boy to Walk

347 Baseball

1988. 25th Anniv of St. Joseph's Catholic Hospital. Multicoloured.

1693	10 c. Type **346**	10	10
1694	10 c. Medical staff and hospital	10	10
1695	35 c. Monk, child, candle and hospital	65	65
1696	$1 Map behind doctor with nurse holding baby	1·90	1·90

1988. Olympic Games, Seoul. Multicoloured.

1697	10 c. Type **347**	10	10
1698	35 c. Hurdling	65	65
1699	45 c. Fencing	80	80
1700	80 c. Synchronised swimming	1·40	1·40
1701	$1 Yachting	1·75	1·75

348 Monkey Bridge

349 Tending Crops

1988.

1703	10 c. Type **348**	10	10
1704	35 c Sasa players (horiz)	40	60
1705	45 c. Snake dancers	75	75

1988. 10th Anniv of International Fund for Agricultural Development. Multicoloured.

1706	10 c. Type **349**	10	10
1707	35 c. Farmers tending livestock and spraying crops	40	60

350 Destruction of Royal Exchange, 1838

1988. 300th Anniv of Lloyd's of London. Multicoloured.

1708	10 c. Type **350**	10	10
1709	35 c. Britten Norman Islander airplane (horiz)	60	60
1710	45 c. "Chevron Antwerp" (tanker) (horiz)	70	75
1711	$1 "Lakonia" (liner) ablaze, 1963	1·75	1·75

351 Honouring Head of Operational Smile Team

1989. 3rd Anniv of Second Republic.

1712	**351**	10 c. black and blue	10	10
1713		35 c. black and red	40	60
1714	–	50 c. black and mauve	85	85

DESIGN: 50 c. Pres. Samuel Doe at John F. Kennedy Memorial Hospital.

1989. Presidents of United States (5th series). As T **308**. Multicoloured.

1715	$1 George Bush	1·60	1·60

352 "Harmony"

353 Union Glass Factory, Gardersville, Monrovia

1989. Liberia–Japan Friendship. 50th Anniv of Rissho Kosei-Kai (lay Buddhist association). Multicoloured.

1716	10 c. Type **352**	10	10
1717	10 c. Nikkyo Niwano (founder and president of association)	10	10
1718	10 c. Rissho Kosei-Kai headquarters, Tokyo	10	10
1719	50 c. Eternal Buddha, Great Sacred Hall	85	85

1989. 15th Anniv of Mano River Union. Mult.

1721	10 c. Type **353**	15	10
1722	35 c. Presidents of Guinea, Sierra Leone and Liberia	40	30
1723	45 c. Monrovia–Freetown highway	55	45
1724	50 c. Flags, map and mail van	85	85
1725	$1 Presidents at 1988 Summit	1·60	1·60

354 Symbols of International Co-operation

357 Recovery Ship U.S.S. "Okinawa"

1989. World Telecommunications Day.

1726	**354**	50 c. multicoloured	85	85

1989. 20th Anniv of First Manned Landing on Moon. Multicoloured.
1728 10 c. Type **357** 30 10
1729 35 c. Edwin Aldrin, Neil Armstrong and Michael Collins (crew) (28 × 28 mm) 40 60
1730 45 c. "Apollo 11" flight emblem (28 × 28 mm) 80 80
1731 $1 Aldrin descending to Moon's surface 1·75 1·75

358 Renovation of Statue of Liberty

360 Nehru and Flag

1989. "Philexfrance '89" International Stamp Exhibition, Paris, and "World Stamp Expo '89" International Stamp Exhibition, Washington D.C. Multicoloured.
1733 25 c. Type **358** 30 20
1734 25 c. French contingent at statue centenary celebrations 30 20
1735 25 c. Statue, officials and commemorative plaque 30 20

1989. Birth Centenary of Jawaharlal Nehru (Indian statesman). Multicoloured.
1737 45 c. Type **360** 55 70
1738 50 c. Nehru 60 80

361 Close View of Station

1990. New Standard A Earth Satellite Station. Multicoloured.
1739 10 c. Type **361** 15 10
1740 35 c. Distant view of station 40 55

362 Emblem

1990. 25th Anniv of United States Educational and Cultural Foundation in Liberia. Multicoloured.
1741 10 c. Type **362** 15 10
1742 45 c. Similar to Type **362** but differently arranged 55 70

363 Flags, Arms, Map and Union Emblem

364 Bomi County

1990. 10th Anniv of Pan-African Postal Union.
1743 **363** 35 c. multicoloured 40 55

1990. County Flags. Multicoloured.
1744 10 c. Type **364** 10 10
1745 10 c. Bong 10 10
1746 10 c. Grand Bassa 10 10
1747 10 c. Grand Cape Mount 10 10
1748 10 c. Grand Gedeh 10 10
1749 10 c. Grand Kru 10 10
1750 10 c. Lofa 10 10
1751 10 c. Margibi 10 10
1752 10 c. Maryland 10 10
1753 10 c. Montserrado 10 10
1754 10 c. Nimba 10 10
1755 10 c. Rivercress 10 10
1756 10 c. Sinoe 10 10
1757 35 c. Type **364** 40 55
1758 35 c. Bong 40 55
1759 35 c. Grand Bassa 40 55
1760 35 c. Grand Cape Mount 40 55
1761 35 c. Grand Gedeh 40 55
1762 35 c. Grand Kru 40 55
1763 35 c. Lofa 40 55
1764 35 c. Margibi 40 55
1765 35 c. Maryland 40 55
1766 35 c. Montserrado 40 55
1767 35 c. Nimba 40 55
1768 35 c. Rivercress 40 55
1769 35 c. Sinoe 40 55
1770 45 c. Type **364** 50 70
1771 45 c. Bong 50 70
1772 45 c. Grand Bassa 50 70
1773 45 c. Grand Cape Mount 50 70
1774 45 c. Grand Gedeh 50 70
1775 45 c. Grand Kru 50 70
1776 45 c. Lofa 50 70
1777 45 c. Margibi 50 70
1778 45 c. Maryland 50 70
1779 45 c. Montserrado 50 70
1780 45 c. Nimba 50 70
1781 45 c. Rivercress 50 70
1782 45 c. Sinoe 50 70
1783 50 c. Type **364** 80 80
1784 50 c. Bong 80 80
1785 50 c. Grand Bassa 80 80
1786 50 c. Grand Cape Mount 80 80
1787 50 c. Grand Gedeh 80 80
1788 50 c. Grand Kru 80 80
1789 50 c. Lofa 80 80
1790 50 c. Margibi 80 80
1791 50 c. Maryland 80 80
1792 50 c. Montserrado 80 80
1793 50 c. Nimba 80 80
1794 50 c. Rivercress 80 80
1795 50 c. Sinoe 80 80
1796 $1 Type **364** 1·60 1·60
1797 $1 Bong 1·60 1·60
1798 $1 Grand Bassa 1·60 1·60
1799 $1 Grand Cape Mount 1·60 1·60
1800 $1 Grand Gedeh 1·60 1·60
1801 $1 Grand Kru 1·60 1·60
1802 $1 Lofa 1·60 1·60
1803 $1 Margibi 1·60 1·60
1804 $1 Maryland 1·60 1·60
1805 $1 Montserrado 1·60 1·60
1806 $1 Nimba 1·60 1·60
1807 $1 Rivercress 1·60 1·60
1808 $1 Sinoe 1·60 1·60

365 Lady Elizabeth Bowes-Lyon as Girl

368 Boxing

367 Clasped Hands and Map

1991. 90th Birthday (1990) of Queen Elizabeth the Queen Mother. Multicoloured.
1809 10 c. Type **365** 15 10
1810 $2 As Duchess of York (29 × 36½ mm) 3·25 3·25

1991. National Unity. Multicoloured.
1812 35 c. Type **367** 40 50
1813 45 c. National flag and map of Africa (ECOMOG (West African States Economic Community peace-keeping forces)) 50 65
1814 50 c. Brewer, Konneh and Michael Francis (co-chairmen) and national flag (All-Liberia Conference) 60 75

1992. Olympic Games, Barcelona. Multicoloured.
1815 45 c. Type **368** 60 65
1816 50 c. Football 70 75
1817 $1 Weightlifting 1·40 1·50
1818 $2 Water polo 3·00 3·00

369 "Disarm Today"

1993. Peace and Redevelopment. Multicoloured.
1820 50 c. Type **369** 70 45
1821 $1 "Join your Parents and build Liberia" 1·40 85
1822 $2 "Peace must prevail in Liberia" 2·75 1·75

OFFICIAL STAMPS

1892. 1892 stamps optd **OFFICIAL.**
O 87 **7** 1 c. red 30 40
O 88 2 c. blue 30 50
O 89 **8** 4 c. black and green 2·50 4·00
O104 **9** 5 c. on 6 c. green (No. 89) 1·00 1·75
O 90 6 c. green 60 90
O 91 **10** 8 c. black and brown 1·00 1·25
O 92 **11** 12 c. red 1·50 1·75
O 93 **12** 16 c. lilac 2·00 2·50
O 94 **13** 24 c. green on yellow 1·40 1·75
O 95 **12** 32 c. blue 3·00 4·50
O 96 **15** $1 black and blue 15·00 18·00
O 97 **13** $2 brown on buff 10·00 12·00
O 98 **17** $5 black and red 12·00 15·00

1894. 1892 stamps optd **O S.**
O119 **7** 1 c. red 30 60
O120 2 c. blue 35 70
O121 **8** 4 c. black and green 2·75 3·00
O122 **10** 8 c. black and brown 1·50 2·00
O123 **11** 12 c. red 1·75 2·50
O124 **12** 16 c. lilac 2·50 3·00
O125 **13** 24 c. green on yellow 2·00 2·50
O126 **12** 32 c. blue 3·50 4·00
O127 **$1** black and blue 20·00 22·00
O128 **$2** brown on buff 12·50 16·00
O129 **$5** black and red 70·00 70·00

1894. 1894 stamp in different colours optd **O S.** Imperf or roul.
O130 **24** 5 c. green and lilac 1·75 2·00

1898. 1897 stamps optd **O S.**
O157 **9** 1 c. purple 35 35
O158 1 c. green 35 35
O159 **15** 2 c. black and bistre 1·50 2·00
O160 2 c. black and red 2·00 2·50
O161 **8** 5 c. black and lake 2·25 1·75
O162 5 c. black and blue 2·50 2·50
O163 **10** 10 c. blue and yellow 1·00 1·25
O164 **11** 15 c. black 1·00 1·50
O165 **12** 20 c. red 1·25 2·00
O166 **13** 25 c. green 1·50 2·00
O167 **12** 30 c. blue 2·00 2·75
O168 **35** 50 c. black and brown 1·75 2·50

†1903. Stamp of 1903, but different colour, optd **O S.**
O210 **40** 3 c. green 20 15

1904. Nos. O104 and 167 surch **ONE O S.** and bars or **O S 2** and bars.
O222 **9** 1 c. on 5 c. on 6 c. green 1·10 1·10
O223 **12** 2 c. on 30 c. blue 6·75 6·75

†1906. Stamps of 1906, but different colours, optd **O S.**
O237 **50** 1 c. black and green 50 50
O238 **51** 2 c. black and red 15 8
O239 – 5 c. black and blue 2·00 35
O240 – 10 c. black and violet 5·00 60
O241 – 15 c. black and brown 4·00 75
O242 – 20 c. black and green 5·00 75
O243 – 25 c. grey and purple 60 15
O244 – 30 c. brown 50 15
O245 – 50 c. green and brown 90 20
O246 – 75 c. black and blue 3·00 75
O247 – $1 black and green 1·00 25
O248 **52** $2 black and purple 1·50 25
O249 **53** $5 black and orange 3·50 30

†1909. Stamps of 1909, but different colours, optd **O S.** 10 c. perf or roul.
O262 **55** 1 c. black and green 15 10
O263 – 2 c. brown and red 15 10
O264 **56** 5 c. black and blue 1·00 15
O266 **57** 10 c. blue and black 50 25
O267 – 15 c. black and purple 50 25
O268 – 20 c. green and bistre 1·25 45
O269 – 25 c. green and blue 70 50
O270 – 30 c. blue 1·00 40
O271 – 50 c. green and brown 2·25 40
O272 – 75 c. black and violet 1·50 40

1910. No. O266 surch **3 CENTS INLAND POSTAGE.** Perf or roul.
O276 **57** 3 c. on 10 c. blue & black 90 45

1914. Official stamps surch: (A) **1914 2 CENTS.** (B) **+ 2 c.** (C) **5.** (D) **CENTS 20 OFFICIAL.**
O291 **57** + 2 c. on 3 c. on 10 c. blue and black (B) (No. O275) 60 1·25
O284 – 2 c. on 25 c. grey and pur (A) (No. O243) 15·00 7·50
O285 – 5 c. on 30 c. blue (C) (No. O270) 11·00 4·50
O286 – 20 c. on 75 c. black and violet (D) (No. O272) 11·00 4·50

1914. No. 233 surch **CENTS 20 OFFICIAL.**
O287 20 c. on 75 c. black and brown 11·00 4·50

1915. Official stamps of 1906 and 1909 surch in different ways.
O325 – 1 c. on 2 c. brown and red (No. O263) 2·25 2·50
O326 **56** 2 c. on 5 c. black and blue (No. O264) 2·50 3·00
O310 – 2 c. on 15 c. black and purple (No. O267) 95 1·25
O311 – 2 c. on 25 c. green and blue (No. O269) 5·50 5·50
O312 – 5 c. on 20 c. green and bistre (No. O268) 1·25 1·50
O313 – 5 c. on 30 c. green and brown (No. O270) 5·50 5·50
O314 – 10 c. on 50 c. green and brown (No. O271) 6·50 7·50
O316 – 20 c. on 75 c. black and violet (No. O272) 2·75 3·50
O317 – 25 c. on $1 black and green (No. O247) 11·00 12·00
O318 **52** 50 c. on $2 black and purple (No. O248) 13·00 15·00
O320 **53** $1 on $5 black and orange (No. O249) 15·00 18·00

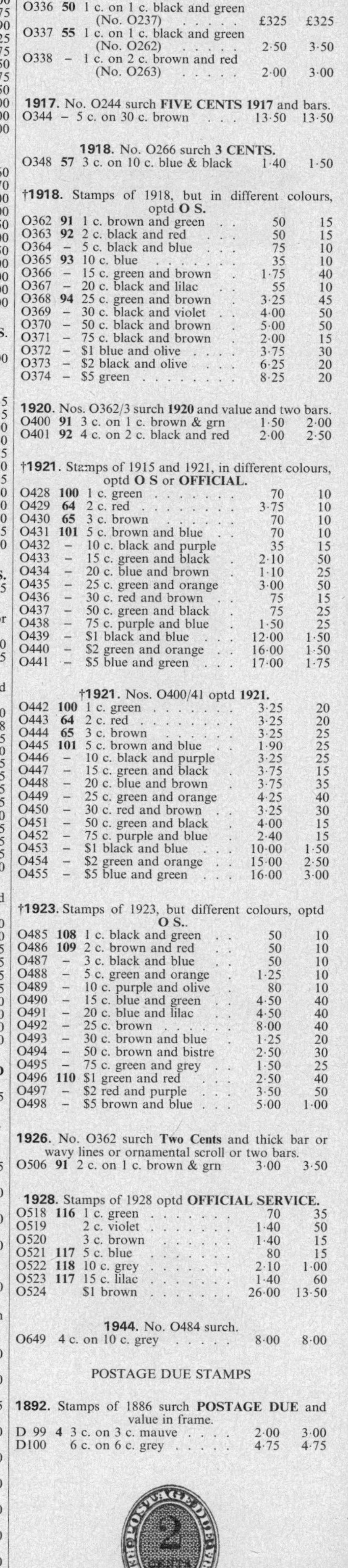

1915. No. O168 surch **10 10** and ornaments and bars.
O321 **35** 10 c. on 50 c. black & brn 9·75 9·75

1915. Military Field Post. Official stamps surch **L E F 1 c.**
O336 **50** 1 c. on 1 c. black and green (No. O237) £325 £325
O337 **55** 1 c. on 1 c. black and green (No. O262) 2·50 3·50
O338 – 1 c. on 2 c. brown and red (No. O263) 2·00 3·00

1917. No. O244 surch **FIVE CENTS 1917** and bars.
O344 – 5 c. on 30 c. brown 13·50 13·50

1918. No. O266 surch **3 CENTS.**
O348 **57** 3 c. on 10 c. blue & black 1·40 1·50

†1918. Stamps of 1918, but in different colours, optd **O S.**
O362 **91** 1 c. brown and green 50 15
O363 **92** 2 c. black and red 50 15
O364 – 5 c. black and blue 75 10
O365 **93** 10 c. blue 35 10
O366 – 15 c. green and brown 1·75 40
O367 – 20 c. black and lilac 55 10
O368 **94** 25 c. green and brown 3·25 45
O369 – 30 c. black and violet 4·00 50
O370 – 50 c. black and brown 5·00 50
O371 – 75 c. black and brown 2·00 15
O372 – $1 blue and olive 3·75 30
O373 – $2 black and olive 6·25 20
O374 – $5 green 8·25 20

1920. Nos. O362/3 surch **1920** and value and two bars.
O400 **91** 3 c. on 1 c. brown & grn 1·50 2·00
O401 **92** 4 c. on 2 c. black and red 2·00 2·50

†1921. Stamps of 1915 and 1921, in different colours, optd **O S** or **OFFICIAL.**
O428 **100** 1 c. green 70 10
O429 **64** 2 c. red 3·75 10
O430 **65** 3 c. brown 70 10
O431 **101** 5 c. brown and blue 70 10
O432 – 10 c. black and purple 35 15
O433 – 15 c. green and black 2·10 50
O434 – 20 c. blue and brown 1·10 25
O435 – 25 c. green and orange 3·00 50
O436 – 30 c. red and brown 75 15
O437 – 50 c. green and black 75 25
O438 – 75 c. purple and blue 1·50 25
O439 – $1 black and blue 12·00 1·50
O440 – $2 green and orange 16·00 1·50
O441 – $5 blue and green 17·00 1·75

†1921. Nos. O400/41 optd **1921.**
O442 **100** 1 c. green 3·25 20
O443 **64** 2 c. red 3·25 20
O444 **65** 3 c. brown 3·25 25
O445 **101** 5 c. brown and blue 1·90 25
O446 – 10 c. black and purple 3·25 25
O447 – 15 c. green and black 3·75 15
O448 – 20 c. blue and brown 3·75 35
O449 – 25 c. green and orange 4·25 40
O450 – 30 c. red and brown 3·25 30
O451 – 50 c. green and black 4·00 15
O452 – 75 c. purple and blue 2·40 15
O453 – $1 black and blue 10·00 1·50
O454 – $2 green and orange 15·00 2·50
O455 – $5 blue and green 16·00 3·00

†1923. Stamps of 1923, but different colours, optd **O S.**
O485 **108** 1 c. black and green 50 10
O486 **109** 2 c. brown and red 50 10
O487 – 3 c. black and blue 50 10
O488 – 5 c. green and orange 1·25 10
O489 – 10 c. purple and olive 80 10
O490 – 15 c. blue and green 4·50 40
O491 – 20 c. blue and lilac 4·50 40
O492 – 25 c. brown 8·00 40
O493 – 30 c. brown and blue 1·25 20
O494 – 50 c. brown and bistre 2·50 30
O495 – 75 c. green and grey 1·50 25
O496 **110** $1 green and red 2·50 40
O497 – $2 red and purple 3·50 50
O498 – $5 brown and blue 5·00 1·00

1926. No. O362 surch **Two Cents** and thick bar or wavy lines or ornamental scroll or two bars.
O506 **91** 2 c. on 1 c. brown & grn 3·00 3·50

1928. Stamps of 1928 optd **OFFICIAL SERVICE.**
O518 **116** 1 c. green 70 35
O519 2 c. violet 1·40 50
O520 3 c. brown 1·40 15
O521 **117** 5 c. blue 80 15
O522 **118** 10 c. grey 2·10 1·00
O523 **117** 15 c. lilac 1·40 60
O524 $1 brown 26·00 13·50

1944. No. O484 surch.
O649 4 c. on 10 c. grey 8·00 8·00

POSTAGE DUE STAMPS

1892. Stamps of 1886 surch **POSTAGE DUE** and value in frame.
D 99 **4** 3 c. on 3 c. mauve 2·00 3·00
D100 6 c. on 6 c. grey 4·75 4·75

D 23

1894.

No.	Type	Description	Unused	Used
D110	D 23	2 c. black and orange on yellow	95	1·00
D111		4 c. blk & red on rose	95	1·00
D112		6 c. blk & brn on buff	95	1·00
D113		8 c. black & blue on bl	1·00	1·50
D114		10 c. black and green on mauve	1·25	2·00
D115		20 c. black and violet on grey	1·25	2·00
D116		40 c. black and brown on green	2·10	2·50

REGISTRATION STAMPS

R 22

1893.

No.	Type	Description	Unused	Used
R105	R 22	(10 c.) black (Buchanan)	£275	£350
R106		(10 c.) black ("Grenville")	£1000	£1250
R107		(10 c.) black (Harper)	£1000	£1250
R108		(10 c.) black (Monrovia)	40·00	£175
R109		(10 c.) blk (Robertsport)	£500	£575

1894. Surch **10 CENTS 10** twice.

No.	Type	Description	Unused	Used
R140	R 22	10 c. blue on pink (Buchanan)	3·75	3·75
R141		10 c. green on buff (Harper)	3·75	3·75
R142		10 c. red on yellow (Monrovia)	3·75	3·75
R143		10 c. red on blue (Robertsport) . . .	3·75	3·75

R 42. Pres. Gibson

†1904.

No.	Type	Description	Unused	Used
R211	R 42	10 c. black and blue (Buchanan)	1·50	25
R212		10 c. black and red ("Grenville")	1·50	25
R213		10 c. black and green (Harper)	1·50	25
R214		10 c. black and violet (Monrovia)	1·50	25
R215		10 c. black and purple (Robertsport) . . .	1·50	25

R 96. Patrol Boat "Quail"

1919. Roul or perf.

No.	Type	Description	Unused	Used
R388	R 96	10 c. blue and black (Buchanan)	90	5·75
R389		10 c. black and brown ("Grenville")	90	7·50
R390		10 c. black and green (Harper)	90	5·25
R391		10 c. blue and violet (Monrovia)	90	5·75
R392		10 c. black and red (Robertsport) . . .	90	7·50

R 106. Gabon Viper

†1921.

No.	Type	Description	Unused	Used
R456	R 106	10 c. black and red (Buchanan)	23·00	2·50
R457		10 c. black and red (Greenville)	14·00	2·50
R458		10 c. black and blue (Harper)	18·00	2·50
R459		10 c. black and orange (Monrovia)	14·00	2·50
R460		10 c. black and green (Robertsport) . . .	14·00	2·50

†1921. Optd **1921.**

No.	Type	Description	Unused	Used
R461	R 106	10 c. black and lake	17·00	4·25
R462		10 c. black and red	17·00	4·25
R463		10 c. black and blue	17·00	4·25
R464		10 c. black and orange	17·00	4·25
R465		10 c. black and green	17·00	4·25

R 111. Sailing Skiff (Buchanan)

†1923. Various sea views.

No.	Type	Description	Unused	Used
R499	R 111	10 c. red and black	8·50	55
R500	–	10 c. green and black	8·50	55
R501	–	10 c. orange and black	8·50	55
R502	–	10 c. blue and black	8·50	55
R503	–	10 c. violet and black	8·50	55

DESIGNS: No. R500, Lighter (Greenville); R501, Full-rigged sailing ship (Harper); R502, "George Washington" (liner) (Monrovia); R503, Canoe (Robertsport).

1941. No. 576 surch **REGISTERED 10 CENTS 10.**

No.	Description	Unused	Used
R592	10 c. on 5 c. brown (postage)	1·40	1·40
R593	10 c. on 5 c. brown (air) . .	1·40	1·40

No. R593 is additionally optd with airplane and **AIR MAIL**.

SPECIAL DELIVERY STAMPS

1941. No. 576 surch with postman and **SPECIAL DELIVERY 10 CENTS 10.**

No.	Description	Unused	Used
S590	10 c. on 5 c. brown (postage)	1·40	1·40
S591	10 c. on 5 c. brown (air) . .	1·40	1·40

No. S591 is additionally optd with airplane and **AIR MAIL**.

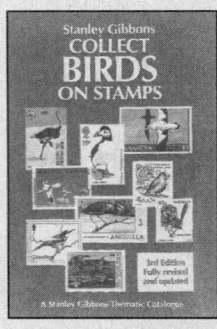

LIBYA Pt. 8; Pt. 13

A former Italian colony in N. Africa, comprising the governorates of Cyrenaica and Tripolitania. From the end of 1951 an independent kingdom including the Fezzan also. Following a revolution in 1969 the country became the Libyan Arab Republic.

1912. 100 centesimi = 1 lira
1952. 1000 milliemes = 1 Libyan pound
1972. 1000 dirhams = 1 dinar

A. ITALIAN COLONY.

1912. Stamps of Italy optd **LIBIA** (No. 5) or **Libia** (others).

1 **30** 1 c. brown 10 55
2 **31** 2 c. brown 10 25
3 **37** 5 c. green 10 10
4 10 c. red 10 10
5 **41** 15 c. black . . . . 18·00 1·10
6 **37** 15 c. grey . . . . 1·90 3·25
7 **33** 20 c. orange 25 25
8 **41** 20 c. orange . . . . 1·10 2·75
9 **39** 25 c. blue 45 35
10 40 c. brown . . . . 70 1·00
11 **33** 45 c. olive . . . . 7·50 9·50
12 **39** 50 c. mauve . . . . 2·25 85
13 60 c. red . . . . 4·25 9·50
14 **34** 1 l. brown and green . . . . 24·00 1·90
15 5 l. blue and red £120 £150
16 10 l. olive and red . . . . . 9·50 35·00

1915. Red Cross stamps of Italy optd **LIBIA.**

17 **53** 10 c. + 5 c. red . . . . . . 80 3·50
18 **54** 15 c. + 5 c. grey . . . . . 3·75 8·00
19 20 c. on 15 c. + 5 c. grey . . 3·75 8·00
20 20 c. + 5 c. orange . . . . 1·25 4·75

1916. No. 100 of Italy optd **LIBIA.**

21 **41** 20 c. on 15 c. grey . . . . . 16·00 4·50

4 Roman Legionary

5 Goddess of Plenty

6 Roman Galley leaving Tripoli

7 Victory

9 "Libyan Sibyl" by Michelangelo

10 Bedouin Woman

1921.

22 **4** 1 c. brown and black . . . 20 90
23 2 c. brown and black . . . 20 90
24 5 c. green and black . . . 40 55
50 7½ c. brown and black . . . 30 1·25
51 **5** 10 c. pink and black . . . 10 10
52 15 c. orange and brown . . 1·90 60
41 **9** 20 c. green 30 10
27 **5** 25 c. blue and deep blue . . 30 15
54 **6** 30 c. brown and black . . . 10 35
42 **9** 40 c. brown . . . . 1·10 40
55 **6** 50 c. green and black . . . 10 10
30 55 c. violet and black . . . 1·90 5·00
43 **9** 60 c. blue 30 10
57 **7** 75 c. red and purple . . . 10 10
58a 1 l. brown . . . . 1·25 10
59 **6** 1 l. 25 blue and indigo . . . 10 10
44 **9** 1 l. 75 orange 10 10
45 2 l. red . . . . 1·60 80
46 2 l. 55 violet . . . . . . 1·60 2·75
32 **7** 5 l. blue and black . . . . 9·00 7·00
33 10 l. green and blue . . . . 40·00 55·00

1922. Victory stamps of Italy optd **LIBIA.**

34 **62** 5 c. green . . . . 30 1·75
35 10 c. red . . . . 30 1·75
36 15 c. grey . . . . 35 3·00
37 25 c. blue . . . . 35 3·00

1922. Nos. 9 and 12 of Libya surch.

38 **39** 40 c. on 50 c. mauve . . . . 1·10 1·40
39 80 c. on 25 c. blue . . . . . 1·60 5·00

1928. Air. Air stamps of Italy optd **Libia.**

64 **88** 50 c. red . . . . 2·75 4·50
64 80 c. brown and purple . . . 5·00 19·00

1928. Types of Italy optd **LIBIA** (No. 67) or **Libia** (others).

65 **92** 7½ c. brown . . . . 5·00 15·00
66 **34** 1 l. 25 blue . . . . 23·00 11·00
67 **91** 1 l. 75 brown . . . . 28·00 1·25

1936. 10th Tripoli Trade Fair.

68 **10** 50 c. violet . . . . 70 1·40
69 1 l. 25 blue . . . . 90 4·25

1936. Air. Nos. 96 and 99 of Cyrenaica optd **LIBIA.**

70 – 50 c. violet 80 10
71 **17** 1 l. black . . . . 2·75 19·00

1937. Air. Stamps of Tripolitania optd **LIBIA.**

72 **18** 50 c. red 20 10
73 60 c. orange 35
74 75 c. blue . . . . 35 12·00
75 80 c. purple . . . . 35 12·00
76 **19** 1 l. blue 90 60
77 1 l. 20 brown . . . . 35 15·00
78 1 l. 50 orange 35
79 5 l. green 35

11 Triumphal Arch

12 Roman Theatre, Sabrata

1937. Inauguration of Coastal Highway.

80 **11** 50 c. red (postage) . . . . 1·10 2·75
81 1 l. 25 blue . . . . 1·10 6·50

82 **12** 50 c. purple (air) . . . . . 1·10 3·75
83 1 l. black . . . . 1·10 6·00

1937. 11th Tripoli Trade Fair. Optd **XI FIERA DI TRIPOLI.**

84 **11** 50 c. red (postage) . . . . 4·00 12·00
85 1 l. 25 blue . . . . 4·00 12·00

86 **12** 50 c. purple (air) . . . . . 4·00 12·00
87 1 l. black . . . . 4·00 12·00

14 Benghazi Waterfront

1938. 12th Tripoli Trade Fair.

88 **14** 5 c. brown (postage) . . . 15 35
89 – 10 c. sepia 15 35
90 **14** 25 c. green 35 35
91 – 50 c. violet 35 20
92 **14** 75 c. red . . . . 40 1·60
93 – 1 l. 25 blue . . . . 50 1·75
DESIGN: 10 c., 50 c., 1 l. 25, Fair Buildings.

94 50 c. olive (air) 70 75
95 1 l. blue . . . . 70 2·75
DESIGN—VERT: View of Tripoli.

16 Statue of Augustus

17 Eagle and Serpent

1938. Birth Bimillenary of Augustus.

96 **16** 5 c. olive (postage) 15 85
97 – 10 c. red 15 85
98 **16** 25 c. green 40 65
99 – 50 c. mauve 40 35
100 **16** 75 c. red . . . . 60 1·40
101 – 1 l. 25 blue . . . . 60 1·40

102 **17** 50 c. olive (air) . . . . . 35 1·10
103 1 l. mauve . . . . 50 2·50
DESIGN: 10, 50 c., 1 l. 25, Statue of Goddess of Plenty.

18 Agricultural Landscape

1939. 13th Tripoli Trade Fair. Inscr "XIII FIERA CAMPIONARIA DE TRIPOLI" etc.

104 **18** 5 c. olive (postage) 10 55
105 – 20 c. brown 30 55
106 **18** 50 c. mauve 35 30
107 – 75 c. red 40 90
108 **18** 1 l. 25 blue 40 90

109 – 25 c. green (air) . . . . . 25 1·10
110 – 50 c. green 30 90
111 – 1 l. mauve . . . . 35 1·10
DESIGNS: 20, 75 c. Ghadames; 25 c., 1 l. Arab, camel and Fiat G18V airliner over desert; 50 c. Fiat G18V airliner over Fair entrance.

19 Buildings

1940. Naples Exhibition.

112 **19** 5 c. brown (postage) 10 35
113 – 10 c. orange 10 35
114 – 25 c. green 50 85
115 **19** 50 c. violet 50 85
116 – 75 c. red . . . . 50 1·25
117 – 1 l. 25 blue . . . . 50 1·40
118 – 2 l. + 75 c. red . . . . . 50 2·00
DESIGNS—HORIZ: 10, 75 c., 2 l. Oxen and plough. VERT: 25 c., 1 l. 25, Mosque.

119 – 50 c. black (air) . . . . . 30 1·40
120 – 1 l. brown . . . . 30 1·40
121 – 2 l. + 75 c. blue . . . . . 55 2·25
122 – 5 l. + 2 l. 50 brown . . . . 55 2·25
DESIGNS—HORIZ: 50 c., 2 l. Savoia Marchetti S.M.75 airplane over city; 1, 5 l. Savoia Marchetti S-73 airplane over oasis.

19a Hitler and Mussolini

1941. Rome-Berlin Axis Commemoration.

123 **19a** 5 c. orange (postage) . . . 10 3·00
124 10 c. brown . . . . 10 3·00
125 20 c. purple . . . . 40 3·00
126 25 c. green . . . . 40 3·00
127 50 c. violet . . . . 40 3·00
128 75 c. red . . . . 40 5·00
129 1 l. 25 blue . . . . 40 5·00

130 50 c. green (air) . . . . . . 45 10·00

B. INDEPENDENT.

ليبيا — -- ليبيا -- ٤ ليرة ع. — -- ليبيا -- ٨ فرنك

LIBYA (20) — 4 MAL. LIBYA (21) — 8 FRANCS LIBYA (22)

1951. Stamps of Cyrenaica optd. (a) For use in Cyrenaica, optd as T **20.**

131 **24** 1 m. brown 15 15
132 2 m. red 20 20
133 3 m. yellow 25 25
134 4 m. green . . . . 30·00 18·00
135 5 m. brown 35 35
136 8 m. orange 40 40
137 10 m. violet 60 60
138 12 m. red 85 85
139 20 m. blue . . . . 1·25 1·25
140 **25** 50 m. blue and brown . . . 11·00 11·00
141 100 m. red and black . . . 25·00 22·00
142 200 m. violet and blue . . . 42·00 38·00
143 500 m. yellow and green . . £120 £110

(b) For use in Tripolitania. Surch as T **21** in Military Authority lire.

151 **24** 1 mal. on 2 m. red 25 25
152 2 mal. on 4 m. green . . . 25 25
153 4 mal. on 8 m. orange . . . 25 25
154 5 mal. on 10 m. violet . . . 35 35
155 6 mal. on 12 m. red 35 35
156 10 mal. on 20 m. blue . . . 65 65
157 **25** 24 mal. on 50 m. blue and brown . . . . 2·50 2·50
158 48 mal. on 100 m. red . . . 7·00 7·00
159 96 mal. on 200 m. violet and blue . . . . 22·00 22·00
160 240 mal. on 500 m. yellow and green . . . . 60·00 60·00

(c) For use in the Fezzan. Surch as T **22.**

166 **24** 2 f. on 2 m. red 20 20
167 4 f. on 4 m. green 30 30
168 8 f. on 8 m. orange 35 40
169 10 f. on 10 m. violet 50 50
170 12 f. on 12 m. red 75 75
171 20 f. on 20 m. blue . . . . 1·40 1·40
172 **25** 48 f. on 50 m. blue & brn . . 40·00 40·00
173 96 f. on 100 m. red and black 40·00 40·00
174 192 f. on 200 m. violet and blue . . . . 90·00 80·00
175 480 f. on 500 m. yellow and green £150 £140

23 King Idris

مؤتمر البريد العربي القاهرة ١٥ مارس ١٩٥٥ (28)

30

1952.

176 **23** 2 m. brown 10 10
177 4 m. grey 10 10
178 5 m. green . . . . 9·00 35
179 8 m. red 40 25
180 **23** 10 m. violet . . . . 9·00 15
181 12 m. red 75 15
182 20 m. blue . . . . 9·50 45
183 25 m. brown . . . . 9·50 45
184 – 50 m. blue and brown . . . 1·25 65
185 – 100 m. red and black . . . 2·50 1·40
186 – 200 m. violet and blue . . 4·50 2·50
187 – 500 m. orange and green . 14·00 9·00
Nos. 184/7 are larger.

1955. Arab Postal Union. As T **96a** of Syria but inscr "LIBYE" at top.

200 5 m. brown 90 60
201 10 m. green . . . . 1·25 90
202 30 m. violet . . . . 1·90 1·40

1955. 2nd Arab Postal Congress, Cairo. Nos. 200/2 optd with T **28.**

203 5 m. brown 40 30
204 10 m. green 70 50
205 30 m. violet . . . . 1·40 85

1955. No. 177 surch.

206 **23** 5 m. on 4 m. grey 65 45

1955.

207 **30** 1 m. black on yellow . . . 10 10
208 2 m. bistre . . . . 1·00 50
209 2 m. brown 10 10
210 3 m. blue 10 10
211 4 m. black . . . . 1·25 50
212 4 m. lake 20 15
213 5 m. green 40 20
214 10 m. lilac 65 25
215 18 m. red 15 10
216 20 m. orange 25 15
217 30 m. blue 50 20
218 35 m. brown 65 25
219 40 m. lake 75 40
220 50 m. olive 85 25
221 – 100 m. purple and slate . . 1·25 50
222 – 200 m. lake and blue . . . 5·00 95
223 – 500 m. orange and green . 9·00 5·00
224 – £L1 green, brown on yellow 12·00 7·50
Nos. 221/4 are larger 27 x 32 mm.
See also Nos. 242/57.

33 Immam's Tomb at Djaghboub

34 Map of Libya

1956. Death Centenary of Imam Essayed Mohamed Aly el Senussi.

225 **33** 5 m. green 20 20
226 10 m. lilac 35 20
227 15 m. red 40 40
228 30 m. blue 80 60

1956. 1st Anniv of Admission to U.N.

229 **34** 15 m. buff and blue . . . 30 15
230 35 m. buff, purple & blue . 65 30

35

36

1957. Arab Postal Congress, Tripoli.

231 **35** 15 m. blue 25 65
232 500 m. brown . . . . . . 8·50 4·50

1958. 10th Anniv of Declaration of Human Rights.

233 **36** 10 m. violet 20 15
234 15 m. green 25 20
235 30 m. blue 65 50

37 F.A.O. Emblem and Date Palms

39

1959. 1st Int Dates Conf, Tripoli.

236 **37** 10 m. black and violet . . 20 15
237 15 m. black and green . . 25 20
238 45 m. black and blue . . . 60 50

1960. Inauguration of Arab League Centre, Cairo. As T **154a** of Syria. but with Arms of Libya and inscr "LIBYA".

239 10 m. black and green 25 20

1960. World Refugee Year.

240 **39** 10 m. black and violet 25 15
241 45 m. black and blue 65 50

1960. As Nos. 207 etc. On coloured paper.

242 **30** 1 m. black on grey 10 10
243 2 m. brown on buff 10 10
244 3 m. indigo on blue 10 10
245 4 m. lake on red 10 10
246 5 m. green on green 10 10
247 10 m. lilac on violet 10 10
248 15 m. sepia on buff 10 10
249 20 m. orange on orange 20 10
250 30 m. red on pink 20 15
251 40 m. lake on red 30 20
252 45 m. blue on blue 35 20
253 50 m. olive on bistre 35 20
254 – 100 m. purple & slate on blue 60 35
255 – 200 m. lake & blue on blue 1·60 90
256 – 500 m. orange & green on green 14·00 3·50
257 – £L1 green & brown on brn 14·00 8·50

40 Palm Tree and Radio Mast

41 Military Watchtower (medallion)

1960. 3rd Arab Telecommunications Conf. Tripoli.

258 **40** 10 m. violet 15 10
259 15 m. turquoise 20 10
260 45 m. lake 70 35

1961. Army Day.

261 **41** 5 m. brown and green 20 10
262 15 m. brown and blue 30 15

42 Zelten Field and Marsa Brega Port

1961. Inaug of First Libyan Petrol Pipeline.

263 **42** 15 m. green and buff 25 10
264 50 m. brown and lavender 75 40
265 100 m. blue and light blue 1·75 50

43 Broken Chain and Agricultural Scenes

1961. 10th Anniv of Independence.

266 **43** 15 m. sepia, turquoise and green 15 10
267 – 50 m. sepia, brown & buff 45 25
268 – 100 m. sepia, blue & salmon 1·10 45

DESIGNS—(embodying broken chain): 50 m. Modern highway and buildings; 100 m. Industrial machinery.

44 Tuareg Camel Riders

1962. Int. Fair, Tripoli.

269 **44** 10 m. chestnut and brown 25 10
270 – 15 m. green and purple 40 25
271 – 50 m. blue and green 1·00 80

DESIGNS: 15 m. Well; 50 m. Oil derrick.

45 Campaign Emblem

46 Ahmed Rafik

1962. Malaria Eradication.

273 **45** 15 m. multicoloured 25 20
274 50 m. multicoloured 60 45

1962. 1st Death Anniv of Ahmed Rafik el Mehdawi (poet).

276 **46** 15 m. green 15 10
277 20 m. brown 25 20

47 Scout Badge and Handclasp

48 City within Oildrop

1962. 3rd Boy Scouts' Meeting, Tripoli.

278 **47** 5 m. sepia, red and yellow 10 10
279 – 10 m. sepia, yellow & blue 20 10
280 – 15 m. sepia, yellow & grey 25 20

DESIGNS: 10 m. Scouts and badge; 15 m. Badge and camp.

1962. Inauguration of Essider Terminal, Sidrah Oil Pipeline.

282 **48** 15 m. purple and green 20 15
283 50 m. olive and brown 60 45

49 Red Crescent encircling Globe

1963. Int. Red Cross Centenary.

284 **49** 10 m. multicoloured 20 15
285 15 m. multicoloured 25 20
286 20 m. multicoloured 40 30

50 Rainbow over Map of Tripoli

1963. International Trade Fair, Tripoli.

287 **50** 15 m. multicoloured 25 20
288 30 m. multicoloured 35 20
289 50 m. multicoloured 70 35

51 Palm and Well

52 "Emancipation"

1963. Freedom from Hunger.

290 **51** 10 m. green, brown & blue 20 10
291 – 15 m. ochre, purple & grn 25 20
292 – 45 m. sepia, blue & salmon 50 35

DESIGNS: 15 m. Camel and sheep; 45 m. Farmer sowing and tractor.

1963. 15th Anniv of Declaration of Human Rights.

293 **52** 5 m. brown and blue 10 10
294 15 m. purple and blue 20 10
295 50 m. green and blue 45 30

54 Map and Fair Entrance

55 Child playing in Sun

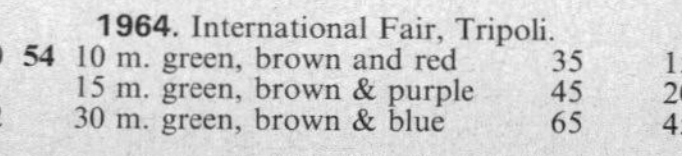

1964. International Fair, Tripoli.

300 **54** 10 m. green, brown and red 35 15
301 15 m. green, brown & purple 45 20
302 30 m. green, brown & blue 65 45

1964. Children's Day. Sun gold.

303 **55** 5 m. violet, red and pink 10 10
304 – 15 m. brown, bistre & buff 20 15
305 **55** 45 m. violet, blue & lt blue 60 35

DESIGN: 15 m. Child in bird's nest.

56 Lungs and Stethoscope

1964. Anti-Tuberculosis Campaign.

307 **56** 20 m. violet 50 25

57 Crown and Map

58 Libyan Woman, Silk Moth and Cocoon

1964. 1st Anniv of Libyan Union.

308 **57** 5 m. orange and green 15 10
309 50 m. yellow and blue 60 25

1964. Emancipation of Libyan Women.

310 **58** 10 m. blue and green 15 10
311 20 m. blue and yellow 25 35
312 35 m. blue and pink 40 45

59 Flags and Scout Salute

60 Bayonet

1964. Libyan Scouts. Multicoloured.

314 10 m. Type **59** 35 20
315 20 m. Scout badge and saluting hands 60 35

1964. Foundation of the Senussi Army.

317 **60** 10 m. brown and green 15 10
318 20 m. black and orange 25 15

61 Ahmed Bahloul (poet)

62 Football

1964. Ahmed Bahloul El-Sharef Commem.

319 **61** 15 m. purple 20 10
320 20 m. blue 35 20

1964. Olympic Games, Tokyo. Rings in Gold.

321 5 m. black and blue (Type **62**) 25 20
322 10 m. black & purple (Cycling) 25 20
323 20 m. black and red (Boxing) 25 20
324 30 m. black and buff (Runner) 35 25
325 35 m. black and olive (High-diving) 35 25
326 50 m. black & grn (Hurdling) 35 25

Nos. 321/6 were arranged together se-tenant in the sheets, each block of six being superimposed with the Olympic "rings" symbol.

63 A.P.U. Emblem

64 I.C.Y. Emblem

1964. 10th Anniv of Arab Postal Union.

328 **63** 10 m. blue and yellow 10 10
329 15 m. brown and lilac 20 10
330 30 m. brown and green 65 35

1965. International Co-operation Year.

331 **64** 5 m. gold & blue (postage) 25 10
332 15 m. gold and red 65 25
333 50 m. gold and violet (air) 75 35

65 European Bee Eater

1965. Birds. Multicoloured.

335 5 m. Long-legged buzzard 65 15
336 10 m. Type **65** 85 15
337 15 m. Black-bellied sandgrouse 1·25 15
338 20 m. Houbara bustard 1·50 25
339 30 m. Spotted sandgrouse 1·90 45
340 40 m. Barbary partridge 2·25 65

The 5 m. and 40 m. are vert.

66 Fair Emblem

1965. International Trade Fair, Tripoli.

341 **66** 50 m. multicoloured 35 20

67 Compass, Rocket and Balloons

1965. World Meteorological Day.

342 **67** 10 m. multicoloured 10 10
343 15 m. multicoloured 20 15
344 50 m. multicoloured 60 45

68 I.T.U. Emblem and Symbols

1965. Centenary of I.T.U.

345 **68** 10 m. brown 10 10
346 20 m. purple 15 10
347 50 m. mauve 40 25

69 Lamp and Burning Library

70 Rose

1965. Reconstitution of Burnt Algiers Library.

348 **69** 15 m. multicoloured 20 10
349 50 m. multicoloured 45 25

1965. Flowers. Multicoloured.

351 1 m. Type **70** 10 10
352 2 m. Iris 10 10
353 3 m. Cactus flower 10 10
354 4 m. Sunflower 20 10

71 Sud Aviation Super Caravelle over Globe

72 Forum, Cyrene

1965. Inaug of Kingdom of Libya Airlines.

355 **71** 5 m. multicoloured 10 10
356 10 m. multicoloured 20 10
357 15 m. multicoloured 40 10

1965.

358	72	50 m. olive and blue . . .	35	25
359	–	100 m. brown and blue . .	65	45
360	–	200 m. blue and purple . .	1·60	65
361	–	500 m. green and red . . .	3·25	1·60
362	–	£L1 brown and green . . .	6·50	3·50

DESIGNS—VERT: 100 m. Trajan's Arch, Leptis Magna; 200 m. Apollo's Temple, Cyrene. HORIZ: 500 m. Antonine Temple, Sabratha; £L1 Theatre, Sabratha.

73 "Helping Hands"

1966. Air. Nubian Monuments Preservation.

363	73	10 m. brown and bistre . .	20	10
364		15 m. brown and green . .	25	10
365		40 m. brown and chestnut	50	25

74 Germa Mausoleum

1966.

367	74	70 m. violet and brown . .	60	35

See also No. E368.

75 Globe and Satellites

1966. International Trade Fair, Tripoli.

369	75	15 m. black, gold & green	20	10
370		45 m. black, gold and blue	40	20
371		55 m. black, gold & purple	55	30

76 League Centre, Cairo, and Emblem

77 W.H.O. Building

1966. Arab League Week.

372	76	20 m. red, green and black	10	10
373		55 m. blue, red and black	35	25

1966. Air. Inauguration of W.H.O. Headquarters, Geneva.

374	77	20 m. black, yellow & blue	20	10
375		50 m. black, green and red	40	25
376		65 m. black, salmon & lake	50	40

78 Tuareg with Camel

80 Leaping Deer

1966. Tuaregs.

378	78	10 m. red	20	20
379	–	20 m. blue	35	30
380	–	50 m. multicoloured . . .	90	50

DESIGNS—VERT: 20 m. As Type **78** but positions of Tuareg and camel reversed. HORIZ: (62 x 39 mm). 50 m. Tuareg with camel (different).

1966. 1st Arab Girl Scouts Camp (5 m.) and 7th Arab Boy Scouts Camp (25 and 65 m.). Multicoloured.

382		5 m. Type **80**	10	10
383		25 m. Boy scouts	20	10
384		65 m. Camp emblem (vert) . .	45	25

81 Airline Emblem

82 U.N.E.S.C.O. Emblem

1966. Air. 1st Anniv of Kingdom of Libya Airlines.

385	81	25 m. multicoloured . . .	20	15
386		60 m. multicoloured . . .	45	35
387		85 m. multicoloured . . .	65	50

1967. 20th Anniv of U.N.E.S.C.O.

388	82	15 m. multicoloured . . .	20	10
389		25 m. multicoloured . . .	40	20

83 Castle of Columns, Tolemaide

85 Fair Emblem

84 "British Confidence" (tanker) at Oil Terminal

1967. Tourism.

390	83	25 m. black, brown & violet	20	10
391	–	55 m. brown, violet & black	40	25

DESIGN—HORIZ: 55 m. Sebba Fort.

1967. Inaug of Marsa al Hariga Oil Terminal.

392	84	60 m. multicoloured . . .	85	30

1967. International Fair, Tripoli.

393	85	15 m. multicoloured . . .	25	10
394		55 m. multicoloured . . .	40	25

86 I.T.Y. Emblem

87 Running

1967. International Tourist Year.

395	86	5 m. black and blue . . .	10	10
396		10 m. blue and black . . .	10	10
397		45 m. black, blue and pink	30	15

1967. Mediterranean Games, Tunisia. Designs showing action "close-ups".

398	87	5 m. black, orange and blue	10	10
399	–	10 m. black, brown & blue	10	10
400	–	15 m. black, violet and blue	10	10
401	–	45 m. black, red and blue	30	25
402	–	75 m. black, green and blue	45	30

DESIGNS: 10 m. Throwing the javelin; 15 m. Cycling; 45 m. Football; 75 m. Boxing.

88 Open Book and Arab League Emblem

89 Human Rights Emblem

1967. Literacy Campaign.

403	88	5 m. orange and violet . .	10	10
404		10 m. green and violet . .	10	10
405		15 m. purple and violet . .	15	10
406		25 m. blue and violet . . .	20	15

1968. Human Rights Year.

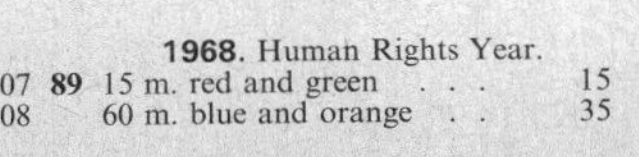

407	89	15 m. red and green . . .	15	10
408		60 m. blue and orange . .	35	25

90 Cameleers, Fokker Friendship, Oil Rig and Map

1968. International Fair, Tripoli.

409	90	55 m. multicoloured	60	30

91 Arab League Emblem

1968. Arab League Week.

410	91	10 m. red and blue	10	10
411		45 m. green and orange . .	35	25

92 Children "Wrestling" (statue)

93 W.H.O. Emblem and Reaching Hands

1968. Children's Day. Multicoloured.

412		25 m. Type **92**	20	15
413		55 m. Libyan mother and children	40	25

1968. 20th Anniv of W.H.O.

414	93	25 m. blue and purple . . .	25	15
415		55 m. brown and blue . . .	40	25

94 Oil Pipeline Map

1968. Inauguration of Zueitina Oil Terminal.

416	94	10 m. multicoloured	20	10
417		60 m. multicoloured	55	25

95 "Teaching the People"

1968. "Eliminate Illiteracy".

418	95	5 m. mauve	10	10
419		10 m. orange	10	10
420		15 m. blue	10	10
421		20 m. green	20	20

96 Conference Emblem

1968. 4th Session of Arab Labour Ministries Conference, Tripoli.

422	96	10 m. multicoloured	10	10
423		15 m. multicoloured	20	10

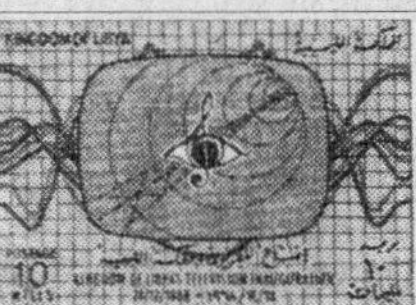

97 Treble Clef, Eye and T.V. Screen

1968. Inauguration of Libyan Television Service.

424	97	10 m. multicoloured . . .	10	10
425		30 m. multicoloured . . .	35	20

98 Bridge, Callipers and Road Sign

1968. Opening of Wadi El Kuf Bridge.

426	98	25 m. multicoloured . . .	15	15
427		60 m. multicoloured . . .	35	25

99 Melons

100 Fair Emblem

1969. Fruits. Multicoloured.

428		5 m. Type **99**	10	10
429		10 m. Dates	10	10
430		15 m. Lemons	10	10
431		20 m. Oranges	15	10
432		25 m. Peaches	20	15
433		35 m. Pears	40	25

1969. 8th International Trade Fair, Tripoli.

434	100	25 m. multicoloured . . .	15	10
435		35 m. multicoloured . . .	25	15
436		40 m. multicoloured . . .	30	20

101 Hoisting Weather Balloon

1969. World Meteorological Day.

437	101	60 m. multicoloured . . .	45	30

102 Family on Staircase within Cogwheel

103 I.L.O. Emblem

1969. 10th Anniv of Libyan Social Insurance.

438	102	15 m. multicoloured . . .	15	10
439		55 m. multicoloured . . .	30	25

1969. 50th Anniv of I.L.O.

440	103	10 m. green, black & turq	10	10
441		60 m. green, black and red	35	25

104 Emblem and Desert Scene

1969. African Tourist Year.

442	104	15 m. multicoloured . . .	15	10
443		30 m. multicoloured . . .	30	25

105 Members of the Armed Forces and Olive Branch

106 Dish Aerial and Flags

1969. Revolution of 1st September.

No.	Type	Description		
444	105	5 m. multicoloured	25	10
445		10 m. multicoloured	35	20
446		15 m. multicoloured	55	25
447		25 m. multicoloured	85	40
448		45 m. multicoloured	1·00	60
449		60 m. multicoloured	1·75	70

On Nos. 444/9 the value is in white and the designer's name appears at the foot of design.

1970. 5th Anniv of Arab Satellite Communications Co-operation Agreement.

No.	Type	Description		
450	106	15 m. multicoloured	25	15
451		20 m. multicoloured	40	20
452		25 m. multicoloured	50	25
453		40 m. multicoloured	65	40

107 Arab League Flag, Arms and Map

1970. Silver Jubilee of Arab League.

No.	Type	Description		
454	107	10 m. sepia, green & blue	10	10
455		15 m. brown, green & orge	15	15
456		20 m. purple, grn & olive	25	25

1970. Revolution of 1st September. Designs as T **105**, but without imprint "M. A. Siala" at foot, and figures of value differently inscr

No.	Type	Description		
457	87	5 m. multicoloured	25	10
458		10 m. multicoloured	35	20
459		15 m. multicoloured	55	25
460		25 m. multicoloured	85	40
461		45 m. multicoloured	1·00	60
462		60 m. multicoloured	1·75	70

108 New Headquarters Building

109 Arms and Soldiers

1970. New U.P.U. Headquarters Building, Berne.

No.	Type	Description		
463	108	10 m. multicoloured	15	10
464		25 m. multicoloured	20	20
465		60 m. multicoloured	40	30

1970. Nos. 358 and 360/2 with "KINGDOM OF LIBYA" inscriptions obliterated.

No.	Type	Description		
465a	72	50 m. olive and blue		
466	–	200 m. blue and purple		
467	–	500 m. green and pink		
468	–	£L1 brown and green		

These stamps were sold only for use on parcel post items. Other values may exist so overprinted, but were unauthorised.

See also Nos. 518/23.

1970. Evacuation of Foreign Military Bases in Libya.

No.	Type	Description		
469	109	15 m. black and red	15	15
470		25 m. yellow, blue & red	20	20
471		45 m. yellow, red & green	50	30

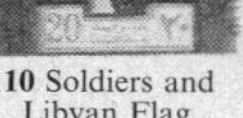
110 Soldiers and Libyan Flag

111 U.N. Emblem, Dove and Scales

1970. 1st Anniv of Libyan Arab Republic.

No.	Type	Description		
472	110	20 m. multicoloured	25	15
473		25 m. multicoloured	40	15
474		30 m. multicoloured	65	35

1970. 25th Anniv of United Nations.

No.	Type	Description		
475	111	5 m. brown, red & green	25	10
476		10 m. green, red & emerald	40	15
477		60 m. green, red and blue	95	40

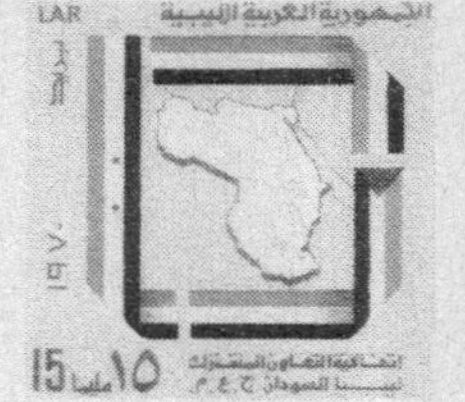
112 Map and Flags

113 Dove, U.N. Emblem and Globe

1970. Signing of Tripoli Charter of Co-operation.

No.	Type	Description		
478	112	15 m. green, black & red	75	40

1971. 10th Anniv of U.N. De-colonisation Declaration.

No.	Type	Description		
479	113	15 m. multicoloured	25	15
480		20 m. multicoloured	40	20
481		60 m. multicoloured	95	40

114 Education Year Emblem

115 Palestinian Guerrilla

1971. International Education Year.

No.	Type	Description		
482	114	5 m. brown, red & black	15	10
483		10 m. green, red & black	25	10
484		20 m. blue, red & black	50	15

1971. "Al-Fatah" Movement for the Liberation of Palestine.

No.	Type	Description		
485	115	5 m. multicoloured	15	10
486		10 m. multicoloured	25	15
487		100 m. multicoloured	90	55

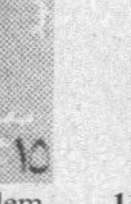
116 Fair Emblem

117 O.P.E.C. Emblem

1971. 9th International Trade Fair, Tripoli.

No.	Type	Description		
488	116	15 m. multicoloured	15	10
489		30 m. multicoloured	35	20

1971. Organization of Petroleum Exporting Countries (O.P.E.C.).

No.	Type	Description		
490	117	10 m. brown and yellow	15	10
491		70 m. violet and pink	60	40

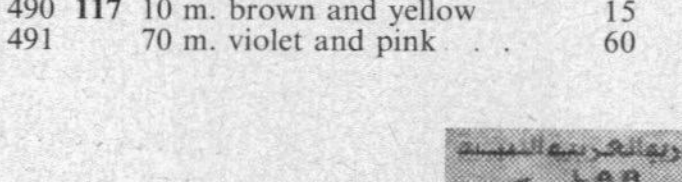

118 Global Symbol

119 Soldier, Torch and Flag

1971. World Telecommunications Day (Nos. 494/5) and Pan-African Telecommunications Network.

No.	Type	Description		
492	–	5 m. multicoloured	10	10
493	–	15 m. multicoloured	10	10
494	118	25 m. multicoloured	20	15
495		35 m. multicoloured	50	25

DESIGN: 5 m., 15 m. Telecommunications map of Africa.

1971. 1st Anniv of Evacuation of Foreign Troops.

No.	Type	Description		
496	119	5 m. multicoloured	10	10
497		10 m. multicoloured	15	10
498		15 m. multicoloured	20	15

120 Ramadan Suehli

121 Palm and Dates

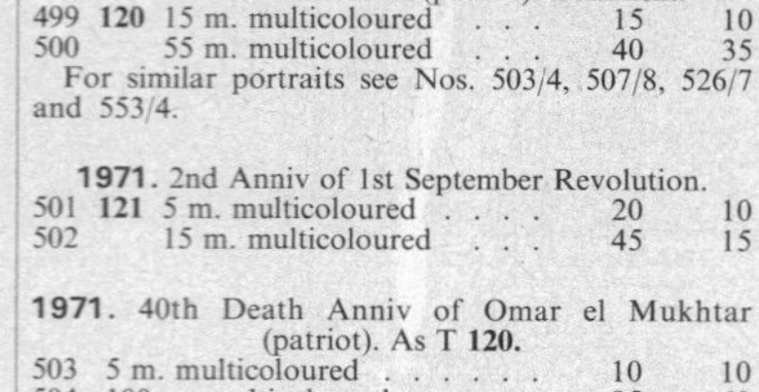

1971. Ramadan Suehli (patriot). Commem.

No.	Type	Description		
499	120	15 m. multicoloured	15	10
500		55 m. multicoloured	40	35

For similar portraits see Nos. 503/4, 507/8, 526/7 and 553/4.

1971. 2nd Anniv of 1st September Revolution.

No.	Type	Description		
501	121	5 m. multicoloured	20	10
502		15 m. multicoloured	45	15

1971. 40th Death Anniv of Omar el Mukhtar (patriot). As T **120**.

No.	Type	Description		
503		5 m. multicoloured	10	10
504		100 m. multicoloured	95	60

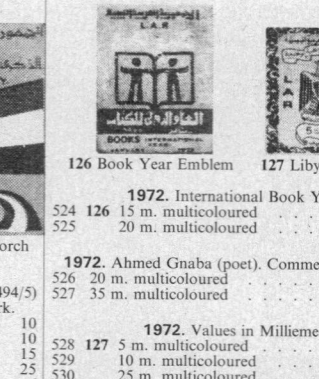

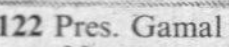
122 Pres. Gamal Nasser

123 Racial Equality Year Emblem

1971. 1st Death Anniv of Pres. Nasser of Egypt.

No.	Type	Description		
505	122	5 m. black, green & pur	10	10
506		15 m. black, purple & grn	15	10

1971. 21st Death Anniv of Ibrahim Usta Omar (poet). As T **120**.

No.	Type	Description		
507		25 m. multicoloured	25	15
508		30 m. multicoloured	45	20

1971. Racial Equality Year.

No.	Type	Description		
509	123	25 m. multicoloured	25	15
510		35 m. multicoloured	35	15

124 A.P.U. Emblem

125 Arab Postal Union. Emblem and Envelopes

1971. 25th Anniv of Founding of Arab Postal Union at Sofar Conference.

No.	Type	Description		
511	124	5 m. multicoloured	10	10
512		10 m. multicoloured	20	10
513		15 m. multicoloured	15	10

1971. 10th Anniv of African Postal Union. Mult.

No.	Type	Description		
514		10 m. Type **125**	10	10
515		15 m. Type **125**	15	10
516		25 m. A.P.U. Emblem and dove with letter	25	15
517		55 m. As 25 m.	50	35

1971. Nos. 423/33 with "KINGDOM OF LIBYA" inscriptions obliterated.

No.	Type	Description		
518		5 m. Type **99**		
519		10 m. Dates		
520		15 m. Lemons		
521		20 m. Oranges		
522		25 m. Peaches		
523		35 m. Pears		

126 Book Year Emblem

127 Libyan Arms

1972. International Book Year.

No.	Type	Description		
524	126	15 m. multicoloured	15	10
525		20 m. multicoloured	25	20

1972. Ahmed Gnaba (poet). Commem. As T **120**.

No.	Type	Description		
526		20 m. multicoloured	25	10
527		35 m. multicoloured	35	20

1972. Values in Milliemes.

No.	Type	Description		
528	127	5 m. multicoloured	10	10
529		10 m. multicoloured	10	10
530		25 m. multicoloured	15	10
531		30 m. multicoloured	20	10
532		35 m. multicoloured	25	10
533		40 m. multicoloured	25	15
534		45 m. multicoloured	35	15
535		55 m. multicoloured	45	20
536		60 m. multicoloured	75	35
537		90 m. multicoloured	75	40

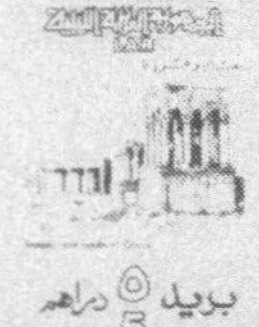
128 Tombs, Ghirza

129 Fair Emblem

1972. Libyan Antiquities. Multicoloured.

No.	Type	Description		
538		5 m. Type **128**	10	10
539		10 m. Cufic inscription, Ajdabiya	10	10
540		15 m. Marcus Aurelius' Arch, Tripoli (horiz)	15	10
541		25 m. Exchanging Weapons (cave painting, Wadi Zigza)	20	15
542		55 m. Garamantian chariot (wall drawing, Wadi Zigza)	50	25
543		70 m. "Libya crowning Cyrene" (Roman relief, Cyrene)	75	45

1972. 10th Int Trade Fair, Tripoli.

No.	Type	Description		
544	129	25 m. multicoloured	20	15
545		35 m. multicoloured	25	20
546		50 m. multicoloured	50	25
547		70 m. multicoloured	65	35

130 Heart and Skeletal Arm

131 "Unity" Symbol on Map

1972. World Health Day.

No.	Type	Description		
548	130	15 m. multicoloured	65	25
549		25 m. multicoloured	95	40

1972. 1st Anniv of Libyan-Egyptian Federation Agreement.

No.	Type	Description		
550	131	15 m. yellow, blue & black	10	10
551		20 m. yellow, green & emer	20	10
552		25 m. yellow, red & black	35	20

1972. Birth Centenary (1970) of Suleiman el Baruni (writer). As T **120**.

No.	Type	Description		
553		10 m. multicoloured	25	15
554		70 m. multicoloured	65	50

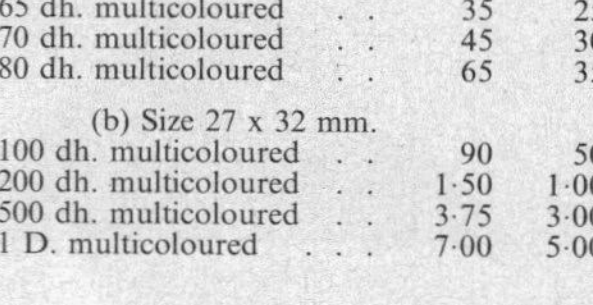

1972. New Currency (Dirhams and Dinars). As Type **127**. (a) Size 19 x 24 mm.

No.	Type	Description		
555	127	15 dh. multicoloured	10	10
556		65 dh. multicoloured	35	25
557		70 dh. multicoloured	45	30
558		80 dh. multicoloured	65	35

(b) Size 27 x 32 mm.

No.	Type	Description		
559	127	100 dh. multicoloured	90	50
560		200 dh. multicoloured	1·50	1·00
561		500 dh. multicoloured	3·75	3·00
562		1 D. multicoloured	7·00	5·00

132

1972.

No.	Type	Description		
563	132	5 m. multicoloured	95	15
564		20 m. multicoloured	3·50	40
565		50 m. multicoloured	8·50	1·40

Nos. 563/5 were also issued with the Arabic face values expressed in the new currency.

See also Nos. 657/9.

133 Environmental Emblem

134 Olympic Emblems

1972. U.N. Environmental Conservation Conference, Stockholm.

No.	Type	Description		
566	133	15 dh. multicoloured	20	10
567		55 dh. multicoloured	45	35

1972. Olympic Games, Munich.

No.	Type	Description		
568	134	25 dh. multicoloured	65	35
569		35 dh. multicoloured	90	65

135 Symbolic Tree and "Fruit"

136 Dome of the Rock

1972. 3rd Anniv of 1st September Revolution.

No.	Type	Description		
570	135	15 dh. multicoloured	15	10
571		25 dh. multicoloured	35	15

1973. Dome of the Rock, Jerusalem.

No.	Type	Description		
572	136	10 dh. multicoloured	10	10
573		25 dh. multicoloured	20	15

137 Nicolas Copernicus **138** Libyan Eagle and Fair

1973. 500th Birth Anniv of Copernicus. Mult.
574 15 dh. Type **137** 15 10
575 25 dh. "Copernicus in his Observatory" (horiz) 25 15

1973. 11th International Trade Fair, Tripoli.
576 **138** 5 dh. multicoloured . . . 15 10
577 10 dh. multicoloured . . . 20 10
578 15 dh. multicoloured . . . 25 15

139 Blind Persons and Occupations **140** Map and Laurel

1973. Role of the Blind in Society.
579 **139** 20 dh. multicoloured . . . 1·25 40
580 25 dh. multicoloured . . . 3·25 1·25

1973. 10th Anniv of Organization of African Unity.
584 **140** 15 dh. multicoloured . . . 20 10
585 25 dh. multicoloured . . . 40 20

141 Interpol H.Q., Paris

1973. 50th Anniv of International Criminal Police Organization (Interpol).
586 **141** 10 dh. multicoloured . . . 10 10
587 15 dh. multicoloured . . . 15 10
588 25 dh. multicoloured . . . 20 20

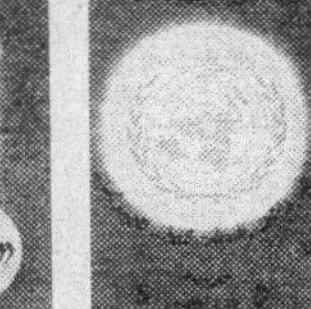
142 Map and Emblems **143** W.M.O. Emblem

1973. Census.
589 **142** 10 dh. blue, black & red 95 20
590 25 dh. green, black & blue 1·25 45
591 35 dh. orange, black & grn 2·25 65

1973. W.M.O. Centenary.
592 **143** 5 dh. blue, black and red 10 10
593 10 dh. blue, black & green 15 10

144 Footballers

1973. 2nd Palestine Cup Football Championship.
594 **144** 5 dh. brown and green . . 20 20
595 25 dh. brown and red . . 35 15

145 Revolutionary Torch **146** "Writing Ability"

1973. 4th Anniv of September 1st Revolution.
596 **145** 15 dh. multicoloured . . . 20 10
597 25 dh. multicoloured . . . 35 10

1973. Literacy Campaign.
598 **146** 25 dh. multicoloured . . 25 15

147 Doorway of Old City Hall **148** Militiamen and Flag

1973. Cent of Tripoli Municipality. Mult.
599 10 dh. Type **147** 20 10
600 25 dh. Khondok fountain . . 25 10
601 35 dh. Clock tower 35 15

1973. Libyan Militia.
602 **148** 15 dh. multicoloured . . 15 10
603 25 dh. multicoloured . . 25 10

149 Arabic Quotation from Speech of 15 April 1973

1973. Declaration of Cultural Revolution by Col. Gaddafi. Multicoloured.
604 25 dh. Type **149** 20 10
605 70 dh. As Type **149** but text in English 60 30

150 Ploughing with Camel **151** Human Rights Emblem

1973. 10th Anniv of World Food Programme.
606 **150** 10 dh. multicoloured . . 10 10
607 25 dh. multicoloured . . 20 10
608 35 dh. multicoloured . . 30 15

1973. 25th Anniv of Declaration of Human Rights.
609 **151** 25 dh. red, purple & blue 20 10
610 70 dh. red, green and blue 50 30

152 Mullet **154** Emblem formed with National Flags

153 Lookout Post and Scout Salute

1973. Fishes. Multicoloured.
611 5 dh. Type **152** 10 10
612 10 dh. Seabream 15 10
613 15 dh. Perch 20 10
614 20 dh. Seaperch 30 15
615 25 dh. Tunny 45 20

1974. 20th Anniv of Scouting in Libya.
616 **153** 5 dh. multicoloured . . . 25 10
617 20 dh. multicoloured . . 75 20
618 25 dh. multicoloured . . 1·50 45

1974. 12th International Trade Fair, Tripoli.
619 **154** 10 dh. multicoloured . . 20 10
620 25 dh. multicoloured . . 25 15
621 35 dh. multicoloured . . 40 35

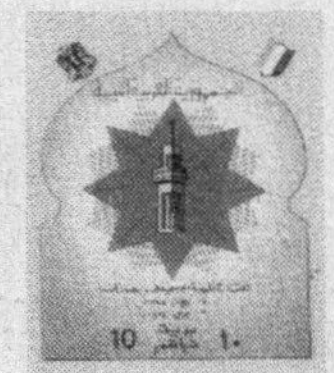
155 Family within Protective Hands **156** Minaret within Star

1974. World Health Day.
622 **155** 5 dh. multicoloured . . . 15 10
623 25 dh. multicoloured . . . 25 20

1974. Inauguration of Benghazi University.
624 **156** 10 dh. multicoloured . . . 20 10
625 25 dh. multicoloured . . . 35 15
626 35 dh. multicoloured . . . 50 25

157 U.P.U. Emblem within Star **158** Traffic Lights and Signs

1974. Centenary of U.P.U.
627 **157** 25 dh. multicoloured . . . 1·60 40
628 70 dh. multicoloured . . . 3·50 90

1974. Motoring and Touring Club of Libya.
629 **158** 5 dh. multicoloured . . . 10 10
630 10 dh. multicoloured . . . 15 10
631 25 dh. multicoloured . . . 15 10

159 Tank, Refinery and Pipeline **160** W.P.Y. Emblem and People

1974. 5th Anniv of 1st September Revolution.
632 **159** 5 dh. multicoloured . . . 10 10
633 20 dh. multicoloured . . . 15 10
634 25 dh. multicoloured . . . 15 10
635 35 dh. multicoloured . . . 20 15

1974. World Population Year.
637 **160** 25 dh. multicoloured . . . 20 10
638 35 dh. multicoloured . . . 25 20

161 **162** Congress Emblem

1975. 13th International Trade Fair, Tripoli. Libyan Costumes.
639 **161** 5 dh. multicoloured . . . 10 10
640 – 10 dh. multicoloured . . . 10 10
641 – 15 dh. multicoloured . . . 10 10
642 – 20 dh. multicoloured . . . 20 10
643 – 25 dh. multicoloured . . . 20 10
644 – 50 dh. multicoloured . . . 45 20
DESIGNS: 10 dh. to 50 dh. Various costumes.

1975. Arab Workers' Congress.
645 **162** 10 dh. multicoloured . . . 10 10
646 25 dh. multicoloured . . . 15 15
647 35 dh. multicoloured . . . 25 15

163 Teacher at Blackboard **164** Human Figures, Text and Globe

1975. Teachers' Day.
648 **163** 10 dh. multicoloured . . 10 10
649 25 dh. multicoloured . . 20 10

1975. World Health Day.
650 **164** 20 dh. multicoloured . . 15 10
651 25 dh. multicoloured . . 20 10

165 Readers and Bookshelves **166** Festival Emblem

1975. Arab Book Exhibition.
652 **165** 10 dh. multicoloured . . 10 10
653 20 dh. multicoloured . . 20 10
654 25 dh. multicoloured . . 25 15

1975. 2nd Arab Youth Festival.
655 **166** 20 dh. multicoloured . . 15 10
656 25 dh. multicoloured . . 20 15

1975. As Nos. 563/5 but without "L.A.R.".
657 **132** 5 dh. black, orange & blue 10 10
658 20 dh. black, yellow & bl 20 10
659 50 dh. black, green & blue 35 15

167 Games Emblem **168** Dove of Peace

1975. 7th Mediterranean Games, Algiers.
660 **167** 10 dh. multicoloured . . 10 10
661 25 dh. multicoloured . . 20 10
662 50 dh. multicoloured . . 35 20

1975. 6th Anniv of September 1st Revolution. Multicoloured.
663 25 dh. Type **168** 20 10
664 70 dh. Peace dove with different background 50 25

169 Khalil Basha Mosque **170** Arms and Crowds

1975. Mosques. Multicoloured.
666 5 dh. Type **169** 10 10
667 10 dh. Sidi Abdulla El Shaab 10 10
668 15 dh. Sidi Ali El Fergani . . 10 10
669 20 dh. Al Kharruba (vert) . . 15 10
670 25 dh. Katiktha (vert) 20 10
671 30 dh. Murad Agha (vert) . . 20 15
672 35 dh. Maulai Mohamed (vert) 25 15

1976. National People's Congress.
673 **170** 35 dh. multicoloured . . 20 10
674 40 dh. multicoloured . . 25 10

171 Dialogue Emblem **172** Woman blowing Bugle

1976. Islamic-Christian Dialogue Seminar.
675 **171** 40 dh. multicoloured . . 25 15
676 115 dh. multicoloured . . 75 30

1976. International Trade Fair, Tripoli. Mult.
677 10 dh. Type **171** 10 10
678 20 dh. Lancer 15 10
679 30 dh. Drummer 20 10
680 40 dh. Bagpiper 25 20
681 100 dh. Woman with jug on head 70 35

173 Early and Modern Telephones

1976. Telephone Centenary. Multicoloured.
682 40 dh. Type **173** 25 15
683 70 dh. Alexander Graham Bell 75 25

174 Mother and Child

175 Hands supporting Eye

1976. International Children's Day.
685 **174** 85 dh. multicoloured . . . 45 30
686 110 dh. multicoloured . . 65 40

1976. World Health Day.
687 **175** 30 dh. multicoloured . . . 20 10
688 35 dh. multicoloured . . . 20 10
689 40 dh. multicoloured . . . 25 15

176 Little Bittern

1976. Libyan Birds. Multicoloured.
690 5 dh. Type **176** 45 20
691 10 dh. Great grey shrike . . . 85 30
692 15 dh. Fulvous babbler . . . 1·25 40
693 20 dh. European bee eater (vert) 1·60 55
694 25 dh. Hoopoe . . . . 1·90 75

177 Barabekh Plant

178 Cycling

1976. Natural History Museum. Multicoloured.
695 10 dh. Type **177** 10 10
696 15 dh. Fin whale (horiz) . . . 15 10
697 30 dh. Lizard (horiz) 20 10
698 40 dh. Elephant's skull (horiz) 25 15
699 70 dh. Bonnelli's eagle . . . . 1·50 40
700 115 dh. Barbary sheep 75 40

1976. Olympic Games, Montreal. Multicoloured.
701 15 dh. Type **178** 10 10
702 25 dh. Boxing 20 10
703 70 dh. Football 50 20

179 Global "Tree"

180 Agricultural and Industrial Symbols

1976. Non-Aligned Countries' Colombo Conference.
705 **179** 115 dh. multicoloured . . 50 35

1976. 7th Anniv of Revolution.
706 **180** 30 dh. multicoloured . . . 15 10
707 40 dh. multicoloured . . . 20 15
708 100 dh. multicoloured . . 40 30

181 Various Sports

182 Chessboard and Pieces

1976. 5th Arab Games, Damascus.
710 **181** 15 dh. multicoloured . . 10 10
711 30 dh. multicoloured . . 15 10
712 100 dh. multicoloured . . 50 30

1976. Arab Chess Olympiad, Tripoli.
714 **182** 15 dh. multicoloured . . 30 15
715 30 dh. multicoloured . . 60 30
716 100 dh. multicoloured . . 1·25 50

183 Ratima

186 Kaaba, Mecca

184 Emblem and Text

1976. Libyan Flora. Multicoloured.
717 15 dh. Type **183** 15 10
718 20 dh. "Sword of Crow" . . 15 10
719 35 dh. Lasef 20 10
720 40 dh. Yadid 30 15
721 70 dh. Esparto grass 60 25

1976. International Archives Council.
722 **184** 15 dh. multicoloured . . 10 10
723 35 dh. multicoloured . . 15 10
724 70 dh. multicoloured . . 30 20

1976. Pilgrimage to Mecca.
729 **186** 15 dh. multicoloured . . 10 10
730 30 dh. multicoloured . . 15 10
731 70 dh. multicoloured . . 30 20
732 100 dh. multicoloured . . 45 30

187

188 Basket

1977. Coil Stamps.
733 **187** 5 dh. multicoloured . . . 10 10
734 20 dh. multicoloured . . . 10 10
735 50 dh. multicoloured . . 25 15

1977. 15th International Trade Fair, Tripoli. Mult.
736 10 dh. Type **188** 10 10
737 20 dh. Leather bag 10 10
738 30 dh. Vase 15 10
739 40 dh. Slippers 20 15
740 50 dh. Saddle 25 15

189 Girl with Flowers

1977. Children's Day. Multicoloured.
742 10 dh. Type **189** 10 10
743 30 dh. Clothes shop 15 10
744 40 dh. Orchard 20 15

190 Fighters and Machine-gun

191 Protected Child

1977. 9th Anniv of Battle of Al-Karamah.
745 **190** 15 dh. multicoloured . . . 10 10
746 25 dh. multicoloured . . . 15 10
747 70 dh. multicoloured . . . 35 25

1977. World Health Day.
748 **191** 15 dh. multicoloured . . . 10 10
749 30 dh. multicoloured . . . 15 10

192 A.P.U. Emblem

1977. 25th Anniv of Arab Postal Union.
750 **192** 15 dh. multicoloured . . . 10 10
751 20 dh. multicoloured . . . 15 10
752 40 dh. multicoloured . . . 20 15

193 Maps of Libya and Africa

194 Heart on Map of Libya

1977. Organization of African Unity Conference, Tripoli.
753 **193** 40 dh. multicoloured . . . 45 20
754 70 dh. multicoloured . . . 55 30

1977. Red Crescent Commemoration.
755 **194** 5 dh. multicoloured . . . 10 10
756 10 dh. multicoloured . . . 15 10
757 30 dh. multicoloured . . . 30 15

195 Messenger and Jet Fighter

1977. Communications Progress. Multicoloured.
758 20 dh. Type **195** 15 10
759 25 dh. Arab rider and Concorde 30 15
760 60 dh. Satellite and aerial . . . 30 20
761 115 dh. Television relay via satellite 65 35
762 150 dh. Camel rider and Boeing 727 airliner loading . . . . 1·25 60
763 200 dh. "Apollo-Soyuz" link 1·25 65

196 Mosque

197 Archbishop Capucci

1977. Libyan Mosques.
765 **196** 40 dh. multicoloured . . . 20 15
766 – 50 dh. multicoloured . . . 25 15
767 – 70 dh. multicoloured . . . 30 20
768 – 90 dh. multicoloured . . . 40 30
769 – 100 dh. multicoloured . . 45 35
770 – 115 dh. multicoloured . . 55 40
DESIGNS: 50 dh. to 115 dh. Various mosques. The 50 dh. and 100 dh. are vertical.

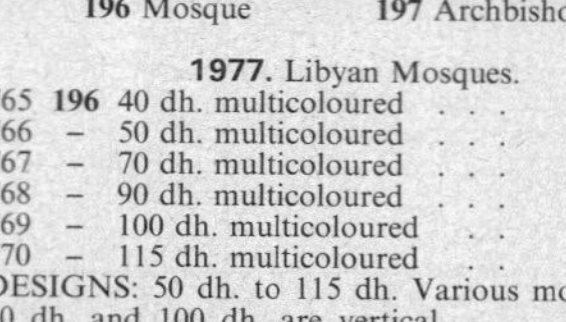

1977. 3rd Anniv of Archbishop Capucci's Imprisonment.
771 **197** 30 dh. multicoloured . . . 15 10
772 40 dh. multicoloured . . . 20 15
773 115 dh. multicoloured . . . 55 35

198 Clasped Hands and Emblems

1977. 8th Anniv of Revolution.
774 **198** 15 dh. multicoloured . . 10 10
775 30 dh. multicoloured . . 15 10
776 85 dh. multicoloured . . 45 25

199 Swimming

1977. Arab School Sports. Multicoloured.
778 5 dh. Type **199** 10 10
779 10 dh. Handball (horiz) . . . 10 10
780 15 dh. Football 15 10
781 25 dh. Table tennis (horiz) . . 25 20
782 40 dh. Basketball 35 25

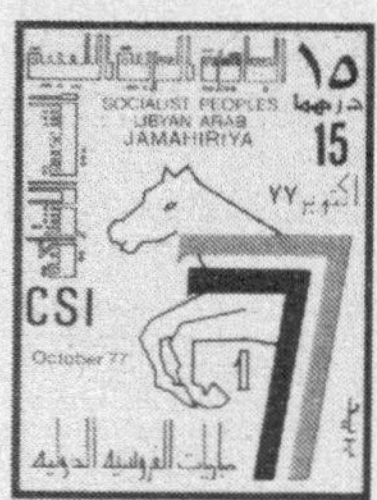

200 Championship Emblem

1977. 1st International Turf Championships, Tripoli. Multicoloured.
783 5 dh. Horse jumping (facing left) 10 10
784 10 dh. Arab horseman 10 10
785 15 dh. Type **200** 15 10
786 45 dh. Horse jumping fence (facing right) 30 15
787 115 dh. Arab horseman racing 60 40

201 Dome of the Rock

202 Fort, and Hands writing Arabic Script in Book

1977. Palestine Welfare.
789 **201** 5 dh. multicoloured . . . 10 10
790 10 dh. multicoloured . . 10 10

1977. "The Green Book". Multicoloured.
791 35 dh. Type **202** 15 10
792 40 dh. Type **202** (text in English) 20 15
793 115 dh. Dove with "Green Book" and map 55 40

203 Emblem

1977. World Standards Day.
794 **203** 5 dh. multicoloured . . . 10 10
795 15 dh. multicoloured . . 10 10
796 30 dh. multicoloured . . 15 10

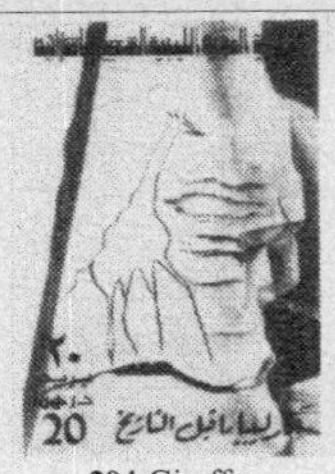
204 Giraffe

1978. Rock Drawings from Wadi Mathendous. Multicoloured.
797 10 dh. Crocodiles (horiz) . . . 10 10
798 15 dh. Elephant hunt (horiz) 10 10
799 20 dh. Type **204** 15 10
800 30 dh. Antelope (horiz) . . . 20 15
801 40 dh. Elephant (horiz) . . . 25 20

205 Silver Pendant **206** Compass and Lightning Flash

1978. 16th Tripoli International Fair.
802 **205** 5 dh. silver, black and red 10 10
803 – 10 dh. silver, black & violet 10 10
804 – 20 dh. silver, black & green 10 10
805 – 25 dh. silver, black & blue 15 10
806 – 115 dh. silver, black & blue 60 35
DESIGNS: 10 dh. Silver ornamental plate; 20 dh. Necklace with three pendants; 25 dh. Crescent-shaped silver brooch; 115 dh. Silver armband.

1978. Arab Cultural Education Organisation.
807 **206** 30 dh. multicoloured . . . 20 15
808 115 dh. multicoloured . . 75 35

207 Dancing a Round

1978. Children's Day. Children's Paintings. Multicoloured.
809 40 dh. Type **207** 20 15
810 40 dh. Children with placards 20 15
811 40 dh. Shopping street 20 15
812 40 dh. Playground 20 15
813 40 dh. Wedding ceremony . . 20 15

208 Brickwork Clenched Fist

1978. The Arabs.
814 **208** 30 dh. multicoloured . . . 20 15
815 115 dh. multicoloured . . 60 35

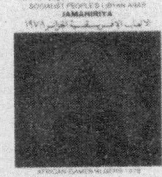

209 Blood Pressure Meter **211** Games Emblem

210 Microwave Antenna

1978. World Hypertension Month.
816 **209** 30 dh. multicoloured . . . 15 15
817 115 dh. multicoloured . . 55 35

1978. World Telecommunications Day.
818 **210** 30 dh. multicoloured . . 15 15
819 115 dh. multicoloured . . 60 35

1978. Third African Games, Algiers.
820 **211** 15 dh. copper, violet & blk 10 10
821 30 dh. silver, lilac & black 15 10
822 115 dh. gold, purple & blk 60 35

212 Aerial View of Airport **213** Ankara

1978. Inauguration of Tripoli International Airport. Multicoloured.
823 40 dh. Type **212** 30 10
824 115 dh. Terminal building . . 95 40

1978. Turkish-Libyan Friendship.
825 **213** 30 dh. multicoloured . . 15 10
826 35 dh. multicoloured . . 15 10
827 115 dh. multicoloured . . 60 35

214 "Armed Forces" **215** Crater

1978. 9th Anniv of 1st September Revolution. Multicoloured.
828 30 dh. Type **214** 40 15
829 35 dh. Tower, Green Book and symbols of progress 15 10
830 115 dh. "Industry" 50 35

1978. Second Symposium on Geology of Libya. Multicoloured.
832 30 dh. Type **215** 15 10
833 40 dh. Oasis 20 15
834 115 dh. Crater (different) . . 50 35

216 "Green Book" and Different Races

1978. International Anti-Apartheid Year.
835 **216** 30 dh. multicoloured . . 15 10
836 40 dh. multicoloured . . 20 15
837 115 dh. multicoloured . . 50 35

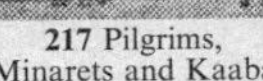

217 Pilgrims, Minarets and Kaaba **218** Clasped Hands and Globe

1978. Pilgrimage to Mecca.
838 **217** 5 dh. multicoloured . . . 10 10
839 10 dh. multicoloured . . 10 10
840 15 dh. multicoloured . . 10 10
841 20 dh. multicoloured . . 15 10

1978. U.N. Conference for Technical Co-operation between Developing Countries.
842 **218** 30 dh. multicoloured . . 15 10
843 40 dh. multicoloured . . 20 15
844 115 dh. multicoloured . . 50 35

219 Workers, Rifles, Torch and Flag **220** Human Figure and Scales

1978. Arab Countries Summit Conference. Multicoloured.
845 30 dh. Type **219** 15 10
846 40 dh. Map of Middle East, eagle and crowd (horiz) 20 15
847 115 dh. As 40 dh. 50 35
848 145 dh. Type **219** 60 45

1978. 30th Anniv of Declaration of Human Rights.
849 **220** 15 dh. multicoloured . . . 10 10
850 30 dh. multicoloured . . . 20 15
851 115 dh. multicoloured . . . 50 35

221 Horse Racing and Fort **222** Lilienthal's Biplane Glider

1978. Libyan Study Centre.
852 **221** 20 dh. multicoloured . . . 15 10
853 40 dh. multicoloured . . . 20 15
854 115 dh. multicoloured . . 50 35

1978. 75th Anniv of First Powered Flight. Mult.
855 20 dh. Type **222** 10 10
856 25 dh. Lindbergh's "Spirit of St. Louis" 10 10
857 30 dh. Admiral Richard Byrd's Trimotor "Floyd Bennett" . 90 25
858 50 dh. Bleriot 5190 Santos Dumont flying boat and airship "Graf Zeppelin" 1·25 35
859 115 dh. Wright brothers and Wright Type A 50 40

223 Libyans, Torch and Laurel Wreath **224** Mounted Dorcas Gazelle Head

1979.
861 **223** 5 dh. multicoloured . . . 10 10
862 10 dh. multicoloured . . 10 10
863 15 dh. multicoloured . . 10 10
864 30 dh. multicoloured . . 20 10
865 50 dh. multicoloured . . 20 10
866 60 dh. multicoloured . . 25 15
867 70 dh. multicoloured . . 30 15
868 100 dh. multicoloured . . 45 25
869 115 dh. multicoloured . . 50 30
870 200 dh. multicoloured . . 75 45
871 250 dh. multicoloured . . 1·25 1·10
871 500 dh. multicoloured . . 1·90 95
872 1000 dh. multicoloured 4·00 2·50
872a 1500 dh. multicoloured 7·00 6·25
872b 2500 dh. multicoloured 11·00 10·00
Nos. 861/9 measure 18 x 23 mm and Nos. 870/2b 26 x 32 mm.

1979. Coil Stamps.
873 **224** 5 dh. multicoloured . . . 15 10
874 20 dh. multicoloured . . . 25 10
875 50 dh. multicoloured . . . 45 25

225 Tortoise

1979. Libyan Animals. Multicoloured.
876 5 dh. Type **225** 10 10
877 10 dh. Addax (vert) 10 10
878 15 dh. Algerian hedgehog . . . 20 10
879 20 dh. North African crested porcupine 20 10
880 30 dh. Dromedaries 30 15
881 35 dh. Wild cat (vert) 40 15
882 45 dh. Dorcas gazelle (vert) . . 50 25
883 115 dh. Cheetah . . . . 1·10 40

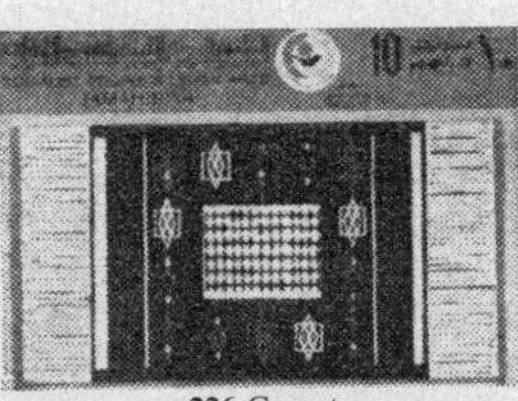
226 Carpet

1979. 17th Tripoli International Trade Fair.
884 **226** 10 dh. multicoloured . . . 10 10
885 – 15 dh. multicoloured . . . 10 10
886 – 30 dh. multicoloured . . 15 10
887 – 45 dh. multicoloured . . 15 10
888 – 115 dh. multicoloured . . 50 35
DESIGNS: 15 dh. to 115 dh. Different carpets.

227 Aircraft and People

1979. International Year of the Child. Children's Paintings (1st series). Multicoloured.
889 20 dh. Type **227** 10 10
890 20 dh. Shepherd with flock . . 10 10
891 20 dh. Open air cafe 10 10
892 20 dh. Boat in storm 10 10
893 20 dh. Policeman on traffic duty 10 10
See also Nos. 975/9.

228 World Map, Koran and Symbols of Arab Achievements **229** Radar Tower and Map

1979. The Arabs.
894 **228** 45 dh. multicoloured . . 20 15
895 70 dh. multicoloured . . 30 20

1979. World Meteorological Day.
896 **299** 15 dh. multicoloured . . 10 10
897 30 dh. multicoloured . . 15 10
898 50 dh. multicoloured . . 20 15

230 Medical Care

1979. World Health Day.
899 **230** 40 dh. multicoloured . . 20 15

231 "Carpobrotus acinaciformis" **232** Farmer and Sheep

1979. Libyan Flowers. Multicoloured.
900 10 dh. Type **231** 10 10
901 15 dh. "Caralluma europaea" 10 10
902 20 dh. "Arum cirenaicum" . . 10 10
903 35 dh. "Lavatera arborea" . . 20 15
904 40 dh. "Capparis spinosa" . . 20 15
905 50 dh. "Ranunculus asiaticus" 25 15

1979. 10th Anniv of Revolution. Mult.
906 15 dh. Type **232** 10 10
907 15 dh. Crowd with Green Book 10 10
908 15 dh. Oil field 10 10
909 15 dh. Refinery 10 10
910 30 dh. Dish aerial 15 10
911 30 dh. Hospital 15 10
912 30 dh. Doctor examining patient 15 10
913 30 dh. Surgeon 15 10
914 40 dh. Street, Tripoli 20 15
915 40 dh. Steel mill 20 15
916 40 dh. Tanks 20 15
917 40 dh. Tuareg horsemen . . . 20 15
918 70 dh. Revolutionaries and Green Book 35 20
919 70 dh. Crowd within map of Libya 35 20
920 70 dh. Mullah 35 20
921 70 dh. Student 35 20

233 Volleyball

234 Emblem

1979. "Universiada '79" World University Games, Mexico City. Multicoloured.
923 45 dh. Type **233** 20 15
924 115 dh. Football 60 30

1979. Third World Telecommunications Exhibition, Geneva.
925 **234** 45 dh. multicoloured . . . 20 15
926 115 dh. multicoloured . . 60 30

235 Seminar Emblem and Crowd

1979. International Seminar on the "Green Book". Multicoloured.
927 10 dh. Type **235** 10 10
928 35 dh. Seminar in progress . . 20 15
929 100 dh. Colonel Gaddafi with "Green Book" 50 30
No. 928 is horizontal, 70 x 43 mm.

236 Horsemen in Town

1979. Evacuation of Foreign Forces. Multicoloured.
931 30 dh. Type **236** 15 10
932 40 dh. Tuareg horsemen . . . 20 15

237 Football Match

1979. Mediterranean Games, Split.
934 **237** 15 dh. multicoloured . . . 10 10
935 30 dh. multicoloured . . . 15 10
936 70 dh. multicoloured . . . 35 20

238 Cyclist and Emblem

1979. Junior Cycling Championships, Tripoli. Multicoloured.
937 15 dh. Type **238** 10 10
938 30 dh. Cyclists and emblem . 15 10

239 Horse-jumping

1979. Pre-Olympics. Multicoloured.
939 45 dh. Type **239** 20 15
940 60 dh. Javelin 30 15
941 115 dh. Hurdles 60 30
942 160 dh. Football 70 40
Nos. 939/42 exist from sheets on which an overall Moscow Olympics emblem in silver was superimposed on the stamps.

240 Figure clothed in Palestinian Flag

241 Ploughing

1979. Solidarity with Palestinian People.
944 **240** 30 dh. multicoloured . . 15 10
945 115 dh. multicoloured . . 60 30

1980. World Olive Oil Year.
946 **241** 15 dh. multicoloured . . 10 10
947 30 dh. multicoloured . . 15 10
948 45 dh. multicoloured . . 20 15

242 Hockey (left)

243 Pipes

1980. National Sports. Multicoloured.
949 10 dh. Type **242** 10 10
950 10 dh. Hockey (right) 10 10
951 10 dh. Leap-frog (left) . . . 10 10
952 10 dh. Leap-frog (right) . . . 10 10
953 15 dh. Long jump (left) . . . 10 10
954 15 dh. Long jump (right) . . 10 10
955 15 dh. Ball catching (left) . . 10 10
956 15 dh. Ball catching (right) . 10 10
957 20 dh. Wrestling (left) 10 10
958 20 dh. Wrestling (right) . . . 10 10
959 20 dh. Stone throwing (left) . 10 10
960 20 dh. Stone throwing (right) 10 10
961 30 dh. Tug-of-war (left) . . . 15 10
962 30 dh. Tug-of-war (right) . . 15 10
963 30 dh. Jumping (left) 15 10
964 30 dh. Jumping (right) 15 10
965 45 dh. Horsemen (left) . . . 20 15
966 45 dh. Horsemen (right) . . . 20 15
967 45 dh. Horsemen with whips (left) 20 15
968 45 dh. Horsemen with whips (right) 20 15
Nos. 949/68 were issued together, divided into se-tenant blocks of four within the sheet, each horizontal pair forming a composite design.

1980. 18th Tripoli International Fair. Multicoloured.
969 5 dh. Drum (horiz) 10 10
970 10 dh. Drum (different) (horiz) 10 10
971 15 dh. Type **243** 10 10
972 20 dh. Bagpipes (horiz) . . . 10 10
973 25 dh. Stringed instrument and bow (horiz) 15 10

1980. International Year of the Child (1979) (2nd issue). As T **227**. Multicoloured.
975 20 dh. "Horse Riding" . . . 10 10
976 20 dh. "Beach scene" 10 10
977 20 dh. "Fish" 10 10
978 20 dh. "Birthday party" . . . 10 10
979 20 dh. "Sheep Festival" . . . 10 10

244 Mosque and Kaaba

1980. 400th Anniv of Hejira.
980 **244** 50 dh. multicoloured . . 25 15
981 115 dh. multicoloured . . 60 30

245 Surgical Operation and Hospital

1980. World Health Day.
982 **245** 20 dh. multicoloured . . . 10 10
983 50 dh. multicoloured . . . 25 15

246 Battle of Shoghab "Shahat", 1913

1980. Battles (1st series). Multicoloured.
984 20 dh. Gardabia, 1915 . . . . 20 15
986 20 dh. Type **246** 10 10
988 20 dh. Fundugh al-Shibani "Garian" 10 10
990 20 dh. Yefren 10 10
992 20 dh. Ghira "Brak" 20 15
994 20 dh. El Hani (Shiat) 35 15
996 20 dh. Sebah 20 15
998 20 dh. Sirt 10 10
985 35 dh. Gardabia 10 10
987 35 dh. Shoghab "Shahat" . . . 20 15
989 35 dh. Fundagh al-Shibani "Garian" 20 15
991 35 dh. Yefren 20 15
993 35 dh. Ghira "Brak" 20 15
995 35 dh. El Hani (Shiat) 60 25
997 35 dh. Sebah 20 15
999 35 dh. Sirt 10 10
The two values commemorating each battle were issued in se-tenant pairs, each pair forming a composite design.
See also Nos. 1027/50, 1132/51 and 1232/39.

247 Flame

248 Ghadames

1980. Sheikh Zarruq Festival.
1000 **247** 40 dh. multicoloured . . 20 15
1001 115 dh. multicoloured . . 60 30

1980. Arabian Towns Organization. Mult.
1003 15 dh. Type **248** 10 10
1004 30 dh. Derna 15 10
1005 50 dh. Ahmad Pasha Mosque, Tripoli 25 15

249 Guides on Hike

1980. 14th Pan-Arab Scout Jamboree. Multicoloured.
1006 15 dh. Type **249** 10 10
1007 30 dh. Guides cooking . . . 15 10
1008 50 dh. Cub Scouts cooking . 25 15
1009 115 dh. Scouts map-reading 60 30

250 Oil Refinery

1980. 11th Anniv of Revolution. Multicoloured.
1011 5 dh. Type **250** 10 10
1012 10 dh. Recreation and youth 10 10
1013 15 dh. Agriculture 10 10
1014 25 dh. Boeing 727-200 airplane and liner 50 15
1015 40 dh. Education 20 15
1016 115 dh. Housing 60 30

HAVE YOU READ THE NOTES AT THE BEGINNING OF THIS CATALOGUE?
These often provide the answers to the enquiries we receive.

251 Camels, Map of Libya and Conference Emblem

1980. World Tourism Conference, Manila. Mult.
1018 45 dh. Type **251** 20 15
1019 115 dh. Emblem, map and camel riders 60 30

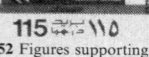

252 Figures supporting O.P.E.C. Emblem

253a Map of Libya and Science Symbols

253 Death of Omar el Mukhtar

1980. 20th Anniv of Organization of Petroleum Exporting Countries. Multicoloured.
1020 45 dh. O.P.E.C. emblem and globe 20 15
1021 115 dh. Type **252** 60 30

1980. 49th Death Anniv of Omar el Mukhtar (patriot).
1022 **253** 20 dh. multicoloured . . 10 10
1023 35 dh. multicoloured . . 20 15

1980. Birth Millenary of Avicenna (philosopher) and School Scientific Exhibition. Multicoloured.
1025 45 dh. Type **253a** 20 15
1026 115 d. Avicenna and Exhibition Emblem 60 30

1981. Battles (2nd series). As T **246.** Mult.
1027 20 dh. Zuara 10 10
1029 20 dh. Tawargha 10 10
1031 20 dh. Dernah 10 10
1033 20 dh. Bir Tagreft 10 10
1035 20 dh. Funduk El Jamel "Misurata" 10 10
1037 20 dh. Sidi El Khemri "Gusbat" 10 10
1039 20 dh. El Khoms 10 10
1041 20 dh. Roghdalin "Menshia" 10 10
1043 20 dh. Ain Zara "Tripoli" . 10 10
1045 20 dh. Rughbat el Naga "Benina" 10 10
1047 20 dh. Tobruk 10 10
1049 20 dh. Ikshadia "Werfella" 10 10
1028 35 dh. Zuara 15 15
1030 35 dh. Tawargha 15 15
1032 35 dh. Dernah 15 15
1034 35 dh. Bir Tagreft 15 15
1036 35 dh. Funduk El Jamel "Misurata" 15 15
1038 35 dh. Sidi El Khemri "Gusbat" 15 15
1040 35 dh. El khoms 15 15
1042 35 dh. Roghdalin "Menshia" 15 15
1044 35 dh. Ain Zara "Tripoli" . 15 15
1046 35 dh. Rughbat el Naga "Benina" 15 15
1048 35 dh. Tobruk 15 15
1050 35 dh. Ikshadia "Werfella" 15 15
The two values commemorating each battle were issued in se-tenant pairs, each pair forming a composite design.

254 Tent, Trees and Sun

1981. Children's Day. Children's Paintings. Multicoloured.
1051 20 dh. Type **254** 10 10
1052 20 dh. Women 10 10
1053 20 dh. Picnic 10 10
1054 20 dh. Aeroplane and playing children 10 10
1055 20 dh. Mosque and man with camel 10 10

255 Central Bank

257 Crowd and "Green Book" Stamp of 1977

256 Pots

1981. 25th Anniv of Central Bank of Libya.
1056 **255** 45 dh. multicoloured . . 15 15
1057 115 dh. multicoloured . . 35 35

1981. Tripoli International Fair. Multicoloured.
1059 5 dh. Type **256** 10 10
1060 10 dh. Silver coffee pot (vert) 10 10
1061 15 dh. Long-necked vase (vert) 10 10
1062 45 dh. Round-bellied vase . . 15 15
1063 115 dh. Jug 35 35

1981. People's Authority Declaration.
1064 **257** 50 dh. multicoloured . . 15 15
1065 115 dh. multicoloured . . 35 35

258 Tajoura Hospital, Medical Complex, Patients, receiving Treatment and W.H.O. Emblem

1981. World Health Day.
1066 **258** 45 dh. multicoloured . . 15 15
1067 115 dh. multicoloured . . 35 35

259 Eye and Man on Crutches

1981. International Year of Disabled People.
1068 **259** 20 dh. green, blue & blk . 10 10
1069 – 45 dh. green, blk & blue . 15 15
1070 – 115 dh. blue and green . . 35 35
DESIGNS: 45 dh. Globe and I.Y.D.P. emblem; 115 dh. Hands holding shield with I.Y.D.P. emblem, eye and man on crutch.

260 Horse

1981. Libyan Mosaics. Multicoloured.
1071 10 dh. Type **260** 10 10
1072 20 dh. Ship 10 10
1073 30 dh. Birds, fish and flowers 10 10
1074 40 dh. Leopard 15 15
1075 50 dh. Man playing musical instrument 15 15
1076 115 dh. Fishes 35 35

INDEX

Countries can be quickly located by referring to the index at the end of this volume.

261 Racial Discrimination Emblem

262 Jet Fighters and Sud Aviation Alouette III Helicopter (left-hand stamp)

1981. International Year Against Racial Discrimination.
1077 **261** 45 dh. multicoloured . . 25 25
1078 50 dh. multicoloured . . 30 30

1981. 12th Anniv of Revolution.
1079 **262** 5 dh. blue and light blue 15 10
1080 – 5 dh. blue and light blue 15 10
1081 – 5 dh. blue and light blue 10 10
1082 – 5 dh. blue and light blue 10 10
1083 – 10 dh. black and blue . 10 10
1084 – 10 dh. black and blue . 10 10
1085 – 10 dh. black and blue . 10 10
1086 – 10 dh. black and blue . 10 10
1087 – 15 dh. brown & lt brown 10 10
1088 – 15 dh. brown & lt brown 10 10
1089 – 15 dh. brown & lt brown 10 10
1090 – 15 dh. brown & lt brown 10 10
1091 – 20 dh. blue and green . 15 15
1092 – 20 dh. blue and green . 15 15
1093 – 20 dh. blue and green . 15 15
1094 – 20 dh. blue and green . 15 15
1095 – 25 dh. brown and yellow 15 15
1096 – 25 dh. brown and yellow 15 15
1097 – 25 dh. brown and yellow 15 15
1098 – 25 dh. brown and yellow 15 15
DESIGNS—VERT: No. 1080, Jet fighter (right-hand stamp); Nos. 1081/2, Parachutists; Nos. 1083/4, Tank parade; Nos. 1085/6, Marching frogmen; Nos. 1087/8, Anti-aircraft rocket trucks; Nos. 1089/90, Missile trucks. HORIZ: Nos. 1091/2, Marching sailors; Nos. 1093/4, Jeeps and anti-aircraft rocket trucks; Nos. 1095/6, Armoured vehicles and landrovers; Nos. 1097/8, Tank parade.
Each pair forms a horizontal composite design, the first number being the left-hand stamp in each instance.

263 Wheat and Plough

1981. World Food Day.
1100 **263** 45 dh. multicoloured . . 25 25
1101 200 dh. multicoloured . 95 95

264 "Pseudotergumia fidia"

1981. Butterflies. Multicoloured.
1102 5 dh. Type **264** 15 10
1103 5 dh. "Chazara prieuri" (sun in background) 15 10
1104 5 dh. "Polygonia c-album" (trees in background) . . 15 10
1105 5 dh. "Colias crocea" (mosque in background) 15 10
1106 10 dh. "Anthocharis bellia" (face value bottom right) 15 10
1107 10 dh. "Pandoriana pandora" (face value bottom left) . 15 10
1108 10 dh. "Melanargia ines" (face value top right) 15 10
1109 10 dh. "Charaxes jasius" (face value top left) 15 10
1110 15 dh. "Nymphales antiopa" (face value bottom right) 30 30
1111 15 dh. "Eurodryas desfontainii" (face value bottom left) . 30 30
1112 15 dh. "Iphiclides podalirius" (face value top right) . . . 30 30
1113 15 dh. "Glaucopsyche melanops" (face value top left) 30 30
1114 25 dh. "Spialia sertorius" (face value bottom right) . . . 50 45
1115 25 dh. "Pieris brassicae" (face value bottom left) . . . 50 45
1116 25 dh. "Lysandra albicans" (face value top right) . . . 50 45
1117 25 dh. "Celastrina argiolus" (face value top left) . . . 50 45
The four designs of each value were issued together in small sheets of four, showing composite background designs.

265 Grapes

266 I.Y.D.P. Emblem and Globe

1981. Fruit. Multicoloured.
1119 5 dh. Type **265** 10 10
1120 10 dh. Dates 10 10
1121 15 dh. Lemons 10 10
1122 20 dh. Oranges 15 15
1123 35 dh. Barbary figs 20 20
1124 55 dh. Pomegranate 30 30

1981. International Year of Disabled Persons.
1125 **266** 45 dh. multicoloured . . 25 25
1126 115 dh. multicoloured . . 55 55

267 Animals (looking right)

1982. Libyan Mosaics. Multicoloured.
1127 45 dh. Type **267** 25 25
1128 45 dh. Orpheus 25 25
1129 45 dh. Animals (looking left) 25 25
1130 45 dh. Fishes 25 25
1131 45 dh. Fishermen 25 25
1132 45 dh. Fishes and ducks . . . 25 25
1133 45 dh. Farm 25 25
1134 45 dh. Birds and fruit 25 25
1135 45 dh. Milking 25 25

268 Koran Texts leading to Ka'aba

269 Grinding Flour

1982. Third Koran Reading Contest. Multicoloured.
1136 10 dh. Type **249** 10 10
1137 35 dh. Koran and formation of the World 20 20
1138 115 dh. Reading the Koran 55 55

1982. Battles (3rd series). As T **246**. Multicoloured.
1140 20 dh. Hun "Gioffra" 15 15
1142 20 dh. Gedabia 15 15
1144 20 dh. El Asaba "Gianduba" 15 15
1146 20 dh. El Habela 15 15
1148 20 dh. Suk El Ahad "Tarhuna" 15 15
1150 20 dh. El Tangi 15 15
1152 20 dh. Sokna 15 15
1154 20 dh. Wadi Smalus "Jabel El Akdar" 15 15
1156 20 dh. Sidi Abuagela "Agelat" 15 15
1158 20 dh. Sidi Surur "Zeliten" 15 15
1160 20 dh. Kuefia 15 15
1162 20 dh. Abunjeim 15 15
1141 35 dh. Hun "Gioffra" 20 20
1143 35 dh. Gedabia 20 20
1145 35 dh. El Asaba "Gianduba" 20 20
1147 35 dh. El Habela 20 20
1149 35 dh. Suk El Ahad "Tarhuna" 20 20
1151 35 dh. El Tangi 20 20
1153 35 dh. Sokna 20 20
1155 35 dh. Wadi Smalus "Jabel El Akdar" 20 20
1157 35 dh. Sidi Abuagela "Agelat" 20 20
1159 35 dh. Sidi Surur "Zeliten" 20 20
1161 35 dh. Kuefia 20 20
1163 35 dh. Abunjeim 20 20
The two values commemorating each battle were issued in se-tenant pairs, each pair forming a composite design.

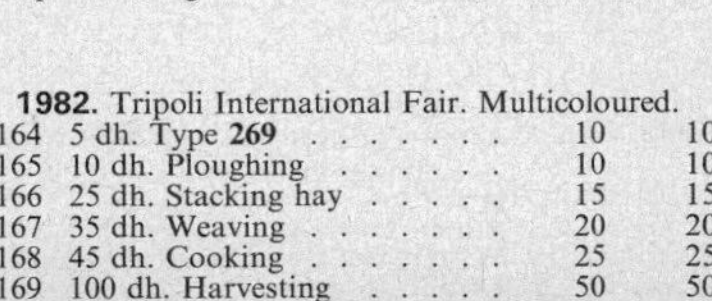

1982. Tripoli International Fair. Multicoloured.
1164 5 dh. Type **269** 10 10
1165 10 dh. Ploughing 10 10
1166 25 dh. Stacking hay 15 15
1167 35 dh. Weaving 20 20
1168 45 dh. Cooking 25 25
1169 100 dh. Harvesting 50 50

270 "ALFATAH" forming Farm Vehicle

1982. People's Authority Declaration. Multicoloured.
1170 100 dh. Type **270** 50 50
1171 200 dh. Colonel Gaddafi, old man, "Green Book" and guns 95 95
1172 300 dh. Rejoicing crowd . . 1·40 1·40

271 Scout flying Model Airship

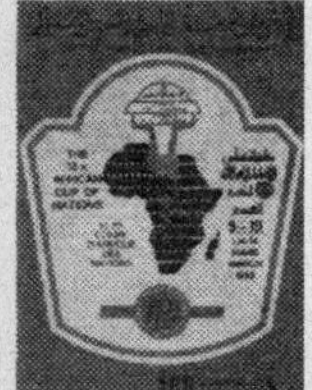

272 Map of Africa and A.F.C. Emblem

1982. 75th Anniv of Boy Scout Movement. Mult.
1173 100 dh. Type **271** 50 50
1174 200 dh. Scouts helping injured dog 95 95
1175 300 dh. Scout reading to old man . . . . 1·40 1·40
1176 400 dh. Scout with model rocket 1·90 1·90

1982. African Football Cup Competition.
1178 **272** 100 dh. multicoloured . 50 50
1179 200 dh. multicoloured . 95 95

273 Footballer

1982. World Cup Football Championship, Spain. Multicoloured.
1180 45 dh. Type **273** 25 25
1181 100 dh. Footballer (different) 50 50
1182 200 dh. As No. 1173 . . . . 95 95
1183 300 dh. Footballer and goalkeeper . . . . 1·40 1·40

274 Palestinian Children

275 Lanner Falcon

1982. Palestinian Children's Day. Multicoloured.
1185 20 dh. Type **274** 15 15
1186 20 dh. Girl with dish 15 15
1187 20 dh. Child with turban . . 15 15
1188 20 dh. Young child 15 15
1189 20 dh. Young boy 15 15

1982. Birds. Multicoloured.
1190 15 dh. Type **275** 35 30
1191 15 dh. Common swift . . . 35 30
1192 15 dh. Peregrine falcon . . . 35 30
1193 15 dh. Greater flamingo . . 35 30
1194 25 dh. Whitethroat 60 40
1195 25 dh. Turtle dove 60 40
1196 25 dh. Black-bellied sandgrouse 60 40
1197 25 dh. Egyptian vulture . . . 60 40
1198 45 dh. Golden oriole . . . . 1·00 70
1199 45 dh. European bee eater . 1·00 70
1200 45 dh. Common kingfisher . 1·00 70
1201 45 dh. Common roller . . . 1·00 70
1202 95 dh. Barbary partridge . . 1·90 1·40
1203 95 dh. Barn owl . . . . . . 1·90 1·40
1204 95 dh. Cream-coloured courser 1·90 1·40
1205 95 dh. Hoopoe . . . . 1·90 1·40
The four designs of each value were printed together in se-tenant blocks of four, forming a composite design.

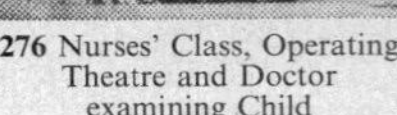

276 Nurses' Class, Operating Theatre and Doctor examining Child

277 Map of Libya and A.P.U. Emblem

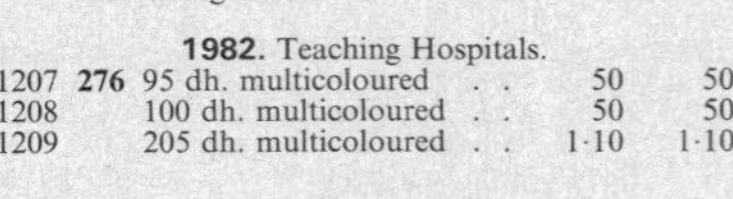

1982. Teaching Hospitals.

1207	**276**	95 dh. multicoloured	50	50
1208		100 dh. multicoloured	50	50
1209		205 dh. multicoloured	1·10	1·10

1982. 30th Anniv of Arab Postal Union.

1210	**277**	100 dh. multicoloured	50	50
1211		200 dh. multicoloured	95	95

278 19th-century Chinese King and diagram of Fischer v Spassky, 1972

1982. World Chess Championship, Moscow. Mult.

1212	100 dh. Type **278**	50	50
1213	100 dh. African king and diagram of Karpov v Korchnoi, 1978	50	50
1214	100 dh. Modern bishop and diagram of Smyslov v Karpov, 1971	50	50
1215	100 dh. 19th-century European rook and diagram of Tal v Vadasz, 1977	50	50

Nos. 1212/15 were printed together, se-tenant, forming a composite design.

279 Hexagonal Pattern

1982. World Telecommunications Day.

1217	**279**	100 dh. multicoloured	50	50
1218		200 dh. multicoloured	95	95

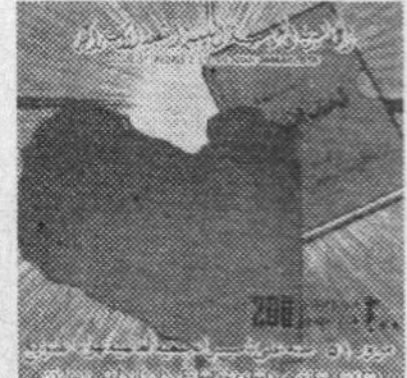

280 Map of Libya and "Green Book"

1982. 51st Anniv of International Philatelic Federation (F.I.P.).

1219	**280**	200 dh. multicoloured	95	95

281 Family & Flag

283 Palm Tree and Red Crescent

282 Pres. Gaddafi and Jet Aircraft

1982. Organization of African Unity Summit. Multicoloured.

1221	50 dh. Type **281**	30	30
1222	100 dh. Map, dove and symbols of industry and agriculture	50	50
1223	200 dh. Pres. Gaddafi and crowd with "Green Book" (65 x 36 mm.)	95	95

1982. 13th Anniv of Revolution. Multicoloured.

1225	15 dh. Type **282**	15	10
1226	20 dh. Gaddafi, soldiers and rockets	15	10
1227	30 dh. Gaddafi, sailors and naval vessels	50	25
1228	45 dh. Gaddafi, soldiers and tanks	25	25
1229	70 dh. Gaddafi, and armed forces	35	35
1230	100 dh. Gaddafi and women soldiers	50	50

1982. 25th Anniv of Libyan Red Crescent. Multicoloured.

1232	100 dh. Type **283**	50	50
1233	200 dh. "25" within crescents	95	95

284 Globe, Dove and Rifle

286 Philadelphus

285 Gaddafi, Crowd, "Green Book" and Emblems

1982. Solidarity with Palestinian People.

1234	**284**	100 dh. black, mauve and green	45	40
1235		200 dh. black, blue and green	90	80

1982. Al Fateh University Symposium on the "Green Book". Multicoloured.

1236	100 dh. Type **285**	50	45
1237	200 dh. Gaddafi, "Green Book", map and emblems	1·00	95

1983. Flowers. Multicoloured.

1238	25 dh. Type **286**	15	10
1239	25 dh. Hypericum	15	10
1240	25 dh. Antirrhinum	15	10
1241	25 dh. Lily	15	10
1242	25 dh. Capparis	15	10
1243	25 dh. Tropaeolum	15	10
1244	25 dh. Roses	15	10
1245	25 dh. Chrysanthemum	15	10
1246	25 dh. "Nigella damascena"	15	10
1247	25 dh. "Guilladia lanceolata"	15	10
1248	25 dh. Dahlia	15	10
1249	25 dh. "Dianthus caryophyllus"	15	10
1250	25 dh. "Notobasis syriaca"	15	10
1251	25 dh. "Nerium oleander"	15	10
1252	25 dh. "Iris histroides"	15	10
1253	25 dh. "Scolymus hispanicus"	15	10

287 Customs Council Building, Brussels, and Warrior on Horseback

288 Camel

1983. 30th Anniv of Customs Co-operation Council. Multicoloured.

1254	25 dh. Type **287**	15	10
1255	50 dh. Customs building	25	20
1256	100 dh. Customs building and warrior with sword	50	45

1983. Battles (4th series). As T **246**. (a) Battle of Ghaser Ahmed.

1257	50 dh. multicoloured	25	20
1258	50 dh. multicoloured	25	20

(b) Battle of Sidi Abuarghub.

1259	50 dh. multicoloured	25	20
1260	50 dh. multicoloured	25	20

(c) Battle of Ghar Yunes.

1261	50 dh. multicoloured	25	20
1262	50 dh. multicoloured	25	20

(d) Battle of Bir Otman.

1263	50 dh. multicoloured	25	20
1264	50 dh. multicoloured	25	20

(e) Battle of Sidi Sajeh.

1265	50 dh. multicoloured	25	20
1266	50 dh. multicoloured	25	20

(f) Battle of Ras el-Hamam.

1267	50 dh. multicoloured	25	20
1268	50 dh. multicoloured	25	20

(g) Battle of Zawiet Ishghefa.

1269	50 dh. multicoloured	25	20
1270	50 dh. multicoloured	25	20

(h) Battle of Wadi Essania.

1271	50 dh. multicoloured	25	20
1272	50 dh. multicoloured	25	20

(i) Battle of El-Meshiashta.

1273	50 dh. multicoloured	25	20
1274	50 dh. multicoloured	25	20

(j) Battle of Gharara.

1275	50 dh. multicoloured	25	20
1276	50 dh. multicoloured	25	20

(k) Battle of Abughelan.

1277	50 dh. multicoloured	20	20
1278	50 dh. multicoloured	20	20

(l) Battle of Mahruka.

1279	50 dh. multicoloured	20	20
1280	50 dh. multicoloured	20	20

The two values for each battle were printed together in se-tenant pairs, forming composite designs.

1983. Farm Animals. Multicoloured.

1281	25 dh. Type **288**	15	10
1282	25 dh. Cow	15	10
1283	25 dh. Horse	15	10
1284	25 dh. Bull	15	10
1285	25 dh. Goat	15	10
1286	25 dh. Sheep dog	15	10
1287	25 dh. Ewe	15	10
1288	25 dh. Ram	15	10
1289	25 dh. Duck	15	10
1290	25 dh. Guinea fowl	15	10
1291	25 dh. Rabbit	15	10
1292	25 dh. Pigeon	15	10
1293	25 dh. Turkey	15	10
1294	25 dh. Cockerel	15	10
1295	25 dh. Hen	15	10
1296	25 dh. Goose	15	10

289 Musician with Twin-horned Pipe

1983. Tripoli International Fair. Multicoloured.

1297	40 dh. Type **289**	20	15
1298	45 dh. Bagpipes (horiz)	25	20
1299	50 dh. Horn	25	20
1300	55 dh. Flute (horiz)	30	25
1301	75 dh. Pipe	40	35
1302	100 dh. Man and woman at well	50	45

290 Phoenician Galley

1983. 25th Anniv of International Maritime Organization. Multicoloured.

1303	100 dh. Type **290**	80	55
1304	100 dh. Ancient Greek galley	80	55
1305	100 dh. Ancient Egyptian ship	80	55
1306	100 dh. Roman sailing ship	80	55
1307	100 dh. Viking longship	80	55
1308	100 dh. Libyan xebec	80	55

291 Motorist

1983. Children's Day. Multicoloured.

1309	20 dh. Type **291**	10	10
1310	20 dh. Tractor and trailer	10	10
1311	20 dh. Child with dove and globe	10	10
1312	20 dh. Scout camp	10	10
1313	20 dh. Dinosaur	10	10

292 Pres. Gaddafi with Children

1983. World Health Day. Multicoloured.

1314	25 dh. Type **292**	15	10
1315	50 dh. Gaddafi and old man in wheelchair	25	20
1316	100 dh. Gaddafi visiting sick girl (horiz)	50	45

293 Gaddafi, Map and "Green Book"

294 Economic Emblems on Map of Africa

1983. First World "Green Book" Symposium. Multicoloured.

1317	50 dh. Type **293**	25	20
1318	70 dh. Syposium in session and emblem (56 x 37 mm)	35	30
1319	80 dh. Gaddafi, "Green Book", emblem and "Jamahiriya"	40	35

1983. 25th Anniv of African Economic Committee.

1321	**294**	50 dh. multicoloured	25	20
1322		100 dh. multicoloured	50	45
1323		250 dh. multicoloured	1·25	1·10

296 "Labrus bimaculatus"

1983. Fishes. Multicoloured.

1325	25 dh. Type **296**	15	10
1326	25 dh. "Trigoporus lastoviza"	15	10
1327	25 dh. "Thalassoma pavo"	15	10
1328	25 dh. "Apogon imberbis"	15	10
1329	25 dh. "Scomber scombrus"	15	10
1330	25 dh. "Spondyliosoma cantharus"	15	10
1331	25 dh. "Trachinus draco"	15	10
1332	25 dh. "Blennius pavo"	15	10
1333	25 dh. "Scorpaena notata"	15	10
1334	25 dh. "Serranus scriba"	15	10
1335	25 dh. "Lophius piscatorius"	15	10
1336	25 dh. "Uranoscopus scaber"	15	10
1337	25 dh. "Auxis thazard"	15	10
1338	25 dh. "Zeus faber"	15	10
1339	25 dh. "Dactylopterus volitans"	15	10
1340	25 dh. "Umbrina cirrosa"	15	10

297 "Still-life" (Gauguin)

1983. Paintings. Multicoloured.

1341	50 dh. Type **297**	25	20
1342	50 dh. Abstract	25	20
1343	50 dh. "The Conquest of Tunis by Charles V" (Rubens)	25	20
1344	50 dh. "Arab Band in Horse-drawn Carriage"	25	20
1345	50 dh. "Apotheosis of Gaddafi" (vert)	25	20
1346	50 dh. Horses (detail of Raphael's "The Triumph of David over the Assyrians") (vert)	25	20
1347	50 dh. "Workers" (vert)	25	20
1348	50 dh. "Sunflowers" (Van Gogh) (vert)	25	20

298 Basketball

1983. Olympic Games, Los Angeles. Mult.

1349 10 dh. Type **298** 10 10
1350 15 dh. High jumping 10 10
1351 25 dh. Running 15 10
1352 50 dh. Gymnastics 25 20
1353 100 dh. Windsurfing 65 45
1354 200 dh. Shot-putting 1·00 95

299 I.T.U. Building, Antenna and W.C.Y. Emblem

1983. World Communications Year.

1356 **299** 10 dh. multicoloured 10 10
1357 50 dh. multicoloured 25 20
1358 100 dh. multicoloured 50 45

300 "The House is to be served by its Residents"

1983. Extracts from the Green Book. Mult.

1359 10 dh. Type **300** 10 10
1360 15 dh. "Power, wealth and arms are in the hands of the people" 10 10
1361 20 dh. "Masters in their own castles" (vert) 10 10
1362 35 dh. "No democracy without popular congresses" 20 15
1363 100 dh. "The authority of the people" (vert) 50 45
1364 140 dh. "The Green Book is the guide of humanity for final release" 75 70

301 Handball

1983. 2nd African Youth Festival. Multicoloured.

1366 100 dh. Type **301** 50 45
1367 100 dh. Basketball 50 45
1368 100 dh. High jumping 50 45
1369 100 dh. Running 50 45
1370 100 dh. Football 50 45

302 Marching Soldiers

1983. 14th Anniv of September Revolution. Mult.

1371 65 dh. Type **302** 35 30
1372 75 dh. Weapons and communications training 40 35
1373 90 dh. Women with machine-guns and bazookas 45 40
1374 100 dh. Machine-gun training 50 45
1375 150 dh. Bazooka training 75 70
1376 250 dh. Rifle training 1·25 1·10

303 Saluting Scouts

1983. Scout Jamborees. Multicoloured.

1378 50 dh. Type **303** 25 20
1379 100 dh. Scouts around camp fire 50 45

EVENTS. 50 dh. Second Islamic Scout Jamboree; 100 dh. 15th Pan Arab Scout Jamboree.

304 Traffic Cadets

305 Saadun

1983. Traffic Day. Multicoloured.

1381 30 dh. Type **304** 15 15
1382 70 dh. Traffic policeman 35 30
1383 200 dh. Police motorcyclists 1·00 95

1983. 90th Birth Anniv of Saadun (patriot soldier).

1384 **305** 100 dh. multicoloured 50 45

306 Walter Wellman's airship "America", 1910

1983. Bicentenary of Manned Flight. Mult.

1385 100 dh. Type **306** 1·00 55
1386 100 dh. Airship "Nulli Secundus", 1907 1·00 55
1387 100 dh. Jean-Baptiste Meusnier's balloon design, 1784 1·00 55
1388 100 dh. Blanchard and Jeffries' Channel crossing, 1785 (vert) 1·00 55
1389 100 dh. Pilatre de Rozier's hydrogen/hot-air balloon flight, 1784 (vert) 1·00 55
1390 100 dh. First Montgolfier balloon, 1783 (vert) 1·00 55

307 Globe and Dove

1983. Solidarity with Palestinian People.

1393 **307** 200 dh. green, blue & blk 1·00 95

308 Gladiators fighting

1983. Mosaics. Multicoloured.

1394 50 dh. Type **308** 25 20
1395 50 dh. Gladiators fighting (different) 25 20
1396 50 dh. Gladiators and slave 25 20
1397 50 dh. Two musicians 25 20
1398 50 dh. Three musicians 25 20
1399 50 dh. Two gladiators 25 20
1400 50 dh. Two Romans and bound victim 25 20
1401 50 dh. Leopard and man hunting deer 25 20
1402 50 dh. Deer and man with boar 25 20

309 Traditional Architecture

1983. Achievements of the Revolution. Mult.

1403 10 dh. Type **309** 10 10
1404 15 dh. Camels drinking and mechanization of farming 10 10
1405 20 dh. Computer operator and industrial scene 10 10
1406 35 dh. Modern architecture 15 10
1407 100 dh. Surgeons and nurses treating patients and hospital 45 40
1408 140 dh. Airport and airplane 1·25 75

310 Flooding a River Bed

311 Mahmud Burkis

1983. Colonel Gaddafi–River Builder. Multicoloured.

1410 50 dh. Type **310** 20 15
1411 50 dh. Irrigation pipe and agricultural produce 20 15
1412 100 dh. Colonel Gaddafi, irrigation pipe and farmland (62 x 44 mm) 45 40
1413 100 dh. Colonel Gaddafi and map (68 x 32 mm) 45 40
1414 150 dh. Colonel Gaddafi explaining irrigation project (35 x 32 mm) 70 65

Nos. 1410/12 were printed together in se-tenant strips of three forming a composite design.

1984. Personalities. Multicoloured.

1416 100 dh. Type **311** 45 40
1417 100 dh. Ahmed el-Bakbak 45 40
1418 100 dh. Mohamed el-Misurati 45 40
1419 100 dh. Mahmud Ben Musa 45 40
1420 100 dh. Abdulhamid el-Sherif 45 40
1421 100 dh. Mehdi el-Sherif 45 40
1422 100 dh. Mahmud Mustafa Dreza 45 40
1423 100 dh. Hosni Fauzi el-Amir 45 40
1424 100 dh. Ali Haidar el-Saati 45 40
1425 200 dh. Ahmed el-Feghi Hasan 90 80
1426 200 dh. Bashir el-Jawab 90 80
1427 200 dh. Ali el-Gariani 90 80
1428 200 dh. Muktar Shakshuki 90 80
1429 200 dh. Abdurrahman el-Busayri 90 80
1430 200 dh. Ibbrahim Bakir 90 80
1431 200 dh. Mahmud el-Janzuri 90 80

312 Windsurfing

313 Col. Gaddafi with Schoolchildren

1984. Water Sports. Multicoloured.

1432 25 dh. Type **312** 20 10
1433 25 dh. Dinghy sailing (orange and red sails) 20 10
1434 25 dh. Dinghy sailing (mauve sails) 20 10
1435 25 dh. Hang-gliding on water skis 20 10
1436 25 dh. Water-skiing 20 10
1437 25 dh. Angling from boat 20 10
1438 25 dh. Men in speed boat 20 10
1439 25 dh. Water-skiing (different) 20 10
1440 25 dh. Fishing 20 10
1441 25 dh. Canoeing 20 10
1442 25 dh. Surfing 20 10
1443 25 dh. Water-skiing (different) 20 10
1444 25 dh. Scuba diving 20 10
1445 25 dh. Diving 20 10
1446 25 dh. Swimming in snorkel and flippers 20 10
1447 25 dh. Scuba diving for fish 20 10

1984. African Children's Day. Multicoloured.

1448 50 dh. Type **313** 20 15
1449 50 dh. Colonel Gaddafi and children in national dress 20 15
1450 100 dh. Colonel Gaddafi on map and children at various activities (62 x 43 mm) 70 40

314 Women in National, Casual and Military Dress

1984. Libyan Women's Emancipation. Multicoloured.

1451 55 dh. Type **314** 25 20
1452 70 dh. Women in traditional, casual and military dress (vert) 30 25
1453 100 dh. Colonel Gaddafi and women in military dress 45 40

315 Theatre, Sabratha

1984. Roman Ruins of Cyrenaica. Multicoloured.

1454 50 dh. Type **315** 20 15
1455 60 dh. Temple, Cyrene 25 20
1456 70 dh. Monument, Sabratha (vert) 30 25
1457 100 dh. Amphitheatre, Leptis Magna 45 40
1458 150 dh. Temple, Cyrene (different) 70 65
1459 200 dh. Basilica, Leptis Magna 90 80

316 Silver Dirham, 115 h.

318 Muktar Shiaker Murabet

317 Men at Tea Ceremony

1984. Arabic Islamic Coins (1st series).

1460 **316** 200 dh. silver, yellow and black 90 85
1461 – 200 dh. silver, mauve and black 90 85
1462 – 200 dh. silver, green and black 90 85
1463 – 200 dh. silver, orange and black 90 85
1464 – 200 dh. silver, blue and black 90 85

DESIGNS: No. 1461, Silver dirham, 93 h; 1462, Silver dirham, 121 h; 1463, Silver dirham, 49 h; 1464, Silver dirham, 135 h.

See also Nos. 1643/5.

1984. International Trade Fair, Tripoli. Mult.

1465 25 dh. Type **317** 15 10
1466 35 dh. Woman making tea 15 15
1467 45 dh. Men taking tea 20 15
1468 55 dh. Family taking tea 25 20
1469 75 dh. Veiled women pouring tea 35 30
1470 100 dh. Robed men taking tea 45 40

1984. Musicians. Multicoloured.

1471 100 dh. Type **318** 45 40
1472 100 dh. El-Aref el-Jamal 45 40
1473 100 dh. Ali Shiaalia 45 40
1474 100 dh. Bashir Fehmi 45 40

319 Playing among Trees

1984. Children's Day. Designs showing children's paintings. Multicoloured.

1475 20 dh. Type **319** 10 10
1476 20 dh. A rainy day 10 10
1477 20 dh. Weapons of war . . . 10 10
1478 20 dh. Playing on the swing 10 10
1479 20 dh. Playing in the park . . 10 10

320 Crest and "39"

1984. 39th Anniv of Arab League.

1480 **320** 30 dh. multicoloured . . 15 15
1481 40 dh. multicoloured . . 20 15
1482 50 dh. multicoloured . . 25 20

321 Red Four-seater Car

1984. Motor Cars and Locomotives. Mult.

1483 100 dh. Type **321** 45 40
1484 100 dh. Red three-seater car 45 40
1485 100 dh. Yellow two-seater car with three lamps 45 40
1486 100 dh. Covered red four-seater car 45 40
1487 100 dh. Yellow two-seater car with two lamps 45 40
1488 100 dh. Cream car with spare wheel at side 45 40
1489 100 dh. Green car with spare wheel at side 45 40
1490 100 dh. Cream four-seater car with spare wheel at back . 45 40
1491 100 dh. Locomotive pulling wagon and coach 70 35
1492 100 dh. Purple and blue locomotive 70 35
1493 100 dh. Cream locomotive . . 70 35
1494 100 dh. Lavender and brown locomotive 70 35
1495 100 dh. Lavender and black locomotive with red wheels 70 35
1496 100 dh. Cream and red locomotive 70 35
1497 100 dh. Purple and black locomotive with red wheels 70 35
1498 100 dh. Green and orange locomotive 70 35

322 Stylised People and Campaign Emblem

1984. World Health Day. Anti-Polio Campaign. Multicoloured.

1499 20 dh. Type **322** 10 10
1500 30 dh. Stylised people and 1981 20 dh. stamp 15 15
1501 40 dh. Stylised people and Arabic emblem 20 15

323 Man making Slippers

1984. Handicrafts. Multicoloured.

1502 150 dh. Type **323** 70 65
1503 150 dh. Man making decorative harness 70 65
1504 150 dh. Women forming cotton into skeins 70 65
1505 150 dh. Woman spinning by hand 70 65
1506 150 dh. Man weaving 70 65
1507 150 dh. Women weaving . . 70 65

324 Telephones, Dial and Mail

1984. Postal and Telecommunications Union Congress. Multicoloured.

1508 50 dh. Type **324** 25 20
1509 50 dh. Woman working at computer console, dial and man working on computer 25 20
1510 100 dh. Satellite, map, laurel branches and telephone handset 45 40

325 Armed Soldiers and Civilians

326 Children behind Barbed Wire

1984. Abrogation of 17th May Treaty. Multicoloured.

1511 50 dh. Type **325** 25 20
1512 50 dh. Map, dove and burning banner 25 20
1513 50 dh. Soldiers shaking hands and crowd with banners (30 x 40 mm) 25 20
1514 100 dh. Hands tearing treaty, Gaddafi and crowd (62 x 40 mm) 45 40
1515 100 dh. Gaddafi addressing crowd 45 40

Nos. 1512/14 were printed together in se-tenant strips of three, forming a composite design.

1984. Child Victims of Invasion Day. Multicoloured.

1516 70 dh. Torn flags on barbed wire 30 25
1517 100 dh. Type **326** 45 40

327 "The Party System Aborts Democracy"

328 Man in Brown Robes

1984. Quotations from "The Green Book". Multicoloured.

1518 100 dh. Type **327** 45 40
1519 100 dh. Colonel Gaddafi . . 45 40
1520 100 dh. "Partners not wage-workers" 45 40
1521 100 dh. "No representation in lieu of the people. Representation is falsification" 45 40
1522 100 dh. The Green Book . . 45 40
1523 100 dh. "Committees everywhere" 45 40
1524 100 dh. "Forming parties splits societies" 45 40
1525 100 dh. Skyscraper and earthmover 45 40
1526 100 dh. "No democracy without popular congresses" . . . 45 40

1984. Costumes. Multicoloured.

1527 100 dh. Type **328** 45 40
1528 100 dh. Woman in green dress and red shawl 45 40
1529 100 dh. Man in ornate costume and turban 45 40
1530 100 dh. Man in short trousers and plain shirt 45 40
1531 100 dh. Woman in shift and trousers with white shawl 45 40
1532 100 dh. Man in long white robe and red shawl 45 40

329 Footballer tackling

1984. World Cup Football Championship. Multicoloured.

1533 70 dh. Type **329** 30 25
1534 70 dh. Footballers in magenta and green shirts 30 25
1535 70 dh. Footballers in orange and lemon shirts 30 25
1536 70 dh. Goalkeeper failing to save ball 30 25
1537 70 dh. Footballers in yellow and brown shirts 30 25
1538 70 dh. Top of Trophy and footballer in green striped shirt 30 25
1539 70 dh. Top of Trophy and footballers in blue and pink shirts 30 25
1540 70 dh. Footballers in black and white striped and green and red striped shirts 30 25
1541 70 dh. Footballers in green and red striped shirts 30 25
1542 70 dh. Foot of trophy and footballers in orange striped and blue shirts 30 25
1543 70 dh. Foot of trophy and goalkeeper 30 25
1544 70 dh. Goalkeeper saving headed ball 30 25
1545 70 dh. Referee and footballers 30 25
1546 70 dh. Footballers in white with red striped sleeves and orange shirts 30 25
1547 70 dh. Footballers in white and green striped and orange shirts 30 25
1548 70 dh. Footballer in pink shirt 30 25

Nos. 1533/48 were printed in sheetlets of 16 stamps, the backgrounds to the stamps forming an overall design of a stadium.

330 Football

331 Palm Trees

1984. Olympic Games, Los Angeles. Mult.

1549 100 dh. Type **330** 45 40
1550 100 dh. Swimming 45 40
1551 100 dh. Throwing the discus 45 40
1552 100 dh. Windsurfing 70 40
1553 100 dh. Basketball 45 40
1554 100 dh. Running 45 40

1984. 9th World Forestry Congress. Mult.

1556 100 dh. Four types of forest 45 40
1557 200 dh. Type **331** 90 85

332 Modern Building

1984. 15th Anniv of Revolution. Multicoloured.

1558 25 dh. Type **332** 15 10
1559 25 dh. Front of building . . . 15 10
1560 25 dh. Building by pool . . . 15 10
1561 25 dh. Col. Gaddafi (three-quarter portrait) 15 10
1562 25 dh. High-rise block 15 10
1563 25 dh. Crane and mosque . . 15 10
1564 25 dh. Motorway interchange 15 10
1565 25 dh. House and garden . . 15 10
1566 25 dh. Shepherd and flock . . 15 10
1567 25 dh. Combine harvester . . 15 10
1568 25 dh. Tractors 15 10
1569 25 dh. Scientific equipment 15 10
1570 25 dh. Col Gaddafi (full face) 15 10
1571 25 dh. Water pipeline 15 10
1572 25 dh. Lighthouse 15 10
1573 25 dh. Liner at quay 30 10

333 Armed Man

334 Soldier flogging Civilian

1984. Evacuation of Foreign Forces. Mult. (a) As T **333.**

1574 50 dh. Type **333** 25 20
1575 50 dh. Armed man (different) 25 20
1576 100 dh. Men on horseback charging (62 x 40 mm) . . 45 40

(b) As T **334.**

1577 100 dh. Type **334** 45 40
1578 100 dh. Girl on horse charging soldiers 45 40
1579 100 dh. Mounted soldiers and wounded being tended by women 45 40

335 Woman riding Skewbald Showjumper

1984. Equestrian Events. Multicoloured.

1580 25 dh. Type **335** 15 10
1581 25 dh. Man riding black showjumper (stands in background) 15 10
1582 25 dh. Jockey riding chestnut horse (stands in background) 15 10
1583 25 dh. Man on chestnut horse jumping in cross-country event 15 10
1584 25 dh. Man riding bay horse in showjumping competition 15 10
1585 25 dh. Woman on black horse in dressage competition . . . 15 10
1586 25 dh. Man on black horse in dressage competition . . . 15 10
1587 25 dh. Woman riding chestnut horse in cross-country event 15 10
1588 25 dh. Jockey riding bay horse 15 10
1589 25 dh. Woman on bay horse in dressage competition . . . 15 10
1590 25 dh. Man on grey horse in dressage competition . . . 15 10
1591 25 dh. Jockey riding grey steeplechaser 15 10
1592 25 dh. Woman riding grey showjumper 15 10
1593 25 dh. Woman riding through water in cross-country competition 15 10
1594 25 dh. Woman on chestnut horse in cross-country competition 15 10
1595 25 dh. Man riding dun showjumper 15 10

Nos. 1580/95 were printed together in sheetlets of 16 stamps, the backgrounds of the stamps forming an overall design of an equestrian ring.

336 Man cleaning Corn

337 Map and Pharmaceutical Equipment

1984. Traditional Agriculture. Multicoloured.

1596 100 dh. Type **336** 45 40
1597 100 dh. Man using oxen to draw water from well 45 40
1598 100 dh. Man making straw goods 45 40
1599 100 dh. Shepherd with sheep 45 40
1600 100 dh. Man treating animal skin 45 40
1601 100 dh. Man climbing coconut tree 45 40

1984. 9th Conference of Arab Pharmacists Union.

1602 **337** 100 dh. multicoloured . 45 40
1603 200 dh. multicoloured . 90 80

338 Crowd with Banner showing Map of North Africa

1984. Arab-African Unity. Multicoloured.
1604 100 dh. Type **338** 45 40
1605 100 dh. Crowd and men holding flags 45 40

339 1982 and 1983 Solidarity Stamps and Map of Palestine

1984. Solidarity with Palestinian People.
1606 **339** 100 dh. multicoloured . . 45 40
1607 150 dh. multicoloured . . 70 65

340 Boeing 747SP, 1975

1984. 40th Anniv of International Civil Aviation Organization. Multicoloured.
1608 70 dh. Type **340** 50 30
1609 70 dh. Concorde, 1969 . . . 50 30
1610 70 dh. Lockheed TriStar 500, 1978 . . . . 50 30
1611 70 dh. Airbus Industrie A310, 1982 . . . . 50 30
1612 70 dh. Tupolev Tu-134A, 1962 50 30
1613 70 dh. Shorts 360, 1981 . . . 50 30
1614 70 dh. Boeing 727-100, 1963 . 50 30
1615 70 dh. Sud Aviation Caravelle 10R, 1965 . . . . 50 30
1616 70 dh. Fokker Friendship, 1955 50 30
1617 70 dh. Lockheed Constellation, 1946 . . . . 50 30
1618 70 dh. Martin M-130 flying boat, 1955 . . . . 50 30
1619 70 dh. Douglas DC-3, 1936 . . 50 50
1620 70 dh. Junkers Ju-52/3m, 1932 50 30
1621 70 dh. Lindbergh's "Spirit of St. Louis", 1927 . . . . 50 30
1622 70 dh. De Havilland Moth, 1925 50 30
1623 70 dh. Wright Flyer I, 1903 . 50 30

Nos. 1608/23 were printed together in sheetlets of 16 stamps, the backgrounds of the stamps forming an overall design of a runway.

341 Coin **342** Mother and Son

1984. 20th Anniv of African Development Bank. Multicoloured.
1624 50 dh. Type **341** 25 20
1625 70 dh. Map of Africa and "20" 30 25
1626 100 dh. "20" and symbols of industry and agriculture . . 45 40

1985. U.N.I.C.E.F. Child Survival Campaign. Multicoloured.
1627 70 dh. Type **342** 30 20
1628 70 dh. Couple and children 30 20
1629 70 dh. Col. Gaddafi and children 30 20
1630 70 dh. Boys in uniform . . . 30 20

343 Mohamed Hamdi **344** Pipeline, River, Plants and Map

1985. Musicians and Instruments. Multicoloured.
1631 100 dh. Kamel el-Ghadi . . 45 35
1632 100 dh. Fiddle rebab 45 35
1633 100 dh. Ahmed el-Khogia . . 45 35
1634 100 dh. Violin 45 35
1635 100 dh. Mustafa el-Fallah . 45 35
1636 100 dh. Zither 45 35
1637 100 dh. Type **343** 45 35
1638 100 dh. Mask 45 35

1985. Col. Gaddafi–River Builder. Multicoloured.
1639 100 dh. Type **344** 45 35
1640 100 dh. Water droplet, river and flowers 45 35
1641 100 dh. Dead tree with branch thriving in water droplet . 45 35

345 Gold Dinar, 105 h.

1985. Arabic Islamic Coins (2nd series). Mult.
1643 200 dh. Type **345** 90 80
1644 200 dh. Gold dinar, 91 h. . . 90 80
1645 200 dh. Gold dinar, 77 h. . . 90 80

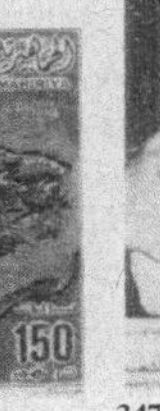

346 Fish **347** Gaddafi in Robes and Hat

1985. Fossils. Multicoloured.
1647 150 dh. Type **346** 65 55
1648 150 dh. Frog 65 55
1649 150 dh. Mammal 65 55

1985. People's Authority Declaration. Mult.
1650 100 dh. Type **347** 45 35
1651 100 dh. Gaddafi in black robe holding book 45 35
1652 100 dh. Gaddafi in dress uniform without cap . . . 45 35
1653 100 dh. Gaddafi in black dress uniform with cap . . . 45 35
1654 100 dh. Gaddafi in white dress uniform 45 35

348 Cymbal Player

1985. International Trade Fair, Tripoli. Mult.
1655 100 dh. Type **348** 45 35
1656 100 dh. Piper and drummer 45 35
1657 100 dh. Drummer and bagpipes player 45 35
1658 100 dh. Drummer 45 35
1659 100 dh. Tambour player . . 45 35

349 Goalkeeper catching Ball **350** Emblem, Radio Transmitter and Satellite

1985. Children's Day. Multicoloured.
1660 20 dh. Type **349** 10 10
1661 20 dh. Child on touchline with ball 10 10
1662 20 dh. Letters of alphabet as players 10 10
1663 20 dh. Goalkeeper saving ball 10 10
1664 20 dh. Player heading ball . . 10 10

1985. International Communications Development Programme.
1665 **350** 30 dh. multicoloured . . 15 10
1666 70 dh. multicoloured . . 35 25
1667 100 dh. multicoloured . . 45 35

351 Nurses and Man in Wheelchair **352** "Mytilidae"

1985. World Health Day. Multicoloured.
1668 40 dh. Type **351** 15 10
1669 60 dh. Nurses and doctors . . 25 15
1670 100 dh. Nurse and child . . . 45 35

1986. Sea Shells. Multicoloured.
1671 25 dh. Type **352** 25 10
1672 25 dh. "Muricidae" 25 10
1673 25 dh. "Cardiidae" 25 10
1674 25 dh. "Corallophilidae" . . 25 10
1675 25 dh. "Muricidae" (different) 25 10
1676 25 dh. "Muricacea" 25 10
1677 25 dh. "Turridae" 25 10
1678 25 dh. "Argonautidae" . . . 25 10
1679 25 dh. "Tonnidae" 25 10
1680 25 dh. "Aporrhaidae" 25 10
1681 25 dh. "Trochidae" 25 10
1682 25 dh. "Cancellariidae" . . . 25 10
1683 25 dh. "Epitoniidae" 25 10
1684 25 dh. "Turbnidae" 25 10
1685 25 dh. "Mitridae" 25 10
1686 25 dh. "Pectinidae" 25 10

Nos. 1671/86 were printed se-tenant, the backgrounds forming an overall design of the sea bed.

353 Books and Emblem **354** Girls Skipping

1985. International Book Fair, Tripoli.
1687 **353** 100 dh. multicoloured . . 45 35
1688 200 dh. multicoloured . . 90 80

1985. International Youth Year. Multicoloured.
1689 20 dh. Type **354** 10 10
1690 20 dh. Boys playing with stones 10 10
1691 20 dh. Girls playing hopscotch 10 10
1692 20 dh. Boys playing with sticks 10 10
1693 20 dh. Boys playing with spinning top 10 10

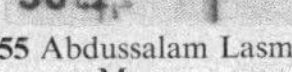

355 Abdussalam Lasmar Mosque **356** Jamila Zemerli

1985. Minarets. Multicoloured.
1695 50 dh. Type **355** 20 15
1696 50 dh. Zaoviat Kadria Mosque 20 15
1697 50 dh. Zaoviat Amura Mosque 20 15
1698 50 dh. Gurgi Mosque 20 15
1699 50 dh. Mizran Mosque . . . 20 15
1700 50 dh. Salem Mosque 20 15
1701 50 dh. Ghat Mosque 20 15
1702 50 dh. Ahmed Karamanli Mosque 20 15
1703 50 dh. Atya Mosque 20 15
1704 50 dh. El Kettani Mosque . . 20 15
1705 50 dh. Benghazi Mosque . . 20 15
1706 50 dh. Derna Mosque 20 15
1707 50 dh. El Derug Mosque . . 20 15
1708 50 dh. Ben Moussa Mosque 20 15
1709 50 dh. Ghadames Mosque . . 20 15
1710 50 dh. Abdulwahab Mosque 20 15

1985. Teachers' Day. Multicoloured.
1711 100 dh. Type **356** 45 35
1712 100 dh. Hamida El-Anezi . . 45 35

HAVE YOU READ THE NOTES AT THE BEGINNING OF THIS CATALOGUE?
These often provide the answers to the enquiries we receive.

357 "Philadelphia" exploding **358** Gaddafi and Followers

1985. Battle of the "Philadelphia". Multicoloured.
1713 50 dh. Type **357** 60 20
1714 50 dh. Men with swords . . 60 20
1715 100 dh. Men fighting and ship's rigging (59 x 45 mm) . . . 1·25 45

Nos. 1713/15 were printed together, se-tenant, forming a composite design.

1986. Colonel Gaddafi's Islamic Pilgrimage. Multicoloured.
1716 200 dh. Gaddafi writing . . 90 80
1717 200 dh. Gaddafi praying . . 90 80
1718 200 dh. Gaddafi, crowds and Kaaba 90 80
1719 200 dh. Gaddafi and mirror 90 80
1720 200 dh. Type **358** 90 80

359 "Leucopaxillus lepistoides"

1985. Mushrooms. Multicoloured.
1722 50 dh. Type **359** 30 15
1723 50 dh. "Amanita caesarea" . 30 15
1724 50 dh. "Coriolus hirsutus" . 30 15
1725 50 dh. "Cortinarius subfulgens" 30 15
1726 50 dh. "Dermocybe pratensis" 30 15
1727 50 dh. "Macrolepiota excoriata" 30 15
1728 50 dh. "Amanita curtipes" . 30 15
1729 50 dh. "Trametes ljubarskyi" 30 15
1730 50 dh. "Pholiota aurivella" . 30 15
1731 50 dh. "Boletus edulis" . . . 30 15
1732 50 dh. "Geastrum sessile" . . 30 15
1733 50 dh. "Russula sanguinea" . 30 15
1734 50 dh. "Cortinarius herculeus" 30 15
1735 50 dh. "Pholiota lenta" . . . 30 15
1736 50 dh. "Amanita rubescens" 30 15
1737 50 dh. "Seleroderma polyrhizum" 30 15

Nos. 1722/37 were printed together, se-tenant, the backgrounds of the stamps forming an overall design of map of Mediterranean.

360 Woman in Purple Striped Dress **361** "In Need Freedom is Latent"

1985. Traditional Women's Costumes. Multicoloured.
1738 100 dh. Type **360** 45 35
1739 100 dh. Woman in robes covering her face 45 35
1740 100 dh. Woman in colourful robes with heavy jewellery 45 35
1741 100 dh. Woman in long blue striped dress 45 35
1742 100 dh. Woman in red dress and trousers 45 35

1985. Quotations from "The Green Book".
1743 **361** 100 dh. lt grn, grn & blk 45 35
1744 – 100 dh. multicoloured . 45 35
1745 – 100 dh. lt grn, grn & blk 45 35
1746 – 100 dh. lt grn, grn & blk 45 35
1747 – 100 dh. multicoloured . 45 35
1748 – 100 dh. lt grn, grn & blk 45 35
1749 – 100 dh. lt grn, grn & blk 45 35
1750 – 100 dh. multicoloured . 45 35
1751 – 100 dh. lt grn, grn & blk 45 35

DESIGNS: No. 1744, Gaddafi in uniform reading; 1745, "To make a party you split society"; 1746, "Public sport is for all the masses"; 1747, "Green Books" and doves; 1748, "Wage-workers are a type of slave, however improved their wages may be"; 1749, "People are only harmonious with their own arts and heritages"; 1750, Gaddafi addressing crowd; 1751, "Democracy means popular rule not popular expression".

362 Tree and Citrus Fruits

1985. 16th Anniv of Revolution. Multicoloured.

1752 100 dh. Type **362** . . . 45 35
1753 100 dh. Oil pipeline and tanks 45 35
1754 100 dh. Capital and olive branch . . . 45 35
1755 100 dh. Mosque and modern buildings . . . 45 35
1756 100 dh. Flag and mountains 45 35
1757 100 dh. Telecommunications 45 35

363 Zauiet Amoura, Janzour **364** Players in Red No. 5 and Green Shirts

1985. Mosque Gateways. Multicoloured.

1759 100 dh. Type **363** . . . 45 35
1760 100 dh. Shiaieb El-Ain, Tripoli 45 35
1761 100 dh. Zauiet Abdussalam El-Asmar, Zliten . . . 45 35
1762 100 dh. Karamanli, Tripoli . 45 35
1763 100 dh. Gurgi, Tripoli . . . 45 35

1985. Basketball. Multicoloured.

1764 25 dh. Type **364** . . . 15 10
1765 25 dh. Players in green number 7 and red shirts . . . 15 10
1766 25 dh. Players in green number 8 and red shirts . . . 15 10
1767 25 dh. Players in red number 6 and green shirts . . . 15 10
1768 25 dh. Players in red number 4 and green number 7 shirts 15 10
1769 25 dh. Players in green numbers 6 and 5 and red number 9 shirts . . . 15 10
1770 25 dh. Basket and one player in red and two in green shirts 15 10
1771 25 dh. Players in red number 8 and green number 7 shirts 15 10
1772 25 dh. Two players in green shirts and two in red shirts, one number 4 . . . 15 10
1773 25 dh. Players in red numbers 4 and 7 and green shirts . . 15 10
1774 25 dh. Players in red numbers 4 and 9 and green numbers 7 and 4 shirts . . . 15 10
1775 25 dh. Players in red number 6 and green shirts . . . 15 10
1776 25 dh. Players in red number 9 and green number 8 shirts 15 10
1777 25 dh. Players in red number 8 and green number 5 shirts 15 10
1778 25 dh. Players in red number 4 and green shirts . . . 15 10
1779 25 dh. Players in red number 5 and green number 10 shirts 15 10

Nos. 1764/79 were printed together se-tenant, the backgrounds of the stamps forming an overall design of baseball court and basket.

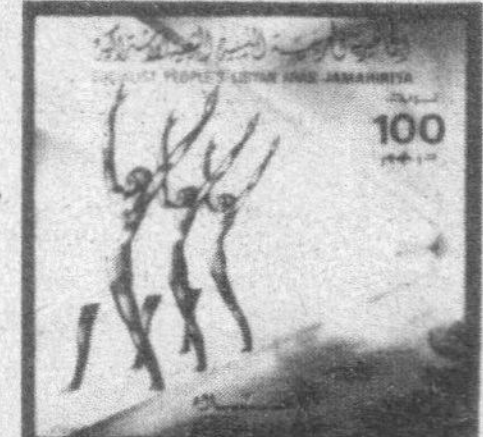

365 People in Light Ray

1985. Evacuation of Foreign Forces. Multicoloured.

1780 100 dh. Man on crutches in web and light shining on tree . 45 35
1781 100 dh. Hands pulling web away from man . . . 45 35
1782 100 dh. Type **365** . . . 45 35

MINIMUM PRICE

The minimum price quoted is 10p which represents a handling charge rather than a basis for valuing common stamps. For further notes about prices, see introductory pages.

366 Stockbook, Magnifying Glass and Stamps **337** Players

1985. Stamp Day. "Italia '85" International Stamp Exhibition, Rome. Multicoloured.

1783 50 dh. Man and desk on flying stamp above globe . . . 20 15
1784 50 dh. Type **366** . . . 20 15
1785 50 dh. Stamps escaping from wallet . . . 20 15

1986. World Cup Football Championship, Mexico (1st issue). Multicoloured.

1786 100 dh. Type **367** . . . 45 35
1787 100 dh. Players in red and white number 10 and yellow shirts 45 35
1788 100 dh. Goalkeeper and player defending goal against attack 45 35
1789 100 dh. Goalkeeper diving to make save . . . 45 35
1790 100 dh. Goalkeeper jumping to make save . . . 45 35
1791 100 dh. Player in red and white shirt tackling player in lime shirt . . . 45 35

See also Nos. 1824/9.

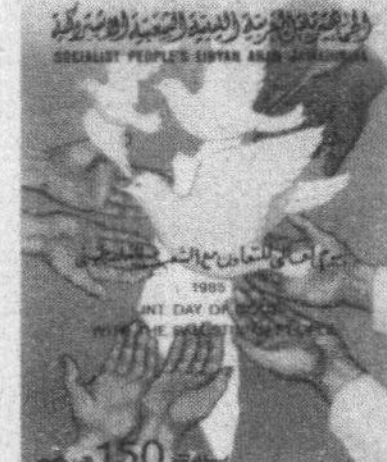

368 Hands releasing Dove

1985. Solidarity with Palestinian People.

1793 **368** 100 dh. multicoloured . 45 35
1794 150 dh. multicoloured . 45 35

370 Headquarters and Dish Aerial **371** Paper and Quill in Hand

1986. 1st Anniv of General Posts and Telecommunications Corporation.

1807 **370** 100 dh. multicoloured . 40 30
1808 150 dh. multicoloured . 60 50

1986. Peoples' Authority Declaration. Multicoloured.

1809 50 dh. Type **371** . . . 20 15
1810 50 dh. Paper and globe in hand 20 15
1811 100 dh. "Green Books" and dove (53 x 37 mm) . . . 40 30

372 Flute

1986. International Trade Fair, Tripoli. Mult.

1812 100 dh. Type **372** . . . 40 30
1813 100 dh. Drums . . . 40 30
1814 100 dh. Double pipes . . . 40 30
1815 100 dh. Tambourines . . . 40 30
1816 100 dh. Drum hung from shoulder . . . 40 30

373 Boy Scout with Fish on Hook

1986. Children's Day. Multicoloured.

1817 50 dh. Type **373** . . . 20 15
1818 50 dh. Boy on camel . . . 20 15
1819 50 dh. Boy catching butterflies 20 15
1820 50 dh. Boy playing drum . . 20 15
1821 50 dh. Boy and giant goalkeeper on football pitch . . . 20 15

374 Emblem, Man and Skull in Blood Droplet

1986. World Health Day. Multicoloured, background colours given.

1822 **374** 250 dh. silver . . . 1·00 80
1823 250 dh. gold . . . 1·00 80

375 Footballers

1986. World Cup Football Championship, Mexico (2nd issue). Multicoloured.

1824 50 dh. Type **375** . . . 20 15
1825 50 dh. Player jumping over player on ground . . . 20 15
1826 50 dh. Referee and players . . 20 15
1827 50 dh. Goalkeeper trying to save ball . . . 20 15
1828 50 dh. Player about to tackle 20 15
1829 50 dh. Player jumping over ball 20 15

376 Peas **377** Health Programmes

1986. Vegetables. Multicoloured.

1831 50 dh. Type **376** . . . 20 15
1832 50 dh. Marrow . . . 20 15
1833 50 dh. Beans . . . 20 15
1834 50 dh. Aubergine . . . 20 15
1835 50 dh. Corn on the cob . . . 20 15
1836 50 dh. Tomato . . . 20 15
1837 50 dh. Red pepper . . . 20 15
1838 50 dh. Zucchini . . . 20 15
1839 50 dh. Garlic . . . 20 15
1840 50 dh. Cabbage . . . 20 15
1841 50 dh. Cauliflower . . . 20 15
1842 50 dh. Celery . . . 20 15
1843 50 dh. Onions . . . 20 15
1844 50 dh. Carrots . . . 20 15
1845 50 dh. Potato . . . 20 15
1846 50 dh. Radishes . . . 20 15

Nos. 1831/46 were printed together in sheetlets of 16 stamps, the backgrounds of the stamps forming an overall design of a garden.

1986. Jamahiriya Thought. Multicoloured.

1847 50 dh. Type **377** . . . 20 15
1848 50 dh. Education programmes 20 15
1849 100 dh. "Green Book", agricultural scenes and produce (agriculture programmes) (62 x 41 mm) 40 30

378 Gaddafi studying Plane

1986. Colonel Gaddafi, "Great man-made River Builder". Multicoloured.

1850 100 dh. Type **378** . . . 40 30
1851 100 dh. Gaddafi showing planned route on map . . 40 30
1852 100 dh. Gaddafi and old well 40 30
1853 100 dh. Gaddafi in desert . . 40 30
1854 100 dh. Gaddafi and pipe . . 40 30
1855 100 dh. Gaddafi at pumping station . . . 40 30
1856 100 dh. Gaddafi and storage tank . . . 40 30
1857 100 dh. Workers' hut . . . 40 30
1858 100 dh. Water in cupped hands and irrigation equipment . 40 30
1859 100 dh. Gaddafi turning wheel at opening ceremony . . . 40 30
1860 100 dh. Laying pipes . . . 40 30
1861 100 dh. Pipe sections on lorries 40 30
1862 100 dh. Gaddafi in robes holding "Green Book" . . 40 30
1863 100 dh. Boy giving Gaddafi bowl of fruit . . . 40 30
1864 100 dh. Boy drinking from tap 40 30
1865 100 dh. Gaddafi praying . . 40 30

379 Gaddafi with Children

1986. Colonel Gaddafi, "Man of Peace". Multicoloured.

1866 100 dh. Type **379** . . . 40 30
1867 100 dh. Reading book in tent 40 30
1868 100 dh. With his mother . . 40 30
1869 100 dh. Praying in tent with his sons . . . 40 30
1870 100 dh. Talking to hospital patient . . . 40 30
1871 100 dh. Driving tractor . . . 40 30

380 General Dynamics F-111 Exploding above Man with injured Child

381 Gaddafi, Ruined buildings and Stretcher-bearers

1986. Battle of the U.S.S. "Philadelphia" and American Attack on Libya. Multicoloured.

(a) As T **380**.

1872 50 dh. Type **380** . . . 40 25
1873 50 dh. American aircraft carrier and escaping family . . . 40 25
1874 100 dh. "Philadelphia" exploding (59 x 38 mm) . . 1·00 50

(b) As T **381**.

1875 70 dh. Type **381** . . . 30 20
1876 70 dh. Burning wreckage of car and man and boy in rubble 30 20
1877 70 dh. Woman and child by burning ruin . . . 30 20
1878 70 dh. Men running from bomb strike . . . 30 20
1879 70 dh. Covered body and rescue workers searching ruins . . 30 20
1880 70 dh. Libyans and General Dynamics F-111 airplane tail and wing . . . 50 25
1881 70 dh. Libyans waving fists 30 20
1882 70 dh. Rescue workers lifting child from rubble . . . 30 20
1883 70 dh. Weeping women and soldier carrying baby . . 30 20
1884 70 dh. Libyans and glare of explosion . . . 30 20
1885 70 dh. Libyans and General Dynamics F-111 airplane wing and nose . . . 50 25
1886 70 dh. Man carrying girl . . 30 20
1887 70 dh. Coffins held aloft by crowd . . . 30 20
1888 70 dh. Crowd carrying pictures of Gaddafi . . . 30 20
1889 70 dh. Wounded being tended 30 20
1890 70 dh. Hands tending wounded baby . . . 30 20

(c) Size 89 x 32 mm.

1891 100 dh. General Dynamics F-111 bombers, Gaddafi and anti-aircraft rockets . . 80 35

Nos. 1872/4 were printed together in se-tenant strips of three within the sheet, each strip forming a composite design.

382 "The House must be served by its own Tenant"

1986. Quotations from the "Green Book".

1892 **382** 100 dh. lt grn, grn & blk . . . 40 30
1893 – 100 dh. multicoloured . . 40 30
1894 – 100 dh. lt grn, grn & blk 40 30
1895 – 100 dh. lt grn, grn & blk 40 30
1896 – 100 dh. multicoloured . . 40 30
1897 – 100 dh. lt grn, grn & blk 40 30
1898 – 100 dh. lt grn, grn & blk 40 30
1899 – 100 dh. multicoloured . . 40 30
1900 – 100 dh. lt grn, grn & blk 40 30

DESIGNS: No. 1893, Gaddafi; 1894, "The Child is raised by his mother"; 1895, "Democracy is the Supervision of the People by the People"; 1896, "Green Books"; 1897, "Representation is a Falsification of Democracy"; 1898, "The Recognition of Profit is an Acknowledgement of Exploitation"; 1899, Vase of roses, iris, lilies and jasmine; 1900, "Knowledge is a Natural Right of every Human Being which Nobody has the Right to deprive him of under any Pretext".

383 Map, Chrysanthemum and Health Services

1986. 17th Anniv of Revolution. Multicoloured.

1901 200 dh. Type **383** 80 70
1902 200 dh. Map, sunflower and agriculture programme . . 80 70
1903 200 dh. "Sunflowers" (Van Gogh) 80 70
1904 200 dh. Map, rose and defence programme 80 70
1905 200 dh. Map, campanula and oil exploration programme 80 70

384 Moroccan and Libyan Women

1986. Arab-African Union. Multicoloured.

1906 250 dh. Type **384** . . . . . . 1·00 80
1907 25 dh. Libyan and Moroccan horsemen . . . . 1·00 80

385 Libyan Horseman

1986. Evacuation of Foreign Forces. Multicoloured.

1908 50 dh. Type **385** 20 15
1909 100 dh. Libyan horsemen trampling Italian soldiers 40 30
1910 150 dh. Italian soldiers charging 60 50

386 Globe and Rose

1986. International Peace Year. Multicoloured, background colours given.

1911 **386** 200 dh. green 80 70
1912 200 dh. blue 80 70

387 Brick "Fists" and Maps within Laurel Wreath

1986. Solidarity with Palestinian People. Multicoloured, background colours given.

1913 **387** 250 dh. blue . . . . . . 1·00 80
1914 250 dh. red . . . . . . 1·00 80

388 Drummer

1986. Folk Music. Multicoloured.

1915 70 dh. Type **388** 30 20
1916 70 dh. Masked stick dancer 30 20
1917 70 dh. Woman dancer with pot headdress 30 20
1918 70 dh. Bagpipe player . . . 30 20
1919 70 dh. Tambour player . . . 30 20

389 Gazelles

1987. Endangered Animals. Sand Gazelle. Multicoloured.

1920 100 dh. Type **389** 40 30
1921 100 dh. Mother and calf . . 40 30
1922 100 dh. Gazelle drinking . . 40 30
1923 100 dh. Gazelle lying down 40 30

390 Oil Derricks and Crowd **391** Sheep and Shepherd

1987. People's Authority Declaration. Multicoloured.

1924 500 dh. Type **390** . . . . . 2·00 1·75
1925 500 dh. Buildings and crowd 2·00 1·75
1926 1000 dh. Gaddafi addressing crowd and globe (40 x 38 mm) 3·75 3·25

1987. 18th Anniv of Revolution. Multicoloured.

1927 150 dh. Type **391** 60 50
1928 150 dh. Col. Gaddafi in robes 60 50
1929 150 dh. Mosque 60 50
1930 150 dh. Water flowing from irrigation pipe 60 50
1931 150 dh. Combine harvester . 60 50
1932 150 dh. Col. Gaddafi in army uniform with microphone 60 50
1933 150 dh. Harvesting crop . . 60 50
1934 150 dh. Irrigation 60 50
1935 150 dh. Soldier with rifle . . 60 50
1936 150 dh. Buildings behind Libyan with rifle 60 50
1937 150 dh. Fountain 60 50
1938 150 dh. Buildings and beach 60 50
1939 150 dh. Fort and girls . . . 60 50
1940 150 dh. Children and hand on rifle butt 60 50
1941 150 dh. Theatre 60 50
1942 150 dh. Couple 60 50

392 Omar Abed Anabi al Mansusri

1988. Personalities. Multicoloured.

1943 100 dh. Type **392** 40 30
1944 200 dh. Ahmed Ali al Emrayd 80 70
1945 300 dh. Khalifa Said Ben Asker 1·25 1·00
1946 400 dh. Mohamed Ben Farhat Azawi . . . . 1·60 1·40
1947 500 dh. Mohamed Souf al Lafi al Marmori . . . . 2·00 1·75

393 Gaddafi and Crowd with Raised Fists around Earthmover Bucket

1988. Freedom Festival Day.

1948 **393** 100 dh. multicoloured . . 40 30
1949 150 dh. multicoloured . . 60 50
1950 250 dh. multicoloured . . 1·00 85

394 Woman and Children running

1988. 2nd Anniv of American Attack on Libya. Multicoloured.

1951 150 dh. Type **394** 60 50
1952 150 dh. Gaddafi playing chess with boy 60 50
1953 150 dh. Gaddafi and children 60 50
1954 150 dh. Gaddafi in robes . . 60 50
1955 150 dh. Gaddafi and boys praying 60 50
1956 150 dh. Gaddafi and injured girl 60 50
1957 150 dh. Gaddafi in robes with children (horiz) 60 50
1958 150 dh. Gaddafi making speech (horiz) 60 50
1959 150 dh. Gaddafi and family (horiz) 60 50

395 Roses

1988. 19th Anniv of Revolution.

1961 **395** 100 dh. multicoloured . . 40 30
1962 250 dh. multicoloured . . 1·00 80
1963 300 dh. multicoloured . . 1·25 1·00
1964 500 dh. multicoloured . . 2·10 1·75

396 Relay **397** Dates

1988. Olympic Games, Seoul. Multicoloured.

1965 150 dh. Type **396** 60 50
1966 150 dh. Cycling 60 50
1967 150 dh. Football 60 50
1968 150 dh. Tennis 60 50
1969 150 dh. Running 60 50
1970 150 dh. Showjumping 60 50

1988. The Palm Tree. Multicoloured.

1972 500 dh. Type **397** . . . . . . 2·10 1·75
1973 1000 dh. Tree . . . . 4·00 3·50

398 Petrol Bomb, Sling and Map **399** Globe, Declaration and Dove

1988. Palestinian "Intifada" Movement. Mult.

1974 100 dh. Type **398** 40 30
1975 200 dh. Boy holding stones (45 x 38 mm) 80 70
1976 300 dh. Map and flag . . . 1·25 1·00

1989. People's Authority Declaration.

1977 **399** 260 dh. multicoloured . 1·10 65
1978 500 dh. multicoloured . 2·00 1·25

400 Crowd and Green Books (½ size illustration)

1989. 20th Anniv of Revolution. Multicoloured.

1979 150 dh. Type **400** 60 40
1980 150 dh. Soldiers, Colonel Gaddafi and water pipeline 60 40
1981 150 dh. Military hardware, Gaddafi in uniform, education, communications and medicine 60 40
1982 150 dh. Armed horsemen . . 60 40
1983 150 dh. U.S.S. "Philadelphia" exploding . . . . 1·00 55

401 Execution Victims, Soldiers and Colonel Gaddafi

1989. 78th Anniv of Deportation of Libyans to Italy. Multicoloured.

1985 100 dh. Type **401** 40 25
1986 100 dh. Colonel Gaddafi and Libyans 40 25
1987 100 dh. Soliders, deportees and Gaddafi 40 25
1988 100 dh. Deportees on jetty and in boats 55 25
1989 100 dh. Gaddafi and corpses 40 25

402 Demoliton of Wall **403** Emblem of Committee for supporting "Intifida"

1989. "Demolition of Borders".

1991 **402** 150 dh. multicoloured . 60 40
1992 200 dh. multicoloured . 80 55

1989. Palestinian "Intifida" Movement. Mult.

1993 100 dh. Type **403** 40 25
1994 300 dh. Crowd of youths . . 1·25 85
1995 500 dh. Emblem (1st anniv of declaration of State of Palestine) . . . . 2·00 1·25

404 Circulation Diagram and Annafis

1989. Ibn Annafis (physician) Commemorative.

1996 **404** 100 dh. multicoloured . 40 25
1997 150 dh. multicoloured . 60 40

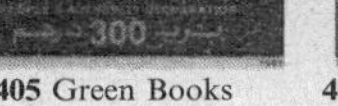

405 Green Books and Fort **406** Libyan People and Soldier

1990. People's Authority Declaration.

1998 **405** 300 dh. multicoloured . 1·25 85
1999 500 dh. multicoloured . 2·00 1·25

1990. 20th Anniv of American Forces Evacuation.

2000 **406** 100 dh. multicoloured . 40 25
2001 400 dh. multicoloured . 1·60 1·00

407 Eagle **408** Anniversary Emblem

1990. 21st Anniv of Revolution.
2002 **407** 100 dh. multicoloured 40 25
2003 400 dh. multicoloured 1·60 1·00
2004 1000 dh. multicoloured 4·00 2·75

1990. 30th Anniv of Organization of Petroleum Exporting Countries.
2006 **408** 100 dh. multicoloured 40 25
2007 400 dh. multicoloured 1·60 1·00

409 I.L.Y. Emblem and Figures **410** Player, Globe and Ball

1990. International Literacy Year.
2008 **409** 100 dh. multicoloured 40 25
2009 300 dh. multicoloured 1·25 85

1990. World Cup Football Championship, Italy.
2010 **410** 100 dh. multicoloured 40 25
2011 400 dh. multicoloured 1·60 1·00
2012 500 dh. multicoloured 2·00 1·25

411 Hand holding Ears of Wheat **412** Members' Flags

1990. World Food Day. Multicoloured.
2014 500 dh. Type **411** 2·00 1·25
2015 2000 dh. Ploughing 8·25 5·25

1991. 2nd Anniv of Union of Arab Maghreb.
2016 **412** 100 dh. multicoloured 40 25
2017 300 dh. multicoloured 1·25 85

413 Flame, Scroll and Koran

1991. People's Authority Declaration.
2018 **413** 300 dh. multicoloured 1·25 85
2019 400 dh. multicoloured 1·60 1·00

414 Girl and International Year of the Child Emblem **415** World Health Organization Emblem

1991. Children's Day. Multicoloured.
2020 100 dh. Type **414** 40 25
2021 400 dh. Boy and Day of the African Child emblem 1·60 1·00

1991. World Health Day. Multicoloured.
2022 100 dh. Type **415** 40 25
2023 200 dh. As Type **415** but with emblem additionally inscr "W.H.O. O.M.S." 80 55

416 Wadi el Hayat **417** Digging Riverbed and laying Pipes

1991. Scenes from Libya. Multicoloured.
2024 100 dh. Type **416** 50 25
2025 250 dh. Mourzuk (horiz) 1·25 65
2026 500 dh. Ghadames (horiz) 2·40 1·25

1991. Great Man-made River. Multicoloured.
2027 50 dh. Type **417** 25 15
2028 50 dh. Col. Gaddafi, agricultural projects and livestock (59 x 37 mm) 25 15
2029 50 dh. Produce 25 15
Nos. 2027/9 were printed together, se-tenant, forming a composite design.

418 "22", Roses and Broken Chain

1991. 22nd Anniv of Revolution. Multicoloured.
2030 300 dh. Type **418** 1·40 70
2031 400 dh. "22" within wheat/cogwheel wreath and broken chain 1·90 95

419 Emblem and Globe

1991. "Telecom 91" International Telecommunications Exhibition, Geneva. Multicoloured.
2033 100 dh. Type **419** 50 25
2034 500 dh. Buldings and dish aerial (horiz) 2·40 1·25

420 Monument and Soldier

1991. 80th Anniv of Deportation of Libyans to Italy. Multicoloured.
2035 100 dh. Type **420** 50 25
2036 400 dh. Naval transport, Libyans and soldiers 2·50 95

421 Map

1991. Arab Unity.
2038 **421** 50 dh. multicoloured 20 10
2039 100 dh. multicoloured 40 20

422 Lorry **424** State Arms

423 Gaddafi and Camels

1991. Paris–Dakar Trans-Sahara Rally. Multicoloured.
2040 50 dh. Type **422** 20 10
2041 50 dh. Blue lorry 20 10
2042 50 dh. African Product lorry 20 10
2043 50 dh. Tomel lorry 20 10
2044 50 dh. All-terrain vehicle No. 173 20 10
2045 50 dh. Mitsuski all-terrain vehicle 20 10
2046 50 dh. Michedop all-terrain vehicle 20 10
2047 50 dh. All-terrain vehicle No. 401 20 10
2048 50 dh. Motor cycle No. 100 20 10
2049 50 dh. Rider pushing red motor cycle 20 10
2050 50 dh. Rider pushing white motor cycle 20 10
2051 50 dh. Motor cycle No. 98 20 10
2052 50 dh. Motor cycle No. 101 20 10
2053 50 dh. Motor cycle No. 80 20 10
2054 50 dh. Motor cycle No. 12 20 10
2055 50 dh. Motor cycle No. 45 20 10

1992. "Gaddafi, Man of Peace 1992". Multicoloured, colour of frame given.
2056 **423** 100 dh. green 40 20
2057 100 dh. grey 40 20
2058 100 dh. red 40 20
2059 100 dh. ochre 40 20

1992.
2061 **424** 100 dh. green, brn & yell 40 20
2062 150 dh. green, brn & grey 60 30
2063 200 dh. green, brown & bl 85 45
2064 250 dh. green, brn & orge 1·10 55
2065 300 dh. green, brn & vio 1·25 65
2066 400 dh. green, brn & mve 1·75 90
2067 450 dh. emerald, brn & grn 1·90 95

425 1991 100 dh. Stamp, Tweezers, Magnifying Glass and Stamps

1992. 3rd Anniv of Union of Arab Maghreb.
2068 **425** 75 dh. multicoloured 30 15
2069 80 dh. multicoloured 35 20

426 Horse-drawn Carriage

1992. International Trade Fair, Tripoli. Mult.
2070 50 dh. Type **426** 20 10
2071 100 dh. Horse-drawn cart 40 20

427 Emblem **429** Fish with Spines

428 Emblem and Camel Rider

1992. People's Authority Declaration.
2072 **427** 100 dh. multicoloured 40 20
2073 150 dh. multicoloured 60 30

1992. African Tourism Year.
2074 **428** 50 dh. multicoloured 20 10
2075 100 dh. multicoloured 40 20

1992. Fishes. Multicoloured.
2076 100 dh. Type **429** 40 20
2077 100 dh. Pike 40 20
2078 100 dh. Fish with seven spines on back 40 20
2079 100 dh. Light brown fish with continuous dorsal fin 40 20
2080 100 dh. Fish with four spines on back 40 20
2081 100 dh. Red fish with whiskers 40 20

430 Horsewoman with Rifle **431** Long Jumping

1992. Horse Riders. Multicoloured.
2082 100 dh. Type **430** 40 20
2083 100 dh. Man on rearing white horse 40 20
2084 100 dh. Man on brown horse with ornate bridle 40 20
2085 100 dh. Roman soldier on brown horse 40 20
2086 100 dh. Man in blue coat on brown horse 40 20
2087 100 dh. Arab on white horse 40 20

1992. Olympic Games, Barcelona. Multicoloured.
2089 50 dh. Type **431** 20 10
2090 50 dh. Throwing the discus 20 10
2091 50 dh. Tennis 20 10

432 Palm Trees

1992. Achievements of the Revolution. Mult.
2093 100 dh. Type **432** 40 20
2094 150 dh. Ingots and foundry 60 30
2095 250 dh. Container ship 1·10 55
2096 300 dh. Airplane 1·25 65
2097 400 dh. Assembly hall 1·75 90
2098 500 dh. Water pipes and Gaddafi 2·10 1·10

433 Gaddafi **434** Laurel Wreath, Torch and "23"

1992. Multicoloured, background colours given.
2099 **433** 500 dh. green 2·10 1·10
2100 1000 dh. pink 4·25 2·25
2101 2000 dh. blue 8·25 4·25
2102 5000 dh. violet 21·00 10·50
2103 6000 dh. orange 25·00 12·50

1992. 23rd Anniv of Revolution. Multicoloured.
2104 50 dh. Type **434** 20 10
2105 100 dh. Laurel wreath, flag, sun and "23" 40 20

435 Antelope drinking **436** Horse and Broken Chain

1992. Oases. Multicoloured.
2107 100 dh. Type **435** 40 20
2108 200 dh. Sun setting behind camel train (vert) 85 45
2109 300 dh. Camel rider 1·25 65

1992. Evacuation of Foreign Forces. Multicoloured.
2110 75 dh. Type **436** 30 15
2111 80 dh. Flag and broken chain 35 20

437 Monument and Dates

1992. 81st Anniv of Deportation of Libyans to Italy.
2112 **437** 100 dh. multicoloured 40 20
2113 250 dh. multicoloured 1·10 55

438 Dome of the Rock and Palestinian

1992. Palestinian "Intifida" Movement. Mult.
2114 100 dh. Type **438** 40 20
2115 300 dh. Map, Dome of the Rock, flag and fist (vert) 1·25 65

439 Red and White Striped Costume

1992. Women's Costumes. Multicoloured.
2116 50 dh. Type **439** 20 10
2117 50 dh. Large red hat with silver decorations, white tunic and red wrap 20 10
2118 50 dh. Brown and orange striped costume with small gold necklace and horseshoe brooch 20 10
2119 50 dh. Purple and white costume 20 10
2120 50 dh. Orange striped costume 20 10

CONCESSIONAL LETTER POST

1929. No. CL227 of Italy optd **LIBIA.**
CL68 **CL 93** 10 c. blue 11·00 12·00

1941. No. CL267 of Italy optd **LIBIA.**
CL123 **CL 109** 10 c. brown 3·50 4·25

EXPRESS LETTER STAMPS

A. ITALIAN ISSUES.

1915. Express Letter stamps of Italy optd **Libia.**
E17 **E 35** 25 c. red 7·00 7·00
E18 **E 41** 30 c. blue and red 4·50 14·00

1921. As Type **E 17** of Somalia, but inscr "LIBIA".
E34 30 c. red and blue 1·10 2·75
E35 50 c. brown and red 1·60 4·25
E42 60 c. brown and red 2·50 7·00
E43 2 l. red and blue 5·00 15·00
Nos. E34 and E43 are inscr "EXPRES".

1922. Nos. E17/18 surch.
E40 **E 35** 60 c. on 25 c. red 3·75 7·00
E41 **E 41** 1 l. 60 on 30 c. blue and red 5·00 17·00

1926. Nos. E42/3 surch.
E62 70 c. on 60 c. brown and red 3·25 7·00
E64 1 l. 25 on 60 c. brown and red 2·75 1·00
E63 2 l. 50 on 2 l. red and blue 3·75 14·00

B. INDEPENDENT ISSUE

1966. Design similar to T **74** inscr "EXPRES".
E368 90 m. red and green 85 65
DESIGN—HORIZ: 90 m. Saracen Castle, Zuela.

OFFICIAL STAMPS

1952. Optd **Official** in English and Arabic.
O192 **23** 2 m. brown 40 35
O193 4 m. grey 65 50
O194 5 m. green 3·25 2·50
O195 8 m. red 2·25 75
O196 10 m. violet 3·00 2·25
O197 12 m. red 4·25 4·50
O198 20 m. blue 7·00 4·50
O199 25 m. brown 9·00 5·00

PARCEL POST STAMPS

Unused prices are for complete stamps.

1915. Parcel Post stamps of Italy optd **LIBIA** on each half of the stamp.
P17 **P 53** 5 c. brown 60 20
P18 10 c. blue 60 20
P19 20 c. black 80 20
P20 25 c. red 85 20
P21 50 c. orange 1·60 20
P22 1 l. violet 1·40 20
P23 2 l. green 1·90 20
P24 3 l. yellow 2·25 20
P25 **P 53** 4 l. grey 2·25 20
P26 10 l. purple 30·00 6·00
P27 12 l. brown 55·00 6·00
P28 15 l. olive 55·00 8·00
P29 20 l. purple 55·00 9·50

1927. Parcel Post stamps of Italy optd **LIBIA** on each half of the stamp.
P62 **P 92** 5 c. brown £8000
P63 10 c. blue 1·40 30
P64 25 c. red 1·40 30
P65 30 c. blue 20 30
P66 50 c. orange 55·00 7·00
P67 60 c. red 20 30
P68 1 l. violet 19·00 3·00
P69 2 l. green 24·00 3·00
P70 3 l. yellow 70 30
P71 4 l. grey 70 30
P72 10 l. mauve £160 11·00
P73 20 l. purple £160 11·00

POSTAGE DUE STAMPS

A. ITALIAN ISSUES.

1915. Postage Due stamps of Italy optd **Libia.**
D17 **D 12** 5 c. purple and orange 40 1·90
D18 10 c. purple and orange 60 1·90
D19 20 c. purple and orange 1·10 3·25
D20 30 c. purple and orange 1·40 3·25
D21 40 c. purple and orange 1·90 3·25
D22 50 c. purple and orange 1·25 3·25
D23 60 c. purple and orange 2·25 4·75
D24 60 c. brown and orange 38·00 70·00
D25 1 l. purple and blue 1·25 75
D26 2 l. purple and blue 19·00 32·00
D27 5 l. purple and blue 24·00 45·00

1934. Postage Due stamps of Italy optd **LIBIA.**
D68 **D 141** 5 c. brown 15 70
D69 10 c. blue 15 70
D70 20 c. red 80 55
D71 25 c. green 80 55
D72 30 c. orange 80 1·10
D73 40 c. brown 80 1·75
D74 50 c. violet 1·10 20
D75 60 c. blue 1·60 2·75
D76 **D 142** 1 l. orange 1·40 20
D77 2 l. green 24·00 4·50
D78 5 l. violet 48·00 15·00
D79 10 l. blue 7·00 15·00
D80 20 l. red 7·00 17·00

B. INDEPENDENT ISSUES

1951. Postage Due stamps of Cyrenaica optd. (a) For use in Cyrenaica. Optd as T **20.**
D144 **D 26** 2 m. brown 4·00 5·00
D145 4 m. green 4·00 5·00
D146 8 m. red 6·00 7·00
D147 10 m. orange 7·50 10·00
D148 20 m. yellow 12·00 14·00
D149 40 m. blue 25·00 22·00
D150 100 m. black 35·00 28·00

(b) For use in Tripolitania. Surch as T **21.**
D161 **D 26** 1 mal. on 2 m. brown 3·75 3·25
D162 2 mal. on 4 m. green 6·00 6·00
D163 4 mal. on 8 m. red 9·50 9·50
D164 10 mal. on 20 m. yellow 19·00 19·00
D165 20 mal. on 40 m. blue 32·00 35·00

D 25

D 53 Government Building, Tripoli

1952.
D188 **D 25** 2 m. brown 40 25
D189 5 m. green 65 50
D190 10 m. red 90 65
D191 50 m. blue 2·50 1·50

1964.
D296 **D 53** 2 m. brown 10 10
D297 6 m. green 20 10
D298 10 m. red 20 15
D299 50 m. blue 40 30

D 185 Men in Boat

1976. Ancient Mosaics. Multicoloured.
D725 5 dh. Type **D 185** 10 10
D726 10 dh. Head of Medusa 10 10
D727 20 dh. Peacock 10 10
D728 50 dh. Fish 25 15

LIECHTENSTEIN Pt. 8

A small independent principality lying between Austria and Switzerland.

1912. 100 heller = 1 krone
1921. 100 rappen = 1 franc. (Swiss)

1 Prince John II 2 3

1912.
1 **1** 5 h. green 8·00 11·00
2 10 h. red 50·00 7·00
3 25 h. blue 60·00 26·00

1917.
7 **2** 3 h. violet 1·60 1·10
8 5 h. green 1·60 1·10
9 **3** 10 h. red 1·60 1·10
10 15 h. brown 1·60 1·10
11 20 h. green 1·60 1·10
12 25 h. blue 1·60 1·10

1918. 60th Anniv of Prince John's Accession. As T **3** but dated "1858–1918" in upper corners.
13 **3** 20 h. green 65 1·10

1920. Optd with a scroll pattern.
14 **2** 5 h. green 2·00 5·50
15 **3** 10 h. red 2·00 5·50
16 25 h. blue 2·00 5·50

1920. Surch.
17 **2** 40 h. on 3 h. violet 2·00 5·50
18 **3** 1 k. on 15 h. brown 2·00 5·50
19 2½ k. on 20 h. green 2·00 5·50

7

8 Castle of Vaduz

1920. Imperf.
20 **7** 5 h. bistre 15 3·50
21 10 h. orange 15 3·50
22 15 h. blue 15 3·50
23 20 h. brown 15 3·50
24 25 h. green 15 3·50
25 30 h. grey 15 3·50
26 40 h. red 15 3·50
27 **8** 1 k. blue 15 3·50

9 Prince John I

10 Arms

1920. Perf.
28 **7** 5 h. bistre 15 40
29 10 h. orange 15 40
30 15 h. blue 15 40
31 20 h. brown 15 40
32 – 25 h. olive 15 40
33 **7** 30 h. grey 15 40
34 – 40 h. red 15 40
35 – 50 h. green 15 40
36 – 60 h. brown 15 40
37 – 80 h. red 15 40
38 **8** 1 k. lilac 15 40
39 – 2 k. blue 25 70
40 **9** 5 k. grey 50 1·25
41 – 7½ k. slate 65 1·50
42 **10** 10 k. yellow 75 2·00
DESIGNS—VERT: As Type **8**: 25 h. St. Mamertus Chapel; 40 h. Gutenberg Castle; 50 h. Courtyard, Vaduz Castle; 60 h. Red House, Vaduz; 80 h. Church Tower, Schaan; 2 k. Bendern. As Type **9**: 7½ k. Prince John II.

11 Madonna

15 St. Mamertus Chapel

14 Arms 16 Vaduz

1920. Prince John's 80th Birthday. Imperf or perf.
43 **11** 50 h. olive 30 1·10
44 80 h. red 30 1·10
45 2 k. blue 30 1·10

1921. Surch **2 Rp.** and bars.
47 **7** 2 r. on 10 h. orge (No. 21) 35 16·00

1921.
47a **14** 2 r. yellow 55 8·00
48 2½ r. brown 55 8·00
49 3 r. orange 55 8·00
50 5 r. olive 7·50 1·25
51 7½ r. blue 3·75 25·00
65 10 r. green 20·00 1·10
53 13 r. brown 7·50 60·00
54 15 r. violet 14·00 12·00
55 **15** 20 r. black and violet 55·00 1·00
56 – 25 r. black and red 2·00 1·75
57 – 30 r. black and green 60·00 8·00
66 – 30 r. black and blue 15·00 1·10
58 – 35 r. black and brown 3·25 8·50
59 – 40 r. black and blue 5·00 2·75
60 – 50 r. black and olive 7·00 2·75
61 – 80 r. black and grey 20·00 55·00
62 **16** 1 f. black and lake 40·00 30·00
DESIGNS—As Type **15**: 25 r. Vaduz Castle; 30 r. Bendern; 35 r. Prince John II; 40 r. Church Tower at Schaan; 50 r. Gutenberg Castle; 80 r. Red House, Vaduz.

1924. Surch.
63 **14** 5 on 7½ r. blue 1·00 2·00
64 10 on 13 r. brown 60 1·25

19 Vinedresser

21 Government Bldg. and Church, Vaduz

1924.
67 **19** 2½ r. mauve and green 1·25 4·75
68 5 r. blue and brown 2·25 70
69 7½ r. brown and green 1·40 4·75
70 – 10 r. green 9·00 55
71 **19** 15 r. green and purple 6·50 25·00
72 – 20 r. red 32·00 70
73 **21** 1½ f. blue 75·00 75·00
DESIGN—As Type **19**: 10, 20 r. Castle of Vaduz.

22 Prince John II

23

1925. Charity. 85th Birthday of Prince.
74 **22** 10 + 5 r. green 35·00 13·00
75 20 + 5 r. red 18·00 13·00
76 30 + 5 r. blue 5·50 4·25

1927. Charity. 87th Birthday of Prince. Arms multicoloured.
77 **23** 10 + 5 r. green 6·50 17·00
78 20 + 5 r. lake 6·50 17·00
79 30 + 5 r. blue 6·50 14·00

24 Salvage work by Austrian soldiers

1928. Flood Relief.
80 – 5 r. + 5 r. brown and red 18·00 17·00
81 – 10 r. + 10 r. brown & green 17·00 21·00
82 **24** 20 r. + 10 r. brown and red 17·00 21·00
83 – 30 r. + 10 r. brown & blue 17·00 21·00
DESIGNS—HORIZ: 5 r. Railway bridge; 10 r. Ruggell; 30 r. Salvage work by Swiss soldiers.

26 Prince John II, 1858-1928

1928. 70th Anniv of Accession of John II.
84 – 10 r. olive and brown 1·75 3·25
85 – 20 r. olive and red 3·00 5·50
86 – 30 r. olive and blue 17·00 14·00
87 – 60 r. olive and mauve 45·00 60·00
88 **26** 1 f. 20 blue 40·00 80·00
89 1 f. 50 sepia 70·00 £160
90 2 f. lake 70·00 £160
91 5 f. green 70·00 £170
DESIGN—VERT: 10 r. to 60 r. Prince John II.

28 Prince Francis I **31** Girl Vintager

32 Prince Francis I and Princess Elsa **34** Monoplane over Vaduz Castle and Rhine Valley

1929. Accession of Prince Francis I.

92	–	10 r. green	60	2·50
93	**28**	20 r. red	75	3·50
94	–	30 r. blue	1·75	15·00
95	–	70 r. brown	16·00	85·00

PORTRAITS: 10 r. Prince Francis I when a boy; 30 r. Princess Elsa; 70 r. Prince Francis I and Princess Elsa.

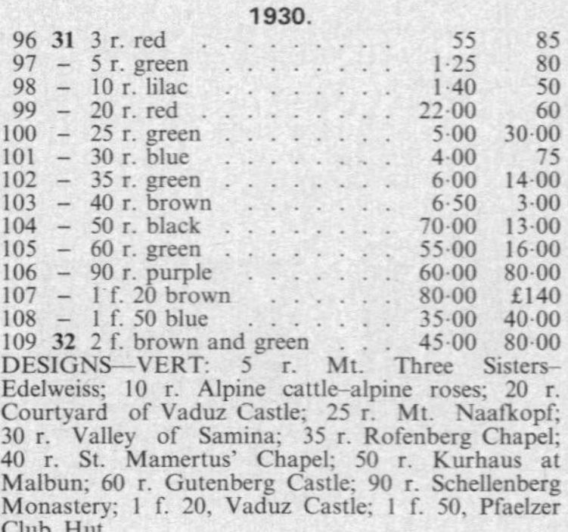

1930.

96	**31**	3 r. red	55	85
97	–	5 r. green	1·25	80
98	–	10 r. lilac	1·40	50
99	–	20 r. red	22·00	60
100	–	25 r. green	5·00	30·00
101	–	30 r. blue	4·00	75
102	–	35 r. green	6·00	14·00
103	–	40 r. brown	6·50	3·00
104	–	50 r. black	70·00	13·00
105	–	60 r. green	55·00	16·00
106	–	90 r. purple	60·00	80·00
107	–	1 f. 20 brown	80·00	£140
108	–	1 f. 50 blue	35·00	40·00
109	**32**	2 f. brown and green	45·00	80·00

DESIGNS—VERT: 5 r. Mt. Three Sisters–Edelweiss; 10 r. Alpine cattle–alpine roses; 20 r. Courtyard of Vaduz Castle; 25 r. Mt. Naafkopf; 30 r. Valley of Samina; 35 r. Rofenberg Chapel; 40 r. St. Mamertus' Chapel; 50 r. Kurhaus at Malbun; 60 r. Gutenberg Castle; 90 r. Schellenberg Monastery; 1 f. 20, Vaduz Castle; 1 f. 50, Pfaelzer Club Hut.

1930. Air.

110	–	15 r. sepia	5·00	8·00
111	–	20 r. green	12·00	13·00
112	–	25 r. brown	6·00	22·00
113	–	35 r. blue	12·00	22·00
114	**34**	45 r. green	25·00	55·00
115		1 f. red	38·00	35·00

DESIGNS—VERT: 15 r., 20 r. Biplane over mountains. HORIZ: 25 r., 35 r. Biplane over Vaduz Castle.

35 Airship "Graf Zeppelin" over Alps

1931. Air.

116	**35**	1 f. green	38·00	80·00
117	–	2 f. blue	80·00	£225

DESIGN: 2 f. Airship "Graf Zeppelin" (different).

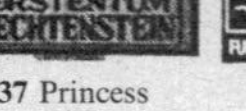

37 Princess Elsa **38** Mt. Naafkopf **39** Prince Francis I

1932. Youth Charities.

118	–	10 r. + 5 r. green	16·00	25·00
119	**37**	20 r. + 5 r. red	16·00	25·00
120	–	30 r. + 10 r. blue	16·00	32·00

DESIGNS—VERT: Smaller: 22×29 mm. 10 r. Arms of Liechtenstein. As Type **37**: 30 r. Prince Francis.

1933.

121	**38**	25 r. orange	£190	50·00
122	–	90 r. green	7·50	65·00
123	–	1 f. 20 brown	80·00	£200

DESIGNS: 90 r. Gutenberg Castle; 1 f. 20, Vaduz Castle.

1933. Prince Francis's 80th Birthday.

124	**39**	10 r. violet	18·00	30·00
125		20 r. red	18·00	30·00
126		30 r. blue	18·00	30·00

40 **41** "Three Sisters"

42 Vaduz Castle **44** Prince Francis I

45 Arms of Liechtenstein **46** Golden Eagle

1933.

127	**40**	3 r. red	15	45
128	**41**	5 r. green	2·25	50
129	–	10 r. violet	50	40
130	–	15 r. red	20	85
131	–	20 r. red	50	45
132	–	25 r. brown	18·00	42·00
133	–	30 r. blue	3·25	90
134	–	35 r. green	70	5·50
135	–	40 r. brown	90	3·50
136	**42**	50 r. brown	18·00	13·00
137	–	60 r. red	1·25	4·75
138	–	90 r. green	5·50	16·00
139	–	1 f. 20 lake	1·75	16·00
140	–	1 f. 50 lake	2·00	21·00
141	–	2 f. brown	55·00	£150
142	**44**	3 f. blue	75·00	£150
143	**45**	5 f. purple	£350	£850

DESIGNS—VERT: As Type **41**: 10 r. Schaan Church; 15 r. Bendern am Rhein; 20 r. Town Hall, Vaduz; 25 r. Saminatal. As Type **44**: 2 f. Princess Elsa. HORIZ: As Type **42**: 30 r. Saminatal; 35 r. Schellenberg ruins; 40 r. Government Building, Vaduz; 60 r. Vaduz Castle; 90 r. Gutenberg Castle; 1 f. 20, Pfalzer Hut, Bettlerjoch; 1 f. 50, Valuna.

See also Nos. 174, 225/6 and 258.

1934. Air.

145	**46**	10 r. violet	8·00	20·00
146	–	15 r. orange	18·00	30·00
147	–	20 r. red	18·00	30·00
148	–	30 r. blue	18·00	30·00
149	–	50 r. green	14·00	25·00

DESIGNS: 10 r. to 20 r. Golden eagles in flight; 30 r. Osprey in nest; 50 r. Golden eagle on rock.

1935. Air. No. 115 surch **60 Rp.**

150	**34**	60 r. on 1 f. red	24·00	40·00

49 "Hindenburg" and Schaan Church

1936. Air.

151	**49**	1 f. red	26·00	65·00
152	–	2 f. violet	22·00	65·00

DESIGN: 2 f. "Graf Zeppelin" over Schaan Airport.

51 Masescha am Triesenberg **52** Schellenberg Castle

1937.

154	–	3 r. brown	15	50
155	**51**	5 r. green and buff	15	20
156	–	10 r. violet and buff	15	15
157	–	15 r. black and buff	20	60
158	–	20 r. red and buff	20	30
159	–	25 r. brown and buff	55	2·00
160	–	30 r. blue and buff	3·00	60
161	**52**	40 r. green and buff	2·25	1·50
162	–	50 c. brown and buff	85	2·00
163	–	60 r. purple and buff	2·25	2·00
164	–	90 r. violet and buff	9·00	13·00
165	–	1 f. purple and buff	2·00	10·00
166	–	1 f. 20 brown and buff	8·00	20·00
167	–	1 f. 50 grey and buff	2·50	20·00

DESIGNS—VERT: As Type **51**: 3 r. Schalun ruins; 10 r. Knight and Vaduz Castle; 15 r. Upper Saminatal; 20 r. Church and Bridge at Bendern; 25 r. Steg Chapel and girl. HORIZ: As Type **52**: 30 r. Farmer and orchard, Triesenberg; 50 r. Knight and Gutenberg Castle; 60 r. Baron von Brandis and Vaduz Castle; 90 r. "Three Sisters" mountain; 1 f. Boundary-stone on Luziensteig; 1 f. 20, Minstrel and Gutenberg Castle; 1 f. 50, Lawena (Schwarzhorn).

53 Roadmakers at Triesenberg

1937. Workers' Issue.

168	–	10 r. mauve	80	70
169	**53**	20 r. red	1·10	1·25
170	–	30 r. blue	1·50	1·50
171	–	50 r. brown	1·00	2·50

DESIGNS: 10 r. Bridge at Malbun; 30 r. Binnen Canal Junction; 50 r. Francis Bridge, near Planken.

1938. Death of Prince Francis I.

174	**44**	3 f. black on yellow	8·50	65·00

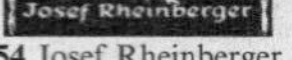

54 Josef Rheinberger **55** Black-headed Gulls

1939. Birth Centenary of Rheinberger (composer).

175	**54**	50 r. green	75	3·25

1939. Air.

176	–	10 r. violet (Barn swallows)	40	45
177	**55**	15 r. orange	65	1·50
178	–	20 r. red (Herring gull)	1·75	45
179	–	30 r. blue (Common buzzard)	1·60	1·25
180	–	50 r. green (Northern goshawk)	5·00	2·00
181	–	1 f. red (Lammergeier)	4·25	13·00
182	–	2 f. violet Lammergeier	4·00	13·00

56 Offering Homage to First Prince

1939. Homage to Francis Joseph II.

183	**56**	20 r. red	60	1·40
184		30 r. blue	60	1·40
185		50 r. green	60	1·40

57 Francis Joseph II

1939.

186	–	2 f. green on cream	6·00	32·00
187	–	3 f. violet on cream	4·50	32·00
188	**57**	5 f. brown on cream	11·00	20·00

DESIGNS: 2 f. Cantonal Arms; 3 f. Arms of Principality.

58 Prince John when a Child

1940. Birth Centenary of Prince John II.

189	**58**	20 r. red	40	1·50
190	–	30 r. blue	55	2·50
191	–	50 r. green	1·00	8·00
192	–	1 f. violet	6·00	55·00
193	–	1 f. 50 black	4·50	45·00
194	–	3 f. brown	3·50	20·00

DESIGNS—HORIZ: As Type **58**: Portraits of Prince John in early manhood (30 r.), in middle age (50 r.) and in later life (1 f.), and Memorial tablet (1 f. 50). VERT: As Type **44**: 3 f. Framed portrait of Prince John II.

60 Wine Press

1941. Agricultural Propaganda.

195	–	10 r. brown	35	80
196	**60**	20 r. red	60	1·25
197	–	30 r. blue	60	2·00
198	–	50 r. green	1·60	13·00
199	–	90 r. violet	1·60	15·00

DESIGNS: 10 r. Harvesting maize; 30 r. Sharpening scythe; 50 r. Milkmaid and cow; 90 r. Girl wearing traditional headdress.

61 Madonna and Child **62** Prince Hans Adam

1941.

200	**61**	10 f. red on buff	45·00	95·00

1941. Princes (1st issue).

201	**62**	20 r. red	30	1·25
202	–	30 r. blue (Wenzel)	35	2·00
203	–	1 f. grey (Anton Florian)	1·40	14·00
204	–	1 f. 50 green (Joseph)	1·50	14·00

See also Nos. 210/13 and 217/20.

63 St. Lucius preaching

1942. 600th Anniv of Separation from Estate of Montfort.

205	**63**	20 r. red on pink	90	80
206	–	30 r. blue on pink	90	2·00
207	–	50 r. green on pink	1·75	6·00
208	–	1 f. brown on pink	2·25	12·00
209	–	2 f. blue on pink	2·25	12·00

DESIGNS: 30 r. Count of Montfort replanning Vaduz; 50 r. Counts of Montfort-Werdenberg and Sargans signing treaty; 1 f. Battle of Gutenberg; 2 f. Homage to Prince of Liechtenstein.

64 Prince John Charles **65** Princess Georgina

1942. Princes (2nd issue).

210	**64**	20 r. red	30	80
211	–	30 r. blue (Francis Joseph I)	45	1·50
212	–	1 f. purple (Alois I)	1·40	13·00
213	–	1 f. 50 brown (John I)	1·40	13·00

1943. Marriage of Prince Francis Joseph II and Countess Georgina von Wildczek.

214	–	10 r. purple	45	80
215	**65**	20 r. red	45	80
216	–	30 r. blue	45	80

PORTRAITS—VERT: 10 r. Prince Francis Joseph II. HORIZ (44×25 mm): 30 r. Prince and Princess.

66 Alois II **67** Marsh Land

1943. Princes (3rd issue).

217	**66**	20 r. brown	30	65
218	–	30 r. blue	60	1·25
219	–	1 f. brown	90	6·50
220	–	1 f. 50 green	90	6·50

PORTRAITS—HORIZ: 30 r. John II; 1 f. Francis I; 1 f. 50, Francis Joseph II.

1943. Completion of Irrigation Canal.

221	**67**	10 r. violet	20	40
222	–	30 r. blue	40	1·90
223	–	50 r. green	75	7·00
224	–	2 f. brown	2·00	11·00

DESIGNS: 30 r. Draining the canal; 50 r. Ploughing reclaimed land; 2 f. Harvesting.

1943. Castles. As T **41**.

225		10 r. grey (Vaduz)	40	35
226		20 r. brown (Gutenberg)	55	80

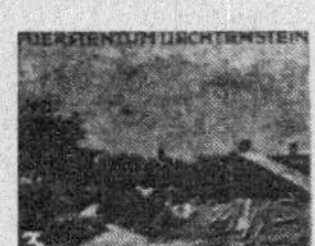
69 Planken

70 Prince Francis Joseph II

1944. Various designs. Buff backgrounds.

No.	Type	Description	Unused	Used
227	69	3 r. brown	15	20
228	–	5 r. green (Bendern)	15	10
228a	–	5 r. brown (Bendern)	28·00	60
229	–	10 r. violet (Triesen)	20	10
230	–	15 r. blue (Ruggell)	30	85
231	–	20 r. red (Vaduz)	30	20
232	–	25 r. purple (Triesenberg)	30	1·00
233	–	30 r. blue (Schaan)	30	25
234	–	40 r. brown (Balzers)	60	1·10
235	–	50 r. grey (Mauren)	70	1·50
236	–	60 r. green (Schellenberg)	3·75	4·25
237	–	90 r. olive (Eschen)	3·75	4·50
238	–	1 f. red (Vaduz Castle)	2·25	3·75
239	–	1 f. 20 brown (Valunatal)	2·50	5·00
240	–	1 f. 50 blue (Lawena)	2·50	5·00

1944.

No.	Type	Description	Unused	Used
241	70	2 f. brown	4·75	14·00
242	–	3 f. green	3·00	11·00

DESIGN: 3 f. Princess Georgina.
See also Nos. 302/3.

72

73

1945. Birth of Crown Prince Johann Adam Pius (known as Prince Hans Adam).

No.	Type	Description	Unused	Used
243	72	20 r. brown, yellow and gold	1·00	40
244		30 r. blue, yellow and gold	1·00	1·40
245		100 r. grey, yellow and gold	2·25	5·00

1945.

No.	Type	Description	Unused	Used
246	73	5 f. blue on buff	19·00	28·00
247		5 f. brown on buff	24·00	38·00

74 First Aid

75 St. Lucius

1945. Red Cross. Cross in red.

No.	Type	Description	Unused	Used
248	–	10 r. + 10 r. violet on buff	1·25	1·50
249	74	20 r. + 20 r. red on buff	1·25	2·25
250	–	1 f. + 1 f. 40 grey on buff	8·00	22·00

DESIGNS: 10 r. Mother and children; 1 f. Nurse and invalid.

1946.

No.	Type	Description	Unused	Used
251	75	10 f. grey on buff	35·00	28·00

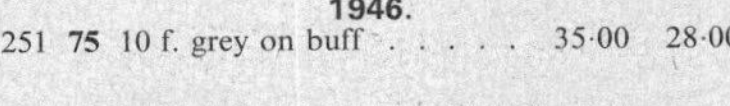

76 Red Deer

79 Wilbur Wright

1946. Wild Life.

No.	Type	Description	Unused	Used
252	76	20 r. red	2·25	2·25
255	–	20 r. red (Chamois)	4·00	4·00
283	–	20 r. red (Roebuck)	8·50	3·75
253	–	30 r. blue (Arctic hare)	3·00	3·00
256	–	30 r. blue (Alpine marmot)	5·50	4·25
284	–	30 r. green (Black grouse)	22·00	6·00
285	–	80 r. brown (Eurasian badger)	35·00	38·00
254	–	1 f. 50 olive (Capercaillie)	9·50	11·00
257	–	1 f. 50 brown (Golden eagle)	9·50	14·00

1947. Death of Princess Elsa. As No. 141.

No.	Type	Description	Unused	Used
258	–	2 f. black on yellow	3·50	12·00

1948. Air. Pioneers of Flight.

No.	Type	Description	Unused	Used
259	–	10 r. green	65	20
260	–	15 r. violet	65	1·10
261	–	20 r. brown	80	20
262	–	25 r. red	1·25	1·90
263	–	40 r. blue	1·75	1·00
264	–	50 r. blue	1·75	1·75
265	–	1 f. purple	2·50	3·00
266	–	2 f. purple	4·50	4·75
267	79	5 f. green	5·50	6·50
268	–	10 f. black	32·00	16·00

PORTRAITS: 10 r. Leonardo da Vinci; 15 r. Joseph Montgolfier; 20 r. Jakob Degen; 25 r. Wilhelm Kress; 40 r. E. G. R. Robertson; 50 r. William Henson; 1 f. Otto Lilienthal; 2 f. Salomon Andree; 10 f. Icarus.

80 "Ginevra de Benci" (Da Vinci)

82 Posthorn and Map of World

1949. Paintings. Size 27 × 31 mm.

No.	Type	Description	Unused	Used
269	80	10 r. green	45	30
270	–	20 r. red	1·25	60
271	–	30 r. brown	3·00	1·25
272	–	40 r. blue	6·00	65
273	–	50 r. violet	5·00	6·50
274	–	60 r. grey	11·00	5·50
275	–	80 r. brown	2·50	4·00
276	–	90 r. green	11·00	5·00
277	–	120 r. mauve	2·50	4·75

DESIGNS: 20 r. "Portrait of a Young Girl" (Rubens); 30 r. Self-portrait of Rembrandt in plumed hat; 40 r. "Stephan Gardiner, Bishop of Winchester" (Quentin Massys); 50 r. "Madonna and Child" (Hans Memling); 60 r. "Franz Meister in 1456" (Jehan Fouquet); 80 r. "Lute Player" (Orazio Gentileschi); 90 r. "Portrait of a Man" (Bernhardin Strigel); 120 r. "Portrait of a Man (Duke of Urbino)" (Raphael).

1949. No. 227 surch **5 Rp.** and bars.

No.	Type	Description	Unused	Used
278	69	5 r. on 3 r. brown and buff	60	40

1949. 75th Anniv of U.P.U.

No.	Type	Description	Unused	Used
279	82	40 r. blue	3·00	3·75

83 Rossauer Castle

86 Boy cutting Loaf

1949. 250th Anniv of Acquisition of Domain of Schellenberg.

No.	Type	Description	Unused	Used
280	83	20 r. purple	2·00	2·00
281	–	40 r. blue	7·00	6·50
282	–	1 f. 50 red	9·50	8·50

DESIGN—HORIZ: 40 r. Bendern Church. VERT: 1 f. 50, Prince Johann Adam I.

1950. Surch **100 100**.

No.	Type	Description	Unused	Used
286	82	100 r. on 40 r. blue	23·00	42·00

1951. Agricultural scenes.

No.	Type	Description	Unused	Used
287	86	5 r. red	20	10
288	–	10 r. green	45	10
289	–	15 r. brown	4·50	5·00
290	–	20 r. sepia	1·00	20
291	–	25 r. red	4·50	4·50
292	–	30 r. green	3·25	55
293	–	40 r. blue	8·50	7·00
294	–	50 r. brown	7·50	3·00
295	–	60 r. brown	7·00	3·00
296	–	80 r. brown	9·00	8·00
297	–	90 r. olive	18·00	4·75
298	–	1 f. violet	55·00	6·00

DESIGNS: 10 r. Man whetting scythe; 15 r. Mowing; 20 r. Girl and sweet corn; 25 r. Haywain; 30 r. Gathering grapes; 40 r. Man with scythe; 50 r. Herdsman with cows; 60 r. Ploughing; 80 r. Girl carrying basket of fruit; 90 r. Woman gleaning; 1 f. Tractor hauling corn.

87 "Lock on the Canal" (Aelbert Cuyp)

88 "Willem von Heythuysen, Burgomaster of Haarlem" (Frans Hals)

1951. Charity. Paintings.

No.	Type	Description	Unused	Used
299	87	10 r. + 10 r. olive	8·00	6·00
300	88	20 r. + 10 r. sepia	8·00	12·00
301	–	40 r. + 10 r. blue	8·00	8·00

DESIGN—As Type **87**: 40 r. "Landscape" (Jacob van Ruysdael).

90 Vaduz Castle

96 Lord Baden-Powell

1951.

No.	Type	Description	Unused	Used
302	70	2 f. blue	13·00	30·00
303	–	3 f. brown	£150	90·00
304	90	5 f. green	£170	£150

DESIGN: 3 f. Princess Georgina.

1952. No. 281 surch **1.20**

No.	Type	Description	Unused	Used
308		1 f. 20 on 40 r. blue	23·00	45·00

1952. Paintings from Prince's Collection. (a) As T **80** but size 25 × 30 mm.

No.	Type	Description	Unused	Used
309		10 r. green	80	70
305		20 r. plum	32·00	3·00
307		40 r. deep blue	12·00	5·00
312		40 r. blue	27·00	38·00

PAINTINGS: No. 309, "Portrait of a Young Man" (A. G.). 305, "Portrait" (Giovanni Salvoldo). 307, "St. John" (Andrea Del Sarto). 312, "Leonhard, Count of Hag" (Hans von Kulmbach).

(b) As T **88** ($22\frac{1}{2} \times 24$ mm).

No.	Type	Description	Unused	Used
310		20 r. bistre	12·00	2·00
306		30 r. olive	22·00	6·00
311		30 r. brown	25·00	6·50

PAINTINGS: No. 310, "St. Nicholas" (Bartholomaus Zeitblom); 306, "Madonna and Child" (Giovanni Botticelli); 311, "St. Christopher" (Lucas Cranach the elder).

1953. 14th International Scout Conf.

No.	Type	Description	Unused	Used
313	96	10 r. green	1·60	1·40
314		20 r. brown	13·00	2·00
315		25 r. red	11·00	15·00
316		40 r. blue	9·00	5·00

97 Alemannic Ornamental Disc, (c. A. D. 600)

98 Prehistoric Walled Settlement, Borscht

1953. Opening of National Museum, Vaduz.

No.	Type	Description	Unused	Used
317	97	10 r. brown	8·00	12·00
318	98	20 r. green	8·00	10·00
319	–	1 f. 20 blue	42·00	26·00

DESIGN—VERT: 1 f. 20, Rossen jug (3000 B. C.).

99 Footballers

100 Madonna and Child

1954. Football.

No.	Type	Description	Unused	Used
320	99	10 r. brown and red	1·90	80
321	–	20 r. deep green and green	6·50	1·25
322	–	25 r. deep brown & brown	16·00	28·00
323	–	40 r. violet and grey	14·00	8·00

DESIGNS—HORIZ: 20 r. Footballer kicking ball; 25 r. Goal-keeper; 40 r. Two footballers.
For stamps in similar designs see Nos. 332/5, 340/3, 351/4 and 363/6.

1954. Nos. 299/301 surch in figures.

No.	Type	Description	Unused	Used
324	87	35 r. on 10 r. + 10 r. olive	3·00	2·00
325	88	60 r. on 20 r. + 10 r. sepia	15·00	9·00
326	–	65 r. on 40 r. + 10 r. blue	5·00	7·00

1954. Termination of Marian Year.

No.	Type	Description	Unused	Used
327	100	20 r. brown	2·00	2·00
328		40 r. green	15·00	17·00
329		1 f. sepia	16·00	16·00

101 Princess Georgina

102 Crown Prince John Adam Pius

1955.

No.	Type	Description	Unused	Used
330	–	2 f. brown	65·00	35·00
331	73	3 f. green	65·00	35·00

PORTRAIT: 2 f. Prince Francis Joseph II.

1955. Mountain Sports designs as T **99**.

No.	Type	Description	Unused	Used
332		10 r. plum and turquoise	90	70
333		20 r. myrtle and bistre	5·00	70
334		25 r. sepia and blue	15·00	14·00
335		40 r. olive and red	15·00	6·00

DESIGNS: 10 r. Slalom racer; 20 r. Mountaineer hammering in piton; 25 r. Skier; 40 r. Mountaineer resting on summit.

1955. 10th Anniv of Liechtenstein Red Cross. Cross in red.

No.	Type	Description	Unused	Used
336	102	10 r. blue	1·25	60
337	–	20 r. green	4·50	1·75
338	–	40 r. bistre	6·50	7·00
339	–	60 r. lake	6·50	3·50

PORTRAITS—VERT: 20 r. Prince Philip; 40 r. Prince Nicholas; 60 r. Princess Nora.

1956. Athletic designs as T **99**.

No.	Type	Description	Unused	Used
340		10 r. green and brown	80	60
341		20 r. purple and green	3·00	70
342		40 r. brown and blue	4·50	4·50
343		1 f. brown and red	10·00	12·00

DESIGNS: 10 r. Throwing the javelin; 20 r. Hurdling; 40 r. Pole vaulting; 1 f. Running.

103

104 Prince Francis Joseph II

1956. 150th Anniv of Sovereignty of Liechtenstein.

No.	Type	Description	Unused	Used
344	103	10 r. purple and gold	2·00	75
345		1 f. 20 blue and gold	9·00	3·50

1956. 50th Birthday of Prince Francis Joseph II.

No.	Type	Description	Unused	Used
346	104	10 r. green	1·40	40
347		15 r. blue	3·00	2·50
348		25 r. purple	3·25	2·50
349		60 r. brown	7·00	2·50

1956. Gymnastic designs as T **99**.

No.	Type	Description	Unused	Used
351		10 r. olive and pink	1·25	75
352		15 r. purple and green	4·50	6·00
353		25 r. green and drab	6·00	7·00
354		1 f. 50 sepia and yellow	16·00	14·00

DESIGNS: 10 r. Somersaulting; 15 r. Vaulting; 25 r. Exercising with rings; 1 f. 50, Somersaulting on parallel bars.

105 Norway Spruce

106 Lord Baden-Powell

1957. Liechtenstein Trees and Bushes.

No.	Type	Description	Unused	Used
355	105	10 r. purple	3·50	1·75
356	–	20 r. lake	3·50	70
357	–	1 f. green	5·50	5·50

DESIGNS: 20 r. Wild rose bush; 1 f. Silver birch.
See also Nos. 369/71, 375/7 and 401/3.

1957. 50th Anniv of Boy Scout Movement and Birth Centenary of Lord Baden-Powell (founder).

No.	Type	Description	Unused	Used
358	–	10 r. blue	1·00	1·25
359	106	20 r. brown	1·00	1·25

DESIGN: 10 r. Torchlight procession.

107 St. Mamertus Chapel

108 Relief Map of Liechtenstein

1957. Christmas.

No.	Type	Description	Unused	Used
360	107	10 r. sepia	70	20
361	–	40 r. blue	2·75	6·00
362	–	1 f. 50 brown	8·00	9·50

DESIGNS: (from St. Mamertus Chapel); 40 r. Altar shrine; 1 f. 50 "Pieta" (sculpture).
See also Nos. 372/4 and 392/4.

1958. Sports designs as T **99**.

No.	Type	Description	Unused	Used
363		15 r. purple and blue	1·00	1·25
364		30 r. olive and purple	4·75	6·00
365		40 r. slate and salmon	7·50	7·50
366		90 r. sepia and apple	2·50	3·50

DESIGNS: 15 r. Swimmer; 30 r. Fencers; 40 r. Tennis player; 90 r. Racing cyclists.

1958. Brussels International Exhibition.

No.	Type	Description	Unused	Used
367	108	25 r. violet, ochre and red	35	55
368		40 r. violet, blue and red	45	55

1958. Liechtenstein Trees and Bushes. As T **105**.

No.	Type	Description	Unused	Used
369		20 r. brown (Sycamore)	3·00	60
370		50 r. green (Holly)	12·00	3·50
371		90 r. violet (Yew)	3·00	2·75

1958. Christmas. As T **107**.

No.	Type	Description	Unused	Used
372		20 r. myrtle	2·50	2·25
373		35 r. violet	2·50	2·25
374		80 r. sepia	2·75	2·25

DESIGNS: 20 r. "St. Maurice and St. Agatha"; 35 r. "St. Peter"; 80 r. St. Peter's Chapel, Mals-Balzers.

1959. Liechtenstein Trees and Bushes. As T **105**.

No.	Type	Description	Unused	Used
375		20 r. lilac (Larch)	4·50	2·25
376		50 r. red (Red-berried elder)	4·00	2·25
377		90 r. green (Linden)	3·50	3·00

109

111 Harvester

110 Flags of Vaduz Castle and Rhine Valley

1959. Pope Pius XII Mourning.
378 **109** 30 r. purple and gold . . 65 75

1959. Views.
379 – 5 r. brown 10 10
380 **110** 10 r. purple 10 10
381 – 20 r. mauve 25 10
382 – 30 r. red 30 15
383 – 40 r. green 75 35
384 – 50 r. blue 45 30
385 – 60 r. blue 65 40
386 **111** 75 r. brown . . . . . . 1·00 1·25
387 – 80 r. green 75 55
388 – 90 r. purple 90 65
389 – 1 f. brown 90 50
390 – 1 f. 20 red . . . . . . 1·25 1·00
390a – 1 f. 30 green . . . . . . 1·00 90
391 – 1 f. 50 blue . . . . . . 1·50 1·00
DESIGNS—HORIZ: 5 r. Bendern Church; 20 r. Rhine Dam; 30 r. Gutenberg Castle; 40 r. View from Schellenberg; 50 r. Vaduz Castle; 60 r. Naafkopf-Falknis Mountains (view from the Bettlerjoch); 1 f. 20, Harvesting apples; 1 f. 30, Farmer and wife; 1 f. 50, Saying grace at table. VERT: 80 r. Alpine haymaker; 90 r. Girl in vineyard; 1 f. Mother in kitchen.

1959. Christmas. As T **107.**
392 5 r. myrtle 50 15
393 60 r. olive . . . . 5·00 4·50
394 1 f. purple . . . . 4·50 2·50
DESIGNS: 5 r. Bendern Church belfry; 60 r. Relief on bell of St. Theodul's Church; 1 f. Sculpture on tower of St. Lucius's Church.

112 Bell Ranger Helicopter

1960. Air. 30th Anniv of 1st Liechtenstein Air Stamps.
395 **112** 30 r. orange . . . . 2·00 2·25
396 – 40 r. blue . . . . 3·50 2·25
397 – 50 r. purple . . . . 8·50 4·00
398 – 75 r. green . . . . 1·50 2·50
DESIGNS (Airliners in flight): 40 r. Boeing 707; 50 r. Convair Coronado; 75 r. Douglas DC-8.

1960. World Refugee Year. Surch **WELT-FLUCHTLINGS JAHR 1960,** uprooted tree and new value.
399 **108** 30 + 10 r. on 40 r. violet, blue and red 60 85
400 50 + 10 r. on 25 r. violet, ochre and red . . . . . 80 1·40

1960. Liechtenstein Trees and Bushes. As T **105.**
401 20 r. brown (Beech) . . . . . 6·00 3·50
402 30 r. purple (Juniper) . . . . 6·00 7·00
403 50 r. turquoise (Pines) . . . . 19·00 9·00

114 Europa "Honeycomb"

1960. United Europe.
404 **114** 50 r. multicoloured . . . 85·00 45·00

115 Princess Gina

116 Heinrich von Frauenberg

1960.
404a – 1 f. 70 violet 80 85
405 **115** 2 f. blue . . . . 1·40 1·40
406 – 3 f. brown . . . . 1·40 1·50
PORTRAITS: 1 f. 70, Crown Prince Hans Adam; 3 f. Prince Francis Joseph II.

1961. Minnesingers (1st issue). Multicoloured. Reproduction from the Manessian Manuscript of Songs.
407 15 r. Type **116** 30 35
408 25 r. Ulrich von Liechtenstein . . 50 50
409 35 r. Ulrich von Gutenberg . . 60 70
410 1 f. Konrad von Altstatten . . 1·40 1·50
411 1 f. 50 Walther von der Vogelweide . . . . 7·25 12·00
See also Nos. 415/8 and 428/31.

117 "Power Transmission"

118 Clasped Hands

1961. Europa.
412 **117** 50 r. multicoloured . . . 20 25

1962. Europa.
413 **118** 50 r. red and blue 40 40

119 Campaign Emblem

120 Pieta

1962. Malaria Eradication.
414 **119** 50 r. turquoise 35 35

1962. Minnesingers (2nd issue). As T **116.** Mult.
415 20 r. King Konradin 20 20
416 30 r. Kraft von Toggenburg . . 60 60
417 40 r. Heinrich von Veldig . . 60 60
418 2 f. Tannhauser . . . . . . 1·50 1·50

1962. Christmas.
419 **120** 30 r. mauve 40 40
420 – 50 r. orange 55 55
421 – 1 f. 20 blue 95 95
DESIGNS: 50 r. Fresco with angel; 1 f. 20, View of Mauren.
See also Nos. 438/40.

121 Prince Francis Joseph II

122 Milk and Bread

1963. 25th Anniv of Reign of Prince Francis Joseph II.
422 **121** 5 f. green . . . . 3·50 2·75

1963. Freedom from Hunger.
423 **122** 50 r. brown, purple & red . . 35 35

123 "Angel of Annunciation"

124 "Europa"

1963. Red Cross Cent. Cross in red; background grey.
424 **123** 20 r. olive and green . . 25 25
425 – 80 r. violet and mauve . . 60 60
426 – 1 f. grey and blue 80 80
DESIGNS: 80 r. "The Epiphany"; 1 f. "Family".

1963. Europa.
427 **124** 50 r. multicoloured . . . 75 65

1963. Minnesingers (3rd issue). As T **116.** Mult.
428 25 r. Heinrich von Sax . . . 25 25
429 30 r. Kristan von Hamle . . 40 40
430 75 r. Werner von Teufen . . 75 75
431 1 f. 70 Hartmann von Aue . . 1·50 1·50

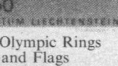

125 Olympic Rings and Flags

126 Arms of Counts of Werdenberg, Vaduz

1964. Olympic Games, Tokyo.
432 **125** 50 r. red, black and blue . . 30 30

1964. Arms (1st issue). Multicoloured.
433 20 f. Type **126** 15 15
434 30 f. Barons of Brandis 20 20
435 80 r. Counts of Sulz 65 65
436 1 f. 50 Counts of Hohenems . . 90 90
See also Nos. 443/6.

127 Roman Castle, Schaan

128 P. Kaiser

1964. Europa.
437 **127** 50 f. multicoloured . . . . 1·10 70

1964. Christmas. As T **120.**
438 10 r. purple 10 10
439 40 r. blue 25 25
440 1 f. 30 purple 80 80
DESIGNS: 10 r. Masescha Chapel; 40 r. "Mary Magdalene" (altar paintings); 1 f. 30, "St. Sebastian, Madonna and Child, and St. Roche" (altar painting).

1964. Death Centenary of Peter Kaiser (historian).
441 **128** 1 f. green on cream 30 45

129 "Madonna" (wood sculpture, c. 1700)

130 Europa "Links" (ancient belt-buckle)

1965.
442 **129** 10 f. red . . . . 5·50 3·50

1965. Arms (2nd issue). As T **126.** Multicoloured.
443 20 r. Von Schellenberg 15 15
444 30 r. Von Gutenberg 20 20
445 80 r. Von Frauenberg 70 70
446 1 f. Von Ramschwag 70 70

1965. Europa.
447 **130** 50 r. brown, grey and blue . . 30 40

131 "Jesus in the Temple"

132 Princess Gina and Prince Franz (after painting by Pedro Leitao)

1965. Birth Centenary of Ferdinand Nigg (painter).
448 – 10 r. deep green and green . 10 10
449 – 30 r. brown and orange . . 15 15
450 **131** 1 f. 20 green and blue . . 40 40
DESIGNS—VERT: 10 r. "The Annunciation"; 30 r. "The Magi".

1965. Special Issue.
451 **132** 75 r. multicoloured 30 40
See also No. 457.

133 Telecommunications Symbols

134 Tree ("Wholesome Earth")

1965. Centenary of I.T.U.
452 **133** 25 r. multicoloured 20 20

1966. Nature Protection.
453 **134** 10 r. green and yellow . . 10 10
454 – 20 r. indigo and blue . . 15 15
455 – 30 r. blue and green . . 15 15
456 – 1 f. 50 red and yellow . . 45 45
DESIGNS: 20 r. Bird ("Pure Air"); 30 r. Fish ("Clean Water"); 1 f. 50, Sun ("Protection of Nature").

1966. Prince Franz Joseph II's 60th Birthday. As T **132,** but with portrait of Prince Franz and inscr "1906–1966".
457 – 1 f. multicoloured 30 45

135 Arms of Herren von Richenstein

136 Europa "Ship"

1966. Arms of Triesen Families. Multicoloured.
458 20 r. Type **135** 15 15
459 30 r. Junker Vaistli 20 20
460 60 r. Edle von Trisun 25 25
461 1 f. 20 Die von Schiel 50 50

1966. Europa.
462 **136** 50 r. multicoloured . . . 30 30

137 Vaduz Parish Church

138 Cogwheels

1966. Restoration of Vaduz Parish Church.
463 **137** 5 r. green and red 10 10
464 – 20 r. purple and bistre . . 15 10
465 – 30 r. blue and red 20 20
466 – 1 f. 70 brown and green . . 60 90
DESIGNS: 20 r. St. Florin; 30 r. Madonna; 1 f. 70, God the Father.

1967. Europa.
467 **138** 50 r. multicoloured . . . 30 30

139 "The Man from Malanser"

141 "Alpha and Omega"

1967. Liechtenstein Sagas. (1st series). Multicoloured.
468 20 r. Type **139** 10 10
469 30 r. "The Treasure of Gutenberg" 15 15
470 1 f. 20 "The Giant of Guflina" . . 40 40
See also Nos. 492/4 and 516/18.

1967. Christian Symbols. Multicoloured.
472 20 r. Type **141** 10 10
473 30 r. "Tropaion" (Cross as victory symbol) 10 10
474 70 r. Christ's monogram . . . 30 30

142 Father J. B. Buchel (educator, historian and poet)

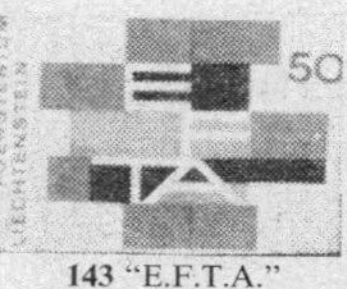

143 "E.F.T.A."

1967. Buchel Commemorative.
475 **142** 1 f. lake and green . . . 35 35

1967. European Free Trade Association.
476 **143** 50 r. multicoloured . . . 30 25

144 "Peter and Paul", Mauren

145 Campaign Emblem

1967. "Patrons of the Church". Multicoloured.
477 5 r. "St. Joseph", Planken . 10 10
478 10 r. "St. Lawrence", Schaan . 10 10
479 20 r. Type **144** 15 10
480 30 r. "St. Nicholas", Balzers . 20 10
480a 40 r. "St. Sebastian", Nendeln . 45 25
481 50 r. "St. George", Schellenberg . 35 20
482 60 r. "St. Martin", Eschen . 50 30
483 70 r. "St. Fridolin", Ruggell . 55 40
484 80 r. "St. Gallus", Triesen . 65 45

485 1 f. "St. Theodolus", Triesenberg 70 40
486 1 f. 20 "St. Anna", Vaduz Castle 85 70
487 1 f. 50 "St. Marie", Bendern-Camprin . . . . . . 1·10 80
488 2 f. "St. Lucius", (patron saint of Liechtenstein) . . . . . 1·50 1·10

1967. "Technical Assistance".
489 **145** 50 r. + 20 r. multicoloured 30 30

146 Europa "Key"

1968. Europa.
490 **146** 50 r. multicoloured . . . 30 25

147 Arms of Liechtenstein and Wilczek

148 Sir Rowland Hill

1968. Silver Wedding Anniv of Prince Francis Joseph II and Princess Gina.
491 **147** 75 r. multicoloured . . . 45 40

1968. Liechtenstein Sagas (2nd series). As T **139.** Multicoloured.
492 30 r. "The Treasure of St. Mamerten" 20 15
493 50 r. "The Hobgoblin in the Bergerwald" 25 25
494 80 r. "The Three Sisters" . . . 40 40

1968. "Pioneers of Philately". (1st series).
495 **148** 20 r. green 15 10
496 – 30 r. brown 20 15
497 – 1 f. black 50 40
PORTRAITS: 30 r. Philippe de Ferrari; 1 f. Maurice Burrus.
See also Nos. 504/5 and 554/6.

150 Arms of Liechtenstein

151 Colonnade

1969.
498 **150** 3 f. 50 brown . . . . . . 1·50 1·25

1969. Europa.
499 **151** 50 r. multicoloured . . . 30 30

152 "Biology"

1969. 250th Anniv of Liechtenstein. Multicoloured.
500 10 r. Type **152** 10 10
501 30 r. "Physics" 20 15
502 50 r. "Astronomy" 40 30
503 80 r. "Art" 60 60

1969. "Pioneers of Philately" (2nd series). As T **148.**
504 80 r. brown 40 40
505 1 f. 20 blue 60 60
PORTRAITS: 80 r. Carl Lindenberg; 1 f. 20, Theodore Champion.

153 Arms of St. Luzi Monastery

154 Symbolic "T"

1969. Arms of Church Patrons. Multicoloured.
506 20 r. St. Johann's Abbey . . . 20 10
507 30 r. Type **153** 25 20
508 30 r. Ladies' Priory, Schanis 25 20
509 30 r. Knights Hospitallers, Feldkirch 25 20
510 50 r. Pfafers Abbey 35 30
511 50 r. Weingarten Abbey . . . 35 30
512 75 r. St. Gallen Abbey . . . 70 50
513 1 f. 20 Ottobeuren Abbey . . 1·10 80
514 1 f. 50 Chur Episcopate . . . 1·40 90

1969. Centenary of Liechtenstein Telegraph System.
515 **154** 30 r. multicoloured . . . 15 15

1969. Liechtenstein Sagas (3rd series). As T **139.** Multicoloured.
516 20 r. "The Cheated Devil" . . 15 15
517 50 r. "The Fiery Red Goat" . . 40 25
518 60 r. "The Grafenberg Treasure" 50 35

155 Orange Lily

156 "Flaming Sun"

1970. Nature Conservation Year. Multicoloured.
519 20 r. Type **155** 20 15
520 30 r. Wild orchid 40 20
521 50 r. Ranunculus 55 40
522 1 f. 20 Bog bean . . . . . . 1·10 1·00
See also Nos. 532/5 and 548/51.

1970. Europa.
523 **156** 50 r. yellow, blue & green 30 30

157 Prince Wenzel

158 Prince Francis Joseph II

1970. 25th Anniv of Liechtenstein Red Cross.
524 **157** 1 f. multicoloured 45 45

1970.
526 – 1 f. 70 green 80 80
526a – 2 f. 50 blue . . . . . . 1·25 1·25
527 **158** 3 f. black . . . . 1·40 1·40
DESIGNS: 1 f. 70, Prince Hans Adam; 2 f. 50, Princess Gina.

159 "Mother and Child" (R. Schadler)

160 Bronze Boar (La Tene period)

1970. Christmas.
528 **159** 30 r. multicoloured . . . 20 15

1971. National Museum Inauguration
529 **160** 25 r. black, blue & ultram 15 15
530 – 30 r. brown and green . . 20 15
531 – 75 r. multicoloured . . . 60 40
DESIGNS: 30 r. Ornamental peacock (Roman, 2nd-century); 75 r. Engraved bowl (13th-century).

161 Europa Chain

1971. Liechtenstein Flowers (2nd series). As T **155.** Multicoloured.
532 10 r. Cyclamen 10 10
533 20 r. Moonwort 15 15
534 50 r. Superb pink 40 35
535 1 f. 50 Alpine columbine . . 1·25 1·00

1971. Europa.
536 **161** 50 r. yellow, blue & black 30 30

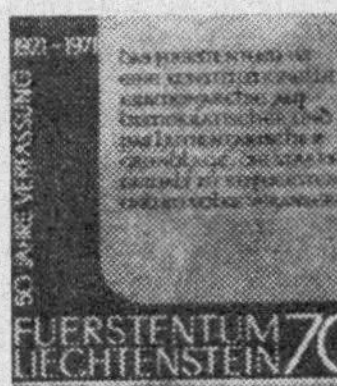

162 Part of Text

163 Cross-country Skiing

1971. 50th Anniv of 1921 Constitution. Mult.
537 70 r. Type **162** 60 50
538 80 r. Princely crown 65 55

1971. Winter Olympic Games, Sapporo, Japan (1972). Multicoloured.
539 15 r. Type **163** 15 10
540 40 r. Ice hockey 30 25
541 65 r. Downhill skiing 45 40
542 1 f. 50 Figure skating 95 95

164 "Madonna and Child" (sculpture, Andrea della Robbia)

165 Gymnastics

1971. Christmas.
543 **164** 30 r. multicoloured 20 15

1972. Olympic Games, Munich. Multicoloured.
544 10 r. Type **165** 10 10
545 20 r. High jumping 15 15
546 40 r. Running 30 25
547 60 r. Throwing the discus . . . 40 35

1972. Liechtenstein Flowers (3rd series). As T **155.** Multicoloured.
548 20 r. Sulphur anemone 15 15
549 30 r. Turk's-cap lily 25 20
550 60 r. Alpine centaury 55 40
551 1 f. 20 Reed-mace 85 75

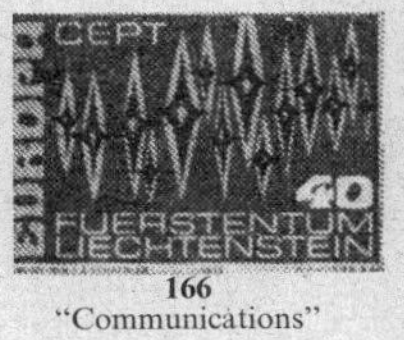

166 "Communications"

168 "Faun"

1972. Europa.
552 **136** 40 r. multicoloured 30 25

1972. "Pioneers of Philately" (3rd series). As T **148.**
554 30 r. green 25 25
555 40 r. purple 30 30
556 1 f. 30 blue . . . . 1·10 85
PORTRAITS: 30 r. Emilio Diena; 40 r. Andre de Cock; 1 f. 30, Theodore E. Steinway.

1972. "Natural Art". Motifs fashioned from roots and branches. Multicoloured.
557 20 r. Type **168** 15 15
558 30 r. "Dancer" 20 20
559 1 f. 10 "Owl" 65 65

169 "Madonna with Angels" (F. Nigg)

170 Lawena Springs

1972. Christmas.
560 **169** 30 r. multicoloured 25 20

1972. Landscapes.
561 – 5 r. purple and yellow . . 10 10
562 **170** 10 r. green and light green 10 10
563 – 15 r. brown and green . . 10 10
564 – 25 r. purple and blue . . . 25 20
565 – 30 r. lilac and brown . . . 30 10
566 – 40 r. mauve and brown . . 40 20
567 – 50 r. blue and lilac 30 20
568 – 60 r. green and yellow . . 30 30
569 – 70 r. blue and light blue . 35 35
570 – 80 r. green and light green 40 40
571 – 1 f. brown and green . . . 60 45
572 – 1 f. 30 blue and green . . 75 75
573 – 1 f. 50 brown and blue . . 75 75
574 – 1 f. 80 brown & lt brown 1·25 1·10
575 – 2 f. brown and blue . . . 1·60 1·00
DESIGNS: 5 r. Silum; 15 r. Ruggeller Reed; 25 r. Steg Kirchlispitz; 30 r. Feld Schellenberg; 40 r. Rennhof Mauren; 50 r. Tidrufe; 60 r. Eschner Riet; 70 r. Mittagspitz; 80 r. Schaan Forest; 1 f. St. Peter's Chapel, Mals; 1 f. 30, Frommenhaus; 1 f. 50, Ochsenkopt; 1 f. 80, Hehlawangspitz; 2 f. Saminaschlucht.

171 Europa "Posthorn"

1973. Europa.
576 **171** 30 r. multicoloured . . . 25 20
577 40 r. multicoloured . . . 35 30

172 Nautilus Goblet

173 Arms of Liechtenstein

1973. Treasures from Prince's Collection (1st issue). Drinking Vessels. Multicoloured.
578 30 r. Type **172** 25 20
579 70 r. Ivory tankard 60 45
580 1 f. 10 Silver cup 80 70
See also Nos. 589/92.

1973.
581 **173** 5 f. multicoloured . . . . 3·00 2·40

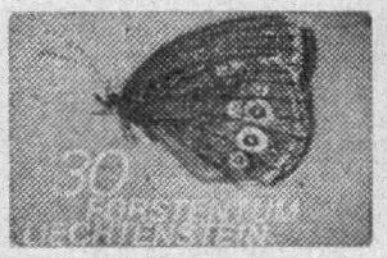

174 False Ringlet

175 "Madonna" (Bartolomeo di Tommaso da Foligno)

1973. Small Fauna of Liechtenstein (1st series). Multicoloured.
582 30 r. Type **174** 35 20
583 40 r. Curlew . . . . 1·25 30
584 60 r. Edible frog 55 40
585 80 r. Grass snake 70 55
See also Nos. 596/9.

1973. Christmas.
586 **175** 30 r. multicoloured . . . 25 20

176 "Shouting Horseman" (sculpture, Andrea Riccio)

177 Footballers

1974. Europa. Multicoloured.
587 30 r. Type **176** 25 20
588 40 r. "Squatting Aphrodite" (sculpture, Antonio Susini) 35 30

1974. Treasures from Prince's Collection (2nd issue). Porcelain. As T **172.** Multicoloured.
589 30 r. Vase, 19th century . . . 25 20
590 50 r. Vase, 1740 . . . . 40 30
591 60 r. Vase, 1830 . . . . 50 40
592 1 f. Vase, c. 1700 . . . . . . 80 75

1974. World Cup Football Championship, West Germany.
593 **177** 80 f. multicoloured . . . 70 55

178 Posthorn and U.P.U. Emblem

179 Bishop Marxer

1974. Centenary of Universal Postal Union.
594 **178** 40 r. black, green & gold 30 25
595 60 r. black, red and gold 40 40

1974. Small Fauna of Liechtenstein (2nd series). As T **174.** Multicoloured.
596 15 r. Mountain newt 15 10
597 25 r. Adder 20 15
598 70 r. Cynthia's fritillary (butterfly) . . . . 1·75 60
599 1 f. 10 Three-toed woodpecker 2·25 85

1974. Death Centenary of Bishop Franz Marxer.
600 **179** 1 f. multicoloured 40 50

180 Prince Francis Joseph II and Princess Gina

1974.
601 180 10 f. brown and gold . . . 4·50 4·50

181 "St. Florian" 182 Prince Constantin

1974. Christmas. Local Art. Glass Paintings. Mult.
602 30 r. Type 181 20 15
603 50 r. "St. Wendelin" 35 30
604 60 r. "St. Mary, Anna and Joachim" 45 40
605 70 r. "Jesus in Manger" 55 50

1975. Royal Princes.
606 182 70 r. green and gold 55 50
607 – 80 r. purple and gold 70 60
608 – 1 f. 20 blue and gold 95 85
PORTRAITS: 80 r. Prince Maximilian; 1 f. 20, Prince Alois.

183 "Cold Sun" (M. Frommelt) 184 Imperial Cross

1975. Europa. Multicoloured.
609 30 r. Type 183 25 20
610 60 r. "Village" (L. Jager) 55 45

1975. Imperial Insignia. (1st series). Multicoloured.
611 30 r. Type 184 25 20
612 60 r. Imperial sword 40 35
613 1 f. Imperial orb 80 70
614 1 f. 30 Coronation robe (50×32 mm) 10·00 8·50
615 2 f. Imperial crown 2·00 1·75
See also Nos. 670/3.

185 "Red Cross Activities" 186 St. Mamerten, Triesen

1975. 30th Anniv of Liechtenstein Red Cross.
616 185 60 r. multicoloured 45 35

1975. European Architectural Heritage Year. Multicoloured.
617 40 r. Type 186 25 25
618 50 r. Red House, Vaduz 30 30
619 70 r. Prebendary buildings, Eschen 50 60
620 1 f. Gutenberg Castle, Balzers 75 85

187 Speed Skating 188 "Daniel in the Lions' Den"

1975. Winter Olympic Games, Innsbruck (1976). Multicoloured.
621 20 r. Type 187 15 10
622 25 r. Ice hockey 20 15
623 70 r. Downhill skiing 60 50
624 1 f. 20 Slalom 90 85

1975. Christmas and Holy Year. Capitals in Chur Cathedral.
625 188 30 r. violet and gold 25 20
626 – 60 r. green and gold 50 40
627 – 90 r. red and gold 95 65
DESIGNS: 60 r. "Madonna"; 90 r. "St. Peter".

189 Mouflon 190 Crayfish

1976. Europa. Ceramics by Prince Hans von Liechtenstein. Multicoloured.
628 40 r. Type 189 50 25
629 80 r. "Pheasant and Brood" 75 60

1976. World Wildlife Fund. Multicoloured.
630 25 r. Type 190 20 20
631 40 r. Turtle 30 30
632 70 r. European otter 60 65
633 80 r. Lapwing 2·00 90

191 Roman Fibula 193 Judo

1976. 75th Anniv of Liechtenstein Historical Society.
634 191 90 r. multicoloured 60 60

1970. Olympic Games, Montreal. Multicoloured.
636 35 r. Type 193 25 20
637 50 r. Volleyball 35 35
638 80 r. Relay 50 50
639 1 f. 10 Long jumping 70 75

194 "Singing Angels" 195 "Pisces"

1976. 400th Birth Anniv (1977) of Peter Paul Rubens (painter). Multicoloured.
640 50 r. Type 194 50 50
641 70 r. "Sons of Rubens" 75 85
642 1 f. "Daughters of Cecrops" (49×39 mm) 3·50 4·25

1976. Signs of the Zodiac (1st series). Multicoloured.
643 20 r. Type 195 15 15
644 40 r. "Aries" 30 25
645 80 r. "Taurus" 50 55
646 90 r. "Gemini" 70 75
See also Nos. 666/9 and 710/13.

196 "Child Jesus of Prague" 197 Sarcophagus Statue, Chur Cathedral

1976. Christmas. Monastic Works in Wax. Mult.
647 20 r. Type 196 15 10
648 50 r. "The Flight into Egypt" (vert) 40 35
649 80 r. "Holy Trinity" (vert) 60 55
650 1 f. 50 "Holy Family" 1·10 1·00

1976. Bishop Ortlieb von Brandis of Chur Commemoration.
651 197 1 f. 10 brown and gold 70 65

199 Map of Liechtenstein, 1721 (J. Heber) 200 Coin of Emperor Constantine II

1977. Europa. Multicoloured.
664 40 r. Type 199 20 20
665 80 r. "View of Vaduz, 1815" (F. Bachmann) 45 45

1977. Signs of the Zodiac (2nd series). As T 195. Multicoloured.
666 40 r. "Cancer" 25 20
667 70 r. "Leo" 45 45
668 80 r. "Virgo" 55 55
669 1 f. 10 "Libra" 65 70

1977. Imperial Insignia (2nd series). As T 184. Multicoloured.
670 40 r. Holy Lance and Reliquary with Particle of the Cross 30 25
671 50 r. "St. Matthew" (Imperial Book of Gospels) 35 30
672 80 r. St. Stephen's Purse 55 55
673 90 r. Tabard of Imperial Herald 75 75

1977. Coins (1st series). Multicoloured.
674 35 r. Type 200 30 25
675 70 r. Lindau Brakteat 50 50
676 80 r. Coin of Ortlieb von Brandis 60 60
See also Nos. 707/9.

201 Frauenthal Castle, Styria 202 Children in Costume

1977. Castles.
677 201 20 r. green and gold 15 15
678 – 50 r. red and gold 30 30
679 – 80 r. lilac and gold 45 50
680 – 90 r. blue and gold 50 60
DESIGNS: 50 r. Gross-Ullersdorf, Moravia; 80 r. Liechtenstein Castle, near Modling, Austria; 90 r. Palais Liechtenstein, Alserbachstrasse, Vienna.

1977. Liechtenstein National Costumes. Mult.
681 40 r. Type 202 25 25
682 70 r. Two girls in traditional costume 40 45
683 1 f. Woman in festive costume 60 65

203 Princess Tatjana

1977. Princess Tatjana.
684 203 1 f. 10 lt brn, brn & gold 1·00 80

204 "Angel" 205 Palais Liechtenstein, Bankgasse, Vienna

1977. Christmas. Sculptures by Erasmus Kern. Multicoloured.
685 20 r. Type 204 15 15
686 50 r. "St. Rochus" 30 30
687 80 r. "Madonna" 45 55
688 1 f. 50 "God the Father" 85 1·00

1978. Europa.
689 205 40 r. blue and gold 30 25
690 – 80 r. red and gold 70 55
DESIGN: 80 r. Feldsberg Castle.

206 Farmhouse, Triesen 207 Vaduz Castle

1978. Buildings. Multicoloured.
691 10 r. Type 206 10 10
692 20 r. Upper village of Triesen 15 10
693 35 r. Barns at Balzers 30 20
694 40 r. Monastery building, Bendern 30 10
695 50 r. Rectory tower, Balzers-Mals 40 25
696 70 r. Rectory, Mauren 50 30
697 80 r. Farmhouse, Schellenberg 70 45
698 90 r. Rectory, Balzers 75 70
699 1 f. Rheinberger House, Vaduz 80 55
700 1 f. 10 Vaduz Mitteldorf 90 70
701 1 f. 50 Town Hall, Triesenberg 1·25 95
702 2 f. National Museum and Administrator's residence, Vaduz 1·50 1·10

1978. 40th Anniv of Prince Francis Joseph II's Accession. Royal Residence. Multicoloured.
703 40 r. Type 207 40 40
704 50 r. Courtyard 40 40
705 70 r. Hall 65 65
706 80 r. High Altar, Castle Chapel 75 75

208 Coin of Prince Charles 209 "Portrait of a Piebald" (J. von Hamilton and A. Faistenberger)

1978. Coins (2nd series). Multicoloured.
707 40 r. Type 208 30 30
708 50 r. Coin of Prince John Adam 40 40
709 80 r. Coin of Prince Joseph Wenzel 65 65

1978. Signs of the Zodiac (3rd series). As T 195. Multicoloured.
710 40 r. "Scorpio" 30 25
711 50 r. "Sagittarius" 40 35
712 80 r. "Capricorn" 65 60
713 1 f. 50 "Aquarius" 1·25 1·10

1978. Paintings. Multicoloured.
714 70 r. Type 209 50 50
715 80 r. "Portrait of a Blackish Brown Stallion" (J. von Hamilton) 65 65
716 1 f. 10 "Golden Carriage of Prince Joseph Wenzel" (Martin von Meytens) (48½×38 mm) 85 85

210 "Adoration of the Shepherds" 211 Mailplane "St. Gallen" over Schaan

1978. Christmas. Church Windows, Triesenberg. Multicoloured.
717 20 r. Type 210 15 15
718 50 r. "Enthroned Madonna with St. Joseph" 40 30
719 80 r. "Adoration of the Magi" 70 65

1979. Europa. Multicoloured.
720 40 r. Type 211 45 45
721 80 r. Airship "Graf Zeppelin" over Vaduz Castle 70 70

212 Child Drinking 213 Ordered Wave-field

1979. International Year of the Child. Multicoloured.
722 80 r. Type 212 40 50
723 90 r. Child eating 50 60
724 1 f. 10 Child reading 55 70

1979. 50th Anniv of International Radio Consultative Committee (CCIR).
725 213 50 r. blue and black 40 30

214 Abstract Composition 215 Sun rising over Continents

1979. Liechtenstein's Entry into Council of Europe.
726 **214** 80 r. multicoloured . . . 70 55

1979. Development Aid.
727 **215** 1 f. multicoloured 80 70

216 Arms of Carl Ludwig von Sulz

217 Sts. Lucius and Florian (fresco, Waltensberg-Vuorz Church)

1979. Heraldic Windows in the Liechtenstein National Museum. Multicoloured.
728 40 r. Type **216** 30 25
729 70 r. Arms of Barbara von Sulz 65 55
730 1 f. 10 Arms of Ulrich von Ramschwag and Barbara von Hallwil 90 80

1979. Patron Saints.
731 **217** 20 f. multicoloured . . . 8·00 8·50

218 Base of Ski Slope, Valuna

1979. Winter Olympic Games, Lake Placid (1980). Multicoloured.
732 40 r. Type **218** 35 25
733 70 r. Malbun and Ochsenkopf 65 55
734 1 f. 50 Ski-lift, Sareis . . . . 1·25 1·00

219 "The Annunciation"

1979. Christmas. Embroideries by Ferdinand Nigg. Multicoloured.
735 20 r. Type **219** 15 10
736 50 r. "Christmas" 40 30
737 80 r. "Blessed are the Peacemakers" 60 50

220 Maria Leopoldine von Esterhazy (bust by Canova)

221 Arms of Andreas Buchel, 1690

1980. Europa.
738 **220** 40 r. green, turq & gold . 35 35
739 – 80 r. brown, red and gold 50 50
DESIGN: 80 r. Maria Theresia von Liechtenstein (after Martin von Meytens).

1980. Arms of Bailiffs (1st series). Multicoloured.
740 40 r. Type **221** 30 25
741 70 r. Georg Marxer, 1745 . . 60 55
742 80 r. Luzius Frick, 1503 . . . 70 60
743 1 f. 10 Adam Oehri, 1634 . . 85 80
See also Nos. 763/6, and 788/91.

222 3 r. Stamp of 1930

223 Milking Pail

1980. 50th Anniv of Postal Museum.
744 **222** 80 r. lake, turq & grey . . 65 60

1980. Alpine Dairy Farming Implements. Mult.
745 20 r. Type **223** 15 15
746 50 r. Wooden heart dairy herd descent marker 40 30
747 80 r. Butter churn 65 55

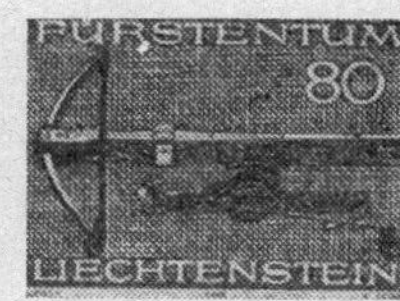
224 Crossbow

1980. Hunting Weapons.
748 **224** 80 r. brown and lilac . . 70 60
749 – 90 r. black and green . . 80 70
750 – 1 f. 10 black and brown 90 80
DESIGNS: 90 r. Spear and knife; 1 f. 10 Rifle and powder-horn.

225 Triesenberg Costumes

1980. Costumes. Multicoloured.
751 40 r. Type **225** 30 25
752 70 r. Dancers, Schellenberg . 65 55
753 80 r. Brass band, Mauren . . 70 65

226 Beech Trees, Matrula (spring)

227 Angel bringing Shepherds Good Tidings

1980. The Forest in the Four Seasons. Multicoloured.
754 40 r. Type **226** 30 30
755 50 r. Firs in the Valorsch (summer) 45 40
756 80 r. Beech tree, Schaan (autumn) 70 60
757 1 f. 50 Edge of forest at Oberplanken (winter) . . . 1·25 1·25

1980. Christmas. Multicoloured.
758 20 r. Type **227** 15 15
759 50 r. Crib 40 30
760 80 r. Epiphany 65 60

228 National Day Procession

230 Scout Emblems

1981. Europa. Multicoloured.
761 40 r. Fireworks at Vaduz Castle 35 25
762 80 r. Type **228** 75 65

1981. Arms of Bailiffs (2nd series). As T **221**. Multicoloured.
763 40 r. Anton Meier, 1748 . . . 30 25
764 70 r. Kaspar Kindle, 1534 . . 60 50
765 80 r. Hans Adam Negele, 1600 70 60
766 1 f. 10 Peter Matt, 1693 . . . 90 80

1981. 50th Anniv of Boy Scout and Girl Guide Movements.
768 **230** 20 r. multicoloured . . . 30 15

231 Symbols of Disability

232 St. Theodul (sculpture)

1981. International Year of Disabled People.
769 **231** 40 r. multicoloured . . . 30 25

1981. 1600th Birth Anniv of St. Theodul.
770 **232** 80 r. multicoloured . . . 65 55

233 "Xanthoria parietina" **234** Gutenberg Castle

1981. Mosses and Lichens. Multicoloured.
771 40 r. Type **233** 30 25
772 50 r. "Parmelia physodes" . . 50 40
773 70 r. "Sphagnum palustre" . . 65 55
774 80 r. "Amblystegium serpens" 80 65

1981. Gutenberg Castle. Multicoloured.
775 20 r. Type **234** 20 15
776 40 r. Courtyard 30 25
777 50 r. Parlour 40 35
778 1 f. 10 Great Hall 95 85

235 Cardinal Karl Borromaus von Mailand

236 St. Nicholas blessing Children

1981. Famous Visitors to Liechtenstein (1st series). Multicoloured.
779 40 r. Type **235** 30 30
780 70 r. Johann Wolfgang von Goethe (writer) 65 60
781 80 r. Alexander Dumas the younger (writer) 75 65
782 1 f. Hermann Hesse (writer) . 85 80
See also Nos. 804/7 and 832/5.

1981. Christmas. Multicoloured.
783 20 r. Type **236** 15 15
784 50 r. Adoration of the Kings 40 30
785 80 r. Holy Family 70 55

237 Peasant Revolt, 1525

1982. Europa. Multicoloured.
786 40 r. Type **237** 40 30
787 80 r. King Wenceslaus with Counts (Imperial direct rule, 1396) 85 65

1982. Arms of Bailiffs (3rd series). As T **221**. Multicoloured.
788 40 r. Johann Kaiser, 1664 . . 40 30
789 70 r. Joseph Anton Kaufmann, 1748 . . . . 70 60
790 80 r. Christoph Walser, 1690 80 75
791 1 f. 10 Stephen Banzer, 1658 1·10 1·00

238 Triesenberg Sports Ground

239 Crown Prince Hans Adam

1982. World Cup Football Championship, Spain. Multicoloured.
792 15 r. Type **238** 20 15
793 25 r. Eschen/Mauren playing fields 25 25
794 1 f. 80 Rheinau playing fields, Balzers . . . . 1·75 1·60

1982. "Liba 82" Stamp Exhibition. Multicoloured.
795 1 f. Type **239** 90 85
796 1 f. Princess Marie Aglae . . . 90 85

240 Tractor (agriculture)

1982. Rural Industries. Multicoloured.
797 30 r. Type **240** 30 25
798 50 r. Cutting flowers (horticulture) 50 40
799 70 r. Workers with logs (forestry) 70 65
800 150 r. Worker and milk (dairy farming) . . . . 1·50 1·40

241 "Neu-Schellenberg"

243 Angel playing Lute

1982. 150th Birth Anniv of Mortiz Menzinger (artist). Multicoloured.
801 40 r. Type **241** 30 25
802 50 r. "Vaduz" 55 40
803 100 r. "Bendern" 90 80

1982. Famous Visitors to Liechtenstein (2nd series). As T **235**. Multicoloured.
804 40 r. Emperor Maximilian I (after Benhard Strigel) . . . 30 25
805 70 f. Georg Jenatsch (liberator of Grisons) 65 50
806 80 r. Angelika Kaufmann (artist, self-portrait) 75 60
807 1 f. St. Fidelis of Sigmaringen 1·00 90

1982. Christmas. Details from High Altar by Jakob Russ, Chur Cathedral. Multicoloured.
808 20 r. Type **243** 15 15
809 50 r. Madonna and child . . 45 35
810 80 r. Angel playing organ . . 70 60

244 Notker Balbulus of St. Gall

245 Shrove Thursday

1983. Europa. Multicoloured.
811 40 r. Type **244** 30 25
812 80 r. Hildegard of Bingen . . 70 55

1983. Shrovetide and Lent Customs. Mult.
813 40 r. Type **245** 30 25
814 70 r. Shrovetide carnival . . . 55 50
815 1 f. 80 Lent Sunday bonfire . . 1·40 1·40

246 River Bank

247 "Schaan"

1983. Anniversaries and Events. Multicoloured.
816 20 r. Type **246** 30 20
817 40 r. Montgolfier Brothers' balloon 35 30
818 50 r. Airmail envelope 50 35
819 80 r. Plant and hands holding spade 70 65
EVENTS: 20 r. Council of Europe river and coasts protection campaign; 40 r. Bicentenary of manned flight; 50 r. World Communications Year; 80 r. Overseas aid.

1983. Landscape Paintings by Anton Ender. Mult.
820 40 r. Type **247** 35 25
821 50 r. "Gutenberg Castle" . . 55 45
822 200 r. "Steg Reservoir" . . . 2·00 2·00

248 Princess Gina

249 Pope John Paul II

1983. Multicoloured.
823 2 f. 50 Type **248** . . . . . . 2·25 1·75
824 3 f. Prince Francis Joseph II 2·75 2·00

1983. Holy Year.
825 **249** 80 r. multicoloured . . . 75 60

250 Snowflakes and Stripes **251** Seeking Shelter

1983. Winter Olympic Games, Sarajevo. Mult.

826 40 r. Type **250** . . . 35 25
827 80 r. Snowflake . . . 75 65
828 1 f. 80 Snowflake and rays . . 1·75 1·75

1983. Christmas. Multicoloured.

829 20 r. Type **251** . . . 15 15
830 50 r. Infant Jesus . . . 50 35
831 80 r. Three Kings . . . 75 65

1984. Famous Visitors to Liechtenstein (3rd series). As T **235**. Multicoloured.

832 40 r. Aleksandr Vassilievich Suvorov (Russian General) 40 30
833 70 r. Karl Rudolf von Buol-Schauenstein, Bishop of Chur 65 60
834 80 r. Carl Zuckmayer (dramatist) 75 65
835 1 f. Curt Goetz (actor) . . . 95 90

253 Bridge

1984. Europa. 25th Anniv of C.E.P.T.

836 **253** 50 r. light blue and blue . 50 40
837 80 r. red and brown . . . 75 70

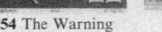

254 The Warning Messenger **255** Pole Vaulting

1984. Liechtenstein Legends. The Destruction of Trisona. Each brown, grey and blue.

838 35 r. Type **254** . . . 30 25
839 50 r. The buried town . . . 55 40
840 80 r. The spared family . . 80 70

1984. Olympic Games, Los Angeles. Mult.

841 70 r. Type **255** . . . 60 55
842 80 r. Throwing the discus . . 70 65
843 1 f. Putting the shot . . . 85 80

256 Currency (trade and banking)

1984. Occupations. Multicoloured.

844 5 r. Type **256** . . . 10 10
845 10 r. Plumber adjusting pipe (building trade) . . 15 10
846 20 r. Operating machinery (industry–production) . . 20 15
847 35 r. Draughtswoman (building trade–planning) . . 35 20
848 45 r. Office worker and world map (industry–sales) . . 50 35
849 50 r. Cook (tourism) . . . 55 30
850 60 r. Carpenter (building trade–interior decoration) . . 70 45
851 70 r. Doctor injecting patient (medical services) . . 75 60
852 80 r. Scientist (industrial research) . . . 80 55
853 100 r. Bricklayer (building trade) 90 65
854 120 r. Flow chart (industry–administration) . . 1·25 1·10
855 150 r. Handstamping covers (post and communications) 1·60 1·00

257 Princess Marie **258** Annunciation

1984. Multicoloured.

856 1 f. 70 Type **257** . . . 1·50 1·25
857 2 f. Prince Hans Adam . . . 2·00 1·50

1984. Christmas. Multicoloured.

858 35 r. Type **258** . . . 30 25
859 50 r. Holy Family . . . 50 40
860 80 r. The Three Kings . . . 80 70

259 Apollo and the Muses playing Music (detail from 18th-century harpsichord lid)

1985. Europa. Music Year. Multicoloured.

861 50 r. Type **259** . . . 60 50
862 80 r. Apollo and the Muses playing music (different) . . 80 75

260 St. Elisabeth Convent, Schaan

1985. Monasteries. Multicoloured.

863 50 r. Type **260** . . . 50 40
864 1 f. Schellenberg Convent . . 1·00 1·00
865 1 f. 70 Gutenberg Mission, Balzers . . . 1·75 1·75

261 Princess Gina and handing out of Rations **262** Justice

1985. 40th Anniv of Liechtenstein Red Cross. Multicoloured.

866 20 r. Type **261** . . . 30 30
867 50 r. Princess Gina and Red Cross ambulance . . . 75 75
868 120 r. Princess Gina with refugee children . . . 1·50 1·50

1985. Cardinal Virtues. Multicoloured.

869 35 r. Type **262** . . . 30 30
870 50 r. Temperance . . . 50 50
871 70 r. Prudence . . . 70 70
872 1 f. Fortitude . . . 1·10 1·10

264 "Portrait of a Canon" (Quentin Massys) **265** Halberd used by Charles I's Bodyguard

1985. Paintings from Metropolitan Museum, New York. Multicoloured.

874 50 r. Type **264** . . . 60 60
875 1 f. "Clara Serena Rubens" (Rubens) . . . 1·50 1·50
876 1 f. 20 "Duke of Urbino" (Raphael) . . . 1·25 1·25

1985. Guards' Weapons and Armour. Mult.

877 35 r. Type **265** . . . 35 30
878 50 r. Morion used by Charles I's bodyguard . . . 70 70
879 80 r. Halberd used by Carl Eusebius's bodyguard . . 90 90

266 Frankincense **267** Puppets performing Tragedy

1985. Christmas. Multicoloured.

880 35 r. Type **266** . . . 35 25
881 50 r. Gold . . . 60 50
882 80 r. Myrrh . . . 90 90

1985. Theatre. Multicoloured.

883 50 r. Type **267** . . . 70 70
884 80 r. Puppets performing comedy 90 90
885 1 f. 50 Opera . . . 1·75 1·75

268 Courtyard **269** Barn Swallows

1986. Vaduz Castle. Multicoloured.

886 20 r. Type **268** . . . 20 15
887 25 r. Keep . . . 40 30
888 50 r. Castle . . . 60 45
889 90 r. Inner gate . . . 75 60
890 1 f. 10 Castle from gardens . . 1·40 1·25
891 1 f. 40 Courtyard (different) . . 1·75 1·40

1986. Europa. Birds. Multicoloured.

892 50 r. Type **269** . . . 1·00 75
893 90 r. European robin . . . 1·50 1·75

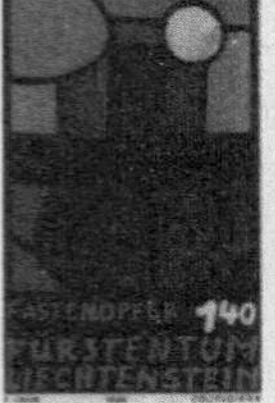

270 "Offerings" **271** Palm Sunday

1986. Lenten Fast.

894 **270** 1 f. 40 multicoloured . . . 1·50 1·50

1986. Religious Festivals. Multicoloured.

895 35 r. Type **271** . . . 40 30
896 50 r. Wedding . . . 70 60
897 70 r. Rogation Day procession 90 80

272 Karl Freiherr Haus von Hausen **273** Francis Joseph II

1986. 125th Anniv of Liechtenstein Land Bank.

898 **272** 50 r. brown, ochre & buff 55 55

1986. 80th Birthday of Prince Francis Joseph II.

899 **273** 3 f. 50 multicoloured . . . 3·00 2·75

274 Roebuck in Ruggeller Riet **275** Cabbage and Beetroot

1986. Hunting. Multicoloured.

900 35 r. Type **274** . . . 45 45
901 50 r. Chamois at Rappenstein 80 80
902 1 f. 70 Stag in Lawena . . . 2·25 2·25

1986. Field Crops. Multicoloured.

903 50 r. Type **275** . . . 70 70
904 80 r. Red cabbages . . . 1·00 1·00
905 90 r. Potatoes, onions and garlic 1·25 1·25

276 Archangel Michael **277** Silver Fir

1986. Christmas. Multicoloured.

906 35 r. Type **276** . . . 35 30
907 50 r. Archangel Gabriel . . . 70 70
908 90 r. Archangel Raphael . . . 1·40 1·40

1986. Tree Bark. Multicoloured.

909 35 r. Type **277** . . . 30 30
910 90 r. Norway spruce . . . 1·40 1·40
911 1 f. 40 Pedunculate oak . . . 1·90 1·90

278 Gamprin Primary School **280** Niklaus von Flue

1987. Europa. Multicoloured.

912 50 r. Type **278** . . . 60 60
913 90 r. Schellenberg parish church 1·40 1·40

1986. 500th Death Anniv of Niklaus von Flue (martyr).

914 **280** 1 f. 10 multicoloured . . 1·25 1·25

281 Miller's Thumb **282** Princes Alois (frame as in first stamps)

1987. Fishes (1st series). Multicoloured.

915 50 r. Type **281** . . . 70 70
916 90 r. Brook trout . . . 1·25 1·25
917 1 f. 10 European grayling . . 1·75 1·75

See also Nos. 959/61.

1987. 75th Anniv of First Liechtenstein Stamps.

918 **282** 2 f. multicoloured . . . 2·40 2·40

283 Staircase **284** Arms

1987. Liechtenstein City Palace, Vienna. Multicoloured.

919 35 r. Type **283** . . . 35 30
920 50 r. Minoritenplatz doorway 70 70
921 90 r. Staircase (different) . . 1·25 1·25

1987. 275th Anniv of Transfer of County of Vaduz to House of Liechtenstein.

922 **284** 1 f. 40 multicoloured . . 1·50 1·50

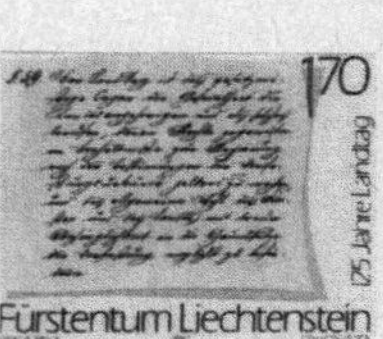

285 Constitution Charter, 1862 **286** St. Matthew

1987. 125th Anniv of Liechtenstein Parliament.

923 **285** 1 f. 70 multicoloured . . 1·75 1·75

1987. Christmas. Illuminations from "Golden Book" of Pfafers Abbey. Multicoloured.

924 35 r. Type **286** . . . 35 30
925 50 r. St. Mark . . . 75 75
926 60 r. St. Luke . . . 85 85
927 90 r. St. John . . . 1·40 1·40

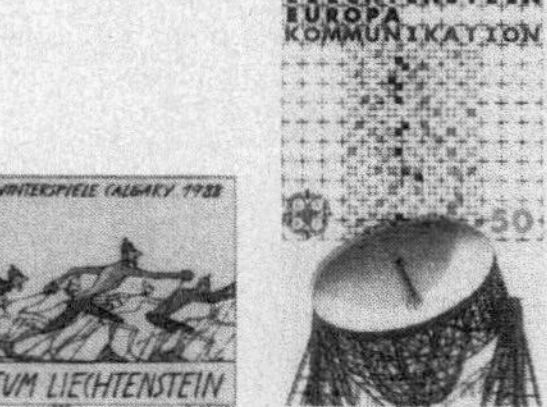

287 "The Toil of the Cross-Country Skier" **288** Dish Aerial

1987. Winter Olympic Games, Calgary (1988). Multicoloured.

928 25 r. Type **287** . . . 30 30
929 90 r. "The Courageous Pioneers of Skiing" . . . 1·40 1·40
930 1 f. 10 "As our Grandfathers used to ride on a Bobsled" 1·60 1·60

1988. Europa. Transport and Communications. Mult.
931 50 r. Type **258** 50 50
932 90 r. Maglev monorail . . . . 1·25 1·25

289 Agriculture

1988. European Campaign for Rural Areas. Multicoloured.
933 80 r. Type **289** . . . . 1·00 1·00
934 90 r. Village centre . . . . . 1·40 1·40
935 1 f. 70 Road . . . . 1·75 1·75

290 Headphones on Books (Radio Broadcasts)

292 St. Barbara's Shrine, Balzers

1988. Costa Rica–Liechtenstein Cultural Co-operation.
936 **290** 50 r. multicoloured . . . 65 65
937 – 1 f. 40 red, brown and green 2·00 2·00
DESIGN: 1 f. 40, Man with pen and radio (Adult education).

1988. Wayside Shrines. Multicoloured.
939 25 r. Type **292** 40 40
940 35 r. Shrine containing statues of Christ, St. Peter and St. Paul at Oberdorf, Vaduz 50 50
941 50 r. St. Anthony of Egypt's shrine, Fallagass, Ruggel . . 85 85

293 Cycling

294 Joseph and Mary

1988. Olympic Games, Seoul. Multicoloured.
942 50 r. Type **293** 70 70
943 80 r. Gymnastics . . . . . . 1·25 1·25
944 90 r. Running . . . . 1·50 1·50
945 1 f. 40 Equestrian event . . . 2·10 2·10

1988. Christmas. Multicoloured.
946 35 r. Type **294** 35 30
947 50 r. Baby Jesus 70 70
948 90 r. Wise Men presenting gifts to Jesus . . . . 1·40 1·40

295 Letter beside Footstool (detail)

296 "Cat and Mouse"

1988. "The Letter" (portrait of Marie-Theresa, Princesse de Lamballe by Anton Hickel). Multicoloured.
949 50 r. Type **295** 65 65
950 90 r. Desk and writing materials (detail) . . . . 1·10 1·10
951 2 f. "The Letter" (complete painting) . . . . 2·00 2·00

1989. Europa. Children's Games. Multicoloured.
952 50 r. Type **296** 90 90
953 90 r. "Hide and Seek" . . . . 1·50 1·50

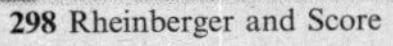

298 Rheinberger and Score

299 Little Ringed Plover

1989. 150th Birth Anniv of Josef Gabriel Rheinberger (composer).
954 **298** 2 f. 90 black, blue & pur 3·00 3·00

1989. Endangered Animals. Multicoloured.
955 25 r. Type **299** 40 40
956 35 r. Green tree frog 50 50
957 50 r. "Libelloides coccajus" (owl-fly) 75 75
958 90 r. Polecat . . . . 1·50 1·50

1989. Fishes (2nd series). As T **281**. Multicoloured.
959 50 r. Pike 60 60
960 1 f. 10 Lake trout . . . . . . 1·40 1·40
961 1 f. 40 Stone loach . . . . . 1·90 1·90

301 Return of Cattle from Alpine Pastures

302 Falknis

1989. Autumn Customs. Multicoloured.
962 35 r. Type **301** 40 40
963 50 r. Peeling corn cobs . . . 65 65
964 80 r. Cattle market . . . . . 1·10 1·10

1989. Mountains. Watercolours by Josef Schadler.
965 – 5 r. multicoloured 10 10
966 – 10 r. multicoloured . . . 10 10
967 – 35 r. multicoloured . . . 30 25
968 – 40 r. multicoloured . . . 35 25
969 – 45 r. multicoloured . . . 40 30
970 **302** 50 r. multicoloured . . . 45 35
971 – 60 r. multicoloured . . . 55 40
972 – 70 r. multicoloured . . . 65 50
973 – 75 r. multicoloured . . . 70 55
974 – 80 r. violet, brown & black 75 60
975 – 1 f. multicoloured 90 70
976 – 1 f. 20 multicoloured . . 1·10 85
977 – 1 f. 50 multicoloured . . 1·40 1·00
978 – 1 f. 60 multicoloured . . 1·50 1·10
979 – 2 f. multicoloured . . . . 1·90 1·90
DESIGNS: 5 r. Augstenberg; 10 r. Hahenespiel; 35 r. Nospitz; 40 r. Ochsenkopf; 45 r. Three Sisters; 60 r. Kuhgrat; 70 r. Galinakopf; 75 r. Plassteikopf; 80 pf. Naafkopf; 1 f. Schonberg; 1 f. 20, Bleikaturm; 1 f. 50, Garselliturm; 1 f. 60, Schwarzhorn; 2 f. Scheienkopf.

303 "Melchior and Balthasar"

304 Mace Quartz

1989. Christmas. Details of triptych by Hugo van der Goes. Multicoloured.
981 35 r. Type **303** 50 50
982 50 r. "Kaspar and Holy Family" (27 × 34 mm) 75 70
983 90 r. "St. Stephen" . . . . . 1·25 1·25

1989. Minerals. Multicoloured.
984 50 r. Type **304** 80 80
985 1 f.10 Globe pyrite . . . . . 1·50 1·50
986 1 f. 50 Calcite . . . . 2·10 2·10

305 Nendeln Forwarding Agency, 1864

306 Penny Black

1990. Europa. Post Office Buildings. Mult.
987 50 r. Type **305** 70 70
988 90 r. Vaduz post office, 1976 1·10 1·10

1990. 150th Anniv of the Penny Black.
989 **306** 1 f. 50 multicoloured . . 1·90 1·90

307 Footballers

308 Tureen, Oranges and Grapes

1990. World Cup Football Championship, Italy.
990 **307** 2 f. multicoloured . . . . 2·40 2·40

1990. 9th Death Anniv of Benjamin Steck (painter). Multicoloured.
991 50 r. Type **308** 70 70
992 80 r. Apples and pewter bowl 1·00 1·00
993 1 f. 50 Basket, apples, cherries and pewter jug . . . . . . 1·90 1·90

309 Princess Gina

310 Ring-necked Pheasant

1990. Prince Francis Joseph II and Princess Gina Commemoration. Multicoloured.
994 2 f. Type **309** . . . . 2·40 2·40
995 3 f. Prince Francis Joseph II 3·50 3·50

1990. Game Birds. Multicoloured.
996 25 r. Type **310** 30 30
997 50 r. Black grouse 60 60
998 2 f. Mallard . . . . 2·40 2·40

311 Annunciation

312 St. Nicholas

1990. Christmas. Paintings. Multicoloured.
999 35 r. Type **311** 45 45
1000 50 r. Nativity 60 60
1001 90 r. Adoration of the Magi 1·00 1·00

1990. Winter Customs. Multicoloured.
1002 35 r. Type **312** 45 45
1003 50 r. Awakening on New Year's Eve 60 60
1004 1 f. 50 Giving New Year greetings . . . . 1·60 1·60

313 Mounted Courier

314 "Olympus 1" Satellite

1990. 500th Anniv of Regular European Postal Services.
1005 **313** 90 r. multicoloured . . . 1·00 1·00

1991. Europa. Europe in Space. Multicoloured.
1006 50 r. Type **314** 55 55
1007 90 r. "Meteosat" satellite . . 95 95

315 St. Ignatius de Loyola (founder of Society of Jesus)

316 U.N. Emblem and Dove

1991. Anniversaries. Multicoloured.
1008 80 r. Type **315** (500th birth anniv) 85 85
1009 90 r. Wolfgang Amadeus Mozart (composer, death bicentenary) 95 95

1991. Admission to U.N. Membership (1990).
1010 **316** 2 f. 50 multicoloured . . 2·75 2·75

317 Non-Commissioned Officer and Private

318 "Near Maloja" (Giovanni Giacometti)

1991. 125th Anniv of Last Mobilization of Liechtenstein's Military Contingent (to the Tyrol). Multicoloured.
1011 50 r. Type **317** 55 55
1012 70 r. Tunic, chest and portrait 75 55
1013 1 f. Officer and private . . . 1·10 1·10

1991. 700th Anniv of Swiss Confederation Paintings by Swiss artists. Multicoloured.
1014 50 r. Type **318** 55 55
1015 80 r. "Rhine Valley" (Ferdinand Gehr) 85 85
1016 90 r. "Bergell" (Augusto Giacometti) 95 95
1017 1 f. 10 "Hoher Kasten" (Hedwig Scherrer) . . . . 1·25 1·25

319 Stampless and Modern Covers

320 Princess Marie

1991. "Liba 92" National Stamp Exhibition, Vaduz.
1018 **319** 90 r. multicoloured . . . 90 90

1991. Multicoloured.
1019 3 f. Type **320** . . . . 3·00 3·00
1020 3 f. 40 Prince Hans Adam II 3·50 3·50

321 Virgin of the Annunciation (exterior of left wing)

322 Cross-country Skiers and Testing for Drug Abuse

1991. Christmas. Details of the altar from St. Mamertus Chapel, Triesen. Multicoloured.
1021 50 r. Type **321** 50 50
1022 80 r. Madonna and Child (wood-carving attr. Jorg Syrlin, inner shrine) . . . 80 80
1023 90 r. Angel Gabriel (exterior of right wing). 90 90

1991. Winter Olympic Games, Albertville. Mult.
1024 70 r. Type **322** 70 70
1025 80 r. Ice hockey player tackling opponent and helping him after fall 80 80
1026 1 f. 60 Downhill skier and fallen skier caught in safety net 1·60 1·60

323 Relay Race, Drugs and Shattered Medal

324 Aztecs

1992. Olympic Games, Barcelona. Multicoloured.
1027 50 r. Type **323** 45 45
1028 70 r. Cycling road race . . . 65 65
1029 2 f. 50 Judo . . . . 2·25 2·25

1992. Europa. 500th Anniv of Discovery of America by Columbus. Multicoloured.
1030 80 r. Type **324** 75 75
1031 90 r. Statue of Liberty and New York skyline 85 85

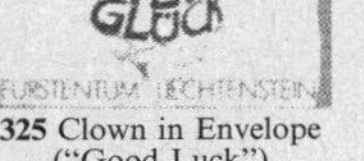

325 Clown in Envelope ("Good Luck")

327 "Blechnum spicant"

1992. Greetings Stamps. Multicoloured.
1032 50 r. Type **325** 45 45
1033 50 r. Wedding rings in envelope and harlequin violinist . . . 45 45
1034 50 r. Postman blowing horn (31 × 21 mm) 45 45
1035 50 r. Flying postman carrying letter sealed with heart (31 × 21 mm) 45 45

1992. Ferns. Multicoloured.
1037 40 r. Type **327** 35 35
1038 50 r. Maidenhair spleenwort 45 45
1039 70 r. Hart's-tongue 65 65
1040 2 f. 50 "Asplenium rutamuraria" 2·25 2·25

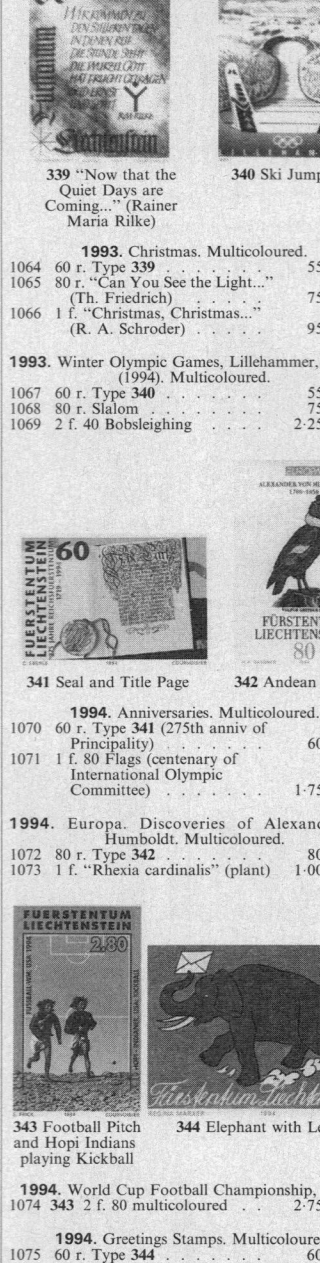

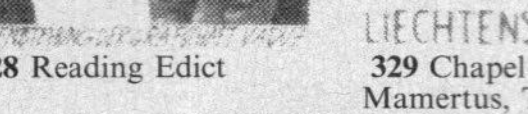
328 Reading Edict **329** Chapel of St. Mamertus, Triesen

1992. 650th Anniv of County of Vaduz.
1041 **328** 1 f. 60 multicoloured 1·50 1·50

1992. Christmas. Multicoloured.
1042 50 r. Type **329** 45 45
1043 90 r. Crib, St. Gallus's Church, Triesen 85 85
1044 1 f. 60 St. Mary's Chapel, Triesen 1·50 1·50

330 Crown Prince Alois **331** "Nafkopf and Huts, Steg"

1992.
1045 **330** 2 f. 50 multicoloured 2·25 2·25

1993. Paintings by Hans Gantner. Multicoloured.
1046 50 r. Type **331** 45 45
1047 60 r. "Hunting Lodge, Sass" 55 55
1048 1 f. 80 "Red House, Vaduz" 1·60 1·60

332 "910805" (Bruno Kaufmann) **333** "Tale of the Ferryman" (painting)

1993. Europa. Contemporary Art. Multicoloured.
1049 80 r. Type **332** 70 70
1050 1 f. "The Little Blue" (Evi Kliemand) 90 90

1993. Tibetan Collection in the National Museum. Multicoloured.
1051 60 r. Type **333** 55 55
1052 80 r. Religious dance mask 75 75
1053 1 f. "Tale of the Fish" (painting) 95 95

334 "Tree of Life" **335** "The Black Hatter"

1993. Missionary Work.
1054 **334** 1 f. 80 multicoloured 1·75 1·75

1993. Homage to Liechtenstein.
1055 **335** 2 f. 80 multicoloured 2·75 2·75

337 Origanum **338** Eurasian Badger

1993. Flowers. Illustrations from "Hortus Botanicus Liechtenstein". Multicoloured.
1057 50 r. Type **337** 50 50
1058 60 r. Meadow sage 55 55
1059 1 f. Seseli annuum 95 95
1060 2 f. 50 Large self-heal 2·40 2·40

1993. Animals. Multicoloured.
1061 60 r. Type **338** 55 55
1062 80 r. Beech marten 75 75
1063 1 f. Red fox 95 95

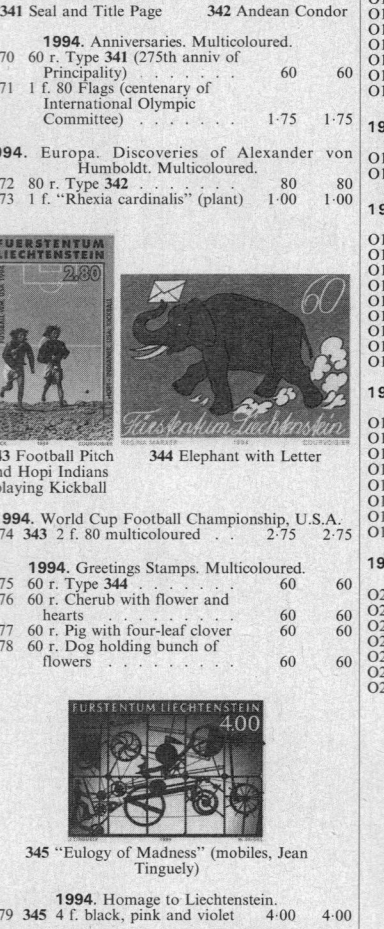

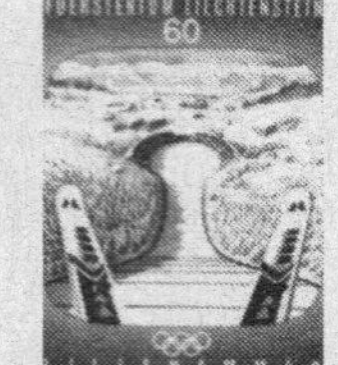
339 "Now that the Quiet Days are Coming..." (Rainer Maria Rilke) **340** Ski Jumping

1993. Christmas. Multicoloured.
1064 60 r. Type **339** 55 55
1065 80 r. "Can You See the Light..." (Th. Friedrich) 75 75
1066 1 f. "Christmas, Christmas..." (R. A. Schroder) 95 95

1993. Winter Olympic Games, Lillehammer, Norway (1994). Multicoloured.
1067 60 r. Type **340** 55 55
1068 80 r. Slalom 75 75
1069 2 f. 40 Bobsleighing 2·25 2·25

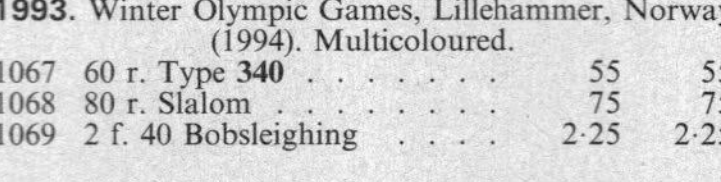

341 Seal and Title Page **342** Andean Condor

1994. Anniversaries. Multicoloured.
1070 60 r. Type **341** (275th anniv of Principality) 60 60
1071 1 f. 80 Flags (centenary of International Olympic Committee) 1·75 1·75

1994. Europa. Discoveries of Alexander von Humboldt. Multicoloured.
1072 80 r. Type **342** 80 80
1073 1 f. "Rhexia cardinalis" (plant) 1·00 1·00

343 Football Pitch and Hopi Indians playing Kickball **344** Elephant with Letter

1994. World Cup Football Championship, U.S.A.
1074 **343** 2 f. 80 multicoloured 2·75 2·75

1994. Greetings Stamps. Multicoloured.
1075 60 r. Type **344** 60 60
1076 60 r. Cherub with flower and hearts 60 60
1077 60 r. Pig with four-leaf clover 60 60
1078 60 r. Dog holding bunch of flowers 60 60

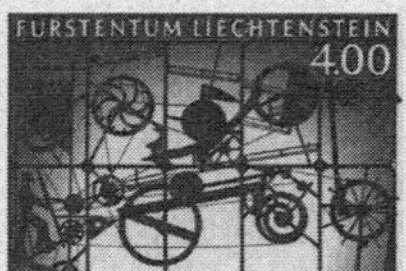

345 "Eulogy of Madness" (mobiles, Jean Tinguely)

1994. Homage to Liechtenstein.
1079 **345** 4 f. black, pink and violet 4·00 4·00

346 Spring

1994. Seasons of the Vine. Multicoloured.
1080 60 r. Type **346** 60 60
1081 60 r. Vine leaves (Summer) 60 60
1082 60 r. Trunk in snowy landscape (Winter) 60 60
1083 60 r. Grapes (Autumn) 60 60

Nos. 1080/3 were issued together, se-tenant, forming a composite design.

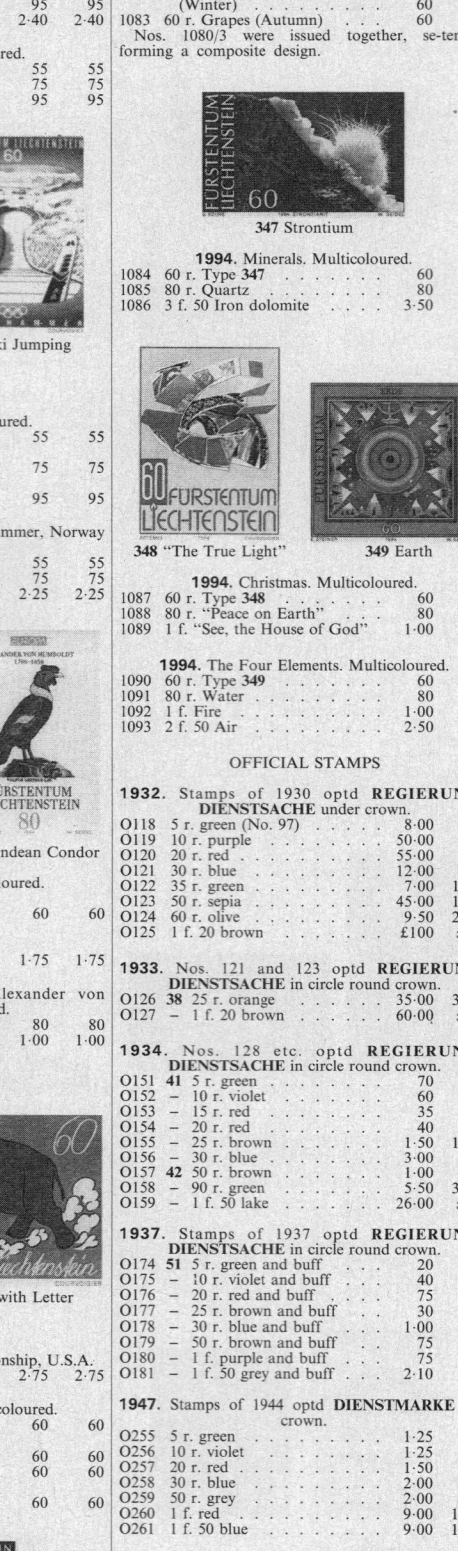

347 Strontium

1994. Minerals. Multicoloured.
1084 60 r. Type **347** 60 60
1085 80 r. Quartz 80 80
1086 3 f. 50 Iron dolomite 3·50 3·50

348 "The True Light" **349** Earth

1994. Christmas. Multicoloured.
1087 60 r. Type **348** 60 60
1088 80 r. "Peace on Earth" 80 80
1089 1 f. "See, the House of God" 1·00 1·00

1994. The Four Elements. Multicoloured.
1090 60 r. Type **349** 60 60
1091 80 r. Water 80 80
1092 1 f. Fire 1·00 1·00
1093 2 f. 50 Air 2·50 2·50

OFFICIAL STAMPS

1932. Stamps of 1930 optd **REGIERUNGS DIENSTSACHE** under crown.
O118 5 r. green (No. 97) 8·00 8·00
O119 10 r. purple 50·00 8·00
O120 20 r. red 55·00 8·00
O121 30 r. blue 12·00 8·00
O122 35 r. green 7·00 18·00
O123 50 r. sepia 45·00 13·00
O124 60 r. olive 9·50 28·00
O125 1 f. 20 brown £100 £250

1933. Nos. 121 and 123 optd **REGIERUNGS DIENSTSACHE** in circle round crown.
O126 **38** 25 r. orange 35·00 32·00
O127 – 1 f. 20 brown 60·00 £225

1934. Nos. 128 etc. optd **REGIERUNGS DIENSTSACHE** in circle round crown.
O151 **41** 5 r. green 70 1·50
O152 – 10 r. violet 60 1·25
O153 – 15 r. red 35 1·40
O154 – 20 r. red 40 1·40
O155 – 25 r. brown 1·50 11·00
O156 – 30 r. blue 3·00 4·50
O157 **42** 50 r. brown 1·00 2·00
O158 – 90 r. green 5·50 30·00
O159 – 1 f. 50 lake 26·00 £130

1937. Stamps of 1937 optd **REGIERUNGS DIENSTSACHE** in circle round crown.
O174 **51** 5 r. green and buff 20 50
O175 – 10 r. violet and buff 40 90
O176 – 20 r. red and buff 75 1·25
O177 – 25 r. brown and buff 30 1·25
O178 – 30 r. blue and buff 1·00 70
O179 – 50 r. brown and buff 75 90
O180 – 1 f. purple and buff 75 5·50
O181 – 1 f. 50 grey and buff 2·10 9·00

1947. Stamps of 1944 optd **DIENSTMARKE** and crown.
O255 5 r. green 1·25 60
O256 10 r. violet 1·25 85
O257 20 r. red 1·50 85
O258 30 r. blue 2·00 1·40
O259 50 r. grey 2·00 3·00
O260 1 f. red 9·00 10·00
O261 1 f. 50 blue 9·00 10·00

O 86 **O 198** Government Building, Vaduz

1950. Buff paper.
O287 **O 86** 5 r. purple and grey 10 10
O288 10 r. olive and red 10 10
O289 20 r. brown and blue 15 15
O290 30 r. lake and red 30 25
O291 40 r. blue and brown 30 30
O292 55 r. green and red 1·00 1·00
O293 60 r. grey and red 1·00 1·00
O294 80 r. orange and grey 75 75
O295 90 r. sepia and blue 80 1·00
O296 1 f. 20 green & orange 1·50 1·50

1968. White paper.
O495 **O 86** 5 r. brown and orange 10 10
O496 10 r. violet and red 10 10
O497 20 r. red and green 15 15
O498 30 r. green and red 25 25
O499 50 r. blue and red 40 40
O500 60 r. orange and blue 50 50
O501 70 r. red and green 60 60
O502 80 r. green and red 70 70
O503 95 r. green and red 1·00 1·00
O504 1 f. purple & turquoise 90 90
O505 1 f. 20 brown & turq 1·40 1·40
O506 2 f. brown and orange 1·60 1·60

1976.
O652 **O 198** 10 r. brown and violet 10 10
O653 20 r. red and blue 15 15
O654 35 r. blue and red 20 20
O655 40 r. violet and green 25 25
O656 50 r. green and mauve 30 30
O657 70 r. purple and green 40 40
O658 80 r. green and purple 50 50
O659 90 r. violet and blue 60 60
O660 1 f. grey and purple 65 65
O661 1 f. 10 brown and blue 70 70
O662 1 f. 50 green and red 90 90
O663 2 f. orange and blue 1·40 1·40
O664 5 f. purple and orange 3·75 3·50

POSTAGE DUE STAMPS

D 11 **D 25** **D 58**

1920.
D43 **D 11** 5 h. red 10 25
D44 10 h. red 10 25
D45 15 h. red 10 25
D46 20 h. red 10 25
D47 25 h. red 15 30
D48 30 h. red 15 30
D49 40 h. red 15 30
D50 50 h. red 15 30
D51 80 h. red 15 30
D52 1 k. blue 20 50
D53 2 k. blue 20 50
D54 5 k. blue 20 50

1928.
D84 **D 25** 5 r. orange and violet 1·00 2·50
D85 10 r. orange and violet 1·25 2·50
D86 15 r. orange and violet 2·50 10·00
D87 20 r. orange and violet 2·50 2·50
D88 25 r. orange and violet 2·50 7·50
D89 30 r. orange and violet 7·00 11·00
D90 40 r. orange and violet 8·00 12·00
D91 50 r. orange and violet 8·50 15·00

1940.
D189 **D 58** 5 r. red and blue 1·25 4·25
D190 10 r. red and blue 50 75
D191 15 r. red and blue 75 4·50
D192 20 r. red and blue 80 1·25
D193 25 r. red and blue 1·40 3·25
D194 30 r. red and blue 3·00 5·00
D195 40 r. red and blue 3·00 4·50
D196 50 r. red and blue 3·00 5·50

LITHUANIA Pt. 10

A country on the Baltic Sea, under Russian rule until occupied by the Germans in the first World War (see German Eastern Command). It was an independent republic from 1918 to 1940, when it was incorporated into the U.S.S.R.

Lithuania declared its independence in 1990, and the U.S.S.R. formally recognised the republic in 1991.

1918. 100 skatiku = 1 auksinas2
1922. 100 centu = 1 litas
1990. 100 kopeks = 1 rouble
1992. Talons
1993. 100 centu = 1 litas

1 2

1918.

3	**1**	10 s. black on buff	50·00	20·00
4		15 s. black on buff	50·00	20·00
5		20 s. black on buff	3·25	2·40
6		30 s. black on buff	3·25	2·40
7		40 s. black on buff	3·25	2·40
8		50 s. black on buff	3·25	2·40

1919.

9	**2**	10 s. black on buff	5·00	1·90
10		15 s. black on buff	5·00	1·90
11		20 s. black on buff	5·00	1·90
12		30 s. black on buff	5·00	1·90

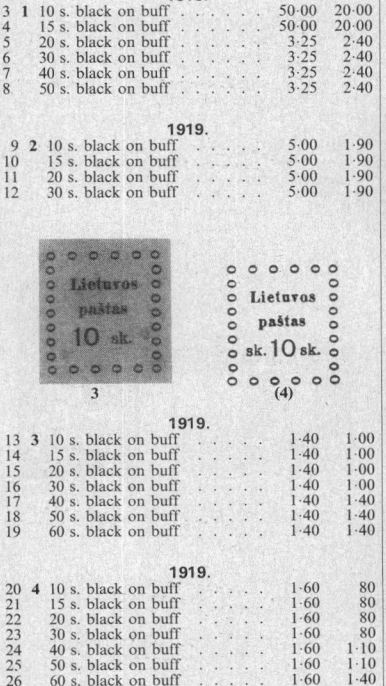

3 (4)

1919.

13	**3**	10 s. black on buff	1·40	1·00
14		15 s. black on buff	1·40	1·00
15		20 s. black on buff	1·40	1·00
16		30 s. black on buff	1·40	1·00
17		40 s. black on buff	1·40	1·40
18		50 s. black on buff	1·40	1·40
19		60 s. black on buff	1·40	1·40

1919.

20	**4**	10 s. black on buff	1·60	80
21		15 s. black on buff	1·60	80
22		20 s. black on buff	1·60	80
23		30 s. black on buff	1·60	80
24		40 s. black on buff	1·60	1·10
25		50 s. black on buff	1·60	1·10
26		60 s. black on buff	1·60	1·40

5 Arms

6

7

1919. "auksinas" in lower case letters on 1 to 5 a.

40	**5**	10 s. pink	15	15
50		10 s. orange	15	10
51		15 s. violet	15	10
52		20 s. blue	15	10
43		30 s. orange	15	15
53		30 s. bistre	15	10
54		40 s. brown	15	10
55	**6**	50 s. green	15	10
56		60 s. red and violet	15	10
57		75 s. red and yellow	15	10
37	**7**	1 a. red and grey	35	20
38		3 a. red and brown	35	20
39		5 a. red and green	40	30

1921. As T **4**, but "AUKSINAS" or "AUKSINAI" in capital letters.

58	**7**	1 a. red and grey	15	10
59		3 a. red and brown	25	15
60		5 a. red and green	40	25

11 Lithuania receiving Independence

12 Lithuania arises

1920. 2nd Anniv of Independence.

65	**11**	10 s. lake	2·00	2·00
66		15 s. lilac	2·00	2·00
67		20 s. blue	2·00	2·00
68	**12**	30 s. brown	2·00	2·00
69	–	40 s. green and brown	2·00	2·00
70	**12**	50 s. red	2·00	2·00
71		60 s. lilac	2·00	2·00
72	–	80 s. red and violet	2·00	2·00
73	–	1 a. red and green	2·00	2·00
74	–	3 a. red and brown	2·00	2·00
75	–	5 a. red and green	2·00	2·00

DESIGNS—VERT: 40 s., 80 s., 1 a. Lithuania with chains broken; 3, 5 a. (25×25 mm) Arms.

16 Arms

17 Vytautas

1920. National Assembly.

76	**16**	10 s. red	30	25
77		15 s. violet	45	35
78	**17**	20 s. green	45	35
79	**16**	30 s. brown	45	45
80	–	40 s. violet and green	45	45
81	**17**	50 s. brown and orange	45	45
82		60 s. red and orange	55	45
83	–	80 s. red, grey and black	55	55
84	–	1 a. yellow and black	55	55
85	–	3 a. green and black	65	65
86	–	5 a. violet and black	1·60	1·60

DESIGNS—As Type **17**: 40 s., 80 s. Gediminas. As Type **16**: 1 a. to 5 a. Sacred Oak and Altar.

20 Sower

21 Kestutis

22 Reaper

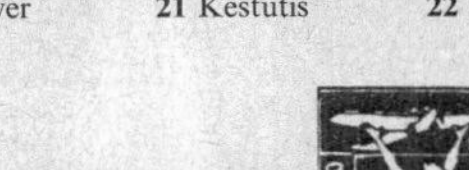
23

28 Allegory of Flight

24 Flying Posthorn

25 Junkers F-13 over R. Niemen

1921.

87	**20**	10 s. red	15	1·40
88		15 s. mauve	15	1·60
89		20 s. blue	10	10
90	**22**	30 s. brown	40	4·00
91	**21**	40 s. red	15	10
92	**22**	50 s. olive	10	10
93		60 s. mauve and green	30	5·00
94	**21**	80 s. red and orange	20	15
95		1 a. green and brown	15	10
96		2 a. red and blue	15	10
97	**23**	3 a. blue and brown	40	85
124	**20**	4 a. blue and yellow	30	20
98	**23**	5 a. red and grey	50	2·00
125	**20**	8 a black and green	65	20
99	**23**	10 a. mauve and red	1·00	35
100		25 a. green and brown	1·10	65
101		100 a. grey and red	4·00	10·00

1921. Air. Inauguration of Kaunas-Konigsberg Air Service.

102	**24**	20 s. blue	1·00	85
103		40 s. orange	1·00	85
104		60 s. green	1·00	65
105		80 s. red	1·10	1·00
106	**25**	1 a. green and red	2·00	1·25
107	–	2 a. brown and blue	2·00	1·50
108	–	5 a. grey and yellow	2·75	2·75

DESIGNS—As Type **25**: 2 a. Three Junkers F-13 monoplanes; 5 a. Junkers F-13 over Gediminas Castle.

1921. Air. Inauguration of Air Mail Service.

109	**28**	20 s. lilac and orange	1·10	1·50
110		40 s. red and blue	1·10	1·50
111		60 s. olive and blue	1·10	1·60
112		80 s. green and yellow	1·10	1·60
113		1 a. blue and green	1·10	1·60
114		2 a. red and grey	1·10	1·50
115		5 a. green and purple	1·10	1·50

1922. Surch **4 AUKSINAI** with or without frame.

116	**6**	4 a. on 75 s. red and yellow	40	40

30 Junkers F-13

1922. Air.

118	**30**	1 a. red and brown	1·60	2·25
119		3 a. green and violet	1·60	1·40
120		5 a. yellow and blue	1·60	2·50

31 Gediminas Castle

33 Pte. Luksis

1922. Air.

121	**31**	2 a. red and blue	1·00	90
122		4 a. red and brown	1·00	90
123		10 a. blue and black	2·40	1·90

1922. "De jure" Recognition of Lithuania by League of Nations. Inscr "LIETUVA DE JURE".

126	**33**	20 s. red and black	35	35
127	–	40 s. violet and green	25	15
128	–	50 s. blue and purple	25	15
129	–	60 s. orange and violet	25	15
130	–	1 a. blue and red	25	20
131	–	2 a. brown and blue	35	35
132	–	3 a. blue and brown	35	35
133	–	4 a. purple and green	35	35
134	–	5 a. red and brown	35	35
135	–	6 a. blue	45	35
136	–	8 a. yellow and blue	65	35
137	–	10 a. green and violet	1·00	1·00

DESIGNS—VERT: 40 s. Lt. Juozapavicius; 50 s. Dr. Basanavicius; 60 s. Mrs. Petkevicaite; 1 a. Prof. Voldemaras; 2 a. Dovidaitis; 3 a. Dr. Slezevicius; 4 a. Dr. Galvanauskas; 5 a. Dr. Grinius; 6 a. Dr. Stulginskis; 8 a. Pres. Smetona. HORIZ: (39×27 mm): 10 a. Stauguitis, Pres. Smetona and Silingas.

1922. Surch.

138	**5**	1 c. on 10 s. orange (postage)	25	5·00
139		1 c. on 15 s. violet	25	5·00
143		1 c. on 20 s. blue	25	5·00
144		1 c. on 30 s. orange	35·00	60·00
145		1 c. on 30 s. bistre	15	40
146		1 c. on 40 s. brown	50	4·00
148	**22**	1 c. on 50 s. olive	10	10
149	**6**	2 c. on 50 s. green	65	4·00
150		2 c. on 60 s. red and violet	10	10
151		2 c. on 75 s. red and yellow	75	5·00
152	**20**	3 c. on 10 s. red	1·50	6·00
153		3 c. on 15 s. mauve	15	15
154		3 c. on 20 s. blue	20	3·25
155	**22**	3 c. on 30 s. brown	1·60	8·25
156	**21**	3 c. on 40 s. red	15	60
157	**7**	3 c. on 1 a. (No. 37)	85·00	£130
158		3 c. on 1 a. (No. 58)	15	1·25
159		3 c. on 3 a. (No. 38)	70·00	£120
160		3 c. on 3 a. (No. 59)	10	65
161		3 c. on 5 a. (No. 39)	40·00	50·00
162		3 c. on 5 a. (No. 60)	10	80
163	**22**	5 c. on 50 s. olive	10	10
164		5 c. on 60 s. mauve & green	85	15·00
165	**21**	5 c. on 80 s. red & orange	10	40
166	**6**	5 c. on 4 a. on 75 s. red and yellow	30	12·50
168	**21**	10 c. on 1 a. green & brown	25	10
169		10 c. on 2 a. red and blue	10	10
170	**20**	15 c. on 4 a. blue & yellow	10	10
171	**23**	25 c. on 3 a. blue and green	5·00	25·00
172		25 c. on 5 a. red and grey	1·60	6·75
173		25 c. on 10 a. mauve & red	1·00	1·60
174	**20**	30 c. on 8 a. black & green	65	35
175	**23**	50 c. on 25 a. green & brown	1·50	3·00
176		1 l. on 100 a grey and red	2·75	3·25
177	**24**	10 c. on 20 s. blue (air)	1·40	3·75
178		10 c. on 40 s. orange	1·40	5·75
179		10 c. on 60 s. green	1·10	5·75
180		10 c. on 80 s. red	1·40	5·75
181	**25**	20 c. on 1 a. green and red	4·75	12·50
182	–	20 c. on 2 a. (No. 107)	8·00	18·00
183	**31**	25 c. on 2 a. red and blue	1·00	85
184		30 c. on 4 a. red and brown	1·00	80
185	–	50 c. on 5 a. (No. 108)	1·40	1·25
186	**31**	50 c. on 10 a. blue & black	65	1·25
187	**30**	1 l. on 5 a. yellow & blue	12·50	27·00

38 Wayside Cross

39 Ruins of Kaunas Castle

40 Seminary Church

1923.

201	**38**	2 c. brown	60	30
202		3 c. green	85	25
203		5 c. green	85	10
204		10 c. violet	2·00	10
189		15 c. red	1·40	10
190		20 c. green	1·40	15
191		25 c. blue	1·40	10
206		36 c. brown	7·50	65
192	**39**	50 c. green	1·40	15
193		60 c. red	1·40	10
194	**40**	1 l. orange and green	6·75	10
195		3 l. red and grey	5·25	55
196		5 l. brown and blue	10·00	90

43 Arms of Memel

44 Ruins of Trakai

1923. Union of Memel with Lithuania.

210	**43**	1 c. red and green	1·10	1·25
211	–	2 c. mauve	1·10	1·25
212	–	3 c. yellow	1·25	1·25
213	**43**	5 c. buff and blue	1·40	1·25
214	–	10 c. red	1·50	1·50
215	–	15 c. green	1·50	1·50
216	**44**	25 c. violet	2·40	2·40
217	–	30 c. red	2·75	3·25
218	–	60 c. green	2·75	3·25
219	–	1 l. green	3·00	3·00
220	–	2 l. red	6·75	10·00
221	**44**	3 l. blue	7·50	10·00
222	–	5 l. blue	10·00	11·50

DESIGNS—As Type **43**: 3 c., 2 l. Chapel of Biruta; 10 c., 15 c. War Memorial Kaunas; As Type **44**: 2, 30 c. Arms of Lithuania; 60 c., 5 l. Memel Lighthouse; 1 l. Memel Harbour.

45

46

1924. Air.

223	**45**	20 c. yellow	1·40	85
224		40 c. green	1·40	85
225		60 c. red	1·60	65
226	**46**	1 l. brown	3·25	55

1924. Charity. War Orphans Fund. Surch **KARO NASLAICIAMS** and premium.

227	**38**	2 c. + 2 c. brown (postage)	1·00	90
228		3 c. + 3 c. olive	1·00	90
229		5 c. + 5 c. green	1·00	90
231		10 c. + 10 c. violet	1·40	1·50
232		15 c. + 15 c. red	1·50	1·50
233		20 c. + 20 c. olive	2·00	2·00
235		25 c. + 25 c. blue	4·75	4·75
236		36 c. + 34 c. brown	5·00	5·00
237	**39**	50 c. + 50 c. green	5·00	5·00
238		60 c. + 60 c. red	6·75	6·75
239	**40**	1 l. + 1 l. orange and green	6·75	6·75
240		3 l. + 2 l. red and grey	11·50	11·50
241		5 l. + 3 l. brown and blue	17·00	17·00
242	**45**	20 c. + 20 c. yellow (air)	6·75	6·75
243		40 c. + 40 c. green	6·75	6·75
244		60 c. + 60 c. red	6·75	6·75
245	**46**	1 l. + 1 l. brown	8·50	9·00

49 Swallow carrying Letter

56

57

1926. Air.

246	**49**	20 c. red	70	30
247		40 c. orange and mauve	70	30
248		60 c. black and blue	2·10	40

1926. Charity. War Invalids. Nos. 227/39 surch with new values and small ornaments.

249	**38**	1 c. + 1 c. on 2 c. + 2 c.	55	65
250		2 c. + 2 c. on 3 c. + 3 c.	55	65
251		2 c. + 2 c. on 5 c. + 5 c.	55	65
253		5 c. + 5 c. on 10 c. + 10 c.	1·40	1·40
254		5 c. + 5 c. on 15 c. + 15 c.	1·40	1·40
255		10 c. + 10 c. on 20 c. + 20 c.	1·40	1·40
257		10 c. + 10 c. on 25 c. + 25 c.	3·25	3·25
258		14 c. + 14 c. on 36 c. + 34 c.	4·00	4·00
259	**39**	20 c. + 20 c. on 50 c. + 50 c.	3·25	3·25
260		25 c. + 25 c. on 60 c. + 60 c.	5·00	5·00
261	**40**	30 c. + 30 c. on 1 l. + 1 l.	8·25	8·25

1926. Charity. War Orphans. Nos. 227/39 surch **V.P.** and new values in circular ornament.

262	**38**	1 c. + 1 c. on 2 c. + 2 c.	55	65
263		2 c. + 2 c. on 3 c. + 3 c.	55	65
264		2 c. + 2 c. on 5 c. + 5 c.	55	65
266		5 c. + 5 c. on 10 c. + 10 c.	1·40	1·40
267		10 c. + 10 c. on 15 c. + 15 c.	1·40	1·25
268		15 c. + 15 c. on 20 c. + 20 c.	1·60	1·40
270		15 c. + 15 c. on 25 c. + 25 c.	3·25	3·25
271		19 c. + 19 c. on 36 c. + 34 c.	3·25	3·25
272	**39**	25 c. + 25 c. on 50 c. + 50 c.	4·00	4·00
273		30 c. + 30 c. on 60 c. + 60 c.	6·75	6·75
274	**40**	50 c. + 50 c. on 1 l. + 1 l.	10·00	10·00

1927.

275 **56** 2 c. orange 55 10
276 3 c. brown 55 10
277 5 c. green . . . . 1·10 10
278 10 c. violet . . . . 2·00 10
279 15 c. red . . . . 1·60 10
280 25 c. blue . . . . 1·60 10
283 30 c. blue . . . . 5·25 10

1927. Dr. Basanavicius Mourning issue.

285 **57** 15 c. red . . . . 1·40 40
286 25 c. blue . . . . 1·40 40
287 50 c. green . . . . 1·40 50
288 60 c. violet . . . . 2·75 1·40

58 "Vytis" of the Lithuanian Arms

1927.

289 **58** 1 l. green and grey . . . . 1·25 65
290 3 l. violet and green . . . . 3·25 50
291 5 l. brown and grey . . . . 6·25 1·25

59 President Antanas Smetona

60 Lithuania liberated

1928. 10th Anniv of Independence.

292 **59** 5 c. green and brown . . . 15 10
293 10 c. black and violet . . . 15 10
294 15 c. brown and orange . . 15 10
295 25 c. slate and blue 50 10
296 **60** 50 c. purple and blue . . . 90 20
297 60 c. black and red . . . . 1·10 35
298 – 1 l. brown . . . . 1·40 1·00

DESIGN—HORIZ: 1 l. Lithuania's resurrection (angel and soldiers). Dated 1918-1928.

62

63

64 J. Tubelis

66 Railway Station, Kaunas

1930. 500th Death Anniv of Grand Duke Vytautas. (a) Postage.

299 **62** 2 c. brown 25 10
300 3 c. violet and brown . . . 25 10
301 5 c. red and green 25 10
302 10 c. green and violet . . . 25 10
303 15 c. violet and red 25 10
304 30 c. purple and blue . . . 50 10
305 36 c. olive and purple . . . 35 15
306 50 c. blue and green . . . 35 20
307 60 c. red and blue 60 35
308 **63** 1 l. purple, grey and green 2·00 65
309 3 l. violet, pink and mauve 2·75 1·25
310 5 l. red, grey and brown . . 5·00 1·40
311 10 l. black and blue . . . 15·00 10·00
312 25 l. green and brown . . . 32·00 48·00

(b) Air.

313 **64** 5 c. brown, yellow & black 35 35
314 10 c. black, drab and blue 40 40
315 15 c. blue, grey and purple 40 40
316 – 20 c. red, orange & brown 1·00 55
317 – 40 c. violet, lt blue and blue 1·40 80
318 – 60 c. black, lilac and green 1·60 1·40
319 – 1 l. black, lilac and red . . 3·00 1·50

DESIGNS—HORIZ: 20 c., 40 c. Vytautas and Kaunas; 60 c., 1 l. Vytautas and Smetona.

1932. Orphans' Fund. Imperf or perf.

320 **66** 5 c. blue and brown 30 30
321 10 c. purple and brown . . 30 30
322 – 15 c. brown and green . . . 30 30
323 – 25 c. blue and green . . . 45 50
324 – 50 c. grey and olive . . . . 1·00 1·60
325 – 60 c. grey and mauve . . . 1·40 5·00
326 – 1 l. blue and grey . . . . . 2·00 2·75
327 – 3 l. purple and green . . . 3·00 5·00

DESIGNS—As Type **66**: 15, 25 c. "The Two Pines" (painting); 50 c. G.P.O. VERT. 60 c., 1, 3 l. Vilnius Cathedral.

68 Map of Lithuania, Memel and Vilna

1932. Air. Orphans' Fund. Imperf or perf.

328 **68** 5 c. red and green 25 25
329 10 c. purple and brown . . 25 25
330 – 15 c. blue and buff 40 40
331 – 20 c. black and brown . . 2·40 2·00
332 – 40 c. purple and yellow . . 3·25 3·25
333 – 60 c. blue and buff . . . . 4·00 6·00
334 – 1 l. purple and green . . . 5·00 6·00
335 – 2 l. blue and green . . . . 5·00 6·75

DESIGNS: 15, 20 c. Airplane over R. Niemen; 40, 60 c. Town Hall, Kaunas; 1, 2 l. Vytautas Church, Kaunas.

69 Vytautas escapes from Prison

71 Coronation of Mindaugas

1932. 15th Anniv of Independence. Imperf or perf.

336 **69** 5 c. purple and red (postage) 50 50
337 10 c. brown and grey . . . 50 50
338 – 15 c. green and red 50 50
339 – 25 c. brown and purple . . 1·00 1·60
340 – 50 c. brown and green . . 1·40 2·40
341 – 60 c. red and green . . . . 1·60 5·00
342 – 1 l. black and blue . . . . 2·00 3·25
343 – 3 l. green and purple . . . 2·75 6·75

344 – 5 c. lilac and green (air) . 15 20
345 – 10 c. red and green 15 25
346 **71** 15 c. brown and violet . . . 20 30
347 – 20 c. black and red 45 45
348 – 40 c. black and purple . . 1·00 2·00
349 – 60 c. black and orange . . 1·40 6·00
350 – 1 l. green and violet . . . 2·10 3·25
351 – 2 l. brown and blue . . . 3·00 6·00

DESIGNS–POSTAGE. As Type **69**: 15, 25 c. Vytautas and Jagello preaching the gospel; 50, 60 c. Battle of Grunewald; 1, 3 l. Proclamation of Independence. AIR. As Type **71**: 5, 10 c. Battle of Saules; 40 c. Gediminas in Council; 60 c. Founding of Vilnius; 1 l. Russians surrendering to Gediminas; 2 l. Algirdas before Moscow.

72 A. Visteliauskas

1933. 50th Anniv of Publication of "Ausra".

352 **72** 5 c. red and green 20 25
353 10 c. red and blue 20 25
354 – 15 c. red and orange . . . 20 25
355 – 25 c. brown and blue . . . 85 1·00
356 – 50 c. blue and green . . . 1·25 1·60
357 – 60 c. deep brown & lt brn 3·00 5·00
358 – 1 l. purple and red . . . . 3·25 4·25
359 – 3 l. purple and blue . . . 5·75 6·75

PORTRAITS: 15, 25 c. P. Vileisis; 50, 60 c. J. Sliupas; 1, 3 l. J. Basanavicius.

73 Trakai Castle

1933. Air. 550th Death Anniv of Grand Duke Kestutis.

360 **73** 5 c. blue and green 20 35
361 10 c. brown and violet . . 20 35
362 – 15 c. violet and blue . . . 20 35
363 – 20 c. purple and brown . . 55 80
364 – 40 c. purple and blue . . . 1·40 1·90
365 – 60 c. blue and red . . . . 2·25 7·75
366 – 1 l. blue and green . . . . 2·75 6·75
367 – 2 l. green and violet . . . 4·00 10·00

DESIGNS: 15, 20 c. Kestutis encounters Birute; 40, 60 c. Birute; 1, 2 l. Kestutis and Algirdas.

74 Mother and Child

75 J. Tumas Vaizgantas

1933. Child Welfare. (a) Postage.

373 **74** 5 c. brown and green . . . 15 20
374 10 c. blue and red 15 20
375 – 15 c. purple and green . . . 20 25
376 – 25 c. black and orange . . 65 1·00
377 – 50 c. red and green . . . . 1·00 1·60
378 – 60 c. orange and black . . 2·40 5·00
379 – 1 l. blue and brown . . . 2·75 5·00
380 – 3 l. green and purple . . . 4·75 8·25

DESIGNS—VERT: 15, 25 c. Boy reading a book; 50, 60 c. Boy with building bricks; 1, 3 l. Mother and child weaving.

(b) Air. Various medallion portraits in triangular frames.

381 – 5 c. blue and red 15 15
382 – 10 c. green and violet . . . 15 15
383 **75** 15 c. brown and green . . . 15 15
384 20 c. blue and red 25 35
385 – 40 c. green and lake . . . . 1·40 1·60
386 – 60 c. brown and blue . . . 1·75 3·75
387 – 1 l. blue and yellow . . . . 2·40 3·75
388 – 2 l. lake and green . . . . 3·75 6·00

DESIGNS: 5, 10 c. Maironis; 40, 60 c. Vincas Kudirka; 1, 2 l. Zemaite.

76 Captains S. Darius and S. Girenas

78 "Flight" mourning over Wreckage

81 President A. Smetona

1934. Air. Death of Darius and Girenas (trans-Atlantic airmen).

389 **76** 20 c. red and black 10 10
390 – 40 c. blue and red 10 10
391 **76** 60 c. violet and black . . . 10 10
392 **78** 1 l. black and red 35 15
393 – 3 l. orange and green . . . 1·00 2·00
394 – 5 l. blue and brown . . . . 4·00 4·25

DESIGNS—HORIZ: 40 c. Bellanca monoplane "Lituanica" over Atlantic. VERT: 3 l. "Lituanica" and globe; 5 l. "Lituanica" and Vytis.

1934. President's 60th Birthday.

395 **81** 15 c. red . . . . 3·25 10
396 30 c. green . . . . 6·75 15
397 60 c. blue . . . . 13·50 70

82

83

84 Gleaner

85

1934.

398 **82** 2 c. red and orange 25 10
399 5 c. green 30 10
400 **83** 10 c. brown . . . . 1·00 10
401 **84** 25 c. brown and green . . . 2·40 10
402 **83** 35 c. red . . . . 2·40 10
403 **84** 50 c. blue . . . . 4·00 10
404 **85** 1 l. purple and red . . . . 17·00 10
405 3 l. green 20 10
406 – 5 l. purple and blue 20 20
407 – 10 l. brown and yellow . . . 1·60 1·25

DESIGNS—HORIZ: as Type **85**: 5 l., 10 l. Knight. For design as Type **82** but smaller, see Nos. 411/12.

1935. Air. Honouring Atlantic Flyer Vaitkus. No. 390 optd **F. VAITKUS nugalejo Atlanta 21-22-IX-1935.**

407a – 40 c. blue and red £300 £325

87 Vaitkus and Air Route

88 President Smetona

1936. Air. Vaitkus' New York–Ireland Flight.

408 **87** 15 c. purple . . . . 1·25 45
409 30 c. green . . . . 1·60 1·10
410 60 c. blue . . . . 2·75 1·10

1936. As T **82** but smaller (18 × 23 mm).

411 **82** 2 c. orange 10 10
412 5 c. green 10 10

1936.

413 **88** 15 c. red . . . . 4·00 10
414 30 c. green . . . . 11·50 10
415 60 c. blue . . . . 6·75 10

89

90 Archer

1937.

416 **89** 10 c. green . . . . 1·10 10
417 25 c. mauve 10 10
418 35 c. red 60 10
419 50 c. brown 30 10
419a 1 l. blue 15 30

1938. 1st National Olympiad Fund.

420 **90** 5 c. + 5 c. green . . . . . 8·25 10·00
421 – 15 c. + 5 c. red . . . . . 9·25 10·00
422 – 30 c. + 10 c. blue . . . . 13·50 13·50
423 – 60 c. + 15 c. brown . . . 20·00 20·00

DESIGNS: 15 c. Throwing the javelin; 30 c. Diving; 60 c. Relay runner breasting tape.

1938. Scouts' and Guides' National Camp Fund. Nos. 420/3 optd **TAUTINE SKAUCIU** (or **SKAUTU**) **STOVYKLA** and badge.

424 **90** 5 c. + 5 c. green . . . . . 10·00 10·00
425 – 15 c. + 5 c. red . . . . . 10·00 10·00
426 – 30 c. + 10 c. blue . . . . 10·00 13·50
427 – 60 c. + 15 c. brown . . . 20·00 22·00

92 President Smetona

93 Scoring a Goal

1939. 20th Anniv of Independence.

428 – 15 c. red 30 10
429 **92** 30 c. green 85 45
430 – 35 c. mauve . . . . 1·00 55
431 **92** 60 c. blue . . . . 1·40 85

DESIGN: 15, 35 c. Dr. Basanvicius proclaiming Lithuanian independence.

1939. 3rd European Basketball Championship and Physical Culture Fund.

432 – 15 c. + 10 c. brown . . . 6·75 6·75
433 **93** 30 c. + 15 c. green . . . . 6·75 6·75
434 – 60 c. + 40 c. violet . . . . 17·00 20·00

DESIGNS—VERT: 15 c. Scoring a goal. HORIZ: (40½ × 36 mm); 60 c. International flags and ball.

1939. Recovery of Vilnius. Nos. 428/31 optd **VILNIUS 1939-X-10** and trident.

435 – 15 c. red 55 30
436 **92** 30 c. green . . . . 1·00 40
437 – 35 c. mauve . . . . 1·10 55
438 **92** 60 c. blue . . . . 1·50 85

95 Vytis

96 Vilnius

1940. "Liberty" Issue.

439 **95** 5 c. brown 10 10
440 – 10 c. green 65 30
441 – 15 c. orange 10 10
442 – 25 c. brown 10 30
443 – 30 c. green 10 10
444 – 35 c. orange 10 45

DESIGNS: 10 c. Angel; 15 c. Woman releasing a dove; 25 c. Mother and children; 30 c. "Liberty Bell"; 35 c. Mythical animal.

1940. Recovery of Vilnius.

445 **96** 15 c. brown 30 15
446 – 30 c. green 85 25
447 – 60 c. blue . . . . 1·60 90

DESIGNS—VERT: 30 c. Portrait of Gediminas. HORIZ: 60 c. Ruins of Trakai Castle.

1940. Incorporation of Lithuania in U.S.S.R. Optd **LTSR 1940 VII 21.**

448 **82** 2 c. red and orange 15 40
449 **95** 5 c. brown 15 40
450 – 10 c. green (No. 440) . . . 4·00 5·00
451 – 15 c. orange (No. 441) . . 15 50
452 – 25 c. brown (No. 442) . . 20 75
453 – 30 c. green (No. 443) . . . 25 80
454 – 35 c. orange (No. 444) . . 60 1·50
455 **89** 50 c. brown . . . . 50 1·40

From 1940 to 1990 Lithuania used stamps of Russia.

99 Angel and Map

1990. No gum. Imperf.

456 **99** 5 k. green 10 10
457 10 k. lilac 20 20
458 20 k. blue 40 40
459 50 k. red . . . . 1·50 1·50

1990. No gum. Imperf (simulated perfs).

460 **99** 5 k. green and brown . . . 10 10
461 10 k. purple and brown . . 20 20
462 20 k. blue and brown . . . 40 40
463 50 k. red and brown . . . 1·00 1·00

100 Vytis

101 Hill of Crosses, Siauliai

1991.

464 **100** 10 k. black, gold & brown 20 20
465 15 k. black, gold & green 30 30
466 20 k. black, gold and blue 40 40
467 30 k. black, gold and red 60 60
468 40 k. black and gold . . . 20 20
469 50 k. black, gold & violet . 25 25
470 **101** 50 k. brown, chestnut & blk 1·00 1·00
471 **100** 100 k. black, gold & green 50 50
472 – 200 k. brown, chestnut & blk 3·25 3·25
473 **100** 500 k. black, gold & blue . 2·40 2·40

DESIGN: As T **101**–200 k. Lithuanian Liberty Bell.
See also Nos. 482 and 488/9.

102 Liberty Statue, Kaunas

103 Angel with Trumpet

1991. National Day.

480 **102** 20 k. mauve, silver & blk 40 40

1991. 1st Anniv of Declaration of Independence from U.S.S.R.

481 **103** 20 k. dp green & green . . 40 40

1991. No gum. Imperf (simulated perfs).

482 **100** 15 k. green 30 30

104 Wayside Crosses

1991.

483 **104** 40 k. green and silver 55 55
484 – 70 k. brown, buff & gold 95 95
485 – 100 k. brown, yell & silver 1·40 1·40

DESIGNS: 70 k. "Madonna" (icon from Pointed Gate Chapel, Vilnius); 100 k. Towers of St. Anne's Church, Vilnius.

105 Candle

1991. 50th Anniv of Resistance to Soviet and German Occupations.

486 **105** 20 k. yellow, black & bis 40 40
487 – 50 k. rose, black and red 1·00 1·00
488 – 70 k. multicoloured . . . 1·10 1·10

DESIGNS: 50 k. Shield pierced by swords; 70 k. Sword and wreath.

1991. No gum. Imperf.

489 **100** 25 k. black and brown . . 50 50
490 30 k. black and purple . . 60 60

106 World Map and Games Emblem

107 Lithuanian Flag on Ice-axe and Mt. Everest

1941. 4th International Lithuanians' Games.

491 **106** 20 k. green, black & yell 40 40
492 – 50 k. green, black & yell 1·40 1·40

DESIGN: 50 k. Symbolic female athlete.

1991. Lithuanian Expedition to Mt. Everest.

493 **107** 20 k. multicoloured . . . 40 40
494 70 k. multicoloured . . . 1·75 1·75

108 Trakai Castle

109 Black Storks

1991. 650th Death Anniv of Grand Duke Gediminas. Each brown, ochre and green.

495 30 k. Type **108** 60 60
496 50 k. Gediminas 75 75
497 70 k. Vilnius in 14th century 1·10 1·10

1991. Birds in the Red Book. Multicoloured.

498 30 k. + 15 k. Type **109** . . . 90 90
499 50 k. Common cranes . . . . 1·00 1·00

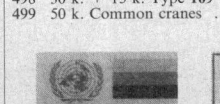

110 U.N. and National Emblems and National Flag

111 National Team Emblem and Colours

1992. Admission to U.N.O.

500 **110** 100 k. multicoloured . . 50 50

1992. Winter Olympic Games, Albertville, and Summer Games, Barcelona. Multicoloured.

501 50 k. + 25 k. Type **111** . . . 35 35
502 130 k. Winter Games emblem 60 60
503 280 k. Summer Games emblem 1·10 1·10

112 Slipper Orchid

113 Goosander ("Mergus merganser")

1992. Plants in the Red Book. Multicoloured.

504 200 k. Type **112** 65 65
505 300 k. Sea holly . . . . . . 1·00 1·00

1992. Birds of the Baltic. No value expressed.

506 **113** B (15 t.) black and green 20 20
507 – B (15 t.) brown, blk & grn 20 20
508 – B (15 t.) sepia, brn & grn 20 20
509 – B (15 t.) brown, blk & grn 20 20

DESIGNS: No. 506, Osprey ("Pandion haliaetus"); 507, Black-tailed godwit ("Limosa limosa"); 509, Common shelduck ("Tadorna tadorna").

114 Kedainiai

115 Couple

1992. Arms. Multicoloured.

510 2 t. Type **114** 15 15
511 3 t. Vilnius 20 20
512 10 t. State arms 65 65

See also Nos. 531/3 and 569/71.

1992. Costumes of Suvalkija.

513 **115** 2 t. multicoloured 15 15
514 – 5 t. multicoloured 30 30
515 – 7 t. multicoloured 45 45

DESIGNS: 5, 7 t. Different costumes.

116 Zapyskis Church

1993. Churches.

516 **116** 3 t. black and stone . . . 15 15
517 – 10 t. black and blue . . . 55 55
518 – 15 t. black and grey . . . 85 85

DESIGNS: 10 t. Church of St. Peter and St. Paul, Vilnius; 15 t. Church of the Resurrection, Kaunas.

1993. Nos. 467, 490 and 468 surch.

519 **100** 1 t. on 30 k. blk, gold & red 10 10
520 1 t. on 30 k. black & pur 10 10
521 3 t. on 40 k. black & gold 35 35

118 Jonas Basanavicius (statesman)

1993. National Day. No value expressed.

522 **118** A (3 t.) red, cinnamon and brown 15 15
523 – B (15 t.) green, stone and brown 85 85

DESIGN: No. 523, Jonas Vileisis (politician).

119 Vytautas

120 Simonas Daukantas (historian)

1993. 600th Anniv (1987) of Accession of Grand Duke Vytautas.

524 – 5 t. gold, red and black . . 25 25
525 **119** 10 t. green, black and red 55 55
526 – 15 t. black, yellow & red 80 80

DESIGNS: 5 t. Seal; 15 t. "Battle of Grunwald" (Jan Matejka).

1993. Birth Anniversaries. Each brown and yellow.

528 1000 t. Type **120** (bicent) . . . 50 50
529 2000 t. Vydunas (125th anniv) 1·25 1·25
530 4500 t. Vincas Mykolaitis-Putinas (philosopher, centenary) . . . . 2·75 2·75

1993. Town Arms. As T **114**. Multicoloured.

531 5 c. Skuodas 10 10
532 30 c. Telsiai 10 10
533 50 c. Klaipeda 20 20

121 "Watchtower" (M. K. Ciurlionis)

122 State Arms

1993. World Unity Day (5 t.) and Transatlantic Flight (80 t.). Multicoloured.

534 5 c. Type **121** 10 10
535 80 c. Steponas Dariaus and Stasys Gireno 30 30

1993. No value expressed.

536 **122** A, green, brown and red 10 10
537 B, red, green and bistre 30 30

123 Pope John Paul II and View of Siluva

124 Couple

1993. Papal Visit. Multicoloured.

538 60 c. Type **123** 20 20
539 60 c. Pope and Hill of Crosses 20 20
540 80 c. Pope and Kaunas . . . 30 30
541 80 c. Pope and Ausra Gates, Vilnius 30 30

1993. Costumes of Dzukai.

542 **124** 60 c. multicoloured . . . 20 20
543 – 80 c. multicoloured . . . 30 30
544 – 1 l. multicoloured 35 35

DESIGNS: 80 c. to 1 l. Different costumes.

125 Klaipeda Post Office

1993. 75th Anniv of First Lithuanian Postage Stamps.

545 **125** 60 c. multicoloured . . . 20 20
546 – 60 c. multicoloured . . . 20 20
547 – 80 c. multicoloured . . . 25 25
548 – 1 l. black, brown and green 30 30

DESIGNS: No. 546, Kaunas post office; 547, Ministry for Post and Information, Vilnius; 548, First Lithuanian stamp.

126 "The Ladle Carver" (A. Gudaitis)

127 European Pond Turtle

1993. Europa. Contemporary Art.

549 **126** 80 c. multicoloured . . . 25 25

1993. Pond Life. Multicoloured.

550 80 c. Type **127** 25 25
551 1 l. Running toad 30 30

128 Games Emblem and Team Colours

130 Kristijonas Donelaitis

129 Antanas Smetona (President 1919–22 and 1926–40)

1994. Winter Olympic Games, Lillehammer, Norway.

552 **128** 1 l. 10 multicoloured . . 35 35

1994. National Day.

553 **129** 1 l. red and black 30 30
554 – 1 l. brown and black . . . 30 30

DESIGN: No. 554, Aleksandras Stulginskis (President 1922–26).

1994. Writers. Each cream, brown and orange.

555 60 c. Type **130** 20 20
556 80 c. Vincas Kudirka 25 25
557 1 l. Jonas Maciulis Maironis . 30 30

131 State Arms

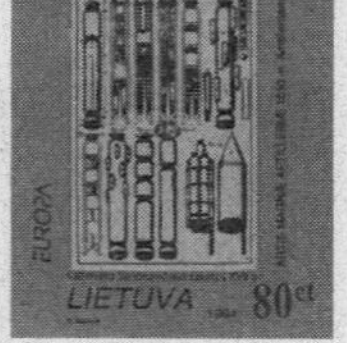
132 Rockets by Kazimieras Simonavicius (illus from "Artis Magnae Artilleriae")

1994.
558 **131** 5 c. brown 10 10
559 10 c. lilac 10 10
560 20 c. green 10 10

1994. Europa. Inventions and Discoveries.
561 **132** 80 c. multicoloured . . . 25 25

133 Couple

134 Music Note, Globe and Flag

1994. 19th-century Costumes of Zemaiciai (Lowlands).
563 **133** 5 c. multicoloured 10 10
564 – 80 c. multicoloured . . . 25 25
565 – 1 l. multicoloured 30 30
DESIGNS: 80 c., 1 l., Different costumes from Zemaiciai.

1994. Lithuanians of the World Song Festival.
566 **134** 10 c. multicoloured . . . 10 10

135 State Arms

136 Common Bat

1994.
567 **135** 2 l. multicoloured 65 65
568 3 l. multicoloured 95 95

1994. Town Arms. As T **114** but size 25 × 32 mm. Multicoloured.
569 10 c. Punia 10 10
570 60 c. Alytus 20 20
571 80 c. Perloja 25 25

1994. Mammals. Multicoloured.
572 20 c. Type **136** 10 10
573 20 c. Fat dormouse 10 10

137 Kaunas Town Hall

138 Madonna and Child

1994. Town Halls.
574 **137** 10 c. black and mauve . . 10 10
575 – 60 c. black and blue . . . 20 20
576 – 80 c. black and green . . 25 25
DESIGNS: 60 c. Kedainiai; 80 c. Vilnius.

1994. Christmas.
577 **138** 20 c. multicoloured . . . 10 10

LOMBARDY AND VENETIA Pt. 2

Formerly known as Austrian Italy. Although these provinces used a different currency the following issues were valid throughout Austria. Lombardy was annexed by Sardinia in 1859 and Venetia by Italy in 1866.

1850. 100 centesimi = 1 lira
1858. 100 soldi = 1 florin
100 kreuzer = 1 gulden

1 Arms of Austria

1850. Imperf.
1c **1** 5 c. orange . . . . £950 55·00
2c 10 c. black . . . . £1000 42·00
7 15 c. red £325 75
4 30 c. brown . . . . £1300 3·50
5e 45 c. blue . . . . £4250 8·50

1859. As T **4** and **5** of Austria (Emperor Francis Joseph I) but value in soldi. Perf.
16 **5** 2 s. yellow . . . . £275 50·00
17 **4** 3 s. black £900 £150
18 3 s. green . . . . £225 50·00
19 **5** 5 s. red . . . . £120 2·25
20 10 s. brown . . . . £180 23·00
21 15 s. blue . . . . £1100 40·00

3 Emperor Francis Joseph I

4 Arms of Austria

1861.
25 **3** 5 s. red . . . . £900 1·40
26 10 s. brown . . . . £900 13·00

1863.
27 **4** 2 s. yellow . . . . 55·00 £110
33 3 s. green . . . . 12·00 9·00
34 5 s. red . . . . 1·75 1·00
35 10 s. blue . . . . 11·00 3·00
36 15 s. brown . . . . 55·00 38·00

JOURNAL STAMPS

J 5

1858. Imperf.
J22 **J 5** 1 k. black £1100 £3000
J23 2 k. red . . . . £130 40·00
J24 4 k. red £25000 £3000

LOURENCO MARQUES Pt. 9

A Portuguese colony in E. Africa, now part of Mozambique, whose stamps it uses.

1895. 1000 reis = 1 milreis
1913. 100 centavos = 1 escudo

1895. "Figures" key-type Inscr "LOURENCO MARQUES".
1 R 5 r. yellow 20 15
2 10 r. mauve 25 15
3 15 r. brown 40 35
4 20 r. lilac 40 35
10 25 r. green 30 15
12 50 r. blue 35 15
18 75 r. red 80 40
14 80 r. green . . . . 1·25 90
7 100 r. brown on yellow . . . 85 50
16 150 r. red on rose 90 75
8 200 r. blue on blue . . . . 1·50 1·00
9 300 r. blue on brown . . . 1·50 1·00

1895. 700th Death Anniv of St. Anthony. Optd **L. MARQUES CENTENARIO DE S. ANTONIO MDCCCXCV** on (a) "Embossed" key-type inscr "PROVINCIA DE MOCAMBIQUE".
19 Q 5 r. black . . . . 5·00 4·50
20 10 r. green . . . . 7·50 5·00
21 20 r. red . . . . 9·00 6·00
22 25 r. purple . . . . 11·00 8·00
23 40 r. brown . . . . 9·00 7·50
27a 50 r. blue . . . . 6·00 5·00
25 100 r. brown . . . . 17·00 12·00
26 200 r. violet . . . . 13·00 12·00
27 300 r. orange . . . . 20·00 17·00

(b) "Figures" key-type inscr "MOCAMBIQUE"
28 R 5 r. orange . . . . 5·00 4·00
29 10 r. mauve . . . . 9·00 7·50
30 50 r. blue . . . . 14·00 8·00
35 75 r. red . . . . 15·00 10·00
32 80 r. green . . . . 25·00 18·00
33 100 r. brown on yellow . . 27·00 25·00
35a 150 r. red on rose . . . . 17·00 14·00

1897. No. 9 surch **50** reis.
36 **R** 50 r. on 300 r. blue on brown 50·00 42·00

1898. "King Carlos" key-type inscr "LOURENCO MARQUES".
37 S 2½ r. grey 15 15
38 5 r. orange 15 15
39 10 r. green 15 15
40 15 r. brown 15 15
83 15 r. green 25 20
41 20 r. lilac 30 15
42 25 r. green 35 15
84 25 r. red 20 15
43 50 r. blue 50 15
85 50 r. brown 45 30
86 65 r. blue . . . . 2·00 1·75
44 75 r. red 80 65
87 75 r. purple 60 50
45 80 r. mauve 70 55
46 100 r. blue on blue 50 25
88 115 r. brown on pink . . . 2·10 2·00
89 130 r. brown on yellow . . 2·25 2·00
47 150 r. brown on yellow . . 90 80
48 200 r. purple on pink . . . 1·60 70
49 300 r. blue on pink . . . . 1·00 75
90 400 r. blue on yellow . . . 2·25 2·00
50 500 r. black on blue . . . 1·25 1·25
51 700 r. mauve on yellow . . . 3·50 2·50

1899. Green and brown fiscal stamps of Mozambique, as T **9** of Macao, bisected and each half surch **Correio de Lourenco Marques** and value. Imperf.
55 – 5 r. on half of 10 r. 60 30
56 – 25 r. on half of 10 r. . . . 60 30
57 – 50 r. on half of 30 r. . . . 60 30
58 – 50 r. on half of 800 r. . . . 90 50

1899. Nos. 44 and 86 surch **50 Reis**.
91 S 50 r. on 65 r. blue . . . . . 1·00 1·00
59 50 r. on 75 r. red . . . . . 1·25 1·00

1902. "Figures" and "Newspaper" key-types surch.
60 V 65 r. on 2½ r. brown . . . . 1·10 1·00
62 R 65 r. on 5 r. yellow . . . . 1·10 1·00
63 65 r. on 15 r. brown . . . . 1·10 1·00
64 65 r. on 20 r. lilac . . . . . 1·10 1·00
66 115 r. on 10 r. mauve . . . 1·10 1·00
67 115 r. on 200 r. blue on bl . . 1·10 1·00
68 115 r. on 300 r. bl on brn . . 1·10 1·00
70 130 r. on 25 r. green . . . . 1·10 1·00
72 130 r. on 80 r. green 85 75
73 130 r. on 150 r. red on rose . 85 75
74 400 r. on 50 r. blue . . . . 3·00 1·75
76 400 r. on 75 r. red . . . . 2·50 2·00
78 400 r. on 100 r. brown on yellow . . . . 1·75 1·25

1902. "King Carlos" key-type inscr "LOURENCO MARQUES" optd **PROVISORIO**.
79 S 15 r. brown 70 50
80 25 r. green 60 35
81 50 r. blue 80 55
82 75 r. red . . . . 1·25 70

1911. "King Carlos" key-type inscr "LOURENCO MARQUES" optd **REPUBLICA**.
92 S 2½ r. grey 10 10
93 5 r. orange 10 10
94 10 r. green 20 15
95 15 r. green 20 15
96 20 r. lilac 35 20
97 25 r. red 20 15
98 50 r. brown 35 25
99 75 r. purple 35 25
100 100 r. blue on blue 35 25
178 115 r. brown on pink . . . 35 35
102 130 r. brown on yellow . . . 30 30
103 200 r. purple on pink . . . 30 30
104 400 r. blue on yellow . . . 60 35
105 500 r. black on blue 70 60
106 700 r. mauve on yellow . . . 75 60

1913. Surch **REPUBLICA LOURENCO MARQUES** and value on "Vasco da Gama" issues of (a) **Portuguese Colonies**.
107 ¼ c. on 2½ r. green 50 45
108 ½ c. on 5 r. red 50 45
109 1 c. on 10 r. purple 35 35
110 2½ c. on 25 r. green 35 35
111 5 c. on 50 r. blue 50 45
112 7½ c. on 75 r. brown 85 75
113 10 c. on 100 r. brown . . . 65 45
114 15 c. on 150 r. bistre 40 40

(b) **Macao**.
115 ¼ c. on ½ a. green 60 45
116 ½ c. on 1 a. red 60 45
117 1 c. on 2 a. purple 40 45
118 2½ c. on 4 a. green 40 45
119 5 c. on 8 a. blue 60 45
120 7½ c. on 12 a. brown . . . . 1·00 85
121 10 c. on 16 a. brown 75 45
122 15 c. on 24 a. bistre 75 45

(c) **Timor**.
123 ¼ c. on ½ a. green 60 45
124 ½ c. on 1 a. red 60 45
125 1 c. on 2 a. purple 40 45
126 2½ c. on 4 a. green 40 45
127 5 c. on 8 a. blue 60 45
128 7½ c. on 12 a. brown . . . . 1·00 85
129 10 c. on 16 a. brown 75 45
130 15 c. on 24 a. bistre 75 45

1914. "Ceres" key-type inscr "LOURENCO MARQUES".
147 U ¼ c. olive 10 10
148 ½ c. black 10 10
149 1 c. green 10 10
150 1½ c. brown 15 15
151 2 c. red 15 15
152 2½ c. violet 15 15
153 5 c. blue 20 20
154 7½ c. brown 20 20
155 8 c. grey 20 20
140 10 c. brown 70 30
157 15 c. red 40 40
142 U 20 c. green 50 40
143 30 c. brown on green . . . 50 40
144 40 c. brown on red . . . 2·75 1·75
145 50 c. orange on pink . . . 90 80
146 1 e. green on blue . . . . 1·00 80

1914. Provisionals of 1902 overprinted **REPUBLICA**.
166 R 115 r. on 10 r. mauve . . 30 30
167 115 r. on 200 r. bl on bl . . 35 30
168 115 r. on 300 r. blue on brown 30 30
161 130 r. on 25 r. green . . . 50 40
164 130 r. on 80 r. green . . . 35 30
169 130 r. on 150 r. red on rose 30 30
184 400 r. on 50 r. blue . . . 60 45
185 400 r. on 75 r. red 75 20

1915. Nos. 93 and 148 perf. diagonally and each half surch ½.
170 S ½ on half of 5 r. orange . . 1·00 90
171 U ¼ on half of ½ c. black . . 1·00 90
Prices of Nos. 170/1 are for whole stamps.

1915. Surch **Dois centavos**.
172 S 2 c. on 15 r. (No. 83) . . . 40 35
173 2 c. on 15 c. (No. 95) . . . 40 35

1918. Red Cross Fund. "Ceres" key-type inscr "LOURENCO MARQUES", optd **9-3-18** and Red Cross or surch with value in figures and bars also.
188 U ¼ c. olive 50 50
189 ½ c. black 50 50
190 1 c. green 50 50
191 2½ c. violet 50 50
192 5 c. blue 50 50
193 10 c. red . . . . 1·00 90
194 20 c. on 1½ c. brown . . . 1·00 90
195 30 c. brown on green . . . 1·00 90
196 40 c. on 2 c. red . . . . . 1·00 90
197 50 c. on 7½ c. brown . . . 1·00 90
198 70 c. on 8 c. grey . . . . 1·00 90
199 1 e. on 15 c. red . . . . . 1·00 90

1920. No. 166 surch **Um quarto de centavo**.
200 R ¼ c. on 115 r. on 10 r. mauve 25 20

1920. No. 152 surch in figures or words.
201 U 1 c. on 2½ c. violet 20 15
202 1½ c. on 2½ c. violet . . . 20 15
203 4 c. on 2½ c. violet 20 15
For other surcharges on "Ceres" key-type of Lourenco Marques, see Mozambique Nos. 309/10 and Nos. D44 and 46.

NEWSPAPER STAMPS

1893. "Newspaper" key-type inscr "LOURENCO MARQUES".
N1 V 2½ r. brown 15 15

1895. 700th Death Anniv of St. Anthony. "Newspaper" key-type inscr "MOCAMBIQUE" optd. **L. MARQUES CENTENARIO DE S. ANTONIO MDCCCXCV**.
N36 V 2½ r. brown . . . . 2·50 2·00

LUBECK Pt. 7

Formerly one of the free cities of the Hanseatic League. In 1868 joined the North German Confederation.

16 schillinge = 1 mark

1

3

1859. Imperf.
9 **1** ½ s. lilac . . . . 14·50 £1300
10 1 s. orange . . . . 26·00 £1300
3 2 s. brown . . . . 16·00 £200
4 2½ s. red . . . . 40·00 £600
6 4 s. green . . . . 16·00 £325

1863. Rouletted.
11 **3** ½ s. green . . . . 38·00 65·00
13 1 s. orange £110 £120
14 2 s. red . . . . 20·00 50·00
16 2½ s. blue . . . . 45·00 £325
17 4 s. bistre . . . . 35·00 95·00

4

5

1864. Imperf.
19 **4** 1¼ s. brown . . . . 21·00 48·00

1865. Roul.
21 **5** 1½ s. mauve . . . . 20·00 75·00

LUXEMBOURG Pt. 4

An independent Grand Duchy lying between Belgium and the Saar District. Under German Occupation from 1940 to 1944.

1852. 12½ centimes = 1 silver groschen
100 centimes = 1 franc
1940. 100 pfennig = 1 reichsmark
1944. 100 centimes = 1 franc (Belgian)

1 Grand Duke William III 3 4

1852. Imperf.

2	**1**	10 c. black	£2000	35·00
3a		1 s. red	£1300	60·00

1859. Imperf or roul.

23	**3**	1 c. brown	32·00	3·50
21		1 c. orange	30·00	5·50
17		2 c. black	12·00	9·00
8		4 c. yellow	£180	£160
20		4 c. green	32·00	19·00
10	**4**	10 c. blue	£190	11·00
24		10 c. purple	£100	1·40
25		10 c. lilac	£110	1·40
28		12½ c. red	£170	4·50
30		20 c. brown	£110	6·00
12		25 c. brown	£375	£250
32		25 c. blue	£850	8·50
13		30 c. purple	£300	£180
14		37½ c. green	£300	£170
35		37½ c. bistre	£300	£275
39		40 c. orange	32·00	80·00

1872. Surch **UN FRANC**. Roul.

37	**4**	1 f. on 37½ c. bistre	£1000	70·00

1874. Perf.

64	**3**	1 c. brown	7·00	5·50
65		2 c. black	6·00	1·00
42		4 c. green	1·00	8·00
43		5 c. yellow	£170	15·00
67	**4**	10 c. lilac	£160	70
61		12½ c. red	£180	£160
69		20 c. brown	40·00	13·00
70		25 c. blue	£250	2·75
71		30 c. red	2·50	19·00
55		40 c. orange	75	8·00

1879. Surch **Un Franc**. Perf.

56	**4**	1 f. on 37½ c. bistre	6·00	20·00

7 Agriculture and Trade 8 Grand Duke Adolf 9

1882.

116	**7**	1 c. grey	15	25
117		2 c. brown	10	20
118		4 c. bistre	35	1·00
119		5 c. green	50	20
120		10 c. red	6·00	20
98		12½ c. blue	1·00	18·00
122		20 c. orange	3·00	1·50
123		25 c. blue	£150	1·00
101		30 c. green	17·00	12·00
124		50 c. brown	65	6·00
103		1 f. lilac	70	20·00
104		5 f. orange	27·00	£120

1891.

127	**8**	10 c. red	15	25
145		12½ c. green	50	50
146		20 c. orange	8·00	50
147		25 c. blue	40	30
148		30 c. green	1·00	1·00
149		37½ c. green	2·00	3·00
150		50 c. brown	6·00	3·50
151		1 f. purple	18·00	5·00
135		2½ f. black	1·00	15·00
136		5 f. lake	30·00	45·00

1895.

152	**9**	1 c. grey	1·00	30
153		2 c. brown	10	20
154		4 c. bistre	15	70
155		5 c. green	1·25	20
156		10 c. red	5·00	20

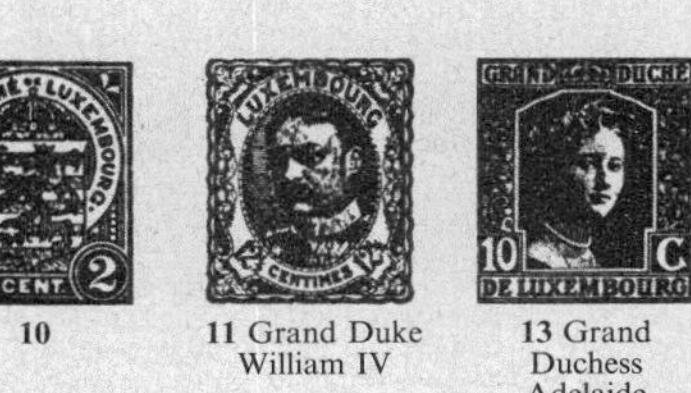

10 11 Grand Duke William IV 13 Grand Duchess Adelaide

1906.

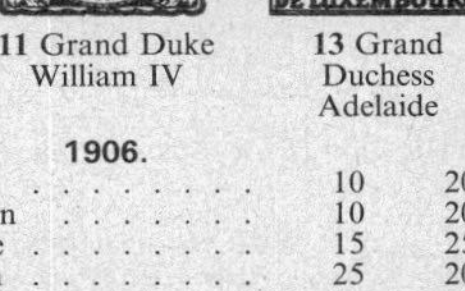

157	**10**	1 c. grey	10	20
158		2 c. brown	10	20
159		4 c. bistre	15	25
160		5 c. green	25	20
231		5 c. mauve	15	20
161		6 c. lilac	10	30
161a		7½ c. orange	10	2·50
162	**11**	10 c. red	80	20
163		12½ slate	1·00	40
164		15 c. brown	1·00	60
165		20 c. orange	1·50	50
166		25 c. blue	38·00	30
166a		30 c. olive	55	50
167		37½ c. green	55	50
168		50 c. brown	1·75	60
169		87½ c. blue	1·25	8·00
170		1 f. purple	3·00	1·00
171		2½ f. red	40·00	80·00
172		5 f. purple	7·00	40·00

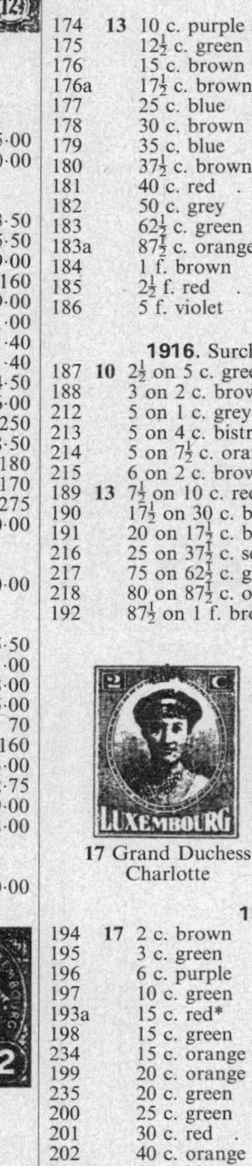

1912. Surch **62½ cts.**

173	**11**	62½ c. on 87½ c. blue	1·00	2·00
173a		62½ c. on 2½ f. red	1·00	3·50
173b		62½ c. on 5 f. purple	40	1·50

1914.

174	**13**	10 c. purple	10	20
175		12½ c. green	10	20
176		15 c. brown	10	20
176a		17½ c. brown	10	40
177		25 c. blue	10	20
178		30 c. brown	10	40
179		35 c. blue	10	40
180		37½ c. brown	10	40
181		40 c. red	20	40
182		50 c. grey	20	40
183		62½ c. green	30	2·25
183a		87½ c. orange	30	2·25
184		1 f. brown	80	25
185		2½ f. red	40	2·50
186		5 f. violet	7·00	35·00

1916. Surch in figures and bars.

187	**10**	2½ on 5 c. green	10	20
188		3 on 2 c. brown	10	20
212		5 on 1 c. grey	10	20
213		5 on 4 c. bistre	10	40
214		5 on 7½ c. orange	10	20
215		6 on 2 c. brown	20	25
189	**13**	7½ on 10 c. red	10	20
190		17½ on 30 c. brown	10	40
191		20 on 17½ c. brown	10	20
216		25 on 37½ c. sepia	10	20
217		75 on 62½ c. green	10	20
218		80 on 87½ c. orange	10	20
192		87½ on 1 f. brown	50	5·50

17 Grand Duchess Charlotte 18 Vianden Castle

1921. Perf.

194	**17**	2 c. brown	10	20
195		3 c. green	10	20
196		6 c. purple	10	20
197		10 c. green	10	20
193a		15 c. red*	10	20
198		15 c. green	10	20
234		15 c. orange	10	20
199		20 c. orange	10	30
235		20 c. green	10	20
200		25 c. green	10	20
201		30 c. red	10	20
202		40 c. orange	10	20
203		50 c. blue	10	40
236		50 c. red	10	20
204		75 c. red	10	1·10
237		75 c. blue	10	20
205		80 c. black	10	85
206a	**18**	1 f. red	10	30
238		1 f. blue	10	50
207	–	2 f. blue	50	50
239	–	2 f. brown	1·10	1·50
208	–	5 f. violet	15·00	6·00

DESIGNS—As Type **18**: 2 f. Factories at Esch; 5 f. Bridge over Alzette.

*No. 193a was originally issued on the occasion of the birth of Crown Prince Jean.

See also Nos. 219/20.

21 Monastery at Clervaux

1921. War Monument Fund.

209	**21**	10 c. + 5 c. green	15	3·00
210	–	15 c. + 10 c. orange	15	5·00
211	–	25 c. + 10 c. green	15	3·00

DESIGNS—HORIZ: 15 c. Pfaffenthal; 25 c. as Type **26**.

1922. Philatelic Exhibition. Imperf.

219	**17**	25 c. green	1·40	5·00
220		30 c. red	1·40	5·00

26 Luxembourg

28 Echternach

1923.

222a	**26**	10 f. black	2·75	8·00

1923. Unveiling of War Memorial by Prince Leopold of Belgium. Nos. 209/11 surch **27 mai 1923** and additional values.

223	**21**	10 + 5 + 25 c. green	1·00	13·00
224	–	15 + 10 + 25 c. orange	1·00	20·00
225	–	25 + 10 + 25 c. green	1·00	13·00

1923.

226a	**28**	3 f. blue	60	50

1924. Charity. Death of Grand Duchess Marie Adelaide. Surch **CARITAS** and new value.

227	**13**	12½ c. + 7½ c. green	10	1·50
228		35 c. + 10 c. blue	10	1·50
229		2½ f. + 1 f. red	35	20·00
230		5 f. + 2 f. violet	35	15·00

1925. Surch **5**.

240	**17**	5 on 10 c. green	10	20

31 32 Grand Duchess Charlotte

1925. Anti-T.B. Fund.

241	**31**	5 c. + 5 c. violet	10	60
242		30 c. + 5 c. orange	10	2·00
243		50 c. + 5 c. brown	10	4·00
244		1 f. + 10 c. blue	25	12·00

1926.

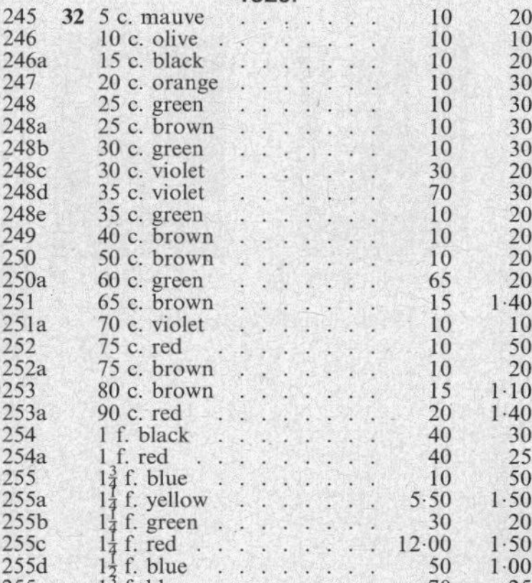

245	**32**	5 c. mauve	10	20
246		10 c. olive	10	10
246a		15 c. black	10	20
247		20 c. orange	10	30
248		25 c. green	10	30
248a		25 c. brown	10	30
248b		30 c. green	10	30
248c		30 c. violet	30	20
248d		35 c. violet	70	30
248e		35 c. green	10	20
249		40 c. brown	10	20
250		50 c. brown	10	20
250a		60 c. green	65	20
251		65 c. brown	15	1·40
251a		70 c. violet	10	10
252		75 c. red	10	50
252a		75 c. brown	10	20
253		80 c. brown	15	1·10
253a		90 c. red	20	1·40
254		1 f. black	40	30
254a		1 f. red	40	25
255		1¾ f. blue	10	50
255a		1¼ f. yellow	5·50	1·50
255b		1¼ f. green	30	20
255c		1¼ f. red	12·00	1·50
255d		1½ f. blue	50	1·00
255e		1¾ f. blue	70	25

33 Prince Jean

34 Grand Duchess and Prince Felix

1926. Child Welfare.

256	**33**	5 c. + 5 c. black and mauve	10	50
257		40 c. + 10 c. black & green	10	1·00
258		50 c. + 15 c. black & yellow	10	1·00
259		75 c. + 20 c. black & red	20	10·00
260		1 f. 50 c. + 30 c. blk and bl	20	10·00

1927. International Philatelic Exhibition.

261	**34**	25 c. purple	1·00	10·00
262		50 c. green	1·50	12·00
263		75 c. red	1·00	10·00
264		1 f. black	1·00	10·00
265		1½ f. blue	1·00	10·00

35 Princess Elisabeth 36 Clervaux

1927. Child Welfare.

266	**35**	10 c. + 5 c. black and blue	10	50
267		50 c. + 10 black & brown	10	1·00
268		75 c. + 20 c. black & orge	10	1·25
269		1 f. + 30 c. black and red	20	10·00
270		1½ f. + 50 c. black & blue	20	10·00

1927. Stamps of 1921 and 1926 surch.

270a	**32**	10 on 30 c. green	30	40
271	**17**	15 on 20 c. green	10	20
272	**32**	15 on 25 c. green	20	60
273	**17**	35 on 40 c. orange	10	20
274	**32**	60 on 65 c. brown	10	40
275	**17**	60 on 75 c. blue	10	20
276	**32**	60 on 75 c. red	10	40
277	**17**	60 on 80 c. black	20	40
278	**32**	60 on 80 c. brown	15	50
278a		70 on 75 c. brown	3·50	30
278b		75 on 90 c. red	1·00	40
278c		1¾ on 1½ f. blue	2·25	1·50

1928. Perf.

279a	**37**	2 f. black	75	60

See also No. 339.

38 Princess Marie Adelaide 39 Princess Marie Gabrielle

1928. Child Welfare.

280	**38**	10 c. + 5 c. purple & green	20	1·00
281		60 c. + 10 c. olive & brown	30	3·50
282		75 c. + 15 c. green and red	50	5·00
283		1 f. + 25 c. brown & green	1·00	16·00
284		1½ f. + 50 c. blue & yellow	1·00	16·00

1928. Child Welfare.

285	**39**	10 c. + 10 c. green & brn	20	50
286		35 c. + 15 c. brown & grn	70	5·00
287		75 c. + 30 c. black and red	70	7·00
288		1¼ f. + 50 c. green and red	2·00	20·00
289		1¾ f. + 75 c. black & blue	2·00	25·00

40 Prince Charles 41 Arms of Luxembourg

1930. Child Welfare.

290	**40**	10 c. + 5 c. brown & green	20	70
291		75 c. + 10 c. green & brn	1·25	4·00
292		1 f. + 25 c. violet and red	2·50	12·00
293		1¼ f. + 75 c. black & yell	4·00	20·00
294		1¾ f. + 1 f. 50 brown & bl	4·50	20·00

1930.

295	**41**	5 c. red	50	30
296		10 c. green	60	20

42 Biplane over the Alzette 43 Luxembourg, Lower Town

1931. Air.

296a	**42**	50 c. green	55	1·00
297		75 c. brown	50	1·00
298		1 f. red	50	1·25
299		1¼ f. purple	50	1·50
300		1¾ f. blue	50	1·50
300a		3 f. black	1·00	4·50

1931.

301	**43**	20 f. green	2·75	15·00

44 Princess Alix 45 Countess Ermesinde 46 Emperor Henry VII

1931. Child Welfare.

302	**44**	10 c. + 5 c. grey & brown	20	1·00
303		75 c. + 10 c. green and red	3·00	12·00
304		1 f. + 25 c. grey and green	5·00	25·00
305		1¼ f. + 75 c. green & violet	5·00	25·00
306		1¾ f. + 1 f. 50 grey & blue	10·00	50·00

1932. Child Welfare.

307	**45**	10 c. + 5 c. brown	30	80
308		75 c. + 10 c. violet	2·00	12·00
309		1 f. + 25 c. red	8·00	35·00
310		1¼ f. + 75 c. lake	8·00	35·00
311		1¾ f. + 1 f. 50 blue	8·00	35·00

1933. Child Welfare.

312	**46**	10 c. + 5 c. brown	30	80
313		75 c. + 10 c. purple	3·00	15·00
314		1 f. + 25 c. red	10·00	35·00
315		1¼ f. + 75 c. brown	12·00	45·00
316		1¾ f. + 1 f. 50 blue	12·00	55·00

INDEX

Countries can be quickly located by referring to the index at the end of this volume.

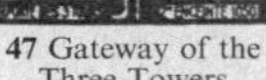

47 Gateway of the Three Towers — 48 Arms of John the Blind

1934.
317 47 5 f. green 1·00 6·00

1934. Child Welfare.
318 48 10 c. + 5 c. violet 10 70
319 35 c. + 10 c. green 2·50 10·00
320 75 c. + 15 c. red 2·50 10·00
321 1 f. + 25 c. red 13·00 50·00
322 1¼ f. + 75 c. orange 15·00 55·00
323 1¾ f. + 1½ f. blue 14·00 55·00

50 Surgeon

1935. International Relief Fund for Intellectuals.
324 – 5 c. violet 15 1·40
325 – 10 c. red 30 1·40
326 – 15 c. olive 30 2·00
327 – 20 c. orange 45 2·50
328 – 35 c. green 80 3·50
329 – 50 c. black 90 5·00
330 – 70 c. green 2·50 6·00
331 50 1 f. red 2·00 7·00
332 – 1 f. 25 turquoise 8·00 55·00
333 – 1 f. 75 blue 10·00 55·00
334 – 2 f. brown 32·00 £120
335 – 3 f. brown 45·00 £160
336 – 5 f. blue 70·00 £300
337 – 10 f. purple £180 £500
338 50 20 f. green £200 £600
DESIGNS — HORIZ: 5 c., 10 f. Schoolteacher; 15 c., 3 f. Journalist; 20 c. 1 f. 75, Engineer; 35 c., 1 f. 25, Chemist. VERT: 10 c., 2 f. "The Arts"; 50 c., 5 f. Barrister; 70 c. University.
This set was sold at the P.O. at double face value.

1935. Esch Philatelic Exhibition. Imperf.
339 37 2 f. (+ 50 c.) black 4·25 13·00

52 Vianden — 53 Charles I

1935.
340 52 10 f. green 1·40 10·00

1935. Child Welfare.
341 53 10 c. + 5 c. violet 10 40
342 35 c. + 10 c. green 30 60
343 70 c. + 20 c. brown 70 1·50
344 1 f. + 25 c. red 12·00 40·00
345 1 f. 25 + 75 c. brown 12·00 40·00
346 1 f. 75 + 1 f. 50 blue 12·00 50·00

54 Town Hall — 55 Wenceslas I — 56 Wenceslas II

1936. 11th Int Philatelic Federation Congress.
347 54 10 c. brown 20 50
348 35 c. green 30 1·00
349 70 c. orange 35 1·50
350 1 f. red 1·00 9·00
351 1 f. 25 violet 1·60 12·00
352 1 f. 75 blue 1·00 10·00

1936. Child Welfare.
353 55 10 c. + 5 c. brown 10 30
354 35 c. + 10 c. green 20 60
355 70 c. + 20 c. slate 40 80
356 1 f. + 25 c. red 2·00 12·00
357 1 f. 25 + 75 c. violet 4·00 30·00
358 1 f. 75 + 1 f. 50 blue 4·00 18·00

1937. Child Welfare.
360 56 10 c. + 5 c. black and red 10 40
361 35 c. + 10 c. green & pur 20 50
362 70 c. + 20 c. red and blue 20 50
363 1 f. + 25 c. red and green 1·00 12·00
364 1 f. 25 + 75 c. purple and brown 1·25 15·00
365 1 f. 75 + 1 f. 50 blue and black 1·25 16·00

57 St. Willibrord — 61 Sigismond of Luxembourg

1938. Echternach Abbey Restoration Fund (1st issue). 1200th Death Anniv of St. Willibrord.
366 57 35 c. + 10 c. green 25 50
367 – 70 c. + 10 c. black 70 60
368 – 1 f. 25 + 25 c. red 90 2·00
369 – 1 f. 75 + 50 c. blue 1·50 2·00
370 – 3 f. + 2 f. red 5·00 8·00
371 – 5 f. + 5 f. violet 5·00 8·00
DESIGNS—As Type **57**: 70 c. Town Hall, Echternach; 1 f. 25, Pavilion, Echternach Municipal Park; 31×51 mm. 1 f 75, St. Willibrord (from miniature); 42×38 mm: 3 f. Echternach Basilica; 5 f. Whitsuntide dancing procession.
See also Nos. 492/7 and 569/70.

1938. Child Welfare.
372 61 10 c. + 5 c. black & mauve 10 40
373 35 c. + 10 c. black & green 20 50
374 70 c. + 20 c. black & brn 30 50
375 1 f. + 25 c. black and red 1·60 14·00
376 1 f. 25 + 75 c. black & grey 1·60 14·00
377 1 f. 75 + 1 f. 50 black and blue 1·90 20·00

62 Arms of Luxembourg — 63 William I

1939. Centenary of Independence.
378 62 35 c. green 15 20
379 63 50 c. orange 25 20
380 – 70 c. green 10 20
381 – 75 c. olive 50 1·00
382 – 1 f. red 1·25 2·00
383 – 1 f. 25 violet 15 20
384 – 1 f. 75 blue 15 20
385 – 3 f. brown 30 50
386 – 5 f. black 30 6·50
387 – 10 f. red 1·00 8·00
PORTRAITS—As Type **63**: 70 c. William II; 75 c. William III; 1 f. Prince Henry; 1 f. 25 Grand Duke Adolphe; 1 f. 75 William IV; 3 f. Marie-Anne, wife of William IV; 5 f. Grand Duchess Marie Adelaide; 10 f. Grand Duchess Charlotte.

1939. Surch in figures.
388 32 30 c. on 60 c. green 10 1·25

65 Allegory of Medicinal Spring — 66 Prince Jean

1939. Mondorf-les-Bains Propaganda.
389 65 2 f. red 30 2·50

1939. 20th Anniv of Reign and of Royal Wedding.
390 66 10 c. + 5 c. brn on cream 10 30
391 – 35 c. + 10 c. green on cream 20 1·00
392 – 70 c. + 20 c. black on cream 55 1·50
393 66 1 f. + 25 c. red on cream 2·50 30·00
394 – 1 f. 25 + 75 c. violet on cream 3·25 40·00
395 – 1 f. 75 + 1 f. 50 blue on cream 4·00 60·00
PORTRAITS: 35 c., 1 f. 25, Prince Felix. 70 c., 1 f. 75, Grand Duchess Charlotte.

1940. Anti-T.B. Fund. Surch with Cross of Lorraine and premium.
396 65 2 f. + 50 c. grey 1·00 12·00

1940-4 GERMAN OCCUPATION.

1940. T 94 of Germany optd **Luxembourg**.
397 94 3 pf. brown 10 35
398 4 pf. slate 10 50
399 5 pf. green 10 50
400 6 pf. green 10 35
401 8 pf. orange 10 35
402 10 pf. brown 10 50
403 12 pf. red 10 35
404 15 pf. red 20 65
405 20 pf. blue 20 1·10
406 25 pf. blue 40 1·25
407 94 30 pf. olive 20 65
408 40 pf. mauve 40 1·25
409 50 pf. black and green 40 1·75
410 60 pf. black and red 60 5·00
411 80 pf. black and blue 3·00 16·00
412 100 pf. black and yellow 60 4·50

1940. Types of Luxembourg surch.
413 32 3 Rpf. on 15 c. black 10 50
414 4 Rpf. on 20 c. orange 10 50
415 5 Rpf. on 35 c. green 10 50
416 6 Rpf. on 10 c. green 10 50
417 8 Rpf. on 25 c. brown 10 50
418 10 Rpf. on 40 c. brown 10 50
419 12 Rpf. on 60 c. green 10 50
420 15 Rpf. on 1 f. red 15 3·25
421 20 Rpf. on 50 c. brown 10 1·00
422 25 Rpf. on 5 c. mauve 35 3·25
423 30 Rpf. on 70 c. violet 15 1·00
424 40 Rpf. on 75 c. brown 15 1·00
425 50 Rpf. on 1¼ f. greeen 15 1·00
426 65 60 Rpf. on 2 f. red 65 16·00
427 47 80 Rpf. on 5 f. green 20 3·25
428 52 100 Rpf. on 10 f. green 20 3·25

1941. Nos. 739/47 of Germany optd **Luxembourg**.
429 3 pf. + 2 pf. brown 20 55
430 4 pf. + 3 pf. grey 20 55
431 5 pf. + 3 pf. green 20 55
432 6 pf. + 4 pf. green 20 55
433 8 pf. + 4 pf. orange 20 55
434 12 pf. + 6 pf. red 20 55
435 15 pf. + 10 pf. purple 1·25 7·50
436 25 pf. + 15 pf. blue 1·00 7·50
437 40 pf. + 35 pf. red 1·00 7·50

1944. INDEPENDENCE REGAINED

70 Grand Duchess Charlotte — 71 "Britannia"

1944.
438 70 5 c. brown 10 10
439 10 c. slate 10 10
440 20 c. orange 20 10
441 25 c. brown 10 10
442 30 c. red 30 30
443 35 c. green 15 30
444 40 c. blue 30 30
445 50 c. violet 10 10
445a 60 c. orange 1·50 15
446 70 c. red 15 20
447 70 c. green 50 70
448 75 c. brown 30 20
449 1 f. olive 10 10
450 1¼ f. orange 20 20
451 1½ f. orange 30 15
452 1¾ f. blue 30 30
453 2 f. red 3·50 15
454 2½ f. mauve 6·50 5·50
455 3 f. green 50 50
456 3½ f. blue 60 85
457 5 f. green 20 20
458 10 f. red 30 1·40
459 20 f. blue 50 16·00

1945. Liberation.
460 – 60 c. + 1 f. 40 green 10 20
461 – 1 f. 20 + 1 f. 80 red 10 20
462 71 2 f. 50 + 3 f. 50 blue 10 20
463 – 4 f. 20 + 4 f. 80 violet 10 20
DESIGNS: 60 c. Ship symbol of Paris between Cross of Lorraine and Arms of Luxembourg; 1 f. 20, Man killing snake between Arms of Russia and Luxembourg; 4 f. 20, Eagle between Arms of U.S.A. and Luxembourg.

72 Statue of the Madonna in Procession

73 Altar and Shrine of the Madonna

1945. Our Lady of Luxembourg.
464 72 60 c. + 40 c. green 20 80
465 – 1 f. 20 + 80 c. red 20 80
466 – 2 f. 50 + 2 f. 50 blue 30 4·00
467 – 5 f. 50 + 6 f. 50 violet 95 50·00
468 73 20 f. + 20 f. brown 95 50·00
DESIGNS: As Type **72**: 1 f. 20, The Madonna; 2 f. 50, The Madonna and Luxembourg; 5 f. 50, Portal of Notre Dame Cathedral.

74 Lion of Luxembourg — 75 Members of the Maquis

1945.
469 74 20 c. black 20 20
470 30 c. green 20 20
470a 60 c. violet 30 20
471 75 c. brown 30 20
472 1 f. 20 red 20 20
473 1 f. 50 violet 20 20
474 2 f. 50 blue 30 30

1945. National War Victims Fund.
475 75 20 c. + 30 c. green & buff 20 1·00
476 – 1 f. 50 + 1 f. red and buff 20 1·00
477 – 3 f. 50 + 3 f. 50 blue & buff 40 10·00
478 – 5 f. + 10 f. brown & buff 30 10·00
DESIGNS: 1 f. 50, Mother and children; 3 f. 50, Political prisoner; 5 f. Executed civilian.

76 — 77 John the Blind, King of Bohemia

1946. Air.
479 – 1 f. green and blue 20 20
480 76 2 f. brown and yellow 20 20
481 – 3 f. brown and yellow 20 20
482 – 4 f. violet and grey 30 30
483 76 5 f. purple and yellow 25 25
484 – 6 f. purple and blue 30 30
485 – 10 f. brown and yellow 1·00 30
486 76 20 f. blue and grey 1·25 1·00
487 – 50 f. green and light green 2·00 1·00
DESIGNS: 1, 4, 10 f. Airplane wheel; 3, 6, 50 f. Airplane engine and castle.

1946. 600th Death Anniv of John the Blind.
488 77 60 c. + 40 c. green & grey 15 1·50
489 1 f. 50 + 50 c. red & buff 25 2·00
490 3 f. 50 + 3 f. 50 blue & grey 95 22·00
491 5 f. + 10 f. brown & grey 50 18·00

78 Exterior Ruins of St. Willibrord Basilica — 79 St. Willibrord

1947. Echternach Abbey Restoration (2nd issue). Inscr "ECHTERNACH".
492 78 20 c. + 10 c. black 30 30
493 – 60 c. + 10 c. green 60 50
494 – 75 c. + 25 c. red 1·00 80
495 – 1 f. 50 c. + 50 c. brown 1·25 80
496 – 3 f. 50 c. + 2 f. 50 blue 4·00 3·75
497 79 25 f. + 25 f. purple 25·00 25·00
DESIGNS—As Type **78**: 60 c. Statue of Abbot Bertels; 75 c. Echternach Abbey emblem; 1 f. 50, Ruined interior of Basilica; 3 f. 50, St. Irmine and Pepin II carrying model of Abbey.

80 U.S. Military Cemetery, Hamm — 82 Michel Lentz (national poet)

1947. Honouring Gen. George S. Patton.
498 80 1 f. 50 red and buff 20 20
499 – 3 f. 50 blue and buff 1·25 2·00
500 80 5 f. green and grey 1·25 1·40
501 – 10 f. purple and grey 5·00 32·00
PORTRAIT: 3 f. 50, 10 f. Gen. G. S. Patton.

1947. National Welfare Fund.
502 82 60 c. + 40 c. brown & buff 55 60
503 1 f. 50 + 50 c. pur & buff 55 60
504 3 f. 50 + 3 f. 50 blue & grey 5·50 18·00
505 10 f. + 5 f. green and grey 5·50 19·00

83 L'Oesling **85** "Dicks" (Edmund de la Fontaine) **86** Grand Duchess Charlotte

1948. Tourist Propaganda.
505a – 2 f. 50 brown & chocolate 1·50 40
505b – 3 f. violet 6·00 1·25
505c – 4 f. blue 4·00 1·25
506 **83** 7 f. brown 22·00 80
507 – 10 f. green 1·75 20
508 – 15 f. red 2·00 40
509 – 20 f. blue 2·00 40
DESIGNS—HORIZ: 2 f. 50, Television transmitter, Dudelange; 3 f. Radio Luxembourg; 4 f. Victor Hugo's house, Vianden; 10 f. River Moselle; 15 f. Mining district. VERT: 20 f. Luxembourg.

1948. National Welfare Fund.
510 **85** 60 c. + 40 c. brown & bis 45 50
511 1 f. 50 + 50 c. red & pink 60 70
512 3 f. 50 + 3 f. 50 blue & grey 9·50 15·00
513 10 f. + 5 f. green and grey 8·50 15·00

1948.
513a **86** 5 c. orange 10 10
513b 10 c. blue 10 10
514 15 c. olive 15 10
514a 20 c. purple 20 10
515 25 c. grey 20 10
515a 30 c. olive 20 10
515b 40 c. red 30 30
515c 50 c. orange 40 15
516 60 c. bistre 30 20
517 80 c. green 30 20
518 1 f. red 1·00 10
518a 1 f. 20 black 1·00 30
518b 1 f. 25 brown 1·00 40
519 1 f. 50 turquoise 1·00 10
520 1 f. 60 grey 1·00 1·00
521 2 f. purple 1·00 10
521a 2 f. 50 red 1·75 10
521b 3 f. blue 13·00 40
521c 3 f. 50 red 4·00 40
522 4 f. blue 4·00 40
522a 5 f. violet 11·00 40
523 6 f. purple 6·50 40
524 8 f. green 5·50 80

87 Date-stamp and Map

1949. 75th Anniv of U.P.U.
525 **87** 80 c. green, lt green & black 50 60
526 2 f. 50 red, pink and black 2·25 1·50
527 4 f. ultramarine, blue & black 3·75 5·50
528 8 f. brown, buff and black 12·00 25·00

88 Michel Rodange **89** Young Girl

1949. National Welfare Fund.
529 **88** 60 c. + 40 c. green & grey 50 50
530 2 f. + 1 f. purple & claret 5·00 6·00
531 4 f. + 2 f. blue and grey 8·00 12·00
532 10 f. + 5 f. brown & buff 8·00 14·00

1950. War Orphans Relief Fund.
533 – 60 c. + 15 c. turquoise 1·50 50
534 **89** 1 f. + 20 c. red 4·00 1·25
535 – 2 f. + 30 c. brown 2·00 1·25
536 **89** 4 f. + 75 c. blue 12·00 15·00
537 – 8 f. + 3 f. black 32·00 42·00
538 **89** 10 f. + 5 f. purple 32·00 42·00
DESIGN: 60 c., 2 f., 8 f. Mother and boy.

90 J. A. Zinnen (composer) **91** Ploughman and Factories

1950. National Welfare Week.
539 **90** 60 c. + 10 c. violet & grey 55 30
540 2 f. + 15 c. red and buff 1·00 40
541 4 f. + 15 c. blue and grey 5·00 7·00
542 8 f. + 5 f. brown and buff 22·00 25·00

1951. To Promote United Europe.
543 **91** 80 c. green and light green 10·00 10·00
544 – 1 f. violet and light violet 5·50 50
545 – 2 f. brown and grey 25·00 50
546 **91** 2 f. 50 red and orange 26·00 21·00
547 – 3 f. brown and yellow 45·00 32·00
548 – 4 f. blue and light blue 60·00 40·00
DESIGNS: 1, 3 f. Map, people and "Rights of Man" Charter; 2, 4 f. Scales balancing "United Europe" and "Peace".

92 L. Menager (composer)

1951. National Welfare Fund.
549 **92** 60 c. + 10 c. black & grey 40 40
550 2 f. + 15 c. green and grey 40 40
551 4 f. + 15 c. blue and grey 4·00 3·00
552 8 f. + 5 f. purple and grey 25·00 30·00

92a T 1 and **86**

92b T 1

1952. National Philatelic Exhibition ("CENTILUX") and Stamp Centenary.
552a **92a** 80 c. black, purple and green (air) 50 50
552b 2 f. 50 black, pur & red 1·50 1·50
552c 4 f. black, purple & blue 3·00 3·00
552d 8 f. black, purple & red 50·00 55·00
552e 10 f. black, purple & brn 40·00 45·00
552f **92b** 2 f. black and green (postage) 35·00 50·00
552g 4 f. red and green 35·00 50·00

93 Hurdling

1952. 15th Olympic Games, Helsinki.
553 **93** 1 f. black and green 60 30
554 – 2 f. black and light brown (Football) 2·00 30
555 – 2 f. 50 black and pink (Boxing) 4·00 90
556 – 3 f. blk & drab (Water polo) 5·00 90
557 – 4 f. black & blue (Cycling) 25·00 6·50
558 – 8 f. black & lilac (Fencing) 16·00 3·75

94 J. B. Fresez (painter) **95** Prince Jean and Princess Josephine Charlotte

1952. National Welfare Fund.
559 **94** 60 c. + 15 c. green & blue 40 40
560 2 f. + 25 c. brown & orange 40 40
561 4 f. + 25 c. violet and grey 3·00 4·00
562 8 f. + 4 f. 75 purple & lt pur 26·00 32·00

1953. Royal Wedding.
563 **95** 80 c. violet & deep mauve 45 35
564 1 f. 20 deep brown & brown 45 35
565 2 f. deep green and green 1·25 35
566 3 f. deep purple and purple 1·25 50
567 4 f. deep blue and blue 5·50 1·00
568 9 f. brown and red 5·50 1·00

96 Echternach Basilica **97** Pierre D'Aspelt

1953. Echternach Abbey Restoration (3rd issue).
569 **96** 2 f. red 3·50 35
570 – 2 f. 50 olive 5·00 5·50
DESIGN: 2 f. 50, Interior of Basilica.

1953. 7th Birth Centenary of Pierre D'Aspelt.
571 **97** 4 f. black 7·00 4·25

98 "Candlemas Singing" **99** Foils, Mask and Gauntlet

1953. National Welfare Fund.
572 **98** 25 c. + 15 c. carmine and red 30 40
573 – 80 c. + 20 c. blue & brown 30 40
574 – 1 f. 20 + 30 c. green & turq 70 80
575 **98** 2 f. + 25 c. brown and red 30 40
576 – 4 f. + 50 c. blue & turquoise 4·75 7·00
577 – 7 f. + 3 f. 35 lilac & violet 13·00 18·00
DESIGNS: 80 c., 4 f. "The Rattles"; 1 f. 20, 7 f. "The Easter-eggs".

1954. World Fencing Championships.
578 **99** 2 f. deep brown and brown on cream 4·00 50

100 Fair Emblem **101** Earthenware Whistle

1954. Luxembourg International Fair.
579 **100** 4 f. multicoloured 9·50 2·75

1954. National Welfare Fund.
580 **101** 25 c. + 5 c. red & orange 40 50
581 – 80 c. + 20 c. grey & black 40 50
582 – 1 f. 20 + 30 c. green and cream 1·50 1·50
583 **101** 2 f. + 25 c. brown & buff 60 60
584 – 4 f. + 50 c. dp blue & blue 5·00 7·00
585 – 7 f. + 3 f. 45 violet & mve 24·00 25·00
DESIGNS: 80 c., 4 f. Sheep and drum; 1 f. 20, 7 f. Merry-go-round horses.

102 Tulips **103**

1955. Mondorf-les-Bains Flower Show.
586 **102** 80 c. red, green & brown 30 30
587 – 2 f. yellow, green and red 40 30
588 – 3 f. purple, green & emer 3·50 3·50
589 – 4 f. orange, green & blue 5·50 5·50
FLOWERS: 2 f. Daffodils; 3 f. Hyacinths; 4 f. Parrot tulips.

1955. 1st National Crafts Exhibition.
590 **103** 2 f. black and grey 1·00 25

104 "Charter" **105** "Christmas Day"

1955. 10th Anniv of U.N.
591 **104** 80 c. blue and black 45 50
592 – 2 f. brown and red 3·25 15
593 – 4 f. red and blue 2·25 3·00
594 – 9 f. green and brown 75 75
SYMBOLIC DESIGNS: 2 f. "Security"; 4 f. "Justice"; 9 f. "Assistance".

1955. National Welfare Fund.
595 – 25 c. + 5 c. red and pink 30 30
596 **105** 80 c. + 20 c. black & grey 30 30
597 – 1 f. 20 + 30 c. deep green and green 60 80
598 – 2 f. + 25 c. deep brown and brown 60 30
599 **105** 4 f. + 50 c. blue & lt blue 6·00 10·00
600 – 7 f. + 3 f. 45 pur & mve 12·00 14·00
ALLEGORICAL DESIGNS: 25 c., 2 f. "St. Nicholas's Day"; 1 f. 20, 7 f. "Twelfth Night".

1956. Mondorf-les-Bains Flower Show. As T **102** but inscription at top in one line. Multicoloured.
601 2 f. Anemones 65 30
602 3 f. Crocuses 2·50 2·25

1956. Roses. As T **102** but inscr at top "LUXEMBOURG–VILLE DES ROSES". Multicoloured.
603 2 f. 50 Yellow roses 6·00 4·50
604 4 f. Red roses 3·00 2·25

108 Steel Plant and Girder **109** Blast Furnaces and Map

1956. 50th Anniv of Esch-sur-Alzette.
605 **108** 2 f. red, black and turq 1·75 40

1956. European Coal and Steel Community. Inscr as in T **109**.
606 **109** 2 f. red 30·00 1·00
607 – 3 f. blue 30·00 22·00
608 – 4 f. green 6·00 4·25
DESIGNS—VERT: 3 f. Girder supporting City of Luxembourg. HORIZ: 4 f. Chain and miner's lamp.

110 **111** Luxembourg Central Station

1956. Europa.
609 **110** 2 f. black and brown £200 25
610 3 f. red and orange 40·00 40·00
611 4 f. deep blue and blue 2·25 3·00

1956. Electrification of Luxembourg Railways.
612 **111** 2 f. sepia and black 3·00 50

112 I. de la Fontaine **113** Arms of Echternach

1956. Council of State Centenary. Inscr as in T **112**.
613 **112** 2 f. sepia 1·00 30
614 – 7 f. purple 2·00 80
DESIGN: 7 f. Grand Duchess Charlotte.

1956. National Welfare Fund. Inscr "CARITAS 1956". Arms. Multicoloured.
615 25 c. + 5 c. Type **113** 25 30
616 80 c. + 20 c. Esch-sur-Alzette 25 30
617 1 f. 20 + 30 c. Grevenmacher 30 45
618 2 f. + 25 c. Type **113** 25 30
619 4 f. + 50 c. Esch-sur-Alzette 2·25 3·50
620 7 f. + 3 f. 45 Grevenmacher 6·00 11·00

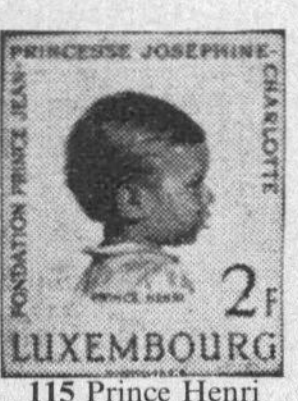

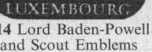

114 Lord Baden-Powell and Scout Emblems **115** Prince Henri

1957. Birth Centenary of Lord Baden-Powell, and 50th Anniv of Scouting Movement.
621 **114** 2 f. brown and green 1·00 30
622 – 2 f. 50 red and violet 2·25 3·75
DESIGN: 2 f. 50, as Type **114** but showing Girl Guide emblems.

1957. "Prince Jean and Princess Josephine-Charlotte Foundation" Child Welfare Clinic.
623 **115** 2 f. dp brown and brown . . 1·00 20
624 – 3 f. dp green and green . . 2·50 2·75
625 – 4 f. deep blue and blue . . 2·00 2·75
DESIGNS—HORIZ: 3 f. Children's Clinic Project. VERT: 4 f. Princess Marie-Astrid.

116 "Peace" **117** Fair Entrance and Flags

1957. Europa.
626 **116** 2 f. brown . . . . 2·00 15
627 3 f. red . . . . 35·00 15·00
628 4 f. purple . . . . 30·00 15·00

1957. National Welfare Fund. Arms as T **113** inscr "CARITAS 1957". Multicoloured.
629 25 c. + 5 c. Luxembourg . . 30 40
630 80 c. + 20 c. Mersch 30 40
631 1 f. 20 + 30 c. Vianden . . . 40 50
632 2 f. + 25 c. Luxembourg . . . 30 30
633 4 f. + 50 c. Mersch . . . . 2·00 4·25
634 7 f. + 3 f. 45 Vianden . . . . 4·75 7·50

1958. 10th Anniv of Luxembourg Int Fair.
635 **117** 2 f. multicoloured 15 15

118 Luxembourg Pavilion **119** St. Willibrord holding Child (after Puseel)

1958. Brussels Exhibition.
636 **118** 2 f. 50 blue and red . . . 15 15

1958. 1300th Birth Anniv of St. Willibrord.
637 – 1 f. red 20 30
638 **119** 2 f. 50 sepia 25 15
639 – 5 f. blue 60 90
DESIGNS: 1 f. St. Willibrord and St. Irmina holding inscribed plaque; 5 f. St. Willibrord and Suppliant. (Miracle of the wine-cask).

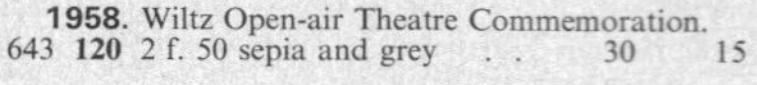
119a Europa **120** Open-air Theatre at Wiltz

1958. Europa.
640 **119a** 2 f. 50 blue and red . . . 15 15
641 3 f. 50 brown and green . . 20 25
642 5 f. red and blue 50 75

1958. Wiltz Open-air Theatre Commemoration.
643 **120** 2 f. 50 sepia and grey . . 30 15

121 Vineyard **122** Grand Duchess Charlotte

1958. Bimillenary of Moselle Wine Industry.
644 **121** 2 f. 50 brown and green 30 15

1958. National Welfare Fund. Arms as T **113** inscr "CARITAS 1958". Multicoloured.
645 30 c. + 10 c. Capellen 30 30
646 1 f. + 25 c. Diekirch 30 30
647 1 f. 50 + 25 c. Redange . . . 50 50
648 2 f. 50 + 50 c. Capellen . . . 30 30
649 5 f. + 50 c. Diekirch . . . . 1·50 4·00
650 8 f. 50 + 4 f. 60 Redange . . 4·25 7·50

1959. 40th Anniv of Accession of Grand Duchess Charlotte.
651 **122** 1 f. 50 dp green and green 35 25
652 2 f. 50 brown and lt brown 35 20
653 5 f. lt blue & ultramarine 75 90

123 N.A.T.O. Emblem **123a** Europa

1959. 10th Anniv of N.A.T.O.
654 **123** 2 f. 50 blue and olive . . 15 10
655 8 f. 50 blue and brown . . 40 40

1959. Mondorf-les-Bains Flower Show. As T **102** but inscr "1959".
656 1 f. violet, yellow and turquoise 25 30
657 2 f. 50 red, green and blue . . 30 20
658 3 f. blue, green and purple . . 50 70
FLOWERS: 1 f. Iris; 2 f. 50, Peony; 3 f. Hortensia.

1959. Europa.
659 **123a** 2 f. 50 green 40 15
660 5 f. blue 55 75

124 Early Locomotive and First Bars of Hymn "De Feierwon"

1959. Railways Centenary.
661 **124** 2 f. 50 blue and red . . . 1·25 40

1959. National Welfare Fund. Arms as T **113** inscr "CARITAS 1959". Multicoloured.
662 30 c. + 10 c. Clervaux . . . 30 30
663 1 f. + 25 c. Remich 30 30
664 1 f. 50 + 25 c. Wiltz 50 50
665 2 f. 50 + 50 c. Clervaux . . . 30 30
666 5 f. + 50 c. Remich . . . . 1·00 2·00
667 8 f. 50 + 4 f. 60 Wiltz . . . 4·25 11·00

125 Refugees seeking Shelter **126** Steel Worker

1960. World Refugee Year.
668 **125** 2 f. 50 blue and salmon 15 15
669 – 5 f. blue and violet . . . 20 35
DESIGN—HORIZ: 5 f. "The Flight into Egypt" (Biblical scene).

1960. 10th Anniv of Schuman Plan.
670 **126** 2 f. 50 lake 20 15

127 European School, Luxembourg **128** Grand Duchess Charlotte

1960. European School Commemoration.
671 **127** 5 f. black and blue . . . 1·25 1·00

1960.
672 **128** 10 c. red 10 20
673 20 c. red 10 20
673a 25 c. orange 20 20
674 30 c. drab 10 20
675 50 c. green 50 20
676 1 f. violet 50 10
677 1 f. 50 mauve 50 15
678 2 f. turquoise 60 10
679 2 f. 50 purple . . . . . 1·50 15
680 3 f. dull purple . . . . 2·75 10
680a 3 f. 50 turquoise . . . . 3·00 2·00
681 5 f. brown . . . . . . 1·75 20
681a 6 f. turquoise . . . . . 2·75 20

129 Heraldic Lion, and Tools

1960. 2nd National Crafts Exhibition.
682 **129** 2 f. 50 multicoloured . . 90 20

129a Conference Emblem **130** Princess Marie-Astrid

1960. Europa.
683 **129a** 2 f. 50 green and black 20 15
684 5 f. black and red 30 25

1960. National Welfare Fund. Inscr "CARITAS 1960". Centres and inscr in sepia.
685 **130** 30 c. + 10 c. blue 20 20
686 – 1 f. + 25 c. pink 20 20
687 – 1 f. 50 + 25 c. turquoise 40 50
688 **130** 2 f. 50 + 50 c. yellow . . 35 25
689 – 5 f. + 50 c. lilac . . . . 75 1·60
690 – 8 f. 50 + 4 f. 60 sage . . . 4·75 11·00
DESIGNS: Princess Marie-Astrid standing (1, 5 f.), sitting with book on lap (1 f. 50, 8 f. 50).

131 Great Spotted Woodpecker **132** Patton Monument, Ettelbruck

1961. Animal Protection Campaign. Inscr "PROTECTION DES ANIMAUX".
691 **131** 1 f. multicoloured 40 15
692 – 1 f. 50 buff, blue and black 25 25
693 – 3 f. brown, buff and violet 40 40
694 – 8 f. 50 multicoloured . . 70 50
DESIGNS—VERT: 8 f. 50, Dachshund. HORIZ: 1 f. 50, Cat; 3 f. Horse.

1961. Tourist Publicity.
695 **132** 2 f. 50 blue and black . . 20 20
696 – 2 f. 50 green 20 20
DESIGN—VERT: No. 696, Clervaux.

133 Doves **134** Prince Henri

1961. Europa.
697 **133** 2 f. 50 red 10 10
698 5 f. blue 20 20

1961. National Welfare Fund. inscr "CARITAS 1961". Centres and inscr in sepia.
699 **134** 30 c. + 10 c. mauve . . . 20 20
700 – 1 f. + 25 c. lavender . . . 20 20
701 – 1 f. 50 + 25 c. salmon . . 35 45
702 **134** 2 f. 50 + 50 c. green . . . 35 30
703 – 5 f. + 50 c. yellow . . . . 70 1·60
704 – 8 f. 50 + 4 f. 60 grey . . . 2·00 5·50
DESIGNS: Prince Henri when young boy (1, 5 f.); youth in formal dress (1 f. 50, 8 f. 50).

135 Cyclist carrying Cycle **136** Europa "Tree"

1962. World Cross-country Cycling Championships, Esch-sur-Alzette.
705 **135** 2 f. 50 multicoloured . . . 30 15
706 – 5 f. multicoloured (Emblem) 30 40

1962. Europa.
707 **136** 2 f. 50 multicoloured . . . 15 10
708 5 f. brown, green & purple 15 20

137 St. Laurent's Church, Diekirch **138** Prince Jean and Princess Margaretha as Babies

1962.
709 **137** 2 f. 50 black and brown 30 15

1962. National Welfare Fund. inscr "CARITAS 1962". Centres and inscr in sepia.
710 **138** 30 c. + 10 c. buff 20 20
711 – 1 f. + 25 c. blue 20 20
712 – 1 f. 50 + 25 c. olive . . . 30 40
713 – 2 f. 50 + 50 c. pink . . . 30 25
714 – 5 f. + 50 c. green . . . . 65 1·50
715 – 8 f. 50 + 4 f. 60 violet . . 1·60 4·50
PORTRAITS—VERT: 1 f., 2 f. 50, Prince Jean and: 2 f. 50, 5 f. Princess Margaretha, at various stages of childhood. HORIZ: 8 f. 50, The Royal Children.

139 Blackboard **140** Benedictine Abbey, Munster

1963. 10th Anniv of European Schools.
716 **139** 2 f. 50 green, red and grey 10 10

1963. Millenary of City of Luxembourg and International Philatelic Exhibition. (a) Horiz views.
717 – 1 f. blue 15 30
718 **140** 1 f. 50 red 15 30
719 – 2 f. 50 green 15 30
720 – 3 f. brown 15 30
721 – 5 f. violet 15 30
722 – 11 f. blue . . . . 1·10 1·75
VIEWS: 1 f. Bock Rock; 2 f. 50, Rham Towers; 3 f. Grand Ducal Palace; 5 f. Castle Bridge; 11 f. Millenary Buildings.

(b) Vert multicoloured designs.
723 1 f. "Three Towers" Gate . . 10 10
724 1 f. 50 Great Seal 15 15
725 2 f. 50 "The Black Virgin" (statue), St. John's Church 15 15
726 3 f. Citadel 15 15
727 5 f. Town Hall 35 70

141 Colpach Castle **142** "Human Rights"

1963. Red Cross Centenary.
728 **141** 2 f. 50 red and slate . . . 15 10

1963. 10th Anniv of European "Human Rights" Convention.
729 **142** 2 f. 50 blue on gold . . . 20 10

143 "Co-operation" **144** Trout snapping Bait

1963. Europa.
730 **143** 3 f. green, orange & turq 20 10
731 6 f. orange, red & brown 20 25

1963. World Fishing Championships, Wormeldange.
732 **144** 3 f. slate 15 15

145 Telephone Dial **146** St. Roch (patron saint of bakers)

1963. Inauguration of Automatic Telephone System.
733 **145** 3 f. green, black and blue 15 15

1963. National Welfare Fund. Patron Saints of Crafts and Guilds. Inscr "CARITAS 1963". Multicoloured.
734 50 c. + 10 c. Type **146** . . . 15 15
735 1 f. + 25 c. St. Anne (tailors) 15 15
736 2 f. + 25 c. St. Eloi (smiths) 15 15
737 3 f. + 50 c. St. Michel (haberdashers) 15 15
738 6 f. + 50 c. St. Barthelemy (butchers) . . . . . 1·25 2·00
739 10 f. + 5 f. 90 St. Thibaut (seven crafts) . . . . . 2·00 3·00

147 Power House **148** Barge entering Canal

1964. Inauguration of Vianden Reservoir.
740 **147** 2 f. blue, brown and red . . . 20 15
741 – 3 f. light blue, turq & red . . . 20 15
742 – 6 f. brown, blue and green . . . 30 15
DESIGNS—HORIZ: 3 f. Upper reservoir. VERT: 6 f. Lohmuhle Dam.

1964. Inauguration of Moselle Canal.
743 **148** 3 f. indigo and blue . . . 30 15

149 Europa "Flower" **150** Students thronging "New Athenaeum"

1964. Europa.
744 **149** 3 f. blue, brown & cream . . . 15 10
745 6 f. sepia, green & yellow . . . 15 20

1964. Opening of "New Athenaeum" (education centre).
746 **150** 3 f. black and green . . . 10 10

150a King Baudouin, Queen Juliana and Grand Duchess Charlotte

1964. 20th Anniversary of "BENELUX".
747 **150a** 3 f. brown, yellow & blue . . . 10 10

151 Grand Duke Jean and Princess Josephine-Charlotte **152** Three Towers

1964. Accession of Grand Duke Jean.
748 **151** 3 f. deep blue & lt blue . . . 30 10
749 6 f. sepia and light brown . . . 30 20

1964. National Welfare Fund. Inscr "CARITAS 1964". Multicoloured.
750 50 c. + 10 c. Type **152** . . . 15 15
751 1 f. + 25 c. Grand Duke Adolphe Bridge . . . 15 15
752 2 f. + 25 c. Lower Town . . . 15 15
753 3 f. + 50 c. Type **152** . . . 15 15
754 6 f. + 50 c. Grand Duke Adolphe Bridge . . . 1·00 1·50
755 10 f. + 5 f. 90 Lower Town . . . 1·00 2·00

153 Rotary Emblem and Cogwheels **154** Grand Duke Jean

1965. 60th Anniv of Rotary International.
756 **153** 3 f. multicoloured . . . 15 10

1965.
757 **154** 25 c. brown . . . 10 10
758 50 c. red . . . 10 10
759 1 f. blue . . . 10 10
760 1 f. 50 purple . . . 10 10
761a 2 f. red . . . 10 10
762 2 f. 50 orange . . . 10 10
763a 3 f. green . . . 20 10
763b 3 f. 50 brown . . . 20 20
764a 4 f. purple . . . 20 10
764ba 5 f. green . . . 20 10
765a 6 f. lilac . . . 30 10
765b 7 f. orange . . . 30 10
765c **154** 8 f. blue . . . 50 10
766 9 f. green . . . 40 20
766a 10 f. black . . . 60 10
767 12 f. red . . . 50 10
767a 14 f. blue . . . 50 40
767b 16 f. green . . . 70 25
767c 18 f. green . . . 80 30
767d 20 f. blue . . . 80 20
767e 22 f. brown . . . 80 60

155 I.T.U. Emblem and Symbols

1965. Centenary of I.T.U.
768 **155** 3 f. blue, lake and violet . . . 10 10

156 Europa "Sprig" **157** "The Roman Lady of the Titelberg"

1965. Europa.
769 **156** 3 f. turquoise, red and black . . . 15 10
770 6 f. brown, blue and green . . . 15 20

1965. National Welfare Fund. Fairy Tales. Inscr "CARITAS 1965". Multicoloured.
771 50 c. + 10 c. Type **157** . . . 15 20
772 1 f. + 25 c. "Schappchen, the Huntsman" . . . 15 20
773 2 f. + 25 c. "The Witch of Koerich" . . . 15 20
774 3 f. + 50 c. "The Goblins of Schoendels" . . . 15 20
775 6 f. + 50 c. "Tollchen, Watchman of Hesperange" . . . 30 1·00
776 10 f. + 5 f. 90 "The Old Spinster of Heispelt" . . . 75 2·75

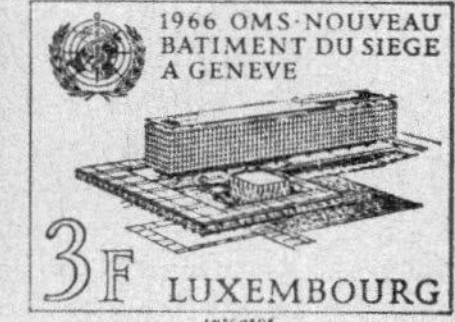

158 "Flag" and Torch **159** W.H.O. Building

1966. 50th Anniv of Luxembourg Workers' Union.
777 **158** 3 f. red and grey . . . 10 10

1966. Inaug. of W.H.O. Headquarters, Geneva.
778 **158** 3 f. green . . . 10 10

160 Golden Key **161** Europa "Ship"

1966. Tercentenary of Solemn Promise to Our Lady of Luxembourg.
779 **160** 1 f. 50 green . . . 10 20
780 – 2 f. red . . . 10 20
781 – 3 f. blue . . . 10 20
782 – 6 f. brown . . . 20 30
DESIGNS: 2 f. Interior of Luxembourg Cathedral (after painting by J. Martin); 3 f. Our Lady of Luxembourg (after engraving by R. Collin); 6 f. Gallery pillar, Luxembourg Cathedral (after sculpture by D. Muller).

1966. Europa.
783 **161** 3 f. blue and grey . . . 10 10
784 6 f. green and brown . . . 20 20

162 Diesel Locomotive

1966. Luxembourg Railwaymen's Philatelic Exhibition. Multicoloured.
785 1 f. 50 Type **162** . . . 30 25
786 3 f. Electric locomotive . . . 30 20

163 Grand Duchess Charlotte Bridge **164** Kirchberg Building and Grand Duke Adolphe Railway Bridge

1966. Tourism.
787 **163** 3 f. lake . . . 10 10
See also Nos. 807/8, 828 and 844/5.

1966. "Luxembourg-European Centre".
788 **164** 1 f. 50 green . . . 20 20
789 – 13 f. blue (Robert Schuman monument) . . . 30 15

165 "Mary, Veiled Matron of Wormeldange" **166** City of Luxembourg, 1850 (after engraving by N. Liez)

1966. National Welfare Fund. Luxembourg Fairy Tales. Multicoloured.
790 50 c. + 10 c. Type **165** . . . 10 20
791 1 f. 50 + 25 c. "Jekel Warden of the Wark" . . . 10 20
792 2 f. + 25 c. "The Black Gentleman of Vianden" . . . 10 20
793 3 f. + 50 c. "The Gracious Fairy of Rosport" . . . 15 20
794 6 f. + 1 f. "The Friendly Shepherd of Donkolz" . . . 35 1·00
795 13 f. + 6 f. 90 "The Little Sisters of Trois-Vierges" . . . 45 2·25

1967. Centenary of Treaty of London.
796 **166** 3 f. brown, blue and green . . . 25 10
797 – 6 f. red, brown and blue . . . 20 30
DESIGN—VERT: 6 f. Plan of Luxembourg fortress c. 1850 (after T. de Cederstolpe).

167 Cogwheels **168** Lion on Globe

1967. Europa.
798 **167** 3 f. purple, grey and buff . . . 15 10
799 6 f. sepia, purple and blue . . . 15 20

1967. 50th Anniv of Lions International.
800 **168** 3 f. yellow, purple & black . . . 10 10

169 European Institutions Building, Luxembourg **170** Hikers and Hostel

1967. N.A.T.O. Council Meeting, Luxembourg.
801 **169** 3 f. turquoise and green . . . 10 10
802 6 f. red and pink . . . 25 35

1967. Luxembourg Youth Hostels.
803 **170** 1 f. 50 multicoloured . . . 10 15

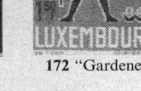

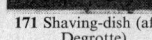

171 Shaving-dish (after Degrotte) **172** "Gardener"

1967. "200 Years of Luxembourg Pottery".
804 **171** 1 f. 50 multicoloured . . . 10 15
805 – 3 f. multicoloured . . . 20 15
DESIGN—VERT: 3 f. Vase, circa 1820.

1967. "Family Gardens" Congress, Luxembourg.
806 **172** 1 f. 50 orange and green . . . 10 15

1967. Tourism. As T **163**.
807 3 f. indigo and blue . . . 20 15
808 3 f. purple, green and blue . . . 20 15
DESIGNS—HORIZ: No. 807, Moselle River and quayside, Mertert. VERT: No. 808, Moselle, Church and vines, Wormeldange.

173 Prince Guillaume **174** Football

1967. National Welfare Fund. Royal Children and Residence.
809 **173** 50 c. + 10 c. brown & buff . . . 15 20
810 – 1 f. 50 + 25 c. brown & bl . . . 15 20
811 – 2 f. + 25 c. brown & red . . . 15 20
812 – 3 f. + 50 c. brown & yell . . . 40 20
813 – 6 f. + 1 f. brown & lav . . . 40 1·00
814 – 13 f. + 6 f. 90 brn, grn & bl . . . 45 2·75
DESIGNS: 1 f. 50, Princess Margaretha; 2 f. Prince Jean; 3 f. Prince Henri; 6 f. Princess Marie-Astrid; 13 f. Berg Castle.

1968. Olympic Games, Mexico.
815 – 50 c. light blue and blue . . . 10 15
816 **174** 1 f. 50 green & emerald . . . 10 15
817 – 2 f. yellow and green . . . 10 15
818 – 3 f. lt orange and orange . . . 10 10
819 – 6 f. green and blue . . . 15 20
820 – 13 f. red and crimson . . . 30 30
DESIGNS: 50 c. Diving; 2 f. Cycling; 3 f. Running; 6 f. Walking; 13 f. Fencing.

175 Europa "Key" **176** Thermal Bath Pavilion, Mondorf-les-Bains

1968. Europa.
821 **175** 3 f. brown, black & green . . . 10 10
822 6 f. green, black & orange . . . 20 30

1968. Mondorf-les-Bains Thermal Baths.
823 **176** 3 f. multicoloured . . . 15 10

177 Fair Emblem

1968. 20th Anniv of Luxembourg Int. Fair.
824 **177** 3 f. multicoloured . . . 15 10

178 Village Project **179** "Blood Transfusion"

1968. Luxembourg SOS Children's Village.
825 **178** 3 f. purple and green . . . 10 10
826 – 6 f. black, blue and purple . . . 20 30
DESIGN—VERT: 6 f. Orphan with foster-mother.

1968. Blood Donors of Luxembourg Red Cross.
827 **179** 3 f. red and blue . . . 20 10

180 Fokker Friendship over Luxembourg **181** Cap Institute

1968. Tourism.
828 **180** 50 f. dp blue, brown & bl . . . 1·75 40

1968. National Welfare Fund. Luxembourg Handicapped Children.
829 **181** 50 c. + 10 c. brown and blue . . . 15 20
830 – 1 f. 50 + 25 c. brn and grn . . . 15 20
831 – 2 f. + 25 c. brown & yell . . . 20 30
832 – 3 f. + 50 c. brown & blue . . . 25 20
833 – 6 f. + 1 f. brown & buff . . . 40 1·00
834 – 13 f. + 6 f. 90 brown and pink . . . 85 3·00
DESIGNS: 1 f. 50, Deaf and dumb child; 2 f. Blind child; 3 f. Nurse supporting handicapped child; 6 f. and 13 f. Mentally handicapped children (different).

183 Colonnade

1969. Europa.

836 **183** 3 f. multicoloured 15 10
837 6 f. multicoloured 30 30

184 "The Wooden Horse" (Kutter)

1969. 75th Birth Anniv of Joseph Kutter (painter). Multicoloured.

838 3 f. Type **184** 50 15
839 6 f. "Luxembourg" (Kutter) 50 30

185 ILO Emblem

186 National Colours

1969. 50th Anniv of Int Labour Organization.

840 **185** 3 f. gold, violet and green 10 10

1969. 25th Anniv of "BENELUX" Customs Union.

841 **186** 3 f. multicoloured 20 10

187 N.A.T.O. Emblem

188 Ear of Wheat and Agrocentre, Mersch

1969. 20th Anniv of N.A.T.O.

842 **187** 3 f. orange and brown . . 20 10

1969. "Modern Agriculture".

843 **188** 3 f. grey and green 10 10

189 Echternach

190 Vianden Castle

1969. Tourism.

844 **189** 3 f. indigo and blue . . . 20 10
845 – 3 f. blue and green 20 10
DESIGN: No. 845, Wiltz.

1969. National Welfare Fund. Castles (1st series). Multicoloured.

846 50 c. + 10 c. Type **190** . . . 15 20
847 1 f. 50 + 25 c. Lucilinburhuc 15 20
848 2 f. + 25 c. Bourglinster . . . 15 20
849 3 f. + 50 c. Hollenfels 15 20
850 6 f. + 1 f. Ansembourg . . . 45 1·50
851 13 f. + 6 f. 90 Beaufort . . . 65 3·00
See also Nos. 862/7.

191 Pasque Flower

192 Firecrest

1970. Nature Conservation Year. Multicoloured.

852 3 f. Type **191** 20 10
853 6 f. West European hedgehogs 60 40

1970. 50 Years of Bird Protection.

854 **192** 1 f. 50 green, black & orge 50 15

193 "Flaming Sun"

1970. Europa.

855 **193** 3 f. multicoloured 10 10
856 6 f. multicoloured 20 30

194 Road Safety Assoc. Emblem and Traffic

1970. Road Safety.

857 **194** 3 f. black, red and lake . 30 15

195 "Empress Kunegonde and Emperor Henry II" (stained-glass windows, Luxembourg Cathedral)

1970. Centenary of Luxembourg Diocese.

858 **195** 3 f. multicoloured 15 20

196 Population Pictograph

197 Facade of Town Hall, Luxembourg

1970. Population Census.

859 **196** 3 f. red, blue and green 15 10

1970. 50th Anniv of Union of Four Suburbs with Luxembourg City.

860 **197** 3 f. brown, ochre & blue 15 10

198 U.N. Emblem

199 Monks in the Scriptorium

1970. 25th Anniv of United Nations.

861 **198** 1 f. 50 violet and blue . . 10 10

1970. National Welfare Fund. Castles (2nd series). Designs as T **190**.

862 50 c. + 10 c. Clervaux . . . 15 20
863 1 f. 50 + 25 c. Septfontaines 15 20
864 2 f. + 25 c. Bourschied . . . 15 20
865 3 f. + 50 c. Esch-sur-Sure . . 15 20
866 6 f. + 1 f. Larochette . . . . 60 1·50
867 13 f. + 6 f. 90 Brandenbourg 1·10 3·25

1971. Medieval Miniatures produced at Echternach. Multicoloured.

868 1 f. 50 Type **199** 10 15
869 3 f. Vine-growers going to work 15 10
870 6 f. Vine-growers at work and returning home 25 20
871 13 f. Workers with spades and hoe 45 55

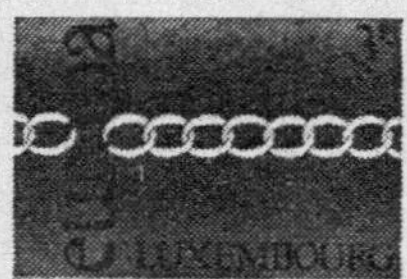
200 Europa Chain

1971.

872 **200** 3 f. black, brown and red 20 15
873 6 f. black, brown & green 35 50

201 Olympic Rings and Arms of Luxembourg

202 "50" and Emblem

1971. Int. Olympic Committee Meeting, Luxembourg.

874 **201** 3 f. red, gold and blue . . 10 10

1971. 50th Anniv of Luxembourg's Christian Workers' Union (L.C.G.B.).

875 **202** 3 f. purple, orange & yell 10 10

203 Artificial Lake, Upper Sure Valley

204 Child with Coin

1971. Man-made Landscapes.

876 **203** 3 f. blue, grey and brown 40 20
877 – 3 f. brown, green and blue 40 25
878 – 15 f. black, blue & brown 60 20
DESIGNS: No. 877, Water-processing plant, Esch-sur-Sure; No. 878, ARBED (United Steelworks) Headquarters Building, Luxembourg.

1971. Schoolchildren's Saving Campaign.

879 **204** 3 f. multicoloured 30 10

205 "Bethlehem Children"

206 Coins of Belgium and Luxembourg

1971. National Welfare Fund. "The Nativity"–wood-carvings in Beaufort Church. Multicoloured.

880 1 f. + 25 c. Type **205** 30 20
881 1 f. 50 + 25 c. "Shepherds" 30 20
882 3 f. + 50 c. "Virgin, Child Jesus and St. Joseph" 30 20
883 8 f. + 1 f. "Herdsmen" . . . 1·25 2·00
884 18 f. + 6 f. 50 "One of the Magi" 2·00 5·00

1972. 50th Anniv of Belgium-Luxembourg Economic Union.

885 **206** 1 f. 50 silver, black & grn 15 15

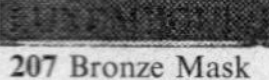
207 Bronze Mask (1st cent.)

208 "Communications"

1972. Gallo-Roman Exhibits from Luxembourg State Museum. Multicoloured.

886 1 f. Samian bowl (2nd cent) (horiz) 15 15
887 3 f. Type **207** 30 15
888 8 f. Limestone head (2nd/3rd century) 60 80
889 15 f. Glass "head" flagon (4th century) 50 60

1972. Europa.

890 **208** 3 f. multicoloured 40 10
891 8 f. multicoloured 85 85

209 Archer

210 R. Schuman (after bronze by R. Zilli)

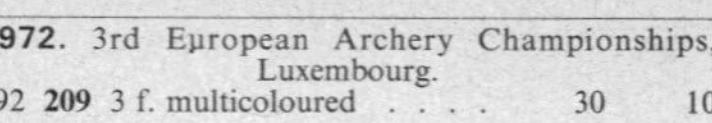

1972. 3rd European Archery Championships, Luxembourg.

892 **209** 3 f. multicoloured 30 10

1972. 20th Anniv of Establishment of European Coal and Steel Community in Luxembourg.

893 **210** 3 f. green and grey . . . 40 15

211 National Monument

212 "Renert"

1972. Monuments and Buildings.

894 **211** 3 f. brown, green & violet 50 15
895 – 3 f. brown, green and blue 50 15
DESIGN: No. 895, European Communities' Court of Justice.

1972. Cent of Publication of Michel Rodange's "Renert" (satirical poem).

896 **212** 3 f. multicoloured 30 10

213 "Angel"

214 "Epona on Horseback"

1972. National Welfare Fund. Stained Glass Windows in Luxembourg Cathedral. Multicoloured.

897 1 f. + 25 c. Type **213** 15 20
898 1 f. 50 + 25 c. "St. Joseph" 15 20
899 3 f. + 50 c. "Holy Virgin with Child Jesus" 15 20
900 8 f. + 1 f. "People of Bethlehem" 1·00 2·00
901 18 f. + 6 f. 50 "Angel" (facing left) . . . . 3·00 7·00

1973. Archaeological Relics. Multicoloured.

902 1 f. Type **214** 15 20
903 4 f. "Panther attacking swan" (horiz) 30 10
904 8 f. Celtic gold coin . . . . . 1·10 1·10
905 15 f. Bronze boar (horiz) . . 90 65

215 Europa "Posthorn"

216 Bee on Honeycomb

1973. Europa.

906 **215** 4 f. orange, blue & violet 35 10
907 8 f. green, yellow & purple 90 1·00

1973. Bee-keeping.

908 **216** 4 f. multicoloured 30 10

217 Nurse and Child

218 Capital, Vianden Castle

1973. Day Nurseries in Luxembourg.

909 **217** 4 f. multicoloured 30 10

1973. Romanesque Architecture in Luxembourg.

910 **218** 4 f. purple and green . . 20 10
911 – 8 f. blue and brown . . . 45 75
DESIGN: 8 f. Detail of altar, St. Irmina's Chapel, Rosport.

219 Labour Emblem

220 J. de Busleyden

1973. 50th Anniv of Luxembourg Board of Labour.
912 **219** 3 f. multicoloured 20 10

1973. 500th Anniv of Great Council of Malines.
913 **220** 4 f. purple and brown 20 10

221 Monument, Wiltz

222 Joachim and St. Anne

1973. National Strike Monument.
914 **221** 4 f. green, brown and grey 20 10

1973. National Welfare Fund. "The Nativity". Details from 16th-century reredos, Hachiville Hermitage. Multicoloured.
915 1 f. + 25 c. Type **222** 15 20
916 3 f. + 25 c. "Mary meets Elizabeth" 15 20
917 4 f. + 50 c. "Magus presenting gift" 20 20
918 8 f. + 1 f. "Shepherds at the manger" 75 2·00
919 15 f. + 7 f. "St. Joseph with Candle" 2·25 6·00

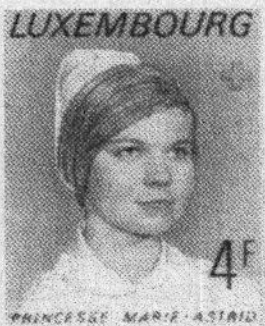

223 Princess Marie-Astrid, Association President

224 Flame Emblem

1974. Luxembourg Red Cross Youth Association.
920 **223** 4 f. multicoloured 60 15

1974. 50th Anniv of Luxembourg Mutual Insurance Federation.
921 **224** 4 f. multicoloured 20 10

225 Seal of Henry VII, King of the Romans

226 "Hind" (A. Tremont)

1974. Seals in Luxembourg State Archives.
922 **225** 1 f. brown, yellow & pur 10 10
923 – 3 f. brown, yellow & grn 20 25
924 – 4 f. dark brown, yell & brn 30 10
925 – 19 f. brown, yell & bl 75 90
DESIGNS: 3 f. Equestrian seal of John the Blind, King of Bohemia; 4 f. Municipal seal of Diekirch; 19 f. Seal of Marienthal Convent.

1974. Europa. Sculptures. Multicoloured.
926 4 f. Type **226** 40 10
927 8 f. "Abstract" (L. Wercollier) 1·00 1·25

227 Churchill Memorial, Luxembourg

228 Diagram of Fair

1974. Birth Centenary of Sir Winston Churchill.
928 **227** 4 f. multicoloured 30 10

1974. New International Fair, Luxembourg-Kirchberg.
929 **228** 4 f. multicoloured 20 10

229 "Theis the Blind" (artist unknown)

230 "Crowning of St. Cecily and St. Valerien" (Hollenfels Church)

1974. 150th Death Anniv of "Theis the Blind" (Mathias Schou, folk singer).
930 **229** 3 f. multicoloured 20 30

1974. Gothic Architecture.
931 **230** 4 f. brown, green & violet 30 30
932 – 4 f. black, brown & blue 30 20
DESIGN: No. 932, Interior of Septfontaines Church.

231 U.P.U. Emblem on "100"

1974. Centenary of Universal Postal Union.
933 **231** 4 f. multicoloured 20 10
934 8 f. multicoloured 50 70

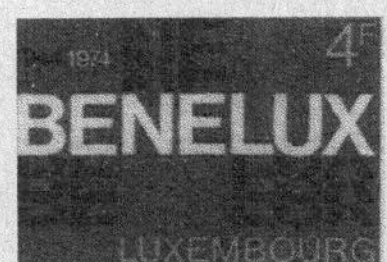

232 "Benelux"

1974. 30th Anniv of Benelux (Customs Union).
935 **232** 4 f. turquoise, green & bl 60 15

233 Differdange

1974. Tourism.
936 **233** 4 f. purple 45 15

234 "Annunciation"

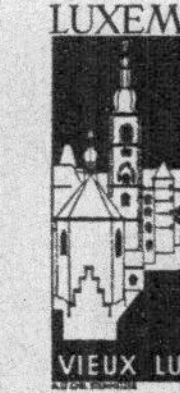

236 The Fish Market, Luxembourg

1974. National Welfare Fund. Illustrations from "Codex Aureus Epternacensis". Multicoloured.
937 1 f. + 25 c. Type **234** 15 20
938 3 f. + 25 c. "Visitation" 15 20
939 4 f. + 50 c. "Nativity" 20 20
940 8 f. + 1 f. "Adoration of the Magi" 90 2·00
941 15 f. + 7 f. "Presentation at the Temple" 1·75 5·00

1975. European Architectural Heritage Year.
943 **236** 1 f. green 70 20
944 – 3 f. brown 1·25 30
945 – 4 f. lilac 1·40 15
946 – 19 f. red 1·50 1·00
DESIGNS—HORIZ: 3 f. Bourglinster Castle; 4 f. Market Square, Echternach. VERT: 19 f. St. Michael's Square, Mersch.

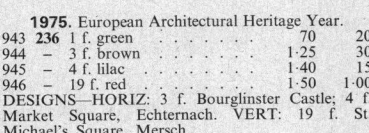

237 "Joseph Kutter" (self-portrait)

238 Dr. Albert Schweitzer

1975. Luxembourg Culture, and Europa. Paintings. Multicoloured.
947 1 f. Type **237** 15 15
948 4 f. "Remich Bridge" (N. Klopp) (horiz) 1·00 20
949 8 f. "Still Life" (J. Kutter) (horiz) 2·00 1·90
950 20 f. "The Dam" (D. Lang) 1·25 45

1975. Birth Centenary of Dr. Albert Schweitzer (medical missionary).
951 **238** 4 f. blue 1·00 15

239 Robert Schuman, G. Martino and P.-H. Spaak

240 Civil Defence Emblem

1975. 25th Anniv of Robert Schuman Declaration for European Unity.
952 **239** 4 f. black, gold and green 1·00 15

1975. 15th Anniv of Civil Defence Reorganization.
953 **240** 4 f. multicoloured 60 10

241 Ice Skating

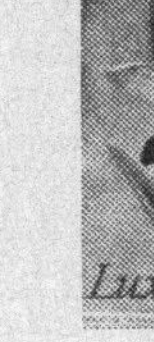

242 Fly Orchid

1975. Sports. Multicoloured.
954 **241** 3 f. purple, blue and green 45 25
955 – 4 f. brown, grn & dp brn 65 15
956 – 15 f. blue, brown & green 1·40 65
DESIGNS — HORIZ: 4 f. Water-skiing. VERT: 15 f. Rock-climbing.

1975. National Welfare Fund. Protected Plants (1st series). Multicoloured.
957 1 f. + 25 c. Type **242** 20 20
958 3 f. + 25 c. Pyramid orchid 40 35
959 4 f. + 50 c. Marsh helleborine 50 15
960 8 f. + 1 f. Pasque flower 1·50 2·00
961 15 f. + 7 f. Bee orchid 3·50 6·00
See also Nos. 976/80 and 997/1001.

243 Grand Duchess Charlotte (80th)

244 7th-century Disc-shaped Brooch

1976. Royal Birthdays. Multicoloured.
962 6 f. Type **243** 1·00 20
963 6 f. Prince Henri (21st) 1·00 20

1976. Luxembourg Culture. Ancient Treasures from Merovingian Tombs. Multicoloured.
964 2 f. Type **244** 15 20
965 5 f. 5th-6th cent. glass beaker (horiz) 30 30
966 6 f. Ancient pot (horiz) 30 15
967 12 f. 7th cent. gold coin 1·00 1·00

245 Soup Tureen

1976. Europa. 19th century Pottery. Multicoloured.
968 6 f. Type **245** 50 15
969 12 f. Bowl 1·25 1·25

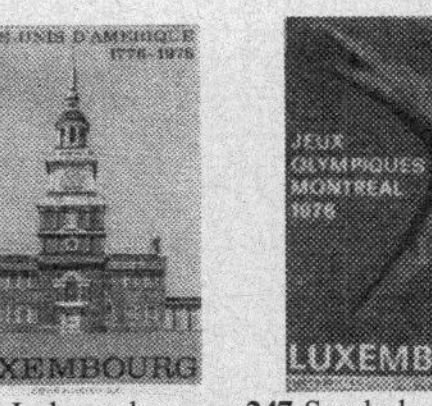

246 Independence Hall, Philadelphia

247 Symbol representing "Strength and Impetus"

1976. Bicentenary of American Revolution.
970 **246** 6 f. multicoloured 30 10

1976. Olympic Games, Montreal.
971 **247** 6 f. gold, magenta and mauve 20 10

248 Association Emblem and "Sound Vibrations"

249 "Virgin and Child"

1976. 30th Anniv of "Jeunesses Musicales" (Youth Music Association).
972 **248** 6 f. multicoloured 30 10

1976. Renaissance Art. Multicoloured.
973 6 f. Type **249** 30 10
974 12 f. Bernard de Velbruck, Lord of Beaufort (funeral monument) 50 80

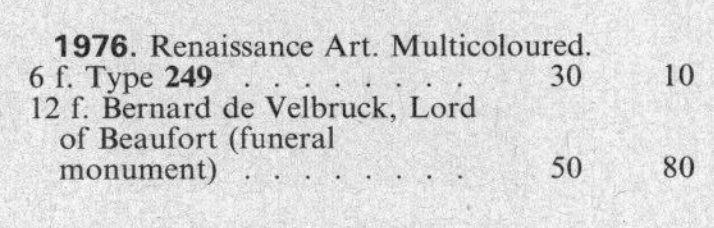

250 Alexander Graham Bell

1976. Telephone Centenary.
975 **250** 6 f. green 30 10

1976. National Welfare Fund. Protected Plants (2nd series). As T **242**. Multicoloured.
976 2 f. + 25 c. Gentian 20 20
977 5 f. + 25 c. Wild daffodil 20 20
978 6 f. + 50 c. Red helleborine (orchid) 40 25
979 12 f. + 1 f. Late spider orchid 1·25 1·50
980 20 f. + 8 f. Twin leaved squill 3·25 5·00

251 Johann von Goethe (poet)

252 Fish Market, Luxembourg

1977. Luxembourg Culture. Famous Visitors to Luxembourg.
981 **251** 2 f. purple 15 10
982 – 5 f. violet 25 20
983 – 6 f. black 60 15
984 – 12 f. violet 1·25 75
DESIGNS: 5 f. Joseph Mallard William Turner (painter); 6 f. Victor Hugo (writer); 12 f. Franz Liszt (musician).

1977. Europa. Multicoloured.
985 6 f. Type **252** 35 10
986 12 f. Grand Duke Adolphe railway bridge and European Investment Bank 90 1·00

253 Esch-sur-Sure

254 Marguerite de Busbach (founder)

1977. Tourism.
987 **253** 5 f. blue 50 20
988 – 6 f. brown 40 10
DESIGNS 6 f. Ehnen.

1977. Anniversaries. Multicoloured.
989 6 f. Type **254** 40 15
990 6 f. Louis Braille (after Filippi) 40 15
ANNIVERSARIES: No. 989, 350th anniv of foundation of Notre Dame Congregation; No. 990, 125th death anniv

256 St. Gregory the Great **257** Head of Medusa

1977. Baroque Art. Sculpture from Feulen Parish Church pulpit attributed to J.-G. Scholtus.
992 **256** 6 f. purple 40 15
993 – 12 f. grey 80 80
DESIGN: 12 f. St. Augustine.

1977. Roman Mosaic at Diekirch.
994 **257** 6 f. multicoloured 60 20

258 Scene from "Orpheus and Eurydice" (Gluck)

1977. 25th Wiltz International Festival.
995 **258** 6 f. multicoloured 60 15

259 Map of E.E.C. and "Europa" (R. Zilli)

1977. 20th Anniv of Rome Treaties.
996 **259** 6 f. multicoloured 40 15

1977. National Welfare Fund. Protected Plants (3rd series). As T **242**. Multicoloured.
997 2 f. + 25 c. Lily of the valley 15 15
998 5 f. + 25 c. Columbine . . . 30 25
999 6 f. + 50 c. Mezereon . . . 50 25
1000 12 f. + 1 f. Early spider orchid 1·75 1·50
1001 20 f. + 8 f. Spotted orchid 3·00 5·00

262 Charles IV **263** Head of Our Lady of Luxembourg

1978. Europa.
1004 **262** 6 f. lilac 40 10
1005 – 12 f. red . . . . 1·25 1·00
DESIGN: 12 f. Pierre d'Aspelt (funeral monument, Mainz Cathedral).

1978. Anniversaries. Multicoloured.
1006 6 f. Type **263** (300th anniv of election as patron saint) . . 40 15
1007 6 f. Trumpeters (135th anniv of Grand Ducal Military Band) 65 15

264 Emile Mayrisch (after T. van Rysselberghe) **265** Child with Ear of Millet

1978. 50th Death Anniv of Emile Mayrisch (iron and steel magnate).
1008 **264** 6 f. multicoloured 55 15

1978. "Solidarity 1978". Multicoloured.
1009 2 f. Type **265** (Terre des Hommes) 10 20
1010 5 f. Flower and lungs (70th anniv of Luxembourg Anti-Tuberculosis League) . . . 30 20
1011 6 f. Open cell (Amnesty International and 30th anniv of Declaration of Human Rights) 35 15

266 Perfect Ashlar **267** "St. Matthew"

1978. 175th Anniv of Luxembourg Grand Lodge.
1012 **266** 6 f. blue 60 15

1979. National Welfare Fund. Glass Paintings (1st series). Multicoloured.
1013 2 f. + 25 c. Type **267** . . . 15 20
1014 5 f. + 25 c. "St. Mark" . . 30 30
1015 6 f. + 50 c. "Nativity" . . . 40 30
1016 12 f. + 1 f. "St. Luke" . . 1·25 1·00
1017 20 f. + 8 f. "St. John" . . . 2·00 4·50
See also Nos. 1035/9 and 1055/8.

268 Denarius of Gaius Julius Caesar **269** Mondorf-les-Bains

1979. Luxembourg Culture. Roman Coins in the State Museum. Multicoloured.
1018 5 f. Type **268** 30 15
1019 6 f. Sestertius of Faustina 1 50 15
1020 9 f. Follis of Helena 80 50
1021 26 f. Solidus of Valens . . . 1·75 1·40
See also Nos. 1040/3 and 1060/3.

1979. Tourism.
1022 **269** 5 f. green, brown & blue 25 20
1023 – 6 f. red 75 10
DESIGN: 6 f. Luxembourg Central Station.

270 Stage Coach **271** Antoine Meyer (poet)

1979. Europa. Multicoloured.
1024 6 f. Type **270** . . . . 1·75 15
1025 12 f. Old wall telephone (vert) 1·75 1·50

1979. Anniversaries.
1026 – 2 f. purple 35 20
1027 **271** 5 f. red 35 20
1028 – 6 f. turquoise 35 20
1029 – 9 f. grey-black 40 25
DESIGNS—36×36 mm: 2 f. Michel Pintz on trial (after L. Piedboeuf) and monument to rebels (180th anniv of peasant uprising against French). 22×36 mm: 5 f. Type **271** (150th anniv of first publication in Luxembourg dialect); 6 f. S. G. Thomas (cent of purchase of Thomas patent for steel production); 9 f. "Abundance crowning Work and Saving" (ceiling painting by August Vinet) (50th anniv of Stock Exchange).

272 "European Assembly" **273** Blindfolded Cherub with Chalice

1979. First Direct Elections to European Assembly.
1030 **272** 6 f. multicoloured . . . 2·25 60

1979. Rococo Art. Details from altar of St. Michael's Church by Barthelemy Namur. Multicoloured.
1031 6 f. Type **273** 40 15
1032 12 f. Cherub with anchor . . 70 70

MINIMUM PRICE

The minimum price quoted is 10p which represents a handling charge rather than a basis for valuing common stamps. For further notes about prices, see introductory pages.

274 Child with Traffic Symbol Balloons jumping over Traffic

1979. International Year of the Child.
1033 **274** 2 f. blue, brown and red 15 15

275 Radio Waves, "RTL" and Dates

1979. 50th Anniv of Broadcasting in Luxembourg.
1034 **275** 6 f. blue and red 50 15

1979. National Welfare Fund. Glass Paintings (2nd series). As T **267**. Multicoloured.
1035 2 f. + 25 c. "Spring" 15 15
1036 5 f. + 25 c. "Summer" . . . 30 30
1037 6 f. + 50 c. "Charity" . . . 40 30
1038 12 f. + 1 f. "Autumn" . . . 80 1·50
1039 20 f. + 8 f. "Winter" . . . . 1·50 4·50

1980. Luxembourg Culture. Medieval Coins in the State Museum. As T **268**. Multicoloured.
1040 2 f. Grosso of Emperor Henry VII 20 20
1041 5 f. Grosso of John the Blind of Bohemia 20 20
1042 6 f. "Mouton d'or" of Wenceslas I and Jeanne, Duke and Duchess of Brabant 80 15
1043 20 f. Grosso of Wenceslas II, Duke of Luxembourg . . . 1·60 80

276 State Archives Building **277** Jean Monnet (statesman)

1980. Tourism.
1044 **276** 6 f. purple, ultram & bl 50 15
1045 – 6 f. red and brown . . . 60 15
DESIGN—VERT: No. 1045, Ettelbruck Town Hall.

1980. Europa.
1046 **277** 6 f. black 50 15
1047 – 12 f. olive . . . . 1·00 85
DESIGN: 12 f. St. Benedict of Nursia (founder of Benedictine Order) (statue in Echternach Abbey).

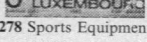

278 Sports Equipment **279** Gloved Hand protecting Worker from Machinery

1980. "Sports for All".
1048 **278** 6 f. black, orange & grn 1·40 30

1980. 9th World Congress on the Prevention of Accidents at Work and Occupational Diseases, Amsterdam.
1049 – 2 f. multicoloured 20 15
1050 **279** 6 f. brown, grey and red 40 15
DESIGN—VERT: 2 f. Worker pouring molten iron.

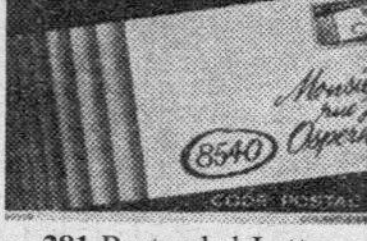

280 "Mercury" (Jean Mich) **281** Postcoded Letter

1980. Art Nouveau Sculpture. Statues beside entrance to State Savings Bank.
1051 **280** 8 f. lilac 45 15
1052 – 12 f. blue 55 60
DESIGN: 12 f. "Ceres" (Jean Mich).

1980. Postcode Publicity.
1053 **281** 4 f. brown, ochre and red 35 15

282 Policemen and Patrol Car

1980. 50th Anniv of National Police Force.
1054 **282** 8 f. multicoloured . . . 80 20

1980. National Welfare Fund. Glass Paintings (3rd series). As T **267**. Multicoloured.
1055 4 f. + 50 c. "St. Martin" . . 30 20
1056 6 f. + 50 c. "St. Nicholas" 30 25
1057 8 f. + 1 f. "Virgin and child" 40 1·00
1058 30 f. + 10 f. "St. George" . 2·25 4·50

1981. Luxembourg Culture. Coins in the State Museum. As T **268**.
1060 4 f. Patagon of Philip IV of Spain, 1635 . . . . 25 20
1061 6 f. 12 sols coin of Maria Theresa, 1775 . . . . . . 30 20
1062 8 f. 12 sols coin of Emperor Joseph II, 1789 . . . . . 30 15
1063 30 f. Siege crown of Emperor Francis II, 1795 . . . . . 1·40 80

284 European Parliament Building, Luxembourg **285** Cock-shaped Whistle sold at Easter Monday Market

1981. Tourism.
1064 **284** 8 f. brown and blue . . 30 15
1065 – 8 f. red and blue 30 15
DESIGN: No. 1065, National Library.

1981. Europa. Multicoloured.
1066 8 f. Procession of beribboned sheep and town band to local fair 40 15
1067 12 f. Type **285** 60 50

286 Staunton Knight on Chessboard **287** Prince Henri and Princess Maria Teresa

1981. Anniversaries.
1068 **286** 4 f. multicoloured . . . 40 15
1069 – 8 f. ochre, brown & silver 40 15
1070 – 8 f. multicoloured . . . 40 15
DESIGNS—VERT: 4 f. Type **286** (50th anniv of Luxembourg Chess Federation); 8 f. (1070), Passbook and State Savings Bank (125th anniv of State Savings Bank). HORIZ: 8 f. (1069), First Luxembourg banknote (125th anniv of International Bank of Luxembourg's issuing rights).

1981. Royal Wedding.
1071 **287** 8 f. multicoloured . . . 50 40

288 Gliders over Useldange **289** Flame

1981. Aviation. Multicoloured.
1072 8 f. Type **288** 30 15
1073 16 f. Cessna 172F Skyhawk and 182H Skylane sports planes 55 60
1074 35 f. Boeing 747-200F 182H over Luxembourg-Findel airport terminal . . . . . 1·25 85

1981. Energy Conservation.
1075 **289** 8 f. multicoloured . . . 30 15

290 Arms of Petange

291 "Apple Trees in Blossom" (Frantz Seimetz)

1981. National Welfare Fund. Arms of Local Authorities (1st series). Multicoloured.
1076 4 f. + 50 c. Type **290** 15 15
1077 6 f. + 50 c. Larochette . . . 25 25
1078 8 f. + 1 f. "Adoration of the Magi" (School of Rubens) 40 30
1079 16 f. + 2 f. Stadtbredimus 80 1·50
1080 35 f. + 12 f. Weiswampach 2·50 5·00
See also Nos. 1097/1101 and 1119/23.

1982. Luxembourg Culture. Landscapes through the Four Seasons. Multicoloured.
1081 4 f. Type **291** 20 15
1082 6 f. "Landscape" (Pierre Blanc) 30 30
1083 8 f. "The Larger Hallerbach" (Guido Oppenheim) . . . 45 15
1084 16 f. "Winter Evening" (Eugene Mousset) 70 70

292 Cross of Hinzert and Statue "Political Prisoner" (Lucien Wercollier)

293 Treaty of London, 1867, and Luxembourg Fortress

1982. National Monument of the Resistance and Deportation, Notre-Dame Cemetery.
1085 **292** 8 f. multicoloured 40 15

1982. Europa. Multicoloured.
1086 8 f. Type **293** 50 15
1087 16 f. Treaty of Paris, 1951, and European Coal and Steel Community Building, Luxembourg 90 75

294 St. Theresa of Avila (wood statue, Carmel Monastery)

295 State Museum

1982. Anniversaries. Multicoloured.
1088 4 f. Type **294** (400th death anniv) 30 15
1089 8 f. Raoul Follereau (social worker for lepers, 5th death anniv) 50 15

1982. Tourism.
1090 **295** 8 f. brown, blue & black 50 15
1091 – 8 f. buff, black and blue 75 15
DESIGN: No. 1091, Luxembourg Synagogue.

296 Bourscheid Castle

297 Key in Lock

1982. Classified Monuments (1st series).
1092 **296** 6 f. blue 30 15
1093 – 8 f. red 50 15
DESIGN—HORIZ: 8 f. Vianden Castle.
See also Nos. 1142/3, and 1165/6.

1982. Anniversaries. Multicoloured.
1094 4 f. Type **297** (50th anniv of International Youth Hostel Federation) 50 15
1095 8 f. Scouts holding hands around globe (75th anniv of Scouting Movement) (vert) 60 15

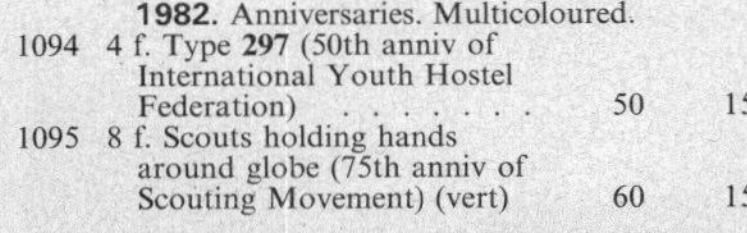

HAVE YOU READ THE NOTES AT THE BEGINNING OF THIS CATALOGUE?
These often provide the answers to the enquiries we receive.

298 Monument to Civilian and Military Deportation

1982. Civilian and Military Deportation Monument, Hollerich Station.
1096 **298** 8 f. multicoloured . . . 40 15

1982. National Welfare Fund. Arms of Local Authorities (2nd series) and Stained Glass Window (8 f.). As T **290**. Multicoloured.
1097 4 f. + 50 c. Bettembourg . . 25 20
1098 6 f. + 50 c. Frisange 30 25
1099 8 f. + 1 f. "Adoration of the Shepherds" (Gustav Zanter, Hoscheid parish church) . 45 30
1100 16 f. + 2 f. Mamer . . . . 90 1·30
1101 35 f. + 12 f. Heinerscheid . 2·25 5·00

299 Modern Fire Engine

300 "Mercury" (Auguste Tremont)

1983. Centenary of National Federation of Fire Brigades. Multicoloured.
1102 8 f. Type **299** 65 15
1103 16 f. Hand fire-pump (18th century) . . . . 1·25 65

1983. Anniversaries and Events.
1104 **300** 4 f. multicoloured . . . 20 20
1105 – 6 f. multicoloured . . . 50 30
1106 – 8 f. brown, black and blue 50 15
1107 – 8 f. deep blue and blue 50 15
DESIGNS: No. 1104, Type **300** (25th Congress of International Association of Foreign Exchange Dealers); 1105, N.A.T.O. emblem surrounded by flags of member countries (25th anniv of N.A.T.O.); 1106, Echternach Cross of Justice (30th Congress of International Union of Barristers); 1107, Globe and customs emblem (30th anniv of Customs Co-operation Council).

301 Robbers attacking Traveller

1983. Europa. Miniatures from "Codex Aureus Escorialensis", illustrating Parable of the Good Samaritan. Multicoloured.
1108 8 f. Type **301** 75 20
1109 16 f. Good Samaritan helping traveller . . . . 1·25 80

302 Initial "H" from "Book of Baruch"

303 Despatch Rider and Postcode

1983. Luxembourg Culture. Echternach Abbey Giant Bible. Multicoloured.
1110 8 f. Type **302** 45 20
1111 35 f. Initial "B" from letter of St. Jerome to Pope Damasius I . . . . 1·50 1·25

1983. World Communications Year. Mult.
1112 8 f. Type **303** 80 20
1113 8 f. Europan Communications Satellite (horiz) . . . . . 1·25 30

304 St. Lawrence's Church, Diekirch

305 Basketball

1983. Tourism.
1114 **304** 7 f. orange, brown and blue 30 15
1115 – 10 f. orange, brown & bl 40 20
DESIGN—HORIZ: 10 f. Dudelange Town Hall.

1983. Anniversaries and Events. Multicoloured.
1116 7 f. Type **305** (50th anniv of Luxembourg basketball Federation) 55 20
1117 10 f. Sheepdog (European Working Dog Championships) 80 20
1118 10 f. City of Luxembourg ("The Green Heart of Europe") 80 20

1983. National Welfare Fund. Arms of Local Authorities (3rd series) and Painting. As T **290**. Multicoloured.
1119 4 f. + 1 f. Winseler 30 20
1120 7 f. + 1 f. Beckerich 40 30
1121 10 f. + 1 f. "Adoration of the Shepherds" (Lucas Bosch) 50 35
1122 16 f. + 2 f. Feulen . . . . . 1·10 1·50
1123 40 f. + 13 f. Mertert . . . . 2·75 5·00

306 Lion and First Luxembourg Stamp

307 Pedestrian Precinct

1984. Anniversaries. Each black, red and blue.
1124 10 f. Type **306** 70 30
1125 10 f. Lion and ministry buildings 70 30
1126 10 f. Lion and postman's bag 70 30
1127 10 f. Lion and locomotive . . 70 30
ANNIVERSARIES: No. 1124, 50th anniv of Federation of Luxembourg Philatelic Societies; 1125, 75th anniv of Civil Service Trade Union Movement; 1126, 75th anniv of Luxembourg Postmen's Trade Union; 1127, 125th anniv of Luxembourg Railways.

1984. Environmental Protection. Multicoloured.
1128 7 f. Type **307** 30 30
1129 10 f. City of Luxembourg sewage treatment plant . . 40 20

308 Hands supporting European Parliament Emblem

309 Bridge

1984. 2nd Direct Elections to European Parliament.
1130 **308** 10 f. multicoloured . . . 60 20

1984. Europa. 25th Anniv of European Post and Telecommunications Conference.
1131 **309** 10 f. green, dp. grn & blk 1·00 20
1132 16 f. orange, brown & blk 2·00 75

310 "The Smoker" (David Teniers the Younger)

311 "The Race" (Jean Jacoby)

1984. Paintings. Multicoloured.
1133 4 f. Type **310** 50 30
1134 7 f. "Young Turk caressing his Horse" (Eugene Delacroix) (horiz) 70 30
1135 10 f. "Ephiphany" (Jan Steen) (horiz) . . . . 1·00 20
1136 50 f. "The Lacemaker" (Pieter van Slingelandt) . . . . . 3·50 1·50

1984. Olympic Games, Los Angeles.
1137 **311** 10 f. orange, black & bl 65 20

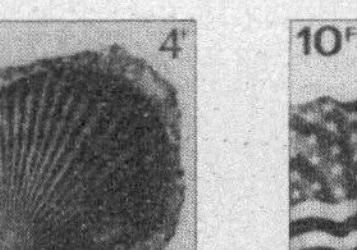

312 "Pecten sp."

313 "American Soldier" (statue by Michel Heitz at Clervaux)

1984. Luxembourg Culture. Fossils in the Natural History Museum. Multicoloured.
1138 4 f. Type **312** 45 20
1139 7 f. "Gryphaea arcuata" . . 85 35
1140 10 f. "Coeloceras raquinianum" (ammonite) . . . . 1·60 15
1141 16 f. "Dapedius sp." (fish) . 1·50 95

1984. Classified Monuments (2nd series). As T **296**.
1142 7 f. turquoise 35 30
1143 10 f. brown 45 15
DESIGNS: 7 f. Hollenfels Castle; 10 f. Larochette Castle.

1984. 40th Anniv of Liberation.
1144 **313** 10 f. black, red and blue 1·25 20

314 Infant astounded by Surroundings

315 Jean Bertels (abbot of Echternach Abbey)

1984. National Welfare Fund. The Child. Mult.
1145 4 f. + 1 f. Type **314** 40 40
1146 7 f. + 1 f. Child dreaming . 60 60
1147 10 f. + 1 f. "Nativity (crib, Steinsel church) . . . . . 1·00 50
1148 16 f. + 2 f. Child sulking . . 2·50 2·50
1149 40 f. + 13 f. Girl admiring flower . . . . 7·00 8·00

1985. Luxembourg Culture. Portrait Medals in State Museum (1st series). Multicoloured.
1150 4 f. Type **315** (steatite medal, 1595) 20 20
1151 7 f. Emperor Charles V (bronze medal, 1537) 30 30
1152 10 f. King Philip II of Spain (silver medal, 1555) 40 20
1153 30 f. Maurice of Orange-Nassau (silver medal, 1615) . . . . 1·25 90
See also Nos. 1173/6.

316 Fencing

317 Papal Arms

1985. Anniversaries. Multicoloured.
1154 10 f. Type **316** (50th anniv of Luxembourg Fencing Federation) 60 20
1155 10 f. Benz "Velo" (centenary of automobile) 60 20
1156 10 f. Teleph[illegible]vithin concentr[illegible]les (centenary of Luxembourg telephone service) 60 20

1985. Visit of Pope John Paul II.
1157 **317** 10 f. multicoloured . . . 60 20

318 Treble Clef within Map of National Anthem

320 Little Owl

1965. Europa. Music Year. Multicoloured.
1158 10 f. Type **318** (Grand Duke Adolphe Union of choral, instrumental and folklore societies) . . . . 1·25 30
1159 16 f. Neck of violin, music school and score of Beethoven's Violin Concerto opus 61 . . . . 2·25 95

1985. Endangered Animals. Multicoloured.
1161 4 f. Type **320** . . . . 1·00 30
1162 7 f. European wildcat (horiz) 1·50 30
1163 10 f. Red admiral (horiz) . . 2·00 30
1164 50 f. European tree frog . . 5·00 1·25

1985. Classified Monuments (3rd series). As T **296**.
1165 7 f. red 50 20
1166 10 f. green 50 15
DESIGNS—HORIZ: 7 f. Echternach orangery. VERT: 10 f. Mohr de Waldt house.

321 Mansfeld Arms (book binding)

322 Application

1985. Luxembourg Culture.
1167 **321** 10 f. multicoloured . . . 50 30

1985. National Welfare Fund. Multicoloured.
1168 4 f. + 1 f. Type **322** 40 30
1169 7 f. + 1 f. Friendship 60 50
1170 10 f. + 1 f. "Adoration of the Magi" (16th century alabaster sculpture) . . . . 1·00 50
1171 16 f. + 2 f. Child identifying with his favourite characters 2·50 2·50
1172 40 f. + 13 f. Shame . . . . 7·50 9·00

1986. Luxembourg Culture. Portrait Medals in State Museum (2nd series). As T **315**.
1173 10 f. multicoloured 50 30
1174 12 f. multicoloured 60 20
1175 18 f. black, grey and blue . . 80 50
1176 20 f. multicoloured . . . . . 1·25 50
DESIGNS: 10 f. Count of Monterey (silver medal, 1675); 12 f. Louis XIV of France (silver medal, 1684); 18 f. Pierre de Weyms (president of Provincial Council) (pewter medal, 1700); 20 f. Duke of Marlborough (silver medal, 1706).

323 Bee on Flower

324 Forest and City

1986. Anniversaries. Multicoloured.
1177 12 f. Type **323** (centenary of Federation of Luxembourg Beekeeper's Association) . 80 20
1178 12 f. Table tennis player (50th anniv of Luxembourg Table Tennis Federation) 80 20
1179 11 f. Mosaic of woman with water jar (centenary of Mondorf State Spa) . . . 80 20

1986. Europa. Multicoloured.
1180 12 f. Type **324** 75 15
1181 20 f. Mankind, industry and countryside . . . . 1·50 75

325 Fort Thungen

326 Schuman

1986. Luxembourg Town Fortifications. Mult.
1182 15 f. Type **325** 60 50
1183 18 f. Invalids' Gate (vert) . . 80 50
1184 50 f. Malakoff Tower (vert) . 2·00 1·50

1986. Birth Centenary of Robert Schuman (politician).
1185 **326** 2 f. black and red 10 10
1186 10 f. black and blue . . . 40 30

327 Road through Red Triangle on Map

328 Ascent to Chapel of the Cross, Grevenmacher

1986. European Road Safety Year.
1187 **337** 10 f. multicoloured . . . 75 20

1986. Tourism.
1188 **328** 12 f. multicoloured . . . 70 30
1189 – 12 f. brown, stone & red 70 30
DESIGN: No. 1189, Relief from Town Hall facade, Esch-sur-Alzette.

329 Presentation of Letter of Freedom to Echternach (after P. H. Witkamp)

330 Annunciation

1986. 800th Birth Anniv of Countess Ermesinde of Luxembourg.
1190 **329** 12 f. brown and stone . 50 30
1191 – 30 f. buff, black and grey 1·50 80
DESIGN: 30 f. Seal, 1238.

1986. National Welfare Fund. Illustrations from 15th-century "Book of Hours". Multicoloured.
1192 6 f. + 1 f. Type **330** . . . . 1·00 30
1193 10 f. + 1 f. Angel appearing to shepherds 50 40
1194 12 f. + 2 f. Nativity . . . . 1·00 50
1195 18 f. + 2 f. Adoration of the Magi . . . . 2·50 2·50
1196 20 f. + 8 f. Flight into Egypt 5·00 5·00

331 Garden Dormouse

332 Network Emblem

1987. Endangered Animals. Multicoloured.
1197 6 f. Type **331** 50 30
1198 10 f. Banded agrion (vert) . 65 55
1199 12 f. Dipper (vert) . . . . . 1·25 55
1200 25 f. Salamander . . . . . 2·00 80

1987. 50th Anniversaries. Multicoloured.
1201 12 f. Type **332** (Amateur Short Wave Network) 55 30
1202 12 f. Anniversary Emblem (International Fair) . . . 55 30

333 "St. Bernard of Siena and St. John the Baptist"

334 National Swimming Centre (Roger Taillibert)

1987. Paintings by Giovanni Ambrogio Bevilacqua in State Museum. Multicoloured.
1203 10 f. Type **333** 50 40
1204 18 f. "St. Jerome and St. Francis of Assisi" 90 60

1987. Europa. Architecture. Multicoloured.
1205 12 f. Type **334** . . . . 1·00 30
1206 20 f. European Communities' Court of Justice . . . . . 2·00 80

335 "Consecration" (stained glass window by Gustav Zanter)

336 Charles Metz (first President) (after Jean-Baptiste Fresez)

1987. Millenary of St. Michael's Church. Multicoloured.
1207 12 f. Type **335** 50 30
1208 20 f. Baroque organ-chest . 1·10 70

1987. Chamber of Deputies.
1209 **336** 6 f. brown 30 20
1210 – 12 f. blue 50 40
DESIGN: 12 f. Chamber of Deputies building.

337 Hennesbau, Niederfeulen

338 Annunciation

1987. Rural Architecture. Each ochre, brown and blue.
1211 10 f. Type **337** 60 30
1212 12 f. 18th-century dwelling house converted to health centre, Mersch 60 30
1213 100 f. 18th-century house converted to Post Office, Bertrange . . . . 4·00 1·75

1987. National Welfare Fund. Illustrations from 15th-century Paris "Book of Hours". Multicoloured.
1214 6 f. + 1 f. Type **338** 70 50
1215 10 f. + 1 f. Visitation . . . . 1·25 1·00
1216 12 f. + 2 f. Adoration of the Magi . . . . 1·50 1·00
1217 18 f. + 2 f. Presentation in the Temple . . . . 2·00 2·00
1218 20 f. + 8 f. Flight into Egypt 4·00 5·00

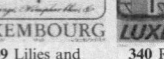

339 Lilies and Water-lily

340 Rail, Road and Water Transport

1988. Luxembourg Culture. Flower Illustrations by Pierre-Joseph Redoute. Multicoloured.
1219 6 f. Type **339** 75 30
1220 10 f. Primulas and double narcissus 75 40
1221 12 f. Tulips and chrysanthemums . . . . . 1·50 20
1222 50 f. Irises and gorterias . . . 2·50 1·25

1988. European Conference of Ministers of Transport, Luxembourg (1223) and 25th Anniv of Eurocontrol (air safety organization) (1224). Multicoloured.
1223 12 f. Type **340** 60 35
1224 20 f. Boeing 747 airplane . . 1·25 80

342 Wiltz Town Hall and Cross of Justice

1988. Tourism. Multicoloured.
1226 10 f. Type **342** 70 30
1227 12 f. Differdange Castle (vert) 70 30
See also Nos. 1254/5 and 1275/6.

343 Athletes

1988. 50th Anniv of League of Luxembourg Student Sports Associations.
1228 **343** 12 f. multicoloured . . . 60 15

344 Automated Mail Sorting

1988. Europa. Transport and Communications. Multicoloured.
1229 12 f. Type **344** . . . . 1·50 20
1230 20 f. Electronic communications . . . . 2·00 90

345 Jean Monnet (statesman, birth centenary)

346 Emblem and Flame

1988. European Anniversaries.
1231 **345** 12 f. pink, brown and light brown 75 20
1232 – 12 f. brown and green . 1·25 20
DESIGN: No. 1232, European Investment Bank headquarters, Kirchberg (30th anniv).

1988. Olympic Games, Seoul.
1233 **346** 12 f. multicoloured 60 15

347 Septfontaines Castle

348 Annunciation to Shepherds

1988. Doorways.
1234 **347** 12 f. black and brown . 45 15
1235 – 25 f. black and green . . 90 80
1236 – 50 f. black and brown . 1·75 1·25
DESIGNS: 25 f. National Library; 50 f. Holy Trinity Church.

1988. National Welfare Fund. Illustrations from 16th-century "Book of Hours". Multicoloured.
1237 9 f. + 1 f. Type **348** 60 40
1238 12 f. + 2 f. Adoration of the Magi 70 40
1239 18 f. + 2 f. Madonna and Child 2·25 2·25
1240 20 f. + 8 f. Pentecost . . . 2·75 2·75

349 C. M. Spoo (promoter of Luxembourgish)

350 Grand Ducal Family Vault Bronze (Auguste Tremont)

1989. Anniversaries.
1241 **349** 12 f. black, red & brown 60 25
1242 – 18 f. multicoloured . . . 90 50
1243 – 20 f. red, black and grey 1·25 75
DESIGNS: 12 f. Type **349** (75th death anniv); 18 f. Stylized inking pad (125th anniv of Book Workers' Federation); 20 f. Henri Dunant (founder of International Red Cross) (75th anniv of Luxembourg Red Cross).

1989. 150th Anniv of Independence.
1244 **350** 12 f. multicoloured . . . 60 30

351 "Astra" Satellite and Map on T.V. Screens

352 Cyclist

1989. Launch of 16-channel T.V. Satellite.
1245 **351** 12 f. multicoloured . . . 60 30

1989. Start in Luxembourg of Tour de France Cycling Race.
1246 **352** 9 f. multicoloured . . . 70 30

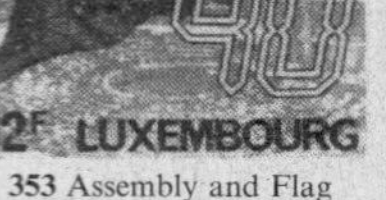
353 Assembly and Flag

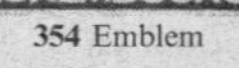
354 Emblem

1989. 40th Anniv of Council of Europe.
1247 **353** 12 f. multicoloured . . . 70 30

1989. Centenary of Interparliamentary Union.
1248 **354** 12 f. yellow, blue & ind 70 30

355 Hands

356 "Three Children in a Park" (anon)

1989. 3rd Direct Elections to European Parliament.
1249 **355** 12 f. multicoloured . . . 70 30

1989. Europa. Children's Games and Toys. Multicoloured.
1250 12 f. Type **356** 75 30
1251 20 f. "Child with Drum" (anon) 1·75 95

357 Grand Duke Jean

358 Charles IV

1989. 25th Anniv of Accession of Grand Duke Jean.
1252 **357** 3 f. black and orange . . 10 10
1253 9 f. black and green . . . 50 30

1989. Tourism. As T **342**. Multicoloured.
1254 12 f. Clervaux Castle 50 30
1255 18 f. 1st-century bronze wild boar, Titelberg 90 65

1989. Luxembourg History. Stained Glass Windows by Joseph Oterberger, Luxembourg Cathedral. Multicoloured.
1256 12 f. Type **358** 75 30
1257 20 f. John the Blind . . . . 1·25 85
1258 25 f. Wenceslas II . . . . . 1·25 85

359 St. Lambert and St. Blase, Fennange

360 Funfair (650th anniv of Schueberfouer)

1989. National Welfare Fund. Restored Chapels (1st series). Multicoloured.
1259 9 f. + 1 f. Type **359** 50 30
1260 12 f. + 2 f. St. Quirinus, Luxembourg (horiz) . . . 60 50
1261 18 f. + 3 f. St. Anthony the Hermit, Reisdorf (horiz) . 1·50 1·50
1262 25 f. + 8 f. The Hermitage, Hachiville . . . . 2·00 2·00
See also Nos. 1280/3 and 1304/7.

1990. Anniversaries.
1263 **360** 9 f. multicoloured . . . 45 30
1264 – 12 f. brown, pink & black 55 30
1265 – 18 f. multicoloured . . . 90 50
DESIGNS: 12 f. Batty Weber (writer, 50th death anniv); 18 f. Dish aerial (125th anniv of International Telecommunications Union).

361 Troops at Fortress

1990. Luxembourg Culture. Etchings of the Fortress by Christoph Wilhelm Selig. Multicoloured.
1266 9 f. Type **361** 60 30
1267 12 f. Soldiers by weir 70 40
1268 20 f. Distant view of fortress 1·25 60
1269 25 f. Walls . . . . 1·75 90

362 Paul Eyschen (75th anniv)

363 "Psallus pseudoplatini" (male and female) on Maple

1990. Statesmen's Death Anniversaries.
1270 **362** 9 f. brown and blue . . 50 30
1271 – 12 f. blue and brown . . 60 40
DESIGN: 12 f. Emmanuel Servais (centenary).

1990. Centenary of Luxembourg Naturalists' Society.
1272 **363** 12 f. multicoloured . . . 70 40

364 General Post Office, Luxembourg City

365 Hammelsmarsch Fountain (Will Lofy)

1990. Europa. Post Office Buildings.
1273 **364** 12 f. black and brown . 75 30
1274 – 20 f. black and blue . . 1·50 70
DESIGN—VERT: 20 f. Esch-sur-Alzette Post Office.

1990. Tourism. As T **342**. Multicoloured.
1275 12 f. Mondercange administrative offices . . . 65 30
1276 12 f. Schifflange town hall and church 65 30

1990. Fountains. Multicoloured.
1277 12 f. Type **365** 60 30
1278 25 f. Doves Fountain . . . 1·25 80
1279 50 f. Maus Ketty Fountain, Mondorf-les-Bains (Will Lofy) . . . . 2·25 1·50

366 Congregation of the Blessed Virgin Mary, Vianden

368 "Geastrum varians"

1990. National Welfare Fund. Restored Chapels (2nd series). Multicoloured.
1280 9 f. + 1 f. Type **366** 60 40
1281 12 f. + 2 f. Notre Dame, Echternach (horiz) . . . 70 50
1282 18 f. + 3 f. Consoler of the Afflicted, Grentzingen (horiz) 1·25 1·25
1283 25 f. + 8 f. St. Pirmin, Kaundorf . . . . 1·75 1·75

1991. Fungi. Illustrations by Pierre-Joseph Redoute. Multicoloured.
1285 14 f. Type **368** . . . . 1·00 40
1286 14 f. "Agaricus (Gymnopus) thiebautii" . . . . . . 1·00 40
1287 18 f. "Agaricus (Lepiota) lepidocephalus" . . . . . 1·50 75
1288 25 f. "Morchella favosa" . . 2·00 1·25

369 "View from the Trier Road"

370 Dicks (after Jean Goedert)

1991. Luxembourg Culture. 50th Death Anniv of Sosthene Weis (painter). Multicoloured.
1289 14 f. Type **369** 80 40
1290 18 f. "Vauban Street and the Viaduct" . . . . 1·00 60
1291 25 f. "St. Ulric Street" (vert) 1·50 75

1991. Death Centenary of Edmond de la Fontaine (pen-name Dicks) (poet).
1292 **370** 14 f. multicoloured . . . 70 40

371 Claw grasping Piece of Metal (after Emile Kirscht)

372 National Miners' Monument, Kayl

1991. 75th Anniv of Trade Union Movement in Luxembourg.
1293 **371** 14 f. multicoloured . . . 70 40

1991. Tourism. Multicoloured.
1294 14 f. Type **372** 75 40
1295 14 f. Magistrates' Court, Redange-sur-Attert (horiz) 75 40

373 Earth and Orbit of "Astra 1A" and "1B" Satellites

374 Telephone

1991. Europa. Europe in Space. Multicoloured.
1296 14 f. Type **373** 90 40
1297 18 f. Betzdorf Earth Station 1·50 85

1991. Posts and Telecommunications.
1298 **374** 4 f. brown 50 20
1299 – 14 f. blue 60 20
DESIGN: 14 f. Postbox.

375 1936 International Philatelic Federation Congress Stamp

376 Girl's Head

1991. 50th Stamp Day.
1300 **375** 14 f. multicoloured . . . 60 40
The stamp illustrated on No. 1300 incorrectly shows a face value of 10 f.

1991. Mascarons (stone faces on buildings) (1st series).
1301 **376** 14 f. black, buff & brown 60 40
1302 – 25 f. black, buff and pink 1·25 80
1303 – 50 f. black, buff and blue 2·25 1·60
DESIGNS: 25 f. Woman's head; 50 f. Man's head.
See also Nos. 1320/22.

377 Chapel of St. Donatus, Arsdorf

378 Jean-Pierre Pescatore Foundation

1991. National Welfare Fund. Restored Chapels (3rd series). Multicoloured.
1304 14 f. + 2 f. Type **377** 80 60
1305 14 f. + 2 f. Chapel of Our Lady of Sorrows, Brandenbourg (horiz) 80 60
1306 18 f. + 3 f. Chapel of Our Lady, Luxembourg (horiz) 1·25 1·25
1307 25 f. + 7 f. Chapel of the Hermitage, Wolwelange . . 1·75 1·75

1992. Buildings. Multicoloured.
1308 14 f. Type **378** 55 35
1309 14 f. Higher Technology Institute, Kirchberg 55 35
1310 14 f. New Fairs and Congress Centre, Kirchberg 55 35

379 Inner Courtyard, Bettembourg Castle

1992. Tourism. Multicoloured.
1311 18 f. Type **379** 75 45
1312 25 f. Walferdange Railway Station . . . . 1·00 60

380 Athlete (detail of mural, Armand Strainchamps)

1992. Olympic Games, Barcelona.
1313 **380** 14 f. multicoloured . . . 55 35

381 Luxembourg Pavilion

382 Lions Emblem

1992. "Expo '92" World's Fair, Seville.
1314 **381** 14 f. multicoloured . . . 55 35

1992. 75th Anniv of Lions International.
1315 **382** 14 f. multicoloured . . . 55 35

383 Memorial Tablet (Lucien Wercollier)

384 Nicholas Gonner (editor)

1992. 50th anniv of General Strike.
1316 **383** 18 f. brown, grey and red 75 45

1992. Europa. 500th anniv of Discovery of America by Columbus. Luxembourg Emigrants to America.
1317 **384** 14 f. brown, black and grn 55 35
1318 – 22 f. blue, black & orange 90 55
DESIGN: 22 f. Nicolas Becker (writer).

385 Star and European Community Emblem

386 Posthorn and Letters

1992. Single European Market.
1319 **385** 14 f. multicoloured . . . 55 35

1992. Mascarons (2nd series). As T **376**.
1320 14 f. black, buff and green 55 35
1321 22 f. black, buff and blue . 90 55
1322 50 f. black, buff and purple 2·00 1·25
DESIGNS: 14 f. Ram's head; 22 f. Lion's head; 50 f. Goat's head.

1992. 150th Anniv of Post and Telecommunications Office. Designs showing stained glass windows by Auguste Tremont. Multicoloured.
1323 14 f. Type **386** 55 35
1324 22 f. Post rider 90 55
1325 50 f. Telecommunications . . 2·00 1·25

387 Hazel Grouse

388 Grand Duke Jean

1992. National Welfare Fund. Birds (1st series). Multicoloured.
1326 14 f. + 2 f. Type **387** 65 50
1327 14 f. + 2 f. Golden oriole (vert) 65 50
1328 18 f. + 3 f. Black stork . . 85 85
1329 22 f. + 7 f. Red kite (vert) . 1·10 1·10
See also Nos. 1364/7 and 1383/6.

1993.
1330 **388** 1 f. black and yellow . . 10 10
1332 5 f. black and yellow . . 20 10
1334 7 f. black and brown . . 30 20
1337 14 f. black and purple . . 55 35
1338 15 f. black and green . . 55 35
1340 18 f. black and yellow . 75 45
1341 20 f. black and red . . . 75 45
1343 22 f. black and green . . 90 55
1345 25 f. black and blue . . 1·00 60
1349 100 f. black and brown . 3·75 2·25

389 Old Ironworks Cultural Centre, Steinfort

1993. Tourism. Multicoloured.
1350 14 f. Type **389** 55 35
1351 14 f. "Children with Grapes" Fountain, Schwebsingen . . 55 35

390 Collage by Maurice Esteve

1993. New Surgical Techniques.
1352 **390** 14 f. multicoloured . . . 55 35

391 Hotel de Bourgogne (Prime Minister's offices)

1993. Historic Houses. Multicoloured.
1353 14 f. Type **391** 55 35
1354 20 f. Simons House (now Ministry of Agriculture) . . 85 50
1355 50 f. Cassal House . . . . . 2·00 1·25

392 "Rezlop" (Fernand Roda)

1993. Europa. Contemporary Art. Multicoloured.
1356 14 f. Type **392** 55 35
1357 22 f. "So Close" (Sonja Roef) 90 55

393 Monument (detail D. Donzelli), Tetange Cemetery

LUXEMBOURG
394 Emblem

1993. 75th Death Anniv of Jean Schortgen (first worker elected to parliament).
1358 **393** 14 f. multicoloured . . . 55 35

1993. Centenary of Artistic Circle of Luxembourg.
1359 **394** 14 f. mauve and violet . 55 35

395 European Community Ecological Label

396 Tram Motor Unit No. 1 (Transport Museum, Luxembourg)

1993. Protection of Environment.
1360 **395** 14 f. blue, grn & emer . . 55 35

1993. Museum Exhibits. Multicoloured.
1361 14 f. Type **396** 55 35
1362 22 f. Iron ore tipper wagon (National Mining Museum, Rumelange) 85 55
1363 60 f. Horse-drawn carriage (Arts and Ancient Crafts Museum, Wiltz) . . . . . 2·25 1·40

1993. National Welfare Fund. Birds (2nd series). As T **387**. Multicoloured.
1364 14 f. + 2 f. Snipe ("Becassine") 65 50
1365 14 f. + 2 f. Kingfisher ("Martin-Pecheur") (vert) 65 50
1366 18 f. + 3 f. Little ringed plover ("Petit Gravelot") 85 85
1367 22 f. + 7 f. Sand martin ("Hirondelle de Rivage") (vert) . . . . 1·25 1·25

LUXEMBOURG 14 JOSEPH KUTTER 1894–1941
397 "Snow-covered Landscape" (Joseph Kutter)

1994. Artists' Birth Centenaries. Multicoloured.
1368 14 f. Type **397** 60 40
1369 14 f. "The Moselle" (Nico Klopp) 60 40

398 Members' Flags

LUXEMBOURG 14 21e CONGRÈS DE GÉNÉALOGIE ET D'HÉRALDIQUE
399 17th-Century Herald's Tabard

1994. 4th Direct Elections to European Parliament.
1370 **398** 14 f. multicoloured . . . 60 40

1994. Congresses. Multicoloured.
1371 14 f. Type **399** (21st International Genealogy and Heraldry Congress) . . . 60 40
1372 18 f. International Police Association emblem on map (14th World Congress) . . 75 45

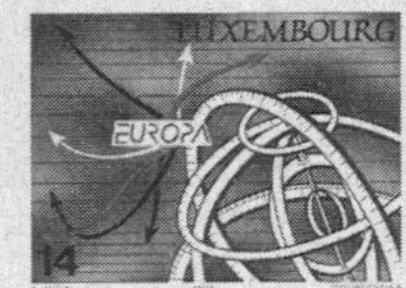

400 Arrows and Terrestrial Globe

1994. Europa. Discoveries. Multicoloured.
1373 14 f. Type **400** 60 40
1374 22 f. Chart, compass rose and sails 90 55

401 "Family" (Laura Lammar)

1994. International Year of the Family.
1375 **401** 25 f. multicoloured . . . 1·00 60

402 Crowds cheering American Soldiers

1994. 50th Anniv of Liberation.
1376 **402** 14 f. multicoloured . . . 60 40

403 Western European Union Emblem (40th anniv)

1994. Anniversaries and Campaigns.
1377 **403** 14 f. blue, lilac and ultramarine 60 40
1378 – 14 f. multicoloured . . . 60 40
1379 – 14 f. multicoloured . . . 60 40
DESIGNS—No. 1378, Emblem (25th anniv in Luxembourg of European Communities' Office for Official Publications); 1379, 10th-century B.C. ceramic bowl from cremation tomb, Bigelbach (European Bronze Age Campaign).

404 Munster Abbey (General Finance Inspectorate)

1994. Former Refuges now housing Government Offices. Multicoloured.
1380 15 f. Type **404** 65 40
1381 25 f. Holy Spirit Convent (Ministry of Finance) . . . 1·00 60
1382 60 f. St. Maximine Abbey of Trier (Ministry of Foreign Affairs) . . . . 2·50 1·50

1994. National Welfare Fund. Birds (3rd series). As T **387**. Multicoloured.
1383 14 f. + 2 f. Stonechat ("Traquet Patre") (vert) 65 50
1384 14 f. + 2 f. Common partridge ("Perdix Grise") 65 60
1385 18 f. + 3 f. Blue-headed wagtail ("Bergeronnette Printaniere") 85 85
1386 22 f. + 7 f. Great grey shrike ("Pie-Grieche Grise") (vert) 1·25 1·25

OFFICIAL STAMPS

1875. Stamps of 1859–72 optd **OFFICIEL**. Roul.
O79 **3** 1 c. brown . . . . 22·00 40·00
O80 2 c. black . . . . 22·00 40·00
O81 **4** 10 c. lilac £2250 £2500
O82 12½ c. red £450 £550
O83 20 c. brown . . . . 40·00 60·00
O84 25 c. blue £250 £150
O85 30 c. purple . . . . 28·00 70·00
O88 40 c. orange £170 £250
O87 1 f. on 37½ c. bistre (No. 37) £140 18·00

1875. Stamps of 1874–79 optd **OFFICIEL**. Perf.
O 89 **3** 1 c. brown . . . . 7·00 30·00
O 90 2 c. black . . . . 8·00 30·00
O 91 4 c. green £100 £140
O 92 5 c. yellow . . . . 50·00 70·00
O 93a **4** 10 c. lilac . . . . 80·00 £100
O111 12½ c. red . . . . 55·00 80·00
O 98 20 c. brown . . . .
O 99a 25 c. blue . . . . 2·00 2·50
O 96 1 f. on 37½ c. bistre (No. 56) 30·00 50·00

1881. Stamp of 1859 optd **S. P.** Roul.
O116 **3** 40 c. orange . . . . 30·00 70·00

1881. Stamps of 1874–79 optd **S. P.** Perf.
O128 **3** 1 c. brown . . . . 7·00 8·00
O129 2 c. black . . . . 8·00 10·00
O118 4 c. green £180 £200
O123 5 c. yellow . . . . 70·00 90·00
O124 **4** 10 c. lilac £100 £130
O131 12½ c. red £120 £160
O132 20 c. brown . . . . 65·00 80·00
O133 25 c. blue . . . . 65·00 80·00
O134 30 c. red . . . . 65·00 80·00
O120 1 f. on 37½ c. bistre (No. 56) 26·00 50·00

1882. Stamps of 1882 optd **S. P.**
O141 **7** 1 c. grey 25 40
O142 2 c. brown 25 40
O143 4 c. olive 25 50
O144 5 c. green 30 60
O181 10 c. red . . . . 11·00 15·00
O158 12½ c. blue . . . . 2·00 5·00
O159 20 c. orange . . . . 2·00 4·00
O183 25 c. blue . . . . 16·00 22·00
O149 30 c. olive . . . . 4·00 9·00
O150 50 c. brown . . . . 1·00 3·00
O151 1 f. lilac . . . . 1·00 4·00
O152 5 f. orange . . . . 12·00 24·00

1891. Stamps of 1891 optd **S. P.**
O188 **8** 10 c. red 25 50
O191 12½ c. green . . . . 7·00 7·00
O192 20 c. orange . . . . 10·00 9·00
O193 25 c. blue 30 55
O194 30 c. green . . . . 8·50 9·00
O195 37½ c. green . . . . 9·00 9·00
O196 50 c. brown . . . . 8·00 10·00
O197 1 f. purple . . . . 8·00 12·00
O198 2½ f. black . . . . 38·00 75·00
O199 5 f. lake . . . . 27·00 55·00

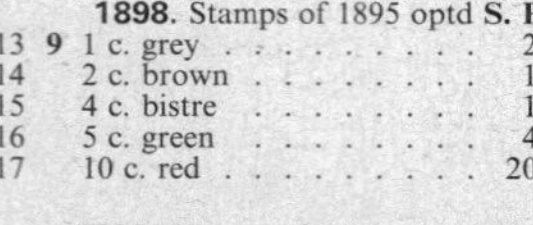

1898. Stamps of 1895 optd **S. P.**
O213 **9** 1 c. grey . . . . 2·00 2·00
O214 2 c. brown . . . . 1·25 1·50
O215 4 c. bistre . . . . 1·25 1·50
O216 5 c. green . . . . 4·00 5·00
O217 10 c. red . . . . 20·00 38·00

1908. Stamps of 1906 optd **Officiel**.
O218 **10** 1 c. grey 10 30
O219 2 c. brown 10 30
O220 4 c. bistre 10 30
O221 5 c. green 10 30
O271 5 c. mauve 10 30
O222 6 c. lilac 10 30
O223 7½ c. yellow 10 30
O224 10 c. red 20 40
O225 12½ c. slate 20 50
O226 15 c. brown 30 50
O227 20 c. orange 30 60
O228 25 c. blue 30 60
O229 30 c. olive . . . . 3·00 6·00
O230 37½ c. green 50 60
O231 50 c. brown . . . . 80 1·25
O232 87½ c. blue . . . . 2·00 3·50
O233 1 f. purple . . . . 3·00 4·00
O234 2½ f. red . . . . 60·00 60·00
O235 5 f. purple . . . . 50·00 50·00

1915. Stamps of 1914 optd **Officiel**.
O236 **13** 10 c. purple 20 70
O237 12½ c. green 20 70
O238 15 c. brown 20 70
O239 17½ c. brown 20 70
O240 25 c. blue 20 70
O241 30 c. brown . . . . 1·50 4·50
O242 35 c. blue . . . . 20 1·25
O243 37½ c. brown . . . . 20 1·50
O244 40 c. red . . . . 30 1·25
O245 50 c. grey . . . . 30 1·00
O246 62½ c. green . . . . 30 1·50
O247 87½ c. orange . . . . 30 1·75
O248 1 f. brown . . . . 30 1·50
O249 2½ f. red . . . . 30 2·50
O250 5 f. violet . . . . 30 3·00

1922. Stamps of 1921 optd **Officiel**.
O251 **17** 2 c. brown 10 20
O252 3 c. green 10 20
O253 6 c. purple 10 40
O272 10 c. green 10 30
O273 15 c. green 10 30
O274 15 c. orange 10 30
O256 20 c. orange 10 40
O275 20 c. green 10 30
O257 25 c. green 10 40
O258 30 c. red 10 40
O259 40 c. orange 10 40
O260 50 c. blue 20 60
O276 50 c. red 20 50
O261 75 c. red 20 60
O277 75 c. blue 20 50
O266 80 c. black 20 50
O263 **18** 1 f. red . . . . 30 2·00
O278 1 f. blue . . . . 30 1·00
O267 – 2 f. blue . . . . 1·00 2·00
O279 – 2 f. brown . . . . 1·50 4·00
O269 – 5 f. violet . . . . 5·00 10·00

1922. Stamps of 1923 optd **Officiel**.
O268b **28** 3 f. blue . . . . 40 1·75
O270 **26** 10 f. black . . . . 8·00 25·00

1926. Stamps of 1926 optd **Officiel**.
O280 **32** 5 c. mauve 10 20
O281 10 c. green 10 20
O298 15 c. black 30 80
O282 20 c. orange 10 20
O283 25 c. green 10 20
O300 25 c. brown 20 60
O301 30 c. green . . . . 30 1·40
O302 30 c. violet 30 80
O303 35 c. violet 30 80
O304 35 c. green 30 80
O286 40 c. brown 10 20
O287 50 c. brown 10 20
O307 60 c. green 30 60
O288 65 c. brown 10 40
O308 70 c. violet . . . . 3·00 6·00
O289 75 c. red 10 40
O309 75 c. brown 30 60
O291 80 c. brown 10 40
O292 90 c. red 20 60
O293 1 f. black 20 50
O312 1 f. red . . . . 40 1·60
O294 1¼ f. blue 10 50
O313 1¼ f. yellow . . . . 2·00 6·00
O314 1¼ f. green . . . . 1·90 4·00
O315 1½ f. blue . . . . 30 1·40
O316 1¾ f. blue . . . . 40 1·50

1928. Stamp of 1928 optd **Officiel**.
O317 **37** 2 f. black . . . . 40 1·50

1931. Stamp of 1931 optd **Officiel**.
O318 **43** 20 f. green . . . . 2·00 7·00

1934. Stamp of 1934 optd **Officiel**.
O319 **47** 5 f. green . . . . 1·40 5·00

1935. No. 340 optd **Officiel**.
O341 **52** 10 f. green . . . . 1·25 6·00

POSTAGE DUE STAMPS

D **12**. Arms of Luxembourg

D 77

1907.
D173 D **12** 5 c. black and green . 10 20
D174 10 c. black and green 1·10 20
D175 12½ c. black and green 30 80
D176 20 c. black and green 60 80
D177 25 c. black and green 10·00 1·25
D178 50 c. black and green 50 3·00
D179 1 f. black and green . 30 3·00

1920. Surch.
D193 D **12** 15 on 12½ c. blk & grn 1·00 6·00
D194 30 on 25 c. blk & grn 1·25 7·00

1922.
D221 D **12** 5 c. red and green . . 20 40
D222 10 c. red and green . . 20 30
D223 20 c. red and green . . 20 30
D224 25 c. red and green . . 20 30
D225 30 c. red and green . . 40 30
D226 35 c. red and green . . 40 20
D227 50 c. red and green . . 40 30
D228 60 c. red and green . . 30 30
D229 70 c. red and green . . 40 30
D230 75 c. red and green . . 40 20
D231 1 f. red and green . . 20 50
D232 2 f. red and green . . 40 6·50
D233 3 f. red and green . . 1·25 13·00

1946.

D488	D 77	5 c. green	30	30
D489		10 c. green	30	30
D490		20 c. green	30	30
D491		30 c. green	30	30
D492		50 c. green	30	30
D493		70 c. green	40	55
D494		75 c. green	1·25	30
D495		1 f. red	30	30
D496		1 f. 50 red	30	30
D497		2 f. red	30	30
D498		3 f. red	40	30
D499		5 f. red	60	30
D500		10 f. red	1·00	1·50
D501		20 f. red	3·00	16·00

MACAO Pt. 9

A Portuguese territory in China at the mouth of the Canton River.

1884. 1,000 reis = 1 milreis
1894. 78 avos = 1 rupee
1913. 100 avos = 1 pataca

1884. "Crown" key-type inscr "MACAU".

1	P	5 r. black	2·25	1·75
2		10 r. orange	3·50	3·00
21		10 r. green	3·25	3·00
3		20 r. olive	6·00	6·00
27		20 r. red	6·50	4·75
13		25 r. red	2·00	1·25
22		25 r. lilac	1·90	1·60
14		40 r. blue	7·00	5·50
23		40 r. yellow	4·75	3·50
15		50 r. green	9·50	6·50
24		50 r. blue	1·90	1·25
31		80 r. grey	9·00	7·00
7		100 r. lilac	3·00	2·25
17		200 r. orange	4·50	3·25
9		300 r. brown	4·00	3·25

1885. "Crown" key type of Macao surch in Reis diagonally and with bar.

19	P	80 r. on 100 r. lilac	6·00	5·00

1885. "Crown" key type of Macao surch thus **5 Reis** diagonally and with bar.

32	P	5 r. on 25 r. red	2·25	2·00
33		10 r. on 25 r. red	3·75	3·00
38		10 r. on 50 r. green	17·00	15·00
35		20 r. on 50 r. green	3·25	2·50
40		40 r. on 50 r. green	13·00	11·00

1885. "Crown" key-type of Macao surch with figure of value only and bar.

41	P	5 on 25 r. red	2·50	2·25
42a		10 on 50 r. green	2·75	2·25

1887. "Crown" key-type of Macao surch horizontally with new value and bar.

43	P	5 r. on 80 r. grey	2·25	2·00
46		5 r. on 100 r. lilac	7·00	6·00
44		10 r. on 80 r. grey	3·75	3·50
47		10 r. on 200 r. orange	12·00	10·00
45		20 r. on 80 r. grey	4·25	3·50

9

1887. Fiscal stamps as **T 9** surch **CORREIO** and new value.

50	5 r. on 10 r. green and brown	16·00	14·00
51	5 r. on 20 r. green and brown	16·00	14·00
52	5 r. on 60 r. green and brown	16·00	14·00
53	10 r. on 10 r. green and brown	20·00	15·00
54	10 r. on 60 r. green and brown	22·00	17·00
55	40 r. on 20 r. green and brown	20·00	16·00

1888. "Embossed" key-type inscr "PROVINCIA DE MACAU".

56	Q	5 r. black	2·00	1·75
57		10 r. green	2·00	1·75
58		20 r. red	2·50	1·75
59		25 r. mauve	3·50	2·25
67		40 r. brown	3·25	2·25
68		50 r. blue	2·25	1·75
69		80 r. grey	2·50	2·00
70		100 r. brown	2·50	2·00
71		200 r. lilac	5·50	3·50
72		300 r. orange	6·50	3·75

1892. No. 71 surch **30 30**.

73	Q	30 on 200 r. lilac	5·00	4·50

1894. "Embossed" key-type of Macao surch **PROVISORIO**, value and Chinese characters.

75b	Q	1 a. on 5 r. black	70	50
76		3 a. on 20 r. red	2·25	1·75
77		4 a. on 25 r. mauve	2·25	1·40
89		5 a. on 30 on 200 r. lilac (No. 73)	4·00	3·75
78		6 a. on 40 r. brown	2·75	1·40
79		8 a. on 50 r. blue	4·50	2·25
80		13 a. on 80 r. grey	3·25	2·75
81		16 a. on 100 r. brown	3·25	2·75
88		31 a. on 200 r. lilac	8·00	6·00
83		47 a. on 300 r. orange	8·00	6·00

1894. "Figures" key-type inscr "MACAU".

91	R	5 r. yellow	1·25	90
92		10 r. mauve	1·25	90
93		15 r. brown	1·50	1·25
94		20 r. lilac	1·50	1·25
95		25 r. green	4·00	3·00
96		50 r. blue	5·00	4·50
97		75 r. red	4·50	4·00
98		80 r. green	4·25	3·50
99		100 r. brown on buff	3·25	3·25
100		150 r. red on rose	4·00	3·25
101		200 r. blue on blue	4·50	4·00
102		300 r. blue on brown	5·50	5·00

1898. As Vasco da Gama types of Portugal but inscr "MACAU".

104	½ a. green	1·00	70
105	1 a. red	1·00	70
106	2 a. purple	1·10	70
107	4 a. green	1·10	70
108	8 a. blue	1·40	1·00
109	12 a. brown	2·25	1·60
110	16 a. brown	2·25	1·50
111	24 a. bistre	2·25	2·00

1898. "King Carlos" key-type inscr "MACAU". Name and value in black.

112	S	½ a. grey	30	20
113		1 a. yellow	40	20
114		2 a. green	45	25
115		2½ a. brown	70	55
116		3 a. lilac	70	55
174		3 a. grey	80	75
117		4 a. green	1·00	80
175		4 a. red	80	75
176		5 a. brown	90	80
177		6 a. brown	95	80
119		8 a. blue	1·10	80
178		8 a. brown	1·75	1·40
120		10 a. blue	1·10	80
121		12 a. red	1·75	1·25
179		12 a. purple	5·50	4·25
122		13 a. mauve	1·75	1·25
123		15 a. green	4·50	3·50
124		16 a. blue on blue	2·00	1·75
181		18 a. brown on pink	4·50	3·25
125		20 a. brown on yellow	2·00	1·75
126		24 a. brown on yellow	2·00	1·75
127		31 a. purple on pink	2·25	1·90
128		47 a. blue on pink	3·50	2·75
183		47 a. blue on yellow	6·00	4·25
129		78 a. black on blue	4·50	4·00

1900. "King Carlos" key-type of Macao surch **PROVISORIO** and new value.

132	S	5 on 13 a. mauve	90	70
133		10 on 16 a. blue on blue	1·00	80
134		15 on 24 a. brown on yell	1·25	1·00
135		20 on 31 a. purple on pink	1·25	1·00

1902. Various types of Macao surch.

138	Q	6 a. on 5 r. black	90	70
142	R	6 a. on 5 r. yellow	80	60
136	P	6 a. on 10 r. orange	2·00	1·75
137		6 a. on 10 r. green	1·25	1·10
139	Q	6 a. on 10 r. green	90	70
143	R	6 a. on 10 r. mauve	1·00	70
144		6 a. on 15 r. brown	1·00	70
145		6 a. on 25 r. green	85	60
140	Q	6 a. on 40 r. brown	90	70
146	R	6 a. on 80 r. green	85	65
148		6 a. on 100 r. brn on buff	85	60
149		6 a. on 200 r. blue on blue	90	60
151	V	18 a. on 2½ r. brown	1·25	1·10
153	Q	18 a. on 20 r. red	1·75	1·25
162	R	18 a. on 20 r. lilac	2·10	1·50
154	Q	18 a. on 25 r. mauve	12·00	9·50
163	R	18 a. on 50 r. blue	2·10	1·75
165		18 a. on 75 r. red	2·25	1·75
155	Q	18 a. on 80 r. grey	15·00	15·00
156		18 a. on 100 r. brown	2·50	2·25
158	Q	18 a. on 200 r. lilac	15·00	14·00
160		18 a. on 300 r. orange	2·50	2·00

1902. "King Carlos" type of Macao optd **PROVISORIO**.

168	S	2 a. green	2·25	1·60
169		4 a. green	2·00	1·50
170		8 a. blue	2·00	1·50
171		10 a. blue	2·00	1·50
172		12 a. red	3·75	2·75

1905. No. 179 surch **10 AVOS** and bar.

184	S	10 a. on 12 a. purple	2·25	2·00

1910. "Due" key-type of Macao, but with words "PORTEADO" and "RECEBER" cancelled.

185	W	½ a. green	1·00	80
186		1 a. green	1·00	80
187		2 a. grey	1·10	1·00

1911. "King Carlos" key-type of Macao optd **REPUBLICA**.

188	S	½ a. grey	25	20
189		1 a. orange	25	20
190		2 a. green	25	20
191		3 a. grey	25	20
192		4 a. red	70	65
193		5 a. brown	70	65
194		6 a. brown	70	65
195		8 a. brown	70	65
196		10 a. blue	70	65
197		13 a. lilac	90	70
198		16 a. blue on blue	90	70
199		18 a. brown on pink	1·75	1·60
200		20 a. brown on cream	1·75	1·60
201		31 a. purple on pink	1·75	1·60
202		47 a. blue and yellow	3·00	3·25
203		78 a. black and blue	3·75	3·25

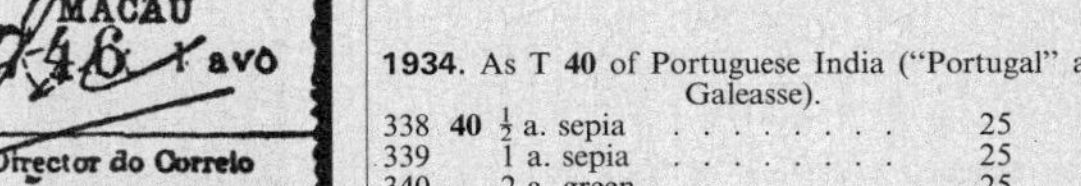

30 32

1911. Fiscal stamp surch **POSTAL 1 AVO** and bar.

204	30	1 a. on 5 r. brown, yellow and black	85	70

1911. Stamps bisected and surch.

205	S	2 a. on half of 4 a. red (No. 175)	1·00	1·00
206		5 a. on half of 10 a. blue (No. 120)	2·00	2·00
207		5 a. on half of 10 a. blue (No. 171)	1·75	1·75

1911.

208	32	1 a. black	80·00	80·00
209		2 a. black	85·00	85·00

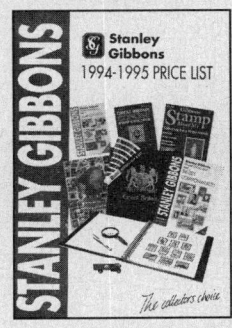

1913. Provisionals of 1902 surch in addition with new value and bars over old value and optd **REPUBLICA**.

212	R	2 a. on 18 a. on 20 r. lilac (No. 162)	90	80
213		2 a. on 18 a. on 50 r. blue (No. 163)	90	80
215		2 a. on 18 a. on 75 r. red (No. 165)	90	80
216		2 a. on 18 a. on 150 r. red on rose (No. 166)	90	80

1913. Provisionals of 1902 optd **REPUBLICA**.

218	Q	6 a. on 5 r. (No. 138)	1·25	1·10
284	R	6 a. on 5 r. (No. 142)	75	65
217	P	6 a. on 10 r. (No. 137)	3·00	2·50
285	Q	6 a. on 10 r. (No. 139)	55	40
286	R	6 a. on 10 r. (No. 143)	55	40
287		6 a. on 15 r. (No. 144)	45	40
288		6 a. on 25 r. (No. 145)	45	40
220	Q	6 a. on 40 r. (No. 140)	1·40	1·10
289	R	6 a. on 80 r. (No. 146)	45	40
291		6 a. on 100 r. (No. 148)	95	70
292		6 a. on 200 r. (No. 149)	45	40
283	S	10 a. on 12 a. (No. 184)	40	35
293	V	18 a. on 2½ r. (No. 151)	70	45
229	Q	18 a. on 20 r. (No. 153)	1·75	1·60
295	R	18 a. on 20 r. (No. 162)	95	85
296		18 a. on 50 r. (No. 163)	1·10	95
298		18 a. on 75 r. (No. 165)	1·10	1·00
230	Q	18 a. on 100 r. (No. 156)	7·50	7·00
299	R	18 a. on 150 r. (No. 166)	1·10	1·00
233	Q	18 a. on 300 r. (No. 160)	3·00	3·00
300	R	18 a. on 300 r. (No. 167)	1·10	1·00

1913. Stamps of 1911 issue surch.

252	S	½ a. on 5 a. brown	80	70
255		1 a. on 13 a. lilac	80	70
253		4 a. on 8 a. brown	1·25	95

1913. Vasco da Gama stamps of Macao optd **REPUBLICA**, and the 12 a. surch **10 A**.

256	½ a. green	60	45
257	1 a. red	60	45
258	2 a. purple	60	45
259	4 a. green	60	45
260	8 a. blue	95	70
261	10 a. on 12 a. brown	1·75	1·00
262	16 a. brown	1·10	80
263	24 a. bistre	1·60	1·10

1913. "Ceres" key-type inscr "MACAU".

264	U	½ a. olive	35	25
265		1 a. black	35	25
311		1½ a. green	25	20
208		2 a. green	35	25
313		3 a. orange	1·00	1·00
267		4 a. red	90	35
315		4 a. yellow	1·00	1·00
268		5 a. brown	1·00	75
269		6 a. violet	1·00	70
270		8 a. brown	1·00	70
271		10 a. blue	1·00	70
272		12 a. brown	1·00	70
320		14 a. mauve	2·50	2·00
273		16 a. grey	2·00	1·40
274		20 a. brown	2·25	1·75
322		24 a. green	2·50	2·00
323		32 a. brown	2·25	2·00
275		40 a. purple	2·25	1·75
324		56 a. red	3·75	2·75
276		58 a. brown on green	3·50	2·50
325		72 a. brown	6·50	4·00
277		76 a. brown on red	4·25	3·75
278		1 p. orange on pink	4·50	4·00
326		1 p. orange	10·00	8·00
279		3 p. green on blue	16·00	12·00
327		3 p. blue	23·00	22·00
328		5 p. red	32·00	38·00

1915. Nos. 170/1 optd **REPUBLICA**.

281	S	8 a. blue	40	35
282		10 a. blue	40	35

1919. Surch.

301	U	½ a. on 5 a. brn (No. 268)	5·50	4·50
330		1 a. on 24 a. grn (No. 322)	70	65
302	R	2 a. on 6 a. on 25 r. green (No. 288)	9·00	9·00
303		2 a. on 6 a. on 80 r. green (No. 289)	5·00	4·50
304	S	"2 avos" on 6 a. (No. 202)	7·50	6·00
331	U	2 a. on 32 a. (No. 323)	70	65
332		4 a. on 12 a. (No. 272)	70	65
333		5 a. on 6 a. vio (No. 269)	2·00	1·75
334		7 a. on 8 a. brn (No. 270)	1·10	1·00
335		12 a. on 14 a. (No. 320)	1·10	1·00
336		15 a. on 16 a. (No. 273)	1·10	1·00
337		20 a. on 56 a. red (No. 324)	1·60	1·40

1934. As T **40** of Portuguese India ("Portugal" and Galeasse).

338	40	½ a. sepia	25	25
339		1 a. sepia	25	25
340		2 a. green	25	25
341		3 a. mauve	25	25
342		4 a. black	35	25
343		5 a. grey	35	25
344		6 a. brown	35	25
345		7 a. red	35	30
346		8 a. blue	35	30
347		10 a. red	55	50
348		12 a. blue	55	50
349		14 a. olive	55	50
350		15 a. red	55	50
351		20 a. orange	55	50
352		30 a. green	1·50	1·00
353		40 a. violet	1·50	1·00
354		50 a. brown	2·75	1·50
355		1 p. blue	8·00	2·40
356		2 p. brown	11·00	4·25
357		3 p. green	14·25	7·25
358		5 p. mauve	27·00	11·00

1936. Air. Stamps of 1934 optd. **Aviso** and with Greek characters or surch also.

359 **40** 2 a. green 90 80
360 3 a. mauve 90 80
361 5 a. on 6 a. brown 90 80
362 7 a. red 90 80
363 8 a. blue . . . . 1·60 1·40
364 15 a. red . . . . 5·50 2·75

54 Vasco da Gama **56** Aircraft over Globe

1938. Name and value in black.

365 **54** 1 a. olive (postage) 20 20
366 2 a. brown 20 20
367 3 a. violet 20 20
368 4 a. green 20 20
369 – 5 a. red 20 20
370 – 6 a. slate 20 20
371 – 8 a. purple 20 20
372 – 10 a. mauve 40 40
373 – 12 a. red 40 40
374 – 15 a. orange 40 40
375 – 20 a. blue 50 45
376 – 40 a. black . . . . 1·10 70
377 – 50 a. brown . . . . 1·10 70
378 – 1 p. red . . . . 3·50 1·50
379 – 2 p. olive . . . . 7·50 3·25
380 – 3 p. blue . . . . 12·00 4·50
381 – 5 p. brown . . . . 20·00 70·00
382 **56** 1 a. red (air) 15 15
383 2 a. violet 15 15
384 3 a. orange 25 25
385 5 a. blue 35 30
386 10 a. red 65 35
387 20 a. green 95 75
388 50 a. brown . . . . 1·40 95
389 70 a. red . . . . 2·75 1·40
390 1 p. mauve . . . . 6·00 2·40

DESIGNS: Nos. 369/71, Mousinho de Albuquerque; Nos. 372/4, Henry the Navigator; Nos. 375/7, Dam; Nos. 378/81, Afonso de Albuquerque.

1940. Surch.

391 **40** 1 a. on 6 a. brn (No. 344) 1·50 1·00
394 2 a. on 6 a. brn (No. 344) 90 80
395 3 a. on 6 a. brn (No. 344) 90 80
401 – 3 a. on 6 a. slate (No. 370) 10·00 9·00
396 **40** 5 a. on 7 a. red (No. 345) 90 80
397 5 a. on 8 a. blue (No. 346) 90 80
398 8 a. on 30 a. (No. 352) . . 1·90 1·75
399 8 a. on 40 a. (No. 353) . . 1·90 1·75
400 8 a. on 50 a. (No. 354) . . 1·90 1·75

61 Mountain Fort **62** Our Lady of Fatima

1948.

410 – 1 a. brown and orange . . 30 25
427 – 1 a. violet and pink . . . 45 35
411 **61** 2 a. purple 30 20
428 2 a. brown and yellow . . 45 35
412 – 3 a. purple 35 30
429 – 3 a. orange 80 35
413 – 8 a. red 35 20
430 – 8 a. grey 80 35
414 – 10 a. purple 75 30
431 – 10 a. brown and orange . . 90 45
415 – 20 a. blue 75 30
416 – 30 a. grey . . . . 1·10 40
432 – 30 a. blue . . . . 1·75 85
417 – 50 a. brown and buff . . . 1·50 55
433 – 50 a. olive and green . . . 3·00 95
418 – 1 p. green . . . . 11·00 2·75
419 – 1 p. blue . . . . 8·50
434 – 1 p. brown . . . . 4·25 1·60
420 – 2 p. red . . . . 10·00 2·25
421 – 3 p. green . . . . 12·00 3·00
422 – 5 p. violet . . . . 18·00 4·00

DESIGNS—HORIZ: 1 a. Macao house; 3 a. Macao; 8 a. Pria, Grande Bay; 10 a. Leal Senado Sq; 20 a. St. Jerome Hill; 30 a. Street scene; 50 a. Goddess Ma; 5 p. Forest road. VERT: 1 p. Cerco Gateway; 2 p. Barra Pagoda; 3 p. Post Office.

1948. Honouring the Statue of Our Lady of Fatima.

423 **62** 8 a. red . . . . 2·00 1·40

64 Globe and Letter **65** Bells and Dove

1949. 75th Anniv of U.P.U.

424 **64** 32 a. purple . . . . 30·00 8·00

1950. Holy Year.

425 32 a. black . . . . 1·75 1·25
426 50 a. red . . . . 1·75 1·25

DESIGN: 50 a. Angel holding candelabra.

66 Arms and Dragon

1950.

435 **66** 1 a. yellow on cream . . . 30 35
436 2 a. green on green 30 35
437 10 a. purple on green . . . 30 35
438 10 a. mauve on green . . . 30 35

67 F. Mendes Pinto **68** Junk

1951.

439 **67** 1 a. indigo and blue . . . 15 10
440 – 2 a. brown and green . . . 15 10
441 – 3 a. green & light green . . 20 10
442 – 6 a. violet and blue . . . 30 15
443 – 10 a. brown and orange . . 90 30
444 **67** 20 a. purple & lt purple . . 2·75 80
445 – 30 a. brown and green . . 2·75 80
446 – 50 a. red and orange . . . 6·50 2·25
447 – 1 p. ultramarine & blue . . 4·50 1·25
448 – 3 p. black and blue . . . 16·00 3·00
449 **68** 5 p. brown and orange . . 32·00 11·00

DESIGNS—As Type **67**: 2, 10 a. St. Francis Xavier; 3, 50 a. J. Alvares; 6, 30 a. L. de Camoens. As Type **68**: HORIZ:. 1 p. Sampan. VERT: 3 p. Junk.

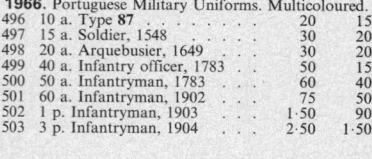

69 Our Lady of Fatima **71** St. Raphael Hospital

1951. Termination of Holy Year.

450 **69** 60 a. mauve and pink . . 1·50 1·25

1952. 1st Tropical Medicine Congress, Lisbon.

451 **71** 6 a. mauve and black . . 80 60

72 St. Francis Xavier Statue **73** The Virgin

1952. 400th Death Anniv of St. Francis Xavier.

452 **72** 3 a. black on cream . . . 20 20
453 – 16 a. brown on buff . . . 80 40
454 – 40 a. black on blue . . . . 1·60 80

DESIGNS: 16 a. Miraculous Arm of St. Francis; 40 a. Tomb of St. Francis.

1953. Missionary Art Exhibition.

455 **73** 8 a. brown and drab . . . 25 25
456 10 a. blue and brown . . . 95 30
457 50 a. green and drab . . . 2·25 1·25

74 Honeysuckle **75** Portuguese Stamp of 1853 and Arms of Portuguese Overseas Provinces

1953. Flowers.

458 **74** 1 a. yellow, green and red 10 10
459 – 3 a. purple, green & yellow 10 10
460 – 5 a. red, green and brown 15 15
461 – 10 a. multicoloured . . . 15 15
462 – 16 a. yellow, green & brown 15 15
463 – 30 a. pink, brown & green 20 15
464 – 39 a. multicoloured 30 25
465 – 1 p. yellow, green & purple 1·40 65
466 – 3 p. red, brown and grey . 2·75 1·10
467 – 5 p. yellow, green and red 5·00 1·50

FLOWERS: 3 a. Myosotis; 5 a. Dragon claw; 10 a. Nunflower; 16 a. Narcissus; 30 a. Peach blossom; 39 a. Lotus blossom; 1 p. Chrysanthemum; 3 p. Plum blossom; 5 p. Tangerine blossom.

1954. Portuguese Postage Stamp Centenary.

468 **75** 10 a. multicoloured 50 50

76 Father M. de Nobrega and Sao Paulo **77** Map of Macao

1954. 4th Centenary of Sao Paulo.

469 **76** 39 a. multicoloured . . . . 1·00 85

1956. Map multicoloured. Values in red, inscr in brown. Colours given are of the backgrounds.

470 **77** 1 a. drab 10 10
471 3 a. slate 10 10
472 5 a. brown 10 10
473 10 a. buff 10 10
474 30 a. blue 30 15
475 40 a. green 45 25
476 90 a. grey . . . . 1·50 55
477 1 p. 50 pink . . . . 2·00 1·40

78 Exhibition Emblem and Atomic Emblems **79** "Cinnamomum camphora"

1958. Brussels International Exhibition.

478 **78** 70 a. multicoloured 55 55

1958. 6th International Congress of Tropical Medicine.

479 **79** 20 a. multicoloured . . . . 2·00 1·60

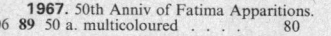

80 Globe girdled by Signs of the Zodiac **81** Boeing 707 over Ermida da Penha

1960. 500th Death Anniv of Prince Henry the Navigator.

480 **80** 2 p. multicoloured 70 60

1960. Air. Multicoloured.

481 50 a. Praia Grande Bay . . . 60 30
482 76 a. Type **81** 80 45
483 3 p. Macao . . . . 1·60 60
484 5 p. Mong Ha . . . . 2·75 1·00
485 10 p. Shore of Praia Grande Bay 5·50 1·00

82 Hockey **83** "Anopheles hycranus"

1962. Sports. Multicoloured.

486 10 a. Type **82** 35 30
487 16 a. Wrestling 95 60
488 20 a. Table tennis 80 45
489 50 a. Motor cycling 80 45
490 1 p. 20 Relay racing . . . . 1·40 1·25
491 2 p. 50 Badminton . . . . . 2·40 2·40

1962. Malaria Eradication.

492 **83** 40 a. multicoloured 55 55

84 Bank Building **85** I.T.U. Emblem and St. Gabriel

1964. Centenary of National Overseas Bank.

493 **84** 20 a. multicoloured . . . . 1·10 1·00

1965. Centenary of I.T.U.

494 **85** 10 a. multicoloured 70 60

86 Infante Dom Henrique Academy and Visconde de Sao Januario Hospital **87** Drummer, 1548

1966. 40th Anniv of National Revolution.

495 **86** 10 a. multicoloured 70 60

1966. Portuguese Military Uniforms. Multicoloured.

496 10 a. Type **87** 20 15
497 15 a. Soldier, 1548 . . . . . 30 20
498 20 a. Arquebusier, 1649 . . . 30 20
499 40 a. Infantry officer, 1783 . . 50 15
500 50 a. Infantryman, 1783 . . . 60 40
501 60 a. Infantryman, 1902 . . . 75 50
502 1 p. Infantryman, 1903 . . . 1·50 90
503 3 p. Infantryman, 1904 . . . 2·50 1·50

88 O. E. Carmo and Patrol Boat "Vega" **89** Arms of Pope Paul VI, and "Golden Rose"

1967. Centenary of Military Naval Assn. Mult.

504 10 a. Type **88** 60 35
505 20 a. Silva Junior and sail frigate "Don Fernando" . . . . . 1·90 1·10

1967. 50th Anniv of Fatima Apparitions.

506 **89** 50 a. multicoloured 80 75

90 Cabral Monument, Lisbon **91** Adm. Gago Coutinho with Sextant

1968. 500th Birth Anniv of Pedro Cabral (explorer). Multicoloured.

507 20 a. Type **90** 50 40
508 70 a. Cabral's statue, Belmonte 1·00 80

1969. Birth Centenary of Admiral Gago Coutinho.

509 **91** 20 a. multicoloured 30 30

92 Church and Convent of Our Lady of the Reliquary, Vidigueira **93** L. A. Rebello da Silva

1969. 500th Birth Anniv of Vasco da Gama (explorer).

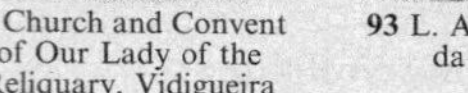

510 **92** 1 p. multicoloured 45 45

1969. Centenary of Overseas Administrative Reforms.

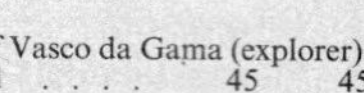

511 **93** 90 a. multicoloured 45 45

94 Bishop D. Belchoir Carneiro

95 Facade of Mother Church, Golega

1969. 400th Anniv of Misericordia Monastery, Macao.
512 **94** 50 a. multicoloured 45 30

1969. 500th Birth Anniv of King Manoel I.
513 **95** 30 a. multicoloured 45 35

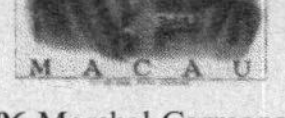
96 Marshal Carmona

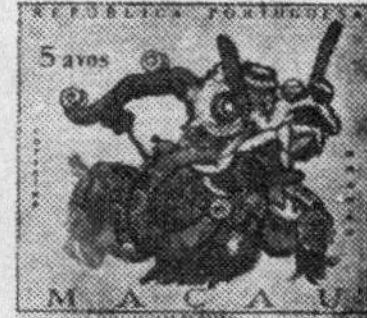
97 Dragon Mask

1970. Birth Centenary of Marshal Carmona.
514 **96** 5 a. multicoloured. 40 30

1971. Chinese Carnival Masks. Multicoloured.
515 5 a. Type **97** 20 20
516 10 a. Lion mask 35 35

98 Portuguese Traders at the Chinese Imperial Court

100 Seaplane "Santa Cruz" arriving at Rio de Janeiro

99 Hockey

101 Lyre Emblem and Theatre Facade

1972. 400th Anniv of Camoens' "The Lusiads" (epic poem).
517 **98** 20 a. multicoloured 1·50 1·10

1972. Olympic Games, Munich.
518 **99** 50 a. multicoloured 40 30

1972. 50th Anniv of First Flight from Lisbon to Rio de Janeiro.
519 **100** 5 p. multicoloured 3·75 2·75

1972. Centenary of Dom Pedro V Theatre, Macao.
520 **101** 2 p. multicoloured 1·25 1·10

102 W.M.O. Emblem

103 Visconde de Sao Januario

1973. Centenary of W.M.O.
521 **102** 20 a. multicoloured 70 60

1974. Centenary of Visconde de Sao Januario Hospital. Multicoloured.
522 15 a. Type **103** 25 15
523 60 a. Hospital buildings of 1874 and 1974 65 35

104 Chinnery (self-portrait)

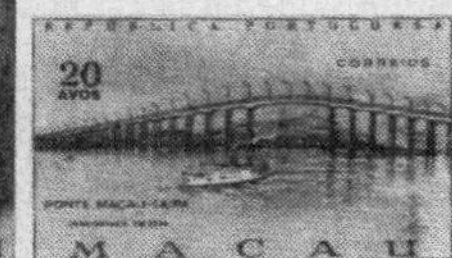
105 Macao-Taipa Bridge

1974. Birth Bicent of George Chinnery (painter).
524 **104** 30 a. multicoloured 80 60

1975. Inauguration of Macao–Taipa Bridge. Multicoloured.
525 20 a. Type **105** 50 35
526 2 p. 20 View of Bridge from below 1·75 1·00

106 Man waving Banner

1975. 1st Anniv of Portuguese Revolution.
527 **106** 10 a. multicoloured 1·00 1·00
528 1 p. multicoloured 2·25 2·00

107 Pou Chai Pagoda

1976. Pagodas. Multicoloured.
529 10 p. Type **107** 3·50 1·25
530 20 p. Tin Hau Pagoda 6·00 2·25

108 Symbolic Figure

1977. Legislative Assembly.
531 **108** 5 a. blue, dp blue & black 1·50 80
532 2 p. brown and black 4·00 1·75
533 5 p. yellow, green & black 5·00 3·75

1979. Nos. 462, 464, 469, 482, 523 and 526 surch.
536 – 10 a. on 16 a. yellow, green and brown 1·75 1·25
537 – 30 a. on 39 a. multicoloured 1·75 1·25
538 **76** 30 a. on 39 a. multicoloured 8·00 5·50
539 – 30 a. on 60 a. multicoloured 2·75 2·00
540 **81** 70 a. on 76 a. multicoloured 9·00 1·00
541 – 2 p. on 2 p. 20 multicoloured 2·40 1·75

111 Camoes and Macao Harbour

113 Buddha and Macao Cathedral

1981. 400th Death Anniv (1980) of Camoes (Portuguese poet).
542 **111** 10 a. multicoloured 20 20
543 30 a. multicoloured 20 20
544 1 p. multicoloured 50 35
545 3 p. multicoloured 1·60 95

1981. Transcultural Psychiatry Symposium.
547 **113** 15 a. multicoloured 15 15
548 40 a. multicoloured 15 15
549 50 a. multicoloured 20 15
550 60 a. multicoloured 25 20
551 1 p. multicoloured 35 25
552 2 p. 20 multicoloured 80 45

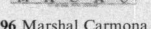

115 Health Services Buildings

1982. Buildings.
554 – 10 a. grey, blue & yellow 10 10
555 – 20 a. black, green & lt grn 10 10
556 **115** 30 a. green, grey & stone 10 10
557 – 40 a. yellow, lt grn & grn 10 10
558 – 60 a. orange, chocolate and brown 15 10
559 – 80 a. pink, green & brown 15 10
560 – 90 a. purple, blue and red 20 10
561 – 1 p. multicoloured 20 10
562 – 1 p. 50 yellow, brn & grey 30 15
563 – 2 p. purple, ultramarine and blue 35 20
564 – 2 p. 50 ultramarine, red and blue 50 30
565 – 3 p. yellow, dp grn & grn 65 40
566 – 7 p. 50 lilac, blue and& red 1·40 85
567 – 10 p. grey, lilac & mauve 1·90 1·10
568 – 15 p. yellow, brown & red 2·75 1·50
DESIGNS: 10 a. Social Welfare Institute; 20 a. Holy House of Mercy; 40 a. Guia lighthouse; 60 a. St. Lawrence's Church; 80 a. St. Joseph's Seminary; 90 a. Pedro V Theatre; 1 p. Cerco city gate; 1 p. 50, St. Domenico's Church; 2 p. Luis de Camoes Museum. 2 p. 50 Ruins of St. Paul's Church; 3 p. Palace of St. Sancha (Governor's residence); 7 p. 50, Senate House; 10 p. Schools Welfare Service building; 15 p. Barracks of the Moors (headquarters of Port Captaincy and Maritime Police).

116 Heng Ho (Moon goddess)

117 Aerial View of Macao, Taipa and Coloane Islands

1982. Autumn Festival. Multicoloured.
569 40 a. Type **116** 15 15
560 1 p. Decorated gourds 30 15
561 2 p. Paper lantern 60 40
562 5 p. Warrior on lion 1·40 1·00

1982. Macao's Geographical Situation. Multicoloured.
573 50 a. Type **117** 20 15
574 3 p. Map of South China 90 70

118 "Switchboard Operators" (Lou Sok Man)

1983. World Communications Year. Children's Drawings. Multicoloured.
575 60 a. Type **118** 20 15
576 3 p. Postman and pillar box (Lai Sok Pek) 90 70
577 6 p. Globe with methods of communication (Loi Chak Keong) 2·00 1·10

119 "Asclepias curassavica"

120 Galleon and Map of Macao (left)

1983. Medicinal Plants. Multicoloured.
578 20 a. Type **119** 25 25
579 40 a. "Acanthus ilicifolius" 30 30
580 60 a. "Melastoma sanguineum" 55 35
581 70 a. Indian lotus ("Nelumbo nucifera") 75 40
582 1 p. 50 "Bombax malabaricum" 1·40 90
583 2 p. 50 "Hibiscus mutabilis" 2·25 1·40

1983. 16th Century Portuguese Discoveries. Multicoloured.
585 4 p. Type **120** 1·60 1·25
586 4 p. Galleon, astrolabe and map of Macao (right) 1·60 1·25
Nos. 585/6 were printed together, se-tenant, forming a composite design.

MINIMUM PRICE

The minimum price quoted is 10p which represents a handling charge rather than a basis for valuing common stamps. For further notes about prices, see introductory pages.

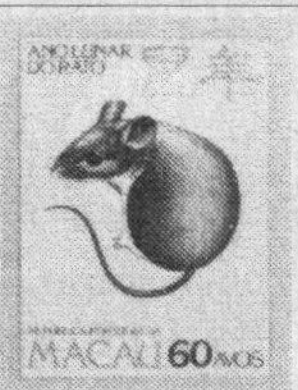
121 Rat

122 Detail of first Macao Stamp, 1884

1984. New Year. "Year of the Rat".
587a **121** 60 a. multicoloured 1·75 1·60

1984. Centenary of Macao Postage Stamps.
588 **122** 40 a. black and red 20 15
589 3 p. black and red 80 55
590 5 p. black and brown 1·25 90

123 Jay

1984. "Ausipex 84" International Stamp Exhibition, Melbourne. Birds. Multicoloured.
592 30 a. White-breasted kingfisher 25 15
593 40 a. Type **123** 25 15
594 50 a. Japanese white eye 40 20
595 70 a. Hoopoe 55 30
596 2 p. 50 Peking robin 1·25 75
597 6 p. Mallard 2·75 1·90

124 Hok Lou T'eng

1984. "Philakorea 84" International Stamp Exhibition, Seoul. Fishing Boats. Multicoloured.
598 20 a. Type **124** 20 15
599 60 a. Tai Tong 40 25
600 2 p. Tai Mei Chai 1·00 60
601 5 p. Ch'at Pong T'o 2·00 1·50

125 Ox and Moon

126 Open Hand with Stylized Doves

1985. New Year. Year of the Ox.
602a **125** 1 p. multicoloured 1·10 1·10

1985. International Youth Year. Multicoloured.
603 2 p. 50 Type **126** 65 35
604 3 p. Open hands and plants 75 40

127 President Ramalho Eanes

1985. Visit of President Eanes of Portugal.
605 **127** 1 p. 50 multicoloured 70 30

128 Riverside Scene

129 "Euploea midamus"

1985. 25th Anniv of Luis de Camoes Museum. Paintings by Cheng Chi Yun. Multicoloured.
606 2 p. 50 Type **128** 60 40
607 2 p. 50 Man on seat and boy filling jar from river 60 40
608 2 p. 50 Playing harp in summerhouse 60 40
609 2 p. 50 Three men by river 60 40

1985. World Tourism Day. Butterflies. Mult.

610 30 a. Type **129** 15 10
611 50 a. "Hebomoia glaucippe" 25 15
612 70 a. "Lethe confusa" 35 20
613 2 p. "Heliophorus epicles" . . 80 45
614 4 p. "Euthalia phemius seitzi" 1·25 70
615 7 p. 50 "Troides helena" . . . 2·25 90

130 Tou (sailing barge) **131** Tiger and Moon

1985. "Italia '85" International Stamp Exhibition, Rome. Cargo Boats. Multicoloured.

617 50 a. Type **130** 30 25
618 70 a. "Veng Seng Lei" (motor junk) 40 25
619 1 p. "Tong Heng Long No. 2" (motor junk) 60 25
620 6 p. "Fong Vong San" (container ship) . . . . 3·00 1·75

1986. New Year. Year of the Tiger.

621 **131** 1 p. 50 multicoloured . . 90 40

132 View of Macao **133** Suo-na

1986. Macao, "the Past is still Present".

622 **132** 2 p. 20 multicoloured . . 75 45

1986. "Ameripex '86" International Stamp Exn, Chicago. Musical Instruments. Multicoloured.

623 20 a. Type **133** 10 10
624 50 a. Sheng (pipes) 15 15
625 60 a. Er-hu (bowed instrument) 20 15
626 70 a. Ruan (string instrument) 25 20
627 5 p. Cheng (harp) . . . . . . 1·50 80
628 8 p. Pi-pa (lute) . . . . . . 2·00 95

134 Hydrofoil

1986. "Stockholmia 86" International Stamp Exhibition. Passenger Ferries. Multicoloured.

630 10 a. Type **134** 20 20
631 40 a. "Tejo" (hovercraft) . . . 25 20
632 3 p. "Tercera" (jetfoil) . . . 1·40 80
633 7 p. 50 High speed ferry . . . 3·75 3·00

135 Taipa Fortress **136** Sun Yat-sen

1986. 10th Anniv of Security Forces. Fortresses. Multicoloured.

634 2 p. Type **135** 90 90
635 2 p. St. Paul on the Mount . . 90 90
636 2 p. St. Francis 90 90
637 2 p. Guia 90 90

Nos. 634/7 were printed together, se-tenant, forming a composite design.

1986. 120th Birth Anniv of Dr. Sun Yat-sen.

638 **136** 70 a. multicoloured . . . 1·75 1·25

137 Hare and Moon **138** Wa To (physician)

1987. New Year. Year of the Hare.

640 **137** 1 p. 50 multicoloured . . 55 20

1987. Shek Wan Ceramics. Multicoloured.

641 2 p. 20 Type **138** 45 35
642 2 p. 20 Choi San, God of Fortune 45 35
643 2 p. 20 Yi, Sun God 45 35
644 2 p. 20 Cung Kuei, Keeper of Demons 45 35

139 Dragon Boats

1987. Dragon Boat Festival. Multicoloured.

645 50 a. Type **139** 20 15
646 5 p. Dragon boat figure-head 1·40 75

140 Circular Fan **141** Fantan

1987. Fans. Multicoloured.

647 30 a. Type **140** 10 10
648 70 a. Folding fan with tree design 15 10
649 1 p. Square-shaped fan with peacock design 45 15
650 6 p. Heart-shaped fan with painting of woman and tree 1·25 1·00

1987. Casino Games. Multicoloured.

652 20 a. Type **141** 10 10
653 40 a. Cussec 15 10
654 4 p. Baccarat 85 65
655 7 p. Roulette . . . . 1·40 90

142 Goods Hand-cart **143** Dragon and Moon

1987. Traditional Vehicles. Multicoloured.

656 10 a. Type **142** 10 10
657 70 a. Open sedan chair . . . 20 10
658 90 a. Rickshaw 20 20
659 10 p. Cycle rickshaw . . . . 2·00 1·25

1988. New Year. Year of the Dragon.

661 **143** 2 p. 50 multicoloured . . 40 30

144 West European Hedgehog

1988. Protected Mammals. Multicoloured.

662 3 p. Type **144** 60 50
663 3 p. Eurasian badger 60 50
664 3 p. European otter 60 50
665 3 p. Chinese pangolin 60 50

145 Breastfeeding

1988. 40th Anniv of W.H.O. Multicoloured.

666 60 a. Type **145** 15 10
667 80 a. Vaccinating child . . . 20 10
668 2 p. 40 Donating blood . . . 35 25

146 Bicycles

1988. Transport. Multicoloured.

669 20 a. Type **146** 10 10
670 50 a. Lambretta and Vespa . . 10 10
671 3 p. 30 Open-sided motor car 55 45
672 5 p. Renault delivery truck, 1912 80 70

147 Hurdling **148** Intelpost (electronic mail)

1988. Olympic Games, Seoul. Multicoloured.

674 40 a. Type **147** 10 10
675 60 a. Basketball 15 10
676 1 p. Football 20 10
677 8 p. Table tennis . . . . . . 1·25 90

1988. New Postal Services. Multicoloured.

679 13 p. 40 Type **148** . . . . . . 2·25 2·00
680 40 p. Express Mail Service (EMS) 6·00 5·00

149 B.M.W. Saloon Car **150** Snake and Moon

1988. 35th Macao Grand Prix. Multicoloured.

681 80 a. Type **149** 20 10
682 2 p. 80 Motor cycle 40 30
683 7 p. Formula 3 car . . . . . . 1·25 90

1989. New Year. Year of the Snake.

685 **150** 3 p. multicoloured 50 40

151 Water Carrier **152** White Building

1989. Traditional Occupations (1st series). Multicoloured.

686 50 a. Type **151** 10 10
687 1 p. Tan-kya (boat) woman . . 20 10
688 4 p. Tin-tin man (pedlar) . . . 60 50
689 5 p. Tao-fu-fa (soya bean cheese) vendor 80 70

See also Nos. 714/17 and 743/6.

1989. Paintings by George Vitalievich Smirnoff in Luis Camoes Museum Multicoloured.

690 2 p. Type **152** 30 20
691 2 p. Building with railings . . 30 20
692 2 p. Street scene 30 20
693 2 p. White, thatched cottage 30 20

153 Common Cobra **154** Talu

1989. "Philexfrance 89" International Stamp Exhibition, Paris. Snakes of Macao. Multicoloured.

694 2 p. 50 Type **153** 40 30
695 2 p. 50 Banded krait ("Bungarus fasciatus") 40 30
696 2 p. 50 Bamboo pit viper ("Trimeresurus albolabris") 40 30
697 2 p. 50 Rat snake ("Elaphe radiata") 40 30

1989. Traditional Games. Multicoloured.

698 10 a. Type **154** 10 10
699 60 a. Triol (marbles) 10 10
700 3 p. 30 Chiquia (shuttlecock) 50 40
701 5 p. Chinese chequers 50 40

155 Piaggio P-136L Flying Boat **156** Malacca

1989. Aircraft. Multicoloured.

702 50 a. Type **155** 10 10
703 70 a. Martin M-130 flying boat 15 10
704 2 p. 80 Fairey IIID seaplane . 65 55
705 4 p. Hawker Osprey seaplane 1·00 65

1989. "World Stamp Expo '89" International Stamp Exhibition, Washington D.C. Portuguese Presence in Far East. Multicoloured.

707 40 a. Type **156** 10 10
708 70 a. Thailand 10 10
709 90 a. India 15 10
710 2 p. 50 Japan 40 30
711 7 p. 50 China . . . . 1·10 85

157 Horse and Moon **159** Long-finned Grouper ("Epinephelus megachir")

1990. New Year. Year of the Horse.

713 **157** 4 p. multicoloured 60 50

1990. Traditional Occupations (2nd series). As T **151**. Multicoloured.

714 30 a. Long-chau singer . . . 10 10
715 70 a. Cobbler 10 10
716 1 p. 50 Travelling penman . . 20 10
717 7 p. 50 Fisherman with wide nets 1·25 1·00

1990. Fishes. Multicoloured.

719 2 p. 40 Type **159** 30 20
720 2 p. 40 Malabar snapper ("Lutianus malabaricus") . . 30 20
721 2 p. 40 Snakehead ("Ophiocepalus maculatus") 30 20
722 2 p. 40 Common paradise fish ("Macropodus opercularis") 30 20

160 Porcelain

1990. "New Zealand 1990" International Stamp Exhibition, Auckland. Industrial Diversification. Multicoloured.

723 3 p. Type **160** 40 30
724 3 p. Furniture 40 30
725 3 p. Toys 40 30
726 3 p. Artificial flowers 40 30

161 Cycling **162** Rose by Lazaro Luis

1990. 11th Asian Games, Peking. Multicoloured.

728 80 a. Type **161** 10 10
729 1 p. Swimming 15 10
730 3 p. Judo 40 30
731 4 p. 20 Shooting 55 40

1990. Compass Roses. Designs showing roses from ancient charts by cartographer named. Mult.

733 50 a. Type **162** 15 15
734 1 p. Diogo Homem 15 25
735 3 p. 50 Diogo Homem (different) 75 55
736 6 p. 50 Fernao Vaz Dourado 1·40 60

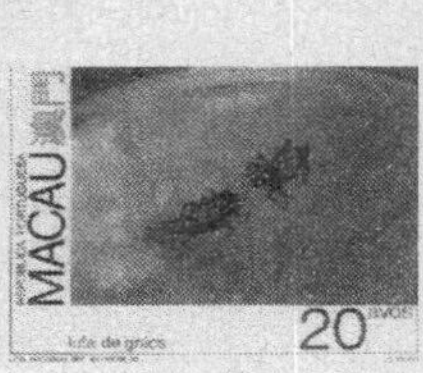

163 Cricket Fight **164** Goat and Moon

1990. Betting on Animals. Multicoloured.
738 20 a. Type **163** 10 10
739 80 a. Hwamei fight 25 15
740 1 p. Greyhound racing 15 10
741 10 p. Horse racing 1·40 1·00

1991. New Year. Year of the Goat.
742 **164** 4 p. 50 multicoloured 60 35

1991. Traditional Occupations (3rd series). As T **151**. Multicoloured.
743 80 a. Knife-grinder 10 10
744 1 p. 70 Flour-puppets vendor 20 10
745 3 p. 50 Street barber 45 25
746 4 p. 20 Fortune-teller 55 35

165 Swollen Harp ("Harpa harpa")

1991. Sea Shells. Multicoloured.
747 3 p. Type **165** 70 40
748 3 p. Oil lamp cone ("Tonna zonata") 70 40
749 3 p. Skeleton shell ("Murex pecten") 70 40
750 3 p. Rosary shell ("Chieoreus rosarius") 70 40

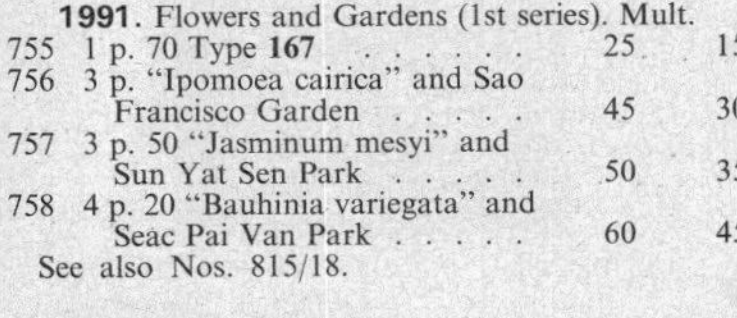

166 Character and Backcloth **167** "Delonix regia" and Lou Lim Ioc Garden

1991. Chinese Opera. Multicoloured.
751 **166** 60 a. multicoloured 10 10
752 – 80 a. multicoloured 10 10
753 – 1 p. multicoloured 15 10
754 – 10 p. multicoloured 1·40 1·00
DESIGNS: Nos. 752/4, Different backcloths and costumes.

1991. Flowers and Gardens (1st series). Mult.
755 1 p. 70 Type **167** 25 15
756 3 p. "Ipomoea cairica" and Sao Francisco Garden 45 30
757 3 p. 50 "Jasminum mesyi" and Sun Yat Sen Park 50 35
758 4 p. 20 "Bauhinia variegata" and Seac Pai Van Park 60 45
See also Nos. 815/18.

168 Portuguese Traders unloading Boats **169** Firework Display

1991. Cultural Exchange. Nambam Paintings attr. Kano Domi. Multicoloured.
760 4 p. 20 Type **168** 85 55
761 4 p. 20 Portuguese traders displaying goods to buyers 60 45

1991. Christmas. Multicoloured.
763 1 p. 70 Type **169** 15 15
764 3 p. Father Christmas 45 30
765 3 p. 50 Man dancing 50 35
766 4 p. 20 January 1st celebrations 60 45

170 Concertina Door

1992. Doors and Windows. Multicoloured.
767 1 p. 70 Type **170** 30 20
768 3 p. Window with four shutters 50 35
769 3 p. 50 Window with two shutters 60 45
770 4 p. 20 Louvred door 70 50

171 Monkey and Moon **172** T'it Kuai Lei

1992. New Year. Year of the Monkey.
771 **171** 4 p. 50 multicoloured 75 55

1992. Gods of Chinese Mythology (1st series). Multicoloured.
772 3 p. 50 (1) Type **172** 60 45
773 3 p. 50 (2) Chong Lei Kun 60 45
774 3 p. 50 (3) Cheong Kuo Lou on donkey 60 45
775 3 p. 50 (4) Loi Tong Pan 60 45
See also Nos. 796/9.

173 Lion Dance **174** High Jumping

1992. "World Columbian Stamp Expo '92", Chicago. Chinese Dances. Multicoloured.
776 1 p. Type **173** 15 10
777 2 p. 70 Lion dance (different) 45 30
778 6 p. Dragon dance 1·00 75

1992. Olympic Games, Barcelona. Multicoloured
779 80 a. Type **174** 15 10
780 4 p. 20 Badminton 70 50
781 4 p. 70 Roller hockey 80 60
782 5 p. Yachting 85 60

175 Na Cha Temple

1992. Temples (1st series). Multicoloured.
784 1 p. Type **175** 15 10
785 1 p. 50 Kun Iam 25 15
786 1 p. 70 Hong Kon 30 20
787 6 p. 50 A Ma 1·10 80
See also Nos. 792/5.

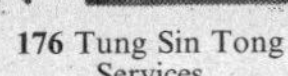

176 Tung Sin Tong Services **177** Rooster and Dragon

1992. Centenary of Tung Sin Tong (medical and educational charity).
788 **176** 1 p. multicoloured 15 10

1992. Portuguese-Chinese Friendship.
789 **177** 10 p. multicoloured 1·75 1·75

178 Cock **179** Children carrying Banners

1992. New Year. Year of the Cock.
791 **178** 5 p. multicoloured 85 60

1993. Temples (2nd series). As T **175**. Mult.
792 50 a. T'am Kong 10 10
793 2 p. T'in Hau 35 25
794 3 p. 50 Lin Fong 60 45
795 8 p. Pau Kong 1·40 1·00

1993. Gods of Chinese Mythology (2nd series). As T **172**. Multicoloured.
796 3 p. 50 (1) Lam Ch'oi Wo flying on crane 60 45
797 3 p. 50 (2) Ho Sin Ku (goddess) on peach blossom 60 45
798 3 p. 50 (3) Hon Seong Chi crossing sea on basket of flowers 60 45
799 3 p. 50 (4) Ch'ou Kuok K'ao crossing river on plank 60 45

1993. Chinese Wedding. Multicoloured.
800 3 p. Type **179** 50 35
801 3 p. Bride 50 35
802 3 p. Bridegroom 50 35
803 3 p. Wedding guests 50 35
Nos. 800/3 were issued together, se-tenant, forming a composite design.

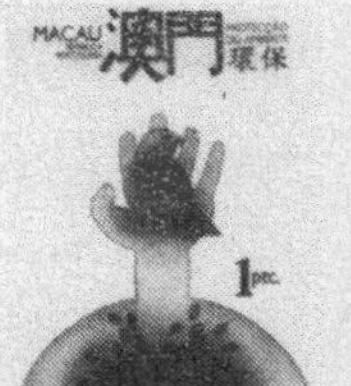

180 Bird perched on Hand **181** Long-eared Owl

1993. Environmental Protection.
805 **180** 1 p. multicoloured 15 10

1993. Birds of Prey. Multicoloured.
806 3 p. Type **181** 50 35
807 3 p. Barn owl ("Tyto alba") 50 35
808 3 p. Peregrine falcon ("Falco peregrinus") 50 35
809 3 p. Golden eagle ("Aquila obrysaetos") 50 35

182 Town Hall

1993. Union of Portuguese-speaking Capital Cities.
811 **182** 1 p. 50 green, blue & red 25 15

183 Portuguese Missionaries

1993. 450th Anniv of First Portuguese Visit to Japan. Multicoloured.
812 50 a. Japanese man with musket 10 10
813 3 p. Type **183** 50 35
814 3 p. 50 Traders carrying goods 60 45

184 "Spathodea campanulata" and Luis de Camoes Garden

1993. Flowers and Gardens (2nd series). Multicoloured.
815 1 p. Type **184** 15 10
816 2 p. "Tithonia diversifolia" and Montanha Russa Garden 35 25
817 3 p. "Rhodomyrtus tomentosa" and Cais Garden 50 35
818 8 p. "Passiflora foetida" and Flora Garden 1·40 1·00

185 Caravel

1993. Sailing Ships. Multicoloured.
820 1 p. Type **185** 15 10
821 2 p. Caravel (different) 35 25
822 3 p. 50 Nau 60 45
823 4 p. 50 Galleon 75 55

186 Saloon Car

1993. 40th Anniv of Macao Grand Prix. Multicoloured.
825 1 p. 50 Type **186** 25 15
826 2 p. Motor cycle 35 25
827 4 p. 50 Racing car 75 55

187 Chow-chow and Moon

1994. New Year. Year of the Dog.
828 **187** 5 p. multicoloured 85 60

188 Map and Prince Henry (½-size illustration)

1994. 600th Birth Anniv of Prince Henry the Navigator.
829 **188** 3 p. multicoloured 50 35

189 Lakeside Hut

1994. Birth Bicentenary of George Chinnery (artist). Multicoloured.
830 3 p. 50 Type **189** 55 40
831 3 p. 50 Fisherman on sea wall 55 40
832 3 p. 50 Harbour 55 40
833 3 p. 50 Sao Tiago Fortress 55 40

190 Lai Sis Exchange

1994. Spring Festival of Lunar New Year. Multicoloured.
835 1 p. Type **190** 15 10
836 2 p. Flower and tangerine tree decorations 30 20
837 3 p. 50 Preparing family meal 55 40
838 4 p. 50 Paper decorations bearing good wishes 70 50

191 "Longevity" **192** Footballer

1994. Chinese Gods. Multicoloured.
839 3 p. Type **191** 50 35
840 3 p. "Prosperity" 50 35
841 3 p. "Happiness" 50 35

1994. World Cup Football Championship, U.S.A.
843 2 p. Type **192** 30 20
844 3 p. Tackling 50 35
845 3 p. 50 Heading ball 55 40
846 4 p. 50 Goalkeeper saving goal 70 50

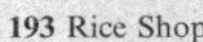

193 Rice Shop **194** Astrolabe

1994. Traditional Chinese Shops. Multicoloured.

848		1 p. Type **193**	15	10
849		1 p. 50 Medicinal tea shop	25	15
850		2 p. Salt-fish shop	30	20
851		3 p. 50 Pharmacy	55	40

1994. Nautical Instruments. Multicoloured.

852		3 p. Type **194**	50	35
853		3 p. 50 Quadrant	55	40
854		4 p. 50 Sextant	70	50

195 Fencing

1994. 12th Asian Games, Hiroshima. Multicoloured.

855		1 p. Type **195**	15	10
856		2 p. Gymnastics	30	20
857		3 p. Water-polo	50	35
858		3 p. 50 Pole vaulting	55	40

196 Nobre de Carvalho Bridge

1994. Bridges. Multicoloured.

859		1 p. Type **196**	15	10
860		8 p. Friendship Bridge	1·25	90

197 Carp **199** Pig and Moon

198 Angel's Head (stained glass window, Macao Cathedral)

1994. Good Luck Signs. Multicoloured.

861		3 p. Type **197**	50	35
862		3 p. 50 Peaches	55	40
863		4 p. 50 Water-lily	70	50

1994. Religious Art. Multicoloured.

864		50 a. Type **198**	10	10
865		1 p. Holy Ghost (stained glass window, Macao Cathedral)	15	10
866		1 p. 50 Silver sacrarium	25	15
867		2 p. Silver salver	30	20
868		3 p. "Escape to Egypt" (ivory statuette)	50	35
869		3 p. 50 Gold and silver cup	55	40

1995. New Year. Year of the Pig.

870	**199**	5 p. 50 multicoloured	90	75

CHARITY TAX STAMPS

The notes under this heading in Portugal also apply here.

1919. Fiscal stamp optd **TAXA DE GUERRA**.

C305		2 a. green	1·75	1·25
C306		11 a. green	2·25	2·00

The above was for use in Timor as well as Macao.

1925. Marquis de Pombal issue of Portugal but inscr "MACAU".

C329	C **73**	2 a. red	60	60
C330	–	2 a. red	60	60
C331	C **75**	2 a. red	60	60

C **48** Our Lady of Charity (altarpiece, Macao Cathedral)

1930.

C332	C **48**	5 a. brown and buff	5·50	4·50

1945. As Type C **48** but values in Arabic and Chinese numerals left and right, at bottom of design.

C486		1 a. olive and green	20	20
C487		2 a. purple and grey	20	20
C415		5 a. brown and yellow	4·00	3·75
C416		5 a. blue and pale blue	3·50	3·00
C417		10 a. green and pale green	3·00	2·50
C470		10 a. blue and green	25	20
C418		15 a. orange & pale orange	2·50	2·00
C419		20 a. red and orange	4·50	4·00
C489		20 a. brown and yellow	30	20
C414		50 a. lilac and buff	4·00	3·75
C472		50 a. red and pink	3·00	2·00

1981. No. C487 and similar higher (fiscal) values surch **20 avos** and Chinese characters.

C546		20 a. on 2 a. purple on grey	35	35
C534		20 a. on 1 p. green & lt grn	80	50
C535		20 a. on 3 p. black and pink	45	25
C536		20 a. on 5 p. brown & yellow		

1981. No. C418 surch **10 avos** and Chinese characters.

C553		10 a. on 15 a. orange and pale orange	25	25

NEWSPAPER STAMPS

1892. "Embossed" key-type of Macao surch **JORNAES** and value in figures.

N73	Q	2½ r. on 10 r. green	65	50
N74		2½ r. on 40 r. brown	65	50
N74		2½ r. on 80 r. grey	65	50

1893. "Newspaper" key-type inscr "Macau".

N79	V	2½ r. brown	45	40

1894. "Newspaper" key-type of Macao surch ½ **avo PROVISORIO** and Chinese characters.

N82	V	½ a. on 2½ r. brown	70	60

POSTAGE DUE STAMPS

1904. "Due" key-type inscr "MACAU".

D184	W	½ a. green	35	35
D185		1 a. green	40	40
D186		2 a. grey	40	40
D187		4 a. brown	40	40
D188		5 a. orange	85	60
D189		8 a. brown	85	60
D190		12 a. brown	1·25	60
D191		20 a. blue	2·25	2·00
D192		40 a. red	2·50	2·25
D193		50 a. orange	6·00	6·00
D194		1 p. lilac	12·00	9·00

1911. "Due" key-types of Macao optd **REPUBLICA**.

D204	W	½ a. green	30	30
D205		1 a. green	30	30
D206		2 a. grey	30	30
D207		4 a. brown	30	30
D208		5 a. orange	30	30
D209		8 a. brown	30	30
D287		12 a. brown	65	40
D211		20 a. blue	1·00	80
D212		40 a. red	1·75	1·40
D290		50 a. orange	2·50	2·25
D214		1 p. lilac	4·50	3·75

1925. Marquis de Pombal issue, as Nos. C329/31 optd **MULTA**.

D329	C **73**	4 a. red	45	45
D330	–	4 a. red	45	45
D331	C **75**	4 a. red	45	45

1947. As Type D **1** of Portuguese Colonies, but inscr "MACAU".

D410	D **1**	1 a. black and purple	70	70
D411		2 a. black and violet	70	70
D412		4 a. black and blue	70	70
D413		5 a. black and brown	70	70
D414		8 a. black and purple	70	70
D415		12 a. black and brown	70	70
D416		20 a. black and green	1·25	1·25
D417		40 a. black and red	2·10	2·10
D418		50 a. black and yellow	3·75	3·75
D419		1 p. black and blue	3·75	3·75

1949. Postage stamps of 1934 surch **PORTEADO** and new value.

D424	**40**	1 a. on 4 a. black	60	60
D425		2 a. on 6 a. brown	60	60
D426		4 a. on 8 a. blue	60	60
D427		5 a. on 10 a. red	70	60
D428		8 a. on 12 a. blue	70	70
D429		12 a. on 30 a. green	1·25	1·10
D430		20 a. on 40 a. violet	1·25	1·10

1951. Optd **PORTEADO** or surch also.

D439	**66**	1 a. yellow on cream	25	25
D440		2 a. green on green	25	25
D441		7 a. on 10 a. mauve on green	25	25

D **70**

1952. Numerals in red. Name in black.

D451	D **70**	1 a. blue and green	10	10
D452		3 a. brown and salmon	10	10
D453		5 a. slate and blue	10	10
D454		10 a. red and blue	20	20
D455		30 a. blue and brown	25	25
D456		1 p. brown & grey	1·10	1·10

MACEDONIA Pt. 3

Part of Austro-Hungarian Empire until 1918 when it became part of Yugoslavia. Separate stamps were issued during German Occupation in the Second World War.

In 1991 Macedonia became an independent republic.

A. GERMAN OCCUPATION

100 stotinki = 1 lev

Македония

8. IX. 1944

1 лв.

(1)

1944. Stamps of Bulgaria, 1940-44. (a) Surch as T **1**.

G1		1 l. on 10 st. orange	3·75	9·25
G2		3 l. on 15 st. blue	3·75	9·25

(b) Surch similar to T **1** but larger.

G3		6 l. on 10 st. blue	6·25	14·00
G4		9 l. on 15 st. green	6·25	14·00
G5		9 l. on 15 st. green	7·75	19·00
G6		15 l. on 4 l. black	15·00	40·00
G7		20 l. on 7 l. blue	15·00	40·00
G8		30 l. on 14 l. brown	30·00	75·00

B. INDEPENDENT REPUBLIC

1991. 100 paras = 1 dinar
1992. 100 deni (de.) = 1 denar (d.)

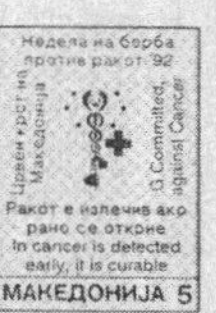

1 Trumpeters **2** Emblems and Inscriptions

1991. Obligatory Tax. Independence.

1	**1**	2 d. 50 black and orange	50	50

1992. Obligatory Tax. Anti-cancer Week. (a) T **2** showing Red Cross symbol at bottom left.

2	**2**	5 d. mauve, black and blue	75	75
3	–	5 d. multicoloured	75	75
4	–	5 d. multicoloured	75	75
5	–	5 d. multicoloured	75	75

DESIGNS: No. 3, Flowers, columns and scanner; 4, Scanner and couch; 5, Computer cabinet.

(b) As T **2** but with right-hand inscr reading down instead of up and without Red Cross symbol.

6		5 d. mauve, black & blue (as No. 2)	75	75
7		5 d. multicoloured (as No. 3)	75	75
8		5 d. multicoloured (as No. 4)	75	75
9		5 d. multicoloured (as No. 5)	75	75

3 Red Cross Aircraft dropping Supplies

1992. Obligatory Tax. Red Cross Week. Multicoloured.

10		10 d. Red Cross slogans	40	40
11		10 d. Type **3**	40	40
12		10 d. Treating road accident victim	40	40
13		10 d. Evacuating casualties from ruined building	40	40

The three pictoral designs are taken from children's paintings.

4 "Skopje Earthquake" **6** Nurse with Baby

5 "Wood-carvers Petar and Makarie" (icon), St. Joven Bigorsk Monastery, Debar

1992. Obligatory Tax. Solidarity Week.

14	4	20 d. black and mauve	50	50
15	–	20 d. multicoloured	50	50
16	–	20 d. multicoloured	50	50
17	–	20 d. multicoloured	50	50

DESIGNS: No. 15, Red Cross nurse with child; 16, Mothers carrying toddlers at airport; 17, Family at airport.

1992. 1st Anniv of Independence.

18	5	30 d. multicoloured	50	50

For 40 d. in same design see No. 33.

1992. Obligatory Tax. Anti-tuberculosis Week. Multicoloured.

19	20 d. Anti-tuberculosis slogans	40	40
20	20 d. Type **6**	40	40
21	20 d. Nurse giving oxygen	40	40
22	20 d. Baby in cot	40	40

7 "The Nativity" (fresco, Slepce Monastery)

9 Radiography Equipment

8 Mixed Bouquet

1992. Christmas. Multicoloured.

23	100 d. Type **7**	10	10
24	500 d. "Madonna and Child" (fresco), Zrze Monastery	50	50

1993. Obligatory Tax. Red Cross Fund. Multicoloured.

25	20 d. Red Cross slogans	40	40
26	20 d. Marguerites	40	40
27	20 d. Carnations	40	40
28	20 d. Type **8**	40	40

1993. Obligatory Tax. Anti-cancer Week. Multicoloured.

29	20 d. Anti-cancer slogans	25	25
30	20 d. Type **9**	25	25
31	20 d. Overhead treatment unit	25	25
32	20 d. Scanner	25	25

1993. As No. 18 but changed value.

33	5	40 d. multicoloured	30	30

10 Macedonian Flag

1993.

34	10	10 d. multicoloured	15	15
35		40 d. multicoloured	50	50
36		50 d. multicoloured	60	60

11 Roach

1993. Fishes from Lake Ohrid. Multicoloured.

37	50 d. Type **11**	10	10
38	100 d. Ohrid trout	20	20
39	1000 d. Type **11**	1·00	1·00
40	2000 d. As No. 38	2·25	2·25

12 Crucifix, St. George's Monastery

1993. Easter.

41	12	300 d. multicoloured	1·25	1·25

13 Diagram of Telecommunications Cable and Map

1993. Opening of Trans-Balkan Telecommunications Line.

42	13	500 d. multicoloured	75	75

14 Red Cross Worker with Baby

1993. Obligatory Tax. Red Cross Week. Multicoloured.

43	50 d. Red Cross inscriptions	20	20
44	50 d. Type **14**	20	20
45	50 d. Physiotherapist and child in wheelchair	20	20
46	50 d. Stretcher party	20	20

15 Unloading U.N.I.C.E.F. Supplies from Lorry

1993. Obligatory Tax. Solidarity Week.

47	–	50 de. black, mauve and silver	20	20
48	15	50 de. multicoloured	20	20
49	–	50 de. multicoloured	20	20
50	–	50 de. multicoloured	20	20

DESIGNS: No. 47, "Skopje Earthquake"; 49, Labelling parcels in warehouse; 50, Consignment of parcels on fork-lift truck.

16 U.N. Emblem and Rainbow

1993. Admission to United Nations Organization.

51	16	10 d. multicoloured	1·50	1·50

17 "Insurrection" (detail) (B. Lazeski)

19 Tapestry

18 Children in Meadow

1993. 90th Anniv of Macedonian Insurrection.

52	17	10 d. multicoloured	1·50	1·50

1993. Obligatory Tax. Anti-tuberculosis Week. Multicoloured.

54	50 de. Anti-tuberculosis slogans	25	25
55	50 de. Type **18**	25	25
56	50 de. Bee on flower	25	25
57	50 de. Goat behind boulder	25	25

1993. Centenary of Founding of Inner Macedonia Revolutionary Organization.

58	19	4 d. multicoloured	25	25

20 "The Nativity" (fresco from St. George's Monastery, Rajcica)

1993. Christmas. Multicoloured.

60	2 d. Type **20**	10	10
61	20 d. "The Three Kings" (fresco from Slepce Monastery)	1·25	1·25

21 Lily

1994. Obligatory Tax. Anti-cancer Week. Multicoloured.

62	1 d. Red Cross and anti-cancer emblems	20	20
63	1 d. Type **21**	20	20
64	1 d. Mushroom	20	20
65	1 d. Swans on lake	20	20

1994. Nos. 1, 18 and 34 surch.

66	5	2 d. on 30 d. multicoloured	35	35
67	1	8 d. on 2 d. 50 black and orange	1·60	1·60
68	6	15 d. on 10 d. multicoloured	2·75	2·75

MADAGASCAR AND DEPENDENCIES Pt. 6

A large island in the Indian Ocean off the east coast of Africa. French Post Offices operated there from 1885.

In 1896 the island was declared a French colony, absorbing Diego-Suarez and Ste. Marie de Madagascar in 1898 and Nossi-Be in 1901.

Madagascar became autonomous as the Malagasy Republic in 1958.

100 centimes = 1 franc

A. FRENCH POST OFFICES.

1889. Stamps of French Colonies "Commerce" type surch with value in figures.

1	J	05 on 10 c. black on lilac	£475	£150
2		05 on 25 c. black on red	£475	£140
4		05 on 40 c. red on yellow	£110	70·00
5		5 on 10 c. black on lilac	£160	90·00
6		5 on 25 c. black on red	£160	95·00
7		15 on 25 c. black on red	£110	70·00
3		25 on 40 c. red on yellow	£425	£120

5

1891. No gum. Imperf.

9	5	5 c. black on green	£100	17·00
10		10 c. black on blue	70·00	22·00
11		15 c. blue on blue	75·00	24·00
12		25 c. brown on buff	14·00	8·50
13		1 f. black on yellow	£800	£200
14		5 f. black and lilac on lilac	£1500	£900

1895. Stamps of France optd **POSTE FRANCAISE Madagascar**.

15	10	5 c. green	4·75	3·75
16		10 c. black on lilac	30·00	19·00
17		15 c. blue	40·00	7·00
18		25 c. black on red	55·00	6·00
19		40 c. red on yellow	45·00	12·00
20		50 c. red	65·00	12·00
21		75 c. brown on orange	60·00	27·00
22		1 f. olive	85·00	18·00
23		5 f. mauve on lilac	£110	50·00

1896. Stamps of France surch with value in figures in oval.

29	10	5 c. on 1 c. black on blue	£4000	£1500
30		15 c. on 2 c. brown on yell	£1500	£750
31		25 c. on 3 c. grey	£1700	£750
32		25 c. on 4 c. red on grey	£4250	£1400
33		25 c. on 40 c. red on yellow	£900	£550

B. FRENCH COLONY

1896. "Tablet" key-type inscr "MADAGASCAR ET DEPENDANCES".

1	D	1 c. black & red on blue	50	50
2		2 c. brown & blue on buff	60	60
2a		2 c. brown & blk on buff	2·75	2·75
3		4 c. brown & bl on grey	85	40
17		5 c. green and red	75	30
6		10 c. black & blue on lilac	4·75	60
18		10 c. red and blue	1·00	25
7		15 c. blue and red	6·00	55
19		15 c. grey and red	1·10	30
8		20 c. red & blue on green	3·50	85
9		25 c. black & red on pink	4·75	40
20		25 c. blue and red	12·50	14·00
10		30 c. brown & bl on drab	4·75	1·50
21		35 c. black & red on yell	28·00	3·50
11		40 c. red & blue on yellow	5·25	1·00
12		50 c. red & blue on pink	6·75	85
22		50 c. brown & red on blue	20·00	16·00
13		75 c. violet & red on orge	2·25	1·50
14		1 f. green and red	7·00	1·90
15		1 f. green and blue	12·50	8·00
16		5 f. mauve & blue on lilac	25·00	16·00

1902. "Tablet" key-type stamps as above surch.

27	D	0,01 on 2 c. brown and blue on buff	4·50	3·00
27a		0,01 on 2 c. brown and black on buff	2·50	4·00
29		0,05 on 30 c. brown and blue on drab	3·50	3·50
23		05 on 50 c. red and blue on pink	2·00	1·50
31		0,10 on 50 c. red and blue on pink	3·00	3·50
24		10 on 5 f. mauve and blue on lilac	14·00	12·00
32		0,15 on 75 c. violet and red on orange	1·75	1·75
33		0,15 on 1 f. green & red	1·75	2·50
25		15 on 1 f. green and red	3·50	1·75

1902. Nos. 59 and 61 of Diego-Suarez surch.

35	D	0,05 on 30 c. brown and blue on drab	85·00	£100
36		0,10 on 50 c. red and blue on pink	£3250	£3000

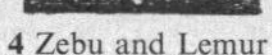
4 Zebu and Lemur

5 Transport in Madagascar

1903.

No.	Type	Description	Unused	Used
38	4	1 c. purple	55	30
39		2 c. brown	50	50
40		4 c. brown	55	55
41		5 c. green	4·75	55
42		10 c. red	5·00	50
43		15 c. red	5·00	65
44		20 c. orange	3·00	1·25
45		25 c. blue	20·00	1·50
46		30 c. red	22·00	8·00
47		40 c. lilac	20·00	3·25
48		50 c. brown	35·00	13·50
49		75 c. yellow	38·00	14·50
50		1 f. green	38·00	23·00
51		2 f. blue	50·00	24·00
52		5 f. black	50·00	55·00

1908.

No.	Type	Description	Unused	Used
53a	5	1 c. green and violet	10	20
54		2 c. green and red	10	20
55		4 c. brown and green	10	25
56		5 c. olive and green	40	15
90		5 c. red and black	20	10
57		10 c. brown and pink	25	15
91		10 c. olive and green	20	20
92		10 c. purple and brown	30	20
58		15 c. red and lilac	30	20
93		15 c. green and olive	25	40
94		15 c. red and blue	90	1·00
59		20 c. brown and orange	25	30
60		25 c. black and blue	1·25	25
95		25 c. black and violet	40	15
61		30 c. black and brown	1·25	1·40
96		30 c. brown and red	45	40
97		30 c. purple and green	50	30
98		30 c. light green and green	80	80
62		35 c. black and red	95	60
63		40 c. black and brown	65	60
64		45 c. black and green	50	50
99		45 c. red and scarlet	50	75
100		45 c. purple and lilac	85	90
65		50 c. black and violet	50	45
101		50 c. black and blue	45	20
102		50 c. yellow and black	60	25
103		60 c. violet on pink	50	65
104		65 c. blue and black	70	75
66		75 c. black and red	45	35
105		85 c. red and green	85	1·25
67		1 f. green and brown	45	30
106		1 f. blue	65	70
107		1 f. green and mauve	3·50	3·75
108		1 f. 10 green and brown	85	1·00
68		2 f. green and blue	2·25	95
69		5 f. brown and violet	7·50	3·75

1912. "Tablet" key-type surch.

No.	Type	Description	Unused	Used
70	D	05 on 15 c. grey and red	35	30
71		05 on 20 c. red and blue on green	40	65
72		05 on 30 c. brown and blue on drab	40	65
73		10 on 75 c. violet and red on orange	3·00	6·00
81		0.60 on 75 c. violet and red on orange	4·50	4·50
82		1 f. on 5 f. mauve and blue on lilac	45	85

1912. Surch.

No.	Type	Description	Unused	Used
74	4	05 on 2 c. brown	25	45
75		05 on 20 c. orange	35	50
76		05 on 30 c. red	35	80
77		10 on 40 c. lilac	50	95
78		10 on 50 c. brown	85	2·00
79		10 on 75 c. brown	2·50	4·50
83		1 f. on 5 f. black	20·00	20·00

1915. Surch 5c and red cross.

No.	Type	Description	Unused	Used
80	5	10 c. + 5 c. brown and pink	50	90

1921. Surch **1 cent**.

No.	Type	Description	Unused	Used
84	5	1 c. on 15 c. red and lilac	40	70

1921. Type **5** (some colours changed) surch.

No.	Type	Description	Unused	Used
109	5	25 c. on 15 c. red and lilac	40	45
85		0,25 on 35 c. black and red	3·00	3·00
86		0,25 on 40 c. black & brown	2·50	2·75
87		0,25 on 45 c. black & green	2·00	2·25
110		25 c. on 2 f. green and blue	30	40
112		25 c. on 5 f. brown & violet	50	60
88		0,30 on 40 c. black & brown	1·10	1·10
113		50 c. on 1 f. green & brown	80	20
89		0,60 on 75 c. black and red	1·90	2·00
114		60 on 75 c. violet on pink	40	40
115		65 c. on 75 c. black and red	90	1·50
116		85 c. on 45 c. black & green	90	1·50
117		90 c. on 75 c. pink and red	45	55
118		1 f. 25 on 1 f. blue	30	40
119		1 f. 50 on 1 f. lt blue & blue	50	20
120		3 f. on 5 f. violet and green	1·50	1·00
121		10 f. on 5 f. mauve and red	4·50	3·25
122		20 f. on 5 f. blue and mauve	6·25	5·50

MINIMUM PRICE

The minimum price quoted is 10p which represents a handling charge rather than a basis for valuing common stamps. For further notes about prices, see introductory pages.

14 Sakalava Chief

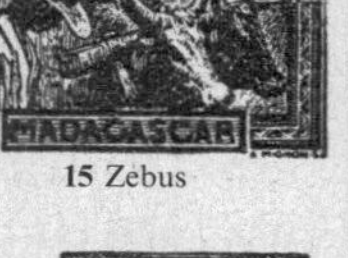
15 Zebus

17 Betsileo Woman

18 General Gallieni

1930.

No.	Type	Description	Unused	Used
123	18	1 c. blue	20	40
124	15	1 c. green and blue	20	25
125	14	2 c. brown and red	10	10
177	18	3 c. blue	15	25
126	14	4 c. mauve and brown	15	35
127	15	5 c. red and green	15	15
128	–	10 c. green and red	10	10
129	17	15 c. red	10	10
130	15	20 c. blue and brown	20	20
131	–	25 c. brown and lilac	20	10
132	17	30 c. green	40	30
133	14	40 c. red and green	30	35
134	17	45 c. lilac	55	50
178	18	45 c. green	35	40
179		50 c. brown	20	10
180		60 c. mauve	15	30
136	15	65 c. mauve and brown	55	25
181	18	70 c. red	35	35
137	17	75 c. brown	50	25
138	15	90 c. red	85	80
182	18	90 c. brown	30	15
139	–	1 f. blue and brown	1·00	90
140	–	1 f. red and scarlet	45	45
140a	–	1 f. 25 brown and blue	95	75
183	18	1 f. 40 orange	50	35
141	14	1 f. 50 ultramarine & blue	4·50	1·25
142		1 f. 50 red and brown	50	55
278		1 f. 50 brown and red	20	50
184	18	1 f. 60 violet	50	40
143	14	1 f. 75 red and brown	2·50	1·00
185	18	2 f. red	35	20
186a		3 f. green	55	60
146	14	5 f. brown and mauve	70	40
147	18	10 f. orange	2·75	1·90
148	14	20 f. blue and brown	1·40	1·40

DESIGN—VERT. 10 c., 25 c., 1 f., 1 f. 25, Hova girl.

1931. "Colonial Exhibition" key-types inscr "MADAGASCAR".

No.	Type	Description	Unused	Used
149	E	40 c. black and green	55	55
150	F	50 c. black and mauve	1·25	70
151	G	90 c. black and red	85	90
152	H	1 f. 50 black and blue	1·40	1·00

19 Bloch 120 over Madagascar

20 J. Laborde and Tananarivo Palace

1935. Air.

No.	Type	Description	Unused	Used
153	19	50 c. red and green	50	55
154		90 c. red and green	35	40
155		1 f. 25 red and lake	35	40
156		1 f. 50 red and blue	40	45
157		1 f. 60 red and blue	20	25
158		1 f. 75 red and orange	5·25	3·25
159		2 f. red and blue	50	30
160		3 f. red and orange	35	30
161		3 f. 65 red and black	35	40
162		3 f. 90 red and green	30	30
163		4 f. red and carmine	35·00	1·90
164		4 f. 50 red and black	18·00	80
165		5 f. red and green	45	40
166		6 f. red and mauve	40	40
167		6 f. 90 red and purple	40	40
168		8 f. red and mauve	70	90
169		8 f. 50 red and green	80	95
170		9 f. red and green	45	50
171		12 f. red and brown	55	65
172		12 f. 50 red and violet	1·25	95
173		15 f. red and orange	60	60
174		16 f. red and green	1·25	1·25
175		20 f. red and brown	1·90	1·40
176		50 f. red and blue	3·25	3·00

1937. International Exhibition, Paris. As Nos. 168/73 of St.-Pierre et Miquelon.

No.	Description	Unused	Used
187	20 c. violet	60	75
188	30 c. green	75	85
189	40 c. red	50	50
190	50 c. brown and agate	45	60
191	90 c. red	45	60
192	1 f. 50 blue	45	90

1938. 60th Death Anniv of Jean Laborde (explorer).

No.	Type	Description	Unused	Used
193	20	35 c. green	35	45
194		55 c. violet	40	45
195		65 c. red	35	50
196		80 c. purple	45	40
197		1 f. red	35	30
198		1 f. 25 red	45	40
199		1 f. 75 blue	90	35
200		2 f. 15 brown	1·75	1·25
201		2 f. 25 blue	75	75
202		2 f. 50 brown	40	45
203		10 f. green	60	60

1938. Int. Anti-Cancer Fund. As T **22** of Mauritania.

No.	Description	Unused	Used
204	1 f. 75 + 50 c. blue	3·75	6·00

1939. New York World's Fair. As T **28** of Mauritania.

No.	Description	Unused	Used
205	1 f. 25 red	75	80
206	2 f. 25 blue	80	85

1939. 150th Anniv of French Revolution. As T **29** of Mauritania.

No.	Description	Unused	Used
207	45 c. + 25 c. green and black (postage)	4·75	5·75
208	70 c. + 30 c. brown and black	5·25	5·75
209	90 c. + 35 c. orange and black	4·75	5·75
210	1 f. 25 + 1 f. red and black	4·75	5·75
211	2 f. 25 + 2 f. blue and black	5·00	5·75
212	4 f. 50 + 4 f. black and orange (air)	9·00	10·00

1942. Surch **50** and bars.

No.	Type	Description	Unused	Used
213	15	50 on 65 c. mauve & brown	95	35

1942. Free French Administration. Optd **FRANCE LIBRE** or surch also.

No.	Type	Description	Unused	Used
214	14	2 c. brown and red (postage)	65	65
215	18	3 c. blue	85·00	90·00
216	15	0,05 on 1 c. green and blue	50	60
217	20	0,10 on 55 c. violet	75	90
218	17	15 c. red	6·25	6·25
219	20	0,30 on 65 c. red	50	60
220	15	0 f. 50 on 0,05 on 1 c. green and blue	50	65
221		50 on 65 c. mauve & brown	55	25
222	18	50 on 90 c. brown	40	20
223	15	65 c. mauve and brown	65	65
224	18	70 c. red	55	60
225	20	80 c. purple	1·40	1·40
226	–	1,00 on 1 f. 25 brown and blue (No. 140a)	1·40	1·40
227	20	1,00 on 1 f. 25 red	5·00	5·00
228	18	1 f. 40 orange	60	60
229	5	1 f. 50 on 1 f. blue	90	85
230	14	1 f. 50 ultramarine & blue	90	90
231		1 f. 50 red and brown	90	90
232	18	1,50 on 1 f. 60 violet	55	55
233	14	1,50 on 1 f. 75 red & brown	55	50
234	20	1,50 on 1 f. 75 blue	55	55
235	18	1 f. 60 violet	50	60
236	20	2,00 on 2 f. 15 brown	50	50
237		2 f. 25 blue	55	55
238	–	2 f. 25 blue (No. 206)	55	55
239	20	2 f. 50 brown	2·00	2·25
240	5	10 f. on 5 f. mauve & red	5·50	5·25
241	20	10 f. green	2·75	3·00
242	5	20 f. on 5 f. blue & mauve	7·75	8·00
243	14	20 f. blue and brown	£550	£650
244	19	1,00 on 1 f. 25 red and lake (air)	3·00	3·25
245		1 f. 50 red and blue	3·75	3·75
246		1 f. 75 red and orange	55·00	60·00
247		3,00 on 3 f. 65 red & black	65	25
248		8 f. red and purple	80	75
249		8,00 on 8 f. 50 red & green	60	30
250		12 f. red and brown	1·75	1·60
251		12 f. 50 red and violet	90	85
252		16 f. red and green	3·25	3·25
253		50 f. red and blue	2·75	2·75

24 Traveller's Tree

29 Gen. Gallieni

1943. Free French Issue.

No.	Type	Description	Unused	Used
254	24	5 c. brown	10	25
255		10 c. mauve	10	10
256		25 c. green	10	20
257		30 c. orange	10	10
258		40 c. blue	20	20
259		80 c. purple	10	10
260		1 f. blue	15	15
261		1 f. 50 c. red	20	15
262		2 f. yellow	15	10
263		2 f. 50 c. blue	20	25
264		4 f. blue and red	20	10
265		5 f. green and black	45	15
266		10 f. red and blue	60	20
267		20 f. violet and brown	40	40

1943. Free French Administration. Air. As T **30** of New Caledonia, but inscr "MADAGASCAR".

No.	Description	Unused	Used
268	1 f. orange	40	40
269	1 f. 50 c. red	40	40
270	5 f. purple	40	40
271	10 f. black	40	40
272	25 f. blue	85	45
273	50 f. green	1·40	70
274	100 f. red	50	80

1944. Mutual Aid and Red Cross Funds. As T **31** of New Caledonia.

No.	Description	Unused	Used
275	5 f. + 20 f. green	50	80

1944. Surch **1 f. 50**.

No.	Type	Description	Unused	Used
276	24	1 f. 50 on 5 c. brown	35	55
277		1 f. 50 on 10 c. mauve	50	80

1945. Eboue. As T **32** of New Caledonia.

No.	Description	Unused	Used
279	2 f. black	20	35
280	25 f. green	50	85

1946. Air. Victory. As T **34** of New Caledonia.

No.	Description	Unused	Used
281	8 f. red	40	40

1945. Surch with new value.

No.	Type	Description	Unused	Used
282	24	50 c. on 5 c. brown	35	35
283		60 c. on 5 c. brown	40	45
284		70 c. on 5 c. brown	35	40
285		1 f. 20 on 5 c. brown	35	35
286		2 f. 40 on 25 c. green	35	45
287		3 f. on 25 c. green	30	30
288		4 f. 50 on 25 c. green	45	50
289		15 f. on 2 f. 50 blue	35	45

1946. Air. From Chad to the Rhine. As Nos. 300/305 of New Caledonia.

No.	Description	Unused	Used
290	5 f. blue	75	85
291	10 f. red	80	90
292	15 f. green	80	90
293	20 f. brown	1·00	1·10
294	25 f. violet	1·25	1·40
295	50 f. red	1·10	1·40

1946.

No.	Type	Description	Unused	Used
296	–	10 c. green (postage)	10	25
297	–	30 c. orange	10	25
298	–	40 c. olive	10	25
299	–	50 c. purple	10	10
300	–	60 c. blue	10	25
301	–	80 c. green	10	25
302	–	1 f. sepia	10	10
303	–	1 f. 20 green	20	20
304	29	1 f. 50 red	10	10
305	–	2 f. black	10	10
306	–	3 f. purple	10	10
307	–	3 f. 60 red	60	60
308	–	4 f. blue	25	20
309	–	5 f. orange	35	15
310	–	6 f. blue	20	10
311	–	10 f. lake	25	25
312	–	15 f. brown	35	20
313	–	20 f. blue	45	35
314	–	25 f. brown	80	45
315	–	50 f. blue and red (air)	90	45
316	–	100 f. brown and red	1·75	85
317	–	200 f. brown and green	3·50	2·00

DESIGNS—As T **29**. VERT: 10 to 50 c. Native with spear; 6, 10 f. Gen. Duchesne; 15, 20, 25 f. Lt.-Col. Joffre. HORIZ: 60, 80 c. Zebus; 1 f., 1 f. 20, Sakalava man and woman; 3 f. 60, 4, 5 f. Betsimisaraka mother and child. 49×28 mm: 50 f. Aerial view of Port of Tamatave. 28×51 mm: 100 f. Allegory of flight. 51×28 mm: Douglas DC-2 airplane and map of Madagascar.

36 Gen. Gallieni and View

1946. 50th Anniv of French Protectorate.

No.	Type	Description	Unused	Used
318	36	10 f. + 5 f. purple	35	45

1948. Air. Discovery of Adelie Land, Antarctic. No. 316 optd **TERRE ADELIE DUMONT D'URVILLE 1840**.

No.	Type	Description	Unused	Used
319	–	100 f. brown and red	35·00	50·00

1949. Air. 75th Anniv of U.P.U. As T **38** of New Caledonia.

No.	Description	Unused	Used
320	25 f. multicoloured	2·75	1·90

1950. Colonial Welfare Fund. As T **39** of New Caledonia.

No.	Description	Unused	Used
321	10 f. + 2 f. purple and green	3·50	4·00

38 Cacti and Succulents

39 Long-tailed Ground Roller

40 Woman and Forest Road

1952.
322 **38** 7 f. 50 green & blue (postage) 70 35
323 **39** 8 f. lake 1·25 35
324 15 f. blue and green 2·75 30
325 – 50 f. green and blue (air) 2·25 40
326 – 100 f. black, brown & blue 8·50 1·50
327 – 200 f. brown and green 12·50 4·50
328 **40** 500 f. brown, sepia & green 21·00 5·00
DESIGNS—As Type **40**: 50 f. Palm trees; 100 f. Antsirabe Viaduct; 200 f. Ring-tailed lemurs.

1952. Military Medal Centenary As T **40** of New Caledonia.
329 15 f. turquoise, yellow & green 1·50 1·90

1954. Air. 10th Anniv of Liberation. As T **42** of New Caledonia.
330 15 f. purple and violet 2·00 1·50

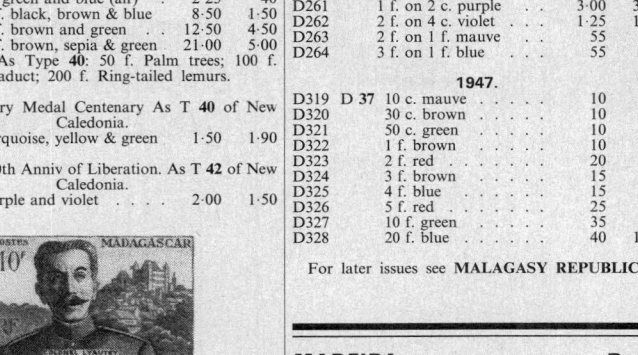

41 Marshal Lyautey

1954. Birth Centenary of Marshal Lyautey.
331 **41** 10 f. indigo, blue & ultram 65 10
332 40 f. lake, grey and black 1·00 10

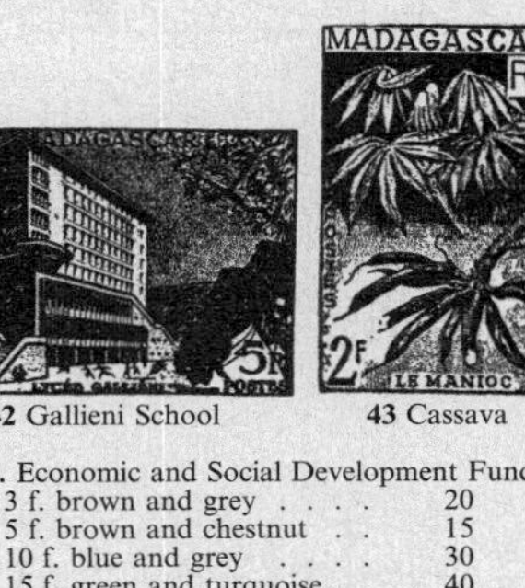

42 Gallieni School **43** Cassava

1956. Economic and Social Development Fund.
333 – 3 f. brown and grey 20 10
334 **42** 5 f. brown and chestnut 15 10
335 – 10 f. blue and grey 30 15
336 – 15 f. green and turquoise 40 15
DESIGNS: 3 f. Tamatave and tractor; 10 f. Dredging canal; 15 f. Irrigation.

1956. Coffee. As T **44** of New Caledonia.
337 20 f. sepia and brown 40 15

1957. Plants.
338 **43** 2 f. green, brown and blue 25 10
339 – 4 f. red, brown and green 25 15
340 – 12 f. green, brown & violet 45 15
DESIGNS: 4 f. Cloves; 12 f. Vanilla.

PARCEL POST STAMPS

1919. Receipt stamp of France surch **MADAGASCAR ET DEPENDANCES 0fr.10 COLIS POSTAUX.**
P81 0 f. 10 on 10 c. grey 2·75 2·75

1919. Fiscal stamp of Madagascar surch **COLIS POSTAUX 0f.10.**
P82 0 f. 10 on 1 f. pink 70·00 42·00

1919. Fiscal stamps surch **Madagascar et Dependances** (in capitals on No. P83) **COLIS POSTAUX 0f.10.**
P83 0 f. 10 pink 6·25 4·75
P84 0 f. 10 red and green 1·50 1·25
P85 0 f. 10 black and green 1·75 1·25

POSTAGE DUE STAMPS

1896. Postage Due stamps of Fr. Colonies optd **Madagascar et DEPENDANCES.**
D17 U 5 c. blue 5·00 4·75
D18 10 c. brown 5·00 4·25
D19 20 c. yellow 4·50 5·00
D20 30 c. red 5·50 5·00
D21 40 c. mauve 50·00 30·00
D22 50 c. violet 6·00 5·00
D23 1 f. green 55·00 35·00

D 6 Governor's Palace, Tananarive
D 37

1908.
D70 **D 6** 2 c. red 10 10
D71 4 c. violet 10 15
D72 5 c. green 10 20
D73 10 c. red 10 20
D74 20 c. olive 10 30
D75 40 c. brown on cream 15 30
D76 50 c. brown on blue 15 25
D77 60 c. red 20 45
D78 1 f. blue 25 55

1924. Surch in figures.
D123 **D 6** 60 c. on 1 f. red 1·00 1·40
D124 2 f. on 1 f. purple 45 60
D125 3 f. on 1 f. blue 45 60

1942. Free French Administration. Optd **FRANCE LIBRE** or surch also.
D254 **D 6** 10 c. red 55 65
D255 20 c. green 55 65
D256 **D 6** 0,30 on 5 c. green 55 65
D257 40 c. brown on cream 55 65
D258 50 c. brown and blue 55 65
D259 60 c. red 55 65
D260 1 f. blue 55 65
D261 1 f. on 2 c. purple 3·00 3·50
D262 2 f. on 4 c. violet 1·25 1·50
D263 2 f. on 1 f. mauve 55 65
D264 3 f. on 1 f. blue 55 65

1947.
D319 **D 37** 10 c. mauve 10 25
D320 30 c. brown 10 25
D321 50 c. green 10 25
D322 1 f. brown 10 25
D323 2 f. red 20 30
D324 3 f. brown 15 30
D325 4 f. blue 15 40
D326 5 f. red 25 45
D327 10 f. green 35 55
D328 20 f. blue 40 1·00

For later issues see **MALAGASY REPUBLIC.**

MADEIRA Pt. 9

A Portuguese island in the Atlantic Ocean off the N.W. coast of Africa. Regarded as part of Portugal for administrative purposes, it now uses Portuguese stamps. Some separate issues for Madeira were introduced from 1980 onwards.

1868. 1000 reis = 1 milreis
1912. 100 centavos = 1 escudo

Nos. 1/77 are stamps of Portugal optd **MADEIRA.**

1868. With curved value label. Imperf.
1 **14** 20 r. olive 90·00 70·00
2 50 r. green 90·00 70·00
3 80 r. orange £100 75·00
4 100 r. lilac £100 75·00

1868. With curved value label. Perf.
10 **14** 5 r. black 20·00 18·00
13 10 r. yellow 42·00 38·00
14 20 r. olive 65·00 55·00
15b 25 r. red 25·00 4·00
16 50 r. green 85·00 70·00
17 80 r. orange 90·00 70·00
19 100 r. mauve 85·00 70·00
20 120 r. blue 55·00 35·00
21 240 r. mauve £200 £190

1871. With straight value label.
57 **15** 5 r. black 3·50 2·25
31 10 r. yellow 12·00 9·00
72a 10 r. green 26·00 20·00
32 15 r. brown 6·50 4·50
49 20 r. olive 13·00 10·00
50 25 r. red 5·00 1·60
51 50 r. green 27·00 11·00
71 50 r. blue 55·00 28·00
27 80 r. orange 40·00 32·00
53 100 r. mauve 35·00 24·00
38 120 r. blue 55·00 38·00
55 150 r. blue 85·00 75·00
74 150 r. yellow £130 £110
39 240 r. mauve £275 £225
67 300 r. lilac 35·00 30·00

1880. Stamps of 1880.
75 **16** 5 r. black 12·00 11·00
78 25 r. grey 12·00 5·00
78b 25 r. brown 12·00 5·00
77 **17** 25 r. grey 12·00 11·00

1898. Vasco da Gama. As Nos. 378/85 of Portugal.
134 2½ r. green 1·25 75
135 5 r. red 1·25 75
136 10 r. purple 2·00 90
137 25 r. green 1·25 75
138 50 r. blue 3·00 1·75
139 75 r. brown 4·00 3·25
140 100 r. brown 3·50 2·75
141 150 r. brown 6·00 5·00
For Nos. 134/41 with **REPUBLICA** optd, see Nos. 455/62 of Portugal.

6 Ceres

7 20 r. Stamp, 1868

1929. Funchal Museum Fund.
148 **6** 3 c. violet 20 20
149 4 c. yellow 20 20
150 5 c. blue 20 20
151 6 c. brown 25 25
152 10 c. red 25 25
153 15 c. green 25 25
154 16 c. brown 25 25
155 25 c. red 30 30
156 32 c. green 30 30
157 40 c. brown 30 30
158 50 c. black 30 30
159 64 c. turquoise 35 35
160 80 c. brown 35 35
161 96 c. red 40 40
162 1 e. black 40 40
163 1 e. 20 red 35 35
164 1 e. 60 blue 35 35
165 2 e. 40 yellow 75 75
166 3 e. 36 olive 80 80
167 **6** 4 e. 50 red 80 80
168 7 e. blue 1·50 1·50

1980. 112th Anniv of First Overprinted Madeira Stamps.
169 **7** 6 e. 50 black, bistre & green 15 10
170 – 19 e. 50 black, purple & red 40 25
DESIGN: 19 e. 50, 100 r. stamp, 1868.

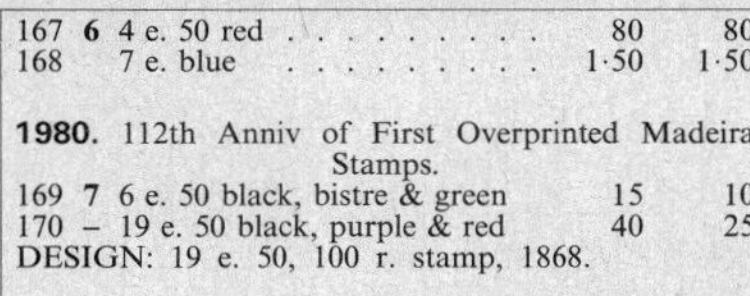

8 Ox Sledge

1980. World Tourism Conference, Manila, Philippines. Multicoloured.
172 50 c. Type **8** 10 10
173 1 e. Wine and grapes 10 10
174 5 e. Map of Madeira 15 10
175 6 e. 50 Basketwork 20 10
176 8 e. Orchid 35 20
177 30 e. Fishing boat 80 35

9 O Bailinho (folk dance)

1981. Europa.
178 **9** 22 e. multicoloured 50 30

10 Portuguese Caravel approaching Madeira
11 "Dactylorhiza foliosa"

1981. 560th Anniv (1980) of Discovery of Madeira. Multicoloured.
180 8 e. Type **10** 25 10
181 33 e. 50 Prince Henry the Navigator and map of Atlantic Ocean 85 40

1981. Regional Flowers. Multicoloured.
182 7 e. Type **11** 10 10
183 8 e. 50 "Geranium maderense" 15 10
184 9 e. "Goodyera macrophylla" 15 10
185 10 e. "Armeria maderensis" 15 10
186 12 e. 50 "Matthiola maderensis" 20 10
187 20 e. "Isoplexis sceptrum" 35 20
188 27 e. "Viola paradoxa" 40 20
189 30 e. "Erica maderensis" 40 25
190 33 e. 50 "Scilla maderensis" 50 30
191 37 e. 50 "Cirsium latifolium" 55 30
192 50 e. "Echium candicans" 85 55
193 100 e. "Clethra arborea" 1·40 65

12 First Sugar Mill
13 Dancer holding Dolls on Staff

1982. Europa.
199 **12** 33 e. 50 multicoloured 1·00 40

1982. O Brinco Dancing Dolls. Multicoloured.
201 27 e. Type **13** 60 40
202 33 e. 50 Dancers 80 50

14 Los Levadas Irrigation Channels

1983. Europa.
203 **14** 37 e. 50 multicoloured 90 30

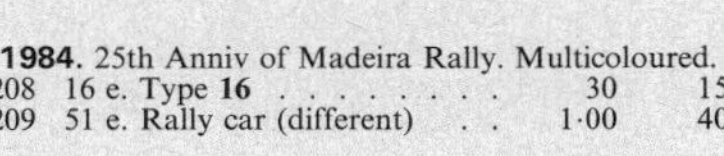

15 Flag of Madeira **16** Rally Car

1983. Flag.
205 **15** 12 e. 50 multicoloured 30 10

1984. Europa. As T **398** of Portugal but additionally inscr "MADEIRA".
206 51 e. multicoloured 95 50

1984. 25th Anniv of Madeira Rally. Multicoloured.
208 16 e. Type **16** 30 15
209 51 e. Rally car (different) 1·00 40

17 Basket Sledge **18** Braguinha Player

1984. Transport (1st series). Multicoloured.
210 16 e. Type **17** 20 10
211 35 e. Hammock 40 30
212 40 e. Borracheiros (wine carriers) 50 30
213 51 e. Local sailing boat 70 35
See also Nos. 218/21.

1985. Europa.
214 **18** 60 e. multicoloured 1·40 55

19 Black Scabbard Fish

1985. Fishes (1st series). Multicoloured.
216 40 e. Type **19** 70 30
217 60 e. Moon fish 1·10 45
See also Nos. 222/3 and 250/3.

1985. Transport (2nd series). As T **17**. Multicoloured.
218 20 e. Ox sledge 20 10
219 40 e. Mountain railway 50 35
220 46 e. Fishing boat and basket used by pesquitos (itinerant fish sellers) 65 35
221 60 e. Coastal ferry 75 40

1986. Fishes (2nd series). As T **19**. Multicoloured.
222 20 e. Big eye tuna 40 10
223 75 e. Red bream 1·40 55

20 Cory's Shearwater and Tanker

1986. Europa.
224 **20** 68 e. 50 multicoloured 1·25 60

21 Sao Lourenco Fort, Funchal

1986. Fortresses. Multicoloured.
226 22 e. 50 Type **21** 20 10
227 52 e. 50 Sao Joao do Pico Fort, Funchal 45 30
228 68 e. 50 Sao Tiago Fort, Funchal 60 35
229 100 e. Nossa Senhora do Amparo Fort, Machico 90 80

22 Firecrest

24 Funchal Cathedral

23 Social Services Centre, Funchal (Raul Chorao Ramalho)

1987. Birds (1st series). Multicoloured.

230 25 e. Type **22** 35 15
231 57 e. Trocaz pigeon 65 35
232 74 e. 50 Barn owl 85 45
233 125 e. Soft-plumaged petrel . . 1·25 80

See also Nos. 240/3.

1987. Europa. Architecture.

234 **23** 74 e. 50 multicoloured . . 90 45

1987. Historic Buildings. Multicoloured.

236 51 e. Type **24** 45 20
237 74 e. 50 Old Town Hall, Santa Cruz 65 30

25 "Maria Cristina" (mail boat)

1988. Europa. Transport and Communications.

238 **25** 80 e. multicoloured 75 40

1988. Birds (2nd series). As T **22**. Multicoloured.

240 27 e. European robin 30 15
241 60 e. Rock sparrow 50 25
242 80 e. Chaffinch 80 45
243 100 e. European sparrow hawk 90 55

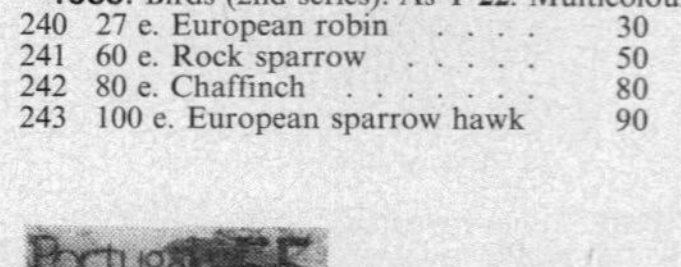

26 Columbus and Funchal House

27 Child flying Kite

1988. Christopher Columbus's Houses in Madeira. Multicoloured.

244 55 e. Type **26** 40 20
245 80 e. Columbus and Porto Santo house (horiz) 70 35

1989. Europa. Children's Games and Toys.

246 **27** 80 e. multicoloured 65 30

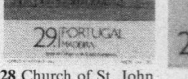

28 Church of St. John the Evangelist

29 Silver Hatchetfish

1989. "Brasiliana 89" Stamp Exhibition, Rio de Janeiro. Madeiran Churches. Multicoloured.

248 29 e. Type **28** 20 10
249 87 e. St. Clara's Church and Convent 65 35

1989. Fishes (3rd series). Multicoloured.

250 29 e. Type **29** 25 10
251 60 e. "Pseudolepidaplois scrofa" 45 20
252 87 e. Rainbow wrasse 70 35
253 100 e. Scorpion fish 80 40

30 Zarco Post Office

31 Bananas

1990. Europa. Post Office Buildings.

254 **30** 80 e. multicoloured . . . 60 30

1990. Sub-tropical Fruits. Multicoloured.

256 5 e. Type **31** 10 10
256b 10 e. Thorn apple 10 10
257 32 e. Avocado 25 10
257b 35 e. Mangoes 30 15
257c 38 e. Tomatoes 35 15
258 60 e. Sugar apple 45 20
258b 65 e. Surinam cherries . . . 50 25
258c 70 e. Brazilian guavas . . . 55 25
258d 85 e. Delicious fruits 80 35
259 100 e. Passion fruit 80 35
260 110 e. Papayas 90 40
261 125 e. Guava . . . . 1·10 50

32 Tunny Boat

1990. Boats. Multicoloured.

270 32 e. Type **32** 25 10
271 50 e. Desert Islands boat . . . 50 20
272 70 e. Maneiro type of fishing boat 60 35
275 95 e. Chavelha type of fishing boat 85 40

33 Trocaz Pigeon

1991. The Trocaz Pigeon. Multicoloured.

274 35 e. Type **33** 35 15
275 35 e. Two pigeons 35 15
276 35 e. Pigeon on nest 35 15
277 35 e. Pigeon alighting on twig 35 15

Nos. 264/7 were issued together, se-tenant, forming a composite design.

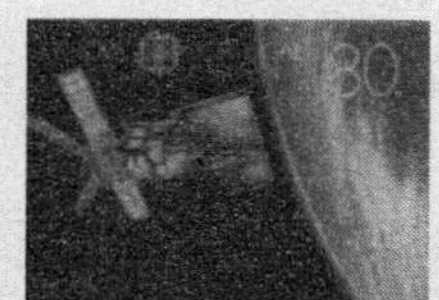

34 European Remote Sensing ("ERSI") Satellite

1991. Europa. Europe in Space.

278 **34** 80 e. multicoloured . . . 65 30

35 Columbus and Funchal House

1992. Europa. 500th Anniv of Discovery of America by Columbus.

280 **35** 85 e. multicoloured . . . 80 35

36 "Gaviao" (ferry)

1992. Island Boats. Multicoloured.

281 38 e. Type **36** 35 15
282 65 e. "Independencia" (catamaran ferry) 65 25
283 85 e. "Madeirense" (car ferry) 85 40
284 120 e. "Funchalense" (freighter) 1·10 55

37 "Shadow thrown by Christa Maar" (Lourdes Castro)

39 Window of St. Francis's Convent, Funchal

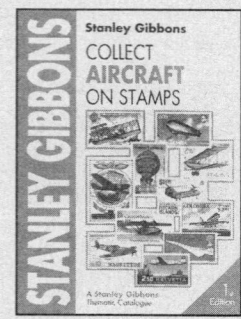

38 Seals Swimming

1993. Europa. Contemporary Art.

285 **37** 90 e. multicoloured 70 30

1993. Mediterranean Monk Seal. Multicoloured.

287 42 e. Type **38** 30 15
288 42 e. Seal basking 30 15
289 42 e. Two seals on rocks . . . 30 15
290 42 e. Mother suckling young 30 15

Nos. 287/90 were issued together, se-tenant, forming a composite design.

1993. Regional Architecture. Multicoloured.

291 42 e. Type **39** 30 15
292 130 e. Window of Mercy, old hospital . . . . 1·00 45

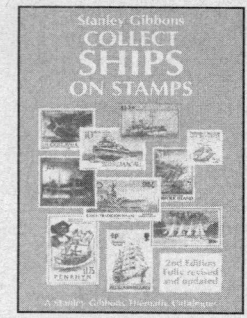

40 Native of Cape of Good Hope and Explorer with Model Caravel

1994. Europa. Discoveries.

293 **40** 100 e. multicoloured 80 35

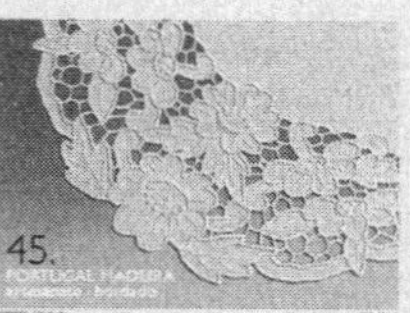

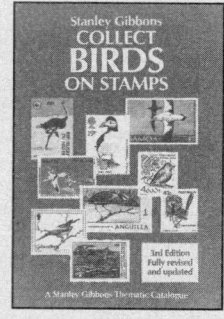

41 Embroidery

1994. Traditional Crafts. Multicoloured.

295 45 e. Type **41** 35 15
296 75 e. Tapestry 60 30
297 100 e. Boots 80 35
298 140 e. Wicker chair back . . . 1·10 50

42 Funchal

1994. District Arms. Multicoloured.

299 45 e. Type **42** 35 15
300 140 e. Porto Santo . . . . . . 1·10 50

CHARITY TAX STAMPS

The note under this heading in Portugal also applies here.

1925. Marquis de Pombal stamps of Portugal inscr "MADEIRA".

C142 C **73** 15 c. grey 70 70
C143 – 15 c. grey 70 70
C144 C **75** 15 c. grey 70 70

NEWSPAPER STAMP

1876. Newspaper stamp of Portugal optd **MADEIRA**.

N69 N **17** 2½ r. green . . . . . . 3·25 1·40

POSTAGE DUE STAMPS

1925. Marquis de Pombal stamps as Nos. C 1/3 optd **MULTA**.

D145 C **73** 30 c. grey 70 70
D146 – 30 c. grey 70 70
D147 C **75** 30 c. grey 70 70

MALAGASY REPUBLIC Pt. 6; Pt. 13

The former areas covered by Madagascar and Dependencies were renamed the Malagasy Republic within the French Community on 14 Oct., 1958.

1958. 100 centimes = 1 franc
1976. 5 francs = 1 ariary

1958. 10th Anniv of Declaration of Human Rights. As T **48** of New Caledonia.
1 10 f. brown and blue 65 45

1959. Tropical Flora. As T **47** of New Caledonia.
2 6 f. green, brown and yellow . . 15 10
3 25 f. multicoloured 40 15
DESIGNS—HORIZ: 6 f. "Datura"; 25 f. Poinsettia.

1 Malagasy Flag and Assembly Hall

1959. Proclamation of Malagasy Republic and "French Community" Commemorative (60 f.).
4 **1** 20 f. red, green and purple . . 30 20
5 – 25 f. red, green and grey . . . 40 25
6 – 60 f. multicoloured 75 45
DESIGNS—VERT: 25 f. Malagasy flag on map of Madagascar; 60 f. Natives holding French and Malagasy flags.

2 "Chionaema pauliani" (butterfly)

3 Reafforestation

1960.
7 – 30 c. multicoloured (postage) 15 10
8 – 40 c. brown, choc & green . . 15 10
9 – 50 c. turquoise and purple . . 15 10
10 **2** 1 f. red, purple and black . . 20 15
11 – 3 f. black, red and olive . . 35 20
12 – 5 f. green, brown and red . . 10 10
13 – 6 f. yellow and green . . . 10 10
14 – 8 f. black, green and red . . 15 10
15 – 10 f. green, brown & turq . . 20 10
16 – 15 f. green and brown . . . 25 15
17 – 30 f. multicoloured (air) . . 75 25
18 – 40 f. brown and turquoise . . 85 30
19 – 50 f. multicoloured . . . . 2·50 50
20 – 100 f. multicoloured . . . . 4·00 85
21 – 200 f. yellow and violet . . 7·50 1·50
22 – 500 f. brown, blue and green 7·50 2·00
BUTTERFLIES—As Type **2**: 30 c. Purple-tip; 40 c. "Acraea hova"; 50 c. Clouded mother-of-pearl; 3 f. "Hypolimnas dexithea". 48 × 27 mm: 50 f. "Charaxes antamboulou"; 100 f. Sunset moth. 27 × 48 mm: 200 f. Tailed comet moth.
OTHER DESIGNS—As Type **2**: HORIZ: 5 f. Sisal; 8 f. Pepper; 15 f. Cotton. VERT: 6 f. Ylang ylang (flower); 10 f. Rice. 48½ × 27 mm: 30 f. Sugar-cane trucks; 40 f. Tobacco plantation; 500 f. Mandrare Bridge.

1960. Trees Festival.
23 **3** 20 f. brown, green and ochre 35 25

4

5 Pres. Philibert Tsiranana

1960. 10th Anniv of African Technical Co-operation Commission.
24 **4** 25 f. lake and green 45 35

1960.
25 **5** 20 f. brown and green 30 15

6 Young Athletes

7 Pres. Tsiranana

1960. 1st Youth Games, Tananarive.
26 **6** 25 f. brown, chestnut & blue 50 30

1960.
27 **7** 20 f. black, red and green . . 25 10

1960. Independence. Surch + **10 F FETES DE L'INDEPENDANCE**.
28 **7** 20 f. + 10 f. black, red & grn 55 35

9 Ruffed Lemur

1961. Lemurs.
29 – 2 f. purple & turq (postage) 15 15
30 **9** 4 f. black, brown and myrtle 20 15
31 – 12 f. brown and green . . . 50 30
32 – 65 f. brown, sepia and myrtle (air) . . . . 1·75 65
33 – 85 f. black, sepia and green 2·25 1·00
34 – 250 f. purple, black and turq 6·50 2·75
LEMURS—VERT: As Type **9**: 2 f. Grey gentle lemur; 12 f. Mongoose-lemur. 48 × 27 mm: 65 f. Diadem sifaka; 85 f. Indris; 250 f. Verreaux's sifaka.

10 Diesel Train

11 U.N. and Malagasy Flags, and Govt. Building, Tananarive

1962.
35 **10** 20 f. myrtle 90 20
36 – 25 f. blue 35 15
DESIGN: 25 f. President Tsirianana Bridge.

1962. Admission into U.N.O.
37 **11** 25 f. multicoloured 35 20
38 85 f. multicoloured 95 55

1962. Malaria Eradication. As T **43** of Mauritania.
39 25 f. + 5 f. green 50 50

12 Ranomafana

1962. Tourist Publicity.
40 **12** 10 f. purple, myrtle and blue (postage) 20 15
41 – 30 f. purple, blue and myrtle 40 15
42 – 50 f. blue, myrtle and purple 60 25
43 – 60 f. myrtle, purple and blue 80 35
44 – 100 f. brown, myrtle and blue (air) . . . . 1·75 95
DESIGNS—As Type **12**: 30 f. Tritriva Lake; 50 f. Foulpointe; 60 f. Fort Dauphin. 27 × 47½ mm: 100 f. Boeing 707 airliner over Nossi-Be.

13 G.P.O., Tamatave

1962. Stamp Day.
45 **13** 25 f. + 5 f. brown, myrtle and blue 35 40

14 Malagasy and U.N.E.S.C.O. Emblems

15 Hydro-electric Station

1962. U.N.E.S.C.O. Conference on Higher Education in Africa, Tananarive.
46 **14** 20 f. black, green and red . 35 25

1962. 1st Anniv of Union of African and Malagasy States. As T **45** of Mauritania.
47 30 f. green 45 35

1962. Malagasy Industrialisation.
48 **15** 5 f. multicoloured 10 10
49 – 8 f. multicoloured 15 10
50 – 10 f. multicoloured 20 10
51 – 15 f. brown, black and blue 35 15
52 – 20 f. multicoloured 35 20
DESIGNS—HORIZ: 8 f. Atomic plant; 15 f. "Esso Gasikara" (tanker); 20 f. Hertzian aerials at Tananarive-Fianarantsoa. VERT: 10 f. Oilwell.

16 Globe and Factory

1963. International Fair, Tamatave.
53 **16** 25 f. orange and black . . . 30 20

1963. Freedom from Hunger. As T **51** of Mauritania.
54 25 f. + 5 f. lake, brown & red 60 60

17 Douglas DC-8 Airliner

1963. Air. Malagasy Commercial Aviation.
55 **17** 500 f. blue, red and green . . 8·50 3·25

18 Central Post Office, Tananarive

19 Madagascar Blue Pigeon

1963. Stamp Day.
56 **18** 20 f. + 5 f. brown & turq 30 35

1963. Malagasy Birds and Orchids (8 f. to 12 f.). Multicoloured. (a) Postage as T **19**.
57 1 f. Type **19** 60 30
58 2 f. Blue Madagascar coucal . . 60 30
59 3 f. Madagascar red fody . . . 60 30
60 6 f. Madagascar pygmy kingfisher 70 30
61 8 f. "Gastrorchis humblotii" . . 20 15
62 10 f. "Eulophiella roempleriana" 30 25
63 12 f. "Angraceum sesquipedale" 30 25

(b) Air. Horiz: 49½ × 28 mm.
64 40 f. Helmet bird . . . . . . 2·50 45
65 100 f. Pitta-like Ground roller 5·50 1·00
66 200 f. Crested wood ibis . . . . 12·00 3·00

20 Centenary Emblem and Map

21 U.P.U. Monument, Berne, and Map of Malagasy

1963. Red Cross Centenary.
67 **20** 30 f. multicoloured 80 60

1963. Air. African and Malagasy Posts and Telecommunications Union. As T **56** of Mauritania.
68 85 f. multicoloured . . . . . . 1·00 90

1963. Air. 2nd Anniv of Malagasy's admission to U.P.U.
69 **21** 45 f. blue, red and turquoise 50 25
70 85 f. blue, red and violet . . 90 50

22 Arms of Fianarantsoa

23 Flame, Globe and Hands

1963. Town Arms (1st series). Multicoloured.
71 1 f. 50 Antsirabe 10 10
72 5 f. Antalaha 15 10
73 10 f. Tulear 20 10
74 15 f. Majunga 30 15
75 20 f. Type **22** 40 15
75a 20 f. Manajary 25 10
76 25 f. Tananarive 45 15
76a 30 f. Nossi Be 35 15
77 50 f. Diego-Suarez 85 50
77a 90 f. Antsohihy . . . . . . 1·40 55
See also Nos. 174/7 and 208/9.

1963. 15th Anniv of Declaration of Human Rights.
78 **23** 60 f. ochre, bronze & mauve 55 45

24 Met Station, Tananarive

1964. Air. World Meteorological Day.
79 **24** 90 f. brown, blue and grey 1·50 1·25

25 Postal Cheques and Savings Bank Building, Tananarive

26 Scouts beside Camp-fire

1964. Stamp Day.
80 **25** 25 f. + 5 f. brown, bl & grn 50 60

1964. 40th Anniv of Malagasy Scout Movement.
81 **26** 20 f. multicoloured 55 25

27 Symbolic Bird and Globe within "Egg"

28 Statuette of Woman

1964. "Europafrique".
82 **27** 45 f. brown and green . . . 45 35

1964. Malagasy Art.
83 **28** 6 f. brown, blue and indigo (postage) 25 15
84 – 30 f. brown, bistre & green 45 20
85 – 100 f. brown, red & vio (air) 1·50 95
DESIGNS: 30 f. Statuette of squatting vendor. 27 × 48½ mm: 100 f. Statuary of peasant family, ox and calf.

1964. French, African and Malagasy Co-operation. As T **68** of Mauritania.
86 25 f. brown, chestnut and black 40 25

29 Tree on Globe

30 Cithern

1964. University of Malagasy Republic.
87 **29** 65 f. black, red and green 50 25

1965. Malagasy Musical Instruments.
88 – 3 f. brown, blue and mauve (postage) 20 10
89 **30** 6 f. sepia, purple and green 25 10
90 – 8 f. brown, black and green 35 10
91 – 25 f. multicoloured 90 50
92 – 200 f. brown, orange and green (air) . . . . 4·00 2·25
DESIGNS—As Type **30**: 3 f. Kabosa (lute); 8 f. Hazolahy (sacred drum). LARGER–VERT: 35½ × 48 mm: 25 f. "Valiha Player" (after E. Ralambo). 27 × 48 mm: 200 f. Bara violin.

31 Foulpointe Post Office

1965. Stamp Day.
93 **31** 20 f. brown, green & orange 20 15

32 I.T.U. Emblem 33 J.-J. Rabearivelo (poet)

1965. I.T.U. Centenary.
94 **32** 50 f. green, blue and red . . 1·00 45

1965. Rabearivelo Commemorative.
95 **33** 40 f. brown and orange . . 40 25

34 Nurse weighing Baby

1965. Air. International Co-operation Year.
96 **34** 50 f. black, bistre and blue 60 35
97 – 100 f. purple, brown & blue 1·25 60
DESIGN: 100 f. Boy and girl.

35 Pres. Tsiranana 36 Bearer

1965. Pres. Tsiranana's 55th Birthday.
98 **35** 20 f. multicoloured 25 15
99 25 f. multicoloured 30 20

1965. Postal Transport.
102 – 3 f. violet, blue and brown 30 15
103 – 4 f. blue, brown and green 25 15
104 **36** 10 f. multicoloured 25 15
105 – 12 f. multicoloured 30 20
106 – 20 f. multicoloured 50 20
107 – 25 f. multicoloured 50 20
108 – 30 f. red, brown and blue 1·25 60
109 – 65 f. brown, blue & violet 1·50 50
DESIGNS—HORIZ: 3 f. Early car; 4 f. Filanzane (litter); 12 f. Pirogue; 20 f. Horse-drawn mail-cart; 25 f. Bullock cart; 30 f. Early railway postal carriage; 65 f. Hydrofoil, "Porthos", Betsiboka.

37 Diseased Hands

1966. World Leprosy Day.
110 **37** 20 f. purple, red and green 35 20

38 Planting Trees

1966. Reafforestation Campaign.
111 **38** 20 f. violet, brown & turq 35 20

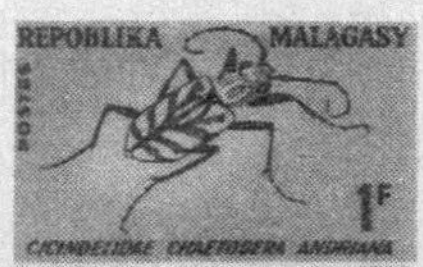

39 "Cicindelidae chaetodera andriana"

1966. Malagasy Insects. Multicoloured.
112 1 f. Type **39** 10 10
113 6 f. "Mantodea tisma freiji" 20 10
114 12 f. "Cerambycini mastododera nodicollis" 45 20
115 45 f. "Trachelophoru giraffa" 85 30

40 Madagascar 1 c. Stamp of 1903 41 Betsileo Dance

1966. Stamp Day.
116 **40** 25 f. bistre and red 35 25

1966. Folk Dances. Multicoloured.
117 2 f. Bilo Sakalava dance (vert) (postage) 15 10
118 5 f. Type **41** 25 15
119 30 f. Antandroy dance (vert) 55 20
120 200 f. Southern Malagasy dancer (air) . . . . 3·50 1·50
121 250 f. Sakalava Net Dance . 4·00 2·25
Nos. 120/1 are size 27 × 48 mm.

43 "Tree" of Emblems

1966. O.C.A.M. Conference, Tananarive.
122 **43** 25 f. multicoloured 30 15
The above was issued with "Janvier 1966" obliterated by bars, and optd "**JUIN 1966**".

44 Singing Anthem 45 U.N.E.S.C.O. Emblem

1966. National Anthem.
123 **44** 20 f. brn, mauve and green 25 10

1966. 20th Anniv of U.N.E.S.C.O.
124 **45** 30 f. blue, bistre and red . 35 20

46 Lions Emblem 47 Harvesting Rice

1967. 50th Anniv of Lions Int.
125 **46** 30 f. multicoloured 40 20

1967. International Rice Year.
126 **47** 20 f. multicoloured 30 15

48 Adventist Temple, Tanambao-Tamatave

1967. Religious Buildings (1st series).
127 **48** 3 f. ochre, blue and green 10 10
128 – 5 f. lilac, purple and green 10 10
129 – 10 f. purple, blue and green 25 10
BUILDINGS—VERT: 5 f. Catholic Cathedral, Tananarive. HORIZ: 10 f. Mosque, Tamatave.
See also Nos. 148/50.

49 Raharisoa at Piano

1967. 4th Death Anniv of Norbert Raharisoa (composer).
130 **49** 40 f. multicoloured 55 20

50 Jean Raoult's Bleriot XI, 1911

1967. "History of Malagasy Aviation".
131 **50** 5 f. brown, blue and green (postage) 35 15
132 – 45 f. black, blue & brown 90 35
133 – 500 f. black, blue and ochre (air) . . . . 8·75 3·75
DESIGNS: 45 f. Bernard Bougault and flying boat, 1926. 48 × 27 mm: 500 f. Jean Dagnaux and Breguet 19A2 biplane, 1927.

51 Ministry of Communications, Tananarive 52 Church, Torch and Map

1967. Stamp Day.
134 **51** 20 f. green, blue & orange 25 15

1967. Air. 5th Anniv of U.A.M.P.T. As T **101** of Mauritania.
135 100 f. mauve, bistre and red 1·25 60

1967. Centenary of Malagasy Lutheran Church.
136 **52** 20 f. multicoloured 30 15

53 Map and Decade Emblem 54 Woman's Face and Scales of Justice

1967. Int Hydrological Decade.
137 **53** 90 f. brown, red and blue 85 45

1967. Women's Rights Commission.
138 **54** 50 f. blue, ochre and green 50 25

55 Human Rights Emblem 56 Congress and W.H.O. Emblems

1968. Human Rights Year.
139 **55** 50 f. red, green and black 40 25

1968. Air. 20th Anniv of W.H.O. and Int Medical Sciences Congress, Tananarive.
140 **56** 200 f. red, blue and ochre 2·00 1·25

57 International Airport, Tananarive-Ivato

1968. Air. Stamp Day.
141 **57** 500 f. blue, green & brown 4·25 3·00

1968. Nos. 33 and 38 surch.
142 **11** 20 f. on 85 f. (postage) . . 40 30
143 – 20 f. on 85 f. (No. 33) (air) 50 30

59 "Industry and Construction" 61 Isotry Protestant Church, Fitiavana, Tananarive

60 Church and Open Bible

1968. Five-Year Plan. (1st issue).
144 **59** 10 f. plum, red and green 15 10
145 – 20 f. black, red and green 20 15
146 – 40 f. blue, brown & ultram 85 35
DESIGNS—VERT: 20 f. "Agriculture". HORIZ: 40 f. "Transport".
See also Nos. 156/7.

1968. 150th Anniv of Christianity in Madagascar.
147 **60** 20 f. multicoloured 25 10

1968. Religious Buildings (2nd series).
148 **61** 4 f. brown, green and red 10 10
149 – 12 f. brown, blue and violet 20 10
150 – 50 f. indigo, blue and green 45 25
DESIGNS: 12 f. Catholic Cathedral, Fianarantsoa; 50 f. Aga Khan Mosque, Tananarive.

62 President Tsiranana and Wife 63 Cornucopia, Coins and Map

1968. 10th Anniv of Republic.
151 **62** 20 f. brown, red and yellow 20 10
152 30 f. brown, red and blue 25 15

1968. 50th Anniv of Malagasy Savings Bank.
154 **63** 20 f. multicoloured 25 10

64 "Dance of the Whirlwind"

1968. Air.
155 **64** 100 f. multicoloured . . . 1·10 65

65 Malagasy Family

1968. Five Year Plan (2nd issue).
156 **65** 15 f. red, yellow and blue 15 10
157 – 45 f. multicoloured 40 25
DESIGN—VERT: 45 f. Allegory of "Achievement".

1968. Air. "Philexafrique" Stamp Exn., Abidjan (1969) (1st issue). As T **113a** of Mauritania.
158 100 f. multicoloured . . . . . 1·75 80
DESIGN: 100 f. "Young Woman sealing a Letter". (J. B. Santerre).

1969. Air. "Philexafrique" Stamp Exn., Abidjan, Ivory Coast (2nd issue). As T **114a** of Mauritania.
159 50 f. red, green and drab . . 1·00 90
DESIGN: 50 f. Malagasy Arms, map and Madagascar stamp of 1946.

68 "Queen Adelaide receiving Malagasy Mission, London" (1836-37)

1969.
160 **68** 250 f. multicoloured . . . 3·00 2·50

69 Hand with Spanner, Cogwheels and I.L.O. Emblem

1969. 50th Anniv of I.L.O.
161 **69** 20 f. multicoloured 25 15

70 Post and Telecommunications Building, Tananarive

1969. Stamp Day.
162 **70** 30 f. multicoloured 35 20

71 Map, Steering Wheel and Vehicles

72 President Tsiranana making Speech

1969. 20th Anniv of Malagasy Motor Club.
163 **71** 65 f. multicoloured 60 35

1969. 10th Anniv of President Tsiranana's Assumption of Office.
164 **72** 20 f. multicoloured 20 10

73 Bananas

74 Start of Race and Olympic Flame

1969. Fruits.
165 **73** 5 f. green, brown and blue 15 10
166 – 15 f. red, myrtle and green 30 10
DESIGN: 15 f. Lychees.

1969. Olympic Games, Mexico (1968).
167 **74** 15 f. brown, red and green 25 20

75 "Malagasy Seashore, East Coast" (A. Razafinjohany)

1969. Air. Paintings by Malagasy Artists. Multicoloured.
168 100 f. Type **75** . . . . . . 1·25 80
169 150 f. "Sunset on the High Plateaux" (H. Ratovo) . . . 2·50 1·40

76 Imerino House, High Plateaux

77 Ambalavao Arms

1969. Malagasy Traditional Dwellings (1st series).
170 – 20 f. red, blue and green . 20 10
171 – 20 f. brown, red and blue 20 10
172 **76** 40 f. red, blue and indigo 40 20
173 – 60 f. purple, green & blue 60 25

HOUSES—HORIZ: 20 f. (No. 170), Tsimihety hut, East Coast; 60 f. Betsimisaraka dwellings, East Coast. VERT: 20 f. (No. 171), Betsileo house, High Plateaux.
See also Nos. 205/6.

1970. Town Arms (2nd series). Multicoloured.
174 10 f. Type **77** 20 10
175 25 f. Morondava 35 15
176 25 f. Ambatondrazaka . . . 35 15
177 80 f. Tamatave 90 35
See also Nos. 208/9.

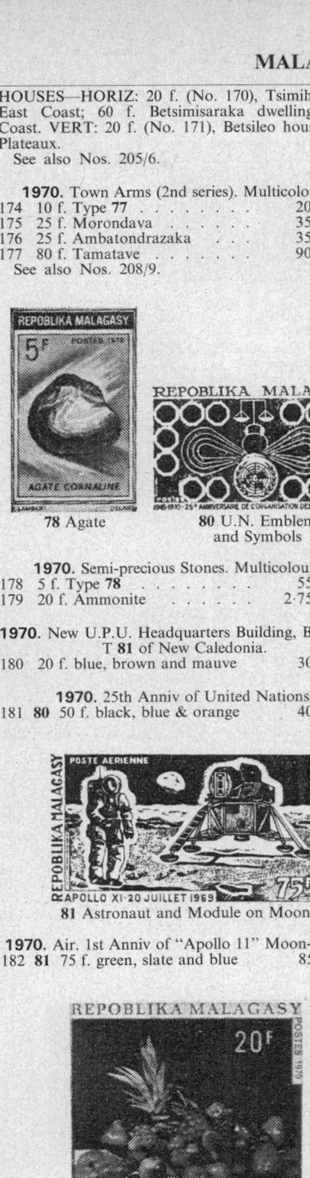

78 Agate

80 U.N. Emblem and Symbols

1970. Semi-precious Stones. Multicoloured.
178 5 f. Type **78** 55 20
179 20 f. Ammonite . . . . . . 2·75 80

1970. New U.P.U. Headquarters Building, Berne. As T **81** of New Caledonia.
180 20 f. blue, brown and mauve 30 20

1970. 25th Anniv of United Nations.
181 **80** 50 f. black, blue & orange 40 25

81 Astronaut and Module on Moon

1970. Air. 1st Anniv of "Apollo 11" Moon-landing.
182 **81** 75 f. green, slate and blue 85 40

82 Malagasy Fruits

1970.
183 **82** 20 f. multicoloured 30 15

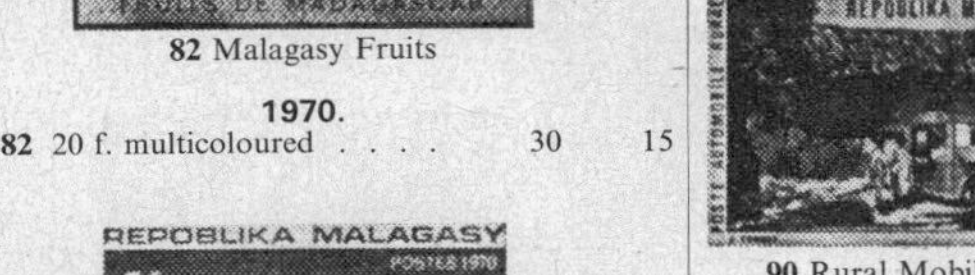

83 "Volute delessertiana"

1970. Sea-shells (1st series). Multicoloured.
184 5 f. Type **83** 50 15
185 10 f. "Murex tribulus" . . . 65 25
186 20 f. "Spondylus" . . . . . 1·40 50

84 Aye-aye

1970. Int Nature Conservation Conference, Tananarive.
187 **84** 20 f. multicoloured 40 30

85 Boeing 737 in Flight

1970. Air.
188 **85** 200 f. red, green and blue 2·40 1·25

86 Pres. Tsiranana

87 Calcite

1970. Pres. Tsiranana's 60th Birthday.
189 **86** 30 f. brown and green . . . 30 15

1971. Minerals Multicoloured.
190 12 f. Type **87** 75 20
191 15 f. Quartz . . . . 1·10 35

88 Soap Works, Tananarive

1971. Malagasy Industries.
192 **88** 5 f. multicoloured 15 10
193 – 15 f. black, brown and blue 25 10
194 – 50 f. multicoloured 55 15
DESIGNS: 15 f. Chrome works, Comina-Andriamena; 50 f. Textile complex, Sotema-Majunga.

89 Globe and Emblems

1971. Council Meeting of Common Market Countries with African and Malagasy Associated States, Tananarive.
195 **89** 5 f. multicoloured 15 15

90 Rural Mobile Post Office

91 Gen. De Gaulle

1971. Stamp Day.
196 **90** 25 f. multicoloured 35 15

1971. Death (1970) of Gen. Charles de Gaulle.
197 **91** 30 f. black, red and blue . . 70 35

92 Palm Beach Hotel, Nossi-Be

93 Forestry Emblem

1971. Malagasy Hotels.
198 **92** 25 f. multicoloured 30 20
199 – 65 f. brown, blue & green 60 30
DESIGN: 65 f. Hilton Hotel, Tananarive.

1971. Forest Preservation Campaign.
200 **93** 3 f. multicoloured 15 10

MINIMUM PRICE

The minimum price quoted is 10p which represents a handling charge rather than a basis for valuing common stamps. For further notes about prices, see introductory pages.

94 Jean Ralaimongo

96 Vezo Dwellings, South-east Coast

1971. Air. Malagasy Celebrities.
201 **94** 25 f. brown, red & orange 30 15
202 – 65 f. brown, myrtle & green 40 25
203 – 100 f. brown, ultram & bl 90 40
CELEBRITIES: 65 f. Albert Sylla; 100 f. Joseph Ravoahangy Andrianavalona.

1971. Air. 10th Anniv of African and Malagasy Posts and Telecommunications Union. As T **139a** of Mauritania.
204 100 f. U.A.M.P.T. H.Q. Brazzaville, and painting "Mpisikidy" (G. Rakotovao) 1·00 60

1971. Malagasy Traditional Dwellings (2nd series). Multicoloured.
205 5 f. Type **96** 15 10
206 10 f. Antandroy hut, South coast 20 10

97 "Children and Cattle in Meadow" (G. Rasoaharijaona)

1971. 25th Anniv of U.N.I.C.E.F.
207 **97** 50 f. multicoloured 65 30

1972. Town Arms (3rd series). As T **77**. Mult.
208 1 f. Maintirano Arms 10 10
209 25 f. Fenerive-Est 35 20

99 Cable-laying train

1972. Co-axial Cable Link, Tananarive-Tamatave.
210 **99** 45 f. brown, green and red 1·40 80

100 Telecommunications Station

1972. Inauguration of Philibert Tsiranana Satellite Communications Station.
211 **100** 85 f. multicoloured . . . 75 45

101 Pres. Tsiranana and Voters

102 "Moped" Postman

1972. Presidential Elections.
212 **101** 25 f. multicoloured . . . 40 35

1972. Stamp Day.
213 **102** 10 f. multicoloured . . . 40 20

1972. De Gaulle Memorial. No. 197 surch **MEMORIAL +20F.**
214 **91** 30 f. + 20 f. blk, red & bl 60 60

104 Exhibition. Emblem and Stamps

105 Road and Monument

1972. 2nd National Stamp Exn, Antanarive.
215 **104** 25 f. multicoloured . . . 35 30
216 40 f. multicoloured . . . 60 35
217 100 f. multicoloured . . . 1·25 75

1972. Opening of Andapa-Sambava Highway.
219 **105** 50 f. multicoloured . . . 35 25

106 Petroleum Refinery, Tamatave
107 R. Rakotobe

1972. Malagasy Economic Development.
220 **106** 2 f. blue, green and yellow 20 10
221 – 100 f. multicoloured . . . 2·40 40
DESIGN: 100 f. "3600 CV" railway locomotive.

1972. Air. 1st Death Anniv of Rene Rakotobe (poet).
222 **107** 40 f. brown, purple & orge 40 20

108 College Buildings

1972. 150th Anniv of Razafindrahety College, Tananarive.
223 **108** 10 f. purple, brown & blue 15 10

109 Volleyball

1972. African Volleyball Championships.
224 **109** 12 f. black, orange & brn 40 15

110 Runners breasting Tape

1972. Air. Olympic Games, Munich. Multicoloured.
225 100 f. Type **110** . . . . 1·00 60
226 200 f. Judo . . . . 1·75 90

111 Hospital Complex

1972. Inauguration of Ravoahangy Andrianavalona Hospital.
227 **111** 6 f. multicoloured 20 15

112 Mohair Goat

1972. Air. Malagasy Wool Production.
228 **112** 250 f. multicoloured . . . 3·50 2·25

113 Ploughing with Oxen

1972. Agricultural Expansion.
229 **113** 25 f. multicoloured . . . 25 15

114 "Virgin and Child" (15th-cent. Florentine School)

1972. Air. Christmas. Religious Paintings. Mult.
230 85 f. Type **114** 85 55
231 150 f. "Adoration of the Magi" (A. Mantegna) (horiz) . . . 2·00 85

115 Betsimisarka Women

1972. Traditional Costumes. Multicoloured.
232 10 f. Type **115** 20 10
233 15 f. Merina mother and child 30 20

116 Astronauts on Moon
117 "Natural Produce"

1973. Air. Moon Flight of "Apollo 17".
234 **116** 300 f. purple, brown & grey 3·00 1·75

1973. 10th Anniv of Malagasy Freedom from Hunger Campaign Committee.
235 **117** 25 f. multicoloured . . . 30 15

118 "The Entombment" (Grunewald)

1973. Air. Easter. Multicoloured.
236 100 f. Type **118** . . . . . . 1·00 55
237 200 f. "The Resurrection" (Grunewald) (vert) . . . . 2·00 1·10

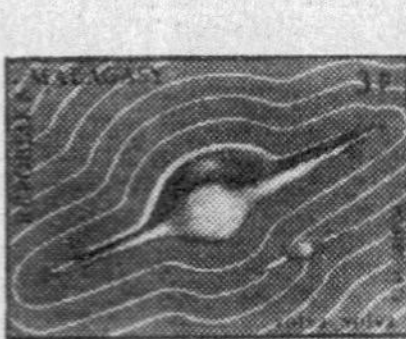
119 "Volva volva" Shell
120 Postal Courier, Tsimandoa

1973. Sea-shells (2nd series). Multicoloured.
238 3 f. Type **119** 15 10
239 10 f. "Lambischiragra" 25 20
240 15 f. "Harpa major" 50 30
241 25 f. Type **119** 70 45
242 40 f. As 15 f. . . . . 1·10 50
243 50 f. As 10 f. . . . . 2·25 60

1973. Stamp Day.
244 **120** 50 f. blue, green & brown 45 20

121 "Africa" within Scaffolding
122 "Cameleon campani"

1973. 10th Anniv of Organization of African Unity.
245 **121** 25 f. multicoloured 30 15

1973. Malagasy Chameleons. Multicoloured.
246 1 f. Type **122** 10 10
247 5 f. "Cameleon nasutus" (male) 10 10
248 10 f. "Cameleon nasutus" (female) 15 10
249 40 f. As 5 f. 55 25
250 60 f. Type **122** 85 35
251 85 f. As 10 f. . . . . 1·25 65

123 Excursion Carriage

1973. Air. Early Malagasy Railways. Multicoloured.
252 100 f. Type **123** . . . . 1·75 80
253 150 f. Steam locomotive . . . 2·50 1·25

124 "Cypripedium"

1973. Orchids. Multicoloured.
254 10 f. Type **124** 30 15
255 25 f. "Nepenthes pervillei" . . 50 20
256 40 f. As 25 f. . . . . 1·00 35
257 100 f. Type **124** . . . . 2·25 85

1973. Pan African Drought Relief. No. 235 surch **SECHERESSE SOLIDARITE AFRICAINE** and value.
258 **117** 100 f. on 25 f. multicoloured 1·10 60

126 Dish Aerial and Met. Station
128 Greater Dwarf Lemur

1973. Air. W.M.O. Centenary.
259 **126** 100 f. orange, blue & blk 1·25 65

1973. 12th Anniv of African and Malagasy Posts and Telecommunications. As T **155a** of Mauritania.
260 100 f. red, violet and green . . 90 45

1973. Malagasy Lemurs.
261 **128** 5 f. brown, green & pur (postage) 30 15
262 – 25 f. brown, sepia & green 80 35
263 – 150 f. brn, grn & sepia (air) 2·25 1·25
264 **128** 200 f. brown, turq & blue 3·25 1·75
DESIGN—VERT: 25 f., 150 f. Weasel-lemur.

129 Pres. Kennedy

1973. Air. 10th Death Anniv of Pres. John Kennedy.
265 **129** 300 f. multicoloured . . . 2·25 1·75

130 Footballers

1973. Air. World Cup Football Championships. West Germany.
266 **130** 500 f. mauve, brown and light brown . . . . . . 5·50 2·50

CURRENCY. Issues from No. 267 to No. 389 have face values shown as "Fmg". This abbreviation denotes the Malagasy Franc which was introduced in 1966.

131 Copernicus, Satellite and Diagram

1974. Air. 500th Birth Anniv of Copernicus.
267 **131** 250 f. blue, brown & green 2·75 1·50

1974. No. 76a surch
268 25 f. on 30 f. multicoloured . 25 15

133 Agricultural Training
135 Family and House

134 Male Player, and Hummingbird on Hibiscus

1974. 25th World Scouting Conference, Nairobi, Kenya.
269 **133** 4 f. grey, blue and green (postage) 10 10
270 – 15 f. purple, green & blue 20 15
271 – 100 f. ochre, red & blue (air) 80 45
272 – 300 f. brown, blue & black 2·75 1·50
DESIGNS—VERT: 15 f. Building construction. HORIZ: 100 f. First Aid training; 300 f. Fishing.

1974. Air. Asia, Africa and Latin America Table-Tennis Championships, Peking.
273 **134** 50 f. red, blue and brown 80 30
274 – 100 f. red, blue and violet 1·60 70
DESIGN: 100 f. Female player, and stylised bird.

1974. World Population Year.
275 **135** 25 f. red, orange and blue 25 10

INDEX

Countries can be quickly located by referring to the index at the end of this volume.

136 Micheline Rail Car

1974. Air. Malagasy Railway Locomotives.
276 **136** 50 f. green, red & brown 65 40
277 – 85 f. red, blue and green 1·10 50
278 – 200 f. blue, lt blue & brn 2·75 1·25
DESIGNS: 85 f. Track-inspection trolley; 200 f. Garratt steam locomotive.

137 U.P.U. Emblem and Letters

1974. Air. Centenary of U.P.U.
279 **137** 250 f. red, blue and violet 1·75 1·40

138 Rainibetsimisaraka

1974. Rainibetsimisaraka Commemoration.
280 **138** 25 f. multicoloured 35 20

1974. Air. West Germany's Victory in World Cup Football Championships. No. 266 optd **R.F.A. 2 HOLLANDE 1.**
281 **130** 500 f. mauve, brown & light brown 4·75 2·50

140 "Apollo" and "Soyuz" spacecraft

1974. Air. Soviet–U.S. Space Co-operation.
282 **140** 150 f. orange, green & blue 1·10 60
283 – 250 f. green, blue & brn 2·00 1·00
DESIGN: No. 283, As Type **140** but different view.

141 Marble Slabs

143 Faces and Maps

1974. Marble Industry. Multicoloured.
284 4 f. Type **141** 25 15
285 25 f. Quarrying 75 25

1974. Air. Universal Postal Union. Centenary (2nd issue). No. 279 optd **100 ANS COLLABORATION INTERNATIONALE.**
286 **137** 250 f. red, blue and violet 1·40 1·00

1974. Europafrique.
287 **143** 150 f. brown, red & orange 1·40 70

144 "Food in Hand"

1974. "Freedom from Hunger".
288 **144** 80 f. blue, brown & grey 65 35

145 "Coton"

146 Malagasy People

1974. Malagasy Dogs. Multicoloured.
289 50 f. Type **145** 1·40 45
290 100 f. Hunting dog 2·00 1·10

1974. Founding of "Fokonolona" Commune.
291 **146** 5 f. multicoloured 15 10
292 10 f. multicoloured 15 10
293 20 f. multicoloured 20 10
294 60 f. multicoloured 60 30

147 "Discovering Talent"

1974. National Development Council.
295 **147** 25 f. multicoloured 20 10
296 35 f. multicoloured 30 15

148 "Adoration of the Magi" (David)

149 Malagasy Girl and Rose

1974. Air. Christmas. Multicoloured.
297 200 f. Type **148** 1·75 95
298 300 f. "Virgin of the Cherries and Child" (Metzys) 3·00 1·25

1975. International Women's Year.
299 **149** 100 f. brown, orange & grn 85 40

150 Colonel Richard Ratsimandrava (Head of Government)

1975.
300 **150** 15 f. brown, black & yell 15 10
301 25 f. brown, black & blue 20 15
302 100 f. brown, black & grn 80 35

151 Sofia Bridge

1975.
303 **151** 45 f. multicoloured 50 20

152 U.N. Emblem and Part of Globe

1975. Air. 30th Anniv of U.N. Charter.
304 **152** 300 f. multicoloured 2·25 1·25

153 De Grasse (after Mauzaisse) and "Randolph"

1975. Bicentenary of American Revolution. (1st issue). Multicoloured.
305 40 f. Type **153** (postage) 55 25
306 50 f. Lafayette, "Lexington" and H.M.S. "Edward" 65 30
307 100 f. D'Estaing and "Languedoc" (air) 1·25 50
308 200 f. Paul Jones, "Bonhomme Richard" and H.M.S. "Serapis" 2·25 1·10
309 300 f. Benjamin Franklin, "Millern" and "Montgomery" 3·25 1·60

154 "Euphorbia viguieri"

1975. Malagasy Flora. Multicoloured.
311 15 f. Type **154** (postage) 25 15
312 25 f. "Hibiscus rosesinensis" 40 20
313 30 f. "Plumeria rubra acutitolia" 55 20
314 40 f. "Pachypodium rosulatum" 1·00 30
315 85 f. "Turraea sericea" (air) 1·75 1·00

1975. Air. "Apollo" - "Soyuz" Space Link Nos. 282/3 optd **JONCTION 17 JUILLET 1975.**
316 **140** 150 f. orange, grn & blue 1·00 60
317 – 250 f. green, blue & brown 2·00 1·00

156 Temple Frieze

1975. Air. "Save Borobudur Temple" (in Indonesia) Campaign.
318 **156** 50 f. red, orange and blue 1·00 50

157 "Racial Unity"

159 Lily Waterfall

158 Pryer's Woodpecker

1975. Namibia Day.
319 **157** 50 f. multicoloured 45 20

1975. International Exposition, Okinawa. Fauna. Multicoloured.
320 25 f. Type **158** (postage) 2·00 35
321 40 f. Ryukyu rabbit 50 20
322 50 f. Toad 70 30
323 75 f. Tortoise 1·10 40
324 125 f. Sika deer (air) 1·50 55

1975. Lily Waterfall. Multicoloured.
326 25 f. Type **159** 40 15
327 40 f. Lily Waterfall (distant view) 60 15

160 Hurdling

1975. Air. "Pre-Olympic Year". Olympic Games, Montreal (1976). Multicoloured.
328 75 f. Type **160** 60 35
329 200 f. Weightlifting (vert) 1·50 75

161 Bobsleigh "Fours"

1975. Winter Olympic Games, Innsbruck. Multicoloured.
330 75 f. Type **161** (postage) 50 25
331 100 f. Ski-jumping 80 35
332 140 f. Speed-skating 1·25 50
333 200 f. Cross-country skiing (air) 1·75 75
334 245 f. Downhill skiing 2·00 90

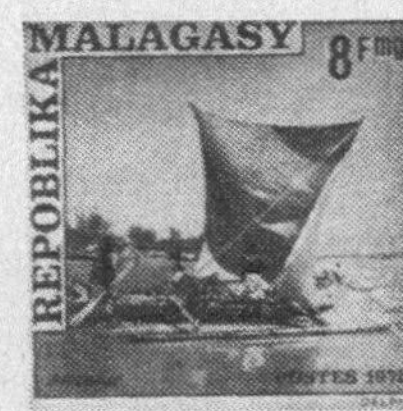

162 Pirogue

1975. Malagasy Sailing-vessels. Multicoloured.
336 8 f. Type **162** 15 15
337 45 f. Malagasy schooner 60 25

163 Canoeing

1976. Olympic Games, Montreal. Multicoloured.
338 40 f. Type **163** (postage) 25 15
339 50 f. Sprinting and hurdling 35 20
340 100 f. Putting the shot, and long-jumping (air) 65 35
341 200 f. Gymnastics-horse and parallel bars 1·40 75
342 300 f. Trampoline-jumping and high-diving 2·00 1·00

164 "Apollo 14" Lunar Module and Flight Badge

1976. Air. 5th Anniv of "Apollo 14" Mission.
344 **164** 150 f. blue, red and green 1·25 65

1976. Air. 5th Anniv of "Apollo 14" Mission. No. 344 optd **5e Anniversaire de la mission APOLLO XIV.**
345 **164** 150 f. blue, red and green 1·25 75

166 "Graf Zeppelin" over Fujiyama

1976. 75th Anniv of Zeppelin. Multicoloured.
346 40 f. Type **166** (postage) . . . 35 15
347 50 f. "Graf Zeppelin" over Rio de Janeiro 40 15
348 75 f. "Graf Zeppelin" over New York 80 25
349 100 f. "Graf Zeppelin" over Sphinx and pyramids . . . 95 35
350 200 f. "Graf Zeppelin" over Berlin (air) . . . . 2·00 75
351 300 f. "Graf Zeppelin" over London . . . . 3·00 1·00

167 "Prevention of Blindness"

1976. World Health Day.
353 **167** 100 f. multicoloured . . . 1·25 55

168 Aragonite

1976. Minerals and Fossils. Multicoloured.
354 25 f. Type **168** 50 15
355 50 f. Fossilised wood 85 30
356 150 f. Celestyte . . . . 2·75 1·10

169 Alexander Graham Bell and Early Telephone

1976. Telephone Centenary. Multicoloured.
357 25 f. Type **169** 15 10
358 50 f. Cable maintenance, 1911 30 15
359 100 f. Telephone operator and switchboard, 1895 . . . . . 60 25
360 200 f. "Emile Baudot" cable ship 1·75 70
361 300 f. Man with radio-telephone 2·00 80

170 Children reading Book

1976. Children's Books Promotion. Multicoloured.
363 10 f. Type **170** 15 10
364 25 f. Children reading book (vert) 35 15

1976. Medal winners, Winter Olympic Games, Innsbruck. Nos. 330/4 optd **VAINQUEUR** and medal winner.
365 75 f. Type **161** (postage) . . . 50 25
366 100 f. Ski-jumping 80 40
367 140 f. Skating . . . . 1·25 50
368 200 f. Cross-country skiing (air) 1·40 75
369 245 f. Downhill skiing . . . . 1·90 1·00
OPTS: 75 f. **ALLEMAGNE FEDERALE**; 100 f. **KARL SCHNABL, AUTRICHE**; 140 f. **SHEILA YOUNG, ETATS-UNIS**; 200 f. **IVAR FORMO, NORVEGE**; 245 f. **ROSI MITTERMAIER, ALLEMAGNE DE L'OUEST**.

The subject depicted on No. 367 is speed-skating, an event in which the gold medal was won by J. E. Storholt, Norway.

1976. Bicentenary of American Revolution. (2nd issue). Nos. 305/9 optd **"4 JUILLET 1776-1976"**.
371 **153** 40 f. multicoloured (postage) 35 25
372 – 50 f. multicoloured . . . 40 30
373 – 100 f. multicoloured (air) 75 50
374 – 200 f. multicoloured . . . 1·50 85
375 – 300 f. multicoloured . . . 2·25 1·25

173 Descent Trajectory

1976. "Viking" Landing on Mars. Multicoloured.
377 75 f. Type **173** 40 20
378 100 f. "Viking" landing module separation 60 25
379 200 f. "Viking" on Martian surface . . . . 1·25 55
380 300 f. "Viking" orbiting Mars 2·00 80

174 Rainandriamampandry
175 Doves over Globe

1976. 30th Anniv of Treaties signed by Rainandriamampandry (Foreign Minister).
382 **174** 25 f. multicoloured . . . 30 20

1976. Indian Ocean – "Zone of Peace". Multicoloured.
383 60 f. Type **175** 35 20
384 160 f. Doves flying across Indian Ocean (horiz) . . . . . . 1·10 55

1976. Olympic Games Medal – winners. Nos. 338/342 optd with names of two winners on each stamp.
385 **163** 40 f. multicoloured (postage) 25 15
386 – 50 f. multicoloured . . . 35 25
387 – 100 f. multicoloured (air) 70 40
388 – 200 f. multicoloured . . . 1·40 65
389 – 300 f. multicoloured . . . 2·00 1·00
OVERPRINTS: 40 f. **V. DIBA, A. ROGOV**; 50 f. **H. CRAWFORD, J. SCHALLER**; 100 f. **U. BEYER, A. ROBINSON**; 200 f. **N. COMANECI, N. ANDRIANOV**; 300 f. **K. DIBIASI, E. VAYTSEKHOVSKAIA**.

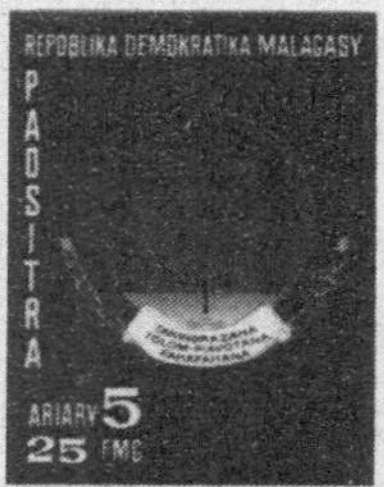

177 Malagasy Arms

1976. 1st Anniv of Malagasy Democratic Republic.
391 **177** 25 f. multicoloured . . . 20 10

178 Rabezavana (Independence Movement leader)

1977. National Heroes. Multicoloured.
392 25 f. Type **178** 20 10
393 25 f. Lt. Albert Randriamaromanana . . . 20 10
394 25 f. Ny Avana Ramanantoanina (politician) 20 10
395 100 f. Fasam-Pirenena National Mausoleum, Tananarive (horiz) 75 40

179 Family

1977. World Health Day.
396 **179** 5 f. multicoloured 15 10

180 Medical School, Antananarivo

1977. 80th Anniv of Medical School Antananarivo.
397 **180** 250 f. multicoloured . . . 1·75 95

181 Rural Post Van

1977. Rural Mail.
398 **181** 35 f. multicoloured 30 15

182 Morse Key and Man with Headphones

1977. 90th Anniv of Antananarivo–Tamatave Telegraph.
399 **182** 15 f. multicoloured 15 10

183 Academy Emblem

1977. 75th Anniv of Malagasy Academy.
400 **183** 10 f. multicoloured 15 10

184 Lenin and Russian Flag

1977. 60th Anniv of Russian Revolution.
401 **184** 25 f. multicoloured 15 10

185 Raoul Follereau

1978. 25th Anniv of World Leprosy Day.
402 **185** 5 f. multicoloured 20 10

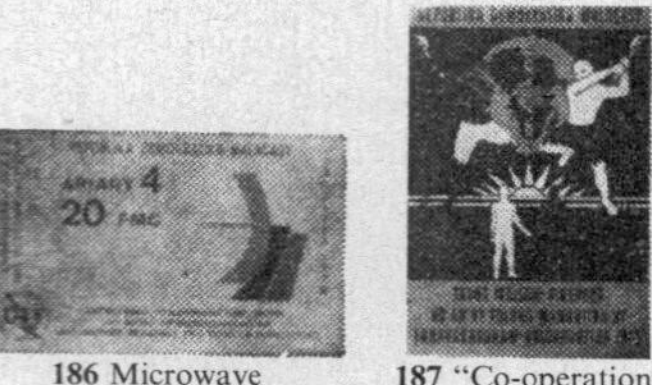
186 Microwave Antenna
187 "Co-operation"

1978. World Telecommunications Day.
403 **186** 20 f. multicoloured 15 10

1978. Anti-Apartheid Year.
404 **187** 60 f. red, black & yellow 40 25

188 Children with Instruments of Revolution

189 Tractor, Factory and Labourers

1978. "Youth–Pillar of the Revolution".
405 **188** 25 f. multicoloured . . . 75 45

1978. Socialist Co-operatives.
406 **189** 25 f. multicoloured . . . 15 10

190 Women at Work
191 Children with Books, Instruments and Fruit

1979. "Women, Pillar of the Revolution".
407 **190** 40 f. multicoloured . . . 25 15

1979. International Year of the Child.
408 **191** 10 f. multicoloured . . . 20 10

192 Ring-tailed Lemur
193 J. V. S. Razakandraina

1979. Animals. Multicoloured.
409 25 f. Type **192** (postage) . . . 25 15
410 125 f. Black lemur . . . . . 1·10 30
411 1000 f. Malagasy civet . . . . 8·00 2·25
412 20 f. Tortoise (air) 20 20
413 95 f. Black lemur (different) . 1·00 40

1979. J. V. S. Razakandraina (poet) Commem.
414 **193** 25 f. multicoloured . . . 15 10

194 "Centella asiatica"

1979. Medicinal Plant.
415 **194** 25 f. multicoloured . . . 15 10

195 Map of Malagasy and Ste. Marie Telecommunications Station

1979. Telecommunications.
416 **195** 25 f. multicoloured . . . 20 10

196 Post Office, Antsirabe

1979. Stamp Day.
417 **196** 500 f. multicoloured . . . 2·75 1·10

197 Palestinians with Flag

1979. Air. Palestinian Solidarity.
418 **197** 60 f. multicoloured . . . 50 20

198 Concorde and Map of Africa

1979. 20th Anniv of ASECNA (African Air Safety Organization).
419 **198** 50 f. multicoloured . . . 60 20

199 Lenin addressing Meeting

1980. 110th Birth Anniv of Lenin.
420 **199** 25 f. multicoloured . . . 20 10

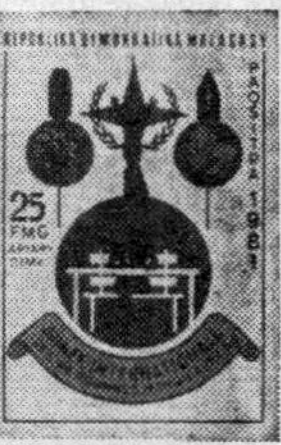

200 Taxi-Bus **201** Map illuminated by Sun

1980. 5th Anniv of Socialist Revolution.
421 **200** 30 f. multicoloured . . . 20 10

1980. 20th Anniv of Independence.
422 **210** 75 f. multicoloured . . . 50 30

202 Military Parade

1980. 20th Anniv of Army.
423 **202** 50 f. multicoloured . . . 35 15

203 Joseph Raseta

1980. Dr. Joseph Raseta Commemoration.
424 **203** 30 f. multicoloured . . . 20 10

204 Anatirova Temple

1980. Anatirova Temple Centenary.
425 **204** 30 f. multicoloured . . . 20 10

205 Boxing

1980. Olympic Games, Moscow. Multicoloured.
426 30 f. Hurdling 20 10
427 75 f. Type **205** 45 25
428 250 f. Judo . . . . 1·50 75
429 500 f. Swimming . . . . . . 2·75 1·50

206 Emblem, Map and Sun

1980. 5th Anniv of Malagasy Democratic Republic.
430 **206** 30 f. multicoloured . . . 20 10

207 Skier

1981. Winter Olympic Games, Lake Placid (1980).
431 **207** 175 f. multicoloured . . . 1·10 55

208 "Angraecum leonis" **209** Handicapped Student

1981. Flowers. Multicoloured.
432 5 f. Type **208** 10 10
433 80 f. "Angraecum famosum" 60 25
434 170 f. "Angraecum sesquipedale" 1·25 55

1981. International Year of Disabled People. Multicoloured.
435 25 f. Type **209** 20 10
436 80 f. Disabled carpenter . . . 55 25

210 Ribbons forming Caduceus, I.T.U. and W.H.O. Emblems

1981. World Telecommunications Day.
437 **210** 15 f. blue, black & yellow 15 10
438 45 f. multicoloured . . . 35 15

211 Valentina Tereshkova (first woman in space)

1981. Space Achievements. Multicoloured.
439 30 f. Type **211** 15 10
440 80 f. Astronaut on Moon . . . 55 25
441 90 f. Yuri Gagarin (first man in space) 65 30

212 Raphael-Louis Rafiringa

1981. Raphael-Louis Rafiringa Commemoration.
442 **212** 30 f. multicoloured 20 10

213 Child writing Alphabet

1981. World Literary Day.
443 **213** 30 f. multicoloured 20 10

214 Ploughing and Sowing

1981. World Food Day.
444 **214** 200 f. multicoloured . . . 1·25 60

215 Magistrates' Oath

1981. Renewal of Magistrates' Oath.
445 **215** 30 f. mauve and black . . 20 10

216 "Dove"

1981. Birth Centenary of Pablo Picasso.
446 **216** 80 f. multicoloured 60 25

217 U.P.U. Emblem and Malagasy Stamps

1981. 20th Anniv of Admission to U.P.U.
447 **217** 5 f. multicoloured 10 10
448 30 f. multicoloured . . . 20 10

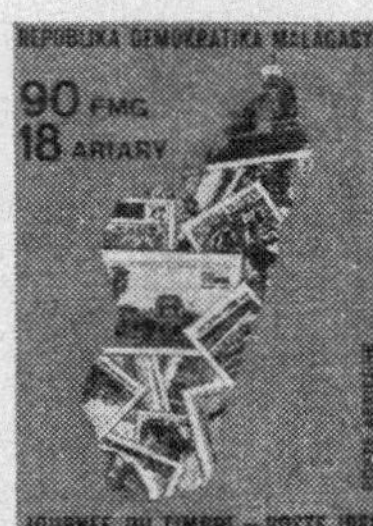

218 Stamps forming Map of Malagasy

1981. Stamp Day.
449 **218** 90 f. multicoloured . . . 65 30

219 Hook-billed Vanga

1982. Birds. Multicoloured.
450 25 f. Type **219** 75 30
451 30 f. Courol 75 30
452 200 f. Madagascar fish eagle (vert) . . . . 4·50 1·90

220 Vaccination **221** Jeannettee Mpihira

1982. Centenary of Discovery of Tubercule Bacillus.
453 **220** 30 f. multicoloured . . . 30 15

1982. Jeannette Mpihira Commemoration.
454 **221** 30 f. multicoloured . . . 20 10

222 Woman's Head formed from Map of Africa **223** Pierre Louis Boiteau

1982. Air. 20th Anniv of Panafrican Women's Organization.
455 **222** 80 f. multicoloured . . . 60 30

1982. Pierre Louis Boiteau Commemoration.
456 **223** 30 f. multicoloured . . . 20 15

224 Andekaleka Dam

1982. Air. Andekaleka Hydro-electric Complex.
457 **224** 80 f. multicoloured . . . 60 30

225 "Sputnik I"

1982. 25th Anniv of First Artificial Satellite. Multicoloured.

458 10 f. Type **225** 10 10
459 80 f. Yuri Gagarin 60 30
460 100 f. "Soyuz-Salyut" space station 75 35

226 Heading Ball

1982. World Cup Football Championship, Spain. Multicoloured.

461 30 f. Type **226** 20 10
462 40 f. Running with ball . . . 30 15
463 80 f. Tackle 60 30

227 Ploughing, Sowing and F.A.O. Emblem

1982. World Food Day.

465 **227** 80 f. multicoloured . . . 50 30

228 Bar Scene

1982. 150th Anniv of Edouard Manet (artist). Multicoloured.

466 5 f. Type **228** 15 15
467 30 f. Woman in white 25 10
468 170 f. Man with pipe . . . . 1·40 65

229 "Lutianus sebae"

1982. Fishes. Multicoloured.

470 5 f. Type **229** 15 15
471 20 f. "Istiophorus platypterus" 20 15
472 30 f. "Pterois volitans" 25 15
473 50 f. "Thunnus albacares" . . 40 15
474 200 f. "Epinephelus fasciatus" 1·75 65

230 Fort Mahavelona

1982. Landscapes. Multicoloured.

476 10 f. Type **230** (postage) . . . 10 10
477 30 f. Ramena coast 20 10
478 400 f. Jacarandas in flower (air) 2·75 1·50

231 Flags of Russia and Malagasy, Clasped Hands and Tractors

1982. 60th Anniv of U.S.S.R. Multicoloured.

479 10 f. Type **231** 10 10
480 15 f. Flags, clasped hands and radio antenna 10 10
481 30 f. Map of Russia, Kremlin and Lenin 15 10
482 150 f. Flags, clasped hands, statue and arms of Malagasy 1·00 45

232 Television, Drums, Envelope and Telephone

1983. World Communications Year. Multicoloured.

483 30 f. Type **232** 15 10
484 80 f. Stylized figures holding cogwheel 55 25

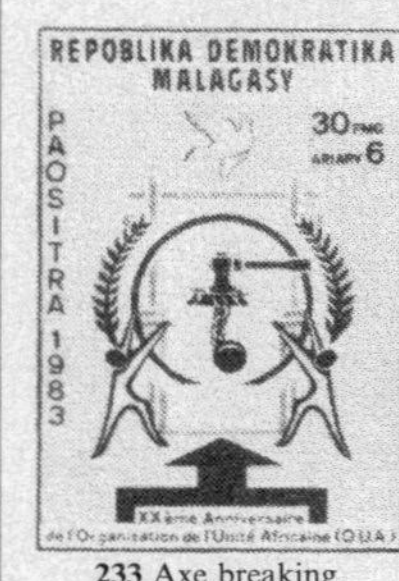

233 Axe breaking Chain on Map of Africa
234 Henri Douzon

1983. 20th Anniv of Organization of African Unity.

485 **233** 30 f. multicoloured . . . 20 10

1983. Henri Douzon (lawyer) Commemorative.

486 **234** 30 f. multicoloured . . . 20 10

237 Ruffed Lemur

1984. Lemurs. Multicoloured.

489 30 f. Type **237** 35 20
490 30 f. Verreaux's sifaka . . . 35 20
491 30 f. Lesser mouse-lemur (horiz) 35 20
492 30 f. Aye-aye (horiz) 35 20
493 200 f. Indri (horiz) . . . . . 2·00 1·10

238 Ski-jumping

1984. Winter Olympic Games, Sarajevo. Mult.

495 20 f. Type **238** 15 10
496 30 f. Ice-hockey 20 10
497 30 f. Downhill skiing 20 10
498 30 f. Speed skating 20 10
499 200 f. Ice-dancing . . . . . . 1·40 70

239 Renault, 1907

1984. Early Motor Cars. Multicoloured.

501 15 f. Type **239** 20 10
502 30 f. Benz, 1896 . . . . 30 15
503 30 f. Baker, 1901 . . . . . . 30 15
504 30 f. Blake, 1901 . . . . 30 15
505 200 f. F.I.A.L., 1908 . . . . . 2·00 75

240 Pastor Ravelojaona
241 "Noli me Tangere"

1984. Pastor Ravelojaona (encylopedist) Commemoration.

507 **240** 30 f. multicoloured 20 15

1984. 450th Death Anniv of Correggio. Paintings by Artist.

508 **241** 5 f. multicoloured 10 10
509 – 20 f. multicoloured 15 10
510 – 30 f. multicoloured 25 15
511 – 80 f. multicoloured 45 25
512 – 200 f. multicoloured . . . 1·40 65

242 Paris Landmarks and Emblem
243 Football

1984. 60th Anniv of International Chess Federation. Multicoloured.

514 5 f. Type **242** 15 15
515 20 f. Wilhelm Steinitz and stylized king 20 15
516 30 f. Vera Menchik and stylized queen 35 15
517 30 f. Anatoly Karpov and trophy 35 15
518 215 f. Nona Gaprindashvili and trophy . . . . 2·75 90

1984. Olympic Games, Los Angeles.

520 **243** 100 f. multicoloured . . . 45 30

244 "Eudaphaenura splendens"
245 Ralaimongo

1984. Butterflies. Multicoloured.

521 15 f. Type **244** 20 15
522 50 f. "Acraea hova" 60 20
523 50 f. "Othreis boesae" 60 20
524 50 f. "Pharmocophagus antenor" 60 20
525 200 f. "Epicausis smithii" . . . 2·25 1·00

1984. Birth Centenary of Jean Ralaimongo (politician).

527 **245** 50 f. multicoloured 30 15

246 Children in Brief-case
247 "Disa incarnata"

1984. 25th Anniv of Children's Rights Legislation.

528 **246** 50 f. multicoloured . . . 40 15

1984. Orchids. Multicoloured.

529 20 f. Type **247** (postage) . . . 20 10
530 235 f. "Eulophiella roempleriana" . . . . . . 2·25 85
531 50 f. "Eulophiella roempleriana" (horiz) (air) 60 25
532 50 f. "Grammangis ellisii" (horiz) 60 25
533 50 f. "Grammangis spectabilis" 60 25

248 U.N. Emblem and Cotton Plant
249 "Sun Princess" (Sadio Diouf)

1984. 20th Anniv of United Nations Conference on Commerce and Development.

535 **248** 100 f. multicoloured . . . 60 30

1984. 40th Anniv of International Civil Aviation Organization.

536 **249** 100 f. multicoloured . . . 65 30

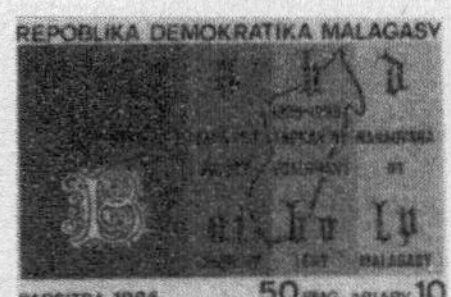

250 Bible, Map and Gothic Letters

1985. 150th Anniv of First Bible in Malagasy Language.

537 **250** 50 f. brown, pink and black 30 15

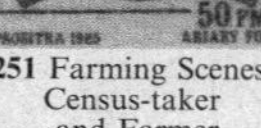

251 Farming Scenes, Census-taker and Farmer
252 Lap-dog

1985. Agricultural Census.

538 **251** 50 f. grey, black and mauve 30 15

1985. Cats and Dogs. Multicoloured.

539 20 f. Type **252** 20 15
540 20 f. Siamese cat 20 15
541 50 f. Abyssinian cat (vert) . . 60 20
542 100 f. Cocker spaniel (vert) . 1·25 35
543 235 f. Poodle . . . . 2·50 90

253 Russian Soldiers in Berlin

1985. 40th Anniv of Victory in Second World War.

545 20 f. Type **253** 15 10
546 50 f. Arms of French squadron and fighter planes 40 15
547 100 f. Victory parade, Red Square, Moscow 75 30
548 100 f. French troops entering Paris (vert) 75 30

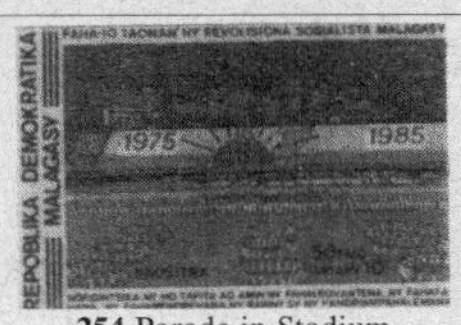
254 Parade in Stadium

1985. 10th Anniv of Malagasy Democratic Republic.
549 **254** 50 f. multicoloured . . . 40 15

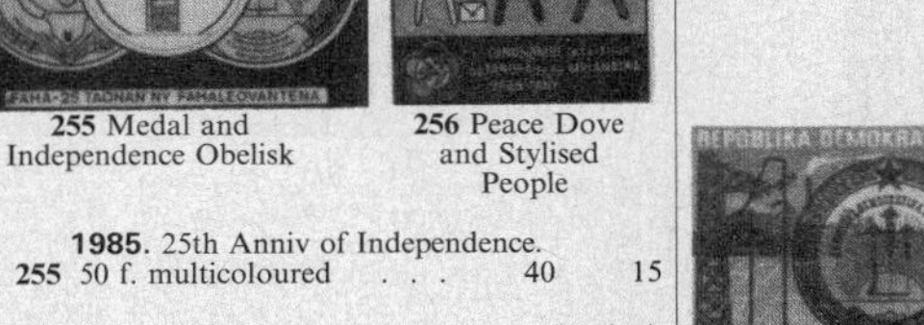
255 Medal and Independence Obelisk

256 Peace Dove and Stylised People

1985. 25th Anniv of Independence.
550 **255** 50 f. multicoloured . . . 40 15

1985. 12th World Youth and Students' Festival, Moscow.
551 **256** 50 f. multicoloured . . . 40 15

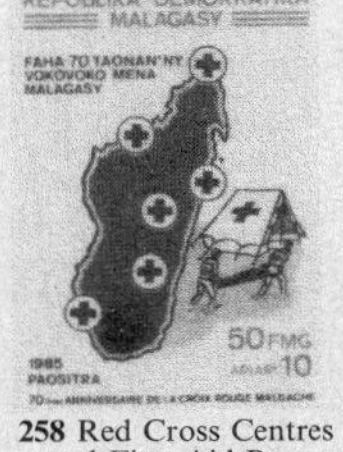
257 I.Y.Y. Emblem and Map of Madagascar

258 Red Cross Centres and First Aid Post

1985. International Youth Year.
552 **257** 100 f. multicoloured . . . 60 25

1985. 70th Anniv of Malagasy Red Cross.
553 **258** 50 f. multicoloured . . . 60 25

259 "View of Sea at Saintes-Maries" (Vincent van Gogh)

260 Indira Gandhi

1985. Impressionist Paintings. Multicoloured.
554 20 f. Type **259** 20 10
555 20 f. "Rouen Cathedral in the Evening" (Claude Monet) (vert) 15 10
556 45 f. "Young Girls in Black" (Pierre-Auguste Renoir) (vert) 30 20
557 50 f. "Red Vineyard at Arles" (van Gogh) 30 20
558 100 f. "Boulevard des Capucines, Paris" (Monet) 85 40

1985. Indira Gandhi (Indian Prime Minister) Commemoration.
560 **260** 100 f. multicoloured . . . 80 30

261 Figures and Dove on Globe and Flag

262 "Aeranthes grandiflora"

1985. 40th Anniv of U.N.O.
561 **261** 100 f. multicoloured . . . 65 25

1985. Orchids. Multicoloured.
562 20 f. Type **262** 20 10
563 45 f. "Angraecum magdalenae" and "Nephele oenopion" (insect) (horiz) 35 15
564 50 f. "Aerangis stylosa" . . . 35 15
565 100 f. "Angraecum eburneum longicalcar" and "Hippotion batschi" (insect) 80 35
566 100 f. "Angraecum sesquipedale" and "Xanthopan morganipredicta" (insect) . 80 35

263 Russian and Czechoslovakian Cosmonauts

1985. Russian "Interkosmos" Space Programme. Multicoloured.
568 20 f. Type **263** 15 10
569 20 f. Russian and American flags and "Apollo"–"Soyuz" link 15 10
570 50 f. Russian and Indian cosmonauts 30 15
571 100 f. Russian and Cuban cosmonauts 50 25
572 200 f. Russian and French cosmonauts . . . . 1·25 60

264 Emblem in "10"

265 Headquarters

1985. 10th Anniv of Malagasy Democratic Republic.
574 **264** 50 f. multicoloured . . . 30 15

1986. 10th Anniv of ARO (State insurance system).
575 **265** 50 f. yellow and brown . 30 15

266 "David and Uriah" (Rembrandt)

268 Sombrero, Football and Player

267 Comet

1986. Foreign Paintings in Hermitage Museum, Leningrad. Multicoloured.
576 20 f. Type **266** 20 10
577 50 f. "Portrait of Old Man in Red" (Rembrandt) 50 30
578 50 f. "Danae" (Rembrandt) (horiz) 50 30
579 50 f. "Marriage of Earth and Water" (Rubens) 50 30
580 50 f. "Portrait of Infanta Isabella's Maid" (Rubens) 50 30

1968. Air. Appearance of Halley's Comet.
582 **267** 150 f. multicoloured . . . 1·00 50

1986. Russian Paintings in the Tretyakov Gallery, Moscow. As T **266**. Multicoloured.
583 20 f. "Fruit and Flowers" (I. Khroutsky) (horiz) 15 10
584 50 f. "The Rooks have Returned" (A. Savrasov) . 30 20
585 50 f. "Unknown Woman" (I. Kramskoi) (horiz) 30 20
586 50 f. "Aleksandr Pushkin" (O. Kiprenski) 30 20
587 100 f. "March, 1895" (I. Levitan) (horiz) 60 40

1986. World Cup Football Championship, Mexico.
589 **268** 150 f. multicoloured . . . 1·10 30

269 Child Care

270 Jungle Cat

1986. U.N.I.C.E.F. Child Survival Campaign.
590 **269** 60 f. multicoloured . . . 40 15

1986. Wild Cats. Multicoloured.
591 10 f. Type **270** 20 10
592 10 f. Wild cat 20 10
593 60 f. Caracal 45 20
594 60 f. Leopard cat 45 20
595 60 f. Serval 45 20

271 Dove above Hands holding Globe

1986. International Peace Year. Multicoloured.
597 60 f. Type **271** 40 15
598 150 f. Doves above emblem and map . . . . 1·00 45

272 U.P.U. Emblem on Dove

273 U.P.U. Emblem on Globe

1986. World Post Day.
599 **272** 60 f. multicoloured (postage) 40 15
600 150 f. blue, black and red (air) . . . . 1·10 50

1986. Air. 25th Anniv of Admission to U.P.U.
601 **273** 150 f. multicoloured . . . 1·10 50

274 Giant Madagascar Coucal

1986. Birds. Multicoloured.
602 60 f. Type **274** . . . . 1·10 40
603 60 f. Crested Madagascar coucal 1·10 40
604 60 f. Rufous vangas (vert) . . 1·10 40
605 60 f. Red-tailed vangas (vert) 1·10 40
606 60 f. Sicklebill . . . . 1·10 40

275 Tortoise

1987. Endangered Animals. Multicoloured.
608 60 f. Type **275** 50 20
609 60 f. Crocodile 50 20
610 60 f. Crested wood ibis (vert) 50 20
611 60 f. Black coucal 50 20

276 Crowd in "40"

1987. 40th Anniv of Anti-Colonial Uprising.
613 **276** 60 f. brown, red & yellow 35 15
614 – 60 f. multicoloured 35 15
DESIGN: No. 614, Hands in broken manacles, map, rifleman and spearman.

277 Emblems, Map and Pictogram

1987. 1st Indian Ocean Towns Games.
615 **277** 60 f. multicoloured 35 15
616 150 f. multicoloured . . . 1·10 35

278 "Sarimanok"

1987. The "Sarimanok" (replica of early dhow). Multicoloured.
617 60 f. Type **278** 40 15
618 150 f. "Sarimanok" (different) 1·10 35

279 Coffee Plant

280 Rifle Shooting and Satellite

1987. 25th Anniv of African and Malagasy Coffee Producers Organization. Multicoloured.
619 60 f. Type **279** 35 15
620 150 f. Map showing member countries . . . . 1·10 35

1987. Winter Olympic Games, Calgary (1988). Multicoloured.
621 60 f. Type **280** 25 10
622 150 f. Slalom 60 20
623 250 f. Luge . . . . 1·25 40
624 350 f. Speed skating . . . . . 1·40 50
625 400 f. Ice hockey . . . . . . 1·60 60
626 450 f. Ice skating (pairs) . . . 2·00 70

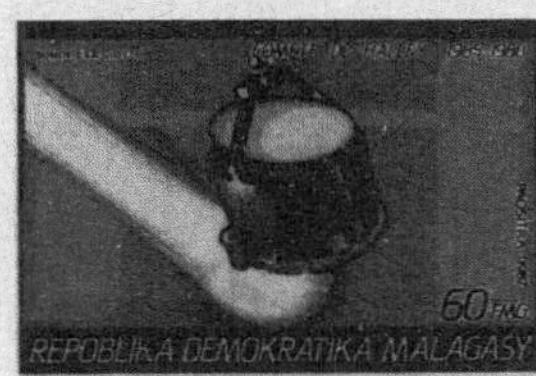
281 "Giotto" Space Probe

1987. Appearance of Halley's Comet (1986). Space Probes. Multicoloured.
628 60 f. Type **281** 25 10
629 150 f. "Vega 1" 60 20
630 250 f. "Vega 2" . . . . 1·25 40
631 350 f. "Planet A 1" . . . . . 1·40 50
632 400 f. "Planet B 1" . . . . . 1·60 60
633 450 f. "I.C.E." . . . . 2·00 70

282 Piper Aztec

283 Rabearivelo

1987. Air. 25th Anniv of Air Madagascar. Multicoloured.
635 60 f. Type **282** 40 20
636 60 f. De Havilland Twin Otter 40 20
637 150 f. Boeing 747-200 . . . . 1·00 40

1987. 50th Death Anniv of Jean-Joseph Rabearivelo (poet).
638 **283** 60 f. multicoloured . . . 30 15

284 Communications Equipment Robot and Print-out Paper

285 Emblem

1987. National Telecommunications Research Laboratory.
639 **284** 60 f. green, black and red 30 15

1987. 150th Anniv of Execution of Rafaravavy Rasalama (Christian martyr).
640 **285** 60 f. black, deep blue and blue 30 15

286 Hand using Key and Telegraphist

1987. Centenary of Antananarivo–Tamatave Telegraph.

641 **286** 60 f. multicoloured . . . 30 15

287 Bartholomeu Dias and Departure from Palos, 1492

1987. 500th Anniv (1992) of Discovery of America by Columbus. Multicoloured.

642 60 f. Type **287** 20 10
643 150 f. Route around Samana Cay and Henry the Navigator 45 20
644 250 f. Columbus and crew disembarking, 1492, and A. de Marchena 75 30
645 350 f. Building Fort Navidad and Paolo del Pozzo Toscanelli 1·10 40
646 400 f. Columbus in Barcelona, 1493, and Queen Isabella of Spain . . . . 1·25 50
647 450 f. Columbus and "Nina" 1·50 50

288 Showjumping and "Harlequin" (Picasso)

1987. Olympic Games, Barcelona (1992). Multicoloured.

649 60 f. Type **288** (postage) . . . 15 10
650 150 f. Weightlifting and Barcelona Cathedral 40 20
651 250 f. Hurdling and Canaletas Fountain 70 30
652 350 f. High jumping and Parc d'Attractions . . . . . . 1·00 40
653 400 f. Gymnast on bar and church (air) . . . . 1·40 50
654 450 f. Gymnast with ribbon and Triumphal Arch . . . . . . 1·50 50

289 Anniversary Emblem, T.V. Tower and Interhotel "Berlin"

290 Musician and Dancers

1987. 750th Anniv of Berlin.

656 **289** 150 f. multicoloured . . . 25 15

1987. Schools Festival.

657 **290** 60 f. multicoloured . . . 15 10

291 Madagascar Pasteur Institute and Pasteur

1987. Centenary of Pasteur Institute, Paris.

658 **291** 250 f. multicoloured . . . 60 25

292 "After the Shipwreck" (Eugene Delacroix)

1987. Paintings in Pushkin Museum of Fine Arts, Moscow. Multicoloured.

659 10 f. Type **292** 15 10
660 60 f. "Jupiter and Callisto" (Francois Boucher) (vert) . 15 10
661 60 f. "Still Life with Swan" (Frans Snyders) 15 10
662 60 f. "Chalet in the Mountains" (Gustave Courbet) 15 10
663 150 f. "At the Market" (Joachim Bueckelaer) 40 15

293 Emblem

294 Family and House on Globe

1987. 10th Anniv of Pan-African Telecommunications Union.

665 **293** 250 f. multicoloured . . . 40 20

1988. International Year of Shelter for the Homeless (1987). Multicoloured.

666 80 f. Type **294** 15 10
667 250 f. Hands forming house protecting family from rain 35 20

295 Lenin addressing Crowd

1988. 70th Anniv of Russian Revolution. Mult.

668 60 f. Type **295** 15 10
669 60 f. Revolutionaries 15 10
670 150 f. Lenin in crowd 25 15

296 Broad-nosed Gentle Lemur

1988. Endangered Species. Multicoloured.

671 60 f. Type **296** 15 10
672 150 f. Diadem sifaka 20 15
673 250 f. Indri 35 15
674 350 f. Ruffed lemur 60 25
675 550 f. Purple herons (horiz) . . 90 70
676 1500 f. Nossi-be chameleon (horiz) . . . . 2·40 1·25

297 Ice Skating

1988. Winter Olympic Games, Calgary. Mult.

678 20 f. Type **297** 10 10
679 60 f. Speed-skating 10 10
680 60 f. Slalom 10 10
681 100 f. Cross-country skiing . 20 10
682 250 f. Ice hockey 45 20

298 Dove, Axe breaking Chain and Map

1988. 25th Anniv of Organization of African Unity.

684 **298** 80 f. multicoloured 15 10

299 Institute Building

1988. 20th Anniv of National Posts and Telecommunications Institute.

685 **299** 80 f. multicoloured 15 10

300 College

1988. Centenary of St. Michael's College.

686 **300** 250 f. multicoloured . . . 30 20

301 Pierre and Marie Curie in Laboratory

302 Emblem

1988. 90th Anniv of Discovery of Radium.

687 **301** 150 f. brown and mauve 40 15

1988. 10th Anniv of Alma-Ata Declaration (on health and social care).

688 **302** 60 f. multicoloured 15 10

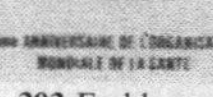

303 Emblem

304 Ring-tailed Lemurs on Island

1988. 40th Anniv of W.H.O.

689 **303** 150 f. brown, blue and black 20 15

1988. 50th Anniv of Tsimbazaza Botanical and Zoological Park. Multicoloured.

690 20 f. Type **304** 15 10
691 80 f. Ring-tailed lemur with young (25 × 37 mm) 20 10
692 250 f. Palm tree and ring-tailed lemur within "Zoo" (47 × 32 mm) 40 20

305 Hoopoe and Blue Madagascar Coucal

306 Cattle grazing

1988. Scouts, Birds and Butterflies. Multicoloured.

694 80 f. Type **305** 30 20
695 250 f. "Chrysiridia croesus" (butterfly) 40 20
696 270 f. Weaver and red forest fody 70 35
697 350 f. "Papilio dardanus" (butterflies) 60 40
698 550 f. Crested Madagascar coucal . . . . 1·25 75
699 1500 f. "Argema mittrei" (butterfly) . . . . 2·50 2·00

1988. 10th Anniv of International Fund for Agricultural Development.

701 **306** 250 f. multicoloured . . . 30 20

307 Karl Bach and Clavier

308 Books

1988. Musicians' Anniversaries. Multicoloured.

702 80 f. Type **307** (death bicentenary) 15 10
703 250 f. Franz Schubert and piano (160th death) 40 15
704 270 f. Georges Bizet and scene from "Carmen" (150th birth) 40 20
705 350 f. Claude Debussy and scene from "Pelleas et Melisande" (70th death) 50 25
706 550 f. George Gershwin at piano writing score of "Rhapsody in Blue" (90th birth) 75 45
707 1500 f. Elvis Presley (10th death (1987)) . . . . 2·50 1·25

1988. "Ecole en Fete" Schools Festival.

709 **308** 80 f. multicoloured . . . 15 10

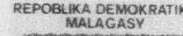

309 "Black Sea Fleet at Feodosiya" (Ivan Aivazovski)

310 "Tragocephala crassicornis"

1988. Paintings of Sailing Ships. Multicoloured.

710 20 f. Type **309** 25 15
711 80 f. "Lesnoie" (N. Semenov) 25 15
712 80 f. "Seascape with Sailing Ships" (Simon de Vlieger) 25 15
713 100 f. "Orel" (N. Golitsine) (horiz) 30 15
714 250 f. "Naval Battle Exercises" (Adam Silo) 75 25

1988. Endangered Beetles. Multicoloured.

716 20 f. Type **310** 15 10
717 80 f. "Polybothris symptuosa-gema" 15 10
718 250 f. "Euchroea auripigmenta" 50 25
719 350 f. "Stellognata maculata" 70 35

311 Stretcher Bearers and Anniversary Emblem

312 Symbols of Human Rights

1988. 125th Anniv of International Red Cross. Multicoloured.

720 80 f. Type **311** 15 10
721 250 f. Red Cross services, emblem and Henri Dunant (founder) 35 20

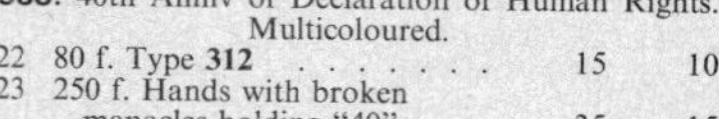

1988. 40th Anniv of Declaration of Human Rights. Multicoloured.

722 80 f. Type **312** 15 10
723 250 f. Hands with broken manacles holding "40" . . 35 15

313 Mercedes-Benz "Blitzen-Benz", 1909

1989. Cars and Trains. Multicoloured.

724 80 f. Type **313** 15 10
725 250 f. Micheline "ZM 517 Tsikirity" Antananarivo-Moramanga line 35 15
726 270 f. Bugatti coupe binder, "41" 40 20
727 350 f. German class "1020" electric locomotive 60 25
728 1500 f. Souleze "710" diesel train, Malagasy 2·25 1·25
729 2500 f. Opel racing car, 1913 3·50 2·00

314 Tyrannosaurus

1989. Prehistoric Animals. Multicoloured.

731 20 f. Type **314** 15 10
732 80 f. Stegosaurus 20 10
733 250 f. Arsinoitherium 40 15
734 450 f. Triceratops 80 30

315 "Tahitian Girls"

1989. Woman in Art. Multicoloured.

736 20 f. Type **315** 10 10
737 80 f. "Portrait of a Girl" (Jean-Baptiste Greuze) 15 10
738 80 f. "Portrait of a Young Woman" (Titian) 15 10
739 100 f. "Woman in Black" (Auguste Renoir) 20 10
740 250 f. "The Lace-maker" (Vasily Tropinine) 35 15

316 "Sobennikoffia robusta"

317 Nehru

1989. Orchids. Multicoloured.

742 5 f. Type **316** 15 10
743 10 f. "Grammangis fallax" (horiz) 15 10
744 80 f. "Angraecum sororium" 20 10
745 80 f. "Cymbidiella humblotii" 20 10
746 250 f. "Oenia oncidiiflora" 60 20

1989. Birth Centenary of Jawaharlal Nehru (Indian statesman).

748 **317** 250 f. multicoloured 45 15

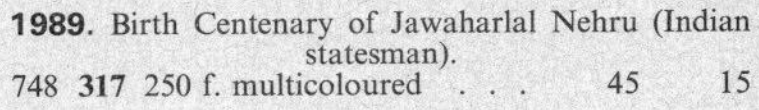

318 Mahamasina Sports Complex, Lake Anosy and Ampefiloha Quarter

1989. Antananarivo. Multicoloured.

749 5 f. Type **318** 10 10
750 20 f. Andravoahangy and Anjanahary Quarters 10 10
751 80 f. Zoma market and Faravohitra Quarter 15 10
752 80 f. Andohan' Analekely Quarter and 29 March Column 15 10
753 250 f. Avenue de l'Independance and Jean Ralaimongo Column 35 15
754 550 f. Lake Anosy, Queen's Palace and Andohalo School 70 35

319 Rose Quartz

1989. Ornamental Minerals. Multicoloured.

755 80 f. Type **319** 20 10
756 250 f. Fossilized wood 60 20

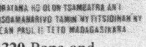

320 Pope and Rasoamanarivo **321** Map and Runner with Torch

1989. Visit of Pope John Paul II and Beatification of Victoire Rasoamanarivo. Multicoloured.

757 80 f. Type **320** 20 10
758 250 f. Map and Pope 55 20

1989. Town Games.

759 **321** 80 f. + 20 f. multicoloured 15 15

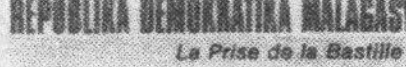

322 "Storming the Bastille"

1989. Bicentenary of French Revolution (1st issue).

760 **322** 250 f. multicoloured 35 15

See also Nos. 773/5.

323 Mirabeau and Gabriel Riqueti at Meeting of States General

1989. "Philexfrance 89" International Stamp Exhibition, Paris. Multicoloured.

761 250 f. Type **323** 30 15
762 350 f. Camille Desmoulins' call to arms 45 20
763 1000 f. Lafayette and crowd demanding bread 1·25 60
764 1500 f. Trial of King Louis XVI 2·00 80
765 2500 f. Assassination of Marat 3·25 1·25

324 "Mars 1"

1989. Space Probes. Multicoloured.

767 20 f. Type **324** 10 10
768 80 f. "Mars 3" 15 10
769 80 f. "Zond 2" 15 10
770 250 f. "Mariner 9" 35 15
771 270 f. "Viking 2" 40 20

325 "Liberty guiding the People" (Eugene Delacroix)

1989. Bicentenary of French Revolution (2nd issue). Multicoloured.

773 5 f. Type **325** (postage) 10 10
774 80 f. "La Marseillaise" (Francois Rude) 15 10
775 250 f. "Oath of the Tennis Court" (Jacques Louis David) (air) 35 15

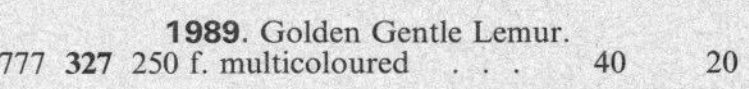

326 Rene Cassin (founder) **327** Mother and Young on Bamboo

1989. 25th Anniv of International Human Rights Institute for French Speaking Countries.

776 **326** 250 f. multicoloured 30 15

1989. Golden Gentle Lemur.

777 **327** 250 f. multicoloured 40 20

328 Footballer and Cavour Monument, Turin

1989. World Cup Football Championship, Italy. Multicoloured.

778 350 f. Type **328** 50 20
779 1000 f. Footballer and Christopher Columbus monument, Genoa 1·40 50
780 1500 f. Florentine footballer, 1530, and "David" (sculpture, Michelangelo) 2·00 75
781 2500 f. Footballer and "Rape of Proserpina" (sculpture, Bernini), Rome 3·25 1·40

329 Pennant Coralfish

1990. Fishes. Multicoloured.

783 5 f. Type **329** 10 10
784 20 f. Snub-nosed parasitic eel (vert) 10 10
785 80 f. Southern guitar-fish (vert) 15 10
786 250 f. Red-banded grouper 40 15
787 320 f. Common hammerhead shark 55 20

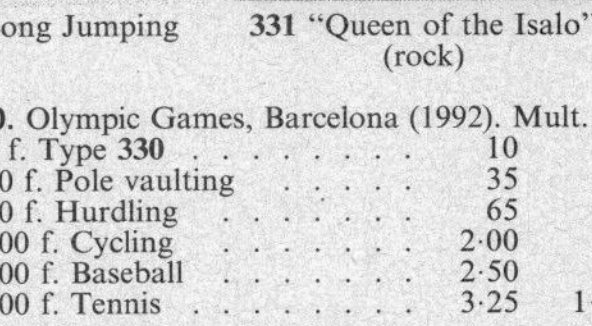

330 Long Jumping **331** "Queen of the Isalo" (rock)

1990. Olympic Games, Barcelona (1992). Mult.

789 80 f. Type **330** 10 10
790 250 f. Pole vaulting 35 15
791 550 f. Hurdling 65 25
792 1500 f. Cycling 2·00 60
793 2000 f. Baseball 2·50 80
794 2500 f. Tennis 3·25 1·25

1990. Natural Features. Multicoloured.

796 70 f. Type **331** 15 10
797 150 f. Lonjy Island (as T **332**) 25 15

332 Pipe

1990. Sakalava Craft. Multicoloured.

798 70 f. Type **332** 15 10
799 150 f. Combs (as T **331**) 25 15

333 Emblem and Projects

1990. 25th Anniv of African Development Bank.

800 **333** 80 f. multicoloured 15 10

334 "Voyager II" and Neptune

1990. 20th Anniv of First Manned Landing on Moon. Multicoloured.

801 80 f. Type **334** 15 10
802 250 f. Hughes Hercules flying boat, Boeing 747 airliner and flying boat "of the future" 40 15
803 550 f. "Noah" satellite tracking elephants 70 25
804 1500 f. Venus and "Magellan" space probe 1·25 55
805 2000 f. Halley's Comet and Concorde 2·25 90
806 2500 f. "Apollo 11" landing capsule and crew 3·00 1·00

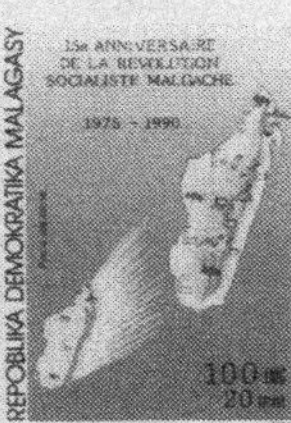

335 Liner on Globe **336** Maps showing Development between 1975 and 1990

1990. 30th Anniv of International Maritime Organization.

808 **335** 250 f. ultramarine, bl & blk 45 15

1990. Air. 15th Anniv of Malagasy Socialist Revolution.

809 **336** 100 f. multicoloured 15 10
810 – 350 f. black and grey 45 25

DESIGN: 350 f. Presidential Palaces, 1975 and 1990.

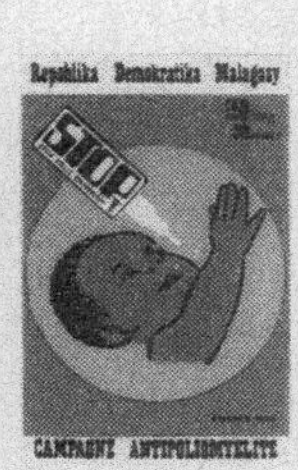

337 Oral Vaccination **338** Four-man Bobsleigh

1990. Anti-Polio Campaign.

811 **337** 150 f. multicoloured 30 15

1990. Winter Olympic Games, Albertville (1992). Multicoloured.

812 350 f. Type **338** 40 20
813 1000 f. Speed skating 1·25 40
814 1500 f. Cross-country skiing 2·00 65
815 2500 f. Downhill skiing 3·00 1·10

339 Society Emblem **340** Mascot

1990. Air. 25th Anniv of Malagasy Bible Society.

817	**339**	25 f. multicoloured	10	10
818	–	100 f. blue, black & green	15	10

DESIGN—VERT: 100 f. Society emblem.

1990. 3rd Indian Ocean Island Games, Malagasy (1st issue).

819	**340**	100 f. + 20 f. on 80 f. + 20 f. multicoloured	15	15
820		350 f. + 20 f. on 250 f. + 20 f. multicoloured	45	40

The games were originally to be held in 1989 and the stamps were printed for release then. The issued stamps are handstamped with the correct date and new value.

See also Nos. 822/3.

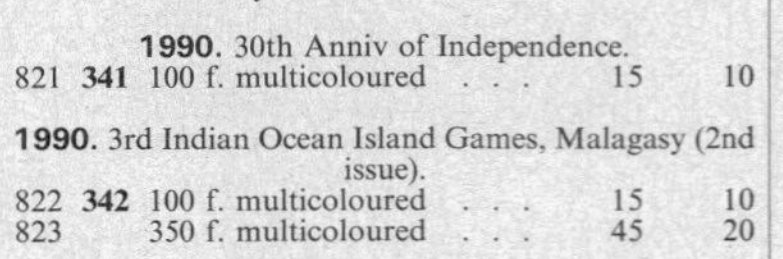

341 Symbols of Agriculture and Industry — **342** Torch

1990. 30th Anniv of Independence.

821	**341**	100 f. multicoloured	15	10

1990. 3rd Indian Ocean Island Games, Malagasy (2nd issue).

822	**342**	100 f. multicoloured	15	10
823		350 f. multicoloured	45	20

343 Envelopes forming Map and Mail Transportation

1990. Air. World Post Day.

824	**343**	350 f. multicoloured	75	30

344 Ho Chi Minh — **345** "Avahi laniger"

1990. Birth Centenary of Ho Chi Minh (President of North Vietnam, 1945–69).

825	**344**	350 f. multicoloured	40	20

1990. Lemurs. Multicoloured.

826	10 f. Type **345**	10	10
827	20 f. "Lemur fulvus albifrons"	10	10
828	20 f. "Lemur fulvus sanfordi"	10	10
829	100 f. "Lemur fulvus collaris"	25	15
830	100 f. "Lepulemur ruficaudatus"	25	15

346 "Tridacna squamosa" — **347** Letters in Book

1990. Shells. Multicoloured.

832	40 f. Type **346**	25	15
833	50 f. "Terebra dimidiata" and "Terebra subulata"	35	15

1990. International Literacy Year. Multicoloured.

834	20 f. Type **347**	10	10
835	100 f. Open book and hand holding pen (horiz)	20	15

348 Cep — **349** De Gaulle, Leclerc and Parod under Arc de Triomphe, 1944

1991. Fungi. Multicoloured.

836	25 f. Type **348**	10	10
837	100 f. Butter mushroom	10	10
838	350 f. Fly agaric	25	10
839	450 f. Scarlet-stemmed boletus	35	15
840	680 f. Flaky-stemmed witches' mushroom	50	25
841	800 f. Brown birch bolete	55	25
842	900 f. Orange birch bolete	65	30

1991. Multicoloured.

844	100 f. Type **349**	10	10
845	350 f. "Galileo" space probe near Jupiter	25	10
846	800 f. Crew of "Apollo 11" on moon	55	25
847	900 f. De Gaulle and Free French emblem, 1942	65	30
848	1250 f. Concorde aircraft and German "ICE" high speed train	1·40	55
849	2500 f. Gen. Charles de Gaulle (French statesman)	1·90	95

350 Industrial and Agricultural Symbols and Arms — **351** Baobab Tree

1991. 15th Anniv (1990) of Republic.

851	**350**	100 f. multicoloured	10	10

1991. Trees. Multicoloured.

852	140 f. Type **351**	10	10
853	500 f. "Dideria madagascariensis"	35	15

352 Whippet

1991. Dogs. Multicoloured.

854	30 f. Type **352**	10	10
855	50 f. Japanese spaniel	10	10
856	140 f. Toy terrier	10	10
857	350 f. Chow-chow	25	10
858	500 f. Chihuahua	35	15
859	800 f. Afghan hound	55	25
860	1140 f. Papillon	85	40

POSTAGE DUE STAMPS

D **13** Independence Obelisk

1962.

D45	D **13**	1 f. green	10	10
D46		2 f. brown	10	10
D47		3 f. violet	10	10
D48		4 f. slate	10	10
D49		5 f. red	10	10
D50		10 f. green	15	15
D51		20 f. purple	20	20
D52		40 f. blue	50	45
D53		50 f. red	75	70
D54		100 f. black	1·40	1·25

APPENDIX

The following stamps have either been issued in excess of postal needs or have not been available to the public in reasonable quantities at face value.

1987.

Winter Olympic Games, Calgary (1988). 1500 f. (on gold foil).

1989.

Scout and Butterfly. 5000 f. (on gold foil).

"Philexfrance 89" Int. Stamp Exhibition, Paris. 5000 f. (on gold foil).

World Cup Football Championship, Italy. 5000 f. (on gold foil).

1990.

Winter Olympic Games, Albertville (1992). 5000 f. (on gold foil).

1991.

Birth Centenary of De Gaulle. 5000 f. (on gold foil).

MALI Pt. 6; Pt. 13

Federation of French Sudan and Senegal, formed in 1959 as an autonomous republic within the French Community. In August 1960 the Federation was split up and the French Sudan part became the independent Mali Republic.

100 centimes = 1 franc

A. FEDERATION.

1 Map, Flag, Mali and Torch

1959. Establishment of Mali Federation.

1	**1**	25 f. multicoloured	50	50

2

1959. Air. 300th Anniv of St. Louis, Senegal.

2	**2**	85 f. multicoloured	1·50	1·25

3 Parrot Fish — **4** Violet Starling

1960. (a) Postage. Fish as T **3**.

3	**3**	5 f. orange, blue and bronze	30	15
4	–	10 f. black, brown & turquoise	30	25
5	–	15 f. brown, slate and blue	40	25
6	–	20 f. black, bistre and green	50	35
7	–	25 f. yellow, sepia and green	60	40
8	–	30 f. red, purple and blue	80	50
9	–	85 f. red, blue and green	1·75	1·50

(b) Air. Birds as T **4**.

10	**4**	100 f. multicoloured	5·50	1·60
11	–	200 f. multicoloured	12·00	5·00
12	–	500 f. multicoloured	32·00	13·50

DESIGNS—HORIZ: 10 f. Trigger fish; 15 f. Batfish; 20 f. Threadfish; 25 f. Butterfly fish; 30 f. Surgeon; 85 f. Sea bream; 200 f. Bateleur. VERT: 500 f. Common gonolek.

1960. 10th Anniv of African Technical Co-operation Commission. As T **4** of Malagasy Republic.

13	25 f. purple and violet	1·00	75

B. REPUBLIC.

1960. Nos. 6, 7, 9 and 10/12 optd **REPUBLIQUE DU MALI** and bar or bars or surch also.

14	20 f. black, bistre and green (postage)	1·25	60
15	25 f. red, purple and blue	1·75	60
16	85 f. red, blue and green	3·00	1·50
17	100 f. multicoloured (air)	4·50	1·50
18	200 f. multicoloured	7·00	3·25
19	300 f. on 500 f. multicoloured	12·00	5·50
20	500 f. multicoloured	25·00	14·00

7 Pres. Mamadou Konate

1961.

21	**7**	20 f. sepia & green (postage)	25	15
22	–	25 f. black and purple	35	15
23	**7**	200 f. sepia and red (air)	3·00	1·00
24	–	300 f. black and green	4·25	1·25

DESIGN: 25, 300 f. President Keita. Nos. 23/4 are larger 27 × 38 mm.

8 U.N. Emblem, Flag and Map

1961. Air. Proclamation of Independence and Admission into U.N.
25 **8** 100 f. multicoloured . . . . 1·25 90

9 Sankore Mosque, Timbuktu

1961. Air.
26 **9** 100 f. brown, blue and sepia 1·75 55
27 – 200 f. brown, red and green 4·00 1·50
28 – 500 f. green, brown and blue 11·00 3·25
DESIGN: 200 f. View of Timbuktu; 500 f. Arms and view of Bamako.

10 Africans learning Vowels

1961. 1st Anniv of Independence.
29 **10** 25 f. multicoloured 45 30

11 Sheep at Pool

12 African Map and King Mohammed V of Morocco

1961.
30 **11** 50 c. sepia, myrtle and red . 15 15
31 **A** 1 f. bistre, green and blue . 15 15
32 **B** 2 f. red, green and blue . . . 15 15
33 **C** 3 f. brown, green and blue . 15 15
34 **D** 4 f. blue, green and bistre . 15 15
35 **11** 5 f. purple, green and blue . 20 15
36 **A** 10 f. brown, myrtle & blue . 20 15
37 **B** 15 f. brown, green & blue . 20 15
38 **C** 20 f. red, green and blue . . 30 25
39 **D** 25 f. brown and blue 40 20
40 **11** 30 f. brown, green & violet . 55 30
41 **A** 40 f. brown, green & blue . 1·25 30
42 **B** 50 f. lake, green and blue . . 50 30
43 **C** 60 f. brown, green and blue . 15 15
44 **D** 85 f. brown, bistre & blue . 1·75 35
DESIGNS: A, Oxen at pool. B, House of Arts, Mail. C, Land tillage. D, Combine-harvester in rice field.

1962. 1st Anniv of African Conf, Casablanca.
45 **12** 25 f. multicoloured 25 15
46 50 f. multicoloured 50 20

13 Patrice Lumumba

1962. 1st Death Anniv of Patrice Lumumba (Congo leader).
47 **13** 25 f. brown and bistre . . . 20 20
48 100 f. brown and green . . . 75 50

1962. Malaria Eradication. As T **43** of Mauritania.
49 25 f. + 5 f. blue 50 60

14 Pegasus and U.P.U. Emblem

1962. 1st Anniv of Admission into U.P.U.
50 **14** 85 f. multicoloured . . . . 1·00 65

14a Posthorn on Map of Africa

15 Sansanding Dam

1962. African Postal Union Commem.
51 **14a** 25 f. green and brown . . 25 20
52 85 f. orange and green . . 75 50

1962.
53 **15** 25 f. black, green and blue 30 20
54 – 45 f. multicoloured . . . . 1·10 50
DESIGN—HORIZ: 45 f. Cotton plant.

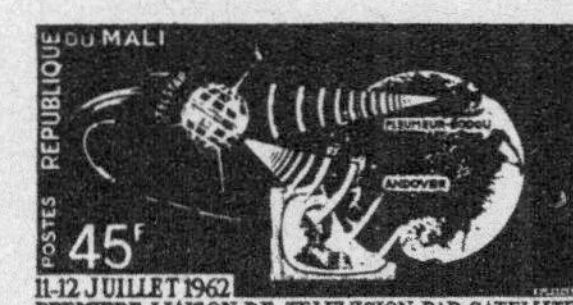

16 "Telstar" Satellite, Globe and Television Receiver

1962. 1st Trans-Atlantic Telecommunications Satellite Link.
55 **16** 45 f. brown, violet and lake 70 40
56 55 f. violet, olive and green 80 60

17 Soldier and Family

18 Bull's Head, Laboratory Equipment and Chicks

1962. Mali–Algerian Solidarity.
57 **17** 25 f. + 5 f. multicoloured . 30 30

1963. Zoological Research Centre, Sobuta.
58 **18** 25 f. turq & brn (postage) . 35 25
59 – 200 f. turquoise, purple and bistre (air) . . . . 3·00 1·25
DESIGN: 200 f. As Type **18** but horiz 47 × 27 mm.

19 Tractor and Campaign Emblem

1963. Freedom from Hunger.
60 **19** 25 f. purple, black and blue 35 20
61 45 f. brown, green & turq . 65 35

20 Balloon and W.M.O. Emblem

1963. Atmospheric Research.
62 **20** 25 f. multicoloured 30 20
63 45 f. multicoloured 60 35
64 60 f. multicoloured 80 50

21 Race Winners

22 Centenary Emblem and Globe

1963. Youth Week. Multicoloured.
65 5 f. Type **21** 15 10
66 10 f. Type **21** 20 15
67 20 f. Acrobatic dance 35 20
68 85 f. Football . . . . 1·40 55
Nos. 67/8 are horiz.

1963. Red Cross Centenary. Inscr in black.
69 **22** 5 f. multicoloured 20 15
70 10 f. red, yellow and grey . . 30 20
71 85 f. red, yellow and grey . . 1·10 60

23 Stretcher case entering Aero 145 Ambulance Airplane

1963. Air.
72 **23** 25 f. brown, blue and green 35 20
73 – 55 f. blue, ochre and brown 1·00 40
74 – 100 f. blue, brown and green 1·60 75
DESIGNS: 55 f. Douglas DC-3 airliner on tarmac; 100 f. Illyushin Il-18 airliner taking off.

24 South African Crowned Crane standing on Giant Tortoise

26 "Kaempferia aethiopica"

25 U.N. Emblem, Doves and Banner

1963. Air. Fauna Protection.
75 **24** 25 f. brown, red and orange 1·75 50
76 200 f. multicoloured . . . . 5·50 2·10

1963. Air. 15th Anniv of Declaration of Human Rights.
77 **25** 50 f. yellow, red and green 75 40

1963. Tropical Flora. Multicoloured.
78 30 f. Type **26** 45 25
79 70 f. "Bombax costatum" . . . 1·40 50
80 100 f. "Adenium honghel" . . . 2·75 65

27 Pharaoh and Cleopatra, Philae

28 Locust on Map of Africa

1964. Air. Nubian Monuments Preservation.
81 **27** 25 f. brown and purple . . . 60 25
82 55 f. olive and purple . . . . 1·40 50

1964. Anti-Locust Campaign.
83 **28** 5 f. brown, green and purple 20 15
84 – 10 f. brown, green and olive 30 20
85 – 20 f. brown, green and bistre 50 25
DESIGNS—VERT: 10 f. Locust and map. HORIZ: 20 f. Air-spraying, locust and village.

29 Football

1964. Olympic Games, Tokyo.
86 **29** 5 f. purple, green and red . 15 10
87 – 10 f. brown, blue and sepia 20 20
88 – 15 f. red and violet 25 20
89 – 85 f. green, brown & violet 1·00 70
DESIGNS—VERT: 10 f. Boxing; 15 f. Running and Olympic Flame. HORIZ: 85 f. Hurdling. Each design has a stadium in the background.

30 Solar Flares

32 Map of Vietnam

31 President Kennedy

1964. Int. Quiet Sun Years.
90 **30** 45 f. olive, red and blue . . 60 35

1964. Air. 1st Death Anniv of Pres. Kennedy.
91 **31** 100 f. multicoloured . . . . 1·40 1·25

1964. Mali–South Vietnam Workers' Solidarity Campaign.
92 **32** 30 f. multicoloured 30 20

33 Knysna Turacos

1965. Air. Birds.
93 **33** 100 f. green, blue and red . 4·75 1·60
94 – 200 f. black, red and blue . 11·00 3·25
95 – 300 f. black, ochre and green 16·00 4·50
96 – 500 f. red, brown and green 24·00 8·25
BIRDS—VERT: 200 f. Abyssinian ground hornbills; 300 f. Egyptian vultures. HORIZ: 500 f. Goliath herons.

34 I.C.Y. Emblem and U.N. Headquarters

36 Abraham Lincoln

35 African Buffalo

1965. Air. International Co-operation Year.
97 **34** 55 f. ochre, purple and blue 75 40

1965. Animals.
98 – 1 f. brown, blue and green 10 10
99 **35** 5 f. brown, orange & green 15 10
100 – 10 f. brown, mauve & green 40 25
101 – 30 f. brown, green and red 75 30
102 – 90 f. brown, grey and green 2·25 95
ANIMALS—VERT: 1 f. Waterbuck; 10 f. Scimitar oryx; 90 f. Giraffe. HORIZ: 30 f. Leopard.

1965. Death Centenary of Abraham Lincoln.
103 **36** 45 f. multicoloured 60 40
104 55 f. multicoloured 65 50

MINIMUM PRICE

The minimum price quoted is 10p which represents a handling charge rather than a basis for valuing common stamps. For further notes about prices, see introductory pages.

37 Hughes' Telegraph
38 "Lungs" and Mobile X-Ray Unit (Anti-T.B.)

1965. Centenary of I.T.U.
105 – 20 f. black, blue & orange 30 25
106 **37** 30 f. green, brn & orange 45 25
107 – 50 f. green, brown & orge 75 45
DESIGNS—VERT: 20 f. Denis's Pneumatic tube; 50 f. Lescurre's heliograph.

1965. Mali Health Service.
108 **38** 5 f. violet, red and crimson 15 15
109 – 10 f. green, bistre and red 25 15
110 – 25 f. green and brown . . . 40 20
111 – 45 f. green and brown . . . 75 40
DESIGNS: 10 f. Mother and children (Maternal and Child Care); 25 f. Examining patient (Marchoux Institute); 45 f. Nurse (Biological Laboratory).

39 Diving

1965. 1st African Games, Brazzaville, Congo.
112 **39** 5 f. red, brown and blue . . 15 10
113 – 15 f. turquoise, brown and red (Judo) 60 30

40 Pope John XXIII
41 Sir Winston Churchill

1965. Air. Pope John Commemoration.
114 **40** 100 f. multicoloured . . . 1·90 75

1965. Air. Churchill Commemoration.
115 **41** 100 f. blue and brown . . . 1·75 75

42 Dr. Schweitzer and Young African

1965. Air. Dr. Albert Schweitzer Commemoration.
116 **42** 100 f. multicoloured . . . 2·00 75

43 Leonov

1966. International Astronautic Conference, Athens (1965). Multicoloured.
117 100 f. Type **43** . . . . 1·60 60
118 100 f. White . . . . 1·60 60
119 300 f. Cooper, Conrad, Leonov and Beliaiev (vert) . . . . . 4·25 2·00

44 Vase, Quill and Cornet

1966. World Festival of Negro Arts, Dakar, Cameroun.
120 **44** 30 f. black, red and ochre 30 20
121 – 55 f. red, black and green 60 35
122 – 90 f. brown, orange & blue 1·10 60
DESIGNS: 55 f. Mask, brushes and palette, microphones; 90 f. Dancers, Mask, patterned cloth.

45 W.H.O. Building

1966. Inaug of W.H.O. Headquarters, Geneva.
123 **45** 30 f. green, blue and yellow 40 20
124 45 f. red, blue and yellow 60 35

46 Fisherman with Net

1966. River Fishing.
125 **46** 3 f. brown and blue . . . 15 15
126 – 4 f. purple, blue and brown 20 15
127 – 20 f. purple, green and blue 35 15
128 **46** 25 f. purple, blue and green 50 20
129 – 60 f. purple, lake and green 85 35
130 – 85 f. plum, green and blue 1·25 50
DESIGNS: 4 f., 60 f. Collective shore fishing; 20 f., 85 f. Fishing pirogue.

47 Papal Arms, U.N. and Peace Emblems

1966. Air. Pope Paul's Visit to U.N.
131 **47** 200 f. blue, green & turq . 2·50 1·10

48 Initiation Ceremony
49 People and U.N.E.S.C.O. Emblem

1966. Mali Pioneers. Multicoloured.
132 5 f. Type **48** 15 15
133 25 f. Pioneers dancing 50 20

1966. Air. 20th Anniv of U.N.E.S.C.O.
134 **49** 100 f. red, green and blue 1·75 70

50 Footballers, Globe, Cup and Football

1966. Air. World Cup Football Championships, England.
135 **50** 100 f. multicoloured . . . 1·75 70

51 Cancer ("The Crab")
52 U.N.I.C.E.F. Emblem and Children

1966. Air. 9th International Cancer Congress, Tokyo.
136 **51** 100 f. multicoloured . . . 1·60 55

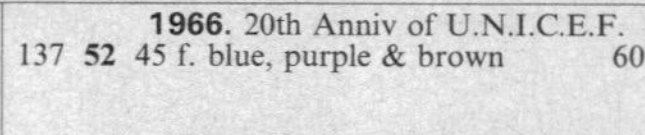

1966. 20th Anniv of U.N.I.C.E.F.
137 **52** 45 f. blue, purple & brown 60 25

53 Inoculating Cattle

1967. Campaign for Preventing Cattle Plague.
138 **53** 10 f. multicoloured 25 10
139 30 f. multicoloured 50 20

54 Desert Vehicles in Pass

1967. Air. Crossing of the Hoggar (1924).
140 **54** 200 f. green, brown & vio 4·50 2·25

55 "Diamant" Rocket and Francesco de Lana-Terzis's "Aerial Ship"
56 Ancient City

1967. Air. French Space Rockets and Satellites.
141 **55** 50 f. blue, turquoise & pur 70 30
142 – 100 f. lake, purple & turq 1·40 50
143 – 200 f. purple, olive and blue 2·40 1·00
DESIGNS: 100 f. Satellite "A 1" and Jules Verne's "rocket"; 200 f. Satellite "D 1" and Da Vinci's "bird-powered" flying machine.

1967. International Tourist Year.
144 **56** 25 f. orange, blue and violet 30 20

57 Amelia Earhart and Mail Route-map

1967. Air. 30th Anniv of Amelia Earhart's Flight, via Gao.
145 **57** 500 f. multicoloured . . . . 7·00 3·25

58 "The Bird Cage"
59 Scout Emblems and Rope Knots

1967. Air. Picasso Commemoration. Designs showing paintings. Multicoloured.
146 50 f. Type **58** . . . . 1·00 30
147 100 f. "Paul as Harlequin" . . 1·75 70
148 250 f. "The Pipes of Pan" . . 3·50 1·50
See also Nos. 158/9 and 164/7.

1967. Air. World Scout Jamboree, Idaho.
149 **59** 70 f. red and green . . . . 1·00 30
150 – 100 f. black, lake and green 1·25 45
DESIGN: 100 f. Scout with "walkie-talkie" radio.

60 "Chelorrhina polyphemus"
61 School Class

1967. Insects.
151 **60** 5 f. green, brown and blue 30 20
152 – 15 f. purple, brown & green 50 25
153 – 50 f. red, brown and green 1·10 55
INSECTS—HORIZ: 15 f. "Ugada grandicollis"; 50 f. "Phymateus cinctus".

1967. International Literacy Day.
154 **61** 50 f. black, red and green 60 20

62 "Europafrique"
63 Lions Emblem and Crocodile

1967. Europafrique.
155 **62** 45 f. multicoloured 70 25

1967. 50th Anniv of Lions International.
156 **63** 90 f. multicoloured 95 55

64 "Water Resources"
65 Block of Flats, Grenoble

1967. International Hydrological Decade.
157 **64** 25 f. black, blue and bistre 30 20

1967. Air. Toulouse-Lautrec Commemoration. Paintings as T **58**. Multicoloured.
158 100 f. "Gazelle" (horse's head) (horiz) . . . . 2·00 1·10
159 300 f. "Gig drawn by Cob" (vert) 4·75 2·25

1968. Air. Winter Olympic Games, Grenoble.
160 **65** 50 f. brown, green and blue 70 35
161 – 150 f. brown, blue and ultramarine . . . . . 1·60 65
DESIGN: 150 f. Bob-sleigh course, Huez mountain.

66 W.H.O. Emblem

1968. 20th Anniv of W.H.O.
162 **66** 90 f. blue, lake and green 70 30

67 Human Figures and Entwined Hearts

1968. World "Twin Towns" Day.
163 **67** 50 f. red, violet and green 40 15

1968. Air. Flower Paintings. As T **58**. Mult.
164 50 f. "Roses and Anemones" (Van Gogh) 50 25
165 150 f. "Vase of Flowers" (Manet) 1·50 55
166 300 f. "Bouquet of Flowers" (Delacroix) . . . . 3·00 1·10
167 500 f. "Marguerites" (Millet) 4·50 2·00
SIZES: 50 f., 300 f. 40 × 41½ mm: 150 f. 36 × 47½ mm: 500 f. 50 × 36 mm.

68 Dr. Martin Luther King   **69** "Draisienne" Bicycle, 1809

1968. Air. Martin Luther King Commemoration.
168 **68** 100 f. black, pink & purple . . 85 35

1968. Veteran Bicycles and Motor Cars.
169 **69** 2 f. brown, mauve and green (postage) 20 15
170 – 5 f. red, blue and bistre . . 30 20
171 – 10 f. blue, brown and green 50 25
172 – 45 f. black, green & brown 80 40
173 – 50 f. red, green & brn (air) 1·00 25
174 – 100 f. blue, mauve & bistre 2·00 60
DESIGNS—HORIZ: 5 f. De Dion-Bouton, 1894; 45 f. Panhard-Levassor, 1914; 100 f. Mercedes-Benz, 1927. VERT: 10 f. Michaux Bicycle, 1861; 50 f. "Bicyclette, 1918".

70 Books, Graph and A.D.B.A. Emblem

1968. 10th Anniv of International African Libraries and Archives Development Association.
175 **70** 100 f. red, black and brown 65 30

71 Football

1968. Air. Olympic Games, Mexico. Multicoloured.
176 100 f. Type **71** 75 40
177 150 f. Long-jumping (vert) . . 1·25 60

1968. Air. "Philexafrique" Stamp Exhibition, Abidjan, Ivory Coast, 1969 (1st issue). As T **113a** of Mauritania. Multicoloured.
178 200 f. "The Editors" (F. M. Granet) . . . . 2·00 1·50

1969. Air. "Philexafrique" Stamp Exn., Abidjan, Ivory Coast (2nd issue). As T **114a** of Mauritania.
179 100 f. purple, red and violet 1·25 1·25
DESIGN: 100 f. Carved animal and French Sudan stamp of 1931.

1969. Air. Birth Bicentenary of Napoleon Bonaparte. Multicoloured. As T **114b** of Mauritania.
180 150 f. "Napoleon Bonaparte, First Consul" (Gros) . . . . 2·25 1·25
181 200 f. "The Bivouac–Battle of Austerlitz" (Lejeune) (horiz) 4·00 1·75

73 Montgolfier Balloon

1969. Air. Aviation History. Multicoloured.
182 50 f. Type **73** 50 20
183 150 f. Ferdinand Ferber's Glider No. 5 . . . . 1·50 40
184 300 f. Concorde . . . . 3·00 1·40

74 African Tourist Emblem

1969. African Tourist Year.
185 **74** 50 f. red, green and blue 25 20

75 "O.I.T." and I.L.O. Emblem

1969. 50th Anniv of I.L.O.
186 **75** 50 f. violet, blue and green 30 20
187 60 f. slate, red and brown 35 20

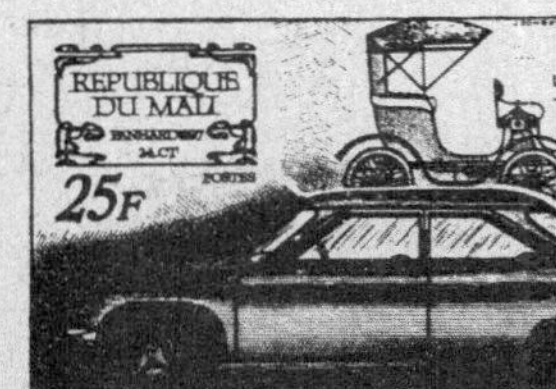

76 Panhard of 1897 and Model "24-CT"

1969. French Motor Industry.
188 **76** 25 f. lake, black and bistre (postage) 50 20
189 – 30 f. green and black . . . 60 20
190 – 55 f. red, black and purple (air) . . . . 1·00 35
191 – 90 f. blue, black and red 1·40 45
DESIGNS: 30 f. Citroen of 1923 and Model "DS-21"; 55 f. Renault of 1898 and Model "16"; 90 f. Peugeot of 1893 and Model "404".

77 Clarke (Australia), 10,000 metres (1965)

1969. Air. World Athletics Records.
192 **77** 60 f. brown and blue . . . 30 25
193 – 90 f. brown and red . . . 45 25
194 – 120 f. brown and green . . 55 35
195 – 140 f. brown and slate . . 70 35
196 – 150 f. black and red . . . 85 50
DESIGNS: 90 f. Lusis (Russia), Javelin (1968); 120 f. Miyake (Japan), Weightlifting (1967); 140 f. Matson (U.S.A.), Shot-putting (1968); 150 f. Keino (Kenya), 3,000 metres (1965).

78 Hollow Blocks

1969. International Toy Fair, Nuremberg.
197 **78** 5 f. red, yellow and grey . 15 10
198 – 10 f. multicoloured 15 10
199 – 15 f. green, red and pink . 20 10
200 – 20 f. orange, blue and red 25 15
DESIGNS: 10 f. Toy donkey on wheels; 15 f. "Ducks"; 20 f. Model car and race-track.

79 "Apollo 8", Earth and Moon

1969. Air. Moon Flight of "Apollo 8".
201 **79** 2,000 f. gold . . . . 14·00 14·00
This stamp is embossed on gold foil.

1969. Air. 1st Man on the Moon. Nos. 182/4 optd **L'HOMME SUR LA LUNE JUILLET 1969** and Apollo 11.
202 50 f. multicoloured 95 65
203 150 f. multicoloured . . . . 2·00 1·25
204 300 f. multicoloured . . . . 3·25 2·50

81 Sheep

1969. Domestic Animals.
205 **81** 1 f. olive, brown and green 10 10
206 – 2 f. brown, grey and red . 10 10
207 – 10 f. olive, brown and blue 20 10
208 – 35 f. slate and red . . . 60 30
209 – 90 f. brown and blue . . . 1·25 55
ANIMALS: 2 f. Goat; 10 f. Donkey; 35 f. Horse; 90 f. Dromedary.

1969. 5th Anniv of African Development Bank. As T **122a** of Mauritania.
210 50 f. brown, green and purple 25 20
211 90 f. orange, green and brown 45 20

83 "Mona Lisa" (Leonardo da Vinci)

1969. Air. 450th Death Anniv of Leonardo da Vinci.
212 **83** 500 f. multicoloured . . . . 4·00 3·25

84 Vaccination   **85** Mahatma Gandhi

1969. Campaign against Smallpox and Measles.
213 **84** 50 f. slate, brown & green 40 15

1969. Air. Birth Centenary of Mahatma Gandhi.
214 **85** 150 f. brown and green . . 1·60 55

1969. 10th Anniv of Aerial Navigation Security Agency for Africa and Madagascar (A.S.E.C.N.A.). As T **94a** of Niger.
215 100 f. green 60 25

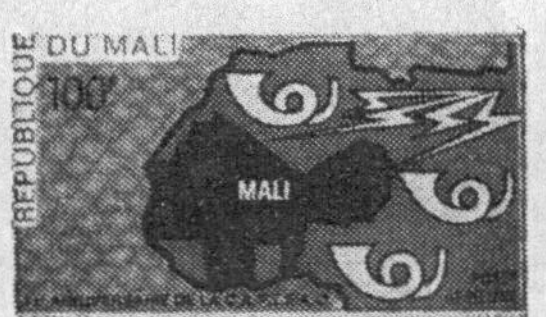

87 West African Map and Posthorns

1970. Air. 11th Anniv of West African Postal Union (C.A.P.T.E.A.O.).
216 **87** 100 f. multicoloured 60 35

1970. Air. Religious Paintings. As T **83**. Mult.
217 100 f. "Virgin and Child" (Van der Weydan School) 70 40
218 150 f. "The Nativity" (The Master of Flamalle) . . . . 1·10 65
219 250 f. "Virgin, Child and St. John the Baptist" (Low Countries School) . . . . 2·40 1·40

89 Franklin D. Roosevelt   **91** Lenin

90 Women of Mali and Japan

1970. Air. 25th Death Anniv of Franklin D. Roosevelt.
220 **89** 500 f. black, red and blue 3·50 2·00

1970. "EXPO 70" World Fair, Osaka, Japan.
221 **90** 100 f. orange, brown & blue 60 20
222 – 150 f. red, green & yellow 80 30
DESIGN: 150 f. Flags and maps of Mali and Japan.

1970. Air. Birth Centenary of Lenin.
223 **91** 300 f. black, green & flesh 2·25 1·00

92 Verne and Moon Rockets

1970. Air. Jules Verne "Prophet of Space Travel". Multicoloured.
224 50 f. Type **92** 60 25
225 150 f. Moon orbit . . . . . . 1·50 50
226 300 f. Splashdown . . . . . 2·25 1·10

93 I.T.U. Emblem and Map

1970. World Telecommunications Day.
227 **93** 90 f. red, brown and sepia 60 25

1970. New U.P.U. Headquarters Building, Berne. As Type **81** of New Caledonia.
228 50 f. brown, green and red . . 30 20
229 60 f. brown, blue and mauve 40 20

1970. Air. Space Flight of "Apollo 13". Nos. 224/6 optd **APOLLO XIII EPOPEE SPATIALE 11-17 AVRIL 1970** in three lines.
230 50 f. multicoloured 40 25
231 150 f. multicoloured . . . . . 1·10 45
232 300 f. multicoloured . . . . . 2·00 1·25

96 "Intelsat 3" Satellite

1970. Air. Space Telecommunications.
233 **96** 100 f. indigo, blue & orange 60 35
234 – 200 f. purple, grey and blue 1·25 50
235 – 300 f. brown, orge & slate 2·25 1·10
236 – 500 f. brown, blue & indigo 3·50 1·60
DESIGNS: 200 f. "Molnya I" satellite; 300 f. Dish aerial, Type PB **2**; 500 f. "Symphony Project" satellite.

97 Auguste and Louis Lumiere, Jean Harlow and Marilyn Monroe

1970. Air. Lumiere Brothers (inventors of the cine camera). Commemoration.
237 **97** 250 f. multicoloured . . . 2·50 1·25

98 Footballers

1970. Air. World Cup Football Championships, Mexico.
238 **98** 80 f. green, brown and red 50 25
239 200 f. red, brown and blue 1·25 55

99 Rotary Emblem, Map and Antelope   **100** "Supporting United Nations"

1970. Air. Rotary International.
240 **99** 200 f. multicoloured . . . 1·75 60

1970. Air. 25th Anniv of U.N.O.
241 **100** 100 f. blue, brown & violet 70 35

101 Page from 11th century Baghdad Koran

1970. Air. Ancient Muslim Art. Multicoloured.
242 50 f. Type **101** 50 25
243 200 f. "Tree and wild Animals" (Jordanian mosaic, c.730) . 1·25 55
244 250 f. "The Scribe" (Baghdad miniature, 1287) . . . . . . 2·00 90

1970. Air. Moon Landing of "Luna 16". Nos. 234/5 surch **LUNA 16 PREMIERS PRELEVEMENTS AUTOMATIQUES SUR LA LUNE SEPTEMBRE 1970** and new values.
245 150 f. on 200 f. purple, grey and blue . . . . 1·00 40
246 250 f. on 300 f. brown, orange and grey . . . . 1·50 60

103 G.P.O., Bamako

1970. Public Buildings.
247 **103** 30 f. olive, green & brown 20 20
248 – 40 f. purple, brown & grn 30 20
249 – 60 f. grey, green and red 40 20
250 – 80 f. brown, green and grey 50 25
BUILDINGS: 40 f. Chamber of Commerce, Bamako; 60 f. Ministry of Public Works, Bamako; 80 f. Town Hall, Segou.

104 Pres. Nasser

106 Gallet "0-30-T" Locomotive

105 "The Nativity" (Antwerp School 1530)

1970. Air. Pres. Gamal Nasser of Egypt. Commemoration.
251 **104** 1000 f. gold . . . . 7·50 7·50

1970. Air. Christmas. Paintings. Multicoloured.
252 100 f. Type **105** 70 40
253 250 f. "Adoration of the Shepherds" (Memling) . . . 1·60 95
254 300 f. "Adoration of the Magi" (17th century Flemish school) 2·25 1·25

1970. Mali Railway Locomotives from the Steam Era (1st series).
255 **106** 20 f. black, red and green 1·40 1·25
256 – 40 f. black, green & brown 1·75 1·60
257 – 50 f. black, green & brown 2·10 1·90
258 – 80 f. black, red and green 3·00 2·75
259 – 100 f. black, green & brn 3·50 3·25
LOCOMOTIVES: 40 f. Felou "0-3-0T"; 50 f. Bechevel "2-3-0T"; 80 f. "231"; 100 f. Type "411".
See also Nos. 367/70.

107 Scouts crossing Log-bridge

1970. Scouting in Mali. Multicoloured.
260 5 f. Type **107** 20 15
261 30 f. Bugler and scout camp (vert) 35 15
262 100 f. Scouts canoeing . . . 90 35

108 Bambara de San Mask

109 General De Gaulle

1971. Mali Masks and Ideograms. Multicoloured.
263 29 f. Type **108** 15 10
264 25 f. Dogon de Bandiagara mask 20 10
265 59 f. Kanaga ideogram . . . 45 15
266 89 f. Bambara ideogram . . . 60 25

1971. Air. Charles De Gaulle Commem. Die-stamped on gold foil.
267 **109** 2000 f. gold, red and blue 30·00 30·00

110 Alfred Nobel

111 Tennis Player (Davis Cup)

1971. Air. 75th Death Anniv of Alfred Nobel (philanthropist).
268 **110** 300 f. red, brown & green 2·25 1·25

1971. Air. World Sporting Events.
269 **111** 100 f. slate, purple & blue 75 25
270 – 150 f. olive, brown & grn 1·40 40
271 – 200 f. brown, olive & blue 2·00 60
DESIGNS—HORIZ: 150 f. Steeplechase (inscr "Derby at Epsom" but probably represents the Grand National). VERT: 200 f. Yacht (America Cup).

112 Youth, Sun and Microscope

1971. 50th Anniv of 1st B.C.G. Vaccine Innoculation.
272 **112** 100 f. brown, green & red 85 40

113 "The Thousand and One Nights"

1971. Air. "Tales of the Arabian Nights". Mult.
273 120 f. Type **113** 70 30
274 180 f. "Ali Baba and the Forty Thieves" . . . . 1·00 40
275 200 f. "Aladdin's Lamp" . . 1·40 50

114 Scouts, Japanese Horseman and Mt. Fuji

1971. 13th World Scout Jamboree, Asagiri, Japan.
276 **114** 80 f. plum, green and blue 60 20

115 Rose between Hands

116 Rural Costume

1971. 25th Anniv of U.N.I.C.E.F.
277 **115** 50 f. brown, red and orge 30 20
278 – 60 f. blue, green & brown 40 20
DESIGN—VERT: 60 f. Nurses and children.

1971. National Costumes. Multicoloured.
279 5 f. Type **116** 15 10
280 10 f. Rural costume (female) 20 15
281 15 f. Tuareg 20 15
282 60 f. Embroidered "boubou" 45 20
283 80 f. Women's ceremonial costume 60 25

117 Olympic Rings and Events

1971. Air. Olympic Games Publicity.
284 **117** 80 f. blue, purple & green 40 20

118 Telecommunications Map

1971. Pan-African Telecommunications Network Year.
285 **118** 50 f. multicoloured 25 20

119 "Mariner 4" and Mars

1971. Air. Exploration of Outer Space.
286 **119** 200 f. green, blue & brown 1·25 50
287 – 300 f. blue, plum & purple 1·75 60
DESIGN: 300 f. "Venera 5" and Venus.

120 "Santa Maria" (1492)

1971. Air. Famous Ships.
288 **120** 100 f. brown, violet & blue 70 35
289 – 150 f. violet, brown & grn 1·25 45
290 – 200 f. green, blue and red 1·60 75
291 – 250 f. red, blue and black 2·25 90
DESIGNS: 150 f. "Mayflower" (1620); 200 f. Battleship "Potemkin" (1905); 250 f. Liner "Normandie" (1935).

121 "Hibiscus rose-sinensis"

1971. Flowers. Multicoloured.
292 20 f. Type **121** 20 10
293 50 f. "Euphorbia pulcherrima" 45 15
294 60 f. "Adenium obesum" . . . 70 20
295 80 f. "Allamanda cathartica" 1·00 25
296 100 f. "Satanocrater berhautii" 1·25 35

122 Allegory of Justice

1971. 25th Anniv of Int Court of Justice, The Hague.
297 **122** 160 f. chocolate, red & brn 80 35

123 Nat King Cole

124 Statue of Olympic Zeus (by Phidias)

1971. Air. Famous Negro Musicians. Multicoloured.
298 130 f. Type **123** . . . . . . 1·25 25
299 150 f. Erroll Garner . . . . . 1·25 30
300 270 f. Louis Armstrong . . . 1·75 45

1971. Air. "The Seven Wonders of the Ancient World".
301 **124** 70 f. blue, brown & purple 35 20
302 – 80 f. black, brown & blue 40 20
303 – 100 f. blue, red and violet 50 25
304 – 130 f. black, purple & blue 75 30
305 – 150 f. brown, green & bl 1·10 35
306 – 270 f. blue, brown & pur 1·60 75
307 – 280 f. blue, purple & brn 2·00 85
DESIGNS—VERT: 80 f. Pyramid of Cheops, Egypt; 130 f. Pharos of Alexandria; 270 f. Mausoleum of Halicarnassos; 280 f. Colossus of Rhodes. HORIZ: 100 f. Temple of Artemis, Ephesus; 150 f. Hanging Gardens of Babylon.

125 "Family Life" (carving)

1971. 15th Anniv of Social Security Service.
308 **125** 70 f. brown, green and red 40 20

126 Slalom-skiing and Japanese Girl

128 Hands clasping Flagpole

127 "Santa Maria della Salute" (Caffi)

1972. Air. Winter Olympic Games, Sapporo, Japan.
309 **126** 150 f. brown, green & orge 1·00 35
310 – 200 f. green, brown & red 1·50 55
DESIGN: 200 f. Ice-hockey and Japanese actor.

1972. Air. U.N.E.S.C.O. "Save Venice" Campaign. Multicoloured.
312 130 f. Type **127** 70 35
313 270 f. "Rialto Bridge" . . . . 1·40 60
314 280 f. "St. Mark's Square" (vert) 1·60 70

1972. Air. Int Scout Seminar, Cotonou, Dahomey.
315 **128** 200 f. green, orange & brn 1·40 55

129 Heart and Red Cross Emblems

1972. Air. World Heart Month.
316 **129** 150 f. red and blue . . . . 1·00 40

130 Football

1972. Air. Olympic Games, Munich (1st issue). Sports and Munich Buildings.
317 **130** 50 f. blue, brown & green 25 20
318 – 150 f. blue, brown & green 70 30
319 – 200 f. blue, brown & green 80 50
320 – 300 f. blue, brown & green 1·25 70
DESIGNS—VERT: 150 f. Judo; 200 f. Hurdling. HORIZ: 300 f. Running.
See also Nos. 357/62.

131 "Apollo 15" and Lunar Rover

1972. Air. History of Transport Development.
322 **131** 150 f. red, green and lake 80 40
323 – 250 f. red, blue and green 2·00 1·00
DESIGN: 250 f. Montgolfier's balloon and Cugnot's steam car.

132 "UIT" on T.V. Screen

1972. World Telecommunications Day.
324 **132** 70 f. black, blue and red 40 20

133 Clay Funerary Statue **134** Samuel Morse and Early Telegraph

1972. Mali Archaeology. Multicoloured.
325 30 f. Type **133** 20 15
326 40 f. Female Figure (wood-carving) 30 20
327 50 f. "Warrior" (stone-painting) 40 20
328 100 f. Wrought-iron ritual figures 1·00 35

1972. Death Centenary of Samuel Morse (inventor of telegraph).
329 **134** 80 f. purple, green and red 45 20

135 "Cinderella" **136** Weather Balloon

1972. Air. Charles Perrault's Fairy Tales.
330 **135** 70 f. green, red and brown 45 20
331 – 80 f. brown, red and green 50 25
332 – 150 f. violet, purple & blue 1·10 35
DESIGNS: 80 f. "Puss in Boots"; 150 f. "The Sleeping Beauty".

1972. World Meteorological Day.
333 **136** 130 f. multicoloured . . . 60 30

137 Astronauts and Lunar Rover

1972. Air. Moon Flight of "Apollo 16".
334 **137** 500 f. brown, violet & grn 3·00 1·25

138 Book Year Emblem

1972. Air. International Book Year.
335 **138** 80 f. gold, green and blue 40 25

139 Sarakole Dance, Kayes **140** Learning the Alphabet

1972. Traditional Dances. Multicoloured.
336 10 f. Type **139** 25 15
337 20 f. Malinke dance, Bamako 30 15
338 50 f. Hunter's dance, Bougouni 45 20
339 70 f. Bambara dance, Segou . 60 20
340 80 f. Dogon dance, Sanga . . 70 30
341 120 f. Targuie dance, Timbukto 1·25 45

1972. International Literacy Day.
342 **140** 80 f. black and green . . 40 15

141 Statue and Musical Instruments **142** Club Banner

1972. First Anthology of Malinenne Music.
343 **141** 100 f. multicoloured . . . 70 30

1972. Air. 10th Anniv of Bamako Rotary Club.
344 **142** 170 f. purple, blue and red 1·00 40

143 Aries the Ram

1972. Signs of the Zodiac.
345 **143** 15 f. brown and purple 25 20
346 – 15 f. black and brown . . 25 20
347 – 35 f. blue and red 40 25
348 – 35 f. red and green . . . 40 25
349 – 40 f. brown and blue . . 50 30
350 – 40 f. brown and purple . 50 30
351 – 45 f. red and blue 60 35
352 – 45 f. green and red . . . 60 35
353 – 65 f. blue and violet . . . 90 35
354 – 65 f. brown and violet . . 90 35
355 – 90 f. blue and mauve . . 1·40 65
356 – 90 f. green and mauve . . 1·40 65
DESIGNS: No. 346, Taurus the Bull; No. 347, Gemini the Twins; No. 348, Cancer the Crab; No. 349, Leo the Lion; No. 350, Virgo the Virgin; No, 351, Libra the Scales; No. 352, Scorpio the Scorpion; No. 353, Sagittarius the Archer; No, 354, Capricornus the Goat; No. 355, Aquarius the Water-carrier; No. 356, Pisces the Fish.

1972. Air. Olympic Games, Munich (2nd issue). Sports and Locations of Games since 1952. As Type **130**.
357 70 f. blue, brown and red . . 25 15
358 90 f. green, red and blue . . 35 20
359 140 f. olive, green and brown 60 20
360 150 f. brown, green and red . . 65 25
361 170 f. blue, brown and purple 75 30
362 210 f. blue, red and green . . . 90 40
DESIGNS—VERT: 70 f. Boxing, Helsinki Games (1952); 150 f. Weightlifting, Tokyo Games (1964). HORIZ: 90 f. Hurdling, Melbourne Games (1956); 140 f. 200 metres, Rome Games (1960); 170 f. Swimming, Mexico Games (1968); 210 f. Throwing the javelin, Munich Games (1972).

1972. Medal Winners, Munich Olympic Games. Nos. 318/20 and 362 optd with events and names, etc.
363 150 f. blue, brown and green 70 30
364 200 f. blue, brown and green 90 40
365 210 f. blue, red and green . . . 90 40
366 300 f. blue, brown and green 1·25 70
OVERPRINTS: 150 f. **JUDO RUSKA 2 MEDAILLES D'OR**; 200 f. **STEEPLE KEINO MEDAILLE D'OR**; 210 f. **MEDAILLE D'OR 90 m. 48**; 300 f. **100 m.-200m BORZOV 2 MEDAILLES D'OR**

1972. Mali Locomotives (2nd series). As T **106.**
367 10 f. blue, green and red . . . 1·25 1·00
368 30 f. blue, green and brown 2·50 2·25
369 60 f. blue, brown and green 3·00 2·75
370 120 f. purple, green and black 5·00 4·50
LOCOMOTIVES: 10 f. First Locomotive to arrive at Bamako, 1906; 30 f. Locomotive from the Thies–Bamako line, 1920; 60 f. Type "141" locomotive, Thies–Bamako line, 1927;. 120 f. Alsthom "BB" coupled diesels, Dakar–Bamako line, 1947.

146 Emperor Haile Selassie

1972. Air. 80th Birth Anniv of Emperor Haile Selassie.
371 **146** 70 f. multicoloured 30 20

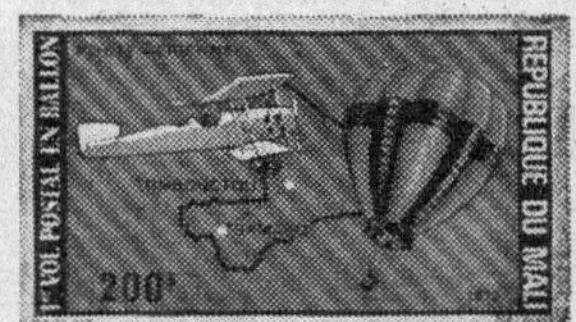

147 Balloon, Breguet 14T Biplane and Map

1972. Air. First Mali Airmail Flight by Balloon, Bamako to Timbuktu. Multicoloured.
372 200 f. Type **147** . . . . 1·00 45
373 300 f. Balloon, Concorde and map . . . . 1·40 60

148 High-Jumping

1973. 2nd African Games, Lagos, Nigeria. Mult.
374 70 f. Type 148 . . . . 30 20
375 270 f. Throwing the discus . . 1·25 60
376 280 f. Football . . . . 1·40 65

149 14th-century German Bishop **150** Interpol Headquarters, Paris

1973. Air. World Chess Championship, Reykjavik, Iceland.
377 **149** 100 f. lt blue, blue & brn 1·25 35
378 – 200 f. red, lt red & black 2·50 75
DESIGN: 200 f. 18th-century Indian knight (elephant).

1973. 50th Anniv of International Criminal Police Organization (Interpol).
379 **150** 80 f. multicoloured 65 20

151 Emblem and Dove with letter **152** "Fauna Protection" Stamp of 1963

1973. 10th Anniv (1971) of African Postal Union.
380 **151** 70 f. multicoloured . . . 35 20

1973. Air. Stamp Day.
381 **152** 70 f. orange, red & brown 1·25 30

153 Astronauts on Moon **155** Handicapped Africans

154 Copernicus

1973. Moon Mission of "Apollo" 17.
382 **153** 250 f. brown and blue . . 1·60 65

1973. 500th Birth Anniv of Copernicus.
384 **154** 300 f. purple and blue . . 2·00 1·10

1973. "Help the Handicapped".
385 **155** 70 f. orange, black and red 35 20

156 Dr. G. A. Hansen

1973. Centenary of Hansen's Identification of the Leprosy Bacillus.
386 **156** 200 f. green, black and red 1·60 60

157 Bentley and Alfa Romeo, 1930

1973. 50th Anniv of Le Mans 24 hour Endurance Race.
387 **157** 50 f. green, orange & blue 35 15
388 – 100 f. green, blue and red 75 25
389 – 200 f. blue, green and red 1·75 50
DESIGNS: 100 f. Jaguar and Talbot, 1953; 200 f. Matra and Porsche, 1952.

158 Scouts around Camp-fire

1973. International Scouting Congress, Addis Ababa and Nairobi.
390 **158** 50 f. brown, red and blue 30 15
391 – 70 f. brown, red and blue 40 20
392 – 80 f. red, brown and green 50 20
393 – 130 f. green, blue & brown 70 30
394 – 270 f. red, violet and grey 1·40 60
DESIGNS—VERT: 70 f. Scouts saluting flag; 130 f. Lord Baden-Powell. HORIZ: 80 f. Standard-bearers; 270 f. Map of Africa and Scouts and Guides in ring.

159 Swimming and National Flags

1973. First Afro-American Sports Meeting, Bamako.
395 **159** 70 f. green, red and blue . . . 30 20
396 – 80 f. green, red and blue . . . 35 25
397 – 330 f. blue and red . . . . 1·50 70
DESIGNS—VERT: 80 f. Throwing the discus and javelin. HORIZ: 330 f. Running.

1973. Pan-African Drought Relief. No. 296 surch **SECHERESSE SOLIDARITE AFRICAINE** and value.
398 200 f. on 100 f. multicoloured . . . 1·10 65

1973. Air. African Fortnight, Brussels. As T **168a** of Niger.
399 70 f. violet, blue and brown . . . 30 20

162 "Perseus" (Cellini)
164 "Apollo 11" First Landing

163 Stephenson's "Rocket" and French "Buddicom" Locomotive

1973. Air. Famous Sculptures.
400 **162** 100 f. green and red . . . 55 25
401 – 150 f. purple and red . . . 85 35
402 – 250 f. green and red . . . 1·50 65
DESIGNS: 150 f. "Pieta" (Michelangelo). 250 f. "Victory of Samothrace".

1973. Air. Famous Locomotives.
403 **163** 100 f. black, blue & brown 1·25 60
404 – 150 f. multicoloured . . . 1·60 65
405 – 200 f. blue, slate and brown 2·50 1·00
DESIGNS: 150 f. Union Pacific and Santa Fe Railroad locomotives; 200 f. "Mistral" and "Tokaido" trains.

1973. Conquest of the Moon.
406 **164** 50 f. purple, red & brown . . 25 20
407 – 75 f. grey, blue and red . . 30 20
408 – 100 f. slate, brown and blue . 55 30
409 – 280 f. blue, green and red . 1·25 65
410 – 300 f. blue, red and green . 1·50 80
DESIGNS: 75 f. "Apollo 13" Recovery capsule; 100 f. "Apollo 14" Lunar trolley; 280 f. "Apollo 15" Lunar rover; 300 f. "Apollo 17" lift off from Moon.

165 Picasso
166 Pres. John Kennedy

1973. Air. Pablo Picasso (artist). Commem.
411 **165** 500 f. multicoloured . . . 2·75 1·25

1973. Air. 10th Death Anniv of Pres. Kennedy.
412 **166** 500 f. black, purple & gold 2·50 1·25

1973. Air. Christmas. As T **105** but dated "1973". Multicoloured.
413 100 f. "The Annunciation" (V. Carpaccio) (horiz) 50 25
414 200 f. "Virgin of St. Simon" (F. Baroccio) . . . . 1·25 50
415 250 f. "Flight into Egypt" (A. Solario) . . . . 1·60 70

167 Player and Football
168 Cora

1973. Air. World Football Cup Championships, West Germany.
416 **167** 150 f. red, brown & green . 75 35
417 – 250 f. green, brown & violet 1·50 60
DESIGN: 250 f. Goalkeeper and ball.

1973. Musical Instruments.
419 **168** 5 f. brown, red and green . 20 10
420 – 10 f. brown and blue . . 20 10
421 – 15 f. brown, red & yellow . 25 15
422 – 20 f. brown and red . . . 30 15
423 – 25 f. brown, red & yellow . 35 15
424 – 30 f. black and blue . . . 50 20
425 – 35 f. sepia, brown and red . 60 20
426 – 40 f. brown and red . . . 65 30
DESIGNS—HORIZ: 10 f. Balafon. VERT: 15 f. Djembe; 20 f. Guitar; 25 f. N'Djarka; 30 f. M'Bolon; 35 f. Dozo N'Goni; 40 f. N'Tamani.

169 "Musicians" (mosaic)

1974. Roman Frescoes and Mosaics from Pompeii.
427 **169** 150 f. red, brown and grey . 75 35
428 – 250 f. brown, red & orange 1·25 60
429 – 350 f. brown, orange and olive . . . . 1·75 75
DESIGNS—VERT: 250 f. "Alexander the Great" (mosaic); 350 f. "Bacchante" (fresco).

170 Corncob, Worker and "Kibaru" Newspaper
171 Sir Winston Churchill

1974. 2nd Anniv of Rural Press.
430 **170** 70 f. brown and green . . 35 20

1974. Air. Birth Cent of Sir Winston Churchill.
431 **171** 500 f. black . . . . . . 2·50 1·50

172 Chess-pieces on Board

1974. Air. 21st Chess Olympiad, Nice.
432 **172** 250 f. indigo, red and blue 2·50 75

173 "The Crucifixion" (Alsace School c. 1380)

1974. Air. Easter. Multicoloured.
433 400 f. Type **173** . . . . 1·60 1·00
434 500 f. "The Entombment" (Titian) (horiz) . . . . . 2·25 1·25

174 Lenin

1974. Air. 50th Death Anniv of Lenin.
435 **174** 150 f. purple and violet . . 70 30

175 Goalkeeper and Globe
177 Full-rigged Sailing Ship and Modern Liner

176 Horse-jumping Scenes

1974. World Cup Football Championships, West Germany.
436 **175** 270 f. red, green and lilac 1·25 80
437 – 280 f. blue, brown and red 1·60 80
DESIGN: 280 f. World Cup emblem on football.

1974. Air. World Equestrian Championships, La Baule.
438 **176** 130 f. brown, lilac and blue 1·50 60

1974. Centenary of Universal Postal Union.
439 **177** 80 f. purple, lilac & brown 55 25
440 – 90 f. orange, grey and& blue 40 30
441 – 270 f. purple, olive & grn 2·00 90
DESIGNS: 90 f. Breguet 14T biplane and Douglas DC-8; 270 f. Early steam and modern electric trains.
See also Nos. 463/4.

178 "Skylab" over Africa

1974. Air. Survey of Africa by "Skylab" Space Station.
442 **178** 200 f. indigo, blue & orge 1·00 40
443 – 250 f. blue, purple & orge 1·25 60
DESIGN: 250 f. Astronaut servicing cameras.

1974. Air. 11th Arab Scout Jamboree, Lebanon. Nos. 391/2 surch **130 f. 11e JAMBOREE ARABE AOUT 1974 LIBAN** or **170 f. CONGRES PAN-ARABE LIBAN AOUT 1974**.
444 130 f. on 70 f. brown, red & bl 70 40
445 170 f. on 80 f. blue, grn & red 75 50

1974. Air. 5th Anniv of First landing on Moon. Nos. 408/9 surch **130 f. 1er DEBARQUEMENT SUR LA LUNE 20-VII-69** or **300 f. 1er PAS SUR LA LUNE 21-VII-69**.
446 130 f. on 100 f. slate, brown and blue 70 45
447 300 f. on 280 f. blue, grn & red 1·40 70

1974. West Germany's Victory in World Cup Football Championships. Nos. 436/7 surch **R.F.A. 2 HOLLANDE 1** and value.
448 **175** 300 f. on 270 f. red, green and lilac . . . . . . 1·40 80
449 – 330 f. on 280 f. blue, brown and red . . . . 1·60 80

182 Weaver
183 River Niger near Gao

1974. Crafts and Craftsmen. Multicoloured.
450 50 f. Type **182** 25 15
451 60 f. Potter 30 15
452 70 f. Smith 40 20
453 80 f. Wood-carver 55 20

1974. Mali Views. Multicoloured.
454 10 f. Type **183** 15 10
455 20 f. "The Hand of Fatma" (rock formation, Hombori) (vert) . . 15 10
456 40 f. Waterfall, Gouina . . . 35 15
457 70 f. Hill-dwellings, Dogon (vert) 60 20

184 "C3-PLM" (1906) and "150-P" (1939) Locomotives

1974. Air. Steam Locomotives.
458 **184** 90 f. indigo, red and blue . 75 40
459 – 120 f. brown, orange & bl 85 50
460 – 210 f. brown, orange & bl 1·60 70
461 – 330 f. black, green & blue 2·40 1·40
DESIGNS: 120 f. Baldwin "2-2-0" (1870) and Pacific (1920) locomotives; 210 f. "241-A1" (1925) and Buddicom (1847) locomotives; 330 f. Hudson (1938) and "La Gironde" (1839) locomotives.

185 Skiing

1974. Air. 50th Anniv of Winter Olympics.
462 **185** 300 f. red, blue and green 1·40 80

1974. Berne Postal Convention. Cent. Nos. 439 and 441 surch **9 OCTOBRE 1974** and value.
463 **177** 250 f. on 80 f. purple, lilac and brown . . . . . . 1·40 80
464 – 300 f. on 270 f. purple, olive and green . . . . . . 1·90 80

187 Mao Tse-tung and Great Wall of China
188 "The Nativity" (Memling)

1974. 25th Anniv of Chinese People's Republic.
465 **187** 100 f. blue, red and green . 50 30

1974. Air. Christmas. Multicoloured.
466 290 f. Type **188** . . . . 1·25 70
467 310 f. "Virgin and Child" (Bourgogne School) . . . . 1·50 75
468 400 f. "Adoration of the Magi" (Schongauer) . . . . . . 1·90 1·10

189 Raoul Follereau (missionary)
191 Dr. Schweitzer

190 Electric Train and Boeing 707

1974. Air. Raoul Follereau, "Apostle of the Lepers".
469 **189** 200 f. blue . . . . 1·25 55
469a 200 f. brown . . . . . . 1·75 1·10

1974. Air. Europafrique.
470 **190** 100 f. green, brown & bl 1·75 65
471 110 f. blue, violet & brn 1·75 65

1975. Birth Centenary of Dr Albert Schweitzer.
472 **191** 150 f. turquoise, grn & blue 90 40

192 Patients making Handicrafts and Lions International Emblem

1975. 5th Anniv of Samanko (Leprosy rehabilitation village). Multicoloured.
473 90 f. Type **192** 50 20
474 100 f. View of Samanko . . . 60 25

193 "The Pilgrims at Emmaus" (Champaigne)

1975. Air. Easter. Multicoloured.
475 200 f. Type **193** 90 45
476 300 f. "The Pilgrims at Emmaus" (Veronese) . . . . 1·25 60
477 500 f. "Christ in Majesty" (Limoges enamel) (vert) . . 2·25 1·25

194 "Journey to the Centre of the Earth"

1975. Air. 70th Death Anniv of Jules Verne.
478 **194** 100 f. green, blue & brn 45 25
479 – 170 f. brown, bl & lt brn 75 35
480 – 190 f. blue, turquoise & brn 1·25 55
481 – 220 f. brown, purple & bl 1·50 60
DESIGNS: 170 f. Jules Verne and "From the Earth to the Moon"; 90 f. Giant octopus–"Twenty Thousand Leagues Under the Sea"; 220 f. "A Floating City".

195 Head of "Dawn" (Tomb of the Medici) **197** Astronaut

196 "Tetrodon fahaka"

1975. Air. 500th Birth Anniv of Michelangelo (artist). Multicoloured.
482 400 f. Type **195** . . . . 1·75 1·10
483 500 f. "Moses" (marble statue, Rome) . . . . 2·25 1·25

1975. Fishes (1st series).
484 **196** 60 f. brown, yellow & grn 50 20
485 – 70 f. black, brown & grey 55 25
486 – 80 f. multicoloured . . . 70 25
487 – 90 f. blue, grey and green 1·00 35
488 – 110 f. black and blue . . . 1·25 45
DESIGNS: 70 f. "Malopterurus electricus"; 80 f. "Citharinus latus"; 90 f. "Hydrocyon forskali"; 110 f. "Lates niloticus".
See also Nos. 544/8.

1975. Air. Soviet–U.S. Space Co-operation.
489 **197** 290 f. red, blue and black 1·10 50
490 – 300 f. red, blue and black 1·10 60
491 – 370 f. green, purple & blk 1·40 80
DESIGNS: 300 f. "America and Russia". 370 f. New York and Moscow landmarks.

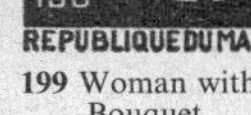

198 Einstein and Equation **199** Woman with Bouquet

1975. Air. 20th Death Anniv of Albert Einstein.
492 **198** 90 f. blue, purple & brown 55 30
See also Nos. 504, 507 and 519.

1975. International Women's Year.
493 **199** 150 f. red and green . . . 70 35

200 Morris "Oxford", 1913

1975. Early Motor-cars.
494 **200** 90 f. violet, brown & blue 50 20
495 – 130 f. red, grey and blue 80 25
496 – 190 f. deep blue, green and blue . . . . 1·25 40
497 – 230 f. brown, blue and red 1·50 45
DESIGNS—MOTOR-CARS: 130 f. Franklin "E", 1907; 190 f. Daimler, 1900; 230 f. Panhard & Levassor, 1895.

201

1975. Air. "Nordjamb 75" World Scout Jamboree, Norway.
498 **201** 100 f. blue, brown & lake 55 25
499 – 150 f. green, brown & bl 75 30
500 – 290 f. lake, brown & blue 1·40 75
DESIGNS: 150 f., 290 f. Scouts and emblem (different).

202 Lafayette and Battle Scene

1975. Air. Bicentenary of American Revolution. Mult.
501 290 f. Type **202** . . . . 1·50 65
502 300 f. Washington and battle scene . . . . 1·50 65
503 370 f. De Grasse and Battle of the Chesapeake, 1781 . . . 1·90 95

1975. 20th Death Anniv of Sir Alexander Fleming (scientist). As T **198**.
504 150 f. brown, purple and blue 80 35

204 Olympic Rings

1975. Air. "Pre-Olympic Year".
505 **204** 350 f. violet and blue . . 1·00 65
506 – 400 f. blue . . . . 1·10 80
DESIGNS: 400 f. Emblem of Montreal Olympics (1976).

1975. Birth Bicentenary of Andre-Marie Ampere. As T **198**.
507 90 f. brown, red and violet . 45 20

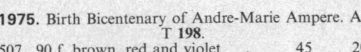

205 Tristater of Carthage

1975. Ancient Coins.
508 **205** 130 f. black, blue & purple 50 25
509 – 170 f. black, green & brn 70 35
510 – 190 f. black, green & red 1·00 65
511 – 260 f. black, blue & orange 1·75 1·25
COINS: 170 f. Decadrachm of Syracuse; 190 f. Tetradrachm of Acanthe; 260 f. Didrachm of Eretrie.

1975. Air. "Apollo–Soyuz" Space Link. Nos. 489/91 optd **ARRIMAGE 17 Juil. 1975.**
512 **197** 290 f. red, blue and black 1·25 65
513 – 300 f. red, blue and black 1·25 65
514 – 370 f. green, purple & blk 1·50 95

207 U.N. Emblem and Names of Agencies forming "ONU"

1975. 30th Anniv of United Nations Charter.
515 **207** 200 f. blue and green . . . 70 45

208 "The Visitation" (Ghirlandaio)

1975. Air. Christmas. Religious Paintings.
516 290 f. Type **208** . . . . 1·40 55
517 300 f. "Nativity" (Fra Filippo Lippi School) . . . . 1·40 65
518 370 f. "Adoration of the Magi" (Velasquez) . . . . 1·60 1·10

1975. Air. 50th Death Anniv of Clement Ader (aviation pioneer). As T **198**.
519 100 f. purple, red and blue 55 20

209 Concorde in Flight

1976. Air. Concorde's First Commercial Flight.
520 **209** 500 f. multicoloured . . . 3·50 1·50

210 Figure-Skating **211** Alexander Graham Bell

1976. Air. Winter Olympic Games, Innsbruck. Multicoloured.
521 120 f. Type **210** 50 25
522 420 f. Ski-jumping . . . . . . 1·50 65
523 430 f. Skiing (slalom) . . . . . 1·50 75

1976. Telephone Centenary.
524 **211** 180 f. blue, brown and light brown 65 35

212 Chameleon

1976. Reptiles. Multicoloured.
525 20 f. Type **212** 20 15
526 30 f. Lizard 25 15
527 40 f. Tortoise 30 20
528 90 f. Python 65 25
529 120 f. Crocodile . . . . 1·10 50

213 Nurse and Patient **215** Constructing Orbital Space Station

214 Dr. Adenauer and Cologne Cathedral

1976. Air. World Health Day.
530 **213** 130 f. multicoloured . . . 55 25

1976. Birth Centenary Dr. Konrad Adenauer.
531 **214** 180 f. purple and brown 90 40

1976. Air. "The Future in Space".
532 **215** 300 f. deep blue, blue and orange . . . . 1·25 60
533 – 400 f. blue, red and purple 1·90 90
DESIGN: 400 f. Sun and space-ship with solar batteries.

216 American Bald Eagle and Liberty Bell

1976. Air. American Revolution. Bicentenary and "Interphil '76" Int. Stamp Exn, Philadelphia.
534 **216** 100 f. blue, purple & black 1·00 20
535 – 400 f. brown, blue & blk 3·50 85
536 – 440 f. violet, green & blk 2·75 85
DESIGNS—HORIZ: 400 f. Warships and American bald eagle. VERT: 440 f. Red Indians and American bald eagle.

217 Running **218** Scouts marching

1976. Air. Olympic Games, Montreal.
537 **217** 200 f. black, brown & red 70 40
538 – 250 f. brown, green & bl 80 50
539 – 300 f. black, blue & green 1·25 60
540 – 400 f. black, blue & green 1·60 90
DESIGNS: 250 f. Swimming; 300 f. Handball; 440 f. Football.

1976. Air. 1st All-African Scout Jamboree, Nigeria.
541 **218** 140 f. brown, blue & green 70 35
542 – 180 f. brown, green & grey 1·00 40
543 – 200 f. violet and brown . 1·10 50
DESIGNS—HORIZ: 180 f. Scouts tending calf. VERT: 200 f. Scout surveying camp at dusk.

1976. Fishes (2nd series). As T **196**.
544 100 f. black and blue 50 20
545 120 f. yellow, brown & green 55 25
546 130 f. turquoise, brown & blk 65 25
547 150 f. yellow, drab and green 75 30
548 220 f. black, green and brown 1·25 50
DESIGNS: 100 f. "Heterotis niloticus"; 120 f. "Synodontis budgetti"; 130 f. "Heterobranchus bidorsalis"; 150 f. "Tilapia mondodi"; 220 f. "Alestes malerolepidotus".

220 Scenes from Children's Book

221 "Roi de L'Air"

1976. Literature for Children.
549 **220** 130 f. grey, green and red . . . 45 25

1976. First Issue of "L'Essor" Newspaper.
550 **221** 120 f. multicoloured . . . 1·00 30

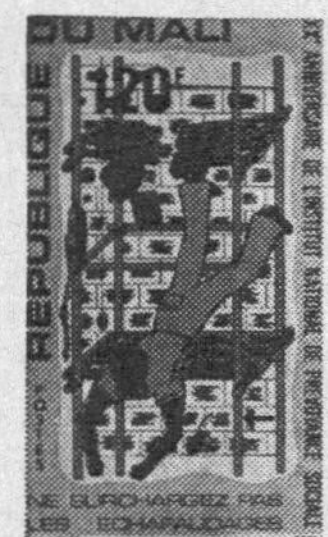
222 Fall from Scaffolding

1976. 20th Anniv of National Social Insurance.
551 **222** 120 f. multicoloured . . . 35 25

223 Moenjodaro

1976. Air. U.N.E.S.C.O. "Save Moenjodaro" (Pakistan) Campaign.
552 **223** 400 f. purple, blue & black 1·75 80
553 – 500 f. red, yellow and blue 2·00 1·25
DESIGN: 500 f. Effigy, animals and remains.

224 Freighter, Vickers Viscount 800 and Map

1976. Air. Europafrique.
554 **224** 200 f. purple and blue . . 1·10 45

225 Cascade of Letters

1976. 25th Anniv of U.N. Postal Administration.
555 **225** 120 f. orange, green & lilac 45 25

226 Moto Guzzi "254" (Italy)

1976. Motorcycling.
556 **266** 90 f. red, grey and brown 45 20
557 – 120 f. violet, blue & black 55 25
558 – 130 f. red, grey and green 70 25
559 – 140 f. blue, green and grey 90 30
DESIGNS: 120 f. B.M.W. "900" (Germany); 130 f. Honda "Egli" (Japan); 140 f. Motobecane "LT3" (France).

INDEX

Countries can be quickly located by referring to the index at the end of this volume.

227 "The Nativity" (Taddeo Gaddi)

1976. Air. Christmas. Religious Paintings. Mult.
560 280 f. Type **227** . . . . 1·25 50
561 300 f. "Adoration of the Magi" (Hans Memling) . . . . . 1·40 60
562 320 f. "The Nativity" (Carlo Crivelli) . . . . 1·50 75

228 Muscat Fishing Boat

1976. Ships.
563 **228** 160 f. purple, green & blue 65 30
564 – 180 f. green, red and blue 65 35
565 – 190 f. purple, blue & green 70 40
566 – 200 f. green, red and blue 75 40
DESIGNS: 180 f. Cochin Chinese junk; 190 f. Dunkirk lightship "Ruytingen"; 200 f. Nile felucca.

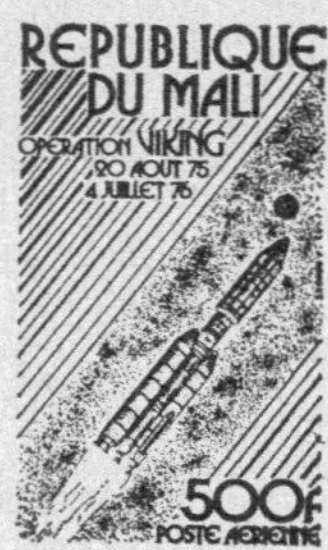
229 Rocket in Flight

1976. Air. Operation "Viking".
567 **229** 500 f. blue, red and lake 1·75 1·25
568 – 1000 f. lake, blue and deep blue . . . . 3·00 1·90
DESIGN: 1000 f. Spacecraft on Mars.

230 Pres. Giscard d'Estaing and Sankore Mosque, Timbuktu

1977. Air. Visit of Pres. Giscard d'Estaing of France.
570 **230** 430 f. multicoloured . . . 2·00 80

231 Rocket on Launch-pad, Newton and Apple

1977. Air. 250th Death Anniv of Isaac Newton.
571 **231** 400 f. purple, red & green 2·00 75

232 Prince Philip and Queen Elizabeth II

1977. Air. "Personalities of Decolonisation". Mult.
572 180 f. Type **232** 65 35
573 200 f. General De Gaulle (vert) 1·10 50
574 250 f. Queen Wilhelmina of the Netherlands (vert) 75 55
575 300 f. King Baudouin and Queen Fabiola of Belgium . . . . 1·10 70
576 480 f. Crowning of Queen Elizabeth II (vert) . . . . 2·00 1·25

233 Lindbergh and "Spirit of St. Louis"

1977. Air. 50th Anniv of Lindbergh's Transatlantic Flight.
577 **233** 420 f. orange and violet . . 1·90 85
578 – 430 f. blue, orange & green 1·90 85
DESIGN: 430 f. "Spirit of St. Louis" crossing the Atlantic.

234 Village Indigobird

236 Printed Circuit

235 Louis Braille and Hands reading Book

1977. Mali Birds. Multicoloured.
579 15 f. Type **234** 45 15
580 25 f. Yellow-breasted barbet 75 15
581 30 f. Vitelline masked weaver 75 55
582 40 f. Carmine bee eater 90 60
583 50 f. Senegal parrot 90 60

1977. 125th Death Anniv of Louis Braille (inventor of "Braille" system of reading and writing for the blind").
584 **235** 200 f. blue, red and green . 1·10 45

1977. World Telecommunications Day.
585 **236** 120 f. red and brown . . . 35 20

236a Chateau Sassenage, Grenoble

1977. Air. 10th Anniv of International French Language Council.
586 **236a** 300 f. multicoloured . . . 1·00 50

237 Airship LZ-1 over Lake Constance

1977. Air. History of the Zeppelin.
587 **237** 120 f. green, brown & blue 55 25
588 – 130 f. deep blue, brown and blue 55 25
589 – 350 f. red, blue and deep blue 1·60 75
590 – 500 f. deep blue, green and blue . . . . 2·25 95
DESIGNS: 130 f. "Graf Zeppelin" over Atlantic; 350 f. Burning of "Hindenburg" at Lakehurst; 500 f. Count Ferdinand von Zeppelin and "Graf Zeppelin" at mooring mast.

238 "Anaz imperator"

1977. Insects. Multicoloured.
591 5 f. Type **238** 20 15
592 10 f. "Sphadromantis viridis" 25 15
593 20 f. "Vespa tropica" 25 15
594 35 f. "Melolontha melolantha" 30 15
595 60 f. Stag beetle 55 20

239 Knight and Rook

240 Henri Dunant

1977. Chess Pieces.
596 **239** 120 f. black, green & brn 1·00 30
597 – 130 f. green, red and black 1·10 30
598 – 300 f. green, red and blue 2·50 75
DESIGNS—VERT: 130 f. Pawn and Bishop. HORIZ: 300 f. King and Queen.

1977. Air. Nobel Peace Prize Winners. Multicoloured.
599 600 f. Type **240** (founder of Red Cross) . . . . 2·00 1·00
600 700 f. Martin Luther King . . 2·25 1·10

241 Ship

242 "Head of Horse"

1977. Europafrique.
601 **241** 400 f. multicoloured . . . 1·25 75

1977. 525th Birth Anniv of Leonardo da Vinci.
602 **242** 200 f. brown and black . 75 50
603 – 300 f. brown . . . . . 1·10 60
604 – 500 f. red . . . . 2·00 85
DESIGNS: 300 f. "Head of Young Girl"; 500 f. Self-portrait.

243 Footballers

245 Dome of the Rock

244 Friendship Hotel

1977. Air. Football Cup Elimination Rounds.
605 – 180 f. brown, green & orge 50 30
606 **243** 200 f. brown, green & orge 60 35
607 – 420 f. grey, green and lilac 1·25 70
DESIGNS—HORIZ: 180 f. Two footballers; 420 f. Tackling.

1977. Inauguration of Friendship Hotel, Bamako.
608 **244** 120 f. multicoloured . . . 35 25

1977. Palestinian Welfare.
609 **245** 120 f. multicoloured . . . 55 20
610 180 f. multicoloured . . . 70 30

246 Mao Tse-tung and "Comatex" Hall, Bamako

1977. Air. Mao Tse-tung Memorial.
611 **246** 300 f. red . . . . 1·25 50

1977. Air. First Commercial Paris–New York Flight by Concorde. Optd **PARIS-NEW YORK 22.11.77.**
612 **209** 500 f. multicoloured . . . 7·00 4·50

248 "Adoration of the Magi" (Rubens)

1977. Air. Christmas. Details from "Adoration of the Magi" by Rubens.
613 **248** 400 f. multicoloured . . . 1·25 75
614 – 500 f. multicoloured . . . 1·60 95
615 – 600 f. multicoloured . . . 2·00 1·10
The 600 f. is a horizontal design.

249 "Hercules and the Nemean Lion"

1978. 400th Birth Anniv of Peter Paul Rubens. Multicoloured.
616 200 f. "Battle of the Amazons" (horiz) 70 35
617 300 f. "Return from Labour in the Fields" (horiz) . . . . . 1·00 55
618 500 f. Type **249** . . . . 1·75 95

250 Schubert and Mute Swans

1978. Air. 150th Death Anniv of Franz Schubert (composer). Multicoloured.
619 300 f. Schubert and bars of music (vert) . . . . 1·50 60
620 420 f. Type **250** . . . . 4·00 70

251 Cook and Shipboard Scene

1978. Air. 250th Birth Anniv of Captain James Cook.
621 **251** 200 f. blue, red and violet 1·25 40
622 – 300 f. brown, blue & green 1·75 70
DESIGN: 300 f. Capt. Cook meeting natives.

252 African and Chained Building

1978. World Anti-Apartheid Year.
623 **252** 120 f. violet, brown & blue 40 20
624 – 130 f. violet, blue & orge 40 20
625 – 180 f. brown, pur & orge 60 30
DESIGNS: 130 f. Statue of Liberty and Africans walking to open door; 180 f. African children and mule in fenced enclosure.

253 Players and Ball **254** "Head of Christ"

1978. Air. World Cup Football Championship, Argentina.
626 **253** 150 f. red, green & brown 60 30
627 – 250 f. red, brown & green 1·25 45
628 – 300 f. red, brown and blue 1·50 50
DESIGNS—VERT: 250 f. HORIZ: 300 f. Different football scenes.

1978. Air. Easter. Works by Durer.
630 **254** 420 f. green and brown . 1·60 75
631 – 430 f. blue and brown . . 1·60 75
DESIGN: 430 f. "The Resurrection".

255 Red-cheeked Cordon-bleu

1978. Birds. Multicoloured.
632 20 f. Type **255** 20 15
633 30 f. Black-faced fire finch . . 45 20
634 50 f. Red-billed fire finch . . 55 40
635 70 f. African collared dove . 95 40
636 80 f. White-billed buffalo weaver 1·40 50

256 C-3 "Trefle"

1978. Air. Birth Centenary of Andre Citroen (automobile pioneer).
637 **256** 120 f. brown, lake & green 60 20
638 – 130 f. grey, orange & blue 70 25
639 – 180 f. blue, green and red 1·10 30
640 – 200 f. black, red and lake 1·25 40
DESIGNS: 130 f. B-2 "Croisiere Noir" track-laying vehicle, 1924; 180 f. B-14 G Saloon, 1927; 200 f. Model-11 front-wheel drive car, 1934.

1978. 20th Anniv of Bamako Lions Club. Nos. 473/4 surch **XXe ANNIVERSAIRE DU LIONS CLUB DE BAMAKO 1958-1978** and value.
641 120 f. on 90 f. Type **192** . . 45 20
642 130 f. on 100 f. View of Samanko 55 30

258 Names of 1978 U.P.U. members forming Map of the World

1978. Centenary of U.P.U. Foundation Congress, Paris.
643 **258** 120 f. green, orange & mve 45 20
644 – 130 f. yellow, red & green 45 20
DESIGN: 130 f. Names of 1878 member states across globe.

259 Desert Scene

1978. Campaign against Desertification.
645 **259** 200 f. multicoloured . . . 70 35

260 Mahatma Gandhi **262** Dominoes

261 "Dermestes bromius"

1978. 30th Anniv of Gandhi's Assassination.
646 **260** 140 f. brown, red & black 85 30

1978. Insects. Multicoloured.
647 15 f. Type **261** 20 15
648 25 f. "Calosoma sp." 25 15
649 90 f. "Lopocerus variegatus" 45 20
650 120 f. "Coccinella septempunctata" 55 25
651 140 f. "Goliathus giganteus" 70 30

1978. Social Games.
652 **362** 100 f. black, green and red 40 20
653 – 130 f. red, black and blue . 85 25
DESIGN: 130 f. Bridge hand.

263 Ostrich on Nest (Syrian Manuscript)

1978. Air. Europafrique. Multicoloured.
654 100 f. Type **263** . . . . 1·25 20
655 110 f. Common zebra (Mansur miniature) 50 30

1978. Air. World Cup Football Championship Finalists. Nos. 626/8 optd with results.
656 **253** 150 f. red, green & brown 60 25
657 – 250 f. red, brown & green 1·00 45
658 – 300 f. red, brown & blue 1·25 60
OPTS: 150 f. **CHAMPION 1978 ARGENTINE**; 250 f. **2e HOLLANDE**: 300 f. **3e BRESIL 4e ITALIE**.

265 Coronation Coach

1978. Air. 25th Anniv of Coronation of Queen Elizabeth II. Multicoloured.
660 500 f. Type **265** . . . . . . 1·50 70
661 1000 f. Queen Elizabeth II . . 2·75 1·40

266 Aristotle and African Animals **267** Douglas DC-3 and U.S.A. 1918 24 c. stamp

1978. 2300th Death Anniv of Aristotle (Greek philosopher).
662 **266** 200 f. brow red and grn 90 35

1978. Air. History of Aviation.
663 **267** 80 f. deep blue, red & blue 35 15
664 – 100 f. multicoloured . . . 40 20
665 – 120 f. black, blue and red 50 25
666 – 130 f. green, red & black 55 30
667 – 320 f. violet, blue & red . 1·25 65
DESIGNS: 100 f. Stampe and Renard SV-4 and Belgium Balloon stamp of 1932; 120 f. Clement Ader's Avion III and France Concorde stamp of 1976; 130 f. Junkers Ju–52/3m and Germany Biplane stamp of 1919; 320 f. Mitsubishi A6M Zero-Sen and Japan Pagoda stamp of 1951.

268 "The Annunciation"

1978. Air. Christmas. Works by Durer.
668 **268** 420 f. brown and black . 1·25 60
669 – 430 f. brown and green . 1·25 60
670 – 500 f. black and brown . 1·60 75
DESIGNS: 430 f. "Virgin and Child"; 500 f. "Adoration of the Magi".

269 Launch of "Apollo 8" and Moon

1978. Air. 10th Anniv of First Manned Flight around the Moon.
671 **269** 200 f. red, green and violet 60 30
672 – 300 f. violet, green and red 1·10 50
DESIGN: 300 f. "Apollo 8" in orbit around the Moon.

270 U.N. and Human Rights Emblems

1978. 30th Anniv of Declaration of Human Rights.
673 **270** 180 f. red, blue and brown 60 35

271 Concorde and Clement Ader's "Eole"

1979. Air. 3rd Anniv of First Commercial Concorde Flight. Multicoloured.
674 120 f. Type **271** 60 25
675 130 f. Concorde and Wright Flyer 1 . . . . 70 30
676 200 f. Concorde and "Spirit of St. Louis" . . . . 1·25 45

1979. Air. "Philexafrique" Stamp Exhibition, Libreville, Gabon (1st issue) and International Stamp Fair, Essen, West Germany. As T **262** of Niger. Multicoloured.
677 200 f. Ruff (bird) and Lubeck 1859 ½ s. stamp . . . . . . 1·00 70
678 200 f. Dromedary and Mali 1965 200 f. stamp . . . . . . 1·75 1·25
See also Nos. 704/5.

1979. Air. Birth Centenary of Albert Einstein (physicist). No. 492 surch **"1879–1979" 130F.**
679 **198** 130 f. on 90 f. blue, purple and brown 55 30

273 "Christ carrying the Cross"

1979. Air. Easter. Works by Durer.
680 **273** 400 f. black and turquoise . . 1·40 60
681 – 430 f. black and red . . . 1·40 60
682 – 480 f. black and blue . . . 1·60 1·00
DESIGNS: 430 f. "Christ on the Cross"; 480 f. "The Great Lamentation".

274 Basketball and St. Basil's Cathedral, Moscow

275 African Manatee

1979. Air. Pre-Olympic Year. Multicoloured.
683 420 f. Type **274** . . . . 1·50 75
684 430 f. Footballer and Kremlin . . 1·50 75

1979. Endangered Animals. Multicoloured.
685 100 f. Type **275** 45 20
686 120 f. Chimpanzee 55 30
687 130 f. Topi 65 35
688 180 f. Gemsbok 80 40
689 200 f. Giant eland 90 55

276 Child and I.Y.C. Emblem

1979. International Year of the Child.
690 **276** 120 f. green, red & brown . . 40 20
691 – 200 f. purple and green . . 70 35
692 – 300 f. brown, mauve and deep brown . . . . . . 1·00 50
DESIGNS: 200 f. Girl and scout with birds; 300 f. Children with calf.

277 Judo

1979. World Judo Championships, Paris.
693 **277** 200 f. sepia, red and ochre . . 80 40

278 Wave Pattern and Human Figures

279 Goat's Head and Lizard Fetishes

1979. World Telecommunications Day.
694 **278** 120 f. multicoloured . . . 35 20

1979. World Museums Day. Multicoloured.
695 90 f. Type **279** 30 15
696 120 f. Seated figures (wood carving) 40 20
697 130 f. Two animal heads and figurine (wood carving) . . 50 25

280 Rowland Hill and Mali 1961 25 f. stamp

281 Cora Players

1979. Death Centenary of Sir Rowland Hill.
698 **280** 120 f. multicoloured . . . 40 20
699 – 130 f. red, blue and green . . 40 20
700 – 180 f. black, green & blue . . 60 30
701 – 200 f. black, red & purple . . 70 35
702 – 300 f. blue, deep blue and red 1·25 50
DESIGNS: 130 f. Airship "Graf Zeppelin" and Saxony stamp of 1850; 180 f. Concorde and France stamp of 1849; 200 f. Stage coach and U.S.A. stamp of 1849; 300 f. U.P.U. emblem and Penny Black.

1979.
703 **281** 200 f. multicoloured . . . 1·00 40

282 Sankore Mosque and "Adenium obesum"

1979. "Philexafrique" Exhibition, Libreville, Gabon (2nd issue).
704 **282** 120 f. multicoloured . . . 90 55
705 – 300 f. red, blue and orange 1·90 1·25
DESIGN: 300 f. Horseman and satellite.

283 Map of Mali showing Conquest of Desert

1979. Operation "Sahel Vert". Multicoloured.
706 200 f. Type **283** 70 30
707 300 f. Planting a tree . . . . 1·10 50

284 Lemons

285 Sigmund Freud

1979. Fruit (1st series). Multicoloured.
708 10 f. Type **284** 15 10
709 60 f. Pineapple 30 15
710 100 f. Papaw 50 15
711 120 f. Sweet-sops 55 20
712 130 f. Mangoes 65 25
See also Nos. 777/81.

1979. 40th Death Anniv of Sigmund Freud (psychologist).
713 **285** 300 f. sepia and violet . . 1·25 60

286 Caillie and Camel approaching Fort

1979. 180th Birth Anniv of Rene Caillie (explorer).
714 **286** 120 f. sepia, brown & blue . . 50 20
715 – 130 f. blue, green & brown . . 60 25
DESIGN: 130 f. Rene Caillie and map of route across Sahara.

287 "Eurema brigitta"

1979. Butterflies and Moths (1st series). Mult.
716 100 f. Type **281** 60 20
717 120 f. "Papilio pylades" 65 20
718 130 f. "Melanitis leda satyridae" . 80 40
719 180 f. "Gonimbrasis belina occidentalis" . . . . . . 1·25 45
720 200 f. "Bunaea alcinoe" . . . 1·50 50
See also Nos. 800/4.

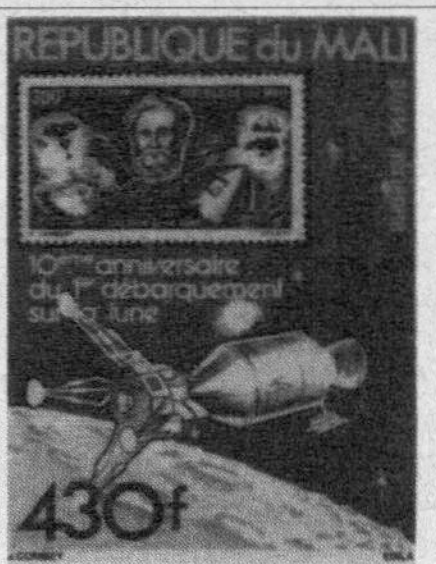

288 Mali 1970 300 f. Stamp and Modules orbiting Moon

1979. Air. 10th Anniv of First Moon Landing.
721 430 f. Type **288** . . . . 1·40 60
722 500 f. 1973 250 f. stamp and rocket launch . . . . 1·60 95

289 Capt. Cook and H.M.S. "Resolution" off Kerguelen Islands

1979. Air. Death Bicent of Captain James Cook.
723 300 f. Type **289** . . . . 1·50 80
724 400 f. Capt. Cook and H.M.S. "Resolution" off Hawaii . . 2·25 1·10

290 Menaka Greyhound

1979. Dogs. Multicoloured.
725 20 f. Type **290** 20 15
726 50 f. Water spaniel 35 15
727 70 f. Beagle 45 15
728 80 f. Newfoundland 55 20
729 90 f. Sheepdog 70 20

291 David Janowski

1979. Air. Chess Grand-masters.
730 **291** 100 f. red and brown . . . 70 30
731 – 140 f. red, brown and blue . 1·00 30
732 – 200 f. blue, violet & green . 1·60 50
733 – 300 f. brown, ochre & red . 2·00 70
DESIGNS: 140 f. Alexander Alekhine; 200 f. Willi Schlage; 300 f. Efim Bogoljubow.

292 "The Adoration of the Magi" 1511 (detail, Durer)

1979. Air. Christmas. Works by Durer.
734 **292** 300 f. brown and orange . 1·00 50
735 – 400 f. brown and blue . . 1·25 75
736 – 500 f. brown and green . . 1·60 95
DESIGNS: 400 f. "Adoration of the Magi" (1503); 500 f. "Adoration of the Magi" (1511, different).

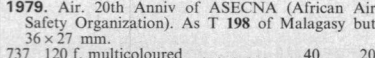

1979. Air. 20th Anniv of ASECNA (African Air Safety Organization). As T **198** of Malagasy but 36 × 27 mm.
737 120 f. multicoloured 40 20

293 Globe, Rotary Emblem and Diesel Train

294 African Ass

1980. Air. 75th Anniv of Rotary International. Multicoloured.
738 220 f. Type **293** . . . . 1·25 50
739 250 f. Globe, Rotary emblem and Douglas DC-10 airliner . . 1·00 45
740 430 f. Bamako Rotary Club and emblem . . . . 1·40 75

1980. Protected Animals. Multicoloured.
741 90 f. Type **294** 50 20
742 120 f. Addax 60 20
743 130 f. Cheetahs 65 35
744 140 f. Barbary sheep 70 45
745 180 f. African buffalo 90 50

295 Speed Skating

1980. Air. Winter Olympics Game, Lake Placid. Multicoloured.
746 200 f. Type **295** 70 30
747 300 f. Ski jump . . . . 1·10 60

296 Stephenson's "Rocket" and Mali 30 f. Stamp, 1972

1980. Air. 150th Anniv of Liverpool and Manchester Railway.
749 **296** 200 f. blue, brown & green . 90 45
750 – 300 f. black, brown & turq . 1·60 80
DESIGN: 300 f. "Rocket" and Mali; 50 f. railway stamp, 1970.

297 Horse Jumping

1980. Air. Olympic Games, Moscow.
751 **297** 200 f. green, brown & blue . 70 30
752 – 300 f. blue, brown & green . 1·00 50
753 – 400 f. red, green & lt green . 1·50 75
DESIGN: 300 f. Sailing. 400 f. Football.

298 Solar Pumping Station, Koni

1980. Solar Energy. Multicoloured.
755 90 f. Type **298** 30 15
756 100 f. Solar capture tables, Dire 35 15
757 120 f. Solar energy cooker . . 50 20
758 130 f. Solar generating station, Dire 55 25

299 Nioro Horse

1980. Horses. Multicoloured.
759 100 f. Mopti 50 15
760 120 f. Type **299** 55 15
761 130 f. Koro 65 20
762 180 f. Lake zone horse 80 35
763 200 f. Banamba 95 40

300 "Head of Christ" (Maurice Denis)

1980. Air. Easter.
764 **300** 480 f. red and brown . . . 1·60 95
765 – 500 f. brown and red . . . 1·60 95
DESIGN: 500 f. "Christ before Pilate" (Durer).

301 Kepler and Diagram of Earth's Orbit

1980. Air. 350th Death Anniv of J. Kepler (astronomer).
766 **301** 200 f. lt blue, blue & red 80 35
767 – 300 f. mauve, violet & grn 1·25 55
DESIGN: 300 f. Kepler, Copernicus and diagram of solar system.

302 Pluto and Diagram of Orbit

1980. Air. 50th Anniv of Discovery of Planet Pluto.
768 **302** 402 f. blue, grey & mauve 1·90 85

303 "Lunokhod 1" (10th Anniv)

1980. Air. Space Events.
769 **303** 480 f. black, red and blue 1·50 85
770 – 500 f. grey, blue and red 1·50 85
DESIGN: 500 f. "Apollo" - "Soyuz" link-up.

304 Fleming and Laboratory

1980. Sir Alexander Fleming (discoverer of penicillin). Commemoration.
771 **304** 200 f. green, sepia & brn 80 35

305 Avicenna, Medical Instruments and Herbs
306 Pilgrim at Mecca

1980. Birth Millenary of Avicenna (Arab physician and philosopher).
772 **305** 120 f. blue, red and brown 40 20
773 – 180 f. dp brn, turq & brn 60 25
DESIGN: 180 f. Avicenna as teacher.

1980. 1400th Anniv of Hegira. Multicoloured.
774 120 f. Type **306** 40 15
775 130 f. Praying hands 40 20
776 180 f. Pilgrims (horiz) 60 30

1980. Fruit (2nd series). As T **284**. Multicoloured.
777 90 f. Guavas 45 20
778 120 f. Cashews 50 20
779 130 f. Oranges 65 25
780 140 f. Bananas 75 25
781 180 f. Grapefruit 90 35

307 Rochambeau and French Fleet at Rhode Island, 1780

1980. Air. French Support for American Independence.
782 **307** 420 f. brown, turq & red 1·50 75
783 – 430 f. black, blue and red 1·50 80
DESIGN: 430 f. Rochambeau, Washington and Eagle.

308 Dove and U.N. Emblem

1980. 60th Anniv of League of Nations.
784 **308** 200 f. blue, red and violet 60 35

309 Scene from "Around the World in 80 Days"

1980. Air. 75th Death Anniv of Jules Verne (writer).
785 **309** 100 f. red, green & brown 1·50 75
786 – 100 f. brown, chestnut and turquoise . . . . 1·50 30
787 – 150 f. green, brn & dp brn 1·00 40
788 – 150 f. blue, violet & dp bl 1·00 40
DESIGNS: No. 786, Concorde; No. 787, "From the Earth to the Moon"; No. 788, Astronaut on Moon.

310 Xylophone, Mask and Emblem

1980. Sixth Arts and Cultural Festival, Bamako.
789 **310** 120 f. multicoloured . . . 40 20

311 Map of Africa and Asia
313 Conference Emblem

1980. 25th Anniv of Afro-Asian Bandung Conference.
790 **311** 300 f. green, red and blue 90 55

1980. Air. Olympic Medal Winners. Nos. 751/3 optd
791 200 f. green, brown and blue 70 35
792 300 f. blue, brown and green 1·00 55
793 400 f. red, green & light green 1·40 75
OVERPRINTS: 200 f. **CONCOURS COMPLET INDIVIDUEL ROMAN (It.) BLINOV (Urss) SALNIKOV (Urss)**; 300 f. **FINN RECHARDT (Fin.) MAYRHOFER (Autr.) BALACHOV (Urss)**; 400 f. **TCHECOSLOVAQUIE ALLEMAGNE DE L'EST URSS**.

1980. World Tourism Conference, Manila. Mult.
795 120 f. Type **313** 35 15
796 180 f. Encampment outside fort and Conference emblem . . 50 30

314 Dam and Rural Scene

1980. 20th Anniv of Independence. Multicoloured.
797 100 f. Type **314** 40 15
798 120 f. National Assembly Building 40 20
799 130 f. Independence Monument (vert) 45 25

1980. Butterflies. (2nd series). As T **287** but dated "1980". Multicoloured.
800 50 f. "Uterheisa pulchella" (postage) 30 20
801 60 f. "Mylothis chloris pieridae" 40 20
802 70 f. "Hypolimnas mishippus" 50 20
803 80 f. "Papilio demodocus" . . 65 20
804 420 f. "Denaus chrysippus" (48 × 36 mm) (air) . . . . . 2·25 1·25

315 Pistol firing Cigarette and Target over Lungs

1980. Anti-Smoking Campaign.
805 **315** 200 f. multicoloured . . . 75 35

316 Train, Boeing 737 and Globe

1980. Europafrique.
806 **316** 300 f. multicoloured . . . 1·25 60

317 Map of West Africa and Agricultural Symbols
318 Gen. de Gaulle and Map of France

1980. 5th Anniv of West African Economic Council. Multicoloured.
807 100 f. Type **317** 35 15
808 120 f. "Transport" . . . . . . 1·40 45
809 130 f. "Industry" 45 25
810 140 f. "Energy" 50 25

1980. Air. 10th Death Anniv of Gen. Charles de Gaulle. Multicoloured.
811 420 f. Type **318** . . . . . . 1·75 75
812 430 f. De Gaulle and Cross of Lorraine . . . . 1·75 75

319 "Tokaido" (Japan) and Mali 1972 10 f. Stamp

1980. Air. Locomotives.
813 **319** 120 f. blue, green and red 65 20
814 – 130 f. green, blue and red 75 25
815 – 200 f. orange, black & grn 1·00 40
816 – 480 f. black, red and green 2·50 95
DESIGNS—HORIZ: 130 f. "RTG" train of Amtrack, U.S.A. and 20 f. locomotive stamp of 1970; 200 f. "Rembrandt" train, Germany and 100 f. locomotive stamp of 1970. VERT: 480 f. "TGV 001" express train, France and 80 f. locomotive stamp of 1970.

320 "Flight into Egypt" (Rembrandt)
321 Nomo Dogon

1980. Air. Christmas. Multicoloured.
817 300 f. "St. Joseph showing the infant Jesus to St. Catherine" (Lorenzo Lotto) (horiz) . . 1·00 55
818 400 f. Type **320** . . . . . . 1·40 80
819 500 f. "Christmas Night" (Gauguin) (horiz) . . . . . 1·60 90

1980. 5th Anniv of African Posts and Telecommunications Union. As T **292** of Niger.
820 130 f. multicoloured 40 20

1981. Statuettes. Multicoloured.
821 60 f. Type **321** 20 15
822 70 f. Senoufo fertility symbol 25 15
823 90 f. Bamanan fertility statuette 35 15
824 100 f. Senoufo captives snuff-box 40 15
825 120 f. Dogon fertility statuette 50 20

322 "Self-portrait" (Blue period)
323 Mambie Sidibe

1981. Birth Bicentenary of Pablo Picasso (artist).
826 **322** 1000 f. multicoloured . . 3·25 1·75

1981. Mali Thinkers and Savants.
827 **323** 120 f. brown, buff and red 40 20
828 – 130 f. brown, buff & black 40 25
DESIGN: 130 f. Amadou Hampate Ba.

324 Mosque and Ka'aba
325 Tackle

1981. 1400th Anniv of Hejira.
829 **324** 120 f. multicoloured . . . 40 20
830 180 f. multicoloured . . . 60 30

1981. Air. World Cup Football Championship Eliminators. Multicoloured.
831 100 f. Type **325** 40 20
832 200 f. Heading the ball 85 35
833 300 f. Running for ball . . . 1·40 50

326 Kaarta Zeba **327** Crinum de Moore "Crinum moorei"

1981. Cattle. Multicoloured.
835 20 f. Type **326** 15 15
836 30 f. Peul du Macina sebu . . 15 15
837 40 f. Maure zebu 25 15
838 80 f. Touareg zebu 50 15
839 100 f. N'Dama cow 60 20

1981. Flowers. Multicoloured.
840 50 f. Type **327** 30 15
841 100 f. Double rose hibiscus "Hibiscus rosa-sinensis" . . 70 15
842 120 f. Pervenche "Catharanthus roseus" 80 20
843 130 f. Frangipani "Plumeria rubra" 80 25
844 180 f. Orgueil de Chine "Caesalpinia pulcherrima" 1·25 40

328 Mozart and Musical Instruments

1981. Air. 225th Birth Anniv of Mozart. Mult.
845 420 f. Type **328** . . . . 1·75 85
846 430 f. Mozart and musical instruments (different) . . . 1·75 85

329 "The Fall on the Way to Calvary" (Raphael) **330** Yuri Gagarin

1981. Air. Easter.
847 500 f. Type **329** . . . . 1·50 85
848 600 f. "Ecce Homo" (Rembrandt) . . . . 2·00 1·25

1981. Air. Space Anniversaries and Events.
849 **330** 200 f. blue, black and red 75 30
850 – 200 f. blue, black & lt blue 75 30
851 – 380 f. multicoloured . . . 1·25 55
852 – 430 f. violet, black & blue 1·50 70
DESIGNS—VERT: No. 849, Type **330**: first man in space (20th anniv); No. 850, Alan Shepard, first American in space (20th anniv); No. 851, Saturn and moons (exploration of Saturn). HORIZ: No. 852, Sir William Herschel, and diagram of Uranus, (Discovery bicentenary)

331 Blind and Sighted Faces **332** Caduceus (Telecommunications and Health)

1981. International Year of Disabled People.
853 **331** 100 f. light brown, brown and green 35 15
854 – 120 f. violet, blue and purple 45 20
DESIGN: 120 f. Mechanical hand and human hand with spanner.

1981. World Telecommunications Day.
855 **332** 130 f. multicoloured . . . 40 25

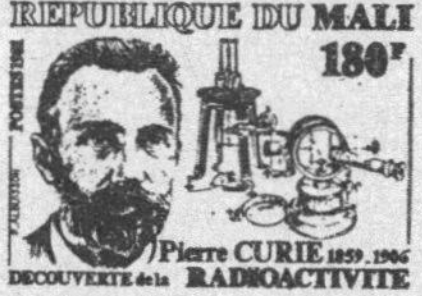

333 Pierre Curie and Instruments

1981. 75th Death Anniv of Pierre Curie (discoverer of radioactivity).
856 **333** 180 f. blue, black & orange 90 30

334 Scouts at Well and Dorcas Gazelle

1981. 4th African Scouting Conference, Abidjan. Multicoloured.
857 110 f. Type **334** 55 30
858 160 f. Scouts signalling and patas monkey . . . . 1·00 60
859 300 f. Scouts saluting and cheetah (vert) . . . . . . 1·50 85

1981. Air. World Railway Speed Record. No. 816 optd **28 fevrier 1981/Record du monde de vitesse–380 km/h**.
861 480 f. black, red and blue . . 2·25 90

336 Columbus, Fleet and U.S. Columbus Stamp of 1892

1981. Air. 475th Death Anniv of Christopher Columbus.
862 **336** 180 f. brown, black & bl 80 40
863 – 200 f. green, blue & brown 1·00 40
864 – 260 f. black, violet and red 1·50 60
865 – 300 f. lilac, red and green 1·60 70
DESIGNS—VERT: 200 f. "Nina" and 1 c. Columbus stamp of Spain; 260 f. "Pinta" and 5 c. Columbus stamp of Spain. HORIZ: 300 f. "Santa Maria" and U.S. 3 c. Columbus stamp.

1981. 23rd World Scouting Conference, Dakar. Nos. 857/9 optd **"DAKAR 8 AOUT 1981/28e CONFERENCE MOUNDIALE DU SCOUTISME"**.
866 **334** 110 f. multicoloured . . . 40 20
867 – 160 f. multicoloured . . . 50 30
868 – 300 f. multicoloured . . . 1·25 55

338 Space Shuttle after Launching

1981. Air. Space Shuttle. Multicoloured.
870 200 f. Type **338** 75 30
871 500 f. Space Shuttle in orbit . 2·00 75
872 600 f. Space Shuttle landing . 2·25 1·25

339 "Harlequin on a Horse"

1981. Air. Birth Centenary of Pablo Picasso. Mult.
874 600 f. Type **339** . . . . 2·50 1·25
875 750 f. "Child with Pigeon" . . 3·00 1·40

340 Prince Charles, Lady Diana Spencer and St. Paul's Cathedral

1981. Air. British Royal Wedding. Multicoloured.
876 500 f. Type **340** . . . . 1·25 75
877 700 f. Prince Charles, Lady Diana Spencer and coach . . 1·75 1·10

342 Maure Sheep **343** Heinrich von Stephan (founder of U.P.U.), Latecoere 28 and Concorde

1981. Sheep. Multicoloured.
886 10 f. Type **342** 15 10
887 25 f. Peul sheep 20 10
888 140 f. Sahael sheep 50 25
889 180 f. Touareg sheep 75 35
890 200 f. Djallonke ram 85 35

1981. Universal Postal Union Day.
891 **343** 400 f. red and green . . . 1·60 70

344 Woman drinking from Bowl

1981. World Food Day.
892 **344** 200 f. brown, orge & mve 65 30

345 "The Incarnation of the Son of God" (detail, Grunewald)

1981. Air. Christmas. Multicoloured.
893 500 f. Type **345** . . . . 1·75 75
894 700 f. "The Campori Madonna" (Correggio) . . . . 2·25 1·25

347 Transport and Hands holding Map of Europe and Africa

1981. Europafrique.
896 **347** 700 f. blue, brown & orge 3·00 1·60

348 Guerin, Calmette, Syringe and Bacillus

1981. 60th Anniv of First B.C.G. Innoculation.
897 **348** 200 f. brown, violet & blk 85 40

1982. Air. World Chess Championship, Merano. Nos. 731 and 733 optd.
898 140 f. red, brown and blue . . 1·10 50
899 300 f. brown, ochre and red . 2·00 75
OPTS: 140 f. **ANATOLI KARPOV VICTOR KORTCHNOI MERANO (ITALIE) (Octobre-Novembre 1981**; 300 f. **Octobre-Novembre 1981 ANATOLI KARPOV Champion du Monde 1981**.

350 "Nymphaea lotus"

1982. Flowers. Multicoloured.
900 170 f. Type **350** 75 35
901 180 f. "Bombax costatum" . . 80 35
902 200 f. "Parkia biglobosa" . . 85 40
903 220 f. "Gloriosa simplex" . . 1·10 45
904 270 f. "Satanocrater berhautii" 1·25 50

351 Lewis Carroll and Characters from "Alice" Books

1982. Air. 150th Birth Anniv of Lewis Carroll. (Revd. Charles Dodgson).
905 110 f. Type **351** 55 25
906 130 f. Characters from "Alice" books 60 30
907 140 f. Characters from "Alice" books (different) 75 30

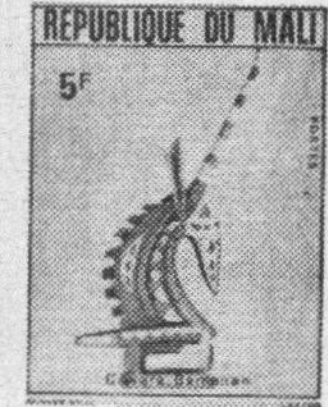

352 "George Washington" (Gilbert Stuart) **353** Ciwara Bamanan

1982. Air. 250th Birth Anniv of George Washington.
908 **352** 700 f. multicoloured . . . 2·00 1·25

1982. Masks. Multicoloured.
909 5 f. Type **353** 10 10
910 35 f. Kanga Dogon 15 10
911 180 f. N Domo Bamanan . . 1·00 40
912 200 f. Cimier (Sogoninkum Bamanan . . . . 1·00 40
913 250 f. Kpelie Senoufo . . . . 1·10 45

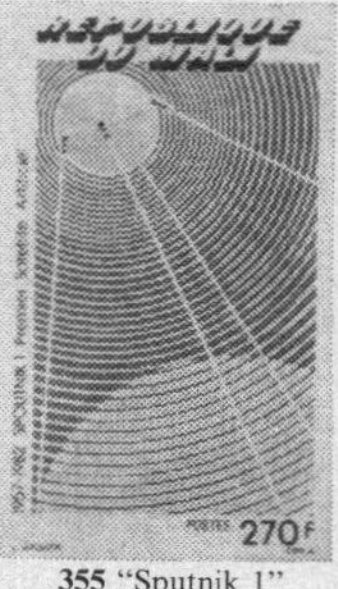

354 Football **355** "Sputnik 1"

1982. Air. World Cup Football Championship, Spain.
914 **354** 220 f. multicoloured . . . 80 45
915 – 420 f. multicoloured . . . 1·50 90
916 – 500 f. multicoloured . . . 1·75 90
DESIGNS: 420 f., 500 f. Football scenes.

1982. 25th Anniv of First Artificial Satellite.
918 **355** 270 f. violet, blue and red 1·25 50

356 Lord Baden-Powell, Tent and Scout Badge

1982. Air. 125th Birth Anniv of Lord Baden-Powell.
919 300 f. Type **356** . . . . 1·50 50
920 500 f. Saluting scout . . . . . 2·25 90

357 "The Transfiguration" (Fra Angelico)

1982. Air. Easter. Multicoloured.
921 680 f. Type **357** . . . . 2·00 1·25
922 1000 f. "Pieta" (Giovanni Bellini) 3·00 1·90

358 Doctor giving Child Oral Vaccine   **360** "En Bon Ami" (N'Teri)

359 Lions Emblem and Blind Person

1982. Anti-Polio Campaign.
923 **358** 180 f. multicoloured 80 35

1982. Lions Club Blind Day.
924 **359** 260 f. orange, blue and red 1·25 50

1982. Hairstyles. Multicoloured.
925 140 f. Type **360** 35 30
926 150 f. Tucked-in pony tail . . 60 35
927 160 f. "Pour l'Art" 70 45
928 180 f. "Bozo Kun" 75 50
929 270 f. "Fulaw Kun" . . . . . 1·25 60

361 Arms Stamp of Mali and France

1982. Air. "Philexfrance 82" International Stamp Exhibition, Paris. Multicoloured.
930 180 f. Type **361** 60 35
931 200 f. Dromedary caravan and 1979 "Philexafrique II" stamp 1·00 70

362 Fire-engine, 1850

1982. Fire-engines. Multicoloured.
932 180 f. Type **362** 85 35
933 200 f. Fire-engine, 1921 . . . 1·25 40
934 270 f. Fire-engine, 1982 . . . 1·50 50

HAVE YOU READ THE NOTES AT THE BEGINNING OF THIS CATALOGUE?
These often provide the answers to the enquiries we receive.

363 Gobra

1982. Zebu. Cattle. Multicoloured.
935 10 f. Type **363** 10 10
936 60 f. Azaouak 25 15
937 110 f. Maure 35 25
938 180 f. Toronke 65 35
939 200 f. Peul Sambourou . . . 75 40

1982. Air. World Cup Football Championship Winners. Nos. 914/16 optd.
940 **354** 220 f. multicoloured . . . 75 45
941 – 420 f. multicoloured . . . 1·50 90
942 – 500 f. multicoloured . . . 1·75 90
OPTS: 220 f. **1 ITALIE 2 RFA 3 POLOGNE**; 420 f. **POLOGNE FRANCE 3-2**; 500 f. **ITALIE RFA 3-1**.

365 "Urchin with Cherries"

1982. Air. 150th Birth Anniv of Edouard Manet (painter).
944 **365** 680 f. multicoloured . . . 2·50 1·25

366 "Virgin and Child" (detail) (Titian)   **367** Wind-surfing

1982. Air. Christmas. Multicoloured.
945 500 f. Type **366** . . . . 1·50 90
946 1000 f. "Virgin and Child" (Giovanni Bellini) . . . 2·75 1·90

1982. Introduction of Wind-surfing as Olympic Event. Multicoloured.
947 200 f. Type **367** 80 45
948 270 f. Wind-surfer . . . . . 1·25 55
949 300 f. Wind-surfer (different) 1·40 55

368 Goethe

1982. Air. 150th Death Anniv of Goethe (poet).
950 **368** 500 f. brown, light brown and black . . . . . . 1·75 90

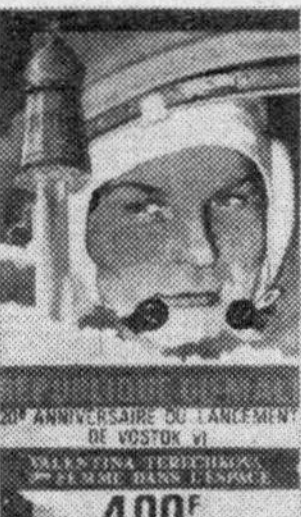

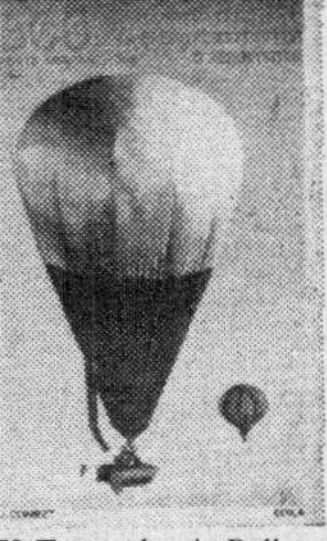

369 Valentina Tereshkova   **370** Transatlantic Balloon "Double Eagle II"

1983. Air. 20th Anniv of Launching of Vostok VI.
951 **369** 400 f. multicoloured . . . 1·25 75

1983. Air. Bicentenary of Manned Flight. Mult.
952 500 f. Type **370** . . . . 2·00 90
953 700 f. Montgolfier balloon . . 2·50 1·25

371 Football

1983. Air. Olympic Games, Los Angeles. Mult.
954 180 f. Type **371** 50 30
955 270 f. Hurdles 75 40
956 300 f. Windsurfing . . . . . . 1·10 55

372 "The Transfiguration" (detail)   **373** Martin Luther King

1983. Air. Easter. Multicoloured.
957 400 f. Type **372** . . . . 1·25 75
958 600 f. "The Entombment" (detail from Baglioni Retable) . . . 2·00 1·10

1983. Celebrities.
959 **373** 800 f. brown, blue & pur 2·50 1·40
960 – 800 f. brown, red & dp red 2·50 1·40
DESIGN: No. 960, President Kennedy.

374 Oua Hairstyle   **375** "Family of Acrobats with Monkey"

1983. Hairstyles. Multicoloured.
961 180 f. Type **374** 60 30
962 200 f. Nation (Diamani) . . . 70 30
963 270 f. Rond Point 90 40
964 300 f. Naamu-Naamu . . . . 1·00 45
965 500 f. Bamba-Bamba . . . . . 2·50 1·40

1983. Air. 10th Death Anniv of Picasso.
966 **375** 680 f. multicoloured . . . 2·00 1·25

376 Lions Club Emblem and Lions

1983. Air. Lions and Rotary Clubs. Mult.
967 700 f. Type **376** . . . . 2·25 2·00
968 700 f. Rotary Club emblem, container ship, diesel railcar and Boeing 737 airliner . . . 4·50 2·50

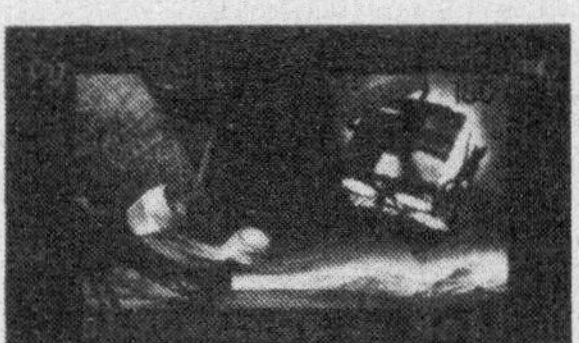

377 Satellite, Antenna and Telephone

1983. World Communications Year.
969 **377** 180 f. multicoloured . . . 55 30

378 Lavoisier and Apparatus   **379** Banzoumana Sissoko

1983. Bicent. of Lavoisier's Analysis of Water.
970 **378** 300 f. green, brown & blue 1·10 50

1983. Mali Musicians. Multicoloured.
971 200 f. Type **379** 75 30
972 300 f. Batourou Sekou Kouyate 1·25 45

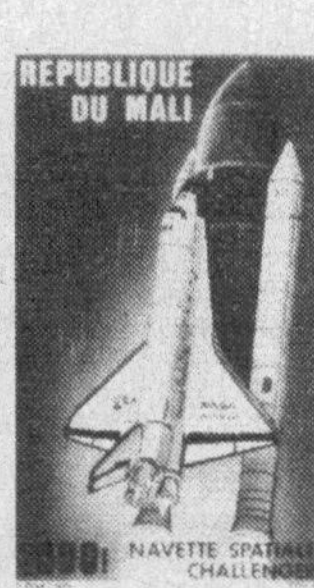

380 Nicephore Niepce and Camera   **381** Space Shuttle "Challenger"

1983. 150th Death Anniv of Nicephore Niepce (pioneer of photography).
973 **380** 400 f. blue, green & dp grn 1·40 65

1983. Air. Space Shuttle.
974 **381** 1000 f. multicoloured . . 3·00 1·75

382 Young People and Map of Africa

1983. 2nd Panafrican Youth Festival. Mult.
975 240 f. Type **382** 75 40
976 270 f. Hands reaching for map of Africa 75 40

383 Mercedes, 1914

1983. Air. Paris–Dakar Rally. Multicoloured.
977 240 f. Type **383** . . . . 1·25 40
978 270 f. Mercedes SSK, 1929 . . 1·25 50
979 500 f. Mercedes W 196, 1954 2·25 80

384 Liner and U.P.U. Emblem   **385** Pawn and Bishop

1983. U.P.U. Day.
981 **384** 240 f. red, black and blue 1·25 50

1983. Air. Chess Pieces.
982 **385** 300 f. grey, violet and green 1·60 60
983 – 420 f. green, pink and grey 2·00 85
984 – 500 f. blue, dp blue & green 2·75 1·00
DESIGNS: 420 f. Rook and knight; 500 f. King and queen.

386 "Canigiani Madonna"

1983. Air. Christmas. 500th Birth Anniv of Raphael. Multicoloured.

986 700 f. Type **386** . . . . . 2·00 1·00
987 800 f. "Madonna of the Lamb" 2·25 1·25

387 Sahara Goat

1984. Goats. Multicoloured.

988 20 f. Type **387** 15 10
989 30 f. Billy goat 20 10
990 50 f. Billy goat (different) . . 25 15
991 240 f. Kaarta goat . . . . . . 1·00 40
992 350 f. Southern goat . . . . . 1·40 75

388 "Leopold Zborowski" (Modigliani)
389 Henri Dunant (founder of Red Cross)

1984. Air. Birth Centenary of Modigliani (painter).

993 **388** 700 f. multicoloured . . . 2·50 1·25

1984. Air. Celebrities.

994 **389** 400 f. dp blue, red & blue 1·50 65
995 – 540 f. dp blue, red & blue 1·60 85
DESIGN: 540 f. Abraham Lincoln.

390 Sidney Bechet

1984. Air. Jazz Musicians. Multicoloured.

996 470 f. Type **390** . . . . 2·25 75
997 500 f. Duke Ellington . . . . 2·25 80

391 Microlight Aircraft

1984. Air. Microlight Aircraft. Multicoloured.

998 270 f. Type **391** . . . . . . 1·00 40
999 350 f. Lazor Gemini motorized hang-glider . . . . 1·25 55

392 Weightlifting

1984. Air. Olympic Games, Los Angeles. Multicoloured.

1000 265 f. Type **392** 75 40
1001 440 f. Show jumping 90 70
1002 500 f. Hurdles . . . . 1·10 80

393 "Crucifixion" (Rubens)

1984. Air. Easter.

1004 **393** 940 f. brown & dp brown 3·00 1·50
1005 – 970 f. brown and red . . 3·00 1·50
DESIGN—HORIZ: 970 f. "The Resurrection" (Mantegna).

1984. Currency revaluation. Various stamps surch. (i) U.P.U. Day (No. 981).

1006 **384** 120 f. on 240 f. red, black and blue (postage) . . 1·10 50

(ii) Goats (Nos. 988/92)

1007 **387** 10 f. on 20 f. mult . . . 10 10
1008 – 15 f. on 30 f. mult . . . 15 10
1009 – 25 f. on 50 f. mult . . . 20 15
1010 – 125 f. on 240 f. mult . . 95 40
1011 – 175 f. on 350 f. mult . . 1·75 65

(iii) Paris–Dakar Rally (No. 977)

1012 **383** 120 f. on 240 f. mult (air) 1·10 40

395 Mercedes "Simplex"

1984. Air. 150th Birth Anniv of Gottlieb Daimler (motor car designer).

1035 **395** 350 f. olive, blue and mauve 2·25 1·10
1036 – 470 f. green, violet and plum . . . . 3·00 1·50
1037 – 485 f. blue, violet and plum 3·25 1·75
DESIGNS: 470 f. Mercedes-Benz Type "370 S"; 485 f. Mercedes-Benz "500 S EC".

396 Farm Workers

1984. Progress in Countryside and Protected Essences. Multicoloured.

1038 5 f. Type **396** 10 10
1039 90 f. Carpentry 60 30
1040 100 f. Tapestry making . . . 70 35
1041 135 f. Metal work 80 40
1042 515 f. "Borassus flabelifer" 3·25 1·90
1043 1225 f. "Vitelaria paradoxa" 7·50 3·75

397 Emblem and Child

1984. United Nations Children's Fund.

1044 **397** 120 f. red, brown and green 80 40
1045 – 135 f. red, blue and brown 90 50
DESIGN: 135 f. Emblem and two children.

398 U.P.U. Emblem, Anchor and Hamburg

1984. Universal Postal Union Congress, Hamburg.

1046 **398** 135 f. mauve, green and blue 80 40

1984. Air. Olympic Winners, Los Angeles. No. 1000/1002 optd.

1047 135 f. on 265 f. Optd **HALTERES 56 KGS / 1. WU (CHINE). 2. LAI (CHINE). 3. KOTAKA (JAPON)** . . 80 40
1048 220 f. on 440 f. Optd **DRESSAGE / PAR EQUIPES / 1. RFA 2. SUISSE / 3. SUEDE** . . . 1·10 75
1049 250 f. on 500 f. Optd **ATHLETISME 3000 METRES STEEPLE / 1. KORIR (KENYA). / 2. MAHMOUD (FRANCE). / 3. DIEMER (E-U).** . . . . 1·40 1·00

400 Emblem

1984. 10th Anniv of Economic Community of West Africa.

1051 **400** 350 f. multicoloured . . . 1·75 1·10

401 Dimetrodon

1984. Prehistoric Animals. Multicoloured.

1052 10 f. Type **401** 15 15
1053 25 f. Iguanodon (vert) 25 15
1054 30 f. Archaeopteryx (vert) . . 45 30
1055 120 f. Type **401** . . . . . . 1·50 45
1056 175 f. As No. 1053 . . . . . 1·75 70
1057 350 f. As No. 1054 . . . . . 3·50 2·50
1058 470 f. Triceratops . . . . . . 5·00 2·50

402 "Virgin and Child between St. Joseph and St. Jerome" (detail, Lorenzo Lotto)

1984. Air. Christmas.

1059 **402** 500 f. multicoloured . . . 3·00 1·60

1984. Drought Aid. No. 758 surch.

1060 **403** 470 f. on 130 f. mult . . 2·75 1·75

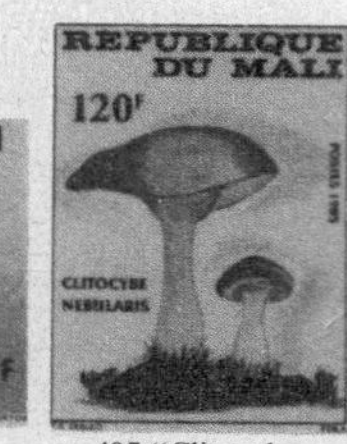

404 Horse Galloping
405 "Clitocybe nebularis"

1985. Horses. Multicoloured.

1061 90 f. Type **404** 70 35
1062 135 f. Beledougou horse . . . 1·25 40
1063 190 f. Nara horse . . . . . . 1·50 70
1064 530 f. Trait horse . . . . . . 4·50 2·00

1985. Fungi. Multicoloured.

1065 120 f. Type **405** . . . . . . 1·50 55
1066 200 f. "Lepiota cortinarius" 2·00 85
1067 485 f. "Agaricus semotus" . . 5·00 2·00
1068 525 f. "Lepiota procera" . . 5·25 2·25

406 Emile Marchoux and Marchoux Institute

1985. Health. Multicoloured.

1069 120 f. Type **406** (World Lepers' Day and 40th anniv of Marchoux Institute) (postage) 80 30
1070 135 f. Lions' emblem and Samanto Village (15th anniv) 85 35
1071 470 f. Laboratory technicians and polio victim (anti-polio campaign) (air) . . . . . 3·50 1·50

407 Profiles and Emblem

1985. 15th Anniv of Technical and Cultural Co-operation Agency.

1072 **407** 540 f. green and brown 3·50 1·90

408 Common Kingfisher

1985. Air. Birth Bicentenary of John J. Audubon (ornithologist). Multicoloured.

1073 180 f. Type **408** . . . . . . 1·40 75
1074 300 f. Great bustard (vert) . 2·25 1·25
1075 470 f. Ostrich (vert) . . . . 3·50 2·00
1076 540 f. Ruppell's griffon . . . 3·75 2·50

409 National Pioneers Movement Emblem

1985. International Youth Year. Multicoloured.

1077 120 f. Type **409** 80 40
1078 190 f. Boy leading oxen . . . 1·40 70
1079 500 f. Sports motifs and I.Y.Y. emblem . . . . 3·50 1·75

410 Sud Aviation Caravelle, Boeing 727-200 and Agency Emblem

1985. Air. 25th Anniv of Aerial Navigation Security Agency for Africa and Madagascar (ASECNA).

1080 **410** 700 f. multicoloured . . 4·50 2·50

411 Lion, and Scouts collecting Wood

1985. Air. "Philexafrique" Stamp Exhibition, Lome. Multicoloured.

1081 200 f. Type **411** . . . . . . 1·50 1·25
1082 200 f. Satellite, dish aerial and globe . . . . 1·50 1·25

412 U.P.U. Emblem, Computer and Reservoir (Development)

1985. "Philexafrique" Stamp Exhibition, Lome, Togo (2nd issue). Multicoloured.
1083 250 f. Type **412** . . . . 1·75 1·25
1084 250 f. Satellite, girls writing and children learning from television (Youth) . . . . 1·75 1·25

413 Grey Cat

1986. Cats. Multicoloured.
1085 150 f. Type **413** . . . . . . 1·50 60
1086 200 f. White cat . . . . . . 2·25 80
1087 300 f. Tabby cat . . . . . . 2·50 1·10

414 Hands releasing Doves and Globe

1986. Anti-apartheid Campaign. Multicoloured.
1088 100 f. Type **414** 65 40
1089 120 f. People breaking chain around world 85 50

415 Comet and Diagram of Orbit

1986. Air. Appearance of Halley's Comet.
1090 **415** 300 f. multicoloured . . 2·25 1·25

416 Internal Combustion Engine

1986. Air. Centenaries of First Motor Car with Internal Combustion Engine and Statue of Liberty. Multicoloured.
1091 400 f. Type **416** . . . . . . 3·00 1·50
1092 600 f. Head of statue, and French and American flags 4·00 2·25

417 Robeson

1986. Air. 10th Death Anniv of Paul Robeson (singer).
1093 **417** 500 f. multicoloured . . 4·00 2·00

418 Women tending Crop

1986. World Communications Day.
1094 **418** 200 f. multicoloured . . 1·50 80

419 Players

1986. World Cup Football Championship, Mexico. Multicoloured.
1095 160 f. Type **419** . . . . . . 1·40 65
1096 225 f. Player capturing ball 1·90 90

420 Watt

1986. 250th Birth Anniv of James Watt (inventor).
1098 **420** 110 f. multicoloured . . 85 45

421 Eberth and Microscope **422** Chess Pieces on Board

1986. Air. 60th Death Anniv of Karl Eberth (discoverer of typhoid bacillus).
1099 **421** 550 f. multicoloured . . 4·00 1·90

1986. Air. World Chess Championship, London and Leningrad. Multicoloured.
1100 400 f. Type **422** . . . . . . 3·50 1·75
1101 500 f. Knight and board . . 4·50 2·25

1986. World Cup Winners. Nos. 1095/6 optd **ARGENTINE 3 R.F.A. 2.**
1102 160 f. multicoloured . . . . 1·25 85
1103 225 f. multicoloured . . . . 1·60 1·00

424 Head

1986. Endangered Animals. Giant Eland. Mult.
1105 5 f. Type **424** 10 10
1106 20 f. Standing by dead tree 25 10
1107 25 f. Stepping over fallen branch 25 10
1108 200 f. Mother and calf . . . 1·90 95

425 Mermoz and "Croix du Sud"

1986. Air. 50th Anniv of Disappearance of Jean Mermoz (aviator). Multicoloured.
1109 150 f. Type **425** . . . . . . 1·25 60
1110 600 f. CAMS 53 flying boat and monoplane . . . . 4·25 2·25
1111 625 f. Map and seaplane "Comte de la Vaulx" . . . 4·50 2·50

1986. 10th Anniv of Concorde's First Commercial Flight. Nos. 674/6 surch **1986–10e Anniversaire du 1er Vol Commercial Supersonique**.
1112 175 f. on 120 f. Type **271** . . 1·40 80
1113 225 f. on 130 f. Concorde and Wright Flyer I 1·75 1·00
1114 300 f. on 200 f. Concorde and Lindbergh's "Spirit of St. Louis" . . . . 2·75 1·50

427 Hansen and Follereau

1987. Air. 75th Death Anniv of Gerhard Hansen (discoverer of bacillus) and 10th Death Anniv of Raoul Follereau (leprosy pioneer).
1115 **427** 500 f. multicoloured . . 3·50 1·90

428 Model "A", 1903

1987. 40th Death Anniv of Henry Ford (motor car manufacturer). Multicoloured.
1116 150 f. Type **428** . . . . 1·25 55
1117 200 f. Model "T", 1923 . . . 1·75 75
1118 225 f. "Thunderbird", 1968 1·75 95
1119 300 f. "Continental", 1963 . . 2·00 1·25

429 Konrad Adenauer **431** Scenes from "The Jazz Singer"

430 Runners and Buddha's Head

1987. Air. 20th Death Anniv of Konrad Adenauer (German statesman).
1120 **429** 625 f. stone, brown and red 4·00 2·25

1987. Air. Olympic Games, Seoul (1988). (1st issue).
1121 **430** 400 f. black and brown 2·00 1·40
1122 – 500 f. dp green, grn & red 2·75 1·75
DESIGN: 500 f. Footballers.
See also Nos. 1133/4.

1987. Air. 60th Anniv of First Talking Picture.
1123 **431** 550 f. red, brn & dp brn 4·00 2·25

432 "Apis florea"

1987. Bees. Multicoloured.
1124 100 f. Type **432** 80 50
1125 150 f. "Apis dorsata" . . . . 1·40 70
1126 175 f. "Apis adonsonii" . . . 1·60 80
1127 200 f. "Apis mellifera" . . . 1·75 1·00

433 Map, Dove and Luthuli

1987. Air. 20th Death Anniv of Albert John Luthuli (Nobel Peace Prize winner).
1128 **433** 400 f. mauve, blue & brn 2·50 1·50

434 Profiles and Lions Emblem

1987. Air. Lions International and Rotary International. Multicoloured.
1129 500 f. Type **434** . . . . 3·00 1·75
1130 500 f. Clasped hands and Rotary emblem . . . . . . 3·00 1·75

435 Anniversary Emblem and Symbols of Activities

1988. 30th Anniv of Lions International in Mali.
1131 **435** 200 f. multicoloured . . 1·25 75

436 Emblem and Doctor examining Boy

1988. 40th Anniv of W.H.O.
1132 **436** 150 f. multicoloured . . 1·10 60

437 Coubertin and Ancient and Modern Athletes

1988. Air. Olympic Games, Seoul (2nd issue). 125th Birth Anniv of Pierre de Coubertin (founder of modern games). Multicoloured.
1133 240 f. Type **437** . . . . 1·10 90
1134 400 f. Stadium, Olympic rings and sports pictograms . . 1·90 1·40

438 "Harlequin"

1988. Air. 15th Death Anniv of Pablo Picasso (painter).
1135 **438** 600 f. multicoloured . . 4·00 2·25

439 Concorde and Globe

1988. Air. 15th Anniv of First North Atlantic Crossing by Concorde.
1136 **439** 500 f. multicoloured . . 3·75 2·00

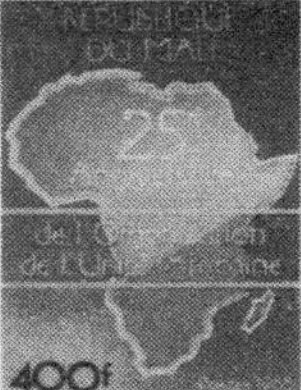

440 Pres. Kennedy **442** Map

1988. 25th Death Anniv of John Fitzgerald Kennedy (American President).
1137 **440** 640 f. multicoloured . . 4·00 2·40

1988. Mali Mission Hospital, Mopti. No. 1132 surch **MISSION MALI HOPITAL de MOPTI 300F** and **MEDECINS DU MONDE** emblem.
1138 **436** 300 f. on 150 f. mult 2·40 1·75

1988. 25th Anniv of Organization of African Unity.
1139 **442** 400 f. multicoloured . . 2·50 1·25

443 Map, Leaf and Stove

1989. Air. "Improved Stoves: For a Green Mali". Multicoloured.
1140 5 f. Type **443** 10 10
1141 10 f. Tree and stove 10 10
1142 25 f. Type **443** 15 10
1143 100 f. As No. 1141 60 35

444 Astronauts on Moon

1989. Air. 20th Anniv of First Manned Moon Landing.
1144 **444** 300 f. blue, purple & grn 2·00 1·25
1145 – 500 f. purple, blue & brn 3·25 1·75
DESIGN: 500 f. Astronauts on moon (diff).

445 Emblem and Crossed Syringes

1989. Vaccination Programme. Multicoloured.
1146 20 f. Type **445** 15 10
1147 30 f. Doctor vaccinating woman 20 10
1148 50 f. Emblem and syringes 40 15
1149 175 f. Doctor vaccinating child 1·40 65

446 Emblem

1989. 25th Anniv of International Law Institute of French-speaking Countries.
1150 **446** 150 f. multicoloured 1·10 55
1151 200 f. multicoloured 1·40 70

447 Crowd

448 U.P.U. Emblem and Hands holding Envelopes

1989. Air. Bicentenary of French Revolution and "Philexfrance 89" International Stamp Exn, Paris.
1152 **447** 400 f. red, blue & purple 2·50 1·25
1153 – 600 f. violet, pur & mve 3·50 2·00
DESIGN: 600 f. Marianne and Storming of Bastille.

1989. World Post Day.
1154 **448** 625 f. multicoloured 3·50 2·25

449 Pope and Cathedral

1990. Visit of Pope John Paul II.
1155 **449** 200 f. multicoloured 1·60 80

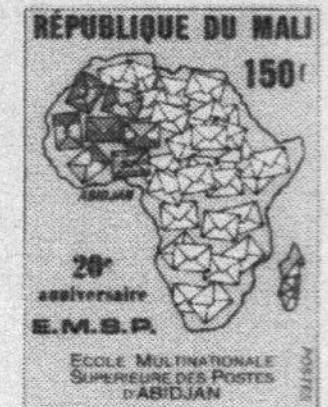

450 Envelopes on Map

1990. 20th Anniv of Multinational Postal Training School, Abidjan.
1156 **450** 150 f. multicoloured 1·25 55

451 Footballers

1990. Air. World Cup Football Championship, Italy. Multicoloured.
1157 200 f. Type **451** 1·50 75
1158 225 f. Footballers (different) 1·75 85

1990. World Cup Result. Nos. 1157/8 optd. Mult.
1160 200 f. **ITALIE : 2 / ANGLETERRE** : 1 1·50 85
1161 225 f. **R.F.A. : 1 / ARGENTINE** : 0 1·75 85

453 Pres. Moussa Traore and Bamako Bridge

1990. 30th Anniv of Independence.
1163 **453** 400 f. multicoloured 2·50 1·50

454 Man writing and Adults learning to Read

455 Woman carrying Water and Cattle at Well

1990. International Literacy Year.
1164 **454** 150 f. multicoloured 1·25 55
1165 200 f. multicoloured 1·50 75

1991. Lions Club (1166) and Rotary International (1167) Projects. Multicoloured.
1166 200 f. Type **455** (6th anniv of wells project) 1·40 75
1167 200 f. Bamako branch emblem and hand (30th anniv of anti-polio campaign) 1·40 75

456 Sonrai Dance, Takamba

457 Bank Emblem and Map of France

1991. Dances. Multicoloured.
1168 50 f. Type **456** 30 15
1169 100 f. Malinke dance, Mandiani 60 30
1170 150 f. Bamanan dance, Kono 90 50
1171 200 f. Dogon dance, Songho 1·10 75

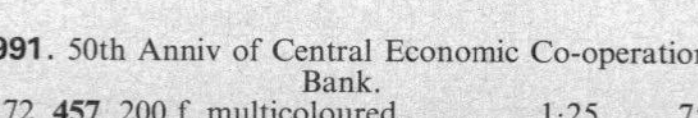

1991. 50th Anniv of Central Economic Co-operation Bank.
1172 **457** 200 f. multicoloured 1·25 75

458 Women with Torch and Banner

1992. National Women's Movement for the Safeguarding of Peace and National Unity.
1173 **458** 150 f. multicoloured 75 40

1992. Various stamps surch.
1174 – 25 f. on 470 f. mult (No. 1058) (postage) 15 10
1175 **420** 30 f. on 110 f. mult 15 10
1176 – 50 f. on 300 f. mult (No. 1087) 25 15
1177 – 50 f. on 1225 f. mult (No. 1043) 25 15
1178 – 150 f. on 135 f. mult (No. 1070) 75 40
1179 – 150 f. on 190 f. mult (No. 1063) 75 40
1180 – 150 f. on 190 f. mult (No. 1078) 75 40
1181 **400** 150 f. on 350 f. mult 75 40
1182 – 150 f. on 485 f. mult (No. 1067) 75 40
1183 – 150 f. on 525 f. mult (No. 1068) 75 40
1184 – 150 f. on 530 f. mult (No. 1064) 75 40
1185 **440** 200 f. on 640 f. mult 1·00 50
1186 – 240 f. on 350 f. mult (No. 1057) 1·25 65
1187 **448** 240 f. on 625 f. mult 1·25 65
1188 **410** 20 f. on 700 f. mult (air) 10 10
1189 **415** 20 f. on 300 f. mult 10 10
1190 – 25 f. on 470 f. mult (No. 1071) 15 10
1191 **408** 30 f. on 180 f. mult 15 10
1192 – 30 f. on 500 f. purple, blue and brown (No. 1145) 15 10
1193 – 100 f. on 540 f. mult (No. 1076) 50 25
1194 **438** 100 f. on 600 f. mult 50 25
1195 **444** 150 f. on 300 f. blue, purple and green 75 40
1196 **447** 150 f. on 400 f. red, blue and purple 75 40
1197 – 200 f. on 300 f. mult (No. 1074) 1·00 50
1198 – 240 f. on 600 f. violet, purple & mve (No. 1153) 1·25 65

1992. (a) Postage. No. 1095 surch **150 f "Euro 92"**.
1199 **419** 150 f. on 160 f. mult 75 40

(b) Air. No. 1134 surch **150F "Barcelone 92"**.
1200 150 f. on 400 f. multicoloured 75 40

OFFICIAL STAMPS

O **9** Dogon Mask

O **30** Mail Flag and Emblems

1961.
O26 O **9** 1 f. violet 10 10
O27 2 f. red 10 10
O28 3 f. slate 10 10
O29 5 f. turquoise 15 15
O30 10 f. brown 20 15
O31 25 f. blue 35 15
O32 30 f. red 40 20
O33 50 f. myrtle 70 25
O34 85 f. purple 1·10 65
O35 100 f. green 1·40 65
O36 200 f. purple 2·75 1·40

1964. Centre and flag multicoloured; frame colour given.
O 90 O **30** 1 f. green 10 10
O 91 2 f. lavender 10 10
O 92 3 f. slate 10 10
O 93 5 f. purple 10 10
O 94 10 f. blue 15 10
O 95 25 f. ochre 20 15
O 96 30 f. green 25 15
O 97 50 f. orange 35 15
O 98 85 f. brown 50 20
O 99 100 f. red 65 30
O100 200 f. blue 1·50 60

O **341** Arms of Gao

1981. Town Arms. Multicoloured.
O878 5 f. Type O **341** 10 10
O879 15 f. Tombouctou 10 10
O880 50 f. Mopti 20 10
O881 180 f. Segou 60 30
O882 200 f. Sikasso 80 30
O883 680 f. Koulikoro 2·50 95
O884 700 f. Kayes 2·75 1·25
O885 1000 f. Bamako 4·00 1·50

1984. Nos. O878/85 surch.
O1013 15 f. on 5 f. Type O **341** 15 10
O1014 50 f. on 15 f. Tombouctou 30 15
O1015 120 f. on 50 f. Mopti 70 25
O1016 295 f. on 180 f. Segou 2·00 90
O1017 470 f. on 200 f. Sikasso 3·00 1·50
O1018 515 f. on 680 f. Koulikoro 3·50 1·90
O1019 845 f. on 700 f. Kayes 6·00 2·50
O1020 1225 f. on 1000 f. Bamako 7·50 3·75

POSTAGE DUE STAMPS

D **9** Bambara Mask

1961.
D26 D **9** 1 f. black 10 10
D27 2 f. blue 10 10
D28 5 f. mauve 20 10
D29 10 f. orange 25 15
D30 20 f. turquoise 50 25
D31 25 f. purple 65 30

D **28** "Polyptychus roseus"

1964. Butterflies and Moths. Multicoloured.
D83 1 f. Type D **28** 10 10
D84 1 f. "Deilephila nerii" 10 10
D85 2 f. "Bunaea alcinoe" 15 15
D86 2 f. "Gynanisa maja" 15 15
D87 3 f. "Teracolus eris" 35 30
D88 3 f. "Colotis antevippe" 35 30
D89 5 f. "Manatha microcera" 35 30
D90 5 f. "Charaxes epijasius" 35 30
D91 10 f. "Hypokopelates otraeda" 45 35
D92 10 f. "Lipaphnaeus leonina" 45 35
D93 20 f. "Lobobunaea christyi" 75 70
D94 20 f. "Gonimbrasia hecate" 75 70
D95 25 f. "Hypolimnas misippus" 1·10 90
D96 25 f. "Castopsilia florella" 1·10 90

1984. Nos. D83/96 surch.
D1021 5 f. on 1 f. Type D **28** 10 10
D1022 5 f. on 1 f. "Deilephila nerii" 10 10
D1023 10 f. on 2 f. "Bunaea alcinoe" 10 10
D1024 10 f. on 2 f. "Gynanisa maja" 10 10
D1025 15 f. on 3 f. "Teracolus eris" 15 10
D1026 15 f. on 3 f. "Colotis antevippe" 15 10
D1027 25 f. on 5 f. "Manatha microcera" 15 15
D1028 25 f. on 5 f. "Charaxes epijasius" 15 15
D1029 50 f. on 10 f. "Hypokopelates otraeda" 30 30
D1030 50 f. on 10 f. "Lipaphnaeus leonina" 30 30
D1031 100 f. on 20 f. "Lobobunaea christyi" 60 60
D1032 100 f. on 20 f. "Gonimbrasia hecate" 60 60
D1033 125 f. on 25 f. "Hypolimnas misippus" 75 75
D1034 125 f. on 25 f. "Catopsilia florella" 75 75

MANAMA Pt. 19

A dependency of Ajman.

100 dirhams = 1 riyal

1966. Nos. 10, 12, 14 and 18 of Ajman surch. Manama in English and Arabic and new value.

1	40 d. on 40 n.p. multicoloured	40	25
2	70 d. on 70 n.p. multicoloured	40	25
3	1 r. 50 on 1 r. 50 multicoloured	1·25	75
4	10 r. on 10 r. multicoloured	6·00	6·00

1967. Nos. 140/8 of Ajman optd. **MANAMA** in English and Arabic. (a) Postage.

5	15 d. blue and brown	10	10
6	30 d. brown and black	15	10
7	50 d. black and brown	35	20
8	70 d. violet and black	60	30
	(b) Air.		
9	1 r. green and brown	60	40
10	2 r. mauve and black	1·40	90
11	3 r. black and brown	2·00	1·75
12	5 r. brown and black	3·50	3·50
13	10 r. blue and brown	6·50	6·50

APPENDIX

The following stamps have either been issued in excess of postal needs or have not been available to the public in reasonable quantities at face value. Such stamps may later be given full listing if there is evidence of regular postal use.

1966.

New Currency Surcharges. Stamps of Ajman surch. **Manama** in English and Arabic and new value.

(a) Nos. 19/20 and 22/4 (Kennedy). 10 d. on 10 n.p., 15 d. on 15 n.p., 1 r. on 1 r., 2 r. on 2 r., 3 r. on 3 r.

(b) Nos. 27, 30 and 35/6 (Olympics). 5 d. on 5 n.p., 25 d. on 25 n.p., 3 r. on 3 r., 5 r. on 5 r.

(c) Nos. 70/2 and 75 (Churchill). 50 d. on 50 n.p., 75 d. on 75 n.p., 1 r. on 1 r., 5 r. on 5 r.

(d) Nos. 85/8 (Space). Air 50 d. on 50 n.p., 1 r. on 1 r., 3 r. on 3 r., 5 r. on 5 r.

1967.

World Scout Jamboree, Idaho. Postage 30, 70 d., 1 r.; Air 2, 3, 4 r.

Olympic Games, Mexico (1968). Postage 35, 65, 75 d., 1 r.; Air 1 r. 25, 2, 3, 4 r.

Winter Olympic Games, Grenoble (1968). Postage 5, 35, 60, 75 d.; Air 1, 1 r. 25, 2, 3 r.

Paintings by Renoir and Terbrugghen. Air 35, 65 d., 1, 2 r.×3.

1968.

Paintings by Velazquez. Air 1 r.×2, 2 r.×2.

Costumes. Air 30 d.×2, 70 d.×2, 1 r.×2, 2 r.×2.

Olympic Games, Mexico. Postage 1 r.×4; Air 2 x 4 r.

Satellites and Spacecraft. Air 30 d.×2, 70 d.×2, 1 r.×2, 2 r.×2, 3 r.×2.

Human Rights Year. Kennedy Brothers and Martin Luther King. Air 1 r.×3, 2 r.×3.

Sports Champions, Famous Footballers. Postage 15, 20, 50, 75 d., 1 r.; Air 10 r.

Heroes of Humanity. Circular designs on gold or silver foil. 60 d.×12.

Olympic Games, Mexico. Circular designs on gold or silver foil. Air 3 r.×8.

Mothers' Day. Paintings. Postage 1 r.×6.

Kennedy Brothers Commem. Postage 2 r.; Air 5 r.

Cats. (1st series). Postage 1, 2, 3 d.; Air 2, 3 r.

5th Death Anniv of Pres. Kennedy. Air 10 r.

Space Exploration. Postage 5, 10, 15, 20, 25 d.; Air 15 r.

Olympic Games, Mexico. Gold Medals. Postage 2 r.×4; Air 5 r.×4.

Christmas. Air 5 r.

1969.

Sports Champions. Cyclists. Postage 1, 2, 5, 10, 15, 20 d.; Air 12 r.

Sports Champions. German Footballers. Postage 5, 10, 15, 20, 25 d.; Air 10 r.

Sports Champions. Motor-racing Drivers. Postage 1, 5, 10, 15, 25 d.; Air 10 r.

Motor-racing Cars. Postage 1, 5, 10, 15, 25 d.; Air 10 r.

Sports Champions. Boxers. Postage 5, 10, 15, 20 d.; Air 10 r.

Sports Champions. Baseball Players. Postage 1, 2, 5, 10, 15 d.; Air 10 r.

Birds. Air 1 r.×11.

Roses. 1 r.×6.

Animals. Air 1 r.×6.

Paintings by Italian Artists. 5, 10, 15, 20 d., 10 r.

Great Composers. Air 5, 10, 25 d., 10 r.

Paintings by French Artists. 1 r.×4.

Nude Paintings. Air 2 r.×4.

Kennedy Brothers. Air 2, 3, 10 r.

Olympic Games, Mexico. Gold Medal Winners. Postage 1, 2 d., 10 r.; Air 10 d., 5, 10 r.

Paintings of the Madonna. Postage 10 d.; Air 10 r.

Space Flight of "Apollo 9". Optd. on 1968 Exploration issue. Air 15 r.

Space Flight of "Apollo 10". Optd. on 1968 Space Exploration issue. Air 15 r.

1st Death Anniv of Gagarin. Optd. on 1968 Space Exploration issue. 5 d.

2nd Death Anniv of Edward White (astronaut). Optd. on 1968 Space Exploration issue. 10 d.

1st Death Anniv of Robert Kennedy. Optd. on 1969 Kennedy Brothers issue. Air 2 r.

Olympic Games, Munich (1972). Optd. on 1969 Mexico Gold Medal Winners issue. Air 10 d., 5, 10 r.

Moon Mission of "Apollo 11". Air 1, 2, 3 r.

Christmas. Paintings by Breughel. Postage 1, 2, 4, 5, 10 d.; Air 6 r.

1970.

"Soyuz" and "Apollo" Space Programmes. Postage 1, 2, 4, 5, 10 d.; Air 3, 5 r.

Kennedy and Eisenhower Commem. Embossed on gold foil. Air 20 r.

Lord Baden-Powell Commem. Embossed on gold foil. Air 20 r.

World Cup Football Championships, Mexico. Postage 20, 40, 60, 80 d., 1 r.; Air 3 r.

Brazil's Victory in World Cup Football Championships. Optd. on 1970 World Cup issue. Postage 20, 40, 60, 80 d., 1 r.; Air 3 r.

Paintings by Michelangelo. Postage 1, 2, 4, 5, 10 d.; Air 6 r.

World Fair "Expo 70", Osaka, Japan. Air 25, 50, 75 d., 1, 2, 3, 12 r.

Paintings by Renoir. Postage 1, 2, 5, 6, 10 d.; Air 5, 12 r.

Olympic Games, Rome, Tokyo, Mexico and Munich. Postage 15, 30, 50, 70 d.; Air 2, 5 r.

Winter Olympic Games, Sapporo (1972) (1st issue). Postage 2, 3, 4, 10 d.; Air 2, 5 r.

Christmas. Flower Paintings by Brueghel. Postage 5, 20, 25, 30, 50 d.; Air 60 d., 1, 2 r.

1971.

Winter Olympic Games, Sapporo (2nd issue). Postage 1, 2, 3, 4, 5, 6, 8, 10, 12, 15, 20, 25, 30, 35, 40, 50 d.; Air 75 d, 1, 2, 2 r. 50.

Roses. Postage 5, 20, 25, 30, 50 d.; Air 60 d., 1, 2 r.

Birds. Postage 5, 20, 25, 30, 50 d.; Air 60 d., 1, 2 r.

Paintings by Modigliani. Air 25, 50, 60, 75 d., 1 r. 50, 3 r.

Paintings by Rubens. Postage 1, 2, 3, 4, 5, 10 d.; Air 2, 3 r.

"Philatokyo '72" Stamp Exhibition, Paintings by Hokusai and Hiroshige. Postage 10, 15, 20, 25, 50, 75 d.; Air 1, 2 r.

25th Anniv of United Nations. Optd on 1970 Christmas issue. Postage 5, 20, 25, 30, 50 d.; Air 60 d., 1, 2 r.

British Military Uniforms. Postage 5, 20, 25, 30, 50 d.; Air 60 d., 1, 2 r.

Space Flight of "Apollo 14". Postage 15, 25, 50, 60, 70 d.; Air 5 r.

Space Flight of "Apollo 15". Postage 25, 40, 50, 60 d.; Air 1, 6 r.

13th World Scout Jamboree, Asagiri, Japan. (1st issue). Postage 1, 2, 3, 5, 7, 10, 12, 15, 20, 25, 30, 35, 40, 50, 65, 80 d.; Air 1, 1 r. 25, 1 r. 50, 2 r.

World Wild Life Conservation. Postage 1, 2, 3, 5, 7, 10, 12, 15, 20, 25, 30, 35, 40, 50, 65, 80 d.; Air 1 r., 1 r. 25, 1 r. 50, 2 r.

13th World Scout Jamboree, Asagiri, Japan. (2nd issue). Stamps Postage 10, 15, 20, 25, 50, 75 d.; Air 1, 2 r.

Winter Olympic Games, Sapporo (3rd issue). Postage 1, 2, 3, 4, 5, 10 d.; Air 2, 3 r.

Cats (2nd series). Postage 15, 25, 40, 60 d.; Air 3, 10 r.

Lions International Club. Optd. on 1971 Uniforms issue. Postage 2, 20, 25, 30, 50 d.; Air 60 d., 1, 2 r.

Paintings of Ships. Postage 15, 20, 25, 30, 50 d.; Air 60 d., 1, 2 r.

Great Olympic Champions. Postage 25, 50, 75 d. 1 r.; Air 5 r.

Prehistoric Animals. Postage 15, 20, 25, 30, 50, 60 d.; Air 1, 2 r.

Footballers. Postage 5, 10, 15, 20, 40 d.; Air 5 r.

Royal Visit of Queen Elizabeth II to Japan. Postage 10, 20, 30, 40, 50 d.; Air 2, 3 r.

Fairy Tales. Stories by Hans Andersen. Postage 1, 2, 4, 5, 10 d.; Air 3 r.

World Fair, Philadelphia (1976). American Paintings. Postage 20, 25, 50, 60, 75 d.; Air 3 r.

Fairy Tales. Well-known stories. Postage 1, 2, 4, 5, 10 d.; Air 3 r.

Space Flight of "Apollo 16". Postage 20, 30, 40, 50, 60 d.; Air 3, 4 r.

Tropical Fishes. Postage 1, 2, 3, 4, 5, 10 d.; Air 2, 3 r.

European Tour of Emperor Hirohito of Japan. Postage 1, 2, 4, 5, 10 d.; Air 6 r.

Meeting of Pres. Nixon and Emperor Hirohito of Japan in Alaska. Optd. on 1971 Emperor's Tour issue. Air 6 r.

2500th Anniv of Persian Empire. Postage 10, 20, 30, 40, 50 d.; Air 3 r.

Space Flight of "Apollo 15" and Future Developments in Space. Postage 10, 15, 20, 25, 50 d.; Air 1, 2 r.

1972.

150th Death Anniv (1971) of Napoleon. Postage 10, 20, 30, 40 d.; Air 1, 2, 3, 4 r.

1st Death Anniv of Gen. de Gaulle. Postage 10, 20, 30, 40 d.; Air 1, 2, 3, 4 r.

Paintings from the "Alte Pinakothek", Munich. Postage 5, 10, 15, 20, 25 d.; Air 5 r.

"Tour de France" Cycle Race. Postage 5, 10, 15, 20, 25, 30, 35, 40, 45, 50, 55, 60 d.; Air 65, 70, 75, 80, 85, 90, 95 d., 1 r.

Cats and Dogs. Postage 10, 20, 30, 40, 50 d.; Air 1 r.

25th Anniv of U.N.I.C.E.F. Optd. on 1971 World Scout Jamboree, Asagiri (2nd issue). Postage 10, 15, 20, 25, 50, 75 d.; Air 1, 2 r.

Past and Present Motorcars. Postage 10, 20, 30, 40, 50 d.; Air 1 r.

Military Uniforms. 1 r.×11.

The United Arab Emirates Ministry of Communications took over the Manama postal service on 1 August 1972. Further stamps inscribed "Manama" issued after that date were released without authority and had no validity.

MANCHUKUO Pt. 17

Issues for the Japanese puppet Government set up in 1932 under President (later Emperor) Pu Yi.

100 fen = 1 yuan

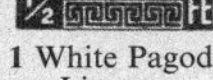

1 White Pagoda, Liaoyang

2 Pu Yi, later Emperor Kang-teh

1932. (a) With five characters in top panel as T **1** and **2**.

1	**1**	$\frac{1}{2}$ f. brown	75	25
2		1 f. lake	75	10
25		$1\frac{1}{2}$ f. mauve	1·50	75
4		2 f. slate	2·25	20
27		3 f. brown	2·50	10
6		4 f. olive	50	10
7		5 f. green	75	15
8		6 f. red	2·75	40
9		7 f. grey	1·25	20
10		8 f. brown	9·00	6·00
11		10 f. orange	1·50	15
12	**2**	13 f. brown	3·50	4·25
13		15 f. red	15·00	75
14		16 f. blue	12·00	2·25
15		20 f. brown	2·75	40
16		30 f. orange	3·25	1·25
17		50 f. green	3·75	70
31		1 y. violet	17·00	6·50
		(b) With six characters in top panel.		
40	**1**	$\frac{1}{2}$ f. sepia	25	10
41		1 f. lake	25	10
42		$1\frac{1}{2}$ f. mauve	60	40
43		3 f. brown	40	10
44		5 f. blue	8·50	60
45		5 f. slate	3·50	40
46		6 f. red	1·00	15
47		7 f. grey	1·25	40
48		9 f. orange	1·25	20
55		10 f. blue	4·25	10
56	**2**	13 f. brown	3·75	4·25
49		15 f. red	2·00	25
50		18 f. green	12·00	3·50
51		20 f. sepia	2·25	20
52		30 f. brown	3·35	35
53		50 f. olive	3·75	30
54		1 y. violet	10·00	3·50

3 Map and Flags **6** Emperor's Palace

1933. 1st Anniv of Republic.

19	**3**	1 f. orange	1·00	1·00
20	–	2 f. green	7·50	7·50
21	**3**	4 f. red	1·00	50
22	–	10 f. blue	11·00	11·00

DESIGN: 2, 10 f. Council Hall, Hsinking.

1934. Enthronement of Emperor.

32	**6**	$1\frac{1}{2}$ f. brown	1·00	40
33	–	3 f. red	1·00	20
34	**6**	6 f. green	4·25	3·75
35	–	10 f. blue	5·75	3·75

DESIGN: 3 f., 10 f. Phoenixes.

1934. Stamps of 1932 surch with four Japanese characters.

36	**1**	1 f. on 4 f. olive (No. 6)	3·50	2·25
38		3 f. on 4 f. olive (No. 6)	22·00	18·50
39	**2**	3 f. on 16 f. blue (No. 14)	6·50	6·50

In No. 38 the left hand upper character of the surcharge consists of three horizontal lines.

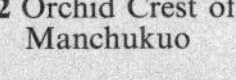

12 Orchid Crest of Manchukuo

13 Changpai Mountain and Sacred Lake

1935. China Mail.

64	**12**	2 f. green	45	15
65		$2\frac{1}{2}$ f. violet	35	15
66	**13**	4 f. green	1·00	30
67		5 f. blue	25	10
68	**12**	8 f. yellow	1·75	30
60	**13**	12 f. red	4·50	2·25
70		13 f. brown	50	15

15 Mt. Fuji

16 Phoenixes

1935. Visit of Emperor Kang-teh to Japan.

71	**15**	$1\frac{1}{2}$ f. green	1·00	80
72	**16**	3 f. orange	1·00	25
73	**15**	6 f. red	3·25	3·25
74	**16**	10 f. blue	3·25	2·50

17 Symbolic of Accord

19 State Council Building, Hsinking

20 Chengte Palace, Jehol

1936. Japan–Manchukuo Postal Agreement.

75	**17**	$1\frac{1}{2}$ f. sepia	1·75	1·50
76	–	3 f. mauve	1·50	25
77	**17**	6 f. red	6·50	6·50
78	–	10 f. blue	5·50	3·50

DESIGN—HORIZ: 3 f., 10 f. Department of Communications.

1936.

79	**19**	$\frac{1}{2}$ f. brown	25	15
80		1 f. red	25	10
81		$1\frac{1}{2}$ f. violet	2·50	2·00
82	A	2 f. green	20	10
83	**19**	3 f. brown	25	15
84	B	4 f. green	20	10
149	**19**	5 f. grey	10	1·00
86	A	6 f. red	75	10
87	B	7 f. black	1·00	10
88		9 f. red	75	20
89	**20**	10 f. blue	40	10
90	B	12 f. orange	25	10
91		13 f. brown	10·00	20·00
92		15 f. red	1·25	30
93	C	18 f. green	7·50	7·50
94		19 f. green	3·50	1·50
95	A	20 f. brown	1·50	35
96	**20**	30 f. brown	1·75	30
97	D	38 f. blue	6·50	6·00
98		39 f. blue	1·00	1·00
99	A	50 f. green	2·25	30
154	**20**	1 y. violet	45	2·75

DESIGNS: A, Carting soya-beans; B. Peiling Mausoleum; C, Airplane and grazing sheep (domestic and China air mail); D, Fokker F.VII b/3m airplane over R. Sungari bridge (air mail to Japan).

21 Sun rising over Fields

22 Shadowgraph of old and new Hsinking

1937. 5th Anniv of Founding of State.

101	**21**	$1\frac{1}{2}$ f. red	5·00	6·00
102	**22**	3 f. green	1·50	1·75

1937. China Mail. Surch in Chinese characters.

108	**12**	$2\frac{1}{2}$ f. on 2 f. green	2·75	2·00
110	**13**	5 f. on 4 f. green	2·75	2·50
111		13 f. on 12 f. brown	9·50	7·00

27 Pouter Pigeon and Hsinking

1937. Completion of Five Year Reconstruction Plan for Hsinking.

112	**27**	2 f. mauve	2·00	1·00
113	–	4 f. red	2·00	25
114	**27**	10 f. green	6·50	4·00
115	–	20 f. blue	7·50	5·00

DESIGN: 4, 20 f. Flag over Imperial Palace.

29 Manchukuo

30 Japanese Residents Assn. Building

1937. Japan's Relinquishment of Extra-territorial Rights.

116 **29** 2 f. red . . . . 1·00 25
117 **30** 4 f. green . . . . 2·75 75
118 8 f. orange . . . . 3·25 2·00
119 – 10 f. blue . . . . 2·75 50
120 – 12 f. violet . . . . 3·50 3·00
121 – 20 f. brown . . . . 4·75 2·75

DESIGNS—As Type **30**: 10, 20 f. Dept. of Communications Bldg. HORIZ: 12 f. Ministry of Justice.

32 "Twofold Happiness"

33 Red Cross on Map and Globe

1937. New Year's Greetings.

122 **32** 2 f. red and blue . . . . . 2·00 30

1938. Inaug of Manchukuo Red Cross Society.

123 **33** 2 f. red . . . . 1·00 1·25
124 4 f. green . . . . 1·00 25

34 Map of Railway Lines

35 "Asia" Express

1939. Completion of 10,000 Kilometres of Manchurian Railways.

125 **34** 2 f. blue and orange . . . 1·50 1·75
126 **35** 4 f. deep blue and blue . . 1·50 1·75

36 Manchurian Cranes over Shipmast

37 Census Official and Manchukuo

38 Census Slogans in Chinese and Mongolian

1940. 2nd Visit of Emperor Kang-teh to Japan.

127 **36** 2 f. purple . . . . 75 1·50
128 4 f. green . . . . 75 1·50

1940. National Census.

129 **37** 2 f. brown and yellow . . . 55 1·50
130 **38** 4 f. deep green and green . 55 1·50

39 Message of Congratulation

40 Dragon Dance

1940. 2600th Anniv of Founding of Japanese Empire.

131 **39** 2 f. red . . . . 15 1·50
132 **40** 4 f. blue . . . . 15 1·50

41 Recruit

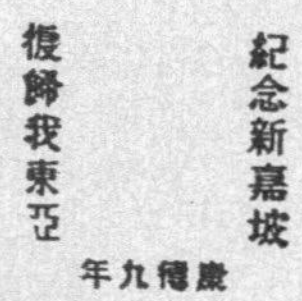
42

1941. Enactment of Conscription Law.

133 **41** 2 f. red . . . . 40 1·50
134 4 f. blue . . . . 55 1·50

1942. Fall of Singapore. Stamps of 1936 optd with T **42**.

135 A 2 f. green . . . . 85 2·00
136 B 4 f. olive . . . . 85 2·00

43 Kenkoku Shrine

44 Achievement of Fine Crops

45 Women of Five Races Dancing

46 Map of Manchukuo

1942. 10th Anniv of Founding of State.

137 **43** 2 f. red 15 75
138 **44** 3 f. orange . . . . 1·75 2·25
139 **43** 4 f. lilac 25 75
140 **45** 6 f. green . . . . 1·75 2·50
141 **46** 10 f. red on yellow . . . . 60 1·50
142 – 20 f. blue on yellow . . . 65 1·50

DESIGN—HORIZ: 20 f. Flag of Manchukuo.

1942. 1st Anniv of "Greater East Asia War". Stamps of 1936 optd with native characters above date **8.12.8**.

143 **19** 3 f. brown . . . . 75 1·75
144 A 6 f. red . . . . 75 1·75

1943. Labour Service Law Proclamation. Stamps of 1936 optd with native characters above heads of pick and shovel.

145 **19** 3 f. brown . . . . 75 1·75
146 A 6 f. red . . . . 75 1·75

49 Nurse and Stretcher

50 Furnace at Anshan Plant

1943. 5th Anniv of Manchukuo Red Cross Society.

147 **49** 6 f. green . . . . 50 2·50

1943. 2nd Anniv of "Greater East Asia War".

148 **50** 6 f. red . . . . 50 2·50

51 Chinese characters

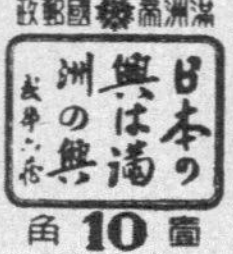
52 Japanese characters

53 "One Heart One Soul"

1944. Friendship with Japan. (a) Chinese characters

155 **51** 10 f. red 25 75
156 40 f. green . . . . 75 1·00

(b) Japanese characters.

157 **52** 10 f. red 25 75
158 40 f. green . . . . 75 1·00

1945. 10th Anniv of Emperor's Edict.

159 **53** 10 f. red . . . . 1·25 4·50

MARIANA ISLANDS Pt. 7

A group of Spanish Islands in the Pacific Ocean of which Guam was ceded to the U.S.A. and the others to Germany. The latter are now under U.S. Trusteeship.

100 pfennig = 1 mark

1899. German stamps optd **Marianen**.

7 **8** 3 pf. brown . . . . 12·00 32·00
8 5 pf. green . . . . 14·00 32·00
9 **9** 10 pf. red . . . . 18·00 38·00
10 20 pf. blue . . . . 22·00 £110
11 25 pf. orange . . . . . . 60·00 £160
12 50 pf. brown . . . . . . 60·00 £190

1901. "Yacht" key-type inscr "MARIANEN".

13 N 3 pf. brown 70 90
14 5 pf. green 70 90
15 10 pf. red . . . . 70 2·75
16 20 pf. blue . . . . 1·00 6·00
17 25 pf. black & red on yell 1·25 13·00
18 30 pf. black & orge on buff 1·25 13·00
19 40 pf. black and red . . . 1·25 13·00
20 50 pf. black & pur on buff 1·40 15·00
21 80 pf. black & red on rose 2·00 24·00
22 O 1 m. red . . . . 2·75 70·00
23 2 m. blue . . . . 4·50 90·00
24 3 m. black . . . . 6·50 £130
25 5 m. red and black £130 £500

MARIENWERDER Pt. 7

A district of E. Prussia where a plebiscite was held in 1920. As a result the district remained part of Germany. After the War of 1939-45 it was returned to Poland and reverted to its original name of Kwidzyn.

100 pfennig = 1 mark.

1

1920.

1 **1** 5 pf. green 25 25
2 10 pf. red 20 15
3 15 pf. grey 30 35
4 20 pf. brown 15 15
5 25 pf. blue 40 45
6 30 pf. orange 85 65
7 40 pf. brown 40 45
8 50 pf. violet 40 40
9 60 pf. brown . . . . 2·75 2·50
10 75 pf. brown 65 75
11 1 m. brown and green . . . 60 55
12 2 m. purple . . . . 4·50 2·40
13 3 m. red . . . . 4·00 3·25
14 5 m. blue and red . . . . . 24·00 17·00

1920. Stamps of Germany inscr "DEUTSCHES REICH" (a) optd **Commission Interalliee Marienwerder**.

15 **10** 5 pf. green . . . . 10·00 20·00
16 20 pf. blue . . . . 3·00 10·00
17 50 pf. black & pur on buff £300 £600
18 75 pf. black and green . . 2·00 5·00
19 80 pf. black and red on rose 60·00 £110
25 **12** 1 m. red . . . . 2·25 4·50
26 1 m. 25 green . . . . . . 2·50 5·00
27 1 m. 50 brown . . . . . . 3·25 7·00
28 **13** 2 m. 50 purple . . . . . . 2·25 4·50

(b) optd **Commission interalliee Marienwerder** and surch also.

21 **24** 1 m. on 2 pf. grey . . . . 20·00 35·00
22 2 m. on $2\frac{1}{2}$ pf. grey . . . 7·00 12·00
23 **10** 3 m. on 3 pf. brown . . . 7·50 14·00
24 **24** 5 m. on $7\frac{1}{2}$ pf. orange . . . 8·50 14·00

1920. As T **1**, with inscription at top changed to "PLEBISCITE".

29 5 pf. green . . . . 2·25 2·00
30 10 pf. red . . . . 2·25 2·00
31 15 pf. grey . . . . 8·50 10·00
32 20 pf. brown . . . . 1·25 1·50
33 25 pf. blue . . . . 11·00 11·00
34 30 pf. orange . . . . 1·00 80
35 40 pf. brown 70 50
36 50 pf. violet . . . . 1·40 1·00
37 60 pf. brown . . . . 4·00 3·75
38 75 pf. brown . . . . 5·00 5·00
39 1 m. brown and green . . . 75 60
40 2 m. purple 90 85
41 3 m. red . . . . 1·40 1·10
42 5 m. blue and red . . . . . 2·00 1·25

MARSHALL ISLANDS Pts 7, 22

A group of islands in the Pacific Ocean, a German protectorate from 1885. From 1920 to 1947 it was a Japanese mandated territory and from 1947 part of the United States Trust Territory of the Pacific Islands, using United States stamps. In 1984 it assumed control of its postal services.

A. GERMAN PROTECTORATE

100 pfennig = 1 mark.

1897. Stamps of Germany optd: (a) Optd **Marschall-Inseln.**

G1 **8** 3 pf. brown £120 £450
G2 5 pf. green £100 £400
G3 **9** 10 pf. red . . . . 30·00 £110
G4 20 pf. blue . . . . 30·00 £110

(b) Optd **Marshall-Inseln.**

G 5 **8** 3 pf. brown . . . . 3·00 5·00
G 6 5 pf. green . . . . 7·50 5·50
G 7 **9** 10 pf. red . . . . 10·00 14·00
G 8 20 pf. blue . . . . 13·00 23·00
G 9 25 pf. orange . . . . . . 17·00 40·00
G10 50 pf. brown . . . . . . 27·00 48·00

1901. "Yacht" key-type inscr "MARSHALL INSELN".

G11 N 3 pf. brown . . . . 60 1·00
G12 5 pf. green . . . . 60 1·10
G13 10 pf. red . . . . 60 4·00
G14 20 pf. blue . . . . 75 9·00
G15 25 pf. black & red on yell 80 15·00
G16 30 pf. blk & orge on buff 80 15·00
G17 40 pf. black and red . . . 80 15·00
G18 50 pf. blk & pur on buff 1·10 20·00
G19 80 pf. blk & red on rose 2·00 32·00
G20 O 1 m. red . . . . 3·25 75·00
G21 2 m. blue . . . . 4·50 £120
G22 3 m. black . . . . 7·00 £190
G23 5 m. red and black £110 £500

B. REPUBLIC

100 cents = 1 dollar

1 Canoe

1984. Inauguration of Postal Independence. Multicoloured.

1 20 c. Type **1** 55 30
2 20 c. Fishes and net 55 30
3 20 c. Navigational stick-chart . 55 30
4 20 c. Islet with coconut palms . 55 30

2 Mili Atoll

3 German Marshall Islands 1900 3 pf. Optd Stamp

1984. Maps. Multicoloured.

5 1 c. Type **2** 10 10
6 3 c. Likiep Atoll 10 10
7 5 c. Ebon Atoll 15 10
8 10 c. Jaluit Atoll 15 10
9 13 c. Ailinginae Atoll 25 15
10 14 c. Wotho Atoll 25 15
11 20 c. Kwajalein and Ebeye Atolls 40 20
12 22 c. Enewetak Atoll 40 20
13 28 c. Ailinglaplap Atoll . . . 65 35
14 30 c. Majuro Atoll 65 25
15 33 c. Namu Atoll 70 40
16 37 c. Rongelap Atoll 75 45
16a 39 c. Taka and Utirik Atolls 75 45
16b 44 c. Ujelang Atoll 85 50
16c 50 c. Aur and Maloclap Atolls 1·00 65
17 $1 Arno Atoll . . . . 2·25 75
18 $2 Wotje and Erikub Atolls . 4·00 2·50
19 $5 Bikini Atoll . . . . . . 10·00 8·00
20 $10 Mashallese stick chart (31 × 31 mm) . . . . . . 16·00 13·00

1984. 19th Universal Postal Union Congress Philatelic Salon, Hamburg.

21 **3** 40 c. brown, black & yellow 75 50
22 – 40 c. brown, black & yellow 75 50
23 – 40 c. blue, black and yellow 75 50
24 – 40 c. multicoloured 75 50

DESIGNS: No. 22, German Marshall Islands 1901 3 pf. "Yacht" stamp; 23, German Marshall Islands 1897 20 pf. stamp; 24, German Marshall Islands 1901 5 m. "Yacht" stamp.

4 Common Dolphin

1984. "Ausipex 84" International Stamp Exhibition, Melbourne. Dolphins. Multicoloured.

25 20 c. Type **4** 55 35
26 20 c. Risso's dolphin 55 35
27 20 c. Spotter dolphins 55 35
28 20 c. Bottle-nosed dolphin . . 55 35

5 Star over Bethlehem and Text

6 Traditional Chief and German and Marshallese Flags

1984. Christmas. Multicoloured.

29 20 c. Type **5** 50 30
30 20 c. Desert landscape 50 30
31 20 c. Two kings on camels . . 50 30
32 20 c. Third king on camel . . 50 30

1984. 5th Anniv of Constitution. Multicoloured.

33 20 c. Type **6** 45 30
34 20 c. Pres. Amata Kabua and American and Marshallese flags 45 30
35 20 c. Admiral Chester W. Nimitz and Japanese and Marshallese flags 45 30
36 20 c. Trygve H. Lie (first Secretary-General of United Nations) and U.N. and Marshallese flags 45 30

7 Leach's Storm Petrel

1985. Birth Bicentenary of John J. Audubon (ornithologist). Multicoloured.

37	22 c. Type **7** (inscr "Fork-tailed Petrel") (postage)	65	30
38	22 c. Pectoral sandpiper	65	30
39	44 c. Brown booby (inscr "Booby Gannet") (air)	1·25	80
40	44 c. Whimbrel (inscr "Great Esquimaux Curlew")	1·25	80

8 Black-spotted Triton

1985. Sea Shells (1st series). Multicoloured.

41	22 c. Type **8**	65	35
42	22 c. Monodon murex	65	35
43	22 c. Diana conch	65	35
44	22 c. Great green turban	65	35
45	22 c. Rose-branch murex	65	35

See also Nos. 85/9, 131/5 and 220/4.

9 Woman as Encourager and Drum

1985. International Decade for Women. Mult.

46	22 c. Type **9**	50	30
47	22 c. Woman as Peacemaker and palm branches	50	30
48	22 c. Woman as Nurturer and pounding stone	50	30
49	22 c. Woman as Benefactress and lesser frigate bird	50	30

Nos. 46/9 were printed together in se-tenant blocks of four within the sheet, each block forming a composite design.

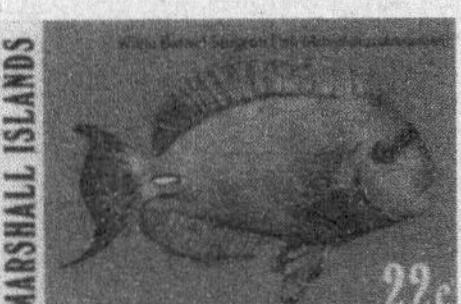

10 White-barred Surgeon Fish

1985. Lagoon Fishes. Multicoloured.

50	22 c. Type **10**	60	40
51	22 c. White-blotched squirrel fish	60	40
52	22 c. White-spotted boxfish	60	40
53	22 c. Saddleback butterfly fish	60	40

11 Basketball

1985. International Youth Year. Multicoloured.

54	22 c. Type **11**	45	30
55	22 c. Elderly woman recording for oral history project	45	30
56	22 c. Islander explaining navigational stick charts	45	30
57	22 c. Dancers at inter-atoll music and dance competition	45	30

12 American Board of Commissions for Foreign Missions Stock Certificate

1985. Christmas. "Morning Star I" (first Christian missionary ship to visit Marshall Islands). Multicoloured.

58	14 c. Type **12**	30	15
59	22 c. Launching of "Morning Star I", 1856	45	30
60	33 c. Departure from Honolulu, 1857	70	50
61	44 c. Entering Ebon Lagoon, 1857	80	60

13 "Giotto" and Section of Comet Tail

1985. Appearance of Halley's Comet. Designs showing comet over Roi-Namur Island. Multicoloured.

62	22 c. Space shuttle and comet	1·00	55
63	22 c. "Planet A" space probe and dish aerial	1·00	55
64	22 c. Type **13**	1·00	55
65	22 c. "Vega" satellite and buildings on island	1·00	55
66	22 c. Sir Edmund Halley, satellite communications ship and airplane	1·00	55

Nos. 62/6 were printed together, se-tenant, forming a composite design.

14 Mallow

1985. Medicinal Plants. Multicoloured.

67	22 c. Type **14**	50	35
68	22 c. Half-flower	50	35
69	22 c. "Guettarda speciosa"	50	35
70	22 c. Love-vine	50	35

15 Triton's Trumpet

1986. World Wildlife Fund. Marine Life. Mult.

71	14 c. Type **15**	45	30
72	14 c. Giant clam	45	30
73	14 c. Small giant clam	45	30
74	14 c. Coconut crab	45	30

16 Consolidated PBY-5A Catalina Amphibian

1986. Air. "Ameripex 86" International Stamp Exhibition, Chicago. Mail Planes. Multicoloured.

75	44 c. Type **16**	85	65
76	44 c. Grumman SA-16 Albatross	85	65
77	44 c. Douglas DC-6B	85	65
78	44 c. Boeing 727-100	85	65

17 Islanders in Outrigger Canoe

1986. 40th Anniv of Operation Crossroads (atomic bomb tests on Bikini Atoll). Multicoloured.

80	22 c. Type **17**	55	35
81	22 c. Advance landing of amphibious DUKW from U.S.S. "Sumner"	55	35
82	22 c. Loading "LST 1108" (tank landing ship) for islanders' departure	55	35
83	22 c. Man planting coconuts as part of reclamation programme	55	35

1986. Sea Shells (2nd series). As T **8**. Multicoloured.

85	22 c. Rose murex	55	35
86	22 c. Orange spider conch	55	35
87	22 c. Red-mouth frog shell	55	35
88	22 c. Laciniate conch	55	35
89	22 c. Giant frog shell	55	35

18 Blue Marlin

1986. Game Fishes. Multicoloured.

90	22 c. Type **18**	50	40
91	22 c. Wahoo	50	40
92	22 c. Dolphin fish	50	40
93	22 c. Yellowfin tuna	50	40

19 Flowers (top left)

1986. International Peace Year. Multicoloured.

94	22 c. Type **19** (Christmas) (postage)	50	35
95	22 c. Flowers (top right)	50	35
96	22 c. Flowers (bottom left)	50	35
97	22 c. Flowers (bottom right)	50	35
98	44 c. Head of Statue crowned with flowers (24 × 39 mm) (cent of Statue of Liberty) (air)	1·00	70

Nos. 94/7 were issued together, se-tenant, in blocks of four within the sheet, each block forming a composite design of mixed flower arrangement.

20 Girl Scout giving Plant to Patient

1986. Air. 20th Anniv of Marshall Island Girl Scouts and 75th Anniv (1987) of United States Girl Scout Movement. Multicoloured.

99	44 c. Type **20**	90	70
100	44 c. Giving salute	90	70
101	44 c. Girl scouts holding hands in circle	90	70
102	44 c. Weaving pandana and palm branch mats	90	70

21 Wedge-tailed Shearwater

1987. Air. Sea Birds. Multicoloured.

103	44 c. Type **21**	90	70
104	44 c. Red-footed booby	90	70
105	44 c. Red-tailed tropic bird	90	70
106	44 c. Lesser frigate bird	90	70

22 "James T. Arnold", 1854

1987. Whaling Ships. Multicoloured.

107	22 c. Type **22**	60	45
108	22 c. "General Scott", 1859	60	45
109	22 c. "Charles W. Morgan", 1865	60	45
110	22 c. "Lucretia", 1884	60	45

23 "Spirit of St. Louis" and Congressional Medal of Honour, 1927

1987. Aviators. Multicoloured.

111	33 c. Type **23**	70	45
112	33 c. Charles Lindbergh and Chance Vought F4U Corsair, Marshall Islands, 1944	70	45
113	39 c. William Bridgeman and Consolidated B-24 Liberator bomber, Kwajalein, 1944	80	60
114	39 c. Bridgeman and Douglas Skyrocket, 1951	80	60
115	44 c. John Glenn and Chance Vought F4U Corsair fighters, Marshall Islands, 1944	1·00	75
116	44 c. Glenn and "Friendship 7" space capsule	1·00	75

24 Lockheed Electra taking off from Lae, New Guinea

1987. Air. "Capex '87" International Stamp Exhibition, Toronto. 50th Anniv of Amelia Earhart's Round the World Flight Attempt. Multicoloured.

117	44 c. Type **24**	90	65
118	44 c. U.S. Coastguard cutter "Itasca" waiting off Howland Island for Electra	90	65
119	44 c. Islanders and crashed Electra on Mili Atoll	90	65
120	44 c. Japanese patrol boat "Koshu" recovering Electra	90	65

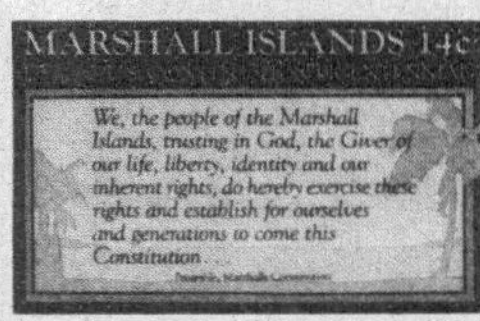

25 "We, the people of the Marshall Islands ..."

1987. Bicentenary of United States of America Constitution. Multicoloured.

122	14 c. Type **25**	30	25
123	14 c. Marshall Is. and U.S.A. emblems	30	25
124	14 c. "We the people of the United States..."	30	25
125	22 c. "All we have and are today as a people..."	45	25
126	22 c. Marshall Is. and U.S.A. flags	45	25
127	22 c. "... to establish Justice..."	45	25
128	44 c. "With this Constitution..."	85	75
129	44 c. Marshall Is. stick chart and U.S. Liberty Bell	85	75
130	44 c. "... to promote the general Welfare..."	85	75

The three designs of each value were printed together, se-tenant, the left hand stamp of each strip bearing quotations from the preamble to the Marshall Islands Constitution and the right hand stamp, quotations from the United States Constitution preamble.

1987. Sea Shells (3rd series). As T **8**. Multicoloured.

131	22 c. Magnificent cone	60	35
132	22 c. Partridge tun	60	35
133	22 c. Scorpion spider conch	60	35
134	22 c. Hairy triton	60	35
135	22 c. Chiragra spider conch	60	35

26 Planting Coconut

1987. Copra Industry. Multicoloured.

136	44 c. Type **26**	80	65
137	44 c. Making copra	80	65
138	44 c. Bottling extracted coconut oil	80	65

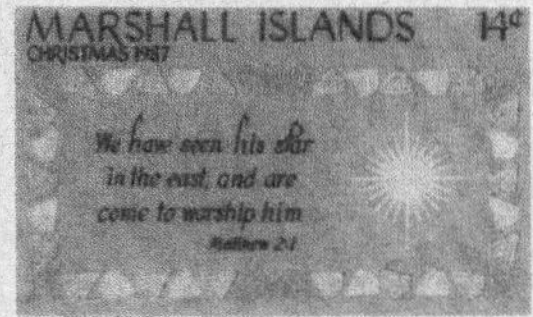

27 "We have seen his star in the east..."

1987. Christmas. Multicoloured.

139	14 c. Type **27**	35	25
140	22 c. "Glory to God in the highest;..."	50	30
141	33 c. "Sing unto the Lord a new song..."	70	40
142	44 c. "Praise him in the cymbals and dances;..."	95	65

28 Eastern Reef Heron

1988. Shore and Water Birds. Multicoloured.
143 44 c. Type **28** . . . 75 50
144 44 c. Bar-tailed godwit . . . 75 50
145 44 c. Blue-faced booby . . . 75 50
146 44 c. Common shoveler . . . 75 50

29 Damselfish **30** Javelin Thrower

1988. Fishes. Multicoloured.
147 1 c. Type **29** . . . 10 10
148 3 c. Blackface butterfly fish . . 10 10
149 14 c. Hawkfish . . . 20 10
150 15 c. Balloonfish . . . 20 10
151 17 c. Trunk fish . . . 25 15
152 22 c. Lyretail wrasse . . . 30 20
153 25 c. Parrotfish . . . 30 20
154 33 c. White-spotted boxfish . . 40 25
155 36 c. Spotted boxfish . . . 45 30
156 39 c. Surgeonfish . . . 50 40
157 44 c. Long-snouted butterfly fish 55 45
158 45 c. Trumpetfish . . . 55 45
159 56 c. Sharp nosed puffer . . . 70 50
160 $1 Seahorse . . . 1·25 70
161 $2 Ghost pipefish . . . 2·50 1·50
162 $5 Big spotted triggerfish . . 6·00 4·50
163 $10 Blue jacks (50 × 28 mm) . 12·00 9·00

1988. Olympic Games, Seoul. Multicoloured.
166 15 c. Type **30** . . . 25 15
167 15 c. Drawing javelin back and star . . . 25 15
168 15 c. Javelin drawn back fully (value at left) . . . 25 15
169 15 c. Commencing throw (value at right) . . . 25 15
170 15 c. Releasing javelin . . . 25 15
171 25 c. Runner and star (left half) 35 25
172 25 c. Runner and star (right half) 35 25
173 25 c. Runner (value at left) . . 35 25
174 25 c. Runner (value at right) . 35 25
175 25 c. Finish of race . . . 35 25

Nos. 166/70 were printed together, se-tenant, forming a composite design of a javelin throw with background of the Marshallese flag. Nos. 171/5 were similarly arranged forming a composite design of a runner and flag.

31 "Casco" sailing through Golden Gate of San Francisco

1988. Centenary of Robert Louis Stevenson's Pacific Voyages. Multicoloured.
176 25 c. Type **31** . . . 50 35
177 25 c. "Casco" at the Needles of Ua-Pu, Marquesas . . . 50 35
178 25 c. "Equator" leaving Honolulu . . . 50 35
179 25 c. Chieftain's canoe, Majuro Lagoon . . . 50 35
180 25 c. Bronze medallion depicting Stevenson by Augustus St. Gaudens, 1887 . . . 50 35
181 25 c. "Janet Nicoll" (inter-island steamer), Majuro Lagoon . 50 35
182 25 c. Stevenson's visit to maniap of King Tembinoka of Gilbert Islands . . . 50 35
183 25 c. Stevenson in Samoan canoe, Apia Harbour . . . 50 35
184 25 c. Stevenson on horse Jack at Valima (Samoan home) . . 50 35

32 Spanish Ragged Cross Ensign (1516-1785) and Magellan's Ship "Vitoria"

1988. Exploration Ships and Flags. Multicoloured.
185 25 c. Type **32** . . . 50 35
186 25 c. British red ensign (1707–1800), "Charlotte" and "Scarborough" . . . 50 35
187 25 c. American flag and ensign (1837–45), U.S.S. "Flying Fish" and U.S.S. "Peacock" 50 35
188 25 c. German flag and ensign (1867–1919) and "Planet" . 50 35

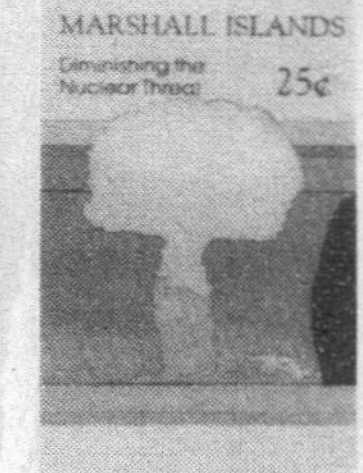

33 Father Christmas in Sleigh **34** Nuclear Test on Bikini Atoll

1988. Christmas. Multicoloured.
189 25 c. Type **33** . . . 35 25
190 25 c. Reindeer over island with palm huts and trees . . . 35 25
191 25 c. Reindeer over island with palm trees . . . 35 25
192 25 c. Reindeer and flying fish 35 25
193 25 c. Reindeer over island with outrigger canoe . . . 35 25

1988. 25th Anniv of Assassination of John F. Kennedy (American President). Multicoloured.
194 25 c. Type **34** . . . 40 25
195 25 c. Kennedy signing Test Ban Treaty . . . 40 25
196 25 c. Kennedy . . . 40 25
197 25 c. Kennedy using hot-line between Washington and Moscow . . . 40 25
198 25 c. Peace Corps volunteers 40 25

35 "SV-5D PRIME" Vehicle Launch from Vandenberg Air Force Base

1988. Kwajalein Space Shuttle Tracking Station. Multicoloured.
199 25 c. Type **35** (postage) . . 45 30
200 25 c. Re-entry of "SV-5D" . 45 30
201 25 c. Recovery of "SV-5D" off Kwajalein . . . 45 30
202 25 c. Space shuttle "Discovery" over Kwajalein . . . 45 30
203 45 c. Shuttle and astronaut over Rongelap (air) . . . 75 55

Nos. 199/202 were printed together, se-tenant, forming a composite design.

36 1918 Typhoon Monument, Majuro

1989. Links with Japan. Multicoloured.
204 45 c. Type **36** . . . 80 55
205 45 c. Japanese seaplane base and railway, Djarret Islet, 1940s 80 55
206 45 c. Japanese fishing boats . 80 55
207 45 c. Japanese skin-divers . . 80 55

37 "Island Woman"

1989. Links with Alaska. Oil Paintings by Claire Fejes. Multicoloured.
208 45 c. Type **37** . . . 75 55
209 45 c. "Kotzebue, Alaska" . . 75 55
210 45 c. "Marshallese Madonna" 75 55

38 Dornier Do-228

1989. Air. Airplanes. Multicoloured.
212 12 c. Type **38** . . . 30 20
214 36 c. Boeing 737 . . . 55 40
215 39 c. Hawker Siddeley H.S.748 65 45
216 45 c. Boeing 727 . . . 75 55

1989. Sea Shells (4th series). As T **8**. Mult.
220 25 c. Pontifical mitre . . . 55 35
221 25 c. Tapestry turban . . . 55 35
222 25 c. Flame mouthed helmet . 55 35
223 25 c. Prickly Pacific drupe . . 55 35
224 25 c. Blood mouthed conch . . 55 35

40 Wandering Tattler

1989. Birds. Multicoloured.
226 45 c. Type **40** . . . 85 60
227 45 c. Turnstone . . . 85 60
228 45 c. Pacific golden plover . . 85 60
229 45 c. Sanderling . . . 85 60

41 "Bussard" (German cruiser) and 1897 Ship's Post Cancellation

1989. "Philexfrance 89" International Stamp Exhibition, Paris. Marshall Islands Postal History. Multicoloured.
230 25 c. Type **41** . . . 80 50
231 25 c. First Day Cover bearing first Marshall Islands stamps and U.S. 10 c. stamp . 80 50
232 25 c. Consolidated PBY-5 Catalina flying boats, floating Fleet Post Office ("L.S.T. 119"), Majuro, and 1944 U.S. Navy cancellation . . . 80 50
233 25 c. Nakajima A6M2 "Rufe" seaplane, mailboat off Mili Island and Japanese cancellation . . . 80 50
234 25 c. Majuro Post Office . . 80 50
235 25 c. Consolidated PBY-5A Catalina amphibian, outrigger canoe and 1951 U.S. civilian mail cancellation . . . 80 50
236 45 c. "Morning Star V" (missionary ship) and 1905 Jaluit cancellation . . . 85 55
237 45 c. 1906 registered cover with Jaluit cancellation . . . 85 55
238 45 c. "Prinz Eitel Freiderich" (auxiliary cruiser) and 1914 German ship's post cancellation . . . 85 55
239 45 c. "Scharnhorst" (cruiser) leading German Asiatic Squadron and 1914 ship's post cancellation . . . 85 55

Nos. 230/5 were printed together, se-tenant, Nos. 231 and 234 forming a composite design to commemorate the 5th anniversary of Marshall Islands Independent Postal Service.

Since August 1989 a considerable number of stamps have appeared, issued on behalf of the Republic of the Marshall Islands. It has only been possible to confirm postal use of the following definitive issues.

44 White-capped Noddy

1990. Birds. Multicoloured.
249 1 c. Type **44** . . . 10 10
250 5 c. Red-tailed tropic bird . . 10 10
251 9 c. Whimbrel . . . 10 10
252 10 c. Sanderling . . . 15 15
253 12 c. Black-naped tern . . . 15 15
254 15 c. Wandering tattler . . . 20 20
255 20 c. Bristle-thighed curlew . . 25 25
256 22 c. Greater scaup . . . 30 30
257 23 c. Common (inscr "Northern") shoveler . . . 30 30
258 25 c. Common (inscr "Brown") noddy . . . 35 35
259 27 c. Sooty tern . . . 35 35
260 28 c. Sharp-tailed sandpiper . . 35 35
261 29 c. Wedge-tailed shearwater 40 40
262 30 c. American (inscr "Pacific") golden plover . . . 40 40
263 35 c. Brown booby . . . 45 45
264 36 c. Red-footed booby . . . 50 50
265 40 c. White tern . . . 55 55
266 45 c. Common teal . . . 60 60
267 50 c. Great frigate bird . . . 65 65
268 52 c. Crested tern (inscr "Great Crested Tern") . . . 70 70
269 65 c. Lesser sand plover . . . 85 85
270 75 c. Little tern . . . 1·00 1·00
271 $1 Eastern (inscr "Pacific") reef heron . . . 1·40 1·40
272 $2 Masked booby . . . 2·50 2·50

45 "Britannia"

1993. Ships. Multicoloured. (a) Size 35 × 21 mm.
278 15 c. Type **45** . . . 20 20
279 19 c. "Micro Palm" (inter-island ship) . . . 25 35
281 23 c. H.M.S. "Cornwallis" (sail frigate) . . . 30 30
282 24 c. U.S.S. "Dolphin" (schooner) . . . 30 30
285 29 c. "Morning Star I" (missionary brigantine) . . 40 40
291 50 c. U.S.S. "Lexington" (aircraft carrier) . . . 65 65
292 52 c. H.M.S. "Serpent" (brig) 70 70
294 75 c. "Scarborough" (British transport) . . . 1·00 1·00

(b) Size 46 × 27 mm.
295 $1 Enewetak outrigger canoe 1·40 1·40
296 $2 Jaluit outrigger canoe . . 2·50 2·50

MARTINIQUE Pt. 6

An island in the West Indies, now an overseas department using the stamps of France.

100 centimes = 1 franc

1886. Stamp of French Colonies, "Commerce" type.
(a) Surch **MARTINIQUE** and new value.
3 J 01 on 20 c. red on green . . . 8·75 9·00
1 5 on 20 c. red on green . . . 30·00 26·00
4 05 on 20 c. red on green . . . 7·00 4·50
2 5 c. on 20 c. red on green £10000 £10000
6 015 on 20 c. red on green 35·00 35·00
5 15 on 20 c. red on green . . . £130 £110

(b) Surch **MQE 15 c.**
7 J **15** c. on 20 c. red on green . . 60·00 55·00

1888. Stamps of French Colonies, "Commerce" type, surch **MARTINIQUE** and value, thus **01 c.**
10 01 c. on 4 c. brn on grey 7·00 1·75
11 05 c. on 4 c. brn on grey £800 £675
12 05 c. on 10 c. black & lilac 60·00 30·00
13 05 c. on 20 c. red on green 12·50 9·25
14 05 c. on 30 c. brn on drab 16·00 14·50
15a 05 c. on 35 c. blk on yell 10·00 7·75
16 05 c. on 40 c. red on yell 32·00 25·00
17 15 c. on 4 c. brn on grey £7000 £6000
18 15 c. on 20 c. red on green 70·00 50·00
19 15 c. on 25 c. blk on pink 9·25 8·00
20 15 c. on 75 c. red on pink £110 90·00

1891. Postage Due stamps of French Colonies surch **TIMBRE-POSTE MARTINIQUE** and value in figures.
21 U 05 c. on 5 c. black . . . . 7·75 7·00
25 05 c. on 10 c. black . . . . 4·25 5·00
22 05 c. on 15 c. black . . . . 5·50 4·00
23 15 c. on 20 c. black . . . . 8·00 5·50
24 15 c. on 30 c. black . . . . 8·00 6·50

1891. Stamp of French Colonies, "Commerce" type, surch **TIMBRE-POSTE 01c. MARTINIQUE.**

1892. Stamp of French Colonies, "Commerce" type, surch **1892 MARTINIQUE** and new value.
31 15 c. on 25 c. black on pink 15·00 15·00

1892. "Tablet" key-type inscr "MARTINIQUE", in red (1, 5, 15, 25, 75 c., 1 f.) or blue (others).
33 D 1 c. black on blue 80 80
34 2 c. brown on buff 90 85
35 4 c. brown on grey 90 85
36 5 c. green on green . . . . 1·25 45
37 10 c. black on lilac . . . . 5·50 70
47 10 c. red . . . . 1·75 50
38 15 c. blue . . . . 21·00 3·50
48 15 c. grey . . . . 6·25 70
39 20 c. red on green . . . . 10·00 4·00
40 25 c. black on pink . . . . 11·50 1·00
49 25 c. blue . . . . 8·50 7·50
41 30 c. brown on drab . . . . 21·00 7·75
50 35 c. black on yellow . . . . 9·50 4·75
42 40 c. red on yellow . . . . 21·00 7·50
43 50 c. red on pink . . . . 20·00 9·75
51 50 c. brown on blue . . . . 21·00 15·00
44 75 c. brown on orange . . . 20·00 10·00
45 1 f. green . . . . 16·00 8·25
52 2 f. violet on pink . . . . . 65·00 50·00
53 5 f. mauve on lilac . . . . 75·00 60·00

1903. Postage Due stamp of French Colonies surch **TIMBRE POSTE 5 F. MARTINIQUE COLIS POSTAUX.**
53a U 5 f. on 60 c. brown on buff £400 £425
Despite the surcharge Nos. 53a was for use on letters as well as parcels.

1904. Surch **10 c.**
55 10 c. on 5 f. mve on lilac . . . 6·25 6·25

1904. Surch **1904 0f10.**
57 0 f. 10 on 40 c. red on yell 10·50 10·50
58 0 f. 10 on 50 c. red on pink 10·50 10·50
59 0 f. 10 on 75 c. brown on orange 9·75 9·75
60 0 f. 10 on 1 f. green . . . . . 10·50 10·50
61 0 f. 10 on 5 f. mve on lilac . . . £140 £140

13 Martinique Woman

15 Woman and Sugar Cane

14 Fort-de-France

1908.
62 **13** 1 c. chocolate and brown 15 20
63 2 c. brown and green . . . 15 25
64 4 c. brown and purple . . . 15 25
65 5 c. brown and green . . . 25 15
87 5 c. brown and orange . . . 15 15
66 10 c. brown and red . . . 45 25
88 10 c. olive and green . . . 20 30
89 10 c. red and purple . . . 20 25
67 15 c. red and purple . . . 15 30
90 15 c. olive and green . . . 20 30
91 **13** 15 c. red and blue 50 70
68 20 c. brown and lilac . . . 50 55
69 **14** 25 c. brown and blue . . . 75 20
92 25 c. brown and orange . . 25 15
93 30 c. brown and red . . . 35 35
94 30 c. red and carmine . . . 20 35
95 30 c. brown and lt brown 20 25
96 30 c. green and blue . . . 70 75
71 35 c. brown and lilac . . . 30 45
72 40 c. brown and green . . 30 40
73 45 c. chocolate and brown 35 45
74 50 c. brown and red . . . 75 45
97 50 c. brown and blue . . . 70 75
98 50 c. green and red 30 20
99 60 c. pink and blue . . . 20 30
100 65 c. brown and violet . . 90 95
75 75 c. brown and black . . 70 60
101 75 c. blue and deep blue . 20 30
102 75 c. blue and brown . . . 1·40 1·50
103 90 c. carmine and red . . 3·25 3·25
76 **15** 1 f. brown and red 40 40
104 1 f. blue 30 40
105 1 f. green and red . . . . 95 1·25
106 1 f. 10 brown and violet . 2·00 2·00
107 1 f. 50 light blue and blue 3·50 3·50
77 2 f. brown and grey . . . 1·90 1·00
108 3 f. mauve on pink . . . . 5·25 5·25
78 5 f. brown and red . . . . 6·25 6·00

1912. Stamps of 1892 surch.
79 05 on 15 c. grey 50 45
80 05 on 25 c. black on pink . . 75 85
81 10 on 40 c. red on yellow . . . 90 1·00
82 10 on 5 f. mauve on lilac . . 1·25 1·40

1915. Surch **5c** and red cross.
83 **13** 10 c. + 5 c. brown and red 1·00 1·00

1920. Surch in figures.
115 **13** 0,01 on 2 c. brown and grn 1·10 1·40
109 0,01 on 15 c. red and purple 25 35
110 0,02 on 15 c. red and purple 15 35
84 05 on 1 c. chocolate & brn 1·00 1·00
111 0,05 on 15 c. red and pur 25 35
116 0,05 on 20 c. brown & lilac 1·25 1·40
85 10 on 2 c. brown and green 85 90
117 **14** 0,15 on 30 c. brown & red 6·50 7·00
86 **13** 25 on 15 c. red and purple 65 70
121 25 c. on 15 c. red & purple 25 35
119 **14** 0,25 on 50 c. brown and red £170 £170
120 0,25 on 50 c. brown & blue 2·75 3·00
122 **15** 25 c. on 2 f. brown & grey 20 35
123 25 c. on 5 f. brown and red 95 60
112 **14** 60 on 75 c. pink and blue 20 35
113 65 on 45 c. brown & lt brn 60 70
114 85 on 75 c. brown & black 65 80
124 90 c. on 75 c. carmine and red 1·90 2·00
125 **15** 1 f. 25 on 1 f. blue 20 30
126 1 f. 50 on 1 f. ultramarine and blue 70 80
127 3 f. on 5 f. green and red 1·25 1·40
128 10 f. on 5 f. red and green 6·00 6·25
129 20 f. on 5 f. violet & brown 9·25 9·00

1931. "Colonial Exhibition" key-types inscr "MARTINIQUE".
130 E 40 c. black and green . . 2·25 2·25
131 F 50 c. black and mauve . . 2·00 2·00
132 G 90 c. black and red . . . 2·25 2·25
133 H 1 f. 50 black and blue . . 2·25 2·25

26 Basse Pointe Village

27 Government House, Fort-de-France

28 Martinique Woman

1933.
134 **26** 1 c. red on pink 15 25
135 **27** 2 c. blue 15 30
136 3 c. purple 20 30
137 **26** 4 c. green 15 30
138 **27** 5 c. purple 15 25
139 **26** 10 c. black on pink 15 25
140 **27** 15 c. black on red 15 25
141 **28** 20 c. brown 15 25
142 **26** 25 c. purple 20 35
143 **27** 30 c. green 25 25
144 30 c. blue 25 30
145 **28** 35 c. green 25 35
146 40 c. brown 25 35
147 **27** 45 c. brown . . . . 1·00 1·10
148 45 c. green 30 45
149 50 c. red 20 15
150 **26** 55 c. red 45 55
151 60 c. blue 25 35
152 **28** 65 c. red on blue 35 30
153 70 c. purple 35 30
154 **26** 75 c. brown 50 50
155 **27** 80 c. violet 35 35
156 **26** 90 c. red . . . . 1·10 95
157 90 c. purple 35 40
158 **27** 1 f. black on green . . . . 1·10 30
159 1 f. red 40 40
160 **28** 1 f. 25 violet 45 45
161 1 f. 25 red 45 40
162 **28** 1 f. 40 blue 40 40
163 **27** 1 f. 50 blue 35 35
164 1 f. 60 brown 45 45
165 **28** 1 f. 75 green . . . . 5·50 2·50
166 1 f. 75 blue 40 35
167 **26** 2 f. blue on green 40 30
168 **28** 2 f. 25 blue 50 45
169 **26** 2 f. 50 purple 55 60
170 **28** 3 f. purple 25 25
171 5 f. red on pink 70 40
172 **26** 10 f. blue on blue 45 30
173 **27** 20 f. red on yellow 85 65

30 Belain d'Esnambuc, 1635

31 Schoelcher and Abolition of Slavery, 1848

1935. West Indies Tercentenary.
174 **30** 40 c. brown . . . . 1·10 1·00
175 50 c. red . . . . 1·10 1·00
176 1 f. 50 blue . . . . 8·00 8·00
177 **31** 1 f. 75 red . . . . 7·25 7·50
178 5 f. brown . . . . 7·25 7·50
179 10 f. green . . . . 5·25 5·50

1937. International Exhibition, Paris. As Nos. 168/73 of St.-Pierre et Miquelon.
180 20 c. violet 85 95
181 30 c. green 85 95
182 40 c. red 85 95
183 50 c. brown and agate . . . . 80 1·10
184 90 c. red . . . . 90 1·10
185 1 f. 50 blue . . . . 1·00 1·10

1938. Int. Anti-Cancer Fund. As T **22** of Mauritania.
186 1 f. 75 + 50 c. blue . . . . . 6·50 6·50

1939. New York World's Fair. As T **28** of Mauritania.
187 1 f. 25 red 70 70
188 2 f. 25 blue 70 70

1939. 150th Anniv of French Revolution. As T **29** of Mauritania.
189 45 c. + 25 c. green and black 4·50 4·50
190 70 c. + 30 c. brown and black 4·50 4·50
191 90 c. + 35 c. orange and black 4·50 4·50
192 1 f. 25 + 1 f. red and black . 4·50 4·50
193 2 f. 25 + 2 f. blue and black . 4·50 4·50

1944. Mutual Aid and Red Cross Funds. As T **31** of New Caledonia.
194 5 f. + 20 f. violet 65 80

1945. Eboue. As T **32** of New Caledonia.
195 2 f. black 20 35
196 25 f. green 55 65

1945. Surch.
197 **27** 1 f. on 2 c. blue 40 40
198 **26** 2 f. on 4 c. olive 40 40
199 **27** 3 f. on 2 c. blue 40 40
200 **28** 5 f. on 65 c. red on blue . . 60 60
201 10 f. (DIX f.) on 65 c. red on blue 60 60
202 **27** 20 f. (VINGT f.) on 3 c. purple 75 75

33 Victor Schoelcher

1945.
203 **33** 10 c. blue and violet 15 30
204 30 c. brown and red 20 30
205 40 c. blue and light blue . . 25 35
206 50 c. red and purple 30 30
207 60 c. orange and yellow . . 30 40
208 70 c. purple and brown . . 30 40
209 80 c. green and light green 30 40
210 1 f. blue and light blue . . 30 40
211 1 f. 20 violet and purple . . 30 40
212 1 f. 50 red and orange . . . 30 40
213 2 f. black and grey 30 40
214 2 f. 40 red and pink 75 90
215 3 f. pink and light pink . . . 30 20
216 4 f. ultramarine and blue . . 35 25
217 4 f. 50 turquoise and green . 50 35
218 5 f. light brown and brown . 40 50
219 10 f. purple and mauve . . . 50 30
220 15 f. red and pink 60 45
221 20 f. olive and green 80 75

1945. Air. As T **30** of New Caledonia.
222 50 f. green 50 35
223 100 f. red 55 45

1946. Air. Victory. As T **34** of New Caledonia.
224 8 f. blue 50 75

1946. Air. From Chad to the Rhine. As Nos. 300/305 of New Caledonia.
225 5 f. orange 40 50
226 10 f. green 40 50
227 15 f. red 50 60
228 20 f. brown 50 60
229 25 f. blue 60 70
230 50 f. grey 80 90

34 Martinique Woman

39 Mountains and Palms

35 Local Fishing Boats and Rocks

40 West Indians and Flying Boat

1947.
231 **34** 10 c. lake (postage) 20 30
232 30 c. blue 15 25
233 50 c. brown 15 30
234 **35** 60 c. green 25 35
235 1 f. lake 25 35
236 1 f. 50 violet 25 35
237 – 2 f. green 60 45
238 – 2 f. 50 brown 60 50
239 – 3 f. blue 45 45
240 – 4 f. brown 45 45
241 – 5 f. green 40 45
242 – 6 f. mauve 45 45
243 – 10 f. blue 75 65
244 – 15 f. lake 90 85
245 – 20 f. brown . . . . . . 1·25 1·00
246 **39** 25 f. violet . . . . 1·40 1·25
247 40 f. green . . . . 1·50 1·40
248 **40** 50 f. purple (air) . . . . . 2·50 2·00
249 – 100 f. green . . . . 3·75 2·50
250 – 200 f. violet . . . . 38·00 15·00

DESIGNS—HORIZ: As Type **35**: 2 f. to 3 f. Gathering sugar cane; 4 f. to 6 f. Mount Pele; 10 f. to 20 f. Fruit products. As Type **40**—VERT: 100 f. Aeroplane over landscape. HORIZ: 200 f. Wandering albatross in flight.

POSTAGE DUE STAMPS

1927. Postage Due stamps of France optd **MARTINIQUE.**
D130 D **11** 5 c. blue 50 85
D131 10 c. brown . . . . . 80 1·00
D132 20 c. olive . . . . . . 90 1·00
D133 25 c. red . . . . . . 1·25 1·50
D134 30 c. red . . . . . . 1·60 1·75
D135 45 c. green . . . . . 1·75 1·75
D136 50 c. purple . . . . . 3·50 3·75
D137 60 c. green . . . . . 4·25 4·25
D138 1 f. red on yellow . . 5·25 5·25
D139 2 f. mauve . . . . . 7·25 7·50
D140 3 f. red . . . . 8·25 8·25

D **29** Fruit

D **43** Map of Martinique

1933.
D174 D **29** 5 c. blue on green . . 15 40
D175 10 c. brown 20 40
D176 20 c. blue 60 65
D177 25 c. red on pink . . 60 65
D178 30 c. purple 40 45
D179 45 c. red on yellow . . 30 35
D180 50 c. brown 45 75
D181 60 c. green 45 75
D182 1 f. black on red . . . 65 90
D183 2 f. purple 55 75
D184 3 f. blue on blue . . . 70 85

1947.
D251 D **43** 10 c. blue 15 20
D252 30 c. green 15 30
D253 50 c. blue 15 30
D254 1 f. orange 20 35
D255 2 f. purple 45 60
D256 3 f. purple 45 60
D257 4 f. brown 55 70
D258 5 f. red 60 70
D259 10 f. black . . . . . 90 1·25
D260 20 f. green . . . . . 90 1·25

MAURITANIA Pt. 6; Pt. 13

A French colony extending inland to the Sahara, incorporated in French West Africa from 1945 to 1959. In 1960 Mauritania became an independent Islamic republic.

1906. 100 centimes = 1 franc.
1973. 100 cents = 1 ouguiya (um).

1906. "Faidherbe", "Palms" and "Balay" key-types inscr "MAURITANIE" in blue (10, 40 c., 5 f.) or red (others).

1 I 1 c. grey . . . 25 25
2 2 c. brown . . . 50 40
3 4 c. brown on blue . . . 75 50
4 5 c. green . . . 45 50
5 10 c. pink . . . 4·50 3·00
6 J 20 c. black on blue . . . 11·00 8·50
7 25 c. blue . . . 4·50 3·25
8 30 c. brown on pink . . . 70·00 40·00
9 35 c. black on yellow . . . 4·25 3·00
10 40 c. red on blue . . . 4·50 3·50
11 45 c. brown on green . . . 4·25 3·50
12 50 c. violet . . . 4·50 3·50
13 75 c. green on orange . . . 4·00 3·50
14 K 1 f. black on blue . . . 9·50 8·00
15 2 f. blue on pink . . . 35·00 30·00
16 5 f. red on yellow . . . £100 85·00

6 Merchants crossing Desert

1913.

18 6 1 c. brown and lilac . . . 10 20
19 2 c. blue and black . . . 10 20
20 4 c. black and violet . . . 15 25
21 5 c. green and light green . . . 25 40
37 5 c. red and purple . . . 10 25
22 10 c. orange and pink . . . 55 75
38 10 c. green and light green . . . 10 25
39 10 c. pink on blue . . . 15 30
23 15 c. black and brown . . . 30 40
24 20 c. orange and brown . . . 20 45
25 25 c. ultramarine and blue . . . 80 85
40 25 c. red and green . . . 40 65
26 30 c. pink and green . . . 50 80
41 30 c. orange and red . . . 50 70
42 30 c. yellow and black . . . 15 35
43 30 c. light green and green . . . 70 95
27 35 c. violet and brown . . . 25 45
44 35 c. light green and green . . . 25 50
28 40 c. green and brown . . . 70 1·10
29 45 c. brown and orange . . . 35 55
30 50 c. pink and lilac . . . 35 50
45 50 c. ultramarine and blue . . . 40 50
46 50 c. blue and green . . . 40 60
47 60 c. violet on pink . . . 15 35
48 65 c. blue and brown . . . 50 70
31 75 c. brown and blue . . . 40 70
49 85 c. brown and green . . . 40 60
50 90 c. pink and red . . . 85 90
32 1 f. black and red . . . 40 65
51 1 f. 10 red and mauve . . . 6·50 6·75
52 1 f. 25 brown and blue . . . 1·10 1·25
53 1 f. 50 blue and light blue . . . 70 75
54 1 f. 75 red and green . . . 70 75
55 1 f. 75 ultramarine and blue . . . 75 70
33 2 f. violet and orange . . . 1·00 1·40
56 3 f. mauve on pink . . . 1·00 1·40
34 5 f. blue and violet . . . 1·40 1·50

1915. Surch **5c** and red cross.

35 6 10 c. + 5 c. orange and pink . . . 40 70
36 15 c. + 5 c. black and brown . . . 40 75

1922. Surch in figures and bars (some colours changed).

60 6 25 c. on 2 f. violet and orange . . . 60 60
57 60 on 75 c. violet on pink . . . 50 70
58 65 on 15 c. black and brown . . . 1·00 1·40
59 85 on 75 c. brown and blue . . . 75 1·10
61 90 c. on 75 c. pink and red . . . 1·40 1·40
62 1 f. 25 on 1 f. ultram and blue . . . 55 75
63 1 f. 50 on 1 f. blue and lt blue . . . 65 80
64 3 f. on 5 f. mauve and brown . . . 5·00 5·00
65 10 f. on 5 f. green and mauve . . . 4·25 4·50
66 20 f. on 5 f. orange and blue . . . 4·25 4·50

1931. "Colonial Exhibition" key-types inscr "MAURITANIE".

67 E 40 c. green and black . . . 5·00 5·25
68 F 50 c. purple and black . . . 2·50 2·50
69 G 90 c. red and black . . . 2·50 2·50
70 H 1 f. 50 blue and black . . . 2·50 2·50

1937. International Exhibition, Paris. As Nos. 168/73 of St.-Pierre et Miquelon.

71 20 c. violet . . . 60 75
72 30 c. green . . . 60 80
73 40 c. red . . . 50 75
74 50 c. brown . . . 50 70
75 90 c. red . . . 50 80
76 1 f. 50 blue . . . 55 80

22 Pierre and Marie Curie

1938. International Anti-Cancer Fund.

76b 22 1 f. 75 + 50 c. blue . . . 3·50 5·00

23 Man on Camel

24 Warriors

25 Encampment

26 Mauritanians

1938.

77 23 2 c. purple . . . 15 30
78 3 c. blue . . . 10 30
79 4 c. lilac . . . 10 30
80 5 c. red . . . 10 30
81 10 c. red . . . 20 35
82 15 c. violet . . . 15 30
83 24 20 c. red . . . 10 30
84 25 c. blue . . . 30 55
85 30 c. purple . . . 20 30
86 35 c. green . . . 35 55
87 40 c. red . . . 35 50
88 45 c. green . . . 35 45
89 50 c. violet . . . 35 55
90 25 55 c. lilac . . . 55 70
91 60 c. violet . . . 40 50
92 65 c. green . . . 40 55
93 70 c. red . . . 50 60
94 80 c. blue . . . 95 1·00
95 90 c. lilac . . . 40 55
96 1 f. red . . . 90 1·10
97 1 f. green . . . 25 45
98 1 f. 25 red . . . 50 90
99 1 f. 40 blue . . . 50 65
100 1 f. 50 violet . . . 45 70
101 1 f. 60 brown . . . 90 1·00
102 26 1 f. 75 blue . . . 75 70
103 2 f. lilac . . . 60 75
104 2 f. 25 blue . . . 45 65
105 2 f. 50 brown . . . 65 80
106 3 f. green . . . 50 70
107 5 f. red . . . 60 90
108 10 f. purple . . . 90 1·40
109 20 f. red . . . 95 1·40

27 Rene Caillie (explorer)

1939. Caillie.

110 27 90 c. orange . . . 50 80
111 2 f. violet . . . 50 80
112 2 f. 25 blue . . . 50 80

28

1939. New York World's Fair.

113 28 1 f. 25 red . . . 45 65
114 2 f. 25 blue . . . 45 65

29 Storming the Bastille

1939. 150th Anniv of French Revolution.

115 29 45 c. + 25 c. green & black . . . 4·75 5·00
116 70 c. + 30 c. brown & black . . . 4·75 5·00
117 90 c. + 35 c. orange & black . . . 4·75 5·00
118 1 f. 25 + 1 f. red and black . . . 4·75 5·00
119 2 f. 25 + 2 f. blue & black . . . 4·75 5·00

30 Twin-engine Airliner over Jungle

1940. Air.

120 30 1 f. 90 blue . . . 45 60
121 2 f. 90 red . . . 45 60
122 4 f. 50 green . . . 45 60
123 4 f. 90 olive . . . 60 75
124 6 f. 90 orange . . . 65 85

1941. National Defence Fund. Surch **SECOURS NATIONAL** and value.

124a + 1 f. on 50 c. (No. 89) . . . 2·00 2·00
124b + 2 f. on 80 c. (No. 94) . . . 4·00 4·00
124c + 2 f. on 1 f. 50 (No. 100) . . . 4·00 4·00
124d + 3 f. on 2 f. (No. 103) . . . 4·00 4·00

31a Ox Caravan

1942. Marshal Petain issue.

124e 31a 1 f. green . . . 20 1·25
124f 2 f. 50 blue . . . 15 1·25

1942. Air. Colonial Child Welfare Fund. As Nos. 98g/i of Niger.

124g 1 f. 50 + 3 f. 50 green . . . 15
124h 2 f. + 6 f. brown . . . 15
124i 3 f. + 9 f. red . . . 15

1942. Air. Imperial Fortnight. As No. 98j of Niger.

124j 1 f. 20 + 1 f. 80 blue and red . . . 15

32 Twin-engine Airliner over Camel Caravan

1942. Air. T **32** inscr "MAURITANIE" at foot.

124k 32 50 f. orange and yellow . . . 75 1·10

1944. Surch

125 25 3 f. 50 on 65 c. green . . . 25 20
126 4 f. on 65 c. green . . . 30 35
127 5 f. on 65 c. green . . . 40 60
128 10 f. on 65 c. green . . . 40 50
129 27 15 f. on 90 c. orange . . . 65 70

ISLAMIC REPUBLIC.

35 Flag of Republic

37 Well

38 Slender-billed Gull

1960. Inauguration of Islamic Republic.

130 35 25 f. bistre, green and brown on rose . . . 40 35

1960. 10th Anniv of African Technical Co-operation Commission. As T **4** of Malagasy Republic.

131 25 f. blue and turquoise . . . 40 35

1960.

132 37 50 c. purple & brn (postage) . . . 10 10
133 – 1 f. bistre, brown and green . . . 10 10
134 – 2 f. brown, green and blue . . . 15 10
135 – 3 f. red, sepia and turquoise . . . 20 20
136 – 4 f. buff and green . . . 20 20
137 – 5 f. chocolate, brown & red . . . 15 10
138 – 10 f. blue, black & brown . . . 20 15
139 – 15 f. multicoloured . . . 40 15
140 – 20 f. brown and green . . . 30 15
141 – 25 f. blue and green . . . 50 15
142 – 30 f. blue, violet & bistre . . . 50 15
143 – 50 f. brown and green . . . 80 40
144 – 60 f. purple, red and green . . . 1·25 40
145 – 85 f. brown, sepia & blue . . . 3·50 1·50
146 – 100 f. brown, chocolate and blue (air) . . . 6·00 2·75
147 – 200 f. myrtle, brn and sepia . . . 14·00 5·75
148 38 500 f. sepia, blue & brn . . . 30·00 11·50

DESIGNS—VERT: (As Type **37**) 2 f. Harvesting dates; 5 f. Harvesting millet; 25, 30 f. Seated dance; 50 f. "Telmidi" (symbolic figure); 60 f. Metalsmith; 85 f. Scimitar oryx; 100 f. Greater flamingo; 200 f. African spoonbill. HORIZ: 3 f. Barbary sheep; 4 f. Fennec foxes; 10 f. Cordwainer; 15 f. Fishing-boat; 20 f. Nomad school.

39 Flag and Map

43 Campaign Emblem

42 European, African and Boeing 707 Airliners

1960. Proclamation of Independence.

149 39 25 f. green, brown and chest . . . 50 50

1962. Air. Air Afrique Airline.

150 42 100 f. green, brown & bistre . . . 1·75 1·10

1962. Malaria Eradication.

151 43 25 f. + 5 f. olive . . . 50 50

44 U.N. Headquarters and View of Nouakchott

1962. Admission to U.N.O.

152 44 15 f. brown, black and blue . . . 20 20
153 25 f. brown, myrtle and blue . . . 35 35
154 85 f. brown, purple and blue . . . 1·00 1·00

45 Union Flag

1962. 1st Anniv of Union of African and Malagasy States.

155 45 30 f. blue . . . 45 45

46 Eagle and Crescent over Nouakchott

1962. 8th Endemic Diseases Eradication Conference, Nouakchott.

156 46 30 f. green, brown and blue . . . 45 35

47 Diesel Mineral Train

1962.

157 47 50 f. multicoloured . . . 2·25 85

1962. Air. 1st Anniv of Admission to U.N.O. As T **44** but views from different angles and inscr "1 er ANNIVERSAIRE 27 OCTOBRE 1962".

158 100 f. blue, brown & turquoise . . . 1·10 90

49 Map and Agriculture

1962. 2nd Anniv of Independence.

159 49 30 f. green and purple . . . 45 30

50 Congress Representatives

1962. 1st Anniv of Unity Congress.
160 **50** 25 f. brown, myrtle & blue 45 40

51 Globe and Emblem

1962. Freedom from Hunger.
161 **51** 25 f. + 5 f. blue, brown & pur 55 55

52 Douglas DC-3 Airliner over Nouakchott Airport

1963. Air. Creation of National Airline.
162 **52** 500 f. myrtle, brown & blue 12·00 4·50

53 Open-cast Mining, Zouerate

1963. Air. Mining Development. Multicoloured.
163 100 f. Type **53** . . . . 2·50 60
164 200 f. Port-Etienne . . . . . 4·50 1·75

54 Striped Hyena   56 "Posts and Telecommunications"

1963. Animals.
165 **54** 50 c. black, brown & myrtle 10 10
166 – 1 f. black, blue and buff . . 10 10
167 – 1 f. 50 brown, olive & pur 20 15
168 – 2 f. purple, green and red 15 15
169 – 5 f. bistre, blue and ochre . 25 20
170 – 10 f. black and ochre . . . 40 20
171 – 15 f. purple and blue . . . 40 20
172 – 20 f. bistre, purple and blue 50 20
173 – 25 f. ochre, brown & turq 70 25
174 – 30 f. bistre, brown and blue 1·25 30
175 – 50 f. bistre, brown & green 1·75 60
176 – 60 f. bistre, brown & turq 2·25 90
ANIMALS—HORIZ: 1 f. Spotted hyena; 2 f. Guinea baboons; 10 f. Leopard; 15 f. Bongos; 20 f. Aardvark; 30 f. North African crested porcupine; 60 f. Chameleon. VERT: 1 f. 50, Cheetah; 5 f. Dromedaries; 25 f. Patas monkeys; 50 f. Dorcas gazelle.

1963. Air. African and Malagasy Posts and Telecommunications Union.
177 **56** 85 f. multicoloured . . . . 1·00 65

57 "Telstar" Satellite

1963. Air. Space Telecommunications.
178 **57** 50 f. brown, purple & green 65 45
179 – 100 f. blue, brown and red 1·25 80
180 – 150 f. turquoise and brown 2·25 1·50
DESIGNS: 100 f. "Syncom" satellite, 150 f. "Relay" satellite.

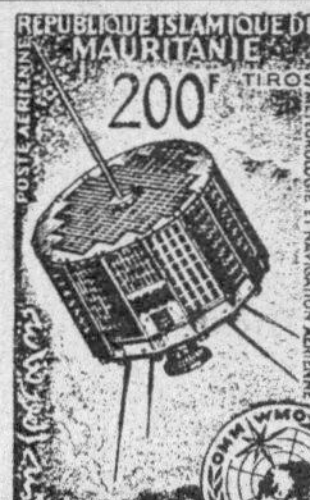

58 "Tiros" Satellite   60 U.N. Emblem, Sun and Birds

59 Airline Emblem

1963. Air. World Meteorological Day.
181 **58** 200 f. brown, blue & green 3·50 1·75

1963. Air. 1st Anniv of "Air Afrique" and DC-8 Service Inauguration.
182 **59** 25 f. multicoloured 50 25

1963. Air. 15th Anniv of Declaration of Human Rights.
183 **60** 100 f. blue, violet & purple 1·25 85

61 Cogwheels and Wheat   62 Lichtenstein's Sandgrouse

1964. Air. European–African Economic Convention.
184 **61** 50 f. multicoloured . . . . 1·10 70

1964. Air. Birds.
185 **62** 100 f. ochre, brown & green 7·50 1·60
186 – 200 f. black, brown & blue 12·00 3·75
187 – 500 f. slate, red and green 26·00 10·00
DESIGNS: 200 f. Reed cormorant; 500 f. Dark chanting goshawk.

63 Temple, Philae

1964. Air. Nubian Monuments Preservation.
188 **63** 10 f. brown, black and blue 45 30
189 25 f. slate, brown and blue 70 60
190 60 f. chocolate, brown & bl 1·50 1·10

64 W.M.O. Emblem. Sun and Lightning   65 Radar Antennae and Sun Emblem

1964. World Meteorological Day.
191 **64** 85 f. blue, orange & brown 1·25 80

1964. International Quiet Sun Years.
192 **65** 25 f. red, green and blue . 35 25

66 Bowl depicting Horse-racing

1964. Air. Olympic Games, Tokyo.
193 **66** 15 f. brown and bistre . . . 30 25
194 – 50 f. brown and blue 60 50
195 – 85 f. brown and red . . . . 1·10 1·00
196 – 100 f. brown and green . . 1·50 1·25
DESIGNS—VERT: 50 f. Running (vase); 85 f. Wrestling (vase). HORIZ: 100 f. Chariot-racing (bowl).

67 Grey Mullet   68 "Co-operation"

1964. Marine Fauna.
197 **67** 1 f. green, blue and brown 15 15
198 – 5 f. purple, green & brown 20 15
199 – 10 f. green, ochre and blue 35 20
200 – 60 f. slate, green and brown 2·00 85
DESIGNS—VERT: 5 f. Lobster ("Panulirus mauritanicus"); 10 f. Lobster ("Panulirus regius"). HORIZ: 60 f. Meagre.

1964. French, African and Malagasy Co-operation.
201 **68** 25 f. brown, green & mauve 40 30

69 Pres. Kennedy   70 "Nymphaea lotus"

1964. Air. 1st Death Anniv of Pres. Kennedy.
202 **69** 100 f. multicoloured . . . . 1·40 1·00

1965. Mauritanian Flowers.
203 **70** 5 f. green, red and blue . . 15 15
204 – 10 f. green, ochre & purple 25 15
205 – 20 f. brown, red and sepia 45 20
206 – 45 f. turquoise, purple & grn 1·10 60
FLOWERS—VERT: 10 f. "Acacia gommier"; 45 f. "Caralluma retrospiciens". HORIZ: 20 f. "Adenium obesum".

71 "Hardine"   72 Abraham Lincoln

1965. Musical Instruments and Musicians.
207 **71** 2 f. brown, bistre and blue 15 15
208 – 8 f. brown, bistre and red 30 15
209 – 25 f. brown, black & green 60 20
210 – 40 f. black, blue and violet 80 35
DESIGNS: 8 f. "Tobol" (drums); 25 f. "Tidinit" ("Violins"); 40 f. Native band.

1965. Death Centenary of Abraham Lincoln.
211 **72** 50 f. multicoloured 70 35

73 Early Telegraph and Relay Satellite

1965. Air. Centenary of I.T.U.
212 **73** 250 f. green, mauve & blue 4·25 3·25

74 Palms in the Adrar

1965. "Tourism and Archaeology" (1st series).
213 **74** 1 f. green, brown and blue 10 10
214 – 4 f. brown, red and blue . . 15 10
215 – 15 f. multicoloured . . . 30 20
216 – 60 f. sepia, brown and green 90 45
DESIGNS—VERT: 4 f. Chinguetti Mosque. HORIZ: 15 f. Clay-pits; 60 f. Carved doorway, Qualata.
See also Nos. 255/8.

75 "Attack on Cancer" (the Crab)   76 Wooden Tea Service

1965. Air. Campaign against Cancer.
217 **75** 100 f. red, blue and ochre 1·50 60

1965. Native Handicrafts.
218 **76** 3 f. brown, ochre and slate 15 15
219 – 7 f. purple, orange and blue 20 20
220 – 25 f. brown, black and red 35 20
221 – 50 f. red, green and orange 75 35
DESIGNS—VERT: 7 f. Snuff-box and pipe; 25 f. Damasquine dagger. HORIZ: 50 f. Mederdra chest.

77 Nouakchott Wharf   78 Sir Winston Churchill

1965. Mauritanian Development.
222 – 5 f. green and brown . . . 90 60
223 **77** 10 f. red, turquoise and blue 15 10
224 – 30 f. red, brown and purple 1·75 60
225 – 85 f. violet, lake and blue 1·25 55
DESIGNS—VERT: 5 f., 30 f. Choum Tunnel. HORIZ: 85 f. Nouakchott Hospital.

1965. Air. Churchill Commem.
226 **78** 200 f. multicoloured . . . 2·50 1·25

79 Rocket "Diamant"

1966. Air. French Satellites.
227 **79** 30 f. green, red and blue . 50 25
228 – 60 f. purple, blue & turquoise 1·00 45
229 – 90 f. lake, violet and blue 1·50 75
DESIGNS—HORIZ: 60 f. Satellite "A 1" and Globe; 90 f. Rocket "Scout" and satellite "FR 1".

80 Dr. Schweitzer and Hospital Scene

1966. Air. Schweitzer Commem.
230 **80** 50 f. multicoloured . . . . 1·10 50

81 Stafford, Schirra and "Gemini 6"

1966. Air. Space Flights. Multicoloured.
231 50 f. Type **81** 60 25
232 100 f. Borman, Lovell and "Gemini 7" . . . . 1·25 60
233 200 f. Beliaiev, Leonov and "Voskhod 2" . . . . 2·50 1·25

82 African Woman and Carved Head

1966. World Festival of Negro Arts, Dakar.
234 **82** 10 f. black, brown & grn 20 10
235 – 30 f. purple, black and blue 35 20
236 – 60 f. purple, red and orange 75 45
DESIGNS: 30 f. Dancers and hands playing cornet; 60 f. Cine-camera and village huts.

83 "Dove" over Map of Africa **84** Satellite "D 1"

1966. Air. Organization of African Unity. (O.A.U.).
237 **83** 100 f. multicoloured . . . 1·00 50

1966. Air. Launching of Satellite "D 1".
238 **84** 100 f. plum, brown & blue 1·10 75

85 Breguet 14T2 Salon

1966. Air. Early Aircraft.
239 **85** 50 f. indigo, blue and bistre 80 25
240 – 100 f. green, purple & blue 1·75 50
241 – 150 f. turquoise, brn & blue 2·50 75
242 – 200 f. indigo, blue & purple 3·50 1·25
AIRCRAFT: 100 f. Farman Goliath; 150 f. Couzinet "Arc en Ciel"; 200 f. Latecoere 28-3 seaplane "Comte de la Vaulx".

86 "Acacia ehrenbergiana"

1966. Mauritanian Flowers. Multicoloured.
243 10 f. Type **86** 25 15
244 15 f. "Schouwia purpurea" . . 35 15
245 20 f. "Ipomaea asarifolia" . . 45 20
246 25 f. "Grewia bicolor" . . . 55 25
247 30 f. "Pancratium trianthum" 90 25
248 60 f. "Blepharis linariifolia" . 1·40 55

87 DC-8F and "Air Afrique" Emblem

1966. Air. Inauguration of Douglas DC-8F Air Services.
249 **87** 30 f. grey, black and red . 40 15

88 "Raft of the Medusa" (after Gericault)

1966. Air. 150th Anniv of Shipwreck of the "Medusa".
250 **88** 500 f. multicoloured . . . 9·00 6·50

89 "Myrina silenus" **90** "Hunting" (petroglyph from Tenses, Adrar)

1966. Butterflies. Multicoloured.
251 5 f. Type **89** 30 20
252 30 f. "Colotis danae" . . . . 1·00 40
253 45 f. "Hypolimnas misippus" 1·75 60
254 60 f. "Danaus chrysippus" . . 2·50 85

1966. Tourism and Archaeology (2nd series).
255 **90** 2 f. chestnut and brown . 15 15
256 – 3 f. brown and blue . . . 20 20
257 – 30 f. green and red 55 25
258 – 50 f. brown, green & pur . 1·25 80
DESIGNS: 3 f. "Fighting" (petroglyph from Tenses, Adrar); 30 f. Copper jug (from Le Mreyer, Adrar); 50 f. Camel and caravan.

91 Cogwheels and Ears of Wheat

1966. Air. Europafrique.
259 **91** 50 f. multicoloured 70 40

92 U.N.E.S.C.O. Emblem

1966. 20th Anniv of U.N.E.S.C.O.
260 **92** 30 f. multicoloured 45 20

93 Olympic Village, Grenoble

1967. Publicity for Olympic Games (1968).
261 – 20 f. brown, blue and green 30 20
262 **93** 30 f. brown, green and blue 40 30
263 – 40 f. brown, purple & blue 60 40
264 – 100 f. brown, green & blk 1·10 70
DESIGNS—VERT: 20 f. Old and new buildings, Mexico City; 40 f. Ice rink, Grenoble and Olympic torch. HORIZ: 100 f. Olympic stadium, Mexico City.

94 South African Crowned Crane **95** Globe, Rockets and Eye

1967. Air. Birds. Multicoloured.
265 100 f. Type **94** . . . . 3·75 1·50
266 200 f. Great egret . . . . . . 7·50 2·10
267 500 f. Ostrich . . . . 16·00 6·75

1967. Air. World Fair, Montreal.
268 **95** 250 f. brown, blue & black 2·25 1·25

96 Prosopis **97** Jamboree Emblem and Scout Kit

1967. Trees.
269 **96** 10 f. green, blue and brown 20 10
270 – 15 f. green, blue and purple 25 15
271 – 20 f. green, purple and blue 30 15
272 – 25 f. brown and green . . . 40 20
273 – 30 f. brown, green and red 55 25
TREES: 15 f. Jujube; 20 f. Date palm; 25 f. Peltophorum; 30 f. Baobab.

1967. World Scout Jamboree, Idaho.
274 **97** 60 f. blue, green and brown 70 35
275 – 90 f. blue, green and red . . 1·10 50
DESIGN—HORIZ: 90 f. Jamboree emblem and scouts.

98 Weaving **99** Atomic Symbol

1967. Advancement of Mauritanian Women.
276 **98** 5 f. red, black and violet . . 15 10
277 – 10 f. black, violet and green 20 10
278 – 20 f. black, purple and blue 35 15
279 – 30 f. blue, black and brown 45 25
280 – 50 f. black, violet & indigo 70 30
DESIGNS—VERT: 10 f. Needlework; 30 f. Laundering. HORIZ: 20 f. Nursing; 50 f. Sewing (with machines).

1967. Air. International Atomic Energy Agency.
281 **99** 200 f. blue, green and red . 2·25 1·10

100 Cattle

1967. Campaign for Prevention of Cattle Plague.
282 **100** 30 f. red, blue and green . 35 25

101 Map of Africa, Letters and Pylons

1967. Air. 5th Anniv of U.A.M.P.T.
283 **101** 100 f. green, brown & pur 1·00 60

102 "Francois of Rimini" (Ingres) **103** Currency Tokens

1967. Air. Death Centenary of Jean Ingres (painter). Multicoloured.
284 90 f. Type **102** . . . . 1·10 60
285 200 f. "Ingres in his Studio" (Alaux) . . . . 2·10 1·25
See also Nos. 306/8.

1967. 5th Anniv of West African Monetary Union.
286 **103** 30 f. grey and orange . . . 35 15

104 "Hyphaene thebaica" **105** Human Rights Emblem

1967. Mauritanian Fruits.
287 **104** 1 f. brown, green & purple 15 10
288 – 2 f. yellow, green & brown 15 10
289 – 3 f. olive, green and violet 15 10
290 – 4 f. red, green and brown 15 10
291 – 5 f. orange, brown & green 20 10
FRUITS—HORIZ: 2 f. "Balanites aegyptiaca"; 4 f. "Ziziphus lotus". VERT: 3 f. "Adansonia digitata"; 5 f. "Phoenix dactylifera".

1968. Human Rights Year.
292 **105** 30 f. yellow, green & black 30 20
293 50 f. yellow, brown & black 55 35

106 Chancellor Adenauer **108** Mosque, Nouakchott

107 Skiing

1968. Air. Adenauer Commemoration.
294 **106** 100 f. sepia, brown & blue 1·25 60

1968. Air. Olympic Games, Grenoble and Mexico.
296 **107** 20 f. purple, indigo & blue 30 10
297 – 30 f. brown, green & plum 35 15
298 – 50 f. green, blue and ochre 55 25
299 – 100 f. green, red & brown 1·00 50
DESIGNS—VERT: 30 f. Horse-vaulting; 50 f. Ski-jumping. HORIZ: 100 f. Hurdling.

1968. Tourism. Multicoloured.
300 30 f. Type **108** 25 20
301 45 f. Amogjar Pass 35 20
302 90 f. Cavaliers' Tower, Boutilimit 65 35

109 Man and W.H.O. Emblem

1968. Air. 20th Anniv of W.H.O.
303 **109** 150 f. blue, purple & brn . 1·50 75

110 U.N.E.S.C.O. Emblem and "Movement of Water"

1968. International Hydrological Decade.
304 **110** 90 f. green and lake . . . 70 40

111 U.P.U. Building, Berne

1968. Admission of Mauritania to U.P.U.
305 **111** 30 f. brown and red . . . 35 20

1968. Air. Paintings by Ingres. As T **102**. Mult.
306 100 f. "Man's Torso" . . . . 1·10 65
307 150 f. "The Iliad" . . . . . . 1·75 95
308 250 f. "The Odyssey" . . . . 2·75 1·60

112 Land-yachts crossing Desert

113 Dr. Martin Luther King

1968. Land-yacht Racing.
309 **112** 30 f. blue, yellow & orange . . 45 25
310 – 40 f. purple, blue & orange . . 55 30
311 – 60 f. green, yellow & orge . . 85 50
DESIGNS—HORIZ: 40 f. Racing on shore. VERT: 60 f. Crew making repairs.

1968. Air. "Apostles of Peace".
312 **113** 50 f. brown, blue and olive . 1·00 40
313 – 50 f. brown and blue . . . 60 25
DESIGN: No. 313, Mahatma Gandhi.

113a "Surprise Letter" (C. A. Coypel)

114 Donkey and Foal

1968. Air. "Philexafrique" Stamp Exn Abidjan, Ivory Coast, (1969) (1st issue).
315 **113a** 100 f. multicoloured . . 1·75 1·75

1968. Domestic Animals. Multicoloured.
316 5 f. Type **114** 15 10
317 10 f. Ewe and lamb 20 15
318 15 f. Dromedary and calf . . 25 15
319 30 f. Mare and foal 45 25
320 50 f. Cow and calf 70 35
321 90 f. Goat and kid . . . . . . 1·40 50

114a Forest Scene and Stamp of 1938

1969. Air. "Philexafrique" Stamp Exhibition, Abidjan, Ivory Coast (2nd issue).
322 **114a** 50 f. purple, green & brown 1·10 1·10

114b "Napoleon at Council of Five Hundred" (Bouchot)

115 Map and I.L.O. Emblem

1969. Air. Birth Bicentenary of Napoleon Bonaparte. Multicoloured.
323 50 f. **114b** . . . . 1·50 90
324 90 f. "Napoleon's Installation by the Council of State" (Conder) 2·00 1·25
325 250 f. "The Farewell of Fontainebleau" (Vernet) . . 5·00 3·25

1969. 50th Anniv of I.L.O.
326 **115** 50 f. multicoloured . . . 50 25

MINIMUM PRICE

The minimum price quoted is 10p which represents a handling charge rather than a basis for valuing common stamps. For further notes about prices, see introductory pages.

116 Monitor Lizard

117 Date Palm, "Parlatoria blanchardi" and "Pharoscymus anchorage"

1969. Reptiles. Multicoloured.
327 5 f. Type **116** 25 20
328 10 f. Horned viper 45 30
329 30 f. Black-collared cobra . . 1·10 35
330 60 f. Rock python . . . . . 1·75 1·10
331 85 f. Nile crocodile . . . . . 2·75 1·40

1969. Date-palms. Protection Campaign.
332 **117** 30 f. blue, red and green . 30 15

118 Camel and Emblem

1969. Air. African Tourist Year.
333 **118** 50 f. purple, blue & orange 70 35

119 Dancers and Baalbek Columns

1969. Baalbek Festival, Lebanon.
334 **119** 100 f. brown, red and blue 1·25 55

120 "Apollo 8" and Moon

1969. Air. Moon Flight of "Apollo 8". Embossed on gold foil.
335 **120** 1,000 f. gold . . . . . . 14·00 14·00

121 Wolde (marathon)

122a Bank Emblem

122 London–Istanbul Route-Map

1969. Air. Gold Medal Winners, Mexico Olympic Games.
336 **121** 30 f. red, brown and blue . 25 15
337 – 70 f. red, brown and green . 50 30
338 – 150 f. green, bistre and red 1·25 70
DESIGNS: 70 f. Beamon (athletics); 150 f. Vera Caslavska (gymnastics).

1969. Air. London–Sydney Motor Ralley.
339 **122** 10 f. brown, blue & purple 15 10
340 – 20 f. brown, blue & purple 30 15
341 – 50 f. brown, blue & purple 60 25
342 – 70 f. brown, blue & purple 85 30
ROUTE-MAPS: 20 f. Ankara-Teheran; 50 f. Kandahar–Bombay; 70 f. Perth-Sydney.

1969. 5th Anniv of African Development Bank. Multicoloured.
344 **122a** 30 f. brown, green & blue 30 15

123 Pendant

124 Sea-water Desalination Plant, Nouakchott

1969. Native Handicrafts.
345 **123** 10 f. brown and purple . . 20 15
346 – 20 f. red, black and blue . 40 20
DESIGN—HORIZ: 20 f. Rahla headdress.

1969. Economic Development.
347 **124** 10 f. blue, purple and red . 20 15
348 – 15 f. black, lake and blue . 25 15
349 – 30 f. black, purple & blue . 30 20
DESIGNS: 15 f. Fishing quay, Nouadhibou; 30 f. Meat-processing plant, Kaedi.

125 Lenin

126 "Sternocera interrupta"

1970. Birth Centenary of Lenin.
350 **125** 30 f. black, red and blue . 30 20

1970. Insects.
351 **126** 5 f. black, buff and brown 25 15
352 – 10 f. brown, yellow & lake 35 15
353 – 20 f. olive, purple & brown 50 25
354 – 30 f. violet, green & brn 80 45
355 – 40 f. brown, blue and lake 1·50 70
INSECTS: 10 f. "Anoplocnemis curvipes"; 20 f. "Julodis aequinoctialis"; 30 f. "Thermophilum sexmaculatum marginatum"; 40 f. "Plocaederus denticornis".

127 Footballers and Hemispheres

128 Japanese Musician, Emblem and Map on Palette

1970. World Cup Football Championships, Mexico.
356 **127** 25 f. multicoloured 30 20
357 – 30 f. multicoloured 35 20
358 – 70 f. multicoloured 70 30
359 – 150 f. multicoloured . . . 1·60 75
DESIGNS: 30, 70, 150 f. As Type **127**, but with different players.

1970. New U.P.U. Headquarters Building. As T **81** of New Caledonia.
360 30 f. red, brown and green . . 35 20

1970. Air. "EXPO 70" World Fair, Osaka, Japan. Multicoloured.
361 50 f. Type **128** 50 20
362 75 f. Japanese fan 75 35
363 150 f. Stylised bird, map and boat . . . . 1·40 80

129 U.N. Emblem and Examples of Progress

1970. Air. 25th Anniv of U.N.O.
364 **129** 100 f. green, brown & blue 1·00 60

130 Vladimir Komarov

131 Descent of "Apollo 13"

1970. Air. "Lost Heroes of Space" (1st series).
365 **130** 150 f. brown, orge & slate 1·50 70
366 – 150 f. brown, blue and slate 1·50 70
367 – 150 f. brown, orge & slate 1·50 70
HEROES: No. 366, Elliott See; 367, Yuri Gagarin. See also Nos. 376/8.

1970. Air. Space Flight of "Apollo 13".
369 **131** 500 f. red, blue and gold . 5·00 5·00

132 Woman in Traditional Costume

133 Arms and State House

1970. Traditional Costumes. As T **132**.
370 **132** 10 f. orange and brown . 20 15
371 – 30 f. blue, red and brown 40 20
372 – 40 f. brown, purple & red 50 30
373 – 50 f. blue and brown . . 70 35
374 – 70 f. brown, chocolate & blue 90 45

1970. Air. 10th Anniv of Independence.
375 **133** 100 f. multicoloured . . . 1·00 45

1970. Air. "Lost Heroes of Space" (2nd series). As T **130**.
376 150 f. brown, blue & turquoise 1·50 70
377 150 f. brown, blue & turquoise 1·50 70
378 150 f. brown, blue and orange 1·50 70
HEROES: No. 376, Roger Chaffee; No. 377, Virgil Grissom; No. 378, Edward White.

134 Greek Wrestling

1971. Air. "Pre-Olympics Year".
380 **134** 100 f. brown, purple & bl 1·10 75

135 People of Different Races

1971. Racial Equality Year.
381 **135** 30 f. plum, blue & brown 30 15
382 – 40 f. black, red and blue 35 20
DESIGN—VERT: 40 f. European and African hands.

136 Pres. Nasser

1971. Air. Pres. Gamal Nasser of Egypt Commemoration.
383 **136** 100 f. multicoloured . . . 85 40

137 Gen. De Gaulle in Uniform

138 Scout Badge, Scout and Map

1971. De Gaulle Commem. Multicoloured.
384 40 f. Type **137** . . . . 1·25 60
385 100 f. De Gaulle as President of France . . . . 2·75 1·40

1971. Air. 13th World Scout Jamboree, Asagiri, Japan.
387 **138** 35 f. multicoloured . . . 40 20
388 40 f. multicoloured . . . 50 20
389 100 f. multicoloured . . . 1·25 45

139 Diesel Locomotive

1971. Miferma Iron-ore Mines. Multicoloured.
390 35 f. Iron ore train . . . . . 1·10 60
391 100 f. Type **139** . . . . . . 2·40 1·40
Nos. 390/1 form a composite design.

139a Headquarters, Brazzaville, and Ardin Musicians

1971. Air. 10th Anniv of African and Malagasy Posts and Telecommunications Union.
392 **139a** 100 f. multicoloured . . 1·10 60

140 A.P.U. Emblem and Airmail Envelope

1971. Air. 10th Anniv of African Postal Union.
393 **140** 35 f. multicoloured . . . 40 25

141 U.N.I.C.E.F. Emblem and Child

1971. 25th Anniv of U.N.I.C.E.F.
394 **141** 35 f. black, brown & blue 35 20

142 "Moslem King" (c. 1218)

1972. Air. Moslem Miniatures. Multicoloured.
395 35 f. Type **142** 45 20
396 40 f. "Enthroned Prince" (Egypt, c. 1334) 60 25
397 100 f. "Pilgrims' Caravan" (Maquamat, Baghdad 1237) 1·50 70

1972. Air. U.N.E.S.C.O. "Save Venice" Campaign. As T **127** of Mali. Multicoloured.
398 45 f. "Quay and Ducal Palace" (Carlevaris) (vert) 60 25
399 100 f. "Grand Canal" (Canaletto) . . . . 1·40 60
400 250 f. "Santa Maria della Salute" (Canaletto) . . . . 3·00 1·50

143 Hurdling

1972. Air. Olympic Games, Munich.
401 **143** 75 f. purple, orange & grn 55 30
402 100 f. purple, blue & brn 75 40
403 200 f. purple, lake & green 1·60 70

144 Nurse tending Baby

145 Samuel Morse and Morse Key

1972. Mauritanian Red Crescent Fund.
405 **144** 35 f. + 5 f. multicoloured 60 60

1972. World Telecommunications Day. Mult.
406 35 f. Type **145** 35 20
407 40 f. "Relay" satellite and hemispheres 45 20
408 75 f. Alexander Graham Bell and early telephone 70 35

146 Spirifer Shell

1972. Fossil Shells. Multicoloured.
409 25 f. Type **146** . . . . 1·00 35
410 75 f. Trilobite . . . . 2·75 1·10

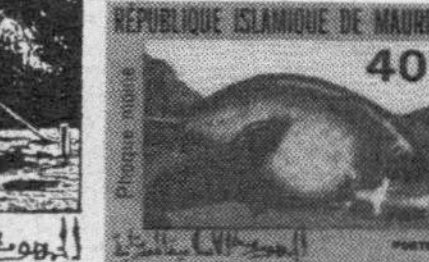

147 "Luna 16" and Moon Probe

151 Mediterranean Monk Seal with Young

149 Africans and 500 f. Coin

1972. Air. Russian Exploration of the Moon.
411 **147** 75 f. brown, blue & green 60 30
412 – 100 f. brown, grey & violet 90 50
DESIGN—HORIZ: 100 f. "Lunokhod 1".

1972. Air. Gold Medal-Winners, Munich. Nos. 401/3 optd as listed below.
413 **143** 75 f. purple, orange & grn 60 30
414 100 f. purple, blue & brn 80 50
415 200 f. purple, lake & green 1·60 1·00
OVERPRINTS: 75 f. **110m. HAIES MILBURN MEDAILLE D'OR**; 100 f. **400m. HAIES AKII-BUA MEDAILLE D'OR**; 200 f. **3,000m. STEEPLE KEINO MEDAILLE D'OR**.

1972. 10th Anniv of West African Monetary Union.
416 **149** 35 f. grey, brown & green 30 20

1973. Air. Moon Flight of "Apollo 17". No. 267 surch **Apollo XVII Decembre 1972** and value.
417 250 f. on 500 f. multicoloured 4·00 2·00

1973. Seals. Multicoloured.
418 40 f. Type **151** (postage) . . . 1·25 50
419 135 f. Head of Mediterranean monk seal (air) . . . . . 3·75 2·00

152 "Lion and Crocodile" (Delacroix)

1973. Air. Paintings by Delacroix. Mult.
420 100 f. Type **152** . . . . 1·50 75
421 250 f. "Lion attacking Forest Hog" . . . . 3·25 2·00

153 "Horns of Plenty"

1973. 10th Anniv of World Food Programme.
422 **153** 35 f. multicoloured 30 20

154 U.P.U. Monument, Berne, and Globe

1973. World U.P.U. Day.
423 **154** 100 f. blue, orange & grn 1·00 65

155 Nomad Encampment and Eclipse

1973. Total Eclipse of the Sun.
424 **155** 35 f. purple and green . . 35 20
425 – 40 f. purple, red and blue 45 20
426 – 140 f. purple and red . . . 1·60 75
DESIGNS—VERT: 40 f. Rocket and Concorde. HORIZ: 140 f. Observation team.

1973. "Drought Relief". African Solidarity. No. 320 surch **SECHERESSE SOLIDARITE AFRICAINE** and value.
428 20 u. on 50 f. multicoloured . 65 45

155a Crane with Letter and Union Emblem

1973. 12th Anniv of African and Malagasy Posts and Telecommunications Union.
429 **155a** 20 u. brown, lt brn & orge 70 45

157 Detective making Arrest and Fingerprint

1973. 50th Anniv of International Criminal Police Organization (Interpol).
430 **157** 15 u. violet, red & brown . 1·10 45

1974. Various stamps surch with values in new currency. (a) Postage.

(i) Nos. 345/6.
431 **123** 27 u. on 10 f. brown & purple . . . . 1·50 70
432 – 28 u. on 20 f. red, black and blue . . . . 1·75 90

(ii) Nos. 351/5.
433 **126** 5 u. on 5 f. black, buff and brown 70 50
434 – 7 u. on 10 f. brown, yellow and lake 60 30
435 – 8 u. on 20 f. olive, pur and brown 70 35
436 – 10 u. on 30 f. violet, purple and brown . . . . . . 1·00 45
437 – 20 u. on 4 f. brown, blue and lake . . . . 2·00 1·10

(iii) Nos. 409/10.
438 **146** 5 u. on 25 f. multicoloured 60 40
439 – 15 u. on 75 f. multicoloured 1·75 1·00

(iv) No. 418.
440 **151** 8 u. on 40 f. multicoloured 90 45

(b) Air.
(i) Nos. 395/7.
441 **142** 7 u. on 35 f. multicoloured 40 20
442 – 8 u. on 40 f. multicoloured 40 20
443 – 20 u. on 100 f. multicoloured 1·50 70

(ii) No. 419.
444 – 27 u. on 135 f. multicoloured 2·25 85

(iii) Nos. 420/1.
445 **152** 20 u. on 100 f. multicoloured 1·60 70
446 – 50 u. on 250 f. multicoloured 3·75 2·00

(iv) Nos. 424/6.
447 **155** 7 u. on 35 f. purple and green 45 20
448 – 8 u. on 40 f. purple, red and blue 45 20
449 – 28 u. on 140 f. purple and red 1·90 70

159 Footballers

161 Sir Winston Churchill

160 Jules Verne and Scenes from Books

1974. Air. World Cup Football Championships, West Germany.
450 **159** 7 u. multicoloured 40 20
451 8 u. multicoloured 40 20
452 20 u. multicoloured . . . . 1·10 50

1974. Air. Jules Verne "Prophet of Space Travel" and "Skylab" Flights Commemoration.
454 **160** 70 u. silver . . . . 4·50 4·50
455 – 70 u. silver . . . . 4·50 4·50
456 **160** 250 u. gold . . . . 12·00 12·00
457 – 250 u. gold . . . . 12·00 12·00
DESIGNS: Nos. 455, 457, "Skylab" in Space.

1974. Air. Birth Centenary of Sir Winston Churchill.
458 **161** 40 u. red and purple . . . 1·75 95

162 U.P.U. Monument and Globes

1974. Centenary of U.P.U.
459 **162** 30 u. red, green and deep green . . . . 1·25 75
460 50 u. red, light blue and blue 2·00 1·25

163 5 Ouguiya Coin and Banknote

1974. 1st Anniv of Introduction of Ouguiya Currency.
461 **163** 7 u. black, green & blue 35 20
462 – 8 u. black, mauve & green 40 20
463 – 20 u. black, blue and red 1·00 50
DESIGNS: 8 u. 10 ouguiya coin and banknote; 20 u. 20 ouguiya coin and banknote.

164 Lenin

166 Two Hunters

1974. Air. 50th Death Anniv of Lenin.
464 **164** 40 u. green and red . . . 2·00 95

1974. Treaty of Berne Centenary. Nos. 459/60 optd **9 OCTOBRE 100 ANS D'UNION POSTALE INTERNATIONALE.**
465 **162** 30 u. red, green and deep green . . . . 1·60 80
466 50 u. red, light blue and blue 2·00 1·25

1975. Nos. 287/91 surch in new currency.
467 – 1 u. on 5 f. orange, brown and green 10 10
468 – 2 u. on 4 f. red, green and brown 15 15
469 – 3 u. on 2 f. yellow, green and brown 20 15
470 **104** 10 u. on 1 f. brown, green and purple 60 20
471 – 12 u. on 3 f. olive, green and violet 75 30

1975. Rock-carvings, Zemmour.
472 **166** 4 u. red and brown 40 15
473 – 5 u. purple 45 25
474 – 10 u. blue and light blue . 80 35
DESIGNS—VERT: 5 u. Ostrich. HORIZ: 10 u. Elephant.

167 Mauritanian Women

1975. Air. International Women's Year.
475 **167** 12 u. purple, brown & bl 50 25
476 – 40 u. purple, brown & bl 1·75 85
DESIGNS: 40 u. Head of Mauritanian woman.

168 Combined European and African Heads

169 Dr. Schweitzer

1975. Europafrique.
477 **168** 40 u. brown, red & bistre . 1·60 95

1975. Birth Centenary of Dr. Albert Schweitzer.
478 **169** 60 u. olive, brown & green 2·50 1·50

1975. Pan-African Drought Relief. Nos. 301/2 surch **SECHERESSE SOLIDARITE AFRICAINE** and value.
479 15 u. on 45 f. multicoloured . 1·00 50
480 25 u. on 90 f. multicoloured . 1·40 75

171 Akoujt Plant and Man with Camel

172 Fair Emblem

1975. Mining Industry.
481 **171** 10 u. brown, blue & orge 1·00 30
482 – 12 u. blue, red and brown 1·25 40
DESIGN: 12 u. Mining operations.

1975. Nouakchott National Fair.
483 **172** 10 u. multicoloured . . . 40 25

173 Throwing the Javelin

1975. Air. "Pre-Olympic Year". Olympic Games, Montreal (1976).
484 **173** 50 u. red, green & brown 1·60 1·40
485 – 52 u. blue, brown and red 1·75 1·40
DESIGN: 52 u. Running.

174 Commemorative Medal

1975. 15th Anniv of Independence. Multicoloured.
486 10 u. Type **174** 50 30
487 12 u. Map of Mauritania . . 60 35

175 "Soyuz" Cosmonauts Leonov and Kubasov

1975. "Apollo-Soyz" Space Link. Multicoloured.
488 8 u. Type **175** (postage) . . . 45 20
489 10 u. "Soyuz" on launch-pad 55 25
490 20 u. "Apollo" on launch-pad (air) 70 45
491 50 u. Cosmonauts meeting astronauts . . . . 2·00 1·00
492 60 u. Parachute splashdown . 2·25 1·25

176 Foot-soldier of Lauzun's Legion

1976. Bicentenary of American Independence. Multicoloured.
494 8 u. Type **176** (postage) . . . 60 20
495 10 u. "Green Mountain" infantryman 70 20
496 20 u. Lauzun Hussar's officer (air) 90 40
497 50 u. Artillery officer of 3rd Continental Regiment . . . 2·40 1·00
498 60 u. Grenadier of Gatinais' Regiment . . . . . . 3·00 1·25

1976. 10th Anniv of Arab Labour Charter. No. 408 surch **10e ANNIVERSAIRE DE LA CHARTE ARABE DU TRAVAIL** in French and Arabic.
500 12 u. on 75 f. blue, blk & grn 55 30

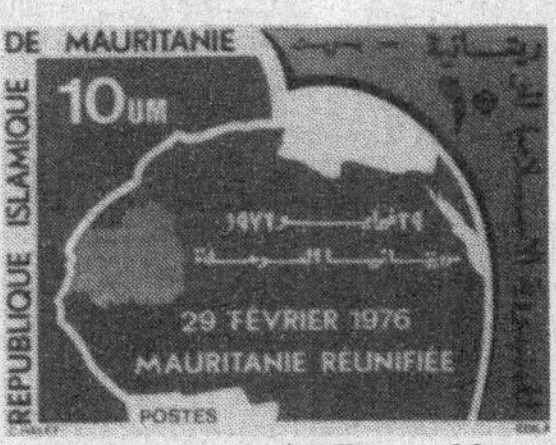

178 Commemorative Text on Map

1976. Reunification of Mauritania.
501 **178** 10 u. green, lilac and deep green 45 30

181 Running

1976. Air. Olympic Games, Montreal.
514 **181** 10 u. brown, green and violet 40 25
515 – 12 u. brown, green and violet 50 35
516 – 52 u. brown, green and violet 1·75 1·25
DESIGNS: 12 u. Vaulting (gymnastics); 52 u. Fencing.

182 LZ-4 at Friedrichshafen

1976. 75th Anniv of Zeppelin Airship. Mult.
517 5 u. Type **182** (postage) 25 15
518 10 u. "Schwaben" over German Landscape 40 20
519 12 u. "Hansa" over Heligoland 50 25
520 20 u. "Bodensee" and Doctor H. Durr . . . . 2·25 75
521 50 u. "Graf Zeppelin" over Capitol, Washington (air) . . 2·25 90
522 60 u. "Graf Zeppelin II" crossing Swiss Alps . . . . 3·00 1·25

183 Temple and Bas-relief

1976. U.N.E.S.C.O. "Save Moenjodaro" (Pakistan) Campaign.
524 **183** 15 u. multicoloured . . . 80 40

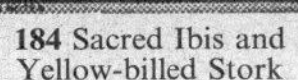

184 Sacred Ibis and Yellow-billed Stork

185 Alexander Graham Bell, Early Telephone and Satellite

1976. Air. Mauritanian Birds. Multicoloured.
525 50 u. Type **184** . . . . 4·25 1·75
526 100 u. Marabou storks (horiz) 7·50 3·75
527 200 u. Long-crested and Martial eagles . . . . 15·00 6·50

1976. Telephone Centenary.
528 **185** 10 u. blue, lake and red . . 50 25

186 Mohammed Ali Jinnah

1976. Birth Centenary of Mohammed Ali Jinnah (first Governor-General of Pakistan).
529 **186** 10 u. multicoloured . . . 35 20

MINIMUM PRICE

The minimum price quoted is 10p which represents a handling charge rather than a basis for valuing common stamps. For further notes about prices, see introductory pages.

187 Capsule Assembly

1977. "Viking" Space Mission. Multicoloured.
530 10 u. Misson Control (horiz) . 50 15
531 12 u. Type **187** 55 20
532 20 u. "Viking" in flight (horiz) (air) 80 25
533 50 u. "Viking" over Mars (horiz) 2·00 60
534 60 u. Parachute descent . . . 2·25 65

188 Bush Hare

1977. Mauritanian Animals. Multicoloured.
536 5 u. Type **188** 30 15
537 10 u. Golden jackals 55 30
538 12 u. Warthogs 75 40
539 14 u. Lion and lioness 85 50
540 15 u. African elephants . . . 1·75 80

189 Frederic and Irene Joliot-Curie (Chemistry, 1935)

1977. Nobel Prize-winners. Multicoloured.
541 12 u. Type **189** (postage) . . . 75 15
542 15 u. Emil von Behring and nurse inoculating patient (1901) . 75 20
543 14 u. George Bernard Shaw and scene from "Androcles and the Lion" (1925) (air) 75 30
544 55 u. Thomas Mann and scene from "Joseph and his Brethren" (1929) . . . . . 1·90 60
545 60 u. International Red Cross and scene on Western Front (Peace Prize) (1917) . . . . 2·25 70

190 A.P.U. Emblem

1977. 25th Anniv of Arab Postal Union.
547 **190** 12 u. multicoloured . . . 45 30

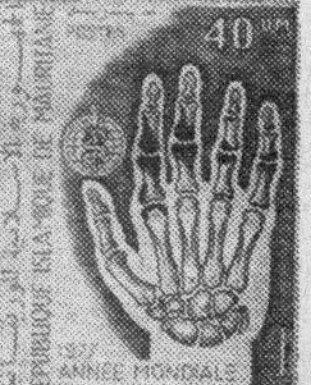

191 Oil Lamp

192 Skeleton of Hand

1977. Pottery from Tegdaoust.

548 **191** 1 u. olive, brown and blue 10 10
549 – 2 u. mauve, brown & blue 15 10
550 – 5 u. orange, brown & blue 25 10
551 – 12 u. brown, green and red 55 20

DESIGNS: 2 u. Four-handled tureen; 5 u. Large jar; 12 u. Narrow-necked jug.

1977. World Rheumatism Year.

552 **192** 40 u. orange, brown & grn 2·00 1·25

193 Holy Kaaba, Mecca

1977. Air. Pilgrimage to Mecca.

553 **193** 12 u. multicoloured . . . 60 40

194 Charles Lindbergh and "Spirit of St. Louis"

1977. History of Aviation. Multicoloured.

554 12 u. Type **194** 50 15
555 14 u. Clement Ader and "Eole" 60 25
556 15 u. Louis Bleriot and Bleriot XI 70 25
557 55 u. General Italo Balbo and Savoia Marchetti S-55X flying boats . . . . 2·25 70
558 60 u. Concorde . . . . 2·50 85

195 Dome of the Rock **197** "Helene Fourment and Her Children" (Rubens)

196 Two Players

1977. Palestinian Welfare.

560 **195** 12 u. multicoloured . . . 70 30
561 14 u. multicoloured . . . 80 35

1977. World Cup Football Championships–Elimination Rounds. Multicoloured.

562 12 u. Type **196** (postage) . . . 40 15
563 14 u. Sir Alf Ramsey and Wembley Stadium 50 20
564 15 u. A "throw-in" 60 20
565 50 u. Football and emblems (air) 2·00 60
566 60 u. Eusebio Ferreira . . . . 2·40 1·00

1977. 400th Birth Anniv of Rubens. Paintings. Multicoloured.

568 12 u. Type **197** 50 15
569 14 u. "The Marquis of Spinola" 60 20
570 67 u. "The Four Philosophers" 2·25 75
571 69 u. "Steen Castle and Park" (horiz) . . . . 2·50 85

198 Addra Gazelles

1978. Endangered Animals. Multicoloured.

573 5 u. Scimitar oryx (horiz) . . 35 15
574 12 u. Type **198** 65 25
575 14 u. African manatee (horiz) 80 35
576 55 u. Barbary sheep . . . . . 3·00 1·00
577 60 u. African elephant (horiz) 3·25 1·25
578 100 u. Ostrich . . . . 4·50 1·75

199 Clasped Hands and President Giscard d'Estaing of France

1978. Air. Franco-African Co-operation. Embossed on foil.

579 **199** 250 u. silver . . . . . . 7·00 7·00
580 500 u. gold . . . . 14·00 14·00

199a Earth-mover and Route Map **200** Footballers

1978. Nouakchott–Nema Highway. Mult.

580a 12 u. Type **199a** . . . . 2·00 1·50
580b 14 u. Bulldozer and route map 2·25 1·75

1978. World Cup Football Championship, Argentina. Multicoloured.

581 12 u. Type **200** 40 20
582 14 u. World Cup 50 25
583 20 u. F.I.F.A. flag and football 85 35

201 Raoul Follereau and St. George fighting Dragon

1978. 25th Anniv of Raoul Follereau Foundation.

585 **201** 12 u. brown and green . 70 40

202 Emblem and People holding Hands **203** Charles de Gaulle

1978. International Anti-Apartheid Year.

586 – 25 u. brown, blue and red 90 60
587 **202** 30 u. brown, blue & green 1·10 70

DESIGN—HORIZ: 25 u. Emblem and people behind fence.

1978. Personalities. Multicoloured.

588 12 u. Type **203** 90 30
589 14 u. King Baudouin of Belgium 90 30
590 55 u. Queen Elizabeth II (25th anniv of Coronation) . . . 2·00 90

1978. Air. "Philexafrique" Stamp Exhibition, Libreville (Gabon) (1st issue), and 2nd International Stamp Fair, Essen (West Germany). As T **262** of Niger. Multicoloured.

591 20 u. Water rail and Hamburg 1859 ½ s. stamp . . . . . . 1·00 65
592 20 u. Spotted hyena and Mauritania 1967 100 f. South African crowned crane stamp 1·00 65

See also Nos. 619/20.

1978. Argentina's Victory in World Cup Football Championship. Nos. 562/6 optd **ARGENTINE–PAYS BAS 3-1** in English and Arabic.

593 **196** 12 u. mult (postage) . . . 50 25
594 – 14 u. multicoloured . . . 55 30
595 – 15 u. multicoloured . . . 65 30
596 – 50 u. multicoloured (air) . 1·75 1·10
597 – 60 u. multicoloured . . . 2·25 1·40

205 View of Nouakchott

1978. 20th Anniv of Nouakchott.

599 **205** 12 u. multicoloured . . . 45 30

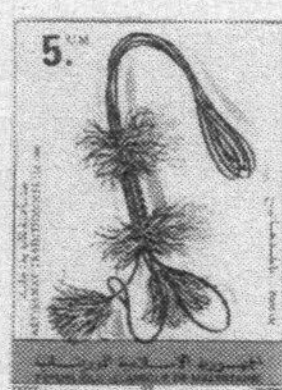

206 Human Rights Emblem **208** Key Chain

207 Wright Flyer I and Clement Ader's Avion III

1978. 30th Anniv of Declaration of Human Rights.

600 **206** 55 u. red and blue . . . . 1·60 1·25

1979. Air. 75th Anniv of First Powered Flight.

601 **207** 15 u. grey, red and blue 75 35
602 – 40 u. violet, blue & brn 1·75 1·10

DESIGN: 40 u. Concorde and Wright Flyer I.

1979. Handicrafts. Multicoloured.

603 5 u. Type **208** 25 15
604 7 u. Tooth-brush case 30 20
605 10 u. Knife sheath 45 25

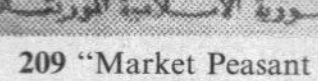

209 "Market Peasant and Wife" **210** Seated Buddha, Temple of Borobudur

1979. 450th Birth Anniv of Albrecht Durer (artist).

606 **209** 12 u. black and red . . . 50 25
607 – 14 u. black and red . . . 60 25
608 – 55 u. black and red . . . 1·60 75
609 – 60 u. black and red . . . 1·90 1·00

DESIGNS: 14 u. "Young Peasant and his Wife"; 55 u. "Mercenary with Banner"; 60 u. "St. George and the Dragon".

1979. U.N.E.S.C.O. Campaign for Preservation of Historic Monuments. Multicoloured.

611 12 u. Type **210** 50 30
612 14 u. Carthaginian warrior and hunting dog 60 30
613 55 u. Erechtheum Caryatid, Acropolis. . . . . 1·75 1·25

211 Rowland Hill and Paddle-steamer "Sirius"

1979. Death Centenary of Sir Rowland Hill. Multicoloured.

614 12 u. Type **211** 50 25
615 14 u. Hill and "Great Republic" (paddle-steamer) 65 25
616 55 u. Hill and "Mauretania I" (liner) . . . . 2·00 60
617 60 u. Hill and "Stirling Castle" (liner) . . . . 2·50 85

212 Satellite over Earth

1979. "Philexafrique" Exhibition, Libreville (2nd issue).

619 – 12 u. multicoloured . . . 60 50
620 **212** 30 u. red, blue and lilac . 1·40 1·25

DESIGN—HORIZ: 12 u. Embossed leather cushion cover.

213 Mother and Children **215** Sprinter on Starting-blocks

1979. International Year of the Child. Multicoloured.

621 12 u. Type **213** 45 25
622 14 u. Mother with sleeping baby 55 35
623 40 u. Children playing with ball 1·50 90

1979. 10th Anniv of "Apollo 11" Moon Landing. Nos. 530/4 optd **ALUNISSAGE APOLLO XI JUILLET 1969**, with Lunar module, or surch also.

624 10 u. Mission Control (horiz) (postage) 40 25
625 12 u. Type **187** 45 30
626 14 u. on 20 u. "Viking" in flight (horiz) (air) 60 25
627 50 u. "Viking" over Mars (horiz) 1·60 1·00
628 60 u. Parachute descent . . . 1·90 1·10

1979. Pre-Olympic Year. Multicoloured.

630 12 u. Type **215** 35 15
631 14 u. Female runner 40 15
632 55 u. Male runner leaving start 1·50 60
633 60 u. Hurdling . . . . 1·60 60

215a "Scomberesox saurus"

1979. Fishes. Multicoloured.

634a 1 u. Type **215a** 10 10
634b 2 u. Swordfish 10 10
634c 3 u. "Trigla lucerna" 15 15

216 Ice Hockey

1979. Winter Olympic Games, Lake Placid (1980). Ice Hockey. Multicoloured.

635 10 u. Type **216** 40 20
636 12 u. Saving a goal 45 25
637 14 u. Goalkeeper and player . . 55 25
638 55 u. Two players . . . . . . 2·00 60
639 60 u. Goalkeeper . . . . . . 2·25 65
640 100 u. Tackle . . . . 3·50 1·25

217 Woman pouring out Tea

1980. Taking Tea.

641 **217** 1 u. multicoloured 10 10
642 5 u. multicoloured 20 10
643 12 u. multicoloured . . . 45 20

218 Koran, World Map and Symbols of Arab Achievements

1980. The Arabs.

644 **218** 12 u. multicoloured . . . 40 25
645 15 u. multicoloured . . . 50 30

1980. Winter Olympics Medal Winners. Nos. 635/40 optd.

646 10 u. **Medaille de bronze SUEDE** 35 20
647 12 u. **MEDAILLE DE BRONZE SUEDE** 40 20
648 14 u. **Medaille d'argent U.R.S.S.** 45 25
649 55 u. **MEDAILLE D'ARGENT U.R.S.S.** . . . . 1·50 80
650 60 u. **MEDAILLE D'OR ETATS-UNIS** . . . . 1·75 90
651 100 u. **Medaille d'or ETATS-UNIS** . . . . 3·00 1·50

220 Holy Kaaba, Mecca **221** Mother and Child

1980. Pilgrimage to Mecca. Multicoloured.

652 10 u. Type **220** 40 20
653 50 u. Pilgrims outside Mosque 1·60 1·10

1980. World Red Cross Societies Day.

654 **221** 20 u. multicoloured . . . 70 40

222 Crowd greeting Armed Forces

1980. Armed Forces Festival.

655 **222** 12 u. multicoloured . . . 35 20
656 14 u. multicoloured . . . 40 25

223 Horse jumping Bar **224** Trees on Map of Mauritania

1980. Olympic Games, Moscow. Multicoloured.

657 10 u. Type **223** 30 20
658 20 u. Water polo 55 30
659 50 u. Horse jumping brick wall (horiz) . . . . 1·40 55
660 70 u. Horse jumping stone wall 1·90 75

1980. Tree Day.

662 **224** 12 u. multicoloured . . . 35 20

225 "Rembrandt's Mother"

1980. Paintings by Rembrandt. Multicoloured.

663 10 u. "Self-portrait" 30 20
664 20 u. Type **225** 55 30
665 50 u. "Portrait of a Man in Oriental Costume" . . . . 1·40 55
666 70 u. "Titus Lisant" . . . . 1·90 75

226 Footballers

1980. Air. World Cup Football Championship, Spain (1982). Multicoloured.

668 10 u. Type **226** 30 20
669 12 u. Goalkeeper and players . 35 20
670 14 u. Goalkeeper catching ball 40 25
671 20 u. Fighting for possession . 55 30
672 67 u. Tackle . . . . 1·90 75

1980. Olympic Medal Winners. Nos. 657/60 optd.

674 10 u. **VAINQUEUR KOWALLZYK (POL)** . . 30 20
675 20 u. **VAINQUEUR THEURER (AUTR)** 55 30
676 50 u. **VAINQUEUR URSS** . 1·40 55
677 70 u. **VAINQUEUR ROMAN (IT)** . . . . 1·90 75

228 Giovi "Mastodont"

1980. Locomotives. Multicoloured.

679 10 u. Type **228** 40 15
680 12 u. SNIM-SEM diesel ore train 45 15
681 14 u. Steam locomotive of Chicago, Milwaukee and St. Paul Railway 55 20
682 20 u. Bury steam locomotive 1837 . . . . 75 25
683 67 u. Steam locomotive of French Reseau du Nord line 2·50 55
684 100 u. Steam locomotive of Berlin–Potsdam line . . . . 3·75 95

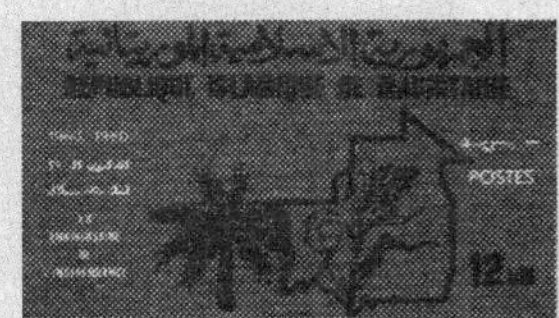

229 Palm Tree, Crescent and Star, Maize and Map

1980. 20th Anniv of Independence.

685 **229** 12 u. multicoloured . . . 40 20
686 15 u. multicoloured . . . 50 30

230 El Haram Mosque

1981. 15th Century of Hegira. Multicoloured.

687 2 um. Type **230** 10 10
688 12 um. Medine Mosque . . . 40 20
689 14 um. Chinguetti Mosque . 50 30

231 Space Shuttle in Orbit

1981. Air. Space Shuttle. Multicoloured.

690 12 um. Type **231** 40 20
691 20 um. Shuttle and space station 70 30
692 50 um. Shuttle performing experiment . . . . 1·60 75
693 70 um. Shuttle landing . . . . 2·25 1·00

232 "The Harlequin"

1981. Air. Birth Centenary of Pablo Picasso. Multicoloured.

695 12 um. Type **232** 50 20
696 20 um. "Vase of Flowers" . . 75 30
697 50 um. "Three Women at a Fountain" (horiz) . . . . 1·40 75
698 70 um. "Dinard Landscape" (horiz) . . . . 2·25 1·00
699 100 um. "Le Dejeuner sur l'Herbe" (horiz) . . . . . . 3·00 1·50

233 I.Y.D.P. Emblem

1981. International Year of Disabled People.

700 **233** 12 um. violet, gold & blue 45 30

234 Open Landau

1981. British Royal Wedding. Multicoloured.

701 14 um. Type **234** 40 20
702 18 um. Light carriage 45 20
703 77 um. Closed coupe . . . . . 1·40 1·10

235 George Washington

1981. Bicentenary of Battles of Yorktown and Chesapeake Bay. Multicoloured.

705 14 um. Type **235** 45 25
706 18 um. Admiral de Grasse . . 55 25
707 63 um. Surrender of Cornwallis at Yorktown (horiz) . . . . 1·75 95
708 81 um. Battle of Chesapeake Bay (horiz) . . . . 2·25 1·50

236 Columbus and "Pinta"

1981. 450th Death Anniv of Christopher Columbus. Multicoloured.

709 19 um. Type **236** . . . . . . 1·00 40
710 55 um. Columbus and "Santa Maria" . . . . 2·75 1·10

237 Wheat and F.A.O. Emblem **238** Kemal Ataturk

1981. World Food Day.

711 **237** 19 um. multicoloured . . 60 40

1981. Birth Centenary of Kemal Ataturk (Turkish statesman).

712 **238** 63 um. multicoloured . . 2·00 1·25

239 Eastern White Pelicans

1981. Birds of the Arguin. Multicoloured.

713 2 um. Type **239** 30 15
714 18 um. Greater flamingoes . . 1·25 70

240 Hand holding Torn Flag

1981. Battle of Karameh Commemoration.

715 **240** 14 um. multicoloured . . 45 30

241 "Dermochelys coiacer"

1981. Turtles. Multicoloured.

716 1 um. Type **241** 20 15
717 3 um. "Chelonia mydas" . . 30 15
718 4 um. "Eretmochelys imbricata" 35 15

242 Sea Scouts

1982. 75th Anniv of Boy Scout Movement. Multicoloured.

719 14 um. Type **242** 55 25
720 19 um. Scouts boarding rowing boat 90 35
721 22 um. Scouts in rowing boat 1·00 40
722 92 um. Scouts in yacht . . . 3·00 1·25

243 Deusenberg, 1921

1982. 75th Anniv of French Grand Prix Motor Race. Multicoloured.
724 7 um. Type **243** 40 20
725 12 um. Alfa Romeo, 1932 . . 50 20
726 14 um. Juan Fangio 60 35
727 18 um. Renault, 1979 . . . . 75 40
728 19 um. Niki Lauda 75 45

244 A.P.U. Emblem **245** Hexagonal Pattern

1982. 30th Anniv of Arab Postal Union.
730 **244** 14 um. orange and brown 45 30

1982. World Telecommunications Day.
731 **245** 21 um. multicoloured . . 65 45

246 Environmental Emblem on Map

1982. 10th Anniv of U.N. Environmental Programme.
732 **246** 14 um. blue and light blue 45 30

247 Princess of Wales

1982. 21st Birthday of Princess of Wales. Mult.
733 21 um. Type **247** 75 35
734 77 um. Princess of Wales (different) . . . . 2·40 1·10

248 Straw Hut

1982. Traditional Houses. Multicoloured.
736 14 um. Type **248** 45 30
737 18 um. Thatched hut 55 45
738 19 um. Tent 60 45

1982. Birth of Prince William of Wales. Nos. 701/3 surch **NAISSANCE ROYALE 1982**.
739 14 um. Type **234** 45 35
740 18 um. Light carriage 55 40
741 77 um. Closed coupe . . . . . 2·40 1·25

1982. Air. World Cup Football Championship Results. Nos. 668/72 optd **ITALIE 3 ALLEMAGNE (R.F.A.) 1**.
743 10 um. Type **226** 40 25
744 12 um. Goalkeeper punching ball 40 30
745 14 um. Goalkeeper catching ball 45 30
746 20 um. Three players 70 40
747 67 um. Tackle . . . . 2·25 1·40

251 Cattle at Collinaire Dam, Hodh El Gharbi

1992. Agricultural Development.
749 14 um. Type **251** . . . . . . 1·25 1·10
750 18 um. Irrigation canal, Gorgol 1·75 1·25

252 Desert Rose

1982. Desert Rose.
751 **252** 21 um. multicoloured . . 1·50 1·00

253 Montgolfier Balloon, 1783

1983. Bicent of Manned Flight. Multicoloured.
752 14 um. Type **253** 65 20
753 18 um. Charles's hydrogen balloon ascent, 1783 (horiz) 65 30
754 19 um. Goodyear Aerospace airship 65 30
755 55 um. Nieuport 11 "Bebe" biplane (horiz) . . . . . . 1·75 70
756 63 um. Concorde (horiz) . . 3·00 1·00
757 77 um. "Apollo 11" on Moon 2·50 1·00
No. 754 is wrongly inscribed "Zeppelin".

254 Ouadane

1983. Protection of Ancient Sites. Multicoloured.
758 14 um. Type **254** 40 25
759 18 um. Chinguetti 50 30
760 24 um. Oualata 70 45
761 30 um. Tichitt . . . . 1·00 55

255 Manuscript **256** I.M.O. Emblem

1983. Ancient Manuscripts. Multicoloured.
762 2 um. Type **255** 10 10
763 5 um. Decorated manuscript . 15 15
764 7 um. Shield-shaped patterned manuscript 25 20

1983. 25th Anniv of I.M.O.
765 **256** 18 um. multicoloured . . 50 30

257 W.C.Y. Emblem

1983. World Communications Year.
766 **257** 14 um. multicoloured . . 55 30

258 Customs Emblems

1983. 30th Anniv of Customs Co-operation Council.
767 **258** 14 um. multicoloured . . 45 30

259 Pilatre de Rozier and Montgolfier Balloon **260** Grinding Stone

1983. Bicentenary of Manned Flight. Mult.
768 10 um. Type **259** (postage) . . 40 20
769 14 um. John Wise and balloon "Atlantic" 50 30
770 25 um. Charles Renard and Renard and Krebs' airship "La France" (horiz) 85 35
771 100 um. Henri Juillot and Lebaudy-Juillot airship "Patrie" (air) (horiz) . . . . 3·75 1·25

1983. Prehistoric Grindstones. Multicoloured.
773 10 um. Type **260** 50 30
774 14 um. Pestle and mortar . . . 75 40
775 18 um. Grinding dish . . . . 1·00 60

261 Basketball

1983. Pre-Olympic Year. Multicoloured.
776 1 um. Type **261** (postage) . . . 10 10
777 20 um. Wrestling 60 25
778 50 um. Show-jumping . . . . 1·50 80
779 77 um. Running (air) . . . . . 2·25 1·25

262 Lord Baden-Powell (founder of Scout Movement)

1984. Celebrities. Multicoloured.
781 5 um. Type **262** (postage) . . . 15 10
782 14 um. Goethe (poet) 45 20
783 25 um. Rubens and detail of painting "The Virgin and Child" 75 45
784 100 um. P. Harris (founder of Rotary International) (air) . 3·00 1·40

263 Tunny

1984. Fishing Resources. Multicoloured.
786 1 um. Type **263** 10 10
787 2 um. Mackerel 10 10
788 5 um. Hake 25 15
789 14 um. Chinchard 70 45
790 18 um. Building a fishing boat 85 55

264 Durer and "Madonna and Child"

1984. Multicoloured.
791 10 um. Type **264** (postage) . . 35 20
792 12 um. "Apollo 11" and astronaut (15th anniv of first manned Moon landing) . . 40 25
793 50 um. Chess pieces and globe 2·00 80
794 77 um. Prince and Princess of Wales (air) . . . . 2·25 1·40

265 Start of Race

1984. Olympic Games, Los Angeles. Multicoloured.
796 14 um. Type **265** 40 25
797 18 um. Throwing the discus (vert) 55 25
798 19 um. Hurdling (vert) 55 25
799 44 um. Throwing the javelin (vert) . . . . 1·25 65
800 77 um. High jumping . . . . 2·00 1·25

266 Feeding Dehydrated Child from Glass **267** Aerial View of Complex

1984. Infant Survival Campaign. Multicoloured.
802 1 um. Type **266** 10 10
803 4 um. Breast-feeding baby . . 15 10
804 10 um. Vaccinating baby . . . 30 20
805 14 um. Weighing baby 45 30

1984. Nouakchott Olympic Complex.
806 **267** 14 um. multicoloured . . 50 40

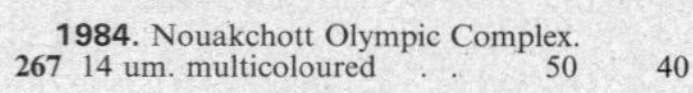

268 Tents and Mosque Courtyard

1984. Pilgrimage to Mecca. Multicoloured.
807 14 um. Type **268** 50 30
808 18 um. Tents and courtyard (different) 75 40

269 Emblem

1984. 10th Anniv of West African Economic Community.
809 **269** 14 um. multicoloured . . 45 30

270 S. van den Berg (windsurfing)

1984. Air. Olympic Games Yachting Gold Medallists. Multicoloured.
810 14 um. Type **270** 55 25
811 18 um. R. Coutts ("Finn" class) 75 25
812 19 um. Spain ("470" class) . . 1·00 25
813 44 um. U.S.A. ("Soling" class) 1·90 60

1984. Drought Relief. No. 537 surch **Aide au Sahel 84.**
815 18 um. on 10 um. multicoloured 70 50

272 Profiles and Emblem

1985. 15th Anniv of Technical and Cultural Co-operation Agency.
816 **272** 18 um. blue, deep blue and red 60 45

273 Animal drinking in Water droplet and Skeletons

274 Replanting Trees

1985. Campaign against Drought. Multicoloured.
817 14 um. Type **273** . . . . . . 1·10 50
818 18 um. Lush trees by river in water droplet and dead trees 1·10 50

1985. Anti-desertification Campaign. Multicoloured.
819 10 um. Type **274** 35 25
820 14 um. Animals fleeing from forest fire 55 30
821 18 um. Planting grass to hold sand dunes 65 50

275 Emblem

1985. 30th Anniv (1984) of Arab League.
822 **275** 14 um. green and black . 45 30

276 Map, I.Y.Y. Emblem and Youths

1985. Air. "Philexafrique" Stamp Exhibition, Lome. Multicoloured.
823 40 um. Type **276** (International Youth Year) . . . . . . 1·50 1·25
824 40 um. Nouadhibou oil refinery 1·50 1·25

277 Bonaparte's Gulls

1985. Air. Birth Bicentenary of John J. Audubon (ornithologist). Multicoloured.
825 14 um. Wester tanager and scarlet tanager 80 35
826 18 um. Type **277** . . . . . . 1·00 40
827 19 um. Blue jays . . . . . . 1·10 60
828 44 um. Black skimmer . . . . 3·25 2·00

278 "Der Adler", 1835

1985. Anniversaries. Multicoloured.
830 12 um. Type **278** (German railways. 150th anniv) . . . 60 25
831 18 um. Class 10 locomotive, 1956 (German railways. 150th anniv) 90 25
832 44 um. Johann Sebastian Bach (composer, 300th birth anniv European Music Year) . . . 1·60 70
833 77 um. Georg Frederick Handel (composer, 300th birth anniv European Music Year) . . 2·75 1·25
834 90 um. Statue of Liberty (centenary) (vert) . . . . . 2·75 1·40

279 Globe and Emblem

1985. World Food Day.
836 **279** 18 um. multicoloured . . 55 35

280 Tending Sheep and reading Book

1985. Air. "Philexafrique" Stamp Exhibition, Lome, Togo (2nd issue). Multicoloured.
837 50 um. Type **280** . . . . . . 2·00 1·50
838 50 um. Dock, iron ore mine and train . . . . 2·00 1·50

281 Map showing Industries

1985. 25th Anniv of Independence.
839 **281** 18 um. multicoloured . . 60 40

282 Development

1986. International Youth Year. Multicoloured.
840 18 um. Type **282** 60 30
841 22 um. Re-afforestation (voluntary work) 70 40
842 25 um. Hands reaching from globe to dove (peace) (vert) 75 50

283 Latecoere Seaplane "Comte de la Vaulx" and Map

1986. Air. 55th Anniv (1985) of First Commercial South Atlantic Flight. Multicoloured.
843 18 um. Type **283** 60 35
844 50 um. Piper Twin Commanche airplanes crossing between maps of Africa and South America . . . . 1·75 1·25

284 Toujounine Earth Receiving Station

1986.
845 **284** 25 um. multicoloured . . 90 50

285 Heads of Mother and Pup

1986. World Wildlife Fund. Mediterranean Monk Seal. Multicoloured.
846 2 um. Type **285** 20 15
847 5 um. Mother and pup on land 25 15
848 10 um. Mother and pup swimming 40 15
849 18 um. Seal family 80 25

286 Player and 1970 25 f. Stamp

1986. Air. World Cup Football Championship, Mexico. Multicoloured.
851 8 um. Type **286** 25 10
852 18 um. Player and 1970 30 f. stamp 60 20
853 22 um. Player and 1970 70 f. stamp 70 30
854 25 um. Player and 1970 150 f. stamp 85 35
855 40 um. Player and World Cup trophy on "stamp" . . . . . 1·25 60

287 Weaving

1986.
857 **287** 18 um. multicoloured . . . 60 35

288 Emblem, Boeing 737, Douglas DC-10 and Map

1986. Air. 25th Anniv of Air Afrique.
858 **288** 26 um. multicoloured . . . 1·00 40

289 Indian, "Santa Maria" and Route Map

1987. 500th Anniv (1992) of Discovery of America by Christopher Columbus. Multicoloured.
859 2 um. Type **289** (postage) . . . 10 10
860 22 um. Indian, "Nina" and map 65 30
861 35 um. Indian, "Pinta" and map 1·10 50
862 150 um. Indian, map and Christopher Columbus (air) 4·50 1·60

290 J. H. Dort, Comet Picture and Space Probe "Giotto"

1986. Appearance of Halley's Comet. Multicoloured.
864 5 um. Type **290** (postage) . . 15 10
865 18 um. William Huggins (astronomer) and "Ariane" space rocket 60 20
866 26 um. E. J. Opik and space probes "Giotto" and "Vega" 80 30
867 80 um. F. L. Whipple and "Planet A" space probe (air) 2·75 1·25

291 Astronauts

1986. "Challenger" Astronauts Commemoration. Multicoloured.
869 7 um. Type **291** (postage) . . 20 10
870 22 um. Judith Resnik and astronaut 60 30
871 32 um. Ellison Onizuka and Ronald McNair . . . . . . 1·00 45
872 43 um. Christa Corrigan McAuliffe (air) . . . . . . 1·50 60

292 Sea Bream

1986. Fishes and Birds. Multicoloured.
874 4 um. Type **292** 20 15
875 22 um. White spoonbills . . . 1·50 70
876 32 um. Bridled terns . . . . . 1·75 90
877 98 um. Sea trout . . . . . . 3·25 2·25
See also Nos. 896/900.

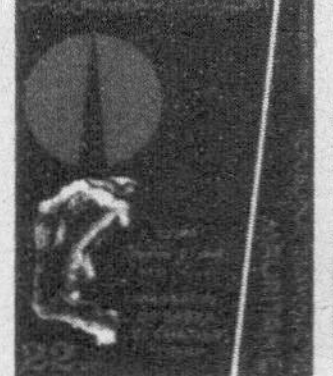

293 Arrow through Victim

294 Fisherman

1986. 4th Anniv of Massacre of Palestinian Refugees in Sabra and Shatila Camps, Lebanon.
878 **293** 22 um. black, gold & red . 80 40

1986. World Food Day.
879 **294** 22 um. multicoloured . . 80 40

295 Dome of the Rock

1987. "Arab Jerusalem".
880 **295** 22 um. multicoloured . . 80 40

296 Boxing

1987. Air. Olympic Games, Seoul (1988) (1st issue). Multicoloured.
881 30 um. Type **296** 80 40
882 40 um. Judo . . . . 1·00 55
883 50 um. Fencing . . . . 1·25 70
884 75 um. Wrestling . . . . . . 2·00 1·10
See also Nos. 902/5.

297 Cordoue Mosque

1987. 1200th Anniv of Cordoue Mosque.
886 **297** 30 um. multicoloured . . 1·00 50

298 Women's Slalom

1987. Air. Winter Olympic Games, Calgary (1988). Multicoloured.
887 30 um. Type **298** . . . . . . 1·10 40
888 40 um. Men's speed skating . 1·40 55
889 50 um. Ice hockey . . . . . . 1·60 75
890 75 um. Women's downhill skiing 2·50 1·10

299 Adults at Desk

1987. Literacy Campaign. Multicoloured.
892 18 um. Type **299** 60 40
893 20 um. Adults and children reading 80 50

300 People queueing for Treatment

1987. World Health Day.
894 **300** 18 um. multicoloured . . 70 40

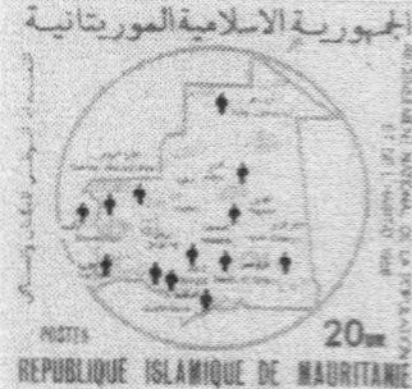

301 Map within Circle

1988. National Population and Housing Census.
895 **301** 20 um. multicoloured . . 60 35

1988. Fishes and Birds. Horiz designs as T **292**. Multicoloured.
896 1 um. White wrasse 10 10
897 7 um. Trigger fish 30 15
898 15 um. Striped bonitos 50 30
899 18 um. Cormorants 70 40
900 80 um. Royal terns . . . . . 3·00 2·00

302 People with Candles 303 Hammer-Throwing

1988. 40th Anniv of W.H.O.
901 **302** 30 um. multicoloured . . 1·00 40

1988. Air. Olympic Games, Seoul (2nd issue). Multicoloured.
902 20 um. Type **303** 50 25
903 24 um. Discus 60 30
904 30 um. Putting the shot . . . 80 40
905 150 um. Javelin throwing . . 4·00 2·10

1988. Winter Olympic Games Gold Medal Winners. Nos. 887/90 optd.
907 30 um. Optd **Medaille d'or/Vreni Schneider (Suisse)** . . . . . 1·00 50
908 40 um. Optd **Medaille d'or/1500 m./Andre Hoffman (R.D.A.)** 1·10 75
909 50 um. Optd **Medaille d'or/ U.R.S.S.** . . . . 1·50 1·00
910 75 um. Optd **Medaille d'or/ Marina Kiehl (R.F.A.)** . . . 2·25 1·50

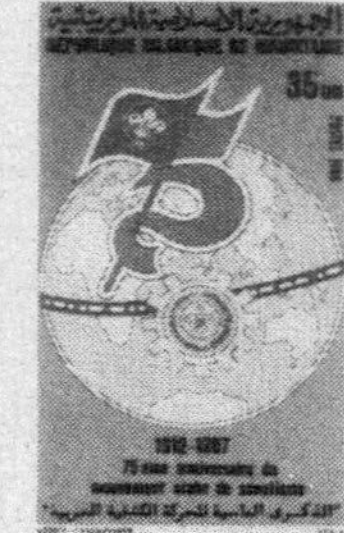

305 Flags and Globe

1988. 75th Anniv of Arab Scout Movement.
912 **305** 35 um. multicoloured . . 1·25 55

306 Men at Ballot Box

1988. 1st Municipal Elections. Multicoloured.
913 20 um. Type **306** 60 30
914 24 um. Woman at ballot box . . 80 40

307 Emblem 308 Ploughing with Oxen

1988. 25th Anniv of Organization of African Unity.
915 **307** 40 um. multicoloured . . 1·25 60

1988. 10th Anniv of International Agricultural Development Fund.
916 **308** 35 um. multicoloured . . 1·10 70

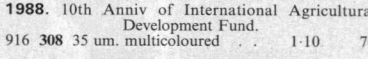

309 Port Activities

1989. 1st Anniv of Nouakchott Free Port.
917 **309** 24 um. multicoloured . . 1·25 65

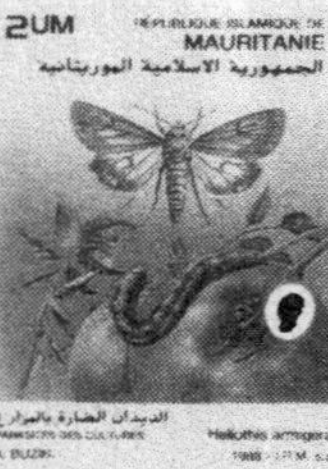
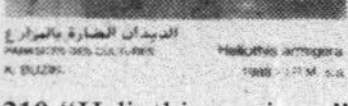

310 "Heliothis armigera" 311 "Nomadacris septemfasciata"

1989. Plant Pests. Multicoloured.
918 2 um. Type **310** 15 15
919 6 um. "Aphis gossypii" . . . 20 15
920 10 um. "Agrotis ypsilon" . . 35 15
921 20 um. "Chilo sp." 75 30
922 24 um. "Plitella xylostella" . 85 40
923 30 um. "Henosepilachna elaterii" 1·25 55
924 42 um. "Trichoplusia ni" . . 1·50 70

1989. Locusts. Multicoloured.
925 5 um. Type **311** 15 10
926 20 um. Locusts mating 60 30
927 24 um. Locusts emerging from chrysallis 70 40
928 40 um. Locusts flying . . . . 1·25 75
929 88 um. Locust (different) . . . 3·00 1·25

312 Men of Different Races embracing 313 Footballers

1989. "Philexfrance '89" Int Stamp Exn, Paris, and Bicent of French Revolution.
930 **312** 35 um. multicoloured . . . 1·10 60

1989. World Cup Football Championship, Italy (1990) (1st issue).
931 **313** 20 um. multicoloured . . . 70 40
See also Nos. 937/41.

314 Attan'eem Migat, Mecca

1989. Pilgrimage to Mecca.
932 **314** 20 um. multicoloured . . . 75 30

315 Emblem 317 Youths

1989. 25th Anniv of African Development Bank.
933 **315** 37 um. black and mauve . 1·00 50

316 Carpet

1989.
934 **316** 50 um. multicoloured . . . 1·50 80

1989. 2nd Anniv of Palestinian "Intifida" Movement.
935 **317** 35 um. multicoloured . . . 1·25 50

318 Member Countries' Leaders (½ size illustration)

1990. 1st Anniv of Arab Maghreb Union.
936 **318** 50 um. multicoloured . . . 1·50 70

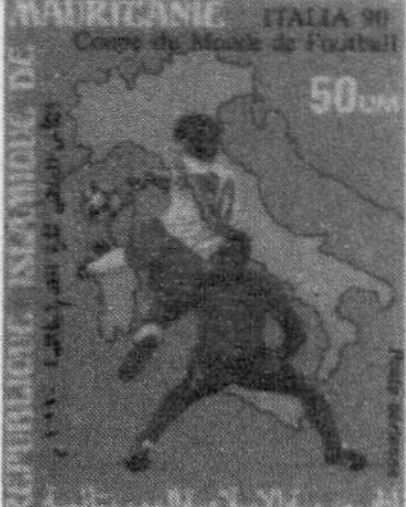

319 Players 320 Envelopes on Map

1990. Air. World Cup Football Championship, Italy (2nd issue).
937 **319** 50 um. multicoloured . . 1·50 50
938 – 60 um. multicoloured . . 1·90 60
939 – 70 um. multicoloured . . 2·00 75
940 – 90 um. multicoloured . . 2·75 75
941 – 150 um. multicoloured . . 4·50 1·25
DESIGNS: 60 to 150 um. Show footballers.

1990. 20th Anniv of Multinational Postal Training School, Abidjan.
942 **320** 50 um. multicoloured . . 1·10 50

321 Books and Desk

1990. International Literacy Year.
943 **321** 60 um. multicoloured . . 1·75 1·00

322 Maps and Earth-moving Vehicles

1990. Mineral Resources.
944 **322** 60 um. multicoloured . . 2·25 1·25

323 Dressage 324 Emblem

1990. Olympic Games, Barcelona (1992). Mult.
945 5 um. Type **323** (postage) . . 20 15
946 50 um. Archery . . . . 1·40 40
947 60 um. Throwing the hammer 1·50 50
948 75 um. Football . . . . . . 2·00 50
949 90 um. Basketball . . . . . . 2·75 65
950 220 um. Table tennis (air) . . 6·00 1·40

1990. 2nd Anniv of Declaration of State of Palestine.
952 **234** 85 um. multicoloured . . 1·75 1·10

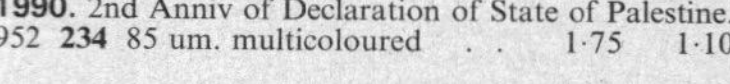

325 Camp

1990. Integration of Repatriates from Senegal. Multicoloured.
953 50 um. Type **325** 90 60
954 75 um. Women's sewing group 1·25 1·00
955 85 um. Water collection . . . 1·40 1·00

326 Map, Dove and Mandela

1990. Release from South African Prison of Nelson Mandela.

956	**326**	85 um. multicoloured . .	1·60	1·10

327 Downhill skiing

1990. Winter Olympic Games, Albertville (1992). Multicoloured.

957	60 um. Type **327** (postage) . .	1·00	60
958	75 um. Cross-country skiing .	1·50	75
959	90 um. Ice hockey	1·75	95
960	220 um. Figure skating (pairs) (air)	3·75	2·25

328 Blue Leg

1991. Scouts, Fungi and Butterflies. Multicoloured.

962	5 um. Type **328** (postage) . .	15	10
963	50 um. "Agaricus bitorquis edulis"	1·40	60
964	60 um. "Bunea alcinoe" (butterfly)	2·00	75
965	90 um. "Salamis cytora" (butterfly)	2·50	1·10
966	220 um. "Bronze boletus" . .	4·50	2·25
967	75 um. "Cyrestis camillus" (butterfly) (air)	2·00	85

329 Dish Aerials and Transmitting Tower

330 Woman carrying Bucket of Water

1991. 30th Anniv of Independence. Multicoloured.

968	50 um. Type **329**	1·00	65
969	60 um. Container ship in dock	2·00	85
970	100 um. Workers in field . . .	1·75	1·00

1991. World Meteorological Day.

972	**330**	100 um. multicoloured . .	1·75	1·10

331 Health Centre

1991. 20th Anniv of Medecins sans Frontieres (international medical relief organization).

973	**331**	60 um. multicoloured . .	70	45

332 Cats

1991. Domestic Animals. Multicoloured.

974	50 um. Type **332**	55	35
975	60 um. Basenji dog	70	45

333 Globe and Stylized Figures

1991. World Population Day.

976	**333**	90 um. multicoloured . .	1·00	60

334 Blind Woman with Sight restored

1991. Anti-blindness Campaign.

977	**334**	50 um. multicoloured . .	55	35

335 Nouakchott Electricity Station

1991. 2nd Anniv of Nouakchott Electricity Station.

978	**335**	50 um. multicoloured . .	55	35

OFFICIAL STAMPS

O **41** Cross of Trarza

O **179**

1961.

O150	O **41**	1 f. purple and blue .	10	10
O151		3 f. myrtle and red . .	10	10
O152		5 f. brown and green	10	10
O153		10 f. blue and turquoise	20	10
O154		15 f. orange and blue	30	15
O155		20 f. green and myrtle	35	20
O156		25 f. red and orange .	40	30
O157		30 f. green and purple	45	30
O158		50 f. sepia and red . .	1·00	45
O159		100 f. blue and orange	1·60	75
O160		200 f. red and green .	3·00	1·60

1976.

O502	O **179**	1 u. multicoloured .	10	10
O503		2 u. multicoloured .	15	10
O504		5 u. multicoloured .	20	15
O505		10 u. multicoloured	40	20
O506		12 u. multicoloured	55	30
O507		40 u. multicoloured	1·75	1·00
O508		50 u. multicoloured	2·25	1·25

POSTAGE DUE STAMPS

1906. Stamps of 1906 optd **T** in a triangle.

D18	I	5 c. green and red	—	27·00
D19		10 c. pink and blue . . .	—	27·00
D20	J	20 c. black & red on blue	—	40·00
D21		25 c. blue and red	—	40·00
D22		30 c. brown & red on pink	—	£110
D23		50 c. violet and red . . .	—	£110
D24	K	1 f. black & red on blue .	—	£160

1906. "Natives" key-type inscr "MAURITANIE" in blue (10, 30 c.) or red (others).

D25	L	5 c. green	1·25	1·25
D26		10 c. purple	1·75	1·75
D27		15 c. blue on blue . . .	4·00	3·25
D28		20 c. black on yellow . .	6·00	6·00
D29		30 c. red on cream . . .	6·00	6·75
D30		50 c. violet	9·25	9·25
D31		60 c. black on buff . . .	6·50	6·75
D32		1 f. black on pink	11·50	9·25

1914. "Figure" key-type inscr "MAURITANIE".

D35	M	5 c. green	10	25
D36		10 c. red	15	25
D37		15 c. grey	15	30
D38		20 brown	15	30
D39		30 c. blue	25	40
D40		50 c. black	50	95
D41		60 c. orange	40	50
D42		1 f. violet	60	80

1927. Surch in figures.

D67	M	2 f. on 1 f. purple . . .	1·25	1·75
D68		3 f. on 1 f. brown . . .	1·25	2·00

D **40** Qualata Motif

D **55** Ruppell's Griffon

1961.

D150	D **40**	1 f. yellow and purple	10	10
D151		2 f. grey and red . . .	10	10
D152		5 f. pink and red . . .	20	15
D153		10 f. green and myrtle .	25	15
D154		15 f. brown and drab	30	15
D155		20 f. blue and red . . .	35	20
D156		25 f. red and green . .	55	35

1963. Birds. Multicoloured.

D177	50 c. Type D **55**	45	20
D178	50 c. Common crane	45	20
D179	1 f. Eastern white pelican . .	55	25
D180	1 f. Garganey	55	25
D181	2 f. Golden oriole	65	25
D182	2 f. Variable sunbird	65	25
D183	5 f. Great snipe	75	55
D184	5 f. Common shoveler . . .	75	55
D185	10 f. Vulturine guineafowl .	1·40	1·00
D186	10 f. Black stork	1·40	1·00
D187	15 f. Grey heron	1·60	1·40
D188	15 f. White stork	1·60	1·40
D189	20 f. Paradise whydah . . .	1·90	1·60
D190	20 f. Red-legged partridge .	1·90	1·60
D191	25 f. Little stint	2·25	2·00
D192	25 f. Arabian bustard . . .	2·25	2·00

D **180**

1976.

D509	D **180**	1 u. multicoloured . .	10	10
D510		3 u. multicoloured . .	15	15
D511		10 u. multicoloured	35	35
D512		12 u. multicoloured	40	40
D513		20 u. multicoloured	70	70

APPENDIX

The following stamps have either been issued in excess of postal needs or have not been available to the public in a reasonable quantities at face value. Such stamps may later be given full listing if there is evidence of regular postal use.

1962.

World Refugee Year (1960). Optd on 1960–61 Definitive issue, 30, 50, 60 f.

Olympic Games in Rome (1960) and Tokyo (1964). Surch on 1960–61 Definitive issue 75 f. on 15 f., 75 f. on 20 f.

European Steel and Coal Community and Exploration of Iron-ore in Mauritania. Optd on 1960–61 Definitive issue. Air 500 f.

Malaria Eradication. Optd on 1960–61 Definitive issue. Air. 100, 200 f.

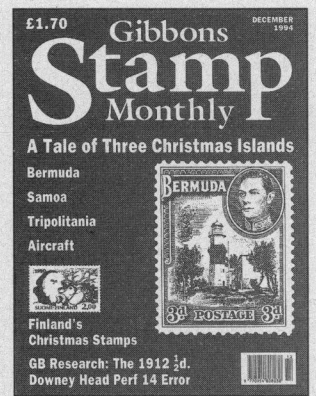

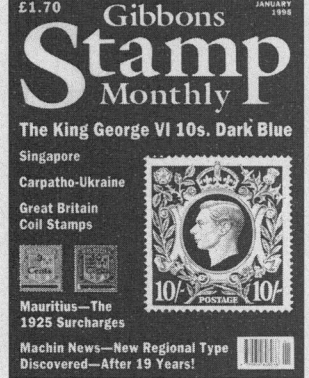

MAYOTTE Pt. 6

One of the Comoro Is. adjacent to Madagascar.

100 centimes = 1 franc

1892. "Tablet" key-type inscr "MAYOTTE".
1 D 1 c. black and red on blue 40 40
2 2 c. brown & blue on buff 50 50
3 4 c. brown & blue on grey 70 60
4 5 c. green & red on green 1·50 1·00
5 10 c. black & blue on lilac 2·00 2·00
15 10 c. red and blue 26·00 20·00
6 15 c. blue and red 6·00 4·00
16 15 c. grey and red 60·00 45·00
7 20 c. red & blue on green 5·25 4·50
8 25 c. black & red on pink 3·75 2·50
17 25 c. blue and red 4·00 3·50
9 30 c. brown & bl on drab 8·25 5·75
18 35 c. black & red on yellow 2·50 2·50
10 40 c. red & blue on yellow 6·75 5·75
19 45 c. black on green 7·50 6·00
11 50 c. red and blue on pink 12·50 8·00
20 50 c. brown & red on blue 6·25 8·25
12 75 c. brown & red on orge 14·00 9·00
13 1 f. green and red 10·50 8·00
14 5 f. mauve & blue on lilac 70·00 60·00

1912. Surch in figures.
21 D 05 on 20 c. brown and blue on buff 90 90
22 05 on 4 c. brown and blue on grey 35 30
23 05 on 15 c. blue and red 50 50
24 05 on 20 c. red and blue on green 50 60
25 05 on 25 c. black and red on pink 50 60
26 05 on 30 c. brown and blue on drab 60 65
27 10 on 40 c. red and blue on yellow 50 70
28 10 on 45 c. black and red on green 55 55
29 10 on 50 c. red and blue on pink 1·50 1·75
30 10 on 75 c. brown and red on orange 85 1·00
31 10 on 1 f. green and red 1·00 1·10

MECKLENBURG-SCHWERIN Pt. 7

In northern Germany. Formerly a Grand Duchy, Mecklenburg-Schwerin joined the North German Confederation in 1868.

48 schilling = 1 thaler

1

2

1856. Imperf.
1a 1 ¼ s. red 9·50 8·00
1 4/4 s. red £130 £110
3 2 3 s. yellow 75·00 42·00
4 5 s. blue £200 £250
See note below No. 7.

1864. Roul.
5a 1 ¼ s. red £120 £140
6a ¼ s. red 6·00 6·00
5 4/4 s. red £2250 £1800
6 4/4 s. red 48·00 48·00
11 2 2 s. purple £200 £225
9 3 s. yellow £150 95·00
7 5 s. bistre £130 £225

Nos. 1, 1a, 5, 5a have a dotted background, Nos 6 and 6a a plain background. Prices for Nos. 1a, 5a and 6a are for quarter stamps; prices for Nos. 1, 5 and 6 are for the complete stamp (four quarters) as illustrated in Type **1**.

MECKLENBURG-STRELITZ Pt. 7

In northern Germany. Formerly a Grand Duchy, Mecklenburg-Strelitz joined the North German Confederation in 1868.

30 silbergroschen = 1 thaler

1

2

1864. Roul. Various frames.
2 1 ¼ sgr. orange £150 £2250
3 ⅓ sgr. green 50·00 £1200
6 1 sch. mauve £275 £3500
7 2 1 sgr. red £130 £190
9 2 sgr. blue 28·00 £750
11 3 sgr. bistre 28·00 £1200

MEMEL Pt. 7

A seaport and district on the Baltic Sea, formerly part of Germany. Under Allied control after the 1914–18 war, it was captured and absorbed by Lithuania in 1923 and returned to Germany in 1939. From 1945 the area has been part of Lithuania.

1920. 100 pfennig = 1 mark
16.4.23. 100 centu = 1 litas

1920. Stamps of France surch **MEMEL** and **pfennig** or **mark** with figure of value.
1 18 5 pf. on 5 c. green 10 20
2 10 pf. on 10 c. red 10 20
3 20 pf. on 25 c. blue 10 20
4 30 pf. on 30 c. orange 10 20
5 40 pf. on 20 c. brown 10 20
6 50 pf. on 35 c. violet 10 35
7 13 60 pf. on 40 c. red & blue 20 55
8 80 pf. on 45 c. green & blue 15 35
9 1 m. on 50 c. brown & lav 10 20
10 1 m. 25 on 60 c. violet & bl 70 1·75
11 2 m. on 1 f. red and yellow 15 25
12 3 m. on 2 f. orange & green 9·00 22·00
13 3 m. on 5 f. blue and yellow 9·50 22·00
14 4 m. on 2 f. orange & green 15 35
15 10 m. on 5 f. blue & yellow 1·50 4·00
16 20 m. on 5 f. blue & yellow 30·00 55·00

1920. Stamps of Germany inscr "DEUTSCHES REICH" optd **Memel-gebiet** or **Memelgebiet**.
17 10 5 pf. green 20 35
18 10 pf. red 2·00 6·50
19 10 pf. orange 15 35
20 24 15 pf. purple 2·25 6·00
21 10 20 pf. blue 15 15
22 30 pf. black & orge on buff 1·25 2·00
23 30 pf. blue 15 35
24 40 pf. black and red 10 15
25 50 pf. black & pur on buff 10 15
26 60 pf. olive 45 2·00
27 75 pf. black and green 2·00 5·00
28 80 pf. blue 90 2·75
29 1 m. red 20 45
30 1 m. 25 green 11·00 26·00
31 2 m. 50 brown 3·50 7·00
32 13 2 m. blue 1·50 3·25
33 2 m. 50 red 9·50 22·00

The following are all surch on stamps of France.

1921. Stamps of 1920 further surch in large figures.
34 18 15 on 10 pf. on 10 c. red 15 35
35 15 on 20 pf. on 25 c. blue 20 55
36 15 on 50 pf. on 35 c. violet 15 45
37 13 60 on 40 pf. on 20 c. brown 15 15
38 75 on 60 pf. on 40 c. red and blue 40 1·00
39 1,25 on 1 m. on 50 c. brown and lavender 15 40
40 5,00 on 2 m. on 1 f. red and yellow 45 1·25

1921. Surch **MEMEL** and **Pfennig** or **Mark** with figure of value.
54 18 5 pf. on 5 c. orange 10 20
55 10 pf. on 10 c. red 40 1·10
56 10 pf. on 10 c. green 10 20
57 15 pf. on 10 c. green 10 30
58 20 pf. on 20 c. brown 2·75 8·50
59 20 pf. on 25 c. blue 2·75 8·50
60 25 pf. on 5 c. orange 10 15
61 30 pf. on 30 c. red 40 1·75
86 35 pf. on 35 c. violet 10 20
64 13 40 pf. on 40 c. red and blue 10 15
62 15 50 pf. on 50 c. blue 10 15
41 13 60 pf. on 40 c. red and blue 2·25 6·50
87 15 75 pf. on 15 c. green 10 15
63 18 75 pf. on 35 c. violet 10 15
65 13 80 pf. on 45 c. green & blue 10 15
88 18 1 m. on 25 c. blue 10 15
66 13 1 m. on 40 c. red and blue 10 15
89 18 1¼ m. on 30 c. red 10 20
67 13 1 m. 25 on 60 c. violet & bl 10 20
68 1 m. 50 on 45 c. green & bl 10 25
90 2 m. on 45 c. green & blue 10 20
69 2 m. on 1 f. red and green 10 20
91 2¼ m. on 40 c. red and blue 10 20
92 2½ m. on 60 c. violet & blue 20 25
113 18 3 m. on 5 c. orange 10 1·10
70 13 3 m. on 60 m. violet & blue 45 85
93 4 m. on 45 c. green & blue 10 15
71 5 m. on 1 f. red and green 15 45
114 15 6 m. on 15 c. green 15 80
94 13 6 m. on 60 c. violet & blue 10 15
72 6 m. on 2 f. orange & green 15 45
115 18 8 m. on 30 c. red 35 2·25
95 13 9 m. on 1 f. red and green 15 30
73 9 m. on 5 f. blue and buff 20 60
116 10 m. on 45 c. green & blue 35 1·00
43 10 m. on 5 f. blue and buff 55 1·40
96 12 m. on 40 c. red and blue 15 30
117 20 m. on 40 c. red and blue 35 1·60
44 20 m. on 45 c. green & blue 2·75 10·00
97 20 m. on 2 f. orange & grn 15 40
118 30 m. on 60 c. violet & blue 35 1·50
98 30 m. on 5 f. blue and buff 2·25 6·50
119 40 m. on 1 f. red and green 35 1·75
99 50 m. on 2 f. orange & grn 7·00 18·00
120 80 m. on 2 f. orange & grn 35 1·75
121 100 m. on 5 f. blue & buff 45 3·00

1921. Air. Optd **FLUGPOST** in double-lined letters.
47 13 60 pf. on 40 c. red and blue (No. 7) 22·00 60·00
48 60 pf. on 40 c. red and blue (No. 41) 2·00 6·50
49 80 pf. on 45 c. green & blue 2·00 6·00
50 1 m. on 50 c. brown & lav 1·40 4·50
51 2 m. on 1 f. red and yellow 2·00 4·50
52 3 m. on 60 c. violet and blue (No. 42) 2·00 6·50
53 4 m. on 2 f. orange & green 2·25 10·00

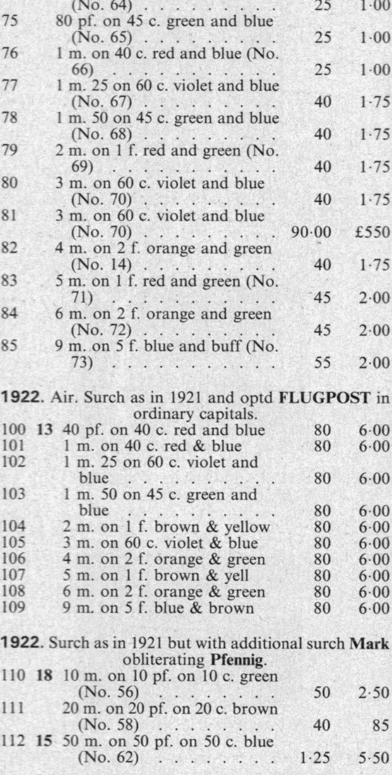

1922. Air. Optd **Flugpost** in script letters.
74 13 40 pf. on 40 c. red and blue (No. 64) 25 1·00
75 80 pf. on 45 c. green and blue (No. 65) 25 1·00
76 1 m. on 40 c. red and blue (No. 66) 25 1·00
77 1 m. 25 on 60 c. violet and blue (No. 67) 40 1·75
78 1 m. 50 on 45 c. green and blue (No. 68) 40 1·75
79 2 m. on 1 f. red and green (No. 69) 40 1·75
80 3 m. on 60 c. violet and blue (No. 70) 40 1·75
81 3 m. on 60 c. violet and blue (No. 70) 90·00 £550
82 4 m. on 2 f. orange and green (No. 14) 40 1·75
83 5 m. on 1 f. red and green (No. 71) 45 2·00
84 6 m. on 2 f. orange and green (No. 72) 45 2·00
85 9 m. on 5 f. blue and buff (No. 73) 55 2·00

1922. Air. Surch as in 1921 and optd **FLUGPOST** in ordinary capitals.
100 13 40 pf. on 40 c. red and blue 80 6·00
101 1 m. on 40 c. red & blue 80 6·00
102 1 m. 25 on 60 c. violet and blue 80 6·00
103 1 m. 50 on 45 c. green and blue 80 6·00
104 2 m. on 1 f. brown & yellow 80 6·00
105 3 m. on 60 c. violet & blue 80 6·00
106 4 m. on 2 f. orange & green 80 6·00
107 5 m. on 1 f. brown & yell 80 6·00
108 6 m. on 2 f. orange & green 80 6·00
109 9 m. on 5 f. blue & brown 80 6·00

1922. Surch as in 1921 but with additional surch **Mark** obliterating **Pfennig**.
110 18 10 m. on 10 pf. on 10 c. green (No. 56) 50 2·50
111 20 m. on 20 pf. on 20 c. brown (No. 58) 40 85
112 15 50 m. on 50 pf. on 50 c. blue (No. 62) 1·25 5·50

1923. Nos. 64 and 67 with additional surch.
122 13 (40) Mark on 40 pf. on 40 c. red and blue 40 1·25
123 "80" on 1 m. 25 on 60 c. violet and blue 40 1·75

1923. Nos. 90 and 88 surch with large figures.
124 13 10 on 2 m. on 45 c. green and blue 85 2·50
125 18 25 on 1 m. on 25 c. blue 85 2·50

LITHUANIAN OCCUPATION

The port and district of Memel was captured by Lithuanian forces in 1923 and incorporated in Lithuania.

1

5

1923. Surch **KLAIPEDA (MEMEL)** and value over curved line and **MARKIU**.
1 1 10 m. on 5 c. blue 35 75
2 25 m. on 5 c. blue 35 75
3 50 m. on 25 c. red 35 75
4 100 m. on 25 c. red 50 1·40
5 400 m. on 1 l. brown 1·25 2·50

1923. Surch **Klaipeda (Memel)** and value over two straight lines and **Markiu**.
6 1 10 m. on 5 c. blue 65 1·75
7 25 m. on 5 c. blue 65 1·75
8 50 m. on 25 c. red 65 1·75
9 100 m. on 25 c. red 65 1·75
10 400 m. on 1 l. brown 70 2·25
11 500 m. on 1 l. brown 70 2·25

1923. Surch **KLAIPEDA (Memel)** and value over four stars and **MARKIU**.
12 1 10 m. on 5 c. blue 55 1·75
13 20 m. on 5 c. blue 55 1·75
14 25 m. on 24 c. red 55 1·75
15 50 m. on 25 c. red 65 2·25
16 100 m. on 1 l. brown 80 2·75
17 200 m. on 1 l. brown 80 2·75

1923.
18 5 10 m. brown 20 45
19 20 m. yellow 20 45
20 25 m. orange 20 45
21 40 m. violet 20 45
22 50 m. green 75 85
23 100 m. red 40 40
24 300 m. olive 2·50 45·00
25 400 m. brown 45 65
26 500 m. purple 2·50 45·00
27 1,000 m. blue 65 80

7 Memel Port

8 Memel Arms

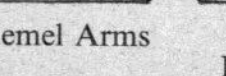

9 Memel Lighthouse

1923. Uniting of Memel with Lithuania and amalgamation of Memel Harbours.
28 7 40 m. olive 2·50 10·00
29 50 m. brown 2·50 10·00
30 80 m. green 2·50 10·00
31 100 m. red 2·50 10·00
32 8 200 m. blue 2·50 10·00
33 300 m. brown 2·50 10·00
34 400 m. purple 2·50 10·00
35 500 m. orange 2·50 10·00
36 600 m. olive 2·50 10·00
37 9 800 m. blue 2·50 10·00
38 1000 m. purple 2·50 10·00
39 2000 m. red 2·50 10·00
40 3000 m. green 2·50 10·00

1923. No. 123 of Memel surch **Klaipeda**, value and large **M** between bars, sideways.
41 100 on 80 on 1 m. 25 on 60 c. 3·25 8·50
42 400 m. on 80 on 1 m. 25 on 60 c. 3·25 8·50
43 500 m. on 80 on 1 m. 25 on 60 c. 3·25 8·50

1923. Surch (thin or thick figures) in **CENT.** or **LITAS** and bars.
60 5 2 c. on 10 m. brown 1·25 5·50
44 2 c. on 20 m. yellow 2·25 3·25
45 2 c. on 50 m. green 2·25 3·25
63 3 c. on 10 m. brown 2·00 5·50
46 3 c. on 40 m. violet 2·50 3·50
47 3 c. on 300 m. olive 2·50 3·50
48 5 c. on 100 m. red 2·50 3·50
49 5 c. on 300 m. olive 3·00 4·25
50 10 c. on 400 m. brown 5·00 7·00
67 15 c. on 25 m. orange 70·00 £350
51 30 c. on 500 m. purple 3·00 3·50
68 50 c. on 1000 m. blue 1·50 4·75
69 1 l. on 1000 m. blue 3·25 9·00

1923. Surch in **CENTU** and bars.
53 5 2 c. on 300 m. olive 3·75 6·25
54 3 c. on 300 m. olive 3·75 6·25
55 10 c. on 25 m. orange 3·75 6·25
56 15 c. on 25 m. orange 3·75 6·25
57 20 c. on 500 m. purple 3·75 6·25
58 30 c. on 500 m. purple 3·75 6·25
59 50 c. on 500 m. purple 10·00 17·00

1923. Surch in **CENT.** or **LITAS**.
70 7 15 c. on 40 m. olive 3·25 12·00
71 30 c. on 50 m. brown 2·50 6·50
72 30 c. on 80 m. green 3·25 10·00
73 30 c. on 100 m. red 2·50 6·50
74 8 50 c. on 200 m. blue 3·25 10·00
75 50 c. on 300 m. brown 2·50 6·50
76 50 c. on 400 m. purple 3·25 11·00
77 50 c. on 500 m. orange 2·50 6·50
78 1 l. on 600 m. olive 3·25 11·00
79 9 1 l. on 800 m. blue 3·25 11·00
80 1 l. on 1000 m. purple 3·25 11·00
81 1 l. on 2000 m. red 3·25 11·00
82 1 l. on 3000 m. green 3·25 11·00

1923. Surch in large figures and **Centu** and bars reading upwards.
83 1 10 c. on 25 m. on 5 c. blue (No. 2) 17·00 40·00
84 15 c. on 100 m. on 25 c. red (No. 4) 20·00 £110
85 30 c. on 400 m. on 1 l. brown (No. 5) 4·00 16·00
86 60 c. on 50 m. on 25 c. red (No. 8) 20·00 £130

1923. Surch in large figures and **CENT.** and bars.
87 7 15 c. on 50 m. brown £225 £450
88 25 c. on 100 m. red £110 £225
89 8 30 c. on 300 m. brown £180 £1000
90 60 c. on 500 m. orange £110 £900

1923. Surch in **Centu** or **Centai** (25 c.) between bars.
91 5 15 c. on 10 m. brown 5·00 20·00
92 15 c. on 20 m. yellow 2·25 10·00
93 15 c. on 25 m. orange 2·75 12·00
94 15 c. on 40 m. violet 2·25 10·00
95 15 c. on 50 m. green 1·50 8·00
96 15 c. on 100 m. red 1·50 8·00
97 15 c. on 400 m. brown 1·25 6·00
98 15 c. on 1000 m. blue 45·00 £250
99 25 c. on 10 m. brown 3·25 16·00
100 25 c. on 20 m. yellow 2·25 9·50
101 25 c. on 25 m. orange 2·75 12·00
102 25 c. on 40 m. violet 2·25 10·00
103 25 c. on 50 m. green 1·40 7·50
104 25 c. on 100 m. red 1·40 7·50
105 25 c. on 400 m. brown 1·25 6·00
106 25 c. on 1000 m. blue 50·00 £275
107 30 c. on 10 m. brown 4·50 19·00
108 30 c. on 20 m. yellow 2·50 10·00
109 30 c. on 25 m. orange 3·25 12·00
110 30 c. on 40 m. violet 2·50 10·00
111 30 c. on 50 m. green 1·40 6·50
112 30 c. on 100 m. red 1·40 7·00
113 30 c. on 400 m. brown 1·25 6·00
114 30 c. on 1000 m. blue 45·00 £250

MEXICO Pt. 15

A republic of Central America. From 1864–67 an Empire under Maximilian of Austria.

8 reales = 100 centavos = 1 peso

1 Miguel Hidalgo y Costilla 2

1856. With or without optd district name. Imperf.

1c	1	½ r. blue	12·50	14·00
8c		½ r. black on buff	12·50	17·00
6		1 r. orange	11·00	1·60
9b		1 r. black on green	2·50	2·75
7b		2 r. green	10·50	1·60
10c		2 r. black on red	1·40	3·25
4b		4 r. red	55·00	75·00
11b		4 r. black on yellow	22·00	35·00
12a		4 r. red on yellow	50·00	60·00
5c		8 r. lilac	75·00	95·00
13a		8 r. black on brown	48·00	95·00
14a		8 r. green on brown	60·00	80·00

1864. Perf.

15a	2	1 r. red	10	
16a		2 r. blue	15	
17a		4 r. brown	25	
18a		1 p. black	95	

3 Arms of Mexico 4 Emperor Maximilian

1864. Imperf.

30	3	3 c. brown	£600	£1200
19a		½ r. brown	85·00	£225
31		½ r. purple	35·00	28·00
31c		½ r. grey	40·00	40·00
32b		1 r. blue	8·25	5·00
33		2 r. orange	2·50	1·60
34		4 r. green	55·00	32·00
35b		8 r. red	80·00	48·00

1864. Imperf.

40	4	7 c. purple	£225	£2500
36c		7 c. grey	32·00	60·00
41		13 c. blue	3·75	5·50
42		25 c. orange	3·25	5·00
39c		50 c. green	11·50	11·50

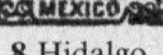

7 Hidalgo 8 Hidalgo 9 Hidalgo

10 Hidalgo 15 Benito Juarez 16

1868. Imperf or perf.

67	7	6 c. black on brown	4·50	2·50
68		12 c. black on green	1·90	60
69		25 c. blue on pink	3·50	45
70b		50 c. black on yellow	60·00	7·50
71		100 c. black on brown	60·00	22·00
76		100 c. brown on brown	95·00	28·00

1872. Imperf or perf.

87	8	6 c. green	6·25	6·25
88		12 c. blue	80	65
94		25 c. red	3·50	75
90		50 c. yellow	70·00	16·00
91		100 c. lilac	48·00	25·00

1874. Various frames. Perf.

102a	9	4 c. orange	3·50	6·25
97	10	5 c. brown	2·10	1·40
98	9	10 c. black	85	50
105		10 c. orange	85	50
99	10	25 c. blue	35	30
107	9	50 c. green	7·00	6·25
108		100 c. red	9·50	8·25

1879.

115	15	1 c. brown	1·90	1·75
116		2 c. violet	1·75	1·50
117		5 c. orange	1·25	60
118		10 c. blue	1·60	1·25
127a		10 c. brown	1·25	
128		12 c. brown	3·25	3·25
129		18 c. brown	3·75	3·25
130		24 c. mauve	3·75	3·25
119		25 c. red	4·00	4·75
132		25 c. brown	2·10	
120		50 c. green	6·25	6·00
134	15	50 c. yellow	35·00	38·00
121		85 c. violet	11·00	9·50
122		100 c. black	12·50	11·00
137		100 c. orange	40·00	48·00

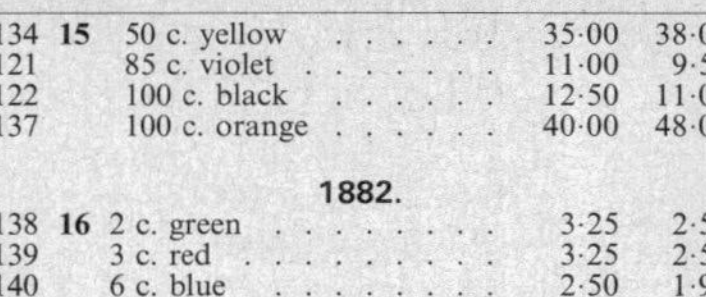

1882.

138	16	2 c. green	3·25	2·50
139		3 c. red	3·25	2·50
140		6 c. blue	2·50	1·90

17 Hidalgo 18

1884.

141	17	1 c. green	1·25	15
142		2 c. green	1·90	25
157		2 c. red	6·25	1·40
143		3 c. green	3·75	80
158		3 c. brown	8·75	2·50
144		4 c. green	5·00	80
159		4 c. red	12·50	7·50
145		5 c. green	5·00	60
160		5 c. blue	8·75	1·60
146		6 c. green	4·50	45
161		6 c. brown	10·00	2·50
147		10 c. green	4·75	15
162		10 c. orange	7·50	45
148		12 c. green	8·75	1·25
163		12 c. brown	16·00	3·75
149		20 c. green	25·00	95
150		25 c. green	45·00	1·90
164		25 c. blue	55·00	8·75
151		50 c. green	40	1·25
152		1 p. blue	40	4·75
153		2 p. blue	40	8·75
154		5 p. blue	£120	80·00
155		10 p. blue	£170	95·00

1886.

196	18	1 c. green	30	10
209		2 c. red	35	10
167		3 c. lilac	2·50	1·25
189		3 c. red	30	10
198		3 c. orange	95	35
168		4 c. lilac	4·50	95
211		4 c. red	75	50
199		4 c. orange	1·10	50
191		5 c. blue	20	10
170		6 c. lilac	5·00	60
213		6 c. red	95	60
200		6 c. orange	1·40	35
171		10 c. lilac	5·00	15
193		10 c. red	10	10
185a		10 c. brown	8·75	1·90
201		10 c. orange	7·50	35
172		12 c. lilac	5·00	3·25
215		12 c. red	3·25	3·75
173		20 c. lilac	40·00	22·00
194		20 c. red	50	20
202		20 c. orange	12·50	1·60
174		25 c. lilac	16·00	3·75
217		25 c. red	95	25
203		25 c. orange	4·00	1·10
206		5 p. red	£350	£225
207		10 p. red	£550	£350

19 Foot Postman 20 Mounted Postman and Pack Mules 21 Statue of Cuauhtemoc

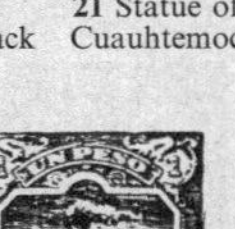

22 Mailcoach 23 Steam Train

1895.

253	19	1 c. green	20	10
219		2 c. red	30	10
220		3 c. brown	30	10
221	20	4 c. orange	1·50	25
257	21	5 c. blue	35	10
223	22	10 c. purple	50	10
224	20	12 c. olive	8·25	3·75
225	22	15 c. blue	4·00	80
226		20 c. red	4·00	40
227		50 c. mauve	12·00	4·75
228	23	1 p. brown	23·00	11·50
229		5 p. red	80·00	48·00
230		10 p. blue	£130	85·00

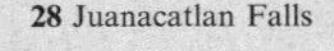

27 28 Juanacatlan Falls

29 Popocatepetl 30 Cathedral, Mexico

1899. Various frames for T **27**.

266	27	1 c. green	80	10
276		1 c. purple	60	10
267		2 c. red	2·40	10
277		2 c. green	80	10
268		3 c. brown	1·60	10
278		4 c. red	2·50	20
269		5 c. blue	2·50	10
279		5 c. orange	45	10
270		10 c. brown and purple	3·25	15
280		10 c. orange and blue	2·50	10
271		15 c. purple and lavender	4·25	10
272		20 c. blue and red	4·75	15
273a	28	50 c. black and purple	19·00	1·25
281		50 c. black and red	40·00	3·50
274	29	1 p. black and blue	42·00	1·90
275	30	5 p. black and red	£130	6·25

32 Josefa Ortiz 40 Hidalgo at Dolores

1910. Centenary of First Independence Movement.

282	32	1 c. purple	10	10
283	–	2 c. green	10	10
284	–	3 c. brown	25	10
285	–	4 c. red	1·25	20
286	–	5 c. orange	10	10
287	–	10 c. orange and blue	80	10
288	–	15 c. lake and slate	4·50	20
289	–	20 c. blue and lake	2·50	10
290	40	50 c. black and brown	6·25	95
291	–	1 p. black and blue	7·50	1·10
292	–	5 p. black and red	28·00	2·75

DESIGNS: As Type **32**: 2 c. L. Vicario; 3 c. L. Rayon; 4 c. J. Aldama; 5 c. M. Hidalgo; 10 c. I. Allende; 15 c. E. Gonzalez; 20 c. M. Abasolo. As Type **40**: 1 p. Mass on Mt. of Crosses; 5 p. Capture of Granaditas.

REVOLUTIONARY PROVISIONALS

For full list of the provisional issues made during the Civil War from 1913 onwards, see the Stanley Gibbons Part 15 (Central America) Catalogue.

CONSTITUTIONALIST GENERAL ISSUES.

CT 1

1914. "Transitorio".

CT1	CT 1	1 c. blue	20	15
CT2		2 c. green	30	15
CT3		4 c. blue	7·00	1·60
CT4		5 c. green	7·00	1·90
CT9		5 c. green	10	10
CT5		10 c. red	15	15
CT6		20 c. brown	25	25
CT7		50 c. red	1·60	2·10
CT8		1 p. violet	8·75	10·00

The words of value on No. CT4, are 2 × 14 mm and on No. CT9 are 2½ × 16 mm.

1914. Victory of Torreon. Nos. CT1/7 optd **Victoria de TORREON ABRIL 2 - 1914**.

CT10	CT 1	1 c. blue	95·00	80·00
CT11		2 c. green	£110	95·00
CT12		4 c. blue	£130	£160
CT13		5 c. green	11·50	12·50
CT14		10 c. red	60·00	60·00
CT15		20 c. brown	£1100	£1100
CT16		50 c. red	£1200	£1200

CT 3 CT 4

1914. Handstamped with Type CT 3.

(a) Nos. D 282/6.

CT17	D 1	1 c. blue	8·75	10·00
CT18		2 c. blue	8·75	10·00
CT19		4 c. blue	8·75	10·00
CT20		5 c. blue	8·75	10·00
CT21		10 c. blue	8·75	10·00

(b) Nos. 282/92.

CT22	32	1 c. purple	35	30
CT23	–	2 c. green	95	80
CT24	–	3 c. brown	95	80
CT25	–	4 c. red	1·60	1·25
CT26	–	5 c. orange	20	10
CT27	–	10 c. orange and blue	1·90	1·25
CT28	–	15 c. lake and slate	3·25	1·90
CT29	–	20 c. blue and lake	6·25	3·75
CT30	40	50 c. black and brown	7·50	5·00
CT31	–	1 p. black and blue	16·00	6·25
CT32	–	5 p. black and red	£100	95·00

1914.

CT33	CT 4	1 c. pink	80	12·50
CT34		2 c. green	80	11·50
CT35		3 c. orange	80	12·50
CT36		5 c. red	60	5·00
CT37		10 c. green	60	22·00
CT38		25 c. blue	10·00	

CT 5

1914. "Denver" issue.

CT39	CT 5	1 c. blue	15	20
CT40		2 c. green	15	15
CT41		3 c. orange	25	15
CT42		5 c. red	25	15
CT43		10 c. red	35	40
CT44		15 c. mauve	60	1·10
CT45		50 c. yellow	1·25	1·60
CT46		1 p. violet	5·25	7·50

1914. Optd **GOBIERNO CONSTITUCIONALISTA**.

(a) Nos. 279 and 271/2.

CT50	–	5 c. orange	48·00	35·00
CT51	–	15 c. purple and lavender	95·00	95·00
CT52	–	20 c. blue and red	£300	£250

(b) Nos. D282/6.

CT53	D 32	1 c. blue	1·10	1·10
CT54		2 c. blue	1·25	1·25
CT55		4 c. blue	9·50	9·50
CT56		5 c. blue	9·50	9·50
CT57		10 c. blue	1·60	1·60

(c) Nos. 282/92.

CT58	32	1 c. purple	10	10
CT59	–	2 c. green	10	10
CT60	–	3 c. brown	20	20
CT61	–	4 c. red	25	25
CT62	–	5 c. orange	10	10
CT63	–	10 c. orange and blue	10	10
CT64	–	15 c. lake and slate	35	30
CT65	–	20 c. blue and lake	35	35
CT66	40	50 c. black and brown	1·10	75
CT67	–	1 p. black and blue	4·75	3·25
CT68	–	5 p. black and red	25·00	19·00

CONVENTIONIST ISSUES

(CV 1) Villa-Zapata Monogram

1914. Optd with Type CV 1. (a) Nos. 266/75.

CV 1	27	1 c. green	60·00	
CV 2		2 c. red	60·00	
CV 3		3 c. brown	32·00	
CV 4		5 c. blue	60·00	
CV 5		10 c. brown and purple	60·00	
CV 6		15 c. purple and lavender	60·00	
CV 7		20 c. blue and red	60·00	
CV 8	28	50 c. black and red	£160	
CV 9	29	1 p. black and blue	£160	
CV10	30	5 p. black and red	£300	

(b) Nos. 276/80.

CV11	27	1 c. purple	60·00	
CV12		2 c. green	60·00	
CV13		4 c. red	60·00	
CV14		5 c. orange	7·75	
CV15		10 c. orange and blue	48·00	

(c) Nos. D282/6.

CV16	D 32	1 c. blue	6·00	6·25
CV17		2 c. blue	6·00	6·25
CV18		4 c. blue	6·00	6·25
CV19		5 c. blue	6·00	6·25
CV20		10 c. blue	60·00	6·25

(d) Nos. 282/92.

CV21	32	1 c. purple	40	40
CV22	–	2 c. green	45	20
CV23	–	3 c. brown	30	30
CV24	–	4 c. red	1·25	1·25
CV25	–	5 c. orange	10	10
CV26	–	10 c. orange and blue	95	95
CV27	–	15 c. lake and slate	95	95
CV28	–	20 c. blue and lake	95	95
CV29	40	50 c. black and brown	6·25	6·25
CV30	–	1 p. black and blue	9·50	9·50
CV31	–	5 p. black and red	95·00	95·00

CONSTITUTIONALIST PROVISIONAL ISSUES

CT 10 CT 11 Carranza Monogram

1914. Nos. 282/92 handstamped with Type CT **10**.

CT69	32	1 c. purple	6·00	5·50
CT70	–	2 c. green	6·00	5·50
CT71	–	3 c. brown	6·00	5·50

CT72 – 4 c. red . . . . 7·50 7·00
CT73 – 5 c. orange 90 90
CT74 – 10 c. orange and blue . . 7·00 6·25
CT75 – 15 c. lake and slate . . . 7·00 6·25
CT76 – 20 c. blue and lake . . . 8·75 5·75
CT77 **40** 50 c. black and brown . . 19·00 19·00
CT78 – 1 p. black and blue . . . 28·00
CT79 – 5 p. black and red . . . £100

1915. Optd with Type CT **11**. (a) No. 271.
CT80 – 15 c. purple and lavender 50·00 50·00

(b) No. 279.
CT81 – 5 c. orange . . . . 12·50 12·50

(c) Nos. D282/6.
CT82 D **32** 1 c. blue . . . . . . 7·00
CT83 2 c. blue . . . . . . 7·00
CT84 4 c. blue . . . . . . 7·00
CT85 5 c. blue . . . . . . 7·00
CT86 10 c. blue . . . . . . 7·00

(d) Nos. 282/92.
CT87 **32** 1 c. purple 35 35
CT88 – 2 c. green 35 30
CT89 – 3 c. brown 35 35
CT90 – 4 c. red . . . . 1·25 1·25
CT91 – 5 c. orange 10 10
CT92 – 10 c. orange and blue . . 75 75
CT93 – 15 c. lake and slate . . . 75 75
CT94 – 20 c. blue and lake . . . 75 75
CT95 **40** 50 c. black and brown . . 6·25 6·25
CT96 – 1 p. black and blue . . . 9·50 9·50
CT97 – 5 p. black and red . . . 95·00 95·00

GENERAL ISSUES.

43 Coat of Arms 44 Statue of Cuauhtemoc 45 Ignacio Zaragoza

1915. Portraits as T **45**. Roul or perf.
293 **43** 1 c. violet 10 10
294 **44** 2 c. green 20 15
304 **45** 3 c. brown 20 15
305 4 c. red (Morelos) 20 20
306 5 c. orange (Madero) . . . 25 15
307 10 c. blue (Juarez) 15 10

46 Map of Mexico 47 Lighthouse, Veracruz

48 Post Office, Mexico City

1915.
299 **46** 40 c. grey 30 30
433 40 c. mauve . . . . 1·25 25
300 **47** 1 p. grey and brown . . . 35 60
411 1 p. grey and blue . . . 22·00 60
301 **48** 5 p. blue and lake . . . . 5·00 5·50
412 5 p. grey and green 50 60

(49) 50 V. Carranza

1916. Silver Currency. Optd with T **49**. (a) No. 271.
309 – 15 c. purple and lavender . . £250 £250

(b) No. 279
309a – 5 c. orange . . . . 55·00 55·00

(c) Nos. 282/92.
310 **32** 1 c. purple . . . . 2·10 3·25
311 – 2 c. green 25 15
312 – 3 c. brown 25 15
313 – 4 c. red . . . . 3·75 5·00
314 – 5 c. orange 10 10
315 – 10 c. orange and blue . . . 60 95
316 – 15 c. lake and slate . . . 1·10 1·90
317 – 20 c. blue and lake . . . 1·10 1·90
318 **40** 50 c. black and brown . . 5·25 3·25
319 – 1 p. black and blue . . . 9·50 4·00
320 – 5 p. black and red . . . 95·00 80·00

(d) Nos. CT1/3 and CT5/8.
320b CT **1** 1 c. blue . . . . . . 15·00
320c 2 c. green . . . . . . 7·50
320d 4 c. blue £160
320e 10 c. red . . . . . . 1·40
320f 20 c. brown . . . . . 1·90
320g 50 c. red . . . . . . 9·50
320h 1 p. violet . . . . . 15·00

(e) Nos. CT39/46.
321 CT **5** 1 c. blue . . . . 2·40 12·00
322 2 c. green . . . . 2·40 7·00
323 3 c. orange . . . . . . 45 7·00
324 5 c. red . . . . 45 7·00
325 10 c. red . . . . 45 3·25
326 15 c. mauve . . . . . . 45 7·00
327 50 c. yellow . . . . . . 70 8·00
328 1 p. violet . . . . . . 6·00 15·00

(f) Nos. CT58/68.
329 **32** 1 c. purple . . . . 1·60 2·50
330 – 2 c. green 35 30
331 – 3 c. brown 30 30
332 – 4 c. red 30 30
333 – 5 c. orange 50 15
334 – 10 c. orange and blue . . 35 30
335 – 15 c. lake and slate . . . 40 40
336 – 20 c. blue and lake . . . 40 40
337 **40** 50 c. black and brown . . 4·75 3·75
338 – 1 p. black and blue . . 10·00 10·00
339 – 5 p. black and red . . . 95·00 85·00

(g) Nos. CV22/9.
340 **32** 1 c. purple . . . . 7·00 9·50
341 – 2 c. green 75 45
342 – 3 c. brown . . . . 2·00 2·75
343 – 4 c. red . . . . 8·25 9·50
344 – 5 c. orange . . . . 2·75 3·75
345 – 10 c. orange and blue . . 7·50 8·75
346 – 15 c. lake and slate . . . 7·50 8·75
347 – 20 c. blue and lake . . . 7·50 8·75

(h) Nos. CT87/97.
348 **32** 1 c. purple . . . . 1·60 2·10
349 – 2 c. green 30 30
350 – 3 c. brown 25 20
351 – 4 c. red . . . . 3·25 3·75
352 – 5 c. orange 40 10
353 – 10 c. orange and blue . . 75 1·25
354 – 15 c. lake and slate . . . 60 30
355 – 20 c. blue and red . . . 60 55
356 **40** 50 c. black and brown . . 4·75 5·50
357 – 1 p. black and blue . . . 7·00 7·50

1916. Carranza's Triumphal Entry into Mexico City.
358 **50** 10 c. brown . . . . 7·50 8·25
359 10 c. blue 60 30

(51)

1916. Optd with T **51**. (a) Nos. D282/6.
360 D **32** 5 c. on 1 c. blue . . . . 1·60 1·60
361 10 c. on 2 c. blue . . . 1·60 1·60
362 20 c. on 4 c. blue . . . 1·60 1·60
363 25 c. on 5 c. blue . . . 1·60 1·60
364 60 c. on 10 c. blue . . . 75 75
365 1 p. on 1 c. blue . . . 75 75
366 1 p. on 2 c. blue . . . 75 75
367 1 p. on 4 c. blue . . . 40 40
368 1 p. on 5 c. blue . . . 1·60 1·60
369 1 p. on 10 c. blue . . . 1·60 1·60

(b) Nos. 282, 286 and 283.
370 **32** 5 c. on 1 c. purple . . . 10 10
371 10 c. on 1 c. purple . . . 10 10
372 – 20 c. on 5 c. orange . . . 10 10
373 – 25 c. on 5 c. orange . . . 15 15
374 – 60 c. on 2 c. green . . . 10·50 12·50

(c) Nos. CT39/40.
375 CT **5** 60 c. on 1 c. blue . . . 1·90 3·75
376 60 c. on 2 c. green . . . 1·90 3·75

(d) Nos. CT58, CT62 and CT59.
377 **32** 5 c. on 1 c. purple . . . 10 10
378 – 10 c. on 1 c. purple . . . 60 60
379 – 25 c. on 5 c. purple . . . 15 15
380 – 60 c. on 2 c. green . . . £130 £170

(e) No. CV25.
381 – 25 c. on 5 c. orange . . . 15 10

(f) Nos. CT87, CT91 and CT88.
382 **32** 5 c. on 1 c. purple . . . 9·50 12·50
383 – 10 c. on 1 c. purple . . . 3·25 4·75
385 – 25 c. on 5 c. orange . . . 50 95
386 – 60 c. on 2 c. green . . . £140

1916. Nos. D282/6 surch **GPM** and value.
387 D **32** $2.50 on 1 c. blue . . . 60 60
388 $2.50 on 2 c. blue . . . 6·25 6·25
389 $2.50 on 4 c. blue . . . 6·25 6·25
390 $2.50 on 5 c. blue . . . 6·25 6·25
391 $2.50 on 10 c. blue . . 6·25 6·25

52a Arms 53 Zaragoza

1916.
392 **52a** 1 c. purple 15 15

1917. Portraits. Roul or perf.
393 **53** 1 c. violet 25 10
393a 1 c. grey 70 20
394 – 2 c. green (Vazquez) . . . 35 10
395 – 3 c. brown (Suarez) . . . 35 10
396 – 4 c. red (Carranza) . . . 60 20
397 – 5 c. blue (Herrera) . . . 85 10
398 – 10 c. blue (Madero) . . . 1·40 10
399 – 20 c. lake (Dominguez) . . 14·00 35
400 – 30 c. purple (Serdan) . . 38·00 60
401 – 30 c. black (Serdan) . . . 45·00 60

1919. Red Cross Fund. Surch with cross and premium.
413 5 c. + 3 c. blue (No. 397) . . 9·00 9·50
414 10 c. + 5 c. blue (No. 398) . 11·00 9·50

56 Meeting of Iturbide and Guerrero

1921. Centenary of Declaration of Independence.
415 **56** 10 c. brown and blue . . . 9·50 1·90
416 – 10 p. black and brown . . . 9·50 22·00
DESIGN: 10 p. Entry into Mexico City.

58 Golden Eagle

1922. Air.
454 **58** 25 c. sepia and lake 70 20
455 25 c. sepia and green . . . 75 25
456 50 c. red and blue . . . . . 1·00 35

59 Morelos Monument 60 Fountain and Aqueduct

61 Pyramid of the Sun, Teotihuacan 62 Castle of Chapultepec

63 Columbus Monument 74 Benito Juarez

64 Juarez Colonnade 65 Monument to Dona Josefa Ortiz de Dominguez

66 Cuauhtemoc Monument 68 Ministry of Communications

69 National Theatre and Palace of Fine Arts

1923. Roul or perf.
436 **59** 1 c. brown 25 10
437 **60** 2 c. red 15 10
438 **61** 3 c. brown 10 10
429 **62** 4 c. green 60 10
440 **63** 4 c. green 15 10
441 5 c. orange 10 10
453 **74** 8 c. orange 15 10
423 **64** 10 c. brown . . . . 4·75 10
442 **66** 10 c. lake 15 10
443 **65** 20 c. blue 35 10
426 **66** 30 c. green . . . . 35·00 2·50
432 **64** 30 c. green 45 10
434 **68** 50 c. brown 30 10
435 **69** 1 p. blue and lake 50 25

70 72 Sr. Francisco Garcia y Santos

73 Post Office, Mexico City

1926. 2nd Pan-American Postal Congress. Inscr as in T **70/3**.
445 **70** 2 c. red . . . . 1·25 35
446 – 4 c. green . . . . 1·25 40
447 **70** 5 c. orange . . . . 1·25 25
448 – 10 c. red . . . . 1·90 25
449 **72** 20 c. blue . . . . 1·90 50
450 30 c. green . . . . 3·25 1·90
451 40 c. mauve . . . . 6·25 1·60
452 **73** 1 p. blue and brown . . . 12·50 3·75
DESIGN—As Type **70**: 4 c., 10 c. Map of North and South America.

1929. Child Welfare. Optd **Protection a la Infancia**.
457 **59** 1 c. brown 25 15

77 79 Capt. Emilio Carranza

1929. Obligatory Tax. Child Welfare.
459 **77** 1 c. violet 10 10
461 2 c. green 20 10
462 5 c. brown 15 10

1929. Air. 1st Death Anniv of Carranza (airman).
463 **79** 5 c. sepia and green . . . 55 30
464 10 c. red and sepia 65 35
465 15 c. green and violet . . 1·90 60
466 20 c. black and sepia . . . 60 35
467 50 c. black and red . . . . 3·75 1·25
468 1 p. sepia and black . . . 7·75 1·75

80

1929. Air. Perf or roul (10, 15, 20, 50 c.), roul (5, 25 c.), perf (others).
476a **80** 5 c. blue 10 10
477 10 c. violet 10 10
478 15 c. red 15 10
479 20 c. brown 75 10
480 25 c. purple 45 40
472 30 c. black 10 10
473 35 c. blue 15 10
481 50 c. red 45 35
474 1 p. blue and black . . . 60 30
475 5 p. blue and red . . . . 2·50 2·10
476 10 p. brown and violet . . 3·75 4·50

81 87

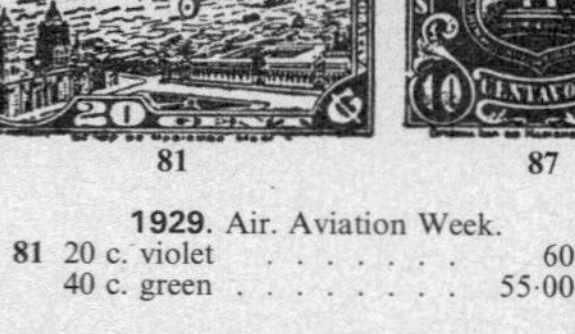

1929. Air. Aviation Week.
482 **81** 20 c. violet 60 50
483 40 c. green . . . . 55·00 48·00

1930. 2nd Pan-American Postal Congress issue optd **HABILITADO 1930**.
484 **70** 2 c. red . . . . 2·10 1·40
485 – 4 c. green . . . . 2·10 1·25
486 **70** 5 c. orange . . . . 2·10 1·10
487 – 10 c. red . . . . 3·75 1·25
488 **72** 20 c. blue . . . . 5·00 1·90
489 30 c. green . . . . 4·50 2·10
490 40 c. mauve . . . . 6·25 4·50
491 **73** 1 p. blue and brown . . . 5·50 3·75

1930. Air. National Tourist Congress. Optd **Primer Congreso Nacional de Turismo. Mexico. Abril 20-27 de 1930.**
492 **80** 10 c. violet (No. 477) . . . 1·25 60

1930. Obligatory Tax. Child Welfare. Surch **HABILITADO $0.01**.
494 **77** 1 c. on 2 c. green 30 15
495 1 c. on 5 c. brown 60 15

1930. Air. Optd **HABILITADO 1930.**
496 **79** 5 c. sepia and green 3·50 2·75
497 15 c. green and violet 5·50 4·75

1930. Air. Optd **HABILITADO Aereo 1930-1931.**
498 **79** 5 c. sepia and green 3·75 4·00
499 10 c. red and sepia 2·10 2·50
500 15 c. green and violet 4·00 4·50
501 20 c. black and sepia 4·50 3·50
502 50 c. black and red 8·75 6·25
503 1 p. sepia and black 2·50 1·75

1931. Obligatory Tax. Child Welfare. No. CT58 optd **PRO INFANCIA.**
504 **32** 1 c. purple 20 15

1931. Fourth Centenary of Puebla.
505 **87** 10 c. brown and blue 1·60 25

88 **92** Fray Bartolome de las Casas

1931. Air. Aeronautic Exhibition.
506 **88** 25 c. lake 2·00 1·60

1931. Nos. 446/52 optd **HABILITADO 1931.**
508 – 4 c. green 35·00
509 **70** 5 c. orange 6·25
510 – 10 c. red 6·25
511 **72** 20 c. blue 6·25
512 30 c. green 11·00
513 40 c. mauve 16·00
514 **73** 1 p. blue and brown 14·00

1931. Air. Surch **HABILITADO Quince centavos.** Perf. or rouletted.
516 **80** 15 c. on 20 c. sepia 20 10

1932. Air. Surch in words and figures. Perf. or roul.
517 **88** 20 c. on 25 c. lake 30 15
521 **80** 30 c. on 20 c. sepia 15 10
519 **58** 40 c. on 25 c. sepia & lake 90 65
520 40 c. on 25 c. sepia & green 25·00 25·00
522 **80** 80 c. on 25 c. (No. 480) 90 60

1932. Air. 4th Death Anniv of Emilio Carranza. Optd **HABILITADO AEREO–1932.**
523 **79** 5 c. sepia and green 3·75 3·25
524 10 c. red and sepia 3·25 1·90
525 15 c. green and violet 3·75 2·50
526 20 c. black and sepia 3·25 1·75
527 50 c. black and red 22·00 22·00

1933. Roul.
528 **92** 15 c. blue 15 10

93 Mexican Geographical and Statistical Society's Arms
94 National Theatre and Palace of Fine Arts

1933. 21st Int Statistical Congress and Centenary of Mexican Geographical and Statistical Society.
529 **93** 2 c. green (postage) 75 20
530 5 c. brown 1·10 25
531 10 c. blue 35 10
532 1 p. violet 32·00 38·00
533 **94** 20 c. violet and red (air) 2·10 85
534 30 c. violet and brown 4·25 3·75
535 1 p. violet and green 42·00 45·00

95 Mother and Child
98 Nevada de Toluca

1934. National University. Inscr "PRO-UNIVERSIDAD".
543 **95** 1 c. orange (postage) 10 10
544 – 5 c. green 1·00 15
545 – 10 c. lake 1·25 30
546 – 20 c. blue 5·00 3·25
547 – 30 c. black 8·75 7·50
548 – 40 c. brown 15·00 10·00
549 – 50 c. blue 28·00 32·00
550 – 1 p. black and red 32·00 30·00
551 – 5 p. brown and black £120 £160
552 – 10 p. violet and brown £500 £650
DESIGNS: 5 c. Archer; 10 c. Festive headdress; 20 c. Woman decorating pot; 30 c. Indian and Inca Lily; 40 c. Potter; 50 c. Sculptor; 1 p. Gold craftsman; 5 p. Girl offering fruit; 10 p. Youth burning incense.

553 **98** 20 c. orange (air) 1·75 1·75
554 – 30 c. purple and mauve 3·50 4·25
555 – 50 c. brown and green 4·00 6·25
556 – 75 c. green and black 4·75 8·75
557 – 1 p. blue and green 5·00 6·25
558 – 5 p. blue and brown 26·00 60·00
559 – 10 p. red and blue 80·00 £130
560 – 20 p. red and brown £475 £750
DESIGNS—Airplane over: 30 c. Pyramids of the Sun and Moon, Teotihuacan; 50 c. Mt. Ajusco; 75 c. Mts. Ixtaccihuatl and Popocatepetl; 1 p. Bridge over R. Papagallo; 5 p. Chapultepec Castle entrance; 10 p. Orizaba Peak, Mt. Citlaltepetl; 20 p. Girl and Aztec calendar stone.

101 Zapoteca Indian Woman
110 Coat of Arms

1934. Pres. Cardenas' Assumption of Office. Designs as Type **101** and **110**. Imprint "OFICINA IMPRESORA DE HACIENDA-MEXICO" at foot of stamp. (a) Postage.
561 – 1 c. orange 30 10
562 **101** 2 c. green 30 10
563 – 4 c. red 45 15
564 – 5 c. brown 30 10
565 – 10 c. blue 40 10
565a – 10 c. violet 80 10
566 – 15 c. blue 2·50 15
567 – 20 c. green 1·25 10
567a – 20 c. blue 85 10
568 – 30 c. red 35 10
653 – 30 c. blue 40 10
569 – 40 c. brown 40 10
570 – 50 c. black 45 10
571 **110** 1 p. red and brown 1·60 10
572 – 5 p. violet and orange 4·75 55
DESIGNS: 1 c. Yalalteca Indian; 4 c. Revolution Monument; 5 c. Los Remedios Tower; 10 c. Cross of Palenque; 15 c. Independence Monument, Mexico City; 20 c. Independence Monument, Puebla; 30 c. "Heroic Children" Monument, Mexico City; 40 c. Sacrificial Stone; 50 c. Ruins of Mitla, Oaxaca; 5 p. Mexican "Charro" (Horseman).

112 Mictlantecuhtli
120 "Peasant admiration"

(b) Air.
573 **112** 5 c. black 20 10
574 – 10 c. brown 45 10
575 – 15 c. green 90 10
576 – 20 c. red 1·90 10
577 – 30 c. olive 35 10
577a – 40 c. blue 60 10
578 – 50 c. green 1·60 10
579 – 1 p. red and green 2·50 10
580 **120** 5 p. black and red 4·50 25
DESIGNS—HORIZ: 10 c. Temple at Quetzalcoatl; 15 c. Aeroplane over Citlaltepetl; 20 c. Popocatepetl; 30 c. Pegasus; 50 c. Uruapan Pottery; 1 p. "Warrior Eagle". VERT: 40 c. Aztec Idol.

121 Tractor
122 Arms of Chiapas

1935. Industrial Census.
581 **121** 10 c. violet 2·50 25

1935. Air. Amelia Earhart Flight to Mexico. No. 576 optd **AMELIA EARHART VUELO DE BUENA VOLUNTAD MEXICO 1935.**
581a 20 c. red £1900 £2500

1935. Annexation of Chiapas Centenary.
582 **122** 10 c. blue 35 15

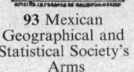

123 E. Zapata
124 Francisco Madero

1935. 25th Anniv of Revolutionary Plans of Ayala and San Luis Potosi.
583 **123** 10 c. violet (postage) 35 10
584 **124** 20 c. red (air) 20 10

129 Nuevo Laredo Road
131 Rio Corona Bridge

1936. Opening of Nuevo Laredo Highway (Mexico City-U.S.A.).
591 – 5 c. red & green (postage) 15 10
592 – 10 c. grey 25 10
593 **129** 20 c. green and brown 75 50
DESIGNS: As Type **129**: 5 c. Symbolical Map of Mexico–U.S.A. road; 10 c. Matalote Bridge.

594 – 10 c. blue (air) 30 10
595 **131** 20 c. orange and violet 30 10
596 – 40 c. green and blue 40 30
DESIGNS: As Type **131**: 10 c. Tasquillo Bridge over Rio Tula; 40 c. Guayalejo Bridge.

1936. 1st Congress of Industrial Medicine and Hygiene. Optd **PRIMER CONGRESO NAL DE HIGIENE V. MED. DEL TRABAJO.**
597 – 10 c. violet (No. 565a) 30 20

1937. As Nos. 561/4, 565a and 576, but smaller. Imprint at foot changed to "TALLERES DE IMP.(RESION) DE EST.(AMPILLAS) Y VALORES-MEXICO".
708 1 c. orange (postage) 25 10
709 2 c. green 25 10
600 4 c. red 40 10
601 5 c. brown 35 10
602 10 c. violet 25 10
603 20 c. red (air) 80 10

134 Blacksmith

1938. Carranza's "Plan of Guadelupe". 25th Anniv Inscr "CONMEMORATIVO PLAN DE GUADALUPE", etc.
604 **134** 5 c. brown & blk (postage) 30 10
605 – 10 c. brown 10 10
606 – 20 c. orange and brown 3·25 50
607 – 20 c. blue and red (air) 20 10
608 – 40 c. red and blue 45 15
609 – 1 p. blue and yellow 3·00 1·40
DESIGNS—VERT: 10 c. Peasant revolutionary; 20 c. Preaching revolt. HORIZ: 20 c. Horseman; 40 c. Biplane; 1 p. Mounted horseman.

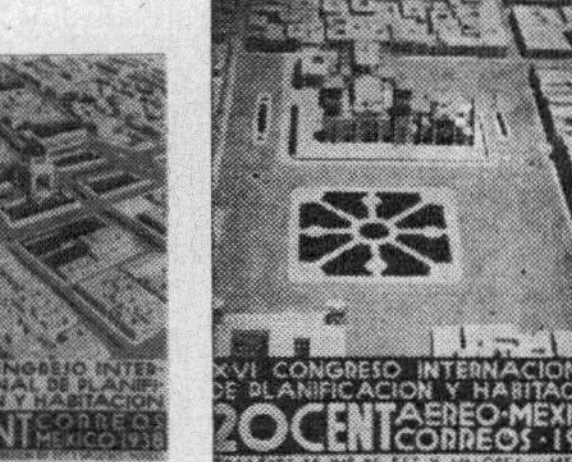

140 Arch of the Revolution
141 Cathedral and Constitution Square

1938. 16th Int Town Planning and Housing Congress, Mexico City. Inscr as in T **140/1**.
610 **140** 5 c. brown (postage) 80 30
611 – 5 c. olive 1·60 1·40
612 – 10 c. orange 8·75 7·00
613 – 10 c. brown 30 10
614 – 20 c. black 2·10 2·50
615 – 20 c. lake 11·50 9·50
DESIGNS: As Type **140**: 10 c. National Theatre; 20 c. Independence Column.

616 **141** 20 c. red (air) 15 10
617 – 20 c. violet 8·75 6·25
619 – 40 c. green 4·50 3·25
620 – 1 p. slate 4·50 3·25
621 – 1 p. light blue 4·50 3·25
DESIGNS: As Type **141**: 40 c. Chichen Itza Ruins (Yucatan); 1 p. Acapulco Beach.

142 Mosquito and Malaria Victim

1939. Obligatory Tax. Anti-Malaria Campaign.
622 **142** 1 c. blue 95 10

INDEX

Countries can be quickly located by referring to the index at the end of this volume.

143 Statue of an Indian
144 Statue of Woman Pioneer and Child

1939. Tulsa Philatelic Convention, Oklahoma.
623 **143** 10 c. red (postage) 20 10
624 **144** 20 c. brown (air) 50 20
625 40 c. green 1·25 60
626 1 p. violet 80 45

145 Mexican Pavilion, World's Fair
146 Morelos Statue on Mexican Pavilion

1939. Air. F. Sarabia non-stop Flight to New York. Optd **SARABIA Vuela MEXICO-NUEVA YORK.**
626a **146** 20 c. blue and red £160 £300

1939. New York World's Fair.
627 **145** 10 c. green & bl (postage) 30 10
628 **146** 20 c. green (air) 60 25
629 40 c. purple 1·60 60
630 1 p. brown and red 1·00 50

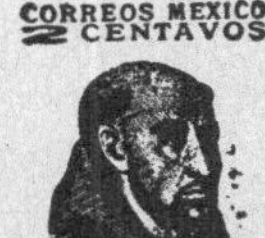

147 J. de Zumarraga
152 "Building"

154 "Transport"

1939. 400th Anniv of Printing in Mexico.
631 **147** 2 c. black (postage) 35 10
632 – 5 c. green 35 10
633 – 10 c. red 10 10
634 – 20 c. blue (air) 10 10
635 – 40 c. green 30 10
636 – 1 p. red and brown 55 35
DESIGNS: 5 c. First printing works in Mexico; 10 c. Antonio D. Mendoza; 20 c. Book frontispiece; 40 c. Title page of first law book printed in America; 1 p. Oldest Mexican Colophon.

1939. National Census. Inscr "CENSOS 1939 1940".
637 **152** 2 c. red (postage) 60 10
638 – 5 c. green 10 10
639 – 10 c. brown 10 10
640 **154** 20 c. blue (air) 70 25
641 – 40 c. orange 35 10
642 – 1 p. violet and blue 1·75 35
DESIGNS: As Type **152**: 5 c. "Agriculture"; 10 c. "Commerce". As Type **154**: 40 c. "Industry"; 1 p. "Seven Censuses".

155 "Penny Black"
156 Roadside Monument

1940. Centenary of First Adhesive Postage Stamps.

643 **155** 5 c. yellow & black (postage) 45 25
644 10 c. purple 10 10
645 20 c. red and blue 15 10
646 1 p. red and grey 4·50 2·50
647 5 p. blue and black 23·00 19·00

648 5 c. green and black (air) 45 30
649 10 c. blue and brown 35 10
650 20 c. violet and red 25 10
651 1 p. brown and red 2·10 3·25
652 5 p. brown and green 25·00 35·00

1940. Opening of Highway from Mexico City to Guadalajara.

654 **156** 6 c. green 35 10

159 Original College at Patzcuaro

1940. 4th Centenary of National College of St. Nicholas de Hidalgo.

655 – 2 c. violet (postage) 65 25
656 – 5 c. red 40 10
657 – 10 c. olive 40 10

658 **159** 20 c. green (air) 20 10
659 – 40 c. orange 25 10
660 – 1 p. violet, brown & orange 60 45

DESIGNS—VERT: 2 c. V. de Quiroga; 5 c. M. Ocampo; 10 c. St. Nicholas College Arms; 40 c. Former College at Morelia. HORIZ: 1 p. Present College at Morelia.

163 Pirate Galleon

1940. 400th Anniv of Campeche. Inscr as in T **163**.

661 – 10 c. red & brown (postage) 1·90 60

662 **163** 20 c. brown and red (air) 70 35
663 – 40 c. green and black 75 25
664 – 1 p. black and blue 3·25 1·90

DESIGNS: 10 c. Campeche City Arms; 40 c. St. Miguel Castel; 1 p. Temple of San Francisco.

165 Helmsman

166 Miguel Hidalgo y Costilla

1940. Inauguration of Pres. Camacho.

665 **165** 2 c. orange & black (postage) 1·00 30
666 5 c. blue and brown 3·75 2·10
667 10 c. olive and brown 1·40 40

668 20 c. grey & orange (air) 1·25 60
669 40 c. brown and green 1·25 95
670 1 p. purple and red 2·10 1·25

1940. Compulsory Tax. Dolores Hidalgo Memorial Fund.

671 **166** 1 c. red 30 10

168 Javelin throwing **169** Dark Nebula in Orion

1941. National Athletic Meeting.

675 **168** 10 c. green 2·10 25

1942. Inauguration of Astro-physical Observatory at Tonanzintla, Puebla.

676 **169** 2 c. blue & violet (postage) 80 50
677 – 5 c. blue 5·50 1·25
678 – 10 c. blue and orange 5·50 25

679 – 20 c. blue and green (air) 7·75 1·90
680 – 40 c. blue and red 7·00 2·50
681 – 1 p. black and orange 7·00 2·75

DESIGNS: 5 c. Solar Eclipse; 10 c. Spiral Galaxy of the "Hunting Dog"; 20 c. Extra-Galactic Nebula in Virgo; 40 c. Ring Nebula in Lyra; 1 p. Russell Diagram.

171 Ruins of Chichen-Itza **172** Merida Nunnery

1942. 400th Anniv of Merida. Inscr as in T **171/2**.

682 **171** 2 c. brown (postage) 70 30
683 – 5 c. red 1·40 30
684 – 10 c. violet 80 10

685 **172** 20 c. blue (air) 95 25
686 – 40 c. green 1·40 1·25
687 – 1 p. red 1·60 1·25

DESIGNS—VERT: 5 c. Mayan sculpture; 10 c. Arms of Merida; 40 c. Montejo University Gateway. HORIZ: 1 p. Campanile of Merida Cathedral.

173 "Mother Earth" **175** Hidalgo Monument

1942. 2nd Inter-American Agricultural Conference.

688 **173** 2 c. brown (postage) 40 20
689 – 5 c. blue 1·90 55
690 – 10 c. orange 60 25

691 – 20 c. green (air) 1·25 25
692 – 40 c. brown 75 25
693 – 1 p. violet 1·60 1·25

DESIGNS: 5 c. Sowing wheat; 10 c. Western Hemisphere carrying torch; 20 c. Corn; 40 c. Coffee; 1 p. Bananas.

1942. 400th Anniv of Guadalajara.

694 **175** 2 c. brown & bl (postage) 15 15
695 – 5 c. red and black 60 25
696 – 10 c. blue and red 60 20

697 – 20 c. black and green (air) 80 35
698 – 40 c. green and olive 1·10 50
699 – 1 p. violet and brown 80 60

DESIGNS—VERT: 5 c. Government Palace; 10 c. Guadalajara. HORIZ: 20 c. St. Paul's Church, Zapopan; 40 c. Sanctuary of Our Lady of Guadalupe; 1 p. Arms of Guadalajara.

186 Saltillo Athenaeum, Coahuila

1942. 75th Anniv of Saltillo Athenaeum.

700 **186** 10 c. black 90 20

189 Birthplace of Allende

1943. 400th Anniv of San Miguel de Allende.

701 – 2 c. blue (postage) 50 15
702 – 5 c. brown 55 15
703 – 10 c. black 2·10 50

704 – 20 c. green (air) 45 30
705 **189** 40 c. purple 60 30
706 – 1 p. red 1·75 1·60

DESIGNS—VERT: 2 c. Cupola de las Monjas; 5 c. Gothic Church; 10 c. Gen. de Allende. HORIZ: 20 c. San Miguel de Allende; 1 p. Church seen through cloisters.

190 "Liberty" **192** Dr. de Castorena **194** "Flight"

1944.

707 **190** 12 c. brown 20 10

1944. 3rd National Book Fair.

732 **192** 12 c. brown (postage) 40 10

733 – 25 c. green (air) 45 10

DESIGN: 25 c. Microphone, book and camera.

1944. Air.

734 **194** 25 c. brown 30 10

195 Hands clasping Globe

1945. Inter-American Conference.

735 **195** 12 c. red (postage) 25 10
736 1 p. green 45 10
737 5 p. brown 3·50 2·75
738 10 p. black 6·25 5·00

739 25 c. orange (air) 10 10
740 1 p. green 15 10
741 5 p. blue 1·25 1·10
742 10 p. red 3·50 2·75
743 20 p. blue 7·25 7·00

196 La Paz Theatre, San Luis Potosi

1945. Reconstruction of La Paz Theatre, San Luis Potosi.

744 **196** 12 c. pur & blk (postage) 20 10
745 1 p. blue and black 30 10
746 5 p. red and black 3·50 3·25
747 10 p. green and black 7·75 7·50

748 30 c. green (air) 10 10
749 1 p. purple and green 15 10
750 5 p. black and green 1·40 1·25
751 10 p. blue and green 2·75 2·10
752 20 p. green and black 6·00 5·25

197 Fountain of Diana the Huntress **198** Removing Bandage

1945.

753 **197** 3 c. violet 40 10

1945. Literacy Campaign.

754 **198** 2 c. blue (postage) 15 10
755 6 c. orange 20 10
756 12 c. blue 20 10
757 1 p. olive 25 10
758 5 p. red and black 2·10 1·90
759 10 p. green and blue 12·50 12·50

760 30 c. green (air) 10 10
761 1 p. red 15 10
762 5 p. blue 1·60 1·40
763 10 p. red 2·75 2·75
764 20 p. brown and green 13·00 12·50

199 Founder of National Post Office **200** O.N.U., Olive Branch and Globe

201 O.N.U. and Flags of United Nations

1946. Foundation of Posts in Mexico in 1580.

765 **199** 8 c. black 60 10

1946. United Nations.

766 **200** 2 c. olive (postage) 15 10
767 6 c. brown 15 10
768 12 c. blue 10 10
769 1 p. green 30 10
770 5 p. red 3·25 3·25
771 10 p. blue 14·00 12·50

772 **201** 3 c. brown (air) 10 10
773 1 p. grey 10 10
774 5 p. green and brown 70 50
775 10 p. brown and sepia 2·75 2·00
776 20 p. red and slate 6·00 4·75

202 Zacatecas City Arms **205** Don Genaro Codina and Zacatecas

1946. 400th Anniv of Zacatecas.

777 **202** 2 c. brown (postage) 25 10
778 – 12 c. blue 15 10
779 – 1 p. mauve 30 10
780 – 5 p. red 3·50 1·90
781 – 10 p. black and blue 19·00 6·25

DESIGNS: 1 p. Statue of Gen. Ortega; 5 p. R. L. Velarde (poet); 10 p. F. G. Salinas.

782 – 30 c. grey (air) 10 10
783 **205** 1 p. green and brown 15 10
784 – 5 p. green and red 1·60 1·60
785 – 10 p. brown and green 5·50 2·75

PORTRAITS: 30 c. Fr. Margil de Jesus; 5 p. Gen. Enrique Estrada; 10 p. D. Fernando Villalpando.

207 Learning Vowels **208** Postman

1946. Education Plan.

786 **207** 1 c. sepia 20 10

1947.

787 **208** 15 c. blue 15 10

209 Roosevelt and First Mexican Stamp **210** 10 c. U.S.A. 1847 and Mexican Eagle

1947. U.S.A. Postage Stamp Centenary.

788 **209** 10 c. brown (postage) 80 60
789 – 15 c. green 10 10

790 – 25 c. blue (air) 35 20
791 **210** 30 c. black 25 10
792 – 1 p. blue and red 50 15

DESIGNS: 15 c. as Type **209** but vert, 25 c., 1 p. as Type **210** but horiz.

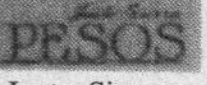

213 Justo Sierra **214** Ministry of Communications

212 Douglas DC4

1947.

795 **213** 10 p. green and brown (postage) 55·00 9·50
796 **214** 20 p. mauve and green 80 1·25

793 – 10 p. red and brown (air) 75 80
794 **212** 20 p. red and blue 1·50 1·25

DESIGN—HORIZ: 10 p. E. Carranza.

215 Manuel Rincon

217 Vicente Suarez

1947. Battle Centenaries. Portraits of "Child Heroes" etc., Inscr "1er CENTENARIO CHAPULTEPEC ("CHURUBUSCO" or "MOLINO DEL REY") 1847 1947".

797 – 2 c. black (postage) . . . 30 10
798 – 5 c. red 15 10
799 – 10 c. brown 15 10
800 – 15 c. green 15 10
801 **215** 30 c. olive 20 10
802 – 1 p. blue 30 15
803 – 5 p. red and blue . . . . 1·25 1·25

DESIGNS—VERT: 2 c. Francisco Marquez; 5 c. Fernando Montes de Oca; 10 c. Juan Escutin; 15 c. Agustin Melgar; 1 p. Lucas Balderas; 5 p. Flag of San Blas Battalion.

804 **217** 25 c. violet (air) 15 10
805 – 30 c. blue 15 10
806 – 50 c. green 25 10
807 – 1 p. violet 30 10
808 – 5 p. brown and blue . . . 80 80

DESIGNS—HORIZ: 30 c. Juan de la Barrera; 50 c. Military Academy; 1 p. Pedro Maria Anaya; 5 p. Antonio de Leon.

218 Puebla Cathedral

221 Dance of the Half Moons, Puebla

1950. (a) Postage. As T **218**.

835 – 3 c. blue 15 10
874 – 5 c. brown 25 10
875 – 10 c. green . . . . . . 1·50 10
876 – 15 c. green 20 10
877e **218** 20 c. blue 30 10
840 – 30 c. red 25 10
879 – 30 c. brown 35 10
880b – 40 c. orange 95 10
1346b – 50 c. blue 10 10
1327b – 80 c. green 35 10
843 – 1 p. brown . . . . . . 2·75 10
1346f – 1 p. green 10 10
1011ab – 1 p. grey 30 10
1327d – 3 p. red 55 10
1012a – 5 p. blue and green . . 1·10 60
1013ab – 10 p. black and blue . . 2·50 1·25
846 – 20 p. violet and green . 6·25 6·25
1014a – 20 p. violet and black . 5·00 2·50
1327e – 50 p. orange and green . 6·25 4·75

DESIGNS: 3 c, 3 p. La Purisima Church, Monterrey; 5 c. Modern building, Mexico City; 10 c. Convent of the Nativity, Tepozlan; 15 c, 50 p. Benito Juarez; 30 c., 80 c. Indian dancer, Michoacan; 40 c. Sculpture, Tabasco; 50 c. Carved head, Veracruz; 1 p. Actopan Convent and carved head; 5 p. Galleon, Campeche; 10 p. Francisco Madero; 20 p. Modern building, Mexico City.

(b) Air. As T **221**.

897 – 5 c. blue 15 10
898 – 10 c. brown 85 15
899a – 20 c. red 35 10
850 – 25 c. brown 60 10
851 – 30 c. olive 15 10
852 – 35 c. violet . . . . . . 1·25 10
1327f – 40 c. blue 10 10
904c – 50 c. green 35 10
1056 – 80 c. red 60 70
906a **221** 1 p. grey 45 10
1327h – 1 p. 60 red 60 10
1327i – 1 p. 90 red 35 10
907a – 2 p. brown . . . . . . 6·25 25
908 – 2 p. 25 purple 60 45
1327j – 4 p. 30 blue 45 10
1017a – 5 p. orange and brown . 2·75 35
1327k – 5 p. 20 lilac 70 25
1327l – 5 p. 60 green . . . . . 1·40 30
895 – 10 p. blue and black . . 3·00 60
1019a – 20 p. blue and red . . . 4·50 4·75

DESIGNS: 5 c., 1 p. 90 Bay of Acapulco; 10 c., 4 p. 30, Dance of the Plumes, Oaxaca; 20 c. Mayan frescoes, Chiapas; 25 c., 2 p. 25, 5 p. 60, Masks, Michoacan; 30 c. Cuauhtemoc; 35 c., 2 p., 5 p. 20, Taxco, Guerrero; 40 c. Sculpture, San Luis Potosi; 50 c., 1 p. 60, Ancient carvings, Chiapas; 80 c. University City, Mexico City; 5 p. Architecture, Queretaro; 10 p. Hidalgo; 20 p. National Music Conservatoire, Mexico City.

222 Arterial Road

224 Train and Map

1950. Opening of Mexican Section of Pan-American Highway. Inscr "CARRETERA INTER-NACIONAL 1950".

860 – 15 c. violet (postage) . . 30 10
861 **222** 20 c. blue 20 10

862 – 25 c. pink (air) . . . . . 1·60 20
863 – 35 c. green 10 10

DESIGNS—HORIZ: 15 c. Bridge; 25 c. Pres. M. Aleman, bridge and map; 35 c. B. Juarez and map.

1950. Inauguration of Mexico–Yucatan Rly.

864 – 15 c. purple (postage) . . 80 10
865 **224** 20 c. red 25 10

866 – 25 c. green (air) 25 10
867 – 35 c. blue 40 30

DESIGNS—VERT: 15 c. Rail-laying. HORIZ: 25 c. Diesel trains; 35 c. M. Aleman and suspension bridge.

227 Hands and Globe

1950. 75th Anniv of U.P.U.

868 – 50 c. violet (postage) . . 25 10

869 – 25 c. red (air) 35 10
870 **227** 80 c. blue 30 20

DESIGNS—HORIZ: 25 c. Aztec runner. VERT: 50 c. Letters "U.P.U.".

228 Miguel Hidalgo 229

1953. Birth Bicentenary of Hidalgo.

871 **228** 20 c. sepia & blue (postage) 1·10 10

872 – 25 c. lake and blue (air) . 35 10
873 **229** 35 c. green 35 10

DESIGN: As Type **229**: 25 c. Full face portrait.

231 Aztec Athlete 232 View and Mayan Bas-relief

1954. 7th Central American and Caribbean Games.

918 **231** 20 c. blue & pink (postage) 55 10

919 **232** 25 c. brown and green (air) 35 15
920 – 35 c. turquoise and purple 30 10

DESIGN: 35 c. Stadium.

233 234

1954. Mexican National Anthem Centenary.

921 **233** 5 c. lilac & blue (postage) 45 15
922 20 c. brown and purple . 55 10
923 1 p. green and red . . . 30 20

924 **234** 25 c. blue and lake (air) 45 15
925 35 c. purple and blue . . 20 10
926 80 c. green and blue . . 25 15

235 Torchbearer and Stadium 236 Aztec God and Map

1955. 2nd Pan-American Games, Mexico City. Inscr "II JUEGOS DEPORTIVOS PANAMERICANOS".

927 **235** 20 c. green & brn (postage) 40 10

928 **236** 25 c. blue and brown (air) 30 10
929 – 35 c. brown and red . . . 30 10

DESIGN: As Type **236**: 35 c. Stadium and map.

237 Olin Design

238 Feathered Serpent and Mask

1956. Mexican Stamp Centenary.

930 **237** 5 c. green & brn (postage) 30 10
931 – 10 c. blue and grey 30 10
932 – 30 c. purple and red . . . 20 10
933 – 50 c. brown and blue . . . 25 10
934 – 1 p. black and green . . . 35 10
935 – 5 p. sepia and bistre . . . 1·25 1·40

DESIGNS: As Type **237**: 10 c. Tohtli bird; 30 c. Zochitl flower; 50 c. Centli corn; 1 p. Mazatl deer; 5 p. Teheutli man's head.

937 **238** 5 c. black (air) 15 10
938 – 10 c. blue 15 10
939 – 50 c. purple 10 10
940 – 1 p. violet 15 10
941 – 1 p. 20 mauve 15 10
942 – 5 p. turquoise 50 50

DESIGNS: As Type **238**: 10 c. Bell tower, coach and Viceroy Enriquez de Almanza; 50 c. Morelos and cannon; 1 p. Mother, child and mounted horseman; 1 p. 20, Sombrero and spurs; 5 p. Emblems of food and education and pointing hand.

239 Stamp of 1856

1956. Centenary Int Philatelic Exn, Mexico City.

944 **239** 30 c. blue and brown . . . 45 15

240 F. Zarco

241 V. Gomez Farias and M. Ocampo

1956. Inscr "CONSTITUYENTE(S) DE 1857".

945 – 25 c. brown (postage) . . 35 10
946 – 45 c. blue 15 10
947 – 60 c. purple 15 10
1346d **240** 70 c. blue 20 10
1327c – 2 p. 30 blue 55 10

949 **241** 15 c. blue (air) 20 10
1327g – 60 c. green 15 15
950 – 1 p. 20 violet and green . 35 15
951 **241** 2 p. 75 purple 50 30

PORTRAITS: As T **240** (postage): 25, 45 c., 2 p. 30, G. Prieto; 60 c. P. Arriagan. As T **41** (air): 60 c., 1 p. 20, L. Guzman and I. Ramirez.

242 Paricutin Volcano

1956. Air. 20th International Geological Congress.

952 **242** 50 c. violet 30 10

243 Map of Central America and the Caribbean

1956. Air. 4th Inter-American Congress of Caribbean Tourism.

953 **243** 25 c. blue and grey 20 10

244 Assembly of 1857 245 Mexican Eagle and Scales

1957. Centenary of 1857 Constitution.

958 – 30 c. gold & lake (postage) 35 10
959 **244** 1 p. green and sepia . . . 25 10

960 **245** 50 c. brown & green (air) 20 10
961 – 1 p. lilac and blue 30 15

DESIGNS—VERT: 30 c. Emblem of Constitution. HORIZ: 1 p. (Air), "Mexico" drafting the Constitution.

246 Globe, Weights and Dials

1957. Air. Centenary of Adoption of Metric System in Mexico.

962 **246** 50 c. black and silver . . 30 10

247 Train Disaster

248 Oil Derrick

1957. Air. 50th Anniv of Heroic Death of J. Garcia (engine driver) at Nacozari.

963 **247** 50 c. purple and red . . . 20 25

1958. 20th Anniv of Nationalization of Oil Industry.

964 **248** 30 c. black & bl (postage) 25 10
965 – 5 p. red and blue . . . . 2·50 2·50

966 – 50 c. green and black (air) 10 10
967 – 1 p. black and red 20 10

DESIGNS—HORIZ: 50 c. Oil storage tank and "AL SERVICIO DE LA PATRIA" ("At the service of the Fatherland"); 1 p. Oil refinery at night. VERT: 5 p. Map of Mexico and silhouette of oil refinery.

249 Angel, Independence Monument, Mexico City

250 U.N.E.S.C.O. Headquarters, Paris

1958. Air. 10th Anniv of Declaration of Human Rights.

968 **249** 50 c. blue 20 10

1959. Inauguration of U.N.E.S.C.O. Headquarters Building, Paris.

969 **250** 30 c. black and purple . . 30 10

251 U.N. Headquarters, New York

252 President Carranza

1959. U.N. Economic and Social Council Meeting, Mexico City.

970 **251** 30 c. blue and yellow . . 30 10

1960. "President Carranza Year" (1959) and his Birth Centenary.

971 **252** 30 c. pur & grn (postage) 20 10

972 – 50 c. violet & salmon (air) 20 10

DESIGN—HORIZ: 50 c. Inscription "Plan de Guadalupe Constitucion de 1917" and portrait as Type **252**.

253 Alexander von Humboldt (statue)

254 Alberto Braniff's Voisin "Boxkite" and Bristol Britannia

1960. Death Centenary of Alexander von Humboldt (naturalist).
973 **253** 40 c. green and brown . . 20 10

1960. Air. 50th Anniv of Mexican Aviation.
974 **254** 50 c. brown and violet . . 40 10
975 1 p. brown and green . . 40 15

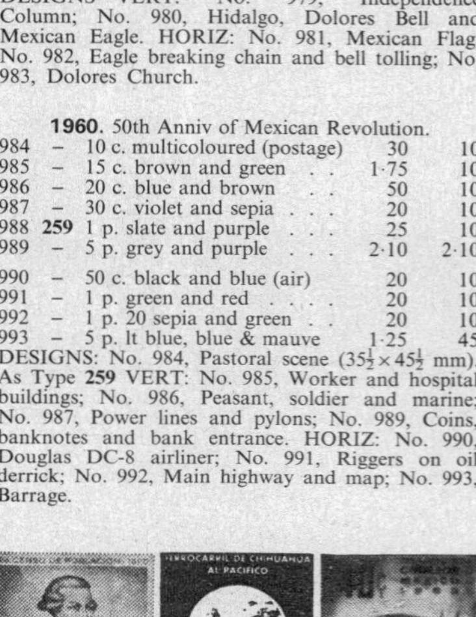

255 Francisco I. Madero
257 Dolores Bell
259 Children at Desk, University and School Buildings

1960. Visit to Mexico of Members of Elmhurst Philatelic Society (American Society of Mexican Specialists). Inscr "HOMENAJE AL COLECCIONISTA".
976 **255** 10 p. sepia, green and purple (postage) . . . . 22·00 26·00
977 – 20 p. sepia, green and purple (air) . . . . 26·00 50·00
DESIGN: As No. 1019a 20 p. National Music Conservatoire inscr "MEX. D.F.".

1960. 150th Anniv of Independence.
978 **257** 30 c. red & grn (postage) 60 10
979 – 1 p. sepia and green . . . 25 10
980 – 5 p. blue and purple . . . 3·25 3·25
981 – 50 c. red and green (air) 15 10
982 – 1 p. 20 sepia and blue . . 20 10
983 – 5 p. sepia and green . . . 2·75 1·10
DESIGNS—VERT: No. 979, Independence Column; No. 980, Hidalgo, Dolores Bell and Mexican Eagle. HORIZ: No. 981, Mexican Flag; No. 982, Eagle breaking chain and bell tolling; No. 983, Dolores Church.

1960. 50th Anniv of Mexican Revolution.
984 – 10 c. multicoloured (postage) 30 10
985 – 15 c. brown and green . . 1·75 10
986 – 20 c. blue and brown . . 50 10
987 – 30 c. violet and sepia . . . 20 10
988 **259** 1 p. slate and purple . . . 25 10
989 – 5 p. grey and purple . . . 2·10 2·10
990 – 50 c. black and blue (air) 20 10
991 – 1 p. green and red 20 10
992 – 1 p. 20 sepia and green . . 20 10
993 – 5 p. lt blue, blue & mauve 1·25 45
DESIGNS: No. 984, Pastoral scene ($35\frac{1}{2} \times 45\frac{1}{2}$ mm). As Type **259** VERT: No. 985, Worker and hospital buildings; No. 986, Peasant, soldier and marine; No. 987, Power lines and pylons; No. 989, Coins, banknotes and bank entrance. HORIZ: No. 990, Douglas DC-8 airliner; No. 991, Riggers on oil derrick; No. 992, Main highway and map; No. 993, Barrage.

261 Count S. de Revillagigedo
262 Railway Tunnel
263 Mosquito Globe and Instruments

1960. Air. National Census.
994 **261** 60 c. black and lake . . . 35 10

1961. Opening of Chihuahua State Railway.
995 **262** 40 c. black & grn (postage) 25 25
996 – 60 c. blue and black (air) 20 30
997 – 70 c. black and blue . . . 20 10
DESIGNS—HORIZ: 60 c. Railway track and outline map of Mexico; 70 c. Railway viaduct.

1962. Malaria Eradication.
998 **263** 40 c. brown and blue . . 25 10

264 Pres. Goulart of Brazil
265 Soldier and Memorial Stone

1962. Visit of President of Brazil.
999 **264** 40 c. bistre 65 10

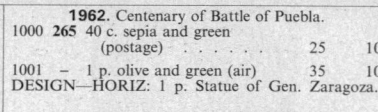

1962. Centenary of Battle of Puebla.
1000 **265** 40 c. sepia and green (postage) 25 10
1001 – 1 p. olive and green (air) 35 10
DESIGN—HORIZ: 1 p. Statue of Gen. Zaragoza.

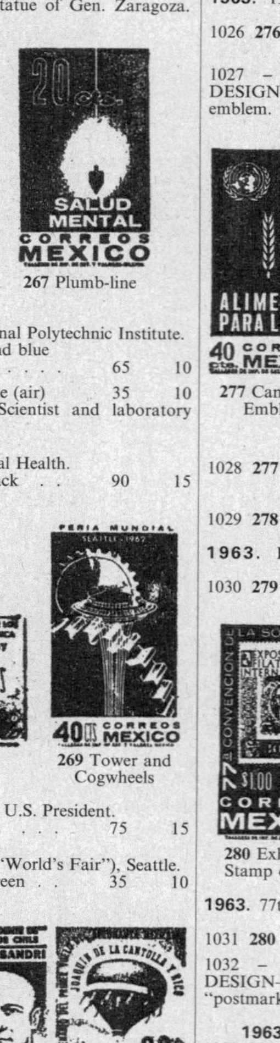

266 Draughtsman and Surveyor
267 Plumb-line

1962. 25th Anniv of National Polytechnic Institute.
1002 **266** 40 c. turquoise and blue (postage) 65 10
1003 – 1 p. olive and blue (air) 35 10
DESIGN—HORIZ: 1 p. Scientist and laboratory assistant.

1962. Mental Health.
1004 **267** 20 c. blue and black . . 90 15

268 Pres. J. F. Kennedy
269 Tower and Cogwheels

1962. Air. Visit of U.S. President.
1005 **268** 80 c. blue and red . . . 75 15

1962. "Century 21" Exn. ("World's Fair"), Seattle.
1006 **269** 40 c. black and green . . 35 10

270 Globe and O.E.A. Emblem
271 Pres. Alessandri of Chile
272 Balloon over Mexico City

1962. Inter-American Economic and Social Council.
1007 **270** 40 c. sepia & grey (post) 25 10
1008 – 1 p. 20 sepia & violet (air) 35 15
DESIGN—HORIZ: 1 p. 20, Globe, Scroll and O.E.A. emblem.

1962. Visit of President of Chile.
1009 **271** 20 c. brown 45 10

1962. Air. 1st Mexican Balloon Flight Centenary
1010 **272** 80 c. black and blue . . 90 25

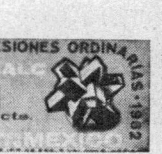

273 "ALALC" Emblem
274 Pres. Betancourt of Venezuela

1963. Air. 2nd "ALALC" Session.
1023 **273** 80 c. purple and orange 65 20

1963. Visit of President of Venezuela.
1024 **274** 20 c. blue 35 10

275 Petroleum Refinery
276 Congress Emblem

1963. Air. 25th Anniv of Nationalization of Mexican Petroleum Industry.
1025 **275** 80 c. slate and orange . . 35 10

1963. 19th International Chamber of Commerce Congress, Mexico City.
1026 **276** 40 c. brown and black (postage) 45 10
1027 – 80 c. black and blue (air) 55 20
DESIGN—HORIZ: 80 c. World map and "C.I.C." emblem.

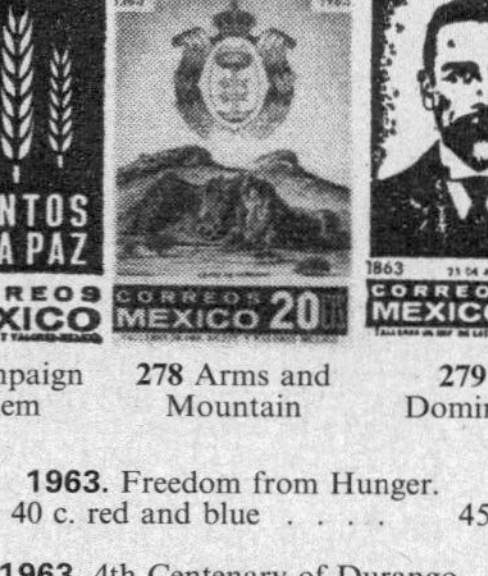

277 Campaign Emblem
278 Arms and Mountain
279 B. Dominguez

1963. Freedom from Hunger.
1028 **277** 40 c. red and blue 45 15

1963. 4th Centenary of Durango.
1029 **278** 20 c. brown and blue . . 45 15

1963. Birth Centenary of B. Dominguez (revolutionary).
1030 **279** 20 c. olive and green . . 45 15

280 Exhibition Stamp of 1956
281 Pres. Tito

1963. 77th American Philatelic Society Convention, Mexico City.
1031 **280** 1 p. brown & bl (postage) 60 45
1032 – 5 p. red (air) . . . . . . 1·40 75
DESIGN—HORIZ: 5 p. EXMEX "stamp" and "postmark".

1963. Air. Visit of President of Yugoslavia.
1033 **281** 2 p. green and violet . . 1·10 30

283 Part of U.I.A. Building
284 Red Cross on Tree
285 Pres. Estenssoro

1963. Air. International Architects' Day.
1034 **283** 80 c. grey and blue . . . 45 15

1963. Red Cross Centenary.
1035 **284** 20 c. red & grn (postage) 30 15
1036 – 80 c. red and green (air) . 70 25
DESIGN—HORIZ: 80 c. Red Cross on dove.

1963. Visit of President of Bolivia.
1037 **285** 40 c. purple and brown 45 15

286 Jose Morelos
287 Don Quixote as Skeleton

1963. 150th Anniv of First Anahuac Congress.
1038 **286** 40 c. bronze and green 40 15

1963. Air. 50th Death Anniv of Jose Posada (satirical artist).
1039 **287** 1 p. 20 black 75 20

288 University Arms
289 Diesel Train

1963. 90th Anniv of Sinaloa University.
1040 **288** 40 c. bistre and green . . 45 15

1963. 11th Pan-American Railways Congress, Mexico City.
1041 **289** 20 c. brn & blk (postage) 55 30
1042 – 1 p. 20 blue and violet (air) 50 20
DESIGN: 1 p. 20, Steam and diesel locomotives and horse-drawn tramcar.

290 "F.S.T.S.E." Emblem
291 Mrs. Roosevelt, Flame and U.N. Emblem

1964. 25th Anniv of Workers' Statute.
1075 **290** 20 c. sepia and orange . 30 10

1964. Air. 15th Anniv of Declaration of Human Rights.
1076 **291** 80 c. blue and orange . . 50 10

292 Pres. De Gaulle

1964. Air. Visit of President of France.
1077 **292** 2 p. blue and brown . . 1·25 35

293 Pres. Kennedy and Pres. A. Lopez Mateos

1964. Air. Ratification of Chamizal Treaty (1963).
1078 **293** 80 c. black and blue . . 55 15

294 Queen Juliana and Arms
295 Academy Emblem

1964. Air. Visit of Queen Juliana of the Netherlands.
1079 **294** 20 c. bistre and blue . . 70 15

1964. Centenary of National Academy of Medicine.
1080 **295** 20 c. gold and black . . 30 10

296 Lieut. Jose Azueto and Cadet Virgillo Uribe

1964. Air. 50th Anniv of Heroic Defence of Veracruz.
1081 **296** 40 c. green and brown . 30 10

297 Arms and World Map

1964. Air. International Bar Assn Conf, Mexico City.
1082 **297** 40 c. blue and brown . . 45 10

298 Colonel G. Mendez 299 Dr. Jose Rizal 300 Zacatecas

1964. Centenary of Battle of the Jahuactal Tabasco.
1083 **298** 40 c. olive and brown . . 35 10

1964. 400 Years of Mexican–Philippine Friendship. Inscr "1564 AMISTAD MEXICANO–FILIPINA 1964".
1084 **299** 20 c. blue & grn (postage) 35 10
1085 – 40 c. blue and violet . . 40 10
1086 – 80 c. blue & lt blue (air) 1·40 25
1087 – 2 p. 75 black and yellow 1·75 70
DESIGNS—As Type **299**: VERT: 40 c. Legaspi. HORIZ: 80 c. Galleon. LARGER (44 × 36 mm): 2 p. 75, Ancient map of Pacific Ocean.

1964. 50th Anniv of Conquest of Zacatecas.
1088 **300** 40 c. green and red . . . 40 10

301 Morelos Theatre, Aguascalientes 302 Andres Manuel del Rio

1965. 50th Anniv of Aguascalientes Convention.
1089 **301** 20 c. purple and grey . . 30 10

1965. Andres M. del Rio Commemoration.
1090 **302** 30 c. black 35 10

303 Netzahualcoyotl Dam 304 J. Morelos (statue)

1965. Air. Inauguration of Netzahualcoyotl Dam.
1091 **303** 80 c. slate and purple . . 30 10

1965. 150th Anniv (1964) of First Constitution.
1092 **304** 40 c. brown and green . 40 10

305 Microwave Tower 306 Fir Trees

1965. Air. Centenary of I.T.U.
1093 **305** 80 c. blue and indigo . . 40 20
1094 – 1 p. 20 green and black 45 20
DESIGN: 1 p. 20, Radio-electric station.

1965. Forest Conservation.
1095 **306** 20 c. green and blue . . 30 10
The inscription "!CUIDALOS!" means "CARE FOR THEM!".

307 I.C.Y. Emblem

1965. International Co-operation Year.
1096 **307** 40 c. brown and green . 25 10

308 Camp Fire and Tent

1965. Air. World Scout Conference, Mexico City.
1097 **308** 30 c. ultramarine & blue 40 20

309 King Baudouin and Queen Fabiola

1965. Air. Visit of Belgian King and Queen.
1098 **309** 2 p. blue and green . . 75 20

310 Mexican Antiquities and Unisphere 311 Dante (after R. Sanzio)

1965. Air. New York World's Fair.
1099 **310** 80 c. green and yellow . . 30 15

1965. Air. Dante's 700th Birth Anniv.
1100 **311** 2 p. red . . . . 1·00 55

312 Sling-thrower 313 Jose M. Morelos y Pavon (leader of independence movement)

1965. Olympic Games (1968) Propaganda (1st series). Museum pieces.
1101 **312** 20 c. blue & olive (postage) 45 10
1102 – 40 c. sepia and red . . . 15 10
1103 – 80 c. slate and red (air) 35 10
1104 – 1 p. 20 indigo and blue 45 15
1105 – 2 p. brown and blue . . 35 10
DESIGNS—As Type **312**: VERT: 40 c. Batsman. HORIZ: 2 p. Ball game. HORIZ (36 × 20 mm): 80 c. Fieldsman. 1 p. 20, Scoreboard.

1965. 150th Anniv of Morelos's Execution.
1108 **313** 20 c. black and blue . . 30 10

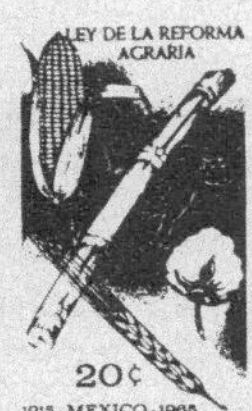

314 Agricultural Produce 315 Ruben Dario

1966. Centenary of Agrarian Reform Law.
1109 **314** 20 c. red 30 10
1110 – 40 c. black 40 10
DESIGN: 40 c. Emilio Zapata, pioneer of agrarian reform.

1966. Air. 50th Death Anniv of Ruben Dario (Nicaraguan poet).
1111 **315** 1 p. 20 sepia 55 20

316 Father Andres de Urdaneta and Compass Rose 317 Flag and Postal Emblem

1966. Air. 400th Anniv of Father Andres de Urdaneta's Return from the Philippines.
1112 **316** 2 p. 75 black 85 45

1966. 9th Postal Union of Americas and Spain Congress (U.P.A.E.), Mexico City.
1113 **317** 40 c. blk & grn (postage) 35 10
1114 – 80 c. black & mauve (air) 30 15
1115 – 1 p. 20 black and blue . . 35 15
DESIGNS—VERT: 80 c. Flag and posthorn. HORIZ: 1 p. 20, U.P.A.E. emblem and flag.

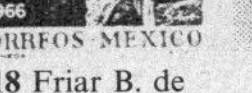

318 Friar B. de Las Casas 319 E.S.I.M.E. Emblem and Diagram

1966. 400th Death Anniv of Friar Bartolome de Las Casas ("Apostle of the Indies").
1116 **318** 20 c. black on buff . . . 35 10

1966. 50th Anniv of Higher School of Mechanical and Electrical Engineering.
1117 **319** 20 c. green and grey . . . 30 10

320 U Thant and U.N. Emblem 321 "1966 Friendship Year"

1966. Air. U.N. Secretary-General U Thant's Visit to Mexico.
1118 **320** 80 c. black and blue . . . 30 15

1966. Air. "Year of Friendship" with Central American States.
1119 **321** 80 c. green and red . . . 25 10

322 F.A.O. Emblem 323 Running and Jumping

1966. International Rice Year.
1120 **322** 40 c. green 30 10

1966. Olympic Games (1968) Propaganda (2nd series).
1121 **323** 20 c. black & bl (postage) 55 10
1122 – 40 c. black and lake . . . 25 10
1124 – 80 c. black & brown (air) 35 10
1125 – 2 p. 25 black and green 55 25
1126 – 2 p. 75 black and violet 60 35
DESIGNS: 40 c. Wrestling. LARGER (57 × 20 mm): 80 c. Obstacle race; 2 p. 25, American football; 2 p. 75, Lighting Olympic flame.

324 U.N.E.S.C.O. Emblem

1966. Air. 20th Anniv of U.N.E.S.C.O.
1128 **324** 80 c. multicoloured . . . 30 10

325 Constitution of 1917 326 Earth and Satellite 327 Oil Refinery

1967. 50th Anniv of Mexican Constitution.
1129 **325** 40 c. black (postage) . . 45 10
1130 – 80 c. brown & ochre (air) 35 10
DESIGN: 80 c. President V. Carranza.

1967. Air. World Meteorological Day.
1131 **326** 80 c. blue and black . . . 30 20

1967. 7th World Petroleum Congress, Mexico City.
1132 **327** 40 c. black and blue . . 30 10

328 Nayarit Indian 329 Degollado Theatre

1967. 50th Anniv of Nayarit State.
1133 **328** 20 c. black and green . . 30 10

1967. Cent. of Degollado Theatre, Guadalajara.
1134 **329** 40 c. brown and mauve 10 10

330 Mexican Eagle and Crown 331 School Emblem

1967. Centenary of Triumph over the Empire.
1135 **330** 20 c. black and ochre . . 30 10

1967. Air. 50th Anniv of Military Medical School.
1136 **331** 80 c. green and yellow . 35 15

332 Capt. H. Ruiz Gavino 333 Marco Polo

1967. Air. 50th Anniv of 1st Mexican Airmail Flight. Pachuca–Mexico City.
1137 **332** 80 c. brown and black . 30 10
1138 – 2 p. brown and black . . 70 20
DESIGN—HORIZ: 2 p. De Havilland D.H.6A biplane.

1967. Air. International Tourist Year.
1139 **333** 80 c. red and black . . . 20 10

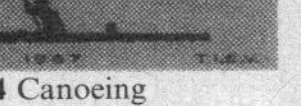

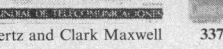

334 Canoeing 335 A. del Valle-Arizpe (writer)

1967. Olympic Games (1968) Propaganda (3rd series).
1140 **334** 20 c. black & bl (postage) 20 10
1141 – 40 c. black and red . . . 15 10
1142 – 50 c. black and green . . 15 10
1143 – 80 c. black and violet . . 25 10
1144 – 2 p. black and orange . 40 15
1146 – 80 c. black & mauve (air) 15 10
1147 – 1 p. 20 black and green 15 10
1148 – 2 p. black and lemon . . 60 20
1149 – 5 p. black and yellow . . 1·00 35
DESIGNS: 40 c. Basketball; 50 c. Hockey; 80 c. (No. 1143), Cycling; 80 c. (No. 1146), Diving; 1 p. 20, Running; 2 p. (No. 1144), Fencing; 2 p. (No. 1148), Weightlifting; 5 p. Football.

1967. Centenary of Fuente Athenaeum, Saltillo.
1151 **335** 20 c. slate and brown . . 30 10

336 Hertz and Clark Maxwell 337 P. Moreno

1967. Air. International Telecommunications Plan Conference, Mexico City.
1152 **336** 80 c. green and black . . 30 10

1967. 150th Death Anniv of Pedro Moreno (revolutionary).
1153 **337** 40 c. black and blue . . 30 15

338 Gabino Berreda (founder of Preparatory School) **339** Exhibition Emblem

1968. Centenary of National Preparatory and Engineering Schools.
1154 **338** 40 c. red and blue . . . 35 10
1155 – 40 c. blue and black . . . 35 10
DESIGN: No. 1155, Staircase, Palace of Mining.

1968. Air. "Efimex '68" International Stamp Exn, Mexico City.
1156 **339** 80 c. green and black . . 25 30
1157 2 p. red and black . . . 25 30
The emblem reproduces the "Hidalgo" Official stamp design of 1884.

1968. Olympic Games (1968) Propaganda (4th series). Designs as T **334**, but inscr "1968".
1158 20 c. black & olive (postage) 25 10
1159 40 c. black and purple . . . 25 10
1160 50 c. black and green . . . 25 10
1161 80 c. black and mauve . . . 25 10
1162 1 p. black and brown . . . 1·50 25
1163 2 p. black and grey . . . . 1·75 95
1165 80 c. black and blue (air) . . 30 10
1166 1 p. black and turquoise . . 35 15
1167 2 p. black and yellow . . . 35 20
1168 5 p. black and brown . . . 80 70
DESIGNS: 20 c. Wrestling; 40 c. Various sports; 50 c. Water-polo; 80 c. (No. 1161), Gymnastics; 80 c. (No. 1165), Yachting; 1 p. (No. 1162), Boxing; 1 p. (No. 1166), Rowing; 2 p. (No. 1163), Pistol-shooting; 2 p. (No. 1167), Volleyball; 5 p. Horse-racing.

340 Dr. Martin Luther King

1968. Air. Martin Luther King Commemorative.
1170 **340** 80 c. black and grey . . 35 15

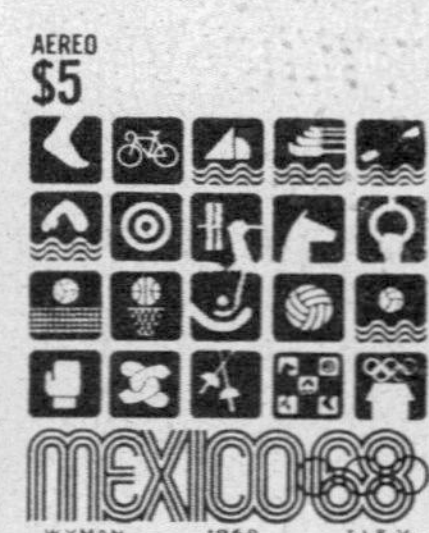

341 Olympic Flame **342** Emblems of Games

1968. Olympic Games, Mexico. (i) Inaug. Issue.
1171 **341** 10 p. multicoloured . . . 2·00 1·25

(ii) Games Issue. Multicoloured designs as T **341**. (20, 40, 50 c. postage and 80 c., 1, 2 p. air) or as T **342** (others).
1172 20 c. Dove of Peace on map (postage) 25 10
1173 40 c. Stadium 30 10
1174 50 c. Telecommunications Tower, Mexico City . . . 30 10
1175 2 p. Palace of Sport, Mexico City 55 25
1176 5 p. Cultural symbols of Games 1·50 80
1178 80 c. Dove and Olympic rings (air) 15 10
1179 1 p. "The Discus-thrower" . . 15 10
1180 2 p. Olympic medals 45 25
1181 5 p. Type **342** . . . . . . 1·75 85
1182 10 p. Line-pattern based on "Mexico 68" & rings . . . 1·50 95

343 Arms of Vera Cruz **344** "Father Palou" (M. Guerrero)

1969. 450th Anniv of Vera Cruz.
1185 **343** 40 c. multicoloured . . 30 10

1969. Air. 220th Anniv of Arrival in Mexico of Father Serra (coloniser of California).
1186 **344** 80 c. multicoloured . . 35 10
It was intended to depict Father Serra in this design, but the wrong detail of the painting by Guerrero, which showed both priests, was used.

345 Football and Spectators

1969. Air. World Cup Football Championship (1st issue). Multicoloured.
1187 80 c. Type **345** 25 10
1188 2 p. Foot kicking ball . . . 35 10
See also Nos. 1209/10.

346 Underground Train

1969. Inauguration of Mexico City Underground Railway System.
1189 **346** 40 c. multicoloured . . 20 10

347 Mahatma Gandhi **348** Footprint on Moon

1969. Air. Birth Centenary of Mahatma Gandhi.
1190 **347** 80 c. multicoloured . . . 30 10

1969. Air. 1st Man on the Moon.
1191 **348** 2 p. black 30 25

349 Bee and Honeycomb **350** "Flying" Dancers and Los Nichos Pyramid, El Tajin

1969. 50th Anniv of I.L.O.
1192 **349** 40 c. brown, blue & yell 20 10

1969. Tourism (1st series). Multicoloured.
1193 40 c. Type **350** 25 10
1193a 40 c. Puerto Vallarta, Jalisco (vert) 25 10
1194 80 c. Acapulco (air) 60 15
1195 80 c. Pyramid, Teotihuacan 60 15
1196 80 c. "El Caracol" (Maya ruin), Yucatan 60 15
See also Nos. 1200/2 and 1274/7.

351 Red Crosses and Sun **352** "General Allende" (D. Rivera)

1969. Air. 50th Anniv of League of Red Cross Societies.
1197 **351** 80 c. multicoloured . . . 30 10

1969. Birth Bicent of General Ignacio Allende ("Father of Mexican Independence").
1198 **352** 40 c. multicoloured . . . 20 10

353 Dish Aerial **354** Question Marks

1969. Air. Inauguration of Satellite Communications Station, Tulancingo.
1199 **353** 80 c. multicoloured . . . 35 10

1969. Tourism (2nd series). As T **350** but dated "1970". Multicoloured.
1200 40 c. Puebla Cathedral . . . 40 10
1201 40 c. Anthropological Museum, Mexico City 40 10
1202 40 c. Belaunzaran Street, Guanajuato 40 10

1970. 9th National and 5th Agricultural Census. Multicoloured.
1204 20 c. Type **354** 30 10
1205 40 c. Horse's head and agricultural symbols 25 10

355 Diagram of Human Eye

1970. 21st International Opthalmological Congress, Mexico City.
1206 **355** 40 c. multicoloured . . . 25 10

356 Cadet Ceremonial Helmet and Kepi **357** Jose Pino Suarez

1970. 50th Anniv of Military College Reorganization.
1207 **356** 40 c. multicoloured . . . 20 10

1970. Birth Centenary (1969) of Jose Maria Pino Suarez (statesman).
1208 **357** 40 c. multicoloured . . . 20 10

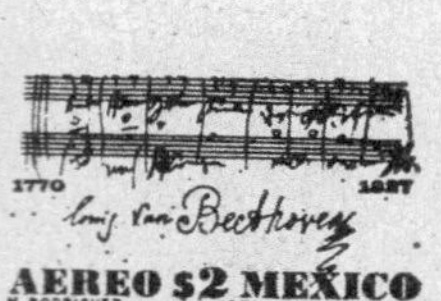

358 Football and Masks **360** Composition by Beethoven

1970. Air. World Cup Football Championship (2nd issue). Multicoloured.
1209 80 c. Type **358** 30 15
1210 2 p. Football and Mexican idols 25 25

1970. Air. Birth Bicentenary of Beethoven.
1212 **360** 2 p. multicoloured . . . 50 25

361 Arms of Celaya **362** "General Assembly"

1970. 400th Anniv of Celaya.
1213 **361** 40 c. multicoloured . . . 20 10

1970. Air. 25th Anniv of U.N.O.
1214 **362** 80 c. multicoloured . . . 30 10

363 "Eclipse de Sol" **364** "Galileo" (Susterman)

1970. Total Eclipse of the Sun (7.3.70).
1215 **363** 40 c. black 20 10

1971. Air. Conquest of Space. Early Astronomers. Multicoloured.
1216 2 p. Type **364** 25 10
1217 2 p. "Kepler" (unknown artist) 25 10
1218 2 p. "Sir Isaac Newton" (Kneller) 25 10

365 "Sister Juana" (M. Cabrera)

1971. Air. Mexican Arts and Sciences (1st series). Paintings. Multicoloured.
1219 80 c. Type **365** 40 15
1220 80 c. "El Paricutin" (volcano) (G. Murillo) 40 15
1221 80 c. "Men of Flames" (J. C. Orozco) 40 15
1222 80 c. "Self-portrait" (J. M. Velasco) 40 15
1223 80 c. "Mayan Warriors" ("Dresden Codex") 40 15
See also Nos. 1243/7, 1284/8, 1323/7, 1351/5, 1390/4, 1417/21, 1523/7, 1540/4, 1650/4, 1688/92, 1834 and 1845.

366 Stamps from Venezuela, Mexico and Colombia

1971. Air. "Philately for Peace". Latin-American Stamp Exhibitions 1968–70.
1224 **366** 80 c. multicoloured . . . 35 15

367 Lottery Balls

1971. Bicentenary of National Lottery.
1225 **367** 40 c. black and green . . 25 10

368 "Francisco Clavijero" (P. Carlin)

1971. Air. Return of the Remains of Francisco Javier Clavijero (historian) to Mexico (1970).
1226 **368** 2 p. brown and green . . 50 25

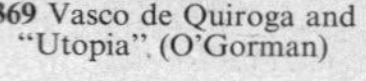

369 Vasco de Quiroga and "Utopia", (O'Gorman) **370** "Amado Nervo" (artist unknown)

1971. 500th Birth Anniv of Vasco de Quiroga, Archbishop of Michoacan.
1227 **369** 40 c. multicoloured . . . 20 10

1971. Birth Centenary of Amado Nervo (writer).
1228 **370** 80 c. multicoloured . . . 20 10

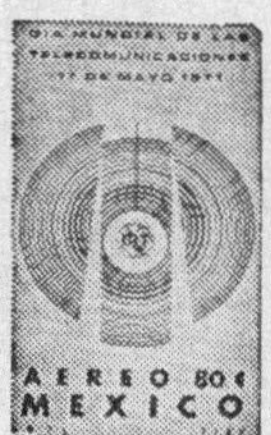

371 I.T.U. Emblem

372 "Mariano Matamoros" (D. Rivera)

1971. Air. World Telecommunications Day.
1229 **371** 80 c. multicoloured . . . 25 10

1971. Air. Birth Bicentenary of Mariano Matamoros (patriot).
1230 **372** 2 p. multicoloured . . . 45 25

373 "General Guerrero" (O'Gorman)

374 Loudspeaker and Sound Waves

1971. Air. 150th Anniv of Independence from Spain.
1231 **373** 2 p. multicoloured . . . 45 25

1971. 50th Anniv of Radio Broadcasting in Mexico.
1232 **374** 40 c. black, blue & green 25 10

375 Pres. Cardenas and Banners

376 Stamps of Venezuela, Mexico, Colombia and Peru

1971. 1st Death Anniv of General Lazaro Cardenas.
1233 **375** 40 c. black and lilac . . . 25 10

1971. Air. "EXFILIMA 71" Stamp Exhibition Lima, Peru.
1234 **376** 80 c. multicoloured . . . 45 15

377 Abstract of Circles

378 Piano Keyboard

1971. Air. 25th Anniv of U.N.E.S.C.O.
1235 **377** 80 c. multicoloured . . . 30 15

1971. 1st Death Anniv of Agustin Lara (composer).
1236 **378** 40 c. black, blue & yellow 30 10

379 "Mental Patients"

380 City Arms of Monterrey

1971. Air. 5th World Psychiatric Congress, Mexico City.
1237 **379** 2 p. multicoloured . . . 25 20

1971. 375th Anniv of Monterrey.
1238 **380** 40 c. multicoloured . . . 10 10

381 Durer's Bookplate

1971. Air. 500th Anniv of Albrecht Durer (artist).
1239 **381** 2 p. black and brown . 40 25

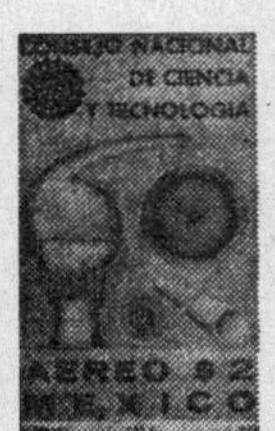

382 Scientific Symbols

383 Emblem of Mexican Cardiological Institute

1972. Air. 1st Anniv of National Council of Science and Technology.
1240 **382** 2 p. multicoloured . . . 20 10

1972. World Health Month. Multicoloured.
1241 40 c. Type **383** (postage) . . 10 10
1242 80 c. Heart specialists (air) . 10 10

1972. Air. Mexican Arts and Sciences (2nd series). Portraits. As T **365**.
1243 80 c. brown and black . . . 75 15
1244 80 c. green and black . . . 75 15
1245 80 c. brown and black . . . 75 15
1246 80 c. blue and black 75 15
1247 80 c. red and black 75 15
PORTRAITS: Nos. 1243, King Netzahualcoyotl of Texcoco (patron of the arts); No. 1244, J. R. de Alarcon (lawyer); No. 1245, J. J. Fernandez de Lizardi (writer); No. 1246, E. G. Martinez (poet); No. 1247, R. L. Velardo (author).

384 Rotary Emblems

385 Indian Laurel and Fruit

1972. Air. 50th Anniv of Rotary Movement in Mexico.
1248 **384** 80 c. multicoloured . . 10 10

1972. Centenary of Chilpancingo as Capital of Guerrero State.
1249 **385** 40 c. black, gold & green 10 10

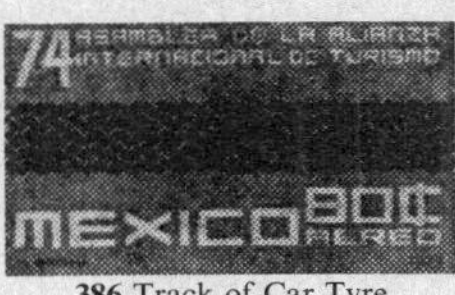

386 Track of Car Tyre

1972. Air. 74th Assembly of International Tourist Alliance, Mexico City.
1250 **386** 80 c. black and grey . . 10 10

387 First issue of "Gaceta De Mexico"

388 Emblem of Lions Organization

1972. 250th Anniv of Publication of "Gaceta De Mexico". (1st newspaper to be published in Latin America).
1251 **387** 40 c. multicoloured . . 10 10

1972. Lions' Clubs Convention, Mexico City.
1252 **388** 40 c. multicoloured . . 10 10

389 "Zaragoza" (cadet sail corvette)

390 "Margarita Maza de Juarez" (artist unknown)

1972. 75th Anniv of Naval Academy, Veracruz.
1253 **389** 40 c. multicoloured . . . 30 10

1972. Death Centenary of Pres. Benito Juarez.
1254 **390** 20 c. mult (postage) . . . 35 10
1255 – 40 c. multicoloured . . . 35 10
1256 – 80 c. black and blue (air) 10 10
1257 – 1 p. 20 multicoloured . . 15 10
1258 – 2 p. multicoloured . . . 20 10
DESIGNS: 40 c. "Benito Juarez" (D. Rivera); 80 c. Page of Civil Register with Juarez signature; 1 p. 20, "Benito Juarez" (P. Clave); 2 p. "Benito Juarez" (J. C. Orozco).

391 "Emperor Justinian I" (mosaic)

392 Atomic Emblem

1972. 50th Anniv of Mexican Bar Association.
1259 **391** 40 c. multicoloured . . . 55 10

1972. Air. 16th General Conference of Int Atomic Energy Organization, Mexico City.
1260 **392** 2 p. black, blue and grey 15 10

393 Caravel on "Stamp"

394 "Sobre las Olas" (sheet-music cover by O'Brandstetter)

1972. Stamp Day of the Americas.
1261 **393** 80 c. violet and brown . . 15 10

1972. Air. 28th International Authors' and Composers' Society Congress, Mexico City.
1262 **394** 80 c. brown 15 10

395 "Mother and Child" (G. Galvin)

1972. Air. 25th Anniv of U.N.I.C.E.F.
1263 **395** 80 c. multicoloured . . . 50 10

396 "Father Pedro de Gante" (Rodriguez y Arangorti)

397 Olympic Emblems

1972. Air. 400th Death Anniv of Father Pedro de Gante (founder of first school in Mexico).
1264 **396** 2 p. multicoloured . . . 25 10

1972. Olympic Games, Munich.
1265 **397** 40 c. multicoloured (postage) 10 10
1266 – 80 c. multicoloured (air) 15 10
1267 – 2 p. black, green and blue 25 10
DESIGNS—HORIZ: 80 c. "Football". VERT: 2 p. Similar to Type **397**.

398 Books on Shelves

400 "Footprints on the Americas"

399 Fish ("Pure Water")

1972. Int Book Year.
1268 **398** 40 c. multicoloured . . . 10 10

1972. Anti-Pollution Campaign.
1269 **399** 40 c. black & bl (postage) 10 10
1270 – 80 c. black and blue (air) 15 10
DESIGN–VERT: 80 c. Pigeon on cornice ("Pure Air").

1972. Air. Tourist Year of the Americas.
1271 **400** 80 c. multicoloured . . . 15 10

401 Stamps of Mexico, Colombia, Venezuela, Peru and Brazil

1973. Air. "EXFILBRA 72" Stamp Exhibition, Rio de Janeiro, Brazil.
1272 **401** 80 c. multicoloured . . . 15 10

402 "Metlac Viaduct" (J. M. Velasco)

1973. Centenary of Mexican Railways.
1273 **402** 40 c. multicoloured . . . 90 10

403 Ocotlan Abbey

1973. Tourism (3rd series). Multicoloured.
1274 40 c. Type **403** (postage) . . 20 10
1275 40 c. Indian hunting dance, Sonora (vert) 20 10
1276 80 c. Girl in local costume (vert) (air) 35 15
1277 80 c. Sport fishing, Lower California 35 10

404 "God of the Winds"

1973. Air. Centenary of W.M.O.
1278 **404** 80 c. black, blue & mauve 35 10

405 Copernicus 406 Cadet

1973. Air. 500th Birth Anniv of Copernicus (astronomer).
1279 **405** 80 c. green 15 10

1973. 150th Anniv of Military College.
1280 **406** 40 c. multicoloured . . . 10 10

407 "Francisco Madero" (D. Rivera) 408 Antonio Narro (founder)

1973. Birth Centenary of Pres. Francisco Madero.
1281 **407** 40 c. multicoloured . . . 10 10

1973. 50th Anniv of "Antonio Narro" Agricultural School, Saltillo.
1282 **408** 40 c. grey 10 10

409 San Martin Statue 410 Caryon Molecules

1973. Air. Argentina's Gift of San Martin Statue to Mexico City.
1283 **409** 80 c. multicoloured . . . 15 10

1973. Air. "Mexican Arts and Sciences". (3rd series). Astronomers. As T **365** but dated "1973".
1284 80 c. green and red 10 10
1285 80 c. multicoloured 10 10
1286 80 c. multicoloured 10 10
1287 80 c. multicoloured 10 10
1288 80 c. multicoloured 10 10

DESIGNS: No. 1284, Aztec "Sun" stone; No. 1285, Carlos de Siguenza y Gongora; No. 1286, Francisco Diaz Covarrubias; No. 1287, Joaquin Gallo; No. 1288, Luis Enrique Erro.

1973. 25th Anniv of Chemical Engineering School.
1289 **410** 40 c. black, yellow & red 10 10

411 Fist with Pointing Finger 412 "EXMEX 73" Emblem

1974. Promotion of Exports.
1294 **411** 40 c. black and green . . 10 10

1974. "EXMEX 73" National Stamp Exhibition, Cuernavaca.
1295 **412** 40 c. black (postage) . . 10 10
1296 – 80 c. multicoloured (air) 15 10

DESIGN: 80 c. Cortes' Palace, Cuernavaca.

413 Manuel Ponce

1974. 25th Death Anniv (1973) of Manuel M. Ponce (composer).
1297 **413** 40 c. multicoloured . . 10 10

414 Gold Brooch, Mochica Culture

1974. Air. Exhibition of Peruvian Gold Treasures, Mexico City.
1298 **414** 80 c. multicoloured . . 15 10

415 C.E.P.A.L. Emblem and Flags 416 Baggage

1974. Air. 25th Anniv of U.N. Economic Commission for Latin America (C.E.P.A.L.).
1299 **415** 80 c. multicoloured . . 15 10

1974. Air. 16th Confederation of Latin American Tourist Organizations (C.O.T.A.L.) Convention, Acapulco.
1300 **416** 80 c. multicoloured . . 15 10

417 Silver Statuette 419 "Dancing Dogs" (Indian statuette)

418 "The Enamelled Saucepan" (Picasso)

1974. 1st International Silver Fair, Mexico City.
1301 **417** 40 c. multicoloured . . 10 10

1974. Air. 1st Death Anniv of Pablo Picasso (artist).
1302 **418** 80 c. multicoloured . . 15 10

1974. 6th Season of Dog Shows.
1303 **419** 40 c. multicoloured . . 10 10

420 Mariano Azuela

1974. Birth Cent (1973) of Mariano Azuela (writer).
1304 **420** 40 c. multicoloured . . 10 10

421 Tepotzotlan Viaduct

1974. National Engineers' Day.
1305 **421** 40 c. black and blue . . . 55 15

422 R. Robles (surgeon)

1974. 25th Anniv of W.H.O.
1306 **422** 40 c. brown and green . . 10 10

423 U.P.U. Emblem

1974. "Exfilmex 74" Inter-American Stamp Exhibition, Mexico City.
1307 **423** 40 c. black and green on yellow (postage) 10 10
1308 80 c. black and brown on yellow (air) 15 10

424 Demosthenes 426 Map and Indian Head

425 Lincoln Standard Biplane

1974. 2nd Spanish-American Reading and Writing Studies Congress, Mexico City.
1309 **424** 20 c. green and brown . . 35 10

1974. Air. 50th Anniv of "Mexicana" (Mexican Airlines). Multicoloured.
1310 80 c. Type **425** 15 10
1311 2 p. Boeing 727-200 jetliner . . 40 10

1974. 150th Anniv of Union with Chiapas.
1312 **426** 20 c. green and brown . . 10 10

427 "Sonar Waves"

1974. Air. 1st International Electrical and Electronic Communications Congress, Mexico City.
1313 **427** 2 p. multicoloured . . . 15 10

428 S. Lerdo de Tejada 429 Manuscript of Constitution

1974. Centenary of Restoration of Senate.
1314 **428** 40 c. black and blue . . 10 10

1974. 150th Anniv of Federal Republic.
1315 **429** 40 c. black and green . . 10 10

430 Ball in Play

1974. Air. 8th World Volleyball Championships, Mexico City.
1316 **430** 2 p. black, brown & orge 15 10

432 F. C. Puerto 433 Mask, Bat and Catcher's Glove

1974. Air. Birth Centenary of Felipe Carrillo Puerto (politician and journalist).
1318 **432** 80 c. brown and green . 10 10

1974. Air. 50th Anniv of Mexican Baseball League.
1319 **433** 80 c. brown and green . 10 10

434 U.P.U. Monument

1974. Centenary of U.P.U.
1320 **434** 40 c. brown and blue (postage) 10 10
1321 – 80 c. multicoloured (air) 10 10
1322 – 2 p. brown and green . . 20 10

DESIGNS: 80 c. Man's face as letter-box, Colonial period; 2 p. Heinrich von Stephan, founder of U.P.U.

1974. Air. Mexican Arts and Sciences (4th series). Music and Musicians. As T **365** but dated "1974". Multicoloured.
1323 80 c. "Musicians" – Mayan painting, Bonampak . . . 15 10
1324 80 c. First Mexican-printed score, 1556 . . . . 15 10
1325 80 c. Angela Peralta (soprano and composer) 15 10
1326 80 c. "Miguel Lerdo de Tejada" (composer) 15 10
1327 80 c. "Silvestre Revueltas" (composer) (bronze by Carlos Bracho) 15 10

435 I.W.Y. Emblem 436 Economic Charter

1975. Air. International Women's Year.
1328 **435** 1 p. 60 black and red . . 15 10

1975. Air. U.N. Declaration of Nations' Economic Rights and Duties.
1329 **436** 1 p. 60 multicoloured . . 15 10

437 Jose Maria Mora

439 Dr. M. Jimenez

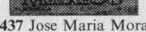

438 Balsa raft "Acali"

1975. 150th Anniv of Federal Republic.
1330 **437** 20 c. multicoloured . . . 10 10

1975. Air. Trans-Atlantic Voyage of "Acali". Canary Islands to Yucatan (1973).
1331 **438** 80 c. multicoloured . . . 30 10

1975. Air. 5th World Gastroenterological Congress.
1332 **439** 2 p. multicoloured . . . 15 10

440 Aztec Merchants with Goods ("Codex Florentino")

1975. Centenary (1974) of Mexican Chamber of Commerce.
1333 **440** 80 c. multicoloured . . . 10 10

441 Miguel de Cervantes Saavedra (Spanish author)

442 4-reales Coin of 1675

1975. Air. 3rd International Cervantes Festival, Guanajuato.
1334 **441** 1 p. 60 red and black . . 15 10

1975. Air. International Numismatics Convention "Mexico 74".
1335 **442** 1 p. 60 bronze and blue 15 10

443 Salvador Novo

1975. Air. 1st Death Anniv of Salvador Novo (poet and writer).
1336 **443** 1 p. 60 multicoloured . . 15 10

444 "Self-portrait" (Siqueiros)

1975. Air. 1st Death Anniv of David Alfaro Siqueiros (painter).
1337 **444** 1 p. 60 multicoloured . 15 10

445 General Juan Aldama (detail from mural by Diego Rivera)

1975. Birth Bicentenary (1974) of General Aldama.
1338 **445** 80 c. multicoloured . . 10 10

446 U.N. and I.W.Y. Emblems

1975. Air. International Women's Year and World Conference.
1339 **446** 1 p. 60 blue and pink . 15 10

447 Eagle and Snake ("Codex Duran")

1975. 650th Anniv of Tenochtitlan (now Mexico City). Multicoloured.
1340 80 c. Type **447** (postage) . . 10 10
1341 1 p. 60 Arms of Mexico City (air) 15 10

448 Domingo F. Sarmiento (educator and statesman)

449 Teachers' Monument, Mexico City

1975. Air. 1st International Congress of "Third World" Educators, Acapulco.
1342 **448** 1 p. 60 green and brown 15 10

1975. Air. Mexican–Lebanese Friendship.
1343 **449** 4 p. 30 green and brown 25 10

450 Games' Emblem

1975. Air. 7th Pan-American Games, Mexico City.
1344 **450** 1 p. 60 multicoloured . 15 10

INDEX

Countries can be quickly located by referring to the index at the end of this volume.

451 Julian Carrillo (composer)

452 Academy Emblem

1975. Birth Centenary of J. Carrillo.
1345 **451** 80 c. brown and green . . 10 10

1975. Cent of Mexican Languages Academy.
1346 **452** 80 c. yellow and brown 10 10

453 University Building

1975. 50th Anniv of Guadalajara University.
1347 **453** 80 c. black, brown & pink 10 10

454 Dr. Atl

455 Road Builders

1975. Air. Atl (Gerardo Murillo-painter and writer). Birth Centenary.
1348 **454** 4 p. 30 multicoloured . . 25 10

1975. "50 Years of Road Construction" and 15th World Road Congress, Mexico City.
1349 **455** 80 c. black & green (post) 10 10
1350 – 1 p. 60 black & blue (air) 15 10
DESIGN: 1 p. 60, Congress emblem.

1975. Air. Mexican Arts and Sciences (5th series). As T **365**, but dated "1975". Multicoloured.
1351 1 p. 60 Title page, F. Hernandez' "History of New Spain" 15 10
1352 1 p. 60 A. L. Herrera (naturalist) 15 10
1353 1 p. 60 Page from "Badiano Codex" (Aztec herbal) . . . 15 10
1354 1 p. 60 A. Rosenblueth Stearns (neurophysiologist) 15 10
1355 1 p. 60 A. A. Duges (botanist and zoologist) 15 10

456 Car Engine Parts

457 Aguascalientes Cathedral

1975. Mexican Exports. Multicoloured.
1356 – 5 c. blue (postage) . . . 35 10
1471 – 20 c. black 35 10
1356b – 40 c. brown 30 10
1356c **456** 50 c. blue 35 10
1472 50 c. black 10 10
1473 – 80 c. red 10 10
1474 – 1 p. violet and yellow 10 10
1358a – 1 p. black and orange 10 10
1475 – 2 p. blue and turquoise 55 10
1476 – 3 p. brown 25 10
1359b – 4 p. red and brown . . 25 10
1359e – 5 p. brown 10 10
1359ed – 6 p. red 10 10
1359ee – 6 p. grey 10 10
1359f – 7 p. blue 10 10
1359g – 8 p. brown 10 10
1359h – 9 p. blue 10 10
1479 – 10 p. lt green and green 95 45
1360ac – 10 p. red 10 10
1360ad – 15 p. orange and brown 15 10
1360b – 20 p. black 15 10
1360bc – 20 p. black and red . . 10 10
1360be – 25 p. brown 25 10
1360bh – 35 p. yellow and mauve 25 10
1360bk – 40 p. yellow and brown 25 10
1360bl – 40 p. gold and green . 25 10
1360bm – 40 p. black 10 10
1360c – 50 p. multicoloured . . 1·25 35
1360d – 50 p. yellow and blue 35 20
1360da – 50 p. red and green . . 35 20
1360db – 60 p. brown 30 15
1360dc – 70 p. brown 35 20
1360de – 80 p. gold and mauve 20 50
1360df – 80 p. blue 80 50
1360dg – 90 p. blue and green . 1·25 55
1360e – 100 p. red, green and grey 70 35
1360ea – 100 p. brown 10 10
1360f – 200 p. yellow, green and grey . . . . 1·90 30
1360fb – 200 p. yellow and green 10 10
1360g – 300 p. blue, red and grey 60 60
1360gb – 300 p. blue and red . . 15 10
1360h – 400 p. bistre, brown and grey 95 35
1360hb – 450 p. brown & mauve 20 10
1360i – 500 p. green, orange and grey . . . . 1·90 30
1360ib – 500 p. grey and blue . 20 10
1360j – 600 p. multicoloured . 30 10
1360k – 700 p. black, red and green 35 10
1360kb – 750 p. black, red and green 30 10
1360l – 800 p. brown & dp brown 40 10
1360m **456** 900 p. black 50 10
1360n – 950 p. blue 40 20
1481a – 1000 p. black, red and grey 50 20
1360pa – 1000 p. red and black 40 8
1360q – 1100 p. grey 60 30
1360r – 1300 p. red, green and grey 60 30
1360rb – 1300 p. red and green 50 25
1360rg – 1400 p. black 50 20
1360s – 1500 p. brown 55 45
1360t – 1600 p. orange 65 30
1360u – 1700 p. green and deep green 70 30
1360w – 1900 p. blue and green 2·25 75
1481b – 2000 p. black and grey 1·25 50
1360xa – 2000 p. black 80 55
1360y – 2100 p. black, orange and grey 80 55
1360ya – 2100 p. black and red 80 55
1360yb – 2200 p. red 90 60
1360z – 2500 p. blue and grey 95 65
1360za – 2500 p. blue 95 65
1630zc – 2800 p. black . . . . 1·10 75
1481c – 3000 p. green, grey and orange . . . . . . 1·75 75
1360zf **456** 3600 p. black and grey 1·50 1·00
1360zg – 3900 p. grey and blue 1·60 1·10
1481d – 4000 p. yellow, grey and red . . . . 2·40 1·25
1360zj – 4800 p. red, green and grey . . . . 1·90 1·25
1481e – 5000 p. grey, green and orange . . . . . . 3·00 1·50
1360zn – 6000 p. green, yellow and grey . . . . 2·40 1·60
1360zq – 7200 p. multicoloured 3·00 2·00
1361 – 30 c. bronze (air) . . . 30 10
1482 – 50 c. green and brown 10 10
1361a – 80 c. blue 10 10
1483 – 1 p. 60 black & orange 10 10
1484 – 1 p. 90 red and green 15 10
1361d – 2 p. gold and blue . . 25 10
1485 – 2 p. 50 red and green 10 10
1361e – 4 p. yellow and brown 25 10
1361f – 4 p. 30 mauve & green 10 20
1361g – 5 p. blue and yellow . 95 20
1361h – 5 p. 20 black and red 25 25
1361i – 5 p. 60 green & yellow 10 30
1488 – 10 p. green and light green 55 40
1361j – 20 p. black, red and green 2·75 85
1361k – 50 p. multicoloured . . 1·60 95

DESIGNS—POSTAGE. 5 c., 6, 1600 p. Steel tubes; 20 c., 40 (1360bm), 1400, 2800 p. Laboratory flasks; 40 c., 100 p. (1360ea) Cup of coffee; 80 c., 10 (1360ac), 2200 p. Steer marked with beef cuts; 1, 3000 p. Electric cable; 2, 90, 1900 p. Sea shell; 3, 60 p. Men's shoes; 4 p. Ceramic tiles; 5, 1100 p. Chemical formulae; 7, 8, 9, 80 (1360df), 2500 p. Textiles; 10 (1479), 1700 p. Tequila; 15 p. Honeycomb; 20 (1360b), 2000 p. Wrought iron; 20 (1360bc), 2100 p. Bicycles; 25, 70, 1500 p. Hammered copper vase; 35, 40 (1360bk/bl), 50 (1360d), 80 p. (1360de) Books; 50 (1360c), 600 p. Jewellery; 50 (1360da), 4800 p. Tomato; 100 (1360e), 1300 p. Strawberries; 200, 6000 p. Citrus fruit; 300 p. Motor vehicles; 400, 450 p. Printed circuit; 500 (1360i), 5000 p. Cotton boll; 500 (1360ib), 3900 p. Valves (petroleum) industry; 700, 750, 7200 p. Film; 800 p. Construction materials; 1000 p. Farm machinery; 4000 p. Bee and honeycomb. AIR. 30 c. Hammered copper vase; 50 c. Electronic components; 80 c. Textiles; 1 p. 60, Bicycles; 1 p. 90, Valves (petroleum) industry; 2 p. Books; 2 p. 50, Tomato; 4 p. Bee and honeycomb; 4 p. 30, Strawberry; 5 p. Motor vehicles; 5 p. 20, Farm machinery; 5 p. 60, Cotton boll; 10 p. Citrus fruit; 20 p. Film; 50 p. Cotton.

1975. 400th Anniv of Aguascalientes.
1362 **457** 50 c. black and green . . 35 10

458 J. T. Bodet

460 "Death of Cuautemoc" (Chavez Morado)

459 "Fresco" (J. C. Orozco)

1975. 1st Death Anniv of Jaime T. Bodet (author and late Director-General of U.N.E.S.C.O.).
1363 **458** 80 c. brown and blue . . 10 10

1975. 150th Anniv of Mexican Supreme Court of Justice.
1364 **459** 80 c. multicoloured . . . 10 10

1975. 450th Death Anniv of Emperor Cuautemoc.
1365 **460** 80 c. multicoloured . . . 10 10

461 Allegory of Irrigation

1976. 50th Anniv of Nat Irrigation Commission.
1366 **461** 80 c. deep blue and blue 10 10

462 City Gateway

1976. 400th Anniv of Leon de los Aldamas, Guanajuato.
1367 **462** 80 c. yellow and purple 10 10

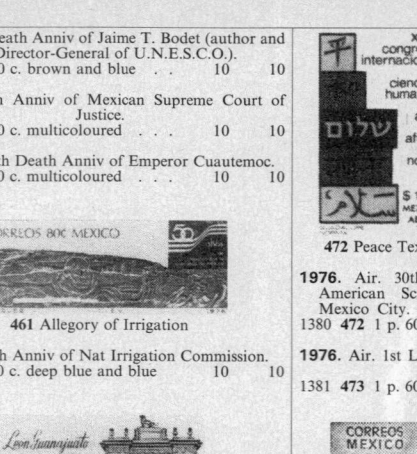

463 Early Telephone **464** Gold Coin

1976. Air. Telephone Centenary.
1368 **463** 1 p. 60 black and grey . 10 10

1976. Air. 4th Int Numismatics Convention.
1369 **464** 1 p. 60 gold, brown & blk 10 10

465 Tlaloc (Aztec god of rain) and Calles Dam

1976. Air. 12th Int Great Dams Congress.
1370 **465** 1 p. 60 purple and green 20 10

466 Perforation Gauge

1976. Air. "Interphil '76" International Stamp Exhibition, Philadelphia.
1371 **466** 1 p. 60 black, red & blue 20 10

467 Rainbow over Industrial Skyline **476** Liberty Bell

1976. Air. U.N. Conf on Human Settlements.
1372 **487** 1 p. 60 multicoloured . . 20 10

1976. Air. Bicentenary of American War of Independence.
1378 **470** 1 p. 60 blue and mauve 20 10

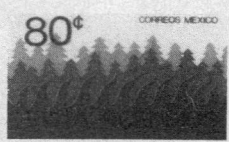

471 Forest Fire

1976. Fire Prevention Campaign.
1379 **471** 80 c. multicoloured 10 10

472 Peace Texts **473** Children on TV Screen

1976. Air. 30th International Asian and North American Science and Humanities Congress, Mexico City.
1380 **472** 1 p. 60 multicoloured . 15 10

1976. Air. 1st Latin-American Forum on Children's Television.
1381 **473** 1 p. 60 multicoloured . 20 10

474 Scout's Hat **475** Exhibition Emblem

1976. 50th Anniv of Mexican Boy Scout Movement.
1382 **474** 80 c. olive and brown . 10 10

1976. "Mexico Today and Tomorrow" Exhibition.
1383 **475** 80 c. black, red & turq . 10 10

476 New Buildings **477** Dr. R. Vertiz

1976. Inaug of New Military College Buildings.
1384 **476** 50 c. brown and ochre . 10 10

1976. Centenary of Opthalmological Hospital of Our Lady of the Light.
1385 **477** 80 c. brown and black . 10 10

478 Guadalupe Basilica

1976. Inauguration of Guadalupe Basilica.
1386 **478** 50 c. bistre and black . 10 10

479 "40" and Emblem

1976. 40th Anniv of National Polytechnic Institute.
1387 **479** 80 c. black, red and green 10 10

480 Blast Furnace

1976. Inauguration of Lazaro Cardenas Steel Mill, Las Truchas.
1388 **480** 50 c. multicoloured . . 10 10

481 Natural Elements

1976. Air. World Urbanisation Day.
1389 **481** 1 p. 60 multicoloured . . 10 10

1976. Air. Mexican Arts and Sciences (6th series). As T **365** but dated "1976". Multicoloured.
1390 1 p. 60 black and red 10 10
1391 1 p. 60 multicoloured 10 10
1392 1 p. 60 black and yellow . . . 10 10
1393 1 p. 60 multicoloured 10 10
1394 1 p. 60 brown and black . . . 10 10
DESIGNS: No. 1390, "The Signal" (Angela Gurria); No. 1391, "The God of Today" (L. Ortiz Monasterio); No. 1392, "The God Coatlicue" (traditional Mexican sculpture); No. 1393, "Tiahuicole" (Manuel Vilar); No. 1394, "The Horseman" (Manuel Tolsa).

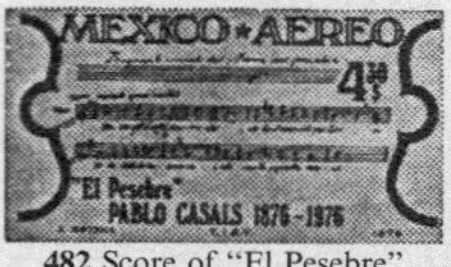

482 Score of "El Pesebre"

1977. Air. Birth Centenary of Pablo Casals (cellist).
1395 **482** 4 p. 30 blue and brown 15 10

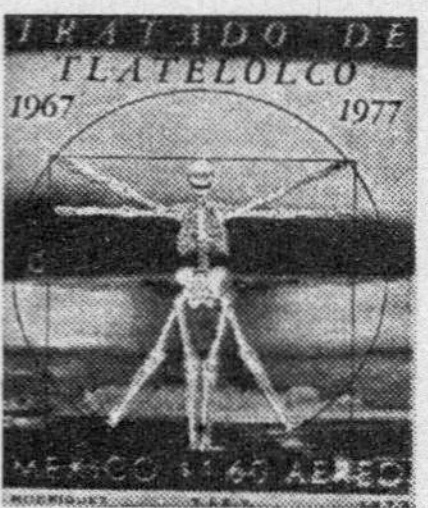

483 "Man's Destruction"

1977. Air. 10th Anniv of Treaty of Tlatelolco.
1396 **483** 1 p. 60 multicoloured . . 10 10

484 Saltillo Cathedral **485** Light Switch, Pylon and Engineers

1977. 400th Anniv of Founding of Saltillo.
1397 **484** 80 c. brown and yellow 10 10

1977. 40 years of Development in Mexico. Federal Electricity Commission.
1398 **485** 80 c. multicoloured . . . 10 10

486 Footballers

1977. Air. 50th Anniv of Mexican Football Federation.
1399 **486** 1 p. 60 multicoloured . . 10 10
1400 – 4 p. 30 yellow, blue & blk 15 10
DESIGN: 4 p. 30, Football emblem.

487 Hands and Scales

1977. Air. 50th Anniv of Federal Council of Reconciliation and Arbitration.
1401 **487** 1 p. 60 orange, brn & blk 10 10

488 Flags of Spain and Mexico **489** Tlaloc (weather god)

1977. Resumption of Diplomatic Relations with Spain.
1402 **488** 50 c. multicoloured (postage) 10 10
1403 80 c. multicoloured . . . 10 10
1404 – 1 p. 60 black & grey (air) 10 10
1405 – 1 p. 90 red, grn & lt grn 10 10
1406 – 4 p. 30 grey, brown & grn 15 10
DESIGNS: 1 p. 60, Arms of Mexico and Spain; 1 p. 90, Maps of Mexico and Spain; 4 p. 30, President Jose Lopez Portillo and King Juan Carlos.

1977. Air. Centenary of Central Meterological Observatory.
1407 **489** 1 p. 60 multicoloured . . 10 10

490 Ludwig van Beethoven **491** A. Serdan

1977. Air. 150th Death Anniv of Beethoven.
1408 **490** 1 p. 60 green and brown 10 10
1409 4 p. 30 red and blue . . 15 10

1977. Birth Centenary of Aquiles Serdan (revolutionary martyr).
1410 **491** 80 c. black, turq & grn 10 10

492 Mexico City–Guernavaca Highway

1977. Air. 25th Anniv of First National Highway.
1411 **492** 1 p. 60 multicoloured . . 10 10

493 Poinsettia **494** Arms of Campeche

1977. Christmas.
1412 **493** 50 c. multicoloured . . . 10 10

1977. Air. Bicentenary of Naming of Campeche.
1413 **494** 1 p. 60 multicoloured . . 10 10

495 Tractor and Dam

1977. Air. U.N. Desertification Conference, Mexico City.
1414 **495** 1 p. 60 multicoloured . . 10 10

496 Congress Emblem

1977. Air. 20th World Education, Hygiene and Recreation Congress.
1415 **496** 1 p. 60 multicoloured . . 10 10

497 Freighter "Rio Yaqui" **498** Mayan Dancer

1977. Air. 60th Anniv of National Merchant Marine.
1416 **497** 1 p. 60 multicoloured . . 40 10

1977. Air. Mexican Arts and Sciences (7th series). Pre-colonial statuettes.
1417 **498** 1 p. 60 red, black & pink 10 10
1418 – 1 p. 60 blue, black and lt blue 10 10
1419 – 1 p. 60 grey, black and yellow 10 10
1420 – 1 p. 60 green, black and turquoise 10 10
1421 – 1 p. 60 red, black and grey . 10 10
DESIGNS: No. 1418, Aztec god of dance; No. 1419, Snake dance; No. 1420, Dancer, Monte Alban; No. 1421, Dancer, Totonaca.

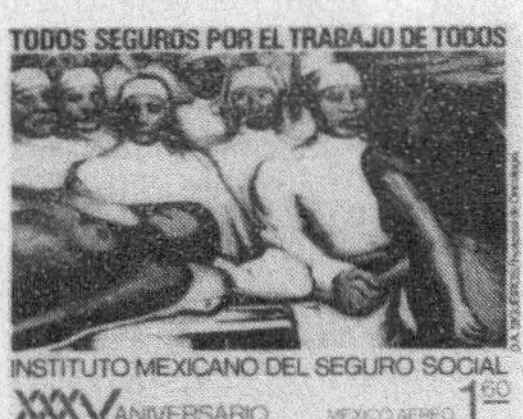
499 Hospital Scene

1978. Air. 35th Anniv of Mexican Social Insurance Institute. Multicoloured.
1422 1 p. 60 Type **499** 10 10
1423 4 p. 30 Workers drawing benefits 15 10

500 Moorish Fountain

1978. Air. 450th Anniv of Chiapa de Corzo, Chiapas.
1424 **500** 1 p. 60 multicoloured . . 10 10

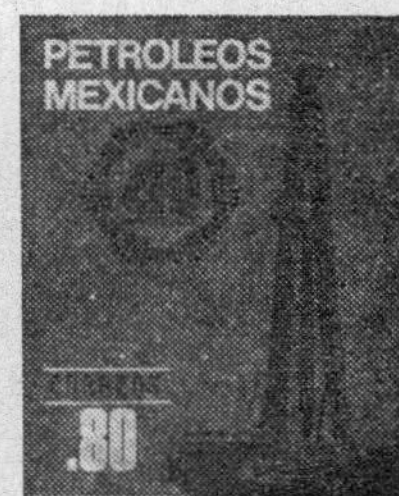
501 Telephones, 1878 and 1978 **502** Oilwell

1978. Centenary of Mexican Telephone.
1425 **501** 80 c. red and salmon . . 10 10

1978. 40th Anniv of Nationalization of Oil Resources.
1426 **502** 80 c. red and salmon (postage) 10 10
1427 – 1 p. 60 blue and red (air) 10 10
1428 – 4 p. 30 black, light blue and blue 35 10
DESIGNS: 1 p. 60, General I. Cardenas (President, 1938); 4 p. 30, Oil rig, Gulf of Mexico.

INDEX

Countries can be quickly located by referring to the index at the end of this volume.

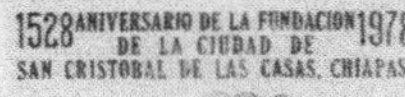

503 Arms of San Cristobal de las Casas

1978. Air. 450th Anniv of San Cristobal de las Casas, Chiapas.
1429 **503** 1 p. 60 purple, pink and black 10 10

504 Fairchild FC-71 Mail Plane **506** Blood Pressure Gauge and Map of Mexico

505 Globe and Cogwheel

1978. Air. 50th Anniv of First Mexican Airmail Route.
1430 **504** 1 p. 60 multicoloured . 20 10
1431 4 p. 30 multicoloured . 30 10

1978. Air. World Conference on Technical Co operation between Underdeveloped Countries. Multicoloured.
1432 1 p. 60 Type **505** 10 10
1433 4 p. 30 Globe and cogwheel joined by flags 15 10

1978. Air. World Hypertension Month and World Health Day.
1434 **506** 1 p. 60 blue and red . . 10 10
1435 – 4 p. 30 salmon and blue 15 10
DESIGN: 4 p. 30, Hand with stethoscope.

507 Kicking Ball **508** Francisco (Pancho) Villa

1978. Air. World Cup Football Championship, Argentina.
1436 **507** 1 p. 60 bl, lt orge & orge 10 10
1437 – 1 p. 90 blue, brn & orge 10 10
1438 – 4 p. 30 blue, grn & orge 15 10
DESIGNS: 1 p. 90, Saving a goal; 4 p. 30, Footballer.

1978. Air. Birth Centenary of Francisco Villa (revolutionary leader).
1439 **508** 1 p. 60 multicoloured . 10 10

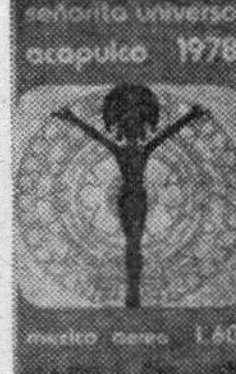
509 Emilio Carranza Stamp of 1929 **510** Woman and Calendar Stone

1978. Air. 50th Anniv of Mexico–Washington Flight by Emilio Carranza.
1440 **509** 1 p. 60 red and brown . 10 10

1978. Air. Miss Universe Contest, Acapulco.
1441 **510** 1 p. 60 black, brn & red 10 10
1442 1 p. 90 black, brn & grn 10 10
1443 4 p. 30 black, brn & red 15 10

511 Alvaro Obregon (J. Romero)

1978. Air. 50th Death Anniv of Alvaro Obregon (statesman).
1444 **511** 1 p. 60 multicoloured . . 10 10

512 Institute Emblem

1978. 50th Anniv of Pan-American Institute for Geography and History.
1445 **512** 80 c. blue and black (postage) 10 10
1446 – 1 p. 60 green & blk (air) 10 10
1447 – 4 p. 30 brown and black 15 10
DESIGNS: 1 p. 60, 4 p. 30, Designs as Type **512**, showing emblem.

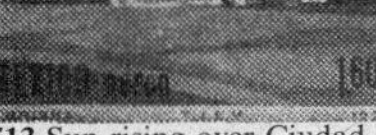
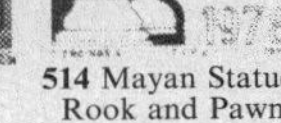

513 Sun rising over Ciudad Obregon **514** Mayan Statue, Rook and Pawn

1978. Air. 50th Anniv of Ciudad Obregon.
1448 **513** 1 p. 60 multicoloured . . 10 10

1978. Air. World Youth Team Chess Championship, Mexico City.
1449 **514** 1 p. 60 multicoloured . . 10 10
1450 4 p. 30 multicoloured . . 20 10

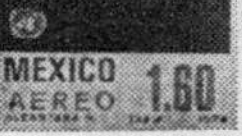
515 Aristotle **516** Mule Deer

1978. Air. 2300th Death Anniv of Aristotle.
1451 **515** 1 p. 60 grey, blue and yellow 10 10
1452 – 4 p. 30 grey, red and yellow 20 10
DESIGN: 4 p. 30, Statue of Aristotle.

1978. Air. World Youth Team Chess Championship, Mexico City.
1453 1 p. 60 Type **516** 20 10
1454 1 p. 60 Ocelot 20 10
See also Nos. 1548/9, 1591/2, 1638/9 and 1683/4.

517 Man's Head and Dove **518** "Dahlia coccinea". ("Dalia" on stamp)

1978. Air. International Anti-Apartheid Year.
1455 **517** 1 p. 60 grey, red and black 10 10
1456 – 4 p. 30 grey, lilac and black 15 10
DESIGN: 4 p. 30, Woman's head and dove.

1978. Mexican Flowers (1st series). Multicoloured.
1457 50 c. Type **518** 10 10
1458 80 c. "Plumeria rubra" . . . 10 10
See also Nos. 1550/1, 1593/4, 1645/6, 1681/2, 1791/2 and 1913/14.

519 Emblem **520** Dr. Rafael Lucio

1978. Air. 12th World Architects' Congress.
1459 **519** 1 p. 60 red, black and orange 10 10

1978. Air. 11th International Leprosy Congress.
1460 **520** 1 p. 60 green 10 10

521 Franz Schubert and "Death and the Maiden" **522** Decorations and Candles

1978. Air. 150th Death Anniv of Franz Schubert (composer).
1461 **521** 4 p. 30 brown, black and green 15 10

1978. Christmas. Multicoloured.
1462 50 c. Type **522** (postage) . . 10 10
1463 1 p. 60 Children and decoration (air) 10 10

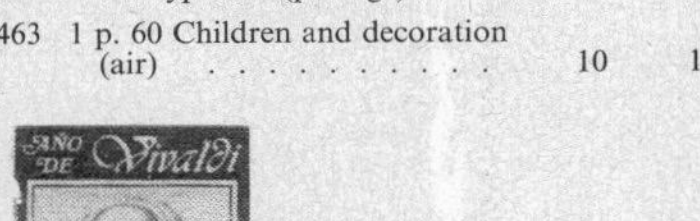

523 Antonio Vivaldi **524** Wright Flyer III

1978. Air. 300th Birth Anniv of Antonio Vivaldi (composer).
1464 **523** 4 p. 30 red, stone and brown 15 10

1978. Air. 75th Anniv of First Powered Flight.
1465 **524** 1 p. 60 orge, yell & mve 15 10
1466 – 4 p. 30 yellow, red & flesh 30 10
DESIGN: 4 p. 30, Side view of Wright Flyer I.

525 Albert Einstein and Equation

1979. Air. Birth Centenary of Albert Einstein (physicist).
1467 **525** 1 p. 60 multicoloured . . 10 10

526 Arms of Hermosillo **527** Sir Rowland Hill

1979. Centenary of Hermosillo, Sonora.
1468 **526** 80 c. multicoloured . . . 10 10

1979. Air. Death Centenary of Sir Rowland Hill.
1469 **527** 1 p. 60 multicoloured . . 10 10

528 "Children" (Adriana Blas Casas)

1979. Air. International Year of the Child.
1470 **528** 1 p. 60 multicoloured . . 10 10

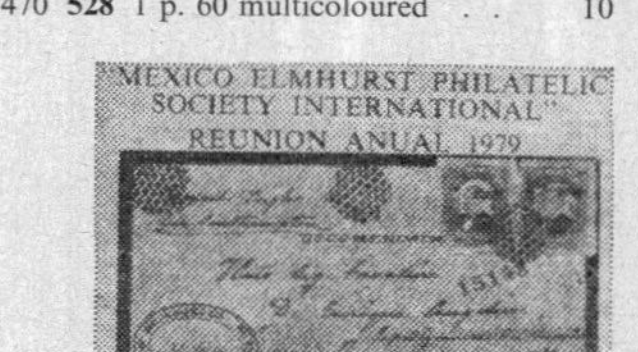

529 Registered Letter from Mexico to Rome, 1880

1979. Air. "Mepsipex 79", Third International Exhibition of Elmhurst Philatelic Society, Mexico City.
1499 **529** 1 p. 60 multicoloured . . 10 10

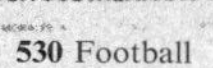

530 Football **531** Josefa Ortiz de Dominguez

1979. "Universiada 79", 10th World University Games, Mexico City (1st issue).
1500 **530** 50 c. grey, black and blue (postage) 10 10
1501 – 80 c. multicoloured . . . 10 10
1502 – 1 p. multicoloured . . . 10 10
1504 – 1 p. 60 multicoloured (air) 10 10
1505 – 4 p. 30 multicoloured . . 15 10
DESIGNS—VERT: 80 c. Aztec ball player; 1 p. Wall painting of athletes; 1 p. 60, Games emblem; 4 p. 30, Flame and doves.
See also Nos. 1514/19.

1979. 150th Death Anniv of Josefa Ortiz de Dominguez (Mayor of Queretaro).
1507 **531** 80 c. pink, black and bright pink 10 10

532 "Allegory of National Culture" (Alfaro Siqueiros)

1979. 50th Anniv of National University's Autonomy. Multicoloured.
1508 80 c. Type **532** (postage) . . 10 10
1509 3 p. "The Conquest of Energy" (Chavez Morado) 20 10
1510 1 p. 60 "The Return of Quetzalcoatl" (Chavez Morado) (air) 10 10
1511 4 p. 30 "Students reaching for Culture" (Alfaro Siqueiros) 15 10

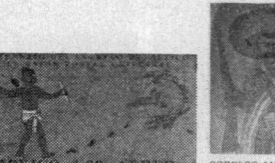

533 Messenger and U.P.U. Emblem **534** Emiliano Zapata (after Diego Rivera)

1979. Air. Centenary of Mexico's Admission to U.P.U.
1512 **533** 1 p. 60 yellow, black and brown 10 10

1979. Birth Centenary of Emiliano Zapata (revolutionary).
1513 **534** 80 c. multicoloured . . . 10 10

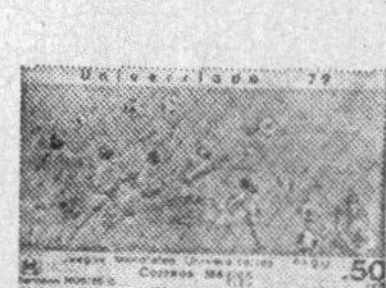
535 Football **536** Tepoztlan, Morelos

1979. "Universiada '79", 10th World University Games, Mexico City (2nd issue). Multicoloured.
1514 50 c. Type **535** (postage) . . 10 10
1515 80 c. Volleyball 10 10
1516 1 p. Basketball 10 10
1518 1 p. 60 Tennis (air) 10 10
1519 5 p. 50 Swimming 30 20

1979. Tourism (1st series). Multicoloured.
1526 80 c. Type **536** (postage) . . 10 10
1527 80 c. Mexcaltitan, Nayarit 10 10
1528 1 p. 60 Agua Azul waterfall, Chipas (air) 10 10
1529 1 p. 60 King Coliman statue, Colima 10 10
See also Nos. 1631/4 and 1675/8.

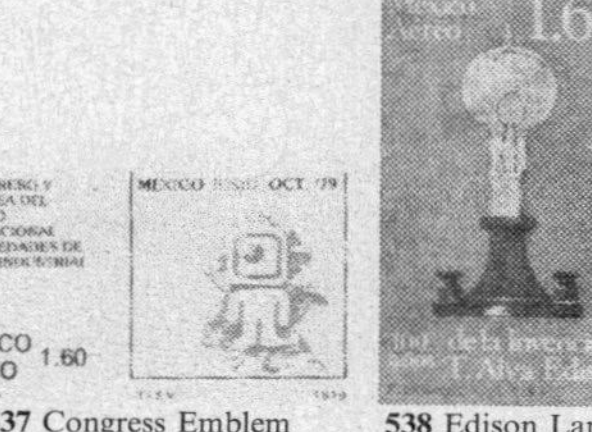

537 Congress Emblem **538** Edison Lamp

1979. Air. 11th Congress and Assembly of International Industrial Design Council.
1530 **537** 1 p. 60 black, mauve and turquoise 10 10

1979. Air. Centenary of Electric Light.
1531 **538** 1 p. 60 multicoloured . 10 10

539 Martin de Olivares (postmaster) **540** Assembly Emblem

1979. 400th Anniv of Royal Proclamation of Mail Services in the New World. Multicoloured.
1532 80 c. Type **539** (postage) . . 10 10
1533 1 p. 60 Martin Enriquez de Almanza (viceroy of New Spain) (air) 10 10
1534 5 p. 50 King Philip II of Spain 35 20

1979. Air. 8th General Assembly of Latin American Universities Union.
1536 **540** 1 p. multicoloured . 10 10

541 Shepherd **542** Moon Symbol from Mexican Codex

1979. Christmas. Multicoloured.
1537 50 c. Type **541** (postage) . . 10 10
1538 1 p. 60 Girl and Christmas tree (air) 10 10

1979. Air. 10th Anniv of First Man on Moon.
1539 **542** 2 p. 50 multicoloured . 15 10

543 Church, Yanhuitlan

1980. Air. Mexican Arts and Sciences (8th series). Multicoloured.
1540 1 p. 60 Type **543** 10 10
1541 1 p. 60 Monastery, Yuriria . 10 10
1542 1 p. 60 Church, Tlayacapan 10 10
1543 1 p. 60 Church, Actopan . . 10 10
1544 1 p. 60 Church, Acolman . . 10 10

544 Steps and Snake's Head

1980. National Pre-Hispanic Monuments (1st series). Multicoloured.
1545 80 c. Type **544** (postage) . . . 10 10
1546 1 p. 60 Doble Tlaloc (rain god) (air) 10 10
1547 5 p. 50 Coyolzauhqui (moon goddess) 35 20
See also Nos. 1565/7 and 1605/7.

1980. Mexican Fauna (2nd series). As T **516**. Multicoloured.
1548 80 c. Common turkey (postage) 35 10
1549 1 p. 60 Greater flamingo (air) 80 25

1980. Mexican Flowers (2nd series). As T **518**. Multicoloured.
1550 80 c. "Tajetes erecta" (postage) 15 10
1551 1 p. 60 "Vanilla planifolia" (air) . 25 10

545 Jules Verne

1980. Air. 75th Death Anniv of Jules Verne (author).
1552 **545** 5 p. 50 brown and black 35 20

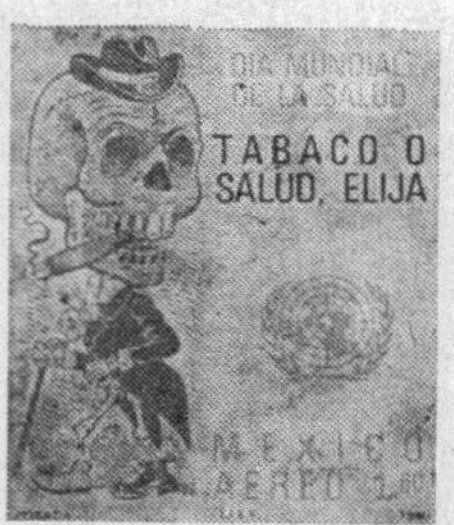

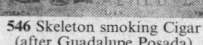

546 Skeleton smoking Cigar (after Guadalupe Posada) **547** China Poblana, Puebla

1980. Air. World Health Day. Anti-Smoking Campaign.
1553 **546** 1 p. 60 purple, blue & red 10 10

1980. National Costumes (1st series). Multicoloured.
1554 50 c. Type **547** (postage) . . . 10 10
1555 80 c. Jarocha, Veracruz . . . 10 10
1556 1 p. 60 Chiapaneca, Chiapas (air) 10 10
See also Nos. 1588/90.

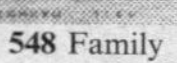

548 Family **549** Cuauhtemoc (last Aztec Emperor)

1980. 10th Population and Housing Census.
1557 **548** 3 p. black and silver . . . 20 10

1980. Pre-Hispanic Personages (1st series). Multicoloured.
1558 80 c. Type **549** 10 10
1559 1 p. 60 Nezahualcoyotl (governor of Tetzcoco) . . 10 10
1560 5 p. 50 Eight Deer Tiger's Claw (11th Mixtec king) 35 20
See also Nos. 1642/4 and 1846/8.

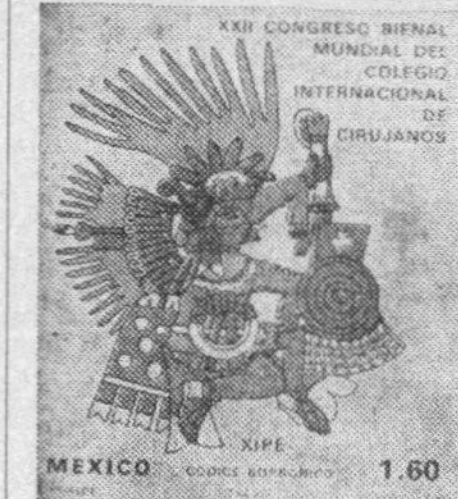

550 Xipe (Aztec god of medicine) **551** Bronze Medal

1980. 22nd World Biennial Congress of International College of Surgeons, Mexico City.
1561 **550** 1 p. 60 multicoloured . . 10 10

1980. Olympic Games, Moscow.
1562 **551** 1 p. 60 bronze, black and turquoise 10 10
1563 – 3 p. silver, black and blue 20 10
1564 – 5 p. 50 gold, black & red 35 20
DESIGNS: 3 p. Silver medal; 5 p. 50, Gold medal.

1980. National Pre-Hispanic Monuments (2nd series). As T **554**. Multicoloured.
1565 80 c. Sacred glass 10 10
1566 1 p. 60 Stone snail 10 10
1567 5 p. 50 Chac Mool (god) . . 35 20

552 Sacromonte Sanctuary, Amecameca

1980. Colonial Architecture (1st series).
1568 **552** 2 p. 50 grey and black . 20 10
1569 – 2 p. 50 grey and black . 20 10
1570 – 3 p. grey and black . . . 25 10
1571 – 3 p. grey and black . . . 25 10
DESIGNS—HORIZ: No. 1552, St. Catherine's Convent, Patzcuaro; No. 1554, Hermitage, Cuernavaca. VERT: No. 1553, Basilica, Culiapan.
See also Nos. 1617/20, 1660/3, 1695/8 and 1784/7.

553 Quetzalcoatl (god) **554** Arms of Sinaloa

1980. World Tourism Conference, Manila, Philippines.
1572 **553** 2 p. 50 multicoloured . . 15 10

1980. 150th Anniv of Sinaloa State.
1573 **554** 1 p. 60 multicoloured . . 10 10

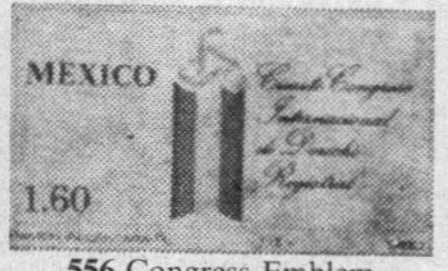

555 Straw Angel **556** Congress Emblem

1980. Christmas. Multicoloured.
1574 50 c. Type **555** 10 10
1575 1 p. 60 Poinsettia in a jug . . 10 10

1980. 4th International Civil Justice Congress.
1576 **556** 1 p. 60 multicoloured . . 10 10

557 Glass Demijohn and Animals **558** "Simon Bolivar" (after Paulin Guerin)

1980. Mexican Crafts (1st series). Multicoloured.
1577 50 c. Type **557** 10 10
1578 1 p. Poncho 10 10
1579 3 p. Wooden mask 20 15
See also Nos. 1624/6.

1980. 150th Death Anniv of Simon Bolivar.
1580 **558** 4 p. multicoloured . . . 30 20

559 Vicente Guerrero **560** Valentin Gomez Farias

1981. 150th Death Anniv of Vicente Guerrero (liberator).
1581 **559** 80 c. multicoloured . . . 10 10

1981. Birth Bicentenary of Valentin Gomez Farias.
1582 **560** 80 c. black and green . . 10 10

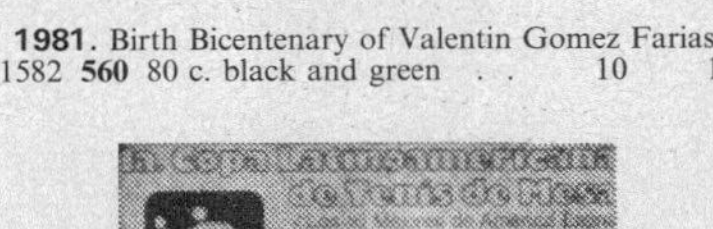

561 Table Tennis Balls in Flight

1981. 1st Latin-American Table Tennis Cup.
1583 **561** 4 p. multicoloured . . . 30 20

562 Jesus Gonzalez Ortega **563** Gabino Barreda

1981. Death Centenary of Jesus Gonzalez Ortega.
1584 **562** 80 c. lt brown & brown 10 10

1981. Death Centenary of Gabino Barreda (politician).
1585 **563** 80 c. pink, black & green 10 10

564 Benito Juarez **565** Foundation Monument

1981. 175th Birth Anniv of Benito Juarez (patriot).
1586 **564** 1 p. 60 grn, brn & lt brn 15 10

1981. 450th Anniv of Puebla City.
1587 **565** 80 c. multicoloured . . . 10 10

1981. National Costumes (2nd series). Vert designs as T **547**. Multicoloured.
1588 50 c. Purepecha, Michoacan 10 10
1589 80 c. Charra, Jalisco 10 10
1590 1 p. 60 Mestiza, Yucatan . . 15 10

1981. Mexican Fauna (3rd series). Vert designs as T **516**. Multicoloured.
1591 80 c. Northern Mockingbird 45 15
1592 1 p. 60 Mountain Trogon . . 85 40

1981. Mexican Flowers (3rd series). Vert designs as T **518**. Multicoloured.
1593 80 c. Avocado 10 10
1594 1 p. 60 Cacao 15 10

566 "Martyrs of Cananea" (David A. Siqueiros)

1981. 75th Anniv of Martyrs of Cananea.
1595 **566** 1 p. 60 multicoloured . 15 10

567 Toy Drummer with One Arm **568** Arms of Queretaro

1981. International Year of Disabled People.
1596 **567** 4 p. multicoloured . . . 30 20

1981. 450th Anniv of Queretaro City.
1597 **568** 80 c. multicoloured . . 10 10

569 Mexican Stamp of 1856 and Postal Service Emblem

1981. 125th Anniv of First Mexican Stamp.
1598 **569** 4 p. multicoloured . . . 30 20

570 Sir Alexander Fleming **572** St. Francisco Xavier Claver

571 Union Congress Building and Emblem

1981. Birth Centenary of Sir Alexander Fleming (discoverer of penicillin).
1599 **570** 5 p. blue and orange . . 35 10

1981. Opening of New Union Congress Building.
1600 **571** 1 p. 60 green and red . . 10 10

1981. 250th Birth Anniv of St. Francis Xavier Claver.
1601 **572** 80 c. multicoloured . . 10 10

573 "Desislava" (detail of Bulgarian Fresco)

1981. 1300th Anniv of Bulgarian State. Mult.
1602 1 p. 60 Type **573** 10 10
1603 4 p. Horse-headed cup from Thrace 25 20
1604 7 p. Madara Horseman (relief) 40 30

1981. Pre-Hispanic Monuments. As T **544**. Multicoloured.
1605 80 c. Seated God 10 10
1606 1 p. 60 Alabaster deer's head 15 10
1607 4 p. Jade Fish 30 20

574 Pablo Picasso

1981. Birth Centenary of Pablo Picasso (artist).
1608 **574** 5 p. deep green & green 35 20

575 Shepherd **576** Wheatsheaf

1981. Christmas. Multicoloured.
1609 50 c. Type **575** 10 10
1610 1 p. 60 Praying girl 15 10

1981. World Food Day.
1611 **576** 4 p. multicoloured . . . 25 15

577 Thomas Edison, Lightbulb and Gramophone

1981. 50th Death Anniv of Thomas Edison (inventor).
1612 **577** 4 p. stone, brown & green 25 15

578 Co-operation Emblem and Wheat

1981. International Meeting on Co-operation and Development, Cancun.
1613 **578** 4 p. blue, grey and black 25 20

579 Globe and Diesel Locomotive

1981. 15th Pan-American Railway Congress.
1614 **579** 1 p. 60 multicoloured . . 35 10

580 Film Frame

1981. 50th Anniv of Mexican Sound Movies.
1615 **580** 4 p. grey, black and green 25 20

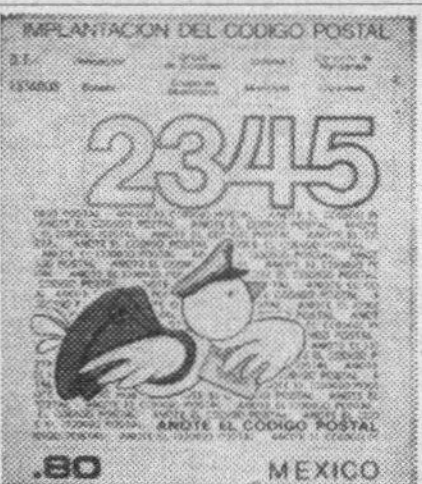

581 Postcode and Bird delivering Letter

1981. Inauguration of Postcodes.
1616 **581** 80 c. multicoloured . . . 10 10

1981. Colonial Architecture (2nd series). As T **522**. Multicoloured.
1617 4 p. Mascarones House . . . 25 15
1618 4 p. La Merced Convent . . 25 15
1619 5 p. Chapel of the Third Order, Texcoco 30 20
1620 5 p. Father Tembleque Aqueduct, Otumba 30 20

582 "Martyrs of Rio Blanco" (Orozco)

1982. 75th Anniv of Martyrs of Rio Blanco.
1621 **582** 80 c. multicoloured . . . 10 10

583 Ignacio Lopez Rayon

1982. 150th Death Anniv of Ignacio Lopez Rayon.
1622 **583** 1 p. 60 green, red & black 10 10

584 Postal Headquarters

1982. 75th Anniv of Postal Headquarters.
1623 **584** 4 p. pink and green . . . 25 20

1982. Mexican Crafts (2nd series). As T **557**. Multicoloured.
1624 50 c. "God's Eye" (Huichol art) 10 10
1625 1 p. Ceramic snail 10 10
1626 3 p. Tiger mask 20 15

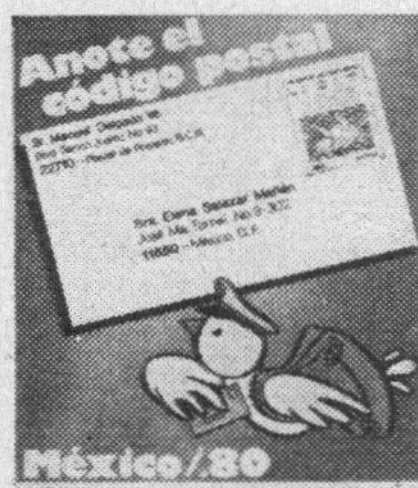

585 Postcoded Letter and Bird

1982. Postcode Publicity.
1627 **585** 80 c. multicoloured . . . 10 10

586 Dr. Robert Koch and Cross of Lorraine

1982. Centenary of Discovery of Tubercle Bacillus.
1628 **586** 4 p. multicoloured . . . 15 10

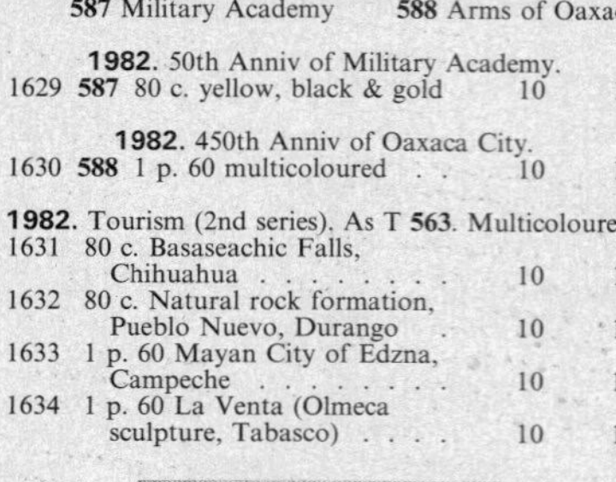

587 Military Academy **588** Arms of Oaxaca

1982. 50th Anniv of Military Academy.
1629 **587** 80 c. yellow, black & gold 10 10

1982. 450th Anniv of Oaxaca City.
1630 **588** 1 p. 60 multicoloured . . 10 10

1982. Tourism (2nd series). As T **563**. Multicoloured.
1631 80 c. Basaseachic Falls, Chihuahua 10 10
1632 80 c. Natural rock formation, Pueblo Nuevo, Durango . 10 10
1633 1 p. 60 Mayan City of Edzna, Campeche 10 10
1634 1 p. 60 La Venta (Olmeca sculpture, Tabasco) 10 10

589 Footballers

1982. World Cup Football Championship, Spain. Multicoloured.
1635 1 p. 60 Type **589** 10 10
1636 4 p. Dribbling 15 10
1637 7 p. Tackling 25 15

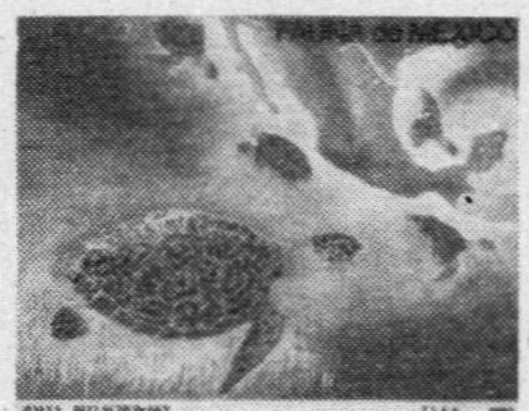

590 Hawksbill Turtles

1982. Mexican Fauna. Multicoloured.
1638 1 p. 60 Type **590** 10 10
1639 4 p. Grey Whales 15 30

591 Vicente Guerrero

1982. Birth Bicentenary of Vicente Guerrero (independence fighter).
1640 **591** 80 c. multicoloured . . . 10 10

592 Symbols of Peace and Communication

1982. Second U.N. Conference on the Exploration and Peaceful Uses of Outer Space, Vienna.
1641 **592** 4 p. multicoloured . . . 10 10

1982. Pre-Hispanic Personalities (2nd series). As T **549**. Multicoloured.
1642 80 c. Tariacuri 10 10
1643 1 p. 60 Acamapichtli 10 10
1644 4 p. Ten Deer Tiger's breastplate 10 10

593 Pawpaw ("Carica papaya")

1982. Mexican Flora. Multicoloured.
1645 80 c. Type **593** 10 10
1646 1 p. 60 Maize ("Zea mays") 10 10

594 Astrologer

1982. Native Mexican Codices. Florentine Codex. Multicoloured.
1647 80 c. Type **594** 10 10
1648 1 p. 60 Arriving at School . 10 10
1649 4 p. Musicians 10 10

595 Manuel Gamio (anthropologist)

1982. Mexican Arts and Scientists. Multicoloured.
1650 1 p. 60 Type **595** 10 10
1651 1 p. 60 Isaac Ochoterena (biologist) 10 10
1652 1 p. 60 Angel Maria Garibay (philologist) 10 10
1653 1 p. 60 Manuel Sandoval Vallarta (nuclear physicist) 10 10
1654 1 p. 60 Guillermo Gonzalez Camarena (electronics engineer) 10 10

596 State Archives Building

1982. Inaug of State Archives Building.
1655 **596** 1 p. 60 black and green 10 10

597 Dove and Peace Text

1982. Christmas. Multicoloured.
1656 50 c. Type **597** 10 10
1657 1 p. 60 Dove and Peace text (different) 10 10

598 Hands holding Food

1982. Mexican Food System.
1658 **598** 1 p. 60 multicoloured . 10 10

MINIMUM PRICE

The minimum price quoted is 10p which represents a handling charge rather than a basis for valuing common stamps. For further notes about prices, see introductory pages.

599 "Revolutionary Mexico" Stamp, 1956

1982. Inauguration of Revolution Museum, Chihuahua.
1659 **599** 1 p. 60 grey and green . . 10 10

1982. Colonial Architecture (3rd series). As T **552**. Multicoloured.
1660 1 p. 60 College of Sts. Peter and Paul, Mexico City 10 10
1661 8 p. Convent of Jesus Maria, Mexico City 15 10
1662 10 p. Open Chapel, Tlalmanalco 20 15
1663 14 p. Convent, Actopan . . . 25 20

600 Alfonso Garcia Robles and Laurel **601** Jose Vasconcelos

1982. Alfonso Garcia Robles (Nobel Peace Prize Winner) Commemoration.
1664 **600** 1 p. 60 grey, black & gold 10 10
1665 – 14 p. pink, black & gold 25 20
DESIGN: 14 p. Robles and medal.

1982. Birth Centenary of Jose Vasconcelos (philosopher).
1666 **601** 1 p. 60 black and blue . . 10 10

602 W.C.Y. Emblem and Methods of Communication

1983. World Communications Year.
1667 **602** 16 p. multicoloured . . . 20 15

603 Sonora State Civil War Stamp, 1913

1983. "Herfilex 83" Mexican Revolution Stamp Exhibition.
1668 **603** 6 p. brown, black & green 10 10

604 "Nauticas Mexico" (container ship), World Map and I.M.O. Emblem

1983. 25th Anniv of International Maritime Organization.
1669 **604** 16 p. multicoloured . . . 80 20

605 Doctor treating Patient

1983. Constitutional Right to Health Protection.
1670 **605** 6 p. green and red . . . 10 10

606 Valentin Gomez Farias (founder) and Arms of Society

1983. 150th Anniv of Mexican Geographical and Statistical Society.
1671 **606** 6 p. multicoloured . . . 10 10

607 Football

1983. Second World Youth Football Championship, Mexico.
1672 **607** 6 p. black and green . . 10 10
1673 13 p. black and red . . . 15 10
1674 14 p. black and blue . . 20 15

1983. Tourism. As T **536**. Multicoloured.
1675 6 p. Federal Palace, Queretaro 10 10
1676 6 p. Water tank, San Luis Potosi 10 10
1677 13 p. Cable car, Zacatecas . 15 10
1678 14 p. Carved head of Kohunlich, Quintana Roo 20 15

608 Bolivar on Horseback

1983. Birth Bicentenary of Simon Bolivar.
1679 **608** 21 p. multicoloured . . . 25 15

609 Angela Peralta **610** Agave

1983. Death Centenary of Angela Peralta (opera singer).
1680 **609** 9 p. light brown & brown 10 10

1983. Mexican Flora and Fauna (5th series). Multicoloured.
1681 9 p. Type **610** 10 10
1682 9 p. Sapodilla 10 10
1683 9 p. Swallowtail 30 10
1684 9 p. Boa constrictor 10 10

611 Two Candles

1983. Christmas. Multicoloured.
1685 9 p. Type **611** 10 10
1686 20 p. Three candles 25 15

612 S.C.T. Emblem

1983. Integral Communications and Transport System.

1687	**612**	13 p. blue and black . .	15	10

613 Carlos Chavez (musician)

1983. Mexican Arts and Sciences (10th series). Contemporary Artists. Multicoloured.

1688	**613**	9 p. brown, light brown and deep brown	10	10
1689	–	9 p. brown, light brown and deep brown	10	10
1690	–	9 p. deep brown, light brown and brown . .	10	10
1691	–	9 p. light brown, deep brown and brown . .	10	10
1692	–	9 p. deep brown, stone and brown	10	10

DESIGNS: No. 1689, Francisco Goitia (painter); No. 1690, S. Diaz Miron (poet); No. 1691, Carlos Bracho (sculptor); No. 1692, Fanny Anitua (singer).

614 Orozco (self-portrait)

1983. Birth Centenary of Jose Clemente Orozco (artist).

1693	**614**	9 p. multicoloured . . .	10	10

615 Human Rights Emblem

1983. 35th Anniv of Human Rights Declaration.

1694	**615**	20 p. deep blue, yellow and blue	25	15

1983. Colonial Architecture (4th series). As T **552**. Each grey and black.

1695	9 p. Convent, Malinalco . .	10	10
1696	20 p. Cathedral, Cuernavaca	25	15
1697	21 p. Convent, Tepeji del Rio	25	15
1698	24 p. Convent, Atlatlahucan	30	20

616 Antonio Caso and Books

1983. Birth Centenary of Antonio Caso (philospher).

1699	**616**	9 p. blue, lilac and red .	10	10

617 Joaquin Velazquez

1983. Bicentenary of Royal Legislation on Mining.

1700	**617**	9 p. multicoloured . . .	10	10

618 Book and Envelopes

1984. Centenary of First Postal Laws.

1701	**618**	12 p. multicoloured . .	15	10

619 Children dancing around Drops of Anti-Polio Serum

1984. World Anti-Polio Campaign.

1702	**619**	12 p. multicoloured . .	15	10

620 Muscovy Duck

1984. Mexican Fauna (6th series). Multicoloured.

1703	12 p. Type **620**	40	20
1704	20 p. Red-billed whistling duck	65	30

621 Xoloitzcuintle Dog

1984. World Dog Show.

1705	**621**	12 p. multicoloured . .	15	10

622 Bank Headquarters

1984. Centenary of National Bank.

1706	**622**	12 p. multicoloured . .	15	10

623 Hands holding Trees

624 Throwing the Discus

1984. Protection of Forest Resources.

1707	**623**	20 p. multicoloured . . .	20	15

1984. Olympic Games, Los Angeles. Multicoloured.

1708	14 p. Type **624**	15	15
1709	20 p. Show jumping	20	15
1710	23 p. Gymnastics (floor exercise)	25	20
1711	24 p. Diving	25	20
1712	25 p. Boxing	25	20
1713	26 p. Fencing	25	20

625 Mexican and Russian Flags

1984. 60th Anniv of Diplomatic Relations with U.S.S.R.

1715	**625**	23 p. multicoloured . . .	25	20

626 Hand holding U.N. emblem

1984. International Population Conference.

1716	**623**	20 p. multicoloured . . .	20	15

627 Gen. Mugica

1984. Birth Centenary of General Francisco Mugica (politician).

1717	**627**	14 p. brown and black . .	15	15

628 Emblem and Dates

629 Airline Emblem

1984. 50th Anniv of Economic Culture Fund.

1718	**628**	14 p. brown, black and red	15	15

1984. 50th Anniv of Aeromexico (state airline).

1719	–	14 p. multicoloured . . .	15	15
1720	**629**	20 p. black and red . . .	20	15

DESIGN—36 × 44 mm: 14 p. "Red Cactus" (sculpture, Sebastian).

630 Palace of Fine Arts

1984. 50th Anniv of Palace of Fine Arts.

1721	**630**	14 p. blue, black and brown	15	15

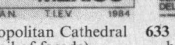

631 Metropolitan Cathedral (detail of facade)

633 Dove and Hand holding Flame

632 Coatzacoalcos Bridge

1984. 275th Anniv of Chihuahua City.

1722	**631**	14 p. brown and black .	15	15

1984. Inaug of Coatzacoalcos Bridge.

1723	**632**	14 p. multicoloured . . .	15	15

1984. World Disarmament Week.

1724	**633**	20 p. multicoloured . . .	20	15

634 Christmas Tree and Toy Train

1984. Christmas. Multicoloured.

1725	14 p. Type **634**	45	15
1726	20 p. Breaking the pinata (balloon filled with gifts) (vert)	20	15

635 Ignacio Manuel Altamirano

1984. 150th Birth Anniv of Ignacio Manuel Altamirano (politician and journalist).

1727	**635**	14 p. red and black . . .	15	15

636 Maps, Graph and Text

1984. 160th Anniv of State Audit Office.

1728	**636**	14 p. multicoloured . . .	15	15

637 Half a Football and Mexican Colours

1984. Mexico, Site of 1986 World Cup Football Championship. Multicoloured.

1729 20 p. Type **637** 20 15
1730 24 p. Football and Mexican colours 25 20

638 Romulo Gallegos **639** State Arms and Open Register

1984. Birth Centenary of Romul Gallegos.

1731 **638** 20 p. black and blue . . 20 15

1984. 125th Anniv of Mexican Civil Register.

1732 **639** 24 p. blue 25 20

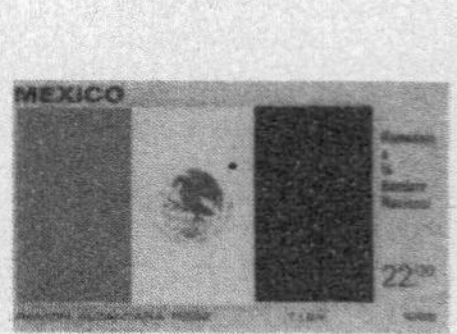

640 Mexican Flag **641** Johann Sebastian Bach

1985. 50th Anniv of National Flag.

1733 **640** 22 p. multicoloured . . . 25 20

1985. 300th Birth Anniv of Johann Sebastian Bach (composer).

1734 **641** 35 p. red and black . . . 15 30

642 I.Y.Y. Emblem **643** Children and Fruit within Book

1985. International Youth Year.

1735 **642** 35 p. purple, gold and black 15 30

1985. Child Survival Campaign.

1736 **643** 36 p. multicoloured . . . 15 10

644 Commemorative Medallion

1985. 450th Anniv of State Mint.

1737 **644** 35 p. gold, mauve & blue 15 10

645 Victor Hugo, Text and Gateway

1985. Death Centenary of Victor Hugo (novelist).

1738 **645** 35 p. grey 15 10

646 Hidalgo 8 r. Stamp, 1856

1985. "Mexifil 85" Stamp Exhibition.

1739 **646** 22 p. grey, black and purple 10 10
1740 – 35 p. grey, black and blue 15 10
1741 – 36 p. multicoloured . . 15 10

DESIGNS: 35 p. Carranza 10 c. stamp, 1916; 36 p. Juarez 50 p. stamp, 1975.

647 Rockets, Satellite, Nurse and Computer Operator

1985. Launching of First Morelos Satellite. Multicoloured.

1743 22 p. Type **647** 10 10
1744 36 p. Camera, dish aerial, satellite and computers . . 15 10
1745 90 p. Camera, dish aerial, satellite, television and couple telephoning 25 20

Nos. 1743/5 were printed together, se-tenant, forming a composite design.

648 Conifer

1985. 9th World Forestry Congress, Mexico.

1747 **648** 22 p. brown, black and green 10 10
1748 – 35 p. brown, black and green 15 10
1749 – 36 p. brown, black and green 15 10

DESIGNS: 35 p. Silk-cotton trees; 36 p. Mahogany tree.

649 Martin Luis Guzman

1985. Mexican Arts and Sciences (11th series). Contemporary Writers.

1750 **649** 22 p. grey and blue . . 10 10
1751 – 22 p. grey and blue . . 10 10
1752 – 22 p. grey and blue . . 10 10
1753 – 22 p. grey and blue . . 10 10
1754 – 22 p. grey and blue . . 10 10

DESIGNS: No. 1751, Augustin Yanez; 1752, Alfonso Reyes; 1753, Jose Ruben Romero; 1754, Artemio de Valle-Arizpe.

650 Miguel Hidalgo

1985. 175th Anniv of Independence Movement. Each green, black and red.

1755 22 p. Type **650** 10 10
1756 35 p. Jose Ma. Morelos . . . 10 10
1757 35 p. Ignacio Allende 10 10
1758 36 p. Leona Vigario 10 10
1759 110 p. Vicente Guerrero . . . 20 15

651 San Ildefonso

1985. 75th Anniv of National University. Mult.

1761 26 p. Type **651** 10 10
1762 26 p. Emblem 10 10
1763 40 p. Modern building . . . 10 10
1764 45 p. 1910 crest and Justo Sierra (founder) 10 10
1765 90 p. University crest 15 10

652 Rural and Industrial Landscapes

1985. 25th Anniv of Inter-American Development Bank.

1766 **652** 26 p. multicoloured . . . 10 10

653 Guns and Doves **654** Hands and Dove

1985. United Nations Disarmament Week.

1767 **653** 36 p. multicoloured . . . 10 10

1985. 40th Anniv of U.N.O.

1768 **654** 26 p. multicoloured . . . 10 10

655 "Girls Skipping" (Mishinoya K. Maki)

1985. Christmas. Children's Paintings. Mult.

1769 26 p. Disabled and able-bodied children playing (Margarita Salazar) 10 10
1770 35 p. Type **655** 10 10

656 Soldadera

1985. 75th Anniv of 1910 Revolution. Each red, black and green.

1771 26 p. Type **656** 10 10
1772 35 p. Pancho Villa 10 10
1773 40 p. Emiliano Zapata . . . 10 10
1774 45 p. Venustiano Carranza . . 10 10
1775 110 p. Francisco I. Madero . 20 15

657 "Vigilante" (Federico Silva)

1985. 2nd "Morelos" Telecommunications Satellite Launch.

1777 – 26 p. black and blue . . 10 10
1778 **657** 35 p. grey, pink and black 10 10
1779 – 45 p. multicoloured . . . 10 10

DESIGNS—VERT: 26 p. "Cosmonaut" (sculpture by Sebastian). HORIZ: 45 p. "Mexican Astronaut" (painting by Cauduro).

658 "Mexico" holding Book

1985. 25th Anniv of Free Textbooks National Commission.

1781 **658** 26 p. multicoloured . . . 10 10

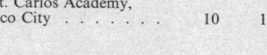

659 Olympic Stadium, University City

1985. World Cup Football Championship, Mexico. Each grey and black.

1782 26 p. Type **659** 10 10
1783 45 p. Azteca Stadium 10 10

1985. Colonial Architecture (5th series). Vert designs as T **552**. Each brown and black.

1784 26 p. Vizcayan College, Mexico City 10 10
1785 35 p. Counts of Heras y Soto Palace, Mexico City . . . 10 10
1786 40 p. Counts of Calimaya Palace, Mexico City . . . 10 10
1787 45 p. St. Carlos Academy, Mexico City 10 10

661 Luis Enrique Erro Planetarium

1986. 50th Anniv of National Polytechnic Institute. Multicoloured.

1788 40 p. Type **661** 10 10
1789 65 p. National School of Arts and Crafts 10 10
1790 75 p. Founders, emblem and "50" 10 10

1985. Mexican Flowers (6th series). As T **518**. Multicoloured.

1791 40 p. Calabash 10 10
1792 65 p. "Nopalea coccinellifera" (cactus) 10 10

663 Doll

1986. World Health Day.

1793 **663** 65 p. multicoloured . . . 10 10

HAVE YOU READ THE NOTES AT THE BEGINNING OF THIS CATALOGUE?

These often provide the answers to the enquiries we receive.

664 Halley and Comet

1986. Appearance of Halley's Comet.
1794 **664** 90 p. multicoloured . . . 15 10

665 Emblem

1986. Centenary of Geological Institute.
1795 **665** 40 p. multicoloured . . . 10 10

666 "Three Footballers with Berets"

1986. World Cup Football Championship, Mexico (2nd issue). Paintings by Angel Zarraga. Multicoloured.
1796 30 p. Type **666** 10 10
1797 40 p. "Portrait of Ramon Novaro" 10 10
1798 65 p. "Sunday" 10 10
1799 70 p. "Portrait of Ernest Charles Gimpel" 10 10
1800 90 p. "Three Footballers" . . 15 10

667 Ignacio Allende

1986. 175th Death Annivs of Independence Heroes. Multicoloured.
1802 40 p. Type **667** 10 10
1803 40 p. Miguel Hidalgo (after J. C. Orozco) 10 10
1804 65 p. Juan Aldama 10 10
1805 75 p. Mariano Jimenez . . . 10 10

668 Mexican Arms over "FTF"

669 Nicolas Bravo

1986. 50th Anniv of Fiscal Tribunal.
1806 **668** 40 p. black, blue & grey 10 10

1986. Birth Bicentenary of Nicolas Bravo (independence fighter).
1807 **669** 40 p. multicoloured . . . 10 10

670 "Zapata Landscape"

1986. Paintings by Diego Rivera. Multicoloured.
1808 50 p. Type **670** 10 10
1809 80 p. "Nude with Arum Lilies" 10 10
1810 110 p. "Vision of a Sunday Afternoon Walk on Central Avenue" (horiz) 20 15

671 Guadalupe Victoria

1986. Birth Bicentenary of Guadalupe Victoria (first President).
1811 **671** 50 p. multicoloured . . 10 10

672 People depositing Produce

1986. 50th Anniv of National Depositories.
1812 **672** 40 p. multicoloured . . 10 10

673 Pigeon above Hands holding Posthorn

674 Emblem

1986. World Post Day.
1813 **673** 120 p. multicoloured . . 20 15

1986. Foundation of National Commission to Mark 500th Anniv (1992) of Discovery of America.
1814 **674** 50 p. black and red . . 10 10

675 Ministry of Mines

676 Liszt

1986. 15th Pan-American Roads Congress.
1815 **675** 80 p. grey and black . . 10 10

1986. 175th Birth Anniv of Franz Liszt (composer).
1816 **676** 100 p. brown and black 15 10

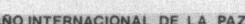

677 U.N. and "Pax Cultura" Emblems

1986. International Peace Year.
1817 **677** 80 p. blue, red and black 10 10

678 Jose Maria Pino Suarez (1st Vice-President of Revolutionary Govt.)

1986. Famous Mexicans buried in The Rotunda of Illustrious Men (1st series).
1818 **678** 50 p. multicoloured . . . 10 10
See also Nos. 1823/4, 1838 and 1899.

679 King

680 "Self-portrait"

1986. Christmas. Multicoloured.
1819 50 p. Type **679** 10 10
1820 80 p. Angel 10 10

1986. Birth Centenary of Diego Rivera (artist).
1821 **680** 80 p. multicoloured . . . 10 10

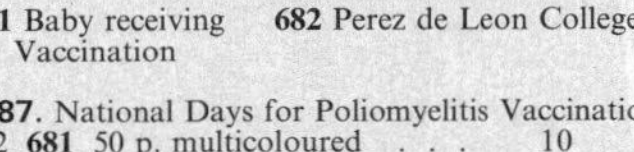

681 Baby receiving Vaccination

682 Perez de Leon College

1987. National Days for Poliomyelitis Vaccination.
1822 **681** 50 p. multicoloured . . . 10 10

1987. Famous Mexicans buried in The Rotunda of Illustrious Men (2nd series). As T **678**. Mult.
1823 100 p. Jose Maria Iglesias . . 10 10
1824 100 p. Pedro Sainz de Baranda 10 10

1987. Centenary of Higher Education.
1825 **682** 100 p. multicoloured . . 10 10

683 Kino and Map

1987. 300th Anniv of Father Eusebio Francisco Kino's Mission to Pimeria Alta.
1826 **683** 100 p. multicoloured . . 10 10

684 Baby's Head

1987. Child Immunization Campaign.
1827 **684** 100 p. deep blue & blue 10 10

685 Staircase

686 "5th of May, 1862, and the Siege of Puebla" Exhibition Poster, 1887

1987. 50th Anniv of Puebla Independent University.
1828 **685** 200 p. grey, pink and black 10 10

1987. 125th Anniv of Battle of Puebla.
1829 **686** 100 p. multicoloured . . 10 10

687 Stylized City

1987. "Metropolis 87" World Association of Large Cities Congress.
1830 **687** 310 p. red, black and green 45 30

688 Lacquerware Tray, Uruapan, Michoacan

689 Genaro Estrada (author and pioneer of democracy)

1987. Handicrafts. Multicoloured.
1831 100 p. Type **688** 10 10
1832 200 p. Woven blanket, Santa Ana Chiautempan, Tlaxcala 10 10
1833 230 p. Ceramic jar with lid, Puebla, Puebla 15 10

1987. Mexican Arts and Sciences (12th series).
1834 **689** 100 p. brown, black and pink 10 10
See also Nos. 1845, 1880 and 1904/5.

BANCO NACIONAL DE COMERCIO EXTERIOR

690 "Native Traders" (mural, P. O'Higgins)

1987. 50th Anniv of National Foreign Trade Bank.
1835 **690** 100 p. multicoloured . . 10 10

691 Diagram of Longitudinal Section through Ship's Hull

1987. 400th Anniv of Publication of First Shipbuilding Manual in America, Diego Garcia de Palacio's "Instrucion Nautica".
1836 **691** 100 p. green, blue & brn 10 10

692 Man carrying Sack of Maize Flour

1987. 50th Anniv of National Food Programme.
1837 **692** 100 p. multicoloured . . 10 10

1987. Mexicans in Rotunda of Illustrious Men (3rd series). As T **678**. Multicoloured.
1838 100 p. Leandro Valle 10 10

693 "Self-portrait with Skull"

1987. Paintings by Saturnino Herran.
1839 **693** 100 p. brown and black 15 10
1840 – 100 p. multicoloured . . 15 10
1841 – 400 p. multicoloured . . 60 50
DESIGNS: No. 1840, "The Offering"; 1841, "Creole with Shawl".

694 Flags of Competing Countries

1987. 10th Pan-American Games, Indianapolis.
1842 **694** 100 p. multicoloured . . 10 10
1843 – 200 p. black, red and green 10 10
DESIGN: 200 p. Running.

695 Electricity Pylon

1987. 50th Anniv of Federal Electricity Commission.
1844 **695** 200 p. multicoloured . . 10 10

1987. Mexican Arts and Sciences (13th series). As T **689**. Multicoloured.
1845 100 p. J. E. Hernandez y Davalos (author) 10 10

1987. Pre-Hispanic Personages (3rd series). As T **549**. Multicoloured.
1846 100 p. Xolotl (Chichimeca commander) 10 10
1847 200 p. Nezahualpilli (leader of Tezcoco tribe) 10 10
1848 400 p. Motecuhzoma Ilhuicamina (leader of Tenochtitlan tribe) 45 10

$100
GRAN PREMIO DE MEXICO
T.I.E.V. 1987

696 Stylized Racing Car

1987. Mexico Formula One Grand Prix.
1849 **696** 100 p. multicoloured . . 10 10

697 Mexican Cultural Centre, Mexico City
698 "Santa Maria" and 1922 Mexican Festival Emblem

1987. Mexican Tourism.
1850 **697** 100 p. multicoloured . . 10 10

1987. 500th Anniv of "Meeting of Two Worlds" (discovery of America by Columbus) (1st issue).
1851 **698** 150 p. multicoloured . . 30 15
See also Nos. 1902, 1941, 1979, 2038 and 2062/6.

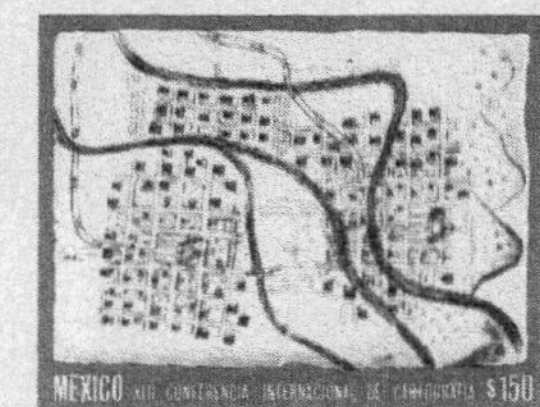

699 16th-century Spanish Map of Mexico City

1987. 13th International Cartography Conference.
1852 **699** 150 p. multicoloured . . 10 10

1987. Mexican Tourism. As T **697**. Multicoloured.
1853 150 p. Michoacan 15 10
1854 150 p. Garcia Caves, Nuevo Leon 10 10
1855 150 p. View of Mazatlan, Sinaloa 10 10

700 Pre-Hispanic Wedding Ceremony

1987. Native Codices. Mendocino Codex. Mult.
1856 150 p. Type **700** 10 10
1857 150 p. Moctezuma's council chamber 10 10
1858 150 p. Foundation of Tenochtitlan 10 10

701 Dove with Olive Twig

1987. Christmas.
1859 **701** 150 p. mauve 10 10
1860 – 150 p. blue 10 10
DESIGN: No. 1860, As T **701** but dove facing left.

702 "Royal Ordinance for the Carriage of Maritime Mail" Title Page

1987. World Post Day.
1861 **702** 150 p. green and grey . . 10 10

MEXICO $250

703 Circle of Flags

1987. 1st Meeting of Eight Latin-American Presidents, Acapulco. Multicoloured.
1863 250 p. Type **703** 10 10
1864 500 p. Flags and doves . . . 25 10

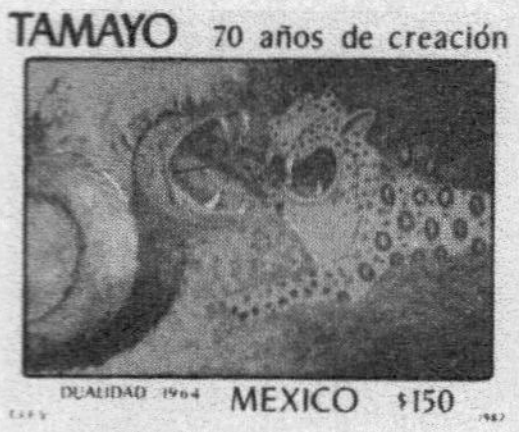

704 "Dualidad 1964"

1987. Rufino Tamayo (painter). "70 Years of Creativity".
1865 **704** 150 p. multicoloured . . 10 10

705 Train on Metlac Railway Bridge

1987. 50th Anniv of Railway Nationalization.
1866 **705** 150 p. multicoloured . . 35 10

706 Stradivarius at Work (detail, 19th-century engraving)

1987. 250th Death Anniv of Antonio Stradivarius (violin-maker).
1867 **706** 150 p. light violet and violet 10 10

SUPREMA CORTE DE JUSTICIA
TRIBUNAL CONSTITUCIONAL
Manuel Crescencio Rejon
MEXICO $300

707 Statue of Manuel Crescensio Rejon (promulgator of Yucatan State Constitution)

1988. Constitutional Tribunal, Supreme Court of Justice.
1868 **707** 300 p. multicoloured . . 15 10

708 American Manatee

1988. Animals. Multicoloured.
1869 300 p. Type **708** 15 10
1870 300 p. Mexican mole salamander 15 10

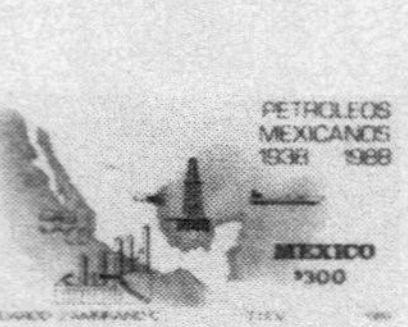

709 Map and Oil Industry Symbols

710 "The Vaccination"

1988. 50th Anniv of Pemex (Nationalized Petroleum Industry).
1871 **709** 300 p. blue and black . . 20 10
1872 – 300 p. multicoloured . . 15 10
1873 – 500 p. multicoloured . . 25 10
DESIGNS:—36 × 43 mm: No. 1872, PEMEX emblem. 43 × 36 mm: No. 1873, "50" and oil exploration platform.

1988. World Health Day (1874) and 40th Anniv of W.H.O. (1875). Paintings by Diego Rivera.
1874 **710** 300 p. brown and green 15 10
1875 – 300 p. multicoloured . . 15 10
DESIGN:—43 × 36 mm: No. 1875, "The People demand Health".

711 "Death Portrait" (Victor Delfin)

1988. 50th Death Anniv of Cesar Vallejo (painter and poet). Multicoloured.
1876 300 p. Type **711** 15 10
1877 300 p. Portrait by Arnold Belkin and "Hoy me palpo..." . . 15 10
1878 300 p. Portrait as in T **711** but larger (30 × 35 mm) . . . 15 10
1879 300 p. Portrait as in No. 1877 but larger (23 × 35 mm) . . 15 10

1988. Mexican Arts and Sciences (14th series). As T **689**.
1880 300 p. brown, black and violet 15 10
DESIGN: 300 p. Carlos Pellicer (poet).

712 Girl and Boy holding Stamp in Tweezers

1988. "Mepsirrey '88" Stamp Exhibition, Monterrey. Multicoloured.
1881 300 p. Type **712** 15 10
1882 300 p. Envelope with "Monterrey" hand-stamp 15 10
1883 500 p. Exhibition emblem . . 25 10

713 Hernandos Rodriguez Racing Circuit, Mexico City

1988. Mexico Formula One Grand Prix.
1884 **713** 500 p. multicoloured . . 25 10

714 Lopez Verlarde and Rose

715 Emblem

1988. Birth Centenary of Ramon Lopez Verlarde (poet). Multicoloured.
1885 300 p. Type **714** 15 10
1886 300 p. Abstract 15 10

1988. 50th Anniv of Military Sports.
1887 **715** 300 p. multicoloured . . 15 10

MORE DETAILED LISTS
are given in the Stanley Gibbons Catalogues referred to in the country headings. For lists of current volumes see introduction

716 Chrysanthemum, Container Ship and Flags

1988. Centenary of Mexico–Japan Friendship, Trade and Navigation Treaty.
1888 **716** 500 p. multicoloured . . 35 10

717 Map 718 Runners

1988. Oceanographical Assembly.
1889 **717** 500 p. multicoloured . . 25 10

1988. Olympic Games Seoul.
1890 **718** 500 p. multicoloured . . 25 10

719 Boxer and Flags

1988. 25th Anniv of World Boxing Council.
1892 **719** 500 p. multicoloured . . 25 10

720 Hospital and Emblem

1988. 125th Anniv of Red Cross.
1893 **720** 300 p. grey, red and black 15 10

721 Posada

1988. 75th Death Anniv of Jose Guadalupe Posada (painter).
1894 **721** 300 p. black and silver . 15 10

722 "Danaus plexippus"

1988. Endangered Insects. The Monarch Butterfly. Multicoloured.
1895 300 p. Type **722** 30 10
1896 300 p. Butterflies on wall . . 30 10
1897 300 p. Butterflies on leaves . 30 10
1898 300 p. Caterpillar, butterfly and chrysalis 30 10

1988. Mexicans in Rotunda of Illustrious Persons (4th series). As T **678**. Multicoloured.
1899 300 p. Manuel Sandoval Vallarta 15 10

723 Envelopes forming Map

1988. World Post Day.
1900 **723** 500 p. black and blue . 20 10

724 Indian and Monk writing

1988. 500th Anniv of "Meeting of Two Worlds" (2nd issue). Yanhuitian Codex.
1902 **724** 500 p. multicoloured . 20 10

725 Man watering Plant

1988. World Food Day. "Rural Youth".
1903 **725** 500 p. multicoloured . . 20 10

1988. Mexican Arts and Sciences (15th series). As T **689**.
1904 300 p. black and grey . . . 15 10
1905 300 p. brown, black & yellow 15 10
DESIGNS: No. 1904, Alfonso Caso; 1905, Vito Alessio Robles.

726 Act

1988. 175th Anniv of Promulgation of Act of Independence.
1906 **726** 300 p. flesh and brown 15 10

727 "Self-portrait 1925" 728 Children and Kites

1988. 25th Death Anniv of Antonio Ruiz (painter). Multicoloured.
1907 300 p. Type **727** 15 10
1908 300 p. "La Malinche" . . . 15 10
1909 300 p. "March Past" 15 10

1988. Christmas. Multicoloured.
1910 300 p. Type **728** 15 10
1911 300 p. Food (horiz) 15 10

729 Emblem

1988. 50th Anniv of Municipal Workers Trade Union.
1912 **729** 300 p. black and brown 15 10

1988. Mexican Flowers (7th series). As T **518**. Multicoloured.
1913 300 p. "Mimosa tenuiflora" 15 10
1914 300 p. "Ustilago maydis" . . 15 10

731 "50" and Emblem

1989. 50th Anniv of State Printing Works.
1915 **731** 450 p. brown, grey & red 20 10

732 Arms and Score of National Anthem

1989. 145th Anniv of Dominican Independence.
1916 **732** 450 p. multicoloured . . 20 10

733 Emblem

1989. Centenary of International Boundary and Water Commission.
1917 **733** 1100 p. multicoloured . . 50 50

734 Emblem

1989. 10th International Book Fair, Mineria.
1918 **734** 450 p. multicoloured . . 20 10

735 Composer at Work

1989. 25th Anniv of Society of Authors and Composers.
1919 **735** 450 p. multicoloured . . 20 10

736 People

1989. Anti-Aids Campaign.
1920 **736** 450 p. multicoloured . . 20 10

737 Vicario 738 Statue of Reyes

1989. Birth Bicentenary of Leona Vicario (Independence fighter).
1921 **737** 450 p. brown, deep brown and black 20 10

1989. Birth Centenary of Alfonso Reyes (writer).
1922 **738** 450 p. multicoloured . . 20 10

739 Speeding Cars

1989. Mexico Formula One Grand Prix.
1923 **739** 450 p. multicoloured . . 20 10

740 Sea and Mountains 741 Huehuetcotl (god)

1989. 14th Travel Agents' Meeting, Acapulco.
1924 **740** 1100 p. multicoloured . . 50 50

1989. 14th International Congress on Ageing.
1925 **741** 450 p. pink, black and stone 20 10

742 Revolutionary and Battle Site

1989. 75th Anniv of Battle of Zacatecas.
1926 **742** 450 p. black 20 10

743 Catchers

1989. Baseball Professionals' Hall of Fame. Multicoloured.
1927 550 p. Type **743** 20 10
1928 550 p. Striker 20 10
Nos. 1927/8 were printed together, se-tenant, forming a composite design.

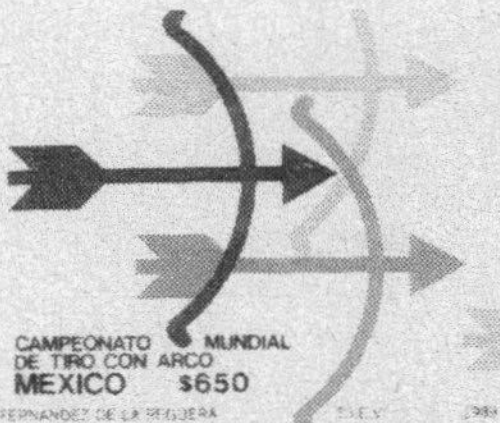

744 Bows and Arrows

1989. World Archery Championships, Switzerland. Multicoloured.
1929 650 p. Type **744** 25 10
1920 650 p. Arrows and target . . 25 10
Nos. 1929/30 were printed together, se-tenant, forming a composite design.

745 Arms

1989. Centenary of Tijuana.
1931 **745** 1100 p. multicoloured . . 50 20

746 Storming the Bastille

1989. Bicentenary of French Revolution.
1932 **746** 1300 p. multicoloured . . 60 50

747 Mina

1989. Birth Bicentenary of Francisco Xavier Mina (independence fighter).
1933 **747** 450 p. multicoloured . . 20 10

748 Cave Paintings

1989. 25th Anniv of National Anthropological Museum, Chapultepec.
1934 **748** 450 p. multicoloured . . 20 10

749 Runners

1989. 7th Mexico City Marathon.
1935 **749** 450 p. multicoloured . . 20 10

750 Printed Page

1989. 450th Anniv of First American and Mexican Printed Work.
1936 **750** 450 p. multicoloured . . 20 10

751 Posthorn and Cancellations

1989. World Post Day.
1937 **751** 1100 p. multicoloured . 50 20

752 "Aguascalientes in History" (Osvaldo Barra)

1989. 75th Anniv of Aguascalientes Revolutionary Convention.
1936 **752** 450 p. multicoloured . . 20 10

753 Patterns

1989. America. Pre-Columbian Culture.
1939 450 p. Type **753** 20 10
1940 450 p. Traditional writing . 20 10

754 Old and New World Symbols

755 Cross of Lorraine

1989. 500th Anniv of "Meeting of Two Worlds" (3rd issue).
1941 **754** 1300 p. multicoloured . 60 25

1989. 50th Anniv of Anti-tuberculosis National Committee.
1942 **755** 450 p. multicoloured . . 20 10

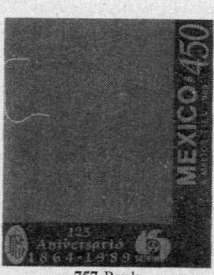

756 Mask of God Murcielago

1989.
1943 **756** 450 p. green, black & mve 20 10

758 Cortines

759 Man with Sparkler

1989. Birth Centenary of Adolfo Ruiz Cortines (President, 1952–58).
1945 **758** 450 p. multicoloured . . 20 10

1989. Christmas. Multicoloured.
1946 450 p. Type **759** 20 10
1947 450 p. People holding candles (horiz) 20 10

760 Emblem

1989. 50th Anniv of National Institute of Anthropology and History.
1948 **760** 450 p. gold, red & black 20 10

761 Steam Locomotive, Modern Train and Felipe Pescador

1989. 80th Anniv of Nationalization of Railways.
1949 **761** 450 p. multicoloured . . 20 10

762 Bridge

1990. Opening of Tampico Bridge.
1950 **762** 600 p. black, gold & red 20 10

763 Smiling Children

1990. Child Vaccination Campaign.
1951 **763** 700 p. multicoloured . . 25 10

764 People in Houses

1990. 11th General Population and Housing Census.
1952 **764** 700 p. green, yell & lt grn 25 10

765 Stamp under Magnifying Glass

1990. 10th Anniv of Mexican Philatelic Association.
1953 **765** 700 p. multicoloured . . 25 10

766 Archive

1990. Bicentenary of National Archive.
1954 **766** 700 p. blue 25 10

767 Emblem and "90"

1990. 1st International Poster Biennale.
1955 **767** 700 p. multicoloured . . 25 10

768 Messenger, 1790

1990. "Stamp World London 90" International Stamp Exhibition.
1956 **768** 700 p. yellow, red & black 25 10

769 Penny Black

1990. 150th Anniv of the Penny Black.
1957 **769** 700 p. black, red & gold 25 10

770 National Colours and Pope John Paul II

1990. Papal Visit.
1958 **770** 700 p. multicoloured . . 25 10

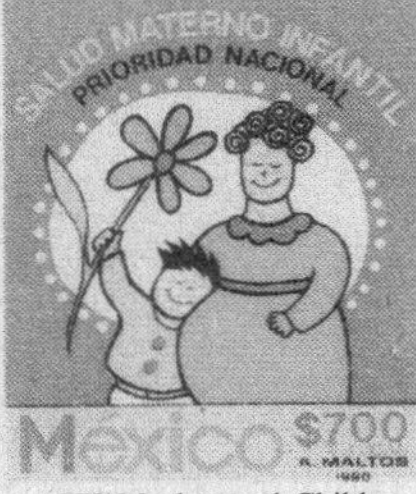

771 Church **772** Mother and Child

1990. 15th Travel Agents' Congress.
1959 **771** 700 p. multicoloured . . 25 10

1990. Mother and Child Health Campaign.
1960 **772** 700 p. multicoloured . . 25 10

773 Smoke Rings forming Birds **774** Globe as Tree

1990. World Anti-Smoking Day.
1961 **773** 700 p. multicoloured . . 25 10

1990. World Environment Day.
1962 **774** 700 p. multicoloured . . 25 10

775 Racing Car and Chequered Flag

1990. Mexico Formula One Grand Prix.
1963 **775** 700 p. black, red & green 25 10

776 Aircraft Tailfin

1990. 25th Anniv of Airports and Auxiliary Services.
1964 **776** 700 p. multicoloured . . 25 10

777 Family

1990. United Nations Anti-drugs Decade.
1965 **777** 700 p. multicoloured . . 25 10

778 Tree Trunk

1990. Forest Conservation.
1966 **778** 700 p. multicoloured . . 25 10

779 Emblem

1990. "Solidarity".
1967 **779** 700 p. multicoloured . . 25 10
See also No. 2047.

780 Columns and Native Decoration

1990. World Heritage Site. Oaxaca.
1968 **780** 700 p. multicoloured . . 25 10

781 Elegant Tern

1990. Conservation of Rasa Island, Gulf of California.
1969 **781** 700 p. grey, black & red 70 20

782 Institute Activities

1990. 25th Anniv of Mexican Petroleum Institute.
1970 **782** 700 p. blue and black . 25 10

783 National Colours, City Monuments and Runners

1990. 18th International Mexico City Marathon.
1971 **783** 700 p. black, red & green 25 10

784 Facade

1990. 50th Anniv of Colima University.
1972 **784** 700 p. multicoloured . . 25 10

785 Abstract

1990. Mexico City Consultative Council.
1973 **785** 700 p. multicoloured . . 25 10

786 Electricity Worker

1990. 30th Anniv of Nationalization of Electricity Industry.
1974 **786** 700 p. multicoloured . . 25 10

787 Violin and Bow

1990. 50th Death Anniv of Silvestre Revueltas (violinist).
1975 **787** 700 p. multicoloured . . 25 10

788 Building

1990. 450th Anniv of Campeche.
1976 **788** 700 p. multicoloured . . 25 15

789 Crossed Rifle and Pen **790** Emblem

1990. 80th Anniv of San Luis Plan.
1977 **789** 700 p. multicoloured . . 25 15

1990. 14th World Supreme Councils Conference.
1978 **790** 1500 p. multicoloured . . 55 35

791 Spanish Tower and Mexican Pyramid

1990. 500th Anniv of "Meeting of Two Worlds" (4th issue).
1979 **791** 700 p. multicoloured . . 25 15

792 Glass of Beer, Ear of Barley and Hop **793** Carving

1990. Centenary of Brewing Industry.
1980 **792** 700 p. multicoloured . . 25 15

1990. Bicentenary of Archaeology in Mexico.
1981 **793** 1500 p. multicoloured . . 55 35

794 Ball-game Field **795** Globe and Poinsettia

1990. 16th Central American and Caribbean Games. Multicoloured.
1982 750 p. Type **794** 30 20
1983 750 p. Amerindian ball-game player 30 20
1984 750 p. Amerindian ball-game player (different) (horiz) . 30 20
1985 750 p. Yutsil and Balam (mascots) (horiz) 30 20

1990. Christmas. Multicoloured.
1986 700 p. Type **795** 25 15
1987 700 p. Fireworks and candles 25 15

796 Dog (statuette)

1990. 50th Anniv of Mexican Canine Federation.
1988 **796** 700 p. multicoloured . . 25 15

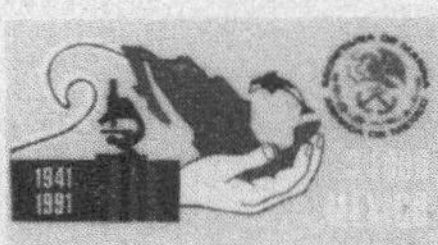

797 Microscope, Dolphin and Hand holding Map

1991. 50th Anniv of Naval Secretariat.
1989 **797** 1000 p. gold, black & bl 40 25

798 Means of Transport

1991. Accident Prevention.
1990 **798** 700 p. multicoloured . . 40 15

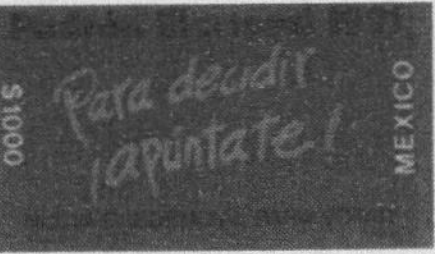

799 Products in Bags **800** "In order to Decide, Register"

1991. 15th Anniv of National Consumer Institute.
1991 **799** 1000 p. multicoloured . . 40 25

1991. Electoral Register.
1992 **800** 1000 p. orange, grn & blk 40 25

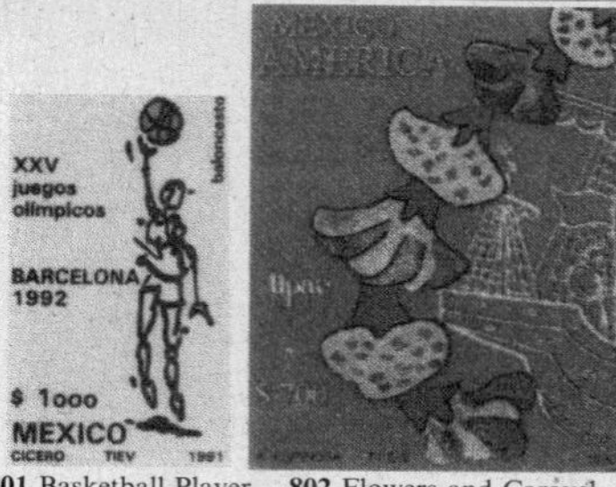

801 Basketball Player **802** Flowers and Caravel

1991. Olympic Games, Barcelona (1992). (1st issue).
1993 **801** 1000 p. black and yellow 40 25
See also Nos. 2050, 2057 and 2080/9.

1991. America (1990). Natural World. Mult.
1994 700 p. Type **802** 40 15
1995 700 p. Right half of caravel, parrot and flowers 40 15
Nos. 1994/5 were issued together, se-tenant, forming a composite design.

803 Children in Droplet

1991. Children's Month. Vaccination Campaign.
1996 **803** 1000 p. multicoloured . . 40 25

804 Map **805** Dove and Children

1991. World Post Day (1990).
1997 **804** 1500 p. multicoloured . . 55 35

1991. Children's Days for Peace and Development.
1998 **805** 1000 p. multicoloured . . 40 25

806 Dove **807** Mining

1991. Family Health and Unity.
1999 **806** 1000 p. multicoloured . . 40 25

1991. 500th Anniv of Mining.
2000 **807** 1000 p. multicoloured . . 40 25

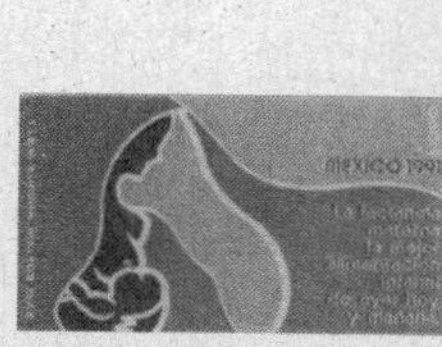

808 Mother feeding Baby **809** Emblem

1991. Breastfeeding Campaign.
2001 **808** 1000 p. buff, blue & brn 40 25

1991. 16th Tourism Fair, Acapulco.
2002 **809** 1000 p. green & dp green 40 25

810 Rotary Emblem and Independence Monument, Mexico City **811** "Communication"

1991. Rotary International Convention. "Let us Preserve the Planet Earth".
2003 **810** 1000 p. gold and blue . 40 25

1991. Centenary of Ministry of Transport and Communications (S.C.T.). Multicoloured.
2004 1000 p. Type **811** 40 35
2005 1000 p. Boeing 737 landing . 40 25
2006 1000 p. Facsimile machine . 40 25
2007 1000 p. Van 40 25
2008 1000 p. Satellites and Earth 40 25
2009 1000 p. Railway freight cars on bridge 40 25
2010 1000 p. Telephone users . . 40 25
2011 1000 p. Road bridge over road 40 25
2012 1000 p. Road bridge and cliffs 40 25
2013 1000 p. Stern of container ship and dockyard 40 25
2014 1000 p. Television camera and presenter 40 25
2015 1000 p. Front of truck at toll gate 40 25
2016 1000 p. Roadbuilding ("Solidarity") 40 25
2017 1500 p. Boeing 737 and control tower 55 35
2018 1500 p. Part of fax machine, transmitters and dish aerials on S.C.T. building 55 35
2019 1500 p. Satellite (horiz) . . . 55 35
2020 1500 p. Railway locomotives 55 35
2021 1500 p. S.C.T. building . . . 55 35
2022 1500 p. Road bridge over ravine 55 35
2023 1500 p. Bow of container ship and dockyard 55 35
2024 1500 p. Bus at toll gate . . . 55 35
2025 1500 p. Rear of truck and trailer at toll gate 55 35
Nos. 2005/25 were issued together, se-tenant, each block containing several composite designs.

812 Jaguar

1991. Lacandona Jungle Conservation.
2026 **812** 1000 p. black, orge & red 40 25

813 Driver and Car **814** Emblem and Left-hand Sections of Sun and Earth

1991. Mexico Formula 1 Grand Prix.
2027 **813** 1000 p. multicoloured . 40 25

1991. Total Eclipse of the Sun. Multicoloured.
2028 1000 p. Type **814** 40 25
2029 1000 p. Emblem and right-hand sections of sun and Earth 40 25
2030 1500 p. Emblem and centre of sun and Earth showing north and central America . . . 55 35
Nos. 2028/30 were issued together, se-tenant, forming a composite design.

815 "Solidarity" (Rufino Tamayo) **816** Bridge

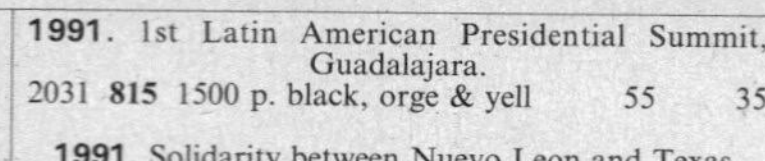

1991. 1st Latin American Presidential Summit, Guadalajara.
2031 **815** 1500 p. black, orge & yell 55 35

1991. Solidarity between Nuevo Leon and Texas.
2032 **816** 2000 p. multicoloured . . 1·10 75

817 Runners **819** Emblem

818 Cogwheel

1991. 9th Mexico City Marathon.
2033 **817** 1000 p. multicoloured . . 40 25

1991. 50th Anniv (1990) of National Chambers of Industry and Commerce.
2034 **818** 1500 p. multicoloured . . 55 35

1991. 55th Anniv of Federation Fiscal Tribunal.
2035 **819** 1000 p. silver and blue . . 40 25

820 National Colours forming Emblem

1991. "Solidarity–Let us Unite in order to Progress".
2036 **820** 1000 p. multicoloured . . 40 25

821 Dove with Letter **822** World Map

1991. World Post Day.
2037 **821** 1000 p. multicoloured . . 40 25

1991. 500th Anniv of "Meeting of Two Worlds" (5th issue).
2038 **822** 1000 p. multicoloured . . 40 25

823 Caravel, Sun and Trees

1991. America. Voyages of Discovery. Mult.
2039 1000 p. Type **823** 40 25
2040 1000 p. Storm cloud, caravel and broken snake 40 25

824 Flowers and Pots

1991. Christmas. Multicoloured.
2041 1000 p. Type **824** 40 25
2042 1000 p. Children with decoration 40 25

825 Abstract

1991. Carlos Merida (artist) Commemoration.
2043 **825** 1000 p. multicoloured . . 40 25

826 Score and Portrait

1991. Death Bicentenary of Wolfgang Amadeus Mozart (composer).
2044 **826** 1000 p. multicoloured . . 40 25

827 Kidney Beans and Maize

1991. Self-sufficiency in Kidney Beans and Maize.
2045 **827** 1000 p. multicoloured . . 40 25

828 City Plan

1991. 450th Anniv of Morelia.
2046 **828** 1000 p. brown, stone and red 40 25

1991. "Solidarity". As No. 1967 but new value.
2047 **779** 1000 p. multicoloured . . 40 25

829 Merida

1992. 450th Anniv of Merida.
2048 **829** 1300 p. multicoloured . . 60 40

830 Colonnade

1992. Bicentenary of Engineering Training in Mexico.
2049 **830** 1300 p. blue and red . . 60 40

831 Horse Rider

1992. Olympic Games, Barcelona (2nd issue).
2050 **831** 2000 p. multicoloured . . 90 60

MINIMUM PRICE

The minimum price quoted is 10p which represents a handling charge rather than a basis for valuing common stamps. For further notes about prices, see introductory pages.

832 City Arms

1992. 450th Anniv of Guadalajara. Multicoloured.
2051 1300 p. Type **832** 60 40
2052 1300 p. "Guadalajara Town Hall" (Jorge Navarro) . . 60 40
2053 1300 p. "Guadalajara Cathedral" (Gabriel Flores) 60 40
2054 1900 p. "Founding of Guadalajara" (Rafael Zamarripa) 85 55
2055 1900 p. Anniversary emblem (Ignacio Vazquez) 85 55

833 Children and Height Gauge **834** Olympic Torch and Rings

1992. Child Health Campaign.
2056 **833** 2000 p. multicoloured . . 90 60

1992. Olympic Games, Barcelona (3rd issue).
2057 **834** 2000 p. multicoloured . . 90 60

835 Horse and Racing Car

1992. "500th Anniv of the Wheel and the Horse in America". Mexico Formula 1 Grand Prix.
2058 **835** 1300 p. multicoloured . . 60 40

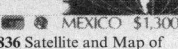

836 Satellite and Map of Americas **837** Human Figure and Cardiograph

1992. "Americas Telecom '92" Telecommunications Exhibition.
2059 **836** 1300 p. multicoloured . . 60 40

1992. World Health Day.
2060 **837** 1300 p. black, red & blue 60 40

838 Emblem

1992. 60th Anniv of Military Academy.
2061 **838** 1300 p. red, yellow & blk 60 40

839 "Inspiration of Christopher Columbus" (Jose Maria Obregon) **840** Complex

1992. 500th Anniv of "Meeting of Two Worlds" (6th issue). "Granada 92" International Stamp Exhibition.
2062 1300 p. Type **839** 60 40
2063 1300 p. "Racial Encounter" (Jorge Gonazalez Camarena) 60 40
2064 2000 p. "Origin of the Sky" (Selden Codex) 90 60
2065 2000 p. "Quetzalcoatl and Tezcatlipoca" (Borhomico Codex) 90 60
2066 2000 p. "From Spaniard and Indian, mestizo" 90 60

1992. National Medical Centre.
2068 **840** 1300 p. multicoloured . 60 40

841 Children, Dove and Globe **842** New-born Baby

1992. Children's Rights.
2069 **841** 1300 p. multicoloured . 60 40

1992. Traditional Childbirth.
2070 **842** 1300 p. multicoloured . 60 40

1992. "World Columbian Stamp Expo '92", Chicago. Nos. 2062/6 optd **WORLD COLUMBIAN STAMP EXPO '92 MAY 22-31, 1992 - CHICAGO** and emblem.
2071 1300 p. mult (No. 2062) . . 50 35
2072 1300 p. mult (No. 2063) . . 50 35
2073 2000 p. mult (No. 2064) . . 80 55
2074 2000 p. mult (No. 2065) . . 80 55
2075 2000 p. mult (No. 2066) . . 80 55

845 Arms of Colleges

1992. Bicentenary of Mexico Notary College.
2078 **845** 1300 p. multicoloured . 50 35

846 Trees and Cacti

1992. Tree Day.
2079 **846** 1300 p. multicoloured . 50 35

847 Boxing **848** Athlete

1992. Olympic Games, Barcelona (4th issue). Mult.
2080 1300 p. Type **847** 50 35
2081 1300 p. High jumping . . . 50 35
2082 1300 p. Fencing 50 35
2083 1300 p. Shooting 50 35
2084 1300 p. Gymnastics 50 35
2085 1900 p. Rowing 75 50
2086 1900 p. Running 75 50
2087 1900 p. Football 75 50
2088 1900 p. Swimming 75 50
2089 2000 p. Equestrian 80 55

1992. 10th Mexico City Marathon.
2091 **848** 1300 p. multicoloured . 50 35

849 Emblem

1992. "Solidarity".
2092 **849** 1300 p. multicoloured . 50 35

851 Television, Map and Radio

1992. 50th Anniv of National Chamber of Television and Radio Industry.
2094 **851** 1300 p. multicoloured . . 50 35

852 Letter orbiting Globe

1992. World Post Day.
2095 **852** 1300 p. multicoloured . . 50 35

853 Satellite above South and Central America and Flags

1992. American Cadena Communications System.
2096 **853** 2000 p. multicoloured . . 80 55

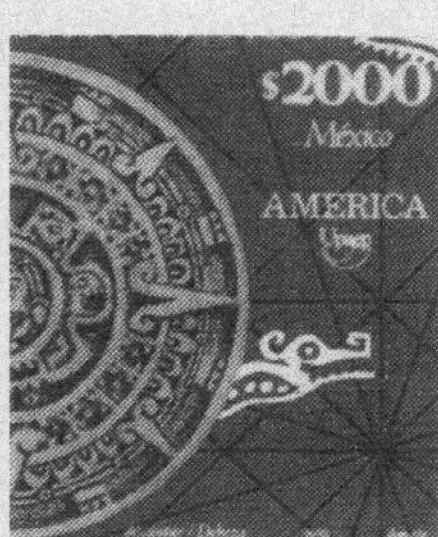

854 Gold Compass Rose

1992. America. 500th Anniv of Discovery of America by Columbus. Multicoloured.
2097 2000 p. Type **854** 80 55
2098 2000 p. Compass rose (different) and fish 80 55
Nos. 2097/8 were issued together, se-tenant, forming a composite design.

855 Scroll

1992. 400th Anniv of San Luis Potosi.
2099 **855** 1300 p. black and mauve 50 35

856 Berrendos Deer

1992. Conservation.
2100 **856** 1300 p. multicoloured . . 50 35

857 Schooner, Landing Ship, Emblem and Sailors **858** Christmas Tree, Children and Crib

1992. Navy Day.
2101 **857** 1300 p. multicoloured . . 50 35

1992. Christmas. Children's Drawings. Mult.
2102 1300 p. Type **858** 50 35
2103 2000 p. Street celebration (horiz) 80 55

Currency Reform. 1 (new) peso = 1000 (old) pesos.

859 Anniversary Emblem **860** Emblem

1993. 50th Anniv of Mexican Social Security Institute (1st issue).
2104 **859** 1 p. 50 green, gold & blk 60 40
See also Nos. 2110 and 2152/3.

1993. Centenary of Mexican Opthalmological Society.
2105 **860** 1 p. 30 multicoloured . . 50 35

861 Children **862** Society Arms and Founders

1993. Children's Month.
2106 **861** 1 p. 30 multicoloured . . 50 35

1993. 160th Anniv of Mexican Geographical and Statistical Society.
2107 **862** 1 p. 30 multicoloured . . 50 35

863 1824 Constitution **864** Gomez, Children and Hospital

1993. 150th Death Anniv of Miguel Ramos Arizpe, "Father of Federalism".
2108 **863** 1 p. 30 multicoloured . . 50 35

1993. 50th Anniv of Federico Gomez Children's Hospital.
2109 **864** 1 p. 30 multicoloured . . 50 35

865 Doctor with Child

1993. 50th Anniv of Mexican Social Security Institute (2nd issue). Medical Services.
2110 **865** 1 p. 30 multicoloured . . 50 35

866 Mother feeding Baby

1993. "Health begins at Home".
2111 **866** 1 p. 30 multicoloured . . 50 35

867 Seal and Map

1993. Upper Gulf of California Nature Reserve.
2112 **867** 1 p. 30 multicoloured . . 50 35

868 Cantinflas

1993. Mexican Film Stars. Mario Moreno (Cantinflas).
2113 **868** 1 p. 30 black and blue . 50 35
See also Nos. 2156/60.

869 Campeche

1993. Tourism. Multicoloured.

2114	90 c. Type **869**	35	25
2115	1 p. Guanajuato	40	25
2116	1 p. 30 Colima	50	35
2117	1 p. 90 Michoacan (vert)	75	50
2118	2 p. Coahuila	80	55
2119	2 p. 20 Queretaro	90	60
2120	2 p. 50 Sonora	1·00	65
2121	2 p. 80 Zacatecas (vert)	1·10	75
2122	3 p. 70 Sinaloa	1·50	1·00
2123	4 p. 40 Yucatan	1·75	1·10
2124	4 p. 80 Chiapas	1·90	1·25
2125	6 p. Mexico City	2·40	1·60

870 Dr. Maximiliano Ruiz Castaneda

1993. 50th Anniv of Health Service. Multicoloured.

2126	1 p. 30 Type **870**	50	35
2127	1 p. 30 Dr. Bernardo Sepulveda Gutierrez	50	35
2128	1 p. 30 Dr. Ignacio Chavez Sanchez	50	35
2129	1 p. 30 Dr. Mario Salazar Mallen	50	35
2130	1 p. 30 Dr. Gustavo Baz Prada	50	35

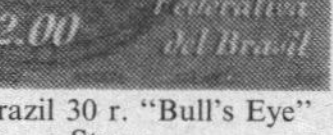

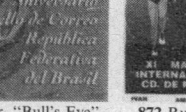

871 Brazil 30 r. "Bull's Eye" Stamp

872 Runners

1993. 150th Anniv of First Brazilian Stamps.
2131 **871** 2 p. multicoloured . . . 80 55

1993. 11th Mexico City Marathon.
2132 **872** 1 p. 30 multicoloured . . 50 35

873 Emblem

874 Open Book and Symbols

1993. "Solidarity".
2133 **873** 1 p. 30 multicoloured . . 50 35

1993. 50th Anniv of Monterrey Institute of Technology and Higher Education. Multicoloured.
2134 1 p. 30 Type **874** 50 35
2135 2 p. Buildings and mountains 80 55
Nos. 2134/5 were issued together, se-tenant, forming a composite design.

875 Cogwheels and Emblem

876 Torreon

1993. 75th Anniv of Concamin.
2136 **875** 1 p. 30 multicoloured . 50 35

1993. Centenary of Torreon.
2137 **876** 1 p. 30 multicoloured . 50 35

877 Emblem

1993. "Europalia 93 Mexico" Festival.
2138 **877** 2 p. multicoloured . . . 80 55

878 Globe in Envelope

879 Gen. Guadalupe Victoria

1993. World Post Day.
2139 **878** 2 p. multicoloured . . . 80 55

1993. 150th Death Anniv of General Manuel Guadalupe Victoria (first President, 1824–28).
2140 **879** 1 p. 30 multicoloured . . 50 35

880 Emblem

881 Hands protecting Foetus

1993. National Civil Protection System and International Day for Reduction of Natural Disasters.
2141 **880** 1 p. 30 red, blk and yell 50 35

1993. United Nations Decade of International Law.
2142 **881** 2 p. multicoloured . . . 80 55

882 Torch Carrier

1993. 20th National Wheelchair Games.
2143 **882** 1 p. 30 multicoloured . 50 35

883 Peon y Contreras

1993. 150th Birth Anniv of Jose Peon y Contreras (poet, dramatist and founder of National Romantic Theatre).
2144 **883** 1 p. 30 violet and black 50 35

884 Peacock

885 Presents around Trees

1993. America. Endangered Birds. Multicoloured.
2145 2 p. Type **884** 80 55
2146 2 p. Quetzal on branch (horiz) 80 55

1993. Christmas. Multicoloured.
2147 1 p. 30 Type **885** 50 35
2148 1 p. 30 Three wise men (horiz) 50 35

886 Satellites orbiting Earth

1993. "Solidarity".
2149 **886** 1 p. 30 multicoloured . . 50 35

887 School and Arms

1993. 125th Anniv of National Preparatory School.
2150 **887** 1 p. 30 multicoloured . . 50 35

888 Emblem on Map

1993. 55th Anniv of Municipal Workers Trade Union.
2151 **888** 1 p. 30 multicoloured . . 50 35

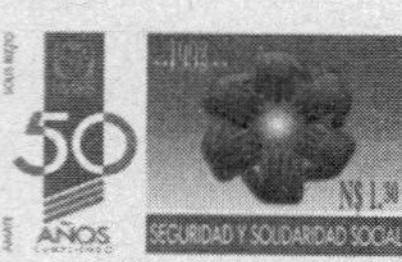

889 Hands

1993. 50th Anniv of Mexican Social Security Institute (3rd issue). Multicoloured.
2152 1 p. 30 Type **889** (social security) 50 35
2153 1 p. 30 Ball, building blocks, child's painting and dummy (day nurseries) 50 35

890 Mezcala Solidarity Bridge

1993. Tourism. Multicoloured.
2154 1 p. 30 Type **890** 50 35
2155 1 p. 30 Mexico City–Acapulco motorway 50 35

1993. Mexican Film Stars. As T **868**.

2156	1 p. 30 black and blue	50	35
2157	1 p. 30 black and orange	50	35
2158	1 p. 30 black and green	50	35
2159	1 p. 30 black and violet	50	35
2160	1 p. 30 black and pink	50	35

DESIGNS:—No, 2156, Pedro Armendariz in "Juan Charrasqueado"; 2157, Maria Felix in "The Lover"; 2158, Pedro Infante in "Necesito dinero"; 2159, Jorge Negrete in "It is not enough to be a Peasant"; 2160, Dolores del Rio in "Flor Silvestre".

891 Estefania Castaneda Nunez

1994. 72nd Anniv of Secretariat of Public Education. Educationists. Multicoloured.

2161	1 p. 30 Type **891**	50	35
2162	1 p. 30 Lauro Aguirre Espinosa	50	35
2163	1 p. 30 Rafael Ramirez Castaneda	50	35
2164	1 p. 30 Moises Saenz Garza	50	35
2165	1 p. 30 Gregorio Torres Quintero	50	35
2166	1 p. 30 Jose Vasconcelos	50	35
2167	1 p. 30 Rosaura Zapato Cano	50	35

892 Zapata (after H. Velarde)

893 Emblem and Worker

1994. 75th Death Anniv of Emiliano Zapata (revolutionary).
2168 **892** 1 p. 30 multicoloured . . 50 35

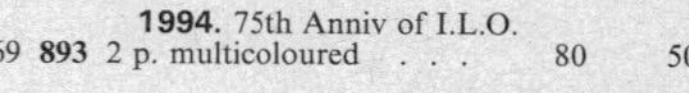

1994. 75th Anniv of I.L.O.
2169 **893** 2 p. multicoloured . . . 80 50

894 Map and Emblem

895 "Earth and Communication" (frieze, detail)

1994. 50th Anniv of National Schools Building Programme Committee.
2170 **894** 1 p. 30 multicoloured . . 50 35

1994. 3rd Death Anniv of Francisco Zuniga (sculptor).
2171 **895** 1 p. 30 multicoloured . . 50 35

896 Flower and Children

1994. Children's Organization for Peace and Development.
2172 **896** 1 p. 30 multicoloured . . 50 35

897 Greater Flamingo

1994. DUMAC Nature Protection Organization.
2173 **897** 1 p. 30 multicoloured . . 50 35

898 Children and Silhouette of Absentee

1994. Care and Control of Minors.
2174 **898** 1 p. 30 black and green . 50 35

899 Man and Letters **900** Route Map

1994. 34th World Advertising Congress, Cancun.
2175 **899** 2 p. multicoloured . . . 80 35

1994. 50th Anniv of National Association of Importers and Exporters.
2176 **900** 1 p. 30 multicoloured . . 50 35

901 Head and Emblem

1994. International Telecommunications Day.
2177 **901** 2 p. multicoloured . . . 80 55

902 Animals

1994. Yumka Wildlife Centre, Villahermosa.
2178 **902** 1 p. 30 multicoloured . . 50 35

903 Town Centre

1994. U.N.E.S.C.O. World Heritage Site, Zacatecas.
2179 **903** 1 p. 30 multicoloured . . 50 35

EXPRESS LETTER STAMPS

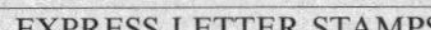

E 55 Express Service Messenger

1919.
E445 **E 55** 20 c. black and red . . 35 15

E 95

1934.
E536 **E 95** 10 c. blue and red . . 15 30

E 121 Indian Archer **E 222**

1934. New President's Assumption of Office. Imprint "OFICINA IMPRESORA DE HACIENDA–MEXICO".
E581 **E 121** 10 c. violet . . . . . 1·00 20

1938. Imprint "TALLERES DE IMP. DE EST. Y VALORES-MEXICO".
E610 **E 121** 10 c. violet 55 20
E731 20 c. orange 25 30

1940. Optd **1940.**
E665 **E 55** 20 c. black and red . . 20 15

1950.
E860 **E 222** 25 c. orange 20 10
E910 – 60 c. green . . . . . 1·10 35
DESIGN: 60 c. Hands and letter.

E 244

E 245

1956.
E 954 **E 244** 35 c. purple 25 10
E1065 50 c. green 45 10
E 956 **E 245** 80 c. red 50 80
E1066 1 p. 20 lilac . . . . 1·50 75
E1346p **E 244** 2 p. orange 20 15
E1346q **E 245** 5 p. blue 20 60

E 468 Watch Face

1979.
E1373 **E 468** 2 p. black & orange 10 60

INSURED LETTER STAMPS

IN 125 Safe **IN 222** P.O. Treasury Vault

1935. Inscr as in Type IN **125**.
IN583 – 10 c. red . . . . . 1·10 30
IN733 – 50 c. blue 75 25
IN734 **IN 125** 1 p. green 75 35
DESIGNS: 10 c. Bundle of insured letters; 50 c. Registered mailbag.

1950.
IN911 **IN 222** 20 c. blue 15 10
IN912 40 c. purple 15 10
IN913 1 p. green 20 10
IN914 5 p. green and blue 65 60
IN915 10 p. blue and red 3·00 1·50

IN 469 Padlock

1976.
IN1374 **IN 469** 40 c. black & turq 10 10
IN1522 1 p. black & turq 10 10
IN1376 2 p. black and blue 10 10
IN1380 5 p. black & turq 10 10
IN1524 10 p. black & turq 10 10
IN1525 20 p. black & turq 10 10
IN1383 50 p. black & turq 95 95
IN1384 100 p. black & turq 60 60
The 5, 10, 20 p. exist with the padlock either 31 or 32½ mm high.

OFFICIAL STAMPS

O 18 Hidalgo

1884. No value shown.
O156 **O 18** Red 30 20
O157 Brown 15 10
O158 Orange 80 15
O159 Green 30 15
O160 Blue 45 35

1894. Stamps of 1895 handstamped **OFICIAL**.
O231 **19** 1 c. green . . . . 3·75 1·25
O232 2 c. red . . . . 4·50 1·25
O233 3 c. brown . . . . 3·75 1·25
O234 **20** 4 c. orange . . . . . . 5·50 2·50
O235 **21** 5 c. blue . . . . 7·50 2·50
O236 **22** 10 c. purple . . . . . . 7·00 50
O237 **20** 12 c. olive . . . . 15·00 6·25
O238 **22** 15 c. blue . . . . 8·75 3·75
O239 20 c. red . . . . 8·75 3·75
O240 50 c. mauve . . . . . . 19·00 9·50
O241 **23** 1 p. brown . . . . 48·00 19·00
O242 5 p. red . . . . £110 55·00
O243 10 p. blue £190 £100

1899. Stamps of 1899 handstamped **OFICIAL**.
O276 **27** 1 c. green . . . . 9·50 60
O286 1 c. purple . . . . 8·75 95
O277 2 c. red . . . . 12·50 95
O287 2 c. green . . . . 8·75 95
O278 3 c. brown . . . . 12·50 60
O288 4 c. red . . . . 16·00 45
O279 5 c. blue . . . . 12·50 1·10
O289 5 c. orange . . . . 16·00 3·25
O280 10 c. brown and purple 16·00 1·40
O290 10 c. orange and blue . . 19·00 95
O281 15 c. purple and lavender 16·00 1·40
O282 20 c. blue and red . . . . 19·00 45
O283 **28** 50 c. black and purple . . 38·00 6·25
O291 50 c. black and red . . . 48·00 6·25
O284 **29** 1 p. black and blue . . . 80·00 6·25
O285 **30** 5 p. black and red . . . . 50·00 19·00

1911. Independence stamps optd **OFICIAL**.
O301 **32** 1 c. purple . . . . 1·25 1·25
O302 – 2 c. green 75 45
O303 – 3 c. brown . . . . 1·25 45
O304 – 4 c. red . . . . 1·90 45
O305 – 5 c. orange . . . . 3·25 1·75
O306 – 10 c. orange and blue . . 1·90 45
O307 – 15 c. lake and slate . . . 3·25 2·00
O308 – 20 c. blue and lake . . . 2·50 45
O309 **40** 50 c. black and brown . . 8·75 3·75
O310 – 1 p. black and blue . . . 15·00 6·25
O311 – 5 p. black and red . . . . 55·00 32·00

1915. Stamps of 1915 optd **OFICIAL**.
O321 **43** 1 c. violet 30 55
O322 **44** 2 c. green 30 55
O323 **45** 3 c. brown 30 55
O324 4 c. red 30 55
O325 5 c. orange 30 55
O326 10 c. blue 30 55

1915. Stamps of 1915 optd **OFICIAL**.
O318 **46** 40 c. grey . . . . 2·50 2·75
O455 40 c. mauve . . . . 3·75 1·90
O319 **47** 1 p. grey and brown . . . 3·25 3·75
O456 1 p. grey and blue . . . . 9·50 6·25
O320 **48** 5 p. blue and lake . . . . 19·00 16·00
O457 5 p. grey and green . . . 55·00 95·00

1916. Nos. O301/11 optd with T **49**.
O358 **32** 1 c. purple . . . . 1·90
O359 – 2 c. green 30
O360 – 3 c. brown 35
O361 – 4 c. red . . . . 2·00
O362 – 5 c. orange 35
O363 – 10 c. orange and blue . . 35
O364 – 15 c. lake and slate . . . 35
O365 – 20 c. blue and lake . . . 40
O366 **40** 50 c. black and brown . 55·00
O367 – 1 p. black and blue . . . 3·25
O368 – 5 p. black and red . . . £1600

1918. Stamps of 1917 optd **OFICIAL**.
O424 **53** 1 c. violet . . . . 1·25 60
O446 1 c. grey 30 20
O447 – 2 c. green 20 20
O448 – 3 c. brown 25 20
O449 – 4 c. red . . . . 3·75 45
O450 – 5 c. blue 20 20
O451 – 10 c. blue 30 15
O452 – 20 c. lake . . . . 2·50 2·50
O454 – 30 c. black . . . . 3·75 1·40

1923. No. 416 optd **OFICIAL**.
O485 10 p. black and brown . . . 60·00 95·00

1923. Stamps of 1923 optd **OFICIAL**.
O471 **59** 1 c. brown 20 20
O473 **60** 2 c. red 25 25
O475 **61** 3 c. brown 55 40
O461 **62** 4 c. green . . . . 1·90 1·90
O476 **63** 4 c. green 40 40
O477 5 c. orange 70 65
O489 **74** 8 c. orange . . . . 3·75 2·50
O479 **66** 10 c. lake 55 55
O480 **65** 20 c. blue . . . . 3·25 2·50
O464 **64** 30 c. green 35 25
O467 **68** 50 c. brown 55 55
O469 **69** 1 p. blue and lake . . . . 4·75 4·75

1929. Air. Optd **OFICIAL**.
O501 **80** 5 c. blue (roul) 45 25
O502 **81** 20 c. violet 55 55
O492 **58** 25 c. sepia and lake . . . 3·50 2·75
O490 25 c. sepia and green . . . 1·75 1·25

1929. Air. As 1926 Postal Congress stamp optd **HABILITADO Servicio Oficial Aereo.**
O493 **70** 2 c. black . . . . 26·00 26·00
O494 – 4 c. black . . . . 26·00 26·00
O495 **70** 5 c. black . . . . 26·00 26·00
O496 – 10 c. black . . . . 26·00 26·00
O497 **72** 20 c. black . . . . 26·00 26·00
O498 30 c. black . . . . 26·00 26·00
O499 40 c. black . . . . 26·00 26·00
O500 **73** 1 p. black £950 £950

O 85

1930. Air.
O503 **O 85** 20 c. grey . . . . . . 2·75 2·75
O504 35 c. violet 40 95
O505 40 c. blue and brown 50 90
O506 70 c. sepia and violet 50 95

1931. Air. Surch **HABILITADO Quince centavos.**
O515 **O 85** 15 c. on 20 c. grey . . 45 45

1932. Air. Optd **SERVICIO OFICIAL** in one line.
O532 **80** 10 c. violet (perf or roul) 30 30
O533 15 c. red (perf or roul) . 85 85
O534 20 c. sepia (roul) 85 85
O531 **58** 50 c. red and blue 90 70

1932. Stamps of 1923 optd **SERVICIO OFICIAL** in two lines.
O535 **59** 1 c. brown 15 15
O536 **60** 2 c. red 10 10
O537 **61** 3 c. brown 95 95
O538 **63** 4 c. green . . . . 3·25 2·50
O539 5 c. red . . . . 3·75 2·50
O540 **66** 10 c. lake . . . . 1·10 75
O541 **65** 20 c. blue . . . . 4·75 3·25
O544 **64** 30 c. green . . . . 2·50 95
O545 **46** 40 c. mauve . . . . 4·75 1·90
O546 **68** 50 c. brown 80 95
O547 **69** 1 p. blue and lake 95 95

1933. Air. Optd **SERVICIO OFICIAL** in two lines.
O553 **58** 50 c. red and blue . . . 1·00 70

1933. Air. Optd **SERVICIO OFICIAL** in two lines.
O548 **80** 5 c. blue (No. 476a) . . . 30 30
O549 10 c. violet (No. 477) . . 30 30
O550 20 c. sepia (No. 479) . . 30 60
O551 50 c. lake (No. 481) . . . 40 95

1934. Optd **OFICIAL**.
O565 **92** 15 c. blue 35 35

1938. Nos. 561/71 optd **OFICIAL**.
O622 1 c. orange . . . . 70 1·25
O623 2 c. green 45 45
O624 4 c. red 45 45
O625 10 c. violet 45 80
O626 20 c. blue 55 80
O627 30 c. red . . . . 70 1·25
O628 40 c. brown . . . . 70 1·25
O629 50 c. black . . . . 1·00 1·00
O630 1 p. red and brown . . . . 2·50 3·75

PARCEL POST STAMPS

P 167 Mail Train

1941.
P732 **P 167** 10 c. red . . . . . . 1·75 40
P733 20 c. violet . . . . . 2·00 50

P 228 Mail Train

1951.

P916 P 228 10 c. pink . . . . . . 1·25 15
P917 20 c. violet . . . . . 1·75 25

POSTAGE DUE STAMPS

D 32

1908.

D282 D 32 1 c. blue . . . . 1·00 1·00
D283 2 c. blue . . . . 1·00 1·00
D284 4 c. blue . . . . 1·00 1·00
D285 5 c. blue . . . . 1·00 1·100
D286 10 c. blue . . . . . . 1·00 1·00

MICRONESIA Pt. 22

A group of islands in the Pacific, from 1899 to 1914 part of the German Caroline Islands. Occupied by the Japanese in 1914 the islands were from 1920 a Japanese mandated territory, and from 1947 part of the United States Trust Territory of the Pacific Islands, using United States stamps. Micronesia assumed control of its postal services in 1984.

100 cents = 1 dollar

1 Yap

1984. Inauguration of Postal Independence. Maps. Multicoloured.

1 20 c. Type **1** 60 45
2 20 c. Truk 60 45
3 20 c. Pohnpei 60 45
4 20 c. Kosrae 60 45

2 Fernandez de Quiros

3 Boeing 727-100

1984.

5 2 1 c. blue 10 10
6 – 2 c. brown 10 10
7 – 3 c. blue 10 10
8 – 4 c. green 10 10
9 – 5 c. brown and olive 10 10
10 – 10 c. purple 15 10
11 – 13 c. blue 20 10
11a – 15 c. red 20 10
12 – 17 c. brown 25 10
13 2 19 c. purple 30 10
14 – 20 c. green 30 10
14a – 22 c. green 30 15
14b – 25 c. orange 30 15
15 – 30 c. red 45 15
15a – 36 c. blue 50 20
16 – 37 c. violet 50 20
16a – 45 c. green 60 30
17 – 50 c. brown and sepia . . . 80 35
18 – $1 olive . . . . 1·50 85
19 – $2 blue . . . . 3·00 1·50
20 – $5 brown . . . . 8·00 4·50
20a – $10 blue . . . . 15·00 11·00

DESIGNS: 2, 20 c. Louis Duperrey; 3, 30 c. Fyodor Lutke; 4, 37 c. Jules Dumont d'Urville; 5 c. Men's house, Yap; 10, 45 c. Sleeping Lady (mountains), Kosrae; 13, 15 c. Liduduhriap waterfall, Pohnpei; 17, 25 c. Tonachau Peak, Truk; 22, 36 c. "Senyavin" (full-rigged sailing ship); 50 c. Devil mask, Truk; $1 Sokehs Rock, Pohnpei; $2 Outrigger canoes, Kosrae; $5 Stone money, Yap; $10 Official seal.

1984. Air. Multicoloured.

21 28 c. Type **3** 55 30
22 35 c. Grumman SA-16 Albatros flying boat 70 50
23 40 c. Consolidated PBY-5A Catalina amphibian 90 60

4 Truk Post Office

1984. "Ausipex 84" International Stamp Exhibition, Melbourne. Multicoloured.

24 20 c. Type **4** (postage) 50 20
25 28 c. German Caroline Islands 1919 3 pf. yacht stamp (air) 60 40
26 35 c. German 1900 20 pf. stamp optd for Caroline Islands . . 70 50
27 40 c. German Caroline Islands 1915 5 m. yacht stamp . . . 80 65

5 Baby in Basket

1984. Christmas. Multicoloured.

28 20 c. Type **5** (postage) 50 25
29 28 c. Open book showing Christmas scenes (air) . . . 60 40
30 35 c. Palm tree decorated with lights 70 50
31 40 c. Women preparing food . 80 65

6 U.S.S. "Jamestown" (warship)

1985. Ships.

32 6 22 c. black & brn (postage) 65 35
33 – 33 c. black and lilac (air) . . 85 50
34 – 39 c. black and green . . . . 1·00 70
35 – 44 c. black and red . . . . 1·40 85

DESIGNS: 33 c. "L'Astrolabe" (D'Urville's ship); 39 c. "La Coquille" (Duperrey's ship); 44 c. "Shenandoah" (Confederate warship).

7 Lelu Protestant Church, Kosrae

1985. Christmas.

36 7 22 c black and orange (postage) 70 30
37 – 33 c. black and violet (air) . 95 50
38 – 44 c. black and green . . . . 1·50 70

DESIGNS: 33 c. Dublon Protestant Church; 44 c. Pohnpei Catholic Church.

8 "Noddy Tern"

1985. Birth Bicentenary of John J. Audubon (ornithologist). Multicoloured.

39 22 c. Type **8** (postage) 70 50
40 22 c. "Turnstone" 70 50
41 22 c. "Golden Plover" 70 50
42 22 c. "Black-bellied Plover" . 70 50
43 44 c. "Sooty Tern" (air) . . . 1·25 80

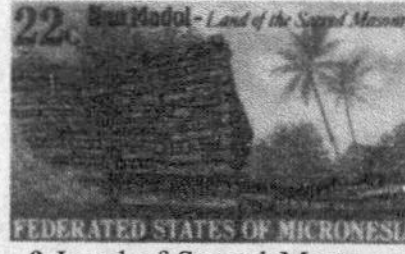

9 Land of Sacred Masonry

1985. Nan Madol, Pohnpei. Multicoloured.

44 22 c. Type **9** (postage) 45 25
45 33 c. Nan Tauas inner courtyard (air) 60 45
46 39 c. Nan Tauas outer wall . . 75 60
47 44 c. Nan Tauas burial vault . . 90 70

10 Doves, "LOVE" and Hands

12 Bully Hayes

1986. Anniversaries and Events. Multicoloured.

48 22 c. Type **10** (Interntional Peace Year) 60 35
49 44 c. Halley's comet . . . . . 1·40 80
50 44 c. "Trienza" (cargo liner) arriving at jetty (40th anniv of return of Nauruans from Truk) 1·40 80

1986. Nos. 1/4 surch.

51 22 c. on 20 c. Type **1** 55 45
52 22 c. on 20 c. Truk 55 45
53 22 c. on 20 c. Pohnpei 55 45
54 22 c. on 20 c. Kosrae 55 45

1986. "Ameripex 86" International Stamp Exhibition, Chicago. Bully Hayes (buccaneer). Multicoloured.

55 22 c. Type **12** (postage) 50 30
56 33 c. Angelo (crew member) forging Hawaii 5 c. blue stamp (air) 65 50
57 39 c. "Leonora" sinking off Kosrae 75 60
58 44 c. Hayes escaping capture on Kosrae 95 75
59 75 c. Cover of book "Bully Hayes, Buccaneer" by Louis Becke 1·50 1·25

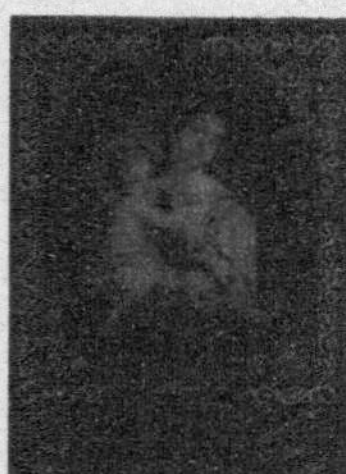
13 "Madonna and Child"

1986. Christmas. "Madonna and Child" Paintings.

61 – 5 c. multicoloured (postage) 15 10
62 – 22 c. multicoloured 70 30
63 – 33 c. multicoloured (air) . . 95 65
64 13 44 c. multicoloured . . . . . 1·25 1·00

14 Passports on Globe

1986. 1st Micronesian Passport.

65 14 22 c. blue, black and yellow 60 35

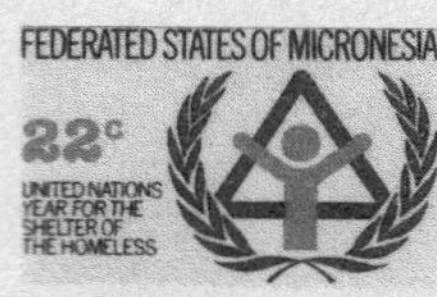

15 Emblem (International Year of Shelter for the Homeless)

1987. Anniversaries and Events.

66 15 22 c. blue, red and black (postage) 35 30
67 – 33 c. green, red and black (air) 50 40
68 – 39 c. blue, black and red . . 60 50
69 – 44 c. blue, red and black . . 75 60

DESIGNS: 33 c. Dollar sign (bicentenary of dollar currency); 39 c. Space capsule (25th anniv of first American to orbit Earth); 44 c. "200 USA" (bicentenary of US constitution).

16 Archangel Gabriel appearing to Mary

1987. Christmas. Multicoloured.

71 22 c. Type **16** (postage) 40 30
72 33 c. Joseph praying and Mary with baby Jesus (air) 60 45
73 39 c. Shepherds with their sheep 75 60
74 44 c. Wise men 90 75

17 Spanish Missionary and Flag

1988. Micronesian History. Multicoloured.

75 22 c. Type **17** (postage) 50 35
76 22 c. Natives producing copra and German flag 50 35
77 22 c. School pupils and Japanese flag 50 35
78 22 c. General store and U.S. flag 50 35
79 44 c. Traditional boatbuilding and fishing skills (air) . . . . . 1·00 75
80 44 c. Welcoming tourists from Douglas DC-10 airliner and divers investigating World War II wreckage . . . . 1·00 75

18 Ponape White Eye

19 Marathon

1988. Birds. Multicoloured.

81 3 c. Type **18** (postage) 10 10
82 14 c. Truk monarch 25 10
83 22 c. Ponape starling 35 20
84 33 c. Truk white eye (air) . . . 55 35
85 44 c. Blue-faced parrot finch . 75 60
86 $1 Yap monarch . . . . 1·50 1·25

1988. Olympic Games, Seoul. Multicoloured.

87 25 c. Type **19** 45 25
88 25 c. Hurdling 45 25
89 45 c. Basketball 70 55
90 45 c. Volleyball 70 55

20 Girls decorating Tree

1988. Christmas. Multicoloured.

91 25 c. Type **20** 45 30
92 25 c. Dove with mistletoe in beak and children holding decorations 45 30
93 25 c. Boy in native clothing and girl in floral dress sitting at base of tree 45 30
94 25 c. Boy in T-shirt and shorts and girl in native clothing sitting at base of tree 45 30

Nos. 91/4 were printed together in blocks of four, se-tenant, forming a composite design.

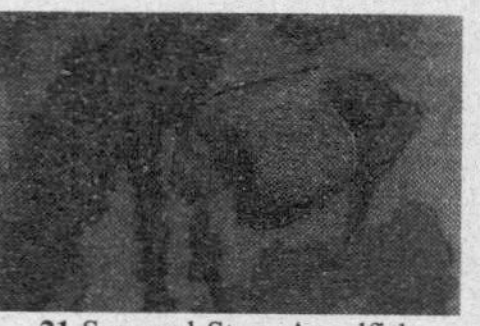
21 Sun and Stars Angelfish

1988. Truk Lagoon, "Micronesia's Living War Memorial". Multicoloured.

95 25 c. Type **21** 40 30
96 25 c. Jellyfish and shoal of small fishes 40 30
97 25 c. Snorkel divers 40 30
98 25 c. Two goldenjack (black-striped fishes facing left) . . 40 30
99 25 c. Blacktip reef shark . . . 40 30
100 25 c. Deck railings of wreck and fishes 40 30
101 25 c. Squirrelfish (red fish) . . 40 30
102 25 c. Batfish and aircraft cockpit 40 30
103 25 c. Three Moorish idols (fishes with long dorsal fins) . . . 40 30
104 25 c. Four barracuda and shoal 40 30
105 25 c. Two spot-banded butterfly fishes (facing alternate directions) 40 30
106 25 c. Three-spot damselfish and aircraft propeller 40 30
107 25 c. Foxface (fish) and shoal 40 30
108 25 c. Lionfish (fish with spines) 40 30
109 25 c. Scuba diver 40 30
110 25 c. Tubular corals 40 30
111 25 c. Ornate butterfly fish and brain coral 40 30
112 25 c. Clown fish, clam and sea plants 40 30

Nos. 95/112 were printed together, se-tenant, in sheetlets of 18 stamps, the backgrounds of the stamps forming an overall design of the remains of a Japanese ship and "Zero" fighter plane on the Lagoon bed colonized by marine life.

22 Flag of Pohnpei

1989. Air. State Flags. Multicoloured.
113 45 c. Type **22** 85 60
114 45 c. Truk 85 60
115 45 c. Kosrae 85 60
116 45 c. Yap 85 60

23 Plumeria and Headdress

1989. Mwarmwarms (floral decorations). Multicoloured.
117 45 c. Type **23** 85 60
118 45 c. Hibiscus and lei 85 60
119 45 c. Jasmine and Yap religious mwarmwarm 85 60
120 45 c. Bougainvillea and Truk dance mwarmwarm 85 60

24 White Shark

1989. Sharks. Multicoloured.
121 25 c. Type **24** 65 40
122 25 c. Hammerhead shark . . . 65 40
123 45 c. Tiger shark (vert) . . . . 1·10 75
124 45 c. Great white shark (vert) 1·10 75

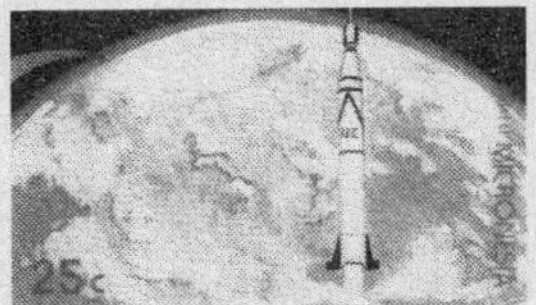

26 "Explorer 1" Satellite over North America

1989. 20th Anniv of First Manned Landing on the Moon. Multicoloured.
126 25 c. Bell XS-15 rocket plane . 40 30
127 25 c. Type **26** 40 30
128 25 c. Ed White on space walk during "Gemini 4" mission 40 30
129 25 c. "Apollo 18" spacecraft 40 30
130 25 c. "Gemini 4" space capsule over South America 40 30
131 25 c. Space shuttle "Challenger" 40 30
132 25 c. Italian "San Marco 2" satellite 40 30
133 25 c. Russian "Soyuz 19" spacecraft 40 30
134 25 c. Neil Armstrong descending ladder to Moon's surface during "Apollo 11" mission 40 30
135 $2.40 Lunar module "Eagle" on Moon (34 × 46 mm) . . . 3·50 2·75

Nos. 126/34 were printed together in se-tenant sheetlets of nine stamps, the backgrounds of the stamps forming an overall design of Earth as viewed from the Moon.

27 Horse's Hoof

1989. Sea Shells. Multicoloured.
136 1 c. Type **27** 10 10
137 3 c. Rare spotted cowrie . . . 10 10
138 15 c. Commercial trochus . . 20 10
139 20 c. General cone 25 10
140 25 c. Triton's trumpet 30 20
141 30 c. Laciniated conch 35 25
142 36 c. Red-mouthed olive . . . 45 35
143 45 c. Map cowrie 55 45
144 50 c. Textile cone 60 50
145 $1 Orange spider conch . . . 1·25 1·00
146 $2 Golden cowrie . . . . . . 2·50 2·00
147 $5 Episcopal mitre . . . . . 6·00 4·50

28 Oranges

1989. "World Stamp Expo '89" International Stamp Exhibition, Washington D.C. "Kosrae–The Garden State". Multicoloured.
155 25 c. Type **28** 45 30
156 25 c. Limes 45 30
157 25 c. Tangerines 45 30
158 25 c. Mangoes 45 30
159 25 c. Coconuts 45 30
160 25 c. Breadfruit 45 30
161 25 c. Sugar cane 45 30
162 25 c. Kosrae house 45 30
163 25 c. Bananas 45 30
164 25 c. Children with fruit and flowers 45 30
165 25 c. Pineapples 45 30
166 25 c. Taro 45 30
167 25 c. Hibiscus 45 30
168 25 c. Ylang ylang 45 30
169 25 c. White ginger 45 30
170 25 c. Plumeria 45 30
171 25 c. Royal poinciana 45 30
172 25 c. Yellow allamanda . . . 45 30

29 Angel over Micronesian Village

1989. Christmas. Multicoloured.
173 25 c. Type **29** 50 25
174 45 c. Truk children dressed as Three Kings 75 60

30 Young Kingfisher and Sokehs Rock, Pohnpei

1990. World Wide Fund for Nature. Micronesian Kingfisher and Micronesian Pigeon.
175 10 c. Type **30** 15 10
176 15 c. Adult kingfisher and rain forest, Pohnpei 25 15
177 20 c. Pigeon flying over lake at Sleeping Lady, Kosrae . . 35 25
178 25 c. Pigeon perched on leaf, Tol Island, Truk 45 35

31 Wooden Whale Stamp and "Lyra"

1990. "Stamp World London 90" International Stamp Exhibition. 19th-century British Whaling Ships. Multicoloured.
179 45 c. Type **31** 55 45
180 45 c. Harpoon heads and "Prudent" 55 45
181 45 c. Carved whale bone and "Rhone" 55 45
182 45 c. Carved whale tooth and "Sussex" 55 45

33 Beech 18 over Kosrae Airport
34 School Building

1990. Air. Airplanes. Multicoloured.
185 22 c. Type **33** 30 15
186 36 c. Boeing 727 landing at Truk 50 30
187 39 c. Britten Norman Islander over Pohnpei 50 30
188 45 c. Beech Queen Air over Yap 60 35

1990. 25th Anniv of Pohnpei Agriculture and Trade School. Multicoloured.
190 25 c. Type **34** 25 15
191 25 c. Fr. Costigan (founder) and students 25 15
192 25 c. Fr. Hugh Costigan . . . 25 15
193 25 c. Ispahu Samuel Hadley (Metelanim chief) and Fr. Costigan 25 15
194 25 c. Statue of Liberty, New York City Police Department badge and Empire State Building 25 15

36 Loading Mail Plane at Pohnpei Airport

1990. Pacific Postal Transport. Multicoloured.
196 25 c. Type **36** 35 20
197 45 c. Launch meeting "Nantaku" (inter-island freighter) in Truk Lagoon to exchange mail, 1940 65 40

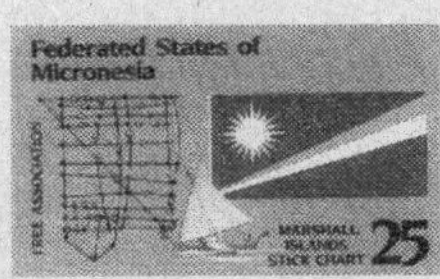

37 Marshallese Stick Chart, Outrigger Canoe and Flag

1990. 4th Anniv of Ratification of Micronesia and Marshall Islands Compacts of Free Association. Multicoloured.
198 25 c. Type **37** 35 20
199 25 c. Frigate bird, U.S.S. "Constitution" (frigate), U.S. flag and bald eagle 35 20
200 25 c. Micronesian outrigger canoe and flag 35 20

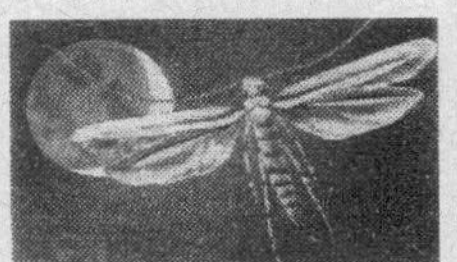
38 "Caloptilia sp." and New Moon

1990. Moths. Multicoloured.
201 45 c. Type **38** 60 50
202 45 c. "Anticrates sp." (inscr "Yponomeatidae") and waxing moon 60 50
203 45 c. "Cosmopterigidae" family and full moon 60 50
204 45 c. "Cosmopteridigae" family and waning moon 60 50

39 Cherub above Roof
41 Hawksbill Turtle returning to Sea

1990. Christmas. "Micronesian Holy Night". Multicoloured.
205 25 c. Type **39** 30 20
206 25 c. Two cherubs and Star of Bethlehem 30 20
207 25 c. Cherub blowing horn . . 30 20
208 25 c. Lambs, goat, pig and chickens 30 20
209 25 c. Native wise men offering gifts to Child 30 20
210 25 c. Children and dog beside lake 30 20
211 25 c. Man blowing conch shell 30 20
212 25 c. Adults and children on path 30 20
213 25 c. Man and children carrying gifts 30 20

Nos. 205/13 were printed together, se-tenant, forming a composite design.

1991. Sea Turtles. Multicoloured.
215 29 c. Type **41** 45 25
216 29 c. Green turtles swimming underwater 45 25
217 50 c. Hawksbill turtle swimming underwater 45 25
218 50 c. Leatherback turtle swimming underwater . . . 45 25

42 Boeing E-3 Sentry

1991. Operations Desert Shield and Desert Storm (liberation of Kuwait). Multicoloured.
219 29 c. Type **42** 40 25
220 29 c. Grumman F-14 Tomcat 40 25
221 29 c. U.S.S. "Missouri" (battleship) 40 25
222 29 c. Multiple Launch Rocket System 40 25
223 $2.90 Great frigate bird with yellow ribbon and flag of Micronesia (50 × 37 mm) . . 3·75 2·75

43 "Evening Flowers, Toloas, Truk"

1991. "Phila Nippon '91" International Stamp Exhibition, Tokyo. 90th Birth Anniv (1992) of Paul Jacoulet (artist). Micronesian Ukiyo-e Prints by Jacoulet. Multicoloured.
225 29 c. Type **43** 40 25
226 29 c. "The Chief's Daughter, Mogomog" 40 25
227 29 c. "Yagourouh and Mio, Yap" 40 25
228 50 c. "Yap Beauty and Orchids" 70 45
229 50 c. "The Yellow-Eyed Boys, Ohlol" 70 45
230 50 c. "Violet Flowers, Tomil, Yap" 70 45

44 Sheep and Holy Family

1991. Christmas. Shell Cribs. Multicoloured.
232 29 c. Type **44** 40 25
233 40 c. Three Kings arriving at Bethlehem 55 35
234 50 c. Sheep around manger . 65 45

45 Pohnpei Fruit Bat

1991. Pohnpei Rain Forest. Multicoloured.
235 29 c. Type **45** 40 25
236 29 c. Purple-capped fruit dove 40 25
237 29 c. Micronesian kingfisher 40 25
238 29 c. Birdnest fern 40 25
239 29 c. Island swiftlets 40 25
240 29 c. Pohnpei white-eye ("Long-billed white-eye") 40 25
241 29 c. Brown noddy 40 25
242 29 c. Pohnpei lory 40 25
243 29 c. Pohnpei flycatcher . . . 40 25
244 29 c. Caroline ground dove . . 40 25
245 29 c. White-tailed tropic bird 40 25
246 29 c. Micronesian honeyeater 40 25
247 29 c. Ixora 40 25
248 29 c. Pohnpei fantail 40 25
249 29 c. Grey white-eye 40 25
250 29 c. Blue-faced parrot finch 40 25
251 29 c. Cicadabird 40 25
252 29 c. Green skink 40 25

Nos. 235/52 were issued together, se-tenant, forming a composite design.

46 Britten Norman Islander and Outrigger Canoe
47 Volunteers learning Crop Planting

1992. Air. Multicoloured.
253 40 c. Type **46** 55 35
254 50 c. Boeing 727-200 airliner and outrigger canoe (different) . 65 45

1992. 25th Anniv of Presence of United States Peace Corps in Micronesia. Multicoloured.
255 29 c. Type **47** 40 25
256 29 c. Education 40 25
257 29 c. Pres. John Kennedy announcing formation of Peace Corps 40 25
258 29 c. Public health nurses . . 40 25
259 29 c. Recreation 40 25

48 Queen Isabella of Spain

1992. 500th Anniv of Discovery of America by Christopher Columbus. Multicoloured.

260		29 c. Type **48**	40	25
261		29 c. "Santa Maria"	40	25
262		29 c. Christopher Columbus	40	25

49 Flags

1992. 1st Anniv of U. N. Membership.

264	**49**	29 c. multicoloured	40	25
265		50 c. multicoloured	65	45

50 Bouquet

1992. Christmas.

266	**50**	29 c. multicoloured	40	25

MIDDLE CONGO — Pt. 6

One of three colonies into which Fr. Congo was divided in 1906. Became part of Fr. Equatorial Africa in 1937. Became part of the Congo Republic within the French Community on 28th November, 1958.

100 centimes = 1 franc

1 Leopard in Ambush

2 Bakalois Woman

3 Coconut Palms, Libreville

1907.

1	**1**	1 c. olive and brown	10	10
2		2 c. violet and brown	10	10
3		4 c. blue and brown	10	10
4		5 c. green and blue	10	10
21		5 c. yellow and blue	35	45
5		10 c. red and blue	15	10
22		10 c. green and light green	1·25	1·25
6		15 c. purple and pink	85	55
7		20 c. brown and blue	1·25	1·00
8	**2**	25 c. blue and green	45	35
23		25 c. green and grey	35	45
9		30 c. pink and green	55	45
24		30 c. red	75	75
10		35 c. brown and blue	55	55
11		40 c. green and brown	55	55
12		45 c. violet and orange	2·10	1·90
13		50 c. green and orange	75	70
25		50 c. blue and green	85	85
14		75 c. brown and blue	3·50	2·50
15	**3**	1 f. green and violet	6·00	4·50
16		2 f. violet and green	5·00	3·25
17		5 f. blue and pink	18·00	16·00

1916. Surch **5c** and red cross.

20	**1**	10 c. + 5 c. red and blue	45	55

1924. Surch **AFRIQUE EQUATORIALE FRANCAISE** and new value.

26	**3**	25 c. on 2 f. green and violet	35	35
27		25 c. on 5 f. pink and blue	35	35
28		65 on 1 f. brown and orange	45	55
29		85 on 1 f. brown and orange	55	55
30	**2**	90 on 75 c. scarlet and red	65	55
31		1 f. 25 on 1 f. ultramarine & bl	25	25
32		1 f. 50 on 1 f. blue & ultram	85	65
33		3 f. on 5 f. pink and brown	1·10	85
34		10 f. on 5 f. green and red	5·50	4·00
35		20 f. on 5 f. purple and brown	8·00	5·50

1924. Optd **AFRIQUE EQUATORIALE FRANCAISE.**

36	**1**	1 c. olive and brown	15	20
37		2 c. violet and brown	20	20
38		4 c. blue and brown	20	20
39		5 c. yellow and blue	20	20
40		10 c. green and light green	20	20
41		10 c. red and grey	20	20
42		15 c. purple and pink	25	25
43		20 c. brown and blue	25	25
44		20 c. green and light green	25	25
45		20 c. brown and mauve	45	25
46	**2**	25 c. green and grey	25	25
47		30 c. red	45	25
48		30 c. grey and mauve	20	10
49		30 c. deep green and green	25	25
50		35 c. brown and blue	25	25
51		40 c. green and brown	40	25
52		45 c. violet and orange	75	45
53		50 c. blue and green	50	25
54		50 c. yellow and black	25	15
55		65 c. brown and blue	1·10	90
56		75 c. brown and blue	35	25
57		90 c. red and pink	2·25	1·60
58	**3**	1 f. green and violet	75	55
59		1 f. 10 mauve and brown	1·75	1·10
60		1 f. 50 ultramarine and blue	3·25	2·40
61		2 f. violet and green	85	65
62		3 f. mauve on pink	3·50	3·00
63		5 f. blue and pink	2·50	1·25

1931. "Colonial Exhibition" key-types inscr "MOYEN CONGO".

65	E	40 c. green and black	2·00	1·90
66	F	50 c. mauve and black	1·10	1·00
67	G	90 c. red and black	1·40	1·10
68	H	1 f. 50 blue and black	2·00	1·10

15 Mindouli Viaduct

1933.

69	**15**	1 c. brown	10	50
70		2 c. blue	10	50
71		4 c. olive	10	50
72		5 c. red	20	30
73		10 c. green	40	50
74		15 c. purple	75	1·25
75		20 c. red on rose	4·50	3·00
76		25 c. orange	75	75
77		30 c. green	1·75	1·25
78	–	40 c. brown	85	55
79	–	45 c. black on green	90	65
80	–	50 c. purple	55	35
81	–	65 c. red on green	55	45
82	–	75 c. black on red	5·50	3·50
83	–	90 c. red	55	55
84	–	1 f. red	55	45
85	–	1 f. 25 green	90	60
86	–	1 f. 50 blue	3·25	1·50
87	–	1 f. 75 violet	1·00	75
88	–	2 f. olive	85	65
89	–	3 f. black on red	1·75	1·60
90	–	5 f. grey	8·00	6·50
91	–	10 f. black	35·00	18·00
92	–	20 f. brown	22·00	14·00

DESIGNS: 40 c. to 1 f. 50 Pasteur Institute, Brazzaville; 1 f. 75 to 20 f. Government Building, Brazzaville.

POSTAGE DUE STAMPS

1928. Postage Due type of France optd **MOYEN-CONGO A. E. F.**

D64	D **11**	5 c. blue	25	25
D65		10 c. brown	25	25
D66		20 c. olive	55	55
D67		25 c. red	55	55
D68		30 c. red	55	55
D69		45 c. green	55	55
D70		50 c. purple	65	75
D71		60 c. brown on cream	95	95
D72		1 f. red on cream	1·00	1·00
D73		2 f. red	1·75	1·90
D74		3 f. violet	3·25	3·25

D 13 Village

1930.

D75	D **13**	5 c. olive and blue	35	45
D76		10 c. brown and red	55	55
D77		20 c. brown and green	1·50	1·50
D78		25 c. brown and blue	2·00	2·25
D79		30 c. green and brown	3·00	3·25
D80		45 c. olive and green	3·00	3·25
D81		50 c. brown and mauve	3·00	3·25
D82		60 c. black and violet	3·50	3·50
D83	–	1 f. black and brown	6·00	6·00
D84	–	2 f. brown and mauve	6·50	6·50
D85	–	3 f. brown and red	6·50	6·50

DESIGN: 1 to 3 f. "William Guinet" (steamer) on the River Congo.

D 17 "Le Djoue"

1933.

D 93	D **17**	5 c. green	40	45
D 94		10 c. blue on blue	45	45
D 95		20 c. red on yellow	55	55
D 96		25 c. red	55	55
D 97		30 c. red	65	75
D 98		45 c. purple	65	75
D 99		50 c. black	1·25	1·25
D100		60 c. black on red	1·75	1·75
D101		1 f. red	2·50	2·50
D102		2 f. orange	3·75	3·75
D103		3 f. blue	6·25	6·25

For later issues see **FRENCH EQUATORIAL AFRICA.**

MODENA — Pt. 8

A state in Upper Italy, formerly a duchy and now part of Italy. Used stamps of Sardinia after the cessation of its own issues in 1860. Now uses Italian stamps.

100 centesimi = 1 lira

1 Arms of Este

5 Cross of Savoy

1852. Imperf.

9	**1**	5 c. black on green	10·00	23·00
3		10 c. black on pink	£200	55·00
4		15 c. black on yellow	15·00	13·00
5		25 c. black on buff	18·00	14·00
12		40 c. black on blue	19·00	85·00
13		1 l. black on white	35·00	£1800

1859. Imperf.

48	**5**	5 c. green	£600	£500
50		15 c. brown	£1000	£2250
51		15 c. grey	£130	
53		20 c. black	£900	75·00
54		20 c. lilac	30·00	£400
56		40 c. red	80·00	£700
58		80 c. brown	80·00	£15000

NEWSPAPER STAMPS

1853. As T **1** but in the value tablet inscr "B.G. CEN" and value. Imperf.

N3	**1**	9 c. black on mauve	£140	40·00
N4		10 c. black on lilac	20·00	£160

N 4

1859. Imperf.

N5	N **4**	10 c. black	£400	£1800

MOHELI — Pt. 6

An island in the Comoro Archipelago adjacent to Madagascar. A separate French dependency until 1914 when the whole archipelago was placed under Madagascar whose stamps were used until 1950. Now part of the Comoro Islands.

100 centimes = 1 franc

1906. "Tablet" key-type inscr "MOHELI" in blue (2, 4, 10, 20, 30, 40 c., 5 f.) or red (others).

1	D	1 c. black on blue	85	80
2		2 c. brown on buff	85	60
3		4 c. brown on grey	90	1·10
4		5 c. green	1·25	1·00
5		10 c. red	1·60	1·00
6		20 c. red on green	6·00	4·00
7		25 c. blue	6·25	3·00
8		30 c. brown on drab	9·50	7·00
9		35 c. black on yellow	4·75	2·25
10		40 c. red on yellow	7·00	4·25
11		45 c. black on green	45·00	30·00
12		50 c. brown on blue	13·00	8·00
13		75 c. brown on orange	13·00	11·50
14		1 f. green	8·50	8·25
15		2 f. violet on pink	21·00	19·00
16		5 f. mauve on lilac	90·00	75·00

1912. Surch in figures.

17	D	05 on 4 c. brown and blue on grey	55	70
18		05 on 20 c. red and blue on green	90	2·00
19		05 on 30 c. brown and blue on drab	80	1·00
20		10 on 40 c. red and blue on yellow	80	1·00
21		10 on 45 c. black and red on green	60	80
22		10 on 50 c. brown and red on blue	90	1·25

MOLDOVA — Pt. 10

Formerly Moldavia, a constituent republic of the Soviet Union. Moldova declared its sovereignty within the Union in 1990 and became independent in 1991.

1991. 100 kopeks = 1 rouble
1993. Kupon (temporary currency)
1993. 100 bani = 1 leu

1 Arms

2 Codrii Nature Reserve

1991. 1st Anniv of Declaration of Sovereignty. Multicoloured. Imperf.

1		7 k. Type **1**	10	10
2		13 k. Type **1**	20	20
3		30 k. Flag (35 × 23 mm)	45	45

1992.

4	**2**	25 k. multicoloured	45	45

3 Arms

4 Tupolev Tu-144

1992.

5	**3**	35 k. green	10	10
6		50 k. red	20	20
7		65 k. brown	30	30
8		1 r. purple	45	45
9		1 r. 50 blue	75	75

1992. Air.
15 **4** 1 r. 75 red 30 30
16 2 r. 50 mauve 45 45
17 7 r. 75 violet . . . . 1·50 1·50
18 8 r. 50 green . . . . 1·90 1·90
See also Nos. 70/3.

5 European Bee Eater **6** St. Panteleimon Church

1992. Birds. Multicoloured.
19 50 k. Type **5** 20 20
20 65 k. Golden oriole 25 25
21 2 r. 50 Green woodpecker . . . 65 65
22 6 r. Common roller . . . . . . 1·10 1·10
23 7 r. 50 Hoopoe . . . . 1·25 1·25
24 15 r. European cuckoo . . . . 2·50 2·50
See also Nos. 63/9.

1992. Centenary (1991) of St. Panteleimon Church, Chisinau.
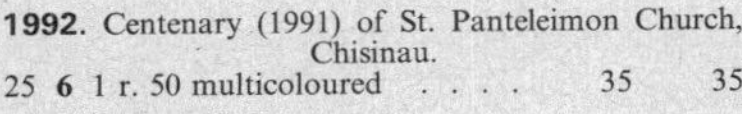
25 **6** 1 r. 50 multicoloured 35 35

7 Wolf suckling Romulus and Remus **9** High Jumping

1992. Trajan Memorial, Chisinau.
26 **7** 5 r. multicoloured 95 95

1992. Various stamps of Russia surch **MOLDOVA** and value.
27 2 r. 50 on 4 k. red (No. 4672) 25 25
28 6 r. on 3 k. red (No. 4671) . . 65 65
29 8 r. 50 on 4 k. red (No. 4672) 95 95
30 10 r. on 3 k. turq (No. 5941) . 1·25 1·25

1992. Olympic Games, Barcelona. Multicoloured.
31 35 k. Type **9** 10 10
32 65 k. Wrestling 45 45
33 1 r. Archery 65 65
34 2 r. 50 Swimming . . . . . . 1·00 1·00
35 10 r. Show jumping . . . . . . 1·50 1·50

1992. Moldovan Olympic Games Medal Winners. Nos. 33/4 optd.
37 1 r. Archery (optd **NATALIA VALEEV / bronz** and emblem) 50 50
38 2 r. 50 Swimming (optd **IURIE BASCATOV / argint** and emblem) . . . . 1·40 1·40

12 Moldovan Flag, Statue of Liberty and U.N. Emblem and Building

1992. Admission of Moldova to U.N.O. Mult.
40 1 r. 30 Type **12** 15 15
41 12 r. As Type **12** but with motifs differently arranged . . . . . 1·25 1·25

13 Moldovan Flag and Prague Castle

1992. Admission of Moldova to European Security and Co-operation Conf Multicoloured.
42 2 r. 50 Type **13** 20 20
43 25 r. Helsinki Cathedral and Moldovan flag . . . . 1·60 1·60

1992. Nos. 4533, 4670/1 of Russia surch **MOLDOVA**, new value and bunch of grapes.
44 – 45 k. on 2 k. mauve . . . 15 15
45 – 46 k. on 2 k. mauve . . . 15 15
46 **1753** 63 k. on 1 k. green 25 25
47 – 63 k. on 3 k. red 25 25
48 **1753** 70 k. on 1 k. green 15 15
49 4 r. on 1 k. green 80 80

15 Carpet and Pottery **16** Galleon

1992. Folk Art.
50 **15** 7 r. 50 multicoloured . . . 2·50 2·50

1992. 500th Anniv of Discovery of America by Columbus. Multicoloured.
51 1 r. Type **16** 15 15
52 6 r. Carrack . . . . 1·10 1·10
53 6 r. Caravel . . . . 1·10 1·10

17 Letter Sorter, Train, State Flag and U.P.U. Emblem

1992. Admission to U.P.U. Multicoloured.
55 5 r. Type **17** 95 95
56 10 r. Douglas DC-10 airplane, computerized letter sorting equipment, state flag and U.P.U. emblem . . . . . . 1·75 1·75

18 Aesculapius Snake

1993. Protected Animals. Snakes. Multicoloured.
57 3 r. Type **18** 35 35
58 3 r. Aesculapius in tree 35 35
59 3 r. Aesculapius on path . . . 35 35
60 3 r. Aesculapius on rock . . . 35 35
61 15 r. Grass snake . . . . 1·10 1·10
62 25 r. Adder . . . . 3·00 3·00
Nos. 57/60 were issued together, se-tenant, forming a composite design.

1993. Birds. As Nos. 19/24 but with values changed and additional design. Multicoloured.
63 2 r. Type **5** 10 10
64 3 r. As No. 20 . . . . 10 10
65 5 r. As No. 21 . . . . 15 15
66 10 r. As No. 22 . . . . 30 30
67 15 r. As No. 23 . . . . 65 65
68 50 r. As No. 24 . . . . 1·50 1·50
69 100 r. Barn swallow . . . . . 2·75 2·75

1993. Air.
70 **4** 25 r. red 55 55
71 45 r. brown . . . . 1·10 1·10
72 50 r. green . . . . 1·40 1·40
73 90 r. blue . . . . 2·40 2·40

19 Arms **20**

1993.
74 **19** 2 k. blue 10 10
75 3 k. purple 10 10
76 6 k. green 10 10
77 – 10 k. violet and green . . . 10 10
78 – 15 k. violet and green . . . 10 10
79 – 20 k. violet and grey . . . 15 15
80 – 30 k. violet and yellow . . 20 20
81 – 50 k. violet and red 50 50
82 **20** 100 k. multicoloured . . . 1·00 1·00
83 250 k. multicoloured . . . 2·75 2·75
DESIGN: 10 to 50 k. Similar to Type **19** but with inscription and value at foot differently arranged.

21 Red Admiral **22** "Tulipa bibersteiniana"

1993. Butterflies and Moths. Multicoloured.
94 6 b. Type **21** 10 10
95 10 b. Swallowtail 15 15
96 50 b. Peacock 75 75
97 250 b. Emperor moth . . . . . 3·75 3·75

1993. Flowers. Multicoloured.
98 6 b. Type **22** 20 20
99 15 b. Lily of the valley 45 45
100 25 b. Snowdrop 70 70
101 30 b. Peony 90 90
102 50 b. Snowdrop . . . . 1·50 1·50
103 90 b. Pasque flower . . . . . 2·75 2·75

23 Dragos Voda (1352–53) **24** "Story of One Life" (M. Grecu)

1993. 14th-century Princes of Moldavia. Multicoloured.
105 6 b. Type **23** 15 15
106 25 b. Bogdan Voda I (1359–65) 25 25
107 50 b. Latcu Voda (1365–75) . . 50 50
108 100 b. Petru I Musat (1375–91) 1·00 1·00
109 150 b. Roman Voda Musat (1391–94) . . . . 1·50 1·50
110 200 b. Stefan I (1394–99) . . . 2·10 2·10

1993. Europa. Contemporary Art. Multicoloured.
111 3 b. Type **24** 10 10
112 150 b. "Coming of Spring" (I. Vieru) . . . . 2·10 1·10

25 Biathletes **27** State Arms

1994. Winter Olympic Games, Lillehammer, Norway. Multicoloured.
113 3 b. Type **25** 10 10
114 150 b. Close-up of biathlete shooting . . . . 2·10 2·10

1994. No. 4533 of Russia surch **MOLDOVA**, grapes and value.
115 **1753** 3 b. on 1 k. green 10 10
116 25 b. on 1 k. green . . . 40 40
117 50 b. on 1 k. green . . . 90 90

1994.
118 **27** 1 b. multicoloured 10 10
120 10 b. multicoloured 10 10
121 30 b. multicoloured 10 10
122 38 b. multicoloured 10 10
123 45 b. multicoloured 15 15
125 75 b. multicoloured 30 15
127 1 l. 50 multicoloured . . . 55 55
128 1 l. 80 multicoloured . . . 60 60
129 2 l. 50 mult (24 × 29 mm) . 75 75
130 4 l. 50 multicoloured . . . 1·25 1·25
131 5 l. 40 multicoloured . . . 1·40 1·40
132 6 l. 90 multicoloured . . . 1·50 1·50
133 7 l. 20 mult (24 × 29 mm) . 1·75 1·75
134 13 l. mult (24 × 29 mm) . . 3·50 3·30
135 24 l. mult (24 × 29 mm) . . 7·00 7·00

28 Launch of "Titan II" Rocket **29** Maria Cibotari (singer)

1994. Europa. Inventions and Discoveries. 25th Anniv of First Manned Moon Landing. Multicoloured.
136 1 b. Type **28** 10 10
137 45 b. Ed White (astronaut) on space walk ("Gemini 4" flight, 1965) 10 10
138 2 l. 50 Lunar module landing, 1969 . . . . 1·10 1·10

1994. Entertainers' Death Anniversaries. Mult.
139 3 b. Type **29** (45th) 10 10
140 90 b. Dumitru Caraciobanu (actor, 14th) 25 25
141 150 b. Eugeniu Coca (composer, 40th) 45 45
142 250 b. Igor Vieru (actor, 11th) 1·25 1·25

30 Preparing Stamp Design

1994. Stamp Day.
143 **30** 10 b. black, blue and mauve 10 10
144 – 45 b. black, mauve and yellow 25 25
145 – 2 l. multicoloured . . . . 1·10 1·10
DESIGNS: 45 b. Printing stamps; 2 l. Checking finished sheets.

31 Pierre de Coubertin (founder)

1994. Centenary of International Olympic Committee. Multicoloured.
146 60 b. Type **31** 20 20
147 1 l. 50 Rings and "Paris 1994" centenary congress emblem 65 65

MONACO Pt. 6

A principality on the S. coast of France including the town of Monte Carlo.

100 centimes = 1 French franc

1 Prince Charles III — 2 Prince Albert — 4 War Widow and Monaco

1885.
1 **1** 1 c. olive 7·50 8·50
2 2 c. lilac 20·00 18·00
3 5 c. blue 35·00 26·00
4 10 c. brown on yellow 40·00 30·00
5 15 c. red £150 9·00
6 25 c. green £350 45·00
7 40 c. blue on red 32·00 27·00
8 75 c. black on red 80·00 50·00
9 1 f. black on yellow £1000 £350
10 5 f. red on green £2500 £1500

1891.
11 **2** 1 c. green 40 50
12 2 c. purple 40 50
13 5 c. blue 25·00 2·00
22 5 c. green 45 25
14 10 c. brown on yellow 70·00 9·00
23 10 c. red 1·00 30
15 15 c. pink £100 4·00
24 15 c. brown on yellow 1·50 60
25 15 c. green 1·75 1·75
16 25 c. green £225 25·00
26 25 c. blue 4·25 1·50
17 40 c. black on pink 2·00 1·25
18 50 c. brown on orange 3·50 3·00
19 75 c. brown on buff 15·00 8·00
20 1 f. black on yellow 12·00 6·00
21 5 f. red on green 80·00 40·00
28 5 f. mauve £180 £170
29 5 f. green 20·00 22·00

1914. Surcharged **+5c.**
30 **2** 10 c. + 5 c. red 3·75 4·50

1919. War Orphans Fund.
31 **4** 2 c. + 3 c. mauve 10·00 13·00
32 5 c. + 5 c. green 6·50 9·50
33 15 c. + 10 c. red 6·50 9·50
34 25 c. + 15 c. blue 15·00 24·00
35 50 c. + 50 c. brown on orge 70·00 90·00
36 1 f. + 1 f. black on yellow £250 £300
37 5 f. + 5 f. red £850 £950

1920. Princess Charlotte's Marriage. Nos. 33/7 optd **20 mars 1920** or surch also.
38 **4** 2 c. + 3 c. on 15 c. + 10 c. 28·00 28·00
39 2 c. + 3 c. on 25 c. + 15 c. 28·00 28·00
40 2 c. + 3 c. on 50 c. + 50 c. 28·00 28·00
41 5 c. + 5 c. on 1 f. + 1 f. 28·00 28·00
42 5 c. + 5 c. on 5 f. + 5 f. 28·00 28·00
43 15 c. + 10 c. red 17·00 20·00
44 25 c. + 15 c. blue 7·00 7·00
45 50 c. + 50 c. brown on orge 30·00 35·00
46 1 f. + 1 f. black on yellow 40·00 42·00
47 5 f. + 5 f. red £5000 £5000

1921. Princess Antoinette's Baptism. Optd **28 DECEMBRE 1920** or surch also.
48 **2** 5 c. green 45 50
49 75 c. brown on buff 3·50 5·00
50 2 f. on 5 f. mauve 27·00 35·00

1922. Surch.
51 **2** 20 c. on 15 c. green 1·00 1·00
52 25 c. on 10 c. red 55 60
53 50 c. on 1 f. black on yellow 4·25 5·00

8 Prince Albert I — 9 St. Devote Viaduct

1922.
54 **8** 25 c. brown 2·25 3·25
55 – 30 c. green 65 1·10
56 – 30 c. red 40 45
57 **9** 40 c. brown 50 50
58 – 50 c. blue 3·75 4·00
59 – 60 c. grey 20 25
60 – 1 f. black on yellow 20 20
61a – 2 f. red 40 35
62 – 5 f. brown 28·00 32·00
63 – 5 f. green on blue 5·00 6·50
64 – 10 f. red 11·00 13·00
DESIGNS: As Type **9**: 30 c., 50 c. Oceanographic Museum; 60 c., 1 f., 2 f. The Rock; 5 f., 10 f. Prince's Palace, Monaco.

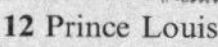

12 Prince Louis — 13 Prince Louis and Palace

1923.
65 **12** 10 c. green 35 35
66 15 c. red 50 50
67 20 c. brown 30 30
68 25 c. purple 25 30
69 **13** 50 c. blue 25 30

1924. Surch with new value and bars.
70 **2** 45 c. on 50 c. brown on orge 50 50
71 75 c. on 1 f. black on yellow 30 30
72 85 c. on 5 f. green 30 30

14 — 15 — 16

17 St. Devote Viaduct

1924.
73 **14** 1 c. grey 10 10
74 2 c. brown 10 10
75 3 c. mauve 1·75 45
76 5 c. orange 20 20
77 10 c. blue 10 10
78 **15** 15 c. green 10 10
79 15 c. violet 1·50 80
80 20 c. mauve 15 10
81 20 c. pink 20 10
82 25 c. pink 10 10
83 25 c. red on yellow 15 15
84 30 c. orange 10 10
85 40 c. brown 15 10
86 40 c. blue on blue 15 10
87 45 c. black 70 40
88 **16** 50 c. green 15 15
89 **15** 50 c. brown on yellow 10 10
90 **16** 60 c. brown 10 15
91 **15** 60 c. green on green 10 10
92 75 c. green on green 20 15
93 75 c. red on yellow 15 10
94 75 c. black 40 20
95 80 c. red on yellow 25 20
96 90 c. red on yellow 75 75
97 **17** 1 f. black on yellow 20 15
98 1 f. 05 mauve 20 35
99 1 f. 10 green 8·00 3·50
100 **15** 1 f. 25 blue on blue 15 15
101 1 f. 50 blue on blue 1·40 90
102 – 2 f. brown and mauve 70 60
103 – 3 f. lilac and red on yellow 12·00 6·50
104 – 5 f. red and green 5·00 3·75
105 – 10 f. blue and brown 12·00 10·00
DESIGN—As Type **17**: 2 f. to 10 f. Monaco.

1926. Surch.
106 **15** 30 c. on 25 c. pink 20 10
107 50 c. on 60 c. green on grn 70 15
108 **17** 50 c. on 1 f. 05 mauve 40 35
109 50 c. on 1 f. 10 green 4·50 2·75
110 **15** 50 c. on 1 f. 25 blue on blue 35 30
111 1 f. 25 on 1 f. blue on blue 35 20
112 – 1 f. 50 on 2 f. brown and mauve (No. 102) 2·50 2·25

20 Prince Charles III, Louis II and Albert I

1928. International Philatelic Exn, Monte Carlo.
113 **20** 50 c. red 65 65
114 1 f. 50 blue 65 65
115 3 f. violet 65 65

20a — 21 Palace Entrance

22 St. Devote's Church — 23 Prince Louis II

1933.
116 **20a** 1 c. plum 10 10
117 2 c. green 10 10
118 3 c. purple 10 10
119 5 c. red 10 10
120 10 c. blue 10 10
121 15 c. violet 75 70
122 **21** 15 c. red 40 10
123 20 c. brown 40 10
124 A 25 c. sepia 60 30
125 **22** 30 c. green 70 30
126 **23** 40 c. sepia 1·10 1·10
127 B 45 c. brown 2·25 60
128 **23** 50 c. violet 1·00 60
129 C 65 c. green 2·00 40
130 D 75 c. blue 2·40 1·25
131 **23** 90 c. red 3·25 2·00
132 **22** 1 f. brown 14·00 5·00
133 D 1 f. 25 red 3·00 2·00
134 **23** 1 f. 50 blue 16·00 6·50
135 A 1 f. 75 red 18·00 4·00
136 1 f. 75 red 15·00 5·00
137 B 2 f. blue 4·25 2·00
138 **21** 3 f. violet 10·00 3·00
139 A 3 f. 50 orange 38·00 22·00
140 **22** 5 f. purple 14·00 9·00
141 A 10 f. blue 85·00 32·00
142 C 20 f. black £130 85·00
DESIGNS—As Type **21**—HORIZ: A, The Prince's Residence; B, The Rock of Monaco; C, Palace Gardens; D, Fortifications and Harbour.
For other stamps in Type **20a** see Nos. 249, etc.

1933. Air. Surch with Bleriot XI airplane and **1f50.**
143 – 1 f. 50 on 5 f. red and green (No. 104) 22·00 22·00

28 Palace Gardens

1937. Charity.
144 **28** 50 c. + 50 c. green 1·75 2·25
145 – 90 c. + 90 c. red 1·75 2·25
146 – 1 f. 50 + 1 f. 50 blue 3·50 4·50
147 – 2 f. + 2 f. violet 5·50 5·50
148 – 5 f. + 5 f. red 60·00 60·00
DESIGNS—HORIZ: 90 c. Exotic gardens; 1 f. 50, The Bay of Monaco. VERT: 2, 5 f. Prince Louis II.

1937. Postage Due stamps optd **POSTES** or surch also.
149 D **18** 5 on 10 c. violet 70 70
150 10 c. violet 70 70
151 15 on 30 c. bistre 70 70
152 20 on 30 c. bistre 70 70
153 25 on 60 c. red 1·25 1·25
154 30 c. bistre 1·90 1·75
155 40 on 60 c. red 2·00 1·60
156 50 on 60 c. red 2·00 2·00
157 65 on 1 f. blue 1·60 1·60
158 85 on 1 f. blue 3·50 3·50
159 1 f. blue 4·50 4·50
160 2 f. 15 on 2 f. red 5·50 5·50
161 2 f. 25 on 2 f. red 11·00 11·00
162 2 f. 50 on 2 f. red 18·00 18·00

31 Prince Louis II — 33 Monaco Hospital

1938.
164 **31** 55 c. brown 1·75 70
165 65 c. violet 16·00 7·00
166 70 c. brown 15 15
167 90 c. violet 15 15
168 1 f. red 3·25 2·50
169 1 f. 25 red 20 15
170 1 f. 75 blue 7·00 4·50
171 2 f. 25 blue 20 15

1938. Anti-Cancer Fund. 40th Anniv of Discovery of Radium.
172 – 65 c. + 25 c. green 5·00 5·00
173 **33** 1 f. 75 + 50 c. blue 6·00 6·00
DESIGN—VERT: 65 c. Pierre and Marie Curie.

34 The Cathedral — 38 Monaco Harbour

1939.
174 **34** 20 c. mauve 15 15
175 – 25 c. brown 30 20
176 – 30 c. green 20 20
177 – 40 c. red 20 20
178 – 45 c. purple 20 20
179 – 50 c. green 25 15
180 – 60 c. red 20 20
181 – 60 c. green 20 20
182 **38** 70 c. lilac 35 20
183 75 c. green 35 20
184 – 1 f. black 20 20
185 – 1 f. 30 brown 20 20
186 – 2 f. purple 20 20
187 – 2 f. 50 red 16·00 9·50
188 – 2 f. 50 blue 70 30
189 **38** 3 f. red 40 20
190 **34** 5 f. blue 1·40 60
191 – 10 f. green 80 65
192 – 20 f. blue 1·00 65
DESIGNS—VERT: 25, 40 c., 2 f. Place St. Nicholas; 30, 60 c., 20 f. Palace Gateway; 50 c., 1 f., 1 f. 30, Palace of Monaco. HORIZ: 45 c., 2 f. 50, 10 f. Aerial view of Monaco.

40 Louis II Stadium — 41 Lucien

1939. Inauguration of Louis II Stadium, Monaco.
198 **40** 10 f. green 95·00 95·00

1939. National Relief. XVI–XVIII-century portrait designs and view.
199 **41** 5 c. + 5 c. black 1·00 1·00
200 – 10 c. + 10 c. purple 1·00 1·00
201 – 45 c. + 15 c. green 3·00 3·00
202 – 70 c. + 30 c. mauve 4·50 5·00
203 – 90 c. + 35 c. violet 5·50 6·50
204 – 1 f. + 1 f. blue 15·00 15·00
205 – 2 f. + 2 f. red 16·00 18·00
206 – 2 f. 25 + 1 f. 25 blue 28·00 28·00
207 – 3 f. + 3 f. red 40·00 40·00
208 – 5 f. + 5 f. red 60·00 65·00
DESIGNS—VERT: 10 c. Honore II; 45 c. Louis I; 70 c. Charlotte de Gramont; 90 c. Antoine I; 1 f. Marie de Lorraine; 2 f. Jacques I; 2 f. 25, Louise-Hippolyte; 3 f. Honore III. HORIZ: 5 f. The Rock of Monaco.

1939. 8th International University Games. As T **40** but inscr. "VIIIeme JEUX UNIVERSITAIRES INTERNATIONAUX 1939".
209 40 c. green 75 90
210 70 c. brown 85 1·00
211 90 c. violet 1·00 1·25
212 1 f. 25 red 1·00 1·25
213 2 f. 25 blue 2·50 2·50

1940. Red Cross Ambulance Fund. As Nos. 174/92 in new colours surch with Red Cross and premium.
214 **34** 20 c. + 1 f. violet 1·25 2·25
215 – 25 c. + 1 f. green 1·25 2·25
216 – 30 c. + 1 f. red 1·25 2·25
217 – 40 c. + 1 f. blue 1·25 2·25
218 – 45 c. + 1 f. red 1·25 2·25
219 – 50 c. + 1 f. brown 1·25 2·25
220 – 60 c. + 1 f. green 1·25 2·25
221 **38** 75 c. + 1 f. black 1·90 2·25
222 – 1 f. + 1 f. red 1·75 2·40
223 – 2 f. + 1 f. slate 1·75 2·40
224 – 2 f. 50 + 1 f. green 7·00 6·50
225 **38** 3 f. + 1 f. blue 9·50 7·75
226 **34** 5 f. + 1 f. black 9·50 7·75
227 – 10 f. + 5 f. blue 17·00 17·00
228 – 20 f. + 5 f. purple 25·00 25·00

44 Prince Louis II

1941.
229 **44** 40 c. red 20 20
230 80 c. green 20 20
231 1 f. violet 10 10
232 1 f. 20 green 10 10
233 1 f. 50 red 10 10
234 1 f. 50 violet 10 10
235 2 f. green 10 10
236 2 f. 40 red 10 10
237 2 f. 50 blue 35 35
238 4 f. blue 10 10

45 — 46

1941. National Relief Fund.
239 **45** 25 c. + 25 c. purple 50 1·00
240 **46** 50 c. + 25 c. brown 50 1·00
241 75 c. + 50 c. purple 1·25 1·60
242 **45** 1 f. + 1 f. blue 1·25 1·60
243 **46** 1 f. 50 + 1 f. 50 red 1·40 2·25
244 **45** 2 f. + 2 f. green 1·40 2·25
245 **46** 2 f. 50 + 2 f. blue 1·60 2·75
246 **45** 3 f. + 3 f. brown 1·75 2·75
247 **46** 5 f. + 5 f. green 4·50 2·75
248 **45** 10 f. + 8 f. sepia 10·00 6·00

1941. New values and colours.

249 **20a** 10 c. black 10 10
250 – 30 c. red (as No. 176) . . 20 15
251 **20a** 30 c. green 10 10
252 40 c. red 10 10
253 50 c. violet 10 10
362 **34** 50 c. brown 10 10
254 **20a** 60 c. blue 10 10
363 – 60 c. pink (as No. 175) . . 10 15
255 **20a** 70 c. brown 10 10
256 **34** 80 c. green 10 10
257 – 1 f. brown (as Nos. 178) . . 10 10
258 **38** 1 f. 20 blue 15 15
259 – 1 f. 50 blue (as Nos. 175) . 15 15
260 **38** 2 f. blue 10 10
261 – 2 f. green (as No. 179) . . 10 10
262 – 3 f. black (as No. 175) . . 10 10
364 – 3 f. purple (as No. 176) . . 20 20
391 – 3 f. green (as No. 175) . . 40 20
263 **34** 4 f. mauve 10 20
365 – 4 f. green (as No. 175) . . 20 20
264 – 4 f. 50 violet (as No. 179) . 10 10
265 – 5 f. green (as No. 176) . . 10 10
392 – 5 f. green (as No. 178) . . 20 10
393 – 5 f. red (as No. 176) . . . 35 35
266 – 6 f. violet (as No. 179) . . 20 30
368 – 8 f. brown (as No. 179) . . 65 40
267 **34** 10 f. blue 10 10
370 – 10 f. brown (as No. 179) . 1·00 45
394 **38** 10 f. yellow 60 20
268 15 f. red 20 15
269 – 20 f. brown (as No. 178) . 20 15
373 – 20 f. red (as No. 178) . . 45 25
270 **38** 25 f. green 90 60
374 25 f. black . . . . 17·00 8·50
397 – 25 f. blue (as No. 176) . . 13·50 8·50
398 **25** f. red (as No. 179) . . . 90 55
399 – 30 f. blue (as No. 176) . . 2·75 2·75
400 – 35 f. blue (as No. 179) . . 3·00 1·10
401 **34** 40 f. red . . . . 2·25 2·00
402 50 f. violet . . . . 2·00 65
403 – 65 f. violet (as No. 178) . 3·50 3·75
404 **34** 70 f. yellow . . . . 3·75 5·00
405 – 75 f. green (as No. 175) . 8·75 4·50
406 – 85 f. red (as No. 175) . . 6·00 4·50
407 – 100 f. turquoise (as No. 178) 4·50 4·50

47 Caudron Rafale over Monaco

48 Propeller and Palace

49 Arms, Airplane and Globe

50 Charles II

1942. Air.

271 **47** 5 f. green 20 20
272 10 f. blue 20 30
273 **48** 15 f. brown 55 35
274 – 20 f. brown 55 45
275 – 50 f. purple . . . . 3·00 1·75
276 **49** 100 f. red and purple . . . 3·00 1·75

DESIGNS—VERT: 20 f. Pegasus. HORIZ: 50 f. Common gull over Bay of Monaco.

1942. National Relief Fund. Royal Personnages.

277 – 2 c. + 3 c. blue 10 10
278 **50** 5 c. + 5 c. red 10 10
279 – 10 c. + 5 c. black 10 10
280 – 20 c. + 10 c. green 10 10
281 – 30 c. + 30 c. purple . . . 10 10
282 – 40 c. + 40 c. red 10 10
283 – 50 c. + 50 c. violet . . . 10 10
284 – 75 c. + 75 c. purple . . . 10 10
285 – 1 f. + 1 f. green 10 10
286 – 1 f. 50 + 1 f. red 10 10
287 – 2 f. 50 + 2 f. 50 violet . . 1·50 2·25
288 – 3 f. + 3 f. blue . . . . . 1·50 2·25
289 – 5 f. + 5 f. sepia . . . . 2·00 3·50
290 – 10 f. + 5 f. purple . . . 2·00 3·50
291 – 20 f. + 5 f. blue . . . . 2·25 4·00

PORTRAITS: 2 c. Rainier Grimaldi; 10 c. Jeanne Grimaldi; 20 c. Charles Auguste, Goyon de Matignon; 30 c. Jacques I; 40 c. Louise-Hippolyte; 50 c. Charlotte Grimaldi; 75 c. Marie Charles Grimaldi; 1 f. Honore III; 1 f. 50, Honore IV; 2 f. 50, Honore V; 3 f. Florestan I; 5 f. Charles III; 10 f. Albert I; 20 f. Princess Marie-Victoire.

52 Prince Louis II

1943.

292 **52** 50 f. violet 55 55

53 St. Devote

54 Blessing the Sea

55 Arrival of St. Devote at Monaco

1944. Charity. Festival of St. Devote.

293 **53** 50 c. + 50 c. brown . . . 15 15
294 – 70 c. + 80 c. blue 15 15
295 – 80 c. + 70 c. green . . . 15 15
296 – 1 f. + 1 f. purple 15 15
297 – 1 f. 50 + 1 f. 50 red . . . 15 15
298 **54** 2 f. + 2 f. purple 20 30
299 – 5 f. + 2 f. violet 35 35
300 – 10 f. + 40 f. blue 35 35
301 **55** 20 f. + 60 f. blue . . . . 2·75 3·25

DESIGNS—VERT: 70 c., 1 f. Various processional scenes; 1 f. 50, Burning the boat; 10 f. Trial scene. HORIZ: 80 c. Procession; 5 f. St. Devote's Church.

1945. Air. For War Dead and Deported Workers. As Nos. 272/6 (colours changed) surch.

302 1 f. + 4 f. on 10 f. red . . . 35 35
303 1 f. + 4 f. on 15 f. brown . . 35 35
304 1 f. + 4 f. on 20 f. brown . . 35 35
305 1 f. + 4 f. on 50 f. blue . . . 35 35
306 1 f. + 4 f. on 100 f. purple . 35 35

57 Prince Louis II **58**

1946.

361 **57** 30 c. black 10 10
389 50 c. olive 10 10
390 1 f. violet 10 10
307 2 f. 50 green 15 10
308 3 f. mauve 15 10
366 5 f. brown 20 15
309 6 f. red 15 10
367 6 f. purple . . . . 1·00 20
310 10 f. blue 15 10
369 10 f. orange 10 10
371 12 f. red . . . . 1·60 50
395 12 f. slate . . . . 2·75 2·00
396 15 f. lake . . . . 2·75 2·25
372 18 f. blue . . . . 3·75 2·75
311 **58** 50 f. grey . . . . 90 1·10
312 100 f. red . . . . 1·25 1·60

59 Child Praying

60 Nurse and Baby

1946. Child Welfare Fund.

313 **59** 1 f. + 3 f. green 20 20
314 2 f. + 4 f. red 20 20
315 4 f. + 6 f. blue 20 20
316 5 f. + 40 f. mauve 55 55
317 10 f. + 60 f. red 55 55
318 15 f. + 100 f. blue 90 90

1946. Anti-tuberculosis Fund.

319 **60** 2 f. + 8 f. blue 35 35

1946. Air. Optd **POSTE AERIENNE** over Sud Ouest Cassiopees airplane.

320 **58** 50 f. grey . . . . 1·75 1·40
321 100 f. red . . . . 2·75 2·00

INDEX

Countries can be quickly located by referring to the index at the end of this volume.

62 Steamship and Chart

1946. Stamp Day.

322 **62** 3 f. + 2 f. blue 20 20

63

1946. Air.

323 **63** 40 f. red 60 40
324 50 f. brown 70 50
325 100 f. green . . . . 1·40 1·00
326 200 f. violet . . . . 1·50 1·40
326a 300 f. blue & ultramarine . 28·00 35·00
326b 500 f. green & deep green . 22·00 30·00
326c 1000 f. violet and brown . 28·00 35·00

64 Pres. Roosevelt and Palace of Monaco

66 Pres. Roosevelt

1946. President Roosevelt Commemorative.

327 **66** 10 c. mauve (postage) . . . 10 10
328 – 30 c. blue 15 15
329 **64** 60 c. green 15 15
330 – 1 f. sepia 30 30
331 – 2 f. + 3 f. green 55 55
332 – 3 f. violet . . . . 1·00 1·00
333 – 5 f. red (air) 30 30
334 – 10 f. black 60 40
335 **66** 15 f. + 10 f. orange . . . 75 65

DESIGNS—HORIZ: 30 c., 5 f. Rock of Monaco; 2 f. Viaduct and St. Devote. VERT: 1 f., 3 f., 10 f. Map of Monaco.

67 Prince Louis II

68 Pres. Roosevelt as a Philatelist

69 Statue of Liberty and New York Harbour

70 Prince Charles III

1947. Participation in the Centenary International Philatelic Exhibition, New York. (a) Postage.

336 **67** 10 f. blue . . . . 2·00 2·00

(b) Air. Dated "1847 1947".

337 **68** 50 c. violet 40 35
338 – 1 f. 50 mauve 30 25
339 – 3 f. orange 30 20
340 – 10 f. blue . . . . 2·00 2·00
341 **69** 15 f. red . . . . 3·00 3·00

DESIGNS—HORIZ: As Type **68**: 1 f. 50 G.P.O., New York; 3 f. Oceanographic Museum, Monte Carlo. As Type **69**: 10 f. Bay of Monaco.

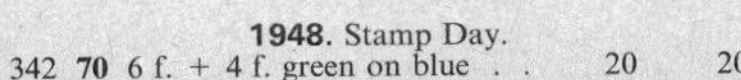

1948. Stamp Day.

342 **70** 6 f. + 4 f. green on blue . . 20 20

71 Diving

72 Tennis

1948. Olympic Games, Wembley. Inscr "JEUX OLYMPIQUES 1948".

343 – 50 c. green (postage) . . . 15 15
344 – 1 f. red 15 15
345 – 2 f. blue 40 40
346 – 2 f. 50 red . . . . 1·00 1·00
347 **71** 4 f. slate . . . . 1·50 1·50
348 – 5 f. + 5 f. brown (air) . . 4·50 7·25
349 – 6 f. + 9 f. violet . . . . 6·50 9·50
350 **72** 10 f. + 15 f. red . . . . 11·00 16·00
351 – 15 f. + 25 f. blue . . . . 15·00 25·00

DESIGNS—HORIZ: 50 c. Hurdling; 15 f. Yachting. VERT: 1 f. Running; 2 f. Throwing the discus; 2 f. 50, Basketball; 5 f. Rowing; 6 f. Skiing.

75 The Salmacis Nymph

77 F. J. Bosio (wrongly inscr. "J. F.")

1948. Death Centenary of Francois Joseph Bosio (sculptor).

352 **75** 50 c. green (postage) . . . 10 10
353 – 1 f. red 20 20
354 – 2 f. blue 30 30
355 – 2 f. 50 violet 80 80
356 **77** 4 f. mauve . . . . 1·40 1·40
357 – 5 f. + 5 f. blue (air) . . . 3·75 6·50
358 – 6 f. + 9 f. green . . . . 5·50 8·25
359 – 10 f. + 15 f. red . . . . 6·00 8·75
360 – 15 f. + 25 f. brown . . . 7·75 12·00

DESIGNS—VERT: 1, 5 f. Hercules struggling with Achelous; 2, 6 f. Aristaeus (Garden God); 15 f. The Salmacis Nymph (36 × 48 mm). HORIZ: 2 f. 50, 10 f. Hyacinthus awaiting his turn to throw a quoit.

79 Exotic Gardens

80 "Princess Alice II"

1949. Birth Centenary of Prince Albert I.

375 – 2 f. blue (postage) 25 20
376 **79** 3 f. green 10 10
377 – 4 f. brown and blue . . . 20 20
378 **80** 5 f. red 40 40
379 – 6 f. violet 45 45
380 – 10 f. sepia 80 65
381 – 12 f. pink . . . . 1·25 85
382 – 18 f. orange and brown . . 2·50 2·50
383 – 20 f. brown (air) 30 55
384 – 25 f. blue 30 55
385 – 40 f. green 55 80
386 – 50 f. green, brown & black . 65 1·10
387 – 100 f. red . . . . 3·00 4·00
388 – 200 f. orange . . . . . . 5·50 7·00

DESIGNS—HORIZ: 2 f. Yacht "Hirondelle I" (1870); 4 f. Oceanographic Museum, Monaco; 10 f. "Hirondelle II" (1914); 12 f. Albert harpooning whale; 18 f. Buffalo (Palaeolithic mural); 20 f. Constitution Day, 1911; 25 f. Paris Institute of Palaeontology; 200 f. Coin with effigy of Albert. VERT: 6 f. Statue of Albert at tiller; 40 f. Anthropological Museum; 50 f. Prince Albert I; 100 f. Oceanographic Institute, Paris.

83 Palace of Monaco and Globe

1949. 75th Anniv of U.P.U.

410 **83** 5 f. green (postage) 10 10
411 10 f. orange . . . . 2·75 2·75
412 15 f. red 20 25
413 25 f. blue (air) 55 45
414 40 f. sepia and brown . . . 45 65
415 50 f. blue and green . . . 55 75
416 100 f. blue and red . . . . 1·50 1·60

84 Prince Rainier III and Monaco Palace

85 Prince Rainier III

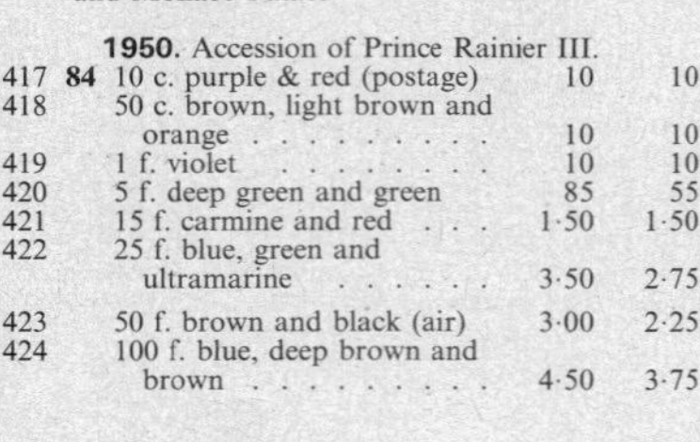

1950. Accession of Prince Rainier III.

417 **84** 10 c. purple & red (postage) 10 10
418 50 c. brown, light brown and orange 10 10
419 1 f. violet 10 10
420 5 f. deep green and green 85 55
421 15 f. carmine and red 1·50 1·50
422 25 f. blue, green and ultramarine 3·50 2·75
423 50 f. brown and black (air) 3·00 2·25
424 100 f. blue, deep brown and brown 4·50 3·75

1950.

425 **85** 50 c. violet 10 10
426 1 f. brown 10 10
434 5 f. green 6·00 2·25
427 6 f. green 65 20
428 8 f. green 3·50 1·10
429 8 f. orange 90 35
435 10 f. orange 10·00 4·50
430 12 f. blue 1·25 25
431 15 f. red 2·25 35
432 15 f. blue 1·10 20
433 18 f. red 3·00 80

86 Prince Albert I

87 Edmond and Jules de Goncourt

1951. Unveiling of Prince Albert Statue.

436 **86** 15 f. blue 6·00 4·00

1951. 50th Anniv of Goncourt Academy.

437 **87** 15 f. purple 3·50 3·50

88 St. Vincent de Paul

90 St. Peter's Keys and Papal Bull

89 Judgement of St. Devote

1951. Holy Year.

438 **88** 10 c. blue, ultram & red 15 15
439 – 50 c. violet and red 15 15
440 **89** 1 f. green and brown 20 20
441 **90** 2 f. red and purple 30 30
442 – 5 f. green 30 30
443 – 12 f. violet 40 40
444 – 15 f. red 2·75 2·00
445 – 20 f. brown 4·00 2·50
446 – 25 f. blue 5·00 2·75
447 – 40 f. violet and mauve 6·50 3·50
448 – 50 f. brown and olive 7·75 5·00
449 – 100 f. brown 25·00 15·00

DESIGNS—TRIANGULAR: 50 c. Pope Pius XII. As Type **90**—HORIZ: 5 f. Mosaic. VERT: 12 f. Prince Rainier III in St. Peter's; 15 f. St. Nicholas of Patara; 20 f. St. Romain; 25 f. St. Charles Borromeo; 40 f. Coliseum; 50 f. Chapel of St. Devote. As Type **89**: VERT: 100 f. Rainier of Westphalia.

93 Wireless Mast and Monaco

94 Seal of Prince Rainier III

1951. Monte Carlo Radio Station.

450 **93** 1 f. orange, red and blue 55 20
451 15 f. purple, red and violet 2·75 55
452 30 f. brown and blue 10·00 2·00

1951.

453 **94** 1 f. violet 65 30
454 5 f. black 2·50 1·10
512 5 f. violet 2·25 65
513 6 f. red 2·75 80
455 8 f. red 4·50 2·50
514 8 f. brown 3·25 1·10
456 15 f. green 9·00 5·00
515 15 f. blue 11·00 2·50
457 30 f. blue 14·00 7·00
516 30 f. green 14·00 4·00

95 Gallery of Hercules

1952. Monaco Postal Museum.

460 **95** 5 f. chestnut and brown 30 30
461 15 f. violet and purple 55 30
462 30 f. indigo and blue 1·00 40

96 Football

1953. 15th Olympic Games, Helsinki. Inscr "HELSINKI 1952".

463 – 1 f. mauve & violet (postage) 20 15
464 **96** 2 f. blue and green 20 20
465 – 3 f. pale and deep blue 25 20
466 – 5 f. green and brown 70 30
467 – 8 f. red and lake 1·25 80
468 – 15 f. brown, green and blue 90 55
469 – 40 f. black (air) 9·00 6·50
470 – 50 f. violet 9·00 6·50
471 – 100 f. green 14·00 10·00
472 – 200 f. red 18·00 11·00

DESIGNS: 1 f. Basketball; 3 f. Yachting; 5 f. Cycling; 8 f. Gymnastics; 15 f. Louis II Stadium, Monaco; 40 f. Running; 50 f. Fencing; 100 f. Rifle target and Arms of Monaco; 200 f. Olympic torch.

97 "Journal Inedit"

1953. Centenary of Publication of Journal by E. and J. de Goncourt.

473 **97** 5 f. green 40 25
474 15 f. brown 1·50 50

98 Physalia, Yacht "Princess Alice", Prince Albert, Richet and Portier

1953. 50th Anniv of Discovery of Anaphylaxis.

475 **98** 2 f. violet, green and brown 10 10
476 5 f. red, lake and green 40 25
477 15 f. lilac, blue and green 2·25 1·10

99 F. Ozanam

100 St. Jean-Baptiste de la Salle

1954. Death Centenary of Ozanam (founder of St. Vincent de Paul Conferences).

478 **99** 1 f. red 10 10
479 – 5 f. blue 25 25
480 **99** 15 f. black 1·25 55

DESIGN: 5 f. Outline drawing of Sister of Charity.

1954. St. J.-B. de la Salle (educationist).

481 **100** 1 f. red 10 10
482 – 5 f. sepia 25 25
483 **100** 15 f. blue 1·25 40

DESIGN: 5 f. Outline drawing of De la Salle and two children.

101 102 103

1954. Arms.

484 – 50 c. red, black and mauve 10 10
485 – 70 c. red, black and blue 10 10
486 **101** 80 c. red, black and green 10 10
487 – 1 f. red, black and blue 10 10
488 **102** 2 f. red, black and orange 10 10
489 – 3 f. red, black and green 10 10
490 **103** 5 f. multicoloured 10 10

DESIGNS—HORIZ: 50 c. as Type **101**. VERT: 70 c., 1, 3 f. as Type **102**.

104 Seal of Prince Rainier III

1954. Precancelled.

491 **104** 4 f. red 65 20
492 5 f. blue 20 10
493 8 f. green 65 30
494 8 f. purple 55 20
495 10 f. green 20 10
496 12 f. violet 2·75 80
497 15 f. orange 80 55
498 20 f. green 80 55
499 24 f. brown 5·50 2·75
500 30 f. blue 1·10 65
501 40 f. brown 3·25 1·00
502 45 f. red 2·25 1·00
503 55 f. blue 5·50 1·60

See also Nos. 680/3.

105 Lambarene

106 Dr. Albert Schweitzer

1955. 80th Birthday of Dr. Schweitzer (humanitarian).

504 **105** 2 f. green, turquoise and blue (postage) 10 10
505 **106** 5 f. blue and green 65 65
506 – 15 f. purple, black and green 1·75 1·75
507 – 200 f. slate, green and blue (air) 28·00 17·00

DESIGNS—As Type **106**: 15 f. Lambarene Hospital. HORIZ—(48 × 27 mm): 200 f. Schweitzer and jungle scene.

107 Common Cormorants

1955. Air.

508a – 100 f. indigo and blue 15·00 12·00
509 – 200 f. black and blue 18·00 9·50
510 – 500 f. grey and green 30·00 16·00
511a **107** 1,000 f. black, turquoise and green 75·00 45·00

DESIGNS—As Type **107**: 100 f. Roseate tern; 200 f. Herring gull; 500 f. Wandering albatrosses.

108 Eight Starting Points

109 Prince Rainier III

1955. 25th Monte Carlo Car Rally.

517 **108** 100 f. red and brown 60·00 50·00

1955.

518 **109** 6 f. purple and green 10 10
519 8 f. violet and red 10 10
520 12 f. green and red 20 10
521 15 f. blue and purple 30 15
522 18 f. blue and orange 60 20
523 20 f. turquoise 70 30
524 25 f. black and orange 45 20
525 30 f. sepia and blue 11·00 3·75
526 30 f. violet 2·00 75
527 35 f. brown 3·50 90
528 50 f. lake and green 2·75 90

See also Nos. 627/41.

110 "La Maison a Vapeur"

111 "The 500 Millions of the Begum"

113 U.S.S. "Nautilus"

112 "Round the World in Eighty Days"

1955. 50th Death Anniv of Jules Verne (author). Designs illustrating his works.

529 – 1 f. blue & brown (postage) 10 10
530 – 2 f. sepia, indigo and blue 10 10
531 **110** 3 f. blue, black and brown 10 10
532 – 5 f. sepia and red 10 10
533 **111** 6 f. grey and sepia 25 25
534 – 8 f. turquoise and olive 35 35
535 – 10 f. sepia, turquoise & ind 80 80
536 **112** 15 f. red and brown 75 55
537 – 25 f. black and green 1·75 1·10
538 **113** 30 f. black, purple & turq 4·00 3·25

539	–	200 f. indigo & blue (air)	24·00	22·00

DESIGNS—As Type **111**—VERT: 1 f. "Five Weeks in a Balloon". HORIZ: 5 f. "Michael Strogoff"; 8 f. "Le Superbe Orenoque". As Type **110**: HORIZ: 2 f. "A Floating Island"; 10 f. "Journey to the Centre of the Earth"; 25 f. "20,000 Leagues under the Sea"; 200 f. "From Earth to Moon".

114 "The Immaculate Virgin" (F. Brea)

1955. Marian Year.

540	**114**	5 f. green, grey and brown	20	20
541	–	10 f. green, grey & brown	30	30
542	–	15 f. brown and sepia	40	40

DESIGNS—As Type **114**: 10 f. "Madonna" (L. Brea). As Type **113**: 15 f. Bienheureux Rainier.

115 Rotary Emblem

1955. 50th Anniv of Rotary International.

543	**115**	30 f. blue and yellow	70	70

116 George Washington
118 President Eisenhower

117 Abraham Lincoln

1956. 5th International Stamp Exhibition, New York.

544	**116**	1 f. violet and lilac	10	10
545	–	2 f. lilac and purple	10	10
546	**117**	3 f. blue and violet	10	10
547	**118**	5 f. red	20	20
548	–	15 f. brown and chocolate	45	45
549	–	30 f. black, indigo & blue	2·25	1·75
550	–	40 f. brown	1·60	1·60
551	–	50 f. red	2·25	2·25
552	–	100 f. green	2·75	2·75

DESIGNS—As Type **117**: 2 f. F. D. Roosevelt. As Type **116**—HORIZ: 15 f. Monaco Palace in the 18th century; 30 f. Landing of Columbus. LARGER (48×36 mm): 50 f. Aerial view of Monaco Palace in the 18th century; 100 f. Louisiana landscape in 18th century. As Type **118**: 40 f. Prince Rainier III.

120

1956. 7th Winter Olympic Games, Cortina d'Ampezzo and 16th Olympic Games, Melbourne.

553	–	15 f. brown, green & pur	90	55
554	**120**	30 f. red	1·50	1·00

DESIGN: 15 f. "Italia" ski-jump.

1956. Nos. D482/95 with "TIMBRE TAXE" barred out and some surch also. (a) Postage.

555	2 f. on 4 f. slate and brown	30	30
556	2 f. on 4 f. brown and slate	30	30
557	3 f. lake and green	35	35
558	3 f. green and lake	35	35
559	5 f. on 4 f. slate and brown	30	30
560	5 f. on 4 f. brown and slate	30	30
561	10 f. on 4 f. slate and brown	55	55
562	10 f. on 4 f. brown and slate	55	55
563	15 f. on 5 f. violet and blue	1·00	1·00
564	15 f. on 5 f. blue and violet	1·00	1·00
565	20 f. violet and blue	2·00	1·40
566	20 f. blue and violet	2·00	1·40
567	25 f. on 20 f. violet and blue	4·50	2·25
568	25 f. on 20 f. blue and violet	4·50	2·25
569	30 f. on 10 f. indigo and blue	5·50	4·50
570	30 f. on 10 f. blue and indigo	5·50	4·50
571	40 f. on 50 f. brown and red	7·75	4·50
572	40 f. on 50 f. red and brown	7·75	4·50
573	50 f. on 100 f. green and purple	11·00	6·50
574	50 f. on 100 f. purple and green	11·00	10·00

(b) Air. Optd **POSTE AERIENNE** also.

575	100 f. on 20 f. violet and blue	8·00	8·00
576	100 f. on 20 f. blue and violet	8·00	8·00

121 Route Map from Glasgow

1956. 26th Monte Carlo Car Rally.

577	**121**	100 f. brown and red	17·00	14·00

122 Princess Grace and Prince Rainier III

1956. Royal Wedding.

578	**122**	1 f. black & grn (postage)	10	10
579		2 f. black and red	10	10
580		3 f. black and blue	20	15
581		5 f. black and green	55	25
582		15 f. black and brown	80	40
583		100 f. brown & purple (air)	90	60
584		200 f. brown and red	1·10	65
585		500 f. brown and grey	2·50	2·00

123 Princess Grace
124 Princess Grace with Princess Caroline

1957. Birth of Princess Caroline.

586	**123**	1 f. grey	10	10
587		2 f. olive	10	10
588		3 f. brown	10	10
589		5 f. red	10	10
590		15 f. pink	10	10
591		25 f. blue	50	10
592		30 f. violet	50	10
593		50 f. red	1·00	20
594		75 f. orange	1·50	40

1958. Birth of Prince Albert.

595	**124**	100 f. black	4·50	3·50

125 Order of St. Charles
126 Route Map from Munich

1958. Centenary of Creation of National Order of St. Charles.

596	**125**	100 f. multicoloured	1·60	1·40

1958. 27th Monte Carlo Rally.

597	**126**	100 f. multicoloured	5·50	5·00

127 Statue of the Holy Virgin and Popes Pius IX and Pius XII

1958. Centenary of Apparition of Virgin Mary at Lourdes.

598	**127**	1 f. grey & brown (postage)	10	10
599	–	2 f. violet and blue	10	10
600	–	3 f. sepia and green	10	10
601	–	5 f. blue and sepia	10	10
602	–	8 f. multicoloured	15	15
603	–	10 f. multicoloured	15	10
604	–	12 f. multicoloured	20	15
605	–	20 f. myrtle and purple	30	20
606	–	35 f. myrtle, bistre and brown	40	30
607	–	50 f. blue, green and lake	65	55
608	–	65 f. turquoise and blue	90	70
609	–	100 f. grey, myrtle and blue (air)	1·40	1·10
610	–	200 f. brown and chestnut	2·00	1·75

DESIGNS—VERT: (26½×36 mm): 2 f. St. Bernadette; 3 f. St. Bernadette at Bartres; 5 f. The Miracle of Bourriette; 20 f. St. Bernadette at prayer; 35 f. St. Bernadette's canonization. (22×36 mm): 8 f. Stained-glass window. As Type **127**: 50 f. St. Bernadette, Pope Pius XI, Mgr. Laurence and Abbe Peyramale. HORIZ: (48×36 mm): 10 f. Lourdes grotto; 12 f. Interior of Lourdes grotto. (36×26½ mm): 65 f. Shrine of St. Bernadette; (48×27 mm): 100 f. Lourdes Basilica; 200 f. Pope Pius X and subterranean interior of Basilica.

128 Princess Grace and Clinic

1959. Opening of new hospital block in "Princess Grace" Clinic, Monaco.

611	**128**	100 f. grey, brown & green	1·25	80

129 U.N.E.S.C.O. Headquarters, Paris, and Cultural Emblems

1959. Inaug. of U.N.E.S.C.O. Headquarters Building.

612	**129**	25 f. multicoloured	15	10
613	–	50 f. turquoise, black & ol	35	30

DESIGN: 50 f. As Type **129** but with heads of children and letters of various alphabets in place of the emblems.

130 Route Map from Athens
131 Prince Rainier and Princess Grace

1959. 28th Monte Carlo Rally.

614	**130**	100 f. blue, red & grn on blue	4·00	3·50

1959. Air.

615	**131**	300 f. violet	7·75	3·75
616		500 f. blue	13·50	6·00

See also Nos. 642/3.

132 "Princess Caroline" Carnation

1959. Flowers.

617	**132**	5 f. mve, grn and brn	10	10
618	–	10 f. on 3 f. pink, green and brown	10	10
619	–	15 f. on 1 f. yellow & green	15	10
620	–	20 f. purple and green	35	25
621	–	25 f. on 6 f. red, yellow and green	55	30
622	–	35 f. pink and green	1·40	80
623	–	50 f. green and sepia	1·40	80
624	–	85 f. on 65 f. lavender, bronze and green	2·00	1·40
625	–	100 f. red and green	3·25	2·00

FLOWERS—As Type **132**: 10 f. "Princess Grace" carnation; 100 f. "Grace of Monaco" rose. VERT: (22×36 mm): 15 f. Mimosa; 25 f. Geranium. HORIZ: (36×22 mm): 20 f. Bougainvillea; 35 f. "Laurier" rose; 50 f. Jasmine; 85 f. Lavender.

(New currency. 100 (old) francs = 1 (new franc.)

133 "Uprooted Tree"
134 Oceanographic Museum

1960. World Refugee Year.

626	**133**	25 c. green, blue and black	15	15

1960. Prince Rainier types with values in new currency.

627	**109**	25 c. blk & orge (postage)	10	10
628		30 c. violet	20	10
629		40 c. red and brown	20	10
630		45 c. brown and grey	30	10
631		50 c. red and green	40	20
632		50 c. red and brown	40	10
633		60 c. brown and green	50	20
634		60 c. brown and purple	90	30
635		65 c. blue and brown	5·50	1·00
636		70 c. blue and plum	80	10
637		85 c. green and violet	1·00	40
638		95 c. blue	1·50	40
639		1 f. 10 blue and brown	1·50	80
640		1 f. 30 brown and red	2·75	1·10
641		2 f. 30 purple and orange	1·40	45
642	**131**	3 f. violet (air)	35·00	13·00
643		5 f. blue	35·00	16·00

1960.

644	–	5 c. green, black and blue	10	10
645	**134**	10 c. brown and blue	15	10
646	–	10 c. blue, violet and green	10	10
647	–	40 c. purple, grn & dp grn	45	10
648	–	45 c. brown, green & blue	2·00	20
649	–	70 c. brown, red and green	40	20
650	–	80 c. red, green and blue	90	40
651	–	85 c. black, brown & grey	5·25	1·10
652	–	90 c. red, blue and black	1·00	40
653	–	1 f. multicoloured	1·25	25
654	–	1 f. 15 black, red and blue	1·25	65
655	–	1 f. 30 brown, green & bl	80	35
656	–	1 f. 40 orange, green & vio	2·00	80

DESIGNS—HORIZ: 5 c. Palace of Monaco; 10 c. (No. 646), Aquatic Stadium; 40, 45, 80 c., 1 f. 40, Aerial view of Palace; 70, 85, 90 c., 1 f. 15, 1 f. 30, Court of Honour, Monaco Palace; 1 f. Palace floodlit.

134a St. Devote

1960. Air.

668	**134a**	2 f. violet, blue and green	1·40	75
669		3 f. brown, green and blue	2·00	1·10
670		5 f. red	3·50	90
671		10 f. brown, grey and green	5·50	3·25

135 Sea Horse

136 Route Map from Lisbon

1960. Marine Life and Plants. (a) Marine Life.
672 – 1 c. red and turquoise . . . 10 10
673 – 12 c. brown and blue . . 55 10
674 **135** 15 c. green and red . . . 65 10
675 – 20 c. multicoloured . . . 60 10
DESIGNS—HORIZ: 1 c. "Macrocheira kampferi" (crab); 20 c. "Pterois volitans". VERT: 12 c. "Fasciolaria trapezium" (shell).

(b) Plants.
676 – 2 c. multicoloured 10 10
677 – 15 c. orange, brown & olive 65 10
678 – 18 c. multicoloured 55 10
679 – 20 c. red, olive and brown . 55 10
PLANTS—VERT: 2 c. "Selenicereus sp."; 15 c. "Cereus sp."; 18 c. "Aloe ciliaris"; 20 c. "Nopalea dejecta".

1960. Prince Rainier Seal type with values in new currency. Precancelled.
680 **104** 8 c. purple 65 20
681 20 c. green . . . . 1·00 35
682 40 c. brown . . . . 1·60 65
683 55 c. blue . . . . 4·50 1·00

1960. 29th Monte Carlo Rally.
684 **136** 25 c. black, red and blue on blue . . . . 1·40 1·40

137 Stamps of Monaco 1885, France and Sardinia, 1860

1960. 75th Anniv of 1st Stamp.
685 **137** 25 c. bistre, blue and violet 70 70

138 Aquarium

1960. 50th Anniv of Oceanographic Museum, Monaco.
686 – 5 c. black, blue and purple 20 15
687 **138** 10 c. grey, brown and grn 35 35
688 – 15 c. black, bistre and blue 20 15
689 – 20 c. black, blue & mauve 45 20
690 – 25 c. turquoise 90 65
691 – 50 c. brown and blue . . 1·75 1·00
DESIGNS—VERT: 5 c. Oceanographic Museum (similar to Type **134**). HORIZ: 15 c. Conference Hall; 20 c. Hauling-in catch; 25 c. Museum, aquarium and under-water research equipment; 50 c. Prince Albert, "Hirondelle I" (schooner) and "Princess Alice" (steam yacht).

139 Horse-jumping

1960. Olympic Games.
692 **139** 5 c. brown, red and green 10 10
693 – 10 c. brown, blue & green 20 20
694 – 15 c. red, brown & purple 20 20
695 – 20 c. black, blue and green 2·00 2·00
696 – 25 c. purple, turq & grn 55 55
697 – 50 c. purple, blue & turq . 90 90
DESIGNS: 10 c. Swimming; 15 c. Long jumping; 20 c. Throwing the javelin; 25 c. Free-skating; 50 c. Skiing.

140 Rally Badge, Old and Modern Cars

1961. 50th Anniv of Monte Carlo Rally.
698 **140** 1 f. violet, red and brown 1·40 1·00

141 Route Map from Stockholm

142 Marine-life

1961. 30th Monte Carlo Rally.
699 **141** 1 f. multicoloured . . . . 1·10 1·10

1961. World Aquariological Congress. Orange network background.
700 **142** 25 c. red, sepia and violet 15 15

143 Leper in Town of Middle Ages

145 Insect within Protective Hand

144 Semi-submerged Sphinx of Ouadi-es-Saboua

1961. Sovereign Order of Malta.
701 **143** 25 c. black, red and brown 15 15

1961. U.N.E.S.C.O. Campaign for Preservation of Nubian Monuments.
702 **144** 50 purple, blue and brown 65 65

1962. Nature Preservation.
703 **145** 25 c. mauve and purple . 15 15

146 Chevrolet, 1912

1961. Veteran Motor Cars.
704 1 c. brown, green and chestnut 10 10
705 2 c. blue, purple and red . . 10 10
706 3 c. purple, black and mauve 10 10
707 4 c. blue, brown and violet . 10 10
708 5 c. green, red and olive . . . 10 10
709 10 c. brown, red and blue . . 10 10
710 15 c. green and turquoise . . 15 15
711 20 c. brown, red and violet . 20 20
712 25 c. violet, red and brown . 35 35
713 30 c. lilac and green 60 60
714 45 c. green, purple and brown 1·40 1·10
715 50 c. blue, red and brown . . 1·40 1·10
716 65 c. brown, red and grey . . 1·40 1·10
717 1 f. blue, red and violet . . . 2·75 2·75
MOTOR CARS: 1 c. Type **146**: 2 c. Peugeot, 1898; 3 c. Fiat, 1901; 4 c. Mercedes, 1901; 5 c. Rolls Royce, 1903;. 10 c. Panhard-Lavassor, 1899; 15 c. Renault, 1898; 20 c. Ford "N", 1906 (wrongly inscr "FORD-S-1908"); 25 c. Rochet-Schneider, 1894; 30 c. FN-Herstal, 1901; 45 c. De Dion Bouton, 1900; 50 c. Buick, 1910; 65 c. Delahaye, 1901; 1 f. Cadillac, 1906.

147 Racing Car and Race Route

1962. 20th Monaco Motor Grand Prix.
718 **147** 1 f. purple . . . . 1·40 1·00

148 Route Map from Oslo

1962. 31st Monte Carlo Rally.
719 **148** 1 f. multicoloured . . . . 1·10 90

149 Louis XII and Lucien Grimaldi

1962. 450th Anniv of Recognition of Monegasque Sovereignty by Louis XII.
720 **149** 25 c. black, red and blue 20 20
721 – 50 c. brown, lake and blue 20 20
722 – 1 f. red, green and brown 55 55
DESIGNS: 50 c. Parchment bearing declaration of sovereignty; 1 f. Seals of two Sovereigns.

150 Mosquito and Swamp

1962. Malaria Eradication.
723 **150** 1 f. green and olive 50 30

151 Sun, Bouquet and "Hope Chest"

1962. National Multiple Sclerosis Society, New York.
724 **151** 20 c. multicoloured 15 10

152 Harvest Scene

1962. Europa.
725 **152** 25 c. brown, green and blue (postage) 15 15
726 50 c. olive and turquoise 25 25
727 1 f. olive and purple . . . 55 55
728 – 2 f. slate, brown and green (air) . . . . 1·00 90
DESIGN: 2 f. Mercury in flight over Europe.

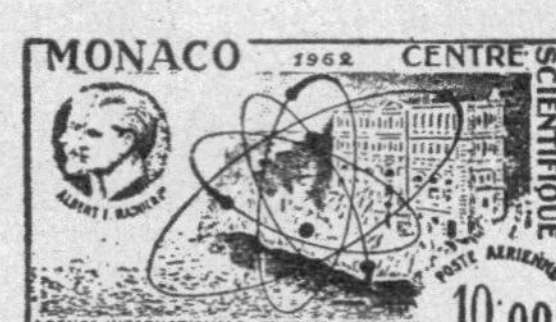

153 Atomic Symbol and Scientific Centre, Monaco

1962. Air. Scientific Centre, Monaco.
729 **153** 10 f. violet, brown & blue 5·50 5·00

154 Yellow Wagtails

155 Galeazzi's Diving Turret

1962. Protection of Birds useful to Agriculture.
730 **154** 5 c. yellow, brown & green 10 10
731 – 10 c. red, bistre and purple 10 10
732 – 15 c. multicoloured . . . 15 10
733 – 20 c. sepia, green & mauve 15 10
734 – 25 c. multicoloured . . . 50 20
735 – 30 c. brown, blue & myrtle 60 40
736 – 45 c. brown and violet . . 90 50
737 – 50 c. black, olive & turq 1·40 60
738 – 85 c. multicoloured . . . 1·90 1·10
739 – 1 f. sepia, red and green 2·50 1·25
BIRDS: 10 c. European robins; 15 c. Goldfinches; 20 c. Blackcaps; 25 c. Greater spotted woodpeckers; 30 c. Nightingale; 45 c. Barn owls; 50 c. Common starlings; 85 c. Red crossbills; 1 f. White storks.

1962. Underwater Exploration.
740 – 5 c. black, violet and blue 10 10
741 **155** 10 c. blue, violet & brown 10 10
742 – 25 c. bistre, green and blue 10 10
743 – 45 c. black, blue and green 35 25
744 – 50 c. green, bistre and blue 35 35
745 – 85 c. blue and turquoise 65 60
746 – 1 f. brown, green and blue 90 90
DESIGNS—HORIZ: 5 c. Divers; 25 c. Williamson's photosphere (1914) and bathyscape "Trieste"; 45 c. Klingert's diving-suit (1797) and modern diving-suit; 50 c. Diving saucer; 85 c. Fulton's "Nautilus" (1800) and modern submarine; 1 f. Alexander the Great's diving bell and Beebe's bathysphere.

156 Donor's Arm and Globe

158 Feeding Chicks in Nest

157 "Ring-a-ring o' Roses"

1962. 3rd Int Blood Donors' Congress' Monaco.
747 **156** 1 f. red, sepia and orange 40 40

1963. U.N. Children's Charter.
748 **157** 5 c. red, blue and ochre . 10 10
749 **158** 10 c. green, sepia and blue 10 10
750 – 15 c. blue, red and green 10 10
751 – 20 c. multicoloured . . . 10 10
752 – 25 c. blue, purple & brown 20 20
753 – 50 c. multicoloured . . . 30 30
754 – 95 c. multicoloured . . . 65 45
755 – 1 f. purple, red & turq . . 1·10 90
DESIGNS—As Type **157**: 1 f. Prince Albert and Princess Caroline; Children's paintings as Type **158**: HORIZ: 15 c. Children on scales; 50 c. House and child. VERT: 20 c. Sun's rays and children of three races; 25 c. Mother and child; 95 c. Negress and child.

159 Ship's Figurehead

160 Racing Cars

1963. International Red Cross Centenary.
756 **159** 50 c. red, brown & turquoise 25 25
757 – 1 f. multicoloured 55 55
DESIGN—HORIZ: 1 f. Moynier, Dunant and Dufour.

1963. European Motor Grand Prix.
758 **160** 50 c. multicoloured . . . 40 35

161 Emblem and Charter

1963. Founding of Lions Club of Monaco.
759 **161** 50 c. blue, bistre and violet 40 40

162 Hotel des Postes and U.P.U. Monument, Berne

1963. Paris Postal Conference Centenary.
760 **162** 50 c. lake, green & yellow 30 30

163 "Telstar" Satellite and Globe

1963. 1st Link Trans-Atlantic T.V. Satellite.
761 **163** 50 c. brown, green & pur . 40 40

164 Route Map from Warsaw

1963. 32nd Monte Carlo Rally.
762 **164** 1 f. multicoloured 90 80

165 Feeding Chicks

1963. Freedom from Hunger.
763 **165** 1 f. multicoloured 50 50

166 Allegory

1963. 2nd Ecumenical Council, Vatican City.
764 **166** 1 f. turquoise, green and red 40 40

167 Henry Ford and Ford "A" Car of 1903

1963. Birth Centenary of Henry Ford (motor pioneer).
765 **167** 20 c. green and purple . . 20 20

168 H. Garin (winner of 1903 race) cycling through Village

1963. 50th "Tour de France" Cycle Race.
766 **168** 25 c. green, brown & blue 20 20
767 – 50 c. sepia, green & blue 25 25
DESIGN: 50 c. Cyclist passing Desgrange Monument, Col du Galibier, 1963.

169 P. de Coubertin and Discus-thrower

1963. Birth Centenary of Pierre de Coubertin (reviver of Olympic Games).
768 **169** 1 f. brown, red and lake . 40 40

170 Roland Garros and Morane Saulnier Type I

1963. Air. 50th Anniv of 1st Aerial Crossing of Mediterranean Sea.
769 **170** 2 f. sepia and blue . . . 1·10 90

171 Route Map from Paris **173** "Europa"

172 Children with Stamp Album

1963. 33rd Monte Carlo Rally.
770 **171** 1 f. red, turquoise and blue 70 60

1963. "Scolatex" International Stamp Exn, Monaco.
771 **172** 50 c. blue, violet and red 20 20

1963. Europa.
772 **173** 25 c. brown, red and green 20 20
773 50 c. sepia, red and& blue 30 30

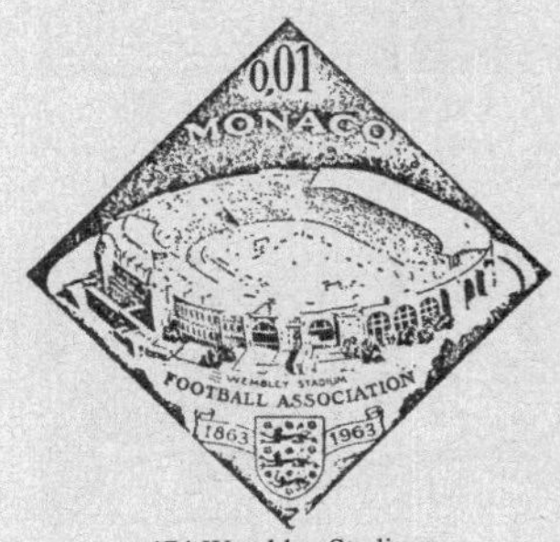

174 Wembley Stadium

1963. Cent of (English) Football Association.
774 **174** 1 c. violet, green and red 10 10
775 – 2 c. red, black and green 10 10
776 – 3 c. orange, olive and red 10 10
777 – 4 c. multicoloured 10 10
Multicoloured horiz designs depicting (a) "Football through the Centuries".
778 10 c. "Calcio", Florence (16th cent) 10 10
779 15 c. "Soule", Brittany (19th cent) 10 10
780 20 c. English military college (after Cruickshank, 1827) . 10 10
781 25 c. English game (after Overend, 1890) 10 10
(b) "Modern Football".
782 30 c. Tackling 20 20
783 50 c. Saving goal 55 55
784 95 c. Heading ball 80 80
785 1 f. Corner kick . . . . 1·00 1·00
DESIGNS—As Type **174**: 4 c. Louis II Stadium, Monaco. This stamp is optd in commemoration of the Association Sportive de Monaco football teams in the French Championships and in the Coupe de France, 1962–63. HORIZ: (36×22 mm): 2 c. Footballer making return kick; 3 c. Goalkeeper saving ball.
Nos. 778/81 and 782/5 were respectively issued together in sheets and arranged in blocks of 4 with a football in the centre of each block.

175 Communications in Ancient Egypt, and Rocket

1964. "PHILATEC 1964" Int Stamp Exn, Paris.
786 **175** 1 f. brown, indigo & blue . 40 40

176 Reproduction of Rally Postcard Design

1964. 50th Anniv of 1st Aerial Rally, Monte Carlo.
787 1 c. olive, blue & grn (postage) 10 10
788 2 c. bistre, brown and blue . . 10 10
789 3 c. brown, blue and green . . 10 10
790 4 c. red, turquoise and blue . 10 10
791 5 c. brown, red and violet . . 10 10
792 10 c. violet, brown and blue . 10 10
793 15 c. orange, brown and blue . 10 10
794 20 c. sepia, green and blue . 20 10
795 25 c. brown, blue and red . . 30 10
796 30 c. myrtle, purple and blue . 40 20
797 45 c. sepia, turquoise & brn . . 55 35
798 50 c. ochre, olive and violet . . 65 45
799 65 c. red, slate and turquoise 90 55
800 95 c. turquoise, red and bistre 1·40 90
801 1 f. brown, blue and turquoise 1·50 1·00
802 5 f. sepia, blue & brown (air) 3·00 3·00
DESIGNS: 1 c. Type **176**. 48×27 mm—Rally planes: 2 c. Renaux's Farman M.F.7 floatplane; 3 c. Espanet's Nieuport 4 seaplane; 4 c. Moineau's Breguet HU-3 seaplane; 5 c. Roland Garros' Morane Saulnier Type I seaplane; 10 c. Hirth's WDD Albatros seaplane; 15 c. Prevost's Deperdussin Monocoque Racer. Famous planes and flights: 20 c. Vickers–Vimy (Ross Smith: London–Port Darwin, 1919); 25 c. Douglas World Cruiser seaplane (U.S. World Flight, 1924); 30 c. Savoia Marchetti S-55M flying boat "Santa Maria" (De Pinedo's World Flight, 1925); 45 c. Fokker F. VIIa/3m "Josephine Ford" (Flight over North Pole, Byrd and Bennett, 1925); 50 c. Ryan NYP Special "Spirit of St. Louis" (1st solo crossing of N. Atlantic, Lindbergh, 1927); 65 c. Breguet 19 "Point d'Interrogation" (Paris–New York, Coste and Bellonte, 1930); 95 c. Latecoere 28-3 seaplane "Comte de la Vaulx" (Dakar–Natal, first S. Atlantic airmail flight, Mermoz, 1930); 1 f. Dornier Do-X flying boat (Germany–Rio de Janeiro, Christiansen, 1930); 5 f. Convair B-58 Hustler (New York–Paris in 3 hours, 19' 41" Major Payne, U.S.A.F., 1961).

177 Aquatic Stadium **178** Europa "Flower"

1964. Precancelled.
803 **177** 10 c. multicoloured . . . 1·50 20
803a 15 c. multicoloured . . . 75 20
804 25 c. turquoise, blue & blk 75 20
805 50 c. violet, turq & blk . 1·40 65
The "1962" date has been obliterated with two bars.
See also Nos. 949/51a and 1227/1230.

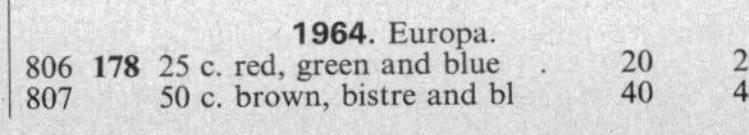

1964. Europa.
806 **178** 25 c. red, green and blue . 20 20
807 50 c. brown, bistre and bl 40 40

179 Weightlifting

1964. Olympic Games, Tokyo and Innsbruck.
808 **179** 1 c. red, brown and blue (postage) 10 10
809 – 2 c. red, green and olive . 10 10
810 – 3 c. blue, brown and red . 10 10
811 – 4 c. green, olive and red . 10 10
812 – 5 f. red, brown and blue (air) 2·25 2·25
DESIGNS: 2 c. Judo; 3 c. Pole vaulting; 4 c. Archery; 5 f. Bobsleighing.

180 Pres. Kennedy and Space Capsule

1964. Pres. Kennedy Commemoration.
813 **180** 50 c. indigo and blue . . 40 40

181 Monaco and Television Set

1964. 5th Int Television Festival, Monte Carlo.
814 **181** 50 c. brown, blue and red 30 30

182 F. Mistral and Statue

1964. 50th Death Anniv of Frederic Mistral (poet).
815 **182** 1 f. brown and olive . . . 35 35

183 Scales of Justice

1964. 15th Anniv of Declaration of Human Rights.
816 **183** 1 f. green and brown . . 40 40

184 Route Map from Minsk

1964. 34th Monte Carlo Rally.
817 **184** 1 f. brown, turq & ochre 55 40

185 FIFA Emblem

1964. 60th Anniv of Federation Internationale de Football Association (FIFA).
818 **185** 1 f. bistre, blue and red . 60 60

186 "Syncom 2" and Globe

1965. Cent of I.T.U.
819 **186** 5 c. green & ultra (postage) 10 10
820 – 10 c. chestnut, brown & bl 10 10
821 – 12 c. purple, red and grey 10 10
822 – 18 c. blue, red and purple 10 10
823 – 25 c. violet, bistre & purple 10 10
824 – 30 c. bistre, brown & sepia 20 20
825 – 50 c. blue and green . . . 25 25
826 – 60 c. blue and brown . . 25 25
827 – 70 c. sepia, orange & blue 40 40
828 – 95 c. black, indigo & blue 65 65
829 – 1 f. brown and blue . . . 90 90
830 – 10 f. green, blue and brown (air) . . . . 4·00 4·00

DESIGNS—As Type **186**: HORIZ: 10 c. "Echo 2"; 18 c. "Lunik 3"; 30 c. A. G. Bell and telephone; 50 c. S. Morse and telegraph; 60 c. E. Belin and "belinograph". VERT: 12 c. "Relay"; 10 f. Monte Carlo television transmitter. LARGER (48½ × 27 mm): 25 c. "Telstar" and Pleumeur-Bodou Station; 70 c. Roman beacon and Chappe's telegraph; 95 c. Cable-laying ships "Great Eastern" and "Alsace"; 1 f. E. Branly, G. Marconi and English Channel.

187 Europa "Sprig"

1965. Europa.
831 **187** 30 c. brown and green . . 15 15
832 60 c. violet and red . . . 30 30

188 Monaco Palace (18th cent)

1966. 750th Anniv of Monaco Palace.
833 **188** 10 c. violet, green and blue 10 10
834 – 12 c. bistre, blue and black 10 10
835 – 18 c. green, black & blue 15 15
836 – 30 c. brown, black & blue 20 20
837 – 60 c. green, blue & bistre 30 30
838 – 1 f. 30 brown and green 80 80

DESIGNS: (Different views of Palace): 12 c. 17th century; 18 c. 18th century; 30 c. 19th century; 60 c. 19th century; 1 f. 30, 20th century.

189 Dante

1966. 700th Anniv of Dante's Birth.
839 **189** 30 c. green, deep green and red 20 20
840 – 60 c. blue, turquoise & grn 40 40
841 – 70 c. black, green and red 55 55
842 – 95 c. blue, violet & purple 80 80
843 – 1 f. turquoise, blue & dp bl 80 80

DESIGNS: (Scenes from Dante's works): 60 c. Dante harassed by the panther (envy); 70 c. Crossing the 5th circle; 95 c. Punishment of the arrogant; 1 f. Invocation of St. Bernard.

190 "The Nativity"

1966. World Assn. of Children's Friends (A.M.A.D.E.).
844 **190** 30 c. brown 20 20

191 Route Map from London

1966. 35th Monte Carlo Rally.
845 **191** 1 f. blue, purple and red . 55 55

192 Princess Grace with Children

1966. Air. Princess Stephanie's 1st Birthday.
846 **192** 3 f. brown, blue and violet 2·00 1·60

193 Casino in 19th Century **194** Europa "Ship"

1966. Centenary of Monte Carlo.
847 – 12 c. black, red and blue (postage) 10 10
848 **193** 25 c. multicoloured . . . 10 10
849 – 30 c. multicoloured . . . 10 10
850 – 40 c. multicoloured . . . 20 20
851 – 60 c. multicoloured . . . 30 30
852 – 70 c. blue and lake . . . 65 65
853 – 95 c. black and purple . .
854 – 1 f. 30 purple, brown and chestnut 90 90
855 – 5 f. lake, ochre and blue (air) 2·25 2·25

DESIGNS—VERT: 12 c. Prince Charles III. HORIZ: 40 c. Charles III Monument; 95 c. Massenet and Saint-Saens; 1 f. 30, Faure and Ravel. LARGER (48 × 27 mm): 30 c. F. Blanc, originator of Monte Carlo, and view of 1860; 60 c. Prince Rainier III and projected esplanade; 70 c. Rene Blum and Diaghilev, ballet character from "Petrouchka". (36 × 36 mm): 5 f. Interior of Opera House, 1879.

1966. Europa.
856 **194** 30 c. orange 15 15
857 60 c. green 25 25

195 Prince Rainier and Princess Grace **197** "Learning to Write"

196 Prince Albert I and Yachts "Hirondelle I" and "Princess Alice"

1966. Air.
858 **195** 2 f. slate and red 90 40
859 3 f. slate and green . . . 2·00 70
860 5 f. slate and blue . . . 2·25 90
861 10 f. slate and bistre . . 4·50 3·00
862 20 f. brown and orange . 50·00 30·00

1966. 1st International Oceanographic History Congress, Monaco.
861 **196** 1 f. lilac and blue . . . . 1·40 1·00

1966. 20th Anniv of U.N.E.S.C.O.
862 **197** 30 c. purple and mauve . . 10 10
863 60 c. brown and blue . . . 25 25

198 T.V. Screen, Cross and Monaco Harbour **200** W.H.O. Building

199 "Precontinent III"

1966. 10th Meeting of International Catholic Television Association (U.N.D.A.), Monaco.
864 **198** 60 c. red, purple & crimson 20 15

1966. 1st Anniv of Underwater Research Craft "Precontinent III".
865 **199** 1 f. yellow, brown & blue . 35 30

1966. Inaug of W.H.O. Headquarters, Geneva.
866 **200** 30 c. brown, grn and blue 10 10
867 60 c. brown, red and green 20 20

201 Bugatti, 1931 **202** Dog (Egyptian bronze)

1967. 25th Motor Grand Prix, Monaco. Multicoloured. (a) Postage.
868 1 c. Type **201** 10 10
869 2 c. Alfa-Romeo, 1932 . . . . 10 10
870 5 c. Mercedes, 1936 . . . . 10 10
871 10 c. Maserati, 1948 . . . . 10 10
872 18 c. Ferrari, 1955 . . . . . 10 10
873 20 c. Alfa-Romeo, 1950 . . . 10 10
874 25 c. Maserati, 1957 . . . . 15 15
875 30 c. Cooper-Climax, 1958 . . 15 15
876 40 c. Lotus-Climax, 1960 . . 20 20
877 50 c. Lotus-Climax, 1961 . . 40 20
878 60 c. Cooper-Climax, 1962 . . 65 40
879 70 c. B.R.M., 1963-6 . . . . 80 55
880 1 f. Walter Christie, 1907 . . 1·00 80
881 2 f. 30 Peugeot, 1910 . . . . 2·00 1·50

(b) Air. Diamond. 50 × 50 mm.
882 3 f. black and blue . . . . . 1·50 1·25

DESIGN: Panhard-Phenix, 1895.

1967. Int Cynological Federation Congress, Monaco.
883 **202** 30 c. black, purple & green 25 25

203 View of Monte Carlo

1967. International Tourist Year.
884 **203** 30 c. brown, green & blue 15 10

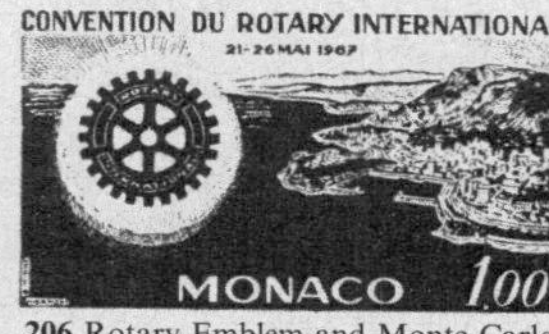

204 Pieces on Chessboard

1967. Int Chess Grand Prix, Monaco.
885 **204** 60 c. black, plum and blue 65 50

205 Melvin Jones (founder), Lions Emblem and Monte Carlo

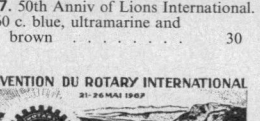

1967. 50th Anniv of Lions International.
886 **205** 60 c. blue, ultramarine and brown 30 20

206 Rotary Emblem and Monte Carlo

1967. Rotary International Convention.
887 **206** 1 f. bistre, blue and green 40 30

207 Fair Buildings

1967. World Fair, Montreal.
888 **207** 1 f. red, slate and blue . . 30 30

208 Squiggle on Map of Europe **209** Cogwheels

1967. European Migration Committee (C.I.M.E.).
889 **208** 1 f. brown, bistre and blue 30 25

1967. Europa.
890 **209** 30 c. violet, purple and red 20 20
891 60 c. green, turq & emerald 30 30

1967. 9th Int Hydrographic Congress, Monaco.
892 **210** 1 f. brown, blue and green 35 30

210 Dredger and Coastal Chart

211 Marie Curie and Scientific Equipment

1967. Birth Centenary of Marie Curie.
893 **211** 1 f. blue, olive & brown . 35 30

212 Skiing

1967. Winter Olympic Games, Grenoble.
894 **212** 2 f. 30 brown, blue & slate 1·00 80

213 "Prince Rainier I" (E. Charpentier)

1967. Paintings. "Princes and Princesses of Monaco". Multicoloured.
895 1 f. Type **213** 40 40
896 1 f. "Lucien Grimaldi" (A. di Predis) 40 40
See also Nos. 932/3, 958/9, 1005/6, 1023/4, 1070/1, 1108/9, 1213/14, 1271/2, 1325, 1380/1, 1405/6, 1460/1 and 1531/2.

214 Putting the Shot

1968. Olympic Games, Mexico.
897 **214** 20 c. blue, brown and green (postage) 10 10
898 – 30 c. brown, blue & plum 10 10
899 – 60 c. blue, purple and red 20 20
900 – 70 c. red, blue and ochre 25 25
901 – 1 f. blue, brown and orange 50 50
902 – 2 f. 30 olive, blue and lake 1·10 1·10
903 – 3 f. blue, violet & grn (air) 1·50 1·25
DESIGNS: 30 c. High-jumping; 60 c. Gymnastics; 70 c. Water-polo; 1 f. Greco-Roman wrestling; 2 f. 30, Gymnastics (different); 3 f. Hockey.

215 "St. Martin"

1968. 20th Anniv of Monaco Red Cross.
904 **215** 2 f. 30 blue and brown . . 90 90

216 "Anemones" (after Raoul Dufy)

217 Insignia of Prince Charles III and Pope Pius IX

1968. Monte Carlo Floral Exhibitions.
905 **216** 1 f. multicoloured 55 55

1968. Centenary of "Nullius Diocesis" Abbey.
906 **217** 10 c. brown and red . . . 10 10
907 – 20 c. red, green and brown 10 10
908 – 30 c. brown and blue . . 20 20
909 – 60 c. brown, blue & green 25 25
910 – 1 f. indigo, bistre and blue 40 40
DESIGNS—VERT: 20 c. "St. Nicholas" (after Louis Brea); 30 c. "St. Benedict" (after Simone Martini); 60 c. Subiaco Abbey. HORIZ: 1 f. Old St. Nicholas' Church (on site of present cathedral).

218 Europa "Key"

1968. Europa.
911 **218** 30 c. red and orange . . 20 20
912 60 c. blue and red 30 30
913 1 f. brown and green . . 90 65

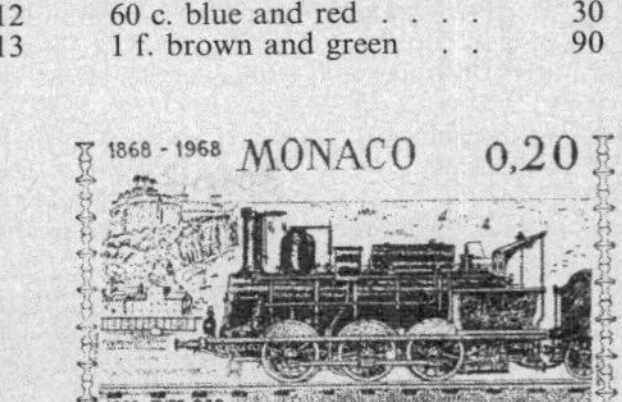

219 Type 0-3-0 Steam Locomotive (1868)

1968. Centenary of Nice–Monaco Railway.
914 **219** 20 c. black, blue & purple 30 25
915 – 30 c. black, blue and olive 40 35
916 – 60 c. black, blue and ochre 90 40
917 – 70 c. black, violet & brown 1·40 75
918 – 1 f. black, blue and red . 2·00 1·40
919 – 2 f. 30 blue, black and red 2·75 2·40
DESIGNS: 30 c. Type "C-220" steam locomotive (1898); 60 c. Type "230-C" steam locomotive (1910); 70 c. Type "231-F" steam locomotive (1925); 1 f. Type "241-A" steam locomotive (1952); 2 f. 30, Type "BB" electric locomotive (1968).

220 Chateaubriand and Combourg Castle

1968. Birth Centenary of Chateaubriand (novelist).
920 **220** 10 c. plum, green & myrtle 10 10
921 – 20 c. violet, purple & blue 10 10
922 – 25 c. brown, violet & blue 10 10
923 – 30 c. violet, choc & brn . 15 15
924 – 60 c. brown, grn & red . 25 25
925 – 2 f. 30 brown, mve & blue 90 90
Scenes from Chateaubriand's novels: 20 c. "Le Genie du Christianisme"; 25 c. "Rene"; 30 c. "Le Dernier Abencerage"; 60 c. "Les Martyrs"; 2 f. 30, "Atala".

221 Law Courts, Paris, and statues–"La France et la Fidelite"

1968. Birth Centenary of J. F. Bosio (Monegasque sculptor).
926 **221** 20 c. brown and purple . 10 10
927 – 25 c. brown and red . . . 10 10
928 – 30 c. blue and green . . 10 10
929 – 60 c. green and myrtle . . 25 20
930 – 2 f. 30 black and slate . . 75 65
DESIGNS—VERT: (26 × 36 mm): 25 c. "Henry IV as a Child"; 30 c. "J. F. Bosio" (lithograph); 60 c. "Louis XIV". HORIZ: As Type **221**: 2 f. 30, "Napoleon I, Louis XVIII and Charles X".

222 W.H.O. Emblem

1968. 20th Anniv of W.H.O.
931 **222** 60 c. multicoloured . . . 25 20

1968. Paintings. "Princes and Princesses of Monaco". As T **213**. Multicoloured.
932 1 f. "Prince Charles II" (Mimault) 30 30
933 2 f. 30 "Princess Jeanne Grimaldi" (Mimault) . . . 70 70

223 The Hungarian March

1969. Death Centenary of Hector Berlioz (composer).
934 **223** 10 c. brown, violet and green (postage) 10 10
935 – 20 c. brown, olive & mauve 10 10
936 – 25 c. brown, blue & mauve 10 10
937 – 30 c. black, green & black 10 10
938 – 40 c. red, black and slate 10 10
939 – 50 c. brown, slate & purple 15 15
940 – 70 c. brown, slate & green 25 20
941 – 1 f. black, mauve & brown 35 25
942 – 1 f. 15 black, blue & turq 50 40
943 – 2 f. black, blue & grn (air) 90 80
DESIGNS—HORIZ: 20 c. Mephistopheles appears to Faust; 25 c. Auerbach's tavern; 30 c. Sylphs' ballet; 40 c. Minuet of the goblins; 50 c. Marguerite's bedroom; 70 c. "Forests and caverns"; 1 f. The journey to Hell; 1 f. 15, Heaven; All scenes from Berlioz's "The Damnation of Faust". VERT: 2 f. Bust of Berlioz.

224 "St. Elisabeth of Hungary"

1969. Monaco Red Cross.
944 **224** 3 f. blue, brown and red 1·40 1·10

225 "Napoleon I" (P. Delaroche)

1969. Birth Bicentenary of Napoleon Bonaparte.
945 **225** 3 f. multicoloured . . . . 1·10 1·00

226 Colonnade

227 "Head of Woman" (Da Vinci)

1969. Europa.
946 **226** 40 c. red and purple . . . 30 10
947 70 c. blue, brown & black 80 45
948 1 f. ochre, brown and blue 1·00 65

1969. Precancelled. As T **177**. No date.
949 22 c. brown, blue and black . 35 10
949a 26 c. violet, blue and black . 40 15
949b 30 c. multicoloured 65 15
950 35 c. multicoloured 45 10
950a 45 c. multicoloured 65 10
951 70 c. black and blue 65 35
951a 90 c. green, blue and black 1·25 35

1969. 450th Death Anniv of Leonardo da Vinci.
952 **227** 30 c. brown 10 10
953 – 40 c. red and brown . . . 15 10
954 – 70 c. green 25 20
955 – 80 c. sepia 35 25
956 – 1 f. 15 brown 55 45
957 – 3 f. brown . . . . 1·40 80
DRAWINGS: 40 c. Self-portrait; 70 c. "Head of an Old Man"; 80 c. "Head of St. Madeleine"; 1 f. 15, "Man's Head"; 3 f. "The Condottiere".

1969. Paintings. "Princes and Princesses of Monaco". As T **213**. Multicoloured.
958 1 f. "Prince Honore II" (Champaigne) 35 35
959 3 f. "Princess Louise-Hippolyte" (Champaigne) . . . . 1·00 1·00

228 Marine Fauna, King Alfonso XIII of Spain and Prince Albert I of Monaco

229 I.L.O. Emblem

1969. 50th Anniv of Int Commission for Scientific Exploration of the Mediterranean, Madrid.
960 **228** 40 c. blue and black . . . 20 20

1969. 50th Anniv of I.L.O.
961 **229** 40 c. multicoloured . . . 20 20

230 Aerial View of Monaco and T.V. Camera

1969. 10th International Television Festival.
962 **230** 40 c. purple, lake and blue 15 15

231 J.C.C. Emblem

1969. 25th Anniv of Junior Chamber of Commerce.
963 **231** 40 c. violet, bistre and blue 15 15

232 Alphonse Daudet and Scenes from "Lettres"

1969. Centenary of Daudet's "Lettres de Mon Moulin".
964 **232** 30 c. lake, violet and green 10 10
965 – 40 c. green, brown & blue 20 20
966 – 70 c. multicoloured . . . 30 25
967 – 80 c. violet, brown & grn 30 30
968 – 1 f. 15 brown, orange & bl 50 50
DESIGNS: (Scenes from the book): 40 c. "Installation" (Daudet writing); 70 c. "Mule, Goat and Wolf"; 80 c. "Gaucher's Elixir" and "The Three Low Masses"; 1 f. 15, Daudet drinking, "The Old Man" and "The Country Sub-Prefect".

233 Conference Building, Albert I and Rainier III

1970. Interparliamentary Union's Spring Meeting, Monaco.
969 **233** 40 c. black, red and purple 15 10

234 Baby Common Seal

1970. Protection of Baby Seals.
970 **234** 40 c. drab, blue and purple 40 30

235 Japanese Print

236 Dobermann

1970. Expo 70.
971 **235** 20 c. brown, green and red . . . 10 10
972 – 30 c. brown, buff & green . . . 25 20
973 – 40 c. bistre and violet . . . 15 15
974 – 70 c. grey and red . . . 50 50
975 – 1 f. 15 red, green & purple . . . 55 55
DESIGNS—VERT: 30 c. Manchurian Cranes (birds); 40 c. Shinto temple gateway. HORIZ: 70 c. Cherry blossom; 1 f. 15, Monaco Palace and Osaka Castle.

1970. International Dog Show, Monte Carlo.
976 **236** 40 c. black and brown . . 65 40

237 Apollo

1970. 20th Anniv of World Federation for Protection of Animals.
977 **237** 30 c. black, red and blue . 40 20
978 – 40 c. brown, blue & green . 40 20
979 – 50 c. brown, ochre & blue . 55 40
980 – 80 c. brown, blue & green . 80 55
981 – 1 f. brown, bistre and slate . 1·50 90
982 – 1 f. 15 brown, green & blue . 2·00 1·10
DESIGNS—HORIZ: 40 c. Basque ponies; 50 c. Common seal. VERT: 80 c. Chamois; 1 f. White-tailed sea eagles; 1 f. 15, European otter.

238 "St. Louis" (King of France)

1970. Monaco Red Cross.
983 **238** 3 f. green, brown and slate . 1·25 1·10
See also Nos. 1022, 1041, 1114, 1189 and 1270.

239 "Roses and Anemones" (Van Gogh)

1970. Monte Carlo Flower Show.
984 **239** 3 f. multicoloured . . . . 1·50 1·25
See also Nos. 1042 and 1073.

240 Moon Plaque, Presidents Kennedy and Nixon

1970. 1st Man on the Moon (1969). Multicoloured.
985 40 c. Type **240** 15 10
986 80 c. Astronauts on Moon . . 65 40

241 New U.P.U. Building and Monument

242 "Flaming Sun"

1970. New U.P.U. Headquarters Building.
987 **241** 40 c. brown, black & green 15 10

1970. Europa.
988 **242** 40 c. purple 20 10
989 80 c. green 55 30
990 1 f. blue 90 55

243 Camargue Horse

1970. Horses.
991 **243** 10 c. slate, olive and blue (postage) 10 10
992 – 20 c. brown, olive and blue 20 10
993 – 30 c. brown, green & blue 20 15
994 – 40 c. grey, brown & slate 30 20
995 – 50 c. brown, olive & blue 65 35
996 – 70 c. brown, orange & grn 1·00 65
997 – 85 c. blue, green and olive 1·50 90
998 – 1 f. 15 black, green & blue 2·00 1·40
999 – 3 f. multicoloured (air) . 1·50 1·40
HORSES—HORIZ: 20 c. Anglo-Arab; 30 c. French saddle-horse; 40 c. Lippizaner; 50 c. Trotter; 70 c. English thoroughbred; 85 c. Arab; 1 f. 15, Barbary. DIAMOND (50 × 50 mm): 3 f. Rock-drawings of horses in Lascaux grotto.

244 Dumas, D'Artagnan and the Three Musketeers

1970. Birth Centenary of Alexandre Dumas (pere) (author).
1000 **244** 30 c. slate, brown & blue 10 10

245 Henri Rougier and Voisin "Boxkite"

1970. 60th Anniv of First Mediterranean Flight.
1001 **245** 40 c. brown, blue & slate 20 10

246 De Lamartine and scene from "Meditations Poetiques"

1970. 150th Birth Anniv of A. de Lamartine (writer).
1002 **246** 80 c. brown, blue & turq 30 15

247 Beethoven

1970. Birth Bicentenary of Beethoven.
1003 **247** 1 f. 30 brown and red . 1·00 65

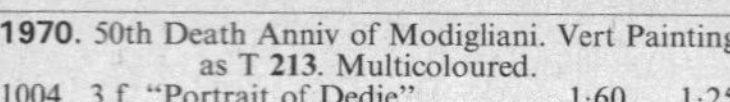
1970. 50th Death Anniv of Modigliani. Vert Painting as T **213**. Multicoloured.
1004 3 f. "Portrait of Dedie" . . . 1·60 1·25

1970. Paintings. "Princes and Princesses of Monaco". As T **213**.
1005 1 f. red and black 30 30
1006 3 f. multicoloured . . . . . . 1·00 90
PORTRAITS: 1 f. "Prince Louis I" (F. de Troy); 3 f. "Princess Charlotte de Gramont" (S. Bourdon).

248 Cocker Spaniel

249 Razorbill

1971. International Dog Show, Monte Carlo.
1007 **248** 50 c. multicoloured . . . 1·40 90
See also Nos. 1036, 1082, 1119, 1218 and 1239.

1971. Campaign Against Pollution of the Sea.
1008 **249** 50 c. indigo and blue . . 65 35

250 Hand holding Emblem

1971. 7th Int Blood-Donors Federation Congress.
1009 **250** 80 c. red, violet and grey . 35 30

251 Sextant, Scroll and Underwater Scene

1971. 50th Anniv of Int Hydrographic Bureau.
1010 **251** 80 c. brown, grn & slate . 40 30

252 Detail of Michelangelo painting ("The Arts")

1971. 25th Anniv of U.N.E.S.C.O.
1011 **252** 30 c. brown, blue & vio 10 10
1012 – 50 c. blue and brown . . 20 10
1013 – 80 c. brown and green . . 30 15
1014 – 1 f. 30 green 40 40
DESIGNS—VERT: 50 c. Alchemist and dish aerial ("Sciences"); 1 f. 30, Prince Pierre of Monaco (National U.N.E.S.C.O. Commission). HORIZ: 80 c. Ancient scribe, book and T.V. screen ("Culture").

253 Europa Chain

1971. Europa.
1015 **253** 50 c. red 30 10
1016 80 c. blue 65 40
1017 1 f. 30 green . . . . . 1·40 90

254 Old Bridge, Sospel

1971. Protection of Historic Monuments.
1018 **254** 50 c. brown, blue & green 15 10
1019 – 80 c. brown, green & grey 25 15
1020 – 1 f. 30 red, green & brn 55 40
1021 – 3 f. slate, blue and olive 1·10 1·00
DESIGNS—HORIZ: 80 c. Roquebrune Chateau; 1 f. 30, Grimaldi Chateau, Cagnes-sur-Mer. VERT: 3 f. Roman "Trophy of the Alps", La Turbie.

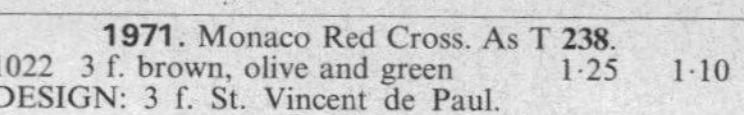
1971. Monaco Red Cross. As T **238**.
1022 3 f. brown, olive and green 1·25 1·10
DESIGN: 3 f. St. Vincent de Paul.

1972. Paintings. "Princes and Princesses of Monaco". As T **213**. Multicoloured.
1023 1 f. "Prince Antoine I" (Rigaud) 40 20
1024 3 f. "Princess Marie de Lorraine" (18th-cent. French School) . . . . 1·10 1·00

255 La Fontaine and Animal Fables (350th)

1972. Birth Annivs. (1971).
1025 **255** 50 c. brown, emer & grn 30 20
1026 – 1 f. 30 purple, blk & red 55 40
DESIGNS: 1 f. 30, Baudelaire, nudes and cats (150th).

256 Saint-Saens and scene from Opera, "Samson and Delilah"

1972. 50th Death Anniv (1971) of Camile Saint-Saens.
1027 **256** 90 c. brown and sepia . 40 25

257 Battle Scene

1972. 400th Anniv (1971) of Battle of Lepanto.
1028 **257** 1 f. blue, brown and red 60 40

258 "Christ before Pilate" (engraving by Durer)

1972. 500th Birth Anniv (1971) of Albrecht Durer.
1029 **258** 2 f. black and brown . . 1·00 80

259 "The Cradle" (B. Morisot)

1972. 25th Anniv (1971) of U.N.I.C.E.F.
1030 **259** 2 f. multicoloured . . . 90 65

INDEX

Countries can be quickly located by referring to the index at the end of this volume.

260 "Gilles" (Watteau)

1972. 250th Death Anniv (1971) of Watteau.
1031 **260** 3 f. multicoloured . . . . 1·40 1·25

261 Santa Claus

1972. Christmas (1971).
1032 **261** 30 c. red, blue and brown 10 10
1033 50 c. red, green & orange 25 10
1034 90 c. red, blue and brown 40 20

262 Steam Locomotive and Modern Turbo Express

1972. 50th Anniv of International Railway Union.
1035 **262** 50 c. purple, lilac and red 50 30

1972. Int Dog Show, Monte Carlo. As T **248**.
1036 60 c. multicoloured . . . . . 1·40 90
DESIGN: 60 c. Great Dane.

263 "Pollution Kills"

1972. Anti-Pollution Campaign.
1037 **263** 90 c. brown, green & blk 50 30

264 Ski-jumping

1972. Winter Olympic Games, Sapporo, Japan.
1038 **264** 90 c. black, red and green 40 30

265 "Communications" 266 "SS. Giovanni e Paolo" (detail, Canaletto)

1972. Europa.
1039 **265** 50 c. blue and orange . 80 30
1040 90 c. blue and green . . 1·50 1·00

1972. Monaco Red Cross. As T **238**.
1041 3 f. brown and purple . . . 1·25 1·10
DESIGN: 3 f. St. Francis of Assisi.

1972. Monte Carlo Flower Show. As T **239**.
1042 3 f. multicoloured . . . . . 2·00 1·00
DESIGN: 3 f. "Vase of Flowers" (Cezanne).

1972. U.N.E.S.C.O. "Save Venice" Campaign.
1043 **266** 30 c. red 25 20
1044 – 60 c. violet 35 20
1045 – 2 f. blue . . . . 1·10 1·00
DESIGNS—27×48 mm: 60 c. "S. Pietro di Castello" (F. Guradi). As Type **266**: 2 f. "Piazetta S. Marco" (B. Bellotto).

267 Dressage

1972. Olympic Games, Munich. Equestrian Events.
1046 **267** 60 c. brown, blue & lake 40 40
1047 – 90 c. lake, brown & blue 90 90
1048 – 1 f. 10 blue, lake & brown 1·25 1·25
1049 – 1 f. 40 brown, lake & blue 2·25 2·25
DESIGNS: 90 c. Cross country; 1 f. 10, Show jumping (wall); 1 f. 40, Show jumping (parallel bars).

268 Escoffier and Birthplace

1972. 125th Birth Anniv of Auguste Escoffier (master chef).
1050 **268** 45 c. black and brown . 25 15

269 Drug Addiction 270 Globe, Birds and Animals

1972. Campaign Against Drugs.
1051 **269** 50 c. red, brown & orange 25 20
1052 90 c. green, brown & blue 35 30
See also Nos. 1088/91 and 1280/1.

1972. 17th Int Congress of Zoology, Monaco.
1053 **270** 30 c. green, brown & red 15 10
1054 – 50 c. brown, purple and red 30 10
1055 **270** 90 c. blue, brown & red 40 20
DESIGN—HORIZ: 50 c. Similar to Type **270**.

271 Bouquet 272 "The Nativity" and Child's face

1972. Monte Carlo Flower Show, 1973 (1st issue). Multicoloured.
1056 30 c. Lilies in vase 20 10
1057 50 c. Type **271** 65 20
1058 90 c. Flowers in Vase . . . 1·00 65
See also Nos. 1073, 1105/7, 1143/4, 1225/6, 1244, 1282/3 and 1316/17.

1972. Christmas.
1059 **272** 30 c. grey, blue & purple 10 10
1060 50 c. red, purple & brown 20 10
1061 90 c. violet, plum & pur 40 20

273 Louis Bleriot and Bleriot XI

1972. Birth Anniversaries.
1062 **273** 30 c. blue and brown . . 15 10
1063 – 50 c. blue, turquoise and new blue 40 30
1064 – 90 c. brown and buff . . 55 35
DESIGNS AND ANNIVERSARIES: 30 c. (birth centenary); 50 c. Amundsen and polar scene (birth centenary); 90 c. Pasteur and laboratory scene (150th birth anniv).

274 "Gethsemane"

1972. Protection of Historical Monuments. Frescoes by J. Canavesio. Chapel of Notre-Dame des Fontaines, La Brigue.
1065 **274** 30 c. red 10 10
1066 – 50 c. grey 20 15
1067 – 90 c. green 40 25
1068 – 1 f. 40 red 55 40
1069 – 2 f. purple . . . . . . 1·10 65
DESIGNS: 50 c. "Christ Outraged"; 90 c. "Ascent to Calvary"; 1 f. 40, "The Resurrection"; 2 f. "The Crucifixion".

1972. Paintings. "Princes and Princesses of Monaco". As T **213**. Multicoloured.
1070 1 f. "Prince Jacques 1" (N. Largilliere) 40 25
1071 3 f. "Princess Louise-Hippolyte" (J. B. Vanloo) . 1·25 1·00

1973. Monte Carlo Flower Show. (2nd issue). As T **239**.
1073 3 f. 50 multicoloured . . . . 3·00 2·25
DESIGN: 3 f. 50, "Bouquet of Flowers".

276 Europa "Posthorn"

1973. Europa.
1074 **276** 50 c. orange . . . . . . 1·10 40
1075 90 c. green . . . . 2·50 1·60

277 Moliere and Characters from "Le Malade Imaginaire" 278 Colette, Cat and Books

1973. 300th Death Anniv of Moliere.
1076 **277** 20 c. red, brown and blue 30 20

1973. Birth Anniversaries.
1077 **278** 30 c. black, blue and red 35 20
1078 – 45 c. multicoloured . . . 1·40 50
1079 – 50 c. lilac, purple & blue 30 20
1080 – 90 c. multicoloured . . . 45 30
DESIGNS AND ANNIVERSARIES—HORIZ: 30 c., Type **278** (nature writer, birth cent); 45 c. J.-H. Fabre and insects (entomologist, 150th birth anniv); 90 c. Sir George Cayley and his "convertiplane" (aviation pioneer, birth bicent). VERT: 50 c. Blaise Pascal (philosopher and writer, 350th birth anniv).

279 E. Ducretet, "Les Invalides" and Eiffel Tower

1973. 75th Anniv of Eugene Ducretet's First Hertzian Radio Link.
1081 **279** 30 c. purple and brown . 20 15

1973. International Dog Show, Monte Carlo. As T **248**. Inscr "1973". Multicoloured.
1082 45 c. Alsatian . . . . 3·75 2·25

280 C. Peguy and Chartres Cathedral

1973. Birth Bicentenary of Charles Peguy (writer).
1083 **280** 50 c. brown, mauve & grey 30 25

281 Telecommunications Equipment 282 Stage Characters

1973. 5th World Telecommunications Day.
1084 **281** 60 c. violet, blue & brown 30 20

1973. 5th World Amateur Theatre Festival.
1085 **282** 60 c. lilac, blue and red . 35 20

283 Ellis and Rugby Tackle

1973. 150th Anniv of Founding of Rugby Football by William Web Ellis.
1086 **283** 90 c. red, lake and brown 55 35

284 St. Theresa

1973. Birth Centenary of St. Theresa of Lisieux.
1087 **284** 1 f. 40 multicoloured . . 65 40

285 Drug Addiction

1973. Campaign Against Drugs.
1088 **285** 50 c. red, green and blue 20 15
1089 – 50 c. multicoloured . . . 20 15
1090 **285** 90 c. violet, green and red 40 30
1091 – 90 c. multicoloured . . . 60 40
DESIGN: Nos. 1089, 1091, Children, syringes and addicts.

286 "Institution of the Creche" (Giotto)

1973. 750th Anniv of St. Francis of Assisi Creche.
1092 **286** 30 c. purple (postage) . . 30 20
1093 – 45 c. red 55 30
1094 – 50 c. brown 80 30
1095 – 1 f. green . . . . . . 1·40 80
1096 – 2 f. brown . . . . . . 2·50 1·60
1097 – 3 f. blue (air) . . . . . 2·00 1·60
DESIGN—HORIZ: 45 c. "The Nativity" (School of F. Lippi); 50 c. "The Birth of Jesus Christ" (Giotto). VERT: 1 f. "The Nativity" (15th century miniature); 2 f. "The Birth of Jesus" (Fra Angelico); 3 f. "The Nativity" (Flemish school).

287 Country Picnic

1973. 50th Anniv of National Committee for Monegasque Traditions.
1098 **287** 10 c. blue, green & brown 10 10
1099 – 20 c. violet, blue & green 10 10
1100 – 30 c. sepia, brown & grn 15 15
1101 – 45 c. red, violet & purple 20 20
1102 – 50 c. black, red & brown 30 30
1103 – 60 c. red, violet and blue 30 30
1104 – 1 f. violet, blue & brown 45 45
DESIGNS—VERT: 20 c. Maypole dance. HORIZ: 30 c. "U Bradi" (local dance); 45 c. St. Jean fire-dance; 50 c. Blessing the Christmas loaf; 60 c. Blessing the sea Festival of St. Devote; 1 f. Corpus Christi procession.

1973. Monte Carlo Flower Show, 1974. As T **271**. Multicoloured.
1105 45 c. Roses and Strelitzia . . 55 25
1106 60 c. Mimosa and myosotis . 90 40
1107 1 f. "Vase of Flowers" (Odilon Redon) . . . . 2·00 1·00

1973. Paintings. "Princes and Princesses of Monaco". As T **213**. Multicoloured.
1108 2 f. "Charlotte Grimaldi" (in day dress, P. Gobert) . . . 1·00 90
1109 2 f. "Charlotte Grimaldi" (in evening dress, P. Gobert) . 1·00 90

289 U.P.U. Emblem and Symbolic Heads **290** Farman, Farman F.60 Goliath and Farman H.F.III

1974. Centenary of Universal Postal Union.
1111 **289** 50 c. purple and brown . 25 10
1112 – 70 c. multicoloured . . . 35 20
1113 – 1 f. 10 multicoloured . . 80 55
DESIGNS: 70 c. Hands holding letters; 1 f. 10, "Countries of the World" (famous buildings).

1974. Monaco Red Cross. As T **238**.
1114 3 f. blue, green and purple . 1·25 1·25
DESIGN: 3 f. St. Bernard of Menthon.

1974. Birth Centenary of Henry Farman (aviation pioneer).
1115 **290** 30 c. brown, purple & bl 10 10

291 Marconi, Circuit Plan and Destroyers

1974. Birth Centenary of Guglielmo Marconi (radio pioneer).
1116 **291** 40 c. red, dp blue & blue 20 10

292 Duchesne and "Penicillium glaucum"

1974. Birth Centenary of Ernest Duchesne (microbiologist).
1117 **292** 45 c. black, blue & purple 25 10

293 Forest and Engine

1974. 60th Death Anniv of Fernand Forest (motor engineer and inventor).
1118 **293** 50 c. purple, red & black 20 10

1974. International Dog Show, Monte Carlo. As T **248**, inscr "1974".
1119 60 c. multicoloured . . . . 2·40 1·40
DESIGN: 60 c. Schnauzer.

294 Ronsard and Characters from "Sonnet to Helene"

1974. 450th Birth Anniv of Pierre de Ronsard (poet).
1120 **294** 70 c. brown and red . . 40 35

295 Sir Winston Churchill (after bust by O. Nemon) **297** "The King of Rome" (Bosio)

296 Interpol Emblem, and Views of Monaco and Vienna

1974. Birth Centenary of Sir Winston Churchill.
1121 **295** 1 f. brown and grey . . 50 30

1974. 60th Anniv of 1st International Police Judiciary Congress and 50th Anniv of International Criminal Police Organization (Interpol).
1122 **296** 2 f. blue, brown & green 1·00 80

1974. Europa. Sculptures by J. F. Bosio.
1123 **297** 45 c. green and brown . 1·10 65
1124 – 1 f. 10 bistre and brown 1·75 1·10
DESIGN: 1 f. 10, "Madame Elizabeth".

298 "The Box" (A. Renoir)

1974. "The Impressionists". Multicoloured.
1126 1 f. Type **298** . . . . . . 1·40 65
1127 1 f. "The Dance Class" (E. Degas) . . . . . . 1·40 65
1128 2 f. "Impression-Sunrise" (C. Monet) (horiz) . . . . 2·50 1·10
1129 2 f. "Entrance to Voisins Village" (C. Pissarro) (horiz) 2·50 1·10
1130 2 f. "The Hanged Man's House" (P. Cezanne) (horiz) 2·50 1·10
1131 2 f. "Floods at Port Marly" (A. Sisley) (horiz) . . . . 2·50 1·10

299 Tigers and Trainer

1974. 1st International Circus Festival, Monaco.
1132 **299** 2 c. brown, green & blue 10 10
1133 – 3 c. brown and purple 10 10
1134 – 5 c. blue, brown and red 10 10
1135 – 45 c. brown, black & red 40 20
1136 – 70 c. multicoloured . . 65 30
1137 – 1 f. 10 brown, grn & red 1·25 65
1138 – 5 f. green, blue & brown 4·25 2·75
DESIGNS—VERT: 3 c. Performing horse; 45 c. Equestrian act; 1 f. 10, Acrobats; 5 f. Trapeze act. HORIZ: 5 c. Performing elephants; 70 c. Clowns.

300 Honore II on Medal

1974. 350th Anniv of Monegasque Numismatic Art.
1139 **300** 60 c. green and red . . . 25 35

301 Marine Flora and Fauna

1974. 24th Congress of the International Commission for the Scientific Exploration of the Mediterranean. Multicoloured.
1140 45 c. Type **301** 40 20
1141 70 c. Sea-bed flora and fauna 80 30
1142 1 f. 10 Sea-bed flora and fauna (different) . . . . . . 1·60 55
Nos. 1141/2 are larger, size 52 × 31 mm.

1974. Monte Carlo Flower Show. As T **271**. Multicoloured.
1143 70 c. Honeysuckle and violets 65 40
1144 1 f. 10 Iris and chrysanthemums 1·10 65

302 Prince Rainier III (F. Messina) **303**

1974.
1145 **302** 60 c. green (postage) . . 30 15
1146 80 c. red 40 25
1147 80 c. green 40 10
1148 1 f. brown 90 35
1149 1 f. red 50 10
1149a 1 f. green 40 10
1149b 1 f. 10 green 40 10
1150 1 f. 20 violet . . . . . 1·75 1·40
1150a 1 f. 20 red 65 10
1150b 1 f. 20 green 65 10
1151 1 f. 25 blue 80 55
1151a 1 f. 30 red 65 15
1152 1 f. 40 red 80 10
1152a 1 f. 50 black 75 40
1153 1 f. 60 grey 80 20
1153a 1 f. 70 blue 90 40
1153b 1 f. 80 blue . . . . . 1·00 50
1154 2 f. mauve . . . . . 2·00 75
1154a 2 f. 10 brown . . . . . 1·10 55
1155 2 f. 30 violet . . . . . 1·10 55
1156 2 f. 50 black . . . . . 1·75 90
1157 9 f. violet . . . . . 5·00 2·50
1158 **303** 10 f. violet (air) . . . . 4·00 1·75
1159 15 f. red . . . . . . 6·50 3·50
1160 20 f. blue . . . . . . 8·50 4·50

304 Coastline, Monte Carlo **305** "Haagocereus chosicensis"

1974.
1161 **304** 25 c. blue, green & brown 25 10
1162 – 25 c. brown, green & blue 20 20
1163 – 50 c. brown and blue . . 35 10
1164 **304** 65 c. blue, brown & green 30 20
1165 – 70 c. multicoloured . . . 30 20
1166 **304** 1 f. 10 brown, green & bl 90 30
1167 – 1 f. 10 black, brown & bl 55 30
1168 – 1 f. 30 brown, green & bl 65 30
1169 – 1 f. 40 green, grey & brn 1·10 40
1170 – 1 f. 50 green, blue & blk 1·00 55
1171 – 1 f. 70 brown, green & bl 1·60 1·00
1172 – 1 f. 80 brown, green & bl 1·10 65
1173 – 2 f. 30 brown, grey & bl 1·40 90
1174 – 3 f. brown, grey & green 3·50 1·50
1175 – 5 f. brown, green & blue 5·50 2·00
1176 – 6 f. 50 brown, blue & grn 3·00 2·00
DESIGNS—VERT: 50 c. Palace clock tower; 70 c. Botanical gardens; 1 f. 30, Monaco Cathedral; 1 f. 40, 1 f. 50, Prince Albert I statue and Museum; 3 f. Fort Antoine. HORIZ: 25 c. (1162), 1 f. 70, "All Saints" Tower; 1 f. 10, (1167), Palais de Justice; 1 f. 80, 5 f. 50, La Condamine; 2 f. 30, North Galleries of Palace; 6 f. 50, Aerial view of hotels and harbour.

1975. Plants. Multicoloured.
1180 10 c. Type **305** 10 10
1181 20 c. "Matucana madisoniarum" 10 10
1182 30 c. "Parodia scopaioides" . 35 10
1183 85 c. "Mediolobivia arachnacantha" . . . . . 1·10 40
1184 1 f. 90 "Matucana yanganucensis" . . . . . 2·25 1·25
1185 4 f. "Echinocereus marksianus" 4·50 2·50

306 "Portrait of a Sailor" (P. Florence) **308** "Prologue"

307 "St. Bernardin de Sienne"

1975. Europa.
1186 **306** 80 c. purple . . . . . 1·10 65
1187 – 1 f. 20 blue . . . . . 1·60 90
DESIGN: 1 f. 20, "St. Devote" (Ludovic Brea).

1975. Monaco Red Cross.
1189 **307** 4 f. blue and purple . . 2·25 1·50

1975. Centenary of "Carmen" (opera by Georges Bizet).
1190 **308** 30 c. violet, brown & blk 10 10
1191 – 60 c. grey, green and red 20 10
1192 – 80 c. green, brown & blk 40 25
1193 – 1 f. 40 purple, brown and ochre 80 60
DESIGNS—HORIZ: 60 c. Lilla Pastia's tavern; 80 c. "The Smuggler's Den"; 1 f. 40, "Confrontation at Seville".

309 Saint-Simon **310** Dr. Albert Schweitzer

1975. 300th Birth Anniv of Louis de Saint-Simon (writer).
1194 **309** 40 c. blue 25 15

1975. Birth Centenary of Dr. Schweitzer (Nobel Peace Prize Winner).
1195 **310** 60 c. red and brown . . 40 20

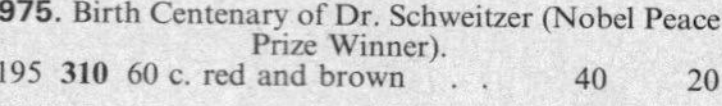

311 "Stamp" and Calligraphy

1975. "Arphila 75" International Stamp Exhibition, Paris.
1196 **311** 80 c. brown and orange . 50 35

312 Seagull and Sunrise

1975. International Exposition, Okinawa.
1197 **312** 85 c. blue, green & orange 55 30

313 Pike smashing Crab

1975. Anti-Cancer Campaign.
1198 **313** 1 f. multicoloured 65 30

314 Christ with Crown of Thorns

1975. Holy Year.
1199 **314** 1 f. 15 black, brn & pur 70 40

315 Villa Sauber, Monte Carlo

1975. European Architectural Heritage Year.
1200 **315** 1 f. 20 green, brown & bl 90 55

316 Woman's Head and Globe

1975. International Women's Year.
1201 **316** 1 f. 20 multicoloured . . 90 60

317 Rolls-Royce "Silver Ghost" (1907)

1975. Evolution of the Motor Car.
1202 **317** 5 c. blue, green & brown 10 10
1203 – 10 c. indigo and blue . . 10 10
1204 – 20 c. blue, ultram & blk . 20 10
1205 – 30 c. purple and mauve . 40 20
1206 – 50 c. blue, purple & mve 80 40
1207 – 60 c. red and green . . . 1·10 65
1208 – 80 c. indigo and blue . . 1·60 90
1209 – 85 c. brown, orge & grn . 2·25 1·50
1210 – 1 f. 20 blue, red and green 2·25 1·60
1211 – 1 f. 40 green and blue . . 3·50 2·00
1212 – 5 f. 50 blue, emerald and green . . . . 9·00 5·50
MOTOR CARS: 10 c. Hispano-Suiza "H.6B" (1926); 20 c. Isotta Fraschini "8A" (1928); 30 c. Cord "L.29"; 50 c. Voisin "V12" (1930); 60 c. Duesenberg "SJ" (1933); 80 c. Bugatti "57 C" (1938); 85 c. Delahaye "135 M" (1940); 1 f. 20, Cisitalia "Pininfarina" (1945); 1 f. 40, Mercedes-Benz "300 SL" (1955); 5 f. 50, Lamborghini "Countach" (1974).

1975. Paintings. "Princes and Princesses of Monaco". As T **213**. Multicoloured.
1213 2 f. "Prince Honore III" . . 1·10 65
1214 4 f. "Princess Catherine de Brignole" . . . . 2·50 1·60

318 Dog behind Bars 319 Maurice Ravel

1975. 125th Birth Anniv of Gen. J. P. Delmas de Grammont (author of Animal Protection Code).
1215 **318** 60 c. black and brown . . 65 40
1216 – 80 c. black and brown . . 90 65
1217 – 1 f. 20 green and purple 1·40 70
DESIGNS—VERT: 80 c. Cat chased up tree. HORIZ: 1 f. 20, Horse being ill-treated.

1975. International Dog Show, Monte Carlo. As T **248**, but inscr "1975". Multicoloured.
1218 60 c. black and purple . . . 2·00 1·10
DESIGN: 60 c. French poodle.

1975. Birth Centenaries of Musicians.
1219 **319** 60 c. brown and purple . 55 30
1220 – 1 f. 20 black and purple 1·00 80
DESIGN: 1 f. 20, Johann Strauss (the younger).

320 Circus Clown 322 Andre Ampere with Electrical Meter

321 Monaco Florin Coin, 1640

1975. 2nd International Circus Festival.
1221 **320** 80 c. multicoloured . . 80 40

1975. Monaco Numismatics.
1222 **321** 60 c. brown and blue . . 50 30
See also Nos. 1275, 1320 and 1448.

1975. Birth Centenary of Andre Ampere (physicist).
1223 **322** 85 c. indigo and blue . . 60 35

323 "Lamentations for the Dead Christ"

1975. 500th Birth Anniv of Michelangelo.
1224 **323** 1 f. 40 olive and black . 80 60

1975. Monte Carlo Flower Show (1976). As T **271**. Multicoloured.
1225 60 c. Bouquet of wild flowers 90 35
1226 80 c. Ikebana flower arrangement . . . . . . 1·00 40

1975. Precancelled. Surch.
1227 42 c. on 26 c. violet, blue and black (No. 949a) 1·40 60
1228 48 c. on 30 c. red, blue, lilac & black (No. 949b) . . . . 2·00 80
1229 70 c. on 45 c. blue, violet, turq & black (No. 950a) . . . . 3·50 1·25
1230 1 f. 35 on 90 c. green, blue and black (No. 951a) . . . . 4·50 2·00

325 Prince Pierre de Monaco

1976. 25th Anniv of Literary Council of Monaco.
1231 **325** 10 c. black 10 10
1232 – 20 c. blue and red . . . 20 10
1233 – 25 c. blue and red . . . 20 10
1234 – 30 c. brown 20 15
1235 – 50 c. blue, red and purple 30 20
1236 – 60 c. brown, grn & lt brn 40 25
1237 – 80 c. purple and blue . . 65 40
1238 – 1 f. 20 violet, blue & mve 1·10 90
COUNCIL MEMBERS—HORIZ: 20 c. A. Maurois and Colette; 25 c. Jean and Jerome Tharaud; 30 c. E. Henriot, M. Pagnol and G. Duhamel; 50 c. Ph. Heriat, J. Supervielle and L. Pierard; 60 c. R. Dorgeles, M. Achard and G. Bauer; 80 c. F. Hellens, A. Billy and Mgr. Grente; 1 f. 20, J. Giono, L. Pasteur Vallery-Radot and M. Garcon.

326 Dachshunds

1976. International Dog Show, Monte Carlo.
1239 **326** 60 c. multicoloured . . . 2·50 1·50

327 Bridge Table and Monte Carlo Coast

1976. 5th Bridge Olympiad, Monte Carlo.
1240 **327** 60 c. brown, green & red 55 30

328 Alexander Graham Bell and Early Telephone

1976. Telephone Centenary.
1241 **328** 80 c. brown, light brown and grey 50 30

329 Federation Emblem on Globe

1976. 50th Anniv of International Philatelic Federation.
1242 **329** 1 f. 20 red, blue & green . 80 60

330 U.S.A. 2 c. Stamp, 1926

1976. Bicent of American Revolution.
1243 **330** 1 f. 70 black and purple . 1·10 80

331 "The Fritillaries" (Van Gogh)

1976. Monte Carlo Flower Show.
1244 **331** 3 f. multicoloured . . . . 4·75 3·00

332 Diving 333 Decorative Plate

1976. Olympic Games, Montreal.
1245 **332** 60 c. brown and blue . . 25 20
1246 – 80 c. blue, brown & green 40 30
1247 – 85 c. blue, green & brown 50 40
1248 – 1 f. 20 brown, green & bl 80 60
1249 – 1 f. 70 brown, blue & grn 1·00 1·00
DESIGNS—VERT: 80 c. Gymnastics; 85 c. Hammer-throwing. HORIZ: 1 f. 20, Rowing; 1 f. 70, Boxing.

1976. Europa. Monegasque Ceramics. Multicoloured.
1251 80 c. Type **333** 80 60
1252 1 f. 20 Grape-harvester (statuette) . . . . 1·10 80

334 Palace Clock Tower 335 "St. Louise de Marillac" (altar painting)

1976. Precancelled.
1254 **334** 50 c. red 60 30
1255 52 c. orange 30 15
1256 54 c. green 40 20
1257 60 c. green 60 40
1258 62 c. mauve 40 20
1259 68 c. yellow 60 30
1260 90 c. violet 90 65
1261 95 c. red 65 35
1262 1 f. 05 brown 60 35
1263 1 f. 60 blue . . . . . . 1·50 90
1264 1 f. 70 turquoise . . . . 1·50 60
1265 1 f. 85 brown . . . . . 1·25 80

1976. Monaco Red Cross.
1270 **335** 4 f. black, purple & green 2·25 1·40

1976. Paintings. "Princes and Princesses of Monaco". As T **213**.
1271 2 f. purple . . . . 1·10 80
1272 4 f. multicoloured . . . . 2·25 1·40
DESIGNS: 2 f. "Prince Honore IV"; 4 f. "Princess Louise d'Aumont-Mazarin".

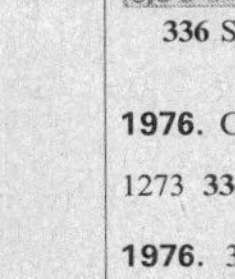
336 St. Vincent-de-Paul 337 Marie de Rabutin Chantal

1976. Centenary of St. Vincent-de-Paul Conference, Monaco.
1273 **336** 60 c. black, brown & blue 30 20

1976. 350th Birth Anniv of Marquise de Sevigne (writer).
1274 **337** 80 c. black, violet and red 40 25

338 Monaco 2 g. "Honore II" Coin, 1640

1976. Monaco Numismatics.
1275 **338** 80 c. blue and green . . 55 30

339 Richard Byrd, "Josephine Ford", Airship "Norge" and Roald Amundsen

1976. 50th Anniv of First Flights over North Pole.
1276 **339** 85 c. black, blue & green 1·0 65

340 Gulliver and Lilliputians 341 Girl's Head and Christmas Decorations

1976. 250th Anniv of Jonathan Swift's "Gulliver's Travels".
1277 **340** 1 f. 20 multicoloured . . 60 45

1976. Christmas.
1278 **341** 60 c. multicoloured . . . 40 20
1279 1 f. 20 green, orge & pur 65 40

342 "Drug" Dagger piercing Man and Woman
343 Circus Clown

1976. Campaign against Drug Abuse.
1280 **342** 80 c. blue, orge & bronze 50 30
1281 1 f. 20 lilac, purple & brn 75 40

1976. Monte Carlo Flower Show (1977). As T **271**. Multicoloured.
1282 80 c. Flower arrangement . . 80 40
1283 1 f. Bouquet of flowers . . . 1·40 65

1976. 3rd International Circus Festival, Monte Carlo.
1284 **343** 1 f. multicoloured . . . . 1·00 55

344 Schooner "Hirondelle"

1977. 75th Anniv of Publication of "Career of a Navigator" by Prince Albert I (1st issue). Illustrations by L. Tinayre.
1285 **344** 10 c. brown, blue & turq 10 10
1286 – 20 c. black, brown & lake 10 10
1287 – 30 c. green, blue & orge 15 15
1288 – 80 c. black, blue and red 35 25
1289 – 1 f. black and brown . . 55 30
1290 – 1 f. 25 olive, green & vio 65 40
1291 – 1 f. 40 brown, olive & grn 1·00 80
1292 – 1 f. 90 blue, lt blue & red 1·40 1·25
1293 – 2 f. 50 brown, blue and turquoise . . . . . . 2·25 2·00
DESIGNS—VERT: 20 c. Prince Albert I; 1 f. Helmsman; 1 f. 90, Bringing in the trawl. HORIZ: 30 c. Crew-members; 80 c. "Hirondelle" in a gale; 1 f. 25, Securing the lifeboat; 1 f. 40, Shrimp fishing; 2 f. 50, Capture of a moon-fish.
See also Nos. 1305/13.

345 Pyrenean Sheep and Mountain Dogs

1977. International Dog Show, Monte Carlo.
1294 **345** 80 c. multicoloured . . . 2·25 1·10

346 "Maternity" (M. Cassatt)

1977. World Association of the "Friends of Children".
1295 **346** 80 c. deep brown, brown and black 55 35

347 Archers

1977. 10th International Archery Championships.
1296 **347** 1 f. 10 black, brown & bl 60 40

INDEX

Countries can be quickly located by referring to the index at the end of this volume.

348 Charles Lindbergh and "Spirit of St. Louis"

1977. 50th Anniv of Lindbergh's Transatlantic Flight.
1297 **348** 1 f. 90 light blue, blue and brown . . . . 1·60 1·00

349 "Harbour, Deauville"

1977. Birth Centenary of Raoul Dufy (painter).
1298 **349** 2 f. multicoloured . . . 2·25 2·00

350 "Portrait of a Young Girl"
351 "L'Oreillon" Tower

1977. 400th Birth Anniv of Peter Paul Rubens (painter).
1299 **350** 80 c. orange, brn & blk . 40 30
1300 – 1 f. red 65 35
1301 – 1 f. 40 orange and red . 1·40 90
DESIGNS: 1 f. "Duke of Buckingham"; 1 f. 40, "Portrait of a Child".

1977. Europa. Monaco Views.
1302 **351** 1 f. brown and blue . . 90 30
1303 – 1 f. 40 blue, brown and bistre . . . . 1·40 65
DESIGN: 1 f. 40, St. Michael's Church, Menton.

1977. 75th Anniv of Publication of "Career of a Navigator" by Prince Albert I (2nd issue). Illustrations by L. Tinayre. As T **344**.
1305 10 c. black and blue 10 10
1306 20 c. blue 10 10
1307 30 c. blue, light blue and green 20 20
1308 80 c. brown, black and green 30 30
1309 1 f. grey and green 50 30
1310 1 f. 25 black, brown and lilac 60 40
1311 1 f. 40 purple, blue & brown 90 60
1312 1 f. 90 black, blue and light blue 1·50 1·25
1313 3 f. blue, brown and green . 2·25 1·60
DESIGNS—HORIZ: 10 c. "Princess Alice" (steam yacht) at Kiel; 20 c. Ship's laboratory; 30 c. "Princess Alice" in ice floes; 1 f. Polar scene; 1 f. 25, Bridge of "Princess Alice" during snowstorm; 1 f. 40, Arctic camp; 1 f. 90, Ship's steam launch in floating ice; 3 f. "Princess Alice" passing iceberg. VERT: 80 c. Crewmen in Arctic dress.

352 Santa Claus and Sledge
353 Face, Poppy and Syringe

1977. Christmas.
1314 **352** 80 c. red, green and blue 35 25
1315 1 f. 40 multicoloured . . 65 35

1977. Monte Carlo Flower Show. As T **271**. Mult.
1316 80 c. Snapdragons and campanula 80 40
1317 1 f. Ikebana . . . . 1·00 65

1977. Campaign Against Drug Abuse.
1318 **353** 1 f. black, red and violet 55 30

354 Clown and Flags

1977. 4th International Festival of Circus, Monaco.
1319 **354** 1 f. multicoloured . . . . 1·00 55

355 Gold Coin of Honore II

1977. Monaco Numismatics.
1320 **355** 80 c. brown and red . . . 50 35

356 Mediterranean divided by Industry

1977. Protection of the Mediterranean Environment.
1321 **356** 1 f. black, green and blue 60 35

357 Dr. Guglielminetti and Road Tarrers

1977. 75th Anniv of First Experiments at Road Tarring in Monaco.
1322 **357** 1 f. 10 black, bistre and brown 50 35

358 F.M.L.T. Badge and Monte Carlo

1977. 50th Anniv of Monaco Lawn Tennis Federation.
1323 **358** 1 f. blue, red and brown 60 30

359 Wimbledon and First Championships

1977. Centenary of Wimbledon Lawn Tennis Championships.
1324 **359** 1 f. 40 grey, green & brown 1·00 55

1977. Paintings. "Princes and Princesses of Monaco". As T **213**. Multicoloured.
1325 6 f. "Prince Honore V" . . . 3·00 1·60

360 St. Jean Bosco

1977. Monaco Red Cross. Monegasque Art.
1326 **360** 4 f. green, brown & blue 2·00 1·10

1978. Precancelled. Surch.
1327 **334** 58 c. on 54 c. green . . . 60 30
1328 73 c. on 68 c. yellow . . 70 40
1329 1 f. 15 on 1 f. 05 brown 1·00 65
1330 2 f. on 1 f. 85 brown . . 1·75 1·10

362 Aerial Shipwreck from "L'Ile Mysterieuse"

1978. 150th Birth Anniv of Jules Verne.
1331 **362** 5 c. brown, red and olive 10 10
1332 – 25 c. turquoise, blue & red 10 10
1333 – 30 c. blue, brown & lt blue 15 10
1334 – 80 c. black, green & orge 35 20
1335 – 1 f. brown, lake and blue 55 30
1336 – 1 f. 40 bistre, brown and green 80 65
1337 – 1 f. 70 brown, lt blue and blue . . . . 1·10 80
1338 – 5 f. 50 violet and blue . 3·00 2·25
DESIGNS: 25 c. The abandoned ship from "L'Ile Mysterieuse"; 30 c. The secret of the island from "L'Ile Mysterieuse"; 80 c. "Robur the Conqueror"; 1 f. "Master Zacharius"; 1 f. 40, "The Castle in the Carpathians"; 1 f. 70, "The Children of Captain Grant"; 5 f. 50, Jules Verne and allegories.

363 Aerial View of Congress Centre

1978. Inauguration of Monaco Congress Centre.
1339 **363** 1 f. brown, blue and green 40 30
1340 – 1 f. 40 blue, brown & grn 65 40
DESIGN: 1 f. 40, View of Congress Centre from sea.

364 Footballers and Globe

1978. World Cup Football Championship, Argentina.
1341 **364** 1 f. blue, slate and green 65 55

365 Antonio Vivaldi
366 "Ramoge" (research vessel) and Grimaldi Palace

1978. 300th Birth Anniv of Antonio Vivaldi (composer).
1342 **365** 1 f. brown and red . . . 60 40

1978. Environment Protection. "RAMOGE" Agreement.
1343 **366** 80 c. multicoloured . . . 40 25
1344 – 1 f. red, blue and green 65 40
DESIGN—HORIZ: (48 × 27 mm): 1 f. Map of coastline between St. Raphael and Genes.

367 Monaco Cathedral
368 Monaco Congress Centre

1978. Europa. Monaco Views.
1345 **367** 1 f. green, brown & blue 80 45
1346 – 1 f. 40 brown, green & bl 1·25 65
DESIGN: 1 f. 40, View of Monaco from the east.

1978. Precancelled.
1348 **368** 61 c. orange 30 10
1349 64 c. green 30 10
1350 68 c. blue 30 10
1351 78 c. purple 40 20
1352 83 c. violet 40 20
1353 88 c. orange 40 20
1354 1 f. 25 brown 70 30
1355 1 f. 30 red 65 40
1356 1 f. 40 green 65 40
1357 2 f. 10 blue . . . . . . 1·50 75
1358 2 f. 25 orange . . . . . 1·40 80
1359 2 f. 35 mauve . . . . . 1·10 80

369 "Cinderella"

1978. 350th Birth Anniv of Charles Perrault (writer).
1360 **369** 5 c. red, olive and violet 10 10
1361 – 25 c. black, brown & mve 10 10
1362 – 30 c. green, lake & brown 15 10
1363 – 80 c. multicoloured . . . 25 20
1364 – 1 f. red, brown and olive 40 30
1365 – 1 f. 40 mauve, ultram & blue 75 65
1366 – 1 f. 70 green, blue & grey 1·00 65
1367 – 1 f. 90 multicoloured . . 1·25 90
1368 – 2 f. 50 blue, orange & grn 1·50 1·10
DESIGNS: 25 c. "Puss in Boots"; 30 c. "The Sleeping Beauty"; 80 c. "Donkey's Skin"; 1 f. "Little Red Riding Hood"; 1 f. 40, "Bluebeard"; 1 f. 70, "Tom Thumb"; 1 f. 90, "Riquet with a Tuft"; 2 f. 50, "The Fairies".

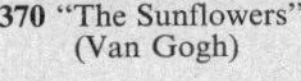

370 "The Sunflowers" (Van Gogh) **371** Afghan Hound

1978. Monte Carlo Flower Show (1979) and 125th Birth Anniv of Vincent Van Gogh. Multicoloured.
1369 1 f. Type **370** . . . . 1·40 65
1370 1 f. 70 "The Iris" (Van Gogh) 2·00 1·10

1978. International Dog Show, Monte Carlo. Multicoloured.
1371 1 f. Type **371** . . . . 1·50 1·00
1372 1 f. 20 Borzoi . . . . 2·50 1·40

372 Girl with Letter **374** Juggling Seals

373 Catherine and William Booth

1978. Christmas.
1373 **372** 1 f. brown, blue and red 55 40

1978. Centenary of Salvation Army.
1374 **373** 1 f. 70 multicoloured . . 1·00 70

1978. 5th International Circus Festival, Monaco.
1375 **374** 80 c. orange, black & blue 40 20
1376 – 1 f. multicoloured 65 35
1377 – 1 f. 40 brown, mauve and bistre . . . . 1·00 35
1378 – 1 f. 90 blue, lilac and mauve 1·40 1·10
1379 – 2 f. 40 multicoloured . . 2·00 1·50
DESIGNS—HORIZ: 1 f. 40, Horseback acrobatics; 1 f. 90, Musical monkeys; 2 f. 40, Trapeze. VERT: 1 f. Lion tamer.

1978. Paintings. "Princes and Princesses of Monaco". As T **213**. Multicoloured.
1380 2 f. "Prince Florestan I" (G. Dauphin) . . . . . . 1·10 90
1381 4 f. "Princess Caroline Gilbert de la Metz" (Marie Verroust) 2·25 1·90

377 "Jongleur de Notre-Dame" (Massenet)

1979. Centenary of "Salle Garnier" (Opera House) (1st issue).
1384 **377** 1 f. blue, orange & mauve 40 20
1385 – 1 f. 20 violet, blk & turq 65 30
1386 – 1 f. 50 maroon, grn & turq 80 65
1387 – 1 f. 70 multicoloured . . 1·10 90
1388 – 2 f. 10 turquoise & violet 1·50 1·10
1389 – 3 f. multicoloured . . 2·00 1·40
DESIGNS—HORIZ: 1 f. 20, "Hans the Flute Player" (L. Ganne); 1 f. 50, "Don Quixote" (J. Massenet); 2 f. 10, "The Child and the Sorcerer" (M. Ravel); 3 f. Charles Garnier (architect) and south facade of Opera House. VERT: 1 f. 70, "L'Aiglon" (A. Honegger and J. Ibert).
See also Nos. 1399/1404.

378 Flower, Bird and Butterfly

1979. International Year of the Child. Children's Paintings.
1390 **378** 50 c. pink, green & black 20 15
1391 – 1 f. slate, green & orange 45 25
1392 – 1 f. 20 slate, orange & mve 65 30
1393 – 1 f. 50 yellow, brown & bl 90 55
1394 – 1 f. 70 multicoloured . . 1·10 65
DESIGNS: 1 f. Horse and Child; 1 f. 20, "The Gift of Love"; 1 f. 50, "Peace in the World"; 1 f. 70, "Down with Pollution".

379 Armed Foot Messenger

1979. Europa.
1395 **379** 1 f. 20 brown, green & bl 65 30
1396 – 1 f. 50 brown, turq & bl 80 40
1397 – 1 f. 70 brown, green & bl 95 70
DESIGNS: 1 f. 50, 18th cent felucca; 1 f. 70, Arrival of 1st train at Monaco.

380 "Instrumental Music" (G. Boulanger) (detail of Opera House interior)

1979. Centenary of "Salle Garnier" (Opera House) (2nd issue).
1399 – 1 f. brown, orange & turq 55 20
1400 – 1 f. 20 multicoloured . . 65 40
1401 – 1 f. 50 multicoloured . . 1·00 65
1402 – 1 f. 70 blue, brown & red 1·40 1·00
1403 – 2 f. 10 red, violet & black 1·60 1·10
1404 **380** 3 f. green, brown and light green . . . . 2·10 1·50
DESIGNS: As Type **377**. HORIZ: 1 f. "Les Biches" (F. Poulenc); 1 f. 20, "The Sailors" (G. Auric); 1 f. 70, "Gaiete Parisienne" (J. Offenbach). VERT: 1 f. 50, "La Spectre de la Rose" (C. M. Weber) (after poster by Jean Cocteau); 2 f. 10, "Salome" (R. Strauss).

1979. Paintings. "Princes and Princesses of Monaco". As T **213**. Multicoloured.
1405 3 f. "Prince Charles III" (B. Biard) . . . . 1·40 1·00
1406 4 f. "Antoinette de Merode" 1·75 1·40

381 St. Pierre Claver **382** "Princess Grace" Orchid

1979. Monaco Red Cross.
1407 **381** 5 f. multicoloured . . . 2·25 1·75

1979. Monte Carlo Flora 1980.
1408 **382** 1 f. multicoloured . . . 1·40 80

383 "Princess Grace" Rose **384** Clown balancing on Ball

1979. Monte Carlo Flower Show.
1409 **383** 1 f. 20 multicoloured . . 1·60 90

1979. 6th International Circus Festival.
1410 **384** 1 f. 20 multicoloured . . 1·00 65

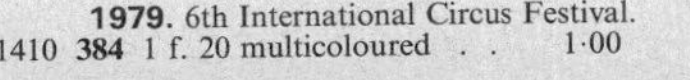

385 Sir Rowland Hill and Penny Black **386** Albert Einstein

1979. Death Centenary of Sir Rowland Hill.
1411 **385** 1 f. 70 brown, blue & blk 65 45

1979. Birth Centenary of Albert Einstein (physicist).
1412 **386** 1 f. 70 brown, grey & red 60 50

387 St. Patrick's Cathedral **388** Nativity Scene

1979. Centenary of St. Patrick's Cathedral, New York.
1413 **387** 2 f. 10 black, blue & brn . 1·00 60

1979. Christmas.
1414 **388** 1 f. 20 blue, orange & mve 40 25

389 Early Racing Cars

1979. 50th Anniv of Grand Prix Motor Racing.
1415 **389** 1 f. multicoloured 50 30

390 Arms of Charles V and Monaco

1979. 450th Anniv of Visit of Emperor Charles V.
1416 **390** 1 f. 50 brown, blue & blk 60 40

391 Setter and Pointer

1979. International Dog Show, Monte Carlo.
1417 **391** 1 f. 20 multicoloured . . 20 10

392 Spring

1980. Precancels. The Seasons.
1418 **392** 76 c. brown and green . . 35 20
1419 88 c. olive, emerald & grn 35 20
1420 – 99 c. green and brown . . 45 30
1421 – 1 f. 14 green, emer & brn 45 30
1422 – 1 f. 60 brown, grey & deep brown 90 65
1423 – 1 f. 84 lake, grey & brown 90 55
1424 – 2 f. 65 brown, lt blue & bl 1·40 90
1425 – 3 f. 05, brown, bl & slate 1·50 1·00
DESIGNS: 99 c., 1 f. 14, Summer; 1 f. 60, 1 f. 84, Autumn; 2 f. 65, 3 f. 05, Winter.

394 Paul P. Harris (founder) and View of Chicago

1980. 75th Anniv of Rotary International.
1434 **394** 1 f. 80 olive, blue & turq 90 65

395 Gymnastics

1980. Olympic Games, Moscow and Lake Placid.
1435 **395** 1 f. 10 blue, brn & grey 30 20
1436 – 1 f. 30 red, brown & blue 40 30
1437 – 1 f. 60 red, blue & brown 55 40
1438 – 1 f. 80 brown, bis & grn 65 40
1439 – 2 f. 30 grey, violet & mve 1·00 65
1440 – 4 f. green, blue & brown 1·40 1·25
DESIGNS: 1 f. 30, Handball; 1 f. 60, Pistol shooting; 1 f. 80, Volleyball; 2 f. 30, Ice hockey; 4 f. Skiing.

396 Colette (novelist) **397** "La Source"

1980. Europa. Each black, green and red.
1441 1 f. 30 Type **396** 35 25
1442 1 f. 80 Marcel Pagnol (writer) 45 30

1980. Birth Bicentenary of Jean Ingres (artist).
1444 **397** 4 f. multicoloured . . . 4·00 2·25

398 Montaigne **399** Guillaume Apollinaire (after G. Pieret)

1980. 400th Anniv of Publication of Montaigne's "Essays".
1445 **398** 1 f. 30 black, red and blue 50 25

1980. Birth Centenary of Guillaume Apollinaire (poet).
1446 **399** 1 f. 10 brown 40 30

400 Congress Centre

1980. Kiwanis International European Convention.
1447 **400** 1 f. 30 black, blue and red 50 25

401 Honore II Silver Ecu, 1649

1980. Numismatics.
1448 **401** 1 f. 50 black and blue . 65 40

MINIMUM PRICE

The minimum price quoted is 10p which represents a handling charge rather than a basis for valuing common stamps. For further notes about prices, see introductory pages.

402 Lhassa Apso and Shih Tzu

1980. International Dog Show, Monte Carlo.
1449 **402** 1 f. 30 multicoloured . . 2·00 1·25

403 "The Princess and the Pea"

1980. 175th Birth Anniv of Hans Christian Andersen.
1450 **403** 70 c. sepia, red & brown 25 20
1451 – 1 f. 30 blue, turq & red 35 25
1452 – 1 f. 50 black, blue & turq 65 55
1453 – 1 f. 60 red, black & brn 80 70
1454 – 1 f. 80 yellow, brn & turq 1·00 75
1455 – 2 f. 30 brown, pur & vio 1·40 90
DESIGNS: 1 f. 30, "The Little Mermaid"; 1 f. 50, "The Chimneysweep and Shepherdess"; 1 f. 60, "The Brave Little Lead Soldier"; 1 f. 80, "The Little Match Girl"; 2 f. 30, "The Nightingale".

404 "The Road" (M. Vlaminck)

1980. 75th Anniv of 1905 Autumn Art Exhibition. Multicoloured.
1456 2 f. Type **404** . . . . 1·50 65
1457 3 f. "Woman at Balustrade" (Van Dongen) . . . . . . 2·50 1·25
1458 4 f. "The Reader" (Henri Matisse) . . . . 3·00 2·00
1459 5 f. "Three Figures in a Meadow" (A. Derain) . . 4·25 2·40

1980. Paintings. "Princes and Princesses of Monaco". As T **213**. Multicoloured.
1460 4 f. "Prince Albert I" (L. Bonnat) . . . . 1·60 1·25
1461 4 f. "Princess Marie Alice Heine" (. Maeterlinck) . . 1·60 1·25

405 "Sunbirds"

1980. Monaco Red Cross.
1462 **405** 6 f. red, bistre and brown 2·75 2·00

406 "MONACO" balanced on Tightrope

1980. Seventh International Circus Festival, Monaco.
1463 **406** 1 f. 30 red, turquoise & blue 1·00 55

407 Children and Nativity

1980. Christmas.
1464 **407** 1 f. 10 blue, carmine and red 35 25
1465 2 f. 30 violet, orange and pink 85 55

1980. Monte Carlo Flower Show, 1981. As T **383**. Multicoloured.
1466 1 f. 30 "Princess Stephanie" Rose 80 40
1467 1 f. 80 Ikebana . . . . 1·50 80

408 "Alcyonium" 409 Fish with Hand for Tail

1980. Marine Fauna. Multicoloured.
1468 5 c. "Spirographis spallanzanli" 10 10
1469 10 c. "Anemonia sulcata" . 10 10
1470 15 c. "Leptopsammia pruvoit" 10 10
1471 20 c. "Pteroides" 10 10
1472 30 c. "Paramuricea clavata" (horiz) 30 10
1473 40 c. Type **408** 30 10
1474 50 c. "Corallium rubrum" . 40 20
1475 60 c. "Calliactis parasitica" (horiz) 50 20
1476 70 c. "Cerianthus membranaceus" (horiz) . . 60 30
1477 1 f. "Actinia equina" (horiz) 80 30
1478 2 f. "Protula" (horiz) . . . 2·00 50

1981. "Respect the Sea".
1479 **409** 1 f. 20 multicoloured . . 60 40

410 Prince Rainier and Princess Grace

1981. Royal Silver Wedding.
1480 **410** 1 f. 20 black and green . 1·00 40
1481 1 f. 40 black and red . . 1·10 65
1482 1 f. 70 black and green . 1·50 80
1483 1 f. 80 black and brown 1·75 1·10
1484 2 f. black and blue . . . 2·50 1·50

411 Mozart (after Lorenz Vogel) 412 Palm Cross

1981. 225th Birth Anniv of Wolfgang Amadeus Mozart (composer).
1485 **411** 2 f. brown, dp brn & bl 1·40 60
1486 – 2 f. 50 blue, brn & dp brn 1·50 1·00
1487 – 3 f. 50 dp brown, bl & brn 2·25 1·75
DESIGNS—HORIZ: 2 f. 50, "Mozart at 7 with his Father and Sister" (engraving by Delafoose after drawing by Carmontelle); 3 f. 50 ,"Mozart directing Requiem two Days before his Death" (painting by Baude).

1981. Europa. Multicoloured.
1488 **412** 1 f. 40 green, brown & red 35 25
1489 – 2 f. multicoloured . . . 60 40
DESIGN: 2 f. Children carrying palm crosses.

413 Paris Football Stadium, Cup and Footballer

1981. 25th Anniv of European Football Cup.
1491 **413** 2 f. black and blue . . . 90 55

414 I.Y.D.P. Emblem and Girl in Wheelchair

1981. International Year of Disabled Persons.
1492 **414** 1 f. 40 blue and green . 55 40

415 Palace flying Old Flag, National Flag, and Monte Carlo

1981. Centenary of National Flag.
1493 **415** 2 f. red, blue and brown . 85 55

416 Oceanographic Institute, Paris and Oceanographic Museum, Monaco

1981. 75th Anniv of Oceanographic Institute.
1494 **416** 1 f. 20 blue, black & brn 50 40

417 Bureau Building and "Faddey Bellingshausen" (hydrographic research ship)

1981. 50th Anniv of Int Hydrographic Bureau.
1495 **417** 2 f. 50 sepia, brown & light brown . . . . 1·00 80

418 Rough Collies and Shetland Sheepdogs

1981. International Dog Show, Monte Carlo.
1496 **418** 1 f. 40 multicoloured . . 2·00 1·50

419 Rainier III and Prince Albert 420 Arctic Scene and Map

1981. (a) 23 × 28 mm.
1497 **419** 1 f. 40 green (postage) . . 50 10
1498 1 f. 60 red 60 10
1499 1 f. 60 green 50 10
1500 1 f. 70 green 50 10
1501 1 f. 80 red 60 10
1502 1 f. 80 green 55 10
1503 1 f. 90 green 90 40
1504 2 f. red 75 10
1505 2 f. green 75 10
1506 2 f. 10 red 90 10
1507 2 f. 20 red 60 10
1508 2 f. 30 blue . . . . . . 1·50 80
1509 2 f. 50 brown . . . . . . 1·00 30
1510 2 f. 60 blue . . . . . . 1·60 65
1511 2 f. 80 blue . . . . . . 1·90 75
1512 3 f. blue . . . . 2·00 65
1513 3 f. 20 blue . . . . . . 1·60 75
1514 3 f. 40 blue . . . . . . 2·00 90
1515 3 f. 60 blue . . . . . . 1·75 40
1516 4 f. brown . . . . . . 1·60 40
1517 5 f. 50 black . . . . . . 2·50 *80
1518 10 f. purple . . . . . . 2·50 1·10
1519 15 f. green . . . . . . 6·00 1·40
1520 20 f. blue . . . . 5·50 2·00

(b) 36 × 27 mm.
1521 – 5 f. violet (air) . . . . . . 1·75 60
1522 – 10 f. red . . . . 4·00 1·25
1523 – 15 f. green . . . . . . 5·50 1·75
1524 – 20 f. blue . . . . 7·00 2·50
1525 – 30 f. brown . . . . . . 6·50 3·50
DESIGN: Nos. 1521/5, Double portrait and monograms.

1981. 1st International Congress on Discovery and History of Northern Polar Regions, Rome.
1530 **421** 1 f. 50 multicoloured . . 1·00 55

1981. Paintings. "Princes and Princesses of Monaco". Vert designs as T **213**. Multicoloured.
1531 3 f. "Prince Louis II" (P.-A. de Laszlo) . . . . . 1·25 90
1532 5 f. "Princess Charlotte" (P.-A. de Laszlo) . . . . . 2·00 1·75

422 Hercules fighting the Nemean Lion

1981. Monaco Red Cross. The Twelve Labours of Hercules (1st series).
1533 **422** 2 f. 50 + 50 c. green, brown and red . . . . 1·00 90
1534 – 3 f. 50 + 50 c. blue, green and red . . . . 1·40 1·10
DESIGN: 3 f. 50, Slaying the Hydra of Lerna.
See also Nos. 1584/5, 1631/2, 1699/1700, 1761/2 and 1794/5.

423 Ettore Bugatti (racing car designer) (Cent) 424 Eglantines and Morning Glory

1981. Birth Anniversaries.
1535 **423** 1 f. indigo, blue and red 60 30
1536 – 2 f. black, blue & brown 70 55
1537 – 2 f. 50 brown, black and red 1·25 65
1538 – 4 f. multicoloured . . . 2·50 1·75
1539 – 4 f. multicoloured . . . 2·50 1·75
DESIGNS: No. 1536, George Bernard Shaw (dramatist, 125th anniv); 1537, Fernand Leger (painter, centenary). LARGER: 37 × 48 mm: 1538, Pablo Picasso (self-portrait) (centenary); 1539, Rembrandt (self-portrait) (375th anniv).

1981. Monte Carlo Flower Show (1982). Mult.
1540 1 f. 40 Type **424** 90 40
1541 2 f. "Ikebana" (painting by Ikenobo) . . . . 1·40 80

425 "Catherine Deneuve" 426 Tiger, Clown, Acrobat and Elephants

1981. 1st International Rose Show, Monte Carlo.
1542 **425** 1 f. 80 multicoloured . . 1·40 75

1981. 8th International Circus Festival, Monaco.
1543 **426** 1 f. 40 violet, mve & blk 1·00 65

427 Praying Children and Nativity

1981. Christmas.
1544 **427** 1 f. 20 blue, mauve & brn 40 25

428 "Lancia-Stratos" Rally Car

1981. 50th Monte Carlo Rally (1982).
1545 **428** 1 f. blue, red & turquoise 65 40

430 "Hoya bella" **431** Spring

1981. Plants in Exotic Garden. Multicoloured.
1547 1 f. 40 Type **430** . . . . . . 2·00 70
1548 1 f. 60 "Bolivicereus samaipatanus" . . . . . . 1·75 70
1549 1 f. 80 "Trichocereus grandiflorus" (horiz) . . . 1·75 75
1550 2 f. "Argyroderma roseum" . 1·00 30
1551 2 f. 30 "Euphorbia milii" . . 1·75 70
1552 2 f. 60 "Echinocereus fitchii" (horiz) . . . . 1·75 70
1553 2 f. 90 "Rebutia heliosa" (horiz) 1·90 1·10
1554 4 f. 10 "Echinopsis multiplex cristata" (horiz) . . . . . 2·75 1·60

1982. Precancels. The Seasons of the Peach Tree.
1555 **431** 97 c. mauve and green . 40 25
1556 – 1 f. 25 green, orge & mve 50 30
1557 – 2 f. 03 brown 90 65
1558 – 3 f. 36 brown and blue . 1·25 1·00
DESIGNS: 1 f. 25, Summer; 2 f. 03, Autumn; 3 f. 36, Winter.

432 Nutcracker **433** Capture of Monaco Fortress, 1297

1982. Birds from Mercantour National Park.
1559 **432** 60 c. black, brown & grn 50 40
1560 – 70 c. black and mauve . 90 50
1561 – 80 c. red, black & orange 1·00 50
1562 – 90 c. black, red and blue 1·10 70
1563 – 1 f. 40 brown, blk & red 1·75 1·40
1564 – 1 f. 60 brown, black & blue 2·50 1·50
DESIGNS—VERT: 70 c. Black grouse; 80 c. Rock partridge; 1 f. 60, Golden eagle. HORIZ: 90 c. Wallcreeper; 1 f. 40, Rock ptarmigan.

1982. Europa.
1565 **433** 1 f. 60 blue, brown and red 50 30
1566 – 2 f. 30 blue, brown and red 75 45
DESIGN: 2 f. 30, Signing the Treaty of Peronne, 1641.

434 Old Quarter

1982. Fontvieille.
1568 **434** 1 f. 40 blue, brown & grn 50 20
1569 – 1 f. 60 light brown, brown and red 65 20
1570 – 2 f. 30 purple . . . . . . 1·00 55
DESIGNS: 1 f. 60, Land reclamation; 2 f. 30, Urban development.

435 Stadium

1982. Fontvieille Sports Stadium (1st series).
1571 **435** 2 f. 30 green, brown & blue 1·00 65
See also No. 1616.

436 Arms of Paris

1982. "Philexfrance" International Stamp Exhibition, Paris.
1572 **436** 1 f. 40 red, grey and deep red 55 40

437 Old English Sheepdog

1982. International Dog Show, Monte Carlo. Multicoloured.
1573 60 c. Type **437** . . . . . . 1·25 65
1574 1 f. Briard . . . . 1·75 1·00

438 Monaco Cathedral and Arms

1982. Creation of Archbishopric of Monaco (1981).
1575 **438** 1 f. 60 black, blue and red 65 40

439 St. Francis of Assisi **440** Dr. Robert Koch

1982. 800th Birth Anniv of St. Francis of Assisi.
1576 **439** 1 f. 40 grey and light grey 60 30

1982. Centenary of Discovery of Tubercle Bacillus.
1577 **440** 1 f. 40 purple and lilac . 80 40

441 Lord Baden-Powell **443** St. Hubert (18th-century medallion)

1982. 125th Birth Anniv of Lord Baden-Powell (founder of Boy Scout Movement).
1578 **441** 1 f. 60 brown and black 90 55

1982. 29th Meeting of International Hunting Council, Monte Carlo.
1580 **443** 1 f. 60 multicoloured . . 65 55

444 Books, Reader and Globe

1982. International Bibliophile Association General Assembly, Monte Carlo.
1581 **444** 1 f. 60 blue, purple & red 65 40

445 "Casino, 1870"

1982. Monaco in the "Belle Epoque" (1st series). Paintings by Hubert Clerissi. Multicoloured.
1582 3 f. Type **445** . . . . 1·40 90
1583 5 f. "Porte d'Honneur, Royal Palace, 1893" . . . . . . 2·50 1·40
See also Nos. 1629/30, 1701/2, 1763/4, 1801/2, 1851/2, 1889/90 and 1965/6.

1982. Monaco Red Cross. The Twelve Labours of Hercules (2nd series). As T **422**.
1584 2 f. 50 + 50 c. green, red and bright red . . . . 1·00 1·00
1585 3 f. 50 + 50 c. brown, blue and red . . . . 1·40 1·40
DESIGNS: 2 f. 50, Capturing the Erymanthine Boar. 3 f. 50, Shooting the Stymphalian Birds.

446 Nicolo Paganini (violinist and composer, bicent) **447** Vase of Flowers

1982. Birth Anniversaries.
1586 **446** 1 f. 60 brown and purple 75 55
1587 – 1 f. 80 red, mauve & brn 90 55
1588 – 2 f. 60 green and red . . 1·25 75
1589 – 4 f. multicoloured . . . . 3·00 1·40
1590 – 4 f. multicoloured . . . . 3·00 1·40
DESIGNS—VERT: No. 1587, Anna Pavlova (ballerina, centenary); 1588, Igor Stravinsky (composer, centenary). HORIZ: (47 × 36 mm): 1589, "In a Boat" (Edouard Manet, 150th anniv); 1590, "The Black Fish" (Georges Braque, centenary).

1982. Monte Carlo Flower Show (1983). Mult.
1591 1 f. 60 Type **447** . . . . . . 1·00 40
1592 2 f. 60 Ikebana arrangement . 2·00 65

448 Bowl of Flowers **449** The Three Kings

1982.
1593 **448** 1 f. 60 multicoloured . . 1·00 40

1982. Christmas.
1594 **449** 1 f. 60 green, blue & orge 55 30
1595 – 1 f. 80 green, blue & orge 65 30
1596 – 2 f. 60 green, blue & orge 1·00 55
DESIGNS: 1 f. 80, The Holy Family; 2 f. 60, Shepherds and angels.

450 Prince Albert I and Polar Scene

1982. Centenary of First International Polar Year.
1598 **450** 1 f. 60 brown, green & bl 1·10 75

451 Viking Longships off Greenland

1982. Millenary of Discovery of Greenland by Erik the Red.
1599 **451** 1 f. 60 blue, brown & blk 1·40 65

452 Julius Caesar in the Port of Monaco ("Aeneid", Book VI)

1982. 2000th Death Anniv of Virgil (poet).
1600 **452** 1 f. 80 deep blue, blue and brown . . . . 1·10 65

453 Spring **454** Tourism

1983. Precancels. The Seasons of the Apple Tree.
1601 **453** 1 f. 05 purple, green and yellow 35 30
1602 – 1 f. 35 lt green, dp grn & turquoise 40 40
1603 – 2 f. 19 red, brown & grey 80 55
1604 – 3 f. 63 yellow and brn . 1·50 1·00
DESIGNS: 1 f. 35, Summer; 2 f. 19, Autumn; 3 f. 63, Winter.

1983. 50th Anniv of Exotic Garden. Mult.
1605 1 f. 80 Type **454** 75 65
1606 2 f. Cactus plants (botanical collections) . . . . 1·10 75
1607 2 f. 30 Cactus plants (international flower shows) 1·40 1·10
1608 2 f. 60 Observatory grotto (horiz) . . . . 1·50 90
1609 3 f. 30 Museum of Prehistoric Anthropology (horiz) . . . 2·00 1·50

455 Alaskan Malamute **457** St. Charles Borromee and Church

1983. International Dog Show, Monte Carlo.
1610 **455** 1 f. 80 multicoloured . . 1·75 1·10

1983. Centenary of St. Charles Church, Monte Carlo.
1612 **457** 2 f. 60 deep blue, blue and green 90 65

458 Montgolfier Balloon, 1783 **459** Franciscan College

1983. Europa.
1613 **458** 1 f. 80 blue, brown & grey 55 30
1614 – 2 f. 60 grey, blue & brown 75 40
DESIGN: 2 f. 60, Space shuttle.

1983. Centenary of Franciscan College, Monte Carlo.
1616 **459** 2 f. grey, brown and red 65 40

460 Stadium

1983. Fontvieille Sports Stadium (2nd series).
1617 **460** 2 f. green, blue & brown 65 40

461 Early and Modern Cars

1983. Centenary of Petrol-driven Motor Car.
1618 **461** 2 f. 90 blue, brown & green 1·40 1·10

462 Blue Whale

1983. International Commission for the Protection of Whales.
1619 **462** 3 f. 30 blue, light blue and grey . . . . 2·75 1·75

463 Dish Aerial, Pigeon, W.C.Y. Emblem and Satellite

1983. World Communications Year.
1620 **463** 4 f. lilac and mauve . . . 1·25 1·00

464 Smoking Moor

1983. Nineteenth Century Automata from the Galea Collection. Multicoloured.
1621 50 c. Type **464** 15 10
1622 60 c. Clown with diabolo . . 20 10
1623 70 c. Smoking monkey . . . 20 15
1624 80 c. Peasant with pig 30 15
1625 90 c. Buffalo Bill smoking . . 40 15
1626 1 f. Snake charmer 40 15
1627 1 f. 50 Pianist 65 40
1628 2 f. Young girl powdering herself . . . . 1·00 65

1983. Monaco in the "Belle Epoque" (2nd series). As T **445**. Multicoloured.
1629 3 f. "The Beach, 1902" . . . 1·75 1·10
1630 5 f. "Cafe de Paris, 1905" . . 2·50 1·75

1983. Monaco Red Cross. The Twelve Labours of Hercules (3rd series). As T **422**.
1631 2 f. 50 + 50 c. brn, bl & red 1·10 1·00
1632 3 f. 50 + 50 c. vio, mauve & red 1·40 1·25
DESIGNS: 2 f. 50, Capturing the Hind of Ceryneia; 3 f. 50, Cleaning the Augean stables.

465 Johannes Brahms (composer)

1983. Birth Anniversaries.
1633 **465** 3 f. deep brown, brown and green . . . . 1·10 75
1634 – 3 f. black, brown and red 1·10 75
1635 – 4 f. multicoloured . . . . 2·50 1·60
1635 – 4 f. multicoloured . . . . 2·50 1·60
DESIGNS—HORIZ: No. 1633, Type **465** (150th anniv); 1634, Giacomo Puccini (composer) and scene from "Madame Butterfly" (125th anniv). VERT: (37 × 48 mm): 1635, "Portrait of a Young Man" (Raphael (artist), 500th anniv); 1636, "Cottin Passage" (Utrillo (artist), centenary).

466 Circus Performers

467 Bouquet

1983. 9th International Circus Festival, Monaco.
1637 **466** 2 f. blue, red and green . 1·00 65

1983. Monte Carlo Flower Show (1984). Mult.
1638 1 f. 60 Type **467** 90 35
1639 2 f. 60 Arrangement of poppies 1·40 65

468 Provencale Creche

1983. Christmas.
1640 **468** 2 f. multicoloured . . . . 1·00 55

469 Nobel Literature Prize Medal

1983. 150th Birth Anniv of Alfred Nobel (inventor of dynamite and founder of Nobel Prizes).
1641 **469** 2 f. black, grey and red . 75 55

470 O. F. Ozanam (founder) and Paris Headquarters **471** "Tazerka" (oil rig)

1983. 150th Anniv of Society of St. Vincent de Paul.
1642 **470** 1 f. 80 violet and purple 65 40

1983. Oil Industry.
1643 **471** 5 f. blue, brown & turq . 1·75 1·10

474 Skater and Stadium

1984. Winter Olympic Games, Sarajevo.
1646 **474** 2 f. blue, green and turquoise 65 55
1647 – 4 f. blue, violet & purple 1·40 75
DESIGN: 4 f. Skater and snowflake.

475 Bridge

476 Balkan Fritillary

1984. Europa. 25th Anniv of European Post and Telecommunications Conference.
1648 **475** 2 f. blue 65 30
1649 3 f. green . . . . 1·00 75

1984. Butterflies and Moths in Mercantour National Park. Multicoloured.
1651 1 f. 60 Type **476** 75 40
1652 2 f. "Zygaena vesubiana" . . 1·00 55
1653 2 f. 80 False mnestra ringlet 1·40 75
1654 3 f. Small apollo (horiz) . . 1·40 75
1655 3 f. 60 Southern swallowtail (horiz) . . . . 1·75 1·40

477 Auvergne Pointer **478** Sanctuary and Statue of Virgin

1984. International Dog Show, Monte Carlo.
1656 **477** 1 f. 60 multicoloured . . 1·40 75

1984. Our Lady of Laghet Sanctuary.
1657 **478** 2 f. blue, brown and green 65 40

479 Piccard's Stratosphere Balloon "F.N.R.S."

480 Concert

1984. Birth Centenary of Auguste Piccard (physicist).
1658 **479** 2 f. 80 black, green & bl 90 55
1659 – 4 f. blue, green & turq 1·40 75
DESIGN: 4 f. Bathyscaphe.

1984. 25th Anniv of Palace Concerts.
1660 **480** 3 f. 60 blue and deep blue 1·40 75

481 Place de la Visitation

482 Spring

1984. Bygone Monaco (1st series). Paintings by Hubert Clerissi.
1661 **481** 5 c. brown 10 15
1662 – 10 c. red 10 10
1663 – 15 c. violet 10 10
1664 – 20 c. blue 10 10
1665 – 30 c. blue 15 10
1666 – 40 c. green 20 10
1667 – 50 c. red 20 10
1668 – 60 c. blue 20 10
1669 – 70 c. orange 60 10
1670 – 80 c. green 20 10
1671 – 90 c. mauve 25 20
1672 – 1 f. blue 30 15
1673 – 2 f. black 60 25
1674 – 3 f. red . . . . 1·00 40
1675 – 4 f. blue . . . . 1·10 80
1676 – 5 f. green . . . . 1·10 65
1677 – 6 f. green . . . . 1·75 75
DESIGNS: 10 c. Town Hall; 15 c. Rue Basse; 20 c. Place Saint-Nicolas; 30 c. Quai du Commerce; 40 c. Rue des Iris; 50 c. Ships in harbour; 60 c. St. Charles's Church; 70 c. Religious procession; 80 c. Olive tree overlooking harbour; 90 c. Quayside; 1 f. Palace Square; 2 f. Fishing boats in harbour; 3 f. Bandstand; 4 f. Railway station; 5 f. Mail coach; 6 f. Monte Carlo Opera House.
See also Nos. 2015/27.

1984. Precancels. The Seasons of the Quince.
1678 **482** 1 f. 14 red and green . . 30 30
1679 – 1 f. 47 dp green & green 40 40
1680 – 2 f. 38 olive, turquoise & green 75 55
1681 – 3 f. 95 green . . . . . . 1·40 1·00
DESIGNS: 1 f. 47, Summer; 2 f. 38, Autumn; 3 f. 95, Winter.

483 Shepherd **485** Bowl of Mixed Flowers

484 Gargantua and Cattle

1984. Christmas. Crib Figures from Provence. Multicoloured.
1682 70 c. Type **483** 25 15
1683 1 f. Blind man 35 20
1684 1 f. 70 Happy man 65 35
1685 2 f. Spinner 75 40
1686 2 f. Angel playing trumpet . . 75 40
1687 2 f. 40 Garlic seller . . . . . 1·00 50
1688 3 f. Drummer . . . . 1·40 65
1689 3 f. 70 Knife grinder . . . . 1·60 90
1690 4 f. Elderly couple . . . . . 1·75 1·10

1984. 450th Anniv of First Edition of "Gargantua" by Francois Rabelais.
1691 **484** 2 f. black, red and brown 65 40
1692 – 2 f. black, red and blue 65 40
1693 – 4 f. green . . . . 1·40 1·00
DESIGNS:—As T **484**: No. 1692, Panurge's sheep. 36 × 48 mm: 1693, Francois Rabelais.

1984. Monte Carlo Flower Show (1985). Mult.
1694 2 f. 10 Type **485** . . . . . 1·00 40
1695 3 f. Ikebana arrangement . . 1·60 65

486 Television Lights and Emblem

1984. 25th International Television Festival, Monte Carlo.
1696 **486** 2 f. 10 blue, grey and mauve 65 40
1697 – 3 f. grey, blue and red . . 1·00 65
DESIGN: 3 f. "Golden Nymph" (Grand Prix).

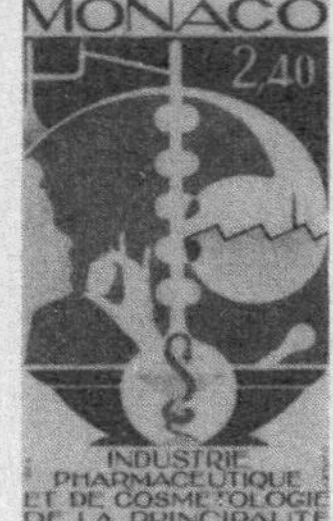

487 Chemical Equipment

1984. Pharmaceutical and Cosmetics Industry.
1698 **487** 2 f. 40 blue, deep blue and green 75 35

1984. Monaco Red Cross. The Twelve Labours of Hercules (4th series). As T **422**.
1699 3 f. + 50 c. brown, light brown and red . . . . 1·10 1·00
1700 4 f. + 50 c. green, brown and red . . . . 1·40 1·25
DESIGNS: 3 f. Killing the Cretan bull; 4 f. Capturing the Mares of Diomedes.

1984. Monaco in the "Belle Epoque" (3rd series). Paintings by Hubert Clerissi. As T **445**. Mult.
1701 4 f. "Grimaldi Street, 1908" (vert) . . . . 1·60 1·25
1702 5 f. "Railway Station, 1910" (vert) . . . . 2·50 1·60

489 "Woman with Chinese Vase"

1984. 150th Birth Anniv of Edgar Degas (artist).
1704 **489** 6 f. multicoloured . . . 2·50 2·00

490 Spring

1985. Precancels. Seasons of the Cherry.
1705 **490** 1 f. 22 olive, green and blue 30 30
1706 – 1 f. 57 red, green and yellow 40 40
1707 – 2 f. 55 orange and brown 75 55
1708 – 4 f. 23 purple, green and blue . . . . 1·40 90
DESIGNS: 1 f. 57, Summer; 2 f. 55, Autumn; 4 f. 23, Winter.

491 First Stamp

1985. Centenary of First Monaco Stamps.
1709 **491** 1 f. 70 green 65 30
1710 2 f. 10 red 80 10
1711 3 f. blue . . . . 1·40 40

493 "Berardia subacaulis"

495 Nadia Boulanger (composer)

1985. Flowers in Mercantour National Park. Mult.

1724 1 f. 70 Type **493** 65 35
1725 2 f. 10 "Saxifraga florulenta" (vert) 75 40
1726 2 f. 40 "Fritillaria moggridgei" (vert) . . . . 1·00 65
1727 3 f. "Sempervivum allionii" (vert) . . . . 1·25 90
1728 3 f. 60 "Silene cordifolia" (vert) 1·40 1·10
1729 4 f. "Primula allionii" . . . . 1·75 1·50

1985. 25th Anniv of First Musical Composition Competition.

1731 **495** 1 f. 70 brown 55 30
1732 – 2 f. 10 blue 75 40
DESIGN: 2 f. 10, Georges Auric (composer).

496 Stadium and Runners

1985. Inauguration of Louis II Stadium, Fontvieille, and Athletics and Swimming Championships.

1733 **496** 1 f. 70 brown, red and violet 55 40
1734 – 2 f. 10 blue, brown and green 65 40
DESIGN: 2 f. 10, Stadium and swimmers.

497 Prince Antoine I

1985. Europa.

1735 **497** 2 f. 10 blue 65 30
1736 – 3 f. red . . . . 1·00 50
DESIGN: 3 f. John-Baptiste Lully (composer).

498 Museum, "Hirondelle" (schooner) and "Denise" (midget submarine)

1985. 75th Anniv of Oceanographic Museum.

1738 **498** 2 f. 10 black, green and blue 75 40

499 Boxer

1985. International Dog Show, Monte Carlo.

1739 **499** 2 f. 10 multicoloured . . 1·60 90

500 Scientific Motifs

1985. 25th Anniv of Scientific Centre.

1740 **500** 5 f. blue, black and violet 1·00 55

501 Children and Hands holding Seedling and Emblem

502 Regal Angelfish

1985. International Youth Year.

1741 **501** 3 f. brown, green and light brown . . . . 1·00 55

1985. Fishes in Oceanographic Museum Aquarium (1st series). Multicoloured.

1742 1 f. 80 Type **502** 75 55
1743 1 f. 90 Type **502** . . . . . . 1·25 55
1744 2 f. 20 Powder blue tang surgeonfish 90 40
1745 3 f. 20 "Chaetodon collare" 1·40 1·00
1746 3 f. 40 As No. 1745 . . . . 2·25 1·10
1747 3 f. 90 Spotted triggerfish . 2·00 1·40
1748 7 f. Fishes in aquarium (36 × 48 mm) . . . . 3·00 2·00
See also Nos. 1857/62.

504 Rome Buildings and Emblem

1985. "Italia '85" International Stamp Exhibition, Rome.

1750 **504** 4 f. black, green and red 1·40 90

505 Clown **506** Decorations

1985. 11th International Circus Festival, Monaco.

1751 **505** 1 f. 80 multicoloured . . 1·00 55

1985. Christmas.

1752 **506** 2 f. 20 multicoloured . . 90 40

507 Ship and Marine Life **508** Arrangement of Roses, Tulips and Jonquil

1985. Fish Processing Industry.

1753 **507** 2 f. 20 blue, turquoise and brown 65 40

1985. Monte Carlo Flower Show (1986). Mult.

1754 2 f. 20 Type **508** . . . . . . 1·00 55
1755 3 f. 20 Arrangement of chrysanthemums and heather 1·50 1·00

509 Globe and Satellite

1985. European Telecommunications Satellite Organization.

1756 **509** 3 f. black, blue and violet 1·10 65

510 Sacha Guitry (actor, centenary)

1985. Birth Anniversaries.

1757 **510** 3 f. orange and brown 1·00 55
1758 – 4 f. blue, brown and mauve 1·40 75
1759 – 5 f. turquoise, blue and grey 1·75 1·10
1760 – 6 f. blue, brown and black 2·00 1·25
DESIGNS: 4 f. Wilhelm and Jacob Grimm (folklorists, bicentenaries); 5 f. Frederic Chopin and Robert Schumann (composers, 175th annivs); 6 f. Johann Sebastian Bach and Georg Friedrich Handel (composers, 300th annivs).

1985. Monaco Red Cross. The Twelve Labours of Hercules (5th series). As T **422**.

1761 3 f. + 70 c. green, deep red and red . . . . 1·10 90
1762 4 f. + 80 c. brown, bl & red 1·25 1·10
DESIGNS: 3 f. The Cattle of Geryon; 4 f. The Girdle of Hippolyte.

1985. Monaco in the "Belle Epoque" (4th series). As T **445**, showing paintings by Hubert Clerissi. Multicoloured.

1763 4 f. "Port of Monaco, 1912" . 1·50 1·10
1764 6 f. "Avenue de la Gare 1920" 2·75 2·00

512 Spring

1986. Precancels. Seasons of the Hazel Tree.

1766 **512** 1 f. 28 brown, green & bl 30 30
1767 – 1 f. 65 green, brn & yell 40 40
1768 – 2 f. 67 grey, brown and deep brown 75 55
1769 – 4 f. 44 green and brown 1·40 90
DESIGNS: 1 f. 65, Summer; 2 f. 67, Autumn; 4 f. 44, Winter.

513 Ancient Monaco

1986. 10th Anniv of "Annales Monegasques" (historical review).

1770 **513** 2 f. 20 grey, blue and brown 65 35

514 Scotch Terriers

1986. International Dog Show, Monte Carlo.

1771 **514** 1 f. 80 multicoloured . . 2·25 1·10

515 Mouflon **516** Research Vessel "Ramoge"

1986. Mammals in Mercantour National Park. Multicoloured.

1772 2 f. 20 Type **515** 65 30
1773 2 f. 50 Ibex 75 55
1774 3 f. 20 Chamois . . . . 1·00 75
1775 3 f. 90 Alpine marmot (vert) . 1·40 90
1776 5 f. Arctic hare (vert) . . . . 1·75 1·40
1777 7 f. 20 Stoat (vert) . . . . . 2·40 2·00

1986. Europa. Each green, blue and red.

1778 2 f. 20 Type **516** 80 40
1779 3 f. 20 Underwater nature reserve, Larvotto beach . . 1·00 65

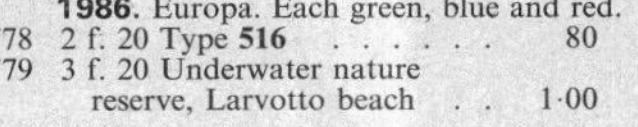

517 Prince Albert I and National Council Building

1986. Anniversaries and Events.

1781 **517** 2 f. 50 brown and green . . 75 55
1782 – 3 f. 20 brown, red and black 1·10 90
1783 – 3 f. 90 purple and red . . 1·50 1·10
1784 – 5 f. green, red and blue . 1·75 1·25
DESIGNS—HORIZ: 2 f. 50, Type **517** (75th anniv of First Constitution); 3 f. 20, Serge Diaghilev and dancers (creation of new Monte Carlo ballet company); 3 f. 90, Henri Rougier and Turcat-Mery car (75th Anniv of first Monte Carlo Rally). VERT: 5 f. Flags and Statue of Liberty (centenary).

518 Chicago and Flags

1986. "Ameripex '86" International Stamp Exhibition, Chicago.

1785 **518** 5 f. black, red and blue 1·75 1·00

520 Comet, Telescopes and 1532 Chart by Apian

1986. Appearance of Halley's Comet.

1787 **520** 10 f. blue, brown & green 3·00 2·00

521 Monte Carlo and Congress Centre

1986. 30th International Insurance Congress.

1788 **521** 3 f. 20 blue, brown & grn 1·00 55

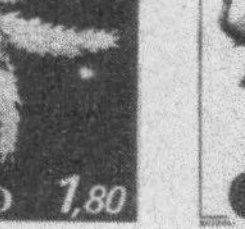

522 Christmas Tree Branch and Holly **523** Clown's Face and Elephant on Ball

1986. Christmas. Multicoloured.

1789 1 f. 80 Type **522** 65 25
1790 2 f. 50 Christmas tree branch and poinsettia 90 35

1986. 12th International Circus Festival, Monaco.

1791 **523** 2 f. 20 multicoloured . . 1·10 40

524 Posy of Roses and Acidanthera **525** Making Plastic Mouldings for Car Bodies

1986. Monte Carlo Flower Show (1987). Mult.

1792 2 f. 20 Type **524** . . . . . . 1·10 40
1793 3 f. 90 Lilies and beech in vase 1·75 1·00

1986. Monaco Red Cross. The Twelve Labours of Hercules (6th series). As T **422**.

1794 3 f. + 70 c. green, yell & red 1·10 75
1795 4 f. + 80 c. blue, brn & red . 1·25 1·00
DESIGNS: 3 f. The Golden Apples of the Hesperides; 4 f. Capturing Cerberus.

1986. Plastics Industry.

1796 **525** 3 f. 90 turquoise, red and grey . . . . 1·40 55

526 Scenes from "Le Cid" (Pierre Corneille)

1986. Anniversaries.

1797 **526** 4 f. dp brown and brown 1·40 90
1798 – 5 f. brown and blue . . 1·75 75
DESIGNS: 4 f. Type **526** (350th anniv of first performance); 5 f. Franz Liszt (composer) and bible (175th birth anniv).

527 Horace de Saussure, Mont Blanc and Climbers

1986. Bicentenary of First Ascent of Mont Blanc by Dr. Paccard and Jacques Balmat.
1799 **527** 5 f. 80 blue, red & black . . . 1·75 1·25

528 "The Olympic Diver" (Emma de Sigaldi)

1986. 25th Anniv of Unveiling of "The Olympic Diver" (statue).
1800 **528** 6 f. multicoloured . . . . 2·00 1·10

1986. Monaco in the "Belle Epoque" (5th series). Paintings by Hubert Clerissi. As T **445**. Mult.
1801 6 f. "Bandstand and Casino, 1920" (vert) . . . . 2·25 1·40
1802 7 f. "Avenue du Beau Rivage, 1925" (vert) . . . . 3·25 2·00

530 Spring

1987. Precancels. Seasons of the Chestnut.
1804 **530** 1 f. 31 green, yell & brn 30 30
1805 – 1 f. 69 green and brown 40 40
1806 – 2 f. 74 brown, yell & bl 75 65
1807 – 4 f. 56 brown, grn & grey 1·40 1·10
DESIGNS: 1 f. 69, Summer; 2 f. 74, Autumn; 4 f. 56, Winter.

531 Golden Hunter

1987. Insects in Mercantour National Park. Multicoloured.
1808 1 f. Type **531** 40 20
1809 1 f. 90 Golden wasp (vert) . . 65 30
1810 2 f. Green tiger beetle 65 30
1811 2 f. 20 Brown aeshna (vert) . 75 40
1812 3 f. Leaf beetle . . . . 1·10 65
1813 3 f. 40 Grasshopper (vert) . . 1·40 90

532 St. Devote Church **533** Dogs

1987. Centenary of St. Devote Parish Church.
1814 **532** 1 f. 90 brown 55 25

1987. International Dog Show, Monte Carlo.
1815 **533** 1 f. 90 grey, black & brn 1·00 40
1816 – 2 f. 70 black and green 1·75 80
DESIGN: 2 f. 70, Poodle.

534 Stamp Album

1987. Stamp Day.
1817 **534** 2 f. 20 red, purple and mauve 65 20

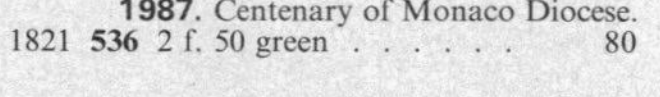

535 Louis II Stadium, Fontvieille **536** Cathedral

1987. Europa. Each blue, green and red.
1818 2 f. 20 Type **535** 65 30
1819 3 f. 40 Crown Prince Albert Olympic swimming pool . 1·10 55

1987. Centenary of Monaco Diocese.
1821 **536** 2 f. 50 green 80 30

538 Lawn Tennis

1987. 2nd European Small States Games, Monaco.
1823 **538** 3 f. black, red and purple 1·25 65
1824 – 5 f. blue and black . . . 1·75 1·00
DESIGN: 5 f. Sailing dinghies and windsurfer.

539 "Red Curly Tail" (Alexander Calder)

1987. "Monte Carlo Sculpture 1987" Exhibition.
1825 **539** 3 f. 70 multicoloured . . 1·25 80

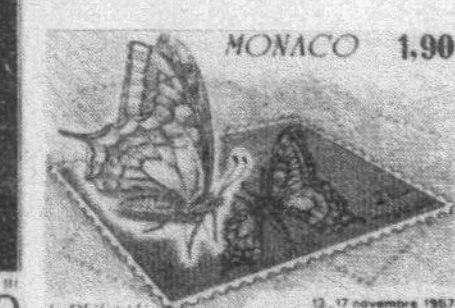

540 Prince Rainier III **541** Swallowtail on Stamp

1987. 50th Anniv of Monaco Stamp Issuing Office.
1826 **540** 4 f. blue . . . . 1·40 1·40
1827 – 4 f. red . . . . 1·40 1·40
1828 – 8 f. black . . . . 2·50 2·50
DESIGNS: No. 1827, Prince Louis II. (47 × 37 mm): 1829, Villa Miraflores.

1987. International Stamp Exhibition.
1829 **541** 1 f. 90 deep green and green 55 25
1830 2 f. 20 purple and red . 65 45
1831 2 f. 50 purple and mauve 90 60
1832 3 f. 40 deep blue and blue 1·25 90

542 Festival Poster (J. Ramel) **543** Christmas Scenes

1987. 13th International Circus Festival, Monaco (1988).
1833 **542** 2 f. 20 multicoloured . . 1·10 30

1987. Christmas.
1834 **543** 2 f. 20 red 60 20

544 Strawberry Plants and Campanulas in Bowl **545** Obverse and Reverse of Honore V 5 f. Silver Coin

1987. Monte Carlo Flower Show (1988). Mult.
1835 2 f. 20 Type **544** 75 25
1836 3 f. 40 Ikebana arrangement of water lilies and dog roses (horiz) . . . . 1·25 50

1987. 150th Anniv of Revival of Monaco Coinage.
1837 **545** 2 f. 50 black and red . . 75 40

546 Graph, Factory, Electron Microscope and Printed Circuit

1987. Electro-Mechanical Industry.
1838 **546** 2 f. 50 blue, green and red 75 40

547 St. Devote

1987. Monaco Red Cross. St. Devote, Patron Saint of Monaco (1st series). Multicoloured.
1839 4 f. Type **547** . . . . 1·40 65
1840 5 f. St. Devote and her nurse 1·75 90
See also Nos. 1898/9, 1956/7, 1980/1, 2062/3 and 2101/2.

548 Oceanographic Museum and I.A.E.A. Headquarters, Vienna

1987. 25th Anniv of International Marine Radioactivity Laboratory, Monaco.
1842 **548** 5 f. black, brown and blue 1·50 1·00

549 Jouvet

1987. Birth Centenary of Louis Jouvet (actor).
1843 **549** 3 f. black . . . . 1·10 65

550 River Crossing

1987. Bicentenary of First Edition of "Paul and Virginia" by Bernardin de Saint-Pierre.
1844 **550** 3 f. green, orange and blue 90 65

551 Marc Chagall (painter)

1987. Anniversaries.
1845 **551** 4 f. black and red . . . . 1·40 75
1846 – 4 f. purple, red and brown 1·40 75
1847 – 4 f. red, blue and brown . 1·40 65
1848 – 4 f. green, brown & pur 1·40 65
1849 – 5 f. blue, brown and green 1·60 90
1850 – 5 f. brown, green and blue 1·60 90
DESIGNS: No. 1845, Type **551** (birth centenary); 1846, Chapel of Ronchamp and Charles Edouard Jeanneret (Le Corbusier) (architect, birth centenary); 1847, Sir Isaac Newton (mathematician) and diagram (300th anniv of publication of "Principia Mathematica"); 1848, Key and Samuel Morse (inventor, 150th Anniv of Morse telegraph); 1849, Wolfgang Amadeus Mozart and scene from "Don Juan" (opera, bicentenary of composition); 1850, Hector Berlioz (composer) and scene from "Mass for the Dead" (150th anniv of composition).

1987. Monaco in the "Belle Epoque" (6th series). As T **445** showing paintings by Hubert Clerissi. Multicoloured.
1851 6 f. "Main Ramp to Palace Square, 1925" (vert) . . . 2·00 1·40
1852 7 f. "Monte Carlo Railway Station, 1925" (vert) . . . 3·00 2·00

552 Coat of Arms **553** Spanish Hogfish

1987.
1853 **552** 2 f. multicoloured . . . 50 30
1854 2 f. 20 multicoloured . . 65 30

1988. Fishes in Oceanographic Museum Aquarium (2nd series). Multicoloured.
1857 2 f. Type **553** 75 30
1858 2 f. 20 Longnose butterfly fish ("Chelmon rostratus") . . 90 30
1859 2 f. 50 Harlequin filefish ("Oxymonacanthus longirostrus") 90 55
1860 3 f. Blue trunkfish . . . . . 1·00 40
1861 3 f. 70 Lionfish . . . . . . 1·40 65
1862 7 f. Moon wrasse (horiz) . . 2·00 1·25

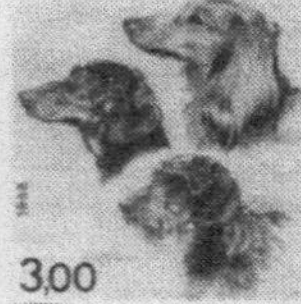

554 Spring **556** Dachshunds

1988. Precancels. Seasons of the Pear Tree. Multicoloured.
1863 1 f. 36 Type **554** 30 30
1864 1 f. 75 Summer 40 40
1865 2 f. 83 Autumn 75 65
1866 4 f. 72 Winter . . . . 1·40 1·10
See also Nos. 1952/5.

1988. European Dachshunds Show, Monte Carlo.
1868 **556** 3 f. multicoloured . . . 1·40 75

557 Children of different Races around Globe **558** Satellite Camera above Man with World as Brain

1988. 25th Anniv of World Association of Friends of Children.
1869 **557** 5 f. green, brown & blue 1·60 1·00

1988. Europa. Transport and Communications. Each black, brown and red.
1870 2 f. 20 Type **558** 65 30
1871 3 f. 60 High-speed mail train and aircraft propeller . . . 1·40 65

559 Coxless Four

1988. Centenary of Monaco Nautical Society (formerly Regatta Society).
1873 **559** 2 f. blue, green and red . 65 30

560 Jean Monnet (statesman) **561** "Leccinum rotundifoliae"

1988. Birth Centenaries.
1874 **560** 2 f. black, brown & blue 1·75 75
1875 – 2 f. black and blue . . . 1·75 75
DESIGN: No. 1875, Maurice Chevalier (entertainer).

1988. Fungi in Mercantour National Park. Multicoloured.
1876 2 f. Type **561** 65 30
1877 2 f. 20 Crimson wax cap . . 75 30
1878 2 f. 50 "Pholiota flammans" . 90 55
1879 2 f. 70 "Lactarius lignyotus" 1·00 75
1880 3 f. Goaty smell (vert) . . . 1·10 75
1881 7 f. "Russula olivacea" (vert) 2·75 1·75

562 Nansen

563 Church and "Miraculous Virgin"

1988. Centenary of First Crossing of Greenland by Fridtjof Nansen (Norwegian explorer).
1882 **562** 4 f. violet . . . . 1·60 75

1988. Restoration of Sanctuary of Our Lady of Laghet.
1883 **563** 5 f. multicoloured . . . . 1·60 1·00

564 Anniversary Emblem

1988. 40th Anniv of W.H.O.
1884 **564** 6 f. red and blue . . . . 1·75 1·25

565 Anniversary Emblem

1988. 125th Anniv of Red Cross.
1885 **565** 6 f. red, grey and black . 1·75 1·25

566 Congress Centre

1988. 10th Anniv of Monte Carlo Congress Centre.
1886 **566** 2 f. green 55 30
1887 – 3 f. red 90 55
DESIGN: 3 f. Auditorium.

1988. Monaco in the "Belle Epoque" (7th series). Paintings by Hubert Clerissi. As T **445**. Mult.
1889 6 f. "Steam packet in Monte Carlo Harbour, 1910" . . 2·00 1·40
1890 7 f. "Place de la Gare, 1910" 2·50 1·40

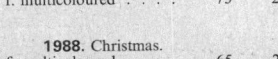

568 Festival Poster (J. Ramel)

569 Star Decoration

1988. 14th International Circus Festival, Monaco (1989).
1891 **568** 2 f. multicoloured 75 20

1988. Christmas.
1892 **569** 2 f. multicoloured 65 25

570 Arrangement of Fuchsias, Irises, Roses and Petunias

571 Models

1988. Monte Carlo Flower Show (1989).
1893 **570** 3 f. multicoloured . . . 1·10 40

1988. Ready-to-Wear Clothing Industry.
1894 **571** 3 f. green, orange & black 75 35

572 Lord Byron (bicentenary)

574 "Le Nain and his Brothers" (Antoine Le Nain)

1988. Writers' Birth Anniversaries.
1895 **572** 3 f. black, brown and blue 90 55
1896 – 3 f. purple and blue . . 90 55
DESIGN: No. 1896, Pierre de Marivaux (300th anniv).

1988. Monaco Red Cross. St. Devote, Patron Saint of Monaco (2nd series). As T **547**. Multicoloured.
1898 4 f. Roman governor Barbarus arriving at Corsica . . . . 1·25 65
1899 5 f. St. Devote at the Roman senator Eutychius's house 1·60 1·00

1988. Artists' Birth Anniversaries.
1900 **574** 5 f. brown olive and red 1·60 90
1901 – 5 f. black, green and blue 1·60 90
DESIGNS: No. 1912, Type **574** (400th anniv): 1913, "The Great Archaeologists" (bronze statue, Giorgio de Chirico) (centenary).

575 Sorcerer

1989. Rock Carvings in Mercantour National Park. Multicoloured.
1902 2 f. Type **575** 55 25
1903 2 f. 20 Oxen in yoke 55 25
1904 3 f. Hunting implements . . 90 40
1905 3 f. 60 Tribal chief . . . . . 1·00 55
1906 4 f. Puppet (vert) . . . . . 1·10 65
1907 5 f. Jesus Christ (vert) . . . 1·50 90

576 Rue des Spelugues

577 Prince Rainier

1989. Old Monaco (1st series). Multicoloured.
1908 2 f. Type **576** 90 40
1909 2 f. 20 Place Saint Nicolas . 1·00 45
See also Nos. 1969/70 and 2090/1.

1989.
1910 **577** 2 f. blue and azure . . . 65 10
1911 2 f. 10 blue and azure . 55 10
1912 2 f. 20 brown and pink . 75 10
1913 2 f. 20 blue and azure . 40 10
1914 2 f. 30 brown and pink . 55 10
1915 2 f. 40 blue and azure . 55 10
1916 2 f. 50 brown and pink . 55 10
1918 2 f. 80 brown and pink . 60 10
1920 3 f. 20 blue and cobalt . 75 30
1922 3 f. 40 blue and cobalt . 70 20
1923 3 f. 60 blue and cobalt . 1·00 30
1924 3 f. 70 blue and cobalt . 80 30
1925 3 f. 80 purple and lilac . 90 30
1927 4 f. purple and lilac . . 85 20
1930 5 f. brown and pink . . 1·10 40
1932 10 f. dp green and green 2·00 1·00
1934 15 f. blue and grey . . . 3·25 1·10
1936 20 f. red and pink . . . 4·00 1·60
1938 25 f. black and grey . . 5·50 1·60
1940 40 f. brown and pink . . 8·75 2·75

578 Yorkshire Terrier

1989. International Dog Show, Monte Carlo.
1941 **578** 2 f. 20 multicoloured . . 90 55

579 Magician, Dove and Cards

1989. 5th Grand Prix of Magic, Monte Carlo.
1942 **579** 2 f. 20 black, blue & red . 55 30

580 Nuns and Monks around "Our Lady of Misericorde"

1989. 350th Anniv of Archiconfrerie de la Misericorde.
1943 **580** 3 f. brown, black and red 75 40

581 Charlie Chaplin (actor) and Film Scenes

1989. Birth Centenaries.
1944 – 3 f. green, blue & mauve 75 55
1945 **581** 4 f. purple, green and red 1·50 90
DESIGN: 3 f. Jean Cocteau (writer and painter), scene from "The Double-headed Eagle" and frescoes in Villefrance-sur-Mer chapel.

583 Boys playing Marbles

586 "Artist's Mother" (Philibert Florence)

1989. Europa. Children's Games. Each mauve, brown and grey.
1947 2 f. 20 Type **583** 65 30
1948 3 f. 60 Girls skipping . . . . 1·00 55

1989. Precancels. As Nos. 1863/6 but values changed. Multicoloured.
1952 1 f. 39 Type **554** 30 20
1953 1 f. 79 Summer 40 30
1954 2 f. 90 Autumn 75 55
1955 4 f. 84 Winter . . . . 1·40 90

1989. Monaco Red Cross. St. Devote, Patron Saint of Monaco (3rd series). As T **547**. Multicoloured.
1956 4 f. St. Devote beside the dying Eutychius . . . . 1·25 65
1957 5 f. Barbarus condemns St. Devote to torture for refusing to make a sacrifice to the gods 1·50 75

1989. Artists' 150th Birth Anniversaries.
1958 **586** 4 f. brown . . . . 1·25 65
1959 - 6 f. multicoloured . . . . . 1·75 1·10
1960 - 8 f. multicoloured . . . . . 2·25 1·50
DESIGNS—HORIZ: 6 f. "Molesey Regatta" (Alfred Sisley). VERT: 8 f. "Farmyard at Auvers" (Paul Cezanne).

587 Poinsettia, Christmas Roses and Holly

1989. Christmas.
1961 **587** 2 f. multicoloured . . . 90 20

588 Map and Emblem

1989. Centenary of Interparliamentary Union.
1962 **588** 4 f. black, green and red 1·10 65

590 Monaco Palace, White House, Washington, and Emblem

1989. 20th U.P.U. Congress, Washington D.C.
1964 **590** 6 f. blue, brown and black 1·60 1·25

1989. Monaco in the "Belle Epoque" (8th series). Paintings by Hubert Clerissi. As T **445**. Mult.
1965 7 f. "Barque in Monte Carlo Harbour, 1915" (vert) . . 2·00 1·50
1966 8 f. "Gaming Tables, Casino, 1915" (vert) . . . . 2·25 1·75

591 World Map

592 Clown and Horses

1989. 10th Anniv of Monaco Aide et Presence (welfare organization).
1967 **591** 2 f. 20 brown and red . 65 30

1989. 15th International Circus Festival, Monte Carlo.
1968 **592** 2 f. 20 multicoloured . . 1·00 40

1990. Old Monaco (2nd series). Paintings by Claude Rosticher. As T **576**. Multicoloured.
1969 2 f. 10 La Rampe Major . . 75 40
1970 2 f. 30 Town Hall Courtyard 90 45

593 Phalaenopsis "Princess Grace"

594 Bearded Collie

1990. International Garden and Greenery Exposition, Osaka, Japan. Multicoloured.
1971 2 f. Type **593** 55 30
1972 3 f. Iris "Grace Patricia" . . . 75 40
1973 3 f. "Paphiopedilum" "Prince Rainier III" 75 40
1974 4 f. "Cattleya" "Principessa Grace" . . . . 1·00 55
1975 5 f. Rose "Caroline of Monaco" 1·25 90

1990. International Dog Show, Monte Carlo.
1976 **594** 2 f. 30 multicoloured . . 90 40

595 Noghes and Racing Car

1990. Birth Centenary of Antony Noghes (founder of Monaco Grand Prix and Monte Carlo Rally).
1977 **595** 3 f. red, lilac and black . 90 40

596 Cyclist and Lancia Rally Car

1990. Centenary of Automobile Club of Monaco (founded as Cycling Racing Club).
1978 **596** 4 f. blue, brown & purple 1·10 55

597 Telephone, Satellite and Dish Aerial

1990. 125th Anniv of I.T.U.
1979 **597** 4 f. lilac, mauve and blue 1·10 65

1990. Monaco Red Cross. St. Devote, Patron Saint of Monaco (4th series). As T **547**. Multicoloured.
1980 4 f. St. Devote being flogged 1·25 65
1981 5 f. Placing body of St. Devote in fishing boat . . . . . . 1·50 1·75

598 Sir Rowland Hill and Penny Black

1990. 150th Anniv of Penny Black.
1982 **598** 5 f. blue and black . . . 1·50 1·00

599 "Post Office, Place de la Mairie" **601** Anatase

1990. Europa. Post Office Buildings. Paintings by Hubert Clerissi. Multicoloured.
1983 2 f. 30 Type **599** 65 30
1984 3 f. 70 "Post Office, Avenue d'Ostende" . . . . 1·10 60

1990. Minerals in Mercantour National Park. Mult.
1987 2 f. 10 Type **601** 55 25
1988 2 f. 30 Albite 55 25
1989 3 f. 20 Rutile 75 35
1990 3 f. 80 Chlorite . . . . 1·00 50
1991 4 f. Brookite (vert) . . . . . 1·00 55
1992 6 f. Quartz (vert) . . . . . . 1·40 90

602 Powerboat **603** Pierrot writing (mechanical toy)

1990. World Offshore Powerboat Racing Championship.
1993 **602** 2 f. 30 brown, red & blue 1·25 75

1990. Philatelic Round Table.
1994 **603** 3 f. blue 75 35

604 Christian Samuel Hahnemann (founder of homeopathy)

1990. Bicentenaries.
1995 **604** 3 f. purple, green & black 75 35
1996 – 5 f. chestnut, brown & bl 1·40 70
DESIGN: 5 f. Jean-Francois Champollion (Egyptologist) and hieroglyphics (birth bicentenary).

605 Monaco Heliport, Fontvieille **606** Petanque Player

1990. 30th International Civil Airports Association Congress, Monte Carlo.
1997 **605** 3 f. black, red and brown 75 35
1998 – 5 f. black, blue & brown 1·40 60
DESIGN: 5 f. Aerospatiale Ecureuil helicopters over Monte Carlo Congress Centre.

1990. 26th World Petanque Championship.
1999 **606** 6 f. blue, brown & orange 1·60 80

607 Spring **608** Miller on Donkey

1990. Precancels. Seasons of the Plum Tree. Multicoloured.
2000 1 f. 46 Type **607** 30 20
2001 1 f. 89 Summer 40 30
2002 3 f. 06 Autumn 65 55
2003 5 f. 10 Winter . . . . . . 1·10 90

1990. Christmas. Crib figures from Provence. Multicoloured.
2004 2 f. 30 Type **608** 55 20
2005 3 f. 20 Woman carrying faggots 75 30
2006 3 f. 80 Baker . . . . 1·10 55
See also Nos. 2052/4, 2097/9, 2146/8 and 2191/3.

610 Pyotr Ilich Tchaikovsky (composer) **611** Clown playing Concertina

1990. 150th Birth Anniversaries.
2008 **610** 5 f. blue and green . . . 1·40 75
2009 – 5 f. bistre and blue . . . 1·40 65
2010 – 7 f. multicoloured . . . 1·60 1·10
DESIGNS:—As T **610**: No. 2009, "Cathedral" (Auguste Rodin, sculptor). 48 × 37 mm: "The Magpie" (Claude Monet, painter).

1991. 16th International Circus Festival, Monte Carlo.
2011 **611** 2 f. 30 multicoloured . . 55 25
See also No. 2069.

1991. Bygone Monaco (2nd series). Paintings by Hubert Clerissi. As T **481**.
2015 20 c. purple 10 10
2017 40 c. green 10 10
2018 50 c. red 10 10
2019 60 c. blue 15 10
2020 70 c. green 15 10
2021 80 c. blue 20 15
2022 90 c. lilac 30 15
2023 1 f. blue 30 15
2024 2 f. red 45 30
2025 3 f. black . . . . 1·10 80
2027 7 f. grey and black . . . . 1·50 1·10
DESIGNS: 20 c. Rock of Monaco and Fontvieille; 40 c. Place du Casino; 50 c. Place de la Cremaillere and railway station; 60 c. National Council building; 70 c. Palace and Rampe Major; 80 c. Avenue du Beau Rivage; 90 c. Fishing boats, Fontvieille; 1 f. Place d'Armes; 2 f. Marche de la Condamine; 3 f. Yacht; 7 f. Oceanographic Museum.

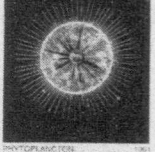

612 Abdim's Stork **613** Phytoplankton

1991. International Symposium on Bird Migration. Multicoloured.
2029 2 f. Type **612** 50 35
2030 3 f. Broad-tailed humming birds 85 60
2031 4 f. Garganeys . . . . 1·00 70
2032 5 f. Eastern broad-billed roller 1·40 1·00
2033 6 f. European bee eaters . . . 1·60 1·25

1991. Oceanographic Museum (1st series).
2034 **613** 2 f. 10 multicoloured . . 55 30
See also Nos. 2095/6.

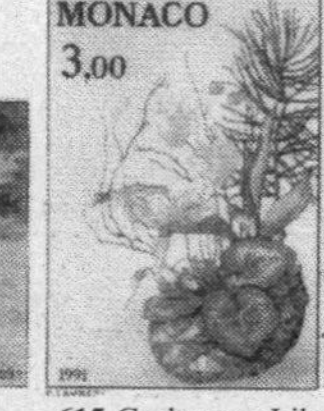

614 Schnauzer **615** Cyclamen, Lily-of-the-Valley and Pine Twig in Fir-cone

1991. International Dog Show, Monte Carlo.
2035 **614** 2 f. 50 multicoloured . . 65 40

1991. Monte Carlo Flower Show.
2036 **615** 3 f. multicoloured 75 40

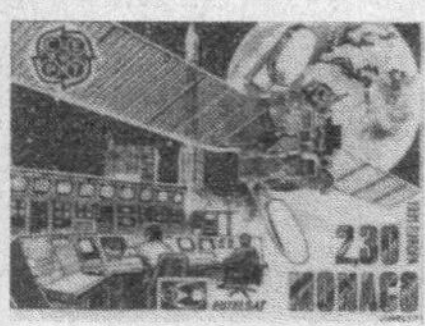

616 Corals **617** Control Room, "Eutelsat" Satellite and Globe

1991. "Joys of the Sea" Exhibition. Multicoloured.
2037 2 f. 20 Type **616** 55 40
2038 2 f. 40 Coral necklace 55 40

1991. Europa. Europe in Space. Each blue, black and green.
2039 2 f. 30 Type **617** 55 30
2040 3 f. 20 Computer terminal, "Inmarsat" satellite, research ship transmitting signal and man with receiving equipment 90 60

618 Cross-country Skiers and Statue of Skiers by Emma de Sigaldi

1991. 1992 Olympic Games. (a) Winter Olympics, Albertville.
2042 **618** 3 f. green, blue and olive . 70 75
2043 – 4 f. green, blue and olive . 1·00 1·00

(b) Olympic Games, Barcelona.
2044 – 3 f. green, lt brown & brown 75 75
2045 – 5 f. black, brown and green 1·25 1·25
DESIGNS: No. 2043, Right-hand part of statue and cross-country skiers; 2044, Track, relay runners and left part of statue of relay runners by Emma de Sigaldi; 2045, Right part of statue, view of Barcelona and track.

619 Head of "David" (Michelangelo), Computer Image and Artist at Work **620** Prince Pierre, Open Book and Lyre

1991. 25th International Contemporary Art Prize.
2046 **619** 4 f. green, dp green & lilac 1·00 65

1991. 25th Anniv of Prince Pierre Foundation.
2047 **620** 5 f. black, blue & brown 1·25 90

621 Tortoises

1991. Hermann's Tortoise. Multicoloured.
2048 1 f. 25 Type **621** 25 20
2049 1 f. 25 Head of tortoise . . . 25 20
2050 1 f. 25 Tortoise in grass . . . 25 20
2051 1 f. 25 Tortoise emerging from among plants 25 20

1991. Christmas. As T **608** showing crib figures from Provence. Multicoloured.
2052 2 f. 50 Consul 50 20
2053 3 f. 50 Arlesian woman . . . 70 30
2054 4 f. Mayor 90 40

622 Norway Spruce

1991. Conifers in Mercantour National Park. Multicoloured.
2055 2 f. 50 Type **622** 50 20
2056 3 f. 50 Silver fir 70 30
2057 4 f. "Pinus uncinata" 90 30
2058 5 f. Scots pine (vert) . . . . 1·10 55
2059 6 f. Arolla pine . . . . . . 1·40 75
2060 7 f. European larch (vert) . . 1·60 90

1991. Monaco Red Cross. St. Devote, Patron Saint of Monaco (5th series). As T **547**. Multicoloured.
2062 4 f. 50 Fishing boat carrying body caught in storm . . . 1·10 90
2063 5 f. 50 Dove guiding boat-man to port of Monaco . . . . 1·40 1·10

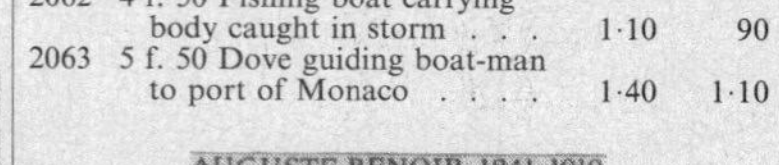

624 "Portrait of Claude Monet"

1991. 150th Birth Anniv of Auguste Renoir (painter).
2064 **624** 5 f. multicoloured . . . 1·10 65

625 Prince Honore II of Monaco

1991. 350th Anniv of Treaty of Peronne (giving French recognition of sovereignty of Monaco). Paintings by Philippe de Champaigne. Mult.
2065 6 f. Type **625** . . . . 1·40 75
2066 7 f. King Louis XIII of France 1·60 90

626 Princess Grace (after R. Samini)

1991. 10th Anniv of Princess Grace Theatre.
2067 **626** 8 f. multicoloured . . . . 1·60 1·10

1992. 16th International Circus Festival, Monte Carlo. As No. 2011 but value and dates changed.
2069 **611** 2 f. 50 multicoloured . . 55 30
The 1991 Festival was cancelled.

628 Two-man Bobsleighs

1992. Winter Olympic Games, Albertville (7 f.), and Summer Games, Barcelona (8 f.).
2070 **628** 7 f. blue, turquoise & blk 1·50 90
2071 – 8 f. purple, blue and green 1·75 1·00
DESIGN: 8 f. Football.

630 Spring

1992. Precancels. Seasons of the Walnut Tree. Mult.
2073 1 f. 60 Type **630** 35 20
2074 2 f. 08 Summer 50 30
2075 2 f. 98 Autumn 70 40
2076 5 f. 28 Winter . . . . 1·25 75

631 Golden Labrador

1992. International Dog Show, Monte Carlo.
2077 **631** 2 f. 20 multicoloured . . 50 30

632 Racing along Seafront **633** Mixed Bouquet

1992. 50th Monaco Grand Prix.
2078 **632** 2 f. 50 black, purple & bl 60 35

1992. 25th Monte Carlo Flower Show.
2079 **633** 3 f. 40 multicoloured . . 80 45

634 Ford Sierra Rally Car

1992. 60th Monte Carlo Car Rally.
2080 **634** 4 f. black, green and red 95 55

636 "Pinta" off Palos

1992. Europa. 500th Anniv of Discovery of America by Columbus. Multicoloured.
2082 2 f. 50 Type **636** 60 40
2083 3 f. 40 "Santa Maria" in the Antilles 80 60
2084 4 f. "Nina" off Lisbon . . . 95 75

637 Produce

1992. "Ameriflora" Horticultural Show, Columbus, Ohio. Multicoloured.
2086 4 f. Type **637** 95 55
2087 5 f. Vase of mixed flowers . 1·10 70

638 Prince Rainier I and Fleet (detail of fresco by E. Charpentier, Spinola Palace, Genoa)

1992. Columbus Exhibition, Genoa (6 f.), and "Expo '92" World's Fair, Seville (7 f.).
2088 **638** 6 f. brown, red and blue 1·50 1·10
2089 – 7 f. brown, red and blue 1·60 1·10
DESIGN: 7 f. Monaco pavilion.

1992. Old Monaco (3rd series). Paintings by Claude Rosticher. As T **576**. Multicoloured.
2090 2 f. 20 La Porte Neuve (horiz) 50 30
2091 2 f. 50 La Placette Bosio (horiz) 60 35

639 "Christopher Columbus"

1992. "Genova '92" International Thematic Stamp Exhibition. Roses. Multicoloured.
2092 3 f. Type **639** 70 40
2093 4 f. "Prince of Monaco" . . 95 55

640 Lammergeier

1992.
2094 **640** 2 f. 20 orange, blk & grn 50 30

1992. Oceanographic Museum (2nd series). As T **613**. Multicoloured.
2095 2 f. 20 "Ceratium ranipes" . 50 30
2096 2 f. 50 "Ceratium hexacanthum" 60 35

1992. Christmas. As T **608** showing crib figures from Provence. Multicoloured.
2097 2 f. 50 Basket-maker 60 35
2098 3 f. 40 Fishwife 80 45
2099 5 f. Rural constable . . . . 1·10 70

641 "Seabus" (tourist submarine)

1992.
2100 **641** 4 f. blue, red and brown 1·00 80

642 Burning Boat Ceremony, St. Devote's Eve

1992. Monaco Red Cross. St. Devote, Patron Saint of Monaco (6th series).
2101 **642** 6 f. red, blue and brown . 1·50 1·10
2102 – 8 f. purple, orange & red 1·90 1·10
DESIGN: 8 f. Procession of reliquary, St. Devote's Day.

643 Athletes, Sorbonne University and Coubertin

1992. Centenary of Pierre de Coubertin's Proposal for Revival of Olympic Games.
2103 **643** 10 f. blue . . . . 2·25 1·40

644 Baux de Provence and St. Catherine's Chapel

1992. Titles of Princes of Monaco. Marquis of Baux de Provence.
2104 **644** 15 f. multicoloured . . . 3·50 2·10

646 Clown and Tiger **647** Short-toed Eagles

1993. 17th Int Circus Festival, Monte Carlo.
2106 **646** 2 f. 50 multicoloured . . 60 35

1993. Birds of Prey in Mercantour National Park.
2107 **647** 2 f. chestnut, brown and orange 45 30
2108 – 3 f. indigo, orange & blue 70 45
2109 – 4 f. brown, ochre & blue 95 55
2110 – 5 f. brown, chestnut and green . . . . 1·10 70
2111 – 6 f. brown, mauve & grn 1·40 85
DESIGNS—HORIZ: 3 f. Peregrine falcon. VERT: 4 f. Eagle owl; 5 f. Honey buzzard; 6 f. Tengmalm's owl.

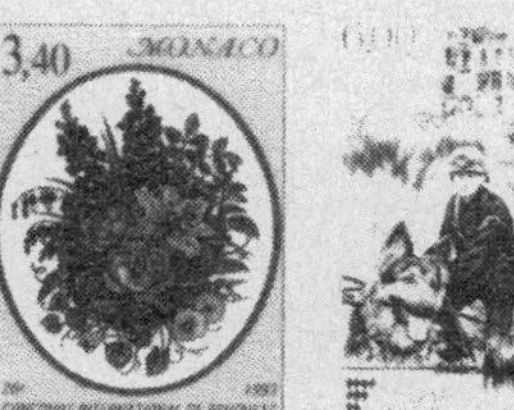

650 Mixed Bouquet **652** Fire Fighting and Rescue

651 Pennants, Auditorium and Masks

1993. Monte Carlo Flower Show.
2114 **650** 3 f. 40 multicoloured . . 80 50

1993. 10th International Amateur Theatre Festival.
2115 **651** 4 f. 20 multicoloured . . 1·00 60

1993. World Civil Protection Day.
2116 **652** 6 f. black, red and green . 1·40 85

653 Newfoundland **654** Golfer

1993. International Dog Show, Monte Carlo.
2117 **653** 2 f. 20 multicoloured . . 50 30

1993. 10th Monte Carlo Open Golf Tournament.
2118 **654** 2 f. 20 multicoloured . . 50 30

655 Princess Grace **656** Mirror and Candelabra

1993. 10th Death Anniv (1992) of Princess Grace.
2119 **655** 5 f. blue . . . . 1·10 70

1993. 10th Antiques Biennale.
2120 **656** 7 f. multicoloured . . . 1·60 1·00

657 "Echinopsis multiplex" **658** Monte Carlo Ballets

1993. Cacti.
2121 **657** 2 f. 50 green, pur & yell 60 35
2122 – 2 f. 50 green and purple 60 35
2123 – 2 f. 50 green, pur & yell 60 35
2124 – 2 f. 50 green and yellow 60 35
DESIGNS: No. 2122, "Zygocactus truncatus"; 2123, "Echinocereus procumbens"; 2124, "Euphorbia virosa".
See also Nos. 2154/66.

1993. Europa. Contemporary Art.
2125 **658** 2 f. 50 black, brn & pink 60 35
2126 – 4 f. 20 grey and brown 1·00 60
DESIGN: 4 f. 20, "Evolution" (sculpture, Emma de Sigaldi).

660 State Arms and Olympic Rings

1993. 110th International Olympic Committee Session, Monaco.
2129 **660** 2 f. 80 red, brown & blue 65 40
2130 – 2 f. 80 blue, lt blue & red 60 40
2131 – 2 f. 80 brown, blue & red 65 40
2132 – 2 f. 80 blue, lt blue & red 65 40
2133 – 2 f. 80 brown, blue & red 65 40
2134 – 2 f. 80 blue, lt blue & red 65 40
2135 – 2 f. 80 brown, blue & red 65 40
2136 – 2 f. 80 blue, lt blue & red 65 40
2137 – 4 f. 50 multicoloured . . 1·00 60
2138 – 4 f. 50 black, yellow & bl 1·00 60
2139 – 4 f. 50 red, yellow & blue 1·00 60
2140 – 4 f. 50 black, yellow & bl 1·00 60
2141 – 4 f. 50 red, yellow & blue 1·00 60
2142 – 4 f. 50 black, yellow & bl 1·00 60
2143 – 4 f. 50 red, yellow & blue 1·00 60
2144 – 4 f. 50 red, yellow & blue 1·00 60
DESIGNS: Nos. 2129, 2137, Type **660** 2130, Bobsleighing; 2131, Skiing; 2132, Yachting; 2133, Rowing; 2134, Swimming; 2135, Cycling; 2136, 2144, Commemorative inscription; 2138, Gymnastics (rings exercise); 2139, Judo; 2140, Fencing; 2141, Hurdling; 2142, Archery; 2143, Weightlifting.

661 Examining 1891 1 c. Stamp

1993. Centenary of Monaco Philatelic Union.
2145 **661** 2 f. 40 multicoloured . . 55 35

1993. Christmas. Crib figures from Provence. As T **608**. Multicoloured.
2146 2 f. 80 Donkey 65 40
2147 3 f. 70 Shepherd holding lamb 85 55
2148 4 f. 40 Ox lying down in barn 1·00 60

662 Grieg, Music and Trolls

1993. 150th Birth Anniv of Edvard Grieg (composer).
2149 **662** 4 f. blue 95 60

663 Abstract Lithograph

664 Monaco Red Cross Emblem

1993. Birth Centenary of Joan Miro (painter and sculptor).
2150 **663** 5 f. multicoloured . . . . 1·10 70

1993. Monaco Red Cross.
2151 **664** 5 f. red, yellow and black 1·10 70
2152 – 6 f. red and black . . . . 1·40 85
DESIGN: 6 f. Crosses inscribed with fundamental principles of the International Red Cross.

665 "St. Joseph the Carpenter"

1993. 400th Birth Anniv of Georges de la Tour (painter).
2153 **665** 6 f. multicoloured . . . . 1·40 85

1994. Cacti. As Nos. 2121/4 but values changed and additional designs.
2154 20 c. green, purple & yell . . 10 10
2155 30 c. green and purple . . . 10 10
2156 40 c. green and yellow . . . 10 10
2157 50 c. green, red and olive . . 15 10
2158 60 c. green, red yellow . . . 15 10
2159 70 c. green, red and blue . . 15 10
2160 80 c. green, orange and red . 20 15
2164 2 f. green, red and yellow . . 50 35
2166 4 f. green, purple and yellow 95 60
DESIGNS: 30 c. "Zygocactus truncatus"; 40 c. "Euphorbia virosa"; 50 c. "Selenicereus grandiflorus"; 60 c. "Opuntia basilaris"; 70 c. "Aloe plicatilis"; 80 c. "Opuntia hybride"; 2 f. "Aporocactus flagelliformis"; 4 f. "Echinocereus procumbens".

666 Festival Poster

667 Artist/Poet

1994. 18th Int Circus Festival, Monte Carlo.
2168 **666** 2 f. 80 multicoloured . . 65 40

1994. Mechanical Toys.
2169 **667** 2 f. 80 blue 65 40
2170 – 2 f. 80 red 65 40
2171 – 2 f. 80 purple 65 40
2172 – 2 f. 80 green 65 40
DESIGNS: No. 2170, Bust of Japanese woman; 2171, Shepherdess with sheep; 2172, Young Parisienne.

669 King Charles Spaniels

1994. International Dog Show, Monte Carlo.
2175 **669** 2 f. 40 multicoloured . . 60 40

670 Couple, Leaves and Pollution

671 Iris

1994. Monaco Committee of Anti-tuberculosis and Respiratory Diseases Campaign.
2176 **670** 2 f. 40 + 60 c. mult . . 75 60

1994. Monte Carlo Flower Show.
2177 **671** 4 f. 40 multicoloured . . 1·10 70

672 Levitation Trick

1994. 10th Monte Carlo Magic Grand Prix.
2178 **672** 5 f. blue, black and red . 1·25 75

673 Ingredients and Dining Table overlooking Harbour

1994. 35th Anniv of Brotherhood of Cordon d'Or French Chefs.
2179 **673** 6 f. multicoloured . . . 1·50 90

674 Isfjord, Prince Albert I, Map of Spitzbergen and "Princess Alice II"

1994. Europa. Discoveries made by Prince Albert I. Each black, blue and red.
2180 2 f. 80 Type **674** 70 45
2181 4 f. 50 Oceanographic Museum, mirrorbelly and "Eryoneicus alberti" (crustacean) . . . 1·10 70

675 Olympic Flag and Sorbonne University

676 Dolphins through Porthole

1994. Centenary of International Olympic Committee.
2183 **675** 3 f. multicoloured . . . 75 45

1994. Economic Institute of the Rights of the Sea Conference, Monaco.
2184 **676** 6 f. multicoloured . . . 1·50 90

677 Family around Tree of Hearts

678 Footballer's Legs and Ball

1994. International Year of the Family.
2185 **677** 7 f. green, orange and blue 1·75 1·10

1994. World Cup Football Championship, U.S.A.
2186 **678** 8 f. red and black . . . . 2·00 1·25

679 Athletes and Villa Miraflores

1994. Inauguration of New Seat of International Amateur Athletics Federation.
2187 **679** 8 f. blue, purple and bistre 2·00 1·25

680 De Dion Bouton, 1903

1994. Vintage Car Collection of Prince Rainier III.
2188 **680** 2 f. 80 black, brown and mauve 70 45

681 Emblem and Monte Carlo

682 Emblem and Korean Scene

1994. 1st Association of Postage Stamp Catalogue Editors and Philatelic Publications Grand Prix.
2189 **681** 3 f. multicoloured 75 45

1994. 21st Universal Postal Union Congress, Seoul.
2190 **682** 4 f. 40 black, blue and red 1·10 70

1994. Christmas. As T **608** showing crib figures from Provence. Multicoloured.
2191 2 f. 80 Virgin Mary 70 45
2192 4 f. 50 Baby Jesus . . . . . . 1·10 70
2193 6 f. Joseph . . . . 1·50 90

683 Prince Albert I

684 Three Ages of Voltaire (writer, 300th anniv)

1994. Inaug of Stamp and Coin Museum. Coins.
2194 **683** 3 f. stone, brown and red 75 45
2195 – 4 f. grey, brown and red . 1·00 60
2196 – 7 f. stone, brown and red 1·75 1·10
DESIGNS: 4 f. Arms of House of Grimaldi; 7 f. Prince Rainier III.

1994. Birth Anniversaries.
2198 **684** 5 f. green . . . . 1·25 75
2199 – 6 f. brown and purple . . 1·50 90
DESIGN—HORIZ: 6 f. Sarah Bernhardt (actress, 150th anniv).

685 Heliport and Helicopter

1994. 50th Anniv of International Civil Aviation Organization.
2200 **685** 5 f. green, black and blue 1·25 75
2201 – 7 f. brown, black and red 1·75 1·10
DESIGN: 7 f. Harbour and helicopter.

687 Blood Vessels on Woman (anti-cancer)

1994. Monaco Red Cross. Health Campaigns.
2203 **687** 6 f. blue, black and red . 1·50 90
2204 – 8 f. green, black and red 2·00 1·25
DESIGN: 8 f. Tree and woman (anti-AIDS).

688 Robinson Crusoe and Friday

1994. Anniversaries. Multicoloured.
2205 7 f. Type **688** (275th anniv of publication of "Robinson Crusoe" by Daniel Defoe) 1·75 1·10
2206 9 f. "The Snake Charmer" (150th birth anniv of Henri Rousseau, painter) . . . . 2·25 1·40

POSTAGE DUE STAMPS

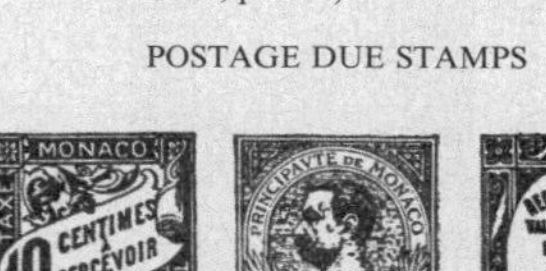
D 3 D 4

D **18**

1906.
D 29a D 3 1 c. green 20 30
D 30 5 c. green 35 45
D 31a 10 c. red 25 30
D 32 10 c. brown £350 £110
D 33 15 c. purple on cream 1·40 1·00
D113 20 c. bistre on buff . . 15 15
D 34 30 c. blue 30 35
D114 40 c. mauve 15 15
D 35 50 c. brown on buff . 2·75 2·50
D115 50 c. green 15 15
D116 60 c. black 40 40
D117 60 c. mauve . . . . . 10·00 13·50
D118 1 f. purple on cream . 10 10
D119 2 f. red 30 30
D120 3 f. red 30 30
D121 5 f. blue 40 40

1910.
D36 D 4 1 c. olive 20 25
D37 10 c. lilac 30 35
D38 30 c. bistre £170 £170

1919. Surch.
D39 D 4 20 c. on 10 c. lilac . . . 1·75 2·50
D40 40 c. on 30 c. bistre . . 1·75 2·50

1925.
D106 D 18 1 c. olive 15 20
D107 10 c. violet 15 20
D108 30 c. bistre 15 30
D109 60 c. red 15 30
D110 1 f. blue . . . . . . 55·00 48·00
D111 2 f. red . . . . 90·00 70·00

1925. Surch **1 franc a percevoir.**
D112 D 3 1 f. on 50 c. brown on buff 65 65

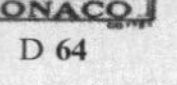

D **64** D **65**

1946.
D327 D 64 10 c. black 10 10
D328 30 c. violet 10 10
D329 50 c. blue 10 10
D330 1 f. green 15 15
D331 2 f. brown 15 15
D332 3 f. mauve 20 20

D333		4 f. red	30	35
D334	D 65	5 f. brown	20	20
D335		10 f. blue	30	30
D336		20 f. turquoise	40	45
D337		50 f. red and mauve	32·00	48·00
D338		100 f. red and green	5·00	9·00

D **99** Early Steam Locomotive

1953.

D478	–	1 f. red and green	10	10
D479	–	1 f. green and red	10	10
D480	–	2 f. turquoise and blue	10	10
D481	–	2 f. blue and turquoise	10	10
D482	D 99	3 f. lake and green	20	20
D483	–	3 f. green and lake	20	20
D484	–	4 f. slate and brown	15	15
D485	–	4 f. brown and slate	15	15
D486	–	5 f. violet and blue	40	40
D487	–	5 f. blue and violet	40	40
D488	–	10 f. indigo and blue	5·50	5·50
D489	–	10 f. blue and indigo	5·50	5·50
D490	–	20 f. violet and blue	1·75	1·75
D491	–	20 f. blue and violet	1·75	1·75
D492	–	50 f. brown and red	4·50	4·50
D493	–	50 f. red and brown	4·50	4·50
D494	–	100 f. green and purple	7·50	7·50
D495	–	100 f. purple and green	11·00	11·00

TRIANGULAR DESIGNS: Nos. D478, Pigeons released from mobile loft; D479, Sikorsky S-51 helicopter; D480, Brig; D481, "United States" (liner); D483, Streamlined steam locomotive; D484, Santos-Dumont's monoplane No. 20 Demoiselle; D485, De Havilland Comet 1 airliner; D486, Old motor car; D487, "Sabre" racing-car; D488, Leonardo da Vinci's flying machine; D489, Postal rocket; D490, Mail balloon, Paris, 1870; D491, Airship "Graf Zeppelin"; D492, Postilion; D493, Motor cycle messenger; D494, Mail coach; D495, Railway mail van.

D **140** 18th-Century Felucca

1960.

D698	D 140	1 c. brown, grn & bl	55	55
D699	–	2 c. sepia, bl & grn	15	15
D700	–	5 c. purple, blk & turq	15	25
D701	–	10 c. black, grn & bl	10	10
D702	–	20 c. purple, grn & bl	80	80
D703	–	30 c. brown, bl & grn	90	90
D704	–	50 c. blue, brn & myrtle	80	80
D705	–	1 f. brown, myrtle & bl	1·60	1·60

DESIGNS: 2 c. Paddle-steamer "La Palmaria"; 5 c. Arrival of first railway train at Monaco; 10 c. 15th-16th-century armed messenger; 20 c. 18th-century postman; 30 c. "Charles III" (paddle-steamer); 50 c. 17th-century courier; 1 f. Mail coach (19th-century).

D **393** Prince's Seal

D **492** Coat of Arms

1980.

D1426	D 393	5 c. red and brown	10	10
D1427		10 c. orange and red	10	10
D1428		15 c. violet and red	10	10
D1429		20 c. green and red	10	10
D1430		30 c. blue and red	15	15
D1431		40 c. bistre and red	20	20
D1432		50 c. violet and red	25	25
D1433		1 f. grey and blue	40	40
D1434		2 f. brown & black	90	80
D1435		3 f. red and green	1·40	1·10
D1436		4 f. green and red	1·75	1·50
D1437		5 f. brown & mauve	2·25	1·75

1985.

D1712	D 492	5 c. multicoloured	10	10
D1713		10 c. multicoloured	10	10
D1714		15 c. multicoloured	10	10
D1715		20 c. multicoloured	10	10
D1716		30 c. multicoloured	10	10
D1717		40 c. multicoloured	10	10
D1718		50 c. multicoloured	10	10
D1719		1 f. multicoloured	30	30
D1720		2 f. multicoloured	65	65
D1721		3 f. multicoloured	1·00	1·00
D1722		4 f. multicoloured	1·40	1·40
D1723		5 f. multicoloured	1·50	1·50

INDEX

Countries can be quickly located by referring to the index at the end of this volume.

MONGOLIA Pt. 10

A republic in Central Asia between China and Russia, independent since 1921.

1924. 100 cents = 1 dollar (Chinese)
1926. 100 mung = 1 tugrik

1 Eldev-Otchir Symbol

2 Soyombo Symbol

1924. Inscr in black.

1	1	1 c. brown, pink and grey on bistre	3·25	3·25
2		2 c. brown, blue and red on brown	3·25	2·75
3		5 c. grey, red and yellow	20·00	14·00
4		10 c. blue and brown on blue	7·50	5·50
5		20 c. grey, blue and white on blue	12·00	8·50
6		50 c. red and orange on pink	20·00	14·00
7		$1 bistre, red and white on yellow	32·00	22·00

Stamps vary in size according to the face value.

1926. Fiscal stamps as T **2** optd **POSTAGE** in frame in English and Mongolian.

8	2	1 c. blue	6·50	6·50
9		2 c. buff	7·50	7·50
10		5 c. purple	8·50	8·50
11		10 c. green	10·00	10·00
12		20 c. brown	13·00	13·00
13		50 c. brown and yellow	£120	£120
14		$1 brown and pink	£325	£375
15		$5 red and olive	£350	

Stamps vary in size according to the face value.

4 State Emblem: Soyombo Symbol **5**

1926. New Currency.

16	4	5 m. black and lilac	4·00	4·00
17		20 m. black and blue	3·50	3·50

1926.

18	5	1 m. black and yellow	1·00	80
19		2 m. black and brown	1·10	90
20		5 m. black and lilac (A)	2·00	1·40
28		5 m. black and lilac (B)	13·00	8·50
21		10 m. black and blue	1·40	1·10
30		20 m. black and blue	14·00	8·00
22		25 m. black and green	3·00	1·75
23		40 m. black and yellow	4·50	2·00
24		50 m. black and brown	6·00	3·25
25		1 t. black, green and brown	14·00	6·50
26		3 t. black, yellow and red	30·00	25·00
27		5 t. black, red and purple	45·00	40·00

In (A) the Mongolian numerals are in the upper and in (B) in the lower value tablets.

These stamps vary in size according to the face value.

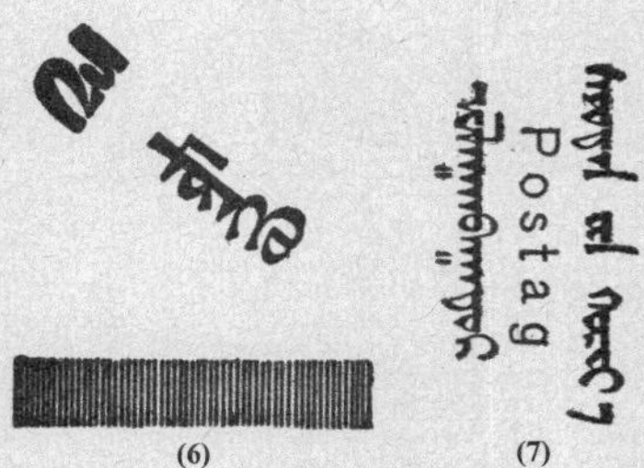

(6) (7)

1930. Surch as T **6**.

32	5	10 m. on 1 m. black & yellow	20·00	30·00
33		20 m. on 2 m. black & brown	30·00	30·00
34		25 m. on 40 m. black & yell	35·00	35·00

1931. Optd with T **7**.

35	2	1 c. blue	17·00	8·00
36		2 c. buff	12·00	6·00
37		5 c. purple	18·00	6·00
38		10 c. green	18·00	6·00
39		20 c. brown	27·00	8·50
40		50 c. brown and yellow	70·00	70·00
41		$1 brown and pink		

1931. Surch **Postage** and value in "Menge".

43	2	5 m. on 5 c. purple	18·00	6·00
44		10 m. on 10 c. green	30·00	15·00
45		20 m. on 20 c. brown	40·00	20·00

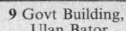

9 Govt Building, Ulan Bator

11 Sukhe Bator

12 Lake and Mountain Scenery

1932.

46	–	1 m. brown	1·40	1·00
47	–	2 m. red	1·40	1·00
48	–	5 m. blue	35	30
49	9	10 m. green	35	30
50	–	15 m. brown	35	30
51	–	20 m. red	35	30
52	–	25 m. violet	45	30
53	11	40 m. black	45	40
54	–	50 m. blue	35	30
55	12	1 t. green	60	50
56	–	3 t. violet	1·75	1·25
57	–	5 t. brown	10·00	7·50
58	–	10 t. blue	17·00	13·00

DESIGNS—As Type **9**: 1 m. Weavers; 5 m. Machinist. As Type **11**: 2 m. Telegraphist; 15 m. Revolutionary soldier carrying flag; 20 m. Mongols learning Latin alphabet; 25 m. Soldier; 50 m. Sukhe Bator's monument. As Type **12**: 3 t. Sheep-shearing; 5 t. Camel caravan; 10 t. Lassoing wild horses (after painting by Sampilon).

13 Mongol Man

14 Camel Caravan

1943. Network background in similar colour to stamps.

59	13	5 m. green	3·50	3·50
60	–	10 m. blue	6·00	3·75
61	–	15 m. red	7·00	5·00
62	14	20 m. brown	11·00	9·00
63	–	25 m. brown	11·00	11·00
64	–	30 m. red	12·00	12·00
65	–	45 m. purple	17·00	17·00
66	–	60 m. green	28·00	28·00

DESIGNS—VERT: 10 m. Mongol woman; 15 m. Soldier; 30 m. Arms of the Republic; 45 m. Portrait of Sukhe Bator, dated 1894–1923. HORIZ: 25 m. Secondary school; 60 m. Pastoral scene.

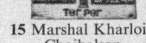

15 Marshal Kharloin Choibalsan

17 Victory Medal

16 Choibalsan and Sukhe Bator

1945. 50th Birthday of Choibalsan.

67	15	1 t. black	7·50	7·50

1946. 25th Anniv of Independence. As T **16/17**.

68	–	30 m. bistre	4·50	3·50
69	16	50 m. purple	5·50	4·00
70	–	60 m. brown	5·50	5·50
71	–	60 m. black	8·00	5·50
72	17	80 m. brown	7·50	7·50
73	–	1 t. blue	11·00	12·00
74	–	2 t. brown	14·00	16·00

DESIGNS—VERT: ($21\frac{1}{2}\times32$ mm): 30 m. Choibalsan, aged four. As Type **17**: 60 m. (No. 71), Choibalsan when young man; 1 t. 25th Anniversary Medal; 2 t. Sukhe Bator. HORIZ: As Type **16**: 60 m. (No. 70), Choibalsan University.

17a Flags of Communist Bloc

1951. Struggle for Peace.

75	17a	1 t. multicoloured	7·50	7·50

17b Lenin (after P. Vasilev)

19 Sukhe Bator

18 State Shop

1951. Honouring Lenin.

76	17b	3 t. multicoloured	16·00	16·00

1951. 30th Anniv of Independence.

77	–	15 m. green on azure	3·25	3·25
78	18	20 m. orange	3·25	3·25
79	–	20 m. multicoloured	3·75	3·75
80	–	25 m. blue on azure	3·75	3·75
81	–	30 m. multicoloured	4·25	4·25
82	–	40 m. violet on pink	4·50	4·50
83	–	50 m. brown on azure	9·00	9·00
84	–	60 m. black on pink	8·00	8·00
85	19	2 t. brown	15·00	15·00

DESIGNS—HORIZ: (As Type **18**): 15 m. Alti Hotel; 40 m. State Theatre, Ulan Bator; 50 m. Pedagogical Institute. $55\frac{1}{2}\times26$ mm: 25 m. Choibalsan University. VERT: (As Type **19**): 20 m. (No. 79); 30 m. Arms and flag; 60 m. Sukhe Bator Monument.

20 School-children

1952. Culture.

86	–	5 m. brown on pink	2·00	1·75
87	20	10 m. blue on pink	2·50	2·50

DESIGN: 5 m. New houses.

21 Choibalsan in National Costume

22 Choibalsan and Farm Worker

1953. 1st Death Anniv of Marshal Choibalsan. As T **21/22**.

88	21	15 m. blue	2·50	2·75
89	22	15 m. green	2·50	2·75
90	21	20 m. green	5·00	6·00
91	22	20 m. sepia	2·50	2·50
92	–	20 m. blue	2·50	2·50
93	–	30 m. sepia	3·25	3·25
94	–	50 m. brown	3·25	3·25
95	–	1 t. red	4·00	4·00
96	–	1 t. purple	4·00	4·00
97	–	2 t. red	4·00	4·00
98	–	3 t. purple	5·00	5·00
99	–	5 t. red	19·00	19·00

DESIGNS: As Type **21**: 1 t. (96); 2 t. Choibalsan in uniform. 33×48 mm: 3, 5 t. Busts of Choibalsan and Sukhe Bator. 33×46 mm: 50 m., 1 t. (95), Choibalsan and young pioneer. 48×33 mm: 20 m. (92); 30 m. Choibalsan and factory hand.

23 Arms of the Republic

23a Lenin

1954.

100	23	10 m. red	6·50	4·00
101		20 m. red	11·00	5·00
102		30 m. red	6·00	4·50
103		40 m. red	7·00	4·50
104		60 m. red	6·50	4·50

1955. 85th Birth Anniv of Lenin.

105	23a	2 t. blue	3·75	2·00

23b Flags of the Communist Bloc

24 Sukhe Bator and Choibalsan

1955. Struggle for Peace.

106	23b	60 m. multicoloured	1·00	55

1955.

107	24	30 m. green	30	20
108	–	30 m. blue	50	20
109	–	30 m. red	40	40
110	–	40 m. purple	1·00	40
111	–	50 m. brown	1·00	45
112	–	1 t. multicoloured	2·75	1·25

DESIGNS—HORIZ: 30 m. blue, Lake Khobsogol; 50 m. Choibalsan University. VERT: 30 m. red, Lenin Statue, Ulan Bator; 40 m. Sukhe Bator and dog; 1 t. Arms and flag of the Republic.

24a Train linking Ulan Bator and Moscow

25 Arms of the Republic

1956. Mongol–Soviet Friendship. Multicoloured.

113	1 t. Type 24a	22·00	10·00
114	2 t. Flags of Mongolia and Russia	3·50	2·00

1956.

115	25	20 m. brown	50	30
116		30 m. brown	65	35
117		40 m. blue	80	45
118		60 m. green	1·00	65
119		1 t. red	1·60	80

26 Hunter and Golden Eagle

27 Arms

27a Wrestlers

1956. 35th Anniv of Independence.

120	26	30 m. brown	32·00	16·00
121	27	30 m. blue	5·00	4·00
122	27a	60 m. green	15·00	15·00
123	–	60 m. orange	15·00	15·00

DESIGN: As Type 26: 60 m. (No. 123), Children. Also inscr "xxxv".

28

29

1958. With or without gum.

124	28	20 m. red	1·50	1·00

1958. 13th Mongol People's Revolutionary Party Congress. With or without gum.

125	29	30 m. red and salmon	3·00	3·25

1958. As T 27a but without "xxxv". With or without gum.

126	50 m. brown on pink	5·00	3·75

30 Dove and Globe

1958. 4th Congress of International Women's Federation, Vienna. With or without gum.

127	30	60 m. blue	3·25	2·00

31 Ibex

32 Yak

1958. Mongolian Animals. As T 31/2.

128	–	30 m. pale blue	12·00	2·50
129	–	30 m. turquoise	12·00	2·50
130	31	30 m. green	3·00	1·50
131		30 m. turquoise	3·00	1·00
132	32	60 m. bistre	3·50	2·00
133		60 m. orange	3·50	1·25
134	–	1 t. blue	5·00	2·50
135	–	1 t. light blue	4·00	1·75
136	–	1 t. red	5·00	3·25
137	–	1 t. red	4·00	2·00

DESIGNS—VERT: 30 m. (Nos. 128/9), Dalmatian pelicans. HORIZ: 1 t. (Nos. 134/5), Yak, facing right; 1 t. (Nos. 136/7), Bactrian camels.

33 Goat

34 "Tulaga"

1958. Mongolian Animals.

138	33	5 m. sepia and yellow	15	10
139	–	10 m. sepia and green	20	10
140	–	15 m. sepia and lilac	35	10
141	–	20 m. sepia and blue	35	10
142	–	25 m. sepia and red	40	10
143	–	30 m. purple and mauve	50	10
144	33	40 m. green	50	10
145	–	50 m. brown and salmon	60	20
146	–	60 m. blue	80	20
147	–	1 t. bistre and yellow	1·75	50

ANIMALS: 10 m., 30 m. Ram; 15 m., 60 m. Stallion; 20 m., 50 m. Bull; 25 m., 1 t. Bactrian camel.

1959.

148	34	1 t. multicoloured	3·25	1·10

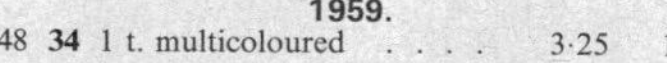

35 Taming a Wild Horse

1959. Mongolian Sports. Centres and inscriptions multicoloured: frame colours given below.

149	35	5 m. yellow and orange	20	10
150	–	10 m. purple	20	10
151	–	15 m. yellow and green	20	10
152	–	20 m. lake and red	25	10
153	–	25 m. blue	40	15
154	–	30 m. yellow, green & turq	55	15
155	–	70 m. red and yellow	70	30
156	–	80 m. purple	1·10	60

DESIGNS: 10 m. Wrestlers; 15 m. Introducing young rider; 20 m. Archer; 25 m. Galloping horseman; 30 m. Archery contest; 70 m. Hunting a wild horse; 80 m. Proclaiming a champion.

36 Child Musician

1959. Mongolian Youth Festival (1st issue).

157	36	5 m. purple and blue	20	10
158	–	10 m. brown and green	25	10
159	–	20 m. green and purple	25	10
160	–	25 m. blue and green	50	25
161	–	40 m. violet and myrtle	95	40

DESIGNS—VERT: 10 m. Young wrestlers; 20 m. Youth on horse; 25 m. Artists in national costume. HORIZ: 40 m. Festival parade.

37 Festival Badge

38 Kalmuck Script

1959. Mongolian Youth Festival (2nd issue).

162	37	30 m. purple and blue	30	20

1959. Mongolists' Congress. Designs as T 38 incorporating "MONGOL" in various scripts.

163	–	30 m. multicoloured	5·00	5·00
164	–	40 m. red, blue and yellow	5·00	5·00
165	38	50 m. multicoloured	7·00	7·00
166	–	60 m. red, blue and yellow	11·00	11·00
167	–	1 t. yellow, turquoise & orge	14·00	14·00

SCRIPTS (29½ × 42½ mm): 30 m. Stylized Ulghur; 40 m. Soyombo; 60 m. Square (Pagspa). (21½ × 31 mm): 1 t. Cyrillic.

39 Military Monument

40 Herdswoman and Lamb

1959. 20th Anniv of Battle of Khalka River.

168	–	40 m. red, brown & yellow	55	15
169	39	50 m. multicoloured	55	15

DESIGN: 40 m. Mounted horseman with flag (emblem), inscr "AUGUST 1959 HALHIN GOL".

1959. 2nd Meeting of Rural Economy Co-operatives.

170	40	30 m. green	3·50	3·50

41 Sable

1959. Mongolian Fauna.

171	41	5 m. purple, yellow & blue	15	10
172	–	10 m. multicoloured	60	10
173	–	15 m. black, green and red	45	10
174	–	20 m. purple, blue and red	45	15
175	–	30 m. myrtle, purple & grn	50	15
176	–	50 m. black, blue and green	1·10	30
177	–	1 t. black, green and red	1·75	40

ANIMALS—HORIZ: (58 × 21 mm): 10 m. Ring-necked pheasants; 20 m. European otter; 50 m. Saiga; 1 t. Siberian musk deer. As Type 41: 15 m. Muskrat; 30 m. Argali.

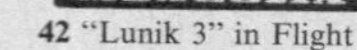
42 "Lunik 3" in Flight

44 "Flower" Emblem

43 Motherhood Badge

1959. Launching of "Lunik 3" Rocket.

178	42	30 m. yellow and violet	65	25
179	–	50 m. red, green and blue	80	35

DESIGN—HORIZ: 50 m. Trajectory of "Lunik 3" around the Moon.

1960. International Women's Day.

180	43	40 m. bistre and blue	50	15
181	44	50 m. yellow, green & blue	75	30

45 Lenin

46 Larkspur

1960. 90th Birth Anniv of Lenin.

182	45	40 m. red	60	15
183		50 m. violet	40	30

1960. Flowers.

184	46	5 m. blue, green and bistre	15	10
185	–	10 m. red, green and orange	20	10
186	–	15 m. violet, green & bistre	25	10
187	–	20 m. yellow, green & olive	30	10
188	–	30 m. violet, green & emer	35	15
189	–	40 m. orange, green & violet	65	15
190	–	50 m. violet, green and blue	85	35
191	–	1 t. mauve, green & lt green	1·60	80

FLOWERS: 10 m. Tulip; 15 m. Jacob's ladder; 20 m. Asiatic globe flower; 30 m. Clustered bellflower; 40 m. Grass of Parnassus; 50 m. Meadow cranes-bill; 1 t. "Begonia vansiana".

47 Horse-jumping

1960. Olympic Games. Inscr "ROMA 1960" or "ROMA MCMLX". Centres in greenish grey.

192	47	5 m. red, black & turquoise	10	10
193	–	10 m. violet and yellow	15	10
194	–	15 m. turquoise, black & red	20	20
195	–	20 m. red and blue	20	10
196	–	30 m. ochre, black & green	35	10
197	–	50 m. blue and turquoise	50	10
198	–	70 m. green, black & violet	60	30
199	–	1 t. mauve and green	90	50

DESIGNS—DIAMOND SHAPED: 10 m. Running; 20 m. Wrestling; 50 m. Gymnastics; 1 t. Throwing the discus. As Type 47: 15 m. Diving; 30 m. Hurdling; 70 m. High jumping.

48

1960. Red Cross.

200	48	20 m. red, yellow and blue	70	25

49 Newspapers

1960. 40th Anniv of Mongolian Newspaper "Unen" ("Truth").

201	49	20 m. buff, green and red	20	10
202		30 m. red, yellow and green	30	15

50 Hoopoe

1961. Mongolian Song-birds.
203 – 5 m. mauve, black and grn 70 25
204 **50** 10 m. red, black and green 80 25
205 – 15 m. yellow, black & green 90 35
206 – 20 m. green, black & bistre 1·10 35
207 – 50 m. blue, black and red 1·60 35
208 – 70 m. yellow, black & mve 1·75 65
209 – 1 t. mauve, orange & black 2·25 90
BIRDS: As Type **50**: 15 m. Golden oriole; 20 m. Siberian capercaillie. Inverted triangulars: 5 m. Rose-coloured starling; 50 m. Eastern broad-billed roller; 70 m. Tibetan sandgrouse; 1 t. Mandarin.

51 Foundry Worker 52 Patrice Lumumba

1961. 15th Anniv of World Federation of Trade Unions.
210 **51** 30 m. red and black 30 10
211 – 50 m. red and violet 35 20
DESIGN—HORIZ: 50 m. Hemispheres.

1961. Patrice Lumumba (Congolese politician) Commemoration.
212 **52** 30 m. brown 1·50 1·00
213 50 m. purple 2·00 1·25

53 Bridge 54 Gagarin with Capsule

1961. 40th Anniv of Independence (1st issue). Mongolian Modernization.
214 **53** 5 m. green 10 10
215 – 10 m. blue 10 10
216 – 15 m. red 15 10
217 – 20 m. brown 15 10
218 – 30 m. blue 20 15
219 – 50 m. green 30 20
220 – 1 t. violet 50 25
DESIGNS: 10 m. Shoe-maker; 15 m. Store at Ulan Bator; 30 m. Government Building, Ulan Bator; 50 m. Machinist; 1 t. Ancient and modern houses. (59 × 20½ mm): 20 m. Choibalsan University.
See also Nos. 225/32, 233/41, 242/8 and 249/56.

1961. World's First Manned Space Flight. Mult.
221 20 m. Type **54** 50 15
222 30 m. Gagarin and globe (horiz) 60 30
223 50 m. Gagarin in capsule making parachute descent 90 60
224 1 t. Globe and Gagarin (horiz) 1·40 90

55 Postman with Reindeer

1961. 40th Anniv of Independence (2nd issue). Mongolian Postal Service.
225 **55** 5 m. red, brown and blue (postage) 15 10
226 – 15 m. violet, brown & bistre 30 10
227 – 20 m. blue, black and green 20 10
228 – 25 m. violet, bistre & green 30 15
229 – 30 m. green, black & lav 3·50 80
230 – 10 m. orange, black and green (air) 35 10
231 – 50 m. black, pink and green 1·00 25
232 – 1 t. multicoloured 1·10 35
DESIGNS: Postman with: 10 m. Horses; 15 m. Camels; 20 m. Yaks; 25 m. Postman on quayside; 30 m. Diesel mail train; 50 m. Ilyushin Il-14M mail plane over map; 1 t. Postal emblem.

56 Rams

1961. 40th Anniv of Independence (3rd issue). Animal Husbandry.
233 **56** 5 m. black, red and blue 10 10
234 – 10 m. black, green & purple 15 10
235 – 15 m. black, red and green 20 10
236 – 20 m. sepia, blue & brown 25 10
237 – 25 m. black, yellow & green 30 15
238 – 30 m. black, red and violet 35 15
239 – 40 m. black, green and red 40 15
240 – 50 m. black, brown & blue 65 25
241 – 1 t. black, violet and olive 90 50
DESIGNS: 10 m. Oxen; 15 m. Camels; 20 m. Pigs and poultry; 25 m. Angora goats; 30 m. Mongolian horses; 40 m. Ewes; 50 m. Cows; 1 t. Combine-harvester.

57 Children Wrestling

1961. 40th Anniv of Independence (5th issue). Mongolian Sports.
242 **57** 5 m. multicoloured 15 10
243 – 10 m. sepia, red and green 20 10
244 – 15 m. purple blue & yellow 25 10
245 – 20 m. red, black and green 40 25
246 – 30 m. purple, green & lav 80 30
247 – 50 m. indigo, orange & blue 1·00 35
248 – 1 t. purple, blue and grey 1·60 70
DESIGNS: 10 m. Horse-riding; 15 m. Children on camel and pony; 20 m. Falconry; 30 m. Skiing; 50 m. Archery; 1 t. Dancing.

58 Young Mongol

1961. 40th Anniv of Independence (6th issue). Mongolian Culture.
249 **58** 5 m. purple and green 10 10
250 – 10 m. blue and red 10 10
251 – 15 m. brown and blue 15 10
252 – 20 m. green and violet 25 10
253 – 30 m. red and blue 35 15
254 – 50 m. violet and bistre 80 20
255 – 70 m. green and mauve 90 25
256 – 1 t. red and blue 1·25 70
DESIGNS—HORIZ: 10 m. Mongol chief; 70 m. Orchestra; 1 t. Gymnast. VERT: 15 m. Sukhe Bator Monument; 20 m. Young singer; 30 m. Young dancer; 50 m. Dombra-player.

59 Mongol Arms 60 Congress Emblem

1961. Arms multicoloured; inscr in blue; background colours given.
257 **59** 5 m. salmon 15 10
258 10 m. lilac 20 10
259 15 m. brown 25 10
260 20 m. turquoise 35 10
261 30 m. ochre 45 15
262 50 m. mauve 50 20
263 70 m. olive 60 25
264 1 t. orange 1·00 35

1961. 5th World Federation of Trade Unions Congress, Moscow.
265 **60** 30 m. red, yellow and blue 30 15
266 50 m. red, yellow and sepia 35 20

61 Dove, Map and Globe

1962. Admission of Mongolia to U.N.O.
267 **61** 10 m. multicoloured 20 10
268 – 30 m. multicoloured 30 15
269 – 50 m. multicoloured 40 15
270 – 60 m. multicoloured 60 25
271 – 70 m. multicoloured 70 35
DESIGNS: 30 m. U.N. Emblem and Mongol Arms; 50 m. U.N. and Mongol flags; 60 m. U.N. Headquarters and Mongolian Parliament building; 70 m. U.N. and Mongol flags, and Assembly.

62 Football, Globe and Flags

1962. World Cup Football Championship, Chile. Multicoloured.
272 10 m. Type **62** 10 10
273 30 m. Footballers, globe and ball 25 10
274 50 m. Footballers playing in stadium 40 15
275 60 m. Goalkeeper saving goal 50 25
276 70 m. Stadium 1·10 35

63 D. Natsagdorj 64 Torch and Handclasp

1962. 3rd Congress of Mongolian Writers.
277 **63** 30 m. brown 20 15
278 50 m. green 30 15

1962. Afro-Asian People's Solidarity.
279 **64** 20 m. multicoloured 15 10
280 30 m. multicoloured 25 20

65 Flags of Mongolia and U.S.S.R 67 Victory Banner

1962. Mongol-Soviet Friendship.
281 **65** 30 m. multicoloured 25 10
282 50 m. multicoloured 35 20

1962. Malaria Eradication. Nos. 1849/91 optd with Campaign emblem and **LUTTE CONTRE LE PALUDISME**.
283 **46** 5 m. 20 20
284 – 10 m. 20 20
285 – 15 m. 20 20
286 – 20 m. 20 20
287 – 30 m. 40 30
288 – 40 m. 40 30
289 – 50 m. 55 50
290 – 1 t. 1·10 80

1962. 800th Birth Anniv of Genghis Khan.
291 **67** 20 m. multicoloured 5·50 5·50
292 – 30 m. multicoloured 5·50 5·50
293 – 50 m. black, brown and red 12·00 12·00
294 – 60 m. buff, blue and brown 12·00 12·00
DESIGNS: 30 m. Engraved lacquer tablets; 50 m. Obelisk; 60 m. Genghis Khan.

68 Perch

1962. Fish. Multicoloured.
295 5 m. Type **68** 15 10
296 10 m. Burbot 15 10
297 15 m. Arctic grayling 20 10
298 20 m. Bullhead 30 15
299 30 m. Pike–perch 45 20
300 50 m. Sturgeon 70 30
301 70 m. Dace 95 45
302 1 t. 50 Sculpin 1·50 70

69 Sukhe Bator

1963. 70th Birth Anniv of Sukhe Bator.
303 **69** 30 m. blue 15 10
304 60 m. lake 30 20

70 Dog "Laika" and "Sputnik 2"

1963. Space Flights. Multicoloured.
305 5 m. Type **70** 20 10
306 15 m. Rocket blasting off 35 10
307 25 m. "Lunik 2" (1959) 35 15
308 70 m. Nikolaev and Popovich 65 35
309 1 t. Rocket "Mars" (1962) 90 55
SIZES: As Type **70**: 70 m., 1 t. VERT: (21 × 70 mm): 15 m., 25 m.

71 Children packing Red Cross Parcels

1963. Red Cross Centenary Multicoloured.
310 20 m. Type **71** 35 10
311 30 m. Blood transfusion 45 15
312 50 m. Doctor treating child 60 20
313 60 m. Ambulance at street accident 75 20
314 1 t. 30 Centenary emblem 90 40

72 Karl Marx 73 Woman

1963. 145th Birth Anniv of Karl Marx.
315 **72** 30 m. blue 20 10
316 60 m. lake 25 20

1963. 5th World Congress of Democratic Women, Moscow.
317 **73** 30 m. multicoloured 25 20

74 "Inachis io"

1963. Mongolian Butterflies. Multicoloured.

318 5 m. Type **74** 30 10
319 10 m. "Gonepteryx rhamni L." 35 10
320 15 m. "Aglais urticae L." . . 85 15
321 20 m. "Parnassius apollo L." . 55 20
322 30 m. "Papilio machaon L." . 85 25
323 60 m. "Agrodiaetus damon Schiff" . . . . 1·25 45
324 1 t. "Limenitis populi L." . . 1·75 60

75 Globe and Scales of Justice

1963. 15th Anniv of Declaration of Human Rights.

325 **75** 30 m. red, blue and brown 20 15
326 60 m. black, blue & yellow 30 20

76 "Coprinus comatus"

1964. Mushrooms. Multicoloured.

327 5 m. Type **76** 25 10
328 10 m. "Lactarius torminosus" 35 15
329 15 m. "Psalliota campestris" . 45 15
330 20 m. "Russula delica" . . . 50 15
331 30 m. "Ixocomus granulatus" . 75 20
332 50 m. "Lactarius scobiculatus" 1·00 45
333 70 m. "Lactarius deliciosus" . 1·40 60
334 1 t. "Ixocomus variegatus" . . 1·90 80

77 Lenin when a Young Man

1964. 60th Anniv of London Bolshevik (Communist) Party.

335 **77** 30 m. red and brown . . . 30 30
336 50 m. ultramarine and blue 35 30

78 Gymnastics

1964. Olympic Games, Tokyo. Multicoloured.

337 5 m. Type **78** 10 10
338 10 m. Throwing the javelin . . 10 10
339 15 m. Wrestling 10 10
340 20 m. Running 20 10
341 30 m. Horse-jumping 30 15
342 50 m. High-diving 40 20
343 60 m. Cycling 65 30
344 1 t. Emblem of Tokyo Games 90 50

79 Congress Emblem

1964. 4th Mongolian Women's Congress.

345 **79** 30 m. multicoloured . . . 35 20

80 "Lunik 1"

1964. Space Research. Multicoloured.

346 5 m. Type **80** 15 10
347 10 m. "Vostoks 1 and 2" . . 15 10
348 15 m. "Tiros" (vert) 20 10
349 20 m. "Cosmos" (vert) . . . 20 10
350 30 m. "Mars Probe" (vert) . . 30 10
351 60 m. "Luna 4" (vert) . . . 45 15
352 80 m. "Echo 2" 60 25
353 1 t. Radio telescope 65 45

81 Horseman and Flag

1964. 40th Anniv of Mongolian Constitution.

354 **81** 25 m. multicoloured . . . 30 10
355 50 m. multicoloured . . . 35 20

82 Marine Exploration

1965. International Quiet Sun Year. Multicoloured.

356 5 m. Type **82** (postage) . . . 30 10
357 10 m. Weather balloon . . . 15 10
358 60 m. Northern Lights . . . 60 20
359 80 m. Geomagnetic emblems . 70 25
360 1 t. Globe and I.Q.S.Y. emblem 1·10 50

361 15 m. Weather satellite (air) . 40 10
362 20 m. Antarctic exploration . 3·00 55
363 30 m. Space exploration . . . 55 15

83 Horses Grazing

1965. Mongolian Horses. Multicoloured.

364 5 m. Type **83** 30 10
365 10 m. Hunting with golden eagles 80 15
366 15 m. Breaking-in wild horse 45 15
367 20 m. Horses racing 45 15
368 30 m. Horses jumping 55 15
369 60 m. Hunting wolves 70 25
370 80 m. Milking a mare 85 40
371 1 t. Mare and colt . . . . . 1·40 60

84 Farm Girl with Lambs

1965. 40th Anniv of Mongolian Youth Movement.

372 **84** 5 m. orange, bistre & green 10 10
373 – 10 m. bistre, blue and red 15 10
374 – 20 m. ochre, red and violet 20 15
375 – 30 m. lilac, brown & green 45 20
376 – 50 m. orange, buff and blue 75 45

DESIGNS: 10 m. Young drummers; 20 m. Children around campfire; 30 m. Young wrestlers; 50 m. Emblem.

85 Chinese Perch

1965. Mongolian Fishes. Multicoloured.

377 5 m. Type **85** 20 10
378 10 m. "Brachymistrax lenok" . 20 10
379 15 m. Siberian sturgeon . . . 25 15
380 20 m. Taimen 35 15
381 30 m. Banded catfish 55 20
382 60 m. Amur catfish 85 20
383 80 m. Pike 90 40
384 1 t. River perch . . . . 1·25 60

86 Marx and Lenin

87 I.T.U. Emblem and Symbols

1965. Organization of Socialist Countries' Postal Administrations Conference, Peking.

385 **86** 10 m. black and red 25 15

1965. Air. I.T.U. Centenary.

386 **87** 30 m. blue and bistre . . . 40 15
387 50 m. red, bistre and blue 60 20

88 Sable

1966. Mongolian Fur Industry.

388 **88** 5 m. purple, black & yellow 15 10
389 – 10 m. brown, black & grey 15 10
390 – 15 m. brown, black & blue 25 10
391 – 20 m. multicoloured 25 10
392 – 30 m. brown, black & mve 35 10
393 – 60 m. brown, black & green 55 25
394 – 80 m. multicoloured 85 40
395 – 1 t. blue, black and olive . . 1·90 50

DESIGNS (Fur animals): HORIZ: 10 m. Red fox; 30 m. Pallas's Cat; 60 m. Beech marten. VERT: 15 m. European otter; 20 m. Cheetah; 80 m. Stoat; 1 t. Woman in fur coat.

89 W.H.O. Building

1966. Inauguration of W.H.O. Headquarters, Geneva.

396 **89** 30 m. blue, gold and green . 35 15
397 50 m. blue, gold and red . . 50 20

90 Footballers

1966. World Cup Football Championships. Multicoloured.

398 10 m. Type **90** 15 10
399 30 m. Footballers (different) . 25 10
400 60 m. Goalkeeper saving goal 40 25
401 80 m. Footballers (different) . 65 30
402 1 t. World Cup flag . . . . . 1·10 35

92 Sukhe Bator and Parliament Buildings, Ulan Bator

1966. 15th Mongolian Communist Party Congress.

404 **92** 30 m. multicoloured . . . 15 10

93 Wrestling

95 State Emblem

1966. World Wrestling Championships Toledo (Spain). Similar wrestling designs.

405 **93** 10 m. black, mauve & pur 10 10
406 – 30 m. black, mauve & grey 20 15
407 – 60 m. black, mauve & brn 30 15
408 – 80 m. black, mauve & lilac 40 20
409 – 1 t. black, mauve and turq 55 20

1966. 45th Anniv of Independence. Mult.

411 30 m. Type **95** 75 20
412 50 m. Sukhe Bator, emblems of agriculture and industry (horiz) . . . . 1·75 30

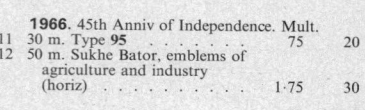

96 "Physochlaena physaloides"

97 Child with Dove

1966. Flowers. Multicoloured.

413 5 m. Type **97** 20 10
414 10 m. Onion 20 10
415 15 m. Red lily 25 10
416 20 m. "Thermopsis lanceolata" 35 10
417 30 m. "Amygdalus mongolica" 50 20
418 60 m. Bluebeard 60 30
419 80 m. "Piptanthus mongolicus" 75 40
420 1 t. "Iris bungei" 95 55

1966. 60th Birth Anniv of D. Natsagdorj. Nos. 277/8 optd **1906 1966.**

420a **63** 30 m. brown . . . . . . 6·50 6·50
420b 50 m. green . . . . . . 6·50 6·50

1966. Children's Day. Multicoloured.

421 10 m. Type **97** 20 10
422 15 m. Children with reindeer . 20 10
423 20 m. Boys wrestling 25 10
424 30 m. Boy riding horse . . . 50 15
425 60 m. Children on camel . . . 60 20
426 80 m. Shepherd boy with sheep 75 25
427 1 t. Boy archer . . . . 1·40 55

The 15 m., 30 m. and 80 m. are horiz.

98 "Proton 1"

1966. Space Satellites. Multicoloured.

428 5 m. "Vostok 2" (vert) 10 10
429 10 m. Type **93** 10 10
430 15 m. "Telstar 1" (vert) 15 10
431 20 m. "Molniya 1" (vert) 15 10
432 30 m. "Syncom 3" (vert) 20 15
433 60 m. "Luna 9" (vert) 40 15
434 80 m. "Luna 12" (vert) 60 30
435 1 t. Mars and photographs taken by "Mariner 4" 85 40

99 Tarbosaurus **100** Congress Emblem

1966. Prehistoric Animals. Multicoloured.

436 5 m. Type **99** 40 10
437 10 m. Talararus 40 10
438 15 m. Protoceratops 55 15
439 20 m. Indricotherium 55 15
440 30 m. Saurolophus 90 20
441 60 m. Mastodon 1·40 30
442 80 m. Mongolotherium 1·60 45
443 1 t. Mammuthus 1·75 70

1967. 9th International Students' Union Congress.

444 **100** 30 m. ultramarine and blue 25 15
445 50 m. blue and pink 35 20

101 Sukhe Bator and Mongolian and Soviet Soldiers **102** Vietnamese Mother and Child

1967. 50th Anniv of October Revolution.

446 **101** 40 m. multicoloured 35 20
447 – 60 m. multicoloured 40 25

DESIGN: 60 m. Lenin, and soldiers with sword.

1967. Help for Vietnam.

448 **102** 30 m. + 20 m. brown, red and blue 30 25
449 50 m. + 30 m. brown, blue and red 50 40

103 Figure Skating

1967. Winter Olympic Games, Grenoble. Mult.

450 5 m. Type **103** 10 10
451 10 m. Speed skating 10 10
452 15 m. Ice hockey 30 10
453 20 m. Skijumping 40 10
454 30 m. Bob sleighing 45 20
455 60 m. Figure skating (pairs) 60 30
456 80 m. Downhill skiing 80 40

104 Bactrian Camel and Calf

1968. Young Animals. Multicoloured.

458 5 m. Type **104** 15 10
459 10 m. Yak 15 10
460 15 m. Lamb 20 10
461 20 m. Foal 30 10
462 30 m. Calf 30 10
463 60 m. Bison 40 15
464 80 m. Roe deer 55 30
465 1 t. Reindeer 80 40

105 Prickly Rose

ДЭХБ
20 ЖИЛ
WHO
(**106**)

1968. Mongolian Berries.

466 **105** 5 m. ultramarine on blue 15 10
467 – 10 m. brown on buff 15 10
468 – 15 m. emerald on green 20 10
469 – 20 m. red on cream 20 10
470 – 30 m. red on pink 25 10
471 – 60 m. brown on orange 45 20
472 – 80 m. turquoise on blue 60 25
473 – 1 t. red on cream 80 40

DESIGNS: 10 m. Blackcurrant; 15 m. Gooseberry; 20 m. Crabapple; 30 m. Strawberry; 60 m. Redcurrant; 80 m. Cowberry; 1 t. Sea buckthorn.

1968. 20th Anniv of World Health Organization. Nos. 396/7 optd with T **106**.

474 **89** 30 m. blue, gold and green 2·50 2·50
475 50 m. blue, gold and red 2·50 2·50

107 Human Rights Emblem **109** "Portrait of artist Sharab" (A. Sangatzohyo)

108 "Das Kapital"

1968. Human Rights Year.

476 **107** 30 m. green and blue 30 10

1968. 150th Birth Anniv of Karl Marx. Mult.

477 30 m. Type **108** 20 10
478 50 m. Karl Marx 35 20

1968. Mongolian Paintings. Multicoloured.

479 5 m. Type **109** 15 10
480 10 m. "On Remote Roads" (A. Sangatzohyo) 20 10
481 15 m. "Camel Calf" (B. Avarzad) 25 10
482 20 m. "The Milk" (B. Avarzad) 30 15
483 30 m. "The Bowman" (B. Gombosuren) 50 30
484 80 m. "Girl Sitting on a Yak" (A. Sangatzohyo) 70 40
485 1 t. 40 "Cagan Dara Ekke" (Janaivajara) 1·25 75

110 Volleyball

1968. Olympic Games, Mexico. Multicoloured.

487 5 m. Type **110** 10 10
488 10 m. Wrestling 10 10
489 15 m. Cycling 15 10
490 20 m. Throwing the javelin 15 10
491 30 m. Football 15 15
492 60 m. Running 35 25
493 80 m. Gymnastics 55 25
494 1 t. Weightlifting 90 40

111 Hammer and Spade

1968. 7th Anniv of Darkhan Town.

496 **111** 50 m. orange and blue 20 10

112 Gorky **113** "Madonna and Child" (Boltraffio)

1968. Birth Centenary of Maksim Gorky (writer).

497 **112** 60 m. ochre and blue 20 10

1968. 20th Anniv (1966) of U.N.E.S.C.O. Paintings by European Masters in National Gallery, Budapest. Multicoloured.

498 5 m. Type **113** 15 10
499 10 m. "St. Roch healed by an angel" (Moretto of Brescia) 20 10
500 15 m. "Madonna and Child with St. Anne" (Macchietti) 25 10
501 20 m. "St. John on Patmos" (Cano) 35 15
502 30 m. "Young lady with viola da gamba" (Kupetzky) 35 15
503 80 m. "Study of a head" (Amerling) 60 50
504 1 t. 40 "The death of Adonis" (Furini) 1·25 75

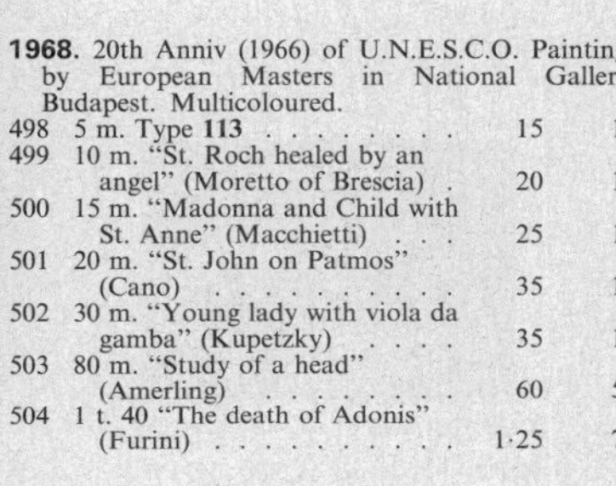

114 Paavo Nurmi (running)

1969. Olympic Games' Gold-medal Winners. Multicoloured.

506 5 m. Type **114** 10 10
507 10 m. Jesse Owens (running) 10 10
508 15 m. F. Blankers-Koen (hurdling) 15 10
509 20 m. Laszlo Papp (boxing) 15 10
510 30 m. Wilma Rudolph (running) 25 15
511 60 m. Boris Sahlin (gymnastics) 35 20
512 80 m. D. Schollander (swimming) 40 25
513 1 t. A. Nakayama (ring exercises) 80 45

115 Bayit Costume (woman)

1969. Mongolian Costumes. Multicoloured.

515 5 m. Type **115** 20 10
516 10 m. Torgut (man) 20 10
517 15 m. Sakhchin (woman) 25 10
518 20 m. Khalka (woman) 35 10
519 30 m. Daringanga (woman) 40 15
520 60 m. Mingat (woman) 55 20
521 80 m. Khalka (man) 75 25
522 1 t. Barga (woman) 1·25 40

116 Emblem and Helicopter Rescue

1969. 30th Anniv of Mongolian Red Cross.

523 **116** 30 m. red and blue 60 20
524 – 50 m. red and violet 50 25

DESIGN: 50 m. Shepherd and ambulance.

117 Yellow Lion's-foot

1969. Landscapes and Flowers. Multicoloured.

525 5 m. Type **117** 15 10
526 10 m. Variegated pink 15 10
527 15 m. Superb pink 25 10
528 20 m. Meadow cranesbill 25 10
529 30 m. Mongolian pink 40 15
530 60 m. Asiatic globe flower 50 15
531 80 m. Long-lipped larkspur 70 30
532 1 t. Saxaul 85 40

118 "Bullfight" (O. Tsewegdjaw)

1969. 10th Anniv of Co-operative Movement. Paintings in National Gallery, Ulan Bator. Mult.

533 5 m. Type **118** 10 10
534 10 m. "Colts Fighting" (O. Tsewegdjaw) 10 10
535 15 m. "Horse-herd" (A. Sengetsohyo) 20 10
536 20 m. "Camel Caravan" (D. Damdinsuren) 20 10
537 30 m. "On the Steppe" (N. Tsultem) 35 15
538 60 m. "Milking Mares" (O. Tsewegdjaw) 40 15
539 80 m. "Off to School" (B. Avarzad) 50 30
540 1 t. "After Work" (G. Odon) 80 40

120 Army Crest

БНМАУ-ыг
тунхагласны
45
жилийн ой
1969—XI—26
(**121**)

1969. 30th Anniv of Battle of Khalka River.

543 **120** 50 m. multicoloured 30 10

1969. 45th Anniv of Mongolian People's Republic. Nos. 411/12 optd with T **121**.

544 **95** 30 m. multicoloured 1·50 1·40
545 – 50 m. multicoloured 3·00 2·10

122 "Sputnik 3"

1969. Exploration of Space. Multicoloured.

546 5 m. Type **122** 15 10
547 10 m. "Vostok 1" 15 10
548 15 m. "Mercury 7" 20 10
549 20 m. Space-walk from "Voskhod 2" 30 10
550 30 m. "Apollo 8" in Moon orbit 40 15
551 60 m. Space-walk from "Soyuz 5" 45 25
552 80 m. "Apollo 12" and Moon landing 55 30

123 Wolf

1970. Wild Animals. Multicoloured.

No.	Description		
554	5 m. Type **123**	25	10
555	10 m. Brown bear	30	10
556	15 m. Lynx	55	10
557	20 m. Wild Boar	55	10
558	30 m. Elk	60	20
559	60 m. Bobak marmot	70	20
560	80 m. Argali	80	35
561	1 t. "Hun Hunter and Hound" (tapestry)	90	50

124 "Lenin Centenary" (silk panel, Cerenhuu)

1970. Birth Centenary of Lenin. Multicoloured.

No.	Description		
562	20 m. Type **124**	15	10
563	50 m. "Mongolians meeting Lenin" (Sangatzohyo) (horiz)	30	15
564	1 t. "Lenin" (Mazhig)	45	20

125 "Fairy Tale" Pavilion

1970. "EXPO 70" World Fair, Osaka, Japan.

No.	Description		
565 **125**	1 t. 50 multicoloured	65	55

126 Footballers

1970. World Cup Football Championships, Mexico.

No.	Description		
567 **126**	10 m. multicoloured	15	10
568 –	20 m. multicoloured	15	10
569 –	30 m. multicoloured	20	10
570 –	50 m. multicoloured	25	10
571 –	60 m. multicoloured	45	15
572 –	1 t. multicoloured	55	15
573 –	1 t. 30 multicoloured	70	40

DESIGNS: Nos. 568/73, Different football scenes.

127 Common Buzzard

1970. Birds of Prey. Multicoloured.

No.	Description		
575	10 m. Type **127**	60	10
576	20 m. Tawny owls	80	10
577	30 m. Northern goshawk	95	15
578	50 m. White-tailed sea eagle	1·00	20
579	60 m. Peregrine falcon	1·50	40
580	1 t. Common kestrels	1·75	40
581	1 t. 30 Black kite	2·10	50

128 Soviet Memorial, Treptow, Berlin

129 Mongol Archery

1970. 25th Anniv of Victory in Second World War.

No.	Description		
582 **128**	60 m. multicoloured	35	15

1970. Mongolian Traditional Life. Multicoloured.

No.	Description		
583	10 m. Type **129**	30	15
584	20 m. Bodg-gegeen's Palace, Ulan Bator	30	15
585	30 m. Mongol horsemen	30	20
586	40 m. "The White Goddess-Mother"	30	25
587	50 m. Girl in National costume	65	45
588	60 m. "Lion's Head" (statue)	75	45
589	70 m. Dancer's mask	85	65
590	80 m. Gateway, Bogd-gegeen's Palace	1·00	1·00

131 I.E.Y. and U.N. Emblems with Flag

1970. International Education Year.

No.	Description		
592 **131**	60 m. multicoloured	25	15

132 Horseman, "50" and Sunrise

1970. 50th Anniv of National Press.

No.	Description		
593 **132**	30 m. multicoloured	35	20

133 "Vostok 3" and "4"

1971. Space Research. Multicoloured.

No.	Description		
594	10 m. Type **133**	15	10
595	20 m. Space-walk from "Voskhod 2"	15	15
596	30 m. "Gemini 6" and "7"	15	15
597	50 m. Docking of "Soyuz 4" and "5"	25	20
598	60 m. "Soyuz 6", "7" and "8"	35	20
599	80 m. "Apollo 11" and lunar module	50	35
600	1 t. "Apollo 13" damaged	60	30
601	1 t. 30 "Luna 16"	75	30

No. 594 is incorrectly inscribed "Vostok 2–3". The date refers to flight of "Vostoks 3" and "4".

134 Sukhe Bator addressing Meeting

1971. 50th Anniv of Revolutionary Party. Mult.

No.	Description		
603	30 m. Type **134**	15	10
604	60 m. Horseman with flag	25	10
605	90 m. Sukhe Bator with Lenin	30	15
606	1 t. 20 Mongolians with banner	40	25

136 Tsam Mask

1971. Mongol Tsam Masks.

No.	Description		
608 **136**	10 m. multicoloured	15	10
609 –	20 m. multicoloured	25	10
610 –	30 m. multicoloured	30	10
611 –	50 m. multicoloured	35	10
612 –	60 m. multicoloured	45	20
613 –	1 t. multicoloured	80	30
614 –	1 t. 30 multicoloured	1·00	50

DESIGNS: Nos. 609/14, Different dance masks.

137 Banner and Party Emblems

1971. 16th Revolutionary Party Congress.

No.	Description		
615 **137**	60 m. multicoloured	20	10

138 Steam Locomotive

1971. "50 Years of Transport Development". Multicoloured.

No.	Description		
616	20 m. Type **138**	60	15
617	30 m. Diesel locomotive	65	15
618	40 m. Russian "Urals" truck	65	15
619	50 m. Russian "Moskovich 412" car	75	15
620	60 m. Polikarpov Po-2 biplane	90	25
621	80 m. Antonov AN-24B airliner	1·10	40
622	1 t. Lake steamer "Sukhe Bator"	2·00	70

139 Soldier

140 Emblem and Red Flag

1971. 50th Anniv of People's Army and Police. Multicoloured.

No.	Description		
623	60 m. Type **139**	40	10
624	1 t. 50 Policeman and child	85	20

1971. 50th Anniv of Revolutionary Youth Organization.

No.	Description		
625 **140**	60 m. multicoloured	30	20

141 Mongolian Flag and Year Emblem

1971. Racial Equality Year.

No.	Description		
626 **141**	60 m. multicoloured	30	15

142 "The Old Man and the Tiger"

1971. Mongolian Folk Tales. Multicoloured.

No.	Description		
627	10 m. Type **142**	20	10
628	20 m. "The Boy Giant-killer"	20	10
629	30 m. Cat and mice	20	10
630	50 m. Mongolians riding on eagle	25	10
631	60 m. Girl on horseback ("The Wise Bride")	40	15
632	80 m. King and courtiers with donkey	55	20
633	1 t. Couple kneeling before empty throne ("Story of the Throne")	80	25
634	1 t. 30 "The Wise Bird"	95	40

143 Yaks

1971. Livestock Breeding. Multicoloured.

No.	Description		
635	20 m. Type **143**	20	10
636	30 m. Bactrian camels	20	10
637	40 m. Sheep	25	10
638	50 m. Goats	40	10
639	60 m. Cattle	50	20
640	80 m. Horses	60	25
641	1 t. Pony	95	45

144 Cross-country Skiing

1972. Winter Olympic Games, Sapporo, Japan. Multicoloured.

No.	Description		
642	10 m. Type **144**	25	10
643	20 m. Bobsleighing	30	10
644	30 m. Figure skating	30	10
645	50 m. Slalom skiing	35	10
646	60 m. Speed skating	40	15
647	80 m. Downhill skiing	55	20
648	1 t. Ice hockey	70	25
649	1 t. 30 Pairs figure skating	85	40

145 "Horse-breaking" (A. Sengatzohyo)

1972. Paintings by Contemporary Artists from the National Gallery, Ulan Bator. Multicoloured.

No.	Description		
651	10 m. Type **145**	15	10
652	20 m. "Black Camel" (A. Sengatzohyo)	20	10
653	30 m. "Jousting" (A. Sengatzohyo)	25	10
654	50 m. "Wrestling Match" (A. Sengatzohyo)	30	10
655	60 m. "Waterfall" (A. Sengatzohyo)	40	10
656	80 m. "Old Musician" (U. Yadamsuren)	50	20
657	1 t. "Young Musician" (U. Yadamsuren)	60	25
658	1 t. 30 "Ancient Prophet" (B. Avarzad)	85	40

147 "Calosoma fischeri"

1972. Insects. Multicoloured.

660 10 m. Type **147** 20 10
661 20 m. "Mylabris mongolica" . 25 10
662 30 m. "Sternoplax zichyi" . . 30 10
663 50 m. "Rhaebus komarovi" . 40 15
664 60 m. "Meloe centripubens" . 55 15
665 80 m. "Eodorcadion mongolicum" 75 25
666 1 t. "Platyope maongolica" . . 90 30
667 1 t. 30 "Lixus nigrolineatus" . 1·40 50

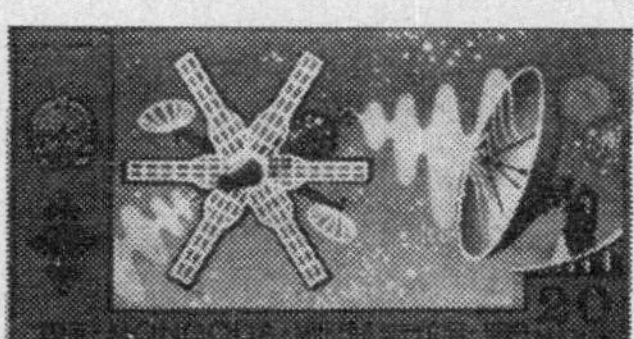

149 Satellite and Dish Aerial ("Telecommunications")

1972. Air. National Achievements. Multicoloured.

669 20 m. Type **149** 20 10
670 30 m. Horse-herd ("Livestock Breeding") 30 10
671 40 m. Diesel train and Tupolev Tu-144 aircraft ("Transport") 90 15
672 50 m. Corncob and farm ("Agriculture") 35 15
673 60 m. Ambulance and hospital ("Public Health") 70 20
674 80 m. Actors ("Culture") . . . 70 25
675 1 t. Factory ("Industry") . . . 75 40

150 Globe, Flag and Dish Aerial

1972. Air. World Telecommunications Day.

676 **150** 60 m. multicoloured . . . 40 15

151 Running

1972. Olympic Games, Munich. Multicoloured.

677 10 m. Type **151** 15 10
678 15 m. Boxing 15 10
679 20 m. Judo 20 10
680 25 m. High jumping 20 10
681 30 m. Rifle-shooting 30 15
682 60 m. Wrestling 45 20
683 80 m. Weightlifting 55 25
684 1 t. Mongolian flag and Olympic emblems 80 45

152 E.C.A.F.E. Emblem

1972. 25th Anniv of E.C.A.F.E.

686 **152** 60 m. blue, gold and red . 20 10

153 Mongolian Racerunner

1972. Reptiles. Multicoloured.

687 10 m. Type **153** 20 10
688 15 m. Radde's toad 25 10
689 20 m. Halys viper 85 10
690 25 m. Toad-headed agama . . 40 15
691 30 m. Asiatic grass frog . . . 55 15
692 60 m. Plate-tailed geckol . . 70 25
693 80 m. Steppe ribbon snake . . 85 35
694 1 t. Mongolian agama . . . . 1·25 55

154 "Technical Knowledge"

1972. 30th Anniv of Mongolian State University. Multicoloured.

695 50 m. Type **154** 35 10
696 60 m. University building . . 45 15

155 "Madonna and Child with St. John the Baptist and a Holy Woman" (Bellini)

1972. Air. U.N.E.S.C.O. "Save Venice" Campaign. Paintings. Multicoloured.

697 10 m. Type **155** 15 10
698 20 m. "The Transfiguration" (Bellini) (vert) 20 10
699 30 m. "Blessed Virgin with the Child" (Bellini) (vert) . . . 25 10
700 50 m. "Presentation of the Christ in the Temple" (Bellini) . . 40 15
701 60 m. "St. George" (Bellini) (vert) 50 20
702 80 m. "Departure of Ursula" (detail, Carpaccio) (vert) . 65 35
703 1 t. "Departure of Ursula" (different detail, Carpaccio) 85 45

156 Manlay-Bator Damdinsuren

157 Spassky Tower, Moscow Kremlin

1972. National Heroes. Multicoloured.

705 10 m. Type **156** 15 10
706 20 m. Ard Ayus in chains (horiz) 25 10
707 50 m. Hatan-Bator Magsarzhav 40 15
708 60 m. Has-Bator on the march (horiz) 55 20
709 1 t. Sukhe Bator 85 30

1972. 50th Anniv of U.S.S.R.

710 **157** 60 m. multicoloured . . . 50 15

158 Snake and "Mars 1"

1972. Air. Animal Signs of the Mongolian Calendar and Progress in Space Exploration. Multicoloured.

711 60 m. Type **158** 70 25
712 60 m. Horse and "Apollo 8" (square) 70 25
713 60 m. Sheep and "Electron 2" (square) 70 25
714 60 m. Monkey and "Explorer 6" 70 25
715 60 m. Dragon and "Mariner 2" 70 25
716 60 m. Pig and "Cosmos 110" (square) 70 25
717 60 m. Dog and "Ariel 2" (square) 70 25
718 60 m. Cockerel and "Venus 1" 70 25
719 60 m. Hare and "Soyuz 5" . . 70 25
720 60 m. Tiger and "Gemini 7" (square) 70 25
721 60 m. Ox and "Venus 4" (square) 70 25
722 60 m. Rat and "Apollo 15" lunar rover 70 25

The square designs are size 40×40 mm.

159 Swimming Gold Medal (Mark Spitz, U.S.A.)

1972. Gold Medal Winners, Munich Olympic Games. Multicoloured.

723 5 m. Type **159** 15 10
724 10 m. High jumping (Ulrike Meyfarth, West Germany) . 25 10
725 20 m. Gymnastics (Savao Kato, Japan) 25 10
726 30 m. Show jumping (Andras Balczo, Hungary) 35 10
727 60 m. Running (Lasse Viren, Finland) 50 20
728 80 m. Swimming (Shane Gould, Australia) 70 25
729 1 t. Putting the shot (Anatoli Bondarchuk, U.S.S.R.) . . . 85 35

160 Monkey on Cycle

1973. Mongolian Circus (1st series). Mult.

731 5 m. Type **160** 20 10
732 10 m. Seal with ball 20 10
733 15 m. Bear on mono-wheel . . . 30 10
734 20 m. Acrobat on camel . . . 30 10
735 30 m. Acrobat on horse . . . 50 10
736 50 m. Clown playing flute . . 60 15
737 60 m. Contortionist 70 30
738 1 t. New Circus Hall, Ulan Bator 1·00 45

See also Nos. 824/30.

161 Mounted Postman

162 Sukhe Bator receiving Traditional Gifts

1973.

739 **161** 50 m. brown (postage) . . 60 10
740 – 60 m. green . . . . 1·75 15
741 – 1 t. purple . . . . 1·00 20
742 – 1 t. 50 blue (air) . . . . . 1·75 25

DESIGNS: 60 m. Diesel train; 1 t. Mail truck; 1 t. 50, Antonov An-24 airliner.

1973. 80th Birth Anniv of Sukhe Bator. Mult.

743 10 m. Type **162** 15 10
744 20 m. Holding reception . . . 25 10
745 50 m. Leading army 35 10
746 60 m. Addressing council . . . 45 10
747 1 t. Giving audience (horiz) . . 65 20

163 W.M.O. Emblem and Meteorological Symbols

1973. Air. Centenary of World Meteorological Organization.

748 **163** 60 m. multicoloured . . . 45 15

164 "Copernicus" (anon)

167 Marx and Lenin

Нэгдлийн Холбооны IV Их Хурал 1973–6–11

(166)

1973. 500th Birth Anniv of Nicholas Copernicus (astronomer). Multicoloured.

749 50 m. Type **164** 40 15
750 60 m. "Copernicus in his Observatory" (J. Matejko) (55×35 mm) 50 15
751 1 t. "Copernicus" (Jan Matejko) 70 30

1973. 4th Agricultural Co-operative Congress, Ulan Bator. No. 538 optd with T **166**.

754 60 m. multicoloured . . . . .

1973. 9th Organization of Socialist States Postal Ministers Congress, Ulan Bator.

755 **167** 60 m. multicoloured . . . 30 15

168 Russian Stamp and Emblems

1973. Air. Council for Mutual Economic Aid Posts and Telecommunications Conference, Ulan Bator. Multicoloured.

756 30 m. Type **168** 30 15
757 30 m. Mongolia 45 20
758 30 m. Bulgaria 45 20
759 30 m. Hungary 45 20
760 30 m. Czechoslovakia 45 20
761 30 m. German Democratic Republic 45 20
762 30 m. Cuba 45 20
763 30 m. Rumania 45 20
764 30 m. Poland 70 20

169 Common Shelduck

1973. Aquatic Birds. Multicoloured.

765 5 m. Type **169** 40 10
766 10 m. Black-throated diver . . 55 10
767 15 m. Bar-headed geese . . . 85 15
768 30 m. Great crested grebe . . 1·10 20
769 50 m. Mallard . . . . 1·60 40
770 60 m. Mute swan . . . . . . 1·90 40
771 1 t. Greater scaups . . . . . 2·25 50

170 Siberian Weasel

1973. Small Fur Animals. Multicoloured.

772 5 m. Type **170** 20 10
773 10 m. Siberian chipmunk 20 10
774 15 m. Siberian flying squirrel 20 10
775 20 m. Eurasian badger 25 15
776 30 m. Eurasian red squirrel 35 15
777 60 m. Wolverine 70 30
778 80 m. American mink 85 45
779 1 t. Arctic hare 1·25 60

171 Launching "Soyuz" Spacecraft

1973. Air. "Apollo" and "Soyuz" Space Programmes. Multicoloured.

780 5 m. Type **171** 15 10
781 10 m. "Apollo 8" 15 10
782 15 m. "Soyuz 4" and "5" linked 20 15
783 20 m. "Apollo 11" module on Moon 20 15
784 30 m. "Apollo 14" after splash-down 30 15
785 50 m. Triple flight by "Soyuz 6", "7" and "8" 35 20
786 60 m. "Apollo 16" lunar rover 45 25
787 1 t "Lunokhod 1" 65 30

172 Global Emblem

1973. 15th Anniv of Review "Problems of Peace and Socialism".

789 **172** 60 m. red, gold and blue 35 15

173 Alpine Aster

1973. Mongolian Flowers. Multicoloured.

790 5 m. Type **173** 15 10
791 10 m. Mongolian catchfly 25 10
792 15 m. "Rosa davurica" 30 10
793 20 m. Mongolian dandelion 40 15
794 30 m. "Rhododendron dahuricum" 55 20
795 50 m. "Clematis tangutica" 70 40
796 60 m. Siberian primrose 85 55
797 1 t. Pasque flower 1·25 65

174 "Limenitis populi"

1974. Butterflies and Moths. Multicoloured.

798 5 m. Type **174** 30 10
799 10 m. "Arctia hebe" 35 10
800 15 m. "Rhyparia purpurata" 40 10
801 20 m. "Catocala pacta" 55 10
802 30 m. "Isoceras kaszabi" 70 15
803 50 m. "Celerio costata" 1·00 30
804 60 m. "Arctia caja" 1·10 40
805 1 t. "Diacrisia sannio" 1·50 50

175 "Hebe Namshil" (L. Merdorsh)

176 Comecon Headquarters, Moscow

1974. Mongolian Opera and Drama. Multicoloured.

806 15 m. Type **175** 25 10
807 20 m. "Sive Hiagt" (D. Luvsansharav) (horiz) 25 10
808 25 m. "Edre" (D. Namdag) 30 10
809 30 m. "The Three Khans of Sara-gol" (horiz) 40 15
810 60 m. "Amarsana" (B. Damdinsuren) 65 20
811 80 m. "Edre" (different scene) 80 25
812 1 t. "Edre" (different scene) 1·25 55

1974. Air. 25th Anniv of Communist Council for Mutual Economic Aid ("Comecon").

813 **176** 60 m. multicoloured 30 20

177 Government Building and Sukhe Bator Monument, Ulan Bator

1974. 50th Anniv of Renaming of Capital as Ulan Bator.

814 **177** 60 m. multicoloured 30 20

179 Mounted Courier

1974. Air. Centenary of U.P.U. Multicoloured.

816 50 m. Type **179** 1·50 40
817 50 m. Reindeer mail sledge 1·50 40
818 50 m. Mail coach 1·50 40
819 50 m. Balloon post 2·00 40
820 50 m. Lake steamer "Sukhe Bator" and Polikarpov Po-2 biplane 2·25 40
821 50 m. Mail train and P.O. truck 1·75 40
822 50 m. Rocket in orbit 1·50 40

180 Performing Horses

1974. Mongolian Circus (2nd series). Multicoloured.

824 10 m. Type **180** (postage) 20 10
825 20 m. Juggler (vert) 30 10
826 30 m. Elephant on ball (vert) 40 15
827 40 m. Performing yak 60 20
828 60 m. Acrobats (vert) 75 25
829 80 m. Trick cyclist (vert) 1·10 45
830 1 t. Contortionist (vert) (air) 1·10 45

181 "Training a Young Horse"

1974. Int Children's Day. Drawings by Lhamsurem. Multicoloured.

831 10 m. Type **181** 20 10
832 20 m. "Boy with Calf" 30 10
833 30 m. "Riding untamed Horse" 35 10
834 40 m. "Boy with Foal" 45 20
835 60 m. "Girl dancing with Doves" 60 20
836 80 m. "Wrestling" 65 30
837 1 t. "Hobby-horse Dance" 1·10 45

182 Archer on Foot

1974. "Nadam" Sports Festival. Multicoloured.

838 10 m. Type **182** 20 10
839 20 m. "Kazlodanie" (Kazakh mounted game) 30 10
840 30 m. Mounted archer 40 10
841 40 m. Horse-racing 50 20
842 60 m. Bucking horse-riding 60 20
843 80 m. Capturing wild horse 70 30
844 1 t. Wrestling 80 45

183 Giant Panda

1974. Bears. Multicoloured.

845 10 m. Brown bear 15 10
846 20 m. Type **183** 25 10
847 30 m. Giant Panda 45 15
848 40 m. Brown bear 45 20
849 60 m. Sloth bear 70 30
850 80 m. Asiatic black bear 80 50
851 1 t. Brown bear 1·40 65

184 Red Deer

1974. Games Reserves. Fauna. Multicoloured.

852 10 m. Type **184** 15 10
853 20 m. Eurasian beaver 30 10
854 30 m. Leopard 40 15
855 40 m. Herring gull 85 30
856 60 m. Roe deer 80 30
857 80 m. Argali 85 35
858 1 t. Siberian musk deer 1·40 65

185 Detail of Buddhist Temple, Palace of Bogdo Gegen

1974. Mongolian Architecture. Multicoloured.

859 10 m. Type **185** 20 10
860 15 m. Buddhist temple (now museum) 20 10
861 30 m. "Charity" Temple, Ulan Bator 40 15
862 50 m. Yurt (tent) 55 20
863 80 m. Arbour in court-yard 75 40

186 Spassky Tower, Moscow, and Sukhe Bator Statue, Ulan Bator

187 Proclamation of the Republic

1974. Brezhnev's Visit to Mongolia.

864 **186** 60 m. multicoloured 30 20

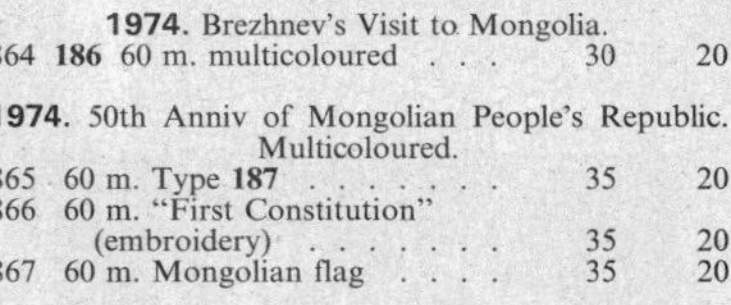

1974. 50th Anniv of Mongolian People's Republic. Multicoloured.

865 60 m. Type **187** 35 20
866 60 m. "First Constitution" (embroidery) 35 20
867 60 m. Mongolian flag 35 20

188 Gold Decanter

1974. Goldsmiths' Treasures of the 19th Century. Multicoloured.

868 10 m. Type **188** 20 10
869 20 m. Silver jug 30 10
870 30 m. Night lamp 35 10
871 40 m. Tea jug 45 20
872 60 m. Candelabra 55 20
873 80 m. Teapot 75 30
874 1 t. Silver bowl on stand 1·00 40

189 Lapwing

1974. Protection of Water and Nature Conservation. Multicoloured.

875 10 m. Type **189** (postage) 50 10
876 20 m. Sturgeon 45 10
877 30 m. Marsh marigolds 50 15
878 40 m. Dalmatian pelican 90 20
879 60 m. Perch 75 25
880 80 m. Sable 90 40
881 1 t. Hydrologist with jar of water (air) 1·00 40

190 U.S. Mail Coach

1974. Centenary of U.P.U. Multicoloured.

883 10 m. Type **190** 15 10
884 20 m. French postal cart 20 10
885 30 m. Changing horses, Russian mail and passenger carriage 35 15
886 40 m. Swedish postal coach with caterpillar tracks 45 20
887 50 m. First Hungarian mail van 50 25
888 60 m. German Daimler-Benz mail van and trailer 65 40
889 1 t. Mongolian postal courier 95 55

191 Red Flag

193 Mongolian Woman

192 "Zygophyllum xanthoxylon" (½-size illustration)

1975. 30th Anniv of Victory.
891 **191** 60 m. multicoloured . . . 35 20

1975. 12th International Botanical Conference. Rare Medicinal Plants. Multicoloured.
892 10 m. Type **192** 25 10
893 20 m. "Incarvillea potaninii" . 35 10
894 30 m. "Lancea tibetica" . . . 55 15
895 40 m. "Jurinea mongolica" . . 55 20
896 50 m. "Saussurea involucrata" 70 20
897 60 m. "Allium mongolicum" . 80 30
898 1 t. "Adonis mongolica" . . . 1·40 40

1975. International Women's Year.
899 **193** 60 m. multicoloured . . . 45 20

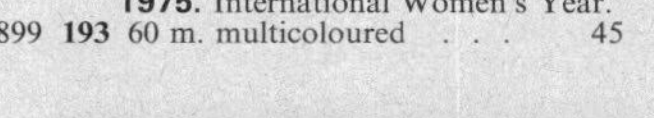

194 "Soyuz" on Launch-pad

1975. Air. Joint Soviet–American Space Project. Multicoloured.
900 10 m. Type **194** 10 10
901 20 m. Launch of "Apollo" . . 15 10
902 30 m. "Apollo" and "Soyuz" spacecraft 30 10
903 40 m. Docking manoeuvre . . 35 20
904 50 m. Spacecraft docked together 45 20
905 60 m. "Soyuz" in orbit 50 30
906 1 t. "Apollo" and "Soyuz" spacecraft and communications satellite . . 80 40

195 Child and Lamb

1975. International Children's Day. Multicoloured.
908 10 m. Type **195** 20 10
909 20 m. Child riding horse . . . 40 10
910 30 m. Child with calf 40 10
911 40 m. Child and "orphan camel" 40 15
912 50 m. "The Obedient Yak" . . 50 25
913 60 m. Child riding on swan . . 60 30
914 1 t. Two children singing . . . 95 45
See also Nos. 979/85.

196 Pioneers tending Tree

Тээвэр—50
1975—7—15.
(197)

1975. 50th Anniv of Mongolian Pioneer Organization. Multicoloured.
915 50 m. Type **196** 30 15
916 60 m. Children's study circle . 50 20
917 1 t. New emblem of Mongolian pioneers 65 30

1975. 50th Anniv of Public Transport. Nos. 616/22 optd with T **197**.
918 **138** 20 m. multicoloured . . . 2·50 2·50
919 – 30 m. multicoloured . . . 2·50 2·50
920 – 40 m. multicoloured . . . 1·90 1·90
921 – 50 m. multicoloured . . . 1·90 1·90
922 – 60 m. multicoloured . . . 2·50 2·50
923 – 80 m. multicoloured . . . 3·00 3·00
924 – 1 t. multicoloured . . . . 3·75 3·75

198 Argali

1975. Air. South Asia Tourist Year.
925 **198** 1 t. 50 multicoloured . . 90 40

199 Golden Eagle attacking Red Fox

1975. Hunting Scenes. Multicoloured.
926 10 m. Type **199** 55 10
927 20 m. Lynx-hunting (vert) . . 45 10
928 30 m. Hunter stalking bobak marmots 50 15
929 40 m. Hunter riding on reindeer (vert) 60 20
930 50 m. Shooting wild boar . . 60 25
931 60 m. Wolf in trap (vert) . . 75 35
932 1 t. Hunters with brown bear 1·00 50

200 "Mesocottus haitej"

1975. Fishes. Multicoloured.
933 10 m. Type **200** 20 10
934 20 m. "Pseudaspius lepto cephalus" 30 10
935 30 m. "Oreoleuciscus potanini" 35 15
936 40 m. "Tinca tinca" 45 20
937 50 m. "Coregonus lavaretus" 65 25
938 60 m. "Erythroculter mongolicus" 75 30
939 1 t. "Carassius auratus" . . . 1·25 55

201 "Morin Hur" (musical instrument)

202 Revolutionary with Banner

1975. Mongolian Handicrafts. Multicoloured.
940 10 m. Type **201** 15 10
941 20 m. Saddle 25 10
942 30 m. Headdress 30 10
943 40 m. Boots 40 15
944 50 m. Cap 50 20
945 60 m. Pipe and tobacco pouch 60 25
946 1 t. Fur hat 90 40

1975. 70th Anniv of 1905 Russian Revolution.
947 **202** 60 m. multicoloured . . . 35 20

203 "Taming a Wild Horse"

1975. Mongolian Paintings. Multicoloured.
948 10 m. Type **203** 10 10
949 20 m. "Camel Caravan" (horiz) 25 10
950 30 m. "Man playing Lute" . . 35 10
951 40 m. "Woman adjusting Headdress" (horiz) 40 15
952 50 m. "Woman in ceremonial Costume" 40 25
953 60 m. "Woman fetching Water" 50 30
954 1 t. "Woman playing Yaga" (musical instrument) 75 40

204 Ski Jumping

205 "House of Young Technicians"

1975. Winter Olympic Games, Innsbruck. Multicoloured.
956 10 m. Type **204** 10 10
957 20 m. Ice hockey 30 10
958 30 m. Slalom skiing 35 10
959 40 m. Bobsleighing 45 15
960 50 m. Rifle shooting (biathlon) 55 25
961 60 m. Speed skating 60 25
962 1 t. Figure skating 90 45

1975. Public Buildings.
964 **205** 50 m. blue 40 10
965 – 60 m. green 50 15
966 – 1 t. brown 70 25
DESIGNS: 60 m. Hotel, Ulan Bator; 1 t. "Museum of the Revolution".

206 "Molniya" Satellite

1976. Air. 40th Anniv of Mongolian Meteorological Office.
967 **206** 60 m. blue and yellow . . 55 20

209 "National Economy" Star

1976. 17th Mongolian People's Revolutionary Party Congress, Ulan Bator.
970 **209** 60 m. multicoloured . . . 35 20

210 Archery

1976. Olympic Games, Montreal. Multicoloured.
971 10 m. Type **210** 15 10
972 20 m. Judo 20 10
973 30 m. Boxing 35 10
974 40 m. Gymnastics 35 15
975 60 m. Weightlifting 45 20
976 80 m. High jumping 55 25
977 1 t. Rifle shooting 80 35

1976. Int Children's Day. As T **195**. Mult.
979 10 m. Gobi Desert landscape . 20 10
980 20 m. Horse-taming 30 10
981 30 m. Horse-riding 35 10
982 40 m. Pioneers' camp 45 20
983 60 m. Young musician 60 20
984 80 m. Children's party 80 30
985 1 t. Mongolian wrestling . . . 1·00 45

211 Cavalry Charge

1976. 55th Anniv of Revolution. Multicoloured.
986 60 m. Type **211** (postage) . . 65 20
987 60 m. Man and emblem (vert) 65 20
988 60 m. "Industry and Agriculture" (air) 65 20

213 Osprey

1976. Protected Birds. Multicoloured.
990 10 m. Type **213** 50 10
991 20 m. Griffon vulture 65 10
992 30 m. Lammergeier 90 15
993 40 m. Marsh harrier . . . . . 1·10 15
994 60 m. European black vulture 1·40 20
995 80 m. Golden eagle . . . . . 1·60 25
996 1 t. Tawny eagle . . . . . . 1·90 30

214 "Rider on Wild Horse"

1976. Paintings by O. Tsewegdjaw. Multicoloured.
997 10 m. Type **214** 15 10
998 20 m. "The First Nadam" (game on horse-back) (horiz) 20 10
999 30 m. "Harbour on Khobsogol Lake" (horiz) 55 15
1000 40 m. "Awakening the Steppe" (horiz) 45 20
1001 80 m. "Wrestling" (horiz) . . . 60 25
1002 1 t. "The Descent" (yak hauling timber) . . . . 1·00 50

215 "Industrial Development"

1976. Mongolian–Soviet Friendship.
1003 **215** 60 m. multicoloured . . 90 20

216 John Naber of U.S.A. (Swimming)

217 Tablet on Tortoise

1976. Olympic Games, Montreal. Gold Medal Winners. Multicoloured.

1004 10 m. Type **216** 10 10
1005 20 m. Nadia Comaneci of Rumania (gymnastics) . . 15 10
1006 30 m. Kornelia Ender of East Germany (swimming) . . . 30 10
1007 40 m. Mitsuo Tsukahara of Japan (gymnastics) 40 15
1008 60 m. Gregor Braun of West Germany (cycling) 50 25
1009 80 m. Lasse Viren of Finland (running) 60 30
1010 1 t. Nikolai Andrianov of U.S.S.R. (gymnastics) . . . 70 35

1976. Archaeology.

1012 **217** 50 m. brown and blue . . 40 15
1013 – 60 m. black and green . . 40 15

DESIGN: 60 m. 6th-century stele.

218 R-1 Biplane

1976. Aircraft. Multicoloured.

1014 10 m. Type **218** 20 10
1015 20 m. Polikarpov R-5 biplane 30 10
1016 30 m. Kalinin K-5 . . . . . . 40 10
1017 40 m. Polikarpov Po-2 biplane 45 15
1018 60 m. Polikarpov I-16 jet fighter 60 20
1019 80 m. Yakovlev Ya-6 Air 6 . 75 35
1020 1 t. Junkers F-13 . . . . . . 95 40

219 Dancers in Folk Costume

1977. Mongolian Folk Dances. Multicoloured.

1021 10 m. Type **219** 25 10
1022 20 m. Dancing girls in 13th-century costume 35 10
1023 30 m. West Mongolian dance 45 10
1024 40 m. "Ekachi" dance . . . 50 15
1025 60 m. "Bielge" ("Trunk") dance 80 20
1026 80 m. "Hodak" dance 95 30
1027 1 t. "Dojarka" dance . . . . 1·10 45

220 Gravitational Effects on "Pioneer"

1977. 250th Death Anniv of Sir Isaac Newton (mathematician). Multicoloured.

1028 60 m. Type **220** (postage) . . 45 15
1029 60 m. Apple tree (25 × 32 mm) 45 15
1030 60 m. Planetary motion and sextant 45 15
1031 60 m. Sir Isaac Newton (25 × 32 mm) 45 15
1032 60 m. Spectrum of light . . . 45 15
1033 60 m. Attraction of Earth . . 45 15
1034 60 m. Laws of motion of celestial bodies (25 × 32 mm) 45 15
1035 60 m. Space-walking (air) . . 45 15
1036 60 m. "Pioneer 10" and Jupiter 45 15

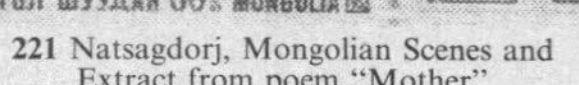

221 Natsagdorj, Mongolian Scenes and Extract from poem "Mother"

1977. Natsagdorj (poet) Commem. Mult.

1037 60 m. Type **221** 40 25
1038 60 m. Border stone, landscape and extract from poem "My Homeland" 40 25

222 Horse Race

1977. Horses. Multicoloured.

1039 10 m. Type **222** 20 10
1040 20 m. Girl on white horse . 25 10
1041 30 m. Rangeman on brown horse 30 10
1042 40 m. Tethered horses . . . 40 20
1043 60 m. White mare with foal . 55 20
1044 80 m. Brown horse with shepherd 70 30
1045 1 t. White horse 85 45

223 "Mongolemys elegans"

1977. Prehistoric Animals. Multicoloured.

1046 10 m. Type **223** 30 10
1047 20 m. "Embolotherium ergiliense" 45 10
1048 30 m. "Psittacosaurus mongoliensis" 55 15
1049 40 m. Enthelodon 70 20
1050 60 m. "Spirocerus kiakhtensis" 1·00 25
1051 80 m. Hipparion . . . . . . 1·40 40
1052 1 t. "Bos primigenius" . . . 1·60 55

225 Child feeding Lambs

226 Industrial Plant and Transport

1977. Children's Day and 1st Balloon Flight in Mongolia. Multicoloured.

1054 10 m. + 5 m. Type **225** . . 30 15
1055 20 m. + 5 m. Boy playing flute and girl dancing 45 15
1056 30 m. + 5 m. Girl chasing butterflies 55 20
1057 40 m. + 5 m. Girl with ribbon 60 25
1058 60 m. + 5 m. Girl with flowers 70 40
1059 80 m. + 5 m. Girl with bucket 80 50
1060 1 t. + 5 m. Boy going to school 1·00 60

1977. Erdenet (New Town).

1062 **226** 60 m. multicoloured . . 75 20

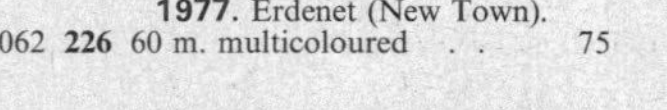

227 Trade Unions Emblem

1977. Air. 11th Mongolian Trade Unions Congress.

1063 **227** 60 m. multicoloured . . 50 15

228 Mounting Bell-shaped Gear on Rocket. (Illustration reduced. Actual size 66 × 26 mm)

1977. Air. 11th Anniv of "Intercosmos" Co-operation. Multicoloured.

1064 10 m. Type **228** 10 10
1065 20 m. Launch of "Intercosmos 3" 20 10
1066 30 m. Tracking ship "Kosmonaut Yury Gargarin" 60 15
1067 40 m. Observation of lunar eclipse 50 20
1068 60 m. Earth station's multiple antennae 70 25
1069 80 m. Magnetosphere examination, Van Allen Zone 90 35
1070 1 t. Meteorological satellites . 1·25 65

229 Fire-fighters' Bucket Chain

1977. Mongolian Fire-fighting Services. Multicoloured.

1072 10 m. Type **229** 20 10
1073 20 m. Horse-drawn hand pump 30 10
1074 30 m. Horse-drawn steam pump 40 15
1075 40 m. Fighting forest fire . . 50 20
1076 60 m. Mobile foam extinguisher 70 25
1077 80 m. Modern fire engine . . 85 30
1078 1 t. Mil Mi-8 helicopter spraying fire . . . . 1·25 45

230 "Molniya" Satellite and Dish Aerial on TV Screen

1977. 40th Anniv of Technical Institute.

1079 **230** 60 m. blue, black & grey 45 20

231 "Aporia crataegi"

1977. Butterflies and Moths. Multicoloured.

1080 10 m. Type **231** 20 10
1081 20 m. "Gastropacha quercifolia" 35 15
1082 30 m. "Colias chrysoteme" . 50 15
1083 40 m. "Dasychira fascelina" . 70 20
1084 60 m. "Malocosoma neustria" 1·00 25
1085 80 m. "Diacrisia sannio" . . 1·40 35
1086 1 t. "Heodes virgaureae" . . 1·60 50

232 Lenin Museum

1977. Inauguration of Lenin Museum, Ulan Bator.

1087 **232** 60 m. multicoloured . . . 40 20

233 Cruiser "Aurora" and Soviet Flag

1977. 60th Anniv of Russian Revolution. Mult.

1088 50 m. Type **233** 60 15
1089 60 m. Dove and globe (horiz) 50 15
1090 1 t. 50 Freedom banner around the globe (horiz) 75 35

234 Giant Pandas

1977. Giant Pandas. Multicoloured.

1091 10 m. Eating bamboo shoot (vert) 20 10
1092 20 m. Type **234** 35 10
1093 30 m. Female and cub in washtub (vert) 45 15
1094 40 m. Male and cub with bamboo shoot 60 20
1095 60 m. Female and cub (vert) 80 30
1096 80 m. Family (horiz) . . . . 1·40 50
1097 1 t. Male on hind legs (vert) 1·60 65

236 Montgolfier Balloon

1977. Air. Airships and Balloons. Multicoloured.

1099 20 m. Type **236** 25 10
1100 30 m. Airship "Graf Zeppelin" over North Pole 30 10
1101 40 m. Airship "Osoaviachim" over the Arctic 40 15
1102 50 m. Airship "North" . . . 55 20
1103 60 m. Aereon 340 design . . 65 20
1104 80 m. Nestrenko's planned airship 70 35
1105 1 t. 20 "Flying Crane" airship 1·00 60

237 Ferrari "312-T2"

1978. Racing Cars. Multicoloured.

1107 20 m. Type **237** 25 10
1108 30 m. Ford McLaren "M-23" 30 10
1109 40 m. Soviet experimental car 40 20
1110 50 m. Japanese Mazda . . . 50 20
1111 60 m. Porsche "936-Turbo" . 60 25
1112 80 m. Model of Soviet car . 65 25
1113 1 t. 20 American rocket car "Blue Flame" 95 40

238 "Boletus variegatus". (Illustration reduced. Actual size 75 × 25 mm)

1978. Mushrooms. Multicoloured.

1114 20 m. Type **238** 35 15
1115 30 m. "Russula cyanoxantha" 50 15
1116 40 m. "Boletus aurantiacus" 60 20
1117 50 m. "Boletus scaber" . . . 70 25
1118 60 m. "Russula flava" . . . 80 30
1119 80 m. "Lactarius resimus" . . 1·00 45
1120 1 t. 20 "Flammula spumosa" 1·40 65

239 A. F. Mozhaiski and Monoplane

1978. Air. History of Aviation. Multicoloured.

1121 20 m. Type **239** 20 10
1122 30 m. Henri Farman and Farman H.F.III biplane . 25 10
1123 40 m. Geoffrey de Havilland and De Havilland FE.1 biplane 30 15
1124 50 m. Charles Lindbergh and "Spirit of St. Louis" . . . 45 20
1125 60 m. Shagdarsuren, Dembral, biplane and glider 55 20
1126 80 m. Chalkov, Baidukov, Beliadov and Tupolev ANT-25 . . . . 65 35
1127 1 t. 20 A. N. Tupolev and Tu-154 . . . . 90 55

240 Footballers and View of Rio de Janeiro

1978. World Cup Football Championship, Argentina. Multicoloured.

1129	20 m. Type **240**	20	10
1130	30 m. Footballers and Old Town Tower, Berne	25	10
1131	40 m. Footballers and Stockholm Town Hall	30	15
1132	50 m. Footballers and University of Chile	40	20
1133	60 m. Footballers, Houses of Parliament and Tower of London	55	25
1134	80 m. Footballers and Theatre Degolladeo of Guadalajara, Mexico	60	25
1135	1 t. 20 Footballers and Munich Town Hall	85	40

241 Mongolian Youth and Girl

1978. Mongolian Youth Congress, Ulan Bator.

1137	**241** 60 m. multicoloured	35	15

242 Eurasian Beaver and 1954 Canadian Beaver Stamp

1978. "CAPEX '78". International Stamp Exhibition, Toronto. Multicoloured.

1138	20 m. Type **242**	20	10
1139	30 m. Tibetan sandgrouse and Canada S.G. 620	40	10
1140	40 m. Black-throated diver and Canada S.G. 495	50	10
1141	50 m. Argali and Canada S.G. 449	70	35
1142	60 m. Brown bear and Canada S.G. 447	80	40
1143	80 m. Elk and Canada S.G. 448	90	45
1144	1 t. 20 Herring gull and Canada S.G. 474	1·50	25

243 Marx, Engels and Lenin

1978. 20th Anniv of Review "Problems of Peace and Socialism".

1146	**243** 60 m. red, gold and black	40	15

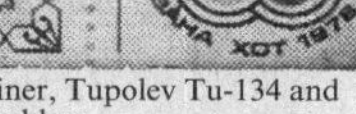

244 Map of Cuba, Liner, Tupolev Tu-134 and Emblem

1978. Air. 11th World Youth Festival, Havana.

1147	**244** 1 t. multicoloured	90	20

245 "Open-air Repose"

1978. 20th Anniv of Philatelic Co-operation between Mongolia and Hungary. Paintings by P. Angalan. Multicoloured.

1148	1 t. 50 Type **245**	90	90
1149	1 t. 50 "Winter Night"	90	90
1150	1 t. 50 "Saddling"	90	90

247 Butterfly Dog

1978. Dogs. Multicoloured.

1152	10 m. Type **247**	20	10
1153	20 m. Black Mongolian sheepdog	25	10
1154	30 m. Puli (Hungarian sheepdog)	35	15
1155	40 m. St. Bernard	40	20
1156	50 m. German shepherd dog	55	25
1157	60 m. Mongolian watchdog	65	25
1158	70 m. Semoyedic Spitz	75	35
1159	80 m. Laika (space dog)	90	35
1160	1 t. 20 Black and white poodles and cocker spaniel	1·10	55

248 Open Book showing Scenes from Mongolian Literary Works

1978. 50th Anniv of Mongolian Writers' Association.

1161	**248** 60 m. blue and red	35	15

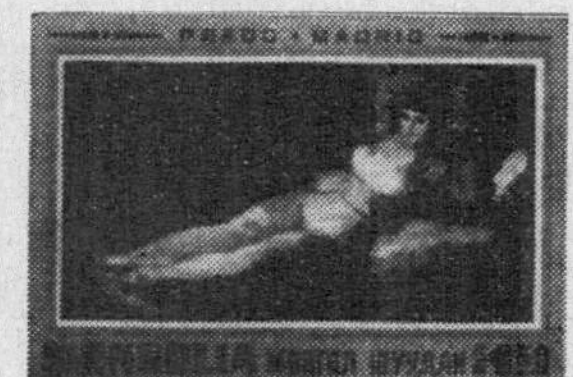

249 "Dressed Maja" (Goya - 150th Death Anniv)

1978. Painters' Anniversaries. Multicoloured.

1162	1 t. 50 Type **249**	90	90
1163	1 t. 50 "Ta Matete" (Gaugin - 75th death anniv)	90	90
1164	1 t. 50 "Bridge at Arles" (Van Gogh - 125th birth anniv)	90	90

250 Young Bactrian Camel

1978. Bactrian Camels. Multicoloured.

1166	20 m. Camel with Foal	25	15
1167	30 m. Type **250**	30	15
1168	40 m. Two camels	45	20
1169	50 m. Woman leading loaded camel	55	25
1170	60 m. Camel in winter coat	70	30
1171	80 m. Camel-drawn water waggon	90	45
1172	1 t. 20 Camel racing	1·25	60

251 Flags of COMECON Countries

1979. 30th Anniv of Council of Mutual Economic Assistance.

1173	**251** 60 m. multicoloured	35	25

MINIMUM PRICE

The minimum price quoted is 10p which represents a handling charge rather than a basis for valuing common stamps. For further notes about prices, see introductory pages.

252 Children riding Camel

1979. International Year of the Child. Multicoloured.

1174	10 m. + 5 m. Type **252**	15	15
1175	30 m. + 5 m. Children feeding chickens	25	15
1176	50 m. + 5 m. Children with deer	35	15
1177	60 m. + 5 m. Children picking flowers	45	20
1178	70 m. + 5 m. Children watering tree	50	25
1179	80 m. + 5 m. Young scientists	60	35
1180	1 t. + 5 m. Making music and dancing	80	50

253 Silver Tabby

1978. Domestic Cats. Multicoloured.

1182	10 m. Type **253**	20	10
1183	30 m. White Persian	35	15
1184	50 m. Red Persian	55	15
1185	60 m. Blue-cream Persian	70	20
1186	70 m. Siamese	80	30
1187	80 m. Smoke Persian	90	35
1188	1 t. Birman	1·25	50

254 "Potaninia mongolica"

1189	10 m. Type **254**	20	10
1190	30 m. "Sophora alopecuroides"	30	10
1191	50 m. "Halimodendron halodendron"	35	15
1192	60 m. "Myosotis asiatica"	50	20
1193	70 m. "Scabiosa comosa"	50	30
1194	80 m. "Leucanthemum sibiricum"	60	30
1195	1 t. "Leontopodium ochroleucum"	80	45

255 Finland v. Czechoslovakia

1979. World Ice Hockey Championships, Moscow. Multicoloured.

1196	10 m. Type **255**	15	10
1197	30 m. West Germany v. Sweden	30	10
1198	50 m. U.S.A. v. Canada	50	20
1199	60 m. Russia v. Sweden	60	20
1200	70 m. Canada v. Russia	65	25
1201	80 m. Swedish goalkeeper	75	25
1202	1 t. Czechoslovakia v. Russia	1·00	35

256 Lambs (Sanzhid)

1979. Agriculture Paintings. Multicoloured.

1203	10 m. Type **256**	10	10
1204	30 m. "Milking camels" (Budbazar)	20	10
1205	50 m. "Aircraft bringing help" (Radnabazar)	40	15
1206	60 m. "Herdsmen" (Budbazar)	40	15
1207	70 m. "Milkmaids" "Nanzadsguren) (vert)	50	30
1208	80 m. "Summer Evening" (Sanzhid)	70	40
1209	1 t. "Country Landscape" (Tserendondog)	80	50

257 First Mongolian and Bulgarian Stamps

1979. Death Centenary of Sir Rowland Hill, and "Philaserdica 79" International Stamp Exn, Sofia. Each black, grey and brown.

1211	1 t. Type **257**	1·50	1·00
1212	1 t. American mail coach	1·50	1·00
1213	1 t. Travelling post office, London-Birmingham railway	1·50	1·00
1214	1 t. Paddle-steamer "Hindoostan"	1·75	1·00

258 Stephenson's "Rocket"

1979. Development of Railways. Multicoloured.

1215	10 m. Type **258**	25	10
1216	20 m. German "Der Adler" locomotive, 1835	30	10
1217	30 m. American locomotive, 1860	40	10
1218	40 m. Mongolian locomotive, 1931	50	15
1219	50 m. Mongolian locomotive, 1936	55	20
1220	60 m. Mongolian locomotive, 1970	65	25
1221	70 m. Japanese high-speed electric train, 1963	80	30
1222	80 m. French "Orleans" aerotrain	90	40
1223	1 t. 20 Russian experimental jet train "Rapidity"	1·00	50

259 Flags of Mongolia and Russia

262 East German Flag, Berlin Buildings and "Soyuz 31"

260 Pallas's Cat

1979. 40th Anniv of Battle of Khalka River.

1224	**259** 60 m. gold, red and yellow	40	35
1225	– 60 m. red, yellow & blue	40	35

DESIGN: No. 1225, Ribbons, badge and military scene.

1979. Wild Cats. Multicoloured.

1226	10 m. Type **260**	15	10
1227	30 m. Lynx	30	15
1228	50 m. Tiger	55	25
1229	60 m. Snow leopard	65	25
1230	70 m. Leopard	75	35
1231	80 m. Cheetah	80	35
1232	1 t. Lion	1·25	50

1979. 30th Anniv of German Democratic Republic (East Germany).

1234	**262** 60 m. multicoloured	60	30

263 Demoiselle Crane

1979. Air. Protected Birds. Multicoloured.

1235	10 m. Type **263**	35	10
1236	30 m. Barred warbler	55	10
1237	50 m. Ruddy shelduck	65	15
1238	60 m. Azure-winged magpie	75	15
1239	70 m. Goldfinch	75	20
1240	80 m. Great tit	85	25
1241	1 t. Golden oriole	1·10	30

264 "Venus 5" and "6"

1979. Air. Space Research. Multicoloured.

1242	10 m. Type **264**	10	10
1243	30 m. "Mariner 5"	20	10
1244	50 m. "Mars 3"	35	20
1245	60 m. "Viking 1" and "2"	40	20
1246	70 m. "Luna 1", "2" and "3"	45	25
1247	80 m. "Lunokhod 2"	50	25
1248	1 t. "Apollo 15" Moon-rover	65	40

265 Cross-country Skiing

1980. Winter Olympic Games, Lake Placid. Multicoloured.

1250	20 m. Type **265**	20	10
1251	30 m. Biathlon	25	15
1252	40 m. Ice hockey	30	20
1253	50 m. Ski jumping	40	25
1254	60 m. Slalom	50	30
1255	80 m. Speed skating	60	30
1256	1 t. 20 Four-man bobsleigh	85	45

266 "Andrena scita"

1980. Air. Wasps and Bees. Multicoloured.

1258	20 m. Type **266**	25	15
1259	30 m. "Paravespula germanica"	30	20
1260	40 m. "Perilampus ruficornis"	40	25
1261	50 m. "Bombus terrestris"	60	30
1262	60 m. "Apis mellifera"	70	35
1263	80 m. "Stilbum cyanurum"	80	45
1264	1 t. 20 "Parnopes grandior"	1·25	60

267 Weightlifting

1980. Olympic Games, Moscow. Multicoloured.

1266	20 m. Type **267**	15	10
1267	30 m. Archery	20	15
1268	40 m. Gymnastics	25	15
1269	50 m. Running	35	20
1270	60 m. Boxing	40	25
1271	80 m. Judo	50	25
1272	1 t. 20 Cycling	75	40

268 Zlin Akrobat Specials

1980. Air. World Acrobatic Championship, Oshkosh, Wisconsin. Multicoloured.

1274	20 m. Type **268**	25	10
1275	30 m. Socata Sportsman	30	10
1276	40 m. Grumman Yankee	40	15
1277	50 m. MJ-2 Tempete	55	20
1278	60 m. Pitts S-2A biplane	65	25
1279	80 m. Hirth Acrostar	75	35
1280	1 t. 20 Yakovlev Yak-50	1·00	60

269 Swimming

1980. Olympic Medal Winners. Multicoloured.

1282	20 m. Type **269**	15	10
1283	30 m. Fencing	20	10
1284	50 m. Judo	30	15
1285	60 m. Athletics	40	20
1286	80 m. Boxing	50	25
1287	1 t. Weightlifting	55	30
1288	1 t. 20 Kayak-canoe	75	35

270 Sukhe Bator

271 Gubarev

1980. Mongolian Politicians.

1290	**270** 60 m. brown	40	20
1291	– 60 m. blue	40	20
1292	– 60 m. turquoise	40	20
1293	– 60 m. bronze-green	40	20
1294	– 60 m. deep green	40	20
1295	– 60 m. red	40	20
1296	– 60 m. brown	40	20

DESIGNS—VERT: No. 1291, Marshal Choibalsan; No. 1292, Yu. Tsedenbal aged 13; No. 1293, Tsedenbal as soldier, 1941; No. 1294, Pres. Tsedenbal in 1979; No. 1295, Tsedenbal with children. HORIZ: No. 1296, Tsedenbal and President Brezhnev of Russia.

1980. "Intercosmos" Space Programme. Multicoloured.

1297	40 m. Type **271**	30	20
1298	40 m. Czechoslovak stamp showing Gubarev and Remek	30	20
1299	40 m. P. Klimuk	30	20
1300	40 m. Polish stamp showing M. Hermaszewski	30	20
1301	40 m. V. Bykovsky	30	20
1302	40 m. East German stamp showing S. Jahn	30	20
1303	40 m. N. Rukavishnikov	30	20
1304	40 m. Bulgarian stamp showing G. Ivanov	30	20
1305	40 m. V. Kubasov	30	20
1306	40 m. Hungarian stamp showing Kubasov and B. Farkas	30	20

272 Benz, 1885

1980. Classic Cars. Multicoloured.

1307	20 m. Type **272**	25	10
1308	30 m. "President" Czechoslovakia, 1897	30	10
1309	40 m. Armstrong Siddeley, 1904	35	25
1310	50 m. Russo-Balt, 1909	45	20
1311	60 m. Packard, 1909	50	20
1312	80 m. Lancia, 1911	70	30
1313	1 t. 60 "Marne" taxi, 1914	1·40	60

273 Adelie Penguin

276 "The Shepherd speaking the Truth"

1980. Antarctic Exploration. Multicoloured.

1315	20 m. Type **273**	55	15
1316	30 m. Blue whales	70	20
1317	40 m. Wandering albatross and Jacques Cousteau's bathysphere	95	30
1318	50 m. Weddell seals and mobile research station	90	30
1319	60 m. Emperor penguins	1·25	35
1320	70 m. Great skuas	1·50	40
1321	80 m. Killer whales	1·60	55
1322	1 t. 20 Adelie penguins, research station, Ilyushin Il-18B airplane and tracked vehicle	2·25	75

1980. Nursery Tales. Multicoloured.

1326	20 m. Type **276**	25	10
1327	30 m. Children under umbrella and rainbow ("Above them the Sky is always clear")	30	10
1328	40 m. Children on sledge and skis ("Winter's Joys")	35	15
1329	50 m. Girl watching boy playing flute ("Little Musicians")	40	15
1330	60 m. Boys giving girl leaves ("Happy Birthday")	55	20
1331	80 m. Children with flowers and briefcase ("First Schoolday")	65	30
1332	1 t. 20 Girls dancing ("May Day")	90	40

277 Soldier

1981. 60th Anniv of Mongolian People's Army.

1334	**277** 60 m. multicoloured	60	30

278 Economy Emblems within Party Initials

1981. 60th Anniv of Mongolian Revolutionary People's Party.

1335	**278** 60 m. gold, red and black	45	25

279 Motocross

1981. Motor Cycle Sports. Multicoloured.

1336	10 m. Type **279**	15	10
1337	20 m. Tour racing	25	10
1338	30 m. Ice racing	30	15
1339	40 m. Road racing	40	20
1340	50 m. Motocross (different)	50	25
1341	60 m. Road racing (different)	55	25
1342	70 m. Speedway	60	30
1343	80 m. Sidecar racing	70	35
1344	1 t. 20 Road racing (different)	95	45

280 Cosmonauts entering Space Capsule

1981. Soviet–Mongolian Space Flight. Mult.

1345	20 m. Type **280**	30	10
1346	30 m. Rocket and designer S. P. Korolev	35	10
1347	40 m. "Vostok 1" and Yuri Gagarin	40	15
1348	50 m. "Soyuz"–"Sallyut" space station	50	20
1349	60 m. Spectral photography	60	25
1350	80 m. Crystal and space station	70	30
1351	1 t. 20 Space complex, Moscow Kremlin and Sukhe Bator statue, Ulan Bator	90	45

281 Ulan Bator Buildings and 1961 Mongolian Stamp

1981. Stamp Exhibitions.

1353	**281** 1 t. multicoloured	1·75	80
1354	– 1 t. multicoloured	1·75	80
1355	– 1 t. black, blue and magenta	1·75	80
1356	– 1 t. multicoloured	1·75	80

DESIGNS: No. 1353, Type **281** (Mongolian stamp exhibition); No. 1354, Wurttemberg stamps of 1947 and 1949 and view of Old Stuttgart ("Naposta '81" exhibition); No. 1355, Parliament building and sculpture, Vienna, and Austrian stamp of 1933 ("WIPA 1981" exhibition); No. 1356, Japanese stamp of 1964, cherry blossom and girls in Japanese costume ("Japex '81" exhibition, Tokyo).

282 Star and Industrial and Agricultural Scenes

1981. 18th Mongolian Revolutionary People's Party Congress.

1357	**282** 60 m. multicoloured	45	25

284 Sheep Farming

1981. "Results of the People's Economy". Multicoloured.

1359	20 m. Type **284**	30	10
1360	30 m. Transport	70	15
1361	40 m. Telecommunications	90	15
1362	50 m. Public health service	50	20
1363	60 m. Agriculture	60	25
1364	80 m. Electrical industry	70	30
1365	1 t. 20 Housing	1·00	45

286 Pharaonic Ship (15th century B.C.)

1981. Sailing Ships. Multicoloured.

No.	Description		
1367	10 m. Type **286**	30	10
1368	20 m. Mediterranean sailing ship (9th century)	40	15
1369	40 m. Hanse kogge (12th century) (vert)	60	20
1370	50 m. Venetian felucca (13th century) (vert)	75	30
1371	60 m. Columbus's "Santa Maria" (vert)	90	35
1372	80 m. Cook's H.M.S. "Endeavour" (vert)	1·00	50
1373	1 t. "Poltava" (18th-century Russian ship of the line) (vert)	1·40	60
1374	1 t. 20 American schooner (19th century) (vert)	1·60	75

287 Arms of Mongolia and Russia

1981. Soviet–Mongolian Friendship Pact.

No.	Description		
1375	**287** 60 m. red, blue and gold	45	25

288 "Hendrickje in Bed"

290 White-tailed Sea Eagle and German 1 m. "Zeppelin" Stamp

289 Billy Goat (pawn)

1981. 375th Birth Anniv of Rembrandt (artist). Multicoloured.

No.	Description		
1376	20 m. "Flora"	20	10
1377	30 m. Type **288**	25	15
1378	40 m. "Young Woman with Earrings"	40	20
1379	50 m. "Young girl in the Window"	45	25
1380	60 m. "Hendrickje like Flora"	55	30
1381	80 m. "Saskia with Red Flower"	70	35
1382	1 t. 20 "The Holy Family with Drape" (detail)	85	45

1981. Mongolian Chess Pieces. Multicoloured.

No.	Description		
1384	20 m. Type **289**	50	15
1385	40 m. Horse-drawn cart (rook)	75	25
1386	50 m. Camel (bishop)	90	35
1387	60 m. Horse (knight)	1·25	40
1388	80 m. Lion (queen)	1·60	60
1389	1 t. 20 Man with dog (king)	2·00	85

1981. Air. 50th Anniv of "Graf Zeppelin" Polar Flight. Multicoloured.

No.	Description		
1391	20 m. Type **290**	40	15
1392	30 m. Arctic Fox and German 2 m. "Zeppelin" stamp	40	20
1393	40 m. Walrus and German 4 m. "Zeppelin" stamp	50	25
1394	50 m. Polar Bear and Russian 30 k. "Zeppelin" stamp	60	30
1395	60 m. Snowy Owl and Russian 35 k. "Zeppelin" stamp	1·00	20
1396	80 m. Atlantic Puffin and Russian 1 r. "Zeppelin" stamp	1·25	20
1397	1 t. 20 Northern sealion and Russian 2 r. "Zeppelin" stamp	1·50	65

291 Circus Camel and Circus Building, Ulan Bator

1981. Mongolian Sport and Art. Multicoloured.

No.	Description		
1399	10 m. Type **291**	10	10
1400	20 m. Horsemen and stadium (National holiday cavalcade)	20	15
1401	40 m. Wrestling and Ulan Bator stadium	40	25
1402	50 m. Archers and stadium	55	30
1403	60 m. Folk singer-dancer and House of Culture	65	35
1404	80 m. Girl playing jatga (folk instrument) and Ulan Bator Drama Theatre	80	40
1405	1 t. Ballet dancers and Opera House	1·25	50
1406	1 t. 20 Exhibition Hall and statue of man on bucking horse	1·40	70

292 Mozart and scene from "The Magic Flute"

1981. Composers. Multicoloured.

No.	Description		
1407	20 m. Type **292**	40	15
1408	30 m. Beethoven and scene from "Fidelio"	50	20
1409	40 m. Bartok and scene from "The Miraculous Mandarin"	60	25
1410	50 m. Verdi and scene from "Aida"	80	35
1411	60 m. Tchaikovsky and scene from "The Sleeping Beauty"	90	40
1412	80 m. Dvorak and score of "New World" symphony	1·25	50
1413	1 t. 20 Chopin, piano, score and quill pens	1·60	75

293 "Mongolian Women in Everyday Life" (detail, Davaakhuu)

294 Gorbatko

1981. International Decade for Women. Mult.

No.	Description		
1414	20 m. Type **293**	25	10
1415	30 m. "Mongolian Women in Everyday Life" (different detail)	35	15
1416	40 m. "National Day" (detail, Khishigbaiar)	40	20
1417	50 m. "National Day" (detail) (different)	50	25
1418	60 m. "National Day" (detail) (different)	60	35
1419	80 m. "Ribbon Weaver" (Ts. Baidi)	85	40
1420	1 t. 20 "Expectant Mother" (Senghesokhio)	1·25	65

1981. "Intercosmos" Space Programme. Mult.

No.	Description		
1422	50 m. Type **294**	50	30
1423	50 m. Vietnam stamp showing Gorbatko and Pham Tuan	50	30
1424	50 m. Romanenko	50	30
1425	50 m. Cuban stamp showing Tamayo	50	30
1426	50 m. Dzhanibekov	50	30
1427	50 m. Mongolian stamp showing Dzhanibekov and Gurrugchaa	50	30
1428	50 m. Popov	50	30
1429	50 m. Rumanian stamp showing "Salyut" space station and "Soyuz" space ship	50	30

295 Karl von Drais Bicycle, 1816

1982. History of the Bicycle. Multicoloured.

No.	Description		
1430	10 m. Type **295**	20	10
1431	20 m. Macmillan bicycle, 1838	30	10
1432	40 m. First American pedal bicycle by Pierre Lallament, 1866	50	20
1433	50 m. First European pedal bicycle by Ernest Michaux	55	25
1434	60 m. "Kangaroo" bicycle, 1877	60	30
1435	80 m. Coventry Rotary Tandem, 1870s	75	45
1436	1 t. Chain-driven bicycle, 1878	95	60
1437	1 t. 20 Modern bicycle	4·50	2·40

296 Footballers (Brazil, 1950)

1982. World Cup Football Championship, Spain. Multicoloured.

No.	Description		
1439	10 m. Type **296**	15	10
1440	20 m. Switzerland, 1954	25	10
1441	40 m. Sweden, 1958	40	20
1442	50 m. Chile, 1962	55	25
1443	60 m. England, 1966	60	30
1444	80 m. Mexico, 1970	75	40
1445	1 t. West Germany, 1974	95	50
1446	1 t. 20 Argentina, 1978	1·25	55

297 Trade Union Emblem and Economic Symbols

299 Dimitrov

1982. 12th Mongolian Trade Unions Congress.

No.	Description		
1448	**297** 60 m. multicoloured	50	30

1982. Birth Centenary of Georgi Dimitrov (Bulgarian statesman).

No.	Description		
1450	**299** 60 m. black, grey & gold	55	30

300 Chicks

1982. Young Animals. Multicoloured.

No.	Description		
1451	10 m. Type **300**	20	10
1452	20 m. Colt	30	15
1453	30 m. Lamb	40	20
1454	40 m. Roe deer fawn	50	25
1455	50 m. Bactrian camel	65	30
1456	60 m. Kid	70	35
1457	70 m. Calf	80	40
1458	1 t. 20 Wild piglet	1·10	60

301 Coal-fired Industry

1982. Coal Mining.

No.	Description		
1459	**301** 60 m. multicoloured	70	30

302 Emblem

304 Revsomol Emblem within "Flower"

INDEX

Countries can be quickly located by referring to the index at the end of this volume.

303 Siberian Pine

1982. 18th Revsomol Youth Congress.

No.	Description		
1460	**302** 60 m. multicoloured	55	30

1982. Trees. Multicoloured.

No.	Description		
1461	20 m. Type **303**	25	15
1462	30 m. Siberian fir	35	20
1463	40 m. Poplar	45	25
1464	50 m. Siberian larch	55	30
1465	60 m. Scots pine	65	35
1466	80 m. Birch	75	45
1467	1 t. 20 Spruce	1·10	60

1982. 60th Anniv of Revsomol Youth Organization.

No.	Description		
1449	**304** 60 m. multicoloured	55	30

305 World Map and Satellite

1982. Air. I.T.U. Delegates' Conference, Nairobi.

No.	Description		
1469	**305** 60 m. multicoloured	70	30

306 Japanese "Iseki-6500" Tractor

1982. Tractors. Multicoloured.

No.	Description		
1470	10 m. Type **306**	15	10
1471	20 m. West German "Deutz-DX230"	25	10
1472	40 m. British "Bonser"	40	20
1473	50 m. American "International-884"	55	25
1474	60 m. French Renault "TX 145-14"	60	30
1475	80 m. Russian "Belarus-611"	75	40
1476	1 t. Russian "K-7100"	95	50
1477	1 t. 20 Russian "DT-75"	1·10	55

307 Fish and Lake Hevsgel

1982. Landscapes and Animals. Multicoloured.

No.	Description		
1478	20 m. Type **307**	35	15
1479	30 m. Zavkhan Highlands and sheep	40	20
1480	40 m. Lake Hovd and Eurasian beaver	50	25
1481	50 m. Lake Uvs and horses	65	30
1482	60 m. Bajankhongor Steppe and goitred gazelle	80	35
1483	80 m. Bajan-Elgii Highlands and rider with golden eagle	1·50	35
1484	1 t. 20 Gobi Desert and bactrian camels	1·40	65

308 "Sputnik 1"

1982. Air. Second U.N. Conference on the Exploration and Peaceful Uses of Outer Space. Multicoloured.

1485 60 m. Type **308** 60 30
1486 60 m. "Sputnik 2" and Laika (first dog in space) 60 30
1487 60 m. "Vostok 1" and Yuri Gagarin (first man in space) 60 30
1488 60 m. "Venera 8" 60 30
1489 60 m. "Vostok 6" and V. Tereshkova (first woman in space) 60 30
1490 60 m. Aleksei Leonov and space walker 60 30
1491 60 m. Neil Armstrong and astronaut on Moon's surface 60 30
1492 60 m. V. Dzhanibekov, Jean-Loup Chretien and "Soyuz T-6" 60 30

309 Montgolfier Brothers' Balloon, 1783

1982. Air. Bicentenary of Manned Flight. Mult.

1494 20 m. Type **309** 30 10
1495 30 m. Blanchard and Jefferies crossing the channel, 1785 . 40 20
1496 40 m. Green's flight to Germany in "Royal Vauxhall", 1836 55 25
1497 50 m. Andree's North Pole flight in "Oernen", 1897 . 60 30
1498 60 m. First Gordon Bennett balloon race, Paris, 1906 . 70 35
1499 80 m. First stratosphere flight in "F.N.R.S.", Switzerland, 1931 . . . . 90 45
1500 1 t. 20 USSR VR-62 flight, 1933 1·25 65

310 Sorcerer tells Mickey Mouse to clean up Quarters

1983. Drawings from "The Sorcerer's Apprentice" (section of Walt Disney's film "Fantasia"). Mult.

1502 25 m. Type **310** 20 10
1503 35 m. Mickey notices Sorcerer has left his cap behind . . 30 15
1504 45 m. Mickey puts cap on and commands broom to fetch water 35 20
1505 55 m. Broom carrying water . 40 25
1506 65 m. Mickey sleeps while broom continues to fetch water, flooding the room . . 50 30
1507 75 m. Mickey uses axe on broom to try to stop it . . 55 35
1508 85 m. Each splinter becomes a broom which continues to fetch water 65 40
1509 1 t. 40 Mickey, clinging to Sorcerer's Book of Spells, caught in whirlpool . . . . 1·00 55
1510 2 t. Mickey handing cap back to Sorcerer . . . . 1·40 75

311 Foal with Mother

1983. "The Foal and the Hare" (folk tale). Mult.

1512 10 m. Type **311** 10 10
1513 20 m. Foal wanders off alone 15 10
1514 30 m. Foal finds sack 25 15
1515 40 m. Foal unties sack . . . 30 15
1516 50 m. Wolf jumps out of sack 40 20
1517 60 m. Hare appears as wolf is about to eat foal 45 25
1518 70 m. Hare tricks wolf into re-entering sack 50 30
1519 80 m. Hare ties up sack with wolf inside 60 35
1520 1 t. 20 Hare and foal look for foal's mother 90 50

312 Antonov An-24B Aircraft

1983. Tourism. Multicoloured.

1524 20 m. Type **312** 35 10
1525 30 m. Skin tent 35 15
1526 40 m. Roe deer 40 20
1527 50 m. Argali 55 25
1528 60 m. Imperial eagle . . . . 1·25 30
1529 80 m. Khan Museum, Ulan Bator 90 40
1530 1 t. 20 Sukhe Bator statue, Ulan Bator . . . . 1·00 60

313 Rose

1983. Flowers. Multicoloured.

1531 20 m. Type **313** 30 10
1532 30 m. Dahlia 40 15
1533 40 m. Marigold 50 20
1534 50 m. Narcissus 60 25
1535 60 m. Viola 70 30
1536 80 m. Tulip 85 40
1537 1 t. 20 Sunflower . . . . . 1·25 60

314 Border Guard

1983. 50th Anniv of Border Guards.

1538 **314** 60 m. multicoloured . . 1·00 40

316 Karl Marx

1983. Death Centenary of Karl Marx.

1540 **316** 60 m. red, gold and blue 70 40

317 Agriculture

1983. 18th Communist Party Congress Five Year Plan. Multicoloured.

1541 10 m. Type **317** 15 10
1542 20 m. Power industry . . . 25 10
1543 30 m. Textile industry . . . 30 15
1544 40 m. Science in industry and agriculture 45 25
1545 60 m. Improvement of living standards 60 35
1546 80 m. Communications . . . 1·40 50
1547 1 t. Children (education) . . 1·00 60

318 Young Inventors

1983. Children's Year. Multicoloured.

1548 10 m. Type **318** 15 10
1549 20 m. In school 25 10
1550 30 m. Archery 40 15
1551 40 m. Shepherdess playing flute 50 20
1552 50 m. Girl with deer 65 30
1553 70 m. Collecting rocks and mushrooms . . . . 1·00 50
1554 1 t. 20 Girl playing lute and boy singing . . . . 1·25 60

319 Skating

1983. 10th Anniv of Children's Fund. Multicoloured.

1555 20 m. Type **319** 15 15
1556 30 m. Shepherds 25 15
1557 40 m. Tree-planting 50 25
1558 50 m. Playing by the sea . . . 65 35
1559 60 m. Carrying water 80 40
1560 80 m. Folk dancing . . . . . 1·00 65
1561 1 t. 20 Ballet . . . . 1·75 85

320 Pallas's Pika

1983. Small Mammals. Multicoloured.

1563 20 m. Type **320** 35 20
1564 30 m. Long-eared jerboa . . . 45 25
1565 40 m. Eurasian red squirrel . . 55 30
1566 50 m. Daurian hedgehog . . 65 40
1567 60 m. Harvest mouse 80 45
1568 80 m. Eurasian water shrew . 1·25 70
1569 1 t. 20 Siberian chipmunk . . 1·75 95

322 Bobsleighing

1984. Winter Olympic Games, Sarajevo. Mult.

1571 20 m. Type **322** 30 15
1572 30 m. Cross-country skiing . 40 20
1573 40 m. Ice hockey 55 30
1574 50 m. Speed skating 65 35
1575 60 m. Ski jumping 75 40
1576 80 m. Ice dancing . . . . . . 1·25 70
1577 1 t. 20 Biathlon (horiz) . . . 1·60 90

323 Mail Van

1984. World Communications Year. Multicoloured.

1579 10 m. Type **323** 15 10
1580 20 m. Earth receiving station 30 20
1581 40 m. Airliner 75 30
1582 50 m. Central Post Office, Ulan Bator 70 35
1583 1 t. Transmitter . . . . . . 1·10 70
1584 1 t. 20 Diesel train . . . . . 2·50 1·00

325 Cycling

326 Flag, Rocket and Coastal Scene

1587 20 m. Gymnastics (horiz) . . 25 15
1588 30 m. Type **325** 35 20
1589 40 m. Weightlifting 45 25
1590 50 m. Judo 55 30
1591 60 m. Archery 65 35
1592 80 m. Boxing 90 60
1593 1 t. 20 High jumping (horiz) 1·25 75

1984. 25th Anniv of Cuban Revolution.

1595 **326** 60 m. multicoloured . . 80 40

328 Douglas DC-10

329 Speaker, Radio and Transmitter

1984. Air. Civil Aviation. Multicoloured.

1597 20 m. Type **328** 35 15
1598 30 m. Airbus Industrie A300B2 55 20
1599 40 m. Concorde 70 30
1600 50 m. Boeing 747-200 . . . 85 35
1601 60 m. Ilyushin Il-62M . . . 1·00 40
1602 80 m. Tupolev Tu-154 . . . 1·40 70
1603 1 t. 20 Ilyushin Il-86 . . . . 1·75 85

1984. 50th Anniv of Mongolian Broadcasting.

1605 **329** 60 m. multicoloured . . 75 40

330 Silver and Gold Coins

332 Sukhe Bator Statue

331 Golden Harp

1984. 60th Anniv of State Bank.

1606 **330** 60 m. multicoloured . . 75 40

1984. Scenes from Walt Disney's "Mickey and the Beanstalk" (cartoon film). Multicoloured.

1607 25 m. Type **331** 20 10
1608 35 m. Mickey holding box of magic beans 30 15
1609 45 m. Mickey about to eat bean 40 20
1610 55 m. Mickey looking for magic bean 50 25
1611 65 m. Goofy, Mickey and Donald at top of beanstalk 55 30
1612 75 m. Giant holding Mickey 60 35
1613 85 m. Giant threatening Mickey 80 40
1614 140 m. Goofy, Mickey and Donald cutting down beanstalk . . . . 1·40 65
1615 2 t. Goofy and Donald rescuing golden harp . . . . 1·60 75

1984. 60th Anniv of Ulan Bator City.
1617 **332** 60 m. multicoloured . . 75 40

333 Arms, Flag and Landscape
334 Rider carrying Flag

1984. 60th Anniv of Mongolian People's Republic.
1618 **333** 60 m. multicoloured . . 75 40

1984. 60th Anniv of Mongolian People's Revolutionary Party.
1619 **334** 60 m. multicoloured . . 75 40

335 Gaetan Boucher (speed skating)

1984. Winter Olympic Gold Medal Winners. Multicoloured.
1620 20 m. Type **335** 30 10
1621 30 m. Eirik Kvalfoss (biathlon) 40 20
1622 40 m. Marja-Liisa Hamalainen (cross-country skiing) . . . 55 25
1623 50 m. Max Julen (slalom) . . 70 35
1624 60 m. Jens Weissflog (ski jumping) (vert) 85 40
1625 80 m. W. Hoppe and D. Schauerhammer (two-man bobsleigh) (vert) . . . . . 1·25 60
1626 1 t. 20 J. Valova and O. Vassiliev (pairs figure skating) (vert) . . . . 1·75 85

336 Donshy Mask

1984. Traditional Masks. Multicoloured.
1628 20 m. Type **336** 10 10
1629 30 m. Zamandi 10 10
1630 40 m. Ulaan-Yadam 15 10
1631 50 m. Lkham 20 10
1632 60 m. Damdinchoizhoo . . . 25 10
1633 80 m. Ochirvaan 30 15
1634 1 t. 20 Namsrai 50 25

337 Collie

1984. Dogs. Multicoloured.
1636 20 m. Type **337** 10 10
1637 30 m. German shepherd . . . 10 10
1638 40 m. Papillon 15 10
1639 50 m. Cocker spaniel 20 10
1640 60 m. Terrier puppy (diamond-shaped) 25 10
1641 80 m. Dalmatians (diamond-shaped) 30 15
1642 1 t. 20 Mongolian shepherd . 50 25

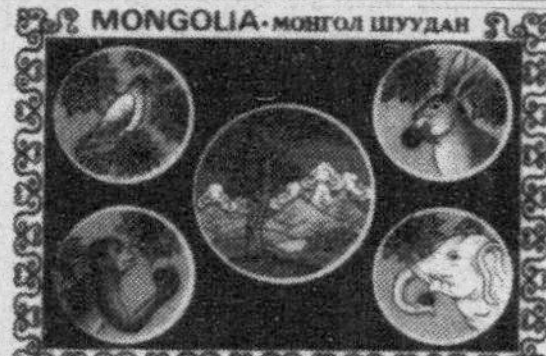
338 Four Animals and Tree

1984. "The Four Friendly Animals" (fairy tale). Multicoloured.
1643 10 m. Type **338** 10 10
1644 20 m. Animals discussing who was the oldest 10 10
1645 30 m. Monkey and elephant beside tree 10 10
1646 40 m. Elephant as calf and young tree 15 10
1647 50 m. Monkey and young tree 20 10
1648 60 m. Hare and young tree . 25 10
1649 70 m. Dove and sapling . . 30 15
1650 80 m. Animals around mature tree 30 15
1651 1 t. 20 Animals supporting each other so that dove could reach fruit 50 25

339 Fawn

1984. Red Deer. Multicoloured.
1653 50 m. Type **339** 20 10
1654 50 m. Stag 20 10
1655 50 m. Adults and fawn by river 20 10
1656 50 m. Doe in woodland . . 20 10

340 Flag and Pioneers
342 Black Stork

341 Shar Tarlan

1985. 60th Anniv of Mongolian Pioneer Organization.
1657 **340** 60 m. multicoloured . . 25 10

1985. Cattle. Multicoloured.
1658 20 m. Type **341** 10 10
1659 30 m. Bor khalium 10 10
1660 40 m. Sarlag 15 10
1661 50 m. Dornod talin bukh . . 20 10
1662 60 m. Char tarlan 25 15
1663 80 m. Nutgiin uulderiin unee 30 15
1664 1 t. 20 Tsagaan tolgoit . . . 50 25

1985. Birds. Multicoloured.
1666 20 m. Type **342** 10 10
1667 30 m. White-tailed sea eagle 10 10
1668 40 m. Great white crane . . 15 10
1669 50 m. Heude's parrotbill . . 20 10
1670 60 m. Crane 25 15
1671 80 m. Japanese white-necked crane 30 15
1672 1 t. 20 Rough-legged buzzard 50 25

343 Footballers
344 Monument

1985. World Junior Football Championship, U.S.S.R.
1674 **343** 20 m. multicoloured . . . 10 10
1675 – 30 m. multicoloured . . . 10 10
1676 – 40 m. multicoloured . . . 15 10
1677 – 50 m. multicoloured . . . 20 10
1678 – 60 m. multicoloured . . . 25 10
1679 – 80 m. multicoloured . . . 30 15
1680 – 1 t. 20 multicoloured . . 50 25
DESIGNS: 30 m. to 1 t. 20 Different footballing scenes.

1985. 40th Anniv of Victory in Europe.
1682 **344** 60 m. multicoloured . . . 25 15

345 Snow Leopards

1985. The Snow Leopard. Multicoloured.
1683 50 m. Type **345** 20 10
1684 50 m. Leopard 20 10
1685 50 m. Leopard on cliff ledge . 20 10
1686 50 m. Mother and cubs . . . 20 10

346 Moscow Kremlin and Girls of Different Races
347 Monument

1985. 12th World Youth and Students' Festival, Moscow.
1687 **346** 60 m. multicoloured . . . 25 10

1985. 40th Anniv of Victory in Asia.
1688 **347** 60 m. multicoloured . . . 25 10

348 "Rosa dahurica"

1985. Plants. Multicoloured.
1689 20 m. Type **348** 10 10
1690 30 m. False chamomile . . . 10 10
1691 40 m. Dandelion 15 10
1692 50 m. "Saxzitraga nirculus" . 20 10
1693 60 m. Cowberry 25 10
1694 80 m. "Sanguisorba officinalis" 30 15
1695 1 t. 20 "Plantago major" . . 50 25
See also Nos. 1719/25.

349 Camel

1985. The Bactrian Camel. Multicoloured.
1697 50 m. Type **349** 20 10
1698 50 m. Adults and calf . . . 20 10
1699 50 m. Calf 20 10
1700 50 m. Adult 20 10

350 "Soyuz" Spacecraft

1985. Space. Multicoloured.
1701 20 m. Type **350** 10 10
1702 30 m. "Kosmos" satellite . . 10 10
1703 40 m. "Venera-9" satellite . . 15 10
1704 50 m. "Salyut" space station 20 10
1705 60 m. "Luna-9" landing vehicle 25 10
1706 80 m. "Soyuz" rocket on transporter 30 15
1707 1 t. 20 Dish aerial receiving transmission from "Soyuz" 50 25

352 U.N. and Mongolian Flags and U.N. Headquarters, New York
354 Congress Emblem

353 "Tricholoma mongolica"

1985. 40th Anniv of U.N.O.
1710 **352** 60 m. multicoloured . . 25 10

1985. Fungi. Multicoloured.
1711 20 m. Type **353** 10 10
1712 30 m. Chanterelle 10 10
1713 40 m. Boot-lace fungus . . . 15 10
1714 50 m. Caesar's mushroom . . 20 10
1715 70 m. Chestnut mushroom . . 30 15
1716 80 m. Red-staining mushroom 30 15
1717 1 t. 20 Cep 50 25

1986. 19th Mongolian Revolutionary People's Party Congress.
1718 **354** 60 m. multicoloured . . 25 10

1986. Plants. As T **348**. Multicoloured.
1719 20 m. "Valeriana officinalis" 10 10
1720 30 m. "Hyoscymus niger" . . 10 10
1721 40 m. "Ephedra sinica" . . 15 10
1722 50 m. "Thymus gobica" . . 20 10
1723 60 m. "Paeonia anomalia" . 25 10
1724 80 m. "Achilea millefolium" 30 15
1725 1 t. 20 "Rhododendron adamsii" 50 25

355 Scene from Play

1986. 80th Birth Anniv of D. Natsagdorj (writer).
1726 **355** 60 m. multicoloured . . 25 10

356 Thalmann

357 Man wearing Patterned Robe

1986. Birth Centenary of Ernst Thalmann (German politician).
1727 **356** 60 m. multicoloured . . 25 10

1986. Costumes. Multicoloured.
1728 60 m. Type **357** . . 25 10
1729 60 m. Man in blue robe and fur-lined hat with ear flaps . . 25 10
1730 60 m. Woman in black and yellow dress and bolero . . 25 10
1731 60 m. Woman in pink dress patterned with stars 25 10
1732 60 m. Man in cream robe with fur cuffs 25 10
1733 60 m. Man in brown robe and mauve and yellow tunic . . 25 10
1734 60 m. Woman in blue dress with black, yellow and red overtunic 25 10

358 Footballers

1986. World Cup Football Championship, Mexico.
1735 **358** 20 m. multicoloured . . 10 10
1736 – 30 m. multicoloured . . 10 10
1737 – 40 m. multicoloured . . 15 10
1738 – 50 m. multicoloured . . 20 10
1739 – 60 m. multicoloured . . 25 10
1740 – 80 m. multicoloured . . 30 15
1741 – 1 t. 20 multicoloured . . 50 25
DESIGNS: 30 m. to 1 t. 20. Different footballing scenes.

359 Mink

1986. Mink. Multicoloured.
1743 60 m. Type **359** 25 10
1744 60 m. Mink on rock 25 10
1745 60 m. Mink on snow covered branch 25 10
1746 60 m. Two mink 25 10
See also Nos. 1771/4, 1800/3, 1804/7, 1840/3 and 1844/7.

360 "Neptis coenobita"

361 Sukhe Bator Statue

1986. Butterflies and Moths. Multicoloured.
1747 20 m. Type **360** 10 10
1748 30 m. "Colias tycha" 10 10
1749 40 m. "Leptidea amurensis" . 15 10
1750 50 m. "Oeneis tarpenledevi" . 20 10
1751 60 m. "Mesoacidalia charlotta" 25 10
1752 80 m. Eyed hawk moth . . . 30 15
1753 1 t. 20 Large tiger moth . . 50 25

1986. 65th Anniv of Independence.
1754 **361** 60 m. multicoloured . . 25 10

362 Yak and Goats Act

1986. Circus. Multicoloured.
1755 20 m. Type **362** 10 10
1756 30 m. Acrobat 10 10
1757 40 m. Yak act 15 10
1758 50 m. Acrobats (vert) . . . 20 10
1759 60 m. High wire act (vert) . . 25 10
1760 80 m. Fire juggler on camel (vert) 30 15
1761 1 t. 20 Acrobats on camel-drawn cart (vert) 50 25

363 Morin Khuur

364 Flag and Emblem

1986. Musical Instruments. Multicoloured.
1762 20 m. Type **363** 10 10
1763 30 m. Bishguur (wind instrument) 10 10
1764 40 m. Ever buree (wind) . . 15 10
1765 50 m. Shudarga (string) . . 20 10
1766 60 m. Khiil (string) 25 10
1767 80 m. Janchir (string) (horiz) 30 15
1768 1 t. 20 Jatga (string) (horiz) . 50 25

1986. International Peace Year.
1770 **364** 10 m. multicoloured . . 10 10

1986. Przewalski's Horse. As T **359**. Mult.
1771 50 m. Horses grazing on sparsely grassed plain . . 20 10
1772 50 m. Horses grazing on grassy plain 20 10
1773 50 m. Adults with foal . . . 20 10
1774 50 m. Horses in snow . . . 20 10

365 Temple

1986. Ancient Buildings. Multicoloured.
1775 60 m. Type **365** 25 10
1776 60 m. Temple with light green roof and white doors . . . 25 10
1777 60 m. Temple with porch . . 25 10
1778 60 m. White building with three porches 25 10

366 Redhead ("Aythya americana")

1986. Birds. Multicoloured.
1779 60 m. Type **366** 25 10
1780 60 m. Ruffed grouse ("Bonasa umbellus") 25 10
1781 60 m. Whistling swan ("Olor columbianus") 25 10
1782 60 m. Rock pipit ("Anthus spinoletta") 25 10

367 Alfa Romeo "RL Sport", 1922

1986. Cars. Multicoloured.
1783 20 m. Type **367** 10 10
1784 30 m. Stutz "Bearcat", 1912 . 10 10
1785 40 m. Mercedes "Simplex", 1902 . . . . 15 10
1786 50 m. Tatra "11", 1923 . . . 20 10
1787 60 m. Ford Model "T", 1908 25 10
1788 80 m. Vauxhall, 1905 . . . . 30 15
1789 1 t. 20 Russo-Balt "K", 1913 50 25

368 Wilhelm Steinitz and Bardeleben Game, 1895

1986. World Chess Champions. Multicoloured.
1791 20 m. Type **368** 10 10
1792 30 m. Emanuel Lasker and Pilsberi game, 1895 . . . . 10 10
1793 40 m. Alexander Alekhine and Retti game, 1925 . . . . . 15 10
1794 50 m. Mikhail Botvinnik and Capablanca game, 1938 . . 20 10
1795 60 m. Anatoly Karpov and Untsiker game, 1975 . . . 25 10
1796 80 m. Nona Gaprindashvili and Lasarevich game, 1961 . . 30 15
1797 1 t. 20 M. Chirburdanidze and Levitina game, 1984 . . . . 50 25

1986. Saiga Antelope ("Saiga tatarica"). As T **359**. Multicoloured.
1800 60 m. Male 25 10
1801 60 m. Female with calf . . . 25 10
1802 60 m. Male and female . . . 25 10
1803 60 m. Male and female in snow 25 10

1986. Pelicans. As T **359**. Multicoloured.
1804 60 m. Dalmatian pelican ("Pelecanus crispus") . . . 25 10
1805 60 m. Dalmatian pelican preening 25 10
1806 60 m. Eastern white pelican ("Pelecanus onocrotalus") . 25 10
1807 60 m. Eastern white pelicans in flight 25 10

370 Siamese Fighting Fish

1987. Aquarium Fishes. Multicoloured.
1808 20 m. Type **370** 10 10
1809 30 m. Goldfish 10 10
1810 40 m. "Rasbora hengeli" . . 15 10
1811 50 m. "Aequidens sp." . . . 20 10
1812 60 m. Moonfish 25 10
1813 80 m. Green swordtail 30 15
1814 1 t. 20 Angel fish (vert) . . . 50 25

371 Lassooing Horse

1987. Traditional Equestrian Sports. Mult.
1816 20 m. Type **371** 10 10
1817 30 m. Breaking horse 10 10
1818 40 m. Mounted archer 15 10
1819 50 m. Race 20 10
1820 60 m. Horseman snatching flag from ground 25 10
1821 80 m. Tug of war 30 15
1822 1 t. 20 Racing wolf 50 25

372 Grey-headed Green Woodpecker

373 Butterfly Hunting

1987. Woodpeckers. Multicoloured.
1823 20 m. Type **372** 10 10
1824 30 m. Wryneck 10 10
1825 40 m. Great spotted woodpecker 15 10
1826 50 m. White-backed woodpecker 20 10
1827 60 m. Lesser spotted woodpecker 25 10
1828 80 m. Black woodpecker . . 30 15
1829 1 t. 20 Three-toed woodpecker 50 25

1987. Children's Activities. Multicoloured.
1831 20 m. Type **373** 10 10
1832 30 m. Feeding calves 10 10
1833 40 m. Drawing on ground in chalk 15 10
1834 50 m. Football 20 10
1835 60 m. Go-carting 25 10
1836 80 m. Growing vegetables . . 30 15
1837 1 t. 20 Playing string instrument 50 25

374 Industry and Agriculture

1987. 13th Congress and 60th Anniv of Mongolian Trade Union.
1838 **374** 60 m. multicoloured . . 25 10

375 Women in Traditional Costume

376 Flags of Member Countries

1987. 40th Anniv of Mongol–Soviet Friendship.
1839 **375** 60 m. multicoloured . . 25 10

1987. Argali ("Ovis ammon"). As T **359**. Mult.
1840 60 m. On grassy rock (full face) 25 10
1841 60 m. On rock (three-quarter face) 25 10
1842 60 m. Family 25 10
1843 60 m. Close-up of head and upper body 25 10

1987. Swans. As T **359**. Multicoloured.
1844 60 m. Mute Swan ("Cygnus olor") in water 25 10
1845 60 m. Mute swan on land . . 25 10
1846 60 m. Whistling swan ("Cygnus bewickii") 25 10
1847 60 m. Whistling swan, "Cygnus gunus" and mute swan . . 25 10

1987. 25th Anniv of Membership of Council for Mutual Economic Aid.
1848 **376** 60 m. multicoloured . . 25 10

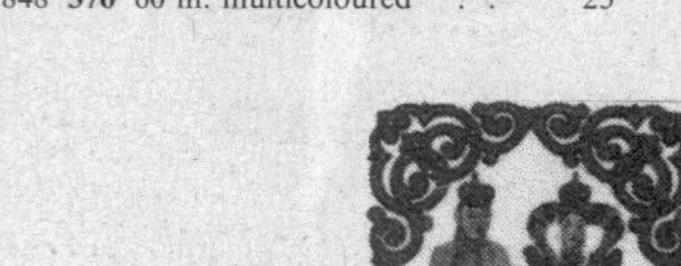

377 Sea Buckthorn

378 Couple in Traditional Costume

1987. Fruits. Multicoloured.
1849 20 m. Type **377** 10 10
1850 30 m. Blackcurrants 10 10
1851 40 m. Redcurrants 15 10
1852 50 m. Redcurrants 20 10
1853 60 m. Raspberries 25 10
1854 80 m. "Padus asiatica" . . . 30 15
1855 1 t. 20 Strawberries 50 25

1987. Folk Art. Multicoloured.
1857 20 m. Type **378** 10 10
1858 30 m. Gold-inlaid baton and pouch 10 10
1859 40 m. Gold and jewelled ornaments 15 10
1860 50 m. Bag and dish 20 10
1861 60 m. Earrings 25 10
1862 80 m. Pipe, pouch and bottle 30 15
1863 1 t. 20 Decorative headdress 50 25

379 Dancer

1987. Dances.
1864 **379** 20 m. multicoloured . . 10 10
1865 – 30 m. multicoloured . . 10 10
1866 – 40 m. multicoloured . . 15 10
1867 – 50 m. multicoloured . . 20 10
1868 – 60 m. multicoloured . . 25 10
1869 – 80 m. multicoloured . . 30 15
1870 – 1 t. 20 multicoloured . . 50 25
DESIGNS: 30 m. to 1 t. 20, Different dances.

381 Scottish Fold

1987. Cats. Multicoloured.
1872 20 m. Type **381** 10 10
1873 30 m. Grey 10 10
1874 40 m. Oriental 15 10
1875 50 m. Abyssinian (horiz) . . 20 10
1876 60 m. Manx (horiz) 25 10
1877 80 m. Black shorthair (horiz) 30 15
1878 1 t. 20 Spotted (horiz) . . . 50 25

382 Mil Mi-V12

1987. Helicopters. Multicoloured.
1880 20 m. Type **382** 10 10
1881 30 m. Westland WG-30 . . . 15 10
1882 40 m. Bell LongRanger II . . 20 10
1883 50 m. Kawasaki-Hughes 369HS 25 10
1884 60 m. Kamov Ka-32 . . . . 30 10
1885 80 m. Mil Mi-17 . . . . . 35 15
1886 1 t. 20 Mil Mi-10K 60 25

383 City Scene 384 Kremlin, Lenin and Revolutionaries

1987. 19th Mongolian People's Revolutionary Party Congress. Multicoloured.
1887 60 m. Type **383** 25 10
1888 60 m. Clothing and mining industries 25 10
1889 60 m. Agriculture 25 10
1890 60 m. Family 25 10
1891 60 m. Workers, factories and fields 25 10
1892 60 m. Building construction . 25 10
1893 60 m. Scientist 25 10

1987. 70th Anniv of Russian October Revolution.
1894 **384** 60 m. multicoloured . . 25 10

385 Seven with One Blow

1987. Walt Disney Cartoons. Mult (a) "The Brave Little Tailor" (Grimm Brothers).
1895 25 m. Type **385** 10 10
1896 35 m. Brought before the King 15 10
1897 45 m. Rewards for bravery . 20 10
1898 55 m. Fight between Mickey and the giant 25 10
1899 2 t. Happy ending 80 40

(b) "The Celebrated Jumping Frog of Calaveras County" (Mark Twain).
1901 65 m. "He'd bet on anything" 25 10
1902 75 m. "He never done nothing but...learn that frog to jump" 30 15
1903 85 m. "What might it be that you've got in that box?" . 35 15
1904 1 t. "40 He got the frog out and filled him full of quail shot" 60 30

386 Head

1987. The Red Fox. Multicoloured.
1906 60 m. Type **386** 25 10
1907 60 m. Vixen and cubs . . . 25 10
1908 60 m. Stalking 25 10
1909 60 m. In the snow 25 10

388 Bobsleighing 389 Sukhe Bator

1988. Air. Winter Olympic Games, Calgary. Mult.
1911 20 m. Type **388** 10 10
1912 30 m. Ski jumping 10 10
1913 40 m. Skiing 15 10
1914 50 m. Biathlon 20 10
1915 60 m. Speed skating 25 10
1916 80 m. Figure skating 30 15
1917 1 t. 20 Ice hockey 50 25

1988. 95th Birth Anniv of Sukhe Bator.
1919 **389** 60 m. multicoloured . . 25 10

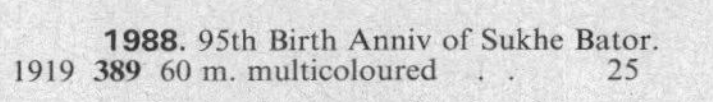

390 "Invitation"

1988. Roses. Multicoloured.
1920 20 m. Type **390** 10 10
1921 30 m. "Meilland" 10 10
1922 40 m. "Pascali" 15 10
1923 50 m. "Tropicana" 20 10
1924 60 m. "Wendy Cussons" . . 25 10
1925 80 m. "Rosa sp" (wrongly inscr "Blue Moon") 30 15
1926 1 t. 20 "Diorama" 50 25

391 "Ukhaant Ekhner"

1988. Puppets. Multicoloured.
1928 20 m. Type **391** 10 10
1929 30 m. "Altan Everte Mungun Turuut" 10 10
1930 40 m. "Aduuchyn Khuu" . 15 10
1931 50 m. "Suulenkhuu" 20 10
1932 60 m. "Khonchyn Khuu" . 25 10
1933 80 m. "Argat Byatskhan Baatar" 30 15
1934 1 t. 20 "Botgochyn Khuu" . 50 25

393 Judo 394 Marx

1988. Olympic Games, Seoul. Multicoloured.
1936 20 m. Type **393** 10 10
1937 30 m. Archery 10 10
1938 40 m. Weightlifting 15 10
1939 50 m. Gymnastics 20 10
1940 60 m. Cycling 25 10
1941 80 m. Running 30 15
1942 1 t. 20 Wrestling 50 25

1988. 170th Birth Anniv of Karl Marx.
1944 **394** 60 m. multicoloured . . . 25 10

395 Couple and Congress Banner 396 "Kosmos"

1988. 19th Revsomol Youth Congress.
1945 **395** 60 m. multicoloured . . . 25 10

1988. Spacecraft and Satellites. Multicoloured.
1946 20 m. Type **396** 10 10
1947 30 m. "Meteor" 10 10
1948 40 m. "Salyut"–"Soyuz" space complex 15 10
1949 50 m. "Prognoz-6" 20 10
1950 60 m. "Molniya-1" 25 10
1951 80 m. "Soyuz" 30 15
1952 1 t. 20 "Vostok" 50 25

397 Buddha 398 Emblem

1988. Religious Sculptures.
1954 **397** 20 m. multicoloured . . . 10 10
1955 – 30 m. multicoloured . . . 10 10
1956 – 40 m. multicoloured . . . 15 10
1957 – 50 m. multicoloured . . . 20 10
1958 – 60 m. multicoloured . . . 25 10
1959 – 80 m. multicoloured . . . 30 15
1960 – 1 t. 20 multicoloured . . . 50 25
DESIGNS: 30 m. to 1 t. 20, Different buddhas.

1988. 30th Anniv of Problems of "Peace and Socialism" (magazine).
1962 **398** 60 m. multicoloured . . . 25 10

399 Eagle

1988. White-tailed Sea Eagle. Multicoloured.
1963 60 m. Type **399** 25 10
1964 60 m. Eagle on fallen branch and eagle landing 25 10
1965 60 m. Eagle on rock 25 10
1966 60 m. Eagle (horiz) 25 10

400 Ass

1988. Asiatic Wild Ass. Multicoloured.
1967 60 m. Type **400** 25 10
1968 60 m. Head of ass 25 10
1969 60 m. Two adults 25 10
1970 60 m. Mare and foal 25 10

401 Athlete 403 U.S.S.R. (ice hockey)

1988. Traditional Sports. Multicoloured.
1971 10 m. Type **401** 10 10
1972 20 m. Horseman 10 10
1973 30 m. Archery 10 10
1974 40 m. Wrestling 15 10
1975 50 m. Archery (different) . . 20 10
1976 70 m. Horsemen (national holiday cavalcade) 30 15
1977 1 t. 20 Horsemen, wrestlers and archers 50 25

1988. Winter Olympic Games Gold Medal Winners. Multicoloured.
1979 1 t. 50 Type **403** 60 30
1980 1 t. 50 Bonnie Blair (speed skating) 60 30
1981 1 t. 50 Alberto Tomba (slalom) 60 30
1982 1 t. 50 Matti Nykanen (ski jumping) (horiz) 60 30

404 Brown Goat

1988. Goats. Multicoloured.
1984 20 m. Type **404** 10 10
1985 30 m. Black goat 10 10
1986 40 m. White long-haired goats 15 10
1987 50 m. Black long-haired goat 20 10
1988 60 m. White goat 25 10
1989 80 m. Black short-haired goat 30 15
1990 1 t. 20 Nanny and kid . . . 50 25

405 Emblem

1989. 60th Anniv of Mongolian Writers' Association.
1992 **405** 60 m. multicoloured . . 25 10

406 Beaver gnawing Trees

1989. Eurasian Beaver. Multicoloured.
1993 60 m. Type **406** 25 10
1994 60 m. Beaver with young . . 25 10
1995 60 m. Beavers beside tree stump and in water 25 10
1996 60 m. Beaver rolling log . . 25 10

407 Dancers

1989. Ballet.

1997	**407**	20 m. multicoloured	10	10
1998	–	30 m. multicoloured	10	10
1999	–	40 m. multicoloured (vert)	15	10
2000	–	50 m. multicoloured	20	10
2001	–	60 m. multicoloured	25	10
2002	–	80 m. multicoloured (vert)	30	15
2003	–	1 t. 20 multicoloured (vert)	50	25

DESIGNS: 30 m. to 1 t. 20, Different dancing scenes.

408 "Ursus pruinosis"

1989. Bears. Multicoloured.

2004	20 m. Type **408**	10	10
2005	30 m. Brown bear	10	10
2006	40 m. Asiatic black bear	15	10
2007	50 m. Polar bear	20	10
2008	60 m. Brown bear	25	10
2009	80 m. Giant panda	30	15
2010	1 t. 20 Brown bear	50	25

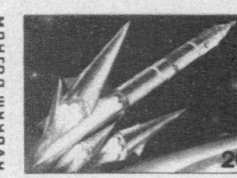

409 "Soyuz" Spacecraft

1989. Space. Multicoloured.

2012	20 m. Type **409**	10	10
2013	30 m. "Apollo"–"Soyuz" link	10	10
2014	40 m. "Columbia" space shuttle (vert)	15	10
2015	50 m. "Hermes" spacecraft	20	10
2016	60 m. "Nippon" spacecraft (vert)	25	10
2017	80 m. "Energy" rocket (vert)	30	15
2018	1 t. 20 "Buran" space shuttle (vert)	50	25

411 Nehru **412** "Opuntia microdasys"

1989. Birth Centenary of Jawaharial Nehru (Indian statesman).

2021	**411**	10 m. multicoloured	10	10

1989. Cacti. Multicoloured.

2022	20 m. Type **412**	10	10
2023	30 m. "Echinopsis multipiex"	10	10
2024	40 m. "Rebutia tephracanthus"	15	10
2025	50 m. "Brasilicactus haselbergii"	20	10
2026	60 m. "Gymnocalycium mihanovichii"	25	10
2027	80 m. "C. strausii"	30	15
2028	1 t. 20 "Horridocactus tuberisvicatus"	50	25

1989. 800th Anniv of Coronation of Genghis Khan. Nos. 291/4 optd **CHINGGIS KHAN CROWNATION 1189.**

2030	**67**	20 m. multicoloured	10	10
2031	–	30 m. multicoloured	10	10
2032	–	50 m. black, brown & red	20	10
2033	–	60 m. buff, blue & brown	25	10

415 Citroen "BX"

1989. Motor Cars. Multicoloured.

2035	20 m. Type **415**	10	10
2036	30 m. Volvo "760 GLF"	10	10
2037	40 m. Honda "Civic"	15	10
2038	50 m. Volga	20	10
2039	60 m. Ford "Granada"	25	10
2040	80 m. Baz "21099"	30	15
2041	1 t. 20 Mercedes "190"	50	25

416 Monument **417** Florence Griffith-Joyner (running)

1989. 50th Anniv of Battle of Khalka River.

2043	**416**	60 m. multicoloured	30	10

1989. Olympic Games Medal Winners. Mult.

2044	60 m. Type **417**	25	10
2045	60 m. Stefano Cerioni (fencing)	25	10
2046	60 m. Gintautas Umaras (cycling)	25	10
2047	60 m. Kristin Otto (swimming)	25	10

418 "Malchin Zaluus" (N. Sandagsuren)

1989. 30th Anniv of Co-operative Movement. Paintings. Multicoloured.

2049	20 m. Type **418**	10	10
2050	30 m. "Tsaatny Tukhai Dursamkh" (N. Sandagsuren) (vert)	10	10
2051	40 m. "Uul Shig Tushigtei" (D. Amgalan)	15	10
2052	50 m. "Goviin Egshig" (D. Amgalan)	20	10
2053	60 m. "Tsagaan Sar" (Ts. Dagvanyam)	25	10
2054	80 m. "Tumen Aduuny Bayar" (M. Butemkh) (vert)	30	15
2055	1 t. 20 "Bilcheer Deer" (N. Tsultem)	50	25

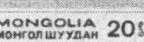

419 Four-man Bobsleighing **420** Victory Medal

1989. Ice Sports. Multicoloured.

2057	20 m. Type **419**	10	10
2058	30 m. Luge	10	10
2059	40 m. Figure skating	15	10
2060	50 m. Two-man bobsleighing	20	10
2061	60 m. Ice dancing	25	10
2062	80 m. Speed skating	30	15
2063	1 t. 20 Ice speedway	50	25

1989. Orders. Designs showing different badges and medals. Multicoloured, background colour given.

2065	**420**	60 m. blue	25	10
2066	–	60 m. orange	25	10
2067	–	60 m. mauve	25	10
2068	–	60 m. violet	25	10
2069	–	60 m. green	25	10
2070	–	60 m. blue	25	10
2071	–	60 m. red	25	10

422 Chu Lha **423** Sukhe Bator Statue

1989. Buddhas. Multicoloured.

2073	20 m. Damdin Sandub	10	10
2074	30 m. Pagwa Lama	10	10
2075	40 m. Type **422**	15	10
2076	50 m. Agwanglobsan	20	10
2077	60 m. Dorje Dags Dan	25	10
2078	80 m. Wangchikdorje	30	15
2079	1 t. 20 Buddha	50	25

1990. New Year.

2081	**423**	10 m. multicoloured	75	35

424 Newspapers and City **425** Emblem

1990. 70th Anniv of "Khuvisgalt Khevlel" (newspaper).

2082	**424**	60 m. multicoloured	65	30

1990. 20th Mongolian People's Revolutionary Party Congress.

2083	**425**	60 m. multicoloured	50	25

426 Male Character

1990. "Mandukhai the Wise" (film).

2084	**426**	20 m. multicoloured	20	10
2085	–	30 m. multicoloured	30	15
2086	–	40 m. multicoloured	45	20
2087	–	50 m. multicoloured	55	30
2088	–	60 m. multicoloured	75	35
2089	–	80 m. multicoloured	90	45
2090	–	1 t. 20 multicoloured	1·25	65

DESIGNS: 30 m. to 1 t. 20, Different characters from the film.

427 Trophy and Players

1990. World Cup Football Championship, Italy.

2092	**427**	20 m. multicoloured	20	10
2093	–	30 m. multicoloured	30	15
2094	–	40 m. multicoloured	40	20
2095	–	50 m. multicoloured	60	30
2096	–	60 m. multicoloured	70	35
2097	–	80 m. multicoloured	95	40
2098	–	1 t. 20 multicoloured	1·25	65

DESIGNS: 30 m. to 1 t. 20, Trophy and different players.

428 Lenin

1990. 120th Birth Anniv of Lenin.

2100	**428**	60 m. black, red and gold	65	30

429 Mother with Fawn

1990. Siberian Musk Deer. Multicoloured.

2101	60 m. Type **429**	65	30
2102	60 m. Deer in wood	65	30
2013	60 m. Deer on river bank	65	30
2014	60 m. Deer in winter landscape	65	30

433 Russian Victory Medal **434** Crane

1990. 45th Anniv of End of Second World War.

2108	**433**	60 m. multicoloured	65	30

1990. The Japanese White-necked Crane. Multicoloured.

2109	60 m. Type **434**	45	25
2110	60 m. Crane feeding (horiz)	45	25
2111	60 m. Cranes flying (horiz)	45	25
2112	60 m. Crane on river bank	45	25

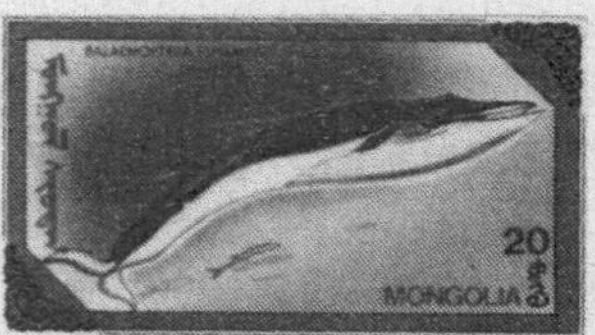

435 Fin Whale

1990. Marine Mammals. Multicoloured.

2113	20 m. Type **435**	15	10
2114	30 m. Humpback whale	25	10
2115	40 m. Narwhal	35	15
2116	50 m. Risso's dolphin	45	20
2117	60 m. Bottle-nosed dolphin	50	25
2118	80 m. Atlantic white-sided dolphin	70	35
2119	1 t. 20 Bowhead whale	90	45

436 Weapons and Black Standard **437** Panda

1990. 750th Anniv of "Secret History of the Mongols" (book). Multicoloured.

2121	10 m. Type **436**	10	10
2122	10 m. Weapons and white standard	10	10
2123	40 m. Brazier (17½ × 22 mm)	30	15

2124 60 m. Genghis Khan ($17\frac{1}{2}\times22$ mm) 55 25
2125 60 m. Horses galloping . . . 55 25
2126 60 m. Tartar camp 55 25
2127 80 m. Men kneeling to ruler . 60 30
2128 80 m. Court 60 30

1990. The Giant Panda. Multicoloured.
2129 10 m. Type **437** 10 10
2130 20 m. Panda eating bamboo . 15 10
2131 30 m. Adult eating bamboo, and cub 25 10
2132 40 m. Panda on tree branch (horiz) 35 15
2133 50 m. Adult and cub resting (horiz) 40 20
2134 60 m. Panda and mountains (horiz) 55 25
2135 80 m. Adult and cub playing (horiz) 60 30
2136 1 t. 20 Panda on snow-covered river bank (horiz) . . . . . 1·25 60

438 Chasmosaurus

1990. Prehistoric Animals. Multicoloured.
2138 20 m. Type **438** 15 10
2139 30 m. Stegosaurus 25 10
2140 40 m. Probactrosaurus . . . 35 15
2141 50 m. Opisthocoelicaudia . . 45 20
2142 60 m. Iguanodon (vert) . . . 50 25
2143 80 m. Tarbosaurus 70 35
2144 1 t. 20 Mamenchisaurus (after Mark Hallett) (60×22 mm) 90 45

439 Lighthouse, Alexandria, Egypt
440 Parrot

1990. Seven Wonders of the World. Mult.
2146 20 m. Type **439** 15 10
2147 30 m. Pyramids of Egypt (horiz) 25 10
2148 40 m. Statue of Zeus, Olympia 35 15
2149 50 m. Colossus of Rhodes . . 45 25
2150 60 m. Mausoleum, Halicarnassus 50 25
2151 80 m. Temple of Artemis, Ephesus (horiz) 70 35
2152 1 t. 20 Hanging Gardens of Babylon 90 45

1990. Parrots.
2154 **440** 20 m. multicoloured . . 15 10
2155 – 30 m. multicoloured . . 25 10
2156 – 40 m. multicoloured . . 35 15
2157 – 50 m. multicoloured . . 45 20
2158 – 60 m. multicoloured . . 55 25
2159 – 80 m. multicoloured . . 75 35
2160 – 1 t. 20 multicoloured . . 90 45
DESIGNS: 30 m. to 1 t. 20, Different parrots.

441 Purple Bear Moth

1990. Moths and Butterflies. Multicoloured.
2162 20 m. Type **441** 15 10
2163 30 m. Great night peacock butterfly 25 10
2164 40 m. Moth 35 15
2165 50 m. Magpie moth 45 20
2166 60 m. Chequered moth . . . 50 25
2167 80 m. Swallowtail 70 35
2168 1 t. 20 Butterfly 90 45

442 Jetsons in Flying Saucer

1991. The Jetsons (cartoon characters). Mult.
2170 20 m. Type **442** 10 10
2171 25 m. Family walking on planet and dragon (horiz) 10 10
2172 30 m. Jane, George, Elroy and dog Astro 10 10
2173 40 m. George, Judy, Elroy and Astro crossing river . . . 15 10
2174 50 m. Flying in saucer (horiz) 35 15
2175 60 m. Jetsons and Cosmo Spacely (horiz) 45 20
2176 70 m. George and Elroy flying with jetpacks . . . . . .
2177 80 m. Elroy (horiz) 55 25
2178 1 t. 20 Judy and Astro watching Elroy doing acrobatics on tree 95 45

443 Dino and Bam-Bam meeting Mongolian Boy with Camel

1991. The Flintstones (cartoon characters). Mult.
2180 25 m. Type **443** 10 10
2181 35 m. Bam-Bam and Dino posing with boy (vert) . . 15 10
2182 45 m. Mongolian mother greeting Betty Rubble, Wilma Flintstone and children . . 20 10
2183 55 m. Barney Rubble and Fred riding dinosaurs 25 10
2184 65 m. Flintstones and Rubbles by river 30 15
2185 75 m. Bam-Bam and Dino racing boy on camel . . . 40 20
2186 85 m. Fred, Barney and Bam-Bam with Mongolian boy 55 25
2187 1 t. 40 Flintstones and Rubbles in car 90 45
2188 2 t. Fred and Barney taking refreshments with Mongolian 1·40 70

444 Party Emblem
445 Bird and Emblem

1991. 70th Anniv of Mongolian People's Revolutionary Party.
2190 **444** 60 m. multicoloured . . 50 25

1991. "Stamp World London 90" International Stamp Exhibition.
2191 **445** 25 m. multicoloured . . 10 10
2192 – 35 m. multicoloured . . 15 10
2193 – 45 m. multicoloured . . 20 10
2194 – 55 m. multicoloured . . 25 10
2195 – 65 m. multicoloured . . 30 10
2196 – 75 m. mult (horiz) . . . 35 10
2197 – 85 m. multicoloured . . 45 15
2198 – 1 t. 40 multicoloured . . 85 40
2199 – 2 t. multicoloured . . . 1·10 55
DESIGNS: 35 m. to 2 t. Different birds.

446 Black Grouse

1991. Birds. Multicoloured.
2201 20 m. Type **446** 15 10
2202 30 m. Common shelduck . . 25 10
2203 40 m. Ring-necked pheasant . 35 15
2204 50 m. Long-tailed duck . . . 50 25
2205 60 m. Hazel grouse 60 30
2206 80 m. Red-breasted merganser 80 40
2207 1 t. 20 Goldeneye . . . . . . 1·10 55

447 Emblem
448 Superb Pink

1991. 70th Anniv of Mongolian People's Army.
2209 **447** 60 m. multicoloured . . . 50 25

1991. Flowers. Multicoloured.
2210 20 m. Type **448** 15 10
2211 30 m. "Gentiana pneumonanthe" (wrongly inscr "puenmonanthe") . . 25 10
2212 40 m. Dandelion 35 15
2213 50 m. Siberian iris 50 25
2214 60 m. Turk's-cap lily 60 30
2215 80 m. "Aster amellus" 80 40
2216 1 t. 20 "Ciszium rivulare" . . 1·10 55

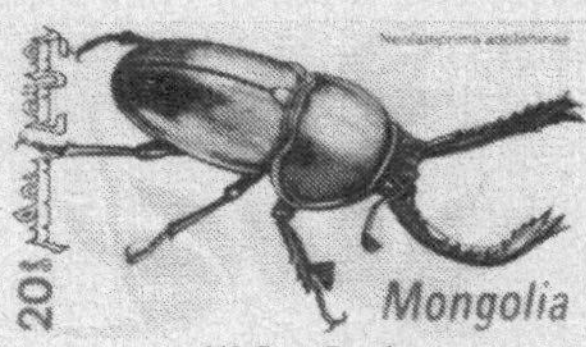

449 Stag Beetle

1991. Beetles. Multicoloured.
2218 20 m. Type **449** 15 10
2219 30 m. "Chelorrhina polyphemus" 25 15
2220 40 m. "Coptolabrus coelestis" 35 15
2221 50 m. "Epepeotes togatus" . 50 25
2222 60 m. Tiger beetle 60 30
2223 80 m. "Macrodontia cervicornis" 80 40
2224 1 t. 20 Hercules beetle . . . . 1·10 55

450 Defend

1991. Buddhas. Multicoloured.
2226 20 m. Type **450** 15 10
2227 30 m. Badmasanhava 25 10
2228 40 m. Avalokitecvara 35 15
2229 50 m. Buddha 50 25
2230 60 m. Mintugwa 60 30
2231 80 m. Shyamatara 70 35
2232 1 t. 20 Samvara . . . . 1·10 55

451 Zebras

1991. African Wildlife. Multicoloured.
2234 20 m. Type **451** 15 10
2235 30 m. Cheetah (wrongly inscr "Cheetan") 25 10
2236 40 m. Black rhinoceros . . . 35 15
2237 50 m. Giraffe (vert) 50 25
2238 60 m. Gorilla 60 30
2239 80 m. Elephants 80 40
2240 1 t. 20 Lion (vert) . . . . . . 1·10 55

452 Communications

1991. Meiso Mizuhara Stamp Exhibition, Ulan-Bator.
2242 **452** 1 t. 20 multicoloured . . 55 25

453 Scotch Bonnet

1991. Fungi. Multicoloured.
2243 20 m. Type **453** 10 10
2244 30 m. Oak mushroom . . . 15 10
2245 40 m. "Hygrophorus marzuelus" 20 10
2246 50 m. Chanterelle 30 15
2247 60 m. Field mushroom . . . 40 20
2248 80 m. Bronze boletus 50 25
2249 1 t. 20 Caesar's mushroom . 85 40
2250 2 t. "Tricholoma terreum" . 1·50 75

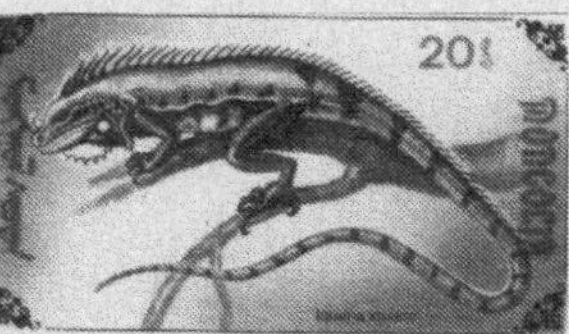
455 Green Iguana

1991. Reptiles. Multicoloured.
2253 20 m. Type **455** 15 10
2254 30 m. Flying gecko 30 15
2255 40 m. Frilled lizard 40 20
2256 50 m. Common cape lizard . 50 25
2257 60 m. Common basilisk . . . 60 30
2258 80 m. Common tegu 80 40
2259 1 t. 20 Marine iguana . . . 1·25 65

456 Warrior

1991. Masked Costumes. Multicoloured.
2261 35 m. Type **456** 15 10
2262 45 m. Mask with fangs . . . 25 10
2263 55 m. Bull mask 40 20
2264 65 m. Dragon mask 50 25
2265 85 m. Mask with beak . . . 60 30
2266 1 t. 40 Old man . . . . . . 1·10 55
2267 2 t. Gold mask with earrings 1·25 60

457 German Shepherd

1991. Dogs. Multicoloured.
2269 20 m. Type **457** 15 10
2270 30 m. Dachshund (vert) . . . 30 15
2271 40 m. Yorkshire terrier (vert) 40 20
2272 50 m. Standard poodle . . . 50 25
2273 60 m. Springer spaniel . . . 60 30
2274 80 m. Norfolk terrier 80 40
2275 1 t. 20 Keeshund . . . . . . 1·25 60

458 Siamese

1991. Cats. Multicoloured.
2277 20 m. Type **458** 15 10
2278 30 m. Black and white longhaired (vert) 30 15
2279 40 m. Ginger red 40 20
2280 50 m. Tabby (vert) 50 25
2281 60 m. Red and white (vert) 60 30
2282 80 m. Maine coon (vert) 80 40
2283 1 t. 20 Blue-eyed white persian (vert) 1·25 60

459 Pagoda

460 Butterfly

1991. "Phila Nippon '91" International Stamp Exhibition, Tokyo. Multicoloured.
2285 1 t. Type **459** 25 10
2286 2 t. Japanese woman 50 25
2287 3 t. Mongolian woman 80 40
2288 4 t. Temple 1·25 60

1991. Butterflies and Flowers. Multicoloured.
2289 20 m. Type **460** 10 10
2290 25 m. Yellow roses 15 10
2291 30 m. Butterfly 20 10
2292 40 m. Butterfly 25 10
2293 50 m. Butterfly 30 15
2294 60 m. Butterfly 35 15
2295 70 m. Red rose 40 20
2296 80 m. Margueritas 50 25
2297 1 t. 20 Lily 75 35

1991. "Expo '90" International Garden and Greenery Exhibition, Osaka. Nos. 2289/97 optd **EXPO '90** and symbol.
2298 20 m. multicoloured 10 10
2299 25 m. multicoloured 15 10
2300 30 m. multicoloured 20 10
2301 40 m. multicoloured 25 10
2302 50 m. multicoloured 30 15
2303 60 m. multicoloured 35 15
2304 70 m. multicoloured 40 20
2305 80 m. multicoloured 50 25
2306 1 t. 20 multicoloured 75 35

462 Poster for 1985 Digital Stereo Re-issue

1991. 50th Anniv (1990) of Original Release of Walt Disney's "Fantasia" (cartoon film). Multicoloured.
2308 1 t. 70 Type **462** 10 10
2309 2 t. 1940 poster for original release 15 10
2310 2 t. 30 Poster for 1982 digital re-issue 20 10
2311 2 t. 60 Poster for 1981 stereo re-issue 25 10
2312 4 t. 20 Poster for 1969 "Psychedelic Sixties" release 45 20
2313 10 t. 1941 poster for original release 1·50 75
2314 15 t. Mlle. Upanova (sketch by Campbell Grant) 1·75 85
2315 16 t. Mickey as the Sorcerer's Apprentice (original sketch) 2·10 1·00

MONG-TSEU (MENGTSZ) Pt. 17

An Indo-Chinese P.O. in Yunnan province, China, closed in 1922.

1903. 100 centimes = 1 franc
1919. 100 cents = 1 piastre

Stamps of Indo-China surcharged.

1903. "Tablet" key-type surch **MONGTZE** and value in Chinese.
1 D 1 c. black and red on buff 3·50 3·50
2 2 c. brown & blue on buff 2·25 2·25
3 4 c. brown & blue on grey 3·50 3·50
4 5 c. green and red 2·75 3·00
5 10 c. red and blue 4·00 4·00
6 15 c. grey and red 5·00 4·50
7 20 c. red and blue on green 5·25 5·25
8 25 c. blue and red 5·75 5·50
9 25 c. black and red on pink £400 £400
10 30 c. brown & bl on drab 4·75 5·00
11 40 c. red & blue on yellow 38·00 38·00
12 50 c. red and blue on pink £190 £190
13 50 c. brown & red on blue 60·00 60·00
14 75 c. brown & red on orge 60·00 60·00
15 1 f. green and red 60·00 60·00
16 5 f. mauve & blue on lilac 60·00 60·00

1906. Surch **Mong-Tseu** and value in Chinese.
17 **8** 1 c. green 90 85
18 2 c. purple on yellow 90 85
19 4 c. mauve on blue 90 85
20 5 c. green 90 85
21 10 c. pink 1·10 1·10
22 15 c. brown on blue 1·10 1·10
23 20 c. red on green 2·00 2·00
24 25 c. blue 2·25 2·25
25 30 c. brown on cream 3·50 3·50
26 35 c. black on yellow 2·50 2·50
27 40 c. black on grey 3·25 3·25
28 50 c. brown 9·50 9·50
29 D 75 c. brown & red on orange 23·00 23·00
30 **8** 1 f. green 11·00 11·00
31 2 f. brown on yellow 27·00 27·00
32 D 5 f. mauve and blue on lilac 60 60
34 **8** 10 f. red on green 80·00 80·00

1908. Surch **MONGTSEU** and value in Chinese.
35 **10** 1 c. black and brown 35 40
36 2 c. black and brown 40 45
37 4 c. black and blue 50 55
38 5 c. black and green 60 60
39 10 c. black and red 85 90
40 15 c. black and violet 95 95
41 **11** 20 c. black and violet 2·50 2·25
42 25 c. black and blue 3·25 3·25
43 30 c. black and brown 2·25 2·00
44 35 c. black and green 2·25 2·00
45 40 c. black and brown 2·25 2·25
46 50 c. black and red 2·25 2·25
47 **12** 75 c. black and orange 5·50 5·50
48 – 1 f. black and red 6·00 6·25
49 – 2 f. black and green 8·00 8·25
50 – 5 f. black and blue 55·00 60·00
51 – 10 f. black and violet 65·00 70·00

1919. Nos. 35/51 further surch in figures and words.
52 **10** $\frac{2}{5}$ c. on 1 c. black & brown 45 45
53 $\frac{4}{5}$ c. on 2 c. black & brown 45 40
54 $1\frac{3}{5}$ c. on 4 c. black & blue 90 90
55 2 c. on 5 c. black and green 55 55
56 4 c. on 10 c. black and red 1·10 1·00
57 6 c. on 15 c. black and violet 1·10 1·00
58 **11** 8 c. on 20 c. black and violet 2·00 2·00
59 10 c. on 25 c. black and blue 1·60 1·60
60 12 c. on 30 c. black & brown 1·60 1·60
61 14 c. on 35 c. black & green 1·60 1·50
62 16 c. on 40 c. black & brown 2·00 2·00
63 20 c. on 50 c. black and red 2·25 2·00
64 **12** 30 c. on 75 c. black & orge 2·00 2·00
65 – 40 c. on 1 f. black and red 4·25 4·25
66 – 80 c. on 2 f. black and green 2·75 2·75
67 – 2 p. on 5 f. black and blue 70·00 75·00
68 – 4 p. on 10 f. black and violet 13·00 13·00

MONTENEGRO Pt. 3

Formerly a monarchy on the Adriatic Sea and part of Yugoslavia. In Italian and German occupation during 1939-45 war.

1874. 100 novcic = 1 florin
1902. 100 heller = 1 krone
1907. 100 para = 1 krone (1910 = 1 perper)

1 Prince Nicholas

Прослава 1493 1893 Штампарије
(2)

1874.
45 **1** 1 n. pale blue 10 15
38 2 n. yellow 2·50 1·90
51 2 n. green 10 15
39 3 n. green 40 50
52 3 n. red 10 15
40 5 n. red 40 40
53 5 n. orange 25 15
19 7 n. mauve 29·00 19·00
41 7 n. pink 40 40
54 7 n. grey 15 20
42 10 n. blue 40 40
55 10 n. purple 10 15
56 15 n. brown 15 15
46 20 n. brown 10 15
7 25 n. purple £225 £200
44 25 n. brown 40 1·50
57 25 n. blue 10 25
47 **1** 30 n. brown 10 15
48 50 n. blue 10 20
49 1 f. green 25 1·40
50 2 f. red 80 2·25

1893. 400th Anniv of Introduction of Printing into Montenegro. Optd with T **2**.
81 **1** 2 n. yellow 20·00 2·50
82 3 n. green 2·50 1·60
83 5 n. red 1·90 90
84 7 n. pink 3·25 1·50
86 10 n. blue 3·25 2·50
87 15 n. bistre 3·50 3·25
89 25 n. brown 3·25 1·50

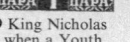

3 Monastery near Cetinje, Royal Mausoleum

1896. Bicentenary of Petrovich Niegush Dynasty.
90 **3** 1 n. brown and blue 10 80
91 2 n. yellow and purple 10 80
92 3 n. green and brown 10 80
93 5 n. brown and green 10 80
94 10 n. blue and yellow 10 80
95 15 n. green and blue 10 80
96 20 n. blue and green 10 80
97 25 n. yellow and blue 10 80
98 30 n. brown and purple 10 80
99 50 n. slate and red 10 70
100 1 f. slate and pink 15 1·25
101 2 f. grey and brown 15 1·25

4

УСТАВ
Constitution
Никољдан
1905
(5)

7

1902.
102 **4** 1 h. blue 15 15
103 2 h. purple 20 15
104 5 h. green 15 10
105 10 h. red 20 10
106a 25 h. blue 15 15
107 50 h. green 35 30
108 1 k. brown 30 30
109 2 k. brown 35 35
110 5 k. orange 50 90

1905. Granting of Constitution. Optd with T **5**.
111 **4** 1 h. blue 15 15
112 2 h. mauve 15 15
113 5 h. green 15 15
114 10 h. red 15 15
124 25 h. blue 15 15
125 50 h. green 15 15
126 1 k. brown 15 15
127 2 k. brown 15 15
119 5 k. orange 50 1·50

1907.
129 **7** 1 p. yellow 10 20
130 2 p. black 10 20
131 5 p. green 65 10
132 10 p. red 1·60 10
133 15 p. blue 10 15
134 20 p. orange 10 20
135 25 p. blue 10 20
136 35 p. brown 15 15
137 50 p. lilac 30 35
138 1 k. red 30 30
139 2 k. green 35 30
140 5 k. red 75 60

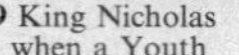
9 King Nicholas when a Youth

10 King Nicholas and Queen Milena

11 Prince Nicholas

12 Nicholas I

1910. Fiftieth Year of King's Reign.
141 **9** 1 p. black 15 10
142 **10** 2 p. purple 15 10
143 – 5 p. green 10 10
144 – 10 p. red 10 10
145 – 15 p. blue 10 10
146 **10** 20 p. olive 25 15
147 – 25 p. blue 15 10
148 – 35 p. brown 50 40
149 – 50 p. violet 20 20
150 – 1 per. lake 30 30
151 – 2 per. green 70 45
152 **11** 5 per. blue 75 75

DESIGNS: As Type **9**: 5 p., 10 p., 25 p., 35 p. Nicholas I in 1910; 15 p. Nicholas I in 1878; 50 p., 1 per., 2 per. Nicholas I in 1890.

1913.
153 **12** 1 p. orange 10 10
154 2 p. purple 10 10
155 5 p. green 10 10
156 10 p. red 10 10
157 15 p. blue 15 15
158 20 p. brown 15 15
159 25 p. blue 15 15
160 35 p. red 40 40
161 50 p. blue 20 20
162 1 per. brown 20 20
163 2 per. lilac 40 40
164 5 per. green 40 40

ITALIAN OCCUPATION

Montenegro
Црна Гора
17-IV-41-XIX
(1)

ЦРНА ГОРА
(2)

1941. Stamps of Yugoslavia optd with T **1**.

(a) Postage. On Nos. 414, etc.
1 **99** 25 p. black 10 45
2 1 d. green 10 45
3 1 d. 50 red 10 45
4 2 d. mauve 10 45
5 3 d. brown 10 45
6 4 d. blue 10 45
7 5 d. blue 1·25 2·25
8 5 d. 50 violet 1·25 2·25
9 6 d. blue 1·25 2·25
10 8 d. brown 1·40 2·25
11 12 d. violet 1·25 2·25
12 16 d. purple 1·25 2·25
13 20 d. blue 50·00 95·00
14 30 d. pink 25·00 45·00

(b) Air. On Nos. 360/7.
15 **80** 50 p. brown 2·50 5·00
16 – 1 d. green 1·75 3·25
17 – 2 d. blue 1·75 3·25
18 – 2 d. 50 red 2·50 5·00
19 **80** 5 d. violet 22·00 38·00
20 – 10 d. red 16·00 32·00
21 – 20 d. green 22·00 45·00
22 – 30 d. blue 16·00 32·00

1941. Stamps of Italy optd with T **2**. (a) On Postage stamps of 1929.
28 **98** 5 c. brown 10 35
29 – 10 c. brown 10 35
30 – 15 c. green 10 35
31 **99** 20 c. red 10 35
32 – 25 c. green 10 35
33 **103** 30 c. brown 10 35
34 50 c. violet 10 35
35 – 75 c. red 10 35
36 – 1 l. 25 blue 10 35

(b) On Air stamp of 1930.
37 **110** 50 c. brown 10 35

1942. Nos. 416, etc., of Yugoslavia optd **Governatorato del Montenegro Valore LIRE**.
43 **99** 1 d. green 25 40
44 1 d. 50 red 11·00 22·00
45 3 d. brown 25 40
46 4 d. blue 30 40
47 5 d. 50 violet 30 40
48 6 d. blue 30 40
49 8 d. brown 30 40
50 12 d. violet 30 40
51 16 d. purple 30 40

1942. Air. Nos. 360/7 of Yugoslavia optd **Governatorato del Montenegro Valore in Lire**.
52 **80** 0.50 l. brown 1·40 3·00
53 – 1 l. green 1·40 3·00
54 – 2 l. blue 1·40 3·00
55 – 2.50 l. red 1·40 3·00
56 **80** 5 l. violet 1·40 3·00
57 – 10 l. brown 1·40 3·00
58 – 20 l. green 55·00 £120
59 – 30 l. blue 12·50 27·00

4 Prince Bishop Peter Njegos and View

1943. National Poem Commemoratives. Each stamp has fragment of poetry inscr at back.
60 **4** 5 c. violet 10 60
61 – 10 c. green 10 60
62 – 15 c. brown 10 60
63 – 20 c. orange 10 60
64 – 25 c. green 15 60
65 – 50 c. mauve 15 60
66 – 1 l. 25 blue 15 85
67 – 2 l. green 30 1·25
68 – 5 l. red on buff 1·75 4·75
69 – 20 l. purple on grey 3·75 11·00

DESIGNS—HORIZ: 10 c. Meadow; 15 c. Country chapel; 20 c. Chiefs Meeting; 25, 50 c. Folk-dancing; 1 l. 25, Taking the Oath; 2 l. Procession; 5 l. Watch over wounded standard-bearer. VERT: 20 l. Portrait of Prince Bishop Peter Njegos.

INDEX

Countries can be quickly located by referring to the index at the end of this volume.

5 Cetinje

1943. Air.
70 **5** 50 c. brown 10 70
71 – 1 l. blue 15 70
72 – 2 l. mauve . . . . 20 1·00
73 – 5 l. green . . . . 45 1·90
74 – 10 l. purple on buff . . . . 3·00 8·00
75 – 20 l. blue on pink . . . . . 5·00 13·00
DESIGNS—HORIZ: 1 l. Coastline; 2 l. Budva; 5 l. Mt. Lovcen; 10 l. Lake of Scutari. VERT: 20 l. Mt. Durmitor.

GERMAN OCCUPATION

1943. Nos. 419/20 of Yugoslavia surch **Deutsche Militaer-Verwaltung Montenegro** and new value in lire.
76 **99** 50 c. on 3 d. brown . . . . 3·00 18·00
77 1 l. on 3 d. brown . . . . 3·00 18·00
78 1 l. 50 on 3 d. brown . . . 3·00 18·00
79 2 l. on 3 d. brown . . . . 6·25 38·00
80 4 l. on 3 d. brown . . . . 6·25 38·00
81 5 l. on 4 d. blue . . . . 6·25 38·00
82 8 l. on 4 d. blue . . . . 7·75 75·00
83 10 l. on 4 d. blue . . . . 14·00 £120
84 20 l. on 4 d. blue . . . . 25·00 £250

1943. Appointment of National Administrative Committee. Optd **Nationaler Verwaltungsausschuss 10.XI.1943**. (a) Postage. On Nos. 64/8.
85 25 c. green . . . . 9·25 £140
86 50 c. mauve . . . . 9·25 £140
87 1 l. 25 blue . . . . 9·25 £140
88 2 l. green . . . . 9·25 £140
89 5 l. red on buff £250 £1900

(b) Air. On Nos. 70/4.
90 **5** 50 c. brown . . . . 17·00 £160
91 1 l. blue . . . . 17·00 £160
92 2 l. mauve . . . . 17·00 £160
93 5 l. green . . . . 17·00 £160
94 10 l. purple on buff £3250 £12000

1944. Refugees Fund. Surch **Fluchtlingshilfe Montenegro** and new value in German currency.
(a) On Nos. 419/20 of Yugoslavia.
95 **99** 0.15 + 0.85 Rm. on 3 d. . . 9·25 £140
96 0.15 + 0.85 Rm. on 4 d. . . 9·25 £140

(b) On Nos. 46/9.
97 – 0.15 + 0.85 Rm. on 25 c. . 9·25 £140
98 – 0.15 + 1.35 Rm. on 50 c. . 9·25 £140
99 – 0.25 + 1.75 Rm. on 1 l. 25 . 9·25 £140
100 – 0.25 + 1.75 Rm. on 2 l. . . 9·25 £140

(c) Air. On Nos. A52/4.
101 **5** 0.15 + 0.85 Rm. on 50 c. . 9·25 £140
102 – 0.25 + 1.25 Rm. on 1 l. . . 9·25 £140
103 – 0.50 + 1.50 Rm. on 2 l. . . 9·25 £140

1944. Red Cross. Surch + **Crveni Krst Montenegro** and new value in German currency. (a) On Nos. 419/20 of Yugoslavia.
104 **99** 0.50 + 2.50 Rm. on 3 d. . 9·25 £110
105 0.50 + 2.50 Rm. on 4 d. . 9·25 £110

(b) On Nos. 64/5.
106 – 0.15 + 0.85 Rm. on 25 c. . 9·25 £110
107 – 0.15 + 1.35 Rm. on 50 c. . 9·25 £110

(c) Air. On Nos. 70/2.
108 **5** 0.25 + 1.75 Rm. on 50 c. . 10·50 £110
109 – 0.25 + 2.75 Rm. on 1 l. . . 10·50 £110
110 – 0.50 + 2 Rm. on 2 l. . . . 10·50 £110

ACKNOWLEDGEMENT OF RECEIPT STAMPS

A 3

A 4

1895.
A90 **A 3** 10 n. blue and red . . . 10 30

1902.
A111 **A 4** 25 h. orange and red . . 40 40

1905. Optd with T **5**.
A130 **A 4** 25 h. orange and red . . 10 15

1907. As T **7**, but letters "A" and "R" in top corners.
A141 **7** 25 p. olive 20 35

1913. As T **12**, but letters "A" and "R" in top corners.
A169 **12** 25 p. olive 20 35

POSTAGE DUE STAMPS

D 3

D 4

D 8

1894.
D90 **D 3** 1 n. red . . . . 1·90 1·25
D91 2 n. green 15 15
D92 3 n. orange 15 15
D93 5 n. green 15 15
D94 **D 3** 10 n. purple 15 15
D95 20 n. blue 15 20
D96 30 n. green 15 20
D97 50 n. pale green 15 20

1902.
D111 **D 4** 5 h. orange 10 10
D112 10 h. olive 15 10
D113 25 h. purple 15 10
D114 50 h. green 15 10
D115 1 k. pale green 20 20

1905. Optd with T **5**.
D120 **D 4** 5 h. orange 25 25
D121 10 h. olive 15 20
D122 25 h. purple 25 25
D123 50 h. green 25 25
D124 1 k. pale green 40 40

1907.
D141 **D 8** 5 p. brown 15 15
D142 10 p. violet 15 15
D143 25 p. red 15 15
D144 50 p. green 15 15

1913. As T **12** but inscr "HОРТОМАРКА" at top.
D165 5 p. grey 50 50
D166 10 p. violet 25 25
D167 25 p. blue 25 25
D168 50 p. red 40 35

ITALIAN OCCUPATION

1941. Postage Due stamps of Yugoslavia optd **Montenegro Upha 17-IV-41-XIX**.
D23 **D 56** 50 p. violet 20 65
D24 1 d. mauve 20 65
D25 2 d. blue 20 65
D26 5 d. orange . . . . . 9·25 18·00
D27 10 d. brown . . . . . 1·60 3·25

1942. Postage Due stamps of Italy optd **UPHATOPA**.
D38 **D 141** 10 c. blue 10 80
D39 20 d. red 10 80
D40 30 c. orange 10 80
D41 50 c. violet 10 80
D42 1 l. orange 20 80

MOROCCO Pt. 13

An independent kingdom, established in 1956, comprising the former French and Spanish International Zones.

A. NORTHERN ZONE.

100 centimes = 1 peseta

1 Sultan of Morocco

2 Polytechnic

1956.
1 **1** 10 c. brown 10 10
2 – 15 c. brown 10 10
3 **2** 25 c. violet 10 10
4 – 50 c. green 25 25
5 **1** 80 c. green 30 30
6 – 2 p. lilac . . . . 2·00 1·60
7 **2** 3 p. blue . . . . 4·00 2·75
8 – 10 p. green . . . . 14·00 11·00
DESIGNS—HORIZ: 15 c., 2 p. Villa Sanjurjo harbour. VERT: 50 c., 10 p. Cultural Delegation building, Tetuan.

3 Lockheed Super Constellation over Lau Dam

1956. Air.
9 **3** 25 c. purple 20 15
10 – 1 p. 40 mauve 35 25
11 **3** 3 p. 40 red . . . . 1·60 1·25
12 – 4 p. 80 purple . . . . . . 2·50 1·75
DESIGN: 1 p. 40, 4 p. 80, Lockheed Super Constellation over Rio Nekor Bridge.

1957. 1st Anniv of Independence. As T **7** but with Spanish inscriptions and currency.
13 80 c. green 35 25
14 1 p. 50 olive . . . . 1·25 80
15 3 p. red . . . . 3·25 2·75

1957. As T **5** but with Spanish inscriptions and currency.
16 30 c. indigo and blue 10 10
17 70 c. purple and brown . . . 20 10
18 80 c. purple 80 15
19 1 p. 50 lake and green . . . 25 15
20 3 p. green 35 15
21 7 p. red . . . . 1·40 40

1957. Investiture of Prince Moulay el Hassan. As T **9** but with Spanish inscriptions and currency.
22 80 c. blue 30 25
23 1 p. 50 green . . . . 1·00 80
24 3 p. red . . . . 2·40 2·25

1957. Nos. 17 and 19 surch.
25 15 c. on 70 c. purple and brown 30 30
26 1 p. 20 on 1 p. 50 lake and green 65 30

1957. 30th Anniv of Coronation of Sultan Sidi Mohammed ben Yusuf. As T **10** but with Spanish inscription and currency.
27 1 p. 20 green and black . . . 35 35
28 1 p. 80 red and black 40 40
29 3 p. violet and black 80 75

B. SOUTHERN ZONE

100 centimes = 1 franc

5 Sultan of Morocco

6 Classroom

7 Sultan of Morocco

1956.
30 **5** 5 f. indigo and blue 20 10
31 10 f. sepia and brown . . . 15 10
32 15 f. lake and green 25 10
33 25 f. purple 70 10
34 30 f. green . . . . 1·40 10
35 50 f. red . . . . 2·10 15
36 70 f. brown and sepia . . . 3·50 60

1956. Education Campaign.
37 – 10 f. violet and purple . . . 1·50 85
38 – 15 f. lake and red . . . . . 1·75 1·25
39 **6** 20 f. green and turquoise . . 1·90 2·00
40 – 30 f. red and lake . . . . . 3·50 3·25
41 – 50 f. blue and indigo . . . 6·00 4·00
DESIGNS: 10 f. Peasants reading book; 15 f. Two girls reading; 30 f. Child reading to old man; 50 f. Child teaching parents the alphabet.

1957. 1st Anniv of Independence.
42 **7** 15 f. green . . . . 1·25 90
43 25 f. olive . . . . 1·75 90
44 30 f. red . . . . 3·25 1·40

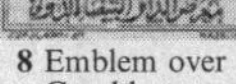
8 Emblem over Casablanca

9 Crown Prince Moulay el Hassan

1957. Air. International Fair, Casablanca.
45 **8** 15 f. green and red 90 60
46 25 f. turquoise . . . . . . 1·75 1·10
47 30 f. brown . . . . 2·25 1·25

1957. Investiture of Crown Prince Moulay el Hassan.
48 **9** 15 f. blue . . . . 1·25 65
49 25 f. green . . . . 1·25 1·00
50 30 f. red . . . . 2·25 1·25

10 King Mohammed V

11 Moroccan Pavilion

1957. 30th Anniv of Coronation of King Mohammed V.
51 **10** 15 f. green and black . . . 60 50
52 25 f. red and black . . . . 1·10 60
53 30 f. violet and black . . . 1·10 90

C. ISSUES FOR THE WHOLE OF MOROCCO.

1958. 100 centimes = 1 franc
1962. 100 francs = 1 dirham

1958. Brussels International Exhibition.
54 **11** 15 f. turquoise 25 20
55 25 f. red 25 25
56 30 f. blue 35 30

12 King Mohammed V and U.N.E.S.C.O. Headquarters, Paris

57 **12** 15 f. green 25 20
58 25 f. lake 25 25
59 30 f. blue 35 30

13 Ben-Smine Sanatorium

14 King Mohammed V on Horseback

1959. "National Aid".
60 **13** 50 f. bistre, green and red . 70 35

1959. King Mohammed V's 50th Birthday.
61 **14** 15 f. lake 40 30
62 25 f. blue 70 35
63 45 f. green 80 45

15 Princess Lalla Amina

16

1959. Children's Week.
64 **15** 15 f. blue 25 20
65 25 f. green 30 25
66 45 f. purple 35 30

1960. Meeting of U.N. African Economic Commission, Tangier.
67 **16** 45 f. green, brown & violet 65 50

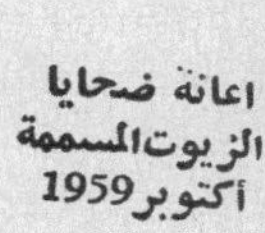
+10 f
اعانة ضحايا
الزيوت المسممة
أكتوبر 1959
(17)

18 Arab Refugees

1960. Adulterated Cooking Oil Victims Relief Fund. Surch as T **17**.
68 **5** 5 f. + 10 f. indigo and blue . 35 30
69 10 f. + 10 f. sepia and brown 45 45
70 15 f. + 10 f. lake and green . 95 60
71 25 f. + 15 f. purple . . . . 1·10 70
72 30 f. + 20 f. green . . . . 1·75 1·60

1960. World Refugee Year.
73 **18** 15 f. black, green and ochre 25 20
74 – 45 f. green and black . . . 35 35
DESIGNS: 45 f. "Uprooted tree" and Arab refugees.

19 Marrakesh

20 Lantern

1960. 900th Anniv of Marrakesh.
75 **19** 100 f. green, brown and blue 80 65

1960. 1100th Anniv of Karaouiyne University.
76 **20** 15 f. purple 25 25
77 – 25 f. blue (Fountain) . . . 35 25
78 – 30 f. brown (Minaret) . . . 90 60
79 – 35 f. black (Frescoes) . . . 1·10 80
80 – 45 f. green (Courtyard) . . 1·60 1·10

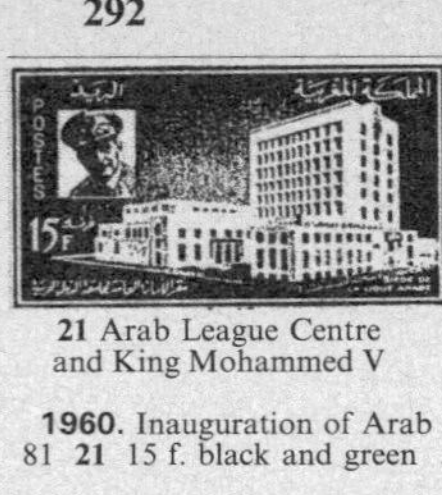

اسبوع التضامن +5f 1380 1960

21 Arab League Centre and King Mohammed V (22)

1960. Inauguration of Arab League Centre, Cairo.
81 21 15 f. black and green 20 20

1960. Solidarity Fund. Nos. 458/9 (Mahakma, Casablanca) of French Morocco surch as T 22.
82 106 15 f. + 3 f. on 18 f. myrtle 55 55
83 + 5 f. on 20 f. lake 80 80

23 Wrestling 24 Runner

1960. Olympic Games.
84 23 5 f. purple, green and violet 10 10
85 – 10 f. chocolate, blue & brn . 15 10
86 – 15 f. brown, blue and green . 20 15
87 – 20 f. purple, blue and bistre 25 20
88 – 30 f. brown, violet and red . 30 25
89 – 40 f. brown, blue and violet 60 25
90 – 45 f. blue, green and purple . 75 35
91 – 70 f. black, blue and brown . 1·10 45
DESIGNS: 10 f. Gymnastics; 15 f. Cycling; 20 f. Weightlifting; 30 f. Running; 40 f. Boxing; 45 f. Sailing; 70 f. Fencing.

1961. 3rd Pan-Arab Games, Casablanca.
92 24 20 f. green 20 15
93 30 f. lake 25 20
94 50 f. blue 40 35

25 Post Office and Letters 26 King Mohammed V and African Map 27 Lumumba and Congo Map

1961. African Postal and Telecommunications Conference, Tangier.
95 25 20 f. purple and mauve . . . 35 30
96 – 30 f. turquoise and green . . 45 35
97 – 90 f. ultramarine and blue . . 85 60
DESIGNS—VERT: 30 f. Telephone operator. HORIZ: 90 f. Sud Aviation Caravelle mail plane over Tangier.

1962. 1st Anniv of African Charter of Casablanca.
98 26 20 f. purple and buff 20 20
99 30 f. indigo and blue 25 25

1962. Patrice Lumumba Commemorative.
100 27 20 f. black and bistre . . . 20 20
101 30 f. black and brown . . . 30 25

28 King Hassan II 29 "Pupils of the Nation"

1962. Air.
102 28 90 f. black 40 15
103 1 d. red 90 15
104 2 d. blue . . . . 1·10 45
105 3 d. green . . . . 1·75 75
106 5 d. violet . . . . 3·50 1·25

1962. Children's Education.
107 29 20 f. blue, red and green . . 35 25
108 30 f. sepia, brown and green 40 35
109 90 f. blue, purple and green 60 50

1962. Arab League Week. As T 76 of Libya.
110 20 f. brown 20 15

30 King Hassan II 31 Scout with Banner

1962.
111 30 1 f. olive 10 10
112 2 f. violet 10 10
113 5 f. sepia 10 10
114 10 f. brown 10 10
115 15 f. turquoise 15 10
116 20 f. purple (18 × 22 mm) 20 10
116a 20 f. purple (17½ × 23½ mm) 30 10
116b 25 f. red 20 10
117 30 f. green 25 10
117a 35 f. slate 25 10
117b 40 f. blue 30 10
118 50 f. purple 40 10
118a 60 f. purple 70 10
119 70 f. blue 95 10
120 80 f. lake . . . . 1·50 15

1962. 5th Arab Scout Jamboree, Rabat.
121 31 20 f. purple and blue . . . 20 15

32 Campaign Emblem and Swamp 33 Aquarium and Fish

1962. Malaria Eradication Campaign.
122 32 20 f. blue and green . . . 20 15
123 – 50 f. lake and green . . . 35 25
DESIGN—VERT: 50 f. Sword piercing mosquito.

1962. Casablanca Aquarium. Multicoloured.
124 20 f. Type 33 . . . . 35 25
125 30 f. Aquarium and eel . . . 35 25

فيضانات 1963 20+5

34 Mounted Postman and 1912 Sherifian Stamp (35)

1962. First National Philatelic Exhibition, Rabat, and Stamp Day.
126 34 20 f. green and brown . . 40 35
127 – 30 f. black and red 50 40
128 – 50 f. bistre and blue . . . 95 50
DESIGNS: 30 f. Postman and circular postmark; 50 f. Sultan Hassan I and octagonal postmark. (Both stamps commemorate 70th anniv of Sherifian post.)

1963. Flood Relief Fund. Surch as T 35.
129 5 20 + 5 f. on 5 f. indigo and blue 40 35
130 30 + 10 f. on 50 f. red . . 50 50

36 King Moulay Ismail 37 Ibn Batota (voyager)

1963. 300th Anniv of Meknes.
131 36 20 f. sepia 25 20

1963. "Famous Men of Maghreb".
132 37 20 f. purple 20 20
133 – 20 f. black 20 20
134 – 20 f. myrtle 25 25
134a 37 40 f. blue 30 10
PORTRAITS: No. 133, Ibn Khaldoun (historian). No. 134, Al Idrissi (geographer).

38 Sugar Beet and Refinery 39 Isis (bas relief)

1963. Freedom from Hunger.
135 38 20 f. black, brown & green . 25 20
136 – 50 f. black, brown & blue . 65 35
DESIGN—VERT: 50 f. Fisherman and tunny.

1963. Nubian Monuments Preservation.
137 – 20 f. black and grey 20 15
138 39 30 f. violet 25 25
139 – 50 f. purple 60 35
DESIGNS—HORIZ: 20 f. Heads of Colossi, Abu Simbel; 50 f. Philae Temple.

40 Agadir before Earthquake

1963. Reconstruction of Agadir.
140 40 20 f. red and blue 35 35
141 30 f. red and blue 45 35
142 – 50 f. red and blue 80 40
DESIGNS: 30 f. is optd with large red cross and date of earthquake, 29th February, 1960; 50 f. Reconstructed Agadir.

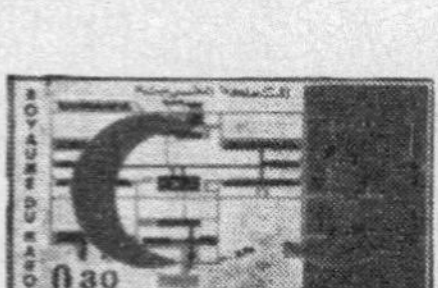
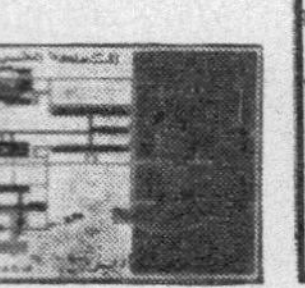

41 Plan of new Agadir Hospital 42 Emblems of Morocco and Rabat

1963. Centenary of International Red Cross.
143 41 30 f. multicoloured 20 20

1963. Opening of Parliament.
144 42 20 f. multicoloured 20 20

43 Hands breaking Chain 44 National Flag

1963. 15th Anniv of Declaration of Human Rights.
145 43 20 f. brown, sepia & green . 20 20

1963. Evacuation of Foreign Troops from Morocco.
146 44 20 f. red, green and black . 25 25

45 "Moulay Abdurrahman" (after Delacroix)

1964. 3rd Anniv of King Hassan's Coronation.
147 45 1 d. multicoloured . . . . 2·25 1·60

46 Map, Chart and W.M.O. Emblem

1964. World Meteorological Day. Multicoloured.
148 20 f. African weather map (postage) (vert) 25 20
149 30 f. Type 46 . . . . 40 35
150 90 f. Globe and weather vane (air) (vert) 60 45

47 Fair Entrance

1964. Air. 20th Anniv of Casablanca Int Fair.
151 47 1 d. red, drab and blue . . 70 60

48 Moroccan Pavilion at Fair

1964. Air. New York World's Fair.
152 48 1 d. multicoloured . . . . 1·00 65

49 Children Playing in the Sun 50 Olympic Torch

1964. Postal Employees' Holiday Settlements.
153 49 20 f. multicoloured 25 20
154 – 30 f. multicoloured 35 25
DESIGN: 30 f. Boy, girl and holiday settlement.

1964. Olympic Games, Tokyo.
155 50 20 f. green, violet and red . 25 25
156 30 f. purple, blue and grn . 35 30
157 50 f. red, blue and green . 40 35

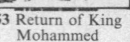

51 Lighthouse and Sultan Mohamed ben Abdurrahman (founder) 52 Tangier Iris

1964. Centenary of Cape Spartel Lighthouse.
158 51 25 f. multicoloured 20 15

1965. Flowers. Multicoloured.
159 25 f. Type 52 . . . . 70 45
160 40 f. Gladiolus (vert) 85 55
161 60 f. Caper (horiz) . . . . . 1·50 1·00

53 Return of King Mohammed 54 Early Telegraph Receiver

1965. 10th Anniv of Return of King Mohammed V from Exile.
162 53 25 f. green 25 20

1965. Centenary of I.T.U. Multicoloured.
163 25 f. Type 54 . . . . 20 20
164 40 f. "TIROS" weather satellite 35 30

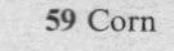

55 I.C.Y. Emblem 59 Corn

1965. International Co-operation Year.
165 **55** 25 f. black and green . . . 25 20
166 60 f. lake 40 35

1965. Seashells. As T **52**. Designs multicoloured; background colours given.
167 25 f. violet 55 25
168 25 f. blue 55 25
169 25 f. yellow 55 25
SEASHELLS: No. 167, "Charonia modifera"; No. 168, "Pitaria chione"; No. 169, "Cymbium neptuni".

1965. Shellfish. As T **52**. Multicoloured.
170 25 f. Helmet Crab 30 20
171 40 f. Mantis shrimp . . . . . 1·25 70
172 1 d. Royal prawn (horiz) . . . 1·75 1·00

1965. Orchids. As T **52**. Multicoloured.
173 25 f. "Ophrys speculum" (vert) 20 20
174 40 f. "Ophrys fusca" (vert) . . 35 25
175 60 f. "Ophrys tenthredinifera" (horiz) . . . . 1·25 90

1966. Agricultural Products (1st issue).
176 **59** 25 f. black and ochre . . . 20 15
See also Nos. 188/9 and 211.

60 Flag, Map and Dove

1966. 10th Anniv of Independence.
177 **60** 25 f. red and green 20 15

61 King Hassan II and Crown

1966. 5th Anniv of King Hassan's Coronation.
178 **61** 25 f. blue, green and red . 20 15

62 Cross-country Runner

1966. 53rd "Cross des Nations" (Cross-country Race).
179 **62** 25 f. green 20 15

63 W.H.O. Building

1966. Inaug. of W.H.O. Headquarters, Geneva.
180 **63** 25 f. black and purple . . . 20 15
181 – 40 f. black and blue 25 20
DESIGN: 40 f. W.H.O. Building (different view).

64 King Hassan and Parachutist

65 Brooch

1966. 10th Anniv of Royal Armed Forces.
182 **64** 25 f. black and gold . . . 35 25
183 – 40 f. black and gold . . . 35 25
DESIGN: 40 f. Crown Prince Hassan kissing hand of King Mohammed.

1966. Palestine Week. As No. 110 but inscr. "SEMAINE DE LA PALESTINE" at foot and dated "1966".
184 25 f. blue 20 15

1966. Red Cross Seminar. Moroccan Jewellery. Multicoloured.
185 25 f. + 5 f. Type **65** 60 45
186 40 f. + 10 f. Pendant 90 55
See also Nos. 203/4, 246/7, 274/5, 287/8, 303/4, 324/5, 370/1, 397/8, 414/15, 450/1 and 493.

66 Rameses II, Abu Simbel

67 Diesel Train

1966. Air. 20th Anniv of U.N.E.S.C.O.
187 **66** 1 d. red and yellow . . . 70 50

1966. Agricultural Products (2nd and 3rd issue.) Designs as T **59**.
188 40 f. multicoloured 25 10
189 60 f. multicoloured 35 20
DESIGNS—VERT: 40 f. Citrus fruits. HORIZ: 60 f. Olives.

1966. Moroccan Transport. Multicoloured.
190 25 f. Type **67** (postage) . . . 75 35
191 40 f. Liner "Maroc" 55 15
192 1 d. Tourist coach 50 20
193 3 d. Sud Aviation Caravelle of Royal Air Maroc ($48\times27\frac{1}{2}$ mm) (air) . . . . 3·25 1·50

68 Shad

1967. Fishes. Multicoloured.
194 25 f. Type **68** 25 20
195 40 f. Pale bonito 35 25
196 1 d. Bluefish . . . . 1·40 90

69 Hilton Hotel, Ancient Ruin and Map

1967. Opening of Hilton Hotel, Rabat.
197 **69** 25 f. black and blue . . . 20 15
198 1 d. purple and blue . . . 50 20

70 Ait Aadel Dam

1967. Inauguration of Ait Aadel Dam.
199 25 f. grey, blue and green . . 25 15
200 40 f. bistre and blue 30 20

71 Moroccan Scene and Lions Emblem

1967. 50th Anniv of Lions Int.
201 **71** 40 f. blue and gold 25 20
202 1 d. green and gold . . . 50 25

1967. Moroccan Red Cross. As T **65**. Mult.
203 60 f. + 5 f. Necklace 65 65
204 1 d. + 10 f. Two bracelets . 1·40 1·40

72 Three Hands and Pickaxe

73 I.T.Y. Emblem

1967. Communal Development Campaign.
205 **72** 25 f. green 20 15

1967. International Tourist Year.
206 **73** 1 d. blue and cobalt . . . 50 35

74 Arrow and Map

75 Horse-jumping

1967. Mediterranean Games, Tunis.
207 **74** 25 f. multicoloured 25 20
208 40 f. multicoloured 30 20

1967. International Horse Show.
209 **75** 40 f. multicoloured 30 20
210 1 d. multicoloured 50 35

1967. Agricultural Products (4th issue). As T **59**.
211 40 f. mult (Cotton plant) . . . 25 15

76 Human Rights Emblem

77 Msouffa Woman

1968. Human Rights Year.
212 **76** 25 f. slate 20 20
213 1 d. lake 35 25

1968. Moroccan Costumes. Multicoloured.
214 10 f. Ait Moussa or Ali . . . 40 25
215 15 f. Ait Mouhad 60 30
216 25 f. Barquemaster of Rabat-Sale 60 35
217 25 f. Townsman 70 35
218 40 f. Townswoman 70 45
219 60 f. Royal Mokhazni 90 60
220 1 d. Type **77** . . . . 1·10 70
221 1 d. Riff . . . . 1·10 70
222 1 d. Zemmour woman . . . . 1·25 85
223 1 d. Meknassa . . . . 1·25 60

78 King Hassan

79 Red Crescent Nurse and Child

1968.
224 **78** 1 f. multicoloured 10 10
225 2 f. multicoloured 10 10
226 5 f. multicoloured 10 10
227 10 f. multicoloured 10 10
228 15 f. multicoloured 10 10
229 20 f. multicoloured 10 10
230 25 f. multicoloured 15 10
231 30 f. multicoloured 15 10
232 35 f. multicoloured 20 10
233 40 f. multicoloured 20 10
234 50 f. multicoloured 50 10
235 60 f. multicoloured 50 10
236 70 f. multicoloured . . . . 3·00 65
237 75 f. multicoloured 70 15
238 80 f. multicoloured 70 20
239 – 90 f. multicoloured . . . . 1·00 20
240 – 1 d. multicoloured . . . . 1·25 20
241 – 2 d. multicoloured . . . . 1·90 35
242 – 3 d. multicoloured . . . . 4·00 80
243 – 5 d. multicoloured . . . . 7·00 2·00
Nos. 239/43 bear a similar portrait of King Hassan, but are larger, $26\frac{1}{2}\times40\frac{1}{2}$ mm.

1968. 20th Anniv of W.H.O.
244 **79** 25 f. brown, red & blue . . 20 10
245 40 f. brown, red & slate . . 25 15

1968. Red Crescent. Moroccan Jewellery. As T **65**. Multicoloured.
246 25 f. Pendant brooch 40 15
247 40 f. Bracelet 85 25

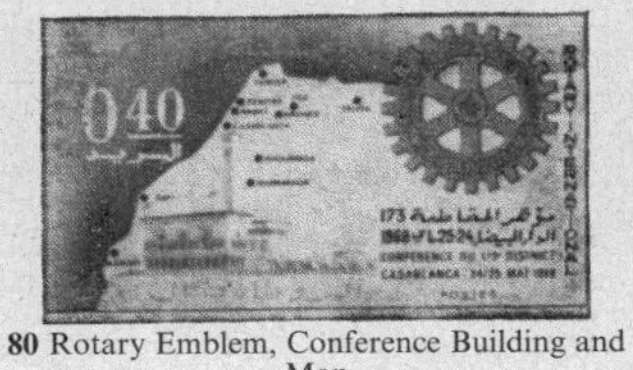

80 Rotary Emblem, Conference Building and Map

1968. Rotary Int District Conf, Casablanca.
248 **80** 40 f. gold, blue and green . . 35 20
249 1 d. gold, ultramarine & blue 75 30

81 Belt Pattern

82 Princess Lalla Meryem

1968. "The Belts of Fez". Designs showing ornamental patterns.
250 **81** 25 f. multicoloured . . . . 1·50 70
251 – 40 f. multicoloured . . . . 1·75 85
252 – 60 f. multicoloured . . . . 2·75 1·25
253 – 1 d. multicoloured . . . . 4·75 2·75

1968. World Children's Day. Multicoloured.
254 25 f. Type **82** 25 20
255 40 f. Princess Lalla Asmaa . . 35 25
256 1 d. Crown Prince Sidi Mohammed 45 55

83 Wrestling

1968. Olympic Games, Mexico. Multicoloured.
257 15 f. Type **83** 15 15
258 20 f. Basketball 15 15
259 25 f. Cycling 15 15
260 40 f. Boxing 25 15
261 60 f. Running 35 15
262 1 d. Football 90 45

84 Silver Crown

85 Costumes of Zagora, South Morocco

1968. Ancient Moroccan Coins.
263 **84** 20 f. silver & purple . . . 20 20
264 – 25 f. gold and purple . . . 25 25
265 – 40 f. silver and green . . . 90 30
266 – 60 f. gold and red . . . . 1·25 65
COINS: 25 f. Gold dinar; 40 f. Silver dirham; 60 f. Gold piece.
See also Nos. 270/1.

1969. Traditional Women's Costumes. Mult.
267 15 f. Type **85** (postage) . . . 85 50
268 25 f. Ait Adidou costumes . . 1·10 75
269 1 d. Ait Ouaouzguit costumes (air) . . . . 1·75 85

1969. 8th Anniv of Coronation of Hassan II. As T **84** (silver coins).
270 1 d. silver and blue . . . . . 3·25 95
271 5 d. silver and violet . . . . 7·50 4·25
COINS: 1 d. One dirham coin of King Mohammed V; 5 d. One dirham coin of King Hassan II.

86 Hands "reading" Braille on Map

1969. Protection of the Blind Week.
272 **86** 25 f. + 10 f. multicoloured 20 15

87 "Actor"

89 King Hassan II

1969. World Theatre Day.
273 **87** 1 d. multicoloured 45 25

1969. 50th Anniv of League of Red Cross Societies. Moroccan Jewellery as T **65**. Multicoloured.
274 25 f. + 5 f. Bracelets 60 45
275 40 f. + 10 f. Pendant 90 55

1969. King Hassan's 40th Birthday.
276 **89** 1 d. multicoloured 90 35

مؤتمر القمة الاسلامى
الرباط ١٥ رجب ١٣٨٩
(**90**)

91 Mahatma Gandhi

1969. Islamic Summit Conf, Rabat (1st issue). No. 240 optd with T **90**.
278 1 d. multicoloured . . . . . . 4·00 3·25

1969. Birth Centenary of Mahatma Gandhi.
279 **91** 40 f. brown and lavender . 20 15

92 I.L.O. Emblem

1969. 50th Anniv of I.L.O.
280 **92** 50 f. multicoloured 25 20

93 King Hassan on Horseback

1969. Islamic Summit Conference, Rabat (2nd issue).
281 **93** 1 d. multicoloured 85 35

94 "Spahi Horseman" (Haram al Glaoui)

1970. Moroccan Art.
282 **94** 1 d. multicoloured 65 30

1970. Flood Victims Relief Fund. Nos. 227/8 surch.
283 **78** 10 f. + 25 f. multicoloured 2·75 2·75
284 15 f. + 25 f. multicoloured 2·75 2·75

96 Drainage System, Fez

97 "Dance of the Guedra" (P. Beaubrun)

1970. 50th Congress of Public and Municipal Health Officials, Rabat.
285 **96** 60 f. multicoloured 35 20

1970. Folklore Festival, Marrakesh.
286 **97** 40 f. multicoloured 25 20

1970. Red Crescent. Moroccan Jewellery as T **65**. Multicoloured.
287 25 f. + 5 f. Necklace 70 65
288 50 f. + 10 t. Pendant . . . . 1·25 1·00

1970. Population Census. No. 189 surch **1970 0,25** and Arabic inscr.
290 25 f. on 60 f. multicoloured . 20 10

99 Dish Aerial, Souk el Arba des Sehoul Communications Station

100 Ruddy Shelduck

1970. 17th Anniv of Revolution.
291 **99** 1 d. multicoloured 45 35

1970. Nature Protection, Wild Birds. Multicoloured.
292 25 f. Type **100** . . . . . . 1·00 35
293 40 f. Houbara bustard . . . 1·60 35

101 I.E.Y. Emblem and Moroccan with Book

1970. International Education Year.
294 **101** 60 f. multicoloured . . . 35 20

102 Symbols of U.N

1970. 25th Anniv of U.N.O.
295 **102** 50 f. multicoloured . . . 20 15

103 League Emblem, Map and Laurel

1970. 25th Anniv of Arab League.
296 **103** 50 f. multicoloured . . . 25 15

104 Olive Grove and Extraction Plant

1970. World Olive-oil Production Year.
297 **104** 50 f. black, brown & green 55 15

105 Es Sounna Mosque

1971. Restoration of Es Sounna Mosque, Rabat.
298 **105** 60 f. multicoloured . . . 25 15

106 "Heart" within Horse

107 King Hassan II and Dam

1971. European and North African Heart Week.
299 **106** 50 f. multicoloured . . . 25 20

1971. 10th Anniv of King Hassan's Accession.
300 **107** 25 f. multicoloured . . . 15 10

108 Palestine on Globe

1971. Palestine Week.
302 **108** 25 f. + 10 f. multicoloured 25 20

1971. Red Crescent, Moroccan Jewellery. As T **65**. Multicoloured.
303 25 f. + 5 f. "Arrow-head" brooch 50 50
304 40 f. + 10 f. Square pendant . 75 65

109 Hands holding Peace Dove

1971. Racial Equality Year.
305 **109** 50 f. multicoloured 20 15

110 Musical Instrument

1971. Protection of the Blind Week.
306 **110** 40 f. + 10 f. multicoloured 20 20

111 Children at Play

112 Shah Mohammed Reza Pahlavi of Iran

1971. International Children's Day.
307 **111** 40 f. multicoloured 20 15

1971. 2,500th Anniv of Persian Empire.
308 **112** 1 d. multicoloured 40 30

113 Aerial View of Mausoleum

1971. Mausoleum of Mohammed V. Multicoloured.
309 25 f. Type **113** 15 15
310 50 f. Tomb of Mohammed V 20 20
311 1 d. Interior of Mausoleum (vert) 40 20

114 Football and Emblem

116 Sun and Landscape

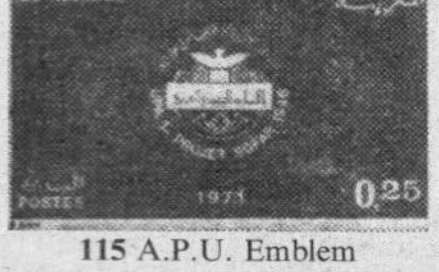

115 A.P.U. Emblem

1971. Mediterranean Games, Izmir, Turkey. Multicoloured.
312 40 f. Type **114** 20 15
313 60 f. Athlete and emblem . . 25 20

1971. 25th Anniv of Founding of Arab Postal Union at Sofar Conference.
314 **115** 25 f. red, blue & light blue 15 10

1971. 50th Anniv of Sherifian Phosphates Office.
315 **116** 70 f. multicoloured . . . 30 20

117 Torch and Book Year Emblem

118 Lottery Symbol

1972. International Book Year.
316 **117** 1 d. multicoloured 40 25

1972. Creation of National Lottery.
317 **118** 25 f. gold, black & brown 15 10

119 Bridge of Sighs

120 Mizmar (double-horned flute)

1972. U.N.E.S.C.O. "Save Venice" Campaign. Multicoloured.
318 25 f. Type **119** 15 15
319 50 f. St. Mark's Basilica (horiz) 20 15
320 1 d. Lion of St. Marks (horiz) 40 20

1972. Protection of the Blind Week.
321 **120** 25 f. + 10 f. multicoloured 20 20

121 Bridge and Motorway

1972. 2nd African Highways Conference, Rabat.
322 **121** 75 f. multicoloured . . . 25 20

122 Moroccan Stamp of 1969, and Postmark

1972. Stamp Day.,
323 **122** 1 d. multicoloured 40 20

1972. Red Crescent. Moroccan Jewellery. As T **65**. Multicoloured.
324 25 f. + 5 f. Jewelled bangles 50 50
325 70 f. + 10 f. Filigree pendant 75 75

123 "Betrothal of Imilchil" (Tayeb Lahlou)

124 Dove on African Map

1972. Folklore Festival, Marrakesh.
326 **123** 60 f. multicoloured . . . 60 35

1972. 9th Organisation of African Unity Summit Conference, Rabat.
327 **124** 25 f. multicoloured . . . 15 15

125 Polluted Beach

1972. U.N. Environmental Conservation Conference, Stockholm.
328 **125** 50 f. multicoloured . . . 25 20

126 Running

127 "Sonchus pinnatifidus"

1972. Olympic Games, Munich.
329 **126** 25 f. red, pink & black . . 15 15
330 – 50 f. violet, lilac & black . 20 15
331 – 75 f. green, yell and blk . 30 20
332 – 1 d. blue, light bl & blk . 35 25
DESIGNS: 50 f. Wrestling; 75 f. Football; 1 d. Cycling.

1972. Moroccan Flowers. (1st series). Multicoloured.
333 25 f. Type **127** 20 15
334 40 f. "Amberboa crupinoides" 25 15
See also Nos. 375/6.

128 Sand Gazelle

129 Rabat Carpet

1972. Nature Protection. Fauna. Multicoloured.
335 25 f. Type **128** 50 25
336 40 f. Barbary sheep 60 25

1972. Moroccan Carpets (1st series). Multicoloured.
337 50 f. Type **129** 75 35
338 75 f. Rabat carpet with "star-shaped" centre . . . . . . 1·00 50
See also Nos. 380/1, 406/7, 433/4, 485/7 and 513.

130 Mother and Child with U.N. Emblem

132 Global Weather Map

131 "Postman" and "Stamp"

1972. International Children's Day.
339 **130** 75 f. blue, yellow & green 35 30

1973. Stamp Day.
340 **131** 25 f. multicoloured . . . 15 10

1973. Centenary of W.M.O.
341 **132** 70 f. multicoloured . . . 35 20

133 King Hassan and Arms

1973.
342 **133** 1 f. multicoloured . . . 10 10
343 2 f. multicoloured . . . 10 10
344 5 f. multicoloured . . . 10 10
345 10 f. multicoloured . . . 10 10
346 15 f. multicoloured . . . 10 10
347 20 f. multicoloured . . . 10 10
348 25 f. multicoloured . . . 10 10
349 30 f. multicoloured . . . 15 10
350 35 f. multicoloured . . . 15 10
351 40 f. multicoloured . . . 3·75 45
352 50 f. multicoloured . . . 20 10
353 60 f. multicoloured . . . 25 15
354 70 f. multicoloured . . . 25 15
355 75 f. multicoloured . . . 30 15
356 80 f. multicoloured . . . 30 20
357 90 f. multicoloured . . . 35 15
358 1 d. multicoloured . . . 1·50 20
359 2 d. multicoloured . . . 3·25 55
360 3 d. multicoloured . . . 4·25 75
361 5 d. mult (brown background) . . . . . 3·25 75
361a 5 d. mult (pink background) 3·50 90

مناظرة
السياحة
1973
(134)

1973. Nat. Tourist Conf. Nos. 324/5 surch with T **134**.
362 **65** 25 f. on 5 f. multicoloured 2·00 2·00
363 70 f. on 10 f. multicoloured 2·00 2·00
On No. 363 the Arabic text is arranged in one line.

135 Tambours

1973. Protection of the Blind Week.
364 **135** 70 f. + 10 f. multicoloured 40 30

136 Kaaba, Mecca, and Mosque, Rabat

1973. Prophet Mohammed's Birthday.
365 **136** 25 f. multicoloured . . . 15 10

137 Roses and M'Gouna

1973. M'Gouna Rose Festival.
366 **137** 25 f. multicoloured . . . 15 10

138 Handclasp and Torch

139 Folk-dancers

1973. 10th Anniv of Organization of African Unity.
367 **138** 70 f. multicoloured . . . 30 15

1973. Folklore Festival, Marrakesh. Multicoloured.
368 50 f. Type **139** 20 15
369 1 d. Folk-musicians 40 25

1973. Red Crescent. Moroccan Jewellery. As T **65**. Multicoloured.
370 25 f. + 5 f. Locket 70 50
371 70 f. + 10 f. Bracelet inlaid with pearls 80 60

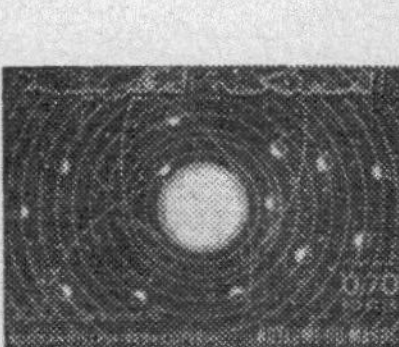
140 Solar System

141 Microscope

1973. 500th Birth Anniv of Nicholas Copernicus.
372 **140** 70 f. multicoloured 35 20

1973. 25th Anniv of W.H.O.
373 **141** 70 f. multicoloured 25 20

142 Interpol Emblem and Fingerprint

1973. 50th Anniv of International Criminal Police Organization (Interpol).
374 **142** 70 f. multicoloured 30 25

1973. Moroccan Flowers (2nd series). As T **127**. Multicoloured.
375 25 f. "Chrysanthemum carinatum" (horiz) 15 10
376 1 d. "Amberboa muricata" . . 75 25

143 Striped Hyena

1973. Nature Protection. Multicoloured.
377 25 f. Type **143** 40 15
378 50 f. Eleonora's Falcon (vert) . 1·75 35

144 Map and Arrows

1973. Meeting of Maghreb Committee for Co-ordination of Posts and Telecommunications, Tunis.
379 **144** 25 f. multicoloured 15 10

1973. Moroccan Carpets (2nd series). As T **129**. Multicoloured.
380 25 f. Carpet from the High Atlas 60 25
381 70 f. Tazenakht carpet 90 50

145 Golf Club and Ball

المؤتمر الاسلامي - لاهور
1394
(146)

1974. International "Hassan II Trophy" Golf Grand Prix, Rabat.
382 **145** 70 f. multicoloured . . . . 2·25 1·25

1974. Islamic Summit Conference, Lahore, Pakistan. No. 281 optd with T **146**.
383 1 d. multicoloured . . . . . . 2·00 1·25

147 Human Rights Emblem

148 Vanadinite

1974. 25th Anniv (1973) of Declaration of Human Rights.
384 **147** 70 f. multicoloured 25 20

1974. Moroccan Mineral Sources. Multicoloured.
385 25 f. Type **148** 25 15
386 70 f. Erythrine 60 35

149 Marrakesh Minaret

150 U.P.U. Emblem and Congress Dates

1974. 173rd District of Rotary International Annual Conference, Marrakesh.
387 **149** 70 f. multicoloured . . . 25 20

1974. Centenary of U.P.U.
388 **150** 25 f. black, red and green 15 10
389 – 1 d. multicoloured 40 25
DESIGN—HORIZ: 1 d. Commemorative scroll.

151 Drummers and Dancers

1974. 15th Folklore Festival, Marrakesh. Multicoloured.
390 25 f. Type **151** 35 15
391 70 f. Juggler with woman . . 85 30

152 Environmental Emblem and Scenes

154 Flintlock Pistol

1974. World Environmental Day.
392 **152** 25 f. multicoloured . . . 20 15

1974. Red Crescent. Moroccan Firearms. Multicoloured.
397 25 f. + 5 f. Type **154** 50 50
398 70 f. + 10 f. Gunpowder box 75 75

155 Stamps, Postmark and Magnifying Glass

≋
الاحصاء الفلاحي
.1،00
(156)

1974. Stamp Day.
399 **155** 70 f. multicoloured . . . 25 20

1974. No. D393 surch with T **156**.
400 1 d. on 5 f. orange, grn & blk 1·50 95

157 World Cup Trophy

158 Erbab (two-string fiddle)

1974. World Cup Football Championship, West Germany.
401 **157** 1 d. multicoloured 45 30

1974. Blind Week.
402 **158** 70 f. + 10 f. multicoloured 30 25
See also No. 423.

160 Double-spurred Francolin

162 Jasmine

1974. Moroccan Animals. Multicoloured.
404 25 f. Type **160** 90 25
405 70 f. Leopard (horiz) 60 40

1974. Moroccan Carpets (3rd series). As T **129**. Multicoloured.
406 25 f. Zemmour carpet 25 10
407 1 d. Beni M'Guild carpet . . . 80 25

1975. Flowers (1st series). Multicoloured.
408 25 f. Type **162** 10 10
409 35 f. Orange lilies 15 10
410 70 f. Poppies 55 35
411 90 f. Carnations 75 50
See also Nos. 417/20.

163 Aragonite

165 "The Water-carrier" (Feu Taieb-Lalou)

1975. Minerals. Multicoloured.
412 50 f. Type **163** 20 15
413 1 d. Agate 35 20
See also Nos. 543 and 563/4.

1975. Red Crescent. Moroccan Jewellery. As T **65**. Multicoloured.
414 25 f. + 5 f. Pendant 50 50
415 70 f. + 10 f. Earring 75 65

1975. "Moroccan Painters".
416 **165** 1 d. multicoloured 75 30

1975. Flowers (2nd series). As T **162**. Multicoloured.
417 10 f. Daisies 10 10
418 50 f. Pelargoniums 20 10
419 60 f. Orange blossom 50 30
420 1 d. Pansies 75 60

166 Collector with Stamp Album

167 Dancer with Rifle

1975. Stamp Day.
421 **166** 40 f. multicoloured . . . 20 10

1975. 16th Nat Folklore Festival, Marrakesh.
422 **167** 1 d. multicoloured 65 30

1975. Blind Week. As T **158**. Multicoloured.
423 1 d. Mandolin 35 25

168 "Animals in Forest" (child's drawing)

1975. Children's Week.
424 **168** 25 f. multicoloured . . . 15 10

169 Games Emblem and Athletes

1975. 7th Mediterranean Games, Algiers.
425 **169** 40 f. multicoloured . . . 15 10

170 Waldrapp

1975. Fauna. Multicoloured.
426 40 f. Type **170** . . . . 1·50 40
427 1 d. Caracal (vert) 90 40
See also Nos. 470/71.

1975. "Green March" (1st issue). Nos. 370/1 optd **1975** and Arabic inscr.
428 25 f. (+ 5 f.) multicoloured . 2·00 2·00
429 70 f. (+ 10 f.) multicoloured 2·00 2·00
The premiums on the stamps are obliterated.

172 King Mohammed V greeting Crowd

1975. 20th Anniv of Independence. Mult.
430 40 f. Type **172** 15 10
431 1 d. King Hassan (vert) . . . 35 20
432 1 d. King Hassan V wearing fez (vert) 35 20

1975. Moroccan Carpets (4th series). As T **129**. Multicoloured.
433 25 f. Ouled Besseba carpet . . 60 35
434 1 d. Ait Ouaouzguid carpet . 90 45
See Nos. 485/7 and 513.

173 Marchers crossing Desert

174 Fez Coin of 1883/4

1975. "Green March" (2nd issue).
435 **173** 40 f. multicoloured . . . 15 10

1976. Moroccan Coins (1st series). Multicoloured.
436 5 f. Type **174** 10 10
437 15 f. Rabat silver coin 1774/5 10 10
438 35 f. Sabta coin, 13/14th centuries 10 10
439 40 f. Type **174** 12 10
440 50 f. As No. 437 . . . . . . 15 10
441 65 f. As No. 438 . . . . . . 50 15
442 1 d. Sabta coin, 12/13th centuries 65 15
See also Nos. 458/67a.
For Nos. 439/40 in smaller size, see Nos. 520/b.

175 Interior of Mosque

1976. Millennium of Ibn Zaidoun Mosque. Multicoloured.
443 40 f. Type **175** 15 10
444 65 f. Interior archways (vert) 20 15

176 Moroccan Family

1976. Family Planning.
445 **176** 40 f. multicoloured 15 10

177 Bou Anania College, Fez

1976. Moroccan Architecture.
446 **177** 1 d. multicoloured 25 20

178 Temple Sculpture

1976. Borobudur Temple Preservation Campaign. Multicoloured.
447 40 f. Type **178** 15 15
448 1 d. View of Temple 30 20

179 Dome of the Rock, Jerusalem

1976. 6th Anniv of Islamic Conference.
449 **179** 1 d. multicoloured 30 20

1976. Red Crescent. Moroccan Jewellery. As T **65**. Multicoloured.
450 40 f. Jewelled purse 15 10
451 1 d. Jewelled pectoral 65 25

180 George Washington, King Hassan I, Statue of Liberty and Mausoleum of Mohammed V

181 Wrestling

1976. Bicentenary of American Revolution. Multicoloured.
452 40 f. Flags of USA and Morocco (horiz) 20 15
453 1 d. Type **180** 65 25

1976. Olympic Games, Montreal. Multicoloured.
454 35 f. Type **181** 10 10
455 40 f. Cycling 15 10
456 50 f. Boxing 20 15
457 1 d. Running 70 25

1976. Moroccan Coins (2nd series). As T **174**. Multicoloured.
458 5 f. Medieval silver mohur . . 10 10
459 10 f. Gold mohur 10 10
460 15 f. Gold coin 10 10
461 20 f. Gold coin (different) . . 10 10
461a 25 f. As No. 437 . . . . . . 10 10
462 30 f. As No. 459 . . . . . . 10 10
463 35 f. Silver dinar 45 10
464 60 f. As No. 458 . . . . . . 20 15
465 70 f. Copper coin 55 15
466 75 f. As No. 463 . . . . . . 25 15
466a 80 f. As No. 460 . . . . . . 20 10
467 75 f. As No. 465 . . . . . . 60 35
467a 3 d. As No. 461 . . . . . . 60 50

182 Early and Modern Telephones with Dish Aerial

1976. Telephone Centenary.
468 **182** 1 d. multicoloured 35 25

183 Gold Medallion

1976. Blind Week.
469 **183** 50 f. multicoloured . . . 20 10

1976. Birds. As T **170**. Multicoloured.
470 40 f. Dark chanting goshawk . 1·10 35
471 1 d. Purple swamphen . . . . 1·60 70
Nos. 470/1 are vert designs.

185 King Hassan, Emblems and Map

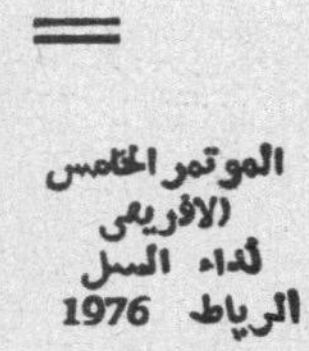

=
المؤتمر الخامس
الأفريقي
لداء السل
الرباط 1976
(186)

1976. 1st Anniv of "Green March".
472 **185** 40 f. multicoloured . . . 15 10

1976. Fifth African Tuberculosis Conference. Nos. 414/15 optd with T **186**.
473 25 f. multicoloured . . . . . 1·25 1·25
474 70 f. multicoloured . . . . . 1·50 1·50

187 Globe and Peace Dove

188 African Nations Cup

1976. Conference of Non-Aligned Countries, Colombo.
475 **187** 1 d. red, black and blue . 30 20

1976. African Nations Football Championship.
476 **188** 1 d. multicoloured 30 20

189 Letters encircling Globe

1977. Stamp Day.
477 **189** 40 f. multicoloured . . . 15 10

190 "Aeonium arboreum"

1977. Flowers. Multicoloured.
478 40 f. Type **190** 30 10
479 50 f. "Malope trifida" (24 × 38 mm) 50 30
480 1 d. "Hesperolaburnum platyclarpum" 60 30

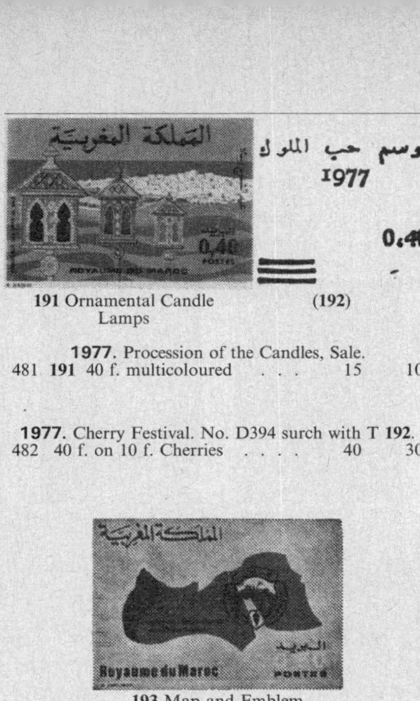

موسم حب الملوك
1977
0,40

191 Ornamental Candle Lamps (192)

1977. Procession of the Candles, Sale.
481 **191** 40 f. multicoloured . . . 15 10

1977. Cherry Festival. No. D394 surch with T **192**.
482 40 f. on 10 f. Cherries 40 30

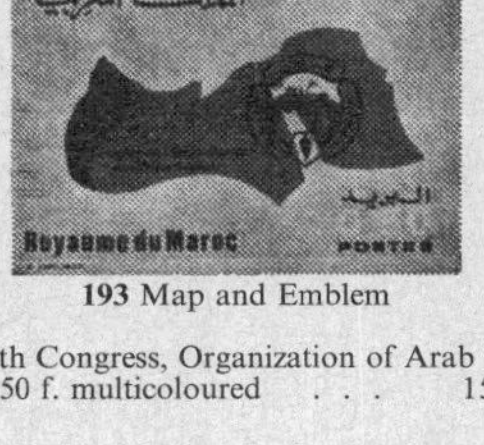

193 Map and Emblem

1977. 5th Congress, Organization of Arab Towns.
483 **193** 50 f. multicoloured . . . 15 10

194 A.P.U. Emblem

1977. 25th Anniv of Arab Postal Union.
484 **194** 1 d. multicoloured 30 20

1977. Carpets (5th series). As T **129**. Multicoloured.
485 35 f. Marmoucha carpet . . . 25 15
486 40 f. Ait Haddou carpet . . . 40 20
487 1 d. Henbel rug, Sale 65 30

195 Zither **196** Mohammed Ali Jinnah

1977. Blind Week.
488 **195** 1 d. multicoloured 35 25

1977. Birth Centenary of Mohammed Ali Jinnah.
489 **196** 70 f. multicoloured . . . 25 20

197 Marcher with Flag

1977. 2nd Anniv of "Green March".
490 **197** 1 d. multicoloured 30 20

198 Assembly Hall

1977. Opening of House of Representatives.
491 **198** 1 d. multicoloured 30 20

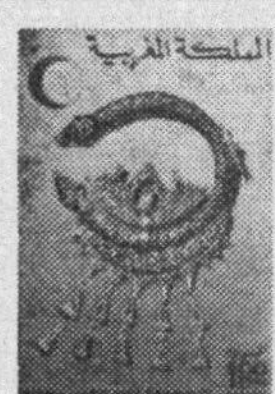

199 Silver Brooch **200** Bowl with Funnel

1977. Red Crescent.
493 **199** 1 d. multicoloured . . . 60 20

1978. Moroccan Copperware. Multicoloured.
494 40 f. Type **200** 10 10
495 1 d. Bowl with cover 70 20

201 Development Emblem **202** Decorative Pot with Lid

1978. Sahara Development. Multicoloured.
496 40 f. Type **201** 10 10
497 1 d. Fishes in net and camels at oasis (horiz) 30 20

1978. Blind Week. Multicoloured.
498 1 d. Type **202** 60 30
499 1 d. Decorative jar 60 30

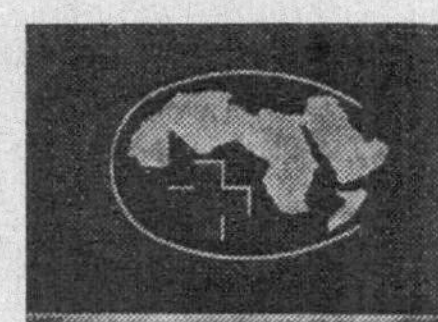

203 Map and Red Cross within Red Crescent

1978. 10th Conference of Arab Red Crescent and Red Cross Societies.
500 **203** 1 d. red and black . . . 30 20

204 View of Fez **205** Dome of the Rock

1978. Rotary International Meeting, Fez.
501 **204** 1 d. multicoloured . . . 30 20

1978. Palestine Welfare.
502 **205** 5 f. multicoloured 10 10
503 10 f. multicoloured . . . 10 10

206 Flautist and Folk Dancers **208** Yacht

207 Sugar Field and Crushing Plant

1978. National Folklore Festival, Marrakesh.
504 **206** 1 d. multicoloured . . . 55 20

1978. Sugar Industry.
505 **207** 40 f. multicoloured . . . 15 10

1978. World Sailing Championships.
506 **208** 1 d. multicoloured 60 20

209 Tree, Tent and Scout Emblem **211** Human Rights Emblem

210 Moulay Idriss

1978. Pan-Arab Scout Festival, Rabat.
507 **209** 40 f. multicoloured 15 10

1978. Moulay Idriss Great Festival.
508 **210** 40 f. multicoloured 15 10

1978. 30th Anniv of Declaration of Human Rights.
509 **211** 1 d. multicoloured 30 20

212 Houses in Agadir **214** Decorated Pot

213 Player, Football and Cup

1979. Southern Moroccan Architecture (1st series). Multicoloured.
510 40 f. Type **212** 15 10
511 1 d. Old fort at Marrakesh . . 60 15
See also Nos. 536 and 562.

1979. Mohammed V Football Cup.
512 **213** 40 f. multicoloured 15 10

1979. Moroccan Carpets (6th series). As T **129**.
513 40 f. Marmoucha carpet . . . 40 15

1979. Blind Week.
514 **214** 1 d. multicoloured 30 20

215 "Procession from a Mosque" **216** Coffee Pot and Heater

1979. Paintings by Mohamed Ben Ali Rbati. Mult.
515 40 f. Type **215** 15 10
516 1 d. "Religious Ceremony in a Mosque" (horiz) 55 20

1979. Red Crescent. Brassware. Multicoloured.
517 40 f. Engraved Circular Boxes . 25 15
518 1 d. Type **216** 60 30

217 Costumed Girls **218** Curved Dagger in Jewelled Sheath

1979. National Folklore Festival, Marrakesh.
519 **217** 40 f. multicoloured . . . 15 10

1979. Moroccan Coins. As T **174**, but smaller, $17\frac{1}{2} \times 22\frac{1}{2}$ mm.
520 40 f. multicoloured 10 10
520b 50 f. multicoloured 10 10

1979. Ancient Weapons.
521 **218** 1 d. black and yellow . . 30 20

219 King Hassan II **221** King Hassan II

220 Festival Emblem

1979. King Hassan's 50th Birthday.
522 **219** 1 d. multicoloured 30 20

1979. 4th Arab Youth Festival, Rabat.
523 **220** 1 d. multicoloured 30 20

1979. "25th Anniv of Revolution of King and People".
524 **221** 1 d. multicoloured 30 20

222 World Map superimposed on Open Book

1979. 50th Anniv of International Bureau of Education.
525 **222** 1 d. brown and yellow . . 30 20

223 Pilgrims in Wuquf, Arafat

1979. Pilgrimage to Mecca.
526 **223** 1 d. multicoloured 30 20

استرجاع اقليم وادى الذهب
1979-8-14
(224)

1979. Recovery of Oued Eddahab Province. Design as No. 497, with face value amended (40 f.), optd with T **224**.
527 40 f. multicoloured 15 10
528 1 d. multicoloured 65 20

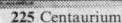

225 Centaurium **226** Children around Globe

1979. Flowers. Multicoloured.
529 40 f. Type **225** 15 10
530 1 d. "Leucanthemum catanance" 55 20

1979. International Year of the Child.
531 **226** 40 f. multicoloured . . . 60 25

227 European Otter **228** Traffic Signs

1979. Wildlife. Multicoloured.
532 40 f. Type **227** 25 15
533 1 d. Moussier's Redstart . . . 1·10 40

1980. Road Safety. Multicoloured.
534 40 f. Type **228** 15 10
535 1 d. Children at crossing . . . 30 20

229 Fortress

1980. South Moroccan Architecture (2nd series).
536 **229** 1 d. multicoloured 30 20

230 Copper Bowl with Lid **231** Pot

1980. Red Crescent. Multicoloured.
537 50 f. Type **230** 15 15
538 70 f. Copper kettle and brazier 35 20

1980. Blind Week.
539 **231** 40 f. multicoloured . . . 15 10

232 Mechanised Sorting Office, Rabat

1980. Stamp Day.
540 **232** 40 f. multicoloured . . . 15 10

233 World Map and Rotary Emblem **234** Leather Bag and Cloth

1980. 75th Anniv of Rotary International.
541 **233** 1 d. multicoloured 30 20

1980. 4th Textile and Leather Exhibition, Casablanca.
542 **234** 1 d. multicoloured 30 20

1980. Minerals (2nd series). As T **163**. Multicoloured.
543 40 f. Gypsum 15 10

235 Peregrine Falcon **236** Diagram of Blood Circulation and Heart

1980. Hunting with Falcon.
544 **235** 40 f. multicoloured . . . 85 20

1980. Campaign against Cardio-vascular Diseases.
545 **236** 1 d. multicoloured . . . 30 20

237 Decade Emblem and Human Figures **238** Harnessed Horse

1980. Decade for Women.
546 **237** 40 f. mauve and blue . . 15 10
547 – 1 d. multicoloured . . . 30 20
DESIGN: 1 d. Decade and United Nations emblems.

1980. Ornamental Harnesses. Multicoloured.
548 40 f. Harnessed horse (different) 15 10
549 1 d. Type **238** 30 20

239 Satellite orbiting Earth and Dish Aerial **240** Light Bulb and Fuel Can

1980. World Meteorological Day.
550 **239** 40 f. multicoloured . . . 15 10

1980. Energy Conservation. Multicoloured.
551 40 f. Type **240** 15 10
552 1 d. Hand holding petrol pump 30 20

241 Conference Emblem

1980. World Tourism Conference, Manila.
553 **241** 40 f. multicoloured . . . 15 10

242 Tree bridging Straits of Gibraltar

1980. European–African Liaison over the Straits of Gibraltar.
554 **242** 1 d. multicoloured . . . 60 20

243 Flame and Marchers

1980. 5th Anniv of "The Green March".
555 **243** 1 d. multicoloured . . . 30 20

244 Holy Kaaba, Mecca **245** "Senecio antheuphorbium"

1980. 1400th Anniv of Hegira. Multicoloured.
556 40 f. Type **244** 15 10
557 1 d. Mosque, Mecca 30 20

1980. Flowers. Multicoloured.
558 40 f. Type **245** 15 10
559 1 d. "Periploca laevigata" . . 60 20

246 Painting by Aherdan **247** Nejjarine Fountain, Fez

1980. Paintings.
560 – 40 f. bistre and brown . . 15 10
561 **246** 1 d. multicoloured 30 20
DESIGN: 40 f. Composition of bird and feathers.

1981. Moroccan Architecture (3rd series).
562 **247** 40 f. multicoloured 10 10

1981. Minerals (3rd series). Vert designs as T **163**. Multicoloured.
563 40 f. Onyx 25 10
564 1 d. Malachite-azurite 55 25

248 King Hassan II **249** King Hassan II

1981. 25th Anniv of Independence. Mult.
565 60 f. Type **248** 10 10
566 60 f. Map, flags, broken chains and "25" 10 10
567 60 f. King V. Mohammed . . 10 10

1981. 20th Anniv of King Hassan's Coronation.
568 **249** 1 d. 30 multicoloured . . . 50 25

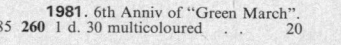

250 "Source" (Jillali Gharbaoul)

1981. Moroccan Painting.
569 **250** 1 d. 30 multicoloured . . . 50 25

251 "Anagalis monelli" **252** King Hassan as Major General

1981. Flowers. Multicoloured.
570 40 f. Type **251** 20 10
571 70 f. "Bubonium intricatum" . 40 15

1981. 25th Anniv of Moroccan Armed Forces.
572 **252** 60 f. lilac, gold and green . 10 10
573 – 60 f. multicoloured 10 10
574 – 60 f. lilac, gold and green . 10 10
DESIGNS: No. 573, Army badge; No. 574, King Mohammed V (founder).

253 Caduceus (Telecommunications and Health) **254** Plate with Pattern

1981. World Telecommunications Day.
575 **253** 1 d. 30 multicoloured . . 20 20

1981. Blind Week. Multicoloured.
576 50 f. Type **254** 10 10
577 1 d. 30 Plate with ship pattern 20 20

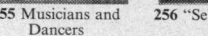

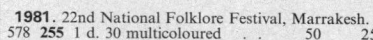

255 Musicians and Dancers **256** "Seboula" Dagger

1981. 22nd National Folklore Festival, Marrakesh.
578 **255** 1 d. 30 multicoloured . . 50 25

1981. Ancient Weapons.
579 **256** 1 d. 30 multicoloured . . 20 20

257 Pestle and Mortar **258** Hands holding I.Y.D.P. Emblem

1981. Red Crescent. Moroccan Copperware. Mult.
580 60 f. Type **257** 25 15
581 1 d. 30 Tripod brazier 55 25

1981. International Year of Disabled People.
582 **258** 60 f. multicoloured . . . 10 10

259 "Iphiclides feisthamelii Lotteri" **260** King Hassan and Marchers

1981. Butterflies (1st series). Multicoloured.
583 60 f. Type **259** 50 25
584 1 d. 30 "Zerynthina rumina africana" . . . . 1·25 60
See also Nos. 609/10.

1981. 6th Anniv of "Green March".
585 **260** 1 d. 30 multicoloured . . 20 20

261 Town Buildings and Congress Emblem

1981. 10th International Twinned Towns Congress, Casablanca.
586 **261** 1 d. 30 multicoloured . . 20 20

262 Dome of the Rock **264** Terminal Building and Runway

1981. Palestinian Solidarity Day.
587 **262** 60 f. multicoloured . . . 10 10

1981. 12th Arab Summit Conference, Fez. Nos. 502/3 surch **1981 0,40**.
588 **205** 40 f. on 5 f. multicoloured 3·00 3·00
588a 40 f. on 10 f. multicoloured 2·00 2·00

1981. 1st Anniv of Mohammed V Airport.
589 **264** 1 d. 30 multicoloured . . 20 20

265 Al Massira Dam

266 King Hassan II

1981. Al Massira Dam.

590 **265** 60 f. multicoloured . . . 10 10

1981.

591 **266** 5 f. red, blue and gold . 10 10
592 10 f. red, yellow and gold 10 10
593 15 f. red, green and gold 10 10
594 20 f. red, pink and gold 10 10
595 25 f. red, lilac and gold 10 10
596 30 f. blue, lt bl & gold . 10 10
597 35 f. blue, yellow & gold 10 10
598 40 f. blue, green and gold 10 10
599 50 f. blue, pink and gold 10 10
600 60 f. blue, lilac and gold 10 10
601 65 f. blue, lilac and gold 10 10
602 70 f. violet, yellow and gold 10 10
603 75 f. violet, green and gold 15 15
604 80 f. violet, pink and gold 15 15
605 90 f. violet, lilac and gold 15 15
605a 1 d. 25 red, mauve & gold 20 15
605b 4 d. brown, yellow and gold 75 55

See also Nos. 624/9, 718/22, 759/61 and 866.

267 Horse Jumping

268 Ait Quaquzguit

1981. Equestrian Sports.

606 **267** 1 d. 30 multicoloured . . 50 25

1982. Carpets (1st series). Multicoloured.

607 50 f. Type **268** 10 10
608 1 d. 30 Ouled Besseba 30 30

See also Nos. 653/4.

1982. Butterflies and Moths (2nd series). As T **259**. Multicoloured.

609 60 f. "Celerio oken lineata" . 35 25
610 1 d. 30 "Mesoacidalia aglaja lyauteyi" 75 55

269 Tree and Emblem

270 Jug

1982. World Forestry Day.

611 **269** 40 f. multicoloured . . . 10 10

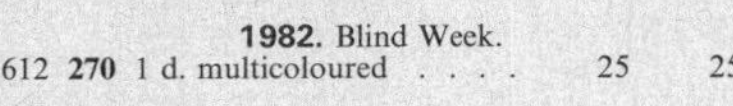
1982. Blind Week.

612 **270** 1 d. multicoloured 25 25

271 Dancers

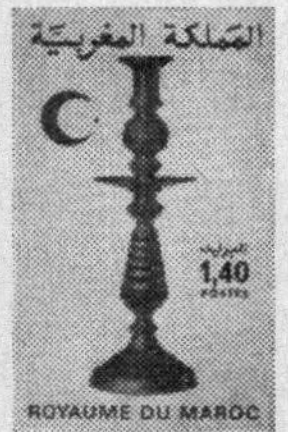
272 Candlestick

1982. Popular Art.

613 **271** 1 d. 40 multicoloured . . 35 35

1982. Red Crescent.

614 **272** 1 d. 40 multicoloured . . 35 35

273 Painting by M. Mezian

274 Buildings and People on Graph

1982. Moroccan Painting.

615 **273** 1 d. 40 multicoloured . . 35 35

1982. Population and Housing Census.

616 **274** 60 f. multicoloured . . . 15 15

275 Dr. Koch, Lungs and Apparatus

276 I.T.U. Emblem

1982. Centenary of Discovery of Tubercle Bacillus.

617 **275** 1 d. 40 multicoloured . . 35 35

1982. I.T.U. Delegates' Conference, Nairobi.

618 **276** 1 d. 40 multicoloured . . 35 35

277 Wheat, Globe, Sea and F.A.O. Emblem

278 Diesel Train and Route Map

1982. World Food Day.

619 **277** 60 f. multicoloured . . . 15 15

1982. Unity Railway.

620 **278** 1 d. 40 multicoloured . . 65 50

279 A.P.U. Emblem

1982. 30th Anniv of Arab Postal Union.

621 **279** 1 d. 40 multicoloured . . 40 15

280 Dome of the Rock and Map of Palestine

281 Red Coral

1982. Palestinian Solidarity.

622 **280** 1 d. 40 multicoloured . . 40 15

1982. Red Coral of Al Hoceima.

623 **281** 1 d. 40 multicoloured . . 70 25

1983. As T **266** but inscribed "1982".

624 1 d. maroon, blue and gold . 25 10
625 1 d. 40 brown, lt brn and gold 35 10
626 2 d. maroon, green and gold . 45 15
627 3 d. brown, yellow and gold . 65 25
628 5 d. brown, green and gold . 1·10 50
629 10 d. brown, orange and gold 2·25 90

282 Moroccan Stamps

283 King Hassan II

1983. Stamp Day.

630 **282** 1 d. 40 multicoloured . . 25 20

1983.

631 **283** 1 d. 40 multicoloured . . 25 20
632 2 d. multicoloured . . 35 30
633 3 d. multicoloured . . 55 50
634 5 d. multicoloured . . 90 45
635 10 d. multicoloured . . 2·25 85

284 Decorated Pot

286 Ornamental Stand

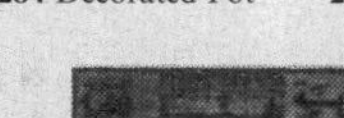

285 Musicians

1983. Blind Week.

636 **284** 1 d. 40 multicoloured . . . 25 20

1983. Popular Arts.

637 **285** 1 d. 40 multicoloured . . . 25 20

1983. Red Crescent.

638 **286** 1 d. 40 multicoloured . . . 25 20

287 Commission Emblem

288 "Tecoma sp."

1983. 25th Anniv of Economic Commission for Africa.

639 **287** 1 d. 40 multicoloured . . . 25 20

1983. Flowers. Multicoloured.

640 60 c. Type **288** 10 10
641 1 d. 40 "Strelitzia sp." 25 20

289 King Hassan II, Map and Sultan of Morocco

1983. 30th Anniv of Revolution.

642 **289** 80 c. multicoloured 20 20

290 Games Emblem and Stylized Sports

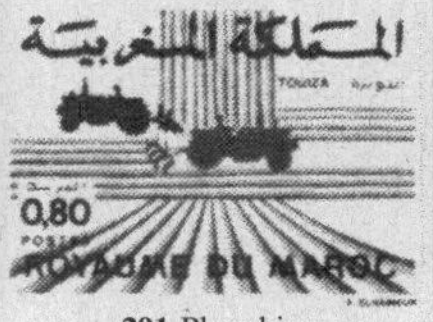

291 Ploughing

1983. 9th Mediterranean Games, Casablanca.

644 **290** 80 c. blue, silver and gold . 20 20
645 – 1 d. multicoloured 20 20
646 – 2 d. multicoloured 60 30

DESIGNS—VERT: 1 d. Games emblem. HORIZ: 2 d. Stylized runner.

1983. Touiza.

648 **291** 80 c. multicoloured 20 20

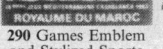

292 Symbol of "Green March"

293 Palestinian formed from Map and Globe

1983. 8th Anniv of "Green March".

649 **292** 80 f. multicoloured 20 15

1983. Palestinian Welfare.

650 **293** 80 f. multicoloured . . . 20 15

294 Ouzoud Waterfall

295 Children's Emblem

1983. Ouzoud Waterfall.

651 **294** 80 f. multicoloured . . . 20 15

1983. Children's Day. Multicoloured.

652 **295** 2 d. multicoloured 35 30

1983. Carpets (2nd series). As T **268**. Mult.

653 60 f. Zemmouri 10 10
654 1 d. 40 Zemmouri (different) . 25 20

296 Transport and W.C.Y. Emblem

1983. World Communications Year.

655 **296** 2 d. multicoloured . . . . 1·25 50

297 Views of Jerusalem and Fez

1984. Twinned Towns.

656 **297** 2 d. multicoloured 40 20

298 Fennec Fox

1984. Animals. Multicoloured.

657 80 f. Type **298** 30 25
658 2 d. Lesser Egyptian jerboa . 60 35

299 Map of League Members and Emblem

(300)

1984. 39th Anniv of League of Arab States.

659 **299** 2 d. multicoloured 40 20

1984. 25th National Folklore Festival, Marrakesh. No. 578 optd with T **300**.

660 **255** 1 d. 30 multicoloured . . 20 15

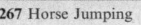

301 "Metha viridis"

302 Decorated Bowl

1984. Flowers. Multicoloured.

661 80 f. Type **301** 20 15
662 2 d. Aloe 40 30

1984. Blind Week.

663 **302** 80 f. multicoloured . . . 20 15

303 Lidded Container **304** Sports Pictograms

1984. Red Crescent.
664 **303** 2 d. multicoloured 40 30

1984. Olympic Games, Los Angeles.
665 **304** 2 d. multicoloured 40 30

305 Dove carrying Children **306** U.P.U. Emblem and Ribbons

1984. International Child Victims' Day.
666 **305** 2 d. multicoloured 40 30

1984. Universal Postal Union Day.
667 **306** 2 d. multicoloured 40 30

307 Hands holding Ears of Wheat **308** Stylized Bird, Airplane and Emblem

1984. World Food Day.
668 **307** 80 f. multicoloured . . . 20 15

1984. 40th Anniv of I.C.A.O.
669 **308** 2 d. multicoloured 40 30

309 Inscribed Scroll

1984. 9th Anniv of "Green March".
670 **309** 80 f. multicoloured . . . 20 15

311 Flag and Dome of the Rock **312** Emblem and People

1984. Palestinian Welfare.
672 **311** 2 d. multicoloured 30 25

1984. 36th Anniv of Human Rights Declaration.
673 **312** 2 d. multicoloured 30 25

313 Aidi **314** Weighing Baby

1984. Dogs. Multicoloured.
674 80 f. Type **313** 15 10
675 2 d. Sloughi 30 25

1985. Infant Survival Campaign.
676 **314** 80 f. multicoloured . . . 15 10

315 Children playing in Garden **316** Sherifian Mail Postal Cancellation, 1892

1985. 1st Moroccan S.O.S. Children's Village.
677 **315** 2 d. multicoloured . . . 30 25

1985. Stamp Day.
678 **316** 2 d. grey, pink and black 30 25
See also Nos. 698/9, 715/16, 757/8, 778/9, 796/7, 818/19 and 841/2.

317 Emblem, Birds, Landscape and Fish **318** Musicians

1985. World Environment Day.
680 **317** 80 f. multicoloured . . . 15 10

1985. National Folklore Festival, Marrakesh.
681 **318** 2 d. multicoloured . . . 75 25

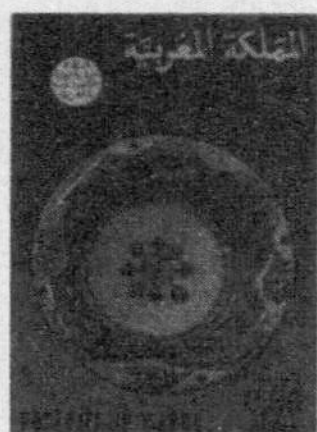

319 Decorated Plate **320** Bougainvillea

1985. Blind Week.
682 **319** 80 f. multicoloured . . . 15 10

1985. Flowers. Multicoloured.
683 80 f. Type **320** 15 10
684 2 d. "Hibiscus rosasinensis" . 70 25

321 Woman in Headdress **323** Map and Emblem

322 Musicians and Dancers

1985. Red Crescent.
685 **321** 2 d. multicoloured . . . 65 25

1985. National Folklore Festival, Marrakesh.
686 **322** 2 d. multicoloured . . . 30 25

1985. 6th Pan-Arab Games.
687 **323** 2 d. multicoloured . . . 30 25

HAVE YOU READ THE NOTES AT THE BEGINNING OF THIS CATALOGUE?
These often provide the answers to the enquiries we receive.

324 Emblem on Globe **325** Emblem

1985. 40th Anniv of U.N.O.
688 **324** 2 d. multicoloured 30 25

1986. International Youth Year.
689 **325** 2 d. multicoloured 30 25

326 Medal **327** Clasped Hands around Flag

1985. 10th Anniv of "Green March".
690 **326** 2 d. multicoloured 30 25

1985. Palestinian Welfare.
691 **327** 2 d. multicoloured 30 25

328 "Euphydryas desfontainii" **329** Arms

1985. Butterflies (1st series). Multicoloured.
692 80 f. Type **328** 45 30
693 2 d. "Colotis evagore" 95 55
See also Nos. 713/14.

1986. 25th Anniv of King Hassan's Coronation. Multicoloured.
694 80 f. Type **329** 15 10
695 2 d. King Hassan II (horiz) . . 30 25

330 Emblem **331** Vase

1986. 26th International Military Medicine Congress.
697 **330** 2 d. multicoloured 30 25

1986. Stamp Day. As T **316**.
698 80 f. orange and black 15 10
699 2 d. green and black 30 25
DESIGNS: 80 f. Sherifian postal seal of Maghzen-Safi; 2 d. Sherifian postal seal of Maghzen-Safi (different).

1986. Blind Week.
700 **331** 1 d. multicoloured 15 10

332 Footballer and Emblem

1986. World Cup Football Championship, Mexico. Multicoloured.
701 1 d. Type **332** 15 10
702 2 d. Cup, pictogram of footballer and emblem 30 25

333 Copper Coffee Pot **334** "Warionia saharae"

1986. Red Crescent.
703 **333** 2 d. multicoloured 30 25

1986. Flowers. Multicoloured.
704 1 d. Type **334** 15 10
705 2 d. "Mandragora autumnalis" 30 25

335 Emblem **336** Dove and Olive Branch

1986. 18th Parachute Championships.
706 **335** 2 d. multicoloured 30 25

1986. International Peace Year.
707 **336** 2 d. multicoloured 30 25

337 Horsemen **338** Book

1986. Horse Week.
708 **337** 1 d. light brown, pink and brown 15 10

1986. 11th Anniv of "Green March".
709 **338** 1 d. multicoloured 15 10

339 Stylized People and Wheat **340** Marrakesh

1986. Fight against Hunger.
710 **339** 2 d. multicoloured 30 25

1986. Aga Khan Architecture Prize.
711 **340** 2 d. multicoloured 30 25

الملتقى العالمي الاول
لخطباء الجمعة

341 Hands holding Wheat (**342**)

1986. "1,000,000 Hectares of Grain".
712 **341** 1 d. multicoloured 15 10

1986. Butterflies (2nd series). As T **328**. Multicoloured.
713 1 d. "Elphinstonia charlonia" 65 35
714 2 d. "Anthocharis belia" . . . 90 85

1987. Stamp Day. As T **316**.
715 1 d. blue and black 15 10
716 2 d. red and black 30 25
DESIGNS: 1 d. Circular postal cancellation of Tetouan; 2 d. Octagonal postal cancellation of Tetouan.

1987. Air. 1st World Reunion of Friday Preachers. Optd with T **342**.
717 **283** 2 d. multicoloured 30 25

1987. Size 25 × 32 mm. Inscribed "1986".
718 **266** 1 d. 60 red, brown and gold 25 20
719 2 d. 50 red, grey and gold 35 25
720 6 d. 50 red, brown and gold 1·25 35
721 7 d. red, brown and gold . 1·40 45
722 8 d. 50 red, lilac and gold 1·60 50

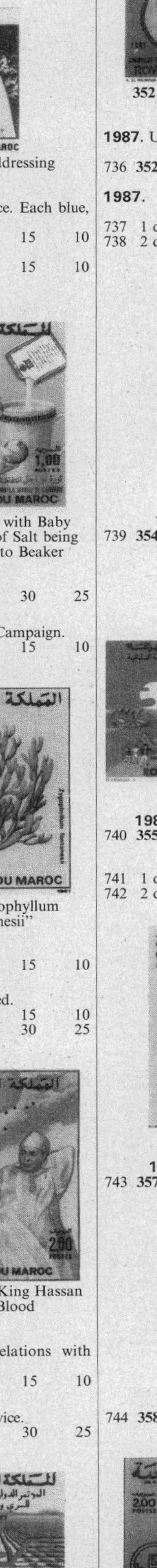

343 Sidi Muhammad ben Yusuf addressing Crowd

1987. 40th Anniv of Tangier Conference. Each blue, silver and black.
723 1 d. Type **343** 15 10
724 1 d. King Hassan II making speech 15 10

344 Copper Lamp

345 Woman with Baby and Packet of Salt being emptied into Beaker

1987. Red Crescent.
726 **344** 2 d. multicoloured 30 25

1987. U.N.I.C.E.F. Child Survival Campaign.
727 **345** 1 d. multicoloured 15 10

346 Decorated Pottery Jug

347 "Zygophyllum fontanesii"

1987. Blind Week.
728 **346** 1 d. multicoloured 15 10

1987. Flowers. Multicoloured.
729 1 d. Type **347** 15 10
730 2 d. "Otanthus maritimus" . . 30 25

348 Arabesque from Door, Dar Batha Palace, Fez

349 Map and King Hassan giving Blood

1987. Bicentenary of Diplomatic Relations with United States of America.
731 **348** 1 d. blue, red & black . . 15 10

1987. Blood Transfusion Service.
732 **349** 2 d. multicoloured 30 25

350 Woman from Melhfa

351 Emblem and Irrigated Field

1987. Sahara Costumes. Multicoloured.
733 1 d. Type **350** 15 10
734 2 d. Man from Derraa 30 25

1987. 13th International Irrigation and Drainage Congress.
735 **351** 1 d. multicoloured 15 10

352 Baby on Hand and Syringe

353 Azurite

1987. United Nations Children's Fund Child Survival Campaign.
736 **352** 1 d. multicoloured . . . 15 10

1987. Mineral Industries Congress, Marrakesh. Multicoloured.
737 1 d. Type **353** 15 10
738 2 d. Wulfenite 30 25

354 "12" on Scroll

1987. 12th Anniv of "Green March".
739 **354** 1 d. multicoloured 15 10

355 Activities

356 Desert Sparrow

1987. Armed Forces Social Services Month.
740 **355** 1 d. multicoloured . . . 15 10

1987. Birds. Multicoloured.
741 1 d. Type **356** 45 20
742 2 d. Barbary partridge . . . 85 50

357 1912 25 m. Stamp and Postmark

1987. 75th Anniv of Moroccan Stamps.
743 **357** 3 d. mauve, black and green 80 40

358 "Cetiosaurus mogrebiensis"

1988. Dinosaur of Tilougguite.
744 **358** 2 d. multicoloured . . . 1·00 25

359 King Mohammed V

360 Map and Player in Arabesque Frame

1988. International Conference on King Mohammed V, Rabat.
745 **359** 2 d. multicoloured . . . 30 25

1988. 16th African Nations Cup Football Competition.
746 **360** 3 d. multicoloured . . . 75 40

361 Boy with Horse

1988. Horse Week.
747 **361** 3 d. multicoloured . . . . 1·10 35

362 Pottery Flask

363 Anniversary Emblem

1988. Blind Week.
748 **362** 3 d. multicoloured 75 35

1988. 125th Anniv of Red Cross.
749 **363** 3 d. black, red and pink . 75 35

364 "Citrullus colocynthis"

365 Breastfeeding Baby

1988. Flowers. Multicoloured.
750 3 d. 60 Type **364** 90 45
751 3 d. 60 "Calotropis procera" . 90 45

1988. U.N.I.C.E.F. Child Survival Campaign.
752 **365** 3 d. multicoloured 40 35

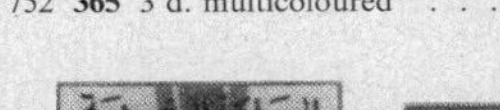

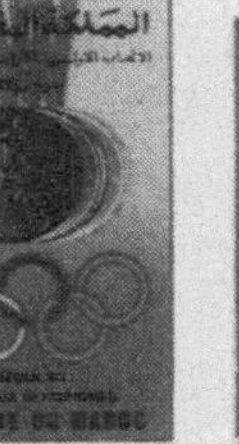

366 Olympic Medals and Rings

367 Greater Bustard

1988. Olympic Games, Seoul.
753 **366** 2 d. multicoloured 30 25

1988. Birds. Multicoloured.
754 3 d. 60 Type **367** . . . . 1·40 45
755 3 d. 60 Greater flamingo . . . 1·40 45

368 "13" on Scroll

اتحاد المغرب العربي

مراكش ـ فبراير 89

(370)

369 Housing of the Ksours and Csbaha

1988. 13th Anniv of "Green March".
756 **368** 2 d. multicoloured 30 25

1988. Stamp Day. As T **316**.
757 3 d. brown and black 40 35
758 3 d. violet and black 40 35
DESIGNS: No. 757, Octagonal postal cancellation of Maghzen el Jadida; 758, Circular postal cancellation of Maghzen el Jadida.

1988. Inscribed "1988".
759 **266** 1 d. 20 blue, lilac & gold . 15 10
760 3 d. 60 red and gold . . . 75 20
761 5 d. 20 brown, bis & gold 1·00 30

1989. Architecture.
762 **369** 2 d. multicoloured 30 25

1989. Union of Arab Maghreb. No. 631 optd with T **370**.
763 **283** 1 d. 40 multicoloured . . 20 15

371 King and Bishop with Chess Symbols

1989. 25th Anniv of Royal Moroccan Chess Federation.
764 **371** 2 d. multicoloured 30 25

372 Copper Vase

373 Ceramic Vase

1989. Red Crescent.
765 **372** 2 d. multicoloured 30 25

1989. Blind Week.
766 **373** 2 d. multicoloured 30 25

374 King Hassan

375 "Cerinthe major"

1989. 60th Birthday of King Hassan II. Mult.
767 2 d. Type **374** 30 25
768 2 d. King Hassan in robes . . 30 25

1989. Flowers. Multicoloured.
770 2 d. Type **375** 30 25
771 2 d. "Narcissus papyraceus" . 30 25

376 Telephone Handset linking Landmarks

1989. World Telecommunications Day.
772 **376** 2 d. multicoloured 30 25

377 Gender Symbols forming Globe, Woman and Eggs

1989. 1st World Fertility and Sterility Congress.
773 **377** 2 d. multicoloured 30 25

378 Desert Wheatear

1989. Birds. Multicoloured.
774 2 d. Type **378** 60 25
775 3 d. Shore lark . . . . 1·50 35

379 House of Representatives

1989. Centenary of Interparliamentary Union.
776 **379** 2 d. multicoloured 30 25

380 Scroll

1989. 14th Anniv of "Green March".
777 **380** 3 d. multicoloured 70 35

1990. Stamp Day. As T **316**.
778 2 d. orange and black 25 20
779 3 d. green and black 70 35
DESIGNS: 2 d. Round postal cancellation of Casablanca; 3 d. Octagonal postal cancellation of Casablanca.

381 Flags forming Map

1990. 1st Anniv of Union of Arab Maghreb.
780 **381** 2 d. multicoloured 25 20

382 Oil Press

1990. 3rd World Olive Year. Multicoloured.
782 2 d. Type **382** 25 15
783 3 d. King Hassan and olives . 40 25

383 Decorated Pot

1990. Blind Week.
784 **383** 2 d. multicoloured 25 15

384 Silver Teapot

1990. Red Crescent.
785 **384** 2 d. multicoloured 25 15

385 Arabic Script and Open Book  **386** Turtle Dove

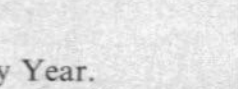

1990. International Literacy Year.
786 **385** 3 d. green, yellow & blk . 40 25

1990. Birds. Multicoloured.
787 2 d. Type **386** 60 30
788 3 d. Hoopoe (horiz) . . . . . 1·00 50

387 "15" on Scroll  **388** "35", Sun's Rays and Flag

1990. 15th Anniv of "Green March".
789 **387** 3 d. multicoloured . . . 40 25

1990. 35th Anniv of Independence.
790 **388** 3 d. multicoloured . . . 40 25

389 Dam

1990.
791 **389** 3 d. multicoloured . . . 40 25

390 Emblem  **392** Projects and Emblem

391 Morse Code Apparatus

1990. 10th Anniv of Royal Academy of Morocco.
792 **390** 3 d. multicoloured . . . 40 25

1990. 20th Anniv of National Postal Museum. Multicoloured.
793 2 d. Type **391** 25 15
794 3 d. Horse-drawn mail wagon, 1913 . . . . 40 25

1991. Stamp Day. As T **316**.
796 2 d. red and black 25 15
797 3 d. blue and black 40 25
DESIGNS: 2 d. Round postal cancellation of Rabat; 3 d. Octagonal postal cancellation of Rabat.

1991. 40th Anniv of United Nations Development Programme.
798 **392** 3 d. turquoise, yell & blk 40 25

393 King Hassan  **394** Mining

1991. 30th Anniv of Enthronement of King Hassan II. Multicoloured.
799 3 d. Type **393** 40 25
800 3 d. King Hassan in robes . . 40 25

1991. 70th Anniv of Mineral Exploitation by Sherifian Phosphates Office.
802 **394** 3 d. multicoloured . . . 40 25

395 Kettle on Stand  **396** Lantern

1991. Blind Week.
803 **395** 3 d. multicoloured 40 25

1991. Red Crescent.
804 **396** 3 d. multicoloured 40 25

397 "Cynara humilis"  **398** Man

1991. Flowers. Multicoloured.
805 3 d. Type **397** 40 25
806 3 d. "Pyrus mamorensis" . . . 40 25

1991. Ouarzazate Costumes. Multicoloured.
807 3 d. Type **398** 45 20
808 3 d. Woman 45 20

1991. Inscribed "1991".
809 **266** 1 d. 35 red, green & gold . 20 10

399 Road  **400** Members' Flags and Map

1991. 19th World Roads Congress, Marrakesh.
810 **399** 3 d. multicoloured 45 20

1991. 4th Ordinary Session of Arab Maghreb Union Presidential Council, Casablanca.
811 **400** 3 d. multicoloured 45 20

401 "16" on Scroll  **402** White Stork

1991. 16th Anniv of "Green March".
812 **401** 3 d. multicoloured 45 20

1991. Birds. Multicoloured.
813 3 d. Type **402** 45 20
814 3 d. European bee eater . . . 45 20

403 Figures and Blood Splash  **405** Zebra and Map of Africa

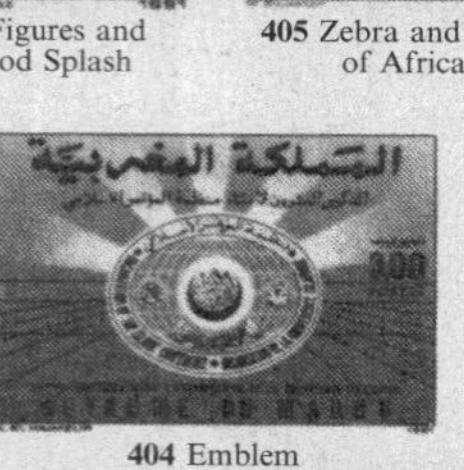

404 Emblem

1991. World AIDS Day.
815 **403** 3 d. multicoloured 45 20

1991. 20th Anniv of Islamic Conference Organization.
816 **404** 3 d. multicoloured 45 20

1991. African Tourism Year.
817 **405** 3 d. multicoloured 45 20

1992. Stamp Day. As T **316**.
818 3 d. green and black 45 20
819 3 d. violet and black 45 20
DESIGNS: No. 818, Circular postal cancellation of Essaouira; No. 819, Octagonal postal cancellation of Essaouira.

406 Satellites around Earth  **407** Bottle

1992. International Space Year.
820 **406** 3 d. multicoloured 45 20

1992. Blind Week.
821 **407** 3 d. multicoloured 45 20

408 Brass Jug 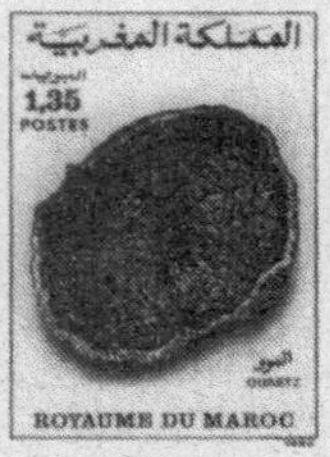 **409** Quartz

1992. Red Crescent.
822 **408** 3 d. multicoloured 45 20

1992. Minerals. Multicoloured.
823 1 d. 35 Type **409** 20 10
824 3 d. 40 Calcite 50 25

410 Woman  **411** "Campanula afra"

1992. Tata Costumes. Multicoloured.
825 1 d. 35 Type **410** 20 10
826 3 d. 40 Man 50 25

1992. Flowers. Multicoloured.
827 1 d. 35 Type **411** 20 10
828 3 d. 40 "Thymus broussonetii" 50 20

412 Olympic Rings and Torch  **414** La Koutoubia, La Giralda (cathedral bell-tower) and Exhibition Emblem

413 Map of Africa and Methods of Transport and Communication

1992. Olympic Games, Barcelona.
829 **412** 3 d. 40 multicoloured . . 50 20

1992. Decade of Transport and Communications in Africa.
830 **413** 3 d. 40 multicoloured . . 50 20

1992. "Expo '92" World's Fair, Seville.
831 **414** 3 d. 40 multicoloured . . 50 20

415 Columbus's Fleet and Route Map

1992. 500th Anniv of Discovery of America by Columbus.
832 **415** 3 d. 40 multicoloured . . 50 20

416 "Ganga cala"

1992. Birds. Multicoloured.
833 3 d. Type **416** 40 20
834 3 d. Griffon vulture ("Gyps fulvus") (vert) 40 20

417 "17" on Scroll

1992. 17th Anniv of "Green March".
835 **417** 3 d. 40 multicoloured . . 50 20

418 Postal Messenger, Route Map and Cancellations

1992. Centenary of Sherifian Post. Multicoloured.
836 1 d. 35 Type **418** 20 10
837 3 d. 40 Postal cancellation, "100" on scroll and Sultan Mulay al-Hassan 50 20

419 Conference Emblem

1992. International Nutrition Conference, Rome.
839 **419** 3 d. 40 multicoloured . . 50 20

420 Douglas DC-9 Airliners on Runway

422 Satellite orbiting Earth

421 Dishes

1992. Al Massira Airport, Agadir.
840 **420** 3 d. 40 multicoloured . . 50 20

1993. Stamp Day. As T **316**.
841 1 d. 70 green and black . . . 25 10
842 3 d. 80 orange and black . . 55 25
DESIGNS: 1 d. 70, Round postal cancellation of Tangier; 3 d. 80, Octagonal postal cancellation of Tangier.

1993. Blind Week.
843 **421** 4 d. 40 multicoloured . . 60 25

1993. World Meteorological Day.
844 **422** 4 d. 40 multicoloured . . 60 25

423 Kettle on Stand

424 Emblem

1993. Red Crescent.
845 **423** 4 d. 40 multicoloured . . 60 25

1993. World Telecommunications Day.
846 **424** 4 d. 40 multicoloured . . 60 25

425 Woman extracting Argan Oil

426 Prince Sidi Mohammed

1993. Argan Oil. Multicoloured.
847 1 d. 70 Type **425** 25 10
848 4 d. 80 Branch and fruit of argan tree 70 30

1993. 30th Birthday of Prince Sidi Mohammed.
849 **426** 4 d. 80 multicoloured . . 70 30

427 King Hassan and Mosque

428 Canopy, Sceptres, Flag and "40" on Sun

1993. Inauguration of King Hassan II Mosque.
850 **427** 4 d. 80 multicoloured . . 70 30

1993. 40th Anniv of Revolution.
851 **428** 4 d. 80 multicoloured . . 70 30

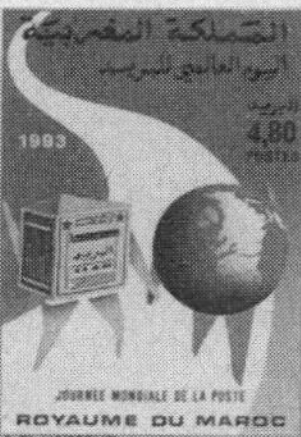

429 Post Box and Globe

430 Emblem

1993. World Post Day.
852 **429** 4 d. 80 multicoloured . . 70 30

1993. Islamic Summer University.
853 **430** 4 d. 80 multicoloured . . 70 30

431 "18" on Scroll

433 Flags, Scroll and "50"

432 Marbled Teal

1993. 18th Anniv of "Green March".
854 **431** 4 d. 80 multicoloured . . . 70 30

1993. Waterfowl. Multicoloured.
855 1 d. 70 Type **432** 25 10
856 4 d. 80 Crested coot 70 30

1994. 50th Anniv of Istaqlal (Independence) Party.
857 **433** 4 d. 80 multicoloured . . . 70 30

434 House

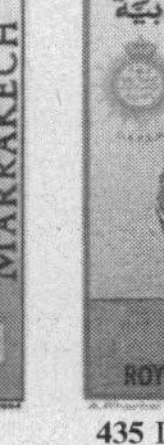

435 Decorated Vase

1994. Signing of Uruguay Round Final Act of General Agreement on Tariffs and Trade, Marrakesh.
858 **434** 1 d. 70 multicoloured . . . 25 10
859 – 4 d. 80 multicoloured . . . 70 30
DESIGN: 4 d. 80, Mosque.

1994. Blind Week.
861 **435** 4 d. 80 multicoloured . . . 70 30

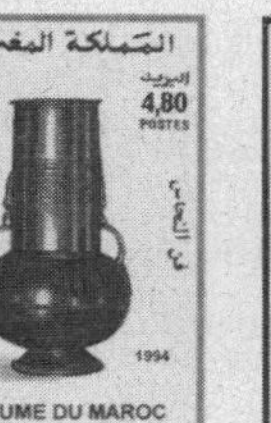

436 Copper Vessel

437 Couple

1994. Red Crescent.
862 **436** 4 d. 80 multicoloured . . . 70 30

1994. National Congress on Children's Rights. Children's Drawings. Multicoloured.
863 1 d. 70 Type **437** 25 10
864 4 d. 80 Couple under sun . . . 70 30

438 Ball, Moroccan and U.S.A. Flags, Pictogram and Trophy

1994. World Cup Football Championship, U.S.A.
865 **438** 4 d. 80 multicoloured . . . 70 30

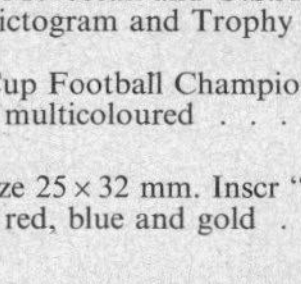

1994. Size 25 × 32 mm. Inscr "1994".
866 **266** 1 d. 70 red, blue and gold . 25 10

439 King Hassan II and Arms

1994. 65th Birthday of King Hassan II. Multicoloured.
867 1 d. 70 Type **439** 25 10
868 4 d. 80 King Hassan II (vert) . 70 30

440 "100" and Rings

441 Saint-Exupery, Route Map and Biplane

1994. Centenary of International Olympic Committee.
869 **440** 4 d. 80 multicoloured . . 70 30

1994. 50th Death Anniv of Antoine de Saint-Exupery (writer and pilot).
870 **441** 4 d. 80 multicoloured . . 70 30

POSTAGE DUE STAMPS

D 53

1965.
D162 D 53 5 f. green . . . . . . 1·50 75
D163 10 f. brown 50 25
D164 20 f. red 50 25
D165 30 f. sepia . . . . . . 1·00 50

D 153. Peaches

1974.
D393 – 5 f. orge, grn & blk 10 10
D394 – 10 f. grn, red & blk 10 10
D395 – 20 f. green & black 15 10
D396 D 153 30 f. orge, grn & blk 20 10
D397 – 40 f. green and black 15 10
D398 – 60 f. orge, grn & blk 20 15
D399 – 80 f. orange, green and black 25 20
D399a – 1 d. multicoloured 20 15
D400 – 1 d. 20 multicoloured 20 15
D401 – 1 d. 60 multicoloured 25 20
D402 – 2 d. multicoloured 30 25
DESIGNS: 60 f., 1 d. 60, Peaches. VERT: 5 f. Oranges; 10 f., 1 d. 20, Cherries; 20 f. Raisins; 40 f. Grapes; 80 f. Oranges; 1 d. Apples; 2 d. Strawberries.

MOSUL Pt. 19

Stamps used by Indian forces in Mesopotamia (now Iraq) at the close of the 1914–18 war.

12 pies = 1 anna; 16 annas = 1 rupee

1919. Turkish Fiscal stamps surch **POSTAGE I.E.F. D** and value in annas.
1 ½ a. on 1 pi. green and red 1·40 1·40
2 1 a. on 20 pa. black on red 1·40 1·60
4 2½ a. on 1 pi. mauve & yellow 1·50 1·50
5 3 a. on 20 pa. green 1·60 2·00
6 3 a. on 20 pa. green & orange 24·00 38·00
7 4 a. on 1 pi. violet 3·00 3·50
8 8 a. on 10 pa. lake 4·25 5·00

MOZAMBIQUE Pt. 9; Pt. 13

Former Overseas Province of Portugal in East Africa, granted independence in 1975.

1876. 1000 reis = 1 milreis
1913. 100 centavos = 1 escudo
1980. 100 centavos = 1 metical

1876. "Crown" key-type inscr "MOCAMBIQUE".
1 P 5 r. black 60 50
11 10 r. yellow 2·00 1·75
19 10 r. green 50 30
3 20 r. bistre 60 35
20 20 r. red £140 90·00
4a 25 r. red 30 20
21 25 r. lilac 1·25 75
14 40 r. blue 5·50 3·00
22 40 r. buff 90 30
6 50 r. green 40·00 12·00
23 50 r. blue 45 30
7 100 r. lilac 40 25
17 200 r. orange 1·50 80
9 300 r. brown 1·25 75

1886. "Embossed" key-type inscr "PROVINCIA DE MOCAMBIQUE".
30 Q 5 r. black 60 35
32 10 r. green 55 35
34 20 r. red 60 35
48 25 r. mauve 3·75 1·90
37 40 r. brown 60 35
38 50 r. blue 80 40
40 100 r. brown 60 35
42 200 r. violet 1·25 90
43 300 r. orange 1·75 1·00

1893. No. 37 surch **PROVISORIO 5 5**.
53 Q 5 on 40 r. brown 30·00 20·00

1894. "Figures" key-type inscr. "MOCAMBIQUE".
56 R 5 r. orange 35 25
57 10 r. mauve 35 25
58 15 r. brown 45 30
59 20 r. lilac 45 25
65 25 r. green 40 15
60 50 r. blue 1·25 35
67 75 r. red 75 50
61 80 r. green 1·25 70
62 100 r. brown on buff 80 55
68 150 r. red on rose 3·50 2·00
64 200 r. blue on blue 1·25 95
69 300 r. blue on brown 2·00 1·50

1895. "Embossed" key-type of Mozambique optd **1195 CENTENARIO ANTONINO 1895**.
71 Q 5 r. black 2·50 2·00
72 10 r. green 2·50 2·25
73 20 r. red 2·75 2·50
74 25 r. mauve 2·75 2·50
75 40 r. brown 2·75 2·75
76 50 r. blue 2·75 2·75
77 100 r. brown 2·75 2·75
78 200 r. lilac 8·50 6·50
79 300 r. orange 8·50 6·50

1897. No. 69 surch **50 reis**.
82 R 50 r. on 300 r. bl on brn 70·00 50·00

1898. Nos. 34 and 37 surch **MOCAMBIQUE** and value.
84 Q 2½ r. on 20 r. red 7·00 5·50
85 5 r. on 40 r. brown 6·00 5·50

1898. "King Carlos" key type inscr "MOCAMBIQUE".
86 S 2½ r. grey 15 15
87 5 r. orange 15 15
88 10 r. green 15 15
89 15 r. brown 1·75 75
138 15 r. green 50 40
90 20 r. lilac 50 25
91 25 r. green 50 25
139 25 r. red 40 15
92 50 r. blue 55 30
140 50 r. brown 1·00 85
141 65 r. blue 3·00 3·00
93 75 r. red 2·75 1·50
142 75 r. purple 1·00 85
94 80 r. mauve 2·75 1·50
95 100 r. blue on blue 1·25 60
143 115 r. brown on pink 3·00 2·50
144 130 r. brown on yellow 3·00 2·50
96 150 r. brown on yellow 2·75 1·50
97 200 r. purple on pink 1·00 70
98 300 r. blue on pink 2·25 1·25
145 400 r. blue on yellow 4·50 3·25
99 500 r. black on blue 5·00 3·00
100 700 r. mauve on yellow 6·00 3·50

1902. Various types surch.
146 S 50 r. on 65 r. blue 1·10 1·00
101 R 65 r. on 10 r. mauve 1·00 90
102 65 r. on 15 r. brown 1·00 90
105 Q 65 r. on 20 r. red 1·50 1·25
106 R 65 r. on 20 r. lilac 1·00 90
108 Q 65 r. on 40 r. brown 2·00 2·00
110 65 r. on 200 r. violet 1·75 1·25
111 V 115 r. on 2½ r. brown 1·00 90
113 Q 115 r. on 5 r. black 75 60
114 R 115 r. on 5 r. orange 1·00 90
115 115 r. on 25 r. green 1·00 90
117 Q 115 r. on 50 r. blue 60 55
120 130 r. on 25 r. mauve 80 50
121 R 130 r. on 75 r. red 1·00 90
122 130 r. on 100 r. brown on buff 2·25 2·25
123 130 r. on 150 r. red on rose 1·25 1·10
124 130 r. on 200 r. bl on bl 2·00 2·00
126 Q 130 r. on 300 r. orange 80 50
128 400 r. on 10 r. green 2·00 2·00
129 R 400 r. on 50 r. blue 60 50
130 400 r. on 80 r. green 60 50
132 Q 400 r. on 100 r. brown 15·00 9·00
133 R 400 r. on 300 r. blue on brown 60 50

1903. "King Carlos" key-type of Mozambique optd **PROVISORIO**.
134 S 15 r. brown 75 40
135 25 r. green 75 40
136 50 r. blue 1·25 90
137 75 r. red 2·00 1·25

1911. "King Carlos" key-type of Mozambique optd **REPUBLICA**.
147 S 2½ r. grey 10 15
148 5 r. orange 15 15
149 10 r. green 40 25
150 15 r. green 15 10
151 20 r. lilac 40 20
152 25 r. red 15 10
153 50 r. brown 15 15
154 75 r. purple 30 25
155 100 r. blue on blue 30 25
156 115 r. brown on pink 40 30
157 130 r. brown on yellow 40 30
158 200 r. purple on pink 80 45
159 400 r. blue on yellow 70 45
160 500 r. black on blue 70 45
161 700 r. mauve on yellow 70 45

1912. "King Manoel" key-type inscr "MOCAMBIQUE" with opt **REPUBLICA**.
162 T 2½ r. lilac 10 10
163 5 r. black 15 10
164 10 r. green 15 10
165 20 r. red 30 25
166 25 r. brown 10 10
167 50 r. blue 20 15
168 75 r. brown 20 15
169 100 r. brown on green 20 15
170 200 r. green on pink 45 40
171 300 r. black on blue 45 40
172 500 r. brown and olive 85 75

1913. Surch **REPUBLICA MOCAMBIQUE** and value on "Vasco da Gama" issues of (a) Portuguese Colonies.
173 ¼ c. on 2½ r. green 45 30
174 ½ c. on 5 r. red 40 30
175 1 c. on 10 r. purple 30 30
176 2½ c. on 25 r. green 30 30
177 5 c. on 50 r. blue 40 30
178 7½ c. on 75 r. brown 75 60
179 10 c. on 100 r. brown 50 45
180 15 c. on 150 r. bistre 40 35

(b) Macao.
181 ¼ c. on ½ a. green 60 50
182 ½ c. on 1 a. red 50 50
183 1 c. on 2 a. purple 35 30
184 2½ c. on 4 a. green 35 30
185 5 c. on 8 a. blue 1·50 1·25
186 7½ c. on 12 a. brown 90 80
187 10 c. on 16 a. brown 60 50
188 15 c. on 24 a. bistre 60 45

(c) Timor.
189 ¼ c. on ½ a. green 60 50
190 ½ c. on 1 a. red 60 50
191 1 c. on 2 a. purple 35 30
192 2½ c. on 4 a. green 35 30
193 5 c. on 8 a. blue 90 70
194 7½ c. on 12 a. brown 90 80
195 10 c. on 16 a. brown 50 45
196 15 c. on 24 a. bistre 60 45

1914. "Ceres" key-type inscr "MOCAMBIQUE".
197 U ¼ c. olive 10 10
198 ½ c. black 10 10
199 1 c. green 10 10
200 1½ c. brown 10 10
201 2 c. red 10 10
270 2 c. grey 10 10
202 2½ c. violet 10 10
255 3 c. orange 10 10
256 4 c. pink 10 10
257 4½ c. grey 10 10
203 5 c. blue 10 10
275 6 c. mauve 10 10
259 7 c. blue 10 10
260 7½ c. brown 10 10
278 8 c. grey 10 10
279 10 c. brown 10 10
280 12 c. brown 10 10
281 12 c. green 10 10
283 15 c. red 10 10
284 20 c. green 15 15
285 24 c. blue 15 15
286 25 c. brown 20 20
209 30 c. brown on green 70 50
287 30 c. green 15 15
295 30 c. lilac on red 70 55
210 40 c. brown on red 75 60
288 40 c. blue 35 15
211 50 c. orange on pink 1·50 1·00
289 50 c. mauve 15 10
297 60 c. brown on red 70 50
290 60 c. blue 40 25
291 60 c. red 40 35
298 80 c. brown on blue 65 40
293 80 c. red 40 20
299 1 e. green on blue 1·00 55
264 1 e. pink 50 30
301 1 e. blue 70 40
300 U 2 e. mauve on red 75 45
302 2 e. purple 40 25
303 5 e. bistre 4·00 1·75
304 10 e. pink 6·50 2·25
305 20 e. green 17·00 7·50

1915. Nos. 136/7 optd **REPUBLICA**.
226 S 50 r. blue 30 25
213 75 r. red 70 40

1915. Provisional issues of 1902 optd **REPUBLICA**.
227 S 50 r. on 65 r. blue 30 25
214 V 115 r. on 2½ r. brown 30 25
216 Q 115 r. on 5 r. black 11·00 11·00
229 R 115 r. on 5 r. orange 30 25
230 115 r. on 25 r. green 30 25
231 130 r. on 75 r. red 30 25
220 130 r. on 100 r. brown on buff 55 45
232 130 r. on 150 r. red on rose 30 25
233 130 r. on 200 r. bl on bl 30 25
223 400 r. on 50 r. blue 65 55
224 400 r. on 80 r. green 65 55
225 400 r. on 300 r. bl on brn 65 55

1918. Charity Tax stamp surch **2½ CENTAVOS**. Roul or perf.
248 C 16 2½ c. on 5 c. red 40 25

1920. Charity Tax stamps surch **CORREIOS** and value in figures.
306 C 15 1 c. on 1 c. green 30 25
307 C 16 1½ c. on 5 c. red 25 20

1920. Charity Tax stamp surch **SEIS CENTAVOS**.
308 C 16 6 c. on 5 c. red 35 30

1921. "Ceres" stamps of 1913 surch.
309 U 10 c. on ½ c. black 70 60
310 30 c. on 1½ c. brown 70 60
316 50 c. on 4 c. pink 50 30
311 60 c. on 2½ c. violet 85 70
328 70 c. on 2 e. purple 25 15
329 1 e. 40 c. on 2 e. purple 30 20

1922. "Ceres" key-type of Lourenco Marques surch.
312 U 10 c. on ½ c. black 40 30
314 30 c. on 1½ c. brown 40 30

1922. Charity Tax stamp surch **2$00**.
315 C 16 $2 on 5 c. red 60 35

1924. 4th Death Centenary of Vasco da Gama. "Ceres" key-type of Mozambique optd **Vasco da Gama 1924**.
317 U 80 c. pink 50 30

1925. Nos. 129 and 130 surch **Republica 40 C**.
318 R 40 c. on 400 r. on 50 r. 30 25
319 40 c. on 400 r. on 80 r. 35 30

1929. "Due" key-type inscr "MOCAMBIQUE" optd **CORREIOS**.
320 W 50 c. lilac 50 40

23 Mousinho de Albuquerque

25 "Portugal" and Camoens' "The Lusiads"

1930. Albuquerque's Victories Commemorative. Vignette in grey.
321 23 50 c. lake and red (Macontene) 3·00 3·00
322 50 c. orange and red (Mujenga) 3·00 3·00
323 50 c. mauve and brown (Coolela) 2·50 2·50
324 50 c. grey and green (Chaimite) 3·00 3·00
325 50 c. blue and indigo (Ibrahimo) 2·50 2·50
326 50 c. blue and black (Mucuto-muno) 2·50 2·50
327 50 c. violet and lilac (Naguema) 2·50 2·50

The above were for compulsory use throughout Mozambique in place of ordinary postage stamps on certain days in 1930 and 1931. They are not listed among the Charity Tax stamps as the revenue was not applied to any charitable fund.

1938. Value in black or red.
330 25 1 c. brown 10 10
331 5 c. sepia 10 10
332 10 c. mauve 10 10
333 15 c. black 10 10
334 20 c. grey 10 10
335 30 c. green 10 10
336 35 c. green 2·50 1·50
337 40 c. red 10 10
338 45 c. blue 20 20
339 50 c. brown 15 15
340 60 c. olive 20 10
341 70 c. brown 20 10
342 80 c. green 20 10
343 85 c. red 50 35
344 1 e. red 20 10
345 1 e. 40 blue 3·50 1·25
346 1 e. 75 blue 2·50 1·00
347 2 e. mauve 75 20
348 5 e. green 1·40 30
349 10 e. brown 3·00 40
350 20 e. orange 12·00 80

1938. As 1938 issue of Macao. Name and value in black.
351 **54** 1 c. olive (postage) 10 10
352 5 c. brown 10 10
353 10 c. red 10 10
354 15 c. purple 10 10
355 20 c. slate 10 10
356 – 30 c. purple 10 10
357 – 35 c. green 10 10
358 – 40 c. brown 10 10
359 – 50 c. mauve 10 10
360 – 60 c. black 15 10
361 – 70 c. violet 15 15
362 – 80 c. orange 15 15
363 – 1 e. red 25 15
364 – 1 e. 75 blue 80 20
365 – 2 e. red 90 35
366 – 5 e. olive 2·00 40
367 – 10 e. blue 4·50 50
368 – 20 e. brown 10·00 55
369 **56** 10 c. red (air) 10 10
370 20 c. violet 10 10
371 50 c. orange 10 10
372 1 e. blue 15 10
373 2 e. red 35 15
374 3 e. green 50 20
375 5 e. brown 85 30
376 9 e. red 1·50 40
377 10 e. mauve 2·25 60

DESIGNS: 30 to 50 c. Mousinho de Albuquerque; 60 c. to 1 e. Dam; 1 e. 75, to 5 e. Henry the Navigator; 10, 20 e. Afonso de Albuquerque.

1938. No. 338 surch **40 centavos**.
378 **25** 40 c. on 45 c. blue 1·60 1·40

26a Route of President's Tour

27 New Cathedral, Lourenco Marques

1938. President Carmona's 2nd Colonial Tour.
379 **26a** 80 c. violet 1·25 85
380 1 e. 75 blue 3·75 2·25
381 3 e. green 5·50 3·00
382 20 e. brown 27·00 18·00

1944. 400th Anniv of Lourenco Marques.
383 **27** 50 c. brown 60 30
384 50 c. green 60 30
385 – 1 e. 75 blue 3·50 80
386 – 20 e. black 2·50 25

DESIGNS—HORIZ: 1 e. 75, Lourenco Marques Central Railway Station; 20 e. Town Hall, Lourenco Marques.
See also No. 405.

1946. Nos. 354, 364 and 375 surch.
387 10 c. on 15 c. purple (postage) 25 20
388 60 c. on 1 e. 75 blue 35 20
289 3 e. on 5 e. brown (air) 2·25 1·25

1947. No. 386a surch.
390 2 e. on 20 e. black 80 30

30 Lockheed Lodestar

1946. Air. Values in black.
391 **30** 1 e. 20 red 85 50
392 1 e. 60 blue 1·00 55
393 1 e. 70 purple 1·75 90
394 2 e. 90 brown 2·75 1·75
395 3 e. green 2·00 1·25

1947. Air. Optd **Taxe percue**. Values in red (50 c.) or black (others).
397 **30** 50 c. black 45 30
398 1 e. pink 45 30
399 3 e. green 75 30
400 4 e. 50 green 1·50 80
401 5 e. lake 1·50 80
402 10 e. blue 5·75 1·60
403 20 e. violet 10·50 4·00
404 50 e. orange 18·00 7·25

1948. As T **27** but without commemorative inscr.
405 4 e. 50 red 90 25

31 Antonio Enes

33 Lourenco Marques

1948. Birth Centenary of Antonio Enes.
406 **31** 50 c. black and cream 50 15
407 5 e. purple and cream 2·25 55

1948.
408 – 5 c. brown 15 25
409 – 10 c. purple 15 10
410 – 20 c. brown 15 10
411 – 30 c. purple 15 10
412 – 40 c. green 15 10
413 33 50 c. grey 15 10
414 – 60 c. red 30 10
415 33 80 c. violet 15 10
416 – 1 e. red 25 10
417 – 1 e. 20 grey 50 20
418 – 1 e. 50 violet 30 15
419 – 1 e. 75 blue 70 15
420 – 2 e. brown 45 10
421 – 2 e. 50 blue . . . . . . 1·75 15
422 – 3 e. olive 65 15
423 – 3 e. 50 olive . . . . . . 1·50 20
424 – 5 e. green . . . . 1·00 15
425 – 10 e. brown . . . . . . 2·50 3·00
426 – 15 e. red . . . . 7·00 1·00
427 – 20 e. orange . . . . . . 10·00 1·00
DESIGNS—VERT: 5, 30 c. Gogogo Peak; 20, 40 c. Zumbo River; 60 c., 3 e. 50, Nhanhangare Waterfall. HORIZ: 10 c., 1 e. 20, Bridge over Zambesi; 1, 5 e. Gathering coconuts; 1 e. 50, 2 e. River Pungue at Beira; 1 e. 75, 3 e. Polana beach, Lourenco Marques; 2 e. 50, 10 e. Bird's eye view of Lourenco Marques; 15, 20 e. Malema River.

1949. Honouring the Statue of Our Lady of Fatima. As T **62** of Macao.
428 50 c. blue 65 35
429 1 e. 20 mauve . . . . 1·75 1·00
430 4 e. 50 green . . . . 6·50 2·00
431 20 e. brown . . . . 13·00 2·75

35 Aircraft and Globe
36 "Balistoides conspicillum"

1949. Air.
432 35 50 c. brown 15 10
433 1 e. 20 violet 20 10
434 4 e. 50 blue 40 15
435 5 e. green 90 30
436 20 e. brown . . . . 2·50 70

1949. 75th Anniv of U.P.U. As T **64** of Macao.
437 4 e. 50 blue 90 40

1950. Holy Year. As Nos. 425/6 of Macao.
438 1 e. 50 orange 35 20
439 3 e. blue 55 30

1951. Fishes. Multicoloured.
440 5 c. Type **36** 15 15
441 10 c. "Chaetodon aurigia" . . . 10 10
442 15 c. "Chaetodon inula" . . . 40 35
443 20 c. "Pterois volitans" . . . 15 10
444 30 c. "Canthigaster margaritatus" 15 10
445 40 c. "Stephanolepis auratus" . 15 10
446 50 c. "Teuthis nigrofuscus" . . 15 10
447 1 e. "Heniochus acuminatus" (vert) 15 10
448 1 e. 50 "Novaculichthys macrolepidotus" 15 10
449 2 e. "Gaterin schotaf" 15 10
450 2 e. 50 "Lutianus kasmira" . . 35 15
451 3 e. "Acauthurus triostegus" . 35 15
452 3 e. 50 "Abalistes stellaris" . . 40 15
453 4 e. "Fistularia petimba" . . . 60 30
454 4 e. 50 "Chaetodon vagabundus" 90 30
455 5 e. "Amblyapistus binotata" . 70 10
456 6 e. "Platax pinnatus" (vert) . 70 15
457 8 e. "Zanclus canescens" (vert) 90 25
458 9 e. "Tetrosomus concatenatus" 90 20
459 10 e. "Dactyloptena orientalis" 3·75 80
460 15 e. "Odonus niger" . . . . 16·00 5·50
461 20 e. "Rhinecanthus aculeatus" 8·00 2·50
462 30 e. "Lactoria cornutus" . . 8·00 2·75
463 50 e. "Lactoria fornasina" . . 15·00 6·00

1951. Termination of Holy Year. As T **69** of Macao.
464 5 e. red and pink . . . . . . 1·00 60

37 Victor Cordon (colonist)
39 Liner and Lockheed Constellation Airplane

1951. Birth Centenary of Cordon.
465 37 1 e. brown and orange . . 65 20
466 5 e. black and blue . . . . 3·00 50

1952. 1st Tropical Medicine Congress. Lisbon. As T **71** of Macao.
467 3 e. orange and blue 50 20
DESIGN: Miguela Bombarda Hospital.

1952. 4th African Tourist Congress.
468 39 1 e. 50 multicoloured . . . 50 30

40 Missionary
41 "Papilio demodocus"

1953. Missionary Art Exhibition.
469 40 10 c. lake and lilac 10 10
470 1 e. lake and green 40 15
471 5 e. black and blue 75 20

1953. Butterflies and Moths. Multicoloured.
472 10 c. Type **41** 10 10
473 15 c. "Amphicallia thelwalli" . 10 10
474 20 c. "Euxanthe wakefieldi" . . 10 10
475 30 c. "Axiocerses harpax" . . 10 10
476 40 c. "Teracolus omphale" . . 10 10
477 50 c. "Papilio dardanus tibullus" 10 10
478 80 c. "Nudaurelia hersilia dido" 15 15
479 1 e. "Aigenia mimosae" . . . 15 10
480 1 e. 50 "Papilio antheus evombaroides" 15 10
481 2 e. "Athletes ethica" . . . . 3·75 25
482 2 e. 30 "Danais chrysippus" . 2·50 20
483 2 e. 50 "Papilio phorcas ansorgei" . . . . 6·00 20
484 3 e. "Arniocera ericata" . . . 75 10
485 4 e. "Pseudaphelia pollinaris" 40 10
486 4 e. 50 "Egybolis vaillantina" 40 10
487 5 e. "Metarctica lateritia" . . 40 10
488 6 e. "Xanthospilopteryx mozambica" 45 15
489 7 e. 50 "Nyctemera leuconoe" 2·50 25
490 10 e. "Charaxes azota" . . . 6·00 80
491 20 e. "Aegocera fervida" . . 8·50 80

42
43 Map of Mozambique

1953. Philatelic Exhibition, Lourenco Marques.
492 42 1 e. multicoloured 65 20
493 3 e. multicoloured . . . . 1·75 40

1953. Portuguese Postage Stamp Centenary. As T **75** of Macao.
494 50 c. multicoloured 30 25

1954. 4th Centenary of Sao Paulo. As T **76** of Macao.
495 3 e. 50 multicoloured 20 10

1954. Multicoloured map; Mozambique territory in colours given.
496 43 10 c. lilac 10 10
497 20 c. yellow 10 10
498 50 c. violet 10 10
499 1 e. orange 10 10
500 2 e. 30 white 35 30
501 4 e. salmon 35 15
502 10 e. green . . . . 1·25 20
503 20 e. brown . . . . 1·75 25

44 Arms of Beira
45 Mousinho de Albuquerque

1954. 1st Philatelic Exhibition, Manica and Sofala.
504 44 1 e. 50 multicoloured . . . 20 15
505 3 e. 50 multicoloured . . . 40 25

1955. Birth Centenary of M. de Albuquerque.
506 45 2 e. black and grey 30 20
507 – 2 e. 50 black, blue & buff . 70 40
DESIGN: 2 e. 50, Equestrian statue of Albuquerque.

46 Arms and Inhabitants
47 Beira

1956. Visit of President to Mozambique. Multicoloured. Background in colours given.
508 46 1 e. cream 15 10
509 2 e. 50 blue 35 20

1957. 50th Anniv of Beira.
510 47 2 e. 50 multicoloured . . . 40 15

1958. 6th International Congress of Tropical Medicine. As T **79** of Macao.
511 1 e. 50 multicoloured 80 45
DESIGN: 1 e. 50, "Strophanthus grandiflorus" (plant).

1958. Brussels International Exn. As T **78** of Macao.
512 3 e. 50 multicoloured 15 10

48 Caravel
49 "Arts and Crafts"

1960. 500th Death Anniv of Prince Henry the Navigator.
513 48 5 e. multicoloured 40 15

1960. 10th Anniv of African Technical Co-operation Commission.
514 49 3 e. multicoloured 25 15

50 Arms of Lourenco Marques
51 Fokker Friendship and De Havilland Dragon Rapide over Route Map

1961. Arms. Multicoloured.
515 5 c. Type **50** 10 10
516 15 c. Chibuto 10 10
517 20 c. Nampula 10 10
518 30 c. Inhambane 10 10
519 50 c. Mozambique (city) . . . 10 10
520 1 e. Matola 15 10
521 1 e. 50 Quelimane 15 10
522 2 e. Mocuba 30 10
523 2 e. 50 Antonio Enes 70 10
524 3 e. Cabral 30 10
525 4 e. Manica 30 15
526 4 e. 50 Pery 30 15
527 5 e. St. Tiago de Tete 35 15
528 7 e. 50 Porto Amelia 55 25
529 10 e. Chinde 90 25
530 20 e. Joao Belo . . . . . . 2·00 35
531 50 e. Beira . . . . 4·00 85

1962. Sports. As T **82** of Macao. Multicoloured.
532 50 c. Water-skiing 10 10
533 1 e. Wrestling 50 15
534 1 e. 50 Gymnastics 25 10
535 2 e. 50 Hockey 60 10
536 4 e. 50 Netball 70 35
537 15 e. Outboard speedboat racing 90 70

1962. Malaria Eradication. Mosquito design as T **83** of Macao. Multicoloured.
538 2 c. 50 "A. funestus" 30 20

1962. 25th Anniv of D.E.T.A. (Mozambique Airline).
539 51 3 e. multicoloured 30 15

52 Lourenco Marques in 1887 and 1962
53 Oil Refinery, Sonarep

1962. 75th Anniv of Lourenco Marques.
540 52 1 e. multicoloured 25 15

1962. Air. Multicoloured.
541 1 e. 50 Type **53** 35 10
542 2 e. Salazar Academy 25 10
543 3 e. 50 Aerial view of Lourenco Marques Port 30 10
544 4 e. 50 Salazar Barrage 30 10
545 5 e. Trigo de Morais Bridge and Dam 35 10
546 20 e. Marcelo Caetano Bridge and Dam . . . . 1·25 35
Each design includes an aircraft in flight.

54 Arms of Mozambique and Statue of Vasco da Gama

55 Nef, 1430

1963. Bicentenary of City of Mozambique.
547 54 3 e. multicoloured 25 15

1963. 10th Anniv of T.A.P. Airline. As T **52** of Portuguese Guinea.
548 2 e. 50 multicoloured 20 15

1963. Evolution of Sailing Ships. Multicoloured.
549 10 c. Type **55** 10 10
550 20 c. Caravel, 1436 (vert) . . 10 10
551 30 c. Caravel, 1460 (vert) . . 10 10
552 50 c. Vasco da Gama's ship "Sao Gabriel", 1497 (vert) . . . 10 10
553 1 e. Don Manuel's nau, 1498 (vert) 40 10
554 1 e. 50 Galleon, 1530 (vert) . 40 10
555 2 e. Nau "Flor de la Mer", 1511 (vert) 40 10
556 2 e. 50 Caravel "Redonda", 1519 40 10
557 3 e. 50 Nau, 1520 (vert) . . . 45 10
558 4 e. Portuguese Indies galley, 1521 . . . . 50 10
559 4 e. 50 "Santa Tereza" (galleon), 1639 (vert) 50 20
560 5 e. Nau "N. Senhora da Conceicao", 1716 (vert) . . 9·75 20
561 6 e. Warship "N. Senhora do Bom Sucesso", 1764 . . . . 65 20
562 7 e. 50 Bomb launch, 1788 . . 90 30
563 8 e. Naval brigantine "Lebre", 1793 . . . . 90 30
564 10 e. Corvette "Andorinha", 1799 . . . . 95 30
565 12 e. 50 Naval schooner "Maria Teresa", 1820 . . . . . . 1·10 55
566 15 e. Warship "Vasco da Gama", 1841 . . . . 1·75 55
567 20 e. Sail frigate "Don Fernando II e Gloria", 1843 (vert) . . 2·25 65
568 30 e. Cadet barque "Sagres I", 1924 (vert) . . . . 3·50 1·10

1964. Centenary of National Overseas Bank. As T **84** of Macao but view of Bank building, Lourenco Marques.
569 1 e. 50 multicoloured 20 15

56 Pres. Tomas
57 State Barge of Joao V, 1728

1964. Presidential Visit.
570 56 2 e. 50 multicoloured . . . 15 10

1964. Portuguese Marine, 18th and 19th Centuries. Multicoloured.
571 15 c. Type **57** 10 10
572 35 c. State barge of Jose I, 1753 10 10
573 1 e. Barge of Alfandega, 1768 30 10
574 1 e. 50 Oarsman of 1780 (vert) 25 10
575 2 e. 50 State barge "Pinto da Fonesca", 1780 . . . . . . 20 10
576 5 e. State barge of Carlota Joaquina, 1790 . . . . . . 25 15
577 9 e. Don Miguel's state barge, 1831 . . . . 45 30

1965. I.T.U. Centenary As T **85** of Macao.
578 1 e. multicoloured 25 15

1966. 40th Anniv of National Revolution. As T **86** of Macao, but showing different building. Multicoloured.
579 1 e. Railway station, Beira and Antonio Enes Academy . . 30 30

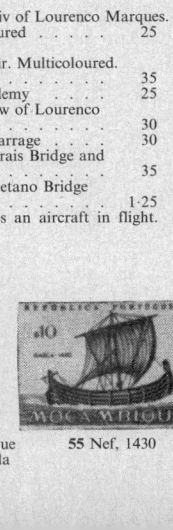

58 Arquebusier, 1560
59 Luis de Camoens (poet)

1967. Portuguese Military Uniforms. Multicoloured.
580 20 c. Type **58** 10 10
581 30 c. Arquebusier, 1640 . . . 10 10
582 40 c. Infantryman, 1777 . . . 15 10
583 50 c. Infantry officer, 1777 . . 15 10
584 80 c. Drummer, 1777 . . . . 30 10
585 1 e. Infantry sergeant, 1777 . 25 10
586 2 e. Infantry major, 1784 . . 20 10
587 2 e. 50 Colonial officer, 1788 . 30 10
588 3 e. Infantryman, 1789 . . . 35 10
589 5 e. Colonial bugler, 1801 . . 40 20
590 10 e. Colonial officer, 1807 . . 55 25
591 15 e. Infantryman, 1817 . . . 70 40

1967. Centenary of Military Naval Association. As T **88** of Macao. Multicoloured.
592 3 e. A. Coutinho and paddle-gunboat "Tete" 30 10
593 10 e. J. Roby and paddle-gunboat "Granada" 50 25

1967. 50th Anniv of Fatima Apparitions. As T **89** of Macao.
594 50 c. "Golden Crown" . . . 10 10

1968. 500th Birth Anniv of Pedro Cabral (explorer). As T **90** of Macao.

595 1 e. Erecting the Cross at Porto Sequro (horiz) 10 10
596 1 e. 50 First mission service in Brazil (horiz) 20 10
597 3 e. Church of Grace, Santarem 30 15

1969. Birth Centenary of Admiral Gago Coutinho. As T **91** of Macao.

598 70 c. Admiral Gago Coutinho Airport, Lourenco Marques (horiz) 25 10

1969. 400th Anniv of Camoens' Visit to Mozambique. Multicoloured.

599 15 c. Type **59** 10 10
600 50 c. Nau (horiz) 10 10
601 1 e. 50 Map of Mozambique, 1554 . . . . 20 10
602 2 e. 50 Chapel of Our Lady of Baluarte (horiz) 15 15
603 5 e. Part of the "Lusiad" (poem) 30 20

1969. 500th Birth Anniv of Vasco da Gama (explorer). As T **92** of Macao. Multicoloured.

604 1 e. Route map of Da Gama's Voyage to India (horiz) . . 15 10

1969. Centenary of Overseas Administrative Reforms. As T **93** of Macao.

605 1 e. 50 multicoloured 10 10

1969. 500th Birth Anniv of King Manoel I. As T **95** of Macao. Multicoloured.

606 80 c. Illuminated arms (horiz) 15 10

1970. Birth Centenary of Marshal Carmona. As T **96** of Macao.

607 5 e. Portrait in ceremonial dress 15 10

60 Fossilized Fern

1971. Rocks, Minerals and Fossils. Mult.

608 15 c. Type **60** 15 10
609 50 c. Fossilized snail 20 10
610 1 e. Stibnite 20 10
611 1 e. 50 Pink beryl 20 10
612 2 e. Endothiodon and fossil skeleton 25 10
613 3 e. Tantalocolumbite 30 10
614 3 e. 50 Verdelite 35 10
615 4 e. Zircon 45 30
616 10 e. Petrified tree-stump . . . 1·50 50

1972. 400th Anniv of Camoens' "The Lusiads" (epic poem). As T **98** of Macao. Multicoloured.

617 4 e. Mozambique Island in 16th century . . . . 1·25 30

1972. Olympic Games, Munich. As T **99** of Macao. Multicoloured.

618 3 e. Hurdling and swimming . 10 10

1972. 50th Anniv of 1st Flight, Lisbon–Rio de Janeiro. As T **100** of Macao. Multicoloured.

619 1 e. Fairey IIID seaplane "Santa Cruz" at Recife 10 10

61 Racing Yachts

1973. World Championships for "Vauriens" Class Yachts, Lourenco Marques.

620 **61** 1 e. multicoloured 15 10
621 – 1 e. 50 multicoloured . . . 15 10
622 – 3 e. multicoloured 25 15

DESIGNS: Nos. 621/2 similar to Type **61**.

1973. Centenary of I.M.O./W.M.O. As T **102** of Macao.

623 2 e. multicoloured 15 15

62 Dish Aerials

1974. Inauguration of Satellite Communications Station Network.

624 **62** 50 c. multicoloured 20 15

63 Bird with "Flag" Wings

1975. Implementation of Lusaka Agreement.

625 **63** 1 e. multicoloured 10 10
626 1 e. 50 multicoloured . . . 10 10
627 2 e. multicoloured 15 10
628 3 e. 50 multicoloured . . . 20 10
629 6 e. multicoloured 40 15

1975. Independence. Optd **INDEPENDENCIA 25 JUN 75**.

631 **43** 10 c. mult (postage) . . . 25 25
632 – 40 c. mult (No. 476) . . . 10 10
633 **62** 50 c. multicoloured . . . 20 15
634 **61** 1 e. multicoloured . . . 30 25
635 – 1 e. 50 mult (No. 621) . . 60 50
636 – 2 e. mult (No. 623) . . . 1·75 1·75
637 – 2 e. 50 mult (No. 535) . . 35 30
638 – 3 e. mult (No. 618) . . . 40 35
639 – 3 e. mult (No. 622) . . . 45 40
640 – 3 e. 50 mult (No. 614) . . 1·75 1·75
641 – 4 e. 50 mult (No. 536) . . 2·00 1·10
642 – 7 e. 50 mult (No. 489) . . 55 30
643 – 10 e. mult (No. 616) . . . 1·00 35
644 – 15 e. mult (No. 537) . . . 1·25 1·10
645 **43** 20 e. multicoloured . . . 1·25 1·10
646 – 3 e. 50 multicoloured (No. 543) (air) 35 25
647 – 4 e. 50 mult (No. 544) . . 40 25
648 – 5 e. mult (No. 545) . . . 90 50
649 – 20 e. mult (No. 546) . . . 1·50 90

66 Workers, Farmers and Children **67** Farm Worker

1975. "Vigilance, Unity, Work". Multicoloured.

650 20 c. Type **66** 10 10
651 30 c. Type **66** 10 10
652 50 c. Type **66** 10 10
653 2 e. 50 Type **66** 15 10
654 4 e. 50 Armed family, workers and dancers 25 15
655 5 e. As No. 654 . . . . . . 35 15
656 10 e. As No. 654 . . . . . . 70 30
657 50 e. As No. 654 . . . . . . 3·00 1·50

1976. Women's Day.

659 **67** 1 e. black and green . . . 10 10
660 – 1 e. 50 black and brown . 10 10
661 – 2 e. 50 black and blue . . 15 10
662 – 10 e. black and red . . . 65 40

DESIGNS: 1 e. 50, Teaching; 2 e. 50, Nurse; 10 e. Mother.

1976. Pres. Kaunda's First Visit to Mozambique. Optd **PRESIDENTE KENNETH KAUNDA PREMEIRA VISITA 20/4/1976**.

663 **63** 2 e. multicoloured 15 10
664 3 e. 50 multicoloured . . . 25 15
665 6 e. multicoloured 50 30

69 Arrival of President Machel **70** Mozambique Stamp of 1876 and Emblem

1976. 1st Anniv of Independence. Mult.

666 50 c. Type **69** 10 10
667 1 e. Proclamation ceremony . 10 10
668 2 e. 50 Signing ceremony . . 15 10
669 7 e. 50 Soldiers on parade . . 40 20
670 20 e. Independence flame . . 1·10 80

1976. Stamp Centenary.

671 **70** 1 e. 50 multicoloured . . . 10 10
672 6 e. multicoloured 30 20

1976. "FACIM" Industrial Fair. Optd **FACIM 1976**.

673 **66** 2 e. 50 multicoloured . . . 30 15

72 Weapons and Flag **73** Thick-tailed Bush baby

1976. Army Day.

674 **72** 3 e. multicoloured 20 10

1977. Animals. Multicoloured.

675 50 c. Type **73** 15 10
676 1 e. Ratel (horiz) 15 10
677 1 e. 50 Temminck's ground pangolin 20 10
678 2 e. Steenbok (horiz) 20 10
679 2 e. 50 Diademed monkey . . 25 10
680 3 e. Hunting dog (horiz) . . . 25 10
681 4 e. Cheetah (horiz) 35 10
682 5 e. Spotted hyena 50 15
683 7 e. 50 Warthog (horiz) 75 25
684 8 e. Hippopotamus (horiz) . . 80 30
685 10 e. White rhinoceros (horiz) . 80 30
686 15 e. Sable antelope . . . . . 1·25 65

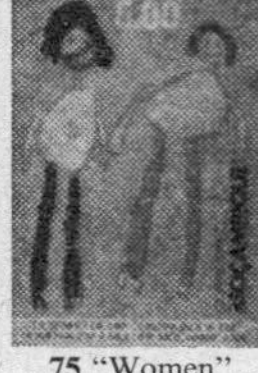

74 Congress Emblem **75** "Women" (child's drawing)

1977. 3rd Frelimo Congress, Maputo. Mult.

687 3 e. Type **74** 15 10
688 3 e. 50 Macheje Monument (site of 2nd Congress) (34 × 24 mm) 20 10
689 20 e. Maputo Monument (23 × 34 mm) . . . . 1·10 50

1977. Mozambique Women's Day.

690 **75** 5 e. multicoloured 25 10
691 15 e. multicoloured 65 25

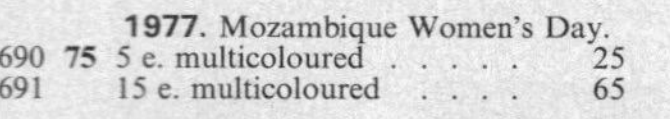

76 Labourer and Farmer **77** Crowd with Arms and Crops

1977. Labour Day.

692 **76** 5 e. multicoloured 25 10

1977. 2nd Anniv of Independence.

693 **77** 50 c. multicoloured 10 10
694 1 e. 50 multicoloured . . . 10 10
695 3 e. multicoloured 15 10
696 15 e. multicoloured 60 25

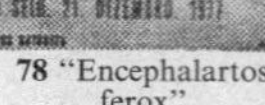

78 "Encephalartos ferox" **79** "Chariesthes bella"

1978. Stamp Day. Nature Protection. Mult.

697 1 e. Type **78** 10 10
698 10 e. Nyala 50 20

1978. Beetles. Multicoloured.

699 50 c. Type **79** 10 10
700 1 e. "Tragocephalus variegata" 10 10
701 1 e. 50 "Monochamus leuconotus" 10 10
702 3 e. "Prosopocera lactator" . . 25 10
703 5 e. "Dinocephalus ornatus" . . 40 10
704 10 e. "Tragiscoschema nigroscriptus" 60 20

80 Violet-crested Turaco **81** Mother and Child

1978. Birds. Multicoloured.

705 50 c. Type **80** 25 10
706 1 e. Lilac-breasted roller . . . 35 10
707 1 e. 50 Red-headed weaver . . 35 10
708 2 e. 50 Violet starling 35 10
709 3 e. Peters's twin-spot 60 10
710 15 e. European bee eater . . . 1·50 35

1978. Global Eradication of Smallpox.

711 **81** 15 e. multicoloured 45 25

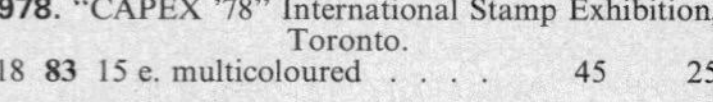

82 "Crinum delagoense" **83** First Stamps of Mozambique and Canada

1978. Flowers. Multicoloured.

712 50 c. Type **82** 10 10
713 1 e. "Gloriosa superba" . . . 10 10
714 1 e. 50 "Eulophia speciosa" . 10 10
715 3 e. "Erithrina humeana" . . 15 10
716 5 e. "Astripomoea malvacea" 40 15
717 10 e. "Kigelia africana" . . . 50 30

1978. "CAPEX '78" International Stamp Exhibition, Toronto.

718 **83** 15 e. multicoloured 45 25

84 Mozambique Flag **85** Boy with Books

1978. 3rd Anniv of Independence. Multicoloured.

719 1 e. Type **84** 10 10
720 1 e. 50 Coat of Arms 10 10
721 7 e. 50 People and Constitution 25 15
722 10 e. Band and National Anthem 30 20

1978. 11th World Youth Festival, Havana. Multicoloured.

724 2 e. 50 Type **85** 10 10
725 3 e. Soldiers 15 10
726 7 e. 50 Harvesting wheat . . . 25 20

86 Czechoslovakian 50 h. Stamp, 1919

1978. "PRAGA '78" International Stamp Exhibition.

727 **86** 15 e. blue, ochre and red . 45 30

87 Football

1978. Stamp Day. Sports. Multicoloured.

729 50 c. Type **87** 10 10
730 1 e. 50 Putting the shot . . . 10 10
731 3 e. Hurdling 15 10
732 7 e. 50 Basketball 35 20
733 12 e. 50 Swimming 45 35
734 25 e. Roller-skate hockey . . 95 60

88 U.P.U. Emblem and Dove

1979. Membership of U.P.U.

735 **88** 20 e. multicoloured 70 45

89 Eduardo Mondlane

1979. 10th Death Anniv of Eduardo Mondlane (founder of FRELIMO). Multicoloured.

736 1 e. Soldier handing gourd to woman . . . 10 10
737 3 e. FRELIMO soldiers . . . 15 10
738 7 e. 50 Children learning to write 30 20
739 12 e. 50 Type **89** . . . 40 30

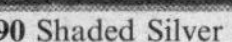

90 Shaded Silver **91** I.Y.C. Emblem

1979. Domestic Cats. Multicoloured.

740 50 c. Type **90** . . . 10 10
741 1 e. 50 Manx cat . . . 10 10
742 2 e. 50 British blue . . . 15 10
743 3 e. Turkish cat . . . 20 10
744 12 e. 50 Long-haired tabby . . 50 30
745 20 e. African wild cat . . . 85 55

1979. Obligatory Tax. International Year of the Child.

746 **91** 50 c. red . . . 15 10

92 Wrestling

1979. Olympic Games, Moscow (1980). Mult.

747 1 e. Type **92** . . . 10 10
748 2 e. Running . . . 10 10
749 3 e. Horse jumping . . . 15 10
750 5 e. Canoeing . . . 15 10
751 10 e. High jump . . . 30 20
752 15 e. Archery . . . 50 40

93 Flowers

1979. International Year of the Child. Multicoloured.

754 50 c. Type **93** . . . 10 10
755 1 e. 50 Dancers . . . 10 10
756 3 e. In the city . . . 15 10
757 5 e. Working in the country . 15 10
758 7 e. 50 Houses . . . 25 15
759 12 e. 50 Transport . . . 90 35

94 Flight from Colonialism

1979. 4th Anniv of Independence. Multicoloured.

760 50 c. Type **94** . . . 10 10
761 2 e. Eduardo Mondlane (founder of FRELIMO) . . . 10 10
762 3 e. Armed struggle, death of Mondlane . . . 15 10
763 7 e. 50 Final fight for liberation 25 15
764 15 e. President Samora Machel proclaims victory . . . 45 35

95 "Scorpaena mossambica"

1979. Tropical Fish. Multicoloured.

766 50 c. Type **95** . . . 10 10
767 1 e. 50 "Caraux speciosus" . . 15 10
768 2 e. 50 "Gobius inhaca" . . 15 10
769 3 e. "Acanthurus lineatus" . . 15 10
770 10 e. "Gobuchthys lemayi" . . 40 20
771 12 e. 50 "Variola louti" . . 60 30

96 Quartz

1979. Minerals. Multicoloured.

772 1 e. Type **96** . . . 10 10
773 1 e. 50 Beryl . . . 10 10
774 2 e. 50 Magnetite . . . 15 10
775 5 e. Tourmaline . . . 30 10
776 10 e. Euxenite . . . 60 20
777 20 e. Fluorite . . . 1·10 45

97 Soldier handing out Guns

1979. 15th Anniv of Fight for Independence.

778 **97** 5 e. multicoloured . . . 25 15

98 Locomotive

1979. Early Locomotives. Designs depicting various locomotives.

779 **98** 50 c. multicoloured . . . 10 10
780 – 1 e. 50 multicoloured . . . 15 10
781 – 3 e. multicoloured . . . 30 10
782 – 7 e. 50 multicoloured . . . 50 15
783 – 12 e. 50 multicoloured . . 80 25
784 – 15 e. multicoloured . . . 90 35

99 Dalmatian

1979. Dogs. Multicoloured.

785 50 c. Basenji (vert) . . . 10 10
786 1 e. 50 Type **99** . . . 15 10
787 3 e. Boxer . . . 15 10
788 7 e. 50 Blue gascon pointer . 35 15
789 12 e. 50 English cocker spaniel 60 25
790 15 e. Pointer . . . 85 30

100 "Papilio nireus"

1979. Stamp Day. Butterflies. Multicoloured.

791 1 e. Type **100** . . . 10 10
792 1 e. 50 "Amauris ochlea" . . 10 10
793 2 e. 50 "Pinacopterix eriphia" 15 10
794 5 e. "Junonia hierta" . . . 35 10
795 10 e. "Nephronia argia" . . . 60 20
796 20 e. "Catacroptera cloanthe" 1·25 55

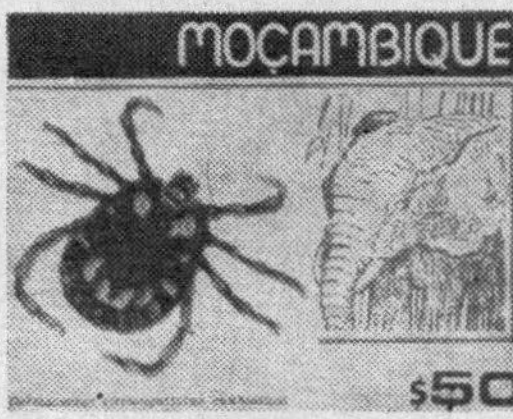

101 "Dermacentor circumguttatus cunhasilvai" and African Elephant

1980. Ticks. Multicoloured.

797 50 c. Type **101** . . . 20 10
798 1 e. 50 "Dermacentor rhinocerinos" and black rhinoceros . . . 30 10
799 2 e. 50 "Amblyomma hebraeum" and giraffe . . . 40 15
800 3 e. "Amblyomma pomposum" and eland . . . 50 15
801 5 e. "Amblyomma theilerae" and cow . . . 60 15
802 7 e. 50 "Amblyomma eburneum" and African buffalo . . . 85 30

102 Ford "Hercules" Bus, 1950

1980. Road Transport. Multicoloured.

803 50 c. Type **102** . . . 10 10
804 1 e. 50 Scania "Marco-polo" bus, 1978 . . . 10 10
805 3 e. Bussing Nag Bus, 1936 . . 15 10
806 5 e. Ikarus articulated bus, 1978 20 10
807 7 e. 50 Ford Taxi, 1929 . . . 40 15
808 12 e. 50 Fiat "131" Taxi, 1978 65 20

103 Soldier and Map of Southern Africa

1980. Zimbabwe Independence.

809 **103** 10 e. blue and brown . . . 40 15

104 Marx, Engels and Lenin

1980. International Workers' Day.

810 **104** 10 e. multicoloured . . . 40 15

105 "Market" (Moises Simbine)

1980. "London 1980" International Stamp Exhibition. Multicoloured.

811 50 c. "Heads" (Malangatana) . 10 10
812 1 e. 50 Type **105** . . . 10 10
813 3 e. "Heads with Helmets" (Malangatana) . . . 15 10
814 5 e. "Women with Goods" (Machiana) . . . 20 10
815 7 e. 50 "Crowd with Masks" (Malangatana) . . . 25 15
816 12 e. 50 "Man and Woman with Spear" (Mankeu) . . . 50 25

106 Telephone

1980. World Telecommunications Day.

817 **106** 15 e. multicoloured . . . 60 25

MINIMUM PRICE

The minimum price quoted is 10p which represents a handling charge rather than a basis for valuing common stamps. For further notes about prices, see introductory pages.

107 Mueda Massacre **108** Crowd waving Tools

1980. 20th Anniv of Mueda Massacre.

818 **107** 15 e. green, brown and red 60 25

1980. 5th Anniv of Independence.

819 – 1 e. black and red . . . 10 10
820 **108** 2 e. multicoloured . . . 10 10
821 – 3 e. multicoloured . . . 15 10
822 – 4 e. multicoloured . . . 20 10
823 – 5 e. black, yellow and red 20 10
824 – 10 e. multicoloured . . . 40 15

DESIGNS—As T **108**: 1 e. Crowd, doctor tending patient, soldier and workers tilling land; 3 e. Crowd with flags and tools; 4 e. Stylised figures raising right hand; 5 e. Hand grasping flags, book and plants; 10 e. Figures carrying banners each with year date. 55×37 mm: 30 e. Soldiers.

109 Gymnastics

1980. Olympic Games, Moscow. Multicoloured.

826 50 c. Type **109** . . . 10 10
827 1 e. 50 Football . . . 10 10
828 2 e. 50 Running . . . 10 10
829 3 e. Volleyball . . . 20 10
830 10 e. Cycling . . . 40 15
831 12 e. 50 Boxing . . . 45 20

110 Narina Trogon

1980. Birds. Multicoloured.

832 1 m. Type **110** . . . 25 10
833 1 m. 50 South African crowned crane . . . 30 10
834 2 m. 50 Bare-throated francolin 30 10
835 5 m. Ostrich . . . 65 10
836 7 m. 50 Spur-winged goose . . 75 15
837 12 m. 50 African fish eagle . . 90 25

111 Family and Census Officer

1980. First General Census.

838 **111** 3 m. 50 multicoloured . . 25 10

112 Animals fleeing from Fire

1980. Campaign against Bush Fires.

839 **112** 3 m. 50 multicoloured . . 25 10

113 "Harpa major"

1980. Stamp Day. Shells. Multicoloured.
840 1 m. Type **113** 10 10
841 1 m. 50 "Lambis chiragra" 15 10
842 2 m. 50 Venus comb shell 20 10
843 5 m. "Architectonia perspectiva" 40 15
844 7 m. 50 "Murex ramosus" 50 20
845 12 m. 50 "Strombus aurisdianae" 85 35

114 Pres. Machel, Electricity Pylons, Aircraft and Lorry

1981. "Decade for Victory over Underdevelopment".
846 **114** 3 m. 50 blue and red 1·00 25
847 – 7 m. 50 brown and green 25 15
848 – 12 m. 50 mauve and blue 50 30
DESIGNS: 7 m. 50, Pres. Machel and armed forces on parade; 12 m. 50, Pres. Machel and classroom scenes.

115 Footballer and Athletic de Bilbao Stadium

1981. World Cup Football Championships, Spain (1982). Multicoloured.
849 1 m. Type **115** 10 10
850 1 m. 50 Valencia, C.F. 10 10
851 2 m. 50 Oviedo C.F. 10 10
852 5 m. R. Betis Balompie 20 10
853 7 m. 50 Real Zaragoza 25 15
854 12 m. 50 R. C.D. Espanol 50 25

116 Giraffe **117** Chitende

1981. Protected Animals. Multicoloured.
856 50 c. Type **116** 10 10
857 1 m. 50 Topi 10 10
858 2 m.50 Aardvark 10 10
859 3 m. African python 10 10
860 5 m. Loggerhead turtle 20 15
861 10 m. Marabou stork 50 30
862 12 m. 50 Saddle-bill stork 80 35
863 15 m. Kori bustard 95 45

1981. Musical Instruments. Multicoloured.
864 50 c. Type **117** 10 10
865 2 m. Pankwe (horiz) 10 10
866 2 m. 50 Kanyembe 10 10
867 7 m. Nyanga (horiz) 30 20
868 10 m. Likuti and M'Petheni (horiz) 70 25

118 Disabled Persons making Baskets

1981. International Year of Disabled People.
869 **118** 5 m. multicoloured 25 15

119 De Havilland Dragon Rapide

1981. Air. Mozambique Aviation History. Mult.
870 50 c. Type **119** 10 10
871 1 m. 50 Junkers Ju 52/3m 10 10
872 3 m. Lockheed Super Electra 20 15
873 7 m. 50 De Havilland Dove 35 30
874 10 m. Douglas DC-3 50 35
875 12 m. 50 Fokker Friendship 75 50

120 Controlled Killing, Marromeu

1981. World Hunting Exhibition, Plovdiv. Mult.
876 2 m. Type **120** 30 15
877 5 m. Traditional hunting Cheringoma 20 15
878 6 m. Tourist hunting, Save 40 30
879 7 m. 60 Marksmanship Gorongosa 40 20
880 12 m. 50 African elephants, Gorongosa 1·25 60
881 20 m. Trap, Cabo Delgado 80 50

121 50 Centavos Coin **122** Sunflower

1981. 1st Anniv of New Currency. Mult.
883 50 c. Type **121** 10 10
884 1 m. One metical coin 10 10
885 2 m. 50 Two meticals 50 coin 10 10
886 5 m. Five meticals coin 20 15
887 10 m. Ten meticals coin 50 25
888 20 m. Twenty meticals coin 1·10 55

1981. Agricultural Resources.
890 **122** 50 c. orange and red 10 10
891 – 1 m. black and red 10 10
892 – 1 m. 50 blue and red 10 10
893 – 2 m. 50 yellow and red 10 10
894 – 3 m. 50 green and red 15 10
895 – 4 m. 50 grey and red 15 10
896 – 10 m. blue and red 40 15
897 – 12 m. 50 brown and red 50 20
898 – 15 m. brown and red 60 25
899 – 25 m. green and red 1·10 40
900 – 40 m. orange and red 1·60 60
901 – 60 m. brown and red 2·25 1·00
DESIGNS: 1 m. Cotton; 1 m. 50, Sisal; 2 m. 50, Cashew; 3 m. 50, Tea; 4 m. 50, Sugar cane; 10 m. Castor oil; 12 m. 50, Coconut; 15 m. Tobacco; 25 m. Rice; 40 m. Maize; 60 m. Groundnut.

123 Archaeological Excavation, Manyikeni

1981. Archaeological Excavation. Mult.
902 1 m. Type **123** 10 10
903 1 m. 50 Hand-axe (Massingir Dam) 10 10
904 2 m. 50 Ninth century bowl (Chibuene) 10 10
905 7 m. 50 Ninth century pot (Chibuene) 30 20
906 12 m. 50 Gold beads (Manyikeni) 50 30
907 20 m. Gong (Manyikeni) 80 50

124 Mapiko Mask

1981. Sculptures. Multicoloured.
908 50 c. Type **124** 10 10
909 1 m. Woman who suffers 10 10
910 2 m. 50 Woman with a child 10 10
911 3 m. 50 The man who makes fire 15 10
912 5 m. Chietane 20 15
913 12 m. 50 Chietane (different) 70 30

125 Broken Loaf on Globe

1981. World Food Day.
914 **125** 10 m. multicoloured 45 25

126 Tanker "Matchedje"

1981. Mozambique Ships. Multicoloured.
915 50 c. Type **126** 10 10
916 1 m. 50 Tug "Macuti" 10 10
917 3 m. Trawler "Vega 7" 20 10
918 5 m. Freighter "Linde" 30 20
919 7 m. 50 Freighter "Pemba" 50 30
920 12 m. 50 Dredger "Rovuma" 95 55

127 "Portunus pelagicus"

1981. Crustaceans. Multicoloured.
921 50 c. Type **127** 10 10
922 1 m. 50 "Scylla serrata" 10 10
923 3 m. "Penacus indicus" 15 10
924 7 m. 50 "Palinurus delagoae" 35 20
925 12 m. 50 "Lysiosquilla maculata" 55 35
926 15 m. "Panulirus ornatus" 80 45

128 "Hypoxis multiceps" **129** Telex Tape, Telephone and Globe

1981. Flowers. Multicoloured.
927 1 m. Type **128** 10 10
928 1 m. 50 "Pelargonium luridun" 10 10
929 2 m. 50 "Caralluma melanathera" 10 10
930 7 m. 50 "Ansellia gigantea" 35 20
931 12 m. 50 "Stapelia leendertsiae" 60 35
932 25 m. "Adenium multiflorum" 1·25 70

1982. 1st Anniv of Mozambique Post and Telecommunications. Multicoloured.
933 6 m. Type **129** 35 20
934 15 m. Winged envelope and envelope forming railway wagon 75 75

130 Diagram of Petrol Engine

1982. Fuel Saving. Multicoloured.
935 5 m. Type **130** 30 15
936 7 m. 50 Speeding car 45 25
937 10 m. Loaded truck 60 35

131 "Pelamis platurus"

1982. Reptiles. Multicoloured.
938 50 c. Type **131** 10 10
939 1 m. 50 "Naja mossambica mossambica" 10 10
940 3 m. "Thelotornis capensis mossambica" 20 15
941 6 m. "Dendroaspis polylepis polylepis" 35 25
942 15 m. "Dispholidus typus" 80 50
943 20 m. "Bitis arietans arietans" 1·25 75

132 Dr. Robert Koch, Bacillus and X-Ray

1982. Centenary of Discovery of Tubercle Bacillus.
944 **132** 20 m. multicoloured 1·40 75

133 Telephone Line **134** Player with Ball

1982. International Telecommunications Union. Plenipotentiary Conference.
945 **133** 20 m. multicoloured 1·00 75

1982. World Cup Football Championship, Spain. Multicoloured.
946 1 m. 50 Type **134** 10 10
947 3 m. 50 Player heading ball 25 15
948 7 m. Two players fighting for ball 40 20
949 10 m. Player receiving ball 60 30
950 20 m. Goalkeeper 1·00 75

135 Political Rally **137** "Vangueria infausta"

1982. 25th Anniv of FRELIMO. Multicoloured.
953 4 m. Type **135** 25 15
954 8 m. Agriculture 45 25
955 12 m. Marching workers 70 35

1982. Fruits. Multicoloured.
956 1 m. Type **137** 10 10
957 2 m. "Mimusops caffra" 10 10
958 4 m. "Sclerocarya caffra" 25 15
959 8 m. "Strychnos spinosa" 45 25
960 12 m. "Salacia kraussi" 70 40
961 32 m. "Trichilia emetica" 1·50 85

138 "Sputnik I" **139** Vigilantes

1982. 25th Anniv of First Articial Satellite. Multicoloured.
962 1 m. Type **138** 10 10
963 2 m. First manned space flight 10 10
964 4 m. First walk in space 25 15
965 8 m. First manned flight to the moon 45 25
966 16 m. "Soyuz"–"Apollo" mission 1·00 70
967 20 m. "Intercosmos" rocket 1·25 70

1982. People's Surveillance Day.
968 **139** 4 m. multicoloured 25 15

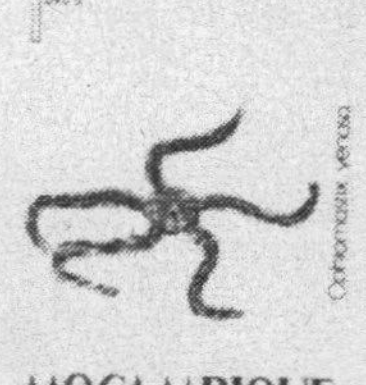

140 Caique **141** "Ophiomostix venosa"

1982. Traditional Boats. Multicoloured.
969 1 m. Type **140** 10 10
970 2 m. Machua 15 10
971 4 m. Calaua (horiz) 30 15
972 8 m. Chitatarro (horiz) 60 25
973 12 m. Cangaia (horiz) 80 35
974 16 m. Chata (horiz) 1·40 60

1982. Starfishes and Sea Urchins. Multicoloured.
975 1 m. Type **141** 10 10
976 2 m. "Protoreaster lincki" . . 10 10
977 4 m. "Tropiometra carinata" . 15 10
978 8 m. "Holothuria scabra" . . 35 20
979 12 m. "Prionocidaris baculosa" 60 35
980 16 m. "Colobocentrotus atnatus" 80 40

142 Soldiers defending Mozambique

1983. 4th Frelimo Party Congress. Multicoloured.
981 4 m. Type **142** 15 10
982 8 m. Crowd waving voting papers 30 20
983 16 m. Agriculture, industry and education 65 40

143 "Codium duthierae"

1983. Seaweeds. Multicoloured.
984 1 m. Type **143** 10 10
985 2 m. "Halimeda cunata" . . . 10 10
986 4 m. "Dictyota liturata" . . . 15 10
987 8 m. "Endorachne binghamiae" 40 20
988 12 m. "Laurencia flexuosa" . . 60 30
989 20 m. "Acrosorium sp." . . . 1·00 55

144 Diving and Swimming

1983. Olympic Games, Los Angeles (1st issue). Multicoloured.
990 1 m. Type **144** 10 10
991 2 m. Boxing 10 10
992 4 m. Basketball 20 10
993 8 m. Handball 35 20
994 12 m. Volleyball 55 30
995 16 m. Running 65 40
996 20 m. Yachting . . . . 1·00 65
See also Nos. 1029/34.

145 Mallet Type Locomotive

1983. Steam Locomotives. Multicoloured.
998 1 m. Type **145** 10 10
999 2 m. Baldwin Series "200" . 15 10
1000 4 m. Henschel Series "1600" . 30 15
1001 8 m. Baldwin Series "05" . . 60 25
1002 16 m. Henschel Garratt type . 1·10 50
1003 32 m. Henschel Series "50" . 2·25 1·00

146 O.A.U. Emblem

1983. 20th Anniv of Organization of African Unity.
1004 **146** 4 m. multicoloured . . . 20 15

147 Four-toed Elephant-shrew

150 "Communications"

148 Aiding Flood Victims

1983. Mozambique Mammals. Multicoloured.
1005 1 m. Type **147** 10 10
1006 2 m. Four-striped grass mouse 15 10
1007 4 m. Vincent's bush squirrel 25 15
1008 8 m. Hottentot mole-rat . . 50 25
1009 12 m. Natal red hare 75 40
1010 16 m. Straw-coloured fruit bat 95 50

1983. 2nd Anniv of Mozambique Red Cross. Multicoloured.
1011 4 m. Type **148** 20 10
1012 8 m. Red Cross lorry . . . 40 20
1013 16 m. First aid demonstration 75 40
1014 32 m. Agricultural worker performing first aid . . . 1·50 75

1983. World Communications Year.
1016 **150** 8 m. multicoloured . . . 60 25

151 Line Fishing

1983. Fishery Resources. Multicoloured.
1017 50 c. Type **151** 10 10
1018 2 m. Chifonho (basket trap) 10 10
1019 4 m. Spear fishing 20 15
1020 8 m. Gamboa (fence trap) . 40 25
1021 16 m. Mono (basket trap) . 1·00 40
1022 20 m. Lema (basket trap) . . 1·25 55

152 Kudu Horn

153 Swimming

1983. Stamp Day. Multicoloured.
1023 50 c. Type **152** 10 10
1024 1 m. Drum communication . 10 10
1025 4 m. Postal runners 20 15
1026 8 m. Mail canoe 40 40
1027 16 m. Mail van 75 40
1028 20 m. Mail train . . . . . . 1·75 1·00

1984. Olympic Games, Los Angeles (2nd issue). Multicoloured.
1029 50 c. Type **153** 10 10
1030 4 m. Football 20 10
1031 8 m. Hurdling 35 20
1032 16 m. Basketball 90 50
1033 32 m. Handball . . . . . . 1·50 80
1034 60 m. Boxing . . . . 2·50 1·50

154 "Trichilia emetica"

1984. Indigenous Trees. Multicoloured.
1035 50 c. Type **154** 10 10
1036 2 m. "Brachystegia spiciformis" 10 10
1037 4 m. "Androstachys johnsonii" 20 10
1038 8 m. "Pterocarpus angolensis" 35 20
1039 16 m. "Milletia stuhlmannii" 80 40
1040 50 m. "Dalbergia melanoxylon" 2·25 1·40

155 Dove with Olive Sprig

1984. Nkomati South Africa–Mozambique Non-aggression Pact.
1041 **155** 4 m. multicoloured . . . 25 10

156 State Arms

1984. Emblems of the Republic. Multicoloured.
1042 4 m. Type **156** 20 10
1043 8 m. State Flag 40 20

157 Makway Dance

1984. "Lubrapex '84" Portuguese–Brazilian Stamp Exhibition, Lisbon. Traditional Mozambican dances. Multicoloured.
1044 4 m. Type **157** 20 10
1045 8 m. Mapiko dance 40 20
1046 16 m. Wadjaba dance . . . . 1·10 50

158 Nampula Museum and Statuette of Woman with Water Jug

1984. Museums. Multicoloured.
1047 50 c. Type **158** 10 10
1048 4 m. Natural History Museum and secretary bird 45 10
1049 8 m. Revolution Museum and soldier carrying wounded comrade 35 20
1050 16 m. Colonial History Museum and cannon 65 40
1051 20 m. National Numismatic Museum and coins . . . . 1·00 65
1052 30 m. St. Paul's Palace and antique chair . . . . 1·25 95

159 "Alestes imberi"

1984. Fishes. Multicoloured.
1053 50 c. Type **159** 10 10
1054 4 m. "Labeo congoro" . . . 20 10
1055 12 m. "Synodontis zambezensis" 60 35
1056 16 m. "Notobranchius rachovii" 75 50
1057 40 m. "Barbus paludinosus" . 2·00 1·25
1058 60 m. "Barilius zambezensis" 2·75 1·75

160 Badge and Laurels

162 Knife and Club

161 Rural Landscape and Emblem

1984. International Fair, Maputo.
1059 **160** 16 m. multicoloured . . 70 50

1984. 20th Anniv of African Development Bank.
1060 **161** 4 m. multicoloured . . . 30 10

1984. Traditional Weapons. Multicoloured.
1061 50 c. Type **162** 10 10
1062 4 m. Axes 20 10
1063 8 m. Spear and shield . . . 35 15
1064 16 m. Bow and arrow . . . 75 35
1065 32 m. Rifle . . . . 1·50 95
1066 50 m. Assegai and arrow . . 2·25 1·60

163 Workers and Emblem

1984. 1st Anniv of Organization of Mozambican Workers.
1067 **163** 4 m. multicoloured . . . 20 10

164 Barue 1902 Postmark

1984. Stamp Day. Postmarks. Multicoloured.
1068 4 m. Type **164** 15 10
1069 8 m. Zumbo postmark and King Carlos 15 r. Mozambique "key type" stamp 35 20
1070 12 m. Mozambique Company postmark and 1935 airmail stamp 55 30
1071 16 m. Macequece postmark and 1937 2 e. Mozambique Company stamp 70 40

165 Keeper and Hive

166 Shot-putter and Emblem

1985. Bee-keeping. Multicoloured.
1072 4 m. Type **165** 15 10
1073 8 m. Worker bee 45 20
1074 16 m. Drone . . . . 1·00 40
1075 20 m. Queen bee . . . . . . 1·40 60

1985. "Olymphilex 85" Olympic Stamps Exhibition, Lausanne.
1076 **166** 16 m. blue, black & red . 75 35

167 Forecasting Equipment and Desert

1985. World Meteorology Day.
1077 **167** 4 m. multicoloured . . . 35 10

168 Map

1985. 5th Anniv of Southern African Development Co-ordination Conference. Multicoloured.
1078 4 m. Type **168** 15 10
1079 8 m. Map and pylon 45 20
1080 16 m. Industry and transport 1·00 50
1081 32 m. Member states' flags . 1·60 95

169 Battle of Mujenga, 1896

1985. 10th Anniv of Independence. Mult.
1082 1 m. Type **169** 10 10
1083 4 m. Attack on Barue by Macombe, 1917 . . . . . 25 10
1084 8 m. Attack on Massangano, 1868 . . . . 55 20
1085 16 m. Battle of Marracuene, 1895, and Gungunhana . . 1·25 50

170 U.N. Building, New York and Flag

1985. 40th Anniv of U.N.O.
1086 **170** 16 m. multicoloured . . 80 50

171 Mathacuzana

1985. Traditional Games and Sports. Multicoloured.
1087 50 c. Type **171** 10 10
1088 4 m. Mudzobo 20 10
1089 8 m. Muravarava (board game) 40 20
1090 16 m. N'tshuwa 90 50

172 "Rana angolensis"

1985. Frogs and Toads. Multicoloured.
1091 50 c. Type **172** 10 10
1092 1 m. "Hyperolius pictus" . . 10 10
1093 4 m. "Ptychadena porosissima" 15 10
1094 8 m. "Afrixalus formasinii" . 50 20
1095 16 m. "Bufo regularis" . . . 95 50
1096 32 m. "Hyperolius marmoratus" . . . . . . 2·00 95

HAVE YOU READ THE NOTES AT THE BEGINNING OF THIS CATALOGUE?
These often provide the answers to the enquiries we receive.

174 "Aloe ferox"

176 Comet and "Giotto" Space Probe

175 Mozambique Company, 1918 10 c. Stamp

1985. Medicinal Plants. Multicoloured.
1099 50 c. Type **174** 10 10
1100 1 m. "Boophone disticha" . 10 10
1101 3 m. 50 "Gloriosa superba" 15 10
1102 4 m. "Cotyledon orbiculata" 15 10
1103 8 m. "Homeria breyniana" . 55 20
1104 50 m. "Haemanthus coccineus" 3·00 1·50

1985. Stamp Day. Multicoloured.
1105 1 m. Type **175** 10 10
1106 4 m. Nyassa Co. 1911 25 r. stamp 15 10
1107 8 m. Mozambique Co. 1918 ½ c. stamp 50 20
1108 16 m. Nyassa Co. 1924 1 c. Postage Due stamp . . . 1·10 50

1986. Appearance of Halley's Comet.
1109 **176** 4 m. blue & light blue . 20 10
1110 – 8 m. violet & light violet 50 20
1111 – 16 m. multicoloured . . 95 50
1112 – 30 m. multicoloured . . 2·00 95
DESIGNS: 8 m. Comet orbits; 16 m. Small and large telescopes, comet and space probe; 30 m. Comet, stars and globe.

177 Vicente

1986. World Cup Football Championship, Mexico. Multicoloured.
1113 3 m. Type **177** 15 10
1114 4 m. Coluna 20 10
1115 8 m. Costa Pereira 40 20
1116 12 m. Hilario 65 35
1117 16 m. Matateu 95 50
1118 50 m. Eusebio . . . . 3·00 1·60

178 Dove and Emblem

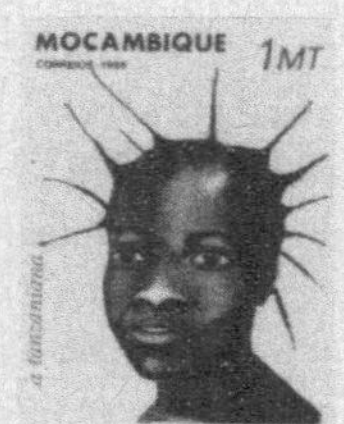

179 "Amanita muscaria"

1986. International Peace Year.
1119 **178** 16 m. multicoloured . . 85 45

1986. Fungi. Multicoloured.
1120 4 m. Type **179** 35 15
1121 8 m. "Lactarius deliciosus" . 65 25
1122 16 m. "Amanita phaloides" . 1·40 60
1123 30 m. "Tricholoma nudum" 2·75 1·10

181 Spiky Style

1986. Women's Hairstyles. Multicoloured.
1125 1 m. Type **181** 10 10
1126 4 m. Beaded plaits 25 10
1127 8 m. Plaited tightly to head . 50 20
1128 16 m. Plaited tightly to head with ponytail . . . . 1·25 55

182 Dugong

1986. Marine Mammals. Multicoloured.
1129 1 m. Type **182** 10 10
1130 8 m. Common dolphin . . . 35 20
1131 16 m. "Neobalena marginata" 1·25 50
1132 50 f. Fin whale . . . . 3·50 1·75

183 Children Studying

1986. 1st Anniv of Continuadores Youth Organization.
1133 **183** 4 m. multicoloured . . . 30 15

184 50 m. Notes

1986. Savings. Multicoloured.
1134 4 m. Type **184** 25 10
1135 8 m. 100 m. notes 50 20
1136 16 m. 500 m. notes . . . . . 1·40 50
1137 30 m. 1000 m. notes . . . . . 2·50 1·25

185 Quelimane Post Office

1986. Stamp Day. Post Offices. Multicoloured.
1138 3 m. Type **185** 20 10
1139 4 m. Maputo 30 10
1140 8 m. Beira 65 20
1141 16 m. Nampula . . . . 1·40 50

186 Pyrite

1987. Minerals. Multicoloured.
1142 4 m. Type **186** 30 10
1143 8 m. Emerald 60 20
1144 12 m. Agate 85 40
1145 16 m. Malachite . . . . . . 1·40 50
1146 30 m. Garnet . . . . 2·25 1·25
1147 50 m. Amethyst . . . . 3·75 1·75

187 Crowd beneath Flag

1987. 10th Anniv of Mozambique Liberation Front.
1148 **187** 4 m. multicoloured . . . 30 15

188 Little Libombos Dam

1987.
1149 **188** 16 m. multicoloured . . 1·40 60

189 Children being Vaccinated

1987. World Health Day. Vaccination Campaign.
1150 **189** 50 m. multicoloured . . 1·60 1·50

190 Common Grenadier

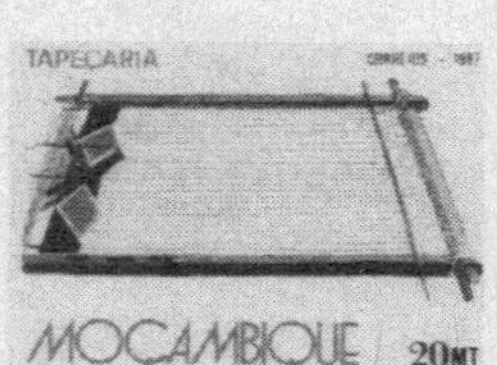

191 Football

1987. Birds. Multicoloured.
1151 3 m. Type **190** 65 40
1152 4 m. Woodland kingfisher . 65 40
1153 8 m. White-fronted bee eater 65 40
1154 12 m. Lesser seedcracker . . 65 40
1155 16 m. Broad-billed roller . . 65 40
1156 30 m. Neergaard's sunbird . 65 40

1987. Olympic Games, Seoul (1988) (1st issue). Multicoloured.
1157 12 m. 50, Type **191** 10 10
1158 25 m. Running 20 10
1159 50 m. Handball 40 20
1160 75 m. Chess . . . . 1·25 30
1161 100 m. Basketball . . . . . 1·25 35
1162 200 m. Swimming . . . . . 1·75 65
See also Nos. 1176/81.

193 Work on Loom

1987. Weaving. Multicoloured.
1164 20 m. Type **193** 15 10
1165 40 m. Triangle and diamond design 40 10
1166 80 m. "Eye" design 70 20
1167 200 m. Red carpet . . . . . 1·75 60

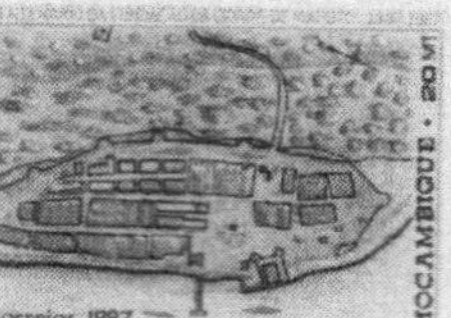

194 Piper "Navajo"

1987. Air. History of Aviation in Mozambique. Multicoloured.
1168 20 m. Type **194** 15 10
1169 40 m. De Havilland Hornet moth 25 10
1170 80 m. Boeing 737 . . . . . 50 20
1171 120 m. Beechcraft King Air . 75 20
1172 160 m. Piper Aztec . . . . 1·00 35
1173 320 m. Douglas DC-10 . . . 2·00 75

195 Early Plan

1987. Centenary of Maputo as City.
1174 **195** 20 m. multicoloured . . 20 15

1987. No. 895 surch **4,00 MT**.

1175		4 m. on 4 m. 50 grey & red	15	10

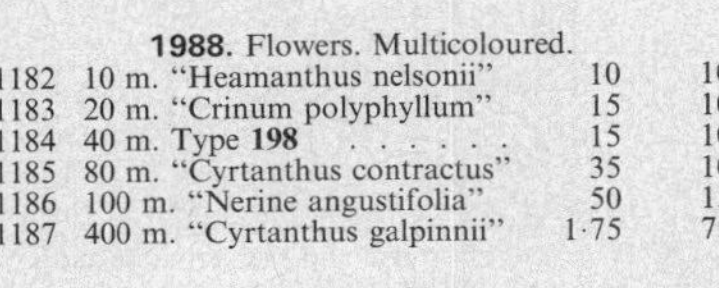

197 Javelin throwing **198** "Boophane disticha"

1988. Olympic Games, Seoul (2nd issue). Mult.

1176		10 m. Type **197**	10	10
1177		20 m. Baseball	10	10
1178		40 m. Boxing	10	10
1179		80 m. Hockey	40	10
1180		100 m. Gymnastics	50	15
1181		400 m. Cycling	1·50	75

1988. Flowers. Multicoloured.

1182		10 m. "Heamanthus nelsonii"	10	10
1183		20 m. "Crinum polyphyllum"	15	10
1184		40 m. Type **198**	15	10
1185		80 m. "Cyrtanthus contractus"	35	10
1186		100 m. "Nerine angustifolia"	50	15
1187		400 m. "Cyrtanthus galpinnii"	1·75	75

199 Man refusing Cigarette

1988. 40th Anniv of W.H.O. Anti-smoking Campaign.

1188	**199**	20 m. multicoloured	20	10

201 Mat

1988. Basketry. Multicoloured.

1190		20 m. Type **201**	10	10
1191		25 m. Basket with lid	10	10
1192		80 m. Basket with handle	20	10
1193		100 m. Fan	30	10
1194		400 m. Dish	1·25	60
1195		500 m. Conical basket	1·60	85

203 Percheron

1988. Horses. Multicoloured.

1197		20 m. Type **203**	15	10
1198		40 m. Arab	20	10
1199		80 m. Pure blood	40	10
1200		100 m. Pony	50	15

204 Machel

1988. 2nd Death Anniv of Samora Machel (President 1975–86).

1201	**204**	20 m. multicoloured	15	10

205 Inhambane

1988. Ports. Multicoloured.

1202		20 m. Type **205**	15	10
1203		50 m. Quelimane (vert)	10	10
1204		75 m. Pemba	15	10
1205		100 m. Beira	35	10
1206		250 m. Nacala (vert)	65	35
1207		500 m. Maputo	1·40	70

206 Mobile Post Office

1988. Stamp Day. Multicoloured.

1208		20 m. Type **206**	10	10
1209		40 m. Posting box (vert)	15	10

207 Maize **208** Mondlane

1989. 5th FRELIMO Congress. Multicoloured.

1210		25 m. Type **207**	10	10
1211		50 m. Hoe	10	10
1212		75 m. Abstract	10	10
1213		100 m. Cogwheels	20	10
1214		250 m. Right-half of cogwheel	50	25

Nos. 1210/14 were printed together, se-tenant, forming a composite design.

1989. 20th Anniv of Assassination of Pres. Mondlane.

1215	**208**	25 m. black, gold & red	15	10

209 "Storming the Bastille" (Thevenin)

1989. Bicentenary of French Revolution. Mult.

1216		100 m. Type **209**	25	10
1217		250 m. "Liberty guiding the People" (Delacroix)	60	35

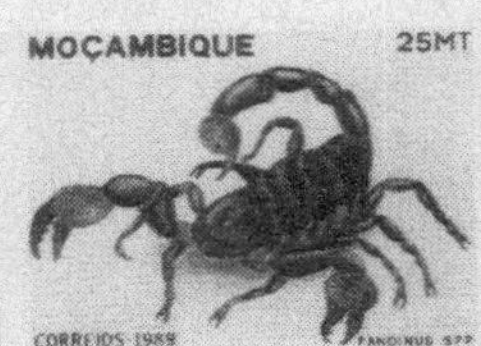

210 "Pandinus sp."

1989. Venomous Animals. Multicoloured.

1219		25 m. Type **210**	10	10
1220		50 m. Egyptian cobra	10	10
1221		75 m. "Bombus sp." (bee)	15	10
1222		100 m. "Paraphysa sp." (spider)	25	10
1223		250 m. "Conus marmoreus"	90	40
1224		500 m. Devil firefish	1·40	70

211 "Acropora pulchra"

1989. Corals. Multicoloured.

1225		25 m. Type **211**	10	10
1226		50 m. "Eunicella papilosa"	15	10
1227		100 m. "Dendrophyla migrantus"	30	10
1228		250 m. "Favia fragum"	50	35

212 Footballers **213** Macuti Lighthouse

1989. World Cup Football Championship, Italy (1990). Designs showing various footballing scenes.

1229	**212**	30 m. multicoloured	10	10
1230	–	60 m. multicoloured	15	10
1231	–	125 m. multicoloured	30	10
1232	–	200 m. multicoloured	50	25
1233	–	250 m. multicoloured	65	35
1234	–	500 m. multicoloured	1·50	70

1989. Lighthouses. Multicoloured.

1235		30 m. Type **213**	15	10
1236		60 m. Pinda	15	10
1237		125 m. Cape Delgado	30	10
1238		200 m. Goa Island	60	25
1239		250 m. Caldeira Point	80	35
1240		500 m. Vilhena	1·50	70

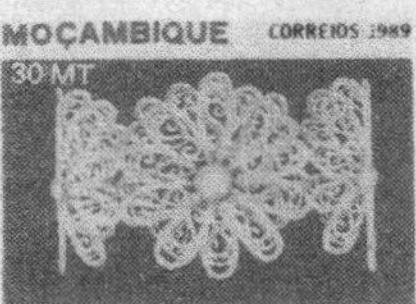

214 Bracelet

1989. Silver Filigree Work.

1241	**214**	30 m. grey, red & black	10	10
1242	–	60 m. grey, blue & black	15	10
1243	–	125 m. grey, red & black	25	10
1244	–	200 m. grey, bl & black	40	25
1245	–	250 m. grey, pur & blk	55	35
1246	–	500 m. grey, grn & blk	1·25	70

DESIGNS: 60 m. Flower belt; 125 m. Necklace; 200 m. Casket; 250 m. Spoons; 500 m. Butterfly.

215 Flag and Soldiers **216** Rain Gauge

1989. 25th Anniv of Fight for Independence.

1247	**215**	30 m. multicoloured	15	10

1989. Meteorological Instruments. Multicoloured.

1248		30 m. Type **216**	10	10
1249		60 m. Radar graph	15	10
1250		125 m. Sheltered measuring instruments	30	10
1251		200 m. Computer terminal	55	25

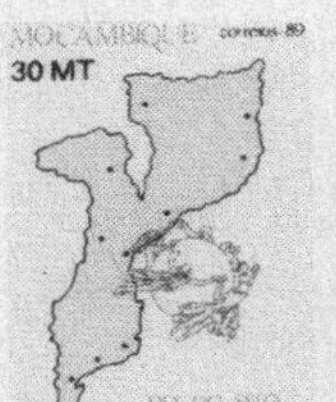

218 Map and U.P.U. Emblem **219** Railway Map

1989. Stamp Day.

1253	**218**	30 m. multicoloured	15	10
1254	–	60 m. black, green & red	15	10

DESIGN: 60 m. Map and Mozambique postal emblem.

1990. 10th Anniv of Southern Africa Development Co-ordination Conference.

1255	**219**	35 m. multicoloured	20	10

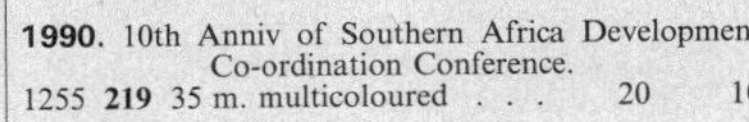

220 Cloth and Woman wearing Dress

1990. Traditional Dresses. Designs showing women wearing different dresses and details of cloth used.

1256	**220**	42 m. multicoloured	10	10
1257	–	90 m. multicoloured	15	10
1258	–	150 m. multicoloured	20	10
1259	–	200 m. multicoloured	25	15
1260	–	400 m. multicoloured	55	40
1261	–	500 m. multicoloured	65	50

221 Sena Fortress, Sofala

1990. Fortresses.

1262	**221**	45 m. blue and black	10	10
1263	–	90 m. blue and black	15	10
1264	–	150 m. multicoloured	20	10
1265	–	200 m. multicoloured	30	15
1266	–	400 m. red and black	55	40
1267	–	500 m. red and black	70	40

DESIGNS: 90 m. Sto. Antonio, Ibo Island; 150 m. S. Sebastiao, Mozambique Island; 200 m. S. Caetano, Sofala; 400 m. Our Lady of Conception, Maputo; 500 m. S. Luis, Tete.

223 Obverse and Reverse of 50 m. Coin

1990. 15th Anniv of Bank of Mozambique.

1269	**223**	100 m. multicoloured	20	10

224 Statue of Eduardo Mondlane (founder of FRELIMO)

1990. 15th Anniv of Independence. Mult.

1270		42 m. 50 Type **224**	10	10
1271		150 m. Statue of Samora Machel (President, 1975–86)	25	15

225 White Rhinoceros

1990. Endangered Animals. Multicoloured.

1272		42 m. 50 Type **225**	15	10
1273		100 m. Dugong	20	10
1274		150 m. African elephant	35	15
1275		200 m. Cheetah	40	15
1276		400 m. Spotted-necked otter	70	40
1277		500 m. Hawksbill turtle	85	50

226 "Dichrostachys cinerea" **227** Pillar Box waving to Kurika

1990. Environmental Protection. Plants. Mult.

1278		42 m. 50 Type **226**	10	10
1279		100 m. Forest fire	20	10
1280		150 m. Horsetail tree	25	10
1281		200 m. Mangrove	30	15
1282		400 m. "Estrato herbaceo" (grass)	65	40
1283		500 m. Pod mahogany	80	50

1990. Kurika (post mascot) at Work. Mult.

1284		42 m. 50 Type **227**	15	10
1285		42 m. 50 Hand cancelling envelopes	15	10
1286		42 m. 50 Leaping across hurdles	15	10
1287		42 m. 50 Delivering post to chicken	15	10

MINIMUM PRICE

The minimum price quoted is 10p which represents a handling charge rather than a basis for valuing common stamps. For further notes about prices, see introductory pages.

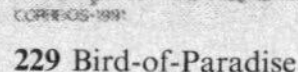

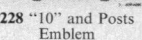

228 "10" and Posts Emblem

229 Bird-of-Paradise Flower

1991. 10th Anniv of National Posts and Telecommunications Enterprises, Mozambique.
1288 **228** 50 m. blue, red & blk . . 15 10
1289 – 50 m. brown, green & black 15 10
DESIGN: No. 1289, "10" and telecommunications emblem.

1991. Flowers. Multicoloured.
1290 50 m. Type **229** 15 10
1291 125 m. Flamingo lily 25 15
1292 250 m. Calla lily 50 30
1293 300 m. Canna lily 55 35

230 Two Hartebeest

231 Mpompine

1991. Lichtenstein's Hartebeest. Multicoloured.
1294 50 m. Type **230** 15 10
1295 100 m. Alert hartebeest . . . 20 10
1296 250 m. Hartebeest grazing . . 50 30
1297 500 m. Mother feeding young 90 60

1991. Maputo Drinking Fountains. Mult.
1298 50 m. Type **231** 10 10
1299 125 m. Chinhambanine . . . 15 10
1300 250 m. S. Pedro-Zaza . . . 25 10
1301 300 m. Xipamanine 35 15

232 Painting by Samate

233 Diving

1991. Paintings by Mozambican Artists. Mult.
1302 180 m. Type **232** 15 10
1303 250 m. Malangatana Ngwenya 20 15
1304 560 m. Malangatana Ngwenya (different) 40 30

1991. Olympic Games, Barcelona (1992). Mult.
1305 10 m. Type **233** 10 10
1306 50 m. Roller hockey 15 10
1307 100 m. Tennis 20 10
1308 200 m. Table tennis 30 10
1309 500 m. Running 50 20
1310 1000 m. Badminton 85 40

234 Proposed Boundaries in 1890 Treaty

236 Skipping

1991. Centenary of Settling of Mozambique Borders. Multicoloured.
1311 600 m. Type **234** 50 25
1312 800 m. Frontiers settled in English-Portuguese 1891 treaty 75 35

1991. Stamp Day. Children's Games. Multicoloured.
1314 40 m. Type **236** 10 10
1315 150 m. Spinning top 10 10
1316 400 m. Marbles 20 10
1317 900 m. Hopscotch 45 20

MORE DETAILED LISTS
are given in the Stanley Gibbons Catalogues referred to in the country headings. For lists of current volumes see introduction

237 "Christ"

238 "Rhisophora mucronata"

1992. Stained Glass Windows. Multicoloured.
1318 40 m. Type **237** 10 10
1319 150 m. "Faith" 10 10
1320 400 m. "IC XC" 20 10
1321 900 m. Window in three sections 45 20

1992. Marine Flowers. Multicoloured.
1322 300 m. Type **238** 15 10
1323 600 m. "Cymodocea ciliata" 30 15
1324 1000 m. "Sophora inhambanensis" 50 25

239 Spears

240 Amethyst Sunbird

1992. "Lubrapex 92" Brazilian–Portuguese Stamp Exhibition, Lisbon. Weapons. Multicoloured.
1325 100 m. Type **239** 10 10
1326 300 m. Tridents 15 10
1327 500 m. Axe 25 10
1328 1000 m. Dagger 50 25

1992. Birds. Multicoloured.
1329 150 m. Type **240** 10 10
1330 200 m. Mosque swallow . . . 10 10
1331 300 m. Red-capped robin chat 15 10
1332 400 m. "Lamprocolius chloropterus" 20 10
1333 500 m. Bush shrike 25 10
1334 800 m. African golden oriole 40 20

241 Emblem

242 Phiane

1992. 30th Anniv of Eduardo Mondlane University.
1335 **241** 150 m. green and brown 10 10

1992. "Genova '92" International Thematic Stamp Exn. Musical Instruments. Multicoloured.
1336 200 m. Type **242** 10 10
1337 300 m. Xirupe (rattle) . . . 15 10
1338 500 m. Ngulula (drum) . . . 25 10
1339 1500 m. Malimba (drum) . . 75 35

243 Children Eating

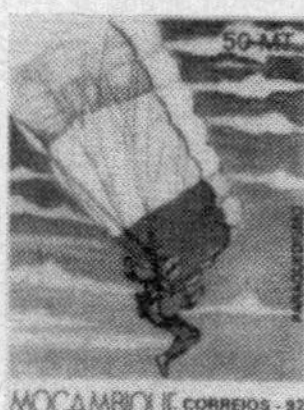
244 Parachutist

1992. International Nutrition Conference, Rome.
1341 **243** 450 m. multicoloured . . 20 10

1992. Parachuting. Multicoloured.
1342 50 m. Type **244** 10 10
1343 400 m. Parachutist and buildings 20 10
1344 500 m. Airplane dropping parachutists 25 10
1345 1500 m. Parachutist (different) 70 35

1992. No. 890 surch **50MT**.
1346 **122** 50 m. on 50 c. orange and red 10 10

246 Order of Peace and Friendship

1993. Mozambique Decorations. Multicoloured.
1347 400 m. Type **246** 20 10
1348 800 m. Bagamoyo Medal . . 40 20
1349 1000 m. Order of Eduardo Mondlane 50 25
1350 1500 m. Veteran of the Struggle for National Liberation Medal 70 35

247 Tree Stumps and Girl Carrying Wood

1993. Pollution. Multicoloured.
1351 200 m. Type **247** 10 10
1352 750 m. Chimneys smoking . . 35 15
1353 1000 m. Tanker sinking . . . 50 25
1354 1500 m. Car exhaust fumes . 70 35

248 Lion (Gorongosa Park, Sofala)

1993. National Parks. Multicoloured.
1355 200 m. Type **248** 10 10
1356 800 m. Giraffes (Banhine Park, Gaza) 40 20
1357 1000 m. Dugongs (Bazoruto Park, Inhambane) 50 25
1358 1500 m. Ostriches (Zinave Park, Inhambane) 70 35

249 Heroes Monument, Maputo

1993. "Brasiliana 93" International Stamp Exhibition, Rio de Janeiro.
1359 **249** 1500 m. multicoloured . . 55 25

250 Conference Emblem

251 "Cycas cercinalis"

1993. National Culture Conference, Maputo.
1360 **250** 200 m. multicoloured . . 10 10

1993. Forest Plants. Multicoloured.
1361 200 m. Type **251** 10 10
1362 250 m. "Cycas revoluta" . . 10 10
1363 900 m. "Encephalartos ferox" 25 10
1364 2000 m. "Equisetum ramosissimum" 50 25

252 "Anacardium occidentale"

1994. Medicinal Plants. Multicoloured.
1365 200 m. Type **252** 10 10
1366 250 m. "Sclerocarya caffra" . 10 10
1367 900 m. "Annona senegalensis" 25 10
1368 2000 m. "Crinum delagoense" 50 25

1994. Various stamps surch.
1369 50 m. on 7 m. 50 multicoloured (No. 905) 10 10
1370 50 m. on 7 m. 50 multicoloured (No. 924) 10 10
1371 50 m. on 7 m. 50 multicoloured (No. 930) 10 10
1372 100 m. on 10 m. blue and red (No. 896) 10 10
1373 100 m. on 12 m. 50 mult (No. 931) 10 10
1374 200 m. on 12 m. 50 brown and red (No. 897) 10 10
1375 250 m. on 12 m. 50 mult (No. 925) 10 10

CHARITY TAX STAMPS

The notes under this heading in Portugal also apply here.

C 15 Arms of Portugal and Mozambique and Allegorical Figures

C 16 Prow of Galley of Discoveries and Symbols of Declaration of War

1916. War Tax Fund. Imperf, roul or perf.
C234 C 15 1 c. green 50 30
C235 C 16 5 c. red 50 30

C 18 "Charity"

C 22 Society's Emblem

1920. 280th Anniv of Restoration of Portugal. Wounded Soldiers and Social Assistance Funds.
C309 C 18 ¼ c. olive 70 70
C310 ½ c. black 80 80
C311 1 c. brown 80 80
C312 2 c. brown 80 80
C313 3 c. lilac 80 80
C314 4 c. green 80 80
C315 – 5 c. green 90 90
C316 – 6 c. blue 90 90
C317 – 7½ c. brown 90 90
C318 – 8 c. yellow 90 90
C319 – 10 c. lilac 90 90
C320 – 12 c. pink 90 90
C321 – 18 c. red 90 90
C322 – 24 c. brown . . . . . 1·10 90
C323 – 30 c. olive . . . . . 1·10 90
C324 – 40 c. red . . . . . . 1·10 90
C325 – 50 c. yellow . . . . . 1·10 90
C326 – 1 e. blue . . . . . . 1·10 90
DESIGNS: 5 c. to 12 c. Wounded soldier and nurse; 18 c. to 1 e. Family scene.

1925. Marquis de Pombal stamps of Portugal, but inscr "MOCAMBIQUE".
C327 C 73 15 c. brown 20 20
C328 – 15 c. brown 20 20
C329 C 75 15 c. brown 20 20

1925. Red Cross. Surch **50 CENTAVOS**.
C330 C 22 50 c. yellow and grey . 60 40

1926. Surch **CORREIOS** and value.
C337 C 22 5 c. yellow and red . . 50 50
C338 10 c. yellow and green 60 60
C339 20 c. yellow and grey . 75 60
C340 30 c. yellow and blue . 75 60
C331 40 c. yellow and grey . 80 60
C341 40 c. yellow and violet 75 60
C332 50 c. yellow and grey . 80 60
C342 50 c. yellow and red . 75 70
C333 60 c. yellow and grey . 80 60
C343 60 c. yellow and brown 75 70
C334 80 c. yellow and grey . 80 60
C344 80 c. yellow and blue . 75 70
C335 1 e. yellow and grey . 90 80
C345 1 e. yellow and olive . 75 70
C336 2 e. yellow and grey . 90 80
C346 2 e. yellow and brown 80 80

C 25

1928. Surch **CORREIOS** and value in black, as in Type C **25**.

No.	Type	Description	Unused	Used
C347	C 25	5 c. yellow and green	1·00	1·00
C348		10 c. yellow and blue	1·00	1·00
C349		20 c. yellow and black	1·00	1·00
C350		30 c. yellow and red	1·00	1·00
C351		40 c. yellow and red	1·00	1·00
C352		50 c. yellow and red	1·00	1·00
C353		60 c. yellow and brown	1·00	1·00
C354		80 c. yellow and brown	1·00	1·00
C355		1 e. yellow and grey	1·00	1·00
C356		2 e. yellow and red	1·00	1·00

C 27

C 29 Pelican

C 28 "Charity"

1929. Value in black.

No.	Type	Description	Unused	Used
C357	C 27	40 c. red and blue	1·00	1·00
C358		40 c. violet and red	1·00	1·00
C359		40 c. violet and olive	1·00	1·00
C360		40 c. red and brown	1·00	1·00
C361		(No value) red & green	1·50	1·50
C362		40 c. blue and brown	1·00	1·00
C363		40 c. blue and orange	1·00	1·00
C364		40 c. red and green	1·00	1·00
C365		40 c. black and yellow	1·50	1·25
C366		40 c. black and brown	1·50	1·40

1942.

No.	Type	Description	Unused	Used
C383	C 28	50 c. red and black	2·50	1·00

1943. Inscr "Colonia de Mocambique". Value in black.

No.	Type	Description	Unused	Used
C384	C 29	50 c. red	2·00	75
C385		50 c. blue	2·00	75
C386		50 c. violet	2·00	75
C387		50 c. brown	2·00	75
C388		50 c. bistre	2·00	75
C389		50 c. blue	2·00	75
C393		50 c. green	2·00	75

1952. Inscr "Provincia de Mocambique". Value in black.

No.	Type	Description	Unused	Used
C514	C 29	30 c. yellow	75	50
C515		50 c. orange	75	50
C469		50 c. green	75	50
C470		50 c. brown	75	50

1957. No. C470 surch.

No.	Type	Description	Unused	Used
C511	C 29	30 c. on 50 c. brown	40	30

C **56** Women and Children C **58** Telegraph Poles and Map

1963.

No.	Type	Description	Unused	Used
C569	C 56	30 c. green, blk & red	10	10
C570		50 c. black, bistre & red	20	10
C571		50 c. black, pink & red	20	10
C572		50 c. black, green & red	20	10
C573		50 c. black, blue & red	20	10
C574		50 c. black, buff & red	20	10
C575		50 c. black, grey & red	20	10
C576		50 c. black, yell & red	15	10
C577		1 e. grey, blk & red	50	25
C578		1 e. black, brn & red	15	10
C578a		1 e. black, mve & red	15	10

1965. Mozambique Telecommunications Improvement. Inscr "TELECOMMUNICACOES".

No.	Type	Description	Unused	Used
C579	C 58	30 c. black, pink & vio	10	10
C580	–	50 c. black, brown & bl	10	10
C581	–	1 e. blk, orge & grn	15	10

DESIGN—19½ × 36 mm: 50 c. 1 e. Telegraph linesman.

A 2 e. 50, in Type C **58** was also issued for compulsory use on telegrams.

NEWSPAPER STAMPS

1893. "Embossed" key-type of Mozambique surch **JORNAES 2½ 2½.**

No.	Type	Description	Unused	Used
N53	Q	2½ r. on 40 r. brown	14·00	9·00

1893. "Embossed" key-type of Mozambique surch **JORNAES 2½ REIS.**

No.	Type	Description	Unused	Used
N54	Q	2½ r. on 40 r. brown	55·00	38·00
N55		5 r. on 40 r. brown	35·00	30·00

1893. "Newspaper" key-type inscribed "MOCAMBIQUE".

No.	Type	Description	Unused	Used
N58	V	2½ r. brown	25	20

POSTAGE DUE STAMPS

1904. "Due" key-type inscr "MOCAMBIQUE".

No.	Type	Description	Unused	Used
D146	W	5 r. green	20	20
D147		10 r. grey	20	20
D148		20 r. brown	20	20
D149		30 r. orange	35	20
D150		50 r. brown	35	20
D151		60 r. brown	1·25	75
D152		100 r. mauve	1·25	75
D153		130 r. blue	75	60
D154		200 r. red	1·10	60
D155		500 r. violet	1·25	60

1911. "Due" key-type of Mozambique optd **REPUBLICA.**

No.	Type	Description	Unused	Used
D162	W	5 r. green	20	20
D163a		10 r. green	20	20
D164		20 r. brown	25	20
D165		30 r. orange	25	20
D166		50 r. brown	25	20
D167		60 r. brown	35	20
D168		100 r. mauve	45	25
D169		130 r. blue	55	40
D170		200 r. red	65	55
D171		500 r. violet	85	60

1917. "Due" key-type of Mozambique, but currency changed.

No.	Type	Description	Unused	Used
D246	W	½ c. green	20	20
D247		1 c. grey	20	20
D248		2 c. brown	20	20
D249		3 c. orange	20	20
D250		5 c. brown	20	20
D251		6 c. brown	20	20
D252		10 c. mauve	20	20
D253		13 c. blue	30	30
D254		20 c. red	30	30
D255		50 c. violet	30	30

1918. Charity Tax stamps optd **PORTEADO.**

No.	Type	Description	Unused	Used
D256	C 15	1 c. green	70	50
D257	C 16	5 c. red	70	50

1922. "Ceres" key-type of Lourenco Marques (½, 1½ c.) and of Mozambique (1, 2½, 4 c.) surch **PORTEADO** and value and bar.

No.	Type	Description	Unused	Used
D316	U	5 c. on ½ c. black	70	50
D317		6 c. on 1 c. green	70	50
D318		10 c. on 1½ c. brown	70	50
D319		20 c. on 2½ c. violet	70	50
D320		50 c. on 4 c. pink	70	50

1924. "Ceres" key-type of Mozambique surch **Porteado** and value.

No.	Type	Description	Unused	Used
D321	U	20 c. on 30 c. green	40	30
D323		50 c. on 60 c. blue	60	40

1925. Marquis de Pombal charity tax designs as Nos. C327/9, optd **MULTA.**

No.	Type	Description	Unused	Used
D327	C 73	30 c. brown	20	20
D328	–	30 c. brown	20	20
D329	C 75	30 c. brown	20	20

1952. As Type D **70** of Macao, but inscr "MOCAMBIQUE". Numerals in red, name in black (except 50 c. in blue).

No.	Description	Unused	Used
D468	10 c. red and green	10	10
D469	30 c. sepia and pink	10	10
D470	50 c. black, blue and grey	10	10
D471	1 e. blue and olive	10	10
D472	2 e. green and yellow	15	15
D473	5 e. brown and stone	25	15

MOZAMBIQUE COMPANY Pt. 9

The Mozambique Company was responsible until 1942 for the administration of Manica and Sofala territory in Portuguese E. Africa from 1891. Now part of Mozambique.

1899. 1000 reis = 1 milreis
1913. 100 centavos = 1 escudo

1892. "Embossed" key-type inscr "PROVINCA DE MOCAMBIQUE" optd **COMPA DE MOCAMBIQUE.**

No.	Type	Description	Unused	Used
10	Q	5 r. black	30	20
2		10 r. green	40	20
3		20 r. red	50	20
4		25 r. mauve	35	25
5		40 r. brown	35	20
6		50 r. blue	40	25
7		100 r. brown	35	25
8		200 r. violet	65	50
9		300 r. orange	65	50

2

1895. Value in black or red (500, 1000 r.).

No.	Type	Description	Unused	Used
33	2	2½ r. yellow	10	10
114		2½ r. grey	50	25
17		5 r. orange	15	10
18		10 r. mauve	20	15
115		10 r. green	30	25
39		15 r. brown	20	15
116		15 r. green	30	25
20		20 r. lilac	15	15
45		25 r. green	20	15
117		25 r. red	40	20
46		50 r. blue	25	20
118		50 r. brown	40	30
109		65 r. blue	25	20
48		75 r. red	25	20
119		75 r. mauve	90	75
50		80 r. green	25	20
52		100 r. brown on buff	30	20
120		100 r. blue on blue	90	75
110		115 r. pink on rose	75	65
121		115 r. brown on rose	1·40	90
111		130 r. green on rose	75	65
122		130 r. brown on yellow	1·40	90
54		150 r. orange on rose	30	20
55		200 r. blue on blue	30	20
123		200 r. lilac on red	1·40	90
56		300 r. blue on brown	30	20
112		400 r. black on blue	75	65
124		400 r. blue on yellow	1·75	1·40
58		500 r. black	40	30
125		500 r. black on blue	1·75	40
126		700 r. mauve on yellow	1·90	1·60
59		1000 r. mauve	45	30

1895. Surch **PROVISORIO 25.**

No.	Type	Description	Unused	Used
105	2	25 on 75 r. red	1·40	1·25
77		25 on 80 r. green	7·00	5·00

1895. No. 6 optd **PROVISORIO.**

No.	Type	Description	Unused	Used
78	Q	50 r. blue	1·75	1·50

1898. Vasco da Gama. Optd **1498 Centenario da India 1898.**

No.	Type	Description	Unused	Used
80	2	2½ r. yellow	60	60
81		5 r. orange	75	65
82		10 r. mauve	75	60
84		15 r. brown	90	80
86		20 r. lilac	1·00	90
87		25 r. green	1·60	1·00
99		50 r. blue	95	90
89		75 r. red	1·60	1·40
91		80 r. green	1·60	1·25
101		100 r. brown on buff	1·75	1·50
102		150 r. orange on red	1·75	1·60
94		200 r. blue on blue	2·25	2·00
104		300 r. blue on brown	3·25	2·25

1900. Surch **25 Reis** and bar.

No.	Type	Description	Unused	Used
106	2	25 r. on 5 r. orange	1·25	75

1900. Perforated through centre and surch **50 REIS.**

No.	Type	Description	Unused	Used
108	2	50 r. on half of 20 r. lilac	40	35

1911. Optd **REPUBLICA.**

No.	Type	Description	Unused	Used
145	2	2½ r. grey	15	10
147		5 r. orange	15	10
148		10 r. green	10	10
150		15 r. green	10	10
151		20 r. lilac	15	10
153		25 r. red	10	10
155		50 r. brown	10	10
156		75 r. mauve	15	10
157		100 r. blue on blue	20	10
159		115 r. brown on red	30	20
160		130 r. brown on yellow	30	20
161		200 r. lilac on red	30	15
162		400 r. blue on yellow	30	15
163		500 r. black on blue	30	15
164		700 r. purple on yellow	35	30

1916. Surch **REPUBLICA** and value in figures.

No.	Type	Description	Unused	Used
166	2	¼ c. on 2½ r. grey	10	10
168		½ c. on 5 r. orange	10	10
170		1 c. on 10 r. green	15	15
173		1½ c. on 15 r. green	15	15
175		2 c. on 20 r. lilac	15	15
178		2½ c. on 25 r. red	15	15
180		5 c. on 50 r. brown	15	15
181		7½ c. on 75 r. mauve	25	15
182		10 c. on 100 r. blue on blue	25	15
183		11½ c. on 115 r. brown on red	50	30
184		13 c. on 130 r. brown on yell	50	25
185		20 c. on 200 r. lilac on red	40	25
186		40 c. on 400 r. blue on yell	40	25
187		50 c. on 500 r. black on blue	45	35
188		70 c. on 700 r. purple on yell	45	35

1917. Red Cross Fund. Optd **REPUBLICA**, red cross and **31.7.17.**

No.	Type	Description	Unused	Used
189	2	2½ r. grey	1·25	1·00
190		10 r. green	1·50	1·25
191		20 r. lilac	1·50	1·25
192		50 r. brown	4·00	2·00
193		75 r. mauve	10·00	8·50
194		100 r. blue	12·00	9·00
195		700 r. purple on yellow	40·00	28·00

1918. Surch **REPUBLICA** and value.

No.	Type	Description	Unused	Used
196	2	¼ c. on 700 r. purple on yellow	70	65
197		2½ c. on 500 r. black on blue	70	65
198		5 c. on 400 r. blue on yellow	70	65

HAVE YOU READ THE NOTES AT THE BEGINNING OF THIS CATALOGUE?
These often provide the answers to the enquiries we receive.

14 Native Village **15** Ivory

33 **36** Tea

1918.

No.	Type	Description	Unused	Used
199	14	¼ c. green and brown	15	15
233		¼ c. black and olive	15	15
200	15	½ c. black	15	15
201	–	1 c. black and green	15	15
202	–	1½ c. green and black	15	15
203	–	2 c. black and red	15	15
235	–	2 c. black and grey	15	15
204	–	2½ c. black and lilac	15	15
236	–	3 c. black and orange	15	15
205	–	4 c. brown and green	15	15
237	–	4 c. black and red	15	15
227	14	4½ c. black and grey	15	15
206	–	5 c. black and blue	15	15
207	–	6 c. blue and purple	25	20
238	–	6 c. black and mauve	15	15
228	–	7 c. black and blue	45	25
208	–	7½ c. green and orange	25	25
209	–	8 c. black and lilac	25	25
210	–	10 c. black and red	50	25
229	–	12 c. black and brown	65	40
241	–	12 c. black and green	25	20
211	–	15 c. black and red	50	25
212	–	20 c. black and green	20	15
251	33	24 c. black and blue	70	60
252	–	25 c. blue and brown	70	60
213	–	30 c. black and brown	30	25
244	–	30 c. black and green	35	25
214	–	40 c. black and green	25	15
246	33	40 c. black and blue	40	25
258	–	45 c. blue	1·50	70
215	–	50 c. black and orange	30	25
247	–	50 c. black and mauve	55	25
230	–	60 c. brown and red	70	45
259	–	70 c. brown	1·25	45
231	–	80 c. brown and blue	1·10	50
248	–	80 c. black and red	75	40
253	–	85 c. black and red	55	40
216	–	1 e. black and green	65	45
249	–	1 e. black and blue	50	40
254	–	1 e. 40 black and blue	1·00	40
232	–	2 e. violet and red	1·50	75
250	–	2 e. black and lilac	1·00	40
255	–	5 e. blue and brown	75	30
256	36	10 e. black and red	80	35
257	–	20 e. black and green	1·00	40

DESIGNS—HORIZ: 1, 3 c. Maize field; 2 c. Sugar factory; 5 c., 2 e. Beira; 20 c. Law Court; 40 c. Mangrove swamp; 43 c. Ivory store; 20 e. R. Zambesi; VERT: 1½ c. India-rubber; 2½ c. River Buzi; 4 c. Tobacco bushes; 6 c. Coffee bushes; 7, 15 c. Steam train; 7½ c. Orange tree; 8, 12 c. Cotton plants; 10, 80 c. Sisal plantation; 25 c., 1 e. 40, Beira; 30 c. Coconut palm; 50, 60 c. Cattle-breeding; 70 c. Gold-mining; 1 e. Mozambique Co's Arms; 5 e. Tapping rubber.

1920. Pictorial issue surch.

No.	Description	Unused	Used
217	½ c. on 30 c. (No. 213)	90	90
218	½ c. on 1 e. (No. 216)	70	60
219	1½ c. on 2½ c. (No. 204)	90	90
220	1½ c. on 5 c. (No. 206)	1·10	70
221	2 c. on 2½ c. (No. 204)	60	50
222	4 c. on 20 c. (No. 212)	90	80
223	4 c. on 40 c. (No. 214)	90	70
224	6 c. on 8 c. (No. 209)	90	70
225	6 c. on 50 c. (No. 215)	90	70

40 Zambesi Bridge

1935. Opening of Zambesi Bridge.

No.	Type	Description	Unused	Used
260	40	1 e. black and blue	2·00	1·00

41 Armstrong Whitworth Atalanta over Beira

1935. Inauguration of Blantyre–Beira–Salisbury Air Route.

No.	Type	Description	Unused	Used
261	41	5 c. black and blue	35	25
262		10 c. black and red	35	25
263		15 c. black and red	35	25
264		20 c. black and green	35	25
265		30 c. black and green	35	25
266		40 c. black and green	50	30
267		45 c. black and blue	50	30
268		50 c. black and purple	50	35
269		60 c. brown and red	85	40
270		80 c. black and red	85	40

42 Armstrong Whitworth Atalanta over Beira

1935. Air.

271 **42** 5 c. black and blue 10 10
272 10 c. black and red 10 10
273 15 c. black and red 10 10
274 20 c. black and green 10 10
275 30 c. black and green 10 10
276 40 c. black and green 10 10
277 45 c. black and blue 10 10
278 50 c. black and purple 10 10
279 60 c. brown and red 10 10
280 80 c. black and red 10 10
281 1 e. black and blue 15 20
282 2 e. black and purple 30 20
283 5 e. blue and brown 55 35
284 10 e. black and red 60 35
285 20 e. black and green 1·25 50

43 Dhow **46** Palms at Beira

45 Crocodile

1937.

286 – 1 c. violet and green 10 10
287 – 5 c. green and blue 10 10
288 **43** 10 c. blue and red 10 10
289 – 15 c. black and red 10 10
290 – 20 c. blue and green 10 10
291 – 30 c. blue and green 10 10
292 – 40 c. black and green 15 10
293 – 45 c. brown and blue 10 10
294 **45** 50 c. green and purple 10 10
295 – 60 c. blue and red 10 10
296 – 70 c. green and brown 10 10
297 – 80 c. green and red 15 10
298 – 85 c. black and brown 20 15
299 – 1 e. black and blue 15 15
300 **46** 1 e. 40 c. green and blue 20 15
301 – 2 e. brown and lilac 50 15
302 – 5 e. blue and brown 60 20
303 – 10 e. black and red 50 30
304 – 20 e. purple and green 1·00 45

DESIGNS—VERT: 21 × 29 mm—1 c. Giraffe; 20 c. Common zebra; 70 c. Native woman; 23 × 31 mm—10 e. Old Portuguese gate, Sena; 20 e. Arms. HORIZ: 29 × 21 mm—5 c. Native huts. 15 c. Caetano fortress, Sofala; 60 c. Leopard; 80 c. Hippopotami; 37 × 22 mm—5 e. Railway bridge over River Zambesi. TRIANGULAR: 30 c. Python; 40 c. White rhinoceros; 45 c. Lion; 85 c. Vasco da Gama's flagship "Sao Gabriel"; 1 e. Native in dugout canoe; 2 e. Greater kudu.

1939. President Carmona's Colonial Tour. Optd **28-VII-1939 Visita Presidencial.**

305 – 30 c. (No. 291) 60 45
306 – 40 c. (No. 292) 60 45
307 – 45 c. (No. 293) 60 45
308 **45** 50 c. green and purple 60 45
309 – 85 c. (No. 298) 60 45
310 – 1 e. (No. 299) 1·00 60
311 – 2 e. (No. 301) 1·25 1·00

49 King Afonso Henriques **51** "Don John IV" after Alberto de Souza

1940. 800th Anniv of Portuguese Independence.

312 **49** 1 e. 75 light blue and blue 65 35

1940. Tercentenary of Restoration of Independence.

313 **51** 40 c. black and blue 20 15
314 50 c. green and violet 20 15
315 60 c. blue and red 20 15
316 70 c. green and brown 20 15
317 80 c. green and red 20 15
318 1 e. black and blue 20 15

CHARITY TAX STAMPS

The notes under this heading in Portugal also apply here.

1932. No. 236 surch **Assistencia Publica 2 Ctvos. 2.**

C260 2 c. on 3 c. black & orge 30 30

C **41** "Charity" C **50**

1934.

C261 C **41** 2 c. black and mauve 35 30

1940.

C313 C **50** 2 c. blue and black 2·75 2·25

C **52**

1941.

C319 C **52** 2 c. red and black 2·75 2·25

NEWSPAPER STAMP

1894. "Newspaper" key-type inscr "MOCAMBIQUE" optd **COMPA DE MOCAMBIQUE.**

N15 V $2\frac{1}{2}$ r. brown 30 25

POSTAGE DUE STAMPS

D **9** D **32**

1906.

D114 D **9** 5 r. green 20 20
D115 10 r. grey 20 20
D116 20 r. brown 20 20
D117 30 r. orange 30 25
D118 50 r. brown 30 25
D119 60 r. brown 1·60 1·50
D120 100 r. mauve 45 45
D121 130 r. blue 2·50 1·60
D122 200 r. red 1·00 65
D123 500 r. lilac 1·25 1·00

1911. Optd **REPUBLICA.**

D166 D **9** 5 r. green 15 15
D167 10 r. grey 15 15
D168 20 r. brown 15 15
D169 30 r. orange 15 15
D170 50 r. brown 15 15
D171 60 r. brown 25 20
D172 100 r. mauve 25 20
D173 130 r. blue 65 65
D174 200 r. red 70 65
D175 500 r. lilac 80 70

1916. Currency changed.

D189 D **9** $\frac{1}{2}$ c. green 10 10
D190 1 c. grey 10 10
D191 2 c. brown 10 10
D192 3 c. orange 10 10
D193 5 c. brown 10 10
D194 6 c. brown 15 15
D195 10 c. mauve 30 30
D196 13 c. blue 65 65
D197 20 c. red 65 65
D198 50 c. lilac 80 80

1919.

D217 D **32** $\frac{1}{2}$ c. green 10 10
D218 1 c. black 10 10
D219 2 c. brown 10 10
D220 3 c. orange 10 10
D221 5 c. brown 10 10
D222 6 c. brown 25 25
D223 10 c. red 25 25
D224 13 c. blue 25 25
D225 20 c. red 40 20
D226 50 c. grey 25 20

MUSCAT AND OMAN Pt. 19

Independent Sultanate in Eastern Arabia. The title of the Sultanate was changed in 1971 to Oman.

1966. 64 baizas = 1 rupee
1970. 1000 baizas = 1 rial saidi

12 Sultan's Crest **14** Nakhai Fort

1966.

94 **12** 3 b. purple 10 15
95 5 b. brown 15 10
96 10 b. brown 20 10
97 A 15 b. black and violet 50 15
98 20 b. black and blue 60 15
99 25 b. black and orange 75 20
100 **14** 30 b. mauve and blue 80 25
101 B 50 b. green and brown 1·00 30
102 C 1 r. blue and orange 2·25 55
103 D 2 r. brown and green 4·00 1·75
104 E 5 r. violet and red 10·00 6·00
105 F 10 r. red and violet 18·00 12·00

DESIGNS—VERT: $21\frac{1}{2} \times 25\frac{1}{2}$ mm: A, Crest and Muscat harbour. HORIZ: (As Type **14**); B, Samail Fort; C, Sohar Fort; D, Nizwa Fort; E, Matrah Fort; F, Mirani Fort.

15 Mina el Fahal

1969. 1st Oil Shipment (July 1967). Multicoloured.

106 20 b. Type **15** 70 35
107 25 b. Storage tanks 1·00 50
108 40 b. Desert oil-rig 1·50 85
109 1 r. Aerial view from "Gemini 4" 3·50 2·25

1970. Designs as issue of 1966, but inscribed in new currency.

110 **12** 5 b. purple 15 10
111 10 b. brown 20 10
112 20 b. brown 40 10
113 A 25 b. black and violet 75 15
114 30 b. black and blue 85 20
115 40 b. black and orange 1·00 25
116 **14** 50 b. mauve and blue 1·50 25
117 B 75 b. green and brown 2·00 50
118 C 100 b. blue and orange 2·50 60
119 D $\frac{1}{4}$ r. brown and green 7·50 3·25
120 E $\frac{1}{2}$ r. violet and red 12·00 7·50
121 F 1 r. red and violet 22·00 13·00

For later issues see **OMAN**.

MYANMAR Pt. 21

Formerly known as Burma.

100 pyas = 1 kyat

81 Fountain, National Assembly Park ($\frac{1}{2}$-size illustration)

1990. State Law and Order Restoration Council.

312 **81** 1 k. multicoloured 1·00 65

1990. As Nos. 258/61 of Burma but inscr "UNION OF MYANMAR".

313 15 p. deep green and green 20 15
314 20 p. black, brown and blue 25 20
315 50 p. violet and brown 45 25
316 1 k. violet, mauve and black 95 65

82 Map and Emblem **83** Nawata Ruby

1990. 40th Anniv of United Nations Development Programme.

322 **82** 2 k. blue, yellow & black 1·90 1·25

1991. Gem Emporium.

323 **83** 50 p. multicoloured 95 65

84 "Grandfather giving Sword to Grandson" (statuette, Nan Win) **85** Emblem

1992. 44th Anniv of Independence. Multicoloured.

324 50 p. Warrior defending personification of Myanmar and map (poster, Khin Thein) 50 40
325 2 k. Type **84** 2·00 1·50

1992. National Sports Festival.

326 **85** 50 p. multicoloured 55 40

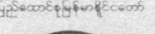

86 Campaign Emblem **87** Fish, Water Droplet and Leaf

1992. Anti-AIDS Campaign.

327 **86** 50 p. red 40 30

1992. International Nutrition Conference, Rome.

328 **87** 50 p. multicoloured 30 20
329 1 k. multicoloured 55 40
330 3 k. multicoloured 1·60 1·10
331 5 k. multicoloured 2·75 1·90

88 Statue **89** Hintha (legendary bird)

1993. National Convention for Drafting of New Constitution.

332 **88** 50 p. multicoloured 25 20
333 3 k. multicoloured 1·50 1·00

1993. Statuettes. Multicoloured.

334 5 k. Type **89** 2·50 1·75
335 10 k. Lawkanat 5·00 3·50

90 Horseman aiming Spear at Target

1993. Festival of Traditional Equestrian Sports, Sittwe.

336 **90** 3 k. multicoloured 1·60 1·10

91 Tree, Globe and Figures **92** Association Emblem

1994. World Environment Day.

337 **91** 4 k. multicoloured 2·00 1·50

1994. 1st Anniv of Union Solidarity and Development Association.

338 **93** 3 k. multicoloured 1·75 1·25

NAKHICHEVAN — Pt. 10

An autonomous province of Azerbaijan, separated from the remainder of the republic by Armenian territory. Nos. 1 and 2 were issued during a period when the administration of Nakhichevan was in dispute with the central government.

100 qopik = 1 manat

1 President Aliev

1993. 70th Birthday of President H. Aliev of Nakhichevan.

1 **1** 5 m. black and red
2 – 5 m. multicoloured

DESIGN: No. 2, Map of Nakhichevan.

NAPLES — Pt. 8

A state on the S.W. coast of Central Italy, formerly part of the Kingdom of Sicily, but now part of Italy.

100 grana = 200 tornesi = 1 ducato

1 Arms under Bourbon Dynasty — 4 Cross of Savoy

1858. The frames differ in each value. Imperf.

No.	Type	Description	Unused	Used
8	1	½ t. blue	£12000	£8000
1		½ g. lake	£650	£170
2		1 g. lake	£180	15·00
3		2 g. lake	£110	4·25
4		5 g. lake	£900	18·00
5		10 g. lake	£2000	65·00
6		20 g. lake	£1700	£275
7		50 g. lake	£42500	£2500

1860. Imperf.

No.	Type	Description	Unused	Used
9	4	½ t. blue	£20000	£3250

NEAPOLITAN PROVINCES — Pt. 8

Temporary issues for Naples and other parts of S. Italy which adhered to the new Kingdom of Italy in 1860.

100 grana = 200 tornesi = 1 ducato

1

1861. Embossed. Imperf.

No.	Type	Description	Unused	Used
2	1	½ t. green	3·25	55·0
5		½ g. brown	£110	80·00
9		1 g. black	£200	5·00
10		2 g. blue	45·00	3·75
15		5 g. red	£130	40·00
18		10 g. orange	£110	70·00
19		20 g. yellow	£400	£700
23		50 g. slate	5·00	£6000

NEPAL — Pt. 21

An independent Kingdom in the Himalayas N. of India.

1861. 16 annas = 1 rupee
1907. 64 pice = 1 rupee
1954. 100 paisa = 1 rupee

1 (1 a.) — 2 (½ a.) — 3 Siva Mahadeva (2 pice)

1881. Imperf or pin-perf.

No.	Type	Description	Unused	Used
34	2	½ a. black	2·00	1·00
35		½ a. orange	£300	£120
26	1	1 a. blue	6·00	5·00
14		1 a. green	26·00	26·00
16c		2 a. violet	12·00	12·00
40		2 a. brown	5·00	3·00
41		4 a. green	4·00	4·00

1907. Various sizes.

No.	Type	Description	Unused	Used
57	3	2 p. brown	20	20
58		4 p. green	60	40
59		8 p. red	40	30
60		16 p. purple	3·00	1·50
61		24 p. orange	3·00	1·00
62		32 p. blue	5·00	1·25
63		1 r. red	9·00	4·00
50		5 r. black and brown	14·00	8·00

5 Swayambhunath Temple, Katmandu — 7 Guheswari Temple, Patan

8 Sri Pashupati (Siva Mahadeva)

1949.

No.	Type	Description	Unused	Used
64	5	2 p. brown	50	40
65	–	4 p. green	50	40
66	–	6 p. pink	1·00	40
67	–	8 p. red	1·00	60
68	–	16 p. purple	1·00	60
69	–	20 p. blue	2·00	1·00
70	7	24 p. red	1·60	60
71	–	32 p. blue	3·00	1·00
72	8	1 r. orange	12·00	6·00

DESIGNS—As Type **5**: 4 p. Pashupatinath Temple, Katmandu; 6 p. Tri-Chundra College; 8 p. Mahabuddha Temple; 16 p. Krishna Mandir Temple, Patan. As Type **7**: 20 p. View of Katmandu; 32 p. The twenty-two fountains, Balaju.

9 King Tribhuvana — 10 Map of Nepal

1954. (a) Size 18 × 22 mm.

No.	Type	Description	Unused	Used
73	9	2 p. brown	1·00	20
74		4 p. green	2·00	60
75		6 p. red	80	20
76		8 p. lilac	60	20
77		12 p. orange	4·00	1·00
		(b) Size 25½ × 29½ mm.		
78	9	16 p. brown	80	20
79		20 p. red	1·60	60
80		24 p. red	1·40	60
81		32 p. blue	2·00	60
82		50 p. mauve	9·00	3·00
83		1 r. red	18·00	5·00
84		2 r. brown	9·00	4·00
		(c) Size 30 × 18 mm.		
85	10	2 p. brown	80	40
86		4 p. green	2·00	60
87		6 p. red	6·00	1·00
88		8 p. lilac	60	40
89		12 p. orange	6·00	1·00
		(d) Size 38 × 21½ mm.		
90	10	16 p. brown	1·00	40
91		20 p. red	1·60	40
92		24 p. red	1·25	40
93		32 p. blue	3·00	80
94		50 p. mauve	11·00	3·00
95		1 r. red	20·00	4·00
96		2 r. brown	9·00	4·00

11 Mechanization of Agriculture — 13 Hanuman Dhoka, Katmandu

1956. Coronation.

No.	Type	Description	Unused	Used
97	11	4 p. green	2·00	1·25
98	–	6 p. red and orange	1·25	60
99	–	8 p. violet	80	40
100	13	24 p. red	2·00	80
101	–	1 r. brown	55·00	48·00

DESIGNS—VERT: As Type **11**: 8 p. Processional elephant. As Type **13**: 6 p. Throne; 1 r. King and Queen and mountains.

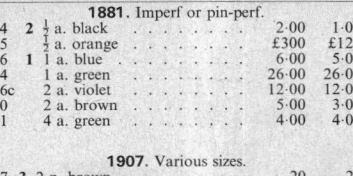

15 U.N. Emblem and Nepalese Landscape — 16 Nepalese Crown

1956. 1st Anniv of Admission into U.N.O.

No.	Type	Description	Unused	Used
102	15	12 p. blue and buff	2·75	1·60

1957. (a) Size 18 × 22 mm.

No.	Type	Description	Unused	Used
103	16	2 p. brown	40	25
104		4 p. green	60	40
105		6 p. red	40	40
106		8 p. lilac	40	40
107		12 p. red	2·25	60
		(b) Size 25½ × 29½ mm.		
108	16	16 p. brown	3·00	1·00
109		20 p. red	5·00	1·40
110		24 p. red	3·00	1·25
111		32 p. blue	4·00	1·40
112		50 p. red	7·00	3·00
113		1 r. salmon	15·00	6·00
114		2 r. orange	7·00	4·00

17 Gaunthali carrying Letter — 18 Temple of Lumbini

1958. Air. Inauguration of Nepalese Internal Airmail Service.

No.	Type	Description	Unused	Used
115	17	10 p. blue	1·10	1·10

1958. Human Rights Day.

No.	Type	Description	Unused	Used
116	18	6 p. yellow	80	80

19 Nepalese Map and Flag

1959. 1st Nepalese Elections.

No.	Type	Description	Unused	Used
117	19	6 p. red and green	30	25

20 Spinning Wheel — 21 King Mahendra

1959. Cottage Industries.

No.	Type	Description	Unused	Used
118	20	2 p. brown	25	25

1959. Admission of Nepal to U.P.U.

No.	Type	Description	Unused	Used
119	21	12 p. blue	30	25

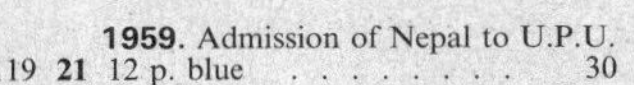

22 Vishnu — 23 Nyatopol Temple, Bhaktapur

1959.

No.	Type	Description	Unused	Used
120	22	1 p. brown	10	10
121	–	2 p. violet	10	10
122	–	4 p. blue	30	20
123	–	6 p. pink	30	15
124	–	8 p. sepia	20	10
125	–	12 p. grey	30	10
126	23	16 p. violet and brown	30	10
127		20 p. lake and blue	1·00	40
128		24 p. red and myrtle	1·00	40
129		32 p. blue and lilac	60	40
130		50 p. myrtle and red	1·00	40
131	–	1 r. blue and brown	6·00	2·00
132	–	2 r. blue and mauve	6·00	3·25
133	–	5 r. red and violet	45·00	38·00

DESIGNS—As Type **22**: HORIZ: 2 p. Krishna; 8 p. Siberian musk deer; 12 p. Indian rhinoceros. VERT: 4 p. Himalayas; 6 p. Gateway, Bhaktapur Palace. As Type **23**: VERT: 1 r., 2 r. Himalayan monal pheasant; 5 r. Satyr tragopan.

24 King Mahendra opening Parliament — 25 Sri Pashupatinath

1959. Opening of 1st Nepalese Parliament.

No.	Type	Description	Unused	Used
134	24	6 p. red	60	60

1959. Temple Renovation.

No.	Type	Description	Unused	Used
135	25	4 p. green (18 × 25 mm)	40	40
136		8 p. red (21 × 28½ mm)	60	40
137		1 r. blue (24½ × 33½ mm)	5·00	3·25

26 Children, Pagoda and Mt. Everest — 27 King Mahendra

1960. Children's Day.

No.	Type	Description	Unused	Used
137a	26	6 p. blue	8·00	6·00

1960. King Mahendra's 41st Birthday.

No.	Type	Description	Unused	Used
138	27	1 r. purple	90	60

See also Nos. 163/4a.

28 Mt. Everest — 29 King Tribhuvana

1960. Mountain Views.

No.	Type	Description	Unused	Used
139	–	5 p. sepia and purple	20	10
140	28	10 p. purple and blue	30	15
141	–	40 p. brown and violet	70	45

DESIGNS: 5 p. Machha Puchhre; 40 p. Manaslu (wrongly inscr. "MANSALU").

1961. 10th Democracy Day.

No.	Type	Description	Unused	Used
142	29	10 p. salmon and brown	10	10

30 Prince Gyanendra cancelling Children's Day Stamps of 1960 — 31 King Mahendra

1961. Children's Day.

No.	Type	Description	Unused	Used
143	30	12 p. orange	20·00	20·00

1961. King Mahendra's 42nd Birthday.

No.	Type	Description	Unused	Used
144	31	6 p. green	20	20
145		12 p. blue	30	30
146		50 p. red	60	60
147		1 r. brown	1·00	1·00

32 Campaign Emblem and House — 33 King Mahendra on horseback

1962. Malaria Eradication.

No.	Type	Description	Unused	Used
148	32	12 p. blue	20	20
149	–	1 r. orange and red	60	60

DESIGN: 1 r. Emblem and Nepalese flag.

1962. King Mahendra's 43rd Birthday.

No.	Type	Description	Unused	Used
150	33	10 p. blue	15	15
151		15 p. brown	20	20
152		45 p. brown	40	40
153		1 r. olive	60	60

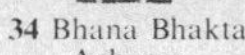

34 Bhana Bhakta Acharya — 35 King Mahendra — 36

1962. Nepalese Poets.

154 **34** 5 p. brown 20 20
155 – 10 p. turquoise 20 20
156 – 40 p. olive 30 30

PORTRAITS: 10 p. Moti Ram Bhakta; 40 p. Sambhu Prasad.

1962.

157 **35** 1 p. red 10 10
158 2 p. blue 10 10
158a 3 p. grey 30 20
159 5 p. bistre 10 10
160 **36** 10 p. purple 10 10
161 40 p. brown 20 20
162 75 p. turquoise . . . . . . 6·00 6·00
162a **35** 75 p. turquoise 80 40
163 **27** 2 r. orange 80 80
164 5 r. green . . . . 1·60 1·60
164a 10 r. violet . . . . 6·00 5·00

No. 158a is smaller, $17\frac{1}{2} \times 20$ mm.

37 Emblems of Learning — 38 Hands holding Lamps

1963. U.N.E.S.C.O. "Education for All" Campaign.

165 **37** 10 p. black 20 10
166 15 p. brown 30 20
167 50 p. violet 50 40

1963. National Day.

168 **38** 5 p. blue 10 10
169 10 p. brown 10 10
170 50 p. mauve 40 30
171 1 r. turquoise 80 40

39 Campaign Symbols — 40 Map of Nepal and Open Hand

1963. Freedom from Hunger.

172 **39** 10 p. orange 20 10
173 15 p. blue 30 20
174 50 p. green 60 40
175 1 r. brown 80 70

1963. Rastruya Panchayat.

176 **40** 10 p. green 10 10
177 15 p. purple 20 20
178 50 p. slate 50 30
179 1 r. violet 80 50

41 King Mahendra — 42 King Mahendra and Highway Map

1963. King Mahendra's 44th Birthday.

180 **41** 5 p. violet 10 10
181 10 p. brown 20 10
182 15 p. green 30 20

1964. Inauguration of East–West Highway.

183 **42** 10 p. orange and blue . . . 10 10
184 15 p. orange and blue . . . 20 10
185 50 p. brown and green . . . 30 20

43 King Mahendra at Microphone — 44 Crown Prince Birendra

1964. King Mahendra's 45th Birthday.

186 **43** 1 p. brown 10 10
187 2 p. slate 10 10
188 2 r. brown 60 60

1964. Crown Prince's 19th Birthday.

189 **44** 10 p. green 50 40
190 15 p. brown 50 40

45 Flag, Kukris, Rings and Torch — 46 Nepalese Family

1964. Olympic Games, Tokyo.

191 **45** 10 p. blue, red and pink . . . 50 40

1965. Land Reform.

192 – 2 p. black and green . . . 20 20
193 – 5 p. brown and green . . . 20 20
194 – 10 p. purple and grey . . . 20 20
195 **46** 15 p. brown and yellow . . . 30 30

DESIGNS: 2 p. Farmer and cattle; 5 p. Ears of corn; 10 p. Grain elevator.

47 Globe and Letters — 48 King Mahendra

1965. Introduction of International Insured and Parcel Service.

196 **47** 15 p. violet 20 20

1965. King Mahendra's 46th Birthday.

197 **48** 50 p. purple 50 40

49 Four Martyrs — 50 I.T.U. Emblem

1965. "Nepalese Martyrs".

198 **49** 15 p. green 25 20

1965. I.T.U. Centenary.

199 **50** 15 p. black and purple . . . 30 20

51 I.C.Y. Emblem — 52 Devkota (poet)

1965. International Co-operation Year.

200 **51** 1 r. multicoloured 60 50

1965. Devkota Commemorative.

201 **52** 15 p. brown 20 20

54 Flag and King Mahendra

1966. Democracy Day.

202 **54** 15 p. red and blue 40 30

55 Siva Parvati and Pashuvati Temple — 56 "Stamp" Emblem

1966. Maha Siva-Ratri Festival.

203 **55** 15 p. violet 25 20

1966. Nepalese Philatelic Exhibition.

204 **56** 15 p. orange and green . . . 30 20

57 King Mahendra — 58 Queen Mother

1966. King Mahendra's 47th Birthday.

205 **57** 15 p. brown and ochre . . 25 20

1966. Queen Mother's 60th Birthday.

206 **58** 15 p. brown 20 20

59 Queen Ratna — 60 Flute-player and Dancer

1966. Children's Day.

207 **59** 15 p. brown and yellow . . 25 20

1966. Krishna Anniv.

208 **60** 15 p. violet and yellow . . 25 20

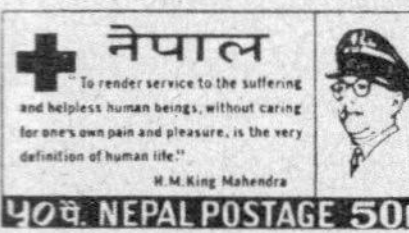

61 "To render service..."

1966. 1st Anniv of Nepalese Red Cross.

209 **61** 50 p. red and green . . . . 2·40 80

62 W.H.O. Building on Flag — 63 Paudyal

1966. Inaug of W.H.O. Headquarters, Geneva.

210 **62** 1 r. violet . . . . 1·25 80

1966. Leknath Paudyal (poet) Commemorative.

211 **63** 15 p. blue 25 20

64 Rama and Sita — 65 Buddha

1967. Rama Navami, 2024, birthday of Rama.

212 **64** 15 p. brown and yellow . . 25 20

1967. Buddha Jayanti, birthday of Buddha.

213 **65** 75 p. purple and orange . . 50 50

66 King Mahendra addressing Nepalese

1967. King Mahendra's 48th Birthday.

214 **66** 15 p. brown and blue . . . 25 25

67 Queen Ratna and Children — 68 Ama Dablam (mountain)

1967. Children's Day.

215 **67** 15 p. brown and cream . . 25 20

1967. International Tourist Year.

216 **68** 5 p. violet (postage) . . . 20 20
217 – 65 p. brown 40 40
218 – 1 r. 80 red and blue (air) . 1·00 80

DESIGNS: 38×20 mm: 65 p. Bhaktapur Durbar Square. $35\frac{1}{2} \times 25\frac{1}{2}$ mm: 1 r. 80 Plane over Kathmandu.

69 Open-air Class

1967. Constitution Day. "Go to the Village" Educational Campaign.

219 **69** 15 p. multicoloured 25 20

70 Crown Prince Birendra, Camp-fire and Scout Emblem

1967. Diamond Jubilee of World Scouting.

220 **70** 15 p. blue 40 30

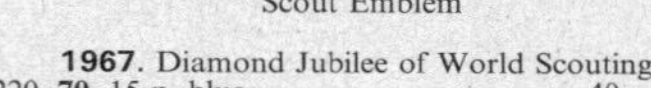

71 Prithvi Narayan Shah (founder of Kingdom) — 72 Arms of Nepal

1968. Bicentenary of the Kingdom.

221 **71** 15 p. blue and red 40 30

1968. National Day.

222 **72** 15 p. blue and red 40 30

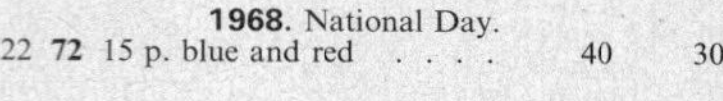

73 W.H.O. Emblem and Nepalese Flag

1968. 20th Anniv of W.H.O.

223 **73** 1 r. 20 blue, red & yellow . 1·75 1·25

74 Sita and Janaki Temple

1968. Sita Jayanti.

224 **74** 15 p. brown and violet . . 30 20

75 King Mahendra, Mountains and Himalayan Monal Pheasant

1968. King Mahendra's 49th Birthday.
225 **75** 15 p. multicoloured 75 30

76 Garuda and Airline Emblem

1968. Air. 10th Anniv of Royal Nepalese Airlines.
226 **76** 15 p. brown and blue . . . 20 20
227 – 65 p. blue 40 40
228 – 2 r. 50 blue and orange . . 1·50 1·25
DESIGNS—DIAMOND ($25\frac{1}{2}\times25\frac{1}{2}$ mm): 65 p. Route-map. HORIZ: As Type **70**: 2 r. 50, Convair Metropolitan airliner over Mount Dhaulagiri.

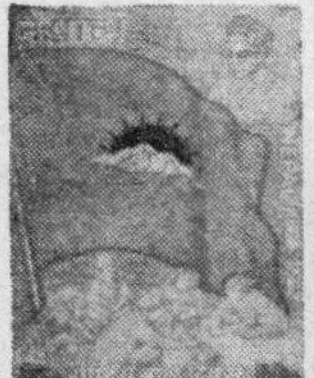

77 Flag, Queen Ratna and Children 78 Human Rights Emblem and Buddha

1968. Children's Day and Queen Ratna's 41st Birthday.
229 **77** 5 p. red, yellow and green . 20 15

1968. Human Rights Year.
230 **78** 1 r. red and green . . . . 1·60 1·25

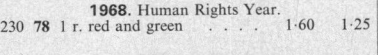

79 Crown Prince Birendra and Dancers

1968. Crown Prince Birendra's 24th Birthday, and National Youth Festival.
231 **79** 25 p. blue 40 30

80 King Mahendra, Flags and U.N. Building, New York 81 Amsu Varma (7th-century ruler)

1969. Nepal's Election to U.N. Security Council.
232 **80** 1 r. multicoloured 60 50

1969. Famous Nepalese.
233 **81** 15 p. violet and green . . . 30 30
234 – 25 p. turquoise 40 40
235 – 50 p. brown 50 50
236 – 1 r. purple and brown . . . 60 50
DESIGNS—VERT: 25 p. Ram Shah (7th-century King of Gurkha); 50 p. Bhimsen Thapa (19th-century Prime Minister). HORIZ: 1 r. Bal Bhadra Kunwar (19th-century warrior).

82 I.L.O. Emblem

1969. 50th Anniv of I.L.O.
237 **82** 1 r. brown and red . . . . 3·00 2·00

83 King Mahendra 85 Queen Ratna, and Child with Toy

84 King Tribhuvana and Queens

1969. King Mahendra's 50th Birthday.
238 **83** 25 p. multicoloured . . . 25 25

1969. 64th Birth Anniv of King Tribhuvana.
239 **84** 25 p. sepia and yellow . . 25 25

1969. National Children's Day.
240 **85** 25 p. red and brown . . . 25 25

86 Rhododendron 87 Durga, Goddess of Victory

1969. Flowers. Multicoloured.
241 25 p. Type **86** 35 30
242 25 p. Narcissus 35 30
243 25 p. Marigold 35 30
244 25 p. Poinsettia 35 30

1969. Durga Pooja Festival.
245 **87** 15 p. black and orange . . 20 20
246 50 p. violet and brown . . 45 40

88 Crown Prince Birendra and Princess Aishwarya

1970. Royal Wedding.
247 **88** 25 p. multicoloured . . . 25 20

89 Produce, Cow and Landscape

1970. Agricultural Year.
248 **89** 25 p. multicoloured . . . 25 20

90 King Mahendra, Mt. Everest and Nepalese Crown

1970. King Mahendra's 51st Birthday.
249 **90** 50 p. multicoloured . . . 40 30

91 Lake Gosainkunda

1970. Nepalese Lakes. Multicoloured.
250 5 p. Type **91** 20 20
251 25 p. Lake Phewa Tal 30 30
252 1 r. Lake Rara Daha 50 50

92 A.P.Y. Emblem

1970. Asian Productivity Year.
253 **92** 1 r. blue 50 40

93 Queen Ratna and Children's Palace, Taulihawa

1970. National Children's Day.
254 **93** 25 p. slate and brown . . . 25 20

94 New Headquarters Building

1970. New U.P.U. Headquarters, Berne.
255 **94** 2 r. 50 brown . . . . 1·00 80

95 U.N. Flag

1970. 25th Anniv of United Nations.
256 **95** 25 p. blue and purple . . . 25 20

96 Durbar Square, Patan

1970. Tourism. Multicoloured.
257 15 p. Type **96** 20 10
258 25 p. Boudhanath Stupa (temple) (vert) 30 20
259 1 r. Mt. Gauri Shankar 50 40

97 Statue of Harihar, Valmiki Ashram 98 Torch within Spiral

1971. Nepalese Religious Art.
260 **97** 25 p. black and brown . . . 25 20

1971. Racial Equality Year.
261 **98** 1 r. red and blue 60 45

99 King Mahendra taking Salute 100 Sweta Bhairab

1971. King Mahendra's 52nd Birthday.
262 **99** 15 p. plum and blue 25 20

1971. Bhairab Images.
263 **100** 15 p. brown and chestnut . 20 20
264 – 25 p. brown and green . . 20 20
265 – 50 p. brown and blue . . . 40 40
DESIGNS: 25 p. Mahankal Bhairab; 50 p. Kal Bhairab.

101 Child presenting Queen Ratna with Garland

1971. National Children's Day.
266 **101** 25 p. multicoloured . . . 25 15

102 Iranian and Nepalese Flags on Map of Iran

1971. 2,500th Anniv of Persian Empire.
267 **102** 1 r. multicoloured 60 40

103 Mother and Child

1971. 25th Anniv of U.N.I.C.E.F.
268 **103** 1 r. blue 60 40

104 Mt. Everest 105 Royal Standard

1971. Himalayan Peaks. Multicoloured.
269 25 p. Type **104** 20 10
270 1 r. Mt. Kanchenjunga . . . 40 30
271 1 r. 80 Mt. Annapurna I . . . 70 50

1972. National Day.
272 **105** 25 p. black and red . . . 25 15

106 Araniko and White Dagoba, Peking 107 Open Book

1972. Araniko (13th-century architect). Commem.
273 **106** 15 p. brown and blue . . 15 10

1972. International Book Year.
274 **107** 2 p. brown and buff . . . 10 10
275 5 p. black and brown . . 10 10
276 1 r. black and blue . . . 50 40

108 Human Heart

1972. World Heart Month.
277 **108** 25 p. red and green . . . 25 20

109 King Mahendra 110 King Birendra

1972. 1st Death Anniv of King Mahendra.
278 **109** 25 p. brown and black . . 25 15

1972. King Birendra's 28th Birthday.
279 **110** 50 p. purple and brown . 30 25

111 Northern Border Costumes
112 Sri Baburam Acharya 

1973. National Costumes. Multicoloured.
280 25 p. Type **111** 20 10
281 50 p. Hill-dwellers 25 20
282 75 p. Katmandu Valley 35 25
283 1 r. Inner Terai 50 35

1973. 85th Birth Anniv of Sri Baburam Acharya (historian).
284 **112** 25 p. drab and red 20 15

113 Nepalese Family

1973. 25th Anniv of W.H.O.
285 **113** 1 r. blue and brown 50 40

114 Birthplace of Buddha, Lumbini

1973. Tourism. Multicoloured.
286 25 p. Type **114** 20 10
287 75 p. Mt. Makalu 30 20
288 1 r. Castle, Gurkha 40 40

115 Transplanting Rice

1973. 10th Anniv of World Food Programme.
289 **115** 10 p. brown & violet 10 10

116 Interpol H.Q., Paris

1973. 50th Anniv of International Criminal Police Organization (Interpol).
290 **116** 25 p. blue and brown 20 15

117 Shri Shom Nath Sigdyal
118 Cow 

1973. 1st Death Anniv of Shri Shom Nath Sigdyal (scholar).
291 **117** 1 r. 25 violet 50 40

1973. Domestic Animals. Multicoloured.
292 2 p. Type **118** 10 10
293 3 r. 25 Yak 90 60

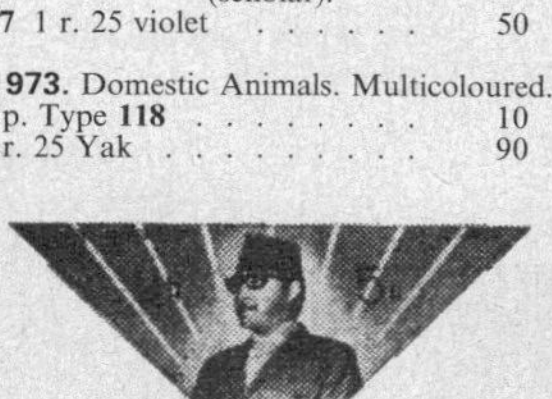

119 King Birendra

1974. King Birendra's 29th Birthday.
294 **119** 5 p. brown and black 10 10
295 15 p. brown and black 15 10
296 1 r. brown and black 40 30

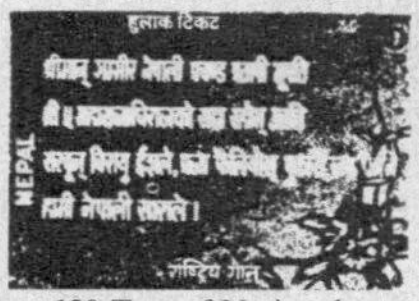

120 Text of National Anthem
121 King Janak seated on Throne 

1974. National Day.
297 **120** 25 p. red 20 10
298 – 1 r. green 30 25
DESIGN: 1 r. Anthem musical score.

1974. King Janak Commemoration.
299 **121** 2 r. 50 multicoloured 1·00 80

122 Emblem and Village

1974. 25th Anniv of SOS Children's Village International.
300 **122** 25 p. blue and red 15 15

123 Football
124 W.P.Y. Emblem 

1974. Nepalese Games. Multicoloured.
301 2 p. Type **123** 10 10
302 2 r. 75 Baghchal (diagram) 60 50

1974. World Population Year.
303 **124** 5 p. blue and brown 10 10

125 U.P.U. Monument, Berne
126 Red Lacewing 

1974. Centenary of U.P.U.
304 **125** 1 r. black and green 40 30

1974. Nepalese Butterflies. Multicoloured.
305 10 p. Type **126** 10 10
306 15 p. Leaf buttefly 40 15
307 1 r. 25 Leaf butterfly (underside) 1·00 70
308 1 r. 75 Red-breasted jezebel 1·25 1·00

127 King Birendra
128 Muktinath 

1974. King Birendra's 30th Birthday.
309 **127** 25 p. black and green 15 15

1974. "Visit Nepal" Tourism. Multicoloured.
310 25 p. Type **128** 20 10
311 1 r. Peacock window, Bhaktapur (horiz) 40 25

129 Guheswari Temple

1975. Coronation of King Birendra. Multicoloured.
312 25 p. Type **129** 20 10
313 50 p. Rara (lake view) 20 10
314 1 r. Throne and sceptre 30 20
315 1 r. 25 Royal Palace, Katmandu 60 30
316 1 r. 75 Pashupatinath Temple 40 40
317 2 r. 75 King Birendra and Queen Aishwarya 60 50
SIZES—HORIZ: 50 p. 37×30 mm. 1 r., 1 r. 25., 2 r. 75, 46×26 mm. VERT: 1 r. 75, 25×31 mm.

130 Tourism Year Emblem

1975. South Asia Tourism Year. Multicoloured.
319 2 p. Type **130** 10 10
320 25 p. Temple stupa (vert) 20 20

131 Tiger

1975. Wildlife Conservation. Multicoloured.
321 2 p. Type **131** 20 20
322 5 p. Swamp deer (vert) 20 20
323 1 r. Lesser panda 40 40

132 Queen Aishwarya and I.W.Y. Emblem

1975. International Women's Year.
324 **132** 1 r. multicoloured 30 20

133 Rupse Falls
134 King Birendra 

1975. Tourism. Multicoloured.
325 2 p. Mt. Ganesh Himal (horiz) 10 10
326 25 p. Type **133** 10 10
327 50 p. Kumari ("Living Goddess") 30 20

1975. King Birendra's 31st Birthday.
328 **134** 25 p. violet and purple 15 10

136 Flag and Map
138 Flags of Nepal and Colombo Plan 

137 Transplanting Rice

1976. Silver Jubilee of National Democracy Day.
330 **136** 2 r. 50 red and blue 50 40

1976. Agriculture Year.
331 **137** 25 p. multicoloured 15 10

1976. 25th Anniv of Colombo Plan.
332 **138** 1 r. multicoloured 30 25

INDEX

Countries can be quickly located by referring to the index at the end of this volume.

139 Running
140 "Dove of Peace" 

1976. Olympic Games, Montreal.
333 **139** 3 r. 25 black and blue 80 60

1976. 5th Non-aligned Countries' Summit Conference.
334 **140** 5 r. blue, yellow and black 1·10 70

141 Lakhe Dance

1976. Nepalese Dances. Multicoloured.
335 10 p. Type **141** 10 10
336 15 p. Maruni dance 10 10
337 30 p. Jhangad dance 20 10
338 1 r. Sebru dance 30 20

142 Nepalese Lily
143 King Birendra 

1976. Flowers. Multicoloured.
339 30 p. Type **142** 30 10
340 30 p. "Meconopsis grandis" 30 10
341 30 p. "Cardiocrinum giganteum" (horiz) 30 10
342 30 p. "Megacodon stylophorus" (horiz) 30 10

1976. King Birendra's 32nd Birthday.
343 **143** 5 p. green 10 10
344 30 p. lake, brown & yell 15 10

144 Liberty Bell

1976. Bicentenary of American Revolution.
345 **144** 10 r. multicoloured 1·50 1·40

145 Kaji Amarsingh Thapa

1977. Thapa (19th-century warrior) Commem.
346 **145** 10 p. brown & lt brown 10 10

146 Terracotta Figurine and Kapilavastu

1977. Tourism.
347 **146** 30 p. violet 10 10
348 – 5 r. brown and green 80 60
DESIGN: 5 r. Ashokan pillar, Lumbini.

147 Great Indian Hornbill
148 Tukuche Himal and Police Flag 

1977. Birds. Multicoloured.
349 5 p. Type **147** 40 10
350 15 p. Cheer pheasant (horiz) 70 10
351 1 r. Green magpie (horiz) 1·10 30
352 2 r. 30 Spiny babbler 2·00 60

1977. 1st Anniv of Ascent of Tukuche Himal.
353 **148** 1 r. 25 multicoloured . . . 30 20

149 Map of Nepal and Scout Emblem
150 Dhanwantari, the Health-giver

1977. 25th Anniv of Scouting in Nepal.
354 **149** 3 r. 50 multicoloured . . . 60 40

1977. Dhanwantari Commemoration.
355 **150** 30 p. green 15 10

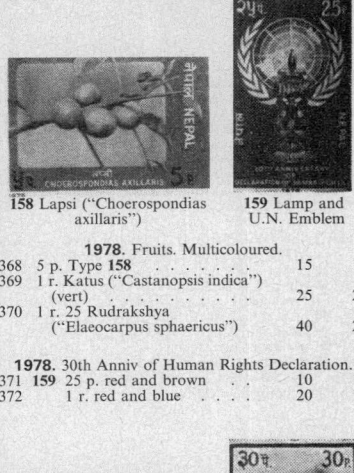

151 Map of Nepal and Flags
152 King Birendra

1977. Colombo Plan. 26th Consultative Committee Meeting, Katmandu.
356 **151** 1 r. multicoloured 20 15

1977. King Birendra's 33rd Birthday.
357 **152** 5 p. brown 10 10
358 1 r. brown 20 20

153 General Post Office, Katmandu, and Seal

1978. Centenary of Nepalese Post Office.
359 **153** 25 p. brown and black . . 10 10
360 – 75 p. ochre and black . . 20 20
DESIGN: 75 p. General Post Office, Katmandu, and early postmark.

154 South-west Face of Mount Everest

1978. 25th Anniv of Ascent of Mount Everest.
361 **154** 2 r. 30 slate and brown . . 50 30
362 – 4 r. blue and green 70 60
DESIGN: 4 r. South face of Mt. Everest.

155 Sun, Ankh and Landscape

1978. World Environment Day.
363 **155** 1 r. orange and green . . 20 15

156 Queen Mother Ratna
157 Rapids, Tripsuli River

1978. Queen Mother's 50th Birthday.
364 **156** 2 r. 30 olive 40 30

1978. Tourism. Multicoloured.
365 10 p. Type **157** 10 10
366 50 p. Window, Nara Devi, Katmandu 15 10
367 1 r. Mahakali dance (vert) . . 25 20

158 Lapsi ("Choerospondias axillaris")
159 Lamp and U.N. Emblem

1978. Fruits. Multicoloured.
368 5 p. Type **158** 15 10
369 1 r. Katus ("Castanopsis indica") (vert) 25 20
370 1 r. 25 Rudrakshya ("Elaeocarpus sphaericus") 40 25

1978. 30th Anniv of Human Rights Declaration.
371 **159** 25 p. red and brown . . 10 10
372 1 r. red and blue 20 15

160 Wright Flyer I and Boeing 727-100

161 King Birendra

1978. Air. 75th Anniv of First Powered Flight.
373 **160** 2 r. 30 blue and brown . 45 30

1978. King Birendra's 34th Birthday.
374 **161** 30 p. blue and brown . . 10 10
375 2 r. brown and violet . . 30 25

162 Red Machchhindranath and Kamroop and Patan Temples

1979. Red Machchhindranath (guardian deity) Festival.
376 **162** 75 p. brown and green . 20 15

163 "Buddha's Birth" (carving, Maya Devi Temple)

164 Planting a Sapling

1979. Lumbini Year.
377 **163** 1 r. yellow and brown . . 20 15

1979. Tree Planting Festival.
378 **164** 2 r. 30 multicoloured . . 50 40

165 Chariot of Red Machchhindranath

166 Nepalese Scouts and Guides

1979. Bhoto Jatra (Vest Show Festival).
379 **165** 1 r. 25 multicoloured . . 25 20

1979. International Year of the Child.
380 **166** 1 r. yellow-brown 25 20

167 Mount Pabil

168 Great Grey Shrike

1979. Tourism.
381 **167** 30 p. green 10 10
382 – 50 p. red and blue 10 10
383 – 1 r. 25 multicoloured . . . 25 25
DESIGNS: 50 p. Yajnashala, Swargadwari. 1 r. 25, Shiva-Parbati (wood carving, Gaddi Baithak Temple).

1979. International World Pheasant Association Symposium, Katmandu. Multicoloured.
384 10 p. Type **168** (postage) . . . 25 20
385 10 r. Fire-tailed sunbird . . . 6·00 3·50
386 3 r. 50 Himalayan monal pheasant (horiz) (air) . . . . 2·10 1·90

169 Lichchhavi Coin (obverse)

170 King Birendra

1979. Coins.
387 **169** 5 p. pink and brown . . . 10 10
388 – 5 p. pink and brown . . . 10 10
389 – 15 p. blue and deep blue . 10 10
390 – 15 p. blue and deep blue . 10 10
391 – 1 r. blue and grey 20 20
392 – 1 r. blue and grey 20 20
DESIGNS: No. 388, Lichchhavi coin (reverse); No. 389, Malla coin (obverse); No. 390, Malla coin (reverse); No. 391, Prithvi Narayan Shah coin (obverse); No. 392, Prithvi Narayan Shah coin (reverse).

1979. King Birendra's 35th Birthday. Multicoloured.
393 25 p. Type **170** 10 10
394 2 r. 30 Reservoir 40 30

171 Samyak Pooja Festival

1980. Samyak Pooja.
395 **171** 30 p. grey, brown & mar . 10 10

172 Sacred Basil ("Ocimum sanctum")

1980. Nepalese Herbs. Multicoloured.
396 5 p. Type **172** 10 10
397 30 p. Valerian ("Valeriana jatamansi jones") 10 10
398 1 r. Nepalese pepper ("Zanthoxylum armatum") . 20 15
399 2 r. 30 Himalayan rhubarb ("Rheum emodi wall") . . . 40 25

173 Gyandil Das

174 Everlasting Flame and Temple, Shirsasthan

1980. Nepalese Writers.
400 **173** 5 p. lilac and ochre 10 10
401 – 30 p. maroon and brown . 10 10
402 – 1 r. olive and blue 15 15
403 – 2 r. 30 blue and green . . 55 25
DESIGNS: 30 p. Siddhidas Amatya; 1 r. Pahalman Singh Swanr; 2 r. 30, Jay Prithvi Bahadur Singh.

1980. Tourism. Multicoloured.
404 10 p. Type **174** 10 10
405 1 r. Godavari Pond 20 15
406 5 r. Mount Dhaulagiri 70 50

175 Bhairab Dancer

176 King Birendra

1980. World Tourism Conference, Manila.
407 **175** 25 r. multicoloured . . . 3·00 2·25

1980. King Birendra's 36th Birthday.
408 **176** 1 r. multicoloured 20 15

177 I.Y.D.P. Emblem and Nepalese Flag

1981. International Year of Disabled Persons.
409 **177** 5 r. multicoloured 80 60

178 Nepal Rastra Bank

179 One Anna Stamp of 1881

1981. 25th Anniv of Nepal Rastra Bank.
410 **178** 1 r. 75 multicoloured . . 25 20

1981. Nepalese Postage Stamp Centenary.
411 **179** 10 p. blue, brown and black 10 10
412 – 40 p. purple, brown and black 10 10
413 – 3 r. 40 green, brown and blk 50 40
DESIGNS: 40 p. 2 anna stamp of 1881; 3 r. 40, 4 a. stamp of 1881.

180 Nepalese Flag and Association Emblem

181 Hand holding Stamp

1981. International Hotel Association, Katmandu. 70th Council Meeting.
415 **180** 1 r. 75 multicoloured . . . 25 20

1981. "Nepal 81" Stamp Exhibition, Katmandu.
416 **181** 40 p. multicoloured . . . 10 10

182 King Birendra

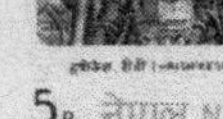
183 Image of Hrishikesh, Ridi

1981. King Birendra's 37th Birthday.
417 **182** 1 r. multicoloured 15 15

1981. Tourism. Multicoloured.
418 5 p. Type **183** 10 10
419 25 p. Tripura Sundari Temple, Baitadi 10 10
420 2 r. Mt. Langtang Lirung . . 25 15

184 Academy Building

185 Balakrishna Sama

1982. 25th Anniv of Royal Nepal Academy.
421 **184** 40 p. multicoloured . . . 10 10

1982. 1st Death Anniv of Balakrishna Sama (writer).
422 **185** 1 r. multicoloured 15 15

186 "Intelsat V" and Dish Aerial **187** Mount Nuptse

1982. Sagarmatha Satellite Earth Station, Balambu.
423 **186** 5 r. multicoloured . . . 75 40

1982. 50th Anniv of Union of International Alpinist Associations. Multicoloured.
424 25 p. Type **187** 10 10
425 2 r. Mount Lhotse (31 × 31 mm) 30 20
426 3 r. Mount Everest (39 × 31 mm) 60 30
Nos. 424/6 were issued together, se-tenant, forming a composite design.

188 Games Emblem and Weights **189** Indra Sarobar Lake

1982. 9th Asian Games, New Delhi.
427 **188** 3 r. 40 multicoloured . . . 50 40

1982. Kulekhani Hydro-electric Project.
428 **189** 2 r. multicoloured 30 20

190 King Birendra **191** N.I.D.C. Emblem

1982. King Birendra's 38th Birthday.
429 **190** 5 p. multicoloured . . . 10 10

1983. 25th Anniv of Nepal Industrial Development Corporation.
430 **191** 50 p. multicoloured . . . 10 10

192 Boeing 727 over Himalayas

1983. 25th Anniv of Royal Nepal Airlines.
431 **192** 1 r. multicoloured 40 15

193 W.C.Y. Emblem and Nepalese Flag **194** Sarangi

1983. World Communications Year.
432 **193** 10 p. multicoloured . . . 10 10

1983. Musical Instruments. Multicoloured.
433 5 p. Type **194** 10 10
434 10 p. Kwota (drum) 10 10
435 50 p. Narashinga (horn) . . . 10 10
436 1 r. Murchunga 20 20

195 Chakrapani Chalise **196** King Birendra and Doves

1983. Birth Centenary of Chakrapani Chalise (poet).
437 **195** 4 r. 50 multicoloured . . 60 45

1983. King Birendra's 39th Birthday.
438 **196** 5 r. multicoloured 70 40

197 Barahkshetra Temple and Image of Barah

1983. Tourism. Multicoloured.
439 1 r. Type **197** 15 10
440 2 r. 50 Temple, Triveni . . . 25 20
441 6 r. Mount Cho-oyu 70 50

198 Auditing Accounts **199** Antenna and Emblem

1984. 25th Anniv of Auditor General.
442 **198** 25 p. multicoloured . . . 10 10

1984. 20th Anniv of Asia-Pacific Broadcasting Union.
443 **199** 5 r. multicoloured 70 60

200 University Emblem **201** Boxing

1984. 25th Anniv of Tribhuvan University.
444 **200** 50 p. multicoloured . . . 15 10

1984. Olympic Games, Los Angeles.
445 **201** 10 r. multicoloured . . . 1·25 80

202 Family and Emblem **203** National Flag and Emblem

1984. 25th Anniv of Nepal Family Planning Association.
446 **202** 1 r. multicoloured 15 10

1984. Social Service Day.
447 **203** 5 p. multicoloured . . . 10 10

204 Gharial **205** "Vishnu as Giant" (stone carving)

1984. Wildlife. Multicoloured.
448 10 p. Type **204** 10 10
449 25 p. Snow leopard 10 10
450 50 p. Blackbuck 20 20

1984. Tourism. Multicoloured.
451 10 p. Type **205** 10 10
452 1 r. Temple of Chhinna Masta Bhagavati and sculpture (horiz) 15 10
453 5 r. Mount Api 70 45

206 King Birendra

1984. King Birendra's 40th Birthday.
454 **206** 1 r. multicoloured 15 10

207 Animals and Mountains **208** Shiva

1985. Sagarmatha (Mt. Everest) National Park.
455 **207** 10 r. multicoloured . . . . 2·00 55

1985. Traditional Paintings. Details of cover of "Siva Dharma Purana". Multicoloured.
456 50 p. Type **208** 10 10
457 50 p. Multi-headed Shiva talking to woman 10 10
458 50 p. Brahma and Vishnu making offering (15 × 22 mm) 10 10
459 50 p. Shiva (different) 10 10
460 50 p. Shiva talking to woman . . 10 10
Nos. 456/60 were printed together, se-tenant, forming a composite design.

209 U.N. Flag **210** Lungs and Bacilli

1985. 40th Anniv of U.N.O.
461 **209** 5 r. multicoloured 60 40

1985. 14th Eastern Regional Tuberculosis Conference.
462 **210** 25 r. multicoloured . . . . 2·75 2·00

211 Flags of Member Countries

1985. 1st South Asian Regional Co-operation Summit.
463 **211** 5 r. multicoloured 60 40

212 Jaleshwar Temple **213** I.Y.Y. Emblem

1985. Tourism. Multicoloured.
464 10 p. Type **212** 10 10
465 1 r. Temple of Goddess Shaileshwari 10 10
466 2 r. Phoksundo Lake 25 15

1985. International Youth Year.
467 **213** 1 r. multicoloured 15 10

214 King Birendra **215** Devi Ghat Hydro-electric Project

1985. King Birendra's 41st Birthday.
468 **214** 50 p. multicoloured . . . 10 10

1985.
469 **215** 2 r. multicoloured 30 20

216 Emblem **217** Royal Crown

1986. 25th Anniv of Panchayat System (partyless government).
470 **216** 4 r. multicoloured 50 40

1986.
471 – 5 p. brown and deep brown 10 10
472 – 10 p. blue 10 10
474 – 50 p. blue 10 10
476 **217** 1 r. brown and light brown 15 10
DESIGNS: 5, 50 p. Pashupati Temple; 10 p. Mayadevi Temple of Lumbini (Buddha's birthplace).

218 Pharping Hydro-electric Station

1986. 75th Anniv of Pharping Hydro-electric Power Station.
480 **218** 15 p. multicoloured . . . 10 10

219 Emblem and Map

1986. 25th Anniv of Asian Productivity Organization.
481 **219** 1 r. multicoloured 15 10

220 Mt. Pumori, Himalayas **221** King Birendra

1986. Tourism. Multicoloured.
482 60 p. Budhanilkantha (statue), Katmandu Valley (38 × 22 mm) 10 10
483 8 r. Type **220** 80 60

1986. King Birendra's 42nd Birthday.
484 **221** 1 r. multicoloured 15 10

222 Emblem **223** Flag and Emblem

1986. International Peace Year.
485 **222** 10 r. multicoloured . . . 90 70

1987. 10th Anniv of National Social Service Co-ordination Council.
486 **223** 1 r. multicoloured 15 10

224 Emblem and Forest

1987. 1st Nepal Scout Jamboree, Katmandu.
487 **224** 1 r. brown, orange & bl . 20 10

225 Ashokan Pillar and Maya Devi

1987. Lumbini, Buddha's Birthplace.
488 **225** 4 r. multicoloured 40 30

226 Emblem **227** Emblem

1987. 3rd South Asian Association for Regional Co-operation Summit, Katmandu.
489 **226** 60 p. gold and red 10 10

1987. 25th Anniv of Rastriya Samachar Samiti (news service).
490 **227** 4 r. purple, blue & red . . 40 30

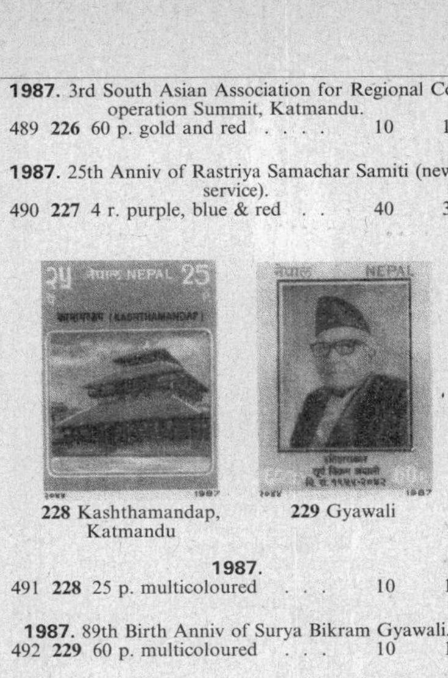

228 Kashthamandap, Katmandu

229 Gyawali

1987.
491 **228** 25 p. multicoloured . . . 10 10

1987. 89th Birth Anniv of Surya Bikram Gyawali.
492 **229** 60 p. multicoloured . . . 10 10

230 Emblem

231 King Birendra

1987. International Year of Shelter for the Homeless.
493 **230** 5 r. multicoloured 50 40

1987. King Birendra's 43rd Birthday.
494 **231** 25 p. multicoloured . . . 10 10

232 Mt. Kanjiroba

1987.
495 **232** 10 r. multicoloured . . . 90 60

233 Crown Prince Dipendra

1988. Crown Prince Dipendra's 17th Birthday.
496 **233** 1 r. multicoloured 15 10

234 Baby in Incubator

1988. 25th Anniv of Kanti Children's Hospital.
497 **234** 60 p. multicoloured . . . 10 10

235 Swamp Deer

236 Laxmi, Goddess of Wealth

1988. 12th Anniv of Royal Shukla Phanta Wildlife Reserve.
498 **235** 60 p. multicoloured . . . 20 10

1988. 50th Anniv of Nepal Bank Ltd.
499 **136** 2 r. multicoloured 20 15

237 Queen Mother

238 Hands protecting Blood Droplet

1988. 60th Birthday of Queen Mother.
500 **237** 5 r. multicoloured 50 40

1988. 25th Anniv of Nepal Red Cross Society.
501 **238** 1 r. red and brown . . . 15 10

239 Temple and Statue

1988. Temple of Goddess Bindhyabasini, Pokhara.
502 **239** 15 p. multicoloured . . . 10 10

240 King Birendra

241 Temple

1988. King Birendra's 44th Birthday.
503 **240** 4 r. multicoloured 40 25

1989. Pashupati Area Development Trust.
504 **241** 1 r. multicoloured 15 10

242 Emblem

243 S.A.A.R.C. Emblem

1989. 10th Anniv of Asia-Pacific Telecommunity.
505 **242** 4 r. green, black & violet 25 15

1989. South Asian Association for Regional Co-operation Year against Drug Abuse and Trafficking.
506 **243** 60 p. multicoloured . . . 10 10

244 King Birendra

245 Child Survival Measures

1989. King Birendra's 45th Birthday.
507 **244** 2 r. multicoloured 20 10

1989. Child Survival Campaign.
508 **245** 1 r. multicoloured 10 10

246 Lake Rara

247 Mt. Amadablam

1989. Rara National Park.
509 **246** 4 r. multicoloured 25 15

1989.
510 **247** 5 r. multicoloured 40 20

248 Crown Prince Dipendra

249 Temple of Manakamana, Gorkha

1989. Crown Prince Dipendra's Coming-of-Age.
511 **248** 1 r. multicoloured 10 10

1990.
512 **249** 60 p. black and blue . . . 10 10

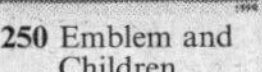

250 Emblem and Children

251 Emblem

1990. 25th Anniv of Nepal Children's Organization.
513 **250** 1 r. multicoloured 10 10

1990. Centenary of Bir Hospital.
514 **251** 60 p. red, blue and yellow 10 10

252 Emblem

253 Goddess and Bageshwori Temple, Nepalgunj

1990. 20th Anniv of Asian–Pacific Postal Training Centre, Bangkok.
515 **252** 4 r. multicoloured 30 15

1990. Tourism. Multicoloured.
516 1 r. Type **253** 10 10
517 5 r. Mt. Saipal (36 × 27 mm) . . 35 25

254 Leisure Activities

1990. South Asian Association for Regional Co-operation Girls' Year.
518 **254** 4 r. 60 multicoloured . . . 35 20

255 King Birendra

256 Koirala

1990. King Birendra's 46th Birthday.
519 **255** 2 r. multicoloured 15 10

1990. 76th Birth Anniv of Bisweswar Prasad Koirala (Prime Minister, 1959–60).
520 **256** 60 p. black, orange and red 10 10

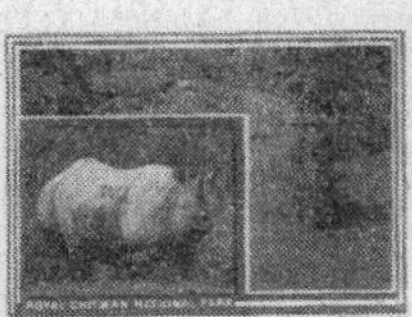

257 Indian Rhinoceros and Lake

258 Flower and Crowd

1991. Royal Chitwan National Park.
521 **257** 4 r. multicoloured 35 20

1991. 1st Anniv of Abrogation of Ban on Political Parties.
522 **258** 1 r. multicoloured 10 10

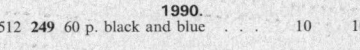

259 Official and Villagers

260 Federation and Jubilee Emblems

1991. National Population Census.
523 **259** 60 p. multicoloured . . . 10 10

1991. 25th Anniv of Federation of Nepalese Chambers of Commerce and Industry.
524 **260** 3 r. multicoloured 20 15

261 Crosses

262 Delegates

1991. 25th Anniv (1990) of Nepal Junior Red Cross.
525 **261** 60 p. red and grey 10 10

1991. 1st Session of Revived Parliament.
526 **262** 1 r. multicoloured 10 10

263 King Birendra making Speech

264 Rama and Janaki (statues) and Vivaha Mandap

1991. Constitution Day.
527 **263** 50 p. multicoloured . . . 10 10

1991. 5th Anniv of Rebuilt Vivaha Mandap Pavilion, Janaki Temple.
528 **264** 1 r. multicoloured 10 10

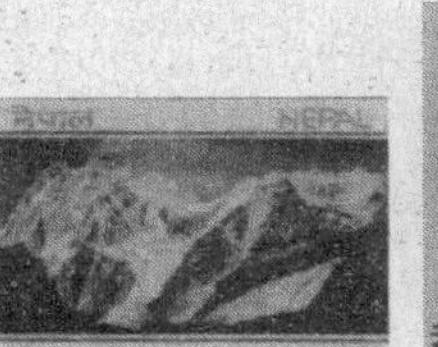

265 Mt. Kumbhakarna

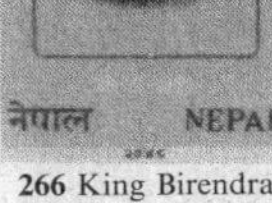

266 King Birendra

1991.
529 **265** 4 r. 60 multicoloured . . 30 15

1991. King Birendra's 47th Birthday.
530 **266** 8 r. multicoloured 50 30

267 Houses

268 Glass magnifying Society Emblem

1991. South Asian Association for Regional Co-operation Year of Shelter.
531 **267** 9 r. multicoloured 50 35

1992. 25th Anniv (1991) of Nepal Philatelic Society.
532 **268** 4 r. multicoloured 25 15

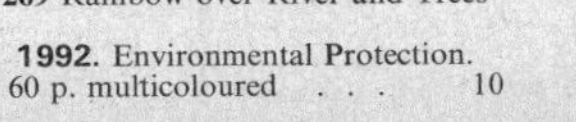

269 Rainbow over River and Trees

1992. Environmental Protection.
533 **269** 60 p. multicoloured . . . 10 10

270 Nutrition, Education and Health Care

1992. Rights of the Child.

534	**270**	1 r. multicoloured	10	10

271 Thakurdwara Temple, Bardiya

272 Bank Emblem

1992. Temples. Multicoloured.

535		75 p. Type **271** (postage)	10	10
536		1 r. Namo Buddha Temple, Kavre	10	10
537		2 r. Narijhowa Temple, Mustang	10	10
538		11 r. Dantakali Temple, Bijayapur (air)	55	35

1992. 25th Anniv of Agricultural Development Bank.

539	**272**	40 p. brown and green	10	10

273 Pin-tailed Green Pigeon

1992. Birds. Multicoloured.

540		1 r. Type **273**	10	10
541		3 r. Bohemian waxwing	15	10
542		25 r. Rufous-tailed desert lark	1·25	80

274 King Birendra exchanging Swords with Goddess Sree Bhadrakali

275 Pandit Kulchandra Gautam

1992. King Birendra's 48th Birthday.

543	**274**	7 r. multicoloured	35	25

1992. Poets. Multicoloured, frame colour given in brackets.

544		1 r. Type **275**	10	10
545		1 r. Chittadhar Hridaya (drab)	10	10
546		1 r. Vidyapati (stone)	10	10
547		1 r. Teongsi Sirijunga (grey)	10	10

276 Shooting and Marathon

277 Barb

1992. Olympic Games, Barcelona.

548	**276**	25 r. multicoloured	1·25	80

1993. Fishes. Multicoloured.

549		25 p. Type **277**	10	10
550		1 r. Marinka	10	10
551		5 r. Indian eel	25	15
552		10 r. "Psilorhynchus pseudecheneis"	50	30

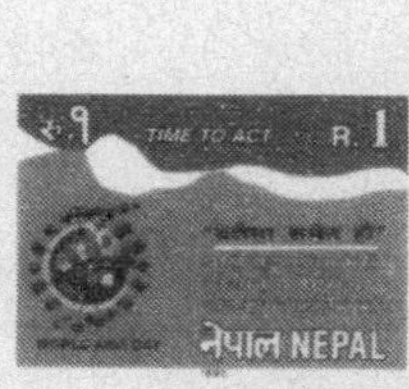

278 Antibodies attacking Globe

279 Tanka Prasad Acharya (Prime Minister, 1956–57)

1993. World AIDS Day.

554	**278**	1 r. multicoloured	10	10

1993. Death Anniversaries. Multicoloured.

555		25 p. Type **279** (1st anniv)	10	10
556		1 r. Sungdare Sherpa (mountaineer) (4th anniv)	10	10
557		7 r. Siddhi Charan Shrestha (poet) (1st anniv)	30	20
558		15 r. Falgunand (religious leader) (44th anniv)	60	40

280 Bagh Bairab Temple, Kirtipur

1993. Holy Places. Multicoloured.

559		1 r. 50 Halesi Mahadev cave (hiding place of Shiva), Khotang	10	10
560		5 r. Devghat (gods' bathing place), Tanahun	20	15
561		8 r. Type **280**	30	20

281 Tushahity Fountain, Sundari Chowk, Patan

282 King Birendra

1993. Tourism. Multicoloured.

562		5 r. Type **281**	20	10
563		8 r. White-water rafting	30	20

1993. King Birendra's 49th Birthday.

564	**282**	10 r. multicoloured	40	25

283 Monument

284 Mt. Everest

1994.

565	**283**	20 p. brown	10	10
566	–	25 p. red	10	10
567	–	30 p. green	10	10
568	**284**	1 r. multicoloured	10	10
569	–	5 r. multicoloured	20	10

DESIGNS—20 × 22 mm: 25 p. State arms. 22 × 20 mm: 30 p. Lumbini. 25 × 15 mm: 5 r. Map of Nepal, crown and state arms and flag.

OFFICIAL STAMPS

O 25 Nepalese Arms and Soldiers

काज सरकारी

(O 28)

1960. (a) Size 30 × 18 mm.

O135	**O 25**	2 p. brown	10	10
O136		4 p. green	10	10
O137		6 p. red	10	10
O138		8 p. violet	10	10
O139		12 p. orange	15	15

(b) Size 38 × 27 mm.

O140	**O 25**	16 p. brown	20	20
O141		24 p. red	35	25
O142		32 p. purple	35	35
O143		50 p. blue	65	55
O144		1 r. red	1·40	1·25
O145		2 r. orange	2·50	2·25

1960. Optd as Type O **28**.

O146	**27**	1 r. purple	50	

1961. Optd with Type O **28**.

O148	**35**	1 p. red	10	10
O149		2 p. blue	10	10
O150		5 p. brown	10	10

NETHERLANDS Pt. 4

A kingdom in the N.W. of Europe on the North Sea.

100 cents = 1 gulden (florin)

1 3 4 King William III

1852. Imperf.

1	**1**	5 c. blue	£425	23·00
2		10 c. red	£600	32·00
3b		15 c. orange	£700	75·00

1864. Perf.

8	**3**	5 c. blue	£300	12·00
9		10 c. red	£425	6·50
10		15 c. orange	£1200	60·00

1867.

47	**4**	5 c. blue	80·00	1·00
30		10 c. red	£130	1·40
46		15 c. brown	£600	26·00
50		20 c. green	£550	20·00
15		25 c. purple	£2250	80·00
16		50 c. gold	£2500	£130

5 6

1869.

58	**5**	$\frac{1}{2}$ c. brown	23·00	2·50
53		1 c. black	£200	55·00
59		1 c. green	11·00	1·00
60		$1\frac{1}{2}$ c. red	£140	80·00
61		2 c. yellow	50·00	8·50
62		$2\frac{1}{2}$ c. mauve	£500	45·00

1872.

91	**6**	5 c. blue	8·00	15
92		$7\frac{1}{2}$ c. brown	35·00	17·00
112		10 c. red	50·00	65
113		$12\frac{1}{2}$ c. grey	60·00	1·25
95		15 c. brown	£350	3·75
96		20 c. green	£450	3·75
97		$22\frac{1}{2}$ c. green	65·00	38·00
98		25 c. lilac	£600	2·50
100		50 c. bistre	£700	8·00
101		1 g. violet	£500	22·00
74	–	2 g. 50 blue and red	£900	85·00

No. 74 is similar to Type **6** but larger and with value and country scrolls transposed.

8

9 Queen Wilhelmina

1876.

138d	**8**	$\frac{1}{2}$ c. red	2·75	10
140		1 c. green	2·25	10
143		2 c. yellow	35·00	2·50
145		$2\frac{1}{2}$ c. mauve	14·00	15

1891.

147a	**9**	3 c. orange	6·00	1·10
148a		5 c. blue	4·00	10
149b		$7\frac{1}{2}$ c. brown	16·00	5·00
150b		10 c. red	23·00	55
151b		$12\frac{1}{2}$ c. grey	22·00	65
152a		15 c. brown	55·00	4·00
153b		20 c. green	55·00	2·00
154a		$22\frac{1}{2}$ c. green	32·00	11·00
155		25 c. mauve	£110	3·00
156a		50 c. bistre	£500	15·00
159	–	50 c. brown and green	70·00	7·50
157	**9**	1 g. violet	£550	55·00
160	–	1 g. green and brown	£180	21·00
161	–	2 g. 50 blue and red	£425	£120
165	–	5 g. red and green	£750	£350

Nos. 159, 160, 161 and 165 are as Type **9** but larger and with value and country scrolls transposed.

11 12 13

1898. Nos. 174 and 176 also exist imperf.

167	**12**	$\frac{1}{2}$ c. lilac	40	15
168		1 c. red	1·00	10
226		$1\frac{1}{2}$ c. blue	3·25	25
170		2 c. brown	3·75	10
171		$2\frac{1}{2}$ c. green	3·25	10
172	**13**	3 c. orange	14·00	2·50
173		3 c. green	1·25	10
227		4 c. purple	1·50	70
228		$4\frac{1}{2}$ c. mauve	3·75	4·00
174		5 c. red	1·50	10
187a		5 c. red and blue	5·00	80
175		$7\frac{1}{2}$ c. brown	60	10
176		10 c. grey	7·00	10
177		$12\frac{1}{2}$ c. blue	3·00	15
178		15 c. brown	80·00	3·25
179		15 c. red and blue	6·00	10
180		$17\frac{1}{2}$ c. mauve	50·00	12·00
181		$17\frac{1}{2}$ c. brown and blue	16·00	85
182		20 c. green	£100	65
183		20 c. grey and green	10·00	30
184		$22\frac{1}{2}$ c. green and brown	9·50	40
185		25 c. blue and pink	9·50	10
230		30 c. purple and mauve	23·00	20
231		40 c. orange and green	38·00	75
186		50 c. red and green	75·00	90
232		50 c. violet and grey	70·00	60
233		60 c. green and olive	38·00	90
202	**11**	1 g. green	55·00	30
203		$2\frac{1}{2}$ g. lilac	£100	2·50
201		5 g. red	£225	4·25
198		10 g. red	£700	£600

14

1906. Society for the Prevention of Tuberculosis.

208	**14**	1 c. (+ 1 c.) red	2·50	2·50
209		3 c. (+ 3 c.) green	25·00	24·00
210		5 c. (+ 5 c.) violet	25·00	7·50

15 Admiral M. A. de Ruyter

16 William I

1907. Birth Tercentenary of Admiral de Ruyter.

211	**15**	$\frac{1}{2}$ c. blue	70	80
212		1 c. red	2·50	2·00
213		$2\frac{1}{2}$ c. red	7·50	2·00

1913. Independence Centenary.

214	**16**	$2\frac{1}{2}$ c. green on green	60	50
215	–	3 c. yellow on cream	90	90
216	–	5 c. red on buff	90	40
217	–	10 c. grey	3·50	1·75
218	**16**	$12\frac{1}{2}$ c. blue on blue	2·50	1·50
219	–	20 c. brown	12·00	9·00
220	–	25 c. blue	13·00	7·50
221	–	50 c. green	32·00	30·00
222	**16**	1 g. red	45·00	15·00
223	–	$2\frac{1}{2}$ g. lilac	£120	50·00
224	–	5 g. yellow on cream	£250	38·00
225	–	10 g. orange	£700	£700

DESIGNS: 3 c., 20 c., $2\frac{1}{2}$ g. William II; 5 c., 25 c., 5 g. William III; 10 c., 50 c., 10 g. Queen Wilhelmina.

1919. Surch **Veertig Cent** (40 c.) or **Zestig Cent** (60 c.).

234	**13**	40 c. on 30 c. purple & mve	25·00	2·50
235		60 c. on 30 c. purple & mve	24·00	3·50

1920. Surch in figures.

238	**13**	4 c. on $4\frac{1}{2}$ c. mauve	4·00	1·40
236	**11**	2.50 on 10 g. red	£150	£120
237	–	2.50 on 10 g. red (225)	£140	90·00

23 24

1921. Air.

239	**23**	10 c. red	1·75	1·25
240		15 c. green	6·00	2·00
241		60 c. blue	16·00	20

1921.

242	**24**	5 c. green	10·00	15
243		$12\frac{1}{2}$ c. red	15·00	1·75
244		20 c. blue	23·00	15

25 Lion in Dutch Garden and Orange Tree (emblematical of Netherlands) — 26 — 27

1923.

248	25	1 c. violet	50	60
249		2 c. orange	5·00	10
250	26	2½ c. green	1·75	70
251	27	4 c. blue	1·25	45

1923. Surch.

252	12	2 c. on 1 c. red	45	20
253		2 c. on 1½ c. blue	45	20
254	13	10 c. on 3 c. green	4·50	15
255		10 c. on 5 c. red	8·50	55
256		10 c. on 12½ c. blue	7·50	55
257a		10 c. on 17½ c. brown & bl	3·00	3·50
258a		10 c. on 22½ c. olive & brn	3·00	3·50

30 — 31

1923. 25th Anniv of Queen's Accession.

259a	31	2 c. green	15	10
260a	30	5 c. green	25	10
261a	31	7½ c. red	40	10
262b		10 c. red	30	10
263		20 c. blue	3·50	55
264		25 c. yellow	6·00	90
265b		35 c. orange	5·50	2·50
266a		50 c. black	16·00	20
267	30	1 g. red	30·00	5·00
268		2½ g. black	£225	£200
269		5 g. blue	£200	£190

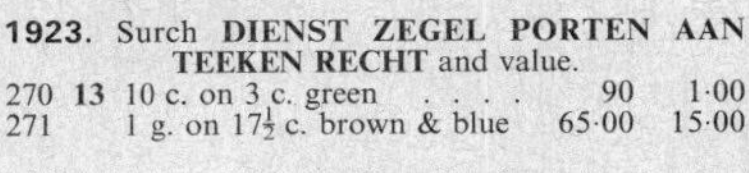

1923. Surch **DIENST ZEGEL PORTEN AAN TEEKEN RECHT** and value.

270	13	10 c. on 3 c. green	90	1·00
271		1 g. on 17½ c. brown & blue	65·00	15·00

33

1923. Culture Fund.

272	33	2 c. + 5 c. blue on pink	17·00	17·00
273	–	10 c. + 5 c. red on pink	17·00	17·00

DESIGN: 10 c. Two women.

35 Carrier Pigeon — 36 Queen Wilhelmina

1924.

330	35	½ c. grey	40	25
423		1 c. red	10	10
332		1½ c. mauve	20	10
424a		1½ c. grey	10	10
425		2 c. orange	10	10
426a		2½ c. green	70	20
427		3 c. green	10	10
427a		4 c. blue	10	10
428	36	5 c. green	15	10
429		6 c. brown	15	10
279		7½ c. yellow	40	10
313		7½ c. violet	2·75	10
314		7½ c. red	20	10
279c		9 c. red and black	1·75	1·60
281		10 c. red	1·40	10
317		10 c. blue	2·00	10
282		12½ c. red	1·75	35
431		12½ c. blue	30	10
320		15 c. blue	7·00	15
432		15 c. yellow	80	10
433		20 c. blue	7·00	10
434		21 c. brown	24·00	90
323		22½ c. brown	7·00	2·50
434a		22½ c. orange	16·00	18·00
435		25 c. green	4·75	10
346		27½ c. grey	3·25	1·50
437		30 c. violet	6·00	10
286c		35 c. brown	32·00	6·50
437a		40 c. brown	12·00	15
329		50 c. green	5·00	15
289		60 c. violet	30·00	85
437c		60 c. black	27·00	90
301		1 g. blue (23×29 mm)	8·00	30
302		2½ g. red (23×29 mm)	85·00	4·00
303		5 g. black (23×29 mm)	£170	2·50

For further stamps in Type 35, see Nos. 546/57.

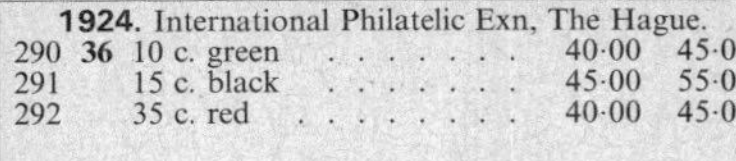

1924. International Philatelic Exn, The Hague.

290	36	10 c. green	40·00	45·00
291		15 c. black	45·00	55·00
292		35 c. red	40·00	45·00

37 — 38 — 39

1924. Dutch Lifeboat Centenary.

293	37	2 c. brown	2·25	2·50
294	38	10 c. brown on yellow	7·00	2·00

1924. Child Welfare.

295	39	2 c. + 2 c. green	90	1·60
296		7½ c. + 3½ c. brown	5·50	7·00
297		10 c. + 2½ c. red	5·50	1·50

40 Arms of South Holland — 46 Queen Wilhelmina — 47 Red Cross Allegory

1925. Child Welfare. Arms as T **40**.

298	–	2 c. + 2 c. green & yell	80	80
299	–	7½ c. + 3½ c. violet & blue	4·00	4·00
300	40	10 c. + 2½ c. red & yellow	3·25	40

ARMS: 2 c. North Brabant; 7½ c. Gelderland.
See also Nos. 350/3 and 359/62.

1926. Child Welfare. Arms as T **40**.

350		2 c. + 2 c. red and silver	40	40
351		5 c. + 3 c. green and blue	1·50	1·25
352		10 c. + 3 c. red and green	2·25	20
353		15 c. + 3 c. yellow & blue	6·00	6·00

ARMS: 2 c. Utrecht; 5 c. Zeeland; 10 c. North Holland; 15 c. Friesland.

1927. 60th Anniv of Dutch Red Cross Society.

354a	46	2 c. + 2 c. red	1·75	2·25
355	–	3 c. + 2 c. green	6·00	8·50
356	–	5 c. + 3 c. blue	70	55
357a	–	7½ c. + 3½ c. blue	5·00	1·60
358	47	15 c. + 5 c. red & blue	12·00	12·00

PORTRAITS: 2 c. King William III; 3 c. Queen Emma; 5 c. Henry, Prince Consort.

1927. Child Welfare. Arms as T **40**.

359		2 c. + 2 c. red and lilac	30	35
360		5 c. + 3 c. green & yellow	1·50	1·40
361		7½ c. + 3½ c. red and black	3·50	30
362		15 c. + 3 c. blue & brown	5·50	5·00

ARMS: 2 c. Drente; 5 c. Groningen; 7½ c. Limburg; 15 c. Overyssel.

48 Sculler — 49 Footballer

1928. Olympic Games, Amsterdam.

363	48	1½ c. + 1 c. green	1·25	70
364	–	2 c. + 1 c. purple	2·00	1·10
365	49	3 c. + 1 c. green	2·00	1·00
366	–	5 c. + 1 c. blue	2·25	80
367	–	7½ c. + 2½ c. orange	2·50	1·00
368	–	10 c. + 2 c. red	7·00	5·50
369	–	15 c. + 2 c. blue	6·50	3·50
370	–	30 c. + 3 c. sepia	25·00	25·00

DESIGNS—HORIZ: 2 c. Fencer. VERT: 5 c. Yachting; 7½ c. Putting the weight; 10 c. Runner; 15 c. Horseman; 30 c. Boxer.

50 Lieut. Koppen

1928. Air.

371	50	40 c. red	45	45
372	–	75 c. green	45	45

DESIGN: 75 c. Van der Hoop.

52 J. P. Minckelers — 53 Mercury

1928. Child Welfare.

373	52	1½ c. + 1½ c. violet	50	35
374	–	5 c. + 3 c. green	80	65
375a	–	7½ c. + 2½ c. red	3·00	25
376a	–	12½ c. + 3½ c. blue	12·00	8·00

PORTRAITS: 5 c. Boerhaave; 7½ c. H. A. Lorentz; 12½ c. G. Huygens.

1929. Air.

377	53	1½ g. black	2·00	1·60
378		4½ g. red	1·50	3·50
379		7½ g. green	21·00	3·75

1929. Surch **21**.

380	36	21 c. on 22½ c. brown	23·00	1·40

55 "Friendship and Security" — 56 Rembrandt and "De Staalmeesters"

1929. Child Welfare.

381	55	1½ c. + 1½ c. grey	1·50	40
382		5 c. + 3 c. green	2·50	65
383		6 c. + 4 c. red	1·75	30
384		12½ c. + 3½ c. blue	15·00	13·00

1930. Rembrandt Society.

385	56	5 c. (+ 5 c.) green	9·00	8·00
386		6 c. (+ 5 c.) black	4·50	1·50
387		12½ c. (+ 5 c.) blue	13·00	15·00

57 Spring — 58 — 59 Queen Wilhelmina

1930. Child Welfare.

388	57	1½ c. + 1½ c. red	1·50	35
389	–	5 c. + 3 c. green	2·25	65
390	–	6 c. + 4 c. purple	2·25	25
391	–	12½ c. + 3½ c. blue	18·00	10·00

DESIGNS (allegorical): 5 c. Summer; 6 c. Autumn; 12½ c. Winter.

1931. Gouda Church Restoration Fund.

392	58	1½ c. + 1½ c. green	13·00	13·00
393		6 c. + 4 c. red	27·00	25·00

1931.

395	–	70 c. blue and red (postage)	26·00	45
395b	–	80 c. green and red	95·00	3·00
394	59	36 c. red and blue (air)	14·00	40

DESIGNS: 70 c. Portrait and factory; 80 c. Portrait and shipyard.

61 Mentally Deficient Child — 62 Windmill and Dykes, Kinderdijk — 63 Gorse (Spring)

1931. Child Welfare.

396	–	1½ c. + 1½ c. red and blue	1·40	50
397	61	5 c. + 3 c. green & purple	2·25	1·25
398	–	6 c. + 4 c. purple & green	1·75	40
399	–	12½ c. + 3½ c. blue & red	28·00	24·00

DESIGNS: 1½ c. Deaf mute; 6 c. Blind girl; 12½ c. Sick child.

1932. Tourist Propaganda.

400	62	2½ c. + 1½ c. green & black	5·50	2·50
401	–	6 c. + 4 c. grey & black	9·00	22·50
402	–	7½ c. + 3½ c. red & black	32·00	23·00
403	–	12½ c. + 2½ c. blue & black	35·00	24·00

DESIGNS: 6 c. Aerial view of Town Hall, Zierikzee; 7½ c. Bridges at Schipluiden and Moerdijk; 12½ c. Tulips.

1932. Child Welfare.

404	63	1½ c. + 1½ c. brown & yell	1·75	35
405	–	5 c. + 3 c. blue and red	1·75	65
406	–	6 c. + 4 c. green & orge	1·75	30
407	–	12½ c. + 3½ c. blue & orange	32·00	20·00

DESIGNS: Child and: 5 c. Cornflower (Summer); 6 c. Sunflower (Autumn); 12½ c. Christmas rose (Winter).

64 Arms of House of Orange — 65 Portrait by Goltzius

1933. 4th Birth Centenary of William I of Orange. T **64** and portraits of William I inscr. "1533", as T **65**.

408	64	1½ c. black	55	15
409	65	5 c. green	1·75	20
410	–	6 c. purple	2·75	10
411	–	12½ c. blue	17·00	3·50

DESIGNS: 6 c. Portrait by Key; 12½ c. Portrait attributed to Moro.

68 Dove of Peace — 69 Projected Monument at Den Helder — 70 "De Hoop" (hospital ship)

1933. Peace Propaganda.

412	68	12½ c. blue	8·50	25

1933. Seamen's Fund.

413	69	1½ c. + 1½ c. red	1·75	1·25
414	70	5 c. + 3 c. green and red	12·00	2·50
415	–	6 c. + 4 c. green	17·00	2·50
416	–	12½ c. + 3½ c. blue	24·00	21·00

DESIGNS: 6 c. Lifeboat; 12½ c. Seaman and Seamen's Home.

73 Pander S.4 Postjager

1933. Air. (Special Flights).

417	73	30 c. green	70	75

74 Child and Star of Epiphany — 75 Princess Juliana

1933. Child Welfare.

418	74	1½ c. + 1½ c. orange & grey	1·50	45
419		5 c. + 3 c. yellow and brown	2·25	60
420		6 c. + 4 c. gold and green	2·50	40
421		12½ c. + 3½ c. silver & blue	24·00	20·00

1934. Crisis stamps.

438	–	5 c. + 4 c. purple	10·00	2·75
439	75	6 c. + 5 c. blue	11·00	5·50

DESIGN: 5 c. Queen Wilhelmina.

76 Dutch Warship — 77 Dowager Queen Emma

1934. Tercentenary of Curacao.

440	–	6 c. black	4·00	10
441	76	12½ c. blue	26·00	2·75

DESIGN: 6 c. Willemstad Harbour.

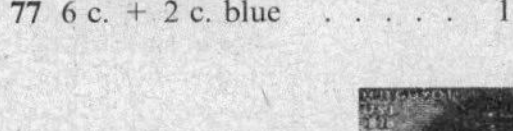

1934. Anti-T.B. Fund.

442	77	6 c. + 2 c. blue	11·00	1·60

78 Destitute child — 79 H. D. Guyot

1934. Child Welfare.

443	78	1½ c. + 1½ c. brown	1·50	50
444		5 c. + 3 c. red	2·25	1·25
445		6 c. + 4 c. green	2·25	25
446		12½ c. + 3½ c. blue	26·00	20·00

1935. Cultural and Social Relief Fund.

447	79	1½ c. + 1½ c. red	1·90	1·90
448	–	5 c. + 3 c. brown	4·50	5·50
449	–	6 c. + 4 c. green	6·00	30
450	–	12½ c. + 3½ c. blue	30·00	6·00

PORTRAITS: 5 c. A. J. M. Diepenbrock; 6 c. F. C. Donders; 12½ c. J. P. Sweelinck.
See also Nos. 456/9, 469/72, 478/82 and 492/6.

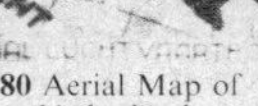

80 Aerial Map of Netherlands **81** Child picking fruit

1935. Air Fund.

451	80	6 c. + 4 c. brown	24·00	11·00

1935. Child Welfare.

452	81	1½ c. + 1½ c. red	60	30
453		5 c. + 3 c. green	1·75	1·25
454		6 c. + 4 c. brown	1·50	30
455		12½ c. + 3½ c. blue	24·00	9·00

1936. Cultural and Social Relief Fund. As T **79**.

456		1½ c. + 1½ c. sepia	85	1·00
457		5 c. + 3 c. green	4·75	3·75
458		6 c. + 4 c. red	1·75	35
459		12½ c. + 3½ c. blue	17·00	3·25

PORTRAITS: 1½ c. H. Kamerlingh Onnes; 5 c. Dr. A. S. Talma; 6 c. Mgr. Dr. H. J. A. M. Schaepman; 12½ c. Desiderius Erasmus.

83 Pallas Athene

1936. Tercentenary of Utrecht University Foundation.

460	83	6 c. red	1·50	20
461	–	12½ c. blue	5·00	4·50

DESIGN: 12½ c. Gisbertus Voetius.

84 Child Herald **85** Scout Movement

1936. Child Welfare.

462	84	1½ c. + 1½ c. slate	50	25
463		5 c. + 3 c. green	2·25	75
464		6 c. + 4 c. brown	2·00	20
465		12½ c. + 3½ c. blue	16·00	5·00

1937. Scout Jamboree.

466	–	1½ c. black and green	15	10
467	85	6 c. brown and black	1·50	10
468	–	12½ c. black and blue	3·00	1·25

DESIGNS: 1½ c. Scout Tenderfoot Badge; 12½ c. Hermes.

1937. Cultural and Social Relief Fund. Portraits as T **79**.

469		1½ c. + 1½ c. sepia	60	60
470		5 c. + 3 c. green	4·75	4·00
471		6 c. + 4 c. purple	1·10	25
472		12½ c. + 3½ c. blue	9·00	1·00

PORTRAITS: 1½ c. Jacob Maris; 5 c. F. de la B. Sylvius; 6 c. J. van den Vondel; 12½ c. A. van Leeuwenhoek.

86 "Laughing Child" by Frans Hals **87** Queen Wilhelmina

1937. Child Welfare.

473	86	1½ c. + 1½ c. black	15	15
474		3 c. + 2 c. green	1·25	1·25
475		4 c. + 2 c. red	60	50
476		5 c. + 3 c. green	50	15
477		12½ c. + 3½ c. blue	7·50	1·75

1938. Cultural and Social Relief Fund. As T **79**.

478		1½ c. + 1½ c. sepia	40	70
479		3 c. + 2 c. green	60	35
480		4 c. + 2 c. red	1·75	2·25
481		5 c. + 3 c. green	2·50	30
482		12½ c. + 3½ c. blue	9·00	1·25

PORTRAITS: 1½ c. M. van St. Aldegonde; 3 c. O. G. Heldring; 4 c. Maria Tesselschade; 5 c. Rembrandt; 12½ c. H. Boerhaave.

1938. 40th Anniv of Coronation.

483	87	1½ c. black	20	10
484		5 c. red	25	10
485		12½ c. blue	3·25	1·40

88 Carrion Crow **89** Boy with flute

1938. Air. (Special Flights).

486	88	12½ c. blue and grey	70	65
790a		25 c. blue and grey	4·50	1·90

1938. Child Welfare.

487	89	1½ c. + 1½ c. black	15	20
488		3 c. + 2 c. brown	40	30
489		4 c. + 2 c. green	75	85
490		5 c. + 3 c. red	35	15
491		12½ c. + 3½ c. blue	9·00	2·00

1939. Cultural and Social Relief Fund. As T **79**.

492		1½ c. + 1½ c. brown	60	60
493		2½ c. + 2½ c. green	3·75	2·75
494		3 c. + 3 c. red	80	1·25
495		5 c. + 3 c. green	2·75	30
496		12½ c. + 3½ c. blue	8·00	1·00

PORTRAITS: 1½ c. M. Maris; 2½ c. Anton Mauve; 3 c. Gerardus van Swieten; 5 c. Nicolas Beets; 12½ c. Pieter Stuyvesant.

91 St. Willibrord's landing in the Netherlands **92** Steam Locomotive "Der Arend" **93** Child and Cornucopia

1939. 12th Death Centenary of St. Willibrord.

497	91	5 c. green	75	10
498	–	12½ c. blue	4·25	2·50

DESIGN: 12½ c. St. Willibrord as Bishop of Utrecht.

1939. Centenary of Netherlands Railway.

499	92	5 c. green	75	15
500	–	12½ c. blue	9·50	3·50

DESIGN: 12½ c. Modern electric locomotive.

1939. Child Welfare.

501	93	1½ c. + 1½ c. black	15	20
502		2½ c. + 2½ c. green	4·50	2·75
503		3 c. + 3 c. red	60	25
504		5 c. + 3 c. green	1·00	10
505		12½ c. + 3½ c. blue	3·75	1·40

94 Queen Wilhelmina **95** Vincent Van Gogh **98** Girl with Dandelion

1940.

506	94	5 c. green	10	10
506a		6 c. brown	65	10
507		7½ c. red	10	10
508		10 c. purple	10	10
509		12½ c. blue	10	10
510		15 c. blue	15	10
510a		17½ c. blue	1·40	80
511		20 c. violet	20	10
512		22½ c. olive	80	95
513		25 c. red	20	10
514		30 c. ochre	45	30
515		40 c. green	95	85
515a		50 c. orange	7·50	60
515b		60 c. purple	6·50	2·50

1940. Cultural and Social Relief Fund.

516	95	1½ c. + 1½ c. brown	1·10	35
517	–	2½ c. + 2½ c. green	3·00	1·25
518	–	3 c. + 3 c. red	2·00	1·00
519	–	5 c. + 3 c. green	4·00	25
520	–	12½ c. + 3½ c. blue	4·00	65

PORTRAITS: 1½ c. E. J. Potgieter; 3 c. Petrus Camper; 5 c. Jan Steen; 12½ c. Joseph Scaliger.

See also Nos. 558/62 and 656/60.

1940. As No. 519, colour changed. Surch.

521		7½ c. + 2½ c. on 5 c. + 3 c. red	35	25

1940. Surch with large figures and network.

522	35	2½ on 3 c. red	85	25
523		5 on 3 c. green	10	20
524		7½ on 3 c. red	10	10
525		10 on 3 c. green	10	15
526		12½ on 3 c. blue	15	30
527		17½ on 3 c. green	35	65
528		20 on 3 c. green	15	15
529		22½ on 3 c. green	50	1·10
530		25 on 3 c. green	25	30
531		30 on 3 c. green	30	50
532		40 on 3 c. green	35	70
533		50 on 3 c. green	50	60
534		60 on 3 c. green	90	1·25
535		70 on 3 c. green	2·00	3·00
536		80 on 3 c. green	2·75	5·50
537		100 on 3 c. green	24·00	35·00
538		250 on 3 c. green	25·00	42·00
539		500 on 3 c. green	25·00	40·00

1940. Child Welfare.

540	98	1½ c. + 1½ c. violet	50	20
541		2½ c. + 2½ c. olive	1·75	90
542		4 c. + 3 c. blue	1·90	1·10
543		5 c. + 3 c. green	2·00	15
544		7½ c. + 3½ c. red	50	15

1941.

546	35	5 c. green	10	10
547		7½ c. red	10	10
548		10 c. violet	10	10
549		12½ c. blue	10	30
550		15 c. blue	20	35
551		17½ c. red	10	15
552		20 c. violet	15	15
553		22½ c. olive	10	30
554		25 c. lake	15	25
555		30 c. brown	3·75	25
556		40 c. green	15	30
557		50 c. brown	10	15

1941. Cultural and Social Relief Fund. As T **95** but inscr "ZOMERZEGEL 31.12.46".

558		1½ c. + 1½ c. brown	60	30
559		2½ c. + 2½ c. green	60	30
560		4 c. + 3 c. red	50	30
561		5 c. + 3 c. green	65	30
562		7½ c. + 3½ c. purple	65	30

PORTRAITS: 1½ c. Dr. A. Mathijsen; 2½ c. J. Ingenhousz; 4 c. Aagje Deken; 5 c. Johan Bosboom; 7½ c. A. C. W. Staring.

100 "Titus Rembrandt" **101** Legionary

1941. Child Welfare.

563	100	1½ c. + 1½ c. black	25	30
564		2½ c. + 2½ c. olive	25	30
565		4 c. + 3 c. blue	25	30
566		5 c. + 3 c. green	25	30
567		7½ c. + 3½ c. red	25	30

1942. Netherlands Legion Fund.

568	101	7½ c. + 2½ c. red	25	50
569	–	12½ c. + 87½ c. blue	3·75	7·00

DESIGN—HORIZ: 12½ c. Legionary with similar inscription.

1943. 1st European Postal Congress. As T **26** but larger (21 × 27½ mm) surch **EUROPEESCHE P T T VEREENIGING 19 OCTOBER 1942 10 CENT.**

570	26	10 c. on 2½ c. yellow	10	15

103 Seahorse **104** Michiel A. de Ruyter

1943. Old Germanic Symbols.

571	103	1 c. black	10	10
572	–	1½ c. red	10	10
573	–	2 c. blue	10	10
574	–	2½ c. green	10	10
575	–	3 c. red	10	10
576	–	4 c. brown	10	10
577	–	5 c. olive	10	10

DESIGNS—VERT: 1½ c. Triple crowned tree; 2½ c. Birds in ornamental tree; 4 c. Horse and rider. HORIZ: 2 c. Swans; 3 c. Trees and serpentine roots; 5 c. Prancing horses.

1943. Dutch Naval Heroes.

578	104	7½ c. red	10	10
579	–	10 c. green	10	10
580	–	12½ c. blue	10	15
581	–	15 c. violet	15	15
582	–	17½ c. grey	10	10
583	–	20 c. brown	10	10
584	–	22½ c. red	10	20
585	–	25 c. purple	25	50
586	–	30 c. blue	10	10
587	–	40 c. grey	10	15

PORTRAITS: 10 c. Johan Evertsen; 12½ c. Maarten H. Tromp; 15 c. Piet Hein; 17½ c. Wilhelm Joseph van Gent; 20 c. Witte de With; 22½ c. Cornelis Evertsen; 25 c. Tjerk Hiddes de Fries; 30 c. Cornelis Tromp; 40 c. Cornelis Evertsen the younger.

105 Mail Cart **106** Child and Doll's House

1943. Stamp Day.

589	105	7½ c. + 7½ c. red	10	10

1944. Child Welfare and Winter Help Funds. Inscr "WINTERHULP" (1½ c. and 7½ c.) or "VOLKSDIENST" (others).

590	106	1½ c. + 3½ c. black	10	20
591	–	4 c. + 3½ c. brown	10	20
592	–	5 c. + 5 c. green	10	20
593	–	7½ c. + 7½ c. red	10	20
594	–	10 c. + 40 c. blue	10	20

DESIGNS: 4 c. Mother and child; 5 c., 10 c. Mother and children; 7½ c. Child and wheatsheaf.

107 Infantryman **111** Queen Wilhelmina

1944.

595	107	1½ c. black	10	10
596	–	2½ c. green	10	10
597	–	3 c. brown	10	10
598	–	5 c. blue	10	10
599	111	7½ c. red	10	10
600		10 c. orange	10	10
601		12½ c. blue	10	10
602		15 c. red	1·75	1·75
603		17½ c. green	1·00	1·40
604		20 c. violet	25	20
605		22½ c. red	75	90
606		25 c. brown	2·25	2·00
607		30 c. green	20	15
608		40 c. purple	2·75	2·75
609		50 c. mauve	1·50	1·25

DESIGNS—HORIZ: 2½ c. "Nieuw Amsterdam" (liner); 3 c. Airman. VERT: 5 c. "De Ruyter" (cruiser).

The above set was originally for use on Netherlands warships serving with the Allied Fleet, and was used after liberation in the Netherlands.

112 Lion and Dragon **113**

1945. Liberation.

610	112	7½ c. orange	10	10

1945. Child Welfare.

611	113	1½ c. + 2½ c. grey	30	25
612		2½ c. + 3½ c. green	30	25
613		5 c. + 5 c. brown	30	25
614		7½ c. + 4½ c. red	30	25
615		12½ c. + 5½ c. blue	30	25

114 Queen Wilhelmina **115** Emblem of Abundance

1946.

616	114	1 g. blue	80	20
617		2½ g. red	£140	9·00
618		5 g. green	£140	30·00
619		10 g. violet	£140	28·00

1946. War Victims' Relief Fund.

620	115	1½ c. + 3½ c. black	50	30
621		2½ c. + 5 c. green	60	60
622		5 c. + 10 c. violet	65	60
623		7½ c. + 15 c. red	45	20
624		12½ c. + 37½ c. blue	95	60

116 Princess Irene **117** Boy on Roundabout

1946. Child Welfare.

625	116	1½ c. + 1½ c. brown	50	50
626	–	2½ c. + 1½ c. green	50	60
627	116	4 c. + 2 c. red	65	65
628	–	5 c. + 2 c. brown	65	65
629	–	7½ c. + 2½ c. red	50	15
630	–	12½ c. + 7½ c. blue	50	65

PORTRAITS: 2½ c., 5 c. Princess Margriet; 7½ c., 12½ c. Princess Beatrix.

1946. Child Welfare.

631	117	2 c. + 2 c. violet	40	40
632		4 c. + 2 c. green	45	50
633		7½ c. + 2½ c. red	45	50
634		10 c. + 5 c. purple	60	15
635		20 c. + 5 c. blue	60	65

118 Numeral **119** Queen Wilhelmina **122** Children

1946.

636	118	1 c. red	10	10
637		2 c. blue	10	10
638		2½ c. orange	8·50	1·75
638a		3 c. brown	10	10
639		4 c. green	20	10
639a		5 c. orange	10	10
639c		6 c. grey	45	10
639d		7 c. red	20	10
639f		8 c. mauve	20	10

1947.

640	119	5 c. green	65	10
641		6 c. black	15	10
642		6 c. blue	40	10
643		7½ c. red	15	20
644		10 c. purple	40	10
645		12½ c. red	60	40
646		15 c. violet	3·25	10
647		20 c. blue	5·00	10
648		22½ c. green	70	70
649		25 c. blue	13·00	10
650		30 c. orange	7·50	20
651		35 c. blue	6·50	50
652		40 c. brown	18·00	50
653	–	45 c. blue	23·00	12·00
654	–	50 c. brown	22·00	25
655	–	60 c. red	23·00	1·75

Nos. 653/5 are as Type **119** but have the inscriptions in colour on white ground.

1947. Cultural and Social Relief Fund. As T **95** but inscr "ZOMERZEGEL...13.12.48".

656		2 c. + 2 c. red	70	50
657		4 c. + 2 c. green	1·50	75
658		7½ c. + 2½ c. violet	2·25	85
659		10 c. + 5 c. brown	2·00	15
660		20 c. + 5 c. blue	1·40	85

PORTRAITS: 2 c. H. van Deventer; 4 c. P. C. Hooft; 7½ c. Johan de Witt; 10 c. J. F. van Royen; 20 c. Hugo Grotius.

1947. Child Welfare.

661	122	2 c. + 2 c. brown	20	10
662	–	4 c. + 2 c. green	1·40	60
663	–	7½ c. + 2½ c. brown	1·75	90
664	–	10 c. + 5 c. lake	1·50	10
665	122	20 c. + 5 c. blue	1·75	90

DESIGN: 4 c. to 10 c. Baby.

124 Ridderzaal, The Hague **125** Queen Wilhelmina

1948. Cultural and Social Relief Fund.

666	124	2 c. + 2 c. brown	1·75	40
667	–	6 c. + 4 c. green	2·00	60
668	–	10 c. + 5 c. red	1·60	15
669	–	20 c. + 5 c. blue	2·00	90

BUILDINGS: 6 c. Palace on the Dam; 10 c. Kneuterdijk Palace; 20 c. Nieuwe Kerk, Amsterdam.

1948. Queen Wilhelmina's Golden Jubilee.

670	125	10 c. red	10	10
671		20 c. blue	2·50	1·60

126 Queen Juliana **127** Boy in Canoe

1948. Coronation.

672	126	10 c. brown	1·50	10
673		20 c. blue	2·75	50

1948. Child Welfare.

674	127	2 c. + 2 c. green	15	10
675	–	5 c. + 3 c. green	2·75	80
676	–	6 c. + 4 c. grey	1·40	15
677	–	10 c. + 5 c. red	45	10
678	–	20 c. + 8 c. blue	2·75	1·10

DESIGNS: 5 c. Girl swimming; 6 c. Boy on toboggan; 10 c. Girl on swing; 20 c. Boy skating.

128 Terrace near Beach

1949. Cultural and Social Relief Fund.

679	128	2 c. + 2 c. yell & blue	1·50	20
680	–	5 c. + 3 c. yell & blue	2·50	2·00
681	–	6 c. + 4 c. green	2·25	50
682	–	10 c. + 5 c. yell & blue	3·25	10
683	–	20 c. + 5 c. blue	2·50	2·25

DESIGNS: 5 c. Hikers in cornfield; 6 c. Campers by fire; 10 c. Gathering wheat; 20 c. Yachts.

129 Queen Juliana **130** **131** Hands reaching for Sunflower

1949.

684	129	5 c. green	50	10
685		6 c. blue	40	10
686		10 c. orange	30	10
687		12 c. red	1·75	1·75
688		15 c. green	3·25	10
689		20 c. blue	3·00	10
690		25 c. brown	12·00	10
691		30 c. violet	7·00	10
692		35 c. blue	15·00	15
693		40 c. purple	28·00	20
694		45 c. orange	1·75	90
695		45 c. violet	35·00	30
696		50 c. green	6·50	15
697		60 c. brown	13·00	15
697a		75 c. red	75·00	1·25
698	130	1 g. red	3·50	10
699		2½ g. brown	£180	2·00
700a		5 g. brown	£400	3·00
701		10 g. violet	£350	14·00

1949. Red Cross and Indonesian Relief Fund.

702	131	2 c. + 3 c. yellow & grey	90	30
703		6 c. + 4 c. yellow & red	65	40
704		10 c. + 5 c. yellow & bl	3·75	25
705		30 c. + 10 c. yellow & brn	10·00	3·00

132 Posthorns and Globe **133** "Autumn"

1949. 75th Anniv of U.P.U.

706	132	10 c. lake	55	10
707		20 c. blue	8·00	2·25

1949. Child Welfare Fund. Inscr "VOOR HET KIND".

708	133	2 c. + 3 c. brown	20	10
709	–	5 c. + 3 c. red	6·00	1·75
710	–	6 c. + 4 c. green	3·00	30
711	–	10 c. + 5 c. grey	20	10
712	–	20 c. + 7 c. blue	5·00	1·60

DESIGNS: 5 c. "Summer"; 6 c. "Spring"; 10 c. "Winter"; 20 c. "New Year".

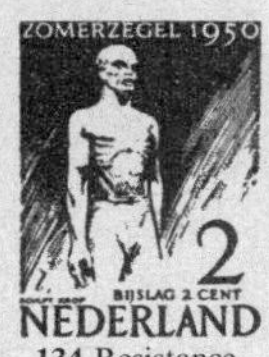

134 Resistance Monument **135** Part of Moerdyk Bridge

1950. Cultural and Social Relief Fund. Inscr "ZOMERZEGEL 1950".

713	134	2 c. + 2 c. brown	1·40	1·25
714	–	4 c. + 2 c. green	10·00	10·00
715	–	5 c. + 3 c. grey	6·50	3·50
716	–	6 c. + 4 c. violet	3·25	75
717	135	10 c. + 5 c. slate	5·00	20
718	–	20 c. + 5 c. blue	14·00	13·00

DESIGNS—VERT: 4 c. Sealing dykes; 5 c. Rotterdam skyscraper. HORIZ: 6 c. Harvesting; 20 c. "Overijssel" (canal freighter).

1950. Surch with bold figure **6**.

719	119	6 c. on 7½ c. red	1·40	10

INDEX

Countries can be quickly located by referring to the index at the end of this volume.

137 Good Samaritan and Bombed Church **138** Janus Dousa

1950. Bombed Churches Rebuilding Fund.

720	137	2 c. + 2 c. olive	4·50	1·75
721		5 c. + 3 c. brown	14·00	14·00
722		6 c. + 4 c. green	10·00	2·00
723		10 c. + 5 c. red	12·00	35
724		20 c. + 5 c. blue	26·00	26·00

1950. 375th Anniv of Leyden University.

725	138	10 c. olive	3·75	10
726	–	20 c. blue	3·75	1·40

PORTRAIT: 20 c. Jan van Hout.

139 Baby and Bees **140** Bergh Castle

1950. Child Welfare. Inscr "VOOR HET KIND".

727	139	2 c. + 3 c. red	20	10
728	–	5 c. + 3 c. olive	8·00	3·50
729	–	6 c. + 4 c. green	3·25	60
730	–	10 c. + 5 c. purple	20	10
731	–	20 c. + 7 c. blue	12·00	11·00

DESIGNS: 5 c. Boy and fowl; 6 c. Girl and birds; 10 c. Boy and fish; 20 c. Girl, butterfly and frog.

1951. Cultural and Social Relief Fund. Castles.

732	–	2 c. + 2 c. violet	2·50	1·25
733	140	5 c. + 3 c. red	8·50	8·00
734	–	6 c. + 4 c. sepia	2·75	60
735	–	10 c. + 5 c. green	6·00	25
736	–	20 c. + 5 c. blue	8·00	8·00

DESIGNS—HORIZ: 2 c. Hillenraad; 6 c. Hernen. VERT: 10 c. Rechteren; 20 c. Moermond.

141 Girl and Windmill **142** Gull **143** Jan van Riebeeck

1951. Child Welfare.

737	141	2 c. + 3 c. green	30	10
738	–	5 c. + 3 c. blue	4·50	4·50
739	–	6 c. + 4 c. brown	4·25	60
740	–	10 c. + 5 c. lake	20	10
741	–	20 c. + 7 c. blue	6·50	6·50

DESIGNS: Each shows boy or girl: 5 c. Crane; 6 c. Fishing nets; 10 c. Factory chimneys; 20 c. Flats.

1951. Air.

742	142	15 g. brown	£250	£120
743		25 g. black	£275	£120

1952. Tercentenary of Landing in South Africa and Van Riebeeck Monument Fund.

744	143	2 c. + 3 c. violet	3·25	3·25
745		6 c. + 4 c. green	8·00	6·50
746		10 c. + 5 c. red	8·50	5·00
747		20 c. + 5 c. blue	5·50	3·00

144 Miner **145** Wild Rose

1952. 50th Anniv of State Mines, Limburg.

748	144	10 c. blue	2·50	10

1952. Cultural and Social Relief Fund. Floral designs inscr "ZOMERZEGEL 1952".

749	145	2 c. + 2 c. grn & red	75	50
750	–	5 c. + 3 c. yell & green	1·25	90
751	–	6 c. + 4 c. green & red	1·50	55
752	–	10 c. + 5 c. grn & orge	2·00	15
753	–	20 c. + 5 c. grn & blue	13·00	12·00

FLOWERS: 5 c. Marsh Marigold; 6 c. Tulip; 10 c. Marguerite; 20 c. Cornflower.

146 Radio Masts **147** Boy feeding Goat

1952. Netherlands Stamp Centenary and Centenary of Telegraph Service.

754	–	2 c. violet	70	10
755	146	6 c. red	20	10
756	–	10 c. green	20	10
757	–	20 c. slate	5·00	2·00

DESIGNS: 2 c. Telegraph poles and train; 10 c. Postman delivering letters, 1852; 20 c. Postman delivering letters, 1952.

1952. International Postage Stamp Ex, Utrecht ("ITEP"). Nos. 754/7 but colours changed.

757a	–	2 c. brown	20·00	15·00
757b	146	6 c. blue	15·00	13·00
757c	–	10 c. lake	15·00	13·00
757d	–	20 c. blue	15·00	13·00

Nos. 757a/d were sold only in sets at the Exhibition at face + 1 g. entrance fee.

1952. Child Welfare.

758	147	2 c. + 3 c. black & olive	15	10
759	–	5 c. + 3 c. black & pink	1·00	80
760	–	6 c. + 4 c. black & green	1·90	50
761	–	10 c. + 5 c. black & orge	20	10
762	–	20 c. + 7 c. black & blue	6·50	6·50

DESIGNS: 5 c. Girl riding donkey; 6 c. Girl playing with dog; 10 c. Boy and cat; 20 c. Boy and rabbit.

1953. Flood Relief Fund. Surch **19 53 10 c + 10 WATERSNOOD**.

763	129	10 c. + 10 c. orange	65	10

149 Hyacinth **150** Red Cross

1953. Cultural and Social Relief Fund.

764	149	2 c. + 2 c. green & violet	60	35
765	–	5 c. + 3 c. green & orge	1·00	1·10
766	–	6 c. + 4 c. yellow & green	1·25	55
767	–	10 c. + 5 c. green & red	2·25	15
768	–	20 c. + 5 c. green & blue	12·00	12·00

FLOWERS: 5 c. African marigold; 6 c. Daffodil; 10 c. Anemone; 20 c. Dutch iris.

1953. Red Cross Fund. Inscr "RODE KRUIS".

769	150	2 c. + 3 c. red and sepia	40	45
770	–	6 c. + 4 c. red and brown	2·75	2·75
771	–	7 c. + 5 c. red and olive	75	50
772	–	10 c. + 5 c. red	60	10
773	–	25 c. + 8 c. red and blue	7·50	6·00

DESIGNS: 6 c. Man with lamp; 7 c. Rescue worker in flooded area; 10 c. Nurse giving blood transfusion; 25 c. Red Cross flags.

151 Queen Juliana **152** Queen Juliana

1953.

775	151	10 c. brown	10	10
776		12 c. turquoise	10	10
777		15 c. red	10	10
777b		18 c. turquoise	20	10
778		20 c. purple	15	10
778b		24 c. olive	40	20
779		25 c. blue	20	10
780a		30 c. orange	40	15
781		35 c. brown	90	10
781a		37 c. turquoise	85	20
782		40 c. slate	35	10
783		45 c. red	40	10
784		50 c. green	35	10
785		60 c. brown	50	10
785a		62 c. red	5·00	3·25
785b		70 c. blue	60	10
786		75 c. purple	50	10
786a		80 c. violet	75	15
786b		85 c. green	1·40	20
786c		95 c. brown	2·25	25
787	152	1 g. red	2·50	10
788		2½ g. green	9·00	10
789		5 g. black	3·50	15
790		10 g. blue	19·00	1·25

153 Girl with Pigeon **154** M. Nijhoff (poet)

1953. Child Welfare. Inscr "VOOR HET KIND".

791	–	2 c. + 3 c. blue & yellow	10	10
792	–	5 c. + 3 c. lake & green	75	85
793	153	7 c. + 5 c. brown & blue	3·00	80
794	–	10 c. + 5 c. lilac & bistre	10	10
795	–	25 c. + 8 c. turq & pink	11·00	12·00

DESIGNS: 2 c. Girl, bucket and spade; 5 c. Boy and apple; 10 c. Boy and tjalk (sailing boat); 25 c. Girl and tulip.

1954. Cultural and Social Relief Fund.
796 **154** 2 c. + 3 c. blue . . . . . 1·75 1·75
797 – 5 c. + 3 c. brown 60 60
798 – 7 c. + 5 c. red . . . . . 2·00 1·40
799 – 10 c. + 5 c. green . . . . 7·50 15
800 – 25 c. + 8 c. purple . . . 14·00 13·00
PORTRAITS: 5 c. W. Pijper (composer); 7 c. H. P. Berlage (architect); 10 c. J. Huizinga (historian); 25 c. Vincent van Gogh (painter).

155 St. Boniface

156 Boy and Model Glider

1954. 1200th Anniv of Martyrdom of St. Boniface.
801 **155** 10 c. blue . . . . 1·75 10

1954. National Aviation Fund.
802 **156** 2 c. + 2 c. green 75 90
803 – 10 c. + 4 c. blue . . . . 2·25 50
PORTRAIT: 10 c. Dr. A. Plesman (aeronautical pioneer).

157 Making Paperchains

158 Queen Juliana

1954. Child Welfare.
804 **157** 2 c. + 3 c. brown 10 10
805 – 5 c. + 3 c. olive 90 65
806 – 7 c. + 5 c. blue . . . . 1·50 50
807 – 10 c. + 5 c. red 10 10
808 – 25 c. + 8 c. blue . . . . 9·50 8·00
DESIGNS—VERT: 5 c. Girl brushing her teeth; 7 c. Boy and toy boat; 10 c. Nurse and child. HORIZ: 25 c. Invalid boy drawing in bed.

1954. Ratification of Statute for the Kingdom.
809 **158** 10 c. red 80 10

159 Factory, Rotterdam

160 "The Victory of Peace"

1955. Cultural and Social Relief Fund.
810 **159** 2 c. + 3 c. brown . . . . 1·25 1·25
811 – 5 c. + 3 c. green 55 35
812 – 7 c. + 5 c. red . . . . 1·25 1·25
813 – 10 c. + 5 c. blue . . . . 1·75 15
814 – 25 c. + 8 c. brown . . . . 13·00 11·00
DESIGNS—HORIZ: 5 c. Post Office, The Hague; 10 c. Town Hall, Hilversum; 25 c. Office Building, The Hague. VERT: 7 c. Stock Exchange, Amsterdam.

1955. 10th Anniv of Liberation.
815 **160** 10 c. red . . . . 1·25 10

161 Microscope and Emblem of Cancer

162 "Willem van Loon" (D. Dircks)

1955. Queen Wilhelmina Anti-Cancer Fund.
816 **161** 2 c. + 3 c. blk & red . . 60 50
817 5 c. + 3 c. green & red . 60 30
818 7 c. + 5 c. purple & red . 85 70
819 10 c. + 5 c. blue and red . 85 10
820 25 c. + 8 c. olive & red . 9·00 7·00

1955. Child Welfare Fund.
821 **162** 2 c. + 3 c. green 10 10
822 – 5 c. + 3 c. red 65 60
823 – 7 c. + 5 c. brown . . . . 3·25 80
824 – 10 c. + 5 c. blue 10 10
825 – 25 c. + 8 c. lilac . . . . 9·00 9·00
PORTRAITS: 5 c. "Portrait of a Boy" (J. A. Backer); 7 c. "Portrait of a Girl" (unknown); 10 c. "Philips Huygens" (A. Hanneman); 25 c. "Constantin Huygens" (A. Hanneman).

163 "Farmer"

1956. Cultural and Social Relief Fund and 350th Birth Anniv of Rembrandt. Details from Rembrandt's paintings.
826 **163** 2 c. + 3 c. slate . . . . 2·25 2·50
827 – 5 c. + 3 c. olive . . . . 1·25 1·25
828 – 7 c. + 5 c. brown . . . . 3·50 3·50
829 – 10 c. + 5 c. green . . . . 10·00 25
830 – 25 c. + 8 c. brown . . . 13·00 15·00
PAINTINGS: 5 c. "Young Tobias with Angel"; 7 c. "Persian wearing Fur Cap"; 10 c. "Old Blind Tobias"; 25 c. Self-portrait 1639.

164 Yacht

165 Amphora

167 "Portrait of a Boy" (Van Scorel)

1956. 16th Olympic Games, Melbourne.
831 **164** 2 c. + 3 c. black & blue . 40 40
832 – 5 c. + 3 c. black & yellow 40 40
833 **165** 7 c. + 5 c. black & brown 1·50 1·25
834 – 10 c. + 5 c. black & grey 3·50 40
835 – 25 c. + 8 c. black & green 8·50 8·50
DESIGNS: As Type **164**: 5 c. Runner; 10 c. Hockey player; 25 c. Water polo player.

1956. Europa. As T **110** of Luxembourg.
836 10 c. black and lake . . . . 1·75 10
837 25 c. black and blue . . . . 50·00 1·75

1956. Child Welfare Fund. 16th century Dutch Paintings.
838 **167** 2 c. + 3 c. grey & cream 10 10
839 – 5 c. + 3 c. olive & cream 50 65
840 – 7 c. + 5 c. purple & cream 3·75 1·50
841 – 10 c. + 5 c. red & cream 10 10
842 – 25 c. + 8 c. blue & cream 8·00 5·50
PAINTINGS: 5 c. "Portrait of a Boy"; 7 c. "Portrait of a Girl"; 10 c. "Portrait of a Girl"; 25 c. "Portrait of Eechie Pieters".

168 "Curacao" (trawler) and Fish Barrels

169 Admiral M. A. de Ruyter

1957. Cultural and Social Relief Fund. Ships.
843 – 4 c. + 3 c. blue . . . . 1·25 90
844 – 6 c. + 4 c. lilac . . . . 1·00 60
845 – 7 c. + 5 c. red . . . . 1·50 95
846 **168** 10 c. + 8 c. green . . . . 3·75 15
847 – 30 c. + 8 c. brown . . . . 7·50 7·00
DESIGNS: 4 c. "Gaasterland" (freighter); 6 c. Coaster; 7 c. "Willem Barendsz" (whale factory ship) and whale; 30 c. "Nieuw Amsterdam" (liner).

1957. 350th Birth Anniv of M. A. de Ruyter.
848 **169** 10 c. orange 75 10
849 – 30 c. blue . . . . . . 5·00 1·75
DESIGN: 30 c. De Ruyter's flagship, "De Zeven Provincien".

170 Blood Donors' Emblem

171 "Europa" Star

1957. 90th Anniv of Netherlands Red Cross Society and Red Cross Fund.
850 **170** 4 c. + 3 c. blue & red . . 75 1·00
851 – 6 c. + 4 c. green & red . . 65 65
852 – 7 c. + 5 c. red & green . . 75 75
853 – 10 c. + 8 c. red & ochre . . 90 10
854 – 30 c. + 8 c. red & blue . . 3·50 3·75
DESIGNS: 6 c. "J. Henry Dunant" (hospital ship); 7 c. Red Cross; 10 c. Red Cross emblem; 30 c. Red Cross on globe.

1957. Europa.
855 **171** 10 c. black and blue . . . 65 10
856 30 c. green and blue . . . 8·00 1·75

172 Portrait by B.J. Blommers

173 Walcheren Costume

1957. Child Fund Welfare. 19th/20th Century Paintings by Dutch Masters.
857 **172** 4 c. + 4 c. red 10 10
858 – 6 c. + 4 c. green . . . . 1·50 80
859 – 8 c. + 4 c. sepia . . . . 2·25 1·75
860 – 12 c. + 9 c. purple 10 10
861 – 30 c. + 9 c. blue . . . . 6·50 8·00
PORTRAITS: Child paintings by: W. B. Tholen (6 c.); J. Sluyters (8 c.); M. Maris (12 c.); C. Kruseman (30 c.).

1958. Cultural and Social Relief Fund. Provincial Costumes.
862 **173** 4 c. + 4 c. blue 80 60
863 – 6 c. + 4 c. ochre 90 80
864 – 8 c. + 4 c. red . . . . . 5·00 1·75
865 – 12 c. + 9 c. brown . . . 2·00 15
866 – 30 c. + 9 c. lilac . . . . 8·00 7·50
COSTUMES: 6 c. Marken; 8 c. Scheveningen; 12 c. Friesland; 30 c. Volendam.

1958. Surch **12 C.**
867 **151** 12 c. on 10 c. brown . . . 80 10

1958. Europa. As T **119a** of Luxembourg.
868 12 c. blue and red 20 10
869 30 c. red and blue 90 70

176 Girl on Stilts and Boy on Tricycle

177 Cranes

1958. Child Welfare Fund. Children's Games.
870 **176** 4 c. + 4 c. blue 10 10
871 – 6 c. + 4 c. red . . . . . 1·50 1·25
872 – 8 c. + 4 c. green . . . . 1·50 1·25
873 – 12 c. + 9 c. red 10 10
874 – 30 c. + 9 c. blue . . . . 5·50 5·50
DESIGNS: 6 c. Boy and girl on scooter; 8 c. Boys playing leap-frog; 12 c. Boys on roller-skates; 30 c. Girl skipping and boy in toy car.

1959. 10th Anniv of N.A.T.O. As T **123** of Luxembourg (N.A.T.O. emblem).
875 12 c. blue and yellow 10 10
876 30 c. blue and red . . . . . 1·00 60

1959. Cultural and Social Relief Fund. Prevention of Sea Encroachment.
877 – 4 c. + 4 c. blue on green . 1·10 1·25
878 – 6 c. + 4 c. brown on grey 90 90
879 – 8 c. + 4 c. violet on blue . 2·25 1·75
880 **177** 12 c. + 9 c. green on yell . 3·75 15
881 – 30 c. + 9 c. black on red . 6·50 6·50
DESIGNS: 4 c. Tugs and caisson; 6 c. Dredger; 8 c. Labourers making fascine mattresses; 30 c. Sand-spouter and scoop.

1959. Europa. As T **123a** of Luxembourg.
882 12 c. red 15 10
883 30 c. green . . . . 2·50 1·50

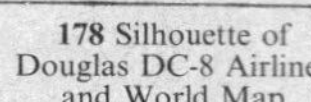

178 Silhouette of Douglas DC-8 Airliner and World Map

179 Child in Play-pen

1959. 40th Anniv of K.L.M. (Royal Dutch Airlines).
884 **178** 12 c. blue and red 20 10
885 – 30 c. blue and green . . 2·00 1·25
DESIGN: 30 c. Silhouette of Douglas DC-8 airliner.

1959. Child Welfare Fund.
886 **179** 4 c. + 4 c. blue & brown . 10 10
887 – 6 c. + 4 c. brown & green 1·75 1·40
888 – 8 c. + 4 c. blue & red . . 3·00 1·50
889 – 12 c. + 9 c. red, black and blue 10 10
890 – 30 c. + 9 c. turquoise and yellow . . . . 4·00 4·00
DESIGNS: 6 c. Boy as "Red Indian" with bow and arrow; 8 c. Boy feeding geese; 12 c. Traffic warden escorting children; 30 c. Girl doing homework.

180 Refugee Woman

181 White Water-lily

1960. World Refugee Year.
891 **180** 12 c. + 8 c. purple . . . 25 15
892 30 c. + 10 c. green . . . 2·00 2·50

1960. Cultural and Social Relief Fund. Flowers.
893 – 4 c. + 4 c. red, green and grey 80 65
894 – 6 c. + 4 c. yellow, green and salmon 50 45
895 **181** 8 c. + 4 c. multicoloured . 2·25 2·50
896 – 12 c. + 8 c. red, green and buff . . . . 2·00 20
897 – 30 c. + 10 c. blue, green and yellow . . . . 5·50 6·00
FLOWERS—VERT: 4 c. "The Princess" tulip; 6 c. Gorse; 12 c. Poppy; 30 c. Blue sea-holly.

182 J. van der Kolk

183 Marken Costume

184 Herring Gull

1960. World Mental Health Year.
898 **182** 12 c. red 50 10
899 – 30 c. blue (J. Wier) . . . 4·00 2·25

1960. Europa. As T **113**a of Norway.
900 12 c. yellow and red 25 10
901 30 c. yellow and blue . . . . 2·75 2·00

1960. Child Welfare Fund. Costumes. Multicoloured portraits.
902 **183** 4 c. + 4 c. slate 30 10
903 – 6 c. + 4 c. ochre . . . . 2·50 1·25
904 – 8 c. + 4 c. turquoise . . . 5·50 2·25
905 – 12 c. + 9 c. violet 30 10
906 – 30 c. + 9 c. grey . . . . 7·00 6·00
DESIGNS: Costumes of: 6 c. Volendam; 8 c. Bunschoten; 12 c. Hindeloopen; 30 c. Huizen.

1961. Cultural and Social Relief Fund. Beach and Meadow Birds.
907 **184** 4 c. + 4 c. slate & yell . . 1·50 1·50
908 – 6 c. + 4 c. sep. & brown 50 40
909 – 8 c. + 4 c. brn & olive . 1·40 1·25
910 – 12 c. + 8 c. blk & blue . 3·00 25
911 – 30 c. + 10 c. blk & green 5·50 4·00
BIRDS—HORIZ: 6 c. Oystercatcher; 12 c. Avocet. VERT: 8 c. Curlew; 30 c. Lapwing.

185 Doves

186 St. Nicholas

1961. Europa.
912 **185** 12 c. brown 10 10
913 30 c. turquoise 30 30

1961. Child Welfare.
914 **186** 4 c. + 4 c. red 10 10
915 – 6 c. + 4 c. blue . . . . . 1·25 90
916 – 8 c. + 4 c. bistre . . . . 1·25 1·25
917 – 12 c. + 9 c. green 10 10
918 – 30 c. + 9 c. orange . . . 3·50 3·25
DESIGNS: 6 c. Epiphany; 8 c. Palm Sunday; 12 c. Whitsuntide; 30 c. Martinmas.

187 Queen Juliana and Prince Bernhard

188 Detail of "The Repast of the Officers of the St. Jorisdoelen" after Frans Hals

1962. Silver Wedding.
919 **187** 12 c. red 15 10
920 30 c. green . . . . 1·50 60

1962. Cultural, Health and Social Welfare Funds.
921 – 4 c. + 4 c. green . . . . 1·25 90
922 – 6 c. + 4 c. black 65 65
923 – 8 c. + 4 c. purple . . . . 1·50 1·50
924 – 12 c. + 8 c. bistre . . . . 1·50 25
925 **188** 30 c. + 10 c. blue . . . . 2·00 2·00
DESIGNS—HORIZ: 4 c. Roman cat (sculpture). VERT: 6 c. Ammonite fossil; 8 c. Pendulum clock (after principle of Huygens); 12 c. Ship's figurehead.

189 Telephone Dial 190 Europa "Tree"

1962. Completion of Netherlands Automatic Telephone System. Inscr "1962".

926 **189** 4 c. red & black 10 10
927 – 12 c. drab and black . . . 20 10
928 – 30 c. ochre, bl & blk . . . 2·75 1·40

DESIGNS—VERT: 12 c. Diagram of telephone network. HORIZ: 30 c. Arch and telephone dial.

1962. Europa.

929 **190** 12 c. black, yellow & bis . 10 10
930 30 c. black, yellow & bl . 90 60

191 "Polder" Landscape (reclaimed area) 192 Children cooking Meal

1962.

935 – 4 c. deep blue and blue . . 10 10
937 **191** 6 c. deep green & green . 40 10
938 – 10 c. dp purple & purple . 10 10

DESIGNS: 4 c. Cooling towers, State mines, Limburg; 10 c. Delta excavation works.

1962. Child Welfare.

940 **192** 4 c. + 4 c. red 10 10
941 – 6 c. + 4 c. bistre 70 55
942 – 8 c. + 4 c. blue . . . . . 1·25 1·25
943 – 12 c. + 9 c. green 10 10
944 – 30 c. + 9 c. lake . . . . 2·25 2·75

DESIGNS—Children: 6 c. Cycling; 8 c. Watering flowers; 12 c. Feeding poultry; 30 c. Making music.

193 Ears of Wheat 194 "Gallery" Windmill

1963. Freedom from Hunger.

945 **193** 12 c. ochre and blue . . . 10 10
946 30 c. ochre and red . . . 1·00 75

1963. Cultural, Health and Social Welfare Funds. Windmill types.

947 **194** 4 c. + 4 c. blue . . . . . 1·00 1·00
948 – 6 c. + 4 c. violet . . . . 1·00 1·00
949 – 8 c. + 4 c. green . . . . 1·40 1·40
950 – 12 c. + 8 c. brown . . . 1·75 25
951 – 30 c. + 10 c. red . . . . 2·00 2·00

WINDMILLS—VERT: 6 c. North Holland polder; 12 c. "Post"; 30 c. "Wip". HORIZ: 8 c. South Holland polder.

195 196 Wayside First Aid Post

1963. Paris Postal Conference Centenary.

952 **195** 30 c. blue, green & blk . . 1·25 1·00

1963. Red Cross Fund and Centenary (8 c.).

953 **196** 4 c. + 4 c. blue and red . 40 40
954 – 6 c. + 4 c. violet and red . 25 30
955 – 8 c. + 4 c. red & black . 90 75
956 – 12 c. + 9 c. brown & red 35 15
957 – 30 c. + 9 c. green & red . 1·25 1·60

DESIGNS: 6 c. "Books" collection-box; 8 c. Crosses; 12 c. "International Aid" (Negro children at meal); 30 c. First aid party tending casualty.

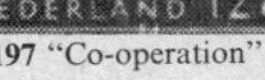

197 "Co-operation" 198 "Auntie Luce sat on a goose ..."

1963. Europa.

958 **197** 12 c. orange and brown . 10 10
959 30 c. orange and green . 1·25 1·00

1963. Child Welfare.

960 **198** 4 c. + 4 c. ultra & bl . . 10 10
961 – 6 c. + 4 c. green & red . 70 65
962 – 8 c. + 4 c. brown & green 90 65
963 – 12 c. + 9 c. violet & yell 10 10
964 – 30 c. + 8 c. blue & pink 1·75 1·75

DESIGNS (Nursery rhymes): 6 c. "In the Hague there lives a count..."; 8 c. "One day I passed a puppet's fair..."; 12 c. "Storky, storky, Billy Spoon...."; 30 c. "Ride on a little pram...".

199 William, Prince of Orange, landing at Scheveningen 200 Knights' Hall, The Hague

1963. 150th Anniv of Kingdom of the Netherlands.

965 **199** 4 c. black, bis & blue . . 10 10
966 5 c. black, red and green 10 10
967 – 12 c. bistre, blue & black 10 10
968 – 30 c. red and black . . . 50 50

DESIGNS: 12 c. Triumvirate: Van Hogendorp, Van Limburg, and Van der Duyn van Maasdam; 30 c. William I taking oath of allegiance.

1964. 500th Anniv of 1st States-General Meeting.

969 **200** 12 c. black and olive . . 15 10

201 Guide Dog for the Blind

1964. Cultural, Health and Social Welfare Funds. Animals.

970 **201** 5 c. + 5 c. red, black and olive 60 50
971 – 8 c. + 5 c. brown, black and red 30 30
972 – 12 c. + 9 c. black, grey and bistre 55 15
973 – 30 c. + 9 c. multicoloured 85 70

DESIGNS: 8 c. Three red deer; 12 c. Three kittens; 30 c. European bison and calf.

202 University Arms 203 Station Signal

1964. 350th Anniv of Groningen University.

974 **202** 12 c. slate 10 10
975 – 30 c. brown 20 15

DESIGN: 30 c. "AG" monogram.

1964. 125th Anniv of Netherlands Railways.

976 **203** 15 c. black and green . . . 20 10
977 – 40 c. black and yellow . . 90 70

DESIGN: 40 c. Electric train at speed.

204 Bible and Dove 205 Europa "Flower"

1964. 150th Anniv of Netherlands Bible Society.

978 **204** 15 c. brown 10 10

1964. Europa.

979 **205** 15 c. green 15 10
980 20 c. brown 35 25

1964. 20th Anniv of "BENELUX". As T **150a** of Luxembourg, but smaller 35 × 22 mm.

981 15 c. violet and flesh 10 10

206 Young Artist 207 Queen Juliana

1964. Child Welfare.

982 **206** 7 c. + 3 c. blue & green . 40 50
983 – 10 c. + 5 c. red, pink and green 35 40
984 – 15 c. + 10 c. yellow, black and bistre 10 10
985 – 20 c. + 10 c. red, sepia and mauve 45 45
986 – 40 c. + 15 c. green & blue 75 70

DESIGNS: 10 c. Ballet-dancing; 15 c. Playing the recorder; 20 c. Masquerading; 40 c. Toy-making.

1964. 10th Anniv of Statute for the Kingdom.

987 **207** 15 c. green 10 10

208 "Killed in Action" (Waalwijk) and "Destroyed Town" (Rotterdam) (monuments) 209 Medal of Knight (Class IV)

1965. "Resistance" Commemoration.

988 **208** 7 c. black and red 10 10
989 – 15 c. black and olive . . . 10 10
990 – 40 c. black and red . . . . 1·25 75

MONUMENTS: 15 c. "Docker" (Amsterdam) and "Killed in Action" (Waalwijk); 40 c. "Destroyed Town" (Rotterdam) and "Docker" (Amsterdam).

1965. 150th Anniv of Military William Order.

991 **209** 1 g. grey 90 55

210 I.T.U. Emblem and "Lines of Communication" 211 Veere

1965. Centenary of I.T.U.

992 **210** 20 c. blue and drab . . . 20 15
993 40 c. brown and blue . . . 65 50

1965. Cultural, Health and Social Welfare Funds.

994 **211** 8 c. + 6 c. black & yell . . 30 45
995 – 10 c. + 6 c. black & turq . 45 40
996 – 18 c. + 12 c. blk & brn . 35 15
997 – 20 c. + 10 c. black & blue 45 40
998 – 40 c. + 10 c. black & grn . 55 55

DESIGNS: (Dutch towns): 10 c. Thorn; 18 c. Dordrecht; 20 c. Staveren; 40 c. Medemblik.

212 Europa "Sprig" 213 Girl's Head

1965. Europa.

999 **212** 18 c. black, red & brn . . 20 10
1000 20 c. black, red & blue . . 30 25

1965. Child Welfare. Multicoloured.

1001 8 c. + 6 c. Type **213** 10 10
1002 10 c. + 6 c. Ship 50 50
1003 18 c. + 12 c. Boy (vert) . . . 10 10
1004 20 c. + 10 c. Duck-pond . . . 65 60
1005 40 c. + 10 c. Tractor . . . . 1·25 80

214 Marines of 1665 and 1965 215 "Help them to a safe Haven" (Queen Juliana)

1965. Tercentenary of Marine Corps.

1007 **214** 18 c. blue and red 10 10

1966. Intergovernmental Committee for European Migration (I.C.E.M.) Fund.

1008 **215** 10 c. + 7 c. yell & blk . . 30 25
1009 40 c. + 20 c. red and blk . 30 15

216 Writing Materials 217 Aircraft in Flight

1966. Cultural, Health and Social Welfare Funds. Gysbert Japicx Commem and 200th Anniv of Netherlands Literary Society. Multicoloured.

1011 10 c. + 5 c. Type **216** . . . 30 35
1012 12 c. + 8 c. Part of MS, Japicx's poem "Wobbelke" 30 35
1013 20 c. + 10 c. Part of miniature, "Knight Walewein" . . . 40 35
1014 25 c. + 10 c. Initial "D" and part of MS, novel, "Ferguut" 50 65
1015 40 c. + 20 c. 16th-cent printery (woodcut) 40 65

1966. Air (Special Flights).

1016 **217** 25 c. multicoloured . . . 30 40

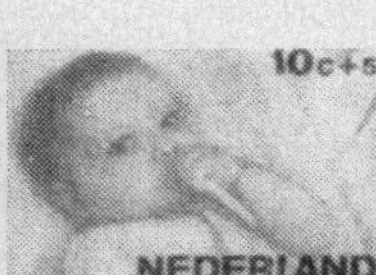

218 Europa "Ship" 219 Infant

1966. Europa.

1017 **218** 20 c. green and yellow . 15 10
1018 40 c. deep blue & blue . 30 15

1966. Child Welfare.

1019 **219** 10 c. + 5 c. red & blue . 10 10
1020 – 12 c. + 8 c. green & red 10 10
1021 – 20 c. + 10 c. blue & red 10 10
1022 – 25 c. + 10 c. purple & bl 80 90
1023 – 40 c. + 20 c. red & green 70 80

DESIGNS: 12 c. Young girl; 20 c. Boy in water; 25 c. Girl with moped; 40 c. Young man with horse.

220 Assembly Hall 221 Whelk Eggs

1967. 125th Anniv of Delft Technological University.

1025 **220** 20 c. sepia and yellow . 10 10

1967. Cultural, Health and Social Welfare Funds. Marine Fauna.

1026 **221** 12 c. + 8 c. brown & grn 20 20
1027 – 15 c. + 10 c. blue, light blue and deep blue 20 20
1028 – 20 c. + 10 c. mult . . . 20 15
1029 – 25 c. + 10 c. purple, brown and bistre 45 50
1030 – 45 c. + 20 c. mult . . . 70 65

DESIGNS: 15 c. Whelk; 20 c. Mussel; 25 c. Jellyfish; 45 c. Crab.

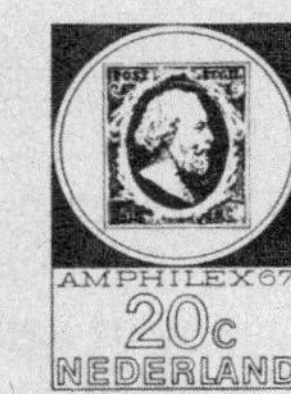

222 Cogwheels 223 Netherlands 5 c. Stamp of 1852

1967. Europa.

1031 **222** 20 c. blue & light blue . 40 10
1032 45 c. purple & lt purple . 1·00 70

1967. "Amphilex 67" Stamp Exn, Amsterdam.

1035 **223** 20 c. blue and black . . 1·90 1·90
1036 – 25 c. red and black . . . 1·90 1·90
1037 – 75 c. green and black . . 1·90 1·90

DESIGNS: 25 c. Netherlands 10 c. stamp of 1864; 75 c. Netherlands 20 c. stamp of 1867.

Nos. 1035/7 were sold at the Exhibition and at post offices at 3 g. 70, which included entrance fee to the Exhibition.

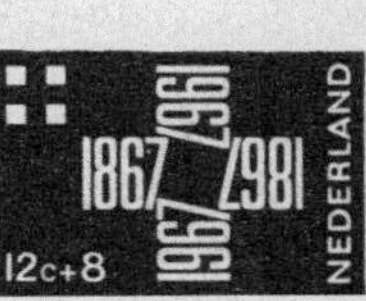

224 "1867-1967" 225 "Porcupine Lullaby"

1967. Centenary of Dutch Red Cross.

No.	Type	Description	Mint	Used
1038		12 c. + 8 c. blue and red	20	20
1039		15 c. + 10 c. red	35	35
1040		20 c. + 10 c. olive and red	20	15
1041		25 c. + 10 c. green & red	35	40
1042		45 c. + 20 c. grey and red	60	70

DESIGNS: 12 c. Type **224**; 15 c. Red crosses; 20 c. "NRK" ("Nederlandsche Rood Kruis") in the form of a cross; 25 c. Maltese cross and "red" crosses; 45 c. "100" in the form of a cross.

1967. Child Welfare. Multicoloured.

No.	Type	Description	Mint	Used
1043		12 c. + 8 c. Type **225**	10	10
1044		15 c. + 10 c. "The Whistling Kettle"	10	10
1045		20 c. + 10 c. "Dikkertje Dap" (giraffe)	10	10
1046		25 c. + 10 c. "The Flower-seller"	70	80
1047		45 c. + 20 c. "Pippeloentje" (bear)	80	95

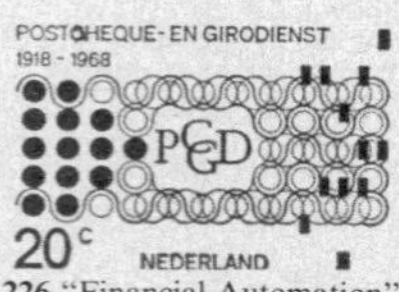

226 "Financial Automation"

1968. 50th Anniv of Netherlands Postal Cheque and Clearing Service.

No.	Type	Description	Mint	Used
1049	**226**	20 c. red, black & yell	15	10

227 St. Servatius' Bridge, Maastricht **228** Europa "Key"

1968. Cultural, Health and Social Welfare Funds. Dutch Bridges.

No.	Type	Description	Mint	Used
1050	**227**	12 c. + 8 c. green	40	50
1051	–	15 c. + 10 c. brown	60	70
1052	–	20 c. + 10 c. red	1·50	25
1053	–	25 c. + 10 c. blue	40	50
1054	–	45 c. + 20 c. blue	60	80

BRIDGES: 15 c. Magere ("Narrow"), Amsterdam; 20 c. Railway, Culemborg; 25 c. Van Brienenoord, Rotterdam; 45 c. Oosterschelde, Zeeland.

1968. Europa.

No.	Type	Description	Mint	Used
1055	**228**	20 c. blue	20	10
1056		45 c. red	70	60

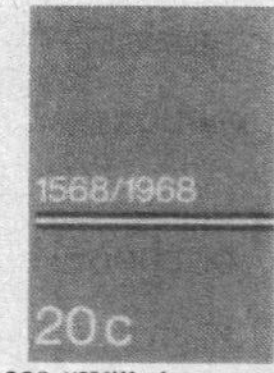

229 "Wilhelmus van Nassouwe" **230** Wright Type A and Cessna 150F

1968. 400th Anniv of Dutch National Anthem, "Wilhelmus".

No.	Type	Description	Mint	Used
1057	**229**	20 c. multicoloured	20	10

1968. Dutch Aviation Anniversaries.

No.	Type	Description	Mint	Used
1058		12 c. black, red & mauve	10	10
1059		20 c. black, emerald & grn	10	10
1060		45 c. black, blue & green	1·25	1·25

DESIGNS AND EVENTS: 12 c. T **230** (60th anniv (1967) of Royal Netherlands Aeronautical Assn); 20 c. Fokker F.II and Fellowship aircraft (50th anniv (1969) of Royal Netherlands Aircraft Factories "Fokker"); 45 c. De Havilland D.H.9B biplane and Douglas DC-9 airliner (50th anniv (1969) of Royal Dutch Airlines "KLM").

231 "Goblin"

1968. Child Welfare.

No.	Type	Description	Mint	Used
1061	**231**	12 c. + 8 c. pink, black and green	10	10
1062	–	15 c. + 10 c. pink, blue and black	10	10
1063	–	20 c. + 10 c. blue, green and black	10	10
1064	–	25 c. + 10 c. red, yellow and black	1·50	1·50
1065	–	45 c. + 20 c. yellow, orange and black	1·75	1·75

DESIGNS: 15 c. "Giant"; 20 c. "Witch"; 25 c. "Dragon"; 45 c. "Sorcerer".

232 "I A O" (Internationale Arbeidsorganisatie)

1969. 50th Anniv of I.L.O.

No.	Type	Description	Mint	Used
1067	**232**	25 c. red and black	35	10
1068		45 c. blue and black	65	65

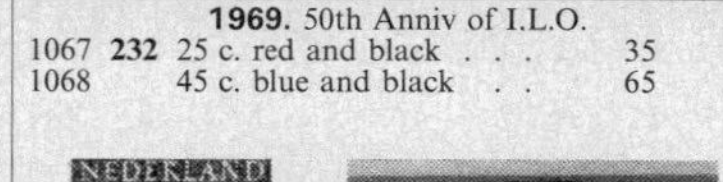

233 Queen Juliana **234** Villa, Huis ter Heide (1915)

1969. (a) Type **233**.

No.	Type	Description	Mint	Used
1069	**233**	25 c. red	1·75	10
1069c		30 c. brown	15	10
1070a		35 c. blue	20	10
1071a		40 c. red	25	10
1072a		45 c. blue	30	10
1073a		50 c. purple	25	10
1073c		55 c. red	20	10
1074a		60 c. blue	20	10
1075		70 c. brown	40	10
1076		75 c. green	45	10
1077		80 c. red	45	10
1077a		90 c. grey	50	10

(b) Size 22 × 33 mm.

No.	Type	Description	Mint	Used
1078	–	1 g. green	50	10
1079	–	1 g. 25 lake	70	10
1080	–	1 g. 50 brown	80	10
1081	–	2 g. mauve	95	10
1082	–	2 g. 50 blue	1·25	10
1083	–	5 g. grey	3·50	10
1084	–	10 g. blue	4·50	80

DESIGNS: 1 g., 1 g. 25, 1 g. 50, 2 g., 2 g. 50, 5 g. and 10 g. similar to Type **233**.

1969. Cultural, Health and Social Welfare Funds. 20th-century Dutch Architecture.

No.	Type	Description	Mint	Used
1085	**234**	12 c. + 8 c. black & brn	70	70
1086	–	15 c. + 10 c. black, red and blue	70	70
1087	–	20 c. + 10 c. black & vio	70	70
1088	–	25 c. + 10 c. brown & grn	70	30
1089	–	45 c. + 20 c. black, blue and yellow	70	70

DESIGNS: 15 c. Private House, Utrecht (1924); 20 c. Open-Air School, Amsterdam (1930); 25 c. Orphanage, Amsterdam (1960); 45 c. Congress Building, The Hague (1969).

235 Colonnade **236** Stylised "Crab" (of Cancer)

1969. Europa.

No.	Type	Description	Mint	Used
1090	**235**	25 c. blue	40	10
1901		45 c. red	1·25	1·10

1969. 20th Anniv of Queen Wilhelmina Cancer Fund.

No.	Type	Description	Mint	Used
1092	**236**	12 c. + 8 c. violet	75	75
1093		25 c. + 10 c. orange	1·00	30
1094		45 c. + 20 c. green	1·40	1·75

1969. 25th Anniv of "BENELUX" Customs Union. As T **186** of Luxembourg.

No.	Type	Description	Mint	Used
1095		25 c. multicoloured	30	10

238 Erasmus

239 Child with Violin

1969. 500th Birth Anniv of Desiderius Erasmus.

No.	Type	Description	Mint	Used
1096	**238**	25 c. purple on green	30	10

1969. Child Welfare.

No.	Type	Description	Mint	Used
1097	–	12 c. + 8 c. black, yellow and blue	10	10
1098	**239**	15 c. + 10 c. black and red	10	10
1099	–	20 c. + 10 c. black, yellow and red	1·90	2·00
1100	–	25 c. + 10 c. black, red and yellow	10	10
1101	–	45 c. + 20 c. black, red and green	1·90	2·00

DESIGNS—VERT: 12 c. Child with recorder; 20 c. Child with drum. HORIZ: 25 c. Three choristers; 45 c. Two dancers.

240 Queen Juliana and "Sunlit Road" **241** Prof. E. M. Meijers (author of "Burgerlijk Wetboek")

1969. 25th Anniv of Statute for the Kingdom.

No.	Type	Description	Mint	Used
1103	**240**	25 c. multicoloured	30	10

1970. Introduction of New Netherlands Civil Code ("Burgerlijk Wetboek").

No.	Type	Description	Mint	Used
1104	**241**	25 c. ultramarine, green and blue	30	10

242 Netherlands Pavilion

243 "Circle to Square"

1970. Expo 70, World Fair, Osaka, Japan.

No.	Type	Description	Mint	Used
1105	**242**	25 c. grey, blue & red	30	10

1970. Cultural, Health and Social Welfare Funds.

No.	Type	Description	Mint	Used
1106	**243**	12 c. + 8 c. black on yell	1·10	1·25
1107	–	15 c. + 10 c. black on silver	1·10	1·25
1108	–	20 c. + 10 c. black	1·10	1·25
1109	–	25 c. + 10 c. black on bl	1·10	70
1110	–	45 c. + 20 c. white on grey	1·10	1·25

DESIGNS: 15 c. Parallel planes in cube; 20 c. Overlapping scales; 25 c. Concentric circles in transition; 45 c. Spirals.

244 "V" Symbol

245 "Flaming Sun"

1970. 25th Anniv of Liberation.

No.	Type	Description	Mint	Used
1111	**244**	12 c. red, blue & brown	40	10

1970. Europa.

No.	Type	Description	Mint	Used
1112	**245**	25 c. red	40	10
1113		45 c. blue	1·60	1·00

246 "Work and Co-operation"

247 Globe on Plinth

1970. Inter-Parliamentary Union Conference.

No.	Type	Description	Mint	Used
1114	**246**	25 c. green, blk & grey	40	10

1970. 25th Anniv of United Nations.

No.	Type	Description	Mint	Used
1115	**247**	45 c. blk, violet and bl	75	70

248 Human Heart

249 Toy Block

1970. Netherlands Heart Foundation.

No.	Type	Description	Mint	Used
1116	**248**	12 c. + 8 c. red, black and yellow	80	80
1117		25 c. + 10 c. red, black and mauve	80	65
1118		45 c. + 20 c. red, black and green	80	80

1970. Child Welfare. "The Child and the Cube".

No.	Type	Description	Mint	Used
1119	**249**	12 c. + 8 c. blue, violet and green	10	10
1120	–	15 c. + 10 c. green, blue and yellow	1·60	1·60
1121	**249**	20 c. + 10 c. mauve, red and violet	1·60	1·60
1122	–	25 c. + 10 c. red, yell and mauve	15	10
1123	**249**	45 c. + 20 c. grey, cream and black	2·00	2·00

DESIGN: 15 c., 25 c. As Type **249**, but showing underside of block.

250 "Fourteenth Census 1971"

1971. 14th Netherlands Census.

No.	Type	Description	Mint	Used
1125	**250**	15 c. purple	15	10

251 "50 years of Adult University Education" **252** Europa Chain

1971. Cultural, Health and Social Welfare Funds. Other designs show 15th-century wooden statues by unknown artists.

No.	Type	Description	Mint	Used
1126	**251**	15 c. + 10 c. black, red and yellow	1·50	1·50
1127	–	20 c. + 10 c. black and green on green	1·00	1·00
1128	–	25 c. + 10 c. black and orange on orge	1·25	60
1129	–	30 c. + 15 c. black and blue on blue	1·50	1·50
1130	–	45 c. + 20 c. black and red on pink	1·50	1·50

STATUES: 20 c. "Apostle Paul"; 25 c. "Joachim and Ann"; 30 c. "John the Baptist and Scribes"; 45 c. "Ann, Mary and Christ-Child" (detail).

1971. Europa.

No.	Type	Description	Mint	Used
1131	**252**	25 c. yellow, red & black	40	10
1132		45 c. yellow, blue & blk	1·60	1·00

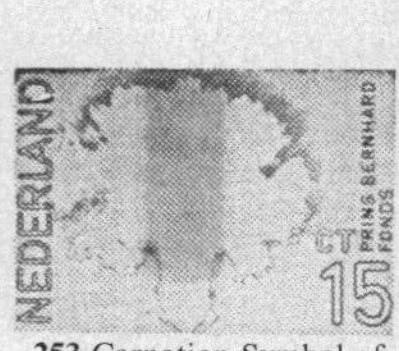

253 Carnation Symbol of Prince Bernhard Fund **254** "The Good Earth"

1971. Prince Bernhard's 60th Birthday.

No.	Type	Description	Mint	Used
1133	**253**	15 c. yellow, grey & blk	15	10
1134	–	20 c. multicoloured	25	15
1135	–	25 c. multicoloured	25	10
1136	–	45 c. + 20 c. black, purple and yellow	2·75	2·75

DESIGNS—HORIZ: 20 c. Panda symbol of World Wildlife Fund. VERT: 25 c. Prince Bernhard; 45 c. Statue, Borobudur Temple, Indonesia.

1971. Child Welfare.

No.	Type	Description	Mint	Used
1137	**254**	15 c. + 10 c. red, purple and black	10	10
1138	–	20 c. + 10 c. mult	30	15
1139	–	25 c. + 10 c. mult	15	10
1140	–	30 c. + 15 c. blue, violet and black	85	70
1141	–	45 c. + 20 c. blue, green and black	1·75	2·00

DESIGNS—VERT: 20 c. Butterfly; 45 c. Reflecting water. HORIZ: 25 c. Sun waving; 30 c. Moon winking.

255 Delta Map **256** "Fruits"

1972. Delta Sea-Defences Plan.

No.	Type	Description	Mint	Used
1143	**255**	20 c. multicoloured	30	10

1972. Cultural, Health and Social Welfare Funds. "Floriade Flower Show" (20 c., 25 c.) and "Holland Arts Festival" (30 c., 45 c.). Mult.

No.	Type	Description	Mint	Used
1144		20 c. + 10 c. Type **256**	1·25	1·00
1145		25 c. + 10 c. "Flower"	1·25	1·00
1146		30 c. + 15 c. "Sunlit Landscape"	1·25	70
1147		45 c. + 25 c. "Music"	1·25	1·00

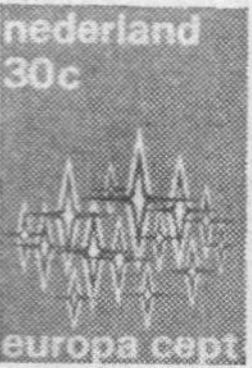

257 "Communications" **258** "There is more to be done in the world than ever before" (Thorbecke)

1972. Europa.

No.	Type	Description	Mint	Used
1148	**257**	30 c. brown and blue	85	10
1149		45 c. brown and orange	1·40	1·25

1972. Death Centenary of J. R. Thorbecke (statesman).

No.	Type	Description	Mint	Used
1150	**258**	30 c. black and blue	30	10

259 Netherlands Flag

260 Hurdling

1972. 400th Anniv of Netherlands Flag.
1151 **259** 20 c. multicoloured . . . 60 15
1152 25 c. multicoloured . . . 1·40 10

1972. Olympic Games, Munich. Multicoloured.
1153 20 c. Type **260** 15 10
1154 30 c. Diving 15 10
1155 45 c. Cycling . . . . 1·00 1·25

261 Red Cross

262 Prince Willem-Alexander

1972. Netherlands Red Cross.
1156 **261** 5 c. red 10 10
1157 – 20 c. + 10 c. red & pink 60 60
1158 – 25 c. + 10 c. red & orge 80 1·00
1159 – 30 c. + 15 c. red & black 75 35
1160 – 45 c. + 25 c. red & blue 85 95
DESIGNS: 20 c. Accident services; 25 c. Blood transfusion; 30 c. Refugee relief; 45 c. Child care.

1972. Child Welfare. Multicoloured.
1161 25 c. + 15 c. Type **262** . . . 15 15
1162 30 c. + 10 c. Prince Johan Friso 70 80
1163 35 c. + 15 c. Prince Constantin 70 10
1164 50 c. + 20 c. The Three Princes 2·00 2·50
Nos. 1162/4 are horiz.

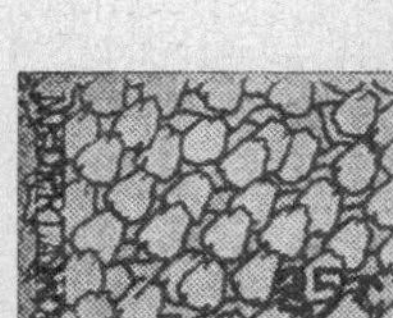

263 Tulips in Bloom

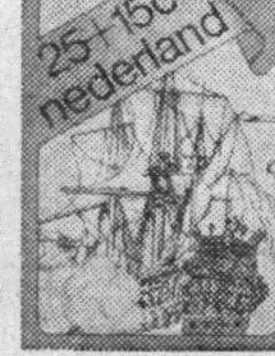

264 "De Zeven Provincien" (De Ruyter's flagship)

1973. Tulip Exports.
1166 **263** 25 c. multicoloured 75 10

1973. Cultural, Health and Social Welfare Funds. Dutch Ships. Multicoloured.
1167 25 c. + 15 c. Type **264** . . . 1·25 1·50
1168 30 c. + 10 c. "W.A. Scholten" (steamship) (horiz) . . . . 1·25 1·50
1169 35 c. + 15 c. "Veendam" (liner) (horiz) . . . . 1·50 1·00
1170 50 c. + 20 c. Fishing boat (from etching by R. Nooms) . . 1·50 1·50

265 Europa "Posthorn"

266 Hockey-players

1973. Europa.
1171 **265** 35 c. lt blue & blue . . . 45 40
1172 50 c. blue and violet . . 80 75

1973. Events and Anniversaries. Multicoloured.
1173 25 c. Type **266** 25 10
1174 30 c. Gymnastics . . . . . . 2·25 55
1175 35 c. Dish aerial (vert) . . . 35 10
1176 50 c. Rainbow 60 60
EVENTS—VERT: 25 c. 75th anniv of Royal Netherlands Hockey Association; 30 c. World Gymnastics Championships, Rotterdam. HORIZ: 35 c. Opening of Satellite Station, Burum; 50 c. Centenary of World Meteorological Organization.

267 Queen Juliana

268 "Co-operation"

1973. Silver Jubilee of Queen Juliana's Accession.
1177 **267** 40 c. multicoloured . . 50 10

1973. International Development Co-operation.
1178 **268** 40 c. multicoloured . . 1·00 10

269 "Chess"

270 Northern Goshawk

1973. Child Welfare.
1179 **269** 25 c. + 15 c. red, yellow and black 65 15
1180 – 30 c. + 10 c. green, mauve and black . . . . . . 1·00 70
1181 – 40 c. + 20 c. yellow, green and black 80 10
1182 – 50 c. + 20 c. blue, yellow and black . . . . . . 2·25 2·25
DESIGNS: 30 c. "Noughts and crosses"; 40 c. "Maze"; 50 c. "Dominoes".

1974. "Nature and Environment". Multicoloured.
1184 25 c. Type **270** . . . . . . 1·90 60
1185 25 c. Tree . . . . 1·25 60
1186 25 c. Fisherman and frog . . 1·25 60
Nos. 1184/6 were issued together se-tenant forming a composite design.

271 Bandsmen (World Band Contest, Kerkrade)

272 Football on Pitch

1974. Cultural, Health and Social Welfare Funds.
1187 **271** 25 c. + 15 c. multicoloured 90 90
1188 – 30 c. + 10 c. multicoloured 90 90
1189 – 40 c. + 20 c. brown, black and red 90 65
1190 – 50 c. + 20 c. purple, black and red 90 90
DESIGNS: 30 c. Dancers and traffic-lights ("Modern Ballet"); 40 c. Herman Heijermans; 50 c. "Kniertje" (character from Heijermans' play "Op hoop van zegan"). The 40 c. and 50 c. commemorate the 50th death anniv of the playwright.

1974. Sporting Events.
1191 **272** 25 c. multicoloured . . 20 10
1192 – 40 c. yellow, red & mve 30 10
DESIGNS AND EVENTS—HORIZ: 25 c. (World Cup Football Championships, West Germany). VERT: 40 c. Hand holding tennis ball (75th anniv of Royal Dutch Lawn Tennis Association).

273 Netherlands Cattle

274 "BENELUX" (30th Anniv of Benelux (Customs Union))

1974. Anniversaries. Multicoloured.
1193 25 c. Type **273** . . . . . . 11·00 1·40
1194 25 c. "Cancer" 15 15
1195 40 c. "Suzanna" (lifeboat) seen through binoculars 20 10
EVENTS AND ANNIVERSARIES: No. 1193, Cent of Netherlands Cattle Herdbook Society; No. 1194, 25th anniv of Queen Wilhelmina Cancer Research Fund; No. 1195, 150th anniv of Dutch Lifeboat Service.

1974. International Anniversaries.
1196 **274** 30 c. green, turq & bl . . 20 10
1197 – 45 c. deep blue, silver & bl 30 10
1198 – 45 c. yellow, blue & blk 30 10
DESIGNS—VERT: No. 1197, NATO emblem (25th anniv); 1198, Council of Europe emblem (25th anniv).

275 Hands with Letters

276 Boy with Hoop

1974. Centenary of Universal Postal Union.
1199 **275** 60 c. multicoloured . . . 40 35

1974. 50th Anniv of Child Welfare Issues. Early Photographs.
1200 **276** 30 c. + 15 c. brown & blk 15 15
1201 – 35 c. + 20 c. brown . . . 40 50
1202 – 45 c. + 20 c. black . . . 40 15
1203 – 60 c. + 20 c. black . . . 1·00 1·40
DESIGNS: 35 c. Child and baby; 45 c. Two young girls; 60 c. Girl sitting on balustrade.

277 Amsterdam

278 St. Hubertus Hunting Lodge, De Hoge Veluwe National Park

1975. Anniversaries. Multicoloured.
1205 30 c. Type **277** 20 10
1206 30 c. Synagogue and map . . 40 15
1207 35 c. Type **277** 35 10
1208 45 c. "Window" in human brain 40 15
ANNIVERSARIES: Nos. 1205, 1207, Amsterdam (700th anniv); No. 1206, Portuguese-Israelite Synagogue, Amsterdam (300th anniv); No. 1208, Leyden University and university education (400th anniv).

1975. Cultural, Health and Social Welfare Funds. National Monument Year. Preserved Monuments. Multicoloured.
1209 35 c. + 20 c. Type **278** . . . 50 50
1210 40 c. + 15 c. Bergijnhof (Beguinage), Amsterdam (vert) 50 50
1211 50 c. + 20 c. "Kuiperspoort" (Cooper's gate), Middelburg (vert) 65 50
1212 60 c. + 20 c. Orvelte village, Drenthe 75 90

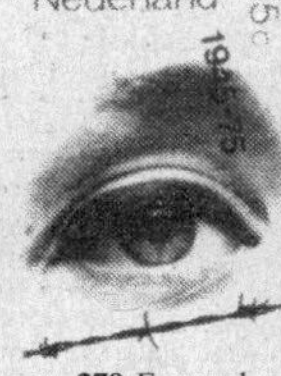

279 Eye and Barbed Wire

280 Company Emblem and "Stad Middelburg" (schooner)

1975. 30th Anniv of Liberation.
1213 **279** 35 c. black and red . . . 30 10

1975. Centenary of Zeeland Shipping Company.
1214 **280** 35 c. multicoloured . . . 30 10

281 Dr. Albert Schweitzer crossing Lambarene River

1975. Birth Centenary of Dr. Schweitzer.
1215 **281** 50 c. multicoloured . . . 40 10

282 Man and Woman on "Playing-card"

283 Braille Reading

1975. International Events. Multicoloured.
1216 35 c. Type **282** (Int Women's Year) 20 10
1217 50 c. Metric scale (Metre Convention centenary) (horiz) 30 10

1975. 150th Anniv of Invention of Braille.
1218 **283** 35 c. multicoloured . . . 30 10

284 Dutch 25 c. Coins

285 "Four Orphans" (C. Simons), Torenstraat Orphanage, Medemblik

1975. Savings Campaign.
1219 **284** 50 c. grey, green & blue . 35 10

1975. Child Welfare. Historic Ornamental Stones. Multicoloured.
1220 35 c. + 15 c. Type **285** . . . 15 15
1221 40 c. + 15 c. "Milkmaid" Kooltuin Alkmaar 45 45
1222 50 c. + 25 c. "Four Sons of Aymon seated on Beyaert", Herengracht 30 10
1223 60 c. + 25 c. "Life at the Orphanage", Molenstraat Orphanage, Gorinchem . . 85 85

286 18th-century Lottery Ticket

287 Numeral

1976. 250th Anniv of National Lottery.
1225 **286** 35 c. multicoloured . . . 30 10

1976.
1226 **287** 5 c. grey 10 10
1227 10 c. blue 10 10
1228 25 c. violet 10 10
1229 40 c. brown 15 10
1230 45 c. blue 30 10
1231 50 c. mauve 30 10
1232 55 c. green 45 10
1233 60 c. yellow 45 10
1234 65 c. brown 45 10
1235 70 c. violet 45 10
1236 80 c. mauve 50 10

288 West European Hedgehog

1976. Cultural, Health and Social Welfare Funds. Nature Protection (40, 75 c.) and Anniversaries. Multicoloured.
1241 40 c. + 20 c. Type **288** . . . 60 60
1242 45 c. + 20 c. Open book (vert) 60 60
1243 55 c. + 20 c. People and organization initials . . . 70 25
1244 75 c. + 25 c. Frog and spawn (vert) 85 85
ANNIVERSARIES: No. 1242, 175th anniv of Primary education and centenary of Agricultural education; No. 1245, 75th anniv of Social Security Bank and legislation.

289 Admiral Michiel de Ruyter (statue)

1976. 300th Death Anniv of Admiral Michiel de Ruyter.
1245 **289** 55 c. multicoloured . . . 35 10

290 Guillaume Groen van Prinsterer

1976. Death Centenary of Guillaume Groen van Prinsterer (statesman).
1246 **290** 55 c. multicoloured . . . 35 10

291 Detail of 18th Century Calendar

1976. Bicentenary of American Revolution.
1247 **291** 75 c. multicoloured . . . 50 35

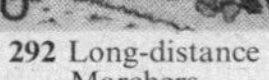

292 Long-distance Marchers　**293** The Art of Printing

1976. Sport and Recreation Anniversaries. Mult.
1248 40 c. Type **292** 20 15
1249 55 c. Runners "photo-finish" 60 15
ANNIVERSARIES: 40 c. 60th Nijmegen Long-Distance March; 55 c. Royal Dutch Athletics Society (75th anniv).

1976. Anniversaries.
1250 **293** 45 c. red and blue . . . 25 10
1251 – 55 c. + 25 c. multicoloured 45 45
DESIGNS AND EVENTS: 45 c. Type **293** (75th anniv of Netherlands Printers' organization); 55 c. Rheumatic patient "Within Care" (50th anniv of Dutch Anti-Rheumatism Association).

294 Dutch Tjalk and Reclaimed Land　**295** Queen Wilhelmina 4½ c. Stamp, 1919

1976. Zuider Zee Project–Reclamation and Urbanization. Multicoloured.
1252 **294** 40 c. blue, olive and red . . 25 10
1253 – 75 c. yellow, red & blue . 50 35
DESIGN: 75 c. Duck flying over reclaimed land.

1976. "Amphilex '77" International Stamp Exhibition, Amsterdam (1977) (1st series). Stamp Portraits of Queen Wilhelmina. Mult.
1254 – 55 c. + 55 c. blue, deep grey and grey 70 75
1255 **295** 55 c. + 55 c. purple, deep grey and grey 70 75
1256 – 55 c. + 55 c. brown, deep grey and grey 70 75
1257 – 75 c. + 75 c. turq, deep grey and grey 70 75
1258 – 75 c. + 75 c. blue, deep grey and grey 70 75
DESIGNS: No. 1254, 5 c. stamp, 1891; No. 1256, 25 c. stamp, 1924; No. 1257, 15 c. stamp, 1940; No. 1258, 25 c. stamp, 1947.
See also Nos. 1273/6.

296 "Football" (J. Raats)

1976. Child Welfare. Children's Paintings. Multicoloured.
1259 40 c. + 20 c. Type **296** . . . 25 25
1260 45 c. + 20 c. "Boat" (L Jacobs) 25 25
1261 55 c. + 20 c. "Elephant" (M. Lugtenburg) 30 10
1262 75 c. + 25 c. "Caravan" (A. Seeleman) 65 80

297 Ballot-paper and Pencil

1977. National Events. Multicoloured.
1264 40 c. "Energy" (vert) 30 10
1265 45 c. Type **297** 40 10
EVENTS: 40 c. "Be wise with energy" campaign; 45 c. Elections to Lower House of States General.
See also No. 1268.

298 Spinoza　**299** Early Type Faces and "a" on Bible Script

1977. 300th Death Anniv of Barach (Benedictus) de Spinoza (philosopher).
1266 **298** 75 c. multicoloured . . 60 30

1977. 500th Anniv of Printing of "Delft Bible".
1267 **299** 55 c. multicoloured . . 40 30

1977. Elections to Lower House of States General. As T **297** but also inscribed "25 MEI '77".
1268 45 c. multicoloured 45 10

300 Altar of Goddess Nehalennia　**301** "Kaleidoscope"

1977. Cultural, Health and Social Welfare Funds. Roman Archaeological Discoveries.
1269 – 40 c. + 20 c. mult . . . 30 30
1270 **300** 45 c. + 20 c. black, stone and green 30 25
1271 – 55 c. + 20 c. black, blue and red 30 20
1272 – 75 c. + 25 c. black, grey and yellow 40 45
DESIGNS: 40 c. Baths, Heerlen; 55 c. Remains of Zwammerdam ship; 75 c. Parade helmet.

1977. "Amphilex 1977" International Stamp Exhibition, Amsterdam (2nd series). As T **295**.
1273 55 c. + 45 c. grn, brn & grey 45 50
1274 55 c. + 45 c. bl, brn & grey 45 50
1275 55 c. + 45 c. bl, brn & grey 45 50
1276 55 c. + 45 c. red, brn & grey 45 50
DESIGNS: No. 1273, Queen Wilhelmina 1 g. stamp, 1898; No. 1274, Queen Wilhelmina 20 c. stamp, 1923; No. 1275, Queen Wilhelmina 12½ c. stamp, 1938; No. 1276, Queen Wilhelmina 10 c. stamp, 1948.

1977. Bicentenary of Netherlands Society for Industry and Commerce.
1278 **301** 55 c. multicoloured . . 30 10

302 Man in Wheelchair and Maze of Steps　**303** Risk of Drowning

1977. Anniversaries.
1279 **302** 40 c. brown, green & bl 20 10
1280 – 45 c. multicoloured . . 25 10
1281 – 55 c. multicoloured . . 35 10
DESIGNS—HORIZ: 40 c. Type **302** (50th anniv of A.V.O. Nederland); 45 c. Diagram of water current (50th anniv of Delft Hydraulic Laboratory). VERT: 55 c. Teeth (centenary of dentists' training in Netherlands).

1977. Child Welfare. Dangers to Children. Mult.
1282 40 c. + 20 c. Type **303** . . . 30 20
1283 45 c. + 20 c. Medicine cabinet (poisons) 30 25
1284 55 c. + 20 c. Balls in road (traffic) 30 20
1285 75 c. + 25 c. Matches (fire) 55 65

304 "Postcode"　**305** Makkum Dish

1978. Introduction of Postcodes.
1287 **304** 40 c. red and blue . . . 20 10
1288 45 c. red and blue . . . 25 10

1978. Cultural, Health and Social Welfare Funds. Multicoloured.
1289 40 c. + 20 c. Anna Maria van Schurman (writer) 30 30
1290 45 c. + 20 c. Passage from letter by Belle de Zuylen (Mme. de Charriere) 30 25
1291 55 c. + 20 c. Delft dish . . 30 25
1292 75 c. + 25 c. Type **305** . . . 40 45

306 "Human Rights" Treaty　**307** Chess

1978. European Series.
1293 **306** 45 c. grey, black and blue 25 10
1294 – 55 c. black, stone and orange 35 10
DESIGN: 55 c. Haarlem Town Hall (Europa).

1978. Sports.
1295 **307** 40 c. multicoloured . . . 50 15
1296 – 45 c. red and blue . . . 50 15
DESIGN: 45 c. The word "Korfbal".

308 Kidney Donor　**309** Epaulettes

1978. Health Care. Multicoloured.
1297 **308** 40 c. black, blue and red . 25 10
1298 – 45 c. multicoloured . . . 30 10
1299 – 55 c. + 25 c. red, grey and black 45 50
DESIGNS—VERT: 45 c. Heart and torch. HORIZ: 55 c. Red crosses on world map.

1978. 150th Anniv of Royal Military Academy, Breda.
1301 **309** 55 c. multicoloured . . . 30 10

310 Verkade as Hamlet

1978. Birth Centenary of Eduard Rutger Verkade (actor and producer).
1302 **310** 45 c. multicoloured . . . 30 10

311 Boy ringing Doorbell

1978. Child Welfare. Multicoloured.
1303 40 c. + 20 c. Type **311** . . . 30 20
1304 45 c. + 20 c. Child reading . 30 20
1305 55 c. + 20 c. Boy writing (vert) 30 15
1306 75 c. + 25 c. Girl and blackboard 40 60

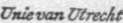

312 Clasped Hands and Arrows　**313** Names of European Community Members

1979. 400th Anniv of Treaty of Utrecht.
1308 **312** 55 c. blue 35 10

1979. First Direct Elections to European Assembly.
1309 **313** 45 c. red, blue and black . 40 10

314 Queen Juliana

1979. Queen Juliana's 70th Birthday.
1310 **314** 55 c. multicoloured . . . 40 10

315 Fragment of "Psalmen Trilogie". (J. Andriessen)　**316** Netherlands Stamps and Magnifying Glass

1979. Cultural, Health and Social Welfare Funds.
1311 **315** 40 c. + 20 c. grey and red 30 30
1312 – 45 c. + 20 c. grey and red 30 25
1313 – 55 c. + 20 c. multicoloured 30 20
1314 – 75 c. + 25 c. multicoloured 40 45
DESIGNS AND EVENTS: 150th anniv of Musical Society; 45 c. Choir. Restoration of St. John's Church, Gouda (stained glass windows); 55 c. Mary (detail, "Birth of Christ"); 75 c. William of Orange (detail, "Relief of Leyden").

1979. Europa and 75th Anniv of Scheveningen Radio. Multicoloured.
1315 55 c. Type **316** 35 10
1316 75 c. Liner and Morse Key . 50 35

317 Map of Chambers of Commerce　**318** Action Shot of Football Match

1979. 175th Anniv of First Dutch Chamber of Commerce, Maastricht.
1317 **317** 45 c. multicoloured . . . 40 15

1979. Anniversaries. Multicoloured.
1318 45 c. Type **318** (centenary of organized football) 35 15
1319 55 c. Women's suffrage meeting (60th anniv of Women's suffrage) (vert) 45 10

319 Porch of Old Amsterdam Theatre

1979. 300th Death Annivs. of Joost van den Vondel (poet) and Jan Steen (painter). Multicoloured.
1320 40 c. Type **319** 20 10
1321 45 c. "Gay Company" (detail) (Jan Steen) 25 10

320 Hindustani Girl on Father's Shoulder (The Right to Love)

1979. Child Welfare. International Year of the Child
1322 **320** 40 c. + 20 c. grey, red and yellow 35 20
1323 – 45 c. + 20 c. grey, red and black 35 15
1324 – 55 c. + 20 c. grey, black and yellow 35 15
1325 – 75 c. + 25 c. black, blue and red 45 60
DESIGNS—HORIZ: 45 c. Chilean child from refugee camp (The Right to Medical Care). VERT: 55 c. Senegalese boy from Sahel area (The Right to Food); 75 c. Class from Albert Cuyp School, Amsterdam (The Right to Education).

321 A. F. de Savornin Lohman　**322** Dunes

1980. Dutch Politicians. Multicoloured.
1327 45 c. Type **321** (Christian Historical Union) 25 10
1328 50 c. P. J. Troelstra (Socialist Party) 25 10
1329 60 c. P. J. Oud (Liberal Party) 35 10

1980. Cultural, Health and Social Welfare Funds. Multicoloured.

1330 45 c. + 20 c. Type **322** . . . 40 30
1331 50 c. + 20 c. Country estate (vert) 40 30
1332 60 c. + 25 c. Lake District . 50 25
1333 80 c. + 35 c. Moorland . . . 65 65

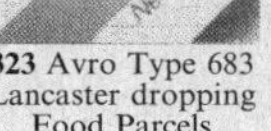

323 Avro Type 683 Lancaster dropping Food Parcels

324 Queen Beatrix and New Church, Amsterdam

1980. 35th Anniv of Liberation. Multicoloured.

1334 45 c. Type **323** 40 15
1335 60 c. Anne Frank (horiz) . . 60 10

1980. Installation of Queen Beatrix.

1336 **324** 60 c. blue, red & yellow . 45 10
1337 65 c. blue, red & yellow . 55 10

325 Young Stamp Collectors

326 "Flight"

1980. "Jupostex 1980" Stamp Exhibition, Eindhoven, and Dutch Society of Stamp Dealers Show, The Hague.

1338 **325** 50 c. multicoloured . . . 30 20

1980. Air. (Special Flights).

1339 **326** 1 g. blue and black . . . 45 45

327 Bridge Players and Cards

328 Road Haulage

1980. Sports Events. Multicoloured.

1340 50 c. Type **327** (Bridge Olympiad, Valkenburg) . . 30 10
1341 60 c. + 25 c. Sportswoman in wheelchair (Olympics for the Disabled, Arnhem and Veenendaal) 50 40

1980. Transport.

1342 **328** 50 c. multicoloured . . . 25 10
1343 – 60 c. blue, brown & blk . 40 10
1344 – 80 c. multicoloured . . . 45 25

DESIGNS: 60 c. Rail transport; 80 c. Motorised canal barge.

329 Queen Wilhelmina

1980. Europa.

1345 **329** 60 c. black, red & blue . 35 10
1346 – 80 c. black, red & blue . 40 20

DESIGN: 80 c. Sir Winston Churchill.

330 Abraham Kuyper (first rector) and University Seal

1980. Centenary of Amsterdam Free University.

1347 **330** 50 c. multicoloured . . . 30 10

331 "Pop-up" Book

332 Saltmarsh

1980. Child Welfare. Multicoloured.

1348 45 c. + 20 c. Type **331** . . . 35 20
1349 50 c. + 20 c. Child flying on a book (vert) 35 35
1350 60 c. + 30 c. Boy reading "Kikkerkoning" (vert) . . 45 20
1351 80 c. + 30 c. Dreaming in a book 60 65

1981. Cultural, Health and Social Welfare Funds. Multicoloured.

1353 45 c. + 20 c. Type **332** . . . 30 30
1354 55 c. + 25 c. Dyke 30 30
1355 60 c. + 25 c. Drain 35 30
1356 65 c. + 30 c. Cultivated land 40 40

333 Parcel (Parcel Post)

1981. P.T.T. Centenaries. Multicoloured.

1357 45 c. Type **333** 25 10
1358 55 c. Telephone, dish aerial and telephone directory page (public telephone service) . 30 10
1359 65 c. Savings bank books, deposit transfer card and savings bank stamps (National Savings Bank) . 35 10

334 Huis ten Bosch Royal Palace, The Hague

1981.

1361 **334** 55 c. multicoloured . . 35 10

335 Carillon

1981. Europa. Multicoloured.

1362 45 c. Type **335** 35 10
1363 65 c. Barrel organ 55 10

336 Council of State Emblem and Maps of 1531 and 1981

1981. 450th Anniv of Council of State.

1364 **336** 65 c. orange, deep orange and red 45 10

337 Marshalling Yard, Excavator and Ship's Screw

1981. Industrial and Agricultural Exports. Multicoloured.

1365 45 c. Type **337** 40 15
1366 55 c. Inner port, cast-iron component and weighing machine 40 15
1367 60 c. Airport, tomato and lettuce 45 40
1368 65 c. Motorway interchange, egg and cheese 55 10

338 "Integration in Society"

1981. Child Welfare. Integration of Handicapped Children. Multicoloured.

1369 45 c. + 25 c. Type **338** . . . 40 20
1370 55 c. + 20 c. "Integration in the Family" (vert) 45 45
1371 60 c. + 25 c. Child vaccinated against polio (Upper Volta project) (vert) 50 50
1372 65 c. + 30 c. "Integration among Friends" 60 20

339 Queen Beatrix

340 Agnieten Chapel and Banners

1981.

1374 **339** 65 c. brown and black . . 40 10
1375 70 c. lilac and black . . 55 10
1376 75 c. pink and black . . . 50 10
1377 90 c. green and black . . 1·25 10
1378 1 g. lilac and black . . . 50 10
1379 1 g. 20 bistre and black . . 80 10
1380 1 g. 40 green and black . 1·75 10
1381 1 g. 50 lilac and black . . 90 10
1382 2 g. bistre and black . . . 1·10 10
1383 2 g. 50 orange and black . 1·50 15
1384 3 g. blue and black . . . 1·50 10
1385 4 g. green and black . . . 2·25 10
1386 5 g. blue and black . . . 2·75 10
1387 6 g. 50 lilac and black . . 5·00 15
1388 7 g. blue and black . . . 4·00 10
1389 7 g. 50 green and black . . 4·25 30

For this design but on uncoloured background see Nos. 1594/1605.

1982. 350th Anniv of University of Amsterdam.

1395 **340** 65 c. multicoloured . . . 50 10

341 Skater

342 Apple Blossom

1982. Centenary of Royal Dutch Skating Association.

1396 **341** 45 c. multicoloured . . . 40 20

1982. Cultural, Health and Social Welfare Funds. Multicoloured.

1397 50 c. + 20 c. Type **342** . . . 40 45
1398 60 c. + 25 c. Anemones . . . 50 45
1399 65 c. + 25 c. Roses 50 45
1400 70 c. + 30 c. African violets . 70 75

343 Stripes in National Colours

1982. Bicentenary of Netherlands–United States Diplomatic Relations.

1401 **343** 50 c. red, blue and black . 40 10
1402 65 c. red, blue and black . 60 20

344 Sandwich Tern and Eider

345 Zebra Crossing

1982. Waddenzee. Multicoloured.

1403 50 c. Type **344** 40 15
1404 70 c. Barnacle Geese 60 15

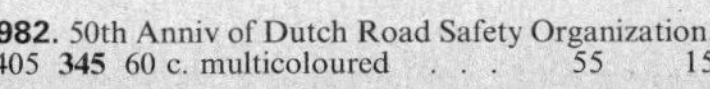

1982. 50th Anniv of Dutch Road Safety Organization.

1405 **345** 60 c. multicoloured . . . 55 15

346 Ground Plan of Enkhuizen Fortifications

347 Aerial view of Palace and Liberation Monument

1982. Europa. Multicoloured.

1406 50 c. Type **346** 40 10
1407 70 c. Part of ground plan of Coevorden fortifications . . 60 10

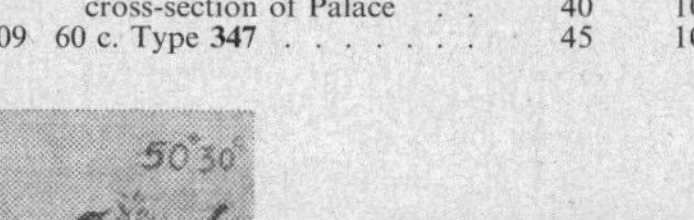

1982. Royal Palace, Dam Square, Amsterdam. Multicoloured.

1408 50 c. Facade, ground plan and cross-section of Palace . . 40 10
1409 60 c. Type **347** 45 10

348 Great Tits and Child

349 Touring Club Activities

1982. Child Welfare. Child and Animal. Mult.

1410 50 c. + 30 c. Type **348** . . . 60 30
1411 60 c. + 20 c. Child arm-in-arm with cat 65 20
1412 65 c. + 20 c. Child with drawing of rabbit 70 85
1413 70 c. + 30 c. Child with palm cockatoo . . . . 1·00 95

1983. Centenary of Royal Dutch Touring Club.

1415 **349** 70 c. multicoloured . . . 65 10

350 Johan van Oldenbarnevelt (statesman) (after J. Houbraken)

351 Newspaper

1983. Cultural, Health and Social Welfare Funds.

1416 **350** 50 c. + 20 c. pink, blue and black 50 40
1417 – 60 c. + 25 c. multicoloured 60 40
1418 – 65 c. + 25 c. multicoloured 75 60
1419 – 70 c. + 30 c. grey, black and gold 80 60

DESIGNS: 60 c. Willem Jansz Blaeu (cartographer) (after Thomas de Keijser); 65 c. Hugo de Groot (statesman) (after J. van Ravesteyn); 70 c. "Saskia van Uylenburch" (portrait of his wife by Rembrandt).

1983. Europa. Multicoloured.

1420 50 c. Type **351** (75th anniv of Netherlands Newspaper Publishers Assoc.) 40 10
1421 70 c. European Communications Satellite and European Telecommunication Satellites Organization members' flags 60 10

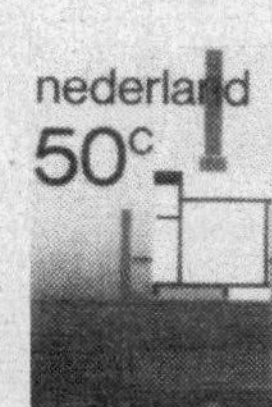

352 "Composition 1922" (P. Mondriaan)

353 "Geneva Conventions"

1983. De Stijl Art Movement. Multicoloured.

1422 50 c. Type **352** 40 10
1423 65 c. Contra construction from "Maison Particuliere" (C. van Eesteren and T. van Doesburg) 60 20

1983. Red Cross.

1424 **353** 50 c. + 25 c. multicoloured 45 45
1425 – 60 c. + 20 c. multicoloured 55 45
1426 – 65 c. + 25 c. multicoloured 70 45
1427 – 70 c. + 30 c. grey, black and red 80 70

DESIGNS: 60 c. Red Cross and text "charity, independence, impartiality"; 65 c. "Socio-medical work"; 70 c. Red Cross and text "For Peace".

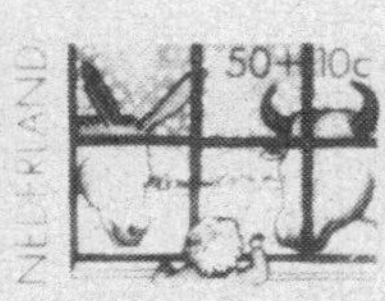

354 Luther's Signature **355** Child looking at Donkey and Ox through Window

1983. 500th Birth Anniv of Martin Luther (Protestant Reformer).

1428 **354** 70 c. multicoloured . . . 40 10

1983. Child Welfare. Child and Christmas. Multicoloured.

1429 50 c. + 10 c. Type **355** . . . 50 50
1430 50 c. + 25 c. Child riding flying snowman 60 20
1431 60 c. + 30 c. Child in bed and star 75 75
1432 70 c. + 30 c. Children dressed as the three kings 80 20

356 Parliament

1984. Second Elections to European Parliament.

1434 **356** 70 c. multicoloured . . . 55 10

357 Lapwings **358** St. Servaas

1984. Cultural, Health and Social Welfare Funds. Pasture Birds. Multicoloured.

1435 50 c. + 20 c. Type **357** . . . 50 35
1436 60 c. + 25 c. Ruffs 70 35
1437 65 c. + 25 c. Redshanks (vert) 80 70
1438 70 c. + 30 c. Black-tailed godwits (vert) 85 80

1984. 1600th Death Anniv of St. Servaas (Bishop of Tongeren and Maastricht).

1439 **358** 60 c. multicoloured . . . 50 10

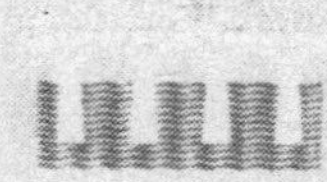

359 Bridge

1984. Europa. 25th Anniv of European Post and Telecommunications Conference.

1440 **359** 50 c. dp blue and blue . 40 10
1441 70 c. green and lt green 70 10

360 Eye and Magnifying Glass

1984. Centenary of Organized Philately in the Netherlands and "Filacento" International Stamp Exhibition, The Hague. Multicoloured.

1442 50 c. + 20 c. Type **360** . . . 40 40
1443 60 c. + 25 c. 1909 cover . . 50 50
1444 70 c. + 30 c. Stamp club meeting, 1949 . . . . 60 60

361 William of Orange (after Adriaen Thomaszoon Key)

1984. 400th Death Anniv of William of Orange.

1446 **361** 70 c. multicoloured . . . 60 10

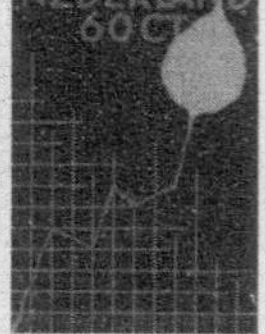

362 Giant Pandas and Globe **363** Graph and Leaf

1984. World Wildlife Fund.

1447 **362** 70 c. multicoloured . . 75 10

1984. 11th International Small Business Congress, Amsterdam.

1448 **363** 60 c. multicoloured . . 55 10

364 Violin Lesson **365** Sunny, First Dutch Guide-Dog

1984. Child Welfare. Strip Cartoons. Multicoloured.

1449 50 c. + 25 c. Type **364** . . . 40 25
1450 60 c. + 20 c. At the dentist . 75 55
1451 65 c. + 20 c. The plumber . 85 85
1452 70 c. + 30 c. The king and money chest 65 35

1985. 50th Anniv of Royal Dutch Guide-Dog Fund.

1454 **365** 60 c. black, ochre and red 60 10

366 Plates and Cutlery on Place-mat **367** Saint Martin's Church, Zaltbommel

1985. Tourism. Multicoloured.

1455 50 c. Type **366** (centenary of Travel and Holidays Association) 40 10
1456 70 c. Kroller-Muller museum emblem, antlers and landscape (50th anniv of De Hoge Veluwe National Park) 60 10

1985. Cultural, Health and Social Welfare Funds. Religious Buildings. Multicoloured.

1457 50 c. + 20 c. Type **367** . . . 60 45
1458 60 c. + 25 c. Winterswijk synagogue and Holy Ark (horiz) 65 55
1459 65 c. + 25 c. Bolsward Baptist church 80 55
1460 70 c. + 30 c. Saint John's Cathedral, 's-Hertogenbosch (horiz) 85 35

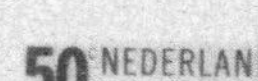

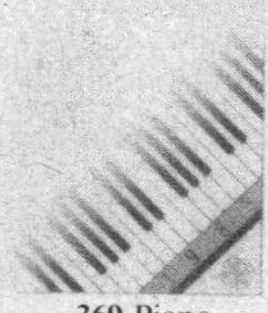

368 Star of David, Illegal Newspapers and Rifle Practice (Resistance Movement) **369** Piano Keyboard

1985. 40th Anniv of Liberation.

1461 **368** 50 c. black, stone & red 50 10
1462 – 60 c. black, stone & blue 55 10
1463 – 65 c. black, stone & orge 60 25
1464 – 70 c. black, stone & grn 65 10

DESIGNS: 60 c. Bombers over houses, "De Vliegende Hollander" (newspaper) and soldier (Allied Forces); 65 c. Soldiers and civilians, "Parool" (newspaper) and American war cemetery, Margraten (Liberation); 70 c. Women prisoners, prison money and Burma Railway (Dutch East Indies).

1985. Europa. Music Year. Multicoloured.

1465 50 c. Type **369** 40 10
1466 70 c. Organ 60 10

370 National Museum, Amsterdam (centenary)

1985. Anniversaries and Events. Multicoloured.

1467 50 c. Type **370** 45 10
1468 60 c. Teacher with students (bicentenary of Amsterdam Nautical College) 55 10
1469 70 c. Ship's mast and rigging ("Sail '85", Amsterdam) . . 70 10

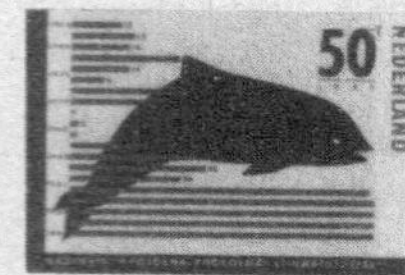

371 Porpoise and Graph

1985. Endangered Animals.

1470 **371** 50 c. black, blue & red . 40 10
1471 – 70 c. black, blue & red . 85 10

DESIGN: 70 c. Seal and PCB molecule structure.

372 Ignition Key and Framed Photograph ("Think of Me")

1985. Child Welfare. Road Safety. Multicoloured.

1472 50 c. + 25 c. Type **372** . . . 60 30
1473 60 c. + 20 c. Child holding target showing speeds . . . 70 70
1474 65 c. + 20 c. Girl holding red warning triangle 85 85
1475 70 c. + 30 c. Boy holding "Children Crossing" sign . 90 20

373 Penal Code Extract

1986. Centenary of Penal Code.

1477 **373** 50 c. black, yell & pur . . 35 10

374 Surveyor with Pole and N.A.P. Water Gauge

1986. 300th Anniv of Height Gauging Marks at Amsterdam.

1478 **374** 60 c. multicoloured . . . 45 10

375 Windmill, Graph and Cloudy Sky

1986. Inaug of Windmill Test Station, Sexbierum.

1479 **375** 70 c. multicoloured . . . 60 10

376 Scales **377** Het Loo Palace Garden, Apeldoorn

1986. Cultural, Health and Social Welfare Funds. Antique Measuring Instruments. Multicoloured.

1480 50 c. + 20 c. Type **376** . . . 45 30
1481 60 c. + 25 c. Clock (vert) . . 55 30
1482 65 c. + 25 c. Barometer (vert) 70 70
1483 70 c. + 30 c. Jacob's staff . . 80 80

1986. Europa. Multicoloured.

1484 50 c. Type **377** 40 10
1485 70 c. Tree with discoloured crown 70 10

378 Cathedral **379** Drees at Binnenhof, 1947

1986. Utrecht Events.

1486 **378** 50 c. multicoloured . . . 45 20
1487 – 60 c. blue, pink and black 65 20
1488 – 70 c. multicoloured . . . 80 10

DESIGNS—VERT: 50 c. Type **378** (completion of interior restoration); 60 c. German House (75th anniv of Heemschut Conservation Society). HORIZ: 70 c. Extract from foundation document (350th anniv of Utrecht University).

1986. Birth Centenary of Dr. Willem Drees (politician).

1489 **379** 55 c. multicoloured . . . 60 10

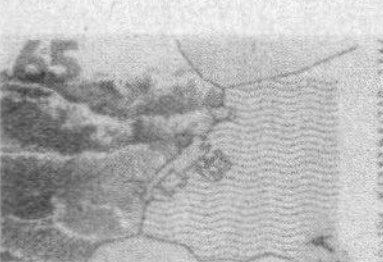

380 Draughts as Biscuits in Saucer **381** Map of Flood Barrier

1986. 75th Anniversary of Royal Dutch Draughts Association (1490) and Royal Dutch Billiards Association (1491). Multicoloured.

1490 75 c. Type **380** 90 15
1491 75 c. Player in ball preparing to play 90 15

1986. Delta Project Completion. Multicoloured.

1492 65 c. Type **381** 70 20
1493 75 c. Flood barrier 90 10

382 Children listening to Music (experiencing) **383** Engagement Picture

1986. Child Welfare. Child and Culture.

1494 55 c. + 25 c. Type **382** . . . 70 70
1495 65 c. + 35 c. Boy drawing (achieving) 80 60
1496 75 c. + 35 c. Children at theatre (understanding) 90 20

1987. Golden Wedding of Princess Juliana and Prince Bernhard.

1498 **383** 75 c. orange, black and gold 75 10

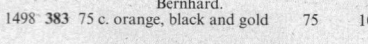

384 Block of Flats and Hut

1987. International Year of Shelter for the Homeless (65 c.) and Centenary of Netherlands Salvation Army (75 c.). Multicoloured.

1499 65 c. Type **384** 60 20
1500 75 c. Army officer, meeting and tramp 80 10

385 Eduard Douwes Dekker (Multatuli) and De Harmonie Club

1987. Writers' Death Annivs. Multicoloured.

1501 55 c. Type **385** (centenary) . 55 20
1502 75 c. Constantijn Huygens and Scheveningseweg, The Hague (300th anniv) 85 10

386 Steam Pumping Station, Nijerk

1987. Cultural Health and Social Welfare Funds. Industrial Buildings.

1503 **386** 55 c. + 30 c. red, grey and black 70 75
1504 – 65 c. + 35 c. grey, black and blue 85 85
1505 – 75 c. + 35 c. grey, yellow and black 90 60

DESIGNS: 65 c. Water tower, Deventer; 75 c. Brass foundry, Joure.

387 Dance Theatre, Scheveningen (Rem Koolhaas)

1987. Europa. Architecture. Multicoloured.

1506 55 c. Type **387** 55 20
1507 75 c. Montessori School, Amsterdam (Herman Hertzberger) 85 10

388 Auction at Broek op Langedijk

1987. Centenary of Auction Sales (55, 75 c.) and 150th Anniv of Groningen Agricultural Society (65 c.). Multicoloured.

1508 55 c. Type **388** 55 20
1509 65 c. Groningen landscape and founders' signatures . . . 65 20
1510 75 c. Auction sale and clock . 75 10

389 Telephone Care Circles

390 Map of Holland

1987. Dutch Red Cross. Multicoloured.

1511 55 c. + 30 c. Type **389** . . . 60 60
1512 65 c. + 35 c. Red cross and hands (Welfare work) . . 75 75
1513 75 c. + 35 c. Red cross and drip (Blood transfusion) 85 45

1987. 75th Anniv of Netherlands Municipalities Union.

1514 **390** 75 c. multicoloured . . . 65 10

391 Noordeinde Palace, The Hague

392 Woodcutter

1987.

1515 **391** 65 c. multicoloured . . . 50 10

1987. Child Welfare. Child and Profession. Multicoloured.

1516 55 c. + 25 c. Type **392** . . . 60 60
1517 65 c. + 35 c. Woman sailor . 75 55
1518 75 c. + 35 c. Woman pilot . 85 25

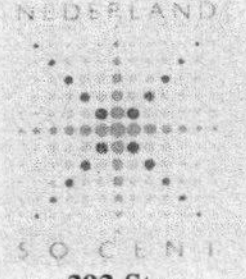

393 Star

394 "Narcissus cyclamineus" "Peeping Tom" and Extract from "I Call You Flowers" (Jan Hanlo)

1987. Christmas.

1520 **393** 50 c. red, blue and green 60 20
1521 50 c. yellow, red and blue 60 20
1522 **393** 50 c. red, blue and yellow 60 20
1523 50 c. yellow, red and green 60 20
1524 50 c. blue, green and red 60 20

The first colour described is that of the St. George's Cross.

1988. "Filacept" European Stamp Exhibition, The Hague. Flowers. Multicoloured.

1525 55 c. + 55 c. Type **394** . . . 90 80
1526 75 c. + 70 c. "Rosa gallica" "Versicolor" and "Roses" (Daan van Golden) . . . 1·10 1·00
1527 75 c. + 70 c. Sea holly and 1270 map of The Hague . . . . 1·10 1·00

395 Quagga

1988. Cultural, Health and Social Welfare Funds. 150th Anniv of Natura Artis Magistra Zoological Society. Multicoloured.

1528 55 c. + 30 c. Type **395** . . . 70 70
1529 65 c. + 35 c. American manatee 80 80
1530 75 c. + 35 c. Orang-utan (vert) 90 45

396 Man's Shoulder

397 Traffic Scene with Lead Symbol crossed Through

1988. 75th Anniv of Netherlands Cancer Institute.

1531 **396** 75 c. multicoloured . . 80 10

1988. Europa. Transport. Multicoloured.

1532 55 c. Type **397** (lead-free petrol) 50 20
1533 75 c. Cyclists reflected in car wing mirror (horiz) . . . 75 10

398 Pendulum, Prism and Saturn

1988. 300th Anniv of England's Glorious Revolution. Multicoloured.

1534 65 c. Type **398** 50 20
1535 75 c. Queen Mary, King William III and 17th-century warship 60 10

399 "Cobra Cat" (Appel)

400 Sailing Ship and Map of Australia

1988. 40th Anniv of Founding of Cobra Painters Group. Multicoloured.

1536 55 c. Type **399** 50 50
1537 65 c. "Kite" (Corneille) . . 55 50
1538 75 c. "Stumbling Horse" (Constant) 60 20

1988. Bicentenary of Australian Settlement.

1539 **400** 75 c. multicoloured . . 70 10

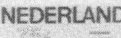

401 Statue of Erasmus, Rotterdam

402 "Rain"

1988. 75th Anniv of Erasmus University, Rotterdam (1540) and Centenary of Concertgebouw Concert Hall and Orchestra (1541).

1540 **401** 75 c. dp green & green . 65 20
1541 – 75 c. violet 65 20

DESIGN: No. 1541, Violin and Concertgebouw concert hall.

1988. Child Welfare. Centenary of Royal Netherlands Swimming Federation. Children's drawings. Multicoloured.

1543 55 c. + 25 c. Type **402** . . . 65 60
1544 65 c. + 35 c. "Getting Ready for the Race" 85 50
1545 75 c. + 35 c. "Swimming Test" 85 30

403 Stars

1988. Christmas.

1547 **403** 50 c. multicoloured . . . 50 10

404 Postal and Telecommunications Services

1989. Privatization of Netherlands PTT.

1548 **404** 75 c. multicoloured . . . 75 10

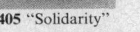

405 "Solidarity"

406 Members' Flags

1989. Trade Unions. Multicoloured.

1549 55 c. Type **405** 40 20
1550 75 c. Talking mouths on hands 50 10

1989. 40th Anniv of N.A.T.O.

1551 **406** 75 c. multicoloured . . . 75 10

407 Boier

408 Boy with Homemade Telephone

1989. Cultural, Health and Social Welfare Funds. Old Sailing Vessels.

1552 **407** 55 c. + 30 c. grn & blk . 30 10
1553 – 65 c. + 35 c. blue & blk . 35 10
1554 – 75 c. + 35 c. brn & blk . 40 10

DESIGNS: 65 c. Fishing smack; 75 c. Clipper.

1989. Europa. Children's Games. Multicoloured.

1555 55 c. Type **408** 50 20
1556 75 c. Girl with homemade telephone 75 10

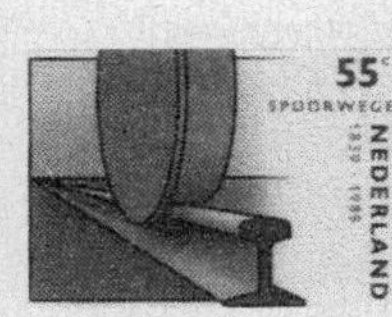

409 Wheel on Rail

410 Boy with Ball and Diagram of Goal Scored in European Championship

1989. 150th Anniv of Netherlands' Railways. Multicoloured.

1557 55 c. Type **409** 60 20
1558 65 c. Locomotives 65 20
1559 75 c. Clock and "The Kiss" (sculpture by Rodin) . . . 70 10

1989. Centenary of Royal Dutch Football Assn.

1560 **410** 75 c. multicoloured . . . 80 10

411 Map

412 Right to Housing

1989. 150th Anniv of Division of Limburg between Netherlands and Belgium.

1561 **411** 75 c. multicoloured . . . 80 10

1989. Child Welfare. 30th Anniv of Declaration of Rights of the Child. Multicoloured.

1562 55 c. + 25 c. Type **412** . . . 60 60
1563 65 c. + 35 c. Right to food . 80 50
1564 75 c. + 35 c. Right to education 90 30

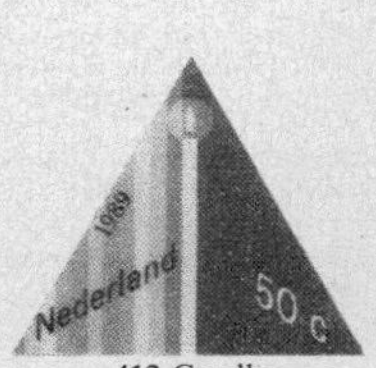

413 Candle

414 "Arms of Leiden" (tulip) and Plan of Gardens in 1601

1989. Christmas.

1566 **413** 50 c. multicoloured . . . 60 10

1990. 400th Anniv of Hortus Botanicus (botanical gardens), Leiden.

1567 **414** 65 c. multicoloured . . . 70 20

415 Pointer on Graduated Scale

416 "Self-portrait" (detail)

1990. Centenary of Labour Inspectorate.

1568 **415** 75 c. multicoloured . . . 70 10

1990. Death Centenary of Vincent van Gogh (painter). Multicoloured.

1569 55 c. Type **416** 75 20
1570 75 c. "Green Vineyard" (detail) 1·25 10

417 Summer's Day

1990. Cultural, Health and Social Welfare Funds. The Weather. Multicoloured.

1571 55 c. + 30 c. Type **417** . . . 60 50
1572 65 c. + 35 c. Clouds and isobars (vert) 75 65
1573 75 c. + 35 c. Satellite weather picture (vert) 90 30

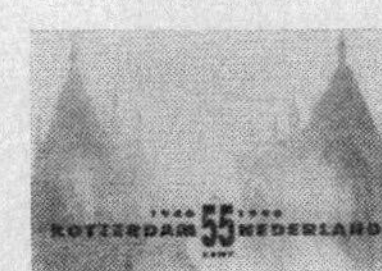

418 Zuiderkerk Ruins

1990. 50th Anniv of German Bombing of Rotterdam.

1574 **418** 55 c. deep brown, brown and black 55 20
1575 – 65 c. multicoloured . . . 65 10
1576 – 75 c. multicoloured . . . 85 10

DESIGNS: 65 c. City plan as stage; 75 c. Girder and plans for future construction.

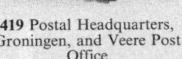

419 Postal Headquarters, Groningen, and Veere Post Office

420 Construction of Indiaman and Wreck of "Amsterdam"

1990. Europa. Post Office Buildings.

1577 – 55 c. grey, mve & brn . . 55 20
1578 **419** 75 c. blue, grn & grey . . 85 10

DESIGN: 55 c. As Type **419** but inscr "Postkantoor Veere".

1990. 3rd Anniv of Dutch East India Company Ships Association (replica ship project) (1579) and "Sail 90", Amsterdam (1580). Multicoloured.

1579 65 c. Type **420** 65 20
1580 75 c. Crew manning yards on sailing ship 95 10

421 Queens Emma, Wilhelmina, Juliana and Beatrix

422 Flames, Telephone Handset and Number

1990. Netherlands Queens of the House of Orange.
1581 **421** 150 c. multicoloured . . 1·50 45

1990. Introduction of National Emergency Number.
1582 **422** 65 c. multicoloured . . . 60 20

423 Girl riding Horse

424 Falling Snow

1990. Child Welfare. Hobbies. Multicoloured.
1583 55 c. + 25 c. Type **423** . . . 75 60
1584 65 c. + 35 c. Girl at computer 85 50
1585 75 c. + 35 c. Young philatelist 90 30

1990. Christmas.
1587 **424** 50 c. multicoloured . . . 50 10

425 Industrial Chimneys, Exhaust Pipes and Aerosol Can (Air Pollution)

1991. Environmental Protection. Multicoloured.
1588 55 c. Type **425** 55 20
1589 65 c. Outfall pipes and chemicals (sea pollution) . 70 20
1590 75 c. Agricultural chemicals, leaking drums and household landfill waste (soil pollution) 90 10

426 German Raid on Amsterdam Jewish Quarter and Open Hand

1991. 50th Anniv of Amsterdam General Strike.
1591 **426** 75 c. multicoloured . . . 75 10

427 Princess Beatrix and Prince Claus on Wedding Day

428 Queen Beatrix

1991. Royal Silver Wedding Anniversary. Mult.
1592 75 c. Type **427** 95 35
1593 75 c. Queen Beatrix and Prince Claus on horseback 95 35

1991.
1594 **428** 75 c. dp green & green . 55 10
1595 80 c. brown & lt brown 60 10
1597 90 c. blue 70 10
1598 1 g. violet 75 10
1600 1 g. 30 blue and violet . 1·00 10
1601 1 g. 40 green and olive . 1·00 10
1602 1 g. 60 purple & mauve 1·25 10
1603 2 g. brown . . . . . 1·50 10
1603a 2 g. 50 purple . . . . 1·75 10
1604 3 g. blue . . . . . . 2·25 10
1605 5 g. red . . . . . . 3·75 10
1706 7 g. 50 violet . . . . 5·50 1·75
1708 10 g. green . . . . . 7·50 2·50

429 "Meadow" Farm, Wartena, Friesland

430 Gerard Philips's Experiments with Carbon Filaments

1991. Cultural, Health and Social Welfare Funds. Traditional Farmhouses. Multicoloured.
1610 55 c. + 30 c. Type **429** . . . 80 50
1611 65 c. + 35 c. "T-house" farm, Kesteren, Gelderland . . . 90 65
1612 75 c. + 35 c. "Courtyard" farm, Nuth, Limburg 95 30

1991. 75th Anniv of Netherlands Standards Institute (65 c.) and Centenary of Philips Organization (others). Multicoloured.
1615 55 c. Type **430** 45 20
1616 65 c. Wiring to Standard NEN 1010 (horiz) 55 20
1617 75 c. Laser beams reading video disc 70 10

431 Man raising Hat to Space

432 Sticking Plaster over Medal

1991. Europa. Europe in Space. Multicoloured.
1618 55 c. Type **431** 60 20
1619 75 c. Ladders stretching into space 80 10

1991. 75th Anniv of Nijmegen International Four Day Marches.
1620 **432** 80 c. multicoloured . . 65 10

433 Jacobus Hendericus van't Hoff

434 Children and Open Book

1991. Dutch Nobel Prize Winners. Multicoloured.
1621 60 c. Type **433** (chemistry, 1901) 50 15
1622 70 c. Pieter Zeeman (physics, 1902) 60 20
1623 80 c. Tobias Michael Carel Asser (peace, 1911) . . . 65 10

1991. Centenary (1992) of Public Libraries in the Netherlands.
1624 **434** 70 c. drab, black & mve 60 20
1625 – 80 c. multicoloured . . 65 10
DESIGN: 80 c. Books on shelf.

435 Girls with Doll and Robot

436 "Greetings Cards keep People in Touch"

1991. Child Welfare. Outdoor Play. Multicoloured.
1626 60 c. + 30 c. Type **435** . . . 75 50
1627 70 c. + 35 c. Bicycle race . . 85 65
1628 80 c. + 40 c. Hide and Seek 95 30

1991. Christmas.
1630 **436** 55 c. multicoloured . . 45 15

437 Artificial Lightning, Microchip and Oscilloscope

1992. 150th Anniv of Delft University of Technology.
1631 **437** 60 c. multicoloured . . 50 15

438 Extract from Code

440 Tulips ("Mondrian does not like Green")

1992. Implementation of Property Provisions of New Civil Code.
1632 **438** 80 c. multicoloured . . 65 10

1992. "Expo '92" World's Fair, Seville. Mult.
1634 70 c. Type **440** 60 20
1635 80 c. "Netherland Expo '92" 65 10

441 Tasman's Map of Staete Landt (New Zealand)

1992. 350th Anniv of Discovery of Tasmania and New Zealand by Abel Tasman.
1636 **441** 70 c. multicoloured . . . 60 20

442 Yellow and Purple Flowers

443 Geometric Planes

1992. Cultural, Health and Social Welfare Funds. "Floriade" Flower Show, Zoetermeer. Multicoloured.
1637 60 c. + 30 c. Water lilies . . 75 50
1638 70 c. + 35 c. Orange and purple flowers 85 65
1639 80 c. + 40 c. Type **442** . . . 95 30

1992. 150th Anniv of Royal Association of Netherlands Architects (60 c.) and Inauguration of New States General Lower House (80 c.). Multicoloured.
1643 60 c. Type **443** 50 15
1644 80 c. Atrium and blue sky (symbolising sending of information into society) . 65 10

444 Globe and Columbus

445 Moneta (Goddess of Money)

1992. Europa. 500th Anniv of Discovery of America by Columbus.
1645 **444** 60 c. multicoloured . . . 50 15
1646 – 80 c. blk, mve & yell . . 65 10
DESIGN—VERT: 80 c. Galleon.

1992. Centenary of Royal Netherlands Numismatics Society.
1647 **445** 70 c. multicoloured . . . 60 20

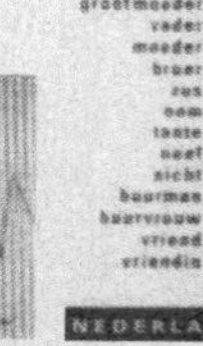

446 Teddy Bear wearing Stethoscope

447 List of Relatives and Friends

1992. Centenary of Netherlands Paediatrics Society.
1648 **446** 80 c. multicoloured . . . 65 10

1992. 50th Anniv of Departure of First Deportation Train from Westerbork Concentration Camp.
1649 **447** 70 c. multicoloured . . . 55 15

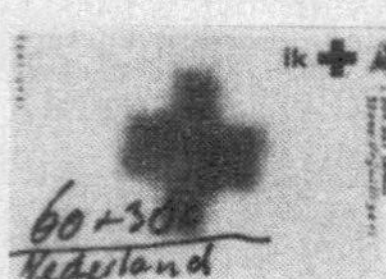

448 Cross

1992. 125th Anniv of Netherlands Red Cross. Multicoloured.
1650 60 c. + 30 c. Type **448** . . . 70 45
1651 70 c. + 35 c. Supporting injured person 80 55
1652 80 c. + 40 c. Red cross on dirty bandage 90 30

449 "United Europe" and European Community Flag

450 Queen Beatrix on Official Birthday, 1992, and at Investiture

1992. European Single Market.
1656 **449** 80 c. multicoloured . . . 60 10

1992. 12½ Years since Accession to the Throne of Queen Beatrix.
1657 **450** 80 c. multicoloured . . . 60 10

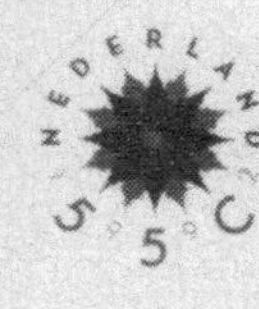

451 Saxophone Player

452 Poinsettia

1992. Child Welfare. Child and Music. Mult.
1658 60 c. + 30 c. Type **451** . . . 70 45
1659 70 c. + 35 c. Piano player . 80 55
1660 80 c. + 40 c. Double bass player 90 30

1992. Christmas.
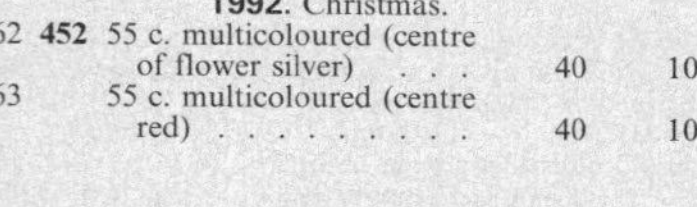
1662 **452** 55 c. multicoloured (centre of flower silver) . . . 40 10
1663 55 c. multicoloured (centre red) 40 10

453 Cycling

1993. Centenary of Netherlands Cycle and Motor Industry Association.
1664 **453** 70 c. multicoloured . . . 55 15
1665 – 80 c. brown, grey & yell 60 10
DESIGN: 80 c. Car.

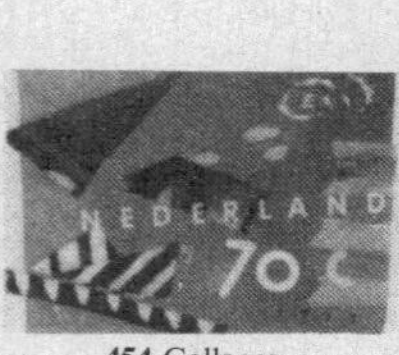

454 Collages

455 Mouth to Mouth Resuscitation

1993. Greetings Stamps. Multicoloured.
1666 70 c. Type **454** 55 10
1667 70 c. Collages (different) . . 55 10

1993. Anniversaries. Multicoloured.
1668 70 c. Type **455** (centenary of Royal Netherlands First Aid Association) 55 10
1669 80 c. Pests on leaf (75th anniv of Wageningen University of Agriculture) 55 10
1670 80 c. Lead driver and horses (bicentenary of Royal Horse Artillery) 60 10

456 Emblems

1993. 150th Anniv of Royal Dutch Notaries Association. Each red and violet.
1671 80 c. Type **456** ("150 Jaar" reading up) 60 10
1672 80 c. As Type **456** but emblems inverted and "150 Jaar" reading down 60 10
Nos. 1671/2 were issued together in horizontal tete-beche pairs, each pair forming a composite design.

457 Large White

458 Elderly Couple

1993. Butterflies. Multicoloured.

1673		70 c. Pearl-bordered fritillary	55	15
1674		80 c. Large tortoiseshell . . .	60	10
1675		90 c. Type **457**	70	20

1993. Cultural, Health and Social Welfare Funds. Senior Citizens' Independence.

1677		70 c. + 35 c. Type **458** . . .	75	50
1678		70 c. + 35 c. Elderly man . .	75	50
1679		80 c. + 40 c. Elderly woman with dog	75	25

459 Radio Orange

460 Sports Pictograms

1993. Radio Orange (Dutch broadcasts from London during Second World War). Multicoloured.

1683		80 c. Type **459**	55	10
1684		80 c. Man listening to radio in secret	55	10

1993. 2nd European Youth Olympic Days. Multicoloured.

1685		70 c. Type **460**	50	15
1686		80 c. Sports pictograms (different)	55	10

461 "The Embodiment of Unity" (Wessel Couzijn)

462 Johannes Diderik van der Waals (Physics, 1910)

1993. Europa. Contemporary Art. Multicoloured.

1687		70 c. Type **461**	50	15
1688		80 c. Architectonic sculpture (Per Kirkeby)	55	10
1689		160 c. Sculpture (Naum Gabo) (vert)	1·10	55

1993. Nobel Prize Winners.

1690	**462**	70 c. blue, black & red .	50	15
1691	–	80 c. mauve, blk & red .	55	10
1692	–	90 c. multicoloured . . .	65	15

DESIGNS: 80 c. Willem Einthoven (medicine, 1924); 90 c. Christiaan Eijkman (medicine, 1929).

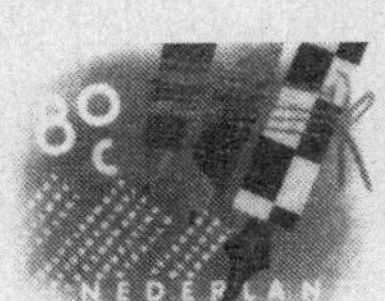

463 Pen and Pencils

1993. Letter Writing Campaign. Multicoloured.

1693		80 c. Type **463**	55	10
1694		80 c. Envelope	55	10

464 "70"

1993. Stamp Day (70 c.) and Netherlands PTT (80 c.). Multicoloured.

1695		70 c. Type **464**	50	15
1696		80 c. Dish aerial and dove carrying letter	55	10

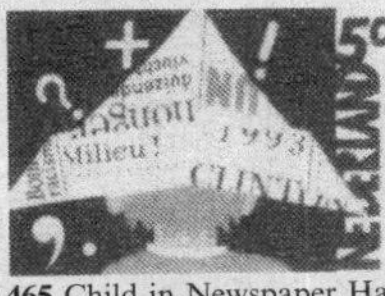
465 Child in Newspaper Hat

1993. Child Welfare. Child and the Media. Multicoloured.

1697		70 c. + 35 c. Type **465** . . .	75	50
1698		70 c. + 35 c. Elephant listening to radio on headphones .	75	50
1699		80 c. + 40 c. Television . .	75	25

466 Candle

1993. Christmas. Multicoloured.

1711		55 c. Type **466**	45	15
1712		55 c. Fireworks	45	15

Both designs have a number of punched holes.

467 "Composition"

1994. 50th Death Anniv of Piet Mondriaan (artist). Multicoloured.

1713		70 c. "The Red Mill" (detail)	55	15
1714		80 c. Type **467**	65	10
1715		90 c. "Broadway Boogie Woogie" (detail)	70	20

468 Barnacle Goose

1994. "Fepapost 94" European Stamp Exhibition, The Hague. Multicoloured.

1716		70 c. + 60 c. Type **468** . . .	1·00	65
1717		80 c. + 70 c. Bluethroat . .	1·25	40
1718		90 c. + 80 c. Garganey . .	1·40	95

469 Downy Rose

1994. Wild Flowers. Multicoloured.

1719		70 c. Type **469**	55	15
1720		80 c. Daisies	65	10
1721		90 c. Wood forgetmenot . .	70	20

470 Airplane

1994. 75th Aircraft Industry Anniversaries.

1723	**470**	80 c. blue and black . .	65	10
1724	–	80 c. grey, red and black	65	10
1725	–	80 c. multicoloured . . .	65	10

DESIGNS: No. 1723, Type **470** (KLM (Royal Dutch Airlines)); 1724, Plan and outline of aircraft and clouds (Royal Netherlands Fokker Aircraft Industries); 1725, Airplane and clouds (National Aerospace Laboratory).

471 Woman using Telephone

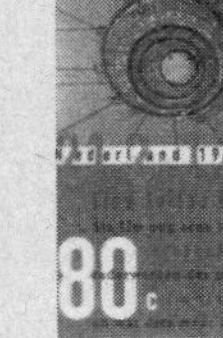

472 Eisinga's Planetarium

1994. Cultural, Health and Social Welfare Funds. Senior Citizens' Security. Multicoloured.

1726		70 c. + 35 c. Type **471** . . .	85	55
1727		80 c. + 40 c. Man using telephone	95	30
1728		90 c. + 35 c. Man using telephone (different) . . .	1·00	65

1994. Anniversaries. Multicoloured.

1732		80 c. Type **472** (250th birth anniv of Eise Eisinga) . . .	65	10
1733		90 c. Astronaut and boot print on Moon surface (25th anniv of first manned Moon landing)	70	20

473 Players Celebrating

1994. World Cup Football Championship, U.S.A.

1734	**473**	80 c. multicoloured . . .	65	10

474 Stock Exchange

1994. Quotation of Netherlands PTT (KPN) on Stock Exchange.

1735	**474**	80 c. multicoloured . . .	65	15

475 Road Sign, Car and Bicycle

1994. Anniversaries and Events. Multicoloured.

1736		70 c. Type **475** (centenary of provision of road signs by Netherlands Motoring Association)	55	15
1737		80 c. Equestrian sports (World Equestrian Games, The Hague)	65	10

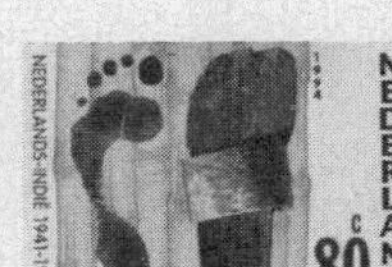

476 Footprint and Sandal

1994. Second World War. Multicoloured.

1738		80 c. Type **476** (war in Netherlands Indies, 1941–45)	65	10
1739		90 c. Soldier, children and aircraft dropping paratroops (50th anniv of Operation Market Garden (Battle of Arnhem)) (vert)	70	20

477 Brandaris Lighthouse, Terschelling

1994. Lighthouses. Multicoloured.

1740		70 c. Type **477**	55	15
1741		80 c. Ameland (vert)	65	10
1742		90 c. Vlieland (vert)	70	20

478 Decorating

1994. Child Welfare. "Together". Multicoloured.

1744		70 c. + 35 c. Type **478** . . .	85	55
1745		80 c. + 40 c. Girl on swing knocking fruit off tree (vert)	95	30
1746		90 c. + 35 c. Girl helping boy onto roof of playhouse (vert)	1·00	65

INDEX

Countries can be quickly located by referring to the index at the end of this volume.

MARINE INSURANCE STAMPS

M 22

1921.

M238	M **22**	15 c. green	4·00	45·00
M239		60 c. red	5·00	65·00
M240		75 c. brown	7·00	70·00
M241	–	1 g. 50 blue	60·00	£500
M242	–	2 g. 25 brown	£120	£700
M243	–	4½ g. black	£170	£900
M244	–	7½ g. red	£300	£1400

DESIGNS (inscr "DRIJVENDE BRANDKAST"): 1 g. 50, 2 g. 25 "Explosion"; 4½ g., 7½ g. Lifebelt.

OFFICIAL STAMPS

1913. Stamps of 1898 optd **ARMENWET.**

O214	**12**	1 c. red	3·50	1·75
O215		1½ c. blue	85	1·40
O216		2 c. brown	6·00	6·00
O217		2½ c. green	14·00	11·00
O218	**13**	3 c. green	3·50	65
O219		5 c. red	3·50	4·00
O220		10 c. grey	29·00	38·00

POSTAGE DUE STAMPS

D 8

D 9

1870.

D76	D **8**	5 c. brown on yellow . .	65·00	10·00
D77		10 c. purple on blue . .	£150	13·00

For same stamps in other colours, see Netherlands Indies, Nos. D1/5.

1881.

D208	D **9**	½ c. black and blue . .	15	15
D182		1 c. black and blue . .	1·25	15
D183		1½ c. black and blue . .	45	20
D184		2½ c. black and blue . .	1·40	15
D209		3 c. black and blue . .	1·50	1·00
D210		4 c. black and blue . .	1·50	1·75
D185		5 c. black and blue . .	10·00	10
D211		6½ c. black and blue . .	35·00	35·00
D212		7½ c. black and blue . .	1·25	40
D186		10 c. black and blue . .	27·00	25
D187		12½ c. black and blue .	23·00	70
D188		15 c. black and blue . .	27·00	60
D189		20 c. black and blue . .	16·00	6·00
D190		25 c. black and blue . .	35·00	45
D181		1 g. red and blue . . .	85·00	22·00

No. D181 is inscribed "EEN GULDEN".

1906. Surch

D213	D **9**	3 c. on 1 g. red & blue	26·00	24·00
D215		4 on 6½ c. black & blue	4·00	5·50
D216		6½ on 20 c. black & blue	3·50	4·50
D214		50 c. on 1 g. red & blue	£130	£120

1907. De Ruyter Commem. stamps surch **PORTZEGEL** and value.

D217	**15**	½ c. on 1 c. red	1·25	1·25
D218		1 c. on 1 c. red	40	40
D219		1½ c. on 1 c. red	35	35
D220		2½ c. on 1 c. red	85	85
D221		5 c. on 2½ c. red	1·25	35
D222		6½ c. on 2½ c. red	3·00	3·00
D223		7½ c. on ½ c. blue	1·75	1·25
D224		10 c. on ½ c. blue	1·50	55
D225		12½ c. on ½ c. blue . . .	4·50	4·50
D226		15 c. on 2½ c. red	6·00	3·00
D227		25 c. on ½ c. blue	8·00	6·50
D228		50 c. on ½ c. blue	35·00	32·00
D229		1 g. on ½ c. blue	55·00	48·00

1912. Re-issue of Type D **9** in one colour.

D230	D **9**	½ c. blue	10	10
D231		1 c. blue	10	10
D232		1½ c. blue	1·00	1·00
D233		2½ c. blue	10	10
D234		3 c. blue	35	35
D235		4 c. blue	10	15
D236		4½ c. blue	4·75	4·75
D237		5 c. blue	10	10
D238		5½ c. blue	4·50	4·50
D239		7 c. blue	2·00	2·25
D240		7½ c. blue	2·25	75
D241		10 c. blue	10	10
D242		12½ c. blue	20	15
D453		15 c. blue	20	10
D244		20 c. blue	20	10
D245		25 c. blue	65·00	60
D246		50 c. blue	40	15

D 25

D 121

1921.

D442 **D 25** 3 c. blue 10 15
D445 6 c. blue 10 15
D446 7 c. blue 15 15
D447 7½ c. blue 20 25
D448 8 c. blue 15 15
D449 9 c. blue 20 25
D450 11 c. blue 11·00 3·00
D247 12 c. blue 15 15
D455 25 c. blue 20 10
D456 30 c. blue 25 10
D458 1 g. red 60 10

1923. Surch in white figures in black circle.

D272 **D 9** 1 c. on 3 c. blue 30 35
D273 2½ c. on 7 c. blue 35 25
D274 25 c. on 1½ c. blue 7·50 35
D275 25 c. on 7½ c. blue 7·50 25

1924. Stamps of 1898 surch **TE BETALEN PORT** and value in white figures in black circle.

D295 **13** 4 c. on 3 c. green 1·25 1·50
D296 **12** 5 c. on 1 c. red 35 10
D297 10 c. on 1½ c. blue 75 15
D298 **13** 12½ c. on 5 c. red 80 15

1947.

D656 **D 121** 1 c. blue 10 10
D657 3 c. blue 10 15
D658 4 c. blue 13·00 80
D659 5 c. blue 10 10
D660 6 c. blue 35 35
D661 7 c. blue 15 15
D662 8 c. blue 15 15
D663 10 c. blue 15 10
D664 11 c. blue 35 35
D665 12 c. blue 55 80
D666 14 c. blue 75 70
D667 15 c. blue 30 10
D668 16 c. blue 85 85
D669 20 c. blue 30 10
D670 24 c. blue 1·25 1·25
D671 25 c. blue 30 10
D672 26 c. blue 1·60 1·75
D673 30 c. blue 65 10
D674 35 c. blue 70 10
D675 40 c. blue 75 10
D676 50 c. blue 85 10
D677 60 c. blue 1·00 25
D678 85 c. blue 17·00 35
D679 90 c. blue 3·50 40
D680 95 c. blue 3·50 35
D681 1 g. red 2·25 10
D682 1 g. 75 red 6·00 25

For stamps as Types D **121**, but in violet, see under Surinam.

INTERNATIONAL COURT OF JUSTICE

Stamps specially issued for use by the Headquarters of the Court of International Justice. Nos. J1 to J36 were not sold to the public in unused condition.

1934. Optd **COUR PER- MANENTE DE JUSTICE INTER- NATIONALE.**

J1 **35** 1½ c. mauve — 40
J2 2½ c. green — 40
J3 **36** 7½ c. red — 80
J4 **68** 12½ c. blue — 27·00
J7 **36** 12½ c. blue — 13·00
J5 15 c. yellow — 1·00
J6 3 c. purple — 1·50

1940. Optd **COUR PER- MANANTE DE JUSTICE INTER- NATIONALE.**

J 9 **94** 7½ c. red — 9·00
J10 12½ c. blue — 9·00
J11 15 c. blue — 9·00
J12 30 c. bistre — 9·00

1947. Optd **COUR INTERNATIONALE DE JUSTICE.**

J13 **94** 7½ c. red — 1·00
J14 10 c. purple — 1·00
J15 12½ c. blue — 1·00
J16 20 c. violet — 1·00
J17 25 c. red — 1·00

J 3 — J 4 Peace Palace, The Hague — J 5 Queen Juliana

1950.

J18 **J 3** 2 c. blue — 7·00
J19 4 c. green — 7·00

1951.

J20 **J 4** 2 c. lake — 50
J21 3 c. blue — 50
J22 4 c. green — 50
J23 5 c. brown — 50
J24 **J 5** 6 c. mauve — 2·75
J25 **J 4** 6 c. green — 85
J26 7 c. red — 85
J27 **J 5** 10 c. green — 15
J28 12 c. red — 1·75
J29 15 c. red — 15
J30 20 c. blue — 20
J31 25 c. brown — 20
J32 30 c. purple — 30
J33 **J 4** 40 c. blue — 30
J34 45 c. red — 35
J35 50 c. mauve — 35
J36 **J 5** 1 g. grey — 70

J 6 Olive Branch and Peace Palace, The Hague

1989.

J37 **J 6** 5 c. black and yellow 10 10
J38 10 c. black and blue 10 10
J39 25 c. black and red 20 20
J41 50 c. black and green 40 40
J42 55 c. black and mauve 40 40
J43 60 c. black and bistre 45 45
J44 65 c. black and green 50 50
J45 70 c. black and blue 55 55
J46 75 c. black and yellow 55 55
J47 80 c. black and green 60 60
J49 1 g. black and orange 75 75
J50 1 g. 50 black and blue 1·10 1·10
J51 1 g. 60 black and brown 1·25 1·25
J54 – 5 g. multicoloured 3·75 3·75
J56 – 7 g. multicoloured 5·25 5·25

DESIGNS: 5, 7 g. Olive branch and column.

NETHERLANDS ANTILLES Pt. 4

Curacao and other Netherlands islands in the Caribbean Sea. In December 1954 these were placed on an equal footing with Netherlands under the Crown.

100 cents = 1 gulden

48 Spanish Galleon

49 Alonso de Ojeda

1949. 450th Anniv of Discovery of Curacao.

306 **48** 6 c. green 3·50 1·75
307 **49** 12½ c. red 3·75 3·50
308 **48** 15 c. blue 3·75 2·25

50 Posthorns and Globe

51 Leap-frog

1949. 75th Anniv of U.P.U.

309 **50** 6 c. red 3·00 2·25
310 25 c. blue 3·00 1·10

1950. As numeral and portrait types of Netherlands but inscr "NED. ANTILLEN".

325 **118** 1 c. brown 10 10
326 1½ c. blue 10 10
327 2 c. orange 10 10
328 2½ c. green 80 15
329 3 c. violet 10 10
329a 4 c. green 45 35
330 5 c. red 10 10
310a **129** 5 c. yellow 25 25
311 6 c. purple 85 10
311a 7½ c. brown 4·00 10
312a 10 c. red 30 30
313 12½ c. green 1·75 15
314a 15 c. blue 35 35
315a 20 c. orange 70 70
316 21 c. black 2·00 1·75
316a 22½ c. green 5·00 10
317a 25 c. violet 80 80
318 27½ c. brown 5·00 1·90
319a 30 c. sepia 80 80
319b 40 c. blue 80 80
320 50 c. olive 9·00 10
321 **130** 1½ g. green 32·00 20
322 2½ g. brown 30·00 70
323 5 g. red 50·00 8·50
324 10 g. purple £200 50·00

1951. Child Welfare.

331 **51** 1½ c. + 1 c. violet 1·75 2·25
332 – 5 c. + 2½ c. brown 11·00 4·50
333 – 6 c. + 2½ c. blue 11·00 4·50
334 – 12½ c. + 5 c. red 11·00 4·50
335 – 25 c. + 10 c. turquoise 11·00 4·50

DESIGNS: 5 c. Kite-flying; 6 c. Girl on swing; 12½ c. Girls playing "Oranges and Lemons"; 25 c. Bowling hoops.

52 Gull over Ship

54 Fort Beekenburg

1952. Seamen's Welfare Fund. Inscr "ZEEMANSWELVAREN".

336 **52** 1½ c. + 1 c. green 1·50 75
337 – 6 c. + 4 c. brown 8·00 3·50
338 – 12½ c. + 7 c. mauve 8·00 3·75
339 – 15 c. + 10 c. blue 10·00 4·00
340 – 25 c. + 15 c. red 8·50 3·50

DESIGNS: 6 c. Sailor and lighthouse; 12½ c. Sailor on ship's prow; 15 c. Tanker in harbour; 25 c. Anchor and compass.

1953. Netherlands Flood Relief Fund. No. 321 surch **22½ Ct. + 7½ Ct. WATERSNOOD NEDER-LAND 1953.**

341 **130** 22½ c. + 7½ c. on 1½ g. 1·10 1·10

1953. 250th Anniv of Fort Beekenburg.

342 **54** 22½ c. brown 3·50 40

55 Aruba Beach

1954. 3rd Caribbean Tourist Assn Meeting.

343 **55** 15 c. blue and buff 3·50 2·50

1954. Ratification of Statute of the Kingdom. As No. 809 of Netherlands.

344 **158** 7½ c. green 70 65

56 "Anglo" Flower

1955. Child Welfare.

345 **56** 1½ c. + 1 c. blue, yellow & turquoise 40 50
346 – 7½ c. + 5 c. red, yellow and violet 3·25 2·25
347 – 15 c. + 5 c. red, grn & olive 3·25 2·50
348 – 22½ c. + 7½ c. red, yellow and blue 3·25 2·25
349 – 25 c. + 10 c. red, yellow and grey 3·25 2·50

FLOWERS: 7½ c. White Cayenne; 15 c. "French" flower; 22½ c. Cactus; 25 c. Red Cayenne.

57 Prince Bernhard and Queen Juliana

1955. Royal Visit.

350 **57** 7½ c. + 2½ c. red 20 20
351 22½ c. + 7½ c. blue 95 95

59 Oil Refinery

1955. 21st Meeting of Caribbean Commission.

352 – 15 c. blue, green & brown 2·50 2·00
353 **59** 25 c. blue, green & brown 4·00 2·50

DESIGN (rectangle, 36×25 mm): 15 c. Aruba Beach.

60 St. Anne Bay

61 Lord Baden-Powell

1956. 10th Anniv of Caribbean Commission.

354 **60** 15 c. blue, red and black 30 25

1957. 50th Anniv of Boy Scout Movement.

355 **61** 6 c. + 1½ c. yellow 50 50
356 7½ c. + 2½ c. green 50 50
357 15 c. + 5 c. red 50 50

62 "Dawn of Health"

1957. 1st Caribbean Mental Health Congress, Aruba.

358 **62** 15 c. black and yellow 30 30

63 Saba

1957. Tourist Publicity. Multicoloured.

359 7½ c. Type **63** 35 35
360 15 c. St. Maarten 35 35
361 25 c. St. Eustatius 35 35

64 Footballer

65 Curacao Intercontinental Hotel

1957. 8th Central American and Caribbean Football Championships.
362 **64** 6 c. + 2½ c. orange 50 70
363 – 7½ c. + 5 c. red . . . . 1·00 1·10
364 – 15 c. + 5 c. green . . . . 1·10 1·10
365 – 22½ c. + 7½ c. blue . . . . 1·10 80
DESIGNS—HORIZ: 7½ c. Caribbean map. VERT: 15 c. Goalkeeper saving ball; 22½ c. Footballers with ball.

1957. Opening of Curacao Inter-continental Hotel.
366 **65** 15 c. blue 30 25

66 Map of Curacao 67 American Kestrel

1957. International Geophysical Year.
367 **66** 15 c. deep blue and blue . . 80 65

1958. Child Welfare. Bird design inscr "VOOR HET KIND". Multicoloured.
368 2½ c. + 1 c. Type **67** 30 25
369 7½ c. + 1½ c. Yellow oriole . . 85 65
370 15 c. + 2½ c. Scaly-breasted ground doves . . . . 1·10 80
371 22½ c. + 2½ c. Brown-throated conure . . . . 1·25 70

68 Greater Flamingoes (Bonaire)

1958. Size 33½ × 22 mm.
372 **68** 6 c. pink and green . . . 7·50 10
373 A 7½ c. yellow and brown . . . 10 10
374 8 c. yellow and blue . . . 10 15
375 B 10 c. yellow and grey . . . 10 10
376 C 12 c. grey and green . . . 15 20
377 D 15 c. blue and green . . . 15 10
377a 15 c. lilac and green . . . 15 10
378 E 20 c. grey and red 20 10
379 A 25 c. green and blue . . . 25 10
380 D 30 c. green and brown . . 30 10
381 E 35 c. pink and grey . . . 35 20
382 C 40 c. green and mauve . . . 40 10
383 B 45 c. blue and violet . . . 50 20
384 **68** 50 c. pink and brown . . . 50 10
385 E 55 c. green and red . . . 65 25
386 **68** 65 c. pink and green . . . 65 30
387 D 70 c. orange and purple . . 70 45
388 **68** 75 c. pink and violet . . . 80 45
389 B 85 c. green and brown . . . 85 60
390 E 90 c. orange and blue . . . 85 70
391 C 95 c. yellow and orange . . 90 70
392 D 1 g. grey and red . . . . 1·00 15
393 A 1½ g. brown and violet . . . 1·40 20
394 C 2½ g. yellow and blue . . . 2·50 30
395 B 5 g. mauve and brown . . . 4·75 85
396 **68** 10 g. pink and blue . . . 8·50 4·00
DESIGNS: A. Dutch Colonial houses (Curacao); B. Mountain and palms (Saba); C. Town Hall (St. Maarten); D. Church tower (Aruba); E. Memorial obelisk (St. Eustatius).
For larger versions of some values see Nos. 653/6.

69 70 Red Cross Flag and Antilles Map

1958. 50th Anniv of Netherlands Antilles Radio & Telegraph Administration.
397 **69** 7½ c. lake and blue 15 15
398 15 c. blue and red 30 30

1958. Neth. Antilles Red Cross Fund. Cross in red.
399 **70** 6 c. + 2 c. brown 30 30
400 7½ c. + 2½ c. green 45 45
401 15 c. + 5 c. yellow 45 45
402 22½ c. + 7½ c. blue 45 45

71 Aruba Caribbean Hotel

1959. Opening of Aruba Caribbean Hotel.
403 **71** 15 c. multicoloured 30 20

72 Zeeland

1959. Curacao Monuments Preservation Fund. Multicoloured.
404 6 c. + 1½ c. Type **72** 80 80
405 7½ c. + 2½ c. Saba Island . . 80 90
406 15 c. + 5 c. Molenplein (vert) 80 90
407 22½ c. + 7½ c. Scharloobrug . 80 90
408 25 c. + 7½ c. Brievengat . . . 80 90

73 Water-distillation Plant 74 Antilles Flag

1959. Inauguration of Aruba Water-distillation Plant.
409 **73** 20 c. light blue and blue . 35 35

1959. 5th Anniv of Ratification of Statute of the Kingdom.
410 **74** 10 c. red, blue & lt blue . 25 25
411 20 c. red, blue and yellow . 30 30
412 25 c. red, blue and green . 30 30

75 Fokker F.XVIII "De Snip" over Caribbean 76 Mgr. Niewindt

1959. 25th Anniv of K.L.M. Netherlands-Curacao Air Service. Each yellow, deep blue and blue.
413 10 c. Type **75** 40 30
414 20 c. Fokker F.XVIII "De Snip" over globe 40 30
415 25 c. Douglas DC-7C "Seven Seas" over Handelskade (bridge), Willemstad . . . 40 15
416 35 c. Douglas DC-8 at Aruba Airport 40 40

1960. Death Centenary of Mgr. M. J. Niewindt.
417 **76** 10 c. purple 35 35
418 20 c. violet 50 50
419 25 c. olive 35 35

77 Flag and Oil-worker 78 Frogman

1960. Labour Day.
420 **77** 20 c. multicoloured . . . 30 30

1960. Princess Wilhelmina Cancer Relief Fund. Inscr "KANKERBESTRIJDING".
421 **78** 10 c. + 2 c. blue . . . . 1·10 1·10
422 – 20 c. + 3 c. multicoloured 1·40 1·25
423 – 25 c. + 5 c. red, blue & blk 1·40 1·25
DESIGNS—HORIZ: 20 c., 25 c. Tropical fishes (different).

79 Child on Bed 80 Governor's Salute to the American Naval Brig "Andrew Doria" at St. Eustatius

1961. Child Welfare. Inscr "voor het kind".
424 6 c. + 2 c. black and green . 25 25
425 10 c. + 3 c. black and red . . 30 30
426 20 c. + 6 c. black and yellow . 30 30
427 25 c. + 8 c. black and orange . 35 35
DESIGNS: 6 c. Type **79**; 10 c. Girl with doll; 20 c. Boy with bucket; 25 c. Children in classroom.

1961. 185th Anniv of 1st Salute to the American Flag.
428 **80** 20 c. multicoloured 70 60

1962. Royal Silver Wedding. As T **187** of Netherlands.
429 10 c. orange 15 15
430 25 c. blue 30 20

81 Jaja (nursemaid) and Child 82 Knight and World Map

1962. Cultural Series.
431 – 6 c. brown and yellow . . . 15 15
432 – 10 c. multicoloured 20 15
433 – 20 c. multicoloured 30 30
434 **81** 25 c. brown, green & blk . 35 30
DESIGNS: 6 c. Corn-masher; 10 c. Benta player; 20 c. Petji kerchief.

1962. 5th International Candidates Chess Tournament, Curacao.
436 **82** 10 c. + 5 c. green 95 60
437 20 c. + 10 c. red 95 60
438 25 c. + 10 c. blue 95 60

1963. Freedom from Hunger. No. 378 surch **TEGEN DE HONGER** wheat sprig and **+10 c.**
439 20 c. + 10 c. grey and red . . 50 50

84 Family Group

1963. 4th Caribbean Mental Health Congress, Curacao.
440 **84** 20 c. buff and blue 30 30
441 – 25 c. red and blue 30 30
DESIGN: 25 c. Egyptian Cross emblem.

85 "Freedom" 86 Hotel Bonaire

1963. Centenary of Abolition of Slavery in Dutch West Indies.
442 **85** 25 c. brown and yellow . . 25 25

1963. Opening of Hotel Bonaire.
443 **86** 20 c. brown 20 20

87 Child and Flowers 88 Test-tube and Flask

1963. Child Welfare. Child Art. Multicoloured.
444 5 c. + 2 c. Type **87** 25 35
445 6 c. + 3 c. Children and flowers 25 35
446 10 c. + 5 c. Girl with ball . . 30 35
447 20 c. + 10 c. Men with flags . 30 35
448 25 c. + 12 c. Schoolboy . . . 30 35
Nos. 445/7 are horiz.

1963. 150th Anniv of Kingdom of the Netherlands. As No. 968 of Netherlands, but smaller, size (26 × 27 mm).
449 25 c. green, red and black . . 20 20

1963. Chemical Industry, Aruba.
450 **88** 20 c. red, light green and green 45 40

89 Winged Letter

1964. 35th Anniv of 1st U.S.–Curacao Flight. Multicoloured.
451 20 c. Type **89** 30 30
452 25 c. Route map, Sikorsky S-38 flying boat and Boeing 707 . 40 30

90 Trinitaria

1964. Child Welfare. Multicoloured.
453 6 c. + 3 c. Type **90** 20 20
454 10 c. + 5 c. Magdalena . . . 25 25
455 20 c. + 10 c. Yellow keiki . . 30 30
456 25 c. + 11 c. Bellisima . . . 30 30

91 Caribbean Map 92 "Six Islands"

1964. 5th Caribbean Council Assembly.
457 **91** 20 c. yellow, red & blue . . 30 20

1964. 10th Anniv of Statute for the Kingdom.
458 **92** 25 c. multicoloured 20 20

93 Princess Beatrix 94 I.T.U. Emblem and Symbols

1965. Visit of Princess Beatrix.
459 **93** 25 c. red 35 30

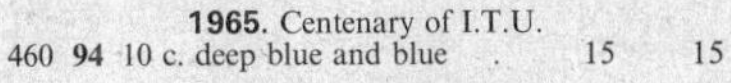

1965. Centenary of I.T.U.
460 **94** 10 c. deep blue and blue . 15 15

95 "Asperalla" (tanker) at Curacao

1965. 50th Anniv of Curacao's Oil Industry. Multicoloured.
461 10 c. Catalytic cracking plant (vert) 20 15
462 20 c. Type **95** 25 15
463 25 c. Super fractionating plant (vert) 25 20

96 Flag and Fruit Market, Curacao 97 Cup Sponges

1965.
464 **96** 1 c. blue, red & green . . . 10 10
465 – 2 c. blue, red and yellow . 10 10
466 – 3 c. blue, red and cobalt . 10 10
467 – 4 c. blue, red and orange . 25 10
468 – 5 c. blue, red and blue . . 10 10
469 – 6 c. blue, red and pink . . 10 10
DESIGNS (Flag and): 2 c. Divi-divi tree; 3 c. Lace; 4 c. Greater flamingoes; 5 c. Church; 6 c. Lobster. Each is inscr with a different place-name.

1965. Child Welfare. Marine Life. Multicoloured.
470 6 c. + 3 c. Type **97** 15 15
471 10 c. + 5 c. Cup sponges (diff) 20 20
472 20 c. + 10 c. Sea anemones on star coral 20 20
473 25 c. + 11 c. Basket sponge and "Brain" coral 30 35

98 Marine and Seascape 99 Budgerigars and Wedding Rings

1965. Tercentenary of Marine Corps.
474 **98** 25 c. multicoloured 20 15

1966. Intergovernmental Committee for European Migration (I.C.E.M.) Fund. As T **215** of Netherlands.
475 35 c. + 15 c. bistre & brown . 20 25

1966. Marriage of Crown Princess Beatrix and Herr Claus von Amsberg.
476 **99** 25 c. multicoloured 40 35

100 Admiral de Ruyter and Map

1966. 300th Anniv of Admiral de Ruyter's Visit to St. Eustatius.

477 **100** 25 c. ochre, violet & blue . 20 15

101 "Grammar" 102 Cooking

1966. 25 years of Secondary Education.

478 **101** 6 c. black, blue & yellow 10 10
479 – 10 c. black, red & green . 10 10
480 – 20 c. black, blue & yellow 15 15
481 – 25 c. black, red and green 20 20

DESIGNS: The "Free Arts", figures representing: 10 c. "Rhetoric" and "Dialect"; 20 c. "Arithmetic" and "Geometry"; 25 c. "Astronomy" and "Music".

1966. Child Welfare. Multicoloured.

482 6 c. + 3 c. Type **102** 10 10
483 10 c. + 5 c. Nursing 10 10
484 20 c. + 10 c. Metal-work fitting 20 20
485 25 c. + 11 c. Ironing 25 25

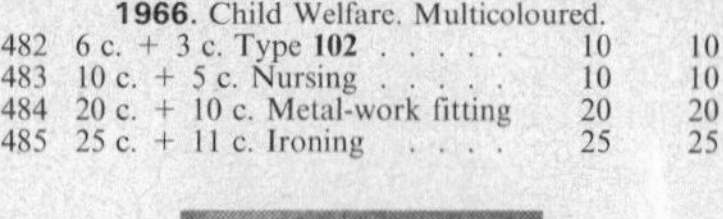

103 "Gelderland" (cruiser)

1967. 60th Anniv of Royal Netherlands Navy League.

486 **103** 6 c. bronze and green . . 10 10
487 – 10 c. ochre and yellow . . 15 15
488 – 20 c. brown and sepia . . 20 15
489 – 25 c. blue and indigo . . 20 20

SHIPS: 10 c. "Pioneer" (schooner); 20 c. "Oscilla" (tanker); 25 c. "Santa Rosa" (liner).

104 M. C. Piar 105 "Heads in Hands"

1967. 150th Death Anniv of Manuel Piar (patriot).

490 **104** 20 c. brown and red . . . 15 15

1967. Cultural and Social Relief Funds.

491 **105** 6 c. + 3 c. black & blue . 10 10
492 10 c. + 5 c. black & mve . 15 15
493 20 c. + 10 c. purple . . . 15 15
494 25 c. + 11 c. blue 15 20

106 "The Turtle and the Monkey" 107 Olympic Flame and Rings

1967. Child Welfare. "Nanzi" Fairy Tales. Mult.

495 6 c. + 3 c. "Princess Long Nose" (vert) 15 15
496 10 c. + 5 c. Type **106** 20 15
497 20 c. + 10 c. "Nanzi (spider) and the Tiger" 25 15
498 25 c. + 11 c. "Shon Arey's Balloon" (vert) 30 20

1968. Olympic Games, Mexico. Multicoloured.

499 10 c. Type **107** 20 20
500 20 c. "Throwing the discus" (statue) 20 20
501 25 c. Stadium and doves . . . 20 20

108 "Dance of the Ribbons"

1968. Cultural and Social Relief Funds.

502 **108** 10 c. + 5 c. multicoloured 15 15
503 15 c. + 5 c. multicoloured 15 15
504 20 c. + 10 c. multicoloured 15 20
505 25 c. + 10 c. multicoloured 20 25

109 Boy with Goat

1968. Child Welfare Fund. Multicoloured.

506 6 c. + 3 c. Type **109** 15 15
507 10 c. + 5 c. Girl with dog . . 15 15
508 20 c. + 10 c. Boy with cat . . 25 25
509 25 c. + 11 c. Girl with duck . 35 35

110 Fokker Friendship 500 111 Radio Pylon, "Waves" and Map

1968. Dutch Antillean Airlines.

510 **110** 10 c. blue, black & yellow 25 20
511 – 20 c. blue, black & brown 25 20
512 – 25 c. blue, black & pink . 25 20

DESIGNS: 20 c. Douglas DC-9; 25 c. Fokker Friendship 500 in flight and Douglas DC-9 on ground.

1969. Opening of Broadcast Relay Station, Bonaire.

513 **111** 25 c. green, dp blue & blue 20 20

112 "Code of Laws" 113 "Carnival"

1969. Centenary of Netherlands Antilles Court of Justice.

514 **112** 20 c. green, gold & lt grn 20 20
515 – 25 c. multicoloured . . . 20 20

DESIGN: 25 c. "Scales of Justice".

1969. Cultural and Social Relief Funds. Antilles' Festivals. Multicoloured.

516 10 c. + 5 c. Type **113** 30 30
517 15 c. + 5 c. "Harvest Festival" 30 30
518 20 c. + 10 c. "San Juan Day" 40 40
519 25 c. + 10 c. "New Years' Day" 40 40

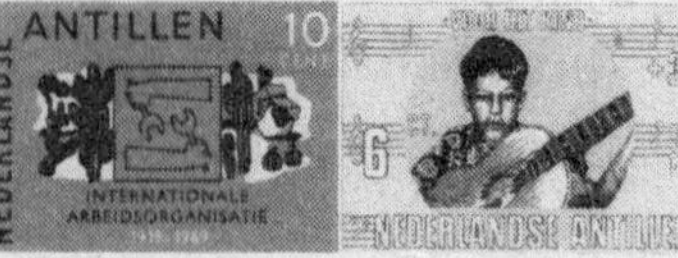

114 I.L.O. Emblem, "Koenoekoe" House and Cacti 115 Boy playing Guitar

1969. 50th Anniv of Int. Labour Organization.

520 **114** 10 c. black and blue . . . 15 15
521 25 c. black and red 15 15

1969. Child Welfare.

522 **115** 6 c. + 3 c. violet & orge 25 25
523 – 10 c. + 5 c. grn & yell . 35 35
524 – 20 c. + 10 c. red and blue 40 40
525 – 25 c. + 11 c. brn & pink 50 50

DESIGNS: 10 c. Girl playing recorder; 20 c. Boy playing "marimula"; 25 c. Girl playing piano.

1969. 15th Anniv of Statute of the Kingdom. As T **240** of the Netherlands, but inscr "NEDERLANDSE ANTILLEN".

526 25 c. multicoloured 25 20

117 Radio Station, Bonaire 118 St. Anna Church, Otrabanda, Curacao

1970. 5th Anniv of Trans-World Religious Radio Station, Bonaire. Multicoloured.

527 10 c. Type **117** 15 15
528 15 c. Trans-World Radio emblem 15 15

1970. Churches of the Netherlands Antilles. Mult.

529 10 c. Type **118** 20 20
530 20 c. "Mikve Israel-Emanuel" Synagogue, Punda, Curacao (horiz) 20 20
531 25 c. Pulpit Fort Church Curacao 20 20

119 "The Press" 120 Mother and Child

1970. Cultural and Social Relief Funds. "Mass-media". Multicoloured.

532 10 c. + 5 c. Type **119** 40 40
533 15 c. + 5 c. "Films" 40 40
534 20 c. + 10 c. "Radio" 45 45
535 25 c. + 10 c. "Television" . . 45 45

1970. Child Welfare. Multicoloured.

536 6 c. + 3 c. Type **120** 45 45
537 10 c. + 5 c. Child with piggy-bank 45 45
538 20 c. + 10 c. Children's Judo . 45 45
539 25 c. + 11 c. "Pick-a-back" . 45 45

121 St. Theresia's Church, St. Nicolaas, Aruba 122 Lions Emblem

1971. 40th Anniv of St. Theresia Parish, Aruba.

540 **121** 20 c. multicoloured 20 20

1971. 25th Anniv of Curacao Lions Club.

541 **122** 25 c. multicoloured 35 25

123 Charcoal Stove 125 Admiral Brion

1971. Cultural and Social Relief Funds. Household Utensils. Multicoloured.

542 10 c. + 5 c. Type **123** 45 45
543 15 c. + 5 c. Earthenware water vessel 45 45
544 20 c. + 10 c. Baking oven . . 45 45
545 25 c. + 10 c. Kitchen implements 45 45

1971. Prince Bernhard's 60th Birthday. Design as No. 1135 of Netherlands.

546 45 c. multicoloured 45 40

1971. 150th Death Anniv of Admiral Pedro Luis Brion.

547 **125** 40 c. multicoloured 30 30

126 Bottle Doll 127 Queen Emma Bridge, Curacao

1971. Child Welfare. Home-made Toys. Mult.

548 15 c. + 5 c. Type **126** 60 60
549 20 c. + 10 c. Simple cart . . . 65 65
550 30 c. + 15 c. Spinning-tops . . 65 65

1971. Views of the Islands. Multicoloured.

551 1 c. Type **127** 10 10
552 2 c. The Bottom, Saba 10 10
553 3 c. Greater flamingoes, Bonaire 30 10
554 4 c. Distillation plant, Aruba . 10 10
555 5 c. Fort Amsterdam, St. Maarten 10 10
556 6 c. Fort Oranje, St. Eustatius 10 10

128 Ship in Dock 129 Steel Band

1972. Inauguration of New Dry Dock Complex, Willemstad, Curacao.

557 **128** 30 c. multicoloured . . . 35 30

1972. Cultural and Social Relief Funds. Folklore. Multicoloured.

558 15 c. + 5 c. Type **129** 75 75
559 20 c. + 10 c. "Seu" festival . 75 75
560 30 c. + 15 c. "Tambu" dance 75 75

130 J. E. Irausquin 131 Dr. M. F. da Costa Gomez

1972. 10th Death Anniv of Juan Enrique Irausquin (Antilles statesman).

561 **130** 30 c. red 30 25

1972. 65th Birth Anniv of Moises F. da Costa Gomez (statesman).

562 **131** 30 c. black and green . . 30 25

132 Child playing with Earth 133 Pedestrian Crossing

1972. Child Welfare. Multicoloured.

563 15 c. + 5 c. Type **132** 85 85
564 20 c. + 10 c. Child playing in water 85 85
565 30 c. + 15 c. Child throwing ball into the air 85 85

1973. Cultural and Social Relief Funds. Road Safety.

566 **133** 12 c. + 6 c. multicoloured 90 80
567 – 15 c. + 7 c. grn, orge & red 90 80
568 – 40 c. + 20 c. multicoloured 90 80

DESIGNS: 15 c. Road-crossing patrol; 40 c. Traffic lights.

134 William III (portrait from stamp of 1873) 135 Map of Aruba, Curacao and Bonaire

1973. Stamp Centenary.

569 **134** 15 c. lilac, mauve & gold 30 25
570 – 20 c. multicoloured . . . 35 30
571 – 30 c. multicoloured . . . 35 30

DESIGNS: 20 c. Antilles postman; 30 c. Postal Service emblem.

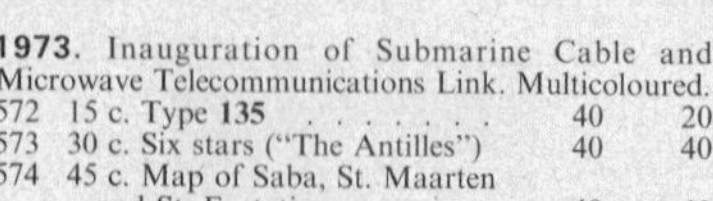

1973. Inauguration of Submarine Cable and Microwave Telecommunications Link. Multicoloured.

572 15 c. Type **135** 40 20
573 30 c. Six stars ("The Antilles") 40 40
574 45 c. Map of Saba, St. Maarten and St. Eustatius 40 40

136 Queen Juliana 137 Jan Eman

1973. Silver Jubilee of Queen Juliana's Reign.

576 **136** 15 c. multicoloured . . . 45 45

1973. 16th Death Anniv of Jan Eman (Aruba statesman).
577 **137** 30 c. black and green . . 30 25

138 "1948–1973" **139** L. B. Scott

1973. Child Welfare Fund. 25th Anniv of 1st Child Welfare Stamps.
578 **138** 15 c. + 5 c. light green, green and blue 85 70
579 – 20 c. + 10 c. brown, green and blue 85 75
580 – 30 c. + 15 c. violet, blue and light blue . . . . . . 1·25 90
DESIGNS: No. 579, Three Children; No. 580, Mother and child.

1974. 8th Death Anniv of Lionel B. Scott (St. Maarten statesman).
582 **139** 30 c. multicoloured . . . 30 30

140 Family Meal **141** Girl combing Hair

1974. Family Planning Campaign. Multicoloured.
583 6 c. Type **140** 10 103
584 12 c. Family at home 25 20
585 15 c. Family in garden 30 20

1974. Cultural and Social Relief Funds. "The Younger Generation". Multicoloured.
586 12 c. + 6 c. Type **141** . . . . 1·00 1·00
587 15 c. + 7 c. "Pop dancers" . 1·00 1·00
588 40 c. + 20 c. Group drummer 1·00 1·00

142 Desulphurisation Plant

1974. 50th Anniv of Lago Oil Co., Aruba. Multicoloured.
589 15 c. Type **142** 45 30
590 30 c. Fractionating towers . . 45 30
591 45 c. Lago refinery at night . . 45 35

143 U.P.U. Emblem **144** "A Carpenter outranks a King"

1974. Centenary of Universal Postal Union.
592 **143** 15 c. gold, green & blk . . 40 35
593 30 c. gold, blue & black . 40 40

1974. Child Welfare. Children's Songs. Mult.
594 15 c. + 5 c. Type **144** 70 70
595 20 c. + 10 c. Footprints ("Let's Do a Ring-dance") 70 70
596 30 c. + 15 c. "Moon and Sun" 70 70

145 Queen Emma Bridge **146** Ornamental Ventilation Grid

1975. Antillean Bridges. Multicoloured.
597 20 c. Type **145** 45 40
598 30 c. Queen Juliana Bridge . . 50 40
599 40 c. Queen Wilhelmina Bridge 65 50

1975. Cultural and Social Welfare Funds.
600 **146** 12 c. + 6 c. multicoloured 65 65
601 – 15 c. + 7 c. brown & stone 65 65
602 – 40 c. + 20 c. multicoloured 65 65
DESIGNS: 15 c. Knight accompanied by buglers (tombstone detail); 40 c. Foundation stone.

147 Sodium Chloride Molecules

1975. Bonaire Salt Industry. Multicoloured.
603 15 c. Type **147** 55 35
604 20 c. Salt incrustation and blocks 55 45
605 40 c. Map of salt area (vert) . 65 45

148 Fokker F.XVIII "De Snip" and Old Control Tower

1975. 40th Anniv of Aruba Airport. Mult.
606 15 c. Type **148** 45 25
607 30 c. Douglas DC-9-30 and modern control tower . . . 45 30
608 40 c. Tail of Boeing 727-200 and "Princess Beatrix" Airport buildings 45 45

149 I.W.Y. Emblem

1975. International Women's Year. Multicoloured.
609 6 c. Type **149** 20 15
610 12 c. "Social Development" . 35 20
611 20 c. "Equality of Sexes" . . 45 30

150 Children making Windmill

1975. Child Welfare. Multicoloured.
612 15 c. + 5 c. Type **150** 70 65
613 20 c. + 10 c. Child modelling clay 70 65
614 30 c. + 15 c. Children drawing pictures 70 65

151 Beach, Aruba **152** J. A. Abraham (statesman)

1976. Tourism. Multicoloured.
615 40 c. Type **151** 60 50
616 40 c. Fish Kiosk, Bonaire . . 60 50
617 40 c. "Table Mountain", Curacao 60 50

1976. Abraham Commemoration.
618 **152** 30 c. purple on brown . . 40 35

153 Dyke Produce **154** Arm holding Child

1976. Agriculture, Animal Husbandry and Fisheries. Multicoloured.
619 15 c. Type **153** 35 25
620 35 c. Cattle 50 40
621 45 c. Fishes 50 50

1976. Child Welfare. "Carrying the Child".
622 **154** 20 c. + 10 c. multicoloured 60 60
623 – 25 c. + 12 c. multicoloured 60 60
624 – 40 c. + 18 c. multicoloured 60 60
DESIGNS—HORIZ: 25 c. VERT: 40 c. Both similar to Type **154** showing arm holding child.

INDEX
Countries can be quickly located by referring to the index at the end of this volume.

155 "Andrew Doria" (naval brig) receiving Salute **156** Carnival ostume

1976. Bicentenary of American Revolution. Multicoloured.
625 25 c. Flags and plaque, Fort Oranje 70 45
626 40 c. Type **155** 70 45
627 55 c. Johannes de Graaff, Governor of St. Eustatius . 70 70

1977. Carnival.
628 – 25 c. multicoloured 45 35
629 **156** 35 c. multicoloured 45 35
630 – 40 c. multicoloured 45 35
DESIGNS: 25 c., 40 c. Women in Carnival costumes.

157 Tortoise (Bonaire) **158** "Ace" Playing Card

1977. Rock Paintings. Multicoloured.
631 25 c. Bird (Aruba) 60 35
632 35 c. Abstract (Curacao) . . . 60 45
633 40 c. Type **157** 75 45

1977. Sixth Central American and Caribbean Bridge Championships. Multicoloured.
634 **158** 20 c. + 10 c. red & black . 50 35
635 – 25 c. + 12 c. multicoloured 50 45
636 – 40 c. + 18 c. multicoloured 65 60
DESIGNS—VERT: 25 c. "King" playing card. HORIZ: 40 c. Bridge hand.

159 "Cordia sebestena" **160** Bells outside Main Store

1977. Flowers. Multicoloured.
639 25 c. Type **159** 40 35
640 40 c. "Albizzia lebbeck" (vert) 50 45
641 55 c. "Tamarindus indica" . . 60 55

1977. 50th Anniv of Spritzer and Fuhrmann (jewellers). Multicoloured.
642 20 c. Type **160** 40 30
643 40 c. Globe basking in sun . . 50 40
644 55 c. Antillean flag and diamond ring 60 60

161 Children with Toy Animal

1977. Child Welfare. Multicoloured.
645 15 c. + 15 c. Type **161** 35 25
646 20 c. + 10 c. Children with toy rabbit 40 40
647 25 c. + 12 c. Children with toy cat 50 45
648 40 c. + 18 c. Children with toy beetle 55 55

162 "The Unspoiled Queen" (Saba)

1977. Tourism. Multicoloured.
650 25 c. Type **162** 15 15
651 35 c. "The Golden Rock" (St. Eustatius) 20 20
652 40 c. "The Friendly Island" (St. Maarten) 25 25

1977. As Nos. 378, 381/2 and 385, but larger, (39 × 22 mm).
653 E 20 c. grey and red . . . . 1·00 1·00
654 35 c. pink and brown . . . 2·50 3·00
655 C 40 c. green and mauve . . 1·25 1·25
656 E 55 c. green and red . . . 1·50 1·50

163 19th-century Chest **164** Water-skiing

1978. 150th Anniv of Netherlands Antilles' Bank. Multicoloured.
657 **163** 15 c. blue & light blue . . 10 10
658 – 20 c. orange and gold . . 10 10
659 – 40 c. green & deep green 20 20
DESIGNS: 20 c. Bank emblem; 40 c. Strong-room door.

1978. Sports Funds. Multicoloured.
660 15 c. + 5 c. Type **164** 10 10
661 20 c. + 10 c. Yachting . . . 15 15
662 25 c. + 12 c. Football 20 20
663 40 c. + 18 c. Baseball 35 35

165 "Erythrina velutina" **166** "Polythysana rubrescens"

1978. Flora of Netherlands Antilles. Multicoloured.
664 15 c. "Delconix regia" 20 15
665 25 c. Type **165** 25 25
666 50 c. "Gualacum officinale" (horiz) 35 30
667 55 c. "Gilricidia sepium" (horiz) 45 45

1978. Butterflies. Multicoloured.
668 15 c. Type **166** 25 15
669 25 c. "Caligo sp." 40 20
670 35 c. "Prepona praeneste" . . 55 35
671 40 c. "Morpho sp." 70 50

167 "Conserve Energy" (English) **168** Red Cross

1978. Energy Conservation.
672 **167** 15 c. orange and black . . 15 15
673 – 20 c. green and black . . 20 20
674 – 40 c. red and black . . 40 40
DESIGNS: As No. 672 but text in Dutch (20 c.) or in Papiamento (40 c.).

1978. 150th Birth Anniv of Henri Dunant (founder of Red Cross).
675 **168** 55 c. + 25 c. red & blue . 30 30

169 Curacao from Sea, and Punched Tape **170** Boy Rollerskating

1978. 70th Anniv of Antilles Telecommunications Corporation (Landsradio). Multicoloured.
677 20 c. Type **169** 25 25
678 40 c. Ship's bridge, punched tape and radio mast 35 35
679 55 c. Satellite and aerial (vert) 50 50

1978. Child Welfare. Multicoloured.
680 15 c. + 5 c. Type **170** 40 35
681 20 c. + 10 c. Boy and girl flying kite 50 40
682 25 c. + 12 c. Boy and girl playing marbles 50 45
683 40 c. + 18 c. Girl riding bicycle 60 55

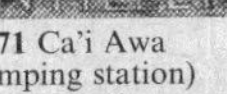

171 Ca'i Awa (pumping station) **172** Aruba Coat of Arms (float)

1978. 80th Death Anniv of Leonard Burlington Smith (entrepreneur and U.S. Consul).

685 **171** 25 c. multicoloured . . . 20 15
686 – 35 c. black, greenish yellow and yellow . . . 25 20
687 – 40 c. multicoloured . . . 35 30

DESIGNS—VERT: 35 c. Leonard Burlington Smith. HORIZ: 40 c. Opening ceremony of Queen Emma Bridge, 1888.

1979. 25th Aruba Carnival. Multicoloured.

688 40 c. + 10 c. Float representing heraldic fantasy . . . 40 35
689 75 c. + 20 c. Type **172** . . . 65 65

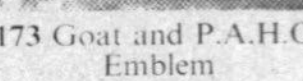

173 Goat and P.A.H.O. Emblem **174** Yacht and Sun

1979. 12th Inter-American Ministerial Meeting on Foot and Mouth Disease and Zoonosis Control, Curacao. Multicoloured.

690 50 c. Type **173** . . . 30 30
691 75 c. Horse and conference emblem . . . 45 45
692 150 c. Cows, flag and Pan-American Health Organization (P.A.H.O.) and W.H.O. emblems . . . 1·00 1·00

1979. 12th International Sailing Regatta, Bonaire. Multicoloured.

694 15 c. + 5 c. Type **174** . . . 15 15
695 35 c. + 25 c. Yachts . . . 35 35
696 40 c. + 15 c. Yacht and globe (horiz) . . . 50 50
697 55 c. + 25 c. Yacht, sun and flamingo . . . 60 60

175 Corps Members **176** "Melochia tomentosa"

1979. 50th Anniv of Curacao Volunteer Corps.

699 **175** 15 c. + 10 c. blue, red and ultramarine . . . 25 20
700 – 40 c. + 20 c. blue, violet and gold . . . 45 40
701 – 1 g. multicoloured . . . 70 65

DESIGNS: 40 c. Sentry in battle dress and emblem; 1 g. Corps emblem, flag and soldier in ceremonial uniform.

1979. Flowers. Multicoloured.

702 25 c. "Casearia tremula" . . . 20 15
703 40 c. "Cordia cylindrostachya" . . . 35 30
704 1 g. 50 Type **176** . . . 1·00 1·00

177 Girls reading Book **178** Dove and Netherlands Flag

1979. International Year of the Child.

705 **177** 20 c. + 10 c. multicoloured . . . 25 25
706 – 25 c. + 12 c. multicoloured . . . 35 30
707 – 35 c. + 15 c. violet, brown and black . . . 50 45
708 – 50 c. + 20 c. multicoloured . . . 60 55

DESIGNS: 25 c. Toddler and cat; 35 c. Girls carrying basket; 50 c. Boy and girl dressing-up.

1979. 25th Anniv of Statute of the Kingdom. Multicoloured.

710 65 c. Type **178** . . . 50 40
711 1 g. 50 Dove and Netherlands Antilles flag . . . 80 90

179 Map of Aruba and Foundation Emblem

1979. 30th Anniv of Aruba Cultural Centre Foundation. Multicoloured.

712 95 c. Type **179** . . . 60 60
713 1 g. Foundation headquarters . . . 70 70

180 Brass Chandelier

1980. 210th Anniv of Fort Church, Curacao.

714 **180** 20 c. + 10 c. yellow, black and brown . . . 20 20
715 – 50 c. + 25 c. mult . . . 50 50
716 – 100 c. multicoloured . . . 65 65

DESIGNS: 50 c. Pipe organ; 100 c. Cupola tower, 1910.

181 Rotary Emblem and Cogwheel

1980. 75th Anniv of Rotary International. Multicoloured.

717 45 c. Rotary emblem . . . 35 35
718 50 c. Globe and cogwheels . . . 40 40
719 85 c. Type **181** . . . 65 65

182 Savings Box

1980. 75th Anniv of Post Office Savings Bank. Multicoloured.

721 25 c. Type **182** . . . 20 20
722 150 c. Savings box (different) . . . 1·00 1·00

183 Queen Juliana Accession Stamp

1980. Accession of Queen Beatrix.

723 **183** 25 c. red, green and gold . . . 20 20
724 – 60 c. green, red and gold . . . 40 40

DESIGN: 60 c. 1965 Royal Visit stamp.

184 Sir Rowland Hill **185** Volleyball

1980. "London 1980" International Stamp Exhibition.

725 **184** 45 c. black and green . . . 35 35
726 – 60 c. black and red . . . 40 40
727 – 1 g. red, black and blue . . . 70 70

DESIGNS: 60 c. "London 1980" logo; 1 g. Airmail label.

1980. Sports Funds.

729 – 25 c. + 10 c. red & black . . . 25 25
730 – 40 c. + 15 c. yellow & blk . . . 35 35
731 **185** 45 c. + 20 c. light green, green and black . . . 50 50
732 – 60 c. + 25 c. pink, orange and black . . . 75 75

DESIGNS: 25 c. Gymnastics (beam exercise); 30 c. Gymnastics (horse vaulting); 60 c. Basketball.

186 White-fronted Dove

1980. Birds. Multicoloured.

734 25 c. Type **186** . . . 25 20
735 60 c. Tropical mockingbird . . . 65 45
736 85 c. Bananaquit . . . 80 70

187 "St. Maarten Landscape" **188** Rudolf Theodorus Palm

1980. Child Welfare. Children's Drawings. Multicoloured.

737 25 c. + 10 c. Type **187** . . . 30 30
738 30 c. + 15 c. "Bonaire House" . . . 35 40
739 40 c. + 20 c. "Child writing on Board" . . . 45 50
740 60 c. + 25 c. "Dancing Couple" (vert) . . . 60 65

1981. Birth Centenary (1980) of Rudolf Theodorus Palm (musician).

742 **188** 60 c. brown and yellow . . . 50 45
743 – 1 g. buff and blue . . . 1·00 85

DESIGN: 1 g. Musical score and hands playing piano.

189 Map of Aruba and TEAM Emblem **190** Boy in Wheelchair

1981. 50th Anniv of Evangelical Alliance Mission (TEAM) in Antilles. Multicoloured.

744 30 c. Type **189** . . . 25 20
745 50 c. Map of Curacao and emblem . . . 50 40
746 1 g. Map of Bonaire and emblem . . . 1·00 85

1981. International Year of Disabled Persons. Multicoloured.

747 25 c. + 10 c. Blind woman . . . 35 35
748 30 c. + 15 c. Type **190** . . . 45 45
749 45 c. + 20 c. Child in walking frame . . . 70 70
750 60 c. + 25 c. Deaf girl . . . 80 80

191 Tennis **192** Gateway

1981. Sports Funds. Multicoloured.

751 30 c. + 15 c. Type **191** . . . 50 50
752 50 c. + 20 c. Swimming . . . 70 70
753 70 c. + 25 c. Boxing . . . 90 90

1981. 125th Anniv of St. Elisabeth's Hospital. Multicoloured.

755 60 c. Type **192** . . . 60 50
756 1 g. 50 St. Elisabeth's Hospital . . . 1·40 1·40

193 Marinus van der Maarel (promoter) **194** Mother and Child

1981. 50th Anniv (1980) of Antillean Boy Scouts Association. Multicoloured.

757 45 c. + 20 c. Wolf Cub and leader . . . 75 75
758 70 c. + 25 c. Type **193** . . . 1·10 1·10
759 1 g. + 50 c. Headquarters, Ronde Klip . . . 1·60 1·60

1981. Child Welfare. Multicoloured.

761 35 c. + 15 c. Type **194** . . . 45 50
762 45 c. + 20 c. Boy and girl . . . 55 60
763 55 c. + 25 c. Child with cat . . . 70 75
764 85 c. + 40 c. Girl with teddy bear . . . 1·10 1·25

195 "Jatropha gossypifolia" **196** Pilot Gig approaching Ship

1981. Flowers. Multicoloured.

766 45 c. "Cordia globosa" . . . 35 35
767 70 c. Type **195** . . . 70 70
768 100 c. "Croton flavens" . . . 85 85

1982. Centenary of Pilotage Service. Mult.

769 70 c. Type **196** . . . 80 80
770 85 c. Modern liner and map of Antilles . . . 1·00 1·00
771 1 g. Pilot boarding ship . . . 1·10 1·10

197 Fencing **198** Holy Ark

1982. Sports Funds.

772 **197** 35 c. + 15 c. mauve and violet . . . 65 50
773 – 45 c. + 20 c. blue and deep blue . . . 85 70
774 – 70 c. + 35 c. multicoloured . . . 1·25 95
775 – 85 c. + 40 c. brown and deep brown . . . 1·40 1·10

DESIGNS: 45 c. Judo; 70 c. Football; 85 c. Cycling.

1982. 250th Anniv of Dedication of Mikve Israel-Emanuel Synagogue, Curacao. Mult.

777 75 c. Type **198** . . . 1·25 90
778 85 c. Synagogue facade . . . 1·40 90
779 150 c. Tebah (raised platform) . . . 1·75 1·40

199 Peter Stuyvesant (Governor) and Flags of Netherlands, Netherlands Antilles and United States **200** Airport Control Tower

1982. Bicentenary of Netherlands–United States Diplomatic Relations.

780 **199** 75 c. multicoloured . . . 1·00 80

1982. International Federation of Air Traffic Controllers.

782 – 35 c. black, ultramarine and blue . . . 50 35
783 **200** 75 c. black, green and light green . . . 1·00 75
784 – 150 c. black, orange and salmon . . . 1·50 1·25

DESIGNS: 35 c. Radar plot trace; 150 c. Radar aerials.

201 Mail Bag **202** Brown Chromis

1982. "Philexfrance 82" International Stamp Exhibition, Paris. Multicoloured.

785 45 c. Exhibition emblem . . . 50 40
786 85 c. Type **201** . . . 95 75
787 150 c. Netherlands Antilles and French flags . . . 1·40 1·25

1982. Fishes. Multicoloured.

789 35 c. Type **202** . . . 70 40
790 75 c. Spotted trunkfish . . . 1·25 75
791 85 c. Blue tang . . . 1·40 1·00
792 100 c. French angelfish . . . 1·50 1·10

203 Girl playing Accordion

1982. Child Welfare. Multicoloured.

793 35 c. + 15 c. Type **203** . . . 80 60
794 75 c. + 35 c. Boy playing guitar . . . 1·40 1·25
795 85 c. + 40 c. Boy playing violin . . . 1·75 1·40

204 Saba House

1982. Cultural and Social Relief Funds. Local Houses. Multicoloured.

797 35 c. + 15 c. Type **204** . . . 70 45
798 75 c. + 35 c. Aruba House . . . 1·25 95
799 85 c. + 40 c. Curacao House . . . 1·40 1·25

205 High Jumping

1983. Sports Funds. Multicoloured.

801 35 c. + 15 c. Type **205** . . . 65 50
802 45 c. + 20 c. Weightlifting . . 1·00 85
803 85 c. + 40 c. Wind-surfing . . 1·50 1·40

206 Natural Bridge, Aruba **207** W.C.Y. Emblem and Means of Communication

1983. Tourism. Multicoloured.

804 35 c. Type **206** 60 50
805 45 c. Lac Bay, Bonaire 75 55
806 100 c. Willemstad, Curacao . . 1·25 1·10

1983. World Communications Year.

807 **207** 1 g. multicoloured . . . . . 1·25 1·10

208 "Curacao" (paddle-steamer) and Post Office Building **209** Mango ("Mangifera indica")

1983. "Brasiliana 83" International Stamp Exhibition, Rio de Janeiro. Multicoloured.

809 45 c. Type **208** 70 60
810 55 c. Brazil flag, exhibition emblem and Netherlands Antilles flag and postal service emblem 75 65
811 100 c. Governor's Palace, Netherlands Antilles, and Sugarloaf Mountain, Rio de Janeiro . . . . 1·25 1·00

1983. Flowers. Multicoloured.

813 45 c. Type **209** 80 65
814 55 c. "Malpighia punicifolia" . 95 75
815 100 c. "Citrus aurantifolia" . 1·50 1·25

210 Boy and Lizard

1983. Child Welfare. Multicoloured.

816 45 c. + 20 c. Type **210** . . . . 1·00 85
817 55 c. + 25 c. Girl watching ants 1·25 1·10
818 100 c. + 50 c. Girl feeding donkey . . . . 2·00 1·75

211 Aruba Water Jar **212** Saba

1983. Cultural and Social Relief Funds. Pre-Columbian Pottery.

820 **211** 45 c. + 20 c. light blue, blue and black . . . . . . 1·10 1·00
821 – 55 c. + 25 c. pink, red and black . . . . 1·25 1·10
822 – 85 c. + 40 c. stone, green and black . . . . 1·50 1·25
823 – 100 c. + 50 c. light brown, brown and black . . . 2·00 1·75

DESIGNS: 55 c. Aruba decorated bowl; 85 c. Curacao human figurine; 100 c. Fragment of Curacao female figurine.

1983. Local Government Buildings. Multicoloured.

824 20 c. Type **212** 20 20
825 25 c. St. Eustatius 25 25
826 30 c. St. Maarten 30 30
827 35 c. Aruba . . . . 1·75 35
828 45 c. Bonaire 45 45
829 55 c. Curacao 55 55
830 60 c. Type **212** 60 60
831 65 c. As No. 825 . . . . . . 65 65
832 70 c. Type **212** 75 75
833 75 c. As No. 826 . . . . . . 75 75
834 85 c. As No. 827 . . . . . . 3·00 1·10
835 85 c. As No. 828 . . . . . . 85 85
836 90 c. As No. 828 . . . . . . 90 90
837 95 c. As No. 829 . . . . . . 95 95
838 1 g. Type **212** . . . . 1·00 1·00
839 1 g. 50 As No. 825 . . . . . 1·40 1·40
841 2 g. 50 As No. 826 . . . . . 2·25 2·25
842 5 g. As No. 828 . . . . 4·25 4·25
843 10 g. As No. 829 . . . . . . 7·50 7·50
844 15 g. Type **212** . . . . 11·00 11·00

213 Note-taking, Type-setting and Front Page of "Amigoe"

1984. Centenary of "Amigoe de Curacao" (newspaper). Multicoloured.

845 45 c. Type **213** 65 55
846 55 c. Printing press and newspapers 75 65
847 85 c. Reading newspaper . . 1·25 1·10

214 W.I.A. and I.C.A.O. Emblems

1984. 40th Anniv of I.C.A.O.

848 **214** 25 c. multicoloured . . . 40 35
849 – 45 c. violet, blue & black 75 60
850 – 55 c. multicoloured . . . 85 70
851 – 100 c. multicoloured . . . 1·40 1·25

DESIGNS: 45 c. I.C.A.O. anniversary emblem; 55 c. A.L.M. and I.C.A.O. emblems; 100 c. Fokker F.XIII airplane "De Snip".

215 Fielder

1984. Sports Funds. 50th Anniv of Curacao Baseball Federation. Multicoloured.

852 25 c. + 10 c. Type **215** . . . 80 60
853 45 c. + 20 c. Batter . . . . 1·25 1·10
854 55 c. + 25 c. Pitcher . . . . 1·50 1·25
855 85 c. + 40 c. Running for base 1·75 1·50

216 Microphones and Radio

1984. Cultural and Social Relief Funds. Radio and Gramophone. Multicoloured.

857 45 c. + 20 c. Type **216** . . . 1·25 1·10
858 55 c. + 25 c. Gramophones and record . . . . 1·50 1·40
859 100 c. + 50 c. Gramophone with horn . . . . 1·90 1·75

217 Bonnet-maker

1984. Centenary of Curacao Chamber of Commerce and Industry. Multicoloured.

860 45 c. Type **217** . . . . 1·10 85
861 55 c. Chamber emblem . . . 1·10 90
862 1 g. "Southward" (liner) passing under bridge . . . . 1·50 1·25

No. 861 is an inverted triangle.

218 Black-faced Grassquit **219** Eleanor Roosevelt and Val-Kill, Hyde Park, New York

1984. Birds. Multicoloured.

863 45 c. Type **218** . . . . 1·10 75
864 55 c. Rufous-collared sparrow . 1·40 1·00
865 150 c. Blue-tailed emerald . . 2·25 1·75

1984. Birth Centenary of Eleanor Roosevelt.

866 **219** 45 c. multicoloured 70 65
867 – 85 c. black, gold & bis . . 1·00 1·00
868 – 100 c. black, yell & red . . 1·10 1·10

DESIGNS: 85 c. Portrait in oval frame; 100 c. Eleanor Roosevelt with children.

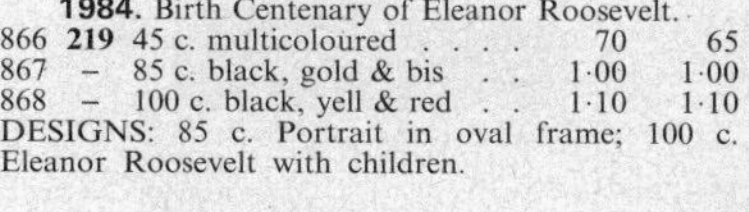

220 Child Reading **221** Adult Flamingo and Chicks

1984. Child Welfare. Multicoloured.

869 45 c. + 20 c. Type **220** . . . . 1·10 1·10
870 55 c. + 25 c. Family reading . 1·40 1·40
871 100 c. + 50 c. Family in church 1·75 1·75

1985. Greater Flamingoes. Multicoloured.

873 25 c. Type **221** 85 60
874 45 c. Young flamingoes . . . 1·10 80
875 55 c. Adult flamingoes . . . . 1·40 90
876 100 c. Flamingoes in various flight positions . . . . . . 2·25 1·40

222 Symbols of Entered Apprentice **223** Players with Ball

1985. Bicentenary of De Vergenoeging Masonic Lodge, Curacao. Multicoloured.

877 45 c. Type **222** . . . . 1·10 75
878 55 c. Symbols of the Fellow Craft 1·40 1·10
879 100 c. Symbols of the Master Mason . . . . 2·50 1·60

1985. Sports Funds. Football. Multicoloured.

880 10 c. + 5 c. Type **223** 40 35
881 15 c. + 5 c. Dribbling ball . . . 50 40
882 45 c. + 20 c. Running with ball 1·10 95
883 55 c. + 25 c. Tackling . . . . 1·40 1·25
884 85 c. + 40 c. Marking player with ball . . . . 1·75 1·60

224 Boy using Computer

1985. Cultural and Social Welfare Funds. International Youth Year. Multicoloured.

885 45 c. + 20 c. Type **224** . . . . 1·25 1·10
886 55 c. + 25 c. Girl listening to records . . . . 1·50 1·40
887 100 c. + 50 c. Boy break-dancing 2·25 2·00

225 U.N. Emblem

1985. 40th Anniv of U.N.O.

888 **225** 55 c. multicoloured . . . . 1·00 85
889 1 g. multicoloured . . . . 1·50 1·40

226 Pierre Lauffer and Poem **227** Eskimo

1985. Papiamentu (Creole language). Multicoloured.

890 45 c. Type **226** 50 50
891 55 c. Wave inscribe "Papiamentu" 75 75

1985. Child Welfare. Multicoloured.

892 5 c. + 5 c. Type **227** 35 20
893 10 c. + 5 c. African child . . . 45 30
894 25 c. + 10 c. Chinese girl . . . 65 50
895 45 c. + 20 c. Dutch girl . . . 1·25 85
896 55 c. + 25 c. Red Indian girl 1·40 1·10

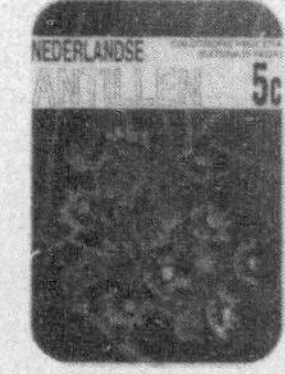

228 "Calotropis procera" **229** Courthouse

1985. Flowers. Multicoloured.

898 5 c. Type **228** 20 10
899 10 c. "Capparis flexuosa" . . 20 15
900 20 c. "Mimosa distachya" . . 45 30
901 45 c. "Ipomoea nil" 75 55
902 55 c. "Heliotropium ternatum" 90 70
903 150 c. "Ipomoea incarnata" . 1·75 1·50

1986. 125th Anniv of Curacao Courthouse. Multicoloured.

904 5 c. Type **229** 15 10
905 15 c. States room (vert) . . . 25 15
906 25 c. Court room 45 35
907 55 c. Entrance (vert) 80 70

230 Sprinting **231** Girls watching Artist at work

1986. Sports Funds. Multicoloured.

908 15 c. + 5 c. Type **230** 60 35
909 25 c. + 10 c. Horse racing . . 85 60
910 45 c. + 20 c. Motor racing . . 1·25 85
911 55 c. + 25 c. Football . . . . 1·40 1·25

1986. Curacao Youth Care Foundation. Multicoloured.

912 30 c. + 15 c. Type **231** . . . 80 55
913 45 c. + 20 c. Children watching sculptor at work . . . . . 1·10 75
914 55 c. + 25 c. Children watching potter at work . . . . . . 1·25 1·10

232 Chained Man

1986. 25th Anniv of Amnesty International. Multicoloured.

915 45 c. Type **232** 80 55
916 55 c. Dove behind bars . . . 90 65
917 100 c. Man behind bars . . . 1·40 1·10

233 Post Office Mail Box **234** Boy playing Football

1986. Mail Boxes. Multicoloured.

918 10 c. Type **233** 15 10
919 25 c. Street mail box on pole . 30 25
920 45 c. Street mail box in brick column 60 45
921 55 c. Street mail box 75 65

1986. Child Welfare. Multicoloured.

922 20 c. + 10 c. Type **234** . . . 50 40
923 25 c. + 15 c. Girl playing tennis 65 55
924 45 c. + 20 c. Boy practising judo 90 75
925 55 c. + 25 c. Boy playing baseball . . . . 1·25 1·10

235 Brothers' First House and Mauritius Vliegendehond

236 Engagement Picture

1986. Centenary of Friars of Tilburg Mission. Multicoloured.

927 10 c. Type **235** 25 15
928 45 c. St. Thomas College and Mgr. Ferdinand E. C. Kieckens 80 55
929 55 c. St. Thomas College courtyard and Fr. F.S. de Beer 90 70

1987. Golden Wedding of Princess Juliana and Prince Bernhard.

930 **236** 1 g. 35 orange, black and gold . . . . 1·75 1·40

237 Map

238 Girls playing Instruments

1987. 150th Anniv of Maduro Holding Inc. Multicoloured.

932 70 c. Type **237** 80 65
933 85 c. Group activities 90 80
934 1 g. 55 Saloman Elias Levy Maduro (founder) . . . . . 1·75 1·50

1987. Cultural and Social Relief Funds.

935 **238** 35 c. + 15 c. multicoloured 70 60
936 – 45 c. + 25 c. light green, green and blue . . . . 1·00 85
937 – 85 c. + 40 c. multicoloured 1·40 1·25

DESIGNS: 45 c. Woman pushing man in wheelchair. 85 c. Bandstand.

239 Map and Emblem

1987. 50th Anniv of Curacao Rotary Club. Multicoloured.

938 15 c. Type **239** 20 15
939 50 c. Zeelandia country house (meeting venue) 65 55
940 65 c. Emblem on map of Curacao 80 65

240 Octagon (house where Bolivar's sisters lived)

1987. 175th Anniv of Simon Bolivar's Exile on Curacao (60, 80 c.) and 50th Anniv of Bolivarian Society (70, 90 c.). Multicoloured.

941 60 c. Type **240** 75 65
942 70 c. Society headquarters, Willemstad, Curacao 80 70
943 80 c. Room in Octagon . . . 1·10 90
944 90 c. Portraits of Manuel Carlos Piar, Simon Bolivar and Pedro Luis Brion . . . . 1·25 1·10

241 Baby

1987. Child Welfare. Multicoloured.

945 40 c. + 15 c. Type **241** . . . 80 70
946 55 c. + 25 c. Child . . . . 1·25 1·10
947 115 c. + 50 c. Youth . . . . 1·75 1·60

242 White-tailed Tropic Birds

1987. 25th Anniv of Netherlands Antilles National Parks Foundation. Multicoloured.

949 70 c. Type **242** 80 60
950 85 c. White-tailed deer . . . 90 75
951 155 c. Iguana . . . . 1·75 1·50

243 Printing Press and Type

1987. 175th Anniv of "De Curacaosche Courant" (periodical and printing shop). Multicoloured.

952 55 c. Type **243** 65 55
953 70 c. Keyboard and modern printing press 85 65

244 William Godden (founder)

1988. 75th Anniv of Curacao Mining Company. Multicoloured.

954 40 c. Type **244** 70 45
955 105 c. Phosphate processing plant . . . . 1·50 1·10
956 155 c. Tafelberg (source of phosphate) . . . . 2·25 1·60

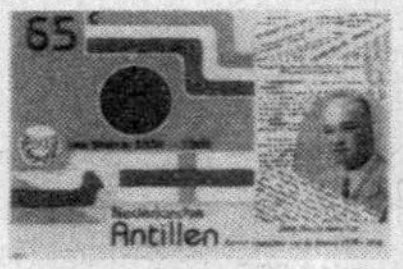

245 Flags, Minutes and John Horris Sprockel (first President)

246 Bridge through "100"

1988. 50th Anniv of Netherlands Antilles Staten (legislative body). Multicoloured.

957 65 c. Type **245** 75 65
958 70 c. Ballot paper and schematic representation of extension of voting rights 75 65
959 155 c. Antilles and Netherlands flags and birds representing five Antilles islands and Aruba 1·50 1·40

1988. Cultural and Social Relief Funds. Centenary of Queen Emma Bridge, Curacao. Mult.

960 55 c. + 25 c. Type **246** . . . 70 65
961 115 c. + 55 c. Willemstad harbour (horiz) . . . . . . 1·40 1·25
962 190 c. + 60 c. Leonard B. Smith (engineer) and flags (horiz) 2·50 2·40

247 Broken Chain

1988. 125th Anniv of Abolition of Slavery. Mult.

963 155 c. Type **247** . . . . . . 1·40 1·25
964 190 c. Breach in slave wall . . 1·60 1·50

248 Flags and Map

249 Charles Hellmund (Bonaire councillor)

1988. 3rd Inter-American Foundation of Cities "Let us Build Bridges" Conference, Curacao. Multicoloured.

965 80 c. Type **248** 90 70
966 155 c. Bridge and globe . . . 1·40 1·25

1988. Celebrities. Multicoloured.

967 55 c. Type **249** 55 45
968 65 c. Atthelo Maud Edwards-Jackson (founder of Saba Electric Company) 60 55
969 90 c. Nicolaas Debrot (Governor of Antilles, 1962-69) . . . . 1·00 90
970 120 c. William Charles de la Try Ellis (lawyer and politician) . 1·10 1·00

250 Child watching Television

251 "Cereus hexagonus"

1988. Child Welfare. Multicoloured.

971 55 c. + 25 c. Type **250** 80 60
972 65 c. + 30 c. Boy with radio . 1·10 85
973 115 c. + 55 c. Girl using computer . . . . 1·50 1·25

1988. Cacti. Multicoloured.

975 55 c. Type **251** 70 45
976 115 c. Melocactus . . . . . . 1·10 85
977 125 c. "Opuntia wentiana" . . 1·25 1·00

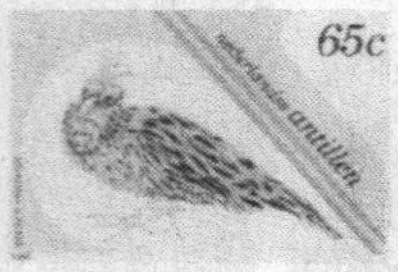

252 Magnifying Glass over 1936 and 1980 Stamps

253 Crested Bobwhite

1989. Cultural and Social Relief Funds. 50th Anniv of Curacao Stamp Association. Multicoloured.

978 30 c. + 10 c. Type **252** 60 40
979 55 c. + 20 c. Picking up stamp with tweezers (winning design by X. Rico in drawing competition) 85 75
980 80 c. + 30 c. Barn owl and stamp album . . . . 1·10 95

Nos. 978/80 were printed together, se-tenant, forming a composite design.

1989. 40th Anniv of Curacao Foundation for Prevention of Cruelty to Animals. Multicoloured.

981 65 c. Type **253** 85 55
982 115 c. Dogs and cats . . . . . 1·40 90

254 "Sun Viking" in Great Bay Harbour, St. Maarten

255 Paula Clementina Dorner (teacher)

1989. Tourism. Cruise Liners. Multicoloured.

983 70 c. Type **254** 70 55
984 155 c. "Eugenio C" entering harbour, St. Annabay, Curacao . . . . 1·40 1·25

1989. Celebrities. Multicoloured.

985 40 c. Type **255** 55 35
986 55 c. John Aniseto de Jongh (pharmacist and politician) . 65 45
987 90 c. Jacobo Jesus Maria Palm (musician) 95 70
988 120 c. Abraham Mendes Chumaceiro (lawyer and social campaigner) . . . . 1·25 1·00

256 Boy and Girl under Tree

257 Hand holding "7"

1989. Child Welfare. Multicoloured.

989 40 c. + 15 c. Type **256** 75 60
990 65 c. + 30 c. Two children playing on shore . . . . . 1·10 85
991 115 c. + 35 c. Adult carrying child . . . . 1·60 1·40

1989. 40th Anniv of Queen Wilhelmina Foundation for Cancer Care. Multicoloured.

993 30 c. Type **257** 40 25
994 60 c. Seated figure and figure receiving radiation treatment 65 55
995 80 c. Figure exercising and Foundation emblem 80 70

258 Fireworks

259 "Tephrosia cinerea"

1989. Christmas. Multicoloured.

997 30 c. Type **258** 40 25
998 100 c. Christmas tree decorations 1·10 85

1990. Flowers. Multicoloured.

999 30 c. Type **259** 35 30
1000 55 c. "Erithalis fruticosa" . . 60 50
1001 65 c. "Evolvulus antillanus" . 70 60
1002 70 c. "Jacquinia arborea" . . 80 65
1003 125 c. "Tournefortia onaphalodes" . . . . . . 1·40 1·25
1004 155 c. "Sesuvium portulacastrum" . . . . . . 1·75 1·40

260 Girl Guides

261 Nun with Child, Flag and Map

1990. Cultural and Social Relief Funds. Mult.

1005 30 c. + 10 c. Type **260** (60th anniv) 50 50
1006 40 c. + 15 c. Totolika (care of mentally handicapped organization) (17th anniv) 65 65
1007 155 c. + 65 c. Boy scout (60th anniv) . . . . 2·50 2·50

1990. Centenary of Arrival of Dominican Nuns in Netherlands Antilles. Multicoloured.

1008 10 c. Type **261** 15 10
1009 55 c. St. Rose Hospital and St. Martin's Home, St. Maarten 65 55
1010 60 c. St. Joseph School, St. Maarten 70 60

262 Goal Net, Ball and Shield

263 Carlos Nicolaas-Perez (philologist and poet)

1990. Multicoloured.

1011 65 c. + 30 c. Type **262** (65th anniv of Sport Unie Brion Trappers football club) . . 1·10 1·10
1012 115 c. + 55 c. Guiding addict from darkness towards sun (anti-drugs campaign) . . 2·25 2·25

1990. Meritorious Antilleans. Multicoloured.

1013 40 c. Type **263** 45 40
1014 60 c. Evert Kruythoff (writer) 65 55
1015 80 c. John de Pool (writer) . 90 75
1016 150 c. Joseph Sickman Corsen (poet and composer) . . . 1·75 1·40

264 Queen Emma

265 Isla Refinery

1990. Dutch Queens of the House of Orange. Multicoloured.

1017 100 c. Type **264** . . . . . . 1·10 90
1018 100 c. Queen Wilhelmina . . 1·10 90
1019 100 c. Queen Juliana . . . . 1·10 90
1020 100 c. Queen Beatrix . . . . 1·10 90

1990. 75th Anniv of Oil Refining on Curacao.

1022 **265** 100 c. multicoloured . . 1·40 1·25

266 Flower and Bees

267 Parcels

1990. Child Welfare. International Literacy Year. Designs illustrating letters of alphabet. Multicoloured.

1023 30 c. + 5 c. Type **266** 40 40
1024 55 c. + 10 c. Dolphins and sun 75 75
1025 65 c. + 15 c. Donkey with bicycle 95 95
1026 100 c. + 20 c. Goat dreaming of house . . . . 1·40 1·40
1027 115 c. + 25 c. Rabbit carrying food on yoke . . . . . . 1·60 1·60
1028 155 c. + 55 c. Lizard, moon and cactus . . . . 2·40 2·40

1990. Christmas. Multicoloured.

1029 30 c. Type **267** (25th anniv of Curacao Lions Club's Good Neighbour project) 35 30
1030 100 c. Mother and child . . . 1·10 90

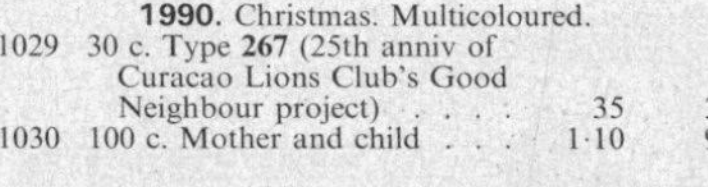

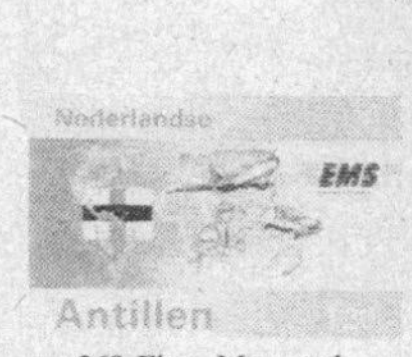

268 Flag, Map and Distribution of Mail

269 Scuba Diver and French Grunt

1991. 6th Anniv of Express Mail Service.

1031 **268** 20 g. multicoloured . . . 18·00 14·00

1991. Fishes. Multicoloured.

1032 10 c. Type **269** 15 10
1033 40 c. Spotted trunkfish . . . 50 40
1034 55 c. Coppersweepers 70 60
1035 75 c. Skindiver and yellow goatfishes 90 75
1036 100 c. Blackbar soldier-fishes 1·25 1·00

270 Children and Stamps

1991. Cultural and Social Relief Funds. Mult.

1037 30 c. + 10 c. Type **270** (12th anniv of Philatelic Club of Curacao) 50 50
1038 65 c. + 25 c. St. Vincentius Brass Band (50th anniv) . . 1·10 1·10
1039 155 c. + 55 c. Games and leisure pursuits (30th anniv of FESEBAKO) (Curacao community centres) . . . . 2·40 2·40

271 "Good Luck"

272 Westpoint Lighthouse, Curacao

1991. Greetings Stamps. Multicoloured.

1040 30 c. Type **271** 35 30
1041 30 c. "Thank You" 35 30
1042 30 c. Couple and family ("Love You") 35 30
1043 30 c. Song birds ("Happy Day") 35 30
1044 30 c. Greater flamingo and medicines ("Get Well Soon") 35 30
1045 30 c. Flowers and balloons ("Happy Birthday") . . . 35 30

1991. Lighthouses. Multicoloured.

1046 30 c. Type **272** 45 40
1047 70 c. Willems Toren, Bonaire 1·00 80
1048 115 c. Klein Curacao lighthouse 1·90 1·60

273 Peter Stuyvesant College

1991. 50th Anniv of Secondary Education in Netherlands Antilles (65 c.) and "Espamer '91" Spain–Latin America Stamp Exhibition, Buenos Aires (125 c.). Multicoloured.

1049 65 c. Type **273** 75 60
1050 125 c. Dancers of Netherlands Antilles, Argentina and Portugal (vert) . . . . . 1·40 1·25

274 Octopus with Letters and Numbers

275 Nativity

1991. Child Welfare. Multicoloured.

1051 40 c. + 15 c. Type **274** . . . 90 90
1052 65 c. + 30 c. Parents teaching arithmetic . . . . 1·25 1·25
1053 155 c. + 65 c. Bird and tortoise with clock . . . . 2·50 2·50

1991. Christmas. Multicoloured.

1055 30 c. Type **275** 35 30
1056 100 c. Angel appearing to shepherds . . . . 1·25 1·00

276 Joseph Alvarez Correa (founder) and Headquarters of S.E.L. Maduro and Sons

277 Fawn

1991. 75th Anniv of Maduro and Curiel's Bank. Multicoloured.

1057 30 c. Type **276** 40 35
1058 70 c. Lion rampant (bank's emblem) and "75" 75 60
1059 155 c. Isaac Haim Capriles (Managing Director, 1954-74) and Scharloo bank branch 1·60 1·40

1992. The White-tailed Deer. Multicoloured.

1060 5 c. Type **277** (postage) . . . 10 10
1061 10 c. Young adults 10 10
1062 30 c. Stag 30 25
1063 40 c. Stag and hind in water 35 30
1064 200 c. Stag drinking (air) . . 1·75 1·40
1065 355 c. Stag calling . . . . . 2·75 2·25

278 Windsurfer

280 "Santa Maria"

1992. Cultural and Social Relief Funds. Olympic Games, Barcelona. Multicoloured.

1066 30 c. + 10 c. Type **278** (award of silver medal to Jan Boersma, 1988 Games) . . 35 35
1067 55 c. + 25 c. Globe, national flag and Olympic rings . . 65 65
1068 115 c. + 55 c. Emblem of National Olympic Committee (60th anniv) . . . . 1·40 1·40

Nos. 1066/8 were issued together, se-tenant, forming a composite design.

1992. "World Columbian Stamp Expo '92", Chicago. Multicoloured.

1070 250 c. Type **280** . . . . . . 2·00 1·60
1071 500 c. Chart and Columbus . 4·00 3·25

281 View of Dock and Town

282 Angela de Lannoy-Willems

1992. Curacao Port Container Terminal. Mult.

1072 80 c. Type **281** 60 50
1073 125 c. Crane and ship . . . 95 80

1992. Celebrities.

1074 **282** 30 c. black, brown & grn 35 20
1075 – 40 c. black, brown & bl . 30 25
1076 – 55 c. black, brown & orge 40 35
1077 – 70 c. black, brown & red 55 45
1078 – 100 c. black, brown & bl . 75 60

DESIGNS: 30 c. Type **282** (first woman Member of Parliament); 40 c. Lodewijk Daniel Gerharts (entrepreneur on Bonaire); 55 c. Cyrus Wilberforce Wathey (entrepreneur on St. Maarten); 70 c. Christian Winkel (Deputy Governor of Antilles); 100 c. Mother Joseph (founder of Roosendaal Congregation (Franciscan welfare sisterhood)).

283 Spaceship

284 Queen Beatrix and Prince Claus

1992. Child Welfare. Multicoloured.

1079 30 c. + 10 c. Type **283** . . . 30 30
1080 70 c. + 30 c. Robot 75 75
1081 100 c. + 40 c. Extra-terrestrial being . . . . 1·00 1·00

1992. 12½ Years since Accession to the Throne of Queen Beatrix (100 c.) and Royal Visit to Netherlands Antilles (others). Designs showing photos of previous visits to the Antilles. Multi.

1083 70 c. Type **284** 55 45
1084 100 c. Queen Beatrix signing book 75 60
1085 175 c. Queen Beatrix and Prince Claus with girl . . . . . . 1·25 1·00

285 Crib

286 Hibiscus

1992. Christmas. Multicoloured.

1086 30 c. Type **285** 25 20
1087 100 c. Mary and Joseph searching for lodgings (vert) 75 60

1993. Flowers. Multicoloured.

1088 75 c. Type **286** 55 45
1089 90 c. Sunflower 70 60
1090 175 c. Ixora . . . . 1·25 1·00
1091 195 c. Rose . . . . 1·50 1·25

287 De Havilland Twin Otter and Flight Paths

288 Pekingese

1993. Anniversaries. Multicoloured.

1092 65 c. Type **287** (50th anniv of Princess Juliana International Airport, St. Maarten) . . . 50 40
1093 75 c. Laboratory worker and National Health Laboratory (75th anniv) 55 45
1094 90 c. De Havilland Twin Otter on runway at Princess Juliana International Airport . . . 70 60
1095 175 c. White and yellow cross (50th anniv of Princess Margriet White and Yellow Cross Foundation for District Nursing) . . . . 1·25 1·00

1993. Dogs. Multicoloured.

1096 65 c. Type **288** 50 40
1097 90 c. Standard Poodle 70 70
1098 100 c. Pomeranian 75 60
1099 175 c. Papillon . . . . 1·25 1·00

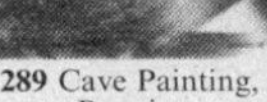

289 Cave Painting, Bonaire

290 "Sun and Sea"

1993. "Brasiliana '93" International Stamp Exhibition, Rio de Janeiro, and Admittance of Antilles to Postal Union of the Americas, Spain and Portugal. Multicoloured.

1100 150 c. Type **289** . . . . . . 1·10 90
1101 200 c. Exhibition emblem and Antilles flag . . . . 1·50 1·25
1102 250 c. Globe and hand signing U.P.A.E.P. agreement . . . 1·90 1·60

1993. "Carib-Art" Exhibition, Curacao. Multicoloured.

1103 90 c. Type **290** 70 60
1104 150 c. "Heaven and Earth" . 1·10 90

291 "Safety in the Home"

1993. Child Welfare. Child and Danger. Mult.

1105 65 c. + 25 c. Type **291** . . . 70 70
1106 90 c. + 35 c. Child using seat belt ("Safety in the Car") (vert) 95 95
1107 175 c. + 75 c. Child wearing armbands ("Safety in the Water") . . . . 1·90 1·90

292 Consulate, Curacao

293 "Mother and Child" (mosaic)

1993. Bicentenary of United States Consul General to the Antilles. Multicoloured.

1109 65 c. Type **292** 50 40
1110 90 c. Arms of Netherlands Antilles and U.S.A. . . . 70 60
1111 175 c. American bald eagle . 2·25 1·00

1993. Christmas. Works by Lucilia Engels-Boskaljon. Multicoloured.

1112 30 c. Type **293** 20 15
1113 115 c. "Madonna and Christ" (painting) 80 65

294 Basset Hound

295 Common Caracara

1994. Dogs. Multicoloured.

1114 65 c. Type **294** 45 35
1115 75 c. Pit bull terrier 55 45
1116 90 c. Cocker spaniel 65 55
1117 175 c. Chow-chow . . . . . 1·25 1·00

1994. Birds. Multicoloured.

1118 50 c. Type **295** 35 30
1119 95 c. Green peafowl 65 55
1120 100 c. Scarlet macaw 70 60
1121 125 c. Troupial 90 75

296 Joseph Husurell Lake (founder of United People's Liberation Front)

297 Players' Legs

1994. Celebrities. Multicoloured.

1122 65 c. Type **296** 45 35
1123 75 c. Efrain Jonckheer (politician and diplomat) . 55 45
1124 100 c. Michiel Martinus Romer (teacher) 70 60
1125 175 c. Carel Nicolaas Winkel (social reformer) . . . . . 1·25 1·00

1994. World Cup Football Championship, U.S.A. Multicoloured.

1126 90 c. Type **297** 60 55
1127 150 c. Foot and ball . . . . 1·10 90
1128 175 c. Referee's whistle and cards . . . . 1·25 1·00

INDEX

Countries can be quickly located by referring to the index at the end of this volume.

298 Chair and Hammer

299 Birds and Dolphin

1994. 75th Anniv of International Labour Organization. Multicoloured.
1129 90 c. Type **298** 60 55
1130 110 c. Heart and "75" 80 65
1131 200 c. Tree 1·40 1·25

1994. Nature Protection. Multicoloured.
1132 10 c. Type **299** 10 10
1133 35 c. Dolphin, pelican and other birds 25 20
1134 50 c. Coral, iguana, lobster and fish 35 30
1135 125 c. Fish, turtle, shell, flamingos and ducks 90 75

300 1945 7½ c. Netherlands Stamp

301 Mother and Child

1994. "Fepapost '94" European Stamp Exhibition, The Hague. Multicoloured.
1137 2 g. 50 Type **300** 1·75 1·40
1138 5 g. 1933 6 c. Curacao stamp 3·50 3·00

1994. Child Welfare. International Year of the Family. Multicoloured.
1140 35 c. + 15 c. Type **301** 35 35
1141 65 c. + 25 c. Father and daughter reading together 60 60
1142 90 c. + 35 c. Grandparents 90 90

POSTAGE DUE STAMPS

1952. As Type D **121** of Netherlands but inscr "NEDERLANDSE ANTILLEN".
D336 1 c. green 10 10
D337 2½ c. green 60 60
D338 5 c. green 20 10
D339 6 c. green 65 50
D340 7 c. green 65 50
D341 8 c. green 65 50
D342 9 c. green 65 50
D343 10 c. green 30 15
D344 12½ c. green 30 15
D345 15 c. green 35 25
D346 20 c. green 35 45
D347 25 c. green 65 10
D348 30 c. green 1·25 1·50
D349 35 c. green 1·50 1·50
D350 40 c. green 1·25 1·50
D351 45 c. green 1·50 1·50
D352 50 c. green 1·25 1·25

NETHERLANDS INDIES Pt. 4

A former Dutch colony, consisting of numerous settlements in the East Indies, of which the islands of Java and Sumatra and parts of Borneo and New Guinea are the most important. Renamed Indonesia in 1948, Independence was granted during 1949. Netherlands New Guinea remained a Dutch possession until 1962 when it was placed under U.N. control, being incorporated with Indonesia in 1963.

100 cents = 1 gulden

1 King William III

2

1864. Imperf.
1 **1** 10 c. red £170 75·00

1868. Perf.
2 **1** 10 c. red £650 £110

1870. Perf.
27 **2** 1 c. green 1·60 1·00
28 2 c. purple £100 75·00
29 2 c. brown 4·50 3·25
30 2½ c. buff 32·00 18·00
12 5 c. green 50·00 3·25
32 10 c. brown 12·00 15
51 12½ c. drab 2·50 80
34 15 c. brown 18·00 50
5 20 c. blue 90·00 1·40
36 25 c. purple 17·00 50
55 30 c. green 28·00 2·25
17 50 c. red 15·00 85
38 2 g. green and purple 85·00 9·00

5

6 Queen Wilhelmina

1883.
89 **5** 1 c. green 50 10
90 2 c. brown 50 10
91 2½ c. buff 65 55
92 3 c. purple 75 10
88 5 c. green 24·00 15·00
93 5 c. blue 7·50 10

1892.
94 **6** 10 c. brown 3·50 15
95 12½ c. grey 7·00 11·00
96 15 c. brown 12·00 60
97 20 c. blue 26·00 65
98 25 c. purple 25·00 90
99 30 c. green 35·00 1·40
100 50 c. red 24·00 55
101 2 g. 50 blue and brown £110 22·00

1900. Netherlands stamps of 1898 surch **NED.-INDIE** and value.
111 **13** 10 c. on 10 c. lilac 1·25 10
112 12½ c. on 12½ c. blue 1·75 45
113 15 c. on 15 c. brown 2·25 15
114 20 c. on 20 c. green 12·00 40
115 25 c. on 25 c. blue & pink 12·00 45
116 50 c. on 50 c. red & green 22·00 55
117 **11** 2½ g. on 2½ g. lilac 38·00 8·50

1902. Surch.
118 **5** ½ on 2 c. brown 20 20
119 2½ on 3 c. purple 25 25

1902. As T **11/13** of Surinam but inscr "NEDERLANDSCH-INDIE".
120 ½ c. lilac 30 10
121 1 c. olive 30 10
122 2 c. brown 2·25 15
123 2½ c. green 1·50 10
124 3 c. orange 1·40 1·00
125 4 c. blue 8·50 7·50
126 5 c. red 3·75 10
127 7½ c. grey 1·75 25
128 10 c. slate 1·00 10
129 12½ c. blue 1·40 10
130 15 c. brown 6·50 1·50
131 17½ c. bistre 2·25 15
132 20 c. grey 1·40 1·40
133 20 c. olive 18·00 10
134 22½ c. olive and brown 3·25 15
135 25 c. mauve 7·00 10
136 30 c. brown 23·00 10
137 50 c. red 14·00 10
138 1 g. lilac 40·00 20
206 1 g. lilac on blue 40·00 4·50
139 2½ g. grey 48·00 1·25
207 2½ g. grey on blue 55·00 25·00

1902. No. 130 optd with horiz bars.
140 15 c. brown 1·10 55

1905. No. 132 surch **10 cent.**
141 10 c. on 20 c. grey 1·60 90

1908. Stamps of 1902 optd **JAVA.**
142 ½ c. lilac 15 20
143 1 c. olive 15 15
144 2 c. brown 1·40 1·40
145 2½ c. green 65 10
146 3 c. orange 50 65
147 5 c. red 1·90 10
148 7½ c. grey 1·75 1·50
149 10 c. slate 45 10
150 12½ c. blue 2·00 40
151 15 c. brown 2·40 2·25
152 17½ c. bistre 1·40 60
153 20 c. olive 7·50 40
154 22½ c. olive and brown 3·75 1·75
155 25 c. mauve 3·25 15
156 30 c. brown 22·00 1·60
157 50 c. red 14·00 45
158 1 g. lilac 38·00 2·00
159 2½ g. grey 55·00 38·00

1908. Stamps of 1902 optd **BUITEN BEZIT.**
160 ½ c. lilac 20 20
161 1 c. olive 25 15
162 2 c. brown 1·25 1·90
163 2½ c. green 55 15
164 3 c. orange 45 90
165 5 c. red 1·90 30
166 7½ c. grey 2·00 2·25
167 10 c. slate 45 10
168 12½ c. blue 6·50 1·60
169 15 c. brown 3·50 1·90
170 17½ c. bistre 1·25 85
171 20 c. olive 6·00 1·25
172 22½ c. olive and brown 5·00 3·00
173 25 c. mauve 3·75 25
174 30 c. brown 14·00 1·60
175 50 c. red 6·00 55
176 1 g. lilac 45·00 2·25
177 2½ g. grey 70·00 55·00

1912. As T **18/19** of Surinam, but inscr "NEDERLANDSCH-INDIE" (T **18**) or "NEDERL-INDIE" (T **19**).
208 **18** ½ c. lilac 10 10
209 1 c. green 15 10
210 2 c. brown 30 10
264 2 c. grey 30 10
211 2½ c. green 1·10 10
265 2½ c. pink 25 10
212 3 c. brown 30 10
266 3 c. green 65 10
213 4 c. blue 55 15
267 4 c. green 1·25 15
268 4 c. bistre 7·00 3·75
214 5 c. pink 70 10
269 5 c. green 85 10
270 5 c. blue 35 10
215 7½ c. brown 35 10
271 7½ c. bistre 35 10
216 **19** 10 c. red 50 10
272 **18** 10 c. lilac 90 10
217 **19** 12½ c. blue 80 10
273 12½ c. red 85 10
274 15 c. blue 6·50 10
218 17½ c. brown 80 10
219 20 c. green 1·40 10
275 20 c. blue 1·40 10
276 20 c. orange 12·00 10
220 22½ c. orange 1·25 50
221 25 c. mauve 1·40 10
222 30 c. grey 1·50 10
277 32½ c. violet and orange 1·40 15
278 35 c. brown 7·00 50
279 40 c. green 1·40 10

1913. As T **20** of Surinam but inscr "NED. INDIE".
223 50 c. green 2·50 10
280 60 c. blue 3·25 10
281 80 c. orange 3·75 10
224 1 g. brown 2·50 10
283 1 g. 75 lilac 14·00 1·75
225 2½ g. pink 9·50 35

1915. Red Cross. Stamps of 1912 surch **+5 cts.** and red cross.
243 1 c. + 5 c. green 3·50 3·25
244 5 c. + 5 c. pink 4·25 4·00
245 10 c. + 5 c. red 6·50 6·50

1917. Stamps of 1902, 1912 and 1913 surch.
246 ½ c. on 2½ c. (No. 211) 20 20
247 1 c. on 4 c. (No. 213) 45 45
250 12½ c. on 17½ c. (No. 218) 25 10
251 12½ c. on 22½ c. (No. 220) 35 10
248 17½ c. on 22½ c. (No. 134) 70 35
252 20 c. on 22½ c. (No. 220) 35 10
249 30 c. on 1 g. (No. 138) 6·00 1·25
253 32½ c. on 50 c. (No. 223) 1·25 10
254 40 c. on 50 c. (No. 223) 3·50 40
255 60 c. on 1 g. (No. 224) 5·50 30
256 80 c. on 1 g. (No. 224) 6·50 75

1922. Bandoeng Industrial Fair. Stamps of 1912 and 1917 optd **3de N. I. JAARBEURS BANDOENG 1922.**
285 1 c. green 6·00 4·50
286 2 c. brown 6·00 4·50
287 2½ c. pink 50·00 60·00
288 3 c. yellow 6·00 5·50
289 4 c. blue 35·00 30·00
290 5 c. green 12·00 8·00
291 7½ c. brown 7·50 4·50
292 10 c. lilac 60·00 75·00
293 12½ c. on 22½ c. orange (No. 251) 6·00 6·00
294 17½ c. brown 3·75 4·50
295 20 c. blue 6·00 4·50

Nos. 285/95 were sold at a premium for 3, 4, 5, 6, 8, 9, 10, 12½, 15, 20 and 22 c. respectively.

33

36 Fokker F.VIIa

1923. Queen's Silver Jubilee.
296 **33** 5 c. green 15 10
297 12½ c. red 15 10
298 20 c. blue 25 10
299 50 c. orange 1·25 50
300 1 g. purple 2·50 30
301 2½ g. grey 23·00 14·00
302 5 g. brown 75·00 95·00

1928. Air. Stamps of 1912 and 1913 surch **LUCHTPOST**, Fokker F.VII airplane and value.
303 10 c. on 12½ c. red 90 90
304 20 c. on 25 c. mauve 2·25 2·25
305 40 c. on 80 c. orange 1·75 1·40
306 75 c. on 1 g. sepia 85 50
307 1½ g. on 2½ g. red 6·00 5·50

1928. Air.
308 **36** 10 c. purple 30 15
309 20 c. brown 75 50
310 40 c. red 1·00 50
311 75 c. green 2·00 15
312 1 g. 50 orange 3·75 50

1930. Air. Surch **30** between bars.
313 **36** 30 c. on 40 c. red 75 15

38 Watch-tower

40 M. P. Pattist in Flight

1930. Child Welfare. Centres in brown.
315 – 2 c. + 1 c. mauve 70 65
316 **38** 5 c. + 2½ c. green 3·75 2·25
317 – 12½ c. + 2½ c. red 2·50 45
318 – 15 c. + 5 c. blue 5·00 4·50

DESIGNS—VERT: 2 c. Bali Temple. HORIZ: 12½ c. Minangkabau Compound; 15 c. Buddhist Temple, Borobudur.

1930. No. 275 surch **12½.**
319 12½ c. on 20 c. blue 35 10

1931. Air. 1st Java–Australia Mail.
320 **40** 1 g. brown and blue 10·00 10·00

41

1931. Air.
321 **41** 30 c. red 2·25 10
322 4½ g. blue 8·00 3·00
323 7½ g. green 9·50 3·25

42 Ploughing

1931. Lepers' Colony.
324 **42** 2 c. + 1 c. brown 2·25 1·50
325 – 5 c. + 2½ c. green 3·50 3·00
326 – 12½ c. + 2½ c. red 2·25 45
327 – 15 c. + 5 c. blue 8·00 6·50

DESIGNS: 5 c. Fishing; 12½ c. Native actors; 15 c. Native musicians.

1932. Air. Surch **50** on Fokker F.VIIa/3m airplane.
328 **36** 50 c. on 1 g. 50 c. orange 2·50 35

44 Plaiting Rattan

45 William of Orange

1932. Salvation Army. Centres in brown.
329 – 2 c. + 1 c. purple 40 30
330 **44** 5 c. + 2½ c. green 2·75 2·00
331 – 12½ c. + 2½ c. red 85 25
332 – 15 c. + 5 c. blue 3·75 3·00

DESIGNS: 2 c. Weaving; 12½ c. Textile worker; 15 c. Metal worker.

1933. 400th Birth Anniv of William I of Orange.
333 **45** 12½ c. red 1·10 15

46 Rice Cultivation   47 Queen Wilhelmina

1933.

335 **46** 1 c. violet 20 10
397 2 c. purple 10 15
337 2½ c. bistre 20 10
338 3 c. green 20 15
339 3½ c. grey 15 15
340 4 c. green 75 10
401 5 c. blue 10 10
342 7½ c. violet . . . . 1·25 10
343 10 c. red . . . . 1·75 10
403 **47** 10 c. red 10 10
334 12½ c. brown . . . . 8·00 25
345 12½ c. red 25 10
404 15 c. blue 10 10
405 20 c. purple 20 10
348 25 c. green . . . . 1·60 10
349 30 c. blue . . . . 2·40 10
350 32½ c. bistre . . . . 7·00 6·00
408 35 c. violet . . . . 3·50 1·10
352 40 c. green . . . . 2·50 10
353 42½ c. yellow . . . . 2·50 20
354 50 c. blue . . . . 3·25 15
355 60 c. blue . . . . 4·00 40
356 80 c. red . . . . 4·50 60
357 1 g. violet . . . . 6·00 30
358 1 g. 75 green . . . . 14·00 13·00
414 2 g. green . . . . 25·00 13·00
359 2 g. 50 purple . . . . 17·00 1·10
415 5 g. bistre . . . . 25·00 5·50

The 50 c. to 5 g. are larger, 30×30 mm.

48 Pander S.4 Postjager

1933. Air. Special Flights.

360 **48** 30 c. blue . . . . 1·40 1·40

49 Woman and Lotus Blossom   53 Cavalryman and Wounded Soldier

1933. Y.M.C.A. Charity.

361 **49** 2 c. + 1 c. brown & purple 70 1·25
362 – 5 c. + 2½ c. brown & green 2·25 1·75
363 – 12½ c. + 2½ c. brown & orge 2·50 25
364 – 15 c. + 5 c. brown & blue 3·25 2·00

DESIGNS: 5 c. Symbolising the sea of life; 12½ c. Y.M.C.A. emblem; 15 c. Unemployed man.

1934. Surch.

365 **36** 2 c. on 10 c. purple 25 45
366 2 c. on 20 c. brown 20 20
367 **41** 2 c. on 30 c. red 35 75
368 **36** 42½ c. on 75 c. green . . . 3·75 25
369 42½ c. on 1 g. 50 orange . . 3·75 35

1934. Anti-Tuberculosis Fund. As T **77** of Netherlands.

370 12½ c. + 2½ c. brown . . . . . 1·25 45

1935. Christian Military Home.

371 – 2 c. + 1 c. brown & purple 1·40 1·25
372 **53** 5 c. + 2½ c. brown & grn . 3·50 2·75
373 – 12½ c. + 2½ c. brown & orge 3·50 25
374 – 15 c. + 5 c. brown & blue 5·00 6·00

DESIGNS: 2 c. Engineer chopping wood; 12½ c. Artilleryman and volcano victim; 15 c. Infantry bugler.

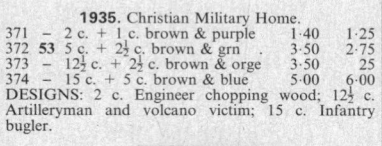

54 Dinner-time   55 Boy Scouts   59 Sifting Rice

1936. Salvation Army.

375 **54** 2 c. + 1 c. purple . . . . 1·25 55
376 5 c. + 2½ c. blue . . . . 1·40 1·10
377 7½ c. + 2½ c. violet . . . 1·40 1·40
378 12½ c. + 2½ c. orange . . . 1·40 25
379 15 c. + 5 c. blue . . . . 2·40 1·90

Nos. 376/9 are larger, 30×27 mm.

1937. Scouts' Jamboree.

380 **55** 7½ c. + 2½ c. green . . . . 1·25 1·10
381 12½ c. + 2½ c. red . . . . 1·25 50

1937. Nos. 222 and 277 surch in figures.

382 10 c. on 30 c. slate . . . . . 2·40 25
383 10 c. on 32½ c. vio & orge . . 2·40 25

1937. Relief Fund. Inscr "A.S.I.B.".

385 **59** 2 c. + 1 c. sepia & orange 1·25 80
386 – 3½ c. + 1½ c. grey . . . . 1·25 80
387 – 7½ c. + 2½ c. green & orge 1·40 85
388 – 10 c. + 2½ c. red & orange 1·40 20
389 – 25 c. + 5 c. blue . . . . 1·40 1·25

DESIGNS: 3½ c. Mother and children; 7½ c. Ox-team ploughing rice-field; 10 c. Ox-team and cart; 20 c. Man and woman.

1938. 40th Anniv of Coronation. As T **87** of Netherlands.

390 2 c. violet 10 15
391 10 c. red 15 10
392 15 c. blue . . . . 1·40 65
393 20 c. red 60 25

62 Douglas DC-2 Airliner   63 Nurse and Child

1938. Air Service Fund. 10th Anniv of Royal Netherlands Indies Air Lines.

394 **62** 17½ c. + 5 c. brown . . . 85 85
395 – 20 c. + 5 c. slate 85 85

DESIGN: 20 c. As Type **62**, but reverse side of airliner.

1938. Child Welfare. Inscr "CENTRAAL MISSIE-BUREAU".

416 **63** 2 c. + 1 c. violet 65 40
417 – 3½ c. + 1½ c. green . . . . 1·10 1·10
418 – 7½ c. + 2½ c. red 80 70
419 – 10 c. + 2½ c. red . . . . 1·00 20
420 – 20 c. + 5 c. blue . . . . 1·25 80

DESIGNS—(23×23 mm): Nurse with child suffering from injuries to eye (3½ c.), arm (7½ c.), head (20 c.) and nurse bathing a baby (10 c.).

63a Group of Natives   64 European Nurse and Patient

1939. Netherlands Indies Social Bureau and Protestant Church Funds.

421 – 2 c. + 1 c. violet 25 15
422 – 3½ c. + 1½ c. green . . . 35 20
423 **63a** 7½ c. + 2½ c. brown . . . 25 20
424 – 10 c. + 2½ c. red . . . . 1·50 75
425 **64** 10 c. + 2½ c. red . . . . 1·50 75
426 – 20 c. + 5 c. blue 50 35

DESIGNS—VERT: 2 c. as Type **63a** but group in European clothes. HORIZ: 3½ c., 10 c. (No. 424) as Type **64**, but Native nurse and patient.

1940. Red Cross Fund. No. 345 surch **10+5 ct** and cross.

428 **47** 10 c. + 5 c. on 12½ c. red . 80 45

68 Queen Wilhelmina   69 Netherlands Coat of Arms

1941. As T **94** of Netherlands but inscr "NED. INDIE" and T **68**.

429 – 10 c. red 20 10
430 – 15 c. blue . . . . 1·10 1·10
431 – 17½ c. orange 35 55
432 – 20 c. mauve . . . . 16·00 27·00
433 – 25 c. green . . . . 23·00 38·00
434 – 30 c. brown . . . . 1·50 30
435 – 35 c. purple . . . . 80·00 £250
436 – 40 c. green . . . . 6·50 2·25
437 – 50 c. red . . . . 1·40 65
438 – 60 c. blue 85 50
439 – 80 c. red . . . . 1·00 75
440 – 1 g. violet . . . . 1·25 25
441 – 2 g. green . . . . 7·00 80
442 – 5 g. bistre £170 £475
443 – 10 g. green . . . . 23·00 17·00
444 **68** 25 g. orange £150 £130

Nos 429/36 measure 18×23 mm., Nos. 431/43 20½×26 mm.

1941. Prince Bernhard Fund for Dutch Forces.

453 **69** 5 c. + 5 c. blue & orange 10 15
454 10 c. + 10 c. blue and red 15 15
455 1 g. + 1 g. blue and grey . 7·50 11·00

70 Doctor and Child   71 Wayangwong Dancer

1941. Indigent Mohammedans' Relief Fund.

456 **70** 2 c. + 1 c. green 40 50
457 – 3½ c. + 1½ c. brown . . . . 2·50 3·25
458 – 7½ c. + 2½ c. violet . . . . 2·00 2·25
459 – 10 c. + 2½ c. red 70 30
460 – 15 c. + 5 c. blue . . . . . 6·50 5·50

DESIGNS: 3½ c. Native eating rice; 7½ c. Nurse and patient; 10 c. Nurse and children; 15 c. Basket-weaver.

1941.

461 – 2 c. red 10 15
462 – 2½ c. purple 15 20
463 – 3 c. green 15 40
464 **71** 4 c. green 15 35
465 – 5 c. blue 10 10
466 – 7½ c. violet 40 10

DESIGNS (dancers): 2 c. Menari; 2½ c. Nias; 3 c. Legon; 5 c. Padjoge; 7½ c. Dyak.

See also Nos. 514/16.

72 Paddyfield   73 Queen Wilhelmina

1945.

467 **72** 1 c. green 20 15
468 – 2 c. mauve 20 30
469 – 2½ c. purple 20 15
470 – 5 c. blue 15 10
471 – 7½ c. olive 45 10
472 **73** 10 c. brown 10 10
473 15 c. blue 10 10
474 17½ c. red 15 15
475 20 c. purple 15 10
476 30 c. grey 25 10
477 – 60 c. grey 60 10
478 – 1 g. green . . . . 1·00 10
479 – 2½ g. orange . . . . 3·25 45

DESIGNS: As Type **72**: 2 c. Lake in W. Java; 2½ c. Medical School, Batavia; 5 c. Seashore; 7½ c. Douglas DC-2 airplane over Bromo Volcano. (30×30 mm): 60 c. to 2½ g. Portrait as Type **73** but different frame.

76 Railway Viaduct near Soekaboemi   81 Queen Wilhelmina

1946.

484 **76** 1 c. green 30 60
485 – 2 c. brown 10 10
486 – 2½ c. red 15 15
487 – 5 c. blue 10 10
488 – 7½ c. blue 15 10

DESIGNS: 2 c. Power station; 3 c. Minangkabau house; 5 c. Tondano scene (Celebes); 7½ c. Buddhist Stupas, Java.

1947. Surch in figures.

502 – 3 c. on 2½ c. red (No. 486) . 10 10
503 – 3 c. on 7½ c. blue (No. 488) 10 10
504 **76** 4 c. on 1 c. green . . . . 45 1·50
505 – 45 c. on 60 c. blue (No. 355) 1·25 90

No. 505 has three bars.

1947. Optd **1947**.

506 **47** 12½ c. red 10 10
507 25 c. green 20 10
508 – 40 c. green (No. 436) . . . 30 10
509 **47** 50 c. blue 50 25
510 80 c. red 75 55
511 – 2 g. green (No. 441) . . . 3·25 45
512 – 5 g. brown (No. 442) . . . 9·50 6·50

1948. Relief for Victims of the Terror. Surch **PELITA 15 + 10 Ct.** and lamp.

513 **47** 15 c. + 10 c. on 10 c. red . 10 10

1948. Dancers. As T **71**.

514 3 c. red (Menari) 10 10
515 4 c. green (Legon) 10 10
516 7½ c. brown (Dyak) 55 55

1948.

517 **81** 15 c. orange 60 60
518 20 c. blue 10 10
519 25 c. green 15 10
520 40 c. green 20 10
521 45 c. mauve 35 45
522 50 c. lake 25 10
523 80 c. red 30 10
524 1 g. violet 25 10
525 10 g. green . . . . 27·00 8·50
526 25 g. orange . . . . 65·00 55·00

Nos. 524/6 are larger 21×26 mm.

1948. Queen Wilhelmina's Golden Jubilee. As T **81** but inscr "1898 1948".

528 15 c. orange 25 15
529 20 c. blue 25 10

1948. As T **126** of Netherlands.

530 15 c. red 30 15
531 20 c. blue 30 10

MARINE INSURANCE STAMPS

1921. As Type M **22** of the Netherlands, but inscribed "NED. INDIE".

M257 15 c. green . . . . 1·75 30·00
M258 60 c. red . . . . 3·50 48·00
M259 75 c. brown . . . . 3·50 50·00
M260 1 g. 50 blue . . . . 24·00 £250
M261 2 g. 25 brown . . . . 30·00 £325
M262 4½ g. black . . . . 65·00 £650
M263 7½ g. red . . . . 85·00 £750

OFFICIAL STAMPS

1911. Stamps of 1892 optd **D** in white on a black circle.

O178 **6** 10 c. brown . . . . 1·00 50
O179 12½ c. grey . . . . 2·25 3·75
O180 15 c. bistre . . . . 2·25 2·00
O181 20 c. blue . . . . 2·25 80
O182 25 c. mauve . . . . 8·00 7·00
O183 50 c. red . . . . 1·75 1·00
O184 2 g. 50, blue and brown . 45·00 45·00

1911. Stamps of 1902 (except No. O185) optd **DIENST**.

O186 ½ c. lilac 10 30
O187 1 c. olive 15 10
O188 2 c. brown 10 10
O185 2½ c. yellow (No. 91) 50 50
O189 2½ c. green . . . . 1·10 1·00
O190 3 c. orange 30 25
O191 4 c. blue 15 10
O192 5 c. red 55 55
O193 7½ c. grey . . . . 2·00 2·25
O194 10 c. slate 15 10
O195 12½ c. blue . . . . 1·60 1·75
O196 15 c. brown 50 50
O197 15 c. brown (No. 140) . . . 26·00
O198 17½ c. bistre . . . . 2·25 1·75
O199 20 c. olive 50 40
O200 22½ c. olive and brown . . . 3·00 2·25
O201 25 c. mauve . . . . 1·75 1·50
O202 30 c. brown 70 40
O203 50 c. red . . . . 11·00 6·00
O204 1 g. lilac . . . . 2·25 1·00
O205 2½ g. grey . . . . 26·00 28·00

POSTAGE DUE STAMPS

1874. As Postage Due stamps of Netherlands. Colours changed.

D56 **D 8** 5 c. yellow £250 £225
D57 10 c. green on yellow . . £110 75·00
D59 15 c. orange on yellow . 16·00 13·00
D60 20 c. green on blue . . . 28·00 9·00

1882. As Type D **2** of Surinam.

D68 2½ c. black and red 30 80
D69 5 c. black and red 20 35
D65 10 c. black and red . . . . . 2·25 2·25
D70 15 c. black and red . . . . . 2·50 2·25
D71 20 c. black and red . . . . . 85·00 35
D82 30 c. black and red . . . . . 1·60 1·90
D72 40 c. black and red . . . . . 1·10 1·50
D73 50 c. black and pink 70 45
D74 75 c. black and red 45 45

1892. As Type D **9** of Netherlands.

D102 2½ c. black and pink . . . 40 25
D103 5 c. black and pink . . . 2·25 10
D104b 10 c. black and pink . . . 2·25 1·75
D105 15 c. black and pink . . . 11·00 1·40
D106b 20 c. black and pink . . . 3·50 1·25
D107 30 c. black and pink . . . 16·00 4·75
D108 40 c. black and pink . . . 11·00 1·25
D109 50 c. black and pink . . . 7·00 65
D110 75 c. black and pink . . . 17·00 3·50

1913. As Type D **9** of Netherlands.

D226 1 c. orange 10 95
D489 1 c. violet 50 80
D227 2½ c. orange 10 10
D527 2½ c. brown 45 75
D228 3½ c. orange 10 95
D491 3½ c. blue 50 80
D229 5 c. orange 10 10
D230 7½ c. orange 10 10
D493 7½ c. green 60 80
D231 10 c. orange 10 10
D494 10 c. mauve 60 80
D232 12½ c. orange . . . . 2·50 10
D448 15 c. orange 65 85
D234 20 c. orange 15 10
D495 20 c. blue 60 90
D235 25 c. orange 15 10
D496 25 c. yellow 75 90
D236 30 c. orange 20 20
D497 30 c. brown . . . . 80 1·00
D237 37½ c. orange . . . . 15·00 13·00
D238 40 c. orange 20 15
D498 40 c. green . . . . 1·25 1·10
D239 50 c. orange . . . . 1·25 10
D499 50 c. yellow . . . . 1·40 1·25
D240 75 c. orange . . . . 2·25 15
D500 75 c. blue . . . . 1·40 1·25
D241 1 g. orange . . . . 4·50 4·75
D452 1 g. blue 45 55
D501 100 c. green . . . . 1·40 1·25

1937. Surch **20**.

D384 **D 5** 20 c. on 37½ c. red . . 25 25

1946. Optd **TE BETALEN PORT** or surch also.

D480 2½ c. on 10 c. red (No. 429) 45 45
D481 10 c. red (No. 429) . . . . 1·00 1·00
D482 20 c. mauve (No. 432) . . . 2·25 2·25
D483 40 c. green (No. 436) . . . 48·00 48·00

For later issues see **INDONESIA**.

MINIMUM PRICE

The minimum price quoted is 10p which represents a handling charge rather than a basis for valuing common stamps. For further notes about prices, see introductory pages.

NETHERLANDS NEW GUINEA Pt. 4

The Western half of the island of New Guinea was governed by the Netherlands until 1962, when control was transferred to the U.N. (see West New Guinea). The territory later became part of Indonesia as West Irian (q.v.).

100 cents = 1 gulden

1950. As numeral and portrait types of Netherlands but inscr "NIEUW GUINEA".

1 118 1 c. grey 15 15
2 2 c. orange 15 15
3 2½ c. olive 15 10
4 3 c. mauve 1·50 1·25
5 4 c. green 1·50 1·00
6 5 c. blue 3·00 15
7 7½ c. brown 35 15
8 10 c. violet 1·75 15
9 12½ c. red 1·75 1·40
10 129 15 c. brown 1·25 50
11 20 c. blue 35 10
12 25 c. red 35 10
13 30 c. blue 6·50 25
14 40 c. green 65 10
15 45 c. brown 3·50 50
16 50 c. orange 65 10
17 55 c. grey 6·00 50
18 80 c. purple 7·00 3·00
19 130 1 g. red 11·00 15
20 2 g. brown 8·50 1·10
21 5 g. green 12·00 1·00

1953. Netherlands Flood Relief Fund. Nos. 6, 10 and 12 surch **hulp nederland 1953** and premium.

22 118 5 c. + 5 c. blue 8·00 8·50
23 129 15 c. + 10 c. brown 8·00 8·50
24 25 c. + 10 c. red 8·00 8·50

5 Lesser Bird of Paradise

6 Queen Juliana

1954.

25 5 1 c. yellow and red 30 10
26 5 c. yellow and brown 35 10
27 – 10 c. brown and blue 40 10
28 – 15 c. brown and yellow 50 10
29 – 20 c. brown and green 90 35

DESIGN: 10, 15, 20 c. Greater bird of paradise.

1954.

30 6 25 c. red 20 10
31 30 c. blue 20 10
32 40 c. orange 1·75 2·00
33 45 c. green 60 85
34 55 c. turquoise 45 10
35 80 c. grey 85 30
36 85 c. brown 90 45
37 1 g. purple 4·50 1·75

1955. Red Cross. Nos. 26/8 surch with cross and premium.

38 5 5 c. + 5 c. yellow and sepia 1·00 85
39 – 10 c. + 10 c. brown & blue 1·00 85
40 – 15 c. + 10 c. brown & lemon 1·00 85

8 Child and Native Hut

10 Papuan Girl and Beach Scene

1956. Anti-Leprosy Fund.

41 – 5 c. + 5 c. green 90 85
42 8 10 c. + 5 c. purple 90 85
43 – 25 c. + 10 c. blue 90 85
44 8 30 c. + 10 c. buff 90 85

DESIGN: 5 c., 25 c. Palm-trees and native hut.

1957. Child Welfare Fund.

51 10 5 c. + 5 c. lake 90 85
52 – 10 c. + 5 c. green 90 85
53 10 25 c. + 10 c. brown 90 85
54 – 30 c. + 10 c. blue 90 85

DESIGN: 10 c., 30 c. Papuan child and native hut.

11 Red Cross and Idol

12 Papuan and Helicopter

1958. Red Cross Fund.

55 11 5 c. + 5 c. multicoloured 1·00 90
56 – 10 c. + 5 c. multicoloured 1·00 90
57 11 25 c. + 10 c. multicoloured 1·00 90
58 – 30 c. + 10 c. multicoloured 1·00 90

DESIGN: 10 c., 30 c. Red Cross and Asman-Papuan bowl in form of human figure.

1959. Stars Mountains Expedition, 1959.

59 12 55 c. brown and blue 1·10 80

13 Blue-crowned Pigeon

14 "Tecomanthe dendrophila"

1959.

60 13 7 c. purple, blue and brown 50 20
61 12 c. purple, blue & green 50 20
62 17 c. purple and blue 50 15

1959. Social Welfare. Inscr "SOCIALE ZORG".

63 14 5 c. + 5 c. red and green 65 45
64 – 10 c. + 5 c. purple, yellow and olive 65 45
65 – 25 c. + 10 c. yellow, green and red 65 45
66 – 30 c. + 10 c. green & violet 65 45

DESIGNS: 10 c. "Dendrobium attenatum Lindley"; 25 c. "Rhododendron zoelleri Warburg"; 30 c. "Boea cf. urvillei".

1960. World Refugee Year. As T **180** of Netherlands.

67 25 c. blue 40 40
68 30 c. ochre 40 70

16 Paradise Birdwing

1960. Social Welfare Funds. Butterflies.

69 16 5 c. + 5 c. multicoloured 80 65
70 – 10 c. + 5 c. bl, blk & salmon 80 65
71 – 25 c. + 10 c. red, sep & yell 85 65
72 – 30 c. + 10 c. multicoloured 85 65

BUTTERFLIES: 10 c. Large green-banded blue; 25 c. Red lacewing; 30 c. Catops owl butterfly.

17 Council Building, Hollandia

1961. Opening of Netherlands New Guinea Council.

73 17 25 c. turquoise 20 30
74 30 c. red 20 30

18 "Scapanes australis"

19 Children's Road Crossing

1961. Social Welfare Funds. Beetles.

75 18 5 c. + 5 c. multicoloured 20 25
76 – 10 c. + 5 c. multicoloured 20 25
77 – 25 c. + 10 c. multicoloured 25 30
78 – 30 c. + 10 c. multicoloured 30 35

BEETLES: 10 c. Brenthid weevil; 25 c. "Neolamprima adolphinae" (stag beetle); 30 c. "Aspidomorpha aurata" (leaf beetle).

1962. Road Safety Campaign. Triangle in red.

79 19 25 c. blue 35 35
80 – 30 c. green (Adults at road crossing) 35 35

1962. Silver Wedding of Queen Juliana and Prince Bernhard. As T **187** of Netherlands.

81 55 c. brown 30 35

21 Shadow of Palm on Beach

22 Lobster

1962. 5th South Pacific Conference, Pago Pago. Multicoloured.

82 25 c. Type **21** 20 35
83 30 c. Palms on beach 20 35

1962. Social Welfare Funds. Shellfish. Multicoloured.

84 5 c. + 5 c. Crab (horiz) 20 20
85 10 c. + 5 c. Type **22** 20 20
86 25 c. + 10 c. Spiny lobster 25 25
87 30 c. + 10 c. Shrimp (horiz) 25 30

POSTAGE DUE STAMPS

1957. As Type D **121** of Netherlands but inscr "NEDERLANDS NIEUW GUINEA".

D45 1 c. red 10 20
D46 5 c. red 50 1·10
D47 10 c. red 1·50 2·25
D48 25 c. red 2·25 70
D49 40 c. red 2·25 85
D50 1 g. blue 3·00 3·75

For later issues see **WEST NEW GUINEA** and **WEST IRIAN**.

NEW CALEDONIA Pt. 6

A French Overseas Territory in the S. Pacific, E. of Australia, consisting of New Caledonia and a number of smaller islands.

100 centimes = 1 franc

1 Napoleon III

1860. Imperf.

1 1 10 c. black £170

Nos. 5/35 are stamps of French Colonies optd or surch.

1881. "Peace and Commerce" type surch **N C E** and new value. Imperf.

5 H 05 on 40 c. red on yellow 17·00 16·00
8a 5 on 40 c. red on yellow 12·00 12·00
9 5 on 75 c. red 28·00 27·00
6a 25 on 35 c. black on orge £100 90·00
7 25 on 75 c. red £250 £190

1886. "Peace and Commerce" (imperf) and "Commerce" types surch **N.C.E. 5c.**

10 J 5 c. on 1 f. green 11·00 11·00
11 H 5 c. on 1 f. green £7000 £7500

1891. "Peace and Commerce" (imperf) and "Commerce" types surch **N.-C.E. 10 c.** in ornamental frame.

13 H 10 c. on 40 c. red on yell 16·00 15·00
14 J 10 c. on 40 c. red on yell 8·25 7·75

1892. "Commerce" type surch **N.-C.E. 10 centimes** in ornamental frame.

15 J 10 c. on 30 c. brn on drab 8·00 8·00

1892. Optd **NLLE CALEDONIE** (a) "Peace and Commerce" type. Imperf.

16 H 20 c. red on green £225 £250
17 35 c. black on orange 40·00 40·00
19 1 f. green £170 £170

(b) "Commerce" type.

20 J 5 c. green on green 9·00 7·50
21 10 c. black on lilac 85·00 42·00
22 15 c. blue 60·00 27·00
23 20 c. red on green 60·00 35·00
24 25 c. brown on yellow 11·00 8·75
25 25 c. black on pink 60·00 8·00
26 30 c. brown on drab 45·00 38·00
27 35 c. black on orange £160 £120
29 75 c. red on pink £120 90·00
30 1 f. green £100 85·00

1892. Surch **N-C-E** in ornamental scroll and new value. (a) "Peace and Commerce" type. Imperf.

31 H 10 on 1 f. green £3500 £2750

(b) "Commerce" type.

32 J 5 on 20 c. red on green 11·00 8·25
34 5 on 75 c. red on pink 7·50 4·75
35 10 on 1 f. green 7·50 5·00

1892. "Tablet" key-type inscr "NLLE CALEDONIE ET DEPENDANCES".

37 D 1 c. black and red on blue 35 30
38 2 c. brown & blue on buff 65 40
39 4 c. brown & blue on grey 90 1·00
55 5 c. green and red 85 50
41 10 c. black & blue on lilac 3·50 2·25
56 10 c. red and blue 4·00 70
42 15 c. blue and red 11·00 80
57 15 c. grey and red 6·00 65
43 20 c. red & blue on green 9·75 6·25
44 25 c. black & red on pink 10·00 3·00
58 25 c. blue and red 8·75 5·75
45 30 c. brown & bl on drab 10·00 6·00
46 40 c. red & blue on yellow 10·00 8·25
47 50 c. red and blue on pink 38·00 16·00
59 50 c. brown & red on blue 40·00 48·00
60 50 c. brown & blue on blue 38·00 35·00
48 75 c. brown & red on orge 19·00 12·50
49 1 f. green and red 22·00 13·50

1899. Stamps of 1892 surch (a) **N-C-E** in ornamental scroll and **5**.

50 D 5 on 2 c. brown & bl on buff 11·00 8·75
51 5 on 4 c. brn & bl on grey 1·90 2·00

(b) **N.C.E.** and **15** in circle.

52 D 15 on 30 c. brown and blue on drab 2·50 2·75
53 15 on 75 c. brown and red on orange 8·50 6·25
54 15 on 1 f. green and red 13·50 12·50

1902. Surch **N.-C.E.** and value in figures.

61 D 5 on 30 c. brown and blue on drab 5·25 4·75
62 15 on 40 c. red and blue on yellow 4·00 3·75

1903. 50th Anniv of French Annexation. Optd **CINQUANTENAIRE 24 SEPTEMBRE 1853 1903** and eagle.

63 D 1 c. black and red on blue 95 75
64 2 c. brown & blue on buff 2·25 1·90
65 4 c. brown & blue on grey 3·50 2·00
66 5 c. green and red 2·75 2·50
69 10 c. black & blue on lilac 4·50 5·50
70 15 c. grey and red 6·50 3·25
71 20 c. red & blue on green 11·00 8·25
72 25 c. black & red on pink 11·00 9·75
73 30 c. brown & bl on drab 13·50 10·50
74 40 c. red & blue on yellow 20·00 13·50
75 50 c. red and blue on pink 35·00 21·00
76 75 c. brown & bl on orge 60·00 55·00
77 1 f. green and red 70·00 65·00

1903. Nos. 64 etc further surch with value in figures within the jubilee opt.

78 D 1 on 2 c. brn & bl on buff 50 45
79 2 on 4 c. brn & bl on grey 1·25 1·10
80 4 on 5 c. green and red 1·25 1·10
82 10 on 15 c. grey and red 1·60 1·75
83 15 on 20 c. red and blue on green 1·75 1·60
84 20 on 25 c. black and red on pink 3·00 2·75

15 Kagu

16

17 "President Felix Faure" (barque)

1905.

85 15 1 c. black on green 15 10
86 2 c. brown 20 15
87 4 c. blue on orange 20 25
88 5 c. green 30 20
112 5 c. blue 25 30
113 10 c. green 50 45
114 10 c. red 30 35
90 15 c. lilac 40 25
91 16 20 c. brown 30 25
92 25 c. blue on green 45 20
115 25 c. red on yellow 30 20
93 30 c. brown on orange 30 40
116 30 c. red 85 90
117 30 c. orange 35 30
94 35 c. black on yellow 25 30
95 40 c. red on green 65 55
96 45 c. red 40 45
97 50 c. red on orange 1·50 1·00
118 50 c. blue 90 85
119 50 c. grey 40 35
120 65 c. blue 35 35
98 75 c. olive 35 35
121 75 c. blue 30 40
122 75 c. violet 60 50
99 17 1 f. blue on green 50 45
123 1 f. blue 90 95
100 2 f. red on blue 1·40 1·10
101 5 f. black on orange 4·00 3·75

1912. Stamps of 1892 surch.

102 D 05 on 15 c. grey and red 40 45
103 05 on 20 c. red and blue on green 40 55
104 05 on 30 c. brown and blue on drab 40 55
105 10 on 40 c. red and blue on yellow 90 95
106 10 on 50 c. brown and blue on blue 95 1·00

1915. Surch **NCE 5** and red cross.

107 15 10 c. + 5 c. red 65 60

1915. Surch **5c** and red cross.

109 15 10 c. + 5 c. red 40 50
110 15 c. + 5 c. lilac 35 45

1918. Surch **5 CENTIMES**.

111 15 5 c. on 15 c. lilac 70 70

1922. Surch **0 05**.

124 15 0.05 on 15 c. lilac 25 45

1924. Types **15/17** (some colours changed) surch.

125 15 25 c. on 15 c. lilac 30 35
126 17 25 c. on 2 f. red on blue 40 50
127 25 c. on 5 f. black on orge 40 50
128 16 60 on 75 c. green 25 35
129 65 on 45 c. purple 70 80
130 85 on 45 c. purple 90 1·00
131 90 on 75 c. red 35 45
132 17 1 f. 25 on 1 f. blue 30 35
133 1 f. 50 on 1 f. blue on blue 60 70
134 3 f. on 5 f. mauve 65 70
135 10 f. on 5 f. green on mve 4·00 4·25
136 20 f. on 5 f. red on yellow 8·50 8·50

22 Pointe des Paletuviers

23 Chief's Hut

24 La Perouse, De Bougainville and "L'Astrolabe"

1928.

137 **22** 1 c. blue and purple 10 20
138 2 c. green and brown 10 30
139 3 c. blue and red 15 25
140 4 c. blue and orange . . . 15 35
141 5 c. brown and blue 15 35
142 10 c. brown and lilac . . . 20 25
143 15 c. blue and brown . . . 20 25
144 20 c. brown and red . . . 20 35
145 25 c. brown and green . . 25 30
146 **23** 30 c. deep green and green 20 30
147 35 c. mauve and black . . 30 20
148 40 c. green and red . . . 25 30
149 45 c. red and blue 50 60
150 45 c. green and deep green 40 50
151 50 c. brown and mauve . . 40 25
152 55 c. red and blue . . . . 1·90 95
153 60 c. red and blue . . . 25 35
154 65 c. blue and brown . . . 45 55
155 70 c. brown and mauve . . 30 40
156 75 c. drab and blue . . . 80 60
157 80 c. green and purple . . 50 40
158 85 c. brown and green . . 75 55
159 90 c. pink and red . . . 40 55
160 90 c. red and brown . . . 50 60
161 **24** 1 f. pink and drab . . . . 3·75 2·00
162 1 f. carmine and red . . . 65 75
163 1 f. green and red 40 50
164 1 f. 10 brown and green . . 8·75 7·50
165 1 f. 25 green and brown . . 55 65
166 1 f. 25 carmine and red . . 40 50
167 1 f. 40 red and blue . . . 40 50
168 1 f. 50 light blue and blue . 35 40
169 1 f. 60 brown and green . . 65 70
170 1 f. 75 orange and blue . . 45 45
171 1 f. 75 blue & ultramarine . 45 50
172 2 f. brown and orange . . 40 50
173 2 f. 25 blue & ultramarine . 45 50
174 2 f. 50 brown 65 70
175 3 f. brown and mauve . . . 45 50
176 5 f. brown and blue 45 50
177 10 f. brown & pur on pink . 80 80
178 20 f. brown & red on yellow 1·40 1·10

1931. "Colonial Exhibition" key-types.

179 E 40 c. green and black . . . 2·50 2·50
180 F 50 c. mauve and black . . . 2·50 2·50
181 G 90 c. red and black . . . 2·50 2·50
182 H 1 f. 50 blue and black . . . 2·50 2·50

1932. Paris-Noumea Flight. Optd with Couzinet 33 airplane and **PARIS-NOUMEA Verneilh-Deve-Munch 5 Avril 1932.**

183 **23** 40 c. olive and red £300 £350
184 50 c. brown and mauve . . . £300 £350

1933. 1st Anniv of Paris-Noumea Flight. Optd **PARIS-NOUMEA Premiere liaison aerienne 5 Avril 1932** and Couzinet 33 airplane.

185 **22** 1 c. blue and purple . . . . 4·75 4·75
186 2 c. green and brown . . . 4·75 4·75
187 4 c. blue and orange . . . 4·75 4·75
188 5 c. brown and blue . . . . 4·75 4·75
189 10 c. brown and lilac . . . 4·75 4·75
190 15 c. blue and brown . . . 4·75 4·75
191 20 c. brown and red . . . 4·75 4·75
192 25 c. brown and green . . 4·75 4·75
193 **23** 30 c. deep green and green 4·50 4·75
194 35 c. mauve and black . . 4·50 4·75
195 40 c. green and red . . . 4·50 4·75
196 45 c. red and blue . . . . 4·50 4·75
197 50 c. brown and mauve . . 4·50 4·75
198 70 c. brown and mauve . . 5·25 5·50
199 75 c. drab and blue . . . 5·25 5·50
200 85 c. brown and green . . 5·25 5·50
201 90 c. pink and red . . . . 5·25 5·50
202 **24** 1 f. pink and drab . . . . 5·25 5·50
203 1 f. 25 green and brown . . 5·25 5·50
204 1 f. 50 light blue & blue . . 5·25 5·50
205 1 f. 75 orange and blue . . 5·00 5·50
206 2 f. brown and orange . . 6·25 6·25
207 3 f. brown and mauve . . . 5·75 6·25
208 5 f. brown and blue . . . 5·75 6·25
209 10 f. brown & pur on pink . 6·00 6·25
210 20 f. brown & red on yellow 6·00 6·25

1937. International Exhibition, Paris. As Nos. 168/73 of St.-Pierre et Miquelon.

211 20 c. violet 60 80
212 30 c. green 65 85
213 40 c. red 60 80
214 50 c. brown and blue . . . 60 75
215 90 c. red 60 85
216 1 f. 50 blue 60 80

DESIGNS—HORIZ: 30 c. Sailing ships; 40 c. Berber, Negress and Annamite; 90 c. France extends torch of civilization; 1 f. 50, Diane de Poitiers. VERT: 50 c. Agriculture.

27 Breguet Saigon Flying Boat over Noumea

1938. Air.

217 **27** 65 c. violet 50 60
218 4 f. 50 red 70 70
219 7 f. green 50 50
220 9 f. blue . . . . 1·40 1·50
221 20 f. orange 85 85
222 50 f. black . . . . 1·75 1·75

1938. Int Anti-Cancer Fund. As T **22** of Mauritania.

223 1 f. 75 + 50 c. blue . . . . . 5·75 7·25

1939. New York World's Fair. As T **28** of Mauritania.

224 1 f. 25 red 70 70
225 2 f. 25 blue 60 70

1939. 150th Anniv of French Revolution. As T **29** of Mauritania.

226 45 c. + 25 c. green and black (postage) . . . . 5·00 5·50
227 70 c. + 30 c. brown & black 5·00 5·50
228 90 c. + 35 c. orange & black 5·00 5·50
229 1 f. 25 + 1 f. red & black . . 5·00 5·50
230 2 f. 25 + 2 f. blue & black . . 5·50 5·00
231 4 f. 50 + 4 f. black and orange (air) . . . . 12·00 17·00

1941. Adherence to General de Gaulle. Optd **France Libre**.

232 **22** 1 c. blue and purple . . . 12·50 12·50
233 2 c. green and brown . . . 12·50 12·50
234 3 c. blue and red . . . . . 12·00 12·50
235 4 c. blue and orange . . . 12·50 12·50
236 5 c. brown and blue . . . 11·50 12·50
237 10 c. brown and lilac . . . 11·50 12·50
238 15 c. blue and brown . . . 12·50 12·50
239 20 c. brown and red . . . 12·50 12·50
240 25 c. brown and green . . 12·50 12·50
241 **23** 30 c. deep green and green 12·50 12·50
242 35 c. mauve and black . . 12·50 12·50
243 40 c. green and red . . . 12·50 12·50
244 45 c. green & deep green . 12·50 12·50
245 50 c. brown and mauve . . 12·50 12·50
246 55 c. red and blue . . . . 12·50 12·50
247 60 c. red and blue . . . . 12·50 12·50
248 65 c. blue and brown . . . 12·50 12·50
249 70 c. brown and mauve . . 12·50 12·50
250 75 c. drab and blue . . . 12·50 12·50
251 80 c. green and purple . . 12·50 12·50
252 85 c. brown and green . . 14·00 14·00
253 90 c. pink and red . . . . 14·00 14·00
254 **24** 1 f. carmine and red . . . 14·00 14·00
255 1 f. 25 green and brown . 14·00 14·00
256 1 f. 40 red and blue . . . 14·00 14·00
257 1 f. 50 light blue & blue . 14·00 14·00
258 1 f. 60 brown and green . 14·00 14·00
259 1 f. 75 orange and blue . . 14·00 14·00
260 2 f. brown and orange . . 14·00 14·00
261 2 f. 25 blue & ultramarine 14·00 14·00
262 2 f. 50 brown . . . . . . 15·00 15·00
263 3 f. brown and mauve . . 15·00 15·00
264 5 f. brown and blue . . . 15·00 15·00
265 10 f. brown & pur on pink 18·00 18·00
266 20 f. brown & red on yellow 20·00 20·00

29 Kagu

30 Fairey FC-1 Airliner

1942. Free French Issue (a) Postage.

267 **29** 5 c. brown 20 30
268 10 c. blue 20 30
269 25 c. green 20 30
270 30 c. red 20 30
271 40 c. green 40 30
272 80 c. purple 40 30
273 1 f. mauve 50 35
274 1 f. 50 red 50 35
275 2 f. black 60 60
276 2 f. 50 blue 60 60
277 4 f. violet 70 45
278 5 f. yellow 80 60
279 10 f. brown . . . . 1·25 85
280 20 f. green . . . . 1·75 1·25

(b) Air.

281 **30** 1 f. orange 45 55
282 1 f. 50 red 45 55
283 5 f. purple 50 60
284 10 f. black 70 70
285 25 f. blue 70 70
286 50 f. green . . . . 95 1·00
287 100 f. red . . . . 1·40 1·25

31

32 Felix Eboue

1944. Mutual Aid and Red Cross Funds.

288 **31** 5 f. + 20 f. red 50 60

1945. Eboue.

289 **32** 2 f. black 40 50
290 25 f. green . . . . 1·10 1·25

1945. Surch.

291 **29** 50 c. on 5 c. brown 55 70
292 60 c. on 5 c. brown 55 70
293 70 c. on 5 c. brown 55 80
294 1 f. 20 on 5 c. brown . . . 30 40
295 2 f. 40 on 25 c. green . . . 40 50
296 3 f. on 25 c. green 40 50
297 4 f. 50 on 25 c. green . . . 60 70
298 15 f. on 2 f. 50 blue . . . . 1·00 1·25

34 "Victory"

1946. Air. Victory.

299 **34** 8 f. blue 50 70

35 Legionaries by Lake Chad

1946. Air. From Chad to the Rhine.

300 **35** 5 f. black 50 70
301 – 10 f. red 75 85
302 – 15 f. blue 70 85
303 – 20 f. brown 70 85
304 – 25 f. green . . . . 90 1·25
305 – 50 f. purple . . . . 90 1·75

DESIGNS: 10 f. Battle of Koufra; 15 f. Tank Battle, Mareth; 20 f. Normandy Landings; 25 f. Liberation of Paris; 50 f. Liberation of Strasbourg.

36 Two Kagus

37 Sud Est Languedoc Airliners over Landscape

1948. (a) Postage.

306 **36** 10 c. purple and yellow . . 10 30
307 30 c. purple and green . . 15 30
308 40 c. purple and brown . . 15 30
309 – 50 c. purple and pink . . . 15 35
310 – 60 c. brown and yellow . . 25 35
311 – 80 c. green & light green . 25 35
312 – 1 f. violet and orange . . . 25 35
313 – 1 f. 20 brown and blue . . 25 35
314 – 1 f. 50 blue and yellow . . 25 35
315 – 2 f. brown and green . . . 30 25
316 – 2 f. 40 red and purple . . 40 35
317 – 3 f. violet and orange . . 3·50 1·00
318 – 4 f. indigo and blue . . . 75 45
319 – 5 f. violet and red 90 60
320 – 6 f. brown and yellow . . 90 80
321 – 10 f. blue and orange . . . 90 70
322 – 15 f. red and blue . . . . 1·00 1·00
323 – 20 f. violet and yellow . . 1·25 1·10
324 – 25 f. blue and orange . . 1·75 1·60

(b) Air.

325 – 50 f. purple and orange . . 3·00 3·00
326 **37** 100 f. blue and green . . 6·25 4·50
327 – 200 f. brown and yellow . . 10·00 8·00

DESIGNS—As T **36**: HORIZ: 50 c. to 80 c. Ducos Sanatorium; 1 f. 50, Porcupine Is; 2 f. to 4 f. Nickel foundry; 5 f. to 10 f. "The Towers of Notre Dame" Rocks. VERT: 15 f. to 25 f. Chief's hut. As T **37**: HORIZ: Sud Est Languedoc airliner over– 50 f. St. Vincent Bay; 200 f. Noumea.

38 People of Five Races, Bomber and Globe

1949. Air. 75th Anniv of U.P.U.

328 **38** 10 f. multicoloured . . . . 3·00 3·50

39 Doctor and Patient

40

1950. Colonial Welfare Fund.

329 **39** 10 f. + 2 f. pur & brn . . 2·25 2·75

1952. Military Medal Centenary.

330 **40** 2 f. red, yell & grn . . . . 2·25 2·75

41 Admiral D'Entrecasteaux

1953. French Administration Centenary Inscr "1853 1953".

331 **41** 1 f. 50 lake and brown . . 4·25 3·75
332 – 2 f. blue and turquoise . . 3·25 2·25
333 – 6 f. brown, blue and red . 7·00 4·50
334 – 13 f. blue and green . . . 7·50 5·25

DESIGNS: 2 f. Mgr. Douarre and church; 6 f. Admiral D'Urville and map; 13 f. Admiral Despointes and view.

42 Normandy Landings, 1944

1954. Air. 10th Anniv of Liberation.

335 **42** 3 f. blue and deep blue . . 4·00 3·50

43 Towers of Notre-Dame (rocks)

44 Coffee

45 Transporting Nickel

1955.

336 **43** 2 f. 50 c. blue, green and sepia (postage) 80 70
337 3 f. blue, brown & green . 5·25 3·00
338 **44** 9 f. deep blue and blue . . 1·40 75
339 **45** 14 f. blue & brown (air) . . 2·50 1·10

46 Dumbea Barrage

47 "Xanthostemon"

1956. Economic and Social Development Fund.

340 **46** 3 f. green and blue . . . . 1·10 65

1958. Flowers.

341 **47** 4 f. multicoloured . . . . 1·60 65
342 – 15 f. red, yellow & green . 3·50 1·25

DESIGN: 15 f. "Hibiscus".

48 "Human Rights"

49 "Brachyrus zebra"

1958. 10th Anniv of Declaration of Human Rights.
343 **48** 7 f. red and blue . . . . . 1·25 95

1959.
344 **49** 1 f. brown and grey 60 45
345 – 2 f. blue, purple and green . 70 40
346 – 3 f. red, blue and green . . 85 45
347 – 4 f. purple, red and green . 70 50
348 – 5 f. bistre, blue and green . 1·40 65
349 – 10 f. multicoloured . . . . 2·00 80
350 – 26 f. multicoloured . . . . 4·25 2·75
DESIGNS—HORIZ: 2 f. Outrigger canoes racing; 3 f. "Lienardella fasciata" (fish); 5 f. Sail Rock, Noumea; 26 f. Fluorescent corals. VERT: 4 f. Fisherman with spear. "Glaucus" and "Spirographe" (corals).

49a The Carved Rock, Bourail

1959. Air.
351 – 15 f. green, brown & red . 3·50 1·50
352 – 20 f. brown and green . . 6·25 2·50
353 – 25 f. black, blue & purple 6·50 2·50
354 – 50 f. brown, green & blue 5·25 3·50
355 – 50 f. brown, green & blue 4·25 2·50
356 – 100 f. brown, green & blue 17·00 9·00
357 **49a** 200 f. brown, green & blue 28·00 13·00
DESIGNS—HORIZ: 15 f. Fisherman with net; 20 f. Nautilus shell; 25 f. Underwater swimmer shooting fish; 50 f. (No. 355), Isle of Pines; 100 f. Corbeille de Yate. VERT: 50 f. (No. 354), Yate barrage.

49b Napoleon III 49c Port-de-France, 1859

1960. Postal Centenary.
358 **15** 4 f. red 75 50
359 – 5 f. brown and lake . . . 75 50
360 – 9 f. brown and turquoise . 90 60
361 – 12 f. black and blue . . . 90 75
362 **49b** 13 f. blue . . . . 2·50 1·60
363 **49c** 19 f. red, green & turq . . 2·75 1·10
364 – 33 f. red, green and blue . 4·00 2·25
DESIGNS—As Type **49c**: HORIZ: 5 f. Girl operating cheque-writing machine; 12 f. Telephone receiver and exchange building; 33 f. As Type **49c** but without stamps in upper corners. VERT: 9 f. Letter-box on tree.

49d Map of Pacific and Palms

1962. 5th South Pacific Conference, Pago-Pago.
365 **49d** 15 f. multicoloured . . . 2·00 1·25

49e Map and Symbols of Meteorology

1962. 3rd Regional Assembly of World Meteorological Association, Noumea.
366 **49e** 50 f. multicoloured . . . 7·50 4·50

50 "Telstar" Satellite and part of Globe

1962. Air. 1st Transatlantic TV Satellite Link.
367 **50** 200 f. turquoise, brn & bl . 26·00 11·00

INDEX

Countries can be quickly located by referring to the index at the end of this volume.

51 Emblem and Globe

1963. Freedom from Hunger.
368 **51** 17 f. blue and purple . . . 2·50 1·50

52 Relay-running 53 Centenary Emblem

1963. 1st South Pacific Games, Suva, Fiji.
369 **52** 1 f. red and green 65 60
370 – 7 f. brown and blue . . . 1·10 65
371 – 10 f. brown and green . . 1·75 1·00
372 – 27 f. blue & deep purple . 4·00 2·25
DESIGNS: 7 f. Tennis; 10 f. Football; 27 f. Throwing the javelin.

1963. Red Cross Centenary.
373 **53** 37 f. red, grey and blue . . 5·50 4·00

54 Globe and Scales of Justice 54a "Bikkia fritillarioides"

1963. 15th Anniv of Declaration of Human Rights.
374 **54** 50 f. red and blue . . . . 5·50 5·00

1964. Flowers. Multicoloured.
375 1 f. "Freycinettia" 60 40
376 2 f. Type **54a** 60 40
377 3 f. "Xanthostemon francii" . 90 70
378 4 f. "Psidiomyrtus locellatus" 1·40 80
379 5 f. "Callistemon suberosum" 1·75 1·00
380 7 f. "Montrouziera sphaeroidea" 4·75 1·40
381 10 f. "Ixora collina" . . . . 4·75 1·40
382 17 f. "Deplanchea speciosa" . 6·75 3·50
The 7 f. and 10 f. are horiz.

54b "Ascidies polycarpa" 54c "Philately"

1964. Corals and Marine Animals from Noumea Aquarium.
383 **54b** 7 f. red, brown and blue (postage) . . . . 1·10 80
384 – 10 f. red and blue . . . . 1·60 65
385 – 17 f. red, green and blue . 3·50 2·00
388 – 13 f. bistre, black and orange (air) . . . . 2·50 1·10
389 – 15 f. green, olive & blue . 3·75 1·25
390 – 25 f. blue and green . . . 6·00 3·75
386 – 27 f. multicoloured . . . 4·50 2·50
387 – 37 f. multicoloured . . . 7·00 3·75
DESIGNS—As T **54b**: VERT: 10 f. "Alcyonium catalai" (coral). HORIZ: 17 f. "Hymenocera elegans" (crab). 48×28 mm: 27 f. Surgeon fish; 37 f. "Phyllobranchus" (sea slug). 48×27 mm: 13 f. "Coris angulata" (fish) (juvenile); 15 f. "Coris angulata"; 25 f. "Coris angulata" (adult).

1964. "PHILATEC 1964" Int Stamp Exn, Paris.
391 **54c** 40 f. brn, grn & vio . . . 6·00 5·50

54d Houailou Mine

1964. Air. Nickel Production at Houailou.
392 **54d** 30 f. multicoloured . . . 3·50 2·50

54e Ancient Greek Wrestling

1964. Air. Olympic Games, Tokyo.
393 **54e** 10 f. sepia, mauve & green 16·00 14·00

55 Weather Satellite 56 "Syncom" Communications Satellite, Telegraph Poles and Morse Key

1965. Air. World Meteorological Day.
394 **55** 9 f. multicoloured . . . . . 2·75 2·25

1965. Air. Centenary of I.T.U.
395 **56** 40 f. pur, brn & blue . . . 10·00 7·50

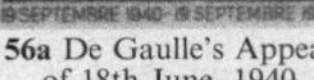
56a De Gaulle's Appeal of 18th June, 1940 56b Amedee Lighthouse

1965. 25th Anniv of New Caledonia's Adherence to the Free French.
396 **56a** 20 f. black, red & blue . . 10·00 6·00

1965. Inauguration of Amedee Lighthouse.
397 **56b** 8 f. bis., bl & green . . . . 1·00 60

56c Rocket "Diamant"

1966. Air. Launching of 1st French Satellite.
398 **56c** 8 f. lake, blue & turq . . . 3·00 1·50
399 – 12 f. lake, blue & turq . . 3·50 2·50
DESIGN: 12 f. Satellite "A1".

56d Games Emblem

1966. Publicity for 2nd South Pacific Games, Noumea.
400 **56d** 8 f. black, red and blue . . 1·10 70

56e Satellite "D1"

1966. Air. Launching of Satellite "D1".
401 **56e** 10 f. brown, blue and buff 2·25 1·50

57 Noumea, 1866 (after Lebreton)

1966. Air. Centenary of Renaming of Port-de-France as Noumea.
402 **57** 30 f. slate, red and blue . . 4·00 2·75

58 Red-throated Parrot Finch 59 U.N.E.S.C.O. Allegory

1966. Birds. Multicoloured.
403 1 f. Type **58** (postage) . . . . 1·50 75
404 1 f. New Caledonian grass warbler 85 60
405 2 f. New Caledonian whistler . 1·10 70
406 3 f. New Caledonian pigeon ("Notou") . . . . 2·50 1·40
407 3 f. White-throated pigeon ("Collier blanc") . . . . . 1·10 80
408 4 f. Kagu . . . . 2·40 1·10
409 5 f. Horned parakeet . . . . 4·25 1·50
410 10 f. Red-faced honeyeater . . 8·50 2·75
411 15 f. New Caledonian friar-bird 4·75 1·90
412 30 f. Sacred kingfisher . . . . 6·50 3·75
413 27 f. Horned parakeet (diff) (air) 5·00 3·00
414 37 f. Scarlet honeyeater . . . 8·50 4·25
415 39 f. Emerald dove . . . . . 7·75 2·75
416 50 f. Cloven-feathered dove . 10·50 5·00
417 100 f. Whistling hawk . . . . 18·00 7·25
Nos. 413/14 are $26\times45\frac{1}{2}$ mm; Nos. 415/17 are $27\frac{1}{2}\times48$ mm.

1966. 20th Anniv of U.N.E.S.C.O.
418 **59** 16 f. purple, ochre and green 1·50 1·00

60 High-jumping

1966. South Pacific Games, Noumea.
419 **60** 17 f. violet, green & lake . 1·75 1·10
420 – 20 f. green, purple & lake . 3·00 1·50
421 – 40 f. green, violet & lake . 3·50 2·25
422 – 100 f. purple, turq & lake . 7·50 4·50
DESIGNS: 20 f. Hurdling; 40 f. Running; 100 f. Swimming.

61 Lekine Cliffs

1967.
424 **61** 17 f. grey, green and blue . 1·75 1·00

62 Ocean Racing Yachts

1967. Air. 2nd Whangarei-Noumea Yacht Race.
425 **62** 25 f. red, blue and green . 4·50 3·00

63 Magenta Stadium

1967. Sport Centres. Multicoloured.
426 10 f. Type **63** . . . . 1·40 60
427 20 f. Ouen-Toro swimming pool 2·50 1·10

64 New Caledonian Scenery

1967. International Tourist Year.
428 **64** 30 f. multicoloured . . . . 4·00 2·00

65 19th-century Postman

1967. Stamp Day.
429 **65** 7 f. red, green & turquoise . 1·40 1·00

66 "Papilio montrouzieri"

1967. Butterflies and Moths.
430 **66** 7 f. blue, black & green (postage) . . . . 1·60 80
431 – 9 f. blue, brown and mve . 2·50 1·10
432 – 13 f. violet, purple & brn . 3·00 1·40
433 – 15 f. yellow, purple & blue . 5·00 2·50
434 – 19 f. orange, brown and green (air) . . . . 4·50 2·75
435 – 29 f. purple, red and blue . 6·00 4·00
436 – 85 f. brown, red & yellow . 14·00 6·75
BUTTERFLIES—As T **66**: 9 f. "Polyura clitarchus"; 13 f. Common eggfly (male), and 15 f. (female). 48 × 27 mm: 19 f. Orange tiger; 29 f. Silver-striped hawk moth; 85 f. "Dellas elipsis".

67 Garnierite (mineral), Factory and Jules Garnier

1967. Air. Centenary of Garnierite Industry.
437 **67** 70 f. multicoloured . . . . 6·75 4·50

67a Lifou Island

1967. Air.
438 **67a** 200 f. multicoloured . . . 11·50 7·50

67b Skier and Snow-crystal

1967. Air. Winter Olympic Games, Grenoble.
439 **67b** 100 f. brn, blue & grn . . 12·00 7·50

68 Bouquet, Sun and W.H.O. Emblem
69 Human Rights Emblem

1968. 20th Anniv of W.H.O.
440 **68** 20 f. blue, red and violet . 2·75 1·50

1968. Human Rights Year.
441 **69** 12 f. red, green & yellow . 1·40 1·00

70 Ferrying Mail-van across Tontouta River

1968. Stamp Day.
442 **70** 9 f. brown, blue and green . 1·75 1·00

71 "Conus geographus"
72 Dancers

1968. Sea Shells.
443 – 1 f. brn, grey & grn (postage) 80 45
444 – 1 f. purple and violet . . . 65 35
445 – 2 f. pur, red and blue . . 65 60
446 – 3 f. brown and green . . . 90 45
447 – 5 f. red, brown & violet . 1·25 65
448 **71** 10 f. brown, grey & bl . . 2·00 1·10
449 – 10 f. yellow, brown & red . 2·00 80
450 – 10 f. black, brown & orge . 1·60 65
451 – 15 f. red, grey and green . 3·50 1·40
452 – 21 f. brown, sepia & green . 3·75 1·25
453 – 22 f. red, brown & bl (air) 3·50 1·75
454 – 25 f. brown and red . . . 3·50 2·00
455 – 33 f. brown and blue . . . 4·50 2·50
456 – 34 f. violet, brown & orge 4·50 2·50
457 – 39 f. brown, grey & green 4·50 2·00
458 – 40 f. black, brown & red . 4·50 2·00
459 – 50 f. red, purple & green . 6·00 3·00
460 – 60 f. brown and green . . 9·00 4·50
461 – 70 f. brown, grey & violet 10·00 4·00
462 – 100 f. brown, black & bl . 17·00 8·50
DESIGNS—VERT: 22 × 36 mm: 1 f. (No. 443) "Strombus epidromis"; 1 f. (No. 444) "Lambis scorpius"; 3 f. "Lambis lambis"; 10 f. (No. 450) "Strombus variabilis". 27 × 48 mm: 22 f. "Strombus sinuatus"; 25 f. "Lambis crocata"; 34 f. "Strombus vomer"; 50 f. "Lambis chiragra". HORIZ: 36 × 22 mm: 2 f. "Murex haustellum"; 5 f. "Murex triremis"; 10 f. (No. 449) "Cypraea cribaria"; 15 f. "Murex rameux"; 21 f. "Cypraea talpe". 48 × 27 mm: 33 f. "Cypraea argus"; 39 f. "Conus lienardi"; 40 f. "Conus cabriti"; 60 f. "Cypraea mappa"; 70 f. "Conux coccineus"; 100 f. "Murex noir".

1968. Air.
463 **72** 60 f. red, blue and green . 6·50 4·00

73 Rally Car

1968. 2nd New Caledonian Motor Safari.
464 **73** 25 f. blue, red and green . 4·50 2·00

74 Caudron C-60 "Aiglon" and Route Map

1969. Air. Stamp Day. 30th Anniv of 1st Noumea-Paris Flight by Martinet and Klein.
465 **74** 29 f. red, blue and violet . 3·50 2·00

75 Concorde in Flight

1969. Air. 1st Flight of Concorde.
466 **75** 100 f. green and light green 22·00 15·00

76 Cattle-dip

1969. Cattle-breeding in New Caledonia.
467 **76** 9 f. brown, green & blue (postage) 90 65
468 – 25 f. violet, brown & grn . 2·50 1·00
469 – 50 f. purple, red & grn (air) 4·00 2·75
DESIGNS: 25 f. Branding. LARGER 48 × 27 mm; 50 f. Stockman with herd.

77 Judo

1969. 3rd South Pacific Games, Port Moresby, Papua New Guinea.
470 **77** 19 f. pur, blue & red (post) 2·75 1·25
471 – 20 f. black, red & green . . 2·75 1·25
472 – 30 f. black & blue (air) . . 3·50 1·75
473 – 39 f. brn, grn and blk . . . 5·50 2·50
DESIGNS—HORIZ: 20 f. Boxing; 30 f. Diving (38 × 27 mm). VERT: 39 f. Putting the shot (27 × 48 mm).

1969. Air. Birth Bicentenary of Napoleon Bonaparte. As T **114b** of Mauritania. Multicoloured.
474 40 f. "Napoleon in Coronation Robes" (Gerard) (vert) . . . 15·00 8·50

78 Douglas DC-4 over Outrigger Canoe

1969. Air. 20th Anniv of Regular Noumea-Paris Air Service.
475 **78** 50 f. green, brown & blue . 4·50 2·75

79 I.L.O. Building Geneva

1969. 50th Anniv of I.L.O.
476 **79** 12 f. brown, violet & salmon 1·10 80

80 "French Wings around the World"

1970. Air. 10th Anniv of French "Around the World" Air Service.
477 **80** 200 f. brown, blue & vio . . 15·00 8·50

81 New U.P.U. Building, Berne

1970. Inauguration of New U.P.U. Headquarters Building, Berne.
478 **81** 12 f. red, grey and brown . 1·40 80

82 Packet Steamer "Natal", 1883

1970. Stamp Day.
479 **82** 9 f. black, green and blue . 2·00 1·00

83 Cyclists on Map

1970. Air. 4th "Tour de Nouvelle Caledonie" Cycle Race.
480 **83** 40 f. brown, blue & lt bl . . 3·50 2·25

84 Mt. Fuji and Japanese Express Train

1970. Air. "EXPO 70" World Fair, Osaka, Japan. Multicoloured.
481 20 f. Type **84** . . . . 2·50 1·10
482 45 f. "EXPO" emblem, map and Buddha . . . . 3·50 1·60

85 Racing Yachts

1971. Air. One Ton Cup Yacht Race Auckland, New Zealand.
483 **85** 20 f. green, red and black . 2·50 1·25

86 Dumbea Mail Train

1971. Stamp Day.
484 **86** 10 f. black, green and red . 2·50 1·25

87 Ocean Racing Yachts

1971. 3rd Whangarei–Noumea Ocean Yacht Race.
485 **87** 16 f. turquoise, green and blue 3·50 1·75

88 Lieut.-Col. Broche and Theatre Map

1971. 30th Anniv of French Pacific Battalion's Participation in Second World War Mediterranean Campaign.
486 **88** 60 f. multicoloured . . . . 5·50 3·50

89 Early Tape Machine
90 Weightlifting

1971. World Telecommunications Day.
487 **89** 19 f. orange, pur & red . . 2·50 1·00

1971. 4th South Pacific Games, Papeete, French Polynesia.
488 **90** 11 f. brn & red (postage) . 1·40 1·25
489 – 23 f. violet, red & blue . . 2·50 1·25
490 – 25 f. green & red (air) . . 2·75 2·00
491 – 100 f. blue, green & red . . 6·50 4·00
DESIGNS—VERT: 23 f. Basketball. HORIZ: 48 × 27 mm: 25 f. Pole-vaulting; 100 f. Archery.

91 Port de Plaisance, Noumea

1971. Air.
492 **91** 200 f. multicoloured . . . 14·50 7·75

92 De Gaulle as President of French Republic, 1970

93 Publicity Leaflet showing De Havilland Gipsy Moth "Golden Eagle"

1971. 1st Death Anniv of General De Gaulle.
493 **92** 34 f. black and purple . . . 6·50 2·75
494 – 100 f. black and purple . . 13·00 6·00
DESIGN: 100 f. De Gaulle in uniform, 1940.

1971. Air. 40th Anniv of 1st New Caledonia to Australia Flight.
495 **93** 90 f. brown, blue & orge . 7·50 4·00

94 Downhill Skiing

1972. Air. Winter Olympic Games, Sapporo, Japan.
496 **94** 50 f. green, red & blue . . 5·00 2·50

95 St. Mark's Basilica, Venice

1972. Air. U.N.E.S.C.O. "Save Venice" Campaign.
497 **95** 20 f. brown, grn and blue . 2·75 1·40

96 Commission Headquarters, Noumea

1972. Air. 25th Anniv of South Pacific Commission.
498 **96** 18 f. multicoloured . . . . 1·50 1·00

97 Couzinet 33 "Le Biarritz" and Noumea Monument

1972. Air. 40th Anniv of 1st Paris–Noumea Flight.
499 **97** 110 f. black, purple & grn . 10·00 6·75

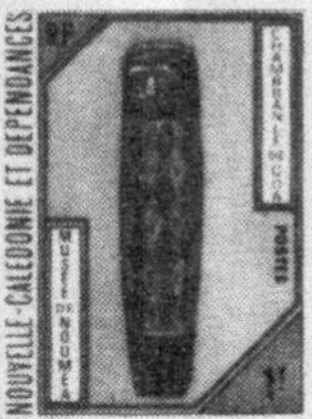

98 Pacific Island Dwelling

99 Goa Door-post

1972. Air. South Pacific Arts Festival, Fiji.
500 **98** 24 f. brown, blue & orange . 2·75 1·50

1972. Exhibits from Noumea Museum.
501 **99** 1 f. red, grn & grey (post) . 75 30
502 – 2 f. black, grn & dull grn . 75 30
503 – 5 f. multicoloured . . . . 1·00 50
504 – 12 f. multicoloured . . . . 2·25 1·00
505 – 16 f. multicoloured (air) . 1·50 1·00
506 – 40 f. multicoloured . . . . 3·00 1·50
DESIGNS: 2 f. Carved wooden pillow; 5 f. Monstrance; 12 f. Tchamba mask; 16 f. Ornamental arrowheads; 40 f. Portico, chief's house.

100 Hurdling over "H" of "MUNICH"

1972. Air. Olympic Games, Munich.
507 **100** 72 f. violet, purple & blue 6·50 3·50

101 New Head Post Office Building, Noumea

1972. Air.
508 **101** 23 f. brown, blue & green 2·25 1·00

102 J.C.I. Emblem

1972. 10th Anniv of New Caledonia Junior Chamber of Commerce.
509 **102** 12 f. multicoloured . . . 1·25 80

103 Forest Scene

1973. Air. Landscapes of the East Coast. Multicoloured.
510 11 f. Type **103** . . . . . . 1·25 80
511 18 f. Beach and palms (vert) . 2·50 1·25
512 21 f. Waterfall and inlet (vert) 3·00 1·40
See also Nos. 534/6.

104 Moliere and Characters

1973. Air. 300th Death Anniv of Moliere (playwright).
513 **104** 50 f. multicoloured . . . 5·50 2·50

105 Tchamba Mask

1973.
514 **105** 12 f. purple (postage) . . 2·50 1·40
515 – 23 f. blue (air) . . . . . 6·50 4·00
DESIGN: 23 f. Concorde in flight.

106 Liner "El Kantara" in Panama Canal

1973. 50th Anniv of Marseilles–Noumea Shipping Service via Panama Canal.
516 **106** 60 f. black, brown & green 5·50 3·00

107 Globe and Allegory of Weather

1973. Air. Centenary of World Meteorological Organization.
517 **107** 80 f. multicoloured . . . . 5·50 2·75

108 DC-10 in Flight

1973. Air. Inauguration of Noumea–Paris DC-10 Air Service.
518 **108** 100 f. grn, brn & blue . . 6·50 3·50

109 "Ovula ovum"

1973. Marine Fauna from Noumea Aquarium. Multicoloured.
519 8 f. "Chaetodon melanotus" (daylight) . . . . 1·40 70
520 14 f. "Chaetodonmelanotus" (nocturnal) . . . . 2·00 1·10
521 3 f. Type **109** (air) 80 35
522 32 f. "Acanthurus olivaceus" (adult and young) . . . . . 4·00 1·75
523 32 f. "Hydatina" . . . . . . 3·50 1·60
524 37 f. "Dolium perdix" . . . . 3·50 1·60

111 Office Emblem

1973. 10th Anniv of Central Schools Co-operation Office.
532 **111** 20 f. blue, yellow & green . 1·60 90

112 New Caledonia Mail-coach, 1880

1973. Air. Stamp Day.
533 **112** 15 f. multicoloured . . . . 1·75 1·10

1974. Air. Landscapes of the West Coast. As T **103**. Multicoloured.
534 8 f. Beach and palms (vert) . . 1·00 65
535 22 f. Trees and mountain . . . 1·75 1·10
536 26 f. Trees growing in sea . . 2·75 1·25

113 Centre Building

1974. Air. Opening of Scientific Studies Centre, Anse-Vata, Noumea.
537 **113** 50 f. multicoloured . . . . 2·50 1·40

114 "Bird" embracing Flora

1974. Nature Conservation.
538 **114** 7 f. multicoloured 65 45

115 18th-century French Sailor

1974. Air. Discovery and Reconnaissance of New Caledonia and Loyalty Islands.
539 – 20 f. violet, red and blue . 1·50 80
540 – 25 f. green, brown & red . 1·50 1·00
541 **115** 28 f. brown, blue & grn . 1·60 1·00
542 – 30 f. blue, brown & red . 2·25 1·40
543 – 36 f. red, brown & blue . 3·50 2·00
DESIGNS—HORIZ: 20 f. Captain Cook, H.M.S. "Endeavour" and map of Grand Terre island; 25 f. La Perouse, "L'Astrolabe" and map of Grand Terre island (reconnaissance of west coast); 30 f. Entrecasteaux, ship and map of Grand Terre island (reconnaissance of west coast); 36 f. Dumont d'Urville, "L'Astrolabe" and map of Loyalty Islands.

116 "Telecommunications"

1974. Air. Centenary of U.P.U.
544 **116** 95 f. orange, pur & grey . 5·00 3·00

117 "Art"

1974. Air. "Arphila 75" International Stamp Exhibition, Paris (1975) (1st issue).
545 **117** 80 f. multicoloured . . . 3·50 2·50
See also No. 554.

118 Hotel Chateau-Royal

1974. Air. Inauguration of Hotel Chateau Royal, Noumea.
546 **118** 22 f. multicoloured . . . 1·40 80

118a Animal Skull, Burnt Tree and Flaming Landscape

1975. "Stop Bush Fires".
547 **118a** 20 f. multicoloured . . . 1·00 65

119 "Cricket"

1975. Air. Tourism. Multicoloured.
548 3 f. Type **119** 80 45
549 25 f. "Bougna" ceremony . . 1·50 80
550 31 f. "Pilou" native dance . . 2·25 1·00

120 "Calanthe veratrifolia"

122 Throwing the Discus

1975. New Caledonian Orchids. Multicoloured.
551 8 f. Type **120** (postage) . . . . 1·10 55
552 11 f. "Lyperanthus gigas" . . 1·40 65
553 42 f. "Eriaxis rigida" (air) . . 3·50 2·00

1975. Air. "Arphila 75" International Stamp Exhibition, Paris (2nd issue).
554 **121** 105 f. purple, green & bl . 5·50 3·00

1975. Air. 5th South Pacific Games, Guam.
555 24 f. Type **122** . . . . 1·50 1·00
556 50 f. Volleyball . . . . 2·50 1·50

123 Festival Emblem

124 Birds in Flight

1975. "Melanesia 2000" Festival, Noumea.
557 **123** 12 f. multicoloured 80 45

1975. 10th Anniv of Noumea Ornithological Society.
558 **124** 5 f. multicoloured 65 40

125 Pres. Pompidou

127 Brown Booby

126 Concordes

1975. Pompidou Commemoration.
559 **125** 26 f. grey and green . . . 1·60 80

1976. Air. First Commercial Flight of Concorde.
560 **126** 147 f. blue and red . . . . 10·00 6·50

1976. Ocean Birds. Multicoloured.
561 1 f. Type **127** 60 40
562 2 f. Blue-faced booby 85 40
563 8 f. Red-footed booby (vert) . 2·00 1·00

128 Festival Emblem

1976. South Pacific Festival of Arts, Rotorua, New Zealand.
564 **128** 27 f. multicoloured . . . 1·50 1·00

129 Lion and Lions' Emblem

130 Early and Modern Telephones

1976. 15th Anniv of Lions Club, Noumea.
565 **129** 49 f. multicoloured . . . 3·00 1·75

1976. Air. Telephone Centenary.
566 **130** 36 f. multicoloured . . . 2·00 1·25

131 Capture of Penbosct

1976. Air. Bicent of American Revolution.
567 **131** 24 f. purple and brown . . 1·50 1·00

132 Bandstand

1976. "Aspects of Old Noumea". Multicoloured.
568 25 f. Type **132** . . . . 1·10 55
569 30 f. Monumental fountain (vert) 1·40 80

133 Athletes

1976. Air. Olympic Games, Montreal.
570 **133** 33 f. violet, red & purple 1·75 1·00

134 "Chick" with Magnifier

1976. Air. "Philately in Schools", Stamp Exhibition, Noumea.
571 **134** 42 f. multicoloured . . . 2·50 1·50

135 Dead Bird and Trees

1976. Nature Protection.
572 **135** 20 f. multicoloured . . . 1·40 65

136 South Pacific Heads

1976. 16th South Pacific Commission Conference.
573 **136** 20 f. multicoloured . . . . 1·25 70

137 Old Town Hall, Noumea

1976. Air. Old and New Town Halls, Noumea. Mult.
574 75 f. Type **137** . . . . 3·75 2·50
575 125 f. New Town Hall . . . . 6·25 3·00

138 Water Carnival

1977. Air. Summer Festival, Noumea.
576 **138** 11 f. multicoloured 80 40

139 "Pseudophyllanax imperialis" (cricket)

1977. Insects.
577 **139** 26 f. emerald, green & brn 1·25 1·00
578 – 31 f. brown, sepia and grn 2·00 1·00
DESIGN: 31 f. "Agrianome fairmairei" (long-horn beetle).

140 Miniature Roadway

1977. Air. Road Safety.
579 **140** 50 f. multicoloured . . . . 2·50 1·25

141 Earth Station

1977. Earth Satellite Station, Noumea.
580 **141** 29 f. multicoloured . . . . 1·40 80

142 "Phajus daenikeri"

1977. Orchids. Multicoloured.
581 22 f. Type **142** . . . . 1·25 80
582 44 f. "Dendrobium finetianum" 2·50 1·25

143 Mask and Palms

1977. La Perouse School Philatelic Exn.
583 **143** 35 f. multicoloured . . . 1·40 1·00

144 Trees

1977. Nature Protection.
584 **144** 20 f. multicoloured . . . 1·00 65

145 Palm Tree and Emblem

1977. French Junior Chambers of Commerce Congress.
585 **145** 200 f. multicoloured . . . 7·75 5·00

146 Young Great Frigate Bird

1977. Great Frigate Birds. Multicoloured.
586 16 f. Type **146** (postage) . . . 1·10 65
587 42 f. Adult male bird (horiz) (air) 3·25 1·75

147 Magenta Airport and Map of Internal Air Network

1977. Air. Airports. Multicoloured.
588 24 f. Type **147** . . . . 1·00 65
589 57 f. La Tontout International Airport, Noumea . . . . 2·50 1·50

1977. Air. 1st Commercial Flight of Concorde, Paris–New York. Optd **22.11.77 PARIS NEW-YORK**.
590 **126** 147 f. blue and red . . . 11·00 9·00

149 Horse and Foal

1977. 10th Anniv of S.E.C.C. (Horse-breeding Society).
591 **149** 5 f. brown, green and blue 80 40

150 "Moselle Bay" (H. Didonna)

1977. Air. Views of Old Noumea (1st series).
592 **150** 41 f. multicoloured . . . 2·50 1·50
593 – 42 f. purple and brown . . 2·50 1·50
DESIGN—49 × 27 mm: 42 f. "Settlers Valley" (J. Kreber).

151 Black-naped Tern

1978. Ocean Birds. Multicoloured.
594 22 f. Type **151** . . . . 1·25 80
595 40 f. Sooty tern . . . . 2·50 1·50

152 "Araucaria montana" 153 "Halityle regularis"

1978. Flora. Multicoloured.
596 16 f. Type **152** (postage) . . . 55 45
597 42 f. "Amyema scandens" (horiz) (air) . . . . 2·50 1·50

1978. Noumea Aquarium.
598 **153** 10 f. multicoloured . . . 65 30

154 Turtle

1978. Protection of the Turtle.
599 **154** 30 f. multicoloured . . . 1·25 80

155 New Caledonian Flying Fox

1978. Nature Protection.
600 **155** 20 f. multicoloured . . . 1·10 65

156 "Underwater Carnival"

1978. Air. Aubusson Tapestry.
601 **156** 105 f. multicoloured . . . 4·25 2·50

157 Pastor Maurice Leenhardt

1978. Birth Centenary of Pastor Maurice Leenhardt.
602 **157** 37 f. sepia, green & orge . 1·50 1·10

158 Hare chasing "Stamp" Tortoise

1978. School Philately (1st series).
603 **158** 35 f. multicoloured . . . 2·25 1·40

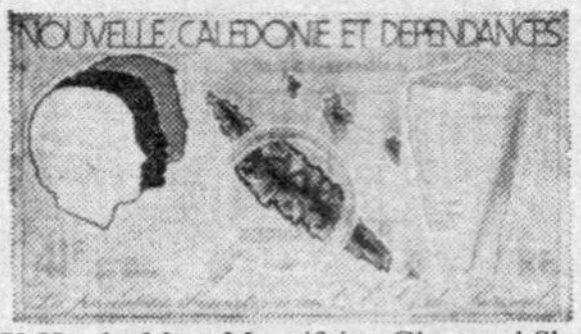

159 Heads, Map, Magnifying Glass and Shell

1978. Air. Thematic Philately at Bourail.
604 **159** 41 f. multicoloured . . . 1·75 1·10

160 Candles 161 Footballer and League Badge

1978. 3rd New Caledonian Old People's Day.
605 **160** 36 f. multicoloured . . . 1·25 80

1978. 50th Anniv of New Caledonian Football League.
606 **161** 26 f. multicoloured . . . 1·25 65

162 "Fauberg Blanchot" (after Lacouture)

1978. Air. Views of Old Noumea.
607 **162** 24 f. multicoloured . . . 1·25 65

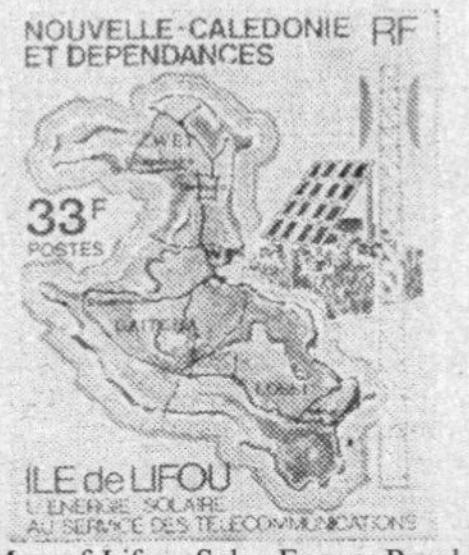

163 Map of Lifou, Solar Energy Panel and Transmitter Mast

1978. Telecommunications through Solar Energy.
608 **163** 33 f. multicoloured . . . 1·40 80

164 Petroglyph, Mere Region 165 Ouvea Island and Outrigger Canoe

1979. Archaeological Sites.
609 **164** 10 f. red 65 45

1979. Islands. Multicoloured.
610 11 f. Type **165** 60 40
611 31 f. Mare Island and ornaments (horiz) 85 60
See also Nos. 629 and 649.

166 Satellite Orbit of Earth

167 19th-century Barque and Modern Container Ship

1979. Air. 1st World Survey of Global Atmosphere.
612 **166** 53 f. multicoloured . . . . 1·50 1·00

1979. Air. Centenary of Chamber of Commerce and Industry.
613 **167** 49 f. mauve, blue & brown 1·50 80

168 Child's Drawing

1979. Air. International Year of the Child.
614 **168** 35 f. multicoloured . . . . 1·40 80

169 House at Artillery Point

1979. Views of Old Noumea.
615 **169** 20 f. multicoloured 85 55

170 "Katsuwonus pelamis"

1979. Air. Sea Fishes (1st series). Multicoloured.
616 29 f. Type **170** . . . . 1·40 65
617 30 f. "Makaira indica" . . . . 1·40 70
See also Nos. 632/3 and 647/8.

171 L. Tardy de Montravel (founder) and View of Port-de-France (Noumea)

1979. Air. 125th Anniv of Noumea.
618 **171** 75 f. multicoloured . . . . 2·75 1·50

172 The Eel Queen (Kanaka legend) 173 Auguste Escoffier

1979. Air. Nature Protection.
619 **172** 42 f. multicoloured . . . . 2·00 1·40

1979. Auguste Escoffier Hotel School.
620 **173** 24 f. brown, green and turquoise 85 55

174 Games Emblem and Catamarans

1979. 6th South Pacific Games, Fiji.
621 **174** 16 f. multicoloured 85 45

175 Children of Different Races, Map and Postmark

1979. Air. Youth Philately.
622 **175** 27 f. multicoloured . . . 90 55

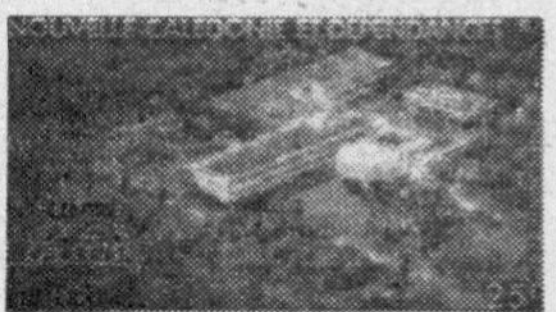

176 Aerial View of Centre

1979. Air. Overseas Scientific and Technical Research Office (O.R.S.T.O.M.) Centre, Noumea.
623 **176** 25 f. multicoloured . . . 90 55

177 "Agathis ovata"

1979. Trees. Multicoloured.
624 5 f. Type **177** 50 20
625 34 f. "Cyathea intermedia" . 1·25 65

178 Rodeo Riding

1979. Pouembout Rodeo.
626 **178** 12 f. multicoloured . . . 80 40

179 Hill, 1860 10 c. Stamp and Post Office

1979. Air. Death Centenary of Sir Rowland Hill.
627 **179** 150 f. black, brn & orge . 4·50 2·50

180 "Bantamia merleti"

1980. Noumea Aquarium. Fluorescent Corals (1st issue).
628 **180** 23 f. multicoloured . . . 90 45
See also No. 646.

1980. Islands. As T **165**. Multicoloured.
629 23 f. Map of Ile des Pins and ornaments (horiz) 80 40

181 Outrigger Canoe

1980. Air.
630 **181** 45 f. blue, turq & indigo . 1·40 1·00

182 Globe, Rotary Emblem, Map and Carving

1980. Air. 75th Anniv of Rotary International.
631 **182** 100 f. multicoloured . . . 3·25 1·75

1980. Air. Sea Fishes (2nd series). As T **170**. Multicoloured.
632 34 f. Angler holding dolphin fish 1·25 80
633 39 f. Fishermen with sailfish (vert) . . . . 1·50 90

183 "Hibbertia virotii" **184** High Jumper, Magnifying Glass, Albums and Plimsoll

1980. Flowers. Multicoloured.
634 11 f. Type **183** 60 40
635 12 f. "Grevillea meisneri" . . 60 40

1980. School Philately.
636 **184** 30 f. multicoloured . . . 80 50

185 Scintex Super Emeraude Airplane and Map

1980. Air. Coral Sea Air Rally.
637 **185** 31 f. blue, green and brn . 1·00 80

186 Sailing Canoe

1980. Air. South Pacific Arts Festival, Port Moresby.
638 **186** 27 f. multicoloured . . . 80 65

187 Road Signs as Road-users

1980. Road Safety.
639 **187** 15 f. multicoloured . . . 60 25

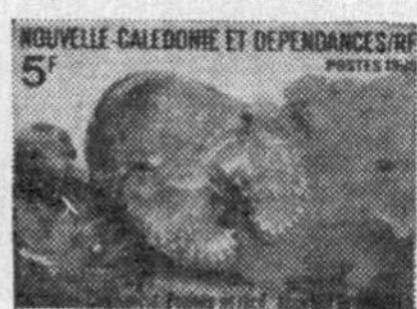

188 "Parribacus caledonicus"

1980. Noumea Aquarium. Marine Animals (1st series). Multicoloured.
640 5 f. Type **188** 30 20
641 8 f. "Panulirus versicolor" . . 40 20
See also Nos. 668/9.

189 Kiwanis Emblem

1980. Air. 10th Anniv of Noumea Kiwanis Club.
642 **189** 50 f. multicoloured . . . 1·50 1·00

190 Sun, Tree and Solar Panel

1980. Nature Protection. Solar Energy.
643 **190** 23 f. multicoloured . . . 90 55

191 Old House, Poulou

1980. Air. Views of Old Noumea (4th series).
644 **191** 33 f. multicoloured . . . 90 65

192 Charles de Gaulle **193** Manta Ray

1980. Air. 10th Death Anniv of Charles de Gaulle (French statesman).
645 **192** 120 f. green, olive & blue 4·50 2·75

1981. Air. Noumea Aquarium. Fluorescent Corals (2nd series). As T **180**. Multicoloured.
646 60 f. "Trachyphyllia geoffroyi" 1·60 90

1981. Sea Fishes (3rd series). Multicoloured.
647 23 f. Type **193** 70 50
648 25 f. Grey Shark 75 50

1981. Islands. As T **165**. Multicoloured.
649 26 f. Map of Belep Archipelago and Diver (horiz) 75 45

194 "Xeronema moorei"

1981. Air. Flowers. Multicoloured.
650 38 f. Type **194** 90 55
651 51 f. "Geissois pruinosa" . . 1·25 75

195 Yuri Gagarin and "Vostok 1"

1981. Air. 20th Anniv of First Men in Space. Multicoloured.
652 64 f. Type **195** . . . . . . 1·50 1·25
653 155 f. Alan Shepard and "Freedom 7" . . . . 4·00 2·50

196 Liberation Cross, "Zealandia" (troopship) and Badge

1981. Air. 40th Anniv of Departure of Pacific Battalion for Middle East.
655 **196** 29 f. multicoloured . . . 1·40 80

197 "Cymbiola rossiniana" **198** Sail Corvette "Constantine"

1981. Shells. Multicoloured.
656 1 f. Type **197** 15 10
657 2 f. "Connus floccatus" . . . 25 20
658 13 f. "Cypraea stolida" (horiz) 65 25

1981. Ships (1st series).
659 **198** 10 f. blue, brown and red . 65 30
660 – 25 f. blue, brown and red . 1·00 65
DESIGN: 25 f. Paddle-gunboat "Le Phoque", 1853.
See also Nos. 680/1 and 725/6.

199 "Echinometra mathaei"

1981. Air. Water Plants. Multicoloured.
661 38 f. Type **199** 90 55
662 51 f. "Prionocidaris verticillata" 1·25 65

200 Broken-stemmed Rose and I.Y.D.P. Emblems

1981. International Year of Disabled Persons.
663 **200** 45 f. multicoloured . . . . 1·40 80

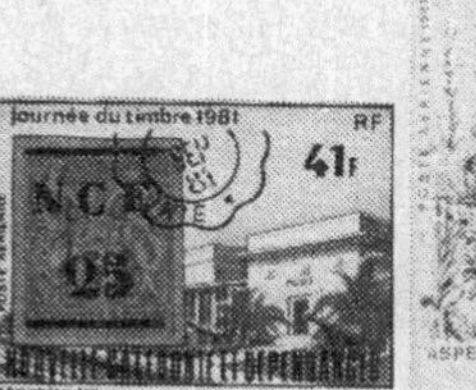

201 25 c. Surcharged Stamp of 1881 **202** Latin Quarter

1981. Air. Stamp Day.
664 **201** 41 f. multicoloured . . . . 1·10 65

1981. Air. Views of Old Noumea.
665 **202** 43 f. multicoloured . . . . 1·10 65

203 Trees and Fish **204** Victor Roffey and "Golden Eagle"

1981. Nature Protection.
666 **203** 28 f. blue, green & brown . 1·10 65

1981. Air. 50th Anniv of First New Caledonia–Australia Airmail Flight.
667 **204** 37 f. black, vio and blue . 90 60

1982. Noumea Aquarium. Marine Animals (2nd series). As T **188**. Multicoloured.
668 13 f. "Calappa calappa" . . . 65 45
669 25 f. "Etisus splendidus" . . . 1·00 65

205 "La Rousette"

1982. Air. New Caledonian Aircraft (1st series).
670 **205** 38 f. brown, red and green 90 55
671 – 51 f. brn, orge & grn . . . 1·10 65
DESIGN: 51 f. "Le Cagou".
See also Nos. 712/13.

206 Chalcantite, Ouegoa

1982. Rocks and Minerals (1st series). Multicoloured.
672 15 f. Type **206** 90 65
673 30 f. Anorthosite, Blue River . 1·25 65
See also Nos. 688/9.

207 De Verneilh, Deve and Munch (air crew), Couzinet 33 "Le Biarritz" and Route Map

1982. Air. 50th Anniv of First Flight from Paris to Noumea.
674 **207** 250 f. mauve, blue and black 5·50 2·75

208 Scout and Guide Badges and Map

1982. Air. 50th Anniv of New Caledonian Scout Movement.
675 **208** 40 f. multicoloured . . . 1·00 65

209 "The Rat and the Octopus" (Canaque legend)

1982. "Philexfrance 82" International Stamp Exhibition, Paris.
676 **209** 150 f. blue, mauve and deep blue . . . . 3·00 2·25

210 Footballer, Mascot and Badge

1982. Air. World Cup Football Championship, Spain.
677 **210** 74 f. multicoloured . . . 1·60 1·00

211 Savanna Trees at Niaoulis **212** Islanders, Map and Kagu

1982. Flora. Multicoloured.
678 20 f. Type **211** 80 45
679 29 f. "Melaleuca quinquenervia" (horiz) . . . . 1·00 55

1982. Ships (2nd series). As T **198**.
680 44 f. blue, purple and brown . 1·00 65
681 59 f. blue, light brown and brown 1·25 80
DESIGNS: 44 f. Naval transport barque "Le Cher"; 59 f. Sloop "Kersaint", 1902.

1982. Air. Overseas Week.
682 **212** 100 f. brown, green & bl . 2·00 1·10

213 Ateou Tribal House   214 Grey's Fruit Dove

1982. Traditional Houses.
683 **213** 52 f. multicoloured . . . 1·40 90

1982. Birds. Multicoloured.
684 32 f. Type **214** . . . . . . 1·40 70
685 35 f. Rainbow lory . . . . . 1·40 70

215 Canoe

1982. Central Office of Education Co-operation office.
686 **215** 48 f. multicoloured . . . 1·25 65

216 Bernheim and Library

1982. Bernheim Library, Noumea.
687 **216** 36 f. brown, purple and blk 90 50

1983. Air. Rocks and Minerals (2nd series). As T **206**. Multicoloured.
688 44 f. Paya gypsum (vert) . . . 1·10 80
689 59 f. Kone silica (vert) . . . . 1·40 90

217 "Dendrobium oppositifolium"

1983. Orchids. Multicoloured.
690 10 f. Type **217** 30 10
691 15 f. "Dendrobium munificum" 40 15
692 29 f. "Dendrobium fractiflexum" 80 35

218 W.C.Y. Emblem, Map of New Caledonia and Globe

1983. Air. World Communications Year.
693 **218** 170 f. multicoloured . . . 3·50 2·00

219 "Crinum asiaticum"

1983. Flowers. Multicoloured.
694 1 f. Type **219** 10 10
695 2 f. "Xanthostemon aurantiacum" 10 10
696 4 f. "Metrosideros demonstrans" (vert) 10 10

220 Wall Telephone and Noumea Post Office, 1890

1983. 25th Anniv of Post and Telecommunications Office. Multicoloured.
697 30 f. Type **220** 70 30
698 40 f. Telephone & Noumea Post Office, 1936 . . . . . . 80 30
699 50 f. Push-button telephone and Noumea Post Office, 1972 . 1·25 40

221 "Laticaudata laticaudata"   224 Volleyball

223 Bangkok Temples

1983. Noumea Aquarium. Sea Snakes. Multicoloured.
701 31 f. Type **221** 80 40
702 33 f. "Laticauda colubrina" . 1·00 40

1983. Air. New Caledonian Aircraft (2nd series). As T **205**. Each red, mauve & brown.
712 46 f. Mignet HM14 "Pou du Ciel" . . . . 1·00 65
713 61 f. Caudron C-600 "Aiglon" 1·25 80

1983. Air. "Bangkok 1983" International Stamp Exhibition.
714 **223** 47 f. multicoloured . . . 1·10 80

1983. 7th South Pacific Games, Western Samoa.
715 **224** 16 f. purple, blue and red 65 40

225 Oueholle

1983. Air.
716 **225** 76 f. multicoloured . . . 1·50 1·00

226 Desert and Water Drop showing Fertile Land   227 Barn Owl

1983. Water Resources.
717 **226** 56 f. multicoloured . . . 1·40 90

1983. Birds of Prey. Multicoloured.
718 34 f. Type **227** . . . . 1·50 80
719 37 f. Osprey . . . . 1·75 95

228 "Young Man on Beach" (R. Mascart)   229 "Conus chenui"

1983. Air. Paintings. Multicoloured.
720 100 f. Type **228** . . . . . . 2·25 1·50
721 350 f. "Man with Guitar" (P. Nielly) . . . . 7·50 4·50

1984. Sea Shells (1st series). Multicoloured.
722 5 f. Type **229** 30 10
723 15 f. "Conus moluccensis" . . 40 15
724 20 f. "Conus optimus" 75 40
See also Nos. 761/2 and 810/11.

230 "St. Joseph" (freighter)

1984. Ships (3rd series). Each black, red and blue.
725 18 f. Type **230** 65 40
726 31 f. "Saint Antoine" (freighter) 75 60

231 "Amphiprion clarkii"

1984. Air. Noumea Aquarium. Fishes. Multicoloured.
727 46 f. Type **231** . . . . 1·10 65
728 61 f. "Centropyge bicolor" . . 1·50 1·10

232 Arms of Noumea   233 "Araucaria columnaris"

1984.
729 **232** 35 f. multicoloured 80 45

1984. Air. Trees. Multicoloured.
730 51 f. Type **233** . . . . 1·25 65
731 67 f. "Pritchardiopsis jeanneneyi" . . . . 1·40 80

234 Tourist Centres

1984. Nature Protection.
732 **234** 65 f. multicoloured . . . . 1·50 80

235 Swimming

1984. Air. Olympic Games, Los Angeles. Multicoloured.
733 50 f. Type **235** . . . . 1·25 90
734 83 f. Windsurfing . . . . . . 1·75 1·25
735 200 f. Marathon . . . . 4·25 3·00

236 "Diplocaulobium ou-hinnae"

1984. Orchids. Multicoloured.
736 16 f. Type **236** 65 40
737 38 f. "Acianthus atepalus" . . 1·00 75

237 Royal Exhibition Hall, Melbourne

1984. Air. "Ausipex 84" International Stamp Exhibition, Melbourne.
738 **237** 150 f. grn, brn & mve . . 3·50 2·50

238 School and Arrow Sign-post   239 Anchor, Rope and Stars

1984. Centenary of Public Education.
740 **238** 59 f. multicoloured . . . 1·10 65

1984. Air. Armed Forces Day.
741 **239** 51 f. multicoloured . . . 1·00 65

240 "Women looking for Crabs" (Mme. Bonnet de Larbogne)

1984. Air. Art. Multicoloured.
742 120 f. Type **240** . . . . . . 2·50 1·50
743 300 f. "Cook discovering New Caledonia" (tapestry by Pilioko) . . . . 6·00 4·00

241 Kagu

1985.
744 **241** 1 f. blue 10 10
745 2 f. green 10 10
746 3 f. orange 10 10
747 4 f. green 15 15
748 5 f. mauve 15 15
749 35 f. red 80 45
750 38 f. red 80 60
751 40 f. red 90 35
For similar design but with "& DEPENDANCES" omitted, see Nos. 837/43.

1985. Sea Shells (2nd series). As T **229**. Multicoloured.
761 55 f. "Conus bullatus" . . . 1·25 80
762 72 f. "Conus lamberti" . . . 1·50 1·00

243 Weather Station transmitting Forecast to Boeing 737 and Trawler

1985. World Meteorology Day.
763 **243** 17 f. multicoloured . . . 45 25

244 Map and Hands holding Red Cross

1985. International Medicines Campaign.
764 **244** 41 f. multicoloured . . . 90 45

245 Electronic Telephone Exchange

1985. Inauguration of Electronic Telephone Equipment.
765 **245** 70 f. multicoloured . . . 1·50 80

246 Marguerite la Foa Suspension Bridge

1985. Protection of Heritage.
766 **246** 44 f. brown, red and blue . 1·00 55

247 Kagu with Magnifying Glass and Stamp

1985. "Le Cagou" Stamp Club.
767 **247** 220 f. multicoloured . . . 4·00 2·50

248 Festival Emblem

1985. 4th Pacific Arts Festival, Papeete. Mult.
769 55 f. Type **248** . . . . 1·25 80
770 75 f. Girl blowing triton shell . 1·50 1·00

249 Flowers, Barbed Wire and Starving Child

1985. International Youth Year.
771 **249** 59 f. multicoloured . . . 1·10 55

250 "Amedee Lighthouse" (M. Hosken)
251 Tree and Seedling

1985. Electrification of Amedee Lighthouse.
772 **250** 89 f. multicoloured . . . 1·75 1·00

1985. "Planting for the Future".
773 **251** 100 f. multicoloured . . . 2·00 1·00

252 De Havilland Dragon Rapide and Route Map

1985. Air. 30th Anniv of First Regular Internal Air Service.
774 **252** 80 f. multicoloured . . . 1·50 1·00

253 Hands and U.N. Emblem

1985. 40th Anniv of U.N.O.
775 **253** 250 f. multicoloured . . . 4·50 2·50

254 School, Map and "Shell"

1985. Air. Jules Garnier High School.
776 **254** 400 f. multicoloured . . . 7·50 4·00

255 Purple Swamphen

1985. Birds. Multicoloured.
777 50 f. Type **255** . . . . 1·00 70
778 60 f. Island thrush . . . . . 1·25 90

256 Aircraft Tail Fins and Eiffel Tower

1986. Air. 30th Anniv of Scheduled Paris–Noumea Flights.
779 **256** 72 f. multicoloured . . . 1·50 90

257 "Rhinopias aphanes"

1986. Noumea Aquarium. Multicoloured.
780 10 f. "Pomacanthus imperator" 25 20
781 17 f. Type **257** 35 25

258 Kanumera Bay, Isle of Pines

1986. Landscapes (1st series). Multicoloured.
782 50 f. Type **258** . . . . . . 1·00 55
783 55 f. Inland village . . . . . 1·10 55
See also Nos. 795/6 and 864/5.

259 "Bavayia sauvagii"

1986. Geckos. Multicoloured.
784 20 f. Type **259** 55 25
785 45 f. "Rhacodactylus leachianus" 1·00 65

INDEX

Countries can be quickly located by referring to the index at the end of this volume.

260 Players and Azteca Stadium

1986. World Cup Football Championship, Mexico.
786 **260** 60 f. multicoloured . . . . 1·10 90

261 Vivarium, Nou Island

1986. Air. Protection of Heritage.
787 **261** 230 f. deep brown, blue and brown . . . . 4·50 2·75

262 Pharmaceutical Equipment

1986. 120th Anniv of First Pharmacy.
788 **262** 80 f. multicoloured . . . . 1·50 1·10

263 "Coelogynae licastioides"

1986. Orchids. Multicoloured.
789 44 f. Type **263** . . . . 1·00 55
790 58 f. "Calanthe langei" . . . . 1·25 80

264 Black-backed Magpie

1986. "Stampex 86" National Stamp Exhibition, Adelaide.
791 **264** 110 f. multicoloured . . . 2·50 2·00

265 Airplane over New Caledonia

1986. Air. Inaugural Flight of "ATR 42".
792 **265** 18 f. multicoloured 35 25

266 Emblem and 1860 Stamp
267 Arms of Mont Dore

1986. Air. "Stockholmia 86" International Stamp Exhibition.
793 **266** 108 f. black, red and lilac . 2·00 1·50

1986.
794 **267** 94 f. multicoloured . . . . 1·75 1·10

1986. Landscapes (2nd series). As T **258**. Multicoloured.
795 40 f. West coast (vert) 80 40
796 76 f. South . . . . 1·50 90

268 Wild Flowers
269 Club Banner

1986. Association for Nature Protection.
797 **268** 73 f. multicoloured . . . 1·50 90

1986. 25th Anniv of Noumea Lions Club.
798 **269** 350 f. multicoloured . . . 6·00 4·50

270 "Moret Bridge" (Alfred Sisley)

1986. Paintings. Multicoloured.
799 74 f. Type **270** . . . . 1·50 90
800 140 f. "Hunting Butterflies" (Berthe Morisot) . . . . . 2·75 1·75

271 Emblem and Sound Waves
272 "Challenge France"

1987. Air. 25th Anniv of New Caledonia Amateur Radio Association.
801 **271** 64 f. multicoloured . . . 1·25 80

1987. America's Cup Yacht Race. Multicoloured.
802 30 f. Type **272** . . . . 1·00 55
803 70 f. "French Kiss" . . . . . 1·50 1·00

273 "Anona squamosa" and "Graphium gelon"

1987. Plants and Butterflies. Multicoloured.
804 46 f. Type **273** . . . . 1·00 65
805 54 f. "Abizzia granulosa" and "Polyura gamma" . . . . . 1·25 80

274 Peaceful Landscape, Earphones and Noisy Equipment

1987. Air. Nature Protection. Campaign against Noise.
806 **274** 150 f. multicoloured . . . 3·00 1·50

275 Isle of Pines Canoe

1987. Canoes. Each brown, green and blue.
807 72 f. Type **275** . . . . 1·40 90
808 90 f. Ouvea canoe . . . . . . 1·75 1·10

276 Town Hall

1987. New Town Hall, Mont Dore.
809 **276** 92 f. multicoloured . . . 1·75 1·10

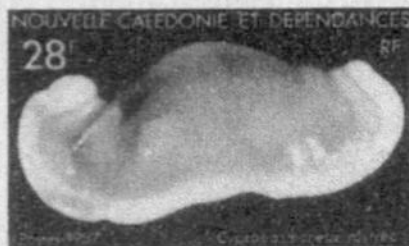

277 "Cypraea moneta"

1987. Sea Shells (3rd series). Multicoloured.
810 28 f. Type **277** 55 45
811 36 f. "Cypraea martini" . . . 80 55

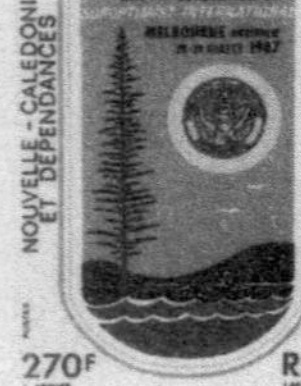

278 Games Emblem 279 Emblem

1987. 8th South Pacific Games. Noumea (1st issue).
812 **278** 40 f. multicoloured . . . 80 55
See also Nos. 819/21.

1987. 13th Soroptimists International Convention, Melbourne.
813 **279** 270 f. multicoloured . . . 5·00 3·25

280 New Caledonia White Eye

1987. Birds. Multicoloured.
814 18 f. Type **280** 45 30
815 21 f. Peregrine falcon (vert) . . 45 30

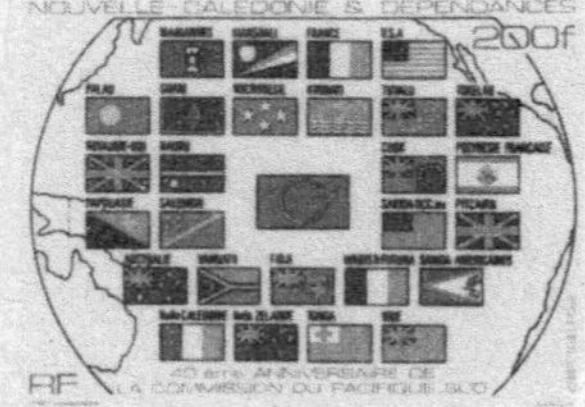

281 Flags on Globe

1987. 40th Anniv of South Pacific Commission.
816 **281** 200 f. multicoloured . . . 3·75 2·25

282 Globe and Magnifying Glass on Map of New Caledonia

1987. Schools Philately.
817 **282** 15 f. multicoloured . . . 35 20

283 Cricketers

1987. Air. French Cricket Federation.
818 **283** 94 f. multicoloured . . . 1·90 1·25

284 Golf

1987. 8th South Pacific Games, Noumea (2nd issue). Multicoloured.
819 20 f. Type **284** 40 20
820 30 f. Rugby football 60 35
821 100 f. Long jumping . . . . 1·75 1·10

285 Arms of Dumbea 287 University

286 Route Map, "L'Astrolabe", "La Boussole" and La Perouse

1988. Air.
822 **285** 76 f. multicoloured . . . 1·40 90

1988. Bicentenary of Disappearance of La Perouse's Expedition.
823 **286** 36 f. blue, brown & red . 80 45

1988. French University of South Pacific, Noumea and Papeete.
824 **287** 400 f. multicoloured . . . 7·25 4·50

288 Zebra Angelfish 289 Mwaringou House, Canala

1988. Noumea Aquarium. Fishes. Multicoloured.
825 30 f. Type **288** 65 40
826 46 f. "Glyphidodontops cyaneus" . . . . 1·00 60

1988. Traditional Huts. Each brown, green and blue.
827 19 f. Type **289** 35 20
828 21 f. Nathalo house, Lifou (horiz) 35 20

290 Anniversary Emblem

1988. 125th Anniv of International Red Cross.
829 **290** 300 f. blue, green and red 6·00 3·25

291 "Ochrosia elliptica"

1988. Medicinal Plants. Multicoloured.
830 28 f. Type **291** (postage) . . . 60 40
831 64 f. "Rauvolfia sevenetii" (air) 1·25 80

292 "Gymnocrinus richeri"

1988.
832 **292** 51 f. multicoloured . . . . 1·10 65

293 Furnished Room and Building Exterior

1988. Bourail Museum and Historical Association.
833 **293** 120 f. multicoloured . . . 2·25 1·50

294 La Perouse sighting Phillip's Fleet in Botany Bay

1988. "Sydpex 88" Stamp Exhibition, Sydney. Multicoloured.
834 42 f. Type **294** 85 70
835 42 f. Phillip sighting "La Boussole" and "L'Astrolabe" 85 70

295 Kagu 297 Laboratory Assistant, Noumea Institute and Pasteur

296 Table Tennis

1988.
837 **295** 1 f. blue 10 10
838 2 f. green 10 10
839 3 f. orange 10 10
840 4 f. green 10 10
841 5 f. mauve 15 10
842 28 f. orange 50 20
843 40 f. red 65 20

1988. Olympic Games, Seoul.
846 **296** 150 f. multicoloured . . . 2·75 1·60

1988. Centenary of Pasteur Institute, Paris.
847 **297** 100 f. red, black and blue . 1·90 1·25

298 Georges Baudoux

1988. Writers.
848 **298** 72 f. brown, green and purple (postage) . . . . 1·40 80
849 – 73 f. brown, bl & blk (air) 1·40 90
DESIGN: 73 f. Jean Mariotti.

299 Map and Emblems

1988. Air. Rotary International Anti-Polio Campaign.
850 **299** 220 f. multicoloured . . . 4·00 2·75

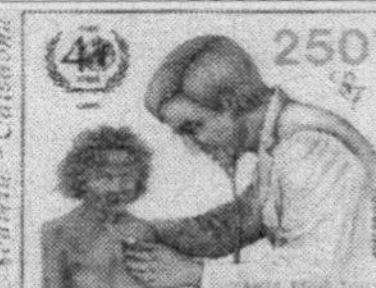

300 Doctor examining Child

1988. 40th Anniv of W.H.O.
851 **300** 250 f. multicoloured . . . 4·50 2·50

301 "Terre des Hommes" (L. Bunckley)

1988. Paintings. Multicoloured.
852 54 f. Type **301** . . . . 1·25 80
853 92 f. "Latin Quarter" (Marik) 2·00 1·25

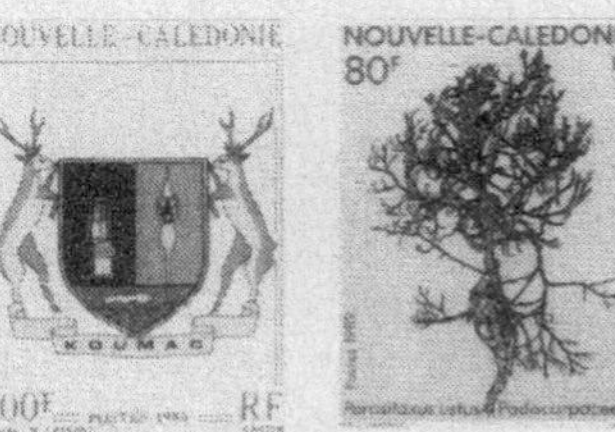

302 Arms of Koumac 303 "Parasitaxus ustus"

1989.
854 **302** 200 f. multicoloured . . . 3·25 2·25

1989. Flowers. Multicoloured.
855 80 f. Type **303** . . . . 1·50 90
856 90 f. "Tristaniopsis guillainii" (horiz) . . . . 1·60 1·00

304 "Plesionika sp"

1989. Marine Life. Multicoloured.
857 18 f. Type **304** 45 20
858 66 f. Waspfish . . . . 1·10 80
859 110 f. "Latiaxis sp." . . . . . 2·00 80

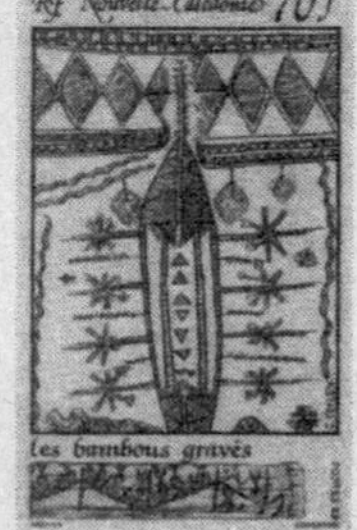

305 "Liberty" 306 Canoe and Diamond Decoration

1989. Bicentenary of French Revolution and "Philexfrance 89" International Stamp Exn, Paris. Multicoloured.
860 40 f. Type **305** (postage) . . . 80 45
861 58 f. "Equality" (air) . . . . 1·10 65
862 76 f. "Fraternity" . . . . . . 1·40 90

1989. Landscapes (3rd series). As T **258**. Mult.
684 180 f. Ouaieme ferry (post) . . 3·25 1·75
685 64 f. "The Broody Hen" (rocky islet), Hienghene (air) . . . 1·25 65

1989. Bamboo Decorations by C. Ohlen. Each black, bistre and orange.
866 70 f. Type **306** (postage) . . . 1·40 80
867 44 f. Animal design (air) . . . 80 55

307 "Hobie Cat 14" Yachts

1989. 10th World "Hobie Cat" Class Catamaran Championship, Noumea.
868 **307** 350 f. multicoloured . . . 6·00 3·50

308 Book Title Pages and Society Members

1989. 20th Anniv of Historical Studies Society.
869 **308** 74 f. black and brown . . 1·40 90

309 Fort Teremba

1989. Protection of Heritage.
870 **309** 100 f. green, brown & blue 1·75 1·10

310 "Rochefort's Escape" (Edouard Manet) 311 Fr. Patrick O'Reilly

1989. Paintings. Multicoloured.
871 130 f. Type **310** . . . . 2·50 1·50
872 270 f. "Self-portrait" (Gustave Courbet) . . . . 4·75 3·00

1990. Writers.
873 **311** 170 f. black and mauve . 3·00 1·75

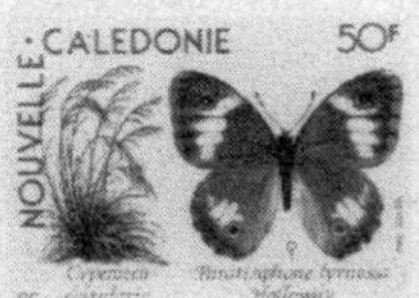

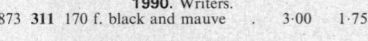

312 Grass and Female Butterfly

1990. "Cyperacea costularia" (grass) and "Paratisiphone lyrnessa" (butterfly). Multicoloured.
874 50 f. Type **312** (postage) . . . 90 55
875 18 f. Grass and female butterfly (different) (air) 35 20
876 94 f. Grass and male butterfly 1·60 1·00

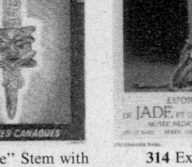

313 "Maize" Stem with Face 314 Exhibit

1990. Kanaka Money.
877 **313** 85 f. olive, orange & grn . 1·60 80
878 – 140 f. orange, black & grn 2·50 1·40
DESIGN: 140 f. "Rope" stem with decorative end.

1990. Jade and Mother-of-pearl Exhibition.
879 **314** 230 f. multicoloured . . . 4·00 2·40

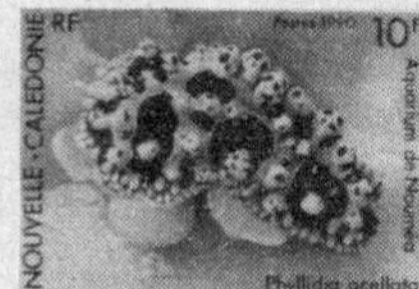
315 "Phyllidia ocellata"

1990. Noumea Aquarium. Sea Slugs. Multicoloured.
880 10 f. Type **315** 25 10
881 42 f. "Chromodoris kuniei" (vert) . . . . 1·00 55

316 Head of "David" (Michelangelo) and Footballers

1990. World Cup Football Championship, Italy.
882 **316** 240 f. multicoloured . . . 4·00 2·40

317 De Gaulle

1990. Air. 50th Anniv of De Gaulle's Call to Resist.
883 **317** 160 f. multicoloured . . . 2·75 1·90

318 Neounda Site

1990. Petroglyphs.
884 **318** 40 f. brown, green and red (postage) 65 45
885 – 58 f. black, brown and blue (air) . . . . 1·00 65
DESIGN—HORIZ: 58 f. Kassducou site.

319 Map and Pacific International Meeting Centre

1990.
886 **319** 320 f. multicoloured . . . 5·00 2·40

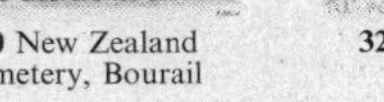
320 New Zealand Cemetery, Bourail 321 Kagu

1990. Air. "New Zealand 1990" International Stamp Exhibition, Auckland. Multicoloured.
887 80 f. Type **320** . . . . 1·40 1·10
888 80 f. Brigadier William Walter Dove . . . . 1·40 1·10

1990.
890 **321** 1 f. blue 10 10
891 2 f. green 10 10
892 3 f. yellow 10 10
893 4 f. green 10 10
894 5 f. violet 10 10
895 9 f. grey 10 10
896 12 f. red 15 10
897 40 f. mauve 50 30
898 50 f. red 65 40
899 55 f. red 70 45

The 5 and 55 f. exist both perforated with ordinary gum and imperforate with self-adhesive gum.

For design with no value expressed see No. 994.

322 "Munidopsis sp" 324 "Gardenia aubryi"

323 Emblem

1990. Air. Deep Sea Animals. Multicoloured.
900 30 f. Type **322** 55 35
901 60 f. "Lyreidius tridentatus" . 1·00 55

1990. Air. 30th South Pacific Conference, Noumea.
902 **323** 85 f. multicoloured . . . . 1·40 90

1990. Flowers. Multicoloured.
903 105 f. Type **324** . . . . 1·60 1·10
904 130 f. "Hibbertia baudouinii" . 2·00 1·40

325 De Gaulle

1990. Air. Birth Centenary of Charles de Gaulle (French statesman).
905 **325** 410 f. blue . . . . 6·75 2·75

326 "Mont Dore, Mountain of Jade" (C. Degroiselle)

1990. Air. Pacific Painters. Multicoloured.
906 365 f. Type **326** (postage) . . . 5·75 3·25
907 110 f. "The Celieres House" (M. Petron) (air) . . . . 1·75 1·40

327 Fayawa-Ouvea Bay

1991. Air. Regional Landscapes. Multicoloured.
908 36 f. Type **327** 65 45
909 90 f. Coastline of Mare . . . . 1·60 90

328 Louise Michel and Classroom

1991. Writers.
910 **328** 125 f. mauve and blue . . 2·00 1·25
911 – 125 f. blue and brown . . 2·00 1·25
DESIGN: No. 911, Charles B. Nething and photographer.

329 Houailou Hut 330 Northern Province

1991. Melanesian Huts. Multicoloured.
912 12 f. Type **329** 20 10
913 35 f. Hienghene hut 55 35

1991. Provinces. Multicoloured.
914 45 f. Type **330** 65 55
915 45 f. Islands Province 65 55
916 45 f. Southern Province . . . 65 55

331 "Dendrobium biflorum"

1991. Orchids. Multicoloured.
917 55 f. Type **331** 90 55
918 70 f. "Dendrobium closterium" 1·10 65

332 Pinecone Fish

1991. Fishes. Multicoloured.
919 60 f. Type **332** . . . . 1·00 55
920 100 f. "Tristigenys niphonia" . 1·60 1·00

333 Research Equipment and Sites

1991. French Scientific Research Institute for Development and Co-operation.
921 **333** 170 f. multicoloured . . . 3·25 1·60

334 Emblem 336 Emblems

335 Map and Dragon

1991. 9th South Pacific Games, Papua New Guinea.
922 **334** 170 f. multicoloured . . . 2·75 1·40

1991. Centenary of Vietnamese Settlement in New Caledonia.
923 **335** 300 f. multicoloured . . . 4·50 2·75

1991. 30th Anniv of Lions International in New Caledonia.
924 **336** 192 f. multicoloured . . . 3·00 1·60

337 Map, "Camden" (missionary brig), Capt. Robert Clark Morgan and Trees

1991. 150th Anniv of Discovery of Sandalwood.
925 **337** 200 f. blue, turquoise & grn 3·00 1·75

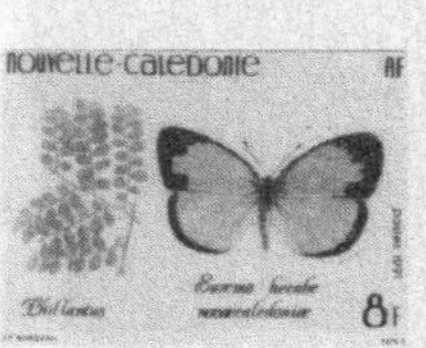

338 "Phillantus" and Common Grass Yellow

1991. "Phila Nippon '91" International Stamp Exhibition, Tokyo. Plants and Butterflies. Mult.
926 8 f. Type **338** 10 10
927 15 f. "Pipturus incanus" and "Hypolimnas octocula" . . 20 10
928 20 f. "Stachytarpheta urticaefolia" and meadow argos 30 20
929 26 f. "Malaisia scandens" and "Cyrestis telamon" 40 20

339 Nickel Processing Plant and Dam

1991. 50th Anniv of Central Economic Co-operation Bank. Multicoloured.
931 76 f. Type **339** . . . . . . 1·25 75
932 76 f. Housing and hotels . . . 1·25 75

340 "Caledonian Cricket" (Marcel Moutouh)

1991. Air. Pacific Painters. Multicoloured.
933 130 f. Type **340** . . . . . . 2·10 1·10
934 435 f. "Saint Louis" (Janine Goetz) . . . . 6·75 4·00

341 Blue River (½ size illustration)

1992. Air. Blue River National Park.
935 **341** 400 f. multicoloured . . . 5·25 3·25

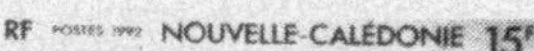

342 La Madeleine Falls

1992. Nature Protection.
937 **342** 15 f. multicoloured . . . 20 15

343 Lapita Pot **345** "Pinta"

344 Barqueta Bridge

1992. Air. Noumea Museum.
939 **343** 25 f. black and orange . 30 20

1992. Air. "Expo '92" World's Fair, Seville.
940 **344** 10 f. multicoloured . . . 15 10

1992. Air. "World Columbian Stamp Expo '92", Chicago. Multicoloured.
941 80 f. Type **345** . . . . . . 1·00 90
942 80 f. "Santa Maria" . . . . 1·00 90
943 80 f. "Nina" . . . . 1·00 90

346 Crane and Kagu within "100"

1992. Centenary of Arrival of First Japanese Immigrants. Multicoloured, background colours given.
945 **346** 95 f. yellow . . . . . . 1·25 75
946 95 f. grey . . . . 1·25 75

347 Synchronised Swimming

1992. Olympic Games, Barcelona.
947 **347** 260 f. multicoloured . . . 3·25 2·00

348 Bell Airacobra, Grumman F4F Wildcat, Barrage Balloon, Harbour and Nissen Huts

1992. 50th Anniv of Arrival of American Forces in New Caledonia.
948 **348** 50 f. multicoloured . . . 65 40

349 "Wahpa" (Paul Mascart)

1992. Air. Pacific Painters.
949 **349** 205 f. multicoloured . . . 2·50 1·50

350 Australian Cattle Dog **352** "Amalda fuscolingua"

351 Entrecasteaux and Fleet

1992. Air. Canine World Championships.
950 **350** 175 f. multicoloured . . . 2·25 1·40

1992. Air. Navigators. Bicentenary of Landing of Admiral Bruni d'Entrecasteaux on West Coast of New Caledonia.
951 **351** 110 f. orange, blue & grn . 1·50 90

1992. Air. Shells. Multicoloured.
952 30 f. Type **352** 55 35
953 50 f. "Cassis abbotti" 85 50

353 Deole

1992. Air. "La Brousse en Folie" (comic strip) by Bernard Berger. Multicoloured.
954 80 f. Type **353** . . . . 1·00 60
955 80 f. Tonton Marcel . . . . . 1·00 60
956 80 f. Tathan . . . . 1·00 60
957 80 f. Joinville . . . . 1·00 60

354 Lagoon

1993. Lagoon Protection.
958 **354** 120 f. multicoloured . . . 1·50 90

355 Harbour (Gaston Roullet)

1993. Air. Pacific Painters.
959 **355** 150 f. multicoloured . . . 1·90 1·25

356 Symbols of New Caledonia

1993. School Philately. "Tourism my Friend".
960 **356** 25 f. multicoloured 30 20

357 Still and Plantation

1993. Air. Centenary of Production of Essence of Niaouli.
966 **357** 85 f. multicoloured . . . 1·10 65

358 Planets and Copernicus

1993. Air. "Polska '93" International Stamp Exhibition, Poznan. 450th Death Anniv of Nicolas Copernicus (astronomer).
967 **358** 110 f. blue, turquoise & grey 1·40 85

359 Noumea Temple

1993. Air. Centenary of First Protestant Church in Noumea.
968 **359** 400 f. multicoloured . . . 5·25 3·25

1993. No. 898 surch **55F.**
969 **321** 55 f. on 50 f. red 70 45

361 Malabou

1993. Air. Regional Landscapes.
970 **361** 85 f. multicoloured . . . 1·10 65

362 Locomotive and Bridge

1993. Air. Centenary of Little Train of Thio.
971 **362** 115 f. red, green and lilac 1·50 90

363 Rochefort **364** "Megastylis paradoxa"

1993. Air. 80th Death Anniv of Henri Rochefort (journalist).
972 **363** 100 f. multicoloured . . . 1·40 85

1993. Air. "Bangkok 1993" International Stamp Exhibition, Thailand. Multicoloured.
973 30 f. Type **364** 40 25
974 30 f. "Vanda coerulea" . . . 40 25

365 Route Map and Boeing 737-300/500

1993. Air. 10th Anniv of Aircalin (national airline).
976 **365** 85 f. multicoloured . . . 1·10 65

366 "Francois Arago" (cable laying ship)

1993. Air. Centenary of New Caledonia–Australia Telecommunications Cable.
977 **366** 200 f. purple, blue & turq 2·50 1·50

367 "Oxypleurodon orbiculatus"

1993. Air. Deep-sea Life.
978 **367** 250 f. multicoloured . . . 3·25 2·00

368 Aircraft, Engine and Hangar

1993. Air. 25th Anniv of Chamber of Commerce and Industry's Management of La Tontouta Airport, Noumea.
979 **368** 90 f. multicoloured . . . 1·25 75

369 First Christmas Mass, 1843 (stained glass window, Balade church)

1993. Air. Christmas.
980 **369** 120 f. multicoloured . . . 1·60 1·00

370 Bourail

1993. Town Arms. Multicoloured.
981 70 f. Type **370** . . . . 1·00 60
982 70 f. Noumea . . . . 1·00 60
983 70 f. Canala . . . . 1·00 60
984 70 f. Kone . . . . 1·00 60
985 70 f. Paita . . . . 1·00 60
986 70 f. Dumbea . . . . 1·00 60
987 70 f. Koumac . . . . 1·00 60
988 70 f. Ponerihouen . . . . . . 1·00 60
989 70 f. Kaamoo Hyehen . . . . 1·00 60
990 70 f. Mont Dore . . . . 1·00 60
991 70 f. Thio . . . . 1·00 60
992 70 f. Kaala-Gomen . . . . . 1·00 60
993 70 f. Touho . . . . 1·00 60

1994. No value expressed.
994 **321** (60 f.) red 85 55

371 Dog, Exhibition Emblem and Chinese Horoscope Signs (New Year)

1994. Air. "Hong Kong '94" International Stamp Exhibition.
995 **371** 60 f. multicoloured . . . 85 55

372 Airbus Industrie A340

1994. Air 1st Paris–Noumea Airbus Flight. Self-adhesive.
997 **372** 90 f. multicoloured . . . 1·25 75

1994. "Philexjeunes '94" Youth Stamp Exhibition, Grenoble. No. 960 optd **PHILEXJEUNES'94 GRENOBLE 22–24 AVRIL**.
998 **356** 25 f. multicoloured . . . 35 25

374 Photograph of Canala Post Office and Post Van

1994. 50th Anniv of Noumea–Canala Postal Service.
999 **374** 15 f. brown, green and blue 20 15

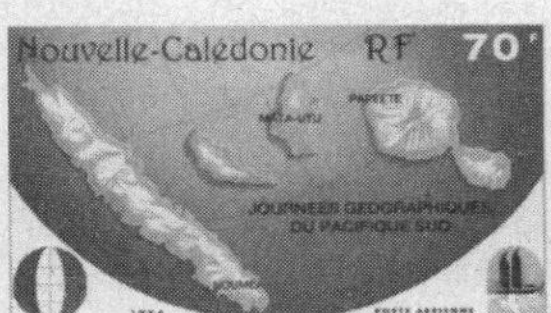

375 Pacific Islands on Globe

1994. Air. South Pacific Geographical Days.
1000 **375** 70 f. multicoloured . . . 1·00 60

376 Post Office, 1859

1994. Postal Administration Head Offices. Mult.
1001 30 f. Type **376** 40 25
1002 60 f. Posts and Telecommunications Office, 1936 . 85 55
1003 90 f. Ministry of Posts and Telecommunications, 1967 1·25 75
1004 120 f. Ministry of Posts and Telecommunications, 1993 1·60 1·00

377 "The Mask Wearer"

1994. Pacific Sculpture.
1005 **377** 60 f. multicoloured . . . 85 55

378 "Legend of the Devil Fish" (Micheline Neporon)

1994. Air. Pacific Painters.
1006 **378** 120 f. multicoloured . . . 1·60 1·00

379 "Chambeyronia macrocarpa" **380** Podtanea Pot

1994.
1007 **379** 90 f. multicoloured . . . 1·25 75

1994. Air. Noumea Museum.
1008 **380** 95 f. multicoloured . . . 1·40 85

381 Trophy, U.S. Flag and Ball

1994. Air. World Cup Football Championship, U.S.A.
1009 **381** 105 f. multicoloured . . . 1·50 90

OFFICIAL STAMPS

O 49 Ancestor Pole **O 110** Carved Wooden Pillow (Noumea Museum)

1958. Inscr "OFFICIEL".
O344 **O 49** 1 f. yellow 45 40
O345 3 f. green 45 40
O346 4 f. purple 45 50
O347 5 f. blue 60 50
O348 9 f. black 70 70
O349 A 10 f. violet 85 70
O350 13 f. green . . . . . . 1·00 80
O351 15 f. blue . . . . . . 1·25 1·00
O352 24 f. mauve . . . . . 1·40 1·10
O353 26 f. orange . . . . . 1·50 1·25
O354 B 50 f. green . . . . . . 3·50 2·50
O355 100 f. brown . . . . . 7·50 4·00
O356 200 f. red . . . . . . 15·00 9·00
DESIGNS: A, B, Different idols.

1973.
O525 **O 110** 1 f. green, blk & yell 20 20
O526 2 f. red, black & grn 20 15
O527 3 f. green, blk & brn 30 20
O528 4 f. green, blk & bl 30 20
O529 5 f. green, blk & mve 45 25
O530 9 f. green, blk & bl 55 45
O531 10 f. green, blk & orge 55 45
O532 11 f. grn, blk & mve 35 20
O533 12 f. green, blk & turq 65 45
O534 15 f. green, blk & lt grn 35 25
O535 20 f. green, blk & red 35 25
O536 23 f. green, blk & red 55 45
O537 24 f. green, blk & bl 45 35
O538 25 f. green, blk & grey 65 45
O539 26 f. green, blk & yell 55 35
O540 29 f. red, black & grn 80 55
O541 31 f. red, black & yell 65 45
O542 35 f. red, black & yell 65 45
O543 36 f. green, blk & mve 65 45
O544 38 f. red, black & brn 65 45
O545 40 f. red, black & bl 65 55
O546 42 f. green, blk & brn 65 45
O547 50 f. green, blk & bl 90 65
O548 58 f. blue, blk & grn 1·00 65
O549 65 f. red, black & mve 1·10 65
O549a 76 f. red, blk & yell 1·40 75
O550 100 f. green, blk & red 1·75 1·25
O551 200 f. green, blk & yell 3·50 2·25

PARCEL POST STAMPS

1926. Optd **Colis Postaux** or surch also.
P137 **17** 50 c. on 5 f. green on mauve 60 90
P138 1 f. blue . . . . 90 1·00
P139 2 f. red on blue . . . . . 1·25 1·40

1930. Optd **Colis Postaux**.
P179 **23** 50 c. brown and mauve . 70 70
P180 **24** 1 f. pink and drab . . . 85 85
P181 2 f. brown and orange . . 1·25 1·25

POSTAGE DUE STAMPS

1903. Postage Due stamps of French Colonies optd **CINQUANTENAIRE 24 SEPTEMBRE 1853 1903** and eagle. Imperf.
D78 U 5 c. blue . . . . 1·40 1·25
D79 10 c. brown . . . . 5·00 4·25
D80 15 c. green . . . . 14·00 5·50
D81 30 c. red . . . . 9·50 7·00
D82 50 c. purple . . . . 45·00 10·50
D83 60 c. brown on buff . . . £160 40·00
D84 1 f. pink . . . . 21·00 9·75
D85 2 f. brown £600 £650

D 18 Outrigger Canoe **D 25** Sambar Stag **D 38**

1906.
D102 **D 18** 5 c. blue on blue . . . 25 30
D103 10 c. brown on buff . 35 50
D104 15 c. green 40 45
D105 20 c. black on yellow . 40 45
D106 30 c. red 50 50
D107 50 c. blue on cream . 80 85
D108 60 c. green on blue . . 75 80
D109 1 f. green on cream . 1·10 1·10

1926. Surch.
D137 **D 18** 2 f. on 1 f. mauve . . 1·90 2·00
D138 3 f. on 1 f. brown . . 1·90 2·00

1928.
D179 **D 25** 2 c. brown and blue . 15 30
D180 4 c. green and red . . 25 35
D181 5 c. grey and orange . 25 35
D182 10 c. blue and mauve . 20 35
D183 15 c. red and olive . . 25 35
D184 20 c. olive and red . . 40 60
D185 25 c. blue and brown . 40 45
D186 30 c. olive and green . 40 55
D187 50 c. red and brown . 75 85
D188 60 c. red and mauve . 80 80
D189 1 f. green and blue . . 95 1·00
D190 2 f. olive and red . . 1·10 1·10
D191 3 f. brown and violet . 1·90 1·75

1948.
D328 **D 38** 10 c. mauve 15 30
D329 30 c. brown 20 30
D330 50 c. green 30 35
D331 1 f. brown 30 35
D332 2 f. red 30 35
D333 3 f. brown 30 35
D334 4 f. blue 45 45
D335 5 f. red 55 60
D336 10 f. green 85 85
D337 20 f. blue . . . . . . 1·60 1·75

D 223 New Caledonian Flying Fox

1983.
D703 **D 223** 1 f. multicoloured . . 10 10
D704 2 f. multicoloured . . 10 10
D705 3 f. multicoloured . . 10 10
D706 4 f. multicoloured . . 20 20
D707 5 f. multicoloured . . 20 20
D708 10 f. multicoloured . 20 20
D709 20 f. multicoloured . 40 40
D710 40 f. multicoloured . 80 80
D711 50 f. multicoloured . 90 90

NICARAGUA Pt. 15

A republic of Central America independent since 1821.

1862. 100 centavos = 1 peso (paper currency)
1912. 100 centavos de cordoba = 1 peso de cordoba (gold currency)
1925. 100 centavos = 1 cordoba

2 Volcanoes 5

1862. Perf or roul.

No.	Type	Description	Unused	Used
13	2	1 c. brown	1·50	75
4		2 c. blue	2·25	75
14		5 c. black	6·00	1·25
18		10 c. red	2·25	1·40
19		25 c. green	2·25	2·40

1882.

No.	Type	Description	Unused	Used
20	5	1 c. green	15	20
21		2 c. red	15	20
22		5 c. blue	15	15
23		10 c. violet	15	60
24		15 c. yellow	30	1·50
25		20 c. grey	50	3·00
26		50 c. violet	70	6·00

6 Locomotive and Telegraph Key 7

1890.

No.	Type	Description	Unused	Used
27	6	1 c. brown	15	25
28		2 c. red	15	25
29		5 c. blue	15	15
30		10 c. grey	15	20
31		20 c. red	15	1·50
32		50 c. violet	15	4·75
33		1 p. brown	20	6·50
34		2 p. green	20	8·50
35		5 p. red	25	16·00
36		10 p. orange	25	23·00

1891.

No.	Type	Description	Unused	Used
37	7	1 c. brown	15	30
38		2 c. red	15	30
39		5 c. blue	15	25
40		10 c. grey	15	35
41		20 c. lake	15	1·75
42		50 c. violet	15	3·00
43		1 p. sepia	15	4·50
44		2 p. green	15	5·00
45		5 p. red	15	12·00
46		10 p. orange	15	15·00

8 First Sight of the New World 9 Volcanoes 10

1892. Discovery of America.

No.	Type	Description	Unused	Used
47	8	1 c. brown	15	25
48		2 c. red	15	25
49		5 c. blue	15	20
50		10 c. grey	15	25
51		20 c. red	15	1·75
52		50 c. violet	15	4·25
53		1 p. brown	15	4·25
54		2 p. green	15	5·00
55		5 p. red	15	14·00
56		10 p. orange	15	18·00

1893.

No.	Type	Description	Unused	Used
57	9	1 c. brown	15	25
58		2 c. red	15	25
59		5 c. blue	15	20
60		10 c. grey	15	25
61		20 c. brown	15	1·40
62		50 c. violet	15	3·50
63		1 p. brown	15	4·25
64		2 p. green	15	5·00
65		5 p. red	15	11·00
66		10 p. orange	15	14·00

1894.

No.	Type	Description	Unused	Used
67	10	1 c. brown	15	25
68		2 c. red	15	25
69		5 c. blue	15	20
70		10 c. grey	15	25
71		20 c. red	15	1·50
72		50 c. violet	15	3·50
73		1 p. brown	15	4·25
74		2 p. green	15	7·50
75		5 p. brown	15	9·00
76		10 p. orange	15	12·00

11 12 Map of Nicaragua 13 Arms of Republic of Central America

1895.

No.	Type	Description	Unused	Used
77	11	1 c. brown	15	20
78		2 c. red	15	20
79		5 c. blue	15	15
80		10 c. grey	15	20
81		20 c. red	15	70
82		50 c. violet	15	3·00
83		1 p. brown	15	4·50
84		2 p. green	15	4·75
85		5 p. red	15	9·25
86		10 p. orange	15	14·50

1896. Date "1896".

No.	Type	Description	Unused	Used
90	12	1 c. violet	15	75
91		2 c. green	15	50
92		5 c. red	15	35
93		10 c. blue	30	65
94		20 c. brown	1·75	3·50
95		50 c. grey	35	4·75
96		1 p. black	35	6·50
97		2 p. red	35	9·00
98		5 p. blue	35	9·00

1897. As T **12**, dated "1897".

No.	Type	Description	Unused	Used
99	12	1 c. violet	25	35
100		2 c. green	25	35
101		5 c. red	25	20
102		10 c. blue	3·75	65
103		20 c. brown	1·50	2·25
104		50 c. grey	5·25	5·75
105		1 p. black	5·25	8·75
106		2 p. red	11·50	11·00
107		5 p. blue	11·50	25·00

1898.

No.	Type	Description	Unused	Used
108	13	1 c. brown	20	20
109		2 c. grey	20	20
110		4 c. lake	20	30
122		5 c. olive	15·00	15
112		10 c. purple	8·75	40
113		15 c. blue	25	1·00
114		20 c. blue	6·00	1·00
115		50 c. yellow	6·00	5·75
116		1 p. blue	30	9·50
117		2 p. brown	11·00	13·00
118		5 p. orange	15·00	19·00

14 15 Mt. Momotombo

1899.

No.	Type	Description	Unused	Used
126	14	1 c. green	10	25
127		2 c. brown	10	25
128		4 c. red	20	25
129		5 c. blue	15	25
130		10 c. orange	15	25
131		15 c. brown	15	40
132		20 c. green	20	70
133		50 c. red	15	1·75
134		1 p. orange	15	5·00
135		2 p. violet	15	12·00
136		5 p. blue	15	14·50

1900.

No.	Type	Description	Unused	Used
137	15	1 c. red	30	10
138		2 c. orange	60	15
139		3 c. green	70	20
140		4 c. olive	90	25
184		5 c. red	75	25
185		5 c. blue	55	15
142		6 c. red	18·00	5·50
186		10 c. mauve	55	10
144		15 c. blue	9·50	35
145		20 c. brown	8·50	30
146		50 c. lake	8·50	1·50
147		1 p. yellow	18·00	6·50
148		2 p. red	7·50	75
149		5 p. black	13·00	2·50

1901. Surch **1901** and value.

No.	Type	Description	Unused	Used
151	15	2 c. on 1 p. yellow	7·00	6·00
169		3 c. on 6 c. red	6·50	3·75
163		4 c. on 6 c. red	5·50	3·50
173		5 c. on 1 p. yellow	9·00	4·25
168		10 c. on 2 p. red	7·00	1·75
152		10 c. on 5 p. black	12·50	10·00
153		20 c. on 2 p. red	12·50	12·50
176		20 c. on 5 p. black	4·75	3·75

1901. Postage Due stamps of 1900 optd **1901 Correos.**

No.	Type	Description	Unused	Used
177	D 16	1 c. red	60	30
178		2 c. orange	45	30
179		5 c. blue	55	45
180		10 c. violet	55	45
181		20 c. brown	75	1·00
182		30 c. green	70	1·00
183		50 c. lake	70	1·00

1902. Surch **1902** and value.

No.	Type	Description	Unused	Used
187	15	15 c. on 2 c. orange	2·50	1·00
188		30 c. on 1 c. red	1·00	3·50

27 Pres. Santos Zelaya 37 Arms

1903. 10th Anniv of Revolution against Sacaza and 1st election of Pres. Zelaya.

No.	Type	Description	Unused	Used
189	27	1 c. black and green	25	45
190		2 c. black and red	50	45
191		5 c. black and blue	25	45
192		10 c. black and orange	25	70
193		15 c. black and lake	45	1·40
194		20 c. black and violet	45	1·40
195		50 c. black and olive	45	3·00
196		1 p. black and brown	45	3·50

1904. Surch.

No.	Type	Description	Unused	Used
205	15	5 c. on 10 c. mauve	75	50
200		15 c. on 10 c. mauve	5·75	3·00

1904. Surch **Vale**, value and wavy lines.

No.	Type	Description	Unused	Used
203	15	5 c. on 10 c. mauve	1·50	35
204		15 c. on 10 c. mauve	40	30

1905.

No.	Type	Description	Unused	Used
206	37	1 c. green	20	15
207		2 c. red	20	15
208		3 c. violet	25	20
280		3 c. orange	25	15
209		4 c. orange	25	20
281		4 c. violet	25	15
282		5 c. blue	25	15
211		6 c. grey	45	30
283		6 c. brown	1·75	1·10
212		10 c. brown	55	20
284		10 c. lake	60	10
213		15 c. olive	55	25
285		15 c. black	60	10
214		20 c. lake	45	25
286		20 c. olive	60	10
215		50 c. orange	1·75	1·40
287		50 c. green	70	35
216		1 p. black	90	90
288		1 p. yellow	70	35
217		2 p. green	90	1·25
289		2 p. red	70	35
218		5 p. violet	1·00	1·50

1906. Surch **Vale** (or **VALE**) and value in one line.

No.	Type	Description	Unused	Used
292	37	2 c. on 3 c. orange	90	75
293		5 c. on 20 c. olive	30	25
247		10 c. on 2 c. red	1·10	45
223		10 c. on 3 c. violet	30	15
248		10 c. on 4 c. orange	1·25	55
291		10 c. on 15 c. black	30	25
250		10 c. on 20 c. lake	1·90	85
252		10 c. on 50 c. orange	1·40	45
234		10 c. on 2 p. green	12·00	7·00
235		10 c. on 5 p. violet	60·00	42·00
226		15 c. on 1 c. green	30	20
229		20 c. on 2 c. red	40	25
230		20 c. on 5 c. blue	45	35
236		35 c. on 6 c. grey	1·60	1·60
232		50 c. on 6 c. grey	45	35
238		1 p. on 5 p. violet	25·00	14·50

51 50 64

1908. Fiscal stamps as T **51** optd **CORREO–1908** or surch **VALE** and value also.

No.	Type	Description	Unused	Used
260	51	1 c. on 5 c. yellow	35	20
261		2 c. on 5 c. yellow	35	25
262		4 c. on 5 c. yellow	65	30
256		5 c. yellow	45	35
257		10 c. blue	35	20
263		15 c. on 50 c. green	45	30
264		35 c. on 50 c. green	2·50	65
258		1 p. brown	20	1·40
259		2 p. grey	20	1·50

1908. Fiscal stamps as T **50** optd **CORREOS–1908** or surch **VALE** and value also.

No.	Type	Description	Unused	Used
268	50	2 c. orange	2·10	1·00
269		4 c. on 2 c. orange	1·00	65
270		5 c. on 2 c. orange	1·10	45
271		10 c. on 2 c. orange	1·10	25

1909. Surch **CORREOS–1909 VALE** and value.

No.	Type	Description	Unused	Used
273	51	1 c. on 50 c. green	2·25	95
274		2 c. on 50 c. green	4·00	1·75
275		4 c. on 50 c. green	4·00	1·75
276		5 c. on 50 c. green	2·25	1·10
277		10 c. on 50 c. green	65	40

1910. Surch **Vale** and value in two lines.

No.	Type	Description	Unused	Used
296	37	2 c. on 3 c. orange	65	35
300		2 c. on 4 c. violet	25	15
301		5 c. on 20 c. olive	25	15
302		10 c. on 15 c. black	30	15
303		10 c. on 50 c. green	20	15
299		10 c. on 1 p. yellow	65	35
305		10 c. on 2 p. red	45	35

1911. Surch **Correos 1911** (or **CORREOS 1911**) and value.

No.	Type	Description	Unused	Used
307	51	2 c. on 5 p. blue	25	30
312		5 c. on 2 p. grey	90	70
308		5 c. on 10 p. pink	55	30
309	51	10 c. on 25 c. lilac	30	20
310		10 c. on 2 p. grey	30	20
311		35 c. on 1 p. brown	30	25

1911. Surch **VALE POSTAL de 1911** and value.

No.	Type	Description	Unused	Used
313	51	5 c. on 25 c. lilac	90	70
314		5 c. on 50 c. green	3·00	3·00
315		5 c. on 5 p. blue	4·00	4·00
317		5 c. on 50 p. red	3·00	3·00
318		10 c. on 50 c. green	70	45

1911. Railway stamps as T **64**, with fiscal surch on the front, surch on back **Vale–cts. CORREO DE 1911.**

No.	Type	Description	Unused	Used
319	64	2 c. on 5 c. on 2 c. blue	55	65
320		05 c. on 5 c. on 2 c. blue	30	40
321		10 c. on 5 c. on 2 c. blue	30	40
322		15 c. on 10 c. on 1 c. red	40	50

1911. Railway stamps, with fiscal surch as last, further surch on front **CORREO** and value.

No.	Type	Description	Unused	Used
323	64	2 c. on 10 c. on 1 c. red	80	80
324		20 c. on 10 c. on 1 c. red	4·00	4·00
325		50 c. on 10 c. on 1 c. red	7·50	7·50

1911. Railway stamps, with fiscal surch as last, surch in addition on front **Correo Vale 1911** and value.

No.	Type	Description	Unused	Used
326	64	2 c. on 10 c. on 1 c. red	15	15
328		5 c. on 5 c. on 2 c. blue	90	80
327		5 c. on 10 c. on 1 c. red	20	125
330		10 c. on 10 c. on 1 c. red	70	50

1911. Railway stamps, with fiscal surch on front, surch in addition **Vale CORREO DE 1911** and value on back.

No.	Type	Description	Unused	Used
331	64	5 c. on 10 c. on 1 c. red		18·00
332		10 c. on 10 c. on 1 c. red		7·00

70 71

1912.

No.	Type	Description	Unused	Used
337	70	1 c. green	25	15
338		2 c. red	25	15
339		3 c. brown	25	15
340		4 c. purple	25	15
341		5 c. black and blue	25	15
342		6 c. brown	25	70
343		10 c. brown	25	15
344		15 c. violet	25	15
345		20 c. brown	25	15
346		25 c. black and green	25	15
347	71	35 c. brown and green	1·10	1·10
348	70	50 c. blue	65	30
349		1 p. orange	90	1·40
350		2 p. green	90	1·75
351		5 p. black	1·60	2·10

1913. Surch **Vale 15 cts Correos 1913.**

No.	Type	Description	Unused	Used
352	71	15 c. on 35 c. brown & grn	30	20

1913. Surch **VALE 1913** and value in "centavos de cordoba".

A. On stamps of 1912 issue.

No.	Type	Description	Unused	Used
353	70	½ c. on 3 c. brown	35	25
354		½ c. on 15 c. violet	20	15
355		½ c. on 1 p. orange	20	15
356		1 c. on 3 c. brown	55	45
357		1 c. on 4 c. purple	20	15
358		1 c. on 50 c. blue	20	15
359		1 c. on 5 p. black	20	15
360		2 c. on 4 c. purple	25	20
361		2 c. on 20 c. brown	2·25	2·75
362		2 c. on 25 c. black & grn	25	15
363	71	2 c. on 35 c. brown & grn	20	35
364	70	2 c. on 50 c. blue	20	90
365		2 c. on 2 p. green	15	15
366		3 c. on 6 c. brown	15	10

B. On Silver Currency stamps of 1912 (Locomotive type).

No.	Type	Description	Unused	Used
367	Z 1	½ c. on 2 c. red	1·40	1·25
368		1 c. on 3 c. brown	95	85
369		1 c. on 4 c. red	95	85
370		1 c. on 6 c. red	95	85
371		1 c. on 20 c. blue	95	85
372		1 c. on 25 c. black & grn	95	85
384		2 c. on 1 c. green	11·00	10·00
373		2 c. on 25 c. black & grn	5·00	4·50
374		5 c. on 35 c. black & grn	95	85
375		5 c. on 50 c. olive	95	85
376		6 c. on 1 p. orange	95	85
377		10 c. on 2 p. brown	95	85
378		1 p. on 5 p. green	95	85

1914. No. 352 surch with new value and **Cordoba** and thick bar over old surch.

No.	Type	Description	Unused	Used
385	71	½ c. on 15 c. on 35 c.	15	10
386		1 c. on 15 c. on 35 c.	20	15

1914. Official stamps of 1913 surch with new value and thick bar through "OFFICIAL".

No.	Type	Description	Unused	Used
387	70	1 c. on 25 c. blue	30	20
388	71	1 c. on 35 c. blue	30	20
389	70	1 c. on 1 p. blue	20	15
391		2 c. on 50 c. blue	20	15
392		2 c. on 2 p. blue	20	15
393		5 c. on 5 p. blue	20	15

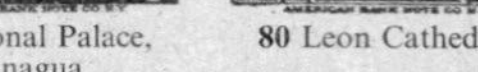

79 National Palace, Managua 80 Leon Cathedral

1914. Various frames.

No.	Type	Description	Unused	Used
394	79	½ c. blue	50	15
395		1 c. green	50	15
396	80	2 c. orange	50	15
397	79	3 c. brown	80	25
398	80	4 c. red	80	25
399	79	5 c. grey	30	10
400	80	6 c. sepia	5·25	3·25
401		10 c. yellow	55	15
402	79	15 c. violet	3·50	1·40
403	80	20 c. grey	6·50	3·25
404	79	25 c. orange	85	20
405	80	50 c. blue	85	25

See also Nos. 465/72, 617/27 and 912/24.

1915. Surch **VALE 5 cts. de Cordoba 1915**.

No.	Type	Description	Unused	Used
406	80	5 c. on 6 c. sepia	1·10	35

1918. Stamps of 1914 surch **Vale–centavos de cordoba**.

No.	Type	Description	Unused	Used
407	80	½ c. on 6 c. sepia	2·00	75
408		½ c. on 10 c. yellow	1·40	25
409	79	½ c. on 15 c. violet	1·40	45
410		½ c. on 25 c. orange	3·00	85
411	80	½ c. on 50 c. blue	1·40	25
440		1 c. on 2 c. orange	90	20
413	79	1 c. on 3 c. brown	1·50	25
414	80	1 c. on 6 c. sepia	7·00	2·10
415		1 c. on 10 c. yellow	13·00	4·75
416	79	1 c. on 15 c. violet	2·40	55
418	80	1 c. on 20 c. grey	1·40	25
420	79	1 c. on 25 c. orange	2·40	70
421	80	1 c. on 50 c. blue	7·75	2·25
422		2 c. on 4 c. red	1·75	25
423		2 c. on 6 c. sepia	13·00	4·75
424		2 c. on 10 c. yellow	13·00	2·50
425		2 c. on 20 c. grey	7·00	2·10
426	79	2 c. on 25 c. orange	3·00	30
427	80	5 c. on 6 c. sepia	5·00	2·50
428	79	5 c. on 15 c. violet	1·75	45

1919. Official stamps of 1915 surch **Vale–centavo de cordoba** and with bar through "OFFICIAL".

No.	Type	Description	Unused	Used
444	80	½ c. on 2 c. blue	30	15
445		½ c. on 4 c. blue	70	15
446	79	1 c. on 3 c. blue	70	25
432		1 c. on 25 c. blue	1·10	20
433	80	2 c. on 50 c. blue	1·10	20
443a		10 c. on 20 c. blue	1·00	40

1921. Official stamps of 1913 optd **Particular** and wavy lines through "OFFICIAL".

No.	Type	Description	Unused	Used
441	70	1 c. blue	90	45
442		5 c. blue	90	35

1921. No. 399 surch **Vale medio centavo**.

No.	Type	Description	Unused	Used
447	79	½ c. on 5 c. black	35	15

1921. Official stamp of 1915 optd **Particular R de C** and bars.

No.	Type	Description	Unused	Used
448	79	1 c. blue	3·50	1·00

1921. Official stamps of 1915 surch **Vale un centavo R de C** and bars.

No.	Type	Description	Unused	Used
449	79	1 c. on 5 c. blue	95	35
450	80	1 c. on 6 c. blue	50	20
451		1 c. on 10 c. blue	65	20
452	79	1 c. on 15 c. blue	1·10	20

90

91 Jose C. del Valle

1921. Fiscal stamps as T **23** surch **R de C Vale** and new value.

No.	Type	Description	Unused	Used
453	90	1 c. on 1 c. red and black	10	10
454		1 c. on 2 c. green and black	10	10
455		1 c. on 4 c. orange and black	10	10
456		1 c. on 15 c. blue and black	10	10

No. 456 is inscr "TIMBRE TELEGRAFICO".

1921. Independence Centenary.

No.	Type	Description	Unused	Used
457	–	½ c. black and blue	30	25
458	91	1 c. black and green	30	25
459	–	2 c. black and red	30	25
460	–	5 c. black and violet	30	25
461	–	10 c. black and orange	20	25
462	–	25 c. black and yellow	30	25
463	–	50 c. black and violet	30	25

DESIGNS: ½ c. Arce; 2 c. Larreinaga; 5 c. F. Chamorro; 10 c. Jerez; 25 c. J. P. Chamorro; 50 c. Dario.

1922. Surch **Vale un centavo R. de C.**

No.	Type	Description	Unused	Used
464	80	1 c. on 10 c. yellow	10	10

1922. As Nos. 394, etc., but colours changed.

No.	Type	Description	Unused	Used
465	79	½ c. green	15	10
466		1 c. violet	15	10
467	80	2 c. red	15	10
468	79	3 c. olive	25	15
469	80	6 c. brown	15	15
470	79	15 c. brown	25	15
471	80	20 c. brown	35	15
472		1 cor. brown	65	35

Nos. 465/72 are size 27×22¾ mm.

For later issues of these types, see Nos. 617/27 and 912/24.

1922. Optd **R. de C**.

No.	Type	Description	Unused	Used
473	79	1 c. violet	10	10

1922. Independence issue of 1921 surch **R. de C. Vale un centavo**.

No.	Type	Description	Unused	Used
474	91	1 c. on 1 c. black and green	55	45
475	–	1 c. on 5 c. black and violet	55	55
476	–	1 c. on 10 c. black and orange	55	30
477	–	1 c. on 25 c. black and yellow	55	25
478	–	1 c. on 50 c. black and violet	25	20

94

99 F. Hernandez de Cordoba

106

1922. Surch **Nicaragua R. de C. Vale un cent.**

No.	Type	Description	Unused	Used
479	94	1 c. yellow	10	10
480		1 c. mauve	10	10
481		1 c. blue	10	10

1922. Surch thus: **Vale 0.01 de Cordoba** in two lines.

No.	Type	Description	Unused	Used
482	80	1 c. on 10 c. yellow	70	25
483		2 c. on 10 c. yellow	70	20

1923. Surch thus: **Vale 2 centavos de cordoba** in three lines.

No.	Type	Description	Unused	Used
484	79	1 c. on 5 c. black	70	15
485	80	2 c. on 10 c. yellow	70	15

1923. Optd **Sello Postal**.

No.	Type	Description	Unused	Used
486	–	½ c. black & blue (No. 457)	5·50	4·25
487	91	1 c. black and green	1·40	70

1923. Independence issue of 1921 surch **R. de C. Vale un centavo de cordoba**.

No.	Type	Description	Unused	Used
488		1 c. on 2 c. black and red	30	30
489		1 c. on 5 c. black and violet	35	15
490		1 c. on 10 c. black and orge	15	15
491		1 c. on 25 c. black and yellow	25	25
492		1 c. on 50 c. black and violet	15	10

1923. Fiscal stamp optd R. de C.

No.	Type	Description	Unused	Used
493	90	1 c. red and black	15	10

1924. Optd **R. de C. 1924** in two lines.

No.	Type	Description	Unused	Used
494	79	1 c. violet	15	15

1924. 400th Anniv of Foundation of Leon and Granada.

No.	Type	Description	Unused	Used
495	99	1 c. green	90	25
496		2 c. red	90	25
497		5 c. blue	65	25
498		10 c. brown	65	45

1925. Optd **R. de C. 1925** in two lines.

No.	Type	Description	Unused	Used
499	79	1 c. violet	15	10

1927. Optd **Resello 1927**.

No.	Type	Description	Unused	Used
525	79	½ c. green	10	10
528		1 c. violet (No. 466)	10	10
555		1 c. violet (No. 473)	15	10
532	80	2 c. red	15	10
533	79	3 c. green	20	10
537	80	4 c. red	9·50	8·00
539	79	5 c. grey	55	20
542	80	6 c. brown	7·75	6·50
543		10 c. yellow	25	15
545	79	15 c. brown	55	25
547	80	20 c. brown	25	15
549	79	25 c. orange	30	15
551	80	50 c. blue	30	15
553		1 cor. brown	35	15

1928. Optd **Resello 1928**.

No.	Type	Description	Unused	Used
559	79	½ c. green	20	15
560		1 c. violet	10	10
561	80	2 c. red	15	10
562	79	3 c. green	15	10
563	80	4 c. red	15	10
564	79	5 c. grey	15	10
565	80	6 c. brown	15	10
566		10 c. yellow	20	10
567	79	15 c. brown	25	20
568	80	20 c. brown	35	20
569	79	25 c. orange	55	20
570	80	50 c. blue	90	10
571		1 cor. brown	75	25

1928. Optd **Correos 1928**.

No.	Type	Description	Unused	Used
574	79	½ c. green	15	10
575		1 c. violet	10	10
576		3 c. olive	55	20
577	80	4 c. red	25	10
578	79	5 c. grey	20	10
579	80	6 c. brown	30	15
580		10 c. yellow	35	15
581	79	15 c. brown	1·00	15
582	80	20 c. brown	1·00	15
583	79	25 c. orange	1·00	20
584	80	50 c. blue	1·00	20
585		1 cor. brown	3·00	1·50

1928. No. 577 surch **Vale 2 cts.**

No.	Type	Description	Unused	Used
586	80	2 c. on 4 c. red	90	25

1928. Fiscal stamp as T **90**, but inscr "TIMBRE TELEGRAFICO" and surch **Correos 1928 Vale** and new value.

No.	Type	Description	Unused	Used
587	90	1 c. on 5 c. blue and black	25	15
588		2 c. on 5 c. blue and black	25	15
589		3 c. on 5 c. blue and black	25	15

1928. Obligatory Tax. No. 587 additionally optd **R. de T**.

No.	Type	Description	Unused	Used
590	90	1 c. on 5 c. blue & black	45	10

1928. As Nos. 465/72 but colours changed.

No.	Type	Description	Unused	Used
591	79	½ c. red	30	15
592		1 c. orange	30	15
593	80	2 c. green	30	15
594	79	3 c. purple	30	20
595	80	4 c. brown	30	20
596	79	5 c. yellow	30	15
597	80	6 c. blue	30	20
598		10 c. blue	65	20
599	79	15 c. red	85	35
600	80	20 c. green	85	35
601	79	25 c. purple	16·00	3·75
602	80	50 c. brown	1·90	70
603		1 cor. violet	3·75	1·75

See also Nos. 617/27 and 912/24.

1928.

No.	Type	Description	Unused	Used
604	106	1 c. purple	20	10
647		1 c. red	25	10

For 1 c. green see No. 925.

1929. Optd **R. de C.**

No.	Type	Description	Unused	Used
605	79	1 c. orange	10	10
628		1 c. olive	15	10

1929. Optd **Correos 1929**.

No.	Type	Description	Unused	Used
606	79	½ c. green	20	15

1929. Optd **Correos 1928**.

No.	Type	Description	Unused	Used
607	99	10 c. brown	55	45

1929. Fiscal stamps as T **90**, but inscr "TIMBRE TELEGRAFICO". A. Surch **Correos 1929 R. de C. C$ 0.01** vert.

No.	Type	Description	Unused	Used
613	90	1 c. on 5 c. blue & black	10	15

B. Surch **Correos 1929** and value.

No.	Type	Description	Unused	Used
611	90	1 c. on 10 c. green and black	20	15
612		2 c. on 5 c. blue and black	20	10

C. Surch **Correos 1929** and value vert and **R. de C.** or **R. de T.** horiz.

No.	Type	Description	Unused	Used
608	90	1 c. on 5 c. blue and black (R. de T.)	20	15
609		2 c. on 5 c. blue and black (R. de T.)	15	15
610		2 c. on 5 c. blue and black (R. de C.)	13·00	70

1929. Air. Optd **Correo Aereo 1929. P.A.A.**

No.	Type	Description	Unused	Used
614	79	25 c. sepia	1·40	1·40
615		25 c. orange	1·00	1·00
616		25 c. violet	90	70

1929. As Nos. 591/603 but colours changed.

No.	Type	Description	Unused	Used
617	79	1 c. green	10	10
618		3 c. blue	25	15
619	80	4 c. blue	25	15
620	79	5 c. brown	30	15
621	80	6 c. drab	30	15
622		10 c. brown	45	15
623	79	15 c. red	65	20
624	80	20 c. orange	80	25
625	79	25 c. violet	20	10
626	80	50 c. green	35	15
627		1 cor. yellow	2·75	90

See also Nos. 912/24.

112 Mt. Momotombo

114 G.P.O. Managua

1929. Air.

No.	Type	Description	Unused	Used
629	112	15 c. purple	25	10
630		20 c. green	70	45
631		25 c. olive	50	30
632		50 c. sepia	80	45
633		1 cor. red	1·10	55

See also Nos. 926/30.

1930. Air. Surch **Vale** and value.

No.	Type	Description	Unused	Used
634	112	15 c. on 25 c. olive	40	30
635		20 c. on 25 c. olive	60	45

1930. Opening of the G.P.O., Managua.

No.	Type	Description	Unused	Used
636	114	½ c. sepia	80	60
637		1 c. red	80	60
638		2 c. orange	65	45
639		3 c. orange	1·00	90
640		4 c. yellow	1·00	90
641		5 c. olive	1·60	1·10
642		6 c. green	1·60	1·10
643		10 c. black	1·60	1·00
644		25 c. blue	3·25	2·40
645		50 c. blue	5·25	3·50
646		1 cor. violet	15·00	7·25

1931. Optd **1931** and thick bar obliterating old overprint "1928".

No.	Type	Description	Unused	Used
648	99	10 c. brown (No. 607)	45	90

1931. No. 607 surch **C $ 0.02**.

No.	Type	Description	Unused	Used
649	99	2 c. on 10 c. brown	55	45

1931. Optd **1931** and thick bar.

No.	Type	Description	Unused	Used
650	99	2 c. on 10 c. brown (498)	55	1·75

1931. Air. Nos. 614/16 surch **1931 Vale** and value.

No.	Type	Description	Unused	Used
651	79	15 c. on 25 c. sepia	90·00	90·00
652		15 c. on 25 c. orange	45·00	45·00
653		15 c. on 25 c. violet	9·00	9·00
654		20 c. on 25 c. violet	9·00	9·00

1931. Optd **1931**.

No.	Type	Description	Unused	Used
656	79	½ c. green	35	10
657		1 c. olive	35	10
665		1 c. orange (No. 605)	10	10
658	80	2 c. red	35	10
659	79	3 c. blue	35	15
660		5 c. yellow	2·10	1·40
661		5 c. sepia	65	20
662		15 c. orange	70	45
663		25 c. sepia	9·00	3·75
664		25 c. violet	3·50	1·50

1931. Air. Surch **1931** and value.

No.	Type	Description	Unused	Used
667	80	15 c. on 25 c. olive	4·75	4·75
668		15 c. on 50 c. sepia	36·00	36·00
669		15 c. on 1 cor. red	90·00	90·00
666		15 c. on 20 c. on 25 c. olive (No. 635)	7·50	7·50

120 G.P.O. before and after the Earthquake

1932. G.P.O. Reconstruction Fund.

No.	Type	Description	Unused	Used
670	120	½ c. green (postage)	90	90
671		1 c. brown	1·25	1·25
672		2 c. red	90	90
673		3 c. blue	90	90
674		4 c. blue	90	90
675		5 c. brown	1·40	1·40
676		6 c. brown	1·40	1·40
677		10 c. brown	2·25	1·50
678		15 c. red	3·50	2·25
679		20 c. orange	2·10	2·10
680		25 c. violet	2·25	2·25
681		50 c. green	2·25	2·25
682		1 cor. yellow	4·50	4·50
683		15 c. mauve (air)	90	75
684		20 c. green	1·10	1·10
685		25 c. brown	5·50	5·50
686		50 c. brown	7·00	7·00
687		1 cor. red	10·50	10·50

1932. Air. Surch **Vale** and value.

No.	Type	Description	Unused	Used
688	112	30 c. on 50 c. sepia	1·40	1·40
689		35 c. on 50 c. sepia	1·40	1·40
690		40 c. on 1 cor. red	1·60	1·60
691		55 c. on 1 cor. red	1·60	1·60

For similar surcharges on these stamps in different colours see Nos. 791/4 and 931/4.

1932. Air. International Air Mail Week. Optd **Semana Correo Aereo Internacional 11-17 Septiembre 1932**.

No.	Type	Description	Unused	Used
692	112	15 c. violet	40·00	40·00

1932. Air. Inauguration of Inland Airmail Service. Surch **Inauguracion Interior 12 Octubre 1932 Vale C$0.08.**

No.	Type	Description	Unused	Used
693	112	8 c. on 1 cor. red	13·00	13·00

1932. Air. Optd **Interior–1932** or surch **Vale** and value also.

No.	Type	Description	Unused	Used
705	120	25 c. brown	4·75	4·75
706		32 c. on 50 c. brown	5·50	5·50
707		40 c. on 1 cor. red	4·25	4·25

1932. Air. Nos. 671, etc., optd **Correo Aereo Interior** in one line and **1932**, or surch **Vale** and value also.

No.	Type	Description	Unused	Used
694	120	1 c. brown	12·00	12·00
695		2 c. red	12·00	12·00
696		3 c. blue	5·50	5·50
697		4 c. blue	5·50	5·50
698		5 c. brown	5·50	5·50
699		6 c. brown	5·50	5·50
700		8 c. on 10 c. brown	5·25	5·25
701		16 c. on 20 c. orange	5·25	5·25
702		24 c. on 25 c. violet	5·25	5·25
703		50 c. green	5·25	5·25
704		1 cor. yellow	5·50	5·50

1932. Air. Surch **Correo Aereo Interior–1932** in two lines and **Vale** and value below.

No.	Type	Description	Unused	Used
710	80	1 c. on 2 c. red	40	40
711	79	2 c. on 3 c. blue	40	40
712	80	3 c. on 4 c. blue	40	40
713	79	4 c. on 5 c. sepia	40	40
714	80	5 c. on 6 c. brown	40	40
715		6 c. on 10 c. brown	40	40
716	79	8 c. on 15 c. orange	40	40
717	80	16 c. on 20 c. orange	40	40
718	79	24 c. on 25 c. violet	85	60
719		25 c. on 25 c. violet	85	60
720	80	32 c. on 50 c. green	85	75
721		40 c. on 50 c. green	95	85
722		50 c. on 1 cor. yellow	1·25	1·25
723		100 c. on 1 cor. yellow	2·50	2·50

127 Wharf, Port San Jorge

128 La Chocolata Cutting

1932. Opening of Rivas Railway.

No.	Type	Description	Unused	Used
726	127	1 c. yellow (postage)	17·00	
727	–	2 c. red	17·00	
728	–	5 c. sepia	17·00	
729	–	10 c. brown	17·00	
730	–	15 c. yellow	17·00	

731 **128** 15 c. violet (air) . . . . . 22·00
732 – 20 c. green . . . . 22·00
733 – 25 c. brown . . . . 22·00
734 – 50 c. sepia . . . . 22·00
735 – 1 cor. red . . . . 22·00
DESIGNS—HORIZ: 2 c. El Nacascolo Halt; 5 c. Rivas Station; 10 c. San Juan del Sur; 15 c. (No. 730), Arrival platform at Rivas; 20 c. El Nacascolo; 25 c. La Cuesta cutting; 50 c. San Juan del Sur Quay; 1 cor. El Estero.

1932. Surch **Vale** and value in words.
736 **79** 1 c. on 3 c. blue 35 15
737 **80** 2 c. on 4 c. blue 30 15

130 Railway Construction

1932. Opening of Leon–Sauce Railway.
739 – 1 c. yellow (postage) . . . 17·00
740 – 2 c. red . . . . 17·00
741 – 5 c. sepia . . . . 17·00
742 **130** 10 c. brown . . . . . . 17·00
743 – 15 c. yellow . . . . . . 17·00
744 – 15 c. violet (air) . . . . . 22·00
745 – 20 c. green . . . . 22·00
746 – 25 c. brown . . . . 22·00
747 – 50 c. sepia . . . . 22·00
748 – 1 cor. red . . . . 22·00
DESIGNS—HORIZ: 1 c. El Sauce; 2 c., 15 c. (No. 744), Bridge at Santa Lucia; 5 c. Santa Lucia; 15 c. (No. 743) Santa Lucia cutting; 20 c. Santa Lucia River Halt; 25 c. Malpaicillo Station; 50 c. Railway panorama; 1 cor. San Andres.

1933. Surch **Resello 1933 Vale** and value in words.
749 **79** 1 c. on 3 c. blue 20 15
750 1 c. on 5 c. sepia 20 15
751 **80** 2 c. on 10 c. brown 20 15

133 Flag of the Race

1933. 441st Anniv of Columbus' Departure from Palos. Roul.
753 **133** ½ c. green (postage) . . . 95 95
754 1 c. green 80 80
755 2 c. red 80 80
756 3 c. red 80 80
757 4 c. orange 80 80
758 5 c. yellow 95 95
759 10 c. brown 95 95
760 15 c. brown 95 95
761 20 c. blue 95 95
762 25 c. blue 95 95
763 30 c. violet . . . . 2·40 2·40
764 50 c. purple . . . . 2·40 2·40
765 1 cor. brown . . . . . . 2·40 2·40
766 1 c. brown (air) 90 90
767 2 c. purple 90 90
768 4 c. violet . . . . 1·50 1·40
769 5 c. blue . . . . 1·40 1·40
770 6 c. blue . . . . 1·40 1·40
771 8 c. brown 45 45
772 15 c. brown 45 45
773 20 c. yellow . . . . 1·40 1·40
774 25 c. orange . . . . 1·40 1·40
775 50 c. red . . . . 1·40 1·40
776 1 cor. green . . . . 9·00 9·00

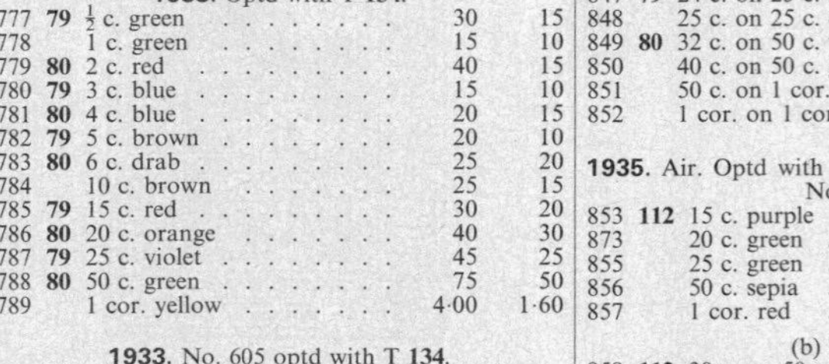

(134) (Facsimile signatures of R. E. Deshon, Minister of Transport and J. R. Sevilla, P.M.G.)

1933. Optd with T **134**.
777 **79** ½ c. green 30 15
778 1 c. green 15 10
779 **80** 2 c. red 40 15
780 **79** 3 c. blue 15 10
781 **80** 4 c. blue 20 15
782 **79** 5 c. brown 20 10
783 **80** 6 c. drab 25 20
784 10 c. brown 25 15
785 **79** 15 c. red 30 20
786 **80** 20 c. orange 40 30
787 **79** 25 c. violet 45 25
788 **80** 50 c. green 75 50
789 1 cor. yellow . . . . . . 4·00 1·60

1933. No. 605 optd with T **134**.
790 **79** 1 c. orange 25 15

1933. Air. Surch **Vale** and value.
791 **112** 30 c. on 50 c. orange . . . 35 15
792 35 c. on 50 c. blue 45 20
793 40 c. on 1 cor. yellow . . . 70 15
794 55 c. on 1 cor. green . . . 70 30

135 Lake Xolotlan

1933. Air. International Airmail Week.
795 **135** 10 c. brown 90 90
796 15 c. violet 75 75
797 25 c. red 85 85
798 50 c. blue 90 90

(136)

1933. Air. Surch as T **136**.
799 **80** 1 c. on 2 c. green 15 15
800 **79** 2 c. on 3 c. olive 15 15
801 **80** 3 c. on 4 c. red 15 15
802 **79** 4 c. on 5 c. blue 15 15
803 **80** 5 c. on 6 c. blue 15 15
804 6 c. on 10 c. sepia . . . 15 10
805 **79** 8 c. on 15 c. brown . . . 20 15
806 **80** 16 c. on 20 c. brown . . . 20 15
807 **79** 24 c. on 25 c. red 15 15
808 25 c. on 25 c. orange . . . 30 30
809 **80** 32 c. on 50 c. violet . . . 30 25
810 40 c. on 50 c. green . . . 40 25
811 50 c. on 1 cor. yellow . . . 40 30
812 1 cor. on 1 cor. red . . . 95 80

1933. Obligatory Tax. As No. 647 optd with T **134**. Colour changed.
813 **106** 1 c. orange 25 15

1934. Air. Surch **Servicio Centroamericano Vale 10 centavos**.
814 **112** 10 c. on 20 c. green . . . 35 35
815 10 c. on 25 c. olive . . . 35 35
See also No. 872.

1935. Optd **Resello 1935**. (a) Nos. 778/9.
816 **79** 1 c. green 10 10
817 **80** 2 c. red 15 10

(b) No. 813 but without T **134** opt.
818 **106** 1 c. orange 15 10

1935. No. 783 surch **Vale Medio Centavo**.
819 **80** ½ c. on 6 c. brown 35 15

1935. Optd with T **134** and **RESELLO-1935** in a box.
820 **79** ½ c. green 20 15
821 **80** ½ c. on 6 c. brown (No. 819) 15 10
822 **79** 1 c. green 25 10
823 **80** 2 c. red 55 10
824 2 c. red (No. 817) 30 10
825 **79** 3 c. blue 30 15
826 **80** 4 c. blue 30 15
827 **79** 5 c. brown 25 10
828 **80** 6 c. drab 30 10
829 10 c. brown 55 20
830 **79** 15 c. red 15 10
831 **80** 20 c. orange 90 25
832 **79** 25 c. violet 30 15
833 **80** 50 c. green 35 25
834 1 cor. yellow 45 35

1935. Obligatory Tax. No. 605 optd with **RESELLO-1935** in a box.
835 **79** 1 c. orange . . . . 25·00

1935. Obligatory Tax. Optd **RESELLO-1935** in a box.
(a) No. 813 without T **134** opt.
836 **106** 1 c. orange 25 15

(b) No. 818.
868 **106** 1 c. orange 20 15

1935. Air. Nos. 799/812 optd with **RESELLO-1935** in a box.
839 **80** 1 c. on 2 c. green 10 10
840 **79** 2 c. on 3 c. olive 20 20
879 **80** 3 c. on 4 c. red 15 15
880 **79** 4 c. on 5 c. blue 15 15
881 **80** 5 c. on 6 c. blue 15 15
882 6 c. on 10 c. sepia . . . 15 15
883 **79** 8 c. on 15 c. brown . . . 15 15
884 **80** 16 c. on 20 c. brown . . . 15 15
847 **79** 24 c. on 25 c. red 35 30
848 25 c. on 25 c. orange . . . 25 25
849 **80** 32 c. on 50 c. violet . . . 20 20
850 40 c. on 50 c. green . . . 30 25
851 50 c. on 1 cor. yellow . . . 45 35
852 1 cor. on 1 cor. red . . . 85 40

1935. Air. Optd with **RESELLO-1935** in a box. (a) Nos. 629/33.
853 **112** 15 c. purple 30 10
873 20 c. green 40 30
855 25 c. green 40 35
856 50 c. sepia 40 35
857 1 cor. red 65 35

(b) Nos. 791/4.
858 **112** 30 c. on 50 c. orange . . . 40 35
859 35 c. on 50 c. blue 40 25
860 40 c. on 1 cor. yellow . . . 40 35
861 55 c. on 1 cor. green . . . 40 30

(c) Nos. 814/5.
862 **112** 10 c. on 20 c. green . . . £300 £300
863 10 c. on 25 c. olive . . . 60 50

1935. Optd with **RESELLO-1935** in a box.
864 **79** ½ c. green (No. 465) 15 10
865 1 c. green (No. 617) 20 10
866 **80** 2 c. red (No. 467) 55 10
867 **79** 3 c. blue (No. 618) 20 15

1936. Surch **Resello 1936 Vale** and value.
869 **79** 1c. on 3 c. blue (No. 618) . 15 10
870 2 c. on 5 c. brown (No. 620) 15 10

1936. Air. Surch **Servicio Centroamericano Vale diez centavos** and **RESELLO-1935** in a box.
871 **112** 10 c. on 25 c. olive 30 30

1936. Obligatory Tax. No. 818 optd **1936**.
874 **106** 1 c. orange 50 20

1936. Obligatory Tax. No. 605 optd with T **134** and **1936**.
875 **79** 1 c. orange 50 20

1936. Air. No. 622 optd **Correo Aereo Centro-Americano Resello 1936**.
876 **80** 10 c. brown 20 20

1936. Air. Nos. 799/800 and 805 optd **Resello 1936**.
885 **80** 1 c. on 2 c. green 25 20
886 **79** 2 c. on 3 c. olive 10 10
887 8 c. on 15 c. brown 25 25

1936. Optd with or without T **37**, surch **1936 Vale** and value.
888 **79** ½ c. on 15 c. red 20 15
889 **80** 1 c. on 4 c. blue 25 15
890 **79** 1 c. on 5 c. brown 25 20
891 **80** 1 c. on 6 c. drab 45 20
892 **79** 1 c. on 15 c. red 25 20
893 **80** 1 c. on 20 c. orange . . . 20 15
895 2 c. on 10 c. brown . . . 30 20
896 **79** 2 c. on 15 c. red 60 50
897 **80** 2 c. on 20 c. orange . . . 55 45
898 **79** 2 c. on 25 c. violet 35 20
900 **80** 2 c. on 50 c. green 35 25
901 2 c. on 1 cor. yellow . . . 35 30
902 3 c. on 4 c. blue 40 30

1936. Optd **Resello 1936**.
903 **79** 3 c. blue (No. 618) 35 25
904 5 c. brown (No. 620) . . . 30 15
905 **80** 10 c. brown (No. 784) . . . 30 20

1936. Air. Surch **1936 Vale and value**.
906 **112** 15 c. on 50 c. brown . . . 30 25
907 15 c. on 1 cor. red 30 25

1936. Fiscal stamps surch **RECONSTRUCCION COMUNICACIONES 5 CENTAVOS DE CORDOBA** and further surch **Vale dos centavos Resello 1936**.
908 **90** 1 c. on 5 c. green 25 10
909 2 c. on 5 c. green 25 10

1936. Obligatory Tax. Fiscal stamps surch **RECONSTRUCCION COMUNICACIONES 5 CENTAVOS DE CORDOBA** and further surch

(a) **1936 R. de C. Vale Un Centavo**.
910 **90** 1 c. on 5 c. green 15 10

(b) **Vale un centavo R. de C. 1936**.
911 **90** 1 c. on 5 c. green 20 10

1937. Colours changed. Size 27 × 22¾ mm.
912 **79** ½ c. black 15 10
913 1 c. red 15 10
914 **80** 2 c. blue 15 10
915 **79** 3 c. brown 15 10
916 **80** 4 c. yellow 20 10
917 **79** 5 c. red 15 10
918 **80** 6 c. violet 20 10
919 10 c. green 20 10
920 **79** 15 c. green 30 10
921 **80** 20 c. brown 30 10
922 **79** 25 c. orange 30 10
923 **80** 50 c. brown 35 15
924 1 cor. blue 40 25

1937. Obligatory Tax. Colour changed.
925 **106** 1 c. green 15 10

1937. Air. Colours changed.
926 **112** 15 c. orange 20 10
927 20 c. red 20 15
928 25 c. black 25 15
929 50 c. violet 45 15
930 1 cor. orange 65 15

1937. Air. Surch **Vale** and value. Colours changed.
931 **112** 30 c. on 50 c. red 30 10
932 35 c. on 50 c. olive 35 10
933 40 c. on 1 cor. green . . . 35 15
934 55 c. on 1 cor. blue 35 30

1937. Air. Surch **Servicio Centroamericano Vale Diez Centavos**.
949 **112** 10 c. on 1 cor. red 30 15

1937. Air. No. 805 (without T **134**) optd **1937**.
950 **79** 8 c. on 15 c. brown 50 15

142 Baseball Player

1937. Obligatory Tax. For 1937 Central American Olympic Games. Optd with ball in red under "OLIMPICO".
951 **142** 1 c. red 35 15
952 1 c. yellow 35 15
953 1 c. blue 35 15
953a 1 c. green 35 15

1937. Nos. 799/809 optd **Habilitado 1937**.
954 **80** 1 c. on 2 c. green 10 10
955 **79** 2 c. on 3 c. olive 10 10
956 **80** 3 c. on 4 c. red 10 10
957 **79** 4 c. on 5 c. blue 10 10
658 **80** 5 c. on 6 c. blue 10 10
959 6 c. on 10 c. brown 10 10
960 **79** 8 c. on 15 c. brown 10 10
661 **80** 16 c. on 20 c. brown . . . 20 20
962 **79** 24 c. on 25 c. red 20 20
963 25 c. on 25 c. orange . . . 20 25
664 **80** 32 c. on 50 c. violet 20 25

144 Presidential Palace, Managua

1937. Air. Inland.
965 **144** 1 c. red 15 10
966 2 c. blue 15 10
967 3 c. olive 15 10
968 4 c. black 15 10
969 5 c. purple 20 10
970 6 c. brown 20 10
971 8 c. violet 20 10
972 16 c. orange 35 25
973 24 c. yellow 20 15
974 25 c. green 50 25

145 Nicaragua

1937. Air. Abroad.
975 **145** 10 c. green 25 10
976 15 c. blue 25 10
977 20 c. yellow 30 25
978 25 c. violet 30 25
979 30 c. red 40 25
980 50 c. orange 60 25
981 1 cor. olive 65 45

146 Presidential Palace

1937. Air. Abroad. 150th Anniv of U.S. Constitution.
982 – 10 c. blue and green . . . 1·10 70
983 **146** 15 c. blue and orange . . 1·10 70
984 – 20 c. blue and red 80 65
985 – 25 c. blue and brown . . . 80 65
986 – 30 c. blue and green . . . 80 65
987 – 35 c. blue and yellow . . . 35 25
988 – 40 c. blue and green . . . 55 40
989 – 45 c. blue and purple . . . 55 40
990 – 50 c. blue and mauve . . . 55 40
991 – 55 c. blue and green . . . 95 60
992 – 75 c. blue and green . . . 55 30
993 – 1 cor. red and blue . . . 75 30
DESIGNS: 10 c. Children's Park, Managua; 20 c. S. America; 25 c. C. America; 30 c. N. America; 35 c. Lake Tiscapa; 40 c. Pan American motor-road; 45 c. Priniomi Park; 50 c. Piedrecitas Park; 55 c. San Juan del Sur; 75 c. Rio Tipitapa; 1 cor. Granada landscape.

146b Diriangen

1937. Air. Day of the Race.
993a **146b** 1 c. green (inland) . . . 15 10
993b 4 c. lake 15 10
993c 5 c. violet 25 15
993d 8 c. blue 15 10
993e 10 c. brown (abroad) . . . 20 10
993f 15 c. blue 20 10
993g 20 c. pink 30 15

147 Letter Carrier

1937. 75th Anniv of Postal Administration.
994 **147** ½ c. green 15 10
995 – 1 c. mauve 15 10
996 – 2 c. brown 15 10
997 – 3 c. violet 30 20
998 – 5 c. blue 30 20
999 – 7½ c. red . . . . 2·50 75
DESIGNS: 1 c. Mule transport; 2 c. Diligence; 3 c. Yacht; 5 c. Packet steamer; 7½ c. Steam mail train.

147a Gen. Tomas Martinez

1938. Air. 75th Anniv of Postal Administration.
999a **147a** 1 c. black and orange (inland) 25 20
999b 5 c. black and violet . . 25 20
999c 8 c. black and blue . . . 30 30
999d 16 c. black and brown . 40 35
999e – 10 c. black and green (abroad) 30 25
999f – 15 c. black and blue . . 40 35
999g – 25 c. black and violet . . 25 25
999h – 50 c. black and red . . 40 30
DESIGNS: 10 c. to 50 c. Gen. Anastasio Somoza.

1938. Surch **1938** and **Vale**, new value in words and **Centavos**.
1000 **79** 3 c. on 25 c. orange . . . 10 10
1001 **80** 5 c. on 50 c. brown . . . 10 10
1002 6 c. on 1 cor. blue 15 15

149 Dario Park

150 Laka Managua

151 President Somoza

1939.
1003 **149** 1½ c. green (postage) . . . 10 10
1004 2 c. red 10 10
1005 3 c. blue 10 10
1006 6 c. brown 10 10
1007 7½ c. green 10 10
1008 10 c. brown 15 10
1009 15 c. orange 15 10
1010 25 c. violet 15 15
1011 50 c. green 30 20
1012 1 cor. yellow 60 45

1013 **150** 2 c. blue (air: inland) . . . 15 15
1014 3 c. olive 15 15
1015 8 c. mauve 15 15
1016 16 c. orange 25 15
1017 24 c. yellow 25 15
1018 32 c. green 35 15
1019 50 c. red 40 15

1020 **151** 10 c. brown (air: abroad) . . 15 10
1021 15 c. blue 15 10
1022 20 c. yellow 15 20
1023 25 c. violet 15 15
1024 30 c. red 20 20
1025 50 c. orange 30 20
1026 1 cor. olive 45 35

1939. Nos. 920/1. Surch **Vale un Centavo 1939**.
1027 **79** 1 c. on 15 c. green 10 10
1028 **80** 1 c. on 20 c. brown 10 10

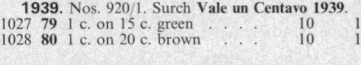

153 Will Rogers and Managua Airport

1939. Air. Will Rogers Commemorative. Inscr "WILL ROGERS/1931/1939".
1029 **153** 1 c. green 10 10
1030 – 2 c. red 10 10
1031 – 3 c. blue 10 10
1032 – 4 c. blue 15 10
1033 – 5 c. red 10 10
DESIGNS: 2 c. Rogers at Managua; 3 c. Rogers in P.A.A. hut; 4 c. Rogers and U.S. Marines; 5 c. Rogers and street in Managua.

156 Senate House and Pres. Somoza

1940. Air. President's Visit to U.S.A. Inscr "AEREO INTERIOR".
1034 – 4 c. brown 15 10
1035 **156** 8 c. brown 10 10
1036 – 16 c. green 15 10
1037 **156** 20 c. mauve 30 15
1038 – 32 c. red 20 20

(b) Inscr "CORREO AEREO INTERNACIONAL".
1039 – 25 c. blue 20 15
1040 – 30 c. black 20 10
1041 **156** 50 c. red 25 40
1042 – 60 c. green 30 35
1043 – 65 c. brown 30 20
1044 – 90 c. olive 40 35
1045 – 1 cor. violet 60 30
DESIGNS: 4 c., 16 c., 25 c., 30 c., 65 c., 90 c. Pres. Somoza addressing Senate; 32 c., 60 c., 1 cor. Portrait of Pres. Somoza between symbols of Nicaragua and New York World's Fair.

158 L. S. Rowe, Statue of Liberty and Union Flags

1940. Air. 50th Anniv of Pan-American Union.
1046 **158** 1 cor. 25 multicoloured . 40 35

159 First Issue of Nicaragua and Sir Rowland Hill

1941. Air. Centenary of First Adhesive Postage stamps.
1047 **159** 2 cor. brown . . . . . 2·25 75
1048 3 cor. blue . . . . . . 7·00 80
1049 5 cor. red . . . . . . 20·00 2·10

1941. Surch **Servicio ordinario/Vale Diez Centavos/de Cordoba**.
1050 **153** 10 c. on 1 c. green . . . 15 10

161 Rube Dario

1941. 25th Death Anniv of Ruben Dario (poet).
1051 **161** 10 c. red (postage) . . . 20 15
1052 20 c. mauve (air) 25 15
1053 35 c. green 30 20
1054 40 c. orange 35 25
1055 60 c. blue 40 35

1943. As No. 1050, but **de Cordoba** omitted.
1056 **153** 10 c. on 1 c. green . . . 10 10

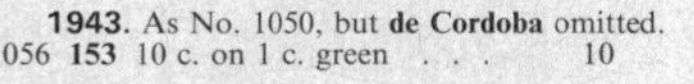

162 "V" for Victory

163 Red Cross

164 Red Cross Workers and Wounded

1943. Victory.
1057 **162** 10 c. red & violet (post) . 10 10
1058 30 c. red and brown . . . 15 10
1059 40 c. red and green (air) . 15 10
1060 60 c. red and blue 20 10

1944. Air. 80th Anniv of Int Red Cross Society.
1061 **163** 25 c. red 40 15
1062 – 50 c. bistre 65 35
1063 **164** 1 cor. green . . . . . . 1·25 1·00
DESIGN—VERT: 50 c. Two Hemispheres.

166 Columbus's Fleet and Lighthouse

165 Columbus and Lighthouse

168 Roosevelt as a Stamp Collector

1945. Honouring Columbus's Discovery of America and Erection of Columbus Lighthouse near Trujillo City, Dominican Republic.
1064 **165** 4 c. black & green (post) . 15 10
1065 6 c. black and orange . . 20 10
1066 8 c. black and red . . . 20 15
1067 10 c. black and blue . . . 30 15
1068 **166** 20 c. grey & green (air) . 40 15
1069 35 c. black and red . . . 70 20
1070 75 c. pink and green . . . 1·25 40
1071 90 c. blue and red . . . 1·50 60
1072 1 cor. blue and black . . 1·75 45
1073 2 cor. 50 red and blue . . 4·50 2·25

1946. President Roosevelt Commemorative Inscr "HOMENAJE A ROOSEVELT".
1074 **168** 4 c. green & black (post) . 15 15
1075 – 8 c. violet and black . . 20 20
1076 – 10 c. blue and black . . 30 25
1077 – 16 c. red and black . . 40 30
1078 – 32 c. brown and black . . 50 25
1079 – 50 c. grey and black . . 50 25
1080 – 25 c. orange & black (air) 20 10
1081 – 75 c. red and black . . . 25 20
1082 – 1 cor. green and black . . 30 30
1083 – 3 cor. violet and black . . 2·25 2·25
1084 – 5 cor. blue and black . . 3·00 3·00
DESIGNS — portraying Roosevelt HORIZ: 8 c., 25 c. with Churchill at the Atlantic Conference; 16 c., 1 cor. with Churchill, De Gaulle and Giraud at the Casablanca Conference; 32 c., 3 cor. with Churchill and Stalin at the Teheran Conference. VERT: 10 c., 75 c. Signing Declaration of War against Japan; 50 c., 5 cor. Head of Roosevelt

171 Managua Cathedral

172 G.P.O., Managua

1947. Managua Centenary Frames in black.
1085 **171** 4 c. red (postage) 10 10
1086 – 5 c. blue 15 10
1087 – 6 c. green 20 15
1088 – 10 c. olive 20 15
1089 – 75 c. brown 30 25
1090 – 5 c. violet (air) 10 10
1091 **172** 20 c. green 15 15
1092 – 35 c. orange 15 15
1093 – 90 c. purple 30 20
1094 – 1 cor. brown 45 35
1095 – 2 cor. 50 purple . . . . 1·00 1·10
DESIGNS—POSTAGE. (as Type **171**): 5 c. Health Ministry; 6 c. Municipal Building; 10 c. College; 75 c. G.P.O., Managua. AIR (as Type **172**): 5 c. College; 35 c. Health Ministry; 90 c. National Bank; 1 cor. Municipal Building; 2 cor. 50 National Palace.

173 San Cristobal Volcano

174 Ruben Dario Monument, Managua

1947. (a) Postage.
1096 **173** 2 c. orange and black . . 10 10
1097 – 3 c. violet and black . . 10 10
1098 – 4 c. grey and black . . . 10 10
1099 – 5 c. red and black . . . 20 10
1100 – 6 c. green and black . . 15 10
1101 – 8 c. brown and black . . 15 10
1102 – 10 c. red and black . . . 25 15
1103 – 20 c. blue and black . . 1·10 25
1104 – 30 c. purple and black . . 70 25
1105 – 50 c. red and black . . 1·90 70
1106 – 1 cor. brown and black . 60 35
DESIGNS—as Type **173**: 3 c. Lion on Ruben Dario's tomb, Leon Cathedral; 4 c. Race Stand; 5 c. Soldiers' Monument; 6 c. Sugar cane; 8 c. Tropical fruits; 10 c. Cotton; 20 c. Horses; 30 c. Coffee plant; 50 c. Prize bullock; 1 cor. Agricultural landscape.

(b) Air.
1107 **174** 5 c. red and green . . . 10 10
1108 – 6 c. orange and black . . 10 10
1109 – 8 c. brown and red . . . 10 10
1110 – 10 c. blue and brown . . 15 10
1111 – 20 c. orange and blue . . 15 10
1112 – 25 c. green and red . . . 20 15
1113 – 35 c. brown and black . . 30 15
1114 – 50 c. black and violet . . 20 10
1115 – 1 cor. red and black . . 45 25
1116 – 1 cor. 50 green & red . . 50 45
1117 – 5 cor. red and brown . . 3·75 3·75
1118 – 10 cor. brown and violet 3·00 3·00
1119 – 25 cor. yellow and green 6·00 6·00
DESIGNS—As Type **174**: 6 c. Baird's tapir; 8 c. Highway and Lake Managua; 10 c. Genizaro Dam; 20 c. Ruben Dario Monument, Managua; 25 c. Sulphur Lagoon, Nejapa; 35 c. Managua Airport; 50 c. Mouth of Rio Prinzapolka; 1 cor. Thermal Baths, Tipitapa; 1 cor. 50, Rio Tipitapa; 5 cor. Embassy building; 10 cor. Girl carrying basket of fruit; 25 cor. Franklin D. Roosevelt Monument, Managua.

175 Soft-ball

176 Pole-vaulting

177 Tennis

178 National Stadium Managua

1949. 10th World Amateur Baseball Championships.
(a) Postage as T **175/6**.
1120 **175** 1 c. brown 10 10
1121 – 2 c. blue 50 15
1122 **176** 3 c. green 25 10
1123 – 4 c. purple 15 15
1124 – 5 c. orange 40 15
1125 – 10 c. green 40 15
1126 – 15 c. red 50 15
1127 – 25 c. blue 50 20
1128 – 35 c. green 80 20
1129 – 40 c. violet . . . . . . 1·75 30
1130 – 60 c. black . . . . . . 1·40 35
1131 – 1 cor. red . . . . 1·50 90
1132 – 2 cor. purple . . . . . . 2·75 1·50
DESIGNS—VERT: 2 c. Scout; 5 c. Cycling; 25 c. Boxing; 35 c. Basket-ball. HORIZ: 4 c. Diving; 10 c. Stadium; 15 c. Baseball; 40 c. Yachting; 60 c. Table tennis; 1 cor. Football; 2 cor. Tennis.

(b) Air as T **177**.
1133 **177** 1 c. red 10 10
1134 – 2 c. black 10 10
1135 – 3 c. red 10 10
1136 – 4 c. black 10 10
1137 – 5 c. blue 35 15
1138 – 15 c. green 65 10
1139 – 25 c. purple . . . . . . 1·25 25
1140 – 30 c. brown . . . . . . 1·00 25
1141 – 40 c. violet 50 25

1142 – 75 c. mauve . . . . . . 2·50 1·60
1143 – 1 cor. blue . . . . 3·00 80
1144 – 2 cor. olive . . . . 1·25 1·00
1145 – 5 cor. green . . . . . . 2·10 2·10
DESIGNS—SQUARE: 2 c. Football; 3 c. Table tennis; 4 c. Stadium; 5 c. Yachting; 15 c. Basketball; 25 c. Boxing; 30 c. Baseball; 40 c. Cycling; 75 c. Diving; 1 cor. Pole-vaulting; 2 cor. Scout; 5 cor. Soft-ball.

1949. Obligatory Tax stamps. Stadium Construction Fund.
1146 **178** 5 c. blue 20 10
1146a 5 c. red 20 10

179 Rowland Hill

180 Heinrich von Stephan

1950. 75th Anniv of U.P.U. Frames in black.
1147 **179** 20 c. red (postage) . . . 15 10
1148 – 25 c. green 15 10
1149 – 75 c. blue 50 50
1150 – 80 c. green 30 25
1151 – 4 cor. blue 85 80
DESIGNS—VERT: 25 c. Portrait as Type **180**; 75 c. Monument, Berne; 80 c., 4 cor. Obverse and reverse of Congress Medal.

1152 – 16 c. red (air) 15 10
1153 **180** 20 c. orange 15 10
1154 – 25 c. black 15 15
1155 – 30 c. red 25 10
1156 – 85 c. green 55 50
1157 – 1 cor. 10 brown 50 35
1158 – 2 cor. 14 green . . . . . 1·25 1·25
DESIGNS—HORIZ: 16 c. Rowland Hill; 25, 30 c. U.P.U. Offices, Berne; 85 c. Monument, Berne; 1 cor. 10, and 2 cor. 14, Obverse and reverse of Congress Medal.

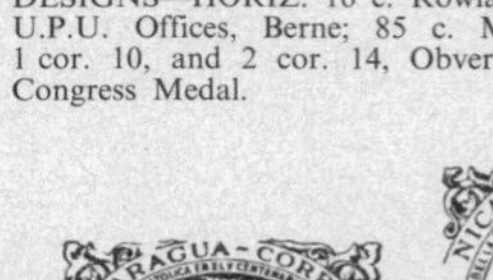
181 Queen Isabella and Columbus's Fleet

182 Isabella the Catholic

1952. 500th Birth Anniv of Isabella the Catholic.
1159 – 10 c. mauve (postage) . . 10 10
1160 **181** 96 c. blue . . . . 1·00 55
1161 – 98 c. red . . . . 1·00 55
1162 – 1 cor. 20 brown 50 40
1163 **182** 1 cor. 76 purple 60 60

1164 2 cor. 30 red (air) . . . . 1·40 1·10
1165 – 2 cor. 80 orange . . . . 1·00 95
1166 – 3 cor. green . . . . . . 3·25 1·50
1167 **181** 3 cor. 30 blue . . . . . 3·25 1·75
1168 – 3 cor. 60 green . . . . . 1·50 1·25
DESIGNS—VERT: 10 c., 3 cor. 60, Queen facing right; 98 c., 3 cor. Queen and "Santa Maria"; 1 cor. 20, 2 cor. 80, Queen and Map of Americas.

183 O.D.E.C.A. Flag

1953. Foundation of Organization of Central American States.
1169 **183** 4 c. blue (postage) . . . 10 10
1170 – 5 c. green 10 10
1171 – 6 c. brown 10 10
1172 – 15 c. olive 20 15
1173 – 50 c. sepia 25 15

1174 – 20 c. red (air) 10 10
1175 **183** 25 c. blue 15 10
1176 – 30 c. brown 15 15
1177 – 60 c. green 25 20
1178 – 1 cor. purple 35 45
DESIGNS: 5 c., 1 cor. Map of C. America; 6 c., 20 c. Hands holding O.D.E.C.A. arms; 15 c., 30 c. Five Presidents of C. America; 50 c., 60 c. Charter and flags.

184 Pres. Solorzano

185 Pres. Arguello

1953. Presidential Series. Portraits in black. (a) Postage. As T **184**.
1179 **184** 4 c. red 10 10
1180 – 6 c. blue (D. M. Chamorro) 10 10
1181 – 8 c. brown (Diaz) 10 10
1182 – 15 c. red (Somoza) . . . 15 10
1183 – 50 c. grn (E. Chamorro) . 20 15

(b) Air. As T **185**.
1184 **185** 4 c. red 10 10
1185 – 5 c. orange (Moncada) . 10 10
1186 – 20 c. blue (J. B. Sacasa) 10 10
1187 – 25 c. blue (Zelaya) . . . 10 10
1188 – 30 c. lake (Somoza) . . . 10 10
1189 – 35 c. green (Martinez) . . 20 20
1190 – 40 c. plum (Guzman) . . 20 20
1191 – 45 c. olive (Cuadra) . . 20 20
1192 – 50 c. red (P. J. Chamorro) 35 25
1193 – 60 c. blue (Zavala) . . . 40 40
1194 – 85 c. brown (Cardenas) . 40 40
1195 – 1 cor. 10 pur (Carazo) . 60 55
1196 – 1 cor. 20 bistre (R. Sacasa) 65 55

186 Sculptor and U.N. Emblem

1954. U.N.O. Inscr "HOMENAJE A LA ONU".
1197 **186** 3 c. drab (postage) . . . 10 10
1198 A 4 c. green 15 10
1199 B 5 c. green 20 10
1200 C 15 c. green 55 20
1201 D 1 cor. turquoise 45 40

1202 E 3 c. red (air) 10 10
1203 F 4 c. orange 10 10
1204 C 5 c. rd 15 10
1205 D 30 c. pink 75 15
1206 B 2 cor. red 80 70
1207 A 3 cor. brown . . . . . 1·50 1·00
1208 **186** 5 cor. purple . . . . . 1·75 1·40
DESIGNS: A, Detail from Nicaragua's Coat of Arms; B, Globe; C, Candle and Nicaragua's Charter; D, Flags of Nicaragua and U.N.; E, Torch; F, Trusting hands.

187 Capt. D. L. Ray

188 North American Sabre

1954. National Air Force. Frames in black. (a) Postage. Frames as T **187**.
1209 **187** 1 c. black 10 10
1210 – 2 c. black 10 10
1211 – 3 c. myrtle 10 10
1212 – 4 c. orange 15 10
1213 – 5 c. green 20 10
1214 – 15 c. turquoise 15 10
1215 – 1 cor. violet 35 25

(b) Air. Frames as T **188**.
1216 – 10 c. black 10 10
1217 **188** 15 c. black 15 10
1218 – 20 c. mauve 15 10
1219 – 25 c. red 20 10
1220 – 30 c. blue 10 10
1221 – 50 c. blue 75 50
1222 – 1 cor. green 65 35
DESIGNS—POSTAGE: 2 c. North American Sabre; 3 c. Douglas Boston; 4 c. Consolidated Liberator; 5 c. North American Texan trainer; 15 c. Pres. Somoza; 1 cor. Emblem. AIR: 10 c. D. L. Ray; 20 c. Emblem; 25 c. Hangars; 30 c. Pres. Somoza; 50 c. North American Texan trainers; 1 cor. Lockheed Lightning airplanes.

189 Rotary Slogans

190a

1955. 50th Anniv of Rotary International.
1223 **189** 15 c. orange (postage) . 10 10
1224 A 20 c. olive 15 15
1225 B 35 c. violet 15 15
1226 C 40 c. red 15 15
1227 D 90 c. black 30 25

1228 D 1 c. red (air) 10 10
1229 A 2 c. blue 10 10
1230 C 3 c. green 10 10
1231 **189** 4 c. violet 10 10
1232 B 5 c. brown 10 10
1233 25 c. turquoise 15 15
1234 **189** 30 c. black 15 10
1235 C 45 c. mauve 30 25
1236 A 50 c. green 25 20
1237 D 1 cor. blue 45 30
DESIGNS—VERT: A, Clasped hands; B, Rotarian and Nicaraguan flags; D, Paul P. Harris. HORIZ: C, World map and winged emblem.

1956. National Exhibition. Surch **Conmemoracion Exposicion Nacional Febrero 4-16, 1956** and value.
1238 5 c. on 6 c. brown (No. 1171) postage 10 10
1239 5 c. on 6 c. blk & blue (1180) 10 10
1240 5 c. on 8 c. brn & blk (1101) 10 10
1241 15 c. on 35 c. violet (1225) . 15 10
1242 15 c. on 80 c. grn & blk (1150) 15 10
1243 15 c. on 90 c. black (1227) . 15 10

1244 30 c. on 35 c. black & green (1189) (air) 10 15
1245 30 c. on 45 c. blk & ol. (1191) 25 15
1246 30 c. on 45 c. mauve (1235) . 25 15
1247 2 cor. on 5 cor. purple (1208) 50 35

1956. Obligatory Tax. Social Welfare Fund.
1247a **190a** 5 c. blue 10 10

191 Gen. J. Dolores Estrada

192 President Somoza

1956. Cent of War of 1856. Inscr as in T **191**.
1248 – 5 c. brown (postage) . . . 10 10
1249 – 10 c. lake 10 10
1250 – 15 c. grey 10 10
1251 – 25 c. red 15 15
1252 – 50 c. purple 30 20

1253 **191** 30 c. red (air) 10 10
1254 – 60 c. brown 20 15
1255 – 1 cor. 50 green 20 35
1256 – 2 cor. 50 blue 30 30
1257 – 10 cor. orange . . . . . 1·90 1·75
DESIGNS—VERT: 5 c. Gen. M. Jerez; 10 c. Gen. F. Chamorro; 50 c. Gen. J. D. Estrada; 1 cor. 50, E. Mangalo; 10 cor. Commodore H. Paulding. HORIZ: 15 c. Battle of San Jocinto; 25 c. Granada in flames; 60 c. Bas-relief; 2 cor. 50, Battle of Rivas.

1957. Air. National Mourning for Pres. G. A. Somoza. Various frames. Inscr as in T **192**. Centres in black.
1258 – 15 c. black 10 10
1259 – 30 c. blue 15 15
1260 **192** 2 cor. violet 80 70
1261 – 3 cor. olive . . . . 1·25 1·10
1262 – 5 cor. sepia . . . . 1·90 1·90

193 Scout and Badge

194 Clasped Hands, Badge and Globe

1957. Birth Centenary of Lord Baden-Powell.
1263 **193** 10 c. olive & violet (post) 10 10
1264 – 15 c. sepia and purple . . 15 15
1265 – 20 c. brown and blue . . 15 15
1266 – 25 c. brown & turquoise . 15 15
1267 – 50 c. olive and red . . . 35 35

1268 **194** 3 c. olive and red (air) . . 15 15
1269 – 4 c. blue and brown . . . 15 15
1270 – 5 c. brown and green . . 15 15
1271 – 6 c. drab and violet . . . 15 15
1272 – 8 c. red and black 15 15
1273 – 30 c. black and green . . 15 15
1274 – 40 c. black and blue . . . 15 15
1275 – 75 c. sepia and purple . . 35 35
1276 – 85 c. grey and red . . . 40 40
1277 – 1 cor. brown and green . 40 40
DESIGNS—VERT: 4 c. Scout badge; 5 c., 15 c. Wolf cub; 6 c. Badge and flags; 8 c. Badge and emblems of scouting; 20 c. Scout; 25 c. A. Harrison; 75 c. Rover Scout; 85 c. Scout. HORIZ: 40 c. Presentation to Pres. Somoza.

195 Pres. Luis Somoza

197 Archbishop of Managua

196 Managua Cathedral

1957. Election of Pres. Somoza. Portrait in brown. (a) Postage. Oval frame.
1278 **195** 10 c. red 10 10
1279 15 c. blue 10 10
1280 35 c. purple 10 10
1281 50 c. brown 15 15
1282 75 c. green 40 40

(b) Air. Rectangular frame.
1283 – 20 c. blue 10 10
1284 – 25 c. mauve 15 10
1285 – 30 c. sepia 15 10
1286 – 40 c. turquoise 15 15
1287 – 2 cor. violet 95 95

1957. Churches and Priests. Centres in olive.
1288 **196** 5 c. green (postage) . . . 10 10
1289 – 10 c. purple 10 10
1290 **197** 15 c. blue 10 10
1291 – 20 c. sepia 15 10
1292 – 50 c. green 20 15
1293 – 1 cor. violet 30 30

1294 **197** 30 c. green (air) 10 10
1295 **196** 60 c. brown 15 15
1296 – 75 c. blue 25 25
1297 – 90 c. red 30 30
1298 – 1 cor. 50 turquoise . . . 35 35
1299 – 2 cor. purple 40 40
DESIGNS—HORIZ: As Type **196**: 20, 90 c. Leon Cathedral; 50 c., 1 cor. 50, La Merced, Granada Church. VERT: As Type **197**: 10, 75 c. Bishop of Nicaragua; 1, 2 cor. Father Mariano Dubon.

198 "Honduras" (freighter)

199 Exhibition Emblem

1957. Nicaraguan Merchant Marine Commemoration. Inscr as in T **198**.
1300 **198** 4 c. black, blue and myrtle (postage) 15 10
1301 – 5 c. violet, blue & brown 15 10
1302 – 6 c. black, blue & red . . 15 10
1303 – 10 c. black, green and sepia 20 10
1304 – 15 c. brown, blue & red . 30 10
1305 – 50 c. brown, blue & violet 30 20

1306 – 25 c. purple, blue and ultramarine (air) . . . 30 10
1307 – 30 c. grey, buff & brown 15 10
1308 – 50 c. bistre, blue & violet 20 20
1309 – 60 c. black, turquoise and purple 55 20
1310 – 1 cor. black, blue & red . 75 30
1311 – 2 cor. 50 brown, blue and black . . . . 1·75 1·00
DESIGNS: 5 c. Gen. A. Somoza, founder of Mamenic (National) Shipping Line, and "Guatemala" (freighter); 6 c. "Guatemala"; 10 c. "Salvador" (freighter); 15 c. Freighter between hemispheres; 25 c. "Managua" (freighter); 30 c. Ship's wheel and world map; 50 c. (No. 1305), Hemispheres and ship; 50 c. (No. 1308), Mamenic Shipping Line flag; 60 c. "Costa Rica" (freighter); 1 cor. "Nicarao" (freighter); 2 cor. 50, Map, freighter and flag.

1958. Air. Brussels International Exn Inscr "EXPOSICION MUNDIAL DE BELGICA 1958".
1312 **199** 25 c. black, yell & grn . 10 10
1313 – 30 c. multicoloured . . . 15 15
1314 – 45 c. black, ochre & blue 15 15
1315 **199** 1 cor. black, blue and dull purple 25 25
1316 – 2 cor. multicoloured . . 25 25
1317 – 10 cor. sepia, purple and blue . . . . 1·40 1·00
DESIGNS: As Type **199**: 30 c., 20 cor. Arms of Nicaragua; 45 c., 10 cor. Nicaraguan Pavilion.

200 Emblems of C. American Republics

201 Arms of La Salle

1958. 17th Central American Lions Convention. Inscr as in T **200**. Emblems (5 c., 60 c.) multicoloured; Lions badge (others) in blue, red, yellow (or orange and buff).
1318 **200** 5 c. blue (postage) . . . 10 10
1319 – 10 c. blue and orange . . 10 10
1320 – 20 c. blue and green . . 10 10
1321 – 50 c. blue and purple . . 15 15
1322 – 75 c. blue and mauve . . 30 25
1323 – 1 cor. 50, blue, salmon and drab 45 45

1324 – 30 c. blue & orge (air) . 10 10
1325 **200** 60 c. blue and pink . . . 20 15
1326 – 90 c. blue 25 20
1327 – 1 cor. 25 blue and olive . 35 30
1328 – 2 cor. blue and green . . 60 50
1329 – 3 cor. blue, red and violet 95 90
DESIGNS—HORIZ: 10 c., 1 cor. 25, Melvin Jones; 20, 30 c. Dr. T. A. Arias; 50, 90 c. Edward G. Barry; 75 c., 2 cor. Lions emblem; 1 cor. 50, 3 cor. Map of C. American Isthmus.

1958. Brothers of the Nicaraguan Christian Schools Commem. Inscr as in T **201**.
1330 **201** 5 c. red, blue & yellow (postage) 10 10
1331 – 10 c. sepia, blue & green 10 10
1332 – 15 c. sepia, brown & bis 10 10
1333 – 20 c. black, red & bistre 10 10
1334 – 50 c. sepia, orange & bis 15 15
1335 – 75 c. sepia, turquoise & grn 25 20
1336 – 1 cor. black, vio & bistre 40 30

1337 **201** 30 c. blue, red & yellow (air) 10 10
1338 – 60 c. sepia, purple & grey 25 20
1339 – 85 c. black, red & blue . 30 25
1340 – 90 c. black, green & ochre 35 35
1341 – 1 cor. 25 black, red and ochre 50 45

1342 – 1 cor. 50 sepia, green and grey 60 55
1343 – 1 cor. 75 blk, brn & bl . 65 55
1344 – 2 cor. sepia, grn & grey . 65 65
DESIGNS—HORIZ: 10, 60 c. Managua Teachers Institute. VERT: 15, 85 c. De La Salle (founder); 20, 90 c. Brother Carlos; 50 c., 1 cor. 50, Brother Antonio; 75 c., 1 cor. 25, Brother Julio; 1 cor., 1 cor. 75, Brother Argeo; 2 cor. Brother Eugenio.

202 U.N. Emblem

203

204

1958. Inaug. of U.N.E.S.C.O. Headquarters Building, Paris. Inscr as in T **202**.
1345 **202** 10 c. blue & mve (postage) 10 10
1346 – 15 c. mauve and blue . . 10 10
1347 – 25 c. brown and green . 10 10
1348 – 40 c. black and red . . 15 15
1349 – 45 c. mauve and blue . 20 20
1350 **202** 50 c. green and brown . 25 25
1351 – 60 c. blue & mauve (air) . 25 15
1352 – 75 c. brown and green . 25 20
1353 – 90 c. green and brown . 30 25
1354 – 1 cor. mauve and blue . 40 30
1355 – 3 cor. red and black . 60 60
1356 – 5 cor. blue and mauve . 1·00 85
DESIGNS—VERT: 15 c. Aerial view of H.Q; 25, 45 c. Facade composed of letters "UNESCO"; 40 c. H.Q. and Eiffel Tower; In oval vignettes–60 c., As 15 c; 75 c., 5 cor., As 25 c.; 90 c., 3 cor. As 40 c.; 1 cor., As Type **202**.

1959. Obligatory Tax. Consular Fiscal stamps surch Serial Nos. in red.
1357 **203** 5 c. on 50 c. blue 10 10
1358 **204** 5 c. on 50 c. blue 10 10

205

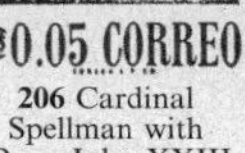

206 Cardinal Spellman with Pope John XXIII

207 Abraham Lincoln

1959. Obligatory Tax.
1359 **205** 5 c. blue 15 10

1959. Cardinal Spellman Commemoration.
1360 **206** 5 c. flesh & grn (postage) 10 10
1361 A 10 c. multicoloured . . . 10 10
1362 B 15 c. red, black and grn . 10 10
1363 C 20 c. yellow and blue . . 10 10
1364 D 25 c. red and blue . . . 10 10
1365 E 30 c. bl, red & yellow (air) 10 10
1366 **206** 35 c. bronze and orange . 10 10
1367 A 1 cor. multicoloured . . 30 30
1368 B 1 cor. 5 red and black . . 35 30
1369 C 1 cor. 50 yellow & blue . 45 35
1370 D 2 cor. blue, violet & red . 55 45
1371 E 5 cor. multicoloured . . 75 55
DESIGNS—VERT: A, Cardinal's Arms; B, Cardinal; D, Cardinal wearing sash. HORIZ: C, Cardinal and Cross; E, Flags of Nicaragua, Vatican City and U.S.A.

1960. 150th Birth Anniv of Abraham Lincoln. Portrait in black.
1372 **207** 5 c. red (postage) 10 10
1373 10 c. green 10 10
1374 15 c. orange 10 10
1375 1 cor. purple 25 25
1376 2 cor. blue 30 45
1377 30 c. blue (air) 10 10
1378 35 c. red 15 10
1379 70 c. purple 20 20
1380 1 cor. 5 green 35 35
1381 1 cor. 50 violet 50 45
1382 – 5 cor. ochre and black . 55 55
DESIGN—HORIZ: 5 cor. Scroll inscr "Dar al que necesite–A. Lincoln".

1960. Air. 10th Anniv of San Jose (Costa Rica) Philatelic Society. Optd **X Aniversario Club Filatelico S. J.–C. R.**
1383 2 cor. red (No. 1206) 70 60
1384 2 cor. 50 blue (No. 1256) . . 75 75
1385 3 cor. green (No. 1166) . . . 1·40 90

1960. Red Cross Fund for Chilean Earthquake Relief Nos. 1372/82 optd **Resello** and Maltese Cross. Portrait in black.
1386 **207** 5 c. red (postage) 10 10
1387 10 c. green 10 10
1388 15 c. orange 10 10
1389 1 cor. purple 25 25
1390 2 cor. blue 30 25
1391 30 c. blue (air) 25 20
1392 35 c. red 20 20
1393 **207** 70 c. purple 25 25
1394 1 cor. 5 green 30 30
1395 1 cor. 50 violet 40 35
1396 – 5 cor. ochre and black . 1·00 1·00

210

1961. Air. World Refugee Year. Inscr "ANO MUNDIAL DEL REFUGIADO".
1397 – 2 cor. multicoloured . . 20 20
1398 **210** 5 cor. ochre, blue & grn 60 60
DESIGN: 2 cor. Procession of refugees.

211 Pres. Roosevelt, Pres. Somoza and Officer

1961. Air. 20th Anniv of Nicaraguan Military Academy.
1399 **211** 20 c. multicoloured . . 10 10
1400 – 25 c. red, blue and black 10 10
1401 – 30 c. multicoloured . . 10 10
1402 – 35 c. multicoloured . . 10 10
1403 – 40 c. multicoloured . . 10 10
1404 – 45 c. black, flesh and red 15 15
1405 **211** 60 c. multicoloured . . 15 15
1406 – 70 c. multicoloured . . 20 20
1407 – 1 cor. 5 multicoloured . 25 25
1408 – 1 cor. 50 multicoloured . 35 35
1409 – 2 cor. multicoloured . . 50 50
1410 – 5 cor. blk, flesh & grey . 70 60
DESIGNS — VERT: 25, 70 c. Flags; 35 c., 1 cor. 50, Standard bearers; 40 c., 2 cor. Pennant and emblem. HORIZ: 30 c., 1 cor. 5 Group of officers; 45 c., 5 cor. Pres. Somoza and Director of Academy.

1961. Air. Consular Fiscal stamps as T **203/4** with serial Nos. in red, surch **Correo Aereo** and value.
1411 20 c. on 50 c. blue 15 10
1412 20 c. on 1 cor. olive . . . 15 10
1413 20 c. on 2 cor. green . . . 15 10
1414 20 c. on 3 cor. red 15 10
1415 20 c. on 5 cor. red 15 10
1416 20 c. on 10 cor. violet . . 15 10
1417 20 c. on 20 cor. brown . . 15 10
1418 20 c. on 50 cor. brown . . 15 10
1419 20 c. on 100 cor. lake . . 15 10

213 I.J.C. Emblem and Global Map of the Americas

215 R. Cabezas

1961. Air. Junior Chamber of Commerce Congress.
1420 2 c. multicoloured 10 10
1421 3 c. black and yellow . . . 10 10
1422 4 c. multicoloured 10 10
1423 5 c. black and red 10 10
1424 6 c. multicoloured 15 10
1425 10 c. multicoloured 10 10
1426 15 c. black, green and blue . 10 10
1427 30 c. black and blue . . . 15 10
1428 35 c. multicoloured . . . 15 10
1429 70 c. black, red and yellow . 20 20
1430 1 cor. 5 multicoloured . . 35 30
1431 5 cor. multicoloured . . . 70 70
DESIGNS—HORIZ: 2 c., 15 c. Type **213**; 4 c., 35 c. "J.C.I." upon Globe. VERT: 3 c., 30 c. I.J.C. emblem; 5 c., 70 c. Scroll; 6 c., 1 cor. 5, Handclasp; 10 c., 5 cor. Regional map of Nicaragua.

1961. Air. 1st Central American Philatelic Convention, San Salvador. Optd **Convencion Filatelica - Centro - America - Panama - San Salvador - 27 Julio 1961.**
1432 **158** 1 cor. 25 multicoloured . 25 25

1961. Air. Birth Centenary of Cabezas.
1433 **215** 20 c. blue and orange . 10 10
1434 – 40 c. purple and blue . . 15 15
1435 – 45 c. sepia and green . . 15 15
1436 – 70 c. green and brown . 25 20
1437 – 2 cor. blue and pink . . 60 40
1438 – 10 cor. purple and turquoise 1·50 1·50
DESIGNS—HORIZ: 40 c. Map and view of Cartago; 45 c. 1884 newspaper; 70 c. Assembly outside building; 2 cor. Scroll; 10 cor. Map and view of Masaya.

216 Official Gazettes

219 "Cattleya skinneri"

1961. Centenary of Regulation of Postal Rates.
1439 **216** 5 c. brown & turquoise . . 10 10
1440 – 10 c. brown and green . . 10 10
1441 – 15 c. brown and red . . . 10 10
DESIGNS: 10 c. Envelopes and postmarks; 15 c. Martinez and Somoza.

1961. Air. Dag Hammarskjold Commem. Nos. 1351/6 optd **Homenaje a Hammarskjold Sept. 18-1961.**
1442 60 c. blue and mauve . . . 30 30
1443 75 c. brown and green . . . 35 35
1444 90 c. green and brown . . . 45 45
1445 1 cor. mauve and blue . . . 50 50
1446 3 cor. red and black 80 80
1447 5 cor. blue and mauve . . . 1·50 1·50

1962. Air. Surch **RESELLO C$ 1.00.**
1448 – 1 cor. on 1 cor. 10 brown (No. 1157) 30 25
1449 **207** 1 cor. on 1 cor. 5 black and green 30 25
See also Nos. 1498/1500a, 1569/70, 1608/14, 1669/76 and 1748/62.

1962. Obligatory Tax. Nicaraguan Orchids. Multicoloured.
1450 5 c. Type **219** 10 10
1451 5 c. "Bletia roezlii" 10 10
1452 5 c. "Sobralia pleiantha" . . 10 10
1453 5 c. "Lycaste macrophylla" . 10 10
1454 5 c. "Schomburgkia tibicinus" 10 10
1455 5 c. "Maxillaria tenuifolia" . 10 10
1456 5 c. "Stanhopea ecornuta" . . 10 10
1457 5 c. "Oncidium ascendens" and "O. cebolleta" 10 10
1458 5 c. "Cycnoches egertonianum" 10 10
1459 5 c. "Hexisia bidentata" . . 10 10

220 U.N.E.S.C.O. "Audience"

NICARAGUA
CORREOS CORREOS
0.02 CENTAVOS 0.02
222 Arms of Nueva Segovia

1962. Air. 15th Anniv of U.N.E.S.C.O.
1460 **220** 2 cor. multicoloured . . . 15 15
1461 – 5 cor. multicoloured . . . 80 80
DESIGN: 5 cor. U.N. and U.N.E.S.C.O. emblems.

1962. Air. Malaria Eradication. Nos. 1425, 1428/31 optd with mosquito surrounded by **LUCHA CONTRA LA MALARIA.**
1462 – 10 c. 35 30
1463 – 35 c. 45 30
1464 – 70 c. 60 45
1465 – 1 cor. 5 . . . . 80 65
1466 – 5 cor. . . . . 1·00 1·25

1962. Urban and Provincial Arms. Arms mult; inscr. black; background colours below.
1467 **222** 2 c. mauve (postage) . . 10 10
1468 – 3 c. blue 10 10
1469 – 4 c. lilac 10 10
1470 – 5 c. yellow 10 10
1471 – 6 c. brown 10 10
1472 **222** 30 c. red (air) 10 10
1473 – 50 c. orange 15 10
1474 – 1 cor. green 25 20
1475 – 2 cor. grey 45 40
1476 – 5 cor. blue 75 60
ARMS: 3 c., 50 c. Leon; 4 c., 1 cor. Managua; 5 c., 2 cor. Granada; 6 c., 5 cor. Rivas.

223 Liberty Bell

1963. Air. 150th Anniv of Independence.
1477 **223** 30 c. drab, blue & black . 15 10

HAVE YOU READ THE NOTES AT THE BEGINNING OF THIS CATALOGUE?
These often provide the answers to the enquiries we receive.

224 Blessing

1963. Air. Death Tercentenary of St. Vincent de Paul and St. Louise de Marillac.
1478 – 60 c. black and orange . 15 10
1479 **224** 1 cor. olive and orange . 25 20
1480 – 2 cor. black and red . . 50 45
DESIGNS—VERT: 60 c. "Comfort" (St. Louise and woman). HORIZ: 2 cor. St. Vincent and St. Louise.

225 "Map Stamp"

226 Cross on Globe

1963. Air. Central American Philatelic Societies Federation Commemoration.
1481 **225** 1 cor. blue and yellow . 30 20

1963. Air. Ecumenical Council, Vatican City.
1482 **226** 20 c. red and yellow . . 15 10

227 Ears of Wheat

228 Boxing

1963. Air. Freedom from Hunger.
1483 **227** 10 c. green & light green 10 10
1484 – 25 c. sepia & yellow . . 15 10
DESIGN: 25 c. Barren tree and campaign emblem.

1963. Air. Sports. Multicoloured.
1485 2 c. Type **228** 10 10
1486 3 c. Running 10 10
1487 4 c. Underwater harpooning 10 10
1488 5 c. Football 10 10
1489 6 c. Baseball 15 10
1490 10 c. Tennis 20 10
1491 15 c. Cycling 20 10
1492 20 c. Motor-cycling 20 10
1493 35 c. Chess 30 15
1494 60 c. Angling 35 20
1495 1 cor. Table-tennis 55 35
1496 2 cor. Basketball 75 55
1497 5 cor. Golf . . . . 1·90 1·10

1964. Air. Surch **Resello or RESELLO** (1500a) and value.
1498 – 5 c. on 6 c. (No. 1424) . 35 10
1499 – 10 c. on 30 c. (No. 1365) 45 15
1500 **207** 15 c. on 30 c. 70 20
1500a **201** 20 c. on 30 c. 15 10
See also Nos. 1448/9, 1569/70, 1608/14 and 1669/76.

1964. Optd **CORREOS.**
1501 5 c. multicoloured (No. 1451) 10 10

231 Flags

232 "Alliance Emblem"

1964. Air. "Centro America".
1502 **231** 40 c. multicoloured . . . 15 15

1964. Air. "Alliance for Progress". Multicoloured.
1503 5 c. Type **232** 10 10
1504 10 c. Red Cross Post . . . 10 10
1505 15 c. Highway 10 10
1506 20 c. Ploughing 10 10
1507 25 c. Housing 15 10
1508 30 c. Presidents Somoza and Kennedy and Eugene Black (World Bank) 15 10
1509 35 c. School and adults . . . 20 15
1510 40 c. Chimneys 25 15
Nos. 1504/10 are horiz.

233 Map of Member Countries
235 Rescue of Wounded Soldier

1964. Air. Central-American "Common Market". Multicoloured.
1511 15 c. Type **233** 10 10
1512 25 c. Ears of wheat 10 10
1513 40 c. Cogwheels 10 10
1514 50 c. Heads of cattle 15 10

1964. Air. Olympic Games, Tokyo. Nos. 1485/7, 1489 and 1495/6 optd **OLIMPIADAS TOKYO-1964**.
1515 2 c. Type **108** 10 10
1516 3 c. Running 10 10
1517 4 c. Underwater harpooning . 10 10
1518 6 c. Baseball 10 10
1519 1 cor. Table-tennis . . . . . 1·10 1·10
1520 2 cor. Basketball . . . . . . 2·25 2·25

1965. Air. Red Cross Centenary. Multicoloured.
1521 20 c. Type **235** 10 10
1522 25 c. Blood transfusion . . . 15 10
1523 40 c. Red Cross and snowbound town 15 15
1524 10 cor. Red Cross and map of Nicaragua . . . . 1·50 1·50

236 Statuettes

1965. Air. Nicaraguan Antiquities. Multicoloured.
1525 5 c. Type **236** 10 10
1526 10 c. Totem 10 10
1527 15 c. Carved dog 10 10
1528 20 c. Composition of "objets d'art" 10 10
1529 25 c. Dish and vase 10 10
1530 30 c. Pestle and mortar . . . 10 10
1531 35 c. Statuettes (different) . . 10 10
1532 40 c. Deity 15 10
1533 50 c. Wine vessel and dish . . 15 10
1534 60 c. Bowl and dish 20 10
1535 1 cor. Urn 45 15
The 15, 25, 35 and 60 c. are horiz.

237 Pres. Kennedy
238 A. Bello

1965. Air. Pres. Kennedy Commemorative.
1536 **237** 35 c. black and green . . 15 10
1537 75 c. black and mauve . . 25 15
1538 1 cor. 10 black & blue . . 35 25
1539 2 cor. black & brown . . 90 55

1965. Air. Death Centenary of Andres Bello (poet and writer).
1540 **238** 10 c. black and brown . . 10 10
1541 15 c. black and blue . . 10 10
1542 45 c. black and purple . . 15 10
1543 80 c. black and green . . 20 15
1544 1 cor. black and yellow . . 25 20
1545 2 cor. black and grey . . 45 45

1965. 9th Central-American Scout Camporee. Nos. 1450/9 optd with scout badge and **CAMPOREE SCOUT 1965**.
1546 5 c. multicoloured 20 20
1547 5 c. multicoloured 20 20
1548 5 c. multicoloured 20 20
1549 5 c. multicoloured 20 20
1550 5 c. multicoloured 20 20
1551 5 c. multicoloured 20 20
1552 5 c. multicoloured 20 20
1553 5 c. multicoloured 20 20
1554 5 c. multicoloured 20 20
1555 5 c. multicoloured 20 20

240 Sir Winston Churchill
241 Pope John XXIII

1966. Air. Churchill Commemorative.
1556 **240** 20 c. mauve & black . . 10 10
1557 – 35 c. green and black . . 15 10
1558 – 60 c. ochre and black . . 15 15
1559 – 75 c. red 20 20
1560 – 1 cor. purple 30 25
1561 **240** 2 cor. violet, lilac & blk . 60 55
1562 – 3 cor. blue and black . . 65 60
DESIGNS—HORIZ: 35 c., 1 cor. Churchill broadcasting. VERT: 60 c., 3 cor. Churchill crossing the Rhine; 75 c. Churchill in Hussars' uniform.

1966. Air. Closure of Vatican Ecumenical Council. Multicoloured.
1564 20 c. Type **241** 10 10
1565 35 c. Pope Paul VI 15 15
1566 1 cor. Archbishop Gonzalez y Robleto 30 25
1567 2 cor. St. Peter's, Rome . . 30 25
1568 3 cor. Papal arms 60 40

1967. Air. Nos. 1533/4 surch **RESELLO** and value.
1569 10 c. on 50 c. multicoloured 10 10
1570 15 c. on 60 c. multicoloured 10 10
See also Nos. 1448/9, 1498/1500a, 1608/14 and 1669/76.

243 Dario and Birthplace

1967. Air. Birth Cent. of Ruben Dario (poet). Designs showing Dario and view. Multicoloured.
1571 5 c. Type **243** 10 10
1572 10 c. Monument, Managua . 10 10
1573 20 c. Leon Cathedral (site of Dario's tomb) 10 10
1574 40 c. Allegory of the centaurs 15 10
1575 75 c. Allegory of the swans . 2·00 75
1576 1 cor. Roman triumphal march 25 20
1577 2 cor. St. Francis and the wolf 45 40
1578 5 cor. "Faith" opposing "Death" 65 60

244 "Megalura peleus"

1967. Air. Butterflies. Multicoloured.
1580 5 c. "Heliconius petiveranua" 10 10
1581 10 c. "Colaenis julia" . . . 10 10
1582 15 c. Type **244** 10 10
1583 20 c. "Aneyluris jurgensii" . 10 10
1584 25 c. "Thecla regalis" . . . 10 10
1585 30 c. "Doriana thia" 10 10
1586 35 c. "Lymnias pixae" . . . 15 10
1587 40 c. "Metamorpho dido" . . 25 10
1588 50 c. "Papilio arcas" 25 15
1589 60 c. "Ananea cleomestra" . . 35 15
1590 1 cor. "Victorina epaphaus" . 60 30
1591 2 cor. "Prepona demophon" . 1·10 50
The 5, 10, 30, 35, 50 c. and 1 cor. are vert.

245 McDivitt and White

1967. Air. Space Flight of McDivitt and White. Multicoloured.
1592 5 c. Type **245** 10 10
1593 10 c. Astronauts and "Gemini 5" on launching pad . . . 10 10
1594 15 c. "Gemini 5" and White in Space 10 10
1595 20 c. Recovery operation at sea 15 10
1596 35 c. Type **245** 15 10
1597 40 c. As 10 c. 15 10
1598 75 c. As 15 c. 20 20
1599 1 cor. As 20 c. 35 25

246 National Flower of Costa Rica

1967. Air. 5th Year of Central American Economic Integration. Designs showing National Flowers of the Central-American Countries. Multicoloured.
1600 40 c. Type **246** 15 10
1601 40 c. Guatemala 15 10
1602 40 c. Honduras 15 10
1603 40 c. Nicaragua 15 10
1604 40 c. El Salvador 15 10

247 Presidents Diaz and Somoza
249 Mangoes

1968. Air. Visit of Pres. Diaz of Mexico.
1605 – 20 c. black 10 10
1606 **247** 40 c. olive 20 10
1607 – 1 cor. brown 35 20
DESIGNS—VERT: 20 c. Pres. Somoza greeting Pres. Diaz; 1 cor. Pres. Diaz of Mexico.

1968. Surch **RESELLO** and value.
1608 – 5 c. on 6 c. (No. 1180) (postage) 10 10
1609 – 5 c. on 6 c. (No. 1471) . . 10 10
1610 – 5 c. on 6 c. (No. 1424) (air) 10 10
1611 – 5 c. on 6 c. (No. 1489) . . 10 10
1612 **156** 5 c. on 8 c. (No. 1035) . . 10 10
1614 – 1 cor. on 1 cor. 50 (No. 1369) 25 20
See also Nos. 1448/9, 1498/1500a, 1569/70 and 1669/76.

1968. Air. Nicaraguan Fruits. Multicoloured.
1615 5 c. Type **249** 10 10
1616 10 c. Pineapples 10 10
1617 15 c. Oranges 10 10
1618 20 c. Pawpaws 10 10
1619 30 c. Bananas 10 10
1620 35 c. Avocado pears 15 10
1621 50 c. Water-melons 15 10
1622 75 c. Cashews 25 15
1623 1 cor. Sapodilla plums . . . 35 20
1624 2 cor. Cocoa beans 45 20

250 "The Crucifixion" (Fra Angelico)

1968. Air. Religious Paintings. Multicoloured.
1625 10 c. Type **250** 10 10
1626 15 c. "The Last Judgement" (Michelangelo) 10 10
1627 35 c. "The Beautiful Gardener" (Raphael) 15 15
1628 2 cor. "The Spoliation of Christ" (El Greco) 45 30
1629 3 cor. "The Conception" (Murillo) 60 45
Nos. 1626/9 are vert.

1968. Air. Pope Paul's Visit to Bogota. Nos. 1625/8 optd **Visita de S. S. Paulo VI C. E. de Bogota 1968**.
1631 **250** 10 c. multicoloured . . . 10 10
1632 – 15 c. multicoloured . . . 10 10
1633 – 35 c. multicoloured . . . 10 10
1634 – 2 cor. multicoloured . . . 30 20

252 Basketball

1969. Air. Olympic Games, Mexico. Mult.
1635 10 c. Type **252** 10 10
1636 15 c. Fencing 10 10
1637 20 c. High-diving 10 10
1638 35 c. Running 10 10
1639 50 c. Hurdling 15 10
1640 75 c. Weightlifting 20 15
1641 1 cor. Boxing 35 20
1642 2 cor. Football 55 55
The 15, 50 c. and 1 cor. are horiz.

253 "Cichlasoma citrinellum"

1969. Air. Fishes. Multicoloured.
1644 10 c. Type **253** 10 10
1645 15 c. "Cichlasoma nicaraguensis" 10 10
1646 20 c. "Cyprinus carpio" (Carp) 10 10
1647 30 c. "Lepisosteus tropicus" (Gar) 10 10
1648 35 c. "Xiphias gladius" (Swordfish) 10 10
1649 50 c. "Phylipuns dormitor" (vert) 15 10
1650 75 c. "Tarpon atlanticus" (Tarpon) (vert) 20 15
1651 1 cor. "Eulamia nicaraguensis" (vert) 30 15
1652 2 cor. "Istiophorus albicans" (Sailfish) (vert) 30 35
1653 3 cor. "Pristis antiquorum" (Sawfish) (vert) 60 40

1969. Air. Various stamps surch **RESELLO** and value.
1655 10 c. on 25 c. (No. 1507) . . 10 10
1656 10 c. on 25 c. (No. 1512) . . 10 10
1657 15 c. on 25 c. (No. 1529) . . 10 10
1658 50 c. on 70 c. (No. 1379) . . 15 10

255 Scenery, Tower and Emblem
258 "Minerals"

1969. Air. "Hemisfair" (1968) Exhibition.
1659 **255** 30 c. blue and red . . . 10 10
1660 35 c. purple and red . . 10 10
1661 75 c. red and blue . . . 15 10
1662 1 cor. purple and black . 30 20
1663 2 cor. purple and green . 55 40

1969. Various stamps surch (a) Optd **CORREO**.
1665 5 c. (No. 1450) 10 10
1666 5 c. (No. 1453) 10 10
1667 5 c. (No. 1454) 10 10
1668 5 c. (No. 1459) 10 10

(b) Optd **RESELLO** and surch.
1670 10 c. on 30 c. (No. 1324) . . 10 10
1671 10 c. on 30 c. (No. 1427) . . 10 10
1669 10 c. on 25 c. (No. 1529) . . 10 10
1672 10 c. on 30 c. (No. 1530) . . 10 10
1673 15 c. on 35 c. (No. 1531) . . 10 10
1674 20 c. on 30 c. (No. 1307) . . 10 10
1675 20 c. on 30 c. (No. 1401) . . 10 10
1676 20 c. on 35 c. (No. 1509) . . 10 10

1969. Air. Nicaraguan Products. Multicoloured.
1677 5 c. Type **258** 10 10
1678 10 c. "Fish" 10 10
1679 15 c. "Bananas" 10 10
1680 20 c. "Timber" 10 10
1681 35 c. "Coffee" 10 10
1682 40 c. "Sugar-cane" 15 10
1683 60 c. "Cotton" 20 10
1684 75 c. "Rice and Maize" . . . 20 15
1685 1 cor. "Tobacco" 30 20
1686 2 cor. "Meat" 35 25

1969. 50th Anniv of I.L.O. Obligatory tax stamps. Nos. 1450/9, optd, **O.I.T. 1919-1969**.
1687 5 c. multicoloured 10 10
1688 5 c. multicoloured 10 10
1689 5 c. multicoloured 10 10
1690 5 c. multicoloured 10 10
1691 5 c. multicoloured 10 10
1692 5 c. multicoloured 10 10
1693 5 c. multicoloured 10 10
1694 5 c. multicoloured 10 10
1695 5 c. multicoloured 10 10
1696 5 c. multicoloured 10 10

260 Girl carrying Tinaja
261 Pele (Brazil)

1970. Air. 8th Inter-American Savings and Loans Conference, Managua.
1697 **260** 10 c. multicoloured . . . 10 10
1698 15 c. multicoloured . . . 10 10
1699 20 c. multicoloured . . . 10 10
1700 35 c. multicoloured . . . 10 10
1701 50 c. multicoloured . . . 15 10
1702 75 c. multicoloured . . . 20 15
1703 1 cor. multicoloured . . . 30 20
1704 2 cor. multicoloured . . 60 40

1970. World Football "Hall of Fame" Poll-winners. Multicoloured.
1705 5 c. Type **261** (postage) . . . 10 10
1706 10 c. Puskas (Hungary) . . . 10 10
1707 15 c. Matthews (England) . . 10 10
1708 40 c. Di Stefano (Argentina) . 10 10
1709 2 cor. Facchetti (Italy) . . . 55 45
1710 3 cor. Yashin (Russia) . . . 70 65

1711 5 cor. Beckenbauer (West Germany) 70 90
1712 20 c. Santos (Brazil) (air) . . 10 10
1713 80 c. Wright (England) . . . 20 15
1714 1 cor. Flags of 16 World Cup Finalists 25 20
1715 4 cor. Bozsik (Hungary) . . . 90 75
1716 5 cor. Charlton (England) . . 1·10 90

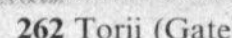

262 Torii (Gate) **263** Module and Astronauts on Moon

1970. Air. EXPO 70, World Fair, Osaka, Japan.
1717 **262** 25 c. multicoloured . . . 10 10
1718 30 c. multicoloured . . . 10 10
1719 35 c. multicoloured . . . 10 10
1720 75 c. multicoloured . . . 25 15
1721 1 cor. 50 multicoloured . . 35 30
1722 3 cor. multicoloured . . 45 35

1970. Air. "Apollo 11" Moon Landing. Mult.
1724 35 c. Type **263** 10 10
1725 40 c. Module landing on Moon 10 10
1726 60 c. Astronauts with U.S. Flag 20 15
1727 75 c. As 40 c. 25 15
1728 1 cor. As 60 c. 35 20
1729 2 cor. Type **263** 40 35

264 F. D. Roosevelt **265** "The Annunciation" (Grunewald)

1970. Air. 25th Death Anniv of Franklin D. Roosevelt.
1730 **264** 10 c. black 10 10
1731 – 15 c. brown and black . . 10 10
1732 – 20 c. green and black . . 10 10
1733 **264** 35 c. purple and black . . 10 10
1734 – 50 c. brown 15 10
1735 **264** 75 c. blue 20 15
1736 – 1 cor. red 25 20
1737 – 2 cor. black 30 35

PORTRAITS: 15 c., 1 cor. Roosevelt with stamp collection; 20 c., 50 c., 2 cor. Roosevelt (full-face).

1970. Air. Christmas. Paintings. Multicoloured.
1738 10 c. Type **265** 10 10
1739 10 c. "The Nativity" (detail, El Greco) 10 10
1740 10 c. "The Adoration of the Magi" (detail, Durer) . . . 10 10
1741 10 c. "Virgin and Child" (J. van Hemessen) 10 10
1742 10 c. "The Holy Shepherd" (Portuguese School, 16th cent.) 10 10
1743 15 c. Type **265** 10 10
1744 20 c. As No. 1739 . . . . . 10 10
1745 35 c. As No. 1740 . . . . . 15 10
1746 75 c. As No. 1741 . . . . . 20 15
1747 1 cor. As No. 1742 . . . . 30 20

1971. Surch **RESELLO** and new value.
1748 30 c. on 90 c. black (No. 1227) (postage) . . . . 10·00 10·00
1749 10 c. on 1 cor. 5 red, black & red (No. 1368) (air) 10 10
1750 10 c. on 1 cor. 5 mult (No. 1407) 10 10
1751 10 c. on 1 cor. 5 mult (No. 1430) 10 10
1752 15 c. on 1 cor. 50 green and red (No. 1116) 10 10
1753 15 c. on 1 cor. 50 green (No. 1255) 10 10
1754 15 c. on 1 cor. 50 yellow and blue (No. 1369) 10 10
1755 15 c. on 1 cor. 50 black and violet (No. 1381) 10 10
1756 20 c. on 85 c. black and red (No. 1276) 15 10
1757 20 c. on 85 c. black, red and blue (No. 1339) 15 10
1758 25 c. on 90 c. black, green and ochre (No. 1440) 15 15
1759 30 c. on 1 cor. 10 black and purple (No. 1195) 15 15
1760 40 c. on 1 cor. 10 brown and black (No. 1157) 65 65
1761 40 c. on 1 cor. 50 mult (No. 1408) 65 65
1762 1 cor. on 1 cor. 10 black and blue (No. 1538) . . . . . 1·60 1·60

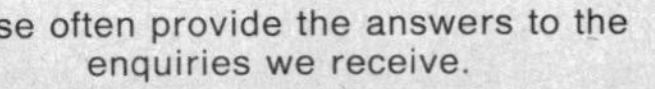

HAVE YOU READ THE NOTES AT THE BEGINNING OF THIS CATALOGUE?
These often provide the answers to the enquiries we receive.

266 Basic Mathematical Equation

1971. Scientific Formulae. "The Ten Mathematical Equations that changed the Face of the Earth". Multicoloured.
1763 10 c. Type **266** (postage) . . 10 10
1764 15 c. Newton's Law 10 10
1765 20 c. Einstein's Law 10 10
1766 1 cor. Tsiolkovsky's Law . . 25 25
1767 2 cor. Maxwell's Law . . . 90 75
1768 25 c. Napier's Law (air) . . 10 10
1769 30 c. Pythagoras' Law . . . 10 10
1770 40 c. Boltzmann's Law . . . 15 10
1771 1 cor. Broglie's Law 30 20
1772 2 cor. Archimedes' Law . . 55 40

267 Peace Emblem

1971. "Is There a Formula for Peace?".
1773 **267** 10 c. blue and black . . 10 10
1774 15 c. blue, black & vio . 10 10
1775 20 c. blue, black & brn . 10 10
1776 40 c. blue, black & grn . 10 10
1777 50 c. blue, black & pur . 15 10
1778 80 c. blue, black & red . 15 15
1779 1 cor. blue, black & grn 30 20
1780 2 cor. blue, black & vio 55 35

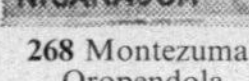

268 Montezuma Oropendola **269** "Moses with the Tablets of the Law" (Rembrandt)

1971. Air. Nicaraguan Birds. Multicoloured.
1781 10 c. Type **268** 35 15
1782 15 c. Turquoise-browed motmot 35 15
1783 20 c. White-throated magpie-jay 45 15
1784 25 c. Scissor-tailed flycatcher 45 15
1785 30 c. Spotted-breasted oriole (horiz) 60 15
1786 35 c. Rufous-naped wren . . 70 15
1787 40 c. Great kiskadee 70 15
1788 75 c. Red-legged honeycreeper (horiz) . . . . 1·25 35
1789 1 cor. Great-tailed grackle (horiz) . . . . 1·50 45
1790 2 cor. Belted kingfisher . . . 2·50 65

1971. "The Ten Commandments". Paintings. Multicoloured.
1791 10 c. Type **269** (postage) . . 10 10
1792 15 c. "Moses and the Burning Bush" (Botticelli) (1st Commandment) 10 10
1793 20 c. "Jepthah's Daughter" (Degas) (2nd Commandment) (horiz) 10 10
1794 30 c. "St. Vincent Ferrer preaching in Verona" (Morone) (3rd Commandment) (horiz) . 10 10
1795 35 c. "Noah's Drunkenness" (Michelangelo) (4th Commandment) (horiz) . 10 10
1796 40 c. "Cain and Abel" (Trevisani) (5th Commandment) (horiz) . 10 10
1797 50 c. "Joseph accused by Potiphar's Wife" (Rembrandt) (6th Commandment) 10 10
1798 60 c. "Isaac blessing Jacob" (Eeckhout) (7th Commandment) (horiz) . 15 10
1799 75 c. "Susannah and the Elders" (Rubens) (8th Commandment) (horiz) . 25 20
1800 1 cor. "Bathsheba after her Bath" (Rembrandt) (9th Commandment) (air) . . . 25 20
1801 2 cor. "Naboth's Vineyard" (Smetham) (10th Commandment) 40 35

270 U Thant and Pres. Somoza

1971. Air. 25th Anniv of U.N.O.
1802 **270** 10 c. brown and red . . . 10 10
1803 15 c. green and emerald . 10 10
1804 20 c. blue & light blue . . 10 10
1805 25 c. red and purple . . . 10 10
1806 30 c. brown & orange . . 10 10
1807 40 c. green and grey . . . 15 10
1808 1 cor. green & sage . . . 25 20
1809 2 cor. brown & light brown 30 35

1972. Olympic Games, Munich. Nos. 1709, 1711, 1713 and 1716 surch **OLIMPIADAS MUNICH 1972**, emblem and value or optd only (5 cor.).
1810 40 c. on 2 cor. multicoloured (postage) 10 10
1811 50 c. on 3 cor. multicoloured . 15 10
1812 20 c. on 80 c. mult (air) . . . 10 10
1813 60 c. on 4 cor. multicoloured . 15 10
1814 5 cor. multicoloured 65 65

272 Figurine and Apoyo Site on Map

1972. Air. Pre-Columbian Art. A. H. Heller's Pottery Discoveries. Multicoloured.
1815 10 c. Type **272** 10 10
1816 15 c. Cana Castilla 10 10
1817 20 c. Catarina 10 10
1818 25 c. Santa Helena 10 10
1819 30 c. Mombacho 10 10
1820 35 c. Tisma 10 10
1821 40 c. El Menco 10 10
1822 50 c. Los Placeres 15 10
1823 60 c. Masaya 15 15
1824 80 c. Granada 20 15
1825 1 cor. Las Mercedes 30 20
1826 2 cor. Nindiri 55 35

273 "Lord Peter Wimsey" (Dorothy Sayers)

1972. Air. 50th Anniv of International Criminal Police Organization (INTERPOL). Famous Fictional Detectives. Multicoloured.
1827 5 c. Type **273** 10 10
1828 10 c. "Philip Marlowe" (Raymond Chandler) . . . 10 10
1829 15 c. "Sam Spade" (D. Hammett) . . . . . . 4·50 10
1830 20 c. "Perry Mason" (Erle Stanley Gardner) . . 10 10
1831 25 c. "Nero Wolfe" (Rex Stout) 10 10
1832 35 c. "C. Auguste Dupin" (Edgar Allan Poe) 10 10
1833 40 c. "Ellery Queen" (F. Dannay and M. Lee) . . 10 10
1834 50 c. "Father Brown" (G. K. Chesterton) 10 10
1835 60 c. "Charlie Chan" (Earl D. Biggers) 15 10
1836 80 c. "Inspector Maigret" (Georges Simenon) 25 15
1837 1 cor. "Hercule Poirot" (Agatha Christie) 25 20
1838 2 cor. "Sherlock Holmes" (A. Conan Doyle) 70 70

274 "The Shepherdess and her Brothers"

1972. Air. Christmas. Scenes from Legend of the Christmas Rose. Multicoloured.
1839 10 c. Type **274** 10 10
1840 15 c. Adoration of the Wise Men 10 10
1841 20 c. Shepherdess crying . . . 10 10
1842 35 c. Angel appears to Shepherdess 10 10
1843 40 c. Christmas Rose 10 10
1844 60 c. Shepherdess thanks angel for roses 15 10
1845 80 c. Shepherdess takes roses to Holy Child 15 15
1846 1 cor. Holy Child receiving roses 20 15
1847 2 cor. Nativity Scene 45 35

275 Sir Walter Raleigh and Elizabethan Galleon

1973. Air. Causes of the American Revolution. Multicoloured.
1849 10 c. Type **275** 30 10
1850 15 c. Signing "Mayflower Compact" 10 10
1851 20 c. Acquittal of Peter Zenger (vert) 10 10
1852 25 c. Acclaiming American resistance (vert) 10 10
1853 30 c. Revenue Stamp (vert) . . 10 10
1854 35 c. "Serpent" slogan–"Join or die" 10 10
1855 40 c. Boston Massacre (vert) . 10 10
1856 50 c. Boston Tea-party . . . 10 10
1857 60 c. Patrick Henry on trial (vert) 15 10
1858 75 c. Battle of Bunker Hill . . 20 10
1859 80 c. Declaration of Independence 20 15
1860 1 cor. Liberty Bell 30 20
1861 2 cor. US seal (vert) 90 60

1973. Nos. 1450/54, 1456 and 1458/9 optd **CORREO**.
1862 **219** 5 c. multicoloured . . . 25 10
1863 – 5 c. multicoloured . . . 25 10
1864 – 5 c. multicoloured . . . 25 10
1865 – 5 c. multicoloured . . . 25 10
1866 – 5 c. multicoloured . . . 25 10
1867 – 5 c. multicoloured . . . 25 10
1868 – 5 c. multicoloured . . . 25 10
1869 – 5 c. multicoloured . . . 25 10

277 Baseball, Player and Map **278** Givenchy, Paris

1973. Air. 20th International Baseball Championships, Managua (1972).
1870 **277** 15 c. multicoloured . . . 10 10
1871 20 c. multicoloured . . . 10 10
1872 40 c. multicoloured . . . 10 10
1873 10 cor. multicoloured . . 1·50 90

1973. World-famous Couturiers. Mannequins. Multicoloured.
1875 1 cor. Type **278** (postage) . . 25 20
1876 2 cor. Hartnell, London . . 40 40
1877 5 cor. Balmain, Paris . . . . 1·00 90
1878 10 c. Lourdes, Nicaragua (air) 10 10
1879 15 c. Halston, New York . . 10 10
1880 20 c. Pino Lancetti, Rome . . 10 10
1881 35 c. Madame Gres, Paris . . 10 10
1882 40 c. Irene Galitzine, Rome . 10 10
1883 80 c. Pedro Rodriguez, Barcelona 15 15

279 Diet Chart

1973. Air. Child Welfare. Multicoloured.
1885 5 c. + 5 c. Type **279** 10 10
1886 10 c. + 5 c. Senora Samoza with baby, and Children's Hospital 10 10
1887 15 c. + 5 c. "Childbirth" . . 10 10
1888 20 c. + 5 c. "Immunisation" . 10 10
1889 30 c. + 5 c. Water purification 10 10
1890 35 c. + 5 c. As No. 1886 . . 10 10
1891 50 c. + 10 c. Alexander Fleming and "Antibiotics" 10 10
1892 60 c. + 15 c. Malaria control 15 10
1893 70 c. + 10 c. Laboratory analysis 15 15
1894 80 c. + 20 c. Gastro-enteritis 20 15
1895 1 cor. + 50 c. As No. 1886 . 30 25
1896 2 cor. Pediatric surgery . . . 45 35

280 Virginia and Father

1973. Christmas. "Does Santa Claus exist?" (Virginia O'Hanlon's letter to American "Sun" newspaper). Multicoloured.

1897 2 c. Type **280** (postage) 10 10
1898 3 c. Text of letter 10 10
1899 4 c. Reading the reply 10 10
1900 5 c. Type **280** 10 10
1901 15 c. As 3 c. 10 10
1902 20 c. As 4 c. 10 10

1903 1 cor. Type **280** (air) 20 15
1904 2 cor. As 3 c. 35 30
1905 4 cor. As 4 c. 75 65

281 Churchill making Speech, 1936

1974. Birth Cent. of Sir Winston Churchill.

1907 **281** 2 c. multicoloured (postage) 10 10
1908 – 3 c. black, blue & brown 10 10
1909 – 4 c. multicoloured 10 10
1910 – 5 c. multicoloured 10 10
1911 – 10 c. brown, green & bl 30 10

1912 – 5 cor. multicoloured (air) 90 80
1913 – 6 cor. black, brown & bl 1·00 90

DESIGNS: 3 c. "The Four Churchills" (wartime cartoon); 4 c. Candle, cigar and "Action" stickers; 5 c. Churchill, Roosevelt and Stalin at Yalta; 10 c. Churchill landing in Normandy, 1944; 5 cor. Churchill giving "V" sign; 6 cor. "Bulldog Churchill" (cartoon).

282 Presentation of World Cup to Uruguay, 1930

1974. World Cup Football Championships. Mult.

1915 1 c. Type **282** (postage) 10 10
1916 2 c. Victorious Italian team, 1934 10 10
1917 3 c. Presentation of World Cup to Italy, 1938 10 10
1918 4 c. Uruguay's winning goal, 1950 10 10
1919 5 c. Victorious West Germany, 1954 10 10
1920 10 c. Rejoicing Brazilian players, 1958 10 10
1921 15 c. Brazilian player holding World Cup, 1962 10 10
1922 20 c. Queen Elizabeth II presenting Cup to Bobby Moore, 1966 10 10
1923 25 c. Victorious Brazilian players, 1970 10 10
1924 10 cor. Football and flags of participating countries, 1974 (air) 1·75 1·75

283 "Malachra sp."

284 Nicaraguan 7½ c. Stamp of 1937

1974. Wild Flowers and Cacti. Multicoloured.

1926 2 c. Type **283** (postage) 10 10
1927 3 c. "Paguira insignis" 10 10
1928 4 c. "Convolvulus sp." 10 10
1929 5 c. "Pereschia autumnalis" 10 10
1930 10 c. "Ipomea tuberosa" 10 10
1931 15 c. "Hibiscus elatus" 10 10
1932 20 c. "Plumeria acutifolia" 10 10

1933 1 cor. "Centrosema sp." (air) 20 20
1934 3 cor. "Hylocereus undatus" 60 55

1974. Centenary of U.P.U.

1935 **284** 2 c. red, grn & blk (postage) 10 15
1936 – 3 c. blue, green & blk 10 10
1937 – 4 c. multicoloured 10 10
1938 – 5 c. brown, mve & blk 10 10
1939 – 10 c. red, brown & blk 10 10
1940 – 20 c. green, blue & blk 10 10

1941 – 40 c. multicoloured (air) 10 10
1942 – 3 cor. green, blk & pink 50 40
1943 – 5 cor. blue, black & lilac 1·00 80

DESIGNS—VERT: 3 c. 5 c. stamp of 1937; 5 c. 2 c. stamp of 1937; 10 c. 1 c. stamp of 1937; 20 c. ½ c. stamp of 1937; 40 c. 10 c. stamp of 1961; 5 cor. 4 cor. U.P.U. stamp of 1950. HORIZ: 4 c. 10 c. air stamp of 1934; 3 cor. 85 c. U.P.U. air stamp of 1950.

1974. Air. West Germany's Victory in World Cup Football Championships. No. 1924 optd TRIUMFADOR ALEMANIA OCCIDENTAL.

1945 10 cor. multicoloured 1·75 1·60

286 Tamandua

1974. Nicaraguan Fauna. Multicoloured.

1947 1 c. Type **286** (postage) 10 10
1948 2 c. Puma 10 10
1949 3 c. Common raccoon 10 10
1950 4 c. Ocelot 10 10
1951 5 c. Kinkajou 10 10
1952 10 c. Coypu 10 10
1953 15 c. Collared peccary 15 10
1954 20 c. Baird's tapir 15 10

1955 3 cor. Red brocket (air) 1·50 1·40
1956 5 cor. Jaguar 2·40 2·00

287 "Prophet Zacharias"

288 Giovanni Martinelli ("Othello")

1975. Christmas. 500th Birth Anniv of Michelangelo. Multicoloured.

1957 1 c. Type **287** (postage) 10 10
1958 2 c. "Christ amongst the Jews" 10 10
1959 3 c. "The Creation of Man" (horiz) 10 10
1960 4 c. Interior of Sistine Chapel, Rome 10 10
1961 5 c. "Moses" 10 10
1962 10 c. "Mouscron Madonna" 10 10
1963 15 c. "David" 10 10
1964 20 c. "Doni Madonna" 10 10

1965 40 c. "Madonna of the Steps" (air) 10 10
1966 80 c. "Pitti Madonna" 15 15
1967 2 cor. "Christ and Virgin Mary" 35 30
1968 5 cor. "Michelangelo" (self-portrait) 75 75

1975. Great Opera Singers. Multicoloured.

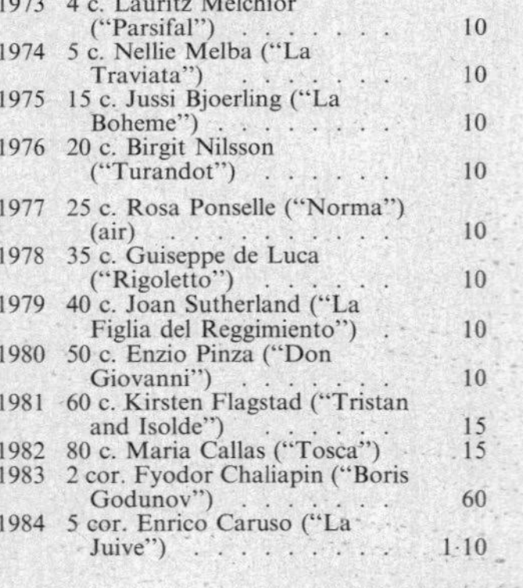

1970 1 c. Type **288** (postage) 10 10
1971 2 c. Tito Gobbi ("Simone Boccaoegra") 10 10
1972 3 c. Lotte Lehmann ("Der Rosenkavalier") 10 10
1973 4 c. Lauritz Melchior ("Parsifal") 10 10
1974 5 c. Nellie Melba ("La Traviata") 10 10
1975 15 c. Jussi Bjoerling ("La Boheme") 10 10
1976 20 c. Birgit Nilsson ("Turandot") 10 10

1977 25 c. Rosa Ponselle ("Norma") (air) 10 10
1978 35 c. Guiseppe de Luca ("Rigoletto") 10 10
1979 40 c. Joan Sutherland ("La Figlia del Reggimiento") 10 10
1980 50 c. Enzio Pinza ("Don Giovanni") 10 10
1981 60 c. Kirsten Flagstad ("Tristan and Isolde") 15 10
1982 80 c. Maria Callas ("Tosca") 15 15
1983 2 cor. Fyodor Chaliapin ("Boris Godunov") 60 35
1984 5 cor. Enrico Caruso ("La Juive") 1·10 60

289 The First Station

290 "The Spirit of 76"

1975. Easter. The 14 Stations of the Cross.

1986 **289** 1 c. multicoloured (postage) 10 10
1987 – 2 c. multicoloured 10 10
1988 – 3 c. multicoloured 10 10
1989 – 4 c. multicoloured 10 10
1990 – 5 c. multicoloured 10 10
1991 – 15 c. multicoloured 10 10
1992 – 20 c. multicoloured 10 10
1993 – 25 c. multicoloured 10 10
1994 – 35 c. multicoloured 10 10

1995 – 40 c. multicoloured (air) 10 10
1996 – 50 c. multicoloured 10 10
1997 – 80 c. multicoloured 15 15
1998 – 1 cor. multicoloured 20 15
1999 – 5 cor. multicoloured 80 65

DESIGNS: 2 c. to 5 cor. Different Stations of the Cross.

1975. Bicentenary of American Independence (1st series). Multicoloured.

2000 1 c. Type **290** (postage) 10 10
2001 2 c. Pitt addressing Parliament 10 10
2002 3 c. Paul Revere's Ride (horiz) 10 10
2003 4 c. Demolishing statue of George III (horiz) 10 10
2004 5 c. Boston Massacre 10 10
2005 10 c. Tax stamp and George III 3d. coin (horiz) 10 10
2006 15 c. Boston Tea Party (horiz) 10 10
2007 20 c. Thomas Jefferson 10 10
2008 25 c. Benjamin Franklin 10 10
2009 30 c. Signing of Declaration of Independence (horiz) 10 10
2010 35 c. Surrender of Cornwallis at Yorktown (horiz) 10 10

2011 40 c. Washington's Farewell (horiz) (air) 10 10
2012 50 c. Washington addressing Congress (horiz) 10 10
2013 2 cor. Washington arriving for Presidential Inauguration (horiz) 70 30
2014 5 cor. Statue of Liberty & flags 75 45

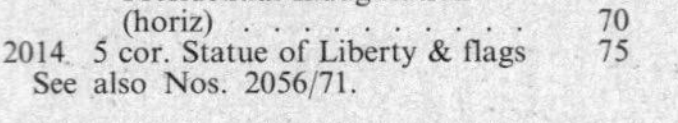

See also Nos. 2056/71.

291 Saluting the Flag

1975. "Nordjamb 75" World Scout Jamboree, Norway. Multicoloured.

2016 1 c. Type **291** (postage) 10 10
2017 2 c. Scout canoe 10 10
2018 3 c. Scouts shaking hands 10 10
2019 4 c. Scout preparing meal 10 10
2020 5 c. Entrance to Nicaraguan camp 10 10
2021 20 c. Scouts meeting 10 10

2022 35 c. Aerial view of camp (air) 10 10
2023 40 c. Scouts making music 10 10
2024 1 cor. Camp-fire 20 15
2025 10 cor. Lord Baden-Powell 1·25 1·10

292 President Somoza

293 "Chess Players" (L. Carracci)

1975. President Somoza's New Term of Office, 1974–1981.

2027 **292** 20 c. multicoloured (postage) 10 10
2028 40 c. multicoloured 10 10

2029 1 cor. multicoloured (air) 20 20
2030 10 cor. multicoloured 1·25 1·10
2031 20 cor. multicoloured 3·25 2·75

1975. Chess. Multicoloured.

2032 1 c. Type **293** (postage) 10 10
2033 2 c. "Arabs playing Chess" (Delacroix) 10 10
2034 3 c. "Cardinals playing Chess" (V. Marais-Milton) 10 10
2035 4 c. "Duke Albrecht V of Bavaria and Anna of Austria at Chess" (H. Muelich) (vert) 10 10
2036 5 c. "Chess game" (14th-century Persian manuscript) 10 10
2037 10 c. "Origins of Chess" (India, 1602) 10 10
2038 15 c. "Napoleon playing Chess in Schonbrunn Palace in 1809" (A. Uniechowski) (vert) 10 10
2039 20 c. "The Chess Game in the House of Count Ingenheim" (J.E. Hummel) 10 10

2040 40 c. "The Chess-players" (T. Eakins) (air) 10 10
2041 2 cor. Fischer v Spassky match, Reykjavik, 1972 55 35
2042 5 cor. "William Shakespeare and Ben Jonson playing Chess" (K. van Mander) 60 50

HAVE YOU READ THE NOTES AT THE BEGINNING OF THIS CATALOGUE?

These often provide the answers to the enquiries we receive.

294 Choir of King's College Cambridge

1975. Christmas. Famous Choirs. Multicoloured.

2044 1 c. Type **294** (postage) 10 10
2045 2 c. Abbey Choir, Einsiedeln 10 10
2046 3 c. Regensburg Cathedral choir 10 10
2047 4 c. Vienna Boys' choir 10 10
2048 5 c. Sistine Chapel choir 10 10
2049 15 c. Westminster Cathedral choir 10 10
2050 20 c. Mormon Tabernacle choir 10 10

2051 50 c. School choir, Montserrat (air) 10 10
2052 1 cor. St. Florian children's choir 20 15
2053 2 cor. "Little Singers of the Wooden Cross" (vert) 45 35
2054 5 cor. Pope with choristers of Pueri Cantores 60 50

295 "The Smoke Signal" (F. Remington)

1976. Bicent of American Revolution (2nd series). "200 Years of Progress". Multicoloured.

2056 1 c. Type **295** (postage) 10 10
2057 1 c. Houston Space Centre 10 10
2058 2 c. Lighting candelabra, 1976 10 10
2059 2 c. Edison's lamp and houses 10 10
2060 3 c. "Agriculture 1776" 10 10
2061 3 c. "Agriculture 1976" 10 10
2062 4 c. Harvard College, 1776 10 10
2063 4 c. Harvard University, 1976 10 10
2064 5 c. Horse and carriage 15 10
2065 5 c. Boeing 747-100 airliner 15 10

2066 80 c. Philadelphia, 1776 (air) 25 15
2067 80 c. Washington, 1976 25 15
2068 2 cor. 75 "Bonhomme Richard" (John Paul Jones's flagship) and H.M.S. "Seraphis", Battle of Flamborough Head 1·50 70
2069 2 cor. 75 U.S.S. "Glenard Phipscomp" (nuclear submarine) 1·50 70
2070 4 cor. Wagon train 90 70
2071 4 cor. "Amtrak" express train 1·90 1·25

296 Italy, 1968

1976. Olympic Games, Victors in Rowing and Sculling. Multicoloured.

2073 1 c. Denmark 1964 (postage) 10 10
2074 2 c. East Germany 1972 10 10
2075 3 c. Type **296** 10 10
2076 4 c. Great Britain 1936 10 10
2077 5 c. France 1952 (vert) 10 10
2078 35 c. U.S.A. 1920 (vert) 10 10

2079 55 c. Russia 1956 (vert) (air) 20 10
2080 70 c. New Zealand 1972 (vert) 20 15
2081 90 c. New Zealand 1968 25 20
2082 20 cor. U.S.A. 1956 2·75 2·50

1976. Air. Olympic Games, Montreal. East German Victory in Rowing Events. No. 2082 optd **REPUBLICA DEMOCRATICA ALEMANA VENCEDOR EN 1976.**

2084 20 cor. multicoloured 2·75 2·50

299 Mauritius 1847 2d. "Post Office"

1976. Rare and Famous Stamps. Multicoloured.

2087 1 c. Type **299** (postage) 10 10
2088 2 c. Western Australia 1854 "Inverted Mute Swan" 30 10
2089 3 c. Mauritius 1847 1d. "Post Office" 10 10
2090 4 c. Jamaica 1920 1s. Inverted Frame 10 10
2091 5 c. U.S. 1918 24 c. Inverted Aircraft 10 10
2092 10 c. Swiss 1845 Basel "Dove" 10 10
2093 25 c. Canada 1959 Seaway Inverted Centre 10 10
2094 40 c. Hawaiian 1851 2 c. "Missionary" (air) 10 10
2095 1 cor. G.B. 1840 "Penny Black" 20 20

2096 2 cor. British Guiana 1850 1 c. Black on Magenta 40 35
2097 5 cor. Honduras 1925 Airmail 25 c. on 10 c. 70 50
2098 10 cor. Newfoundland 1919 "Hawker" Airmail stamp . 1·25 1·10

300 Olga Nunez de Saballos (Member of Parliament)

1977. Air. International Women's Year. Mult.
2100 35 c. Type **300** 10 10
2101 1 cor. Josefa Toledo de Aguerri (educator) 20 20
2102 10 cor. Hope Portocarreo de Samoza (President's wife) . 1·25 1·00

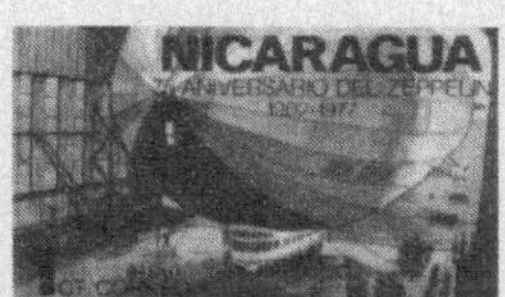

301 "Graf Zeppelin" in Hangar

1977. 75th Anniv of First Zeppelin Flight. Multicoloured.
2104 1 c. Type **301** (postage) . . . 10 10
2105 2 c. "Graf Zeppelin" in flight 10 10
2106 3 c. Giffard's steam-powered dirigible airship, 1852 . . . 15 10
2107 4 c. "Graf Zeppelin" in mooring hangar 15 10
2108 5 c. "Graf Zeppelin" on ground 15 10
2109 35 c. Astra airship "Ville de Paris" (air) 35 15
2110 70 c. "Schwaben" 40 20
2111 3 cor. "Graf Zeppelin" over Lake Constance . . . . . 1·00 65
2112 10 cor. LZ-2 on Lake Constance . . . . 3·75 2·25

302 Lindbergh and Map

1977. 50th Anniv of Lindbergh's Transatlantic Flight. Multicoloured.
2114 1 c. Type **302** (postage) . . . 10 10
2115 2 c. Map and "Spirit of St. Louis" 10 10
2116 3 c. Charles Lindbergh (vert) 10 10
2117 4 c. "Spirit of St. Louis" crossing Atlantic 10 10
2118 5 c. Charles Lindbergh standing by "Spirit of St. Louis" . . 10 10
2119 20 c. Lindbergh, route and "Spirit of St. Louis" . . . 20 15
2120 55 c. Lindbergh landing in Nicaragua (1928) (air) . . 20 15
2121 80 c. "Spirit of St. Louis" and route map 35 15
2122 2 cor. "Spirit of St. Louis" flying along Nicaraguan coast 65 35
2123 10 cor. Passing Momotombo (Nicaragua) . . . . 1·90 1·25

303 Christmas Festival

1977. Christmas. Scenes from Tchaikovsky's "Nutcracker" Suite. Multicoloured.
2125 1 c. Type **303** 10 10
2126 2 c. Doll's dance 10 10
2127 3 c. Clara and snowflakes . . 10 10
2128 4 c. Snow fairy and Prince . . 10 10
2129 5 c. Snow fairies 10 10
2130 15 c. Sugar fairy and prince . 10 10
2131 40 c. Waltz of the Flowers . . 10 10
2132 90 c. Chinese dance 20 15
2133 1 cor. Senora Bonbonierre . . 20 20
2134 10 cor. Arabian dance . . . 1·40 1·25

304 "Mr. and Mrs. Andrews". (Gainsborough)

1978. Paintings. Multicoloured.
2136 1 c. Type **304** (postage) . . . 10 10
2137 2 c. "Giovanna Bacelli" (Gainsborough) 10 10
2138 3 c. "Blue Boy" (Gainsborough) 10 10
2139 4 c. "Francis I" (Titian) . . 10 10
2140 5 c. "Charles V at Battle of Muhlberg" (Titian) . . . 10 10
2141 25 c. "Sacred Love" (Titian) 10 10
2142 5 cor. "Hippopotamus and Crocodile Hunt" (Rubens) (air) 60 50
2143 10 cor. "Duke of Lerma on Horseback" (Rubens) . . 1·75 1·40

305 Gothic Portal with Rose Window, Small Basilica of St. Francis

1978. 750th Anniv of Canonisation of St. Francis of Assisi. Multicoloured.
2145 1 c. Type **305** (postage) . . . 10 10
2146 2 c. St. Francis preaching to birds 10 10
2147 3 c. Painting of St. Francis . 10 10
2148 4 c. Franciscan genealogical tree 10 10
2149 5 c. Portiuncola 10 10
2150 15 c. Autographed blessing . 10 10
2151 25 c. Windows of Large Basilica 10 10
2152 80 c. St. Francis and wolf (air) 15 10
2153 10 cor. St. Francis . . . . . 1·60 1·50

306 Passenger and Freight Locomotive

1978. Centenary of Railway. Multicoloured.
2155 1 c. Type **306** (postage) . . . 10 10
2156 2 c. Light-weight cargo locomotive 10 10
2157 3 c. American locomotive . 10 10
2158 4 c. Baldwin heavy freight locomotive 10 10
2159 5 c. Baldwin light freight and passenger locomotive . . . 10 10
2160 15 c. Presidential Pullman coach 10 10
2161 35 c. Light-weight American locomotive (air) 20 10
2162 4 cor. Baldwin locomotive . 1·75 70
2163 10 cor. Juniata locomotive . 4·75 1·75

307 Mongol Warriors ("Michael Strogoff")

1978. 150th Birth Anniv of Jules Verne. Multicoloured.
2165 1 c. Type **307** (postage) . . . 10 10
2166 2 c. Sea scene ("The Mysterious Island") 10 10
2167 3 c. Sea monsters ("Journey to the Centre of the Earth") . 10 10
2168 4 c. Balloon and African elephant ("Five Weeks in a Balloon") 20 10
2169 90 c. Submarine ("Twenty Thousand Leagues Under the Sea") (air) 40 20
2170 10 cor. Balloon, Indian, steam locomotive and elephant ("Around the World in Eighty Days") . . . . . . 5·50 3·00

308 Icarus

1978. 75th Anniv of History of Aviation. First Powered Flight. Multicoloured.
2172 1 c. Type **308** (postage) . . . 10 10
2173 2 c. Montgolfier balloon (vert) 10 10
2174 3 c. Wright Flyer I 10 10
2175 4 c. Orville Wright in Wright Type A (vert) 10 10
2176 55 c. Vought-Sikorsky VS-300 helicopter prototype (air) . 30 10
2177 10 cor. Space shuttle . . . . 2·10 1·00

309 Ernst Ocwirk and Alfredo di Stefano
310 "St. Peter" (Goya)

1978. World Cup Football Championship, Argentina. Multicoloured.
2179 20 c. Type **309** (postage) . . . 10 10
2180 25 c. Ralk Edstrom and Oswaldo Piazza 10 10
2181 50 c. Franz Beckenbauer and Dennis Law (air) 10 10
2182 5 cor. Dino Zoff and Pele . . 65 50

1978. Christmas. Multicoloured.
2184 10 c. Type **310** (postage) . . . 10 10
2185 15 c. "St. Gregory" (Goya) . . 10 10
2186 3 cor. "The Apostles John and Peter" (Durer) (air) 40 30
2187 10 cor. "The Apostles Paul and Mark" (Durer) . . . . . . 1·40 1·00

311 San Cristobal

1978. Volcanoes and Lakes. Multicoloured.
2189 5 c. Type **311** (postage) . . . 10 10
2190 5 c. Lake de Cosiguina . . . 10 10
2191 20 c. Telica 10 10
2192 20 c. Lake Jiloa 10 10
2193 35 c. Cerro Negro (air) . . . 10 10
2194 35 c. Lake Masaya 10 10
2195 90 c. Momotombo 20 15
2196 90 c. Lake Asososca 20 15
2197 1 cor. Mombacho 20 15
2198 1 cor. Lake Apoyo 20 15
2199 10 cor. Concepcion . . . . . 1·60 80
2200 10 cor. Lake Tiscapa . . . . 1·60 80

312 General O'Higgins

1979. Air. Birth Bicentenary of Bernardo O'Higgins (liberation hero).
2201 **312** 20 cor. multicoloured . . 3·75 1·90

313 Ginger Plant and Broad-tailed Hummingbird

1979. Air. Flowers. Multicoloured.
2202 50 c. Type **313** . . . . 1·25 10
2203 55 c. Orchids 10 10
2204 70 c. Poinsettia 15 10
2205 80 c. "Poro poro" 15 10
2206 2 cor. "Morpho cypris" (butterfly) and Guayacan flowers 50 30
2207 4 cor. Iris 45 30

314 Children with football
315 Indian Postal Runner

316 Einstein and Albert Schweitzer

317 Loggerhead Turtle

1980. Year of Liberation (1979) and Nicaragua's Participation in Olympic Games. Unissued stamps overprinted. (a) International Year of the Child. Mult.
2208 20 c. Children on roundabout (postage) 15 15
2209 90 c. Type **314** (air) 65 65
2210 2 cor. Children with stamps albums . . . . 1·50 1·50
2211 2 cor. 20 Children playing with model train and aircraft . 3·00 2·00
2212 10 cor. Baseball . . . . . . 7·50 7·50

(b) Death Centenary of Sir Rowland Hill. Mult.
2214 20 c. Type **315** (postage) . . 20 20
2215 35 c. Pony express 40 40
2216 1 cor. Pre-stamp letter (horiz) 1·10 1·10
2217 1 cor. 80 Sir Rowland Hill examining sheet of Penny Black stamps (air) . . . . 1·90 1·90
2218 2 cor. 20 Penny Blacks (horiz) 2·40 2·40
2219 5 cor. Nicaraguan Zeppelin flight cover (horiz) . . . . 5·50 5·50

(c) Birth Centenary of Albert Einstein (physicist). Mult.
2221 5 c. Type **316** (postage) . . . 15 15
2222 10 c. Einstein and equation . 25 25
2223 15 c. Einstein and 1939 World Fair pavilion 40 40
2224 20 c. Einstein and Robert Oppenheimer 50 50
2225 25 c. Einstein in Jerusalem . 65 65
2226 1 cor. Einstein and Nobel Prize medal (air) . . . . . . 2·50 2·50
2227 2 cor. 75 Einstein and space exploration . . . . 7·00 7·00
2228 10 cor. Einstein and Mahatma Gandhi . . . . 15·00 15·00

(d) Endangered Turtles. Multicoloured.
2230 90 c. Type **317** 70 70
2231 2 cor. Leatherback turtle . . 1·50 1·50
2232 2 cor. 30 Ridley turtle . . . 1·75 1·75
2233 10 cor. Hawksbilled turtle . . 7·50 7·50

318 Rigoberto Lopez Perez and Crowds pulling down Statue

1980. 1st Anniv of the Revolution. Multicoloured.
2235 40 c. Type **318** 10 10
2236 75 c. Street barricade 10 10
2237 1 cor. "Learn to Read" emblem (vert) 15 10
2238 1 cor. 25 German Pomares Ordonez and jungle fighters 20 15
2239 1 cor. 85 Victory celebrations (vert) 25 15
2240 2 cor. 50 Carlos Fonesca and camp-fire 35 35
2241 5 cor. Gen. Augusto Sandino and flag (vert) 70 55

1980. Literacy Year. Unissued stamps optd **1980 ANO DE LA ALFABETIZACION**. (a) International Year of the Child. As Nos. 2208/12.
2243 – 20 c. Children on roundabout (postage) . 1·00 1·00
2244 **314** 90 c. Children with football (air) . . . . 1·00 1·00
2245 – 2 cor. Children with stamp albums . . . . 1·00 1·00
2246 – 2 cor. 20 Children playing with train and airplane 2·00 2·00
2247 – 10 cor. Baseball . . . . 4·50 4·50

(b) Death Centenary of Sir Rowland Hill. Nos. 2214/16.
2249 **315** 20 c. Indian postal runner 70 70
2250 – 35 c. Pony express . . . 70 70
2251 – 1 cor. Pre-stamp letter (horiz) 70 70

(c) Birth Centenary of Albert Einstein (physicist). As Nos. 2221/8.
2253 5 c. Optd **"YURI GAGARIN/ 12/IV/1961/LER HOMBRE EN EL ESPACIO"** (postage) 1·10 1·10
2254 10 c. Optd **"LURABA 1981"** and space shuttle . . . . . 1·10 1·10

2255 15 c. Optd **"SPACE SHUTTLE"** and craft . . 1·10 1·10
2256 20 c. Optd **ANO DE LA ALFABETIZACION** . . . 1·10 1·10
2257 25 c. Optd **"16/VII/1969/LER HOMBRE A LA LUNA" and "APOLLO XI"** . . . . . 1·10 1·10
2258 1 cor. Optd As No. 2256 (air) 1·10 1·10
2259 2 cor. 75 Optd As No. 2256 . 1·10 1·10
2260 10 cor. 75 Optd **"LUNO-JOD 1"** and vehicle . . . . . . 1·10 1·10

(d) Air. Endangered Species. Turtles. As Nos. 2230/3. Multicoloured.
2262 **317** 90 c. Loggerhead turtle . 1·00 1·00
2263 – 2 cor. Leatherback turtle 1·00 1·00
2264 – 2 cor. 20 Ridley turtle . . 1·00 1·00
2265 – 10 cor. Hawksbill turtle . 1·00 1·00

321 Footballer and El Molinon Stadium

1981. World Cup Football Championships, Spain. (1st issue). Venues. Multicoloured.
2268 5 c. Type **321** 10 10
2269 20 c. Sanchez Pizjuan, Seville 10 10
2270 25 c. San Mames, Bilbao . . 10 10
2271 30 c. Vincent Calderon, Madrid 10 10
2272 50 c. R.C.D. Espanol, Barcelona 10 10
2273 4 cor. New Stadium, Valladolid 55 35
2274 5 cor. Balaidos, Vigo 55 35
2275 10 cor. Santiago Bernabeu, Madrid . . . . 1·10 65
See also Nos. 2325/31.

322 Adult Education

1981. 2nd Anniv of Revolution. Multicoloured.
2277 50 c. Type **322** (postage) . . 10 10
2278 2 cor. 10 Workers marching (air) 30 15
2279 3 cor. Roadbuilding and container ship 65 30
2280 6 cor. Medical services . . . 50 25

323 Allegory of Revolution

1981. 20th Anniv of Sandinista National Liberation Front. Multicoloured.
2281 50 c. Type **323** (postage) . . 10 10
2282 4 cor. Sandinista guerrilla (air) 25 10

324 Postman

1981. 12th Postal Union of the Americas and Spain Congress, Managua. Multicoloured.
2283 50 c. Type **324** (postage) . . 10 10
2284 2 cor. 10 Pony Express (air) . 30 15
2285 3 cor. Postal Headquarters Managua 45 25
2286 6 cor. Government building, globe and flags of member countries 50 25

326 "Nymphaea capensis"

1981. Water Lilies. Multicoloured.
2288 50 c. Type **326** (postage) . . 10 10
2289 1 cor. "Nymphaea daubenyana" 15 10
2290 1 cor. 20 "Nymphaea Marliacea Chromat" 20 10
2291 1 cor. 80 "Nymphaea Dir. Geo. T. Moore" 25 15
2292 2 cor. "Nymphaea lotus" . . 30 15
2293 2 cor. 50 "Nymphaea B.G. Berry" 35 20
2294 10 cor. "Nymphaea Gladstoniana" (air) . . . 60 40

328 "Cheirodon axelrodi"

1981. Tropical Fishes. Multicoloured.
2296 50 c. Type **328** (postage) . . 10 10
2297 1 cor. "Poecilia reticulata" . 15 10
2298 1 cor. 85 "Anostomus anostomus" 25 15
2299 2 cor. 10 "Corydoras arculatus" 30 15
2300 2 cor. 50 "Cynolebias nigripinnis" 35 20
2301 3 cor. 50 "Petrolebias longipinnis" (air) 50 30
2302 4 cor. "Xiphophorus helleri" 55 35

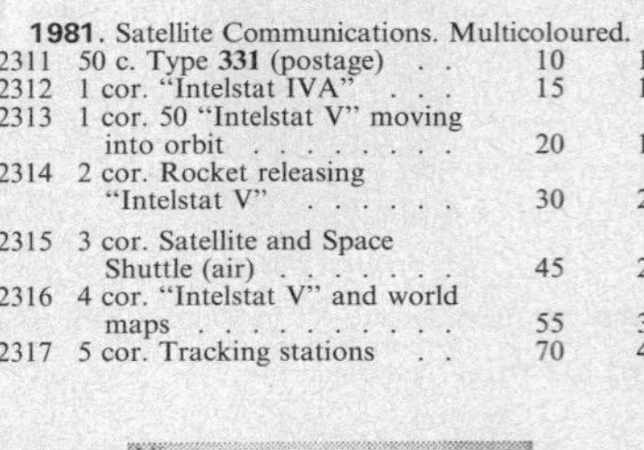

330 Lineated Woodpecker **331** Satellite in Orbit

1981. Birds. Multicoloured.
2304 50 c. Type **330** (postage) . . 30 15
2305 1 cor. 20 Keel-billed toucan (horiz) 60 25
2306 1 cor. 80 Finsch's conure (horiz) 70 35
2307 2 cor. Scarlet macaw 95 40
2308 3 cor. Slaty-tailed trogon (air) 1·25 50
2309 4 cor. Violet sabrewing (horiz) 1·50 60
2310 6 cor. Blue-crowned motmot 2·75 1·00

1981. Satellite Communications. Multicoloured.
2311 50 c. Type **331** (postage) . . 10 10
2312 1 cor. "Intelstat IVA" . . . 15 10
2313 1 cor. 50 "Intelstat V" moving into orbit 20 15
2314 2 cor. Rocket releasing "Intelstat V" 30 20
2315 3 cor. Satellite and Space Shuttle (air) 45 25
2316 4 cor. "Intelstat V" and world maps 55 30
2317 5 cor. Tracking stations . . 70 45

332 Locomotive "El 93" at Lago Granada

1981. Locomotives. Multicoloured.
2318 50 c. Type **332** (postage) . . 15 10
2319 1 cor. Vulcan Iron Works 0-6-0 locomotive, 1946 . . . . 30 10
2320 1 cor. 20 Philadelphia Iron Works 0-6-0 locomotive, 1911 35 10
2321 1 cor. 80 Steam hoist, 1909 . 50 10
2322 2 cor. "U-10B", 1956 . . . 55 10
2323 2 cor. 50 German railbus, 1954 65 15
2324 6 cor. Japanese railbus, 1967 (air) . . . . 1·75 35

333 Heading Ball

1982. World Cup Football Championship, Spain (2nd issue). Multicoloured.
2325 5 c. Type **333** (postage) . . . 10 10
2326 20 c. Running with ball . . . 10 10
2327 25 c. Running with ball (different) 10 10
2328 2 cor. 50 Saving goal 35 20
2329 3 cor. 50 Goalkeeper diving for ball (horiz) 50 30
2330 4 cor. Kicking ball (air) . . . 55 35
2331 10 cor. Tackle (horiz) 60 40

334 Cocker Spaniel

1982. Pedigree Dogs. Multicoloured.
2333 5 c. Type **334** (postage) . . . 10 10
2334 20 c. Alsatian 10 10
2335 25 c. English setter 10 10
2336 2 cor. 50 Brittany spaniel . . 35 20
2337 3 cor. Boxer (air) 45 25
2338 3 cor. 50 Pointer 50 30
2339 6 cor. Collie 60 30

335 Satellite Communications

1982. Air. I.T.U. Congress.
2340 **335** 25 cor. multicoloured . . 2·10 1·50

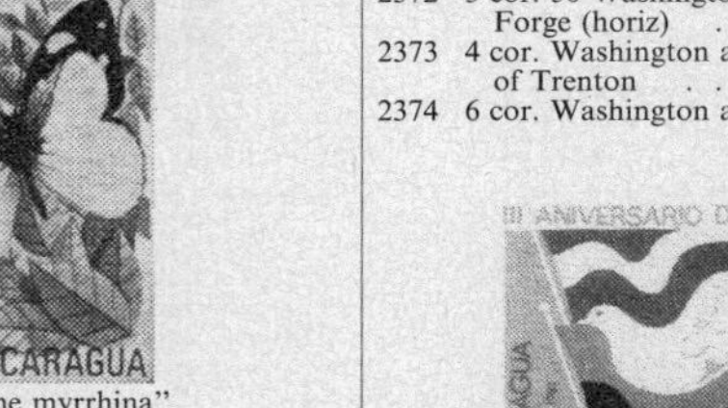

336 "Dynamine myrrhina"

1982. Butterflies. Multicoloured.
2341 50 c. Type **336** (postage) . . . 20 5
2342 1 cor. 20 "Eunica alcmena" . 40 10
2343 1 cor. 50 "Callizona acesta" . 40 12
2344 2 cor. "Adelpha leuceria" . . 60 20
2345 3 cor. "Parides iphidamas" (air) 1·00 30
2346 3 cor. 50 "Consul hippona" . 1·10 35
2347 4 cor. "Morpho peleides" . 1·25 40

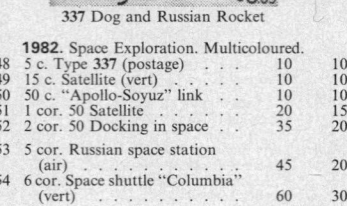

337 Dog and Russian Rocket

1982. Space Exploration. Multicoloured.
2348 5 c. Type **337** (postage) . . . 10 10
2349 15 c. Satellite (vert) 10 10
2350 50 c. "Apollo-Soyuz" link . . 10 10
2351 1 cor. 50 Satellite 20 15
2352 2 cor. 50 Docking in space . . 35 20
2353 5 cor. Russian space station (air) 45 20
2354 6 cor. Space shuttle "Columbia" (vert) 60 30

338 Mailcoach

1982. Centenary of U.P.U. Membership. Multicoloured.
2355 50 c. Type **338** (postage) . . . 10 10
2356 1 cor. 20 "Victoria" (packet steamer) 60 20
2357 3 cor. 50 Railway locomotive (air) . . . . 1·50 15
2358 10 cor. Boeing 727-100 airliner 1·50 1·10

339 Cyclists

1982. 14th Central American and Caribbean Games. Multicoloured.
2359 10 c. Type **339** (postage) . . 10 10
2360 15 c. Swimming (horiz) . . . 10 10
2361 25 c. Basketball 10 10
2362 50 c. Weightlifting 10 10
2363 2 cor. 50 Handball (air) . . . 35 20
2364 3 cor. Boxing (horiz) 45 25
2365 9 cor. Football (horiz) . . . 75 45

341 Washington passing through Trenton

1982. 250th Birth Anniv of George Washington. Multicoloured.
2368 50 c. Mount Vernon, Washington's house (39 × 49 mm) (postage) 10 10
2369 1 cor. Washington signing the Constitution (horiz) . . . 15 10
2370 2 cor. Type **341** 30 20
2371 2 cor. 50 Washington crossing the Delaware (horiz) (air) . 35 20
2372 3 cor. 50 Washington at Valley Forge (horiz) 50 30
2373 4 cor. Washington at the Battle of Trenton 55 35
2374 6 cor. Washington at Princeton 60 55

342 Carlos Fonseca, Dove and Flags

1982. 3rd Anniv of Revolution. Multicoloured.
2375 50 c. Type **342** (postage) . . 10 10
2376 2 cor. 50 Ribbons forming dove (vert) (air) 35 20
2377 1 cor. Augusto Sandino and dove (vert) 55 30
2378 6 cor. Dove 60 55

343 "Vase of Flowers" (R. Penalba)

1982. Paintings. Multicoloured.
2379 25 c. Type **343** (postage) . . 10 10
2380 50 c. "El Gueguense" (M. Garcia) (horiz) 10 10
2381 1 cor. "The Couple" (R. Perez) 15 10
2382 1 cor. 20 "Canales Valley" (A. Mejias) (horiz) 20 10
2383 1 cor. 85 "Portrait of Senora Castellon" (T. Jerez) . . . 25 15
2384 2 cor. "The Vendors" (L. Cerrato) 30 20
2385 9 cor. "Sitting Woman" (A. Morales) (horiz) (air) . 55 35

344 Lenin and Dimitrov, Moscow, 1921

1982. Birth Cent. of Georgi Dimitrov (Bulgarian statesman). Multicoloured.

2387 50 c. Type **344** (postage) . . 10 10
2388 2 cor. 50 Dimitrov & Todor Yikov, Sofia, 1946 (air) . . 35 20
2389 4 cor. Dimitrov and flag . . 55 35

345 Ausberto Narvaez

1982. 26th Anniv of State of Resistance Movement. Multicoloured.

2390 50 c. Type **345** (postage) . . 10 10
2391 2 cor. 50 Cornelio Silva . . . 35 20
2392 4 cor. Rigoberto Lopez Perez (air) 55 35
2393 6 cor. Edwin Castro 60 55

346 Old Ruins at Leon

1982. Tourism. Multicoloured.

2394 50 c. Type **346** (postage) . . 10 10
2395 1 cor. Ruben Dario Theatre and Park, Managua 15 10
2396 1 cor. 20 Independence Square, Granada 20 10
2397 1 cor. 80 Corn Island 25 15
2398 2 cor. Carter Santiago Volcano, Masaya 30 20
2399 2 cor. 50 El Coyotepe Fortress, Masaya (air) 35 20
2400 3 cor. 50 Luis A. Velazquez Park, Managua 50 30

347 Karl Marx and View of Trier

1982. Death Centenary of Karl Marx. Multicoloured.

2401 1 cor. Type **347** (postage) . . 15 10
2402 4 cor. Marx and grave in Highgate Cemetery (air) . . 55 35

348 Stacking Cane and Fruit

1982. World Food Day. Multicoloured.

2403 50 c. Picking Fruit (horiz) . . 10 10
2404 1 cor. Type **348** 15 10
2405 2 cor. Cutting sugar cane (horiz) 30 20
2406 10 cor. F.A.O. and P.A.N. emblems (horiz) 85 65

349 "Santa Maria"

1982. 490th Anniv of Discovery of America. Multicoloured.

2407 50 c. Type **349** (postage) . . 50 15
2408 1 cor. "Nina" . . . . . . 1·00 30
2409 1 cor. 50 "Pinta" . . . . . 1·40 35
2410 2 cor. Columbus and fleet . . 1·60 55
2411 2 cor. 50 Fleet and map of route (air) . . . . 1·75 55
2412 4 cor. Arrival in America . . 55 35
2413 7 cor. Death of Columbus . . 65 60

350 "Lobelia laxiflora" **351** "Micrurus lemniscatus"

1982. Woodland Flowers. Multicoloured.

2415 50 c. Type **350** (postage) . . 10 10
2416 1 cor. 20 "Bombacopsis quinata" 20 10
2417 1 cor. 80 "Mimosa albida" . 25 15
2418 2 cor. "Epidendrum alatum" 30 20
2419 2 cor. 50 Passion flower "Passiflora foetida" wrongly inscr "Pasiflora" (air) . . . 35 20
2420 3 cor. 50 "Clitoria sp." . . . 50 30
2421 5 cor. "Russelia sarmentosa" 70 45

1982. Reptiles. Multicoloured.

2422 10 c. Type **351** (postage) . . 10 10
2423 50 c. Common iguana "Iguana iguana" (horiz) 10 10
2424 2 cor. "Lachesis muta" (snake) (horiz) 30 20
2425 2 cor. 50 Hawksbill turtle "Eretmochelys imbricata" (horiz) (air) 35 20
2426 3 cor. Boa Constrictor "Constrictor constrictor" . 45 25
2427 3 cor. 50 American crocodile "Crocodilus acutus" (horiz) 50 30
2428 5 cor. Diamond-back rattlesnake "Sistrurus catenatus" (horiz) 70 45

352 Tele-cor Building, Managua

1982. Telecommunications Day. Multicoloured.

2429 1 cor. Type **352** (postage) . . 15 10
2430 50 c. Interior of radio transmission room (air) . 10 10

353 Girl with Dove

1983. Air. Non-Aligned States Conference.

2431 **353** 4 cor. multicoloured . . 55 35

354 Jose Marti and Birthplace

1983. 130th Birth Anniv of Jose Marti (Cuban revolutionary).

2432 **354** 1 cor. multicoloured . . 15 10

355 Boxing

356 "Neomarica coerulea"

1983. Olympic Games, Los Angeles (1st issue). Multicoloured.

2433 50 c. Type **355** (postage) . . 10 10
2434 1 cor. Gymnastics 15 10
2435 1 cor. 50 Running 20 15
2346 2 cor. Weightlifting 30 20
2347 4 cor. Discus (air) 55 35
2348 5 cor. Basketball 70 45
2349 6 cor. Cycling 90 55

See also Nos. 2609/15.

1983. Flowers.

2441 **356** 1 cor. blue 15 10
2442 – 1 cor. violet 15 10
2443 – 1 cor. mauve 15 10
2444 – 1 cor. brown 15 10
2445 – 1 cor. green 15 10
2446 – 1 cor. blue 15 10
2447 – 1 cor. green 15 10
2448 – 1 cor. green 15 10
2449 – 1 cor. mauve 15 10
2450 – 1 cor. red 15 10
2451 – 1 cor. grey 15 10
2452 – 1 cor. yellow 15 10
2453 – 1 cor. brown 15 10
2454 – 1 cor. purple 15 10
2455 – 1 cor. green 15 10
2456 – 1 cor. black 15 10

DESIGNS: No. 2442, "Tabebula ochraceae"; 2443, "Laelia sp"; 2444, "Plumeria rubra"; 2445, "Brassavola nodosa"; 2446, "Stachytarpheta indica"; 2447, "Cochiospermum sp"; 2448, "Malvaviscus arboreus"; 2449, "Telecoma stans"; 2450, "Hibiscus rosa-sinensis"; 2451, "Cattleya lueddemanniana"; 2452, "Tagetes erecta"; 2453, "Senecio sp"; 2454, "Sobralia macrantha"; 2455, "Thumbergia alata"; 2456, "Bixa orellana".

See also Nos. 2739/54, 2838/53 and 3087/3102.

357 Momotombo Geo-thermal Electrical Plant

1983. Air. Energy.

2457 **357** 2 cor. 50 multicoloured . 35 20

358 Demonstrating Crowd

1983. Papal Visit.

2458 **358** 50 c. red, black and blue (postage) 10 10
2459 – 1 cor. multicoloured . . . 15 10
2460 – 4 cor. multicoloured (air) 55 35
2461 – 7 cor. multicoloured . . . 1·00 60

DESIGNS: 1 cor. Map of Nicaragua and girl picking coffee; 4 cor. Pres. Cordova Rivas and Pope John Paul II; 7 cor. Pope outside Managua Cathedral.

359 "Xilophanes chiron"

1983. Moths. Multicoloured.

2463 15 c. Type **359** (postage) . . . 10 10
2464 50 c. "Protoparce ochus" . . 15 10
2465 65 c. "Pholus lasbruscae" . . 25 10
2466 1 cor. "Amphypterus gannascus" 30 10
2467 1 cor. 50 "Pholus licaon" . . 40 15
2468 2 cor. "Agrius cingulata" . . 60 25
2469 10 cor. "Rothschildia jurulla" (vert) (air) . . . . 3·25 95

360 Subriava Church, Leon

1983. Monuments. Multicoloured.

2470 50 c. Type **360** (postage) . . . 10 10
2471 1 cor. "La Immaculada" Castle, Rio San Juan 15 10
2472 2 cor. La Recoleccion Church, Leon (vert) 30 20
2473 4 cor. Ruben Dario Monument, Managua (vert) (air) . . . 55 35

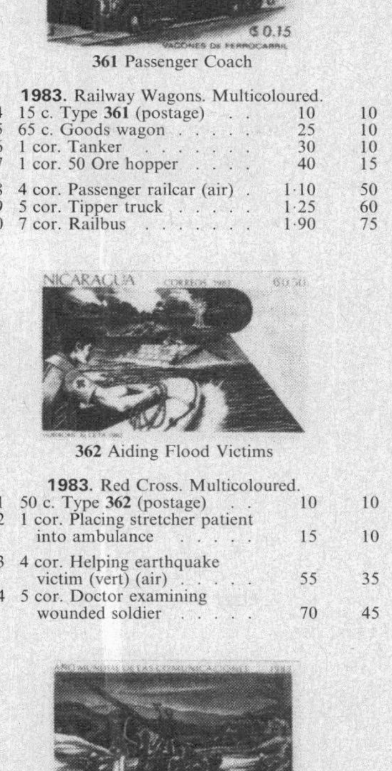

361 Passenger Coach

1983. Railway Wagons. Multicoloured.

2474 15 c. Type **361** (postage) . . 10 10
2475 65 c. Goods wagon 25 10
2476 1 cor. Tanker 30 10
2477 1 cor. 50 Ore hopper 40 15
2478 4 cor. Passenger railcar (air) . 1·10 50
2479 5 cor. Tipper truck . . . . . 1·25 60
2480 7 cor. Railbus . . . . 1·90 75

362 Aiding Flood Victims

1983. Red Cross. Multicoloured.

2481 50 c. Type **362** (postage) . . 10 10
2482 1 cor. Placing stretcher patient into ambulance 15 10
2483 4 cor. Helping earthquake victim (vert) (air) 55 35
2484 5 cor. Doctor examining wounded soldier 70 45

363 Raising Telephone Pole

1983. World Communications Year.

2485 **363** 1 cor. multicoloured . . 15 10

365 Baseball

1983. Ninth Pan-American Games. Multicoloured.

2487 15 c. Type **365** (postage) . . 10 10
2488 50 c. Water polo 10 10
2489 65 c. Running 15 10
2490 1 cor. Basketball (vert) . . . 15 10
2491 2 cor. Weightlifting (vert) . . 30 20
2492 7 cor. Fencing (air) 65 30
2493 8 cor. Gymnastics 70 40

367 Container Ship being Unloaded

1983. 4th Anniv of Revolution. Multicoloured.

2496 1 cor. Type **367** 45 15
2497 2 cor. Telcor building, Leon . 30 20

368 Carlos Fonseca

369 Simon Bolivar on Horseback

1983. Founders of Sandinista National Liberation Front. Multicoloured.

2498 50 c. Escobar, Navarro, Ubeda, Pomares and Ruiz (postage) 10 10
2499 1 cor. Santos Lopez, Borge, Buitrago and Mayorga . . 15 10
2500 4 cor. Type **368** (air) 55 35

1983. Birth Bicentenary of Simon Bolivar. Mult.
2501 50 c. Bolivar and Sandinista guerrilla 10 10
2502 1 cor. Type **369** 15 10

371 Movements of a Pawn

1983. Chess. Multicoloured.
2504 15 c. Type **371** (postage) . . 10 10
2505 65 c. Knight's movements . . 12 10
2506 1 cor. Bishop's movements . . 15 10
2507 2 cor. Rook's movements . . 30 20
2508 4 cor. Queen's movements (air) 55 35
2509 5 cor. King's movements . . 70 45
2510 7 cor. Game in progress . . . 75 60

372 Speed Skating

1983. Winter Olympic Games, Sarajevo (1984) (1st issue). Multicoloured.
2511 50 c. Type **372** (postage) . . 10 10
2512 1 cor. Slalom 15 10
2513 1 cor. 50 Luge 20 15
2514 2 cor. Ski jumping 30 20
2515 4 cor. Figure skating (air) . . 55 35
2516 5 cor. Downhill skiing . . . 70 45
2517 6 cor. Biathlon 90 55

373 Soldiers with German Shepherd Dog **374** "Madonna of the Chair"

1983. Armed Forces.
2519 **373** 4 cor. multicoloured . . 55 35

1983. 500th Birth Anniv of Raphael. Multicoloured.
2520 50 c. Type **374** (postage) . . 10 10
2521 1 cor. "Esterhazy Madonna" 15 10
2522 1 cor. 50 "Sistine Madonna" 20 12
2523 2 cor. "Madonna of the Linnet" 30 20
2524 4 cor. "Madonna of the Meadow" (air) 55 35
2525 5 cor. "Madonna of the Garden" 70 45
2526 6 cor. "Adoration of the Kings" 90 55

375 Pottery Idol

1983. Archaeological Finds. Multicoloured.
2528 50 c. Type **375** (postage) . . 10 10
2529 1 cor. Pottery dish with ornamental lid 15 10
2530 2 cor. Vase with snake design 30 20
2531 4 cor. Pottery dish (air) . . . 55 35

376 Metal being poured into Moulds

1983. Nationalization of Mines. Multicoloured.
2532 1 cor. Type **376** (postage) . . 15 10
2533 4 cor. Workers and mine (air) 55 35

377 Radio Operator and Sinking Liner

1983. "Fracap '83" Congress of Radio Amateurs of Central America and Panama. Multicoloured.
2534 1 cor. Type **377** 45 15
2535 4 cor. Congress emblem and town destroyed by earthquake 55 35

378 Tobacco

1983. Agrarian Reform.
2536 **378** 1 cor. green 15 10
2537 – 2 cor. orange 30 20
2538 – 4 cor. brown 35 35
2539 – 5 cor. blue 45 45
2540 – 6 cor. lavender 55 55
2541 – 7 cor. purple 60 60
2542 – 8 cor. purple 70 65
2543 – 10 cor. brown 90 90

DESIGNS: 2 cor. Cotton; 4 cor. Maize; 5 cor. Sugar; 6 cor. Cattle; 7 cor. Rice; 8 cor. Coffee; 10 cor. Bananas.

See also Nos. 2755/62 and 2854/61.

379 Fire Engine with Ladder

1983. Fire Engines. Multicoloured.
2544 50 c. Type **379** (postage) . . 10 10
2545 1 cor. Water Tanker . . . 15 10
2546 6 cor. Crew vehicle, 1930 . . 90 55
2547 1 cor. 50 Pump with extension fire hoses (air) 20 15
2548 2 cor. Pump with high-pressure tank 30 20
2548a 4 cor. Water tanker 60 40
2549 5 cor. Fire engine, 1910 . . 70 45

380 Jose Marti and General Sandino

1983. Nicaragua-Cuba Solidarity. Multicoloured.
2550 1 cor. Type **380** (postage) . . 15 10
2551 4 cor. Teacher, doctor and welder (air) 55 35

381 "Adoration of the Shepherds" (Hugo van der Gaes) **382** Anniversary Emblem

1983. Christmas. Multicoloured.
2552 50 c. Type **381** (postage) . . 10 10
2553 1 cor. "Adoration of the Kings" (Domenico Ghirlandaio) . 15 10
2554 2 cor. "Adoration of the Shepherds" (El Greco) . . 30 20
2555 7 cor. "Adoration of the Kings" (Konrad von Soest) (air) . 65 30

1984. Air. 25th Anniv of Cuban Revolution.
2557 **382** 4 cor. red, blue and black 45 20
2558 – 6 cor. multicoloured . . 55 30

DESIGN: 6 cor. Fidel Castro and Che Guevara.

INDEX
Countries can be quickly located by referring to the index at the end of this volume.

383 Bobsleigh

1984. Winter Olympic Games, Sarajevo. Mult.
2559 50 c. Type **383** (postage) . . . 10 10
2560 50 c. Biathlon 10 10
2561 1 cor. Slalom 20 15
2562 1 cor. Speed skating 20 15
2563 4 cor. Skiing (air) 45 45
2564 5 cor. Ice dancing 55 55
2565 10 cor. Ski jumping 90 60

384 Chinchilla

1984. Cats. Multicoloured.
2567 50 c. Type **384** (postage) . . . 10 10
2568 50 c. Longhaired white . . . 10 10
2569 1 cor. Red tabby 20 15
2570 2 cor. Tortoiseshell 35 20
2571 4 cor. Burmese 70 45
2572 3 cor. Siamese (air) 50 35
2573 7 cor. Longhaired silver . . . 70 35

385 National Arms **386** Blanca Arauz

1984. 50th Death Anniv of Augusto Sandino. Multicoloured.
2574 1 cor. Type **385** (postage) . . 20 15
2575 4 cor. Augusto Sandino (air) . 35 20

1984. International Women's Day.
2576 **386** 1 cor. multicoloured . . . 20 15

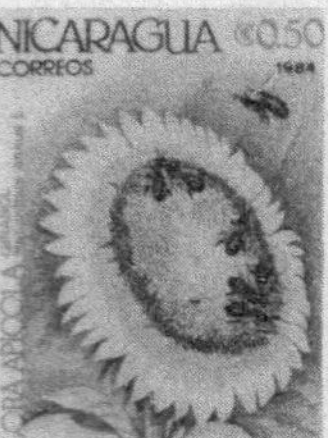

387 Sunflower **388** "Soyuz"

1984. Agricultural Flowers. Multicoloured.
2577 50 c. Type **387** (postage) . . . 10 10
2578 50 c. "Poinsettia pulcherrima" 10 10
2579 1 cor. "Cassia alata" 20 15
2580 2 cor. "Antigonon leptopus" . 35 20
2581 3 cor. "Bidens pilosa" (air) . 50 35
2582 4 cor. "Althaea rosea" . . . 75 45
2583 5 cor. "Rivea corymbosa" . . 85 55

1984. Space Anniversaries. Multicoloured.
2584 50 c. Type **388** (15th anniv of "Soyuz 6", "7" and "8" flights) (postage) 10 5
2585 50 c. "Soyuz" (different) (15th anniv of "Soyuz 6", "7" and "8" flights) 10 5
2586 1 cor. "Apollo II" approaching Moon (15th anniv of 1st manned landing) 20 15
2587 2 cor. "Luna I" (25th anniv of 1st Moon satellite) 35 20
2588 3 cor. "Luna II" (25th anniv of 1st Moon landing) (air) . . 50 35
2589 4 cor. "Luna III" (25th anniv of 1st photographs of far side of Moon) 70 45
2590 9 cor. Rocket (50th anniv of Korolev's book on space flight) . . . . 1·25 75

389 "Noli me Tangere" (detail) **390** Daimler, 1886

1984. 450th Death Anniv of Correggio (artist). Multicoloured.
2591 50 c. Type **389** (postage) . . . 10 10
2592 50 c. "Madonna of St. Jerome" (detail) 10 10
2593 1 cor. "Allegory of Virtue" . . 20 15
2594 2 cor. "Allegory of Pleasure" 35 20
2595 3 cor. "Ganymedes" (detail) (air) 50 35
2596 5 cor. "The Danae" (detail) . 55 55
2597 8 cor. "Leda and the Swan" (detail) . . . . 1·00 60

1984. 150th Birth Anniv of Gottlieb Daimler (automobile designer). Multicoloured.
2599 1 cor. Type **390** (postage) . . 10 10
2600 1 cor. Abadal, 1914 (horiz) . 10 10
2601 2 cor. Ford, 1903 . . . . . 35 20
2602 2 cor. Renault, 1899 . . . . 35 20
2603 3 cor. Rolls Royce, 1910 (horiz) (air) 50 35
2604 4 cor. Metallurgique, 1907 (horiz) 70 45
2605 7 cor. Bugatti "Mod 40" (horiz) 75 50

392 Mail Transport

1984. Air. 19th Universal Postal Union Congress Philatelic Salon, Hamburg.
2607 **392** 15 cor. multicoloured . . 4·00 2·10

393 Basketball

1984. Olympic Games, Los Angeles (2nd issue). Multicoloured.
2609 50 c. Type **393** (postage) . . 10 10
2610 50 c. Volleyball 10 10
2611 1 cor. Hockey 20 15
2612 2 cor. Tennis (air) 35 20
2613 3 cor. Football (horiz) . . . 50 35
2614 4 cor. Water polo (horiz) . . 70 45
2615 9 cor. Soccer (horiz) . . . . 1·10 75

395 Rural Construction Site

1984. 5th Anniv of Revolution. Multicoloured.
2618 5 c. Type **395** (postage) . . . 10 10
2619 1 cor. Pacific-Atlantic Railway locomotive 30 20
2620 4 cor. Ploughing with oxen and tractor (Agrarian reform) (air) 40 20
2621 7 cor. State Council building 75 35

396 "Children defending Nature" (Pablo Herrera Berrios)

1984. U.N.E.S.C.O. Environmental Protection Campaign. Multicoloured.

2622 50 c. Type **396** (postage) 10 10
2623 1 cor. Living and dead forests 20 15
2624 2 cor. Fisherman and dried river bed 35 20
2625 10 cor. Hands holding plants (vert) (air) 85 75

397 Red Cross Airplane and Ambulance

1984. 50th Anniv of Nicaraguan Red Cross. Multicoloured.

2626 1 cor. Type **397** (postage) 30 15
2627 7 cor. Battle of Solferino (125th anniv) (air) 90 45

399 Ventura Escalante and Dominican Republic Flag

1984. Baseball. Multicoloured.

2629 50 c. Type **399** (postage) 10 10
2630 50 c. Danial Herrera and Mexican flag 10 10
2631 1 cor. Adalberto Herrera and Venezuelan flag 20 15
2632 1 cor. Roberto Clemente and Nicaraguan flag 20 15
2633 3 cor. Carlos Colas and Cuban flag (air) 30 35
2634 4 cor. Stanley Cayasso and Argentinian flag 45 45
2635 5 cor. Babe Ruth and U.S.A. flag 55 55

400 Central American Tapir

1984. Wildlife Protection. Multicoloured.

2636 25 c. Type **400** (postage) 10 10
2637 25 c. Young tapir 10 10
2638 3 cor. Close-up of tapir (air) 15 10
2639 4 cor. Mother and young 20 15

401 Football in 1314

1985. World Cup Football Championship, Mexico (1986) (1st issue). Multicoloured.

2640 50 c. Type **401** (postage) 10 10
2641 50 c. Football in 1500 10 10
2642 1 cor. Football in 1872 10 10
2643 1 cor. Football in 1846 10 10
2644 2 cor. Football in 1883 (air) 10 10
2645 4 cor. Football in 1890 20 15
2646 6 cor. Football in 1953 30 20

See also Nos. 2731/7 and 2812/18.

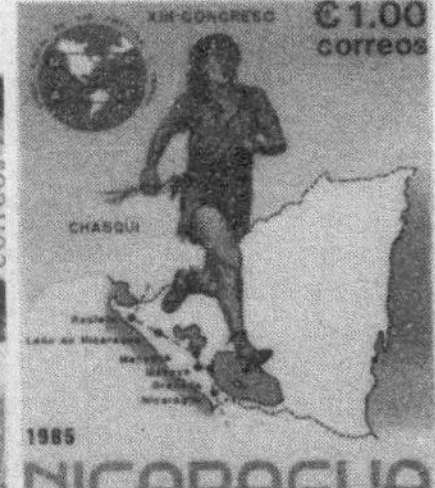

402 "Strobilomyces retisporus" 403 Postal Runner and Map

1985. Fungi. Multicoloured.

2648 50 c. Type **402** (postage) 10 10
2649 50 c. "Boletus calopus" 10 10
2650 1 cor. "Boletus luridus" 10 10
2651 1 cor. "Xerocomus illudens" (air) 10 10
2652 4 cor. "Gyrodon merulioides" 25 15
2653 5 cor. "Tylopilus plumbeoviolaceus" 30 15
2654 8 cor. "Gyroporus castaneus" 50 25

1985. 13th Postal Union of the Americas and Spain Congress. Multicoloured.

2655 1 cor. Type **403** (postage) 10 10
2656 7 cor. Casa Aviocar mail plane over map (air) 45 20

406 Early Steam Engine

1985. 150th Anniv of German Railway. Mult.

2659 1 cor. Type **406** (postage) 15 10
2660 1 cor. Electric locomotive 15 10
2661 9 cor. Steam locomotive No. 88 (air) 50 15
2662 9 cor. Double deck tram 50 15
2663 15 cor. Steam passenger locomotive 75 20
2664 21 cor. Mountain steam locomotive 1·10 30

407 Douglas, 1928

1985. Centenary of Motor Cycle. Multicoloured.

2666 50 c. Type **407** (postage) 10 10
2667 50 c. FN, 1928 10 10
2668 1 cor. Puch, 1938 10 10
2669 2 cor. Wanderer, 1939 (air) 10 10
2670 4 cor. Honda, 1949 10 10
2671 5 cor. BMW, 1984 10 10
2672 7 cor. Honda, 1984 40 10

408 "Matelea quirosii" 409 "Capitulation of German Troops" (P. Krivonogov)

1985. Flowers. Multicoloured.

2673 50 c. Type **408** (postage) 10 10
2674 50 c. "Ipomea nil" 10 10
2675 1 cor. "Lysichitum americanum" 10 10
2676 2 cor. "Clusia sp." (air) 10 10
2677 4 cor. "Vanilla planifolia" 10 10
2678 7 cor. "Stemmadenia obovata" 75 40

1985. 40th Anniv of End of World War II. Mult.

2679 9 cor. 50 Type **409** (postage) 1·00 50
2680 28 cor. Woman behind barbed wire and Nuremberg trial (air) 3·00 1·50

410 Lenin and Red Flag 413 Ring-necked Pheasant

412 Victoria de Julio Sugar Factory

1985. 115th Birth Anniv of Lenin. Multicoloured.

2681 4 cor. Type **410** 10 10
2682 21 cor. Lenin addressing crowd 45 30

1985. Air. 6th Anniv of Revolution. Multicoloured.

2684 9 cor. Type **412** 20 15
2685 9 cor. Soldier and flag 20 15

1985. Domestic Birds. Multicoloured.

2686 50 c. Type **413** 30 10
2687 50 c. Hen 10 10
2688 1 cor. Helmet guineafowl 30 10
2689 2 cor. Goose 15 10
2690 6 cor. Ocellated turkey 70 15
2691 8 cor. Duck 20 10

414 Luis A. Delgadillo 415 Zeledon

1985. International Music Year. Multicoloured.

2692 1 cor. Type **414** (postage) 10 10
2693 1 cor. Masked dancer with floral headdress 10 10
2694 9 cor. Masked procession (air) 65 40
2695 9 cor. Crowd outside church 65 40
2696 15 cor. Masked dancer in brimmed hat 1·10 55
2697 21 cor. Procession resting 1·50 75

1985. Air. Birth Centenary of Benjamin Zeledon.

2698 **415** 15 cor. multicoloured 1·00 55

416 Dunant and Lifeboat

1985. 75th Death Anniv of Henri Dunant (founder of Red Cross). Multicoloured.

2699 3 cor. Type **416** 20 10
2700 15 cor. Dunant and Ilyushin Il-86 and Tupolev Tu-154 aircraft 1·25 55

417 Fire Engine

1985. 6th Anniv of SINACOI Fire Service. Mult.

2701 1 cor. Type **417** (postage) 10 10
2702 1 cor. Fire station 10 10
2703 1 cor. Engine with water jet 10 10
2704 3 cor. Foam tender (air) 10 10
2705 9 cor. Airport fire engine 50 15
2706 15 cor. Engine at fire 85 45
2707 21 cor. Fireman in protective clothing 1·10 75

418 Halley, Masaya Volcano and Comet

1985. Appearance of Halley's Comet. Multicoloured.

2708 1 cor. Type **418** (postage) 10 10
2709 3 cor. Armillary sphere and 1910 trajectory 10 10
2710 3 cor. "Venus" space probe and Tycho Brahe underground observatory 10 10
2711 9 cor. Habermel's astrolabe and comet's path through solar system (air) 50 15
2712 15 cor. Hale Telescope, Mt. Palomar, and Herschel's telescope 85 45
2713 21 cor. Galileo's telescope and sections through telescopes of Newton, Cassegrain and Ritchey 1·25 60

419 Tapir eating

1985. Protected Animals. Baird's Tapir. Mult.

2714 1 cor. Type **419** (postage) 10 10
2715 3 cor. Tapir in water (air) 10 10
2716 5 cor. Tapir in undergrowth 10 10
2717 9 cor. Mother and calf 20 15

420 "Rosa spinosissima"

1986. Wild Roses. Multicoloured.

2718 1 cor. Type **420** 10 10
2719 1 cor. Dog rose ("R. canina") 10 10
2720 3 cor. "R. eglanteria" 10 10
2721 5 cor. "R. rubrifolia" 10 10
2722 9 cor. "R. foetida" 20 15
2723 100 cor. "R. rugosa" 2·00 1·10

421 Crimson Topaz 422 Footballer and Statue

1986. Birds. Multicoloured.

2724 1 cor. Type **421** 10 10
2725 3 cor. Orange-billed nightingale thrush 10 10
2726 3 cor. Troupial 10 10
2727 5 cor. Painted bunting 30 10
2728 10 cor. Frantzius's nightingale thrush 65 30
2729 21 cor. Great horned owl 1·25 75
2730 75 cor. Great kiskadee 4·50 2·40

1986. World Cup Football Championship, Mexico (2nd issue). Multicoloured.

2731 1 cor. Type **422** (postage) 10 10
2732 1 cor. Footballer and sculptured head 10 10
2733 3 cor. Footballer and water holder with man as stem (air) 10 10
2734 3 cor. Footballer and sculpture 10 10
2735 5 cor. Footballer and sculptured head (different) 10 10
2736 9 cor. Footballer and sculpture (different) 20 15
2737 100 cor. Footballer and sculptured snake's head 3·00 1·50

1986. (a) Flowers. As Nos. 2441/56 but values changed.

2739 5 cor. blue 10 10
2740 5 cor. violet 10 10
2741 5 cor. purple 10 10
2742 5 cor. orange 10 10
2743 5 cor. green 10 10
2744 5 cor. blue 10 10
2745 5 cor. green 10 10
2746 5 cor. green 10 10
2747 5 cor. mauve 10 10
2748 5 cor. red 10 10
2749 5 cor. grey 10 10
2750 5 cor. orange 10 10
2751 5 cor. brown 10 10
2752 5 cor. brown 10 10
2753 5 cor. green 10 10
2754 5 cor. black 10 10

DESIGNS: No. 2739, Type **356**; 2740, "Tabebula ochraceae"; 2741, "Laelia sp"; 2742, Frangipani ("Plumeria rubra"); 2743, "Brassavola nodosa"; 2744, "Strachytarpheta indica"; 2745, "Cochlospermum sp"; 2746, "Malvaviscus arboreus"; 2747, "Tecoma stans"; 2748, Chinese hibiscus ("Hibiscus rosa-sinensis"); 2749, "Cattleya lueddemanniana"; 2750, African marigold ("Tagetes erecta"); 2751, "Senecio sp"; 2752, "Sobralia macrantha"; 2753, "Thumbergia alata"; 2754, "Bixa orellana".

(b) Agrarian Reform. As T **378**.
2755 1 cor. brown 10 10
2756 9 cor. violet 20 15
2757 15 cor. purple 30 20
2758 21 cor. red 45 30
2759 33 cor. orange 65 45
2760 42 cor. green 90 55
2761 50 cor. brown . . . . 1·00 65
2762 100 cor. blue . . . . 2·00 1·50
DESIGNS: 1 cor. Type **378**; 9 cor. Cotton; 15 cor. Maize; 21 cor. Sugar; 33 cor. Cattle; 42 cor. Rice; 50 cor. Coffee; 100 cor. Bananas.

423 Alfonso Cortes

1986. National Libraries. Latin American Writers. Multicoloured.
2763 1 cor. Type **423** (postage) . . 10 10
2764 3 cor. Azarias H. Pallais . . 10 10
2765 3 cor. Salomon de la Selva . 10 10
2766 5 cor. Ruben Dario 10 10
2767 9 cor. Pablo Neruda 10 10
2768 15 cor. Alfonso Reyes (air) . 45 25
2769 100 cor. Pedro Henriquez Urena 3·00 1·50

424 Great Britain Penny Black and Nicaragua 1929 25 c. Stamps

1986. Air. 125th Anniv of Nicaraguan Stamps. Designs showing G.B. Penny Black and Nicaragua stamps.
2770 **424** 30 cor. multicoloured . . 90 45
2771 – 40 cor. brown, black and grey . . . . 1·25 60
2772 – 50 cor. red, black and grey 1·50 75
2773 – 100 cor. blue, black and grey . . . . 3·00 1·50
DESIGNS: 40 c. 1903 1 p. stamp; 50 c. 1892 5 p. stamp; 1 p. 1862 2 c. stamp.

425 Sapodilla **426** Rainbow and Globe

1986. 40th Anniv of F.A.O. Multicoloured.
2774 1 cor. Type **425** (postage) . . 10 10
2775 1 cor. Maranon 10 10
2776 3 cor. Tree-cactus 10 10
2777 3 cor. Granadilla 10 10
2778 5 cor. Custard-apple (air) . . 10 10
2779 21 cor. Melocoton 65 35
2780 100 cor. Mamey . . . . . . 3·00 1·50

1986. Air. International Peace Year. Multicoloured.
2781 5 cor. Type **426** 10 10
2782 10 cor. Dove and globe . . . 30 10

427 Lockheed L-1011 TriStar 500

1986. "Stockholmia 86" International Stamp Exhibition. Multicoloured.
2783 1 cor. Type **427** (postage) . . 10 10
2784 1 cor. Yakovlev Yak-40 . . . 10 10
2785 3 cor. B.A.C. One Eleven . . 10 10
2786 3 cor. Boeing 747-100 . . . . 10 10
2787 9 cor. Airbus Industrie A300 (air) 30 10
2788 15 cor. Tupolev Tu-154 . . 45 10
2789 100 cor. Concorde (vert) . . 3·00 1·50

428 "Pinta" and 16th-century Map

1986. 500th Anniv (1992) of Discovery of America by Columbus (1st issue). Multicoloured.
2791 1 cor. Type **428** (postage) . . 45 20
2792 1 cor. "Santa Maria" and "Nina" 45 20
2793 9 cor. Juan de la Cosa (air) . 30 10
2794 9 cor. Christopher Columbus 30 10
2795 21 cor. King and Queen of Spain 65 35
2796 100 cor. Courtiers behind Columbus and Indians . . 3·00 1·50
The designs of the same value and Nos. 2795/6 were printed together in se-tenant pairs within their sheets, Nos. 2791/2 and 2795/6 forming composite designs.
See also Nos. 2903/8.

429 Fonseca and Flags

1986. Air. 25th Anniv of Sandinista Front and 10th Death Anniv of Carlos Fonseca (co-founder).
2798 **429** 15 cor. multicoloured . 10 10

430 Rhinoceros **431** "Theritas coronata"

1986. Air. Endangered Animals. Multicoloured.
2799 15 cor. Type **430** 45 10
2800 15 cor. Zebra 45 10
2801 25 cor. Elephant 75 40
2802 25 cor. Giraffe 75 40
2803 50 cor. Tiger . . . . 1·50 75
2804 50 cor. Mandrill . . . . . . 1·50 75

1986. Butterflies. Multicoloured.
2805 10 cor. Type **431** (post) . . . 20 10
2806 15 cor. "Salamis cacta" (air) . 20 10
2807 15 cor. "Charayes nitebis" . . 20 10
2808 15 cor. "Papilio maacki" . . 20 10
2809 25 cor. "Palaeochrysophonus hippothoe" 20 10
2810 25 cor. "Euphaedro cyparissa" 20 10
2811 30 cor. "Ritra aurea" . . . 20 10

432 Player and French Flag **433** Ernesto Mejia Sanchez

1986. Air. World Cup Football Championship, Mexico (3rd issue). Finalists. Multicoloured. Designs showing footballers and national flags.
2812 10 cor. Type **432** 10 10
2813 10 cor. Argentina 10 10
2814 10 cor. West Germany . . . 10 10
2815 15 cor. England 10 10
2816 15 cor. Brazil 10 10
2817 25 cor. Spain 10 10
2818 50 cor. Belgium (horiz) . . . 10 10

1987. Ruben Dario Cultural Order of Independence. Multicoloured.
2820 10 cor. Type **433** (postage) . . 10 10
2821 10 cor. Fernando Gordillo . . 10 10
2822 10 cor. Francisco Perez Estrada 10 10
2823 15 cor. Order medal (air) . . 10 10
2824 30 cor. Julio Cortazar . . . 20 20
2825 60 cor. Enrique Fernandez Morales 35 25

434 Ice Hockey **435** Development

1987. Winter Olympic Games, Calgary (1988). Multicoloured.
2826 10 cor. Type **434** (postage) . . 10 10
2827 10 cor. Speed skating 10 10
2828 15 cor. Downhill skiing (air) . 10 10
2829 15 cor. Figure skating 10 10
2830 20 cor. Shooting 15 10
2831 30 cor. Slalom 20 10
2832 40 cor. Ski jumping 25 10

1987. U.N.I.C.E.F. Child Survival Campaign. Multicoloured.
2834 10 cor. Type **435** (postage) . . 10 10
2835 25 cor. Vaccination (air) . . . 75 40
2836 30 cor. Oral rehydration therapy 90 45
2837 50 cor. Breastfeeding . . . . 1·50 75

1987. (a) Flowers. As Nos. 2441/56 and 2739/54 but values changed.
2838 10 cor. blue 10 10
2839 10 cor. violet 10 10
2840 10 cor. purple 10 10
2841 10 cor. red 10 10
2842 10 cor. green 10 10
2843 10 cor. blue 10 10
2844 10 cor. green 10 10
2845 10 cor. green 10 10
2846 10 cor. mauve 10 10
2847 10 cor. red 10 10
2848 10 cor. green 10 10
2849 10 cor. orange 10 10
2850 10 cor. brown 10 10
2851 10 cor. purple 10 10
2852 10 cor. turquoise 10 10
2853 10 cor. black 10 10
DESIGNS: No. 2838, Type **356**; 2839, "Tabebula ochraceae"; 2840, "Laelia sp"; 2841, Frangipani; 2842, "Brassavola nodosa"; 2843, "Stachytarpheta indica"; 2844, "Cochlospermum sp"; 2845, "Malvaviscus arboreus"; 2846, "Tecoma stans"; 2847, Chinese hibiscus; 2848, "Cattleya lueddermanniana"; 2849, African marigold; 2850, Senecio sp"; 2851, "Sobralla macrantha"; 2852, "Thumbergia alata"; 2853, "Bixa orellana".

(b) Agrarian Reform. As T **378**. Dated "1987".
2854 10 cor. brown 10 10
2855 10 cor. violet 10 10
2856 15 cor. purple 10 10
2857 25 cor. red 15 10
2858 30 cor. orange 20 10
2859 50 cor. brown 30 20
2860 60 cor. green 35 25
2861 100 cor. blue 65 45
DESIGNS: No. 2854, Type **378**; 2855, Cotton; 2856, Maize; 2857, Sugar; 2858, Cattle; 2859, Coffee; 2860, Rice; 2861, Bananas.

436 Flags and Buildings **438** Tennis Player

437 "Mammuthus columbi"

1987. 77th Interparliamentary Conference, Managua.
2862 **436** 10 cor. multicoloured . . 10 10

1987. Prehistoric Animals. Multicoloured.
2863 10 cor. Type **437** (postage) . . 10 10
2864 10 cor. Triceratops 10 10
2865 10 cor. Dimetrodon 10 10
2866 15 cor. Uintaterium (air) . . 10 10
2867 15 cor. Dinichthys 10 10
2868 30 cor. Pteranodon 60 35
2869 40 cor. Tilosaurus 85 45

1987. "Capex 87" International Stamp Exhibition, Toronto.
2870 10 cor. multicoloured (Type **438**) (postage) 10 10
2871 10 cor. multicoloured 10 10
2872 15 cor. multicoloured (male player) (air) 45 10
2873 15 cor. multicoloured (female player) 45 10
2874 20 cor. multicoloured 60 30
2875 30 cor. multicoloured 60 45
2876 40 cor. multicoloured 85 60
DESIGNS: Nos. 2871/6, Various tennis players.

439 Dobermann Pinscher **441** Levski

440 Modern Wooden Houses

1987. Dogs. Multicoloured.
2878 10 cor. Type **439** (postage) . 10 10
2879 10 cor. Bull mastiff 10 10
2880 15 cor. Japanese spaniel (air) 45 10
2881 15 cor. Keeshond 45 10
2882 20 cor. Chihuahua 60 30
2883 30 cor. St. Bernard 90 45
2884 40 cor. West Gotha spitz . . 85 60

1987. Air. International Year of Shelter for the Homeless. Multicoloured.
2885 20 cor. Type **440** 15 10
2886 30 cor. Modern brick-built houses 20 10

1987. Air. 150th Birth Anniv of Vasil Levski (revolutionary).
2887 **441** 30 cor. multicoloured . . 20 10

442 "Opuntia acanthocarpa major"

1987. Cacti. Multicoloured.
2888 10 cor. Type **442** (postage) . 10 10
2889 10 cor. "Lophocereus schottii" 10 10
2890 10 cor. "Echinocereus engelmanii" 10 10
2891 20 cor. Saguaros (air) . . . 60 30
2892 20 cor. "Lemaireocereus thurberi" 60 30
2893 30 cor. "Opuntia fulgida" . . 90 45
2894 50 cor. "Opuntia ficus indica" 1·50 75

443 High Jumping

1987. 10th Pan-American Games, Indiana. Multicoloured.
2895 10 cor. Type **443** (postage) . 10 10
2896 10 cor. Handball 10 10
2897 15 cor. Running (air) 45 10
2898 15 cor. Gymnastics 45 10
2899 20 cor. Baseball 60 30
2900 30 cor. Synchronised swimming (vert) 90 45
2901 40 cor. Weightlifting (vert) . 1·25 60

445 "Cosmos"

1987. Cosmonautics Day. Multicoloured.
2904 10 cor. Type **445** (postage) . 10 10
2905 10 cor "Sputnik" 10 10
2906 15 cor. "Proton" (air) . . . 45 10
2907 25 cor. "Luna" 75 40
2908 25 cor. "Meteor" 75 40
2909 30 cor. "Electron" 90 45
2910 50 cor. "Mars-1" . . . . . 1·50 75

446 Native Huts and Terraced Hillside

1987. Air. 500th Anniv (1992) of Discovery of America by Christopher Columbus (2nd issue). Multicoloured.

2911	15 cor. Type 446	45	20
2912	15 cor. Columbus's fleet	65	20
2913	20 cor. Spanish soldiers in native village	60	30
2914	30 cor. Mounted soldiers killing natives	90	45
2915	40 cor. Spanish people and houses	1·25	60
2916	50 cor. Church and houses	1·50	75

447 "Atractoteus tropicus gaspar"

1987. World Food Day. Fishes. Multicoloured.

2917	10 cor. Type 447 (postage)	10	10
2918	10 cor. "Tarpon atlanticus"	10	10
2919	10 cor. Cichlid	10	10
2920	15 cor. "Astyana fasciatus" (air)	45	10
2921	15 cor. Midas cichlid	45	10
2922	20 cor. Cichlid (different)	60	30
2923	50 cor. "Carcharhinus nicaraguensis"	1·50	75

448 Lenin 449 "Nativity"

1987. 70th Anniv of Russian Revolution. Mult.

2924	10 cor. Type 448 (postage)	10	10
2925	30 cor. "Aurora" (cruiser) (horiz) (air)	35	15
2926	50 cor. Russian arms	30	20

1987. Christmas. Details of Painting by L. Saenz. Multicoloured.

2927	10 cor. Type 449	10	10
2928	20 cor. "Adoration of the Magi"	60	30
2929	25 cor. "Adoration of the Magi" (close-up detail)	75	40
2930	50 cor. "Nativity" (close-up detail)	1·50	75

1987. Surch.

2931	435	400 cor. on 10 cor. mult (postage)	30	15
2935	440	200 cor. on 20 cor. multicoloured (air)	15	10
2932	–	600 cor. on 50 cor. mult (No. 2837)	40	20
2933	–	1000 cor. on 25 cor. mult (No. 2835)	70	35
2936	–	3000 cor. on 30 cor. mult (No. 2886)	2·10	1·00
2934	–	5000 cor. on 30 cor. mult (No. 2836)	3·50	1·75

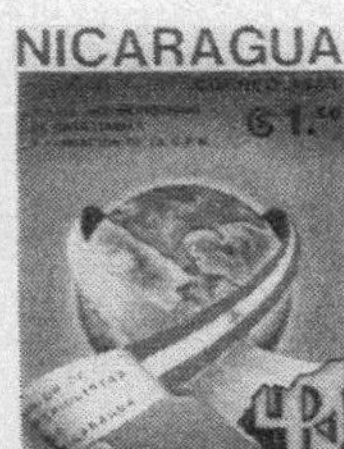

451 Cross-country Skiing 452 Flag around Globe

1988. Winter Olympic Games, Calgary. Mult.

2937	10 cor. Type 451	10	10
2938	10 cor. Rifle-shooting (horiz)	10	10
2939	15 cor. Ice hockey	45	10
2940	20 cor. Ice skating	60	30
2941	25 cor. Downhill skiing	75	40
2942	30 cor. Ski jumping (horiz)	90	45
2943	40 cor. Slalom	1·25	60

1988. 10th Anniv of Nicaragua Journalists' Association. Multicoloured.

2945	1 cor. Type 452 (postage)	10	10
2946	5 cor. Churches of St. Francis Xavier, Sandino and Fatima, Managua, and speaker addressing journalists (42 × 27 mm) (air)	1·25	60

453 Basketball

1988. Olympic Games, Seoul. Multicoloured.

2947	10 cor. Type 453	10	10
2948	10 cor. Gymnastics	10	10
2949	15 cor. Volleyball	45	10
2950	20 cor. Long jumping	60	30
2951	25 cor. Football	75	40
2952	30 cor. Water polo	90	45
2953	40 cor. Boxing	1·25	60

454 Brown Bear

1988. Mammals and their Young. Multicoloured.

2955	10 c. Type 454 (postage)	10	10
2956	15 c. Lion	10	10
2957	25 c. Cocker spaniel	10	10
2958	50 c. Wild boar	15	10
2959	4 cor. Cheetah (air)	55	20
2960	7 cor. Spotted hyena	1·00	40
2961	8 cor. Red fox	1·25	50

455 Slide Tackle

1988. "Essen '88" International Stamp Fair and European Football Championship, Germany. Multicoloured.

2963	50 c. Type 455 (postage)	10	10
2964	1 cor. Footballers	15	10
2965	2 cor. Lining up shot (vert) (air)	30	10
2966	3 cor. Challenging for ball (vert)	50	20
2967	4 cor. Heading ball (vert)	65	25
2968	5 cor. Tackling (vert)	80	30
2969	6 cor. Opponent winning possession	1·00	40

456 Bell JetRanger III

1988. "Finlandia 88" International Stamp Exhibition, Helsinki. Helicopters. Multicoloured.

2971	4 cor. Type 456 (postage)	15	10
2972	12 cor. MBB-Kawasaki BK-117A-3 (air)	20	10
2973	16 cor. Boeing-Vertol B-360	30	10
2974	20 cor. Agusta A.109 MR11	40	10
2975	24 cor. Sikorsky S-61N	55	20
2976	28 cor. Aerospatiale SA.365 Dauphin 2	60	25
2977	56 cor. Sikorsky S-76 Spirit	1·25	50

457 Flags and Map 458 Casimiro Sotelo Montenegro

1988. 9th Anniv of Revolution. Multicoloured.

2979	1 cor. Type 457 (postage)	20	10
2980	5 cor. Landscape and hands releasing dove (air)	80	30

1988. Revolutionaries.

2981	458	4 cor. blue (postage)	15	10
2982	–	12 cor. mauve (air)	20	10
2983	–	16 cor. green	30	10
2984	–	20 cor. red	45	15
2985	–	24 cor. brown	55	20
2986	–	28 cor. violet	65	25
2987	–	50 cor. red	1·25	45
2988	–	100 cor. purple	2·40	1·00

DESIGNS: 12 cor. Ricardo Morales Aviles; 16 cor. Silvio Mayorga Delgado; 20 cor. Pedro Arauz Palacios; 24 cor. Oscar A. Turcios Chavarrias; 28 cor. Julio C. Buitrago Urroz; 50 cor. Jose B. Escobar Perez; 100 cor. Eduardo E. Contreras Escobar.

459 "Acacia baileyana" 460 "Strombus pugilis"

1988. Flowers. Multicoloured.

2989	4 cor. Type 459 (postage)	15	10
2990	12 cor. "Anigozanthos manglesii" (air)	20	10
2991	16 cor. "Telopia speciosissima"	30	10
2992	20 cor. "Eucalyptus ficifolia"	45	15
2993	24 cor. "Boronia heterophylla"	60	25
2994	28 cor. "Callistemon speciosus"	70	30
2995	30 cor. "Nymphaea caerulea" (horiz)	80	35
2996	50 cor. "Clianthus formosus"	1·25	50

1988. Molluscs. Multicoloured.

2997	4 cor. Type 460 (postage)	20	10
2998	12 cor. "Polymita picta" (air)	30	10
2999	16 cor. "Architectonica maximum"	40	10
3000	20 cor. "Pectens laqueatus"	55	10
3001	24 cor. "Guildfordia triumphans"	75	20
3002	28 cor. "Ranella pustulosa"	80	25
3003	50 cor. "Trochus maculatus"	1·75	50

461 Zapotecan Funeral Urn 462 "Chrysina macropus"

1988. 500th Anniv (1992) of Discovery of America by Columbus (3rd issue). Multicoloured.

3004	4 cor. Type 461 (postage)	15	10
3005	12 cor. Mochican ceramic seated figure (air)	20	10
3006	16 cor. Mochican ceramic head	30	10
3007	20 cor. Tainan ceramic vessel	45	10
3008	28 cor. Nazcan vessel (horiz)	65	20
3009	100 cor. Incan ritual pipe (horiz)	2·40	1·00

1988. Beetles. Multicoloured.

3011	4 cor. Type 462 (postage)	15	10
3012	12 cor. "Plusiotis victoriana" (air)	20	10
3013	16 cor. "Ceratotrupes bolivari"	30	10
3014	20 cor. "Gymnetosoma stellata"	50	15
3015	24 cor. "Euphoria lineoligera"	60	20
3016	28 cor. "Euphoria candezei"	70	30
3017	50 cor. "Sulcophanaeus chryseicollis"	1·25	50

463 Dario

1988. Air. Centenary of Publication of "Blue" by Ruben Dario.

3018	463	25 cor. multicoloured	60	20

464 Simon Bolivar, Jose Marti, Gen. Sandino and Fidel Castro

1989. Air. 30th Anniv of Cuban Revolution.

3019	464	20 cor. multicoloured	50	20

465 Pochomil Tourist Centre

1989. Tourism. Multicoloured.

3020	4 cor. Type 465 (postage)	15	10
3021	12 cor. Granada Tourist Centre (air)	20	10
3022	20 cor. Olof Palme Convention Centre	45	15
3023	24 cor. Masaya Volcano National Park	55	20
3024	28 cor. La Boquita Tourist Centre	70	25
3025	30 cor. Xiloa Tourist Centre	75	30
3026	50 cor. Managua Hotel	1·25	50

466 Footballers 467 Downhill Skiing

1989. Air. World Cup Football Championship, Italy (1990).

3028	466	100 cor. multicoloured	10	10
3029	–	200 cor. multicoloured	10	10
3030	–	600 cor. multicoloured	10	10
3031	–	1000 cor. multicoloured	30	10
3032	–	2000 cor. multicoloured	60	10
3033	–	3000 cor. multicoloured	90	40
3034	–	5000 cor. multicoloured	1·50	50

DESIGNS: 200 cor. to 5000 cor. Different footballers.

1989. Air. Winter Olympic Games, Albertville (1992). Multicoloured.

3036	50 cor. Type 467	10	10
3037	300 cor. Ice hockey	10	10
3038	600 cor. Ski jumping	10	10
3039	1000 cor. Ice skating	30	10
3040	2000 cor. Biathlon	60	10
3041	3000 cor. Slalom	90	40
3042	5000 cor. Skiing	1·50	50

468 Water Polo

1989. Air. Olympic Games, Barcelona (1992). Multicoloured.

3044	100 cor. Type 468	10	10
3045	200 cor. Running	10	10
3046	600 cor. Diving	10	10
3047	1000 cor. Gymnastics	30	10
3048	2000 cor. Weightlifting	60	10
3049	3000 cor. Volleyball	90	40
3050	5000 cor. Wrestling	1·50	50

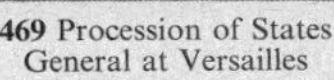

469 Procession of States General at Versailles 470 American Anhinga

1989. "Philexfrance 89" International Stamp Exhibition, Paris, and Bicentenary of French Revolution. Multicoloured.

3052 50 cor. Type **469** (postage) . 15 10
3054 300 cor. Oath of the Tennis Court (36 × 28 mm) (air) . 10 10
3055 600 cor. "The 14th of July" (29 × 40 mm) 10 10
3056 1000 cor. Tree of Liberty (36 × 28 mm) 30 10
3057 2000 cor. "Liberty guiding the People" (Eugene Delacroix) (29 × 40 mm) 60 10
3058 3000 cor. Storming the Bastille (36 × 28 mm) 90 40
3059 5000 cor. Lafayette taking oath (28 × 36 mm) . . . . 1·50 50

1989. Air. "Brasiliana 89" International Stamp Exhibition, Rio de Janeiro. Birds. Multicoloured.

3060 100 cor. Type **470** 10 10
3061 200 cor. Swallow-tailed kite . 10 10
3062 600 cor. Turquoise-browed motmot 10 10
3063 1000 cor. "Setophaga picta" . 30 10
3064 2000 cor. Great antshrike (horiz) 60 10
3065 3000 cor. Northern royal flycatcher 90 40
3066 5000 cor. White-flanked antwren (horiz) . . . . . . 1·50 50

471 Anniversary Emblem

472 Animal-shaped Vessel

1989. Air. 10th Anniv of Revolution.

3068 **471** 300 cor. multicoloured . 10 10

1989. Air. America. Pre-Columbian Artefacts.

3070 **472** 2000 cor. multicoloured . 60 10

Currency Reform. 150000 (old) cordoba = 1 (new) cordoba

The following issues, denominated in the old currency, were distributed by agents but were not issued (each set consists of seven values and is dated "1990"):
"London 90" International Stamp Exhibition. Ships.
World Cup Football Championship, Italy
Olympic Games, Barcelona (1992)
Fungi
Winter Olympic Games, Albertville (1992)

473 Little Spotted Kiwi

1991. "New Zealand 1990" International Stamp Exhibition, Auckland. Birds. Multicoloured.

3071 5 c. Type **473** 10 10
3072 5 c. Takahe 10 10
3073 10 c. Red-fronted parakeet . 10 10
3074 20 c. Weka rail 10 10
3075 30 c. Kagu (vert) 10 10
3076 60 c. Kea 15 10
3077 70 c. Kakapo 15 10

474 Jaguar

1991. 45th Anniv of Food and Agriculture Organization. Animals. Multicoloured.

3079 5 c. Type **474** 10 10
3080 5 c. Ocelot (vert) 10 10
3081 10 c. Black-handed spider monkey (vert) 10 10
3082 20 c. Baird's tapir 10 10
3083 30 c. Nine-banded armadillo . . 10 10
3084 60 c. Coyote 15 10
3085 70 c. Two-toed sloth 15 10

475 Dr. Chamorro

476 Steam Locomotive, Peru

1991. Dr. Pedro Joaquin Chamorro (campaigner for an independent Press).

3086 **475** 2 cor. 25 multicoloured . 50 20

1991. Flowers. As T **356** but with currency inscribed in "oro".

3087 – 1 cor. blue 25 10
3088 – 2 cor. green 45 20
3089 – 3 cor. brown 70 30
3090 – 4 cor. purple 95 40
3091 – 5 cor. red . . . . 1·10 45
3092 – 6 cor. green . . . . . . 1·40 55
3093 **356** 7 cor. blue . . . . . . 1·60 65
3094 – 8 cor. green . . . . . . 1·90 75
3095 – 9 cor. green . . . . . . 2·10 85
3096 – 10 cor. violet . . . . . 2·25 90
3097 – 11 cor. mauve . . . . . 2·50 1·00
3098 – 12 cor. yellow . . . . . 2·75 1·10
3099 – 13 cor. red . . . . . . 3·00 1·25
3100 – 14 cor. green . . . . . 3·25 1·25
3101 – 15 cor. mauve . . . . . 3·50 1·40
3102 – 16 cor. black . . . . . 3·75 1·50

DESIGNS: 1 cor. "Stachytarpheta indica"; 2 cor. "Cochlospermum sp."; 3 cor. "Senecio sp."; 4 cor. "Sobralia macrantha"; 5 cor. Frangipani; 6 cor. "Brassavola nodosa"; 8 cor. "Malvaviscus arboreus"; 9 cor. "Cattleya lueddemanniana"; 10 cor. "Tabebula ochraceae"; 11 cor. "Laelia sp."; 12 cor. African marigold; 13 cor. Chinese hibiscus; 14 cor. "Thumbergia alata"; 15 cor. "Tecoma stans"; 16 cor. "Bixa orellana".

1991. Steam Locomotives of South and Central America. Multicoloured.

3103 25 c. Type **476** 10 10
3104 25 c. Bolivia 10 10
3105 50 c. Argentina 10 10
3106 1 cor. 50 Chile 25 10
3107 2 cor. Colombia 35 10
3108 3 cor. Brazil 50 10
3109 3 cor. 50 Paraguay 60 10

477 Match Scene (West Germany versus Netherlands)

1991. West Germany, Winners of World Cup Football Championship (1990). Multicoloured.

3111 25 c. Type **477** 10 10
3112 25 c. Match scene (West Germany versus Colombia) (vert) 10 10
3113 50 c. West German players and referee 10 10
3114 1 cor. West German players forming wall (vert) 25 10
3115 1 cor. 50 Diego Maradona (Argentina) (vert) 35 15
3116 3 cor. Argentinian players and Italian goalkeeper (vert) . . 70 30
3117 3 cor. 50 Italian players . . 80 30

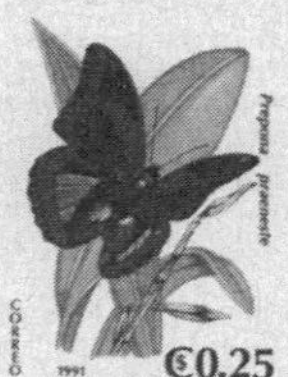

478 "Prepona praeneste"

1991. Butterflies. Multicoloured.

3119 25 c. Type **478** 10 10
3120 25 c. "Anartia fatima" . . . 10 10
3121 50 c. "Eryphanis aesacus" . . 10 10
3122 1 cor. "Heliconius melpomene" 25 10
3123 1 cor. 50 "Chlosyne janais" . 35 15
3124 3 cor. "Marpesia iole" . . . 70 30
3125 3 cor. 50 Rusty-tipped page . 80 30

479 Dove and Cross

1991. 700th Anniv of Swiss Confederation.

3127 **479** 2 cor. 25 red, black and yellow 50 20

480 Yellow-headed Amazon

1991. "Rainforest is Life". Fauna. Multicoloured.

3128 2 cor. 25 Type **480** 50 20
3129 2 cor. 25 Toucan 50 20
3130 2 cor. 25 Scarlet macaw . . . 50 20
3131 2 cor. 25 Quetzal 50 20
3132 2 cor. 25 Black-handed spider monkey 50 20
3133 2 cor. 25 White-throated capuchin 50 20
3134 2 cor. 25 Three-toed sloth . . 50 20
3135 2 cor. 25 Wagler's oropendola 50 20
3136 2 cor. 25 Violet sabrewing . . 50 20
3137 2 cor. 25 Tamandua 50 20
3138 2 cor. 25 Jaguarundi 50 20
3139 2 cor. 25 Boa constrictor . . 50 20
3140 2 cor. 25 Common iguana . . 50 20
3141 2 cor. 25 Jaguar 50 20
3142 2 cor. 25 White-necked jacobin 50 20
3143 2 cor. 25 "Doxocopa clothilda" (butterfly) 50 20
3144 2 cor. 25 "Dismorphia deione" (butterfly) 50 20
3145 2 cor. 25 Golden arrow-poison frog 50 20
3146 2 cor. 25 "Callithomia hezia" (butterfly) 50 20
3147 2 cor. 25 Chameleon 50 20

Nos. 3128/47 were issued together, se-tenant, forming a composite design.

481 "Isochilus major"

1991. Orchids. Multicoloured.

3148 25 c. Type **481** 10 10
3149 25 c. "Cycnoches ventricosum" 10 10
3150 50 c. "Vanilla odorata" . . . 10 10
3151 1 cor. "Helleriella nicaraguensis" 25 10
3152 1 cor. 50 "Barkeria spectabilis" 35 15
3153 3 cor. "Maxillaria hedwigae" 70 30
3154 3 cor. 50 "Cattleya aurantiaca" 80 30

482 Concepcion Volcano

1991. America (1990).

3156 **482** 2 cor. 25 multicoloured . 50 20

483 Warehouse and Flags

1991. 30th Anniv of Central American Bank of Economic Integration.

3157 **483** 1 cor. 50 multicoloured . 35 15

484 "The One-eyed Man"

1991. Death Centenary (1990) of Vincent van Gogh (painter). Multicoloured.

3158 25 c. Type **484** 10 10
3159 25 c. "Head of Countrywoman with Bonnet" 10 10
3160 50 c. "Self-portrait" 10 10
3161 1 cor. "Vase with Carnations and other Flowers" . . . 25 10
3162 1 cor. 50 "Vase with Zinnias and Geraniums" 35 15
3163 3 cor. "Portrait of Tanguy Father" 70 30
3164 3 cor. 50 "Portrait of a Man" (horiz) 80 30

485 Painting by Rafaela Herrera (1st-prize winner)

1991. National Children's Painting Competition.

3166 **485** 2 cor. 25 multicoloured . 50 20

486 Golden Pavilion

1991. "Phila Nippon '91" International Stamp Exhibition, Tokyo. Multicoloured.

3167 25 c. Type **486** 10 10
3168 50 c. Himaji Castle 10 10
3169 1 cor. Head of Bunraku doll 25 10
3170 1 cor. 50 Japanese cranes . . 35 15
3171 2 cor. 50 Phoenix pavilion . 60 25
3172 3 cor. "The Guardian" (statue) 70 30
3173 3 cor. 50 Kabuki actor . . . 80 30

SILVER CURRENCY

The following were for use in all places on the Atlantic coast of Nicaragua where the silver currency was in use. This currency was worth about 50 c. to the peso. Earlier issues (overprints on Nicaraguan stamps) were also issued for Zelaya. These are listed in the Stanley Gibbons Part 15 (Central America) Catalogue.

Z 1

1912.

Z 1	**Z 1**	1 c. green	1·25	65
Z 2		2 c. red	85	40
Z 3		3 c. brown	1·25	60
Z 4		4 c. lake	1·25	50
Z 5		5 c. blue	1·25	50
Z 6		6 c. red	6·75	3·50
Z 7		10 c. grey	1·25	50
Z 8		15 c. lilac	1·25	90
Z 9		20 c. blue	1·25	90
Z10		25 c. black and green	1·60	1·25
Z11		35 c. black and brown	2·25	1·40
Z12		50 c. green	2·25	1·40
Z13		1 p. orange	3·50	2·25
Z14		2 p. brown	6·75	4·25
Z15		5 p. green	13·50	8·75

OFFICIAL STAMPS

Overprinted **FRANQUEO OFICIAL**.

1890. Stamps of 1890.

O37	**6**	1 c. blue	15	35
O38		2 c. blue	15	35
O39		5 c. blue	15	40
O40		10 c. blue	15	45
O41		20 c. blue	15	55
O42		50 c. blue	15	75
O43		1 p. blue	20	1·10
O44		2 p. blue	20	1·60
O45		5 p. blue	20	3·50
O46		10 p. blue	20	6·75

1891. Stamps of 1891.

O47	**7**	1 c. green	15	40
O48		2 c. green	15	40
O49		5 c. green	15	40
O50		10 c. green	15	40
O51		20 c. green	15	70
O52		50 c. green	15	75
O53		1 p. green	15	90
O54		2 p. green	15	90
O55		5 p. green	15	2·25
O56		10 p. green	15	3·50

1892. Stamps of 1892.

O57	**8**	1 c. brown	15	30
O58		2 c. brown	15	30
O59		5 c. brown	15	30
O60		10 c. brown	15	30
O61		20 c. brown	15	50
O62		50 c. brown	15	70
O63		1 p. brown	15	1·10
O64		2 p. brown	15	1·75
O65		5 p. brown	15	2·75
O66		10 p. brown	15	3·50

1893. Stamps of 1893.

O67	**9**	1 c. black	15	30
O68		2 c. black	15	30
O69		5 c. black	15	30
O70		10 c. black	15	30
O71		20 c. black	15	50
O72		25 c. black	15	65
O73		50 c. black	15	70
O74		1 p. black	15	1·00
O75		2 p. black	15	1·25
O76		5 p. black	15	2·75
O77		10 p. black	15	3·50

1894. Stamps of 1894.

O78	**10**	1 c. orange	15	30
O79		2 c. orange	15	30
O80		5 c. orange	15	30
O81		10 c. orange	15	30
O82		20 c. orange	15	30
O83		50 c. orange	15	45
O84		1 p. orange	15	1·00
O85		2 p. orange	15	1·75
O86		5 p. orange	15	3·50
O87		10 p. orange	15	4·50

1895. Stamps of 1895.

O88	**11**	1 c. green	15	30
O89		2 c. green	15	30
O90		5 c. green	15	30
O91		10 c. green	15	30
O92		20 c. green	15	50
O93		50 c. green	15	80
O94		1 p. green	15	80
O95		2 p. green	15	1·25
O96		5 p. green	15	1·90
O97		10 p. green	15	2·40

1896. Stamps of 1896, dated "1896", optd **FRANQUEO OFICIAL** in oval frame.

O 99	**12**	1 c. red	1·50	1·90
O100		2 c. red	1·50	1·90
O101		5 c. red	1·50	1·90
O102		10 c. red	1·50	1·90
O103		20 c. red	1·90	1·90
O104		50 c. red	3·00	3·00
O105		1 p. red	7·25	7·25
O106		2 p. red	7·25	7·25
O107		5 p. red	9·50	9·50

1896. Nos. D99/103 handstamped **Franqueo Oficial**.

O108	**D 13**	1 c. orange	—	4·25
O109		2 c. orange	—	4·25
O110		5 c. orange	—	3·00
O111		10 c. orange	—	3·00
O112		20 c. orange	—	3·00

1897. Stamps of 1897, dated "1897", optd **FRANQUEO OFICIAL** in oval frame.

O113	**12**	1 c. red	2·00	2·00
O114		2 c. red	2·00	2·00
O115		5 c. red	2·00	2·00
O116		10 c. red	1·90	2·10
O117		20 c. red	1·90	2·40
O118		50 c. red	3·00	3·00
O119		1 p. red	8·25	8·25
O120		2 p. red	9·75	9·75
O121		5 p. red	15·00	15·00

1898. Stamps of 1898 optd **FRANQUEO OFICIAL** in oval frame.

O124	**13**	1 c. red	2·00	2·00
O125		2 c. red	2·00	2·00
O126		4 c. red	2·00	2·00
O127		5 c. red	1·50	1·50
O128		10 c. red	2·40	2·40
O129		15 c. red	3·75	3·75
O130		20 c. red	3·75	3·75
O131		50 c. red	5·00	5·00
O132		1 p. red	6·50	6·50
O133		2 p. red	6·50	6·50
O134		5 p. red	6·50	6·50

1899. Stamps of 1899 optd **FRANQUEO OFICIAL** in scroll.

O137	**14**	1 c. green	15	60
O138		2 c. brown	15	60
O139		4 c. red	15	60
O140		5 c. blue	15	40
O141		10 c. orange	15	60
O142		15 c. brown	15	1·25
O143		20 c. green	15	2·00
O144		50 c. red	15	2·00
O145		1 p. orange	15	6·00
O146		2 p. violet	15	6·00
O147		5 p. blue	15	9·00

O 16

O 38

1900.

O148	**O 16**	1 c. purple	45	45
O149		2 c. orange	35	35
O150		4 c. olive	45	45
O151		5 c. blue	90	30
O152		10 c. violet	90	25
O153		20 c. brown	65	25
O154		50 c. lake	90	35
O155		1 p. blue	2·10	1·50
O156		2 p. orange	2·40	2·40
O157		5 p. black	3·00	3·00

1903. Stamps of 1900 surch **OFICIAL** and value, with or without ornaments.

O197	**15**	1 c. on 10 c. mauve	75	1·00
O198		2 c. on 3 c. green	1·00	1·25
O199		4 c. on 3 c. green	3·75	3·75
O200		4 c. on 10 c. mauve	3·75	3·75
O201		5 c. on 3 c. green	45	50

1903. Surch.

O202	**O 16**	10 c. on 20 c. brown	15	15
O203		30 c. on 20 c. brown	15	15
O204		50 c. on 20 c. brown	35	25

1905.

O219	**O 38**	1 c. green	20	20
O220		2 c. red	20	20
O221		5 c. blue	20	20
O222		10 c. brown	20	20
O223		20 c. orange	20	20
O224		50 c. olive	20	20
O225		1 p. lake	20	20
O226		2 p. violet	20	20
O227		5 p. black	20	20

1907. Surch thus: **Vale 10 c**.

O239	**O 38**	10 c. on 1 c. green	55	55
O241		10 c. on 2 c. red	15·00	11·50
O243		20 c. on 2 c. red	13·50	9·00
O245		50 c. on 1 c. green	1·10	1·10
O247		50 c. on 2 c. red	13·50	6·50

1907. Surch thus: **Vale 20 cts** or **Vale $1.00**.

O249	**O 38**	20 c. on 1 c. green	70	70
O250		$1 on 2 c. red	1·10	1·10
O251		$2 on 2 c. red	1·10	1·10
O252		$3 on 2 c. red	1·10	1·10
O253		$4 on 5 c. blue	1·40	1·40

1907. No. 206 surch **OFICIAL** and value.

O256	**49**	10 c. on 1 c. green	9·00	7·75
O257		15 c. on 1 c. green	9·00	7·75
O258		20 c. on 1 c. green	9·00	7·75
O259		50 c. on 1 c. green	9·00	7·75
O260		1 p. on 1 c. green	8·25	7·75
O261		2 p. on 1 c. green	8·25	7·75

1907. Fiscal stamps as T **50** surch thus: **10 cts. CORREOS 1907 OFICIAL 10 cts.**

O262	**50**	10 c. on 2 c. orange	10	10
O263		35 c. on 1 c. blue	10	10
O264		70 c. on 1 c. blue	10	10
O266		1 p. on 2 c. orange	10	15
O267		2 p. on 2 c. orange	10	15
O268		3 p. on 5 c. brown	10	15
O269		4 p. on 5 c. brown	15	15
O270		5 p. on 5 c. brown	15	15

1908. Stamp of 1905 surch **OFICIAL VALE** and value.

O271	**37**	10 c. on 3 c. violet	9·00	7·75
O272		15 c. on 3 c. violet	9·00	7·75
O273		20 c. on 3 c. violet	9·00	7·75
O274		35 c. on 3 c. violet	9·00	7·75
O275		50 c. on 3 c. violet	9·00	7·75

1908. Fiscal stamps as T **50** surch as last but dated 1908.

O276	**50**	10 c. on 1 c. blue	55	35
O277		10 c. on 2 c. orange	75	30
O278		35 c. on 1 c. blue	55	35
O279		35 c. on 2 c. orange	80	45
O280		50 c. on 1 c. blue	55	35
O281		50 c. on 2 c. orange	80	45
O282		70 c. on 2 c. orange	80	45
O283		1 p. on 1 c. blue	23·00	23·00
O284		1 p. on 2 c. orange	80	45
O285		2 p. on 1 c. blue	65	55
O286		2 p. on 2 c. orange	80	45

1909. Stamps of 1905 optd **OFICIAL**.

O290	**37**	10 c. lake	15	15
O291		15 c. black	45	35
O292		20 c. olive	70	55
O293		50 c. green	1·10	70
O294		1 p. yellow	1·25	90
O295		2 p. red	1·75	1·40

1911. Stamps of 1905 optd **OFICIAL** and surch **Vale** and value.

O296	**37**	5 c. on 3 c. orange	3·75	3·75
O297		10 c. on 4 c. violet	3·00	3·00

1911. Railway coupon stamp surch **Timbre Fiscal Vale 10 ctvs** further surch **Correo oficial Vale** and new value. Printed in red.

O334	**64**	10 c. on 10 c. on 1 c.	3·00	3·00
O335		15 c. on 10 c. on 1 c.	3·00	3·00
O336		20 c. on 10 c. on 1 c.	3·00	3·00
O337		50 c. on 10 c. on 1 c.	4·00	4·00
O338		$1 on 10 c. on 1 c.	4·75	7·25
O339		$2 on 10 c. on 1 c.	6·50	10·00

1911. Railway coupon stamps surch **TIMBRE FISCAL VALE 10 ctvs.** further surch **CORREO OFICIAL** and new value. Printed in red.

O340	**64**	10 c. on 10 c. on 1 c.	22·00	17·00
O341		15 c. on 10 c. on 1 c.	22·00	17·00
O342		20 c. on 10 c. on 1 c.	22·00	18·00
O343		50 c. on 10 c. on 1 c.	18·00	15·00

1911. Railway stamp with value of postal surch on back cancelled with thick bar, surch on front **Correo Oficial Vale 1911** and new value. Printed in red.

O344	**64**	5 c. on 10 c. on 1 c.	3·75	4·50
O345		10 c. on 10 c. on 1 c.	4·25	5·25
O346		15 c. on 10 c. on 1 c.	5·00	5·75
O347		20 c. on 10 c. on 1 c.	5·50	8·50
O348		50 c. on 10 c. on 1 c.	6·25	7·50

1912. Railway stamp with whole surch on back cancelled with thick bar, surch on front **Correo Oficial 1912** and new value. Printed in red.

O349	**64**	5 c. on 10 c. on 1 c.	5·50	4·75
O350		10 c. on 10 c. on 1 c.	5·50	4·75
O351		15 c. on 10 c. on 1 c.	5·50	4·75
O352		20 c. on 10 c. on 1 c.	5·50	4·75
O353		25 c. on 10 c. on 1 c.	5·50	4·75
O354		50 c. on 10 c. on 1 c.	5·50	4·75
O355		$1 on 10 c. on 1 c.	5·50	4·75

1913. Stamps of 1912 optd **OFICIAL**.

O356	**70**	1 c. blue	10	10
O357		2 c. blue	10	10
O358		3 c. blue	10	10
O359		4 c. blue	10	10
O360		5 c. blue	10	10
O361		6 c. blue	10	15
O362		10 c. blue	10	15
O363		15 c. blue	10	15
O364		20 c. blue	10	20
O365		25 c. blue	15	15
O366	**71**	35 c. blue	20	20
O367	**70**	50 c. blue	1·10	1·10
O368		1 p. blue	25	25
O369		2 p. blue	25	25
O370		5 p. blue	35	35

1915. Optd **OFICIAL**.

O406	**79**	1 c. blue	15	15
O407	**80**	2 c. blue	15	15
O408	**79**	3 c. blue	15	15
O409	**80**	4 c. blue	15	15
O410	**79**	5 c. blue	15	15
O411	**80**	6 c. blue	15	15
O412		10 c. blue	15	15
O413	**79**	15 c. blue	15	15
O414	**80**	20 c. blue	15	15
O415	**79**	25 c. blue	25	25
O416	**80**	50 c. blue	45	45

1925. Optd **Oficial** or **OFICIAL**.

O513	**79**	½ c. green	10	10
O514		1 c. violet	10	10
O515	**80**	2 c. red	10	10
O516	**79**	3 c. olive	10	10
O517	**80**	4 c. red	10	10
O518	**79**	5 c. black	10	10
O519	**80**	6 c. brown	10	10
O520		10 c. yellow	10	10
O521	**79**	15 c. brown	10	10
O522	**80**	20 c. brown	10	10
O523	**79**	25 c. orange	40	40
O524	**80**	50 c. blue	45	45

1929. Air. Official stamps of 1925 additionally optd **Correo Aereo**.

O618	**79**	25 c. orange	35	35
O619	**80**	50 c. blue	55	55

1931. Stamp of 1924 surch **OFICIAL C$ 0.05 Correos 1928**.

O651	**99**	5 c. on 10 c. brown	25	25

1931. No. 648 additionally surch **OFICIAL** and value.

O652	**99**	5 c. on 10 c. brown	25	25

1931. Stamps of 1914 optd 1931 (except 6 c., 10 c.), and also optd **OFICIAL**.

O670	**79**	1 c. olive (No. 762)	20	20
O707	**80**	2 c. red	6·50	6·50
O671	**79**	3 c. blue	20	20
O672		5 c. sepia	20	20
O673	**80**	6 c. brown	25	25
O675		10 c. brown	25	25
O674		10 c. blue (No. 697)	1·10	1·10
O710	**79**	15 c. orange	70	70
O711		25 c. sepia	70	70
O712		25 c. violet	1·75	1·75

1932. Air. Optd **Correo Aereo OFICIAL** only.

O688	**79**	15 c. orange	45	45
O689	**80**	20 c. orange	50	50
O690	**79**	25 c. violet	50	50
O691	**80**	50 c. green	60	60
O692		1 cor. yellow	60	60

1932. Air. Optd **1931. Correo Aereo OFICIAL**.

O693	**79**	25 c. sepia	25·00	25·00

1932. Optd **OFICIAL**.

O694	**79**	1 c. olive	10	10
O695	**80**	2 c. red	10	10
O696	**79**	3 c. blue	15	10
O697	**80**	4 c. blue	15	10
O698	**79**	5 c. sepia	15	15
O699	**80**	6 c. brown	20	10
O700		10 c. brown	30	25
O701	**79**	15 c. orange	40	25
O702	**80**	20 c. orange	40	30
O703	**79**	25 c. violet	1·25	50
O704	**80**	50 c. green	15	15
O705		1 cor. yellow	20	20

1933. 441st Anniv of Columbus's Departure from Palos. As T **133**, but inscr "CORREO OFICIAL". Roul.

O777		1 c. yellow	60	60
O778		2 c. yellow	60	60
O779		3 c. brown	60	60
O780		4 c. brown	60	60
O781		5 c. brown	60	60
O782		6 c. blue	75	75
O783		10 c. violet	75	75
O784		15 c. purple	75	75
O785		20 c. green	75	75
O786		25 c. green	1·75	1·75
O787		50 c. red	2·25	2·25
O788		1 cor. red	3·50	3·50

1933. Optd with T **134** and **OFICIAL**.

O814	**79**	1 c. green	10	10
O815	**80**	2 c. red	10	10
O816	**79**	3 c. blue	10	10
O817	**80**	4 c. blue	10	10
O818	**79**	5 c. brown	10	10
O819	**80**	6 c. grey	10	10
O820		10 c. brown	10	10
O821	**79**	15 c. red	15	15
O822	**80**	20 c. orange	15	15
O823	**79**	25 c. violet	15	15
O824	**80**	50 c. green	25	25
O825		1 cor. yellow	50	45

1933. Air. Optd with T **134** and **CORREO Aereo OFICIAL**.

O826	**79**	15 c. violet	20	20
O827	**80**	20 c. green	20	20
O828	**79**	25 c. olive	20	20
O829	**80**	50 c. green	35	35
O830		1 cor. red	60	50

1935. Nos. O814/25 optd **RESELLO-1935** in a box.

O864	**79**	1 c. green	10	10
O865	**80**	2 c. red	10	10
O866	**79**	3 c. blue	10	10
O867	**80**	4 c. blue	10	10
O868	**79**	5 c. brown	10	10
O869	**80**	6 c. grey	10	10
O870		10 c. brown	10	10
O871	**79**	15 c. red	15	15
O872	**80**	20 c. orange	15	15
O873	**79**	25 c. violet	15	15
O874	**80**	50 c. green	20	20
O875		1 cor. yellow	35	35

1935. Air. Nos. O826/30 optd **RESELLO-1935** in a box.

O877	**79**	15 c. violet	30	25
O878	**80**	20 c. green	30	25
O879	**79**	25 c. olive	30	30
O880	**80**	50 c. green	90	90
O881		1 cor. red	90	90

(O 141)

O 151 Islets in the Great Lake

1937. Nos. 913, etc., optd with Type O **141**.

O935	**79**	1 c. red	25	15
O936	**80**	2 c. blue	25	15
O937	**79**	3 c. brown	30	25
O938		5 c. red	35	30
O939	**80**	10 c. green	40	35
O940	**79**	15 c. green	50	40
O941		25 c. orange	60	45
O942	**80**	50 c. brown	85	50
O943		1 cor. blue	2·25	1·00

1937. Air. Nos. 926/30 optd with Type O **141**.

O944	**112**	15 c. orange	50	35
O945		20 c. red	50	35
O946		25 c. black	50	45
O947		50 c. violet	50	45
O948		1 cor. orange	50	45

1939.

O1020	O 151	2 c. red	15	15
O1021		3 c. blue	15	15
O1022		6 c. brown	15	15
O1023		7½ c. green	15	15
O1024		10 c. brown	15	15
O1025		15 c. orange	15	15
O1026		25 c. violet	30	30
O1027		50 c. green	45	45

O **152** Pres. Somoza

1939. Air.

O1028	O 152	10 c. brown	30	30
O1029		15 c. blue	30	30
O1030		20 c. yellow	30	30
O1031		25 c. violet	30	30
O1032		30 c. red	30	30
O1033		50 c. orange	40	40
O1034		1 cor. olive	75	75

O **175** Managua Airport

1947. Air.

O1120	O 175	5 c. brown & black	15	10
O1121	–	10 c. blue and black	15	15
O1122	–	15 c. violet & black	15	10
O1123	–	20 c. orange & black	20	10
O1124	–	25 c. blue & black	15	15
O1125	–	50 c. red & black	15	15
O1126	–	1 cor. grey & black	40	35
O1127	–	2 cor. 50 brown and black	75	90

DESIGNS: 10 c. Sulphur Lagoon, Nejapa; 15 c. Ruben Dario Monument, Managua; 20 c. Baird's tapir; 25 c. Genizaro Dam; 50 c. Thermal Baths, Tipitapa; 1 cor. Highway and Lake Managua; 2 cor. 50, Franklin D. Roosevelt Monument, Managua.

O **181** U.P.U. Offices, Berne

1950. Air. 75th Anniv of U.P.U. Inscr as in Type O **181**. Frames in black.

O1159	–	5 c. purple	10	10
O1160	–	10 c. green	10	10
O1161	–	25 c. purple	10	10
O1162	O 181	50 c. orange	15	10
O1163	–	1 cor. blue	35	30
O1164	–	2 cor. 60 black	2·10	1·75

DESIGNS—HORIZ: 5 c. Rowland Hill; 10 c. Heinrich von Stephan;. 25 c. Standehaus, Berne; 1 cor. Monument, Berne; 2 cor. 60, Congress Medal.

1961. Air. Consular Fiscal stamps as T **203/4** with serial Nos. in red, surch **Oficial Aereo** and value.

O1448	10 c. on 1 cor. olive	10	10
O1449	15 c. on 20 cor. brown	10	10
O1450	20 c. on 100 cor. lake	10	10
O1451	25 c. on 50 c. blue	15	10
O1452	35 c. on 50 cor. brown	15	15
O1453	50 c. on 3 cor. red	15	15
O1454	1 cor. on 2 cor. green	25	20
O1455	2 cor. on 5 cor. red	25	45
O1456	5 cor. on 10 cor. violet	60	60

POSTAGE DUE STAMPS

D 13

D 16

1896.

D 99	D 13	1 c. orange	45	1·10
D100		2 c. orange	45	1·10
D101		5 c. orange	45	1·10
D102		10 c. orange	45	1·10
D103		20 c. orange	45	1·10
D104		30 c. orange	45	1·10
D105		50 c. orange	45	1·40

1897.

D108	D 13	1 c. violet	45	1·10
D109		2 c. violet	45	1·10
D110		5 c. violet	45	1·10
D111		10 c. violet	45	1·10
D112	D 13	20 c. violet	75	1·25
D113		30 c. violet	45	90
D114		50 c. violet	45	90

1898.

D124	D 13	1 c. green	15	1·25
D125		2 c. green	15	1·25
D126		5 c. green	15	1·25
D127		10 c. green	15	1·25
D128		20 c. green	15	1·25
D129		30 c. green	15	1·25
D130		50 c. green	15	1·25

1899.

D137	D 13	1 c. red	15	1·25
D138		2 c. red	15	1·25
D139		5 c. red	15	1·25
D140		10 c. red	15	1·25
D141		20 c. red	15	1·25
D142		50 c. red	15	1·25

1900.

D146	D 16	1 c. red	70
D147		2 c. orange	70
D148		5 c. blue	70
D149		10 c. violet	70
D150		20 c. brown	70
D151		30 c. green	1·40
D152		50 c. lake	1·40

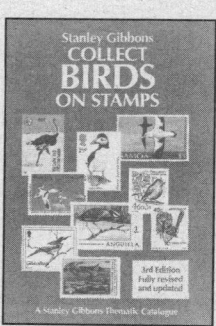

NIGER Pt. 6; Pt. 14

Area south of the Sahara. In 1920 was separated from Upper Senegal and Niger to form a separate colony. From 1944 to 1959 used the stamps of French West Africa.

In 1958 Niger became an autonomous republic within the French Community and on 3 August 1960 an independent republic.

100 centimes = 1 franc

1921. Stamps of Upper Senegal and Niger optd **TERRITOIRE DU NIGER**.

No.	Type	Description	Unused	Used
1	7	1 c. violet and purple	10	30
2		2 c. purple and grey	10	30
3		4 c. blue and black	15	30
4		5 c. chocolate and brown	15	30
5		10 c. green and light green	50	75
25		10 c. pink on blue	10	30
6		15 c. yellow and brown	15	30
7		20 c. black and purple	15	30
8		25 c. green and black	15	30
9		30 c. carmine and red	50	65
26		30 c. red and green	30	50
10		35 c. violet and red	25	40
11		40 c. red and grey	35	50
12		45 c. brown and blue	35	50
13		50 c. blue and ultramarine	40	60
27		50 c. blue and grey	50	70
28		60 c. red	35	55
14		75 c. brown and yellow	45	85
15		1 f. purple and brown	60	80
16		2 f. blue and green	65	90
17		5 f. black and violet	1·25	1·40

1922. Stamps of 1921 surch.

No.	Type	Description	Unused	Used
18	7	25 c. on 15 c. yellow & brown	25	40
19		25 c. on 2 f. blue and green	25	45
20		25 c. on 5 f. black & violet	25	45
21		60 on 75 c. violet on pink	25	45
22		65 on 45 c. brown and blue	75	1·40
23		85 c. on 75 c. brown & yellow	85	1·40
24		1 f. 25 on 1 f. lt blue & blue	60	85

3 Wells

5 Zinder Fort

4 Canoe on River Niger

1926.

No.	Type	Description	Unused	Used
29	3	1 c. green and purple	10	25
30		2 c. red and grey	10	30
31		3 c. brown and mauve	10	30
32		4 c. black and brown	10	30
33		5 c. green and red	10	35
34		10 c. green and blue	10	20
35		15 c. light green and green	40	40
36		15 c. red and lilac	10	25
37	4	20 c. brown and blue	15	30
38		25 c. pink and black	15	30
39		30 c. light green and green	35	55
40		30 c. mauve and yellow	20	40
41		35 c. blue and red on blue	15	30
42		35 c. green and deep green	35	50
43		40 c. grey and purple	25	40
44		45 c. mauve and yellow	55	70
45		45 c. green and turquoise	35	55
46		50 c. green and red on green	25	30
47		55 c. brown and red	50	70
48		60 c. brown and red	40	65
49		65 c. red and green	25	45
50		70 c. red and green	55	70
51		75 c. mauve and grn on pink	70	90
52		80 c. green and purple	80	95
53		90 c. red and carmine	55	70
54		90 c. green and red	55	70
55	5	1 f. green and red	3·00	3·00
56		1 f. orange and red	65	60
57		1 f. red and green	40	55
58		1 f. 10 green and brown	2·25	2·00
59		1 f. 25 red and green	70	75
60		1 f. 25 orange and red	50	70
61		1 f. 40 brown and mauve	50	70
62		1 f. 50 light blue and blue	25	35
63		1 f. 60 green and brown	75	95
64		1 f. 75 brown and mauve	1·40	1·50
65		1 f. 75 ultramarine and blue	65	85
66		2 f. brown and orange	35	50
67		2 f. 25 ultramarine and blue	55	75
68		2 f. 50 brown	65	80
69		3 f. grey and mauve	35	45
70		5 f. black & purple on pink	50	65
71		10 f. mauve and lilac	75	80
72		20 f. orange and green	75	85

1931. "Colonial Exhibition" key types inscr. "NIGER".

No.	Type	Description	Unused	Used
73	E	40 c. green	2·25	2·25
74	F	50 c. mauve	2·00	2·25
75	G	90 c. red	2·50	2·75
76	H	1 f. 50 blue	2·50	2·75

1937. International Exhibition, Paris. As Nos. 168/73 of St.-Pierre et Miquelon.

No.	Type	Description	Unused	Used
77		20 c. violet	60	85
78		30 c. green	60	85
79		40 c. red	55	75
80		50 c. brown and agate	50	70
81		90 c. red	55	85
82		1 f. 50 blue	55	85

1938. Int. Anti-Cancer Fund. As T **22** of Mauritania.

No.	Type	Description	Unused	Used
83		1 f. 75 + 50 c. blue	8·50	9·50

1939. Caille. As T **27** of Mauritania.

No.	Type	Description	Unused	Used
84		90 c. orange	40	55
85		2 f. violet	40	55
86		2 f. 25 blue	40	55

1939. New York World's Fair. As T **28** of Mauritania.

No.	Type	Description	Unused	Used
87		1 f. 25 red	50	60
88		2 f. 25 blue	50	60

1939. 150th Anniv of French Revolution. As T **29** of Mauritania.

No.	Type	Description	Unused	Used
89		45 c. + 25 c. green and black	4·50	5·00
90		70 c. + 30 c. brown and black	4·50	5·00
91		90 c. + 35 c. orange and black	4·75	5·00
92		1 f. 25 + 1 f. red and black	4·50	5·00
93		2 f. 25 + 2 f. blue and black	4·50	5·00

1940. Air. As T **30** of Mauritania.

No.	Type	Description	Unused	Used
94		1 f. 90 blue	50	55
95		2 f. 90 red	45	55
96		4 f. 50 green	60	70
97		4 f. 90 olive	50	60
98		6 f. 90 orange	45	60

1941. National Defence Fund. Surch **SECOURS NATIONAL** and additional value.

No.	Type	Description	Unused	Used
98a	4	+ 1 f. on 50 c. green and red on green	2·00	2·00
98b		+ 2 f. on 80 c. green & pur	3·00	3·00
98c	5	+ 2 f. on 1 f. 50 lt blue & bl	4·25	4·25
98d		+ 3 f. on 2 f. brown & orge	4·25	4·25

5a Zinder Fort

5c "Vocation"

5b Weighing Baby

1942. Marshal Petain issue.

No.	Type	Description	Unused	Used
98e	5a	1 f. green	10	
98f		2 f. 50 blue	10	

1942. Air. Colonial Child Welfare Fund.

No.	Type	Description	Unused	Used
98g	–	1 f. 50 + 3 f. 50 green	20	
98h	–	2 f. + 6 f. brown	15	
98i	5b	3 f. + 9 f. red	15	

DESIGNS: 49×28 mm: 1 f. 50 Maternity Hospital, Dakar; 2 f. Dispensary, Mopti.

1942. Air. Imperial Fortnight.

No.	Type	Description	Unused	Used
98j	5c	1 f. 20 + 1 f. 80 blue & red	10	

1942. Air. As T **32** of Mauritania but inscr "NIGER" at foot.

No.	Type	Description	Unused	Used
98k		50 f. red and yellow	80	1·00

7 Giraffes

8 Carmine Bee Eater

1959. Wild Animals and Birds. Inscr "PROTECTION DE LA FAUNE".

No.	Type	Description	Unused	Used
99	–	50 c. turquoise, green and black (postage)	25	10
100	–	1 f. multicoloured	30	15
101	–	2 f. multicoloured	30	15
102	–	5 f. mauve, black & brown	40	15
103	–	7 f. red, black and green	50	20
104	–	10 f. multicoloured	25	10
105	–	15 f. sepia and turquoise	25	10
106	–	20 f. black and violet	35	10
107	7	25 f. multicoloured	45	10
108		30 f. brown, bistre & green	50	20
109	–	50 f. blue and brown	4·00	80
110	–	60 f. sepia and green	5·50	1·10
111	–	85 f. brown and bistre	2·50	85
112	–	100 f. bistre and green	3·25	85
113	8	200 f. multicoloured (air)	18·00	5·50
114	–	500 f. green, brown & blue	8·50	6·00

DESIGNS—As Type **7**: HORIZ: 50 c., 10 f. African manatee. VERT: 1, 2 f. Crowned Cranes; 5, 7 f. Saddle-bill Stork; 15, 20 f. Barbary sheep; 50, 60 f. Ostriches; 85, 100 f. Lion. As Type **8**: VERT: 500 f. Game animals.

1960. 10th Anniv of African Technical Co-operation Commission. As T **4** of Malagasy Republic.

No.	Type	Description	Unused	Used
115		25 f. brown and ochre	50	40

9 Conseil de l'Entente Emblem

11 Pres. Diori Hamani

1960. 1st Anniv of Conseil de l'Entente.

No.	Type	Description	Unused	Used
116	9	25 f. multicoloured	50	40

1960. Independence. No. 112 surch 200 F and bars and **Independance 3-8-60**.

No.	Type	Description	Unused	Used
117	–	200 f. on 100 f.	9·00	9·00

1960.

No.	Type	Description	Unused	Used
118	11	25 f. black and bistre	35	25

12 U.N. Emblem and Niger Flag

1961. Air. 1st Anniv of Admission into U.N.

No.	Type	Description	Unused	Used
119	12	25 f. red, green & orange	40	25
120		100 f. green, red & emerald	1·40	90

1962. Air. "Air Afrique" Airline. As T **42** of Mauritania.

No.	Type	Description	Unused	Used
121		100 f. violet, black and brown	1·50	75

1962. Malaria Eradication. As T **43** of Mauritania.

No.	Type	Description	Unused	Used
122		25 f. + 5 f. brown	45	45

13 Athletics

1962. Abidjan Games, 1961. Multicoloured.

No.	Type	Description	Unused	Used
123		15 f. Boxing and cycling (vert)	25	15
124		25 f. Basketball and football (vert)	35	20
125		85 f. Type **13**	1·10	55

1962. 1st Anniv of Union of African and Malagasy States. As T **45** of Mauritania.

No.	Type	Description	Unused	Used
126	72	30 f. mauve	40	30

14 Pres. Hamani and Map

15 Running

1962. 4th Anniv of Republic.

No.	Type	Description	Unused	Used
127	14	25 f. multicoloured	35	25

1963. Freedom from Hunger. As T **51** of Mauritania.

No.	Type	Description	Unused	Used
128		25 f. + 5 f. purple, brn & olive	55	55

1963. Dakar Games.

No.	Type	Description	Unused	Used
129	–	15 f. brown and blue	25	15
130	15	25 f. red and brown	35	20
131	–	45 f. black and green	70	40

DESIGNS—HORIZ: 15 f. Swimming. VERT: 45 f. Volleyball.

16 Agadez Mosque

1963. Air. 2nd Anniv of Admission to U.P.U. Multicoloured.

No.	Type	Description	Unused	Used
132		50 f. Type **16**	75	40
133		85 f. Gaya Bridge	1·25	60
134		100 f. Presidential Palace, Niamey	1·25	70

17 Wood-carving

1963. Traditional Crafts. Multicoloured.

No.	Type	Description	Unused	Used
135		5 f. Type **17** (postage)	15	15
136		10 f. Skin-tanning	20	15
137		25 f. Goldsmith	40	20
138		30 f. Mat-making	60	30
139		85 f. Potter	1·40	80
140		100 f. Canoe building (air)	2·00	1·10

The 10 f. and 30 f. are horiz and the 100 f. larger 47×27 mm.

1963. Air. African and Malagasy Posts and Telecommunications Union. As T **56** of Mauritania.

No.	Type	Description	Unused	Used
141		85 f. multicoloured	95	55

1963. Air. Red Cross Centenary. Optd with cross and **Centenaire de la Croix-Rouge** in red.

No.	Type	Description	Unused	Used
142	12	25 f. red, green and orange	60	40
143		100 f. green, red and emerald	1·40	85

19 Costume Museum

1963. Opening of Costume Museum, Niamey. Vert costume designs. Multicoloured.

No.	Type	Description	Unused	Used
144		15 f. Berber woman	20	15
145		20 f. Haussa woman	35	15
146		25 f. Tuareg woman	45	20
147		30 f. Tuareg man	55	20
148		60 f. Djerma woman	1·25	50
149		85 f. Type **19**	1·50	60

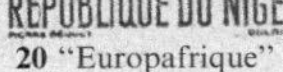

20 "Europafrique"

22 Man and Globe

21 Groundnut Cultivation

1963. Air. European–African Economic Convention.

No.	Type	Description	Unused	Used
150	20	50 f. multicoloured	2·50	2·00

1963. Air. Groundnut Cultivation Campaign.

No.	Type	Description	Unused	Used
151	21	20 f. blue, brown & green	35	20
152	–	45 f. brown, blue & green	75	25
153	–	85 f. multicoloured	1·40	65
154	–	100 f. olive, brown & blue	1·50	90

DESIGNS: 45 f. Camel transport; 85 f. Fastening sacks; 100 f. Dispatch of groundnuts by lorry.

1963. Air. 1st Anniv of "Air Afrique" and DC-8 Service Inauguration. As T **59** of Mauritania.

No.	Type	Description	Unused	Used
155		50 f. multicoloured	70	45

1963. 15th Anniv of Declaration of Human Rights.

No.	Type	Description	Unused	Used
156	22	25 f. blue, brown & green	45	25

23 "Telstar"

1964. Air. Space Telecommunications.
157 **23** 25 f. olive and violet . . . 40 20
158 – 100 f. green and purple . . 1·10 80
DESIGN: 100 f. "Relay".

24 "Parkinsonia aculeata" 25 Statue, Abu Simbel

1964. Flowers. Multicoloured.
159 5 f. Type **24** 60 30
160 10 f. "Russelia equisetiformis" 50 30
161 15 f. "Lantana Camara" . . . 1·00 45
162 20 f. "Agryeia nervosa" . . . 1·00 45
163 25 f. "Luffa Cylindrica" . . . 1·00 45
164 30 f. "Hibiscus rosa-sinensis" . 1·40 60
165 45 f. "Plumierai rubra" . . . 2·00 1·25
166 50 f. "Catharanthus roseus" . . 2·00 1·25
167 60 f. "Caesalpinia pulcherrima" 3·50 1·50
Nos. 164/7 have "REPUBLIQUE DU NIGER" at the top and the value at bottom right.

1964. Air. Nubian Monuments Preservation.
168 **25** 25 f. green and brown . . . 65 45
169 30 f. brown and blue . . . 1·00 70
170 50 f. blue and purple . . . 2·00 1·25

26 Globe and "Tiros" Satellite

1964. Air. World Meteorological Day.
171 **26** 50 f. brown, blue and green 1·10 65

27 Sun Emblem and Solar Flares 28 Convoy of Lorries

1964. International Quiet Sun Years.
172 **27** 30 f. red, violet and sepia . 50 35

1964. O.M.N.E.S. (Nigerian Mobile Medical and Sanitary Organization) Commemoration.
173 **28** 25 f. orange, olive & blue . 40 20
174 – 30 f. multicoloured 50 20
175 – 50 f. multicoloured 80 30
176 – 60 f. purple, orange & turq 90 35
DESIGNS: 30 f. Tending children; 50 f. Tending women; 60 f. Open-air laboratory.

29 Rocket, Stars and Stamp Outline

1964. Air. "PHILATEC 1964" Int Stamp Exn, Paris.
177 **29** 50 f. mauve and blue . . . 85 60

30 European, African and Symbols of Agriculture and Industry 31 Pres. Kennedy

1964. Air. 1st Anniv of European–African Economic Convention.
178 **30** 50 f. multicoloured 65 40

1964. Air. Pres. Kennedy Commemoration.
179 **31** 100 f. multicoloured . . . 1·25 1·10

32 Water-polo

1964. Air. Olympic Games, Tokyo.
180 **32** 60 f. brown, deep green and purple 60 50
181 – 85 f. brown, blue and red . 1·00 60
182 – 100 f. blue, red and green . 1·25 70
183 – 250 f. blue, brown and grn 2·50 1·75
DESIGNS—HORIZ: 85 f. Relay-racing. VERT: 100 f. Throwing the discus; 250 f. Athlete holding Olympic Torch.

1964. French, African and Malagasy Co-operation. As T **68** of Mauritania.
184 50 f. brown, orange & violet . 65 40

33 Azawak Tuareg Encampment

1964. Native Villages. Multicoloured.
185 15 f. Type **33** 20 20
186 20 f. Songhai hut 25 20
187 25 f. Wogo and Kourtey tents 30 20
188 30 f. Djerma hut 40 25
189 60 f. Sorkawa fishermen's encampment 75 30
190 85 f. Hausa urban house . . 1·25 50

34 Doctors and Patient and Microscope Slide 35 Abraham Lincoln

1964. Anti-Leprosy Campaign.
191 **34** 50 f. multicoloured 50 45

1965. Death Centenary of Abraham Lincoln.
192 **35** 50 f. multicoloured 60 50

36 Instruction by "Radio-Vision"

1965. "Human Progress". Inscr as in T **36**.
193 **36** 20 f. brown, yellow & blue 30 20
194 – 25 f. sepia, brown and green 35 20
195 – 30 f. purple, red and green 45 25
196 – 50 f. purple, blue and brown 70 35
DESIGNS: 25 f. Student; 30 f. Adult class; 50 f. Five tribesmen ("Alphabetisation").

37 Ader's Telephone 38 Pope John XXIII

1965. I.T.U. Centenary.
197 **37** 25 f. black, lake and green . 50 25
198 – 30 f. green, purple and red . 60 30
199 – 50 f. green, purple and red . 1·00 50
DESIGNS: 30 f. Wheatstone's telegraph; 50 f. "Telautographe".

1965. Air. Pope John Commemoration.
200 **38** 100 f. multicoloured . . . . 1·40 75

39 Hurdling 40 "Capture of Cancer" (the Crab)

1965. 1st African Games, Brazzaville.
201 **39** 10 f. purple, green & brown 20 15
202 – 15 f. red, brown and grey . 30 15
203 – 20 f. purple, blue & green . 40 20
204 – 30 f. purple, green & lake . 50 25
DESIGNS—VERT: 15 f. Running; 30 f. Long-jumping. HORIZ: 20 f. Pole-vaulting.

1965. Air. Campaign against Cancer.
205 **40** 100 f. brown, black & green 1·40 80

41 Sir Winston Churchill 42 Interviewing

1965. Air. Churchill Commemoration.
206 **41** 100 f. multicoloured . . . . 1·40 80

1965. Radio Club Promotion.
207 **42** 30 f. brown, violet & green . 30 15
208 – 45 f. red, black and buff . . 45 25
209 – 50 f. multicoloured 55 30
210 – 60 f. purple, blue & ochre . 60 40
DESIGNS—VERT: 45 f. Recording; 50 f. Listening to broadcast. HORIZ: 60 f. Listeners debate.

43 "Agricultural and Industrial Workers" 44 Fair Scene and Flags

1965. Air. International Co-operation Year.
211 **43** 50 f. brown, black & bistre . 70 35

1965. Air. International Fair, Niamey.
212 **44** 100 f. multicoloured . . . . 1·10 70

45 Dr. Schweitzer and Diseased Hands

1966. Air. Schweitzer Commemoration.
213 **45** 50 f. multicoloured 80 45

46 "Water Distribution and Control"

1966. Int Hydrological Decade Inauguration.
214 **46** 50 f. blue, orange & violet 70 35

47 Weather Ship "France I"

1966. Air. 6th World Meteorological Day.
215 **47** 50 f. green, purple and blue 1·25 55

48 White and "Gemini" Capsule

1966. Air. Cosmonauts.
216 **48** 50 f. black, brown & green 75 40
217 – 50 f. blue, violet & orange 75 40
DESIGN: No. 217, Leonov and "Voskhod" capsule.

49 Head-dress and Carvings

51 Goalkeeper saving ball 50 "Diamant" Rocket and Gantry

1966. World Festival of Negro Arts, Dakar.
218 **49** 30 f. black, brown & green 45 25
219 – 50 f. violet, brown and blue 60 35
220 – 60 f. lake, violet & brown . 70 40
221 – 100 f. black, red & blue . . 1·25 70
DESIGNS: 50 f. Carved figures and mosaics; 60 f. Statuettes, drums and arch; 100 f. Handicrafts and church.

1966. Air. French Space Vehicles. Multicoloured designs each showing different Satellites.
222 45 f. Type **50** 70 40
223 60 f. "A 1" (horiz) 80 45
224 90 f. "FR 1" (horiz) . . . . 1·00 50
225 100 f. "D 1" (horiz) . . . . . 1·50 75

1966. World Cup Football Championships.
226 – 30 f. red, brown and blue . 55 25
227 **51** 50 f. brown, blue & green . 75 35
228 – 60 f. blue, purple and bistre 85 50
DESIGNS—VERT: 30 f. Player dribbling ball; 60 f. Player kicking ball.

53 Parachutist

52 Cogwheel Emblem and Hemispheres 54 Inoculating Cattle

1966. Air. Europafrique.
229 **52** 50 f. multicoloured 70 45

1966. 5th Anniv of National Armed Forces. Mult.
230 20 f. Type **53** 35 15
231 30 f. Soldiers with standard (vert) 45 20
232 45 f. Armoured patrol vehicle (horiz) 70 30

1966. Air. Inauguration of DC-8F Air Services. As T **87** of Mauritania.
233 30 f. olive, black and grey . . 60 25

1966. Campaign for Prevention of Cattle Plague.
234 **54** 45 f. black, brown & blue . 1·00 50

55 "Voskhod 1" **56** U.N.E.S.C.O. "Tree"

1966. Air. Astronautics.
235 **55** 50 f. blue, indigo and lake . 65 35
236 – 100 f. violet, blue and lake . 1·25 75
DESIGN—HORIZ: 100 f. "Gemini 6" and "7".

1966. 20th Anniv of U.N.E.S.C.O.
237 **56** 50 f. multicoloured 70 25

57 Japanese Gate, Atomic Symbol and Cancer ("The Crab") **58** Furnace

1966. Air. International Cancer Congress, Tokyo.
238 **57** 100 f. multicoloured . . . 1·40 75

1966. Malbaza Cement Works.
239 **58** 10 f. blue, orange & brown 15 10
240 – 20 f. blue and green 30 15
241 – 30 f. brown, grey and blue . 45 20
242 – 50 f. indigo, brown & blue 65 30
DESIGNS—HORIZ: 20 f. Electrical power-house; 30 f. Works and cement silos; 50 f. Installation for handling raw materials.

59 Niamey Mosque

1967. Air.
243 **59** 100 f. blue, green and grey 1·10 70

60 Durer (self-portrait)

1967. Air. Paintings. Multicoloured.
244 50 f. Type **60** 80 60
245 100 f. David (self-portrait) . . 1·50 90
246 250 f. Delacroix (self-portrait) 3·00 2·00
See also Nos. 271/2 and 277/9.

61 Red-billed Hornbill **62** Bob-sleigh Course, Villard-de-Lans

1967. Birds.
247 **61** 1 f. bistre, red and green (postage) 15 15
248 – 2 f. black, brown and green 15 15
249 – 30 f. multicoloured . . . 85 30
249a – 40 f. purple, orange and green . . . . 1·00 50
250 – 45 f. brown, green and blue 1·25 30
250a – 65 f. yell, brown & purple 1·40 60
251 – 70 f. multicoloured . . . . 1·60 75
251a – 250 f. blue, purple and green (48 × 27 mm) (air) . . . 4·75 1·75
BIRDS: 2 f. Lesser pied kingfishers; 30 f. Common gonolek; 40 f. Red bishop; 45 f., 65 f. Little masked weaver; 70 f. Chestnut-bellied sandgrouse; 250 f. Splendid glossy starlings.

1967. Grenoble–Winter Olympics Town (1968).
252 **62** 30 f. brown, blue and green 40 25
253 – 45 f. brown, blue and green 60 30
254 – 60 f. brown, blue and green 80 50
255 – 90 f. brown, blue and green 1·10 65
DESIGNS: 45 f. Ski-jump, Autrans; 60 f. Ski-jump, St. Nizier du moucherotte; 90 f. Slalom course, Chamrousse.

63 Family and Lions Emblem **64** Weather Ship

1967. 50th Anniv of Lions International.
256 **63** 50 f. blue, red and green . 60 35

1967. Air. World Meteorological Day.
257 **64** 50 f. red, black and blue . 1·25 65

65 View of World Fair

1967. Air. World Fair, Montreal.
258 **65** 100 f. black, blue & purple 1·10 50

66 I.T.Y. Emblem and Jet Airliner **67** Scouts around Camp-fire

1967. International Tourist Year.
259 **66** 45 f. violet, green & purple 45 35

1967. World Scout Jamboree, Idaho, U.S.A.
260 **67** 30 f. brown, lake and blue 40 20
261 – 45 f. blue, brown & orge . 60 30
262 – 80 f. lake, slate and bistre . 1·25 50
DESIGNS—HORIZ: 45 f. Jamboree emblem and scouts. VERT: 80 f. Scout cooking meal.

68 Audio-Visual Centre

1967. Air. National Audio-Visual Centre, Niamey.
263 **68** 100 f. violet, blue and green 90 50

69 Carrying Patient **70** "Europafrique"

1967. Nigerian Red Cross.
264 **69** 45 f. black, red and green . 60 20
265 – 50 f. black, red and green . 75 25
266 – 60 f. black, red and green . 1·00 35
DESIGNS: 50 f. Nurse with mother and child; 60 f. Doctor giving injection.

1967. Europafrique.
267 **70** 50 f. multicoloured 60 30

71 Dr. Konrad Adenauer **72** African Women

1967. Air. Adenauer Commemoration.
268 **71** 100 f. brown and blue . . . 1·40 70

1967. Air. 5th Anniv of African and Malagasy Post and Telecommunications Union (U.A.M.P.T.). As T **101** of Mauritania.
270 100 f. violet, green and red . . 1·10 60

1967. Air. Death Centenary of Jean Ingres (painter). Paintings by Ingres. As T **60**. Multicoloured.
271 100 f. "Jesus among the Doctors" (horiz) . . . . . . 1·60 1·00
272 150 f. "Jesus restoring the Keys to St. Peter" (vert) . . . . . 2·25 1·50

1967. U.N. Women's Rights Commission.
273 **72** 50 f. brown, yellow and blue 60 35

1967. 5th Anniv of West African Monetary Union. As T **103** of Mauritania.
274 30 f. green and purple 35 20

73 Nigerian Children **75** Allegory of Human Rights

74 O.C.A.M. Emblem

1967. Air. 21st Anniv of U.N.I.C.E.F.
275 **73** 100 f. brown, blue & green . 1·25 95

1968. Air. O.C.A.M. Conference, Niamey.
276 **74** 100 f. orange, green and blue 1·10 60

1968. Air. Paintings (self-portraits). As T **60**. Multicoloured.
277 50 f. J.-B. Corot 70 40
278 150 f. Goya . . . . 1·90 1·00
279 200 f. Van Gogh . . . . 2·50 1·50

1968. Human Rights Year.
280 **75** 50 f. indigo, brown and blue 60 30

76 Breguet 27 Biplane over Lake

1968. Air. 35th Anniv of 1st France-Niger Airmail Service.
281 **76** 45 f. blue, green and mauve 95 35
282 – 80 f. slate, brown and blue . 1·60 55
283 – 100 f. black, green & blue . 2·50 75
DESIGNS—Potez 25TOE biplane: 80 f. On ground; 100 f. In flight.

77 "Joyous Health"

1968. 20th Anniv of W.H.O.
284 **77** 50 f. indigo, blue and brown 60 35

78 Cyclists of 1818 and 1968

1968. Air. 150th Anniv of Bicycle.
285 **78** 100 f. green and red . . . 1·50 70

79 Beribboned Rope

1968. Air. 5th Anniv of Europafrique.
286 **79** 50 f. multicoloured 65 40

80 Fencing

1968. Air. Olympic Games, Mexico.
287 **80** 50 f. purple, violet & green 50 35
288 – 100 f. black, purple & blue 85 50
289 – 150 f. purple and orange . 1·25 70
290 – 200 f. blue, brown & green 1·75 1·25
DESIGNS—VERT: 100 f. High-diving; 150 f. Weight-lifting. HORIZ: 200 f. Horse-jumping.

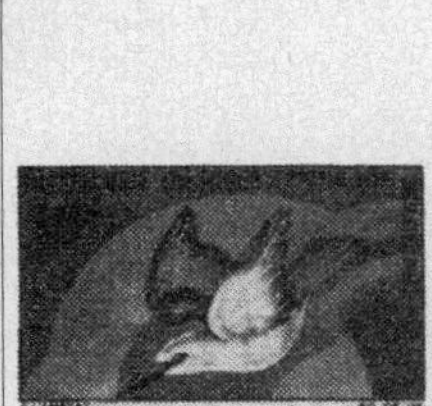

81 Woodland Kingfisher **82** Mahatma Gandhi

1969. Birds. Dated "1968". Multicoloured.
292 5 f. African grey hornbill (postage) 25 10
293 10 f. Type **81** 30 10
294 15 f. Senegal coucal 65 25
295 20 f. Rose-ringed parakeets . 75 40
296 25 f. Abyssinian roller . . . . 1·10 50
297 50 f. Cattle egret . . . . . . 1·50 70
298 100 f. Violet starling (27 × 49 mm) (air) . . . . 3·25 1·40
See also Nos. 372/7, 567/8 and 714/15.

1968. Air. "Apostles of Non-Violence".
299 **82** 100 f. black and yellow . . 1·75 60
300 – 100 f. black and turquoise . 1·00 50
301 – 100 f. black and grey . . . 1·00 50
302 – 100 f. black and orange . . 1·00 50
PORTRAITS: No. 300, President Kennedy; No. 301, Martin Luther King; No. 302, Robert F. Kennedy.

1968. Air. "Philexafrique" Stamp Exhibition., Abidjan (Ivory Coast, 1969) (1st issue). As T **113a** of Mauritania. Multicoloured.
304 100 f. "Pare, Minister of the Interior" (J. L. La Neuville) 1·60 1·60

83 Arms of the Republic

1968. Air. 10th Anniv of Republic.
305 **83** 100 f. multicoloured . . . 1·00 50

1969. Air. Napoleon Bonaparte. Birth Bicentenary. As T **114b** of Mauritania. Multicoloured.
306 50 f. "Napoleon as First Consul" (Ingres) . . . . 1·50 90
307 100 f. "Napoleon visiting the plague victims of Jaffa" (Gros) 2·50 1·25
308 150 f. "Napoleon Enthroned" (Ingres) . . . . 3·50 1·75
309 200 f. "The French Campaign" (Meissonier) . . . . 5·00 2·50

1969. Air. "Philexafrique" Stamp Exhibition, Abidjan, Ivory Coast (2nd issue). As T **114a** of Mauritania.
310 50 f. brown, blue and orange . 1·25 1·00
DESIGN: 50 f. Giraffes and stamp of 1926.

84 Boeing 707 over Rain-cloud and Anemometer

1969. Air. World Meteorological Day.
311 **84** 50 f. black, blue and green 90 35

85 Workers supporting Globe

1969. 50th Anniv of I.L.O.
312 **85** 30 f. red and green 40 20
313 50 f. green and red 50 35

86 Panhard and Levassor (1909)

1969. Air. Veteran Motor Cars.
314 **86** 25 f. green 45 20
315 – 45 f. violet, blue and grey . 55 25
316 – 50 f. brown, ochre and grey 1·10 35
317 – 70 f. purple, red and grey . 1·50 45
318 – 100 f. green, brown and grey 1·75 65
DESIGNS: 45 f. De Dion Bouton 8 (1904); 50 f. Opel "Doktor-wagen" (1909); 70 f. Daimler (1910); 100 f. Vermorel 12/16 (1912).

87 Mother and Child **88** Mouth and Ear

1969. 50th Anniv of League of Red Cross Societies.
319 **87** 45 f. red, brown and blue . 60 25
320 – 50 f. red, grey and green 70 25
321 – 70 f. red, brown and ochre 1·00 40
DESIGNS—VERT: 70 f. Man with Red Cross parcel. HORIZ: 50 f. Symbolic Figures, Globe and Red Crosses.

1969. First French Language Cultural Conf., Niamey.
322 **88** 100 f. multicoloured . . . 1·25 60

89 School Building

1969. National School of Administration.
323 **89** 30 f. black, green and orange 30 20

1969. Air. 1st Man on the Moon. No. 114 optd **L'HOMME SUR LA LUNE JUILLET 1969 APOLLO 11** and moon module.
324 500 f. green, brown & blue . . 6·50 6·50

91 "Apollo 8" and Rocket

1969. Air. Moon Flight of "Apollo 8". Embossed on gold foil.
325 **91** 1,000 f. gold . . . . . . 15·00 15·00

1969. 5th Anniv of African Development Bank. As T **122a** of Mauritania.
326 30 f. brown, green and violet . 35 15

92 Child and Toys

1969. Air. International Toy Fair, Nuremburg.
327 **92** 100 f. blue, brown and green 1·50 50

93 Linked Squares

1969. Air. "Europafrique".
328 **93** 50 f. yellow, black & violet 55 30

94 Trucks crossing Sahara

1969. Air. 45th Anniv of "Croisiere Noire" Trans-Africa Expedition.
329 **94** 50 f. brown, violet and mve 75 35
330 – 100 f. violet, red and blue . 1·50 65
331 – 150 f. multicoloured . . . 2·00 1·25
332 – 200 f. green, indigo and blue 3·00 1·50
DESIGNS: 100 f. Crossing the mountains; 150 f. African children and expedition at Lake Victoria; 200 f. Route Map, European greeting African and Citroen truck.

94a Aircraft, Map and Airport

1969. 10th Anniv of Aerial Navigation Security Agency for Africa and Madagascar (A.S.E.C.N.A.).
333 **94a** 100 f. red . . . . 1·50 70

95 Classical Pavilion

1970. National Museum.
334 **95** 30 f. blue, green and brown 30 15
335 – 45 f. blue, green and brown 45 25
336 – 50 f. blue, brown and green 50 25
337 – 70 f. brown, blue and green 70 40
338 – 100 f. brown, blue and grn 1·10 60
DESIGNS: 45 f. Temporary Exhibition Pavilion; 50 f. Audio-visual Pavilion; 70 f. Local Musical Instruments Gallery; 100 f. Handicrafts Pavilion.

96 Niger Village and Japanese Pagodas **97** Hypodermic "Gun" and Map

1970. Air. "EXPO 70" World Fair, Osaka, Japan (1st issue).
339 **96** 100 f. multicoloured . . . 90 45

1970. One Hundred Million Smallpox Vaccinations in West Africa.
340 **97** 50 f. blue, purple and green 70 30

98 Education Symbols

1970. Air. International Education Year.
341 **98** 100 f. slate, red and purple . 1·00 45

99 Footballer

1970. World Cup Football Competitions, Mexico.
342 **99** 40 f. green, brown and purple 60 25
343 – 70 f. purple, brown and blue 1·00 40
344 – 90 f. red and black . . . . 1·25 60
DESIGNS: 70 f. Football and Globe; 90 f. Two footballers.

100 Rotary Emblems

1970. Air. 65th Anniv of Rotary International.
345 **100** 100 f. multicoloured . . . 1·25 55

101 Bay of Naples and Niger Stamp

1970. Air. 10th "Europafrique" Stamp Exn, Naples.
346 **101** 100 f. multicoloured . . . 1·00 60

102 Clement Ader's "Avion III" and Modern Airplane

1970. Air. Aviation Pioneers.
347 **102** 50 f. grey, blue & red . . . 70 25
348 – 100 f. red, grey & blue . 1·50 60
349 – 150 f. light brown, brown & green . . . . 1·50 75
350 – 200 f. red, bistre and violet 2·25 1·00
351 – 250 f. violet, grey and red . 3·50 1·40
DESIGNS: 100 f. Joseph and Etienne Montgolfier balloon and rocket; 150 f. Isaac Newton and gravity diagram; 200 f. Galileo and rocket in planetary system; 250 f. Leonardo da Vinci's drawing of a "flying machine" and Chanute's glider.

103 Cathode Ray Tube illuminating Books, Microscope and Globe

1970. Air. World Telecommunications Day.
352 **103** 100 f. brown, green and red 1·25 50

1970. Inauguration of New U.P.U. Headquarters Building, Berne. As T **81** of New Caledonia.
353 30 f. red, slate and brown . . 35 20
354 60 f. violet, red and blue . . . 60 30

1970. Air. Safe Return of "Apollo 13". Nos. 348 and 350 optd **Solidarite Spatiale Apollo XIII 11-17 Avril 1970.**
355 100 f. red, slate and blue . . . 1·00 50
356 200 f. red, bistre and violet . . 1·75 75

105 U.N. Emblem, Man, Woman and Doves

1970. Air. 25th Anniv of U.N.O.
357 **105** 100 f. multicoloured . . . 1·00 50
358 150 f. multicoloured . . . 1·50 75

106 Globe and Heads

1970. Air. International French Language Conference, Niamey. Die-stamped on gold foil.
359 **106** 250 f. gold and blue . . . 2·50 2·50

107 European and African Women

1970. Air. "Europafrique".
360 **107** 50 f. red and green . . . 55 30

108 Japanese Girls and "EXPO 70" Skyline

1970. Air. "EXPO 70" World Fair, Osaka, Japan. (2nd issue).
361 **108** 100 f. purple, orange & grn 90 40
362 – 150 f. blue, brown & green 1·25 60
DESIGN: 150 f. "No" actor and "EXPO 70" by night.

109 Gymnast on Parallel Bars **111** Beethoven, Keyboard and Manuscripts

1970. Air. World Gymnastic Championships, Ljubljana.
363 **109** 50 f. blue 50 30
364 – 100 f. green . . . . . . 1·10 55
365 – 150 f. purple . . . . . . 1·75 75
366 – 200 f. red . . . . 2·00 95
GYMNASTS—HORIZ: 100 f. Gymnast on vaulting-horse; 150 f. Gymnast in mid-air. VERT: 200 f. Gymnast on rings.

1970. Air. Moon Landing of "Luna 16". Nos. 349 and 351 surch **LUNA 16 – Sept. 1970 PREMIERS PRELEVEMENTS AUTOMATIQUES SUR LA LUNE** and value.
367 100 f. on 150 f. light brown, brown and green . . . . . 1·10 50
368 200 f. on 250 f. violet, grey and red . . . . 2·40 1·00

1970. Air. Birth Bicentenary of Beethoven. Mult.
369 100 f. Type **111** . . . . . . 1·40 55
370 150 f. Beethoven and allegory, "Hymn of Joy" . . . . . . 2·25 85

112 John F. Kennedy Bridge, Niamey

1970. Air. 12th Anniv of Republic.
371 **112** 100 f. multicoloured . . . 1·10 45

1971. Birds. Designs similar to T **81**. Variously dated between 1970 and 1972. Multicoloured.
372 5 f. African grey hornbill . . 40 20
373 10 f. Woodland kingfisher . . 50 20
374 15 f. Senegal coucal . . . . . 1·10 65
375 20 f. Rose-ringed parakeet . . 1·25 65
376 35 f. Broad-tailed paradise whydah . . . . 1·75 90
377 50 f. Cattle egret . . . . . . 2·25 1·25
The Latin inscription on No. 377 is incorrect, reading "Bulbucus ibis" instead of "Bubulcus ibis".
See also Nos. 714/15.

114 Pres. Nasser

1971. Air. Death of Pres. Gamal Nasser (Egyptian statesman). Multicoloured.

378 100 f. Type **114** 75 40
379 200 f. Nasser waving . . . . . 1·50 75

115 Pres. De Gaulle

1971. Air. De Gaulle Commemoration. Embossed on gold foil.

380 **115** 1000 f. gold . . . . 38·00 38·00

116 "MUNICH" and Olympic Rings

1971. Air. Publicity for 1972 Olympic Games, Munich.

381 **116** 150 f. purple, blue & green 1·25 70

117 "Apollo 14" leaving Moon
118 Symbolic Masks

1971. Air. Moon Mission of "Apollo 14".

382 **117** 250 f. green, orge & blue . 2·25 1·25

1971. Air. Racial Equality Year.

383 **118** 100 f. red, green & blue . 90 40
384 – 200 f. brown, green & blue 1·75 80
DESIGN: 200 f. "Peoples" and clover-leaf emblem.

119 Niamey on World Map

1971. 1st Anniv of French-speaking Countries Co-operative Agency.

385 **119** 40 f. multicoloured . . . 50 25

120 African Telecommunications Map

1971. Air. Pan-African Telecommunications Network.

386 **120** 100 f. multicoloured . . . 75 40

121 African Mask and Japanese Stamp

1971. Air. "PHILATOKYO 71" International Stamp Exhibition, Japan.

387 **121** 50 f. olive, purple & green 65 30
388 – 100 f. violet, red & green 1·10 45
DESIGN: 100 f. Japanese scroll painting and Niger stamp.

122 "Longwood House, St. Helena" (C. Vernet)

1971. Air. 150th Anniv of Napoleon's Death. Paintings. Multicoloured.

389 150 f. Type **122** . . . . 1·75 70
390 200 f. "Napoleon's Body on his Camp-bed" (Marryat) . . . 2·50 90

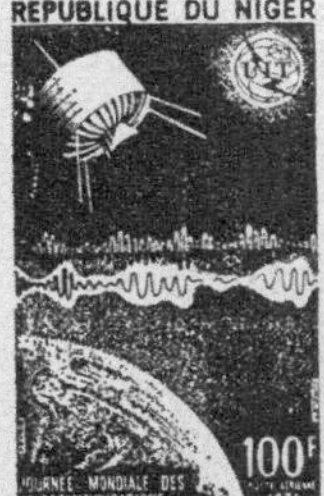

123 Satellite, Radio Waves, and Globe
125 Scout Badges and Mount Fuji

124 Pierre de Coubertin and Discus-throwers

1971. Air. World Telecommunications Day.

391 **123** 100 f. multicoloured . . . 1·10 50

1971. Air. 75th Anniv of Modern Olympic Games.

392 **124** 50 f. red and blue 50 25
393 – 100 f. multicoloured 90 40
394 – 150 f. blue and purple . . 1·40 65
DESIGNS—VERT: 100 f. Male and female athletes holding torch. HORIZ: 150 f. Start of race.

1971. 13th World Scout Jamboree, Asagiri, Japan.

395 **125** 35 f. red, purple & orange 40 20
396 – 40 f. brown, plum and green 45 20
397 – 45 f. green, red and blue . 60 25
398 – 50 f. green, violet and red 70 30
DESIGNS—VERT: 40 f. Scouts and badge; 45 f. Scouts converging on Japan. HORIZ: 50 f. "Jamboree" in rope, and marquee.

126 "Apollo 15" on Moon

1971. Air. Moon Mission of "Apollo 15".

399 **126** 150 f. blue, violet & brn . 1·50 70

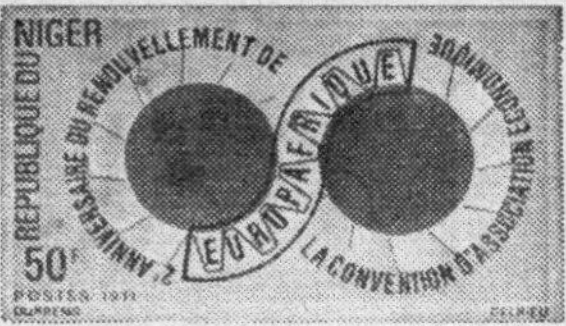

127 Linked Maps

1971. 2nd Anniv of Renewed "Europafrique" Convention, Niamey.

400 **127** 50 f. multicoloured 60 30

128 Gouroumi (Hausa)
129 De Gaulle in Uniform

1971. Musical Instruments.

401 **128** 25 f. brown, green & red . 30 10
402 – 30 f. brown, violet & grn . 35 15
403 – 35 f. blue, green & purple . 35 25
404 – 40 f. brown, orange & grn 45 25
405 – 45 f. ochre, brown & blue . 55 35
406 – 50 f. brown, red & black . 95 45
DESIGNS: 30 f. Molo (Djerma); 35 f. Garaya (Hausa); 40 f. Godjie (Djerma-Sonrai); 45 f. Inzad (Tuareg); 50 f. Kountigui (Sonrai).

1971. Air. 1st Death Anniv of Gen. Charles De Gaulle (French statesman).

407 **129** 250 f. multicoloured . . . 5·00 4·00

1971. Air. 10th Anniv of African and Malagasy Posts and Telecommunications Union. As T **139a** of Mauritania. Multicoloured.

408 100 f. U.A.M.P.T. H.Q. and rural scene 90 45

130 "Audience with Al Hariri" (Baghdad, 1237)

1971. Air. Moslem Miniatures. Multicoloured.

409 100 f. Type **130** . . . . 1·00 45
410 150 f. "Archangel Israfil" (Iraq, 14th-cent.) (vert) . . . . . 1·50 70
411 200 f. "Horsemen" (Iraq, 1210) 2·25 1·25

131 Louis Armstrong
132 "Children of All Races"

1971. Air. Death of Louis Armstrong (American jazz musician). Multicoloured.

412 100 f. Type **131** . . . . 1·50 55
413 150 f. Armstrong playing trumpet . . . . 2·00 85

1971. 25th Anniv of U.N.I.C.E.F.

414 **132** 50 f. multicoloured 60 45

133 "Adoration of the Magi" (Di Bartolo)

1971. Air. Christmas. Paintings. Multicoloured.

415 100 f. Type **133** . . . . . . 1·00 45
416 150 f. "The Nativity" (D. Ghirlandaio) (vert) . . . . 1·50 70
417 200 f. "Adoration of the Shepherds" (Perugino) . . . 2·00 1·00

134 Presidents Pompidou and Hamani

1972. Air. Visit of Pres. Pompidou of France.

418 **134** 250 f. multicoloured . . . 4·75 3·50

135 Ski "Gate" and Cherry Blossom

1972. Air. Winter Olympic Games, Sapporo, Japan.

419 **135** 100 f. violet, red & green . 90 40
420 – 150 f. red, purple & violet 1·25 70
DESIGN—HORIZ: 150 f. Snow crystals and Olympic flame.

1972. Air. U.N.E.S.C.O. "Save Venice" Campaign. As T **145** of Senegal.

422 50 f. multicoloured (vert) . . 50 25
423 100 f. multicoloured (vert) . . 1·00 45
424 150 f. multicoloured (vert) . . 1·50 70
425 200 f. multicoloured . . . . . 2·00 1·00
DESIGNS: Nos. 422/5 depict various details of Guardi's painting, "The Masked Ball".

136 Johannes Brahms and Music
137 Saluting Hand

1972. Air. 75th Death Anniv of Johannes Brahms (composer).

426 **136** 100 f. green, myrtle and red 1·50 55

1972. Air. Int Scout Seminar, Cotonou, Dahomey.

427 **137** 150 f. violet, blue & orange 1·50 60

138 Star Symbol and Open Book

1972. International Book Year.

428 **138** 35 f. purple and green . . 35 20
429 – 40 f. blue and lake . . . 1·00 25
DESIGN: 40 f. Boy reading, galleon and early aircraft.

139 Heart Operation

1972. Air. World Heart Month.

430 **139** 100 f. brown and red . . 1·50 55

140 Bleriot XI crossing the Channel, 1909

1972. Air. Milestones in Aviation History.
431 **140** 50 f. brown, blue & lake . 1·10 50
432 – 75 f. grey, brown & blue . 1·75 60
433 – 100 f. ultramarine, blue and purple . . . . 3·25 1·40
DESIGNS: 75 f. Lindbergh crossing the Atlantic in "Spirit of St. Louis"; 100 f. First flight of Concorde, 1969.

141 Satellite and Universe

1972. Air. World Telecommunications Day.
434 **141** 100 f. brown, purple & red 1·10 45

142 Boxing

1972. Air. Olympic Games, Munich. Sports and Munich Buildings.
435 **142** 50 f. brown and blue . . . 50 20
436 – 100 f. brown and green . . 75 40
437 – 150 f. brown and red . . . 1·25 60
438 – 200 f. brown and mauve . . 1·75 85
DESIGNS—VERT: 100 f. Long-jumping; 150 f. Football. HORIZ: 200 f. Running.

143 A. G. Bell and Telephone

1972. Air. 50th Death Anniv of Alexander Graham Bell (inventor of telephone).
440 **143** 100 f. blue, purple and red 1·10 55

144 "Europe on Africa" Map

1972. Air. "Europafrique" Co-operation.
441 **144** 50 f. red, green and blue . . . 50 25

145 Herdsman and Cattle

146 Lottery Wheel

1972. Medicinal Salt-Ponds at In-Gall. Multicoloured.
442 35 f. Type **145** 50 25
443 40 f. Cattle in salt-pond . . . 60 25

1972. 6th Anniv of National Lottery.
444 **146** 35 f. multicoloured . . . 35 25

147 Postal Runner

1972. Air. U.P.U. Day. Postal Transport.
445 **147** 50 f. brown, green & lake 60 25
446 – 100 f. green, blue & lake . 90 45
447 – 150 f. green, violet & lake 1·75 70
DESIGNS: 100 f. Rural mail van; 150 f. Loading Fokker Friendship mail plane.

1972. 10th Anniv of West African Monetary Union. As T **149** of Mauritania.
448 40 f. grey, violet and brown . . 40 25

1972. Air. Gold Medal Winners. Munich Olympic Games. Nos. 435/8 optd with events and names, etc.
449 **142** 50 f. brown and blue . . 50 20
450 – 100 f. brown and green . . 85 40
451 – 150 f. brown and red . . 1·40 60
452 – 200 f. brown and mauve . 1·75 80
OVERPRINTS: 50 f. **WELTER CORREA MEDAILLE D'OR**; 100 f. **TRIPLE SAUT SANEIEV MEDAILLE D'OR**; 150 f. **FOOTBALL POLOGNE MEDAILLE D'OR**; 200 f. **MARATHON SHORTER MEDAILLE D'OR**.

148 "The Raven and the Fox"

1972. Air. Fables of Jean de la Fontaine.
453 **148** 25 f. black, brown & grn 1·25 40
454 – 50 f. brown, green & pur 60 25
455 – 75 f. brown, green & brn 1·00 45
DESIGNS: 50 f. "The Lion and the Rat"; 75 f. "The Monkey and the Leopard".

149 Astronauts on Moon

1972. Air. Moon Flight of "Apollo 17".
456 **149** 250 f. multicoloured . . . 2·75 1·25

150 Dromedary Race **151** Pole-vaulting

1972. Niger Sports.
457 **150** 35 f. purple, red and blue 75 40
458 – 40 f. lake, brown & green 1·00 60
DESIGN: 40 f. Horse race.

1973. 2nd African Games, Lagos, Nigeria. Mult.
459 35 f. Type **151** 30 25
460 40 f. Basketball 35 25
461 45 f. Boxing 45 25
462 75 f. Football 70 45

152 "Young Athlete" **153** Knight and Pawn

1973. Air. Antique Art Treasures.
463 **152** 50 f. red 50 25
464 – 100 f. violet . . . . 1·00 40
DESIGN: 100 f. "Head of Hermes".

1973. World Chess Championships, Reykjavik, Iceland.
465 **153** 100 f. green, blue & red . 2·50 1·00

154 "Abutilon pannosum" **155** Interpol Badge

1973. Rare African Flowers. Multicoloured.
466 30 f. Type **154** 70 30
467 45 f. "Crotalaria barkae" . . 80 30
468 60 f. "Dichrostachys cinerea" . 1·40 45
469 80 f. "Caralluma decaisneana" 1·60 55

1973. 50th Anniv of International Criminal Police Organization (Interpol).
470 **155** 50 f. multicoloured 85 30

156 Scout with Radio

1973. Air. Scouting in Niger.
471 **156** 25 f. brown, green & red . 25 20
472 – 50 f. brown, green & red . 55 25
473 – 100 f. brown, green & red . 1·25 50
474 – 150 f. brown, green & red . 1·60 70
DESIGNS: 50 f. First Aid; 100 f. Care of animals; 150 f. Care of the environment.

157 Hansen and Microscope **158** Nurse tending Child

1973. Centenary of Dr. Hansen's Discovery of Leprosy Bacillus.
475 **157** 50 f. brown, green & blue . 85 35

1973. 25th Anniv of W.H.O.
476 **158** 50 f. brown, red and blue . 65 25

159 "The Crucifixion" (Hugo van der Goes)

1973. Air. Easter. Paintings. Multicoloured.
477 50 f. Type **159** 55 25
478 100 f. "The Deposition" (Cima de Conegliano) (horiz) . . . 1·10 50
479 150 f. "Pieta" (Bellini) (horiz) . 1·60 65

160 Douglas DC-8 and Mail Van

1973. Air. Stamp Day.
480 **160** 100 f. brown, red & green . 1·50 55

161 W.M.O. Emblem and "Weather Conditions"

1973. Air. Centenary of W.M.O.
481 **161** 100 f. brown, red & grn . 1·10 45

162 "Crouching Lioness" (Delacroix)

1973. Air. Paintings by Delacroix. Multicoloured.
482 130 f. Type **162** . . . . . . 2·00 1·00
483 200 f. "Tigress and Cub" . . . 3·25 1·50

163 Crocodile

1973. Wild Animals from "Park W".
484 **163** 25 f. multicoloured . . . 45 20
485 – 35 f. grey, gold and black 75 30
486 – 40 f. multicoloured . . . 75 30
487 – 80 f. multicoloured . . . 1·25 50
DESIGNS: 35 f. African elephant; 40 f. Hippopotamus; 80 f. Warthog.

164 Eclipse over Mountain

1973. Total Eclipse of the Sun.
488 **164** 40 f. violet 60 30

1973. Air. 24th International Scouting Congress, Nairobi, Kenya. Nos. 473/4 optd **24 Conference Mondiale du Scoutisme NAIROBI, 1973.**
489 100 f. brown, green and red . 1·00 40
490 150 f. brown, green and red . 1·50 60

166 Palomino

1973. Horse-breeding. Multicoloured.
491 50 f. Type **166** 90 30
492 75 f. French trotter . . . . . 1·40 40
493 80 f. English thoroughbred . . 1·50 55
494 100 f. Arab thoroughbred . . . 2·00 65

1973. Pan-African Drought Relief. African Solidarity. No. 436 surch **SECHERESSE SOLIDARITE AFRICAINE** and value.
495 **145** 100 f. on 35 f. multicoloured 1·40 1·00

168 Rudolf Diesel and Engine

1973. 60th Death Anniv of Rudolf Diesel (engineer).
496 **168** 25 f. blue, purple & grey . 55 35
497 – 50 f. grey, green & blue . 95 50
498 – 75 f. blue, black & mauve . 1·40 75
499 – 125 f. blue, red & green . 2·40 90
DESIGNS: 50 f. Type "BB-610 ch" diesel locomotive; 75 f. Type "060-DB" diesel locomotive; 125 f. Type "CC-72004" diesel locomotive.

1973. African and Malagasy Posts and Telecommunications Union. As T **155a** of Mauritania.
500 100 f. red, green and brown . 75 50

168a African Mask and Old Town Hall, Brussels **169** T.V. Set and Class

1973. Air. African Fortnight, Brussels.
501 **168a** 100 f. purple, blue and red 1·00 50

1973. Schools Television Service.
502 **169** 50 f. black, red and blue . . 60 30

1973. 3rd International French Language and Culture Conf., Liege. No. 385 optd **3e CONFERENCE DE LA FRANCOPHONIE LIEGE OCTOBRE 1973.**
503 **110** 40 f. multicoloured . . . 50 25

171 "Apollo" **172** Bees and Honeycomb

1973. Classical Sculptures.
504 **171** 50 f. green and brown . . 60 30
505 – 50 f. black and brown . . 60 30
506 – 50 f. brown and red . . . 60 30
507 – 50 f. purple and red . . . 60 30
DESIGNS: No. 505, "Atlas"; No. 506, "Hercules";. No. 507, "Venus".

1973. World Savings Day.
508 **172** 40 f. brown, red and blue . 45 25

173 "Food for the World" **174** Copernicus and "Sputnik 1"

1973. Air. 10th Anniv of World Food Programme.
509 **173** 50 f. violet, red and blue . 60 30

1973. Air. 500th Birth Anniv of Copernicus (astonomer).
510 **174** 150 f. brown, blue and red 1·40 70

175 Pres. John Kennedy

1973. Air. 10th Death Anniv of U.S. President Kennedy.
511 **175** 100 f. multicoloured . . . 1·00 50

176 Kounta Songhai Blanket **178** Lenin

177 Barges on River Niger

1973. Niger Textiles. Multicoloured.
513 35 f. Type **176** 50 30
514 40 f. Tcherka Snghai blanket (horiz) 70 40

1974. Air. 1st Anniv of Ascent of Niger by "Fleet of Hope".
515 **177** 50 f. blue, green and red . 75 35
516 – 75 f. purple, blue and green 1·00 45
DESIGN: 75 f. "Barban Maza" (tug) and barge.

1974. Air. 50th Death Anniv of Lenin.
517 **178** 50 c. brown 50 30

179 Slalom Skiing

1974. Air. 50th Anniv of Winter Olympic Games.
518 **179** 200 f. red, brown & blue 2·50 1·00

180 Newly-born Baby

1974. World Population Year.
519 **180** 50 f. multicoloured . . . 50 25

181 Footballers and "Global" Ball

1974. Air. World Cup Football Championships, West Germany.
520 **181** 75 f. violet, black and brn 65 35
521 – 150 f. brown, green & turq 1·40 55
522 – 200 f. blue, orange & green 1·75 1·00
DESIGNS: 150f., 200 f. Football scenes similar to Type **181**.

182 "The Crucifixion" (Grunewald)

1974. Air. Easter. Paintings. Multicoloured.
524 50 f. Type **182** 50 25
525 75 f. "Avignon Pieta" (attributed to E. Quarton) 75 35
526 125 f. "The Entombment" (G. Isenmann) . . . . . . 1·25 65

183 Locomotive No. 230k (1948) and U.S.A. Loco No. 2222 (1938)

1974. Famous Railway Locomotives of the Steam Era.
527 **183** 50 f. green, black & violet 80 35
528 – 75 f. green, black & brown 1·25 45
529 – 100 f. multicoloured . . . 1·75 70
530 – 150 f. brown, black & red 2·50 1·00
DESIGNS: 75 f. P.L.M. loco No. C21 (1893); 100 f. U.S.A. "220" (1866) and British "231" (1939) class locomotives; 150 f. Seguin locomotive (1821) and Stephenson's "Rocket" (1829).

184 Map of Member Countries **185** Knights

1974. 15th Anniv of Conseil de l'Entente.
531 **184** 40 f. multicoloured . . . 40 20

1974. Air. 21st Chess Olympiad, Nice.
532 **185** 50 f. brown, blue & indigo 1·25 65
533 – 75 f. purple, brown & green 1·75 75
DESIGN: 75 f. Kings.

186 Marconi and "Elettra" (steam yacht)

1974. Birth Centenary of Guglielmo Marconi (radio pioneer).
534 **186** 50 f. blue, brown & mauve 50 30

187 Astronaut on Palm of Hand **188** Tree on Palm of Hand

1974. Air. 5th Anniv of 1st Landing on Moon.
535 **187** 150 f. brown, blue & ind . 1·25 60

1974. National Tree Week.
536 **188** 35 f. turquoise, grn & brn . 40 30

189 "The Rhinoceros" (Longhi) **190** Camel Saddle

1974. Air. Europafrique.
537 **189** 250 f. multicoloured . . . 5·00 3·00

1974. Handicrafts.
538 **190** 40 f. red, blue & brown . . 45 20
539 – 50 f. blue, red and brown . 55 30
DESIGN: 50 f. Statuettes of horses.

192 Frederic Chopin

1974. 125th Death Anniv of Frederic Chopin.
541 **192** 100 f. black, red & blue . . 1·50 55

1974. Beethoven's Ninth Symphony Commemoration. As T **192**.
542 100 f. lilac, blue and indigo . . 1·50 55
DESIGN: 100 f. Beethoven.

193 European Woman and Douglas DC-8 Airliners **194** "Skylab" over Africa

1974. Air. Centenary of U.P.U.
543 **193** 50 f. turquoise, grn & pur . 50 25
544 – 100 f. blue, mauve & ultram 1·50 60
545 – 150 f. brown, blue & indigo 1·50 80
546 – 200 f. brown, orange & red 1·60 1·25
DESIGNS: 100 f. Japanese woman and electric locomotives; 150 f. American Indian woman and liner; 200 f. African woman and road vehicles.

1974. Air. "Skylab" Space Laboratory.
547 **194** 100 f. violet, brown & blue 1·00 45

195 Don-don Drum **197** "Virgin and Child" (Correggio)

196 Tree and Compass Rose

1974.
548 **195** 60 f. purple, green & red . 90 45

1974. 1st Death Anniv of Tenere Tree (desert landmark).
549 **196** 50 f. brown, blue and ochre 2·00 1·00

1974. Air. Christmas. Multicoloured.
550 100 f. Type **197** . . . . 1·00 35
551 150 f. "Virgin and Child, and St. Hilary" (F. Lippi) . . . . . 1·50 55
552 200 f. "Virgin and Child" (Murillo) . . . . 2·00 95

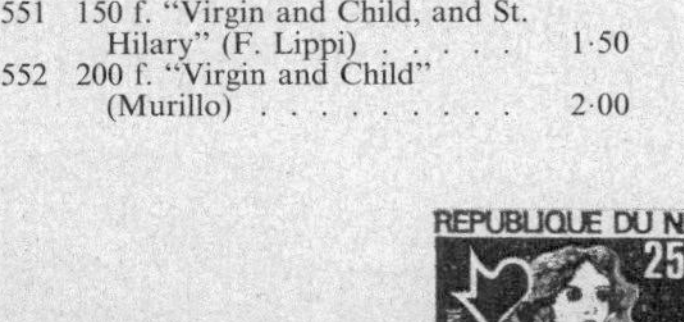

198 "Apollo" Spacecraft **199** European and African Women

1975. Air. "Apollo–Soyuz" Space Test Project.
553 **198** 50 f. green, red and blue . 50 25
554 – 100 f. grey, red and blue . 80 40
555 – 150 f. purple, plum & blue 1·25 60
DESIGNS: 100 f. "Apollo" and "Soyuz" docked; 150 f. "Soyuz" spacecraft.

1975. Air. Europafrique.
556 **199** 250 f. brown, purple & red 2·25 1·75

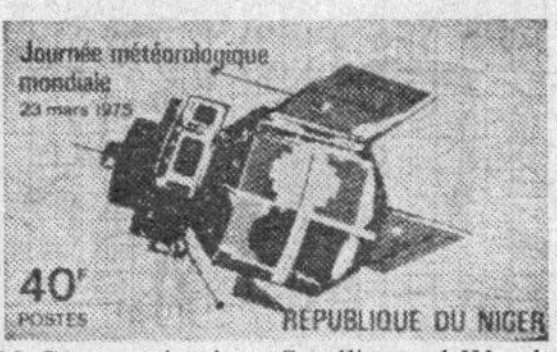

200 Communications Satellite and Weather Map

1975. World Meteorological Day.
557 **200** 40 f. red, black and blue . 40 20

201 "Christ in the Garden of Olives" (Delacroix)

1975. Air. Easter. Multicoloured.
558 75 f. Type **201** 65 35
559 125 f. "The Crucifixion" (El Greco) (vert) . . . . 1·10 50
560 150 f. "The Resurrection" (Limousin) (vert) . . . . . 1·25 75

202 Lt-Col. S. Kountche, Head of State

1975. Air. 1st Anniv of Military Coup.
561 **202** 100 f. multicoloured . . . 1·00 50

203 "City of Truro" (G.W.R., England, 1903)

1975. Famous Locomotives. Multicoloured.
562 50 f. Type **203** 85 35
563 75 f. No. 5003 (Germany, 1937) 1·10 50
564 100 f. "The General" (U.S.A., 1863) . . . . 1·75 75
565 125 f. "BB-15000" Electric (France, 1971) . . . . . . 2·00 90

1975. Birds. As Nos. 296 and 298, but dated "1975". Multicoloured.
567 25 f. Abyssinian Roller (postage) 85 20
568 100 f. Violet Starlings (air) . . 1·90 60

205 "Zabira" Leather Bag **206** African Woman and Child

1975. Niger Handicrafts. Multicoloured.
569 35 f. Type **205** 30 20
570 40 f. Chequered rug 45 25
571 45 f. Flower pot 50 30
572 60 f. Gourd 75 35

1975. International Women's Year.
573 **206** 50 f. blue, brown & red . . 75 50

207 Dr. Schweitzer and Lambarene Hospital

1975. Birth Centenary of Dr. Albert Schweitzer.
574 **207** 100 f. brown, green & blk 1·00 55

208 Peugeot, 1892

1975. Early Motor-cars.
575 **208** 50 f. blue and mauve . . . 60 30
576 – 75 f. purple and blue . . . 1·00 40
577 – 100 f. mauve and green . 1·40 60
578 – 125 f. green and red . . . 1·50 70
DESIGNS: 75 f. Daimler, 1895; 100 f. Fiat, 1899; 125 f. Cadillac, 1903.

HAVE YOU READ THE NOTES AT THE BEGINNING OF THIS CATALOGUE?
These often provide the answers to the enquiries we receive.

209 Tree and Sun **211** Leontini Tetradrachme

210 Boxing

1975. National Tree Week.
579 **209** 40 f. green, orange and red 40 25

1975. Traditional Sports.
580 **210** 35 f. brown, orange & blk 35 20
581 – 40 f. brown, green & blk 40 20
582 – 45 f. brown, blue & black 50 25
583 – 50 f. brown, red and black 55 30
DESIGNS—VERT: 40 f. Boxing; 50 f. Wrestling. HORIZ: 45 f. Wrestling.

1975. Ancient Coins.
584 **211** 50 f. grey, blue and red . 60 20
585 – 75 f. grey, blue & mauve 85 30
586 – 100 f. grey, orange & blue 1·25 40
587 – 125 f. grey, purple & green 1·50 60
COINS: 75 f. Athens tetradrachme; 100 f. Himer diadrachme; 125 f. Gela tetradrachme.

212 Putting the Shot

1975. Air. "Pre-Olympic Year". Olympic Games, Montreal (1976).
588 **212** 150 f. brown and red . . 1·10 55
589 – 200 f. red, chestnut and brown . . . . 1·50 85
DESIGN: 200 f. Gymnastics.

213 Starving Family

1975. Pan-African Drought Relief.
590 **213** 40 f. blue, brown & orange 55 30
591 – 45 f. brown and blue . . 1·10 50
592 – 60 f. blue, green & orange 1·00 40
DESIGNS: 45 f. Animal skeletons; 60 f. Truck bringing supplies.

214 Trading Canoe crossing R. Niger

1975. Tourism. Multicoloured.
593 40 f. Type **214** 50 25
594 45 f. Boubon Camp entrance 55 25
595 50 f. Boubon Camp view . . 60 35

215 U N Emblem and Peace Dove

1975. Air. 30th Anniv of U.N.O.
596 **215** 100 f. light blue and blue 85 40

216 "Virgin of Seville" (Murillo)

1975. Air. Christmas. Multicoloured.
597 50 f. Type **216** 50 35
598 75 f. "Adoration of the Shepherds" (Tintoretto) (horiz) 75 45
599 125 f. "Virgin with Angels" (Master of Burgo d'Osma) . 1·25 75

1975. Air. "Apollo-Soyuz" Space Link. Nos. 533/5 optd **JONCTION 17 Juillet 1975.**
600 **198** 50 f. green, red and blue . 50 25
601 – 100 f. grey, red and blue . 75 45
602 – 150 f. purple, plum & blue 1·25 75

218 "Ashak"

1976. Literacy Campaign. Multicoloured.
603 25 f. Type **218** 15 10
604 30 f. "Kaska" 20 15
605 40 f. "Iccee" 25 15
606 50 f. "Tuuri-nya" 30 20
607 60 f. "Lekki" 35 25

219 Ice-hockey

1976. Winter Olympic Games, Innsbruck, Austria. Multicoloured.
608 40 f. Type **219** (postage) . . . 35 20
609 50 f. Tobogganing 40 20
610 150 f. Ski-jumping . . . . . . 1·25 50
611 200 f. Figure-skating (air) . . . 1·50 75
612 300 f. Cross-country skiing . . 2·00 1·00

220 Early Telephone and Satellite

1976. Telephone Centenary.
614 **220** 100 f. orange, blue & green 85 50

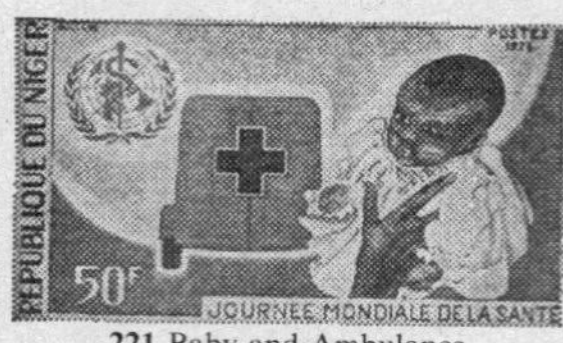

221 Baby and Ambulance

1976. World Health Day.
615 **221** 50 f. red, brown & purple . 50 25

222 Washington crossing the Delaware (after Leutze)

1976. Bicent. of American Revolution. Multicoloured.
616 40 f. Type **222** (postage) . . . 30 15
617 50 f. First soldiers of the Revolution 40 20
618 150 f. Joseph Warren – martyr of Bunker Hill (air) . . . . . 1·10 35
619 200 f. John Paul Jones aboard the "Bonhomme Richard" . 1·50 60
620 300 f. Molly Pitcher – heroine of Monmouth . . . . 2·00 90

223 Distribution of Provisions **225** "Europafrique" Symbols

224 "Hindenburg" crossing Lake Constance

1976. 2nd Anniv of Military Coup. Multicoloured.
622 50 f. Type **223** 35 25
623 100 f. Soldiers with bulldozer (horiz) . . . . 1·10 45

1976. Air. 75th Anniv of Zeppelin Airships. Multicoloured.
624 40 f. Type **224** 40 15
625 50 f. LZ-3 over Wurzberg . . 50 25
626 150 f. L-9 over Friedrichshafen 1·40 55
627 200 f. LZ-2 over Rothenburg (vert) . . . . 1·75 70
628 300 f. "Graf Zeppelin II" over Essen . . . . 3·25 85

1976. "Europafrique".
630 **225** 100 f. multicoloured . . . 1·40 50

226 Plant Cultivation

1976. Communal Works. Multicoloured.
631 25 f. Type **226** 15 10
632 30 f. Harvesting rice 20 15

227 Boxing

1976. Olympic Games, Montreal. Multicoloured.
633 40 f. Type **227** 25 15
634 50 f. Basketball 40 20
635 60 f. Football 45 25
636 80 f. Cycling (horiz) 60 20
637 100 f. Judo (horiz) 70 30

228 Motobecane '125'

1976. Motorcycles.

639 **228** 50 f. violet, brown & turq . . . 60 25
640 – 75 f. green, red & turq . . 85 35
641 – 100 f. brown, orge & pur . 1·25 50
642 – 125 f. slate, olive & black . 1·50 75

DESIGNS: 75 f. Norton "Challenge"; 100 f. B.M.W. "903"; 125 f. Kawasaki "1000".

229 Cultivation Map

1976. Operation "Sahel Vert". Multicoloured.

643 40 f. Type **229** 30 15
644 45 f. Tending plants (vert) . . 35 20
645 60 f. Planting sapling (vert) . . 55 30

1976. International Literacy Day. Nos. 603/7 optd **JOURNEE INTERNATIONALE DE L'ALPHABETISATION**.

646 **218** 25 f. multicoloured . . . 15 15
647 – 30 f. multicoloured . . . 15 15
648 – 40 f. multicoloured . . . 20 15
649 – 50 f. multicoloured . . . 25 20
650 – 60 f. multicoloured . . . 30 20

231 Basket Making

1976. Niger Women's Association. Multicoloured.

651 40 f. Type **231** 35 20
652 45 f. Hairdressing (horiz) . . . 40 25
653 50 f. Making pottery 50 35

232 Wall Paintings

1976. "Archaeology". Multicoloured.

654 40 f. Type **232** 45 25
655 50 f. Neolithic statuettes . . . 50 25
656 60 f. Dinosaur skeleton . . . 90 35

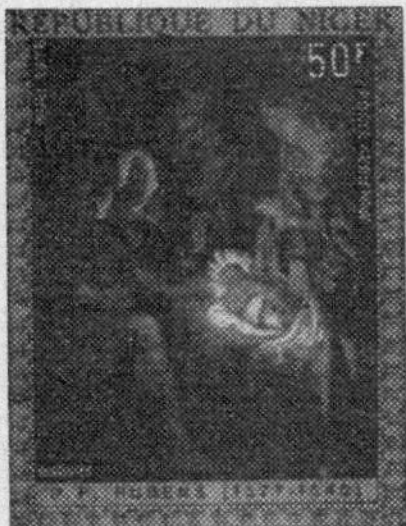

233 "The Nativity" (Rubens)

234 Benin Ivory Mask

1976. Air. Christmas. Multicoloured.

657 50 f. Type **233** 50 25
658 100 f. "Holy Night" (Correggio) 1·10 45
659 150 f. "Adoration of the Magi" (David) (horiz) . . . . . . 1·50 90

1977. 2nd World Festival of Negro-African Arts, Lagos.

660 **234** 40 f. brown 40 20
661 – 50 f. blue 60 30

DESIGNS—HORIZ: 50 f. Nigerian stick dance.

235 Students in Class **236** Examining Patient

1977. Alphabetisation Campaign.

662 **235** 40 f. multicoloured . . . 30 15
663 50 f. multicoloured . . . 40 20
664 60 f. multicoloured . . . 60 20

1977. Village Health. Multicoloured.

665 40 f. Type **236** 50 20
666 50 f. Examining baby 60 30

237 Rocket Launch

1977. "Viking" Space Mission. Multicoloured.

667 50 f. Type **237** (postage) . . . 45 15
668 80 f. "Viking" approaching Mars (horiz) 65 20
669 100 f. "Viking" on Mars (horiz) (air) 65 25
670 150 f. Parachute descent . . . 1·00 30
671 200 f. Rocket in flight . . . . 1·40 45

238 Marabou Stork

1977. Fauna Protection.

673 **238** 80 f. sepia, bis and red . . 1·50 75
674 – 90 f. brown and turquoise 1·25 60

DESIGN: 90 f. Bushbuck.

239 Satellite and Weather Symbols

1977. World Meteorological Day.

675 **239** 100 f. blue, black & turq 1·00 50

240 Gymnastic Exercise

1977. 2nd Youth Festival, Tahoua. Multicoloured.

676 40 f. Type **240** 35 20
677 50 f. High jumping 40 25
678 80 f. Choral ensemble 70 35

241 Red Cross and Children playing

1977. World Health Day. Child Immunisation Campaign.

679 **241** 80 f. red, mauve & orange 75 35

242 Fly, Dagger, and W.H.O. Emblem in Eye

1977. Fight against Onchocerosis (blindness caused by worm infestation).

680 **242** 100 f. blue, grey and red . 1·40 55

243 Guirka Tahoua Dance

1977. "Popular Arts and Traditions". Multicoloured.

681 40 f. Type **243** 45 25
682 50 f. Maifilafili Gaya 50 20
683 80 f. Naguihinayan Loga . . . 80 45

244 Four Cavalrymen

1977. Chiefs' Traditional Cavalry. Multicoloured.

684 40 f. Type **244** 55 25
685 50 f. Chieftain at head of cavalry 65 30
686 60 f. Chieftain and cavalry . . 90 45

245 Planting Crops

1977. "Operation Green Sahel" (recovery of desert).

687 **245** 40 f. multicoloured 50 25

246 Albert John Luthuli (Peace, 1960)

1977. Nobel Prize Winners. Multicoloured.

688 50 f. Type **246** 30 15
689 80 f. Maurice Maeterlinck (Literature, 1911) 55 20
690 100 f. Allan L. Hodgkin (Medicine, 1963) 70 25
691 150 f. Albert Camus (Literature, 1957) . . . . 1·00 35
692 200 f. Paul Ehrlich (Medicine, 1908) . . . . 1·50 40

247 Mao Tse-tung

1977. 1st Death Anniv of Mao Tse-tung (Chinese leader).

694 **247** 100 f. black and red . . . 80 50

248 Vittorio Pozzo (Italy)

1977. World Football Cup Elimination Rounds. Multicoloured.

695 40 f. Type **248** 30 10
696 50 f. Vincente Feola, Spain . . 35 15
697 80 f. Aymore Moreira, Portugal 50 20
698 100 f. Sir Alf Ramsey, England 75 25
699 200 f. Helmut Schon, West Germany . . . . 1·40 45

249 Horse's Head and Parthenon

1977. U.N.E.S.C.O. Commemoration.

701 **249** 100 f. blue, red and pale blue 1·25 60

250 Carrying Water

1977. Women's Work. Multicoloured.

702 40 f. Type **250** 35 30
703 50 f. Pounding maize 40 25

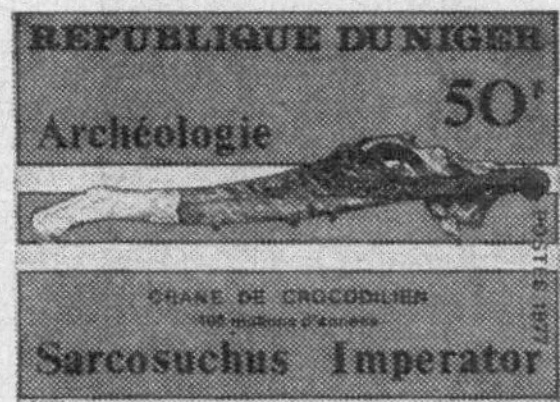

251 Crocodile Skull

1977. Archaeology. Multicoloured.

704 50 f. Type **251** 60 40
705 80 f. Neolithic tools 90 60

252 Paul Follereau and Leper **253** "The Assumption"

1978. 25th Anniv of World Leprosy Day.

706 **252** 40 f. red, blue & orange . 30 15
707 – 50 f. black, red & orange 40 20

DESIGN—HORIZ: 50 f. Follereau and two lepers.

1978. 400th Birth Anniv of Peter Paul Rubens. Paintings. Multicoloured.

708 50 f. Type **253** 30 15
709 70 f. "The Artist and his Friends" (horiz) 40 20
710 100 f. "History of Maria de Medici" 70 25
711 150 f. "Alathea Talbot" . . . 1·10 35
712 200 f. "Portrait of the Marquise de Spinola" . . . . 1·50 40

1978. As Nos. 376/7 but redrawn and background colour of 35 f. changed to blue, 35 f. undated, 50 f. dated "1978".

714 35 f. Broad-tailed paradise whydah 80 35
715 50 f. Cattle egret . . . . . . 1·50 45

The 50 f. is still wrongly inscribed "Balbucus".

254 Putting the Shot

1978. National Schools and University Sports Championships. Multicoloured.

716 40 f. Type **254** 20 15
717 50 f. Volleyball 30 20
718 60 f. Long-jumping 35 20
719 100 f. Throwing the javelin . . 55 35

255 Nurse assisting Patient

1978. Niger Red Cross.

720 **255** 40 f. multicoloured . . . 30 20

256 Station and Dish Aerial

1978. Goudel Earth Receiving Station.

721 **256** 100 f. multicoloured . . . 65 40

257 Football and Flags of Competing Nations

1978. World Cup Football Championship, Argentina. Multicoloured.

722 40 f. Type **257** 25 10
723 50 f. Football in net 35 15
724 100 f. Globe and goal 75 25
725 200 f. Tackling (horiz) . . . . 1·40 55

258 "Fireworks"

1978. Air. 3rd African Games, Algiers. Multicoloured.

727 40 f. Type **258** 25 20
728 150 f. Olympic rings emblem . 1·00 60

259 Niamey Post Office

1978. Niamey Post Office. Multicoloured.

729 40 f. Type **259** 25 15
730 60 f. Niamey Post Office (different) 35 25

260 Aerial View of Water-works

1978. Goudel Water-works.

731 **260** 100 f. multicoloured . . . 55 40

261 R. T. N. Emblem

1978. Air. 20th Anniv of Niger Broadcasting.

732 **261** 150 f. multicoloured . . . 90 60

262 Golden Eagle and Oldenburg 2 g. Stamp of 1859

1978. Air. "Philexafrique" Stamp Exhibition, Libreville, Gabon (1st issue) and Int Stamp Fair, Essen, West Germany. Multicoloured.

733 100 f. Type **262** . . . . . . 1·50 1·25
734 100 f. Giraffes and Niger 1959 2 f. stamp . . . . 1·50 1·25

See also Nos. 769/70

263 Giraffe

265 Dome of the Rock, Jerusalem

1978. Endangered Animals. Multicoloured.

735 40 f. Type **263** 45 25
736 50 f. Ostrich . . . . 1·25 30
737 70 f. Cheetah 75 35
738 150 f. Scimitar oryx (horiz) . . 1·50 75
739 200 f. Addax (horiz) . . . . 2·00 95
740 300 f. Hartebeest (horiz) . . . 2·50 1·25

1978. World Cup Football Championship Finalists. Nos. 695/9 optd.

741 **248** 40 f. multicoloured . . . 30 20
742 – 50 f. multicoloured . . . 40 20
743 – 80 f. multicoloured . . . 55 25
744 – 100 f. multicoloured . . . 65 40
745 – 200 f. multicoloured . . . 1·40 75

OVERPRINTS: 40 f. **EQUIPE QUATRIEME: ITALIE**; 50 f. **EQUIPE TROISIEME: BRESIL**; 80 f. **EQUIPE SECONDE: PAYS BAS**; 100 f. **EQUIPE VAINQUEUR: ARGENTINE**. 200 f. **ARGENTINE - PAYS BAS 3 - 1**.

1978. Palestinian Welfare.

747 **265** 40 f. + 5 f. multicoloured . . 40 30

266 Laying Foundation Stone, and View of University

1978. Air. Islamic University of Niger.

748 **266** 100 f. multicoloured . . . 60 40

267 Tinguizi

268 "The Homecoming" (Daumier)

1978. Musicians. Multicoloured.

749 100 f. Type **267** 75 40
750 100 f. Chetima Ganga (horiz) . 75 40
751 100 f. Dan Gourmou 75 40

1979. Paintings. Multicoloured.

752 50 f. Type **268** 50 20
753 100 f. "Virgin in Prayer" (Durer) 60 20
754 150 f. "Virgin and Child" (Durer) 90 30
755 200 f. "Virgin and Child" (Durer) (different) . . . . . 1·25 40

269 Feeder Tanks

1979. Solar Energy. Multicoloured.

757 40 f. Type **269** 30 20
758 50 f. Solar panels on house roofs (horiz) 40 25

270 Langha Contestants

1979. Traditional Sports. Multicoloured.

759 40 f. Type **270** 25 15
760 50 f. Langha contestants clasping hands 35 20

271 Children with Building Bricks

1979. International Year of the Child. Multicoloured.

761 40 f. Type **271** 25 15
762 100 f. Children with book . . 60 25
763 150 f. Children with model airplane . . . . 1·25 45

272 Rowland Hill, Peugeot Mail Van and French "Ceres" Stamp of 1849

1979. Death Centenary of Sir Rowland Hill. Multicoloured.

764 40 f. Type **272** 25 15
765 100 f. Canoes and Austrian newspaper stamp, 1851 . . . 60 25
766 150 f. "DC-3" aircraft & U.S. "Lincoln" stamp, 1869 . . . 1·10 35
767 200 f. British Advanced Passenger Train and Canada 7½d. stamp, 1857 . . . . . . 1·90 50

273 Zabira Decorated Bag and Niger 45 f. Stamp, 1965

1979. "Philexafrique 2" Exhibition, Gabon (2nd issue).

769 **273** 50 f. multicoloured . . . 65 40
770 – 150 f. blue, red & carmen 1·60 1·10

DESIGNS: 150 f. Talking Heads, world map, satellite and U.P.U. emblem.

274 Alcock and Brown Statue and Vickers Vimy aircraft

1979. 60th Anniv of First Transatlantic Flight.

771 **274** 100 f. multicoloured . . . 1·00 35

275 Djermakoye Palace

1979. Historic Monuments.

772 **275** 100 f. multicoloured . . . 55 40

276 Bororos in Festive Headdress

1979. Annual Bororo Festival. Multicoloured.

773 45 f. Type **276** 30 20
774 60 f. Bororo women in traditional costume (vert) . 35 25

277 Boxing

1979. Pre-Olympic Year.

775 **277** 45 f. multicoloured . . . 30 15
776 – 100 f. multicoloured . . . 55 25
777 – 150 f. multicoloured . . . 85 35
778 – 250 f. multicoloured . . . 1·25 45

DESIGNS: 100 f. to 250 f. Various boxing scenes.

278 Class of Learner-drivers

1979. Driving School.

780 **278** 45 f. multicoloured . . . 30 20

279 Douglas DC-10 over Map of Niger

1979. Air. 20th Anniv of ASECNA (African Air Safety Organization).

781	**279**	150 f. multicoloured . . .	1·10	60

1979. "Apollo 11" Moon Landing. Nos. 667/8, 670/1 optd **alunissage apollo XI juillet 1969** and lunar module.

782	50 f. Type **237** (postage) . . .	30	20
783	80 f. "Viking" approaching Mars (horiz)	50	35
784	150 f. Parachute descent (air) .	90	60
785	200 f. Rocket in flight	1·25	80

281 Four-man Bobsleigh

1979. Winter Olympic Games, Lake Placid (1980). Multicoloured.

787	40 f. Type **281**	25	15
788	60 f. Downhill skiing	35	15
789	100 f. Speed skating	60	25
790	150 f. Two-man bobsleigh . .	90	35
791	200 f. Figure skating	1·10	45

282 Le Gaweye Hotel

1980. Air.

793	**282**	100 f. multicoloured . . .	60	40

283 Sultan and Court

1980. Sultan of Zinder's Court. Multicoloured.

794	45 f. Type **283**	30	20
795	60 f. Sultan and court (different)	40	20

284 Chain Smoker and Athlete — 285 Walking

1980. World Health Day. Anti-Smoking Campaign.

796	**284**	100 f. multicoloured . . .	65	40

1980. Olympic Games, Moscow. Multicoloured.

797	60 f. Throwing the javelin . .	35	15
798	90 f. Type **285**	50	20
799	100 f. High jump (horiz) . . .	55	25
800	300 f. Running (horiz)	1·50	55

1980. Winter Olympic Games Medal Winners. Nos. 787/91 optd.

802	**281**	40 f. **VAINQUEUR R.D.A.**	25	15
803	–	60 f. **VAINQUEUR STENMARK SUEDE** .	30	20
804	–	100 f. **VAINQUEUR HEIDEN Etats-Unis** . .	60	30
805	–	150 f. **VAINQUEURS SCHERER-BENZ Suisse**	90	45
806	–	200 f. **VAINQUEUR COUSINS Grande Bretagne**	1·25	65

287 Village Scene

1980. Health Year.

808	**287**	150 f. multicoloured . . .	75	50

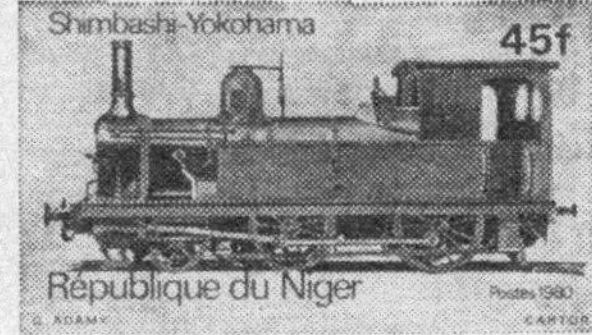

288 Shimbashi-Yokohama Steam Locomotive

1980. Steam Locomotives. Multicoloured.

809	45 f. Type **288**	50	15
810	60 f. American locomotive . .	60	20
811	90 f. German State Railway series 61	1·00	25
812	100 f. Prussian State Railway P2	1·25	40
813	130 f. "L'Aigle"	1·75	50

289 Steve Biko and Map of Africa — 292 U.A.P.T. Emblem

291 Footballer

1980. 4th Death Anniv of Steve Biko (South African Anti-apartheid Worker).

815	**289**	150 f. multicoloured . . .	80	60

1980. Olympic Medal Winners. Nos. 787/800 optd.

816	**285**	60 f. **KULA (URSS)** . .	35	15
817	–	90 f. **DAMILANO (IT)** .	55	25
818	–	100 f. **WZSOLA (POL)** .	60	30
819	–	300 f. **YIFTER (ETH)** . .	1·60	90

1980. World Cup Football Championship, Spain (1982). Various designs showing Football.

821	**291**	45 f. multicoloured . . .	25	15
822	–	60 f. multicoloured . . .	30	15
823	–	90 f. multicoloured . . .	55	20
824	–	100 f. multicoloured . . .	60	25
825	–	130 f. multicoloured . . .	80	30

1980. 5th Anniv of African Posts and Telecommunications Union.

827	**292**	100 f. multicoloured . . .	55	40

293 Earthenware Statuettes

1981. Kareygorou Culture Terracotta Statuettes. Multicoloured.

828	45 f. Type **293**	25	20
829	60 f. Head (vert)	35	20
830	90 f. Head (different) (vert) .	50	30
831	150 f. Three heads	90	50

294 "Self-portrait" — 295 Ostrich

1981. Paintings by Rembrandt. Multicoloured.

832	60 f. Type **294**	40	15
833	90 f. "Portrait of Hendrickje at the Window"	60	20
834	100 f. "Portrait of an Old Man"	65	25
835	130 f. "Maria Trip"	90	35
836	200 f. "Self-portrait" (different)	1·25	45
837	400 f. "Portrait of Saskia" . .	2·25	1·00

1981. Animals. Multicoloured.

839	10 f. Type **295**	50	15
840	20 f. Scimitar oryx	25	15
841	25 f. Addra gazelle	20	15
842	30 f. Arabian bustard	85	30
843	60 f. Giraffe	50	20
844	150 f. Addax	1·00	45

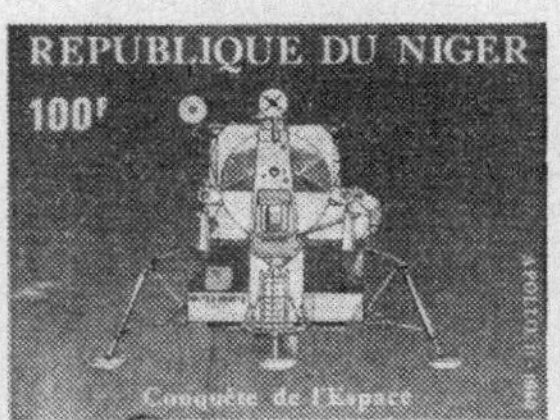

296 "Apollo 11"

1981. Air. Conquest of Space. Multicoloured.

845	100 f. Type **296**	60	25
846	150 f. Boeing 747 SCA carrying space shuttle	1·00	40
847	200 f. Rocket carrying space shuttle	1·25	40
848	300 f. Space shuttle flying over planet	3·00	1·00

297 Tanks — 298 Disabled Archer

1981. 7th Anniv of Military Coup.

849	**297**	100 f. multicoloured . . .	1·00	40

1981. International Year of Disabled People.

850	**298**	50 f. dp. brown, red & brown	50	20
851	–	100 f. brown, red and green	75	40

DESIGN: 100 f. Disabled draughtsman.

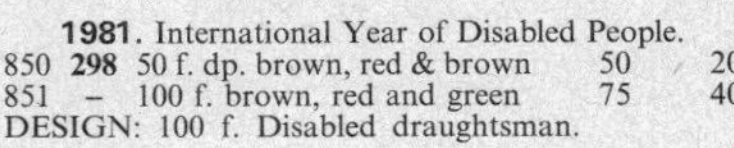

299 Ballet Mahalba

1981. Ballet Mahalba. Multicoloured.

852	100 f. Type **299**	70	35
853	100 f. Ballet Mahalba (different)	70	35

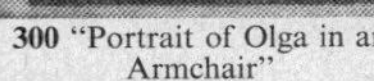

300 "Portrait of Olga in an Armchair" — 301 Mosque and Ka'aba

1981. Air. Birth Centenary of Pablo Picasso (artist). Multicoloured.

854	60 f. Type **300**	40	20
855	90 f. "The Family of Acrobats"	55	25
856	120 f. "The Three Musicians"	70	35
857	200 f. "Paul on a Donkey" .	1·10	55
858	400 f. "Young Girl drawing in an Interior" (horiz)	2·40	1·25

1981. 15th Centenary of Hejira.

859	**301**	100 f. multicoloured . . .	60	35

302 Carriage

1981. British Royal Wedding.

860	**302**	150 f. multicoloured . . .	60	35
861	–	200 f. multicoloured . . .	1·00	55
862	–	300 f. multicoloured . . .	1·25	1·00

DESIGNS: 200 f., 300 f. Similar designs showing carriages.

303 Sir Alexander Fleming — 305 Crops, Cattle and Fish

304 Pen-nibs, Envelope, Flower and U.P.U. Emblem

1981. Birth Centenary of Sir Alexander Fleming (discoverer of Penicillin).

864	**303**	150 f. blue, brown and green	1·25	50

1981. International Letter Writing Week.

865	**304**	65 f. on 45 f. blue and red	40	20
866	–	85 f. on 60 f. blue, orange and black	50	30

DESIGN: 85 f. Quill, hand holding pen and U.P.U. emblem.

1981. World Food Day.

867	**305**	100 f. multicoloured . . .	60	35

306 Tackling

1981. World Cup Football Championship, Spain (1982). Multicoloured.

868	40 f. Type **306**	25	20
869	65 f. Goal keeper fighting for ball	40	30
870	85 f. Passing ball	55	35
871	150 f. Running with ball . . .	1·00	60
872	300 f. Jumping for ball . . .	2·25	1·10

307 Peugeot, 1912

1981. 75th Anniv of French Grand Prix Motor Race. Multicoloured.

874	20 f. Type **307**	25	15
875	40 f. Bugatti, 1924	35	20
876	65 f. Lotus-Climax, 1962 . . .	55	30
877	85 f. Georges Boillot	75	35
878	150 f. Phil Hill	1·10	60

308 "Madonna and Child" (Botticelli) **309** Children watering Plants

1981. Christmas. Various Madonna and Child Paintings by named artists. Multicoloured.
880 100 f. Type **308** 60 40
881 200 f. Botticini . . . . 1·25 75
882 300 f. Botticini (different) . . 2·00 1·10

1982. School Gardens. Multicoloured.
883 65 f. Type **309** 50 30
884 85 f. Tending plants and examining produce 60 35

310 Arturo Toscanini (conductor, 25th death anniv)

1982. Celebrities' Anniversaries. Multicoloured.
885 120 f. Type **310** . . . . 1·00 45
886 140 f. "Fruits on a Table" (Manet, 150th birth anniv) (horiz) 80 55
887 200 f. "L'Estaque" (Braque, birth centenary) (horiz) . . 1·25 60
888 300 f. George Washington (250th birth anniv) . . . . 2·00 90
889 400 f. Goethe (poet, 150th death anniv) . . . . 2·50 1·25
890 500 f. Princess of Wales (21st birthday) . . . . 2·75 1·50

311 Palace of Congresses

1982. Palace of Congresses.
892 **311** 150 f. multicoloured . . . 90 60

312 Martial Arts

1982. 7th Youth Festival, Agadez. Multicoloured.
893 65 f. Type **312** 40 30
894 100 f. Traditional wrestling . . 60 40

313 Planting a Tree

1982. National Re-afforestation Campaign. Multicoloured.
895 150 f. Type **313** . . . . 1·00 60
896 200 f. Forest and desert . . . 1·25 75

MINIMUM PRICE

The minimum price quoted is 10p which represents a handling charge rather than a basis for valuing common stamps. For further notes about prices, see introductory pages.

314 Scouts in Pirogue **315** Map of Africa showing Member States

1982. 75th Anniv of Boy Scout Movement. Mult.
897 65 f. Type **314** 55 30
898 85 f. Scouts inflatable dinghy . 65 30
899 130 f. Scouts in canoe . . . . 1·25 45
900 200 f. Scouts on raft . . . . 1·75 60

1982. Economic Community of West African States.
902 **315** 200 f. yellow, black and blue 1·25 75

316 Casting Net

1982. Niger Fishermen. Multicoloured.
903 65 f. Type **316** 55 30
904 85 f. Net fishing 70 40

1982. Birth of Prince William of Wales. Nos. 860/2 optd **NAISSANCE ROYALE 1982**.
905 **302** 150 f. multicoloured . . . 75 60
906 – 200 f. multicoloured . . . 1·00 75
907 – 300 f. multicoloured . . . 1·40 1·10

318 Hands reaching towards Mosque

1982. 13th Islamic Foreign Ministers Meeting, Niamey.
909 **318** 100 f. multicoloured . . . 60 40

319 "Flautist"

1982. Norman Rockwell Paintings. Multicoloured.
910 65 f. Type **319** 40 25
911 85 f. "Clerk" 50 25
912 110 f. "Teacher and Pupil" . 70 35
913 150 f. "Girl Shopper" 90 50

320 World Map and Satellite

1982. I.T.U. Delegates' Conference, Nairobi.
914 **320** 130 f. blue, light blue and black . . . . 1·00 50

1982. World Cup Football Championship Winners. Nos. 868/72 optd.
915 40 f. Type **306** 25 20
916 65 f. Goal keeper fighting for ball 40 30
917 85 f. Passing ball 45 25
918 150 f. Running with ball . . 90 50
919 300 f. Jumping for ball . . . 1·75 1·10

OVERPRINTS: 40 f. **1966 VAINQUEUR GRANDE - BRETAGNE**; 65 f. **"1970 VAINQUEUR BRESIL"**; 85 f. **"1974 VAINQUEUR ALLEMAGNE (RFA)"**; 150 f. **"1978 VAINQUEUR ARGENTINE"**; 300 f. **"1982 VAINQUEUR ITALIE"**.

322 Laboratory Workers with Microscopes

1982. Laboratory Work. Multicoloured.
921 65 f. Type **322** 60 40
922 115 f. Laboratory workers . . 80 50

323 "Adoration of the Kings"

1982. Air. Christmas. Paintings by Rubens. Multicoloured.
923 200 f. Type **323** . . . . 1·25 50
924 300 f. "Mystic Marriage of St. Catherine" . . . . 2·00 75
925 400 f. "Virgin and Child" . . . 2·50 1·00

324 Montgolfier Balloon

1983. Air. Bicent of Manned Flight. Mult.
926 65 f. Type **324** 45 15
927 85 f. Charles's hydrogen balloon 60 20
928 200 f. Goodyear Aerospace airship (horiz) . . . . 1·25 60
929 250 f. Farman H.F.III biplane (horiz) . . . . 1·50 70
930 300 f. Concorde . . . . . . 3·00 1·40
931 500 f. "Apollo 11" spacecraft . 3·00 1·40

No. 928 is wrongly inscribed "Zeppelin".

325 Harvesting Rice **326** E.C.A. Anniversary Emblem

1983. Self-sufficiency in Food. Multicoloured.
932 65 f. Type **325** 60 30
933 85 f. Planting Rice 80 40

1983. 25th Anniv of Economic Commission for Africa.
934 **326** 120 f. multicoloured . . . 75 40
935 200 f. multicoloured . . . 1·25 70

327 "The Miraculous Draught of Fishes"

1983. 500th Birth Anniv of Raphael. Multicoloured.
936 65 f. Type **327** 60 15
937 85 f. "Grand Ducal Madonna" (vert) 50 20
938 100 f. "The Deliverance of St. Peter" 60 25
939 150 f. "Sistine Madonna" (vert) 1·00 45
940 200 f. "The Fall on the Way to Calvary" (vert) . . . . . 1·10 60
941 300 f. "The Entombment" . . 1·75 80
942 400 f. "The Transfiguration" (vert) . . . . 2·25 1·10
943 500 f. "St. Michael fighting the Dragon" (vert) . . . . . 3·00 1·40

328 Surveying

1983. The Army in the Service of Development. Multicoloured.
944 85 f. Type **328** 60 25
945 150 f. Road building . . . . 1·00 50

329 Palace of Justice

1983. Palace of Justice, Agadez.
946 **329** 65 f. multicoloured . . . 40 20

330 Javelin

1983. Air. Olympic Games, Los Angeles. Mult.
947 85 f. Type **330** 50 20
948 200 f. Shotput . . . . 1·10 60
949 250 f. Throwing the Hammer (vert) . . . . 1·50 70
950 300 f. Discus . . . . 1·75 80

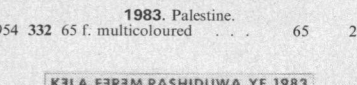

331 Rural Post Vehicle **332** Dome of the Rock

1983. Rural Post Service. Multicoloured.
952 65 f. Type **331** 50 20
953 100 f. Post vehicle and map . 75 30

1983. Palestine.
954 **332** 65 f. multicoloured . . . 65 20

333 Class watching Television

1983. International Literacy Day. Multicoloured.
955 40 f. Type **333** 25 15
956 65 f. Teacher at blackboard (vert) 40 25
957 85 f. Learning weights (vert) . 55 30
958 100 f. Outdoor class 60 35
959 150 f. Woman reading magazine (vert) . . . . 1·00 50

334 Three Dancers

1983. Seventh Dosso Dance Festival. Multicoloured.
960 65 f. Type **334** 50 25
961 85 f. Four dancers 60 35
962 120 f. Two dancers 90 50

335 Post Van **336** Television Antenna and Solar Panel

1983. World Communications Year. Multicoloured.
963 80 f. Type **335** 60 40
964 120 f. Sorting letters 80 40
965 150 f. W.C.Y. emblem (vert) . 1·00 50

1983. Solar Energy in the Service of Television. Multicoloured.
966 85 f. Type **336** 60 30
967 130 f. Land-rover and solar panel 90 45

337 "Hypolimnas misippus"

1983. Butterflies. Multicoloured.
968 75 f. Type **337** 70 35
969 120 f. "Papilio demodocus" . 1·10 50
970 250 f. "Vanessa antiopa" . . 2·00 90
971 350 f. "Charexes jasius" . . . 2·75 1·40
972 500 f. "Danaus chrisippus" . . 4·50 1·75

338 "Virgin and Child with Angels" **339** Samariya Emblem

1983. Air. Christmas. Paintings by Botticelli. Multicoloured.
973 120 f. Type **338** 75 40
974 350 f. "Adoration of the Magi" (horiz) . . . . 2·25 1·00
975 500 f. "Virgin of the Pomegranate" . . . . 3·00 1·25

1984. Samariya.
976 **339** 80 f. black, orange & grn . 50 30

340 Running

1984. Air. Olympic Games, Los Angeles. Mult.
977 80 f. Type **340** 40 20
978 120 f. Pole vault 60 30
979 140 f. High jump 80 30
980 200 f. Triple jump (vert) . . . 1·25 45
981 350 f. Long jump (vert) . . . 2·00 1·00

341 "Alestes bouboni"

1984. Fish.
983 **341** 120 f. multicoloured . . . 1·50 55

342 Obstacle Course

1984. Military Pentathlon. Multicoloured.
984 120 f. Type **342** 80 40
985 140 f. Shooting 95 50

343 Radio Station

1984. New Radio Station.
986 **343** 120 f. multicoloured . . . 85 40

344 Flags, Agriculture and Symbols and Unity and Growth

1984. 25th Anniv of Council of Unity.
987 **344** 65 f. multicoloured . . . 40 25
988 85 f. multicoloured . . . 50 40

345 "Paris" (early steamer)

1984. Ships. Multicoloured.
989 80 f. Type **345** 70 25
990 120 f. "Jacques Coeur" (full-rigged ship) 80 35
991 150 f. "Bosphorus" (full-rigged ship) . . . . 1·25 45
992 300 f. "Comet" (full-rigged ship) 2·25 85

346 Daimler

1984. Motor Cars. Multicoloured.
993 100 f. Type **346** 75 30
994 140 f. Renault . . . . 1·10 45
995 250 f. Delage "D 8" . . . . 1·75 70
996 400 f. Maybach "Zeppelin" . 2·75 90

347 "Rickmer Rickmers" (full-rigged ship)

1984. Universal Postal Union Congress, Hamburg.
997 **347** 300 f. blue, brown and green 2·50 1·50

348 Cattle

1984. Ayerou Market. Multicoloured.
998 80 f. Type **348** 60 40
999 120 f. View of market 90 60

349 Viper

1984.
1000 **349** 80 f. multicoloured . . . 75 40

350 Carl Lewis (100 and 200 metres)

1984. Air. Olympic Games Medal Winners. Multicoloured.
1001 80 f. Type **350** 50 20
1002 120 f. J. Cruz (800 metres) . . 70 40
1003 140 f. A. Cova (10,000 metres) 80 45
1004 300 f. Al Joyner (Triple jump) 1·75 90

351 Emblem

1984. 10th Anniv of Economic Community of West Africa.
1006 **351** 80 f. multicoloured . . . 50 30

352 Emblem and Extract from General Kountche's Speech

1984. United Nations Disarmament Decennials.
1007 **352** 400 f. black and green . . 2·50 1·75
1008 500 f. black and blue . . 3·00 1·75

353 Football

1984. Air. Preliminary Rounds of World Cup Football Championship, Mexico.
1009 **353** 150 f. multicoloured . . . 1·00 45
1010 – 250 f. multicoloured . . . 1·75 80
1011 – 450 f. multicoloured . . . 2·50 1·25
1012 – 500 f. multicoloured . . . 3·00 1·75
DESIGNS: 250 to 500 f. Footballing scenes.

354 "The Visitation" (Ghirlandaio)

1984. Air. Christmas. Multicoloured.
1013 100 f. Type **354** 60 30
1014 200 f. "Virgin and Child" (Master of Saint Verdiana) 1·25 65
1015 400 f. "Virgin and Child" (J. Koning) . . . . 2·50 1·25

1984. Drought Relief. Nos. 895/6 optd **Aide au Sahel 84**.
1016 150 f. multicoloured . . . . . 1·00 80
1017 200 f. multicoloured . . . . . 1·25 1·10

356 Organization Emblem **357** Breast-feeding Baby

1985. 10th Anniv of World Tourism Organization.
1018 **356** 100 f. black, orange and green 70 40

1985. Infant Survival Campaign. Multicoloured.
1019 85 f. Type **357** 70 30
1020 110 f. Feeding baby and changing nappy 90 40

358 Black-necked Stilt

1985. Air. Birth Centenary of John J. Audubon (ornithologist). Multicoloured.
1021 110 f. Type **358** 70 60
1022 140 f. Greater flamingo (vert) 1·00 80
1023 200 f. Atlantic puffin . . . . 1·40 1·25
1024 350 f. Arctic tern (vert) . . . 2·50 1·75

360 Profile and Emblem

1985. 15th Anniv of Technical and Cultural Co-operation Agency.
1026 **360** 110 f. brown, red & vio . 65 40

361 Dancers

1985. 8th Niamey Festival. Multicoloured.
1027 85 f. Type **361** 60 40
1028 110 f. Four dancers (vert) . . 70 50
1029 150 f. Dancers (different) . . 1·00 65

362 Wolf ("White Fang") and Jack London

1985. International Youth Year. Multicoloured.
1030 85 f. Type **362** 60 25
1031 105 f. Woman with lion and Joseph Kessel 75 30
1032 250 f. Capt. Ahab harpooning white whale ("Moby Dick") 1·75 90
1033 450 f. Mowgli on elephant ("Jungle Book") . . . . . 2·75 1·50

363 Two Children on Leaf

1985. "Philexafrique" Stamp Exhibition, Lome, Togo (1st issue). Multicoloured.

1034 200 f. Type **363** . . . . . . 1·25 1·00
1035 200 f. Mining . . . . . . 1·25 1·00

See also Nos. 1064/5.

364 "Hugo with his Son Francois" (A. de Chatillon)

1985. Death Centenary of Victor Hugo (writer).

1036 **364** 500 f. multicoloured . . 3·00 1·75

365 Diesel Train, Satellite and Boeing 737 on Map

1985. Europafrique.

1037 **365** 110 f. multicoloured . . 1·25 55

366 Addax

1985. Endangered Animals. Multicoloured.

1038 50 f. Type **366** 40 15
1039 60 f. Addax (different) (horiz) 45 25
1040 85 f. Two scimitar oryxes (horiz) 55 25
1041 110 f. Oryx 75 35

367 "Oedaleus sp" on Millet **368** Agadez Cross

1985. Vegetation Protection. Multicoloured.

1042 85 f. Type **367** 55 20
1043 110 f. "Dysdercus volkeri" (beetle) 75 35
1044 150 f. Fungi attacking sorghum and millet (horiz) . . . . 1·00 50
1045 210 f. Sudan golden sparrows in tree . . . . 2·50 1·40
1046 390 f. Red-billed queleas in tree 4·00 2·50

1985.

1047 **368** 85 f. green 45 15
1048 – 110 f. brown 55 15

DESIGN: 110 f. Girl carrying water jar on head.

369 Arms, Flags and Agriculture

1985. 25th Anniv of Independence.

1049 **369** 110 f. multicoloured . . 70 40

370 Baobab **371** Man watching Race

1985. Protected Trees. Multicoloured.

1050 110 f. Type **370** 80 50
1051 210 f. "Acacia albida" . . . 1·40 1·00
1052 390 f. Baobab (different) . . 3·00 1·60

1985. Niamey–Bamako Powerboat Race. Mult.

1053 110 f. Type **371** 70 45
1054 150 f. Helicopter and powerboat 1·60 85
1055 250 f. Powerboat and map . 1·75 1·25

1985. "Trees for Niger". As Nos. 1050/2 but new values and optd **DES ARBRES POUR LE NIGER**.

1056 **370** 30 f. multicoloured . . . 25 20
1057 – 85 f. multicoloured . . . 55 40
1058 – 110 f. multicoloured . . 70 55

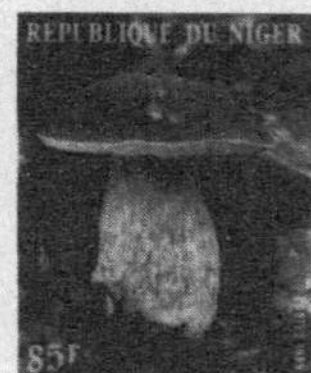

373 "Boletus"

1985. Fungi. Multicoloured.

1059 85 f. Type **373** 80 20
1060 110 f. "Hypholoma fasciculare" 1·25 30
1061 200 f. "Coprinus comatus" . 1·75 70
1062 300 f. "Agaricus arvensis" (horiz) . . . . 2·75 1·00
1063 400 f. "Geastrum fimbriatum" (horiz) . . . . 3·50 1·40

374 First Village Water Pump

1985. "Philexafrique" Stamp Exhibition, Lome, Togo (2nd issue). Multicoloured.

1064 250 f. Type **374** . . . . . . 1·75 1·25
1065 250 f. Handicapped youths playing dili (traditional game) 1·75 1·25

375 "Saving Ant" and Savings Bank Emblem **376** Gouroumi

1985. World Savings Day.

1066 **375** 210 f. multicoloured . . 1·40 85

1985. Musical Instruments. Multicoloured.

1067 150 f. Type **376** . . . . . . 1·10 60
1068 210 f. Gassou (drums) (horiz) 1·60 1·00
1069 390 f. Algaita (flute) . . . . 2·75 1·50

377 "The Immaculate Conception" **379** National Identity Card

378 Comet over Paris, 1910

1985. Air. Christmas. Paintings by Murillo. Mult.

1071 110 f. "Madonna of the Rosary" 65 35
1072 250 f. Type **377** . . . . . . 1·75 90
1073 390 f. "Virgin of Seville" . . 2·50 1·25

1985. Air. Appearance of Halley's Comet. Multicoloured.

1074 110 f. Type **378** 70 35
1075 130 f. Comet over New York 85 40
1076 200 f. "Giotto" satellite . . . 1·50 70
1077 300 f. "Vega" satellite . . . . 2·25 1·00
1078 390 f. "Planet A" space probe 2·50 1·25

1986. Civil Statutes Reform. Each black, green and orange.

1079 85 f. Type **379** 65 30
1080 110 f. Civil registration emblem 75 40

380 Road Signs **381** Oumarou Ganda (film producer)

1986. Road Safety Campaign.

1081 **380** 85 f. black, yellow & red . 75 30
1082 – 110 f. black, red & green . 1·00 40

DESIGN: 110 f. Speed limit sign, road and speedometer ("Watch your speed").

1986. Honoured Artists. Multicoloured.

1083 60 f. Type **381** 35 20
1084 85 f. Idi na Dadaou 50 30
1085 100 f. Dan Gourmou 60 40
1086 130 f. Koungoui (comedian) . 80 45

382 Martin Luther King **384** Statue and F. A. Bartholdi

383 Footballer and 1970 40 f. Stamp

1986. Air. 18th Death Anniv of Martin Luther King (human rights activist).

1087 **382** 500 f. multicoloured . . . 3·25 1·90

1986. Air. World Cup Football Championship, Mexico. Multicoloured.

1088 130 f. Type **383** . . . . . . 1·00 30
1089 210 f. Footballer and 1970 70 f. stamp . . . . 1·25 45
1090 390 f. Footballer and 1970 90 f. stamp . . . . 2·75 1·00
1091 400 f. Footballer and Mexican figure on "stamp" . . . . 2·75 1·00

1986. Air. Centenary of Statue of Liberty.

1093 **384** 300 f. multicoloured . . . 2·25 1·10

385 Truck

1986. "Trucks of Hope". Multicoloured.

1094 85 f. Type **385** 75 30
1095 110 f. Mother and baby (vert) 1·00 40

386 Nelson Mandela and Walter Sisulu **387** Food Co-operatives

1986. International Solidarity with S. African and Namibian Political Prisoners Day. Multicoloured.

1096 200 f. Type **386** . . . . . . 1·50 80
1097 300 f. Nelson Mandela . . . 2·25 1·00

1986. 40th Anniv of F.A.O. Multicoloured.

1098 50 f. Type **387** 30 20
1099 60 f. Anti-desertification campaign 35 25
1100 85 f. Irrigation 50 35
1101 100 f. Rebuilding herds of live-stock 60 40
1102 110 f. Reafforestation . . . 75 45

388 Trees and Woman with Cooking Pots **389** "Sphodromantis sp"

1987. "For a Green Niger". Multicoloured.

1103 85 f. Type **388** 55 30
1104 110 f. Trees, woman and cooking pots (different) . . 70 40

1987. Protection of Vegetation. Useful Insects. Multicoloured.

1105 85 f. Type **389** 60 40
1106 110 f. "Delta sp" 85 50
1107 120 f. "Cicindela sp" 95 65

390 Transmitter, Map and Woman using Telephone

1987. Liptako–Gourma Telecommunications Network.

1108 **390** 110 f. multicoloured . . 80 50

391 Morse Key and Operator, 19th-century

1987. 150th Anniv of Morse Telegraph. Mult.

1109 120 f. Type **391** 75 40
1110 200 f. Samuel Morse (inventor) (vert) . . . . 1·25 70
1111 350 f. Morse transmitter and receiver . . . . 2·25 1·25

392 Tennis Player

1987. Olympic Games, Seoul (1988). Multicoloured.

1112 85 f. Type **392** 50 40
1113 110 f. Pole vaulter 70 40
1114 250 f. Footballer . . . . . . 1·50 90

393 Ice Hockey

1987. Winter Olympic Games, Calgary (1988) (1st issue). Multicoloured.

1116 85 f. Type **393** 60 35
1117 110 f. Speed skating 70 35
1118 250 f. Figure skating (pairs) . . 1·75 90
See also Nos. 1146/9.

394 Long-distance Running

1987. African Games, Nairobi. Multicoloured.

1120 85 f. Type **394** 50 35
1121 110 f. High jumping 60 35
1122 200 f. Hurdling . . . . 1·25 70
1123 400 f. Javelin throwing . . . 2·50 1·40

395 Chief's Stool, Sceptre and Crown

1987. 10th Anniv of National Tourism Office. Multicoloured.

1124 85 f. Type **395** 50 35
1125 110 f. Nomad, caravan and sceptre handle 60 35
1126 120 f. Houses 70 40
1127 200 f. Bridge over River Niger 1·25 70

396 Yaama Mosque at Dawn

1987. Aga Khan Prize. Designs Showing Yaama mosque at various times of day.

1128 **396** 85 f. multicoloured . . . 50 35
1129 – 110 f. multicoloured . . . 60 35
1130 – 250 f. multicoloured . . 1·50 90

397 Court Building

399 Water Drainage

398 "Holy Family of the Sheep" (Raphael)

1987. Appeal Court, Niamey. Multicoloured.

1131 85 f. Type **397** 50 30
1132 110 f. Front entrance 60 35
1133 140 f. Side view 90 55

1987. Christmas.

1134 **398** 110 f. multicoloured . . . 65 40

1988. Health Care. Multicoloured.

1136 85 f. Type **399** 70 40
1137 110 f. Modern sanitation . . 80 40
1138 165 f. Refuse collection . . 1·25 65

400 Singer and Band

402 New Great Market, Niamey

1988. Award of Dan-Gourmou Music Prize.

1139 **400** 85 f. multicoloured . . . 80 50

1988. Winter Olympic Games Winners. Nos. 1116/18 optd.

1140 85 f. **Medaille d'or URSS** . . 50 35
1141 110 f. **Medaille d'or 5.000-10.000 m GUSTAFSON (Suede)** . 60 40
1142 250 f. **Medaille d'or C. CORDEEVA -S. GRINKOV URSS** . . . . 1·50 90

1988.

1143 **402** 85 f. multicoloured . . . 60 40

403 Mother and Child

1988. U.N.I.C.E.F. Child Vaccination Campaign and 40th Anniv of W.H.O. Multicoloured.

1144 85 f. Type **403** 70 40
1145 110 f. Doctor and villagers . . 90 50

404 Kayak

405 Emblem

1988. Air. Olympic Games, Seoul (2nd issue) and 125th Birth Anniv of Pierre de Coubertin (founder of modern Olympic Games). Multicoloured.

1146 85 f. Type **404** 50 20
1147 165 f. Rowing (horiz) 90 50
1148 200 f. Two-man kayak (horiz) 1·25 70
1149 600 f. One-man kayak . . . 3·50 2·00

1988. 25th Anniv of Organization of African Unity.

1151 **405** 85 f. multicoloured . . . 50 30

406 Team working

407 Anniversary Emblem

1988. Dune Stabilisation.

1152 **406** 85 f. multicoloured . . . 60 40

1988. 125th Anniv of International Red Cross.

1153 **407** 85 f. multicoloured . . . 60 30
1154 110 f. multicoloured . . . 80 40

409 Emblem

410 Couple, Globe and Laboratory Worker

1989. Niger Press Agency.

1159 **409** 85 f. black, orange & grn 45 30

1989. Campaign against AIDS.

1160 **410** 85 f. multicoloured . . . 55 30
1161 110 f. multicoloured . . . 85 40

411 Radar, Tanker and Signals

412 General Ali Seybou (Pres.)

1989. 30th Anniv of International Maritime Organization.

1162 **411** 100 f. multicoloured . . . 1·25 60
1163 120 f. multicoloured . . . 1·50 80

1989. 15th Anniv of Military Coup. Mult.

1164 85 f. Type **412** 45 25
1165 110 f. Soldiers erecting flag . 65 35

413 Eiffel Tower

1989. "Philexfrance 89" International Stamp Exhibition, Paris. Multicoloured.

1166 100 f. Type **413** 60 40
1167 200 f. Flags on stamps . . . 1·25 65

414 "Planting a Tree of Liberty"

1989. Bicentenary of French Revolution.

1168 **414** 250 f. multicoloured . . . 1·50 1·00

415 Telephone Dial, Radio Mast, Map and Stamp

416 "Apollo 11" Launch

1989. 30th Anniv of West African Posts and Telecommunications Association.

1169 **415** 85 f. multicoloured . . . 45 30

1989. Air. 20th Anniv of First Manned Landing on Moon. Multicoloured.

1170 200 f. Type **416** . . . . 1·25 65
1171 300 f. Crew . . . . 2·00 1·00
1172 350 f. Astronaut and module on lunar surface . . . . 2·25 1·25
1173 400 f. Astronaut and U.S. flag on lunar surface . . . . . 2·50 1·25

417 Emblem

1989. 25th Anniv of African Development Bank.

1174 **417** 100 f. multicoloured . . . 60 30

418 Before and After Attack, and "Schistocerca gregaria"

1989. Locusts.

1175 **418** 85 f. multicoloured . . . 50 30

419 Auguste Lumiere and 1st Cine Performance, 1895

1989. 35th Death Anniv of Auguste Lumiere and 125th Birth Anniv of Louis Lumiere (photography pioneers). Multicoloured.

1176 150 f. Type **419** 90 55
1177 250 f. Louis Lumiere and first cine-camera, 1894 . . . . . 1·50 85
1178 400 f. Lumiere brothers and first colour cine-camera, 1920 . 2·50 1·25

420 Tractor, Map and Pump

1989. 30th Anniv of Agriculture Development Council.

1179 **420** 75 f. multicoloured . . . 45 30

421 Zinder Regional Museum

422 "Russelia equisetiformis"

1989. Multicoloured.

1180 85 f. Type **421** 45 30
1182 165 f. Temet dunes 90 60

1989. Flowers. Multicoloured.

1183 10 f. Type **422** 15 10
1184 20 f. "Argyreia nervosa" . . . 15 10
1185 30 f. "Hibiscus rosa-sinensis" 20 10
1186 50 f. "Catharanthus roseus" . 35 20
1187 100 f. "Cymothoe sangaris" (horiz) 75 35

423 Emblem

424 Adults learning Alphabet

1990. 10th Anniv of Pan-African Postal Union.

1188 **423** 120 f. multicoloured . . 70 40

1990. International Literacy Year. Multicoloured.

1189 85 f. Type **424** 45 25
1190 110 f. Adults learning arithmetic 65 35

425 Emblem

427 Leland and Child

426 Footballers and Florence

1990. 20th Anniv of Islamic Conference Organization.
1191 **425** 85 f. multicoloured . . . 50 30

1990. Air. World Cup Football Championship, Italy. Multicoloured.
1192 130 f. Type **426** . . . . . . 1·00 40
1193 210 f. Footballers and Verona 1·40 75
1194 500 f. Footballers and Bari . 3·25 1·75
1195 600 f. Footballers and Rome 3·75 2·00

1990. Mickey Leland (American Congressman) Commemoration.
1196 **427** 300 f. multicoloured . . 1·75 1·00
1197 500 f. multicoloured . . 3·00 1·75

428 Emblem

429 Flags and Envelopes on Map

1990. 1st Anniv of National Movement for the Development Society.
1198 **428** 85 f. multicoloured . . . 50 30

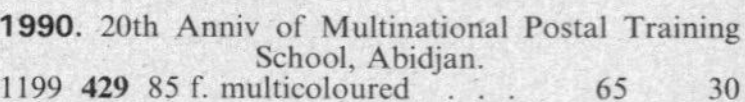

1990. 20th Anniv of Multinational Postal Training School, Abidjan.
1199 **429** 85 f. multicoloured . . . 65 30

430 Gymnastics

1990. Olympic Games, Barcelona (1992). Mult.
1200 85 f. Type **430** 40 25
1201 110 f. Hurdling 60 35
1202 250 f. Running . . . . 1·50 90
1203 400 f. Show jumping . . . . 2·75 1·40
1204 500 f. Long jumping . . . . 3·00 1·75

431 Arms, Map and Flag **432** Emblem

1990. 30th Anniv of Independence.
1206 **431** 85 f. multicoloured . . . 45 30
1207 110 f. multicoloured . . . 65 40

1990. 40th Anniv of United Nations Development Programme.
1208 **432** 100 f. multicoloured . . 50 30

433 The Blusher **434** Christopher Columbus and "Santa Maria"

1991. Butterflies and Fungi. Multicoloured.
1209 85 f. Type **433** (postage) . . . 55 20
1210 110 f. "Graphium pylades" (female) 75 25
1211 200 f. "Pseudacraea hostilia" 1·25 55
1212 250 f. Cracked green russula . 1·50 75
1213 400 f. "Boletus impolitus" (air) 2·50 1·00
1214 500 f. "Precis octavia" . . . 2·75 1·25

1991. 540th Birth of Christopher Columbus. Mult.
1216 85 f. Type **434** (postage) . . . 70 25
1217 110 f. 15th-century Portuguese caravel . . . . 1·00 30
1218 200 f. 16th-century four-masted caravel . . . . 1·60 65
1219 250 f. "Estremadura" (Spanish caravel), 1511 . . . . . . 2·00 85
1220 400 f. "Vija" (Portuguese caravel), 1600 (air) . . . . 3·25 1·10
1221 500 f. "Pinta" . . . . 3·50 1·50

435 Speed Skating

1991. Winter Olympic Games, Albertville (1992). Multicoloured.
1223 110 f. Type **435** 60 25
1224 300 f. Ice-hockey . . . . . 1·25 80
1225 500 f. Women's downhill skiing 2·50 1·25
1226 600 f. Two-man luge . . . . 2·75 1·25

436 Flag and Boy holding Stone **437** Hairstyle

1991. Palestinian "Intifada" Movement.
1227 **436** 110 f. multicoloured . . 75 30

1991. Traditional Hairstyles. Multicoloured.
1228 85 f. Type **437** 20 10
1229 110 f. Netted hairstyle . . . 25 15
1230 165 f. Braided hairstyle . . . 40 20
1231 200 f. Plaited hairstyle . . . 45 25

438 Boubon Market

1991. African Tourism Year. Multicoloured.
1232 85 f. Type **438** 20 10
1233 110 f. Timia waterfalls (vert) 25 15
1234 130 f. Ruins at Assode . . . 30 15
1235 200 f. Tourism Year emblem (vert) 45 25

439 Anatoly Karpov and Gary Kasparov

1991. Anniversaries and Events. Multicoloured.
1236 85 f. Type **439** (World Chess Championship) (postage) . 20 10
1237 110 f. Ayrton Senna and Alain Prost (World Formula 1 motor racing championship) 25 15
1238 200 f. Reading of Declaration of Human Rights and Comte de Mirabeau (bicentenary of French Revolution) . . . 45 25
1239 250 f. Dwight D. Eisenhower, Winston Churchill and Field-Marshal Montgomery (50th anniv of America's entry into Second World War) . . . 60 35
1240 400 f. Charles de Gaulle and Konrad Adenauer (28th anniv of Franco-German Co-operation Agreement) (air) 95 55
1241 500 f. Helmut Kohl and Brandenburg Gate (2nd anniv of German reunification) . 1·10 60

440 Japanese "ERS-1" Satellite

1991. Satellites and Transport. Multicoloured.
1243 85 f. Type **440** (postage) . . 20 10
1244 110 f. Japanese satellite observing Aurora Borealis 25 15
1245 200 f. Louis Favre and "BB 415" diesel locomotive . . 45 25
1246 250 f. "BB-BB301" diesel locomotive 60 35
1247 400 f. "BB-BB302" diesel locomotive (air) 95 55
1248 500 f. Lockheed Stealth fighter-bomber and Concorde . . . 1·10 60

441 Crowd and Emblem on Map **443** Couple adding Final Piece to Globe Jigsaw

442 Timberless House

1991. National Conference (to determine new constitution).
1250 **441** 85 f. multicoloured . . . 20 10

1992.
1251 **442** 85 f. multicoloured . . . 20 10

1992. World Population Day. Multicoloured.
1252 85 f. Type **443** 20 10
1253 110 f. Children flying globe kite (after Robert Parker) . . . 25 15

444 Columbus and Fleet

1992. 500th Anniv of Discovery of America by Columbus.
1254 **444** 250 f. multicoloured . . . 60 35

445 Zaleye

1992. 2nd Death Anniv of Hadjia Haqua Issa (Zaleye) (singer).
1255 **445** 150 f. multicoloured . . . 35 20

446 Conference Emblem **447** College Emblem

1992. International Nutrition Conference, Rome.
1256 **446** 145 f. multicoloured . . . 35 20
1257 350 f. multicoloured . . . 80 45

1993. 30th Anniv of African Meteorology and Civil Aviation College.
1258 **447** 110 f. blue, black & green 25 15

448 Girl planting Sapling

1993. Anti-desertification Campaign.
1259 **448** 85 f. multicoloured . . . 20 10
1260 165 f. multicoloured . . . 40 20

449 Aerosol spraying Globe (Patricia Charets)

1993. World Population Day. Children's Drawings. Multicoloured.
1261 85 f. Type **449** 20 10
1262 110 f. Tree and person with globe as head looking at high-rise tower blocks (Mathieu Chevrault) 25 15

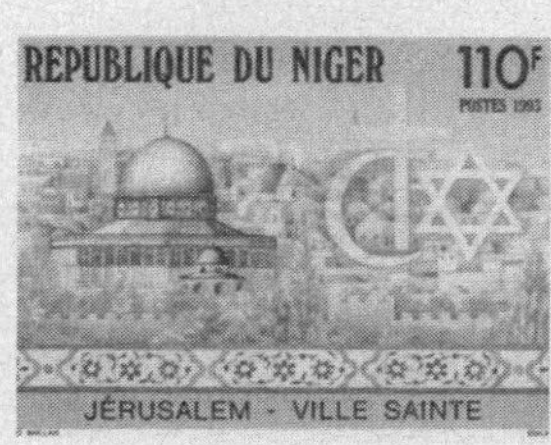

450 Jerusalem

1993. "Jerusalem, Holy City".
1268 **450** 110 f. multicoloured . . 30 15

451 People of Different Races

1994. Award of Nobel Peace Prize to Nelson Mandela and F. W. de Klerk (South African statesmen).
1269 **451** 270 f. multicoloured . . 70 40

OFFICIAL STAMPS

O 13 Djerma Women

1962. Figures of value in black.
O121 **O 13** 1 f. violet 10 10
O122 2 f. green 10 10
O123 5 f. blue 15 10
O124 10 f. red 15 10
O125 20 f. blue 20 15
O126 25 f. orange 25 20
O127 30 f. blue 30 25
O128 35 f. green 35 30
O129 40 f. brown 35 35
O130 50 f. slate 40 40
O131 60 f. turquoise 50 45
O132 85 f. turquoise 70 40
O133 100 f. purple 85 40
O134 200 f. blue . . . . . 1·50 80

1988. As Type **O 13**, but figures of value in same colour as remainder of design.
O1155 **O 13** 5 f. blue 10 10
O1156 10 f. red 10 10
O1157 15 f. yellow 10 10
O1158 20 f. blue 20 10
O1159 45 f. orange 25 20
O1160 50 f. green 30 20

POSTAGE DUE STAMPS

1921. Postage Due stamps of Upper Senegal and Niger "Figure" key-type optd **TERRITOIRE DU NIGER**.

No.	Type	Description	Unused	Used
D18	M	5 c. green	15	50
D19		10 c. red	15	50
D20		15 c. grey	20	60
D21		20 c. brown	20	60
D22		30 c. blue	20	60
D23		50 c. black	25	65
D24		60 c. orange	30	1·00
D25		1 f. violet	50	1·10

D 6 Zinder Fort

1927.

No.	Type	Description	Unused	Used
D73	D 6	2 c. red and blue	10	25
D74		4 c. black and orange	10	25
D75		5 c. violet and yellow	15	25
D76		10 c. violet and red	15	30
D77		15 c. orange and green	15	40
D78		20 c. sepia and red	20	45
D79		25 c. sepia and black	35	50
D80		30 c. grey and violet	60	1·00
D81		50 c. red on green	60	80
D82		60 c. orge, lilac on bl	60	80
D83		1 f. violet & blue on blue	60	75
D84		2 f. mauve and red	60	80
D85		3 f. blue and brown	80	1·00

D 13 Cross of Agadez

1962.

No.	Type	Description	Unused	Used
D123	D 13	50 c. green	10	10
D124		1 f. violet	10	10
D125		2 f. myrtle	10	10
D126	A	3 f. mauve	10	10
D127		5 f. green	15	15
D128		10 f. orange	15	15
D129	B	15 f. blue	15	15
D130		20 f. red	20	20
D131		50 f. brown	40	40

DESIGNS: A, Cross of Iferouane; B, Cross of Tahoua.

D 450 Cross of Iferouane

1993.

No.	Type	Description	Unused	Used
D1263	D 450	5 f. multicoloured	10	10
D1264		10 f. orange & black	10	10
D1265	–	15 f. multicoloured	10	10
D1266	–	20 f. mve, yell & blk	10	10
D1267	–	50 f. multicoloured	10	10

DESIGN: 15 to 50 f. Cross of Tahoua.

NORTH GERMAN CONFEDERATION Pt. 7

The North German Confederation was set up on 1st January, 1868, and comprised the postal services of Bremen, Brunswick, Hamburg Lubeck, Mecklenburg (both), Oldenburg, Prussia (including Hanover, Schleswig-Holstein with Bergedorf and Thurn and Taxis) and Saxony.

The North German Confederation joined the German Reichspost on 4th May, 1871, and the stamps of Germany were brought into use on 1st January, 1872.

Northern District: 30 groschen = 1 thaler
Southern District: 60 kreuzer = 1 gulden

1

3

1868. Roul or perf.

No.	Type	Description	Unused	Used
19	1	$\frac{1}{4}$ g. mauve	15·00	12·00
22		$\frac{1}{3}$ g. green	3·25	65
23		$\frac{1}{2}$ g. orange	3·25	50
25		1 g. red	2·40	30
27		2 g. blue	3·25	40
29		5 g. bistre	7·50	4·00
30	–	1 k. green	10·00	6·50
13	–	2 k. orange	30·00	35·00
33	–	3 k. red	5·50	60
36	–	7 k. blue	8·50	4·00
18	–	18 k. bistre	26·00	65·00

The 1 k. to 18 k. have the figures in an oval.

1869. Perf.

No.	Type	Description	Unused	Used
38	3	10 g. grey	£275	50·00
39	–	30 g. blue	£225	£100

The frame of the 30 g. is rectangular.

OFFICIAL STAMPS

O 5

1870.

No.	Type	Description	Unused	Used
O40	O 5	$\frac{1}{4}$ g. black and brown	22·00	45·00
O41		$\frac{1}{3}$ g. black and brown	14·00	17·00
O42		$\frac{1}{2}$ g. black and brown	2·00	2·50
O43		1 g. black and brown	2·50	35
O44		2 g. black and brown	5·00	2·75
O45		1 k. black and grey	32·00	£225
O46		2 k. black and grey	85·00	£800
O47		3 k. black and grey	28·00	35·00
O48		7 k. black and grey	38·00	£250

NORTH INGERMANLAND Pt. 10

Stamps issued during temporary independence of this Russian territory, which adjoins Finland.

100 pennia = 1 mark

1 18th-century Arms of Ingermanland

4 Gathering Crops

1920.

No.	Type	Description	Unused	Used
1	1	5 p. green	2·25	3·75
2		10 p. red	2·25	3·75
3		25 p. brown	2·25	3·75
4		50 p. blue	2·25	3·75
5		1 m. black and red	20·00	27·00
6		5 m. black and purple	65·00	£110
7		10 m. black and brown	£130	£180

1920. Inscr as in T 2.

No.	Type	Description	Unused	Used
8	–	10 p. blue and green	3·00	5·00
9	–	30 p. green and brown	3·00	5·00
10	–	50 p. brown and blue	3·00	5·00
11	–	80 p. grey and red	3·00	5·00
12	4	1 m. grey and red	15·00	28·00
13	–	5 m. red and violet	10·00	15·00
14	–	10 m. violet and brown	11·00	17·00

DESIGNS—VERT: 10 p. Arms; 30 p. Reaper; 50 p. Ploughing; 80 p. Milking. HORIZ: 5 m. Burning church; 10 m. Zither players.

NORTH WEST RUSSIA Pt. 10

Issues made for use by the various Anti-bolshevist Armies during the Russian Civil War, 1918–20.

100 kopeks = 1 rouble

NORTHERN ARMY

1 "OKCA" = Osobiy Korpus Severnoy Army.—(trans "Special Corps, Northern Army")

1919. As T 1 inscr "OKCA".

No.	Type	Description	Unused	Used
1	1	5 k. purple	10	25
2		10 k. blue	10	25
3		15 k. yellow	10	25
4		20 k. red	10	25
5		50 k. green	10	25

NORTH-WESTERN ARMY

Сѣв. Зап.
Армія
(2)

1919. Arms types of Russia optd as T 2. Imperf or perf.

No.	Type	Description	Unused	Used
6	22	2 k. green	2·50	6·00
16		3 k. red	1·75	5·50
7		5 k. lilac	2·50	6·00
8	23	10 k. blue	3·50	8·00
9	10	15 k. blue and purple	3·25	6·00
10	14	20 k. red and blue	4·50	7·00
11	10	20 k. on 14 k. red and blue	£200	
12		25 k. mauve and green	6·00	11·00
13	14	50 k. green and purple	6·00	11·00
14	15	1 r. orange & brn on brn	12·00	22·00
17	11	3 r. 50 green and red	25·00	35·00
18	22	5 r. blue on green	14·00	22·00
19	11	7 r. pink and green	75·00	£140
15	20	10 r. grey and red on yell	40·00	70·00

1919. No. 7 surch.

No.	Type	Description	Unused	Used
20	22	10 k. on 5 k. red	3·00	5·00

WESTERN ARMY

1919. Stamps of Latvia optd with Cross of Lorraine in circle with plain background. Imperf. (a) Postage stamps.

No.	Type	Description	Unused	Used
21	1	3 k. lilac	22·00	40·00
22		5 k. red	22·00	40·00
23		10 k. blue	£110	£190
24		20 k. orange	22·00	40·00
25		25 k. grey	22·00	40·00
26		35 k. brown	22·00	40·00
27		50 k. violet	22·00	40·00
28		75 k. green	24·00	55·00

(b) Liberation of Riga issue.

No.	Type	Description	Unused	Used
29	4	5 k. red	15·00	35·00
30		15 k. green	15·00	35·00
31		35 k. brown	15·00	35·00

1919. Stamps of Latvia optd with Cross of Lorraine in circle with burele background and characters **3. A** (= "Z. A."). Imperf (a) Postage stamps.

No.	Type	Description	Unused	Used
32	1	3 k. lilac	4·00	8·00
33		5 k. red	4·00	8·00
34		10 k. blue	90·00	£170
35		20 k. orange	8·00	16·00
36		25 k. grey	22·00	45·00
37		35 k. brown	14·00	24·00
38		50 k. violet	14·00	24·00
39		75 k. green	14·00	24·00

(b) Liberation of Riga issue.

No.	Type	Description	Unused	Used
40	4	5 k. red	2·75	6·50
41		15 k. green	2·75	6·50
42		35 k. brown	2·75	6·50

1919. Arms type of Russia surch with Cross of Lorraine in ornamental frame and **LP** with value in curved frame. Imperf or perf.

No.	Type	Description	Unused	Used
43	22	10 k. on 2 k. green	4·50	6·00
54		20 k. on 3 k. red	48·00	75·00
44	23	30 k. on 4 k. red	4·50	7·00
45	22	40 k. on 5 k. red	4·50	7·00
46	23	50 k. on 10 k. blue	4·50	6·00
47	10	70 k. on 15 k. blue & purple	4·50	6·00
48	14	90 k. on 20 k. red & blue	4·50	7·00
49	10	1 r. on 25 k. mauve & grn	4·50	6·00
50		1 r. 50 on 35 k. green & pur	35·00	55·00
51	14	2 r. on 50 k. green & pur	6·00	10·00
52	10	4 r. on 70 k. orange & brn	16·00	24·00
53	15	6 r. on 1 r. orange & brown	16·00	25·00
56	11	10 r. on 3 r. 50 green & pur	38·00	48·00

NORWAY Pt. 11

In 1814 Denmark ceded Norway to Sweden, from 1814 to 1905 the King of Sweden was also King of Norway after which Norway was an independent Kingdom.

1855. 120 skilling = 1 speciedaler
1877. 100 ore = 1 krone

1

3 King Oscar I

1855. Imperf.

No.	Type	Description	Unused	Used
1	1	4 s. blue	£4250	75·00

1856. Perf.

No.	Type	Description	Unused	Used
4	3	2 s. yellow	£300	75·00
6		3 s. lilac	£225	45·00
7		4 s. blue	£120	5·00
11		8 s. lake	£500	18·00

4

5

1863.

No.	Type	Description	Unused	Used
12	4	2 s. yellow	£350	£100
13		3 s. lilac	£325	£250
16		4 s. blue	50·00	4·50
17		8 s. pink	£425	30·00
18		24 s. brown	20·00	70·00

1867.

No.	Type	Description	Unused	Used
21	5	1 s. black	55·00	27·00
23		2 s. brown	10·00	27·00
26		3 s. lilac	£190	55·00
27		4 s. blue	35·00	3·25
29		8 s. red	£255	21·00

6

10 With background shading

A

1872. Value in "Skilling".

No.	Type	Description	Unused	Used
33	6	1 s. green	4·00	19·00
36		2 s. blue	6·50	35·00
39		3 s. red	30·00	3·00
42		4 s. mauve	7·00	30·00
44		6 s. brown	£225	25·00
45		7 s. brown	23·00	30·00

1877. Letters without serifs as Type A. Value in "ore".

No.	Type	Description	Unused	Used
47	10	1 ore brown	3·25	3·50
83		2 ore brown	1·75	2·25
84c		3 ore orange	35·00	2·75
51		5 ore blue	20·00	3·00
85d		5 ore green	27·00	70
86a		10 ore red	26·00	40
55		12 ore green	60·00	11·00
75b		12 ore brown	15·00	11·00
76		20 ore brown	50·00	7·50
87		20 ore blue	35·00	75
88		25 ore mauve	9·00	7·50
61		35 ore green	9·00	8·00
62		50 ore purple	24·00	5·50
63		60 ore blue	22·00	6·50

9 King Oscar II

1878.

No.	Type	Description	Unused	Used
68	9	1 k. green	16·00	5·00
69		1 k. 50 blue	30·00	23·00
70		2 k. brown and red	20·00	16·00

1888. Surch **2 Ore.**

No.	Type	Description	Unused	Used
89a	6	2 ore on 12 ore brown	90	1·00

D

1893. Letters with serifs as Type D.

No.	Type	Description	Unused	Used
133	10	1 ore drab	15	25
134		2 ore brown	15	15
135		3 ore orange	20	10
136		5 ore green	2·25	10

137 **10** 5 ore mauve 30 10
138 7 ore green 30 10
139 10 ore red . . . . 2·75 10
140 10 ore green . . . . 4·00 10
141 12 ore violet 45 50
142a 15 ore brown . . . . . . 2·50 10
143 15 ore blue . . . . . . 2·50 10
144 20 ore blue . . . . . . 4·50 10
145 20 ore green . . . . . . 4·00 10
146 25 ore mauve . . . . . 22·00 15
147 25 ore red . . . . . . 4·00 70
148 30 ore grey . . . . . . 5·00 15
149 30 ore blue . . . . . . 4·75 1·90
150 35 ore green . . . . . . 6·00 4·00
150 35 ore brown . . . . . . 6·00 25
151 40 ore green . . . . . . 2·00 25
152 40 ore blue . . . . . . 16·00 15
153 50 ore red . . . . . . 12·00 20
154 60 ore blue . . . . . . 15·00 20
See also Nos. 279, etc., 529 etc. and 1100/3.

1905. Surch.
122 **5** 1 k. on 2 s. brown . . . . . 20·00 20·00
123 1 k. 50 on 2 s. brown . . . 40·00 40·00
124 2 k. on 2 s. brown . . . . . 35·00 30·00

1906. Surch.
162 **10** 5 ore on 25 ore mauve . . 30 20
125 **6** 15 ore on 4 s. mauve . . . 1·75 2·50
126 30 ore on 7 s. brown . . . 4·50 4·75

15 King Haakon VII **16**

1907.
127 **15** 1 k. green . . . . 20·00 22·00
128 1½ k. blue . . . . 55·00 55·00
129 2 k. red . . . . 70·00 70·00

1910.
155a **16** 1 k. green 25 10
156 1½ k. blue . . . . 1·00 40
157 2 k. red . . . . 1·25 40
158 5 k. violet . . . . 2·25 2·50

17 Constitutional Assembly (after O. Wergeland) **19**

1914. Centenary of Independence.
159 **17** 5 ore green 40 15
160 10 ore red 80 15
161 20 ore blue . . . . 5·50 2·75

1922.
163 **19** 10 ore green . . . . 6·00 10
164 20 ore purple . . . . 8·00 10
165 25 ore red . . . . 18·00 50
166 45 ore blue 85 50

20 **21** **22**

1925. Air. Amundsen's Polar Flight.
167 **20** 2 ore brown . . . . 1·50 1·75
168 3 ore orange . . . . 2·50 2·75
169 5 ore mauve . . . . 4·50 5·50
170 10 ore green . . . . 6·00 6·00
171 15 ore blue . . . . 5·50 6·50
172 20 ore mauve . . . . 9·00 10·00
173 25 ore red . . . . 1·50 1·75

1925. Annexation of Spitzbergen.
183 **21** 10 ore green . . . . 3·00 3·50
184 15 ore blue . . . . 2·50 2·50
185 20 ore purple . . . . 3·50 60
186 45 ore blue . . . . 3·00 3·00

1926. Size 16 × 19½ mm.
187 **22** 10 ore green 40 10
187a 14 ore orange . . . . . . 90 1·25
188 15 ore brown 55 10
189 20 ore purple . . . . . . 15·00 10
189a 20 ore red 45 10
190 25 ore red . . . . . . 6·50 1·25
190a 25 ore brown 60 15
190b 30 ore blue 75 10
191 35 ore brown . . . . . . 45·00 15
191a 35 ore violet . . . . . . 1·50 20
192 40 ore blue . . . . . . 1·75 60
193 40 ore grey . . . . . . 1·50 10
194 50 ore red . . . . . . 1·50 15
195 60 ore blue . . . . . . 1·50 15
For stamps as Type **22** but size 17 × 21 mm, see Nos. 284, etc.

1927. Surcharged with new value and bar.
196 **22** 20 ore on 25 ore red . . . 1·00 80
197 **19** 30 ore on 45 ore blue . . . 7·00 80
198 **21** 30 ore on 45 ore blue . . . 1·50 2·00

24 Akershus Castle **25** Ibsen **28** Abel

1927. Air.
199a **24** 45 ore blue (with frame-lines) 2·25 1·25
323 45 ore blue (without frame-lines) 40 15

1928. Ibsen Centenary.
200 **25** 10 ore green . . . . 4·00 1·50
201 15 ore brown . . . . 1·75 1·75
202 20 ore red . . . . 1·75 35
203 30 ore blue . . . . 2·75 2·00

1929. Postage Due stamps optd **Post Frimerke** or **POST** and thick bar.
204 **D 12** 1 ore brown 25 60
205 4 ore mauve (No. D96a) 20 30
206 10 ore green . . . . . 1·25 1·25
207 15 ore brown . . . . . 1·75 2·00
208 20 ore purple 80 35
209 40 ore blue . . . . . 1·25 40
210 50 ore purple . . . . . 4·75 5·00
211 100 ore yellow . . . . 2·00 1·25
212 200 ore violet . . . . . 3·50 2·00

1929. Death Cent of N. H. Abel (mathematician).
213 **28** 10 ore green . . . . 1·25 40
214 15 ore brown . . . . 1·50 1·25
215 20 ore red 70 15
216 30 ore blue . . . . 1·75 1·25

1929. Surch **14 ORE 14**.
217 **5** 14 ore on 2 s. brown . . . 1·90 2·50

30 St. Olaf (sculpture, Brunlanes Church) **31** Nidaros Trondhjem Cathedral

32 Death of St. Olaf (after P. N. Arbo)

1930. 9th Death Centenary of St. Olaf.
219 **30** 10 ore green . . . . 5·50 25
220 **31** 15 ore sepia and brown . . 60 30
221 **30** 20 ore red 70 15
222 **32** 30 ore blue . . . . 2·25 1·25

33 North Cape and "Bergensfjord" (liner)

1930. Norwegian Tourist Assn. Fund. Size 35½ × 21½ mm.
223 **33** 15 ore + 25 ore brown . . 2·00 3·25
224 20 ore + 25 ore red . . . 20·00 23·00
225 30 ore + 25 ore blue . . . 65·00 75·00
For smaller stamps in this design see Nos. 349/51, 442/66 and 464/6.

34 Radium Hospital

1931. Radium Hospital Fund.
226 **34** 20 ore + 10 ore red . . . 4·00 3·00

35 Bjornson **36** L. Holberg

1932. Birth Cent of Bjornstjerne Bjornson (writer).
227 **35** 10 ore green . . . . 6·00 25
228 15 ore brown 75 85
229 20 ore red 65 15
230 30 ore blue . . . . 1·50 1·25

1934. 250th Birth Anniv of Holberg (writer).
231 **36** 10 ore green . . . . 1·10 25
232 15 ore brown 50 40
233 20 ore red . . . . 8·00 15
234 30 ore blue . . . . 1·75 1·25

37 Dr. Nansen **38** No background shading **38b** King Haakon VII

1935. Nansen Refugee Fund.
235 **37** 10 ore + 10 ore green . . . 1·50 1·60
236 15 ore + 10 ore brown . . 6·50 7·50
237 20 ore + 10 ore red . . . 85 90
238 30 ore + 10 ore blue . . . 6·50 7·00
See also Nos. 275/8.

1937.
279 **38** 1 ore olive 10 10
280 2 ore brown 10 10
281 3 ore orange 10 10
282 5 ore mauve 20 10
283 7 ore green 30 10
413 10 ore grey 30 10
285 12 ore violet 70 80
414 15 ore green . . . . 1·75 10
415 15 ore brown 40 10
416 20 ore brown . . . . 4·00 1·50
417 20 ore green 40 10

1937. As T **22**, but size 17 × 21 mm.
284 **22** 10 ore green 15 10
286 14 ore orange . . . . . . 1·40 1·40
287 15 ore olive 30 10
288a 20 ore red 20 10
289 25 ore brown . . . . . . 1·00 15
289a 25 ore red 30 10
290 30 ore blue . . . . . . 1·00 15
290a 30 ore grey . . . . . . 7·00 20
291 35 ore violet . . . . . . 1·50 10
292 40 ore slate 60 10
292a 40 ore blue . . . . . . 2·25 10
293 50 ore red 70 10
293a 55 ore orange . . . . . . 26·00 10
294 60 ore blue . . . . . . 1·25 10
294a 80 ore brown . . . . . . 22·00 10

1937.
255 **38b** 1 k. green 15 20
256 1 k. 50 blue . . . . 70 1·50
257 2 k. red . . . . 70 3·50
258 5 k. purple . . . . 3·75 30·00

39 Reindeer **41** Joelster in Sunnfjord

1938. Tourist Propaganda.
262 **39** 15 ore brown 50 30
263 – 20 ore red 20 10
264 **41** 30 ore blue 25 10
DESIGN—VERT: 20 ore, Stave Church, Borgund.

1938. Norwegian Tourist Association Fund. As T **33**, but reduced to 27 × 21 mm.
349 **33** 15 ore + 25 ore brown . . 90 1·25
350 20 ore + 25 ore red . . . . 1·10 2·00
351 30 ore + 25 ore blue . . . . 1·60 2·50

42 Queen Maud **43** Lion Rampant **44** Dr. Nansen

1939. Queen Maud Children's Fund.
267 **42** 10 ore + 5 ore green . . . 45 3·50
268 15 ore + 5 ore brown . . . 45 3·50
269 20 ore + 5 ore red . . . . 45 3·50
270 30 ore + 5 ore blue . . . . 45 3·50

1940.
271 **43** 1 k. green 60 10
272 1½ k. blue . . . . 1·00 25
273 2 k. red . . . . 1·25 1·10
274 5 k. purple . . . . 2·75 2·75
See also Nos. 318/21.

1940. National Relief Fund.
275 **44** 10 ore + 10 ore green . . . 2·00 2·00
276 15 ore + 10 ore brown . . . 2·00 2·75
277 20 ore + 10 ore red 60 70
278 30 ore + 10 ore blue . . . . 1·20 1·50

46 Femboring (fishing boat) and Iceberg **47** Colin Archer (founder) and "Colin Archer" lifeboat

1941. Haalogaland Exhibition and Fishermen's Families Relief Fund.
295 **46** 15 ore + 10 ore blue . . . 1·00 3·25

1941. 50th Anniv of National Lifeboat Institution.
296 **47** 10 ore + 10 ore green . . 1·00 1·25
297 15 ore + 10 ore brown . . 1·25 1·60
298 – 20 ore + 10 ore red . . . 60 60
299 – 30 ore + 10 ore blue . . . 2·75 3·75
DESIGN—VERT: 20 ore, 30 ore, "Osloskoyta" (lifeboat).

48 Soldier and Flags **51** Oslo University

1941. Norwegian Legion Support Fund.
300 **48** 20 ore + 80 ore red . . . 21·00 48·00

1941. Stamps of 1937 optd V (= Victory).
301 **38** 1 ore green . . . . 15 2·00
302 2 ore brown . . . . 15 2·75
303 3 ore orange . . . . 15 2·25
304 5 ore mauve 15 20
305 7 ore green . . . . 40 2·75
306 **22** 10 ore green 15 15
307 **38** 12 ore violet . . . . 40 9·00
308 **22** 14 ore orange . . . . 75 8·00
309 15 ore green 15 70
310 20 ore red 15 10
311 25 ore brown 15 30
312 30 ore blue . . . . 40 1·00
313 35 ore violet 40 50
314 40 ore grey 20 40
315 50 ore red . . . . 50 1·50
316 60 ore blue 40 90
317 **43** 1 k. green 40 30
318 1½ k. blue . . . . 1·75 10·00
319 2 k. red . . . . 5·50 35·00
320 5 k. purple . . . . 9·50 55·00

1941. As No. 413, but with "V" incorporated in the design.
321 10 ore green . . . . 40 6·50

1941. Centenary of Foundation of Oslo University Building.
322 **51** 1 k. green . . . . 13·00 30·00

52 Queen Ragnhild's Dream **53** Stiklestad Battlefield

1941. 700th Death Anniv of Snorre Sturlason (historian).
324 **52** 10 ore green 15 10
325 – 15 ore brown 20 30
326 – 20 ore red 15 10
327 – 30 ore blue . . . . 90 1·60
328 – 50 ore violet . . . . 60 1·25
329 **53** 60 ore blue . . . . 60 1·00
DESIGNS (illustrations from "Sagas of Kings")—HORIZ: 15 ore Einar Tambarskjelve at Battle of Svolder; 30 ore King Olav II sails to his wedding; 50 ore Svipdag's men enter Hall of the Seven Kings. VERT: 20 ore Snorre Sturlason.

55 Vidkun Quisling

1942. (a) Without opt.
330 **55** 20 ore + 30 ore red . . . 2·50 9·50
(b) Optd **1-2 1942**.
331 **55** 20 ore + 30 ore red . . . 2·50 9·50

56 Rikard Nordraak **57** Embarkation of the Viking Fleet

1942. Birth Centenary of Rikard Nordraak (composer).
332 **56** 10 ore green . . . . 1·25 1·25
333 **57** 15 ore brown . . . . 1·25 1·60
334 **56** 20 ore red . . . . 1·25 1·25
335 – 30 ore blue . . . . 1·25 1·25
DESIGN—As Type **57**: 30 ore Mountains across sea and two lines of the National Anthem.

1942. War Orphans' Relief Fund. As T **55** but inscr "RIKSTINGET 1942".
336 20 ore + 30 ore red . . . . . 30 2·25

58 J. H. Wessel

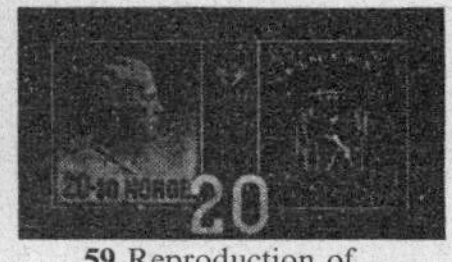

59 Reproduction of Types **55** and **1**

1942. Birth Bicentenary of Wessel (poet).

337	**58**	15 ore brown	15	15
338		20 ore red	15	15

1942. Inaug of European Postal Union, Vienna.

339	**59**	20 ore red	20	50
340		30 ore blue	20	1·10

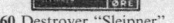

60 Destroyer "Sleipner"

61 Edvard Grieg

1943.

341	**60**	5 ore purple	10	20
342	–	7 ore green	20	20
343	**60**	10 ore green	10	10
344	–	15 ore green	25	40
345	–	20 ore red	10	10
346	–	30 ore blue	85	85
347	–	40 ore green	40	60
348	–	60 ore blue	40	60

DESIGNS: 7 ore, 10 ore, 30 ore Merchant ships in convoy; 15 ore Airman; 20 ore "Vi Vil Vinne" (We will win) written on the highway; 40 ore Soldiers on skis; 60 ore King Haakon VII.

For use on correspondence posted at sea on Norwegian merchant ships and (in certain circumstances) from Norwegian camps in Gt. Britain during the German Occupation of Norway. After liberation all values were put on sale in Norway.

1943. Birth Centenary of Grieg (composer).

352	**61**	10 ore green	30	25
353		20 ore red	30	25
354		40 ore green	30	35
355		60 ore blue	30	35

62 Soldier's Emblem **63** Fishing Station

1943. Soldiers' Relief Fund.

356	**62**	20 ore + 30 ore red	30	2·75

1943. Winter Relief Fund.

357	**63**	10 ore + 10 ore green	70	4·25
358	–	20 ore + 10 ore red	60	3·75
359	–	40 ore + 10 ore grey	60	3·75

DESIGNS: 20 ore Mountain scenery; 40 ore Winter landscape.

64 Sinking of "Baroy" (freighter) **65** Gran's Bleriot XI "Nordsjoen"

1944. Shipwrecked Mariners' Relief Fund.

360	**64**	10 ore + 10 ore green	70	4·25
361	–	15 ore + 10 ore brown	70	4·25
362	–	20 ore + 10 ore red	70	4·25

DESIGNS—HORIZ: 15 ore Cargo liner "Sanct Svithun" attacked by Bristol Blenheim airplane. VERT: 20 ore Sinking of freighter "Irma".

1944. 30th Anniv of First North Sea Flight by Tryggve Gran.

363	**65**	40 ore blue	30	2·00

66 Girl Spinning

67 Arms

68 Henrik Wergeland

1944. Winter Relief Fund. Inscr as in T **66**.

364	**66**	5 ore + 10 ore mauve	30	3·75
365	–	10 ore + 10 ore green	30	3·75
366	–	15 ore + 10 ore purple	30	3·75
367	–	20 ore + 10 ore red	30	3·75

DESIGNS: 10 ore Ploughing; 15 ore Tree felling; 20 ore Mother and children.

1945.

368	**67**	$1\frac{1}{2}$ k. blue	1·10	40

1945. Death Centenary of Wergeland (poet).

369	**68**	10 ore green	25	20
370		15 ore brown	80	80
371		20 ore red	20	10

69 Red Cross Sister **70** Folklore Museum Emblem

1945. Red Cross Relief Fund and Norwegian Red Cross Jubilee.

372	**69**	20 ore + 10 ore red	50	50

1945. 50th Anniv of National Folklore Museum.

373	**70**	10 ore olive	40	30
374		20 ore red	40	20

71 Crown Prince Olav

72 "R.N.A.F."

1946. National Relief Fund.

375	**71**	10 ore + 10 ore green	30	30
376		15 ore + 10 ore brown	30	30
377		20 ore + 10 ore red	30	30
378		30 ore + 10 ore blue	1·00	1·00

1946. Honouring Norwegian Air Force Trained in Canada.

379	**72**	15 ore red	45	40

73 King Haakon VII

74 Fridjof of Nansen, Roald Amundsen and "Fram"

1946.

380	**73**	1 k. green	1·25	10
381		$1\frac{1}{2}$ k. blue	4·00	20
382		2 k. brown	27·00	10
383		5 k. violet	18·00	35

1947. Tercentenary of Norwegian Post Office.

384	–	5 ore mauve	30	10
385	–	10 ore green	30	10
386	–	15 ore brown	55	10
387	–	25 ore red	30	10
388	–	30 ore grey	1·10	30
389	–	40 ore blue	1·60	15
390	–	45 ore violet	3·25	50
391	–	50 ore brown	2·50	15
392	**74**	55 ore orange	4·50	20
393	–	60 ore grey	2·00	80
394	–	80 ore brown	2·00	30

DESIGNS: 5 ore Hannibal Sehested (founder of postal service) and Akershus Castle; 10 ore "Postal-peasant"; 15 ore Admiral Tordenskiold and 18th-century warship; 25 ore Christian M. Falsen; 30 ore Cleng Peerson and "Restaurationen" (emigrant sloop); 40 ore "Constitutionen" (paddle-steamer); 45 ore First Norwegian steam locomotive "Caroline"; 50 ore Svend Foyn and "Spes et Fides" (whale catcher); 60 ore Coronation of King Haakon and Queen Maud in Nidaros Cathedral; 80 ore King Haakon and Oslo Town Hall.

75 Petter Dass **76** King Haakon VII

1947. Birth Tercentenary of Petter Dass (poet).

395	**75**	25 ore red	35	35

1947. 75th Birthday of King Haakon VII.

396	**76**	25 ore orange	35	35

77 Axel Heiberg

80 A. L. Kielland

1948. 50th Anniv of Norwegian Forestry Society and Birth Centenary of Axel Heiberg (founder).

397	**77**	25 ore red	40	30
398		80 ore brown	1·00	30

1948. Red Cross. Surch **25 + 5** and bars.

399	**69**	25 + 5 ore on 20 + 10 ore red	40	50

1949. Stamps of 1937 surch.

400	**22**	25 ore on 20 ore red	50	10
401		45 ore on 40 ore blue	2·25	30

1949. Birth Centenary of Alexander L. Kielland (author).

402	**80**	25 ore red	80	15
403		40 ore blue	80	25
404		80 ore brown	1·25	50

81 Symbolising Universe

82 Pigeons and Globe

1949. 75th Anniv of U.P.U.

405	**81**	10 ore green and purple	50	40
406	**82**	25 ore red	30	15
407	–	40 ore blue	30	30

DESIGN—HORIZ: 40 ore Dove, globe and sign-post.

84 King Harald Haardraade and Oslo Town Hall

85 Child with Flowers

1950. 900th Anniv of Founding of Oslo.

408	**84**	15 ore green	45	60
409		25 ore red	30	15
410		45 ore blue	40	50

1950. Infantile Paralysis Fund.

411	**85**	25 ore + 5 ore red	1·25	1·25
412		45 ore + 5 ore blue	3·50	3·75

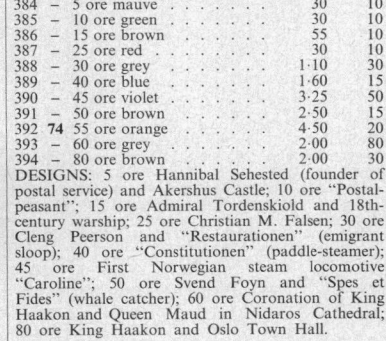

87 King Haakon VII **88** Arne Garborg (after O. Rusti)

1950.

418	**87**	25 ore red	45	10
419		25 ore grey	12·00	10
419a		25 ore green	85	10
420		30 ore grey	6·50	45
421		30 ore red	50	10
422		35 ore red	9·00	10
422a		35 ore red	4·00	10
422b		40 ore purple	1·50	10
423		45 ore blue	1·40	85
424		50 ore brown	1·50	10
425		55 ore orange	1·40	70
426		55 ore blue	1·25	30
427		60 ore blue	8·00	10
427a		65 ore blue	1·25	15
427b		70 ore brown	13·00	15
428		75 ore brown	1·90	15
429		80 ore brown	1·75	10
430		90 ore orange	1·50	15

1951. Birth Centenary Garborg (author).

431	**88**	25 ore red	30	20
432		45 ore blue	1·25	1·25
433		80 ore brown	1·75	1·10

"NOREG" on the stamps was the spelling advocated by Arne Garborg.

89 Ice Skater

92 King Haakon VII

1951. 6th Winter Olympic Games. Inscr "OSLO 1952".

434	**89**	15 ore + 5 ore green	1·90	1·90
435	–	30 ore + 10 ore red	1·90	1·90
436	–	55 ore + 20 ore blue	6·50	6·50

DESIGNS: 30 ore Ski-jumping. LONGER: 55 ore Winter landscape.

1951. Surch in figures.

440	**88**	20 ore on 15 ore green	40	15
437	**87**	30 ore on 25 ore red	40	10

1952. 80th Birthday of King Haakon.

438	**92**	30 ore red and pale red	20	15
439		55 ore blue and grey	60	60

94 "Supplication"

95 Medieval Sculpture

1953. Anti-Cancer Fund.

441	**94**	30 ore + 10 ore red and cream	85	1·10

1953. Norwegian Tourist Association Fund. As T **33** but smaller ($27\frac{1}{2} \times 21$ mm).

442	**33**	20 ore + 10 ore green	8·00	8·00
464		25 ore + 10 ore green	4·50	4·50
443		30 ore + 15 ore red	8·00	8·00
465		35 ore + 15 ore red	6·00	6·00
444		55 ore + 25 ore blue	13·50	13·50
466		65 ore + 25 ore blue	4·50	4·50

1953. 8th Cent of Archbishopric of Nidaros.

445	**95**	30 ore red	30	25

96 1st Railway Steam Locomotive "Caroline" and Horse-drawn Sledge **97** C. T. Nielsen (first Director)

1954. Centenary of Norwegian Railways.

446	**96**	20 ore green	80	30
447	–	30 ore red	80	15
448	–	55 ore blue	1·50	1·25

DESIGNS: 30 ore Diesel express train; 55 ore Engine driver.

1954. Centenary of Telegraph Service.

449	**97**	20 ore black and green	30	30
450	–	30 ore red	30	15
451	–	55 ore blue	1·25	1·00

DESIGNS: 30 ore Radio masts at Tryvannshogda; 55 ore Telegraph linesman on skis.

98 "Posthorn" Type Stamp

100 King Haakon and Queen Maud

1955. Norwegian Stamp Centenary.

452	–	20 ore blue and green	15	20
453	**98**	30 ore deep red and red	15	10
454	–	55 ore blue & grey	25	40

DESIGNS: 20 ore Norway's first stamp; 55 ore "Lion" type stamp.

1955. Stamp Cent and Int Stamp Exn, Oslo. Nos. 452/4 with circular optd **OSLO NORWEX**.

455	–	20 ore blue and green	6·50	8·00
456	**98**	30 ore red & deep red	6·50	8·00
457	–	55 ore blue and grey	6·50	8·00

Nos. 455/7 were only on sale at the Exhibition P.O. at face + 1 k. entrance fee.

1955. Golden Jubilee of King Haakon.

458	**100**	30 ore red	30	15
459		55 ore blue	40	40

101 Crown Princess Martha

101a Whooper Swans

1956. Crown Princess Martha Memorial Fund.

460	**101**	35 ore + 10 ore red	75	1·00
461		65 ore + 10 ore blue	1·50	2·00

1956. Northern Countries' Day.

462	**101a**	35 ore red	1·00	50
463		65 ore blue	1·00	75

102 Jan Mayen Island (after aquarell, H. Mohn) **103** Map of Spitzbergen

1957. Int Geophysical Year. Inscr "INTERN. GEOFYSISK AR 1957–1958".
467 **102** 25 ore green 40 25
468 **103** 35 ore red and grey . . . 40 10
469 – 65 ore green and blue . . 50 40
DESIGN: 65 ore Map of Antarctica showing Queen Maud Land.

104 King Haakon VII **105** King Olav V **106**

1957. 85th Birthday of King Haakon.
470 **104** 35 ore red 15 10
471 65 ore blue 35 35

1958.
472 **105** 25 ore light green 80 10
472a 25 ore green 85 10
473 30 ore violet . . . . . . 1·25 10
474 35 ore red 80 10
474a 35 ore green . . . . . . 2·25 10
475 40 ore red 80 10
475a 40 ore grey . . . . . . 2·50 70
476 45 ore red . . . . 1·00 10
477 50 ore brown . . . . . . 4·00 10
478 50 ore red . . . . 5·00 10
479 55 ore grey . . . . . . 1·50 35
480 60 ore violet . . . . . . 3·75 45
481 65 ore blue . . . . . . 1·75 25
482 80 ore brown . . . . . . 7·00 30
483 85 ore brown . . . . . . 1·25 15
484 90 ore orange . . . . . 1·10 10
485 **106** 1 k. green 50 10
486 1 k. 50 blue . . . . . . 1·25 10
487 2 k. red . . . . 1·50 10
488 5 k. purple . . . . . . 25·00 10
489 10 k. orange . . . . . . 2·75 10

107 Asbjorn Kloster (founder) **108** Society's Centenary Medal

1959. Cent of Norwegian Temperance Movement.
490 **107** 45 ore brown 30 25

1959. 150th Anniv of Royal Norwegian Agricultural Society.
491 **108** 45 ore brown and red . . 25 25
492 90 ore grey and blue . . . 85 1·00

109 Sower **110** White Anemone

1959. Centenary of Norwegian Royal College of Agriculture.
493 **109** 45 ore black and ochre . . 25 25
494 – 90 ore black and blue . . 60 70
DESIGN—VERT: 90 ore Ears of Corn.

1960. Tuberculosis Relief Funds.
495 **110** 45 ore + 10 ore yellow, green and red . . . . . 90 1·00
496 – 90 ore + 10 ore orange, green and blue . . . . 2·50 3·00
DESIGN: 90 ore Blue anemone.

111 Society's Original Seal **112** Refugee Mother and Child

1960. Bicentenary of Royal Norwegian Society of Scientists.
497 **111** 45 ore red on grey . . . 25 15
498 90 ore blue on grey . . . 65 80

1960. World Refugee Year.
499 **112** 45 ore + 25 ore black and red . . . . 1·50 2·00
500 90 ore + 25 ore black and blue . . . . 3·00 4·50

113 Viking Longship

1960. Norwegian Ships.
501 **113** 20 ore black and grey . . 1·00 80
502 – 25 ore black and green . . 1·00 80
503 – 45 ore black and red . . 1·00 15
504 – 55 ore black and brown . 2·00 2·00
505 – 90 ore black and blue . . 1·25 90
SHIPS: 25 ore Hanse kogge; 45 ore "Skomvaer" (barque); 55 ore "Dalfon" (tanker); 90 ore "Bergensfjord" (liner).

113a Conference Emblem **113b** Douglas DC-8

1960. Europa.
506 **113a** 90 ore blue 35 35

1961. 10th Anniv of Scandinavian Airlines System (SAS).
507 **113b** 90 ore blue 30 30

114 Throwing the Javelin **115** Haakonshallen Barracks and Rosencrantz Tower

1961. Norwegian Sport Centenary.
508 **114** 20 ore brown 40 40
509 – 25 ore green 40 40
510 – 45 ore red 40 15
511 – 90 ore purple 70 80
DESIGNS: 25 ore Ice skating; 45 ore Ski jumping; 90 ore Yachting.

1961. 700th Anniv of Haakonshallen.
512 **115** 45 ore black and red . . 30 15
513 1 k. black and green . . 40 25

116 Oslo University **117** Nansen

1961. 150th Anniv of Oslo University.
514 **116** 45 ore red 25 10
515 1 k. 50 blue 45 20

1961. Birth Cent of Nansen (polar explorer).
516 **117** 45 ore black and red . . 25 15
517 90 ore black and blue . . 50 50

118 Amundsen, "Fram" and Dog-team **119** Frederic Passy and Henri Dunant (Winners in 1901)

1961. 50th Anniv of Amundsen's Arrival at South Pole.
518 **118** 45 ore red and grey . . . 50 15
519 – 90 ore deep blue and blue . 90 55
DESIGN: 90 ore Amundsen's party and tent at South Pole.

1961. Nobel Peace Prize.
520 **119** 45 ore red 30 10
521 – 1 k. green 55 20

120 Prof. V. Bjerknes **121** Elrich/Rumpler Taube Monoplane "Start"

1962. Birth Centenary of Prof. Vilhelm Bjerknes (physicist).
522 **120** 45 ore black and red . . . 25 10
523 1 k. 50 black and blue . . 45 25

1962. 50th Anniv of Norwegian Aviation.
524 **121** 1 k. 50 brown and blue . . 70 40

122 Branch of Fir, and Cone **123** Europa "Tree"

1962. Cent of State Forestry Administration.
525 **122** 45 ore grey, black & red . 50 35
526 1 k. grey, black & green . 2·50 20

1962. Europa.
527 **123** 50 ore red 30 10
528 90 ore blue 70 70

125 Reef Knot **126** Camilla Collett **127** Boatload of Wheat

1962.
529 **12** 5 ore red 10 10
529a 10 ore slate 10 10
530 15 ore orange 20 10
530a 20 ore green 10 10
531 25 ore blue 20 10
531ag – 25 ore green 90 10
532 – 30 ore drab . . . . . . 2·25 1·60
532a – 30 ore green 30 10
533 **125** 35 ore green 40 10
533a – 40 ore red . . . . 1·40 10
531aa **12** 40 ore green 10 10
534 – 40 ore green 30 10
534a – 45 ore green 40 25
535 **125** 50 ore red . . . . 2·75 10
535a – 50 ore grey 30 10
531ab **12** 50 ore purple 10 10
536 – 55 ore brown 30 20
536a **125** 60 ore green . . . . . . 6·50 15
537 60 ore red 60 10
531ac **12** 60 ore orange 10 10
537a – 65 ore violet 70 10
538 **125** 65 ore red 30 10
538a – 70 ore brown 30 10
531ad **12** 70 ore yellow 20 10
539 – 75 ore green 30 10
539a – 80 ore red . . . . 2·50 1·00
539b – 80 ore brown 35 10
531ae **12** 80 ore brown 20 10
540 – 85 ore sepia 45 15
540a – 85 ore buff 40 15
540b – 90 ore blue 35 10
531af **12** 90 ore brown 20 10
541 – 100 ore violet 60 10
541a – 100 ore red 50 10
542 – 110 ore red 45 15
542a – 115 ore brown 60 20
543 – 120 ore blue 40 20
543a – 125 ore red 40 10
544 – 140 ore blue 60 35
544a – 750 ore brown 80 10
DESIGNS: 25, 40, 90, 100(2), 110, 120, 125 ore, Runic drawings; 30, 45, 55, 75, 85 ore, Ear of wheat and fish; 65, 80, 140 ore, "Stave" (wooden) church and Aurora Borealis; 115 ore Fragment of Urnes stave-church; 750 ore Sigurd the Dragon-killer testing sword.

For bicolour stamps as T **12** with face values in Kroners see Nos. 1100/3.

1963. 150th Birth Anniv of Camilla Collett (author).
545 **126** 50 ore red 20 10
546 90 ore blue 55 60

1963. Freedom from Hunger.
547 **127** 25 ore bistre 20 30
548 35 ore green 30 30
549 – 50 ore red 30 10
550 – 90 ore blue 60 70
DESIGN—HORIZ: ($37\frac{1}{2}\times21$ mm): 50 ore, 90 ore Birds carrying food on cloth.

128 River Mail Boat **129** Ivar Aasen

1963. Tercentenary of Southern-Northern Norwegian Postal Services.
551 **128** 50 ore red 90 25
552 – 90 ore blue . . . . 1·50 2·00
DESIGN: 90 ore Northern femboring (sailing vessel).

1963. 150th Birth Anniv of Ivar Aasen.
553 **129** 50 ore red and grey . . . 20 10
554 90 ore blue and grey . . . 45 55

The note after No. 433 re "NOREG" also applies here.

130 "Co-operation" **131** "Herringbone" Pattern

1963. Europa.
555 **130** 50 ore orange and red . . 30 10
556 90 ore green and blue . . 1·00 1·00

1963. 150th Anniv of Norwegian Textile Industry.
557 **131** 25 ore green and bistre . 30 35
558 35 ore blue and turquoise 40 55
559 50 ore purple and red . . 30 20

132 Edvard Munch (self-portrait) **133** Eilert Sundt (founder)

1963. Birth Centenary of Edvard Munch (painter and engraver).
560 **132** 25 ore black 20 15
561 – 35 ore green 20 25
562 – 50 ore purple 20 10
563 – 90 ore blue & deep bl . . 50 65
DESIGNS—(Woodcuts): HORIZ: 35 ore "Fecundity"; 50 ore "The Solitaries". VERT: 90 ore "The Girls on the Bridge".

1964. Centenary of Oslo Workers' Society.
564 **133** 25 ore green 20 25
565 – 50 ore purple 20 10
DESIGN: 50 ore Beehive emblem of O.W.S.

134 C. M. Guldberg and P. Waage (chemists) **135** Eidsvoll Manor

1964. Centenary of Law of Mass Action.
566 **134** 35 ore green 40 30
567 55 ore ochre . . . . . . 1·00 1·00

1964. 150th Anniv of Norwegian Constitution.
568 **135** 50 ore grey and red . . . 20 10
569 – 90 ore black and blue . . . 60 60
DESIGN: 90 ore Storting (Parliament House), Oslo.

On 1st June, 1964, a stamp depicting the U.N. refugee emblem and inscr "PORTO BETALT ... LYKKEBREVET 1964" was put on sale. It had a franking value of 50 ore but was sold for 2 k. 50, the balance being for the Refugee Fund. In addition, each stamp bore a serial number representing participation in a lottery which took place in September. The stamp was on sale until 15th July and had validity until 10th August.

136 Harbour Scene **137** Europa "Flower"

1964. Cent of Norwegian Seamen's Mission.
570 **136** 25 ore green and yellow . 30 25
571 90 ore blue and cream . . 80 80

1964. Europa.
572 **137** 90 ore lt blue & dp blue . 75 75

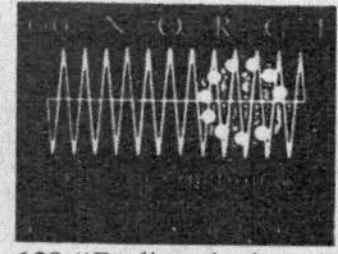

138 H. Anker and O. Arvesen (founders) **139** "Radio-telephone"

1964. Cent of Norwegian Folk High School.
573 **138** 50 ore red 25 10
574 90 ore blue . . . . 1·00 1·00

The note after No. 433 re "NOREG" also applies here.

1965. Cent of I.T.U.
575 **139** 60 ore purple 25 10
576 – 90 ore slate 60 60
DESIGN: 90 ore "T.V. transmission".

140 Dove of Peace and Broken Chain

1965. 20th Anniv of Liberation.
577 **140** 30 ore + 10 ore brown, green and sepia 25 25
578 – 60 ore + 10 ore blue and red 25 20
DESIGN: 60 ore, Norwegian flags.

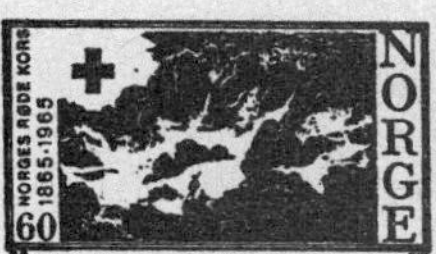

141 Mountain Landscapes **142** Europa "Sprig"

1965. Centenary of Norwegian Red Cross.
579 **141** 60 ore brown and red . . 20 10
580 – 90 ore blue and red . . . 1·60 1·75
DESIGN: 90 ore Coastal view.

1965. Europa.
581 **142** 60 ore red 25 10
582 90 ore blue 60 60

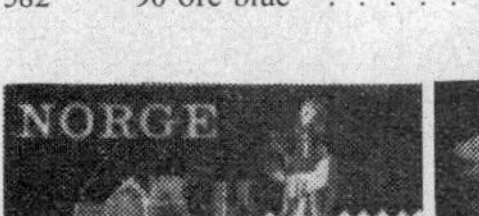

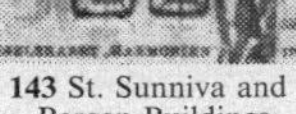

143 St. Sunniva and Bergen Buildings **144** Rondane Mountains (after H. Sohlberg)

1965. Bicentenary of Harmonien Philharmonic Society.
583 – 30 ore black and green . . 25 20
584 **143** 90 ore black and blue . . 50 50
DESIGN—VERT: 30 ore St. Sunniva.

1965. Rondane National Park.
585 **144** 1 k. 50 blue 70 15

145 "Rodoy Skier" (rock carving) **146** "The Bible"

1966. World Skiing Championships, Oslo. Inscr "VM OSLO 1966".
586 **145** 40 ore brown 50 50
587 – 55 ore green . . . . 1·25 1·25
588 – 60 ore brown 50 15
589 – 90 ore blue 90 75
DESIGNS—HORIZ: 55 ore Ski jumper; 60 ore Cross-country skier. VERT: 90 ore Holmenkollen ski jumping tower, Oslo.

1966. 150th Anniv of Norwegian Bible Society.
590 **146** 60 ore red 25 15
591 90 ore blue 45 55

147 Guilloche Pattern **148** J. Sverdrup (after C. Krohg)

1966. 150th Anniv of Bank of Norway.
592 **147** 30 ore green 35 30
593 – 60 ore red (Bank building) 25 15
No. 593 is size 27½ × 21 mm.

1966. 150th Birth Anniv of Johan Sverdrup (statesman).
594 **148** 30 ore green 35 30
595 60 ore purple 30 15

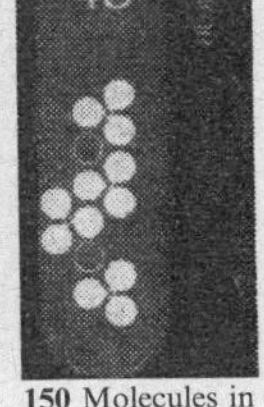

149 Europa "Ship" **150** Molecules in Test-tube

1966. Europa.
596 **149** 60 ore red 30 10
597 90 ore blue 60 60

1966. Birth Centenaries of S. Eyde (industrialist) (1966) and K. Birkeland (scientist) (1967) founders of Norwegian Nitrogen Industry.
598 **150** 40 ore indigo and blue . 75 60
599 – 55 ore mauve and red . . 1·00 90
DESIGN: 55 ore Ear of wheat and conical flask.

151 E.F.T.A. Emblem **152** "Owl" and Three Swords

1967. European Free Trade Assn.
600 **151** 60 ore red 20 10
601 90 ore blue . . . . 80 1·00

1967. 150th Anniv of Higher Military Training.
602 **152** 60 ore brown 40 20
603 90 ore green . . . . . . 1·50 1·25

153 Cogwheels **154** Johanne Dybwad

1967. Europa.
604 **153** 60 ore plum and green . 25 10
605 90 ore violet and blue . . 75 65

1967. Birth Centenary of J. Dybwad (actress).
606 **154** 40 ore blue 20 20
607 60 ore red 20 10

155 I. Skrefsrud (missionary and founder) **156** Climbers on Mountain-top

1967. Centenary of Norwegian Santal Mission.
608 **155** 60 ore brown 20 10
609 – 90 ore blue 50 50
DESIGN—HORIZ: 90 ore Ebenezer Church, Benagaria, Santal, India.

1968. Centenary of Norwegian Mountain Touring Association.
610 **156** 40 ore brown 50 45
611 – 60 ore red 40 15
612 – 90 ore blue 80 60
DESIGNS: 60 ore Mountain cairn and scenery; 90 ore Glitretind peak.

157 "The Blacksmiths" **158** Vinje

1968. Norwegian Handicrafts.
613 **157** 65 ore brown, black & red 25 10
614 90 ore brown, black & bl 55 60

1968. 150th Birth Anniv of Aasmund Vinje (poet).
615 **158** 50 ore brown 20 20
616 65 ore red 20 10
See note below No. 433.

159 Cross and Heart **160** Cathinka Guldberg (first deaconess)

1968. Centenary of Norwegian Lutheran Home Mission Society.
617 **159** 40 ore red and green . . 1·25 1·00
618 65 ore red and violet . . 25 10

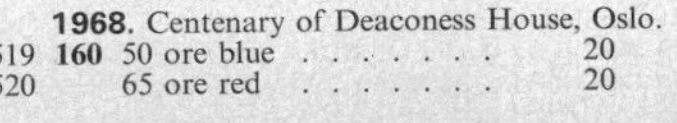
1968. Centenary of Deaconess House, Oslo.
519 **160** 50 ore blue 20 20
520 65 ore red 20 10

161 K. P. Arnoldson and F. Bajer **161a** Viking Ships (from old Swedish coin)

1968. Nobel Peace Prize Winners of 1908.
621 **161** 65 ore brown 30 15
622 90 ore blue 60 50

1969. 50th Anniv of Northern Countries' Union.
623 **161a** 65 ore red 20 10
624 90 ore blue 40 45

162 Transport

1969. Centenary of "Rutebok for Norge" ("Communications of Norway") and Road Safety Campaign.
625 **162** 50 ore green 60 40
626 – 65 ore red and green . . . 25 10
DESIGN: 65 ore Pedestrian-crossing.

163 Colonnade

1969. Europa.
627 **163** 65 ore black and red . . . 25 10
628 90 ore black and blue . . 45 55

164 J. Hjort and Fish Egg **165** Traena Islands

1969. Birth Centenary of Professor Johan Hjort (fisheries pioneer).
629 **164** 40 ore brown and blue . . 50 40
630 – 90 ore blue and green . . 90 80
DESIGN: 90 ore Hjort and polyp.

1969.
631 **165** 3 k. 50 black 60 10

166 King Olav V **167** "Mother and Child"

1969.
632 **166** 1 k. green 45 10
633 1 k. 50 blue 45 10
634 2 k. red 50 10
635 5 k. blue 60 10
636 10 k. brown . . . . . . 1·00 10
637 20 k. brown . . . . . . 2·00 10
637a 50 k. green . . . . . . 5·00 25

1969. Birth Centenary of Gustav Vigeland (sculptor).
638 **167** 65 ore black and red . . . 30 10
639 – 90 ore black and blue . . 70 60
DESIGN: 90 ore "Family" (sculpture).

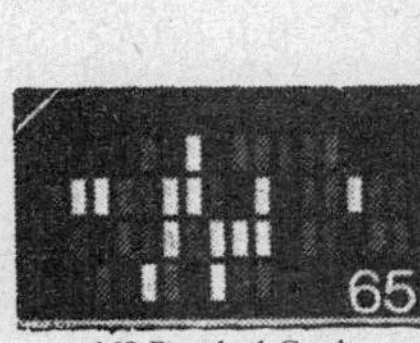

168 Punched Cards **169** Queen Maud

1969. Bicentenary of 1st National Census. Mult.
640 65 ore Type **168** 30 10
641 90 ore "People" (diagram) . . 70 60

1969. Birth Centenary of Queen Maud.
642 **169** 65 ore purple 30 10
643 90 ore blue 70 55

INDEX

Countries can be quickly located by referring to the index at the end of this volume.

170 Wolf **171** "V" Symbol

1970. Nature Conservation Year.
644 **170** 40 ore brown and blue . . 80 35
645 – 60 ore grey and brown . . 80 80
646 – 70 ore brown and blue . . 1·00 15
647 – 100 ore brown and blue . 2·25 1·00
DESIGNS—VERT: 60 ore Pale pasque flower; 70 ore Voringsfossen Falls. HORIZ: 100 ore White-tailed sea eagle.

1970. 25th Anniv of Liberation.
648 **171** 70 ore red and violet . . 1·00 25
649 – 100 ore blue and green . . 1·00 1·00
DESIGN—HORIZ: 100 ore Merchant ships in convoy.

172 "Citizens" **173** Hands reaching for Globe

1970. 900th Anniv of Bergen.
650 **172** 40 ore green 70 50
651 – 70 ore red . . . . 1·40 20
652 – 1 k. blue . . . . 1·00 80
DESIGNS: 70 ore "City in the Mountains"; 1 k. "Ships".

1970. 25th Anniv of United Nations.
653 **173** 70 ore red . . . . 1·25 15
654 100 ore green 80 80

174 G. O. Sars **175** Ball-game

1970. Norwegian Zoologists.
655 **174** 40 ore brown 50 60
656 – 50 ore violet 60 50
657 – 70 ore brown 70 15
658 – 100 ore blue 70 70
ZOOLOGISTS: 50 ore Hans Strom; 70 ore J. E. Gunnerus; 100 ore Michael Sars.

1970. Centenary of Central School of Gymnastics, Oslo.
659 **175** 50 ore brown and blue . . 45 25
660 – 70 ore brown and red . . 55 10
DESIGN—HORIZ: 70 ore "Leapfrog" exercise.

176 Tonsberg's Seal c. 1340

1971. 1100th Anniv of Tonsberg.
661 **176** 70 ore red 30 10
662 100 ore blue 50 45

177 Parliament House, Oslo

1971. Centenary of Introduction of Annual Parliamentary Sessions.
663 **177** 70 ore lilac and red . . . 30 10
664 100 ore green and blue . . 50 40

178 "Helping Hand"

1971. "Help for Refugees".
665 **178** 50 ore green & black . . 40 30
666 70 ore red & black . . . 30 10

179 "Hauge addressing Followers" (A. Tidemand)

1971. Birth Centenary of Hans Nielson Hauge (church reformer).

667 **179** 60 ore black 35 30
668 70 ore brown 25 10

180 Bishop welcoming Worshippers

1971. 900th Anniv of Oslo Bishopric.

669 – 70 ore black and red . . . 30 10
670 **180** 1 k. black and blue . . . 95 80

DESIGN—VERT: 70 ore Masons building first church.

181 Roald Amundsen and Treaty Emblem

182 "The Preacher and the King"

1971. 10th Anniv of Antarctic Treaty.

671 **181** 100 ore red and blue . . . 1·90 1·25

1971. Norwegian Folk Tales. Drawings by Erik Werenskiold.

672 – 40 ore black and green . . 35 10
673 **182** 50 ore black and blue . . 40 15
674 – 70 ore black and purple . . 55 10

DESIGNS—VERT: 40 ore "The Farmer and the Woman"; 70 ore "The Troll and the Girl".

183 Anniversary Symbol

184 3s. "Posthorn" Stamp

1972. 150th Anniv of Norwegian Savings Banks.

675 **183** 80 ore gold and red . . . 40 10
676 1 k. 20 gold and blue . . . 50 45

1972. Centenary of Norwegian "Posthorn" Stamps.

677 **184** 80 ore red and brown . . 30 10
678 1 k. blue and violet . . 40 30

185 Alstad "Picture" Stone (detail)

186 King Haakon VII

1972. 1100th Anniv of Norway's Unification.

680 **185** 50 ore green 45 40
681 – 60 ore brown 70 65
682 – 80 ore red . . . . 1·00 50
683 – 1 k. 20 blue 70 70

DESIGNS: 60 ore Portal, Hemsedal Church (detail); 80 ore Figurehead of Oseberg Viking ship; 1 k. 20, Sword-hilt (Lodingen).

1972. Birth Centenary of King Haakon VII.

684 **186** 80 ore red 70 10
685 1 k. 20 blue 55 55

187 "Joy" (Ingrid Ekrem)

189 "Maud"

1972. "Youth and Leisure".

686 **187** 80 ore mauve 35 10
687 – 1 k. 20 blue 60 60

DESIGN: 1 k. 20, "Solidarity" (Ole Instefjord).

1972. "Interjunex 1972" Stamp Exhib., Oslo. Nos. 686/7 optd **INTERJUNEX 72**.

688 **187** 80 ore mauve . . . . . 1·50 2·00
689 – 1 k. 20 blue . . . . . 1·50 2·00

1972. Norwegian Polar Ships.

690 **189** 60 ore olive and green . . 1·10 60
691 – 80 ore red and black . . 1·10 10
692 – 1 k. 20 blue and red . . . 1·10 80

DESIGNS: 80 ore "Fram" (Amundsen and Nansen's ship); 1 k. 20, "Gjoa".

190 "Little Man"

191 Dr. Hansen and Bacillus Diagram

1972. Norwegian Folk Tales. Drawings of Trolls by Th. Kittelsen.

693 **190** 50 ore black and green . . 30 10
694 – 60 ore black and blue . . 40 35
695 – 80 ore black and pink . . 30 10

TROLLS: 60 ore "The troll who wonders how old he is". 80 ore "Princess riding on a bear".

1973. Centenary of Hansen's Identification of Leprosy Bacillus.

696 **191** 1 k. blue and red 60 10
697 – 1 k. 40 red and blue . . . 80 70

DESIGN: 1 k. 40, As Type **191** but bacillus as seen in modern microscope.

192 Europa "Posthorn"

193 King Olav V

1973. Europa.

698 **192** 1 k. orange, red and deep red 75 10
699 1 k. 40 green, deep green and blue 55 55

1973. Nordic Countries Postal Co-operation. As T **214** of Sweden.

700 1 k. multicoloured 65 10
701 1 k. 40 multicoloured 60 55

1973. King Olav's 70th Birthday.

702 **193** 1 k. brown and red . . . 40 10
703 1 k. 40 brown and blue . . 40 50

194 J. Aall

195 Bone Carving

1973. Birth Centenary of Jacob Aall (industrialist).

704 **194** 1 k. purple 40 10
705 1 k. 40 blue 40 40

1973. Lapp Handicrafts.

706 **195** 75 ore brown and yellow . . 40 25
707 – 1 k. red and yellow . . . 55 10
708 – 1 k. 40 black and blue . . 65 50

DESIGNS: 1 k. Detail of weaving; 1 k. 40, Detail of tin-ware.

196 Yellow Wood Violet

197 Land Surveying

1973. Mountain Flowers. Multicoloured.

709 65 ore Type **196** 40 10
710 70 ore Rock speedwell . . . 50 40
711 1 k. Mountain heath 50 10

1973. Bicentenary of Norwegian Geographical Society.

712 **197** 1 k. red 50 10
713 – 1 k. 40 blue 75 55

DESIGN: 1 k. 40, Old map of Hestbraepiggene (mountain range).

198 Lindesnes

199 "Bridal Procession on Hardanger Fjord" (A. Tidemand and H. Gude)

1974. Norwegian Capes.

714 **198** 1 k. green 50 15
715 – 1 k. 40 blue . . . . . . 1·00 95

DESIGN: 1 k. 40, North Cape.

1974. Norwegian Paintings. Multicoloured.

716 1 k. Type **199** 40 10
717 1 k. 40, "Stugunoset from Filefjell" (J. Dahl) 60 60

200 Gulating Law Manuscript, 1325

201 Trees and Saw Blade

1974. 700th Anniv of King Magnus Lagaboter's Legislation.

718 **200** 1 k. red and brown 30 10
719 – 1 k. 40 blue and brown . . . 35 40

DESIGN: 1 k. 40, King Magnus Lagaboter (sculpture in Stavanger Cathedral).

1974. Industrial Accident Prevention.

720 **201** 85 ore green, deep green and emerald . . . . 1·50 1·10
721 – 1 k. carmine, red and orange 1·00 15

DESIGN: 1 k. Flower and cogwheel.

202 J. H. L. Vogt

203 Buildings of the World

1974. Norwegian Geologists.

722 **202** 65 ore brown and green . . 30 25
723 – 85 ore brown and purple . . 85 75
724 – 1 k. brown and orange . . 45 10
725 – 1 k. 40 brown and blue . . 65 60

DESIGNS: 85 ore V. M. Goldschmidt; 1 k. Th. Kjerulf; 1 k. 40, W. C. Brogger.

1974. Centenary of Universal Postal Union.

726 **203** 1 k. brown and green . . . 30 10
727 – 1 k. 40 blue and brown . . 35 45

DESIGN: 1 k. 40, People of the World.

204 Detail of Chest of Drawers

205 Woman Skier, 1900

1974. Norwegian Folk Art. Rose Painting. Mult.

728 85 ore Type **204** 45 45
729 1 k. Detail of cupboard . . . 30 10

1975. Norwegian Skiing.

730 **205** 1 k. red and green 75 15
731 – 1 k. 40 blue and brown . . 75 55

DESIGN: 1 k. 40, Skier making telemark turn.

206 "Three Women with Ivies" (wrought-iron gates, Vigeland Park)

207 Nusfjord Fishing Harbour, Lofoten Islands

1975. International Women's Year.

732 **206** 1 k. 25 violet and purple . 50 10
733 1 k. 40 blue and turquoise 50 50

1975. European Architectural Heritage Year.

734 **207** 1 k. green 50 35
735 – 1 k. 25 red 40 10
736 – 1 k. 40 blue 50 50

DESIGNS: 1 k. 25, Old Stavanger; 1 k. 40, Roros.

208 Norwegian 1-k. Coin, 1875

1975. Cent of Monetary and Metre Conventions.

737 **208** 1 k. 25 red 30 10
738 – 1 k. 40 blue 50 40

DESIGN: 1 k. 40, O. J. Broch (original Director of the International Bureau of Weights and Measures).

209 Camping and Emblem

1975. World Scout Jamboree, Lillehammer. Mult.

739 1 k. 25 Type **209** 45 15
740 1 k. 40 Skiing and emblem . . 80 60

210 Colonist's Peat House

1975. 150th Anniv of First Emigrations to America.

741 **210** 1 k. 25 brown 80 15
742 – 1 k. 40 blue 70 50

DESIGNS: 1 k. 40, C. Peerson and extract from letter to America, 1874.

211 "Templet" (Temple Mountain), Tempelfjord, Spitzbergen

212 "Television Screen" (T. E. Johnsen)

1975. 50th Anniv of Norwegian Administration of Spitzbergen.

743 **211** 1 k. grey 50 25
744 – 1 k. 25 purple 50 10
745 – 1 k. 40 blue . . . . . . 1·50 1·00

DESIGNS: 1 k. 25, Miners leaving pit; 1 k. 40, Polar bear.

1975. 50th Anniv of Norwegian Broadcasting System. Multicoloured.

746 1 k. 25 Type **212** 30 10
747 1 k. 40 Telecommunications antenna (N. Davidsen) (vert) 50 35

213 "The Annunciation"

214 "Halling" (folk dance)

1975. Paintings from "Altaket" (wooden vault from "Al" (Stave Church), Hallingdal).

748 80 ore Type **213** 30 10
749 1 k. "The Visitation" 30 25
750 1 k. 25 "The Nativity" (30 × 38 mm) 30 10
751 1 k. 40 "The Adoration" (30 × 38 mm) 60 45

1976. Norwegian Folk Dances. Multicoloured.

752 80 ore Type **214** 45 25
753 1 k. "Springar" 45 25
754 1 k. 25 "Gangar" 45 10

215 Silver Sugar Caster, Stavanger, 1770

217 "The Pulpit", Lyse Fjord

216 Bishop's "Mitre" Bowl, 1760

1976. Centenary of Oslo Museum of Applied Art.

755 **215** 1 k. 25 brown, red & rose 20 10
756 – 1 k. 40 violet, blue and light blue 35 40

DESIGN: 1 k. 40, Goblet, Nostetangen Glass-works, 1770.

1976. Europa. Early Products of Herrebo Potteries, Halden.

757 **216** 1 k. 25 mauve and purple 20 10
758 – 1 k. 40 deep blue & blue . 30 40

DESIGN: 1 k. 40, Decorative plate, 1760.

1976. Norwegian Scenery. Multicoloured.
759 1 k. Type **217** 50 25
760 1 k. 25 Peak of Gulleplet ("The Golden Apple"), Balestrand, Sognefjord 50 10

218 Social Development Graph
219 Olav Duun and Cairn, Dun Mountain, Joa Island, Namsen Fjord

1976. Cent of Norwegian Central Statistics Bureau.
761 **218** 1 k. 25 red 20 10
762 – 2 k. blue 30 20
DESIGN: 2 k. National productivity graph.

1976. Birth Centenary of Olav Duun (novelist).
763 **219** 1 k. 25 multicoloured . . 20 10
764 1 k. 40 multicoloured . . 25 30

220 "Slindebirkin" (T. Fearnley)
221 Details of "April"

1976. Norwegian Paintings. Multicoloured.
765 1 k. 25 Type **220** 20 10
766 1 k. 40 "Gamle Furutraer" (L. Hertervig) 25 35

1976. Baldishol Stave Church Tapestry. Mult.
767 80 ore T **221** 20 15
768 1 k. Detail of "May" 20 25
769 1 k. 25 "April" and "May" section of tapestry (48 × 30 mm) 20 15

222 Five Water-lilies

1977. Nordic Countries Co-operation in Nature Conservation and Environment Protection.
770 **222** 1 k. 25 multicoloured . . 25 10
771 1 k. 40 multicoloured . . 25 35

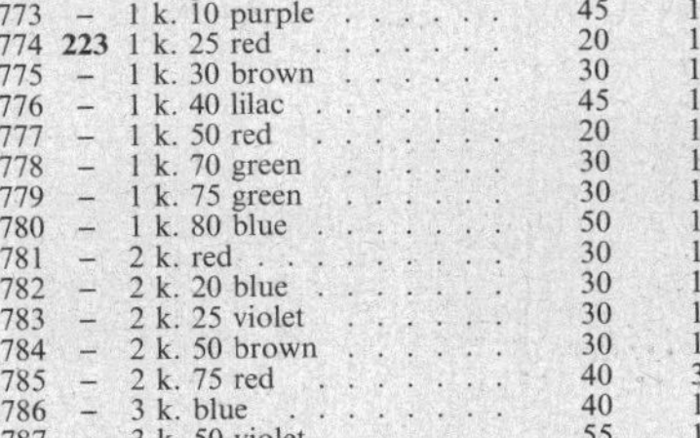

223 Akershus Castle, Oslo
224 Hamnoy, Lofoten Islands

1977.
772 – 1 k. green 15 10
773 – 1 k. 10 purple 45 15
774 **223** 1 k. 25 red 20 10
775 – 1 k. 30 brown 30 10
776 – 1 k. 40 lilac 45 10
777 – 1 k. 50 red 20 10
778 – 1 k. 70 green 30 15
779 – 1 k. 75 green 30 10
780 – 1 k. 80 blue 50 10
781 – 2 k. red 30 10
782 – 2 k. 20 blue 30 15
783 – 2 k. 25 violet 30 15
784 – 2 k. 50 brown 30 10
785 – 2 k. 75 red 40 30
786 – 3 k. blue 40 10
787 – 3 k. 50 violet 55 15
DESIGNS—HORIZ: 1 k. Austraat Manor; 1 k. 10, Trondenes Church, Harstad; 1 k. 30, Steinviksholm Fortress, Asen Fjord; 1 k. 40, Ruins of Hamar Cathedral; 2 k. 20, Tromsdalen Church; 2 k. 50, Loghouse, Breiland; 2 k. 75, Damsgard Palace, Laksevag, near Bergen; 3 k. Ruins of Selje Monastery; 3 k. 50, Lindesnes lighthouse. VERT: 1 k. 50, Stavanger Cathedral; 1 k. 70, Rosenkrantz Tower, Bergen; 1 k. 75, Seamen's commemoration hall, Stavern; 1 k. 80, Torungen lighthouses, Arendal; 2 k. Tofte royal estate, Dovre; 2 k. 25, Oscarshall (royal residence), Oslofjord.

1977. Europa. Multicoloured.
795 1 k. 25 Type **224** 40 10
796 1 k. 80 Huldrefossen (vert) . . 40 40
See note below No. 433.

HAVE YOU READ THE NOTES AT THE BEGINNING OF THIS CATALOGUE?
These often provide the answers to the enquiries we receive.

225 Spruce
226 Paddle-Steamer "Constitutionen" at Arendal

1977. Norwegian Trees.
797 **225** 1 k. green 20 25
798 – 1 k. 25 brown 20 15
799 – 1 k. 80 black 30 35
DESIGNS: 1 k. 25, Fir; 1 k. 80, Birch.

1977. Norwegian Coastal Routes.
800 **226** 1 k. brown 40 25
801 – 1 k. 25 red 60 10
802 – 1 k. 30 green . . . . . . 1·25 1·10
803 – 1 k. 80 blue 60 65
DESIGNS: 1 k. 25, "Vesteraalen" (freighter) off Bodo; 1 k. 30, Ferries "Kong Haakon" and Dronningen at Stavanger, 1893; 1 k. 80, "Nordstjernen" and "Harald Jarl" (ferries).

227 "From the Herring Fishery" (after photo by S.A. Borretzen)
228 "Saturday Evening" (H. Egedius)

1977. Fishery Industry.
804 **227** 1 k. 25 brown and pink . . 20 10
805 – 1 k. 80 blue & light blue . 30 35
DESIGNS: 1 k. 80, Coley and fish hooks.
See note below No. 433.

1977. Norwegian Paintings. Multicoloured.
806 1 k. 25 Type **228** 20 10
807 1 k. 80 "Forest Lake in Lower Telemark" (A. Cappelen) . 30 40

229 "David with the Bells"
230 "Peer and the Buck Reindeer" (after drawing by P. Krohg for "Peer Gynt")

1977. Miniatures from the Bible of Aslak Bolt. Multicoloured.
808 80 ore Type **229** 20 10
809 1 k. "Singing Friars" 20 20
810 1 k. 25 "The Holy Virgin with the Child" (34 × 27 mm) . . . 20 10

1978. 150th Birth Anniv of Henrik Ibsen (dramatist).
811 **230** 1 k. 25 black and buff . . 20 10
812 – 1 k. 80 multicoloured . . 25 30
DESIGN: 1 k. 80, Ibsen (after E. Werenskiold).

231 Heddal Stave Church, Telemark
232 Lenangstindene and Jaegervasstindene, Troms

1978. Europa.
813 **231** 1 k. 25 brown & orange . 25 10
814 – 1 k. 80 green and blue . . 30 40
DESIGN: 1 k. 80, Borgund stave church, Sogn.

1978. Norwegian Scenery. Multicoloured.
815 1 k. Type **232** 30 15
816 1 k. 25 Gaustatoppen, Telemark 35 30

233 King Olav in Sailing-boat

1978. 75th Birthday of King Olav V.
817 **233** 1 k. 25 brown 20 10
818 – 1 k. 80 violet 30 35
DESIGN—VERT: 1 k. 80, King Olav delivering royal speech, opening of Parliament.

234 Amundsen's Polar Flight Stamp of 1925

1978. "Norwex 80" International Stamp Exhibition.
819 **234** 1 k. 25 green and grey . . 85 90
820 – 1 k. 25 blue and grey . . 85 90
821 – 1 k. 25 green and grey . . 85 90
822 – 1 k. 25 blue and grey . . 85 90
823 **234** 1 k. 25 purple and grey . . 85 90
824 – 1 k. 25 red and grey . . 85 90
825 **234** 1 k. 25 purple and grey . . 85 90
826 – 1 k. 25 blue and grey . . 85 90
DESIGNS: Nos. 821/2, 824, 826 Annexation of Spitzbergen stamps of 1925.
On Nos. 819/26 each design incorporates a different value of the 1925 issues.

235 Willow Pipe Player
236 Wooden Doll, c. 1830

1978. Musical Instruments.
827 **235** 1 k. green 30 10
828 – 1 k. 25 red 30 10
829 – 1 k. 80 blue 30 30
830 – 7 k. 50 grey . . . . . . 1·25 25
821 – 15 k. brown . . . . . . 1·75 15
DESIGNS: 1 k. 25, Norwegian violin; 1 k. 80, Norwegian zither; 7 k. 50, Ram's horn; 15 k. Jew's harp.
See note below No. 433.

1978. Christmas. Antique Toys from Norwegian Folk Museum. Multicoloured.
835 80 ore Type **236** 20 10
836 1 k. Toy town, 1896/7 . . . . 20 20
837 1 k. 25 Wooden horse from Torpo, Hallingdal 20 10

237 Ski Jumping at Huseby, 1879
238 "Portrait of Girl" (Stoltenberg)

1979. Centenary of Skiing Competitions at Huseby and Holmenkollen.
838 **237** 1 k. green 30 15
839 – 1 k. 25 red 30 10
840 – 1 k. 80 blue 35 35
DESIGNS: 1 k. 25, Crown Prince Olav ski jumping at Holmenkollen, 1922; 1 k. 80, Cross-country skiing at Holmenkollen, 1976.

1979. International Year of the Child. Mult.
841 1 k. 25 Type **238** 25 10
842 1 k. 80 "Portrait of Boy" (H. C. F. Hosenfelder) 30 30

239 Road to Briksdal Glacier
240 Falkberget (after Harald Dal)

1979. Norwegian Scenery. Multicoloured.
843 1 k. Type **239** 25 15
844 1 k. 25 Skjernoysund, near Mandal 25 10

1979. Birth Centenary of Johan Falkberget (novelist).
845 **240** 1 k. 25 brown 20 10
846 – 1 k. 80 blue 25 35
DESIGN: 1 k. 80, "Ann-Magritt and the Hovi Bullock" (statue by Kristofer Leirdal).

242 Kylling Bridge, Verma, Romsdal

243 Glacier Buttercup

1979. Norwegian Engineering.
848 **242** 1 k. 25 black and brown . 40 10
849 – 2 k. black and blue 35 20
850 – 10 k. brown and bistre . . 1·90 35
DESIGNS: 2 k. Vessingsjo Dam, Nea, Sor-Trondelag; 10 k. "Statfjord A" offshore oil drilling and production platform.

1979. Flowers. Multicoloured.
851 80 ore Type **243** 20 10
852 1 k. Alpine cinquefoil 25 20
853 1 k. 25 Purple saxifrage . . . 25 10
See also Nos. 867/8.

244 Leaf and Emblems
245 Oystercatcher Chick ("Haematopus ostralegus")

1980. Centenary of Norwegian Christian Youth Association. Multicoloured.
854 1 k. Type **244** 15 10
855 1 k. 80 Plant and emblems . . 20 30

1980. Birds (1st series). Multicoloured.
856 1 k. Type **245** 35 15
857 1 k. Mallard chick ("Anas platyrhynchos") 35 15
858 1 k. 25 Dipper ("Cinclus anclus") 35 10
859 1 k. 25 Great tit ("Parus major") 35 10
See also Nos. 869/72, 894/5 and 914/15.

246 Telephone and Dish Aerial

1980. Centenary of Norwegian Telephone Service.
860 **246** 1 k. 25 brown, red & blue 20 10
861 – 1 k. 80 multicoloured . . 30 35
DESIGN: 1 k. 80, Erecting a telephone pole.

248 "Vulcan as an Armourer" (Hassel Jerverk after Bech)

1980. Nordic Countries Co-operation. Cast-iron Stove Ornaments.
863 **248** 1 k. 25 brown 15 10
864 – 1 k. 80 blue 20 30
DESIGN: 1 k. 80, "Hercules at a burning Altar" (Moss Jerverk after Henrich Bech).

249 "Jonsokbal" (N. Astrup)

1980. Norwegian Paintings. Multicoloured.
856 1 k. 25 Type **249** 15 10
857 1 k. 80 "Seljefloyten" (C. Skredsvig) 25 30

1980. Flowers. As T **243**. Multicoloured.
867 80 ore Rowan berries 15 10
868 1 k. Dog rose hips 15 10

1981. Birds (2nd series). As T **245**. Multicoloured.
869 1 k. 30 Lesser white-fronted goose 30 20
870 1 k. 30 Peregrine falcon . . . 30 20
871 1 k. 50 Atlantic puffin 50 10
872 1 k. 50 Black guillemot . . . 50 10

250 Cow

251 "The Mermaid" (painting by Kristen Aanstad on wooden dish from Hol)

1981. Centenary of Norwegian Milk Producers' National Association. Multicoloured.
873 1 k. 10 Type **250** 15 15
874 1 k. 50 Goat 20 10
See note below No. 433.

1981. Europa. Multicoloured.

875 1 k. 50 Type **251** 30 10
876 2 k. 20 "The Proposal" (painting by Ola Hansson on box from Nes) 40 45

252 Weighing Anchor

253 Paddle Steamer "Skibladner"

1981. Sailing Ship Era.

877 **252** 1 k. 30 green 40 30
878 – 1 k. 50 red 35 15
879 – 2 k. 20 blue 70 45

DESIGNS—VERT: 1 k. 50, Climbing the rigging. HORIZ: 2 k. 20, Cadet ship "Christian Radich".

1981. Norwegian Lake Shipping.

880 **253** 1 k. 10 brown 20 20
881 – 1 k. 30 green 20 30
882 – 1 k. 50 red 20 10
883 – 2 k. 30 blue 40 30

DESIGNS: 1 k. 30, "Victoria" (ferry); 1 k. 50, "Faemund II" (ferry); 2 k. 30, "Storegut" (train ferry).

254 Handicapped People as Part of Community

1981. International Year of Disabled Persons.

884 **254** 1 k. 50 pink, red & blue . . 20 10
885 – 2 k. 20 blue, deep blue and red 30 35

DESIGN: 2 k. 20, Handicapped and non-handicapped people walking together.

255 "Interior in Blue" (Harriet Backer)

256 Hajalmar Branting and Christian Lange

1981. Norwegian Paintings. Multicoloured.

886 1 k. 50 Type **255** 20 10
887 1 k. 70 "Peat Moor on Jaeren" (Kitty Lange Kielland) . . . 30 35

1981. Nobel Peace Prize Winners of 1921.

888 **256** 5 k. black 70 35

257 One of the Magi (detail from Skjak tapestry, 1625)

258 Ski Sticks

1981. Tapestries. Multicoloured.

889 1 k. 10 Type **257** 20 10
890 1 k. 30 "Adoration of Christ" (detail from Skjak tapestry, 1625) 20 15
891 1 k. 50 "Marriage in Cana" (pillow slip from Storen, 18th century) (29 × 36 mm) . . . 20 10

1982. World Ski Championships, Oslo.

892 **258** 2 k. red and blue 30 10
893 – 3 k. blue and red 50 35

DESIGN: 3 k. Skis.

1982. Birds (3rd series). As T **245**. Multicoloured.

894 2 k. Bluethroat 40 20
895 2 k. European robin 40 20

259 Nurse

260 King Haakon VII disembarking from "Heimdal" after Election, 1905

1982. Anti-tuberculosis Campaign. Mult.

896 2 k. Type **259** 25 10
897 3 k. Microscope 35 35

1982. Europa.

898 **260** 2 k. brown 40 10
899 – 3 k. blue 50 35

DESIGN: 3 k. Crown Prince Olav greeting King Haakon VII after liberation, 1945.

261 "Girls from Telemark" (Erik Werenskiold)

1982. Norwegian Paintings. Multicoloured.

900 1 k. 75 Type **261** 25 25
901 2 k. "Tone Veli by Fence" (Henrik Sorenson) 25 10

See note below No. 433.

262 Consecration Ceremony, Nidaros Cathedral, Trondheim

1982. 25th Anniv of King Olav V's Reign.

902 **262** 3 k. blue 35 40

263 "Bjorn Bjornson on the Balcony at Aulestad" (Erik Werenskiold)

1982. Writers' Anniversaries. Multicoloured.

903 1 k. 75 Type **263** (150th birth anniv) 25 25
904 2 k. "Sigrid Undset" (after A. C. Svarstad) (birth centenary) . 25 10

264 Construction of Letter "A"

265 Fridtjof Nansen

1982. Centenary of Graphical Union of Norway.

905 **264** 2 k. yellow, green and black 25 15
906 – 3 k. multicoloured 35 35

DESIGN: 3 k. Offset litho printing rollers.

1982. 1922 Nobel Peace Prize-Winner.

907 **265** 3 k. blue 40 35

266 "Christmas Tradition" (Adolf Tidemand)

267 Buhund (farm dog)

1982. Christmas.

908 **266** 1 k. 75 multicoloured . . 25 15

1983. Norwegian Dogs. Multicoloured.

909 2 k. Type **267** 40 25
910 2 k. 50 Elkhound 35 15
911 3 k. 50 Lundehund (puffin hunter) 40 40

268 Mountain Scenery

269 Edvard Grieg with Concerto in A-minor

1983. Nordic Countries' Postal Co-operation "Visit the North". Multicoloured.

912 2 k. 50 Type **268** 25 10
913 3 k. 50 Fjord scenery 35 35

1983. Birds (4th series). As T **245**. Mult.

914 2 k. 50 Barnacle goose 50 25
915 2 k. 50 Little auk 50 25

1983. Europa.

916 **269** 2 k. 50 red 50 10
917 – 3 k. 50 blue & green . . . 50 35

DESIGN—VERT: 3 k. 50, Statue of Niels Henrik Abel (mathematician) by Gustav Vigeland.

270 Arrows forming Posthorn

271 King Olav V and Royal Birch, Molde

1983. World Communications Year. Multicoloured.

918 2 k. 50 Type **270** 25 10
919 3 k. 50 Arrows circling globe . 35 35

1983. 80th Birthday of King Olav V.

920 **271** 5 k. green 65 25

272 Lie

273 Northern Femboring

1983. 150th Birth Anniv of Jonas Lie (author).

921 **272** 2 k. 50 red 30 10

1983. North Norwegian Ships.

922 **273** 2 k. blue and brown . . . 50 20
923 – 3 k. brown and blue . . . 60 40

DESIGNS: 3 k. Northern jekt (sailing vessel).

See note below No. 433.

274 "The Sleigh Ride" (Axel Ender)

275 Post Office Counter

1983. Christmas. Multicoloured.

924 2 k. Type **274** 20 10
925 2 k. 50 "The Guests are arriving" (Gustav Wendel) 25 10

1984. Postal Work. Multicoloured.

926 2 k. Type **275** 25 20
927 2 k. 50 Postal sorting 30 10
928 3 k. 50 Postal delivery 40 35

276 Freshwater fishing

277 Magnetic Meridians and Parallels

1984. Sport Fishing.

929 **276** 2 k. 50 red 30 10
930 – 3 k. green 35 40
931 – 3 k. 50 blue 85 50

DESIGNS: 3 k. Salmon fishing; 3 k. 50, Sea fishing.

1984. Birth Bicentenary of Christopher Hansteen (astronomer and geophysicist).

932 **277** 3 k. 50 blue 40 30
933 – 5 k. red 60 30

DESIGN—VERT: 5 k. Portrait of Hansteen by Johan Gorbitz.

278 Bridge

279 Vegetables, Fruit and Herbs

1984. Europa. 25th Anniv of European Post and Telecommunications Conference.

934 **278** 2 k. 50 multicoloured . . 30 10
935 3 k. 50 multicoloured . . 40 40

1984. Centenary of Norwegian Horticultural Society. Multicoloured.

936 2 k. Type **279** 25 15
937 2 k. 50 Rose and garland of flowers 30 10

280 Honey Bees

281 Holberg (after J. M. Bernigeroth)

1984. Centenaries of Norwegian Beekeeping Society and Norwegian Poultry-breeding Society. Mult.

938 2 k. 50 Type **280** 30 10
939 2 k. 50 Leghorn cock 30 10

See note below No. 433.

1984. 300th Birth Anniv of Ludvig Holberg (writer).

940 **281** 2 k. 50 red 30 10

282 Children reading

284 Karius and Baktus (tooth decay bacteria)

283 Entering Parliamentary Chamber, 2 July 1884

1984. 150th Anniv of "Norsk Penning-Magazin" (1st weekly magazine in Norway).

941 **282** 2 k. 50 purple, blue and red 25 10
942 – 3 k. 50 orange and violet . 35 35

DESIGN: 3 k. 50, 1st edition of "Norsk Penning-Magazin".

1984. Cent. of Norwegian Parliament.

943 **283** 7 k. 50 brown 80 45

1984. Characters from Stories by Thorbjorn Egner. Multicoloured.

944 2 k. Type **284** 30 15
945 2 k. The tree shrew playing guitar 30 15
946 2 k. 50 Kasper, Jesper and Jonatan (Rovers) in Kardemomme Town . . . 80 25
947 2 k. 50 Chief Constable Bastian 40 15

285 Mount Sagbladet (Saw Blade)

286 Return of Crown Prince Olav, 1945

1985. Antarctic Mountains. Multicoloured.

948 2 k. 50 Type **285** 35 15
949 3 k. 50 Mount Hoggestabben (Chopping Block) 45 40

1985. 40th Anniv of Liberation.

950 **286** 3 k. 50 red and blue . . . 60 35

287 Kongsten Fort

1985. 300th Anniv of Kongsten Fort.

951 **287** 2 k. 50 multicoloured . . 30 10

288 Bronze Cannon, 1596 — 289 "Boy and Girl" (detail)

1985. Artillery Anniversaries. Multicoloured.

952 3 k. Type **287** (300th anniv of Artillery) . . . 35 30
953 4 k. Cannon on sledge carriage, 1758 (bicentenary of Artillery Officers Training School) . . 45 35

1985. International Youth Year. Sculptures in Vigeland Park. Multicoloured.

954 2 k. Type **289** 20 20
955 3 k. 50 Bronze fountain (detail) 40 40
See note below No. 433.

290 Torgeir Augundsson (violinist) — 291 Workers at Glomfjord

1985. Europa. Music Year.

956 **290** 2 k. 50 red 50 10
957 – 3 k. 50 blue 60 40
DESIGN: 3 k. 50, Ole Bull (composer and violinist).

1985. Centenary of Electricity in Norway.

958 **291** 2 k. 50 deep red and red . 35 10
959 – 4 k. blue and green . . . 45 40
DESIGN: 4 k. Men working on overhead cable.

293 Carl Deichman on Book Cover — 294 Wreath

1985. Bicentenary of Public Libraries.

961 **293** 2 k. 50 brown and red . . 35 10
962 – 10 k. green . . . . . . 1·25 50
DESIGN—HORIZ: 10 k. Library interior.

1985. Christmas. Multicoloured.

963 2 k. Type **294** 35 10
964 2 k. 50 Bullfinches 50 10

295 Dredger "Berghavn" — 296 Sun

1985. 250th Anniv of Port Authorities and Hydrography in Norway.

965 **295** 2 k. 50 purple, orange & bl 35 10
966 – 5 k. blue, grey & brown . 60 40
DESIGN: 5 k. Sextant and detail of chart No. 1 of Lt. F.C. Grove showing Trondheim sealane, 1791.

1986.

967 **296** 2 k. 10 orange & brown . . 25 10
968 – 2 k. 30 grey and blue . . 35 10
969 – 2 k. 70 pink and red . . 35 10
970 – 4 k. blue and green . . . 40 10
DESIGNS: 2 k. 30, Fishes; 2 k. 70, Flowers; 4 k. Star ornaments.

297 Marksman in Prone Position

1986. World Biathlon Championships. Mult.

977 2 k. 50 Type **297** 35 10
978 3 k. 50 Marksman standing to take aim 45 35

298 Industry and Countryside — 299 Stone Cutter

1986. Europa. Multicoloured.

979 2 k. 50 Type **298** 40 10
980 3 k. 50 Dead and living forest, mountains and butterflies . 60 35

1986. Centenary of Norwegian Craftsmen's Federation.

981 **299** 2 k. 50 red and orange . 35 10
982 – 7 k. blue and red . . . 80 50
DESIGN: 7 k. Carpenter.

300 Moss

1986. Nordic Countries' Postal Co-operation. Twinned Towns. Multicoloured.

983 2 k. 50 Type **300** 50 15
984 4 k. Alesund 75 55
See note below No. 433.

301 Han Polson Egede (missionary) and Map — 303 "Olav Kyrre founds the Diocese in Nidaros"

1986. Birth Anniversaries.

985 **301** 2 k. 10 brown and red . . 30 30
986 – 2 k. 50 red, green & blue 35 10
987 – 3 k. brown and red . . . 45 40
988 – 4 k. purple and lilac . . . 55 40
DESIGNS: 2 k. 10, Type **301** (300th anniv); 2 k. 50, Herman Vildenvey (poet) and poem carved in wall at Stavern (centenary); 3 k. Tore Orjasaeter (poet) and old cupboard from Skjak (centenary); 4 k. Engebret Soot (engineer) and lock gates, Orje (centenary).
See note below No. 433.

1986. Christmas. Stained Glass Windows by Gabriel Kielland from Nidaros Cathedral, Trondheim. Multicoloured.

990 2 k. 10 Type **303** 30 20
991 2 k. 50 "The King and the Peasant at Sul" 30 15

304 Doves — 305 Numeral

1986. International Peace Year.

992 **304** 15 k. red, blue & green . 1·75 75

1987.

993 **305** 3 k. 50 yellow, red & blue 60 20
994 4 k. 50 blue, yellow & grn 65 15

306 Wooden Building

1987. Europa. Multicoloured.

1000 2 k. 70 Type **306** 55 10
1001 4 k. 50 Building of glass and stone 70 20

307 The Final Vote — 309 Funnel-shaped Chanterelle ("Cantharellus tubaeformis")

1987. 150th Anniv of Laws on Local Councils.

1002 **307** 12 k. green . . . . . . 1·60 55

1987. Fungi (1st series). Multicoloured.

1004 2 k. 70 Type **309** 50 15
1005 2 k. 70 The gypsy ("Rozites caperata") 50 15
See also Nos. 1040/1 and 1052/3.

310 Bjornstad Farm from Vaga

1987. Centenary of Sandvig Collections, Maihaugen.

1006 **310** 2 k. 70 dp brn & brn . . 50 15
1007 – 3 k. 50 red and blue . . . 60 40
DESIGN: 3 k. 50, "Horse and Rider" (wooden carving, Christen Erlandsen Listad).

311 Valevag Churchyard

1987. Birth Centenary of Fartein Valen (composer).

1008 **311** 2 k. 30 blue and green . . 50 30
1009 – 4 k. 50 brown 90 35
DESIGN—VERT: 4 k. 50, Farten Valen.
See note below No. 433.

312 "Storm at Sea" (Christian Krohg)

1987. Paintings. Multicoloured.

1010 2 k. 70 Type **312** 50 15
1011 5 k. "The Farm" (Gerhard Munthe) . . . . 1·00 50

314 Cat with Children making Decorations

1987. Christmas. Multicoloured.

1013 2 k. 30 Type **314** 45 15
1014 2 k. 70 Dog with children making gingersnaps . . . 55 15

315 Dales Pony — 316 Capercaillie

1987. Native Ponies.

1015 **315** 2 k. 30 deep brown, green and brown 55 20
1016 – 2 k. 70 buff, brown & bl . 65 15
1017 – 4 k. 50 brown, red and blue 90 45
DESIGNS: 2 k. 70, Fjord pony; 4 k. 50, Nordland pony.
See note below No. 433.

1988. Animals.

1018 – 2 k. 60 deep brown, brown and green 45 10
1019 **316** 2 k. 90 blk, brn & grn . 45 15
1020 – 3 k. brown, grey & grn . 55 10
1021 – 3 k. 20 ultramarine, green and blue 60 20
1022 – 3 k. 80 brown, bl & blk . 55 10
1023 – 4 k. brown, red & green 70 10
1024 – 4 k. 50 brown, grn & bl . 90 10
1025 – 5 k. 50 brn, grey & grn . 1·10 25
1026 – 6 k. 40 brn, blk & grn . 1·25 50
DESIGNS: 2 k. 60, Fox; 3 k. Stoat; 3 k. 20, Mute swan; 3 k. 80, Reindeer; 4 k. Eurasian red squirrel; 4 k. 50, Beaver; 5 k. 50, Lynx; 6 k. 40, Tengmalm's owl.

317 Band

1988. Centenary of Salvation Army in Norway. Multicoloured.

1035 2 k. 90 Type **317** 45 15
1036 4 k. 80 Othilie Tonning (early social worker) and Army nurse 80 40

318 Building Fortress

1988. Military Anniversaries.

1037 **318** 2 k. 50 green 50 20
1038 – 2 k. 90 brown 55 15
1039 – 4 k. 60 blue 90 35
DESIGNS: 2 k. 50, Type **318** (300th anniv of Defence Construction Service); 2 k. 90, Corps members in action (centenary of Army Signals corps); 4 k. 60, Making pontoon bridge (centenary of Engineer Corps).

1988. Fungi (2nd series). As T **309**. Mult.

1040 2 k. 90 Wood blewits 65 15
1041 2 k. 90 Saffron milkcaps . . 65 15

319 Globe — 320 King Olav V

1988. European Campaign for Interdependence and Solidarity of North and South.

1042 **319** 25 k. multicoloured . . . 3·50 75

1988. 85th Birthday of King Olav V.

1043 **320** 2 k. 90 multicoloured . . 70 10

321 "Prinds Gustav" (paddle-steamer) — 322 King Christian IV

1988. Europa. Transport and Communications.

1045 **321** 2 k. 90 black, red & blue 85 10
1046 – 3 k. 80 blue, red & yell . 1·00 60
DESIGN: 3 k. 80, Heroybrua Bridge.

1988. 400th Anniv of Christian IV's Accession to Danish and Norwegian Thrones.

1047 **322** 2 k. 50 black, brn & vio 60 10
1048 – 10 k. multicoloured . . . 2·40 45
DESIGN: 10 k. 1628 silver coin and extract from decree on mining in Norway.

324 Ludvig with Ski Stick — 325 Start and Finish of Race

1988. Christmas. Multicoloured.

1050 2 k. 90 Type **324** 70 10
1051 2 k. 90 Ludvig reading letter 70 10

1989. Fungi (3rd series). As T **309**. Multicoloured.

1052 3 k. Chanterelle ("Cantharellus cibarius") 60 20
1053 3 k. Butter mushroom ("Suillus luteus") 60 20

1989. World Cross-country Championship, Stavanger.

1054 **325** 5 k. multicoloured . . . 1·10 25

MORE DETAILED LISTS

are given in the Stanley Gibbons Catalogues referred to in the country headings. For lists of current volumes see introduction

326 Vardo **327** Setesdal Woman

1989. Town Bicentenaries.

1055 **326** 3 k. blue, red & lt blue . 60 10
1056 – 4 k. purple, blue & orge . 1·00 35
DESIGN: 4 k. Hammerfest.

1989. Nordic Countries' Postal Co-operation. Traditional Costumes. Multicoloured.

1057 3 k. Type **327** 60 10
1058 4 k. Kautokeino man . . . . 1·00 45

328 Children making Snowman **329** Rooster and Cover of 1804 First Reader

1989. Europa. Children's Games. Multicoloured.

1059 3 k. 70 Type **328** 85 50
1060 5 k. Cat's cradle . . . . . 1·50 50
See note below No. 433.

1989. 250th Anniv of Primary Schools.

1061 **329** 2 k. 60 multicoloured . . 85 45
1062 – 3 k. brown 60 10
DESIGN: 3 k. Pocket calculator and child writing.

332 Arnulf Overland (poet, centenary) **333** Star Decoration

1989. Writers' Birth Anniversaries.

1065 **332** 3 k. red and blue 60 10
1066 – 25 k. blue, orange & green 4·50 70
DESIGN: 25 k. Hanna Winsnes (pseudonym Hugo Schwartz) (bicentenary).

1989. Christmas. Tree Decorations. Mult.

1067 3 k. Type **333** 60 10
1068 3 k. Bauble 60 10

334 Larvik Manor **335** Emblem

1989. Manor Houses.

1069 **334** 3 k. brown 60 10
1070 – 3 k. green 60 10
DESIGN: No. 1070, Rosendal Barony.

1990. Winter Cities Events, Tromso.

1071 **335** 5 k. multicoloured . . . 1·00 35

336 Common Spotted Orchid ("Dactylorhiza fuchsii") **337** Merchant Navy, Airforce, Home Guard, "Moses" (coastal gun) and Haakon VII's Monogram

1990. Orchids (1st series). Multicoloured.

1072 3 k. 20 Type **336** 60 10
1073 3 k. 20 Dark red helleborine ("Epipactis atrorubens") 60 10
See also Nos. 1141/2.

1990. 50th Anniv of Norway's Entry into Second World War. Multicoloured.

1074 3 k. 20 Type **337** 60 10
1075 4 k. Second Battle of Narvik, 1940 . . . . 1·00 45

339 Trondheim Post Office **340** "Tordenskiold" (from print by J. W. Tegner after Balthazar Denner)

1990. Europa. Post Office Buildings. Mult.

1077 3 k. 20 Type **339** 75 10
1078 4 k. Longyearbyen Post Office 85 45

1990. 300th Birth Anniv of Admiral Tordenskiold (Peter Wessel). Multicoloured.

1079 3 k. 20 Type **340** 75 10
1080 5 k. Tordenskiold's coat-of-arms . . . . 1·00 45

341 Svendsen **343** "Children and Snowman" (Ragni Engstrom Nilsen)

1990. 150th Birth Anniv of Johan Svendsen (composer and conductor).

1081 **341** 2 k. 70 black and red . . 85 50
1082 – 15 k. brown & yellow . 2·75 50
DESIGN: 15 k. Svendsen Monument (Stinius Fredriksen), Oslo.

1990. Christmas. Children's Prizewinning Drawings. Multicoloured.

1084 3 k. 20 Type **343** 60 10
1085 3 k. 20 "Christmas Church" (Jorgen Ingier) 60 10

344 Nobel Medal and Soderblom

1990. 60th Anniv of Award of Nobel Peace Prize to Nathan Soderblom, Archbishop of Uppsala.

1086 **344** 30 k. brown, blue & red 5·50 70

345 Plan and Elevation of Container Ship and Propeller **346** Satellite transmitting to Tromso

1991. Centenaries of Federation of Engineering Industries (1989) and Union of Iron and Metal Workers.

1087 **345** 5 k. multicoloured . . . 1·00 45

1991. Europa. Europe in Space. Mult.

1088 3 k. 20 Type **346** 60 10
1089 4 k. Rocket leaving Andoya rocket range 90 25

347 Christiansholm Fortress (late 17th-century) **348** Fountain, Vigeland Park, Oslo

1991. 350th Anniv of Kristiansand. Each black, blue and red.

1090 3 k. 20 Type **347** 60 15
1091 5 k. 50 Present day view of Christiansholm Fortress . 1·10 60

1991. Nordic Countries' Postal Co-operation. Tourism. Multicoloured.

1092 3 k. 20 Type **348** 60 10
1093 4 k. Globe, North Cape Plateau 85 45

349 "Skomvaer III" (lifeboat) **352** Posthorn

1991. Centenary of Norwegian Society for Sea Rescue.

1094 **349** 3 k. 20 brown, black & grn 60 25
1095 – 27 k. brown, grey & purple 5·00 2·25
DESIGN—VERT: 27 k. "Colin Archer" (first lifeboat).

1991.

1098 **352** 1 k. black and orange . . 20 10
1099 2 k. red and green 35 10
1100 3 k. green and blue . . . 55 10
1101 4 k. red and orange . . . 75 10
1102 5 k. blue and green . . . 90 10
1103 6 k. red and green . . . 1·10 25
1104 7 k. blue and brown . . . 1·25 25
1105 8 k. green and purple . . 1·50 35
1106 9 k. brown and blue . . . 1·60 45

353 Guisers with Goat Head

1991. Christmas. Guising. Multicoloured.

1120 3 k. 20 Type **353** 60 10
1121 3 k. 20 Guisers with lantern . 60 10

354 Queen Sonja **355** King Harald **356** King Harald

1992.

1122 **354** 2 k. 80 lake, purple & red 50 10
1123 3 k. green, deep green and turquoise 55 10
1124 **355** 3 k. 30 blue, ultramarine and light blue 60 10
1125 3 k. 50 black and grey . . 65 10
1128 5 k. 50 brn, sepia & blk . 1·00 25
1129 5 k. 60 orange, red and vermilion . . . . 1·00 25
1131 6 k. 50 emerald, green and turquoise . . . . 1·25 25
1132 6 k. 60 maroon, purple and brown . . . . 1·25 25
1135 **356** 10 k. green 90 45
1137 20 k. violet . . . . . . 3·75 85
1138 30 k. blue . . . . 6·00 2·40
1139 50 k. green . . . . . . 9·25 1·25

1992. Orchids (2nd series). As T **336**. Mult.

1141 3 k. 30 Lady's slipper orchid ("Cypripedium calceolus") . 60 10
1142 3 k. 30 Fly orchid ("Ophrys insectifera") 60 10

358 "Restauration" (emigrant sloop)

1992. Europa. 500th Anniv of Discovery of America by Columbus. Transatlantic Ships. Multicoloured.

1144 3 k. 30 Type **358** 70 15
1145 4 k. 20 "Stavangerfjord" (liner) and American skyline . . . 1·25 35
See note below No. 433.

359 Norwegian Pavilion, Rainbow and Ship **360** Molde

1992. "Expo '92" World's Fair, Seville. Mult.

1146 3 k. 30 Type **359** 70 10
1147 5 k. 20 Mountains, rainbow, fish and oil rig . . . . . 1·25 25

1992. 250th Anniversaries of Molde and Kristiansund.

1148 **360** 3 k. 30 blue, green & brn 70 10
1149 – 3 k. 30 blue, brown & lt bl 70 10
DESIGN: No. 1149, Kristiansund.

361 Banners and Lillehammer Buildings **363** Gnomes below Pillar Box

1992. Winter Olympic Games, Lillehammer (1994) (1st issue). Multicoloured.

1150 3 k. 30 Type **361** 60 10
1151 4 k. 20 Flags 75 35
See also Nos. 1169/70 and 1175/80.
See note below No. 433.

1992. Christmas. Designs showing Christmas card designs by Otto Moe. Multicoloured.

1153 3 k. 30 Type **363** 60 10
1154 3 k. 30 Gnome posting letter 60 10

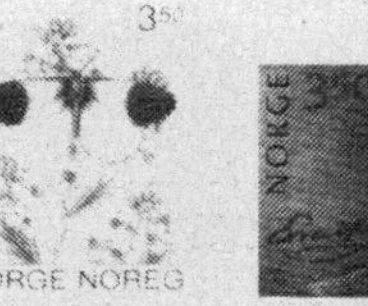

364 Orange-tip ("Anthocaris cardamines") **366** Grieg

1993. Butterflies (1st series). Multicoloured.

1155 3 k. 50 Type **364** 65 10
1156 3 k. 50 Small tortoiseshell ("Aglais urticae") 65 10
See also Nos. 1173/4.

1993. 150th Birth Anniv of Edvard Grieg (composer). Multicoloured.

1158 3 k. 50 Type **366** 65 10
1159 5 k. 50 "Spring" . . . . . . 1·00 25

367 Two-man Kayak on Lake **368** Richard With (founder) and "Vesteraalen"

1993. Nordic Countries' Postal Co-operation. Tourist Activities. Multicoloured.

1160 4 k. Type **367** 75 45
1161 4 k. 50 White-water rafting . 85 55

1993. Centenary of Express Coaster Service.

1162 **368** 3 k. 50 blue, vio & red . 65 10
1163 – 4 k. 50 multicoloured . . 85 25
DESIGN: 4 k. 50, Modern vessel.

369 Handball **370** Johann Castberg (politician)

1993. Sports Events. Multicoloured.

1164 3 k. 50 Type **369** (Women's World Championship, Norway) 65 10
1165 5 k. 50 Cycling (World Championships, Oslo and Hamar) . . . . 1·00 40

1993. Centenary of Workforce Protection Legislation.

1166 **370** 3 k. 50 brown and blue . 65 10
1167 – 12 k. blue and brown . . 2·25 90
DESIGN: 12 k. Betzy Kjelsberg (first woman factory inspector).

372 Torch Bearer on Skis **373** Store Mangen Chapel

1993. Winter Olympic Games, Lillehammer (1994) (2nd issue). Morgedal–Lillehammer Torch Relay. Multicoloured.

1169 3 k. 50 Type **372** 65 10
1170 3 k. 50 Lillehammer 65 10
Nos. 1169/70 were issued together, se-tenant, forming a composite design.

1993. Christmas. Multicoloured.

1171	3 k. 50 Type **373**	65	10
1172	3 k. 50 Stamnes church, Sandnessjoen	65	10

1994. Butterflies (2nd series). As T **364**. Mult.

1173	3 k. 50 Northern clouded yellow	65	10
1174	3 k. 50 Freya's fritillary	65	10

374 Flags

375 Cross-country Skiing

1994. Winter Olympic Games, Lillehammer (3rd issue). Multicoloured.

1175	3 k. 50 Type **374**	65	10
1176	3 k. 50 Flags (different)	65	10
1177	3 k. 50 Lillehammer (church) and rings	65	10
1178	3 k. 50 Lillehammer (ski jump) and rings	65	10
1179	4 k. 50 Flags of European countries	85	25
1180	5 k. 50 Flags of non-European countries	1·00	40

Nos. 1175/8 were issued together, se-tenant, forming a composite design.

1994. Paralympic Games, Lillehammer. Mult.

1181	4 k. 50 Type **375**	80	20
1182	5 k. 50 Downhill skiing	1·00	40

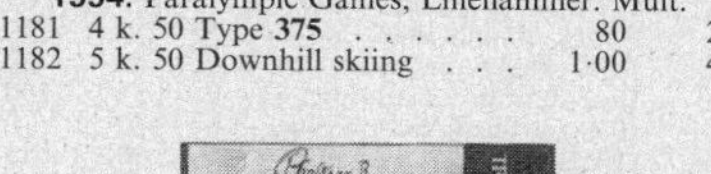

376 King Christian VII's Signature and Seal

1994. Bicentenary of Tromso.

1183	**376**	3 k. 50 red, bistre & brn	65	10
1184	–	4 k. 50 blue, yellow and light blue	85	25

DESIGN: 4 k. 50, Tromsdalen church.

377 Mount Floy Incline Railway, Bergen

1994. Tourism. Multicoloured.

1185	4 k. Type **377**	70	25
1186	4 k. 50 "Svolvaer Goat" (rock formation), Lofoten	85	25
1187	5 k. 50 Beacon, World's End, Tjome	1·00	40

378 Osterdal Farm Buildings

1994. Cent of Norwegian Folk Museum, Bygdoy.

1188	**378**	3 k. multicoloured	60	10
1189	–	3 k. 50 blue, yellow and purple	70	10

DESIGN: 3 k. 50, Horse-drawn sleigh, 1750 (Torsten Hoff).

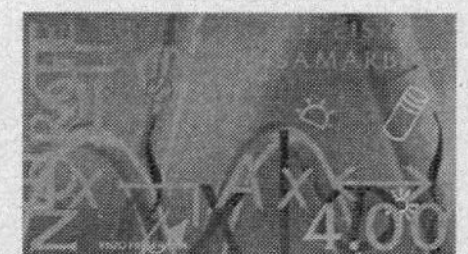

379 Technological Symbols and Formula ("Glass Flasks")

1994. EUREKA (European technology co-operation organization) Conference of Ministers, Lillehammer. Multicoloured.

1190	4 k. Type **379**	80	20
1191	4 k. 50 Technological symbols ("Electronic Chips")	90	25

380 Tram and Street Plan of Oslo, 1894

382 Sledge

1994. Centenary of Electric Trams. Multicoloured.

1192	3 k. 50 Type **380**	70	10
1193	12 k. Modern tram and Oslo route map	2·40	95

1994. Christmas.

1195	**382**	3 k. 50 red and black	70	10
1196	–	3 k. 50 ultramarine, blue and black	70	10

DESIGN: No. 1196, Kick-sledge.

OFFICIAL STAMPS

O 22

O 36

1925.

O187	O **22**	5 ore mauve	20	40
O188		10 ore green	20	15
O189		15 ore blue	60	95
O190		20 ore purple	20	10
O191		30 ore slate	1·60	2·50
O192		40 ore blue	45	35
O193		60 ore blue	2·00	2·50

1929. Surch **2** twice.

O219	O **22**	2 ore on 5 ore mauve	20	40

1933.

O231	O **36**	2 ore brown	30	60
O243		5 ore purple	40	60
O244		7 ore orange	4·75	5·50
O245		10 ore green	30	15
O235		15 ore olive	30	25
O247		20 ore red	30	10
O237		25 ore brown	40	40
O238		30 ore blue	40	40
O248		35 ore mauve	40	30
O249		40 ore grey	40	15
O250		60 ore blue	40	25
O241		70 ore brown	80	1·25
O242		100 ore violet	90	1·00

O 39

O 58 Quisling Emblem

1937.

O267	O **39**	5 ore mauve	40	10
O256		7 ore orange	20	40
O257		10 ore green	15	10
O270		15 ore olive	55	70
O271		20 ore red	10	10
O260		25 ore brown	40	50
O273		25 ore red	20	10
O261		30 ore blue	40	30
O275		30 ore grey	50	20
O276		35 ore purple	15	10
O277		40 ore grey	20	10
O278		40 ore blue	2·00	20
O279		50 ore lilac	50	10
O280		60 ore blue	30	10
O281		100 ore violet	30	10
O282		200 ore orange	1·60	20

1942.

O336	O **58**	5 ore mauve	20	60
O337		7 ore orange	20	60
O338		10 ore green	10	15
O339		15 ore brown	1·25	6·00
O340		20 ore red	10	15
O341		25 ore brown	2·25	13·00
O342		30 ore blue	1·50	11·00
O343		35 ore purple	1·50	9·00
O344		40 ore slate	15	20
O345		60 ore blue	1·25	6·00
O346		1 k. blue	1·25	7·50

1949. Surch **25** and bar.

O402	O **39**	25 ore on 20 ore red	30	15

O 89

O 99

1951.

O434	O **89**	5 ore mauve	40	15
O435		10 ore grey	40	10
O436		15 ore brown	50	20
O437		30 ore red	40	10
O438		35 ore brown	60	40
O439		60 ore blue	60	15
O440		100 ore violet	1·25	25

1955.

O458	O **99**	5 ore purple	15	10
O459		10 ore grey	15	10
O460		15 ore brown	50	60
O461		20 ore green	20	10
O462		25 ore green	40	15
O463		30 ore red	80	40
O464		30 ore green	55	15
O465		35 ore red	30	10
O466		40 ore lilac	60	10
O467		40 ore green	50	15
O468		45 ore red	65	10
O469		50 ore brown	1·50	25
O470		50 ore red	80	10
O471		50 ore blue	30	10
O738		50 ore grey	30	10
O739		60 ore blue	80	85
O473		60 ore red	60	10
O474		60 ore green	1·25	1·40
O475		65 ore red	60	10
O476		70 ore brown	1·75	60
O477		70 ore red	30	10
O478		75 ore brown	6·50	6·50
O479		75 ore green	60	50
O481		80 ore brown	40	10
O741		80 ore red	30	10
O482		85 ore brown	60	80
O483		90 ore orange	60	15
O484		1 k. violet	50	10
O485		1 k. red	30	10
O486		1 k. 10 red	55	30
O744		1 k. 25 red	45	10
O745		1 k. 30 purple	45	30
O746		1 k. 50 red	30	10
O747		1 k. 75 green	60	40
O749		2 k. red	55	10
O487		2 k. green	1·25	10
O750		3 k. violet	75	20
O488		5 k. violet	3·00	35
O752		5 k. blue	1·00	20

POSTAGE DUE STAMPS

D 12

1889. Inscr "at betale" and "PORTOMAERKE".

D95	D **12**	1 ore green	30	40
D96a		4 ore mauve	65	35
D97		10 ore red	1·90	25
D98		15 ore brown	75	40
D99		20 ore blue	1·10	25
D94		50 ore purple	1·90	1·25

1922. Inscr "a betale" and "PORTOMERKE".

D162	D **12**	4 ore mauve	3·50	3·50
D163		10 ore green	1·25	85
D164		20 ore purple	2·50	2·00
D165		40 ore blue	4·50	40
D166		100 ore yellow	14·00	7·50
D167		200 ore violet	38·00	17·50

NOSSI-BE Pt. 6

An island north-west of Madagascar, declared a French protectorate in 1840. In 1901 it became part of Madagascar and Dependencies.

100 centimes = 1 franc

1889. Stamp of French Colonies, "Peace and Commerce" type, surch.

8	H	25 c. on 40 c. red on yellow	£1400	£500

1889. Stamps of French Colonies, "Commerce" type, surch.

4	J	5 c. on 10 c. black on lilac	£1600	£550
2		5 c. on 20 c. red on green	£1800	£700
6		15 on 20 c. red on green	£1500	£550
7		25 on 30 c. brown on drab	£1400	£425
9		25 on 40 c. red on yellow	£1400	£400

1890. Stamps of French Colonies, "Commerce" type, surch (a) **N S B 0 25**.

10	**J**	0.25 on 20 c. red on green	£225	£160
11		0 25 on 75 c. red on pink	£225	£160
12		0 25 on 1 f. green	£225	£160

(b) **N S B 25 c.**

13	J	25 c. on 20 c. red on green	£225	£160
14		25 c. on 75 c. red on pink	£225	£160
15		25 c. on 1 f. green	£225	£160

(c) **N S B 25** in frame.

16	J	25 on 20 c. red on green	£575	£375
17		25 on 75 c. red on pink	£575	£375
18		25 on 1 f. green	£575	£375

1893. Stamps of French Colonies, "Commerce" type, surch **NOSSI-BE** and bar over value in figures.

36	J	25 on 20 c. red on green	23·00	18·00
37		50 on 10 c. black on lilac	25·00	18·00
38		75 on 15 c. blue	£160	£120
39		1 f. on 5 c. green	60·00	50·00

1893. Stamps of French Colonies, "Commerce" type, optd **Nossi Be**.

40	J	10 c. black on lilac	8·00	4·50
41		15 c. blue	8·50	7·00
42		20 c. red on green	60·00	30·00

1894. "Tablet" key-type inscr "NOSSI-BE" in red (1, 5, 15, 25, 75 c., 1 f.) or blue (others).

44	D	1 c. black on blue	60	60
45		2 c. brown on buff	85	75
46		4 c. brown on grey	1·25	75
47		5 c. green on green	1·40	85
48		10 c. black on lilac	3·00	1·90
49		15 c. blue	4·75	2·25
50		20 c. red on green	5·25	3·00
51		25 c. black on pink	6·00	4·25
52		30 c. brown on drab	8·25	5·00
53		40 c. red on yellow	9·00	7·75
54		50 c. red on pink	9·00	6·25
55		75 c. brown on orange	23·00	17·00
56		1 f. green	12·00	9·00

POSTAGE DUE STAMPS

1891. Stamps of French Colonies, "Commerce" type, surch **NOSSI-BE chiffre-taxe A PERCEVOIR** and value.

D19	J	0.20 on 1 c. black on blue	£210	£160
D20		0.30 on 2 c. brown on buff	£210	£160
D21		0.35 on 4 c. brown on grey	£225	£170
D22		0.35 on 20 c. red on green	£250	£170
D23		0.50 on 30 c. brn on drab	70·00	55·00
D24		1 f. on 35 c. blk on orge	£160	£110

1891. Stamps of French Colonies, "Commerce" type, surch **Nossi-Be A PERCEVOIR** and value.

D25	J	5 c. on 20 c. red on green	£160	£110
D26		10 c. on 15 c. blue on blue	£140	£140
D33		0.10 on 5 c. green	10·00	8·25
D27		15 c. on 10 c. blk on lilac	90·00	90·00
D34		0.15 on 20 c. red on green	12·50	11·00
D28		25 c. on 5 c. green on grn	90·00	90·00
D35		0.25 on 75 c. red on pink	£375	£350

NYASSA COMPANY Pt. 9

In 1894 Portugal granted a charter to the Nyassa Company to administer an area in the Northern part of Mozambique, including the right to issue its own stamps. The lease was terminated in 1929 and the administration was transferred to Mozambique whose stamps were used there.

1898. 1000 reis = 1 milreis
1913. 100 centavos = 1 escudo

1898. "Figures" and "Newspaper" key-types inscr "MOCAMBIQUE" optd **NYASSA**.

1	V	2½ r. brown	1·10	1·10
2	R	5 r. orange	1·10	1·10
3		10 r. mauve	1·10	1·10
4		15 r. brown	1·10	1·10
5		20 r. lilac	1·10	1·10
6		25 r. green	1·10	1·10
7		50 r. blue	1·10	1·10
8		75 r. red	1·50	1·25
9		80 r. green	1·50	1·40
10		100 r. brown on buff	1·50	1·40
11		150 r. red on rose	3·25	3·25
12		200 r. blue on blue	2·25	2·25
13		300 r. blue on brown	2·25	2·25

1898. "King Carlos" key-type inscr "MOCAMBIQUE" optd **NYASSA**.

14	S	2½ r. grey	75	65
15		5 r. orange	75	65
16		10 r. green	75	65
17		15 r. brown	90	75
18		20 r. lilac	90	75
19		25 r. green	90	75
20		50 r. blue	90	75
21		75 r. red	90	75
22		80 r. mauve	1·25	1·10
23		100 r. blue on blue	1·25	1·10
24		150 r. brown on yellow	1·25	1·10
25		200 r. purple on pink	1·25	1·10
26		300 r. blue on pink	1·25	1·10

2 Giraffe **3** Dromedaries

1901.

27	**2**	2½ r. brown and black	60	30
28		5 r. violet and black	60	30
29		10 r. green and black	60	30
30		15 r. brown and black	60	30
31		20 r. red and black	60	40
32		25 r. orange and black	60	40
33		50 r. blue and black	60	40
34	**3**	75 r. red and black	70	50
35		80 r. mauve and black	70	50
36		100 r. brown and black	70	50
37		150 r. brown and black	70	50
38		200 r. green and black	75	55
39		300 r. green and black	75	55

1903. Surch in figures and words.

40	**3**	65 r. on 80 r. mauve & blk	50	40
41		115 r. on 150 r. brown & blk	50	40
42		130 r. on 300 r. green & blk	50	40

1903. Optd **PROVISORIO**.

43	**2**	15 r. brown and black	55	45
44		25 r. orange and black	55	45

1910. Optd **PROVISORIO** and surch in figures and words.

50	**2**	5 r. on 2½ r. brown and black	60	45
51	**3**	50 r. on 100 r. brown & black	60	45

9 Dromedaries **12** Vasco de Gama's Flagship "Sao Gabriel"

1911. Optd **REPUBLICA**.

53	**9**	2½ r. violet and black	50	30
54		5 r. black	50	30
55		10 r. green and black	50	30
56	–	20 r. red and black	50	30
57	–	25 r. brown and black	50	30
58	–	50 r. blue and black	50	30
59	–	75 r. brown and black	50	40
60	–	100 r. brown & black on green	50	40
61	–	200 r. green & blk on pink	60	60
62	**12**	300 r. black on blue	1·25	90
63		400 r. brown and black	1·40	1·00
64		500 r. violet and olive	1·75	1·40

DESIGNS—HORIZ: 20, 25, 50 r. Common zebra. VERT: 75, 100, 200 r. Giraffe.

1918. Surch **REPUBLICA** and value in figures.

65	**2**	¼ c. on 2½ c. brown and black	20·00	13·00
66		½ c. on 5 r. violet and black	20·00	13·00
67		1 c. on 10 r. green and black	20·00	13·00
68		1½ c. on 15 r. brown & black	80	60
69		2 c. on 20 r. red and black	60	50
70		3½ c. on 25 r. orange & black	60	50
71		5 c. on 50 r. blue and black	60	50
72	**3**	7½ c. on 75 r. red and black	60	50
73		8 c. on 80 r. mauve and black	60	50
74		10 c. on 100 r. brown & black	60	50
75		15 c. on 150 r. brown & black	75	65
76		20 c. on 200 r. green & black	75	65
77		30 c. on 300 r. green & black	95	80

1919. Nos. 43/4 and 40/2 surch **REPUBLICA** and value in figures.

78	**2**	1½ c. on 15 r. brown & black	2·00	1·50
79		3½ c. on 25 r. orange & blk	70	50
80	**3**	40 c. on 65 r. on 80 r.	4·50	4·50
81		50 c. on 115 r. on 150 r.	1·25	1·00
82		1 c. on 130 r. on 300 r.	1·25	1·00

1921. Stamps of 1911 surch in figures and words.

83	**9**	¼ c. on 2½ r. violet & black	80	80
85		½ c. on 5 r. black	80	80
86		1 c. on 10 r. green & black	80	80
87	**12**	1½ c. on 300 r. black on blue	80	80
88	–	2 c. on 20 r. red and black	80	80
89	–	2½ c. on 25 r. brown & black	80	80
90	**12**	3 c. on 400 r. brown & black	80	80
91	–	5 c. on 50 r. blue and black	80	80
92	–	7½ c. on 75 r. brown & black	80	80
93	–	10 c. on 100 r. brown and black on green	80	80
94	**12**	12 c. on 500 r. violet & olive	80	80
95	–	20 c. on 200 r. green and black on pink	80	80

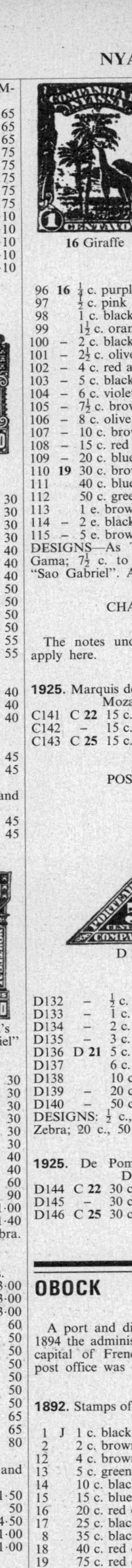

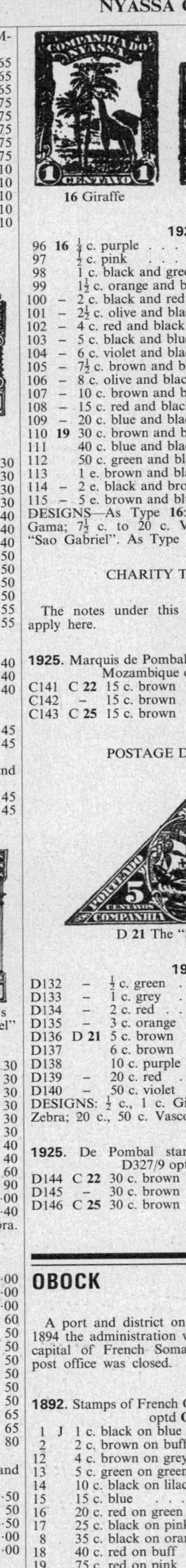

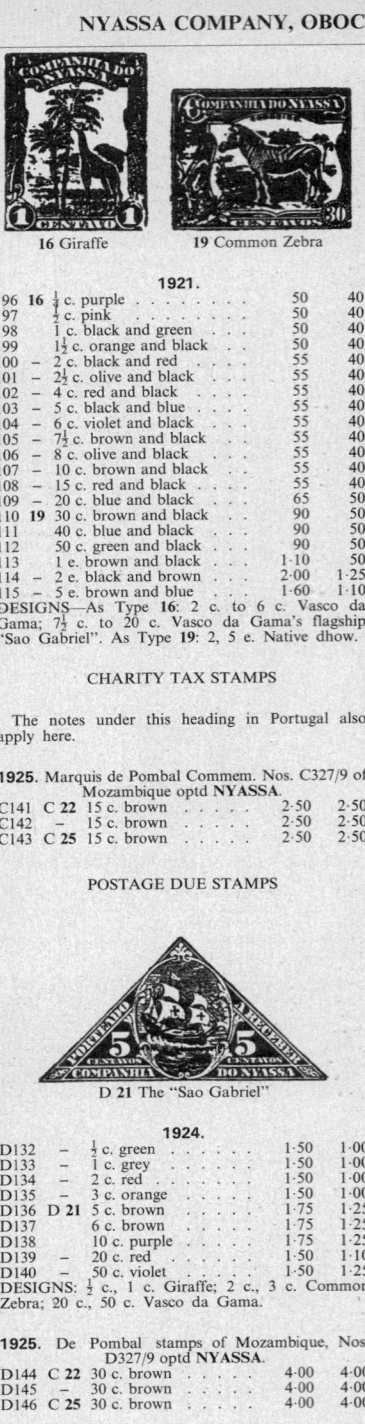

16 Giraffe **19** Common Zebra

1921.

96	**16**	¼ c. purple	50	40
97		½ c. pink	50	40
98		1 c. black and green	50	40
99		1½ c. orange and black	50	40
100	–	2 c. black and red	55	40
101	–	2½ c. olive and black	55	40
102	–	4 c. red and black	55	40
103	–	5 c. black and blue	55	40
104	–	6 c. violet and black	55	40
105	–	7½ c. brown and black	55	40
106	–	8 c. olive and black	55	40
107	–	10 c. brown and black	55	40
108	–	15 c. red and black	55	40
109	–	20 c. blue and black	65	50
110	**19**	30 c. brown and black	90	50
111		40 c. blue and black	90	50
112		50 c. green and black	90	50
113		1 e. brown and black	1·10	50
114	–	2 e. black and brown	2·00	1·25
115	–	5 e. brown and blue	1·60	1·10

DESIGNS—As Type **16**: 2 c. to 6 c. Vasco da Gama; 7½ c. to 20 c. Vasco da Gama's flagship "Sao Gabriel". As Type **19**: 2, 5 e. Native dhow.

CHARITY TAX STAMPS

The notes under this heading in Portugal also apply here.

1925. Marquis de Pombal Commem. Nos. C327/9 of Mozambique optd **NYASSA**.

C141	C **22**	15 c. brown	2·50	2·50
C142	–	15 c. brown	2·50	2·50
C143	C **25**	15 c. brown	2·50	2·50

POSTAGE DUE STAMPS

D **21** The "Sao Gabriel"

1924.

D132	–	½ c. green	1·50	1·00
D133	–	1 c. grey	1·50	1·00
D134	–	2 c. red	1·50	1·00
D135	–	3 c. orange	1·50	1·00
D136	D **21**	5 c. brown	1·75	1·25
D137		6 c. brown	1·75	1·25
D138		10 c. purple	1·75	1·25
D139	–	20 c. red	1·50	1·10
D140	–	50 c. violet	1·50	1·25

DESIGNS: ½ c., 1 c. Giraffe; 2 c., 3 c. Common Zebra; 20 c., 50 c. Vasco da Gama.

1925. De Pombal stamps of Mozambique, Nos. D327/9 optd **NYASSA**.

D144	C **22**	30 c. brown	4·00	4·00
D145	–	30 c. brown	4·00	4·00
D146	C **25**	30 c. brown	4·00	4·00

OBOCK Pt. 6

A port and district on the Somali Coast. During 1894 the administration was moved to Djibouti, the capital of French Somali Coast, and the Obock post office was closed.

1892. Stamps of French Colonies, "Commerce" type, optd **OBOCK**.

1	J	1 c. black on blue	18·00	16·00
2		2 c. brown on buff	21·00	18·00
12		4 c. brown on grey	11·00	9·50
13		5 c. green on green	11·00	9·25
14		10 c. black on lilac	11·50	11·00
15		15 c. blue	12·00	10·50
16		20 c. red on green	25·00	20·00
17		25 c. black on pink	10·00	8·25
8		35 c. black on orange	£250	£250
18		40 c. red on buff	30·00	25·00
19		75 c. red on pink	£190	£160
20		1 f. green	40·00	35·00

1892. Nos. 14, 15, 17 and 20 surch.

39	J	1 on 25 c. black on red	6·00	5·50
40		2 on 10 c. black on lilac	40·00	25·00
41		2 on 15 c. blue	6·25	6·75
42		4 on 15 c. blue	7·00	6·75
43		4 on 25 c. black on red	7·75	7·00
44		5 on 25 c. black on red	11·00	8·25
45		20 on 10 c. black on lilac	50·00	42·00
46		30 on 10 c. black on lilac	65·00	55·00
47		35 on 25 c. black on red	50·00	45·00
48		75 on 1 f. olive	65·00	60·00
49		5 f. on 1 f. olive	£525	£475

1982. "Tablet" key-type inscr "OBOCK" in red (1, 5, 15, 25, 75 c., 1 f.) or blue (others).

50	D	1 c. black on blue	1·40	1·25
51		2 c. brown on buff	60	65
52		4 c. brown on grey	1·50	1·25
53		5 c. green on green	2·25	1·50
54		10 c. black on lilac	3·75	2·25
55		15 c. blue	7·75	5·00
56		20 c. red on green	15·00	12·50
57		25 c. black on pink	14·00	12·50
58		30 c. brown on drab	11·00	9·00
59		40 c. red on yellow	11·00	8·00
60		50 c. red on pink	12·50	8·25
61		75 c. brown on orange	16·00	8·25
62		1 f. green	22·00	18·00

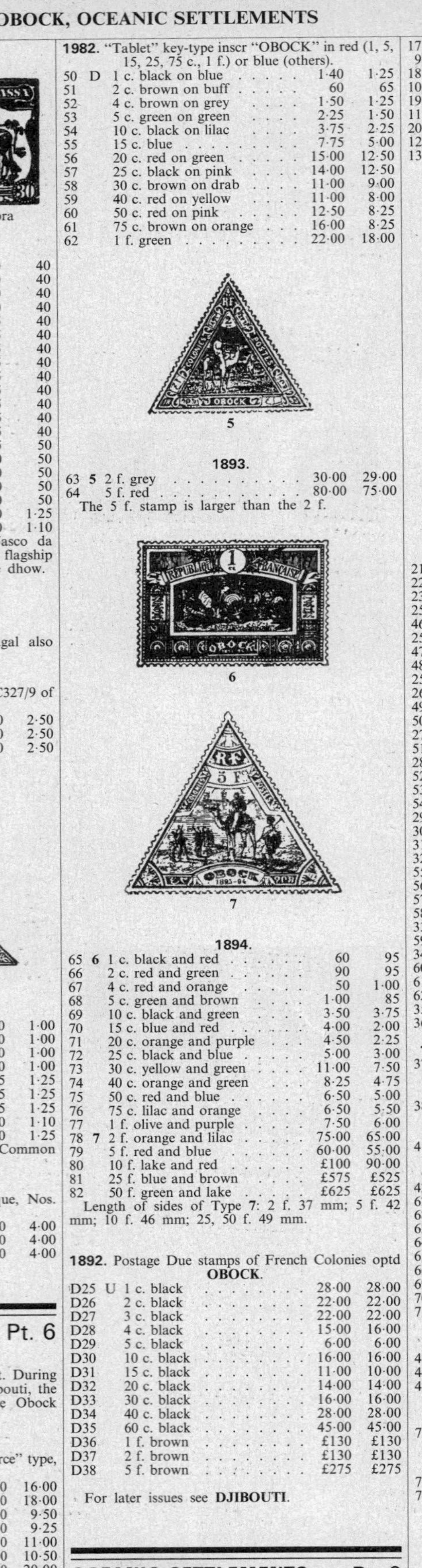

5

1893.

63	**5**	2 f. grey	30·00	29·00
64		5 f. red	80·00	75·00

The 5 f. stamp is larger than the 2 f.

6

7

1894.

65	**6**	1 c. black and red	60	95
66		2 c. red and green	90	95
67		4 c. red and orange	50	1·00
68		5 c. green and brown	1·00	85
69		10 c. black and green	3·50	3·75
70		15 c. blue and red	4·00	2·00
71		20 c. orange and purple	4·50	2·25
72		25 c. black and blue	5·00	3·00
73		30 c. yellow and green	11·00	7·50
74		40 c. orange and green	8·25	4·75
75		50 c. red and blue	6·50	5·00
76		75 c. lilac and orange	6·50	5·50
77		1 f. olive and purple	7·50	6·00
78	**7**	2 f. orange and lilac	75·00	65·00
79		5 f. red and blue	60·00	55·00
80		10 f. lake and red	£100	90·00
81		25 f. blue and brown	£575	£525
82		50 f. green and lake	£625	£625

Length of sides of Type **7**: 2 f. 37 mm; 5 f. 42 mm; 10 f. 46 mm; 25, 50 f. 49 mm.

1892. Postage Due stamps of French Colonies optd **OBOCK**.

D25	U	1 c. black	28·00	28·00
D26		2 c. black	22·00	22·00
D27		3 c. black	22·00	22·00
D28		4 c. black	15·00	16·00
D29		5 c. black	6·00	6·00
D30		10 c. black	16·00	16·00
D31		15 c. black	11·00	10·00
D32		20 c. black	14·00	14·00
D33		30 c. black	16·00	16·00
D34		40 c. black	28·00	28·00
D35		60 c. black	45·00	45·00
D36		1 f. brown	£130	£130
D37		2 f. brown	£130	£130
D38		5 f. brown	£275	£275

For later issues see **DJIBOUTI**.

OCEANIC SETTLEMENTS Pt. 6

Scattered French islands in the E. Pacific Ocean, including Tahiti and the Marquesas.

In 1957 the Oceanic Settlements were renamed French Polynesia.

1892. "Tablet" key-type.

1	D	1 c. black and red on blue	65	60
2		2 c. brown & blue on buff	90	85
3		4 c. brown & blue on grey	1·75	1·25
14		5 c. green and red	80	65
5		10 c. black & blue on lilac	12·00	5·00
15		10 c. red and blue	80	60
6		15 c. blue and red	10·50	4·75
16		15 c. grey and red	1·75	1·40
7		20 c. red & blue on green	9·25	4·00
8		25 c. black & red on pink	27·00	12·50
17	D	25 c. blue and red	7·50	3·25
9		30 c. brown & blue on drab	8·00	6·00
18		35 c. black & red on yellow	2·50	2·00
10		40 c. red & blue on yellow	65·00	45·00
19		45 c. black & red on green	2·75	1·60
11		50 c. red and blue on pink	4·50	3·25
20		50 c. brown & red on blue	£140	£110
12		75 c. brown & red on orge	6·00	4·00
13		1 f. green and red	8·25	6·25

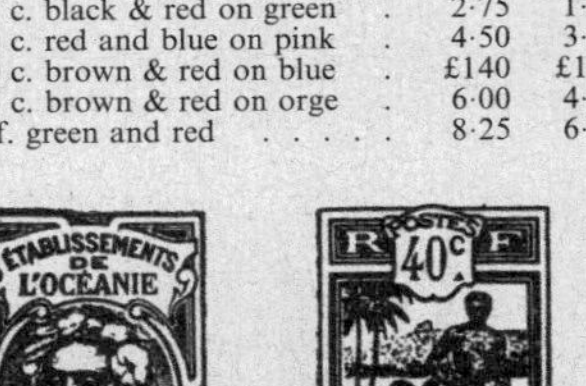

2 Tahitian Woman **3** Kanakas

4 Valley of Fautaua

1913.

21	**2**	1 c. brown and violet	10	25
22		2 c. grey and brown	15	25
23		4 c. blue and orange	15	30
25		5 c. light green and green	30	45
46		5 c. black and blue	30	40
25		10 c. orange and red	40	50
47		10 c. light green and green	35	50
48		10 c. purple & red on blue	60	70
25a		15 c. black and orange	30	35
26		20 c. violet and black	25	35
49		20 c. green	35	50
50		20 c. brown and red	65	70
27	**3**	25 c. blue and ultramarine	45	50
51		25 c. red and violet	50	60
28		30 c. brown and grey	1·75	1·60
52		30 c. red and carmine	75	90
53		30 c. red and black	40	55
54		30 c. green and blue	65	80
29		35 c. red and green	35	40
30		40 c. green and black	40	45
31		45 c. red and orange	35	45
32		50 c. black and brown	7·25	5·50
55		50 c. blue and ultramarine	45	60
56		50 c. blue and grey	45	60
57		60 c. black and green	35	45
58		65 c. mauve and brown	1·25	1·40
33		75 c. violet and purple	1·00	85
59		90 c. mauve and red	8·25	8·25
34	**4**	1 f. black and red	1·40	1·00
60		1 f. 10 brown and mauve	85	85
61		1 f. 40 violet and brown	2·00	2·00
62		1 f. 50 light blue and blue	8·00	8·00
35		2 f. green and brown	2·25	2·00
36		5 f. blue and violet	5·00	5·00

1915. "Tablet" key-type optd **E F O 1915** and bar.

37	D	10 c. red	1·90	1·90

1915. Red Cross. No. 37 surch **5c** and red cross.

38	D	10 c. + 5 c. red	12·00	13·50

1915. Red Cross. Surch **5c** and red cross.

41	**2**	10 c. + 5 c. orange and red	1·10	1·25

1916. Surch.

42	**2**	10 c. on 15 c. black & orange	70	75
67	**4**	25 c. on 2 f. green & brown	50	60
68		25 c. on 5 f. blue and violet	50	60
63	**3**	60 c. on 75 c. brown and blue	20	35
64	**4**	65 on 1 f. brown and blue	80	80
65		85 on 1 f. brown and blue	75	80
66	**3**	90 on 75 c. mauve and red	75	80
69	**4**	1 f. 25 on 1 f. ultramarine & bl	50	60
70		1 f. 50 on 1 f. lt blue & blue	1·00	1·25
71		20 f. on 5 f. mauve and red	12·50	10·00

1921. Surch **1921** and new value.

43	**2**	05 on 2 c. grey and brown	17·00	17·00
44	**3**	10 on 45 c. red and orange	17·00	17·00
45	**2**	25 on 15 c. black and orange	3·75	4·00

1924. Surch **45 c. 1924**.

72	**2**	45 c. on 10 c. orange and red	95	95

1926. Surch in words.

73	**4**	3 f. on 5 f. blue and grey	1·10	90
74		10 f. on 5 f. black and green	3·00	2·50

13 Papetoia Bay

1929.

75	**13**	3 f. sepia and green	4·00	4·00
76		5 f. sepia and blue	6·25	6·75
77		10 f. sepia and red	18·00	20·00
78		20 f. sepia and mauve	22·00	23·00

1931. "International Colonial Exhibition", Paris, key-types.

79	E	40 c. black and green	3·50	3·00
80	F	50 c. black and mauve	3·50	3·25
81	G	90 c. black and red	3·50	3·25
82	H	1 f. 50 black and blue	3·50	3·50

14 Spearing Fish

15 Tahitian Girl

16 Native Gods

1934.

No.	Type	Description	Mint	Used
83	**14**	1 c. black	15	30
84		2 c. red	15	30
85		3 c. blue	15	30
86		4 c. orange	15	35
87		5 c. mauve	35	45
88		10 c. brown	15	30
89		15 c. green	25	35
90		20 c. red	15	30
91	**15**	25 c. blue	35	45
92		30 c. green	65	70
93		30 c. orange	25	35
94	**16**	35 c. green	1·90	1·90
95	**15**	40 c. mauve	30	35
96		45 c. red	4·75	4·50
97		45 c. green	35	45
98		50 c. violet	15	30
99		55 c. blue	2·75	2·75
100		60 c. black	25	35
101		65 c. brown	1·60	1·60
102		70 c. pink	40	45
103		75 c. olive	4·00	4·00
104		80 c. purple	70	65
105		90 c. red	40	45
106	**16**	1 f. brown	40	30
107		1 f. 25 purple	4·75	4·75
108		1 f. 25 red	40	50
109		1 f. 40 orange	40	50
110		1 f. 50 blue	45	50
111		1 f. 60 violet	40	50
112		1 f. 75 green	3·25	3·00
113		2 f. red	35	40
114		2 f. 25 blue	40	50
115		2 f. 50 black	55	60
116		3 f. orange	50	60
117		5 f. mauve	50	70
118		10 f. green	1·50	1·60
119		20 f. brown	2·00	2·00

17 Flying Boat

1934. Air.

No.	Type	Description	Mint	Used
120	**17**	5 f. green	50	60

1937. International Exhibition, Paris. As Nos. 168/73 of St.-Pierre et Miquelon.

No.	Type	Description	Mint	Used
121		20 c. violet	1·10	1·10
122		30 c. green	1·10	1·10
123		40 c. red	1·40	1·40
124		50 c. brown	1·25	1·60
125		90 c. red	1·40	1·90
126		1 f. 50 blue	1·75	2·75

1938. Int. Anti-Cancer Fund. As T **33** of Mauritania.

No.	Type	Description	Mint	Used
127		1 f. 75 + 50 c. blue	8·50	8·75

1939. New York World's Fair. As T **28** of Mauritania.

No.	Type	Description	Mint	Used
128		1 f. 25 red	1·10	1·10
129		2 f. 25 blue	1·10	1·10

1939. 150th Anniv. of French Revolution. As T **29** of Mauritania.

No.	Type	Description	Mint	Used
130		45 c. + 25 c. green and black (postage)	8·75	8·75
131		70 c. + 30 c. brown & black	8·75	8·75
132		90 c. + 35 c. orange & black	8·75	8·75
133		1 f. 25 + 1 f. red and black	8·75	8·75
134		2 f. 25 + 2 f. blue and black	8·75	8·75
135		5 f. + 4 f. black & orge (air)	17·00	17·00

1941. Adherence to General de Gaulle. Optd **FRANCE LIBRE**. (a) Nos. 75/8.

No.	Type	Description	Mint	Used
136	**13**	3 f. brown and green	3·25	
137		5 f. brown and blue	3·25	
138		10 f. brown and red	9·00	
139		20 f. brown and mauve	65·00	
		(b) Nos. 106 and 115/19.		
140	**16**	1 f. brown	2·25	2·75
141		2 f. 50 black	2·50	3·50
142		3 f. red	2·75	3·50
143		5 f. mauve	3·25	3·50
144		10 f. green	35·00	
145		20 f. brown	32·00	
		(c) Air stamp of 1934.		
146	**17**	5 f. green	1·90	1·90

19 Polynesian Travelling Canoe

1942. Free French Issue. (a) Postage.

No.	Type	Description	Mint	Used
147	**19**	5 c. brown	15	30
148		10 c. blue	15	30
149		25 c. green	15	30
150		30 c. red	15	30
151		40 c. green	15	30
152		80 c. purple	15	30
153		1 f. mauve	20	35
154		1 f. 50 red	25	35
155		2 f. black	25	30
156		2 f. 50 blue	60	1·10
157		4 f. violet	40	55
158		5 f. yellow	50	70
159		10 f. brown	75	85
160		20 f. green	90	90
		(b) Air. As T **30** of New Caledonia.		
161		1 f. orange	40	50
162		1 f. 50 red	40	50
163		5 f. purple	50	60
164		10 f. black	75	80
165		25 f. blue	1·10	1·25
166		50 f. green	1·10	1·25
167		100 f. red	1·00	1·25

1944. Mutual Aid and Red Cross Funds. As T **31** of New Caledonia.

No.	Type	Description	Mint	Used
168		5 f. + 20 f. blue	65	80

1945. Surch in figures.

No.	Type	Description	Mint	Used
169	**19**	50 c. on 5 c. brown	25	35
170		60 c. on 5 c. brown	25	35
171		70 c. on 5 c. brown	25	35
172		1 f. 20 on 5 c. brown	25	35
173		2 f. 40 on 25 c. green	60	70
174		3 f. on 25 c. green	35	45
175		4 f. 50 on 25 c. green	70	85
176		15 f. on 2 f. 50 blue	95	1·10

1945. Eboue. As T **32** of New Caledonia.

No.	Type	Description	Mint	Used
177		2 f. black	30	40
178		25 f. green	95	1·10

1946. Air. Victory. As T **34** of New Caledonia.

No.	Type	Description	Mint	Used
179		8 f. green	75	1·10

1946. Air. From Chad to the Rhine. As Nos. 300/5 of New Caledonia.

No.	Type	Description	Mint	Used
180		5 f. red	1·00	1·10
181		10 f. brown	1·00	1·10
182		15 f. green	1·00	1·10
183		20 f. red	1·50	1·50
184		25 f. purple	1·60	1·90
185		50 f. black	2·00	2·25

21 Moorea Coastline

22 Tahitian Girl

23 Wandering Albatross over Moorea

1948. (a) Postage as T **21/22**.

No.	Type	Description	Mint	Used
186	**21**	10 c. brown	15	30
187		30 c. green	15	30
188		40 c. blue	15	30
189	–	50 c. lake	30	40
190	–	60 c. olive	30	40
191	–	80 c. blue	30	40
192	–	1 f. lake	30	40
193	–	1 f. 20 blue	30	40
194	–	1 f. 50 blue	30	40
195	**22**	2 f. brown	50	60
196		2 f. 40 lake	65	70
197		3 f. violet	5·00	1·50
198		4 f. blue	65	65
199	–	5 f. brown	75	70
200	–	6 f. blue	90	75
201	–	9 f. brown, black and red	6·00	5·00
202	–	10 f. olive	2·75	1·25
203	–	15 f. red	3·00	1·50
204	–	20 f. blue	3·50	1·90
205	–	25 f. brown	2·75	2·50
		(b) Air. As T **23**.		
206	–	13 f. light blue and deep blue	6·00	3·75
207	**23**	50 f. lake	13·50	8·75
208	–	100 f. violet	8·50	5·50
209	–	200 f. blue	25·00	16·00

DESIGNS: As T **22**: 50 c. to 80 c. Kanaka fishermen; 9 f. Bora-Bora girl; 1 f. to 1 f. 50 Faa village; 5 f., 6 f., 10 f. Bora-Bora and Pandanus pine; 15 f. to 25 f. Polynesian girls. As T **23**: 13 f. Pahia Peak and palms; 100 f. Airplane over Moorea; 200 f. Wandering albatross over Maupiti Island.

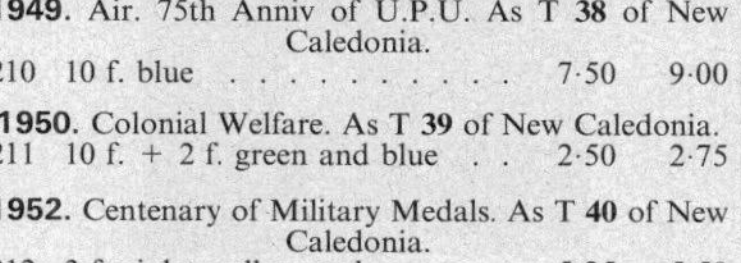

1949. Air. 75th Anniv of U.P.U. As T **38** of New Caledonia.

No.	Type	Description	Mint	Used
210		10 f. blue	7·50	9·00

1950. Colonial Welfare. As T **39** of New Caledonia.

No.	Type	Description	Mint	Used
211		10 f. + 2 f. green and blue	2·50	2·75

1952. Centenary of Military Medals. As T **40** of New Caledonia.

No.	Type	Description	Mint	Used
212		3 f. violet, yellow and green	5·25	5·50

25 "Nafea" (after Gauguin)

26 Schooner in Dry Dock, Papeete

1953. Air. 50th Death Anniv of Gauguin (painter).

No.	Type	Description	Mint	Used
213	**25**	14 f. sepia, red and turquoise	55·00	55·00

1954. Air. 10th Anniv of Liberation. As T **42** of New Caledonia.

No.	Type	Description	Mint	Used
214		3 f. green and turquoise	2·75	2·50

1956. Economic and Social Development Fund.

No.	Type	Description	Mint	Used
215	**26**	3 f. turquoise	1·40	1·00

POSTAGE DUE STAMPS

1926. Postage Due stamps of France surch **Etabts Francais de l'Oceanie 2 francs a percevoir** (No. D80) or optd **Etablissements Francais de l'Oceanie** (others).

No.	Type	Description	Mint	Used
D73	**D 11**	5 c. blue	25	45
D74		10 c. brown	25	45
D75		20 c. olive	65	70
D76		30 c. red	65	70
D77		40 c. red	1·40	1·40
D78		60 c. green	1·40	1·40
D79		1 f. red on yellow	1·25	1·40
D80		2 f. on 1 f. red	1·90	1·90
D81		3 f. mauve	5·50	5·50

D 14 Fautaua Falls

D 24

1929.

No.	Type	Description	Mint	Used
D82	**D 14**	5 c. brown and blue	35	40
D83		10 c. green and orange	35	40
D84		30 c. red and brown	80	80
D85		50 c. brown and green	65	70
D86		60 c. green and violet	1·90	2·00
D87	–	1 f. mauve and blue	1·25	1·40
D88	–	2 f. brown and red	80	80
D89	–	3 f. green and blue	90	95

DESIGN: 1 to 3 f. Polynesian man.

1948.

No.	Type	Description	Mint	Used
D210	**D 24**	10 c. green	15	30
D211		30 c. brown	25	30
D212		50 c. red	25	30
D213		1 f. blue	30	35
D214		2 f. green	50	55
D215		3 f. red	65	70
D216		4 f. violet	75	85
D217		5 f. mauve	1·10	1·25
D218		10 f. blue	2·00	2·25
D219		20 f. lake	2·50	2·75

For later issues see FRENCH POLYNESIA.

OLDENBURG Pt. 7

A former Grand Duchy in North Germany. In 1867 it joined the North German Federation.

72 grote = 1 thaler

1 2 3

1852. Imperf.

No.	Type	Description	Mint	Used
1	**1**	$\frac{1}{3}$ sgr. black on green	£1000	£900
2		$\frac{1}{30}$ th. black on blue	£300	18·00
5		$\frac{1}{15}$ th. black on red	£650	75·00
8		$\frac{1}{10}$ th. black on yellow	£700	75·00

1859. Imperf.

No.	Type	Description	Mint	Used
17	**2**	$\frac{1}{4}$ g. orange	£225	£4500
10		$\frac{1}{3}$ g. black on green	£1900	£2750
19		$\frac{1}{3}$ g. green	£375	£750
21		$\frac{1}{2}$ g. brown	£350	£425
11		1 g. black on blue	£550	30·00
23		1 g. blue	£180	£120
15		2 g. black on red	£800	£550
26		2 g. red	£375	£400
16		3 g. black on yellow	£800	£500
28		3 g. yellow	£375	£400

1862. Roul.

No.	Type	Description	Mint	Used
30	**3**	$\frac{1}{3}$ g. green	£190	£170
32		$\frac{1}{2}$ g. orange	£170	95·00
42		1 g. red	5·00	35·00
36		2 g. blue	£170	35·00
39		3 g. bistre	£170	40·00

OMAN (SULTANATE) Pt. 19

In Jan. 1971, the independent Sultanate of Muscat and Oman was renamed Sultanate of Oman.

NOTE. Labels inscribed "State of Oman" or "Oman Imamate State" are said to have been issued by a rebel administration under the Imam of Oman. There is no convincing evidence that these labels had any postal use within Oman and they are therefore omitted. They can be found, however, used on covers which appear to emanate from Amman and Baghdad.

1000 baizas = rial saidi

1971. Nos. 110/21 of Muscat and Oman optd **SULTANATE of OMAN** in English and Arabic.

No.	Type	Description	Mint	Used
122	**12**	5 b. purple	15	15
123		10 b. brown	20	15
124		20 b. brown	50	15
125	A	25 b. black and violet	80	20
126		30 b. black and blue	90	25
127		40 b. black and orange	1·00	25
128	**14**	50 b. mauve and blue	1·40	30
129	B	75 b. green and brown	1·75	70
130	C	100 b. blue and orange	2·25	70
131	D	$\frac{1}{4}$ r. brown and green	6·50	3·25
132	E	$\frac{1}{2}$ r. violet and red	11·00	1·50
133	F	1 r. red and violet	19·00	14·00

19 Sultan Qabus and Buildings ("Land Development")

1971. National Day. Multicoloured.

No.	Type	Description	Mint	Used
134		10 b. Type **19**	40	15
135		40 b. Sultan in military uniform and Omanis ("Freedom")	1·40	60
136		50 b. Doctors and patients ("Health Services")	1·50	65
137		100 b. Children in class ("Education")	2·75	2·00

1971. No. 94 of Muscat and Oman, optd with **SULTANATE of OMAN** in English and Arabic.

No.	Type	Description	Mint	Used
138		5 b. on 3 b. purple	2·00	2·00

21 Child in Class

1971. 25th Anniv of U.N.I.C.E.F.

No.	Type	Description	Mint	Used
139	**21**	50 b. + 25 b. multicoloured	3·25	3·00

22 Book Year Emblem

1972. Int. Book Year.

No.	Type	Description	Mint	Used
140	**22**	25 b. multicoloured	2·50	1·25

1972. Nos. 110/12 of Muscat and Oman optd with **SULTANATE of OMAN** in English and Arabic.

No.	Type	Description	Mint	Used
141		5 b. purple	50	50
142		10 b. brown	50	50
143		20 b. brown	1·25	1·25

(24)

26 Matrah, 1809

1972. Nos. 102 of Muscat and Oman and 127 of Oman optd with T **24**.

144 25 b. on 1 r. . . . . 5·00 3·75
145 25 b. on 40 b. . . . . 5·00 3·75

1972.

158 **26** 5 b. multicoloured 15 10
147 10 b. multicoloured 25 10
148 20 b. multicoloured 45 15
192 25 b. multicoloured 40 15
193 – 30 b. multicoloured 45 20
194 – 40 b. multicoloured 60 25
195 – 50 b. multicoloured 65 25
196 – 75 b. multicoloured . . . . 1·00 60
154 – 100 b. multicoloured . . . 1·50 45
155 – ¼ r. multicoloured . . . . . 2·75 1·25
156 – ½ r. multicoloured . . . . . 6·50 3·00
157 – 1 r. multicoloured . . . . 13·00 7·50

DESIGNS—(26×21 mm): 30 b. to 75 b. Shinas, 1809. (42×25 mm): 100 b. to 1 r. Muscat, 1809.

29 Government Buildings

1973. Opening of Ministerial Complex.

170 **29** 25 b. multicoloured 65 35
171 100 b. multicoloured . . . 2·75 1·50

30 Oman Crafts (dhow building)

1973. National Day. Multicoloured.

172 15 b. Type **30** 40 20
173 50 b. Seeb International Airport 2·25 1·25
174 65 b. Dhow and tanker . . . 2·00 1·25
175 100 b. "Ship of the Desert" (camel) . . . . 2·75 1·75

31 Aerial View of Port

1974. Inaug of Port Qabus.

176 **31** 100 b. multicoloured . . . 3·00 2·25

32 Map on Open Book

1974. Illiteracy Eradication Campaign. Mult.

177 25 b. Type **32** 50 30
178 100 b. Hands reaching for open book (vert) . . . . 2·25 1·75

33 Sultan Qabus bin Said and Emblems

1974. Centenary of U.P.U.

179 **33** 100 b. multicoloured . . . 1·00 1·25

34 Arab Scribe

1975. "Eradicate Illiteracy".

180 **34** 25 b. multicoloured . . . 1·75 80

35 New Harbour, Mina Raysoot

1975. National Day. Multicoloured.

181 30 b. Type **35** 25 10
182 50 b. Stadium and map . . . 40 20
183 75 b. Water Desalination Plant 65 50
184 100 b. Television Station . . 85 70
185 150 b. Satellite Earth Station and map . . . . 1·25 1·00
186 250 b. Telecommunications symbols and map . . . . . 2·00 2·00

36 Arab Woman and Child with Nurse

1975. International Women's Year. Mult.

187 75 b. Type **36** 55 45
188 150 b. Mother and children (vert) 1·00 1·00

37 Presenting Colours and Opening of Seeb-Nizwa Highway

1976. National Day. Multicoloured.

201 25 b. Type **37** 45 15
202 40 b. Parachutists and harvesting 90 45
203 75 b. Agusta-Bell AB-212 helicopters and Victory Day procession . . . . 1·75 90
204 150 b. Road construction and Salalah T.V. Station . . . 2·00 1·60

38 Great Bath, Moenjodaro

1977. "Save Moenjodaro" Campaign.

205 **38** 125 b. multicoloured . . . 2·50 1·75

39 A.P.U. Emblem

40 Coffee Pots

1977. 25th Anniv of Arab Postal Union.

206 **39** 30 b. multicoloured . . . 70 35
207 75 b. multicoloured . . . 1·90 1·10

1977. National Day. Multicoloured.

208 40 b. Type **40** 40 30
209 75 b. Earthenware pots . . . 70 55
210 100 b. Khor Rori inscriptions 85 65
211 150 b. Silver jewellery . . . 1·40 1·00

1978. Surch in English and Arabic.

212 40 b. on 150 b. mult (No. 185) 7·00 7·00
213 50 b. on 150 b. mult (No. 188) 8·50 8·50
214 75 b. on 250 b. mult (No. 186) 13·00 13·00

42 Mount Arafat Pilgrims and Kaaba

1978. Pilgrimage to Mecca.

215 **42** 40 b. multicoloured . . . . 1·40 75

43 Jalali Fort

1978. National Day. Forts. Multicoloured.

216 20 b. Type **43** 20 15
217 25 b. Nizwa Fort 20 15
218 40 b. Rostaq Fort 35 25
219 50 b. Sohar Fort 40 40
220 75 b. Bahla Fort 55 65
221 100 b. Jibrin Fort 75 85

44 World Map, Koran and Symbols of Arab Achievements

1979. The Arabs.

222 **44** 40 b. multicoloured 45 35
223 100 b. multicoloured . . . 1·40 90

45 Child on Swing

1979. International Year of the Child.

224 **45** 40 b. multicoloured . . . . 1·50 1·00

46 Gas Plant

1979. National Day. Multicoloured.

225 25 b. Type **46** 80 30
226 75 b. Dhow and modern trawler 1·25 1·10

47 Sultan Qabus on Horseback

1979. Armed Forces Day. Multicoloured.

227 40 b. Type **47** . . . . 2·25 75
228 100 b. Soldier . . . . 2·50 1·75

48 Mosque, Mecca

1980. 1400th Anniv of Hegira. Multicoloured.

229 50 b. Type **48** 55 40
230 150 b. Mosque and Kaaba . . 1·75 1·40

49 Bab Alkabir

1980. National Day. Multicoloured.

231 75 b. Type **49** 40 40
232 100 b. Corniche 85 55
233 250 b. Polo match . . . . . . 1·25 1·25
234 500 b. Omani women . . . . 3·00 3·25

50 Sultan and Naval Patrol Boat

1980. Armed Forces Day. Multicoloured.

235 150 b. Type **50** . . . . 1·25 1·00
236 750 b. Sultan and mounted soldiers . . . . 4·50 4·50

51 Policewoman helping Children across Road

1981. National Police Day. Multicoloured.

237 50 b. Type **51** 60 40
238 100 b. Police bandsmen . . . 1·00 80
239 150 b. Mounted police . . . 1·50 1·25
240 ½ r. Police headquarters . . . 4·50 3·50

1981. Nos. 231, 234 and 235/6 surch **POSTAGE** and new value in English and Arabic.

241 **50** 20 b. on 150 b. multicoloured 50 30
242 – 30 b. on 750 b. multicoloured 80 45
243 **49** 50 b. on 75 b. multicoloured 1·40 70
244 – 100 b. on 500 b. multicoloured 2·50 1·40

53 Sultan's Crest

1981. Welfare of Blind.

245 **53** 10 b. black, blue and red . 45 15

54 Palm Tree, Fishes and Wheat

1981. World Food Day.

246 **54** 50 b. multicoloured . . . . 1·40 60

55 Pilgrims at Prayer

1981. Pilgrimage to Mecca.

247 **55** 50 b. multicoloured . . . . 1·40 55

56 Al Razha

1981. National Day. Multicoloured.
248 160 b. Type **56** . . . . 1·25 1·25
249 300 b. Sultan Qabus bin Said . 2·00 2·00

57 Muscat Port, 1981

1981. Retracing the Voyage of Sinbad. Mult.
250 50 b. Type **57** 50 50
251 100 b. "Sohar" (replica of medieval dhow) . . . . . . 1·00 1·00
252 130 b. Map showing route of voyage . . . . 1·25 1·25
253 200 b. Muscat Harbour, 1650 . 1·75 1·75

58 Parachute-drop

1981. Armed Forces Day. Multicoloured.
255 100 b. Type **58** . . . . 1·40 85
256 400 b. Missile-armed corvettes 3·25 3·25

59 Police Launch

1982. National Police Day. Multicoloured.
257 50 b. Type **59** . . . . 1·25 60
258 100 b. Royal Oman Police Band at Cardiff . . . . 1·50 85

60 "Nerium mascatense"

1982. Flora and Fauna. Multicoloured.
259 5 b. Type **60** 10 10
260 10 b. "Dionysia mira" 10 10
261 20 b. "Teucrium mascatense" . 10 10
262 25 b. "Geranium mascatense" 10 10
263 30 b. "Cymatium boschi" (horiz) 15 15
264 40 b. "Acteon eloiseae" (horiz) 15 15
265 50 b. "Cypraea teulerei" (horiz) 20 20
266 75 b. "Cypraea pulchra" (horiz) 30 30
267 100 b. Arabian chukar (25 × 33 mm) . . . . 1·10 60
268 ¼ r. Hoopoe (25 × 33 mm) . . 2·50 2·00
269 ½ r. Arabian tahr (25 × 39 mm) 2·50 2·50
270 1 r. Arabian oryx (25 × 39 mm) 5·00 5·00
Nos. 259/62 show flowers, Nos. 263/6 shells, Nos. 267/8 birds and Nos. 269/70 animals.

61 Palm Tree

1982. Arab Palm Tree Day. Multicoloured.
271 40 b. Type **61** 60 30
272 100 b. Palm tree and nuts . . 1·40 80

62 I.T.U. Emblem

1982. I.T.U. Delegates Conference, Nairobi.
273 **62** 100 b. multicoloured . . . 1·40 80

63 Emblem and Cups

1982. Municipalities Week.
274 **63** 40 b. multicoloured . . . 90 50

64 State Consultative Council Inaugural Session

1982. National Day. Multicoloured.
275 40 b. Type **64** 45 30
276 100 b. Petroleum refinery . . 1·75 80

65 Sultan meeting Troops

1982. Armed Forces Day. Multicoloured.
277 50 b. Type **65** 85 35
278 100 b. Mounted army band . 1·90 90

66 Police Motorcyclist and Headquarters

1983. National Police Day.
279 **66** 50 b. multicoloured . . . 1·25 60

67 Satellite, W.C.Y. Emblem and Dish Aerial

1983. World Communications Year.
280 **67** 50 b. multicoloured . . . 1·25 60

68 Bee Hives

1983. Bee-keeping. Multicoloured.
281 50 b. Type **68** . . . . 1·10 95
282 50 b. Bee collecting nectar . . 1·10 95
Nos. 281/2 were issued together in se-tenant pairs throughout the sheet, each pair forming a composite design.

69 Pilgrims at Mudhalfa

1983. Pilgrimage to Mecca.
283 **69** 40 b. multicoloured . . . . 1·25 60

70 Emblem, Map and Sultan

1983. Omani Youth Year.
284 **70** 50 b. multicoloured . . . . 1·00 55

71 Sohar Copper Mine

1983. National Day. Multicoloured.
285 50 b. Type **71** 85 40
286 100 b. Sultan Qabus University and foundation stone . . . . 1·25 90

72 Machine Gun Post

1983. Armed Forces Day.
287 **72** 100 b. multicoloured . . . 2·25 1·25

73 Police Cadets Parade

1984. National Police Day.
288 **73** 100 b. multicoloured . . . 1·75 1·00

74 Footballers and Cup

1984. 7th Arabian Gulf Cup Football Tournament. Multicoloured.
289 40 b. Type **74** 60 35
290 50 b. Emblem and pictograms of footballers 80 45

75 Stoning the Devil

1984. Pilgrimage to Mecca.
291 **75** 50 b. multicoloured 75 45

76 New Central Post Office and Automatic Sorting Machine

1984. National Day. Multicoloured.
292 130 b. Type **76** 90 85
293 160 b. Map of Oman with telecommunications symbols 1·10 1·00

77 Scouts reading Map

1984. 16th Arab Scouts Conference, Muscat. Multicoloured.
294 50 b. Scouts pegging tent . . 35 30
295 50 b. Type **77** 35 30
296 130 b. Scouts assembled around flag 95 85
297 130 b. Scout, cub, guide, brownie and scout leaders 95 85

78 Sultan, Fighter Planes and "Al Munassir" (landing craft)

1984. Armed Forces Day.
298 **78** 100 b. multicoloured . . . 1·50 85

79 Bell 214ST Helicopter lifting Man from Tanker

1985. National Police Day.
299 **79** 100 b. multicoloured . . . 2·50 1·40

80 Al-Khaif Mosque and Tent, Mina

1985. Pilgrimage to Mecca.
300 **80** 50 b. multicoloured 40 35

81 I.Y.Y. Emblem and Youth holding Olive Branches

1985. International Youth Year. Mult.
301 50 b. Type **81** 35 30
302 100 b. Emblem and young people at various activities 75 60

82 Palace before and after Restoration

1985. Restoration of Jabrin Palace. Mult.
303 100 b. Type **82** 75 60
304 250 b. Restored ceiling . . . . 2·75 2·50

83 Drummers

1985. International Omani Traditional Music Symposium.
305 **83** 50 b. multicoloured 45 35

84 Scenes of Child Care and Emblem

1985. United Nations Children's Fund Child Health Campaign.
306 **84** 50 b. multicoloured 45 35

85 Flags around Map of Gulf

1985. 6th Supreme Council Session of Gulf Co-operation Council, Muscat. Multicoloured.
307 40 b. Type **85** 40 30
308 50 b. Portraits of rulers of Council member countries . 45 35

86 Sultan Qabus University and Students

1985. National Day. Multicoloured.
309 20 b. Type **86** 20 15
310 50 b. Tractor and Oxen ploughing field 45 35
311 100 b. Port Qabus cement factory and Oman Chamber of Commerce 90 75
312 200 b. Road bridge, Douglas DC-10 airliner and communications centre . . . 2·25 1·40
313 250 b. Portrait of Sultan Qabus (vert) . . . . 1·75 1·25

87 Military Exercise at Sea

1985. Armed Forces Day.
314 **87** 100 b. multicoloured . . . 1·50 85

88 "Chaetodon collaris"

1985. Marine Life. Multicoloured.
315 20 b. Type **88** 20 15
316 50 b. "Chaetodon melapterus" 45 35
317 100 c. "Chaetodon gardineri" . 90 75
318 150 b. "Scomberomorus commerson" (horiz) . . . . 1·40 1·00
319 200 b. Lobster (horiz) . . . . 1·60 1·25

89 Frankincense Tree

1985. Frankincense Production.
320 **89** 100 b. multicoloured . . . 70 40
321 3 r. multicoloured . . . . 12·00 8·00

90 Camel Corps Member

1986. National Police Day.
322 **90** 50 b. multicoloured . . . 70 35

91 Cadet Barquentine "Shabab Oman", 1986

1986. Participation of "Shabab Oman" in Statue of Liberty Centenary Celebrations. Multicoloured.
323 50 b. "Sultana" (full-rigged sailing ship), 1840 . . . . 65 45
324 100 b. Type **91** . . . . 1·10 80

92 Crowd around Holy Kaaba

1986. Pilgrimage to Mecca.
326 **92** 50 b. multicoloured . . . 70 35

93 Scouts erecting Tent

1986. 17th Arab Scout Camp, Salalah. Multicoloured.
327 50 b. Type **93** 50 30
328 100 b. Scouts making survey . 1·00 60

94 Sports Complex

1986. Inauguration of Sultan Qabus Sports Complex.
329 **94** 100 b. multicoloured . . . 80 60

95 Mother and Baby, Emblem and Tank on Globe

1986. International Peace Year.
330 **95** 130 b. multicoloured . . . 95 70

INDEX

Countries can be quickly located by referring to the index at the end of this volume.

96 Al-Sahwa Tower

1986. National Day. Multicoloured.
331 50 b. Type **96** 50 30
332 100 b. Sultan Qabus University (inauguration) . . . . 1·00 60
333 130 b. 1966 stamps and F.D.C. cancellation (20th anniv of first Oman stamp issue) (57 × 27 mm) . . . . 1·25 1·10

97 Camel Corps

1987. National Police Day.
334 **97** 50 b. multicoloured 60 35

98 Family

1987. Arabian Gulf Social Work Week.
335 **98** 50 b. multicoloured 45 35

99 Aqueduct

101 Examples of Work and Hand holding Cup

100 Crowd around Holy Kaaba

1987. International Environment Day. Mult.
336 50 b. Greater flamingoes . . . 1·25 40
337 130 b. Type **99** . . . . 1·00 70

1987. Pilgrimage to Mecca. Multicoloured.
338 50 b. Type **100** 45 40
339 50 b. Al-Khaif Mosque and tents, Mina 45 40
340 50 b. Stoning the Devil 45 40
341 50 b. Pilgrims at Mudhalfa . . 45 40
342 50 b. Pilgrims at prayer . . . 45 40
343 50 b. Mount Arafat, pilgrims and Kaaba 45 40

1987. 3rd Municipalities Month.
344 **101** 50 b. multicoloured . . . 40 30

102 Marine Science and Fisheries Centre

1987. National Day. Multicoloured.
345 50 b. Type **102** 40 30
346 130 b. Royal Hospital . . . . 1·00 80

103 Radio Operators

1987. 15th Anniv of Royal Omani Amateur Radio Society.
347 **103** 130 b. multicoloured . . . 85 75

104 Weaver

1988. Traditional Crafts. Multicoloured.
348 50 b. Type **104** 30 25
349 100 b. Potter 55 50
350 150 b. Halwa maker 75 70
351 200 b. Silversmith 90 85

105 Showjumping

106 Emblem

1988. Olympic Games, Seoul. Multicoloured.
353 100 b. Type **105** 45 40
354 100 b. Hockey 45 40
355 100 b. Football 45 40
356 100 b. Running 45 40
357 100 b. Swimming 45 40
358 100 b. Shooting 45 40

1988. 40th Anniv of W.H.O. "Health for All".
359 **106** 100 b. multicoloured . . . 45 40

107 Tending Land and Crops

1988. National Day. Agriculture Year. Mult.
360 100 b. Type **107** 45 40
361 100 b. Livestock 45 40

108 Dhahira Region (woman's)

1989. Costumes. Multicoloured.
363 30 b. Type **108** 15 10
364 40 b. Eastern region (woman's) 20 15
365 50 b. Batinah region (woman's) 25 20
366 100 b. Interior region (woman's) 45 40
367 130 b. Southern region (woman's) 60 50
368 150 b. Muscat region (woman's) 70 60
369 200 b. Dhahira region (man's) 90 85
370 ¼ r. Dhahira region (man's) . 1·00 90
371 ½ r. Southern region (man's) . 1·75 1·50
372 1 r. Muscat region (man's) . . 3·25 3·00

109 Fishing

1989. National Day. Agriculture Year. Mult.
375 100 b. Type **109** 45 40
376 100 b. Agriculture 45 40

110 Flags and Omani State Arms

1989. 10th Supreme Council Session of Arab Co-operation Council, Muscat. Multicoloured.
377 50 b. Type **110** 25 20
378 50 b. Council emblem and Sultan Qabus 25 20

111 Emblem and Map

1990. 5th Anniv (1989) of Gulf Investment Corporation.
379 **111** 50 b. multicoloured . . . 25 20
380 130 b. multicoloured . . . 50 45

112 Emblem and Douglas DC-10 **113** Map

1990. 40th Anniv of Gulf Air.
381 **112** 80 b. multicoloured . . . 50 30

1990. Omani Ophiolite Symposium, Muscat.
382 **113** 80 b. multicoloured . . . 20 10
383 150 b. multicoloured . . . 40 35

114 Ahmed bin Na'aman al-Ka'aby (envoy), "Sultana" and Said bin Sultan

1990. 150th Anniv of First Omani Envoy's Journey to U.S.A.
384 **114** 200 b. multicoloured . . . 85 60

115 Sultan Qabus Rose

1990. 20th Anniv of Sultan Qabus's Accession.
385 **115** 200 b. multicoloured . . . 55 45

116 National Day Emblem

1990. National Day.
386 **116** 100 b. red and green on gold foil 30 25
387 – 200 b. green and red on gold foil 55 45
DESIGN: 200 b. Sultan Qabus.

117 Donor and Recipient

1991. Blood Donation.
389 **117** 50 b. multicoloured . . . 15 10
390 200 b. multicoloured . . 60 50

118 Industrial Emblems

1991. National Day and Industry Year. Mult.
391 100 b. Type **118** 30 25
392 200 b. Sultan Qabus 60 50

119 Weapons, Military Transport and Sultan Qabus

1991. Armed Forces Day.
394 **119** 100 b. multicoloured . . 60 35

120 Interior of Museum and National Flags **121** Satellite Picture of Asia

1992. Inaug of Omani-French Museum, Muscat.
395 **120** 100 b. multicoloured . . 30 25

1992. World Meteorological Day.
397 **121** 220 b. multicoloured . . 80 65

122 Emblem **123** Emblem and Hands protecting Handicapped Child

1992. World Environment Day.
398 **122** 100 b. multicoloured . . 35 30

1992. Welfare of Handicapped Children.
399 **123** 70 b. multicoloured . . . 25 20

124 Sultan Qabus and Books

1992. Publication of Sultan Qabus Encyclopedia of Arab Names.
400 **124** 100 b. multicoloured . . . 35 30

125 Sultan Qabus, Factories and Industry Year Emblem

1992. National Day. Multicoloured.
401 100 b. Type **125** 35 30
402 200 b. Sultan Qabus and Majlis As'shura (Consultative Council) emblem 70 60

126 Mounted Policemen and Sultan Qabus

1993. National Police Day.
403 **126** 80 b. multicoloured . . . 30 25

127 Census Emblem

1993. Population and Housing Census.
404 **127** 100 b. multicoloured . . . 35 30

128 Frigate and Sultan Qabus presenting Colours

1993. Navy Day.
405 **128** 100 b. multicoloured . . . 35 30

129 Youth Year Emblem

1993. National Day. Youth Year. Multicoloured.
406 100 b. Type **129** 35 30
407 200 b. Sultan Qabus 70 60

130 Scout Headquarters and Emblem

1993. 61st Anniv of Scouting in Oman (408) and 10th Anniv of Sultan Qabus as Chief Scout (409). Multicoloured.
408 100 b. Type **130** 35 30
409 100 b. Scout camp and Sultan Qabus 35 30
Nos. 408/9 were issued together, se-tenant, forming a composite design.

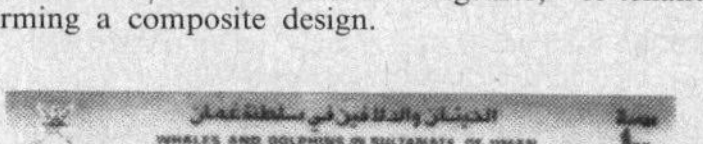

131 Sei Whale and School of Dolphins

1993. Whales and Dolphins in Oman Waters. Multicoloured.
410 100 b. Type **131** 35 30
411 100 b. Sperm whale and dolphins 35 30
Nos. 410/11 were issued together, se-tenant, forming a composite design.

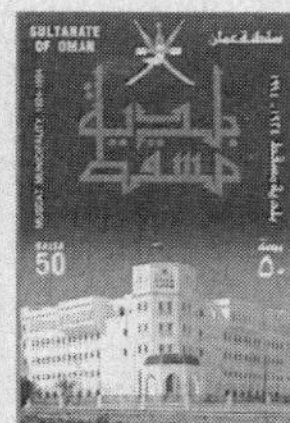
132 Water Drops and Falaj (ancient water system) **133** Municipality Building

1994. World Water Day.
413 **132** 50 b. multicoloured . . . 15 10

1994. 70th Anniv of Muscat Municipality.
414 **133** 50 b. multicoloured . . . 15 10

134 Centenary Emblem and Sports Pictograms

1994. Centenary of International Olympic Committee.
415 **134** 100 b. multicoloured . . . 35 30

PAKHOI Pt. 17

An Indo-Chinese Post Office in China, closed in 1922.

1903. Stamps of Indo-China, "Tablet" key-type, surch **PACKHOI** and value in Chinese.

1 D 1 c. black and red on blue . 3·75 3·75
2 2 c. brown and blue on buff 2·25 2·50
3 4 c. brown and blue on grey 2·00 2·00
4 5 c. green and red . . . . . 1·75 2·00
5 10 c. red and blue . . . . . 1·75 1·75
6 15 c. grey and red . . . . . 1·75 1·75
7 20 c. red and blue on green 3·75 3·75
8 25 c. blue and red . . . . . 2·50 2·50
9 25 c. black and red on pink 3·75 3·75
10 30 c. brown and blue on drab 3·75 3·75
11 40 c. red and blue on yellow 27·00 27·00
12 50 c. red and blue on pink . £200 £200
13 50 c. brown and red on blue 35·00 35·00
14 75 c. brown and red on orange 35·00 35·00
15 1 f. green and red . . . . . 38·00 38·00
16 5 f. mauve and blue on lilac 60·00 60·00

1906. Stamps of Indo-China surch **PAK-HOI** and value in Chinese.

17 **8** 1 c. olive 70 65
18 2 c. red on yellow 70 65
19 4 c. purple on grey 70 65
20 5 c. green 70 65
21 10 c. red 70 65
22 15 c. brown on blue . . . . 2·75 2·75
23 20 c. red on green . . . . . 1·90 1·90
24 25 c. blue . . . . 1·75 1·75
25 30 c. brown on cream . . . . 1·90 1·75
26 35 c. black on yellow . . . . 1·90 1·90
27 40 c. black on grey . . . . . 1·90 1·90
28 50 c. olive on green . . . . 3·50 3·50
29 D 75 c. brown on orange . . . 25·00 25·00
30 **8** 1 f. green . . . . 13·50 13·50
31 2 f. brown on yellow . . . . 22·00 22·00
32 D 5 f. mauve on lilac . . . . 55·00 55·00
33 **8** 10 f. red on green . . . . . 65·00 70·00

1908. Stamps of Indo-China (Native types) surch **PAKHOI** and value in Chinese.

34 **10** 1 c. black and olive 25 30
35 2 c. black and brown 35 40
36 4 c. black and blue 40 45
37 5 c. black and green 55 60
38 10 c. black and red 55 60
39 15 c. black and violet . . . 75 75
40 **11** 20 c. black and violet . . . 75 75
41 25 c. black and blue 90 90
42 30 c. black and brown . . . 1·40 1·50
43 35 c. black and green . . . 1·50 1·50
44 40 c. black and brown . . . 1·40 1·50
45 50 c. black and red . . . . 1·50 1·50
46 **12** 75 c. black and orange . . . 2·75 2·75
47 – 1 f. black and red . . . . 3·50 3·50
48 – 2 f. black and green . . . . 8·00 8·25
49 – 5 f. black and blue . . . . 48·00 50·00
50 – 10 f. black and violet . . . 75·00 75·00

1919. As last surch in addition in figures and words.

51 **10** $\frac{2}{5}$ c. on 1 c. black and olive . . 40 40
52 $\frac{4}{5}$ c. on 2 c. black and brown . 40 45
53 $1\frac{3}{5}$ c. on 4 c. black and blue . . 40 45
54 2 c. on 5 c. black and green . 55 55
55 4 c. on 10 c. black and red . . 1·50 1·50
56 6 c. on 15 c. black & violet . . 55 55
57 **11** 8 c. on 20 c. black & violet . 1·50 1·50
58 10 c. on 25 c. black & blue . 1·75 1·75
59 12 c. on 30 c. black & purple . 70 65
60 14 c. on 35 c. black & green . 45 45
61 16 c. on 40 c. black & brown . 1·10 1·10
62 20 c. on 50 c. black and red . 70 65
63 **12** 30 c. on 75 c. black & orge . 1·10 1·10
64 – 40 c. on 1 f. black and red . 5·25 5·25
65 – 80 c. on 2 f. black & green . 2·25 2·00
66 – 2 pi. on 5 f. black & blue . . 5·50 5·50
67 – 4 pi. on 10 f. black & violet . 11·50 11·50

PALAU Pt. 22

Formerly part of the United States Trust Territory of the Pacific Islands, Palau became a republic on 1 January 1981. Until 1983 it continued to use United States stamps.

100 cents = 1 dollar

1 Preamble to Constitution **2** Palau Fruit Dove

1983. Inaug of Postal Independence. Mult.

1 20 c. Type **1** 60 45
2 20 c. Natives hunting (design from Koror meeting house) 60 45
3 20 c. Preamble to Constitution (different) 60 45
4 20 c. Three fishes (design from Koror meeting house) 60 45

1983. Birds. Multicoloured.

5 20 c. Type **2** 55 40
6 20 c. Morning bird 55 40
7 20 c. Palau white eye (inscr "Giant White-eye") 55 40
8 20 c. Palau fantail 55 40

3 Map Cowrie **4** Humpback Whale

1983. Marine Life. Multicoloured.

9 1 c. Sea fan 10 10
10 3 c. Type **3** 10 10
11 5 c. Jellyfish 15 10
12 10 c. Hawksbill turtle 20 10
13 13 c. Giant clam 25 15
14 14 c. Trumpet triton 30 25
15 20 c. Parrotfish 40 25
16 22 c. Bumphead parrotfish . . 40 30
17 25 c. Soft coral and damsel fish 40 30
17a 28 c. Chambered nautilus . . 55 40
18 30 c. Dappled sea cucumber . 55 40
18a 33 c. Sea anemone and clownfish 55 40
19 37 c. Sea urchin 75 40
19a 39 c. Green sea turtle 75 60
19b 44 c. Pacific sailfish 85 70
20 50 c. Starfish . . . . 1·00 60
21 $1 Squid . . . . 2·00 1·00
22 $2 Dugong . . . . 3·75 2·25
23 $5 Pink sponge . . . . . . 8·50 5·50
24 $10 Spinner dolphin . . . . 15·00 11·00

1983. World Wildlife Fund. Whales. Mult.

25 20 c. Type **4** 70 45
26 20 c. Blue whale 70 45
27 20 c. Fin whale 70 45
28 20 c. Sperm whale 70 45

5 "Spear fishing at New Moon" **6** King Abba Thulle

1983. Christmas. Paintings by Charlie Gibbons. Mult.

29 20 c. Type **5** 55 35
30 20 c. "Taro Gardening" . . . 55 35
31 20 c. "First Child Ceremony" . 55 35
32 20 c. "Traditional Feast at the Bai" 55 35
33 20 c. "Spear Fishing from Red Canoe" 55 35

1983. Bicentenary of Captain Henry Wilson's Voyage to Palau.

34 **6** 20 c. brown, blue & dp blue 50 35
35 – 20 c. brown, blue & dp blue 50 35
36 – 20 c. brown, blue & dp blue 50 35
37 – 20 c. brown, blue & dp blue 50 35
38 – 20 c. brown, blue & dp blue 50 35
39 – 20 c. brown, blue & dp blue 50 35
40 – 20 c. brown, blue & dp blue 50 35
41 – 20 c. brown, blue & dp blue 50 35

DESIGNS—VERT: No. 37, Ludec (King Abba Thulle's wife); 38, Capt. Henry Wilson; 41, Prince Lee Boo. HORIZ: (47 × 20 mm): 35, Mooring in Koror; 36, Village scene in Pelew Islands; 39, Approaching Pelew; 40, Englishman's camp on Ulong.

7 Triton Trumpet

1984. Sea Shells (1st series). Multicoloured.

42 20 c. Type **7** 50 40
43 20 c. Horned helmet 50 40
44 20 c. Giant clam 50 40
45 20 c. Laciniate conch 50 40
46 20 c. Royal cloak scallop . . . 50 40
47 20 c. Triton trumpet (different) 50 40
48 20 c. Horned helmet (different) 50 40
49 20 c. Giant clam (different) . . 50 40
50 20 c. Laciniate conch (different) 50 40
51 20 c. Royal cloak scallop (diff) 50 40

Nos. 43/6 have mauve backgrounds, Nos. 48/51 blue backgrounds.

See also Nos. 145/9, 194/8, 231/5, 256/60 and 515/19.

8 White-tailed Tropic Bird

1984. Air. Birds. Multicoloured.

52 40 c. Type **8** . . . . 1·00 75
53 40 c. White tern (inscr "Fairy Tern") . . . . 1·00 75
54 40 c. White-capped noddy (inscr "Black Noddy") . . . . . . 1·00 75
55 40 c. Black-naped tern . . . . 1·00 75

9 "Oroolong" (Wilson's schooner)

1984. 19th Universal Postal Union Congress Philatelic Salon, Hamburg. Multicoloured.

56 40 c. Type **9** . . . . 1·00 75
57 40 c. Missionary ship "Duff" . 1·00 75
58 40 c. German expeditionary steamer "Peiho" . . . . 1·00 75
59 40 c. German gunboat "Albatros" 1·00 75

10 Spear Fishing

1984. "Ausipex 84" International Stamp Exhibition, Melbourne. Fishing. Multicoloured.

60 20 c. Type **10** 55 35
61 20 c. Kite fishing 55 35
62 20 c. Underwater spear fishing . 55 35
63 20 c. Net fishing 55 35

11 Mountain Apple

1984. Christmas. Multicoloured.

64 20 c. Type **11** 55 35
65 20 c. Beach morning glory . . . 55 35
66 20 c. Turmeric 55 35
67 20 c. Plumeria 55 35

12 Chick

1985. Birth Bicentenary of John J. Audubon (ornithologist). Designs showing Audubon's Shearwater. Multicoloured.

68 22 c. Type **12** (postage) 65 45
69 22 c. Head of shearwater . . . 65 45
70 22 c. Shearwater flying 65 45
71 22 c. Shearwater on lake . . . 65 45
72 44 c. "Audubon's Shearwater" (Audubon) (air) . . . . 1·00 70

13 Borotong (cargo canoe)

1985. Traditional Canoes and Rafts. Multicoloured.

73 22 c. Type **13** 60 45
74 22 c. Kabeki (war canoe) . . . 60 45
75 22 c. Olechutel (bamboo raft) . 60 45
76 22 c. Kaeb (racing/sailing canoe) 60 45

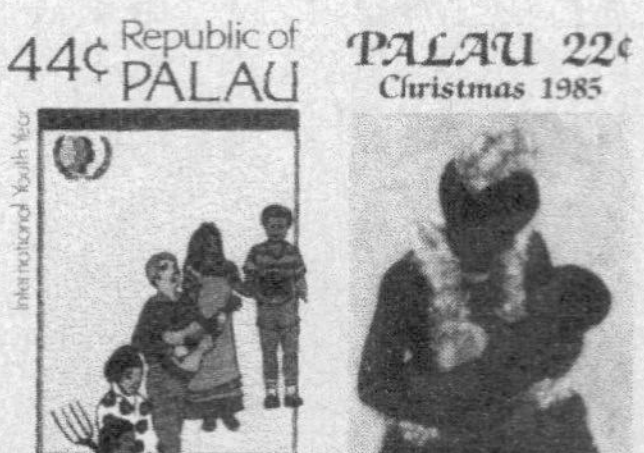

14 Boy with Guitar **16** Mother cuddling Child

15 Raising German Flag at Palau, 1885, and German 1880 20 pf. Stamp

1985. International Youth Year. Multicoloured.

77 44 c. Type **14** 80 60
78 44 c. Boy with fishing rod . . . 80 60
79 44 c. Boy with baseball bat . . 80 60
80 44 c. Boy with spade 80 60

Nos. 77/80 were issued together se-tenant, each block forming a composite design showing a ring of children of different races.

1985. Air. Centenary of Vatican Treaty (granting German trading privileges in Caroline Islands). Multicoloured.

81 44 c. Type **15** . . . . 1·00 75
82 44 c. Early German trading post, Angaur, and Marshall Islands 1899 5 pf. overprinted stamp 1·00 75
83 44 c. Abai (village meeting house) and Caroline Islands 1901 5 m. yacht stamp . . . . 1·00 75
84 44 c. "Cormoran" (German cruiser), 1914, and Caroline Islands 1901 40 pf. yacht stamp 1·00 75

1985. Christmas. Multicoloured.

85 14 c. Mother with child on lap 30 15
86 22 c. Type **16** 45 30
87 33 c. Mother supporting child in arms 70 50
88 44 c. Mother lifting child in air 80 70

17 Consolidated Catalina Amphibian over Natural Bridge

1985. Air. 50th Anniv of First Trans-Pacific Airmail Flight. Multicoloured.

89 44 c. Type **17** . . . . 1·00 65
90 44 c. Douglas DC-6B approaching Airai-Koror Passage . . . . 1·00 65
91 44 c. Grumman Albatross flying boat over Airai Village . . . 1·00 65
92 44 c. Douglas DC-4 landing at Airai . . . . 1·00 65

18 Comet and Kaeb, 1758

1985. Appearance of Halley's Comet. Multicoloured.

94 44 c. Type **18** . . . . 1·10 75
95 44 c. Comet and U.S.S. "Vincennes", 1835 . . . . . 1·10 75
96 44 c. Comet and "Scharnhorst" (German cruiser), 1910 . . . 1·10 75
97 44 c. Comet and tourist cabin cruiser, 1986 . . . . 1·10 75

19 Palau Myiagra Flycatchers

1986. Songbirds. Multicoloured.

98 44 c. Type **19** (inscr "Mangrove Flycatchers") . . . . 1·00 75
99 44 c. Cardinal honeyeaters . . 1·00 75
100 44 c. Blue-faced parrot finches 1·00 75
101 44 c. Grey-brown white eye (inscr "Dusky White-eye") and bridled white eye . . . . . 1·00 75

20 Spear Fisherman

1986. "Ameripex '86" International Stamp Exhibition, Chicago. Sea and Reef World. Multicoloured.

102 14 c. Type **20** 90 55
103 14 c. Olechutel (native raft) . . 90 55
104 14 c. Kaebs (sailing canoes) . . 90 55
105 14 c. Rock islands and sailfish 90 55
106 14 c. Inter-island ferry and flying fishes 90 55
107 14 c. Bone fishes 90 55
108 14 c. Common jacks 90 55
109 14 c. Mackerel 90 55
110 14 c. Sailfishes 90 55
111 14 c. Barracuda 90 55
112 14 c. Trigger fishes 90 55
113 14 c. Dolphin fishes 90 55
114 14 c. Spear fisherman with grouper 90 55
115 14 c. Manta ray 90 55
116 14 c. Marlin 90 55
117 14 c. Parrotfishes 90 55
118 14 c. Wrasse 90 55
119 14 c. Red snappers 90 55
120 14 c. Herring 90 55
121 14 c. Dugongs 90 55
122 14 c. Surgeonfishes 90 55
123 14 c. Leopard ray 90 55
124 14 c. Hawksbill turtle 90 55
125 14 c. Needlefishes 90 55
126 14 c. Tuna 90 55
127 14 c. Octopus 90 55
128 14 c. Clown fishes 90 55
129 14 c. Squid 90 55
130 14 c. Groupers 90 55
131 14 c. Moorish idols 90 55
132 14 c. Queen conch and starfish 90 55
133 14 c. Squirrel fishes 90 55
134 14 c. Starfish and sting rays . 90 55
135 14 c. Lion fish 90 55
136 14 c. Angel fishes 90 55
137 14 c. Butterfly fishes 90 55
138 14 c. Spiny lobster 90 55
139 14 c. Mangrove crab 90 55
140 14 c. Tridacna 90 55
141 14 c. Moray eel 90 55

Nos. 102/41 are each inscribed on the back (over the gum) with the name of the subject featured on the stamp.

Nos. 102/41 were printed together, se-tenant, forming a composite design.

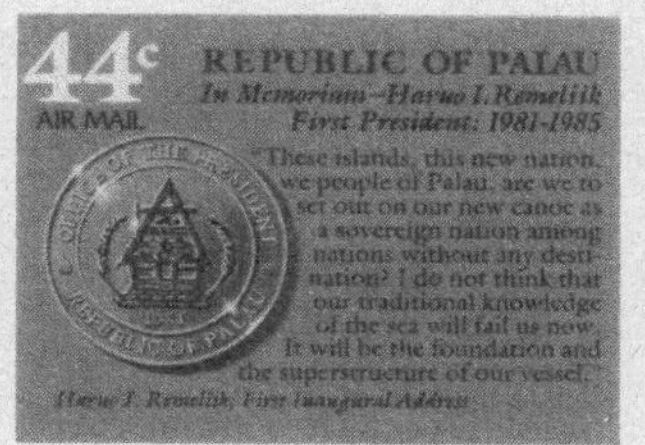

21 Presidential Seal

1986. Air. Haruo I. Remeliik (first President) Commemoration. Multicoloured.

142 44 c. Type **21** 90 60
143 44 c. Kabeki (war canoe) passing under Koror-Babeldaob Bridge 90 60
144 44 c. Presidents Reagan and Remeliik 90 60

1986. Sea Shells (2nd series). As T **7**. Multicoloured.

145 22 c. Commercial trochus . . 55 40
146 22 c. Marble cone 55 40
147 22 c. Fluted giant clam . . . 55 40
148 22 c. Bullmouth helmet . . . 55 40
149 22 c. Golden cowrie 55 40

23 Crab inhabiting Soldier's rusting Helmet

1986. International Peace Year. Multicoloured.

150 22 c. Type **23** (postage) . . . 55 40
151 22 c. Marine life inhabiting airplane 55 40
152 22 c. Rusting tank behind girl 55 40
153 22 c. Abandoned assault landing craft, Airai 55 40
154 22 c. Statue of Liberty, New York (centenary) (air) . . . 1·00 70

24 Gecko

1986. Reptiles. Multicoloured.

155 22 c. Type **24** 60 45
156 22 c. Emerald tree skink . . . 60 45
157 22 c. Estuarine crocodile . . . 60 45
158 22 c. Leatherback turtle . . . 60 45

25 Girl with Guitar and Boy leading Child on Goat

26 Tailed Jay on Soursop

1986. Christmas. Multicoloured.

159 22 c. Type **25** 45 35
160 22 c. Boys singing and girl carrying flowers 45 35
161 22 c. Mother holding baby . . 45 35
162 22 c. Children carrying baskets of fruit 45 35
163 22 c. Girl with white terns . . 45 35

Nos. 159/63 were issued together, se-tenant, forming a composite design.

1987. Butterflies (1st series). Multicoloured.

164 44 c. Type **26** . . . . 1·10 75
165 44 c. Common mormon on sweet orange . . . . 1·10 75
166 44 c. Common eggfly on swamp cabbage . . . . 1·10 75
167 44 c. Oleander butterfly on fig 1·10 75

See also Nos. 223/6.

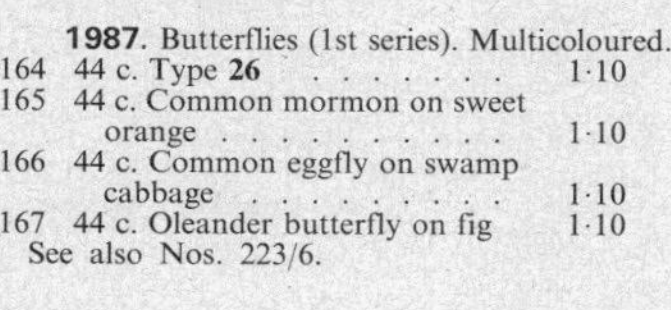

27 Bat flying

28 "Ixora casei"

1987. Air. Palau Fruit Bat. Multicoloured.

168 44 c. Type **27** 95 70
169 44 c. Bat hanging from branch 95 70
170 44 c. Bat feeding 95 70
171 44 c. Head of bat 95 70

1987. Flowers. Multicoloured.

172 1 c. Type **28** 10 10
173 3 c. "Lumnitzera littorea" . . 10 10
174 5 c. "Sonneratia alba" . . . 10 10
175 10 c. Woody vine 15 10
176 14 c. "Bikkia palauensis" . . 20 10
177 15 c. "Limophila aromatica" . 20 10
178 22 c. "Bruguiera gymnorhiza" 30 20
179 25 c. "Fragraea ksid" 30 20
180 36 c. "Ophiorrhiza palauensis" 45 35
181 39 c. "Cerbera manghas" . . 60 40
182 44 c. "Samadera indica" . . 65 45
183 45 c. "Maesa canfieldiae" . . 55 45
184 50 c. "Dolichandrone spathacea" 80 55
185 $1 "Barringtonia racemosa" . 1·50 1·10
186 $2 "Nepenthes mirabilis" . . 2·50 2·00
187 $5 Orchid . . . . 6·00 4·50
188 $10 Bouquet of mixed flowers 12·00 9·00

29 Babeldaob

1987. "Capex '87" International Stamp Exhibition, Toronto. Multicoloured.

190 22 c. Type **29** 40 30
191 22 c. Floating Garden Islands 40 30
192 22 c. Rock Island 40 30
193 22 c. Koror 40 30

1987. Sea Shells (3rd series). As T **7**. Multicoloured.

194 22 c. Black-striped triton . . 50 35
195 22 c. Tapestry turban 50 35
196 22 c. Adusta murex 50 35
197 22 c. Little fox mitre 50 35
198 22 c. Cardinal mitre 50 35

31 "The President shall be the chief executive ..."

1987. Bicentenary of United States of America Constitution. Multicoloured.

199 14 c. Type **31** 25 20
200 14 c. Palau and U.S. Presidents' seals (24 × 37 mm) 25 20
201 14 c. "The executive power shall be vested ..." 25 20
202 22 c. "The legislative power of Palau ..." 35 25
203 22 c. Palau Olbiil Era Kelulau and U.S. Senate seals (24 × 37 mm) 35 25
204 22 c. "All legislative powers herein granted ..." 35 25
205 44 c. "The judicial power of Palau ..." 70 60
206 44 c. Palau and U.S. Supreme Court seals (24 × 37 mm) . . 70 60
207 44 c. "The judicial power of the United States ..." 70 60

The three designs of the same value were printed together in se-tenant strips, the top stamp of each strip bearing extracts from the Palau Constitution and the bottom stamp extracts from the U.S. Constitution.

32 Japanese Mobile Post Office and 1937 Japan ½ s. Stamp

1987. Links with Japan. Multicoloured.

208 14 c. Type **32** 40 30
209 22 c. Phosphate mine and Japan 1942 5 s. stamp 70 50
210 33 c. Douglas DC-2 flying over Badrulchau monuments and Japan 1937 2 s. + 2 s. stamp 85 60
211 44 c. Japanese Post Office, Koror, and Japan 1927 10 s. stamp . . . . 1·10 80

33 Huts, White Tern and Outrigger Canoes

34 Snapping Shrimp and Goby

1987. Christmas. Multicoloured.

213 22 c. Type **33** 45 35
214 22 c. Flying white tern carrying twig 45 35
215 22 c. Holy family in kaeb . . . 45 35
216 22 c. Angel and kaeb 45 35
217 22 c. Outrigger canoes and hut 45 35

Nos. 213/17 were issued together, se-tenant, forming a composite design; each stamp bears a verse of the carol "I Saw Three Ships".

1987. 25th Anniv of World Ecology Movement. Multicoloured.

218 22 c. Type **34** 50 40
219 22 c. Mauve vase sponge and sponge crab 50 40
220 22 c. Pope's damsel fish and cleaner wrasse 50 40
221 22 c. Clown anemone fishes and sea anemone 50 40
222 22 c. Four-coloured nudibranch and banded coral shrimp . . 50 40

1988. Butterflies (2nd series). As T **26**.

223 44 c. Orange tiger on "Tournefotia argentia" . . . 65 55
224 44 c. Swallowtail on "Citrus reticulata" 65 55
225 44 c. Lemon migrant on "Crataeva speciosa" 65 55
226 44 c. "Appias ada" (wrongly inscr "Colias philodice") on "Crataeva speciosa" 65 55

35 Whimbrel

37 Baseball

1988. Ground-dwelling Birds. Multicoloured.

227 44 c. Type **35** 65 55
228 44 c. Chinese little bittern . . 65 55
229 44 c. Rufous night heron . . . 65 55
230 44 c. Banded rail 65 55

1988. Sea Shells (4th series). As T **7**. Mult.

231 25 c. Striped engina 50 35
232 25 c. Ivory cone 50 35
233 25 c. Plaited mitre 50 35
234 25 c. Episcopal mitre 50 35
235 25 c. Isabelle cowrie 50 35

1988. Olympic Games, Seoul. Multicoloured.

237 25 c. + 5 c. Type **37** 45 40
238 25 c. + 5 c. Running 45 40
239 45 c. + 5 c. Diving 80 65
240 45 c. + 5 c. Swimming . . . 80 65

39 Angel Violinist and Singing Cherubs

41 Nicobar Pigeon

1988. Christmas. Multicoloured.

242 25 c. Type **39** 40 30
243 25 c. Angels and children singing 40 30
244 25 c. Children adoring child . 40 30
245 25 c. Angels and birds flying . 40 30
246 25 c. Running children and angels playing trumpets . . 40 30

Nos. 242/6 were issued together, se-tenant, forming a composite design.

1989. Endangered Birds. Multicoloured.

248 45 c. Type **41** . . . . 1·10 75
249 45 c. Palau ground dove . . . 1·10 75
250 45 c. Marianas scrub hen . . 1·10 75
251 45 c. Palau scops owl . . . . 1·10 75

42 Gilled Auricularia

1989. Fungi. Multicoloured.

252 45 c. Type **42** . . . . 1·10 75
253 45 c. Rock mushroom . . . . 1·10 75
254 45 c. Polyporous . . . . . . 1·10 75
255 45 c. Veiled stinkhorn . . . . 1·10 75

43 Robin Redbreast Triton

1989. Sea Shells (5th series). Multicoloured.

256 25 c. Type **43** 60 45
257 25 c. Hebrew cone 60 45
258 25 c. Tadpole triton 60 45
259 25 c. Lettered cone 60 45
260 25 c. Rugose mitre 60 45

44 Cessna 207 Stationair 7

46 Jettison of Third Stage

1989. Air. Airplanes. Multicoloured.

261 36 c. Type **44** 50 40
262 39 c. Embraer Bandeirante . . 60 50
264 45 c. Boeing 727 . . . . . . 70 60

No. 261 is wrongly inscribed "Skywagon"

1989. 20th Anniv of First Manned Landing on Moon. Multicoloured.

267 25 c. Type **46** 40 30
268 25 c. Command Module adjusting position 40 30
269 25 c. Lunar Excursion Module "Eagle" docking 40 30
270 25 c. Space module docking . 40 30
271 25 c. Propulsion for entry into lunar orbit 40 30
272 25 c. Third stage burn 40 30
273 25 c. Command Module orbiting Moon 40 30
274 25 c. Command Module and part of "Eagle" 40 30
275 25 c. Upper part of "Eagle" on Moon 40 30
276 25 c. Descent of "Eagle" . . . 40 30
277 25 c. Nose of rocket 40 30
278 25 c. Reflection in Edwin "Buzz" Aldrin's visor 40 30
279 25 c. Neil Armstrong and flag on Moon 40 30

280 25 c. Footprints and astronaut's oxygen tank 40 30
281 25 c. Upper part of astronaut descending ladder 40 30
282 25 c. Launch tower and body of rocket 40 30
283 25 c. Survival equipment on Aldrin's space suit 40 30
284 25 c. Blast off from lunar surface 40 30
285 25 c. View of Earth and astronaut's legs 40 30
286 25 c. Leg on ladder 40 30
287 25 c. Lift off 40 30
288 25 c. Spectators at launch . . 40 30
289 25 c. Capsule parachuting into Pacific 40 30
290 25 c. Re-entry 40 30
291 25 c. Space Module jettison . 40 30
292 $2.40 "Buzz" Aldrin on Moon (photo by Neil Armstrong) (34 × 47 mm) . . . . 3·50 2·50

Nos. 267/91 were issued together, se-tenant, forming a composite design.

47 Girl as Astronaut

48 Bridled Tern

1989. Year of the Young Reader. Multicoloured.

293 25 c. Type **47** 45 35
294 25 c. Boy riding dolphin . . . 45 35
295 25 c. Cheshire Cat in tree . . 45 35
296 25 c. Mother Goose 45 35
297 25 c. Baseball player 45 35
298 25 c. Girl reading 45 35
299 25 c. Boy reading 45 35
300 25 c. Mother reading to child . 45 35
301 25 c. Girl holding flowers listening to story 45 35
302 25 c. Boy in baseball strip . . 45 35

1989. "World Stamp Expo '89" International Stamp Exhibition, Washington D.C. Stilt Mangrove. Multicoloured.

303 25 c. Type **48** 45 35
304 25 c. Lemon migrant (inscr "Sulphur Butterfly") 45 35
305 25 c. Palua myiagra flycatcher (inscr "Mangrove Flycatcher") 45 35
306 25 c. White-collared kingfisher 45 35
307 25 c. Fruit bat 45 35
308 25 c. Estuarine crocodile . . . 45 35
309 25 c. Rufous night heron . . . 45 35
310 25 c. Stilt mangrove 45 35
311 25 c. Bird's nest fern 45 35
312 25 c. Beach hibiscus tree . . . 45 35
313 25 c. Common eggfly (butterfly) 45 35
314 25 c. Dog-faced watersnake . . 45 35
315 25 c. Jingle shell 45 35
316 25 c. Palau bark cricket . . . 45 35
317 25 c. Periwinkle and mangrove oyster 45 35
318 25 c. Jellyfish 45 35
319 25 c. Striped mullet 45 35
320 25 c. Mussels, sea anemones and algae 45 35
321 25 c. Cardinalfish 45 35
322 25 c. Snappers 45 35

Nos. 303/22 are each inscribed on the back (over the gum) with the name of the subject featured on the stamp.

Nos. 303/22 were issued together, se-tenant, forming a composite design.

49 Angels, Sooty Tern and Audubon's Shearwater

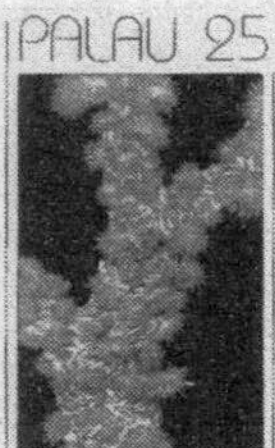

50 Pink Coral

1989. Christmas. Carol of the Birds. Mult.

323 25 c. Type **49** 45 35
324 25 c. Palau fruit dove and angel 45 35
325 25 c. Madonna and child, cherub and birds 45 35
326 25 c. Angel, blue-faced parrot finch, Palau myiagra flycatcher and cardinal honeyeater . . 45 35
327 25 c. Angel, Palau myiagra flycatcher and black-headed gulls 45 35

Nos. 323/7 were printed together, se-tenant, forming a composite design.

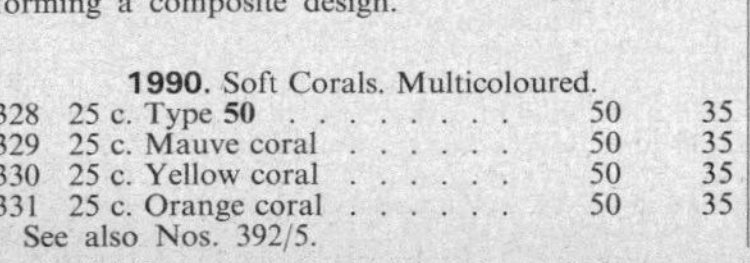

1990. Soft Corals. Multicoloured.

328 25 c. Type **50** 50 35
329 25 c. Mauve coral 50 35
330 25 c. Yellow coral 50 35
331 25 c. Orange coral 50 35

See also Nos. 392/5.

51 Siberian Rubythroat

1990. Forest Birds. Multicoloured.

332 45 c. Type **51** 90 65
333 45 c. Palau bush warbler . . 90 65
334 45 c. Micronesian starling . . 90 65
335 45 c. Slender-billed greybird (inscr "Cicadabird") . . . 90 65

52 Prince Lee Boo, Capt. Henry Wilson and H.M.S. "Victory"

1990. "Stamp World London 90" International Stamp Exhibition. Prince Lee Boo's Visit to England, 1784, and 150th Anniv of the Penny Black. Multicoloured.

336 25 c. Type **52** 30 20
337 25 c. St. James's Palace . . . 30 20
338 25 c. Rotherhithe Docks . . 30 20
339 25 c. Oroolong House, Devon (Capt. Wilson's home) . . 30 20
340 25 c. Vincenzo Lunardi's balloon 30 20
341 25 c. St. Paul's Cathedral . . 30 20
342 25 c. Prince Lee Boo's grave . 30 20
343 25 c. St. Mary's Church, Rotherhithe 30 20
344 25 c. Memorial tablet to Prince Lee Boo 30 20

53 "Corymborkis veratrifolia"

55 White Tern, American Golden Plover and Sanderling

54 Plane Butterfly on Beach Sunflower

1990. "Expo 90" International Garden and Greenery Exposition, Osaka. Orchids. Multicoloured.

346 45 c. Type **53** 55 40
347 45 c. "Malaxis setipes" . . . 55 40
348 45 c. "Dipodium freycinetianum" 55 40
349 45 c. "Bulbophyllum micronesiacum" 55 40
350 45 c. "Vanda teres" 55 40

1990. Butterflies. Multicoloured.

351 45 c. Type **54** 70 55
352 45 c. Painted lady on coral tree 70 55
353 45 c. "Euploea nemertes" on sorcerer's flower 70 55
354 45 c. Meadow argus (inscr "Buckeye") on beach pea . 70 55

1990. Lagoon Life. Multicoloured.

355 25 c. Type **55** 30 20
356 25 c. Bidekill fisherman . . . 30 20
357 25 c. Yacht and insular halfbeaks 30 20
358 25 c. Palauan kaebs 30 20
359 25 c. White-tailed tropic bird 30 20
360 25 c. Spotted eagle ray . . . 30 20
361 25 c. Great barracudas . . . 30 20
362 25 c. Reef needlefish 30 20
363 25 c. Reef blacktip shark . . 30 20
364 25 c. Hawksbill turtle 30 20
365 25 c. Sixfeeler treadfins and octopus 30 20
366 25 c. Batfish and sixfeeler threadfins 30 20
367 25 c. Lionfish and sixfeeler threadfins 30 20
368 25 c. Snowflake moray and sixfeeler threadfins 30 20
369 25 c. Inflated and uninflated porcupine fishes and sixfeeler threadfins 30 20
370 25 c. Regal angelfish, blue-streak cleaner wrasse, blue sea star and corals 30 20
371 25 c. Clown triggerfish and spotted garden eels 30 20
372 25 c. Spotted garden eels . . . 30 20
373 25 c. Blue-lined sea bream, blue-green chromis and sapphire damselfish 30 20
374 25 c. Orangespine unicornfish and whitetipped soldierfish . 30 20
375 25 c. Slatepencil sea urchin and leopard sea cucumber . . . 30 20
376 25 c. Partridge tun shell . . . 30 20
377 25 c. Mandarinfish 30 20
378 25 c. Tiger cowrie 30 20
379 25 c. Feather starfish and orange-fin anemone fish 30 20

Nos. 355/79 were printed together, se-tenant, forming a composite design.

56 "Delphin", 1890, and Card

1990. Pacifica. Mail Transport. Multicoloured.

380 45 c. Type **56** 55 45
381 45 c. Right-hand half of card flown on 1951 inaugural U.S. civilian airmail flight and forklift unloading mail from Boeing 727 airplane 55 45

Nos. 380/1 were issued together, se-tenant, forming a composite design.

57 Girls singing and Boy with Butterfly

1990. Christmas. Multicoloured.

382 25 c. Type **57** 30 20
383 25 c. White terns perching on girl's songbook 30 20
384 25 c. Girl singing and boys playing flute and guitar . . . 30 20
385 25 c. Couple with baby 30 20
386 25 c. Three girls singing . . . 30 20

58 Consolidated B-24S Liberator Bombers over Peleliu

1960. 46th Anniv of U.S. Action in Palau Islands during Second World War.

387 45 c. Type **58** 55 45
388 45 c. Landing craft firing rocket barrage 55 45
389 45 c. 1st Marine division attacking Peleliu 55 45
390 45 c. U.S. Infantryman and Palauan children 55 45

1991. Hard Corals. As T **50**.

392 30 c. Staghorn coral 40 30
393 30 c. Velvet leather coral . . . 40 30
394 30 c. Van Gogh's cypress coral 40 30
395 30 c. Violet lace coral 40 30

59 Statue of Virgin Mary, Nkulangelul Point

1991. Angaur, The Phosphate Island. Mult.

396 30 c. Type **59** 40 30
397 30 c. Angaur Post Office opening day cancellation and kaeb (sailing canoe) (41 × 27 mm) 40 30
398 30 c. Swordfish and Caroline Islands 40 pf. "Yacht" stamp (41 × 27 mm) 40 30
399 30 c. Locomotive at phosphate mine 40 30
400 30 c. Lighthouse Hill and German copra freighter . . 40 30
401 30 c. Dolphins and map showing phosphate mines (41 × 27 mm) 40 30
402 30 c. Estuarine crocodile (41 × 27 mm) 40 30
403 30 c. Workers cycling to phosphate plant 40 30
404 30 c. Freighter loading phosphate 40 30
405 30 c. Hammerhead shark and German overseer (41 × 27 mm) 40 30
406 30 c. Angaur cancellation and Marshall Islands 10 pf. "Yacht" stamp (41 × 27 mm) 40 30
407 30 c. Rear Admiral Graf von Spee and "Scharnhorst" (German cruiser) 40 30
408 30 c. "Emden" (German cruiser) and Capt. Karl von Muller 40 30
409 30 c. Crab-eating macaque (41 × 27 mm) 40 30
410 30 c. Sperm whale (41 × 27 mm) 40 30
411 30 c. H.M.A.S. "Sydney" (cruiser) shelling radio tower 40 30

Nos. 396/411 were issued together, se-tenant, with the centre block of eight stamps forming a composite design of a map of the island.

60 Moorhen

61 Pope Leo XIII and 19th-century Spanish and German Flags

1991. Birds. Multicoloured.

412 1 c. Palau bush warbler . . . 10 10
413 4 c. Type **60** 10 10
414 6 c. Banded rail 10 10
415 19 c. Palau fantail 25 15
416 20 c. Mangrove flycatcher . . 25 15
417 23 c. Purple swamphen . . . 30 20
418 29 c. Palau fruit dove 40 30
419 35 c. Crested tern 45 30
420 40 c. Eastern reef herons (inscr "Pacific Reef-Heron") . . . 55 40
421 45 c. Micronesian pigeon . . . 60 45
422 50 c. Giant frigate bird . . . 65 45
423 52 c. Little pied cormorant . . 70 50
424 75 c. Jungle nightjar . . . . . 1·00 75
425 95 c. Cattle egret . . . . . . 1·25 90
426 $1.34 Sulphur-crested cockatoo 1·75 1·25
427 $2 Blue-faced parrot finch . . 2·75 2·00
428 $5 Eclectus parrots . . . . . 6·75 5·00
429 $10 Palau bush warblers feeding chicks (51 × 28 mm) . . . . 13·00 9·75

1991. Centenary of Christianity in Palau Islands. Multicoloured.

432 29 c. Type **61** 40 30
433 29 c. Ibedul Ilengelekei and Church of the Sacred Heart, Koror, 1920 . . . . 40 30
434 29 c. Marino de la Hoz, Emilio Villar and Elias Fernandez (Jesuit priests executed in Second World War) 40 30
435 29 c. Centenary emblem and Fr. Edwin G. McManus (compiler of Palauan-English dictionary) 40 30
436 29 c. Present Church of the Sacred Heart, Koror . . . 40 30
437 29 c. Pope John Paul II and Palau and Vatican flags . . 40 30

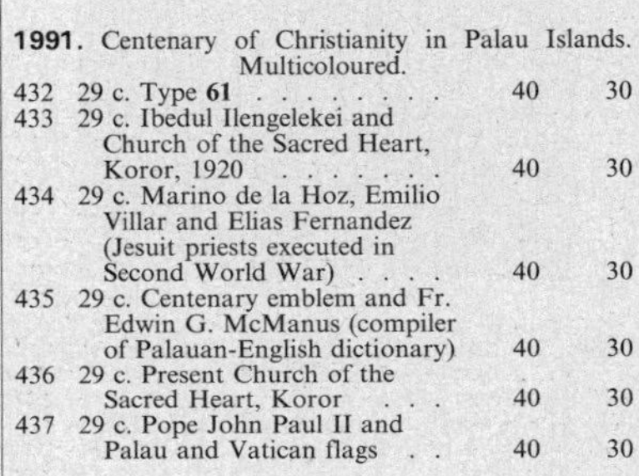

62 Pacific White-sided Dolphin

1991. Pacific Marine Life. Multicoloured.

438 29 c. Type **62** 40 30
439 29 c. Common dolphin . . . 40 30
440 29 c. Rough-toothed dolphin . 40 30
441 29 c. Bottle-nosed dolphin . . 40 30
442 29 c. Common (inscr "Harbor") porpoise 40 30
443 29 c. Head and body of killer whale 40 30
444 29 c. Tail of killer whale, spinner dolphin and yellowfin tuna . 40 30
445 29 c. Dall's porpoise 40 30
446 29 c. Finless porpoise 40 30
447 29 c. Map of Palau Islands and bottle-nosed dolphin . . . 40 30
448 29 c. Dusky dolphin 40 30
449 29 c. Southern right whale dolphin 40 30
450 29 c. Striped dolphin 40 30
451 29 c. Fraser's dolphin 40 30
452 29 c. Peale's dolphin 40 30
453 29 c. Spectacled porpoise . . . 40 30
454 29 c. Spotted dolphin 40 30
455 29 c. Hourglass dolphin . . . 40 30
456 29 c. Risso's dolphin 40 30
457 29 c. Hector's dolphin 40 30

63 McDonnell Douglas Wild Weasel Fighters

1991. Operation Desert Storm (liberation of Kuwait). Multicoloured.

458 20 c. Type **63** 25 20
459 20 c. Lockheed Stealth fighter-bomber 25 20
460 20 c. Hughes Apache helicopter 25 20
461 20 c. "M-109 TOW" missile on "M998 HMMWV" vehicle . 25 20
462 20 c. President Bush of U.S.A. 25 20
463 20 c. M2 "Bradley" tank . . . 25 20
464 20 c. U.S.S. "Ranger" (aircraft carrier) 25 20
465 20 c. PHM-1 (patrol boat) . . 25 20
466 20 c. U.S.S. "Wisconsin" (battleship) 25 20
467 $2.90 Sun, dove and yellow ribbon . . . . 3·75 2·75

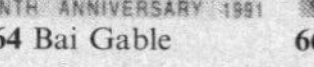

64 Bai Gable **66** "Silent Night, Holy Night!"

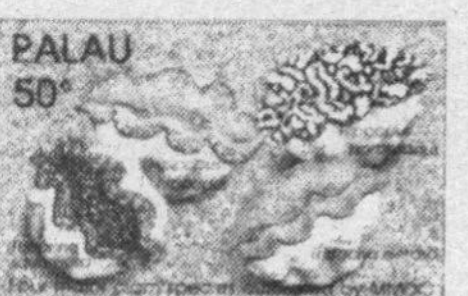

65 "Hippopus hippopus", "Hippopus porcellanus", "Tridacna squamosa" and "Tridacna derasa"

1991. 10th Anniv of Republic of Palau and Palau-Pacific Women's Conference, Koror. Bai (community building) Decorations. Mult. Imperf (self-adhesive) (50 c.) perf (others).

469 29 c. Type **64** (postage) . . . 40 30
470 29 c. Interior of bai (left side) (32 × 48 mm) 40 30
471 29 c. Interior of bai (right side) (32 × 48 mm) 40 30
472 29 c. God of construction . . 40 30
473 29 c. Bubuu (spider) (value at left) (30 × 23 mm) 40 30
474 29 c. Delerrok, the money bird (facing right) (31 × 23 mm) . 40 30
475 29 c. Delerrok (facing left) (31 × 23 mm) 40 30
476 29 c. Bubuu (value at right) (30 × 23 mm) 40 30
477 50 c. Bai gable (as in Type **64**) (24 × 51 mm) (air) 65 45

Nos. 469/76 were issued together, se-tenant, Nos. 470/1 forming a composite design.

1991. Conservation and Cultivation of Giant Clams. Multicoloured.

478 50 c. Type **65** 70 50
479 50 c. Symbiotic relationship between "Tridacna gigas" and "Symbiodinium microadriaticum" 70 50
480 50 c. Hatchery 70 50
481 50 c. Diver measuring clams in sea-bed nursery 70 50
482 50 c. Micronesian Mariculture Demonstration Center, Koror (108 × 16 mm) 70 50

1991. Christmas. Multicoloured.

483 29 c. Type **66** 40 30
484 29 c. "All is calm, all is bright;" 40 30
485 29 c. "Round yon virgin mother and child!" 40 30
486 29 c. "Holy Infant, so tender and mild," 40 30
487 29 c. "Sleep in heavenly peace." 40 30

Nos. 483/7 were issued together, se-tenant, forming a composite design.

67 Flag, Islands and Children

1991. 25th Anniv of Presence of United States Peace Corps in Palau. Children's paintings.

488 29 c. Type **67** 40 30
489 29 c. Volunteers arriving by airplane 40 30
490 29 c. Health care 40 30
491 29 c. Fishing 40 30
492 29 c. Agriculture 40 30
493 29 c. Education 40 30

68 "Zuiho Maru" (trochus shell breeding and marine research)

1991. "Phila Nippon '91" International Stamp Exhibition, Tokyo. Japanese Heritage in Palau. Multicoloured.

494 29 c. Type **68** 40 30
495 29 c. Man carving story board (traditional arts) 40 30
496 29 c. Tending pineapple crop (agricultural training) . . . 40 30
497 29 c. Klidm (stone carving), Koror (archaeological research) 40 30
498 29 c. Teaching carpentry and building design 40 30
499 29 c. Kawasaki "Mavis" flying boat (air transport) 40 30

69 Mitsubishi Zero-Sen attacking Shipping at Pearl Harbor **70** "Troides criton"

1991. Pacific Theatre in Second World War (1st issue). Multicoloured.

501 29 c. Type **69** 40 30
502 29 c. U.S.S. "Nevada" underway from Pearl Harbor 40 30
503 29 c. U.S.S. "Shaw" exploding at Pearl Harbor 40 30
504 29 c. Douglas Dauntless dive bombers attacking Japanese carrier "Akagi" 40 30
505 29 c. U.S.S. "Wasp" sinking off Guadalcanal 40 30
506 29 c. Battle of Philippine Sea 40 30
507 29 c. Landing craft storming Saipan Beach 40 30
508 29 c. U.S. 1st Cavalry on Leyte 40 30
509 29 c. Battle of Bloody Nose Ridge, Peleliu 40 30
510 29 c. U.S. troops landing at Iwo Jima 40 30

See also Nos. 574/83, 601/10 and 681/90.

1992. Butterflies. Multicoloured.

511 50 c. Type **70** 65 45
512 50 c. "Alcides zodiaca" . . . 65 45
513 50 c. "Papilio poboroi" . . . 65 45
514 50 c. "Vindula arsinoe" . . . 65 45

PALAU 29¢

And darkness was upon the face of the deep. And the Spirit of God moved upon the face of the waters. And God said,

Let there be light: and there was light.

71 Common Hairy Triton **73** "And darkness was upon the face of the deep ..."

72 Christopher Columbus

1992. Sea Shells (6th series). Multicoloured.

515 29 c. Type **71** 50 35
516 29 c. Eglantine cowrie 50 35
517 29 c. Sulcate swamp cerith . . 50 35
518 29 c. Black-spined murex . . 50 35
519 29 c. Black-mouth moon . . 50 35

1992. Age of Discovery from Columbus to Drake. Multicoloured.

520 29 c. Type **72** 40 30
521 29 c. Ferdinand Magellan . . 40 30
522 29 c. Sir Francis Drake . . . 40 30
523 29 c. Cloud blowing northerly wind 40 30
524 29 c. Compass rose 40 30
525 29 c. Dolphin and "Golden Hind" (Drake's ship) . . . 40 30
526 29 c. Corn cobs and "Santa Maria" (Columbus's ship) . 40 30
527 29 c. Mythical fishes 40 30
528 29 c. Betel palm, cloves and black pepper 40 303
529 29 c. "Vitoria" (Magellan's ship), Palau Islands, shearwater and crested tern 40 30
530 29 c. White-tailed tropic bird, bicolour parrotfish, pineapple and potatoes 40 30
531 29 c. Compass 40 30
532 29 c. Mythical sea monster . . 40 30
533 29 c. Paddles and astrolabe . . 40 30
534 29 c. Parallel ruler, divider and Inca gold treasure 40 30
535 29 c. Backstaff 40 30
536 29 c. Cloud blowing southerly wind 40 30
537 29 c. Amerigo Vespucci 40 30
538 29 c. Francisco Pizarro 40 30
539 29 c. Vasco Nunez de Balboa . 40 30

With the exception of Nos. 523 and 536 each stamp is inscribed on the back (over the gum) with the names of the subject featured on the stamp.

Nos. 520/39 were issued together, se-tenant, the backgrounds forming a composite design of the hemispheres.

1992. 2nd U.N. Conference on Environment and Development, Rio de Janeiro. The Creation of the World from the Book of Genesis, Chapter 1. Multicoloured.

540 29 c. Type **73** 40 30
541 29 c. Sunlight 40 30
542 29 c. "Let there be a firmament in the midst of the waters, ..." 40 30
543 29 c. Sky and clouds 40 30
544 29 c. "Let the waters under the heaven..." 40 30
545 29 c. Tree 40 30
546 29 c. Waves and sunlight (no inscr) 40 30
547 29 c. Waves and sunlight ("... and it was good.") 40 30
548 29 c. Waves and clouds (no inscr) 40 30
549 29 c. Waves and clouds ("... and it was so.") 40 30
550 29 c. Plants on river bank (no inscr) 40 30
551 29 c. Plants on river bank ("... and it was good.") 40 30
552 29 c. "Let there be lights in the firmament..." 40 30
553 29 c. Comet, planet and clouds 40 30
554 29 c. "Let the waters bring forth abundantly the moving creature..." 40 30
555 29 c. Birds flying and parrot on branch 40 30
556 29 c. "Let the earth bring forth the living creature after his kind..." 40 30
557 29 c. Woman, man and rainbow 40 30
558 29 c. Mountains ("... and it was good.") 40 30
559 29 c. Sun and hills 40 30
560 29 c. Whale and fishes 40 30
561 29 c. Fishes ("... and it was good.") 40 30
562 29 c. Elephants and squirrel . . 40 30
563 29 c. Orchard and cat ("... and it was very good.") 40 30

Nos. 540/63 were issued together, se-tenant, forming six composite designs each covering four stamps.

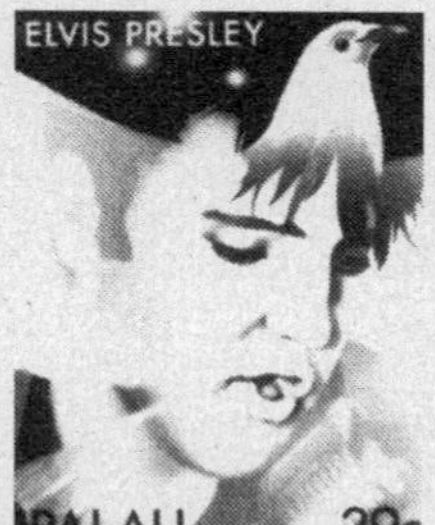

75 Presley and Dove

1992. 15th Death Anniv of Elvis Presley (entertainer). Multicoloured.

565 29 c. Type **75** 40 30
566 29 c. Presley and dove's wing . 40 30
567 29 c. Presley in yellow cape . . 40 30
568 29 c. Presley in white and red shirt (¾ face) 40 30
569 29 c. Presley singing into microphone 40 30
570 29 c. Presley crying 40 30
571 29 c. Presley in red shirt (¾ face) 40 30
572 29 c. Presley in purple shirt (full face) 40 30
573 29 c. Presley (left profile) . . . 40 30

76 Grumman Avenger

1992. Air. Pacific Theatre in Second World War (2nd issue). Aircraft. Multicoloured.

574 50 c. Type **76** 65 45
575 50 c. Curtiss P-40C of the Flying Tigers 65 45
576 50 c. Mitsubishi Zero-Sen . . . 65 45
577 50 c. Hawker Hurricane Mk I . 65 45
578 50 c. Consolidated Catalina flying boat 65 45
579 50 c. Curtiss Hawk 75 . . . . 65 45
580 50 c. Boeing Flying Fortress . 65 45
581 50 c. Brewster Buffalo 65 45
582 50 c. Vickers Supermarine Walrus flying boat 65 45
583 50 c. Curtiss Kittyhawk I . . 65 45

77 "Thus Every Beast"

1992. Christmas. "The Friendly Beasts" (carol). Multicoloured.

584 29 c. Type **77** 40 30
585 29 c. "By Some Good Spell" . 40 30
586 29 c. "In the Stable Dark was Glad to Tell" 40 30
587 29 c. "of the Gift He Gave Emanuel" (angel on donkey) 40 30
588 29 c. "The Gift He Gave Emanuel" (Palauan fruit doves) 40 30

78 Dugong

1993. Animals. Multicoloured.

589 50 c. Type **78** 65 45
590 50 c. Blue-faced (inscr "Masked") booby 65 45
591 50 c. Crab-eating macaque . . 65 45
592 50 c. New Guinea crocodile . . 65 45

79 Giant Deepwater Crab

1993. Seafood. Multicoloured.

593 29 c. Type **79** 40 30
594 29 c. Scarlet shrimp 40 30
595 29 c. Smooth nylon shrimp . . 40 30
596 29 c. Armed nylon shrimp . . 40 30

80 Oceanic Whitetip Shark

1993. Sharks. Multicoloured.

597 50 c. Type **80** 65 45
598 50 c. Great hammerhead shark 65 45
599 50 c. Leopard shark 65 45
600 50 c. Reef blacktip shark . . 65 45

81 U.S.S. "Tranquility" (hospital ship) **82** Girl with Goat

1993. Pacific Theatre in Second World War (3rd issue). Multicoloured.

601 29 c. Capture of Guadalcanal 40 30
602 29 c. Type **81** 40 30
603 29 c. New Guineans drilling . 40 30
604 29 c. Americans land in New Georgia 40 30
605 29 c. U.S.S. "California" (battle ship) 40 30
606 29 c. Douglas Dauntless dive bombers over Wake Island . 40 30
607 29 c. Flame-throwers on Tarawa 40 30
608 29 c. American advance on Makin 40 30
609 29 c. North American B-25 Mitchells bomb Simpson Harbour, Rabaul 40 30
610 29 c. Aerial bombardment of Kwajelein 40 30

1992. Christmas. Multicoloured.

611	29 c. Type **82**	40	30
612	29 c. Children with garlands and goats	40	30
613	29 c. Father Christmas	40	30
614	29 c. Musicians and singer	40	30
615	29 c. Family carrying food	40	30

83 Pterosaur

85 Flukes of Whale's Tail

84 "After Child-birth Ceremony" (Charlie Gibbons)

1993. Monsters of the Pacific. Multicoloured.

616	29 c. Type **83**	40	30
617	29 c. Outrigger canoe	40	30
618	29 c. Head of plesiosaur	40	30
619	29 c. Pterosaur and neck of plesiosaur	40	30
620	29 c. Pterosaur (flying towards left)	40	30
621	29 c. Giant crab	40	30
622	29 c. Tentacles of kraken and two sharks	40	30
623	29 c. Hammerhead shark, tentacle of kraken and neck of plesiosaur	40	30
624	29 c. Head of lake serpent	40	30
625	29 c. Hammerhead shark and neck of serpent	40	30
626	29 c. Kraken	40	30
627	29 c. Ray, tentacles of kraken and body of plesiosaur	40	30
628	29 c. Three fishes and body of plesiosaur	40	30
629	29 c. Butterfly fishes and serpent's claw	40	30
630	29 c. Octopus and body of serpent	40	30
631	29 c. Giant nautilus and body of plesiosaur	40	30
632	29 c. Striped angel fishes	40	30
633	29 c. Lion fish	40	30
634	29 c. Squid	40	30
635	29 c. Shark and body of kronosaur	40	30
636	29 c. Striped shark and sea-bed	40	30
637	29 c. Squid and sea-bed	40	30
638	29 c. Giant nautilus and tail of serpent	40	30
639	29 c. Head of kronosaur	40	30
640	29 c. Lion fish, body of kronosaur and sea-bed	40	30

Nos. 616/40 were issued together, se-tenant, forming a composite design.

1993. International Year of Indigenous Peoples. Multicoloured.

641	29 c. Type **84**	40	30
642	29 c. "Village in Early Palau" (Charlie Gibbons)	40	30

1993. Jonah and The Whale. Multicoloured.

644	29 c. Type **85**	40	30
645	29 c. Bird and part of fluke	40	30
646	29 c. Two birds	40	30
647	29 c. Kaeb (canoe)	40	30
648	29 c. Sun, birds and dolphin	40	30
649	29 c. Shark and whale's tail	40	30
650	29 c. Shoal of brown fishes and part of whale	40	30
651	29 c. Hammerhead shark, shark's tail and fishes	40	30
652	29 c. Two species of fish and shark's head	40	30
653	29 c. Dolphin and fishes	40	30
654	29 c. Small brown and large striped fishes and part of whale	40	30
655	29 c. Two turtles swimming across whale's body	40	30
656	29 c. Shoal of pink fishes and whale's back	40	30
657	29 c. Rays, fishes and top of whale's head	40	30
658	29 c. Two large and shoal of small brown fishes	40	30
659	29 c. Jellyfish and blue fish	40	30
660	29 c. Fishes and whale's dorsal fin	40	30
661	29 c. Whale's eye and corner of mouth	40	30
662	29 c. Opened mouth	40	30
663	29 c. Jonah	40	30
664	29 c. Yellow and black striped fish and corals on sea bed	40	30
665	29 c. Three fishes and sea anemone	40	30
666	29 c. Blue-striped fish and corals on sea bed	40	30
667	29 c. Brown and red striped fish, corals and part of whale's jaw	40	30
668	29 c. Spotted fishes on sea bed	40	30

Nos. 644/68 were issued together, se-tenant, forming a composite design.

86 Manta Ray

1994. "Hong Kong '94" International Stamp Exhibition. Rays. Multicoloured.

669	40 c. Type **86**	50	35
670	40 c. Spotted eagle ray	50	35
671	40 c. Coachwhip ray	50	35
672	40 c. Black-spotted ray	50	35

87 Crocodile's Head

1994. The Estuarine Crocodile. Multicoloured.

673	20 c. Type **87**	25	15
674	20 c. Hatchling and eggs	25	15
675	20 c. Crocodile swimming underwater	25	15
676	20 c. Crocodile half-submerged	25	15

88 Red-footed Booby

1994. Sea Birds. Multicoloured.

677	50 c. Type **88**	65	45
678	50 c. Great frigate bird	65	45
679	50 c. Brown booby	65	45
680	50 c. Little pied cormorant	65	45

89 U.S. Marines capture Kwajalein

1994. Pacific Theatre in Second World War (4th issue). Multicoloured.

681	29 c. Type **89**	35	25
682	29 c. Aerial bombardment of Japanese airbase, Truk	35	25
683	29 c. U.S.S. "284 Tullibee" (Operation Desecrate)	35	25
684	29 c. Landing craft storming Saipan beach	35	25
685	29 c. Shooting down Japanese Zeros, Mariana Islands	35	25
686	29 c. Liberated civilians, Guam	35	25
687	29 c. U.S. troops taking Peleliu	35	25
688	29 c. Securing Angaur	35	25
689	29 c. General MacArthur	35	25
690	29 c. U.S. Army memorial	35	25

90 Allied Warships

1994. 50th Anniv of D-Day (Allied Landings in Normandy). Multicoloured.

691	50 c. C-47 transport aircraft dropping paratroopers	65	45
692	50 c. Type **90**	65	45
693	50 c. Troops disembarking from landing craft	65	45
694	50 c. Tanks coming ashore	65	45
695	50 c. Sherman tank crossing minefield	65	45
696	50 c. Aircraft attacking German positions	65	45
697	50 c. Gliders dropping paratroops behind lines	65	45
698	50 c. Pegasus Bridge	65	45
699	50 c. Allied forces pushing inland	65	45
700	50 c. Beach at end of 6 June, 1944	65	45

PANAMA Pt. 15

Country situated on the C. American isthmus. Formerly a State or Department of Colombia, Panama was proclaimed an independent republic in 1903.

1878. 100 centavos = 1 peso
1906. 100 centesimos = 1 balboa

1 Coat of Arms

3 Map

1878. Imperf. The 50 c. is larger.

1	**1**	5 c. green	15·00	13·50
2		10 c. blue	38·00	35·00
3		20 c. red	24·00	21·00
4		50 c. yellow	9·75	

1887. Perf.

5	**3**	1 c. black on green	50	65
6		2 c. black on pink	1·25	1·00
7		5 c. black on blue	90	35
7a		5 c. black on grey	1·50	45
8		10 c. black on yellow	90	45
9		20 c. black on lilac	90	45
10		50 c. brown	1·50	75

5 Map of Panama **38**

1892.

12a	**5**	1 c. green	15	15
12b		2 c. red	20	20
12c		5 c. blue	90	45
12d		10 c. orange	20	20
12e		20 c. violet	25	25
12f		50 c. brown	30	25
12g		1 p. lake	3·75	2·40

1894. Surch **HABILITADO 1894** and value.

13	**5**	1 c. on 2 c. red	35	35
15	**3**	5 c. on 20 c. black on lilac	1·50	1·00
18		10 c. on 50 c. brown	1·90	1·90

1903. Optd **REPUBLICA DE PANAMA**.

70	**5**	1 c. green	1·25	75
36		2 c. red	55	55
37		5 c. blue	1·25	55
38		10 c. orange	1·25	1·25
39		20 c. violet	2·40	2·40
75	**3**	50 c. brown	14·00	14·00
40	**5**	50 c. brown	6·00	4·25
41		1 p. lake	29·00	24·00

1903. Optd **PANAMA** twice.

53	**5**	1 c. green	25	25
54		2 c. red	25	25
55		5 c. blue	30	30
56		10 c. orange	30	30
64		20 c. violet	90	90
65		50 c. brown	1·50	1·50
66		1 p. lake	3·50	2·75

1904. Optd **Republica de Panama**.

94	**5**	1 c. green	35	35
97		2 c. red	45	45
98		5 c. blue	45	45
99		10 c. orange	45	45
100		20 c. violet	45	45
103	**3**	50 c. brown	1·75	1·75
104	**5**	1 p. lake	9·50	8·25

1905.

151	**38**	½ c. orange	55	45
136		1 c. green	55	40
137		2 c. red	70	55

1906. Surch **PANAMA** twice and new value and thick bar.

138	**5**	1 c. on 20 c. violet	25	25
139		2 c. on 50 c. brown	25	25
140		5 c. on 1 p. lake	55	45

41 Panamanian Flag **42** Vasco Nunez de Balboa

43 F. de Cordoba

44 Arms of Panama

45 J. Arosemena **46** M. J. Hurtado **47** J. de Obaldia

1906.

142	**41**	½ c. multicoloured	40	35
143	**42**	1 c. black and green	40	35
144	**43**	2 c. black and red	55	35
145	**44**	2½ c. red	55	35
146	**45**	5 c. black and blue	1·00	35
147	**46**	8 c. black and purple	55	40
148	**47**	10 c. black and violet	55	35
149	–	25 c. black and brown	1·50	60
150	–	50 c. black	3·75	2·10

DESIGNS: 25 c. Tomas Herrera; 50 c. Jose de Fabrega.

48 Balboa **49** De Cordoba **50** Arms

51 Arosemena **52** Hurtado **53** Obaldia

1909.

152	**48**	1 c. black and green	65	50
153	**49**	2 c. black and red	65	30
154	**50**	2½ c. red	90	30
155	**51**	5 c. black and blue	1·10	30
156	**52**	8 c. black and purple	4·25	2·50
157	**53**	10 c. black and purple	2·10	1·10

56 Balboa viewing Pacific Ocean

57 Balboa reaches the Pacific

1913. 400th Anniv of Discovery of Pacific Ocean.

160	**56**	2½ c. yellow and green	45	40

1915. Panama Exhibition and Opening of Canal.

161	–	½ c. black and olive	45	35
162	–	1 c. black and green	55	35
163	**57**	2 c. black and red	65	35
164	–	2½ c. black and red	65	35
165	–	3 c. black and violet	1·00	35
166	–	5 c. black and blue	1·50	50
167	–	10 c. black and orange	1·50	50
168	–	20 c. black and brown	7·25	2·40

DESIGNS: ½ c. Chorrera Falls; 1 c. Relief Map of Panama Canal; 2½ c. Cathedral Ruins, Old Panama; 3 c. Palace of Arts, National Exhibition; 5 c. Gatun Locks; 10 c. Culebra Cut; 20 c. Archway, S. Domingo Monastery.

62 Balboa Docks

1918. Views on Panama Canal.

178	–	12 c. black and violet	17·00	5·50
179	–	15 c. black and blue	10·00	2·75
180	–	24 c. black and brown	24·00	7·50
181	**62**	50 c. black and orange	25·00	16·00
182	–	1 b. black and violet	35·00	19·00

DESIGNS: 12 c. "Panama" (cargo liner) in Gaillard Cut, north; 15 c. "Panama" in Gaillard Cut, south; 24 c. "Cristobal" (cargo liner) in Gatun Lock; 1 b. "Nereus" (U.S. Navy collier) in San Pedro Miguel Locks.

1919. 400th Anniv of Founding of City of Panama. No. 164 surch **1519 1919 2 CENTESIMOS 2**.

183	2 c. on 2½ c. black and red	45	45

MINIMUM PRICE

The minimum price quoted is 10p which represents a handling charge rather than a basis for valuing common stamps. For further notes about prices, see introductory pages.

64 Arms of Panama

65 Vallarino

68 Bolivar's Speech

70 Hurtado

1921. Independence Cent. Dated "1821 1921".
184 **64** ½ c. orange 55 30
185 **65** 1 c. green 55 25
186 – 2 c. red ("Land Gate", Panama City) 70 30
187 **65** 2½ c. (Bolivar) 95 75
188 – 3 c. violet (Cervantes statue) 95 75
189 **68** 5 c. blue 90 45
190 **65** 8 c. olive (Carlos Ycaza) . 3·50 2·10
191 – 10 c. violet (Government House 1821-1921) . . . . 2·40 85
192 – 15 c. blue (Balboa statue) . 3·00 1·25
193 – 20 c. brown (Los Santos Church) . . . . 5·00 2·40
194 **65** 24 c. sepia (Herrera) . . 5·00 3·00
195 – 50 c. black (Fabrega) . . . 8·75 4·50

1921. Birth Centenary of Manuel Jose Hurtado (writer).
196 **70** 2 c. green 55 35

1923. No. 164 surch **1923 2 CENTESIMOS 2.**
197 2 c. on 2½ c. black and red . . 35 35

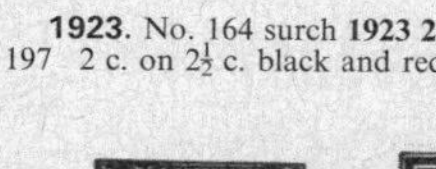

72

73 Simon Bolivar

74 Statue of Bolivar

75 Congress Hall, Panama

1924.
198 **72** ½ c. orange 20 10
199 1 c. green 20 10
200 2 c. red 25 10
201 5 c. blue 35 15
202 10 c. violet 40 20
203 12 c. olive 45 45
204 15 c. blue 55 45
205 24 c. brown . . . . . . 2·25 65
206 50 c. orange . . . . . . 3·75 90
207 1 b. black . . . . 5·50 2·25

1926. Bolivar Congress.
208 **73** ½ c. orange 35 15
209 1 c. green 35 15
210 2 c. red 40 25
211 4 c. grey 40 25
212 5 c. blue 65 40
213 **74** 8 c. purple 75 65
214 10 c. violet 60 60
215 12 c. olive 90 90
216 15 c. blue . . . . . . 1·25 1·10
217 20 c. brown . . . . . . 2·40 1·25
218 **75** 24 c. slate . . . . . . 3·00 1·50
219 50 c. black . . . . . . 7·00 3·50

78 "Spirit of St. Louis" over Map

1928. Lindbergh's Flying Tour.
222 – 2 c. red on rose 55 35
223 **78** 5 c. blue on green 75 55
DESIGN—VERT: 2 c. "Spirit of St. Louis" over Old Panama with opt **HOMENAJE A LINDBERGH.**

1928. 25th Anniv of Independence. Optd **1903. NOV 3 BRE 1928.**
224 **70** 2 c. green 30 20

1929. Air. No. E226 surch with Fokker Universal airplane and **CORREO AEREO 25 25 VEINTICINCO CENTESIMOS.**
225 E **81** 25 c. on 10 c. orange . . 1·10 90

1929. Air. Nos. E226/7 optd **CORREO AEREO** or additionally surch with new value in **CENTESIMOS.**
238 E **81** 5 c. on 10 c. orange . . 55 55
228 10 c. orange 55 55
268 10 c. on 20 c. brown . . 90 55
229 15 c. on 10 c. orange . . 55 55
269 20 c. brown 90 55
230 25 c. on 20 c. brown . . 1·25 1·10

83

87

1930. Air.
231 **83** 5 c. blue 20 10
232 5 c. orange 35 10
233 7 c. red 35 10
234 8 c. black 35 10
235 15 c. green 45 10
236 20 c. red 50 10
237 25 c. blue 55 55

1930. No. 182 optd with airplane and **CORREO AEREO.**
239 1 b. black and violet . . . . 18·00 14·00

1930. Air.
244 **87** 5 c. blue 20 10
245 10 c. orange 35 25
246 30 c. violet . . . . . . 6·75 4·00
247 50 c. red . . . . 1·25 35
248 1 b. black . . . . 6·75 4·25

1930. Bolivar's Death Cent. Surch **1830-1930 17 DE DICIEMBRE UN CENTESIMO.**
249 **73** 1 c. on 4 c. grey 25 20

89 Seaplane over old Panama

92 Manuel Amador Guerrero

1931. Air. Opening of service between Panama City and western provinces.
250 **89** 5 c. blue . . . . 1·00 90

1932. Optd **HABILITADA** or surch also.
251 **64** ½ c. orange (postage) . . . 35 20
252 **73** ½ c. orange 20 20
253 1 c. green 25 20
270 **68** 1 c. on 5 c. blue 45 35
254 **73** 2 c. red 20 20
255 5 c. blue 45 30
256 – 10 c. violet (No. 191) . . . 70 35
258 **74** 10 c. on 12 c. olive . . . 75 40
259 10 c. on 15 c. blue . . . 70 35
257 20 c. brown . . . . . . 1·00 1·10
260 **83** 20 c. on 25 c. blue (air) . . 4·00 55

1932. Birth Centenary of Dr. Guerrero (first president of republic).
261 **92** 2 c. red 45 20

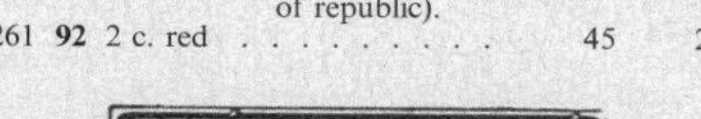

95 National Institute

1934. 25th Anniv of National Institute.
262 – 1 c. green 55 55
263 – 2 c. red 55 55
264 – 5 c. blue 75 60
265 **95** 10 c. brown . . . . . . 2·10 1·00
266 – 12 c. green . . . . . . 3·50 1·50
267 – 15 c. blue . . . . . . 4·75 1·75
DESIGNS—VERT: 1 c. J. D. de Obaldia; 2 c. E. A. Morales; 5 c. Sphinx and Quotation from Emerson. HORIZ: 12 c. J. A. Facio; 15 c. P. Arosemena.

(98)

100 Urraca Monument

INDEX

Countries can be quickly located by referring to the index at the end of this volume.

99 Custom House Ruins, Portobelo

1936. Birth Cent of Pablo Arosemena. (a) Postage. Surch as T **98**, but without **CORREO AEREO.**
271 **72** 2 c. on 24 c. brown 55 45

(b) Air. Surch with T **98.**
272 **72** 5 c. on 50 c. orange 60 50

1936. 4th Spanish-American Postal Congress (1st issue). Inscr "IV CONGRESO POSTAL AMERICO–ESPANOL".
273 **99** ½ c. orange (postage) . . . 40 25
274 – 1 c. green 40 25
275 – 2 c. red 40 25
276 – 5 c. blue 45 30
277 – 10 c. violet 75 45
278 – 15 c. blue 75 60
279 – 20 c. red . . . . 95 1·00
280 – 25 c. brown . . . . . . 1·50 1·40
281 – 50 c. orange . . . . . . 8·00 2·75
282 – 1 b. black . . . . 9·00 7·00
DESIGNS: 1 c. "Panama" (Old tree); 2 c. "La Pollera" (woman in costume); 5 c. Bolivar; 10 c. Ruins of Old Panama Cathedral; 15 c. Garcia y Santos; 20 c. Madden Dam; 25 c. Columbus; 50 c. "Resolute" (liner) in Gaillard Cut; 1 b. Panama Cathedral.

283 **100** 5 c. blue (air) 70 40
284 – 10 c. orange 90 65
285 – 20 c. red . . . . 1·25 1·00
286 – 30 c. violet . . . . . . 2·10 1·90
287 – 50 c. red . . . . 22·00 15·00
288 – 1 b. black . . . . 9·00 6·50
DESIGNS—HORIZ: 10 c. "Man's Genius Uniting the Oceans"; 20 c. Panama; 50 c. San Pedro Miguel Locks; 1 b. Courts of Justice. VERT: 10 c. Balboa Monument.

1937. 4th Spanish-American Postal Congress (2nd issue). Nos. 273/88 optd **UPU.**
289 **99** ½ c. orange (postage) . . . 35 20
290 – 1 c. green 45 20
291 – 2 c. red 45 20
292 – 5 c. blue 45 30
293 – 10 c. violet 75 45
294 – 15 c. blue . . . . . . 4·75 2·40
295 – 20 c. red . . . . 1·10 1·10
296 – 25 c. brown . . . . . . 1·75 90
297 – 50 c. orange . . . . . . 7·00 4·25
298 – 1 b. black . . . . 8·75 7·50

299 **99** 5 c. blue (air) 45 45
300 – 10 c. orange 70 55
301 – 20 c. red 95 75
302 – 30 c. violet . . . . . . 3·50 2·40
303 – 50 c. red . . . . 18·00 18·00
304 – 1 b. black . . . . 11·50 9·50

1937. Optd **1937-38.**
305 **73** ½ c. orange 50 45
306 **65** 1 c. green 30 25
307 **73** 1 c. green 30 25
308 **70** 2 c. green 35 25
309 **73** 2 c. red 35 30

1937. Surch **1937-38** and value.
310 **73** 2 c. on 4 c. grey 45 30
311 **78** 2 c. on 8 c. olive 45 30
312 **74** 2 c. on 8 c. purple 45 30
313 2 c. on 10 c. violet . . . 45 30
314 2 c. on 12 c. olive . . . 45 30
315 – 2 c. on 15 c. (No. 192) . . 45 30
316 **65** 2 c. on 24 c. sepia . . . 45 30
317 2 c. on 50 c. black . . . 45 30

1937. Air. Optd **CORREO AEREO** or surch also.
318 **73** 5 c. blue 45 45
319 **74** 5 c. on 15 c. blue 45 45
320 5 c. on 20 c. brown . . . 45 45
321 **75** 5 c. on 24 c. slate 45 45
322 **62** 5 c. on 1 b. black & violet . 2·50 1·25
323 – 10 c. on 10 c. violet (191) . 1·40 90
324 **75** 10 c. on 50 c. black . . . 1·40 90

105 Fire-Engine

106 Firemen's Monument

107 Fire-Brigade Badge

1937. 50th Anniv of Fire Brigade.
325 – ½ c. orange (postage) . . . 45 25
326 – 1 c. green 45 25
327 – 2 c. red 45 30
328 **105** 5 c. blue 65 30
329 **106** 10 c. violet . . . . . . 1·10 65
330 – 12 c. green . . . . . . 1·50 1·10
331 **107** 5 c. blue (air) 55 35
332 – 10 c. orange 70 45
333 – 20 c. red 90 55
DESIGNS—VERT: ½ c. R. Arango; 1 c. J. A. Guizado; 10 c. (No. 332), F. Arosemena; 12 c. D. H. Brandon; 20 c. J. G. Duque. HORIZ: 2 c. House on fire.

108 Basketball Player

111 Old Panama Cathedral and Statue of Liberty

1938. Air. C. American and Caribbean Olympic Games.
334 **108** 1 c. red 80 30
335 – 2 c. green (Baseball player) 80 15
336 – 7 c. grey (Swimmer) . . . 1·10 35
337 – 8 c. brown (Boxers) . . . 1·10 35
338 – 15 c. blue (Footballer) . . 2·60 1·10
The 1 c. and 15 c. are vert, the rest horiz.

1938. Opening of Aguadulce Normal School, Santiago. Optd **NORMAL DE SANTIAGO JUNIO 5 1938** or surch also.
340 **72** 2 c. red (postage) 30 25
341 **87** 7 c. on 30 c. violet (air) . . 45 45
342 **83** 8 c. on 15 c. green 45 45

1938. 150th Anniv of U.S. Constitution. Flags in red, white and blue.
343 **111** 1 c. black & green (post) . 45 20
344 2 c. black and red . . . 55 25
345 5 c. black and blue . . . 60 45
346 12 c. black and olive . . . 1·10 65
347 15 c. black and blue . . . 1·40 75

348 7 c. black and grey (air) . 50 30
349 8 c. black and blue . . . 70 30
350 15 c. black and brown . . 90 70
351 50 c. black and orange . . 12·00 9·00
352 1 b. black . . . . 12·00 9·00
Nos. 343/7 are without the Douglas DC-3 airliner.

112 Pierre and Marie Curie

113 Gatun Lock

1939. Obligatory Tax. Cancer Research Fund. Dated "1939".
353 **112** 1 c. red 55 15
354 1 c. green 55 15
355 1 c. orange 55 15
356 1 c. blue 55 15

1939. 25th Anniv of Opening of Panama Canal.
357 **113** ½ c. yellow (postage) . . . 1·25 1·25
358 – 1 c. green . . . . 1·50 1·50
359 – 2 c. red 55 15
360 – 5 c. blue . . . . 1·50 20
361 – 10 c. violet . . . . . . 2·00 50
362 – 12 c. olive 75 55
363 – 15 c. blue 75 70
364 – 50 c. orange . . . . . . 1·75 1·25
365 – 1 b. brown . . . . . . 3·50 2·25
DESIGNS: 1 c. "Santa Elena" (liner) in Pedro Miguel Locks; 2 c. Allegory of canal construction; 5 c. "Rangitata" (liner) in Culebra Cut; 10 c. Panama canal ferry; 12 c. Aerial view; 15 c. Gen. Gorgas; 50 c. M. A. Guerrero; 1 b. Woodrow Wilson.

366 – 1 c. red (air) 35 10
367 – 2 c. green 35 15
368 – 5 c. blue 55 20
369 – 10 c. violet 70 25
370 – 15 c. blue 95 35
371 – 20 c. red . . . . 2·50 95
372 – 50 c. brown . . . . . . 3·00 90
373 – 1 b. black . . . . 6·00 4·00
PORTRAITS: 1 c. B. Porras; 2 c. Wm. H. Taft; 5 c. P. J. Sosa; 10 c. L. B. Wise; 15 c. A. Reclus; 20 c. Gen. Goethals; 50 c. F. de Lesseps; 1 b. Theodore Roosevelt.

115 Flags of American Republics

120a "Liberty"

1940. Air. 50th Anniv of Pan-American Union.
374 **115** 15 c. blue 45 30

1940. Air. No. 370 surch **55.**
375 5 c. on 15 c. blue 25 25

No. 363 surch **AEREO SIETE.**
376 7 c. on 15 c. blue 40 30

No. 371 surch **SIETE**.
377 7 c. on 20 c. red 40 30

No. 374 surch **8–8**.
378 115 8 c. on 15 c. blue 40 30

1941. Obligatory Tax. Cancer Research Fund. Optd **LUCHA CONTRA EL CANCER**.
379 72 1 c. green 1·40 1·10

1941. Enactment of New Constitution (a) Postage. Optd **CONSTITUCION 1941**.
380 72 ½ c. orange 35 20
381 1 c. green 35 20
382 2 c. red 35 25
383 5 c. blue 45 20
384 10 c. violet 65 45
385 15 c. blue 1·00 65
386 50 c. orange 5·50 2·50
387 1 b. black 13·00 4·50

(b) Air. Surch **CONSTITUCION 1941 AEREO** and value in figures.
388 E 81 7 c. on 10 c. orange 65 65
389 72 15 c. on 24 c. brown 2·25 1·50

(c) Air. Optd **CONSTITUCION 1941**.
390 83 20 c. red 3·25 2·25
391 87 50 c. red 7·50 4·25
392 1 b. black 17·00 9·00

1941. Obligatory Tax. Cancer Research Fund. Dated "1940".
393 112 1 c. red 45 10
394 1 c. green 45 10
395 1 c. orange 45 10
396 1 c. blue 45 10

1942. Telegraph stamps as T **120a** optd or surch (a) Optd **CORREOS 1942** and (No. 397) surch **2c**.
397 2 c. on 5 c. blue 70 55
398 10 c. violet 90 70

(b) Air. Optd **CORREO AEREO 1942**.
399 20 c. brown 1·75 1·50

123 Flags of Panama and Costa Rica

1942. 1st Anniv of Revised Frontier Agreement between Panama and Costa Rica.
400 123 2 c. red (postage) 30 25
401 15 c. green (air) 60 15

1942. Obligatory Tax. Cancer Research Fund. Dated "1942".
402 112 1 c. violet 45 15

127 Balboa reaches Pacific

129 J. D. Arosemena Normal School **131** A. G. Melendez

1942. (a) Postage stamps.
403 – ½ c. red, blue and violet 10 10
404 – ½ c. blue, orange and red 15 10
405 – 1 c. green 10 10
406 – 1 c. red 10 10
407 – 2 c. red ("ACARRERO") 20 10
408 – 2 c. red ("ACARREO") 45 10
409 – 2 c. black and red 15 10
410 127 5 c. black and blue 20 10
411 – 5 c. blue 30 10
412 – 10 c. orange and red 45 20
413 – 10 c. orange and purple 35 20
414 – 15 c. black and blue 35 55
415 – 15 c. black 35 20
416 – 50 c. black and red 85 60
417 – 1 b. black 1·75 70

DESIGNS—VERT: ½ c. National flag; 1 c. Farm girl; 10 c. Golden Altar, Church of St. Jose; 50 c. San Blas Indian woman and child. HORIZ: 2 c. Oxen drawing sugar cart; 15 c. St. Thomas's Hospital; 1 b. National highway.

(b) Air.
418 – 2 c. red 45 10
419 – 7 c. red 55 20
420 – 8 c. black and brown 20 10
421 – 10 c. black and blue 20 15
422 – 15 c. violet 30 10
423 – 15 c. grey 35 15
424 129 20 c. brown 35 10
425 20 c. green 35 20
426 – 50 c. green 1·25 45
427 – 50 c. red 3·50 2·60
428 – 50 c. blue 60 40
429 – 1 b. orange, yellow & black 1·40 65

DESIGNS—HORIZ: 2 c., 7 c. Sword-fish; 8 c., 10 c. Gate of Glory, Portobelo; 15 c. Taboga Is; 50 c. Fire Brigade H.Q., Panama City; 1 b. Idol (Golden Beast).

1943. Obligatory Tax. Cancer Research Fund. Dated "1943".
433 112 1 c. green 45 15
434 1 c. red 45 15
435 1 c. orange 45 15
436 1 c. blue 45 15

1943. Air.
437 131 3 b. grey 5·50 5·50
438 – 5 b. blue (T. Lefevre) 8·50 7·00

1945. Obligatory Tax. Cancer Research Fund. Dated "1945".
439 112 1 c. red 45 20
440 1 c. green 45 20
441 1 c. orange 45 20
442 1 c. blue 45 20

1946. Obligatory Tax. Cancer Research Fund. Surch **CANCER B/.0.01 1947**.
443 72 1 c. on ½ c. orange 55 15
444 1 c. on 1 c. green 55 15
445 – 1 c. on ½ c. red, blue and violet (No. 403) 45 10
446 72 1 c. on 12 c. olive 45 15
447 1 c. on 24 c. brown 45 15

1947. Air. Surch **AEREO 1947** and value.
448 – 5 c. on 7 c. red (No. 419) 20 20
449 83 5 c. on 8 c. black 20 20
450 – 5 c. on 8 c. black and brown (No. 420) 20 20
451 83 10 c. on 15 c. green 55 35
452 – 10 c. on 15 c. violet (422) 30 25

134 Flag of Panama **135** National Theatre

1947. 2nd Anniv of National Constitutional Assembly.
453 134 2 c. red, deep red and blue (postage) 15 10
454 – 5 c. blue 20 20
455 135 8 c. violet (air) 45 30

DESIGN—As Type **134**: 5 c. Arms of Panama.

1947. Cancer Research Fund. Dated "1947".
456 112 1 c. red 45 10
457 1 c. green 45 10
458 1 c. orange 45 10
459 1 c. blue 45 10

1947. Surch **HABILITADA CORREOS** and value.
460 83 ½ c. on 8 c. black 10 10
461 – ½ c. on 8 c. black and brown (No. 420) 10 10
462 – 1 c. on 7 c. red (No. 419) 15 15
463 135 2 c. on 8 c. violet 20 15

1947. Surch **Habilitada CORREOS B/.0.50**.
464 72 50 c. on 24 c. brown 65 65

138 J. A. Arango **140** Firemen's Monument

1948. Air. Honouring members of the Revolutionary Junta of 1903.
465 – 3 c. black and blue 35 25
466 138 5 c. black and brown 35 25
467 – 10 c. black and orange 35 25
468 – 15 c. black and red 35 55
469 – 20 c. black and red 40 40
470 – 50 c. black 1·75 70
471 – 1 b. black and green 3·00 2·75
472 – 2 b. black and yellow 7·00 6·00

PORTRAITS—HORIZ: 3 c. M. A. Guerrero; 10 c. F. Boyd; 15 c. R. Arias. VERT: 20 c. M. Espinosa; 50 c. C. C. Arosemena (engineer); 1 b. N. de Obarrio; 2 b. T. Arias.

1948. 50th Anniv of Colon Fire Brigade.
473 140 5 c. black and red 20 15
474 – 10 c. black and orange 35 20
475 – 20 c. black and blue 70 40
476 – 25 c. black and brown 70 55
477 – 50 c. black and violet 90 55
478 – 1 b. black and green 1·50 90

DESIGNS—HORIZ: 10 c. Fire engine; 20 c. Fire hose; 25 c. Fire Brigade Headquarters. VERT: 50 c. Commander Walker; 1 b. First Fire-Brigade Commander.

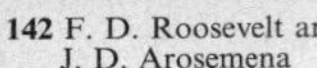
142 F. D. Roosevelt and J. D. Arosemena **144** Roosevelt Monument, Panama

1948. Air. Homage to F. D. Roosevelt.
479 142 5 c. black and red 20 15
480 – 10 c. orange 30 30
481 144 20 c. green 35 35
482 – 50 c. black and blue 40 35
483 – 1 b. black 90 75

DESIGNS—HORIZ: 10 c. Woman with palm symbolizing "Four Freedoms"; 50 c. Map of Panama Canal. VERT: 1 b. Portrait of Roosevelt.

147 Cervantes **148** Monument to Cervantes

1948. 400th Birth Anniv of Cervantes.
484 147 2 c. black and red (post.) 30 15
485 148 5 c. black and blue (air) 20 10
486 – 10 c. black and mauve 35 30

DESIGN—HORIZ: 10 c. Don Quixote and Sancho Panza (inscr as Type **148**).

1949. Air. Jose Gabriel Duque (philanthropist). Birth Centenary No. 486 optd **"CENTENARIO DE/JOSE GABRIEL DUQUE/"18 de Enero de 1949"**.
487 10 c. black & mauve 40 40

1949. Obligatory Tax. Cancer Research Fund. Surch **LUCHA CONTRA EL CANCER** and value.
488 142 1 c. on 5 c. black and red 35 10
489 – 1 c. on 10 c. orange (No. 480) 35 10

1949. Incorporation of Chiriqui Province Cent. Stamps of 1930 and 1942 optd **1849-1949 CHIRIQUI CENTENARIO**. (a) On postage stamps as No. 407. (i) Without surcharge.
491 – 2 c. red 20 10

(ii) Surch **1 UN CENTESIMO 1** also.
490 – 1 c. on 2 c. red 20 10

(b) Air.
492 – 2 c. red (No. 418) 20 20
493 83 5 c. blue 30 30
494 – 15 c. grey (No. 423) 40 40
495 – 50 c. red (No. 427) 1·75 1·75

1949. 75th Anniv of U.P.U. Stamps of 1930 and 1942/3 optd **1874 1949 U.P.U.** No. 625 is also surch. **B/0.25**.
496 – 1 c. grn (No. 405) (postage) 20 10
497 – 2 c. red (No. 407) 30 15
498 127 5 c. blue 45 25
499 – 2 c. red (No. 418) (air) 20 20
500 83 5 c. orange 55 35
501 – 10 c. black and blue (No. 421) 20 20
502 131 25 c. on 3 b. grey 30 30
503 – 50 c. red (No. 427) 1·60 1·60

1949. Cancer Research Fund. Dated "1949".
504 112 1 c. brown 45 10

153 Father Xavier **154** St. Xavier University

1949. Bicentenary of Founding of St. Xavier University.
505 153 2 c. black & red (postage) 25 15
506 154 5 c. black & blue (air) 35 15

155 Dr. Carlos J. Finlay **156** "Aedes aegypti"

1950. Dr. Finlay (medical research worker).
507 155 2 c. black & red (postage) 35 15
508 156 5 c. black & blue (air) 85 40

1950. Death Cent of San Martin. Optd **CENTENARIO del General (or Gral.) Jose de San Martin 17 de Agosto de 1950** or surch also. The 50 c. is optd **AEREO** as well.
509 – 1 c. grn (No. 405) (postage) 15 10
510 – 2 c. on ½ c. (No. 404) 20 10
511 127 5 c. black and blue 25 20
512 – 2 c. red (No. 418) (air) 35 30
513 83 5 c. orange 35 35
514 – 10 c. black & blue (No. 421) 55 45
515 83 25 c. blue 90 70
516 – 50 c. black & violet (No. 477) 1·40 1·00

158 Badge **159** Stadium

1950. Obligatory Tax. Physical Culture Fund. Dated "1950".
517 – 1 c. black and red 70 20
518 158 1 c. black and blue 70 20
519 159 1 c. black and green 70 20
520 – 1 c. black and orange 70 20
521 – 1 c. black and violet 70 20

DESIGNS—VERT: No. 520, as Type **159** but medallion changed and incorporating four "F"s; No. 521, Discus thrower. HORIZ: No. 517, as Type **159** but front of Stadium.

1951. Birth Tercent of Jean-Baptiste de La Salle (educational reformer). Optd **Tercer Centenario del Natalicio de San Juan Baptista de La Salle. 1651-1951.**
522 2 c. black and red (No. 409) 15 15
523 5 c. blue (No. 411) 25 15

1952. Air. Surch **AEREO 1952** and value.
524 2 c. on 10 c. black & blue (No. 421) 20 15
525 5 c. on 10 c. black & blue (No. 421) 25 10
526 1 b. on 5 b. blue (No. 438) 23·00 23·00

1952. Surch **1952** and figure of value.
527 1 c. on ½ c. (No. 404) 15 10

Air. Optd **AEREO** also.
528 5 c. on 2 c. (No. 408) 15 10
529 25 c. on 10 c. (No. 413) 70 65

164 Isabella the Catholic **167** Masthead of "La Estrella"

1952. 500th Birth Anniv of Isabella the Catholic.
530 164 1 c. black & grn (postage) 10 10
531 2 c. black and red 15 10
532 5 c. black and blue 20 15
533 10 c. black and violet 25 20
534 4 c. black and orange (air) 10 10
535 5 c. black and olive 15 10
536 10 c. black and buff 35 30
537 25 c. black and slate 55 35
538 50 c. black and brown 75 45
539 1 b. black 3·00 3·00

1953. Surch **B/.0.01 1953**.
540 1 c. on 10 c. (No. 413) 10 10
541 1 c. on 15 c. black (No. 415) 15 10

1953. Air. No. 421 surch **5 1953**.
542 5 c. on 10 c. black and blue 35 10

1953. Air. Centenary of "La Estrella de Panama", Newspaper.
543 167 5 c. red 20 15
544 10 c. blue 25 25

168 Pres. and Senora Amador Guerrero

1953. 50th Anniv of Panama Republic.
545 – 2 c. violet (postage) 15 10
546 168 5 c. orange 20 10
547 – 12 c. purple 35 15
548 – 20 c. indigo 65 25
549 – 50 c. yellow 90 65
550 – 1 b. blue 2·25 1·00

DESIGNS—VERT: 2 c. Blessing the flat; 50 c. Old Town Hall. HORIZ: 12 c. J. A. Santos and J. De La Ossa; 20 c. Revolutionary council; 1 b. Obverse and reverse of coin.

551 – 2 c. blue (air) 10 10
552 – 5 c. green 15 10
553 – 7 c. grey 20 15
554 – 25 c. black 1·40 70
555 – 50 c. brown 65 70
556 – 1 b. orange 2·25 1·00

DESIGNS—VERT: 2 c. Act of Independence. HORIZ: 5 c. Pres. and Senora Remon Cantera; 7 c. Girl in national costume; 25 c. National flower; 50 c. Salazar, Huertas and Domingo; 1 b. National dance.

1954. Surch in figures.
557 – 3 c. on 1 c. red (No. 406) (postage) 10 10
558 **167** 1 c. on 5 c. red (air) . . . 10 10
559 1 c. on 10 c. blue 10 10

170 Gen. Herrera at Conference Table

1954. Death Centenary of Gen. Herrera.
560 – 3 c. violet (postage) . . . 20 10
561 **170** 6 c. green (air) 15 10
562 – 1 b. black and red . . . . 2·25 2·10
DESIGNS—VERT: 3 c. Equestrian statue. HORIZ: 1 b. Cavalry charge.

171 Rotary Emblem and Map

1955. Air. 50th Anniv of Rotary International.
563 **171** 6 c. violet 15 10
564 21 c. red 55 35
565 1 b. black . . . . 3·50 1·90

172 Tocumen Airport **173** President Remon Cantera

1955.
566 **172** ½ c. brown 10 10

1955. National Mourning for Pres. Remon Cantera.
567 **173** 3 c. blk & pur (postage) . 15 10
568 6 c. black & violet (air) . . 20 15

174 V. de la Guardia y Azala and M. Chiaria **175** F. de Lesseps

1955. Centenary of Cocle Province.
569 **174** 5 c. violet 20 10

1955. 150th Birth Anniv of De Lesseps (engineer).
570 **175** 3 c. lake on pink (postage) 30 10
571 – 25 c. blue on blue . . . . 2·25 1·25
572 – 50 c. violet on lilac . . . 90 60
573 – 5 c. myrtle on green (air) . 20 10
574 – 1 b. black and mauve . . 2·75 1·75
DESIGNS—VERT: 5 c. P. J. Sosa; 50 c. T. Roosevelt. HORIZ: 25 c. First excavations for Panama Canal; 1 b. "Ancon I" (first ship to pass through canal) and De Lesseps.

1955. Air. No. 564 surch.
575 **171** 15 c. on 21 c. red 45 35

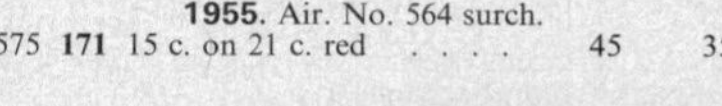

177 Pres. Eisenhower (United States) **178** Bolivar Statue

1956. Air. Pan-American Congress, Panama and 30th Anniv of First Congress.
576 – 6 c. black and blue . . . 30 20
577 – 6 c. black and bistre . . . 30 20
578 – 6 c. black and green . . . 30 20
579 – 6 c. sepia and green . . . 30 20
580 – 6 c. green and yellow . . 30 20
581 – 6 c. green and violet . . . 30 20
582 – 6 c. blue and lilac 30 20
583 – 6 c. green and purple . . 30 20
584 – 6 c. blue and olive . . . 30 20
585 – 6 c. sepia and yellow . . 30 20
586 – 6 c. blue and sepia . . . 30 20
587 – 6 c. green and mauve . . 30 20
588 – 6 c. sepia and red . . . 30 20
589 – 6 c. green and blue . . . 30 20
590 – 6 c. sepia and blue . . . 30 20
591 – 6 c. black and orange . . 30 20
592 – 6 c. sepia and grey . . . 30 20
593 – 6 c. black and pink . . . 30 20
594 **177** 6 c. blue and red 70 35
595 – 6 c. blue and grey 30 20
596 – 6 c. green and brown . . 30 20
597 **178** 20 c. grey 40 55
598 – 50 c. green 75 75
599 – 1 b. sepia . . . . 1·50 95
PRESIDENTIAL PORTRAITS as Type **177**: No. 576, Argentina; 577, Bolivia; 578, Brazil; 579, Chile; 580, Colombia; 581, Costa Rica; 582, Cuba; 583, Dominican Republic; 584, Ecuador; 585, Guatemala; 586, Haiti; 587, Honduras; 588, Mexico; 589, Nicaragua; 590, Panama; 591, Paraguay; 592, Peru; 593, Salvador; 595, Uruguay; 596, Venezuela. As Type **178** — HORIZ: No. 598, Bolivar Hall. VERT: No. 599, Bolivar Medallion.

179 Arms of Panama City **180** Pres. Carlos A. Mendoza

1956. 6th Inter-American Congress of Municipalities, Panama City.
600 **179** 3 c. green (postage) . . . 15 10
601 – 25 c. red (air) 55 35
602 – 50 c. black 65 55
DESIGNS: 25 c. Stone bridge, Old Panama; 50 c. Town Hall, Panama.

1956. Birth Centenary of Pres. Carlos A. Mendoza.
604 **180** 10 c. green and red . . . 20 15

182 Dr. Belisario Porras

1956. Birth Centenary of Dr. Porras.
605 – 15 c. grey (postage) . . . 45 20
606 **182** 25 c. blue and red 65 45
607 – 5 c. green (air) 10 10
608 – 15 c. red 30 25
DESIGNS—HORIZ: 15 c. (No. 605), National Archives; 15 c. (No. 608), St. Thomas's Hospital. VERT: 5 c. Porras Monument.

183 Isthmus Highway **185** Manuel E. Batista

1957. 7th Pan-American Highway Congress.
609 **183** 3 c. green (postage) . . . 15 10
610 – 10 c. black (air) 20 15
611 – 20 c. black and blue . . . 35 35
612 – 1 b. green . . . . 1·75 1·75
DESIGNS—VERT: 10 c. Highway under construction; 20 c. Darien Forest; 1 b. Map of Pan-American Highway.

1957. Air. Surch **1957 X 10 C X**.
614 **173** 10 c. on 6 c. black & violet 20 20

1957. Birth Centenary of Manuel Espinosa Batista (independence leader).
615 **185** 5 c. blue and green . . . 15 10

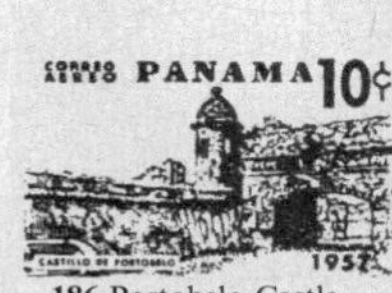

186 Portobelo Castle **189** U.N. Emblem

1957. Air. Buildings. Centres in black.
616 **186** 10 c. grey 25 15
617 – 10 c. purple 25 15
618 – 10 c. violet 25 15
619 – 10 c. grey and green . . . 25 15
620 – 10 c. blue 25 15
621 – 10 c. brown 25 15
622 – 10 c. orange 25 15
623 – 10 c. light blue 25 15
624 – 1 b. red . . . . 2·10 95
DESIGNS—HORIZ: No. 617, San Jeronimo Castle; No. 618, Portobelo Customs-house; No. 619, Panama Hotel; No. 620, Pres. Remon Cantera Stadium; No. 621, Palace of Justice; No. 622, Treasury; No. 623, San Lorenzo Castle. VERT: No. 624, Jose Remon Clinics.

1957. Surch **1957** and value.
625 **172** 1 c. on ½ c. brown 10 10
626 3 c. on ½ c. brown 10 10

1958. Air. Surch **1958** and value.
627 **170** 5 c. on 6 c. green 20 10

1958. Air. 10th Anniv of U.N.O.
628 **189** 10 c. green 20 10
629 21 c. blue 45 35
630 50 c. orange 45 45
631 – 1 b. red, blue and grey . . 1·75 1·40
DESIGN: 1 b. Flags of Panama and United Nations.

1958. No. 547 surch **3 c 1958**.
633 3 c. on 12 c. purple 10 10

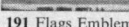

191 Flags Emblem **192** Brazilian Pavilion

1958. 10th Anniv of Organization of American States. Emblem (T **191**) multicoloured within yellow and black circular band; background colours given below.
634 **191** 1 c. grey (postage) 10 10
635 2 c. green 10 10
636 3 c. red 15 10
637 7 c. blue 25 10
638 5 c. blue (air) 15 10
639 10 c. red 20 15
640 – 50 c. black, yellow & grey 35 35
641 **191** 1 b. black . . . . 1·75 1·40
DESIGN—VERT: 50 c. Headquarters building.

1958. Brussels International Exhbition.
642 **192** 1 c. green & yell (postage) 10 10
643 – 3 c. green and blue . . . 15 10
644 – 5 c. slate and brown . . . 15 10
645 – 10 c. brown and blue . . . 20 20
646 – 15 c. violet and grey (air) . 35 35
647 – 50 c. brown and slate . . 60 60
648 – 1 b. turquoise and lilac . . 1·25 1·25
DESIGNS—PAVILIONS: As Type **192**: 3 c. Argentina; 5 c. Venezuela; 10 c. Great Britain; 15 c. Vatican City; 50 c. United States; 1 b. Belgium.

193 Pope Pius XII **194** Children on Farm

1959. Pope Pius XII Commemoration.
650 **193** 3 c. brown (postage) . . . 15 10
651 – 5 c. violet (air) 15 15
652 – 30 c. mauve 30 25
653 – 50 c. grey 75 60
PORTRAITS (Pope Pius XII): 5 c. when Cardinal; 30 c. wearing Papal tiara; 50 c. enthroned.

1959. Obligatory Tax. Youth Rehabilitation Institute. Size 35 × 24 mm.
655 **194** 1 c. grey and red 15 10

195 U.N. Headquarters New York **197** J. A. Facio **198** Football

1959. 10th Anniv of Declaration of Human Rights.
656 **195** 3 c. olive & brown (postage) 10 10
657 – 15 c. green and orange . . 35 25
658 – 5 c. blue and green (air) . 15 10
659 – 10 c. brown and grey . . 20 15
660 – 20 c. slate and brown . . 35 35
661 – 50 c. blue and green . . . 60 60
662 **195** 1 b. blue and red . . . . 1·40 1·25
DESIGNS: 5 c., 15 c. Family looking towards light; 10 c., 20 c. U.N. emblem and torch; 50 c. U.N. flag.

1959. 8th Latin-American Economic Commission Congress. Nos. 656/61 optd **8A REUNION C.E.P.A.L. MAYO 1959** or surch also.
663 **195** 3 c. olive and brown (postage) 10 10
664 – 15 c. green and orange . . 35 20
665 – 5 c. blue and green (air) . 10 10
666 – 10 c. brown and grey . . 25 15
667 – 20 c. slate and brown . . 45 35
668 – 1 b. on 50 c. blue and green 1·60 1·60

1959. 50th Anniv of National Institute.
670 – 3 c. red (postage) 10 10
671 – 13 c. green 30 15
672 – 21 c. blue 40 30
673 **197** 5 c. black (air) 10 10
674 – 10 c. black 20 10
DESIGNS—VERT: 3 c. E. A. Morales (founder); 10 c. Ernesto de la Guardia, Nr; 13 c. A. Bravo. HORIZ: 21 c. National Institute Bldg.

1959. Obligatory Tax. Youth Rehabilitation Institute. As No. 655, but colours changed and inscr. "1959".
675 **194** 1 c. green and black . . . 10 10
676 1 c. blue and black . . . 10 10
See also No. 690.

1959. 3rd Pan-American Games, Chicago. Inscr "III JUEGOS DEPORTIVOS PANAMERICANOS".
677 **198** 1 c. green & grey (postage) 10 10
678 – 3 c. brown and blue . . . 15 10
679 – 20 c. brown and green . . 50 45
680 – 5 c. brown and black (air) 15 10
681 – 10 c. brown and grey . . 25 20
682 – 50 c. brown and blue . . 45 40
DESIGNS: 3 c. Swimming; 5 c. Boxing; 10 c. Baseball; 20 c. Hurdling; 50 c. Basketball.

1960. Air. World Refugee Year. Nos. 554/6 optd **NACIONES UNIDAS ANO MUNDIAL, REFUGIADOS. 1959-1960.**
683 25 c. black 35 35
684 50 c. brown 70 55
685 1 b. orange . . . . 1·50 1·10

200 Administration Building **202** Fencing

1960. Air. 25th Anniv of National University.
686 **200** 10 c. green 15 15
687 – 21 c. blue 30 20
688 – 25 c. blue 50 35
689 – 30 c. black 55 40
DESIGNS: 21 c. Faculty of Science; 25 c. Faculty of Medicine; 30 c. Statue of Dr. Octavio Mendez Pereira (first rector) and Faculty of Law.

1960. Obligatory Tax. Youth Rehabilitation Institute. As No. 655 but smaller (32 × 22 mm) and inscr "1960".
690 **194** 1 c. grey and red 10 10

1960. Olympic Games.
691 **202** 3 c. purple & vio (postage) 10 10
692 – 5 c. green & turquoise . . 20 10
693 – 5 c. red and orange (air) . 10 10
694 – 10 c. black and bistre . . 20 15
695 – 25 c. deep blue and blue . 45 40
696 – 50 c. black and brown . . 60 45
DESIGNS—VERT: 5 c. (No. 692), Football; (No. 693), Basketball; 25 c. Javelin-throwing; 50 c. Runner with Olympic Flame. HORIZ: 10 c. Cycling.

204 "Population"

1960. Air. 6th National Census (5 c.) and Central American Census.
698 **204** 5 c. black 10 10
699 – 10 c. brown 20 15
DESIGN: 10 c. Two heads and map.

205 Boeing 707 Airliner

1960. Air.

700 **205** 5 c. blue 15 10
701 10 c. green 40 20
702 20 c. brown 85 40

206 Pastoral Scene **207** Helen Keller School

1961. Agricultural Census. (16th April).

703 **206** 3 c. turquoise 10 10

1961. 25th Anniv of Lions Club.

705 – 3 c. blue (postage) 10 10
706 **207** 5 c. black (air) 10 10
707 – 10 c. green 20 10
708 – 21 c. blue, red and yellow 40 30

DESIGNS: 3 c. Nino Hospital; 10 c. Children's Colony, Verano; 21 c. Lions emblem, arms and slogan.

1961. Air. Obligatory Tax. Youth Rehabilitation Fund. Surch **1 c "Rehabilitacion de Menores"**.

709 – 1 c. on 10 c. black and bistre (No. 694) 10 10
710 **205** 1 c. on 10 c. green 10 10

1961. Air. Surch **HABILITAD en** and value.

712 **200** 1 c. on 10 c. green 10 10
713 – 1 b. on 25 c. blue and blue (No. 695) . . . . 1·25 1·25

210 Flags of Costa Rica and Panama

1961. Meeting of Presidents of Costa Rica and Panama.

715 **210** 3 c. red & blue (postage) . 15 10
716 – 1 b. black and gold (air) . 1·25 75

DESIGN: 1 b. Pres. Chiari of Panama and Pres. Echandi of Costa Rica.

211 Girl using Sewing-machine

212 Campaign Emblem

1961. Obligatory Tax. Youth Rehabilitation Fund.

717 **211** 1 c. violet 10 10
718 1 c. yellow 10 10
719 1 c. green 10 10
720 1 c. blue 10 10
721 1 c. purple 10 10
722 – 1 c. mauve 10 10
723 – 1 c. grey 10 10
724 – 1 c. blue 10 10
725 – 1 c. orange 10 10
726 – 1 c. red 10 10

DESIGN: Nos. 722/6, Boy sawing wood.

1961. Air. Malaria Eradication.

727 **212** 5 c. + 5 c. red 60 30
728 10 c. + 10 c. blue 60 30
729 15 c. + 15 c. green 60 30

213 Dag Hammarskjold

214 Arms of Panama

1961. Air. Death of Dag Hammarskjold.

730 **213** 10 c. black and grey . . . 20 15

1962. Air. (a) Surch **"Vale B/.0.15"**.

731 **200** 15 c. on 10 c. green 30 20

(b) No, 810 surch **"XX"** over old value and **"VALE B/.1.00"**.

732 – 1 b. on 25 c. deep blue and blue 1·25 75

1962. 3rd Central American Inter-Municipal Co-operation Assembly.

733 **214** 3 c. red, yellow and blue (postage) 10 10
734 – 5 c. black and blue (air) . . 20 10

DESIGN—HORIZ: 5 c. City Hall, Colon.

215 Mercury on Cogwheel

217 Social Security Hospital

1962. 1st Industrial Census.

735 **215** 3 c. red 10 10

1962. Surch **VALE** and value with old value obliterated.

736 **212** 10 c. on 5 c. + 5 c. red . 90 45
737 20 c. on 10 c. + 10 c. blue 1·50 90

1962. Opening of Social Security Hospital, Panama City.

738 **217** 3 c. black and red 10 10

218 Colon Cathedral

221 Col. Glenn and Capsule "Friendship 7"

220 Thatcher Ferry Bridge nearing completion

1962. "Freedom of Worship". Inscr "LIBERTAD DE CULTOS". Centres in black.

739 – 1 c. red and blue (postage) 10 10
740 – 2 c. red and cream . . . 10 10
741 – 3 c. blue and cream . . . 10 10
742 – 5 c. red and green . . . 10 10
743 – 10 c. green and cream . . 20 15
744 – 10 c. mauve and blue . . 20 15
745 – 15 c. blue and green . . 30 20
746 **218** 20 c. red and pink . . . 35 25
747 – 25 c. green and pink . . 45 35
748 – 50 c. blue and pink . . . 60 55
749 – 1 b. violet and cream . . 1·75 1·40

DESIGNS—HORIZ: 1 c. San Francisco de Veraguas Church; 3 c. David Cathedral; 25 c. Orthodox Greek Temple; 1 b. Colon Protestant Church. VERT: 2 c. Panama Old Cathedral; 5 c. Nata Church; 10 c. Don Bosco Temple; 15 c. Virgin of Carmen Church; 50 c. Panama Cathedral.

750 – 5 c. violet and flesh (air) . . 10 10
751 – 7 c. lt mauve and mauve . . 15 10
752 – 8 c. violet and blue . . . 15 10
753 – 10 c. violet and salmon . . 20 10
754 – 10 c. green and light purple 20 20
755 – 15 c. red and orange . . . 25 20
756 – 21 c. sepia and blue . . . 35 30
757 – 25 c. blue and pink . . . 45 35
758 – 30 c. mauve and blue . . 50 45
759 – 50 c. purple and green . . 70 70
760 – 1 b. blue and salmon . . . 1·25 1·10

DESIGNS—HORIZ: 5 c. Cristo Rey Church; 7 c. San Miguel Church; 21 c. Canal Zone Synagogue; 25 c. Panama Synagogue; 50 c. Canal Zone Protestant Church. VERT: 8 c. Santuario Church; 10 c. Los Santos Church; 15 c. Santa Ana Church; 30 c. San Francisco Church; 1 b. Canal Zone Catholic Church.

1962. Air. 9th Central American and Caribbean Games, Jamaica. Nos. 693 and 695 optd **"IX JUEGOS C.A. y DEL CARIBE KINGSTON - 1962"** or surch also.

762 5 c. red and orange 15 15
764 10 c. on 25 c. dp blue and blue 55 50
765 15 c. on 25 c. dp blue and blue 40 35
766 20 c. on 25 c. dp blue and blue 45 45
763 25 c. deep blue and blue . . . 55 50

1962. Opening of Thatcher Ferry Bridge, Canal Zone.

767 **220** 3 c. black & red (postage) 10 10
768 – 10 c. black and blue (air) 20 15

DESIGN: 10 c. Completed bridge.

1962. Air. Col. Glenn's Space Flight.

769 **221** 5 c. red 10 10
770 – 10 c. yellow 20 20
771 – 31 c. blue 45 40
772 – 50 c. green 65 65

DESIGNS—HORIZ: "Friendship": 10 c. Over Earth; 31 c. In space. VERT: 50 c. Col Glenn.

222 U.P.A.E. Emblem

225 F.A.O. Emblem

223 Water Exercise

1963. Air. 50th Anniv of Postal Union of Americas and Spain.

774 **222** 10 c. multicoloured 20 15

1963. 75th Anniv of Panama Fire Brigade.

775 **223** 1 c. blk & green (postage) . 10 10
776 – 3 c. black and blue 10 10
777 – 5 c. black and red 10 10
778 – 10 c. black & orge (air) . . 15 15
779 – 15 c. black and purple . . 20 20
780 – 21 c. blue, gold and red . . 50 45

DESIGNS: 3 c. Brigade officers; 5 c. Brigade president and advisory council; 10 c. "China" pump in action, 1887; 15 c. "Cable 14" station and fire-engine; 21 c. Fire Brigade badge.

1963. Air. Red Cross Cent (1st issue). Nos. 769/71 surch with red cross **1863 1963** and premium.

781 **215** 5 c. + 5 c. red . . . . . . 1·40 1·40
782 – 10 c. + 10 c. yellow . . . 2·75 2·75
783 – 31 c. + 15 c. blue . . . . 2·75 2·75

See also No. 797.

1963. Air. Freedom from Hunger.

784 **225** 10 c. red and green 20 20
785 15 c. red and blue 30 25

1963. Air. 22nd Central American Lions Convention. Optd **"XXII Convencion Leonistica Centroamericana Panama 18-21 Abril 1963"**.

786 **207** 5 c. black 10 10

1963. Air. Surch **HABILITADO Vale B./0.04**.

789 **200** 4 c. in 10 c. green 10 10

1963. Air. Nos. 743 and 769 optd **AEREO** vert.

790 10 c. green and cream 20 15
791 20 c. brown and green 30 25

1963. Air. Freedom of the Press. No. 693 optd **LIBERTAD DE PRENSA 20-VIII-63**.

792 5 c. red and orange 10 10

1963. Air. Visit of U.S. Astronauts to Panama. Optd **"Visita Astronautas Glenn-Schirra Sheppard Cooper a Panama"** or surch also.

793 **221** 5 c. red . . . . 2·50 2·50
794 10 c. on 5 c. red . . . . . 3·25 3·25

1963. Air. Surch **HABILITADO 10 c.**

796 **221** 10 c. on 5 c. red . . . . . 5·50 5·50

1963. Air. Red Cross Centenary (2nd issue). No. 781 surch **"Centenario Cruz Roja Internacional 10 c.** with premium obliterated.

797 **221** 10 c. on 5 c. + 5 c. red . . 6·00 6·00

1963. Surch **VALE** and value.

798 **217** 4 c. on 3 c. black and red (postage) 15 10
799 – 4 c. on 3 c. black, blue and cream (No. 741) 15 10
800 **220** 4 c. on 3 c. black & red . . 15 10
801 – 4 c. on 3 c. black and blue (No. 776) 15 10
802 **182** 10 c. on 25 c. blue & red . 35 15
803 – 10 c. on 25 c. blue (No. 688) (air) 20 15

234 Pres. Orlich (Costa Rica) and Flags

236 Vasco Nunez de Balboa

235 Innsbruck

1963. Presidential Reunion, San Jose (Costa Rica). Multicoloured. Presidents and flags of their countries.

804 1 c. Type **234** (postage) . . . 10 10
805 2 c. Somoza (Nicaragua) . . . 15 15
806 3 c. Villeda (Honduras) . . . 20 15
807 4 c. Chiari (Panama) 25 20
808 5 c. Rivera (El Salvador) (air) 30 30
809 10 c. Ydigoras (Guatemala) . 55 45
810 21 c. Kennedy (U.S.A.) . . . 1·60 1·40

1963. Winter Olympic Games, Innsbruck.

811 ½ c. red and blue (postage) . . 10 10
812 1 c. red, brown and turquoise 10 10
813 3 c. red and blue 25 15
814 4 c. red, brown and green . . 35 20
815 5 c. red, brown & mauve (air) 45 25
816 15 c. red, brown and blue . . 1·10 90
817 21 c. red, brown and myrtle . 2·25 1·90
818 31 c. red, brown and blue . . 3·00 2·25

DESIGNS: ½ c. (expressed "B/0.005"); 3 c. Type **235**: 1 c., 4 c. Speed-skating; 5 c. to 31 c. Skiing (slalom).

1964. 450th Anniv of Discovery of Pacific Ocean.

820 **236** 4 c. grn on flesh (postage) 10 10
821 10 c. violet on pink (air) . 20 20

237 Boy Scout

238 St. Paul's Cathedral, London

1964. Obligatory Tax for Youth Rehabilitation, Institute.

822 **237** 1 c. red 10 10
823 1 c. grey 10 10
824 1 c. light blue 10 10
825 1 c. olive 10 10
826 1 c. violet 10 10
827 – 1 c. brown 10 10
828 – 1 c. orange 10 10
829 – 1 c. turquoise 10 10
830 – 1 c. violet 10 10
831 – 1 c. yellow 10 10

DESIGN: Nos. 827/31, Girl guide.

1964. Air. Ecumenical Council, Vatican City (1st issue). Cathedrals. Centres in black.

832 21 c. red (Type 238) 55 35
833 21 c. blue (Kassa, Hungary) . 55 35
834 21 c. green (Milan) 55 35
835 21 c. black (St. John's, Poland) 55 35
836 21 c. brown (St. Stephen's, Vienna) 55 35
837 21 c. brown (Notre Dame, Paris) 55 35
838 21 c. violet (Moscow) 55 35
839 21 c. violet (Lima) 55 35
840 21 c. red (Stockholm) 55 35
841 21 c. mauve (Cologne) 55 35
842 21 c. bistre (New Delhi) . . . 55 35
843 21 c. deep turquoise (Basel) . 55 35
844 21 c. green (Toledo) 55 35
845 21 c. red (Metropolitan, Athens) 55 35
846 21 c. olive (St. Patrick's, New York) 55 35
847 21 c. green (Lisbon) 55 35
848 21 c. turquoise (Sofia) 55 35
849 21 c. deep brown (New Church, Delft, Netherlands) 55 35
850 21 c. deep sepia (St. George's Patriarchal Church, Istanbul) 55 35
851 21 c. blue (Basilica, Guadalupe, Mexico) 55 35
852 1 b. blue (Panama) . . . . . 1·75 1·75
853 2 b. green (St. Peter's, Rome) 3·00 3·00

See Nos. 882, etc.

1964. As Nos. 749 and 760 but colours changed and optd **HABILITADA**.

855 1 b. blk, red & blue (postage) 1·75 1·60
856 1 b. blk, green & yellow (air) . 1·75 1·25

1964. Air. No. 756 surch **VALE B/.0.50**.

857 50 c. on 21 c. black, sepia and blue 65 40

241 Discus-thrower

1964. Olympic Games, Tokyo.
858 ½ c. ("B/0.005") purple, red, brown and green (postage) . 10 10
859 1 c. multicoloured 10 10
860 5 c. black, red and olive (air) . 35 25
861 10 c. black, red and yellow . . 70 45
862 21 c. multicoloured . . . . . 1·40 90
863 50 c. multicoloured . . . . . 2·75 1·75
DESIGNS: ½ c. Type **241**; 1 c. Runner with Olympic Flame; 5 c. to 50 c. Olympic Stadium, Tokyo, and Mt. Fuji.

1964. Air. Nos. 692 and 742 surch **Aereo B/.0.10**.
865 10 c. on 5 c. green & turquoise 20 15
866 10 c. on 5 c. black, red and green 20 15

243 Space Vehicles (Project "Apollo")

1964. Space Exploration. Multicoloured.
867 ½ c. ("B/0.005") Type **243** (postage) 10 10
868 1 c. Rocket and capsule (Project "Gemini") 10 10
869 5 c. W.M. Schirra (air) 20 20
870 10 c. L.G. Cooper 30 30
871 21 c. Schirra's capsule 75 75
872 50 c. Cooper's capsule . . . . 3·25 3·00

1964. No. 687 surch **Correos B/.0.10**.
874 10 c. on 21 c. blue 15 15

245 Water-skiing

1964. Aquatic Sports. Multicoloured.
875 ½ c. ("B/0.005") Type **245** (postage) 10 10
876 1 c. Underwater-swimming . . 10 10
877 5 c. Fishing (air) 20 10
878 10 c. Sailing (vert) . . . . . . 1·50 60
879 21 c. Speedboat racing . . . . 2·75 1·50
880 31 c. Water polo at Olympic Games, 1964 . . . . 3·50 1·75

1964. Air. Ecumenical Council, Vatican City (2nd issue). Stamps of 1st issue optd **1964**. Centres in black.
882 21 c. red (No. 832) 70 50
883 21 c. green (No. 834) 70 50
884 21 c. olive (No. 836) 70 50
885 21 c. deep sepia (No. 850) . . 70 50
886 1 b. blue (No. 852) . . . . . 2·75 2·00
887 2 b. green (No. 853) . . . . . 5·50 4·50

247 General View

248 Eleanor Roosevelt

1964. Air. New York's World Fair.
889 **247** 5 c. black and yellow . . 30 25
890 – 10 c. black and red . . . 75 60
891 – 15 c. black and green . . 1·25 80
892 – 21 c. black and blue . . . 1·90 1·50
DESIGNS: 10 c., 15 c. Fair pavilions (different); 21 c. Unisphere.

1964. Mrs. Eleanor Roosevelt Commemoration.
894 **248** 4 c. black and red on yellow (postage) 15 10
895 20 c. black and green on buff (air) 50 45

249 Dag Hammarskjold

250 Pope John XXIII

1964. Air. U.N. Day.
897 **249** 21 c. black and blue . . . 70 50
898 – 21 c. blue and black . . . 70 50
DESIGN: No. 898, U.N. Emblem.

1964. Air. Pope John Commemoration.
900 **250** 21 c. black and bistre . . 70 50
901 – 21 c. mult (Papal Arms) . 70 50

251 Slalom Skiing Medals

1964. Winter Olympic Winners' Medals. Medals in gold, silver and bronze.
903 **251** ½ c. ("B/0.005") turquoise (postage) 10 10
904 – 1 c. deep blue 10 10
905 – 2 c. brown 20 15
906 – 3 c. mauve 25 15
907 – 4 c. lake 35 20
908 – 5 c. violet (air) 45 25
909 – 6 c. blue 55 30
910 – 7 c. violet 65 35
911 – 10 c. green 90 50
912 – 21 c. red . . . . 1·40 95
913 – 31 c. blue . . . . . . 2·50 1·40
DESIGNS—Medals for: 1 c., 7 c. Speed-skating; 2 c., 21 c. Bobsleighing; 3 c., 10 c. Figure-skating; 4 c. Ski-jumping; 5 c., 6 c., 31 c. Cross-country skiing. Values in the same design show different medal-winners and country names.

252 Cuvier's Toucan

1965. Birds. Multicoloured.
915 1 c. Type **252** (postage) . . . 40 10
916 2 c. Scarlet macaw 40 10
917 3 c. Black-cheeked woodpecker 65 10
918 4 c. Blue-grey tanager (horiz) 65 15
919 5 c. Troupial (horiz) (air) . . 80 20
920 10 c. Crimson-backed tanager (horiz) . . . . 1·60 30

253 Snapper

1965. Marine Life. Multicoloured.
921 1 c. Type **253** (postage) . . . 10 10
922 2 c. Dolphin 10 10
923 3 c. Shrimp (air) 20 15
924 12 c. Hammerhead 25 20
925 13 c. Atlantic sailfish 30 25
926 25 c. Seahorse (vert) 30 25

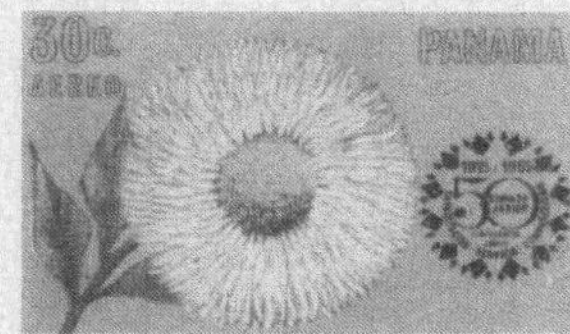

254 Double Daisy and Emblem

1966. Air. 50th Anniv of Junior Chamber of Commerce. Flowers. Multicoloured: background colour given.
927 **254** 30 c. mauve 55 45
928 – 30 c. flesh (Hibiscus) . . . 55 45
929 – 30 c. olive (Mauve orchid) 55 45
930 – 40 c. green (Water lily) . . 60 55
931 – 40 c. blue (Gladiolus) . . . 60 55
932 – 40 c. pink (White orchid) . 60 55
Each design incorporates the Junior Chamber of Commerce Emblem.

1966. Surch (a) Postage.
933 13 c. on 25 c. (No. 747) . . . 30 20

(b) Air.
934 3 c. on 5 c. (No. 680) 10 10
935 13 c. on 25 c. (No. 695) . . . 30 25

265 Chicken

1967. Domestic Animals. Multicoloured.
936 1 c. Type **256** (postage) 10 10
937 3 c. Cockerel 10 10
938 5 c. Pig (horiz) 10 10
939 8 c. Cow (horiz) 15 10
940 10 c. Pekingese dog (air) . . . 25 20
941 13 c. Zebu (horiz) 30 20
942 30 c. Cat 60 50
943 40 c. Horse (horiz) 75 60

257 American Anhinga

1967. Wild Birds. Multicoloured.
944 ½ c. Type **257** 35 10
945 1 c. Resplendent quetzal . . . 35 10
946 3 c. Turquoise-browed motmot 45 10
947 4 c. Red-necked aracari (horiz) 55 15
948 5 c. Chestnut-fronted macaw . 70 15
949 13 c. Belted kingfisher . . . . 1·50 35

258 "Deer" (F. Marc)

1967. Wild Animals. Paintings. Multicoloured.
950 1 c. Type **258** (postage) 10 10
951 3 c. "Cougar" (F. Marc) . . . 10 10
952 5 c. "Monkeys" (F. Marc) . . 10 10
953 8 c. "Fox" (F. Marc) 20 10
954 10 c. "St. Jerome and the Lion" (Durer) (air) 20 15
955 13 c. "The Hare" (Durer) . . . 30 20
956 20 c. "Lady with the Ermine" (Da Vinci) 45 25
957 30 c. "The Hunt" (Delacroix) . 65 45
The 3, 10, 13 and 20 are vert.

259 Map of Panama and People

1969. National Population Census.
958 **259** 5 c. blue 10 10
959 – 10 c. purple 20 15
DESIGN—VERT: 10 c. People and map of the Americas.

260 Cogwheel

1969. 50th Anniv of Rotary Int in Panama.
960 **260** 13 c. black, yellow & blue 20 20

261 Cornucopia and Map

262 Tower and Map

1969. 1st Anniv of 11 October Revolution.
961 **261** 10 c. multicoloured . . . 20 10

1969.
962 **262** 3 c. black and orange . . 10 10
963 – 5 c. green 10 10
964 – 8 c. brown 20 15
965 – 13 c. black and green . . 25 15
966 – 20 c. brown 35 25
967 – 21 c. yellow 35 25
968 – 25 c. green 45 30
969 – 30 c. black 50 45
970 – 34 c. brown 55 45
971 – 38 c. blue 60 45
972 – 40 c. yellow 65 45
973 – 50 c. black and purple . . 85 65
974 – 59 c. purple . . . . . . 1·00 60
DESIGNS—HORIZ: 5 c. Peasants; 13 c. Hotel Continental; 25 c. Del Rey Bridge; 34 c. Panama Cathedral; 38 c. Municipal Palace; 40 c. French Plaza; 50 c. Thatcher Ferry Bridge; 59 c. National Theatre. VERT: 8 c. Nata Church; 20 c. Virgin of Carmen Church; 21 c. Altar, San Jose Church; 30 c. Dr. Arosemena statue.

263 Discus-thrower and Stadium

1970. 11th Central American and Caribbean Games, Panama (1st series).
975 **263** 1 c. multicoloured (postage) 10 10
976 2 c. multicoloured 10 10
977 3 c. multicoloured 10 10
978 5 c. multicoloured 10 10
979 10 c. multicoloured . . . 20 15
980 13 c. multicoloured . . . 25 15
981 – 13 c. multicoloured . . . 25 15
982 **263** 25 c. multicoloured . . . 45 35
983 30 c. multicoloured . . . 55 45
984 – 13 c. multicoloured (air) . 70 20
985 – 30 c. multicoloured . . . 60 45
DESIGNS—VERT: No. 981, "Flor del Espiritu Santo" (flowers); No. 985, Indian girl. HORIZ: No. 984, Thatcher Ferry Bridge and palm.
See also Nos. 986/94.

264 J. D. Arosemena and Stadium

1970. Air. 11th Central American and Caribbean Games, Panama (2nd series). Multicoloured.
986 1 c. Type **264** 10 10
987 2 c. Type **264** 10 10
988 3 c. Type **264** 10 10
989 5 c. Type **264** 10 10
990 13 c. Basketball 20 15
991 13 c. New Gymnasium 20 15
992 13 c. Revolution Stadium . . . 20 15
993 13 c. Panamanian couple in festive costume 20 15
994 30 c. Eternal Flame and stadium 45 35

265 A. Tapia and M. Sosa (first comptrollers)

1971. 40th Anniv of Panamanian Comptroller-General's Office. Multicoloured.
996 3 c. Comptroller-General's Building (1970) (vert) . . . 10 10
997 5 c. Type **265** 10 10
998 8 c. Comptroller-General's emblem (vert) 15 10
999 13 c. Comptroller-General's Building (1955–70) 30 15

266 "Man and Alligator"

267 Map of Panama on I.E.Y. Emblem

1971. Indian Handicrafts.
1000 **266** 8 c. multicoloured . . . 20 15

1971. International Education Year.
1001 **267** 1 b. multicoloured . . . 1·50 1·50

268 Astronaut on Moon

269 Panama Pavilion

1971. Air. "Apollo 11" and "Apollo 12" Moon Missions. Multicoloured.
1002 13 c. Type **268** 35 25
1003 13 c. "Apollo 12" astronauts 35 25

1971. Air. "EXPO 70", World Fair, Osaka, Japan.
1004 **269** 10 c. multicoloured . . . 15 15

270 Conference Text and Emblem

1971. 9th Inter-American Loan and Savings Assn, Conference, Panama City.
1005 **270** 25 c. multicoloured . . . 60 35

271 Panama Flag

1971. Air. American Tourist Year. Multicoloured.
1006 5 c. Type **271** 10 10
1007 13 c. Map of Panama and Western Hemisphere . . . 30 20

272 New U.P.U. H.Q. Building

1971. Inauguration of New U.P.U. Headquarters Building, Berne. Multicoloured.
1008 8 c. Type **272** 20 10
1009 30 c. U.P.U. Monument, Berne (vert) 60 35

273 Cow and Pig

1971. 3rd Agricultural Census.
1010 **273** 3 c. multicoloured . . . 10 10

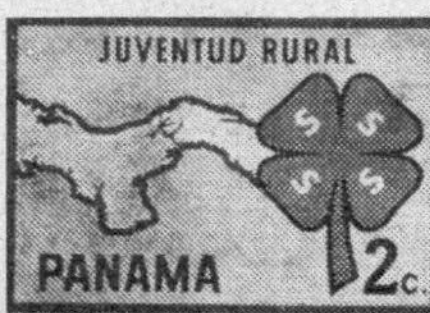
274 Map and "4S" Emblem

1971. "4S" Programme for Rural Youth.
1011 **274** 2 c. multicoloured . . . 10 10

275 Gandhi

276 Central American Flags

1971. Air. Birth Centenary (1969) of Mahatma Gandhi.
1012 **275** 10 c. multicoloured . . . 20 15

1971. Air. 150th Anniv of Central American States' Independence from Spain.
1013 **276** 13 c. multicoloured . . 30 20

277 Early Panama Stamp

278 Altar, Nata Church

1971. Air. 2nd National, Philatelic and Numismatic Exhibition, Panama.
1014 **277** 8 c. blue, black & red . 20 15

1972. Air. 450th Anniv of Nata Church.
1015 **278** 40 c. multicoloured . . 50 45

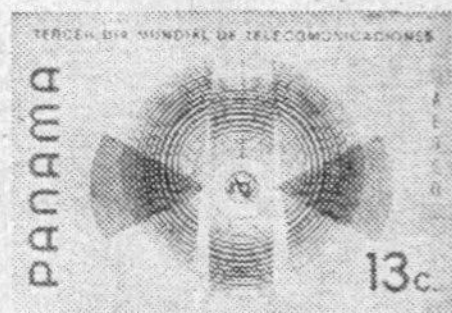
279 Telecommunications Emblem

1972. Air. World Telecommunications Day.
1016 **279** 13 c. black, blue & lt blue 20 15

280 "Apollo 14" Badge

1972. Air. Moon Flight of "Apollo 14".
1017 **280** 13 c. multicoloured . . 60 25

281 Children on See-saw

1972. 25th Anniv (1971) of U.N.I.C.E.F. Multicoloured.
1018 1 c. Type **281** (postage) . . . 10 10
1019 5 c. Boy sitting by kerb (vert) (air) 10 10
1020 8 c. Indian mother and child (vert) 15 10
1021 50 c. U.N.I.C.E.F. emblem (vert) 70 45

282 Tropical Fruits

1972. Tourist Publicity. Multicoloured.
1023 1 c. Type **282** (postage) . . . 10 10
1024 2 c. "Isle of Night" 10 10
1025 3 c. Carnival float (vert) . . 10 10
1026 5 c. San Blas textile (air) . . . 10 10
1027 8 c. Chaquira (beaded collar) 20 10
1028 25 c. Ruined fort, Portobelo . 35 30

283 Map and Flags

284 Baseball Players

1973. Obligatory Tax. Panama City Post Office Building Fund. 7th Bolivar Games.
1030 **283** 1 c. black 10 10

1973. Air. 7th Bolivar Games.
1031 **284** 8 c. red and yellow 15 10
1032 – 10 c. black and blue . . . 20 15
1033 – 13 c. multicoloured . . . 30 20
1034 – 25 c. black, red & green . 55 30
1035 – 50 c. multicoloured . . . 1·25 55
1036 – 1 b. multicoloured . . . 2·50 1·10
DESIGNS—VERT: 10 c. Basketball; 13 c. Flaming torch. HORIZ: 25 c. Boxing; 50 c. Panama map and flag, Games emblem and Bolivar; 1 b. Games' medals.

1973. U.N. Security Council Meeting, Panama City. Various stamps surch **O.N.U.** in laurel leaf and **CONSEJO DE SEGURIDAD 15-21 Marzo 1973** and value.
1037 8 c. on 59 c. (No. 974) (postage) 10 10
1038 10 c. on 1 b. (No. 1001) . . . 15 15
1039 13 c. on 30 c. (No. 969) . . . 20 15
1040 13 c. on 40 c. (No. 1015) (air) 25 15

286 Farming Co-operative

1973. Obligatory Tax. Post Office Building Fund.
1041 **286** 1 c. green and red 10 10
1042 – 1 c. grey and red 10 10
1043 – 1 c. yellow and red . . . 10 10
1044 – 1 c. orange and red . . . 10 10
1045 – 1 c. blue and red 10 10
DESIGNS: No. 1042, Silver coins; No. 1043, V. Lorenzo; No. 1044, Cacique Urraca; No. 1045, Post Office building.
See also Nos. 1061/2.

287 J. D. Crespo (educator)

290 Women's upraised Hands

1973. Famous Panamanians. Multicoloured.
1046 3 c. Type **287** (postage) . . . 10 10
1047 5 c. Isabel Obaldia (educator) (air) 10 10
1048 8 c. N. V. Jaen (educator) . . 20 15
1049 10 c. "Forest Scene" (Roberto Lewis-painter) 20 15
1050 13 c. R. Miro (poet) 35 20
1051 13 c. "Portrait of a Lady" (M. E. Amador-painter) . . 35 20
1052 20 c. "Self-Portrait" (Isaac Benitez-painter) 55 20
1053 21 c. M. A. Guerrero (statesman) 55 25
1054 25 c. Dr. B. Porras (statesman) 55 30
1055 30 c. J. D. Arosemena (statesman) 70 35
1056 34 c. Dr. O. M. Pereira (writer) 90 45
1057 38 c. Dr. R. J. Alfaro (writer) 1·10 50

1973. Air. 50th Anniv of Isabel Obaldia Professional School. Nos. 1047, 1054 and 1056 optd **1923 1973 Godas de Oro Escuela Profesional Isabel Herrera Obaldia** and EP emblem.
1058 5 c. multicoloured 15 10
1059 25 c. multicoloured 55 30
1060 34 c. multicoloured 60 55

1974. Obligatory Tax. Post Office Building Fund. As Nos. 1044/5.
1061 1 c. orange 10 10
1062 2 c. blue 10 10

1974. Surch **VALE** and value.
1063 5 c. on 30 c. black (No. 969) (postage) 10 10
1064 10 c. on 34 c. brown (No. 970) 15 10
1065 13 c. on 21 c. yellow (No. 967) 20 15
1066 1 c. on 25 c. mult (No. 1028) (air) 10 10
1067 3 c. on 20 c. mult (No. 1052) 10 10
1068 8 c. on 38 c. mult (No. 1057) 15 10
1069 10 c. on 34 c. mult (No. 1056) 15 15
1070 13 c. on 21 c. mult (No. 1053) 20 15

1975. Air. International Women's Year.
1071 **290** 17 c. multicoloured . . . 45 20

291 Bayano Dam

1975. Air. 7th Anniv of October 1968, Revolution.
1073 **291** 17 c. black, brown & blue 20 15
1074 – 27 c. blue and green . . 30 25
1075 – 33 c. multicoloured . . . 1·10 30
DESIGNS—VERT: 27 c. Victoria sugar plant, Veraguas, and sugar cane. HORIZ: 33 c. Tocumen International Airport.

1975. Obligatory Tax. Various stamps surch **VALE PRO EDIFICIO** and value.
1076 – 1 c. on 30 c. black (No. 969) (postage) 10 10
1077 – 1 c. on 40 c. yellow (No. 972) 10 10
1078 – 1 c. on 50 c. black & purple (No. 973) 10 10
1079 – 1 c. on 30 c. mult (No. 1009) 10 10
1080 **282** 1 c. on 1 c. multicoloured 10 10
1081 – 1 c. on 2 c. multicoloured (No. 1024) 10 10
1082 **278** 1 c. on 40 c. mult (air) . 10 10
1083 – 1 c. on 25 c. mult (No. 1028) 10 10
1084 – 1 c. on 25 c. mult (No. 1052) 10 10
1085 – 1 c. on 20 c. mult (No. 1054) 10 10
1086 – 1 c. on 30 c. mult (No. 1055) 10 10

1975. Obligatory Tax. Post Office Building Fund. As No. 1045.
1087 1 c. red 10 10

294 Bolivar and Thatcher Ferry Bridge

295 "Evibacus princeps"

1976. 150th Anniv of Panama Congress (1st issue). Multicoloured.
1088 6 c. Type **294** (postage) . . . 10 10
1089 23 c. Bolivar Statue (air) . . . 30 25
1090 35 c. Bolivar Hall, Panama City (horiz) 50 30
1091 41 c. Bolivar and flag . . . 60 40

1976. Marine Fauna. Multicoloured.
1092 2 c. Type **295** (postage) . . . 10 10
1093 3 c. "Ptitosarcus sinuosus" (vert) 10 10
1094 4 c. "Acanthaster planci" . . 10 10
1095 7 c. "Oreaster reticulatus" . . 10 10
1096 17 c. "Diodon hystrix" (vert) (air) 25 15
1097 27 c. "Pocillopora damicornis" 40 25

296 "Simon Bolivar"

1976. 150th Anniv of Panama Congress (2nd issue). Designs showing details of Bolivar Monument or flags of Latin-American countries. Multicoloured.
1099 20 c. Type **296** 30 20
1100 20 c. Argentina 30 20
1101 20 c. Bolivia 30 20
1102 20 c. Brazil 30 20
1103 20 c. Chile 30 20
1104 20 c. "Battle scene" 30 20
1105 20 c. Colombia 30 20
1106 20 c. Costa Rica 30 20
1107 20 c. Cuba 30 20
1108 20 c. Ecuador 30 20
1109 20 c. El Salvador 30 20
1110 20 c. Guatemala 30 20
1111 20 c. Guyana 30 20
1112 20 c. Haiti 30 20
1113 20 c. "Congress assembly" . . 30 20
1114 20 c. "Liberated people" . . 30 20
1115 20 c. Honduras 30 20
1116 20 c. Jamaica 30 20
1117 20 c. Mexico 30 20
1118 20 c. Nicaragua 30 20
1119 20 c. Panama 30 20
1120 20 c. Paraguay 30 20
1121 20 c. Peru 30 20
1122 20 c. Dominican Republic . . 30 20
1123 20 c. "Bolivar and standard-bearer" 30 20
1124 20 c. Surinam 30 20
1125 20 c. Trinidad and Tobago . 30 20
1126 20 c. Uruguay 30 20
1127 20 c. Venezuela 30 20
1128 20 c. "Indian Delegation" . . 30 20

297 Nicanor Villalaz (designer of Panama Arms)

298 National Lottery Building, Panama City

1976. Villalaz Commemoration.
1130 **297** 5 c. blue 10 10

1976. "Progressive Panama".
1131 **298** 6 c. multicoloured . . . 10 10

299 Cerro Colorado, Copper Mine

1976. Air.
1132 **299** 23 c. multicoloured . . . 30 20

300 Contadora Island

1977. Tourism.
1133 **300** 3 c. multicoloured . . . 10 10

301 Secretary-General of Pan-American Union, A. Orfila
302 Signing Ratification of Panama Canal Treaty

1978. Signing of Panama–U.S.A. Treaty. Mult.
1134 3 c. Type **301** 10 10
1135 23 c. Treaty signing scene (horiz) 30 25
1136 40 c. President Carter 55 30
1137 50 c. Gen. O. Torrijos of Panama 70 50
Nos. 1134 and 1136/7 were issued together se-tenant in horizontal stamps of three showing Treaty signing as No. 1135.

1978. Ratification of Panama Canal Treaty.
1138 **302** 3 c. multicoloured . . . 10 10
1139 – 5 c. multicoloured . . . 10 10
1140 – 35 c. multicoloured . . . 50 25
1141 – 41 c. multicoloured . . . 60 30

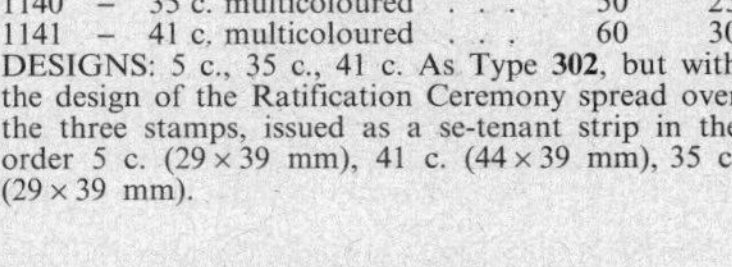
DESIGNS: 5 c., 35 c., 41 c. As Type **302**, but with the design of the Ratification Ceremony spread over the three stamps, issued as a se-tenant strip in the order 5 c. (29 × 39 mm), 41 c. (44 × 39 mm), 35 c. (29 × 39 mm).

303 Colon Harbour and Warehouses

1978. 30th Anniv of Colon Free Zone.
1142 **303** 6 c. multicoloured . . . 10 10

304 Children's Home and Melvin Jones

1978. Birth Centenary of Melvin Jones (founder of Lions International).
1143 **304** 50 c. multicoloured . . . 70 55

305 Pres. Torrijos, "Flavia" (liner) and Children

1979. Return of Canal Zone. Multicoloured.
1144 3 c. Type **305** 10 10
1145 Presidents Torrijos and Carter, liner and flags of Panama and U.S.A. 40 20

306 "75" and Bank Emblem

1979. 75th Anniv of National Bank.
1146 **306** 6 c. black, red and blue . 10 10

307 Rotary Emblem
308 Children inside Heart

1979. 75th Anniv of Rotary International.
1147 **307** 17 c. blue and yellow . . 25 20

1979. International Year of the Child.
1148 **308** 50 c. multicoloured . . 70 45

309 U.P.U. Emblem and Globe
310 Colon Station

1979. 18th Universal Postal Union Congress, Rio de Janeiro.
1149 **309** 35 c. multicoloured . . 50 30

1980. Centenary of Trans-Panamanian Railway.
1150 **310** 1 c. purple and lilac . . 10 25

311 Postal Headquarters, Balboa (inauguration)
318 Boys in Children's Village

1980. Anniversaries and Events.
1151 **311** 3 c. multicoloured . . . 10 10
1152 – 6 c. multicoloured . . . 10 10
1153 – 17 c. multicoloured . . 25 20
1154 – 23 c. multicoloured . . 30 20
1155 – 35 c. blue, black and red 50 30
1156 – 41 c. pink and black . . 60 40
1157 – 50 c. multicoloured . . 70 45
DESIGNS—HORIZ: 17 c. Map of Central America and flags (census of the Americas); 23 c. Tourism and Convention Centre (opening); 35 c. Bank emblem (Inter-American Development Bank, 25th anniv); 41 c. F. de Lesseps (Panama Canal cent); 50 c. Olympic Stadium, Moscow (Olympic Games). VERT: 6 c. National flag (return of Canal Zone).

1980. Olympic Games, Lake Placid and Moscow. (a) Optd **1980 LAKE PLACID MOSCU** and venue emblems.
1158 20 c. (No. 1099) 80 80
1160 20 c. (1101) 80 80
1162 20 c. (1103) 80 80
1164 20 c. (1105) 80 80
1166 20 c. (1107) 80 80
1168 20 c. (1109) 80 80
1170 20 c. (1111) 80 80
1172 20 c. (1113) 80 80
1174 20 c. (1115) 80 80
1176 20 c. 1117) 80 80
1178 20 c. (1119) 80 80
1180 20 c. (1121) 80 80
1182 20 c. (1123) 80 80
1184 20 c. (1125) 80 80
1186 20 c. (1127) 80 80

(b) Optd with Lake Placid Olympic emblems and medals total of country indicated.
1159 20 c. **ALEMANIA D.** (1101) 80 80
1161 20 c. **"AUSTRIA"** (1102) . . 80 80
1163 20 c. **"SUECIA"** (1104) . . . 80 80
1165 20 c. **"U.R.S.S."** (1106) . . . 80 80
1167 20 c. **"ALEMANIA F."** (1108) 80 80
1169 20 c. **"ITALIA"** (1110) . . . 80 80
1171 20 c. **"U.S.A."** (1112) 80 80
1173 20 c. **"SUIZA"** (1114) 80 80
1175 20 c. **"CANADA/GRAN BRETANA"** (1116) . . . 80 80
1177 20 c. **"NORUEGA"** (1118) . 80 80
1179 20 c. **"LICHTENSTEIN"** (1120) 80 80
1181 20 c. **"HUNGRIA/ BULGARIA"** (1122) . . . 80 80
1183 20 c. **"FINLANDIA"** (1124) . 80 80
1185 20 c. **"HOLANDA"** (1126) . 80 80
1187 20 c. **"CHECOSLOVAQUIA/ FRANCIA"** (1128) . . . 80 80
Footnote 1158 etc. occur on 1st, 3rd and 5th rows and Nos. 1160 etc. occur in other rows.

(a) Lake Placid and Moscow and venue with Olympic rings.
1188 20 c. (No. 1099) 80 80
1190 20 c. (1101) 80 80
1192 20 c. (1103) 80 80
1194 20 c. (1105) 80 80
1196 20 c. (1107) 80 80
1198 20 c. (1109) 80 80
1200 20 c. (1111) 80 80
1202 20 c. (1113) 80 80
1204 20 c. (1115) 80 80
1206 20 c. (1117) 80 80
1208 20 c. (1119) 80 80
1210 20 c. (1121) 80 80
1212 20 c. (1123) 80 80
1214 20 c. (1125) 80 80
1216 20 c. (1127) 80 80

(b) Optd with country names as indicated.
1189 20 c. **"RUSIA/ALEMANIA D."** (1101) 80 80
1191 20 c. **"SUECIA/FINLANDIA"** (1102) 80 80
1193 20 c. **"GRECIA/BELGICA/ INDIA"** (1104) 80 80
1195 20 c. **"BULGARIA/CUBA"** (1106) 80 80
1197 20 c. **"CHECOSLOVAQUIA/ YUGOSLAVIA"** (1108) . . 80 80
1199 20 c. **"ZIMBAWE/COREA DEL NORTE/ MONGOLIA"** (1110) . . . 80 80
1201 20 c. **"ITALIA/HUNGRIA"** (1112) 80 80
1203 20 c. **"AUSTRALIA/ DINAMARCA"** (1114) . . 80 80
1205 20 c. **"TANZANIA/MEXICO/ HOLANDA"** (1116) . . . 80 80
1207 20 c. **"RUMANIA/FRANCIA"** (1118) 80 80
1209 20 c. **"BRASIL/ETIOPIA"** (1120) 80 80
1211 20 c. **"IRLANDA/UGANDA/ VENEZUELA"** (1122) . . 80 80
1213 20 c. **"GRAN BRETANA/ POLONIA"** (1124) 80 80
1215 20 c. **"SUIZA/ESPANA/ AUSTRIA"** (1126) 80 80
1217 20 c. **"JAMAICA/LIBANO/ GUYANA"** (1128) 80 80
Footnote Nos. 1188, etc., occur on 1st, 3rd and 5th rows and Nos. 1189 etc., on the others.

1980. Medal Winners at Winter Olympic Games, Lake Placid. (a) Optd with 1980, medals and venue emblems.
1219 20 c. 1980 medals and venue and emblems (No. 1099) 80 80
1221 20 c. As No. 1219 (1101) . . 80 80
1223 20 c. As No. 1219 (1103) . . 80 80
1225 20 c. As No. 1219 (1105) . . 80 80
1227 20 c. As No. 1219 (1107) . . 80 80
1229 20 c. As No. 1219 (1109) . . 80 80
1231 20 c. As No. 1219 (1111) . . 80 80
1233 20 c. As No. 1219 (1113) . . 80 80
1235 20 c. As No. 1219 (1115) . . 80 80
1237 20 c. As No. 1219 (1117) . . 80 80
1239 20 c. As No. 1219 (1119) . . 80 80
1241 20 c. As No. 1219 (1121) . . 80 80
1243 20 c. As No. 1219 (1123) . . 80 80
1245 20 c. As No. 1219 (1125) . . 80 80
1247 20 c. As No. 1219 (1127) . . 80 80

(b) Optd with 1980 medals and venue emblems and Olympic torch and country indicated.
1220 20 c. **"ALEMANIA D."** (1100) 80 80
1222 20 c. **"AUSTRIA"** (1102) . . 80 80
1224 20 c. **"SUECIA"** (1104) . . 80 80
1226 20 c. **"U.R.S.S."** (1106) . . . 80 80
1228 20 c. **"ALEMANIA F."** (1108) 80 80
1230 20 c. **"ITALIA"** (1110) . . . 80 80
1232 20 c. **"U.S.A."** (1112) . . . 80 80
1234 20 c. **"SUIZA"** (1114) . . . 80 80
1236 20 c. **"CANADA/GRAN BRETANA"** (1116) 80 80
1238 20 c. **"NORUEGA"** (1118) . . 80 80
1240 20 c. **"LICHTENSTEIN"** (1120) 80 80
1242 20 c. **"HUNGRIA/ BULGARIA"** (1122) . . . 80 80
1244 20 c. **"FINLANDIA"** (1124) . 80 80
1246 20 c. **"HOLANDIA"** (1126) . 80 80
1248 20 c. **"CHECOSLOVAQUIA/ FRANCIA"** (1128) 80 80
Footnote Nos. 1219, etc., occur in 1st, 3rd and 5th rows and Nos. 1220 occur in others.

1980. World Cup Football Championship, Argentina (1978) and Spain (1980). Optd with
A. Football cup emblems.
B. **"ESPAMER 80"** and "Argentina '78" emblems and inscriptions **"ESPANA '82/CAMPEONATO/ MUNDIAL DE FUTBOL"**.
C. World Cup Trophy and **"ESPANA '82."**.
D. **"ESPANA 82/Football/ Argentina '78/BESPAMER '80 MADRID"**.
E. FIFA globes emblem and **"ESPANA '82/ ARGENTINAA '78/ESPANA '82"**.
F. With ball and inscription as for B.
1249 20 c. No. 1099 (A, C, E) . . 80 80
1250 20 c. No. 1100 (B, D, F) . . 80 80
1251 20 c. No. 1101 (A, C, E) . . 80 80
1252 20 c. No. 1102 (B, D, F) . . 80 80
1253 20 c. No. 1103 (A, C, E) . . 80 80
1254 20 c. No. 1104 (B, D, F) . . 80 80
1255 20 c. No. 1105 (A, C, E) . . 80 80
1256 20 c. No. 1106 (B, D, F) . . 80 80
1257 20 c. No. 1107 (A, C, E) . . 80 80
1258 20 c. No. 1108 (B, D, F) . . 80 80
1259 20 c. No. 1109 (A, C, E) . . 80 80
1260 20 c. No. 1110 (B, D, F) . . 80 80
1261 20 c. No. 1111 (A, C, E) . . 80 80
1262 20 c. No. 1112 (B, D, F) . . 80 80
1263 20 c. No. 1113 (A, C, E) . . 80 80
1264 20 c. No. 1114 (B, D, F) . . 80 80
1265 20 c. No. 1115 (A, C, E) . . 80 80
1266 20 c. No. 1116 (B, D, F) . . 80 80
1267 20 c. No. 1117 (A, C, E) . . 80 80
1268 20 c. No. 1118 (B, D, F) . . 80 80
1269 20 c. No. 1119 (A, C, E) . . 80 80
1270 20 c. No. 1120 (B, D, F) . . 80 80
1271 20 c. No. 1121 (A, C, E) . . 80 80
1272 20 c. No. 1122 (B, D, F) . . 80 80
1273 20 c. No. 1123 (A, C, E) . . 80 80
1274 20 c. No. 1124 (B, D, F) . . 80 80
1275 20 c. No. 1125 (A, C, E) . . 80 80
1276 20 c. No. 1126 (B, D, F) . . 80 80
1277 20 c. No. 1127 (A, C, E) . . 80 80
1278 20 c. No. 1128 (B, D, F) . . 80 80

1980. Obligatory Tax. Children's Village. Multicoloured.
1280 2 c. Type **318** 10 10
1281 2 c. Boy with chicks . . . 10 10
1282 2 c. Working in the fields . . 10 10
1283 2 c. Boys with pig 10 10

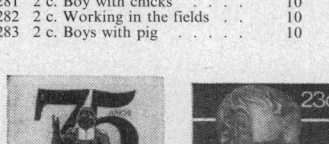

319 Jean Baptiste de la Salle and Map showing La Salle Schools
320 Louis Braille

1981. Education in Panama by the Christian Schools.
1285 **319** 17 c. blue, black and red 25 20

1981. International Year of Disabled People.
1286 **320** 23 c. multicoloured . . . 30 20

321 Statue of the Virgin

1981. 150th Anniv of Apparition of Miraculous Virgin to St. Catharine Laboure.
1287 **321** 35 c. multicoloured . . . 50 35

322 Crimson-backed Tanager

1981. Birds. Multicoloured.
1288 3 c. Type **322** 50 10
1289 6 c. Chestnut-fronted macaw (vert) 60 25
1290 41 c. Violet sabrewing (vert) . 2·50 1·50
1291 50 c. Keel-billed toucan . . . 3·25 1·75

323 "Boy feeding Donkey" (Ricardo Morales)
324 Banner

1981. Obligatory Tax. Christmas. Children's Village. Multicoloured.

1292 2 c. Type **323** 10 10
1293 2 c. "Nativity" (Enrique Daniel Austin) 10 10
1294 2 c. "Bird in Tree" (Jorge Gonzalez) 10 10
1295 2 c. "Church" (Eric Belgrane) 10 10

1981. National Reaffirmation.

1297 **324** 3 c. multicoloured . . . 10 10

325 General Herrera

326 Ricardo J. Alfaro

1982. 1st Death Anniv of General Omar Torrijos Herrera. Multicoloured.

1298 5 c. Aerial view of Panama (postage) 10 10
1299 6 c. Colecito army camp . . 10 10
1300 17 c. Bayano river barrage . . 25 20
1301 50 c. Felipillo engineering works 70 45
1302 23 c. Type **325** (air) 35 25
1303 35 c. Security Council reunion 50 30
1304 41 c. Gen. Omar Torrijos airport . . . . 1·25 45

1982. Birth Centenary of Ricardo J. Alfaro (statesman).

1306 **326** 3 c. black, mauve and blue (postage) 10 10
1307 – 17 c. black and mauve (air) 25 15
1308 – 23 c. multicoloured . . . 30 20

DESIGNS: 17 c. Profile of Alfaro wearing spectacles (as humanist); 23 c. Portrait of Alfaro (as lawyer).

328 Pig Farming

329 Pele (Brazilian footballer)

1982. Obligatory tax. Christmas. Children's Village. Multicoloured.

1309 2 c. Type **328** 10 10
1310 2 c. Gardening 10 10
1311 2 c. Metalwork (horiz) . . . 10 10
1312 2 c. Bee-keeping (horiz) . . . 10 10

1982. World Cup Football Championship, Spain. Multicoloured.

1314 50 c. Italian team (horiz) (postage) 70 45
1315 23 c. Football emblem and map of Panama (air) 30 20
1316 35 c. Type **329** 50 30
1317 41 c. World Cup Trophy . . 60 35

330 Chamber of Trade Emblem

1983. "Expo Comer" Chamber of Trade Exhibition.

1319 **330** 17 c. lt blue, blue, & gold 25 15

331 Dr. Nicolas Solano

332 Pope John Paul II giving Blessing

1983. Air. Birth Centenary (1982) of Dr. Nicolas Solano (anti-tuberculosis pioneer).

1320 **331** 23 c. brown 35 20

1983. Papal Visit. Multicoloured.

1321 6 c. Type **332** (postage) . . . 10 10
1322 17 c. Pope John Paul II . . . 25 15
1323 35 c. Pope and map of Panama (air) 50 30

333 Map of Americas and Sunburst

334 Simon Bolivar

1983. 24th Assembly of Inter-American Development Bank Governors.

1324 **333** 50 c. light blue, blue and gold 70 45

1983. Birth Bicentenary of Simon Bolivar.

1325 **334** 50 c. multicoloured . . 70 45

335 Postal Union of the Americas and Spain Emblem

336 Moslem Mosque

1983. World Communications Day. Mult.

1327 30 c. Type **335** 45 25
1328 40 c. W.C.Y. Emblem . . . 60 40
1329 50 c. Universal Postal Union emblem 70 45
1330 60 c. "Flying Dove" (Alfredo Sinclair) 85 55

1983. Freedom of Worship. Multicoloured.

1332 3 c. Type **336** 10 10
1333 5 c. Bahal temple 10 10
1334 6 c. Church of St. Francis of the Mountains, Veraguas . . 10 10
1335 17 c. Shevet Ahim synagogue 25 15

337 "The Annunciation" (Dagoberto Moran)

338 Ricardo Miro (writer)

1983. Obligatory Tax. Christmas. Children's Village. Multicoloured.

1336 2 c. Type **337** 10 10
1337 2 c. Church and houses (Leonidas Molinar) (vert) . 10 10
1338 2 c. Bethlehem and star (Colon Olmedo Zambrano) (vert) 10 10
1339 2 c. Flight into Egypt (Hector Ulises Velasquez) (vert) . 10 10

1983. Famous Panamanians. Multicoloured.

1341 1 c. Type **338** 10 10
1342 3 c. Richard Newman (educationalist) 10 10
1343 5 c. Cristobal Rodriguez (politician) 10 10
1344 6 c. Alcibiades Arosemena (politician) 10 10
1345 35 c. Cirilo Martinez (educationalist) 50 30

339 "Rural Architecture" (Juan Manuel Cedero)

1983. Paintings. Multicoloured.

1346 1 c. Type **339** 10 10
1347 1 c. "Large Nude" (Manuel Chong Neto) 10 10
1348 3 c. "On another Occasion" (Spiros Vamvas) 10 10
1349 6 c. "Punta Chame" (Guillermo Trujillo) 10 10
1350 28 c. "Neon Light" (Alfredo Sinclair) 30 20
1351 35 c. "The Prophet" (Alfredo Sinclair) (vert) 50 30
1352 41 c. "Highland Girls" (Al Sprague) (vert) 60 40
1353 1 b. "One Morning" (Ignacio Mallol Pibernat) . . . . . 1·40 75

340 Tonosi Double Jug

1984. Archaeological Finds. Multicoloured.

1354 30 c. Type **340** 35 10
1355 40 c. Dish on stand 60 20
1356 50 c. Jug decorated with human face (vert) 70 25
1357 60 c. Waisted bowl (vert) . . 85 35

341 Boxing

342 Roberto Duran

1984. Olympic Games, Los Angeles. Mult.

1359 19 c. Type **341** 35 25
1360 19 c. Baseball 35 25
1361 19 c. Basketball (vert) 35 25
1362 19 c. Swimming (vert) 35 25

1984. Roberto Duran (boxer) Commem.

1363 **342** 26 c. multicoloured . . . 45 30

343 Shooting

1984. Olympic Games, Los Angeles (2nd series). Multicoloured.

1364 6 c. Type **343** (postage) . . . 15 10
1366 30 c. Weightlifting (air) . . . 50 30
1367 37 c. Wrestling 65 45
1368 1 b. Long jump . . . . 1·25 90

344 "Pensive Woman" (Manuel Chong Neto)

345 Map, Pres. Torrijos Herrera and Liner in Canal Lock

1984. Paintings. Multicoloured.

1369 1 c. Type **344** 10 10
1370 3 c. "The Child" (Alfredo Sinclair) (horiz) 10 10
1371 6 c. "A Day in the Life of Rumalda" (Brooke Alfaro) (horiz) 15 10
1372 30 c. "Highlanders" (Al Sprague) 50 10
1373 37 c. "Ballet Interval" (Roberto Sprague) (horiz) 65 15
1374 44 c. "Wood on Chame Head" (Guillermo Trujillo) (horiz) 75 25
1375 50 c. "La Plaza Azul" (Juan Manuel Cedeno) (horiz) . . 60 25
1376 1 b. "Ira" (Spiros Vamvas) (horiz) . . . . 1·25 90

1984. 5th Anniv of Canal Zone Postal Sovereignty.

1377 **345** 19 c. multicoloured . . . 25 25

346 Emblem as Seedling

347 Boy

1984. Air. World Food Day.

1378 **346** 30 c. red, green and blue . 50 45

1984. Obligatory Tax. Christmas. Children's Village. Multicoloured.

1379 2 c. Type **347** 10 10
1380 2 c. Boy in tee-shirt 10 10
1381 2 c. Boy in checked shirt . . 10 10
1382 2 c. Cub scout 10 10

348 American Manatee

1984. Animals. Each in black.

1384 3 c. Type **348** (postage) 10 10
1385 30 c. "Tayra" (air) 60 25
1386 44 c. Jaguarundi 85 40
1387 50 c. White-lipped peccary . 90 40

349 Copper One Centesimo Coins, 1935

1985. Coins. Multicoloured.

1389 3 c. Type **349** (postage) . . . 10 10
1390 3 c. Silver ten centesimo coins, 1904 . . . . 10 10
1391 3 c. Silver five centesimo coins, 1916 . . . . 10 10
1392 30 c. Silver 50 centesimo coins, 1904 (air) 50 30
1393 37 c. Silver half balboa coins, 1962 . . . . 65 45
1394 44 c. Silver balboa coins, 1953 75 50

350 Figures on Map reaching for Dove

351 Tanker in Dock

1985. Contadora Peace Movement.

1395 **350** 10 c. multicoloured . . . 15 10
1396 20 c. multicoloured . . . 30 20
1397 30 c. multicoloured . . . 40 25

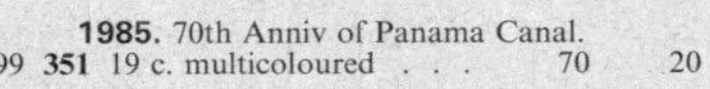

1985. 70th Anniv of Panama Canal.

1399 **351** 19 c. multicoloured . . . 70 20

352 Scouts with Statue of Christ

354 Boys in Cab of Crane

353 "40" on Emblem

1985. Obligatory Tax. Christmas. Children's Village. Multicoloured.

1400 2 c. Type **352** 10 10
1401 2 c. Children holding cards spelling "Feliz Navidad" . 10 10
1402 2 c. Children holding balloons 10 10
1403 2 c. Group of cub scouts . . 10 10

1986. 40th Anniv (1985) of U.N.O.

1405 **353** 23 c. multicoloured . . . 30 20

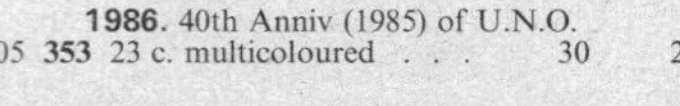

1986. International Youth Year (1985).

1406 **354** 30 c. multicoloured . . . 40 25

355 "Awaiting Her Turn" (Al Sprague)

356 Atlapa Convention Centre

1986. Paintings. Multicoloured.

1407 3 c. Type **355** 10 10
1408 5 c. "Aerobics" (Guillermo Trujillo) (horiz) 10 10
1409 19 c. "House of Cardboard" (Eduardo Augustine) . . . 30 20
1410 30 c. "Tierra Gate" (Juan Manuel Cedeno) (horiz) . . 40 25
1411 36 c. "Supper for Three" (Brood Alfaro) 50 30
1412 42 c. "Tenderness" (Alfredo Sinclair) 60 40
1413 50 c. "Lady of Character" (Manuel Chong Neto) . . 70 45
1414 60 c. "Calla Lilies No. 1" (Maigualida de Diaz) (horiz) 80 55

1986. Miss Universe Contest. Multicoloured.

1415 23 c. Type **356** 30 20
1416 60 c. Emblem 80 55

357 Comet and Globe

358 Angels

1986. Appearance of Halley's Comet.

1417 **357** 23 c. multicoloured . . . 25 15
1418 – 30 c. blue, brown and yellow 35 25

DESIGN: 30 c. Panama la Vieja Cathedral tower.

1986. Obligatory Tax. 20th Anniv of Children's Village. Children's drawings. Multicoloured.

1420 2 c. Type **358** 10 10
1421 2 c. Cupids 10 10
1422 2 c. Indians 10 10
1423 2 c. Angels (different) 10 10

359 Basketball

360 Argentina Player

1986. 15th Central American and Caribbean Games, Santiago. Multicoloured.

1425 20 c. Type **359** 20 10
1426 23 c. Sports 25 15

1986. World Cup Football Championship, Mexico. Multicoloured.

1427 23 c. Type **360** 25 15
1428 30 c. West Germany player . 35 25
1429 37 c. West Germany and Argentina players 45 30

361 Crib

362 Dove and Globe

1986. Christmas. Multicoloured.

1431 23 c. Type **361** 25 15
1432 36 c. Tree and presents . . . 40 25
1433 42 c. As No. 1432 . . . . . 45 30

1986. International Peace Year. Multicoloured.

1434 8 c. Type **362** 10 10
1435 19 c. Profiles and emblem . . 20 10

363 Mask

1987. Tropical Carnival. Multicoloured.

1436 20 c. Type **363** 20 10
1437 35 c. Sun with eye mask . . 40 25

364 Headquarters Building

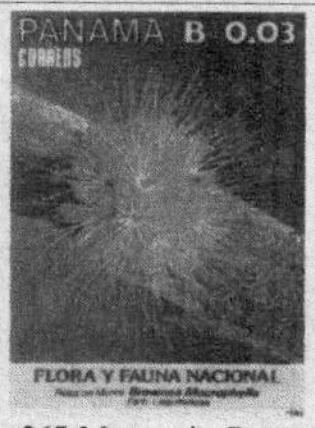

365 Mountain Rose

1987. 50th Anniv (1985) of Panama Lions Club.

1439 **364** 37 c. multicoloured . . 45 30

1987. Flowers and Birds. Multicoloured.

1440 3 c. Type **365** 10 10
1441 5 c. Blue-grey tanager (horiz) 30 10
1442 8 c. Golden cup 10 10
1443 15 c. Tropical kingbird (horiz) 55 10
1444 19 c. "Barleria micans" (flower) 20 10
1445 23 c. Brown pelican (horiz) . 65 15
1446 30 c. "Cordia dentata" (flower) 35 25
1447 36 c. Rufous pigeon (horiz) . 1·10 25

366 Octavio Menendez Pereira (founder) and Anniversary Monument

1987. 50th Anniv (1986) of Panama University.

1448 **366** 19 c. multicoloured . . 20 10

367 Emblem in "40"

368 Heinrich Schutz

1987. 40th Anniv (1985) of F.A.O.

1449 **367** 10 c. brown, yellow and black 10 10
1450 45 c. brown, green and black 50 30

1987. Composers and 7th Anniv (1986) of National Theatre.

1451 **368** 19 c. multicoloured . . 20 10
1452 – 30 c. green, mve & brn . 35 25
1453 – 37 c. brown, blue and deep blue 45 30
1454 – 60 c. green, yell & blk . 70 45

DESIGNS—HORIZ: 30 c. National Theatre. VERT: 37 c. Johann Sebastian Bach; 60 c. Georg Friedrich Handel.

369 Development Projects

370 Horse-drawn Fire Pump, 1887, and Modern Appliance

1987. 25th Anniv (1986) of Inter-American Development Bank.

1455 **369** 23 c. multicoloured . . 25 15

1987. Centenary of Fire Service. Mult.

1456 25 c. Type **370** 30 20
1457 35 c. Fireman carrying boy . 40 25

371 Wrestling

372 "Adoration of the Magi" (Albrecht Nentz)

1987. 10th Pan-American Games, Indianapolis. Multicoloured.

1458 15 c. Type **371** 20 10
1459 25 c. Tennis (vert) 25 15
1460 30 c. Swimming 35 25
1461 41 c. Basketball (vert) . . . 45 30
1462 60 c. Cycling (vert) 70 45

1987. Christmas. Multicoloured.

1464 22 c. Type **372** 25 15
1465 35 c. "The Virgin adored by Angels" (Matthias Grunewald) 40 25
1466 37 c. "Virgin and Child" (Konrad Witz) 45 30

373 Distressed Family and Poor Housing

374 Heart falling into Crack

1987. International Year of Shelter for the Homeless. Multicoloured.

1467 45 c. Type **373** 50 30
1468 50 c. Happy family and stylized modern housing 50 30

1988. Anti-Drugs Campaign.

1469 **374** 10 c. red and orange . . 10 10
1470 17 c. red and green . . . 20 10
1471 25 c. red and blue 30 20

375 Hands and Sapling

376 Breastfeeding

1988. Reafforestation Campaign.

1472 **375** 35 c. deep green and green 40 25
1473 40 c. red and purple . . 45 30
1474 45 c. brown and bistre . . 50 30

1988. U.N.I.C.E.F. Infant Survival Campaign. Multicoloured.

1475 20 c. Type **376** 25 15
1476 31 c. Vaccination 35 25
1477 45 c. Children playing by lake (vert) 50 30

377 Rock Beauty

1988. Fishes. Multicoloured.

1478 7 c. Type **377** 10 10
1479 35 c. French angelfish 40 25
1480 60 c. Black bar soldier fish . . 70 45
1481 1 b. Spotted drum fish . . . 1·25 90

378 Emblem and Clasped Hands

379 "Virgin with Donors"

1988. 75th Anniv of Girl Guide Movement.

1482 **378** 35 c. multicoloured . . . 35 25

1988. Christmas. Anonymous Paintings from Museum of Colonial Religious Art. Mult.

1483 17 c. Type **379** (postage) . . . 20 10
1484 45 c. "Virgin of the Rosary with St. Dominic" 50 30
1485 35 c. "St. Joseph with the Child" (air) 35 25

380 Athletes and Silver Medal (Brazil)

381 St. John Bosco

1989. Seoul Olympic Games Medals. Mult.

1486 17 c. Type **380** (postage) . . . 20 10
1487 25 c. Wrestlers and gold medal (Hungary) 30 20
1488 60 c. Weightlifter and gold medal (Turkey) 70 45
1490 35 c. Boxers and bronze medal (Colombia) (air) 35 25

1989. Death Centenary of St. John Bosco (founder of Salesian Brothers). Multicoloured.

1491 10 c. Type **381** 15 10
1492 20 c. Menor Basilica and St. John with people 25 15

382 Anniversary Emblem

383 "Ancon I" (first ship through Canal)

1989. 125th Anniv of Red Cross Movement.

1493 **382** 40 c. black and red . . . 50 30
1494 – 1 b. multicoloured . . . 1·50 90

DESIGN: 1 b. Red Cross workers putting patient in ambulance.

1989. Air. 75th Anniv of Panama Canal.

1495 **383** 35 c. red, black & yellow 60 40
1496 – 60 c. multicoloured . . . 1·00 80

DESIGN: 60 c. Modern tanker.

384 Barriles Ceremonial Statue

385 "March of the Women on Versailles" (engraving)

1989. America. Pre-Columbian Artefacts. Multicoloured.

1497 20 c. Type **384** 25 15
1498 35 c. Ceramic vase 45 30

1989. Bicent of French Revolution. Mult.

1499 25 c. Type **385** (postage) . . 30 20
1500 35 c. "Storming the Bastille" (air) 45 30
1501 45 c. Birds 55 35

386 "Holy Family"

1989. Christmas. Multicoloured.

1502 17 c. Type **386** 20 10
1503 35 c. 1988 crib in Cathedral . 45 30
1504 45 c. "Nativity" 55 35

The 17 and 45 c. show children's paintings.

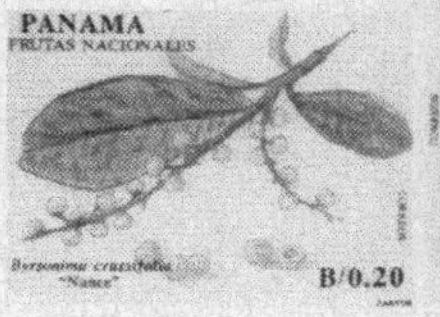

387 "Byrsonima crassifolia"

388 Sinan

1990. Fruit. Multicoloured.

1505 20 c. Type **387** 20 10
1506 35 c. "Bactris gasipaes" . . . 40 25
1507 40 c. "Anacardium occidentale" 40 25

1990. 88th Birthday of Rogelio Sinan (writer).

1508 **388** 23 c. brown and blue . . 25 15

389 Pond Turtle

1990. Reptiles. Multicoloured.

1509 35 c. Type **389** 40 25
1510 45 c. Olive loggerhead turtle 50 35
1511 60 c. Red-footed tortoise . . 65 40

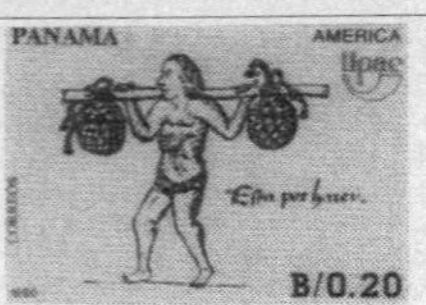

390 Carrying Goods on Yoke (after Oviedo)

1990. America.

1512 **390** 20 c. brown, light brown and gold 20 10
1513 – 35 c. multicoloured . . . 70 50

DESIGN—VERT: 35 c. Warrior wearing gold chest ornament and armbands.

391 Dr. Guillermo Patterson, jun., "Father of Chemistry"

393 St. Ignatius

392 In Sight of Land

1990. Chemistry in Panama.

1514 **391** 25 c. black & turquoise . 25 15
1515 – 35 c. multicoloured . . . 40 25
1516 – 45 c. multicoloured . . . 50 35

DESIGNS: 35 c. Evaporation experiment; 45 c. Books and laboratory equipment.

1991. America. 490th Anniv of Discovery of Panama Isthmus by Rodrigo Bastidas.

1517 **392** 35 c. multicoloured . . . 50 35

1991. 450th Anniv of Society of Jesus and 500th Birth Anniv of St. Ignatius de Loyola (founder).

1518 **393** 20 c. multicoloured . . . 30 20

394 Declaration of Women's Right to Vote

1991. 50th Anniv of First Presidency of Dr. Arnulfo Arias Madrid.

1519 **394** 10 c. brown, stone & gold 15 10
1520 – 10 c. brown, stone & gold 15 10

DESIGN: No. 1520, Department of Social Security headquarters.

395 "Glory to God..." (Luke 2:14) and Score of "Gloria in Excelsis"

1991. Christmas. Multicoloured.

1521 35 c. Type **395** 50 35
1522 35 c. Nativity 50 35

396 Adoration of the Kings

1992. Epiphany.

1523 **396** 10 c. multicoloured . . . 15 10

INDEX

Countries can be quickly located by referring to the index at the end of this volume.

397 Family and Housing Estate

1992. "New Lives" Housing Project.

1524 **397** 5 c. multicoloured . . . 10 10

398 Costa Rican and Panamanian shaking Hands

1992. 50th Anniv (1991) of Border Agreement with Costa Rica. Multicoloured.

1525 20 c. Type **398** 30 20
1526 40 c. Map showing Costa Rica and Panama 55 35
1527 50 c. Presidents Calderon and Arias and national flags . 70 45

399 Pollutants and Hole over Antarctic

1992. "Save the Ozone Layer".

1528 **399** 40 c. multicoloured . . 55 35

400 Exhibition Emblem

1992. "Expocomer 92" 10th International Trade Exhibition, Panama City.

1529 **400** 10 c. multicoloured . . 15 10

401 Portrait

402 Maria Olimpia de Obaldia

1992. 1st Death Anniv of Dame Margot Fonteyn (ballet dancer). Portraits by Pietro Annigoni. Multicoloured.

1530 35 c. Type **401** 50 35
1531 45 c. On stage 60 40

1992. Birth Centenary of Maria Olimpia de Obaldia (poet).

1532 **402** 10 c. multicoloured . . 15 10

403 Athletics Events and Map of Spain

1992. Olympic Games, Barcelona.

1533 **403** 10 c. multicoloured . . 15 10

404 Paca

1992. Endangered Animals.

1534 **404** 5 c. brown, stone & blk . 10 10
1535 – 10 c. black, brn & stone . 15 10
1536 – 15 c. brown, blk & stone . 20 15
1537 – 20 c. multicoloured . . . 30 20

DESIGNS: 10 c. Harpy eagle; 15 c. Jaguar; 20 c. Iguana.

405 Zion Baptist Church, Bocas del Toro

1992. Centenary of Baptist Church in Panama.

1538 **405** 20 c. multicoloured . . . 30 20

406 Columbus's Fleet

1992. America. 500th Anniv of Discovery of America by Columbus. Multicoloured.

1539 20 c. Type **406** 30 20
1540 35 c. Columbus planting flag . 50 35

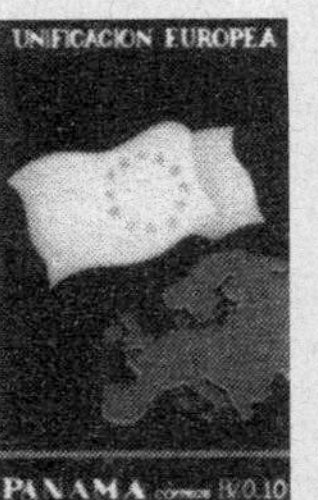

407 Flag and Map of Europe

408 Mascot

1992. European Single Market.

1541 **407** 10 c. multicoloured . . . 15 10

1992. "Expo '92" World's Fair, Seville.

1542 **408** 10 c. multicoloured . . . 15 10

409 Occupations

1992. American Workers' Health Year.

1543 **409** 15 c. multicoloured . . . 20 15

410 Angel and Shepherds

1992. Christmas. Multicoloured.

1544 20 c. Type **410** 30 20
1545 35 c. Mary and Joseph arriving at Bethlehem 50 35

411 Jesus lighting up the Americas

1993. 500th Anniv (1992) of Evangelization of the American Continent.

1546 **411** 10 c. multicoloured . . . 15 10

412 Woman on Crutches and Wheelchair-bound Man

413 Herrera (bust)

1993. National Day of Disabled Persons.

1547 **412** 5 c. multicoloured . . . 10 10

1993. 32nd Death Anniv of Dr. Jose de la Cruz Herrera (essayist).

1548 **413** 5 c. multicoloured . . . 10 10

414 Nutritious Foods and Emblems

1993. International Nutrition Conference, Rome.

1549 **414** 10 c. multicoloured . . . 15 10

415 Caravel and Columbus in Portobelo Harbour

1994. 490th Anniv (1992) of Columbus's Fourth Voyage and Exploration of the Panama Isthmus.

1550 **415** 50 c. multicoloured . . . 65 45

ACKNOWLEDGEMENT OF RECEIPT STAMPS

1898. Handstamped **A. R. COLON COLOMBIA**.
AR24 **5** 5 c. blue . . . . 4·50 3·75
AR25 10 c. orange . . . . 8·00 8·00

1902. Handstamped **AR** in circle.
AR32 **5** 5 c. blue . . . . 3·00 3·00
AR33 10 c. orange . . . . . . 6·00 6·00

1903. No. AR169 of Colombia handstamped **AR** in circle.
AR34 AR **60** 5 c. red . . . . . . 11·00 11·00

AR 37

1904.
AR135 AR **37** 5 c. blue 90 90

1916. Optd **A.R.**
AR177 **50** 2½ c. red 90 90

EXPRESS LETTER STAMPS

1926. Optd **EXPRESO**.
E220 **57** 10 c. black and orange . . 4·25 2·10
E221 20 c. black and brown . . 5·50 2·10

E **81** Cyclist Messenger

1929.
E226 E **81** 10 c. orange 90 70
E227 20 c. brown . . . . . 1·75 1·10

INSURANCE STAMPS

1942. Surch **SEGURO POSTAL HABILITADO** and value.
IN430 5 c. on 1 b. black (No. 373) 45 35
IN431 10 c. on 1 b. brown (No. 365) 70 55
IN432 25 c. on 50 c. brown (No. 372) 1·25 1·25

POSTAGE DUE STAMPS

D **58** San Geronimo Castle Gate, Portobelo

1915.
D169 D **58** 1 c. brown . . . . . . 1·90 30
D170 – 2 c. brown . . . . . . 2·75 25
D171 – 4 c. brown . . . . . . 3·75 55
D172 – 10 c. brown . . . . . 2·75 1·10
DESIGNS—VERT: 2 c. Statue of Columbus. HORIZ: 4 c. House of Deputies. VERT: 10 c. Pedro J. Sosa.
No. D169 is wrongly inscr "CASTILLO DE SAN LORENZO CHAGRES".

D 86

1930.
D240 D **86** 1 c. green 70 25
D241 2 c. red 70 20
D242 4 c. blue 75 30
D243 10 c. violet 75 40

REGISTRATION STAMPS

R 4

1888.
R12 R **4** 10 c. black on grey . . . 6·00 4·00

1897. Handstamped **R COLON** in circle.
R22 **5** 10 c. orange . . . . 4·25 4·00

R 15

1900.
R29 R **15** 10 c. black on blue . . 2·50 2·10
R30 10 c. red . . . . 18·00 15·00

1902. No. R30 surch by hand.
R31 R **15** 20 c. on 10 c. red . . . 15·00 12·00

1903. Type R **85** of Colombia optd **REPUBLICA DE PANAMA**.
R42 20 c. red on blue . . . . . . 27·00
R43 20 c. blue on blue . . . . . . 27·00

1903. Nos. R42/3 surch.
R46 10 c. on 20 c. red on blue . . 50·00 50·00
R47 10 c. on 20 c. blue on blue . . 50·00 50·00

1904. Optd **PANAMA**.
R60 **5** 10 c. orange . . . . 2·10 2·10

1904. Type R **6** of Colombia surch **Panama 10** and bar.
R67 10 c. on 20 c. red on blue . . 38·00 35·00
R68 10 c. on 20 c. blue on blue . . 38·00 35·00

1904. Type R **85** of Colombia optd **Republica de Panama**.
R106 20 c. red on blue . . . . . 5·00 5·00

R 35

1904.
R133 R **35** 10 c. green 70 30

1916. Stamps of Panama surch **R 5 cts**.
R175 **46** 5 c. on 8 c. black & purple 2·10 1·40
R176 **52** 5 c. on 8 c. black & purple 2·10 50

TOO LATE STAMPS

1903. Too Late stamp of Colombia optd **REPUBLICA DE PANAMA**.
L44 L **86** 5 c. violet on red . . . 7·50 5·50

L 36

1904.
L134 L **36** 2½ c. red 70 40

1910. Typewritten optd **Retardo.**
L158 **50** 2½ c. red . . . . 75·00 75·00

1910. Optd **RETARDO.**
L159 **50** 2½ c. red . . . . 38·00 30·00

1916. Surch **RETARDO UN CENTESIMO.**
L174 **38** 1 c. on ½ c. orange . . . 15·00 12·00

APPENDIX

The following stamps have either been issued in excess of postal needs or have not been available to the public in a reasonable quantities at face value. Such stamps may later be given full listing if there is evidence of regular postal use.

1964.
Satellites. Postage ½, 1 c.; Air 5, 10, 21, 50 c.

1965.
Tokyo Olympic Games Medal Winners. Postage ½, 1, 2, 3, 4 c.; Air 5, 6, 7, 10, 21, 31 c.

Space Research. Postage ½, 1, 2, 3 c.; Air 5, 10, 11, 31 c.

400th Birth Anniv of Galileo. Air 10, 21 c.

Peaceful Uses of Atomic Energy. Postage ½, 1, 4 c.; Air 6, 10, 21 c.

Nobel Prize Medals. Air 10, 21 c.

Pres. John Kennedy. Postage ½, 1 c.; Air 10 + 5 c., 21 + 10 c., 31 + 15 c.

1966.
Pope Paul's Visit to U.N. in New York. Postage ½, 1 c.; Air 5, 10, 21, 31 c.

Famous Men. Postage ½ c.; Air 10, 31 c.

Famous Paintings. Postage ½ c.; Air 10, 31 c.

World Cup Football Championships. Postage ½, ½ c.; Air 10, 10, 21, 21 c.

Italian Space Research. Postage ½, 1 c.; Air 5, 10, 21 c.

Centenary of I.T.U. Air. 31 c.

World Cup Winners. Optd on 1966 World Cup Issue. Postage ½, ½ c.; Air. 10, 10, 21, 21 c.

Religious Paintings. Postage ½, 1, 2, 3 c.; Air 21, 21 c.

Churchill and Space Research. Postage ½ c.; Air 10, 31 c.

3rd Death Anniv of Pres. John Kennedy. Postage ½, 1 c.; Air 10, 31 c.

Jules Verne and Space Research. Postage ½, 1 c.; Air 5, 10, 21, 31 c.

1967.
Religious Paintings. Postage ½, 1 c.; Air 5, 10, 21, 31 c.

Mexico Olympics. Postage ½, 1 c.; Air 5, 10, 21, 31 c.

Famous Paintings. Postage 5 c.×3; Air 21 c.×3.

Goya's Paintings. Postage 2, 3, 4 c.; Air 5, 8, 10, 13, 21 c.

1968.
Religious Paintings. Postage 1, 1, 3 c.; Air 4, 21, 21 c.

Mexican President's Visit. Air 50 c., 1 b.

Winter Olympic Games, Grenoble. Postage ½, 1 c.; Air 5, 10, 21, 31 c.

Butterflies. Postage ½, 1, 3, 4 c.; Air 5, 13 c.

Ship Paintings. Postage ½, 1, 3, 4 c.; Air 5, 13 c.

Fishes. Postage ½, 1, 3, 4 c.; Air 5, 13 c.

Winter Olympic Medal Winners. Postage 1, 2, 3, 4, 5, 6, 8 c.; Air 13, 30 c.

Paintings of Musicians. 5, 10, 15, 20, 25, 30 c.

Satellite Transmissions from Panama T.V. (a) Olympic Games, Mexico. Optd on 1964 Satellites issue. Postage ½ c.; Air 50 c. (b) Pope Paul's Visit to Latin America. Postage ½ c.; Air 21 c. (c) Panama Satellite Transmissions. Inauguration (i) optd on Space Research issue of 1965. Postage 5 c.; Air 31 c. (ii) optd on Churchill and Space Research issue of 1966. Postage ½ c.; Air 10 c.

Hunting Paintings. Postage 1, 3, 5, 10 c.; Air 13, 30 c.

Horses and Jockeys. Postage 5, 10, 15, 20, 25, 30 c.

Mexico Olympics. Postage 1, 2, 3, 4, 5, 6, 8 c.; Air 13, 30 c.

1969.
1st Int. Philatelic and Numismatic Exhibition. Optd on 1968 Issue of Mexican Presidents' Visit. Air 50 c., 1 b.

Telecommunications Satellites. Air 5, 10, 15, 20, 25, 30 c.

Provisionals. Surch "Decreto No. 112 (de 6 de marzo de 1969)" and new values on No. 781 and 10 c. + 5 c. and 21 c. + 10 c. of 1965 Issue of 3rd Death Anniv of Pres. John Kennedy. Air 5 c. on 5 c. + 5 c., 5 c. on 10 c. + 5 c., 10 c. on 21 c. + 10 c.

Pope Paul VI. Visit to Latin America. Religious Paintings. Postage 1, 2, 3, 4, 5 c.; Air 6, 7, 8, 10 c.

PAPAL STATES Pt. 8

Parts of Italy under Papal rule till 1870 when they became part of the Kingdom of Italy.

1852. 100 bajocchi = 1 scudo
1866. 100 centesimi = 1 lira

1 2

1852. Papal insignia as in T **1** and **2** in various shapes and frames. Imperf.
1 ½ b. black on grey . . . . . . £225 50·00
5 ½ b. black on purple . . . . . 13·00 £100
10 1 b. black on green . . . . . 22·00 25·00
11 2 b. black on green . . . . . 50·00 3·25
14 2 b. black on white . . . . . 1·75 22·00
15 3 b. black on brown . . . . . 85·00 17·00
16 3 b. black on yellow . . . . . 7·50 80·00
17 4 b. black on brown . . . . £1700 30·00
19 4 b. black on yellow . . . . . 80·00 30·00
21 5 b. black on pink . . . . . £100 4·00
22 6 b. black on lilac . . . . . 90·00 29·00
23 6 b. black on grey . . . . . £250 15·00
25 7 b. black on blue . . . . . £450 28·00
26 8 b. black on white . . . . . £150 14·00
27 50 b. blue £7000 £1300
29 1 s. red £1300 £2500

1867. Same types. Imperf.
30 2 c. black on green . . . . . . 60·00 £130
32 3 c. black on grey £900 £1400
33 5 c. black on blue . . . . . . 70·00 £140
34 10 c. black on orange . . . . . £450 20·00
35 20 c. black on red . . . . . . 60·00 21·00
36 40 c. black on yellow £100 £160
37 80 c. black on pink . . . . . . 90·00 £400

1868. Same types. Perf.
42 2 c. black on green . . . . . . 3·50 24·00
43 3 c. black on grey . . . . . . 18·00 £2500
45 5 c. black on blue . . . . . . 5·50 18·00
46 10 c. black on orange . . . . . 1·25 6·00
50 20 c. black on red . . . . . . 1·25 10·00
49 20 c. black on mauve . . . . . 2·00 10·00
52 40 c. black on yellow . . . . . 1·75 60·00
55 80 c. black on pink . . . . . . 11·00 £250

PARAGUAY
Pt. 20

A republic in the centre of S. America independent since 1811.

1870. 8 reales = 1 peso
1878. 100 centavos = 1 peso
1944. 100 centimos = 1 guarani

1

7

1870. Various frames. Values in "reales". Imperf.
1 **1** 1 r. red . . . . 2·25 2·25
3 2 r. blue . . . . 27·00 27·00
4 3 r. black . . . . 65·00 65·00

1878. Handstamped with large **5**. Imperf.
5 **1** 5 c. on 1 r. red . . . . 25·00 25·00
9 5 c. on 2 r. blue £120 £110
13 5 c. on 3 r. black . . . . . . 85·00 85·00

1879. Prepared for use but not issued (wrong currency). Values in "reales". Perf.
14 **7** 5 r. orange 40
15 10 r. brown 50

1879. Values in "centavos". Perf.
16 **7** 5 c. brown 70 70
17 10 c. green 95 95

1881. Handstamped with large figures.
18 **7** 1 on 10 c. green . . . . . . 3·50 3·50
19 2 on 10 c. green . . . . . . 3·50 3·50

1881. As T **1** (various frames), but value in "centavos". Perf.
20 **1** 1 c. blue 40 40
21a 2 c. red 30 40
22 4 c. brown 40 50

1884. No. 1 handstamped with large **1**. Imperf.
23 **1** 1 c. on 1 r. red . . . . 1·50 1·40

13

24

1884. Perf.
24 **13** 1 c. green 30 15
25 2 c. red 40 15
26 5 c. blue 40 15

1887.
32 **24** 1 c. green 15 15
33a 2 c. red 15 15
34 5 c. blue 30 20
35 7 c. brown 30 25
36 10 c. mauve 45 30
37 15 c. orange 45 30
38 20 c. pink 45 30
50 40 c. blue . . . . 1·50 70
51 60 c. orange 60 30
52 80 c. blue 55 30
53 1 p. green 60 30

25

27 C. Rivarola

1889. Imperf or perf.
40 **25** 15 c. purple 95 95

1892.
42 **27** 1 CENTAVOS grey 15 10
54 1 CENTAVO grey 15 10
43 – 2 c. green 15 10
44 – 4 c. red 10 10
57 – 5 c. purple 15 10
46 – 10 c. violet 30 25
47 – 14 c. brown 30 30
48 – 20 c. red 50 30
49 – 30 c. green 75 30
84 – 1 p. blue 40 25
PORTRAITS: 2 c. S. Jovellano; 4 c. J. Bautista Gil; 5 c. H. Uriarte; 10 c. C. Barreiro; 14 c. Gen. B. Caballero; 20 c. Gen. P. Escobar; 30 c. J. Gonzales; 1 p. J. B. Egusquisa.

1892. 400th Anniv of Discovery of America. No. 46 optd **1492 12 DE OCTUBRE 1892** in oval.
41 10 c. violet . . . . 3·50 1·50

1895. Surch **PROVISORIO 5**.

30 39

1896. Telegraph stamps as T **30** surch **CORREOS 5 CENTAVOS** in oval.

No.	Type	Description	Unused	Used
60	**30**	5 c. on 2 c. brown, blk & grey	45	20
61		5 c. on 4 c. orange, blk & grey	45	20

1898. Surch **Provisorio 10 Centavos.**

No.	Type	Description	Unused	Used
63	**24**	10 c. on 15 c. orange	35	35
62		10 c. on 40 c. blue	25	25

1900. Telegraph stamps as T **30** surch with figures of value twice and bar.

No.	Type	Description	Unused	Used
64	**30**	5 c. on 30 c. green, black and grey	95	70
65		10 c. on 50 c. lilac, black and grey	2·25	1·50

1900.

No.	Type	Description	Unused	Used
76	**39**	1 c. green	10	10
67		2 c. grey	10	10
73		2 c. pink	20	15
68		3 c. brown	10	10
78		4 c. blue	15	10
69		5 c. green	10	10
74		5 c. brown	20	10
79		5 c. lilac	25	10
80		8 c. brown	20	15
71		10 c. red	20	15
72		24 c. blue	45	20
82		28 c. orange	25	35
83		40 c. blue	25	10

1902. Surch **Habilitado en** and new values.

No.	Type	Description	Unused	Used
88	–	1 c. on 14 c. brown (No. 47)	30	20
91	–	1 c. on 1 p. blue (No. 84)	20	15
86	**39**	5 c. on 8 c. brown (No. 80)	35	20
87		5 c. on 28 c. orange (No. 82)	20	30
89	**24**	5 c. on 60 c. orange (No. 51)	20	25
90		5 c. on 80 c. blue (No. 52)	30	25
85	**39**	20 c. on 24 c. blue (No. 72)	35	20

46 47 48

1903.

No.	Type	Description	Unused	Used
92	**46**	1 c. grey	20	15
93		2 c. green	25	20
94a		5 c. blue	25	10
95		10 c. brown	45	20
96		20 c. red	45	25
97		30 c. blue	50	25
98		60 c. violet	75	30

1903.

No.	Type	Description	Unused	Used
99	**47**	1 c. green	15	10
100		2 c. orange	15	10
101		5 c. blue	20	15
102		10 c. violet	30	20
103		20 c. green	50	25
104		30 c. blue	60	30
105		60 c. brown	60	35

1904.

No.	Type	Description	Unused	Used
106	**48**	10 c. blue	35	20

1904. End of successful Revolt against Govt. (begun in August). Surch **PAZ 12 Dic. 1904. 30 centavos.**

No.	Type	Description	Unused	Used
107	**48**	30 c. on 10 c. blue	50	35

50 **51** National Palace, Asuncion

1905.

No.	Type	Description	Unused	Used
108	**50**	1 c. orange	15	10
109		1 c. red	15	10
110		1 c. blue	15	10
112		2 c. green	23·00	
113		2 c. red	15	10
114		5 c. blue	15	10
116		5 c. yellow	15	10
117		10 c. brown	15	10
118		10 c. green	15	10
119		10 c. blue	15	10
120		20 c. lilac	45	35
121		20 c. brown	45	35
122		20 c. green	35	20
123		30 c. blue	45	20
124		30 c. grey	45	20
125		30 c. lilac	50	35
126		60 c. brown	35	25
128		60 c. pink	2·75	95
129	**51**	1 p. black and red	95	80
130		1 p. black and brown	35	35
131		1 p. black and green	35	35
132		2 p. black and blue	35	25
133		2 p. black and red	35	25
134		2 p. black and brown	40	30
135	**51**	5 p. black and red	60	35
136		5 p. black and blue	60	35
137		5 p. black and green	60	35
138		10 p. black and brown	55	35
139		10 p. black and blue	55	35
141		20 p. black and green	1·40	1·25
142		20 p. black and yellow	1·40	1·25
143		20 p. black and purple	1·40	1·25

1907. Surch **Habilitado en** and value and bars.

No.	Type	Description	Unused	Used
159	**50**	5 c. on 1 c. blue	10	10
160		5 c. on 2 c. red	15	10
145		5 c. on 2 c. green	40	25
172	**39**	5 c. on 28 c. orange	95	35
173		5 c. on 40 c. blue	30	25
163	**50**	5 c. on 60 c. brown	15	10
162		5 c. on 60 c. pink	20	15
175		20 c. on 1 c. blue	20	15
180	**24**	20 c. on 2 c. red	1·90	1·50
177	**50**	20 c. on 2 c. red	2·75	2·25
178		20 c. on 30 c. blue	1·10	1·10
179		20 c. on 30 c. lilac	30	30

1907. Official stamps surch **Habilitado en** and value and bars. Where not otherwise stated, the design is as T **50** but with "OFICIAL" below the lion.

No.	Type	Description	Unused	Used
164	–	5 c. on 10 c. green	30	20
149	–	5 c. on 10 c. brown	30	20
150	–	5 c. on 10 c. lilac	30	20
181	**24**	5 c. on 15 c. orange (No. O63)	1·90	1·40
182		5 c. on 20 c. pink (No. O64)	30·00	25·00
166	–	5 c. on 20 c. brown	30	25
151	–	5 c. on 20 c. green	30	20
167	–	5 c. on 20 c. pink	30	25
152	–	5 c. on 20 c. lilac	30	20
157	**46**	5 c. on 30 c. blue (No. O104)	95	85
154	–	5 c. on 30 c. blue	50	50
169	–	5 c. on 30 c. yellow	10	10
168	–	5 c. on 30 c. grey	20	15
183	**24**	5 c. on 50 c. grey (No. O65)	13·50	9·50
158	**46**	5 c. on 60 c. violet (No. O105)	35	25
155	–	5 c. on 60 c. brown	20	15
171	–	5 c. on 60 c. blue	20	10
184	**24**	20 c. on 5 c. blue (No. O60)	1·10	95
174	**46**	20 c. on 5 c. blue (No. O101)	95	75

1907. Official stamps, as T **50** and **51** with "OFICIAL" added, optd **Habilitado** and one bar.

No.	Type	Description	Unused	Used
146		5 c. grey	30	20
148		5 c. blue	25	15
185		1 p. black and orange	35	35
186		1 p. black and red	30	25

1907. Official stamps, as T **51** with "OFFICIAL" added, surch **Habilitado. 1908 UN CENTAVO** and bar.

No.	Type	Description	Unused	Used
188		1 c. on 1 p. black and red	20	20
189		1 c. on 1 p. black and brown	70	50

1908. Optd **1908.**

No.	Type	Description	Unused	Used
190	**50**	1 c. green	10	10
191		5 c. yellow	10	10
192		10 c. brown	10	10
193		20 c. orange	10	10
194		30 c. red	40	30
195		60 c. mauve	30	30
196	**51**	1 p. blue	15	15

1909. Optd **1909.**

No.	Type	Description	Unused	Used
197	**50**	1 c. blue	10	10
198		1 c. red	10	10
199		5 c. green	10	10
200		5 c. orange	10	10
201		10 c. red	20	15
202		10 c. brown	20	15
203		20 c. lilac	20	20
204		20 c. yellow	10	10
205		30 c. brown	45	30
206		30 c. blue	45	30

62 63

65

1910.

No.	Type	Description	Unused	Used
207	**62**	1 c. brown	10	10
208		5 c. lilac	10	10
209		5 c. green	10	10
210		5 c. blue	10	10
211		10 c. green	10	10
212		10 c. violet	10	10
213		10 c. red	10	10
214		20 c. red	10	10
215		50 c. red	45	20
216		75 c. blue	15	10

1911. No. 216 perf diagonally and each half used as 20 c.

No.	Type	Description	Unused	Used
217	**62**	20 c. (½ of 75 c.) blue	15	10

1911. Independence Centenary.

No.	Type	Description	Unused	Used
218	**63**	1 c. black and olive	10	10
219		2 c. black and blue	10	10
220		5 c. black and red	20	10
221		10 c. brown and blue	30	15
222		20 c. blue and olive	30	15
223		50 c. blue and lilac	45	30
224		75 c. purple and olive	45	30

1912. Surch **Habilitada en VEINTE** and thin bar.

No.	Type	Description	Unused	Used
225	**62**	20 c. on 50 c. red	10	10

1913.

No.	Type	Description	Unused	Used
226	**65**	1 c. black	10	10
227		2 c. orange	10	10
228		5 c. mauve	10	10
229		10 c. green	10	10
230		20 c. red	10	10
231		40 c. red	10	10
232		75 c. blue	10	10
233	**65**	80 c. yellow	10	10
234		1 p. blue	10	10
235		1 p. 25 blue	30	10
236		3 p. green	30	10

1918. No. D242 surch **HABILITADO EN 0.05 1918** and bar.

No.	Type	Description	Unused	Used
237		5 c. on 40 c. brown	10	10

1918. Nos. D239/42 optd **HABILITADO 1918.**

No.	Type	Description	Unused	Used
238		5 c. brown	10	10
239		10 c. brown	10	10
240		20 c. brown	10	10
241		40 c. brown	15	10

1918. Surch **HABILITADO EN 0.30 1918** and bar.

No.	Type	Description	Unused	Used
242	**65**	30 c. on 40 c. red	10	10

1920. Surch **HABILITADO en**, value and **1920.**

No.	Type	Description	Unused	Used
243	**65**	50 c. on 80 c. yellow	15	10
244		1 p. 75 on 3 p. green	60	50

1920. Nos. D243/4 optd **HABILITADO 1920** or surch also.

No.	Type	Description	Unused	Used
245		1 p. brown	20	10
246		1 p. on 1 p. 50 brown	35	10

72 Parliament House, Asuncion **75**

1920. Jubilee of Constitution.

No.	Type	Description	Unused	Used
247	**72**	50 c. black and red	30	20
248		1 p. black and blue	50	40
249		1 p. 75 black and blue	20	15
250		3 p. black and yellow	75	25

1920. Surch **50.**

No.	Type	Description	Unused	Used
251	**65**	50 on 75 c. blue	45	10

1921. Surch **50** and two bars.

No.	Type	Description	Unused	Used
252	**62**	50 on 75 c. blue	10	10
253	**65**	50 on 75 c. blue	25	10

1922.

No.	Type	Description	Unused	Used
254	**75**	50 c. blue and red	10	10
255		1 p. brown and blue	10	10

Between 1922 and 1936 many regular postage stamps were overprinted C (= Campana—country), these being used at post offices outside Asuncion but not for mail sent abroad. The prices quoted are for whichever is the cheapest.

77 Starting-point of Conspirators

80 Map

1922. Independence.

No.	Type	Description	Unused	Used
256	**77**	1 p. blue	20	10
258		1 p. blue and red	30	10
259		1 p. grey and purple	30	10
260		1 p. grey and orange	30	10
257		5 p. purple	30	25
261		5 p. brown and blue	30	25
262		5 p. black and green	30	25
263		5 p. blue and red	30	25

1924. Surch **Habilitado en** value and **1924.**

No.	Type	Description	Unused	Used
265	**65**	50 c. on 75 c. blue	10	10
266		$1 on 1 p. 25 blue	10	10
267	–	$1 on 1 p. 50 brown (No. D244)	10	10

1924.

No.	Type	Description	Unused	Used
268	**80**	1 p. blue	10	10
269		2 p. red	15	10
270		4 p. blue	30	10

81 Gen. Jose E. Diaz

82 Columbus

1925.

No.	Type	Description	Unused	Used
271	**81**	50 c. red	10	10
272		1 p. blue	10	10
273		1 p. green	10	10

1925.

No.	Type	Description	Unused	Used
274	**82**	1 p. blue	15	10

1926. Surch **Habilitado en** and new value.

No.	Type	Description	Unused	Used
275	**62**	1 c. on 5 c. blue	10	10
276		$0.02 on 5 c. blue	10	10
277	**65**	7 c. on 40 c. red	10	10
278		15 c. on 75 c. blue	10	10
279	**50**	$0.50 on 60 c. purple (No. 195)	10	10
280	–	$0.50 on 75 c. blue (No. O243)	10	10
281	–	$1.50 on 1 p. 50 brown (No. D244)	15	10
282	**80**	$1.50 on 4 p. blue	10	10

86

87 P. J. Caballero

88 Paraguay

89 Cassel Tower, Asuncion

90 Columbus

1927.

No.	Type	Description	Unused	Used
283	**86**	1 c. red	10	10
284		2 c. orange	10	10
285		7 c. lilac	10	10
286		7 c. green	10	10
287		10 c. green	10	10
288		10 c. red	10	10
290		10 c. blue	10	10
291		20 c. blue	10	10
292		20 c. purple	10	10
293		20 c. violet	10	10
294		20 c. pink	10	10
295		50 c. blue	10	10
296		50 c. red	10	10
323		50 c. orange	10	10
326		50 c. green	10	10
299		50 c. mauve	10	10
300		50 c. pink	10	10
301		70 c. blue	10	10
328	**87**	1 p. green	10	10
329		1 p. red	10	10
330		1 p. purple	10	10
331		1 p. blue	10	10
304		1 p. orange	10	10
332		1 p. violet	10	10
333	**88**	1 p. 50 brown	10	10
334		1 p. 50 lilac	10	10
307		1 p. 50 pink	10	10
335		1 p. 50 blue	10	10
308	–	2 p. 50 bistre	10	10
337	–	2 p. 50 violet	10	10
338	–	3 p. grey	10	10
310	–	3 p. red	10	10
311	–	3 p. violet	10	10
312	**89**	5 p. brown	25	20
340		5 p. violet	10	10
314		5 p. orange	10	10
315	**90**	10 p. red	35	35
317		10 p. blue	35	35
318	**88**	20 p. red	1·10	85
319		20 p. green	1·10	85
320		20 p. purple	1·10	85

DESIGNS—As Type **87**: 2 p. 50, Fulgencio Yegros; 3 p. V. Ignacio Yturbe.

92 Arms of De Salazarde Espinosa, founder of Asuncion

93 Pres. Hayes of U.S.A. and Villa Hayes

1928. Foundation of Asuncion, 1537.

No.	Type	Description	Unused	Used
342	**92**	10 p. purple	95	70

1928. 50th Anniv of Hayes's Decision to award Northern Chaco to Paraguay.

No.	Type	Description	Unused	Used
343	**93**	10 p. brown	2·50	1·10
344		10 p. grey	2·50	1·10

1929. Air. Surch **Correo Aereo Habilitado en** and value.

No.	Type	Description	Unused	Used
357	**86**	$0.95 on 7 c. lilac	20	20
358		$1.90 on 20 c. blue	20	20
345	–	$2.85 on 5 c. purple (No. O239)	60	70
348	–	$3.40 on 3 p. grey (No. 338)	1·40	85
359	**80**	$3.40 on 4 p. blue	30	30
360		$4.75 on 4 p. blue	55	30
346	–	$5.65 on 10 c. green (No. O240)	35	45
361	–	$6.80 on 3 p. grey (No. 338)	35	35
349	**80**	$6.80 on 4 p. blue	1·40	85
347	–	$11.30 on 50 c. red (No. O242)	60	50
350	**89**	$17 on 5 p. brown (A)	1·40	85
362		$17 on 5 p. brown (B)	1·10	1·10

On No. 350 (A) the surcharge is on four lines, and on No. 362 (B) it is in three lines.

95

1929. Air.

352 **95** 2.85 p. green 35 30
353 – 5.65 p. brown 60 30
354 – 5.65 p. red 40 35
355 – 11.30 purple 70 55
356 – 11.30 blue 35 35

DESIGNS: 5.65 p. Carrier pigeon; 11.30 p. Stylized airplane.

1930. Air. Optd **CORREO AEREO** or surch also in words.

363 **86** 5 c. on 10 c. green 10 10
364 5 c. on 70 c. blue 10 10
365 10 c. green 10 10
366 20 c. blue 20 20
367 **87** 20 c. on 1 p. red 30 30
368 **86** 40 c. on 50 c. orange 15 10
369 **87** 1 p. green 35 35
370 – 3 p. grey (No. 338) 35 35
371 **90** 6 p. on 10 p. red 60 50
372 **88** 10 p. on 20 p. red 2·25 2·10
373 10 p. on 20 p. purple 2·25 2·10

101

103

1930. Air.

374 **101** 95 c. blue on blue 40 35
375 95 c. red on pink 40 35
376 – 1 p. 90 purple on blue 40 35
377 – 1 p. 90 red on pink 40 35
378 **103** 6 p. 80 black on blue 40 35
379 6 p. 80 green on pink 45 40

DESIGN: 1 p. 90, Asuncion Cathedral.

104 Declaration of Independence

105

1930. Air. Independence Day.

380 **104** 2 p. 85 blue 40 35
381 3 p. 40 green 35 25
382 4 p. 75 purple 35 25

1930. Red Cross Fund.

383 **105** 1 p. 50 + 50 c. blue 75 70
384 1 p. 50 + 50 c. red 75 70
385 1 p. 50 + 50 c. lilac 75 70

106 Portraits of Archbishop Bogarin

1930. Consecration of Archbishop Bogarin.

386 **106** 1 p. 50 blue 75 60
387 1 p. 50 red 75 60
388 1 p. 50 violet 75 60

1930. Surch **Habilitado en CINCO**.

389 **86** 5 c. on 7 c. green 10 10

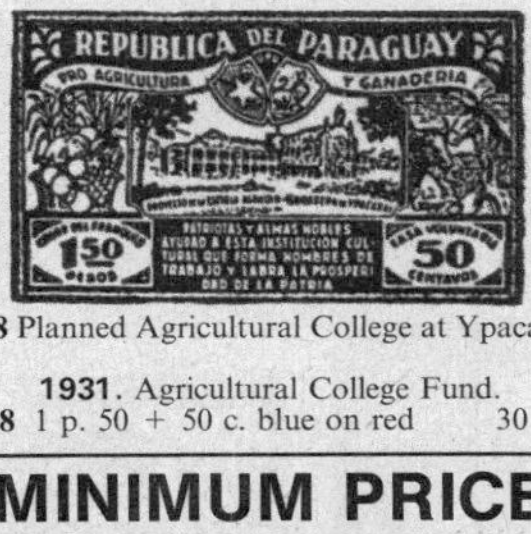

108 Planned Agricultural College at Ypacarai

1931. Agricultural College Fund.

390 **108** 1 p. 50 + 50 c. blue on red 30 30

MINIMUM PRICE

The minimum price quoted is 10p which represents a handling charge rather than a basis for valuing common stamps. For further notes about prices, see introductory pages.

109 Arms of Paraguay

1931. 60th Anniv of First Paraguay Postage Stamps.

391 **109** 10 p. brown 30 25
392 10 p. red on blue 35 25
393 10 p. blue on red 35 25
395 10 p. grey 50 20
396 10 p. blue 20 20

110 Gunboat "Paraguay"

1931. Air. 60th Anniv of Constitution and Arrival of new Gunboats.

397 **110** 1 p. red 20 20
398 1 p. blue 20 20
399 2 p. orange 25 25
400 2 p. brown 25 25
401 3 p. green 50 40
402 3 p. blue 50 45
403 3 p. red 45 40
404 6 p. green 60 60
405 6 p. mauve 75 65
406 6 p. blue 55 50
407 10 p. red 1·60 1·40
408 10 p. green 2·00 1·90
409 10 p. blue 1·10 1·00
410 10 p. brown 1·75 1·60
411 10 p. pink 1·60 1·40

1931. As T **110**.

412 – 1 p. 50 violet 70 35
413 – 1 p. 50 blue 10 10

DESIGN: Gunboat "Humaita".
No. 413 is optd with large **C**.

112 War Memorial

113 Orange Tree and Yerba Mate

114 Yerba Mate

115 Palms

116 Yellow-headed Caracara

1931. Air.

414 **112** 5 c. blue 15 10
415 5 c. green 15 10
416 5 c. red 20 10
417 5 c. purple 15 10
418 **113** 10 c. violet 10 10
419 10 c. red 10 10
420 10 c. brown 10 10
421 10 c. blue 10 10
422 **114** 20 c. red 15 10
423 20 c. blue 20 10
424 20 c. green 20 15
425 20 c. brown 15 10
426 **115** 40 c. green 20 10
426a 40 c. blue 15 10
426b 40 c. red 20 10
427 **116** 80 c. blue 50 15
428 80 c. green 60 20
428a 80 c. red 50 15

1931. Air. Optd with airship "Graf Zeppelin" and **Correo Aereo "Graf Zeppelin"** or surch also.

429 **80** 3 p. on 4 p. blue 4·50 3·75
430 4 p. blue 3·50 3·00

118 Farm Colony

1931. 50th Anniv of Foundation of San Bernardino.

431 **118** 1 p. green 35 20
432 1 p. red 10 10

1931. New Year. Optd **FELIZ ANO NUEVO 1932**.

433 **106** 1 p. 50 blue 60 60
434 1 p. 50 red 60 60

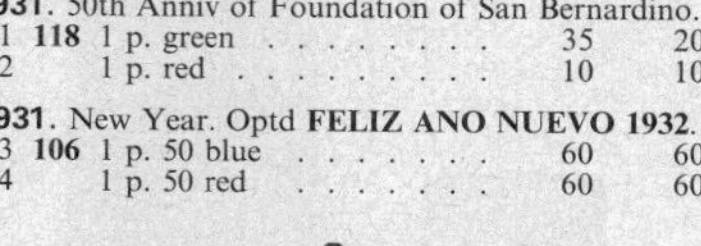

120 "Graf Zeppelin"

1932. Air.

435 **120** 4 p. blue 1·40 1·75
436 8 p. red 2·40 2·00
437 12 p. green 1·90 1·75
438 16 p. purple 3·75 3·00
439 20 p. brown 4·00 3·75

121 Red Cross H.Q

122 (Trans: "Has been, is and will be")

1932. Red Cross Fund.

440 **121** 50 c. + 50 c. pink 25 25

1932. Chaco Boundary Dispute.

441 **122** 1 p. purple 20 10
442 1 p. 50 pink 10 10
443 1 p. 50 brown 10 10
444 1 p. 50 green 10 10
445 1 p. 50 blue 10 10

Nos. 443/5 are optd with a large **C**.

1932. New Year. Surch **CORREOS FELIZ ANO NUEVO 1933** (trans: Happy New Year 1933") and value.

446 **120** 50 c. on 4 p. blue 35 30
447 1 p. on 8 p. red 35 30
448 1 p. 50 on 12 p. green 35 30
449 2 p. on 16 p. purple 35 30
450 5 p. on 20 p. brown 95 75

124 "Graf Zeppelin" over Paraguay

125 "Graf Zeppelin" over Atlantic

1933. Air. "Graf Zeppelin" issue.

451 **124** 4 p. 50 blue 95 75
452 9 p. red 1·90 1·50
453 13 p. 50 green 1·90 1·50
454 **125** 22 p. 50 brown 4·75 3·75
455 45 p. violet 6·75 6·75

126 Columbus's Fleet

1933. 441st Anniv of Departure of Columbus from Palos. Maltese Crosses in violet.

456 **126** 10 c. olive and red 35 15
457 20 c. blue and lake 35 15
458 50 c. red and green 55 30
459 1 p. brown and blue 40 35
460 1 p. 50 green and blue 40 35
461 2 p. green and sepia 1·25 65
462 5 p. lake and olive 2·50 1·25
463 10 p. sepia and blue 2·50 1·25

127 G.P.O., Asuncion

1934. Air.

464 **127** 33 p. 75 blue 1·10 95
468 33 p. 75 red 95 95
466 33 p. 75 green 1·10 95
467 33 p. 75 brown 1·10 95

1934. Air. Optd **1934**.

469 **124** 4 p. 50 blue 1·75 1·75
470 9 p. red 2·25 2·25
471 13 p. 50 green 6·50 6·50
472 **125** 22 p. 50 brown 5·25 5·25
473 45 p. violet 11·00 11·00

1935. Air. Optd **1935**.

474 **124** 4 p. 50 red 2·25 2·25
475 9 p. green 3·25 3·25
476 13 p. 50 brown 9·25 9·25
477 **125** 22 p. 50 purple 8·75 8·75
478 45 p. blue 23·00 23·00

131 Tobacco Plant

1935. Air.

479 **131** 17 p. brown 3·75 3·00
480 17 p. red 6·75 5·00
481 17 p. blue 4·25 3·50
482 17 p. green 2·10 1·75

132 Church of the Incarnation

1935. Air.

483 **132** 102 p. red 2·25 1·75
485 102 p. blue 1·50 1·50
486 102 p. brown 1·50 1·50
487 102 p. violet 75 75
487a 102 p. orange 65 65

1937. Air. Surch **Habilitado en** and value in figures.

488 **127** $24 on 33 p. 75 blue 40 50
489 **132** $65 on 102 p. grey 95 70
490 $84 on 102 p. green 95 60

134 Arms of Asuncion

135 Monstrance

1937. 4th Centenary of Asuncion (1st issue).

491 **134** 50 c. purple and violet 10 10
492 1 p. green and bistre 10 10
493 3 p. blue and red 10 10
494 10 p. yellow and red 15 10
495 20 p. grey and blue 20 20

1937. 1st National Eucharistic Congress.

496 **135** 1 p. red, yellow and blue 10 10
497 3 p. red, yellow and blue 10 10
498 10 p. red, yellow and blue 15 10

136 Oratory of the Virgin of Asuncion

137 Asuncion

1938. 4th Centenary of Asuncion (2nd issue).

499 **136** 5 p. olive 25 10
500 5 p. red 35 10
501 11 p. brown 25 10

1939. Air.

502 **137** 3 p. 40 blue 75 45
503 3 p. 40 green 75 45
504 3 p. 40 brown 75 45

138 J. E. Diaz

1939. Reburial in National Pantheon of Ashes of C. A. Lopez and J. E. Diaz.
505 **138** 2 p. brown and blue . . . 25 15
506 – 2 p. brown and blue . . . 25 15
DESIGN—VERT: No. 506, C. A. Lopez.

139 Pres. Caballero and Senator Decoud

1939. 50th Anniv of Asuncion University.
507 – 50 c. blk & orge (postage) 10 10
508 – 1 p. black and blue . . . 15 10
509 – 2 p. black and red . . . 25 10
510 **139** 5 p. black and blue . . . 35 20

511 28 p. black & red (air) . . 2·50 2·50
512 90 p. black & green . . . 3·00 3·00
DESIGN: Nos. 507/9, Pres. Escobar and Dr. Zubizarreta.

140 Coats of Arms **141** Pres. Baldomir and Flags of Paraguay and Uruguay

1939. Chaco Boundary Peace Conference, Buenos Aires (1st issue).
513 **140** 50 c. blue (postage) . . . 15 10
514 **141** 1 p. olive 15 10
515 A 2 p. green 20 10
516 B 3 p. brown 35 25
517 C 5 p. orange 25 20
518 D 6 p. violet 40 30
519 E 10 p. brown 50 35

520 F 1 p. brown (air) 10 10
521 **140** 3 p. blue 10 10
522 E 5 p. olive 10 15
523 D 10 p. violet 15 15
524 C 30 p. orange 25 15
525 B 50 p. brown 15 25
526 A 100 p. green 25 25
527 **41** 200 p. green . . . . . . 1·50 95
528 – 500 p. black . . . . . . 3·75 3·75
DESIGNS (flag on right is that of country named): A, Benavides (Peru); B, Eagle (USA); C, Alessandri (Chile); D, Vargas (Brazil); E, Ortiz (Argentina); F, Figure of "Peace" (Bolivia); 500 p. (30 × 40 mm), Map of Chaco frontiers.
See also Nos. 536/43.

143 Arms of New York **144** Asuncion–New York Air Route

1939. New York World's Fair.
529 **143** 5 p. red (postage) 20 15
530 10 p. blue 40 30
531 11 p. green 25 45
532 22 p. grey 35 30

533 **144** 30 p. brown (air) . . . . 1·50 1·10
534 80 p. orange . . . . . . 1·75 1·75
535 90 p. violet . . . . . . 3·00 3·00

145 Soldier **147** Waterfall

1940. Chaco Boundary Peace Conference, Buenos Aires (2nd issue). Inscr "PAZ DEL CHACO".
536 **145** 50 c. orange 15 10
537 – 1 p. purple 15 15
538 – 3 p. green 25 20
539 – 5 p. brown 10 25
540 – 10 p. mauve 35 20
541 – 20 p. blue 30 25
542 – 50 p. green 70 35
543 **147** 100 p. black . . . . . 1·50 1·10
DESIGNS: As Type **145**: VERT: 1 p. Water-carrier; 5 p. Ploughing with oxen. HORIZ: 3 p. Cattle Farming. As Type **147**: VERT: 10 p. Fishing in the Paraguay River. HORIZ: 20 p. Bullock-cart; 50 p. Cattle-grazing.

148 Western Hemisphere **149** Reproduction of Paraguay No. 1

1940. 50th Anniv of Pan-American Union.
544 **148** 50 c. orange (postage) . . 10 10
545 1 p. green 10 10
546 5 p. blue 25 10
547 10 p. brown 30 30

548 20 p. red (air) 35 25
549 70 p. blue 35 30
550 100 p. green 40 40
551 500 p. violet . . . . . . 1·75 1·40

1940. Cent of First Adhesive Postage Stamps. Inscr "CENTENARIO DEL SELLO POSTAL 1940".
552 **149** 1 p. purple and green . . 40 35
553 – 5 p. brown and green . . 50 45
554 – 6 p. blue and brown . . 1·10 50
555 – 10 p. black and red . . 1·10 85
DESIGNS: 5 p. Sir Rowland Hill; 6 p., 10 p. Early Paraguayan stamps.

1940. National Mourning for Pres. Estigarribia. Surch **7-IX-40/DUELO NACIONAL/5 PESOS** in black border.
556 **145** 5 p. on 50 c. orange . . . 25 25

152 Dr. Francia **154** Our Lady of Asuncion

1940. Death Centenary of Dr. Francia (dictator).
557 **152** 50 c. red 15 10
558 – 50 c. purple 15 10
559 **152** 1 p. green 15 10
560 – 5 p. blue 15 10
PORTRAIT: Nos. 558 and 560, Dr. Francia seated in library.

1941. Visit of President Vargas of Brazil. Optd **Visita al Paraguay/Agosto de 1941**.
560a 6 p. violet (No. 518) . . . 25 25

1941. Mothers' Fund.
561 **154** 7 p. + 3 p. brown . . . 35 25
562 7 p. + 3 p. violet . . . 35 25
563 7 p. + 3 p. red 35 25
564 7 p. + 3 p. blue 35 25

1942. Nos. 520/2 optd **Habilitado** and bar(s).
565 – 1 p. brown 15 10
566 **140** 3 p. blue 20 10
567 – 5 p. olive 25 10

156 Arms of Paraguay **158** Irala's Vision

1942.
568 **156** 1 p. green 10 10
569 1 p. orange 10 10
570 7 p. blue 10 10
571 7 p. brown 10 10
For other values as Type **156** see Nos. 631, etc.

1942. 4th Centenary of Asuncion.
572 – 2 p. green (postage) . . . 50 40
573 **158** 5 p. red 50 40
574 – 7 p. blue 50 35

575 – 20 p. purple (air) 40 30
576 **158** 70 p. brown . . . . . . 1·10 85
577 – 500 p. olive . . . . . . 3·00 2·75
DESIGNS—VERT: 2 p., 20 p. Indian hailing ships; 7 p., 500 p. Irala's Arms.

160 Columbus sighting America **161** Pres. Morinigo and Symbols of Progress

1943. 450th Anniv of Discovery of America by Columbus.
578 **160** 50 c. violet 25 20
579 1 p. brown 20 10
580 5 p. green 35 20
581 7 p. blue 35 10

1943. Three Year Plan.
582 **161** 7 p. blue 10 10

NOTE: From No. 583 onwards, the currency having been changed, the letter "c" in the value description indicates "centimos" instead of "centavos"

1944. St. Juan Earthquake Fund. Surch **U.P.A.E. Adhesion victimas San Juan y Pueblo Argentino centimos** and bar.
583 – 10 c. on 10 p. brown (No. 519) 40 25

1944. No. 311 surch **Habilitado en un centimo**.
584 1 c. on 3 p. violet 10 10

1944. Surch **1944/5 centimos 5**.
585 **160** 5 c. on 7 p. blue 15 10
586 **161** 5 c. on 7 p. blue 15 10

164 Primitive Indian Postmen **181** Jesuit Relics of Colonial Paraguay

1944.
587 **164** 1 c. black (postage) . . . 10 10
588 – 2 c. brown 15 10
589 – 5 c. olive 20 10
590 – 7 c. blue 15 20
591 – 10 c. green . . . . . . 1·00 45
592 – 15 c. blue 40 25
593 – 50 c. black 35 35
594 – 1 g. red 70 40
DESIGNS—HORIZ: 2 c. Ruins of Humaita Church; 7 c. Marshal Francisco S. Lopez; 1 g. Ytororo Heroes' Monument. VERT: 5 c. First Paraguayan railway locomotive; 10 c. "Tacuary" (paddle-steamer); 15 c. Port of Asuncion; 50 c. Meeting place of Independence conspirators.

595 – 1 c. blue (air) 15 15
596 – 2 c. green 10 10
597 – 3 c. purple 50 20
598 – 5 c. green 20 10
599 – 10 c. violet 20 15
600 – 20 c. brown 15 10
601 – 30 c. blue 25 25
602 – 40 c. olive 15 15
603 – 70 c. red 25 20
604 **181** 1 g. orange 55 40
605 – 2 g. brown 65 55
606 – 5 g. brown . . . . . . 1·50 1·50
607 – 10 g. blue . . . . . . 3·50 3·50
DESIGNS—HORIZ: 1 c. Port of Asuncion; 2 c. First telegraphic apparatus in S. America; 3 c. Paddle-steamer "Tacuary"; 5 c. Meeting Place of Independence Conspirators; 10 c. Antequera Monument; 20 c. First Paraguayan railway locomotive; 40 c. Government House. VERT: 30 c. Ytororo Heroes' Monument; 70 c. As Type **164** but vert: 2 g. Ruins of Humaita Church; 5 g. Oratory of the Virgin; 10 g. Marshal Francisco S. Lopez.
See also Nos. 640/51.

1945. No. 590 surch with figure **5** over ornaments deleting old value.
608 5 c. on 7 c. blue 10 10

186 Clasped Hands and Flags

1945. President Morinigo's Goodwill Visits. Designs of different sizes inscr "CONFRATERNIDAD" between crossed flags of Paraguay and another American country, mentioned in brackets. (a) Postage.
609 **186** 1 c. green (Panama) . . . 10 10
610 3 c. red (Venezuela) . . . 10 10
611 5 c. grey (Ecuador) . . . 10 10
612 2 g. brown (Peru) 85 60

(b) Air.
613 20 c. orange (Colombia) . . 10 30
614 40 c. olive (Bolivia) 10 25
615 70 c. red (Mexico) 10 10
616 1 g. blue (Chile) 25 25
617 2 g. violet (Brazil) 30 30
618 5 g. green (Argentina) . . . 45 45
619 10 g. brown (U.S.A.) . . . 2·25 2·25
The 5 and 10 g. are larger: 32 × 28 and 33½ × 30 mm respectively.

1945. Surch **1945 5 Centimos 5**.
620 **160** 5 c. on 7 p. blue 25 20
621 **161** 5 c. on 7 p. blue 20 20
622 – 5 c. on 7 p. blue (No. 590) 10 20

1945. Surch **1945** and value.
623 **154** 2 c. on 7 p. + 3 p. brown 10 10
624 2 c. on 7 p. + 3 p. violet . 10 10
625 2 c. on 7 p. + 3 p. red . . 10 10
626 2 c. on 7 p. + 3 p. blue . . 10 10
627 5 c. on 7 p. + 3 p. brown 20 10
628 5 c. on 7 p. + 3 p. violet . 20 10
629 5 c. on 7 p. + 3 p. red . . 20 10
630 5 c. on 7 p. + 3 p. blue . . 20 10

1946. As T **156** but inscr "U.P.U." at foot.
631 **156** 5 c. grey 10 10
631a 5 c. pink 10 10
631b 5 c. brown 10 10
686 10 c. blue 10 10
687 10 c. pink 10 10
631c 30 c. green 10 10
631d 30 c. brown 10 10
775 45 c. green 10 10
631e 50 c. mauve 10 10
776 50 c. purple 10 10
858 70 c. brown 10 10
777 90 c. blue 10 10
778 1 g. violet 10 10
860 1 g. 50 mauve 10 10
814 2 g. ochre 10 10
780 2 g. 20 mauve 10 10
781 3 g. brown 10 10
782 4 g. 20 green 10 10
862 4 g. 50 blue 15 10
816 5 g. red 10 10
689 10 g. orange 20 30
784 10 g. green 20 15
818 12 g. 45 green 20 10
819 15 g. orange 25 15
786 20 g. blue 40 30
820 30 g. bistre 20 30
812 50 g. brown 30 25
821 100 g. blue 65 50
See also Nos. 1037/49.

1946. Surch **1946 5 Centimos 5**.
632 **154** 5 c. on 7 p. + 3 p. brown 25 35
633 5 c. on 7 p. + 3 p. violet 25 35
634 5 c. on 7 p. + 3 p. red . 25 35
635 5 c. on 7 p. + 3 p. blue . 25 35

1946. Air. Surch **1946 5 Centimos 5**.
636 5 c. on 20 c. brown (No. 600) 30 30
637 5 c. on 30 c. blue (No. 601) . 30 30
638 5 c. on 40 c. olive (No. 602) . 30 30
639 5 c. on 70 c. red (No. 603) . . 30 30

1946. As Nos. 587/607 but colours changed and some designs smaller.
640 – 1 c. red (postage) 15 15
641 – 2 c. violet 10 10
642 **164** 5 c. blue 10 10
643 – 10 c. orange 10 10
644 – 15 c. olive 15 15
645 **181** 50 c. green 25 30
646 – 1 g. blue 50 30
DESIGNS—VERT: 1 c. Paddle-steamer "Tacuary"; 1 g. Meeting place of Independence Conspirators. HORIZ: 2 c. First telegraphic apparatus in S. America; 10 c. Antequera Monument; 15 c. Ytororo Heroes' Monument.

647 – 10 c. red (air) 10 10
648 – 20 c. green 40 20
649 – 1 g. brown 25 25
650 – 5 g. purple 70 70
651 – 10 g. red . . . . 1·90 1·90
DESIGNS—VERT: 10 c. Ruins of Humaita Church. HORIZ: 20 c. Port of Asuncion; 1 g. Govt. House; 5 g. Marshal Francisco S. Lopez; 10 g. Oratory of the Virgin.

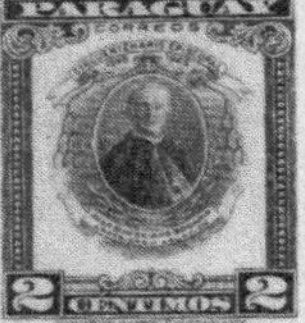

189 Marshal Francisco S. Lopez **190** Archbishop of Paraguay

1947. Various frames.
652 **189** 1 c. violet (postage) . . . 10 10
653 2 c. red 10 10
654 5 c. green 10 10
655 15 c. blue 10 10
656 50 c. green 40 40

657 32 c. red (air) 10 10
658 64 c. brown 25 25
659 1 g. blue 40 40
660 5 g. purple and blue . . . 60 60
661 10 g. green and red . . . 95 95

1947. 50th Anniv of Archbishopric of Paraguay.
662 **190** 2 c. grey (postage) 10 10
663 – 5 c. red 10 10
664 – 10 c. black 10 10
665 – 15 c. green 25 15

666 – 20 c. black (air) 10 10
667 – 30 c. grey 10 10
668 – 40 c. mauve 15 10
669 **190** 70 c. red 25 25
670 – 1 g. lake 30 30
671 – 2 g. red 40 40
672 **190** 5 g. slate and red 70 70
673 – 10 g. brown and green . . 95 95
DESIGNS: 5, 20 c., 10 g. Episcopal Arms; 10, 30, 1 g. Sacred Heart Monument; 15 c., 40 c., 2 g. Vision of projected monument.

194 Torchbearer **195** C. A. Lopez, J. N. Gonzalez and "Paraguari" (freighter)

1948. Honouring the "Barefeet" (political party). Badge in red and blue.

674 194 5 c. red (postage) 10 10
675 15 c. orange 15 10
676 69 c. green (air) 40 40
677 5 g. blue 1·50 1·50

1948. Centenary of Paraguay's Merchant Fleet. Centres in black, red and blue.

678 195 2 c. orange 10 10
679 5 c. blue 15 10
680 10 c. black 20 10
681 15 c. violet 30 10
682 50 c. green 40 20
683 1 g. red 60 25

1949. Air. National Mourning for Archbishop of Paraguay. Surch **DUELO NACIONAL 5 CENTIMOS 5.**

684 190 5 c. on 70 c. red 15 15

1949. Air. Aid to Victims of Ecuadorean Earthquake. No. 667 surch **AYUDA AL ECUADOR 5 + 5** and two crosses.

685 5 c. + 5 c. on 30 c. slate 10 10

198 "Postal Communications"

199 President Roosevelt

1950. Air. 75th Anniv of U.P.U.

691 198 20 c. violet and green 30 30
692 30 c. brown and purple 10 10
693 50 c. green and grey 10 10
694 1 g. brown and blue 10 10
695 5 g. black and red 30 30

1950. Air. Honouring F. D. Roosevelt. Flags in red and blue.

696 199 20 c. orange 10 10
697 30 c. black 10 10
698 50 c. purple 15 10
699 1 g. green 25 25
700 5 g. blue 30 30

1951. 1st Economic Congress of Paraguay. Surch **PRIMER CONGRESO DE ENTIDADES ECONOMICAS DEL PARAGUAY 18-IV-1951** and shield over a block of four stamps.

700a 156 5 c. pink 20 10
700b 10 c. blue 35 25
700c 30 c. green 50 40

Prices are for single stamps. Prices for blocks of four, four times single prices.

200 Columbus Lighthouse

201 Urn

1952. Columbus Memorial Lighthouse.

701 200 2 c. brown (postage) 10 10
702 5 c. blue 10 10
703 10 c. pink 10 10
704 15 c. blue 10 10
705 20 c. purple 10 10
706 50 c. orange 15 10
707 1 g. green 25 25
708 201 10 c. blue (air) 10 10
709 20 c. green 10 10
710 30 c. purple 10 10
711 40 c. pink 10 10
712 50 c. bistre 10 10
713 1 g. blue 15 10
714 2 g. orange 25 20
715 5 g. lake 25 40

202 Isabella the Catholic

203 S. Pettirossi (aviator)

1952. Air. 500th Birth Anniv of Isabella the Catholic.

716 202 1 g. blue 10 10
717 2 g. brown 20 20
718 5 g. green 40 40
719 10 g. purple 40 40

1954. Pettirossi Commemoration.

720 203 5 c. blue (postage) 10 10
721 20 c. red 10 10
722 50 c. purple 10 10
723 60 c. violet 15 10
724 40 c. brown (air) 10 10
725 55 c. green 10 10
726 80 c. blue 10 10
727 1 g. 30 grey 35 35

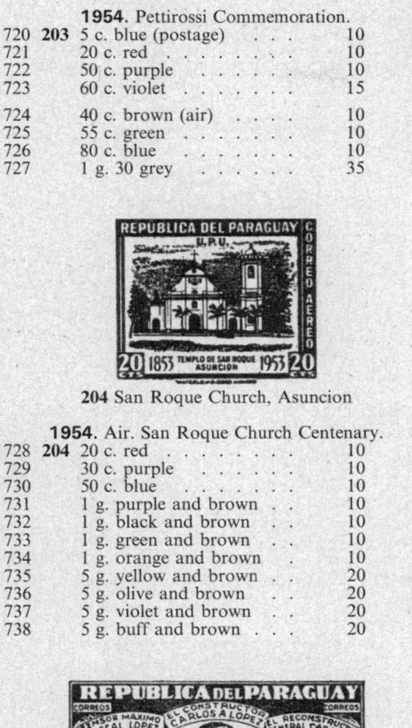
204 San Roque Church, Asuncion

1954. Air. San Roque Church Centenary.

728 204 20 c. red 10 10
729 30 c. purple 10 10
730 50 c. blue 10 10
731 1 g. purple and brown 10 10
732 1 g. black and brown 10 10
733 1 g. green and brown 10 10
734 1 g. orange and brown 10 10
735 5 g. yellow and brown 20 20
736 5 g. olive and brown 20 20
737 5 g. violet and brown 20 20
738 5 g. buff and brown 20 20

205 Marshal Lopez, C. A. Lopez and Gen. Caballero

1954. National Heroes.

739 205 5 c. violet (postage) 10 10
740 20 c. blue 10 10
741 50 c. mauve 10 10
742 1 g. brown 10 10
743 2 g. green 15 10
744 5 g. violet (air) 20 15
745 10 g. olive 35 35
746 20 g. grey 35 30
747 50 g. pink 75 75
748 100 g. blue 2·50 2·50

206 Presidents Stroessner and Peron

1955. Visit of President Peron. Flags in red and blue.

749 206 5 c. brown & buff (postage) 10 10
750 10 c. lake and buff 10 10
751 50 c. grey 10 10
752 1 g. 30 lilac and buff 10 10
753 2 g. 20 blue and buff 20 10
754 60 c. olive and buff (air) 10 10
755 2 g. green 10 10
756 3 g. red 20 10
757 4 g. 10 mauve and buff 30 20

207 Trinidad Campanile

1955. Sacerdotal Silver Jubilee of Mgr. Rodriguez.

758 207 5 c. brown (postage) 10 10
759 – 20 c. brown 10 10
760 – 50 c. brown 10 10
761 – 2 g. 50 green 10 10
762 – 5 g. brown 15 10
763 – 15 g. green 30 20
764 – 25 g. green 35 35
765 207 2 g. blue (air) 10 10
766 – 3 g. green 10 10
767 – 4 g. green 10 10
768 – 6 g. brown 10 10
769 – 10 g. red 20 10
770 – 20 g. brown 30 10
771 – 30 g. green 25 40
772 – 50 g. blue 25 25

DESIGNS—HORIZ: 20 c., 3 g. Cloisters in Trinidad; 5, 10 g. San Cosme Portico; 15, 20 g. Church of Jesus. VERT: 50 c., 4 g. Cornice in Santa Maria; 2 g. 50, 6 g. Santa Rosa Tower; 25, 30 g. Niche in Trinidad; 50 g. Trinidad Sacristy.

208 Angel and Marching Soldiers

209 Soldier and Flags

1957. Chaco Heroes. Inscr "HOMENAJE A LOS HEROES DEL CHACO". Flags in red, white and blue.

787 208 5 c. green (postage) 10 10
788 10 c. red 10 10
789 15 c. blue 10 10
790 20 c. purple 10 10
791 25 c. black 10 10
792 – 30 c. blue 10 10
793 – 40 c. black 10 10
794 – 50 c. lake 10 10
795 – 1 g. turquoise 10 10
796 – 1 g. 30 blue 10 10
797 – 1 g. 50 purple 10 10
798 – 2 g. green 10 10
799 209 10 c. blue (air) 10 10
800 15 c. purple 10 10
801 20 c. red 10 10
802 25 c. blue 10 10
803 50 c. turquoise 10 10
804 1 g. red 10 10
805 – 1 g. 30 purple 10 10
806 – 1 g. 50 blue 10 10
807 – 2 g. green 10 10
808 – 4 g. 10 vermilion and red 10 10
809 – 5 g. black 10 10
810 – 10 g. turquoise 15 15
811 – 25 g. blue 40 15

DESIGNS—HORIZ: Nos. 792/8, Man, woman and flags; Nos. 805/11, "Paraguay" and kneeling soldier.

212 R. Gonzalez and St. Ignatius

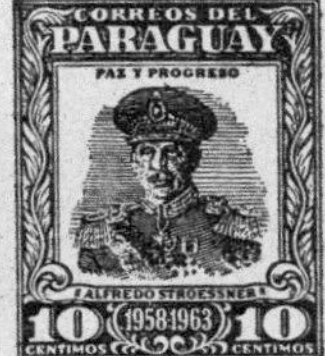
213 President Stroessner

1958. 4th Centenary of St. Ignatius of Loyola.

822 212 50 c. green 10 10
823 – 50 c. brown 10 10
824 – 1 g. 50 violet 10 10
825 – 3 g. blue 10 10
826 212 6 g. 25 red 15 10

DESIGNS—VERT: 50 c. brown; 3 g. Statue of St. Ignatius. HORIZ: 1 g. 50, Jesuit Fathers' house, Antigua.

See also Nos. 1074/81.

1958. Re-election of Pres. Stroessner. Portrait in black.

827 213 10 c. red (postage) 10 10
828 15 c. violet 10 10
829 25 c. green 10 10
830 30 c. lake 10 10
831 50 c. mauve 10 10
832 75 c. blue 10 10
833 5 g. turquoise 10 10
834 10 g. brown 10 15
835 12 g. mauve (air) 40 35
836 18 g. orange 25 40
837 23 g. brown 40 40
838 36 g. green 40 40
839 50 g. olive 50 50
840 65 g. grey 75 75

1959. Nos. 758/72 surch with star enclosed by palm leaves and value.

841 1 g. 50 c. on 5 c. ochre (postage) 10 10
842 1 g. 50 c. on 20 c. brown 10 10
843 1 g. 50 c. on 50 c. purple 10 10
844 3 g. on 2 g. 50 c. olive 10 10
845 6 g. 25 c. on 5 g. brown 10 10
846 20 g. on 15 g. turquoise 35 35
847 30 g. on 25 g. green 50 50
848 4 g. on 2 g. blue (air) 10 10
849 12 g. 45 c. on 3 g. olive 25 20
850 18 g. 15 c. on 6 g. brown 35 30
851 23 g. 40 c. on 10 g. red 25 35
852 34 g. 80 c. on 20 g. bistre 40 50
853 36 g. on 4 g. green 40 30
854 43 g. 95 c. on 30 g. green 50 35
855 100 g. on 50 g. blue 1·10 75

215 U.N. Emblem

216 U.N. Emblem and Map of Paraguay

1959. Air. Visit of U.N. Secretary-General.

856 215 5 g. blue and orange 40 30

1959. Air. U.N. Day.

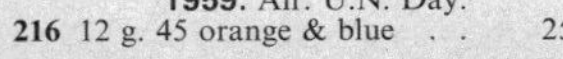
857 216 12 g. 45 orange & blue 25 20

217 Football

218 "Uprooted Tree"

1960. Olympic Games, Rome. Inscr "1960".

863 217 30 c. red & grn (postage) 10 10
864 50 c. purple and blue 10 10
865 75 c. green and orange 10 10
866 1 g. 50 violet and green 10 10
867 – 12 g. 45 blue and red (air) 25 25
868 – 18 g. 15 green and purple 35 35
869 – 36 g. red and green 30 30

DESIGN—AIR: Basketball.

1960. World Refugee Year (1st issue).

870 218 25 c. pink & grn (postage) 10 10
871 50 c. green and red 10 10
872 70 c. brown and mauve 30 25
873 1 g. 50 blue & deep blue 30 30
874 3 g. grey and brown 40 35
875 – 4 g. pink and green (air) 35 50
876 – 12 g. 45 green and blue 70 50
877 – 18 g. 15 orange and red 95 60
878 – 23 g. 40 blue and red 95 1·10

DESIGN—AIR. As Type 218 but with "ANO MUNDIAL" inscr below tree.

See also Nos. 971/7.

219 U.N. Emblem

220 U.N. Emblem and Flags

1960. "Human Rights". Inscr "DERECHOS HUMANOS".

879 219 1 g. red & blue (postage) 10 10
880 – 3 g. orange and blue 10 10
881 – 6 g. orange and green 10 10
882 – 20 g. yellow and red 15 15
883 219 40 g. blue and red (air) 30 30
884 – 60 g. red and green 40 40
885 – 100 g. red and blue 50 50

DESIGNS: 3 g., 60 g. Hand holding scales; 6 g. Hands breaking chain; 20 g., 100 g. "Freedom flame".

1960. U.N. Day. Flags and inscr in blue and red.

886 220 30 c. blue (postage) 10 10
887 75 c. yellow 10 10
888 90 c. mauve 10 10
889 3 g. orange (air) 10 10
890 4 g. green 10 10

221 Bridge with Arms of Brazil and Paraguay

222 Timber Truck

1961. Inauguration of International Bridge between Brazil and Paraguay.

891 221 15 c. green (postage) 10 10
892 30 c. blue 10 10
893 50 c. orange 10 10
894 75 c. blue 10 10
895 1 g. violet 10 10
896 – 3 g. red (air) 15 10
897 – 12 g. 45 lake 30 25
898 – 18 g. 15 green 35 30
899 – 36 g. blue 30 25

DESIGN—HORIZ: Nos. 896/9, Aerial view of bridge.

1961. Paraguayan Progress. Inscr "PARAGUAY EN MARCHA".

900 222 25 c. red & grn (postage) 10 10
901 – 90 c. yellow and blue 10 10
902 – 1 g. red and orange 10 10
903 – 2 g. green and pink 10 10
904 – 5 g. violet and green 15 10
905 222 12 g. 45 blue and buff (air) 40 25
906 – 18 g. 15 violet and buff 55 35
907 – 22 g. blue and orange 30 40
908 – 36 g. yellow, green & blue 60 50

DESIGNS: 90 c., 2 g., 18 g. 15, Motorised timber barge; 1, 5, 22 g. Radio mast; 36 g. Boeing 707 jetliner.

223 P. J. Caballero, J. G. R. de Francia and F. Yegros

224 "Chaco Peace"

1961. 150th Anniv of Independence. (a) 1st issue.
909 **223** 30 c. green (postage) . . . 10 10
910 50 c. mauve 10 10
911 90 c. violet 10 10
912 1 g. 50 blue 10 10
913 3 g. bistre 10 10
914 4 g. blue 10 10
915 5 g. brown 10 10

916 – 12 g. 45 red (air) 20 15
917 – 18 g. 15 blue 30 25
918 – 23 g. 40 green 40 30
919 – 30 g. violet 45 35
920 – 36 g. red 30 50
921 – 44 g. brown 40 35
DESIGN: Nos. 916/21, Declaration of Independence.

(b) 2nd issue. Inscr "PAZ DEL CHACO".
922 **224** 25 c. red (postage) 10 10
923 30 c. green 10 10
924 50 c. brown 10 10
925 1 g. violet 10 10
926 2 g. blue 10 10

927 – 3 g. blue (air) 20 15
928 – 4 g. purple 20 20
929 – 100 g. green 70 60
DESIGN: Nos. 927/9, Clasped hands.

225 Puma

226 Arms of Paraguay

(c) 3rd issue.
930 **225** 75 c. violet (postage) . . . 10 10
931 1 g. 50 brown 10 10
932 4 g. 50 green 15 10
933 10 g. blue 25 20

934 – 12 g. 45 purple (air) . . . 50 40
935 – 18 g. 15 blue 50 50
936 – 34 g. 80 brown 95 95
DESIGN: Nos. 934/6, Brazilian tapir.

(d) 4th issue.
937 **226** 15 c. blue (postage) . . . 10 10
938 25 c. red 10 10
939 75 c. green 10 10
940 1 g. red 10 10

941 3 g. brown (air) 10 10
942 12 g. 45 mauve 25 25
943 36 g. turquoise 30 30
The air stamps have a background pattern of horiz lines.

227 Grand Hotel, Guarani

228 Racquet, Net and Balls

(e) 5th issue.
944 **227** 50 c. grey (postage) . . . 10 10
945 1 g. green 10 10
946 4 g. 50 violet 10 10

947 – 3 g. brown (air) 10 10
948 – 4 g. blue 10 10
949 – 18 g. 15 orange 40 35
950 – 36 g. red 30 50
The air stamps are similar to Type **227** but inscr "HOTEL GUARANI" in upper left corner.
See also Nos. 978/85 and 997/1011.

1961. 28th South American Tennis Championships. Asuncion (1st issue). Centres multicoloured; border colours given.
951 **228** 35 c. pink (postage) . . . 10 10
952 75 c. yellow 10 10
953 1 g. 50 blue 10 10
954 2 g. 25 turquoise 10 10
955 4 g. grey 15 10

956 12 g. 45 orange (air) . . . 40 40
957 20 g. orange 35 70
958 50 g. orange . . . . . . 75 1·75
See also Nos. 978/85.

HAVE YOU READ THE NOTES AT THE BEGINNING OF THIS CATALOGUE?
These often provide the answers to the enquiries we receive.

229

1961. "Europa".
959 **229** 50 c. red, blue and mauve 10 10
960 75 c. red, blue and green 10 10
961 1 g. red, blue and brown 10 10
962 1 g. 50 red, blue & lt blue 10 10
963 4 g. 50 red, blue & yellow 20 20

230 Comm. Alan Shepard and Solar System

231

1961. Commander Shepard's Space Flight.
964 – 10 c. brn & blue (postage) 10 10
965 – 25 c. mauve and blue . . 10 10
966 – 50 c. orange and blue . . 10 10
967 – 75 c. green and blue . . . 10 10

968 **230** 18 g. 15 blue & green (air) 4·50 3·25
969 36 g. blue and orange . . 4·50 3·25
970 50 g. blue and mauve . . 7·00 3·50
DESIGN—HORIZ: Nos. 964/7, Comm. Shepard.

1961. World Refugee Year (2nd issue).
971 **231** 10 c. deep blue and blue (postage) 10 10
972 25 c. purple and orange . 10 10
973 50 c. mauve and pink . . 10 10
974 75 c. blue and green . . . 10 10

975 – 18 g. 15 red and brown (air) 25 25
976 – 36 g. green and red . . . 55 55
977 – 50 g. orange and green . . 70 70
Nos. 975/7 have a different background and frame.

232 Tennis-player

233 Scout Bugler

1962. 150th Anniv of Independence (6th issue) and 28th South American Tennis Championships, Asuncion (2nd issue).
978 **232** 35 c. blue (postage) . . . 10 10
979 75 c. violet 10 10
980 1 g. 50 brown 10 10
981 2 g. 25 green 10 10

982 – 4 g. red (air) 10 10
983 – 12 g. 45 purple 30 30
984 – 20 g. turquoise 25 25
985 – 50 g. brown 40 40
Nos. 982/5 show tennis-player using backhand stroke.

1962. Boy Scouts Commemoration.
986 **233** 10 c. grn & pur (postage) 10 10
987 20 c. green and red . . . 10 10
988 25 c. green and brown . . 10 10
989 30 c. green and emerald . 10 10
990 50 c. green and blue . . 10 10

991 – 12 g. 45 mauve & bl (air) 20 40
992 – 36 g. mauve and green 60 90
993 – 50 g. mauve and yellow 75 90
DESIGN: Nos. 991/3, Lord Baden-Powell.

234 Pres. Stroessner and the Duke of Edinburgh

235 Map of the Americas

1962. Air. Visit of Duke of Edinburgh.
994 **234** 12 g. 45 blue, buff & grn 20 15
995 18 g. 15 blue, pink & red 30 25
996 36 g. blue, yellow & brn . 25 45

1962. 150th Anniv of Independence (7th issue) and Day of the Americas.
997 **235** 50 c. orange (postage) . . 10 10
998 75 c. blue 10 10
999 1 g. violet 10 10
1000 1 g. 50 green 10 10
1001 4 g. 50 red 10 10

1002 – 20 g. mauve (air) 30 20
1003 – 50 g. orange 30 50
DESIGN: 20 g., 50 g. Hands supporting Globe.

236 U.N. Emblem

1962. 150th Anniv of Independence (8th issue).
1004 **236** 50 c. brown (postage) . . 10 10
1005 75 c. purple 10 10
1006 1 g. blue 10 10
1007 2 g. brown 10 10

1008 – 12 g. 45 violet (air) . . . 35 35
1009 – 18 g. 15 green 25 25
1010 – 23 g. 40 red 35 35
1011 – 30 g. red 40 40
DESIGN: Nos. 1008/11, U.N. Headquarters, New York.

237 Mosquito and W.H.O. Emblem

1962. Malaria Eradication.
1012 **237** 30 c. black, blue and pink (postage) 10 10
1013 50 c. black, grn & bistre . 10 10
1014 – 75 c. black, bistre & red . 10 10
1015 – 1 g. black, bistre & grn . 10 10
1016 – 1 g. 50 black, bis & brn . 10 10

1017 **237** 3 g. black, red & bl (air) . 10 10
1018 4 g. black, red & green . 10 10
1019 – 12 g. 45 black, green & brown 25 10
1020 – 18 g. 15 black, red and purple 50 15
1021 – 36 g. black, blue & red . 75 85
DESIGN: Nos. 1014/16, 1019/21, Mosquito on U.N. emblem, and microscope.

238 Football Stadium

239 "Lago Ypoa" (freighter)

1962. World Football Championships, Chile.
1022 **238** 15 c. brn & yell (postage) 10 10
1023 25 c. brown and green . . 10 10
1024 30 c. brown and violet . . 10 10
1025 40 c. brown & orange . . 10 10
1026 50 c. brown and green . . 10 10

1027 – 12 g. 45 black, red and violet (air) 50 25
1028 – 18 g. 15 black, brn & vio 40 45
1029 – 36 g. black, grey & brn . 85 80
DESIGN—HORIZ: Nos. 1027/9, Footballers and Globe.

1962. Paraguayan Merchant Marine Commemoration.
1030 **239** 30 c. brown (postage) . . 10 10
1031 – 90 c. blue 10 10
1032 – 1 g. 50 purple 15 10
1033 – 2 g. green 25 15
1034 – 4 g. 20 blue 35 20

1035 – 12 g. 45 red (air) 30 15
1036 – 44 g. blue 30 45
DESIGNS—HORIZ: 90 c. Freighter; 1 g. 50, "Olympo" (freighter); 2 g. Freighter (diff); 4 g. 20, "Rio Apa" (freighter). VERT: 12 g. 45, 44 g. Ship's wheel.

1962. As Nos. 631, etc., but with taller figures of value.
1037 **156** 50 c. blue 10 10
1038 70 c. lilac 10 10
1039 1 g. 50 violet 10 10
1040 3 g. blue 10 10
1041 4 g. 50 brown 10 10
1042 5 g. mauve 10 10
1043 10 g. mauve 20 10
1044 12 g. 45 blue 20 10
1045 15 g. 45 red 25 10
1046 18 g. 15 purple 10 15
1047 20 g. brown 10 15
1048 50 g. brown 25 30
1049 100 g. grey 55 30

241 Gen. A. Stroessner

242 Popes Paul VI, John XXIII and St. Peter's

1963. Re-election of Pres. Stroessner to Third Term of Office.
1050 **241** 50 c. brn & drab (postage) 10 10
1051 75 c. brown & pink . . . 10 10
1052 1 g. 50 brown & mve . . 10 10
1053 3 g. brown and green . . 10 10

1054 12 g. 45 red and pink (air) 25 20
1055 18 g. 15 green and pink . 35 30
1056 36 g. violet and pink . . 60 40

1964. Popes Paul VI and John XXIII.
1057 **242** 1 g. 50 yell & red (postage) 10 10
1058 3 g. green and red . . . 10 10
1059 4 g. brown and red . . . 10 10

1060 – 12 g. 45 olive & grn (air) 35 20
1061 – 18 g. 15 green & violet . 20 30
1062 – 36 g. green and blue . . 75 60
DESIGNS: Nos. 1060/2, Cathedral, Asuncion.

243 Arms of Paraguay and France

245 Map of the Americas

1964. Visit of French President.
1063 **243** 1 g. 50 brown (postage) . 10 10
1064 – 3 g. blue 10 10
1065 **243** 4 g. grey 10 10

1066 – 12 g. 45 violet (air) . . . 25 20
1067 **243** 18 g. 15 green 40 30
1068 – 36 g. red 75 60
DESIGNS: 3, 12 g. 45, 36 g. Presidents Stroessner and De Gaulle.

1965. 6th Reunion of the Board of Governors of the Inter-American Development Bank. Optd **Centenario de la Epopeya Nacional 1,864-1,870** as in T **245**.
1069 **245** 1 g. 50 green (postage) . 10 10
1070 3 g. pink 10 10
1071 4 g. blue 10 10

1072 12 g. 45 brown (air) . . 20 10
1073 36 g. violet 40 45
The overprint refers to the National Epic of 1864-70, the war with Argentina, Brazil and Uruguay and this inscription occurs on many other issues from 1965 onwards. Nos. 1069/73 without the overprint were not authorised.

246 R. Gonzalez and St. Ignatius

247 Ruben Dario

1966. 350th Anniv of Founding of San Ignacio Guazu Monastery.
1074 **246** 15 c. blue (postage) . . . 10 10
1075 25 c. blue 10 10
1076 75 c. blue 10 10
1077 90 c. blue 10 10

1078 – 3 g. brown (air) 10 10
1079 – 12 g. 45, brown 10 10
1080 – 18 g. 15, brown 20 10
1081 – 23 g. 40 brown 35 25
DESIGNS: Nos. 1078/81, Jesuit Fathers' house, Antigua.
For similar stamps with different inscriptions, see Nos. 822, 824 and 826.

1966. 50th Death Anniv of Ruben Dario (poet).
1082 **247** 50 c. blue 10 10
1083 70 c. brown 10 10
1084 1 g. 50 lake 10 10
1085 3 g. violet 10 10
1086 4 g. turquoise 10 10
1087 5 g. black 10 10

1088 – 12 g. 45 blue (air) . . . 10 10
1089 – 18 g. 15 violet 10 10
1090 – 23 g. 40 brown 35 10
1091 – 36 g. green 50 25
1092 – 50 g. red 30 25
DESIGNS: Nos. 1088/92, Open book inscr "Paraguay de Fuego ..." by Dario.

248 Lions' Emblem on Globe — **249** W.H.O. Emblem

1967. 50th Anniv of Lions International.

1093	**248**	50 c. violet (postage)	10	10
1094		70 c. blue	10	10
1095	–	1 g. 50 blue	10	10
1096	–	3 g. brown	10	10
1097	–	4 g. blue	10	10
1098	–	5 g. brown	10	10
1099	–	12 g. 45 brown (air)	10	10
1100	–	18 g. 15 violet	15	10
1101	–	23 g. 40 purple	20	10
1102	–	36 g. blue	25	25
1103	–	50 g. red	25	25

DESIGNS—VERT: 1 g. 50, 3 g. M. Jones; 4, 5 g. Lions headquarters, Chicago. HORIZ: 12 g. 45, 18 g. 15, Library–"Education"; 23 g. 40, 36 g., 50 g. Medical laboratory–"Health".

1968. 20th Anniv of W.H.O.

1104	**249**	3 g. turquoise (postage)	10	10
1105		4 g. purple	10	10
1106		5 g. brown	10	10
1107		10 g. violet	10	10
1108	–	36 g. brown (air)	40	25
1109	–	50 g. red	45	30
1110	–	100 g. blue	60	35

DESIGN—VERT: Nos. 1108/10, W.H.O. emblem on scroll.

250 — **251**

1969. World Friendship Week.

1111	**250**	50 c. red	10	10
1112		70 c. blue	10	10
1113		1 g. 50 brown	10	10
1114		3 g. mauve	10	10
1115		4 g. green	10	10
1116		5 g. violet	10	10
1117		10 g. purple	20	10

1969. Air. Campaign for Houses for Teachers.

1118	**251**	36 g. blue	40	45
1119		50 g. brown	50	70
1120		100 g. red	95	1·00

252 Pres. Lopez — **253** Paraguay 2 r. Stamp of 1870

1970. Death Centenary of Pres. F. Solano Lopez.

1121	**252**	1 g. brown (postage)	10	10
1122		2 g. violet	10	10
1123		3 g. pink	10	10
1124		4 g. red	10	10
1125		5 g. blue	10	10
1126		10 g. green	10	10
1127		15 g. blue (air)	10	10
1128		20 g. brown	20	10
1129		30 g. green	30	20
1130		40 g. purple	35	25

1970. Centenary of First Paraguayan Stamps.

1131	**253**	1 g. red (postage)	10	10
1132	A	2 g. blue	10	10
1133	B	3 g. brown	10	10
1134	**253**	5 g. violet	10	10
1135	A	10 g. lilac	20	10
1136	B	15 g. purple (air)	30	25
1137	**253**	30 g. green	35	50
1138	A	36 g. red	40	30

DESIGNS: First Paraguay stamps. A, 1 r. B, 3 r.

254 Teacher and Pupil — **255** U.N.I.C.E.F. Emblem

1971. Int Education Year–U.N.E.S.C.O.

1139	**254**	3 g. blue (postage)	10	10
1140		5 g. lilac	10	10
1141		10 g. green	10	10
1142		20 g. red (air)	20	10
1143		25 g. mauve	25	15
1144		30 g. brown	25	20
1145		50 g. green	40	35

1972. 25th Anniv of U.N.I.C.E.F.

1146	**255**	1 g. brown (postage)	10	10
1147		2 g. blue	10	10
1148		3 g. red	10	10
1149		4 g. purple	10	10
1150		5 g. green	10	10
1151		10 g. purple	10	10
1152		20 g. blue (air)	20	10
1153		25 g. green	25	15
1154		30 g. brown	25	20

256 Acaray Dam

1972. Tourist Year of the Americas.

1155	**256**	1 g. brown (postage)	10	10
1156	–	2 g. brown	10	10
1157	–	3 g. blue	10	10
1158	–	5 g. red	10	10
1159	–	10 g. green	10	10
1160	–	20 g. red (air)	25	10
1161	–	25 g. grey	30	15
1162	–	50 g. lilac	1·00	45
1163	–	100 g. mauve	55	40

DESIGNS: 2 g. Statue of Lopez; 3 g. Friendship Bridge; 5 g. Rio Tebicuary Bridge; 10 g. Grand Hotel, Guarani; 20 g. Motor coach; 25 g. Social Service Institute Hospital; 50 g. Liner "Presidente Stroessner"; 100 g. Lockheed Electra airliner.

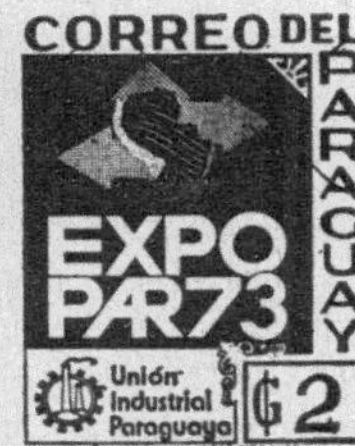

257 O.E.A. Emblem — **258** Exhibition Emblem

1973. 25th Anniv of Organization of American States (O.E.A.).

1164	**257**	1 g. mult. (postage)	10	10
1165		2 g. multicoloured	10	10
1166		3 g. multicoloured	10	10
1167		4 g. multicoloured	10	10
1168		5 g. multicoloured	10	10
1169		10 g. multicoloured	10	10
1170		20 g. multicoloured (air)	20	10
1171		25 g. multicoloured	30	15
1172		50 g. multicoloured	25	35
1173		100 g. multicoloured	55	40

1973. Int Industrial Exhibition, Paraguay.

1174	**258**	1 g. brown (postage)	10	10
1175		2 g. red	10	10
1176		3 g. blue	10	10
1177		4 g. green	10	10
1178		5 g. lilac	10	10
1179		20 g. mauve (air)	20	10
1180		25 g. red	25	10

259 Carrier Pigeon with Letter

1975. Centenary of U.P.U.

1181	**259**	1 g. vio & blk (postage)	10	10
1182		2 g. red and black	10	10
1183		3 g. blue and black	10	10
1184		5 g. blue and black	10	10
1185		10 g. purple and black	10	10
1186		20 g. brown & blk (air)	25	15
1187		25 g. green and black	30	20

260 Institute Buildings

1976. Inauguration (1974) of Institute of Higher Education.

1188	**260**	5 g. violet, red and black (postage)	10	10
1189		10 g. blue, red & black	10	10
1190		30 g. brn, red & blk (air)	25	15

261 Rotary Emblem

1976. 70th Anniv of Rotary International.

1191	**261**	3 g. blue, bistre and black (postage)	10	10
1192		4 g. blue, bistre and mauve	10	10
1193		25 g. blue, bistre and green (air)	30	15

262 Woman and I.W.Y. Emblem

1976. International Women's Year.

1194	**262**	1 g. brown & bl (postage)	10	10
1195		2 g. brown and red	10	10
1196		20 g. brown & green (air)	25	10

263 Black Palms

1977. Flowering Plants and Trees. Multicoloured.

1197	2 g. Type **263** (postage)	10	10
1198	3 g. Mburucuya flowers	10	10
1199	20 g. Marsh rose (tree) (air)	35	25

264 Nanduti Lace — **265** F. S. Lopez

1977. Multicoloured.

1200	1 g. Type **264** (postage)	10	10
1201	5 g. Nanduti weaver	10	10
1202	25 g. Lady holding jar (air)	40	25

1977. 150th Birth Anniv of Marshal Francisco Solano Lopez.

1203	**265**	10 g. brown (postage)	10	10
1204		50 g. blue (air)	40	50
1205		100 g. green	75	60

266 General Bernardino Caballero National College

1978. Cent of National College of Asuncion.

1206	**266**	3 g. red (postage)	10	10
1207		4 g. blue	10	10
1208		5 g. violet	10	10
1209		20 g. brown (air)	20	15
1210		25 g. purple	25	20
1211		30 g. green	35	25

267 Marshal Jose F. Estigarribia, Trumpeter and Flag — **268** Congress Emblem

1978. "Salon de Bronce" Commemoration.

1212	**267**	3 g. purple, blue and red (postage)	10	10
1213		5 g. violet, blue and red	10	10
1214		10 g. grey, blue and red	10	10
1215		20 g. green, bl & red (air)	25	15
1216		25 g. violet, blue and red	30	20
1217		30 g. purple, blue & red	35	25

1979. 22nd Latin American Tourism Congress, Asuncion.

1218	**268**	10 g. black, blue and red (postage)	10	10
1219		50 g. black, blue and red (air)	30	40

269 Spanish Colonial House, Pilar

1980. Bicentenary of Pilar City.

1220	**269**	5 g. mult (postage)	10	10
1221		25 g. multicoloured (air)	30	20

270 Boeing 707

1980. Inauguration of Paraguayan Airlines Boeing 707 Service.

1222	**270**	20 g. mult (postage)	30	10
1223		100 g. multicoloured (air)	1·40	70

271 Seminary, Communion Cup and Bible

1981. Air. Centenary of Metropolitan Seminary, Asuncion.

1224	**271**	5 g. blue	10	10
1225		10 g. brown	10	10
1226		25 g. green	30	20
1227		50 g. black	30	40

272 U.P.U. Monument, Berne

1981. Centenary of Admission to U.P.U.

1228	**272**	5 g. red and black (postage)	10	10
1229		10 g. mauve and black	10	10
1230		20 g. green and black (air)	25	15
1231		25 g. red and black	30	20
1232		50 g. blue and black	30	40

273 St. Maria Mazzarello **275** Sun and Map of Americas

274 Stroessner and Bridge over River Itaipua

1981. Air. Death Centenary of Mother Maria Mazzarello (founder of Daughters of Mary).

1233	**273**	20 g. green and black	25	15
1234		25 g. red and black	30	20
1235		50 g. violet and black	30	40

1983. 25th Anniv of President Stroessner City.

1236	**274**	3 g. grn, bl & blk (postage)	10	10
1237		5 g. red, blue and black	10	10
1238		10 g. violet, blue & blk	10	10
1239		20 g. grey, blue & blk (air)	25	15
1240		25 g. purple, blue & blk	30	20
1241		50 g. blue, grey & black	30	40

1985. Air. 25th Anniv of Inter-American Development Bank.

1242	**275**	3 g. orange, yell & pink	10	10
1243		5 g. orange, yell & mauve	10	10
1244		10 g. orange, yell & mauve	10	10
1245		50 g. orange, yell & brown	10	10
1246		65 g. orange, yellow & bl	15	10
1247		95 g. orange, yell & green	20	15

276 U.N. Emblem **277** 1886 1 c. Stamp

1986. Air. 40th Anniv of U.N.O.

1248	**276**	5 g. blue and brown	10	10
1249		10 g. blue and grey	10	10
1250		50 g. blue and black	10	10

1986. Centenary of First Official Stamp.

1251	**277**	5 g. deep blue, brown and blue (postage)	10	10
1252		15 g. deep blue, brown and blue	10	10
1253		40 g. deep blue, brown and blue	10	10
1254	–	65 g. blue, green and red (air)	15	15
1255	–	100 g. blue, green and red	25	25
1256	–	150 g. blue, green and red	40	40

DESIGNS: 65, 100, 150 g. 1886 7 c. stamp.

278 Integration of the Nations Monument, Colmena

1986. Air. 50th Anniv of Japanese Immigration. Multicoloured.

1257	5 g. La Colmena vineyards (horiz)	10	10
1258	10 g. Flowers of cherry tree and lapacho (horiz)	10	10
1259	20 g. Type **278**	10	10

279 Caballero, Stroessner and Road

1987. Centenary of National Republican Association (Colorado Party).

1260	**279**	5 g. multicoloured (postage)	10	10
1261		10 g. multicoloured	10	10
1262		25 g. multicoloured	10	10
1263	–	150 g. multicoloured (air)	25	40
1264	–	170 g. multicoloured	30	20
1265	–	200 g. multicoloured	35	25

DESIGN: 150 to 200 g. Gen. Bernardino Caballero (President 1881–86 and founder of party), Pres. Alfredo Stroessner and electrification of countryside.

280 Emblem of Visit **281** Silver Mate

1988. Visit of Pope John Paul II.

1266	**280**	10 g. blue and black (postage)	10	10
1267		20 g. blue and black	10	10
1268		50 g. blue and black	15	10
1269	–	100 g. multicoloured (air)	30	20
1270	–	120 g. multicoloured	35	25
1271	–	150 g. multicoloured	45	35

DESIGN—HORIZ: 100 to 150 g. Pope and Caacupe Basilica.

1988. Air. Centenary of New Germany Colony. Multicoloured.

1272	90 g. Type **281**	25	10
1273	105 g. Mate ("Ilex paraguayensis") plantation	30	20
1274	120 g. As No. 1273	35	25

1988. Air. 75th Anniv of Paraguay Philatelic Centre. No. 1249 optd ***75o ANIVERSARIO DE FUNDACION CENTRO FILATELICO DEL PARAGUAY 15 JUNIO-1913 – 1988.**

1275	**276**	10 g. blue and grey	10	10

283 Pres. Stroessner and Government Palace

1988. Air. Re-election of President Stroessner.

1276	**283**	200 g. multicoloured	30	25
1277		500 g. multicoloured	75	90
1278		1000 g. multicoloured	1·50	1·50

1989. "Parafil 89" Stamp Exhibition. Nos. 1268 and 1270 optd **PARAFIL 89.**

1279	**280**	50 g. blue and black (postage)	15	10
1280	–	120 g. multicoloured (air)	35	25

285 Green-winged Macaw

1989. Birds. Multicoloured.

1281	50 g. Type **285** (postage)	15	10
1282	100 g. Brazilian merganser (horiz) (air)	15	10
1283	300 g. Greater rhea (horiz)	45	20
1284	500 g. Toco toucan (horiz)	70	45
1285	1000 g. Bare-faced curassow (horiz)	1·40	1·00
1286	2000 g. Caninde macaw and blue and yellow macaw	2·75	1·90

286 Anniversary Emblem

1990. Centenary of Organization of American States. Multicoloured.

1287	50 g. Type **286**	10	10
1288	100 g. Organization and anniversary emblems (vert)	10	10
1289	200 g. Map of Paraguay	45	15

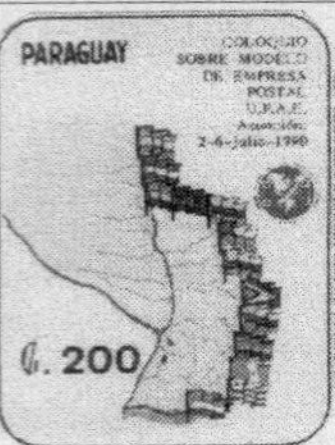

287 Basket **288** Flags on Map

1990. America. Pre-Columbian Life. Mult.

1290	150 g. Type **287** (postage)	15	10
1291	500 g. Guarani post (air)	1·10	95

1990. Postal Union of the Americas and Spain Colloquium. Multicoloured.

1292	200 g. Type **288**	20	15
1293	250 g. First Paraguay stamp	25	15
1294	350 g. Paraguay 1990 America first day cover (horiz)	35	25

289 Planned Building

1990. Centenary of National University. Mult.

1295	300 g. Type **289**	70	55
1296	400 g. Present building	95	75
1297	600 g. Old building	1·40	1·10

290 Guarambare Church

1990. Franciscan Churches. Multicoloured.

1298	50 g. Type **290**	10	10
1299	100 g. Yaguaron Church	25	20
1300	200 g. Ita Church	45	35

1991. Visit of King and Queen of Spain. Nos. 1290/1 optd **Vista de sus Majestades Los Reyes de Espana 22-24 Octubre 1990.**

1301	**287**	150 g. mult (postage)	15	10
1302	–	500 g. multicoloured (air)	1·10	95

292 "Human Rights" (Hugo Pistilli)

1991. 40th Anniv of United Nations Development Programme. Multicoloured.

1303	50 g. Type **292**	10	10
1304	100 g. "United Nations" (sculpture, Hermann Guggiari)	10	20
1305	150 f. First Miguel de Cervantes prize, awarded to Augusto Roa Bastos, 1989	15	10

294 Hands and Ballot Box (free elections)

1991. Democracy. Multicoloured.

1308	50 g. Type **294** (postage)	10	10
1309	100 g. Sun (State and Catholic Church) (vert)	10	10
1310	200 g. Arrows and male and female symbols (human rights) (vert)	15	10
1311	300 g. Dove and flag (freedom of the press) (vert) (air)	25	20
1312	500 g. Woman and child welcoming man (return of exiles)	35	25
1313	3000 g. Crowd with banners (democracy)	2·25	1·75

295 Julio Manuel Morales (gynaecologist)

1991. Medical Professors.

1314	**295**	50 g. mult (postage)	10	10
1315	–	100 g. multicoloured	10	10
1316	–	200 g. multicoloured	15	10
1317	–	300 g. brown, blk & grn	25	20
1318	–	350 g. brown, black and green (air)	25	20
1319	–	500 g. multicoloured	35	25

DESIGNS: 100 g. Carlos Gatti (surgeon); 200 g. Gustavo Gonzalez (symptomatologist); 300 g. Juan Max Boettner (physician and musician); 350 g. Juan Boggino (pathologist); 500 g. Andres Barbero (founder of Paraguayan Red Cross).

1991. "Espamer '91" Spain-Latin America Stamp Exhibition, Buenos Aires. Nos. 1298/1300 optd **ESPAMER 91 BUENOS AIRES 5 14 Jul** and Conquistador in oval.

1323	50 g. multicoloured	10	10
1324	100 g. multicoloured	10	10
1325	200 g. multicoloured	15	10

298 Ruy Diaz de Guzman (historian)

1991. Writers and Musicians. Multicoloured.

1326	50 g. Type **298** (postage)	10	10
1327	100 g. Maria Talavera (war chronicler) (vert)	10	10
1328	150 g. Augusto Roa Bastos (writer and 1989 winner of Miguel de Cervantes Prize) (vert)	10	10
1329	200 g. Jose Asuncion Flores (composer of "La Guarania") (vert) (air)	15	10
1330	250 g. Felix Perez Cardozo (harpist and composer)	20	15
1331	300 g. Juan Carlos Moreno Gonzalez (composer)	25	20

299 Battle of Tavare **300** "Compass of Life" (Alfredo Moraes)

1991. America. Voyages of Discovery. Mult.

1332	100 g. Type **299** (postage)	10	10
1333	300 g. Arrival of Domingo Martinez de Irala in Paraguay (air)	25	20

1991. Paintings. Multicoloured.

1334	50 g. Type **300** (postage)	10	10
1335	100 g. "Callejon Illuminated" (Michael Burt)	10	10
1336	150 g. "Arete" (Lucy Yegros)	10	10
1337	200 g. "Itinerants" (Hugo Bogado Barrios) (air)	15	10
1338	250 g. "Travellers without a Ship" (Bernardo Ismachoviez)	20	15
1339	300 g. "Guarani" (Lotte Schulz)	25	20

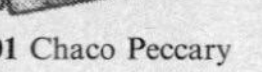

301 Chaco Peccary **302** Geometric Design, Franciscan Church, Caazapa

1992. Endangered Mammals. Multicoloured.
1340 50 g. Type **301** 10 10
1341 100 g. Ocelot (horiz) 10 10
1342 150 g. Brazilian tapir 10 10
1343 200 g. Maned wolf 15 10

1992. 500th Anniv of Discovery of America by Columbus (1st series). Church Roof Tiles. Mult.
1344 50 g. Type **302** 10 10
1345 100 g. Church, Jesuit church, Trinidad 10 10
1346 150 g. Missionary ship, Jesuit church, Trinidad 10 10
1347 200 g. Plant, Franciscan church, Caazapa 15 10
See also Nos. 1367/71.

1992. "Granada '92" International Thematic Stamp Exhibition. Nos. 1344/7 optd **GRANADA '92** and emblem.
1348 50 g. multicoloured 10 10
1349 100 g. multicoloured 10 10
1350 150 g. multicoloured 10 10
1351 200 g. multicoloured 10 10

304 Malcolm L. Norment (founder) and Emblem
305 Southern Hemisphere and Ecology Symbols on Hands

1992. 68th Anniv of Paraguay Leprosy Foundation. Multicoloured.
1352 50 g. Type **304** 10 10
1353 250 g. Gerhard Hansen (discoverer of leprosy bacillus) 20 15

1992. 2nd United Nations Conference on Environment and Development, Rio de Janeiro. Multicoloured.
1354 50 g. Type **305** 10 10
1355 100 g. Butterfly and chimneys emitting smoke 10 10
1356 250 g. Tree and map of South America on globe 20 15

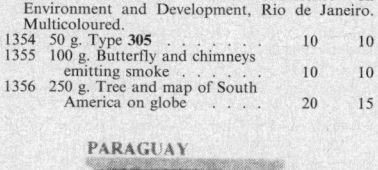

306 Factories and Cotton (economy)

1992. National Population and Housing Census. Multicoloured.
1357 50 g. Type **306** 10 10
1358 200 g. Houses (vert) 15 10
1359 250 g. Numbers and stylized people (population) (vert) . 20 15
1360 300 g. Abacus (education) . . . 25 20

307 Football

1992. Olympic Games, Barcelona. Multicoloured.
1361 50 g. Type **307** 10 10
1362 100 g. Tennis 10 10
1363 150 g. Running 10 10
1364 200 g. Swimming (horiz) . . 15 10
1365 250 g. Judo 20 15
1366 350 g. Fencing (horiz) 25 20

308 Brother Luis Bolanos

1992. 500th Anniv of Discovery of America by Columbus (2nd series). Evangelists. Multicoloured.
1367 50 g. Type **308** (translator of Catechism into Guarani and founder of Guarani Christian settlements) 10 10
1368 100 g. Brother Juan de San Bernardo (Franciscan and first Paraguayan martyr) . 10 10
1369 150 g. St. Roque Gonzalez de Santa Cruz (Jesuit missionary and first Paraguayan saint) 10 10
1370 200 g. Fr. Amancio Gonzalez (founder of Melodia settlement) 15 10
1371 250 g. Mgr. Juan Sinforiano Bogarin (first Archbishop of Asuncion) (vert) 20 15

309 Fleet approaching Shore

1992. America. 500th Anniv of Discovery of America by Columbus. Multicoloured.
1372 150 g. Type **309** (postage) . 10 10
1373 350 g. Christopher Columbus (vert) (air) 25 20

1992. 30th Anniv of United Nations Information Centre in Paraguay. Nos. 1354/6 optd **NACIONES UNIDAS 1992 - 30 ANOS CENTRO INFORMACION OUN EN PARAGUAY**.
1374 50 g. multicoloured 10 10
1375 100 g. multicoloured 10 10
1376 250 g. multicoloured 20 15

1992. Christmas. Nos. 1367/9 optd **Navidad 92**.
1377 50 g. multicoloured 10 10
1378 100 g. multicoloured 10 10
1379 150 g. multicoloured 10 10

1992. "Parafil 92" Paraguay-Argentina Stamp Exhibition, Buenos Aires. Nos. 1372/3 optd **PARAFIL 92**.
1380 150 g. mult (postage) 10 10
1381 350 g. multicoloured (air) . . 25 20

313 Planting and Hoeing

1992. 50th Anniv of Pan-American Agricultural Institute. Multicoloured.
1382 50 g. Type **313** 10 10
1383 100 g. Test tubes 10 10
1384 200 g. Cotton plant in cupped hands 15 10
1385 250 g. Cattle and maize plant 20 15

314 Yolanda Bado de Artecona

1992. Centenary of Paraguayan Writers' College. Multicoloured.
1386 50 g. Type **314** 10 10
1387 100 g. Jose Ramon Silva . . 10 10
1388 150 g. Abelardo Brugada Valpy 10 10
1389 200 g. Tomas Varela 15 10
1390 250 g. Jose Livio Lezcano . 20 15
1391 300 g. Francisco I. Fernandez 25 20

315 Members' Flags and Map of South America
316 Orange Flowers (Gilda Hellmers)

1993. 1st Anniv (1992) of Treaty of Asuncion forming Mercosur (common market of Argentina, Brazil, Paraguay and Uruguay). Multicoloured.
1392 50 g. Type **315** 10 10
1393 50 g. Flags encircling globe showing map of South America 25 20

1993. 50th Anniv of St. Isabel Leprosy Association. Flower paintings by artists named. Multicoloured.
1394 50 g. Type **316** 10 10
1395 200 g. Luis Alberto Balmelli . 15 10
1396 250 g. Lili del Monico 20 15
1397 350 g. Brunilde Guggiari . . 25 20

317 Goethe (after J. Lips) and Manuscript of Poem

1993. Centenary of Goethe College.
1398 **317** 50 g. brown, black & bl . 10 10
1399 – 200 g. multicoloured . . 15 10
DESIGN: 200 g. Goethe (after J. Tischbein).

1993. "Brasiliana 93" International Stamp Exhibition, Rio de Janeiro. Nos. 1398/9 optd **BRASILIANA 93**.
1400 50 g. brown, black and blue . 10 10
1401 200 g. multicoloured 15 10

319 Palace (Michael Burt)

1993. Centenary (1992) of Los Lopez (Government) Palace, Asuncion. Paintings of palace by artists named. Multicolured.
1402 50 g. Type **319** 10 10
1403 100 g. Esperanza Gill 10 10
1404 200 g. Emili Aparici 15 10
1405 250 g. Hugo Bogado Barrios (vert) 15 10

320 Couple sitting on Globe and Emblem

1993. 35th Anniv of World Friendship Crusade.
1406 **320** 50 g. black, blue and mauve 10 10
1407 – 100 g. multicoloured . . 10 10
1408 – 200 g. multicoloured . . 15 10
1409 – 250 g. multicoloured . . 15 10
DESIGNS: 100 g. Dr. Ramon Artemio Bracho (founder), map of Americas and emblem; 200 g. Children and sun emerging from cloud; 250 g. Couple hugging and emblem.

1993. Inauguration of President Juan Carlos Wasmosy. Nos. 1402/5 optd **TRANSMISION DEL MANDO PRESIDENCIAL GRAL. ANDRES RODRIGUEZ ING. JUAN C. WASMOSY 15 DE AGOSTO 1993**.
1410 50 g. multicoloured 10 10
1411 100 g. multicoloured 10 10
1412 200 g. multicoloured 15 10
1413 250 g. multicoloured 15 10

322 "Church of the Incarnation" (Juan Guerra Gaja)

1993. Centenary of Church of the Incarnation. Paintings. Multicoloured.
1414 50 g. Type **322** 10 10
1415 350 g. "Church of the Incarnation" (Hector Blas Ruiz) (horiz) 25 20

323 Bush Dog

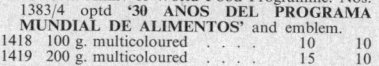

1993. America. Endangered Animals. Multicoloured.
1416 250 g. Type **323** (postage) . . 15 10
1417 50 g. Great anteater (air) . . 10 10

1993. 80th Anniv of World Food Programme. Nos. 1383/4 optd **'30 ANOS DEL PROGRAMA MUNDIAL DE ALIMENTOS'** and emblem.
1418 100 g. multicoloured 10 10
1419 200 g. multicoloured 15 10

325 Children Carol-singing

1993. Christmas. Multicoloured.
1420 50 g. Type **325** 10 10
1421 250 g. Wise men following star 15 10

326 Boy and Girl Scouts

1993. 80th Anniv of Paraguay Scouts Association. Multicoloured.
1422 50 g. Type **326** 10 10
1423 100 g. Boy scouts in camp . 10 10
1424 200 g. Lord Robert Baden-Powell (founder of Scouting movement) 15 10
1425 250 g. Girl scout with flag . 15 10

327 Cecilio Baez

1994. Centenary of First Graduation of Lawyers from National University, Asuncion.
1426 **327** 50 g. red and crimson . . 10 10
1427 – 100 g. yellow and orange 10 10
1428 – 250 g. yellow and green . 15 10
1429 – 500 g. blue and deep blue 30 20
DESIGNS—VERT: 100 g. Benigno Riquelme. HORIZ: 250 g. Emeterio Gonzalez; 500 g. J. Gaspar Villamayor.

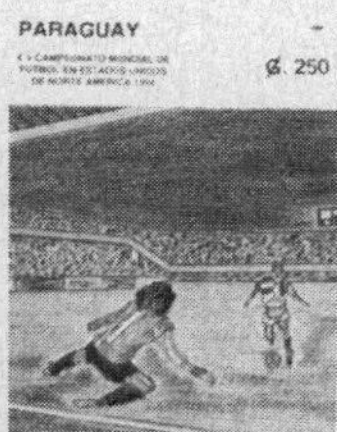

328 Basketball
329 Penalty Kick

1994. 50th Anniv of Phoenix Sports Association. Multicoloured.
1430 50 g. Type **328** 10 10
1431 200 g. Football 15 10
1432 250 g. Pedro Andres Garcia Arias (founder) and tennis (horiz) 15 10

1994. World Cup Football Championship, U.S.A. Multicoloured.

No.	Description	Unused	Used
1433	250 g. Type **329**	15	10
1434	500 g. Tackle	30	20
1435	1000 g. Dribbling ball past opponent	65	50

330 Runner

1994. Centenary of International Olympic Committee. Multicoloured.

No.	Description	Unused	Used
1436	350 g. Type **330**	25	20
1437	400 g. Athlete lighting Olympic Flame	25	20

331 World Map and Emblem

1994. World Congress of International Federation for Physical Education, Asuncion. Multicoloured.

No.	Description	Unused	Used
1438	200 g. Type **331**	15	10
1439	1000 g. Family exercising and flag (vert)	65	50

1994. Brazil, Winners of World Cup Football Championship. Nos. 1433/5 optd **BRASIL Campeon Mundial de Futbol Estados Unidos '94**.

No.	Description	Unused	Used
1440	250 g. multicoloured	15	10
1441	500 g. multicoloured	30	20
1442	1000 g. multicoloured	65	50

1994. 25th Anniv of First Manned Moon Landing. No. 1407 optd **25 Anos, Conquista de la Luna por el hombre 1969 - 1994**.

No.	Description	Unused	Used
1443	100 g. multicoloured	10	10

334 Barrios

1994. 50th Death Anniv of Agustin Pio Barrios Mangore (guitarist). Multicoloured.

No.	Description	Unused	Used
1444	250 g. Type **334**	15	10
1445	500 g. Barrios wearing casual clothes and a hat	30	20

335 Police Commandant, 1913

1994. 151st Anniv of Police Force. Multicoloured.

No.	Description	Unused	Used
1446	50 g. Type **335**	10	10
1447	250 g. Carlos Bernardino Cacabelos (first Commissioner) and Pedro Nolasco Fernandez (first Chief of Asuncion Police Dept)	15	10

336 Maguari Stork

1994. "Parafil 94" Stamp Exhibition. Birds. Multicoloured.

No.	Description	Unused	Used
1448	100 g. Type **336**	10	10
1449	150 g. Yellow-billed cardinal	10	10
1450	400 g. Green kingfisher (vert)	25	20
1451	500 g. Jabiru (vert)	30	20

OFFICIAL STAMPS

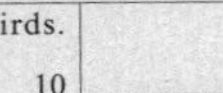

O 14

O 19

O 20

O 37

1886. Various types as O **14**, O **19** and O **20** optd **OFICIAL**. (a) Imperf.

No.	Description	Unused	Used
O32	1 c. orange	2·25	2·25
O33	2 c. violet	2·25	2·25
O34	5 c. orange	2·25	2·25
O35	7 c. green	2·25	2·25
O36	10 c. brown	2·25	2·25
O37	15 c. blue	2·25	2·25
O38	20 c. lake	2·25	2·25

(b) New colours. Perf.

No.	Description	Unused	Used
O39	1 c. green	40	40
O40	2 c. red	40	40
O41	5 c. blue	40	40
O42	7 c. orange	40	40
O43	10 c. lake	40	40
O44	15 c. brown	40	40
O45	20 c. blue	40	40

1889. Stamp of 1889 surch **OFICIAL** and value. Perf.

No.	Type	Description	Unused	Used
O47	**25**	1 on 15 c. purple	1·10	75
O48		2 on 10 c. purple	1·10	75

1889. Stamp of 1889 surch **OFICIAL** and value. Imperf.

No.	Type	Description	Unused	Used
O49	**25**	3 on 15 c. purple	1·10	75
O50		5 on 15 c. brown	1·10	75

1890. Stamps of 1887 optd **OFICIAL** or **Oficial**.

No.	Type	Description	Unused	Used
O58	**24**	1 c. green	10	10
O59		2 c. red	15	10
O60		5 c. blue	15	10
O61		7 c. brown	1·40	75
O55		10 c. mauve	20	15
O63		15 c. orange	20	15
O64		20 c. pink	25	15
O65		50 c. grey	15	15
O86		1 p. green	10	10

1901.

No.	Type	Description	Unused	Used
O73	O **37**	1 c. blue	30	30
O74		2 c. red	10	10
O75		4 c. brown	10	10
O76		5 c. green	10	10
O77		8 c. brown	10	10
O78		10 c. red	10	10
O79		20 c. blue	20	15

1903. Stamps of 1903, optd **OFICIAL**.

No.	Type	Description	Unused	Used
O 99	**46**	1 c. grey	10	10
O100		2 c. green	10	10
O101		5 c. blue	15	10
O102		10 c. brown	10	10
O103		20 c. red	10	10
O104		30 c. blue	10	10
O105		60 c. violet	20	20

1904. As T **50**, but inscr "OFICIAL".

No.	Description	Unused	Used
O106	1 c. green	20	10
O107	1 c. olive	30	10
O108	1 c. orange	35	15
O109	1 c. red	30	20
O110	2 c. orange	20	10
O111	2 c. green	20	10
O112	2 c. red	60	40
O113	2 c. grey	50	30
O114	5 c. blue	25	20
O116	5 c. grey	1·10	75
O117	10 c. lilac	15	10
O118	20 c. lilac	50	30

1913. As T **65**, but inscr "OFICIAL".

No.	Description	Unused	Used
O237	1 c. grey	10	10
O238	2 c. orange	10	10
O239	5 c. purple	10	10
O240	10 c. green	10	10
O241	20 c. red	10	10
O242	50 c. red	10	10
O243	75 c. blue	10	10
O244	1 p. blue	10	10
O245	2 p. yellow	20	20

1935. Optd **OFICIAL**.

No.	Type	Description	Unused	Used
O474	**86**	10 c. blue	10	10
O475		50 c. mauve	10	10
O476	**87**	1 p. orange	10	10
O477	**122**	1 p. 50 green	10	10
O478	–	2 p. 50 violet (No. 337)	10	10

1940. 50th Anniv of Asuncion University. As T **139**, inscr "SERVICIO OFICIAL", but portraits of Pres. Escobar and Dr. Zubizarreta.

No.	Description	Unused	Used
O513	50 c. black and red	10	10
O514	1 p. black and red	10	10
O515	2 p. black and blue	10	10
O516	5 p. black and blue	10	10
O517	10 p. black and blue	10	10
O518	50 p. black and orange	40	10

POSTAGE DUE STAMPS

D 48

1904.

No.	Type	Description	Unused	Used
D106	D **48**	2 c. green	30	30
D107		4 c. green	30	30
D108		10 c. green	30	30
D109		20 c. green	30	30

1913. As T **65**, but inscr "DEFICIENTE".

No.	Description	Unused	Used
D237	1 c. brown	10	10
D238	2 c. brown	10	10
D239	5 c. brown	10	10
D240	10 c. brown	10	10
D241	20 c. brown	10	10
D242	40 c. brown	10	10
D243	1 p. brown	10	10
D244	1 p. 50 brown	10	10

APPENDIX

The following stamps have either been issued in excess of postal needs or have not been available to the public in reasonable quantities at face value. Such stamps may later be given full listing if there is evidence of regular postal use.

1962.

Manned Spacecraft. Postage 15, 25, 30, 40, 50 c.; Air 12 g. 45, 18 g. 15, 36 g.

Previous Olympic Games. (First series). Vert designs. Postage 15, 25, 30, 40, 50 c.; Air 12 g. 45, 18 g. 15, 36 g.

Vatican Council. Postage 50, 70 c., 1 g. 50, 2, 3 g.; Air 5, 10 g., 12 g. 45, 18 g. 15, 23 g. 40, 36 g.

Europa. Postage 4 g.; Air 36 g.

Solar System. Postage 10, 20, 25, 30, 50 c.; Air 12 g. 45, 36 g., 50 g.

1963.

Previous Olympic Games. (Second series). Horiz designs. Postage 15, 25, 30, 40, 50 c.; Air 12 g. 45, 18 g. 15, 36 g.

Satellites and Space Flights. Vert designs. Postage 10, 20, 25, 30, 50 c.; Air 12 g. 45, 36 g., 50 g.

Previous Winter Olympic Games. Postage 10, 20, 25, 30, 50 c.; Air 12 g. 45, 36 g., 50 g.

Freedom from Hunger. Postage 10, 25, 50, 75 c.; Air 18 g. 15, 36 g., 50 g.

"Mercury" Space Flights. Postage 15, 25, 30, 40, 50 c.; Air 12 g. 45, 18 g. 15, 50 g.

Winter Olympic Games. Postage 15, 25, 30, 40, 50 c.; Air 12 g. 45, 18 g. 15, 50 g.

1964.

Tokyo Olympic Games. Postage 15, 25, 30, 40, 50 c.; Air 12 g. 45, 18 g. 15, 50 g.

Red Cross Cent. Postage 10, 25, 30, 50 c.; Air 18 g. 15, 36 g., 50 g.

"Gemini", "Telstar" and "Apollo" Projects. Postage 15, 25, 30, 40, 50 c.; Air 12 g. 45, 18 g. 15, 50 g.

Spacecraft Developments. Postage 15, 25, 30, 40, 50 c.; Air 12 g. 45, 18 g. 15, 50 g.

United Nations. Postage 15, 25, 30, 40, 50 c.; Air 12 g. 45, 18 g. 15, 50 g.

American Space Research. Postage 10, 15, 20, 30, 40 c.; Air 12 g. 45 + 6 g., 18 g. 15 + 9 g., 20 g. + 20 g.

Eucharistic Conference. Postage 20 g. + 10 g., 30 g. + 15 g., 50 g. + 25 g., 100 g. + 50 g.

Pope John Memorial Issue. Postage 20 g. + 10 g., 30 g. + 15 g., 50 g. + 25 g., 100 g. + 50 g.

1965.

Scouts. Postage 10, 15, 20, 30, 50 c.; Air 12 g. 45, 18 g. 15, 36 g.

Tokyo Olympic Games Medals. Postage 15, 25, 30, 40, 50 c.; Air 12 g. 45, 18 g. 15, 50 g.

Famous Scientists. Postage 10, 15, 20, 30, 40 c.; Air 12 g. 45 + 6 g., 18 g. 15 + 9 g., 20 g. + 20 g.

Orchids and Trees. Postage 20, 30, 90 c., 1 g. 50, 4 g. 50.; Air 3 g., 4 g., 66 g.

Kennedy and Churchill. Postage 15, 25, 30, 40, 50 c.; Air 12 g. 45, 18 g. 15, 50 g.

I.T.U. Cent. Postage 10, 15, 20, 30, 40 c.; Air 12 g. 45 + 6 g., 18 g. 15 + 9 g., 20 g. + 10 g.

Pope Paul VI. Visit to United Nations. Postage 10, 15, 20, 30, 50 c.; Air 12 g. 45, 18 g. 15, 36 g.

1966.

"Gemini" Space Project. Postage 15, 25, 30, 40, 50 c.; Air 12 g. 45, 18 g. 15, 50 g.

Events of 1965. Postage 10, 15, 20, 30, 50 c.; Air 12 g. 45, 18 g. 15, 36 g.

Mexico Olympic Games. Postage 10, 15, 20, 30, 50 c.; Air 12 g. 45, 18 g. 15, 36 g.

German Space Research. Postage 10, 15, 20, 30, 50 c.; Air 12 g. 45, 18 g. 15, 36 g.

Famous Writers. Postage 10, 15, 20, 30, 50 c.; Air 12 g. 45, 18 g. 15, 36 g.

Italian Space Research. Postage 10, 15, 20, 30, 50 c.; Air 12 g. 45, 18 g. 15, 36 g.

Moon Missions. Postage 10, 15, 20, 30, 50 c.; Air 12 g. 45, 18 g. 15, 36 g.

Sports Commemorative Issue. Postage 10, 15, 20, 30, 50 c.; Air 12 g. 45, 18 g. 15, 36 g.

3rd Death Anniv of Pres. John Kennedy. Postage 10, 15, 20, 30, 50 c.; Air 12 g. 45, 18 g. 15, 36 g.

Famous Paintings. Postage 10, 15, 20, 30, 50 c.; Air 12 g. 45, 18 g. 15, 36 g.

1967.

Religious Paintings. Postage 10, 15, 20, 30, 50 c.; Air 12 g. 45, 18 g. 15, 36 g.

16th Cent. Religious Paintings. Postage 10, 15, 20, 30, 50 c.; Air 12 g. 45, 18 g. 15, 36 g.

Impressionist Paintings. Postage 10, 15, 20, 30, 50 c.; Air 12 g. 45, 18 g. 15, 36 g.

European Paintings of 17th and 18th Cent. Postage 10, 15, 20, 25, 30, 50 c.; Air 12 g. 45, 18 g. 15, 36 g.

Birth Anniv of Pres. John Kennedy. Postage 10, 15, 20, 25, 30, 50 c.; Air 12 g. 45, 18 g. 15, 36 g.

Sculpture. Postage 10, 15, 20, 25, 30, 50 c.; Air 12 g. 45, 18 g. 15, 50 g.

Mexico Olympic Games. Archaeological Relics. Postage 10, 15, 20, 25, 30, 50 c.; Air 12 g. 45, 18 g. 15, 36 g.

1968.

Religious Paintings. Postage 10, 15, 20, 25, 30, 50 c.; Air 12 g. 45, 18 g. 15, 36 g.

Winter Olympic Games, Grenoble. Paintings. Postage 10, 15, 20, 25, 30, 50 c.; Air 12 g. 45, 18 g. 15, 36 g.

Paraguayan Stamps from 1870-1970. Postage 10, 15, 20, 25, 30, 50 c.; Air 12 g. 45, 18 g. 15, 36 g.

Mexico Olympic Games, Paintings of Children. Postage 10, 15, 20, 25, 30, 50 c.; Air 12 g. 45, 18 g. 15, 36 g. (Sailing ship and Olympic Rings).

Visit of Pope Paul VI to Eucharistic Congress. Religious Paintings. Postage 10, 15, 20, 25, 30, 50 c.; Air 12 g. 45, 18 g. 15, 36 g.

Important Events of 1968. Postage 10, 15, 20, 25, 30, 50 c.; Air 12 g. 45, 18 g. 15, 50 g.

1969.

Gold Medal Winners of 1968 Mexico Olympic Games. Postage 10, 15, 20, 25, 30, 50 c.; Air 12 g. 45, 18 g. 15, 50 g.

Int. Projects in Outer Space. Postage 10, 15, 20, 25, 30, 50 c.; Air 12 g. 45, 18 g. 15, 50 g.

Latin American Wildlife. Postage 10, 10, 15, 15, 20, 20, 25, 25, 30, 30, 50, 50, 75, 75 c; Air 12 g. 45×2, 18 g. 15×2.

Gold Medal Winners in Olympic Football, 1900-1968. Postage 10, 15, 20, 25, 30, 50, 75 c.; Air 12 g. 45, 18 g. 15.

Paraguayan Football Champions, 1930-1966. Postage 10, 15, 20, 25, 30, 50, 75 c.; Air 12 g. 45, 18 g. 15.

Paintings by Goya. Postage 10, 15, 20, 25, 30, 50, 75 c.; Air 12 g. 45, 18 g. 15.

Christmas. Religious Paintings. Postage 10, 15, 20, 25, 30, 50, 75 c.; Air 12 g. 45, 18 g. 15.

1970.

Moon Walk. Postage 10, 15, 20, 25, 30, 50, 75 c.; Air 12 g. 45, 18 g. 15.

Easter. Paintings. Postage 10, 15, 20, 25, 30, 50, 75 c.; Air 12 g. 45, 18 g. 15.

Munich, Olympic Games. Postage 10, 15, 20, 25, 30, 50, 75 c.; Air 12 g. 45, 18 g. 15.

Paintings from the Pinakothek Museum in Munich. Postage 10, 15, 20, 25, 30, 50, 75 c.; Air 12 g. 45, 18 g. 15.

"Apollo" Space Programme. Postage 10, 15, 20, 25, 30, 50, 75 c.; Air 12 g. 45, 18 g. 15.

Space Projects in the Future. Postage 10, 15, 20, 25, 30, 50, 75 c.; Air 12 g. 45, 18 g. 15.

"Expo 70" World Fair, Osaka, Japan. Japanese Paintings. Postage 10, 15, 20, 25, 30, 50, 75 c.; Air 12 g. 45, 18 g. 15, 50 g.

Flower Paintings. Postage 10, 15, 20, 25, 30, 50, 75 c.; Air 12 g. 45, 18 g. 15, 50 g.

Paintings from Prado Museum, Madrid. Postage 10, 15, 20, 25, 30, 50, 75 c.; Air 12 g. 45, 18 g. 15, 50 g.

Paintings by Durer. Postage 10, 15, 20, 25, 30, 50, 75 c.; Air 12 g. 45, 18 g. 15, 50 g.

1971.

Christmas 1970/71. Religious Paintings. Postage 10, 15, 20, 25, 30, 50, 75 c.; Air 12 g. 45, 18 g. 15, 50 g.

Munich Olympic Games 1972. Postage 10, 15, 20, 25, 30, 50, 75 c.; Air 12 g. 45, 18 g. 15, 50 g.

Paintings of Horses and Horsemen. Postage 10, 15, 20, 25, 30, 50, 75 c.; Air 12 g. 45, 18 g. 15, 50 g.

Famous Paintings from the Louvre, Paris. Postage 10, 15, 20, 25, 30, 50, 75 c.; Air 12 g. 45, 18 g. 15, 50 g.

Paintings in the National Museum, Asuncion. Postage 10, 15, 20, 25, 30, 50, 75 c.; Air 12 g. 45, 18 g. 15, 50 g.

Hunting Paintings. Postage 10, 15, 20, 25, 30, 50, 75 c.; Air 12 g. 45, 18 g. 15, 50 g.

Philatokyo '71, Stamp Exhibition, Tokyo. Japanese Paintings. Postage 10, 15, 20, 25, 30, 50, 75 c.; Air 12 g. 45, 18 g. 15, 50 g.

Winter Olympic Games, Sapporo 1972. Japanese Paintings. Postage 10, 15, 20, 25, 30, 50, 75 c.; Air 12 g. 45, 18 g. 15, 50 g.

150th Death Anniv of Napoleon. Paintings. Postage 10, 15, 20, 25, 30, 50, 75 c.; Air 12 g. 45, 18 g. 15, 50 g.

Famous Paintings from the Dahlem Museum, Berlin. Postage 10, 15, 20, 25, 30, 50, 75 c.; Air 12 g. 45, 18 g. 15, 50 g.

1972.

Locomotives (1st series). Postage 10, 15, 20, 25, 30, 50, 75 c.; Air 12 g. 45, 18 g. 15, 50 g.

Winter Olympic Games, Sapporo. Postage 10, 15, 20, 25, 30, 50, 75 c.; Air 12 g. 45, 18 g. 15, 50 g.

Racing Cars. Postage 10, 15, 20, 25, 30, 50, 75 c.; Air 12 g. 45, 18 g. 15, 50 g.

Famous Sailing Ships. Postage 10, 15, 20, 25, 30, 50, 75 c.; Air 12 g. 45, 18 g. 15, 50 g.

Famous Paintings from the Vienna Museum. Postage 10, 15, 20, 25, 30, 50, 75 c.; Air 12 g. 45, 18 g. 15, 50 g.

Famous Paintings from the Asuncion Museum. Postage 10, 15, 20, 25, 30, 50, 75 c.; Air 12 g. 45, 18 g. 15, 50 g.

Visit of the Argentine President to Paraguay. Postage 10, 15, 20, 25, 30, 50, 75 c.; Air 12 g. 45, 18 g. 15.

Visit of President of Paraguay to Japan. Postage 10, 15, 20, 25, 30, 50, 75 c.; Air 12 g. 45, 18 g. 15.

Paintings of Animals and Birds. Postage 10, 15, 20, 25, 30, 50, 75 c.; Air 12 g. 45, 18 g. 15.

Locomotives (2nd series). Postage 10, 15, 20, 25, 30, 50, 75 c.; Air 12 g. 45, 18 g. 15.

South American Fauna. Postage 10, 15, 20, 25, 30, 50, 75 c.; Air 12 g. 45, 18 g. 15.

1973.

Famous Paintings from the Florence Museum. Postage 10, 15, 20, 25, 30, 50, 75 c.; Air 5, 10, 20 g.

South American Butterflies. Postage 10, 15, 20, 25, 30, 50, 75 c.; Air 5, 10, 20 g.

Cats. Postage 10, 15, 20, 25, 30, 50, 75 c.; Air 5, 10, 20 g.

Portraits of Women. Postage 10, 15, 20, 25, 30, 50, 75 c.; Air 5, 10, 20 g.

World Cup Football Championships, West Germany (1974) (1st issue). Postage 10, 15, 20, 25, 30, 50, 75 c.; Air 5, 10, 20 g.

Paintings of Women. Postage 10, 15, 20, 25, 30, 50, 75 c.; Air 5, 10, 20 g.

Birds. Postage 10, 15, 20, 25, 30, 50, 75 c.; Air 5, 10, 20 g.

"Apollo" Moon Missions and Future Space Projects. Postage 10, 15, 20, 25, 30, 50, 75 c.; Air 5, 10, 20 g.

Visit of Pres. Stroessner to Europe and Morocco. Air 5, 10, 25, 50, 150 g.

Folk Costume. 25, 50, 75 c., 1 g., 1 g. 50, 1 g. 75, 2 g. 25.

Flowers. 10, 20, 25, 30, 40, 50, 75 c.

1974.

World Cup Football Championships, West Germany (2nd issue). Air 5, 10, 20 g.

Roses. 10, 15, 20, 25, 30, 50, 75 c.

Famous Paintings from the Gulbenkian Museum, New York. Postage 10, 15, 20, 25, 30, 50, 75 c; Air 5, 10, 20 g.

U.P.U. Cent Postage 10, 15, 20, 25, 30, 50, 75 c.; Air 5, 10, 20 g.

Famous Masterpieces. Postage 10, 15, 20, 25, 30, 50, 75 c.; Air 5, 10, 20 g.

Visit of Pres. Stroessner to France. Air 100 g.

World Cup Football Championships, West Germany (3rd issue). Air 4, 5, 10 g.

Ships. Postage 5, 10, 15, 20, 25, 35, 40, 50 c.

Events of 1974. Air 4 g. (U.P.U.), 5 g. (President of Chile's visit), 10 g. (Pres. Stroessner's visit to South Africa).

Centenary of U.P.U. Air 4, 5, 10, 20 g.

1975.

Paintings. 5, 10, 15, 20, 25, 35, 40, 50 c.

Christmas. (1974) 5, 10, 15, 20, 25, 35, 40, 50 c.

"Expo '75" Okinawa, Japan. Air 4, 5, 10 g.

Paintings from National Gallery, London. 5, 10, 15, 20, 25, 35, 40, 50 c.

Dogs. 10, 15, 20, 25, 35, 40, 50 c.

South American Fauna. 5, 10, 15, 20, 25, 35, 40, 50 c.

"Espana '75". Air 4, 5, 10 g.

500th Birth Anniv of Michelangelo. Postage 5, 10, 15, 20, 25, 35, 40, 50 c.; Air 4, 5, 10 g.

Winter Olympic Games, Innsbruck (1976). Postage 1, 2, 3, 4, 5 g.; Air 10, 15, 20 g.

Olympic Games, Montreal (1976). Gold borders. Postage 1, 2, 3, 4, 5 g.; Air 10, 15, 20 g.

Various Commemorations. Air 4 g. (Zeppelin), 5 g. (1978 World Cup), 10 g. (Nordposta Exhibition).

Bicent. (1976) of American Revolution (1st issue). Paintings of Sailing Ships. 5, 10, 15, 20, 25, 35, 40, 50 c.

Bicent. (1976) of American Revolution (2nd issue). Paintings. 5, 10, 15, 20, 25, 35, 40, 50 c.

Bicent. (1976) of American Revolution (3rd issue). Lunar Rover and American Cars. Air 4, 5, 10 g.

Various Commemorations. Air 4 g. (Concorde), 5 g. (Lufthansa), 10 g. ("Exfilmo" and "Espamer" Stamp Exhibitions).

Paintings by Spanish Artists. Postage 1, 2, 3, 4, 5 g.; Air 10, 15, 20 g.

1976.

Holy Year. Air 4, 5, 10 g.

Cats. 5, 10, 15, 20, 25, 35, 40, 50 c.

Railway Locomotives. Postage 1, 2, 3, 4, 5 g.; Air 10, 15, 20 g.

Butterflies. 5, 10, 15, 20, 25, 35, 40, 50 c.

Domestic Animals. Postage 1, 2, 3, 4, 5 g.; Air 10, 15, 20 g.

Bicentenary of American Revolution (4th issue) and U.S. Postal Service. Postage 1, 2, 3, 4, 5 g.; Air 10, 15, 20 g.

"Paintings and Planets". Postage 1, 2, 3, 4, 5 g.; Air 10, 15, 20 g.

Ship Paintings. Postage 1, 2, 3, 4, 5 g.; Air 10, 15, 20 g.

German Ship Paintings (1st issue). Postage 1, 2, 3, 4, 5 g.; Air 10, 15, 20 g.

Bicentenary of American Revolution (5th issue). Paintings of Cowboys and Indians. Postage 1, 2, 3, 4, 5 g.; Air 10, 15, 20 g.

Gold Medal Winners. Olympic Games, Montreal. Postage 1, 2, 3, 4, 5 g.; Air 10, 15, 20 g.

Paintings by Titian. Postage 1, 2, 3, 4, 5 g.; Air 10, 15, 20 g.

History of the Olympics. Postage 1, 2, 3, 4, 5 g.; Air 10, 15, 20 g.

1977.

Paintings by Rubens (1st issue). Postage 1, 2, 3, 4, 5 g.; Air 10, 15, 20 g.

Bicentenary of American Revolution (6th issue). Astronautics. Postage 1, 2, 3, 4, 5 g.; Air 10, 15, 20 g.

"Luposta 77" Stamp Exn. Zeppelin and National Costumes. Postage 1, 2, 3, 4, 5 g.; Air 10, 15, 20 g.

History of Aviation. Postage 1, 2, 3, 4, 5 g.; Air 10, 15, 20 g.

Paintings. Postage 1, 2, 3, 4, 5 g.; Air 10, 15, 20 g.

German Ship Paintings (2nd issue). Postage 1, 2, 3, 4, 5 g.; Air 10, 15, 20 g.

Nobel Prize-winners for Literature. Postage 1, 2, 3, 4, 5 g.; Air 10, 15, 20 g.

History of World Cup (1st issue). Postage 1, 2, 3, 4, 5 g.; Air 10, 15, 20 g.

History of World Cup (2nd issue). Postage 1, 2, 3, 4, 5 g.; Air 10, 15, 20 g.

1978.

Paintings by Rubens (2nd issue). Postage 1, 2, 3, 4, 5 g.; Air 10, 15, 20 g.

Chess Olympiad, Buenos Aires. Paintings of Chess Games. Postage 1, 2, 3, 4, 5 g.; Air 10, 15, 20 g.

Paintings by Jordaens. Postage 3, 4, 5, 6, 7, 8, 20 g.; Air 10, 25 g.

450th Death Anniv of Durer (1st issue). Postage 3, 4, 5, 6, 7, 8, 20 g.; Air 10, 25 g.

Paintings by Goya. Postage 3, 4, 5, 6, 7, 8, 20 g.; Air 10, 25 g.

Astronautics of the Future. Postage 3, 4, 5, 6, 7, 8, 20 g.; Air 10, 25 g.

Racing Cars. Postage 3, 4, 5, 6, 7, 8, 20 g.; Air 10, 25 g.

Paintings by Rubens (3rd issue). Postage 3, 4, 5, 6, 7, 8, 20 g.; Air 10, 25 g.

25th Anniv of Queen Elizabeth's Coronation (reproduction of stamps). Postage 3, 4, 5, 6, 7, 8, 20 g.; Air 10, 25 g.

Paintings and Stamp Exhibition Emblems. Postage 3, 4, 5, 6, 7, 8, 20 g.; Air 10, 25 g.

Various Commemorations. Air 75 g. (Satellite Earth Station), 500 g. (Coat of Arms), 1000 g. (Pres. Stroessner).

International Year of the Child (1st issue). Snow White and the Seven Dwarfs. Postage 3, 4, 5, 6, 7, 8, 20 g.; Air 10, 25 g.

Military Uniforms. Postage 3, 4, 5, 6, 7, 8, 20 g.; Air 10, 25 g.

1979.

World Cup Football Championship, Argentina. Postage 3, 4, 5, 6, 7, 8, 20 g.; Air 10, 25 g.

Christmas (1978). Paintings of Madonnas. Postage 3, 4, 5, 6, 7, 8, 20 g.; Air 10, 25 g.

History of Aviation. Postage 3, 4, 5, 6, 7, 8, 20 g.; Air 10, 25 g.

450th Death Anniv of Durer (2nd issue). Postage 3, 4, 5, 6, 7, 8, 20 g.; Air 10, 25 g.

Death Centenary of Sir Rowland Hill (1st issue). Reproduction of Stamps. Postage 3, 4, 5, 6, 7, 8, 20 g.; Air 10, 25 g.

International Year of the Child (2nd issue). Cinderella. Postage 3, 4, 5, 6, 7, 8, 20 g.; Air 10, 25 g.

Winter Olympic Games, Lake Placid (1980). Postage 3, 4, 5, 6, 7, 8, 20 g.; Air 10, 25 g.

Sailing Ships. Postage 3, 4, 5, 6, 7, 8, 20 g.; Air 10, 25 g.

International Year of the Child (3rd issue). Cats. Postage 3, 4, 5, 6, 7, 8, 20 g.; Air 10, 25 g.

International Year of the Child (4th issue). Little Red Riding Hood. Postage 3, 4, 5, 6, 7, 8, 20 g.; Air 10, 25 g.

Olympic Games, Moscow (1980). Greek Athletes. Postage 3, 4, 5, 6, 7, 8, 20 g.; Air 10, 25 g.

Centenary of Electric Locomotives. Postage 3, 4, 5, 6, 7, 8, 20 g.; Air 10, 25 g.

1980.

Death Centenary of Sir Rowland Hill (2nd issue). Military Aircraft. Postage 3, 4, 5, 6, 7, 8, 20 g; Air 10, 25 g.

Death Centenary of Sir Rowland Hill (3rd issue). Stamps. Postage 3, 4, 5, 6, 7, 8, 20 g.; Air 10, 25 g.

Winter Olympic Games Medal Winners (1st issue). Postage 3, 4, 5, 6, 7, 8, 20 g.; Air 10, 25 g.

Composers. Scenes from Ballets. Postage 3, 4, 5, 6, 7, 8, 20 g.; Air 20, 25 g.

International Year of the Child (1979) (5th issue). Christmas. Postage 3, 4, 5, 6, 7, 8, 20 g.; Air 10, 25 g.

Exhibitions. Paintings of Ships. Postage 3, 4, 5, 6, 7, 8, 20 g.; Air 10, 25 g.

World Cup Football Championship, Spain (1982) (1st issue). Postage 3, 4, 5, 6, 7, 8, 20 g.; Air 10, 25 g.

World Chess Championship, Merano. Postage 3, 4, 5, 6, 7, 8, 20 g.; Air 10, 25 g.

1981.

Winter Olympic Games Medal Winners (2nd issue). Postage 25, 50 c., 1, 2, 3, 4, 5 g.; Air 5, 10, 30 g.

International Year of the Child (1979) (6th issue). Children and Flowers. Postage 10, 25, 50, 100, 200, 300, 400 g.; Air 75, 500, 1000 g.

"WIPA 1981" International Stamp Exhibition, Vienna. 1980 Composers stamp optd. Postage 4 g.; Air 10 g.

Wedding of Prince of Wales (1st issue). Postage 25, 50 c., 1, 2, 3, 4, 5 g.; Air 5, 10, 30 g.

Costumes and Treaty of Itaipu. 10, 25, 50, 100, 200, 300, 400 g.

Paintings by Rubens. 25, 50 c., 1, 2, 3, 4, 5 g.

Anniversaries and Events. Air 5 g. (250th birth anniv of George Washington), 10 g. (80th birthday of Queen Mother), 30 g. ("Philatokyo '81").

Flight of Space Shuttle. Air. 5, 10, 30 g.

Birth Bicentenary of Ingres. 25, 50 c., 1, 2, 3, 4, 5 g.

World Cup Football Championship, Spain (1982) (2nd issue). Air 5, 10, 30 g.

Birth Centenary of Picasso. 25, 50 c., 1, 2, 3, 4, 5 g.

"Philatelia '81" International Stamp Exhibition, Frankfurt. Picasso Stamps optd. 25, 50 c., 1, 2, 3, 4 g.

"Espamer '81" International Stamp Exhibition. Picasso stamps optd. 25, 50 c., 1, 2, 3, 4 g.

Wedding of Prince of Wales (2nd issue). Postage 25, 50 c., 1, 2, 3, 4, 5 g.; Air 5, 10, 30 g.

International Year of the Child (1979) (7th issue). Christmas. 25, 50 c., 1, 2, 3, 4, 5 g.

Christmas. Paintings. Air 5, 10, 30 g.

1982.

International Year of the Child (1979) (8th issue). Puss in Boots. 25, 50 c., 1, 2, 3, 4, 5 g.

World Cup Football Championship, Spain (3rd issue). Air 5, 10, 30 g.

75th Anniv of Boy Scout Movement and 125th birth Anniv of Lord-Baden Powell (founder). Postage 25, 50 c., 1, 2, 3, 4, 5 g.; Air 5, 10, 30 g.

"Essen 82" International Stamp Exhibition. 1981 International Year of the Child (7th issue) Christmas stamps optd. 25, 50 c., 1, 2, 3, 4 g.

Cats. 25, 50 c., 1, 2, 3, 4, 5 g.

Chess paintings. Air 5, 10, 30 g.

"Philexfrance 82" International Stamp Exhibition. 1981 Ingres stamps optd. 25, 50 c., 1, 2, 3 g.

World Cup Football Championship, Spain (4th issue). Postage 25, 50 c., 1, 2, 3, 4, 5 g.; Air 5, 10, 30 g.

"Philatelia 82" International Stamp Exhibition, Hanover. 1982 Cats issue optd. 25, 50 c., 1, 2, 3, 4, 5 g.

500th Birth Anniv of Raphael (1st issue). 25, 50 c., 1, 2, 3, 4, 5 g.

500th Birth Anniv of Raphael (2nd issue) and Christmas (1st issue). 25, 50 c., 1, 2, 3, 4, 5 g.

World Cup Football Championship Results. Air 5, 10, 30 g.

Christmas (2nd issue). Paintings by Rubens. Air 5, 10, 30 g.

Paintings by Durer. Life of Christ. 25, 50 c., 1, 2, 3, 4, 5 g.

500th Birth Anniv of Raphael (3rd issue) and Christmas (3rd issue). Air 5, 10, 30 g.

1983.

Third International Railways Congress, Malaga (1982). 25, 50 c., 1, 2, 3, 4, 5 g.

Racing Cars. 25, 50 c., 1, 2, 3, 4, 5 g.

Paintings by Rembrandt. Air 5, 10, 30 g.

German Astronautics. Air 5, 10, 30 g.

Winter Olympic Games, Sarajevo (1984). 25, 50 c., 1, 2, 3, 4, 5 g.

Bicentenary of Manned Flight. Air 5, 10, 30 g.

Pope John Paul II. 25, 50 c., 1, 2, 3, 4, 5 g.

Olympic Games, Los Angeles (1984). Air 5, 10, 30 g.

Veteran Cars. Postage 25, 50 c., 1, 2, 3, 4, 5 g.; Air 5, 10, 30 g.

"Brasiliana '83" International Stamp Exhibition and 52nd F.I.P. Congress (1st issue). 1982 World Cup (4th issue) stamps optd. 25, 50 c., 1, 2, 3, 4 g.

"Brasiliana '83" International Stamp Exhibition and 52nd F.I.P. Congress (2nd issue). 1982 Raphael/Christmas stamps optd. 25, 50 c., 1, 2, 3, 4 g.

Aircraft Carriers. 25, 50 c., 1, 2, 3, 4, 5 g.

South American Flowers. Air 5, 10, 30 g.

South American Birds. 25, 50 c., 1, 2, 3, 4, 5 g.

25th Anniv of International Maritime Organization. Air 5, 10, 30 g.

"Philatelia '83" International Stamp Exhibition, Dusseldorf. 1983 International Railway Congress stamps optd. 25, 50 c., 1, 2, 3, 4 g.

"Exfivia - 83" International Stamp Exn, Bolivia. 1982 Durer paintings optd. 25, 50 c., 1, 2, 3, 4 g.

Flowers 10, 25 g.; Chaco soldier 50 g.; Dams, Postage 75 g. Air 100 g.; President, Air 200 g.

1984.

Bicentenary of Manned Flight. 25, 50 c., 1, 2, 3, 4, 5 g.

World Communications Year. Air 5, 10, 30 g.

Dogs. 25, 50 c., 1, 2, 3, 4, 5 g.

Olympic Games, Los Angeles. Air 5, 10, 30 g.

Animals. 10, 25, 50, 75 g.

1983 Anniversaries. Air 100 g. (birth bicentenary of Bolivar), 200 g. (76th anniv of boy scout movement).

Christmas (1983) and New Year. 25, 50 c., 1, 2, 3, 4, 5 g.

Winter Olympic Games, Sarajevo. Air 5, 10, 30 g.

Troubador Knights. 25, 50 c., 1, 2, 3, 4, 5 g.

World Cup Football Championships, Spain (1982) and Mexico (1986). Air 5, 10, 30 g.

International Stamp Fair, Essen. 1983 Racing Cars stamps optd. 25, 50 c., 1, 2, 3, 4 g.

Extinct Animals. 25, 50 c., 1, 2, 3, 4, 5 g.

60th Anniv of International Chess Federation. Air 5, 10, 30 g.

19th Universal Postal Union Congress Stamp Exhibition, Hamburg (1st issue). Sailing Ships. 25, 50 c., 1, 2, 3, 4, 5 g.

19th Universal Postal Union Congress Stamp Exhibition, Hamburg (2nd issue). Troubadour Knights stamp optd. 5 g.

Leaders of the World. British Railway Locomotives. 25, 50 c., 1, 2, 3, 4, 5 g.

50th Anniv of First Lufthansa Europe-South America Direct Mail Flight. Air 5, 10, 30 g.

30th Anniv of Presidency of Alfredo Stroessner. Dam stamp optd. Air 100 g.

"Ausipex 84" International Stamp Exhibition, Melbourne. 1974 U.P.U. Centenary stamps optd. 10, 15, 20, 25, 30, 50, 75 c.

"Phila Korea 1984" International Stamp Exhibition, Seoul. Olympic Games, Los Angeles, and Extinct Animals stamps optd. Postage 5 g.; Air 30 g.

German National Football Championship and Sindelfingen Stamp Bourse. 1974 World Cup stamps (1st issue) optd. 10, 15, 20, 25, 30, 50, 75 c.

Cats. 25, 50 c., 1, 2, 3, 4, 5 g.

Winter Olympic Games Medal Winners. Air 5, 10, 30 g.

Centenary of Motor Cycle. Air 5, 10, 30 g.

1985.

Olympic Games Medal Winners. 25, 50 c., 1, 2, 3, 4, 5 g.

Christmas (1984). Costumes. Air 5, 10, 30 g.

Fungi. 25, 50 c., 1, 2, 3, 4, 5 g.

Participation of Paraguay in Preliminary Rounds of World Cup Football Championship. Air 5, 10, 30 g.

"Interpex 1985" and "Stampex 1985" Stamp Exhibitions. 1981 Queen Mother's Birthday stamp optd. 10 g. × 2.

International Federation of Aero-Philatelic Societies Congress, Stuttgart. 1984 Lufthansa Europe-South America Mail Flight stamp optd. Air 10 g.

Paraguayan Animals and Extinct Animals. 25, 50 c., 1, 2, 3, 4, 5 g.

"Olymphilex 85" Olympic Stamps Exhibition, Lausanne. 1984 Winter Olympics Games Medal Winners stamp optd. 10 g.

"Israphil 85" International Stamp Exhibition, Tel Aviv. 1982 Boy Scout Movement stamp optd. 5 g.

Music Year. Air 5, 10, 30 g.

Birth Bicentenary of John J. Audubon (ornithologist). Birds. 25, 50 c., 1, 2, 3, 4, 5 g.

Railway Locomotives. Air 5, 10, 30 g.

"Italia '85" International Stamp Exhibition, Rome (1st issue). 1983 Pope John Paul II stamp optd. 5 g.

50th Anniv of Chaco Peace (1st issue). 1972 Visit of Argentine President stamp optd. 30 c.

"Mophila 85" Stamp Exhibition, Hamburg. 1984 U.P.U. Congress Stamp Exhibition (1st issue) stamp optd. 5 g.

"Lupo 85" Stamp Exhibition, Lucerne. 1984 Bicentenary of Manned Flight stamp optd. 5 g.

"Expo 85" World's Fair, Tsukuba. 1981 "Philatokyo '81" stamp optd. Air 30 g.

International Youth Year. Mark Twain. 25, 50 c., 1, 2, 3, 4, 5 g.

75th Death Anniv of Henri Dunant (founder of Red Cross). Air 5, 10, 30 g.

150th Anniv of German Railways (1st issue). 25, 50 c., 1, 2, 3, 4, 5 g.

International Chess Federation Congress, Graz. Air 5, 10, 30 g.

50th Anniv of Chaco Peace (2nd issue) and Government Achievements. Postage 10, 25, 50, 75 g.; Air 100, 200 g.

Paintings by Rubens. 25, 50 c., 1, 2, 3, 4, 5 g.

Explorers and their Ships. Air 5, 10, 30 g.

"Italia '85" International Stamp Exhibition, Rome (2nd issue). Paintings. Air 5, 10, 30 g.

1986.

Paintings by Titian. 25, 50 c., 1, 2, 3, 4, 5 g.

International Stamp Fair, Essen. 1985 German Railways stamps optd. 25, 50 c., 1, 2, 3, 4 g.

Fungi. 25, 50 c., 1, 2, 3, 4, 5 g.

"Ameripex '86" International Stamp Exhibition, Chicaco. Air 5, 10, 30 g.

Lawn Tennis (1st issue). Inscriptions in black or red. Air 5, 10, 30 g.

Centenary of Motor Car. 25, 50 c., 1, 2, 3, 4, 5 g.

Appearance of Halley's Comet. Air 5, 10, 30 g.

Qualification of Paraguay for World Cup Football Championship Final Rounds, Mexico (1st issue). 25, 50 c., 1, 2, 3, 4, 5 g.

Tenth Pan-American Games, Indianapolis (1987). 1985 Olympic Games Medal Winners stamp optd. 5 g.

Maybach Cars. 25, 50 c., 1, 2, 3, 4, 5 g.

Freight Trains. Air 5, 10, 30 g.

Qualification of Paraguay for World Cup Football Championship Final Rounds (2nd issue). Air 5, 10, 30 g.

Winter Olympic Games, Calgary (1988) (1st issue). 1983 Winter Olympic Games stamp optd. 5 g.

Centenary of Statue of Liberty. 25, 50 c., 1, 2, 3, 4, 5 g.

Dogs. 25, 50 c., 1, 2, 3, 4, 5 g.

150th Anniv of German Railways (2nd issue). Air 5, 10, 30 g.

Lawn Tennis (2nd issue). 25, 50 c., 1, 2, 3, 4, 5 g.

Visit of Prince Hitachi of Japan. 1972 Visit of President of Paraguay to Japan stamps optd. 10, 15, 20, 25, 30, 50, 75 c.

International Peace Year. Paintings by Rubens. Air 5, 10, 30 g.

Olympic Games, Seoul (1988) (1st issue). 25, 50 c., 1, 2, 3, 4, 5 g.

27th Chess Olympiad, Dubai. 1982 Chess Paintings stamp optd. Air 10 g.

1987.

World Cup Football Championships, Mexico (1986) and Italy (1990). Air 5, 10, 20, 25, 30 g.

12th Spanish American Stamp and Coin Exhibition, Madrid, and 500th Anniv of Discovery of America by Columbus. 1975 South American Fauna and 1983 25th Anniv of I.M.O. stamps optd. Postage 15, 20, 25, 35, 40 g.; Air 10 g.

Tennis as Olympic Sport. 1986 Lawn Tennis (1st issue) stamps optd. Air 10, 30 g.

Olympic Games, Barcelona (1992). 1985 Olympic Games Medal Winners stamps optd. 25, 50 c., 1, 2, 3, 4 g.

"Olymphilex '87" Olympic Stamps Exhibition, Rome. 1985 Olympic Games Medal Winners stamp optd. 5 g.

Cats. 1, 2, 3, 5, 60 g.

Paintings by Rubens (1st issue). 1, 2, 3, 5, 60 g.

Saloon Cars. Air 5, 10, 20, 25, 30 g.

National Topics. Postage 10 g. (steel plant), 25 g. (Franciscan monk), 50 g. (400th anniv of Ita and Yaguaron), 75 g. (450th Anniv of Asuncion); Air 100 g. (airliner), 200 g. (Pres. Stroessner).

"Capex 87" International Stamp Exhibition, Toronto. Cats stamps optd. 1, 2, 3, 5 g.

500th Anniv of Discovery of America by Columbus. 1, 2, 3, 5, 60 g.

Winter Olympic Games, Calgary (1988) (2nd issue). Air 5, 10, 20, 25, 30 g.

Centenary of Colorado Party. National Topics and 1978 Pres. Stroessner stamps optd. Air 200, 1000 g.

750th Anniv of Berlin (1st issue) and "Luposta '87" Air Stamps Exhibition, Berlin. 1, 2, 3, 5, 60 g.

Olympic Games, Seoul (1988) (2nd issue). Air 5, 10, 20, 25, 30 g.

Rally Cars. 1, 2, 3, 5, 60 g.

"Exfivia 87" Stamp Exhibition, Bolivia. National Topics stamps optd. Postage 75 g.; Air 100 g.

"Olymphilex '88" Olympic Stamps Exhibition, Seoul. 1986 Olympic Games, Seoul (1st issue) stamps optd. 2, 3, 4, 5 g.

"Philatelia '87" International Stamp Exhibition, Cologne. 1986 Lawn Tennis (2nd issue) stamps optd. 25, 50 c., 1, 2, 3, 4 g.

Italy-Argentina Match at Zurich to Launch 1990 World Cup Football Championship, Italy. 1986 Paraguay Qualification (2nd issue) stamps optd. Air 10, 30 g.

"Exfilna '87" Stamp Exhibition, Gerona. 1986 Olympic Games, Seoul (1st issue) stamps optd. 25, 50 c.

Spanish Ships. 1, 2, 3, 5, 60 g.

Paintings by Rubens (2nd issue). Air 5, 10, 20, 25, 30 g.

Christmas. Air 5, 10, 20, 25, 30 g.

Winter Olympic Games, Calgary (1988) (3rd issue). 1, 2, 3, 5, 60 g.

1988.

150th Anniv of Austrian Railways. Air 5, 10, 20, 25, 30 g.

"Aeropex 88" Air Stamps Exhibition, Adelaide. 1987 750th Anniv of Berlin and "Luposta '87" stamps optd. 1, 2, 3, 5 g.

"Olympex" Stamp Exhibition, Calgary. 1987 Winter Olympic Games (3rd issue) stamps optd. 1, 2, 3 g.

Olympic Games, Seoul (3rd issue). Equestrian Events. 1, 2, 3, 5, 60 g.

Space Projects. Air 5, 10, 20, 25, 30 g.

750th Anniv of Berlin (2nd issue). Paintings. 1, 2, 3, 5, 60 g.

Visit of Pope John Paul II. 1, 2, 3, 5, 60 g.

"Lupo Wien 88" Stamp Exhibition, Vienna. 1987 National Topics stamp optd. Air 100 g.

World Wildlife Fund. Extinct Animals. 1, 2, 3, 5 g.

Paintings in West Berlin State Museum. Air 5, 10, 20, 25, 30 g.

Bicentenary of Australian Settlement. 1981 Wedding of Prince of Wales (1st issue) optd. 25, 50 c., 1, 2 g.

History of World Cup Football Championship (1st issue). Air 5, 10, 20, 25, 30 g.

New Presidential Period, 1988-1993. 1985 Chaco Peace and Government Achievements issue optd. Postage 10, 25, 50, 75 g.; Air 100, 200 g.

Olympic Games, Seoul (4th issue). Lawn Tennis and Medal. 1, 2, 3, 5, 60 g.

Calgary Winter Olympics Gold Medal Winners. Air 5, 10, 20, 25, 30 g.

History of World Cup Football Championship (2nd issue). Air 5, 10, 20, 25, 30 g.

"Prenfil '88" International Philatelic Press Exhibition, Buenos Aires. "Ameripex '86" stamp optd. Air 30 g.

"Philexfrance 89" International Stamp Exhibition, Paris. 1985 Explorers stamp optd. Air 30 g.

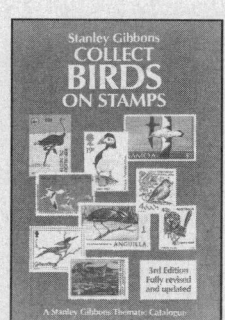

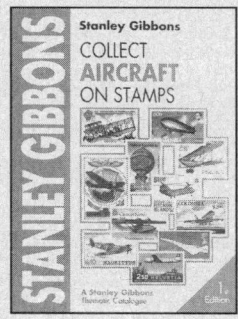

PARMA — Pt. 8

A former Grand Duchy of N. Italy, united with Sardinia in 1860 and now part of Italy.

100 centesimi = 1 lira

1 Bourbon "fleur-de-lis" — **2** — **3**

1852. Imperf.

1	**1**	5 c. black on yellow	38·00	65·00
11		5 c. yellow	£2750	£500
4		10 c. black	38·00	65·00
6		15 c. black on red	£950	22·00
13		15 c. red	£3500	70·00
7		25 c. black on purple	£5500	90·00
14		25 c. brown	£6500	£150
9		40 c. black on blue	£950	£160

1857. Imperf.

17	**2**	15 c. red	£100	£300
19		25 c. purple	£180	80·00
20		40 c. blue	25·00	£300

1859. Imperf.

28	**3**	5 c. green	£850	£2750
30		10 c. brown	£200	£375
31		20 c. blue	£400	£150
33		40 c. red	£300	£5500
35		80 c. yellow	£3250	

NEWSPAPER STAMPS

1853. As T **3**. Imperf.

N1	**3**	6 c. black on red	£170	£200
N3		9 c. black on blue	80·00	£16000

PERU — Pt. 20

A republic on the N.W. coast of S. America independent since 1821.

1857. 8 reales = 1 peso
1858. 100 centavos = 10 dineros = 5 pesetas = 1 peso
1874. 100 centavos = 1 sol
1985. 100 centimos = 1 inti
1991. 100 centimos = 1 sol

7 — **8** — **10** Vicuna

1858. T **7** and similar designs with flags below arms. Imperf.

8	**7**	1 d. blue	75·00	5·00
13		1 peseta red	£100	19·00
5		½ peso yellow	£1300	£225

1862. Various frames. Imperf.

14	**8**	1 d. red	10·00	2·00
20		1 d. green	8·25	1·75
16		1 peseta, brown	55·00	17·00
22		1 peseta, yellow	70·00	21·00

1866. Various frames. Perf.

17	**10**	5 c. green	5·00	60
18	–	10 c. red	5·00	1·10
19	–	20 c. brown	17·00	3·25

See also No. 316.

13 — **14**

1871. 20th Anniv of First Railway in Peru (Lima–Chorillos–Callao). Imperf.

21a	**13**	5 c. red	£110	24·00

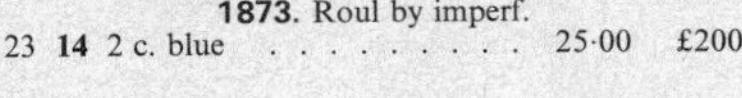

1873. Roul by imperf.

23	**14**	2 c. blue	25·00	£200

15 Sun-god — **16**

20 — **21**

1874. Various frames. Perf.

24	**15**	1 c. orange	40	40
25a	**16**	2 c. violet	40	40
26		5 c. blue	50	25
27		10 c. green	15	15
28		20 c. red	1·60	40
29	**20**	50 c. green	7·50	2·10
30	**21**	1 s. pink	1·25	1·25

For further stamps in these types, see Nos. 278, 279/84 and 314/5.

(**24**) — (**27**) Arms of Chile

1880. Optd with T **24**.

36	**15**	1 c. green	40	40
37	**16**	2 c. red	85	45
39		5 c. blue	1·60	70
40	**20**	50 c. green	23·00	14·50
41	**21**	1 s. red	60·00	38·00

1881. Optd as T **24**, but inscr "LIMA" at foot instead of "PERU".

42	**15**	1 c. green	60	30
43	**16**	2 c. red	11·50	7·50
44		5 c. blue	1·25	45
286		10 c. green	40	50
45	**20**	50 c. green	£375	£200
46	**21**	1 s. red	70·00	45·00

1881. Optd with T **27**.

57	**15**	1 c. orange	30	85
58	**16**	2 c. violet	30	3·25
59		2 c. red	1·40	15·00
60		5 c. blue	45·00	50·00
61		10 c. green	30	1·50
62		20 c. red	65·00	£100

(**28**) — (**28a**)

1882. Optd with T **27** and **28**.

63	**15**	1 c. green	45	65
64	**16**	5 c. blue	45	65
66	**20**	50 c. red	1·40	1·60
67	**21**	1 s. blue	2·75	3·75

1883. Optd with T **28** only.

200	**15**	1 c. green	1·00	1·00
201	**16**	2 c. red	1·00	3·25
202		5 c. blue	1·60	1·60
203	**20**	50 c. pink	48·00	
204	**21**	1 s. blue	25·00	

1883. Handstamped with T **28a** only.

206	**15**	1 c. orange	65	65
210	**16**	5 c. blue	6·25	4·25
211		10 c. green	65	65
216	**20**	50 c. green	5·75	3·00
220	**21**	1 s. red	8·25	5·00

1883. Optd with T **24** and **28a**, the inscription in oval reading "PERU".

223	**20**	50 c. green	£100	50·00
225	**21**	1 s. red	£120	75·00

1883. Optd with T **24** and **28a**, the inscription in oval reading "LIMA".

227	**15**	1 c. green	3·25	3·25
228	**16**	2 c. red	3·25	3·25
232		5 c. blue	5·50	5·00
234	**20**	50 c. green	£120	75·00
236	**21**	1 s. red	£130	£100

1883. Optd with T **28** and **28a**.

238	**15**	1 c. green	85	65
241	**16**	2 c. red	85	60
246		5 c. blue	1·00	65

1884. Optd **CORREOS LIMA** and sun.

277	**16**	5 c. blue	35	25

1886. Re-issue of 1866 and 1874 types.

278	**15**	1 c. violet	25	20
314		1 c. red	30	20
279	**16**	2 c. green	60	10
315		2 c. blue	25	20
280		5 c. orange	30	10
316	**10**	5 c. lake	1·00	35
281	**16**	10 c. black	15	10
317	–	10 c. orange (Llamas)	35	25
282	**16**	20 c. blue	4·25	35
318	–	20 c. blue (Llamas)	5·00	1·10
283	**20**	50 c. red	1·25	35
284	**21**	1 s. brown	1·00	35

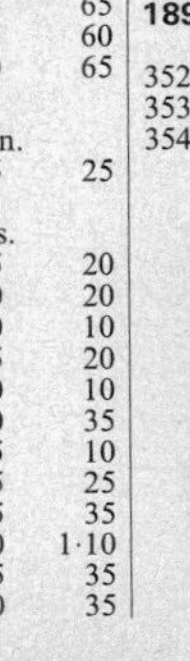

(**71** Pres. R. M. Bermudez) — **73**

1894. Optd with T **71**.

294	**15**	1 c. orange	50	25
295		1 c. green	20	20
296c	**16**	2 c. violet	15	15
297		2 c. red	25	20
298		5 c. blue	2·10	1·50
299		10 c. green	25	20
300	**20**	50 c. green	1·10	1·00

1894. Optd with T **28** and **71**.

301	**16**	2 c. red	20	20
302		5 c. blue	85	30
303	**20**	50 c. red	35·00	25·00
304	**21**	1 s. blue	85·00	75·00

1895. Installation of Pres. Nicolas de Pierola.

328	**73**	1 c. violet	1·00	75
329		2 c. green	1·00	75
330		5 c. yellow	1·00	75
331		10 c. blue	1·00	75
332	–	20 c. orange	1·00	80
333	–	50 c. blue	6·00	3·75
334	–	1 s. lake	32·00	21·00

Nos. 332/4 are larger (30 × 36 mm) and the central device is in a frame of laurel.

See also Nos. 352/4.

75 Atahualpa — **76** Pizarro

77 General de la Mar

1896.

335	**75**	1 c. blue	25	15
336		1 c. green	25	10
337		2 c. blue	20	15
338		2 c. red	20	10
341	**76**	5 c. blue	60	10
340		5 c. green	60	10
342		10 c. yellow	85	20
343		10 c. black	85	10
344		20 c. orange	1·60	25
345	**77**	50 c. red	4·25	50
346		1 s. red	6·25	85
347		2 s. lake	1·90	65

1897. No. D31 optd **FRANQUEO**.

348	D **22**	1 c. brown	25	25

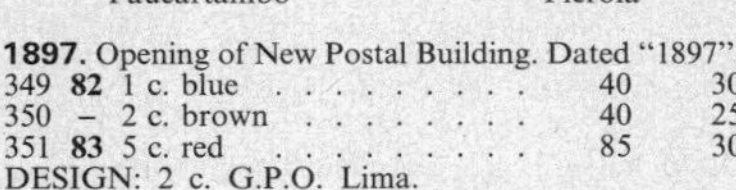

82 Suspension Bridge at Paucartambo — **83** Pres. D. Nicolas de Pierola

1897. Opening of New Postal Building. Dated "1897".

349	**82**	1 c. blue	40	30
350	–	2 c. brown	40	25
351	**83**	5 c. red	85	30

DESIGN: 2 c. G.P.O. Lima.

1899. As Nos. 328/34, but vert inscr replaced by pearl ornaments.

352	**73**	22 c. green	30	15
353	–	5 s. red	1·40	1·40
354	–	10 s. green	£350	£275

84 President Eduardo Lopez de Romana — **85** Admiral Grau

1900.

357	**84**	22 c. black and green	6·75	70

1901. Advent of the Twentieth Century.

358	**85**	1 c. black and green	70	25
359	–	2 c. black and red	70	25
360	–	5 c. black and lilac	1·00	25

PORTRAITS: 2 c. Col. Bolognesi; 5 c. Pres. Romana.

90 Municipal Board of Health Building

1905.

361	**90**	12 c. black and blue	70	25

1907. Surch.

362	**90**	1 c. on 12 c. black & blue	25	20
363		2 c. on 12 c. black & blue	50	35

97 Bolognesi Monument — **98** Admiral Grau

99 Llama — **101** Exhibition Buildings

103 G.P.O., Lima — **107** Columbus

1907.

364	**97**	1 c. black and green	25	15
365	**98**	2 c. purple and red	25	15
366	**99**	4 c. olive	4·50	60
367	–	5 c. black and blue	40	10
368	**101**	10 c. black and brown	1·00	25
369	–	20 c. black and green	19·00	50
370	**103**	50 c. black	19·00	70
371	–	1 s. green and violet	£100	2·10
372	–	2 s. black and blue	£100	85·00

DESIGNS—VERT: As Type **98**: 5 c. Statue of Bolivar. (24 × 33 mm): 2 c. Columbus Monument. HORIZ: As Type **101**: 20 c. Medical School, Lima. (33 × 24 mm): 1 s. Grandstand, Santa Beatrice Race-course, Lima.

1909. Portraits.

373	–	1 c. grey (Manco Capac)	15	15
374	**107**	2 c. green	15	15
375	–	4 c. red (Pizarro)	40	15
376	–	5 c. purple (San Martin)	15	10
377	–	10 c. blue (Bolivar)	55	15
378	–	12 c. blue (de la Mar)	85	25
379	–	20 c. brown (Castilla)	90	40
380	–	50 c. orange (Grau)	4·25	30
381	–	1 s. black and lake (Bolognesi)	8·25	30

See also Nos. 406/13, 431/5, 439/40 and 484/9.

1913. Surch **UNION POSTAL 8 Cts. Sud Americana** in oval.

382	**90**	8 c. on 12 c. black & blue	55	20

1915. As 1896, 1905 and 1907, surch **1915**, and value.

383	**75**	1 c. on 1 c. green	13·50	10·00
384	**97**	1 c. on 1 c. black & green	70	50
385	**98**	1 c. on 2 c. purple & red	1·00	85
386	**76**	1 c. on 10 c. black	85	60
387	**99**	1 c. on 4 c. green	1·60	1·40
388	**101**	1 c. on 10 c. black & brn	35	20
389		2 c. on 10 c. black & brn	85·00	65·00
390	**90**	2 c. on 12 c. black & blue	25	15
391	–	2 c. on 20 c. black and green (No. 369)	11·50	10·00
392	**103**	2 c. on 50 c. black	1·60	1·60

1916. Surch **VALE**, value and **1916**.

393		1 c. on 12 c. blue (378)	15	15
394		1 c. on 20 c. brown (379)	15	15
395		1 c. on 50 c. orange (380)	15	15
396		2 c. on 4 c. red (375)	15	15
397		10 c. on 1 s. black & lake (381)	40	25

1916. Official stamps of 1909 optd **FRANQUEO 1916** or surch **VALE 2 Cts** also.

398	O **108**	1 c. red	15	15
399		2 c. on 50 c. olive	15	15
400		10 c. brown	20	15

1916. Postage Due stamps of 1909 surch **FRANQUEO VALE 2 Cts. 1916**.

401	D **109**	2 c. on 1 c. brown	40	40
402		2 c. on 5 c. brown	15	15
403		2 c. on 10 c. brown	15	15
404		2 c. on 50 c. brown	15	15

1917. Surch **Un Centavo.**
405 1 c. on 4 c. (No. 375) 20 15

1918. Portraits as T **107**.
406 1 c. black & orge (San Martin) 10 10
407 2 c. black & green (Bolivar) . 15 10
408 4 c. black and red (Galvez) . 25 10
409 5 c. black and blue (Pardo) . . 15 10
410 8 c. black and brown (Grau) . 50 25
411 10 c. black & blue (Bolognesi) 35 10
412 12 c. black & lilac (Castilla) . 70 15
413 20 c. black & green (Caceres) . 85 15

126 Columbus at Salamanca University **129** A. B. Leguia

1918.
414 **126** 50 c. black and brown . 4·25 35
415a – 1 s. black and green . . . 10·00 50
416 – 2 s. black and blue . . . 18·00 55
DESIGNS: 1 s. Funeral of Atahualpa; 2 s. Battle of Arica.

1920. New Constitution.
417 **129** 5 c. black and blue . . . 15 15
418 5 c. black and brown . . 15 15

130 San Martin **131** Oath of Independence

132 Admiral Cochrane **137** J. Olaya

1921. Centenary of Independence.
419 **130** 1 c. brown (San Martin) . 25 15
420 2 c. green (Arenales) . . . 25 15
421 4 c. red (Las Heras) . . . 85 50
422 **131** 5 c. brown 35 15
423 **132** 7 c. violet 70 35
424 **130** 10 c. blue (Guisse) 70 35
425 12 c. black (Vidal) . . . . 2·00 40
426 20 c. blk & red (Leguia) . 2·00 70
427 50 c. violet and purple (S. Martin Monument) . 6·00 2·00
428 **131** 1 s. green and red (San Martin and Leguia) . . 10·00 3·00

1923. Surch **CINCO Centavos 1923**.
429 5 c. on 8 c. black and brown (No. 410) 40 20

1924. Surch **CUATRO Centavos 1924**.
430 4 c. on 5 c. (No. 409) 25 15

1924. Portraits as T **107**. Size 18½ × 23 mm.
431 2 c. olive (Rivadeneyra) . . . 10 10
432 4 c. green (Melgar) 10 10
433 8 c. black (Iturregui) . . . . 1·60 1·60
434 10 c. red (A. B. Leguia) . . . 15 10
435 15 c. blue (De la Mar) . . . 50 15
439 1 s. brown (De Saco) . . . . 7·50 85
440 2 s. blue (J. Leguia) . . . . . 19·00 4·25

1924. Monuments.
436 **137** 20 c. blue 70 10
437 20 c. yellow . . . . 1·25 15
438 – 50 c. purple (Bellido) . . . 4·25 35
See also Nos. 484/9.

139 Simon Bolivar **140**

1924. Centenary of Battle of Ayacucho. Portraits of Bolivar.
441 – 2 c. olive 35 10
442 **139** 4 c. green 40 10
443 5 c. black 85 10
444 **140** 10 c. red 40 10
445 – 20 c. blue 85 15
446 – 50 c. lilac . . . . 3·00 50
447 – 1 s. brown . . . . 8·25 2·00
448 – 2 s. blue . . . . 17·00 8·25

1925. Surch **DOS Centavos 1925**.
449 **137** 2 c. on 20 c. blue 85 50

1925. Optd **Plebiscito**.
450 10 c. red (No. 434) 70 70

143 The Rock of Arica **146**

1925. Obligatory Tax. Tacna-Arica Plebiscite.
451 **143** 2 c. orange 25 10
452 5 c. blue . . . . 1·25 50
453 5 c. red 65 40
454 5 c. green 60 40
455 – 10 c. brown . . . . . . 2·50 85
456 – 50 c. green . . . . . . 16·00 7·50
DESIGNS—HORIZ: 39 × 30 mm: 10 c. Soldiers with colours. VERT: 27 × 33 mm: 50 c. Bolognesi Statue.

1927. Obligatory Tax. Figures of value not encircled.
457 **146** 2 c. orange 50 15
458 2 c. brown 50 15
459 2 c. blue 50 15
460 2 c. violet 35 15
461 2 c. green 35 15
462 20 c. red . . . . 2·10 85

1927. Air. Optd **Servicio Aereo**.
463 **9** 50 c. purple (No. 438) . . . 35·00 25·00

148 Pres. A. B. Leguia **149** Rock of Arica

1928. Air.
464 **148** 50 c. green 70 35

1928. Obligatory Tax. Plebiscite Fund.
465 **149** 2 c. mauve 15 10

1929. Surch **Habilitada 2 Cts. 1929**.
466 – 2 c. on 8 c. (No. 410) . . 50 50
468 **137** 15 c. on 20 c. (No. 437) . 70 70

1929. Surch **Habilitada 2 centavos 1929**.
467 2 c. on 8 c. (No. 410) 70 70

1930. Optd **Habilitada Franqueo**.
469 **149** 2 c. mauve 30 30

1930. Surch **Habilitada 2 Cts. 1930**.
470 **137** 2 c. on 20 c. yellow 25 25

1930. Surch **Habilitada Franqueo** 2 Cts. 1930.
471 **148** 2 c. on 50 c. green . . . 25 25

156 Arms of Peru **157** Lima Cathedral

1930. 6th (inscribed "seventh") Pan-American Child Congress.
472 **156** 2 c. green 60 55
473 **157** 5 c. red . . . . 1·40 1·00
474 – 10 c. blue 90 85
475 – 50 c. brown . . . . . . 15·00 10·00
DESIGNS—HORIZ: 10 c. G.P.O., Lima. VERT: 50 c. Madonna and Child.

1930. Fall of Leguia Govt. No. 434 optd with Arms of Peru or surch with new value in four corners also.
477 2 c. on 10 c. red 10 10
478 4 c. on 10 c. red 20 20
479 10 c. red 15 10
476 15 c. on 10 c. red 20 15

159 Simon Bolivar **161** Pizarro

162 The Old Stone Bridge, Lima

1930. Death Centenary of Bolivar.
480 **159** 2 c. brown 35 20
481 4 c. red 70 30
482 10 c. green 35 25
483 15 c. grey 70 50

1930. As T **107** and **137** but smaller 18 × 22 mm.
484 – 2 c. olive (Rivadeneyra) . . 15 10
485 – 4 c. green (Melgar) 15 10
486 – 15 c. blue (De la Mar) . . 50 10
487 **137** 20 c. yellow (Olaya) . . . 1·00 20
488 – 50 c. purple (Bellido) . . . 1·00 25
489 – 1 s. brown (De Saco) . . . 1·60 35

1931. Obligatory Tax. Unemployment Fund. Surch **Habilitada Pro Desocupados 2 Cts.**
490 **159** 2 c. on 4 c. red 70 35
491 2 c. on 10 c. green 50 35
492 2 c. on 15 c. grey 50 35

1931. 1st Peruvian Philatelic Exhibition.
493 **161** 2 c. slate . . . . 1·40 1·10
494 4 c. brown . . . . 1·40 1·10
495 **162** 10 c. red . . . . 1·40 1·10
496 10 c. green and mauve . . 1·40 1·10
497 **161** 15 c. green . . . . . . 1·40 1·10
498 **162** 15 c. red and grey . . . 1·40 1·10
499 15 c. blue and orange . . . 1·40 1·10

163 Manco Capac **164** Oil Well **170**

1931.
500 **163** 2 c. olive 20 10
501 **164** 4 c. green 40 30
502 – 10 c. orange 85 10
503 – 15 c. blue . . . . 1·25 25
504 – 20 c. yellow . . . . . . 4·25 40
505 – 50 c. lilac . . . . 5·00 40
506 – 1 s. brown . . . . 11·00 85
DESIGNS—VERT: 10 c. Sugar Plantation; 15 c. Cotton Plantation; 50 c. Copper Mines. 1 s. Llamas. HORIZ: 20 c. Guano Islands.

1931. Obligatory Tax. Unemployment Fund.
507 **170** 2 c. green 10 10
508 2 c. red 10 10

171 Arms of Piura **172** Parakas

1932. 4th Centenary of Piura.
509 **171** 10 c. blue (postage) . . . 5·00 5·00
510 15 c. violet . . . . 5·00 5·00
511 50 c. red (air) . . . . . . 17·00 16·00

1932. 400th Anniv of Spanish Conquest of Peru. Native designs.
512 **172** 10 c. pur (22 × 19½ mm) . . 15 10
513 – 15 c. lake (25 × 19½ mm) . . 35 10
514 – 50 c. brn (19½ × 22 mm) . . 75 15
DESIGNS: 15 c. Chimu; 50 c. Inca.

175 Arequipa and El Misti **176** Pres. Sanchez Cerro

1932. 1st Anniv of Constitutional Government.
515 **175** 2 c. blue 15 10
527 2 c. black 15 10
528 2 c. green 15 10
516 4 c. brown 15 10
529 4 c. orange 15 10
517 **176** 10 c. red . . . . 11·00 8·25
530 – 10 c. red 50 10
518 – 15 c. blue 35 10
531 – 15 c. mauve 35 10
519 – 20 c. lake 50 10
532 – 20 c. violet 50 15
520 – 50 c. green 70 15
521 – 1 s. orange . . . . . . 5·00 35
533 – 1 s. brown . . . . 6·25 40
DESIGNS—VERT: 10 c. (No. 530), Statue of Liberty; 15 c. to 1 s. Bolivar Monument, Lima.

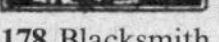

178 Blacksmith **179** Monument of 2nd May to Battle of Callao

1932. Obligatory Tax. Unemployment Fund.
522 **178** 2 c. grey 10 10
523 2 c. violet 10 10

1933. Obligatory Tax. Unemployment Fund.
524 **179** 2 c. violet 15 10
525 2 c. orange 15 10
526 2 c. purple 15 10

181 Hawker Hart Bomber **184** F. Pizarro

185 Coronation of Huascar **186** The Inca

1934. Air.
534 **181** 2 s. blue . . . . 4·50 35
535 5 s. brown . . . . 9·50 70

1934. Obligatory Tax. Unemployment Fund. Optd **Pro-Desocupados**. (a) In one line.
536 **176** 2 c. green 10 10
585 – 2 c. purple (No. 537) . . 10 10

(b) In two lines.
566 – 2 c. purple (No. 537) . . . 10 10

1934.
537 – 2 c. purple 10 10
538 – 4 c. green 15 10
539 **184** 10 c. red 15 10
540 15 c. blue 50 10
541 **185** 20 c. blue . . . . 1·00 15
542 50 c. brown . . . . 1·00 15
543 **186** 1 s. violet . . . . 2·40 35
DESIGNS: 2, 4 c. show the scene depicted in Type **189**.

187 Lake of the Marvellous Cure **188** Grapes

1935. Tercentenary of Founding of Ica.
544 – 4 c. black 65 65
545 **187** 5 c. red 25 65
546 **188** 10 c. mauve . . . . . . 2·75 1·40
547 **187** 20 c. green . . . . 1·00 1·00
548 – 35 c. red . . . . 5·50 3·25
549 – 50 c. brown and orange . 3·75 3·25
550 – 1 s. red and violet . . . . 11·00 8·25
DESIGNS—HORIZ: 4 c. City of Ica; 50 c. Don Diego Lopez and King Philip IV of Spain. VERT: 35 c. Cotton blossom; 1 s. Supreme God of the Nazcas.

189 Pizarro and "The Thirteen"

192 Funeral of Atahualpa

1935. 4th Centenary of Founding of Lima.

551 **189** 2 c. brown (postage) 35 20
552 – 4 c. violet 50 35
553 – 10 c. red 50 20
554 – 15 c. blue 85 40
555 **189** 20 c. grey 1·10 50
556 – 50 c. green 1·60 1·25
557 – 1 s. blue 3·75 2·40
558 – 2 s. brown 8·75 6·75

DESIGNS—HORIZ: 4 c. Lima Cathedral. VERT: 10 c., 50 c. Miss L. S. de Canevaro; 15 c., 2 s. Pizarro; 1 s. The "Tapada" (a veiled woman).

559 **192** 5 c. green (air) 35 20
560 – 35 c. brown 75 35
561 – 50 c. yellow 1·25 70
562 – 1 s. purple 1·75 75
563 – 2 s. orange 1·50 1·50
564 **192** 5 s. purple 6·25 4·25
565 **189** 10 s. blue 23·00 19·00

DESIGNS—HORIZ: 35 c. Airplane near San Cristobal Hill; 50 c., 1 s. Airplane over Avenue of Barefoot Friars. VERT: 2 s. Palace of Torre Tagle.

207 "San Cristobal" (caravel)

1936. Callao Centenary.

567 **207** 2 c. black (postage) 90 20
568 – 4 c. green 45 15
569 – 5 c. brown 45 15
570 – 10 c. blue 45 20
571 – 15 c. green 1·40 25
572 – 20 c. brown 45 25
573 – 50 c. lilac 90 45
574 – 1 s. olive 18·00 1·60
575 – 2 s. purple 11·00 5·00
576 – 5 s. red 15·00 11·50
577 – 10 s. brown and red 38·00 29·00

578 – 35 c. slate (air) 2·10 2·10

DESIGNS—HORIZ: 4 c. La Punta Naval College; 5 c. Independence Square, Callao; 10 c. Aerial view of Callao; 15 c. "Reina del Pacifico" (liner) in Callao Docks and Custom House; 20 c. Plan of Callao, 1746; 35 c. "La Callao" (early locomotive); 1 s. Gunboat "Sacramento"; 10 s. Real Felipe Fortifications. VERT: 50 c. D. Jose de la Mar; 2 s. Don Jose de Velasco; 5 s. Fort Maipo and miniature portraits of Galvez and Nunez.

1936. Obligatory Tax. St. Rosa de Lima Cathedral Construction Fund. Optd **"Ley 8310"**.

579 **179** 2 c. purple 10 10

1936. Surch **Habilitado** and value in figures and words.

580 – 2 c. on 4 c. green (No. 538) (postage) 10 10
581 **185** 10 c. on 20 c. blue 15 15
582 **186** 10 c. on 1 s. violet 20 20

583 **181** 5 c. on 2 s. blue (air) 35 15
584 25 c. on 5 s. brown 70 25

211 Guanay Cormorants

217 Mail Steamer "Inca" on Lake Titicaca

1936.

586 **211** 2 c. brown (postage) 1·50 15
616 – 2 c. green 1·25 15
587 – 4 c. brown 50 25
617 – 4 c. black 25 15
618 – 10 c. red 10 10
619 – 15 c. blue 20 10
590 – 20 c. black 70 15
620 – 20 c. brown 25 15
591 – 50 c. yellow 2·10 50
621 – 50 c. grey 70 15
592 – 1 s. purple 4·25 70
622 – 1 s. blue 1·40 35
593 – 2 s. blue 9·00 2·00
623 – 2 s. violet 3·00 35
594 – 5 s. blue 9·00 3·00
595 – 10 s. brown and violet 50·00 19·00

DESIGNS—VERT: 4 c. Oil well; 10 c. Inca postal runner; 1 s. G.P.O., Lima; 2 s. M. de Amat y Junyent; 5 s. J. A. de Pando y Riva; 10 s. J. D. Condemarin. HORIZ: 15 c. Paseo de la Republica, Lima; 20 c. Municipal Palace and Natural History Museum; 50 c. University of San Marcos, Lima.

See also Nos. 616/23.

596 – 5 c. green (air) 25 10
625 **217** 15 c. blue 70 15
598 – 20 c. grey 90 15
626 – 20 c. green 85 15
627 – 25 c. red 40 10
628 – 30 c. brown 80 15
600 – 35 c. brown 1·60 1·40
601 – 50 c. yellow 25 35
629 – 50 c. red 40 20
630 – 70 c. green 1·25 50
603 – 80 c. black 5·00 3·00
631 – 80 c. green 1·25 30

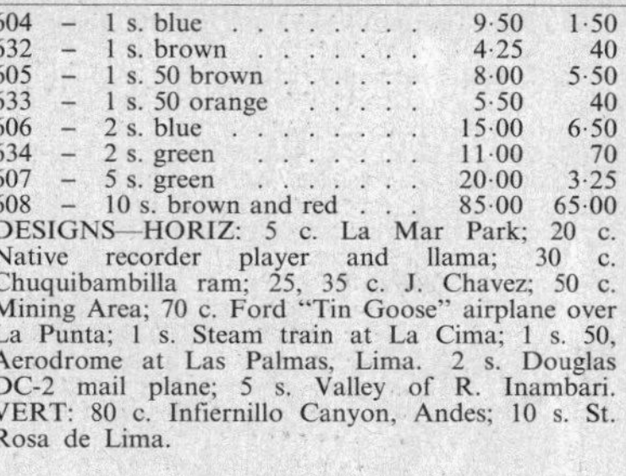

604 – 1 s. blue 9·50 1·50
632 – 1 s. brown 4·25 40
605 – 1 s. 50 brown 8·00 5·50
633 – 1 s. 50 orange 5·50 40
606 – 2 s. blue 15·00 6·50
634 – 2 s. green 11·00 70
607 – 5 s. green 20·00 3·25
608 – 10 s. brown and red 85·00 65·00

DESIGNS—HORIZ: 5 c. La Mar Park; 20 c. Native recorder player and llama; 30 c. Chuquibambilla ram; 25, 35 c. J. Chavez; 50 c. Mining Area; 70 c. Ford "Tin Goose" airplane over La Punta; 1 s. Steam train at La Cima; 1 s. 50, Aerodrome at Las Palmas, Lima. 2 s. Douglas DC-2 mail plane; 5 s. Valley of R. Inambari. VERT: 80 c. Infiernillo Canyon, Andes; 10 s. St. Rosa de Lima.

223 St. Rosa de Lima

1937. Obligatory Tax. St. Rosa de Lima Construction Fund.

609 **223** 2 c. red 15 10

1937. Surch **Habilit.** and value in figures and words.

(a) Postage.

610 1 s. on 2 s. blue (593) 2·10 2·10

(b) Air.

611 15 c. on 30 c. brown (599) 45 40
612 15 c. on 35 c. brown (600) 45 25
613 15 c. on 70 c. green (630) 2·75 2·25
614 25 c. on 80 c. black (603) 2·75 2·25
615 1 s. on 2 s. blue (606) 4·25 3·00

225 Bielovucic over Lima

226 Jorge Chavez

1937. Air. Pan-American Aviation Conf.

635 **225** 10 c. violet 40 10
636 **226** 15 c. green 50 10
637 – 25 c. brown 40 10
638 – 1 s. black 1·90 1·00

DESIGNS—As T **225**: 25 c. Limatambo Airport; 1 s. Peruvian air routes.

229 "Protection" (by John Q. A. Ward)

230 Children's Holiday Camp

1938. Obligatory Tax. Unemployment Fund.

757c **229** 2 c. brown 10 10

1938. Designs as T **230**.

693 **230** 2 c. green 10 10
694 – 4 c. brown 10 10
642 – 10 c. red 20 10
696 – 15 c. blue 10 10
727 – 15 c. turquoise 10 10
644 – 20 c. purple 15 10
740 – 20 c. violet 10 10
698 – 50 c. blue 15 10
741 – 50 c. brown 15 10
699 – 1 s. purple 85 10
742 – 1 s. brown 25 10
700 – 2 s. green 2·50 10
731 – 2 s. blue 55 10
701 – 5 s. brown and violet 5·75 35
732 – 5 s. purple and blue 75 35
702 – 10 s. blue and black 10·00 50
733 – 10 s. black and green 2·50 70

DESIGNS—VERT: 4 c. Chavin pottery; 10 c. Auto-mobile roads in Andes; 20 c. (2) Industrial Bank of Peru; 1 s. (2) Portrait of Toribio de Luzuriaga; 5 s. (2) Chavin Idol. HORIZ: 15 c. (2) Archaeological Museum, Lima; 50 c. (2) Labourers' homes at Lima; 2 s. (2) Fig Tree; 10 s. (2) Mt. Huascaran.

240 Monument on Junin Plains

248 Seal of City of Lima

1938. Air. As T **240**.

650 – 5 c. brown 15 10
743 – 5 c. green 10 10
651 **240** 15 c. brown 15 10
652 – 20 c. red 40 10
653 – 25 c. green 20 10
654 – 30 c. orange 20 10
735 – 30 c. red 15 10
655 – 50 c. green 35 30
736 – 70 c. blue 1·10 10
657 – 80 c. green 60 10
737 – 80 c. red 55 15
658 – 1 s. green 4·50 2·10
705 – 1 s. 50 violet 45 35
738 – 1 s. 50 purple 45 30
660 – 2 s. red and blue 1·60 50
661 – 5 s. purple 8·25 70
662 – 10 s. blue and green 32·00 20·00

DESIGNS—VERT: 20 c. Rear-Admiral M. Villar; 70 c. Infiernillo Canyon; 2 s. Stele from Chavin Temple. HORIZ: 5 c. People's restaurant, Callao; 25 c. View of Tarma; 30 c. Ica River irrigation system; 50 c. Port of Iquitos; 80 c. Mountain roadway; 1 s. Plaza San Martin, Lima; 1 s. 50, Nat. Radio Station, San Miguel; 5 s. Ministry of Public Works; 10 s. Heroe's Crypt, Lima.

1938. 8th Pan-American Congress, Lima.

663 – 10 c. grey (postage) 50 20
664 **248** 15 c. gold, blue, red & blk 85 25
665 – 1 s. brown 1·60 85

DESIGNS (39 × 32½ mm): 10 c. Palace and Square, 1864; 1 s. Palace, 1938.

666 – 25 c. blue (air) 55 50
667 – 1 s. 50 lake 1·50 1·25
668 – 2 s. black 90 45

DESIGNS—VERT: 26 × 37 mm: 25 c. Torre Tagle Palace. HORIZ: 39 × 32½ mm: 1 s. 50, National Congress Building, Lima; 2 s. Congress Presidents, Ferreyros, Paz Soldan and Arenas.

1940. No. 642 surch **Habilitada 5 cts.**

669 5 c. on 10 c. red 15 10

251 National Broadcasting Station

1941. Optd **FRANQUEO POSTAL**.

670 **251** 50 c. yellow 1·60 15
671 1 s. violet 1·60 20
672 2 s. green 3·25 50
673 5 s. brown 19·00 5·50
674 10 s. mauve 29·00 4·25

1942. Air. No. 653 surch **Habilit 0.15**.

675 15 c. on 25 c. green 85 10

253 Map of S. America showing R. Amazon

254 Francisco de Orellana

255 Francisco Pizarro

257 Samuel Morse

1943. 400th Anniv of Discovery of R. Amazon.

676 – 2 c. red 10 10
677 **254** 4 c. grey 15 10
678 **255** 10 c. brown 20 10
679 **253** 15 c. blue 50 20
680 – 20 c. olive 20 15
681 – 25 c. orange 1·40 35
682 **254** 30 c. red 35 20
683 **253** 50 c. green 35 40
685 – 70 c. violet 2·00 70
686 – 80 c. blue 2·00 70
687 – 1 s. brown 3·25 70
688 **255** 5 s. black 6·75 3·25

DESIGNS—As Type **254**: 2, 70 c. Portraits of G. Pizarro and Orellana in medallion; 20, 80 c. G. Pizarro. As Type **253**: 25 c., 1 s. Orellana's Discovery of the R. Amazon.

1943. Surch with Arms of Peru (as Nos. 483, etc) above **10 CTVS**.

689 10 c. on 10 c. red (No. 642) 15 10

1944. Centenary of Invention of Telegraphy.

691 **257** 15 c. blue 15 15
692 30 c. brown 50 20

1946. Surch **Habilitada S/o 0.20**.

706 20 c. on 1 s. purple (No. 699) 25 10

259

261

1947. 1st National Tourist Congress, Lima. Unissued designs inscr "V Congreso Pan Americano de Carretas 1944" optd **Habilitada I Congreso Nac. de Turismo Lima—1947**.

707 **259** 15 c. black and red 25 15
708 – 1 s. brown 35 20
709 – 1 s. 35 green 35 25
710 **261** 3 s. blue 85 50
711 – 5 s. green 1·75 1·25

DESIGNS—VERT: 1 s. Mountain road; 1 s. 35, Forest road. HORIZ: 5 s. Road and house.

1947. Air. 1st Peruvian Int Airways Lima–New York Flight. Optd with PIA badge and **PRIMER VUELO LIMA—NUEVA YORK**.

712 5 c. brown (No. 650) 10 10
713 50 c. green (No. 655) 15 10

263 Basketball Players

1948. Air. Olympic Games.

714 – 1 s. blue 1·25 1·25
715 **263** 2 s. brown 1·60 1·60
716 – 5 s. green 2·75 2·75
717 – 10 s. yellow 3·25 3·25

DESIGNS: 1 s. Map showing air route from Peru to Great Britain; 5 s. Discus thrower; 10 s. Rifleman.

No. 714 is inscr "AEREO" and Nos. 715/17 are optd **AEREO**.

The above stamps exist overprinted **MELBOURNE 1956** but were only valid for postage on one day.

1948. Air. Nos. 653, 736 and 657 surch **Habilitada S/o.** and value.

722 5 c. on 25 c. green 10 10
723 10 c. on 25 c. green 10 10
718 10 c. on 70 c. blue 15 15
719 15 c. on 70 c. blue 15 15
720 20 c. on 70 c. blue 15 15
724 30 c. on 80 c. green 55 15
721 55 c. on 70 c. blue 15 15

263a

263b

1949. Anti-Tuberculosis Fund. Surch **Decreto Ley No. 18** and value.

724a **263a** 3 c. on 4 c. blue 55 10
724b **263b** 3 c. in 10 c. blue 55 10

264 Statue of Admiral Grau

264a "Education"

1949.

726 **264** 10 c. blue and green 10 10

1950. Obligatory Tax. National Education Fund.

851 **264a** 3 c. lake (16½ × 21 mm) 10 10
897 3 c. lake (18 × 21½ mm) 15 10

265 Park, Lima 268 Obrero Hospital, Lima

1951. Air. 75th Anniv of U.P.U. Unissued stamps inscr "VI CONGRESO DE LA UNION POSTAL DE LAS AMREICAS Y ESPANA-1949" optd **U.P.U. 1874-1949.**

745 **265** 5 c. green 10 10
746 – 30 c. red and black . . . 15 10
747 – 55 c. green 15 10
748 – 95 c. turquoise 20 15
749 – 1 s. 50 red 30 25
750 – 2 s. blue 35 30
751 – 5 s. red . . . . 2·10 2·10
752 – 10 s. violet . . . . . . 2·75 3·00
753 – 20 s. blue and brown . . . 4·50 4·50

DESIGNS: 30 c. Peruvian flag; 55 c. Huancayo Hotel; 95 c. Ancash Mtns; 1 s. 50, Arequipa Hotel; 2 s. Coaling Jetty; 5 s. Town Hall, Miraflores; 10 s. Congressional Palace; 20 s. Pan-American flags.

1951. Air Surch **HABILITADA S/O.0.25.**

754 25 c. on 30 c. red (No. 735) . . 15 10

1951. Surch **HABILITADA S/.** and figures.

755 1 c. on 2 c. (No. 693) 10 10
756 5 c. on 15 c. (No. 727) 10 10
757 10 c. on 15 c. (No. 727) . . . 10 10

1951. 5th Pan-American Highways Congress. Unissued "VI CONGRESO DE LA UNION POSTAL" stamps, optd **V Congreso Panamericano de Carreteras 1951**.

758 – 2 c. green 10 10
759 **268** 4 c. red 10 10
760 – 15 c. grey 10 10
761 – 20 c. brown 10 10
762 – 50 c. purple 15 10
763 – 1 s. blue 20 10
764 – 2 s. blue 30 10
765 – 5 s. red . . . . 1·00 1·00
766 – 10 s. brown . . . . 1·75 85

DESIGNS—HORIZ: 2 c. Aguas Promenade; 50 c. Archiepiscopal Palace, Lima; 1 s. National Judicial Palace; 2 s. Municipal Palace; 5 s. Lake Llanganuco, Ancash. VERT: 15 c. Inca postal runner; 20 c. Old P.O., Lima; 10 s. Machu-Picchu ruins.

269 Father Tomas de San Martin and Capt. J. de Aliaga

1951. Air. 4th Cent of S. Marcos University.

767 **269** 30 c. black 10 10
768 – 40 c. blue 15 10
769 – 50 c. mauve 20 10
770 – 1 s. 20 green 30 15
771 – 2 s. grey 35 15
772 – 5 s. multicoloured 90 20

DESIGNS: 40 c. San Marcos University; 50 c. Santo Domingo Convent; 1 s. 20, P. de Peralto Barnuevo, Father Tomas de San Martin and Jose Baquijano; 2 s. Toribio Rodriguez, Jose Hipolito Unanue and Jose Cayetano Heredia; 5 s. University Arms in 1571 and 1735.

270 Engineer's School

1952. (a) Postage.

774 – 2 c. purple 10 10
775 – 5 c. green 15 10
776 – 10 c. green 25 10
777 – 15 c. grey 10 10
777a – 15 c. brown 90 20
829 – 20 c. brown 20 10
779 **270** 25 c. red 15 10
779a 25 c. green 30 10
780 – 30 c. blue 10 10
780a – 30 c. red 15 10
830 – 30 c. mauve 15 10
924 – 50 c. green 20 10
831 – 50 c. purple 15 10
782 – 1 s. brown 30 10
782a – 1 s. blue 30 10
783 – 2 s. turquoise 40 10
783a – 2 s. grey 55 15

DESIGNS—As Type **270**: HORIZ: 2 c. Hotel, Tacna; 5 c. Tuna fishing boat and indigenous fish; 10 c. View of Matarani; 15 c. Steam train; 30 c. Public Health and Social Assistance. VERT: 20 c. Vicuna. Larger (35 × 25 mm): HORIZ: 50 c. Inca maize terraces; 1 s. Inca ruins, Paramonga Fort; 2 s. Agriculture Monument, Lima.

(b) Air.

784 – 40 c. green 30 10
785 – 75 c. brown . . . . 1·50 25
834 – 80 c. red . . . . 1·25 10
786 – 1 s. 25 blue 25 10
787 – 1 s. 50 red 20 10
788 – 2 s. 20 blue 65 15
789 – 3 s. brown 75 25
835 – 3 s. green 50 30
836 – 3 s. 80 orange 85 35
790 – 5 s. brown 50 15
791 – 10 s. brown . . . . 1·50 35
838 – 10 s. red . . . . 1·00 45

DESIGNS—As Type **270**: HORIZ: 40 c. Gunboat "Maranon"; 1 s. 50, Housing Complex. VERT: 75 c., 80 c. Colony Guanay Cormorants. Larger (25 × 25 mm.): HORIZ: 1 s. 25, Corpac-Limatambo Airport; 2 s. 20, 3 s. 80, Inca Observatory, Cuzco; 5 s. Garcilaso (portrait). VERT: 3 s. Tobacco plant, leaves and cigarettes; 10 s. Manco Capac Monument (25 × 37 mm).

See also Nos. 867, etc.

271 Isabella the Catholic

272 "Santa Maria", "Pinta" and "Nina" 273

1953. Air. 500th Birth Anniv of Isabella the Catholic.

792 **271** 40 c. red 20 10
793 **272** 1 s. 25 green . . . . . . 1·40 30
794 **271** 2 s. 15 purple 35 25
795 **272** 2 s. 20 black . . . . . . 3·25 55

1954. Obligatory Tax. National Marian Eucharistic Congress Fund. Roul.

796 **273** 5 c. blue and red 25 10

274 Gen. M. Perez Jimenez 275 Arms of Lima and Bordeaux

1956. Visit of President of Venezuela.

797 **274** 25 c. brown 10 10

1957. Air. Exn. of French Products. Lima.

798 **275** 40 c. lake, blue and green 10 10
799 – 50 c. black, brown & grn 15 10
800 – 1 s. 25 deep blue, green and blue . . . . 1·25 35
801 – 2 s. 20 brown and blue . . 40 30

DESIGNS—HORIZ: 50 c. Eiffel Tower and Lima Cathedral; 1 s. 25, Admiral Dupetit-Thouars and frigate "La Victorieuse"; 2 s. 20, Exhibition building, Pres. Prado and Pres. Coty.

276 1857 Stamp 277 Carlos Paz Soldan (founder)

1957. Air. Centenary of First Peruvian Postage Stamp.

802 – 5 c. black and grey . . . 10 10
803 **276** 10 c. turquoise and mauve 10 10
804 – 15 c. brown and green . . 10 10
805 – 25 c. blue and yellow . . 10 10
806 – 30 c. brown & chocolate . 10 10
807 – 40 c. ochre and black . . 15 10
808 – 1 s. 25 brown and blue . . 35 25
809 – 2 s. 20 red and blue . . . 50 30
810 – 5 s. red and mauve . . . 1·00 1·00
811 – 10 s. violet and green . . 1·60 1·50

DESIGNS: 5 c. Pre-stamp Postmarks; 15 c. 1857 2 r. stamp; 25 c. 1 d. 1858; 30 c. 1 p. 1858 stamp; 40 c. ½ peso 1858 stamp; 1 s. 25, J. Davila Condemarin, Director of Posts, 1857; 2 s. 20, Pres. Ramon Castilla; 5 s. Pres. D. M. Prado; 10 s. Various Peruvian stamps in shield.

1958. Air. Centenary of Lima–Callao Telegraph Service.

812 **277** 40 c. brown and red . . . 10 10
813 – 1 s. green 15 10
814 – 1 s. 25 blue and purple . . 25 15

DESIGNS—VERT: 1 s. Marshal Ramon Castilla. HORIZ: 1 s. 25, Pres. D. M. Prado and view of Callao; No. 814 also commemorates the political centenary of the Province of Callao.

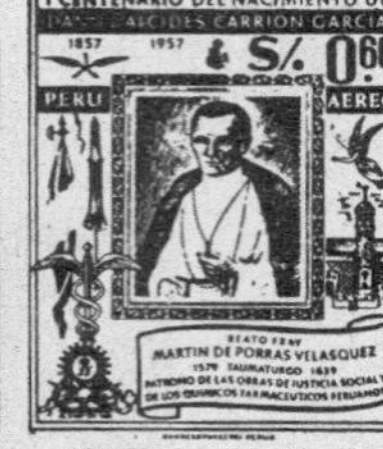

278 Flags of France and Peru 279 Father Martin de Porras Velasquez

1958. Air. "Treasures of Peru" Exhibition, Paris.

815 **278** 50 c. red, blue & dp blue . 10 10
816 – 65 c. multicoloured 10 10
817 – 1 s. 50 brown, purple & bl 25 10
818 – 2 s. 50 purple, turq and green 35 20

DESIGNS—HORIZ: 65 c. Lima Cathedral and girl in national costume; 1 s. 50, Caballero and ancient palace. VERT: 2 s. 50, Natural resources map of Peru.

1958. Air. Birth Centenary of D. A. Carrion Garcia (patriot).

819 **279** 60 c. multicoloured . . . 10 10
820 – 1 s. 20 multicoloured . . . 15 10
821 – 1 s. 50 multicoloured . . . 25 10
822 – 2 s. 20 black 30 20

DESIGNS—VERT: 1 s. 20, D. A. Carrion Garcia. 1 s. 50, J. H. Unanue Pavon. HORIZ: 2 s. 20, First Royal School of Medicine (now Ministry of Government Police, Posts and Telecommunications).

280 Gen. Alvarez Thomas 281 Association Emblems

1958. Air. Death Centenary of Gen. Thomas.

823 **280** 1 s. 10 purple, red & bistre 20 15
824 1 s. 20 black, red & bistre . 25 15

1958. Air. 150th Anniv of Advocates' College, Lima. Emblems in bistre and blue.

825 **281** 80 c. green 10 10
826 1 s. 10 red 15 10
827 1 s. 20 blue 15 10
828 1 s. 50 purple 20 10

282 Piura Arms and Congress Emblem 283

1960. Obligatory Tax. 6th National Eucharistic Congress Fund.

839 **282** 10 c. multicoloured . . . 20 10
839a 10 c. blue and red 20 10

1960. Air. World Refugee Year.

840 **283** 80 c. multicoloured 30 30
841 4 s. 30 multicoloured . . . 50 50

284 Sea Bird bearing Map 285 Congress Emblem

1960. Air. International Pacific Fair, Lima.

842 **284** 1 s. multicoloured 40 15

1960. 6th National Eucharistic Congress, Piura.

843 **285** 50 c. red, black & blue . . 15 10
844 – 1 s. mult (Eucharistic symbols) 25 10

286 1659 Coin

1961. Air. 1st National Numismatic Exhibition, Lima.

845 – 1 s. grey and brown . . . 20 10
846 **286** 2 s. grey and blue 25 15

DESIGNS: 1 s. 1659 coin.

287 "Amazonas" 288 Globe, Moon and Stars

1961. Air. Centenary of World Tour of Cadet Sailing Ship "Amazonas".

847 **287** 50 c. green and brown . . 25 10
848 80 c. red and purple . . . 35 10
849 1 s. black and green . . . 50 10

1961. Air. I.G.Y.

850 **288** 1 s. multicoloured 15 15

289 Olympic Torch 290 "Balloon"

1961. Air. Olympic Games, 1960.

852 **289** 5 c. blue and black . . . 40 35
853 10 s. red and black . . . 70 60

1961. Christmas and New Year.

854 **290** 20 c. blue 30 10

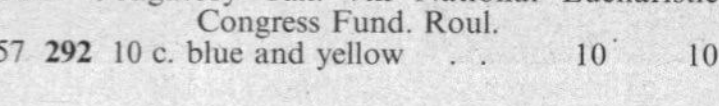

291 Fair Emblem 292 Symbol of Eucharist

1961. Air. 2nd International Pacific Fair, Lima.

855 **291** 1 s. multicoloured 20 15

1962. Obligatory Tax. 7th National Eucharistic Congress Fund. Roul.

857 **292** 10 c. blue and yellow . . 10 10

293 Sculptures "Cahuide" and "Cuauhtemoc"

1962. Air. Peruvian Art Treasures Exhibition, Mexico. 1960. Flags red and green.

859 **293** 1 s. red 15 10
860 – 2 s. turquoise 25 15
861 – 3 s. brown 30 15

DESIGNS: 2 s. Tupac-Amaru and Hidalgo; 3 s. Presidents Prado and Lopez.

294 Frontier Maps

1962. Air. 20th Anniv of Ecuador–Peru Border Agreement.
862 **294** 1 s. 30 blk & red on grey . 25 15
863 1 s. 50 multicoloured . . . 25 15
864 2 s. 50 multicoloured . . . 30 30

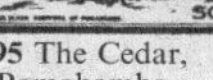

295 The Cedar, Pomabamba — **296** "Man"

1962. Centenary of Pomabamba and Pallasca Ancash.
865 **295** 1 s. green & red (postage) 35 15
866 – 1 s. black and grey (air) 10 10
DESIGN: No. 866, Agriculture, mining, etc, Pallasca Ancash ($31\frac{1}{2} \times 22$ mm.).

1962. As Nos. 774/91 but colours and some designs changed and new values. (a) Postage.
867 20 c. purple 20 10
921 20 c. red 10 10
922 30 c. blue (as No. 776) 10 10
923 40 c. orange (as No. 784) . . . 30 10
871 60 c. black (as No. 774) . . . 25 10
925 1 s. red 10 10

(b) Air.
873 1 s. 30 ochre (as No. 785) . . 2·50 25
874 1 s. 50 purple 35 10
875 1 s. 80 blue (as No. 777) . . . 45 15
876 2 s. green 40 15
926 2 s. 60 green (as No. 783) . . . 30 15
877 3 s. purple 40 15
927 3 s. 60 purple (as No. 789) . . 45 20
878 4 s. 30 orange 55 30
928 4 s. 60 orange (as No. 788) . . 35 25
879 5 s. green 55 35
880 10 s. blue . . . . 1·00 40

1963. Air. Chavin Excavations Fund. Pottery.
881 – 1 s. + 50 c. grey & pink . 15 15
882 – 1 s. 50 + 1 s. grey & blue 15 15
883 – 3 s. + 2 s. 50 grey & green 50 50
884 **296** 4 s. 30 + 3 s. grey and green 85 65
885 – 6 s. + 4 s. grey and olive . 95 85
FIGURES—HORIZ: 1 s. "Griffin"; 1 s. 50, "Eagle"; 3 s. "Cat". VERT: 6 s. "Deity".

297 Campaign and Industrial Emblems — **298** Henri Dunant and Centenary Emblem

1963. Freedom from Hunger.
886 **297** 1 s. bistre & red (postage) 15 10
887 4 s. 30 bistre & grn (air) . 40 40

1964. Air. Red Cross Centenary.
888 **298** 1 s. 30 + 70 c. multicoloured 25 25
889 4 s. 30 + 1 s. 70 mult . . 55 55

299 Chavez and Wing — **300** Alliance Emblem

1964. Air. 50th Anniv of Jorge Chavez's Trans-Alpine Flight.
890 **299** 5 s. blue, purple and brn . 75 35

1964. "Alliance for Progress". Emblem black, green and blue.
891 **300** 40 c. blk & yell (postage) . 10 10
892 – 1 s. 30 black & mauve (air) 15 10
893 **300** 3 s. black and blue . . . 30 25
DESIGN—HORIZ: 1 s. 30, As Type **300**, but with inscription at right.

301 Fair Poster — **302** Net, Flag and Globe

1965. Air. 3rd International Pacific Fair, Lima.
894 **301** 1 s. multicoloured 10 10

1965. Air. Women's World Basketball Championships, Lima.
895 **302** 1 s. 30 violet and red . . . 30 15
896 4 s. 30 bistre and red . . . 45 30

303 St. Martin de Porras (anonymous) — **304** Fair Emblem

1965. Air. Canonisation of St. Martin de Porras (1962). Paintings. Multicoloured.
898 1 s. 30 Type **303** 15 10
899 1 s. 80 "St. Martin and the Miracle of the Animals" (after painting by Camino Brent) 25 10
900 4 s. 30 "St. Martin and the Angels" (after painting by Fausto Conti) 50 25
Porras is wrongly spelt "Porres" on the stamps.

1965. 4th International Pacific Fair, Lima.
901 **304** 1 s. 50 multicoloured . . 15 10
902 2 s. 50 multicoloured . . 20 10
903 3 s. 50 multicoloured . . 30 20

305 Father Christmas and Postmarked Envelope — **312** 2nd May Monument and Battle Scene

1965. Christmas.
904 **305** 20 c. black and red . . . 15 10
905 50 c. black and green . . 20 10
906 1 s. black and blue . . . 30 10
The above stamps were valid for postage only on November 2nd. They were subsequently used as postal employees' charity labels.

1966. Obligatory Tax. Journalists' Fund. (a) Surch **HABILITADO "Fondo del Periodista Peruano" Ley 16078 S/o.0.10.**
907 **264a** 10 c. on 3 c. (No. 897) . 65 10
(b) Surch **Habilitado "Fondo del Periodista Peruano" Ley 16078 S/. 0.10.**
909 **264a** 10 c. on 3 c. (No. 897) . 25 10

1966. Obligatory Tax. Journalists' Fund. No. 857 optd **Periodista Peruano Ley 16078.**
910 **292** 10 c. blue and yellow . . 10 10

1966. Nos. 757c, 851 and 897 surch **XX Habilitado S/. 0.10.**
911 **229** 10 c. on 2 c. brown . . 10 10
912 **264a** 10 c. on 3 c. lake (No. 897) 10 10
912b 10 c. on 3 c. lake (No. 851) 2·00 70

1966. Air. Centenary of Battle of Callao. Mult.
913 1 s. 90 Type **312** 30 20
914 3 s. 60 Monument and sculpture 45 30
915 4 s. 60 Monument and Jose Galvez 50 40

313 Funerary Mask

1966. Gold Objects of Chimu Culture. Multicoloured.
916 1 s. 90 + 90 c. Type **313** . . 35 35
917 2 s. 60 + 1 s. 30 Ceremonial knife (vert) 40 40
918 3 s. 60 + 1 s. 80 Ceremonial urn 60 60
919 4 s. 60 + 2 s. 30 Goblet (vert) 85 85
920 20 s. + 10 s. Ear-ring . . . . 3·25 3·25

314 Civil Guard Emblem

1966. Air. Civil Guard Centenary Multicoloured.
929 90 c. Type **314** 10 10
930 1 s. 90 Emblem and activities of Civil Guard 20 10

INDEX

Countries can be quickly located by referring to the index at the end of this volume.

315 Map and Mountains — **316** Globe

1966. Opening of Huinco Hydro-electric Scheme.
931 **315** 70 c. black, deep blue and blue (postage) 10 10
932 1 s. 90 black, blue and violet (air) 20 15

1967. Air. Peruvian Photographic Exhibition, Lima.
933 – 2 s. 60 red and black . . . 25 15
934 – 3 s. 60 black and blue . . . 35 25
935 **316** 4 s. 60 multicoloured . . . 40 30
DESIGNS: 2 s. 60, "Sun" carving; 3 s. 60, Map of Peru within spiral.

317 Symbol of Construction — **318** "St. Rosa" (from painting by A. Medoro)

1967. Six-year Construction Plan.
936 **317** 90 c. black, gold and mauve (postage) 10 10
937 1 s. 90 black, gold and ochre (air) 15 15

1967. Air. 350th Death Anniv of St. Rosa of Lima. Designs showing portraits of St. Rosa by artists given below. Multicoloured.
938 1 s. 90 Type **318** 30 15
939 2 s. 60 C. Maratta 40 15
940 3 s. 60 Anon., Cusquena School 55 25

319 Vicuna within Figure "5" — **320** Pen-nib made of Newspaper

1967. 5th International Pacific Fair, Lima.
941 **319** 1 s. black, green and gold (postage) 10 10
942 1 s. purple, black and gold (air) 10 10

1967. Obligatory Tax. Journalists' Fund.
943 **320** 10 c. black and red 10 10

321 Wall Reliefs (fishes)

1967. Obligatory Tax. Chan-Chan Excavation Fund.
944 **321** 20 c. black and blue . . . 10 10
945 – 20 c. black and mauve . . 10 10
946 – 20 c. black and brown . . 10 10
947 – 20 c. multicoloured 10 10
948 – 20 c. multicoloured 10 10
949 – 20 c. black and green . . . 10 10
DESIGNS: No. 945, Ornamental pattern; No. 946, Carved "bird"; No. 947, Temple on hillside; No. 948, Corner of Temple; No. 949, Ornamental pattern (birds).

322 Lions' Emblem — **323** Nazca Jug

1967. Air. 50th Anniv of Lions International.
950 **322** 1 s. 60 violet, blue & grey . 15 10

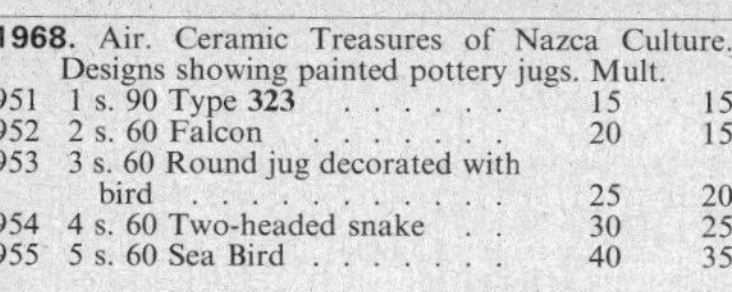

1968. Air. Ceramic Treasures of Nazca Culture. Designs showing painted pottery jugs. Mult.
951 1 s. 90 Type **323** 15 15
952 2 s. 60 Falcon 20 15
953 3 s. 60 Round jug decorated with bird 25 20
954 4 s. 60 Two-headed snake . . 30 25
955 5 s. 60 Sea Bird 40 35

324 Alligator — **325** "Antarqui" (Airline Symbol)

1968. Gold Sculptures of Mochica Culture. Mult.
956 1 s. 90 Type **324** 15 10
957 2 s. 60 Bird 15 10
958 3 s. 60 Lizard 25 15
959 4 s. 60 Bird 30 15
960 5 s. 60 Jaguar 35 20
Nos. 957 and 959 are vert.

1968. Air. 12th Anniv of APSA (Peruvian Airlines).
961 **325** 3 s. 60 multicoloured . . 30 15
962 – 5 s. 60 brown, black & red 45 20
DESIGN: 5 s. 60, Alpaca and stylized Boeing 747.

326 Human Rights Emblem — **327** "The Discus-thrower"

1968. Air. Human Rights Year.
963 **326** 6 s. 50 red, green & brn . 25 20

1968. Air. Olympic Games, Mexico.
964 **327** 2 s. 30 brown, blue & yell 15 10
965 3 s. 50 blue, red & green . 20 15
966 5 s. black, blue and pink . 25 15
967 6 s. 50 purple, brown & bl 35 20
968 8 s. blue, mauve and lilac 40 25
969 9 s. violet, green & orge . 45 30

328

1968. Obligatory Tax. Unissued stamps surch as in T **328**.
970 **328** 20 c. on 50 c. violet, orange and black 40 40
971 20 c. on 1 s. blue, orange and black 40 40

1968. Obligatory Tax. Journalists' Fund. No. 897 surch **Habilitado Fondo Periodista Peruano Ley 17050 S/.** and value.
972 **264a** 20 c. on 3 c. lake 10 10

1968. Christmas. No. 900 surch **PRO NAVIDAD Veinte Centavos R.S. 5-11-68.**
973 20 c. on 4 s. 30 multicoloured 25 20

331 Indian's Head and Wheat — **334** Worker holding Flag and Oil Derrick

333 First Peruvian Coin (obverse and reverse)

1969. Unissued Agrarian Reform stamps, surch as in T **331**. Multicoloured.
974 2 s. 50 on 90 c. Type **331** (postage) 15 10
975 3 s. on 90 c. Man digging . . 15 15
976 4 s. on 90 c. As No. 975 . . . 25 15
977 5 s. 50 on 1 s. 90 Corn-cob and hand scattering cobs (air) . . 30 15
978 6 s. 50 on 1 s. 90 As No. 977 . 40 20

1969. Air. 400th Anniv of 1st Peruvian Coinage.
979 **333** 5 s. black, grey and yellow . . 25 15
980 5 s. black, grey and green . . 25 15

1969. Nationalization of International Petroleum Company's Oilfields and Refinery (9 October, 1968).
981 **334** 2 s. 50 multicoloured . . . 15 10
982 3 s. multicoloured 20 10
983 4 s. multicoloured 25 15
984 5 s. 50 multicoloured . . . 30 20

335 Castilla Monument

336 Boeing 707, Globe and "Kon Tiki" (replica of balsa raft)

1969. Air. Death Centenary of President Ramon Castilla.
985 **335** 5 s. blue and green 30 15
986 – 10 s. brown and purple . . 70 30
DESIGN—(21 × 37 mm): 10 s. President Castilla.

1969. 1st A.P.S.A. (Peruvian Airlines) Flight to Europe.
987 **336** 2 s. 50 mult (postage) . . 20 10
988 3 s. multicoloured (air) . . 30 10
989 4 s. multicoloured 40 10
990 5 s. 50 multicoloured . . . 50 15
991 6 s. 50 multicoloured . . . 60 25

337 Dish Aerial, Satellite and Globe

1969. Air. Inauguration of Lurin Satellite Telecommunications Station, Lima.
992 **337** 20 s. multicoloured . . . 1·00 60

338 Captain Jose A. Quinones Gonzales (military aviator)

1969. Quinones Gonzales Commemoration.
994 **338** 20 s. mult (postage) . . . 1·00 70
995 20 s. multicoloured (air) . 1·00 45

339 W.H.O. Emblem

1969. Air. 20th Anniv (1968) of W.H.O.
996 **339** 5 s. multicoloured 15 15
997 6 s. 50 multicoloured . . . 20 15

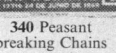

340 Peasant breaking Chains

341 Arms of the Inca Garcilaso de la Vega (historian)

1969. Agrarian Reform Decree.
998 **340** 2 s. 50 deep blue, blue and red (postage) 10 10
999 3 s. purple, lilac and black (air) 10 10
1000 4 s. brown & lt brown . . . 15 10

1969. Air. Garcilaso de la Vega Commem.
1001 **341** 2 s. 40 black, silver & grn . 10 10
1002 – 3 s. 50 black, buff & blue . 15 10
1003 – 5 s. multicoloured . . . 20 15
DESIGNS: 3 s. 50, Title page, "Commentarios Reales", Lisbon, 1609; 5 s. Inca Garcilaso de la Vega.

342 Admiral Grau and Ironclad Warship "Huascar"

1969. Navy Day.
1005 **342** 50 s. multicoloured . . . 3·50 1·75

343 "6" and Fair Flags

1969. 6th International Pacific Fair, Lima.
1006 **343** 2 s. 50 mult (postage) . 10 10
1007 3 s. multicoloured (air) . 15 10
1008 4 s. multicoloured . . . 15 10

344 Father Christmas and Greetings Card

345 Col. F. Bolognesi and Soldier

1969. Christmas.
1009 **344** 20 c. black and red . . . 10 10
1010 20 c. black and orange . 10 10
1011 20 c. black and brown . 10 10

1969. Army Day.
1012 **345** 1 s. 20 black, gold and blue (postage) 10 10
1013 50 s. black, gold and brown (air) . . . . 2·50 1·10

346 Arms of Amazonas

1970. Air. 150th Anniv (1971) of Republic (1st issue).
1014 **346** 10 s. multicoloured . . . 35 30
See also Nos. 1066/70, 1076/80 and 1081/90.

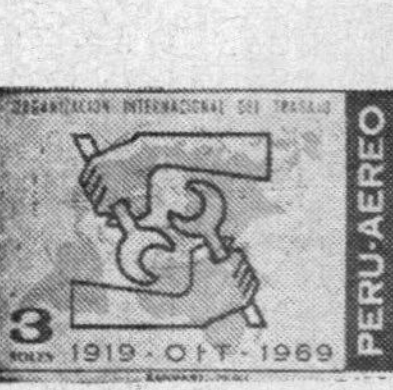

347 I.L.O. Emblem on Map

349 "Puma" Jug

1970. Air. 50th Anniv of I.L.O.
1015 **347** 3 s. deep blue and blue . 15 10

348 "Motherhood"

350 Ministry Building

1970. Air. 24th Anniv of U.N.I.C.E.F.
1016 **348** 5 s. black and yellow . . 25 15
1017 6 s. 50 black and pink . . 35 20

1970. Vicus Culture. Ceramic Art. Multicoloured.
1018 2 s. 50 Type **349** (postage) . . 15 10
1019 3 s. Squatting warrior (statuette) (air) 20 15
1020 4 s. Animal jug 25 15
1021 5 s. 50 Twin jugs 30 20
1022 6 s. 50 Woman with jug (statuette) 40 25

1970. Ministry of Transport and Communications.
1023 **350** 40 c. black and purple . . 10 10
1024 40 c. black and yellow . . 10 10
1025 40 c. black and grey . . . 10 10
1026 40 c. black and red . . . 10 10
1027 40 c. black and brown . . 10 10

351 Anchovy

352 Telephone and Skyline

1970. Fishes. Multicoloured.
1028 2 s. 50 Type **351** (postage) . . 15 10
1029 2 s. 50 Hake 15 10
1030 3 s. Swordfish (air) 15 10
1031 3 s. Yellowfin tuna 15 10
1032 5 s. 50 Wolf-fish 40 15

1970. Air. Nationalization of Lima Telephone Service.
1033 **352** 5 s. multicoloured 30 15
1034 10 s. multicoloured . . . 55 25

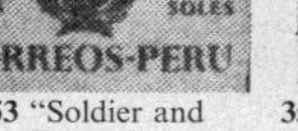

353 "Soldier and Farmer"

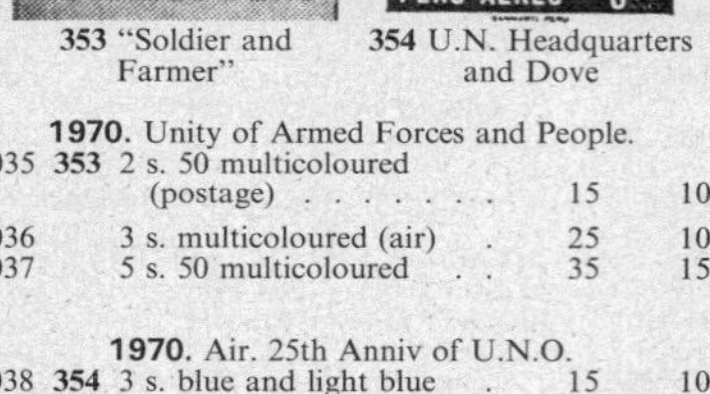

354 U.N. Headquarters and Dove

1970. Unity of Armed Forces and People.
1035 **353** 2 s. 50 multicoloured (postage) 15 10
1036 3 s. multicoloured (air) . 25 10
1037 5 s. 50 multicoloured . . 35 15

1970. Air. 25th Anniv of U.N.O.
1038 **354** 3 s. blue and light blue . 15 10

355 Rotary Emblem

1970. Air. 50th Anniv of Lima Rotary Club.
1039 **355** 10 s. gold, red and black . 75 25

356 Military Parade (Army Staff College, Chorrillos)

1970. Military, Naval and Air Force Academies. Multicoloured.
1040 2 s. 50 Type **356** 35 20
1041 2 s. 50 Parade, Naval Academy, La Punta 35 20
1042 2 s. 50 Parade, Air Force Officer Training School, Las Palmas 35 20

357 Puruchuco, Lima

1970. Tourism. Multicoloured.
1043 2 s. 50 Type **357** (postage) . 15 10
1044 3 s. Chan-Chan-Trujillo, La Libertad (air) 15 10
1045 4 s. Sacsayhuaman, Cuzco . 25 10
1046 5 s. 50 Lake Titicaca, Pomata, Puno 30 15
1047 10 s. Machu-Picchu, Cuzco . 60 30
Nos. 1045/7 are vert.

358 Festival Procession

1970. Air. October Festival, Lima. Multicoloured.
1049 3 s. Type **358** 15 10
1050 4 s. "The Cock-fight" (T. Nunez Ureta) 25 10
1051 5 s. 50 Altar, Nazarenas Shrine (vert) 30 20
1052 6 s. 50 "The Procession" (J. Vinatea Reinoso) . . . 35 25
1053 8 s. "The Procession" (Jose Sabogal) (vert) 50 20

359 "The Nativity" (Cuzco School)

1970. Christmas. Paintings by Unknown Artists. Multicoloured.
1054 1 s. 20 Type **359** 10 10
1055 1 s. 50 "The Adoration of the Magi" (Cuzquena School) 10 10
1056 1 s. 80 "The Adoration of the Shepherds" (Peruvian School) 10 10

360 "Close Embrace" (petroglyph)

1971. Air. "Gratitude for World Help in Earthquake of May 1970".
1057 **360** 4 s. olive, black and red . 25 15
1058 5 s. 50 blue, flesh and red 35 15
1059 6 s. 50 grey, blue and red 40 20

361 "St. Rosa de Lima" (F. Laso)

1971. 300th Anniv of Canonisation of St. Rosa de Lima.
1060 **361** 2 s. 50 multicoloured . . 15 10

362 Tiahuanaco Fabric

1971. Ancient Peruvian Textiles.
1061 **362** 1 s. 20 mult (postage) . . 15 10
1062 – 2 s. 50 multicoloured . . 25 10

1063 – 3 s. multicoloured (air) . 30 10
1064 – 4 s. pink, green & dp grn 40 10
1065 – 5 s. 50 multicoloured . . 55 15
DESIGNS—HORIZ: 2 s. 50, Chancay fabric; 4 s. Chancay lace. VERT: 3 s. Chancay tapestry; 5 s. 50, Paracas fabric.

363 M. Garcia Pumacahua

364 "Cojinova" (Nazca Culture)

1971. 150th Anniv of Independence (2nd issue). National Heroes.
1066 **363** 1 s. 20 blk & red (postage) 10 10
1067 – 2 s. 50 black and blue . . 15 10
1068 – 3 s. black & mve (air) . . 15 10
1069 – 4 s. black and green . . . 15 10
1070 – 5 s. 50 black and brown . 25 15
DESIGNS: 2 s. 50, F. Antonio de Zela; 3 s. T. Rodriguez de Mendoza; 4 s. J. P. Viscardo y Guzman; 5 s. 50, J. G. Condorcanqui, Tupac Amani.
See also Nos. 1076/80 and Nos. 1081/90.

1971. "Traditional Fisheries of Peru". Piscatorial Ceramics. Multicoloured.
1071 1 s. 50 Type **364** (postage) . 15 10
1072 3 s. 50 "Bonito" (Chimu Inca) (air) 30 10
1073 4 s. "Anchoveta" (Mochica) . 40 10
1074 5 s. 50 "Merluza" (Chimu) . 60 15
1075 8 s. 50 "Machete" (Nazca) . 80 25

1971. 150th Anniv of Independence. National Heroes (3rd issue). As T **363**. Multicoloured.
1076 1 s. 20 M. Melgar (postage) . 10 10
1077 2 s. 50 J. Baquijano y Carrillo 15 10
1078 3 s. J. de la Riva Aguero (air) 15 10
1079 4 s. H. Unanue 15 10
1080 5 s. 50 F. J. de Luna Pizarro 25 15

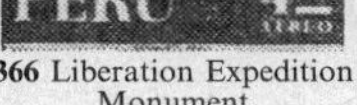

366 Liberation Expedition Monument

367 R. Palma (author and poet)

1971. 150th Anniv of Independence (4th issue). As T **366**. Multicoloured.
1081 1 s. 50 M. Bastidas (post.) . . 10 10
1082 2 s. J. F. Sanchez Carrion . . 10 10
1083 2 s. 50 M. J. Guise 15 10
1084 3 s. F. Vidal (air) 15 10
1085 3 s. 50 J. de San Martin . . . 15 15
1086 4 s. 50 Type **366** 20 15
1087 6 s. "Surrender of the 'Numancia Battalion'" (horiz) (42 × 35 mm) . . . 30 15
1088 7 s. 50 Alvarez de Arenales Monument (horiz) (42 × 39 mm) 35 20
1089 9 s. Monument to Founders of the Republic, Lima (horiz) (42 × 39 mm) 40 20
1090 10 s. "Proclamation of Independence" (horiz) (46 × 35 mm) 50 20

1971. Air. 150th Anniv of National Library.
1091 **367** 7 s. 50 black and brown . 60 25

368 Weightlifting

369 "Gongora portentosa"

1971. Air. 25th World Weightlifting Championships, Huampani, Lima.
1092 **368** 7 s. 50 black and blue . . 60 25

1971. Peruvian Flora (1st series). Orchids. Mult.
1093 1 s. 50 Type **369** 25 10
1094 2 s. "Odontoglossum cristatum" 30 10
1095 2 s. 50 "Mormolyca peruviana" 35 10
1096 3 s. "Trichocentrum pulchrum" 45 15
1097 3 s. 50 "Oncidium sanderae" 35 20
See also Nos. 1170/4 and 1206/10.

370 Family and Flag

371 Schooner "Sacramento" of 1821

1971. Air. 3rd Anniv of October 3rd Revolution.
1098 **370** 7 s. 50 black, red & blue 50 30

1971. Air. 150th Anniv of Peruvian Navy and "Order of the Peruvian Sun".
1100 **371** 7 s. 50 blue & lt blue . . 1·00 30
1101 – 7 s. 50 multicoloured . . 50 25
DESIGN: No. 1101, Order of the Peruvian Sun.

372 "Development and Liberation" (detail)

1971. 2nd Ministerial Meeting of "The 77" Group.
1102 **372** 1 s. 20 multicoloured (postage) 10 10
1103 – 3 s. 50 multicoloured . . 25 10
1104 – 50 s. mult (air) . . . . 2·50 1·25
DESIGNS—As Type **372**: 3 s. 50, 50 s. Detail from the painting "Development and Liberation".

373 "Plaza de Armas, 1843" (J. Rugendas)

1971. "Exfilima" Stamp Exhibition, Lima.
1105 **373** 3 s. black & green . . . 30 10
1106 – 3 s. 50 black and pink . 40 15
DESIGN: 3 s. 50, "Plaza de Armas, 1971" (C. Zeiter).

374 Fair Emblem

375 Army Crest

1971. Air. 7th International Pacific Fair, Lima.
1107 **374** 4 s. 50 multicoloured . . 20 15

1971. 150th Anniv of Peruvian Army.
1108 **375** 8 s. 50 multicoloured . . 60 20

376 "The Flight into Egypt"

1971. Christmas. Multicoloured.
1109 1 s. 80 Type **376** 20 10
1110 2 s. 50 "The Magi" 25 10
1111 3 s. "The Nativity" 35 10

377 "Fishermen" (J. Ugarte Elespuru)

378 Chimu Idol

1971. Social Reforms. Paintings. Mulicoloured
1112 3 s. 50 Type **377** 35 10
1113 4 s. "Threshing Grain in Cajamarca" (Camilo Blas) . 45 10
1114 6 s. "Hand-spinning Huanca Native Women" (J. Sabogal) 60 15

1972. Peruvian Antiquities. Multicoloured.
1115 3 s. 90 Type **378** 35 15
1116 4 s. Chimu statuette 35 15
1117 4 s. 50 Lambayeque idol . . . 45 15
1118 5 s. 40 Mochica collar 55 15
1119 6 s. Lambayeque "spider" pendant 60 15

379 "Pseudopriacanthus serrula"

1972. Peruvian Fishes. Multicoloured.
1120 1 s. 20 Type **379** (postage) . . 15 10
1121 1 s. 50 "Trachichthys mento" 15 10
1122 2 s. 50 "Trachurus symmetricus murphyi" 25 10
1123 3 s. "Pontinus furcirhinus" (air) 30 10
1124 5 s. 50 "Bodianus eclancheri" 55 15

380 "Peruvian Family" (T. Nunez Ureta)

1972. Air. Educations Reforms.
1125 **380** 6 s. 50 multicoloured . . 35 20

381 Mochica Warrior

382 White-tailed Trogon

1972. Peruvian Art (1st series). Mochica Ceramics. Multicoloured.
1126 1 s. 20 Type **381** 15 10
1127 1 s. 50 Warrior's head 15 10
1128 2 s. Kneeling deer 25 10
1129 2 s. 50 Warrior's head (different) 35 10
1130 3 s. Kneeling warrior 40 15
See also Nos. 1180/4.

1972. Air. Peruvian Birds. Multicoloured.
1131 2 s. Type **382** 65 25
1132 2 s. 50 Amazonian umbrellabird 80 25
1133 3 s. Andean cock of the rock 90 30
1134 6 s. 50 Cuvier's toucan . . . 1·90 55
1135 8 s. 50 Blue-crowned motmot 2·25 75

383 "The Harvest" (July)

384 "Quipu" on Map

1972. 400th Anniv of G. Poma de Ayala's "Inca Chronicles". Woodcuts.
1136 **383** 2 s. 50 black and red . . 35 10
1137 – 3 s. black and green . . 60 10
1138 – 2 s. 50 black and pink . . 30 10
1139 – 3 s. black and blue . . . 50 10
1140 – 2 s. 50 black & orange . . 50 10
1141 – 3 s. black and lilac . . . 50 10
1142 – 2 s. 50 black and brown . 35 10
1143 – 3 s. black and green . . . 50 10
1144 – 2 s. 50 black and blue . . 35 10
1145 – 3 s. black and orange . . 50 10
1146 – 2 s. 50 black & mauve . . 35 10
1147 – 3 s. black and yellow . . 50 10
DESIGNS: No. 1137, "Land Purification" (August); No. 1138, "Sowing" (September); No. 1139, "Invocation of the Rains" (October); No. 1140, "Irrigation" (November); No. 1141, "Rite of the Nobility" (December); No. 1142, "Maize Cultivation Rights" (January); No. 1143, "Ripening of the Maize" (February); No. 1144, "Birds in the Maize" (March); No. 1145, "Children as camp-guards" (April); No. 1146, "Gathering the harvest" (May); No. 1147, "Removing the harvest" (June).

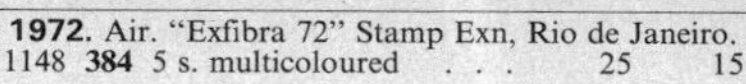
1972. Air. "Exfibra 72" Stamp Exn, Rio de Janeiro.
1148 **384** 5 s. multicoloured . . . 25 15

385 "The Messenger"

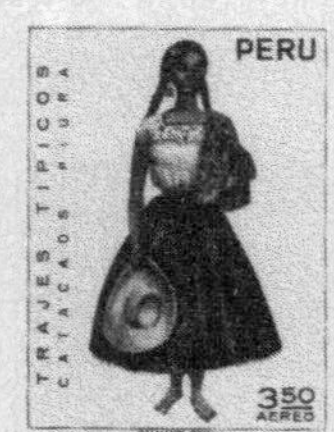

386 Catacaos Woman

1972. Air. Olympic Games, Munich.
1149 **385** 8 s. multicoloured . . . 55 20

1972. Air. Provincial Costumes (1st series). Mult.
1150 2 s. Tupe girl 15 10
1151 3 s. 50 Type **386** 30 10
1152 4 s. Conibo Indian 40 10
1153 4 s. 50 Agricultural worker playing "quena" and drum 40 15
1154 5 s. "Moche" (Trujillo) girl . 40 15
1155 6 s. 50 Ocongate (Cuzco) man and woman 55 40
1156 8 s. "Chucupana" (Ayacucho) girl 60 50
1157 8 s. 50 "Cotuncha" (Junin) girl 70 55
1158 10 s. "Pandilla" dancer . . . 60 60
See also Nos. 1248/9.

387 Ruins of Chavin (Ancash)

1972. Air. 25th Death Anniv Julio C. Tello (archaeologist). Multicoloured.
1159 1 s. 50 "Stone of the 12 Angles", Cuzco (vert) 15 10
1160 3 s. 50 Type **387** 30 10
1161 4 s. Burial-tower, Sillustani (Puno) (vert) 30 10
1162 5 s. Gateway, Chavin (Ancash) 45 15
1163 8 s. "Wall of the 3 Windows", Machu Picchu (Cuzco) . . 55 25

388 "Territorial Waters"

1972. 4th Anniv of Armed Forces Revolution. Mult.
1164 2 s. Agricultural Workers ("Agrarian Reform") (vert) 10 10
1165 2 s. 50 Type **388** 15 10
1166 3 s. Oil rigs ("Nationalisation of Petroleum Industry") (vert) 20 10

389 "The Holy Family" (wood-carving)

1972. Christmas. Multicoloured.
1167 1 s. 50 Type **389** 15 10
1168 2 s. "The Holy Family" (carved Huamanga stone) (horiz) . 15 10
1169 2 s. 50 "The Holy Family" (carved Huamanga stone) . 20 10

390 "Ipomoea purpurea"

391 Inca Poncho

1972. Peruvian Flora (2nd series). Multicoloured.
1170 1 s. 50 Type **390** 15 10
1171 2 s. 50 "Amaryllis ferreyrae" 20 10
1172 3 s. "Liabum excelsum" . . 30 10
1173 3 s. 50 "Bletia catenulata" . 30 10
1174 5 s. "Cantua buxifolia cantuta" 35 20

1973. Air. Ancient Inca Textiles.
1175 **391** 2 s. multicoloured . . . 15 10
1176 – 3 s. 50 multicoloured . . 25 10
1177 – 4 s. multicoloured . . . 25 10
1178 – 5 s. multicoloured . . . 30 12
1179 – 8 s. multicoloured . . . 55 25
DESIGNS: Nos. 1176/9, similar to T **391**.

392 Mochica Cameo and Cups
393 Andean Condor

1973. Air. Peruvian Art (2nd series). Jewelled Antiquities. Multicoloured.
1180 1 s. 50 Type **392** 10 10
1181 2 s. 50 Gold-plated arms and hands (Lambayeque) . . . 15 10
1182 4 s. Bronze effigy (Mochica) . 25 10
1183 5 s. Gold pendants (Nazca) . 30 15
1184 8 s. Gold cat (Mochica) . . . 60 25

1973. Air. Fauna Protection (1st series). Mult.
1185 2 s. 50 Lesser rhea . . . . . 1·25 20
1186 3 s. 50 Giant otter 45 10
1187 4 s. Type **393** . . . . . . 1·75 30
1188 5 s. Vicuna 60 15
1189 6 s. Chilian flamingo . . . . 2·00 35
1190 8 s. Spectacled bear 70 25
1191 8 s. 50 Bush dog (horiz) . . . 60 25
1192 10 s. Short-tailed chinchilla (horiz) 75 30
See also Nos. 1245/6.

394 "The Macebearer" (J. Sabogal)
396 "Spanish Mayor on Horseback"

395 Basketball Net and Map

1973. Air. Peruvian Paintings. Multicoloured.
1193 1 s. 50 Type **394** 10 10
1194 8 s. "Yananacu Bridge" (E. C. Brent) (horiz) . . . 30 15
1195 8 s. 50 "Portrait of a Lady" (D. Hernandez) 35 15
1196 10 s. "Peruvian Birds" (T. N. Ureta) . . . . . . 2·25 30
1197 20 s. "The Potter" (F. Laso) . 1·10 40
1198 50 s. "Reed Boats" (J. V. Reinoso) (horiz) . . 2·75 1·00

1973. Air. 1st World Basketball Festival.
1199 **395** 5 s. green 35 10
1200 20 s. purple 90 40

1973. 170th Birth Anniv of Pancho Fierro (painter). Multicoloured.
1201 1 s. 50 Type **396** 10 10
1202 2 s. "Peasants" 15 10
1203 2 s. 50 "Father Abregu" . . 20 10
1204 3 s. 50 "Dancers" 30 10
1205 4 s. 50 "Esteban Arredondo on horseback" 45 20

1973. Air. Peruvian Flora (3rd series). Orchids. As T **390**. Multicoloured.
1206 1 s. 50 "Lycaste reichenbachii" 20 10
1207 2 s. 50 "Masdevallia amabilis" 30 10
1208 3 s. "Sigmatostalix peruviana" 40 10
1209 3 s. 50 "Porrogossum peruvianum" 40 10
1210 8 s. "Oncidium incarum" . . 60 25

398 Fair Emblem (poster)
399 Symbol of Flight

1973. Air. 8th International Pacific Fair, Lima.
1211 **398** 8 s. red, black and grey . 60 20

1973. Air. 50th Anniv of Air Force Officers' School.
1212 **399** 8 s. 50 multicoloured . . 60 15

400 "The Presentation of the Child"

1973. Christmas. Paintings of the Cuzco School. Multicoloured.
1213 1 s. 50 Type **400** 10 10
1214 2 s. "The Holy Family" (vert) 15 10
1215 2 s. 50 "The Adoration of the Kings" 15 10

401 Freighter "Ilo"

1973. Air. National Development. Multicoloured.
1216 1 s. 50 Type **401** 40 15
1217 2 s. 50 Trawlers 60 15
1218 8 s. B.A.C. One Eleven 200 airliner and seagull . . . 1·00 25

402 House of the Mulberry Tree, Arequipa

1974. Air. "Landscapes and Cities". Mult.
1219 1 s. 50 Type **402** 10 10
1220 2 s. 50 El Misti (peak), Arequipa 15 10
1221 5 s. Giant puya, Cordillera Blanca, Ancash (vert) . . 30 15
1222 6 s. Huascaran (peak), Cordillera Blanca, Ancash 35 15
1223 8 s. Lake Querococha, Cordillera Blanca, Ancash 55 20

403 Peruvian 2 c. Stamp of 1873
405 Church of San Jeronimo, Cuzco

404 Room of the Three Windows, Machu Picchu

1974. Stamp Day and 25th Anniv of Peruvian Philatelic Association.
1224 **403** 6 s. blue and grey . . . 40 15

1974. Air. Archaeological Discoveries. Mult. (a) Cuzco Relics.
1225 3 s. Type **404** 15 10
1226 5 s. Baths of Tampumacchay 25 15
1227 10 s. "Kencco" 45 25

(b) Dr. Tello's Discoveries at Chavin de Huantar. Stone carvings.
1228 3 s. Mythological jaguar . . 15 10
1229 5 s. Rodent ("Vizcacha") . . 25 15
1230 10 s. Chavin warrior 45 25
Nos. 1228/30 are vert designs.

1974. Air. Architectural Treasures. Multicoloured.
1231 1 s. 50 Type **405** 10 10
1232 3 s. 50 Cathedral of Santa Catalina, Cajamarca . . . 20 10
1233 5 s. Church of San Pedro, Zepita, Puno (horiz) . . . 25 10
1234 6 s. Cuzco Cathedral 30 15
1235 8 s. 50 Wall of the Coricancha, Cuzco 55 20

406 "Colombia" Bridge, Tarapoto–Juanjui Highway

1974. "Structural Changes". Multicoloured.
1236 2 s. Type **406** 15 10
1237 8 s. Tayacaja hydro-electric scheme 40 20
1238 10 s. Tablachaca dam 50 25

407 "Battle of Junin" (F. Yanez)

1974. 150th Anniv of Battle of Junin.
1239 **407** 1 s. 50 mult (postage) . . 10 10
1240 2 s. 50 multicoloured . . 10 10
1241 6 s. multicoloured (air) . 30 10

408 "Battle of Ayacucho" (F. Yanez)

1974. 150th Anniv of Battle of Ayacucho.
1242 **408** 2 s. mult (postage) . . . 10 10
1243 3 s. multicoloured 15 10
1244 7 s. 50 mult. (air) 45 15

1974. Air. Fauna Protection (2nd series). As T **393**. Multicoloured.
1245 8 s. Red uakari 50 15
1246 20 s. As 8 s. 85 50

409 Chimu Gold Mask

1974. Air. 8th World Mining Congress, Lima.
1247 **409** 8 s. multicoloured 45 15

1974. Air. Provincial Costumes (2nd series). As T **386**. Multicoloured.
1248 5 s. Horseman in "chalan" (Cajamarca) 35 15
1249 8 s. 50 As 5 s. 60 15

410 Pedro Paulet and Spacecraft

1974. Air. Centenary of U.P.U. and Birth Centenary of Pedro E. Paulet (aviation scientist).
1250 **410** 8 s. violet and blue . . . 40 15

411 Copper Smelter, La Oroya

1974. Expropriation of Cerro de Pasco Mining Complex.
1251 **411** 1 s. 50 blue & deep blue . 10 10
1252 3 s. red and brown . . . 15 10
1253 4 s. 50 green and grey . . 25 15

INDEX

Countries can be quickly located by referring to the index at the end of this volume.

412 "Capitulation of Ayacucho" (D. Hernandez)
413 "Madonna and Child"

1974. Air. 150th Anniv of Spanish Forces' Capitulation at Ayacucho.
1254 **412** 3 s. 50 multicoloured . . 20 10
1255 8 s. 50 multicoloured . . 60 20
1256 10 s. multicoloured . . . 55 25

1974. Christmas. Paintings of the Cuzco Shool. Multicoloured.
1257 1 s. 50 Type **413** (postage) . 10 10
1258 6 s. 50 "Holy Family" (air) . 30 15

414 "Andean Landscape" (T. Nunez Ureta)
415 Map and Civic Centre, Lima

1974. Air. Andean Pact Communications Ministers' Meeting, Cali, Colombia.
1259 **414** 6 s. 50 multicoloured . . 35 15

1975. Air. 2nd General Conference of U.N. Organization for Industrial Development.
1260 **415** 6 s. black, red and grey . 25 15

1975. Air. Various stamps surch.
1261 – 1 s. 50 on 3 s. 60 purple (No. 927) 10 10
1262 – 2 s. on 2 s. 60 green (No. 926) 15 10
1263 – 2 s. on 3 s. 60 purple (No. 927) 15 10
1263a – 2 s. on 3 s. 60 black and blue (No. 934) . . . 10 10
1264 – 2 s. on 4 s. 30 orange (No. 878) 10 10
1265 – 2 s. on 4 s. 30 multicoloured (No. 900) 15 10
1266 – 2 s. on 4 s. 60 orange (No. 928) 10 10
1267 – 2 s. 50 on 4 s. 60 orange (No. 928) 25 10
1268 – 3 s. on 2 s. 60 green (No. 926) 15 10
1294 – 3 s. 50 on 4 s. 60 orange (No. 928) 20 10
1269 – 4 s. on 2 s. 60 green (No. 926) 20 10
1270 – 4 s. on 3 s. 60 purple (No. 927) 20 10
1271 – 4 s. on 4 s. 60 orange (No. 928) 15 10
1295 – 4 s. 50 on 3 s. 80 orange (No. 836) 20 10
1272 – 5 s. on 3 s. 60 purple (No. 927) 20 10
1273 – 5 s. on 3 s. 80 orange (No. 836) 35 10
1296 – 5 s. on 4 s. 30 orange (No. 878) 30 10
1297 – 6 c. on 4 s. 60 orange (No. 928) 40 15
1277 **316** 6 s. on 4 s. 60 multicoloured (No. 935) 45 10
1278 – 7 s. on 4 s. 30 orange (No. 878) 40 15
1279 – 7 s. 50 on 3 s. 60 purple (No. 927) 50 15
1280 – 8 s. on 3 s. 60 purple (No. 927) 50 15
1281 **271** 10 s. on 2 s. 15 purple (No. 794) 40 25
1298 – 10 s. on 2 s. 60 green (No. 926) 60 20
1282 – 10 s. on 3 s. 60 purple (No. 927) 60 25
1283 – 10 s. on 3 s. 60 multicoloured (No. 940) 50 25
1284 – 10 s. on 4 s. 30 orange (No. 878) 25 25
1285 – 10 s. on 4 s. 60 orange (No. 928) 60 25
1286 – 20 s. on 3 s. 60 purple (No. 927) 40 15
1287 – 24 s. on 3 s. 60 multicoloured (No. 953) 1·40 45
1288 – 28 s. on 4 s. 60 multicoloured (No. 954) 85 55
1289 – 32 s. on 5 s. 60 multicoloured (No. 955) 85 65
1290 – 50 s. on 2 s. 60 green (No. 926) . . . . 2·10 1·00
1299 – 50 s. on 3 s. 60 purple (No. 927) . . . . 1·60 1·50
1292 – 100 s. on 3 s. 80 orange (No. 836) . . . . . . 1·60 1·50

417 Lima on World Map

1975. Air. Conference of Non-aligned Countries' Foreign Ministers, Lima.
1311 **417** 6 s. 50 multicoloured . . 40 15

418 Maria Parado de Bellido

1975. "Year of Peruvian Women" and International Women's Year. Multicoloured.
1312 1 s. 50 Type **418** 15 10
1313 2 s. Micaela Bastidas (vert) . 15 10
1314 2 s. 50 Juana Alarco de Dammert 20 10
1315 3 s. I.W.Y. emblem (vert) . . 35 10

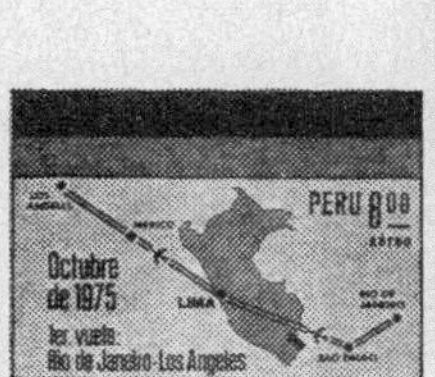

419 Route Map of Flight
420 San Juan Macias

1975. Air. First "Aero–Peru" Flight, Rio de Janeiro–Lima–Los Angeles.
1316 **419** 8 s. multicoloured . . . 30 15

1975. Canonisation of St. Juan Macias.
1317 **420** 5 s. multicoloured . . . 30 10

421 Fair Poster
422 Col. F. Bolognesi

1975. Air. 9th International Pacific Fair, Lima.
1318 **421** 6 s. red, brown & black . 50 15

1975. Air. 159th Birth Anniv of Colonel Francisco Bolognesi.
1319 **422** 20 s. multicoloured . . . 65 35

423 "Nativity"
424 Louis Braille

1976. Air. Christmas (1975).
1320 **423** 6 s. multicoloured . . . 35 15

1976. 150th Anniv of Braille System for Blind.
1321 **424** 4 s. 50 red, black & grey 30 10

426 Inca Postal Runner
427 Map on Riband

1976. Air. 11th UPAE Congress, Lima.
1322 **426** 5 s. black, brown and red 50 10

1976. Air. Re-incorporation of Tacna.
1323 **427** 10 s. multicoloured . . . 30 15

428 Peruvian Flag
429 Police Badge

1976. 1st Anniv of Second Phase of Revolution.
1324 **428** 5 s. red, black and grey . 15 10

1976. Air. 54th Anniv of Peruvian Special Police.
1325 **429** 20 s. multicoloured . . . 55 40

430 "Tree of Badges"
431 Chairman Pal Losonczi

1976. Air. 10th Anniv of Bogota Declaration.
1326 **430** 10 s. multicoloured . . . 30 20

1976. Air. Visit of Hungarian Head of State.
1327 **431** 7 s. black and blue . . . 40 15

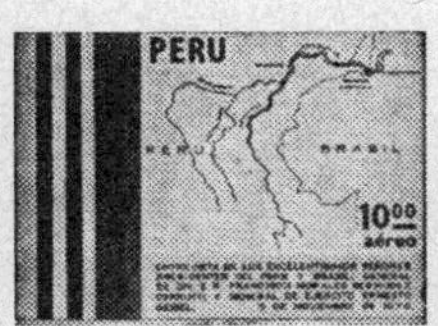

432 "St. Francis of Assisi" (El Greco)
434 "Nativity"

433 Map and National Colours

1976. 750th Death Anniv of St. Francis of Assisi.
1328 **432** 5 s. brown and gold . . 35 10

1976. Air. Meeting of Presidents of Peru and Brazil.
1329 **433** 10 s. multicoloured . . . 30 20

1976. Christmas.
1330 **434** 4 s. multicoloured . . . 30 10

435 Military Monument and Symbols

1977. Air. Army Day.
1331 **435** 20 s. black, buff and red 40 40

436 Map and Scroll
437 Printed Circuit

1977. Air. Visit of Peruvian President to Venezuela.
1332 **436** 12 s. multicoloured . . . 60 25

1977. Air. World Telecommunications Day.
1333 **437** 20 s. red, black & silver 55 40

438 Inca Postal Runner
439 Petrochemical Plant, Map and Tanker

1977.
1334 **438** 6 s. black and turquoise (postage) 40 15
1335 8 s. black and red 40 15
1336 10 s. black and blue . . . 55 25
1337 12 s. black and green . . 55 35
1338 24 s. black and red (air) . 55 50
1339 28 s. black and blue . . . 1·10 50
1340 32 s. black and brown . . . 65 70

1977. Air. Bayovar Petrochemical Complex.
1341 **439** 14 s. multicoloured . . . 1·25 30

440 Arms of Arequipa
441 President Videla

1977. Air. "Gold of Peru" Exhibition, Arequipa.
1342 **440** 10 s. multicoloured . . . 20 10

1977. Air. Visit of President Videla of Argentina.
1343 **441** 36 s. multicoloured . . . 75 25

1977. Various stamps surch **FRANQUEO** and new value.
1344 **325** 6 s. on 3 s. 60 multicoloured 40 15
1345 8 s. on 3 s. 60 multicoloured 45 15
1346 – 10 s. on 5 s. 60 brown, black and red (No. 962) . . . 50 25
1347 **305** 10 s. on 50 c. black & grn 30 10
1348 20 s. on 20 c. black and red 50 20
1349 30 s. on 1 s. black and blue 70 35

444 Fair Emblem and Flags
445 Republican Guard Badge

1977. 10th International Pacific Fair.
1350 **444** 10 s. multicoloured . . . 20 10

1977. 58th Anniv of Republican Guard.
1351 **445** 12 s. multicoloured . . . 25 15

446 Admiral Miguel Grau
447 "The Holy Family"

1977. Air. Navy Day.
1352 **446** 28 s. multicoloured . . . 35 25

1977. Christmas. Multicoloured.
1353 8 s. Type **447** (postage) . . . 10 10
1354 20s. "The adoration of the Shepherds" (air) 50 20

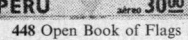

448 Open Book of Flags
449 Inca Head

1978. Air. 8th Meeting of Education Ministers.
1355 **448** 30 s. multicoloured . . . 40 25

1978.
1356 **449** 6 s. green (postage) . . . 10 10
1357 10 s. red 15 10
1358 16 s. brown 20 20
1359 24 s. mauve (air) 30 25
1360 30 s. pink 40 30
1361 65 s. blue 90 70
1362 95 s. blue . . . . 1·00 1·00

450 Emblem and Flags of West Germany, Argentina, Austria and Brazil

1978. World Cup Football Championship, Argentina (1st issue). Multicoloured.
1367 10 s. Type **450** 20 10
1368 10 s. Emblem and flags of Hungary, Iran, Italy and Mexico 20 10
1369 10 s. Emblem and flags of Scotland, Spain, France and Netherlands 20 10
1370 10 s. Emblem and flags of Peru, Poland, Sweden and Tunisia 20 10
See also Nos. 1412/15.

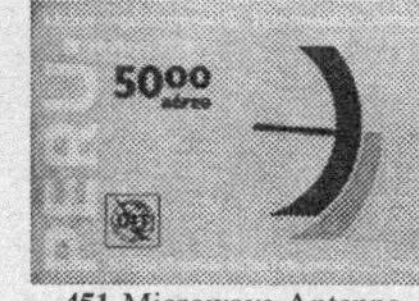

451 Microwave Antenna

1978. Air. 10th World Telecommunications Day.
1371 **451** 50 s. grey, deep blue and blue 75 50

1978. Various stamps surch **Habilitado Dif.-Porte** and value (Nos. 1372/4), **Habilitado R.D. No. 0118** and value (Nos. 1377/8, 1381, 1384, 1390) or with value only (others).
1372 **229** 2 s. on 2 c. brown (postage) 10 10
1373 4 s. on 2 c. brown . . . 10 10
1374 5 s. on 2 c. brown . . . 10 10
1375 **313** 20 s. on 1 s. 90 + 90 c. multicoloured 75 60
1376 – 30 s. on 2 s. 60 + 1 s. 30 mult (No. 917) 60 60
1377 **229** 35 s. on 2 c. brown . . . 25 20
1378 50 s. on 2 c. brown . . . 1·60 1·60
1379 – 55 s. on 3 s. 60 + 1 s. 80 mult (No. 918) 85 85
1380 – 65 s. on 4 s. 60 + 2 s. 30 mult (No. 919) 85 85
1381 – 80 s. on 5 s. 60 mult (No. 960) 60 40
1382 – 85 s. on 20 s. + 10 s. mult (No. 920) . . . . . . 1·25 1·25
1383 – 25 s. on 4 s. 60 mult (No. 954) (air) 20 15
1384 **316** 34 s. on 4 s. 60 mult . . 25 15
1385 **302** 40 s. on 4 s. 30 bistre and red 50 20
1386 **449** 45 s. on 28 s. green . . . 45 25
1387 – 70 s. on 2 s. 60 green (No. 926) 50 40
1388 **449** 75 s. on 28 s. green . . . 75 40
1389 – 105 s. on 5 s. 60 mult (No. 955) . . . . 1·00 85
1390 – 110 s. on 3 s. 60 purple (No. 927) 75 60
1391 – 265 s. on 4 s. 30 mult (No. 900) . . . . 1·90 1·50
The 28 s. value as Type **449** was not issued without a surcharge.

1978. Surch **SOBRE TASA OFICIAL** and value.
1400 **229** 3 s. on 2 s. brown . . . 10 10
1401 6 s. on 2 c. brown . . . 15 10

456 San Martin
457 Elmer Faucett and Stinson-Faucett F-19 and Boeing 727-200 Aircraft

1978. Air. Birth Bicentenary of General Jose de San Martin.
1410 **456** 30 s. multicoloured . . . 40 30

1978. 50th Anniv of Faucett Aviation.
1411 **457** 40 s. multicoloured . . . 50 30

1978. World Cup Football Championship, Argentina (2nd issue). Multicoloured.
1412 16 s. As Type **450** 15 10
1413 16 s. As No. 1368 . . . . . 15 10
1414 16 s. As No. 1369 . . . . . 15 10
1415 16 s. As No. 1370 . . . . . 15 10

458 Nazca Bowl

459 Peruvian Nativity

1978.

1416 **458** 16 s. blue 15 10
1417 20 s. green 15 10
1418 25 s. green 20 15
1419 35 s. red 35 15
1420 45 s. brown 40 25
1421 50 s. black 50 25
1422 55 s. mauve 50 25
1423 70 s. mauve 60 35
1424 75 s. blue 55 40
1425 80 s. brown 55 40
1426 200 s. violet . . . . 1·40 1·00

1978. Christmas.

1436 **459** 16 s. multicoloured . . . 15 10

460 Ministry of Education, Lima

461 Queen Sophia and King Juan Carlos

1979. National Education.

1437 **460** 16 s. multicoloured . . . 15 10

1979. Air. Visit of King and Queen of Spain.

1438 **461** 75 s. multicoloured . . . 60 25

462 Red Cross Emblem

1979. Centenary of Peruvian Red Cross Society.

1439 **462** 16 s. multicoloured . . . 10 10

463 "Naval Battle of Iquique" (E. Velarde)

1979. Pacific War Centenary. Multicoloured.

1440 14 s. Type **463** 20 10
1441 25 s. "Col. Jose Joaquin Inclan" (vert) 30 15
1442 25 s. "Arica Blockade-runner, the Corvette "Union" . . . 40 15
1443 25 s. "Heroes of Angamos" . 40 15
1444 25 s. "Lt. Col. Pedro Ruiz Gallo" (vert) 30 15
1445 85 s. "Marshal Andres H. Caceres" (vert) 45 40
1446 100 s. "Battle of Angamos" (T. Castillo) . . . . 1·40 60
1447 100 s. "Battle of Tarapaca" . 55 45
1448 115 s. "Admiral Miguel Grau" (vert) . . . . 1·00 50
1449 200 s. "Bolognesi's Reply" (Leppiani) . . . . 3·25 2·50
1450 200 s. "Col. Francisco Bolognesi" (vert) . . . . . 1·00 85
1451 200 s. "Col. Alfonso Ugarte" (Morizani) . . . . 1·00 85

A similar 200 s. value, showing the Crypt of the Fallen was on sale for a very limited period only.

464 Billiard Balls and Cue

465 Arms of Cuzco

1979. 34th World Billiards Championship, Lima.

1456 **464** 34 s. multicoloured . . . 30 15

1979. Inca Sun Festival, Cuzco.

1457 **465** 50 s. multicoloured . . . 35 20

466 Flag and Arch

468 Exposition Emblem

1979. 50th Anniv of Re-incorporation of Tacna into Peru.

1458 **466** 16 s. multicoloured . . . 15 10

1979. Surch in figures only.

1459 **229** 7 s. on 2 c. brown . . . 10 10
1460 9 s. on 2 c. brown . . . 10 10
1461 15 s. on 2 c. brown . . 15 10

1979. 3rd World Telecommunications Exhibition, Geneva.

1467 **468** 15 s. orange, blue & grey 10 10

469 Caduceus

470 Fair Emblem on World Map

1979. Int Stomatology Congress, Lima, and 50th Anniv of Peruvian Academy of Stomatology.

1468 **469** 25 s. gold, black & turq 20 15

1979. 11th International Pacific Fair.

1469 **470** 55 s. multicoloured . . . 40 30

471 Regalia of Chimu Chief (Imperial period)

472 Angel with Lute

1979. Rafael Larco Herrera Museum of Archaeology.

1470 **471** 85 s. multicoloured . . . 60 40

1980. Christmas.

1471 **472** 25 s. multicoloured . . . 20 10

1980. Various stamps surch.

1472 **466** 20 s. on 16 s. multicoloured (postage) 15 10
1473 **463** 25 s. on 14 s. multicoloured 30 15
1474 **464** 65 s. on 34 s. multicoloured 45 35
1475 **458** 80 s. on 70 s. mauve . . 55 40
1476 **449** 35 s. on 24 s. mauve (air) 25 15
1477 **438** 45 s. on 32 s. black and brown 30 20

474 "Respect and Comply with the Constitution"

475 Ceramic Vase (Chimu Culture)

1980. Citizens' Duties.

1478 **474** 15 s. turquoise 10 10
1479 – 20 s. red 15 10
1480 – 25 s. blue 20 15
1481 – 30 s. mauve 20 15
1482 – 35 s. black 25 20
1483 – 45 s. green 30 25
1484 – 50 s. brown 35 25

INSCRIPTIONS: 20 s. "Honour your country and protect your interests"; 25 s. "Comply with the elective process"; 30 s. "Comply with your military service"; 35 s. "Pay your taxes"; 45 s. "Work and contribute to national progress"; 50 s. "Respect the rights of others".

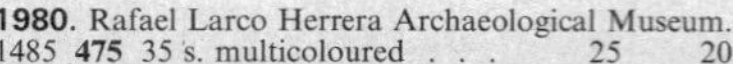

1980. Rafael Larco Herrera Archaeological Museum.

1485 **475** 35 s. multicoloured . . . 25 20

476 "Liberty" and Map of Peru

1980. Return to Democracy.

1486 **476** 25 s. black, buff and red . 20 15
1487 – 35 s. black and red . . . 25 20

DESIGN: 35 s. Handshake.

477 Machu Picchu

478 Rebellion Memorial, Cuzco (Joaquin Ugarte)

1980. World Tourism Conference, Manila.

1488 **477** 25 s. multicoloured . . . 20 15

1980. Bicentenary of Tupac Amaru Rebellion.

1489 **478** 25 s. multicoloured . . . 20 15

See also No. 1503.

479 Nativity

1980. Christmas.

1490 **479** 15 s. multicoloured . . . 10 10

480 Bolivar and Flags

483 Stone Head, Pallasca

482 Presidential Badge of Office, Laurel Leaves and Open Book

1981. 150th Death Anniv of Simon Bolivar.

1491 **480** 40 s. multicoloured . . . 30 20

1981. Various stamps surch.

1492 – 25 s. on 35 s. black and red (No. 1487) 20 15
1493 **482** 40 s. on 25 s. multicoloured 30 20
1494 **458** 85 s. on 200 s. violet . . 60 45
1495 – 100 s. on 115 s. mult (No. 1448) 70 50
1496 **482** 130 s. on 25 s. mult . . . 25 15
1497 140 s. on 25 s. mult . . . 25 15

1981. Re-establishment of Constitutional Government.

1498 **482** 25 s. multicoloured . . . 20 15

1981.

1499 **483** 30 s. violet 20 15
1500 – 40 s. blue 30 20
1501 – 100 s. mauve 70 45
1502 – 140 s. green 95 60

DESIGNS—VERT: 40 s. Stone head, Huamachuco; 100 s. Stone head (Chavin culture). HORIZ: 140 s. Stone puma head (Chavin culture).

484 Tupac Amaru and Micaela Bastidas (sculptures by Miguel Baca Rossi)

485 Post Box, 1859

1981. Bicentenary of Revolution of Tupac Amaru and Micaela Bastidas.

1503 **484** 60 s. multicoloured . . . 40 30

1981. 50th Anniv of Postal and Philatelic Museum, Lima.

1504 **485** 130 s. multicoloured . . 50 60

486 Map of Peru and I.Y.D.P. Emblem

487 Victor Raul Haya de la Torre (President of Constitutional Assembly)

1981. International Year of Disabled Persons.

1505 **486** 100 s. violet, mauve and gold 70 45

1981. Constitution.

1506 **487** 30 s. violet and grey . . 20 15

1981. No. 801 surch.

1507 30 s. on 2 s. 20 brown & blue 20 15
1508 40 s. on 2 s. 20 brown & blue 30 20

1981. 12th International Pacific Fair. No. 801 surch with **12 Feria Internacional del Pacifico 1981 140.**

1509 140 s. on 2 s. 20 brown & blue 95 70

490 Inca Messenger (drawing by Guaman Ponce de Ayala)

493 Inca Pot

1981. Christmas.

1510 **490** 30 s. black and mauve . 20 10
1511 40 s. black and red . . 35 10
1512 130 s. black and green . 45 35
1513 140 s. black and blue . . 45 40
1514 200 s. black and brown . 65 60

1982. Various stamps surch **Habilitado Franq. Postal** and value (Nos. 1520/1) or with value only (others).

1515 **229** 10 s. on 2 c. brown (postage) 15 10
1516 – 10 s. on 10 c. red (No. 642) 10 10
1517 **292** 40 s. on 10 c. blue and yellow 15 10
1518 **273** 70 s. on 5 c. blue and red 35 20
1519 **264a** 80 s. on 3 c. lake . . . 30 15
1520 D **109** 80 s. on 10 c. green . . 30 15
1521 O **108** 80 s. on 10 c. brown . . 30 15
1522 **292** 100 s. on 10 c. blue and yellow 40 20
1523 – 140 s. on 50 c. brown, yellow and red . . . 50 25
1524 – 140 s. on 1 s. mult . . 50 25
1525 **264a** 150 s. on 3 c. lake . . . 40 20
1526 180 s. on 3 c. lake . . . 55 30
1527 200 s. on 3 c. lake . . . 40 40
1528 **273** 280 s. on 5 c. blue and red 60 55
1529 – 40 s. on 1 s. 25 blue and purple (No. 814) (air) 30 15
1530 – 100 s. on 2 s. 20 brown and blue (No. 801) . . . 40 20
1531 – 240 s. on 1 s. 25 blue and purple (No. 814) . . 50 60

Nos. 1523/4 are surcharged on labels for the Seventh Eucharistic Congress which previously had no postal validity.

1982. Indian Ceramics.

1532 **493** 40 s. orange 30 15
1533 80 s. lilac 50 25
1534 – 80 s. red 50 25
1535 **493** 180 s. green . . . . . . 1·25 70
1536 – 240 s. blue 90 60
1537 – 280 s. violet . . . . . . 1·00 70

DESIGNS: 80 s., (No. 1534), 240, 280 s. Nazca fish ceramic.

494 Jorge Basadre (after Oscar Lopez Aliaga)

1982. Jorge Basadre (historian) Commemoration.
1538 **494** 100 s. black and green . 25 20

495 Julio C. Tello (bust, Victoria Macho)

1982. Birth Centenary of Julio C. Tello (archaeologist).
1539 **495** 200 s. green and blue . . 45 30

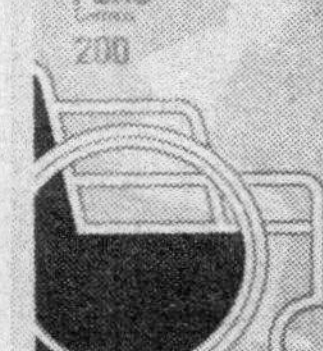

496 Championship Emblem
497 Disabled Person in Wheelchair

1982. 9th World Women's Volleyball Championship, Peru.
1540 **496** 80 s. red and black . . . 20 15

1982. Rights for the Disabled Year.
1541 **497** 200 s. blue and red . . . 50 30

498 Andres A. Caceres Medallion

1982. Centenary of Brena Campaign.
1542 **498** 70 s. brown and grey . . 20 15

499 Footballers
500 Congress Emblem

1982. World Cup Football Championship, Spain.
1543 **499** 80 s. multicoloured . . . 20 15

1982. 16th Int Latin Notaries Congress, Lima.
1544 **500** 500 s. black, gold and red 75 50

501 Bull (clay jar)
502 Pedro Vilcapaza

1982. Handicrafts Year.
1545 **501** 200 s. red, brown and black 50 30

1982. Death Bicentenary of Pedro Vilcapaza (Indian leader).
1546 **502** 240 s. brown and black . 35 35

HAVE YOU READ THE NOTES AT THE BEGINNING OF THIS CATALOGUE?
These often provide the answers to the enquiries we receive.

503 Jose Davila Condemarin (after J. Y. Pastor)
504 "Nativity" (Hilario Mendivil)

1982. Death Cent. of Jose Davila Condemarin (Director General of Posts).
1547 **503** 150 s. black and blue . . 40 25

1982. Christmas.
1548 **504** 280 s. multicoloured . . 40 30

505 Centre Emblem and Hand holding Potatoes

1982. 10th Anniv of International Potato Centre.
1549 **505** 240 s. brown and grey . 35 35

506 Arms of Piura

1982. 450th Anniv of San Miguel de Piura.
1550 **506** 280 s. multicoloured . . 40 40

507 Microscope

1982. Centenary of Discovery of Tubercule Bacillus.
1551 **507** 240 s. green 35 35

508 "St. Theresa of Avila" (Jose Espinoza de los Monteros)
509 Civil Defence Badge and Interlocked Hands

1983. 400th Death Anniv of St. Theresa of Avila.
1552 **508** 100 s. multicoloured . . 25 15

1983. 10th Anniv of Civil Defence System.
1553 **509** 100 s. blue, orange & blk 25 15

510 Silver Shoe

1983. "Peru, Land of Silver".
1554 **510** 250 s. silver, black & bl . 55 35

511 Map of Signatories and 200 Mile Zone

1983. 30th Anniv of Santiago Declaration.
1555 **511** 280 s. brown, blue & blk 40 40

512 Boeing 747-200
513 "75"

1983. 25th Anniv of Lima-Bogota Airmail Service.
1556 **512** 150 s. multicoloured . . . 60 25

1983. 75th Anniv of Lima and Callao State Lotteries.
1557 **513** 100 s. blue and purple . . 20 15

514 Cruiser "Almirante Grau"

1983. Peruvian Navy. Multicoloured.
1558 150 s. Type **514** 75 20
1559 350 s. Submarine "Ferre" . . 1·00 50

1983. Various stamps surch.
1560 **493** 100 s. on 40 s. orange . . 20 15
1561 **498** 100 s. on 70 s. brown and grey 20 15
1562 **496** 100 s. on 80 s. red and black 20 15
1563 **502** 100 s. on 240 s. brown and black 20 15
1564 **505** 100 s. on 240 s. ochre, deep brown and brown . . . 20 15
1565 **507** 100 s. on 240 s. green . . 20 15
1566 **506** 150 s. on 280 s. mult . . 30 15
1567 **511** 150 s. on 280 s. brown, blue and black 30 15
1568 **504** 200 s. on 280 s. mult . . 40 25
1569 **493** 300 s. on 180 s. green . . 55 35
1570 400 s. on 180 s. green . . 75 50
1571 **499** 500 s. on 80 s. mult . . . 95 65

516 Simon Bolivar
517 "Virgin and Child" (Cuzquena School)

1983. Birth Bicentenary of Simon Bolivar.
1572 **516** 100 s. blue and black . . 20 15

1983. Christmas.
1573 **517** 100 s. multicoloured . . . 20 10

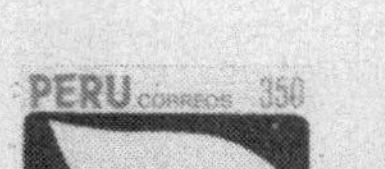

518 Fair Emblem
519 W.C.Y. Emblem

1983. 14th International Pacific Fair.
1574 **518** 350 s. multicoloured . . . 65 40

1984. World Communications Year.
1575 **519** 700 s. multicoloured . . . 1·00 70

520 Leoncio Prado
521 Container Ship at Wharf

1984. Death Centenary (1983) of Colonel Leoncio Prado.
1576 **520** 150 s. bistre and brown . 15 10

1984. Peruvian Industry.
1577 **521** 200 s. purple 40 25
1578 – 300 s. blue 60 25
DESIGN: 300 s. Container ship.

522 Ricardo Palma
523 Pistol Shooting

1984. 150th Birth Anniv (1983) of Ricardo Palma (writer).
1579 **522** 200 s. violet 15 10

1984. Olympic Games, Los Angeles.
1580 **523** 500 s. mauve and black . 45 25
1581 – 750 s. red and black . . 60 30
DESIGN: 750 s. Hurdling.

524 Arms of Callao
525 Water Jar

1984. Town Arms.
1582 **524** 350 s. grey 25 15
1583 – 400 s. brown 30 25
1584 – 500 s. brown 40 30
DESIGNS: 400 s. Cajamarca; 500 s. Ayacucho.

1984. Wari Ceramics (1st series).
1585 **525** 100 s. brown 10 10
1586 – 150 s. brown 15 10
1587 – 200 s. brown 20 10
DESIGNS: 150 s. Llama; 200 s. Vase.
See also Nos. 1616/18.

526 Hendee's Woolly Monkeys
527 Signing Declaration of Independence

1984. Fauna.
1588 **526** 1000 s. multicoloured . . 45 40

1984. Declaration of Independence.
1589 **527** 350 s. black, brown & red 25 15

528 General Post Office, Lima
529 "Canna edulis"

1984. Postal Services.
1590 **528** 50 s. olive 10 10

1984. Flora.
1591 **529** 700 s. multicoloured . . 45 25

530 Grau (after Pablo Muniz)
531 Hipolito Unanue

1984. 150th Anniv of Admiral Miguel Grau. Mult.
1592 600 s. Type **530** 35 20
1593 600 s. Battle of Angamos (45 × 35 mm) 70 30
1594 600 s. Grau's seat, National Congress 35 20
1595 600 s. "Battle of Iquique" (Guillermo Spier) (45 × 35 mm) 70 30

1984. 150th Death Anniv (1983) of Hipolito Unanue (founder of School of Medicine).
1596 **531** 50 s. green 10 10

532 Destroyer "Almirante Guise"

1984. Peruvian Navy.
1597 **532** 250 s. blue 25 15
1598 – 400 s. turquoise & blue . 55 20
DESIGN: 400 s. River gunboat "America".

533 "The Adoration of the Shepherds" **534** Belaunde

1984. Christmas.
1599 **533** 1000 s. multicoloured . . 40 15

1984. Birth Centenary (1983) of Victor Andres Belaunde (diplomat).
1600 **534** 100 s. purple 15 10

535 Street in Cuzco **536** Fair Emblem

1984. 450th Anniv of Founding of Cuzco by the Spanish.
1601 **535** 1000 s. multicoloured . . 40 25

1984. 15th International Pacific Fair, Lima.
1602 **536** 1000 s. blue and red . . 40 25

537 "Foundation of Lima" (Francisco Gonzalez Gamarra) **538** Pope John Paul II

1985. 450th Anniv of Lima.
1603 **537** 1500 s. multicoloured . . 55 30

1985. Papal Visit.
1604 **538** 2000 s. multicoloured . . 45 35

539 Dish Aerial, Huancayo **540** Jose Carlos Mariategui

1985. 15th Anniv (1984) of Entel Peru (National Telecommunications Enterprise).
1605 **539** 1100 s. multicoloured . . 25 15

1985. 60th Death Anniv (1984) of Jose Carlos Mariategui (writer).
1606 **540** 800 s. red 20 15

541 Emblem

1985. 25th Meeting of American Airforces Co-operation System.
1607 **541** 400 s. multicoloured . . 15 10

542 Captain Quinones

1985. 44th Death Anniv of Jose Abelardo Quinones Gonzales (airforce captain).
1608 **542** 1000 s. multicoloured . 25 15

543 Arms of Huancavelica **544** Globe and Emblem

1985.
1609 **543** 700 s. orange 15 15
See also Nos. 1628/9.

1985. 14th Latin-American Air and Space Regulations Days, Lima.
1610 **544** 900 s. blue 25 15

545 Francisco Garcia Calderon (head of 1881 Provisional Government) **546** Cross, Flag and Map

1985. Personalities.
1611 **545** 500 s. green 20 10
1612 – 800 s. green 35 15
DESIGN: 800 s. Oscar Miro Quesada (philosopher and jurist).

1985. 1st Anniv of Constitucion City.
1613 **546** 300 s. multicoloured . . 15 10

547 General Post Office Lima **548** Society Emblem, Satellite and Radio Equipment

1985. Postal Services.
1614 **547** 200 s. grey 10 10

1985. 55th Anniv of Peruvian Radio Club.
1615 **548** 1300 s. blue and orange 35 20

549 Robles Moqo Style Cat Vase **550** St. Francis's Monastry, Lima

1985. Wari Ceramics (2nd series).
1616 **549** 500 s. brown 15 10
1617 – 500 s. brown 15 10
1618 – 500 s. brown 15 10
DESIGNS: No. 1617, Cat, Huaura Style; No. 1618, Llama's head, Robles Moqo style.

1985. Tourism Day.
1619 **550** 1300 s. multicoloured . 30 15

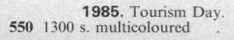

551 Title Page of "Doctrina Christiana" **552** Emblem and Curtiss "Jenny" Airplane

1985. 400th Anniv of First Book printed in South America.
1620 **551** 300 s. black and stone . . 15 10

1985. 40th Anniv of I.C.A.O.
1621 **552** 1100 s. black, blue & red 40 15

553 Humboldt Penguin **554** "Virgin and Child" (Cuzquena School)

1985. Fauna.
1622 **553** 1500 s. multicoloured . . 90 30

1985. Christmas.
1623 **554** 2 i. 50 multicoloured . . 20 10

555 Postman lifting child **556** Cesar Vallejo

1985. Postal Workers' Christmas and Children's Restaurant Funds.
1624 **555** 2 i. 50 multicoloured . . 30 20

1986. Poets.
1625 **556** 800 s. blue 20 10
1626 – 800 s. brown 20 10
DESIGN: No. 1626, Jose Santos Chocano.

557 Arms

1986. 450th Anniv of Trujillo.
1627 **557** 3 i. multicoloured 30 15

1986. Town Arms. As T **543**.
1628 700 s. blue 15 10
1629 900 s. brown 25 15
DESIGNS: 700 s. Huanuco; 900 s. Puno.

558 Stone Carving of Fish **559** "Hymenocallis amancaes"

1986. Restoration of Chan-Chan.
1630 **558** 50 c. multicoloured . . . 10 10

1986. Flora.
1631 **559** 1100 s. multicoloured . . 25 15

560 Alpaca and Textiles **561** St. Rosa de Lima (Daniel Hernandez)

1986. Peruvian Industry.
1632 **560** 1100 s. multicoloured . . 25 15

1986. 400th Birth Anniv of St. Rosa de Lima.
1633 **561** 7 i. multicoloured . . . 70 40

562 Daniel Alcides Carrion **563** Emblems and "16"

1986. Death Centenary (1985) of Daniel Alcides Carrion.
1634 **562** 50 c. brown 10 10

1986. 16th International Pacific Fair, Lima.
1635 **563** 1 i. multicoloured . . . 10 10

564 Woman Handspinning and Boy in Reed Canoe **565** Pedro Vilcapaza

1986. International Youth Year.
1636 **564** 3 i. 50 multicoloured . . 55 20

1986. 205th Anniv of Vilcapaza Rebellion.
1637 **565** 50 c. brown 10 10

566 U.N. Building, New York **567** Fernando and Justo Albujar Fayaque and Manuel Guarniz

1986. 40th Anniv (1985) of U.N.O.
1638 **566** 3 i. 50 multicoloured . . 30 20

1986. National Heroes.
1639 **567** 50 c. brown 10 10

568 Nasturtium **569** Submarine "Casma (R-1)", 1926

1986. Flora.
1640 **568** 80 c. multicoloured . . . 10 10

1986. Peruvian Navy. Each blue.
1641 1 i. 50 Type **569** 45 15
1642 2 i. 50 Submarine "Abtao", 1954 . . . . 80 25

570 Tinta Costumes, Canchis Province　**571** Sacsayhuaman Fort, Cuzco

1986. Costumes.
1643 **570** 3 i. multicoloured 30 20

1986. Tourism Day (1st issue).
1644 **571** 4 i. multicoloured 40 30
See also No. 1654.

572 La Tomilla Water Treatment Plant　**573** "Datura candida"

1986. 25th Anniv of Inter-American Development Bank.
1645 **572** 1 i. multicoloured 10 10

1986. Flora.
1646 **573** 80 c. multicoloured . . . 10 10

574 Pope John Paul and Sister Ana　**575** Chavez, Bleriot XI and Simplon Range

1986. Beatification of Sister Ana of the Angels Monteagudo.
1647 **574** 6 i. multicoloured 65 45

1986. 75th Anniv of Trans-Alpine Flight by Jorge Chavez Dartnell.
1648 **575** 5 i. multicoloured 75 35

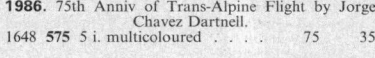

576 Emblem　**577** "Martyrs of Uchuraccay"

1986. National Vaccination Days.
1649 **576** 50 c. blue 10 10

1986. Peruvian Journalists' Fund.
1650 **577** 1 i. 50 black and blue . . 15 10

578 "Canis nudus"　**579** Brigantine "Gamarra"

1986. Fauna.
1651 **578** 2 i. multicoloured 20 15

1986. Navy Day.
1652 **579** 1 i. blue and light blue . 50 20
1653 – 1 i. blue and red 50 20
DESIGN: No. 1653, Battleship "Manco Capac".

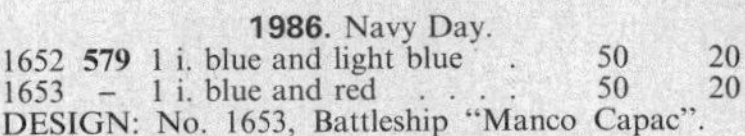

580 Intihuatana Cuzco

1986. Tourism Day (2nd issue).
1654 **580** 4 i. multicoloured . . . 40 30

581 Institute Building

1986. 35th Anniv (1985) of Institute of Higher Military Studies.
1655 **581** 1 i. multicoloured . . . 15 10

582 Children　**583** White-winged Guan

1986. Postal Workers' Christmas and Children's Restaurant Funds.
1656 **582** 2 i. 50 black and brown 30 20

1986. Fauna.
1657 **583** 2 i. multicoloured . . . 55 15

584 Galvez　**585** "St. Joseph and Child" (Cuzquena School)

1986. Birth Centenary (1985) of Jose Galvez Barrenechea (poet).
1658 **584** 50 c. brown 10 10

1986. Christmas.
1659 **585** 5 i. multicoloured . . . 50 30

586 Flags, and Hands holding Cogwheel　**587** Shipibo Costumes

1986. 25th Anniv of "Senati" (National Industrial Training Organization).
1660 **586** 4 i. multicoloured . . . 40 30

1987. Christmas.
1661 **587** 3 i. multicoloured . . . 30 25

588 Harvesting Mashua　**589** Dr. Reiche and Diagram of Nazca Lines

1987. World Food Day.
1662 **588** 50 c. multicoloured . . 10 10

1987. Dr. Maria Reiche (Nazca Lines researcher).
1663 **589** 8 i. multicoloured . . . 80 60

590 Santos　**591** Show Jumping

1987. Mariano Santos (Hero of War of the Pacific).
1664 **590** 50 c. violet 10 10

1987. 50th Anniv of Peruvian Horse Club.
1665 **591** 3 i. multicoloured 30 25

592 Salaverry

1987. 150th Death Anniv (1986) of General Felipe Santiago Salaverry (President, 1835–36).
1666 **592** 2 i. multicoloured 20 15

593 Colca Canyon　**594** 1857 1 & 2 r. Stamps

1987. "Arequipa 87" National Stamp Exhibition.
1667 **593** 6 i. multicoloured 50 30

1987. "Amifil 87" National Stamp Exhibition, Lima.
1668 **594** 1 i. brown, blue and grey 10 10

595 Arguedas　**596** Carving, Emblem and Nasturtium

1987. 75th Birth Anniv (1986) of Jose Maria Arguedas (writer).
1669 **595** 50 c. brown 10 10

1987. Centenary of Arequipa Chamber of Commerce and Industry.
1670 **596** 2 i. multicoloured 20 15

597 Vaccinating Child　**598** De la Riva Aguero

1987. Child Vaccination Campaign.
1671 **597** 50 c. red 10 10

1987. Birth Centenary (1985) of Jose de la Riva Aguero (historian).
1672 **598** 80 c. brown 10 10

599 Porras Barrenechea　**600** Footballers

1987. 90th Birth Anniv of Raul Porras Barrenechea (historian).
1673 **599** 80 c. brown 10 10

1987. World Cup Football Championship, Mexico (1986).
1674 **600** 4 i. multicoloured . . . 20 15

601 Stone Carving of Man

1987. Restoration of Chan-Chan.
1675 **601** 50 c. multicoloured . . . 10 10

602 Comet and "Giotto" Space Probe

1987. Appearance of Halley's Comet (1986).
1676 **602** 4 i. multicoloured . . . 20 15

603 Chavez　**604** Osambela Palace

1987. Birth Centenary of Jorge Chavez Dartnell (aviator).
1677 **603** 2 i. brown, ochre & gold 10 10

1987. 450th Birth Anniv of Lima.
1678 **604** 2 i. 50 multicoloured . . 15 10

605 Machu Picchu

1987. 75th Anniv (1986) of Discovery of Machu Picchu.
1679 **605** 9 i. multicoloured . . . 40 30

606 St. Francis's Church

1987. Cajamarca, American Historical and Cultural Site.
1680 **606** 2 i. multicoloured . . . 10 10

607 National Team, Emblem and Olympic Rings

1988. 50th Anniv (1986) of First Peruvian Participation in Olympic Games (at Berlin).
1681 **607** 1 i. 50 multicoloured . . 10 10

608 Children

1988. 150th Anniv of Ministry of Education.
1682 **608** 1 i. multicoloured 10 10

609 Statue and Pope

1988. Coronation of Virgin of Evangelization, Lima.
1683 **609** 10 i. multicoloured . . . 40 30

610 Emblems **611** Postman and Lima Cathedral

1988. Rotary International Anti-Polio Campaign.
1684 **610** 2 i. blue, gold and red . . 10 10

1988. Postal Workers' Christmas and Children's Restaurant Funds.
1685 **611** 9 i. blue 30 20

612 Flags **613** St. John Bosco

1988. 1st Meeting of Eight Latin American Presidents of Contadora and Lima Groups, Acapulco, Mexico.
1686 **612** 9 i. multicoloured 30 20

1988. Death Centenary of St. John Bosco (founder of Salesian Brothers).
1687 **613** 5 i. multicoloured 20 15

614 Supply Ship "Humboldt" and Globe

1988. 1st Peruvian Scientific Expedition to Antarctica.
1688 **614** 7 i. multicoloured 70 20

615 Clay Wall

1988. Restoration of Chan-Chan.
1689 **615** 4 i. brown and black . . 15 10

616 Vallejo (after Picasso) **617** Journalists at Work

1988. 50th Death Anniv of Cesar Vallejo (poet).
1690 **616** 25 i. black, yellow & brn 50 40

1988. Peruvian Journalists' Fund.
1691 **617** 4 i. blue and brown . . . 10 10

618 1908 2 s. Columbus Monument Stamp **619** "17" and Guanaco

1988. "Exfilima 88" Stamp Exhibition, Lima, and 500th Anniv of Discovery of America by Christopher Columbus.
1692 **618** 20 i. blue, pink & black 20 10

1988. 17th International Pacific Fair, Lima.
1693 **619** 4 i. multicoloured . . . 10 10

620 "Village Band" **621** Dogs

1988. Birth Centenary of Jose Sabogal (painter).
1694 **620** 12 i. multicoloured . . . 15 10

1988. "Canino '88" International Dog Show, Lima.
1695 **621** 20 i. multicoloured . . . 20 10

622 Silva and Score of "Splendour of Flowers" **623** Pope

1988. 50th Death Anniv (1987) of Alfonso de Silva (composer).
1696 **622** 20 i. grey, deep brown and brown 20 10

1988. 2nd Visit of Pope John Paul II.
1697 **623** 50 i. multicoloured . . . 35 25

624 Volleyball **625** Volleyball

1988. Olympic Games, Seoul.
1698 **624** 25 i. multicoloured . . . 20 10

1988. Postal Workers' Christmas and Children's Restaurant Funds. Unissued stamp surch as in T **625**.
1699 **625** 95 i. on 300 s. black and red 60 50

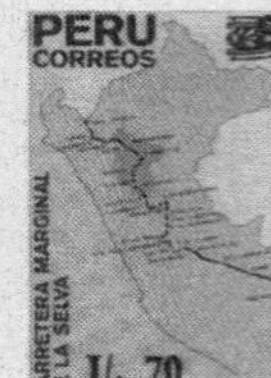
626 Ceramic Vase **627** Map

1988. Chavin Culture. Unissued stamps surch as in T **626**.
1700 **626** 40 i. on 100 s. red . . . 30 20
1701 80 i. on 10 s. black . . . 25 15

1989. Forest Boundary Road. Unissued stamp surch as in T **627**.
1702 **627** 70 i. on 80 s. green, black and blue 40 30

628 Arm **629** Huari Weaving

1989. Laws of the Indies. Unissued stamp surch as in T **628**.
1703 **628** 230 i. on 300 s. brown . . 40 15

1989. Centenary of Credit Bank of Peru.
1704 **629** 500 i. multicoloured . . . 60 20

630 Special Postal Services Emblem **631** Newspaper Offices

1989. Postal Services.
1705 **630** 50 i. blue and green . . . 10 10
1706 – 100 i. red and pink . . . 10 10
DESIGN: 100 i. National Express Post emblem.

1989. 150th Anniv of "El Comercio" (newspaper).
1707 **631** 600 i. multicoloured . . . 50 10

632 Garcilaso de la Vega

1989. 450th Birth Anniv of Garcilaso de la Vega (writer).
1708 **632** 300 i. multicoloured . . . 10 10

633 Emblem

1989. Express Mail Service.
1709 **633** 100 i. red, blue & orange 10 10

634 Dr. Luis Loli Roca (founder of Journalists' Federation)

1989. Peruvian Journalists' Fund.
1710 **634** 100 i. blue, deep blue and black 10 10

635 Relief of Birds

1989. Restoration of Chan-Chan.
1711 **635** 400 i. multicoloured . . . 35 10

MINIMUM PRICE

The minimum price quoted is 10p which represents a handling charge rather than a basis for valuing common stamps. For further notes about prices, see introductory pages.

636 Old Map of South America

1989. Centenary of Lima Geographical Society.
1712 **636** 600 i. multicoloured . . 95 20

637 Painting

1989. 132nd Anniv of Society of Founders of Independence.
1713 **637** 300 i. multicoloured . . 10 10

638 Lake Huacachina

1989. 3rd Meeting of Latin American Presidents of Contadora and Lima Groups, Ica.
1714 **638** 1300 i. multicoloured . . 1·10 60

639 Children buying Stamps for Commemorative Envelopes **641** Vessel with Figure of Doctor examining Patient

640 "Corryocactus huincoensis"

1989. Postal Workers' Christmas and Children's Restaurant Funds.
1715 **639** 1200 i. multicoloured . . 30 20

1989. Cacti. Multicoloured.
1716 500 i. Type **640** 15 10
1717 500 i. "Haagocereus clavispinus" (vert) 15 10
1718 500 i. "Loxanthocereus acanthurus" 15 10
1719 500 i. "Matucana cereoides" (vert) 15 10
1720 500 i. "Trichocereus peruvianus" (vert) 15 10

1989. America. Pre-Columbian Ceramics. Mult.
1721 5000 i. Type **641** . . . . . . 1·60 1·00
1722 5000 i. Vessel with figure of surgeon performing cranial operation . . . . 1·60 1·00

642 Bethlehem Church

1990. Cajamarca, American Historical and Cultural Site.
1723 **642** 600 i. multicoloured . . 15 10

643 Climber in Andes

644 Pope and Virgin of Evangelization

1990. Huascaran National Park. Multicoloured.

1724 900 i. Type **643** 20 15
1725 900 i. Llanganuco Lake (horiz) 20 15
1726 1000 i. "Puya raimondi" (plant) 25 20
1727 1000 i. Snow-covered mountain peak (horiz) 25 20
1728 1100 i. Huascaran Mountain (horiz) 30 25
1729 1100 i. Andean condor over mountain slopes (horiz) 45 35

1990. 2nd Visit of Pope John Paul II.

1730 **644** 1250 i. multicoloured 30 25

645 "Agrias beata" (female)

1990. Butterflies. Multicoloured.

1731 1000 i. Type **645** 35 25
1732 1000 i. "Agrias beata" (male) 35 25
1733 1000 i. "Agrias amydon" (female) 35 25
1734 1000 i. "Agrias sardanapalus" (female) 35 25
1735 1000 i. "Agrias sardanapalus" (male) 35 25

646 Victor Raul Haya de la Torre (President of Constituent Assembly)

647 Emblem

1990. 10th Anniv of Political Constitution.

1736 **646** 2100 i. multicoloured 45 10

1990. 40th Anniv of Peruvian Philatelic Association.

1737 **647** 300 i. brown, blk & cream 10 10

648 Globe and Exhibition Emblem

1990. "Prenfil '88" International Philatelic Literature Exhibition, Buenos Aires.

1738 **648** 300 i. multicoloured 10 10

649 "Republic" (Antoine-Jean Gros)

1990. Bicentenary of French Revolution. Paintings. Multicoloured.

1739 2000 i. Type **649** 40 10
1740 2000 i. "Storming the Bastille" (Hubert Robert) 40 10
1741 2000 i. "Lafayette at the Festival of the Republic" (anon) 40 10
1742 2000 i. "Jean Jacques Rousseau and Symbols of the Revolution" (E. Jeaurat) 40 10

650 "Founding Arequipa" (Teodoro Nunez Ureta)

1990. 450th Anniv of Arequipa.

1734 **650** 50000 i. multicoloured 10 10

651 Pelado Island Lighthouse

1990. Peruvian Navy. Unissued stamps, each light blue and blue, surch as in T **651**.

1744 110000 i. on 200 i. Type **651** 40 25
1745 230000 i. on 400 i. "Morona" (hospital ship) 1·25 60

652 Games Mascot

653 1857 1 r. Stamp and Container Ship

1990. 4th South American Games (1st issue). Multicoloured.

1746 110000 i. Type **652** 25 20
1747 280000 i. Shooting 1·10 60
1748 290000 i. Athletics (horiz) 1·25 65
1749 300000 i. Football 1·25 65

See also Nos. 1753/6.

1990. 150th Anniv of Pacific Steam Navigation Company. Multicoloured. Self-adhesive.

1750 250000 i. Type **653** 1·25 65
1751 350000 i. 1857 2 r. stamp and container ship 1·75 85

654 Postal Van

1990. Postal Workers' Christmas and Children's Restaurant Funds.

1752 **654** 310000 i. multicoloured 75 70

1991. 4th South American Games (2nd issue). As T **652**. Multicoloured.

1753 560000 i. Swimming 1·90 1·10
1754 580000 i. Show jumping (vert) 2·00 1·25
1755 600000 i. Yachting (vert) 2·50 1·40
1756 620000 i. Tennis (vert) 2·10 1·40

655 Maria Jesus Castaneda de Pardo

1991. Red Cross. Unissued stamp surch.

1757 **655** 0.15 i/m. on 2500 i. red 50 25

Note. "i/m" on No. 1757 onwards indicates face value in million intis.

656 Penguins, Scientist and Station

1991. 2nd Peruvian Scientific Expedition to Antarctica. Unissued stamps surch. Multicoloured.

1758 0.40 i/m. on 50000 i. Type **656** 20 10
1759 0.45 i/m. on 80000 i. Station and gull 20 10
1760 0.50 i/m. on 100000 i. Whale, map and station 1·60 10

657 "Siphoonandra elliptica" (plant No. 1 in University herbarium)

658 "Virgin of the Milk"

1991. 300th Anniv of National University of St. Anthony Abad del Cusco. Multicoloured.

1761 10 c. Type **657** 15 10
1762 20 c. Bishop Manuel de Mollinedo y Angulo (first Chancellor) 25 20
1763 1 s. University arms 2·00 1·00

1991. Postal Workers' Christmas and Children's Restaurant Funds. Paintings by unknown artists. Multicoloured.

1764 70 c. Type **658** 1·25 10
1765 70 c. "Divine Shepherdess" 1·25 10

659 Lake

1991. America (1990). The Natural World. Mult.

1766 0.50 i/m. Type **659** 90 10
1767 0.50 i/m. Waterfall (vert) 90 10

660 Sir Rowland Hill and Penny Black

1992. 150th Anniv (1990) of the Penny Black.

1768 **660** 0.40 i/m. black, grey & bl 70 10

661 Arms and College

662 Arms

1992. 150th Anniv (1990) of Our Lady of Guadalupe College.

1769 **661** 0.30 i/m. multicoloured 55 10

1992. 80th Anniv (1991) of Entre Nous Society, Lima (literature society for women).

1770 **662** 10 c. multicoloured 10 10

663 Map

1992. Bolivia–Peru Presidential Meeting, Ilo.

1771 **1663** 20 c. multicoloured 15 10

664 Tacaynamo Idol

665 Raimondi

1992. Restoration of Chan-Chan.

1772 **664** 0.15 i/m. multicoloured 10 10

See note below No. 1757.

1992. Death Centenary of Jose Antonio Raimondi (naturalist).

1773 **665** 0.30 i/m. multicoloured 25 20

See note below No. 1757.

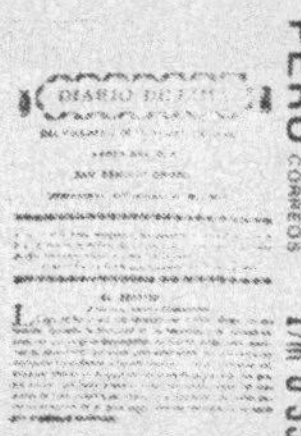

666 First Issue

1992. Bicentenary (1990) of "Diario de Lima" (newspaper).

1774 **666** 35 c. black and yellow 35 15

667 Melgar

1992. Birth Bicentenary (1990) of Mariano Melgar (poet).

1775 **667** 60 c. multicoloured 50 25

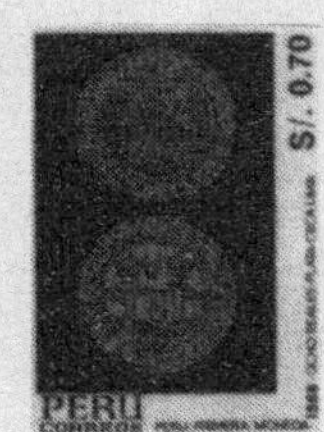

668 1568 Eight Silver Reales Coin

1992. First Peruvian Coinage.

1776 **668** 70 c. multicoloured 70 35

669 Emblem

1992. 75th Anniv of Catholic University of Peru.

1777 **669** 90 c. black and stone 70 35

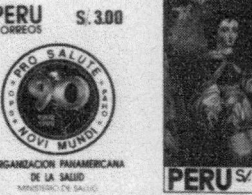

670 Emblem

672 "Virgin of the Spindle" (painting, Santa Clara Monastery, Cuzco)

1992. 90th Anniv of Pan-American Health Organization. Self-adhesive. Imperf.

1778 **670** 3 s. multicoloured 2·40 1·10

1992. Various stamps surch.

1779 – 40 c. on 500 i. multicoloured (1717) 30 15
1780 – 40 c. on 500 i. multicoloured (1718) 30 15
1781 – 40 c. on 500 i. multicoloured (1719) 30 15
1782 – 40 c. on 500 i. multicoloured (1720) 30 15

1783 **493** 50 c. on 180 s. green . . 40 20
1784 **648** 50 c. on 300 i. mult . . . 40 20
1785 **645** 50 c. on 1000 i. mult . . . 40 20
1786 – 50 c. on 1000 i. mult (1732) 40 20
1787 – 50 c. on 1000 i. mult (1733) 40 20
1788 – 50 c. on 1000 i. mult (1734) 40 20
1789 – 50 c. on 1000 i. mult (1735) 40 20
1790 **647** 1 s. on 300 i. brown, black and cream 80 40
1791 **644** 1 s. on 1250 i. mult . . . 80 40
1792 **638** 1 s. on 1300 i. mult . . . 80 40

1993. Self-adhesive. Imperf.
1793 **672** 80 c. multicoloured . . . 65 30

673 Gold Figures

1993. Sican Culture (1st series). Multicoloured. Self-adhesive. Imperf.
1794 2 s. Type **673** . . . . 1·60 80
1795 5 s. Gold foil figure (vert) . . 4·00 2·00
See also Nos. 1814/15.

674 Incan Gold Decoration and Crucifix on Chancay Robe

1993. 500th Anniv of Evangelization of Peru.
1796 **674** 1 s. multicoloured . . . 80 40

675 "The Marinera" (Monica Rojas)

677 "Madonna and Child" (statue)

1993. Paintings of Traditional Scenes. Multicoloured. Self-adhesive. Imperf.
1797 1 s. 50 Type **675** . . . . . . 1·25 60
1798 1 s. 50 "Fruit Sellers" (Angel Chavez) . . . . 1·25 60

1993. Centenary (1991) of Salesian Brothers in Peru. Self-adhesive. Imperf.
1799 **676** 70 c. multicoloured . . . 55 25

677 Francisco Pizarro and Spanish Galleon

1993. America (1991). Voyages of Discovery. Multicoloured.
1800 90 c. Type **677** 55 25
1801 1 s. Spanish galleon and route map of Pizarros' second voyage 60 30
Nos. 1800/1 were issued together, se-tenant, forming a composite design.

678 Gold Mask

1993. Jewels from Funerary Chamber of "Senor of Sipan" (1st series).
1802 **678** 50 c. multicoloured . . . 30 15
See also Nos. 1830/1.

679 Escriva

680 Cherry Blossom and Nazca Lines Hummingbird

1993. 1st Anniv of Beatification of Josemaria Escriva (founder of Opus Dei). Self-adhesive. Imperf.
1803 **679** 30 c. multicoloured . . 20 10

1993. 120th Anniv of Diplomatic Relations and Peace, Friendship, Commerce and Navigation Treaty with Japan. Multicoloured.
1804 1 s. 50 Type **680** 95 45
1805 1 s. 70 Peruvian and Japanese children and Mts. Huascaran (Peru) and Fuji (Japan) . 1·10 55

81 Sea Lions

682 Delgado

1993. Stamp Exhibitions. Multicoloured.
1806 90 c. Type **681** ("Amifil '93" National Stamp Exhibition, Lima) 55 25
1807 1 s. Macaw ("Brasiliana '93" International Stamp Exhibition, Rio de Janeiro) (vert) 60 30

1993. Birth Centenary of Dr. Honorio Delgado (psychiatrist and neurologist). Self-adhesive. Imperf.
1808 **682** 50 c. brown 30 15

683 Morales Macedo

684 "The Sling" (Quechua Indians)

1993. Birth Centenary of Rosalia de Lavalle de Morales Macedo (founder of Society for Protection of Children and of Christian Co-operation Bank). Self-adhesive. Imperf.
1809 **683** 80 c. orange 50 25

1993. Ethnic Groups. Statuettes by Felipe Lettersten. Multicoloured. Self-adhesive. Imperf.
1810 2 s. Type **684** . . . . . . 1·25 60
1811 3 s. 50 "Fire" (Orejon Indians) 2·25 1·10

685 "20" on Stamp

686 "Virgin of Loreta"

1993. 20th International Pacific Fair.
1812 **685** 1 s. 50 multicoloured . . 95 45

1993. Christmas.
1813 **686** 1 s. multicoloured . . . 60 30

687 Artefacts from Tomb, Poma

688 Ceramic Figure

1993. Sican Culture (2nd series). Multicoloured. Self-adhesive. Imperf.
1814 2 s. 50 Type **687** . . . . . 1·50 75
1815 4 s. Gold mask . . . . . . 2·50 1·25

1993. Chancay Culture. Multicoloured. Self-adhesive. Imperf.
1816 10 s. Type **688** . . . . . . 6·25 3·00
1817 20 s. Textile pattern (horiz) . 12·50 6·25

689 "With AIDS There is No Tomorrow"

690 Computer Graphics

1993. International AIDS Day.
1818 **689** 1 s. 50 multicoloured . . 95 45

1994. 25th Anniv of National Council for Science and Technology. Self-adhesive. Imperf.
1819 **690** 1 s. multicoloured 55 25

691 "The Bridge" (woodcut from "New Chronicle and Good Government" by Poma de Ayala)

692 Engraved Mate Dish

1994. Self-adhesive. Imperf.
1820 **691** 20 c. blue 10 10
1821 40 c. orange 20 10
1822 50 c. violet 30 15
For similar design see Nos. 1827/9.

1994. Multicoloured. Self-adhesive. Imperf.
1823 1 s. 50 Type **692** 85 40
1824 1 s. 50 Engraved silver and mate vessel (vert) 85 40
1825 3 s. Figure of bull from Pucara 1·75 85
1826 3 s. Glazed plate decorated with fishes . . . . 1·75 85

693 "The Bridge" (Poma de Ayala)

694 Gold Trinkets

1994.
1827 **693** 30 c. brown 15 10
1828 40 c. black 20 10
1829 50 c. red 30 15

1994. Jewels from Funerary Chamber of Senor de Sipan (2nd series). Multicoloured.
1830 3 s. Type **694** . . . . 1·75 85
1831 5 s. Gold mask (vert) . . . . 2·75 1·25

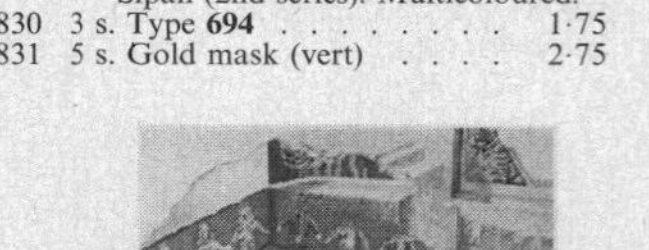

695 El Brujo

1994. Archaeology. El Brujo Complex, Trujillo.
1832 **695** 70 c. multicoloured 40 20

EXPRESS LETTER STAMPS

1908. Optd **EXPRESO**.
E373 **76** 10 c. black . . . . 17·00 12·50
E382 – 10 c. blue (No. 377) . . 21·00 11·50
E383 **101** 10 c. black and brown . 11·50 10·00

OFFICIAL STAMPS

1890. Stamps of 1866 optd **GOBIERNO** in frame.
O287 **15** 1 c. violet . . . . 1·10 1·10
O324 1 c. red . . . . 6·75 6·75
O288 **16** 2 c. green . . . . 1·10 1·10
O325 2 c. blue . . . . 6·75 6·75
O289 5 c. orange . . . . 1·60 1·60
O326 **10** 5 c. lake . . . . 5·50 5·50
O290 **16** 10 c. black 85 45
O291 20 c. blue . . . . 2·50 1·60
O327 20 c. blue (as T **10**) . . . 5·50 5·50
O292 **20** 50 c. red . . . . 3·25 1·40
O293 **21** 1 s. brown . . . . 4·25 3·75

1894. Stamps of 1894 (with "Head" optd) optd **GOBIERNO** in frame.
O305 **15** 1 c. orange (No. 294) . . 19·00 19·00
O306 1 c. green (No. 295) . . 1·10 1·10
O307 **16** 2 c. violet (No. 296) . . 1·10 1·10
O308 2 c. red (No. 297) . . . 90 90
O309 5 c. blue (No. 298) . . . 8·25 7·50
O310 10 c. green (No. 299) . . 3·00 3·00
O311 **20** 50 c. green (No. 300) . . 4·25 4·25

1894. Stamps of 1894 (with "Head" and "Horseshoe" optd) optd **GOBIERNO** in frame.
O312 **16** 2 c. red (No. 301) . . . . 1·60 1·60
O313 5 c. blue (No. 302) . . . 1·60 1·60

1896. Stamps of 1896 optd **GOBIERNO**.
O348 **75** 1 c. blue 10 10
O349 **76** 10 c. yellow . . . . 1·00 25
O350 10 c. black 10 10
O351 **77** 50 c. red 25 20

O 108

1909.
O382 **O 108** 1 c. red 10 10
O572 10 c. brown 40 30
O385 10 c. purple 15 10
O573 50 c. green 35 20

1935. Optd **Servicio Oficial**.
O567 **184** 10 c. red 10 10

PARCEL POST STAMPS.

P 79

1895. Different frames.
P348 **P 79** 1 c. purple . . . . . . 1·90 1·60
P349 2 c. brown . . . . . . 2·10 1·90
P350 5 c. blue . . . . 8·25 5·50
P351 10 c. brown . . . . . 11·50 8·25
P352 20 c. pink . . . . . . 14·00 11·50
P353 50 c. green . . . . . 38·00 32·00

1903. Surch in words.
P361 **P 79** 1 c. on 20 c. pink . . . 10·00 8·25
P362 1 c. on 50 c. green . . 10·00 8·25
P363 5 c. on 10 c. brown . . 65·00 55·00

POSTAGE DUE STAMPS

D 22 **D 23** **D 109**

1874.
D31 **D 22** 1 c. brown 10 10
D32 **D 23** 5 c. red 15 15
D33 10 c. orange 15 15
D34 20 c. blue 30 30
D35 50 c. brown . . . . . 7·50 3·00

1881. Optd with T **24** "LIMA" at foot instead of "PERU").
D47 **D 22** 1 c. brown . . . . . . 3·00 2·00
D48 **D 23** 5 c. red . . . . 5·50 5·00
D49 10 c. orange . . . . . 5·50 5·50
D50 20 c. blue . . . . . . 21·00 17·00
D51 50 c. brown . . . . . 45·00 42·00

1881. Optd **LIMA CORREOS** in double-lined circle.
D52 **D 22** 1 c. brown . . . . . . 4·25 4·25
D53 **D 23** 5 c. red . . . . 5·50 5·00
D54 10 c. orange . . . . . 6·75 5·50
D55 20 c. blue . . . . . . 21·00 17·00
D56 50 c. brown . . . . . 65·00 55·00

1883. Optd with T **24** (inscr "LIMA" instead of "PERU") and also with T **28a**.
D247 **D 22** 1 c. brown . . . . . . 4·25 3·00
D250 **D 23** 5 c. red . . . . 6·25 5·75
D253 10 c. orange . . . . . 6·25 5·75
D256 20 c. blue £375 £375
D258 50 c. brown . . . . . 45·00 35·00

1884. Optd with T **28a** only.
D259 **D 22** 1 c. brown 40 40
D262 **D 23** 5 c. red 20 20
D267 10 c. orange 25 25
D269 20 c. blue 85 35
D271 50 c. brown . . . . . 2·50 75

1894. Optd **LIMA CORREOS** in double-lined circle and with T **28a**.
D275 **D 22** 1 c. brown . . . . 10·50 9·25

1896. Optd **DEFICIT**.
D348 **D 22** 1 c. brown (D31) . . 15 15
D349 **D 23** 5 c. red (D32) . . . 15 15
D350 10 c. orange (D33) . . 45 15
D351 20 c. blue (D34) . . . 55 20
D352 **20** 50 c. red (283) . . . 60 20
D353 **21** 1 s. brown (284) . . . 85 35

1899. As T **73**, but inscr "DEFICIT" instead of "FRANQUEO".
D355 5 s. green . . . . 85 4·25
D356 10 s. brown . . . . 60·00 60·00

1902. Surch **DEFICIT** and value in words.
D361 1 c. on 10 s. (D356) . . . 85 50
D362 5 c. on 10 s. (354) 50 40

1902. Surch **DEFICIT** and value in words.
D363 **D 23** 1 c. on 20 c. (D34) . . 50 40
D364 5 c. on 20 c. (D34) . . 1·25 1·00

1909.

D382	D **109**	1 c. brown	35	15
D419		1 c. purple	15	15
D420		2 c. purple	15	15
D570		2 c. brown	15	15
D383		5 c. brown	35	15
D421		5 c. purple	25	20
D384		10 c. brown	40	15
D422		10 c. purple	40	15
D571		10 c. green	40	15
D385		50 c. brown	60	20
D423		50 c. purple	1·40	50
D424		1 s. purple	10·00	3·00
D425		2 s. purple	19·00	6·75

1935. Optd **Deficit**.

D568	–	2 c. purple (No. 537)	40	40
D569	**184**	10 c. red	50	40

PHILIPPINES Pt. 9; Pt. 22; Pt. 21

A group of islands in the China Sea, E. of Asia, ceded by Spain to the United States after the war of 1898. Under Japanese Occupation from 1941 until 1945. The Philippines became fully independent in 1946. An independent Republic since 1946.

1854. 20 cuartos = 1 real. 8 reales = 1 peso plata fuerte
1864. 100 centimos = 1 peso plata fuerte
1871. 100 centimos = 1 escudo (= $\frac{1}{2}$ peso)
1872. 100 centimos = 1 peseta (= $\frac{1}{5}$ peso)
1876. 1000 milesimas = 100 centavos or centimos = 1 peso
1899. 100 cents = 1 dollar
1906. 100 centavos = 1 peso
1962. 100 sentimos = 1 piso

SPANISH ADMINISTRATION

1

4

5

Queen Isabella II

1854. Imperf.
1 **1** 5 c. orange . . . £1100 £190
3 10 c. red . . . £325 £130
5 1 r. blue . . . £350 £120
7a 2 r. green . . . £475 £110

1859. Imperf.
13 **4** 5 c. orange . . . 10·00 5·00
14 10 c. pink . . . 10·00 6·00

1861. Larger lettering. Imperf.
17 **5** 5 c. orange . . . 18·00 6·50

7

8

13 King Amadeo

1863. Imperf.
19 **7** 5 c. red . . . 10·00 4·50
20 10 c. red . . . 25·00 13·00
21 1 r. mauve . . . £375 £150
22 2 r. blue . . . £325 £140

1863. Imperf.
25 **8** 1 r. green . . . 75·00 28·00

1864. As T **12** of Spain, but value in "centimos de peso". Imperf.
26 $3\frac{1}{8}$ c. black on buff . . . 2·25 1·00
27 $6\frac{2}{8}$ c. green on pink . . . 2·25 80
28 $12\frac{4}{8}$ c. blue on flesh . . . 3·50 80
30 25 c. red . . . 5·00 2·00

1868. Optd **HABILITADO POR LA NACION.**

(a) On 1854 to 1863 issues of Philippines.
41 **7** 5 c. red . . . 35·00 25·00
53 **4** 10 c. pink . . . 65·00 30·00
36 **8** 1 r. green . . . 35·00 10·00
42 **7** 1 r. mauve . . . £375 £225
52 **1** 1 r. blue . . . £1500 £700
43 **7** 2 r. blue . . . £325 £175

(b) On 1864 issues of Philippines.
31 $3\frac{1}{8}$ c. black on buff . . . 10·00 2·75
32 $6\frac{2}{8}$ c. green on pink . . . 10·00 2·75
33 $12\frac{4}{8}$ c. blue on flesh . . . 32·00 15·00
34 25 c. red . . . 13·00 9·00

(c) On Nos. 10/11 of Cuba (as T **9** of Spain but currency changed).
44 1 r. green . . . £110 55·00
45 2 r. red . . . £130 50·00

1871. As T **36** of Spain, but inscr "CORREOS" and currency altered. Perf.
37 5 c. blue . . . 25·00 2·25
38 10 c. green . . . 7·00 2·00
39 20 c. brown . . . 30·00 12·00
40 40 c. red . . . 35·00 6·00

1872.
46 **13** 12 c. red . . . 7·00 2·00
47 16 c. blue . . . 50·00 12·00
48a 25 c. grey . . . 5·00 1·75
49 62 c. mauve . . . 15·00 3·50
50a 1 p. 25 brown . . . 28·00 8·50

1874. As T **42** of Spain, but inscr "FILIPINAS".
54 12 c. lilac . . . 7·50 2·00
55 25 c. blue . . . 2·50 60
56 62 c. red . . . 20·00 1·50
57 1 p. 25 brown . . . 95·00 18·00

1875. As T **45** of Spain, but inscr "FILIPINAS" between rosettes.
58 2 c. red . . . 1·25 40
59 2 c. blue . . . 85·00 35·00
60 6 c. orange . . . 5·50 1·10
61 10 c. blue . . . 2·00 45
62 12 c. mauve . . . 3·00 45
63 20 c. brown . . . 7·50 1·75
64 25 c. green . . . 5·50 45

1878. As T **45** of Spain, but inscr "FILIPINAS" without rosettes.
65 25 m. black . . . 1·25 25
66 25 m. green . . . 27·00 12·00
67 50 m. purple . . . 13·00 3·50
68a ($62\frac{1}{2}$ m.) 0.0625 lilac . . . 22·00 6·50
69 100 m. red . . . 42·00 14·00
70 100 m. green . . . 4·50 1·10
71 125 m. blue . . . 2·25 35
72 200 m. red . . . 13·00 2·75
74 250 m. brown . . . 5·00 1·25

1877. Surch **HABILITADO 12 CS P.T.A.** in frame.
75 12 c. on 2 c. red (No. 58) . . . 30·00 9·00
76 12 c. on 25 m. black (No. 65) . . . 30·00 9·00

1879. Surch **CONVENIO UNIVERSAL DE CORREOS HABILITADO** and value in figures and words.
78 2 c. on 25 m. (No. 66) . . . 23·00 6·00
79 8 c. on 100 m. (No. 69) . . . 20·00 6·00

1880. "Alfonso XII" key-type inscr "FILIPINAS".
97 X 1 c. green . . . 30 10
82a 2 c. red . . . 20 15
83 $2\frac{1}{2}$ c. brown . . . 2·40 15
95 $2\frac{4}{8}$ c. blue . . . 20 10
99 50 m. brown . . . 60 15
85 5 c. lilac . . . 25 15
100 6 c. brown . . . 6·00 1·25
87 $6\frac{2}{8}$ c. green . . . 1·75 75
88 8 c. brown . . . 7·50 1·25
89a 10 c. brown . . . 1·00 10
90 10 c. purple . . . 2·00 1·00
91 10 c. green . . . £150 80·00
92 $12\frac{4}{8}$ c. pink . . . 50 15
93 20 c. brown . . . 1·25 15
94 25 c. brown . . . 1·50 20

1881. "Alfonso XII" key-type inscr "FILIPINAS" with circular surch **HABILITADO CORREOS** or **HABILITADO PA. U. POSTAL** and value in figures and words.
111 X 1 c. on $2\frac{4}{8}$ c. blue . . . 60 40
101 2 c. on $2\frac{1}{8}$ c. brown . . . 2·50 1·10
106 8 c. on 2 c. red . . . 5·50 1·25
107 10 c. cuart. on 2 c. red . . . 3·00 1·25
102 10 c. on $2\frac{4}{8}$ c. blue . . . 5·50 1·00
112 16 cuart. on $2\frac{4}{8}$ c. blue . . . 7·50 1·75
103 20 c. on 8 c. brown . . . 7·50 2·25
113 1 r. on 2 c. red . . . 5·00 1·75
109 1 r. on 5 c. lilac . . . 4·50 2·00
110 1 r. on 8 c. brown . . . 8·50 2·50
105 2 r. on $2\frac{4}{8}$ c. blue . . . 4·50 1·25

25

29

30

31

34

1881. Fiscal and telegraph stamps (a) with circular surch **HABILITADO CORREOS, HABILITADO PARA CORREOS** or **HABILITADO PA. U. POSTAL** and value in figures and words.
115 **25** 2 c. on 10 cuartos bistre . . . 20·00 12·00
129 **29** 2 c. on 200 m. green . . . 4·25 2·00
116 **25** $2\frac{4}{8}$ c. on 10 cuartos bistre . . . 2·50 60
117 $2\frac{4}{8}$ c. on 2 r. blue . . . £140 60·00
124 $6\frac{2}{8}$ c. on $12\frac{4}{8}$ c. lilac . . . 4·75 2·75
118 8 c. on 2 r. blue . . . 7·50 2·00
119 8 c. on 10 c. brown . . . £150 £110
123 16 cmos. on 2 r. blue . . . 5·00 2·00
137 **31** 20 c. on 150 m. blue . . . 22·00 18·00
134 20 c. on 250 m. blue . . . 85·00 70·00
127 **25** 1 r. on 10 cuartos bistre . . . 9·00 3·00
121 1 r. on $12\frac{4}{8}$ c. lilac . . . 6·00 2·50
130 **29** 1 r. on 200 m. green . . . 55·00 32·00
131 1 r. on 1 peso green . . . 25·00 12·00
132 **30** 1 r. on 10 pesetas bistre . . . 35·00 18·00
133 **31** 2 r. on 250 m. blue . . . 8·00 2·50

(b) With two circular surcharges as above, showing two different values.
128 **25** 8 c. on 2 r. on 2 r. blue . . . 17·00 10·00
136 **31** 1 r. on 20 c. on 250 m. bl . . . 8·00 3·75

(c) Optd **HABILITADO PARA CORREOS** in straight lines.
122 **25** 10 cuartos bistre . . . £140 60·00
126 1 r. green . . . 85·00 55·00

1887. Various stamps with oval surch **UNION GRAL. POSTAL HABILITADO** (No. 142) or **HABILITADO PARA COMMUNICACIONES** and new value. (a) "Alfonso XII" key-type inscr "FILIPINAS".
138 X $2\frac{4}{8}$ c. on 1 c. green . . . 1·40 40
139 $2\frac{4}{8}$ c. on 5 c. lilac . . . 1·00 40
140 $2\frac{4}{8}$ c. on 50 m. brown . . . 1·40 90
141 $2\frac{4}{8}$ c. on 10 c. green . . . 1·00 50
142 8 c. on $2\frac{4}{8}$ c. blue . . . 60 30

(b) "Alfonso XII" key-type inscr "FILIPAS-IMPRESOS".
143 X $2\frac{4}{8}$ c. on $\frac{1}{8}$ c. green . . . 30 15

(c) Fiscal and telegraph stamps.
144 **29** $2\frac{4}{8}$ c. on 200 m. green . . . 2·75 1·00
145 $2\frac{4}{8}$ c. on 20 c. brown . . . 8·00 3·75
146 **34** $2\frac{4}{8}$ c. on 1 c. bistre . . . 60 40

1889. Various stamps with oval surch **RECARGO DE CONSUMOS HABILITADO** and new value.

(a) "Alfonso XII" key-type inscr "FILIPINAS".
147 X $2\frac{4}{8}$ c. on 1 c. green . . . 15 15
148 $2\frac{4}{8}$ c. on 2 c. red . . . 10 10
149 $2\frac{4}{8}$ c. on $2\frac{4}{8}$ c. blue . . . 10 10
150 $2\frac{4}{8}$ c. on 5 c. lilac . . . 10 10
151 $2\frac{4}{8}$ c. on 50 m. bistre . . . 10 10
152 $2\frac{4}{8}$ c. on $12\frac{4}{8}$ c. pink . . . 50 50

(b) "Alfonso XII" key-type inscr "FILIPAS-IMPRESOS".
160 X $2\frac{4}{8}$ c. on $\frac{1}{8}$ c. green . . . 15 15

(c) Fiscal and telegraph stamps.
153 **34** $2\frac{4}{8}$ c. on 1 c. bistre . . . 25 25
154 $2\frac{4}{8}$ c. on 2 c. red . . . 25 25
155 $2\frac{4}{8}$ c. on $2\frac{4}{8}$ c. brown . . . 10 10
156 $2\frac{4}{8}$ c. on 5 c. blue . . . 10 10
157 $2\frac{4}{8}$ c. on 10 c. green . . . 10 10
158 $2\frac{4}{8}$ c. on 10 c. mauve . . . 50 60
159 $2\frac{4}{8}$ c. on 20 c. mauve . . . 20 20
161 **25** $17\frac{4}{8}$ c. on 5 p. green . . . 60·00

1890. "Baby" key-type inscr "FILIPINAS".
176 Y 1 c. purple . . . 50 20
188 1 c. red . . . 2·50 1·40
197 1 c. green . . . 1·10 40
162 2 c. red . . . 10 10
177 2 c. purple . . . 20 10
190 2 c. brown . . . 15 10
198 2 c. blue . . . 20 15
163 $2\frac{4}{8}$ c. blue . . . 30 10
178 $2\frac{4}{8}$ c. grey . . . 20 10
165 5 c. blue . . . 30 10
191 5 c. green . . . 20 20
199 5 c. brown . . . 4·00 1·50
181 6 c. purple . . . 20 10
192 6 c. red . . . 40 25
166 8 c. green . . . 20 10
182 8 c. blue . . . 50 20
193 8 c. brown . . . 20 10
167 10 c. green . . . 1·00 20
194 10 c. red . . . 20 10
202 10 c. brown . . . 20 10
168 $12\frac{4}{8}$ c. green . . . 20 10
184 $12\frac{4}{8}$ c. orange . . . 50 10
185 15 c. brown . . . 60 20
195 15 c. red . . . 50 20
203 15 c. green . . . 1·50 75
174 20 c. red . . . 8·00 2·75
186 20 c. brown . . . 1·25 25
196 20 c. purple . . . 3·25 1·25
204 20 c. orange . . . 2·00 75
170 25 c. brown . . . 4·25 75
175 25 c. blue . . . 1·25 25
205 40 c. purple . . . 10·00 2·25
206 80 c. red . . . 15·00 5·50

1897. "Baby" key-type inscr "FILIPINAS" and surch **HABILITADO CORREOS PARA 1897** and value in frame.
212 Y 5 c. on 5 c. green . . . 2·00 1·00
208 15 c. on 15 c. red . . . 2·50 1·50
213 15 c. on 15 c. brown . . . 2·50 1·10
209 20 c. on 20 c. purple . . . 13·00 7·50
214 20 c. on 20 c. brown . . . 4·50 3·00
210 20 c. on 25 c. brown . . . 9·00 7·00

1897. No. 85 surch **HABILITADO CORREOS PARA 1897 5 CENTS 1897** in frame.
215 X 5 c. on 5 c. lilac . . . 3·25 2·00

1898. "Curly Head" key-type inscr "FILIPINAS 1898 y 99".
217 Z 1 m. brown . . . 10 10
218 2 m. brown . . . 10 10
219 3 m. brown . . . 15 10
220 4 m. brown . . . 3·25 65
221 5 m. brown . . . 10 10
222 1 c. violet . . . 10 10
223 2 c. green . . . 10 10
224 3 c. brown . . . 10 10
225 4 c. orange . . . 4·50 3·25
226 5 c. red . . . 15 10
227 6 c. blue . . . 50 25
228 8 c. brown . . . 25 15
229 10 c. red . . . 70 40
230 15 c. olive . . . 70 40
231 20 c. red . . . 70 50
232 40 c. lilac . . . 45 30
233 60 c. black . . . 2·25 1·00
234 80 c. brown . . . 2·25 1·00
235 1 p. green . . . 5·00 3·00
236 2 p. blue . . . 9·00 4·75

STAMPS FOR PRINTED MATTER

1886. "Alfonso XII" key-type inscr "FILIPAS-IMPRESOS".
P138 X 1 m. red . . . 20 10
P139 $\frac{1}{8}$ c. green . . . 20 10
P140 2 m. blue . . . 20 10
P141 5 m. brown . . . 25 10

1890. "Baby" key-type inscr "FILIPAS-IMPRESOS".
P171 Y 1 m. purple . . . 10 10
P172 $\frac{1}{8}$ c. purple . . . 10 10
P173 2 m. purple . . . 10 10
P174 5 m. purple . . . 10 10

1892. "Baby" key-type inscr "FILIPAS-IMPRESOS".
P192 Y 1 m. green . . . 1·75 45
P193 $\frac{1}{8}$ c. green . . . 70 30
P194 2 m. green . . . 1·75 45
P191 5 m. green . . . 80·00 18·00

1894. "Baby" key-type inscr "FILIPAS-IMPRESOS".
P197 Y 1 m. grey . . . 15 10
P198 $\frac{1}{8}$ c. brown . . . 15 10
P199 2 m. grey . . . 15 10
P200 5 m. grey . . . 15 10

1896. "Baby" key-type inscr "FILIPAS-IMPRESOS".
P205 Y 1 m. blue . . . 20 10
P206 $\frac{1}{8}$ c. blue . . . 20 10
P207 2 m. brown . . . 25 10
P208 5 m. blue . . . 1·50 60

UNITED STATES ADMINISTRATION

1899. United States stamps of 1894 (No. 267 etc) optd **PHILIPPINES.**
252 – 1 c. green . . . 2·50 65
253 – 2 c. red . . . 1·25 50
255 – 3 c. violet . . . 4·00 1·60
256 – 4 c. brown . . . 17·00 4·75
257 – 5 c. blue . . . 4·00 1·00
258 – 6 c. purple . . . 20·00 6·00
259 – 8 c. brown . . . 22·00 6·00
260 – 10 c. brown . . . 15·00 3·00
262 – 15 c. green . . . 26·00 6·50
263 **83** 50 c. orange . . . 90·00 38·00
264 – $1 black . . . £325 £190
266 – $2 blue . . . £500 £275
267 – $5 green . . . £1200 £850

1903. United States stamps of 1902 optd **PHILIPPINES.**
268 **103** 1 c. green . . . 3·00 30
269 **104** 2 c. red . . . 5·00 1·25
270 **105** 3 c. violet . . . 55·00 14·00
271 **106** 4 c. brown . . . 60·00 20·00
272 **107** 5 c. blue . . . 8·50 70
273 **108** 6 c. lake . . . 65·00 18·00
274 **109** 8 c. violet . . . 28·00 12·00
275 **110** 10 c. brown . . . 18·00 2·50
276 **111** 13 c. purple . . . 23·00 13·00
277 **112** 15 c. olive . . . 42·00 8·00
278 **113** 50 c. orange . . . £100 30·00
279 **114** $1 black . . . £425 £200
280 **115** $2 blue . . . £1300 £800
281 **116** $5 green . . . £1500 £1000

1904. United States stamp of 1903 optd **PHILIPPINES.**
282 **117** 2 c. red . . . 3·75 1·50

45 Rizal

46 Arms of Manila

1906. Various portraits as T **45** and T **46**.
337 **45** 2 c. green . . . 10 10
338 – 4 c. red (McKinley) . . . 10 10
339 – 6 c. violet (Magellan) . . . 30 10
340 – 8 c. brown (Legaspi) . . . 25 10
341 – 10 c. blue (Lawton) . . . 20 10
288 – 12 c. red (Lincoln) . . . 4·00 1·75
342 – 12 c. orange (Lincoln) . . . 45 15
289 – 16 c. black (Sampson) . . . 3·50 15
298 – 16 c. green (Sampson) . . . 2·00 10
344 – 16 c. olive (Dewey) . . . 1·00 15
290 – 20 c. brown (Washington) . . . 3·50 20
345 – 20 c. yellow (Washington) . . . 35 10
291 – 26 c. brown (Carriedo) . . . 4·50 1·75
346 – 26 c. green (Carriedo) . . . 65 30
292 – 30 c. green (Franklin) . . . 4·75 90
313 – 30 c. blue (Franklin) . . . 2·75 35
347 – 30 c. grey (Franklin) . . . 45 10
293 **46** 1 p. orange . . . 18·00 5·00
363a 1 p. violet . . . 3·50 3·50
294 2 p. black . . . 23·00 1·00
364 2 p. brown . . . 9·00 9·00
350 4 p. blue . . . 20·00 25
351 10 p. green . . . 55·00 4·40

Nos. 288, 289, 298, 290, 291, 292, 313, 293 and 294 exist perf only, the other values perf or imperf.

1926. Air. Madrid–Manila Flight. Stamps as last, optd **AIR MAIL 1926 MADRID-MANILA** and aeroplane propeller.
368 **45** 2 c. green . . . 4·00 3·25
369 4 c. red . . . 5·00 3·75
370 – 6 c. violet . . . 25·00 8·00
371 – 8 c. brown . . . 25·00 9·50
372 – 10 c. blue . . . 25·00 9·50
373 – 12 c. orange . . . 27·00 14·00
374 – 16 c. green (Sampson) . . . £1100 £1000
375 – 16 c. olive (Dewey) . . . 28·00 13·50
376 – 20 c. yellow . . . 28·00 13·50
377 – 26 c. green . . . 28·00 13·50
378 – 30 c. grey . . . 28·00 13·50
383 **46** 1 p. violet . . . £100 65·00
379 2 p. brown . . . £250 £180
380 4 p. blue . . . £425 £275
381 10 p. green . . . £650 £450

49 Legislative Palace

1926. Inauguration of Legislative Palace.
384 **49** 2 c. black and green . . . 40 25
385 4 c. black and red . . . 40 30
386 16 c. black and olive . . . 60 50
387 18 c. black and brown . . . 1·00 55
388 20 c. black and orange . . . 1·25 80
389 24 c. black and grey . . . 1·00 50
390 1 p. black and mauve . . . 45·00 25·00

1928. Air. London–Orient Flight by British Squadron of Seaplanes. Stamps of 1906 optd **L.O.F.** (= London Orient Flight) **1928** and Fairey IIID seaplane.
402 **45** 2 c. green . . . 35 20
403 – 4 c. red . . . 40 30
404 – 6 c. violet . . . 2·40 1·60
405 – 8 c. brown . . . 2·40 2·00
406 – 10 c. blue . . . 2·40 2·00
407 – 12 c. orange . . . 4·00 2·40
408 – 16 c. olive (Dewey) . . . 3·75 2·40
409 – 20 c. yellow . . . 4·00 2·40
410 – 26 c. green . . . 7·50 5·50
411 – 30 c. grey . . . 7·50 5·50
412 **46** 1 p. violet . . . 32·00 32·00

54 Mayon Volcano

57 Vernal Falls, Yosemite National Park, California, wrongly inscr "PAGSANJAN FALLS"

1932.

424 **54** 2 c. green 75 30
425 – 4 c. red 30 20
426 – 12 c. orange 60 50
427 **57** 18 c. red . . . . 24·00 7·00
428 – 20 c. yellow 70 45
429 – 24 c. violet . . . . 1·25 55
430 – 32 c. brown . . . . 1·25 65

DESIGNS—HORIZ: 4 c. Post Office, Manila; 12 c. Freighters at Pier No. 7, Manila Bay; 20 c. Rice plantation; 24 c. Rice terraces; 32 c. Baguio Zigzag.

1932. No. 350 surch in words in double circle.

431 **46** 1 p. on 4 p. blue . . . . . 1·50 30
432 2 p. on 4 p. blue . . . . . 3·00 55

1932. Air. Nos. 424/30 optd with Dornier Do-J flying boat "Gronland Wal" and **ROUND-THE-WORLD FLIGHT VON GRONAU 1932.**

433 2 c. green 30 30
434 4 c. red 30 30
435 12 c. orange 40 40
436 18 c. red . . . . 3·00 2·50
437 20 c. yellow . . . . 1·75 1·50
438 24 c. violet . . . . 1·75 1·50
439 32 c. brown . . . . 1·75 1·50

1933. Air. Stamps of 1906 optd **F. REIN MADRID - MANILA FLIGHT - 1933** under propeller.

440 **45** 2 c. green 30 30
441 – 4 c. red 35 35
442 – 6 c. violet 60 60
443 – 8 c. brown . . . . 1·60 1·25
444 – 10 c. blue . . . . 1·40 90
445 – 12 c. orange . . . . . . 1·25 90
446 – 16 c. olive (Dewey) . . . . 1·25 90
447 – 20 c. orange . . . . . . 1·25 90
448 – 26 c. green . . . . 1·60 1·10
449 – 30 c. grey . . . . 2·00 1·25

1933. Air. Nos. 337 and 425/30 optd with **AIR MAIL** on wings of airplane.

450 2 c. green 40 30
451 4 c. red 15 10
452 12 c. orange 25 10
453 20 c. yellow 25 15
454 24 c. violet 35 15
455 32 c. brown 40 25

66 Baseball

1934. 10th Far Eastern Championship Games.

456 **66** 2 c. brown . . . . 1·50 60
457 – 6 c. blue 45 20
458 – 16 c. purple . . . . 1·25 80

DESIGNS—VERT: 6 c. Tennis; 16 c. Basketball.

69 Dr. J. Rizal

70 Pearl Fishing

1935. Designs as T **69/70** in various sizes (sizes in millimetres).

459 2 c. red (19×22) 10 10
460 4 c. green (34×22) 10 10
461 6 c. brown (22½×28) 15 10
462 8 c. violet (34×22) 20 15
463 10 c. red (34×22) 30 15
464 12 c. black (34×22) 25 20
465 16 c. blue (34×22) 35 15
466 20 c. bistre (19×22) 25 10
467 26 c. blue (34×22) 40 20
468 30 c. red (34×22) 40 30
469 1 p. black & orge (37×27) . . 2·40 90
470 2 p. black & brn (37×27) . . 4·00 1·25
471 4 p. black & blue (37×27) . . 4·00 2·50
472 5 p. black & grn (27×37) . . 9·50 1·75

DESIGNS: 4 c. Woman, Carabao and Ricestalks; 6 c. Filipino girl; 10 c. Fort Santiago; 12 c. Salt springs; 16 c. Magellan's landing; 20 c. "Juan de la Cruz"; 26 c. Rice terraces; 30 c. Blood Compact; 1 p. Barasoain Church; 2 p. Battle of Manila Bay; 4 p. Montalban Gorge; 5 p. George Washington (after painting by John Faed).

INDEX

Countries can be quickly located by referring to the index at the end of this volume.

COMMONWEALTH OF THE PHILIPPINES

83 "Temples of Human Progress"

1935. Inauguration of Commonwealth of the Philippines.

483 **85** 2 c. red 15 15
484 6 c. violet 20 15
485 16 c. blue 20 15
486 36 c. green 40 25
487 50 c. brown 60 50

1935. Air. "China Clipper" Trans-Pacific Air Mail Flight. Optd **P.I.U.S. INITIAL FLIGHT December-1935** and Martin M-130 flying boat.

488 10 c. red (No. 463) 25 20
489 30 c. red (No. 468) 30 35

85 J. Rizal y Mercado

89 Manuel L. Quezon

1936. 75th Birth Anniv of Rizal.

490 **85** 2 c. yellow 10 15
491 6 c. blue 15 15
492 36 c. brown 60 45

1936. Air. Manila-Madrid Flight by Arnaiz and Calvo. Stamps of 1906 surch **MANILA-MADRID ARNACAL FLIGHT–1936** and value.

493 **45** 2 c. on 4 c. red 10 10
494 6 c. on 12 c. orange . . . 15 10
495 16 c. on 26 c. green . . . 20 15

1936. Stamps of 1935 (Nos. 459/72) optd **COMMON-WEALTH** (2 c., 6 c., 20 c.) or **COMMONWEALTH** (others).

496 2 c. red 10 10
497 4 c. green 50 40
526 6 c. brown 10 10
527 8 c. violet 10 10
528 10 c. red 10 10
529 12 c. black 10 10
530 16 c. blue 20 10
531 20 c. bistre 20 10
532 26 c. blue 30 20
505 30 c. red 30 15
534 1 p. black and orange . . . 50 15
535 2 p. black and brown . . . 4·00 75
508 4 p. black and blue . . . . 17·00 2·50
509 5 p. black and green . . . 2·40 1·25

1936. 1st Anniv of Autonomous Government.

510 **89** 2 c. brown 10 10
511 6 c. green 10 10
512 12 c. blue 15 15

90 Philippine Is

92 Arms of Manila

1937. 33rd International Eucharistic Congress.

513 **90** 2 c. green 10 10
514 6 c. brown 15 10
515 12 c. blue 20 10
516 20 c. orange 25 10
517 36 c. violet 35 30
518 50 c. red 45 25

1937.

522 **92** 10 p. grey . . . . 3·50 1·50
523 20 p. brown . . . . 1·75 1·10

1939. Air. 1st Manila Air Mail Exhibition. Surch **FIRST AIR MAIL EXHIBITION Feb 17 to 19, 1939** and value.

548a – 8 c. on 26 c. green (346) . . 60 35
549 **92** 1 p. on 10 p. grey . . . . 3·00 2·40

1939. 1st National Foreign Trade Week. Surch **FIRST FOREIGN TRADE WEEK MAY 21-27, 1939** and value.

551 – 2 c. on 4 c. green (460) . . 10 10
552a **45** 6 c. on 26 c. green (346) . . 20 15
553 **92** 50 c. on 20 p. brown . . . 90 85

101 Triumphal Arch

102 Malacanan Palace

103 Pres. Quezon taking Oath of Office

1939. 4th Anniv of National Independence.

554 **101** 2 c. green 10 10
555 6 c. red 15 10
556 12 c. blue 20 10
557 **102** 2 c. green 10 10
558 6 c. orange 15 10
559 12 c. red 20 10
560 **103** 2 c. orange 10 10
561 6 c. green 15 10
562 12 c. violet 30 15

104 Jose Rizal

105 Filipino Vinta and Boeing 314 Flying Boat

1941.

563 **104** 2 c. green 10 10
623 – 2 c. brown 10 10

In No. 623 the head faces to the right.

1941. Air.

566 **105** 8 c. red 80 75
567 20 c. blue . . . . 1·00 50
568 60 c. green . . . . 1·50 85
569 1 p. sepia 75 60

For Japanese Occupation issues of 1941–45 see **JAPANESE OCCUPATION OF PHILIPPINE ISLANDS.**

1945. Victory issue. Nos. 496, 525/31, 505, 534 and 522/3 optd **VICTORY**.

610 2 c. red 10 10
611 4 c. green 10 10
612 6 c. brown 15 10
613 8 c. violet 20 15
614 10 c. red 20 10
615 12 c. black 25 15
616 16 c. blue 40 15
617 20 c. bistre 40 10
618 30 c. red 70 50
619 1 p. black and orange . . . 1·40 30
620 10 p. grey . . . . 40·00 14·00
621 20 p. brown . . . . 35·00 16·00

INDEPENDENT REPUBLIC

111 "Independence"

113 Bonifacio Monument

1946. Proclamation of Independence.

625 **111** 2 c. red 30 30
626 6 c. green 45 30
627 12 c. blue 70 45

1946. Optd **PHILIPPINES** at top, **50TH ANNIVERSARY MARTYRDOM** in circle and **OF RIZAL 1896-1946** at foot.

628 **104** 2 c. brown (No. 623) . . . 30 20

1947.

629 – 4 c. brown 15 10
630 **113** 10 c. red 20 10
631 – 12 c. blue 25 10
632 – 16 c. grey . . . . 1·50 90
633 – 20 c. brown 45 15
634 – 50 c. green . . . . 1·10 75
635 – 1 p. violet . . . . 2·25 55

DESIGNS—VERT: 4 c. Rizal Monument; 50 c. and 1 p. Avenue of Palm Trees. HORIZ: 12 c. Jones Bridge; 16 c. Santa Lucia Gate; 20 c. Mayon Volcano.

115 Manuel L. Quezon

117 Presidents Quezon and Roosevelt

116 Pres. Roxas taking Oath of Office

1947.

636 **115** 1 c. green 15 10

1947. 1st Anniv of Independence.

638 **116** 4 c. red 20 15
639 6 c. green 50 50
640 16 c. purple . . . . 1·10 75

1947. Air.

641 **117** 6 c. green 60 60
642 40 c. orange . . . . 1·10 1·10
643 80 c. blue . . . . 3·00 3·00

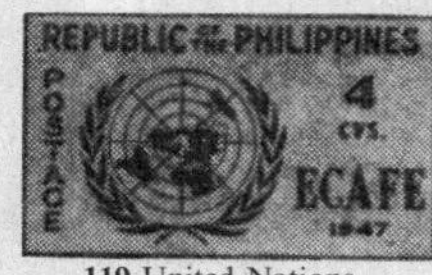

119 United Nations Emblem

121 General MacArthur

1947. Conference of Economic Commission for Asia and Far East, Baguio. Imperf or perf.

648 **119** 4 c. red and pink . . . . 1·50 1·40
649 6 c. violet & light violet . 2·10 2·10
650 12 c. light blue & blue . . 2·50 2·50

1948. 3rd Anniv of Liberation.

652 **121** 4 c. violet 50 20
653 6 c. red . . . . 1·00 65
654 16 c. blue . . . . 1·50 65

122 Threshing Rice

125 Dr. Jose Rizal

1948. United Nations' Food and Agriculture Organization Conference, Baguio.

655 **122** 2 c. green & yell (postage) 85 55
656 6 c. brown and yellow . . 1·00 80
657 18 c. blue & light blue . . 2·75 2·10
658 40 c. red and pink (air) . 14·00 7·50

1948.

662 **125** 2 c. green 15 10

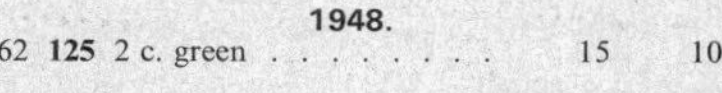

126 Pres. Manuel Roxas

127 Scout and Badge

128 Sampaguita National Flower

1948. President Roxas Mourning Issue.

663 **126** 2 c. black 25 15
664 4 c. black 35 25

1948. 25th Anniv of Philippine Boy Scouts. Perf or imperf.

665 **127** 2 c. green and brown . . 1·10 55
666 4 c. pink and brown . . 1·40 80

1948. Flower Day.

667 **128** 3 c. green and black . . . 35 30

130 Santos, Tavera and Kalaw

131 "Doctrina Christiana" (first book published in Philippines)

1949. Library Rebuilding Fund.

671 **130** 4 c. + 2 c. brown . . . . 1·00 75
672 **131** 6 c. + 4 c. violet . . . . 3·00 2·00
673 – 18 c. + 7 c. blue . . . . 4·00 3·50

DESIGN—VERT: 18 c. Title page of Rizal's "Noli Me Tangere".

132 U.P.U. Monument, Berne

1949. 75th Anniv of U.P.U.

674 132 4 c. green 20 10
675 6 c. violet 20 10
676 18 c. blue 80 25

133 General del Pilar at Tirad Pass
134 Globe

1949. 50th Death Anniv of Gen. Gregorio del Pilar.

678 133 2 c. brown 15 15
679 4 c. green 35 30

1950. 5th International Congress of Junior Chamber of Commerce.

680 134 2 c. violet (postage) 20 10
681 6 c. green 30 10
682 18 c. blue 65 20
683 30 c. orange (air) 50 20
684 50 c. red 90 25

135 Red Lauan Trees
136 Franklin D. Roosevelt

1950. 15th Anniv of Forestry Service.

685 135 2 c. green 30 20
686 4 c. violet 70 25

1950. 25th Anniv of Philatelic Association.

687 136 4 c. brown 35 25
688 6 c. pink 50 35
689 18 c. blue 1·25 90

137 Lions Emblem
138 President Quirino taking Oath of Office

1950. "Lions" International Convention, Manila.

691 137 2 c. orange (postage) 60 60
692 4 c. violet 95 95
693 30 c. green (air) 1·00 70
694 50 c. blue 1·10 95

1950. Pres. Quirino's Inauguration.

696 138 2 c. red 10 10
697 4 c. purple 15 10
698 6 c. green 25 15

1950. Surch **ONE CENTAVO**.

699 125 1 c. on 2 c. green 15 10

140 Dove and Map
141 War Widow and Children

1950. Baguio Conference.

701 140 5 c. green 30 25
702 6 c. red 30 25
703 18 c. blue 70 50

1950. Aid to War Victims.

704 141 2 c. + 2 c. red 10 10
705 – 4 c. + 4 c. violet 40 40
DESIGN: 4 c. Disabled veteran.

142 Arms of Manila
143 Soldier and Peasants

1950. As T **142**. Various arms and frames. (a) Arms inscr "MANILA".

706 5 c. violet 60 45
707 6 c. grey 45 35
708 18 c. blue 60 45

(b) Arms inscr "CEBU".

709 5 c. red 60 45
710 6 c. brown 45 35
711 18 c. violet 60 45

(c) Arms inscr "ZAMBOANGA".

712 5 c. green 60 45
713 6 c. brown 45 35
714 18 c. blue 60 45

(d) Arms inscr "ILOILO".

715 5 c. green 60 45
716 6 c. violet 45 35
717 18 c. blue 60 45

1951. Guarding Peaceful Labour. Perf or imperf.

718 143 5 c. green 20 10
719 6 c. brown 35 35
720 18 c. blue 90 90

144 Philippines Flag and U.N. Emblem
145 Statue of Liberty 

1951. U.N. Day.

721 144 5 c. red 75 35
722 6 c. green 60 35
723 18 c. blue 1·50 1·00

1951. Human Rights Day.

724 145 5 c. green 50 25
725 6 c. orange 65 50
726 18 c. blue 1·50 75

146 Schoolchildren
147 M. L. Quezon

1952. 50th Anniv of Philippine Educational System.

727 146 5 c. orange 60 50

1952. Portraits.

728 147 1 c. brown 10 10
729 – 2 c. black (J. Santos) 10 10
730 – 3 c. red (A. Mabini) 10 10
731 – 5 c. red (M. H. del Pilar) 10 10
842 – 6 c. blue (Dr. J. Rizal) 15 10
732 – 10 c. blue (Father J. Burgos) 15 10
733 – 20 c. red (Lapu-Lapu) 30 10
734 – 25 c. green (Gen. A. Luna) 45 20
735 – 50 c. red (C. Arellano) 85 25
736 – 60 c. red (A. Bonifacio) 1·00 45
737 – 2 p. violet (G. L. Jaena) 3·25 1·00

149 Aurora A. Quezon

1952. Fruit Tree Memorial Fund.

742 149 5 c. + 1 c. blue 15 15
743 6 c. + 2 c. red 40 40
See also No. 925.

150 Milkfish and Map of Oceania
151 "A Letter from Rizal" 

1952. Indo-Pacific Fisheries Council.

744 150 5 c. brown 1·10 65
745 6 c. blue 70 50

1952. Pan-Asiatic Philatelic Exhibition, Manila.

746 151 5 c. blue (postage) 60 15
747 6 c. brown 60 20
748 30 c. red (air) 1·25 1·00

152 Wright Park, Baguio City
153 F. Baltazar (poet)

1952. 3rd Lions District Convention.

749 152 5 c. orange 90 90
750 6 c. green 1·25 1·00

1953. National Language Week.

751 153 5 c. olive 50 35

154 "Gateway to the East"
155 Pres. Quirino and Pres. Sukarno

1953. International Fair, Manila.

752 154 5 c. turquoise 30 15
753 6 c. red 35 15

1953. Visit of President to Indonesia. Flags in yellow, blue and red.

754 155 5 c. blue, yellow & black 20 10
755 6 c. green, yellow & black 25 25

156 Doctor examining patient

1953. 50th Anniv of Philippines Medical Association.

756 156 5 c. mauve 30 25
757 6 c. blue 35 35

1954. Optd **FIRST NATIONAL BOY SCOUTS JAMBOREE APRIL 23-30 1954** or surch also.

758 5 c. red (No. 731) 1·25 1·00
759 18 c. on 50 c. green (No. 634) 2·00 1·50

158 Stamp of 1854, Magellan and Manila P.O.

1954. 1st Philippines Postage Stamps Centenary. Central stamp in orange.

760 158 5 c. violet (postage) 75 50
761 18 c. blue 1·50 1·25
762 30 c. green 3·50 2·10
763 10 c. brown (air) 1·50 1·25
764 20 c. green 2·50 2·00
765 50 c. red 5·00 4·25

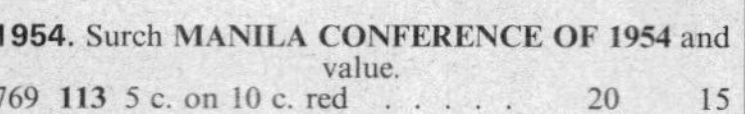

159 Diving
161 "Independence" 

1954. 2nd Asian Games, Manila.

766 – 5 c. blue (Discus) 85 60
767 159 18 c. green 1·40 1·00
768 – 30 c. red (Boxing) 2·00 1·90

1954. Surch **MANILA CONFERENCE OF 1954** and value.

769 113 5 c. on 10 c. red 20 15
770 – 18 c. on 20 c. brown (No. 633) 75 65

1954. Independence. Commemoration.

771 161 5 c. lake 30 25
772 18 c. blue 90 50

162 "The Immaculate Conception" (Murillo)
163 Mayon Volcano and Filipino Vinta 

1954. Marian Year.

773 162 5 c. blue 50 35

1955. 50th Anniv of Rotary International.

774 163 5 c. blue (postage) 40 15
775 18 c. red 1·25 70
776 50 c. green (air) 2·50 1·10

164 "Labour"
165 Pres. Magsaysay

1955. Labour-Management Congress, Manila.

777 164 5 c. brown 50 35

1955. 9th Anniv of Republic.

778 165 5 c. blue 25 20
779 20 c. red 70 70
780 30 c. green 1·25 1·25

166 Lt. J. Gozar

1955. Air. Air Force Heroes.

781 166 20 c. violet 80 15
782 – 30 c. red (Lt. C. F. Basa) 1·10 20
783 166 50 c. green 1·25 30
784 – 70 c. bl (Lt. C. F. Basa) 2·10 1·25

167 Liberty Well

1956. Artesian Wells for Rural Areas.

785 167 5 c. violet 35 35
786 20 c. green 80 65

1956. 5th Conference of World Confederation of Organizations of the Teaching Profession. No. 731 optd **WCOTP CONFERENCE MANILA**.

787 5 c. red 35 35

169 Nurse and War Victims
170 Monument (landing marker) in Leyte

1956. 50th Anniv of Philippines Red Cross.

788 169 5 c. violet and red 50 45
789 20 c. brown and red 65 50

1956. Liberation. Perf or imperf.

790 170 5 c. red 15 15

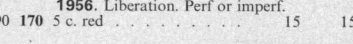

171 St. Thomas's University
172 Statue of the Sacred Heart

1956. University of St. Thomas.
791 **171** 5 c. brown and lake . . . 35 25
792 60 c. brown and mauve . 1·50 1·40

1956. 2nd National Eucharistic Congress and Centenary of the Feast of the Sacred Heart.
793 **172** 5 c. olive 35 30
794 20 c. red 80 75

1956. Surch.
795 5 c. on 6 c. brown (No. 710) . 15 15
796 5 c. on 6 c. brown (No. 713) . 15 15
797 5 c. on 6 c. violet (No. 716) . 15 15

174 Girl Guide, Badge and Camp
175 Pres. Ramon Magsaysay

1957. Girl Guides' Pacific World Camp, Quezon City, and Centenary of Birth of Lord Baden-Powell. Perf or imperf.
798 **174** 5 c. blue 45 45

1957. Death of Pres. Magsaysay.
799 **175** 5 c. black 15 10

176 Sergio Osmena (Speaker) and First Philippine Assembly

1957. 50th Anniv of First Philippine Assembly.
800 **176** 5 c. green 15 15

177 "The Spoliarium" after Juan Luna

1957. Birth Centenary of Juan Luna (painter).
801 **177** 5 c. red 15 10

1957. Inauguration of President C. P. Garcia and Vice-President-elect D. Macapagal. Nos. 732/3 surch **GARCIA-MACAPAGAL INAUGURATION DEC. 30, 1957** and value.
802 5 c. on 10 c. blue 20 20
803 10 c. on 20 c. red 30 30

179 University of the Philippines

1958. Golden Jubilee of University of the Philippines.
804 **179** 5 c. lake 35 15

180 Pres. Garcia
181 Main Hospital Building, Quezon Institute

1958. 12th Anniv of Republic.
805 **180** 5 c. multicoloured . . . 15 10
806 20 c. multicoloured . . . 55 40

1958. Obligatory Tax. T.B. Relief Fund.
807 **181** 5 c. + 5 c. green and red . 20 20
808 10 c. + 5 c. violet and red 40 40

182 The Immaculate Conception and Manila Cathedral

1958. Inauguration of Manila Cathedral.
809 **182** 5 c. multicoloured 25 15

1959. Surch **One Centavo**.
810 1 c. on 5 c. red (No. 731) . . 15 10

1959. 14th Anniv of Liberation. Nos. 704/5 surch.
812 **141** 1 c. on 2 c. + 2 c. red . 10 10
813 – 6 c. on 4 c. + 4 c. violet 15 15

186 Philippines Flag
187 Bulacan Seal

1959. Philippines National Flag Commemoration.
814 **186** 6 c. red, blue and yellow . 15 10
815 20 c. red, blue and yellow 25 20

1959. Bulacan Seal and 60th Anniv of Malolos Constitution.
816 **187** 6 c. green 15 10
817 20 c. red 30 20

1959. Capiz Seal and 11th Death Anniv of Pres. Roxas. As T **187** but with Capiz Seal.
818 6 c. brown 10 10
819 25 c. violet 30 30
The shield within the Capiz seal bears the inset portrait of Pres. Roxas.

1959. Bacolod Seal. As T **187** but with Bacolod Seal.
820 6 c. green 25 15
821 10 c. purple 35 25

188 Scout at Camp Fire
190 Bohol Sanatorium

1959. 10th World Scout Jamboree, Manila.
822 **188** 6 c. + 4 c. red on cream (postage) 15 15
823 6 c. + 4 c. red 35 35
824 – 25 c. + 5 c. bl on cream 60 60
825 – 25 c. + 5 c. blue 75 75
826 – 30 c. + 10 c. green (air) . 60 60
827 – 70 c. + 20 c. brown . . 1·25 1·25
828 – 80 c. + 20 c. violet . . . 1·90 1·90
DESIGNS: 25 c. Scout with bow and arrow; 30 c. Scout cycling; 70 c. Scout with model airplane; 80 c. Pres. Garcia with scout.

1959. Obligatory Tax. T.B. Relief Fund. Nos. 807/8 surch **HELP FIGHT T B** with Cross of Lorraine and value and new design (T **190**).
830 **181** 3 c. + 5 c. on 5 c. + 5 c. 20 20
831 6 c. + 5 c. on 10 c. + 5 c. 20 20
832 **190** 6 c. + 5 c. green and red 20 20
833 25 c. + 5 c. blue and red 45 35

191 Pagoda and Gardens at Camp John Hay

1959. 50th Anniv of Baguio.
834 **191** 6 c. green 15 10
835 25 c. red 35 25

1959. U.N. Day. Surch **6 C UNITED NATIONS DAY**.
836 **132** 6 c. on 18 c. blue 15 10

193 Maria Cristina Falls

1959. World Tourist Conference, Manila.
837 **193** 6 c. green and violet . . . 15 15
838 30 c. green and brown . . 55 40

1959. No. 629 surch **One** and bars.
839 1 c. on 4 c. brown 15 10

195

1959. Centenary of Manila Athenaeum (school).
840 **195** 6 c. blue 10 10
841 30 c. red 45 35

197 Book of the Constitution

1960. 25th Anniv of Philippines Constitution.
844 **197** 6 c. brn & gold (postage) . 15 10
845 30 c. blue & silver (air) . . 40 30

198 Congress Building

1960. 5th Anniv of Manila Pact.
846 **198** 6 c. green 10 10
847 25 c. orange 40 30

199 Sunset, Manila Bay

1960. World Refugee Year.
848 **199** 6 c. multicoloured 15 15
849 25 c. multicoloured 40 30

200 North American F-86 Sabre and Boeing P-12 Fighters
202 Lorraine Cross

1960. Air. 25th Anniv of Philippine Air Force.
850 **200** 10 c. red 30 15
851 20 c. blue 55 35

1960. Surch.
852 **134** 1 c. on 18 c. blue 10 10
853 **161** 5 c. on 18 c. blue 25 20
854 **163** 5 c. on 18 c. red 30 15
855 **158** 10 c. on 18 c. orange & bl 25 15
856 **140** 10 c. on 18 c. blue 25 20

1960. 50th Anniv of Philippine Tuberculosis Society. Lorraine Cross and wreath in red and gold.
857 **202** 5 c. green 15 10
858 6 c. blue 15 10

1960. Obligatory Tax. T.B. Relief Fund. Surch. **6 + 5** and bars and **HELP PREVENT TB**.
859 **181** 6 c. + 5 c. on 5 c. + 5 c. green and red 20 15

204 Pres. Quezon
205 Basketball

1960.
860 **204** 1 c. olive 15 10

1960. Olympic Games.
861 **205** 6 c. brn & grn (postage) . 15 10
862 – 10 c. brown and mauve . . 20 15
863 – 30 c. brn and orge (air) . 60 50
864 – 70 c. purple and blue . . 1·25 1·00
DESIGNS: 10 c. Running; 30 c. Rifle-shooting; 70 c. Swimming.

206 Presidents Eisenhower and Garcia

1960. Visit of President Eisenhower.
865 **206** 6 c. multicoloured 25 15
866 20 c. multicoloured . . . 50 25

207 "Mercury" and Globe

1961. Manila Postal Conference.
867 **207** 6 c. multicoloured (postage) 15 10
868 30 c. multicoloured (air) . 35 25

1961. Surch.
869 20 c. on 25 c. grn (No. 734) . 25 15

1961. 2nd National Scout Jamboree, Zamboanga. Nos. 822/5 surch **2nd National Boy Scout Jamboree Pasonanca Park** and value.
870 10 c. on 6 c. + 4 c. red on cream 15 15
871 10 c. on 6 c. + 4 c. red . . . 50 50
872 30 c. on 25 c. + 5 c. blue on cream 40 40
873 30 c. on 25 c. + 5 c. blue . . 50 50

210 La Salle College

1961. 50th Anniv of La Salle College.
874 **210** 6 c. multicoloured 15 10
875 10 c. multicoloured 25 10

211 Rizal when student, School and University Buildings

1961. Birth Centenary of Dr. Jose Rizal.
876 **211** 5 c. multicoloured 10 10
877 – 6 c. multicoloured 10 10
878 – 10 c. brown and green . . 20 20
879 – 20 c. turquoise and brown 30 30
880 – 30 c. multicoloured . . . 45 35
DESIGNS: 6 c. Rizal and birthplace at Calamba, Laguna; 10 c. Rizal, mother and father; 20 c. Rizal extolling Luna and Hidalgo at Madrid; 30 c. Rizal's execution.

1961. 15th Anniv of Republic. Optd **IKA 15 KAARAWAN Republika ng Pilipinas Hulyo 4, 1961.**
881 **198** 6 c. green 25 25
882 25 c. orange 40 40

213 Roxas Memorial T.B. Pavilion
214 Globe, Plan Emblem and Supporting Hand

1961. Obligatory Tax. T.B. Relief Fund.
883 **213** 6 c. + 5 c. brown and red 20 15

1961. 7th Anniv of Admission of Philippines to Colombo Plan.
884 **214** 5 c. multicoloured 10 10
885 6 c. multicoloured 10 10

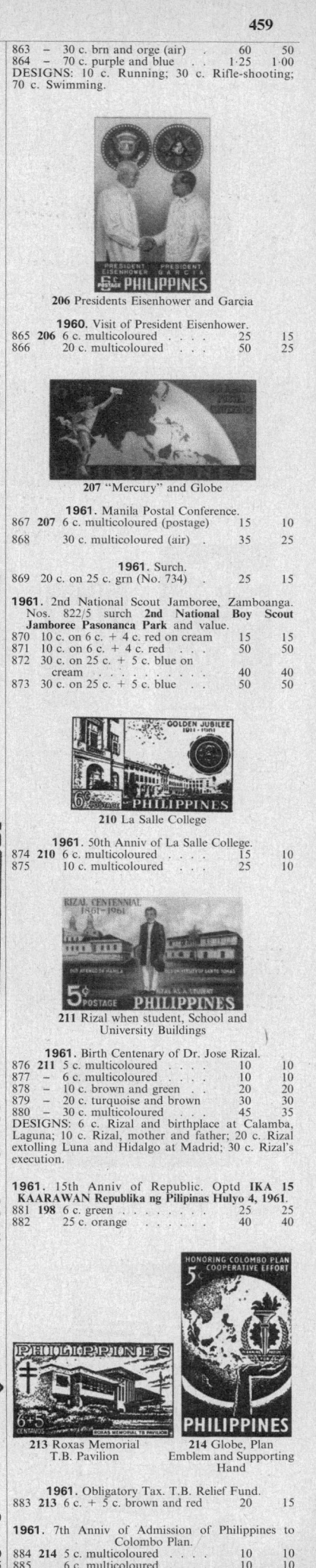

1961. Philippine Amateur Athletic Federation's Golden Jubilee. Surch with P.A.A.F. monogram and **6 c. PAAF GOLDEN JUBILEE 1911 1961.**
886 **200** 6 c. on 10 c. red 25 20

216 Typist

1961. Government Employees' Association Commemoration.
887 **216** 6 c. violet and brown . . 15 10
888 10 c. blue and brown . . 35 20

1961. Inaug. of Pres. Macapagal and Vice Pres. Pelaez. Surch **MACAPAGAL-PELAEZ DEC. 30, 1961 INAUGURATION 6 c.**
889 6 c. on 25 c. vio (No. 819) . . 20 10

1962. Cross obliterated by Arms and surch **6 s** and bars.
890 **181** 6 c. on 5 c. + 5 c. green and red 15 15

220 Waling Waling

221 A. Mabini (statesman)

1962. Orchids in natural colours on blue background.
892 5 c. Type **220** 10 10
893 6 c. White Mariposa 15 15
894 10 c. "Dendrobium sanderii" . 20 20
895 20 c. Sanggumay 35 35

1962. New Currency.
896 – 1 s. brown 10 10
897 **221** 3 s. red 10 10
898 – 5 s. red 10 10
899 – 6 s. brown 15 10
900 – 6 s. blue 15 10
901 – 10 s. purple 15 10
902 – 20 s. blue 25 10
903 – 30 s. red 50 15
904 – 50 s. violet 80 15
905 – 70 s. blue . . . . . . 1·00 45
906 – 1 p. green . . . . . . 2·00 40
907 – 1 p. orange 65 35
PORTRAITS: 1 s. M. L. Quezon; 5 s. M. H. del Pilar; 6 s. (2) J. Rizal (different); 10 s. Father J. Burgos; 20 s. Lapu-Lapu; 30 s. Rajah Soliman; 50 s. C. Arellano; 70 s. S. Osmena; 1 p. (No. 906) E. Jacinto; 1 p. (No. 907) J. M. Panganiban.

225 Pres. Macapagal taking Oath

1962. Independence Day.
915 **225** 6 s. multicoloured 15 10
916 10 s. multicoloured . . . 20 15
917 30 s. multicoloured . . . 35 20

226 Valdes Memorial T.B. Pavilion

1962. Obligatory Tax Stamps. T.B. Relief Fund. Cross in red.
918 **226** 6 s. + 5 s. slate 15 15
919 30 s. + 5 s. blue 45 30
920 70 s. + 5 s. blue . . . . 1·00 80

227 Lake Taal

1962. Malaria Eradication.
921 **227** 6 s. multicoloured 15 15
922 10 s. multicoloured . . . 20 15
923 70 s. multicoloured . . . 1·40 1·00

1962. Bicentenary of Diego Silang Revolt. No. 734 surch **1762 1962 BICENTENNIAL Diego Silang Revolt 20.**
924 20 s. on 25 c. green 30 20

1962. No. 742 with premium obliterated.
925 **149** 5 c. blue 20 15

230 Dr. Rizal playing Chess

1962. Rizal Foundation Fund.
926 **230** 6 s. + 4 s. green & mauve 25 25
927 – 30 s. + 5 s. blue & purple 50 50
DESIGN: 30 s. Dr. Rizal fencing.

1963. Surch.
928 **221** 1 s. on 3 s. red 15 10
929 – 5 s. on 6 s. brown (No. 899) 15 10

1963. Diego Silang Bicentenary Art and Philatelic Exn, G.P.O., Manila. No. 737 surch **1763 1963 DIEGO SILANG BICENTENNIAL ARPHEX** and value.
930 6 c. on 2 p. violet 20 15
931 20 c. on 2 p. violet 25 25
932 70 c. on 2 p. violet 80 65

233 "We want to see ..." (Pres. Roxas)

234 Lorraine Cross on Map

1963. Presidential Sayings (1st issue).
933 **233** 6 s. blue and black . . . 15 10
934 30 s. brown and black . . 50 15
See also Nos. 959/60, 981/2, 1015/6, 1034/5, 1055/6, 1148/9 and 1292/3.

1963. Obligatory Tax. T.B. Relief Fund. Cross in red.
935 **234** 6 s. + 5 s. pink & violet . 15 10
936 10 s. + 5 s. pink & green 15 15
937 50 s. + 5 s. pink & brown 65 45

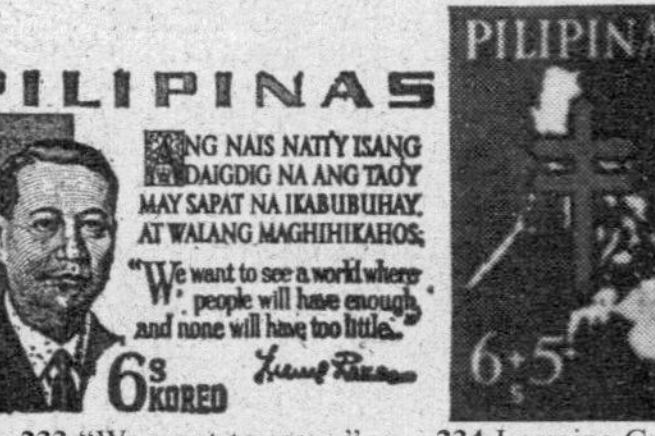

235 Globe and Flags **236** Centenary Emblem

1963. 1st Anniv of Asian-Oceanic Postal Union.
938 **235** 6 s. multicoloured 15 15
939 20 s. multicoloured . . . 20 15

1963. Red Cross Centenary. Cross in red.
940 **236** 5 s. grey and violet . . . 15 10
941 6 s. grey and blue . . . 15 10
942 20 s. grey and green . . . 40 25

237 Tinikling (dance)

1963. Folk Dances. Multicoloured.
943 5 s. Type **237** 20 20
944 6 s. Pandanggo sa Ilaw . . . 20 20
945 10 s. Itik-Itik 20 20
946 20 s. Singkil 35 30

238 Pres. Macapagal and Philippine Family

1963. President's Social-Economic Programme.
947 **238** 5 s. multicoloured 15 10
948 6 s. multicoloured 15 15
949 20 s. multicoloured . . . 30 25

239 Presidents' Meeting

240 Bonifacio and Flag

1963. Visit of President Mateos of Mexico.
950 **239** 6 s. multicoloured 20 15
951 30 s. multicoloured . . . 40 15

1963. Birth Centenary of A. Bonifacio (patriot).
952 **240** 5 s. multicoloured 15 10
953 6 s. multicoloured 15 10
954 25 s. multicoloured 30 25

241 Harvester

242 Bamboo Organ, Catholic Church, Las Pinas

1963. Freedom from Hunger.
956 **241** 6 s. multicoloured (postage) 15 10
957 30 s. multicoloured (air) . 55 40
958 50 s. multicoloured 90 45

1963. Presidential Sayings (2nd issue). As T **233** but with portrait and saying changed.
959 6 s. black and mauve 15 10
960 30 s. black and green 35 15
PORTRAIT AND SAYING: Pres. Magsaysay, "I believe ...".

1964. Las Pinas Organ Commemoration.
961 **242** 5 s. multicoloured 15 10
962 6 s. multicoloured 15 10
963 20 s. multicoloured 40 25

243 A. Mabini (patriot)

245 S.E.A.T.O. Emblems and Flags

244 Negros Oriental T.B. Pavilion

1964. Birth Centenary of A. Mabini.
964 **243** 6 s. gold and violet 15 15
965 10 s. gold and brown . . . 15 15
966 30 s. gold and green . . . 25 15

1964. Obligatory Tax. T.B. Relief Fund. Cross in red.
967 **244** 5 s. + 5 s. purple 15 10
968 5 s. + 5 s. blue 15 10
969 30 s. + 5 s. brown 45 30
970 70 s. + 5 s. green 80 75

1964. 10th Anniv of S.E.A.T.O.
971 **245** 6 s. multicoloured 15 10
972 10 s. multicoloured 20 15
973 25 s. multicoloured 25 20

246 President signing the Land Reform Code **247** Basketball

1964. Agricultural Land Reform Code. President and inscr at foot in brown, red and sepia.
974 **246** 3 s. green (postage) 15 10
975 6 s. blue 15 10
976 30 s. brown (air) 30 25

1964. Olympic Games, Tokyo. Sport in chocolate. Perf or imperf.
977 **247** 6 s. blue and gold 15 15
978 – 10 s. pink and gold . . . 25 15
979 – 20 s. yellow and gold . . 45 25
980 – 30 s. green and gold . . . 60 45
SPORTS: 10 s. Relay-racing; 20 s. Hurdling; 30 s. Football.

1965. Presidential Sayings (3rd issue). As T **233** but with portrait and saying changed.
981 6 s. black and green 15 10
982 30 s. black and purple 35 15
PORTRAIT AND SAYING: Pres. Quirino, "So live ...".

248 Presidents Luebke and Macapagal

1965. Visit of President of German Federal Republic.
983 **248** 6 s. multicoloured 15 10
984 10 s. multicoloured . . . 20 10
985 25 s. multicoloured . . . 35 30

249 Meteorological Emblems

250 Pres. Kennedy

1965. Cent of Philippines Meteorological Services.
986 **249** 6 s. multicoloured 15 10
987 20 s. multicoloured . . . 15 15
988 50 s. multicoloured . . . 50 30

1965. 48th Birth Anniv of Pres. Kennedy.
989 **250** 6 s. multicoloured 20 10
990 10 s. multicoloured . . . 20 15
991 30 s. multicoloured . . . 45 25

251 King Bhumibol and Queen Sirikit, Pres. Macapagal and Wife

1965. Visit of King and Queen of Thailand.
992 **251** 2 s. multicoloured 10 10
993 6 s. multicoloured 15 10
994 30 s. multicoloured . . . 45 25

252 Princess Beatrix and Mrs. Macapagal

1965. Visit of Princess Beatrix of the Netherlands.
995 **252** 2 s. multicoloured 10 10
996 6 s. multicoloured 15 10
997 10 s. multicoloured . . . 20 15

1965. Obligatory Tax. T.B. Relief Fund. Surch.
998 **244** 1 s. + 5 s. on 6 s. + 5 s. 15 10
999 3 s. + 5 s. on 6 s. + 5 s. 20 15

254 Hand holding Cross and Rosary

256 Signing Agreement

1965. 400th Anniv of Philippines Christianisation. Multicoloured.
1000 3 s. Type **254** (postage) . . . 15 10
1001 6 s. Legaspi-Urdaneta, monument 20 10
1002 30 s. Baptism of Filipinos by Father Urdaneta (air) . . 50 30
1003 70 s. "Way of the Cross"–ocean map of Christian voyagers' route, Spain to the Philippines 1·10 65
Nos. 1002/3 are horiz, 48 × 27 mm.

1965. "MAPILINDO" Conference, Manila.
1005 **256** 6 s. blue, red & yellow . 15 10
1006 10 s. multicoloured . . . 15 15
1007 25 s. multicoloured . . . 40 25
The above stamps depict Pres. Sukarno of Indonesia, former Pres. Macapagal of the Philippines and Prime Minister Tunku Abdul Rahman of Malaysia.

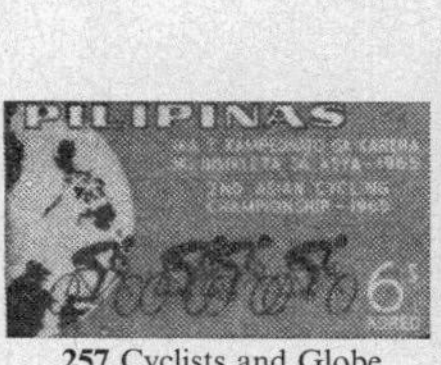

257 Cyclists and Globe **259** Dr. A. Regidor

1965. 2nd Asian Cycling Championships, Philippines.
1008 **257** 6 s. multicoloured . . . 10 10
1009 10 s. multicoloured . . . 20 15
1010 25 s. multicoloured . . . 40 25

1965. Inaug. of Pres. Marcos and Vice-Pres. Lopez. Nos. 926/7 surch **MARCOS-LOPEZ INAUGURATION DEC. 30, 1965** with value and bars.
1011 **230** 10 s. on 6 s. + 4 s. . . . 20 20
1012 – 30 s. on 30 s. + 5 s. . . 50 50

1966. Regidor (patriot) Commemoration.
1013 **259** 6 s. blue 15 10
1014 30 s. brown 25 25

1966. Presidential Sayings (4th issue). As T **233** but with portrait and saying changed.
1015 6 s. black and lake 15 10
1016 30 s. black and blue 35 15
PORTRAIT AND SAYING: Pres. Aguinaldo, "Have faith ...".

1966. Campaign Against Smuggling. No. 900 optd **HELP ME STOP SMUGGLING Pres. MARCOS.**
1017 6 s. blue 20 15

261 Girl Scout

1966. Silver Jubilee of Philippines Girl Scouts.
1018 **261** 3 s. multicoloured . . . 10 10
1019 6 s. multicoloured . . . 15 10
1020 20 s. multicoloured . . . 40 25

262 Pres. Marcos taking Oath

1966. Inauguration (1965) of Pres. Marcos.
1021 **262** 6 s. multicoloured . . . 15 10
1022 20 s. multicoloured . . . 15 15
1023 30 s. multicoloured . . . 25 25

263 Manila Seal and Historical Scenes

1966. Introduction of New Seal for Manila.
1024 **263** 6 s. multicoloured . . . 15 15
1025 30 s. multicoloured . . . 25 15

264 Bank Facade and 1-peso Coin

1966. 50th Anniv of Philippines National Bank. Mult.
1026 6 s. Type **264** 15 10
1027 10 s. Old and new bank buildings 15 15

266 Bank Building

1966. 60th Anniv of Postal Savings Bank.
1029 **266** 6 s. violet, yellow & grn 15 10
1030 10 s. red, yellow & grn . 15 15
1031 20 s. blue, yellow & grn 40 20

1966. Manila Summit Conf. Nos. 1021 and 1023 optd **MANILA SUMMIT CONFERENCE 1966 7 NATIONS** and emblem.
1032 **262** 6 s. multicoloured . . . 15 15
1033 30 s. multicoloured . . . 35 25

1966. Presidential Sayings (5th issue). As T **233** but with portrait and saying changed.
1034 6 s. black and brown 15 10
1035 30 s. black and blue 35 15
PORTRAIT AND SAYING: Pres. Laurel; "No one can love the Filipinos better ...".

1967. 50th Anniv of Lions Int. Nos. 977/80 optd **50th ANNIVERSARY LIONS INTERNATIONAL 1967** and emblem. Imperf.
1036 **247** 6 c. blue and gold . . . 15 15
1037 – 10 c. pink and gold . . 20 15
1038 – 20 c. yellow and gold . . 40 25
1039 – 30 c. green and gold . . 60 60

269 "Succour" (after painting by F. Amorsolo)

1967. 25th Anniv of Battle of Bataan.
1040 **269** 5 s. multicoloured . . . 15 10
1041 20 s. multicoloured . . . 25 15
1042 2 p. multicoloured . . . 2·10 1·25

1967. Nos. 900 and 975 surch.
1043 4 s. on 6 s. blue 15 10
1044 5 s. on 6 s. blue 15 10

271 Stork-billed Kingfisher

1967. Obligatory Tax. T.B. Relief Fund. Birds. Multicoloured.
1045 1 s. + 5 s. Type **271** 15 10
1046 5 s. + 5 s. Rufous hornbill . 60 15
1047 10 s. + 5 s. Philippine eagle 1·10 30
1048 30 s. + 5 s. Great-billed parrot 1·75 55
See also Nos. 1113/6.

272 Gen. MacArthur and Paratroopers landing on Corregidor

1967. 25th Anniv of Battle of Corregidor.
1049 **272** 6 s. multicoloured . . . 10 10
1050 5 p. multicoloured . . . 4·00 3·25

273 Bureau of Posts Building, Manila

1967. 65th Anniv of Philippines Bureau of Posts.
1051 **273** 4 s. multicoloured . . . 20 20
1052 20 s. multicoloured . . . 20 10
1053 50 s. multicoloured . . . 50 40

274 Escaping from Eruption

1967. Obligatory Tax. Taal Volcano Eruption (1965). (1st issue).
1054 **274** 70 s. multicoloured . . . 90 75
For compulsory use on foreign air mail where the rate exceeds 70 s. in aid of Taal Volcano Rehabilitation Committee.
See also No. 1071.

1967. Presidential Sayings (6th issue). As T **233** but with portrait and saying changed.
1055 10 s. black and blue 15 10
1056 30 s. black and violet . . . 35 15
PORTRAIT AND SAYING: Pres. Quezon. "Social justice is far more beneficial ...".

275 "The Holy Family" (Filipino version)

1967. Christmas.
1057 **275** 10 s. multicoloured . . . 15 15
1058 40 s. multicoloured . . . 50 35

276 Pagoda, Pres. Marcos and Chiang Kai-shek

1967. China–Philippines Friendship.
1059 **276** 5 s. multicoloured 10 10
1060 – 10 s. multicoloured . . . 15 15
1061 – 20 s. multicoloured . . . 20 15
DESIGNS: (with portraits of Pres. Marcos and Chiang Kai-shek): 10 s. Gateway, Chinese Garden, Rizal Park, Luneta; 20 s. Chinese Garden, Rizal Park, Luneta.

277 Ayala Avenue, Manila, Inaugural Ceremony and Rotary Badge

1968. 1st Anniv of Makati Centre Post Office, Manila.
1062 **277** 10 s. multicoloured . . . 10 10
1063 20 s. multicoloured . . . 25 25
1064 40 s. multicoloured . . . 50 50

1968. Surch.
1065 – 5 s. on 6 s. (No. 981) . . 10 10
1066 – 5 s. on 6 s. (No. 1034) . . 10 10
1067 **244** 10 s. on 6 s. + 5 s. . . . 10 10

280 Calderon, Barasoain Church and Constitution

1068. Birth Centenary of Felipe G. Calderon (lawyer and author of Malolos Constitution).
1068 **280** 10 s. multicoloured . . . 15 10
1069 40 s. multicoloured . . . 60 40
1070 75 s. multicoloured . . . 1·10 1·00

281 Eruption **282** "Philcomsat", Earth Station and Globe

1968. Taal Volcano Eruption (1965). (2nd issue).
1071 **281** 70 s. multicoloured . . . 90 90

Two issues were prepared by an American Agency under a contract signed with the Philippine postal authority but at the last moment this contract was cancelled by the Philippine Government. In the meanwhile the stamps had been on sale in the U.S.A. but they were never issued in the Philippines and they had no postal validity.
They comprise a set for the Mexican Olympic Games in the values 1, 2, 3 and 15 s. postage and 50, 75 s., 1, 2. p. airmail and a set in memory of J.F. Kennedy and Robert Kennedy in the values 1, 2, 3 s. postage and 5, 10 p. airmail.

1968. Inauguration of "Philcomsat"–POTC Earth Station, Tanay, Rizal, Luzon.
1072 **282** 10 s. multicoloured . . . 20 15
1073 40 s. multicoloured . . . 50 45
1074 75 s. multicoloured . . . 95 80

283 "Tobacco Production" (mural)

1968. Philippines Tobacco Industry.
1075 **283** 10 s. multicoloured . . . 15 15
1076 40 s. multicoloured . . . 60 50
1077 70 s. multicoloured . . . 1·00 85

284 "Kudyapi"

1968. St. Cecilia's Day. Musical Instruments. Mult.
1078 10 s. Type **284** 15 10
1079 20 s. "Ludag" 15 15
1080 30 s. "Kulintangan" 35 30
1081 50 s. "Subing" 50 50

285 Concordia College **286** Children singing Carols

1968. Centenary of Concordia Women's College.
1082 **285** 10 s. multicoloured . . . 15 15
1083 20 s. multicoloured . . . 20 15
1084 70 s. multicoloured . . . 65 50

1968. Christmas.
1085 **286** 10 s. multicoloured . . . 15 15
1086 40 s. multicoloured . . . 50 45
1087 75 s. multicoloured . . . 90 75

287 Philippine Tarsier

1969. Philippines Fauna. Multicoloured.
1088 2 s. Type **287** 15 15
1089 10 s. Tamarau 15 15
1090 20 s. Water buffalo 25 20
1091 75 s. Greater Malay chevrotain 1·25 1·00

288 President Aguinaldo and Cavite Building

1969. Birth Centenary of President Amilio Aguinaldo.
1092 **288** 10 s. multicoloured . . . 20 15
1093 40 s. multicoloured . . . 55 35
1094 70 s. multicoloured . . . 1·00 80

289 Rotary Emblem and "Bastion of San Andres"

1969. 50th Anniv of Manila Rotary Club.
1095 **289** 10 s. mult (postage) . . . 15 15
1096 40 s. multicoloured (air) . . 40 30
1097 75 s. multicoloured . . . 90 70

290 Senator C. M. Recto **291** Jose Rizal College

1969. Recto Commemoration.
1098 **290** 10 s. purple 15 10

1969. Philatelic Week. No. 1051 optd **PHILATELIC WEEK NOV. 24-30, 1968,** etc.
1099 4 s. multicoloured 20 10

1969. Jose Rizal College, Mandaluyong, Rizal.
1100 **292** 10 s. multicoloured . . . 15 15
1101 40 s. multicoloured . . . 60 40
1102 50 s. multicoloured . . . 75 65

1969. 4th National Boy Scout Jamboree, Palayan City. No. 1019 surch **4th NATIONAL BOY SCOUT JAMBOREE PALAYAN CITY - MAY, 1969** and value.
1103 **261** 5 s. on 6 s. multicoloured 20 15

294 Red Cross Emblems and Map
295 Pres. and Mrs. Marcos harvesting Rice

1969. 50th Anniv of League of Red Cross Societies.
1104 **294** 10 s. red, blue and grey . 15 10
1105 40 s. red and blue . . . 50 30
1106 75 s. red, brown & ochre 80 70

1969. "Rice for Progress".
1107 **295** 10 s. multicoloured . . . 15 10
1108 40 s. multicoloured . . . 50 35
1109 75 s. multicoloured . . . 80 70

296 "The Holy Child of Leyte" (statue)

1969. 80th Anniv of Return of the "Holy Child of Leyte" to Tacloban.
1110 **296** 5 s. mult (postage) . . . 10 10
1111 10 s. multicoloured . . . 15 15
1112 40 s. multicoloured (air) . 45 35

1969. Obligatory Tax. T.B. Relief Fund. Birds as T **271**.
1113 1 s. + 5 s. Golden-backed three-toed woodpecker 10 10
1114 5 s. + 5 s. Philippine trogon 50 15
1115 10 s. + 5 s. Johnstone's lorikeet 1·25 35
1116 40 s. + 5 s. Scarlet minivet . 1·75 50

297 Bank Building

1969. Inauguration of Philippines Development Bank, Makati, Rizal.
1117 **297** 10 s. black, blue & green 15 10
1118 40 s. black, red & green . 85 40
1119 75 s. black, brown & grn 1·25 90

298 "Troides magellanus"

1969. Philippine Butterflies. Multicoloured.
1120 10 s. Type **298** 25 15
1121 20 s. "Graphium agamemnon" 30 20
1122 30 s. "Papilio helenus" . . . 55 30
1123 40 s. "Trogonoptera trojana" 80 45

299 Children of the World

1969. 15th Anniv of Universal Children's Day.
1124 **299** 10 s. multicoloured . . . 15 10
1125 20 s. multicoloured . . . 15 15
1126 30 s. multicoloured . . . 25 20

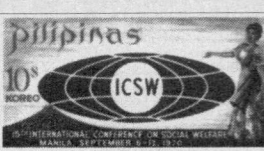

300 Memorial and Outline of Landing

1969. 25th Anniv of U.S. Forces' Landing on Leyte.
1127 **300** 5 s. multicoloured . . . 15 10
1128 10 s. multicoloured . . . 15 15
1129 40 s. multicoloured . . . 50 30

301 Cultural Centre
303 Melchora Aquino

1969. Cultural Centre, Manila.
1130 **301** 10 s. blue 15 15
1131 30 s. purple 35 25

1969. Philatelic Week. Nos. 943/6 (Folk Dances) optd **1969 PHILATELIC WEEK** or optd and surch.
1132 5 s. multicoloured 15 15
1133 5 s. on 6 s. multicoloured . . 15 15
1134 10 s. multicoloured 20 20
1135 10 s. on 20 s. multicoloured 25 20

1969. 50th Death Anniv of Melchora Aquino, "Tandang Sora" (Grand Old Woman of the Revolution).
1136 **303** 10 s. multicoloured . . . 15 10
1137 20 s. multicoloured . . . 25 15
1138 30 s. multicoloured . . . 40 25

1969. 2nd-term Inauguration of President Marcos. No. 1021 surch **PASINAYA, IKA-2 PANUNUNGKULAN PANGULONG FERDINAND E. MARCOS DISYEMBRA 30, 1969.**
1139 **262** 5 s. on 6 s. multicoloured 25 10

305 Ladle and Steel Mills

1970. Iligan Integrated Steel Mills.
1140 **305** 10 s. multicoloured . . . 20 10
1141 20 s. multicoloured . . . 40 20
1142 30 s. multicoloured . . . 60 30

1970. Nos. 900, 962 and 964 surch.
1143 – 4 s. on 6 s. blue 15 10
1144 **242** 5 s. on 6 s. multicoloured 15 10
1145 **243** 5 s. on 6 s. multicoloured 15 10

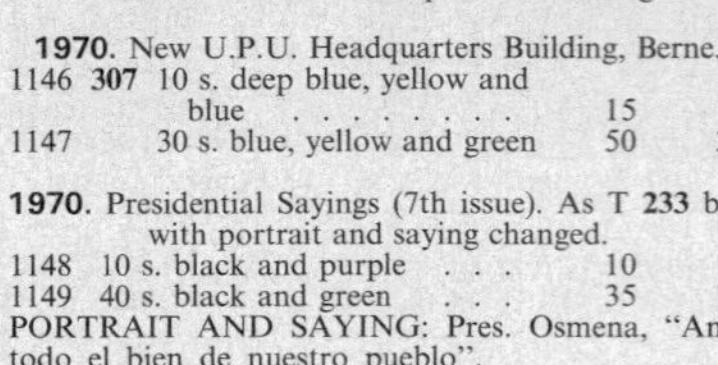

307 New U.P.U. Headquarters Building

1970. New U.P.U. Headquarters Building, Berne.
1146 **307** 10 s. deep blue, yellow and blue 15 10
1147 30 s. blue, yellow and green 50 30

1970. Presidential Sayings (7th issue). As T **233** but with portrait and saying changed.
1148 10 s. black and purple . . . 10 10
1149 40 s. black and green . . . 35 15
PORTRAIT AND SAYING: Pres. Osmena, "Ante todo el bien de nuestro pueblo".

308 Dona Julia V. de Ortigas and T.B. Society Headquarters

1970. Obligatory Tax. T.B. Relief Fund.
1150 **308** 1 s. + 5 s. multicoloured 15 10
1151 5 s. + 5 s. multicoloured 20 20
1152 30 s. + 5 s. multicoloured 70 70
1153 70 s. + 5 s. multicoloured 90 90

309 I.C.S.W. Emblem

1970. 15th Int Conference on Social Welfare.
1154 **309** 10 s. multicoloured . . . 15 15
1155 20 s. multicoloured . . . 30 20
1156 30 s. multicoloured . . . 50 25

310 "Crab" (after sculpture by A. Calder)

1970. "Fight Cancer" Campaign.
1157 **310** 10 s. multicoloured . . . 20 15
1158 40 s. multicoloured . . . 45 25
1159 50 s. multicoloured . . . 65 35

311 Scaled Tridacna

1970. Seashells. Multicoloured.
1160 5 s. Type **311** 10 10
1161 10 s. Royal spiny oyster . . . 25 10
1162 20 s. Venus comb 40 15
1163 40 s. Glory-of-the-Sea cone . 85 40

1970. Nos. 986, 1024 and 1026 surch with new values in figures and letters.
1164 **249** 4 s. on 6 s. 15 10
1165 **263** 4 s. on 6 s. 15 10
1166 **264** 4 s. on 6 s. 15 10

313 The "Hundred Islands" and Ox-cart

1970. Tourism (1st series). Multicoloured.
1167 10 s. Type **313** 15 15
1168 20 s. Tree-house, Pasonanca Park, Zamboanga City . . 20 15
1169 30 s. "Filipino" (statue) and sugar plantation, Negros Island 30 25
1170 2 p. Calesa (horse-carriage) and Miagao Church, Iloilo . . . 1·90 1·10
See also Nos. 1186/9, 1192/5 and 1196/9.

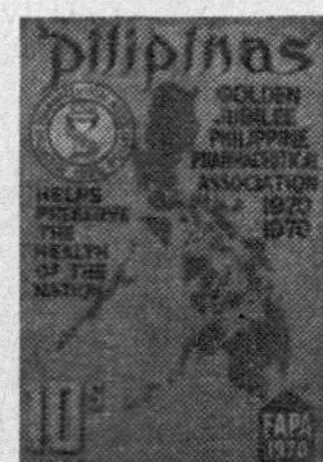

314 Map of the Philippines

1970. Golden Jubilee of Philippine Pharmaceutical Association.
1171 **314** 10 s. multicoloured . . . 15 10
1172 50 s. multicoloured . . . 65 35

1970. U.P.U./A.O.P.U. Regional Seminar, Manila. No. 938 surch **UPU-AOPU REGIONAL SEMINAR NOV. 23–DEC. 5, 1970,** and new value.
1173 **235** 10 s. on 6 s. multicoloured 15 15

1970. Philatelic Week. No. 977 surch **1970 PHILATELIC WEEK** and new value.
1174 **247** 10 s. on 6 s. brown, blue and gold 15 10

317 Pope Paul VI and Map

1970. Pope Paul's Visit to the Philippines.
1175 **317** 10 s. mult (postage) . . 15 10
1176 30 s. multicoloured . . . 30 20
1177 40 s. multicoloured (air) 35 25

318 Mariano Ponce
320 P.A.T.A. Horse and Carriage

1970.
1178 **318** 10 s. red 15 10
1179 – 15 s. brown 15 10
1180 – 40 s. red 35 10
1181 – 1 p. blue 90 35
DESIGNS: 15 s. Josefa Llanes Escoda; 40 s. Gen. Miguel Malvar; 1 p. Julian Felipe.

1971. 20th P.A.T.A. Conference and Workshop, Manila.
1183 **320** 5 s. multicoloured . . . 10 10
1184 10 s. multicoloured . . . 15 15
1185 70 s. multicoloured . . . 50 35

1971. Tourism (2nd series). Views as T **313**. Multicoloured.
1186 10 s. Nayong Pilipino resort . 10 10
1187 20 s. Fish frm, Iloilo 15 10
1188 30 s. Pagsanjan Falls 20 15
1189 5 p. Watch-tower, Punta Cruz 1·60 1·60

321 Emblem and Family

1971. Regional Conference of International Planned Parenthood Federation for South-East Asia and Oceania.
1190 **321** 20 s. multicoloured . . . 15 10
1191 40 s. multicoloured . . . 25 15

1971. Tourism (3rd series). As T **313**. Mult.
1192 10 s. Aguinaldo pearl farm . 15 10
1193 20 s. Coral-diving, Davao . . 20 15
1194 40 s. Taluksengay Mosque . 25 20
1195 1 p. Ifugao woman and Banaue rice-terraces 60 50

1971. Tourism (4th series). As T **313**. Mult.
1196 10 s. Cannon and Filipino vinta, Fort del Pilar 15 10
1197 30 s. Magellan's Cross, Cebu City 15 15
1198 50 s. "Big Jar", Calamba Laguna (Rizal's birthplace) 25 25
1199 70 s. Mayon Volcano and diesel train . . . . 1·75 50

1971. Surch in letters and figures.
1200 **264** 5 s. on 6 s. multicoloured 15 10

323 G. A. Malcolm (founder) and Law Symbols

1971. 60th Anniv of Philippines College of Law.
1201 **323** 15 s. mult (postage) . . 15 15
1202 1 p. multicoloured (air) . 75 70

324 Commemorative Seal

1971. 400th Anniv of Manila.
1203 **324** 10 s. multicoloured (postage) 15 15
1204 1 p. multicoloured (air) . 1·10 75

325 Arms of Faculties

1971. Centenaries of Faculties of Medicine and Surgery, and of Pharmacy, Santo Tomas University.

1205 **325** 5 s. mult (postage) . . . 15 10
1206 2 p. multicoloured (air) . 1·50 1·40

1971. University Presidents' World Congress, Manila. Surch **CONGRESS OF UNIVERSITY PRESIDENTS** emblems and value.

1207 **266** 5 s. on 6 s. violet, yellow and green 15 10

327 "Our Lady of Guia"

1971. 400th Anniv of "Our Lady of Guia", Ermita, Manila.

1208 **327** 10 s. multicoloured . . . 15 15
1209 75 s. multicoloured . . . 60 50

328 Bank and "Customers"

1971. 70th Anniv of First National City Bank.

1210 **328** 10 s. multicoloured . . . 15 10
1211 30 s. multicoloured . . . 30 25
1212 1 p. multicoloured . . . 65 50

1971. Surch in letters and figure.

1213 **259** 4 s. on 6 s. blue 15 10
1214 5 s. on 6 s. blue 15 10

1971. Philatelic Week. Surch **1971 - PHILATELIC WEEK** and new value in letters and figure.

1215 **266** 5 s. on 6 s. violet, yellow and green 15 10

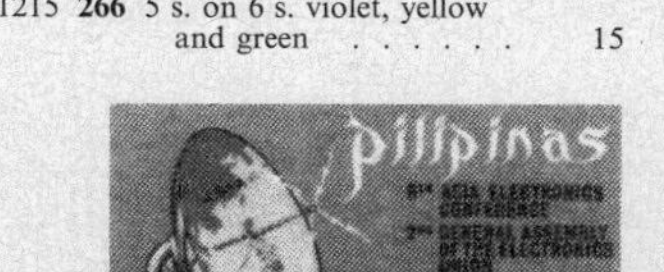

331 Dish Aerial and Events

1972. 6th Asian Electronics Conference, Manila (1971) and Related Events.

1216 **331** 5 s. multicoloured . . . 15 10
1217 40 s. multicoloured . . . 50 35

332 Fathers Burgos, Gomez and Zamora

1972. Centenary of Martyrdom of Fathers Burgos, Gomez and Zamora.

1218 **332** 5 s. multicoloured . . . 10 10
1219 60 s. multicoloured . . . 40 40

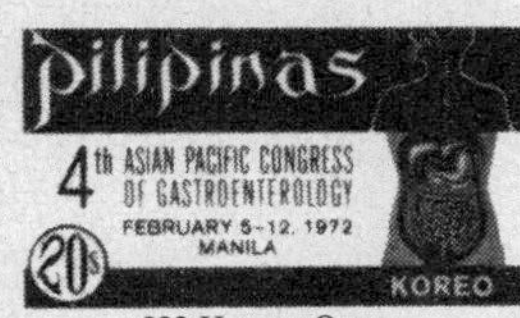

333 Human Organs

1972. 4th Asian-Pacific Gastro-enterological Congress, Manila.

1220 **333** 20 s. mult (postage) . . . 20 15
1221 40 s. multicoloured (air) . 40 35

1972. Surch.

1222 **263** 5 s. on 6 s. multicoloured . 15 10

1972. No. O914 with optd **G.O.** obliterated.

1223 50 s. violet 40 25

1972. Surch.

1224 **245** 10 s. on 6 s. multicoloured 15 10
1225 **451** 10 s. on 6 s. multicoloured 15 10
1226 – 10 s. on 6 s. black & red (No. 1015) 15 10

336 Memorial Gardens, Manila

1972. Tourism. "Visit Asean Lands" Campaign.

1227 **336** 5 s. multicoloured . . . 15 10
1228 50 s. multicoloured . . . 85 25
1229 60 s. multicoloured . . . 1·10 35

337 "KKK" Flag

1972. Evolution of Philippines' Flag.

1230 **337** 30 s. red and blue . . . 30 25
1231 – 30 s. red and blue . . . 30 25
1232 – 30 s. red and blue . . . 30 25
1233 – 30 s. black and blue . . 30 25
1234 – 30 s. red and blue . . . 30 25
1235 – 30 s. red and blue . . . 30 25
1236 – 30 s. red and blue . . . 30 25
1237 – 30 s. red and blue . . . 30 25
1238 – 30 s. black, red and blue 30 25
1239 – 30 s. yellow, red & blue 30 25

FLAGS: No. 1231, Three "K"s in pyramid; No. 1232, Single "K"; No. 1233, "K", skull and crossbones; No. 1234, Three "K"s and sun in triangle; No. 1235, Sun and three "K"s; No. 1236, Ancient Tagalog "K" within sun; No. 1237, Face in sun; No. 1238, Tricolor; No. 1239, Present national flag–sun and stars within triangle, two stripes.

338 Mabol, Santol and Papaya

1972. Obligatory Tax. T.B. Relief Fund. Fruits. Mult.

1240 1 s. + 5 s. Type **338** 10 10
1241 10 s. + 5 s. Bananas, balimbang and mangosteen 15 15
1242 40 s. + 5 s. Guava, mango, duhat and susongkalabac . 30 30
1243 1 p. + 5 s. Orange, pineapple, lanzones and sirhuelas . . 60 60

339 "Scarus frenatus"

1972. Fishes. Multicoloured.

1244 5 s. Type **339** (postage) . . . 10 10
1245 10 s. "Chaetodon kleini" . . 15 10
1246 20 s. "Zanclus cornutus" . . 25 15
1247 50 s. "Holacanthus bispinosus" (air) 70 35

340 Bank Headquarters

1972. 25th Anniv of Philippines Development Bank.

1248 **340** 10 s. multicoloured . . . 15 10
1249 20 s. multicoloured . . . 15 10
1250 60 s. multicoloured . . . 50 35

341 Pope Paul VI

1972. 1st Anniv of Pope Paul's Visit to Philippines.

1251 **341** 10 s. mult (postage) . . . 10 10
1252 50 s. multicoloured . . . 40 35
1253 60 s. multicoloured (air) . 50 50

1972. Various stamps surch.

1254 **240** 10 s. on 6 s. (No. 953) . . 15 10
1255 – 10 s. on 6 s. (No. 959) . . 15 10
1256 **250** 10 s. on 6 s. (No. 989) . . 15 10

343 "La Barca de Aqueronte" (Hidalgo)

1972. 25th Anniv of Stamps and Philatelic Division, Philippines Bureau of Posts. Filipino Paintings. Multicoloured.

1257 5 s. Type **343** 10 10
1258 10 s. "Afternoon Meal of the Rice Workers" (Amorsolo) 10 10
1259 30 s. "Espana y Filipinas" (Luna) (27 × 60 mm) . . . 25 25
1260 70 s. "The Song of Maria Clara" (Amorsolo) 50 50

344 Lamp, Emblem and Nurse

1972. 50th Anniv of Philippine Nurses Assn.

1261 **344** 5 s. multicoloured 10 10
1262 10 s. multicoloured . . . 10 10
1263 70 s. multicoloured . . . 40 35

345 Heart on Map

1972. World Heart Month.

1264 **345** 5 s. red, green & violet . 10 10
1265 10 s. red, green & blue . . 10 10
1266 30 s. red, blue & green . . 25 20

346 "The First Mass" (C. V. Francisco)

1972. 450th Anniv of 1st Mass in Limasawa (1971).

1267 **346** 10 s. mult (postage) . . . 15 15
1268 60 s. multicoloured (air) . 45 40

1972. Asia Pacific Scout Conference, Manila. Various stamps surch **ASIA PACIFIC SCOUT CONFERENCE NOV. 1972**, and value.

1269 **233** 10 s. on 6 s. (No. 933) . . 15 10
1270 **240** 10 s. on 6 s. (No. 953) . . 15 10
1271 – 10 s. on 6 s. (No. 981) . . 15 10

348 Olympic Emblems and Torch

1972. Olympic Games, Munich.

1272 **348** 5 s. multicoloured . . . 10 10
1273 10 s. multicoloured . . . 10 10
1274 70 s. multicoloured . . . 50 40

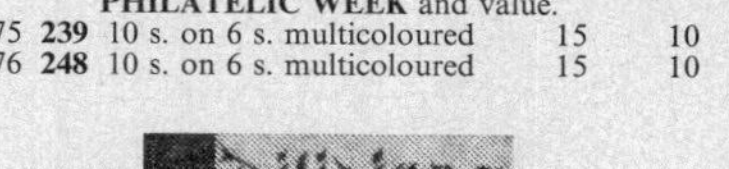

1972. Philatelic Week. Nos. 950 and 983 surch **1972 PHILATELIC WEEK** and value.

1275 **239** 10 s. on 6 s. multicoloured 15 10
1276 **248** 10 s. on 6 s. multicoloured 15 10

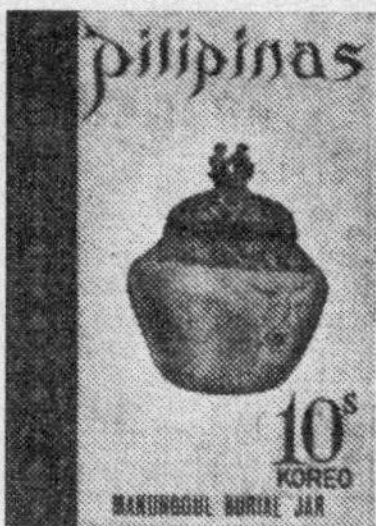

350 Manunggul Burial Jar

1972. Philippine Archaeological Discoveries. Multicoloured.

1277 10 s. Type **350** 15 10
1278 10 s. Ritual earthenware vessel 15 10
1279 10 s. Metal pot 15 10
1280 10 s. Earthenware vessel . . 15 10

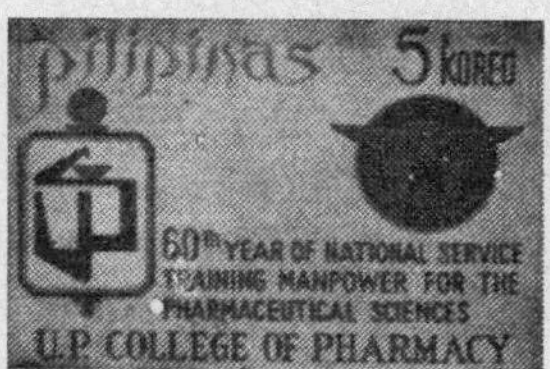

351 Emblems of Pharmacy and University of the Philippines

1972. 60th Anniv of National Training for Pharmaceutical Sciences, University of the Philippines.

1281 **351** 5 s. multicoloured . . . 10 10
1282 10 s. multicoloured . . . 10 10
1283 30 s. multicoloured . . . 25 15

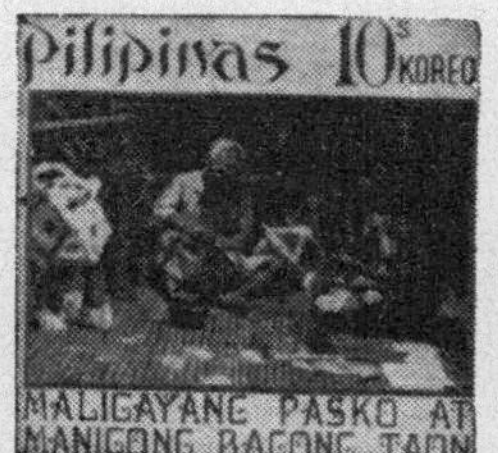

352 "The Lantern-makers" (J. Pineda)

1972. Christmas.

1284 **352** 10 s. multicoloured . . . 10 10
1285 30 s. multicoloured . . . 25 15
1286 50 s. multicoloured . . . 40 35

353 President Roxas and Wife

1972. 25th Anniv of Philippines' Red Cross.

1287 **353** 5 s. multicoloured . . . 10 10
1288 20 s. multicoloured . . . 15 15
1289 30 s. multicoloured . . . 25 20

1973. Nos. 948 and 1005 surch.

1290 **238** 10 s. on 6 s. multicoloured 15 10
1291 **256** 10 s. on 6 s. multicoloured 15 10

1973. Presidential Sayings (8th issue). As T **233**, but with portrait and saying changed.

1292 10 s. black and yellow . . . 15 10
1293 30 s. black and mauve . . . 35 15

PORTRAIT AND SAYING: 10 s., 30 s. Pres. Garcia, "I would rather be right than successful".

355 University Building

1973. 60th Anniv of St. Louis University, Baguio City.
1294 **355** 5 s. multicoloured . . . 10 10
1295 10 s. multicoloured . . . 10 10
1296 75 s. multicoloured . . . 50 45

356 Col. J. Villamor and Air Battle

1973. Villamor Commemoration.
1297 **356** 10 s. multicoloured . . . 15 10
1298 2 p. multicoloured . . . 1·40 1·25

1973. Various stamps surch.
1299 **252** 5 s. on 6 s. multicoloured 10 10
1300 **266** 5 s. on 6 s. multicoloured 10 10
1301 **318** 15 s. on 10 s. red & black 15 10

359 Actor and Stage Performance

1973. 1st "Third-World" Theatre Festival, Manila.
1302 **359** 5 s. multicoloured . . . 10 10
1303 10 s. multicoloured . . . 10 10
1304 50 s. multicoloured . . . 35 20
1305 70 s. multicoloured . . . 55 30

1973. President Marcos' Anti-Smuggling Campaign. No. 1017 surch.
1306 5 s. on 6 s. blue 15 10

1973. 10th Death Anniv of John F. Kennedy. No. 989 surch.
1307 5 s. on 6 s. multicoloured . . 15 10

1973. Compulsory Tax Stamps. T.B. Relief Fund. Nos. 1241/2 surch.
1308 15 s. + 5 s. on 10 s. + 5 s. multicoloured 15 15
1309 60 s. + 5 s. on 40 s. + 5 s. multicoloured 40 40

363 Proclamation Scenes

1973. 75th Anniv of Philippine Independence.
1310 **363** 15 s. multicoloured . . . 10 10
1311 45 s. multicoloured . . . 25 25
1312 90 s. multicoloured . . . 55 55

364 M. Agoncillo (maker of first national flag)

365 Imelda Marcos

1973. Perf or imperf.
1313 – 15 s. violet 15 10
1455 – 30 s. blue 15 10
1456 – 30 s. red 15 10
1314 **364** 60 s. brown 35 35
1315 – 90 s. blue 50 25
1457 – 90 s. green 20 10
1316 – 1 p. 10 blue 65 30
1458 – 1 p. 20 red 35 15
1317 – 1 p. 50 red 90 75
1318 – 1 p. 50 brown 90 35
1319 – 1 p. 80 green . . . . . 1·00 95
1320 – 5 p. blue . . . . 2·75 2·75

DESIGNS: 15 s. Gabriela Silang (revolutionary); 30 s. (No. 1455) Jose Rizal; 30 s. (No. 1456) Rajah Kalantiaw (Panay Chief); 90 s. (No. 1315) Teodoro Yangeo (businessman); 90 s. (No. 1457) Lope K. Santos (father of grammar); 1 p. 10, Pio Valenzuela (physician); 1 p. 20, Gregoria de Jesus (patriot); 1 p. 50, (No. 1317) Pedro Paterno (revolutionary); 1 p. 50, (No. 1318) Teodora Alonso (mother of Jose Rizal); 1 p. 80 E. Evangelista (revolutionary); 5 p. F. M. Guerrero (writer).

1973. Projects Inaugurated by Sra Imelda Marcos.
1321 **365** 15 s. multicoloured . . . 10 10
1322 50 s. multicoloured . . . 30 30
1323 60 s. multicoloured . . . 35 35

366 Malakanyang Palace

1973. Presidential Palace, Manila.
1324 **366** 15 s. mult (postage) . . 10 10
1325 50 s. multicoloured . . . 25 25
1326 60 s. multicoloured (air) 35 35

367 Interpol Emblem 368 Scouting Activities

1973. 50th Anniv of International Criminal Police Organization (Interpol).
1327 **367** 15 s. multicoloured . . . 15 10
1328 65 s. multicoloured . . . 35 20

1973. Golden Jubilee of Philippine Boy Scouts. Perf or imperf.
1329 **368** 15 s. brown and green . 15 10
1330 – 65 s. blue and brown . . 35 30
DESIGN: 65 s. Scouts reading brochure.

369 Bank Emblem, Urban and Agricultural Landscapes

1974. 25th Anniv of Central Bank of the Philippines. Multicoloured.
1331 15 s. Type **369** 15 10
1332 60 s. Bank building, 1949 . . 35 20
1333 1 p. 50 Bank complex, 1974 90 50

370 "Maria Clara" Costume 373 Map of South-East Asia

1974. U.P.U. Centenary. Philippines' Costumes. Multicoloured.
1334 15 s. Type **370** 15 10
1335 60 s. "Balintawak" 35 20
1336 80 s. "Malong" 50 30

1974. Philatelic Week (1973). No. 1303 surch **1973 PHILATELIC WEEK** and value.
1337 **359** 15 s. on 10 s. multicoloured 15 10

1974. 25th Anniv of Philippine "Lionism". Nos. 1297 and 1180 surch **PHILIPPINE LIONISM 1949-1974**, Lion emblem and value.
1338 **356** 15 s. on 10 s. multicoloured 15 10
1339 – 45 s. on 40 s. red 25 20

1974. Asian Paediatrics Congress, Manila. Perf or imperf.
1340 **373** 30 s. red and blue . . . 15 15
1341 1 p. red and green . . . 55 35

374 Gen. Valdes and Hospital

1974. Obligatory Tax. T.B. Relief Fund. Perf or imperf.
1342 **374** 15 s. + 5 s. green & red . 15 15
1343 1 p. 10 + 5 s. blue & red 25 15

1974. Nos. 974, 1024 and 1026 surch.
1344 **246** 5 s. on 3 s. green 15 10
1345 **263** 5 s. on 6 s. mult. 15 10
1346 **264** 5 s. on 6 s. mult. 15 10

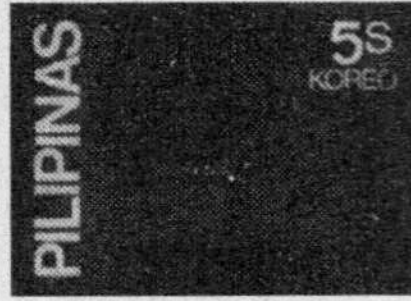

378 W.P.Y. Emblem

1974. World Population Year. Perf or imperf.
1347 **378** 5 s. black and orange . . 10 10
1348 2 p. blue and green . . . 1·00 55

379 Red Feather Emblem

1974. 25th Anniv of Community Chest Movement in the Philippines. Perf or imperf.
1349 **379** 15 s. red and blue 10 10
1350 40 s. red and green . . . 25 15
1351 45 s. red and brown . . . 35 15

381 Sultan Mohammad Kudarat Map, Malayan Prau and Order

1975. Sultan Kudarat of Mindanao Commem.
1352 **381** 15 s. multicoloured . . . 15 10

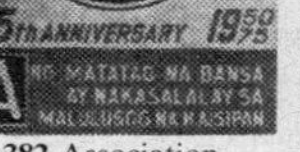
382 Association Emblem 383 Rafael Palma

1975. 25th Anniv of Philippine Mental Health Association. Perf or imperf.
1353 **382** 45 s. green and orange . . 20 15
1354 1 p. green and purple . . 45 35

1975. Birth Centenary of Rafael Palma (educationalist and statesman). Perf or imperf.
1355 **383** 15 s. green 15 10
1356 30 s. brown 15 10

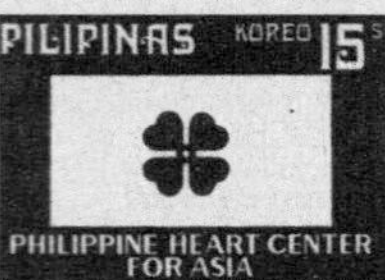

384 Heart Centre Emblem

1975. Inauguration of Philippine Heart Centre for Asia, Quezon City. Perf or imperf.
1356 **384** 15 s. red and blue 15 10
1357 50 s. red and green . . . 20 20

385 Cadet in Full Dress, and Academy Building

1975. 70th Anniv of Philippine Military Academy.
1358 **385** 15 s. multicoloured . . . 15 10
1359 45 s. multicoloured . . . 40 25

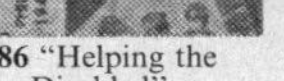

386 "Helping the Disabled" 397 Planting Sapling

1975. 25th Anniv (1974) of Philippines Orthopaedic Association.
1360 **386** 45 s. green 20 15
1361 – 45 s. green (19×35 mm) 20 15
1362 – 45 s. green (19×35 mm) 20 15
1363 – 45 s. green (19×35 mm) 20 15
1364 – 45 s. green 20 15
1365 – 45 s. green 20 15
1366 – 45 s. green (19×35 mm) 20 15
1367 – 45 s. green (19×35 mm) 20 15
1368 – 45 s. green (19×35 mm) 20 15
1369 – 45 s. green 20 15
DESIGNS: Nos. 1361/9. Further details of the mural as Type **386**.
Nos. 1360/9 were issued together se-tenant in blocks of ten (5×2) forming a composite design within the sheet.

1975. Nos. 1153 and 1342/3 surch with Cross of Lorraine and new value.
1370 **374** 5 s. on 15 s. + 5 s. green and red 10 10
1371 **308** 60 s. on 70 s. + 5 s. multicoloured 25 25
1372 **374** 1 p. on 1 p. 10 + 5 s. blue and red 30 25

1975. Forest Conservation. Multicoloured.
1373 45 s. Type **397** 25 15
1374 45 s. Sapling and tree-trunks 25 15

398 Jade Vine 399 Imelda Marcos and I.W.Y. Emblem

1975.
1375 **398** 15 s. multicoloured . . . 15 10

1975. International Women's Year.
1376 **399** 15 s. black, blue & dp bl 15 15
1377 80 s. black, blue and pink 45 35

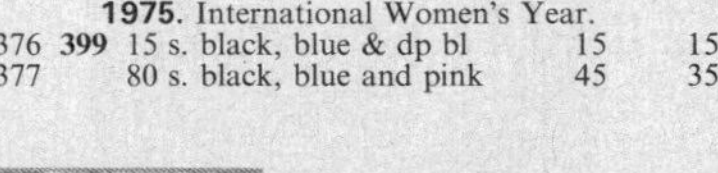

400 Commission Badge 401 Angat River Barrage

1975. 75th Anniv of Civil Service Commission.
1378 **400** 15 s. multicoloured . . . 15 15
1379 50 s. multicoloured . . . 25 15

1975. 25th Anniv of International Irrigation and Drainage Commission.
1380 **401** 40 s. blue and orange . . 15 15
1381 1 p. 50 blue and mauve . 50 40

402 "Welcome to Manila!" 403 N. Romualdez (legislator and writer)

1975. Hong Kong and Shanghai Banking Corporation. Cent of operations in the Philippines.
1382 **402** 1 p. 50 multicoloured . . 1·25 35

1975. Birth Centenaries.
1383 **403** 60 s. lilac 15 10
1384 – 90 s. mauve 35 15
DESIGN: 90 s. General G. del Pilar.

405 Boeing 747-100 Airliner and Martin M-130 Flying Boat

1975. 40th Anniv of First Trans-Pacific China Clipper Airmail Flight. San Francisco–Manila.
1385 **405** 60 s. multicoloured . . . 35 20
1386 1 p. 50 multicoloured . . 90 55

1975. Airmail Exn. Nos. 1314 and 1318 optd **AIRMAIL EXHIBITION NOV. 22-DEC. 9.**
1387 **364** 60 s. brown 25 25
1388 – 1 p. 50 brown 55 55

407 APO Emblem **408** E. Jacinto

1975. 25th Anniv of APO Philatelic Society.
1389 **407** 5 s. multicoloured . . . 15 10
1390 1 p. multicoloured . . . 45 35

1975. Birth Centenary of Emilio Jacinto (military leader).
1391 **408** 65 s. mauve 20 10

409 San Agustin Church **410** "Conducting" Hands

1975. Holy Year. Churches.
1392 **409** 20 s. turquoise 15 15
1393 – 30 s. black and yellow . . 15 15
1394 – 45 s. red and black . . . 20 20
1395 – 60 s. brown, yell & blk . 25 20
DESIGNS—HORIZ: 30 s. Morong Church; 45 s. Taal Basilica. VERT: 60 s. San Sebastian Church.

1976. 50th Anniv of Manila Symphony Orchestra.
1396 **410** 5 s. multicoloured . . . 10 10
1397 50 s. multicoloured . . . 35 25

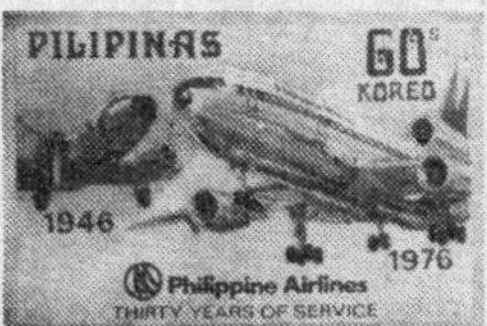

411 Douglas DC-3 and DC-10

1976. 30th Anniv of Philippines Airlines (P.A.L.).
1398 **411** 60 s. multicoloured . . . 30 15
1399 1 p. 50 multicoloured . . 1·10 55

412 Felipe Agoncillo (statesman) **413** University Building

1976. Felipe Agoncillo. Commemoration.
1400 **412** 1 p. 60 black 90 25

1976. 75th Anniv of National University.
1401 **413** 45 s. multicoloured . . . 20 15
1402 60 s. multicoloured . . . 35 20

MORE DETAILED LISTS

are given in the Stanley Gibbons Catalogues referred to in the country headings. For lists of current volumes see introduction

414 "Foresight Prevents Blindness" **415** Emblem on Book

1976. World Health Day.
1403 **1414** 15 s. multicoloured . . 15 10

1976. 75th Anniv of National Archives.
1404 **415** 1 p. 50 multicoloured . 80 65

416 College Emblem and University Tower

1976. 50th Anniv of Colleges of Education and Science, Saint Thomas's University.
1405 **416** 15 s. multicoloured . . . 15 10
1406 50 s. multicoloured . . . 25 20

417 College Building

1976. 50th Anniv of Maryknoll College.
1407 **417** 15 s. multicoloured . . . 15 10
1408 1 p. 50 multicoloured . 75 55

1976. Olympic Games, Montreal. Surch **Montreal 1976 21st OLYMPICS, CANADA.**
1409 **348** 15 s. on 10 s. mult. . . . 15 10

419 Constabulary Headquarters, Manila

1976. 75th Anniv of Philippine Constabulary.
1410 **419** 15 s. multicoloured . . . 15 15
1411 60 s. multicoloured . . . 35 20

420 Land and Aerial Surveying

1976. 75th Anniv of Lands Bureau.
1412 **420** 80 s. multicoloured . . . 35 35

422 Badges of Banking Organizations

1976. International Monetary Fund and World Bank joint Board of Governors Annual Meeting, Manila.
1414 **422** 60 s. multicoloured . . . 25 20
1415 1 p. 50 multicoloured . 75 55

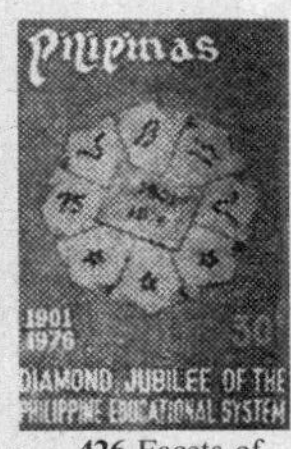

423 Virgin of Antipolo **426** Facets of Education

425 "Going to Church"

1976. 350th Anniv of "Virgin of Antipolo".
1416 **423** 30 s. multicoloured . . . 15 15
1417 90 s. multicoloured . . . 35 25

1976. Philatelic Week. Surch **1976 PHILATELIC WEEK.**
1418 **355** 30 s. on 10 s. mult . . . 15 15

1976. Christmas.
1419 **425** 15 s. multicoloured . . . 10 10
1420 30 s. multicoloured . . . 20 10

1976. 75th Anniv of Philippine Educational System.
1421 **426** 30 s. multicoloured . . . 15 10
1422 75 s. multicoloured . . . 35 25

1977. Surch.
1423 1 p. 20 on 1 p. 10 blue (No. 1316) 55 35
1424 3 p. on 5 p. blue (No. 1320) . 1·10 1·00

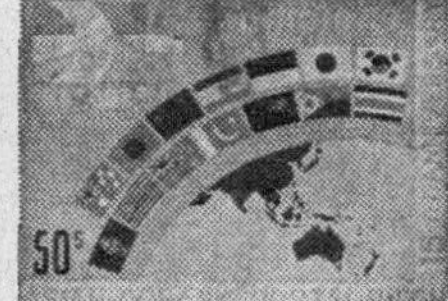

428 Jose Rizal **429** Flags, Map and Emblem

1977. Famous Filipinos. Multicoloured.
1425 30 s. Type **428** 15 10
1426 2 p. 30 Dr. Galicano Apacible 90 60

1977. 15th Anniv of Asian-Oceanic Postal Union.
1427 **429** 50 s. multicoloured . . . 15 10
1428 1 p. 50 multicoloured . . 55 45

430 Worker and Cogwheels **431** Commission Emblem

1977. 10th Anniv of Asia Development Bank.
1429 **430** 90 s. multicoloured . . . 45 35
1430 2 p. 30 multicoloured . . 90 75

1977. National Rural Credit Commission.
1431 **431** 30 s. multicoloured . . . 15 10

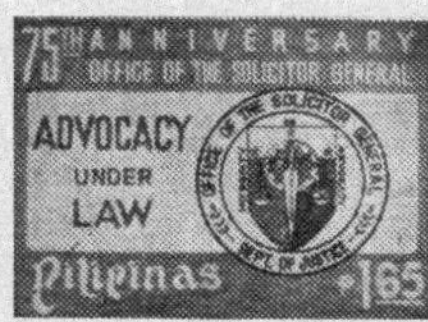

433 Solicitor-General's Emblem

1977. 75th Anniv of Office of Solicitor-General.
1433 **433** 1 p. 65 multicoloured . . 40 25

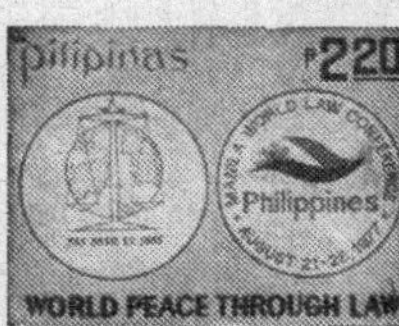

434 Conference Emblem

1977. World Law Conference, Manila.
1434 **434** 2 p. 20 multicoloured . . 70 25

435 A.S.E.A.N. Emblem

1977. 10th Anniv of Association of South East Asian Nationals (A.S.E.A.N.).
1435 **435** 1 p. 50 multicoloured . . 60 35

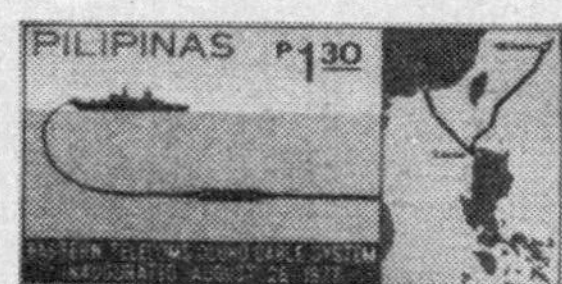

436 Cable Ship "Mercury" and Map

1977. Inauguration of O.L.U.H.O. Cable.
1437 **436** 1 p. 30 multicoloured . . 55 35

437 President Marcos

1977. 60th Birthday of President Marcos.
1438 **437** 30 s. multicoloured . . . 15 10
1439 2 p. 30 multicoloured . . 95 60

438 People raising Flag **439** Bishop Gregorio Aglipay (founder)

1977. 5th Anniv of "New Society".
1440 **438** 30 s. multicoloured . . . 15 10
1441 2 p. 30 multicoloured . . 95 60

1977. 75th Anniv of Aglipayan Church.
1442 **439** 30 s. multicoloured . . . 10 10
1443 90 s. multicoloured . . . 35 20

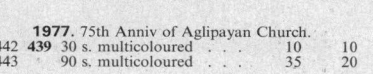

441 Fokker F.7 Trimotor "General New" and World Map

1977. 50th Anniv of Pan-Am International Air Service.
1445 **441** 2 p. 30 multicoloured . . 90 55

442 Eight-pointed Star and Children **445** University Badge

444 Scouts and Map of Philippines

1977. Christmas.
1446 **442** 30 s. multicoloured . . . 15 10
1447 45 s. multicoloured . . . 25 15

1977. Philatelic Week. Surch **1977 PHILATELIC WEEK.**
1448 **407** 90 s. on 1 p. multicoloured 35 20

1977. National Scout Jamboree.
1449 **444** 30 s. multicoloured . . . 35 15

1978. 50th Anniv of Far Eastern University.

1450 **445** 30 s. multicoloured . . . 15 10

446 Sipa Player

1978. "Sipa" (Filipino ball game).

1451 **446** 5 s. multicoloured . . . 10 10

1452 – 10 s. multicoloured . . . 10 10

1453 – 40 s. multicoloured . . . 20 10

1454 – 75 s. multicoloured . . . 40 15

DESIGNS: Nos. 1452/4, Different players.

Nos. 1451/4 were issued together se-tenant forming a composite design.

448 Arms of Meycauayan

1978. 400th Anniv of Meycauayan.

1459 **448** 1 p. 05 multicoloured . . 35 20

449 Horse-drawn Mail Cart

1978. "CAPEX 78" International Philatelic Exhibition, Toronto. Multicoloured.

1460 2 p. 50 Type **449** . . . . . . 1·00 65

1461 5 p. Filipino vinta (sailing canoe) . . . . 2·75 2·00

450 Andres Bonifacio Monument (G. Tolentino)

1978. Andres Bonifacio Monument.

1463 **450** 30 s. multicoloured . . . 15 10

451 Knight, Rook and Globe

1978. World Chess Championship, Baguio City.

1464 **451** 30 s. red and violet . . . 15 10

1465 2 p. red and violet . . . 50 35

452 Miner

1978. 75th Anniv of Benguet Consolidated Mining Company.

1466 **452** 2 p. 30 multicoloured . . 1·25 50

453 Pres. Quezon **455** Pres. Osmena

454 Law Association and Conference Emblems

1978. Birth Centenary of Manuel L. Quezon (former President).

1467 **453** 30 s. multicoloured . . . 15 10

1468 1 p. multicoloured . . . 35 15

1978. 58th International Law Association Conference, Manila.

1469 **454** 2 p. 30 multicoloured . 80 55

1978. Birth Centenary of Sergio Osmena (former President).

1470 **455** 30 s. multicoloured . . . 15 10

1471 1 p. multicoloured . . . 35 15

456 Map of Cable Route and Cable Ship "Mercury"

1978. Inauguration of Philippines–Singapore Submarine Cable.

1472 **456** 1 p. 40 multicoloured . 65 25

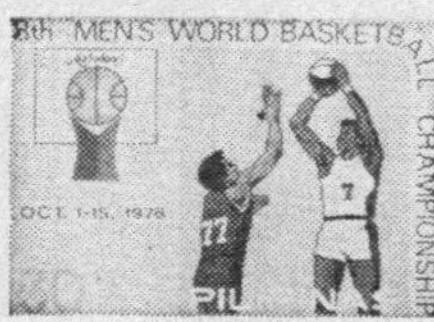

457 Basketball

1978. 8th Men's World Basketball Championships.

1473 **457** 30 s. multicoloured . . . 15 10

1474 2 p. 30 multicoloured . . 80 55

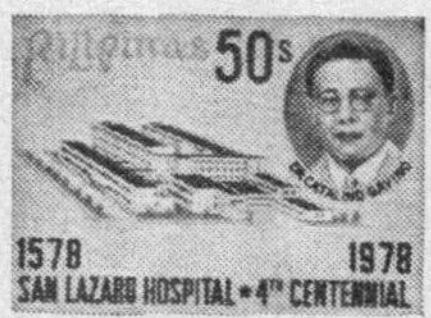

458 Dr. Catalino Gavino and Hospital

1978. 400th Anniv of San Lazaro Hospital.

1475 **458** 50 s. multicoloured . . . 20 10

1476 90 s. multicoloured . . . 35 15

459 Nurse vaccinating Child **461** Man making Telephone-call, Map and Satellite

1978. Global Eradication of Smallpox.

1477 **459** 30 s. multicoloured . . . 15 10

1478 1 p. 50 multicoloured . . 60 35

1978. Philatelic Week. No. 1391 surch **1978 PHILATELIC WEEK 60s.**

1479 **408** 60 s. on 65 s. mauve . . 25 10

1978. 50th Anniv of Philippines Long Distance Telephone Company. Multicoloured.

1480 30 s. Type **461** 20 10

1481 2 p. Woman on telephone and globe 65 45

462 Family travelling in Ox-drawn Cart

1978. Decade of the Filipino Child.

1482 **462** 30 s. multicoloured . . . 10 10

1483 1 p. 35 multicoloured . . 55 20

463 Spanish Colonial Church and Arms

1978. 400th Anniv of Agoo Town.

1484 **463** 30 s. multicoloured . . . 15 10

1485 45 s. multicoloured . . . 20 15

464 Church and Arms

1978. 400th Anniv of Balayan Town.

1486 **464** 30 s. multicoloured . . . 10 10

1487 90 s. multicoloured . . . 35 15

465 Family and Houses **466** Dr. Sison

1978. 30th Anniv of Declaration of Human Rights.

1488 **465** 30 s. multicoloured . . . 10 10

1489 3 p. multicoloured . . . 1·10 65

1978. Dr. Honoria Acosta Sison (first Filipino woman physician) Commemoration.

1490 **466** 30 s. multicoloured . . . 15 10

467 "Chaetodon trifasciatus"

1978. Fishes. Multicoloured.

1491 30 s. Type **467** 10 10

1492 1 p. 20 "Balistoides niger" . . 45 15

1493 2 p. 20 "Rhinecanthus aculeatus" 75 35

1494 2 p. 30 "Chelmon rostratus" . 80 45

1495 5 p. "Chaetodon mertensi" . 1·75 95

1496 5 p. "Euxiphipos xanthometapon" . . . . . 1·75 95

468 Carlos P. Romulo

1979. 80th Anniv of Carlos P. Romulo (1st Asian President of U.N. General Assembly).

1497 **468** 30 s. multicoloured . . . 10 10

1498 2 p. multicoloured . . . 90 45

469 Cogwheel (Rotary Emblem) **470** Rosa Sevilla de Alvero

1979. 60th Anniv of Manila Rotary Club.

1499 **469** 30 s. multicoloured . . . 15 10

1500 2 p. 30 multicoloured . . 95 35

1979. Birth Centenary of Rosa Sevilla de Alvero (writer and educator).

1501 **470** 30 s. mauve 15 10

471 Burning-off Gas and Map

1979. 1st Philippine Oil Production. Nido Complex.

1502 **471** 30 s. multicoloured . . . 20 10

1503 45 s. multicoloured . . . 30 15

472 Merrill's Fruit Dove

1979. Philippine Birds. Multicoloured.

1504 30 s. Type **472** 30 15

1505 1 p. 20 Brown tit-babbler . . 55 45

1506 2 p. 20 Mindoro zone-tailed pigeon . . . . 1·00 50

1507 2 p. 30 Steere's pitta . . . . 1·10 55

1508 5 p. Koch's pitta and red-breasted pitta . . . . . . 2·40 1·25

1509 5 p. Great eared nightjar . . 2·40 1·25

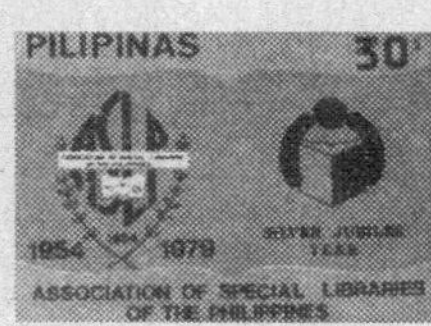

473 Association Emblem

1979. 25th Anniv of Association of Special Libraries of the Philippines.

1510 **473** 30 s. green, black & yell 10 10

1511 75 s. green, black & yell 25 10

1512 1 p. green, black & orge 40 15

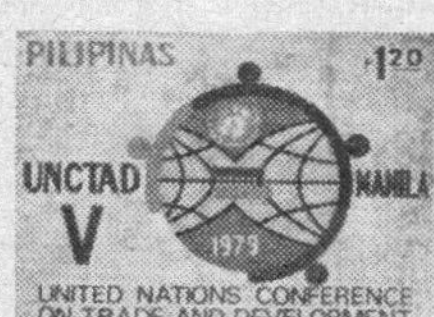

474 Conference Emblem

1979. 5th U.N. Conference on Trade and Development, Manila.

1513 **474** 1 p. 20 multicoloured . . 35 15

1514 2 p. 30 multicoloured . . 90 35

475 Malay Civet

1979. Philippine Animals. Multicoloured.

1515 30 s. Type **475** 10 10

1516 1 p. 20 Crab-eating macaque 45 20

1517 2 p. 20 Javan pig 75 40

1518 2 p. 30 Leopard cat 80 45

1519 5 p. Oriental small-clawed otter 1·75 95

1520 5 p. Malayan pangolin . . . 1·75 95

476 Dish Aerial

1979. World Telecommunications Day. Mult.

1521 90 s. Type **476** 30 10

1522 1 p. 30 World Map 40 15

477 Mussaenda "Dona Evangelina"

1979. Cultivated Mussaendas. Multicoloured.
1523 30 s. Type **477** 10 10
1524 1 p. 20 "Dona Esperanza" . 45 15
1525 2 p. 20 "Dona Hilaria" . . . 75 35
1526 2 p. 30 "Dona Aurora" . . . 80 45
1527 5 p. "Ginning Imelda" . . . 1·75 95
1528 5 p. "Dona Trining" . . . . 1·75 95

478 Manila Cathedral

1979. 400th Anniv of Archdiocese of Manila.
1529 **478** 30 s. multicoloured . . . 10 10
1530 75 s. multicoloured . . . 25 10
1531 90 s. multicoloured . . . 35 15

479 "Bagong Lakas" (patrol boat)

1979. Philippine Navy Foundation Day.
1532 **479** 30 s. multicoloured . . . 25 10
1533 45 s. multicoloured . . . 35 15

1979. Air. 1st Scout Philatelic Exhibition. 25th Anniv of 1st National Jamboree. Surch **1ST SCOUT PHILATELIC EXHIBITION, JULY 4.14.1979 QUEZON CITY AIRMAIL 90s.**
1534 **188** 90 s. on 6 c. + 4 c. red on cream 30 30

481 Afghan Hound

1979. Cats and Dogs. Multicoloured.
1536 30 s. Type **481** 10 10
1537 90 s. Striped tabby cat . . . 35 15
1538 1 p. 20 Dobermann pinscher . 45 20
1539 2 p. 20 Siamese cat 80 25
1540 2 p. 30 Alsatian 90 75
1541 5 p. Chinchilla cat . . . . . 1·75 90

482 Drug Addict breaking Manacles
483 Children flying Kites

1979. "Fight Drug Abuse".
1542 **482** 30 s. multicoloured . . . 10 10
1543 90 s. multicoloured . . . 35 15
1544 1 p. 05 multicoloured . . 40 20

1979. International Year of the Child. Multicoloured.
1545 15 s. Type **483** 10 10
1546 20 s. Boys fighting with catapults 15 10
1547 25 s. Girls dressing-up 15 10
1548 1 p. 20 Boy playing policeman 35 15

484 Hands holding Emblems
485 Anniversary Medal, and 1868 Coin

1979. 80th Anniv of Methodism in the Philippines.
1549 **484** 30 s. multicoloured . . . 15 10
1550 1 p. 35 multicoloured . 45 15

1979. 50th Anniv of Philippine Numismatic and Antiquarian Society.
1551 **485** 30 s. multicoloured . . . 15 10

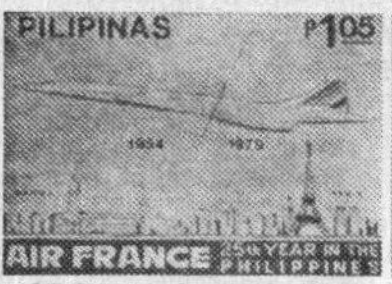

486 Concorde over Manila and Paris
488 "35" and I.A.T.A. Emblem

1979. 25th Anniv of "Air France" Service to the Philippines. Multicoloured.
1552 1 p. 05 Type **486** 60 30
1553 2 p. 20 Concorde over monument . . . . 1·40 55

1979. Philatelic Week. Surch **1979 PHILATELIC WEEK 90s.**
1554 **412** 90 s. on 1 p. 60 black . . 35 15

1979. 35th Annual General Meeting of International Air Transport Association, Manila.
1555 **488** 75 s. multicoloured . . . 30 15
1556 2 p. 30 multicoloured . 85 60

489 Bureau of Local Government Emblem
490 Christmas Greetings

1979. Local Government Year.
1557 **489** 30 s. multicoloured . . . 15 10
1558 45 s. multicoloured . . . 20 15

1979. Christmas. Multicoloured.
1559 30 s. Type **490** 15 10
1560 90 s. Stars 40 25

491 Rheumatism Victim
492 Birthplace, and MacArthur Memorial Foundation

1980. Fourth Congress of Southeast Asia and Pacific Area League Against Rheumatism, Manila.
1561 **491** 30 s. multicoloured . . . 20 10
1562 90 s. multicoloured . . . 45 25

1980. Birth Centenary of General Douglas MacArthur. Multicoloured.
1563 30 s. Type **492** 15 10
1564 75 s. General MacArthur . . 35 15
1565 2 p. 30 Hat, pipe and glasses 1·10 70

493 Columbus and Emblem
495 Tirona, Benitez and University

494 Soldiers and Academy Emblem

1980. 75th Anniv of Knights of Columbus Organization.
1567 **493** 30 s. multicoloured . . . 20 10
1568 1 p. 35 multicoloured . 75 40

1980. 75th Anniv of Philippine Military Academy.
1569 **494** 30 s. multicoloured . . . 20 10
1570 1 p. 20 multicoloured . 65 30

1980. 60th Anniv of Philippine Women's University.
1571 **495** 30 s. multicoloured . . . 20 10
1572 1 p. 05 multicoloured . 55 25

496 Boats and Burning City

1980. 75th Anniv of Rotary International. Different sections of the Francisco painting.
1573 **496** 30 s. multicoloured . . . 20 10
1574 – 30 s. multicoloured . . . 20 10
1575 – 30 s. multicoloured . . . 20 10
1576 – 30 s. multicoloured . . . 20 10
1577 – 30 s. multicoloured . . . 20 10
1578 **496** 2 p. 30 multicoloured . . 1·25 55
1579 – 2 p. 30 multicoloured (As No. 1574) . . . . . . 1·25 55
1580 – 2 p. 30 multicoloured (As No. 1575) . . . . . . 1·25 55
1581 – 2 p. 30 multicoloured (As No. 1576) . . . . . . 1·25 55
1582 – 2 p. 30 multicoloured (As No. 1577) . . . . . . 1·25 55

Nos. 1573/7 and 1578/82 were issued together in se-tenant strips of five, each strip forming a composite design.

497 Mosque and Koran
498 Hand stubbing out Cigarette

1980. 600th Anniv of Islam in the Philippines.
1583 **497** 30 s. multicoloured . . . 20 10
1584 1 p. 30 multicoloured . 65 30

1980. World Health Day. Anti-Smoking Campaign.
1585 **498** 30 s. multicoloured . . . 20 10
1586 75 s. multicoloured . . . 35 20

499 Scouting Activities and Badge

1980. 40th Anniv of Girl Scouting in the Philippines.
1587 **499** 30 s. multicoloured . . . 20 10
1588 2 p. multicoloured . . . 55 25

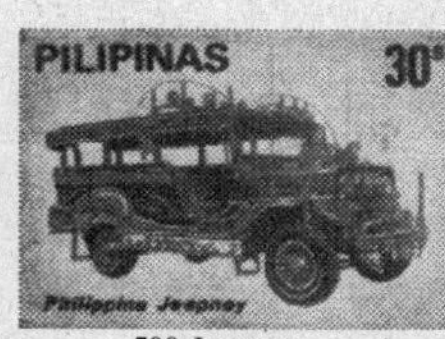

500 Jeepney
501 Association Emblem

1980. The Philippine Jeepney (decorated jeep). Multicoloured.
1589 30 s. Type **500** 20 10
1590 1 p. 20 Side view of Jeepney . 60 30

1980. 7th General Conference of International Association of Universities.
1591 **501** 30 s. multicoloured . . . 80 40
1592 2 p. 30 multicoloured . 1·25 1·10

1980. 82nd Anniv of Independence. Surch **Philippine Independence 82nd Anniversary 1898 1980.**
1593 **412** 1 p. 35 on 1 p. 60 black . 80 40
1594 1 p. 50 on 1 p. 80 green (No. 1319) 90 45

503 Map and Emblems
504 Filipinos and Emblem

1980. 46th Congress of International Federation of Library Associations and Institutions.
1595 **503** 30 s. green and black . . 20 10
1596 75 s. blue and black . . . 40 25
1597 2 p. 30 red and black . . 1·40 75

1980. 5th Anniv of Kabataang Barangay (New Society).
1598 **504** 30 s. multicoloured . . . 20 10
1599 40 s. multicoloured . . . 25 10
1600 1 p. multicoloured . . . 55 30

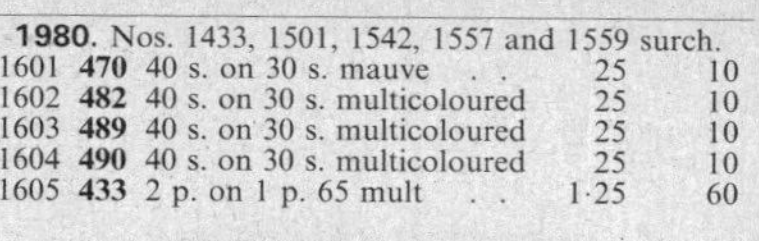

1980. Nos. 1433, 1501, 1542, 1557 and 1559 surch.
1601 **470** 40 s. on 30 s. mauve . . 25 10
1602 **482** 40 s. on 30 s. multicoloured 25 10
1603 **489** 40 s. on 30 s. multicoloured 25 10
1604 **490** 40 s. on 30 s. multicoloured 25 10
1605 **433** 2 p. on 1 p. 65 mult . . 1·25 60

506 Sunset, Filipino Vinta, and Conference Emblem

1980. World Tourism Conference, Manila.
1606 **506** 30 s. multicoloured . . . 25 10
1607 2 p. 30 multicoloured . . 1·25 80

507 Magnifying Glass and Stamps
508 U.N. Headquarters and Philippines' Flag

1980. Stamp Day.
1608 **507** 40 s. multicoloured . . . 25 10
1609 1 p. multicoloured . . . 60 30
1610 2 p. multicoloured . . . 1·25 60

1980. 35th Anniv of U.N.O.
1611 40 s. Type **508** 25 10
1612 3 p. 20 U.N. building, U.N. and Philippines' flags . . . . . 1·75 1·25

509 "Murex alabaster"
510 Interpol Emblem on Globe

1980. Shells. Multicoloured.
1613 40 s. Type **509** 25 10
1614 60 s. "Bursa bubo" 35 20
1615 1 p. 20 "Homalocantha zambol" 65 30
1616 2 p. "Xenophora pallidula" . 1·25 55

1980. 49th Session of Interpol General Assembly, Manila.
1617 **510** 40 s. multicoloured . . . 25 10
1618 1 p. multicoloured . . . 60 25
1619 3 p. 20 multicoloured . . 1·75 1·25

511 University and Faculty Emblems
513 Christmas Tree and Presents

1980. 75th Anniv of Central Philippine University. Multicoloured, background colour given.
1620 **511** 40 s. blue 20 10
1621 3 p. 20 green . . . . . 1·75 1·25

1980. Philatelic Week. No. 1377 surch **1980 PHILATELIC WEEK pl. 20.**
1622 **399** 1 p. 20 on 80 s. black, blue and pink 60 30

1980. Christmas.
1623 **513** 40 s. multicoloured . . . 20 10

1981. Various stamps surch.
1624 **244** 10 s. on 6 s. + 5 s. blue 15 10
1625 **462** 10 s. on 30 s. mult . . . 10 10
1626 **408** 40 s. on 65 s. mauve . . 25 10
1627 **458** 40 s. on 90 s. mult . . . 25 10
1628 **482** 40 s. on 90 s. mult . . . 25 10
1629 – 40 s. on 90 s. mult (No. 1560) 25 10
1630 **448** 40 s. on 1 p. 05 mult . . 25 10
1631 **462** 40 s. on 1 p. 35 mult . . 25 10
1632 **399** 85 s. on 80 s. black, blue and pink (No. 1377) . 45 25
1633 **408** 1 p. on 65 s. mauve (No. 1391) 65 30
1634 **401** 1 p. on 1 p. 50 blue and mauve 60 25
1635 **422** 1 p. on 1 p. 50 mult . . 65 30
1636 – 1 p. 20 on 1 p. 50 brown (No. 1318) 65 35
1637 **433** 1 p. 20 on 1 p. 65 mult . 65 35
1638 – 1 p. 20 on 1 p. 80 grn (No. 1319) 65 35
1639 **401** 2 p. on 1 p. 50 blue and mauve . . . . 1·25 50
1640 **434** 3 p. 20 on 2 p. 20 mult . 1·75 95

1981. 30th Anniv of APO Philatelic Society. Surch **NOV. 30, 1980 APO PHILATELIC SOCIETY PEARL JUBILEE 40S.**
1641 **455** 40 s. on 30 s. mult . . . 25 10

517 Von Stephan and U.P.U. Emblem

1981. 150th Birth Anniv of Heinrich von Stephan (founder of U.P.U.).
1642 **517** 3 p. 20 multicoloured . . 1·75 90

1981. Girls Scouts Camp. No. 1589 surch with **GSP RJASIA. PACIFIC REGIONAL CAMP PHILIPPINES DECEMBER 23, 1980, 40s.**
1643 **500** 40 s. on 30 s. mult . . . 25 10

518 Pope John Paul II **519** Parliamentary Debate

1981. Papal Visit. Multicoloured.
1644 90 s. Type **518** 45 25
1645 1 p. 20 Pope and cardinals . 60 30
1646 2 p. 30 Pope blessing crowd (horiz) . . . . 1·25 60
1647 3 p. Pope and Manila Cathedral (horiz) . . . . 1·60 75

1981. Inter-parliamentary Union Meeting, Manila.
1649 **519** 2 p. multicoloured . . . 1·25 55
1650 3 p. 20 multicoloured . . 1·75 1·00

520 Monument **521** President Aguinaldo's Car

1981. Jose Rizal Monument, Luneta Park.
1651 **520** 40 s. black, yellow & brn 20 10

1981. 50th Anniv of Philippine Motor Association. Multicoloured.
1652 40 s. Type **521** 25 10
1653 40 s. 1930 model car 25 10
1654 40 s. 1937 model car 25 10
1655 40 s. 1937 model car (different) 25 10

522 Bubble Coral

1981. Corals. Multicoloured.
1656 40 s. Type **522** 25 10
1657 40 s. Branching corals . . . 25 10
1658 40 s. Brain coral 25 10
1659 40 s. Table coral 25 10

523 President Marcos and Flag

1981. Inauguration of President Marcos.
1660 **523** 40 s. multicoloured . . . 25 10

524 St. Ignatius de Loyola (founder)

1981. 400th Anniv of Jesuits in the Philippines. Mult.
1662 40 s. Type **524** 25 10
1663 40 s. Dr. Jose P. Rizal and Intramuros Ateneo . . . 25 10
1664 40 s. Father Frederico Faura (director) and Manila Observatory 25 10
1665 40 s. Father Saturnino Urios (missionary) and map of Mindanao 25 10

525 F. R. Castro **526** Pres. Ramon Magsaysay

1981. Chief Justice F. R. Castro.
1667 **525** 40 s. multicoloured . . . 25 10

1981.
1668 – 1 p. brown and black . 65 25
1669 **526** 1 p. 20 brown and black 65 35
1670 – 2 p. red and black . . . 1·25 50
DESIGNS: 1 p. General Gregorio del Pilar; 2 p. Ambrosio R. Bautista.
See also Nos. 1699/1704, 1807/15, 1889 and 2031/3.

527 Man in Wheelchair **528** Early Filipino Writing

1981. International Year of Disabled Persons.
1671 **527** 40 s. multicoloured . . . 25 10
1672 3 p. 20 multicoloured . 1·75 1·00

1981. 24th International Red Cross Conference.
1673 **528** 40 s. black, red and brown 20 10
1674 2 p. black and red . . . 1·25 45
1675 3 p. 20 black, red and lilac 1·75 85

529 Isabel II Gate, Manila

1981.
1676 **529** 40 s. black, red and brown 25 10

530 Concert in Park

1981. Opening of Concert at Park 200.
1677 **530** 40 s. multicoloured . . . 25 10

1981. Philatelic Week. No. 1435 surch **1981 PHILATELIC WEEK** and new value.
1678 **435** 1 p. 20 on 1 p. 50 mult . 65 35

532 Running

1981. 11th South-east Asian Games, Manila.
1679 **532** 40 s. yellow, green & brn 25 10
1680 – 1 p. multicoloured . . . 65 25
1681 – 2 p. multicoloured . . . 1·40 50
1682 – 2 p. 30 multicoloured . . 1·40 65
1683 – 2 p. 80 multicoloured . . 1·75 75
1684 – 3 p. 20 violet and blue . . 1·75 95
DESIGNS: 1 p. Cycling; 2 p. President Marcos and Juan Antonio Samaranch (president of International Olympic Committee); 2 p. 30, Football; 2 p. 80, Shooting; 3 p. 20, Bowling.

533 Manila Film Centre

1982. Manila International Film Festival. Mult.
1685 40 s. Type **533** 25 10
1686 2 p. Front view of trophy . . 1·40 50
1687 3 p. 20 Side view of trophy . 1·90 95

534 Carriedo Fountain **535** Lord Baden-Powell (founder)

1982. Centenary of Manila Metropolitan Waterworks and Sewerage System.
1688 **534** 40 s. blue 25 10
1689 1 p. 20 brown 65 35

1982. 75th Anniv of Boy Scout Movement. Mult.
1690 40 s. Type **535** 25 10
1691 2 p. Scout . . . . 1·40 50

536 Embroidered Banner

1982. 25th Anniv of Children's Museum and Library Inc. Multicoloured.
1692 40 s. Type **536** 25 10
1693 1 p. 20 Children playing . . . 65 35

537 President Marcos presenting Sword of Honour

1982. Military Academy.
1694 **537** 40 s. multicoloured . . . 25 10
1695 1 p. multicoloured . . . 65 30

538 Soldier and Memorial

1982. Bataan Day. Multicoloured.
1696 40 s. Type **538** 25 10
1697 2 p. Doves and rifle . . . . . 1·40 50

1982. Portraits. As T **526**.
1699 40 s. blue 25 10
1700 1 p. red 65 30
1701 1 p. 20 brown 65 35
1702 2 p. purple . . . . 1·25 50
1703 2 p. 30 red . . . . 1·40 55
1704 3 p. 20 blue . . . . 1·50 95
DESIGNS: 40 s. Isabelo de los Reyes (founder of first workers' union); 1 p. Aurora Aragon Quezon (social worker and former First Lady); 1 p. 20, Francisco Dagohoy; 2 p. Juan Sumulong (politician); 2 p. 30, Professor Nicanor Abelardo (composer); 3 p. 20, General Vicente Lim.

539 Worker with Tower Award **541** Green Turtle

1982. Tower Awards (for "Blue Collar" Workers). Multicoloured.
1705 40 s. Type **539** 25 10
1706 1 p. 20 Cogwheel and tower award 65 35

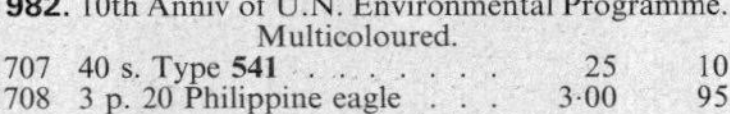
1982. 10th Anniv of U.N. Environmental Programme. Multicoloured.
1707 40 s. Type **541** 25 10
1708 3 p. 20 Philippine eagle . . . 3·00 95

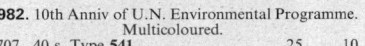

542 K.K.K. Emblem

1982. Inaug of Kilusang Kabuhayan at Kaunlaran (national livelihood movement).
1709 **542** 40 s. green, light green and black 25 10
See also Nos. 1816/17

543 Chemistry Apparatus and Emblem

1982. 50th Anniv of Adamson University.
1710 **543** 40 s. multicoloured . . . 25 10
1711 1 p. 20 multicoloured . . 65 35

544 Dr. Fernando G. Calderon and Emblems

1982. 75th Anniv of College of Medicine, University of the Philippines.
1712 **544** 40 s. multicoloured . . . 25 10
1713 3 p. 20 multicoloured . . 1·75 95

545 President Marcos **546** Hands supporting Family

1982. 65th Birthday of President Marcos.
1714 **545** 40 s. multicoloured . . . 25 10
1715 3 p. 20 multicoloured . . 1·75 95

1982. 25th Anniv of Social Security System.
1717 **546** 40 s. black, orange & blue 25 10
1718 1 p. 20 black, orange and green 65 35

547 Emblem and Flags forming Ear of Wheat

1982. 15th Anniv of Association of South East Asian Nations.
1719 **547** 40 s. multicoloured . . . 25 10

548 St. Theresa of Avila

1982. 400th Death Anniv of St. Theresa of Avila. Multicoloured.

1720 40 s. Type **548** 25 10
1721 1 p. 20 St. Theresa and map of Europe, Africa and Asia . 65 35
1722 2 p. As 1 p. 20 . . . . 1·40 50

549 St. Isabel College

1982. 350th Anniv of St. Isabel College.

1723 **549** 40 s. multicoloured . . . 25 10
1724 1 p. multicoloured . . . 65 30

550 President Marcos signing Decree and Tenant Family

1982. 10th Anniv of Tenant Emancipation Decree.

1725 **550** 40 s. green, brown & blk 25 10

551 "Reading Tree"

1982. Literacy Campaign.

1727 **551** 40 s. multicoloured . . . 25 10
1728 2 p. 30 multicoloured . . 1·40 50

552 Moriones Marinduque (helmeted heads)

1982. 43rd World Congress of Skal Clubs, Manila.

1729 40 s. Type **552** 25 10
1730 2 p. Head in feathered head-dress . . . . 1·40 50

553 Dancers with Parasols

1982. 25th Anniv of Bayanihan Folk Arts Centre. Multicoloured.

1731 40 s. Type **553** 35 10
1732 2 p. 80 Dancers (different) . . 1·50 70

554 Dr. Robert Koch and Bacillus

1982. Cent of Discovery of Tubercule Bacillus.

1733 **554** 40 s. red, blue & black . 25 10
1734 2 p. 80 multicoloured . . 1·75 75

INDEX

Countries can be quickly located by referring to the index at the end of this volume.

555 Father Christmas in Sleigh

1982. Christmas.

1735 **555** 40 s. multicoloured . . . 25 10
1736 1 p. multicoloured . . . 65 30

556 Presidential Couples and Flags

1982. State Visit of Pres. Marcos to United States.

1737 **556** 40 s. multicoloured . . . 20 10
1738 3 p. 20 multicoloured . 1·40 85

557 Woman with Sewing Machine

1982. U.N. World Assembly on Ageing.

1740a **557** 1 p. 20 green & orange 65 35
1741a – 2 p. red and blue . . . 1·40 50

DESIGN: 2 p. Man with carpentry tools.

558 Stamp and Magnifying Glass **559** Eulogio Rodriguez

1983. Philatelic Week.

1742 **558** 40 s. multicoloured . . . 25 10
1743 1 p. multicoloured . . . 65 30

1983. Birth Centenary of Eulogio Rodriguez (former President of Senate).

1744a **559** 40 s. multicoloured . . 25 10
1745 1 p. 20 multicoloured . 65 35

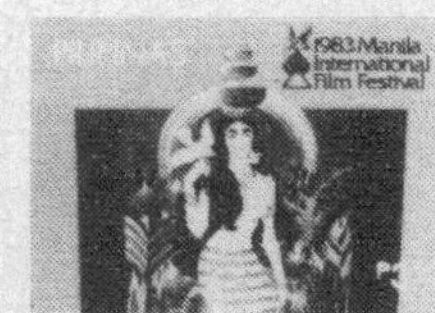

560 Symbolic Figure and Film Frame

1983. Manila International Film Festival.

1746a **560** 40 s. multicoloured . . 25 10
1747a 3 p. 20 multicoloured . 1·50 90

561 Monument

1983. 2nd Anniv of Beatification of Lorenzo Ruiz.

1748 **561** 40 s. yellow, red & blk . 25 10
1749 1 p. 20 multicoloured . 70 35

562 Early Printing Press **563** Emblem and Ship

1983. 390th Anniv of First Local Printing Press.

1750 **562** 40 s. green and black . . 25 10

1983. 25th Anniv of International Maritime Organization.

1751 **563** 40 s. red, blue & black . . 25 10

1983. 7th National Scout Jamboree. No. 1709 optd **7TH B S P NATIONAL JAMBOREE 1983**.

1752 **542** 40 s. green, light green and black 25 10

1983. Nos. 1360/9 surch.

1753 **386** 40 s. on 45 c. green . . . 25 10
1754 – 40 s. on 45 c. green . . . 25 10
1755 – 40 s. on 45 c. green . . . 25 10
1756 – 40 s. on 45 c. green . . . 25 10
1757 – 40 s. on 45 c. green . . . 25 10
1758 – 40 s. on 45 c. green . . . 25 10
1759 – 40 s. on 45 c. green . . . 25 10
1760 – 40 s. on 45 c. green . . . 25 10
1761 – 40 s. on 45 c. green . . . 25 10
1762 – 40 s. on 45 c. green . . . 25 10

566 Calculator Keys

1983. 11th International Organization of Supreme Audit Institutions Congress.

1763 **566** 40 s. deep blue, blue and silver 25 10
1764 – 2 p. 80 multicoloured . . 1·75 75

DESIGN: 2 p. 80, Congress emblem.

567 Smiling Children **568** Detail of Statue

1983. 75th Anniv of Philippine Dental Association.

1766 **567** 40 s. green, purple & brn 20 15

1983. 75th Anniv of University of the Philippines.

1767 **568** 40 s. brown and green . . 20 15
1768 – 1 p. 20 multicoloured . . 60 30

DESIGN: 1 p. 20, Statue and diamond.

569 Yasuhiro Nakasone and Pres. Marcos

1983. Visit of Japanese Prime Minister.

1769 **569** 40 s. multicoloured . . . 20 15

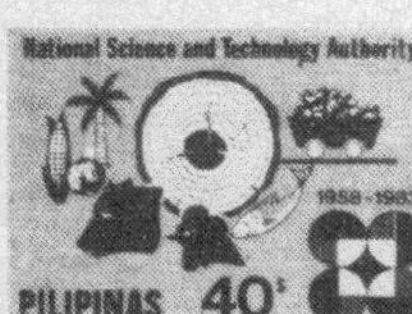

570 Agriculture and Natural Resources

1983. 25th Anniv of National Science and Technology Authority. Multicoloured.

1770 40 s. Type **570** 35 15
1771 40 s. Heart and medical products and food (Health and nutrition) 35 15
1772 40 s. Industrial complex and air (Industry and energy) . . . 35 15
1773 40 s. House, scientific equipment and book (Sciences and social science) 35 15

571 Globes and W.C.Y. Emblem

1983. World Communication Year.

1774 **571** 3 p. 20 multicoloured . . 1·75 85

572 Postman **573** Woman with Tambourine

1983. Bicent of Philippines Postal System.

1775 **572** 40 s. multicoloured . . . 20 15

1983. Christmas. Multicoloured.

1776 40 s. Type **579** 20 15
1777 40 s. Man turning spit (left side) 20 15
1778 40 s. Pig on spit 20 15
1779 40 s. Man turning spit (right side) 20 15
1780 40 s. Man with guitar . . . 20 15

Nos. 1776/80 were issued together in se-tenant strips of five within the sheet, each strip forming a composite design.

574 University Activities

1983. 50th Anniv of Xavier University.

1782 **574** 40 s. multicoloured . . . 20 15
1783 60 s. multicoloured . . . 35 15

575 Woman casting Vote **576** Workers

1983. 50th Anniv of Female Suffrage.

1784 **575** 40 s. multicoloured . . . 20 15
1785 60 s. multicoloured . . . 30 15

1983. 50th Anniv of Ministry of Labour and Employment.

1786 **576** 40 s. multicoloured . . . 20 15
1787 60 s. multicoloured . . . 30 15

577 Cutting Stamp from Envelope **578** Red-vented Cockatoo

1983. Philatelic Week. Multicoloured.

1788 50 s. Type **577** 45 20
1789 50 s. Sorting stamps 45 20
1790 50 s. Soaking stamps 45 20
1791 50 s. Hinging stamp 45 20
1792 50 s. Mounting stamp in album 45 20

1984. Parrots. Multicoloured.

1793 40 s. Type **578** 15 10
1794 2 p. 30 Guaiabero 65 35
1795 2 p. 80 Mountain racket-tailed parrot 85 35
1796 3 p. 20 Great-billed parrot . 1·00 40
1797 3 p. 60 Muller's parrot . . . 1·10 40
1798 5 p. Philippine hanging parrot 1·50 60

579 Princess Tarhata Kiram **580** Nun and Congregation

1984. 5th Death Anniv of Princess Tarhata Kiram.

1799 **579** 3 p. deep green, green and red 65 25

1984. 300th Anniv of Religious Congregation of the Virgin Mary.

1800 **580** 40 s. multicoloured . . . 15 15
1801 60 s. multicoloured . . . 15 15

581 Dona Concha Felix de Calderon

583 Manila

1984. Birth Centenary of Dona Concha Felix de Calderon.
1802 **581** 60 s. green and black . . 10 10
1803 3 p. 60 green and red . . 50 15

1984. Various stamps surch.
1804 **545** 60 s. on 40 s. multicoloured 15 10
1805 **558** 60 s. on 40 s. multicoloured 15 10
1806 – 3 p. 60 on 3 p. 20 blue (No. 1704) 80 30

1984. As Nos. 1700/4 but values changed, and new designs as T **526**.
1807 60 s. brown and black . . . 15 10
1808 60 s. violet and black . . . 15 10
1809 60 s. black 15 10
1810 60 s. blue 20 10
1811 1 p. 80 blue 25 15
1812 2 p. 40 red 35 15
1813 3 p. brown 35 15
1814 3 p. 60 red 45 15
1815 4 p. 20 purple 50 25
DESIGNS: No. 1807, General Artemio Ricarte; 1808, Teodoro M. Kalaw (politician); 1809, Carlos P. Garcia (fourth President); 1810, Quintin Paredes (senator); 1811, General Vicente Lim; 1812, Professor Nicanor Abelardo; 1813, Francisco Dagohoy; 1814, Aurora Aragon Quezon; 1815, Juan Sumulong.

1984.
1816 **542** 60 s. green, light green and black 15 10
1817 60 s. green, red and black 15 15

1984. 150th Anniv of Ayala Corporation.
1818 **583** 70 s. multicoloured . . . 20 10
1819 3 p. 60 multicoloured . . 50 15

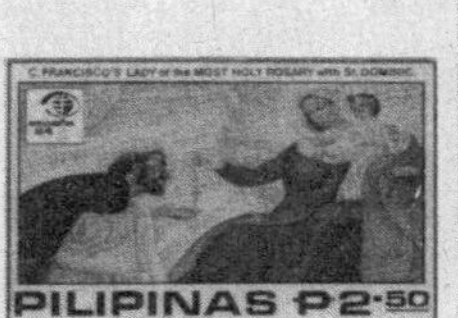

584 "Lady of the Most Holy Rosary with St. Dominic" (C. Francisco)

585 Maria Paz Mendoza Guazon

1984. "Espana 84" International Stamp Exhibition, Madrid. Multicoloured.
1820 2 p. 50 Type **584** 35 15
1821 5 p. "Spoliarum" (Juan Luna) 75 35

1984. Birth Centenary of Dr. Maria Paz Mendoza Guazon.
1823 **585** 60 s. red and blue . . . 15 10
1824 65 s. red and black . . . 15 10

586 "Adolias amlana"

1984. Butterflies. Multicoloured.
1825 60 s. Type **586** 20 10
1826 2 p. 40 "Papilio daedalus" . . 55 25
1827 3 p. "Prothoe franckii semperi" 70 25
1828 3 p. 60 "Troides magellanus" 85 30
1829 4 p. 20 "Yoma sabina vasuki" 1·00 40
1830 5 p. "Chilasa idaeoides" . . 1·10 45

1984. National Children's Book Day. Stamp from miniature sheet (The Monkey and the Turtle) surch **7-17-84 NATIONAL CHILDREN'S BOOK DAY**.
1831 7 p. 20 on 7 p. 50 multicoloured 1·40 80

1984. 420th Anniv of Philippine-Mexican Friendship. Stamp from miniature sheet surch **420TH PHIL-MEXICAN FRIENDSHIP 8.3.84**.
1832 7 p. 20 on 7 p. 50 multicoloured 1·40 80

589 Running

590 The Mansion

1984. Olympic Games, Los Angeles. Multicoloured.
1833 60 s. Type **589** 10 10
1834 2 p. 40 Boxing 40 25
1835 6 p. Swimming . . . . . . 1·10 55
1836 7 p. 20 Windsurfing . . . . 1·40 75
1837 8 p. 40 Cycling . . . . . . 1·60 80
1838 20 p. Running (woman athlete) 3·75 2·00

1984. 75th Anniv of Baguio City.
1840 **590** 1 p. 20 multicoloured . 25 15

1984. 300th Anniv of Our Lady of Holy Rosary Parish. Stamp from miniature sheet surch **9-1-84 300th YR O.L. HOLY ROSARY PARISH**.
1841 7 p. 20 on 7 p. 50 multicoloured 1·40 80

592 Electric Train on Viaduct

1984. Light Railway Transit.
1842 **592** 1 p. 20 multicoloured 20 15

593 Australian and Philippine Stamps and Koalas

1984. "Ausipex 84" International Stamp Exhibition, Melbourne.
1843 **593** 3 p. multicoloured . . . 55 25
1844 3 p. 60 multicoloured . . 65 30

1984. National Museum Week. Stamp from miniature sheet surch **NATIONAL MUSEUM WEEK 10-5-84**.
1846 7 p. 20 on 7 p. 50 multicoloured 1·40 80

1984. Asia Regional Conference of Rotary International. No. 1728 surch **14-17 NOV. 84 R.I. ASIA REGIONAL CONFERENCE**.
1847 **551** 1 p. 20 on 2 p. 30 mult . . 20 15

596 Gold Award

1984. Philatelic Week. Gold Award at "Ausipex 84" to Mario Que. Multicoloured.
1848 1 p. 20 Type **596** 25 15
1849 3 p. Page of Que's exhibit . 35 15

597 Caracao (canoes)

1984. Water Transport. Multicoloured.
1850 60 s. Type **597** 10 10
1851 1 p. 20 Junk 25 10
1852 6 p. Spanish galleon . . . . 1·10 55
1853 7 p. 20 Casco (Filipino cargo prau) . . . . 1·40 65
1854 8 p. 40 Early paddle-steamer 1·60 80
1855 20 p. Modern liner . . . . . 3·75 1·75

599 Anniversary Emblem

1984. 125th Anniv of Ateneo de Manila University.
1857 **599** 60 s. blue and gold . . . 20 10
1858 1 p. 20 blue and silver . 35 25

600 Virgin and Child

602 Abstract

601 Manila-Dagupan Steam Locomotive, 1892

1984. Christmas. Multicoloured.
1859 60 s. Type **600** 20 10
1860 1 p. 20 Holy Family 35 25

1984. Rail Transport. Multicoloured.
1861 60 s. Type **601** 15 10
1862 1 p. 20 Light Railway Transit train, 1984 . . . . 25 10
1863 6 p. Bicol express, 1955 . . . 1·10 55
1864 7 p. 20 Electric tram, 1905 . . 1·40 65
1865 8 p. 40 Commuter train, 1972 1·60 80
1866 20 p. Horse-drawn tram, 1898 3·75 1·75

1984. 10th Anniv of Philippine Jaycees' Ten Outstanding Men Awards. Multicoloured.
1867 60 s. brown background in circle 20 10
1868 60 s. Type **602** 20 10
1869 60 s. red background 20 10
1870 60 s. blue and purple background 20 10
1871 60 s. orange and brown background 20 10
1872 3 p. As No. 1867 . . . . . 40 25
1873 3 p. Type **602** 40 25
1874 3 p. As No. 1869 . . . . . 40 25
1875 3 p. As No. 1870 . . . . . 40 25
1876 3 p. As No. 1871 . . . . . 40 25

603 Tobacco Plant and Dried Leaf

1985. 25th Anniv of Philippine Virginia Tobacco Administration.
1877 **603** 60 s. multicoloured . . . 15 10
1878 3 p. multicoloured . . . 55 25

1985. Philatelic Week, 1984. Nos. 1848/9 optd **Philatelic Week, 1984**.
1879 **596** 1 p. 20 multicoloured . . 20 15
1880 – 3 p. multicoloured . . . 50 35

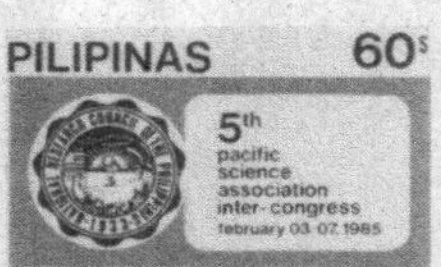

605 National Research Council Emblem

1985. Fifth Pacific Science Association Congress.
1881 **605** 60 s. black, blue and light blue 15 10
1882 1 p. 20 black, blue and orange 40 20

606 "Carmona retusa"

1985. Medicinal Plants. Multicoloured.
1883 60 s. Type **606** 10 10
1884 1 p. 20 "Orthosiphon aristatus" 20 15
1885 2 p. 40 "Vitex negundo" . . . 45 30
1886 3 p. "Aloe barbadensis" . . . 50 35
1887 3 p. 60 "Quisqualis indica" . . 65 45
1888 4 p. 20 "Blumea balsamifera" 75 45

1985. As T **526**.
1889 60 s. brown 20 10
1890 60 s. red 15 10

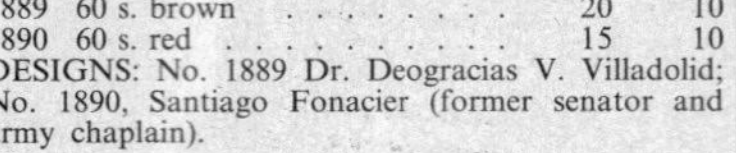

DESIGNS: No. 1889 Dr. Deogracias V. Villadolid; No. 1890, Santiago Fonacier (former senator and army chaplain).

607 "Early Bird" Satellite

1985. 20th Anniv of International Telecommunications Satellite Organization.
1896 **607** 60 s. multicoloured . . . 15 10
1897 3 p. multicoloured . . . 55 25

608 Piebalds

1985. Horses. Multicoloured.
1898 60 s. Type **608** 15 10
1899 1 p. 20 Palominos 25 10
1900 6 p. Bays . . . . 1·25 55
1901 7 p. 20 Browns . . . . . . 1·40 70
1902 7 p. 40 Greys . . . . 1·50 80
1903 20 p. Chestnuts . . . . . . 3·75 1·75

609 Emblem

1985. 25th Anniv of National Tax Research Centre.
1905 **609** 60 s. multicoloured . . . 20 10

610 Transplanting Rice

1985. 25th Anniv of International Rice Research Institute, Los Banos. Multicoloured.
1906 60 s. Type **610** 15 10
1907 3 p. Paddy-fields 35 15

611 Image of Holy Child of Cebu

1985. 420th Anniv of Filipino-Spanish Treaty. Mult.
1908 1 p. 20 Type **611** 25 15
1909 3 p. 60 Rajah Lupas and Miguel Lopez de Lagazpi signing treaty 40 15

613 Family planting Tree

1985. Tree Week. International Year of the Forest.
1911 **613** 1 p. 20 multicoloured . . 25 15

614 Battle of Bessang Pass

615 Vicente Orestes Romualdez

1985. 40th Anniv of Bessang Pass Campaign.
1912 **614** 1 p. 20 multicoloured . . 25 15

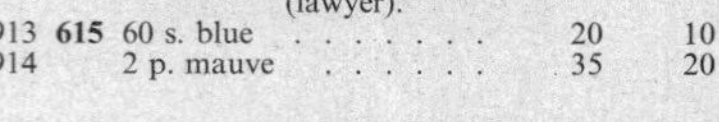

1985. Birth Centenary of Vicente Orestes Romualdez (lawyer).
1913 **615** 60 s. blue 20 10
1914 2 p. mauve 35 20

616 Early Anti-TB Label

1985. 75th Anniv of Philippine Tuberculosis Society. Multicoloured.
1915 60 s. Screening for TB, laboratory work, health education and inoculation . 15 10
1916 1 p. 20 Type **616** 25 15

1985. 45th Anniv of Girl Scout Charter. No. 1409 surch **45th ANNIVERSARY GIRL SCOUT CHARTER**, emblem and new value.
1921 **348** 2 p. 40 on 15 s. on 10 s. multicoloured 30 25
1922 4 p. 20 on 15 s. on 10 s. multicoloured 55 25
1923 7 p. 20 on 15 s. on 10 s. multicoloured 90 45

619 "Our Lady of Fatima"

1985. Marian Year. 2000th Birth Anniversary of Virgin Mary. Multicoloured.
1924 1 p. 20 Type **619** 25 15
1925 2 p. 40 "Our Lady of Beaterio" (Juan Bueno Silva) 30 15
1926 3 p. "Our Lady of Penafrancia" 35 20
1927 3 p. 60 "Our Lady of Guadalupe" 45 25

620 Fishing

1985. International Youth Year. Children's Paintings. Multicoloured.
1928 2 p. 40 Type **620** 30 15
1929 3 p. 60 Picnic 45 15

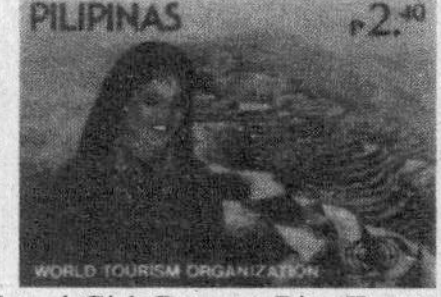

621 Local Girl, Banawe Rice Terraces and Emblem

1985. World Tourism Organization Congress, Sofia.
1930 **621** 2 p. 40 multicoloured . . 30 20

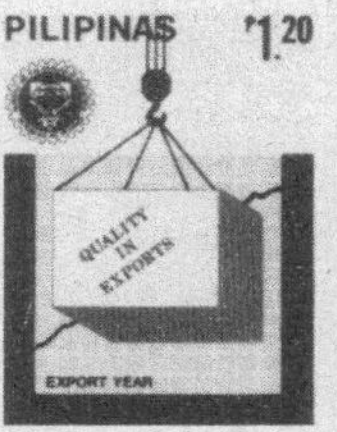

622 Export Graph and Crane lifting Crate

624 Emblem, Doves and Olive Branch

1985. Export Promotion Year.
1931 **622** 1 p. 20 multicoloured . . 25 15

1985. No. 1815 surch.
1932 3 p. 60 on 4 p. 20 purple . . 65 35

1985. 40th Anniv of U.N.O.
1933 **624** 3 p. 60 multicoloured . . 45 25

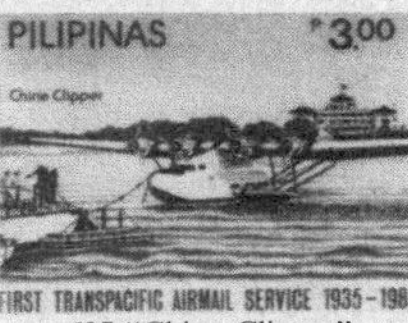

625 "China Clipper"

1985. 50th Anniv of First Trans-Pacific Commercial Flight (San Francisco-Manila). Multicoloured.
1934 3 p. Type **625** 35 20
1935 3 p. 60 Map showing route, "China Clipper" and anniversary emblem . . . 45 25

1985. Philatelic Week. Nos. 1863/4 surch **PHILATELIC WEEK 1985**, No. 1937 further optd **AIRMAIL**.
1936 60 s. on 6 p. mult (postage) . 15 10
1937 3 p. on 7 p. 20 mult (air) . . 55 30

627 Bible and Churches

1985. National Bible Week.
1938 **627** 60 s. multicoloured . . . 15 10
1939 3 p. multicoloured . . . 55 25

628 Panuluyan (enactment of search for an inn)

1985. Christmas. Multicoloured.
1940 60 s. Type **628** 15 10
1941 3 p. Pagdalaw (nativity) . . 55 25

629 Justice holding Scales

630 Rizal and "Noli Me Tangere"

1986. 75th Anniv of College of Law.
1942 **629** 60 s. mauve and black . 15 10
1943 3 p. green, red & black . 55 25
See also No. 2009.

1986. Centenary of Publication of "Noli Me Tangere" (Jose Rizal's first book).
1944 **630** 60 s. violet 10 10
1945 – 1 p. 20 green 25 20
1946 – 3 p. 60 brown 65 30
DESIGNS: 1 p. 20, 3 p. 60, Rizal, "To the Flowers of Heidelberg" and Heidelberg University.

631 Douglas DC-3, 1946

632 Oil Refinery

1986. 45th Anniv of Philippine Airlines. Each red, black and blue.
1947 60 s. Type **631** 10 10
1948 60 s. Douglas DC-4, 1946 . . 15 10
1949 60 s. Douglas DC-6, 1948 . . 15 10
1950 60 s. Vickers Viscount 784, 1957 15 10
1951 2 p. 40 Fokker Friendship, 1960 45 25
1952 2 p. 40 Douglas DC-8-50, 1962 45 25
1953 2 p. 40 B.A.C. One Eleven 500, 1964 . . . . 45 25
1954 2 p. 40 Douglas DC-10-30, 1974 45 25
1955 3 p. 60 Beech 18, 1941 . . 65 30
1956 3 p. 60 Boeing 747-200, 1980 65 30
See also No. 2013.

1986. 25th Anniv of Bataan Refinery.
1957 **632** 60 s. silver and green . . 15 10
1958 – 3 p. silver and blue . . . 55 25
DESIGN—HORIZ: 3 p. Refinery (different).

633 Emblem

1986. "Expo 86" World's Fair, Vancouver.
1959 **633** 60 s. multicoloured . . . 15 10
1960 3 p. multicoloured . . . 55 25

634 Emblem and Industrial and Agricultural Symbols

1986. 25th Anniv of Asian Productivity Organization.
1961 **634** 60 s. black, green & orge 15 10
1962 3 p. black, green & orge . 55 25
1963 3 p. brown (30 × 22 mm) . 55 25

635 1906 2 c. Stamp

637 Corazon Aquino, Salvador Laurel and Hands

1986. "Ameripex 86" International Stamp Exhibition, Chicago.
1964 **635** 60 s. green, black & yell . 15 10
1965 – 3 p. brown, black & grn . 55 25
DESIGN: 3 p. 1935 20 c. stamp.
See also No. 2006.

1986. "People Power". Multicoloured.
1966 60 s. Type **637** 10 10
1967 1 p. 20 Radio antennae, helicopter and people . . . 30 10
1968 2 p. 40 Religious procession . 40 20
1969 3 p. Crowds around soldiers in tanks 50 25

638 Monument and Paco and Taft Schools

1986. 75th Anniv of First La Salle School.
1971 **638** 60 s. brown, lilac and green 10 10
1972 – 2 p. 40 brown, blue & grn 40 20
1973 – 3 p. brown, yellow & grn 50 25
DESIGNS: 2 p. 40, St. Miguel Febres Cordero and Paco School; 3 p. St. Benilde and Taft school; 7 p. 20, Founding brothers of Paco school.

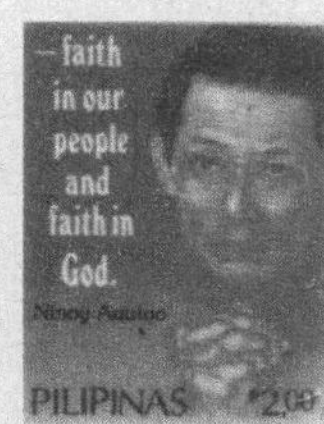

639 Aquino praying

640 "Vanda sanderiana"

1986. 3rd Death Anniv of Benigno S. Aquino, jun.
1975 – 60 s. green 10 10
1976 **639** 2 p. multicoloured . . . 30 15
1977 – 3 p. 60 multicoloured . . 60 25
DESIGNS—VERT: 60 s. Aquino. HORIZ: 3 p. 60, Aquino (different).
See also No. 2007.

1986. Orchids. Multicoloured.
1979 60 s. Type **640** 10 10
1980 1 p. 20 "Epigeneium lyonii" . 20 10
1981 2 p. 40 "Paphiopedilum philippinense" 40 20
1982 3 p. "Amesiella philippinense" 50 25

641 "Christ carrying the Cross"

642 Hospital

1986. 400th Anniv of Quiapo District.
1983 **641** 60 s. red, black and mauve 10 10
1984 – 3 p. 60 blue, blk & grn . 60 25
DESIGN: 3 p. 60, Quiapo Church.

1986. 75th Anniv of Philippine General Hospital.
1985 **642** 60 s. multicoloured . . . 10 10
1986 3 p. multicoloured . . . 50 25
See also No. 2012.

643 Comet and Earth

1986. Appearance of Halley's Comet. Multicoloured.
1987 60 s. Type **643** 10 10
1988 2 p. 40 Comet, Moon and Earth 40 25

644 Handshake

1986. 74th FDI World Dental Congress, Manila. Multicoloured.
1989 60 s. Type **644** 15 10
1990 3 p. Jeepney, Manila 65 35
See also Nos. 2008 and 2011.

645 Butterfly and Beetles

646 Emblem

1986. Philatelic Week and International Peace Year.
1991 **645** 60 s. multicoloured . . . 15 10
1992 – 1 p. blue and black . . . 25 10
1993 – 3 p. multicoloured . . . 65 35
DESIGNS—VERT: 1 p. Peace Year emblem. HORIZ: 3 p. Dragonflies.

1986. 75th Anniv of Manila Young Men's Christian Association.
1994 **646** 2 p. blue 35 15
1995 3 p. 60 red 65 30
See also No. 2010.

647 Old and New Buildings

1986. 85th Anniv of Philippine Normal College.
1996 – 60 s. multicoloured . . . 15 10
1997 **647** 3 p. 60 yellow, brn & bl . 80 40
DESIGN: 60 s. Old and new buildings (different).

648 Mother and Child

651 Emblem

650 Manila Hotel, 1912

1986. Christmas. Multicoloured.
1998 60 s. Type **648** 15 10
1999 60 s. Nativity scene and cow 15 10
2000 60 s. Mother and child with doves 15 10
2001 1 p. Mother and child receiving gifts (horiz) 25 10
2002 1 p. Mother and child beneath arch (horiz) 25 10
2003 1 p. Nativity scene and sheep (horiz) 25 10
2004 1 p. Shepherds around child in manger (horiz) 25 10

1987. No. 1944 surch.
2005 **630** 1 p. on 60 s. violet . . . 15 10

1987. As previous issues but smaller, 22 × 30 mm, 30 × 22mm or 32 × 22 mm (5 p. 50), and values and colours changed.
2006 – 75 s. green (As No. 1965) 10 10
2007 – 1 p. blue (As No. 1975) . 25 10
2008 **644** 3 p. 25 green 65 40
2009 **629** 3 p. 50 brown 75 45
2010 **646** 4 p. blue 65 35
2011 – 4 p. 75 green (As No. 1990) 85 40
2012 **642** 5 p. brown . . . . . . 1·00 60
2013 – 5 p. 50 blue (As No. 1956) 95 45

1987. 75th Anniv of Manila Hotel.
2014 **650** 1 p. brown and black . . 25 15
2015 – 4 p. multicoloured . . . 65 35
2016 – 4 p. 75 multicoloured . . 85 40
2017 – 5 p. 50 multicoloured . . 95 45
DESIGNS: 4 p. Hotel; 4 p. 75, Lobby; 5 p. 50, Staff in ante-lobby.

1987. 50th Anniv of International Eucharistic Congress, Manila. Multicoloured.
2018 75 s. Type **651** 10 10
2019 1 p. Emblem (different) . . . 15 10

1986 SALIGANG BATAS
652 Pres. Cory Aquino taking Oath

1987. Ratification of New Constitution.
2020 **652** 1 p. multicoloured . . . 25 15
2021 – 5 p. 50 blue & brown . . 1·10 55
DESIGN: 5 p. 50, Constitution on open book and dove.
See also No. 2060.

653 Dr. Jose P. Laurel (founder) and Tower

1987. 35th Anniv of Lyceum.
2022 **653** 1 p. multicoloured . . . 10 10
2023 2 p. multicoloured . . . 20 15

654 City Seal, Man with Hawk and Woman with Fruit

1987. 50th Anniv of Davao City.
2024 **654** 1 p. multicoloured . . . 35 10

655 Salary and Policy Loans **656** Emblem and People in Hand

1987. 50th Anniv of Government Service Insurance System. Multicoloured.
2025 1 p. Type **655** 25 15
2026 1 p. 25 Disability and medicare 25 15
2027 2 p. Retirement benefits . . . 35 20
2028 3 p. 50 Survivorship benefits . 65 30

1987. 50th Anniv of Salvation Army in Philippines.
2029 **656** 1 p. multicoloured . . . 15 10

657 Woman, Ballot Box and Map **659** Man with Outstretched Arm

658 Map and Flags as Leaves

1987. 50th Anniv of League of Women Voters.
2030 **657** 1 p. blue and mauve . . 15 10

1987. As T **526**.
2031 1 p. green 15 10
2032 1 p. blue 15 10
2033 1 p. red 15 10
2034 1 p. deep red and red . . . 15 10
DESIGNS: No. 2031, Gen. Vicente Lukban; 2032, Wenceslao Z. Vinzons; 2033, Brigadier General Mateo M. Capinpin (birth centenary); 2034, Jesus Balmori.

1987. 20th Anniv of Association of South-East Asian Nations.
2035 **658** 1 p. multicoloured . . . 15 10

1987. Exports.
2036 **659** 1 p. multicoloured . . . 10 10
2037 – 2 p. green, yell & brn . 20 15
DESIGN: 2 p. Man, cogwheel and factory.
See also No. 2059.

660 Nuns, People and Crucifix within Flaming Heart **661** Statue and Stained Glass Window

1967. 125th Anniv of Daughters of Charity in the Philippines.
2038 **660** 1 p. blue, red and black 15 10

1987. Canonisation of Blessed Lorenzo Ruiz de Manila (first Filipino saint). Multicoloured.
2039 1 p. Type **661** 25 15
2040 5 p. 50 Lorenzo Ruiz praying before execution 75 35

1987. No. 2012 surch **P4.75**.
2042 **642** 4 p. 75 on 5 p. brown . 60 30

663 Nun and Emblem

1987. 75th Anniv of Good Shepherd Sisters in Philippines.
2043 **663** 1 p. multicoloured . . . 15 10

664 Founders

1987. 50th Anniv of Philippines Boy Scouts.
2044 **664** 1 p. multicoloured . . . 15 10

665 Family with Stamp Album

1987. 50th Anniv of Philippine Philatelic Club.
2045 **665** 1 p. multicoloured . . . 15 10

666 Monks, Church and Wrecked Galleon **668** Dove and Letter

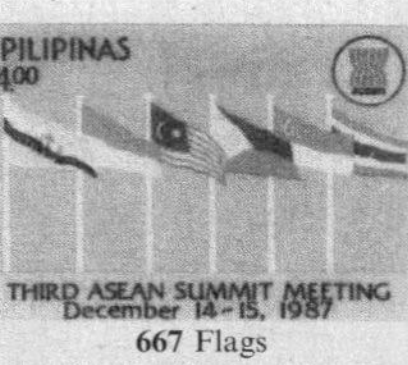

667 Flags

1987. 400th Anniv of Dominican Order in Philippines.
2046 **666** 1 p. black, blue and orange 25 15
2047 – 4 p. 75 multicoloured . . 60 30
2048 – 5 p. 50 multicoloured . . 75 35
DESIGNS: 4 p. 75, J. A. Jeronimo Guerrero and Br. Diego de Sta. Maria and Letran Dominican college; 5 p. 50, Pope and monks.

1987. 3rd Association of South-east Asian Nations Summit Meeting.
2049 **667** 4 p. multicoloured . . . 45 25

1987. Christmas. Multicoloured.
2050 1 p. Type **668** 25 15
2051 1 p. People and star decoration 25 15
2052 4 p. Crowd going to church . 45 25
2053 4 p. 75 Mother and children exchanging gifts 55 25
2054 5 p. 50 Children and bamboo cannons 65 30
2055 8 p. Children at table bearing festive fare 90 45
2056 9 p. 50 Woman at table . . . 1·10 55
2057 11 p. Woman having Christmas meal . . . . 1·25 65

1987. As previous issues but new value (4 p. 75) or smaller, 22 × 32 mm (5 p. 50).
2059 4 p. 75 blue and grey (As No. 2036) 55 30
2060 5 p. 50 green and brown (As No. 2021) 65 30

669 Emblem, Headquarters and Dr. Rizal

1987. 75th Anniv of Philippines Grand Masonic Lodge.
2061 **669** 1 p. multicoloured . . . 15 10

670 Foodstuffs in Split Globe

1987. 40th Anniv of U.N.O. Multicoloured.
2062 1 p. Type **670** (International Fund for Agricultural Development) 15 10
2063 1 p. Means of transport and communications (Asian and Pacific Transport and Communications Decade) . 15 10
2064 1 p. People and hands holding houses (International Year of Shelter for the Homeless) . 15 10
2065 1 p. Happy children playing musical instruments (World Health Day: U.N.I.C.E.F. child vaccination campaign) 15 10

671 Official Seals and Gavel

1988. Opening Session of 1987 Congress. Mult.
2066 1 p. Type **671** 15 10
2067 5 p. 50 Congress in session and gavel 65 40

672 Children and Bosco

1988. Death Centenary of St. John Bosco (founder of Salesian Brothers).
2068 **672** 1 p. multicoloured . . . 15 10
2069 5 p. 50 multicoloured . . 65 40

673 Emblem **675** Envelope with Coded Addresses

1988. Buy Philippine-Made Movement Month.
2070 **673** 1 p. multicoloured . . . 15 15

1988. Various stamps surch **P 3.00**.
2071 – 3 p. on 3 p. 60 brown (No. 1946) 45 25
2072 **646** 3 p. on 3 p. 60 red . . . 45 25
2073 – 3 p. on 3 p. 60 mult (No. 1977) 45 25
2074 – 3 p. on 3 p. 60 blue, black & green (No. 1984) . . . 45 25
2075 **647** 3 p. on 3 p. 60 yellow, brown and blue . . . 45 25

1988. Postal Codes.
2076 **675** 60 s. multicoloured . . . 15 10
2077 1 p. multicoloured . . . 15 10

676 "Vesbius purpureus" **677** Solar Eclipse

1988. Insect Predators. Multicoloured.
2078 1 p. Type **676** 15 10
2079 5 p. 50 "Campsomeris aurulenta" 45 20

1988.
2080 **677** 1 p. multicoloured . . . 15 10
2081 5 p. 50 multicoloured . . 15 10

678 Teodoro **679** Emblem

1988. 101st Birth Anniv of Toribio M. Teodoro (industrialist).
2082 **678** 1 p. lt brown, brn & red 15 10
2083 1 p. 20 blue, brown & red 15 10

1988. 75th Anniv of College of Holy Spirit.
2084 **679** 1 p. brn, gold and blk . 15 10
2085 – 4 p. brown, green & blk 55 25
DESIGN: 4 p. Arnold Janssen (founder) and Sister Edelwina (director).

680 Emblem **681** Luna and Hidalgo

1988. Newly Restored Democracies International Conference.
2086 **680** 4 p. blue, deep blue & blk 55 30

1988. National Juan Luna and Felix Resurreccion Hidalgo Memorial Exhibition.
2087 **681** 1 p. black, yellow & brn 15 10
2088 5 p. 50 black, light brown and brown 70 35

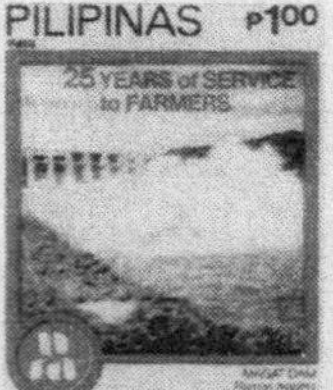

682 Magat Dam, Ramon, Isabela

1988. 25th Anniv of National Irrigation Administration.
2089 **682** 1 p. multicoloured . . . 15 10
2090 5 p. 50 multicoloured . . 70 45

683 Scuba Diving, Siquijor

1988. Olympic Games, Seoul. Multicoloured.
2091 1 p. Type **683** 20 10
2092 1 p. 20 Big game fishing, Aparri, Cagayan 20 15
2093 4 p. Yachting, Manila Central 70 45
2094 5 p. 50 Mountain climbing, Mt. Apo, Davao 95 65
2095 8 p. Golfing, Cebu City, Cebu 1·40 90
2096 11 p. Cycling, Marawi City Tour of Mindanao . . . . 1·90 1·25

1988. Various stamps surch.
2097 1 p. 90 on 2 p. 40 mult (No. 1968) 30 15
2098 1 p. 90 on 2 p. 40 brown, blue & green (No. 1972) 30 15
2099 1 p. 90 on 2 p. 40 mult (No. 1981) 30 15
2100 1 p. 90 on 2 p. 40 mult (No. 1988) 30 15

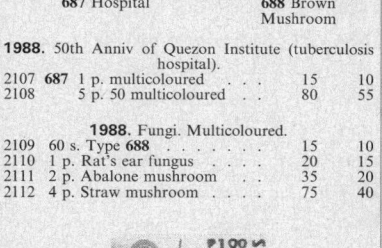

685 Headquarters, Plaza Santa Cruz, Manila
686 Balagtas

1988. Banking Anniversaries. Multicoloured.
2101 1 p. Type **685** (50th anniv of Philippine Int. Commercial Bank) 15 10
2102 1 p. Family looking at factory and countryside (25th anniv of Land Bank) 15 10
2103 5 p. 50 Type **685** 75 50
2104 5 p. 50 As No. 2102 . . . . 75 50

1988. Birth Bicentenary of Francisco Balagtas Baltasco (writer). Each green, brown and yellow.
2105 1 p. Type **686** 15 10
2106 1 p. As Type **686** but details reversed 15 10

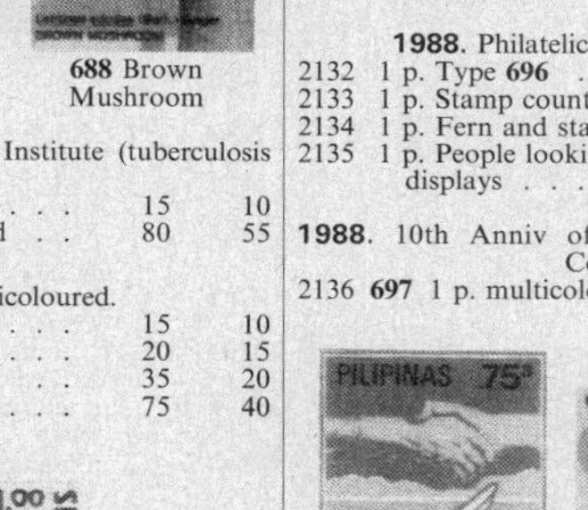

687 Hospital
688 Brown Mushroom

1988. 50th Anniv of Quezon Institute (tuberculosis hospital).
2107 **687** 1 p. multicoloured . . . 15 10
2108 5 p. 50 multicoloured . . 80 55

1988. Fungi. Multicoloured.
2109 60 s. Type **688** 15 10
2110 1 p. Rat's ear fungus 20 15
2111 2 p. Abalone mushroom . . 35 20
2112 4 p. Straw mushroom 75 40

689 Archery

1988. Olympic Games, Seoul. Multicoloured.
2113 1 p. Type **689** 20 10
2114 1 p. 20 Tennis 20 15
2115 4 p. Boxing 60 30
2116 5 p. 50 Athletics 80 40
2117 8 p. Swimming . . . . 1·10 60
2118 11 p. Cycling . . . . 1·60 80

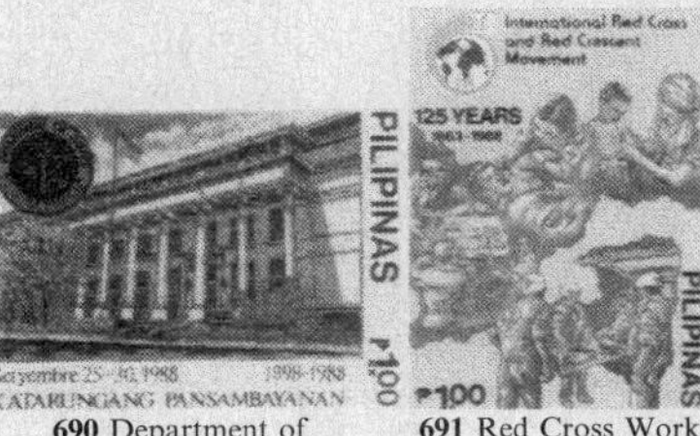

690 Department of Justice
691 Red Cross Work

1988. Law and Justice Week.
2120 **690** 1 p. multicoloured . . . 15 10

1988. 125th Anniv of Red Cross.
2121 **691** 1 p. multicoloured . . . 15 10
2122 5 p. 50 multicoloured . . 75 50

692 Girl and Boy
693 Map and Shrimps

1988. 50th Anniv of Christian Children's Fund.
2123 **692** 1 p. multicoloured . . . 15 10

1988. 50th Anniv of Bacolod City Charter.
2124 **693** 1 p. multicoloured . . . 15 10

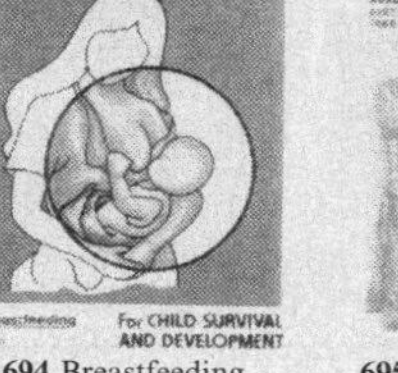

694 Breastfeeding
695 A. A. Quezon

1988. Child Survival Campaign. Multicoloured.
2125 1 p. Type **694** 15 10
2126 1 p. Growth monitoring . . 15 10
2127 1 p. Immunization 15 10
2128 1 p. Oral rehydration . . . 15 10
2129 1 p. Access for the disabled (U.N. Decade of Disabled Persons) 15 10

1988. Birth Centenary of Aurora Aragon Quezon.
2130 **695** 1 p. multicoloured . . . 15 10
2131 5 p. 50 multicoloured . 80 55

696 Post Office
697 Aerials

1988. Philatelic Week. Multicoloured.
2132 1 p. Type **696** 20 15
2133 1 p. Stamp counter 20 15
2134 1 p. Fern and stamp displays 20 15
2135 1 p. People looking at stamp displays 20 15

1988. 10th Anniv of Long Distance Telephone Company.
2136 **697** 1 p. multicoloured . . . 15 10

698 Clasped Hands and Dove
699 Crowd with Banners

1988. Christmas. Multicoloured.
2137 75 s. Type **698** 15 10
2138 1 p. Children making decorations (horiz) 15 15
2139 2 p. Man carrying decorations on yoke (horiz) 30 20
2140 3 p. 50 Christmas tree . . . 55 25
2141 4 p. 75 Candle and stars . . 75 35
2142 5 p. 50 Reflection of star forming heart (horiz) . . . 85 45

1988. Commission on Human Rights (2143) and 40th Anniv of Universal Declaration of Human Rights (2144). Multicoloured.
2143 1 p. Type **699** 15 10
2144 1 p. Doves escaping from cage 15 10

700 Church, 1776
701 Statue and School

1988. 400th Anniv of Malate. Multicoloured.
2145 1 p. Type **700** 15 10
2146 1 p. Our Lady of Remedies Church anniversary emblem 15 10
2147 1 p. Church, 1880 . . . . 15 10
2148 1 p. Church, 1988 . . . . 15 10

1988. 50th Anniv of UST Graduate School.
2149 **701** 1 p. multicoloured . . . 15 10

702 Order's Activities
703 Miguel Z. Ver

1989. 50th Anniv of Oblates of Mary Immaculate.
2150 **702** 1 p. multicoloured . . . 15 10

1989. 47th Anniv of Guerrilla Action against Japanese. Multicoloured.
2151 1 p. Type **703** 15 10
2152 1 p. Eleuterio L. Adevoso . . 15 10

704 Foodstuffs and Gen. Santos
705 Sinulog

1989. 50th Anniv of General Santos City.
2153 **704** 1 p. multicoloured . . . 15 10

1989. "Fiesta Islands '89" (1st series). Mult.
2154 4 p. 75 Type **705** 80 35
2155 5 p. 50 Cenaculo (Lenten festival) 85 45
2156 6 p. Vinta regatta, Iloilo Paraw 1·00 55
See also Nos. 2169/71, 2177/9, 2194/6 and 2210.

706 Tomas B. Mapua
707 Adventure Pool

1989. Birth Centenaries. Multicoloured.
2157 1 p. Type **706** 20 10
2158 1 p. Camilo O. Osias 20 10
2159 1 p. Dr. Olivia D. Salamanca 20 10
2160 1 p. Dr. Francisco S. Santiago 20 10
2161 1 p. Leandro H. Fernandez . 20 10

1989. 26th International Federation of Landscape Architects World Congress, Manila. Multicoloured.
2162 1 p. Type **707** 15 10
2163 1 p. Paco Park 15 10
2164 1 p. Street improvements in Malacanang area 15 10
2165 1 p. Erosion control on upland farm 15 10

708 Palawan Peacock Pheasant
709 Entrance and Statue of Justice

1989. Environment Month. Multicoloured.
2166 1 p. Type **708** 45 10
2167 1 p. Palawan bear cat . . . 15 10

1989. Supreme Court.
2168 **709** 1 p. multicoloured . . . 25 15

1989. "Fiesta Islands '89" (2nd series). As T **705**. Multicoloured.
2169 60 s. Turumba 10 10
2170 75 s. Pahiyas 15 10
2171 3 p. 50 Independence Day . . 50 25

710 Birds, Quill, "Noli Me Tangere" and Flags

1989. Bicentenary of French Revolution and Decade of Philippine Nationalism.
2172 **710** 1 p. multicoloured . . . 15 10
2173 5 p. 50 multicoloured . . 80 55

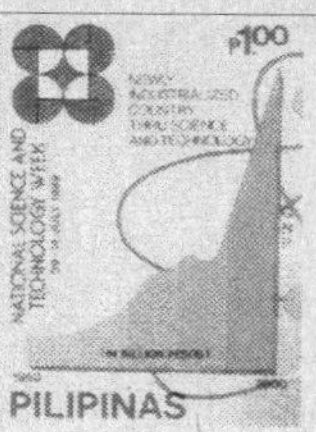

711 Graph
713 Monument, Flag, Civilian and Soldier

1989. National Science and Technology Week. Multicoloured.
2174 1 p. Type **711** 15 10
2175 1 p. "Man" (Leonardo da Vinci) and emblem of Philippine Science High School) 15 10

1989. No. 2060 surch.
2176 4 p. 75 on 5 p. 50 green & brn 70 45

1989. "Fiesta Island 89" (3rd series). As T **705**.
2177 1 p. Pagoda Sa Wawa . . . 30 15
2178 4 p. 75 Cagayan de Oro Fiesta 75 35
2179 5 p. 50 Penafrancia Festival . 85 45

1989. 50th Anniv of National Defence Department.
2180 **713** 1 p. multicoloured . . . 25 10

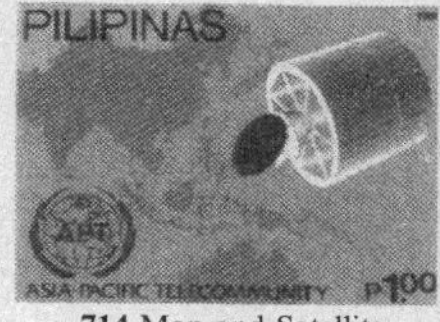

714 Map and Satellite
715 Annunciation

1989. 10th Anniv of Asia–Pacific Telecommunity.
2181 **714** 1 p. multicoloured . . . 25 15

1989. Christmas. Multicoloured.
2182 60 s. Type **715** 10 10
2183 75 s. Mary and Elizabeth . . 10 10
2184 1 p. Mary and Joseph travelling to Bethlehem 15 10
2185 2 p. Search for an inn . . . 30 20
2186 4 p. Magi and star 60 40
2187 4 p. 75 Adoration of shepherds 70 50

716 Lighthouse, Liner and Lifebelt

1989. International Maritime Organization.
2188 **716** 1 p. multicoloured . . . 25 10

717 Spanish Philippines 1854 5 c. and Revolutionary Govt 1898 2 c. Stamps

1989. "World Stamp Expo '89" International Stamp Exhibition, Washington D.C. Multicoloured.
2189 1 p. Type **717** 15 10
2190 4 p. U.S. Administration 1899 50 c. and Commonwealth 1935 6 c. stamps 70 45
2191 5 p. 50 Japanese Occupation 1942 2 c. and Republic 1946 6 c. stamps 80 55

718 Teacher using Stamp as Teaching Aid

1989. Philatelic Week. Philately in the Classroom. Multicoloured.
2192 1 p. Type **718** 15 10
2193 1 p. Children working with stamps 15 10

1989. "Fiesta Islands '89" (4th series). As T **705**.
2194 1 p. Masked festival, Negros 15 10
2195 4 p. 75 Grand Canao, Baguio 75 35
2196 5 p. 50 Fireworks 85 45

719 Heart

1990. 11th World Cardiology Congress, Manila.
2197 **719** 5 p. 50 red, blue & black . . . 85 45

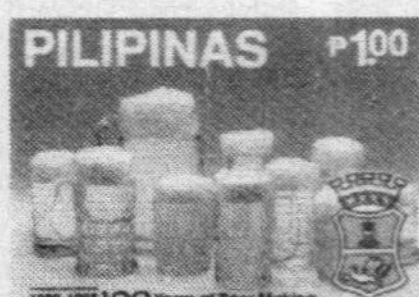

720 Glasses of Beer

1990. Centenary of San Miguel Brewery.
2198 **720** 1 p. multicoloured . . . 15 10
2199 5 p. 50 multicoloured . . 85 45

721 Houses and Family

1990. Population and Housing Census. Multicoloured. Colours of houses given.
2200 **721** 1 p. blue 15 10
2201 1 p. pink 15 10

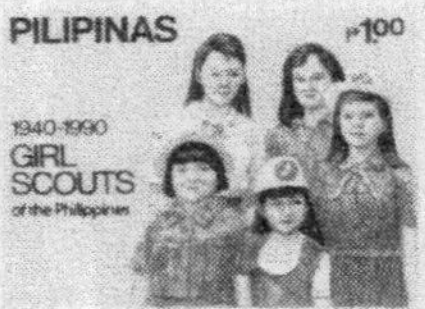

722 Scouts 723 Claro Recto (politician)

1990. 50th Anniv of Philippine Girl Scouts.
2202 **722** 1 p. multicoloured . . . 15 10
2203 1 p. 20 multicoloured . . 15 10

1990. Birth Centenaries. Multicoloured.
2204 1 p. Type **723** 15 10
2205 1 p. Manuel Bernabe (poet) . 15 10
2206 1 p. Guillermo Tolentino (sculptor) 15 10
2207 1 p. Elpidio Quirino (President 1948–53) 15 10
2208 1 p. Dr. Bienvenido Gonzalez (University President, 1937–51) 15 10

724 Badge in Globe

1990. 50th Anniv of Legion of Mary.
2209 **724** 1 p. multicoloured . . . 15 10

1990. "Fiesta Islands '89" (5th series). As No. 2179 but new value.
2210 4 p. multicoloured 60 40

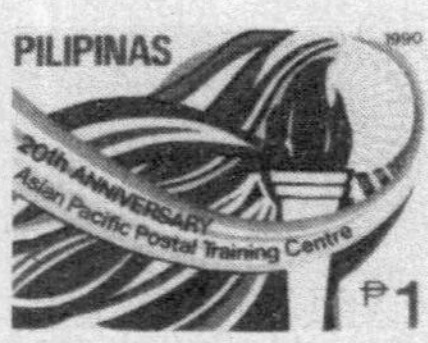

725 Torch

1990. 20th Anniv of Asian–Pacific Postal Training Centre.
2211 **725** 1 p. multicoloured . . . 15 10
2212 4 p. multicoloured . . . 60 40

726 Catechism Class 727 Waling Waling Flowers

1990. National Catechetical Year.
2213 **726** 1 p. multicoloured . . . 15 10
2214 3 p. 50 multicoloured . 50 35

1990. 29th Orient and South-East Asian Lions Forum, Manila. Multicoloured.
2215 1 p. Type **727** 20 10
2216 4 p. Sampaguita flowers . . 65 30

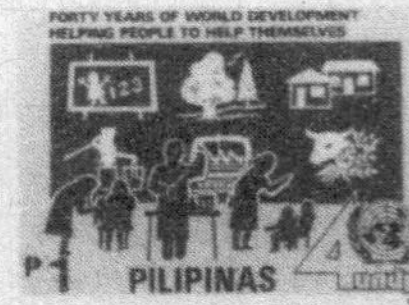

728 Areas for Improvement

1990. 40th Anniv of United Nations Development Programme.
2217 **728** 1 p. multicoloured . . . 15 10
2218 5 p. 50 multicoloured . . 80 55

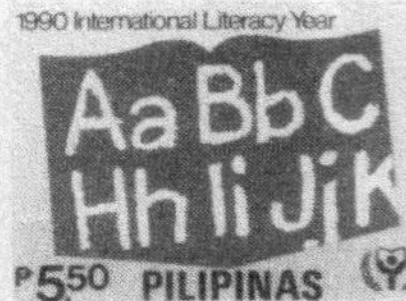

729 Letters of Alphabet

1990. International Literacy Year.
2219 **729** 1 p. green, orange & blk 15 10
2220 5 p. 50 green, yell & blk 80 55

730 "Laughter" (A. Magsaysay-Ho)

1990. Philatelic Week. Multicoloured.
2221 1 p. "Family" (F. Amorsolo) (horiz) 25 15
2222 4 p. 75 "The Builders" (V. Edades) . . . . . . 1·10 55
2223 5 p. 50 Type **730** . . . . . 1·25 65

731 Star

1990. Christmas. Multicoloured.
2224 1 p. Type **731** 15 10
2225 1 p. Stars within stars (Prussian blue background) 15 10
2226 1 p. Red and white star (royal blue background) 15 10
2227 1 p. Gold and red star (green background) 15 10
2228 5 p. 50 Geometric star . . . 80 55

732 Figures

1990. International White Cane Safety Day.
2229 **732** 1 p. black, yellow & blue 25 15

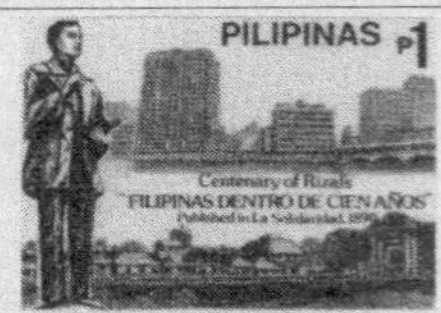

733 La Solidaridad in 1990 and 1890 and Statue of Rizal

1990. Centenary of Publication of "Filipinas Dentro de Cien Anos" by Jose Rizal.
2230 **733** 1 p. multicoloured . . . 25 15

734 Crowd before Figure of Christ 735 Tailplane and Stewardess

1991. 2nd Plenary Council of the Philippines.
2231 **734** 1 p. multicoloured . . . 25 15

1991. 50th Anniv of Philippine Airlines.
2232 **735** 1 p. mult (postage) . . . 15 10
2233 5 p. 50 multicoloured (air) 85 55

736 Gardenia 737 Sheepshank

1991. Flowers. Multicoloured.
2234 60 s. Type **736** 10 10
2235 75 s. Yellow bell 10 10
2236 1 p. Yellow plumeria 15 10
2237 1 p. Red plumeria 15 10
2238 1 p. Pink plumeria 15 10
2239 1 p. White plumeria 15 10
2240 1 p. 20 Nerium 15 10
2241 3 p. 25 Ylang-ylang 55 35
2242 4 p. Pink ixora 55 35
2243 4 p. White ixora 55 35
2244 4 p. Yellow ixora 55 35
2245 4 p. Red ixora 55 35
2246 4 p. 75 Orange bougainvillea . 65 40
2247 4 p. 75 Purple bougainvillea . 65 40
2248 4 p. 75 White bougainvillea . 65 40
2249 4 p. 75 Red bougainvillea . . 65 40
2250 5 p. Canna 65 45
2251 5 p. 50 Red hibiscus . . . 90 60
2252 5 p. 50 Yellow hibiscus . . . 90 60
2253 5 p. 50 White hibiscus . . . 90 60
2254 5 p. 50 Pink hibiscus . . . 90 60
See also Nos. 2322/41 and 2475.

1991. 12th Asia–Pacific and 9th National Boy Scouts Jamboree. Multicoloured.
2255 1 p. Reef knot 20 10
2256 4 p. Type **737** 55 25
2257 4 p. 75 Granny knot . . . 60 30

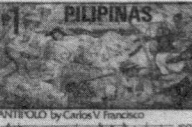

738 Jorge Vargas 739 "Antipolo" (Carlos Francisco) and Score

1991. Birth Centenaries. Multicoloured.
2259 1 p. Type **738** 15 10
2260 1 p. Ricardo Paras 15 10
2261 1 p. Jose Laurel 15 10
2262 1 p. Vicente Fabella 15 10
2263 1 p. Maximo Kalaw 15 10

1991. 400th Anniv of Antipolo.
2264 **739** 1 p. multicoloured . . . 25 15

740 Philippine Eagle

1991. Endangered Species. Philippine Eagle. Mult.
2265 1 p. Type **470** 15 10
2266 4 p. 75 Eagle on branch . . . 65 45
2267 5 p. 50 Eagle in flight . . . 75 50
2268 8 p. Eagle feeding chick . . . 1·10 70

741 Emblem

1991. Centenary of Founding of Society of Lawyers (from 1904 Philippine Bar Association).
2269 **741** 1 p. multicoloured . . . 25 15

742 Flags and Induction Ceremony 743 First Regular Division Emblem

1991. 50th Anniv of Induction of Philippine Reservists into United States Army Forces in the Far East. Background colours given where necessary in brackets.
2270 **742** 1 p. multicoloured . . . 25 15
2272 **743** 2 p. red, black and yellow (1st Regular) 20 15
2273 – 2 p. multicoloured (yellow) (2nd Regular) 20 15
2274 – 2 p. multicoloured (yellow) (11th) 20 15
2275 – 2 p. blue, yellow and black (yellow) (21st) 20 15
2276 **743** 2 p. red and black (1st Regular) 20 15
2277 – 2 p. black, blue and red (2nd Regular) 20 15
2278 – 2 p. multicoloured (white) (11th) 20 15
2279 – 2 p. blue, yellow and black (white) (21st) 20 15
2280 – 2 p. multicoloured (yellow) (31st) 20 15
2281 – 2 p. multicoloured (yellow) (41st) 20 15
2282 – 2 p. multicoloured (yellow) (51st) 20 15
2283 – 2 p. multicoloured (yellow) (61st) 20 15
2284 – 2 p. red, blue and black (31st) 20 15
2285 – 2 p. multicoloured (white) (41st) 20 15
2286 – 2 p. blue, black and red (51st) 20 15
2287 – 2 p. multicoloured (white) (61st) 20 15
2288 – 2 p. multicoloured (yellow) (71st) 20 15
2289 – 2 p. multicoloured (yellow) (81st) 20 15
2290 – 2 p. multicoloured (yellow) (91st) 20 15
2291 – 2 p. multicoloured (yellow) (101st) 20 15
2292 – 2 p. multicoloured (white) (71st) 20 15
2293 – 2 p. multicoloured (white) (81st) 20 15
2294 – 2 p. multicoloured (white) (91st) 20 15
2295 – 2 p. multicoloured (white) (101st) 20 15
2296 – 2 p. blue, black & yellow (Bataan Force) 20 15
2297 – 2 p. yellow, red & blk (yellow) (Philippine) . 20 15
2298 – 2 p. multicoloured (yellow) (Air Corps) 20 15
2299 – 2 p. black, blue & yellow (Offshore Patrol) . . . 20 15
2300 – 2 p. blue and black (Bataan Force) 20 15
2301 – 2 p. yellow, red & black (white) (Philippine) . . 20 15
2302 – 2 p. multicoloured (white) (Air Corps) 20 15
2303 – 2 p. black and blue (Offshore Patrol) . . . 20 15
Nos. 2272/2303 show divisional emblems.

744 Basilio 745 St. John of the Cross

1991. Centenary of Publication of "El Filibusterismo" by Jose Rizal. Each red, green and black.
2304 1 p. Type **744** 15 10
2305 1 p. Simoun 15 10
2306 1 p. Father Florentino . . . 15 10
2307 1 p. Juli 15 10

1991. 400th Death Anniv of St. John of the Cross.
2308 **745** 1 p. multicoloured . . . 25 15

746 Faces (Children's Fund)

1991. United Nations Agencies.
2310 746 1 p. multicoloured . . . 15 10
2311 – 4 p. multicoloured . . . 55 25
2312 – 5 p. 50 black, red & blue 75 35
DESIGNS: 4 p. Hands supporting boatload of people (High Commissioner for Refugees); 5 p. 50, 1951 15 c. and 1954 3 c. U.N. stamps (40th anniv of Postal Administration).

747 "Bayanihan" (Carlos "Botong" Francisco)

1991. Philatelic Week. Multicoloured.
2313 2 p. Type 747 . . . . 30 15
2314 7 p. "Sari-Sari Vendor" (Mauro Malang Santos) 95 45
2315 8 p. "Give Us This Day" (Vicente Manansala) . . . 1·10 55

748 Gymnastics

1991. 16th South-East Asian Games, Manila. Multicoloured.
2316 2 p. Type 748 . . . . 20 15
2317 2 p. Gymnastics (emblem at bottom) 20 15
2318 6 p. Arnis (martial arts) (emblem at left) (vert) . . . 65 45
2319 6 p. Arnis (emblem at right) (vert) 65 45
Designs of the same value were issued together, se-tenant, each pair forming a composite design.

1991. Flowers. As T 736. Multicoloured.
2322 1 p. 50 Type 736 . . . . . . 15 15
2323 2 p. Yellow plumeria 20 20
2324 2 p. Red plumeria 20 20
2325 2 p. Pink plumeria 20 20
2326 2 p. White plumeria 20 20
2327 3 p. Nerium 30 30
2328 5 p. Ylang-ylang 50 50
2329 6 p. Pink ixora 55 55
2330 6 p. White ixora 55 55
2331 6 p. Yellow ixora 55 55
2332 6 p. Red ixora 55 55
2333 7 p. Orange bougainvillea . . 65 65
2334 7 p. Purple bougainvillea . . 65 65
2335 7 p. White bougainvillea . . 65 65
2336 7 p. Red bougainvillea . . . 65 65
2337 8 p. Red hibiscus 75 75
2338 8 p. Yellow hibiscus 75 75
2339 8 p. White hibiscus 75 75
2340 8 p. Pink hibiscus 75 75
2341 10 p. Canna 95 95

750 Church

1991. Christmas. Children's Paintings. Mult.
2342 2 p. Type 750 . . . . 20 15
2343 6 p. Christmas present . . . 60 40
2344 7 p. Santa Claus and tree . . 70 50
2345 8 p. Christmas tree and star . 80 55

751 Basketball Player 752 Monkey firing Cannon

1991. Centenary of Basketball. Multicoloured.
2346 2 p. Type 751 . . . . 25 15
2347 6 p. Basketball player and map (issue of first basketball stamp, 1934) (horiz) . . . 65 30
2348 7 p. Girls playing basketball (introduction of basketball in Philippines, 1904) (horiz) . 75 35
2349 8 p. Basketball players . . . 85 45

1991. New Year. Year of the Monkey.
2351 752 2 p. multicoloured . . . 25 15
2352 6 p. multicoloured . . . 65 30

753 Pres. Aquino and Mailing Centre Emblem

1992. Kabisig Community Projects Organization. Multicoloured.
2353 2 p. Type 753 . . . . 25 15
2354 6 p. Housing 65 30
2355 7 p. Livestock 75 35
2356 8 p. Handicrafts 85 45

754 "Curcuma longa"

1992. Asian Medicinal Plants Symposium, Laguna. Multicoloured.
2357 2 p. Type 754 . . . . 25 15
2358 6 p. "Centella asiatica" . . . 65 30
2359 7 p. "Cassia alata" 75 35
2360 8 p. "Ervatamia pandacaqui" 85 45

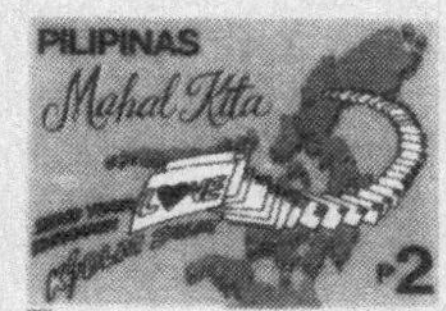

755 "Mahal Kita", Envelopes and Map

1992. Greetings Stamps. Multicoloured.
2361 2 p. Type 755 . . . . 20 15
2362 2 p. As No. 2361 but inscr "I Love You" 20 15
2363 6 p. Heart and doves ("Mahal Kita") 65 35
2364 6 p. As No. 2363 but inscr "I Love You" 65 35
2365 7 p. Basket of flowers ("Mahal Kita") 75 35
2366 7 p. As No. 2365 but inscr "I Love You" 75 35
2367 8 p. Cupid ("Mahal Kita") . 85 45
2368 8 p. As No. 2367 but inscr "I Love You" 85 45

756 Philippine Pavilion and Couple Dancing 757 Our Lady of the Sun

1992. "Expo '92" World's Fair, Seville. Mult.
2369 2 p. Type 756 . . . . 25 15
2370 8 p. Pavilion, preacher and man holding globe 85 45

1992. 300th Anniv of Apparition of Our Lady of the Sun at Porta Vaga.
2372 757 2 p. multicoloured . . . 25 15
2373 8 p. multicoloured . . . 85 45

758 Fish Farming

1992. 75th Anniv of Department of Agriculture. Multicoloured.
2374 2 p. Type 758 . . . . 20 15
2375 2 p. Pig farming 20 15
2376 2 p. Sowing seeds 20 15

759 Race Horses and Emblem 760 Manuel Roxas (President, 1946-48)

1992. 125th Anniv of Manila Jockey Club.
2377 759 2 p. multicoloured . . . 25 15

1992. Birth Centenaries. Multicoloured.
2379 2 p. Type 760 . . . . 20 15
2380 2 p. Natividad Almeda-Lopez (judge) 20 15
2381 2 p. Roman Ozaeta (judge) . 20 15
2382 2 p. Engracia Cruz-Reyes (women's rights campaigner and environmentalist) . . . 20 15
2383 2 p. Fernando Amorsolo (artist) 20 15

761 Queen, Bishop and 1978 30 s. Stamp

1992. 30th Chess Olympiad, Manila. Mult.
2384 2 p. Type 761 . . . . 20 15
2385 6 p. Queen, bishop and 1962 6 s. + 4 s. stamp 60 40

762 Bataan Cross

1992. 50th Anniv of Pacific Theatre in World War II. Multicoloured.
2387 2 p. Type 762 . . . . 20 15
2388 6 p. Map inside "W" 60 40
2389 8 p. Corregidor eternal flame 85 55

763 President Aquino and President-elect Ramos

1992. Election of Fidel Ramos to Presidency.
2391 763 2 p. multicoloured . . . 30 15

764 "Dapitan Shrine" (Cesar Legaspi)

1992. Centenary of Dr. Jose Rizal's Exile to Dapitan. Multicoloured.
2392 2 p. Type 764 . . . . 20 15
2393 2 p. Portrait (after Juan Luna) (vert) 20 15

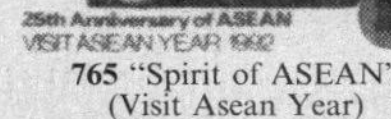

765 "Spirit of ASEAN" (Visit Asean Year) 766 Member of the Katipunan

1992. 25th Anniv of Association of South-East Asian Nations. Multicoloured.
2394 2 p. Type 765 . . . . 20 15
2395 2 p. "ASEAN Sea" (25th Ministerial Meeting and Postal Ministers' Conf) . . 20 15
2396 6 p. Type 765 . . . . 60 40
2397 6 p. As No. 2395 . . . . . . 60 40

1992. Centenary of Katipunan (revolutionary organization). Multicoloured.
2398 2 p. Type 766 . . . . 20 15
2399 2 p. Revolutionaries 20 15
2400 2 p. Plotting (horiz) 20 15
2401 2 p. Attacking (horiz) . . . 20 15

767 Dr. Jose Rizal, Text and Quill

1992. Centenary of La Liga Filipina.
2402 767 2 p. multicoloured . . . 20 15

768 Swimming

1992. Olympic Games, Barcelona. Multicoloured.
2403 2 p. Type 768 . . . . 20 15
2404 7 p. Boxing 70 45
2405 8 p. Hurdling 80 55

769 School, Emblem and Students

1992. Centenaries. Multicoloured.
2407 2 p. Type 769 (Sisters of the Assumption in the Philippines) 20 15
2408 2 p. San Sebastian's Basilica, Manila (centenary (1991) of blessing of fifth construction) (vert) 25 15

770 Masonic Symbols

1992. Centenary of Nilad Lodge (first Filipino Masonic Lodge).
2409 770 2 p. black and green . . 20 15
2410 – 6 p. multicoloured . . . 60 40
2411 – 8 p. multicoloured . . . 80 55
DESIGNS: 6 p. Antonio Luna and symbols; 8 p. Marcelo del Pilar ("Father of Philippine Masonry") and symbols.

771 Ramos taking Oath

1992. Swearing in of President Fidel Ramos. Mult.
2412 2 p. Type 771 . . . . 25 15
2413 8 p. President taking oath in front of flag 85 45

772 Flamingo Guppy

1992. Freshwater Aquarium Fishes (1st series). Multicoloured.

2414 1 p. 50 Type **772** 15 10
2415 1 p. 50 Neon tuxedo guppy 15 10
2416 1 p. 50 King cobra guppy 15 10
2417 1 p. 50 Red-tailed guppy 15 10
2418 1 p. 50 Tiger lacetail guppy 15 10
2419 2 p. Pearl scale goldfish 25 15
2420 2 p. Red-cap goldfish 25 15
2421 2 p. Lionhead goldfish 25 15
2422 2 p. Black moor 25 15
2423 2 p. Bubble-eye 25 15
2424 4 p. Delta topsail variatus 45 25
2425 4 p. Orange spotted hi-fin platy 45 25
2426 4 p. Red lyretail swordtail 45 25
2427 4 p. Bleeding heart hi-fin platy 45 25

See also Nos. 2541/54.

774 Couple

1992. Greetings Stamps. "Happy Birthday". Multicoloured.

2430 2 p. Type **774** 20 15
2431 6 p. Type **774** 60 40
2432 7 p. Balloons and candles on birthday cake 70 50
2433 8 p. As No. 2432 80 55

775 Melon, Beans, Tomatoes and Potatoes

1992. 500th Anniv of Discovery of America by Columbus. Multicoloured.

2434 2 p. Type **775** 20 15
2435 6 p. Maize and sweet potatoes 60 40
2436 8 p. Pineapple, cashews, avocado and water melon 80 55

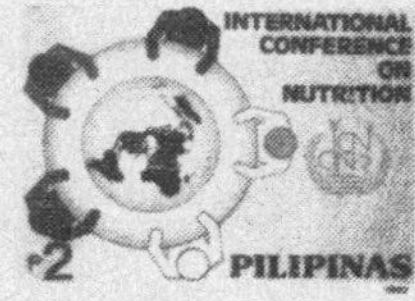

777 Figures around World Map

1992. International Nutrition Conference, Rome.

2438 **777** 2 p. multicoloured 20 15

778 Mother and Child **780** Family and Canoe

1992. Christmas.

2439 **778** 2 p. multicoloured 20 15
2440 – 6 p. multicoloured 60 40
2441 – 7 p. multicoloured 70 50
2442 – 8 p. multicoloured 80 55

DESIGNS: 6 p. to 8 p. Various designs showing mothers and children.

1992. Anti-drugs Campaign. Multicoloured.

2444 2 p. Type **780** 20 15
2445 8 p. Man carrying paddle, children and canoe 80 55

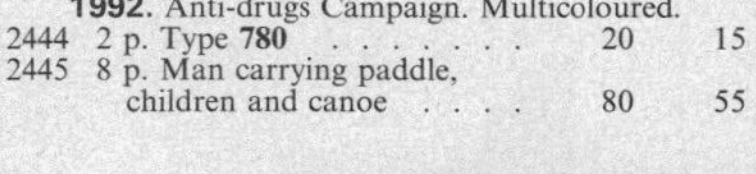

781 Damaged Trees **782** Labuyo (wild cock)

1992. Mt. Pinatubo Fund (for victims of volcanic eruption). Multicoloured.

2446 25 s. Type **781** 10 10
2447 1 p. Mt. Pinatubo erupting 10 10
2448 1 p. Cattle in ash-covered field 10 10
2449 1 p. Refugee settlement 10 10
2450 1 p. People shovelling ash 10 10

1992. New Year. Year of the Cock. Mult.

2451 2 p. Type **782** 20 15
2452 6 p. Maranao Sarimanok (mythical bird) 60 40

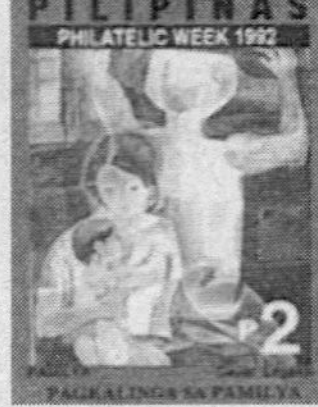

784 Badges of 61st and 71st Divisions, Cebu Area Command **785** "Family" (Cesar Legaspi) (family ties)

1992. Philippine Guerrilla Units of Second World War (1st series). Multicoloured.

2455 2 p. Type **784** 20 15
2456 2 p. Vinzon's Guerrillas and badges of 48th Chinese Guerrilla Squadron and 101st Division 20 15
2457 2 p. Anderson's Command, Luzon Guerrilla Army Forces and badge of Bulacan Military Area 20 15
2458 2 p. President Quezon's Own Guerrillas and badges of Marking's Fil-American Troops and Hunters ROTC Guerrillas 20 15

See also Nos. 2592/5.

1992. Philatelic Week. Multicoloured.

2459 2 p. Type **785** 10 10
2460 6 p. "Pounding Rice" (Nena Saguil) (hard work and industry) 30 20
2461 7 p. "Fish Vendors" (Romeo Tabuena) (flexibility and adaptability) 40 25

786 Black Shama

1992. Endangered Birds. Multicoloured. (a) As T **786**.

2462 2 p. Type **786** 20 15
2463 2 p. Blue-headed fantail 20 15
2464 2 p. Mindoro zone-tailed (inscr "Imperial") pigeon 20 15
2465 2 p. Sulu hornbill 20 15
2466 2 p. Red-vented (inscr "Philippine") cockatoo 20 15

(b) Size 29 × 39 mm.

2467 2 p. Philippine trogon 20 20
2468 2 p. Rufous hornbill 20 20
2469 2 p. White-bellied black woodpecker 20 20
2470 2 p. Spotted wood kingfisher 20 20

(c) Size 36 × 26½ mm.

2471 2 p. Brahminy kite 20 20
2472 2 p. Philippine falconet 20 20
2473 2 p. Eastern reef heron 20 20
2474 2 p. Philippine duck (inscr "Mallard") 20 20

1993. As No. 2235 but value changed.

2475 1 p. multicoloured 10 10

787 Flower (Jasmine) **788** "Euploea mulciber dufresne"

1993. National Symbols. Multicoloured.

2476 60 s. Tree 10 10
2477 1 p. Type **787** 10 10
2478 1 p. 50 Fish 10 10
2479 2 p. Flag 10 10
2480 3 p. Animal (water buffalo) 15 10
2481 5 p. Bird (finches) 25 10
2482 6 p. Leaf (palm) 30 15
2483 7 p. Costume 35 15
2484 8 p. Fruit (mango) 40 20
2485 10 p. House 50 25

See also Nos. 2510/19 and 2563/76.

1993. Butterflies. Multicoloured. (a) As T **788**.

2486 2 p. Type **788** 10 10
2487 2 p. "Cheritra orpheus" 10 10
2488 2 p. "Delias henningia" 10 10
2489 2 p. "Mycalesis ita" 10 10
2490 2 p. "Delias diaphana" 10 10

(b) Size 28 × 35 mm.

2491 2 p. "Papilio rumanzobia" 10 10
2492 2 p. "Papilio palinurus" 10 10
2493 2 p. "Trogonoptera trojana" 10 10
2494 2 p. Tailed jay ("Graphium agamemnon") 10 10

Nos. 2491/4 were issued together, se-tenant, forming a composite design.

790 Nicanor Abelardo **791** Boxing and Judo

1993. Birth Centenaries. Multicoloured.

2497 2 p. Type **790** 10 10
2498 2 p. Pilar Hidalgo-Lim 10 10
2499 2 p. Manuel Viola Gallego 10 10
2500 2 p. Maria Ylagan-Orosa 10 10
2501 2 p. Eulogio B. Rodriguez 10 10

1993. 17th South-East Asian Games, Singapore. Multicoloured.

2502 2 p. Weightlifting, archery, fencing and shooting (79 × 29 mm) 10 10
2503 2 p. Type **791** 10 10
2504 2 p. Athletics, cycling, gymnastics and golf (79 × 29 mm) 10 10
2505 6 p. Table tennis, football, volleyball and badminton (79 × 29 mm) 30 15
2506 6 p. Billiards and bowling 30 15
2507 6 p. Swimming, water polo, yachting and diving (79 × 29 mm) 30 15

793 Flower **794** "Spathoglottis chrysantha"

1993. Centenary of Declaration of Philippine Independence. National Symbols. Multicoloured.

2510 1 p. Flag 10 10
2511 1 p. As No. 2485 10 10
2512 1 p. Costume 10 10
2513 1 p. As No. 2476 10 10
2514 1 p. Type **793** 10 10
2515 1 p. Fruit 10 10
2516 1 p. Leaf 10 10
2517 1 p. As No. 2478 10 10
2518 1 p. As No. 2480 10 10
2519 1 p. As No. 2481 10 10

See also Nos. 2563/76 and 2641/9

1993. Orchids. Multicoloured.

2520 2 p. Type **794** 10 10
2521 2 p. "Arachnis longicaulis" 10 10
2522 2 p. "Phalaenopsis mariae" 10 10
2523 2 p. "Coelogyne marmorata" 10 10
2524 2 p. "Dendrobium sanderae" 10 10
2525 3 p. "Dendrobium serratilabium" 15 10
2526 3 p. "Phalaenopsis equestris" 15 10
2527 3 p. "Vanda merrillii" 15 10
2528 3 p. "Vanda luzonica" 15 10
2529 3 p. "Grammatophyllum martae" 15 10

796 Dog in Window ("Thinking of You")

1993. Greetings Stamps. Multicoloured.

2532 2 p. Type **796** 10 10
2533 2 p. As No. 2532 but inscr "Naaalala Kita" 10 10
2534 6 p. Dog looking at clock ("Thinking of You") 30 15
2535 6 p. As No. 2534 but inscr "Naaalala Kita" 30 15
2536 7 p. Dog looking at calendar ("Thinking of You") 35 15
2537 7 p. As No. 2536 but inscr "Naaalala Kita" 35 15
2538 8 p. Dog with pair of slippers ("Thinking of You") 40 20
2539 8 p. As No. 2538 but inscr "Naaalala Kita" 40 20

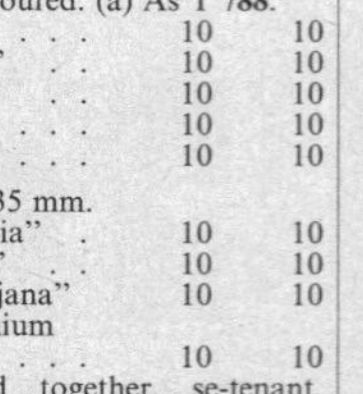

797 Palms and Coconuts **799** Map and Emblem

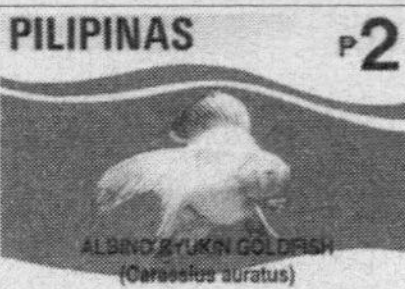

798 Albino Ryukin Goldfish

1993. "Tree of Life".

2540 **797** 2 p. multicoloured 10 10

1993. Freshwater Aquarium Fishes (2nd series). Multicoloured. (a) As T **798**.

2541 2 p. Type **798** 10 10
2542 2 p. Black oranda goldfish 10 10
2543 2 p. Lionhead goldfish 10 10
2544 2 p. Celestial-eye goldfish 10 10
2545 2 p. Pompon goldfish 10 10
2546 2 p. Paradise fish 10 10
2547 2 p. Pearl gourami 10 10
2548 2 p. Red-tailed black shark 10 10
2549 2 p. Tiger barb 10 10
2550 2 p. Cardinal tetra 10 10

(b) Size 29 × 39 mm.

2551 2 p. Pearl-scale angelfish 10 10
2552 2 p. Zebra angelfish 10 10
2553 2 p. Marble angelfish 10 10
2554 2 p. Black angelfish 10 10

1993. Basic Petroleum and Minerals Inc. "Towards Self-sufficiency in Energy".

2556 **799** 2 p. multicoloured 10 10

801 Globe, Scales, Book and Gavel

1993. 16th International Law Conference, Manila. Multicoloured.

2558 2 p. Type **801** 10 10
2559 6 p. Globe, scales, gavel and conference emblem on flag of Philippines (vert) 30 15
2560 7 p. Woman holding scales, conference building and globe 35 15
2561 8 p. Fisherman pulling in nets and emblem (vert) 40 20

802 Our Lady of La Naval (statue) and Galleon

1993. 400th Anniv of Our Lady of La Naval.

2562 **802** 2 p. multicoloured 10 10

1993. National Symbols. As T **793**. Multicoloured.

2563 2 p. Hero (Dr. Jose Rizal) 10 10
2564 2 p. As No. 2485 10 10
2565 2 p. As No. 2512 10 10
2566 2 p. Dance ("Tinikling") 10 10
2567 2 p. Sport (Sipa) 10 10
2568 2 p. As No. 2481 10 10
2570 2 p. As No. 2480 10 10
2571 2 p. Type **793** 10 10
2572 2 p. As No. 2476 10 10
2573 2 p. As No. 2515 10 10
2574 2 p. As No. 2516 10 10
2575 2 p. As No. 2478 10 10
2576 2 p. As No. 2510 10 10

803 Woman and Terraced Hillside

1993. International Year of Indigenous Peoples. Women in traditional costumes. Multicoloured.

2577 2 p. Type **803** 10 10
2578 6 p. Woman, plantation and mountain 30 15
2579 7 p. Woman and mosque 35 15
2580 8 p. Woman and vintas (boats) 40 20

804 Trees

1993. Philatelic Week. "Save the Earth". Multicoloured.

2581 2 p. Type **804** 10 10
2582 6 p. Marine flora and fauna . 30 15
2583 7 p. Bird and irrigation system 35 15
2584 8 p. Effects of industrial pollution 40 20

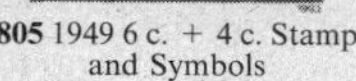

805 1949 6 c. + 4 c. Stamp and Symbols

806 Moon-buggy and Society Emblem

1993. 400th Anniv of Publication of "Doctrina Christiana" (first book published in Philippines).

2585 **805** 2 p. multicoloured . . . 10 10

1993. 50th Anniv of Filipino Inventors Society. Multicoloured.

2586 2 p. Type **806** 10 10
2587 2 p. Rice-harvesting machine 10 10

Nos. 2586/7 were issued together, se-tenant, forming a composite design.

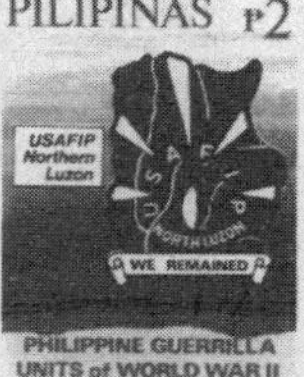

807 Holy Family

808 Northern Luzon

1993. Christmas. Multicoloured.

2588 2 p. Type **807** 10 10
2589 6 p. Church goers 30 15
2590 7 p. Cattle and baskets of food 35 15
2591 8 p. Carol-singers 40 20

1993. Philippine Guerrilla Units of Second World War (2nd series). Multicoloured.

2592 2 p. Type **808** 10 10
2593 2 p. Bohol Area Command . 10 10
2594 2 p. Leyte Area Command . 10 10
2595 2 p. Palawan Special Battalion and Sulu Area Command . 10 10

809 Dove over City (peace and order)

1993. "Philippines 2000" (development plan). Multicoloured.

2596 2 p. Type **809** 10 10
2597 6 p. Means of transport and communications 30 15
2598 7 p. Offices, roads and factories (infrastructure and industry) 35 15
2599 8 p. People from different walks of life (people empowerment) 40 20

810 Shih Tzu

1993. New Year. Year of the Dog. Multicoloured.

2601 2 p. Type **810** 10 10
2602 6 p. Chow 30 15

811 Jamboree Emblem and Flags

1993. 1st Association of South-East Asian Nations Scout Jamboree, Makiling. Multicoloured.

2604 2 p. Type **811** 10 10
2605 6 p. Scout at camp-site, flags and emblem 30 15

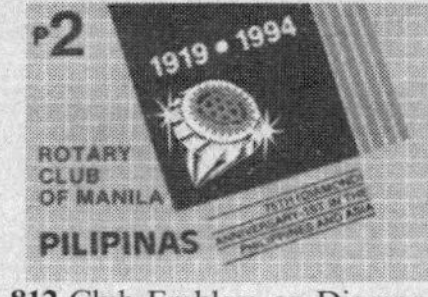

812 Club Emblem on Diamond

1994. 75th Anniv of Manila Rotary Club.

2607 **812** 2 p. multicoloured . . . 10 10

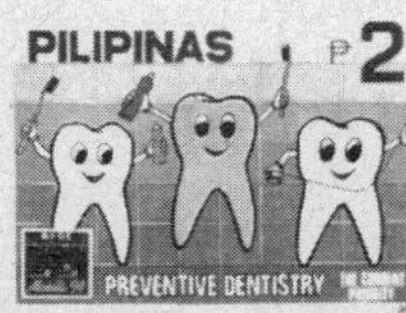

813 Teeth and Dental Hygiene Products

1994. 17th Asian–Pacific Dental Congress, Manila. Multicoloured.

2608 2 p. Type **813** 10 10
2609 6 p. Teeth, flags of participating countries and Philippines circled on globe (vert) . . 30 15

814 "Acropora micropthalma"

1994. Corals. Multicoloured.

2610 2 p. Type **814** 10 10
2611 2 p. "Seriatopora hystrix" . 10 10
2612 2 p. "Acropora latistella" . 10 10
2613 2 p. "Millepora tenella" . . 10 10
2614 2 p. "Millepora tenella" (different) 10 10
2615 2 p. "Pachyseris valenciennesi" 10 10
2616 2 p. "Pavona decussata" . . 10 10
2617 2 p. "Galaxea fascicularis" . 10 10
2618 2 p. "Acropora formosa" . . 10 10
2619 2 p. "Acropora humilis" . . 10 10
2620 2 p. "Isis sp." (vert) 10 10
2621 2 p. "Plexaura sp." (vert) . . 10 10
2622 2 p. "Dendronepthya sp." (vert) 10 10
2623 2 p. "Heteroxenia sp." (vert) 10 10

815 New Year Stamps of 1991 and 1992 bearing Exhibition Emblem

1994. "Hong Kong '94" Stamp Exhibition. Multicoloured.

2625 2 p. Type **815** 10 10
2626 6 p. 1993 New Year stamps . 30 15

816 Class of 1944 Emblem

817 Airplane over Harbour, Man and Cogwheel and Emblem

1994. 50th Anniv of Philippine Military Academy Class of 1944.

2628 **816** 2 p. multicoloured . . . 10 10

1994. Federation of Filipino–Chinese Chambers of Commerce and Industry.

2630 **817** 2 p. multicoloured . . . 10 10

818 "Binabati Kita" and Stork carrying Baby

1994. Greetings Stamps. Multicoloured.

2631 2 p. Type **818** 10 10
2632 2 p. As No. 2631 but inscr "Congratulations" 10 10
2633 2 p. Bouquet ("Binabati Kita") 10 10
2634 2 p. As No. 2633 but inscr "Congratulations" 10 10
2635 2 p. Mortar board, scroll and books ("Binabati Kita") . . 10 10
2636 2 p. As No. 2635 but inscr "Congratulations" 10 10
2637 2 p. Bouquet, doves and heads inside heart ("Binabati Kita") 10 10
2638 2 p. As No. 2637 but inscr "Congratulations" 10 10

OFFICIAL STAMPS

1926. Commemorative issue of 1926 optd **OFFICIAL**.

O391 **49** 2 c. black and green . . . 1·50 80
O392 4 c. black and red . . . 1·50 80
O393 18 c. black and brown . . 5·50 4·50
O394 20 c. black and orange . . 4·50 1·50

1931. Stamps of 1906 optd **O.B.**

O413 2 c. green (No. 337) 10 10
O414 4 c. red (No. 338) 10 10
O415 6 c. violet (No. 339) . . . 10 10
O416 8 c. brown (No. 340) . . . 10 10
O417 10 c. blue (No. 341) . . . 55 10
O418 12 c. orange (No. 342) . . . 30 15
O419 16 c. olive (No. 344) . . . 30 10
O420 20 c. orange (No. 345) . . . 40 10
O421 26 c. green (No. 346) . . . 50 40
O422 30 c. grey (No. 347) 40 30

1935. Nos. 459/68 optd **O.B.**

O473 2 c. red 10 10
O474 4 c. green 10 10
O475 6 c. brown 10 10
O476 8 c. violet 15 15
O477 10 c. red 15 10
O478 12 c. black 20 15
O479 16 c. blue 20 15
O480 20 c. bistre 20 15
O481 26 c. blue 40 35
O482 30 c. red 45 40

1936. Stamps of 1935 Nos. 459/68 optd **O. B. COMMON-WEALTH** (2, 6, 20 c.) or **O. B. COMMONWEALTH** (others).

O538 2 c. red 10 10
O539 4 c. green 10 10
O540 6 c. brown 15 10
O541 8 c. violet 15 10
O542 10 c. red 15 10
O543 12 c. black 15 10
O544 16 c. blue 25 10
O545 20 c. bistre 40 40
O546 26 c. blue 45 45
O547 30 c. red 45 45

1941. Nos. 563 and 623 optd **O. B.**

O565 **104** 2 c. green 10 10
O624 – 2 c. brown 10 10

1948. Various stamps optd **O.B.**

O738 **147** 1 c. brown 10 10
O668 **125** 2 c. green 45 10
O659 – 4 c. brown (No. 629) . . 15 10
O739 – 5 c. red (No. 731) . . . 15 10
O843 – 6 c. blue (No. 842) . . . 15 10
O660 **113** 10 c. red 25 10
O740 – 10 c. blue (No. 732) . . 25 10
O661 – 16 c. slate (No. 632) . . 1·60 60
O669 – 20 c. brown (No. 633) . . 60 15
O741 – 20 c. red (No. 733) . . . 45 15
O670 – 50 c. green (No. 634) . . 1·00 60

1950. Surch **ONE CENTAVO**.

O700 **125** 1 c. on 2 c. grn (No. O668) 15 10

1959. No. 810 optd **O.B.**

O811 1 c. on 5 c. red 10 10

1962. Optd **G.O.**

O908 5 s. red (No. 898) 10 10
O909 6 s. brown (No. 899) 15 10
O910 6 s. blue (No. 900) 15 10
O911 10 s. purple (No. 901) . . . 20 15
O912 20 s. blue (No. 902) 30 15
O913 30 s. red (No. 903) 35 25
O914 50 s. violet (No. 904) 45 35

1970. Optd **G.O.**

O1182 **318** 10 s. red 15 10

OFFICIAL SPECIAL DELIVERY STAMP

1931. No. E353b optd **O.B.**

EO423 20 c. violet 50 35

POSTAGE DUE STAMPS

1899. Postage Due stamps of United States of 1894 optd **PHILIPPINES**.

D268 **D 87** 1 c. red . . . . 3·25 1·50
D269 2 c. red . . . . 3·25 1·25
D270 3 c. red . . . . 12·00 7·00
D271 5 c. red . . . . 8·00 2·50
D272 10 c. red . . . . 10·00 4·00
D273 30 c. red . . . . £180 85·00
D274 50 c. red . . . . £140 80·00

D 51 Post Office Clerk

D 118

1928.

D395 **D 51** 4 c. red 15 15
D396 6 c. red 25 25
D397 8 c. red 25 25
D398 10 c. red 25 25
D399 12 c. red 25 25
D400 16 c. red 30 30
D401 20 c. red 25 25

1937. Surch **3 CVOS. 3**.

D521 **D 51** 3 c. on 4 c. red . . . 20 15

1947.

D644 **D 118** 3 c. red 15 15
D645 4 c. blue 35 30
D646 6 c. olive 45 45
D647 10 c. orange 55 55

SPECIAL DELIVERY STAMPS

1901. Special Delivery stamp of United States of 1888 optd **PHILIPPINES**.

E268 **E 46** 10 c. blue (No. E283) . 85·00 90·00

1907. Special Delivery stamp of United States optd **PHILIPPINES.**

E29 **E 117** 10 c. blue £1500

E 47 Messenger running

1919. Perf (E353), perf or imperf (E353b).

E353 **E 47** 20 c. blue 45 20
E353b 20 c. violet 45 15

1939. Optd **COMMONWEALTH**. Perf.

E550 **E 47** 20 c. violet 30 20

1945. Optd **VICTORY**.

E622 **E 47** 20 c. vio. (No. E550) . 50 50

E 120 Cyclist Messenger and Post Office

1947.

E651 **E 120** 20 c. purple 60 40

E 219 G.P.O. Manila

1962.

E891 **E 219** 20 c. mauve 35 30

POLAND Pt. 5

A country lying between Russia and Germany, originally independent, but divided between Prussia, Austria and Russia in 1772/95. An independent republic since 1918. Occupied by Germany from 1939 to 1945.

1860. 100 kopeks = 1 rouble
1918. 100 pfennig = 1 mark
100 halerzy = 1 korona
100 fenigow = 1 marka
1924. 100 groszy = 1 zloty

1 Russian Arms

2 Sigismund III Vasa Column, Warsaw

1860.
1b **1** 10 k. blue and red £475 £160

1918. Surch **POCZTA POLSKA** and value in fen. as in T **2**.
2 **2** 5 f. on 2 g. brown 70 60
3 – 10 f. on 6 g. green 60 50
4 – 25 f. on 10 g. red . . . . . . 1·90 1·25
5 – 50 f. on 20 g. blue . . . . . . 4·25 3·00
DESIGNS: 6 g. Arms of Warsaw; 10 g. Polish eagle; 20 g. Jan III Sobieski Monument, Warsaw.

1918. Stamps of German Occupation of Poland optd **Poczta Polska** or surch also.
9 **10** 3 pf. brown . . . . 9·00 6·00
10 5 pf. green 40 40
6 **24** 5 on 2½ pf. grey 25 25
7 **10** 5 on 3 pf. brown . . . . . . 2·25 1·25
11 10 pf. red 15 15
12 **24** 15 pf. violet 20 15
13 **10** 20 pf. blue 20 20
8 **24** 25 on 7½ pf. orange 40 30
14 **10** 30 pf. black & orge on buff . . 15 15
15 40 pf. black and red 30 30
16 60 pf. mauve 30 30

1918. Stamps of Austro-Hungarian Military Post (Nos. 69/71) optd **POLSKA POCZTA** and Polish eagle.
17 10 h. green . . . . 5·75 5·25
18 20 h. red . . . . 5·75 5·25
19 45 h. blue . . . . 5·75 5·25

1918. As stamps of Austro-Hungarian Military Post of 1917 optd **POLSKA POCZTA** and Polish eagle or surch also.
20b 3 h. on 3 h. olive . . . . . 18·00 12·50
21 3 h. on 15 h. red . . . . . . 3·75 2·00
22 10 h. on 30 h. green . . . . . 3·75 2·00
23 25 h. on 40 h. olive . . . . . 6·00 2·75
24 45 h. on 60 h. red . . . . . . 5·50 2·75
25 45 h. on 80 h. blue . . . . . 6·00 2·75
28 50 h. green . . . . 38·00 21·00
26 50 h. on 60 h. red . . . . . . 5·50 2·75
29 90 h. violet . . . . 5·50 3·00

1919. Stamps of Austria optd **POCZTA POLSKA**, No. 49 also surch **25**.
30 **49** 3 h. violet £170 £130
31 5 h. green £170 £130
32 6 h. orange . . . . 18·00 12·50
33 10 h. purple £170 £140
34 12 h. blue . . . . 18·00 12·00
35 **60** 15 h. red . . . . 5·25 4·25
36 20 h. green . . . . 60·00 55·00
37 25 h. blue £600 £550
49 **51** 25 on 80 h. brown . . . . . 2·10 1·90
60 30 h. violet . . . . £120 85·00
39 **51** 40 h. green . . . . 12·00 9·50
40 50 h. green . . . . 4·25 3·50
41 60 h. blue . . . . 3·25 3·25
42 80 h. brown . . . . 3·50 3·50
43 90 h. purple £500 £400
44 1 k. red on yellow . . . . . 6·75 4·50
45 **52** 2 k. blue . . . . 3·75 3·75
46 3 k. red . . . . 45·00 38·00
47 4 k. green . . . . 65·00 50·00
48a 10 k. violet £3000 £2500

11

1919. Imperf.
50 **11** 2 h. grey 35 45
51 3 h. violet 35 45
52 5 h. green 25 30
53 6 h. orange . . . . 12·00 15·00
54 10 h. red 25 30
55 15 h. brown 25 30
56 20 h. olive 35 45
57 25 h. red 15 15
58 50 h. blue 25 30
59 70 h. blue 35 45
60 1 k. red and grey 60 75

15 16 17 Agriculture

18 Ploughing in peace

19 Polish Uhlan

1919. For Southern Poland. Value in halerzy or korony. Imperf or perf.
68 **15** 3 h. brown 10 10
69 5 h. green 10 10
70 10 h. orange 10 10
71 15 h. red 10 10
72 **16** 20 h. brown 10 10
85 25 h. blue 10 10
86 50 h. brown 10 10
75 **17** 1 k. green 10 10
88 1 k. 50 brown 90 25
89 2 k. blue . . . . 1·10 25
90 **18** 2 k. 50 purple . . . . . . 1·10 50
91 **19** 5 k. blue . . . . 1·75 90

1919. For Northern Poland. Value in fenigow or marki. Imperf or perf.
104 **15** 3 f. brown 10 10
105 5 f. green 10 10
179 5 f. blue 10 10
106 10 f. purple 10 10
129 10 f. brown 10 10
107 15 f. red 10 10
108 **16** 20 f. blue 10 10
181 20 f. red 10 10
109 25 f. green 10 10
110 50 f. green 10 10
183 50 f. orange 10 10
137 **17** 1 m. violet 20 10
112 1 m. 50 green 60 25
138 2 m. brown 60 10
114 **18** 2 m. 50 brown . . . . . . 1·00 60
139 3 m. brown 30 10
140 **19** 5 m. purple 10 10
141 6 m. red 10 10
142 10 m. red 25 15
143 20 m. green 50 25

1919. 1st Polish Philatelic Exhibition and Polish White Cross Fund. Surch **I POLSKA WYSTAWA MAREK**, cross and new value. Imperf or perf.
116 **15** 5+5 f. green 15 15
117 10+5 f. purple 30 15
118 15+5 f. red 15 15
119 **16** 25+5 f. olive 20 15
120 50+5 f. green 50 30

20

21 Prime Minster Paderewski

22 A. Trampezynski

23 Eagle and Ship

24

1919. 1st Session of Parliament in Liberated Poland. Dated "1919".
121 **20** 10 f. mauve 15 10
122 **21** 15 f. red 15 10
123 **22** 20 f. brown (21 × 25 mm) . . 55 30
124 20 f. brown (17 × 20 mm) . . 1·10 65
125 – 25 f. green . . . . 1·10 65
126 **23** 50 f. blue 35 15
127 – 1 m. violet 40 15
DESIGN—As Type **21**: 25 f. Gen. Pilsudski; As Type **23**: 1 m. Griffin and fasces.

1920.
146 **24** 40 f. violet 10 10
182 40 f. brown 10 10
184 75 f. green 10 10

1920. As T **15**, but value in marks ("Mk").
147 **15** 1 m. red 10 10
148 2 m. green 10 10
149 3 m. blue 10 10
150 4 m. red 10 10
151 5 m. purple 10 10
152 8 m. brown 25 20

1921. Surch **3 Mk**, and bars.
153 **24** 3 m. on 40 f. violet 10 10

1921. Red Cross Fund. Surch with cross and **30MK**.
154 **19** 5 m. + 30 m. purple . . . 3·75 8·00
155 6 m. + 30 m. red . . . . 3·75 8·00
156 10 m. + 30 m. red . . . 8·00 13·00
157 20 m. + 30 m. green . . . 30·00 27·00

28 Sun of Peace

29 Agriculture

1921. New Constitution.
158 **28** 2 m. green . . . . 1·50 1·25
159 3 m. blue . . . . 1·50 1·25
160 4 m. red 70 40
161 **29** 6 m. red 70 40
162 10 m. green . . . . 1·10 40
163 – 25 m. violet . . . . . . 2·25 1·25
164 – 50 m. green and buff . . . 1·50 90
DESIGN: 25, 50 m. "Peace" (Seated women.)

31 Sower

32

1921. Peace Treaty with Russia.
165 **31** 10 m. blue 20 10
166 15 m. brown 25 10
167 20 m. red 20 10

1921.
170 **32** 25 m. violet and buff . . . 10 10
171 50 m. red and buff 10 10
172 100 m. brown and orange . . 10 10
173 200 m. pink and black . . . 10 15
174 300 m. green 15 10
175 400 m. brown 15 10
176 500 m. purple 15 10
177 1000 m. orange 15 10
178 2000 m. violet 15 10

33 Silesian Miner

1922.
185 **33** 1 m. black 10 10
186 1 m. 25 green 10 10
187 2 m. red 10 10
188 3 m. green 10 10
189 4 m. blue 10 10
190 5 m. brown 10 10
191 6 m. orange 10 25
192 10 m. brown 10 10
193 20 m. purple 10 10
194 50 m. olive 10 70
195 80 m. red . . . . 40 1·00
196 100 m. violet . . . . . . 40 1·00
197 200 m. orange . . . . . . 80 1·50
198 300 m. blue . . . . 2·10 3·25

34 Copernicus

39

1923. 450th Birth Anniv of Copernicus (astronomer) and 150th Death Anniv of Konarski (educationist).
199 **34** 1,000 m. slate 60 25
200 – 3,000 m. brown 35 25
201 **34** 5,000 m. red 60 35
DESIGN: 3,000 m. Konarski.

1923. Surch.
202 **32** 10 TYSIECY (= 10000) on 25 m. violet and buff 15 10
206 **15** 20,000 m. on 2 m. green (No. 148) 35 15
204 **31** 25,000 m. on 20 m. red . . 15 10
205 50,000 m. on 10 m. blue . . 15 10
207 **15** 100,000 m. on 5 m. purple (No. 151) 15 10

1924.
208 **39** 10,000 m. purple 25 30
209 20,000 m. green 15 10
210 30,000 m. red 80 30
211 50,000 m. green 85 30
212 100,000 m. brown 60 25
213 200,000 m. blue 60 15
214 300,000 m. mauve 60 30
215 500,000 m. brown . . . . . 60 1·50
216 1,000,000 m. pink . . . . . 60 3·25
217 2,000,000 m. green . . . . 95 12·00

40

41 President Wojciechowski

42

1924. New Currency.
218 **40** 1 g. brown 45 40
219 2 g. brown 45 10
220 3 g. orange 55 10
221 5 g. green 75 10
222 10 g. green 75 10
223 15 g. red 75 10
224 20 g. blue . . . . 3·00 10
225 25 g. red . . . . 4·00 15
226 30 g. violet . . . . 16·00 10
227 40 g. blue . . . . 4·50 30
228 50 g. purple . . . . 3·50 15
229 **41** 1 z. red . . . . 32·00 1·40

1925. National Fund.
230 **42** 1 g. + 50 g. brown . . . . 17·00 20·00
231 2 g. + 50 g. brown . . . . 17·00 20·00
232 3 g. + 50 g. orange . . . . 17·00 20·00
233 5 g. + 50 g. green . . . . 17·00 20·00
234 10 g. + 50 g. green . . . . 17·00 20·00
235 15 g. + 50 g. red . . . . 17·00 20·00
236 20 g. + 50 g. blue . . . . 17·00 20·00
237 25 g. + 50 g. red . . . . 17·00 20·00
238 30 g. + 50 g. violet . . . . 17·00 20·00
239 40 g. + 50 g. blue . . . . 17·00 20·00
240 50 g. + 50 g. purple . . . . 17·00 20·00

43 Holy Gate, Vilna

44 Town Hall, Pozan

48 Galleon

1925.
241 **43** 1 g. brown 25 10
242 – 2 g. olive 50 25
243a – 3 g. blue . . . . 1·40 10
244a **44** 5 g. green . . . . 1·40 10
245a – 10 g. violet . . . . . . 1·40 10
246 – 15 g. red . . . . 1·50 10
247 **48** 20 g. red . . . . 3·00 10
248 **43** 24 g. blue . . . . 8·00 60
249 – 30 g. blue . . . . 3·25 10
250 – 40 g. blue . . . . 3·25 10
251 **48** 45 g. mauve . . . . . . 10·00 40
DESIGNS—As Type **43**: VERT: 2, 30 g. Jan III Sobieski Statue, Lwow. As Type **44**: 3, 10 g. King Sigismund Vasa Column, Warsaw. HORIZ: 15, 40 g. Wawel Castle, Cracow.

49 LVG Schneider Biplane

50 Chopin

1925. Air.
252 **49** 1 g. blue . . . . 65 2·25
253 2 g. orange . . . . 65 2·25
254 3 g. brown . . . . 65 2·25
255 5 g. brown 65 50
256 10 g. green . . . . 1·75 60
257 15 g. mauve . . . . 2·25 75
258 20 g. olive . . . . 12·00 3·50
259 30 g. red . . . . 8·00 1·75
260 45 g. lilac . . . . 11·00 3·75

1927.
261 **50** 40 g. blue . . . . 13·00 1·25

51 Marshal Pilsudski

52 Pres. Moscicki

53

1927.
262 **51** 20 g. red . . . . 2·10 10
262a 25 g. brown . . . . 2·10 15

1927.
263 **52** 20 g. red . . . . 5·25 35

1927. Educational Funds.
264 **53** 10 g. + 5 g. purple on green 8·50 10·00
265 20 g. + 5 g. blue on yellow . 8·50 10·00

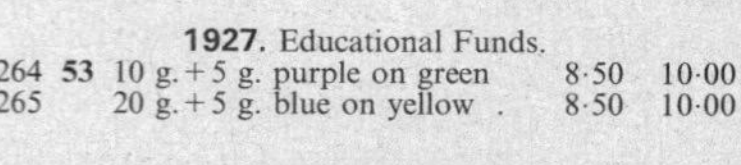

54 Dr. Karl Kaczkowki

55 J. Slowacki (poet)

1927. 4th Int Military Medical Congress, Warsaw.
266 **54** 10 g. green . . . . 3·00 1·00
267 25 g. red . . . . 6·00 2·75
268 40 g. blue . . . . 8·00 2·25

1927. Transfer of Slowacki's remains to Cracow.
269 **55** 20 g. red 5·25 40

56 Marshal Pilsudski — 57 Pres. Moscicki — 58 Gen. Joseph Bem

1928.
272 **56** 50 g. grey 3·25 15
272a 50 g. green 9·00 15
273 **57** 1 z. black on cream 8·75 15

1928.
271 **58** 25 g. red 3·00 20

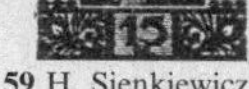

59 H. Sienkiewicz — 60 Slav God, "Swiatowit"

1928. Henryk Sienkiewicz (author).
274 **59** 15 g. blue 1·90 15

1929. National Exhibition Poznan.
275 **60** 25 g. brown 2·40 15

61 — 62 King Jan III Sobieski — 63

1929.
276 **61** 5 g. violet 20 10
277 10 g. green 60 10
278 25 g. brown 40 10

1930. Birth Tercentenary of Jan III Sobieski.
279 **62** 75 g. purple 5·25 20

1930. Centenary of "November Rising" (29th Nov., 1830).
280 **63** 5 g. purple 75 10
281 15 g. blue 3·00 20
282 25 g. lake 1·75 10
283 30 g. red 10·00 3·25

64 Kosciusko, Washington and Pulaski — 65

1932. Birth Bicentenary of George Washington.
284 **64** 30 g. brown on cream 2·75 25

1932.
284a **65** 5 g. violet 15 10
285 10 g. green 15 10
285a 15 g. red 15 10
286 20 g. grey 50 10
287 25 g. bistre 50 10
288 30 g. red 3·00 10
289 60 g. blue 2·50 10

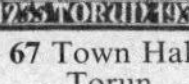

67 Town Hall, Torun — 68 Franciszek Zwirko (airman) and Stanislaw Wigura (aircraft designer)

1933. 700th Anniv of Torun.
290 **67** 60 g. blue on cream 30·00 45

1933. Victory in Flight round Europe Air Race, 1932.
292 **68** 30 g. green 15·00 1·50

1933. Torun Philatelic Exhibition.
293 **67** 60 g. red on cream 17·00 15·00

69 Altar-piece, St. Mary's Church, Cracow

1933. 4th Death Centenary of Veit Stoss (sculptor).
294 **69** 80 g. brown on cream 13·00 1·40

70 "Liberation of Vienna" by J. Matejko

1933. 250th Anniv of Relief of Vienna.
295 **70** 1 z. 20 blue on cream 32·00 12·00

71 Cross of Independence — 73 Marshal Pilsudski and Legion of Fusiliers Badge

1933. 15th Anniv of Proclamation of Republic.
296 **71** 30 g. red 7·75 30

1934. Katowice Philatelic Exhibition. Optd **Wyst. Filat. 1934 Katowice**.
297 **65** 20 g. grey 38·00 26·00
298 30 g. red 38·00 26·00

1934. 20th Anniv of Formation of Polish Legion.
299 **73** 25 g. blue 95 20
300 30 g. brown 2·40 30

1934. Int Air Tournament. Optd **Challenge 1934**.
301 **49** 20 g. olive 14·00 8·50
302 **68** 30 g. green 8·00 2·00

1934. Surch in figures.
303 **69** 25 g. on 80 g. brown on cream 5·25 45
304 **65** 55 g. on 60 g. blue 5·00 25
305 **70** 1 z. on 1 z. 20 blue on cream 17·00 4·00

77 Marshal Pilsudski

1935. Mourning Issue.
306 **77** 5 g. black 70 10
307 15 g. black 70 25
308 25 g. black 1·10 10
309 45 g. black 3·00 1·40
310 1 z. black 5·00 3·00

1935. Optd **Kopiec Marszalka Pilsudskiego**.
311 **65** 15g. red 70 65
312 **73** 25 g. blue 2·50 1·60

79 Pieskowa Skala (Dog's Rock) — 80 Pres. Moscicki

1935.
313 **79** 5 g. blue 40 10
317 – 5 g. violet 15 10
314 – 10 g. green 40 10
318 – 10 g. green 75 10
315 – 15 g. blue 3·25 10
319 – 15 g. lake 30 10
316 – 20 g. black 90 10
320 – 20 g. orange 45 10
321a – 25 g. green 80 10
322 – 30 g. red 1·75 15
323a – 45 g. mauve 1·75 15
324a – 50 g. black 2·25 15
325 – 55 g. blue 6·50 40
326 – 1 z. brown 4·00 90
327 **80** 3 z. brown 2·50 2·25

DESIGNS: 5 g. (No. 317) Monastery of Jasna Gora, Czestochowa; 10 g. (314) Lake Morskie Oko; 10 g. (318) "Batory" (liner) at sea passenger terminal, Gdynia; 15 g. (315) "Pilsudski" (liner); 15 g. (319) University, Lwow; 20 g. (316) Pieniny-Czorsztyn; 20 g. (320) Administrative Buildings, Katowice; 25 g. Belvedere Palace, Warsaw; 30 g. Castle at Mir; 45 h. Castle at Podhorce; 50 g. Cloth Hall, Cracow; 55 g. Raczynski Library, Poznan; 1 z. Vilna Cathedral.

1936. 10th Anniv of Moscicki Presidency. As T **57** but inscr "1926. 3. VI. 1936" below design.
328 **57** 1 z. blue 6·00 5·50

1936. Gordon-Bennett Balloon Race. Optd **GORDON-BENNETT 30. VIII. 1936.**
329 30 g. red (No. 322) 10·50 5·00
330 55 g. blue (No. 325) 10·50 5·00

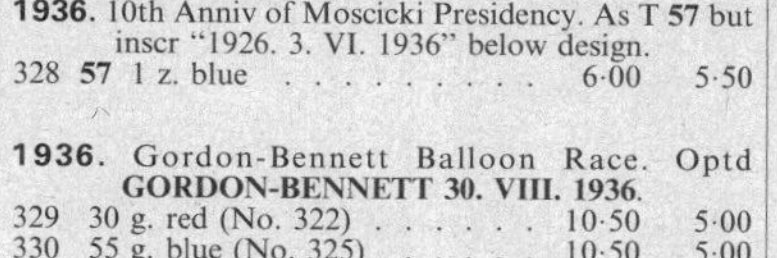

82 Marshal Smigly-Rydz — 83 Pres. Moscicki

1937.
331 **82** 25 g. blue 35 10
332 55 g. blue 50 10
For 25 g. brown see note after No. 273.

1938. President's 70th Birthday.
333 **83** 15 g. grey 20 10
334 30 g. purple 40 10

84 Kosciuszko, Paine and Washington

1938. 150th Anniv of U.S. Constitution.
335 **84** 1 z. blue 1·60 1·40

85a — 86 Marshal Pilsudski

1938. 20th Anniv of Independence.
336 – 5 g. orange 10 10
337 – 10 g. green 10 10
338 **85a** 15 g. brown (A) 15 15
357 15 g. brown (B) 25 20
339 – 20 g. blue 35 10
340 – 25 g. purple 10 10
341 – 30 g. red 55 10
342 – 45 g. black 85 15
343 – 50 g. mauve 1·90 10
344 – 55 g. blue 45 10
345 – 75 g. green 2·75 1·40
346 – 1 z. orange 2·75 1·40
347 – 2 z. red 9·00 7·00
348 **86** 3 z. blue 9·00 13·00

DESIGNS—VERT: 5 g. Boleslaw the Brave; 10 g. Casimir the Great; 20 g. Casimir Jagiellon; 25 g. Sigismund August; 30 g. Stefan Batory; 45 g. Chodkiewicz and Zolkiewski; 50 g. Jan III Sobieski; 55 g. Symbol of Constitution of May 3rd, 1791; 75 g. Kosciuszko, Poniatowski and Dabrowski; 1 z. November Uprising 1830–31; 2 z. Romuald Traugutt.

(A) Type **85a**. (B) as Type **85a** but crossed swords omitted.

87 Teschen comes to Poland — 88 "Warmth"

1938. Acquisition of Teschen.
349 **87** 25 g. purple 1·40 35

1938. Winter Relief Fund.
350 **88** 5 g.+5 g. orange 40 1·70
351 25 g.+10 g. purple 85 1·60
352 55 g.+15 g. blue 1·60 2·50

89 Tatra Mountaineer

1939. International Ski Championship, Zakopane.
353 **89** 15 g. brown 1·00 70
354 25 g. purple 1·50 80
355 30 g. red 2·00 90
356 55 g. blue 7·00 4·50

90 Pilsudski and Polish Legionaries

1939. 25th Anniv of 1st Battles of Polish Legions.
358 **90** 25 g. purple 80 40

1939–1945. GERMAN OCCUPATION.

1939. T **94** of Germany surch **Deutsche Post OSTEN** and value.
359 **94** 6 g. on 3 pf. brown 20 40
360 8 g. on 4 pf. grey 20 30
361 12 g. on 6 pf. green 20 25
362 16 g. on 8 pf. orange 75 1·00
363 20 g. on 10 pf. brown 25 20
364 24 g. on 12 pf. red 25 20
365 30 g. on 15 pf. red 65 85
366 40 g. on 20 pf. blue 50 40
367 50 g. on 25 pf. blue 60 50
368 60 g. on 30 pf. olive 60 25
369 80 g. on 40 pf. mauve 70 70
370 1 z. on 50 pf. black & grn 1·90 1·25
371 2 z. on 100 pf. black & yell 3·75 3·00

1940. Surch **General Gouvernement** and Nazi emblem and value.
372 – 2 g. on 5 g. orge (No. 336) 20 30
373 – 4 g. on 5 g. orge (No. 336) 20 30
374 – 6 g. on 10 g. grn (No. 337) 20 30
375 – 8 g. on 10 g. grn (No. 337) 20 30
376 – 10 g. on 10 g. green (No. 337) 20 30
377 **107** 12 g. on 15 g. brown (No. 338) 20 30
378 16 g. on 15 g. brown (No. 338) 20 30
379 **104** 24 g. on 25 g. blue 20 30
380 – 24 g. on 25 g. purple (No. 340) 80 80
381 – 30 g. on 30 g. red (No. 341) 40 40
382 **110** 30 g. on 5 g.+5 g. orge 40 50
383 **105** 40 g. on 30 g. purple 50 75
384 **110** 40 g. on 25 g.+10 g. pur 40 40
385 – 50 g. on 50 g. mauve (No. 343) 25 40
386 **104** 50 g. on 55 g. blue 40 40
386a D **88** 50 g. on 20 g. green 1·00 1·90
386b 50 g. on 25 g. green 16·00 14·00
386c 50 g. on 30 g. green 40·00 32·00
386d 50 g. on 50 g. green 1·50 1·90
386e 50 g. on 1 z. green 1·50 1·90
387 – 60 g. on 55 g. blue (No. 344) 10·00 8·50
388 – 80 g. on 75 g. green (No. 345) 10·00 8·50
388a **110** 1 z. on 55 g.+15 g. blue 9·00 6·00
389 – 1 z. on 1 z. orge (No. 346) 10·00 8·50
390 – 2 z. on 2 z. red (No. 347) 7·50 6·00
391 **108** 3 z. on 3 z. blue 7·50 6·00
Nos. 386a/e are all postage stamps.

93 Copernicus Memorial, Cracow — 95

1940.
392 – 6 g. brown 25 60
393 – 8 g. brown 25 60
394 – 8 g. black 25 40
395 – 10 g. green 15 15
396 **93** 12 g. green 3·00 25
397 12 g. violet 30 15
398 – 20 g. brown 10 10
399 – 24 g. red 10 10
400 – 30 g. violet 10 15
401 – 30 g. purple 20 30
402 – 40 g. black 20 15
403 – 48 g. brown 70 1·00
404 – 50 g. blue 20 15
405 – 60 g. olive 20 20
406 – 80 g. violet 25 25
407 – 1 z. purple 2·00 1·10
408 – 1 z. green 45 40

DESIGNS: 6 g. Florian gate, Cracow; 8 g. Castle Keep, Cracow; 10 g. Cracow Gate, Lublin; 20 g. Church of the Dominicans, Cracow; 24 g. Wawel Castle, Cracow; 30 g. Old Church in Lublin; 40 g. Arcade, Cloth Hall, Cracow; 48 g. Town Hall, Sandomir; 50 g. Town Hall, Cracow; 60 g. Courtyard of Wawel Castle, Cracow; 80 g. St. Mary's Church, Cracow; 1 z. Bruhl Palace, Warsaw.

1940. Red Cross Fund. As last, new colours, surch with Cross and premium in figures.
409 12 g.+8 g. olive 2·75 2·75
410 24 g.+16 g. olive 2·75 2·75
411 50 g.+50 g. olive 3·25 3·75
412 80 g.+80 g. olive 3·25 3·75

1940. 1st Anniv of German Occupation.
413 **95** 12 g.+38 g. green 1·75 1·90
414 – 24 g.+26 g. red 1·75 1·90
415 – 30 g.+20 g. violet 3·00 2·75
DESIGNS: 24 g. Woman with scarf; 30 g. Fur-capped peasant as Type **96**.

96

1940. Winter Relief Fund.
416 **96** 12 g.+8 g. green . . . . . 1·00 75
417 24 g.+16 g. red . . . . . 1·40 1·50
418 30 g.+30 g. brown . . . . 1·75 1·75
419 50 g.+50 g. blue . . . . . 2·40 2·50

97 Cracow

1941.
420 **97** 10 z. grey and red . . . . 2·25 1·50

98 The Barbican, Cracow
99 Adolf Hitler

1941.
421 **98** 2 z. blue 35 55
422 – 4 z. green 50 70
DESIGN: 4 z. Tyniec Monastery.
See also Nos. 465/8.

1941.
423 **99** 2 g. grey 10 20
424 6 g. brown 10 20
425 8 g. blue 10 20
426 10 g. green 10 10
427 12 g. violet 10 10
428 16 g. orange 35 40
429 20 g. brown 10 15
430 24 g. red 10 10
431 30 g. purple 30 15
432 32 g. green 15 35
433 40 g. blue 10 15
434 48 g. brown 40 40
435 50 g. blue 10 15
436 60 g. olive 10 15
437 80 g. purple 10 15
441 1 z. green 30 40
442 1 z. 20 brown 35 45
443 1 z. 60 blue 45 60

1942. Hitler's 53rd Birthday. As T **99**, but premium inserted in design.
444 30 g.+1 z. purple 30 35
445 50 g.+1 z. blue 30 35
446 1 z. 20+1 z. brown 30 35

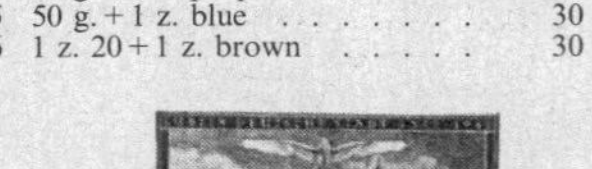

100 Modern Lublin

1942. 600th Anniv of Lublin.
447 – 12 g.+8 g. purple 10 15
448 **100** 24 g.+6 g. brown 10 15
449 – 50 g.+50 g. blue 15 25
450 **100** 1 z.+1 z. green 50 60
DESIGN: 12, 50 g. Lublin, after an ancient engraving.

101 Copernicus
102 Adolf Hitler

1942. 3rd Anniv of German Occupation.
451 – 12 g.+18 g. violet 15 15
452 – 24 g.+26 g. red 15 15
453 – 30 g.+30 g. purple 15 15
454 – 50 g.+50 g. blue 15 20
455 **101** 1 z.+1 z. green 60 35
DESIGNS: 12 g. Velt Stoss (Vit Stvosz); 24 g. Hans Durer; 30 g. J. Schuch; 50 g. J. Elsner.

1943. Hitler's 54th Birthday.
456 **102** 12 g.+1 z. violet 15 20
457 24 g.+1 z. red 15 20
458 84 g.+1 z. green 30 35

1943. 400th Death Anniv of Nicolas Copernicus (astronomer). As No. 455, colour changed, optd **24. MAI 1543 24. MAI 1943.**
459 **101** 1 z.+1 z. purple 60 65

103 Cracow Gate, Lublin
103a Lwow

1943. 3rd Anniv of Nazi Party in German-occupied Poland.
460 **103** 12 g.+38 g. green 10 15
461 – 24 g.+76 g. red 10 15
462 – 30 g.+70 g. purple . . . 10 15
464 – 1 z.+2 z. grey 15 25
DESIGNS: 24 g. Cloth Hall, Cracow; 30 g. Administrative Building, Radom; 50 g. Bruhl Palace, Warsaw; 1 z. Town Hall, Lwow.

1943.
465 – 2 z. green 10 10
466 – 4 z. violet 20 25
467 **103a** 6 z. brown 35 40
468 – 10 z. grey and brown . . 40 50
DESIGNS: 2 z. The Barbican, Cracow; 4 z. Tyniec Monastery; 10 z. Cracow.

104 Adolf Hitler
105 Konrad Celtis

1944. Hitler's 55th Birthday.
469 **104** 12 z.+1 z. green 10 15
470 24 z.+1 z. brown 10 15
471 84 z.+1 z. violet 15 20

1944. Culture Funds.
472 **105** 12 g.+18 g. green 10 10
473 – 24 g.+26 g. red 10 10
474 – 30 g.+30 g. purple . . . 10 10
475 – 50 g.+50 g. blue 20 25
476 – 1 z.+1 z. brown 20 25
PORTRAITS: 24 g. A. Schluter; 30 g. H. Boner; 50 g. Augustus the Strong; 1 z. G. Pusch.

105a Cracow Castle

1944. 5th Anniv of German Occupation.
477a **105a** 10 z.+10 z. black & red 6·00 10·00

1941–45. ISSUES OF EXILED GOVERNMENT IN LONDON.

For correspondence on Polish sea-going vessels and, on certain days, from Polish Military camps in Great Britain.

106 Ruins of Ministry of Finance, Warsaw
107 Vickers-Armstrong Wellington and Hawker Hurricanes used by Poles in Great Britain

1941.
478 – 5 g. violet 15 60
479 **106** 10 g. green 20 70
480 – 25 g. grey . . . . 40 1·25
481 – 55 g. blue . . . . 70 1·75
482 – 75 g. olive . . . . 2·50 4·00
483 – 80 g. red . . . . 2·50 4·00
484 **107** 1 z. blue . . . . 6·00 5·00
485 – 1 z. 50 brown . . . . . 6·00 5·00
DESIGNS—VERT: 5 g. Ruins of U.S. Embassy, Warsaw; 25 g. Destruction of Mickiewicz Monument, Cracow; 1 z. 50, Polish submarine "Orzel". HORIZ: 55 g. Ruins of Warsaw; 75 g. Polish machine-gunners in Great Britain; 80 g. Polish tank in Great Britain.

108 Vickers-Armstrong Wellington and U-boat
109 Merchant Navy

1943.
486 **108** 5 g. red . . . . 1·00 85
487 **109** 10 g. green 60 90
488 – 25 g. violet 60 90
489 – 55 g. blue . . . . 65 1·25
490 – 75 g. brown . . . . . . 1·40 2·00
491 – 80 g. red . . . . 1·75 2·25
492 – 1 z. olive . . . . 3·00 3·00
493 – 1 z. 50 black . . . . . 2·00 4·00
DESIGNS—VERT: 25 g. Anti-tank gun in France; 55 g. Poles at Narvik; 1 z. Saboteurs damaging railway line. HORIZ: 75 g. The Tobruk road; 80 g. Gen. Sikorski visiting Polish troops in Middle East; 1 z. 50, Underground newspaper office.

1944. Capture of Monte Casino. Nos. 482/5 surch **MONTE CASSINO 18 V 1944** and value and bars.
494 – 45 g. on 75 g. olive . . . . 10·00 13·00
495 – 55 g. on 80 g. red . . . . 10·00 13·00
496 **107** 80 g. on 1 z. blue . . . . 10·00 13·00
497 – 1 z. 20 on 1 z. 50 brown . 10·00 13·00

111 Polish Partisans
112 Romuald Traugutt

1945. Relief Fund for Survivors of Warsaw Rising.
498 **111** 1 z.+2 z. green . . . . . 5·25 7·00

1944. INDEPENDENT REPUBLIC.

1944. National Heroes.
499 **112** 25 g. red . . . . 42·00 55·00
500 – 50 g. green . . . . 48·00 65·00
501 – 1 z. blue . . . . 50·00 55·00
PORTRAITS: 50 g. Kosciuszko; 1 z. H. Dabrowski.

113 White Eagle
114 Grunwald Memorial, Cracow

1944.
502 **113** 25 g. red 50 25
503 **114** 50 g. green 50 15

1944. No. 502 surch with value **31.XII. 1943** or **1944** and **K.R.N., P.K.W.N.** or **R.T.R.P.**
504 **113** 1 z. on 25 g. red . . . . . 1·75 2·00
505 2 z. on 25 g. red . . . . . 1·75 2·00
506 3 z. on 25 g. red . . . . . 1·75 2·00

1945. 82nd Anniv of 1863 Revolt against Russia. Surch with value and **22.I.1863**.
507 **112** 5 z. on 25 g. brown . . . 40·00 55·00

1945. Liberation. No. 502 surch **3 zl.** with town names and dates as indicated.
508 3 z. on 25 g. Bydgoszcz 23.1.1945 4·25 5·00
509 3 z. on 25 g. Czestochowa 17.1.1945 . . . . 4·25 5·00
510 3 z. on 25 g. Gniezno 22.1.1945 4·25 5·00
511 3 z. on 25 g. Kalisz 24.1.1945 . 4·25 5·00
512 3 z. on 25 g. Kielce 15.1.1945 . 4·25 5·00
513 3 z. on 25 g. Lodz 19.1.1945 . 4·25 5·00
515 3 z. on 25 g. Radom 16.1.1945 . 4·25 5·00
516 3 z. on 25 g. Warszawa 17.1.1945 10·50 14·00
517 3 z. on 25 g. Zakopane 29.1.1945 6·50 6·50

120 Flag-bearer and War Victim
121 Lodz Factories
123 Grunwald Memorial Cracow

1945. Liberation of Warsaw.
518 **120** 5 z. red . . . . 2·00 2·00

1945. Liberation of Lodz.
519 **121** 1 z. blue 65 20

1945. 151st Anniv of Kosciuszko's Oath of Allegiance. No. 500 surch **5 zl. 24.III.1794.**
520 5 z. on 50 g. green . . . . . 9·00 14·00

1945. Cracow Monuments. Inscr "19.1.1945".
521 **123** 50 g. purple 15 10
522 – 1 z. brown 20 10
523 – 2 z. blue 75 15
524 – 3 z. violet 85 25
525 – 5 z. green . . . . 5·00 7·00
DESIGNS—VERT: 1 z. Kosciuszko Statue; 3 z. Copernicus Memorial. HORIZ: 2 z. Cloth Hall; 5 z. Wawel Castle.

125 H.M.S. "Dragon" (cruiser)

1945. 25th Anniv of Polish Maritime League.
526 **125** 50 g.+2 z. orange . . . . 8·50 6·50
527 – 1 z.+3 z. blue . . . . . 4·50 6·50
528 – 2 z.+4 z. red . . . . . . 3·50 5·50
529 – 3 z.+5 z. olive . . . . . 3·50 5·50
DESIGNS—VERT: 1 z. "Dar Pomorza" (full-rigged cadet ship); 2 z. Naval ensigns. HORIZ: 3 z. Crane and tower, Gdansk.

126 Town Hall, Poznan

1945. Postal Employees Congress.
530 **126** 1 z.+5 z. green . . . . . 18·00 23·00

127 Kosciuszko Memorial, Lodz
128 Grunwald, 1410

1945.
531 **127** 3 z. purple 70 25

1945. 535th Anniv of Battle of Grunwald.
532 **128** 5 z. blue . . . . 8·00 9·00

129 Eagle and Manifesto

1945. 1st Anniv of Liberation.
533 **129** 3 z. red . . . . 10·00 13·00

130 Westerplatte

1945. 6th Anniv of Defence of Westerplatte.
534 **130** 1 z.+9 z. slate . . . . . 20·00 24·00

1945. Surch with new value and heavy bars.
535 **114** 1 z. on 50 g. green . . . 45 15
536a **113** 1 z. 50 on 25 g. red . . . 45 15

133 Crane Tower, Gdansk

1945. Liberation of Gdansk (Danzig). Perf or imperf.
537 **133** 1 z. olive 10 10
538 – 2 z. blue 20 10
539 – 3 z. purple 50 10
DESIGNS—VERT: 2 z. Stock Exchange, Gdansk. HORIZ: 3 z. High Gate, Gdansk.

135 St. John's Cathedral

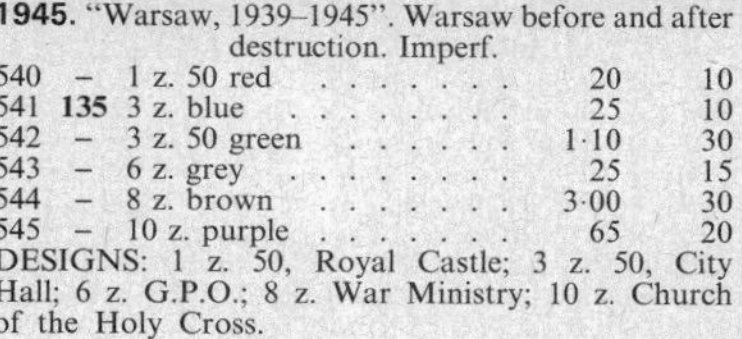

1945. "Warsaw, 1939–1945". Warsaw before and after destruction. Imperf.

540	–	1 z. 50 red	20	10
541	135	3 z. blue	25	10
542	–	3 z. 50 green	1·10	30
543	–	6 z. grey	25	15
544	–	8 z. brown	3·00	30
545	–	10 z. purple	65	20

DESIGNS: 1 z. 50, Royal Castle; 3 z. 50, City Hall; 6 z. G.P.O.; 8 z. War Ministry; 10 z. Church of the Holy Cross.

136 United Workers

1945. Trades' Union Congress.

546	136	1 z. 50+8 z. 50 grey	7·25	8·00

137 Soldiers of 1830 and Jan III Sobieski Statue

1945. 115th Anniv of 1830 Revolt against Russia.

547	137	10 z. grey	8·50	10·50

1946. 1st Anniv of Warsaw Liberation. Nos. 540/5 optd **WARSZAWA WOLNA 17 Styczen 1945-1946.** Imperf.

548	1 z. 50 red	1·75	2·50
549	3 z. blue	1·75	2·50
550	3 z. 50 green	1·75	2·50
551	6 z. grey	1·75	2·50
552	8 z. brown	1·75	2·50
553	10 z. purple	1·75	2·50

139 Insurgent

1946. 83rd Anniv of 1863 Revolt.

554	139	6 z. blue	6·75	8·00

140 Lisunov Li-2 over Ruins of Warsaw

1946. Air.

555	140	5 z. grey	35	10
556		10 z. purple	45	15
557		15 z. blue	2·50	20
558		20 z. purple	1·10	15
559		25 z. green	2·00	35
560		30 z. red	3·00	45

141 Fighting in Spain

1946. Polish Legion in the Spanish Civil War.

561	141	3 z.+5 z. red	4·00	3·75

142 Bydgoszcz

143 "Death" over Majdanek Concentration Camp

1946. 600th Anniv of City of Bydgoszcz.

562	142	3 z+2 z. grey	6·50	6·00

1946. Majdanek Concentration Camp.

563	143	3 z.+5 z. green	3·00	3·00

144 Shield and Soldiers

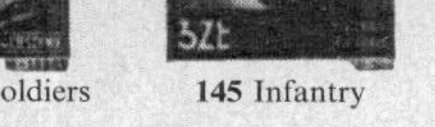

145 Infantry

1946. Uprisings in Upper Silesia (1919–23) and Silesian Campaign against the Germans (1939–45).

564	144	3 z.+7 z. brown	90	65

1946. 1st Anniv of Peace.

565	145	3 z. brown	40	25

146 Polish Coastline

148 Bedzin Castle

147 Pres. Bierut, Premier O. Morawski and Marshal Zymierski

1946. Maritime Festival.

566	146	3 z.+7 z. blue	1·75	2·25

1946. 2nd Anniv of Polish Committee of National Liberation Manifesto.

567	147	3 z. violet	3·25	3·75

1946. Imperf (5z., 10z.) or perf (6 z.).

568	148	5 z. olive	15	10
568a		5 z. brown	20	10
569	–	6 z. black	35	10
570	–	10 z. blue	70	15

DESIGNS—VERT: 6 z. Tombstone of Henry IV. HORIZ: 10 z. Castle at Lanckorona.

149 Crane, Monument and Crane Tower, Gdansk

1946. The Fallen in Gdansk.

571	149	3 z.+12 z. grey	2·00	2·00

150 Schoolchildren at Desk

1946. Polish Work for Education and Fund for International Bureau of Education.

571a	150	3 z.+22 z. red	25·00	42·00
571b	–	6 z.+24 z. blue	25·00	42·00
571c	–	11 z.+19 z. green	25·00	42·00

DESIGNS: 6 z. Court of Jagiellonian University, Cracow; 11 z. Gregory Piramowicz (1735–1801), founder of the Education Commission.

152 Stojalowski, Bojko, Stapinski and Witos

1946. 50th Anniv of Peasant Movement and Relief Fund.

572	152	5 z.+10 z. green	1·25	1·40
573		5 z.+10 z. blue	1·25	1·40
574		5 z.+10 z. olive	1·25	1·40

1947. Opening of Polish Parliament. Surch **+7 SEJM USTAWODAWCZY 19.1.1947.**

575	147	3 z.+7 z. violet	7·25	7·75

1947. 22nd National Ski Championships, Zakopane. Surch **5+15 zl XXII MISTRZOSTWA NARCIARSKIE POLSKI 1947.**

576	113	5+15 z. on 25 g. red	3·25	4·00

1947. No. 569 surch **5 ZL** in outlined figure and capital letters between stars.

577	5 z. on 6 z. black	60	25

156 Home of Emil Zegadlowicz

157 Frederic Chopin (musician)

158 Boguslawski, Modrzejewska and Jaracz (actors)

159 Wounded Soldier, Nurse and Child

1947. Emil Zegadlowicz Commemoration.

578	156	5 z.+15 z. green	1·10	1·40

1947. Polish Culture. Imperf or perf.

579	–	1 z. blue	20	15
580	–	1 z. grey	20	15
581	–	2 z. brown	25	15
582	–	2 z. orange	15	15
583	157	3 z. green	80	20
584		3 z. olive	1·75	30
585	158	5 z. black	55	15
586		5 z. brown	20	15
587	–	6 z. grey	90	20
588	–	6 z. red	35	15
589	–	10 z. grey	1·50	40
590	–	10 z. blue	1·40	25
591	–	15 z. violet	1·50	40
592	–	15 z. brown	1·00	35
593	–	20 z. black	2·25	60
594	–	20 z. purple	1·00	50

PORTRAITS—HORIZ: 1 z. Matejko, Malczewski and Chelmonski (painters); 6 z. Swietochowski, Zeromski and Prus (writers); 15 z. Wyspianski, Slowacki and Kasprowicz (poets). VERT: 2 z. Brother Albert of Cracow; 10 z. Marie Curie (scientist); 20 z. Mickiewicz (poet).

1947. Red Cross Fund.

595	159	5 z.+5 z. grey and red	2·40	3·50

161 Steelworker

163 Brother Albert of Cracow

1947. Occupations.

596	161	5 z. lake	1·00	30
597	–	10 z. green	30	15
598	–	15 z. blue	60	25
599	–	20 z. black	1·00	30

DESIGNS: 10 z. Harvester; 15 z. Fisherman; 20 z. Miner.

1947. Air. Surch **LOTNICZA** bars and value.

600	114	40 z. on 50 g. green	2·00	50
602	113	50 z. on 25 g. red	3·00	1·75

1947. Winter Relief Fund.

603	163	2 z.+18 z. violet	1·10	2·40

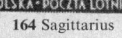

164 Sagittarius

165 Chainbreaker

1948. Air.

604	164	15 z. violet	1·90	25
605		25 z. blue	1·25	15
606		30 z. brown	1·25	40
607		50 z. green	2·40	45
608		75 z. black	2·40	60
609		100 z. orange	2·40	60

1948. Revolution Centenaries.

610	165	15 z. brown	35	15
611	–	30 z. brown	1·25	35
612	–	35 z. green	2·75	60
613	–	60 z. red	1·50	70

PORTRAITS—HORIZ: 30 z. Generals H. Dembinski and J. Bem; 35 z. S. Worcell, P. Sciegienny and E. Dembowski; 60 z. F. Engels and K. Marx.

167 Insurgents

168 Wheel and Streamers

1948. 5th Anniv of Warsaw Ghetto Revolt.

614	167	15 z. black	1·10	1·40

1948. Warsaw–Prague Cycle Race.

615	168	15 z. red and blue	3·00	1·10

169 Cycle Race

170 "Oliwa" under Construction

1948. 7th Circuit of Poland Cycle Race.

616	169	3 z. black	2·00	1·75
617		6 z. brown	2·00	1·75
618		15 z. green	2·75	2·50

1948. Merchant Marine.

619	170	6 z. violet	1·90	1·25
620	–	15 z. red	2·25	2·00
621	–	35 z. grey	3·50	3·25

DESIGNS—HORIZ: 15 z. Freighter at wharf; 35 z. "General M. Zaruski" (cadet ketch).

173 Firework Display

174 "Youth"

1948. Wroclaw Exhibition.

622	173	6 z. blue	40	30
623		15 z. red	65	20
624		18 z. red	1·10	40
625		35 z. brown	1·10	40

1948. International Youth Conf, Warsaw.

626	174	15 z. blue	50	25

175 Roadway, St. Anne's Church and Palace

176 Torun Ramparts and Mail Coach

1948. Warsaw Reconstruction Fund.

627	175	15 z.+5 z. green	25	25

1948. Philatelic Congress, Torun.

628	176	15 z. brown	65	25

177 Steam Locomotive, Clock and Winged Wheel

178 President Bierut

1948. European Railway Conference.

629	177	18 z. blue	5·50	7·75

1948.

629a	178	2 z. orange	10	10
629b		3 z. green	10	10
630		5 z. brown	10	10
631		6 z. black	60	10
631a		10 z. violet	15	10
632		15 z. red	50	10
633		18 z. green	70	20
634		30 z. blue	1·25	20
635		35 z. purple	2·00	40

179 Workers and Flag

1948. Workers' Class Unity Congress, (a) Dated "8 XII 1948".

636 **179** 5 z. red 80 50
637 – 15 z. violet 80 50
638 – 25 z. brown 80 50

(b) Dated "XII 1948".

639 **179** 5 z. plum . . . . 2·25 1·75
640 – 15 z. blue . . . . 2·25 1·75
641 – 25 z. green . . . . 3·00 2·00

DESIGNS: 15 z. Flags and portraits of Engels, Marx, Lenin and Stalin; 25 z. Workers marching and portrait of L. Warynski.

180 Baby 180a Pres. Franklin D. Roosevelt

1948. Anti-tuberculosis Fund. Portraits of babies as T **180**.

642 **180** 3 z.+2 z. green . . . 3·00 2·50
643 – 5 z.+5 z. brown . . . 3·00 2·50
644 – 6 z.+4 z. purple . . . 1·50 2·50
645 – 15 z.+10 . red . . . 1·25 1·75

1948. Air. Honouring Presidents Roosevelt, Pulaski and Kosciuszko.

645a **180a** 80 z. violet . . . 22·00 28·00
645b – 100 z. purple (Pulaski) . 24·00 22·00
645c – 120 z. blue (Kosciuszko) 24·00 22·00

181 Workers

1949. Trades' Union Congress, Warsaw.

646 **181** 3 z. red 90 90
647 – 5 z. blue 90 90
648 – 15 z. green . . . . 1·25 1·25

DESIGNS: 5 z. inscr "PRACA" (Labour), Labourer and tractor; 15 z. inscr "POKOJ" (Peace), Three labourers.

182 Banks of R. Vistula 183 Pres. Bierut

1949. 5th Anniv of National Liberation Committee.

649 **182** 10 z. black . . . . 2·00 1·50
650 **183** 15 z. mauve . . . . 2·00 1·50
651 – 35 z. blue . . . . 2·00 1·50

DESIGN—VERT: 35 z. Radio station, Rasyn.

184 Mail Coach and Map 185 Worker and Tractor

1949. 75th Anniv of U.P.U.

652 **184** 6 z. violet . . . . 1·00 1·25
653 – 30 z. blue (liner) . . . 1·75 1·60
654 – 80 z. green ('plane) . . 3·50 3·50

1949. Congress of Peasant Movement.

655 **185** 5 z. red 85 20
656 10 z. red 20 10
657 15 z. green 20 10
658 35 z. brown . . . . 1·00 70

186 Frederic Chopin 187 Mickiewicz and Pushkin 188 Postman

1949. National Celebrities.

659 – 10 z. purple . . . . 2·00 1·50
660 **186** 15 z. red . . . . 2·75 1·50
661 – 35 z. blue . . . . 2·00 1·50

PORTRAITS: 10 z. Adam Mickiewicz; 35 z. Julius Slowacki.

1949. Polish–Russian Friendship Month.

662 **187** 15 z. violet . . . . 2·40 2·40

1950. 3rd Congress of Postal Workers.

663 **188** 15 z. purple . . . . 2·00 1·40

189 Mechanic, Hangar and Aeroplane 190 President Bierut 195a

1950. Air.

664 **189** 500 z. lake . . . . 5·00 6·75

1950. (a) With frame.

665 **190** 15 z. red 50 15

(b) Without frame. Values in "zloty".

673 **195a** 5 z. green 10 10
674 10 z. red 10 10
675 15 z. blue 85 10
676 20 z. violet 35 10
677 25 z. brown 35 10
678 30 z. red 50 10
679 40 z. brown 70 10
680 50 z. olive . . . . 1·40 20

For values in "groszy" see Nos. 687/94.

191 J. Marchlewski 192 Workers

1950. 25th Death Anniv of Julian Marchlewski (patriot).

666 **191** 15 z. black 65 40

1950. Reconstruction of Warsaw.

667 **192** 5 z. brown 10 10

See also No.695.

193 Worker and Flag 194 Statue

1950. 60th Anniv of May Day Manifesto.

668 **193** 10 z. mauve . . . . 1·60 30
669 – 15 z. olive . . . . 1·60 15

DESIGN—VERT: 15 z. Three workers and flag.

1950. 23rd International Fair, Poznan.

670 **194** 15 z. brown 25 15

195 Dove and Globe 196 Industrial and Agricultural Workers

1950. International Peace Conference.

671 **195** 10 z. green 70 20
672 15 z. brown 30 15

1950. Six Year Reconstruction Plan.

681 **196** 15 z. blue 20 10

See also Nos. 696/e.

197 Hibner, Kniewski, Rutkowski 198 Worker and Dove

1950. 25th Anniv of Revolutionaries' Execution.

682 **197** 15 z. grey . . . . 2·00 60

1950. 1st Polish Peace Congress.

683 **198** 15 z. green 30 10

REVALUATION SURCHARGES. Following a revaluation of the Polish currency, a large number of definitive and commemorative stamps were locally overprinted "Groszy" or "gr". There are 37 known types of overprint and various colours of overprint. We do not list them as they had only local use, but the following is a list of the stamps which were duly authorised for overprinting:—Nos. 579/94, 596/615 and 619/58. Overprints on other stamps are not authorised.

Currency Revalued: 100 old zlotys = 1 new zloty.

199 Dove (after Picasso)

1950. 2nd World Peace Congress, Warsaw.

684 **199** 40 g. blue . . . . 1·60 35
685 45 g. red 30 10

200 General Bem and Battle of Piski

1950. Death Centenary of General Bem.

686 **200** 45 g. blue . . . . 2·75 1·75

1950. As T **195a**. Values in "groszy".

687 **195a** 5 g. violet 10 10
688 10 g. green 10 10
689 15 g. olive 10 10
690 25 g. red 15 10
691 30 g. red 20 10
692 40 g. orange 20 10
693 45 g. blue . . . . 1·25 20
694 75 g. brown 70 10

1950. As No. 667 but value in "groszy".

695 **192** 15 g. green 10 10

1950. As No. 681 but values in "groszy" or "zlotys".

696 **196** 45 g. blue 15 10
696b 75 g. brown 20 10
696d 1 z. 15 green 50 15
696e 1 z. 20 red 35 15

201 Woman and Doves 202 Battle Scene and J. Dabrowski

1951. Women's League Congress.

697 **201** 45 g. red 40 20

1951 80th Anniv of Paris Commune.

698 **202** 45 g. green 30 10

1951. Surch **45gr**.

699 **199** 45 g. on 15 z. red . . . 50 15

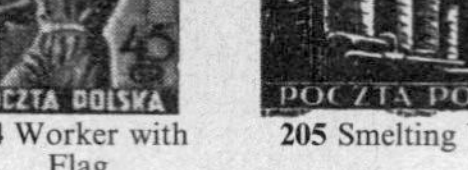

204 Worker with Flag 205 Smelting Works

1951. Labour Day.

700 **204** 45 g. red 40 10

1951.

701 **205** 40 g. blue 15 10
702 45 g. black 15 10
702a 60 g. brown 20 10
702c 90 g. lake 55 10

206 Pioneer and Badge 207 St. Staszic

1951. Int Children's Day. Inscr "I-VI-51"

703 **206** 30 g. olive . . . . 1·00 60
704 – 45 g. blue (Boy, girl and map) . . . . 5·75 60

1951. 1st Polish Scientific Congress. Inscr "KONGRES NAUKI POLSKIEJ"

705 **207** 25 g. red . . . . 2·75 2·75
706 – 40 g. blue 60 20
707 – 45 g. violet . . . . 7·75 65
708 – 60 g. green 60 20
709 – 1 z. 15 purple 90 50
710 – 1 z. 20 grey . . . . 1·75 20

DESIGNS—As Type **207**: 40 g. Marie Curie; 60 g. M. Nencki; 1 z. 15, Copernicus; 1 z. 20, Dove and book. HORIZ—36×21 mm: 45 g. Z. Wroblewski and Olszewski.

209 F. Dzerzhinsky 210 Pres. Bierut, Industry and Agriculture

1951. 25th Death Anniv of Dzerzhinsky (Russian politician).

711 **209** 45 g. brown 25 15

1951. 7th Anniv of People's Republic.

712 **210** 45 g. red 60 15
713 60 g. green . . . . 15·00 5·75
714 90 g. blue . . . . 3·50 70

211 Young People and Globe 213 Sports Badge

1951. 3rd World Youth Festival, Berlin.

715 **211** 40 g. blue 85 25

1951. Surch **45 gr.**

716 **195a** 45 g. on 35 z. orange . . 25 15

1951. Spartacist Games.

717 **213** 45 g. green . . . . 1·10 40

214 Stalin 215 Chopin and Moniuszko

1951. Polish–Soviet Friendship.

718 **214** 45 g. red 15 10
719 90 g. black 35 20

1951. Polish Musical Festival.

720 **215** 45 g. black 30 10
721 90 g. red 90 50

216 Mining Machinery 217 Building Modern Flats

1951. Six Year Plan (Mining).

722 **216** 90 g. brown 25 10
723 1 z. 20 blue 30 10
724 1 z. 20+15 g. orange . . 25 15

1951. Six Year Plan (Reconstruction).

725 **217** 30 g. green 10 10
726 30 g.+15 g. red 20 10
727 1 z. 15 purple 25 10

218 Installing Electric Cables 219 M. Nowotko

1951. Six Year Plan (Electrification).

728 **218** 30 g. black 10 10
729 45 g. red 15 10
730 45 g.+15 g. brown . . . 50 15

1952. 10th Anniv of Polish Workers' Coalition.
731 **219** 45 g. + 15 g. lake 15 10
732 – 90 g. brown 30 15
733 – 1 z. 15 orange 30 15
PORTRAITS: 90 g. P. Finder; 1 z. 15, M. Fornalska.

220 Women and Banner

1952. International Women's Day.
734 **220** 45 g. + 15 g. brown . . . 35 10
735 1 z. 20 red 45 20

221 Gen. Swierczewski

222 Ilyushin Il-12 over Farm

1952. 5th Death Anniv of Gen. Swierczewski.
736 **221** 45 g. + 15 g. brown . . . 35 10
737 90 g. blue 45 25

1952. Air. Aeroplanes and views.
738 – 55 g. blue (Tug and freighters) 40 25
739 **222** 90g. green 35 30
740 – 1 z. 40 purple (Warsaw) . . 50 30
741 – 5 z. black (Steelworks) . . 1·50 40

223 President Bierut

224 Cyclists and City Arms

1952. Pres. Bierut's 60th Birthday.
742 **223** 45 g. + 15 g. red 30 25
743 90 g. green 55 60
744 1 z. 20 + 15 g. blue 70 25

1952. 5th Warsaw–Berlin–Prague Peace Cycle Race.
745 **224** 40 g. blue . . . . 1·50 80

225 Workers and Banner

1952. Labour Day.
746 **225** 45 g. + 15 g. red 15 10
747 75 g. green 40 25

226 J. I. Kraszewski

227 Maria Konopnicka

1952. 140th Birth Anniv of Jozef Ignacy Kraszewski (writer).
748 **226** 25 g. purple 40 25

1952. 110th Birth Anniv of Maria Konopnicka (poet).
749 **227** 30 g. + 15 g. green 45 15
750 1 z. 15 brown 65 45

INDEX

Countries can be quickly located by referring to the index at the end of this volume.

228 H. Kollataj **229** Leonardo da Vinci **231** N. V. Gogol

230 President Bierut and Children

1952. 140th Death Anniv of Hugo Kollataj (educationist and politician).
751 **228** 45 g. + 15 g. brown . . . 15 10
752 1 z. green 25 15

1952. 500th Birth Anniv of Leonardo da Vinci (artist).
753 **229** 30 g. + 15 g. blue 75 35

1952. International Children's Day.
754 **230** 45 g. + 15 g. blue . . . . 2·25 60

1952. Death Centenary of Nikolai Gogol (Russian writer).
755 **231** 25 g. green 60 25

232 Cement Works

233 Swimmers

1952. Construction of Concrete Works, Wierzbica.
756 **232** 3 z. black . . . . 1·25 35
757 10 z. red . . . . 1·60 30

1952. Sports Day.
758 **233** 30 g. + 15 g. blue . . . . 4·50 1·00
759 – 45g. + 15 g. violet . . . . 1·60 15
760 – 1 z. 15 green . . . . . . 1·40 1·40
761 – 1 z. 20 red 85 55
DESIGNS: 45 g. Footballers; 1 z. 15, Runners; 1 z. 20, High jumper.

234 Yachts

1952. Shipbuilders' Day.
762 **234** 30 g. + 15 g. green . . . . 3·00 85
763 – 45 g. + 15 g. blue 75 20
764 – 90 g. plum 75 75
DESIGNS—VERT: 45 g. Full-rigged cadet ship "Dar Pomorza"; 90 g. Shipbuilding worker.

235 Young Workers

236 "New Constitution"

1952. Youth Festival, Warsaw.
765 **235** 30 g. + 15 g. green 35 25
766 – 45 g. + 15 g. red 60 15
767 – 90 g. brown 35 30
DESIGNS—HORIZ: 45 g. Girl and boy students; 90 g. Boy bugler.

1952. Adoption of New Constitution.
768 **236** 45 g. + 15 g. green & brn 1·00 15
769 3 z. violet and brown . . 40 35

237 L. Warynski

238 Jaworzno Power Station

1952. 70th Anniv of Party "Proletariat".
770 **237** 30 g. + 15 g. red 45 15
771 45 g. + 15 g. brown . . . 45 15

1952. Electricity Power Station, Jaworzno.
772 **238** 45 g. + 15 g. red 65 10
773 1 z. black 60 40
774 1 z. 50 green 60 15

239 Frydman

240 Pilot and Glider

1952. Pleniny Mountain Resorts.
775 **239** 45 g. + 15 g. purple 45 10
776 – 60 g. green (Grywald) . . 30 40
777 – 1 z. red (Niedzica) 90 10

1952. Aviation Day.
778 **240** 3 g. + 15 g. green . . . . . 1·40 20
779 – 45 g. + 15 g. red . . . . . 2·25 70
780 – 90 g. blue 40 30
DESIGNS: 45 g. Pilot and Yakovlev Yak-18U; 90 g. Parachutists descending.

241 Avicenna **242** Victor Hugo **243** Shipbuilding

1952. Birth Millenary of Avicenna (Arab physician).
781 **241** 75 g. red 30 15

1952. 150th Birth Anniv of Victor Hugo (French author).
782 **242** 90 g. brown 30 15

1952. Gdansk Shipyards.
783 **243** 5 g. green 15 10
784 15 g. red 15 10

244 H. Sienkiewicz (author)

245 Assault on Winter Palace, Petrograd

1952.
785 **244** 45 g. + 15 g. brown 25 10

1952. 35th Anniv of Russian Revolution. Perf or Imperf.
786 **245** 45 g. + 15 g. red . . . . . 1·00 20
787 60 g. brown 40 30

246 Lenin

247 Miner

248 H. Wieniawski (violinist)

1952. Polish-Soviet Friendship Month.
788 **246** 30 g. + 15 g. purple 30 15
789 45 g. + 15 g. brown 55 25

1952. Miners' Day.
790 **247** 45 g. + 15 g. black 15 10
791 1 z. 20 + 15 g. brown . . . 55 30

1952. 2nd Wieniawski Int Violin Competition.
792 **248** 30 g. + 15 g. green . . . . 1·00 40
793 45 g. + 15 g. violet . . . . 2·75 50

249 Car Factory, Zeran **250** Dove of Peace

1952.
800 – 30 g. + 15 g. blue 20 10
794 **249** 45 g. + 15 g. green 15 10
801 – 60 g. + 20 g. purple 20 10
795 **249** 1 z. 15 brown 55 25
DESIGN: 30, 60 g. Lorry factory, Lublin.

1952. Peace Congress, Vienna.
796 **250** 30 g. green 70 25
797 60 g. blue . . . . 1·25 35

251 Soldier and Flag

253 Karl Marx

254 Globe and Flag

1952. 10th Anniv of Battle of Stalingrad.
798 **251** 60 g. red and green . . . 5·00 1·50
799 80 g. red and grey 60 30

1953. 70th Death Anniv of Marx.
802 **253** 60 g. blue . . . . 17·00 10·00
803 80 g. brown . . . . . . 1·25 30

1953. Labour Day.
804 **254** 60 g. red . . . . 5·00 3·25
805 80 g. red 40 10

255 Cyclists and Arms of Warsaw

256 Boxer

1953. 6th International Peace Cycle Race.
806 – 80 g. green 70 25
807 **255** 80 g. brown 70 25
808 – 80 g. red . . . . 13·00 7·00
DESIGNS: As Type **255**, but Arms of Berlin (No. 806) or Prague (No. 808).

1953. European Boxing Championship, Warsaw. Inscr "17-24. V. 1953".
809 **256** 40 g. lake . . . . 1·00 25
810 80 g. orange . . . . . . 9·00 5·00
811 – 95 g. purple . . . . . . 1·00 90
DESIGN: 95 g. Boxers in ring.

257 Copernicus (after Matejko)

258 "Dalmor" (trawler)

1953. 480th Birth Anniv of Copernicus, (astronomer).
812 **257** 20 g. brown . . . . . . 1·00 30
813 – 80 g. blue . . . . 9·00 8·00
DESIGN—VERT: 80 g. Copernicus and diagram.

1953. Merchant Navy Day.
814 **258** 80 g. green . . . . 1·75 15
815 – 1 z. 35 blue . . . . . . 1·75 3·00
DESIGN: 1 z. 35 "Czech" (freighter).

259 Warsaw Market-place

260 Students' Badge

261 Nurse Feeding Baby

1953. Polish National Day.
816 **259** 20 g. lake 20 10
817 2 z. 35 blue . . . . . . 3·75 3·00

1953. 3rd World Students' Congress, Warsaw. Inscr "III SWIATOWY KONGRESS STUDENTOW". (a) Postage. Perf.
818 – 40 g. brown 15 10
819 **260** 1 z. 35 green 50 10
820 – 1 z. 50 blue . . . . . . 2·25 1·60

(b) Air. Imperf.
821 **260** 55 g. plum . . . . 1·50 40
822 75 g. red 75 75
DESIGNS—HORIZ: 40 g. Students and globe. VERT: 1 z. 50, Woman and dove.

1953. Social Health Service.
823 **261** 80 g. red . . . . 8·00 4·75
824 – 1 z. 75 green 25 15
DESIGN: 1 z. 75, Nurse, mother and baby.

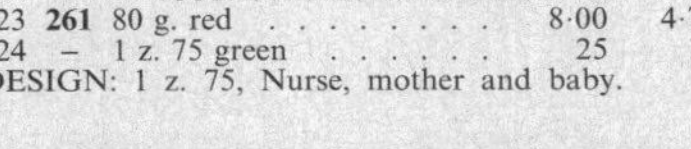

262 M. Kalinowski

263 Jan Kochanowski (poet)

1953. 10th Anniv of Polish People's Army.

No.	Type	Description	Unused	Used
825	262	45 g. brown	3·00	2·75
826	–	80 g. red	60	10
827	–	1 z. 75 olive	60	10

DESIGNS—HORIZ: 80 g. Russian and Polish soldiers. VERT: 1 z. 75, R. Pazinski.

1953. "Renaissance" Commemoration. Inscr "ROK ODRODZENIA".

No.	Type	Description	Unused	Used
828	263	20 g. brown	10	10
829	–	80 g. purple	30	10
830	–	1 z. 35 blue	1·50	1·25

DESIGNS—HORIZ: 80 g. Wawel Castle. VERT: 1 z. 35, Mikolaj Rej (writer).

264 Palace of Science and Culture

265 Dunajec Canyon Pieniny Mts

1953. Reconstruction of Warsaw. Inscr "WARSZAWA".

No.	Type	Description	Unused	Used
831	264	80 g. red	7·25	1·00
832	–	1 z. 75 blue	1·25	25
833	–	2 z. purple	4·00	2·00

DESIGNS: 1 z. 75, Constitution Square; 2 z. Old City Market, Warsaw.

1953. Tourist Series.

No.	Type	Description	Unused	Used
834	–	20 g. lake and blue	15	10
835	–	80 g. lilac and green	2·50	1·50
836	265	1 z. 75 green and brown	70	15
837	–	2 z. black and red	1·00	10

DESIGNS—HORIZ: 20 g. Krynica Spa; 2 z. Clechocinek Spa. VERT: 80 g. Morskie Oko Lake, Tatra Mts.

266 Skiing

267 Infants playing

1953. Winter Sports.

No.	Type	Description	Unused	Used
838	–	80 g. blue	1·25	25
839	266	95 g. green	1·50	25
840	–	2 z. 85 red	4·00	1·90

DESIGNS—VERT: 80 g. Ice-skating; 2 z. 85, Ice-hockey.

1953. Children's Education.

No.	Type	Description	Unused	Used
841	267	10 g. violet	50	10
842	–	80 g. red	75	25
843	–	1 z. 50 green	5·00	2·75

DESIGNS: 80 g. Girls and school; 1 z. 50, Two Schoolgirls writing.

268 Electric Locomotive

269 Mill Girl

1954. Electrification of Railways.

No.	Type	Description	Unused	Used
844	–	60 g. blue	9·00	4·00
845	268	80 g. brown	1·00	25

DESIGN: 60 g. Electric commuter train.

1954. International Women's Day.

No.	Type	Description	Unused	Used
846	269	20 g. green	2·00	1·75
847	–	40 g. blue	50	10
848	–	80 g. brown	50	10

DESIGNS: 40 g. Postwoman; 80 g. Woman driving tractor.

270 Flags and Mayflowers

271 "Warsaw–Berlin–Prague"

1954. Labour Day.

No.	Type	Description	Unused	Used
849	270	40 g. brown	55	30
850		60 g. blue	55	15
851		80 g. red	60	15

1954. 7th Int Peace Cycle Race. Inscr "2–17 MAJ 1954".

No.	Type	Description	Unused	Used
852	271	80 g. brown	70	20
853	–	80 g. blue (Dove and cycle wheel)	70	20

272 Symbols of Labour

273 Glider and Flags

1954. 3rd Trades' Union Congress, Warsaw.

No.	Type	Description	Unused	Used
854	272	25 g. blue	60	25
855		80 g. lake	25	10

1954. International Gliding Competition.

No.	Type	Description	Unused	Used
856	–	45 g. green	60	15
857	273	60 g. violet	1,75	70
858		60 g. brown	1·25	15
859a	–	1 z. 35 blue	1·90	25

DESIGNS: 45 g. Glider and clouds in frame; 1 z. 35, Glider and sky.

274 Paczkow

275 Fencing

1954. Air. Inscr "POCZTA LOTNICZA".

No.	Type	Description	Unused	Used
860	274	60 g. green	25	10
861	–	80 g. red	30	15
862	–	1 z. 15 black	1·40	1·50
863	–	1 z. 50 red	70	10
864	–	1 z. 55 blue	70	10
865	–	1 z. 95 brown	85	15

DESIGNS—Ilyushin Il-12 airplane over: 80 g. Market-place, Kazimierz Dolny; 1 z. 15, Wawel Castle, Cracow; 1 z. 50, Town Hall, Wroclaw; 1 z. 55, Lazienki Palace, Warsaw; 1 z. 95, Cracow Tower, Lublin.

1954. 2nd Spartacist Games (1st issue). Inscr "II OGOLNOPOLSKA SPARTAKIADA".

No.	Type	Description	Unused	Used
866	275	25 g. purple	1·25	35
867	–	60 g. turquoise	1·25	20
868	–	1 z. blue	2·40	40

DESIGNS—VERT: 60 g. Gymnastics. HORIZ: 1 z. Running.

276 Spartacist Games Badge

277 Battlefield

1954. 2nd Spartacist Games (2nd issue).

No.	Type	Description	Unused	Used
869	276	60 g. brown	1·00	20
870		1 z. 55 grey	1·00	30

1954. 10th Anniv of Liberation and Battle of Studzianki.

No.	Type	Description	Unused	Used
871	277	60 g. green	1·50	40
872	–	1 z. blue	5·00	2·75

DESIGN—HORIZ: 1 z. Soldier, airman and tank.

278 Steel Works

1954. 10th Anniv of Second Republic.

No.	Type	Description	Unused	Used
873	–	10 g. sepia and brown	90	10
874	–	20 g. green and red	45	10
876	278	25 g. black and buff	1·50	10
877	–	40 g. brown and yellow	70	10
878	–	45 g. purple and mauve	70	10
880	–	60 g. purple and green	75	10
881	–	1 z. 15 black & turquoise	3·75	20
882	–	1 z. 40 brown and orange	14·00	2·50
883	–	1 z. 55 blue and indigo	3·25	55
884	–	2 z. 10 blue and cobalt	5·00	1·50

DESIGNS: 10 g. Coal mine; 20 g. Soldier and flag; 40 g. Worker on holiday; 45 g. House-builders; 60 g. Tractor and binder; 1 z. 15, Lublin Castle; 1 z. 40, Customers in bookshop; 1 z. 55,"Soldek" (freighter) alongside wharf; 2 z. 10, Battle of Lenino.

279 Signal

280 Picking Apples

1954. Railway Workers' Day.

No.	Type	Description	Unused	Used
885	279	40 g. blue	3·25	50
886	–	60 g. black	2·50	40

DESIGN: 60 g. Night train.

1954. Polish–Russian Friendship.

No.	Type	Description	Unused	Used
887	280	40 g. violet	1·25	60
888		60 g. black	50	15

281 Elblag

282 Chopin and Grand Piano

1954. 500th Anniv of Return of Pomerania to Poland.

No.	Type	Description	Unused	Used
889	281	20 g. red on blue	1·50	60
890	–	45 g. brown on yellow	15	10
891	–	60 g. green on yellow	20	10
892	–	1 z. 40 blue on pink	50	15
893	–	1 z. 55 brown on cream	75	10

VIEWS: 45 g. Gdansk; 60 g. Torun; 1 z. 40, Malbork; 1 z. 55, Olsztyn.

1954. 5th International Chopin Piano Competition, Warsaw (1st issue).

No.	Type	Description	Unused	Used
894	282	45 g. brown	40	10
895		60 g. green	85	10
896		1 z. blue	2·50	1·40

See also Nos. 906/7.

283 Battle Scene

1954. 160th Anniv of Kosciuszko's Insurrection.

No.	Type	Description	Unused	Used
897	283	40 g. olive	40	15
898	–	60 g. brown	60	10
899	–	1 z. 40 black	1·50	70

DESIGNS: 60 g. Kosciuszko on horseback, with insurgents; 1 z. 40, Street battle.

284 European Bison

285 "The Liberator"

1954. Protected Animals.

No.	Type	Description	Unused	Used
900	284	45 g. brown and green	45	15
901	–	60 g. brown and green	45	15
902	–	1 z. 90 brown and blue	90	15
903	–	3 z. brown and turquoise	1·40	60

ANIMALS: 60 g. Elk; 1 z. 90, Chamois; 3 z. Eurasian beaver.

1955. 10th Anniv of Liberation of Warsaw.

No.	Type	Description	Unused	Used
904	285	40 g. brown	1·40	30
905	–	60 g. blue	1·40	50

DESIGN: 60 g. "Spirit of Poland".

286 Bust of Chopin (after L. Isler)

287 Mickiewicz Monument

1955. 5th International Chopin Piano Competition (2nd issue).

No.	Type	Description	Unused	Used
906	286	40 g. brown	30	10
907		60 g. blue	90	20

1955. Warsaw Monuments.

No.	Type	Description	Unused	Used
908	–	5 g. green on yellow	10	10
909	–	10 g. purple on yellow	10	10
910	–	15 g. black on green	10	10
911	–	20 g. blue on pink	10	10
912	–	40 g. violet on lilac	30	10
913	–	45 g. brown on orange	65	20
914	287	60 g. blue on grey	10	10
915	–	1 z. 55 green on grey	1·00	25

MONUMENTS: 5 g. "Siren"; 10 g. Dzerzhinski Statue; 15 g. King Sigismund III Statue; 20 g. "Brotherhood in Arms"; 40 g. Copernicus; 45 g. Marie Curie Statue; 1 z. 55, Kilinski Statue.

288 Flags and Tower

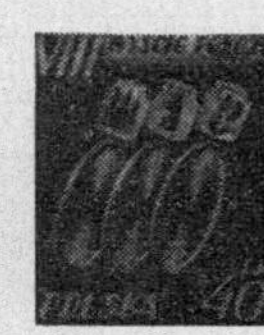
289

1955. 10th Anniv of Russo–Polish Treaty of Friendship.

No.	Type	Description	Unused	Used
916	288	40 g. red	20	10
917		40 g. brown	50	35
918	–	60 g. brown	20	10
919	–	60 g. turquoise	20	10

DESIGN: 60 g. Statue of "Friendship".

1955. 8th International Peace Cycle Race.

No.	Type	Description	Unused	Used
920	289	40 g. brown	45	20
921	–	60 g. blue	25	10

DESIGN: 60 g. "VIII" and doves.

290 Town Hall, Poznan

291 Festival Emblem

1955. 24th International Fair, Poznan.

No.	Type	Description	Unused	Used
922	290	40 g. blue	25	10
923		60 g. red	15	10

1955. Cracow Festival.

No.	Type	Description	Unused	Used
924	291	20 g. multicoloured	50	20
925	–	40 g. multicoloured	25	15
926	291	60 g. multicoloured	1·00	25

No. 925 is as T **291** but horiz and inscr "FESTIWAL SZTUKI", etc.

292 "Peace"

293 Motor Cyclists

1955. 5th International Youth Festival, Warsaw.

No.	Type	Description	Unused	Used
927	–	25 g. brown, pink & yellow	20	10
928	–	40 g. grey and blue	20	10
929	–	45 g. red, mauve & yellow	35	10
930	292	60 g. ultramarine and blue	30	10
931	–	60 g. black and orange	30	10
932	292	1 z. purple and blue	70	50

DESIGNS: 25, 45 g. Pansies and dove; 40, 60 g. (No. 931) Dove and tower.

1955. 13th International Tatra Mountains Motor Cycle Race.

No.	Type	Description	Unused	Used
933	293	40 g. brown	30	10
934		60 g. green	20	10

294 Stalin Palace of Culture and Science, Warsaw

295 Athletes

1955. Polish National Day.

No.	Type	Description	Unused	Used
935	294	60 g. blue	15	10
936		60 g. grey	15	10
937		75 g. green	50	20
938		75 g. brown	50	20

1955. 2nd International Games. Imperf or perf.

No.	Type	Description	Unused	Used
939	295	20 g. brown	15	10
940	–	40 g. purple	20	10
941	–	60 g. blue	35	10
942	–	1 z. red	50	10
943	–	1 z. 35 lilac	70	10
944	–	1 z. 55 green	1·40	50

DESIGNS—VERT: 40 g. Throwing the hammer; 1 z. Net-ball; 1 z. 35, Sculling; 1 z. 55, Swimming. HORIZ: 60 g. Stadium.

296 Szczecin

297 Peasants and Flag

1955. 10th Anniv of Return of Western Territories.
945 **296** 25 g. green 15 10
946 – 40 g. red (Wroclaw) . . . 25 10
947 – 60 g. blue (Zielona Gora) . 45 10
948 – 95 g. black (Opole) . . . 1·25 50

1955. 50th Anniv of 1905 Revolution.
949 **297** 40 g. brown 25 15
950 60 g. red 15 10

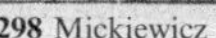
298 Mickiewicz **299** Statue

1955. Death Cent of Adam Mickiewicz (poet).
951 **298** 20 g. brown 20 10
952 **299** 40 g. brown and orange . 20 10
953 – 60 g. brown and green . . 30 10
954 – 95 g. black and red . . . 1·25 50
DESIGNS—As Type **299**: 60 g. Sculptured head; 95 g. Statue.

300 Teacher and Pupil **301** Rook and Hands

1955. 50th Anniv of Polish Teachers' Union.
955 **300** 40 g. brown . . . . 1·25 30
956 – 60 g. blue . . . . 2·25 65
DESIGN: 60 g. Open book and lamp.

1956. 1st World Chess Championship for the Deaf and Dumb, Zakopane.
957 **301** 40 g. red . . . . 4·00 1·00
958 – 60 g. blue . . . . 2·50 10
DESIGNS: 60 g. Knight and hands.

302 Ice Skates **304** Racing Cyclist

303 Officer and "Kilinski" (freighter)

1956. 11th World Students' Winter Sports Championship.
959 **302** 20 g. black and blue . . . 4·00 1·60
960 – 40 g. blue and green . . . 1·00 10
961 – 60 g. red and mauve . . . 1·00 10
DESIGNS: 40 g. Ice-hockey sticks and puck; 60 g. Skis and ski sticks.

1956. Merchant Navy.
962 **303** 5 g. green 15 10
963 – 10 g. red 20 10
964 – 20 g. blue 30 10
965 – 45 g. brown 85 40
966 – 60 g. blue 50 10
DESIGNS: 10 g. Tug and barges; 20 g. "Pokoj" (freighter) in dock; 45 g. Building "Marceli Nowatka" (freighter); 60 g. "Fryderyk Chopin" (freighter) and "Radunia" (trawler).

1956. 9th International Peace Cycle Race.
967 **304** 40 g. blue . . . . 1·10 30
968 60 g. green 20 10

305 Lodge, Tatra Mountains **307** Ghetto Heroes' Monument

1956. Tourist Propaganda.
969 **305** 30 g. green 15 10
970 – 40 g. brown 15 10
971 – 60 g. blue . . . . 1·40 70
972 – 1 z. 15 purple 50 10
DESIGNS: 40 g. Compass, rucksack and map; 60 g. Canoe and map; 1 z. 15, Skis and mountains.

1956. No. 829 surch.
973 10 g. on 80 g. purple 40 20
974 40 g. on 80 g. purple 25 10
975 60 g. on 80 g. purple 25 10
976 1 z. 35 on 80 g. purple . . . 1·25 90

1956. Warsaw Monuments.
977 **307** 30 g. black 15 10
978 – 40 g. brown on green . . . 50 15
979 – 1 z. 55 purple on pink . . 40 15
STATUES: 40 g. Statue of King Jan III Sobieski; 1 z. 55, Statue of Prince Joseph Poniatowski.

308 "Economic Co-operation" **309** Ludwika Wawrzynska (teacher)

1956. Russo–Polish Friendship Month.
980 – 40 g. brown and pink . . 40 20
981 **308** 60 g. red and bistre . . . 25 15
DESIGN: 40 g. Polish and Russian dancers.

1956. Ludwika Wawrzynska Commemoration.
982 **309** 40 g. brown . . . . . . 1·75 25
983 60 g. blue 25 10

310 "Lady with a Weasel" (Leonardo da Vinci) **311** Honey Bee and Hive

1956. International Campaign for Museums.
984 – 40 g. green . . . . 2·25 1·40
985 – 60 g. violet . . . . 1·00 15
986 **310** 1 z. 55 brown . . . . . 2·00 20
DESIGNS: 40 g. Niobe (bust); 60 g. Madonna (Vit Stvosz).

1956. 50th Death Anniv of Jan Dzierzon (apiarist).
987 **311** 40 g. brown on yellow . . 85 30
988 – 60 g. brown on yellow . . 20 10
DESIGN: 60 g. Dr. J. Dzierzon.

312 Fencing **313** 15th-century Postman

1956. Olympic Games. Inscr "MELBOURNE 1956".
989 **312** 10 g. brown and grey . . 15 10
990 – 20 g. lilac and brown . . 20 10
991 – 25 g. black and blue . . 60 15
992 – 40 g. brown and green . . 30 10
993 – 60 g. brown and red . . 50 10
994 – 1 z. 55 brown and violet . 2·50 1·00
995 – 1 z. 55 brown & orange . 1·00 25
DESIGNS: No. 990, Boxing; No. 991, Rowing; No. 992, Steeplechase; No. 993, Javelin throwing; No. 994, Gymnastics. No. 995, Long jumping (Elizabeth Dunska-krzesinska's gold medal).

1956. Re-opening of Postal Museum, Wroclaw.
996 **313** 60 g. black on blue . . . 85 75

314 Snow Crystals and Skier of 1907 **315** Apple Tree and Globe

1957. 50 Years of Skiing in Poland.
997 **314** 40 g. blue 30 10
998 – 60 g. green 30 10
999 – 1 z. purple 70 20
DESIGNS (with snow crystals)—VERT: 60 g. Skier jumping. HORIZ: 1 z. Skier standing.

1957. U.N.O. Commemoration.
1000 **315** 5 g. red and turquoise . 25 15
1001 – 15 g. blue and grey . . 40 15
1002 – 40 g. green and grey . . 70 50
DESIGNS—VERT: 15 g. U.N.O. emblem; 40 g. U.N.O. Headquarters, New York.

316 Skier **317** Winged Letter

1957. 12th Death Annivs of Bronislaw Czech and Hanna Marusarzowna (skiers).
1003 **316** 60 g. brown 90 25
1004 60 g. blue 50 15

1957. Air. 7th Polish National Philatelic Exhibition, Warsaw.
1005 **317** 4 z.+2 z. blue . . . . . 2·75 2·75

318 Foil, Sword and Sabre on Map **319** Dr. S. Petrycy (philosopher)

1957. World Youth Fencing Championships, Warsaw.
1006 **318** 40 g. purple 25 15
1007 – 60 g. red 25 15
1008 – 60 g. blue 20 10
DESIGNS: Nos. 1007/8 are arranged in se-tenant pairs in the sheet and together show two fencers duelling.

1957. Polish Doctors.
1009 **319** 10 g. brown and blue . . 10 10
1010 – 20 g. lake and green . . . 10 10
1011 – 40 g. black and red . . . 10 10
1012 – 60 g. purple and blue . . 40 20
1013 – 1 z. blue and yellow . . . 20 10
1014 – 1 z. 35 brown and green . 15 10
1015 – 2 z. 50 violet and red . . 35 10
1016 – 3 z. brown and violet . . 45 10
PORTRAITS: 20 g. Dr. W. Oczko; 40 g. Dr. J. Sniadecki; 60 g. Dr. T. Chalubinski; 1 z. Dr. W. Bieganski; 1 z. 35, Dr. J. Dietl; 2 z. 50, Dr. B. Dybowski; 3 z. Dr. H. Jordan.

320 Cycle Wheel and Flower **321** Fair Emblem

1957. 10th International Peace Cycle Race.
1017 **320** 60 g. blue 30 15
1018 – 1 z. 50 red (Cyclist) . . . 40 15

1957. 26th International Fair, Poznan.
1019 **321** 60 g. blue 20 10
1020 2 z. 50 green 20 10

322 Carline Thistle **323** Fireman

1957. Wild Flowers.
1021 **322** 60 g. yellow, green & grey 45 10
1022 – 60 g. green and blue . . . 45 10
1023 – 60 g. olive and grey . . . 45 10
1024 – 60 g. purple and green . . 80 10
1025 – 60 g. purple and green . . 45 10
FLOWERS—VERT: No. 1022, Sea holly; No. 1023, Edelweiss; No. 1024, Lady's slipper orchid; No. 1025, Turk's cap lily.

1957. International Fire Brigades Conference, Warsaw. Inscr "KONGRES C.T.I.F. WARSZAWA 1957".
1026 **323** 40 g. black and red . . . 15 10
1027 – 60 g. green and red . . . 15 10
1028 – 2 z. 50 violet and red . . 45 15
DESIGNS: 60 g. Flames enveloping child; 2 z. 50, Ear of corn in flames.

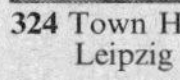

324 Town Hall, Leipzig **325** "The Letter" (after Fragonard)

1957. 4th Int Trade Union Congress, Leipzig.
1029 **324** 60 g. violet 20 10

1957. Stamp Day.
1030 **325** 2 z. 50 green 50 15

326 Red Banner **327** Karol Libelt (founder) **328** H. Wieniawski (violinist)

1957. 40th Anniv of Russian Revolution.
1031 **326** 60 g. red and blue . . . 10 10
1032 – 2 z. 50 brown & black . . 20 10
DESIGN: 2 z. 50, Lenin Monument, Poronin.

1957. Cent of Poznan Scientific Society.
1033 **327** 60 g. red 15 10

1957. 3rd Wieniawski Int Violin Competition.
1034 **328** 2 z. 50 blue 25 15

329 Ilyushin Il-14P over Steel Works **330a** J. A. Komensky (Comenius)

1957. Air.
1035 **329** 90 g. black and pink . . 15 10
1036 – 1 z. 50 brown & salmon 15 10
1037 – 3 z. 40 sepia and buff . 45 10
1038 – 3 z. 90 brown & yellow 90 55
1039 – 4 z. blue and green . . 45 10
1039a – 5 z. lake and lavender . 55 15
1039b – 10 z. brown & turquoise 90 30
1040 – 15 z. violet and blue . . 1·60 35
1040a – 20 z. violet & yellow . 1·75 80
1040b – 30 z. olive and buff . 2·75 1·00
1040c – 50 z. blue and drab . . 7·00 1·90
DESIGNS—Ilyushin Il-14P over: 1 z. 50, Castle Square, Warsaw; 3 z. 40, Market, Cracow; 3 z. 90, Szczecin; 4 z. Karkonosze Mountains; 5 z. Old Market, Gdansk; 10 z. Liw Castle; 15 z. Lublin; 20 z. Cable railway, Kasprowy Wierch; 30 z. Porabka Dam; 50 z. "Batory" (liner).
For stamp as No. 1039b, but printed in purple only, see No.1095.

1957. 300th Anniv of Publication of Komensky's "Opera Didactica Omnia".
1041 **330a** 2 z. 50 red 25 10

331 A. Strug **332** Joseph Conrad and Full-rigged Sailing Ship "Torrens"

1957. 20th Death Anniv of Andrzej Strug (writer).
1042 **331** 2 z. 50 brown 25 10

1957. Birth Centenary of Joseph Conrad (Korzeniowski) (author).
1043 **332** 60 g. brown on green . . 30 10
1044 2 z. 50 blue on pink . . 1·10 10

333 Postman of 1558 **334** Town Hall, Biecz

1958. 400th Anniv of Polish Postal Service (1st issue).
1045 **333** 2 z. 50, purple and blue . 25 10
For similar stamps see Nos. 1063/7.

1958. Ancient Polish Town Halls.
1046 **334** 20 g. green 10 10
1047 – 40 g. brown (Wroclaw) . . 10 10
1048 – 60 g. blue (Tarnow) (horiz) 10 10
1049 – 2 z. 10 lake (Gdansk) . . 15 10
1050 – 2 z. 50 violet (Zamosc) . . 55 25

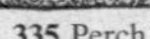

335 Perch

336 Warsaw University

1958. Fishes.
1051 **335** 50 g. yellow, black & blue . . 15 10
1052 – 60 g. blue, indigo & green . . 25 10
1053 – 2 z. 10 multicoloured . . 40 10
1054 – 2 z. 50 green, blk & vio . . 1·25 30
1055 – 6 z. 40 multicoloured . . 1·10 40
DESIGNS—VERT: 60 g. Salmon; 2 z. 10, Pike; 2 z. 50, Trout. HORIZ 6 z. 40, Grayling.

1958. 140th Anniv of Warsaw University.
1056 **336** 2 z. 50 blue 25 10

337 Fair Emblem

338

1958. 27th International Fair, Poznan.
1057 **337** 2z. 50 red and black . . 30 10

1958. 7th International Gliding Championships.
1058 **338** 60 g. black and blue . . 10 10
1059 – 2 z. 50 black and grey . . 30 10
DESIGN: 2 z. 50, As Type **338** but design in reverse.

339 Armed Postman

340 Polar Bear on Iceberg

1958. 19th Anniv of Defence of Gdansk Post Office.
1060 **339** 60 g. blue 25 10

1958. I.G.Y. Inscr as in T **340**.
1061 **340** 60 g. black 15 10
1062 – 2 z. 50 blue 70 15
DESIGN: 2 z. 50, Sputnik and track of rocket.

341 Tomb of Prosper Prowano (First Polish Postmaster) 342 Envelope Quill and Postmark 343 Partisans' Cross

1958. 400th Anniv of Polish Postal Service (2nd issue).
1063 **341** 40 g. purple and blue . . 40 10
1064 – 60 g. black and lilac . . 10 10
1065 – 95 g. violet and yellow . . 10 10
1066 – 2 z. 10 blue and grey . . 60 25
1067 – 3 z. 40 brown & turquoise . 35 20
DESIGNS: 60 g. Mail coach and Church of Our Lady, Cracow; 95 g. Mail coach (rear view); 2 z. 10, 16th-century postman; 3 z. 40, Kogge.
Nos. 1064/7 show various forms of modern transport in clear silhouette in the background.

1958. Stamp Day.
1068 **342** 60 g. green, red & black . 55 40

1958 15th Anniv of Polish People's Army. Polish decorations.
1069 **343** 40 g. buff, black & green 15 10
1070 – 60 g. multicoloured . . 15 10
1071 – 2 z. 50 multicoloured . . 55 15
DESIGNS: 60 g. Virtuti Military Cross; 2 z. 50, Grunwald Cross.

344 "Mail Coach in the Kielce District" (after painting by A. Kedzierskiego)

1958. Polish Postal Service 400th Anniv Exhibition.
1072 **344** 2 z. 50 black on buff . . 85 55

345 Galleon

346 U.N.E.S.C.O Headquarters, Paris

1958. 350th Anniv of Polish Emigration to America.
1073 **345** 60 g. green 15 10
1074 – 2 z. 50 red (Polish emigrants) 30 15

1958. Inauguration of U.N.E.S.C.O. Headquarters Building, Paris.
1075 **346** 2 z. 50 black and green . 55 15

347 S. Wyspianski (dramatist and painter)

348 "Human Rights"

1958. Famous Poles.
1076 **347** 60 g. violet 10 10
1077 – 2 z. 50 green 45 15
PORTRAIT: 2 z. 50, S. Moniuszko (composer).

1958. 10th Anniv of Declaration of Human Rights.
1078 **348** 2 z. 50 lake & brown . . 55 15

349 Party Flag

350 Yacht

1958. 40th Anniv of Polish Communist Party.
1079 **349** 60 g. red and purple . . 10 10

1959. Sports.
1080 **350** 40 g. ultramarine & blue 35 10
1081 – 60 g. purple and salmon 35 10
1082 – 95 g. purple and green . 70 20
1083 – 2 z. blue and green . . 35 20
DESIGNS: 60 g. Archer; 95 g. Footballers; 2 z. Horseman.

351 The "Guilding Hand"

352 Death Cap

1959. 3rd Polish United Workers' Party Congress.
1084 **351** 40 g. black, brown & red 10 10
1085 – 60 g. multicoloured . . 10 10
1086 – 1 z. 55 multicoloured . . 40 10
DESIGNS—HORIZ: 60 g. Hammer and ears of corn. VERT: 1 z. 55, Nowa Huta foundry.

1959. Mushrooms.
1087 **352** 20 g. yellow, brn & grn . 1·60 25
1088 – 30 g. multicoloured . . 30 10
1089 – 40 g. multicoloured . . 65 10
1090 – 60 g. multicoloured . . 65 10
1091 – 1 z. multicoloured . . 1·00 10
1092 – 2 z. 50 brown, grn & bl 1·50 30
1093 – 3 z. 40 multicoloured . . 1·75 35
1094 – 5 z. 60 brown, grn & yell 4·50 1·75
MUSHROOMS: 30 g. Butter mushroom; 40 g. Cep; 60 g. Saffron milk cap; 1 z. Chanterelle; 2 z. 50, Fieldmushroom; 3 z. 40, Fly agaric; 5 z. 60, Brown beech bolete.

1959. Air. 65 Years of Philately in Poland and 6th Polish Philatelic Assn. Congress Warsaw. As No. 1039b but in one colour only.
1095 10 z. purple . . . . 2·75 2·75

353 "Storks" (after Chelmonski)

354 Miner

1959. Polish Paintings.
1096 **353** 40 g. green 15 10
1097 – 60 g. purple 30 10
1098 – 1 z. black 30 10
1099 – 1 z. 50 brown 70 25
1100 – 6 z. 40 blue . . . . . 2·75 1·00
PAINTINGS—VERT: 60 g. "Motherhood" (Wyspianski); 1 z. "Madame de Romanet" (Roda-kowski); 1 z. 50, "Death" (Maiczewski). HORIZ: 6 z. 40, "The Sandmen" (Gierymski).

1959. 3rd Int Miners' Congress, Katowice.
1101 **354** 2 z. 50 multicoloured . . 40 15

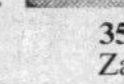

355 Sheaf of Wheat ("Agriculture")

356 Dr L. Zamenhof 357 "Flowering Pink" (Map of Austria)

1959. 15th Anniv of People's Republic.
1102 **355** 40 g. green and black . . 10 10
1103 – 60 g. red and black . . . 10 10
1104 – 1 z. 50 blue and black . . 20 10
DESIGNS: 60 g. Crane ("Building"); 1 z. 50, Corinthian column, and book ("Culture and Science").

1959. Int Esperanto Congress, Warsaw and Birth Centenary of Dr. Ludwig Zamenhof (inventor of Esperanto).
1105 **356** 60 g. black & grn on grn 10 10
1106 1 z. 50 green, red and violet on grey 60 20
DESIGNS: 1 z. 50, Esperanto Star and globe.

1959. 7th World Youth Festival, Vienna.
1107 **357** 60 g. multicoloured . . . 10 10
1108 2 z. 50 multicoloured . . 35 15

358

1959. 30th Anniv of Polish Airlines "LOT".
1109 **358** 60 g. blue, violet & black 15 10

359 Parliament House, Warsaw

1959. 48th Inter-Parliamentary Union Conf, Warsaw.
1110 **359** 60 g. green, red & black . 10 10
1111 2 z. 50 purple, red & blk . 40 15

1959. Baltic States' International Philatelic Exhibition, Gdansk. No. 890 optd **BALPEX I-GDANSK 1959**.
1112 45 g. brown on lemon . . . 60 50

361 Dove and Globe

362 Nurse with Bag

1959. 10th Anniv of World Peace Movement.
1113 **361** 60 g. grey and blue . . . 35 10

1959. 40th Anniv of Polish Red Cross. Cross in red.
1114 **362** 40 g. black and green . . 15 10
1115 – 60 g. brown 15 10
1116 – 2 z. 50 black and red . . 60 30
DESIGNS—VERT: 60 g. Nurse with bottle and bandages. SQUARE—23 × 23 mm: 2 z. 50, J. H. Dunant.

363 Emblem of Polish-Chinese Friendship Society 364

1959. Polish–Chinese Friendship.
1117 **363** 60 g. multicoloured . . . 35 15
1118 2 z. 50 multicoloured . . 25 10

1959. Stamp Day.
1119 **364** 60 g. red, green & turq . 15 10
1120 2 z. 50 blue, grn and red . 30 10

365 Sputnik "3"

1959. Cosmic Flights.
1121 **365** 40 g. black and blue . . 15 10
1122 – 60 g. black and lake . . 30 10
1123 – 2 z. 50 blue and green . 1·25 50
DESIGNS: 60 g. Rocket "Mieczta" encircling Sun; 2 z. 50, Moon rocket "Lunik 2".

366 Schoolgirl

367 Darwin

1959. "1000 Schools for Polish Millennium". Inscr as in T **366**.
1124 **366** 40 g. brown and green . 10 10
1125 – 60 g. red, black & blue . 10 10
DESIGN: 60 g. Children going to school.

1959. Famous Scientists.
1126 **367** 20 g. blue 10 10
1127 – 40 g. olive (Mendeleev) . 10 10
1128 – 60 g. purple (Einstein) . 15 10
1129 – 1 z. 50 brn (Pasteur) . . 20 10
1130 – 1 z. 55 grn (Newton) . . 50 10
1131 – 2 z. 50 violet (Copernicus) 80 50

368 Costumes of Rzeszow 369

1959. Provincial Costumes (1st series).
1132 **368** 20 g. black and green . . 10 10
1133 **369** 20 g. black and green . . 10 10
1134 – 60 g. brown and pink . . 15 10
1135 – 60 g. brown and pink . . 15 10
1136 – 1 z. red and blue 20 10
1137 – 1 z. red and blue 20 10
1138 – 2 z. 50 green and grey . 40 10
1139 – 2 z. 50 green and grey . 40 10
1140 – 5 z. 60 blue and yellow . 1·60 40
1141 – 5 z. 60 blue and yellow . 1·60 40
DESIGNS—Male and female costumes of: Nos. 1134/5, Kurpic; Nos. 1136/7, Silesia; Nos. 1138/9, Mountain regions; Nos. 1140/1, Szamotuly.
See also Nos. 1150/9.

370 Piano

371 Polish 10 k. Stamp of 1860 and Postmark

1960. 150th Birth Anniv of Chopin and Chopin Music Competition, Warsaw.
1142 **370** 60 g. black and violet . . 45 15
1143 – 1 z. 50 black, red & blue 70 15
1144 – 2 z. 50 brown . . . . . 2·00 1·25
DESIGNS—As Type **370**: 1 z. 50, Portion of Chopin's music, 25 × 39½ mm: 2 z. 50, Portrait of Chopin.

1960. Stamp Centenary.
1145 **371** 40 g. red, blue and black 15 10
1146 – 60 g. blue, black & violet 25 10
1147 – 1 z. 35 blue, red and grey 65 35
1148 – 1 z. 55 red, black & green 80 25
1149 – 2 z. 50 green, black & ol 1·40 60
DESIGNS: 1 z. 35, Emblem inscr "1860 1960". Reproductions of Polish stamps: 60 g. No. 356; 1 z. 55, No. 533; 2 z. 50, No. 1030. With appropriate postmarks.

1960. Provincial Costumes (2nd series). As T **368/69**.
1150 40 g. red and blue 10 10
1151 40 g. red and blue 10 10
1152 2 z. blue and yellow . . . 25 10
1153 2 z. blue and yellow . . . 25 10
1154 3 z. 10 turquoise and green . 40 15
1155 3 z. 10 turquoise and green . 40 15
1156 3 z. 40 brown and turquoise 50 20
1157 3 z. 40 brown and turquoise 50 20
1158 6 z. 50 violet and green . . 1·60 40
1159 6 z. 50 violet and green . . 1·60 40
DESIGNS—Male and female costumes of: Nos. 1150/1, Cracow; Nos. 1152/3, Lowicz; Nos. 1154/5, Kujawy; Nos. 1156/7, Lublin; Nos. 1158/9, Lubusz.

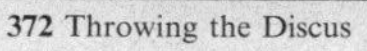

372 Throwing the Discus

373 King Wladislaw Jagiello's Tomb, Wawel Castle

1960. Olympic Games, Rome. Rings and inscr in black.
1160 60 g. blue (T **372**) 15 15
1161 60 g. mauve (Running) . . . 15 15
1162 60 g. violet (Cycling) . . . 15 15
1163 60 g. turq (Show jumping) . . . 15 15
1164 2 z. 50 blue (Trumpeters) . . 70 25
1165 2 z. 50 brown (Boxing) . . . 70 25
1166 2 z. 50 red (Olympic flame) . . 70 25
1167 2 z. 50 green (Long jump) . . 70 25
Stamps of the same value were issued together, se-tenant, forming composite designs illustrating a complete circuit of the stadium track.

1960. 550th Anniv of Battle of Grunwald.
1168 **373** 60 g. brown 25 15
1169 – 90 g. green 55 30
1170 – 2 z. 50 black . . . . . 2·25 1·25
DESIGNS—As Type **373**: 90 g. Proposed Grunwald Monument. HORIZ: 78 × 35½ mm: 2 z. 50, "Battle of Grunwald" (after Jan Matejko).

374 1860 Stamp and Postmark

375 Lukasiewicz (inventor of petrol lamp)

1960. International Philatelic Exn, Warsaw.
1171 **374** 10 z. + 10 z. red, black and blue . . . . 7·75 7·75

1960. Lukasiewicz Commemoration and 5th Pharmaceutical Congress. Poznan.
1172 **375** 60 g. black and yellow . 15 10

376 "The Annunciation"

377 Paderewski

1960. Altar Wood Carvings of St. Mary's Church, Cracow, by Veit Stoss.
1173 **376** 20 g. blue 20 10
1174 – 30 g. brown 15 10
1175 – 40 g. violet 20 10
1176 – 60 g. green 20 10
1177 – 2 z. 50 red 90 30
1178 – 5 z. 60 brown . . . . . 5·50 3·75
DESIGNS: 30 g. "The Nativity"; 40 g. "Homage of the Three Kings"; 60 g. "The Resurrection"; 2 z. 50, "The Ascension"; 5 z. 60, "The Descent of the Holy Ghost".

1960. Birth Centenary of Paderewski.
1179 **377** 2 z. 50 black 35 15

1960. Stamp Day. Optd **DZIEN ZNACZKA 1960**.
1180 **371** 40 g. red, blue & black . 1·40 55

379 Gniezno

380 Great Bustard

1960. Old Polish Towns as T **379**.
1181 5 g. brown 10 10
1182 10 g. green 10 10
1183 20 g. brown 10 10
1184 40 g. red 10 10
1185 50 g. violet 10 10
1186 60 g. lilac 10 10
1187 60 g. blue 10 10
1188 80 g. blue 15 10
1189 90 g. brown 15 10
1190 95 g. green 30 10
1191 1 z. red and lilac 15 10
1192 1 z. 15 green and orange . . 30 10
1193 1 z. 35 mauve and green . . 15 10
1194 1 z. 50 brown and blue . . 30 10
1195 1 z. 55 lilac and yellow . . 30 10
1196 2 z. blue and lilac 20 10
1197 2 z. 10 brown and yellow . . 20 10
1198 2 z. 50 violet and green . . 25 10
1199 3 z. 10 red and grey 30 20
1200 5 z. 60 grey and green . . . 60 25
TOWNS: 10 g. Cracow; 20 g. Warsaw; 40 g. Poznan; 50 g. Plock; 60 g. mauve, Kalisz; 60 g. blue, Tczew; 80 g. Frombork; 90 g. Torum; 95 g. Puck; 1 z. Slupsk; 1 z. 15, Gdansk; 1 z. 35, Wroclaw; 1 z. 50, Szczecin; 1 z. 55, Opole; 2 z. Kolobrzeg; 2 z. 10, Legnica; 2 z. 50, Katowice; 3 z. 10, Lodz; 5 z. 60, Walbrzych.

1960. Birds. Multicoloured.
1201 10 g. Type **380** 20 10
1202 20 g. Raven 20 10
1203 30 g. Common cormorant . . 20 10
1204 40 g. Black stork 35 10
1205 50 g. Eagle owl 65 15
1206 60 g. White-tailed sea eagle . 65 15
1207 75 g. Golden eagle 70 15
1208 90 g. Short-toed eagle . . . 75 25
1209 2 z. 50 Rock thrush . . . . 4·00 1·40
1210 4 z. Common kingfisher . . 3·25 1·00
1211 5 z. 60 Wallcreeper . . . . 5·50 1·10
1212 6 z. 50 Common roller . . . 8·00 2·00

381 Front page of Newspaper "Proletaryat" (1883)

382 Ice-hockey

1961. 300th Anniv of Polish Newspaper Press.
1213 – 40 g. green, blue & black 50 25
1214 **381** 60 g. yellow, red & black 50 25
1215 – 2 z. 50 blue, violet & blk 2·75 2·50
DESIGNS—Newspaper front page: 40 g. "Mercuriusz" (first issue, 1661); 2 z. 50, "Rzeczpospolita" (1944).

1961. 1st Winter Military Spartakiad.
1216 **382** 40 g. black, yellow & lilac 40 10
1217 – 60 g. multicoloured . . 1·00 30
1218 – 1 z. multicoloured . . . 5·50 1·90
1219 – 1 z. 50 black, yell & turq 90 30
DESIGNS: 60 g. Ski jumping; 1 z. Rifle-shooting; 1 z. 50, Slalom.

383 Congress Emblem

384 Yuri Gagarin

1961. 4th Polish Engineers' Conference.
1220 **383** 60 g. black and red . . 15 10

1961. World's 1st Manned Space Flight.
1221 **384** 40 g. black, red and brown 75 20
1222 – 60 g. red, black and blue 75 25
DESIGN: 60 g. Globe and star.

385 Fair Emblem

1961. 30th International Fair, Poznan.
1223 **385** 40 g. black, red and blue 10 10
1224 1 z. 50 black, blue & red 20 10

386 King Mieszko I

1961. Famous Poles (1st issue).
1225 **386** 60 g. black and blue . . 10 10
1226 – 60 g. black and red . . 10 10
1227 – 60 g. black and green . 10 10
1228 – 60 g. black and violet . 70 20
1229 – 60 g. black and brown . 10 10
1230 – 60 g. black and olive . . 10 10
PORTRAITS: No. 1226, King Casimire the Great; No. 1227, King Casmir Jagiellon; No. 1228, Copernicus; No. 1229, A.F. Modrzewski; No. 1230, Kosciuszko.
See also Nos. 1301/6 and 1398/1401.

387 "Leskov" (trawler support ship)

1961. Shipbuilding Industry. Multicoloured.
1231 60 g. Type **387** 25 10
1232 1 z. 55 "Severodvinsk" (depot ship) 40 15
1233 2 z. 50 "Rambutan" (coaster) 70 30
1234 3 z. 40 "Krynica" (freighter) . 1·00 40
1235 4 z. "B 54" freighter . . . . 1·75 70
1236 5 z. 60 "Bavsk" (tanker) . . . 4·50 1·75
SIZES: 2 z. 50, As Type **387**; 5 z. 60 108 × 21 mm; Rest, 81 × 21 mm.

388 Posthorn and Telephone Dial

389 Opole Seal

1961. Communications Minsters' Conference, Warsaw.
1237 **388** 40 g. red, green & blue . 10 10
1238 – 60 g. violet, yellow & purple 15 10
1239 – 2 z. 50 ultram, blue & bis 50 20
DESIGNS: 60 g. Posthorn and radar screen; 2 z. 50, Posthorn and conference emblem.

1961. Polish Western Provinces.
1240 40 g. brown on buff 10 10
1241 40 g. brown on buff 10 10
1242 60 g. violet on pink 10 10
1243 60 g. violet on pink 10 10
1243a 95 g. green on blue 15 10
1243b 95 g. green on blue 15 10
1244 2 z. 50 sage on green 30 15
1245 2 z. 50 sage on green 30 15
DESIGNS—VERT: No. 1240, Type **389**; No. 1242, Henry IV's tomb; No. 1243a, Seal of Conrad II; No. 1244, Prince Barnim's seal. HORIZ: No. 1241, Opole cement works; No. 1243, Wroclaw apartment-house; No. 1243b, Factory interior, Zielona Gora; No. 1245, Szczecin harbour.
See also Nos. 1308/13.

390 Beribboned Paddle

391 Titov and Orbit within Star

1961. 6th European Canoeing Championships. Multicoloured.
1246 40 g. Two canoes within letter "E" 15 10
1247 60 g. Two four-seater canoes at finishing post 15 10
1248 2 z. 50 Type **390** . . . . . . 1·25 40
The 40 g. and 60 g. are horiz.

1961. 2nd Russian Manned Space Flight.
1249 **391** 40 g. black, red and pink 40 10
1250 – 60 g. blue and black . . . 40 10
DESIGN: 60 g. Dove and spaceman's orbit around globe.

392 Monument

393 P.K.O. Emblem and Ant

1961. 40th Anniv of 3rd Silesian Uprising.
1251 **392** 60 g. grey and green . . . 10 10
1252 – 1 z. 55 grey and blue . . 20 10
DESIGN: 1 z. 55, Cross of Silesian uprisers.

1961. Savings Month.
1253 – 40 g. red, yellow & blk . 15 10
1254 **393** 60 g. brown, yell & blk . 15 10
1255 – 60 g. blue, violet & pink . 15 10
1256 – 60 g. green, red & blk . . 15 10
1257 – 2 z. 50 mauve, grey & blk 2·40 1·25
DESIGNS: No. 1253, Savings Bank motif; No. 1255, Bee; No. 1256, Squirrel; No. 1257, Savings Bank book.

394 "Mail Cart" (after J. Chelmonski)

1961. Stamp Day and 40th Anniv of Postal Museum.
1258 **394** 60 g. brown 25 10
1259 60 g. green 25 10

395 Congress Emblem

396 Emblem of Kopasyni Mining Family, 1284

1961. 5th W.F.T.U. Congress, Moscow.
1260 **395** 60 g. black 10 10

1961. Millenary of Polish Mining Industry.
1261 **396** 40 g. purple and orange . 15 10
1262 – 60 g. grey and blue . . . 15 10
1263 – 2 z. 50 green and black . 60 25
DESIGNS: 60 g. 14th-century seal of Bytom; 2 z. 50, Emblem of Int Mine Constructors' Congress, Warsaw, 1958.

397 Child and Syringe

398 Cogwheel and Wheat

1961. 15th Anniv of U.N.I.C.E.F.
1264 **397** 40 g. black and blue . . 10 10
1265 – 60 g. black and orange . 10 10
1266 – 2 z. 50 black & turquoise 60 25
DESIGNS—HORIZ: 60 g. Children of three races. VERT: 2 z. 50, Mother and child, and feeding bottle.

1961. 15th Economic Co-operative Council Meeting, Warsaw.
1267 **398** 40 g. red, yellow & blue . 15 10
1268 – 60 g. red, blue & ultram 15 10
DESIGN: 60 g. Oil pipeline map, E. Europe.

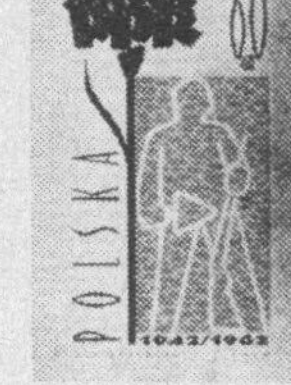

399 Caterpillar-hunter

400 Worker with Flag and Dove

1961. Insects. Multicoloured.
1269 20 g. Type **399** 20 10
1270 30 g. Violet ground beetle . . 20 10
1271 40 g. Alpine longhorn beetle 20 10
1272 50 g. "Cerambyx cerdo" (longhorn beetle) 20 10
1273 60 g. "Carabus auronitens" (ground beetle) 20 10
1274 80 g. Stag beetle 35 10
1275 1 z. 15 Clouded apollo (butterfly) 70 15
1276 1 z. 35 Death's-head hawk moth 45 15
1277 1 z. 50 Scarce swallowtail (butterfly) 90 15
1278 1 z. 55 Apollo (butterfly) . . 90 15
1279 2 z. 50 Red wood ant . . . 1·50 40
1280 5 z. 60 White-tailed bumble bee 8·00 4·25
Nos. 1275/80 are square, 36½ × 36½ mm.

1962. 20th Anniv of Polish Workers' Coalition.
1281 **400** 60 g. brown, blk & red . 15 10
1282 – 60 g. bistre, black & red 15 10
1283 – 60 g. blue, black & red . 15 10
1284 – 60 g. grey, black & red . 15 10
1285 – 60 g. blue, black & red . 15 10
DESIGNS: No. 1282, Steersman; No. 1283, Worker with hammer; No. 1284, Soldier with weapon; No. 1285, Worker with trowel and rifle.

401 Two Skiers Racing

1962. F.I.S. Int. Ski Championships, Zakopane.
1286 **401** 40 g. blue, grey and red . 10 10
1287 40 g. blue, brown & red . 1·00 20
1288 – 60 g. blue, grey and red . 20 10
1289 – 60 g. blue, brown & red . 1·25 70

1290 – 1 z. 50 blue, grey and red 35 10
1291 – 1 z. 50 violet, grey & red 1·75 1·25
DESIGNS—HORIZ: 60 g. Skier racing. VERT: 1 z. 50, Ski jumper.

402 Majdanek Monument

1962. Concentration Camp Monuments.
1292 – 40 g. blue 10 10
1293 **402** 60 g. black 30 10
1294 – 1 z. 50 violet 40 15
DESIGNS—VERT: (20×31 mm): 40 g. Broken carnations and portion of prison clothing (Auschwitz camp); 1 z. 50, Treblinka monument.

403 Racing Cyclist

1962. 15th International Peace Cycle Race.
1295 **403** 60 g. black and blue 20 10
1296 – 2 z. 50 black and yellow 40 10
1297 – 3 z. 40 black and violet 70 25
DESIGNS—74½×22 mm: 2 z. 50, Cyclists & "XV". As Type **403**: 3 z. 40, Arms of Berlin, Prague and Warsaw, and cycle wheel.

405 Lenin Walking

406 Gen. K. Swierczewski-Walter (monument)

1962. 50th Anniv of Lenin's Sojourn in Poland.
1298 **405** 40 g. green & lt green 35 10
1299 – 60 g. lake and pink 15 10
1300 – 2 z. 50 brown & yellow 35 10
DESIGNS: 60 g. Lenin; 2 z. 50, Lenin wearing cap, and St. Mary's Church, Cracow.

1962. Famous Poles (2nd issue). As T **386**.
1301 60 g. black and green 10 10
1302 60 g. black and brown 10 10
1303 60 g. black and blue 50 10
1304 60 g. black and bistre 10 10
1305 60 g. black and purple 10 10
1306 60 g. black and turquoise 10 10
PORTRAITS: No. 1301, A. Mickiewicz (poet); 1302, J. Slowacki (poet); 1303, F. Chopin (composer); 1304, R. Traugutt (patriot); 1305, J. Dabrowski (revolutionary); 1306, Maria Konopnicka (poet).

1962. 15th Death Anniv of Gen. K. Swierczewski-Walter (patriot).
1307 **406** 60 g. black 10 10

1962. Polish Northern Provinces. As T **389**.
1308 60 g. blue and grey 10 10
1309 60 g. blue and grey 10 10
1310 1 z. 55 brown and yellow 20 10
1311 1 z. 55 brown and yellow 20 10
1312 2 z. 50 slate and grey 50 15
1313 2 z. 50 slate and grey 50 15
DESIGNS—VERT: No. 1308, Princess Elizabeth's seal; No. 1310, Gdansk Governor's seal; No. 1312, Frombork Cathedral. HORIZ: No. 1309, Insulators factory, Szczecinek; No. 1311, Gdansk shipyard; No. 1313, Laboratory of Agricultural College, Kortowo.

407 "Crocus scepusiensis" (Borb)

408 "The Poison Well", after J. Malczewski

1962. Polish Protected Plants. Plants in natural colours.
1314 **407** 60 g. yellow 20 10
1315 A 60 g. brown 80 30
1316 B 60 g. pink 20 10
1317 C 90 g. green 25 10
1318 D 90 g. olive 25 10
1319 E 90 g. green 25 10
1320 F 1 z. 50 blue 35 15
1321 G 1 z. 50 green 45 15
1322 H 1 z. 50 turquoise 35 15
1323 I 2 z. 50 green 90 50
1324 J 2 z. 50 turquoise 90 50
1325 K 2 z. 50 blue 1·25 60
PLANTS: A, "Platanthera bifolia" (Rich); B, "Aconitum callibotryon" (Rchb.); C, "Gentiana clusii" (Perr. et Song); D, "Dictamnus albus" (L.); E, "Nymphaca alba" (L.); F, "Daphne mezereum" (L.); G, "Pulsatilla vulgaris" (Mill.); H, "Anemone silvestris" (L.); I, "Trollius europaeus" (L.); J, "Galanthus nivalis" (L.); K, "Adonis vernalis" (L.).

1962. F.I.P. Day ("Federation Internationale de Philatelie").
1326 **408** 60 g. black on cream 30 10

409 Pole Vault

1962. 7th European Athletic Championships, Belgrade. Multicoloured.
1327 40 g. Type **409** 10 10
1328 60 g. 400-metres relay 10 10
1329 90 g. Throwing the javelin 10 10
1330 1 z. Hurdling 10 10
1331 1 z. 50 High-jumping 15 10
1332 1 z. 55 Throwing the discus 15 10
1333 2 z. 50 100-metres final 45 15
1334 3 z. 40 Throwing the hammer 1·10 25

410 "Anopheles sp."

411 Cosmonauts "in flight"

1962. Malaria Eradication.
1335 **410** 60 g. brown & turquoise 10 10
1336 – 1 z. 50 multicoloured 15 10
1337 – 2 z. 50 multicoloured 55 20
DESIGNS: 1 z. 50, Malaria parasites in blood; 2 z. 50, Cinchona plant.

1962. 1st "Team" Manned Space Flight.
1338 **411** 60 g. green, black & violet 15 10
1339 – 2 z. 50 red, black and turquoise 35 15
DESIGN: 2 z. 50, Two stars (representing space-ships) in orbit.

412 "A Moment of Determination" (after painting by A. Kamienski)

413 Mazovian Princes' Mansion, Warsaw

1962. Stamp Day.
1340 **412** 60 g. black 10 10
1341 2 z. 50 brown 45 20

1962. 25th Anniv of Polish Democratic Party.
1342 **413** 60 g. black on red 15 10

414 Cruiser "Aurora"

1962. 45th Anniv of Russian Revolution.
1343 **414** 60 g. blue and red 30 10

415 J. Korczak (bust after Dunikowski)

1962. 20th Death Anniv of Janusz Korczak (child educator).
1344 **415** 40 g. sepia, bistre & brn 15 10
1345 – 60 g. multicoloured 15 10
1346 – 90 g. multicoloured 30 15
1347 – 1 z. multicoloured 30 10
1348 – 2 z. 50 multicoloured 70 40
1349 – 5 z. 60 multicoloured 2·10 90
DESIGNS: 60 g. to 5 z. 60, Illustrations from Korczak's children's books.

416 Old Town, Warsaw

1962. 5th T.U. Congress, Warsaw.
1350 **416** 3 z. 40 multicoloured 45 15

417 Master Buncombe

418 R. Traugutt (insurgent leader)

1962. Maria Konopnicka's Fairy Tale "The Dwarfs and Orphan Mary". Multicoloured.
1351 40 g. Type **417** 45 10
1352 60 g. Lardie the Fox and Master Buncombe 2·25 1·25
1353 1 z. 50 Bluey the Frog making music 60 15
1354 1 z. 55 Peter's kitchen 60 20
1355 2 z. 50 Saraband's concert in Nightingale Valley 75 35
1356 3 z. 40 Orphan Mary and Subearthy 2·40 1·50

1963. Centenary of January (1863) Rising.
1357 **418** 60 g. black, pink & turq 10 10

419 Tractor and Wheat

1963. Freedom from Hunger. Multicoloured.
1358 40 g. Type **419** 10 10
1359 60 g. Millet and hoeing 60 25
1360 2 z. 50 Rice and mechanical harvester 55 15

420 Cocker Spaniel

1963. Dogs.
1361 **420** 20 g. red, black & lilac 15 10
1362 – 30 g. black and red 15 10
1363 – 40 g. ochre, black & lilac 20 10
1364 – 50 g. ochre, black & blue 35 10
1365 – 60 g. black and blue 35 10
1366 – 1 z. black and green 90 30
1367 – 2 z. 50 brown, yell & blk 1·40 40
1368 – 3 z. 40 black and red 3·00 1·40
1369 – 6 z. 50 black and yellow 6·00 3·75
DOGS—HORIZ: 30 g. Sheep-dog; 40 g. Boxer; 2 z. 50, Gun-dog "Ogar"; 6 z. 50, Great dane. VERT: 50 g. Airedale terrier; 60 g. French bulldog; 1 z. French poodle; 3 z. 40, Podhale sheep-dog.

421 Egyptian Galley (15th-century B.C.)

422 Insurgent

1963. Sailing Ships (1st series).
1370 **421** 5 g. brown on bistre 10 10
1371 – 10 g. turquoise on green 15 10
1372 – 20 g. blue on grey 15 10
1373 – 30 g. black on olive 20 10
1374 – 40 g. blue on blue 20 10
1375 – 60 g. purple on brown 35 10
1376 – 1 z. black on blue 40 10
1377 – 1 z. 15 green on pink 65 10
SHIPS: 10 g. Phoenician merchantman (15th cent B.C.); 20 g. Greek trireme (5th cent B.C.); 30 g. Roman merchantman (3rd cent A.D.); 40 g. "Mora" (Norman ship, 1066); 60 g. Hanse kogge (14th cent); 1 z. Hulk (16th cent); 1 z. 15, Carrack (15th cent).
See also Nos. 1451/66.

1963. 20th Anniv of Warsaw Ghetto Uprising.
1378 **422** 2 z. 50 brown and blue 25 10

423 Centenary Emblem

424 Lizard

1963. Red Cross Centenary.
1379 **423** 2 z. 50 red, blue & yellow 60 20

1963. Protected Reptiles and Amphibians. Reptiles in natural colours: inscr in black: background colours given.
1380 **424** 30 g. green 10 10
1381 – 40 g. olive 10 10
1382 – 50 g. brown 15 10
1383 – 60 g. grey 15 10
1384 – 90 g. green 15 10
1385 – 1 z. 15 grey 20 10
1386 – 1 z. 35 blue 20 10
1387 – 1 z. 50 turquoise 45 20
1388 – 1 z. 55 pale blue 40 10
1389 – 2 z. 50 lavender 40 25
1390 – 3 z. green 1·00 30
1391 – 3 z. 40 purple 2·50 1·75
DESIGNS: 40 g. Copperhead (snake); 50 g. Marsh tortoise; 60 g. Grass snake; 90 g. Blindworm; 1 z. 15, Tree toad; 1 z. 35, Mountain newt; 1 z. 50, Crested newt; 1 z. 55, Green toad; 2 z. 50, "Bombina" toad; 3 z. Salamander; 3 z. 40, "Natterjack" (toad).

425 Epee, Foil, Sabre and Knight's Helmet

1963. World Fencing Championships, Gdansk.
1392 **425** 20 g. yellow and brown 10 10
1393 – 40 g. light blue and blue 15 10
1394 – 60 g. vermilion and red 15 10
1395 – 1 z. 15 lt green & green 20 10
1396 – 1 z. 55 red and violet 50 15
1397 – 6 z. 50 yellow, pur & bis 1·60 75
DESIGNS—HORIZ: Fencers with background of: 40 g. Knights jousting; 60 g. Dragoons in sword-fight; 1 z. 15, 18th-century duellists; 1 z. 55, Old Gdansk. VERT: 6 z. 50, Inscription and Arms of Gdansk.

1963. Famous Poles (3rd issue) As T **386**.
1398 60 g. black and brown 10 10
1399 60 g. black and brown 10 10
1400 60 g. black and turquoise 35 10
1401 60 g. black and green 10 10
PORTRAITS: No. 1398, L. Warynski (patriot); No. 1399, L. Krzywicki (economist); No. 1400, M. Sklodowska-Curie (scientist); No. 1401, K. Swierczewski (patriot).

426 Bykovsky and "Vostok 5"

1963. 2nd "Team" Manned Space Flights.
1402 **426** 40 g. black, green & blue 15 10
1403 – 60 g. black, blue & green 15 10
1404 – 6 z. 50 multicoloured 1·10 45
DESIGNS: 60 g. Tereshkova and "Vostok 6"; 6 z. 50, "Vostoks 5 and 6" in orbit.

427 Basketball

1963. 13th European (Men's) Basketball Championships, Wroclaw.
1405 **427** 40 g. multicoloured 10 10
1406 – 50 g. green, black & pink 10 10
1407 – 60 g. black, green & red 10 10
1408 – 90 g. multicoloured 10 10
1409 – 2 z. 50 multicoloured 30 10
1410 – 5 z. 60 multicoloured 1·50 35
DESIGNS: 50 g. to 2 z. 50, As Type **427** but with ball, players and hands in various positions; 5 z. 60, Hands placing ball in net.

428 Missile

1963. 20th Anniv of Polish People's Army. Multicoloured.
1411 20 g. Type **428** 10 10
1412 40 g. "Błyskawica" (destroyer) 15 10
1413 60 g. PZL-106 Kruk (airplane) 15 10
1414 1 z. 15 Radar scanner 15 10
1415 1 z. 35 Tank 20 10
1416 1 z. 55 Missile carrier 30 10
1417 2 z. 50 Amphibious troop carrier 40 10
1418 3 z. Ancient warrior, modern soldier and two swords . . 50 30

429 "A Love Letter" (after Czachorski)

1963. Stamp Day.
1419 **429** 60 g. brown 45 30

1963. Visit of Soviet Cosmonauts to Poland. Nos. 1402/4 optd **23-28 X. 1963** and **w Polsce** together with Cosmonauts names.
1420 **426** 40 g. black, green & blue 25 10
1421 – 60 g. black, blue & green 40 10
1422 – 6 z. 50 multicoloured . . 1·60 1·00

431 Tsiolkovsky's Rocket and Formula
432 Mazurian Horses

1963. "The Conquest of Space". Inscr in black.
1423 **431** 30 g. turquoise 10 10
1424 – 40 g. olive 10 10
1425 – 50 g. violet 10 10
1426 – 60 g. brown 10 10
1427 – 1 z. turquoise 10 10
1428 – 1 z. 50 red 15 10
1429 – 1 z. 55 blue 15 10
1430 – 2 z. 50 purple 30 10
1431 – 5 z. 60 green 90 25
1432 – 6 z. 50 turquoise . . . 1·50 40
DESIGNS: 40 g. "Sputnik 1"; 50 g. "Explorer 1"; 60 g. Banner carried by "Lunik 2"; 1 z. "Lunik 3"; 1 z. 50, "Vostok 1"; 1 z. 55, "Friendship 7"; 2 z. 50, "Vostoks 3 and 4"; 5 z. 60, "Mariner 2"; 6 z. 50, "Mars 1".

1963. Polish Horse-breeding. Multicoloured.
1433 20 g. Arab stallion "Comet" . 10 10
1434 30 g. Wild horses 10 10
1435 40 g. Sokolski horse 15 10
1436 50 g. Arab mares and foals . 15 10
1437 60 g. Type **432** 15 10
1438 90 g. Steeplechasers 25 10
1439 1 z. 55 Arab stallion "Witez II" 50 15
1440 2 z. 50 Head of Arab horse (facing right) 95 15
1441 4 z. Mixed breeds . . . . . 2·25 55
1442 6 z. 50 Head of Arab horse (facing left) . . . . . . 3·25 2·00
SIZES—TRIANGULAR (55×27½ mm): 20, 30 g., 40 g. HORIZ: (75×26 mm): 50, 90 g., 4 z. VERT: as Type **432**: 1 z. 55, 2 z. 50, 6 z. 50.

433 Ice Hockey

1964. Winter Olympic Games, Innsbruck. Mult.
1443 20 g. Type **433** 10 10
1444 30 g. Slalom 10 10
1445 40 g. Downhill skiing 10 10
1446 60 g. Speed skating 10 10
1447 1 z. Ski-jumping 20 10
1448 2 z. 50 Tobogganing 50 10
1449 5 z. 60 Cross-country skiing . 90 25
1450 6 z. 50 Pairs, figure skating . 1·90 70

1964. Sailing Ships (2nd series). As T **421** but without coloured backgrounds. Some new designs.
1451 **421** 5 g. brown 10 10
1452 – 10 g. green 10 10
1453 – 20 g. blue 15 10
1454 – 30 g. bronze 20 10
1455 – 40 g. blue 20 10
1456 – 60 g. purple 20 10
1457 – 1 z. brown 40 10
1458 – 1 z. 15 brown 40 10
1459 – 1 z. 35 blue 40 10
1460 – 1 z. 50 purple 40 10
1461 – 1 z. 55 black 40 10
1462 – 2 z. violet 40 10
1463 – 2 z. 10 green 40 10
1464 – 2 z. 50 mauve 45 10
1465 – 3 z. olive 70 10
1466 – 3 z. 40 brown . . . . . 1·00 10
SHIPS—HORIZ: 10 g. to 1 z. 15, As Nos. 1370/7; 1 z. 50, "Ark Royal" (English galleon, 1587); 2 z. 10, Ship of the line (18th cent); 2 z. 50, Sail frigate (19th cent); 3 z. "Flying Cloud" (clipper, 19th cent). VERT: 1 z. 35, Columbus's "Santa Maria"; 1 z. 55, "Wodnik" (Polish warship, 17th cent); 2 z. Dutch fleute (17th cent); 3 z. 40, "Dar Pomorza" (cadet ship).

434 "Flourishing Tree"

1964. 20th Anniv of People's Republic (1st issue).
1467 **434** 60 g. multicoloured . . 10 10
1468 – 60 g. black, yellow & red 10 10
DESIGN: No. 1468, Emblem composed of symbols of agriculture and industry.
See also Nos. 1497/1506.

435 European Cat
436 Casimir the Great (founder)

1964. Domestic Cats. As T **435**.
1469 30 g. black and yellow . . . 20 10
1470 40 g. multicoloured 20 10
1471 50 g. black, turquoise & yell 20 10
1472 60 g. multicoloured 40 10
1473 90 g. multicoloured 30 10
1474 1 z. 35 multicoloured . . . 30 10
1475 1 z. 55 multicoloured . . . 60 10
1476 2 z. 50 yellow, black & violet 90 50
1477 3 z. 40 multicoloured . . . 2·00 1·00
1478 6 z. 50 multicoloured . . . 4·00 1·75
CATS—European: 30, 40, 60 g., 1 z. 55, 2 z. 50, 6 z. 50, Siamese: 50 g. Persian: 90 g., 1 z. 35, 3 z. 40. Nos. 1472/5 are horiz.

1964. 600th Anniv of Jagiellonian University, Cracow.
1479 **436** 40 g. purple 10 10
1480 – 40 g. green 10 10
1481 – 60 g. violet 10 10
1482 – 60 g. blue 10 10
1483 – 2 z. 50 sepia 60 15
PORTRAITS: No. 1480, Hugo Kollataj (educationist and politician); No. 1481, Jan Dlugosz (geographer and historian); No. 1482, Copernicus (astronomer); No. 1483 (36×37 mm), King Wladislaw Jagiello and Queen Jadwiga.

437 Lapwing

1964. Birds. Multicoloured.
1484 30 g. Type **437** 15 10
1485 40 g. Bluethroat 15 10
1486 50 g. Black-tailed godwit . . 15 10
1487 60 g. Osprey 25 10
1488 90 g. Grey heron 35 10
1489 1 z. 35 Little gull 60 10
1490 1 z. 55 Common shoveler . . 60 15
1491 5 z. 60 Black-throated diver 1·25 50
1492 6 z. 50 Great crested grebe . 1·75 70
Nos. 1487/9 are vert, 35×48 mm.

438 Red Flag on Brick Wall

1964. 4th Polish United Workers' Party Congress, Warsaw. Inscr "PZPR". Multicoloured.
1493 60 g. Type **438** 10 10
1494 60 g. Beribboned hammer . . 10 10
1495 60 g. Hands reaching for Red Flag 10 10
1496 60 g. Hammer and corn emblems 10 10

439 Factory and Cogwheel
441 Battle Scene

440 Gdansk Shipyard

1964. 20th Anniv of People's Republic (2nd issue).
1497 **439** 60 g. black and blue . . . 10 10
1498 – 60 g. black and green . . 10 10
1499 – 60 g. red and orange . . 10 10
1500 – 60 g. blue and grey . . . 10 10
1501 **440** 60 g. blue and green . . . 10 10
1502 – 60 g. violet and mauve . 10 10
1503 – 60 g. brown and violet . . 10 10
1504 – 60 g. bronze and green . . 10 10
1505 – 60 g. purple and red . . . 10 10
1506 – 60 g. brown and yellow . . 10 10
DESIGNS—As Type **439**: No. 1498, Tractor and ear of wheat; No. 1499, Mask and symbols of the arts; No. 1500, Atomic symbol and book. As Type **440**: No. 1502, Lenin Foundry, Nowa Huta; No. 1503, Cement Works, Chelm; No. 1504, Turoszow power station; No. 1505, Petro-chemical plant, Plock; No. 1506, Tarnobrzeg sulphur mine.

1964. 20th Anniv of Warsaw Insurrection.
1507 **441** 60 g. multicoloured . . . 15 10

442 Relay-racing
443 Congress Emblem

1964. Olympic Games, Tokyo. Multicoloured.
1508 20 g. Triple-jumping 10 10
1509 40 g. Rowing 10 10
1510 60 g. Weightlifting 10 10
1511 90 g. Type **442** 10 10
1512 1 z. Boxing 15 10
1513 2 z. 50 Football 35 10
1514 5 z. 60 High jumping (women) 1·00 40
1515 6 z. 50 High-diving . . . . 1·50 75
SIZES: DIAMOND—20 g. to 60 g. SQUARE—90 g. to 2 z. 50. VERT: (23½×36 mm)—5 z. 60, 6 z. 50.

1964. 15th Int Astronautical Congress, Warsaw.
1516 **443** 2 z. 50 black and violet . 40 15

444 Hand holding Hammer
445 S. Zeromski

1964. 3rd Congress of Fighters for Freedom and Democracy Association, Warsaw.
1517 **444** 60 g. red, black & green . 10 10

1964. Birth Cent of Stefan Zeromski (writer).
1518 **445** 60 g. brown 10 10

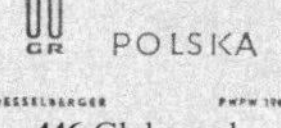

446 Globe and Red Flag
448 Eleanor Roosevelt

447 18th-century Stage Coach (after Brodowski)

1964. Centenary of "First International".
1519 **446** 60 g. black and red . . . 10 10

1964. Stamp Day.
1520 **447** 60 g. green 20 10
1521 60 g. brown 20 10

1964. 80th Birth Anniv of Eleanor Roosevelt.
1522 **448** 2 z. 50 brown 25 10

449 Battle of Studzianki (after S. Zoltowski)

1964. "Poland's Struggle" (World War II) (1st issue).
1523 – 40 g. black 10 10
1524 – 40 g. violet 10 10
1525 – 60 g. blue 15 10
1526 – 60 g. green 15 10
1527 **449** 60 g. bronze 15 10
DESIGNS—VERT: No. 1523, Virtuti Militari Cross; 1524, Westerplatte Memorial, Gdansk; 1525, Bydgoszcz Memorial. HORIZ: No. 1526, Soldiers crossing the Oder (after S. Zoltowski).
See also Nos. 1610/12.

450 Cyclamen
451 Spacecraft of the Future

1964. Garden Flowers. Multicoloured.
1528 20 g. Type **450** 10 10
1529 30 g. Freesia 10 10
1530 40 g. Rose 10 10
1531 50 g. Peony 10 10
1532 60 g. Lily 10 10
1533 90 g. Poppy 15 10
1534 1 z. 35 Tulip 15 10
1535 1 z. 50 Narcissus 65 25
1536 1 z. 55 Begonia 25 10
1537 2 z. 50 Carnation 60 15
1538 3 z. 40 Iris 90 30
1539 5 z. 60 Japanese camelia . . 1·50 70
Nos. 1534/9 are smaller, 26½×37 mm.

1964. Space Research. Multicoloured.
1540 20 g. Type **451** 10 10
1541 30 g. Launching rocket . . . 10 10
1542 40 g. Dog "Laika" and rocket 10 10
1543 60 g. "Lunik 3" and Moon . 10 10
1544 1 z. 55 Satelite 20 10
1545 2 z. 50 "Elektron 2" 50 10
1546 5 z. 60 "Mars 1" . . . . . 1·25 50
1547 6 z. 50+2 z. Gagarin seated in Capsule . . . . 1·75 85

452 "Siren of Warsaw"

1965. 20th Anniv of Liberation of Warsaw.
1548 **452** 60 g. green 10 10

453 Edaphosaurus

1965. Prehistoric Animals (1st series). Multicoloured.
1549 20 g. Type **453** 15 10
1550 30 g. Cryptocleidus 15 10
1551 40 g. Brontosaurus 15 10
1552 60 g. Mesosaurus 15 10
1553 90 g. Stegosaurus 15 10
1554 1 z. 15 Brachiosaurus 20 10
1555 1 z. 35 Styracosaurus 25 10
1556 3 z. 40 Corythosaurus 70 20
1557 5 z. 60 Rhamphorhynchus 1·75 50
1558 6 z. 50 Tyrannosaurus 2·50 60
The 30 g., 60 g., 1 z. 15, 3 z. 40, and 5 z. 60, are vert.
See also Nos. 1639/47.

454 Petro-chemical Works, Plock, and Polish and Soviet Flags

1965. 20th Anniv of Polish-Soviet Friendship Treaty. Multicoloured.
1559 60 g. Seal (vert, 27 × 38½ mm) 10 10
1560 60 g. Type **454** 10 10

455 Polish Eagle and Civic Arms

1965. 20th Anniv of Return of Western and Northern Territories to Poland.
1561 **455** 60 g. red 10 10

456 Dove of Peace

457 I.T.U. Emblem

1965. 20th Anniv of Victory.
1562 **456** 60 g. red and black 10 10

1965. Centenary of I.T.U.
1563 **457** 2 z. 50 black, violet & bl 45 15

458 Clover-leaf Emblem and "The Friend of the People" (journal)

459 "Dragon" Class Yachts

1965. 70th Anniv of Peasant Movement. Mult.
1564 40 g. Type **458** 10 10
1565 60 g. Ears of corn and industrial plant (horiz) 10 10

1965. World Finn Class Sailing Championships, Gdynia. Multicoloured.
1566 30 g. Type **459** 10 10
1567 40 g. "5.5 m." class 10 10
1568 50 g. "Finn" class 15 10
1569 60 g. "V" class 15 10
1570 1 z. 35 "Cadet" class 20 10
1571 4 z. "Star" class 90 30
1572 5 z. 60 "Flying Dutchman" class 1·50 60
1573 6 z. 50 "Amethyst" class 2·25 75
The 50 g., 1 z. 35, 4 z. and 6 z. 50, are horiz.

460 Marx and Lenin

461 17th-Cent Arms of Warsaw

1965. Postal Ministers' Congress, Peking.
1574 **460** 60 g. black on red 15 10

1965. 700th Anniv of Warsaw.
1575 **461** 5 g. red 10 10
1576 – 10 g. green 10 10
1577 – 20 g. blue 10 10
1578 – 40 g. brown 10 10
1579 – 60 g. orange 10 10
1580 – 1 z. 50 black 15 10
1581 – 1 z. 55 blue 20 10
1582 – 2 z. 50 purple 35 10
DESIGNS—VERT: 10 g. 13th-cent antiquities. HORIZ: 20 g. Tombstone of last Masovian dukes; 40 g. Old Town Hall; 60 g. Barbican; 1 z. 50, Arsenal; 1 z. 55, National Theatre; 2 z. 50, Staszic Palace.

463 I.Q.S.Y. Emblem

464 "Odontoglossum grande"

1965. International Quiet Sun Year. Multicoloured. Background colours given.
1584 **463** 60 g. blue 10 10
1585 60 g. violet 10 10
1586 – 2 z. 50 red 35 10
1587 – 2 z. 50 brown 35 10
1588 – 3 z. 40 orange 45 20
1589 – 3 z. 40 olive 45 20
DESIGNS: 2 z. 50, Solar scanner; 3 z. 40, Solar System.

1965. Orchids. Multicoloured.
1590 20 g. Type **464** 15 10
1591 30 g. "Cypripedium hibridum" 15 10
1592 40 g. "Lycaste skinneri" 15 10
1593 50 g. "Cattleya warzewicza" 15 10
1594 60 g. "Vanda sanderiana" 15 10
1595 1 z. 35 "Cypripedium hibridum" 40 10
1596 4 z. "Sobralia" 70 40
1597 5 z. 60 "Disa grandiflora" 1·75 50
1598 6z. 50 "Cattleya labiata" 2·75 1·00
The 30 g. and 1 z. 35, are different designs.

465 Weightlifting

466 "The Post Coach" (after P. Michalowski)

1965. Olympic Games, Tokyo. Polish Medal Winners. Multicoloured.
1599 30 g. Type **465** 10 10
1600 40 g. Boxing 10 10
1601 50 g. Relay-racing 10 10
1602 60 g. Fencing 10 10
1603 90 g. Hurdling (women's 80 m) 10 10
1604 3 z. 40 Relay-racing (women's) 50 10
1605 6 z. 50 "Hop, step and jump" 90 60
1606 7 z. 10 Volleyball (women's) 1·10 50

1965. Stamp Day.
1607 **466** 60 g. brown 15 10
1608 – 2 z. 50 green 25 10
DESIGN: 2 z. 50, "Coach about to leave" (after P. Michalowski).

467 U.N. Emblem

468 Memorial, Holy Cross Mountains

1965. 20th Anniv of U.N.O.
1609 **467** 2 z. 50 blue 30 10

1965. "Poland's Struggle" (World War II) (2nd issue).
1610 **468** 60 g. brown 15 10
1611 – 60 g. green 15 10
1612 – 60 g. brown 15 10
DESIGNS—VERT: No. 1611, Memorial Plaszow. HORIZ: No. 1612, Memorial, Chelm-on-Ner.

469 Wolf

1965. Forest Animals. Multicoloured.
1613 20 g. Type **469** 10 10
1614 30 g. Lynx 10 10
1615 40 g. Red fox 10 10
1616 50 g. Eurasian badger 10 10
1617 60 g. Brown bear 10 10
1618 1 z. 50 Wild boar 70 10
1619 2 z. 50 Red deer 70 15
1620 5 z. 60 European bison 1·60 45
1621 7 z. 10 Elk 2·50 1·00

470 Gig

1965. Horse-drawn Carriages in Lancut Museum. Multicoloured.
1622 20 g. Type **470** 10 10
1623 40 g. Coupe 10 10
1624 50 g. Ladies' "basket" (trap) 10 10
1625 60 g. "Vis-a-vis" 10 10
1626 90 g. Cab 15 10
1627 1 z. 15 Berlinka 20 10
1628 2 z. 50 Hunting brake 50 10
1629 6 z. 50 Barouche 1·40 45
1630 7 z. 10 English brake 2·00 1·00
Nos. 1627/9 are 77 × 22 mm and No. 1630 is 104 × 22 mm.

471 Congress Emblem and Industrial Products

1966. 5th Polish Technicians' Congress, Katowice.
1631 **471** 60 g. multicoloured 15 10

1966. 20th Anniv of Industrial Nationalisation. Designs similar to T **471**. Multicoloured.
1632 60 g. Pithead gear (vert) 15 10
1633 60 g. Freighter 15 10
1634 60 g. Petro-chemical works, Plock 15 10
1635 60 g. Combine-harvester 15 10
1636 60 g. Electric train 20 10
1637 60 g. Exhibition Hall, 35th Poznan Fair 15 10
1638 60 g. Crane (vert) 15 10

1966. Prehistoric Animals (2nd series). As T **453**. Multicoloured.
1639 20 g. Dinichthys 15 10
1640 30 g. Eusthenopteron 15 10
1641 40 g. Ichthyostega 15 10
1642 50 g. Mastodonsaurus 15 10
1643 60 g. Cynognathus 25 10
1644 2 z. 50 Archacopteryx (vert) 40 10
1645 3 z. 40 Brontotherium 60 10
1646 6 z. 50 Machairodus 95 50
1647 7 z. 10 Mammuthus 2·00 95

472 H. Sienkiewicz (novelist)

473 Footballers (Montevideo, 1930)

1966. 50th Death Anniv of Henryk Sienkiewicz.
1648 472 60 g. black on buff 15 10

1966. World Cup Football Championship. Mult.
1649 20 g. Type **473** 10 10
1650 40 g. Rome, 1934 10 10
1651 60 g. Paris, 1938 10 10
1652 90 g. Rio de Janeiro, 1950 10 10
1653 1 z. 50 Berne, 1954 65 15
1654 3 z. 40 Stockholm, 1958 65 15
1655 6 z. 50 Santiago, 1962 1·25 65
1656 7 z. 10 "London", 1966 (elimination match, Glasgow, 1965) 1·75 1·25
Football scenes represent World Cup finals played at the cities stated.

475 Soldier with Flag, and Dove of Peace

476 Women's Relay-racing

1966. 21st Anniv of Victory Day.
1658 **475** 60 g. red and black on silver 10 10

1966. 8th European Athletic Championships, Budapest. Multicoloured.
1659 20 g. Runner starting race 10 10
1660 40 g. Type **476** 10 10
1661 60 g. Throwing the javelin 10 10
1662 90 g. Women's hurdles 10 10
1663 1 z. 35 Throwing the discus 15 10
1664 3 z. 40 Finish of race 55 10
1665 6 z. 50 Throwing the hammer 95 35
1666 7 z. 10 High-jumping 1·25 60
The 20 g., 60 g., 1 z. 35, and 6 z. 50, are vert.

478 White Eagle

479 Flowers and Produce

1966. Polish Millenary (1st issue). Each red and black on gold.
1668 60 g. Type **478** 10 10
1669 60 g. Polish flag 10 10
1670 2 z. 50 Type **478** 30 15
1671 2 z. 50 Polish flag 30 15
See also Nos. 1717/18.

1966. Harvest Festival. Multicoloured.
1672 40 g. Type **479** 25 10
1673 60 g. Woman and loaf 25 10
1674 3 z. 40 Festival bouquet 65 30
The 3 z. 40, is 49 × 48 mm.

480 Chrysanthemum

481 Tourist Map

1966. Flowers. Multicoloured.
1675 10 g. Type **480** 10 10
1676 20 g. Polnsettia 10 10
1677 30 g. Centaury 10 10
1678 40 g. Rose 10 10
1679 60 g. Zinnia 10 10
1680 90 g. Nasturtium 15 10
1681 5 z. 60 Dahlia 90 35
1682 6 z. 50 Sunflower 1·25 45
1683 7 z. 10 Magnolia 2·00 50

1966. Tourism.
1684 **481** 10 g. red 10 10
1685 – 20 g. olive 10 10
1686 – 40 g. blue 10 10
1687 – 60 g. brown 10 10
1688 – 60 g. black 10 10
1689 – 1 z. 15 green 10 10
1690 – 1 z. 35 red 20 10
1691 – 1 z. 55 violet 20 10
1692 – 2 z. green 40 10
DESIGNS: 20 g. Hela Lighthouse; 40 g. Yacht; 60 g. (No. 1687); Poniatowski Bridge, Warsaw; 60 g. (No. 1688), Mining Academy, Kielee; 1 z. 15, Dunajee Gorge; 1 z. 35, Old oaks, Rogalin; 1 z. 55, Silesian Planetarium; 2 z. "Batory" (liner).

482 Roman Capital

1966. Polish Culture Congress.
1693 **482** 60 g. red and brown . . 10 10

483 Stable-man with Percherons

1966. Stamp Day.
1694 **483** 60 g. brown . . 15 10
1695 – 2 z. 50 green . . 25 10
DESIGNS: 2 z. 50, Stablemen with horses and dogs.

484 Soldier in Action

1966. 30th Anniv of Jaroslav Dabrowski Brigade.
1696 **484** 60 g. black, green & red . 15 10

485 Woodland Birds

1966. Woodland Birds. Multicoloured.
1697 10 g. Type **485** . . 25 10
1698 20 g. Green woodpecker . . 25 10
1699 30 g. Jay . . 30 10
1700 40 g. Golden oriole . . 30 10
1701 60 g. Hoopoe . . 30 10
1702 2 z. 50 Redstart . . 65 40
1703 4 z. Siskin . . 2·25 50
1704 6 z. 50 Chaffinch . . 2·25 80
1705 7 z. 10 Great tit . . 2·50 85

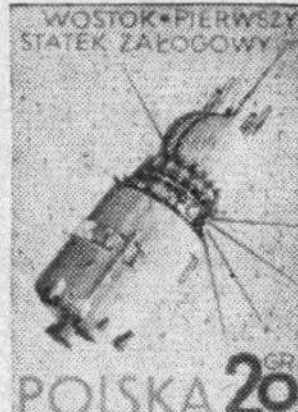

486 Ram (ritual statuette)

487 "Vostok 1"

1966. Polish Archaeological Research.
1706 **486** 60 g. blue . . 15 10
1707 – 60 g. green . . 15 10
1708 – 60 g. brown . . 15 10
DESIGNS—VERT: No. 1707, Plan of Biskupin settlement. HORIZ: No. 1708, Brass implements and ornaments.

1966. Space Research. Multicoloured.
1709 20 g. Type **487** . . 10 10
1710 40 g. "Gemini" . . 10 10
1711 60 g. "Ariel 2" . . 10 10
1712 1 z. 35 "Proton 1" . . 15 10
1713 1 z. 50 "FR 1" . . 25 10
1714 3 z. 40 "Alouette" . . 40 10
1715 6 z. 50 "San Marco 1" . . 1·25 25
1716 7 z. 10 "Luna 9" . . 1·50 40

488 Polish Eagle and Hammer

1966. Polish Millenary (2nd issue).
1717 **488** 40 g. purple, lilac & red . 10 10
1718 – 60 g. purple, green & red 10 10
DESIGN: 60 g. Polish eagle and agricultural and industrial symbols.

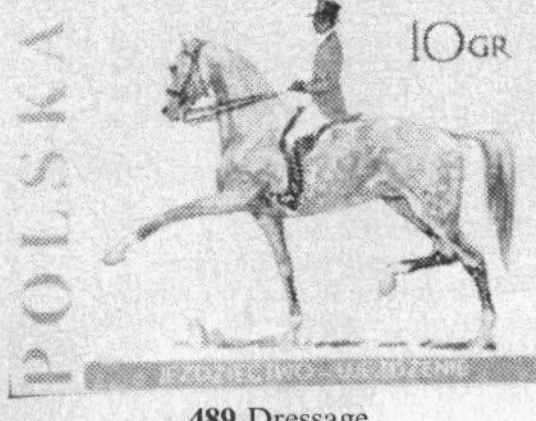

489 Dressage

1967. 150th Anniv of Racehorse Breeding in Poland. Multicoloured.
1719 10 g. Type **489** . . 20 10
1720 20 g. Cross-country racing . 20 10
1721 40 g. Horse-jumping . . 20 10
1722 60 g. Jumping fence in open country . . 30 10
1723 90 g. Horse-trotting . . 35 10
1724 5 z. 90 Playing polo . . 1·00 20
1725 6 z. 60 Stallion "Ofir" . . 1·40 60
1726 7 z. Stallion "Skowronek" . 2·25 85

490 Striped Butterfly

1967. Exotic Fishes. Multicoloured.
1727 5 g. Type **490** . . 10 10
1728 10 g. Imperial angelfish . . 10 10
1729 40 g. Banded butterfly . . 10 10
1730 60 g. Spotted triggerfish . . 10 10
1731 90 g. Undulate triggerfish . 15 10
1732 1 z. 50 Picasso fish . . 25 10
1733 4 z. 50 Black-eyed butterfly . 80 30
1734 6 z. 60 Blue angelfish . . 1·10 60
1735 7 z. Saddleback butterfly . . 1·40 80

491 Auschwitz Memorial

1967. Polish Martyrdom and Resistance, 1939–45.
1736 **491** 40 g. brown . . 10 10
1737 – 40 g. black . . 10 10
1738 – 40 g. violet . . 10 10
DESIGNS—VERT: No. 1737, Auschwitz-Monowitz Memorial; No. 1738, Memorial guide's emblem.
See also Nos. 1770/2, 1798/9 and 1865/9.

492 Cyclists

1967. 20th International Peace Cycle Race.
1739 **492** 60 g. multicoloured . . 15 10

493 Running

1967. Olympic Games (1968). Multicoloured.
1740 20 g. Type **493** . . 10 10
1741 40 g. Horse-jumping . . 10 10
1742 60 g. Relay-running . . 10 10
1743 90 g. Weight-lifting . . 10 10
1744 1 z. 35 Hurdling . . 10 10
1745 3 z. 40 Gymnastics . . 45 15
1746 6 z. 60 High-jumping . . 60 25
1747 7 z. Boxing . . 1·10 65

494 Socialist Symbols

1967. Polish Trade Unions Congress, Warsaw.
1749 **494** 60 g. multicoloured . . 10 10

495 "Arnica montana"

1967. Protected Plants. Multicoloured.
1750 40 g. Type **495** . . 10 10
1751 60 g. "Aquilegia vulgaris" . 10 10
1752 3 z. 40 "Gentiana punctata" . 40 10
1753 4 z. 50 "Lycopodium clavatum" 45 10
1754 5 z. "Iris sibirica" . . 65 15
1755 10 z. "Azalea pontica" . . 1·25 20

496 Katowice Memorial

497 Marie Curie

1967. Inauguration of Katowice Memorial.
1756 **496** 60 g. multicoloured . . 10 10

1967. Birth Centenary of Marie Curie.
1757 **497** 60 g. lake . . 15 10
1758 – 60 g. brown . . 15 10
1759 – 60 g. violet . . 15 10
DESIGNS: No. 1758, Marie Curie's Nobel Prize diploma; No. 1759, Statue of Marie Curie, Warsaw.

498 "Fifth Congress of the Deaf" (sign language)

1967. 5th World Federation of the Deaf Congress, Warsaw.
1760 **498** 60 g. black and blue . . 15 10

499 Bouquet

1967. "Flowers of the Meadow". Multicoloured.
1761 20 g. Type **499** . . 10 10
1762 40 g. Red poppy . . 10 10
1763 60 g. Field bindweed . . 10 10
1764 90 g. Wild pansy . . 15 10
1765 1 z. 15 Tansy . . 15 10
1766 2 z. 50 Corn cockle . . 25 10
1767 3 z. 40 Field seabious . . 50 25
1768 4 z. 50 Scarlet pimpernel . 1·60 40
1769 7 z. 90 Chicory . . 1·75 65

1967. Polish Martyrdom and Resistance, 1939–45 (2nd series). As T **491**.
1770 40 g. blue . . 10 10
1771 40 g. green . . 10 10
1772 40 g. black . . 10 10
DESIGNS—HORIZ: No. 1770, Stutthof Memorial. VERT: No. 1771, Walez Memorial; No. 1772, Lodz-Radogoszcz Memorial.

500 "Wilanow Palace" (from painting by W. Kasprzycki)

1967. Stamp Day.
1773 **500** 60 g. brown and blue . . 15 10

501 Cruiser "Aurora"

1967. 50th Anniv of October Revolution. Each black, grey and red.
1774 60 g. Type **501** . . 30 10
1775 60 g. Lenin . . 30 10
1776 60 g. "Luna 10" . . 30 10

502 Peacock

503 Kosciuszko

1967. Butterflies. Multicoloured.
1777 10 g. Type **502** . . 15 10
1778 20 g. Swallowtail . . 15 10
1779 40 g. Small tortoiseshell . . 15 10
1780 60 g. Camberwell beauty . . 20 10
1781 2 z. Purple emperor . . 35 10
1782 2 z. 50 Red admiral . . 45 10
1783 3 z. 40 Pale clouded yellow . 45 15
1784 4 z. 50 Marbled white . . 2·00 80
1785 7 z. 90 Large blue . . 2·25 80

1967. 150th Death Anniv of Tadeusz Kosciuszko (national hero).
1786 **503** 60 g. chocolate & brown . 10 10
1787 2 z. 50 green and red . . 20 10

504 "The Lobster" (Jean de Heem)

1967. Famous Paintings.
1788 – 20 g. multicoloured . . 20 10
1789 – 40 g. multicoloured . . 10 10
1790 – 60 g. multicoloured . . 10 10
1791 – 2 z. multicoloured . . 25 15
1792 – 2 z. 50 multicolured . . 30 15
1793 – 3 z. 40 multicoloured . . 55 15
1794 **504** 4 z. 50 multicoloured . . 1·00 50
1795 – 6 z. 60 multicoloured . . 1·25 60
DESIGNS (Paintings from the National Museums, Warsaw and Cracow). VERT: 20 g. "Lady with a Weasel" (Leonardo da Vinci); 40 g. "The Polish Lady" (Watteau); 60 g. "Dog fighting Heron" (A. Hondius); 2 z. "Fowler tuning Guitar" (J. B. Greuze); 2 z. 50, "The Tax Collectors" (M. van Reymerswaele); 3 z. 40, "Daria Fiodorowna" (F. S. Rokotov). HORIZ: 6 z. 60, "Parable of the Good Samaritan" (landscape, Rembrandt).

505 W. S. Reymont

1967. Birth Centenary of W. S. Reymont (novelist).
1796 **505** 60 g. brown, red & ochre 10 10

506 J. M. Ossolinski (medallion), Book and Flag

1967. 150th Anniv of Ossolineum Foundation.
1797 **506** 60 g. brown, red & blue . 10 10

1967. Polish Martyrdom and Resistance, 1939-45 (3rd series). As T **491**.
1798 40 g. red . . 10 10
1799 40 g. brown . . 10 10
DESIGNS—VERT: No. 1798, Zagan Memorial. HORIZ: No. 1799, Lambinowice Memorial.

507 Ice Hockey **508** "Puss in Boots"

1968. Winter Olympic Games, Grenoble. Mult.
1800 40 g. Type **507** . . 10 10
1801 60 g. Ski-jumping . . 10 10
1802 90 g. Slalom . . 15 10
1803 1 z. 35 Speed-skating . . 15 10
1804 1 z. 55 Ski-walking . . 15 10
1805 2 z. Tobogganing . . 25 10
1806 7 z. Rifle-shooting on skis . 60 40
1807 7 z. 90 Ski-jumping (different) 1·10 50

1968. Fairy Tales. Multicoloured.
1808 20 g. Type **508** . . 10 10
1809 40 g. "The Raven and the Fox" 10 10
1810 60 g. "Mr. Twardowski" . . 15 10
1811 2 z. "The Fisherman and the Fish" . . 25 10
1812 2 z. 50 "Little Red Riding Hood" . . 35 10
1813 3 z. 40 "Cinderella" . . 50 10
1814 5 z. 50 "The Waif" . . 1·25 50
1815 7 z. "Snow White" . . 1·50 65

509 "Passiflora quadrangularis" 510 "Peace" (poster by H. Tomaszewski)

1968. Flowers. Multicoloured.

1816 10 g. "Clianthus dampieri" . 10 10
1817 20 g. Type **509** 10 10
1818 30 g. "Strelitzia reginae" . . 10 10
1819 40 g. "Coryphanta vivipara" 10 10
1820 60 g. "Odontonia" 10 10
1821 90 g. "Protea cyneroides" . . 15 10
1822 4 z.+2 z. "Abutilon" 75 40
1823 8 z.+4 z. "Rosa polyantha" . 1·90 85

1968. 2nd Int Poster Biennale, Warsaw. Mult.

1824 60 g. Type **510** 10 10
1825 2 z. 50 Gounod's "Faust" (poster by Jan Lenica) . . 20 10

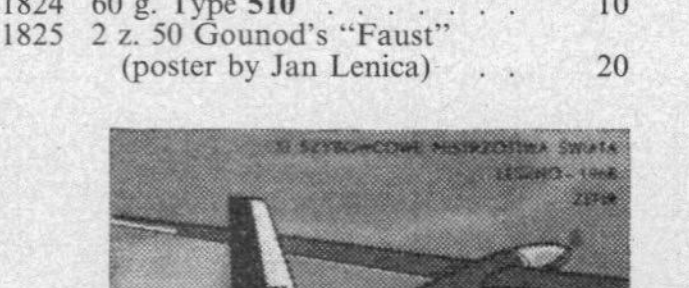

511 Zephyr Glider

1968. 11th World Gliding Championships, Leszno. Gliders. Multicoloured.

1826 60 g. Type **511** 10 10
1827 90 g. Stork 10 10
1828 1 z. 50 Swallow 20 10
1829 3 z. 40 Fly 50 20
1830 4 z. Seal . . . . 1·00 30
1831 5 z. 50 Pirate . . . . 1·25 35

512 Child with "Stamp" 513 Part of Monument

1968. "75 years of Polish Philately". Multicoloured.

1832 60 g. Type **512** 10 10
1833 60 g. Balloon over Poznan . 10 10

1968. Silesian Insurrection Monument, Sosnowiec.

1834 **513** 60 g. black and purple . 10 10

514 Relay-racing

1968. Olympic Games, Mexico. Multicoloured.

1835 30 g. Type **514** 10 10
1836 40 g. Boxing 10 10
1837 60 g. Basketball 10 10
1838 90 g. Long-jumping 10 10
1839 2 z. 50 Throwing the javelin . 20 10
1840 3 z. 40 Gymnastics 35 10
1841 4 z. Cycling 45 30
1842 7 z. 90 Fencing 80 40
1843 10 z.+5 z. Torch runner and Aztec bas-relief . . . . . . 2·00 1·25

The 10 z. is larger, 56×45 mm.

515 "Knight on a Bay Horse" (P. Michalowski)

1968. Polish Paintings. Multicoloured.

1844 40 g. Type **515** 10 10
1845 60 g. "Fisherman" (L. Wyczolkowski) 10 10
1846 1 z. 15 "Jewish Woman with Lemons" (A. Gierymski) . 10 10
1847 1 z. 35 "Eliza Parenska" (S. Wyspianski) 15 10
1848 1 z. 50 "Manifesto" (W. Weiss) 40 20
1849 4 z. 50 "Stanczyk" (Jan Matejko) 40 25
1850 5 z. "Children's Band" (T. Makowski) 65 20
1851 7 z. "Feast II" (Z. Waliszewski) 70 45

The 4 z. 50, 5 z. and 7 z. are horiz.

516 "September, 1939" (Bylina)

1968. 25th Anniv of Polish People's Army. Designs show paintings.

1852 40 g. violet & olive on yellow 10 10
1853 40 g. blue & violet on lilac . 10 10
1854 40 g. green & blue on grey . 10 10
1855 40 g. black & brown on orge 10 10
1856 40 g. purple & green on green 10 10
1857 60 g. brown & ultram on bl 15 10
1858 60 g. purple and grn on grn 15 10
1859 60 g. olive and red on pink . 15 10
1860 60 g. green & brown on red 30 10
1861 60 g. blue & turq on blue . . 20 10

PAINTINGS AND PAINTERS: No. 1852, Type **516**; 1853, "Partisans" (Maciag); 1854, "Lenino" (Bylina); 1855, "Monte Cassino" (Boratynski); 1856, "Tanks before Warsaw" (Garwatowski); 1857, "Neisse River" (Bylina); 1858, "On the Oder" (Mackiewicz); 1859, "In Berlin" (Bylina); 1860, "Blyskawica" (destroyer) (Mokwa); 1861, "Pursuit" (Mikoyan Gurevich MiG-17 aircraft) (Kulisiewicz).

517 "Party Members" (F. Kowarski)

1968. 5th Polish United Workers' Party Congress, Warsaw. Multicoloured designs showing paintings.

1862 60 g. Type **517** 10 10
1863 60 g. "Strike" (S. Lentz) . . 10 10
1864 60 g. "Manifesto" (W. Weiss) 10 10

Nos. 1863/4 are vert.

1968. Polish Martyrdom and Resistance, 1939–45 (4th series). As T **491**.

1865 40 g. grey 10 10
1866 40 g. brown 10 10
1867 40 g. brown 10 10
1868 40 g. blue 10 10
1869 40 g. brown 10 10

DESIGNS—HORIZ: No. 1865, Tomb of Unknown Soldier, Warsaw; No. 1866, Guerillas' Monument, Kartuzy. VERT: No. 1867, Insurgents' Monument, Poznan; No. 1868, People's Guard Insurgents' Monument, Polichno; No. 1869, Rotunda, Zamosc.

518 "Start of Hunt" (W. Kossak)

1968. Paintings. Hunting Scenes. Multicoloured.

1870 20 g. Type **518** 10 10
1871 40 g. "Hunting with Falcon" (J. Kossak) 10 10
1872 60 g. "Wolves' Raid" (A. Wierusz-Kowalski) . . 10 10
1873 1 z. 50 "Home-coming with a Bear" (J. Falat) 40 10
1874 2 z. 50 "The Fox-hunt" (T. Sutherland) 30 10
1875 3 z. 40 "The Boar-hunt" (F. Snyders) 40 15
1876 4 z. 50 "Hunters' Rest" (W. G. Pierow) . . . . 1·50 50
1877 8 z. 50 "Hunting a Lion in Morocco" (Delacroix) . . 1·40 70

519 Maltese Terrier 520 House Sign

1969. Pedigree Dogs. Multicoloured.

1878 20 g. Type **519** 20 10
1879 40 g. Wire-haired fox-terrier . 30 15
1880 60 g. Afghan hound 30 20
1881 1 z. 50 Rough-haired terrier . 30 20
1882 2 z. 50 English setter 60 20
1883 3 z. 40 Pekinese 75 25
1884 4 z. 50 Alsatian . . . . . . 1·60 50
1885 8 z. 50 Pointer . . . . 3·00 1·00

Nos. 1879, 1884 and 1885 are vert.

1969. 9th Polish Democratic Party Congress.

1886 **520** 60 g. red, black & grey . 10 10

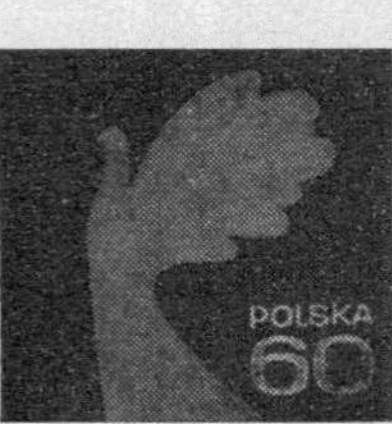

521 "Dove" and Wheat-ears 522 Running

1969. 5th Congress of United Peasant's Party.

1887 **521** 60 g. multicoloured . . . 10 10

1969. 75th Anniv of International Olympic Committee and 50th Anniv of Polish Olympic Committee. Multicoloured.

1888 10 g. Type **522** 10 10
1889 20 g. Gymnastics 10 10
1890 40 g. Weightlifting 10 10
1891 60 g. Throwing the javelin . . 10 10
1892 2 z. 50+50 g. Throwing the discus 20 10
1893 3 z. 40+1 z. Running 30 15
1894 4 z.+1 z. 50 Wrestling . . . 75 25
1895 7 z.+2 z. Fencing . . . . . . 1·40 35

523 Pictorial Map of Swietokrzyski National Park

1969. Tourism (1st series). Multicoloured.

1896 40 g. Type **523** 10 10
1897 60 g. Niedzica Castle (vert) . 10 10
1898 1 z. 35 Kolobrzeg Lighthouse and yacht 30 10
1899 1 z. 50 Szczecin Castle and Harbour 30 10
1900 2 z. 50 Torun and Vistula River 25 10
1901 3 z. 40 Klodzko, Silesia (vert) 35 10
1902 4 z. Sulejow 55 25
1903 4 z. 50 Kazimierz Dolny market-place (vert) . . . 60 25

See also Nos. 1981/5.

524 Route Map and "Opty"

1969. Leonid Teliga's World Voyage in Yacht "Opty".

1904 **524** 60 g. multicoloured . . . 30 10

525 Copernicus (after woodcut by T. Stimer) and Inscription 526 "Memory" Flame and Badge

1969. 500th Birth Anniv (1973) of Copernicus (1st issue).

1905 **525** 40 g. brown, red & yellow 15 10
1906 – 60 g. blue, red & green . 20 10
1907 – 2 z. 50 olive, red & pur . 50 15

DESIGNS: 60 g. Copernicus (after J. Falck) and 15th-century globe; 2 z. 50, Copernicus (after painting by J. Matejko) and diagram of heliocentric system.

See also Nos. 1995/7, 2069/72, 2167/70, 2213/14 and 2217/21.

1969. 5th National Alert of Polish Boy Scout Association.

1908 **526** 60 g. black, red & blue . 10 10
1909 – 60 g. red, black & green 10 10
1910 – 60 g. black, green and red 10 10

DESIGN: No. 1909, "Defence" eagle and badge; No. 1910, "Labour" map and badge.

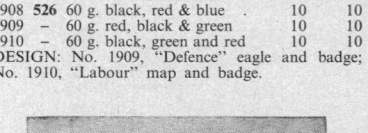

528 Coal-miner

1969. 25th Anniv of Polish People's Republic. Multicoloured.

1911 60 g. Frontier guard and arms 10 10
1912 60 g. Plock Petro-chemical Plant 10 10
1913 60 g. Combine-harvester . . 10 10
1914 60 g. Grand Theatre, Warsaw 10 10
1915 60 g. Curie statue and University, Lublin 10 10
1916 60 g. Type **528** 10 10
1917 60 g. Sulphur-worker 10 10
1918 60 g. Steel-worker 10 10
1919 60 g. Shipbuilder 10 10

Nos. 1911/5 are vert and have white arms embossed in the top portion of the stamps.

529 Astronauts and Module on Moon

1969. 1st Man on the Moon.

1920 **529** 2 z. 50 multicoloured . . 65 35

530 "Motherhood" (S. Wyspianski)

1969. Polish Paintings. Multicoloured.

1921 20 g. Type **530** 10 10
1922 40 g. "Hamlet" (J. Malczewski) 10 10
1923 60 g. "Indian Summer" (J. Chelmonski) 10 10
1924 2 z. "Two Girls" (Olga Bonznanska) (vert) 25 10
1925 2 z. 50 "The Sun of May" (J. Mehoffer) (vert) . . . 15 10
1926 3 z. 40 "Woman combing her Hair" (W. Slewinski) . . 30 20
1927 5 z. 50 "Still Life" (J. Pankiewicz) 65 30
1928 7 z. "Abduction of the King's Daughter" (W. Wojtkiewicz) 1·25 35

531 "Nike" statue 533 Krzczonow (Lublin) Costumes

532 Majdanek Memorial

1969. 4th Congress of Fighters for Freedom and Democracy Association.

1929 **531** 60 g. red, black & brown 10 10

1969. Inaug of Majdanek Memorial.

1930 **532** 40 g. black and mauve . 15 10

1969. Provincial Costumes. Multicoloured.

1931 40 g. Type **533** 10 10
1932 60 g. Lowicz (Lodz) 10 10
1933 1 z. 15 Rozbasrk (Katowice) 15 10
1934 1 z. 35 Lower Silesia (Wroclaw) 15 10
1935 1 z. 50 Opoczno (Lodz) . . . 30 10
1936 4 z. 50 Sacz (Cracow) . . . 60 15
1937 5 z. Highlanders, Cracow . . 50 35
1938 7 z. Kurple (Warsaw) 70 35

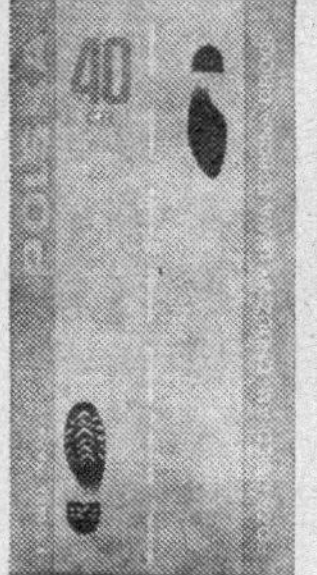

534 "Pedestrians Keep Left"

535 "Welding" and I.L.O. Emblem

1969. Road Safety. Multicoloured.
1939 40 g. Type **534** 10 10
1940 60 g. "Drive Carefully" (horses on road) 10 10
1941 2 z. 50 "Do Not Dazzle" (cars on road at night) 30 15

1969. 50th Anniv of I.L.O.
1942 **535** 2 z. 50 blue and gold . . 25 10

536 "The Bell-founder"

537 "Angel" (19th-century)

1969. Miniatures from Behem's Code of 1505. Multicoloured.
1943 40 g. Type **536** 10 10
1944 60 g. "The Painter" 10 10
1945 1 z. 35 "The Woodcarver" . 15 10
1946 1 z. 55 "The Shoemaker" . . 20 10
1947 2 z. 50 "The Cooper" 25 10
1948 3 z. 40 "The Baker" 30 10
1949 4 z. 50 "The Tailor" 60 30
1950 7 z. "The Bowyer" . . . . . 1·00 40

1969. Polish Folk Sculpture. Multicoloured.
1951 20 g. Type **537** 10 10
1952 40 g. "Sorrowful Christ" (19th-century) 10 10
1953 60 g. "Sorrowful Christ" (19th-cent.) (different) 10 10
1954 2 z. "Weeping Woman" (19th-century) 20 10
1955 2 z. 50 "Adam and Eve" (F. Czajkowski) 20 10
1956 3 z. 40 "Girl with Birds" (L. Kudla) 35 10
1957 5 z. 50+1 z. 50 "Choir" (A. Zegadlo) 80 30
1958 7 z.+1 z. "Organ-grinder" (Z. Skretowicz) 90 50
Nos. 1957/8 are larger, size 25×35 mm.

538 Leopold Staff

1969. Modern Polish Writers.
1959 **538** 40 g. black, olive & green 10 10
1960 – 60 g. black, red and pink 10 10
1961 – 1 z. 35 black, deep blue and blue 10 10
1962 – 1 z. 50 black, vio & lilac 10 10
1963 – 1 z. 55 black, deep green and green 15 10
1964 – 2 z. 50 black, deep blue and blue 20 10
1965 – 3 z. 40 blk, brn and flesh 30 20
DESIGNS: 60 g. Wladyslaw Broniewski; 1 z. 35, Leon Kruczkowski; 1 z. 50, Julian Tuwim; 1 z. 55, Konstanty Ildefons Galczynski; 2 z. 50, Maria Dabrowska; 3 z. 40, Zofia Nalkowska.

539 Nike Monument

1970. 25th Anniv of Liberation of Warsaw.
1966 **539** 60 g. multicoloured . . . 25 10

540 Early Printing Works and Colour Dots

1970. Centenary of Printers' Trade Union.
1967 **540** 60 g. multicoloured . . 10 10

541 Mallard

1970. Game Birds. Multicoloured.
1968 40 g. Type **541** 20 10
1969 60 g. Ring-necked pheasant . 40 10
1970 1 z. 15 Woodcock 30 10
1971 1 z. 35 Ruff 40 10
1972 1 z. 50 Wood pigeon 40 15
1973 3 z. 40 Black grouse 45 15
1974 7 z. Grey partridge . . . . 2·50 1·00
1975 8 z. 50 Capercaillie . . . . 2·75 1·00

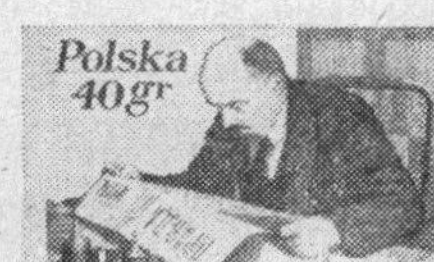

542 Lenin at Desk

1970. Birth Centenary of Lenin.
1976 **542** 40 g. grey and red . . . 10 10
1977 – 60 g. brown and red . . 10 10
1978 – 2 z. 50 black and red . . 20 10
DESIGNS: 60 g. Lenin addressing meeting; 2 z. 50, Lenin at Party conference.

543 Polish and Russian Soldiers in Berlin

1970. 25th Anniv of Liberation.
1980 **543** 60 g. multicoloured . . 15 10

1970. Tourism (2nd series). As T **523**, but with imprint "PWPW 70". Multicoloured.
1981 60 g. Town Hall, Wroclaw (vert) 15 10
1982 60 g. View of Opol 15 10
1983 60 g. Legnica Castle 15 10
1984 60 g. Bolkow Castle 15 10
1985 60 g. Town Hall, Brzeg . . 15 10

544 Polish "Flower"

1970. 25th Anniv of Return of Western Territories.
1986 **544** 60 g. red, silver and green 15 10

545 Movement Flag

546 U.P.U. Emblem and New Headquarters

1970. 75th Anniv of Peasant Movement.
1987 **545** 60 g. multicoloured . . . 10 10

1970. New U.P.U. Headquarters Building, Berne.
1988 **546** 2 z. 50 blue and turquoise 20 10

547 Footballers

548 Hand with "Lamp of Learning"

1970. Gornik Zabrze v. Manchester City, Final of European Cup-winners Cup Championship.
1989 **547** 60 g. multicoloured . . . 20 10

1970. 150th Anniv of Plock Scientific Society.
1990 **548** 60 g. olive, red and black 10 10

549 "Olympic Runners" (from Greek amphora)

1970. 10th Session of Int Olympic Academy.
1991 **549** 60 g. red, yellow & black 10 10
1992 – 60 g. violet, blue & black 10 10
1993 – 60 g. multicoloured . . . 10 10
DESIGNS: No. 1992, "The Archer"; No. 1993, Modern runners.

550 Copernicus (after miniature by Bacciarelli) and Bologna

1970. 500th Birth Anniv (1973) of Copernicus. (2nd issue).
1995 **550** 40 g. green, orange & lilac 15 10
1996 – 60 g. lilac, green & yellow 15 10
1997 – 2 z. 50 brn, blue and green 50 10
DESIGNS: 60 g. Copernicus (after miniature by Lesseur) and Padua; 2 z. 50, Copernicus (by N. Zinck, after lost Goluchowska portrait) and Ferrara.

551 "Aleksander Orlowski" (self-portrait)

1970. Polish Miniatures. Multicoloured.
1998 20 g. Type **551** 10 10
1999 40 g. "Jan Matejko" (self-portrait) 10 10
2000 60 g. "Stefan Batory" (unknown artist) 10 10
2001 2 z. "Maria Leszczynska" (unknown artist) 10 10
2002 2 z. 50 "Maria Walewska" (Marie-Victorie Jacquetot) . 20 10
2003 3 z. 40 "Tadeusz Kosciuszko" (Jan Rustem) 25 10
2004 5 z. 50 "Samuel Linde" (G. Landolfi) 70 40
2005 7 z. "Michal Oginski" (Nanette Windisch) . . . . 1·40 55

552 U.N. Emblem within "Eye"

1970. 25th Anniv of United Nations.
2006 **552** 2 z. 50 multicoloured . . 25 10

553 Piano Keyboard and Chopin's Signature

554 Population Pictograph

1970. 8th International Chopin Piano Competition.
2007 **553** 2 z. 50 black & violet . . 25 10

1970. National Census. Multicoloured.
2008 40 g. Type **554** 10 10
2009 60 g. Family in "house" . . 15 10

555 Destroyer "Piorun". (Illustration reduced. Actual size 77×23 mm)

1970. Polish Warships, World War II.
2010 **555** 40 g. brown 25 10
2011 – 60 g. black 40 15
2012 – 2 z. 50 brown . . . . . 1·00 30
DESIGNS: 60 g. "Orzel" (submarine); 2 z. 50, H.M.S. "Garland" (destroyer loaned to Polish Navy).

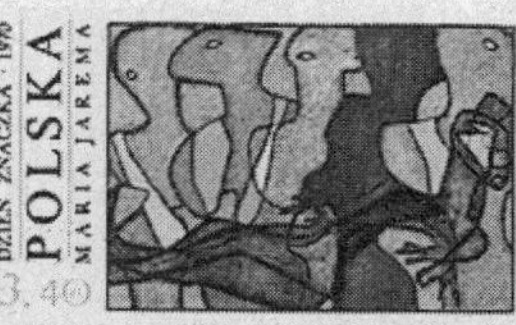

556 "Expressions" (Maria Jarema)

1970. Stamp Day. Contemporary Polish Paintings. Multicoloured.
2013 20 g. "The Violin-cellist" (J. Nowosielski) (vert) . . 10 10
2014 40 g. "View of Lodz" (B. Liberski) (vert) 10 10
2015 60 g. "Studio Concert" (W. Taranczewski) (vert) . 10 10
2016 1 z. 50 "Still Life" (Z. Pronaszko) (vert) . . . 10 10
2017 2 z. "Hanging-up Washing" (A. Wroblewski) (vert) . . 15 10
2018 3 z. 40 Type **556** 25 10
2019 4 z. "Canal in the Forest" (P. Potworowski) 55 20
2020 8 z. 50 "The Sun" (W. Strzeminski) . . . . . 1·10 50

557 "Luna 16" landing on Moon

558 "Stag" (detail from "Daniel" tapestry)

1970. Moon Landing of "Luna 16".
2021 **557** 2 z. 50 multicoloured . . 35 15

1970. Tapestries in Wawel Castle. Multicoloured.
2022 60 g. Type **558** 10 10
2023 1 z. 15 "White Stork" (detail) 30 10
2024 1 z. 35 "Panther fighting Dragon" 15 10
2025 2 z. "Man's Head" (detail "Deluge" tapestry) . . . 20 10
2026 2 z. 50 "Child with Bird" (detail "Adam Tilling the Soil" tapestry) 25 10
2027 4 z. "God, Adam and Eve" (detail "Happiness in Paradise" tapestry) 50 25
2028 4 z. 50 Royal Monogram tapestry 80 35

559 Cadet ship "Dar Pomorza"

1971. Polish Ships. Multicoloured.
2030 40 g. Type **559** 15 10
2031 60 g. Liner "Stefan Batory" . 15 10
2032 1 z. 15 Ice-breaker "Perkun" 25 10

2033 1 z. 35 Lifeboat "R-1" . . . 35 10
2034 1 z. 50 Bulk carrier "Ziemia Szczecinska" 40 10
2035 2 z. 50 Tanker "Beskidy" . . 50 10
2036 5 z. Freighter "Hel" . . . . 1·00 20
2037 8 z. 50 Ferry "Gryf" . . . . 2·10 50

560 Checiny Castle

1971. Polish Castles. Multicoloured.
2038 20 g. Type **560** 10 10
2039 40 g. Wisnicz 10 10
2040 60 g. Bedzin 10 10
2041 2 z. Ogrodzieniec 15 10
2042 2 z. 50 Niedzica 15 10
2043 3 z. 40 Kwidzyn 30 10
2044 4 z. Pieskowa Skala 35 15
2045 8 z. 50 Lidzbark Warminski . 80 60

561 Battle of Pouilly, J. Dabrowski and W. Wroblewski

1971. Centenary of Paris Commune.
2046 **561** 60 g. brown, blue & red . 15 10

562 Plantation **563** "Bishop Marianos"

1971. Forestry Management. Multicoloured.
2047 40 g. Type **562** 10 10
2048 60 g. Forest (27 × 47 mm) . . 10 10
2049 1 z. 50 Tree-felling 30 10

1971. Fresco Discoveries made by Polish Expedition at Faras, Nubia. Multicoloured.
2050 40 g. Type **563** 10 10
2051 60 g. "St. Anne" 10 10
2052 1 z. 15 "Archangel Michael" 10 10
2053 1 z. 35 "The Hermit, Anamon" 10 10
2054 1 z. 50 "Head of Archangel Michael" 15 10
2055 4 z. 50 "Evangelists' Cross" . 35 10
2056 5 z. "Christ protecting a nobleman" 55 25
2057 7 z. "Archangel Michael" (half-length) 65 40

564 Revolutionaries

1971. 50th Anniv of Silesian Insurrection.
2058 **564** 60 g. brown and gold . . 15 10

565 "Soldiers"

1971. 25th Anniv of U.N.I.C.E.F. Children's Drawings. Multicoloured.
2060 20 g. "Peacock" (vert) . . . 10 10
2061 40 g. Type **565** 10 10
2062 60 g. "Lady Spring" (vert) . 10 10
2063 2 z. "Cat and Ball" 15 10
2064 2 z. 50 "Flowers in Jug" (vert) 20 10
2065 3 z. 40 "Friendship" 30 10
2066 5 z. 50 "Clown" (vert) . . . 70 35
2067 7 z. "Strange Planet" 90 40

566 Fair Emblem **567** Copernicus's House, Torun

1971. 40th International Fair, Poznan.
2068 **566** 60 g. multicoloured . . 10 10

1971. 500th Bird Anniv (1973) of Copernicus. (3rd issue). Multicoloured.
2069 40 g. Type **567** 10 10
2070 60 g. Collegium Naius, Jagiellonian University, Cracow (horiz) 10 10
2071 2 z. 50 Olsztyn Castle (horiz) 20 10
2072 4 z. Frombork Cathedral . . 60 25

568 Folk Art Pattern **569** "Head of Worker" (X. Dunikowski)

1971. Folk Art. "Paper Cut-outs" showing various patterns.
2073 **568** 20 g. black, green & bl . 10 10
2074 – 40 g. blue, green & cream 10 10
2075 – 60 g. brown, blue & grey 10 10
2076 – 1 z. 15 purple, brn & buff 10 10
2077 – 1 z. 35 green, red & yell 20 10

1971. Modern Polish Sculpture. Multicoloured.
2078 40 g. Type **569** 10 10
2079 40 g. "Foundryman" (X. Dunikowski) 10 10
2080 60 g. "Miners" (M. Wiecek) 15 10
2081 60 g. "Harvester" (S. Horno-Poplawski) 15 10

570 Congress Emblem and Computer Tapes

1971. 6th Polish Technical Congress, Warsaw.
2083 **570** 60 g. violet and red . . 15 10

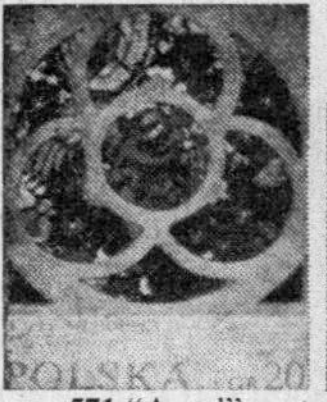

571 "Angel" (J. Mehoffer) **573** PZL P-11C Fighters

572 "Mrs. Fedorowicz" (W. Pruszkowski)

1971. Stained Glass Windows. Multicoloured.
2084 20 g. Type **571** 10 10
2085 40 g. "Lillies" (S. Wyspianski) 10 10
2086 60 g. "Iris" (S. Wyspianski) 10 10
2087 1 z. 35 "Apollo" (S. Wyspianski) 15 10
2088 1 z. 55 "Two Wise Men" (14th-century) 15 10
2089 3 z. 40 "The Flight into Egypt" (14th-century) 30 20
2090 5 z. 50 "Jacob" (14th-century) 60 25
2091 8 z. 50 + 4 z. "Madonna" (15th-century) 90 50

1971. Contemporary Art from National Museum, Cracow. Multicoloured.
2092 40 g. Type **572** 10 10
2093 50 g. "Woman with Book" (T. Czyzeski) 10 10
2094 60 g. "Girl with Chrysanthemums" (O. Boznanska) 10 10
2095 2 z. 50 "Girl in Red Dress" (J. Pankiewicz) (horiz) . . . 15 10
2096 3 z. 40 "Reclining Nude" (L. Chwistek) (horiz) . . . 30 15
2097 4 z. 50 "Strange Garden" (J. Mehoffer) 45 15
2098 5 z. "Wife in White Hat" (Z. Pronaszko) 55 15
2099 7 z. + 1 z. "Seated Nude" (W. Weiss) 75 50

1971. Polish Aircraft of World War II. Multicoloured.
2100 90 g. Type **573** 15 10
2101 1 z. 50 PZL 23A Karas fighters 25 10
2102 3 z. 40 PZL P-37 Los bomber 40 10

574 Royal Castle, Warsaw (pre-1939)

1971. Reconstruction of Royal Castle, Warsaw.
2103 **574** 60 g. black, red and gold 15 10

575 Astronauts in Moon Rover **576** "Lunokhod 1"

1971. Moon Flight of "Apollo 15".
2104 **575** 2 z. 50 multicoloured . . 45 15

1971. Moon Flight of "Lunik 17" and "Lunokhod 1".
2106 **576** 2 z. 50 multicoloured . . 45 15

577 Worker at Wheel **578** Ship-building

1971. 6th Polish United Workers' Party Congress (a) Party Posters.
2108 **577** 60 g. red, blue & grey . . 10 10
2109 60 g. red and grey (Worker's head) 10 10

(b) Industrial Development. Each in gold and red.
2110 60 g. Type **578** 10 10
2111 60 g. Building construction . . 10 10
2112 60 g. Combine-harvester . . . 10 10
2113 60 g. Motor-car production . . 10 10
2114 60 g. Pit-head 10 10
2115 60 g. Petro-chemical plant . . 10 10

579 "Prunus cerasus"

1971. Flowers of Trees and Shrubs. Multicoloured.
2117 10 g. Type **579** 10 10
2118 20 g. "Malusniedzwetzskyana" 10 10
2119 40 g. "Pyrus L." 10 10
2120 60 g. "Prunus persica" . . . 10 10
2121 1 z. 15 "Magnolia kobus" . . 15 10
2122 1 z. 35 "Crategus oxyacantha" 15 10
2123 2 z. 50 "Malus M." 20 10
2124 3 z. 40 "Aesculus carnea" . . 30 10
2125 5 z. "Robinia pseudacacia" . 1·00 25
2126 8 z. 50 "Prunus avium" . . . 1·90 60

580 "Worker" (sculpture, J. Januszkiewicz)

1972. 30th Anniv of Polish Workers' Coalition.
2127 **580** 60 g. black and red . . . 15 10

581 Tobogganing

1972. Winter Olympic Games, Sapporo, Japan. Multicoloured.
2128 40 g. Type **581** 10 10
2129 60 g. Slalom (vert) 10 10
2130 1 z. 65 Biathlon (vert) . . . 30 10
2131 2 z. 50 Ski jumping 45 20

582 "Heart" and Cardiogram Trace **583** Running

1972. World Heart Month.
2133 **582** 2 z. 50 multicoloured . . 20 10

1972. Olympic Games, Munich. Multicoloured.
2134 20 g. Type **583** 10 10
2135 30 g. Archery 10 10
2136 40 g. Boxing 10 10
2137 60 g. Fencing 10 10
2138 2 z. 50 Wrestling 15 10
2139 3 z. 40 Weightlifting 20 10
2140 5 z. Cycling 75 30
2141 8 z. 50 Shooting . . . . . . 1·25 45

584 Cyclists **585** Polish War Memorial, Berlin

1972. 25th International Peace Cycle Race.
2143 **584** 60 g. multicoloured . . . 20 10

1972. "Victory Day, 1945".
2144 **585** 60 g. green 15 10

586 "Rodlo" Emblem **587** Polish Knight of 972 A.D

1972. 50th Anniv of Polish Posts in Germany.
2145 **586** 60 g. ochre, red & green 15 10

1972. Millenary of Battle of Cedynia.
2146 **587** 60 g. multicoloured . . . 15 10

588 Cheetah

1972. Zoo Animals. Multicoloured.

2147 20 g. Type **588** 15 10
2148 40 g. Giraffe (vert) 20 10
2149 60 g. Toco Toucan 30 10
2150 1 z. 35 Chimpanzee 20 10
2151 1 z. 65 Common gibbon . . 30 10
2152 3 z. 40 Crocodile 40 10
2153 4 z. Red kangaroo 70 15
2154 4 z. 50 Tiger (vert) . . . . . 2·75 1·00
2155 7 z. Mountain zebra . . . . 3·00 1·25

589 L. Warynski. (founder) **590** F. Dzerzhinsky

1972. 90th Anniv of Proletarian Party.

2156 **589** 60 g. multicoloured . . . 15 10

1972. 95th Birth Anniv of Feliks Dzerzhinsky (Russian politician).

2157 **590** 60 g. black and red . . . 15 10

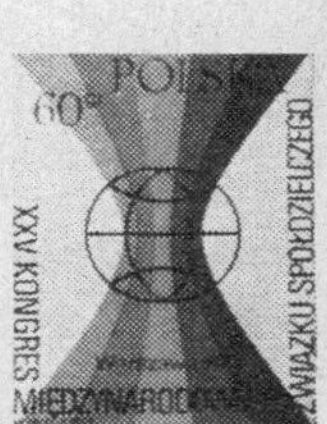

591 Global Emblem **592** Scene from "In Barracks" (ballet)

1972. 25th Int Co-operative Federation Congress.

2158 **591** 60 g. multicoloured . . . 15 10

1972. Death Centenary of Stanislaus Moniuszko (composer). Scenes from Works.

2159 **592** 10 g. violet and gold . . 10 10
2160 – 20 g. black and gold . . 10 10
2161 – 40 g. green and gold . . 10 10
2162 – 60 g. blue and gold . . . 15 10
2163 – 1 z. 15 blue and gold . . 15 10
2164 – 1 z. 35 blue and gold . . 15 10
2165 – 1 z. 55 green and gold . . 15 15
2166 – 2 z. 50 brown and gold . . 50 25

DESIGNS: 20 g. "The Countess" (opera); 40 g. "The Haunted Manor" (opera); 60 g. "Halka" (opera); 1 z. 15, "New Don Quixote" (ballet); 1 z. 35, "Verbum Nobile"; 1 z. 55, "Ideal" (operetta); 2 z. 50, "Pariah" (opera).

593 "Copernicus the Astronomer"

1972. 500th Birth Anniv (1973) of Nicolas Copernicus. (4th issue).

2167 **593** 40 g. black and blue . . 10 10
2168 – 60 g. black and orange . . 15 10
2169 – 2 z. 50 black and red . . 50 10
2170 – 3 z. 40 black and green . . 60 30

DESIGNS: 60 g. Copernicus and Polish eagle; 2 z. 50, Copernicus and Medal; 3 z. 40, Copernicus and page of book.

594 "The Amazon" (P. Michalowski)

1972. Stamp Day. Polish Paintings. Multicoloured.

2172 30 g. Type **594** 10 10
2173 40 g. "Ostafi Laskiewicz" (J. Metejko) 10 10
2174 60 g. "Summer Idyll" (W. Gerson) 10 10
2175 2 z. "The Neapolitan Woman" (A. Kotsis) 15 10
2176 2 z. 50 "Girl Bathing" (P. Szyndler) 20 10
2177 3 z. 40 "The Princess of Thum" (A. Grottger) 30 10
2178 4 z. "Rhapsody" (S. Wyspianski) . . . . . 1·25 45
2179 8 z. 50+4 z. "Young Woman" (J. Malczewski) (horiz) . . 1·50 75

1972. Nos. 1578/9 surch.

2180 50 g. on 40 g. brown 10 10
2181 90 g. on 40 g. brown 15 10
2182 1 z. on 40 g. brown 10 10
2183 1 z. 50 on 60 g. orange . . . 10 10
2184 2 z. 70 on 40 g. brown . . . 20 10
2185 4 z. on 60 g. orange 30 10
2186 4 z. 50 on 60 g. orange . . . 30 10
2187 4 z. 90 on 60 g. orange . . . 50 15

596 "The Little Soldier" (E. Piwowarski)

1972. Children's Health Centre.

2188 **596** 60 g. black and pink . . . 15 10

597 "Royal Castle, Warsaw". (E. J. Dahlberg, 1656) **598** Chalet, Chocholowska Valley

1972. Restoration of Royal Castle, Warsaw.

2189 **597** 60 g. black, violet & bl . 15 10

1972. Tourism. Mountain Chalets. Multicoloured.

2190 40 g. Type **598** 10 10
2191 60 g. Hala Ornak (horiz) . . . 10 10
2192 1 z. 55 Hala Gasienicowa . . 10 10
2193 1 z. 65 Valley of Five Lakes (horiz) 20 10
2194 2 z. 50 Morskie Oko 35 10

599 Trade Union Banners **600** Congress Emblem

1972. 7th Polish Trade Union Congresses.

2195 **599** 60 g. multicoloured . . 15 10

1972. 5th Socialist Youth Union Congress.

2196 **600** 60 g. multicoloured . . 15 10

601 Japanese Azalea

1972. Flowering Shrubs. Multicoloured.

2197 40 g. Type **601** 10 10
2198 50 g. Alpine rose 10 10
2199 60 g. Pomeranian honeysuckle 10 10
2200 1 z. 65 Chinese quince . . . 10 10
2201 2 z. 50 Korean cranberry . . 20 10
2202 3 z. 40 Pontic azalea . . . 30 10
2203 4 z. Delavay's white syringa . 70 25
2204 8 z. 50 Common lilac ("Massena") . . . . 1·50 65

602 Piast Knight (10th-century) **603** Copernicus

1972. Polish Cavalry Through the Ages. Mult.

2205 20 g. Type **602** 10 10
2206 40 g. 13th-century knight . . 10 10
2207 60 g. Knight of Wladyslaw Jagiello's Army (15th-century) (horiz) 10 10
2208 1 z. 35 17th-century hussar . . 10 10
2209 4 z. Lancer of National Guard (18th-century) 60 15
2210 4 z. 50 "Congress Kingdom" cavalry officer 65 20
2211 5 z. Trooper of Light Cavalry (1939) (horiz) . . . . . 1·25 35
2212 7 z. Trooper of People's Army (1945) . . . . 1·40 50

1972. 500th Birth Anniv (1973) of Copernicus (5th issue).

2213 **603** 1 z. brown 15 10
2214 1 z. 50 ochre 20 10

604 Couple with Hammer and Sickle **605** "Copernicus as Young Man" (Bacciarelli)

1972. 50th Anniv of U.S.S.R. Multicoloured.

2215 40 g. Type **604** 10 10
2216 60 g. Red star and globe . . . 10 10

1973. 500th Birth Anniv of Copernicus (6th issue). Multicoloured.

2217 1 z. Type **605** 15 10
2218 1 z. 50 "Copernicus" (anon) . . 15 10
2219 2 z. 70 "Copernicus" (Zinck Nor) 25 10
2220 4 z. "Copernicus" (from Strasbourg clock) 50 25
2221 4 z. 90 "Copernicus" (Jan Matejko) (horiz) 65 35

606 Coronation Sword **607** Statue of Lenin

1973. Polish Art. Multicoloured.

2222 50 g. Type **606** 10 10
2223 1 z. Kruzlowa Madonna (detail) 10 10
2224 1 z. Armour of hussar 10 10
2225 1 z. 50 Carved head from Wavel Castle 10 10
2226 1 z. 50 Silver cockerel 10 10
2227 2 z. 70 Armorial eagle . . . 25 10
2228 4 z. 90 Skarbimierz Madonna 65 35
2229 8 z. 50 "Portrait of Tenczynski" (anon.) . . . . 1·00 50

1973. Unveiling of Lenin's Statue, Nowa Huta.

2230 **607** 1 z. multicoloured . . . 15 10

608 Coded Letter

1973. Introduction of Postal Codes.

2231 **608** 1 z. multicoloured . . . 15 10

609 Wolf

1973. International Hunting Council Congress and 50th Anniv of Polish Hunting Association. Game Animals. Multicoloured.

2232 50 g. Type **609** 10 10
2233 1 z. Mouflon 10 10
2234 1 z. 50 Elk 10 10
2235 2 z. 70 Capercaillie 30 10
2236 3 z. Roe deer 30 10
2237 4 z. 50 Lynx 65 20
2238 4 z. 90 Red deer . . . . . 1·75 35
2239 5 z. Wild boar . . . . . . 2·00 45

610 "Salyut" **611** Open Book and Flame

1973. Cosmic Research. Multicoloured.

2240 4 z. 90 Type **610** 45 25
2241 4 z. 90 "Copernicus" (U.S. satellite) 45 25

1973. 2nd Polish Science Congress, Warsaw.

2242 **611** 1 z. 50 multicoloured . . 15 10

612 Ancient Seal of Poznan **613** M. Nowotko

1973. "Polska 73" Philatelic Exhibition, Poznan. Multicoloured.

2243 1 z. Type **612** 10 10
2244 1 z. 50 Tombstone of N. Tomicki 10 10
2245 2 z. 70 Kalisz paten 25 10
2246 4 z. Bronze gates, Gniezno Cathedral (horiz) 40 20

1973. 80th Birth Anniv of Marceli Nowotko (party leader).

2249 **613** 1 z. 50 black and red . . 15 10

614 Cherry Blossom

1973. Protection of the Environment. Multicoloured.

2250 50 g. Type **614** 10 10
2251 90 g. Cattle in meadow . . . 10 10
2252 1 z. White Stock on nest . . 50 10
2253 1 z. 50 Pond life 15 10
2254 2 z. 70 Meadow flora 25 10
2255 4 z. 90 Ocean fauna 55 30
2256 5 z. Forest life . . . . . . 2·75 45
2257 6 z. 50 Agricultural produce . 1·75 50

615 Motor-cyclist

1973. World Speedway Race Championships, Chorzow.
2258 **615** 1 z. 50 multicoloured . . 15 10

616 "Copernicus" (M. Bacciarelli)

1973. Stamp Day.
2259 **616** 4 z.+2 z. multicoloured . 50 25

617 Tank

1973. 30th Anniv of Polish People's Army. Mult.
2260 1 z. Type **617** 15 10
2261 1 z. Mikoyan Gurevich MiG-21D airplane 20 10
2262 1 z. 50 Guided missile 20 10
2263 1 z. 50 Missile boat 25 10

618 G. Piramowicz and Title Page

1973. Bicent of Nat Educational Commission.
2264 **618** 1 z. brown and yellow . . 10 10
2265 – 1 z. 50 green, & lt green . 15 10
DESIGN: 1 z. 50, J. Sniadecki, H. Kollataj and J. U. Niemcewicz.

619 Pawel Strzelecki (explorer) and Red Kangaroo

1973. Polish Scientists. Multicoloured.
2266 1 z. Type **619** 15 10
2267 1 z. Henryk Arctowski (Polar explorer) and Adelie penguins 35 10
2268 1 z. 50 Stefan Rogozinski (explorer) and "Lucy-Margaret" (schooner) . . . 30 10
2269 1 z. 50 Benedykt Dybowski (zoologist) and sable, Lake Baikal 20 10
2270 2 z. Bronislaw Malinowski (anthropologist) and New Guinea dancers 25 10
2271 2 z. 70 Stefan Drzewiecki (oceanographer) and submarine 35 10
2272 3 z. Edward Strasburger (botanist) and classified plants 35 15
2273 8 z. Ignacy Domeyko (geologist) and Chilean desert landscape 1·40 50

HAVE YOU READ THE NOTES AT THE BEGINNING OF THIS CATALOGUE?
These often provide the answers to the enquiries we receive.

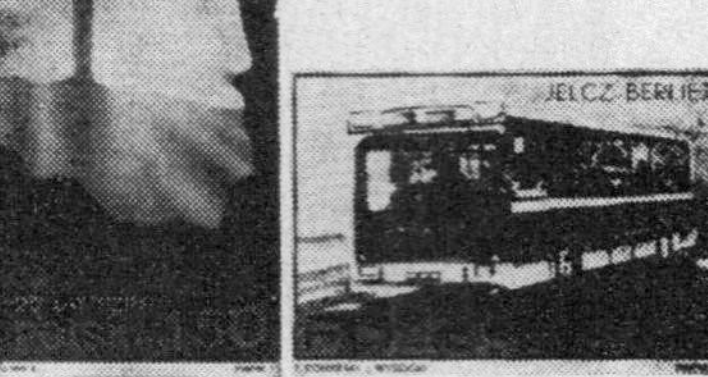

620 Polish Flag **621** Jelcz-Berliet Coach

1973. 25th Anniv of Polish United Workers' Party.
2274 **620** 1 z. 40 red, blue and gold 15 10

1973. Polish Motor Vehicles. Multicoloured.
2275 50 g. Type **621** 10 10
2276 90 g. Jelcz "316" truck . . . 10 10
2277 1 z. Polski-Fiat "126p" saloon 10 10
2278 1 z. 50 Polski-Fiat "125p" saloon and mileage records 10 10
2279 4 z. Nysa "M-521" utility van 40 40
2280 4 z. 50 Star "660" truck . . 75 50

622 Iris **623** Cottage, Kurpie

1974. Flowers. Drawings by S. Wyspianski.
2281 **622** 50 g. purple 10 10
2282 – 1 z. green 10 10
2283 – 1 z. 50 red 10 10
2284 – 3 z. violet 35 10
2285 – 4 z. blue 40 10
2286 – 4 z. 50 green 60 25
FLOWERS: 1 z. Dandelion; 1 z. 50, Rose; 3 z. Thistle; 4 z. Cornflower; 4 z. 50, Clover.

1974. Wooden Architecture. Multicoloured.
2287 1 z. Type **623** 10 10
2288 1 z. 50 Church, Sekowa . . . 10 10
2289 4 z. Town Hall, Sulmierzycc . 30 10
2290 4 z. 50 Church, Lachowice . 35 10
2291 4 z. 90 Windmill, Sobienie Jeziory 55 20
2292 5 z. Orthodox Church, Ulucz 60 30

624 19th-century Mail Coach **625** Cracow Motif

1974. Centenary of Universal Postal Union.
2293 **624** 1 z. 50 multicoloured . . 15 10

1974. "SOCPHILEX IV" Int Stamp Exn, Katowice. Regional Floral Embroideries. Multicoloured.
2294 50 g. Type **625** 10 10
2295 1 z. 50 Lowicz motif . . . 10 10
2296 4 z. Silesian motif 35 15

626 Association Emblem **627** Soldier and Dove

1974. 5th Congress of Fighters for Freedom and Democracy Association, Warsaw.
2298 **626** 1 z. 50 red 15 10

1974. 29th Anniv of Victory over Fascism in Second World War.
2299 **627** 1 z. 50 multicoloured . . 15 10

628 "Comecon" Headquarters, Moscow

1974. 25th Anniv of Council for Mutual Economic Aid.
2300 **628** 1 z. 50 brown, red & blue 15 10

629 World Cup Emblem

1974. World Cup Football Championships, West Germany. Multicoloured.
2301 4 z. 90 Type **629** 50 20
2302 4 z. 90 Players and Olympic Gold Medal of 1972 . . . 50 20

630 Model of 16th-century Galleon **631** Title page of "Chess" by J. Kochanowski

1974. Sailing Ships. Multicoloured.
2304 1 z. Type **630** 25 10
2305 1 z. 50 Sloop "Dal" (1934) . 25 10
2306 2 z. 70 Yacht "Opty" (Teliga's circumnavigation, 1969) . . 35 10
2307 4 z. Cadet ship "Dar Pomorza", 1972 . . . . 65 25
2308 4 z. 90 Yacht "Polonez" (Baranowski's circumnavigation, 1973) 95 35

1974. 10th Inter-Chess Festival, Lublin. Mult.
2309 1 z. Type **631** 20 10
2310 1 z. 50 "Education" (18th-century engraving, D. Chodowiecki) 30 10

632 Lazienkowska Road Junction

1974. Opening of Lazienkowska Flyover.
2311 **632** 1 z. 50 multicoloured . . 15 10

633 Face and Map of Poland **634** Strawberries

1974. 30th Anniv of Polish People's Republic.
2312 **633** 1 z. 50 black, gold & red . 15 10
2313 – 1 z. 50 multicoloured (silver background) 15 10
2314 – 1 z. 50 multicoloured (red background) 15 10
DESIGN—31×43 mm: Nos. 2313/14, Polish "Eagle".

1974. 19th Int Horticultural Congress, Warsaw. Fruits, Vegetables and Flowers. Multicoloured.
2316 50 g. Type **634** 10 10
2317 90 g. Blackcurrants 10 10
2318 1 z. Apples 10 10
2319 1 z. 50 Cucumbers 15 10
2320 2 z. 70 Tomatoes 25 10
2321 4 z. 50 Green Peas 60 20
2322 4 z. 90 Pansies 90 25
2323 5 z. Nasturtiums . . . . . 1·25 30

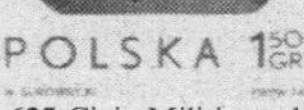

635 Civic Militia and Security Service Emblem **636** "Child in Polish Costume" (L. Orlowski)

1974. 30th Anniv of Polish Civic Militia and Security Service.
2324 **635** 1 z. 50 multicoloured . . 15 10

1974. Stamp Day. "The Child in Polish Costume" Painting. Multicoloured.
2325 50 g. Type **636** 10 10
2326 90 g. "Girl with Pigeon" (anon) 10 10
2327 1 z. "Portrait of a Girl" (S. Wyspianski) 10 10
2328 1 z. 50 "The Orphan from Poronin" (W. Slewinski) . 10 10
2329 3 z. "Peasant Boy" (K. Sichulski) 25 10
2330 4 z. 50 "Florence Page" (A. Gierymski) 40 10
2331 4 z. 90 "Tadeusz and Dog" (P. Michalowski) 50 25
2332 6 z. 50 "Boy with Doe" (A. Kotsis) 70 40

637 "The Crib", Cracow

1974. Polish Art. Multicoloured.
2333 1 z. Type **637** 10 10
2334 1 z. 50 "The Flight to Egypt" (15th-century polyptych) . 15 10
2335 2 z. "King Sigismund III Vasa" (16th-century miniature) . 20 10
2336 4 z. "King Jan Olbracht" (16th-century title-page) 80 25

638 Angler and Fish **639** "Pablo Neruda" (O. Guayasamin)

1974. Polish Folklore. 16th-century Woodcuts (1st series).
2337 **638** 1 z. black 10 10
2338 – 1 z. 50 blue 15 10
DESIGN: 1 z. 50, Hunter and wild animals.
See also Nos. 2525/6.

1974. 70th Birth Anniv of Pablo Neruda (Chilean poet).
2339 **639** 1 z. 50 multicoloured . . 15 10

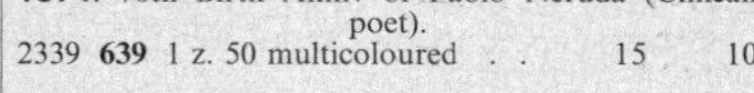

640 "Nike" Memorial and National Opera House

1975. 30th Anniv of Warsaw Liberation.
2340 **640** 1 z. 50 multicoloured . . 15 10

641 Male Lesser Kestrel **642** Broken Barbed Wire

1975. Birds of Prey. Multicoloured.
2341 1 z. Type **641** 30 10
2342 1 z. Lesser kestrel (female) . 30 10
2343 1 z. 50 Red-footed falcon (male) 35 10
2344 1 z. 50 Red-footed falcon (female) 35 10
2345 2 z. European hobby 50 10
2346 3 z. Common kestrel 80 10
2347 4 z. Merlin . . . . 2·10 70
2348 8 z. Peregrine falcon . . . . 3·25 1·40

1975. 30th Anniv of Auschwitz Concentration Camp Liberation.
2349 **642** 1 z. 50 black and red . . 20 10

643 Hurdling

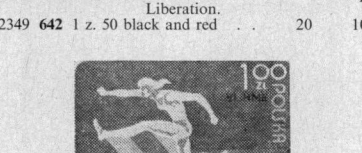

1975. 6th European Indoor Athletic Championships, Katowice. Multicoloured.
2350 1 z. Type **643** 10 10
2351 1 z. 50 Pole vault 15 10
2352 4 z. Triple jump 30 10
2353 4 z. 90 Running 35 15

644 "St. Anne" (Veit Stoss)

1975. "Arphila 1975" International Stamp Exhibition, Paris.
2355 **644** 1 z. 50 multicoloured . . 15 10

645 Globe and "Radio Waves"

1975. International Amateur Radio Union Conference, Warsaw.
2356 **645** 1 z. 50 multicoloured . . 15 10

646 Stone, Pine and Tatra Mountains

647 Hands holding Tulips and Rifle

1975. Centenary of Mountain Guides' Association. Multicoloured.
2357 1 z. Type **646** 10 10
2358 1 z. Gentians and Tatra Mountains 10 10
2359 1 z. 50 Sudety Mountains (horiz) 15 10
2360 1 z. 50 Branch of yew (horiz) 15 10
2361 4 z. Beskidy Mountains . . . 40 15
2362 4 z. Arnica blossoms 40 15

1975. 30th Anniv of Victory over Fascism.
2363 **647** 1 z. 50 multicoloured . . 15 10

648 Flags of Member Countries

1975. 20th Anniv of Warsaw Treaty Organization.
2364 **648** 1 z. 50 multicoloured . . 15 10

649 Hens

1975. 26th European Zoo-technical Federation Congress, Warsaw. Multicoloured.
2365 50 g. Type **649** 10 10
2366 1 z. Geese 10 10
2367 1 z. 50 Cattle 15 10
2368 2 z. Cow 15 10
2369 3 z. Wielkopolska horse . . . 30 10
2370 4 z. Pure-bred Arab horses . 35 10
2371 4 z. 50 Pigs . . . . 1·25 40
2372 5 z. Sheep . . . . 1·75 60

650 "Apollo" and "Soyuz" Spacecraft linked

651 Organization Emblem

1975. "Apollo-Soyuz" Space Project. Multicoloured.
2373 1 z. 50 Type **650** 15 10
2374 4 z. 90 "Apollo" spacecraft . 50 20
2375 4 z. 90 "Soyuz" spacecraft . 50 20

1975. National Health Protection Fund.
2377 **651** 1 z. 50 blue, blk & silver 15 10

652 U.N. Emblem

1975. 30th Anniv of U.N.O.
2378 **652** 4 z. multicoloured . . . 35 15

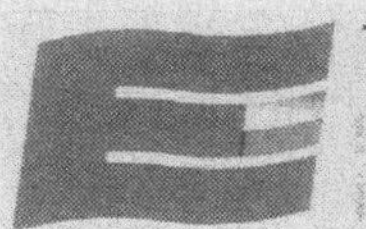

653 Polish Flag within "E" for Europe

1975. European Security and Co-operation Conference, Helsinki.
2379 **653** 4 z. red, blue and black . 35 15

654 "Bolek and Lolek"

1975. Children's Television Characters. Mult.
2380 50 g. Type **654** 10 10
2381 1 z. "Jacek" and "Agatka" . 15 10
2382 1 z. 50 "Reksio" (dog) . . . 15 10
2383 4 z. "Telesfor" (dragon) . . 55 15

655 Institute Emblem

656 Women's Faces

1975. 40th Session of International Statistics Institute.
2384 **655** 1 z. 50 multicoloured . . 15 10

1975. International Women's Year.
2385 **656** 1 z. 50 multicoloured . . 15 10

657 Albatros Biplane

1975. 50th Anniv of First Polish Airmail Stamps. Multicoloured.
2386 2 z. 40 Type **657** 20 10
2387 4 z. 90 Ilyushin Il-62 airplane 45 15

658 "Mary and Margaret" and Polish Settlers

659 Frederic Chopin

1975. Bicentenary of American Revolution. Poles in American Life. Multicoloured.
2388 1 z. Type **658** 20 10
2389 1 z. 50 Polish glass-works, Jamestown 15 10
2390 2 z. 70 Helena Modrzejewska (actress) 15 10
2391 4 z. K. Pulaski (soldier) . . . 30 10
2392 6 z. 40 T. Kosciuzko (soldier) 70 30

1975. 9th International Chopin Piano Competition.
2394 **659** 1 z. 50 black, lilac & gold 15 10

660 "Self-portrait"

661 Market Place, Kazimierz Dolny

1975. Stamp Day. Birth Centenary of Xawery Dunikowski (sculptor). Multicoloured.
2395 50 g. Type **660** 10 10
2396 1 z. "Breath" 10 10
2397 1 z. 50 "Maternity" 15 10
2398 8 z. + 4 z. "Silesian Insurrectionists" 90 45

1975. European Architectural Heritage Year.
2399 **661** 1 z. green 10 10
2400 – 1 z. 50 brown 15 10
DESIGN—VERT: 1 z. 50, Town Hall, Zamosc.

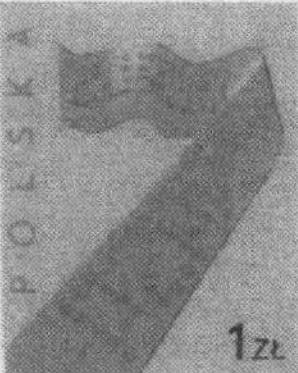

662 "Lodz" (W. Strzeminski)

664 Symbolised Figure "7"

663 Henry IV's Eagle Gravestone Head (14th-century)

1975. "Lodz 75" National Stamp Exhibition.
2401 **662** 4 z. 50 multicoloured . . 40 15

1975. Piast Dynasty of Silesia.
2403 **663** 1 z. green 10 10
2404 – 1 z. 50 brown 10 10
2405 – 4 z. violet 35 15
DESIGNS: 1 z. 50, Seal of Prince Boleslaw of Legnica; 4 z. Coin of last Prince, Jerzy Wilhelm.

1975. 7th Congress of Polish United Workers Party.
2406 **664** 1 z. multicoloured 10 10
2407 – 1 z. 50 red, blue & silver . 15 10
DESIGN: 1 z. 50, Party initials "PZPR".

665 Ski Jumping

1976. Winter Olympic Games, Innsbruck. Mult.
2408 50 g. Type **665** 10 10
2409 1 z. Ice hockey 15 10
2410 1 z. 50 Skiing 20 10
2411 2 z. Skating 20 10
2412 4 z. Tobogganing 35 10
2413 6 z. 40 Biathlon 50 25

666 R. Trevithick's Steam Railway Locomotive, 1803

1976. History of the Railway Locomotive. Mult.
2414 50 g. Type **666** 15 10
2415 1 z. Murray and Blenkinsop's steam locomotive, 1810 . . 15 10
2416 1 z. 50 George Stephenson's locomotive "Rocket", 1829 25 10
2417 1 z. 50 Polish "Universal" Type ET-22 electric locomotive, 1969 . . . . 25 10
2418 2 z. 70 Robert Stephenson's locomotive "North Star", 1837 . . . . 30 10
2419 3 z. Joseph Harrison's steam locomotive, 1840 . . . . . 45 10
2420 4 z. 50 Thomas Roger's steam locomotive, 1855 . . . . . 2·00 45
2421 4 z. 90 Polish Chrzanow Works steam locomotive, 1922 . . 2·00 45

667 Flags of Member Countries

1976. 20th Anniv of Institute for Nuclear Research (C.M.E.A.).
2422 **667** 1 z. 50 multicoloured . . 15 10

668 Early Telephone, Satellite and Radar

1976. Telephone Centenary.
2423 **668** 1 z. 50 multicoloured . . 15 10

669 Jantar Glider

670 Player

1976. Air. Contemporary Aviation.
2424 **669** 5 z. blue 30 15
2425 – 10 z. brown 60 30
2425a – 20 z. olive . . . . . . 1·25 40
2425b – 50 z. lake . . . . 3·00 1·50
DESIGN: 10 z. Mil Mi-6 helicopter; 20 z. PZL-106A agricultural airplane; 50 z. PZL-Mielec TS-11 Iskra jet trainer over Warsaw Castle.

1976. World Ice Hockey Championships, Katowice. Multicoloured.
2426 1 z. Type **670** 10 10
2427 1 z. 50 Player (different) . . 15 10

671 Polish U.N. Soldier

1976. Polish Troops in U.N. Sinai Force.
2428 **671** 1 z. 50 multicoloured . . 15 10

672 "Glory to the Sappers" (S. Kulon) 673 "Interphil 76"

1976. War Memorials. Multicoloured.

2429 1 z. Type **672** 15 10
2430 1 z. 1st Polish Army Monument, Sandau, Laba (B. Koniuszy) 15 10

1976. "Interphil '76" Int Stamp Exn, Philadelphia.

2431 **673** 8 z. 40 multicoloured . . 60 20

674 Wielkopolski Park and Tawny Owl

1976. National Parks. Multicoloured.

2432 90 g. Type **674** 40 15
2433 1 z. Wolinski Park and white-tailed sea eagle 40 15
2434 1 z. 50 Slowinski Park and seagull 50 15
2435 4 z. 50 Bieszezadzki Park and lynx 40 15
2436 5 z. Ojcowski Park and bat . 40 15
2437 6 z. Kampinoski Park and elk 50 25

675 Peace Dove within Globe

1976. 25th Anniv of U.N. Postal Administration.

2438 **675** 8 z. 40 multicoloured . . 60 20

676 Fencing 677 National Theatre

1976. Olympic Games, Montreal. Multicoloured.

2439 50 g. Type **676** 10 10
2440 1 z. Cycling 10 10
2441 1 z. 50 Football 10 10
2442 4 z. 20 Boxing 40 10
2443 6 z. 90 Weightlifting 65 15
2444 8 z. 40 Athletics 75 25

1976. Cent of National Theatre, Poznan.

2446 **677** 1 z. 50 green & orange . 15 10

678 Aleksander Czekanowski and Baikal Landscape 679 "Sphinx"

1976. Death Centenary of Aleksander Czekanowski (geologist).

2447 **678** 1 z. 50 multicoloured . . 15 10

1976. Stamp Day. Corinthian Vase Paintings (7th century B.C.). Multicoloured.

2448 1 z. Type **679** 10 10
2449 1 z. 50 "Siren" (horiz) . . . 10 10
2450 2 z. "Lion" (horiz) 15 10
2451 4 z. 20 "Bull" (horiz) . . . 30 10
2452 4 z. 50 "Goat" (horiz) . . . 35 20
2453 8 z. + 4 z. "Sphinx" (different) 1·10 50

680 Warszawa "M 20"

1976. 25th Anniv of Zeran Motor-car Factory, Warsaw. Multicoloured.

2454 1 z. Type **680** 10 10
2455 1 z. 50 Warszawa "223" . . 10 10
2456 2 z. Syrena "104" 15 10
2457 4 z. 90 Polski - Fiat "125P" 40 20

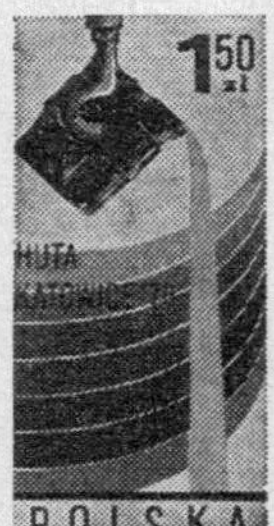

681 Molten Steel Ladle

1976. Huta Katowice Steel Works.

2459 **681** 1 z. 50 multicoloured . . 15 10

682 Congress Emblem 683 "Wirzbieto Epitaph" (painting on wood, 1425)

1976. 8th Polish Trade Unions Congress.

2460 **682** 1 z. 50 orange, bistre and brown 15 10

1976. Polish Art. Multicoloured.

2461 1 z. Type **683** 10 10
2462 6 z. "Madonna and Child" (painted carving, c.1410) . 35 15

684 Tanker "Zawrat" at Oil Terminal, Gdansk

1976. Polish Ports. Multicoloured.

2463 1 z. Type **684** 20 10
2464 1 z. Ferry "Gryf" at Gdansk 20 10
2465 1 z. 50 Loading container ship "General Bem", Gdynia . 40 10
2466 1 z. 50 Liner "Stefan Batory" leaving Gdynia 40 10
2467 2 z. Bulk carrier "Ziemia Szczecinska" loading at Szczecin 55 10
2468 4 z. 20 Loading coal, Swinoujscie 70 15
2469 6 z. 90 Pleasure craft, Kolobrzeg 90 25
2470 8 z. 40 Coastal map . . . . 1·40 35

685 Nurse and Patient 686 Order of Civil Defence Service

1977. Polish Red Cross.

2471 **685** 1 z. 50 multicoloured . . 15 10

1977. Polish Civil Defence.

2472 **686** 1 z. 50 multicoloured . . 15 10

687 Ball in Road

1977. Child Road Safety Campaign.

2473 **687** 1 z. 50 multicoloured . . 15 10

688 Dewberries "Rubus caesius" 689 Computer Tape

1977. Wild Fruits. Multicoloured.

2474 50 g. Type **688** 10 10
2475 90 g. Cowberries 10 10
2476 1z. Wild strawberries 10 10
2477 1 z. 50 Bilberries 15 10
2478 2 z. Raspberries 20 10
2479 4 z. 50 Sloes 40 15
2480 6 z. Rose hips 50 15
2481 6 z. 90 hazelnuts 60 25

1977. 30th Anniv of Russian-Polish Technical Co-operation.

2482 **689** 1 z. 50 multicoloured . . 15 10

690 Pendulum Traces and Emblem

1977. 7th Polish Congress of Technology.

2483 **690** 1 z. 50 multicoloured . . 15 10

691 "Toilet of Venus"

1977. 400th Birth Anniv of Peter Paul Rubens. Multicoloured.

2484 1 z. Type **691** 10 10
2485 1 z. 50 "Bathsheba at the Fountain" 10 10
2486 5 z. "Helena Fourment with Fur Coat" 40 20
2487 6 z. "Self-portrait" 55 35

692 Dove 694 Wolf

693 Cyclist

1977. World Council of Peace Congress.

2489 **692** 1 z. 50 blue, yellow & blk 15 10

1977. 30th International Peace Cycle Race.

2490 **693** 1 z. 50 multicoloured . . 15 10

1977. Endangered Animals. Multicoloured.

2491 1 z. Type **694** 10 10
2492 1 z. 50 Great bustard . . . 40 15
2493 1 z. 50 Common kestrel . . . 40 15
2494 6 z. European otter 50 20

695 "The Violinist" (J. Toorenvliet) 697 H. Wieniawski and Music Clef

696 Midsummer's Day Bonfire

1977. "Amphilex 77" Stamp Exhibition, Amsterdam.

2495 **6** z. multicoloured 40 25

1977. Folk Customs. 19th-century Wood Engravings. Multicoloured.

2496 90 g. Type **696** 10 10
2497 1 z. Easter cock (vert) . . . 10 10
2498 1 z. 50 "Smigus" (dousing of women on Easter Monday, Miechow district) (vert) . . 10 10
2499 3 z. Harvest Festival, Sandomierz district (vert) . 25 10
2500 6 z. Children with Christmas crib (vert) 50 15
2501 8 z. 40 Mountain wedding dance 70 20

1977. Wieniawski International Music Competitions, Poznan.

2502 **697** 1 z. 50 black, red & gold 20 10

698 Apollo ("Parnassius apollo")

1977. Butterflies. Multicoloured.

2503 1 z. Type **698** 20 10
2504 1 z. Large tortoiseshell ("Nymphalis polychloros") 20 10
2505 1 z. 50 Camberwell beauty ("Nymphalis antiopa") . . 25 10
2506 1 z. 50 Swallowtail ("Papilio machaon") 25 10
2507 5 z. High brown fritillary . . 75 15
2508 6 z. 90 Silver-washed fritillary 1·40 65

699 Keyboard and Arms of Slupsk 700 Feliks Dzerzhinsky

1977. Piano Festival, Slupsk.

2509 **699** 1 z. 50 mauve, blk & grn 15 10

1977. Birth Centenary of Feliks Dzerzhinsky (Russian politician).

2510 **700** 1 z. 50 brown and ochre 15 10

701 "Sputnik" circling Earth 702 Silver Dinar (11th century)

1977. 60th Anniv of Russian Revolution and 20th Anniv of 1st Artificial Satellite (1st issue).

2511 **701** 1 z. 50 red and blue . . 15 10

See also No. 2527.

1977. Stamp Day. Polish Coins. Multicoloured.

2513 50 g. Type **702** 10 10
2514 1 z. Cracow grosz, 14th-century 10 10
2515 1 z. 50 Legnica thaler, 17th-century 10 10
2516 4 z. 20 Gdansk guilder, 18th-century 35 10
2517 4 z. 50 Silver 5 z. coin, 1936 35 10
2518 6 z. Millenary 100 z. coin, 1966 60 25

703 Wolin Gate, Kamien Pomorski

704 "Sputnik 1" and "Mercury" Capsule

1977. Architectural Monuments. Multicoloured.
2519 1 z. Type **703** 10 10
2520 1 z. Larch church, Debno . . 10 10
2521 1 z. 50 Monastery, Przasnysz (horiz) 10 10
2522 1 z. 50 Plock cathedral (horiz) 10 10
2523 6 z. Kornik castle (horiz) . . 40 10
2524 6 z. 90 Palace and garden, Wilanow (horiz) 50 25

1977. Polish Folklore. 16th-century woodcuts (2nd series). As T **638**.
2525 4 z. sepia 25 10
2526 4 z. 50 brown 30 10
DESIGNS: 4 z. Bird snaring; 4 z. 50, Bee-keeper and hives.

1977. 20th Anniv of 1st Space Satellite (2nd issue).
2527 **704** 6 z. 90 multicoloured . . 45 35

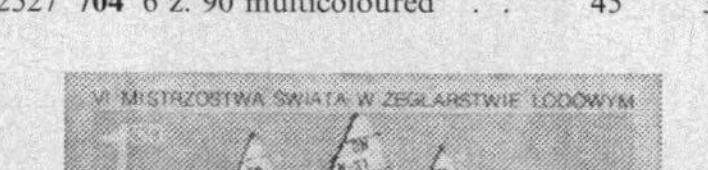

705 DN Category Iceboats

1978. 6th World Ice Sailing Championships.
2528 **705** 1 z. 50 black, grey & blue 15 10
2529 – 1 z. 50 black, grey & blue 15 10
DESIGN: No. 2529, Close-up of DN iceboat.

706 Electric Locomotive and Katowice Station

1978. Railway Engines. Multicoloured.
2530 50 g. Type **706** 10 10
2531 1 z. Py 27 Steam locomotive (Znin-Gasawa narrow-gauge railway) 15 10
2532 1 z. Pm 36 Steam locomotive and Cegielski's factory, Poznan 15 10
2533 1 z. 50 Electric locomotive and Otwock station 15 10
2534 1 z. 50 Steam locomotive and Warsaw Stalowa station . . 15 10
2535 4 z. 50 Steam locomotive Ty 51 and Gdynia station 35 10
2536 5 z. Tr 21 and steam locomotive factory, Chrzanow 40 15
2537 6 z. Cockerill steam locomotive and Vienna station 60 25

707 Czeslaw Tanski and Glider

1978. Aviation History and 50th Anniv of Polish Aero Club. Multicoloured.
2538 50 g. Type **707** 10 10
2539 1 z. Franciszek Zwirko and Stanislaw Wigura with RWD-6 aircraft (vert) . . . 10 10
2540 1 z. 50 Stanislaw Skarzynski and RWD-5 bis monoplane (vert) 15 10
2541 4 z. 20 Mil Mi-2 helicopter (vert) 25 10
2542 6 z. 90 PZL-104 Wilga 35 monoplane 90 20
2543 8 z. 40 SZD-45 Ogar powered glider 80 20

708 Tackle

1978. World Cup Football Championship, Argentina. Multicoloured.
2544 1 z. 50 Type **708** 10 10
2545 6 z. 90 Ball on field (horiz) . 45 20

709 Biennale Emblem

1978. 7th International Poster Biennale, Warsaw.
2546 **709** 1 z. 50 mauve, yell & vio 10 10

711 Polonez Saloon Car

1978. Car Production.
2548 **711** 1 z. 50 multicoloured . . 15 10

712 Fair Emblem

713 Miroslaw Hermaszewski

1978. 50th International Fair, Poznan.
2549 **712** 1 z. 50 multicoloured . . 10 10

1978. First Pole in Space. Multicoloured. With or without date.
2550 1 z. 50 Type **713** 15 10
2551 6 z. 90 M. Hermaszewski and globe 55 15

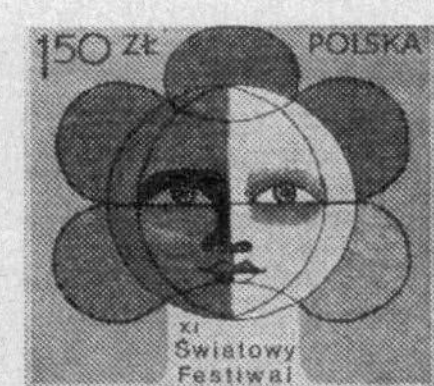

714 Globe containing Face

1978. 11th World Youth and Students Festival, Havana.
2552 **714** 1 z. 50 multicoloured . . 10 10

716 Mosquito and Malaria Organisms

717 Pedunculate Oak

1978. 4th International Congress of Parasitologists, Warsaw and Cracow. Multicoloured.
2554 1 z. 50 Type **716** 15 10
2555 6 z. Tsetse fly and sleeping sickness organism 40 20

1978. Environment Protection. Trees. Multicoloured.
2556 50 g. Norway Maple 10 10
2557 1 z. Type **717** 10 10
2558 1 z. 50 White Poplar 10 10
2559 4 z. 20 Scots Pine 30 10
2560 4 z. 50 White Willow 30 10
2561 6 z. Birch 45 20

719 Communications

1978. 20th Anniv of Socialist Countries Communications Organization.
2563 **719** 1 z. 50 red, lt blue & bl . 10 10

720 "Peace" (Andre Le Brun)

1978.
2564 **720** 1 z. violet 10 10
2565 1 z. 50 turquoise 15 10
2565a 2 z. brown 15 10
2565b 2 z. 50 blue 20 10

721 Polish Unit of U.N. Middle East Force

1978. 35th Anniv of Polish People's Army. Multicoloured.
2566 1 z. 50 Colour party of Tadeusz Kosciuszko 1st Warsaw Infantry Division 15 10
2567 1 z. 50 Mechanised Unit colour party 15 10
2568 1 z. 50 Type **721** 15 10

722 "Portrait of a Young Man" (Raphael)

1978. Stamp Day.
2569 **722** 6 z. multicoloured 35 20

723 Janusz Korczak with Children

724 Wojciech Boguslawski

1978. Birth Centenary of Janusz Korczak (pioneer of children's education).
2570 **723** 1 z. 50 multicoloured . . 15 10

1978. Polish Dramatists. Multicoloured.
2571 50 g. Type **724** 10 10
2572 1 z. Aleksander Fredro . . . 10 10
2573 1 z. 50 Juliusz Slowacki . . . 10 10
2574 2 z. Adam Mickiewicz 15 10
2575 4 z. 50 Stanislaw Wyspianski . 30 10
2576 6 z. Gabriela Zapolska . . . 50 20

725 Polish Combatants' Monument and Eiffel Tower

1978. Monument to Polish Combatants in France, Paris.
2577 **725** 1 z. 50 brown, blue & red 15 10

726 Przewalski Horses

1978. 50th Anniv of Warsaw Zoo. Multicoloured.
2578 50 g. Type **726** 10 10
2579 1 z. Polar bears 10 10
2580 1 z. 50 Indian elephants . . . 20 10
2581 2 z. Jaguars 25 10
2582 4 z. 20 Grey seals 30 10
2583 4 z. 50 Hartebeests 30 10
2584 6 z. Mandrills 45 25

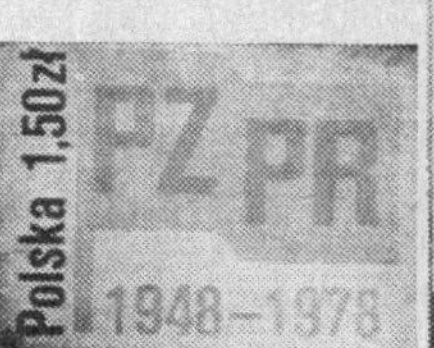

727 Party Flag

728 Stanislaw Dubois

1978. 30th Anniv of Polish Workers' United Party.
2585 **727** 1 z. 50 red, gold and black 10 10

1978. Leaders of Polish Workers' Movement.
2586 **728** 1 z. 50 blue and red . . 10 10
2587 – 1 z. 50 lilac and red . . 10 10
2588 – 1 z. 50 olive and red . . 10 10
2589 – 1 z. 50 brown and red . . 10 10
DESIGNS: No. 2587, Aleksander Zawadzki; No. 2588, Julian Lenski; No. 2589, Aldolf Warski.

729 Ilyushin Il-62M and Fokkerb.VIIb/3m

1979. 50th Anniv of LOT Polish Airlines.
2590 **729** 6 z. 90 multicoloured . . 60 20

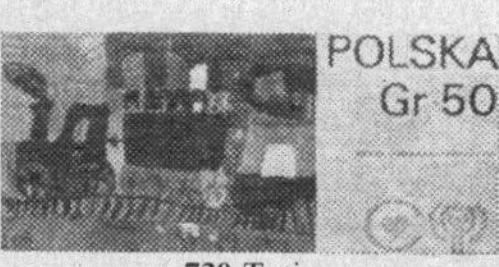

730 Train

1979. International Year of the Child. Children's Paintings. Multicoloured.
2591 50 g. Type **730** 15 10
2592 1 z. "Mother with Children" . 10 10
2593 1 z. 50 Children playing . . 15 10
2594 6 z. Family Group 45 15

731 "Portrait of Artist's Wife with Foxgloves" (Karol Mondrala)

1979. Contemporary Graphics.
2595 – 50 g. lilac 10 10
2596 **731** 1 z. green 10 10
2597 – 1 z. 50 blue 10 10
2598 – 4 z. 50 brown 30 10
DESIGNS—HORIZ: 50 g. "Lightning" (Edmund Bartlomiejezyk). VERT: 1 z. 50, "The Musicians" (Tadeusz Kulisiewicz); 4 z. 50, "Head of a Young Man" (Wladyslaw Skoczylas).

732 A. Frycz Modrzewski (political writer), King Stefan Batory and Jan Zamoyski (chancellor)

1979. 400th Anniv (1978) of Royal Tribunal in Piotrkow Trybunalski.
2599 **732** 1 z. 50 brown and deep brown 15 10

733 Pole Vaulting

1979. 60th Anniv of Polish Olympic Committee. Multicoloured.
2600 1 z. Type **733** 10 10
2601 1 z. 50 High jump 10 10
2602 6 z. Skiing 40 15
2603 8 z. 40 Horse riding 60 25

734 Flounder

1979. Centenary of Polish Angling. Multicoloured.

2605 50 g. Type **734** 10 10
2606 90 g. Perch 10 10
2607 1 z. Greyling 10 10
2608 1 z. 50 Salmon 10 10
2609 2 z. Trout 15 10
2610 4 z. 50 Pike 25 10
2611 5 z. Carp 40 10
2612 6 z. Catfish 45 20

735 "30 Years of RWPG"

1979. 30th Anniv of Council of Mutual Economic Aid.

2613 **735** 1 z. 50 red, ultram and blue 15 10

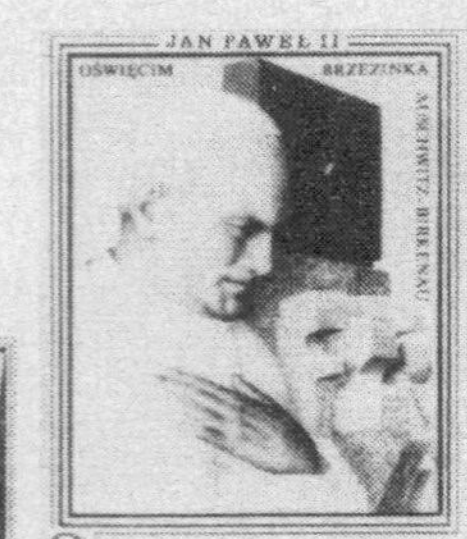

736 Soldier, Civilian and Congress Emblem

738 Pope and Auschwitz Concentration Camp Memorial

737 St. George's Church, Sofia

1979. 6th Congress of Association of Fighters for Liberty and Democracy.

2614 **736** 1 z. 50 red and black 15 10

1979. "Philaserdica 79" International Stamp Exhibition, Sofia, Bulgaria.

2615 **737** 1 z. 50 orge, brn & red 15 10

1979. Visit of Pope John Paul II. Multicoloured.

2616 1 z. 50 Pope and St. Mary's Church, Cracow 25 10
2617 8 z. 40 Type **738** 65 30

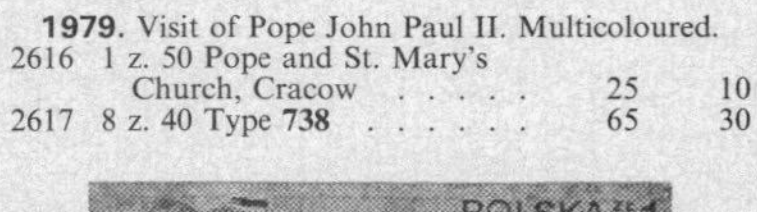

739 River Paddle-steamer "Ksiaze Ksawery" and Old Warsaw

1979. 150th Anniv of Vistula River Navigation. Multicoloured.

2619 1 z. Type **739** 20 10
2620 1 z. 50 River paddle-steamer "General Swierczewski" and Gdansk 25 10
2621 4 z. 50 River tug "Zubr" and Plock 70 10
2622 6 z. Passenger launch "Syrena" and modern Warsaw 1·25 20

740 Statue of Tadeusz Kosciuszko (Marian Konieczny)

741 Mining Machinery

1979. Monument to Tadeusz Kosciuszko in Philadelphia.

2623 **740** 8 z. 40 multicoloured 50 20

1979. Wieliczka Salt Mine.

2624 **741** 1 z. brown and black 10 10
2625 – 1 z. 50 turquoise & black 10 10

DESIGN: 1 z. 50, Salt crystals.

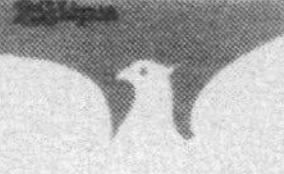

742 Heraldic Eagle

743 Rowland Hill and 1860 Stamp

1979. 35th Anniv of Polish People's Republic.

2626 – 1 z. 50 red, silver and black 15 10
2627 **742** 1 z. 50 red, silver and blue 15 10

DESIGN: No. 2626, Girl and stylized flag.

1979. Death Centenary of Sir Rowland Hill.

2629 **743** 6 z. blue, black & orange 45 15

745 Wojciech Jastrzebowski

746 Monument (Wincenty Kucma)

1979. 7th Congress of International Ergonomic Association, Warsaw.

2631 **745** 1 z. 50 multicoloured 15 10

1979. Unveiling of Monument to Defenders of Polish Post, Gdansk, and 40th Anniv of German Occupation.

2632 **746** 1 z. 50 multicoloured 15 10

747 Radio Mast and Telecommunications Emblem

1979. 50th Anniv of International Radio Communication Advisory Committee.

2634 **747** 1 z. 50 multicoloured 15 10

748 Violin

1979. Wieniawski Young Violinists' Competition, Lublin.

2635 **748** 1 z. 50 blue, orange & grn 15 10

749 Statue of Kazimierz Pulaski, Buffalo (K. Danilewicz)

750 Franciszek Jozwiak (first Commander)

1979. Death Bicentenary of Kazimierz Pulaski (American Revolution Hero).

2636 **749** 8 z. 40 multicoloured 60 20

1979. 35th Anniv of Civic Militia and Security Force.

2637 **750** 1 z. 50 blue and gold 15 10

INDEX

Countries can be quickly located by referring to the index at the end of this volume.

751 Post Office in Rural Area

1979. Stamp Day. Multicoloured.

2638 1 z. Type **751** 10 10
2639 1 z. 50 Parcel sorting machinery 10 10
2640 4 z. 50 Loading containers on train 40 10
2641 6 z. Mobile post office 50 20

752 "The Holy Family" (Ewelina Peksowa)

753 "Soyuz 30-Salyut 6" Complex and Crystal

1979. Polish Folk Art. Glass Paintings. Mult.

2642 2 z. Type **752** 15 10
2643 6 z. 90 "The Nativity" (Zdzislaw Walczak) 55 20

1979. Space Achievements. Multicoloured.

2644 1 z. Type **753** (1st anniv of 1st Pole in space) 10 10
2645 1 z. 50 "Kopernik" and "Copernicus" satellites 15 10
2646 2 z. "Lunik 2" and "Ranger 7" spacecraft (20th anniv of 1st unmanned Moon landing) 15 10
2647 4 z. 50 Yuri Gagarin and "Vostok 1" 40 10
2648 6 z. 90 Neil Armstrong, lunar module and "Apollo 11" (10th anniv of first man on Moon) 50 20

754 Coach and Four

755 Slogan on Map of Poland

1980. 150th Anniv of Sierakow Stud Farm. Mult.

2650 1 z. Type **754** 15 10
2651 2 z. Horse and groom 20 10
2652 2 z. 50 Sulky racing 25 10
2653 3 z. Hunting 30 10
2654 4 z. Horse-drawn sledge 40 10
2655 6 z. Haywain 60 15
2656 6 z. 50 Grooms exercising horses 70 15
2657 6 z. 90 Show jumping 80 20

1980. 8th Polish United Workers' Party Congress. Multicoloured.

2658 2 z. 50 Type **755** 20 10
2659 2 z. 50 Janusz Stann (26 × 46 mm) 20 10

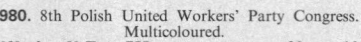

756 Horse Jumping

1980. Olympic Games, Moscow and Winter Olympic Games, Lake Placid. Multicoloured.

2660 2 z. Type **756** 15 10
2661 2 z. 50 Archery 20 10
2662 6 z. 50 Skiing 45 15
2663 8 z. 40 Volleyball 60 25

757 Town Plan and Old Town Hall

1980. 400th Anniv of Zamosc.

2665 **757** 2 z. 50 buff, green & brn 20 10

759 Seals of Poland and Russia

1980. 35th Anniv of Soviet-Polish Friendship Treaty.

2667 **759** 2 z. 50 multicoloured 20 10

760 "Lenin in Cracow" (Zbigniew Pronaszko)

1980. 110th Birth Anniv of Lenin.

2668 **760** 2 z. 50 multicoloured 20 15

761 Workers with Red Flag

1980. 75th Anniv of Revolution of 1905.

2669 **761** 2 z. 50 red, black & yell 20 10

762 Dove

763 Shield with Crests of Member Nations

1980. 35th Anniv of Liberation.

2670 **762** 2 z. 50 multicoloured 20 10

1980. 25th Anniv of Warsaw Pact.

2671 **763** 2 z. grey and red 20 10

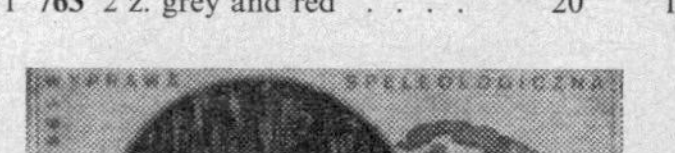

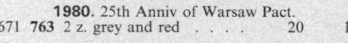

764 Speleological Expedition, Cuba

1980. Polish Scientific Expeditions. Multicoloured.

2672 2 z. Type **764** 15 10
2673 2 z. Antarctic 30 10
2674 2 z. 50 Archaeology, Syria 25 10
2675 2 z. 50 Ethnology, Mongolia 25 10
2676 6 z. 50 Mountaineering, Nepal 45 20
2677 8 z. 40 Paleontology, Mongolia 60 25

765 School and Arms

766 "Clathrus ruber"

1980. 800th Anniv of Malachowski School, Plock.
2678 **765** 2 z. green and black . . 20 10

1980. Fungi. Multicoloured.
2679 2 z. Type **766** 25 10
2680 2 z. "Xerocomus parasiticus" 25 10
2681 2 z. 50 Old man of the woods ("Strobilomyces floccopus") 30 10
2682 2 z. 50 "Phallus hadriani" . . 30 10
2683 8 z. Cauliflower fungus . . . 50 20
2684 10 z. 50 Giant puff-ball . . . 75 40

767 T. Ziolowski and "Lwow"

1980. Polish Merchant Navy School. Cadet Ships and their Captains.
2685 **767** 2 z. black, mauve and violet 30 10
2686 – 2 z. 50 black, light blue and blue 35 10
2687 – 6 z. black, pale green and green 55 15
2688 – 6 z. 50 black, yellow and grey 65 15
2689 – 6 z. 90 black, grey and green 85 20
2690 – 8 z. 40 black, blue and green 90 25
DESIGNS: 2 z. 50, A. Garnuszewski and "Antoni Garnuszewski"; 6 z. A. Ledochowski and "Zenit"; 6 z. 50, K. Porebski and "Jan Turleski"; 6 z. 90, G. Kanski and "Horyzont"; 8 z. 40, Maciejewicz and "Dar Pomorza".

768 Town Hall **769** "Atropa belladonna"

1980. Millenary of Sandomir.
2691 **768** 2 z. 50 brown and black . 20 10

1980. Medicinal Plants. Multicoloured.
2692 2 z. Type **769** 20 10
2693 2 z. 50 "Datura innoxia" . . 25 10
2694 3 z. 40 "Valeriana officinalis" 35 10
2695 5 z. "Menta piperita" . . . 45 10
2696 6 z. 50 "Calendula officinalis" 55 15
2697 8 z. "Salvia officinalis" . . . 70 30

770 Jan Kochanowski **771** U.N. General Assembly

1980. 450th Birth Anniv of Jan Kochanowski (poet).
2698 **770** 2 z. 50 multicoloured . . 20 10

1980. 35th Anniv of U.N.O.
2703 **771** 8 z. 40 brown, blue & red 70 25

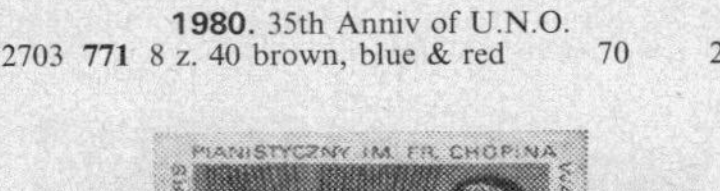

772 Chopin and Trees

1980. 10th International Chopin Piano Competition, Warsaw.
2704 **772** 6 z. 90 multicoloured . . 50 15

773 Postman emptying Post Box

1980. Stamp Day. Multicoloured.
2705 2 z. Type **773** 20 10
2706 2 z. 50 Mail sorting 20 10
2707 6 z. Loading mail onto aircraft 50 15
2708 6 z. 50 Letter boxes 55 15

774 Child embracing Dove

1980. United Nations Declaration on the Preparation of Societies for Life in Peace.
2710 **774** 8 z. 40 multicoloured. . 70 20

775 "Battle of Olszynka Grochowska" (Wojciech Kossak)

1980. 150th Anniv of Battle of Olszynka Grochowska.
2711 **775** 2 z. 50 multicoloured . . 20 10

776 Fire Engine

1980. Warsaw Horse-drawn Vehicles. Mult.
2712 2 z. Type **776** 15 10
2713 2 z. 50 Omnibus 20 10
2714 3 z. Brewery dray 25 10
2715 5 z. Sledge-cab 40 10
2716 6 z. Tram 45 20
2717 6 z. 50 Droshky cab 60 30

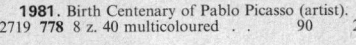

777 "Honour to the Silesian Rebels" (statue by Jan Borowczak) **778** Picasso

1981. 60th Anniv of Silesian Rising.
2718 **777** 2 z. 50 green 15 10

1981. Birth Centenary of Pablo Picasso (artist).
2719 **778** 8 z. 40 multicoloured . . 90 25

779 Balloon of Pilatre de Rozier and Romain, 1785 **780** "Iphigenia" (Anton Maulbertsch)

1981. Balloons. Multicoloured.
2721 2 z. Type **779** 20 10
2722 2 z. Balloon of J. Blanchard and J. Jeffries, 1785 . . . . . 20 10
2723 2 z. 50 Eugene Godard's quiintuple "acrobatic" balloon, 1850 . . . . . 25 10
2724 3 z. F. Hynek and Z. Burzynski's "Kosciuszko", 1933 . . . . 30 10
2725 6 z. Z. Burzynski and N. Wyescki's "Polonia II" 1935 55 15
2726 6 z. 50 Ben Abruzzo, Max Anderson and Larry Newman's "Double Eagle II", 1978 . . . . . . 55 20

1981. "WIPA 1981" International Stamp Exhibition, Vienna.
2728 **780** 10 z. 50 multicoloured . 90 35

781 Wroclaw, 1493 **782** Sikorski

1981. Towns.
2729 – 4 z. violet 30 10
2730 – 5 z. green 50 15
2731 – 6 z. orange 60 15
2732 **781** 6 z. 50 brown 60 20
2733 – 8 z. blue 70 25
DESIGNS—VERT: 4 z. Gdansk, 1652; 5 z. Cracow, 1493. HORIZ: 6 z. Legnica, 1744; 8 z. Warsaw, 1618.

1981. Birth Centenary of General Wladyslaw Sikorski (statesman).
2744 **782** 6 z. 50 multicoloured . . 55 20

783 Faience Vase **784** Congress Emblem

1981. Pottery. Multicoloured.
2745 1 z. Type **783** 15 10
2746 2 z. Porcelain cup and saucer in "Baranowka" design . . . 25 10
2747 2 z. 50 Porcelain jug Korzec manufacture 25 10
2748 5 z. Faience plate with portrait of King Jan III Sobieski by Thiele 50 15
2749 6 z. 50 Faience "Secession" vase 65 20
2750 8 z. 40 Porcelain dish, Cmielow manufacture 80 30

1981. 14th International Architects' Union Congress, Warsaw.
2751 **784** 2 z. yellow, blk and red . 20 10

785 Wild Boar, Rifle and Oak Leaves **786** European Bison

1981. Game Shooting. Multicoloured.
2752 2 z. Type **785** 25 10
2753 2 z. Elk, rifle and fir twigs . . 25 10
2754 2 z. 50 Red fox, shotgun, cartridges and fir branches . 30 10
2755 2 z. 50 Roe deer, feeding rack, rifle and fir branches . . . 30 10
2756 6 z. 50 Mallard, shotgun, basket and reeds . . . . 1·10 30
2757 6 z. 50 Barnacle goose, shotgun and reeds (horiz) . . . . . 1·10 30

1981. Protection of European Bison. Mult.
2758 6 z. 50 Type **786** 75 25
2759 6 z. 50 Two bison, one grazing 75 25
2760 6 z. 50 Bison with calf 75 25
2761 6 z. 50 Calf Feeding 75 25
2762 6 z. 50 Two bison, both looking towards right 75 25

787 Tennis Player

1981. 60th Anniv of Polish Tennis Federation.
2763 **787** 6 z. 50 multicoloured . . 55 15

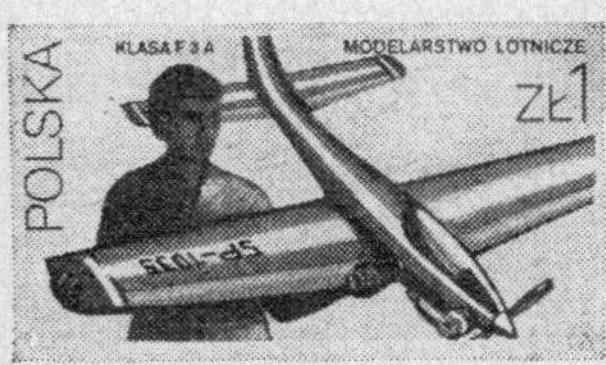

788 Boy with Model Airplane

1981. Model Making. Multicoloured.
2764 1 z. Type **788** 15 10
2765 2 z. Model of "Atlas 2" tug . 30 10
2766 2 z. 50 Cars 30 10
2767 4 z. 20 Man with gliders . . 35 15
2768 6 z. 50 Racing cars 70 15
2769 8 z. Boy with yacht 80 25

789 Disabled Pictogram **791** H. Wieniawski and Violin Head

790 17th-cent Flint-lock Pistol

1981. International Year of Disabled Persons.
2770 **789** 8 z. 40 green, light green and black 75 20

1981. Stamp Day. Antique Weapons. Mult.
2771 2 z. 50 Type **790** 25 10
2772 8 z. 40 17th-century gala sabre 70 20

1981. Wieniawski Young Violinists' Competition.
2773 **791** 2 z. 50 multicoloured . . 25 15

792 Bronislaw Wesolowski **793** F.A.O. Emblem and Globe

1981. Activists of Polish Workers' Movement.
2774 **792** 50 g. green and black . . 10 10
2775 – 2 z. blue and black . . . 15 10
2776 – 2 z. 50 brown and black 20 10
2777 – 6 z. 50 mauve and black 60 25
DESIGNS: 2 z. Malgorzata Fornalska; 2 z. 50, Maria Koszutska; 6 z. 50, Marcin Kasprzak.

1981. World Food Day.
2778 **793** 6 z. 90 brn, orge & yell . 55 25

794 Helena Modrzejewska (actress)

1981. Bicentenary of Cracow Old Theatre.
2779 **794** 2 z. purple, grey and vio 15 10
2780 – 2 z. 50 blue, stone & brn 20 10
2781 – 6 z. 50 violet, bl and grn 50 20
2782 – 8 z. brown, green & red . 80 20
DESIGNS: 2 z. 50, Stanislaw Kozmian (politician, writer and theatre director); 6 z. 50, Konrad Swinarski (stage manager and scenographer); 8 z. Old Theatre building.

796 Gdansk Memorial **797** "Epiphyllopsis gaertneri"

1981. Memorials to the Victims of the 1970 Uprisings.
2784 **796** 2 z. 50+1 z. grey, black and red 50 20
2785 – 6 z. 50+1 z. grey, black and blue . . . . 1·10 90
DESIGN: 6 z. 50, Gdynia Memorial.

1981. Succulent Plants. Multicoloured.
2786 90 g. Type **797** 15 10
2787 1 z. "Cereus tonduzii" . . . 15 10
2788 2 z. "Cylindropuntia leptocaulis" 15 10
2789 2 z. 50 "Cylindropuntia fulgida" 20 10
2790 2 z. 50 "Coralluma lugardi" . 20 10
2791 6 z. 50 "Nopalea cochenillifera" 60 20
2792 6 z. 50 "Lithops helmutii" . . 60 20
2793 10 z. 50 "Cylindropuntia spinosior" . . . . 1·00 35

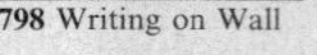
798 Writing on Wall **799** Faience Plate

1982. 40th Anniv of Polish Workers' Coalition.
2794 **798** 2 z. 50 pink, red and black 25 10

1982. Polish Ceramics. Multicoloured.
2795 1 z. Type **799** 15 10
2796 2 z. Porcelain cup and saucer, Korzec 20 10
2797 2 z. 50 Porcelain tureen and sauce-boat, Barnowka . . 25 10
2798 6 z. Porcelain inkpot, Horodnica 60 20
2799 8 z. Faience "Hunter's Tumbler", Lubartow . . . 75 20
2800 10 z. 50 Faience figurine of nobleman, Biala Podlaska . 1·10 40

800 Ignacy Lukasiewicz and Lamp **801** Karol Szymanowski

1982. Death Centenary of Ignacy Lukasiewicz (inventor of petroleum lamp).
2801 **800** 1 z. multicoloured . . . 15 10
2802 – 2 z. multicoloured . . . 20 10
2803 – 2 z. 50 multicoloured . . 30 10
2804 – 3 z. 50 multicoloured . . 35 15
2805 – 9 z. multicoloured . . . 90 25
2806 – 10 z. multicoloured . . . 95 30
DESIGNS: 2 z. to 10 z. Different designs showing lamps.

1982. Birth Centenary of Karol Szymanowski (composer).
2807 **801** 2 z. 50 brown and gold . 25 10

802 RWD 6, 1932

1982. 50th Anniv of Polish Victory in Tourist Aircraft Challenge Competition. Multicoloured.
2808 27 z. Type **802** . . . . 1·50 1·25
2809 31 z. RWD 9 (winner of 1934 Challenge) . . . . 1·90 1·75

803 Henryk Sienkiewicz (literature, 1905) **804** Football as Globe

1982. Polish Nobel Prize Winners.
2811 **803** 3 z. green and black . . 15 10
2812 – 15 z. brown and black . . 65 25
2813 – 25 z. blue . . . . . . 1·50 30
2814 – 31 z. grey and black . . 1·25 70
DESIGNS: 15 z. Wladyslaw Reymont (literature, 1924); 25 z. Marie Curie (physics, 1903, and chemistry, 1911); 31 z. Czeslaw Milosz (literature, 1980).

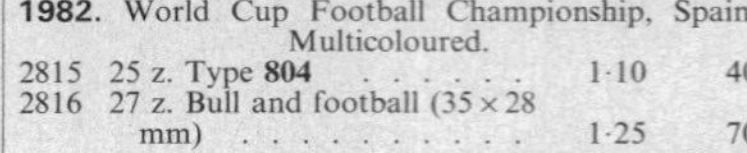
1982. World Cup Football Championship, Spain. Multicoloured.
2815 25 z. Type **804** . . . . . . 1·10 40
2816 27 z. Bull and football (35×28 mm) . . . . 1·25 70

806 Stanislaw Sierakowski and Boleslaw Domanski (former Association presidents) **807** Text around Globe

1982. 60th Anniv of Association of Poles in Germany.
2818 **806** 4 z. 50 red and green . . 55 15

1982. 2nd U.N. Conference on the Exploration and Peaceful Uses of Outer Space, Vienna.
2819 **807** 31 z. multicoloured . . 90 35

1982. No. 2732 surch **10** °°.
2820 10 z. on 6 z. 50 brown . . . 25 10

809 Father Augustyn Kordecki (prior) **810** Marchers with Banner

1982. 600th Anniv of "Black Madonna" (icon) of Jasna Gora. Multicoloured.
2821 2 z. 50 Type **809** 10 10
2822 25 z. "Siege of Jasna Gora by Swedes, 1655" (detail) (horiz) 40 20
2823 65 z. "Black Madonna" . . 1·25 60

1982. Centenary of Proletarian Party.
2825 **810** 6 z. multicoloured . . . 40 10

811 Norbert Barlicki **812** Dr. Robert Koch

1982. Activists of Polish Workers' Movement.
2826 **811** 5 z. light blue, blue and black 15 10
2827 – 6 z. deep green, green and black 20 15
2828 – 15 z. pink, red and black 35 20
2829 – 20 z. mauve, violet and black 60 30
2830 – 29 z. light brown, brown and black 75 45
DESIGNS: 6 z. Pawel Finder; 15 z. Marian Buczek; 20 z. Cezaryna Wojnarowska; 29 z. Ignacy Daszynski.

1982. Centenary of Discovery of Tubercle Bacillus. Multicoloured.
2831 10 z. Type **812** 25 10
2832 25 z. Dr. Odo Bujwid . . . 85 20

813 Carved Head of Woman **813a** Head of Ruler

1982. Carved Heads from Wawel Castle.
2835 **813a** 3 z. 50 brown 15 10
2836 – 5 z. green 20 10
2837 – 5 z. red 20 10
2838 – 10 z. blue 25 10
2839 – 15 z. brown 15 10
2840 – 20 z. grey 45 15
2841 **813a** 20 z. blue 15 10
2842 – 40 z. brown 75 25
2833 **813** 60 z. orange and brn . 1·50 50
2843 – 60 z. green 15 10
2834 – 100 z. ochre & brown . 3·00 1·00
2843a – 200 z. black . . . . . 3·75 1·75
DESIGNS—As T **813**: 100 z. Man. As T **813a**: 5 z. (2836), Warrior; 5 z. (2837); 15 z. Woman wearing chaplet; 10 z. Man in cap; 20 z. (2840), Thinker; 40 z. Man in beret; 60 z. Young man; 200 z. Man.

814 Maximilian Kolbe (after M. Koscielniak) **815** Polar Research Station

1982. Sanctification of Maximilian Kolbe (Franciscan concentration camp victim).
2844 **814** 27 z. multicoloured . . . 90 50

1982. 50th Anniv of Polish Polar Research.
2845 **815** 27 z. multicoloured . . . 2·50 60

816 "Log Floats on Vistula River" (drawing by J. Telakowski) **817** Stanislaw Zaremba

1982. Views of the Vistula River.
2846 **816** 12 z. blue 25 10
2847 – 17 z. blue 30 15
2848 – 25 z. blue 40 20
DESIGNS: 17 z. "Kazimierz Dolny" (engraving by Andriollo); 25 z. "Danzig" (18th-cent engraving).

1982. Mathematicians.
2849 **817** 5 z. lilac, blue and black . 25 10
2850 – 6 z. orange, violet and black 25 10
2851 – 12 z. blue, brown and black 40 10
2852 – 15 z. yellow, brown and black 60 20
DESIGNS: 6 z. Waclaw Sierpinski; 12 z. Zygmunt Janiszewski; 15 z. Stefan Banach.

818 Military Council Medal

1982. 1st Anniv of Military Council.
2853 **818** 2 z. 50 multicoloured . . 25 15

819 Deanery Gate **820** Bernard Wapowski Map, 1526

1982. Renovation of Cracow Monuments (1st series).
2854 **819** 15 z. black, olive & grn . 50 15
2855 – 25 z. black, purple & mve 65 20
DESIGN: 25 z. Gateway of Collegium.
See also Nos. 2904/5, 2968/9, 3029/30, 3116 and 3153.

1982. Polish Maps.
2857 **820** 5 z. multicoloured 15 10
2858 – 6 z. brown, black and red 20 10
2859 – 8 z. multicoloured 25 10
2860 – 25 z. multicoloured . . . 70 25
DESIGNS: 6 z. Map of Prague, 1839; 8 z. Map of Poland from Eugen Romer's Atlas, 1908; 25 z. Plan of Cracow by A. Buchowiecki, 1703, and Astrolabe.

821 "The Last of the Resistance" (Artur Grottger)

1983. 120th Anniv of January Uprising.
2861 **821** 6 z. brown 15 10

822 "Grand Theatre, Warsaw, 1838" (Maciej Zaleski)

1983. 150th Anniv of Grand Theatre, Warsaw.
2862 **822** 6 z. multicoloured . . . 15 10

823 Wild Flowers

1983. Environmental Protection. Multicoloured.
2863 5 z. Type **823** 20 10
2864 6 z. Mute swan and river fishes 35 10
2865 17 z. Hoopoe and trees . . . 1·10 30
2866 30 z. Sea fishes . . . . . . 1·10 45
2867 31 z. European bison and roe deer . . . . 1·10 50
2868 38 z. Fruit . . . . 1·10 60

824 Karol Kurpinski (composer)

1983. Celebrities.
2869 **824** 5 z. lt brown and brown 20 10
2870 – 6 z. purple and violet . 25 10
2871 – 17 z. lt green and green . 60 20
2872 – 25 z. lt brown and brown 75 20
2873 – 27 z. lt blue and blue . . 80 25
2874 – 31 z. lilac and violet . . 90 25
DESIGNS: 6 z. Maria Jasnorzewska Pawlikowska (poetess); 17 z. Stanislaw Szober (linguist); 25 z. Tadeusz Banachiewicz (astronomer and mathematician); 27 z. Jaroslaw Iwaskiewicz (writer); 31 z. Wladyslaw Tatarkiewicz (philosopher and historian).

825 3000 Metres Steeplechase

1983. Sports Achievements.
2875 **825** 5 z. pink and violet . . 20 10
2876 – 6 z. pink, brown & blk . 20 10
2877 – 15 z. yellow and green . 45 15
2878 – 27 z.+5 z. light blue, blue and black . . . . . . 1·00 30
DESIGNS: 6 z. Show jumping; 1 z. Football; 27 z.+5 z. Pole Vault.

826 Ghetto Heroes Monument (Natan Rappaport) **827** Customs Officer and Suitcases

1983. 40th Anniv of Warsaw Ghetto Uprising.
2879 **826** 5 z. lt brown & brown . 15 10

1983. 30th Anniv of Customs Co-operation Council.
2880 **827** 5 z. multicoloured . . . 15 10

828 John Paul II and Jasna Gora Sanctuary

829 Dragoons

1983. Papal Visit. Multicoloured.

2881 31 z. Type **828** . . . . 1·00 30
2882 65 z. Niepokalanow Church and John Paul holding crucifix . 2·25 80

1983. 300th Anniv of Polish Relief of Vienna (1st issue). Troops of King Jan III Sobieski. Multicoloured.

2884 5 z. Type **829** 20 10
2885 5 z. Armoured cavalryman . 20 10
2886 6 z. Infantry non-commissioned officer and musketeer . . . 30 10
2887 15 z. Light cavalry lieutenant 40 20
2888 27 z. "Winged" hussar and trooper with carbine . . . 1·00 40

See also Nos. 2893/6.

830 Arrow piercing "E"

1983. 50th Anniv of Deciphering "Enigma" Machine Codes.

2889 **830** 5 z. red, grey and black . 15 15

831 Torun

1983. 750th Anniv of Torun.

2890 **831** 6 z. multicoloured . . . 30 15

832 Childs Painting

1983. "Order of the Smile" (Politeness Publicity Campaign).

2892 **832** 6 z. multicoloured . . . 15 10

833 King Jan III Sobieski

1983. 300th Anniv of Relief of Vienna (2nd issue). Multicoloured.

2893 5 z. Type **833** 20 10
2894 6 z. King Jan III Sobieski (different) 20 10
2895 6 z. "King Jan III Sobieski on Horseback" (Francesco Trevisani) 20 10
2896 25 z. "King Jan III Sobieski" (Jerzy Eleuter) 90 35

834 Wanda Wasilewska

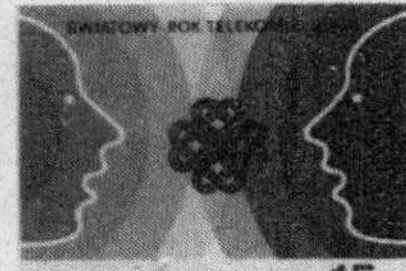

835 Profiles and W.C.Y. Emblem

1983. 40th Anniv of Polish People's Army. Multicoloured.

2898 **834** 5 z. multicoloured . . . 15 10
2899 – 5 z. deep green, green and black 15 10
2900 – 6 z. multicoloured . . . 25 10
2901 – 6 z. multicoloured . . . 25 10

DESIGNS—VERT: No. 2899, General Zygmunt Berling; 2900, "The Frontier Post" (S. Poznanski). HORIZ: No. 2901, "Taking the Oath" (S. Poznanski).

1983. World Communications Year.

2902 **835** 15 z. multicoloured . . 45 20

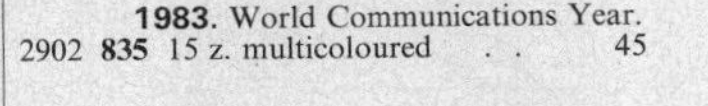

836 Boxing

1983. 60th Anniv of Polish Boxing Federation.

2903 **836** 6 z. multicoloured . . . 20 10

1983. Renovation of Cracow Monuments (2nd series). As T **819**.

2904 5 z. brown, purple & blk . . 20 10
2905 6 z. black, green and blue . 20 15

DESIGNS—HORIZ: 5 z. Cloth Hall. VERT: 6 z. Town Hall tower.

837 Biskupiec Costume

838 Hand with Sword (poster by Zakrzewski and Krolikowski, 1945)

1983. Women's Folk Costumes. Multicoloured.

2906 5 z. Type **837** 20 10
2907 5 z. Rozbark 20 10
2908 6 z. Warmia & Mazuria . . 25 10
2909 6 z. Cieszyn 25 10
2910 25 z. Kurpie . . . . 1·10 30
2911 38 z. Lubusk . . . . 1·60 60

1983. 40th Anniv of National People's Council.

2912 **838** 6 z. multicoloured . . . 20 10

839 Badge of "General Bem" Brigade

840 Dulcimer

1983. 40th Anniv of People's Army.

2913 **839** 5 z. multicoloured . . . 20 10

1984. Musical Instruments (1st series). Mult.

2914 5 z. Type **840** 20 10
2915 6 z. Kettle drum and tambourine 25 10
2916 10 z. Accordion 40 10
2917 15 z. Double bass 50 20
2918 17 z. Bagpipe 60 20
2919 29 z. Country band (wood carvings by Tadeusz Zak) 1·00 30

841 Wincenty Witos

842 "Clematis lanuginosa"

1984. 110th Birth Anniv of Wincenty Witos (leader of Peasants' Movement).

2920 **841** 6 z. brown and green . . 20 10

1984. Clematis. Multicoloured.

2921 5 z. Type **842** 20 10
2922 6 z. "C. tangutica" 25 10
2923 10 z. "C. texensis" 30 15
2924 17 z. "C. alpina" 50 25
2925 25 z. "C. vitalba" . . . . . . 1·00 30
2926 27 z. "C. montana" . . . . . 1·10 35

843 "The Ecstasy of St. Francis" (El Greco)

1984. "Espana 84" International Stamp Exhibition, Madrid.

2927 **843** 27 z. multicoloured . . . 90 25

844 Handball

1984. Olympic Games, Los Angeles, and Winter Olympics, Sarajevo. Multicoloured.

2928 5 z. Type **844** 15 10
2929 6 z. Fencing 20 10
2930 15 z. Cycling 50 15
2931 16 z. Janusz Kusocinski winning 10,000 metres race, 1932 Olympics, Los Angeles . . 70 20
2932 17 z. Stanislawa Walasiewiczowna winning 100 metres race, 1932 Olympics, Los Angeles . . 70 20
2933 31 z. Women's slalom (Winter Olympics) . . . . 1·10 35

845 Monte Cassino Memorial Cross and Monastery

846 "German Princess" (Lucas Cranach)

1984. 40th Anniv of Battle of Monte Cassino.

2935 **845** 15 z. olive and red . . . 45 15

1984. 19th U.P.U. Congress, Hamburg.

2936 **846** 27 z. +10 z. multicoloured 1·10 50

847 "Warsaw from the Praga Bank" (Canaletto)

1984. Paintings of Vistula River. Multicoloured.

2937 5 z. Type **847** 20 10
2938 6 z. "Trumpet Festivity" (A. Gierymski) 25 10
2939 25 z. "The Vistula near Bielany District" (J. Rapacki) . . 90 30
2940 27 z. "Steamship Harbour in the Powisle District" (F. Kostrzewski) . . . . . 1·00 35

848 Order of Grunwald Cross

849 Group of Insurgents

1984. 40th Anniv of Polish People's Republic. Multicoloured.

2941 5 z. Type **848** 20 10
2942 6 z. Order of Revival of Poland 20 10
2943 10 z. Order of Banner of Labour, First Class . . . 30 10
2944 16 z. Order of Builders of People's Poland 55 25

1984. 40th Anniv of Warsaw Uprising. Multicoloured.

2946 4 z. Type **849** 20 10
2947 5 z. Insurgent on postal duty 20 10
2948 6 z. Insurgents fighting . . . 20 10
2949 25 z. Tending wounded . . . 90 35

850 Defence of Oksywie Holm and Col. Stanislaw Dabek

1984. 45th Anniv of German Invasion. Multicoloured.

2950 5 z. Type **850** 20 10
2951 6 z. Battle of Bzura River and Gen. Tadeusz Kutrzeba . . 25 10

See also Nos. 3004/5, 3062, 3126/8, 3172/4 and 3240/3.

851 "Broken Heart" (monument, Lodz Concentration Camp)

1984. Child Martyrs.

2952 **851** 16 z. brown, blue and deep brown 45 15

852 Militiaman and Ruins

1984. 40th Anniv of Security Force and Civil Militia. Multicoloured.

2953 5 z. Type **852** 20 10
2954 6 z. Militiaman in control centre 25 10

853 First Balloon Flight, 1784 (after Chostovski)

1984. Polish Aviation.

2955 **853** 5 z. black, green & mve . 20 10
2956 – 5 z. multicoloured . . . 20 10
2957 – 6 z. multicoloured . . . 20 10
2958 – 10 z. multicoloured . . . 30 15
2959 – 16 z. multicoloured . . . 40 20

2960 – 27 z. multicoloured . . . 90 40
2961 – 31 z. multicoloured . . . 1·10 50

DESIGNS: No. 2956, Michal Scipio del Campo and biplane (1st flight over Warsaw, 1911); 2957, Balloon "Polonez" (winner, Gordon Bennett Cup, 1983); 2958, PWS 101 and Jantar gliders (Lilienthal Medal winners); 2959, PZL-104 Wilga airplane (world precise flight champion, 1983); 2960, Jan Nagorski and Farman M.F.7 floatplane (Arctic zone flights, 1914); 2961, PZL P-37 Los and PZL P-7 aircraft.

854 Weasel

1984. Fur-bearing Animals. Multicoloured.

2962 4 z. Type **854** 20 10
2963 5 z. Stoat 20 10
2964 5 z. Beech marten 25 10
2965 10 z. Eurasian beaver 30 15
2966 10 z. Eurasian otter 30 15
2967 65 z. Alpine marmot . . . . . 2·40 75

1984. Renovation of Cracow Monuments (3rd series). As T **819**.

2968 5 z. brown, black and green . . 20 10
2969 15 z. blue, brown and black . 40 15

DESIGNS—VERT: 5 z. Wawel cathedral. HORIZ: 15 z. Wawel castle (royal residence).

855 Protestant Church, Warsaw

1984. Religious Architecture. Multicoloured.

2970 5 z. Type **855** 15 10
2971 10 z. Saint Andrew's Roman Catholic church, Krakow . 30 10
2972 15 z. Greek Catholic church, Rychwald 45 20
2973 20 z. St. Maria Magdalena Orthodox church, Warsaw 60 20
2974 25 z. Tykocin synagogue, Kaczorow (horiz) 75 25
2975 31 z. Tatar mosque Kruszyiany (horiz) 95 40

856 Steam Fire Hose (late 19th century)

1985. Fire Engines. Multicoloured.

2976 4 z. Type **856** 15 10
2977 10 z. "Polski Fait" 1930s . . 30 10
2978 12 z. "Jelcz 315" fire engine . 35 15
2979 15 z. Manual fire hose, 1899 . 45 15
2980 20 z. "Magirus" fire ladder on "Jelcz" chassis 60 25
2981 30 z. Manual fire hose (early 18th century) . . . . 1·00 45

857 "Battle of Raclawice" (Jan Styka and Wojciech Kossak)

1985.

2982 **857** 27 z. multicoloured . . . 70 25

858 Wincenty Rzymowski

859 Badge on Denim

1985. 35th Death Anniv of Wincenty Rzymowski (founder of Polish Democratic Party).

2983 **858** 10 z. violet and red . . 25 10

1985. International Youth Year.

2984 **859** 15 z. multicoloured . . 40 15

860 Boleslaw III, the Wry-mouthed, and Map

1985. 40th Anniv of Return of Western and Northern Territories to Poland. Multicoloured.

2985 5 z. Type **860** 10 10
2986 10 z. Wladyslaw Gomulka (vice-president of first postwar government) and map . . 35 10
2987 20 z. Piotr Zaremba (Governor of Szczecin) and map . . 60 20

861 "Victory, Berlin 1945" (Joesf Mlynarski)

1985. 40th Anniv of Victory over Fascism.

2988 **861** 5 z. multicoloured . . . 15 10

862 Warsaw Arms and Flags of Member Countries

864 Cadet Ship "Iskra"

863 Wolves in Winter

1985. 30th Anniv of Warsaw Pact.

2989 **862** 5 z. multicoloured . . . 15 10

1985. Protected Animals. The Wolf. Mult.

2990 5 z. Type **863** 15 10
2991 10 z. She-wolf with cubs . . 35 10
2992 10 z. Close-up of wolf . . . 35 10
2993 20 z. Wolves in summer . . 70 20

1985. Musical Instruments (2nd series). As T **840**. Multicoloured.

2994 5 z. Rattle and tarapata . . 15 10
2995 10 z. Stick rattle and berlo . 30 10
2996 12 z. Clay whistles 35 15
2997 20 z. Stringed instruments . 55 20
2998 25 z. Cow bells 75 30
2999 31 z. Wind instruments . . . 90 40

1985. 40th Anniv of Polish Navy.

3000 **864** 5 z. blue and yellow . . 40 10

865 Tomasz Nocznicki

1985. Leaders of Peasants' Movement.

3001 **865** 10 z. green 25 10
3002 – 20 z. brown 50 20

DESIGN: 20 z. Maciej Rataj.

866 Hockey Players

1985. 60th Anniv (1986) of Polish Field Hockey Association.

3003 **866** 5 z. multicoloured 15 10

1985. 46th Anniv of German Invasion. As T **850**. Multicoloured.

3004 5 z. Defence of Wizna and Capt. Wladyslaw Raginis 20 10
3005 10 z. Battle of Mlawa and Col. Wilhelm Liszka-Lawicz . . 60 15

867 Goods Wagon Type "20 K"

1985. PAFAWAG Railway Rolling Stock. Multicoloured.

3006 5 z. Type **867** 20 10
3007 10 z. Electric locomotive, type "201 E" 40 15
3008 17 z. Two-axle coal car, type "OMMK" 65 25
3009 20 z. Passenger car, type "111 A" 85 35

869 Green-winged Teal

1985. Wild Ducks. Multicoloured.

3011 5 z. Type **869** 15 10
3012 5 z. Garganey duck 15 10
3013 10 z. Tufted duck 40 10
3014 15 z. Goldeneye 50 15
3015 25 z. Eider 90 30
3016 29 z. Red-crested pochard . . 1·25 40

870 U.N. Emblem and "Flags"

1985. 40th Anniv of U.N.O.

3017 **870** 27 z. multicoloured . . . 70 25

871 Ballerina

872 "Marysia and Burek in Ceylon"

1985. Bicentenary of Polish Ballet.

3018 **871** 5 z. green, orange & red . 15 10
3019 – 15 z. brown, violet & orge 45 10

DESIGN: 15 z. Male dancer.

1985. Birth Centenary of Stanislaw Ignacy Witkiewicz (artist). Multicoloured.

3020 5 z. Type **872** 15 10
3021 10 z. "Woman with Fox" (horiz) 30 10
3022 10z. "Self-portrait" 30 10
3023 20 z. "Compositions (1917–20)" 55 25
3024 25 z. "Nena Stachurska" . . . 70 30

874 Human Profile

1986. Congress of Intellectuals for Defence of Peaceful Future of the World, Warsaw.

3026 **874** 10 z. ultramarine, violet and blue 25 10

875 Michal Kamienski and Planetary and Comet's Orbits

1985. Appearance of Halley's Comet.

3027 **875** 25 z. blue and brown . . 60 25
3028 – 25 z. deep blue, blue and brown 60 25

DESIGN: No. 3028, "Vega", "Planet A", "Giotto" and "Ice" space probes and comet.

1986. Renovation of Cracow Monuments (4th series). As T **819**.

3029 5 z. dp brown, brown & blk 10 10
3030 10 z. green, brown & black . 30 10

DESIGNS: 5 z. Collegium Maius (Jagiellonian University Museum); 10 z. Kazimierz Town Hall.

876 Sun

877 Grey Partridge

1986. International Peace Year.

3031 **876** 25 z. yellow, light blue and blue 55 20

1986. Game. Multicoloured.

3032 5 z. Type **877** 50 20
3033 5 z. Common rabbit 15 10
3034 10 z. Ring-necked pheasants (horiz) 90 20
3035 10 z. Fallow deer (horiz) . . 30 10
3036 20 z. Hare 60 20
3037 40 z. Argali . . . . 1·25 45

878 Kulczynski

880 Paderewski (composer)

879 "Warsaw Fire Brigade, 1871" (detail, Jozef Brodowski)

1986. 10th Death Anniv (1985) of Stanislaw Kulczynski (politician).

3038 **878** 10 z. light brown and brown 25 10

1986. 150th Anniv of Warsaw Fire Brigade.

3039 **879** 10 z. dp brown & brown 25 10

1986. "Ameripex '86" International Stamp Exhibition, Chicago.

3040 **880** 65 z. blue, black & grey . 1·50 70

881 Footballers

1986. World Cup Football Championship, Mexico.

3041 **881** 25 z. multicoloured . . . 50 20

882 "Wilanow"

1986. Passenger Ferries. Multicoloured.
3042 10 z. Type **882** 55 20
3043 10 z. "Wawel" 55 20
3044 15 z. "Pomerania" 70 30
3045 25 z. "Rogalin" . . . . . . 1·25 50

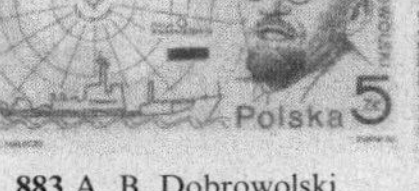

883 A. B. Dobrowolski, Map and Research Vessel "Kopernik"

885 "The Paulinite Church on Skalka in Cracow" (detail), 1627

884 Workers and Emblem

1986. 25th Anniv of Antarctic Agreement.
3047 **883** 5 z. green, black & red . 40 25
3048 – 40 z. lavender, violet and orange . . . . 3·50 85
DESIGN: 40 z. H. Arctowski, map and research vessel "Professor Siedlecki".

1986. 10th Polish United Workers' Party Congress, Warsaw.
3049 **884** 10 z. blue and red . . . 25 10

1986. Treasures of Jasna Gora Monastery. Mult.
3050 5 z. Type **885** 15 10
3051 5 z. "Tree of Jesse", 17th-century 15 10
3052 20 z. Chalice, 18th-century . 40 20
3053 40 z. "Virgin Mary" (detail, chasuble column), 15th-century . . . . 1·00 40

886 Precision Flying (Wacław Nycz)

1986. 1985 Polish World Championship Successes. Multicoloured.
3054 5 z. Type **886** 20 10
3055 10 z. Windsurfing (Malgorzata Palasz-Piasecka) 50 10
3056 10 z. Glider aerobatics (Jerzy Makula) 40 10
3057 15 z. Wrestling (Bogdan Daras) 40 15
3058 20 z. Individual road cycling (Lech Piasecki) 60 20
3059 30 z. Women's modern pentathlon (Barbara Kotowska) . . . . 1·00 35

887 "Bird" in National Costume carrying Stamp

888 Schweitzer

1986. "Stockholmia '86" International Stamp Exhibition.
3060 **887** 65 z. multicoloured . . . 1·50 55

1986. 47th Anniv of German Invasion. As T **850**. Multicoloured.
3062 10 z. Battle of Jordanow and Col. Stanislaw Maczek . . 25 10

1986. 10th Death Anniv (1985) of Albert Schweitzer (medical missionary).
3063 **888** 5 z. brown, lt brown & bl 10 10

889 Airliner and Postal Messenger

890 Basilisk

1986. World Post Day.
3064 **889** 40 z. brown, blue & red 80 35

1986. Folk Tales. Multicoloured.
3066 5 z. Type **890** 15 10
3067 5 z. Duke Popiel (vert) . . . 15 10
3068 10 z. Golden Duck 25 10
3069 10 z. Boruta the Devil (vert) 25 10
3070 20 z. Janosik the Robber (vert) 40 20
3071 50 z. Lajkonik (vert) . . . . 1·10 50

891 Kotarbinski

892 20th-century Windmill, Zygmuntow

1986. Birth Centenary of Tadeusz Kotarbinski (philosopher).
3072 **891** 10 z. deep brown and brown 20 10

1986. Wooden Architecture. Multicoloured.
3073 5 z. Type **892** 10 10
3074 5 z. 17th-century church Baczal Dolny 10 10
3075 10 z. 19th-century Oravian cottage, Zubrzyca Gorna . 25 10
3076 15 z. 18th-century Kashubian arcade cottage, Wdzydze . 30 15
3077 25 z. 19th-century barn, Grzawa 60 20
3078 30 z. 19th-century watermill Siolkowice Stare 90 30

893 Mieszko (Mieczyslaw) I

1986. Polish Rulers (1st series). Drawings by Jan Matejko.
3079 **893** 10 z. brown & green . . 20 10
3080 – 25 z. black and purple . 50 20
DESIGN: 25 z. Queen Dobrawa (wife of Mieszko I).

See also Nos. 3144/5, 3193/4, 3251/2, 3341/2, 3351/2, 3387/8, 3461/4 and 3511/12.

894 Star

1986. New Year.
3081 **894** 25 z. multicoloured . . 45 35

895 Trip to Bielany, 1887

1986. Centenary of Warsaw Cyclists' Society.
3082 **895** 5 z. multicoloured . . . 10 10
3083 – 5 z. brown, light brown and black 10 10
3084 – 10 z. multicoloured . . 25 10
3085 – 10 z. multicoloured . . 25 10
3086 – 30 z. multicoloured . . 60 25
3087 – 50 z. multicoloured . . 1·10 40
DESIGNS: No. 3083, Jan Stanislaw Skrodaki (1895 touring record holder); 3084, Dynasy (Society's headquarters, 1892–1937); 3085, Mieczyslaw Baranski (1896 Kingdom of Poland road cycling champion); 3086, Karolina Kociecka; 3087, Henryk Weiss (Race champion).

896 Lelewel

1986. Birth Bicentary of Joachim Lelewel (historian).
3088 **896** 10 z. + 5 z. multicoloured 30 15

897 Krill and "Antoni Garnuszewski" (cadet freighter)

1987. 10th Anniv of Henryk Arctowski Antarctic Station, King George Island, South Shetlands. Multicoloured.
3089 5 z. Type **897** 10 10
3090 5 z. "Nototenia marmurkowa", "Notothenia rossi" (fishes) and "Zulawy" (supply ship) 10 10
3091 10 z. Southern fulmar and "Pogoria" (cadet brigantine) 50 20
3092 10 z. Adelie penguin and "Gedania" (yacht) . . . 50 20
3093 30 z. Fur seal and "Dziunia" (research vessel) 70 25
3094 40 z. Leopard seals and "Kapitan Ledochowski" (research vessel) 90 35

898 "Portrait of a Woman"

1987. 50th Death Anniv (1986) of Leon Wyczolkowski (artist). Multicoloured.
3095 5 z. "Cineraria Flowers" (horiz) 10 10
3096 10 z. Type **898** 20 10
3097 10 z. "Wooden Church" (horiz) 20 10
3098 25 z. "Beetroot Lifting" . . . 45 20
3099 30 z. "Wading Fishermen" (horiz) 50 25
3100 40 z. "Self-portrait" (horiz) . 70 40

899 "Ravage" (from "War Cycle") and Artur Grottger

1987. 150th Birth Anniv of Artur Grottger (artist).
3101 **899** 15 z. brown and stone . . 20 10

900 Swierczewski

901 Strzelecki

1987. 90th Birth Anniv of General Karol Swierczewski.
3102 **900** 15 z. green and olive . . 20 10

1987. 190th Birth Anniv of Pawel Edmund Strzelecki (scientist and explorer of Tasmania).
3103 **901** 65 z. green 95 45

902 Emblem and Banner

1987. 2nd Patriotic Movement for National Revival Congress.
3104 **902** 10 z. red, blue and brown 15 10

903 CWS "T-1" Motor Car, 1928

1987. Polish Motor Vehicles. Multicoloured.
3105 10 z. Type **903** 15 10
3106 10 z. Saurer-Zawrat bus, 1936 15 10
3107 15 z. Ursus-A lorry, 1928 . . 25 10
3108 15 z. Lux-Sport motor car, 1936 25 10
3109 25 z. Podkowa "100" motor cycle, 1939 . . . . 35 20
3110 45 z. Sokol "600 RT" motor cycle, 1935 . . . . 65 50

904 Royal Palace, Warsaw

1987.
3111 **904** 50 z. multicoloured . . . 75 35

905 Pope John Paul II

1987. 3rd Papal Visit. Multicoloured.
3112 15 z. Type **905** 30 10
3113 45 z. Pope and signature . . 70 35

906 Polish Settler at Kasubia, Ontario

1987. "Capex '87" International Stamp Exhibition, Toronto.
3115 **906** 50 z. + 20 z. multicoloured 95 45

1987. Renovation of Cracow Monuments (5th series). As T **819**.
3116 10 z. lilac, black and green . 15 10
DESIGN: 10 z. Barbican.

907 Ludwig Zamenhof (inventor) and Star

1987. Cent of Esperanto (invented language).
3117 **907** 5 z. brown, green & blk . 80 30

908 "Poznan Town Hall" (Stanislaw Wyspianski)

909 Queen Bee

1987. "Poznan 87" National Stamp Exhibition.
3118 **908** 15 z. brown and orange . 20 10

1987. "Apimondia 87" International Bee Keeping Congress, Warsaw. Multicoloured.
3119 10 z. Type **909** 20 10
3120 10 z. Worker bee 20 10
3121 5 z. Drone 25 15
3122 15 z. Hive in orchard 25 15
3123 40 z. Worker bee on clover flower 70 30
3124 50 z. Forest bee keeper collecting honey 90 50

1987. 48th Anniv of German Invasion. As T **850**. Multicoloured.
3126 10 z. Battle of Mokra and Col. Julian Filipowicz 20 10
3127 10 z. Fighting at Oleszyce and Brig-Gen. Jozef Rudolf Kustron 20 10
3128 15 z. PZL P-7 aircraft over Warsaw and Col. Stefan Pawlikowsi 40 15

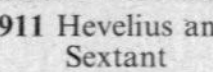

911 Hevelius and Sextant

912 High Jump (World Acrobatics Championships, France)

1987. 300th Death Anniv of Jan Hevelius (astronomer). Multicoloured.
3129 15 z. Type **911** 30 15
3130 40 z. Hevelius and map of constellations (horiz) . . . 70 25

1987. 1986 Polish World Championship Successes. Multicoloured.
3131 10 z. Type **912** 15 10
3132 15 z. Two-man canoe (World Canoeing Championships, Canada) 25 10
3133 20 z. Marksman (Free pistol event, World Marksmanship Championships, East Germany) 40 15
3134 25 z. Wrestlers (World Wrestling Championships, Hungary) 50 20

914 Warsaw Post Office and Ignacy Franciszek Przebendowski (Postmaster General)

1987. World Post Day.
3136 **914** 15 z. green and red . . . 20 10

915 "The Little Mermaid"

916 Col. Stanislaw Wieckowski (founder)

1987. "Hafnia 87" International Stamp Exhibition, Copenhagen. Hans Christain Andersen's Fairy Tales. Multicoloured.
3137 10 z. Type **915** 15 10
3138 10 z. "The Nightingale" . . . 15 10
3139 20 z. "The Wild Swans" . . 30 15
3140 20 z. "The Little Match Girl" 30 15
3141 30 z. "The Snow Queen" . . 50 25
3142 40 z. "The Tin Soldier" . . . 70 30

1987. 50th Anniv of Democratic Clubs.
3143 **916** 15 z. black and blue . . . 20 10

1987. Polish Rulers (2nd series). As T **893**. Drawings by Jan Matejko.
3144 10 z. green and blue 10 10
3145 15 z. blue and ultramarine . . 25 10
DESIGNS: 10 z. Boleslaw I, the Brave; 15 z. Mieszko (Mieczyslaw) II.

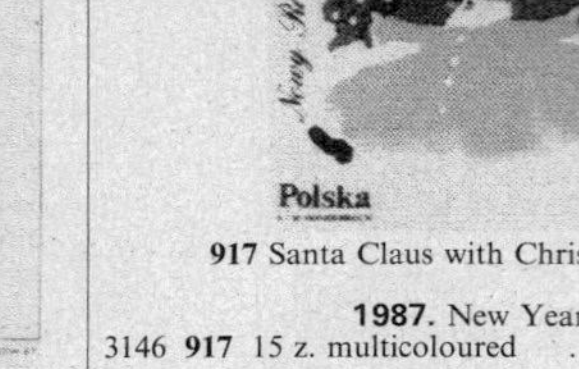

917 Santa Claus with Christmas Trees

1987. New Year.
3146 **917** 15 z. multicoloured . . 20 10

918 Emperor Dragonfly

1988. Dragonflies. Multicoloured.
3147 10 z. Type **918** 20 10
3148 15 z. Four-spotted libellula ("Libellula quadrimaculata") (vert) 35 10
3149 15 z. Banded agrion ("Calopteryx splendens") . 35 10
3150 20 z. "Condulegaster annulatus" (vert) 35 10
3151 30 z. "Sympetrum pedemontanum" 50 15
3152 50 z. "Aeschna viridis" (vert) 90 25

1988. Renovation of Cracow Monuments (6th series). As T **819**.
3153 15 z. yellow, brown & black 15 10
DESIGN: 15 z. Florianska Gate.

919 Composition

1988. International Year of Graphic Design.
3154 **919** 40 z. multicoloured . . 45 15

920 17th-century Friesian Wall Clock with Bracket Case

1988. Clocks and Watches. Multicoloured.
3155 10 z. Type **920** 15 10
3156 10 z. 20th-century annual clock (horiz) 15 10
3157 15 z. 18th-century carriage clock 20 10
3158 15 z. 18th-century French rococo bracket clock . . . 20 10
3159 20 z. 19th-century pocket watch (horiz) 25 10
3160 40 z. 17th-cent tile-case clock from Gdansk by Benjamin Zoll (horiz) 50 25

921 Salmon and Reindeer

1988. "Finlandia 88" International Stamp Exhibition, Helsinki.
3161 **921** 45 z. + 30 z. multicoloured 85 30

922 Triple Jump

924 Wheat as Graph on VDU

1988. Olympic Games, Seoul. Multicoloured.
3162 15 z. Type **922** 20 10
3163 20 z. Wrestling 25 10
3164 20 z. Canoeing 25 10
3165 25 z. Judo 30 15
3166 40 z. Shooting 50 25
3167 55 z. Swimming 65 35

1988. 16th European Conference of Food and Agriculture Organization, Cracow. Multicoloured.
3169 15 z. Type **924** 20 10
3170 40 z. Factory in forest . . . 45 20

925 PZL P-37 Los Bomber

1988. 70th Anniv of Polish Republic (1st issue). 60th Anniv of Polish State Aircraft Works.
3171 **925** 45 z. multicoloured . . . 80 20
See also Nos. 3175, 3177, 3181/88 and 3190/2.

1988. 49th Anniv of German Invasion. As T **850**. Multicoloured.
3172 15 z. Battle of Modlin and Brig.-Gen. Wiktor Thommee 20 10
3173 20 z. Battle of Warsaw and Brig.-Gen. Walerian Czuma 20 10
3174 20 z. Battle of Tomaszow Lubelski and Brig.-Gen. Antoni Szylling 20 10

1988. 70th Anniv of Polish Republic (2nd issue). 50th Anniv of Stalowa Wola Ironworks. As T **925**. Multicoloured.
3175 15 z. View of plant 15 10

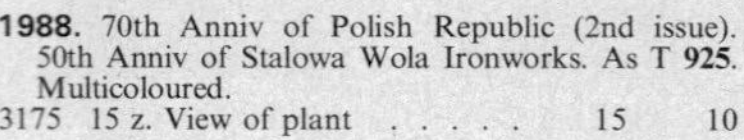

926 Postal Emblem and Tomasz Arciszewski (Postal Minister,1918–19)

927 On the Field of Glory Medal

1988. World Post Day.
3176 **926** 20 z. multicoloured . . . 20 10

1988. 70th Anniv of Polish Republic (3rd issue). 60th Anniv of Military Institute for Aviation Medicine. As T **925**. Multicoloured.
3177 20 z. Hanriot XIV hospital aircraft (38 × 28 mm) . . . 30 10

1988. Polish People's Army Battle Medals (1st series). Multicoloured.
3178 20 z. Type **927** 25 10
3179 20 z. Battle of Lenino Cross . 25 10
See also Nos. 3249/50.

928 "Stanislaw Malachowski" and "Kazimierz Nestor Sapieha"

1988. Bicentenary of Four Years Diet (political and social reforms). Paintings of Diet Presidents by Jozef Peszko.
3180 **928** 20 z. multicoloured . . . 20 10

929 Ignacy Daszynski (politician)

930 Snowman

1988. 70th Anniv of Polish Republic (4th issue). Personalities.
3181 **929** 15 z. green, red & black . 10 10
3182 – 15 z. green, red & black . 10 10
3183 – 20 z. brown, red & black 20 10
3184 – 20 z. brown, red & black 20 10
3185 – 20 z. brown, red & black 20 10
3186 – 200 z. purple, red & black 1·75 50
3187 – 200 z. purple, red & black 1·75 50
3188 – 200 z. purple, red & black 1·75 50
DESIGNS: No. 3182, Wincenty Witos (politician); 3183, Julian Marchlewski (trade unionist and economist); 3184, Stanislaw Wojciechowski (politician); 3185, Wojciech Korfanty (politician); 3186, Ignacy Paderewski (musician and politician); 3187; Marshal Jozef Pilsudski; 3188, Gabriel Narutowicz (President, 1922).

1988. 70th Anniv of Polish Republic (5th issue). As T **925**. Multicoloured.
3190 15 z. Coal wharf, Gdynia Port (65th anniv) (38 × 28 mm) 10 10
3191 20 z. Hipolit Cegielski (founder) and steam locomotive (142nd anniv of H. Cegielski Metal Works, Poznan) (38 × 28 mm) 20 10
3192 40 z. Upper Silesia Tower (main entrance) (60th anniv of International Poznan Fair) 45 20

1988. Polish Rulers (3rd series). Drawings by Jan Matejko. As T **893**.
3193 10 z. deep brown & brown . 10 10
3194 15 z. deep brown & brown . 15 10
DESIGNS: 10 z. Queen Rycheza; 15 z. Kazimierz (Karol Odnowiciel) I.

1988. New Year.
3195 **930** 20 z. multicoloured . . . 20 10

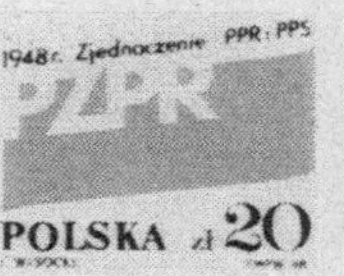

931 Flag

932 "Blysk"

1988. 40th Anniv of Polish United Workers' Party.
3196 **931** 20 z. red and black . . . 20 10

1988. Fire Boats. Multicoloured.
3197 10 z. Type **932** 15 10
3198 15 z. "Plomien" 25 10
3199 15 z. "Zar" 25 10
3200 20 z. "Strazak II" 40 10
3201 20 z. "Strazak 4" 40 10
3202 45 z. "Strazak 25" 80 50

933 Ardennes

934 Wire-haired Dachshund

1989. Horses. Multicoloured.
3203 15 z. Lippizaner (horiz) . . . 10 10
3204 15 z. Type **933** 10 10
3205 20 z. English thoroughbred (horiz) 20 10
3206 20 z. Arab 20 10
3207 30 z. Great Poland race-horse (horiz) 35 10
3208 70 z. Polish horse 75 50

1989. Hunting Dogs. Multicoloured.
3209 15 z. Type **934** 10 10
3210 15 z. Cocker spaniel 10 10
3211 20 z. Czech fousek pointer . 15 10
3212 20 z. Welsh terrier 15 10
3213 25 z. English setter 20 10
3214 45 z. Pointer 40 25

935 Gen. Wladyslaw Anders and Plan of Battle

936 Marianne

1989. 45th Anniv of Battle of Monte Cassino.
3215 **935** 80 z. multicoloured . . . 45 20
See also Nos. 3227, 3247, 3287 and 3327.

1989. Bicentenary of French Revolution.
3216 **936** 100 z. black, red & blue . 60 30

937 Polonia House

1989. Opening of Polonia House (cultural centre), Pultusk.
3218 **937** 100 z. multicoloured . . 60 30

938 Monument (Bohdan Chmielewski)

1989. 45th Anniv of Civic Militia and Security Force.
3219 **938** 35 z. blue and brown . . 70 25

939 Xaweri Dunikowski (artist) **941** Firemen

940 Astronaut

1989. Recipients of Order of Builders of the Republic of Poland. Multicoloured.
3220 35 z. Type **939** 25 10
3221 35 z. Stanislaw Mazur (farmer) 25 10
3222 35 z. Natalia Gasiorowska (historian) 25 10
3223 35 z. Wincenti Pstrowski (initiator of worker performance contests) . . . 25 10

1989. 20th Anniv of First Manned Landing on Moon.
3224 **940** 100 z. multicoloured . . 60 30

1989. World Fire Fighting Congress, Warsaw.
3226 **941** 80 z. multicoloured . . . 45 20

1989. 45th Anniv of Battle of Falaise. As T **935**. Multicoloured.
3227 165 z. Plan of battle and Gen. Stanislaw Maczek (horiz) . 90 45

942 Daisy **943** Museum Emblem

1989. Plants. (a) Perf.
3229 **942** 40 z. green 10 10
3230 – 60 z. violet 15 10
3231 **942** 150 z. red 20 10
3232 – 500 z. mauve 25 15
3233 – 700 z. green 15 10
3234 – 1000 z. blue 80 30

(b) Self-adhesive. Imperf.
3297 – 2000 z. green . . . . . . 1·00 50
3298 – 5000 z. violet . . . . . . 2·50 75
DESIGNS: 60 z. Juniper; 500 z. Wild rose; 700 z. Lily of the valley; 1000 z. Blue cornflower; 2000 z. Water lily; 5000 z. Iris.

1989. 50th Anniv of German Invasion. As T **850**.
3240 25 z. grey, orange & black . . 15 10
3241 25 z. multicoloured 15 10
3242 35 z. multicoloured 25 10
3243 35 z. multicoloured 25 10
DESIGNS: No. 3240, Defence of Westerplatte and Captain Franciszek Dabrowski; 3241, Defence of Hel and Captain B. Przybyszewski; 3242, Battle of Kock and Brig.-Gen. Franciszek Kleeberg; 3243, Defence of Lwow and Brig.-Gen. Wladyslaw Langner.

1989. Caricature Museum.
3244 **943** 40 z. multicoloured . . . 15 10

944 Rafal Czerwiakowski (founder of first university Surgery Department) **945** Emil Kalinski (Postal Minister, 1933–39)

1989. Polish Surgeons' Society Centenary Congress, Cracow.
3245 **944** 40 z. blue and black . . 20 10
3246 – 60 z. green and black . . 25 10
DESIGN: 60 z. Ludwik Rydygier (founder of Polish Surgeons' Society).

1989. 45th Anniv of Landing at Arnhem. As T **935**. Multicoloured.
3247 210 z. Gen. Stanislaw Sosabowski and plan of battle 80 40

1989. World Post Day.
3248 **945** 60 z. multicoloured . . 15 10

1989. Polish People's Army Battle Medals (2nd series). As T **927**. Multicoloured.
3249 60 z. "For Participation in the Struggle for the Rule of the People" 20 10
3250 60 z. Warsaw 1939–45 Medal 20 10

1989. Polish Rulers (4th series). As T **893**. Drawings by Jan Matejko.
3251 20 z. black and grey 10 10
3252 30 z. sepia and brown . . . 10 10
DESIGNS: 20 z. Boleslaw II, the Bold; 30 z. Wladyslaw I Herman.

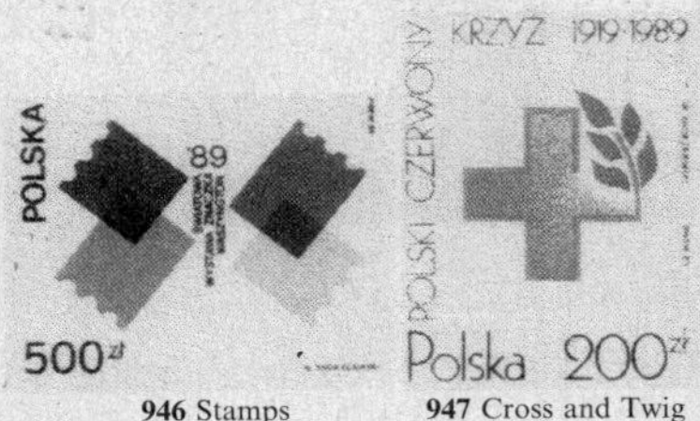

946 Stamps **947** Cross and Twig

1989. "World Stamp Expo '89" International Stamp Exhibition, Washington D.C.
3253 **946** 500 z. multicoloured . . 1·40 70

1989. 70th Anniv of Polish Red Cross.
3254 **947** 200 z. red, green & black 55 25

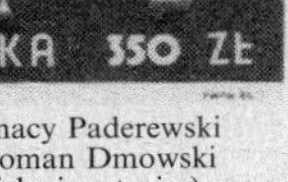

948 Ignacy Paderewski and Roman Dmowski (Polish signatories) **949** Photographer and Medal depicting Maksymilian Strasz

1989. 70th Anniv of Treaty of Versailles.
3255 **948** 350 z. multicoloured . . . 95 45

1989. 150th Anniv of Photography. Multicoloured.
3256 40 z. Type **949** 15 10
3257 60 z. Lens shutter as pupil of eye (horiz) 20 10

1989. No. 2729 surch **500**.
3258 500 z. on 4 z. violet . . . . 1·40 70

951 Painting by Jan Ciaglinski

1989. Flower Paintings by Artists Named. Multicoloured.
3259 25 z. Type **951** 10 10
3260 30 z. Wojciech Weiss 10 10
3261 35 z. Antoni Kolasinski . . . 15 10
3262 50 z. Stefan Nacht-Samborski 15 10
3263 60 z. Jozef Pankiewicz 20 10
3264 85 z. Henryka Beyer 30 10
3265 110 z. Wladyslaw Slewinski . 40 20
3266 190 z. Czeslaw Wdowiszewski 50 30

952 Christ

1989. Icons (1st series). Multicoloured.
3267 50 z. Type **952** 20 15
3268 60 z. Two saints with books 20 15
3269 90 z. Three saints with books 30 20
3270 150 z. Displaying scriptures (vert) 60 30
3271 200 z. Madonna and child (vert) 70 30
3272 350 z. Christ with saints and angels (vert) 80 40
See also Nos. 3345/50.

1990. No. 2839 surch **350 zl**.
3273 350 z. on 15 z. brown 15 10

954 Krystyna Jamroz **955** High Jumping

1990. Singers. Multicoloured.
3274 100 z. Type **954** 10 10
3275 150 z. Wanda Werminska . . 10 10
3276 350 z. Ada Sari 15 10
3277 500 z. Jan Kiepura 20 10

1990. Sports. Multicoloured.
3278 100 z. Yachting 20 10
3279 200 z. Football 20 10
3280 400 z. Type **955** 20 10
3281 500 z. Ice skating 25 10
3282 500 z. Diving 25 10
3283 1000 z. Gymnastics 40 20

956 Kozlowski

1990. Birth Centenary (1989) of Roman Kozlowski (palaeontologist).
3284 **956** 500 z. brown and red . . . 25 10

957 John Paul II **959** Ball and Colosseum

1990. 70th Birthday of Pope John Paul II.
3285 **957** 1000 z. multicoloured . . 45 20

1990. 50th Anniv of Battle of Narvik. As T **935**. Multicoloured.
3287 1500 z. Gen. Zygmunt Bohusz-Szyszko and plan of battle . 45 20

1990. World Cup Football Championship, Italy.
3288 **959** 1000 z. multicoloured . . 70 30

1990. No. 3230 surch **700 zl**.
3289 700 z. on 60 z. violet 35 15

961 Memorial **963** Fresh-water Snail

962 People and "ZUS"

1990. 34th Anniv of 1956 Poznan Uprising.
3290 **961** 1500 z. multicoloured . . 70 30

1990. 70th Anniv of Social Insurance.
3291 **962** 1500 z. blue, mve & yell . 70 30

1990. Shells. No value expressed.
3292 – B (500 z.) lilac 20 10
3293 **963** A (700 z.) green 35 10
DESIGN: B, Viviparous mussel.

964 Cross

1990. 50th Anniv of Katyn Massacre.
3294 **964** 1500 z. black and red . . 70 30

965 Weather Balloon

1990. Polish Hydrology and Meteorology Service. Multicoloured.
3295 500 z. Type **965** 20 10
3296 700 z. Water-height gauge . 35 10

966 Women's Kayak Pairs

1990. 23rd World Canoeing Championships. Multicoloured.
3305 700 z. Type **966** 30 20
3306 1000 z. Men's kayak singles . 50 20

967 Victory Sign **968** Jacob's Ladder

1990. 10th Anniv of Solidarity Trade Union.
3307 **967** 1500 z. grey, black & red 70 30

1990. Flowers. Multicoloured.
3308 200 z. Type **968** 10 10
3309 700 z. Floating heart water fringe ("Nymphoides peltata") 30 15
3310 700 z. Dragonhead ("Dracocephalum ruyschiana") 30 15
3311 1000 z. "Helleborus purpurascens" 50 20
3312 1500 z. Daphne cneorum . . 90 30
3313 1700 z. Campion . . . . . . 1·25 40

969 Serving Dish, 1870–87

1990. Bicentenary of Cmieow Porcelain Works. Multicoloured.
3314 700 z. Type **969** 30 15
3315 800 z. Plate, 1887–90 (vert) . 40 20
3316 1000 z. Cup and saucer, 1887 50 20
3317 1000 z. Figurine of dancer, 1941–44 (vert) 50 20
3318 1500 z. Chocolate box, 1930–90 90 30
3319 2000 z. Vase, 1979 (vert) . . 1·00 40

970 Little Owl **972** Collegiate Church, Tum (12th century)

971 Walesa

1990. Owls. Multicoloured.
3320 200 z. Type **970** 10 10
3321 500 z. Tawny owl 30 10
3322 500 z. Tawny owl (different) . 30 10
3323 1000 z. Short-eared owl . . . 60 20
3324 1500 z. Long-eared owl . . . 90 30
3325 2000 z. Barn owl . . . . . . 1·25 40

1990. Lech Walesa, 1984 Nobel Peace Prize Winner and new President.
3326 **971** 1700 z. multicoloured . . 80 40

1990. 50th Anniv of Battle of Britain. As T **935**. Multicoloured.
3327 1500 z. Emblem of 303 Squadron, Polish Fighter Wing R.A.F. and Hawker Hurricane 70 30

1990. Historic Architecture. Multicoloured.
3328 700 z. Type **972** 30 15
3329 800 z. Reszel castle (11th century) 40 20
3330 1500 z. Chelmno Town Hall (16th century) 90 30
3331 1700 z. Church of the Nuns of the Visitation, Warsaw (18th century) . . . . 1·00 40

973 "King Zygmunt II August" (anon) 974 Silver Fir

1991. Paintings. Multicoloured.
3332 500 z. Type **973** 10 10
3333 700 z. "Adoration of the Magi" (Pultusk Codex) 15 10
3334 1000 z. "St Matthew" (Pultusk Codex) 20 10
3335 1500 z. "Expelling of Merchants from Temple" (Nikolai Haberschrack) 30 15
3336 1700 z. "The Annunciation" (miniature) 35 15
3337 2000 z. "Three Marys" (Nikolai Haberschrack) 40 20

1991. Cones. Multicoloured.
3338 700 z. Type **974** 15 10
3339 1500 z. Weymouth pine . . . 30 15
See also Nos. 3483/4.

975 Radziwill Palace 977 Chmielowski

1991. Admission of Poland into European Postal and Telecommunications Conference.
3340 **975** 1500 z. multicoloured . . 30 15

1991. Polish Rulers (5th series). Drawings by Jan Matejko. As T **893** but surch.
3341 1000 z. on 40 z. black & grn . 25 10
3342 1500 z. on 50 z. black & red . 40 15
DESIGNS: 1000 z. Boleslaw III, the Wry Mouthed; 1500 z. Wladyslaw II, the Exile.
Nos. 3341/2 were not issued unsurcharged.

1991. 75th Death Anniv of Adam Chmielowski ("Brother Albert") (founder of Albertine Sisters).
3343 **977** 2000 z. multicoloured . . 50 15

978 Battle (detail of miniature, Schlackenwerth Codex, 1350)

1991. 750th Anniv of Battle of Legnica.
3344 **978** 1500 z. multicoloured . . 35 15

1991. Icons (2nd series). As T **952**. Mult.
3345 500 z. "Madonna of Nazareth" 10 10
3346 700 z. "Christ the Acheirophyte" 15 10
3347 1000 z. "Madonna of Vladimir" 25 10
3348 1500 z. "Madonna of Kazan" 35 15
3349 2000 z. "St. John the Baptist" 50 20
3350 2200 z. "Christ the Pentocrator" 60 25

1991. Polish Rulers (6th series). Drawings by Jan Matejko. As T **893**.
3351 1000 z. black and red . . . 25 10
3352 1500 z. black and blue . . . 35 15
DESIGNS: 1000 z. Boleslaw IV, the Curly; 1500 z. Mieszko (Mieczyslaw) III, the Old.

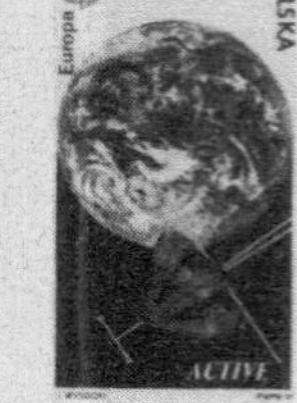

979 Title Page of Constitution 980 Satellite in Earth Orbit

1991. Bicentenary of 3rd May Constitution.
3353 **979** 2000 z. brown, buff & red 50 20
3354 – 2500 z. brown, stone & red 60 25
DESIGNS: 2500 z. "Administration of Oath by Gustav Taubert" (detail, Johann Friedrich Bolt).

1991. Europa. Europe in Space.
3356 **980** 1000 z. multicoloured . 25 10

981 Map and Battle Scene

1991. 50th Anniv of Participation of "Piorun" (destroyer) in Operation against "Bismarck" (German battleship).
3357 **981** 2000 z. multicoloured . 50 20

982 Arms of Cracow 983 Pope John Paul II

1991. European Security and Co-operation Conference Cultural Heritage Symposium, Cracow.
3358 **982** 2000 z. purple and blue . 50 20

1991. Papal Visit. Multicoloured.
3359 1000 z. Type **983** 25 10
3360 2000 z. Pope in white robes . 50 20

984 Chinstrap Penguin 985 Making Paper

1991. 30th Anniv of Antarctic Treaty.
3361 **984** 2000 z. multicoloured . . 50 20

1991. 500th Anniv of Paper Making in Poland.
3362 **985** 2500 z. blue and red . . 60 25

986 Prisoner

1991. Commemoration of Victims of Stalin's Purges.
3363 **986** 2500 z. red and black . 60 25

988 Ball and Basket

1991. Centenary of Basketball.
3365 **988** 2500 z. multicoloured . . 60 25

989 "Self-portrait" (Leon Wyczolkowski)

1991. "Bydgoszcz '91" National Stamp Exn.
3366 **989** 3000 z. green & brown . 70 30

990 Twardowski

1991. 125th Birth Anniv of Kazimierz Twardowski (philosopher).
3368 **990** 2500 z. black and grey . . 50 20

991 Swallowtail

1991. Butterflies and Moths. Multicoloured.
3369 1000 z. Type **991** 20 10
3370 1000 z. Dark crimson underwing ("Mormonia sponsa") 20 10
3371 1500 z. Painted lady ("Vanessa cardui") 30 15
3372 1500 z. Scarce swallowtail ("Iphiclides podalirius") . . 30 15
3373 2500 z. Scarlet tiger moth ("Panaxia dominula") . . . 50 25
3374 2500 z. Peacock ("Nymphalis io") 50 25

992 "The Shepherd's Bow" (Francesco Solimena)

1991. Christmas.
3376 **992** 1000 z. multicoloured . . 20 10

993 Gen. Stanislaw Kopanski and Battle Map

1991. 50th Anniv of Participation of Polish Troops in Battle of Tobruk.
3377 **993** 2000 z. multicoloured . . 45 20

994 Brig.-Gen. Michal Tokarzewski-Karaszewicz 995 Lord Baden-Powell (founder)

1991. World War II Polish Underground Army Commanders.
3378 **994** 2000 z. black and red . . 50 20
3379 – 2500 z. red and violet . . 60 20
3380 – 3000 z. violet and mauve 70 25
3381 – 5000 z. brown and green 1·25 40
3382 – 6500 z. dp brown & brn 1·60 50
DESIGNS: 2500 z. Gen. Broni Kazimierz Sosnkowski; 3000 z. Lt.-Gen. Stefan Rowecki; 5000 z. Lt.-Gen. Tadeusz Komorowski; 6500 z. Brig.-Gen. Leopold Okulicki.

1991. 80th Anniv of Scout Movement in Poland.
3383 **995** 1500 z. yellow and green 35 10
3384 – 2000 z. blue and yellow . 50 20
3385 – 2500 z. violet and yellow 60 20
3386 – 3500 z. brown & yellow . 75 25
DESIGNS: 2000 z. Andrzej Malkowski (Polish founder); 2500 z. "Watch on the Vistula" (Wojciech Kossak); 3500 z. Polish scout in Warsaw Uprising, 1944.

1992. Polish Rulers (7th series). As T **893**.
3387 1500 z. brown and green . . 35 10
3388 2000 z. black and blue . . . 50 20
DESIGNS: 1500 z. Kazimierz II, the Just; 2000 z. Leszek I, the White.

996 Sebastien Bourdon

1992. Self-portraits. Multicoloured.
3389 700 z. Type **996** 15 10
3390 1000 z. Sir Joshua Reynolds 20 10
3391 1500 z. Sir Godfrey Kneller . 25 10
3392 2000 z. Bartolome Esteban Murillo 40 15
3393 2200 z. Peter Paul Rubens . 45 15
3394 3000 z. Diego de Silva y Velazquez 60 25

997 Skiing 998 Manteuffel

1992. Winter Olympic Games, Albertville. Mult.
3395 1500 z. Type **997** 25 10
3396 2500 z. Ice hockey 45 15

1992. 90th Birth Anniv of Tadeusz Manteuffel (historian).
3397 **998** 2500 z. brown 45 15

999 Nicolas Copernicus (astronomer)

1992. Famous Poles. Multicoloured.
3398 1500 z. Type **999** 25 10
3399 2000 z. Frederic Chopin (composer) 40 15
3400 2500 z. Henryk Sienkiewicz (writer) 45 15
3401 3500 z. Marie Curie (physicist) 65 25

1000 Columbus and Left-hand Detail of Map

1992. Europa. 500th Anniv of Discovery of America by Christopher Columbus. Multicoloured.
3403 1500 z. Type **1000** 25 10
3404 3000 z. "Santa Maria" and right-hand detail of Juan de la Costa map, 1500 . . . . . 50 25
Nos. 3403/4 were issued together, se-tenant, forming a composite design.

1001 River Czarna Wiselka

1003 Family and Heart

1002 Prince Jozef Poniatowski

1992. Environmental Protection. River Cascades. Multicoloured.

3405 2000 z. Type **1001** 40 15
3406 2500 z. River Swider 45 15
3407 3000 z. River Tanew 60 20
3408 3500 z. Mickiewicz waterfall . 65 30

1992. Bicentenary of Order of Military Virtue. Multicoloured.

3409 1500 z. Type **1002** 25 10
3410 3000 z. Marshal Jozef Pilsudski 50 25

1992. Children's Drawings. Multicoloured.

3412 1500 z. Type **1003** 25 10
3413 3000 z. Butterfly, sun, bird and dog 50 25

1004 Fencing

1992. Olympic Games, Barcelona. Multicoloured.

3414 1500 z. Type **1004** 25 10
3415 2000 z. Boxing 40 15
3416 2500 z. Running 45 20
3417 3000 z. Cycling 55 25

1006 Statue of Korczak

1992. 50th Death Anniv of Janusz Korczak (educationist).

3419 **1006** 1500 z. black, brn & yell 30 10

1007 Flag and "V"

1008 Wyszinski

1992. 5th Polish Veterans World Meeting.

3420 **1007** 3000 z. multicoloured . 60 30

1992. 11th Death Anniv of Stefan Wyszinski (Primate of Poland) (3421) and 1st Anniv of World Youth Day (3422). Multicoloured.

3421 1500 z. Type **1008** 30 10
3422 3000 z. Pope John Paul II embracing youth 60 30

1009 National Colours encircling World Map

1992. World Meeting of Expatriate Poles, Cracow.

3423 **1009** 3000 z. multicoloured . 60 30

1010 Polish Museum, Adampol

1011 18th-century Post Office Sign, Slonim

1992. 150th Anniv of Polish Settlement at Adampol, Turkey.

3424 **1010** 3500 z. multicoloured . 65 35

1992. World Post Day.

3425 **1011** 3500 z. multicoloured . 65 35

1012 "Dedication" (self-portrait)

1992. Birth Centenary of Bruno Schulz (writer and artist).

3426 **1012** 3000 z. multicoloured . 60 30

1013 "Seated Girl" (Henryk Wicinski)

1992. Polish Sculptures. Multicoloured.

3427 2000 z. Type **1013** 40 15
3428 2500 z. "Portrait of Tytus Czyzewski" (Zbigniew Pronaszko) 45 20
3429 3000 z. "Polish Nike" (Edward Wittig) 60 30
3430 3500 z. "The Nude" (August Zamoyski) 65 35

1014 "10th Theatrical Summer in Zamosc" (Jan Mlodozeniec)

1992. Poster Art (1st series). Multicoloured.

3432 1500 z. Type **1014** 25 10
3433 2000 z. "Red Art" (Franciszek Starowieyski) 40 15
3434 2500 z. "Circus" (Waldemar Swierzy) 45 20
3435 3500 z. "Mannequins" (Henryk Tomaszewski) 65 35

See also Nos. 3502/3 and 3523/4.

1015 Girl skipping with Snake

1992. "Polska '93" International Stamp Exn, Poznan (1st issue). Multicoloured.

3436 1500 z. Type **1015** 25 10
3437 2000 z. Boy on rocking horse with upside-down runners . 40 15
3438 2500 z. Boy firing bird from bow 45 20
3439 3500 z. Girl placing ladder against clockwork giraffe . 65 35

See also Nos. 3452, 3453/6 and 3466/9.

1016 Medal and Soldiers

1992. 50th Anniv of Formation of Polish Underground Army. Multicoloured.

3440 1500 z. Type **1016** 25 10
3441 3500 z. Soldiers 65 35

1017 Church and Star

1018 Wheat

1992. Christmas.

3443 **1017** 1000 z. multicoloured . . 20 10

1992. International Nutrition Conference, Rome. Multicoloured.

3444 1500 z. Type **1018** 25 10
3445 3500 z. Glass, bread, vegetables and jug on table 60 30

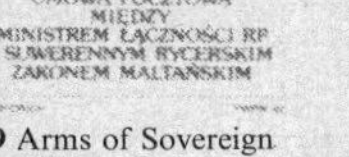

1019 Arms of Sovereign Military Order

1020 Arms, 1295

1992. Postal Agreement with Sovereign Military Order of Malta.

3446 **1019** 3000 z. multicoloured . . 50 25

1992. History of the White Eagle (Poland's arms). Each black, red and yellow.

3447 2000 z. Type **1020** 30 10
3448 2500 z. 15th-century arms . . 40 15
3449 3000 z. 18th-century arms . . 50 25
3450 3500 z. Arms, 1919 . . . . . 60 30
3451 5000 z. Arms, 1990 . . . . . 80 35

1021 Exhibition Emblem and Stylised Stamp

1022 Amber

1992. Centenary of Polish Philately and "Polska '93" International Stamp Exhibition, Poznan (2nd issue).

3452 **1021** 1500 z. multicoloured . . 20 10

1993. "Polska '93" International Stamp Exhibition, Poznan (3rd issue). Amber. Multicoloured.

3453 1500 z. Type **1022** 20 10
3454 2000 z. Pinkish amber . . . 30 10
3455 2500 z. Amber in stone . . . 40 25
3456 3000 z. Amber containing wasp 50 30

1023 Downhill Skier

1024 Flower-filled Heart

1993. Winter University Games, Zakopane.

3458 **1023** 3000 z. multicoloured . 50 30

1993. St. Valentine's Day. Multicoloured.

3459 1500 z. Type **1024** 20 15
3460 3000 z. Heart in envelope . . 50 30

1993. Polish Rulers (8th series). As T **983** showing drawings by Jan Matejko.

3461 1500 z. brown and green . . 20 15
3462 2000 z. black and mauve . . 30 20
3463 2500 z. black and green . . . 40 25
3464 3000 z. dp brown & brown . 50 30

DESIGNS: 1500 z. Wladyslaw Laskonogi; 2000 z. Henryk I; 2500 z. Konrad I of Masovia; 3000 z. Boleslaw V, the Chaste.

1025 Arsenal

1993. 50th Anniv of Attack by Szare Szeregi (formation of Polish Scouts in the resistance forces) on Warsaw Arsenal.

3465 **1025** 1500 z. multicoloured . 20 15

1026 Jousters with Lances

1993. "Polska '93" International Stamp Exhibition, Poznan (4th issue). Jousting at Golub Dobrzyn. Designs showing a modern and a medieval jouster. Multicoloured.

3466 1500 z. Type **1026** 20 15
3467 2000 z. Jousters 30 20
3468 2500 z. Jousters with swords 40 25
3469 3500 z. Officials 60 30

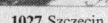

1027 Szczecin

1028 Jew and Ruins

1993. 750th Anniv of Granting of Town Charter to Szczecin.

3470 **1027** 1500 z. multicoloured . . 20 15

1993. 50th Anniv of Warsaw Ghetto Uprising.

3471 **1028** 4000 z. black, yell & bl 65 40

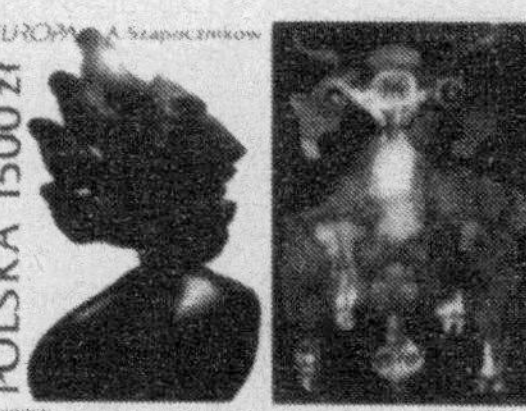

1029 Works by A. Szapocznikow and J. Lebenstein

1993. Europa. Contemporary Art. Multicoloured.

3472 1500 z. Type **1029** 20 15
3473 4000 z. "CXCIX" (S. Gierawski) and "Red Head" (B. Linke) 65 40

1030 "King Alexander Jagiellonczyk in the Sejm" (Jan Laski, 1505)

1993. 500th Anniv of Parliament.
3474 **1030** 2000 z. multicoloured . 30 20

1031 Nullo **1033** Cap

1993. 130th Death Anniv of Francesco Nullo (Italian volunteer in January 1863 Rising).
3475 **1031** 2500 z. multicoloured . 40 25

1993. 3rd World Congress of Cadets of the Second Republic.
3477 **1033** 2000 z. multicoloured . 30 15

1034 Copernicus and Solar System

1993. 450th Death Anniv of Nicolas Copernicus (astronomer).
3478 **1034** 2000 z. multicoloured . 30 15

1035 Fiki Miki and Lion

1993. 40th Death Anniv of Kornel Makuszynski (writer of children's books). Multicoloured.
3479 1500 z. Type **1035** 25 15
3480 2000 z. Billy goat 35 20
3481 3000 z. Fiki Miki 50 30
3482 5000 z. Billy goat riding ostrich 80 45

1993. Cones. As T **974**. Multicoloured.
3483 10000 z. Arolla pine . . . . 1·60 80
3484 20000 z. Scots pine . . . . . 3·25 1·60

1036 Tree Sparrow

1993. Birds. Multicoloured.
3485 1500 z. Type **1036** 25 10
3486 2000 z. Pied wagtail 35 15
3487 3000 z. Syrian woodpecker . 50 25
3488 4000 z. Goldfinch 70 30
3489 5000 z. Common starling . . 80 40
3490 6000 z. Bullfinch . . . . . . 1·00 50

1037 Soldiers Marching

1993. Bicentenary of Dabrowski's "Mazurka" (national anthem) (1st issue).
3491 **1037** 1500 z. multicoloured . 15 10
See also No. 3526.

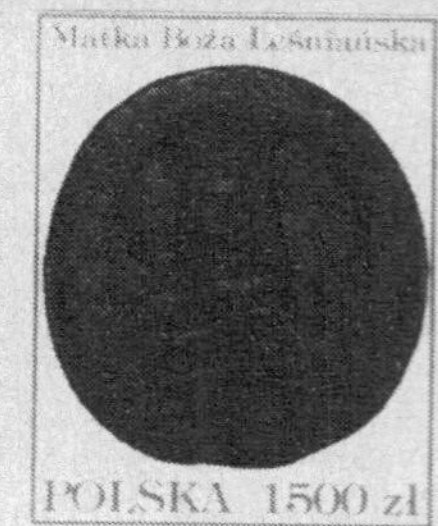

1038 "Madonna and Child" (St. Mary's Basilica, Lesna Podlaska)

1993. Sanctuaries to St. Mary. Multicoloured.
3492 1500 z. Type **1038** 15 10
3493 2000 z. "Madonna and Child" (St. Mary's Church, Swieta Lipka) 20 15

1039 Handley Page Halifax and Parachutes

1993. The Polish Rangers (Second World War air troop).
3494 **1039** 1500 z. multicoloured . 15 10

1040 Trumpet Player

1993. "Jazz Jamboree '93" International Jazz Festival, Warsaw.
3495 **1040** 2000 z. multicoloured . 20 15

1041 Postman **1042** St. Jadwiga (miniature, Schlackenwerther Codex)

1993. World Post Day.
3496 **1041** 2500 z. brown, grey and blue 25 15

1993. 750th Death Anniv of St. Jadwiga of Silesia.
3497 **1042** 2500 z. multicoloured . 15 10

1044 Eagle and Crown **1045** St. Nicholas

1993. 75th Anniv of Republic.
3499 **1044** 4000 z. multicoloured . 40 25

1993. Christmas.
3501 **1045** 1500 z. multicoloured . 15 10

1993. Poster Art (2nd series). As T **1014**. Mult.
3502 2000 z. "Come and see Polish Mountains" (M. Urbaniec) 20 15
3503 5000 z. Production of Alban Berg's "Wozzeck" (J. Lenica) 50 30

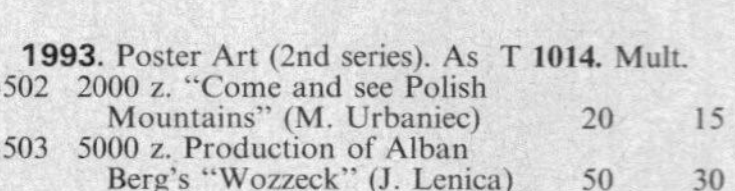

INDEX
Countries can be quickly located by referring to the index at the end of this volume.

1046 Daisy shedding Petals **1047** Cross-country Skiing

1994. Greetings Stamp.
3504 **1046** 1500 z. multicoloured . . 15 10

1994. Winter Olympic Games, Lillehammer, Norway. Multicoloured.
3505 2500 z. Type **1047** 25 10
3506 5000 z. Ski jumping 50 30

1048 Bem and Cannon

1994. Birth Bicentenary of General Jozef Bem.
3508 **1048** 5000 z. multicoloured . . 50 30

1049 Jan Zamojski (founder) **1050** Cracow Battalion Flag and Scythes

1994. 400th Anniv of Zamojski Academy, Zamosc.
3509 **1049** 5000 z. grey, black and brown 50 30

1994. Bicentenary of Tadeusz Kosciuszko's Insurrection.
3510 **1050** 2000 z. multicoloured . . 20 10

1994. Polish Rulers (9th series). Drawings by Jan Matejko. As T **893**.
3511 2500 z. black and blue . . . 25 10
3512 5000 z. black, deep violet and violet 50 30
DESIGN: 2500 z. Leszek II, the Black; 5000 a. Przemysl II.

1051 Oil Lamp, Open Book and Spectacles **1052** "Madonna and Child"

1994. Europa. Inventions and Discoveries. Multicoloured.
3513 2500 z. Type **1051** (invention of modern oil lamp by Ignacy Lukasiewicz) 25 10
3514 6000 z. Illuminated filament forming "man in the moon" (astronomy) 60 40

1994. St. Mary's Sanctuary, Kalwaria Zebrzydowska.
3515 **1052** 4000 z. multicoloured . . 40 25

1053 Abbey Ruins and Poppies

1994. 50th Anniv of Battle of Monte Cassino.
3516 **1053** 6000 z. multicoloured . . 60 40

1054 Mazurka

1994. Traditional Dances. Multicoloured.
3517 3000 z. Type **1054** 30 20
3518 4000 z. Coralski 40 25
3519 9000 z. Krakowiak 90 60

1055 Cogwheels

1994. 75th Anniv of International Labour Organization.
3520 **1055** 6000 z. deep blue, blue and black 60 40

1056 Optic Fibre Cable

1994. 75th Anniv of Polish Electricians Association.
3521 **1056** 4000 z. multicoloured . 40 25

1057 Map of Americas on Football

1994. World Cup Football Championship, U.S.A.
3522 **1057** 6000 z. multicoloured . 60 40

1994. Poster Art (3rd series). As T **1014**. Mult.
3523 4000 z. "Monsieur Fabre" (Wiktor Gorka) 40 25
3524 6000 z. "8th OISTAT Congress" (Hubert Hilscher) (horiz) 60 40

1058 Znaniecki **1059** Polish Eagle and Ribbon

1994. 36th Death Anniv of Professor Florian Znaniecki.
3525 **1058** 9000 z. green, bis & yellow 90 60

1994. Bicentenary of Dabrowski's Mazurka (2nd issue). As T **1037**. Multicoloured.
3526 2500 z. Troops preparing to charge 25 10

1994. 50th Anniv of Warsaw Uprising.
3527 **1059** 2500 z. multicoloured . 25 10

1060 "Stamp" protruding from Pocket **1061** Basilica of St. Brigida, Gdansk

1994. "Philakorea 1994" International Stamp Exhibition, Seoul.
3528 **1060** 4000 z. multicoloured . 25 10

1994. Sanctuaries.
3529 **1061** 4000 z. multicoloured . 25 10

1062 "Nike" (goddess of Victory)

1994. Centenary of International Olympic Committee.
3530 **1062** 4000 z. multicoloured . 25 10

1063 Komeda and Piano Keys

1994. 25th Death Anniv of Krzysztof Komeda (jazz musician).
3531 **1063** 6000 z. multicoloured . 35 15

1064 Catfish ("Ancistrus dolichopterus") **1065** Arms of Polish Post, 1858

1994. Fishes. Multicoloured.
3532 4000 z. Type **1064** 20 10
3533 4000 z. Angel fish ("Pterophyllum scalare") . . 20 10
3534 4000 z. Green swordtail ("Xiphophorus helleri") and neon tetra ("Paracheirodon innesi") . . 20 10
3535 4000 z. Rainbowfish ("Poecilia reticulata") 20 10
Nos. 3532/5 were issued together, se-tenant, forming a composite design.

1994. World Post Day.
3536 **1065** 4000 z. multicoloured . 20 10

1066 Kolbe

1994. Maximilian Kolbe (concentration camp victim) Year.
3537 **1066** 2500 z. multicoloured . 15 10

1067 Pigeon

1994. Pigeons. Multicoloured.
3538 4000 z. Type **1067** 20 10
3539 4000 z. Friar pigeon 20 10
3540 6000 z. Silver magpie pigeon . 35 15
3541 6000 z. Danzig pigeon (black) 35 15

MILITARY POST

I. Polish Corps in Russia, 1918.

1918. Stamps of Russia optd **POCZTA Pol. Korp.** and eagle. Perf or imperf. (70 k.).
M 1 **22** 3 k. red . . . . 40·00 38·00
M 2 **23** 4 k. red . . . . 40·00 38·00
M 3 **22** 5 k. red . . . . 13·00 10·50
M 4 **23** 10 k. blue . . . . 13·00 10·50
M 5 **22** 10 k. on 7 k. bl (No.151) £400 £450
M 6 **10** 15 k. blue and purple . . 2·75 2·50
M 7 **14** 20 k. red and blue . . . 5·25 3·75
M 8 **10** 25 k. mauve and green . 65·00 50·00
M 9 35 k. green and purple . 2·75 2·50
M10 **14** 40 k. green and purple . 10·00 7·50
M11 **10** 70 k. orange and brown (No. 166) £180 £150

1918. Stamps of Russia surch **Pol. Korp.**, eagle and value. (a) Perf on Nos. 92/4.
M12A **22** 10 k. on 3 k. red . . . . 2·50 2·50
M13A 35 k. on 1 k. orange . . 40·00 40·00
M14A 50 k. on 2 k. green . . . 2·75 2·75
M15A 1 r. on 3 k. red . . . . 50·00 50·00

(b) Imperf on Nos. 155/7.
M12B **22** 10 k. on 3 k. red 90 90
M13B 35 k. on 1 k. orange . . 40 40
M14B 50 k. on 2 k. green . . . 90 90
M15B 1 r. on 3 k. red . . . . 1·90 1·90

II. Polish Army in Russia, 1942.

M 3 "We Shall Return"

1942.
M16 **M 3** 50 k. brown £130 £300

NEWSPAPER STAMPS

1919. Newspaper stamps of Austria optd **POCZTA POLSKA**. Imperf.
N50 **N 53** 2 h. brown . . . . . 10·00 10·00
N51 4 h. green . . . . . . 2·40 2·40
N52 6 h. blue . . . . . . 2·40 2·40
N53 10 h. orange . . . . . 38·00 38·00
N54 30 h. red . . . . 6·00 6·00

OFFICIAL STAMPS

O 24 **O 70**

1920.
O128 **O 24** 3 f. red 10 10
O129 5 f. red 10 10
O130 10 f. red 10 10
O131 15 f. red 10 10
O132 25 f. red 10 10
O123 50 f. red 10 10
O134 100 f. red 25 25
O135 150 f. red 30 30
O136 200 f. red 40 40
O137 300 f. red 35 35
O138 600 f. red 50 50

1933. (a) Inscr "ZWYCZAJNA".
O295 **O 70** (No value) mauve . . 75 15
O306 (No value) blue . . . 10 10

(b) Inscr "POLECONA".
O307 **O 70** (No value) red 20 10

O 93

1940. (a) Size 31 × 23 mm.
O392 **O 93** 6 g. brown . . . . . 1·50 1·50
O393 8 g. grey . . . . . . 1·50 1·50
O394 10 g. green . . . . . 1·50 1·50
O395 12 g. green . . . . . 1·75 1·75
O396 20 g. brown . . . . . 1·75 3·00
O397 24 g. red . . . . . . 25·00 1·00
O398 30 g. red . . . . . . 2·25 3·50
O399 40 g. violet . . . . . 2·50 6·00
O400 48 g. olive . . . . . 10·00 7·00
O401 50 g. blue . . . . . . 2·50 2·50
O402 60 g. olive . . . . . 1·75 2·00
O403 80 g. purple . . . . . 1·75 2·00

(b) Size 35 × 26 mm.
O404 **O 93** 1 z. purple and grey . 5·00 5·00
O405 3 z. brown and grey . 5·00 5·00
O406 5 z. orge and grey . . 6·00 6·00

1940. Size 21 × 16 mm.
O407 **O 93** 6 g. brown . . . . . 1·00 1·25
O408 8 g. grey . . . . . . 1·50 1·75
O409 10 g. green . . . . . 2·00 2·00
O410 12 g. green . . . . . 2·00 2·00
O411 **O 93** 20 g. brown . . . . . 1·00 1·25
O412 24 g. red 80 85
O413 30 g. red . . . . . . 1·75 2·00
O414 40 g. violet . . . . . 2·00 2·00
O415 50 g. blue . . . . . . 2·00 2·00

O 102 **O 128** **O 277**

1943.
O456 **O 102** 6 g. brown 10 20
O457 8 g. blue 10 20
O458 10 g. green 10 20
O459 12 g. violet 25 20
O460 16 g. orange 10 30
O461 20 g. olive 15 20
O462 24 g. red 25 20
O463 30 g. purple 15 20
O464 40 g. blue 15 20
O465 60 g. olive 15 20
O466 80 g. purple 20 20
O467 100 g. grey 25 60

1945. No value. (a) With control number below design. Perf or imperf.
O534 **O 128** (5 z.) blue 15 10
O535 (10 z.) red 25 15

(b) Without control number below design. Perf.
O748 **O 128** (60 g.) pale blue . . . 25 10
O805 (60 g.) indigo 65 30
O806 (1.55 z.) red 40 15
The blue and indigo stamps are inscr "ZWYKLA" (Ordinary) and the red stamps "POLECONA" (Registered).

1954. No value.
O871 **O 277** (60 g.) blue 20 10
O872 (1.55 z.) red ("POLECONA") . 40 15

POSTAGE DUE STAMPS

1991. Postage Due Stamps of Austria optd **POCZTA POLSKA**.
D50 **D 55** 5 h. red . . . . 5·75 5·25
D51 10 h. red £1100 £1200
D52 15 h. red . . . . 2·40 2·00
D53 20 h. red £300 £300
D54 25 h. red . . . . 14·00 13·00
D55 30 h. red £550 £475
D56 40 h. red £150 £120
D57 **D 56** 1 k. blue £1700 £1700
D58 5 k. blue £1700 £1700
D59 10 k. blue £6000 £5500

1919. Postage Due Provisionals of Austria optd **POCZTA POLSKA**.
D60 **50** 15 on 36 h. (No. D287) . . £180 £120
D61 50 on 42 h. (No. D289) . . 19·00 19·00

D 20 **D 28** **D 63**

1919. Sold in halerzy or fenigow.
D 92 **D 20** 2 h. blue 10 10
D 93 4 h. blue 10 10
D 94 5 h. blue 10 10
D 95 10 h. blue 10 10
D 96 20 h. blue 10 10
D 97 30 h. blue 10 10
D 98 50 h. blue 10 10
D145 100 h. blue 20 20
D146 200 f. blue 40 30
D147 500 h. blue 25 20
The 20, 100 and 500 values were sold in both currencies.

1919. Sold in fenigow.
D128 **D 20** 2 f. red 25 30
D129 4 f. red 10 10
D130 5 f. red 10 10
D131 10 f. red 10 10
D132 20 f. red 10 10
D133 30 f. red 10 10
D134 50 f. red 10 10
D135 100 f. red 50 30
D136 500 f. red . . . . . . 1·40 70

1921. Stamps of 1919 surch with new value and **doplata**. Imperf.
D154 **11** 6 m. on 15 h. brown . . . 75 75
D155 6 m. on 25 h. red . . . 50 50
D156 20 m. on 10 h. red . . . 95 95
D157 20 m. on 50 h. blue . . . 1·25 1·60
D158 35 m. on 70 h. blue . . . 10·00 12·00

1921. Value in marks. (a) Size 17 × 22 mm.
D159 **D 28** 1 m. blue 20 10
D160 2 m. blue 20 10
D161 4 m. blue 20 10
D162 6 m. blue 20 10
D163 8 m. blue 20 10
D164 20 m. blue 20 10
D165 50 m. blue 20 10
D166 100 m. blue 40 10

(b) Size 19 × 24 mm.
D199 **D 28** 50 m. blue 10 10
D200 100 m. blue 10 10
D201 200 m. blue 10 10
D202 500 m. blue 10 10
D203 **D 28** 1000 m. blue 10 10
D204 2000 m. blue 10 10
D205 10,000 m. blue 10 10
D206 20,000 m. blue 10 10
D207 30,000 m. blue 10 10
D208 50,000 m. blue 20 10
D209 100,000 m. blue . . . 25 10
D210 200,000 m. blue . . . 30 10
D211 300,000 m. blue . . . 30 20
D212 500,000 m. blue . . . 50 15
D213 1,000,000 m. blue . . 95 40
D214 2,000,000 m. blue . . 1·75 40
D215 3,000,000 m. blue . . 1·90 50

1923. Surch.
D216 **D 28** 10,000 on 8 m. blue . 25 10
D217 20,000 on 20 m. blue . 25 20
D218 50,000 on 2 m. blue . 1·50 50

1924. As Type D **28** but value in "groszy" or "zloty". (a) Size 20 × $25\frac{1}{2}$ mm.
D229 **D 28** 1 g. brown 15 15
D230 2 g. brown 15 15
D231 4 g. brown 15 15
D232 6 g. brown 25 15
D233 10 g. brown . . . . . 3·25 15
D234 15 g. brown . . . . . 3·00 20
D235 20 g. brown . . . . . 6·50 20
D236 25 g. brown . . . . . 4·50 20
D237 30 g. brown 85 20
D238 40 g. brown . . . . . 1·10 20
D239 50 g. brown . . . . . 1·10 20
D240 1 z. brown 85 30
D241 2 z. brown 85 30
D242 3 z. brown . . . . . 1·10 1·25
D243 5 z. brown . . . . . 1·10 50

(b) Size 19 × 24 mm.
D290 **D 28** 1 g. brown 20 10
D291 2 g. brown 20 10
D292 10 g. brown . . . . . 1·00 20
D293 15 g. brown . . . . . 1·40 10
D294 20 g. brown . . . . . 3·00 10
D295 25 g. brown . . . . . 27·00 10

1930.
D280 **D 63** 5 g. brown 50 15

1934. Nos. D 79/84 surch.
D301 **D 28** 10 g. on 2 z. brown . 20 15
D302 15 g. on 2 z. brown . 20 15
D303 20 g. on 1 z. brown . 20 15
D304 20 g. on 5 z. brown . 1·90 40
D305 25 g. on 40 g. brown . 50 40
D306 30 g. on 40 g. brown . 70 40
D307 50 g. on 40 g. brown . 70 40
D308 50 g. on 3 z. brown . 1·90 70

1934. No. 273 surch **DOPLATA** and value.
D309 10 g. on 1 z. black on cream 80 10
D310 20 g. on 1 z. black on cream 1·75 45
D311 25 g. on 1 z. black on cream 80 20

D 88 **D 97**

1938.
D350 **D 88** 5 g. green 15 10
D351 10 g. green 15 10
D352 15 g. green 15 10
D353 20 g. green 40 15
D354 25 g. green 15 15
D355 30 g. green 20 15
D356 50 g. green 55 70
D357 1 z. green . . . . . 2·10 1·40

1940. German Occupation.
D420 **D 97** 10 g. orange 35 90
D421 20 g. orange . . . . 35 1·00
D422 30 g. orange . . . . 35 1·00
D423 50 g. orange . . . . 1·25 1·60

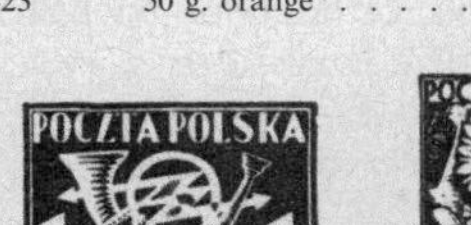

D 126 **D 190**

1945. Size 26 × $19\frac{1}{2}$ mm. Perf.
D530 **D 126** 1 z. brown 10 10
D531 2 z. brown 10 10
D532 3 z. brown 15 15
D533 5 z. brown 20 15

1946. Size 29 × $21\frac{1}{2}$ mm. Perf or imperf.
D646 **D 126** 1 z. brown 10 10
D647 2 z. brown 10 10
D572 3 z. brown 10 10
D573 5 z. brown 10 10
D574 6 z. brown 10 10
D575 10 z. brown 15 15
D649 15 z. brown 20 15
D577 25 z. brown 30 15
D651 100 z. brown 75 25
D652 150 z. brown . . . . 1·40 25

1950.
D665 **D 190** 5 z. red 15 10
D666 10 z. red 15 10
D667 15 z. red 15 10
D668 20 z. red 15 10
D669 25 z. red 25 15
D670 50 z. red 40 15
D671 100 z. red 70 45

1951. Value in "groszy" or "zloty".

D701 D 190 5 g. red 10 10
D702 10 g. red 10 10
D703 15 g. red 10 10
D704 20 g. red 10 10
D705 25 g. red 10 10
D706 30 g. red 15 10
D707 50 g. red 15 15
D708 60 g. red 15 15
D709 90 g. red 25 15
D710 1 z. red 30 25
D711 2 z. red 50 40
D712 5 z. purple 1·60 1·25

1953. As last but with larger figures of value and no imprint below design.

D804 D 190 5 g. brown 10 10
D805 10 g. brown 10 10
D806 15 g. brown 10 10
D807 20 g. brown 10 10
D808 25 g. brown 10 10
D809 30 g. brown 15 10
D810 50 g. brown 20 15
D811 60 g. brown 30 20
D812 90 g. brown 40 35
D813 1 z. brown 50 35
D814 2 z. brown 1·10 80

1980. As Type D 190 but redrawn without imprint.

D2699 1 z. red 10 10
D2700 2 z. drab 10 10
D2701 3 z. violet 25 10
D2702 5 z. brown 45 15

POLISH POST IN DANZIG Pt. 5

For Polish post in Danzig, the port through which Poland had access to the sea between the two Great Wars.

100 groszy = 1 zloty

Stamps of Poland optd **PORT GDANSK**.

1925. Issue of 1924.

R 1 40 1 g. brown 30 60
R 2 2 g. brown 35 1·60
R 3 3 g. orange 35 60
R 4 5 g. green 8·75 3·75
R 5 10 g. green 3·00 1·25
R 6 15 g. red 18·00 3·00
R 7 20 g. blue 1·00 60
R 8 25 g. red 1·00 60
R 9 30 g. violet 1·25 60
R10 40 g. blue 1·25 60
R11 50 g. purple 3·25 80

1926. Issues of 1925–28.

R14 44 5 g. green 1·25 1·00
R15 – 10 g. violet (No. 245a) 1·25 1·00
R16 – 15 g. red (No. 246) 2·40 2·25
R17 48 20 g. red 1·90 1·40
R18 51 25 g. brown 2·75 90
R19 57 1 z. black and cream 18·00 18·00

1929. Issues of 1928/9.

R21 61 5 g. violet 95 80
R22 10 g. green 95 80
R23 59 15 g. blue 1·75 2·40
R24 61 25 g. brown 1·60 80

1933. Stamp of 1928 with vert opt.

R25 57 1 z. black on cream 48·00 60·00

1934. Issue of 1932.

R26 65 5 g. violet 1·90 2·25
R27 10 g. green 20·00 65·00
R28 15 g. red 1·90 2·25

1936. Issue of 1935.

R29 79 5 g. blue (No.313) 2·00 1·75
R31 – 5 g. violet (No.317) 65 1·00
R30 – 15 g. blue (No.315) 2·00 2·75
R32 – 15 g. lake (No.319) 65 1·00
R33 – 25 g. green (No.321a) 2·00 1·25

R 6 Port of Danzig

1938. 20th Anniv of Polish Independence.

R34 R 6 5 g. orange 35 55
R35 15 g. brown 35 55
R36 25 g. purple 35 95
R37 55 g. blue 85 1·75

POLISH POST OFFICE IN TURKEY Pt. 5

Stamps used for a short period for franking correspondence handed in at the Polish Consulate, Constantinople.

100 fenigow = 1 marka

1919. Stamps of Poland of 1919 optd **LEVANT**. Perf.

1 15 3 f. brown 1·40
2 5 f. green 1·40
3 10 f. purple 1·40
4 15 f. red 1·40
5 20 f. blue 1·40
6 25 f. olive 1·40
7 50 f. green 1·40
8 17 1 m. violet 1·40
9 1 m. 50 green 1·40
10 2 m. brown 1·40
11 18 2 m. 50 brown 1·40
12 19 5 m. purple 1·40

PONTA DELGADA Pt. 9

A district of the Azores, whose stamps were used from 1868, and again after 1905.

1000 reis = 1 milreis

1892. As T 26 of Portugal but inscr "PONTA DELGADA".

6 5 r. orange 1·10 70
20 10 r. mauve 1·10 75
8 15 r. brown 1·40 1·25
9 20 r. lilac 1·50 1·10
10 25 r. green 2·40 75
24 50 r.blue 3·00 1·50
25 75 r. red 3·25 2·75
14 80 r. green 4·75 3·75
15 100 r. brown on yellow 5·00 2·75
28 150 r. red on rose 16·00 13·00
16 200 r. blue on blue 20·00 15·00
17 300 r. blue on brown 20·00 16·00

1897. "King Carlos" key-types inscr "PONTA DELGADA".

29 S 2½ r grey 25 20
30 5 r. orange 30 25
31 10 r. green 30 25
32 15 r. brown 3·50 2·75
45 15 r. green 60 50
33 20 r. lilac 65 45
34 25 r. green 95 70
46 25 r. red 40 20
35 50 r. blue 1·10 70
48 65 r. blue 40 35
36 75 r. red 2·00 1·25
49 75 r. brown on yellow 3·75 3·50
37 80 r. mauve 40 35
38 100 r. blue on blue 1·25 75
50 115 r. brown on pink 70 65
51 130 r. brown on yellow 70 65
39 150 r. brown on yellow 70 65
52 180 r. black on pink 70 65
40 200 r. purple on pink 2·75 2·25
41 300 r. blue on pink 2·75 2·25
42 500 r. black on blue 5·00 3·75

PORT LAGOS Pt. 6

French Post Office in the Turkish Empire. Closed in 1898.

25 centimes = 1 piastre

1893. Stamps of France optd **Port-Lagos** and the three higher values surch also in figures and words.

75 10 5 c. green 13·50 10·00
76 10 c. black on lilac 27·00 19·00
77 15 c. blue 55·00 45·00
78 1 p. on 25 c. black on pink 40·00 35·00
79 2 p. on 50 c. red £120 70·00
80 4 p. on 1 f. green 65·00 60·00

PORT SAID Pt. 6

French Post Office in Egypt. Closed 1931.

1902. 100 centimes = 1 franc
1921. 10 milliemes = 1 piastre

1899. Stamps of France optd **PORT SAID**.

101 10 1 c. black on blue 40 50
102 2 c. brown on buff 50 60
103 3 c. grey 75 70
104 4 c. brown on grey 50 80
105 5 c. green 1·25 2·00
107 10 c. black on lilac 4·00 3·50
109 15 c. blue 2·50 4·00
110 20 c. red on green 3·25 4·50
111 25 c. black on pink 1·00 55
112 30 c. brown 4·75 5·00
113 40 c. red on yellow 7·25 4·50
115 50 c. red 9·50 6·00
116 1 f. green 13·00 7·75
117 2 f. brown on blue 42·00 35·00
118 5 f. mauve on lilac 65·00 50·00

1899. No. 107 surch. (a) **25c VINGT-CINQ**.

119 10 25 c. on 10 c. blk on lilac £275 £110

(b) **VINGT-CINQ** only.

121 10 25 c on 10 c blk on lilac 75·00 14·50

1902. "Blanc", "Mouchon" and "Merson" key-types inscr "PORT SAID".

122 A 1 c. grey 10 40
123 2 c. purple 15 35
124 3 c. red 15 20
125 4 c. brown 20 20
126a 5 c. green 65 30
127 B 10 c. red 30 45
128 15 c. red 75 85
128a 15 c. orange 1·10 90
129 20 c. brown 35 60
130 25 c. blue 30 15
131 30 c. mauve 1·75 1·50
132 C 40 c. red and blue 1·25 2·00
133 50 c. brown and lilac 1·00 1·25
134 1 f. red and green 4·25 3·50
135 2 f. lilac and buff 3·75 6·00
136 5 f. blue and buff 14·00 15·00

1915. Red Cross. Surch **5c** and red cross.

137 B 10 c. + 5 c. red 25 80

1921. Surch with value in figures and words (without bars).

151a A 1 m. on 1 c. grey 40 45
152 2 m. on 5 c. green 40 50
153 B 4 m. on 10 c. red 60 95
166a A 5 m. on 1 c. grey 4·00 4·50
167 5 m. on 2 c. purple 6·25 6·25
154 5 m. on 3 c. red 3·75 4·00
141 5 m. on 4 c. brown 4·75 4·75
155 B 6 m. on 15 c. orange 85 1·00
156 6 m. on 15 c. red 5·50 5·50
157 8 m. on 20 c. brown 75 90
168 A 10 m. on 2 c. purple 6·00 6·25
142 10 m. on 4 c. brown 9·50 9·50
158 B 10 m. on 25 c. blue 1·40 1·40
159 10 m. on 30 c. mauve 2·75 3·25
144 12 m. on 30 c. mauve 16·00 16·00
145 A 15 m. on 4 c. brown 3·50 3·75
169 B 15 m. on 15 c. red 27·00 27·00
170 15 m. on 20 c. brown 27·00 27·00
146 C 15 m. on 40 c. red & bl 25·00 25·00
160 15 m. on 50 c. brown and lilac 2·00 2·50
161 B 15 m. on 50 c. blue 2·50 2·00
162 30 m. on 1 f. red & green 1·50 3·00
171 C 30 m. on 50 c. brown & lilac £160 £160
172 60 m. on 50 c. brown and lilac £170 £170
149 60 m. on 2 f. lilac & buff 48·00 48·00
164 60 m. on 2 f. red & green 4·00 4·75
173 150 m. on 50 c. brown and lilac £200 £200
165 150 m. on 5 f. blue & buff 3·75 4·00

1925. Surch with value in figures and words and bars over old value.

174 A 1 m. on 1 c. grey 35 50
175 2 m. on 5 c. green 35 50
176 B 4 m. on 10 c. red 35 50
177 A 5 m. on 3 c. red 40 50
178 B 6 m. on 15 c. orange 60 70
179 8 m. on 20 c. brown 35 60
180 10 m. on 25 c. blue 60 70
181 15 m. on 50 c. blue 70 70
182 C 30 m. on 1 f. red & green 70 95
183 60 m. on 2 f. red & green 70 1·10
184 150 m. on 5 f. bl & buff 1·25 1·27

1927. Altered key-types. Inscr 'Mm' below value.

185 A 3 m. orange 60 75
186 B 15 m. blue 65 75
187 20 m. mauve 90 1·00
188 C 50 m. red and green 1·75 1·90
189 100 m. blue and yellow 2·00 2·50
190 250 m. green and red 4·00 4·25

1927. "French Sinking Fund" issue. As No. 186 (colour changed) surch **+5 Mm Caisse d'Amortissement**.

191 B 15 m. + 5 m. orange 1·25 1·50
192 15 m. + 5 m. mauve 1·25 1·50
193 15 m. + 5 m. brown 1·25 1·50
194 15 m. + 5 m. lilac 1·75 2·75

POSTAGE DUE STAMPS

1921. Postage Due stamps of France surch in figures and words.

D174 D 11 2 m. on 5 c. blue 25·00 25·00
D175 4 m. on 10 c. brown 25·00 25·00
D176 10 m. on 30 c. red 25·00 25·00
D166 12 m. on 10 c. brown 28·00 28·00
D167 15 m. on 5 c. blue 30·00 30·00
D177 15 m. on 50 c. purple 35·00 35·00
D168 30 m. on 20 c. olive 35·00 35·00
D169 30 m. on 50 c. purple £170 £170

For 1928 issues, see Alexandria.

PORTUGAL Pt. 9

A country on the S.W. coast of Europe, a kingdom till 1910, when it became a republic.

1853. 1000 reis = 1 milreis
1912. 100 centavos = 1 escudo

1 Queen Maria II 5 King Pedro V 9 King Luis

1853. Various frames. Imperf.

1 1 5 r. brown £900 £325
4 25 r. blue £350 10·00
6 50 r. green £1100 £300
8 100 r. lilac £5500 £850

1855. Various frames. Imperf.

18 5 5 r. brown £118 14·00
21 25 r. blue £150 6·00
22 25 r. red £100 1·50
13 50 r. green £170 28·00
15 100 r. lilac £275 38·00

1862. Various frames. Imperf.

24 9 5 r. brown 35·00 4·00
28 10 r. yellow 60·00 14·00
30 25 r. red 38·00 1·25
32 50 r. green £225 27·00
34 100 r. lilac £275 32·00

14 King Luis 15

1866. With curved value labels. Imperf.

35 14 5 r. black 48·00 4·00
36 10 r. yellow 85·00 32·00
38 20 r. olive 70·00 25·00
39 25 r. red 95·00 1·25
41 50 r. green £110 26·00
43 80 r. orange £110 26·00
45 100 r. purple £110 35·00
46 120 r. blue £120 22·00

1867. With curved value labels. Perf.

52 14 5 r. black 55·00 12·00
54 10 r. yellow £100 32·00
56 20 r. olive £120 32·00
57 25 r. red 28·00 1·25
60 50 r. green £120 32·00
61 80 r. orange £150 42·00
62 100 r. lilac £130 40·00
64 120 r. blue £130 25·00
67 240 r. mauve £425 £160

1870. With straight value labels. Perf.

No.	Type	Description	Mint	Used
102	15	5 r. black	16·00	2·50
70		10 r. yellow	27·00	8·00
107		10 r. green	38·00	7·00
141		15 r. brown	28·00	4·00
142		20 r. olive	25·00	4·00
79		20 r. red	10·00	70
80		25 r. red	10·00	70
83		50 r. green	45·00	4·50
117		50 r. blue	85·00	12·00
146		80 r. orange	40·00	4·00
153		100 r. mauve	32·00	2·25
93		120 r. blue	£110	28·00
95		150 r. blue	£140	42·00
155		150 r. yellow	65·00	5·00
99		240 r. mauve	£700	£400
156		300 r. mauve	45·00	10·00
128		1000 r. black	£110	22·00

16 King Luis **17**

1880. Various frames for T **16**.

No.	Type	Description	Mint	Used
185	16	5 r. black	7·50	1·00
188		25 r. grey	9·00	50
190		25 r. brown	9·00	50
180	17	25 r. grey	£110	5·50
184	16	50 r. blue	£100	5·00

19 King Luis **26** King Carlos

1882. Various frames.

No.	Type	Description	Mint	Used
229	19	5 r. black	2·25	50
231		10 r. green	10·00	80
232		20 r. red	18·00	5·00
194		25 r. brown	7·50	70
234		25 r. mauve	10·00	35
236		50 r. blue	16·00	90
216		500 r. black	£200	£110
217		500 r. mauve	£100	20·00

1892.

No.	Type	Description	Mint	Used
271	26	5 r. orange	2·50	45
239		10 r. mauve	7·50	90
256		15 r. brown	6·00	1·25
242		20 r. lilac	8·00	2·75
275		25 r. green	9·00	45
244		50 r. blue	12·00	3·00
245		75 r. red	24·00	1·25
262		80 r. green	25·00	15·00
248		100r. brown on yellow	20·00	2·25
265		150 r. red on rose	55·00	15·00
252		200 r. blue on blue	50·00	13·00
267		300 r. blue on brown	65·00	18·00

1892. Optd **PROVISORIO**.

No.	Type	Description	Mint	Used
284	19	5 r. black	3·50	3·25
285		10 r. green	5·00	2·50
295	15	15 r. brown	5·00	3·00
290	19	20 r. red	8·50	5·50
291		25 r. mauve	4·25	2·00
292		50 r. blue	25·00	20·00
293	15	80 r. orange	42·00	32·00

1893. Optd **1893. PROVISORIO** or surch also.

No.	Type	Description	Mint	Used
302	19	5 r. black	7·50	4·50
303		10 r. green	8·00	6·00
304		20 r. red	15·00	13·00
309		20 r. on 25 r. mauve	18·00	11·00
305		25 r. mauve	40·00	32·00
306		50 r. blue	40·00	32·00
310	15	50 r. on 80 r. orange	32·00	42·00
312		75 r. on 80 r. orange	32·00	25·00
308		80 r. orange	40·00	32·00

32 Prince Henry in his Caravel and Family Motto

1894. 500th Birth Anniv of Prince Henry the Navigator.

No.	Type	Description	Mint	Used
314	32	5 r. orange	1·25	1·00
315		10 r. red	1·75	1·00
316		15 r. brown	2·75	1·50
317		20 r. violet	3·00	1·50
318	–	25 r. green	2·50	1·00
319	–	50 r. blue	6·00	2·00
320	–	75 r. red	12·00	4·00
321	–	80 r. green	15·00	4·50
322	–	100 r. brown on buff	9·00	2·50
323	–	150 r. red	22·00	10·00
324	–	300 r. blue on buff	30·00	10·00
325	–	500 r. purple	75·00	25·00
326	–	1000 r. black	95·00	35·00

DESIGNS: 25 r. to 100 r. Prince Henry's fleet; 150 r. to 1000 r. Prince Henry's studies.

35 St. Anthony's Vision **37** St. Anthony ascending into Heaven

1895. 700th Birth Anniv of St. Anthony (Patron Saint).

No.	Type	Description	Mint	Used
327	35	2½ r. black	1·50	1·10
328	–	5 r. orange	1·75	1·10
329	–	10 r. mauve	4·00	2·50
330	–	15 r. brown	6·00	4·00
331	–	20 r. grey	6·00	4·00
332	–	25 r. purple and green	4·00	1·25
333	37	50 r. brown and blue	14·00	10·00
334		75 r. brown and red	20·00	15·00
335		80 r. brown and green	25·00	20·00
336		100 r. black and brown	25·00	13·00
337	–	150 r. red and brown	60·00	45·00
338	–	200 r. blue and brown	60·00	45·00
339	–	300 r. black and brown	85·00	55·00
340	–	500 r. brown and green	£150	£120
341	–	1,000 r. lilac and green	£225	£160

DESIGNS—HORIZ: 5 r. to 25 r. St. Anthony preaching to fishes. VERT: 150 r. to 1,000 r. St. Anthony from picture in Academy of Fine Arts Paris.

39 King Carlos

1895. Numerals of value in black or red.

No.	Type	Description	Mint	Used
342	39	2½ r. grey	10	10
343		5 r. orange	20	10
344		10 r. green	20	10
345		15 r. green	18·00	1·00
346		15 r. brown	27·00	1·50
347		20 r. lilac	25	10
348		25 r. green	22·00	10
349		25 r. red	20	10
351		50 r. blue	25	10
352		65 r. blue	40	10
353		75 r. red	35·00	1·50
354		75 r. brown on yellow	50	20
355		80 r. mauve	80	25
356		100 r. blue on blue	40	10
357		115 r. brown on pink	2·00	1·00
358		130 r. brown on cream	1·50	65
359		150 r. brown on yellow	42·00	9·00
360		180 r. grey on pink	5·00	4·00
361		200 r. puple on pink	1·50	30
362		300 r. blue on pink	1·75	65
363		500 r. black on blue	3·00	2·00

40 Departure of Fleet

43 Muse of History **44** Da Gama and Camoens and "Sao Gabriel" (flagship)

1898. 4th Centenary of Discovery of Route to India by Vasco da Gama.

No.	Type	Description	Mint	Used
378	40	2½ r. green	60	25
379	–	5 r. red	60	25
380	–	10 r. purple	3·50	1·25
381	43	25 r. green	3·00	35
382	44	50 r. blue	4·50	1·50
383	–	75 r. brown	13·00	5·50
384	–	100 r. brown	15·00	5·00
385	–	150 r. brown	25·00	14·00

DESIGNS—HORIZ: 5 r. Arrival at Calicut; 10 r. Embarkation at Rastello; 100 r. Flagship "Sao Gabriel"; 150 r. Vasco da Gama. VERT: 75 r. Archangel Gabriel, Patron Saint of the Expedition.

48 King Manoel II **49**

1910.

No.	Type	Description	Mint	Used
390	48	2½ r. violet	15	10
391		5 r. black	15	10
392		10 r. green	40	20
393		15 r. brown	1·10	50
394		20 r. red	65	35
395		25 r. brown	40	10
396		50 r. blue	65	35
397		75 r. brown	4·25	2·00
398		80 r. grey	1·50	1·25
399		100 r. brown on green	5·50	2·00
400		200 r. green on pink	2·25	1·75
401		300 r. black on blue	3·25	2·25
402	49	500 r. brown and olive	8·00	6·00
403		1,000 r. black and blue	12·00	12·00

1910. Optd **REPUBLICA**.

No.	Type	Description	Mint	Used
404	48	2½ r. violet	20	10
405		5 r. black	20	10
406		10 r. green	1·25	40
407		15 r. brown	40	30
408		20 r. red	2·00	1·10
409		25 r. brown	40	15
410		50 r. blue	3·00	1·10
411		75 r. brown	5·50	2·50
412		80 r. grey	1·50	1·00
413		100 r. brown on green	1·25	25
414		200 r. green on pink	1·50	90
415		300 r. black on blue	2·50	1·50
416	49	500 r. brown and olive	5·50	4·50
417		1,000 r. black and blue	10·00	10·00

1911. Optd **REPUBLICA** or surch also.

No.	Type	Description	Mint	Used
441	40	2½ r. green	20	15
442a	D 48	5 r. black	10	10
443a		10 r. mauve	10	10
444	–	15 r. on 5 r. red (No. 379)	1·10	20
445a	D 48	20 r. orange	60	60
446	43	25 r. green	50	25
447	44	50 r. blue	2·00	1·75
448	–	75 r. brown (No. 383)	15·00	12·00
449	–	80 r. on 150 r. (No. 385)	3·50	2·25
450	–	100 r. brown (No. 384)	2·50	1·50
451	D 48	200 r. brown on buff	25·00	22·00
452		300 r. on 50 r. grey	20·00	16·00
453		500 r. on 100 r. red	15·00	6·50
454	–	1,000 r. on 10 r. (No. 380)	22·00	18·00

1911. Vasco da Gama stamps of Madeira optd **REPUBLICA** or surch also.

No.	Description	Mint	Used
455	2½ r. green	1·50	70
456	15 r. on 5 r. red	1·50	1·00
457	25 r. green	2·50	2·25
458	50 r. blue	4·50	3·50
459	75 r. brown	4·00	2·50
460	80 r. on 150 r. brown	5·00	2·50
461	100 r. brown	12·00	4·25
462	1,000 r. on 10 r. purple	13·00	10·00

56 Ceres **60** Presidents of Portugal and Brazil and Airmen G. Coutinho and S. Cabral

1912.

No.	Type	Description	Mint	Used
484	56	¼ c. olive	10	10
485		½ c. black	10	10
486		1 c. green	75	15
515		1 c. brown	10	10
488		1½ c. brown	2·75	75
516		1½ c. green	10	10
490		2 c. red	2·75	60
517		2 c. yellow	10	10
702		2 c. brown	10	10
492		2½ c. lilac	20	10
521		3 c. red	10	10
703		3 c. blue	10	10
495		3½ c. green	15	10
523		4 c. green	10	10
704		4 c. green	10	10
497		5 c. blue	2·25	20
526		5 c. brown	10	10
499		6 c. purple	20	10
706		6 c. brown	10	10
815		6 c. red	10	10
500		7½ c. brown	3·50	50
529		7½ c. blue	10	15
530		8 c. grey	20	10
531		8 c. green	25	15
532		8 c. orange	30	15
503		10 c. brown	5·50	40
707		10 c. red	10	10
504		12 c. blue	90	35
534		12 c. green	25	15
535		13½ c. blue	45	25
481		14 c. blue on yellow	75	40
536		14 c. purple	35	15
505		15 c. purple	1·00	40
817		15 c. black	15	10
709		16 c. blue	20	15
474		20 c. brown on green	6·50	75
475		20 c. brown on buff	8·00	1·00
539		20 c. brown	35	15
540		20 c. green	35	15
541		20 c. grey	40	15
542		24 c. blue	30	15
543		25 c. pink	35	10
818		25 c. grey	20	10
819		25 c. green	20	10
476		30 c. brown on red	48·00	4·50
477		30 c. brown on yellow	2·50	50
545		30 c. brown	30	15
820		32 c. green	20	10
548		36 c. red	40	15
549		40 c. blue	45	20
550		40 c. brown	35	15
821		40 c. green	15	10
713		48 c. pink	60	30
478		50 c. orange on orange	5·50	75
553		50 c. yellow	50	25
824	56	50 c. red	50	40
554		60 c. blue	60	25
715		64 c. blue	60	45
826		75 c. red	75	25
510		80 c. pink	60	35
558		80 c. violet	1·00	45
827		80 c. green	85	25
559		90 c. blue	1·10	25
717		96 c. red	1·00	75
480		1 e. green on blue	7·00	1·00
561		1 e. lilac	2·50	50
565		1 e. blue	2·50	70
566		1 e. purple	1·00	25
829		1 e. red	2·00	35
562		1 e. 10 brown	2·75	50
563		1 e. 20 green	1·10	30
719		1 e. 20 ochre	4·50	35
830		1 e. 20 brown	1·25	35
831		1 e. 25 blue	1·00	30
568		1 e. 50 lilac	3·50	1·00
720		1 e. 60 blue	1·00	15
721		2 e. green	7·00	25
833		2 e. mauve	10·00	2·50
572		2 e. 40 green	55·00	45·00
573		3 e. pink	45·00	32·00
722		3 e. 20 green	2·50	45
723		4 e. 50 yellow	2·50	45
575		5 e. green	9·50	1·75
724		5 e. brown	42·00	75
725		10 e. red	3·25	55
577		20 e. blue	£110	75·00

1923. Portugal–Brazil Trans-Atlantic Flight.

No.	Type	Description	Mint	Used
578	60	1 c. brown	10	10
579		2 c. orange	10	10
580		3 c. blue	10	10
581		4 c. green	15	15
582		5 c. brown	15	15
583		10 c. brown	15	15
584		15 c. black	20	20
585		20 c. green	20	20
586		25 c. red	30	25
587		30 c. brown	1·10	1·00
588		40 c. brown	20	20
589		50 c. yellow	30	20
590		75 c. purple	35	25
591		1 e. blue	45	35
592		1 e. 50 grey	65	50
593		2 e. green	1·10	1·00

62 Camoens at Ceuta **63** Saving the "Lusiad"

1924. 4th Birth Centenary of Camoens (poet) Value in black.

No.	Type	Description	Mint	Used
600	62	2 c. blue	20	20
601		3 c. orange	20	20
602		4 c. grey	20	20
603		5 c. green	20	20
604		6 c. red	20	20
605	63	8 c. brown	20	20
606		10 c. violet	20	20
607		15 c. olive	20	20
608		16 c. purple	20	20
609		20 c. orange	20	20
610	–	25 c. mauve	25	25
611	–	30 c. brown	25	25
612	–	32 c. green	45	45
613	–	40 c. blue	40	40
614	–	48 c. purple	80	80
615	–	50 c. red	90	90
616	–	64 c. green	95	95
617	–	75 c. violet	1·00	1·00
618	–	80 c. brown	1·00	1·00
619	–	96 c. red	1·00	1·00
620	–	1 e. blue	90	90
621	–	1 e. 20 brown	1·25	1·25
622	–	1 e 50 red	1·00	1·00
623	–	1 e. 60 blue	1·10	1·10
624	–	2 e. green	1·75	1·50
625	–	2 e. 40 green on green	2·50	2·25
626	–	3 e. blue on blue	2·25	2·00
627	–	3 e. 20 black on green	2·25	2·00
628	–	4 e. 50 black on yellow	2·50	2·25
629	–	10 e. brown on red	4·25	3·25
630	–	20 e. violet on mauve	5·50	4·50

DESIGNS—VERT: 25 c. to 48 c. Luis de Camoens; 50 c. to 96 c. 1st Edition of Lusiad; 20 e. Monument to Camoens. HORIZ: 1 e. to 2 e. Death of Camoens; 2 e. 40. to 10 e. Tomb of Camoens.

65 Branco's House at S.Miguel de Seide **67** Camilo Castelo Branco

1925. Birth Centenary of Camilo Castelo Branco (novelist). Value in black.

No.	Type	Description	Mint	Used
631	65	2 c. orange	25	25
632		3 c. green	25	25
633		4 c. blue	25	25
634		5 c. red	25	25
635		6 c. purple	25	25
636		8 c. brown	25	25

637 A 10 c. blue 25 25
638 67 15 c. olive 35 35
639 A 16 c. orange 35 35
640 20 c. violet 35 35
641 67 25 c. red 35 10
642 A 30 c. brown 35 10
643 32 c. green 75 75
644 67 40 c. black and green . . . 45 45
645 A 48 c. purple . . . . 1·25 1·25
646 B 50 c. green . . . . 1·00 1·00
647 64 c. brown . . . . 2·00 2·00
648 75 c. grey . . . . 1·10 1·10
649 67 80 c. brown . . . . 1·00 1·00
650 B 96 c. red . . . . 1·25 1·25
651 1 e. violet . . . . 1·25 1·25
652 1 e. 20 green . . . . 1·25 1·25
653 C 1 e. 50 blue on blue . . . . 6·50 6·50
654 67 1 e. 60 blue . . . . 2·25 2·25
655 C 2 e. green on green . . . . 3·50 3·25
656 2 e. 40 red on orange . . . 18·00 15·00
657 3 e. red on blue . . . . . 25·00 22·00
658 3 e. 20 black on green . . . 18·00 16·00
659 67 4 e. 50 black and red . . . 6·50 5·00
660 C 10 e. brown on buff . . . . 7·50 4·50
661 D 20 e. black on orange . . . 11·00 2·50

DESIGNS—HORIZ: A, Branco's study. VERT: B, Teresa de Albuquerque; C, Mariana and Joao da Cruz; D, Simao de Botelho. Types B/D shows characters from Branco's "Amor de Peredicao".

76 Afonso I, first King of Portugal, 1140

80 Goncalo Mendes da Maia

77 Battle of Aljubarrota

1926. 1st Independence issue. Dated 1926. Centres in black.

671 76 2 c. orange 20 20
672 – 3 c. blue 20 20
673 76 4 c. green 20 20
674 – 5 c. brown 20 20
675 76 6 c. orange 20 20
676 – 15 c. green 20 20
677 76 16 c. blue 55 55
678 77 20 c. violet 55 55
679 – 25 c. red 60 60
680 77 32 c. green 60 60
681 – 40 c. brown 40 40
682 – 46 c. red . . . . 1·25 1·50
683 – 50 c. olive . . . . 1·50 1·75
684 – 64 c. green . . . . 2·00 2·75
685 – 75 c. red . . . . 2·25 2·50
686 – 96 c. red . . . . 3·00 3·75
687 – 1 e. violet . . . . 3·50 4·75
688 77 1 e. 60 blue . . . . 4·75 6·50
689 – 3 e. purple . . . . 14·00 16·00
690 – 4 e. 50 green . . . . 14·00 20·00
691 77 10 e. red . . . . 24·00 30·00

DESIGN—VERT: 25, 40, 50, 75 c. Philippa de Vilhena arms her sons; 64 c., 1 e. Don Joao IV, 1640; 96 c. 3, 4 e. 50, Independence Monument, Lisbon. HORIZ: 3, 5, 15, 46 c. Monastery of D. Joao I.

1926. 1st Independence issue surch. Centres in black.

692 2 c. on 5 c. brown 60 60
693 2 c. on 46 c. red 60 60
694 2 c. on 64 c. green 60 60
695 3 c. on 75 c. red 60 60
696 3 c. on 96 c. red 60 80
697 3 c. on 1 e. violet 60 60
698 4 c. on 1 e. 60 blue . . . . . 2·75 2·75
699 4 c. on 3 e. purple . . . . . 1·60 1·75
700 6 c. on 4 e. 50 green . . . . . 1·60 1·75
701 6 c. on 10 e. red . . . . . 1·75 1·75

1927. 2nd Independence issue. Dated 1927. Centres in black.

726 80 2 c. brown 20 20
727 – 3 c. blue 20 20
728 80 4 c. orange 20 20
729 – 5 c. brown 20 20
730 – 6 c. brown 20 20
731 – 15 c. brown 30 30
732 – 16 c. blue 45 45
733 80 25 c. grey 45 45
734 – 32 c. green . . . . 1·25 1·10
735 – 40 c. green 45 45
736 80 48 c. red . . . . 4·00 3·25
737 – 80 c. violet . . . . 3·75 3·25
738 – 96 c. red . . . . 5·50 4·75
739 – 1 e. 60 blue . . . . 5·50 6·00
740 – 4 e. 50 yellow . . . . 10·00 10·00

DESIGNS—HORIZ: 3, 15, 80 c. Gulmaraes Castle; 6, 32 c. Battle of Montijo. VERT: 5, 16 c., 1 e. 50, Joao das Regras; 40, 96 c. Brites de Aimelda; 4 e. 50, J. P. Ribeiro.

1928. Surch.

742 56 4 c. on 8 c. orange 25 25
743 4 c. on 30 c. brown 25 25
744 10 c. on ¼ c. olive 35 25
745 10 c. on ½ c. black 40 25
746 10 c. on 1 c. brown 35 15
747 10 c. on 4 c. green 25 25
748 10 c. on 4 c. orange 25 25
749 56 10 c. on 5 c. olive 25 25
751 15 c. on 16 c. blue 25 25
752 15 c. on 20 c. brown . . . 13·00 13·00
753 15 c. on 20 c. grey 25 25
754 15 c. on 24 c. turquoise . . 1·10 40
755 15 c. on 25 c. pink 25 20
756 15 c. on 25 c. grey 25 20
757 16 c. on 32 c. green 50 40
758 40 c. on 2 c. yellow 25 25
760 40 c. on 2 c. brown 25 25
761 40 c. on 3 c. blue 25 25
762 40 c. on 50 c. yellow 25 25
763 40 c. on 60 c. blue 50 40
764 40 c. on 64 c. blue 60 50
765 40 c. on 75 c. pink 60 50
766 40 c. on 80 c. violet 40 30
767 40 c. on 90 c. blue . . . . 2·50 1·00
768 40 c. on 1 e. purple 45 35
769 40 c. on 1 e. 10 brown . . . 45 30
770 80 c. on 6 c. red 40 40
771 80 c. on 6 c. brown 40 30
772 80 c. on 48 c. pink 60 40
773 80 c. on 1 e. 50 lilac . . . 75 50
774 96 c. on 1 e. 20 green . . . 1·75 1·10
775 96 c. on 1 e. 20 ochre . . . 1·75 1·25
777 1 $ 60 on 2 e. green . . . 10·00 9·00
778 1 $ 60 on 3 e. 20 bronze . . 3·50 3·00
779 1 $ 60 on 20 e. blue . . . 4·25 3·25

84 Storming of Santarem

1928. 3rd Independence issue. Dated 1928. Centres in black.

780 – 2 c. blue 15 20
781 84 3 c. green 15 20
782 – 4 c. red 15 20
783 – 5 c. olive 15 20
784 – 6 c. brown 30 35
785 84 15 c. grey 40 45
786 – 16 c. purple 40 55
787 – 25 c. blue 50 55
788 – 32 c. green . . . . 95 1·25
789 – 40 c. brown 30 60
790 – 50 c. red . . . . 2·75 2·50
791 84 80 c. grey . . . . 3·25 3·75
792 – 96 c. red . . . . 6·00 7·50
793 – 1 e. mauve . . . . 12·00 13·00
794 – 1 e. 60 blue . . . . 5·00 6·00
795 – 4 e. 50 yellow . . . . 5·00 6·00

DESIGNS—VERT: 2, 25 c., 1 e. 60, G. Paes; 6, 32, 96 c. Joana de Gouveia; 4 e. 50, M. de Albuquerque. HORIZ: 4, 16, 50 c. Battle of Rolica; 5, 40 c., 1 e. Battle of Atoleiros.

1929. Optd **Revalidado.**

805 56 10 c. red 25 15
806 15 c. black 25 15
807 40 c. brown 30 15
808 40 c. green 25 15
810 96 c. red . . . . 2·50 1·50
811 1 e. 60 blue . . . . 6·50 4·00

1929. Telegraph stamp surch **CORREIO 1 $ 60** and bars.

812 – 1 e. 60 on 5 c. brown . . . 5·00 3·25

88 Camoens poem "Lusiads"

89 St. Anthony's Birthplace

1931.

835 88 4 c. brown 10 10
836 5 c. brown 10 10
837 6 c. grey 15 10
838 10 c. purple 10 10
839 15 c. black 15 10
840 16 c. blue 55 20
841 25 c. green . . . . 1·75 10
841a 25 c. blue . . . . 2·00 10
841b 30 c. green 80 10
842 40 c. red . . . . 4·25 10
843 48 c. brown 40 15
844 50 c. brown 20 10
845 75 c. red . . . . 2·50 50
846 80 c. green 25 10
846a 95 c. red . . . . 6·50 2·00
847 1 e. red . . . . 17·00 10
848 1 e. 20 olive . . . . 1·10 60
849 1 e. 25 blue 60 10
849a 1 e. 60 blue . . . . 13·00 1·40
849b 1 e. 75 blue 40 10
850 2 e. violet 25 10
851 4 e. 50 orange 50 10
852 5 e. green 50 10

1931. 700th Death Anniv of St. Anthony.

853 89 15 c. purple 50 20
854 – 25 c. green 50 20
855 – 40 c. brown 75 20
856 – 75 c. red . . . . 8·50 4·25
857 – 1 e. 25 grey . . . . 16·00 8·50
858 – 4 e. 50 purple . . . . 10·00 1·50

DESIGNS—VERT: 25 c. Saint's baptismal font; 40 c. Lisbon Cathedral; 75 c. St. Anthony; 1 e. 25, Santa Cruz Cathedral, Coimbra. HORIZ: 4 e. 50, Saint's tomb, Padua.

90 Don Nuno Alvares Pereira

94 President Carmona

1931. 5th Death Centenary of Pereira.

859 90 15 c. black 50 30
860 25 c. green and black . . . 50 35
861 40 c. orange 75 35
862 75 c. red . . . . 7·00 6·00
863 1 e. 25 blue . . . . 11·00 8·00
864 4 e. 50 green and brown . . 50·00 25·00

1933. Pereira issue of 1931 surch.

865 90 15 c. on 40 c. orange . . . 35 30
866 40 c. on 15 c. black . . . . 1·25 1·10
867 40 c. on 25 c. green & blk . . 40 35
868 40 c. on 75 c. red . . . . 3·00 2·00
869 40 c. on 1 e. 25 blue . . . 3·00 2·00
870 40 c. on 4 e. 50 green and brown . . . . 3·00 2·00

1933. St. Anthony issue of 1931 surch.

871 – 15 c. on 40 c. brown . . . 50 35
872 89 40 c. on 15 c. purple . . . 75 40
873 – 40 c. on 25 c. green . . . 75 30
874 – 40 c. on 75 c. red . . . . 3·00 2·00
875 – 40 c. on 1 e. 25 grey . . . 3·00 2·00
876 – 40 c. on 4 e. 50 purple . . . 3·00 2·00

1934.

877 94 40 c violet . . . . 5·50 10

95

96 Queen Maria

1934. Colonial Exhibition.

878 95 25 c. olive . . . . 2·00 45
879 40 c. red . . . . 5·00 15
880 1 e. 60 blue . . . . 13·00 4·25

1935. 1st Portuguese Philatelic Exhibition.

881 96 40 c. red 65 10

97 Temple of Diana at Evora

98 Prince Henry the Navigator

99 "All for the Nation"

100 Coimbra Cathedral

1935.

882 97 4 c. black 20 10
883 5 c. blue 20 10
884 6 c. brown 20 10
885a 98 10 c. green . . . . 2·50 10
886 15 c. brown 15 10
887 99 25 c. blue . . . . 2·75 10
888 40 c. brown 60 10
889 1 e. red . . . . 1·50 15
890 100 1 e. 75 blue . . . . 28·00 1·25
890a 99 10 e. grey . . . . 6·00 75
890b 20 e. green . . . . 8·00 50

102 Shield and Propeller

103 Symbol of Medicine

1937. Air.

891 102 1 e. 50 blue 50 25
892 1 e. 75 red 80 20
893 2 e. 50 red 70 20
893a 3 e. blue . . . . 5·00 2·50
893b 4 e. green . . . . 9·00 6·50

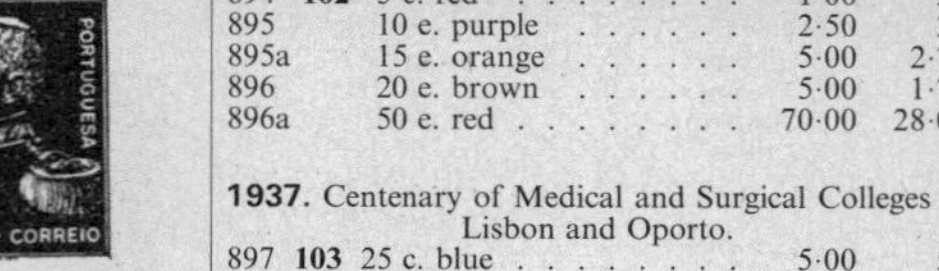

894 102 5 e. red . . . . 1·00 20
895 10 e. purple . . . . 2·50 20
895a 15 e. orange . . . . 5·00 2·75
896 20 e. brown . . . . 5·00 1·75
896a 50 e. red . . . . 70·00 28·00

1937. Centenary of Medical and Surgical Colleges at Lisbon and Oporto.

897 103 25 c. blue . . . . 5·00 50

104 Gil Vicente

106 Grapes

107 Cross of Avis

1937. 400th Death Anniv of Gil Vicente (poet).

898 104 40 c. brown . . . . 6·00 10
899 1 e. red . . . . 1·00 10

1938. Wine and Raisin Congress.

900 106 15 c. violet . . . . 1·00 30
901 25 c. brown . . . . 1·50 60
902 40 c. mauve . . . . 4·50 15
903 1 e. 75 blue . . . . 14·00 6·00

1940. Portuguese Legion.

904 107 5 c. yellow 25 10
905 10 c. violet 35 10
906 15 c. blue 35 10
907 25 c. brown . . . . 7·00 25
908 40 c. green . . . . 12·00 10
909 80 c. green . . . . 1·00 20
910 1 e. red . . . . 14·00 55
911 1 e. 75 blue . . . . 3·75 65

109 Portuguese World Exhibition

113 Sir Rowland Hill

1940. Portuguese Centenaries.

912 109 10 c. red 10 10
913 – 15 c. blue 10 10
914 – 25 c. olive 35 15
915 – 35 c. green 25 20
916 – 40 c. brown 70 10
917 109 80 c. purple . . . . 1·75 15
918 – 1 e. red . . . . 5·00 60
919 – 1 e. 75 blue . . . . 2·50 90

DESIGNS—VERT: 15, 35 c. Statue of King Joao IV; 25 c., 1 e. Monument of Discoveries, Belem; 40 c., 1 e. 75, King Afonso Henriques.

1940. Cent of First Adhesive Postage Stamps.

920 113 15 c. purple 25 15
921 25 c. red 25 15
922 35 c. green 25 20
923 40 c. purple 25 10
924 50 c. green . . . . 4·50 2·00
925 80 c. blue 50 60
926 1 e. red . . . . 5·50 2·50
927 1 e. 75 blue . . . . 2·50 1·25

114 Fish-woman of Nazare

115 Caravel

1941. Costumes.

932 114 4 c. green 15 10
933 – 5 c. brown 15 10
934 – 10 c. purple . . . . 1·25 30
935 – 15 c. green 15 10
936 – 25 c. purple 70 15
937 – 40 c. green 15 10
938 – 80 c. blue . . . . 1·00 80
939 – 1 c. red . . . . 2·50 35
940 – 1 e. 75 blue . . . . 2·50 1·25
941 – 2 e. orange . . . . 13·00 8·50

DESIGNS: 5 c. Woman from Colmbra; 10 c. Vine-grower of Salolo; 15 c. Fish-woman of Lisbon; 25 c. Woman of Olhao; 40 c. Woman of Aveiro; 80 c. Shepherdess of Madeira; 1 e. Spinner of Viana do Castelo; 1 e. 75, Horse-breeder of Ribatejo; 2 e. Reaper of Alentejo;

1943.

942 115 5 c. black 10 10
943 10 c. red 10 10
944 15 c. grey 10 10
945 20 c. violet 10 10
946 30 c. brown 10 10
947 35 c. green 10 10
948 50 c. purple 10 10

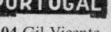

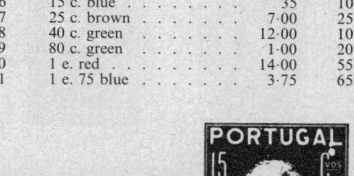

No.	Type	Description	Mint	Used
948a	**115**	80 c. green	1·25	20
949		1 e. red	1·75	10
949a		1 e. lilac	90	10
949b		1 e. 20 red	1·40	10
949c		1 e. 50 olive	11·00	10
950		1 e. 75 blue	7·00	25
950a		1 e. 80 orange	12·50	1·40
951		2 e. red	55	10
951a		2 e. blue	1·75	10
952		2 e. 50 red	90	10
953		3 e. 50 blue	2·75	25
953a		4 e. orange	14·00	90
954		5 e. salmon	40	10
954a		6 e. green	25·00	1·50
954b		7 e. 50 green	7·50	1·50
955		10 e. grey	60	10
956		15 e. green	6·00	30
957		20 e. olive	17·00	10
958		50 e. orange	65·00	35

116 Labourer

117 Mounted Postal Courier

1943. 1st Agricultural Science Congress.

No.	Type	Description	Mint	Used
959	**116**	10 c. blue	30	10
960		50 c. red	40	10

1944. 3rd National Philatelic Exn, Lisbon.

No.	Type	Description	Mint	Used
961	**117**	10 c. brown	15	10
962		50 c. violet	15	10
963		1 e. red	1·25	25
964		1 e. 75 blue	1·25	75

118 Felix Avellar Brotero

120 Vasco da Gama

1944. Birth Bicentenary of Avellar Brotero (botanist).

No.	Type	Description	Mint	Used
965	**118**	10 c. brown	25	10
966	–	50 c. green	50	15
967	–	1 e. red	1·75	30
968	**118**	1 e. 75 blue	1·50	50

DESIGN: 50 c., 1 e. Brotero's statue, Coimbra.

1945. Portuguese Navigators.

No.	Type	Description	Mint	Used
969	–	10 c. brown	15	10
970	–	30 c. orange	15	10
971	–	35 c. green	25	15
972	**120**	50 c. olive	40	10
973	–	1 e. red	1·50	25
974	–	1 e. 75 blue	1·75	70
975	–	2 e. black	2·00	80
976	–	3 e. 50 red	4·00	1·75

PORTRAITS: 10 c. Gil Eanes; 30 c. Joao Gonvalves Zarco; 35 c. Bartolomeu Dias; 1 e. Pedro Alvares Cabral; 1 e. 75, Fernao de Magalhaes (Magellan); 2 e. Frey Goncalo Velho; 3 e. 50, Diogo Cao.

121 President Carmona

122

1945.

No.	Type	Description	Mint	Used
977	**121**	10 c. violet	10	10
978		30 c. brown	10	10
979		35 c. green	15	10
980		50 c. olive	30	10
981		1 e. red	2·75	15
982		1 e. 75 blue	2·40	75
983		2 e. purple	12·00	1·50
984		3 e. 50 slate	7·00	2·75

1945. Naval School Centenary.

No.	Type	Description	Mint	Used
985	**122**	10 c. brown	10	10
986		50 c. green	15	10
987		1 e. red	1·50	25
988		1 e. 75 blue	1·60	1·10

123 Almourol Castle

1946. Portuguese Castles.

No.	Type	Description	Mint	Used
989	–	10 c. purple	10	10
990	–	30 c. brown	15	10
991	–	35 c. olive	20	10
992	–	50 c. grey	25	10
993	**123**	1 e. red	5·50	50
994	–	1 e. 75 blue	4·50	1·00
995	–	2 e. green	12·00	1·25
996	–	3 e. 50 brown	7·00	2·25

DESIGNS: Castles at Silves (10 c.); Leiria (30 c.); Feira (35 c.); Guimaraes (50 c.); Lisbon (1 e. 75); Braganza (2 e.) and Ourem (3 e. 50).

124 "Decree Founding National Bank"

125 Madonna and Child

1946. Centenary of Bank of Portugal.

No.	Type	Description	Mint	Used
997	**124**	50 c. blue	15	10

1946. Tercentenary of Proclamation of St. Mary of Castile as Patron Saint of Portugal.

No.	Type	Description	Mint	Used
998	**125**	30 c. grey	20	15
999		50 c. green	20	10
1000		1 e. red	1·10	45
1001		1 e. 75 blue	1·60	85

126 Caramulo Shepherdess

127 Surrender of the Keys of Lisbon

1947. Regional Costumes.

No.	Type	Description	Mint	Used
1002	**126**	10 c. mauve	15	15
1003	–	30 c. red	15	15
1004	–	35 c. green	15	15
1005	–	50 c. brown	20	10
1006	–	1 e. red	4·25	40
1007	–	1 e. 75 blue	4·00	1·00
1008	–	2 e. blue	17·00	1·50
1009	–	3 e. 50 green	10·00	2·25

COSTUMES: 30 c. Malpique timbrel player; 35 c. Monsanto flautist; 50 c. Woman of Avintes; 1 e. Maia field labourer; 1 e. 75, Woman of Algarve; 2 e. Miranda do Douro bastonet player; 3 e. 50, Woman of the Azores.

1947. 800th Anniv of Recapture of Lisbon from the Moors.

No.	Type	Description	Mint	Used
1010	**127**	5 c. green	10	10
1011		20 c. red	15	15
1012		50 c. violet	25	10
1013		1 e. 75 blue	2·00	1·60
1014		2 e. 50 brown	3·00	3·00
1015		3 e. 50 black	5·00	5·00

128 St. Joao de Brito

1948. Birth Tercentenary of St. Joao de Brito.

No.	Type	Description	Mint	Used
1016	**128**	30 c. green	20	10
1017	–	50 c. brown	20	10
1018	**128**	1 e. red	2·40	60
1019	–	1 e. 75 blue	3·50	1·00

DESIGN: 50 c., 1 e. 75, St. Joao de Brito (different).

130 "Architecture and Engineering"

131 King Joao I

1948. Exhibition of Public Works, and National Congress of Engineering and Architecture.

No.	Type	Description	Mint	Used
1020	**130**	50 c. red	15	10

1949. Portraits.

No.	Type	Description	Mint	Used
1021	**131**	10 c. violet and buff	15	10
1022	–	30 c. green and buff	15	10
1023	–	35 c. green and olive	15	10
1024	–	50 c. blue and light blue	65	15
1025	–	1 e. lake and red	65	10
1026	–	1 e. 75 black and grey	6·00	2·75
1027	–	2 e. blue and light blue	3·00	75
1028	–	3 e. 50 chocolate & brown	11·00	7·50

PORTRAITS: 30 c. Queen Philippa; 35 c. Prince Fernando; 50 c. Prince Henry the Navigator; 1 e. Nun Alvares; 1 e. 75, Joao da Regras; 2 e. Fernao Lopes; 3 e. 50, Afonso Domingues.

132 Statue of Angel

133 Hands and Letter

1949. 16th Congress of the History of Art.

No.	Type	Description	Mint	Used
1029	**132**	1 e. red	3·25	10
1030		5 e. brown	40	10

1949. 75th Anniv of U.P.U.

No.	Type	Description	Mint	Used
1031	**133**	1 e. lilac	15	10
1032		2 e. blue	35	15
1033		2 e. 50 green	1·50	40
1034		4 e. brown	4·50	2·00

134 Our Lady of Fatima

135 Saint and Invalid

1950. Holy Year.

No.	Type	Description	Mint	Used
1035	**134**	50 c. green	35	20
1036		1 e. brown	1·50	10
1037		2 e. blue	2·00	60
1038		5 e. lilac	12·00	2·25

1950. 400th Death Anniv of San Juan de Dios.

No.	Type	Description	Mint	Used
1039	**135**	20 c. violet	25	10
1040		50 c. red	35	10
1041		1 e. green	60	10
1042		1 e. 50 orange	5·00	1·00
1043		2 e. blue	3·25	55
1044		4 e. brown	12·00	2·25

136 G. Junqueiro

137 Fisherman

1951. Birth Centenary of Junqueiro (poet).

No.	Type	Description	Mint	Used
1045	**136**	50 c. brown	1·25	25
1046		1 e. blue	30	10

1951. Fisheries Congress.

No.	Type	Description	Mint	Used
1047	**137**	50 c. green on buff	1·40	40
1048		1 e. purple on buff	35	10

138 Dove and Olive Branch

139 15th Century Colonists

1951. Termination of Holy Year.

No.	Type	Description	Mint	Used
1049	**138**	20 c. brown on buff	20	10
1050		90 c. green and yellow	1·25	50
1051	–	1 e. purple and pink	1·10	10
1052	–	2 e. 30 green and blue	2·00	45

PORTRAIT: 1 e., 2 e. 30, Pope Pius XII.

1951. 500th Anniv of Colonization of Terceira, Azores.

No.	Type	Description	Mint	Used
1053	**139**	50 c. blue	90	30
1054		1 e. brown	90	30

140 Revolutionaries

141 Coach of King Joao VI

1951. 25th Anniv of National Revolution.

No.	Type	Description	Mint	Used
1055	**140**	1 e. purple	1·10	10
1056		2 e. 30 blue	80	60

1952. National Coach Museum.

No.	Type	Description	Mint	Used
1057	–	10 c. purple	15	10
1058	**141**	20 c. olive	15	10
1059	–	50 c. green	25	10
1060	–	90 c. green	1·00	90
1061	–	1 e. orange	50	10
1062	–	1 e. 40 red	2·25	2·25
1063	**141**	1 e. 50 brown	2·75	90
1064	–	2 e. 30 blue	90	40

DESIGNS (coaches of): 10, 90 c. King Felippe II; 50 c., 1 e. 40, Papal Nuncio to Joao V; 1, 2 e. 30, King Jose.

142 "N.A.T.O."

143 Hockey Players

1952. 3rd Anniv of N.A.T.O.

No.	Type	Description	Mint	Used
1065	**142**	1 e. green	5·00	50
1066		3 e. 50 blue	95·00	12·00

1952. 8th World Roller-skating Hockey Championships.

No.	Type	Description	Mint	Used
1067	**143**	1 e. black and blue	2·25	15
1068		3 e. 50 black and brown	3·75	1·40

144 Prof. G. Teixeira

145 Marshal Carmona Bridge

1952. Birth Centenary of Prof. Gomes Teixeira (mathematician).

No.	Type	Description	Mint	Used
1069	**144**	1 e. purple and pink	40	10
1070		2 e. 30 dp blue and blue	2·75	2·00

1952. Centenary of Ministry of Public Works.

No.	Type	Description	Mint	Used
1071	**145**	1 e. brown on cream	40	10
1072	–	1 e. 40 lilac on cream	3·50	2·50
1073	–	2 e. green on cream	1·75	75
1074	–	3 e. 50 blue on cream	3·75	1·25

DESIGNS: 1 e. 40, 28th May Stadium, Braga; 2 e. Coimbra University; 3 e. 50, Salazar Barrage.

146 St. Francis Xavier

147 Medieval Knight

1952. 4th Death Centenary of St. Francis Xavier.

No.	Type	Description	Mint	Used
1075	**146**	1 e. blue	35	10
1076		2 e. purple	45	15
1077		3 e. 50 blue	8·00	4·50
1078		5 e. lilac	14·00	1·90

1953.

No.	Type	Description	Mint	Used
1079	**147**	5 c. green on yellow	10	10
1080		10 c. grey on pink	10	10
1081		20 c. orange on yellow	10	10
1081a		30 c. purple on buff	10	10
1082		50 c. black	10	10
1083		90 c. green on yellow	4·00	25
1084		1 e. brown on pink	10	10
1085		1 e. 40 red	4·00	40
1086		1 e. 50 red on yellow	15	10
1087		2 e. black	15	10
1088		2 e. 30 blue	7·00	25
1089		2 e. 50 black on pink	30	10
1089a		2 e. 50 green on yellow	30	10
1090		5 e. purple on yellow	40	10
1091		10 e. blue on yellow	60	10
1091a		10 e. green on yellow	1·50	10
1092		20 e. brown on yellow	2·00	10
1093		50 e. lilac	2·50	30

148 St. Martin of Dume

149 G. Gomes Fernandes

1953. 14th Centenary of Landing of St. Martin of Dume on Iberian Peninsula.
1094 **148** 1 e. black and grey . . . 50 15
1095 3 e. 50 brown and yellow 3·75 2·75

1953. Birth Centenary of Fernandes (fire-brigade chief).
1096 **149** 1 e. purple and cream . . 70 10
1097 2 e. 30 blue and cream . . 4·75 3·00

150 Club Emblems, 1903 and 1953 **151** Princess St. Joan

1953. 50th Anniv of Portuguese Automobile Club.
1098 **150** 1 e. green 50 10
1099 3 e. 50 brown . . . . . 4·25 2·75

1953. 5th Centenary of Birth of Princess St. Joan.
1100 **151** 1 e. black and green . . 75 15
1101 3 e. 50 dp blue and blue . 4·50 3·00

152 Queen Maria II

1953. Centenary of First Portuguese Stamps. Bottom panel in gold.
1102 **152** 50 c. lake 15 10
1103 1 e. brown 15 10
1104 1 e. 40 purple 80 70
1105 2 e. 30 blue . . . . . . 1·75 1·00
1106 3 e. 50 blue . . . . . . 1·75 1·25
1107 4 e. 50 gold . . . . . . 1·25 90
1108 5 e. olive . . . . 3·25 60
1109 20 e. violet . . . . 20·00 2·00

153 **154**

1954. 150th Anniv of Trade Secretariat.
1110 **153** 1 e. blue 30 10
1111 1 e. 50 brown 60 25

1954. People's Education Plan.
1112 **154** 50 c. blue 10 10
1113 1 e. red 15 10
1114 2 e. green . . . . 6·00 30
1115 2 e. 50 brown . . . . . 5·50 60

155 Cadet and College Banner **156** Father Manuel da Nobrega

1954. 150th Anniv of Military College.
1116 **155** 1 e. brown and green . . 50 10
1117 3 e. 50 blue and green . . 1·75 1·25

1954. 400th Anniv of Sao Paulo.
1118 **156** 1 e. brown 35 10
1119 2 e. 30 blue . . . . . . 10·00 6·50
1120 3 e. 50 green . . . . . 3·50 70
1121 5 e. green . . . . 9·50 1·75

157 King Sancho I, 1154–1211

158 Telegraph Poles

1955. Portuguese Kings.
1122 – 10 c. purple 10 10
1123 **157** 20 c. green 15 10
1124 – 50 c. turquoise 20 10
1125 – 90 c. turquoise 70 70
1126 – 1 e. brown 30 10
1127 – 1 e. 40 red . . . . . . 2·00 1·75
1128 – 1 e. 50 olive . . . . . . 1·00 55
1129 – 2 e. salmon . . . . . . 2·50 1·50
1130 – 2 e. 30 blue . . . . . . 2·50 1·25
KINGS: 10 c. Afonso I; 50 c. Afonso II; 90 c. Sancho II; 1 e. Afonso III; 1 e. 40, Diniz; 1 e. 50, Afonso IV; 2 e. Pedro I; 2 e. 30, Fernando.

1955. Centenary of Electric Telegraph System in Portugal.
1131 **158** 1 e. red and yellow . . . 25 10
1132 2 e. 30 blue and green . 3·75 1·50
1133 3 e. 50 green and yellow 3·75 1·10

159 A. J. Ferreira da Silva **160** Early Steam Locomotive

1956. Birth Centenary of Ferreira da Silva (teacher).
1134 **159** 1 e. blue 20 10
1135 2 e. 30 green . . . . . 2·25 1·75

1956. Centenary of Portuguese Railways.
1136 **160** 1 e. green & dp green . 20 10
1137 – 1 e. 50 blue & turquoise 75 35
1138 – 2 e. brown and bistre . . 6·00 90
1139 **160** 2 e. 50 brown . . . . . 7·00 1·40
DESIGN: 1 e. 50, 2 e. 1956 electric locomotive.

161 Madonna and Child **162** Almeida Garrett (after Barata Feyo)

1956. Mothers' Day.
1140 **161** 1 e. sage and green . . . 20 10
1141 1 e. 50 olive and brown 40 15

1957. Almeida Garrett (writer) Commem.
1142 **162** 1 e. brown 30 10
1143 2 e. 30 violet . . . . . 6·00 3·50
1144 3 e. 50 green . . . . . 1·00 55
1145 5 e. red . . . . 8·00 4·00

163 Cesario Verde **164** Exhibition Emblem

1957. Cesario Verde (poet) Commem.
1146 **163** 1 e brown, buff & olive . 30 10
1147 3 e. 30 black, ol & sage . 60 45

1958. Brussels International Exhibition
1148 **164** 1 e. multicoloured . . . 35 10
1149 3 e. 30 multicoloured . . 90 70

165 St. Elizabeth

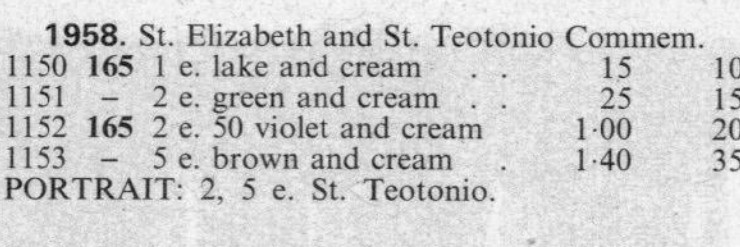

166 Institute of Tropical Medicine, Lisbon

1958. St. Elizabeth and St. Teotonio Commem.
1150 **165** 1 e. lake and cream . . 15 10
1151 – 2 e. green and cream . . 25 15
1152 **165** 2 e. 50 violet and cream . 1·00 20
1153 – 5 e. brown and cream . . 1·40 35
PORTRAIT: 2, 5 e. St. Teotonio.

1958. 6th Int Congress of Tropical Medicine.
1154 **166** 1 e. green and grey . . . 50 10
1155 2 e. 50 blue and grey . . 1·50 55

167 Liner **168** Queen Leonora

1958. 2nd National Merchant Navy Congress.
1156 **167** 1 e. brown, ochre & sepia 70 10
1157 4 e. 50 violet, lav & bl . . 80 60

1958. 500th Birth Anniv of Queen Leonora. Frames and ornaments in bistre, inscriptions and value tablet in black.
1158 **168** 1 e. blue and brown . . . 20 10
1159 1 e. 50 blue 90 30
1160 2 e. 30 blue and green . . 80 30
1161 4 e. 10 blue and grey . . 80 35

169 Arms of Aveiro **170**

1959. Millenary of Aveiro.
1162 **169** 1 e. multicoloured 35 10
1163 5 e. multicoloured . . . . 1·90 55

1960. 10th Anniv of N.A.T.O.
1164 **170** 1 e. black and lilac . . . 50 10
1165 3 e. 50 black and grey . . 1·75 90

171 "Doorway to Peace" **172** Glider

1960. World Refugee Year. Symbol in black.
1166 **171** 20 c. yellow, lemon & brn 10 10
1167 1 e. yellow, green & blue . 30 10
1168 1 e. 80 yellow and green . 30 30

1960. 50th Anniv of Portuguese Aero Club. Multicoloured.
1169 1 e. Type **172** 15 10
1170 1 e. 50 Light monoplane . . . 50 20
1171 2 e. Airplane and parachutes . 80 30
1172 2 e. 50 Model glider . . . . . 1·40 55

173 Padre Cruz (after M. Barata) **174** University Seal

1960. Death Centenary of Padre Cruz.
1173 **173** 1 e. brown 25 10
1174 4 e. 30 blue . . . . 2·25 2·00

1960. 400th Anniv of Evora University.
1175 **174** 50 c. blue 10 10
1176 1 e. brown and yellow . . 15 10
1177 1 e. 40 red 75 75

175 Prince Henry's Arms

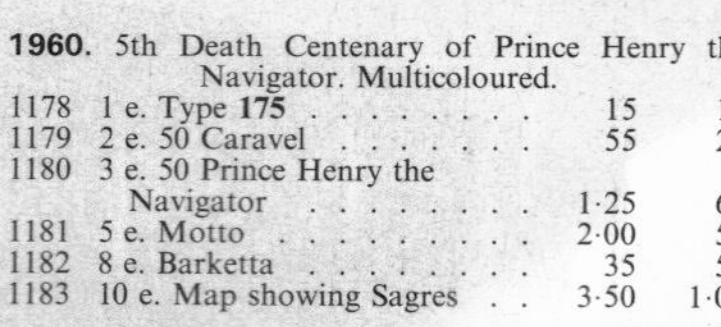

176 Emblems of Prince Henry and Lisbon

1960. 5th Death Centenary of Prince Henry the Navigator. Multicoloured.
1178 1 e. Type **175** 15 10
1179 2 e. 50 Caravel 55 25
1180 3 e. 50 Prince Henry the Navigator . . . . 1·25 65
1181 5 e. Motto . . . . 2·00 50
1182 8 e. Barketta 35 50
1183 10 e. Map showing Sagres . . 3·50 1·00

1960. Europa. As T **129a** of Luxembourg, but size 31 × 21 mm.
1184 1 e. light blue and blue . . . 25 10
1185 3 e. 50 red and lake . . . . 1·75 1·25

1960. 5th National Philatelic Exhibition, Lisbon.
1186 **176** 1 e. blue, black and green 30 10
1187 3 e. 30 blue, black and olive 2·25 2·25

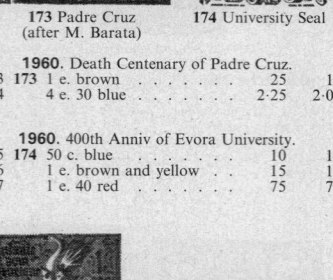

177 Portuguese Flag

178 King Pedro V

1960. 50th Anniv of Republic.
1188 **177** 1 e. multicoloured . . . 10 10

1961. Cent of Lisbon University Faculty of Letters.
1189 **178** 1 e. green and brown . . 30 10
1190 6 e. 50 brown and blue . 70 35

179 Arms of Setubal

180

1961. Centenary of Setubal City.
1191 **179** 1 e. multicoloured . . . 25 10
1192 4 e. 30 multicoloured . . 2·75 2·50

1961. Europa.
1193 **180** 1 e. blue 20 10
1194 1 e. 50 green 50 50
1195 3 e. 50 pink and lake . . 80 80

181 Tomar Gateway

182 National Guardsman

1961. 800th Anniv of Tomar.
1196 – 1 e. multicoloured . . . 30 10
1197 **181** 3 e. 50 multicoloured . . 70 65
DESIGN: 1 e. As Type **181** but without ornamental background.

1962. 50th Anniv of National Republican Guard.
1198 **182** 1 e. multicoloured . . . 10 10
1199 2 e. multicoloured . . . 1·00 30
1200 2 e. 50 multicoloured . . 90 20

183 St. Gabriel (Patron Saint of Telecommunications)

184 Scout Badge and Tents

1962. St. Gabriel Commem.
1201 **183** 1 e. brown and olive . . 35 10
1202 3 e. 50 green, brown & ol 25 25

1962. 18th Int Scout Conference (1961).
1203 **184** 20 c. multicoloured . . . 10 10
1204 50 c. multicoloured . . . 10 10
1205 1 e. multicoloured . . . 40 10
1206 2 e. 50 multicoloured . . 1·40 15
1207 3 e. 50 mulitcoloured . . 40 25
1208 6 e. 50 multicoloured . . 65 40

185 Children with Ball

186 Europa "Honeycomb"

1962. 10th International Paediatrics Congress, Lisbon. Centres in black.
1209 – 50 c. yellow and green . . 10 10
1210 – 1 e. yellow and grey . . 40 10
1211 **185** 2 e. 80 yellow & brown . 50 50
1212 – 3 e. 50 yellow & mauve . 1·00 90
DESIGNS: 50 c. Children with book; 1 e. Inoculating child; 3 e. 50, Weighing baby.

1962. Europa. "EUROPA" in gold.

1213	186	1 e. deep blue and blue	20	10
1214		1 e. 50 dp green & green	60	35
1215		3 e. 50 brown & purple	70	40

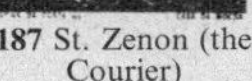

187 St. Zenon (the Courier) 188 Benfica Emblem and European Cup

1962. Stamp Day. Saint in yellow and flesh.

1216	187	1 e. black and purple	15	10
1217		2 e. black and green	60	50
1218		2 e. 80 black and bistre	1·00	1·00

1963. Benfica Club's Double Victory in European Football Cup Championships (1961–62).

1219	188	1 e. multicoloured	70	10
1220		4 e. 30 multicoloured	90	75

189 Campaign Emblem

1963. Freedom from Hunger.

1221	189	1 e. multicoloured	20	10
1222		3 e. 30 multicoloured	60	60
1223		3 e. 50 multicoloured	75	55

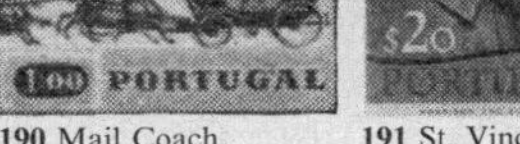

190 Mail Coach 191 St. Vincent de Paul

1963. Centenary of Paris Postal Conference.

1224	190	1 e. blue, light blue and grey	20	10
1225		1 e. 50 multicoloured	60	10
1226		5 e. brown, lilac & orange	30	20

1963. 300th Death Anniv of St. Vincent de Paul. Inscr in gold.

1227	191	20 c. ultram and blue	10	10
1228		1 e. blue and grey	15	10
1229		2 e. 80 black and green	70	65
1230		5 e. grey and mauve	65	55

194 Medieval Knight.

1963. 800th Anniv of Military Order of Avis.

1231	192	1 e. multicoloured	15	10
1232		1 e. 50 multicoloured	25	15
1233		2 e. 50 mulitcoloured	75	45

193 Europa "Dove"

1963. Europa.

1234	193	1 e. grey, blue and black	15	10
1235		2 e. 50 grey, green & blk	85	40
1236		3 e. 50 grey, red & black	1·40	90

194 Supersonic Flight 195 Pharmacist's Jar

1963. 10th Anniv of T.A.P. Airline.

1237	194	1 e. blue and deep blue	20	10
1238		2 e. 50 green and black	60	30
1239		3 e. 50 orange and red	70	60

1964. 400th Anniv of Publication of "Coloquios dos Simples" (Dissertation on Indian herbs and drugs) by Dr. G. d'Orta.

1240	195	50 c. brown, black & bis	10	10
1241		1 e. lake, black & brown	25	10
1242		4 e. 30 blue, blk & grey	2·00	2·25

196 Bank Emblem 197 Sameiro Shrine (Braga)

1964. Centenary of National Overseas Bank.

1243	196	1 e. yellow, olive & blue	15	10
1244		2 e. 50 yellow, olive & grn	85	35
1245		3 e. 50 yellow, olive & brn	50	50

1964. Centenary of Sameiro Shrine

1246	197	1 e. yellow, grey & brn	15	10
1247		2 e. yellow, grey & brn	60	35
1248		5 e. yellow, grn & blue	80	70

198 Europa "Flower" 199 Sun and Globe

1964. Europa.

1249	198	1 e. indigo, light blue and blue	20	10
1250		3 e. 50 brown, orange and purple	80	40
1251		4 e. 30 bronze, yellow and green	1·40	1·25

1964. International Quiet Sun Years.

1252	199	1 e. mulitcoloured	20	10
1253		8 e. multicoloured	70	50

200 Olympic "Rings" 201 E. Coelho (founder)

1964. Olympic Games, Tokyo.

1254	200	20 c. multicoloured	10	10
1255		1 e. multicoloured	15	10
1256		1 e. 50 multicoloured	65	60
1257		6 e. 50 multicoloured	1·00	1·25

1964. Centenary of "Diario de Noticias" (newspaper).

1258	201	1 e. multicoloured	15	10
1259		5 e. multicoloured	65	45

202 Traffic Signals 203 Dom Fernando (second Duke of Braganza)

1965. 1st National Traffic Congress Lisbon.

1260	202	1 e. yellow, red & green	15	10
1261		3 e. 30 green, red & yellow	1·75	1·75
1262		3 e. 50 red, yellow & grn	1·00	55

1965. 500th Anniv of Braganza.

1263	203	1 e. brown and black	10	10
1264		10 e. green and black	75	45

204 Angel and Gateway 205 I.T.U. Emblem

1965. 900th Anniv of Capture of Coimbra from the Moors.

1265	204	1 e. multicoloured	10	10
1266		2 e. 50 multicoloured	85	55
1267		5 e. multicoloured	90	90

1965. Centenary of I.T.U.

1268	205	1 e. olive and brown	15	10
1269		3 e. 50 purple and green	70	50
1270		6 e. 50 blue and green	60	55

206 C. Gulbenkian 207 Red Cross Emblem

1965. 10th Death Anniv of Calouste Gulbenkian (oil industry pioneer and philanthropist).

1271	206	1 e. multicoloured	30	10
1272		8 e. multicoloured	45	40

1965. Centenary of Portuguese Red Cross.

1273	207	1 e. red, green & black	15	10
1274		4 e. red, olive and black	70	45
1275		4 e. 30 red, brown & black	3·50	3·50

208 Europa "Sprig" 209 North American F-86 Sabre Fighter

1965. Europa.

1276	208	1 e. turquoise, blk & blue	15	10
1277		3 e. 50 flesh, brn & lake	85	55
1278		4 e. 30 light green, black and green	2·40	2·50

1965. 50th Anniv of Portuguese Air Force.

1279	209	1 e. red, green and olive	15	10
1280		2 e. red, green & brown	60	25
1281		5 e. red, green and blue	75	75

210 211 Monogram of Christ

1965. 500th Birth Anniv of Gil Vicente (poet and dramatist). Designs depicting characters from Vicente's poems.

1282	210	20 c. multicoloured	10	10
1283	–	1 e. multicoloured	15	10
1284	–	2 e. 50 multicoloured	1·00	20
1285	–	6 e. 50 multicoloured	45	45

1966. Int Committee for the Defence of Christian Civilisation Congress, Lisbon.

1286	211	1 e. violet, gold & bistre	20	10
1287		3 e. 30 black, gold & pur	1·40	1·40
1288		5 e. black, gold and lake	90	60

212 Emblem of Agriculture Construction and Industry 213 Giraldo the "Fearless"

1966. 40th Anniv of National Revolution.

1289	212	1 e. black, blue & grey	10	10
1290		3 e. 50 brown and bistre	75	60
1291		4 e. purple, lake & pink	70	50

1966. 800th Anniv of Reconquest of Evora.

1292	213	1 e. multicoloured	25	10
1293		8 e. multicoloured	50	40

214 Salazar Bridge 215 Europa "Ship"

1966. Inauguration of Salazar Bridge, Lisbon.

1294	214	1 e. red and gold	30	10
1295		2 e. 50 blue and gold	1·00	30
1296	–	2 e. 80 blue and silver	1·10	85
1297	–	4 e. 30 green and silver	1·10	95

DESIGN—VERT: 2 e. 80, 4 e. 30, Salazar Bridge (different view).

1966. Europa.

1298	215	1 e. multicoloured	10	10
1299		3 e. 50 multicoloured	1·25	75
1300		4 e. 50 multicoloured	1·25	1·00

216 C. Pestana (bacteriologist) 217 Bocage

1966. Portuguese Scientists. Portraits in brown and bistre; background colours given.

1301	216	20 c. green	10	10
1302	–	50 c. orange	10	10
1303	–	1 e. yellow	15	10
1304	–	1 e. 50 light brown	15	10
1305	–	2 e. brown	90	10
1306	–	2 e. 50 green	1·00	25
1307	–	2 e. 80 salmon	1·25	1·00
1308	–	4 e. 30 blue	1·60	1·40

SCIENTISTS: 50 c. E. Moniz (neurologist); 1 e. E. A. P. Coutinho (botanist); 1 e. 50, J. C. de Serra (botanist); 2 e. R. Jorge (hygienist and anthropologist); 2 e. 50, J. L. de Vasconcelos (ethnologist); 2 e. 80, M. Lemos (medical historian); 4 e. 30, J. A. Serrano (anatomist).

1966. Birth Bicentenary (1965) of Manuel M. B. du Bocage (poet).

1309	217	1 e. black, green & bistre	10	10
1310		2 e. black, green & brn	35	15
1311		6 e. black, green & grey	55	40

218 Cogwheels 219 Adoration of the Virgin

1967. Europa.

1312	218	1 e. ultramarine, blk & bl	10	10
1313		3 e. 50 brown, black and salmon	80	45
1314		4 e. 30 bronze, black and green	1·40	1·25

1967. 50th Anniv of Fatima Apparitions. Mult.

1315	1 e. Type 219	10	10
1216	2 e. 80 Fatima Church	50	50
1217	3 e. 50 Virgin of Fatima	25	20
1318	4 e. Chapel of the Apparitions	35	30

220 Roman Senators 221 Lisnave Shipyard

1967. New Civil Law Code.

1319	220	1 e. lake and gold	10	10
1320		2 e. 50 blue and gold	75	50
1321		4 e. 30 green and gold	40	50

1967. Inauguration of Lisnave Shipyard, Lisbon.

1322	221	1 e. multicoloured	10	10
1323	–	2 e. 80 multicoloured	35	30
1324	221	3 e. 50 multicoloured	45	20
1325	–	4 e. 30 multicoloured	60	60

DESIGN: 2 e. 80, 4 e. 30, Section of ship's hull and location map.

222 Serpent Symbol 223 Flags of EFTA Countries

1967. 7th European Rheumatological Congress. Lisbon.

1326	222	1 e. multicoloured	10	10
1327		2 e. multicoloured	55	20
1328		5 e. multicoloured	90	80

1967. European Free Trade Association.

1329	223	1 e. multicoloured	10	10
1330		3 e. 50 multicoloured	50	50
1331		4 e. 30 multicoloured	1·75	2·00

224 Tombstones **225** Bento de Goes

1967. Centenary of Abolition of Death Penalty in Portugal.

1332 **224** 1 e. olive 10 10
1333 2 e. brown 50 20
1334 5 e. green 75 75

1968. Bento de Goes Commem.

1335 **225** 1 e. blue, purple and grn 25 10
1336 8 e. purple, green & brn . 45 30

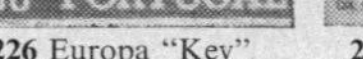

226 Europa "Key" **227** "Maternal Love"

1968. Europa.

1337 **226** 1 e. multicoloured . . . 10 10
1338 3 e. 50 multicoloured . . 75 65
1339 4 e. 30 multicoloured . . 1·60 1·75

1968. 30th Anniv of Organization of Mothers for National Education (O.M.E.N.).

1340 **227** 1 e. black, orge & grey . 15 10
1341 2 e. black, orge & pink . 50 30
1342 5 e. black, orge & blue . 85 1·00

228 "Victory over Disease"

1968. 20th Anniv of W.H.O.

1343 **228** 1 e. multicoloured . . . 15 10
1344 3 e. 50 multicoloured . . 50 30
1345 4 e. 30 multicoloured . . 2·75 3·00

229 Vineyard, Girao

1968. "Lubrapex 1968" Stamp Exhibition "Madeira—Pearl of the Atlantic" Multicoloured.

1346 50 c. Type **229** 10 10
1347 1 e. Firework display 10 10
1348 1 e. 50 Landscape 20 10
1349 2 e. 80 J. Fernandes Vieira (liberator of Pernambuco) . 90 90
1350 3 e. 50 Embroidery 60 50
1351 4 e. 30 J. Goncalves Zarco (navigator) . . . . 2·50 2·50
1352 20 e. "Muschia aurea" . . . 1·75 85

The 2 e. 80 to 20 e. are vert.

230 Pedro Alvares Cabral (from medallion)

1969. 500th Birth Anniv of Pedro Alvares Cabral (explorer).

1353 **230** 1 e. blue 20 10
1354 – 3 e. 50 purple . . . . . 1·75 1·25
1355 – 6 e. 50 multicoloured . . 1·25 80

DESIGNS—VERT: 3 e. 50, Cabral's arms. HORIZ: 6 e. 50, Cabral's fleet (from contemporary documents).

231 Colonnade **232** King Joseph I

1969. Europa.

1356 **231** 1 e. multicoloured . . . 10 10
1357 3 e. 50 multicoloured . . 90 70
1358 4 e. 30 multicoloured . . 1·50 1·40

1969. Centenary of National Press

1359 **232** 1 e. multicoloured . . . 10 10
1360 2 e. multicoloured . . . 65 20
1361 8 e. multicoloured . . . 60 60

233 I.L.O. Emblem **234** J. R. Cabrilho (navigator and coloniser)

1969. 50th Anniv of I.L.O.

1362 **233** 1 e. multicoloured . . . 10 10
1363 3 e. 50 multicoloured . . 50 35
1364 4 e. 30 multicoloured . . 75 75

1969. Bicentenary of San Diego (California)

1365 **234** 1 e. bronze, yell & grn . 10 10
1366 1 e. 50 brown and blue . 70 20
1367 6 e. 50 brown & green . 55 70

235 Vianna da Motta (from painting by C. B. Pinheiro)

1969. Birth Centenary (1968) of Jose Vianna da Motta (concert pianist).

1368 **235** 1 e. multicoloured . . . 30 10
1369 9 e. multicoloured . . . 35 35

236 Coutinho and Fairey IIID Seaplane

1969. Birth Centenary of Gago Coutinho (aviator). Multicoloured.

1370 1 e. Type **236** 15 10
1371 2 e. 80 Coutinho and sextant 75 75
1372 3 e. 30 Type **236** . . . . . 1·25 1·25
1373 4 e. 30 As No. 1371 . . . . 1·25 1·25

237 Vasco da Gama

1969. 500th Birth Anniv of Vasco da Gama. Multicoloured.

1374 1 e. Type **237** 15 10
1375 2 e. 50 Arms of Vasco da Gama 1·60 1·60
1376 3 e. 50 Route map (horiz) . 1·25 75
1377 4 e. Vasca da Gama's fleet (horiz) . . . . 1·00 40

238 "Flaming Sun" **239** Distillation Plant and Pipelines

1970. Europa.

1378 **238** 1 e. cream and blue . . . 20 10
1379 3 e. 50 cream and brown 1·10 60
1380 4 e. 30 cream and green 1·90 60

1970. Inauguration of Porto Oil Refinery.

1381 **239** 1 e. blue 10 10
1382 – 2 e. 80 black and green . 1·00 1·00
1383 **239** 3 e. 30 olive 70 70
1384 – 6 e. brown 65 55

DESIGN: 2 e. 80, 6 e. Catalytic cracking plant and pipelines.

240 Marshal Carmona (from sculpture by L. de Almeida)

1970. Birth Centenary of Marshal Carmona.

1385 **240** 1 e. green 10 10
1386 2 e. 50 blue and red . . . 80 30
1387 7 e. blue 60 60

241 Station Badge

1970. 25th Anniv of Plant Breeding Station.

1388 **241** 1 e. multicoloured 10 10
1389 2 e. 50 multicoloured . . 55 25
1390 5 e. multicoloured 70 45

242 Emblem within Cultural Symbol

1970. Expo 70. Multicoloured.

1391 1 e. Compass (postage) . . . 10 10
1392 5 e. Christian symbol . . . 45 35
1393 6 e. 50 symbolic initials . . . 90 1·00
1394 3 e. 50 Type **242** (air) 35 20

243 Wheel and Star

1970. Centenaries of Covilha (Nos. 1345/6) and Santarem (Nos. 1347/8). Multicoloured.

1395 1 e. Type **243** 10 10
1397 1 e. Castle 10 10
1396 2 e. 80 Ram and weaving frame 1·40 1·40
1398 4 e. Two knights 65 40

244 "Great Eastern" laying Cable

1970. Centenary of Portugal–England Submarine Telegraph Cable.

1399 **244** 1 e. black, blue & green . 15 10
1400 2 e. 50 black, green and cream 80 25
1401 – 2 e. 80 multicoloured . . 1·40 1·40
1402 – 4 e. multicoloured 80 45

DESIGN: 2 e. 80, 4 e. Cable cross-section.

245 Harvesting Grapes **246** Mountain Windmill, Bussaco Hills

1970. Port Wine Industry. Multicoloured.

1403 50 c. Type **245** 10 10
1404 1 e. Harvester and jug . . . 10 10
1405 3 e. 50 Wine-glass and wine barge 60 10
1406 7 e. Wine-bottle and casks . . 60 30

1971. Portuguese Windmills.

1407 **246** 20 c. red, black & brown 10 10
1408 – 50 c. brown, blk & blue . 10 10
1409 – 1 e. purple, blk and grey 10 10
1410 – 2 e. brown, black & mve 50 10
1411 – 3 e. 30 brown, black & bis 1·50 1·25
1412 – 5 e. brown, black & grn . 1·10 30

WINDMILLS: 50 c. Beira Litoral Province; 1 e. "Salolo" type Estremadura Province; 2 e. St. Miguel Azores; 3 e. 30, Porto Santo, Madeira; 5 e. Pico Azores.

247 Europa Chain **248** F. Franco

1971. Europa.

1413 **247** 1 e. green, blue & black . 15 10
1414 3 e. 50 yellow, brn & blk 95 15
1415 7 e. 50 brown, grn & blk 1·50 1·25

1971. Portuguese Sculptors.

1416 **248** 20 c. black 10 10
1417 – 1 e. brown 10 10
1418 – 1 e. 50 brown 20 10
1419a – 2 e. 50 blue 50 10
1420 – 3 e. 50 red 55 15
1421 – 4 e. green . . . . 1·10 1·00

DESIGNS: 1 e. A. Lopes; 1 e. 50, A. de Costa Mota; 2 e. 50, R. Gameiro; 3 e. 50, J. Simoes de Almeida (the Younger); 4 e. F. dos Santos.

249 Pres. Salazar **250** Wolframite

1971. Pres. Antonio Salazar Commemoration

1422 **249** 1 e. brown, green & orge 10 10
1423 5 e. brown, pur & orge . 55 15
1424 10 e. brown, blue & orge 85 45

1971. 1st Spanish–Portuguese–American Congress of Economic Geology. Multicoloured.

1425 1 e. Type **250** 15 10
1426 2 e. 50 Arsenopyrite . . . . 1·25 35
1427 3 e. 50 Beryllium 50 10
1428 6 e. 50 Chalcopyrite 85 45

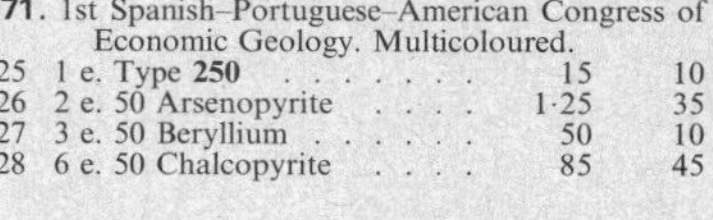

251 Town Gate **252** Weather Equipment

1971. Bicentenary of Castelo Branco. Mult.

1429 1 e. Type **251** 10 10
1430 3 e. Town square and monument 65 40
1431 12 e. 50 Arms of Castelo Branco (horiz) 75 35

1971. 25th Anniv of Portuguese Meteorological Services. Multicoloured.

1432 1 e. Type **252** 10 10
1433 4 e. Weather balloon 75 45
1434 6 e. 50 weather satellite . . . 50 35

253 Drowning Missionaries **254** Man and his Habitat

1971. 400th Anniv of Martyrdom of Brazil Missionaries.

1435 **253** 1 e. black, blue & grey . 10 10
1436 3 e. 30 black, pur & brn 70 70
1437 4 e. 80 black, grn & olive 75 75

1971. Nature Conservation. Multicoloured.

1438 1 e. Type **254** 10 10
1439 3 e. 30 Horses and trees ("Earth") 25 25
1440 3 e. 50 Birds ("The Atmosphere") 35 10
1441 4 e. 50 Fishes ("Water") . . 1·10 80

255 Clerigos Tower, Oporto

1972 Buildings and Views.

1442 – 5 c. grey, black & green . . . 10 5
1443 – 10 c. black, green & blue . . . 10 5
1444 – 30 c. sepia, brown & yell . . . 10 5
1445 – 50 c. blue, orange & blk . . . 8 5
1446p 255 1 e. black, brown & grn . . . 30 10
1447 – 1 e. 50 brown bl & blk . . . 10 10
1448p – 2 e. black, brown & pur . . . 30 10
1449p – 2 e. 50 brown, light brown and grey . . . 10 10
1450 – 3 e. yellow, blk & brn . . . 15 10
1451p – 3 e. 50 green, orge & brn . . . 15 10
1452 – 4 e. black, yellow & bl . . . 40 10
1453 – 4 e. 50 black, brn & grn . . . 65 10
1454 – 5 e. green, brown & blk . . . 3·50 10
1455 – 6 e. brown, green & blk . . . 1·60 20
1456 – 7 e. 50 black, orge & grn . . . 1·00 10
1457 – 8 e. bistre, black & grn . . . 1·50 15
1458 – 10 e. multicoloured . . . 60 10
1459 – 20 e. multicoloured . . . 2·25 10
1460 – 50 e. multicoloured . . . 1·50 20
1461 – 100 e. multicoloured . . . 2·25 50

DESIGNS: 5 c. Aguas Livres aqueduct, Lisbon; 10 c. Lima Bridge; 30 c. Monastery interior, Alcobaca; 50 c. Coimbra University; 1 e. 50, Belem Tower, Lisbon; 2 e. Domus Municipalis, Braganza; 2 e. 50, Castle, Vila de Feira; 3 e. Misericord House, Viana do Castelo; 3 e. 50, Window, Tomar Convent; 4 e. Gateway, Braga; 4 e. 50, Dolmen of Carrazeda; 5 e. Roman Temple, Evora; 6 e. Monastery, Leca do Balio; 7 e. 50, Almourol Castle; 8 e. Ducal Palace, Guimaraes. (31 × 22 mm); 10 e. Cape Girao, Madeira; 20 e. Episcopal Garden, Castelo Branco; 50 e. Town Hall, Sintra; 100 e. Seven cities' Lake, Sao Miguel. Azores.

256 Arms of Pinhel — 257 Heart and Pendulum

1972. Bicentenary of Pinhel's Status as a City. Multicoloured.

1464 1 e. Type **256** . . . 10 10
1465 2 e. 50 Balustrade (vert) . . . 60 15
1466 7 e. 50 Lantern on pedestal (vert) . . . 50 35

1972 World Heart Month.

1467 257 1 e. red and lilac . . . 10 10
1468 – 4 e. red and green . . . 1·25 65
1469 – 9 e. red and brown . . . 50 30

DESIGNS: 4 e. Heart in spiral; 9 e. Heart and cardiogram trace.

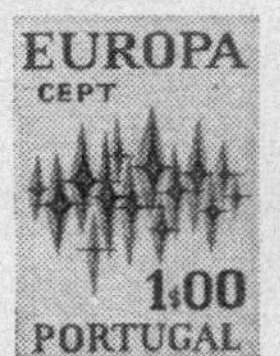

258 "Communications" — 259 Container Truck

1972. Europa.

1470 258 1 e. multicoloured . . . 10 10
1471 3 e. 50 multicoloured . . . 55 25
1472 6 e. multicoloured . . . 1·25 65

1972. 13th International Road Transport Union Congress, Estoril. Multicoloured.

1473 1 e. Type **259** . . . 15 10
1474 4 e. 50 Roof of taxi-cab . . . 1·00 55
1475 8 e. Motor-coach . . . 90 55

260 Football

1972. Olympic Games, Munich. Multicoloured.

1476 50 c. Type **260** . . . 10 10
1477 1 e. Running . . . 10 10
1478 1 e. 50 Show jumping . . . 20 10
1479 3 e. 50 Swimming . . . 30 15
1480 4 e. 50 Sailing . . . 55 40
1481 5 e. Gymnastics . . . 70 40

MINIMUM PRICE

The minimum price quoted is 10p which represents a handling charge rather than a basis for valuing common stamps. For further notes about prices, see introductory pages.

261 Marquis de Pombal — 262 Tome de Sousa

1972. Pombaline University Reforms. Multicoloured.

1482 1 e. Type **261** . . . 10 10
1483 2 e. 50 "The Sciences" (emblems) . . . 80 40
1484 8 e. Arms of Coimbra Univesity . . . 80 65

1972. 150th Anniv of Brazilian Independence. Multicoloured.

1485 1 e. Type **262** . . . 10 10
1486 2 e. 50 Jose Bonifacio . . . 35 15
1487 3 e. 50 Dom Pedro IV . . . 40 15
1488 6 e. Dove and globe . . . 70 30

263 Cabral, Coutinho and Seaplane

1972. 50th Anniv of 1st Lisbon–Rio de Janeiro Flight. Multicoloured.

1489 1 e. Type **263** . . . 15 10
1490 2 e. 50 Route map . . . 30 15
1491 2 e. 80 Type **263** . . . 45 40
1492 3 e. 80 As 2 e. 50 . . . 60 55

264 Camoens

1972. 400th Anniv of Camoens' "Lusiads" (epic poem)

1493 264 1 e. yellow, brown & black . . . 10 10
1494 – 3 e. blue, green & black . . . 60 20
1495 – 10 e. brown, purple & blk . . . 80 45

DESIGNS: 3 e. "Saved from the Sea"; 10 e. "Encounter with Adamastor".

265 Graph and Computer Tapes

1973. Portuguese Productivity Conference, Lisbon. Multicoloured.

1496 1 e. Type **265** . . . 10 10
1497 4 e. Computer scale . . . 60 30
1498 9 e. Graphs . . . 55 25

266 Europa "Posthorn" — 268 Child Running

267 Pres. Medici and Arms

1973. Europa.

1499 266 1 e. multicoloured . . . 10 10
1500 4 e. multicoloured . . . 1·25 35
1501 6 e. multicoloured . . . 1·75 70

1973. Visit of Pres. Medici of Brazil. Mult.

1502 1 e. Type **267** . . . 10 10
1503 2 e. 80 Pres. Medici and globe . . . 40 40
1504 3 e. 50 Type **267** . . . 40 40
1505 4 e. 80 As No. 1503 . . . 35 35

1973. "For the Child".

1506 268 1 e. dp blue, blue & brn . . . 10 10
1507 – 4 e. purple, mauve & brn . . . 70 20
1508 – 7 e. 50 orange, orchre and brown . . . 90 60

DESIGNS: 4 e. Child running (to right); 7 e. 50, Child jumping.

269 Transport and Weather map — 270 Child and Written Text

1973. 25th Anniv of Ministry of Communications. Multicoloured.

1509 1 e. Type **269** . . . 35 10
1510 3 e. 80 "Telecommunications" . . . 30 15
1511 6 e. "Postal Services" . . . 70 45

1973. Bicentenary of Primary State School Education. Multicoloured.

1512 1 e. Type **270** . . . 10 10
1513 4 e. 50 Page of children's primer . . . 55 20
1514 5 e. 30 "Schooldays" (child's drawing) (horiz) . . . 60 35
1515 8 e. "Teacher and children" (horiz) . . . 75 60

271 Early Tram-car — 272 League Badge

1973. Centenary of Oporto's Public Transport System. Multicoloured.

1516 1 e. Horse-drawn tramcar . . . 25 10
1517 3 e. 50 Modern bus . . . 90 50
1518 7 e. 50 Type **271** . . . 1·40 40

Nos. 1516/17 are $31\frac{1}{2} \times 31\frac{1}{2}$ mm.

1973. 50th Anniv of Servicemen's League. Multicoloured.

1519 1 e. Type **272** . . . 10 10
1520 2 e. 50 Servicemen . . . 70 30
1521 11 e. Awards and medals . . . 70 35

273 Death of Nuno Goncalves — 274 Damiao de Gois (after Durer)

1973. 600th Anniv of Defence of Faria Castle by the Alcaide, Nuno Goncalves.

1522 273 1 e. green and yellow . . . 10 10
1523 10 e. purple and yellow . . . 45 30

1974. 400th Death Anniv of Damiao de Gois (scholar and diplomat). Multicoloured.

1524 1 e. Type **274** . . . 10 10
1525 4 e. 50 Title-page of Chronicles of "Prince Dom Joao" . . . 45 20
1526 7 e. 50 Lute and "Dodecahordon" score . . . 55 30

275 "The Exile" (A. Soares dos Reis) — 276 Light Emission

1974. Europa

1527 275 1 e. green, blue and olive . . . 10 10
1528 4 e. green, red and yellow . . . 2·00 40
1529 6 e. dp green, green & bl . . . 2·25 70

1974. Inauguration of Satellite Communications Station Network.

1530 276 1 e. 50 green . . . 10 10
1531 – 4 e. 50 blue . . . 90 50
1532 – 5 e. 30 purple . . . 50 30

DESIGNS: 4 e. 50, Spiral Waves; 5 e. 30, Satellite and Earth.

277 "Diffusion of Hertzian Radio Waves"

1974. Birth Centenary of Guglielmo Marconi (radio pioneer). Multicoloured.

1533 1 e. 50 Type **277** . . . 10 10
1534 3 e. 30 "Radio waves across Space" . . . 60 35
1535 10 e. "Radio waves for Navigation" . . . 1·25 50

278 Early Post-boy and Modern Mail Van

1974. Centenary of U.P.U. Multicoloured.

1536 1 e. 50 Type **278** . . . 10 10
1537 2 e. Hand with letters . . . 40 10
1538 3 e. 30 Sailing packet and modern liner . . . 30 10
1539 4 e. 50 Dove and airliner . . . 50 20
1540 5 e. 30 Hand with letter . . . 40 30
1541 20 e. Early and modern railway locomotives . . . 2·50 1·50

279 Luisa Todi — 280 Arms of Beja

1974. Portuguese Musicians.

1543 279 1 e. 50 purple . . . 10 10
1544 – 2 e. red . . . 1·25 10
1545 – 2 e. 50 brown . . . 80 15
1546 – 3 e. blue . . . 60 25
1547 – 5 e. 30 green . . . 70 40
1548 – 11 e. purple . . . 70 55

PORTRAITS: 2 e. Joao Domingos Bomtempo; 2 e. 50, Carlos Seixas; 3 e. E. Duarte Lobo; 5 e. 30, Joao de Sousa Carvalho; 11 e. Marcos Portugal.

1974. Bimillenary of Beja. Multicoloured.

1549 1 e. 50 Type **280** . . . 10 10
1550 3 e. 50 Beja's inhabitants through the ages . . . 85 60
1551 7 e. Moorish arches . . . 1·40 70

281 "The Annunciation" — 282 Rainbow and Dove

1974. Christmas. Multicoloured.

1552 1 e. 50 Type **281** . . . 10 10
1553 4 e. 50 "The Nativity" . . . 1·60 35
1554 10 e. "The Flight into Egypt" . . . 1·50 40

1974. Portuguese Armed Forces Movement of 25 April.

1555 282 1 e. 50 multicoloured . . . 10 10
1556 3 e. 50 multicoloured . . . 1·60 90
1557 5 e. multicoloured . . . 1·50 35

283 Egas Moniz — 284 Farmer and Soldier

1974. Birth Centenary of Professor Egas Moniz (brain surgeon).

1558 283 1 e. 50 brown & orange . . . 10 10
1559 – 3 e. 30 orange & brown . . . 35 20
1560 – 10 e. grey and blue . . . 1·50 35

DESIGNS: 3 e. 30, Nobel Medicine and Physiology Prize medal, 1949; 10 e. Cerebral angiograph (1927).

1975. Portuguese Cultural Progress and Citizens' Guidance Campaign.
1561 **284** 1 e. 50 multicoloured . . 15 10
1562 3 e. multicoloured . . . 70 20
1563 4 e. 50 multicoloured . . 90 50

285 Hands and Dove of Peace **286** "The Hand of God"

1975. 1st Anniv of Portuguese Revolution. Multicoloured.
1564 1 e. 50 Type **285** 10 10
1565 4 e. 50 Hands and dove . . . 1·40 30
1566 10 e. Peace dove and emblem 1·50 50

1975. Holy Year. Multicoloured.
1567 1 e. 50 Type **286** 10 10
1568 4 e. 50 Hand with cross . . . 1·50 40
1569 10 e. Peace dove . . . . . . 2·00 60

287 "The Horseman of the Apocalypse" (detail of 12th cent manuscript) **288** Assembly Building

1975. Europa. Multicoloured.
1570 1 e. 50 Type **287** 20 10
1571 10 e. "Fernando Pessoa" (poet) (A. Negreiros) . . . . . . 2·50 50

1975. Opening of Portuguese Constituent Assembly.
1572 **288** 2 e. black, red & yellow . 15 10
1573 20 e. black, green & yell . 1·90 90

289 Hiking **290** Planting Tree

1975. 36th International Camping and Caravanning Federation Rally. Multicoloured.
1574 2 e. Type **289** 45 10
1575 4 e. 50 Boating and swimming 80 40
1576 5 e. 30 Caravanning 45 40

1975. 30th Anniv of U.N.O. Multicoloured.
1577 2 e. Type **290** 20 10
1578 4 e. 50 Releasing peace dove . 80 20
1579 20 c. Harvesting corn . . . . 1·50 60

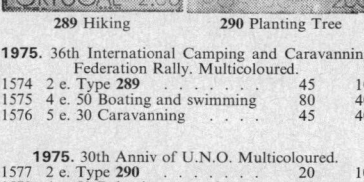

291 Lilienthal Glider and Modern Space Rocket

1975. 26th International Astronautical Federation Congress, Lisbon, Multicoloured.
1580 2 e. Type **291** 20 10
1581 4 e. 50 "Apollo" – "Soyuz" space link 80 40
1582 5 e. 30 R. H. Goddard, R. E. Pelterie, H. Oberth and K. E. Tsiolkovsky (space pioneers) 40 40
1583 10 e. Astronaut and space-ships (70 × 32 mm) . . . . . . 2·25 70

292 Surveying the Land

1975 Centenary of National Geographical Society, Lisbon. Multicoloured.
1584 2 e. Type **292** 20 10
1585 8 e. Surveying the sea . . . 1·00 50
1586 10 e. Globe and people . . . 1·75 60

293 Symbolic Arch **294** Nurse in Hospital Ward

1975. European Architectural Heritage Year.
1587 **293** 2 e. grey, blue & dp blue 20 10
1588 – 8 e. grey and red . . . 1·25 35
1589 – 10 e. multicoloured . . . 1·50 60
DESIGNS: 8 e. Stylized building plan; 10 e. Historical building being protected from development.

1975 International Women's Year. Multicoloured
1590 50 c. Type **294** 10 10
1591 2 e. Woman farm worker . . 65 10
1592 3 e. 50 Woman office worker 75 30
1593 8 e. Woman factory worker . 80 75

295 Pen-nib as Plough Blade

1976. 50th Anniv of National Writers Society.
1595 **295** 3 e. blue and red 25 10
1596 20 e. red and blue . . . 1·75 90

296 First Telephone Set

1976. Telephone Centenary.
1597 **296** 3 e. black, grn & dp grn 45 10
1598 – 10 e. 50 black, red and pink 1·75 55
DESIGNS: 10 e. 50, Alexander Graham Bell.

297 "Industrial Progress" **298** Carved Olive-wood Spoons

1976. National Production Campaign.
1599 **297** 50 c. brown 20 10
1600 – 1 e. green 30 10
DESIGN: 1 e. Consumer goods

1976. Europa. Multicoloured.
1601 3 e. Type **298** 25 10
1602 20 e. Gold ornaments . . . 5·00 2·75

299 Stamp Designing

1976. "Interphil 76". International Stamp Exhibition, Philadelphia. Multicoloured.
1603 3 e. Type **299** 10 10
1604 7 e. 50 Stamp being hand-cancelled 40 30
1605 10 e. Stamp printing 70 35

300 King Fernando promulgating Law

1976. 600th Anniv of Law of "Sesmarias" (uncultivated land). Multicoloured.
1606 3 e. Type **300** 20 10
1607 5 e. Plough and farmers repelling hunters . . . . . 1·10 30
1608 10 e. Corn harvesting . . . 1·40 50

301 Athlete with Olympic Torch

1976. Olympic Games, Montreal. Multicoloured.
1610 3 e. Type **301** 25 10
1611 7 e. Women's relay . . . . . 1·00 75
1612 10 e. 50 Olympic flame . . . 1·50 60

302 "Speaking in the Country"

1976. Literacy Campaign. Multicoloured.
1613 3 e. Type **302** 50 10
1614 3 e. "Speaking at Sea" . . . 50 10
1615 3 e. "Speaking in Town" . . 50 10
1616 3 e. "Speaking at Work" . . 70 10

303 Azure-winged Magpie **304** "Lubrapex" Emblem and Exhibition Hall

1976. "Portucale '77" Thematic Stamp Exhibition, Oporto (1st issue). Multicoloured.
1618 3 e. Type **303** 40 10
1619 5 e. Lynx . . . . 1·00 20
1620 7 e. Portuguese laurel cherry and blue tit . . . . . . 1·25 45
1621 10 e. 50 Little wild carnation and lizard . . . . 1·25 65
See also Nos 1673/8.

1976. "Lubrapex 1976" Luso–Brazilian Stamp Exhibition. Multicoloured.
1622 3 e. Type **304** 15 10
1623 20 e. "Lubrapex" emblem and stamp . . . . 1·90 85

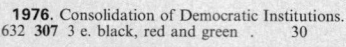

305 Bank Emblem

1976. Centenary of National Trust Fund Bank.
1625 **305** 3 e. multicoloured 10 10
1626 7 e. multicoloured 80 40
1627 15 e. multicoloured . . . 90 60

306 Sheep Grazing **307** "Liberty"

1976 Water Conservation. Protection of Humid Zones. Multicoloured.
1628 1 e. Type **306** 20 10
1629 3 e. Marshland 45 10
1630 5 e. Trout 85 25
1631 10 e. Mallards . . . . 1·60 45

1976. Consolidation of Democratic Institutions.
1632 **307** 3 e. black, red and green . 30 10

308 Examining Child's Eyes

1976. World Health Day. Detection and Prevention of Blindness. Multicoloured.
1633 3 e. Type **308** 15 10
1634 5 e. Welder wearing protective goggles 80 20
1635 10 e. 50 Blind person reading Braille . . . . 1·25 60

309 Hydro-electric Power

1976. Uses of Natural Energy. Multicoloured.
1636 1 e. Type **309** 10 10
1637 4 e. Fossil fuel (oil) 40 10
1638 5 e. Geo-thermic sources . . 50 15
1639 10 e. Wind power 75 35
1640 15 e. Solar energy . . . . . 1·25 55

310 Map of Member Countries **311** Bottle inside Human Body

1977. Admission of Portugal to the Council of Europe.
1641 **310** 8 e. 50 multicoloured . . 60 45
1642 10 e. multicoloured . . . 65 65

1977. 10th Anniv of Portuguese Anti-Alcoholic Society. Multicoloured.
1643 3 e. Type **311** 10 10
1644 5 e. Broken body and bottle 45 15
1645 15 e. Sun behind prison bars and bottle . . . . 1·00 55

312 Forest **313** Exercising

1977. Natural Resources. Forests. Multicoloured.
1646 1 e. Type **312** 10 10
1647 4 e. Cork oaks 30 15
1648 7 e. Logs and trees 75 40
1649 15 e. Trees by the sea 95 85

1977. International Rheumatism Year.
1650 – 4 e. orange, brown & blk 15 10
1651 **313** 6 e. ultramarine, blue and black 65 50
1652 – 10 e. red, mauve & black 70 40
DESIGNS: 4 e. Rheumatism victim; 10 e. Group exercising.

314 Southern Plains **315** John XXI Enthroned

1977. Europa. Multicoloured.
1653 4 e. Type **314** 20 10
1654 8 e. 50 Northern terraced mountains 80 55

1977. 7th Death Centenary of Pope John XXI. Multicoloured.
1656 4 e. Type **315** 20 10
1657 15 e. Pope as doctor 50 25

316 Compass

1977. Camoes Day.
1658 **316** 4 e. multicoloured . . . 15 10
1659 8 e. 50 multicoloured . . 45 45

317 Child and Computer

1977. Permanent Education. Multicoloured.
1660 4 e. Type **317** 25 10
1661 4 e. Flautist and dancers . . 25 10
1662 4 e. Farmer and tractor . . . 25 10
1663 4 e. Students and atomic construction 25 10

318 Pyrite

1977. Natural Resources. The Subsoil. Mult.

1665 4 e. Type **318** 20 10
1666 5 e. Marble 50 15
1667 10 e. Iron ore 65 20
1668 20 e. Uranium . . . . 1·75 75

319 Alexandre Herculano

1977. Death Centenary of Alexandre Herculano (writer and politician).

1669 **319** 4 e. multicoloured 15 10
1670 15 e. multicoloured . . . 60 35

320 Early Locomotive and Peasant Cart (ceramic panel, J. Colaco)

1977. Centenary of Railway Bridge over River Douro. Multicoloured.

1671 4 e. Type **320** 30 10
1672 10 e. Maria Pia bridge (Eiffel) 1·50 1·00

321 Poviero (Northern coast)

1977. "Portucale 77" Thematic Stamp Exhibition, Oporto (2nd issue). Coastal Fishing Boats. Multicoloured.

1673 2 e. Type **321** 35 10
1674 3 e. Sea-going rowing boat, Furadouro 20 10
1675 4 e. Boat from Nazare . . . 25 10
1676 7 e. Caique from Algarve . . 35 15
1677 10 e. Tunny fishing boat, Algarve 65 30
1678 15 e. Boat from Buarcos . . 1·00 45

322 "The Adoration" (Maria do Sameiro A. Santos)

1977. Christmas. Children's Paintings. Mult.

1680 4 e. Type **322** 15 10
1681 7 e. "Star over Bethlehem" (Paula Maria L. David) . . 55 15
1682 10 e. "The Holy Family" (Carla Maria M. Cruz) (vert) . . 60 20
1683 20 e. "Children following the Star" (Rosa Maria M. Cardoso) (vert) . . . . . . 1·75 75

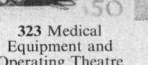

323 Medical Equipment and Operating Theatre

324 Mediterranean Soil

1978. (a) Size 22 × 17 mm.

1684 **323** 50 c. green, blk & red . 10 10
1685 – 1 e. blue, orange and black 10 10
1686 – 2 e. blue, green & brn . 10 10
1687 – 3 e. ochre, olive and black 10 10
1688 – 4 e. green, blue & brn 10 10
1689 – 5 e. blue, green & brn . 15 10
1690 – 5 e. 50 brown, buff and olive 15 10
1691 – 6 e. brown, yell & grn . 25 10
1692 – 6 e. 50 blue, deep blue and olive 15 10
1693 – 7 e. black, grey & bl . . 25 10
1694 – 8 e. ochre, brown and grey 20 10
1694a – 8 e. 50 brown, blk & ochre 25 10
1695 – 9 e. yellow, brn & blk . 20 10
1696 – 10 e. ochre, blk & grn . 25 10
1697 – 12 e. 50 blue, brown and black 20 10
1698 – 16 e. violet, brown and black 25 10

(b) Size 30 × 21 mm.

1699a – 20 e. multicoloured . . 35 15
1700 – 30 e. multicoloured . . 50 20
1701 – 40 e. multicoloured . . 80 15
1702 – 50 e. multicoloured . . 90 15
1703 – 100 e. multicoloured . . 1·75 55
1703a – 250 e. multicoloured . . 3·00 60

DESIGNS: 1 e Old and modern kitchen equipment; 2 e. Telegraph key and masts, microwaves and dish aerial; 3 e. Dressmaking and ready-to-wear clothes; 4 e. Writing desk and computer; 5 e. Tunny fishing boats and modern trawler; 5 e. 50, Manual and mechanical weaver's looms; 6 e. Plough and tractor; 6 e. 50, Monoplane and B.A.C. One Eleven airliner; 7 e. Hand press and modern printing press; 8 e. Carpenter's hand tools and mechanical tool; 8 e. 50, Potter's wheel and modern ceramic machinery; 9 e. Old cameras and modern cine and photo cameras; 10 e. Axe, saw and mechanical saw; 12 e. 50, Navigation and radar instruments; 16 e. Manual and automatic mail sorting; 20 e. Hand tools and building site; 30 e. Hammer, anvil, bellows and industrial complex; 40 e. Peasant cart and lorry; 50 e. Alembic, retorts and modern chemical plant; 100 e. Carpenter's shipyard, modern shipyard and tanker; 250 e. Survey instruments.

1978. Natural Resources. Soil. Mult.

1704 4 e. Type **324** 20 10
1705 5 e. Rock formation 30 10
1706 10 e. Alluvial soil 40 25
1707 20 e. Black soil . . . . . . 1·40 40

325 Pedestrian on Zebra Crossing

1978. Road Safety.

1708 **325** 1 e. blue, black & orge . 10 10
1709 – 2 e. blue, black & grn . 20 10
1710 – 2 e. 50 blue, blk & lt bl . 30 10
1711 – 5 e. blue, black & red . 50 10
1712 – 9 e. blue, blk & brt blue 70 40
1713 – 12 e. 50 blue, blk & brn 1·25 60

DESIGNS: 2 e. Motor cyclist; 2 e. 50, Children in back of car; 5 e. Driver in car; 9 e. View of road from driver's seat; 12 e. 50, Road victim ("Don't drink and drive").

326 Roman Tower of Centum Cellas, Belmonte

327 Roman Bridge, Chaves

1978. Europa. Multicoloured.

1714 10 e. Type **326** 35 10
1715 40 e. Belem Monastery, Lisbon 1·25 65

1978. 19th Century of Chaves (Aquae Flaviae). Multicoloured.

1717 5 e. Type **327** 15 10
1718 20 e. Inscribed tablet from bridge 90 60

328 Running

1978. Sport for All. Multicoloured.

1719 5 e. Type **328** 15 10
1720 10 e. Cycling 30 15
1721 12 e. 50 Swimming 60 60
1722 15 e. Football 55 45

329 Pedro Nunes

1978. 400th Death Anniv of Pedro Nunes (cosmographer). Multicoloured.

1723 5 e. Type **329** 20 10
1724 20 e. Nonio (navigation instrument) and diagram . 1·10 30

330 Trawler, Crates of Fish and Lorry

1978. Natural Resources. Fish. Multicoloured.

1725 5 e. Type **329** 15 10
1726 9 e. Trawler and dockside cranes 25 15
1727 12 e. 50 Trawler, radar and lecture 50 40
1728 15 e. Trawler with echo-sounding equipment and laboratory 70 40

331 Post Rider

1978. Introduction of Post Code. Multicoloured.

1729 5 e. Type **331** 25 10
1730 5 e. Pigeon with letter 25 10
1731 5 e. Sorting letters 25 10
1732 5 e. Pen-nib and post codes . 25 10

332 Symbolic Figure

1978. 30th Anniv of Declaration of Human Rights. Multicoloured.

1733 14 e. Type **332** 30 15
1734 40 e. Similar symbolic figure, but facing right 80 55

333 Sebastiao Magalhaes Lima

1978. 50th Death Anniv of Magalhaes Lima (journalist and pacifist).

1736 **333** 5 e. multicoloured 15 10

334 Portable Post Boxes and Letter Balance

1978. Centenary of Post Museum. Multicoloured.

1737 4 e. Type **334** 15 10
1738 5 e. Morse equipment 15 10
1739 10 e. Printing press and Portuguese stamps of 1853 (125th anniv) 30 15
1740 14 e. Books, bookcase and entrance to Postal Library (centenary) 55 65

335 Emigrant at Railway Station

1979. Portuguese Emigrants. Multicoloured.

1742 5 e. Type **335** 30 10
1743 14 e. Emigrants at airport . . 35 20
1744 17 e. Man greeting child at railway station 90 65

336 Traffic

337 N.A.T.O. Emblem

1979. Fight Against Noise. Multicoloured.

1745 4 e. Type **336** 10 10
1746 5 e. Pneumatic drill 15 10
1747 14 e. Loud hailer 50 25

1979. 30th Anniv of N.A.T.O.

1748 **337** 5 e. blue, red & brown . 10 10
1749 50 e. blue, yellow and red 1·25 1·25

338 Door-to-door Delivery

1979. Europa. Multicoloured.

1751 14 e. Postal messenger delivering letter in cleft stick 30 15
1752 40 e. Type **338** 80 65

339 Children playing Ball

1979. International Year of the Child. Multicoloured.

1754 5 e. 50 Type **339** 15 10
1755 6 e. 50 Mother, baby and dove 15 10
1756 10 e. Child eating 25 10
1757 14 e. Children of different races 35 25

340 Saluting the Flag

1979. Camoes Day.

1759 **340** 6 e. 50 multicoloured . . 15 10

341 Pregnant Woman

1979. The Mentally Handicapped. Multicoloured.

1761 6 e. 50 Type **341** 15 10
1762 17 e. Boy sitting in cage . . 30 30
1763 20 e. Face, and hands holding hammer and chisel 50 40

342 Children reading Book

1979. 50th Anniv of International Bureau of Education. Multicoloured.

1764 6 e. 50 Type **342** 15 10
1765 17 e. Teaching a deaf child . 45 35

343 Water Cart, Caldas de Monchique

1979. "Brasiliana 79" Philatelic Exhibitions. Portuguese Country Carts. Multicoloured.

1766 2 e. 50 Type **343** 10 10
1767 5 e. 50 Wine sledge, Madeira 10 10
1768 6 e. 50 Wine cart, Upper Douro 10 10
1769 16 e. Covered cart, Alentejo 35 30
1770 19 e. Cart, Mogadouro . . . 40 40
1771 20 e. Sand cart, Murtosa . . 40 30

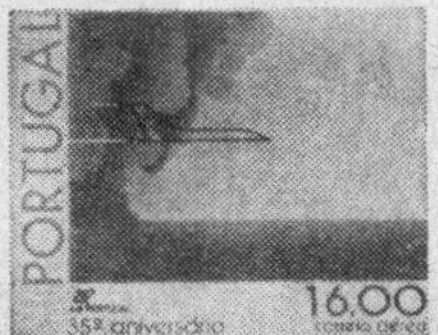

344 Aircraft flying through Storm Cloud

1979. 35th Anniv of TAP National Airline. Multicoloured.
1772 16 e. Type **344** 45 30
1773 19 e. Aircraft and sunset 55 50

345 Antonio Jose de Almeida **346** Family Group

1979. Republican Personalities (1st series).
1774 **345** 5 e. 50 mauve, grey and red 15 10
1775 – 6 e. 50 rose, grey and red 15 10
1776 – 10 e. brown, grey & red 20 10
1777 – 16 e. blue, grey and red 35 25
1778 – 19 e. 50 green, grey and red 40 45
1779 – 20 e. claret, grey and red 40 20
DESIGNS: 6 e. Afonso Costa; 10 e. Teofilo Braga; 16 e. Bernardino Machado; 19 e. 50, Joao Chagas; 20 e. Elias Garcia.
See also Nos. 1787/92.

1979. Towards a National Health Service. Mult.
1780 6 e. 50 Type **346** 15 10
1781 20 e. Doctor examining patient 55 30

347 "The Holy Family"

1979. Christmas. Tile Pictures. Multicoloured.
1782 5 e. 50 Type **347** 15 10
1783 6 e. 50 "Adoration of the Shepherds" 15 10
1784 16 e. "Flight into Egypt" 45 40

348 Rotary Emblem and Globe

1980. 75th Anniv of Rotary International. Mult.
1785 16 e. Type **348** 30 15
1786 50 e. Rotary emblem and torch 1·00 80

349 Jaime Cortesao

1980. Republican Personalities (2nd series).
1787 – 3 e. 50 orange & brown 10 10
1788 – 5 e. 50 green, olive & brn 10 10
1789 – 6 e. 50 lilac and violet 15 10
1790 **349** 11 e. multicoloured 40 50
1791 – 16 e. ochre and brown 40 30
1792 – 20 e. green, blue & lt bl 50 20
DESIGNS: 3 e. 50, Alvaro de Castro; 5 e. 50, Antonio Sergio; 6 e. 50, Norton de Matos; 16 e. Teizeira Gomes; 20 e. Jose Domingues dos Santos.

350 Serpa Pinto

1980. Europa, Multicoloured.
1793 16 e. Type **350** 30 15
1794 60 e. Vasco da Gama 1·00 75

351 Barn Owl

1980. Protection of Species. Animals in Lisbon Zoo. Multicoloured.
1796 6 e. 50 Type **351** 60 10
1797 16 e. Red fox 70 30
1798 19 e. 50 Wolf 1·10 45
1799 20 e. Golden eagle 1·75 45

352 Luis Vaz de Camoes **354** Lisbon and Statue of St. Vincent (Jeronimos Monastery)

353 Pinto in Japan

1980. 400th Death Anniv of Luis Vaz de Camoes (poet).
1801 **352** 6 e. 50 multicoloured 15 10
1802 20 e. multicoloured 40 25

1980. 400th Anniv of Fernao Mendes Pinto's "A Peregrinacao" (The Pilgrimage). Multicoloured.
1803 6 e. 50 Type **353** 15 10
1804 10 e. Sea battle 35 25

1980. World Tourism Conference, Manila, Philippines. Multicoloured.
1805 6 e. 50 Type **354** 15 10
1806 8 e. Lantern Tower, Evora Cathedral 20 15
1807 11 e. Mountain village and "Jesus with top-hat" (Mirando do Douro Cathedral) 30 20
1808 16 e. Canicada dam and "Lady of the Milk" (Braga Cathedral) 55 30
1809 19 e. 50 Aveiro River and pulpit from Santa Cruz Monastery, Coimbra 60 40
1810 20 e. Rocha beach and ornamental chimney, Algarve 60 20

355 Caravel

1980. "Lubrapex 80" Portuguese–Brazilian Stamp Exhibition, Lisbon. Multicoloured.
1811 6 e. 50 Type **355** 20 10
1812 8 e. Nau 25 20
1813 16 e. Galleon 40 30
1814 19 e. 50 Early paddle–steamer with sails 50 40

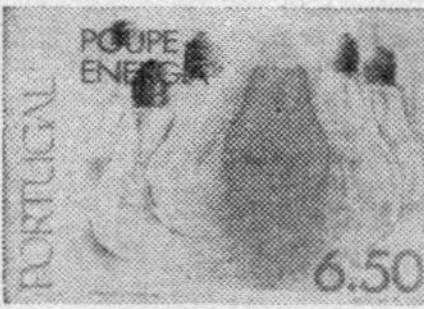

356 Lightbulbs

1980. Energy Conservation. Multicoloured.
1816 6 e. 50 Type **356** 15 10
1817 16 e. Speeding car 50 25

357 Duke of Braganca and Open Book

1980 Bicentenary of Academy of Sciences, Lisbon. Multicoloured.
1818 6 e. 50 Type **357** 15 10
1819 19 e. 50 Uniformed academician, Academy and sextant 60 40

358 Cigarette contaminating Lungs

1980. Anti-Smoking Campaign. Multicoloured.
1820 6 e. 50 Type **358** 20 10
1821 19 e. 50 Healthy figure pushing away hand with cigarette 60 40

359 Head and Computer Punch-card

1981. National Census. Multicoloured.
1822 6 e. 50 Type **359** 15 10
1823 16 e. Houses and punch-card 50 40

360 Fragata, River Tejo **361** "Rajola" Tile from Setubal Peninsula (15th century)

1981. River Boats. Multicoloured.
1824 8 e. Type **360** 25 10
1825 8 e. 50 Rabelo, River Douro 25 10
1826 10 e. Moliceiro, Ria de Aveiro 35 10
1827 16 e. Barco, River Lima 50 25
1828 19 e. 50 Carocho, River Minho 70 35
1829 20 e. Varino, River Tejo 70 20

1981. Tiles (1st issue).
1830 **361** 8 e. 50 multicoloured 25 10
See also Nos. 1843, 1847, 1862, 1871, 1885, 1893, 1902, 1914, 1926, 1935, 1941, 1952, 1970, 1972, 1976, 1983, 1993, 2020 and 2031.

362 Agua Dog

1981. 50th Anniv of Kennel Club of Portugal. Multicoloured.
1832 7 e. Type **362** 25 10
1833 8 e. 50 Serra de Aires 30 10
1834 15 e. Perdigueiro 45 20
1835 22 e. Podengo 65 30
1836 25 e. 50 Castro Laboreiro 75 60
1837 33 e. 50 Serra de Estrella 1·00 50

363 "Agriculture" **364** Dancer and Tapestry

1981. May Day. Multicoloured.
1838 8 e. Type **363** 15 10
1839 25 e. 50 "Industry" 50 45

1981. Europa. Multicoloured.
1840 22 e. Type **364** 40 30
1841 48 e. Painted boat prow, painted plate and shipwright with model boat 80 80

1981. Tiles (2nd issue). Horiz design as T **361**.
1843 8 e. 50 multicoloured 25 10
DESIGN: 8 e. 50, Tracery-pattern tile from Seville (16th century).

365 St. Anthony Writing

1981. 750th Death Anniv of St. Anthony of Lisbon. Multicoloured.
1845 8 e. 50 Type **365** 15 10
1846 70 e. St. Anthony giving blessing 1·40 90

1981. Tiles (3rd series). As T **361**. Mult.
1847 8 e. 50 Arms of Jaime, Duke of Braganca (Seville, 1510) 25 10

366 King Joao II and Caravels

1981. 500th Anniv of King Joao II's Accession. Multicoloured.
1849 8 e. 50 Type **366** 30 10
1850 27 e. King Joao II on horseback 80 50

367 "Dom Luiz" 1862

1981. 125th Anniv of Portuguese Railways. Multicoloured.
1851 8 e. 50 Type **367** 30 10
1852 19 e. Pacific type steam locomotive 1925 70 50
1853 27 e. "Alco 1550" diesel locomotive, 1948 1·00 40
1854 33 e. 50 Alsthom "BB 2600" electric locomotive, 1974 1·25 40

368 "Perrier" Pump, 1856 **369** "Virgin and Child"

1981. Portuguese Fire Engines. Multicoloured.
1855 7 e. Type **368** 20 15
1856 8 e. 50 Ford fire engine, 1927 30 25
1857 27 e. Renault fire pump, 1914 75 25
1858 33 e. 50 Ford "Snorkel" combined hoist and pump, 1978 1·00 75

1981. Christmas Crib Figures. Multicoloured.
1859 7 e. Type **369** 15 15
1860 8 e. 50 "Nativity" 20 10
1861 27 e. "Flight into Egypt" 50 50

1981. Tiles (4th issue). As T **361**. Multicoloured.
1862 8 e. 50 "Pisana" tile, Lisbon (16th century) 20 10

370 St. Francis and Animals **371** Flags of E.E.C. Members

1982. 800th Birth Anniv of St. Francis of Assisi. Multicoloured.
1865 8 e. 50 Type **370** 15 10
1866 27 e. St. Francis helping to build church 60 65

1982. 25th Anniv of European Economic Community.
1867 **371** 27 e. multicoloured 60 40

372 Fort St. Catherina, Lighthouse and Memorial Column

1982. Centenary of Figueira da Foz City. Mult.
1869 10 e. Type **372** 20 10
1870 19 e. Tagus Bridge, shipbuilding yard and trawler 55 50

1982. Tiles (5th issue). As T **361**. Multicoloured.
1871 10 e. Italo-Flemish pattern tile (17th century) 30 10

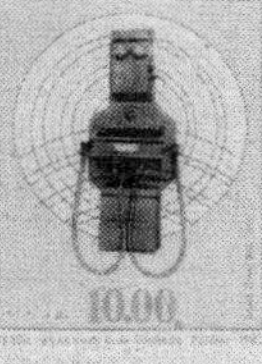

373 "Sagres I" (cadet barque)

374 Edison Gower Bell Telephone, 1883

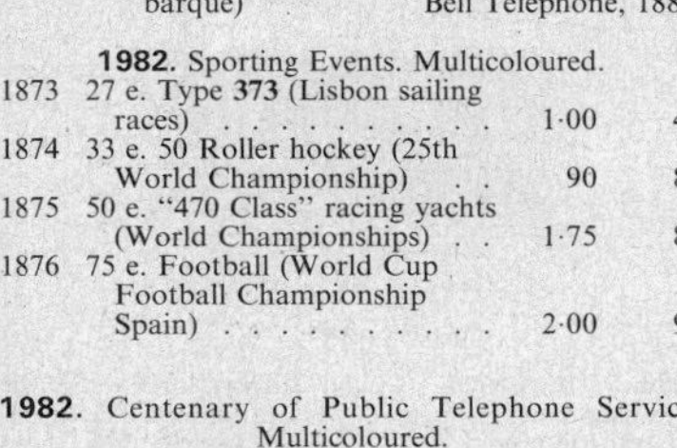

1982. Sporting Events. Multicoloured.

No.	Description	Unused	Used
1873	27 e. Type **373** (Lisbon sailing races)	1·00	40
1874	33 e. 50 Roller hockey (25th World Championship)	90	80
1875	50 e. "470 Class" racing yachts (World Championships)	1·75	85
1876	75 e. Football (World Cup Football Championship Spain)	2·00	90

1982. Centenary of Public Telephone Service. Multicoloured.

No.	Description	Unused	Used
1877	10 e. Type **374**	20	10
1878	27 e. Consolidated telephone, 1887	50	50

375 Embassy of King Manuel to Pope Leo X

1982. Europa.

No.	Type	Description	Unused	Used
1879	**375**	33 e. 50 multicoloured	75	30

376 Pope John Paul II and Shrine of Fatima

277 Dunlin

1982. Papal Visit. Multicoloured.

No.	Description	Unused	Used
1881	10 e. Type **376**	20	10
1882	27 e. Pope and Sameiro Sanctuary	65	50
1883	33 e. 50 Pope and Lisbon Cathedral	85	65

1982. Tiles (6th issue). As T **361**. Multicoloured.

No.	Description	Unused	Used
1885	10 e. Altar front panel depicting oriental tapestry (17th century)	25	10

1982. "Philexfrance 82" International Stamp Exhibition, Paris. Birds. Multicoloured.

No.	Description	Unused	Used
1887	10 e. Type **377**	35	15
1888	19 e. Red-crested pochard	60	40
1889	27 e. Greater flamingo	90	60
1890	33 e. 50 Black-winged stilt	1·10	1·00

378 Dr. Robert Koch

1982. Centenary of Discovery of Tubercle Bacillus. Multicoloured.

No.	Description	Unused	Used
1891	27 e. Type **378**	50	40
1892	33 e. 50 Lungs	60	60

1982. Tiles (7th issue). As T **361**. Multicoloured.

No.	Description	Unused	Used
1893	10 e. Polychromatic quadrilobate pattern, 1630–40	25	10

379 Wine Glass and Stop Sign

1982. "Don't Drink and Drive".

No.	Type	Description	Unused	Used
1895	**379**	10 e. multicoloured	30	10

380 Fairey IIID Seaplane "Lusitania"

1982. "Lubrapex 82" Brazilian–Portuguese Stamp Exhibition, Curitiba. Multicoloured.

No.	Description	Unused	Used
1896	10 e. Type **380**	20	10
1897	19 e. Dornier Do-J Wal flying boat "Argus"	35	30
1898	33 e. 50 Douglas DC-7C "Seven Seas"	60	45
1899	50 e. Boeing 747-282B	90	55

381 Marquis de Pombal

1982. Death Bicentenary of Marquis de Pombal (statesman and reformer).

No.	Type	Description	Unused	Used
1901	**381**	10 e. multicoloured	30	10

1982. Tiles (8th issue). As T **361**. Multicoloured.

No.	Description	Unused	Used
1902	10 e. Monochrome quadrilobate pattern, 1670–90	25	10

382 Gallic Cock and Tricolour

1983. Centenary of French Alliance (French language teaching association).

No.	Type	Description	Unused	Used
1905	**382**	27 e. multicoloured	50	45

383 Lisnave Shipyard

1983. 75th Anniv of Port of Lisbon Administration.

No.	Type	Description	Unused	Used
1906	**383**	10 e. multicoloured	45	15

384 Export Campaign Emblem

1983. Export Promotion

No.	Type	Description	Unused	Used
1907	**384**	10 e. multicoloured	20	15

385 Midshipman, 1782, and Frigate "Vasco da Gama"

386 W.C.Y. Emblem

1983. Naval Uniforms. Multicoloured.

No.	Description	Unused	Used
1908	12 e. 50 Type **385**	30	20
1909	25 e. Seaman and steam corvette "Estefania" 1845	60	25
1910	30 e. Marine sergeant and cruiser "Adamastor" 1900	75	40
1911	37 e. 50 Midshipman and frigate "Joao Belo", 1982	1·10	55

1983. World Cummunications Year. Mult.

No.	Description	Unused	Used
1912	10 e. Type **386**	20	15
1913	33 e. 50 E.C.Y. emblem (diff)	70	60

1983. Tiles (9th issue). As T **361**. Multicoloured.

No.	Description	Unused	Used
1914	12 e. 50 Hunter killing white bull (tile from Saldanha Palace, Lisbon, 17/18th century)	30	10

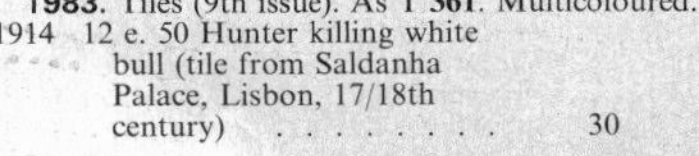

387 Portuguese Helmet (16th century)

1983. "Expo XVII" Council of Europe Exhibition. Multicoloured.

No.	Description	Unused	Used
1916	11 e. Type **387**	20	15
1917	12 e. 50 Astrolabe (16th century)	30	10
1918	25 e. Portuguese caravels (from Flemish tapestry) (16th century)	65	35
1919	30 e. Carved capital (12th century)	60	35
1920	37 e. 50 Hour glass (16th century)	70	35
1921	40 e. Detail from Chinese panel painting (16th-17th century)	75	60

388 Egas Moniz (Nobel Prize winner and brain surgeon)

1983. Europa.

No.	Type	Description	Unused	Used
1923	**388**	37 e. 50 multicoloured	75	30

389 Passenger in Train

1983. European Ministers of Transport Conference.

No.	Type	Description	Unused	Used
1925	**389**	30 e. blue, deep blue and silver	1·25	60

1983. Tiles (10th issue). As T **361**. Multicoloured.

No.	Description	Unused	Used
1926	12 e. 50 Tiles depicting birds (18th century)	30	10

390 Mediterranean Monk Seal

1983. "Brasiliana 83" International Stamp Exhibition Rio de Janeiro. Marine Life. Multicoloured.

No.	Description	Unused	Used
1928	12 e. 50 Type **390**	40	20
1929	30 e. Common dolphin	75	60
1930	37 e. 50 Killer whale	1·00	45
1931	80 e. Humpback whale	2·25	1·00

391 Assassination of Spanish Administrator by Prince John

1983. 600th Anniv of Independence. Mult.

No.	Description	Unused	Used
1933	12 e. 50 Type **391**	30	15
1934	30 e. Prince John proclaimed King of Portugal	60	50

1983. Tiles (11th issue). As T **361**. Multicoloured.

No.	Description	Unused	Used
1935	12 e. 50 Flower pot by Gabriel del Barco (18th century)	30	10

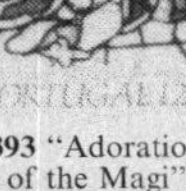

392 Bartolomeu de Gusmao and Model Balloon, 1709

393 "Adoration of the Magi"

1983. Bicentenary of Manned Flight. Mult.

No.	Description	Unused	Used
1937	16 e. Type **392**	30	15
1938	51 e. Montgolfier balloon, 1783	95	65

1983. Christmas. Stained Glass Windows from Monastery of Our Lady of Victory, Batalha. Multicoloured.

No.	Description	Unused	Used
1939	12 e. 50 Type **393**	25	10
1940	30 e. "The Flight into Egypt"	75	45

1983. Tiles (12th issue). As T **361**. Multicoloured.

No.	Description	Unused	Used
1941	12 e. 50 Turkish horseman (18th century)	30	10

394 Siberian Tiger

1983. Centenary of Lisbon Zoo. Multicoloured.

No.	Description	Unused	Used
1944	16 e. Type **394**	55	30
1945	16 e. Cheetah	55	30
1946	16 e. Blesbok	55	30
1947	16 e. White rhino	55	30

395 Fighter Pilot and Hawker Hurricane Mk II, 1954

1983. Air Force Uniforms. Multicoloured.

No.	Description	Unused	Used
1948	16 e. Type **395**	45	15
1949	35 e. Pilot in summer uniform and Republic Thunderjet, 1960	80	35
1950	40 e. Paratrooper in walking-out uniform and Nord Noratlas military transport airplane 1966	95	45
1951	51 e. Pilot in normal uniform and Vought Corsair II, 1966	1·10	60

1984 Tiles (13th issue). As T **36**. Multicoloured.

No.	Description	Unused	Used
1952	16 e. Coat of arms of King Jose I (late 18th century)	30	15

396 "25" on Crate (25th Lisbon International Fair)

1984. Events.

No.	Description	Unused	Used
1954	35 e. Type **396**	55	35
1955	40 e. Wheat rainbow and globe (World Food Day)	75	35
1956	51 e. Hand holding stylised flower (15th International Rehabilitation Congress) (vert)	1·00	60

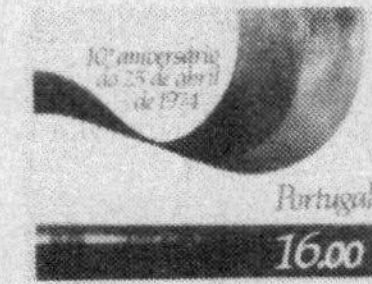

397 National Flag

1984. 10th Anniv of Revolution.

No.	Type	Description	Unused	Used
1957	**397**	16 e. multicoloured	30	15

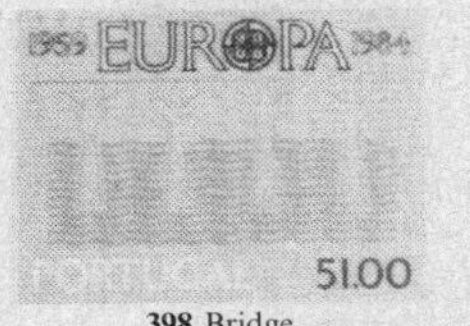

398 Bridge

1984. Europa.

No.	Type	Description	Unused	Used
1958	**398**	51 e. multicoloured	1·00	45

399 "Panel of St. Vincent"

1984. "Lubrapex 84" Portuguese–Brazilian Stamp Exhibition. Multicoloured.

1960 16 e. Type **399** 35 15
1961 40 e. "St. James" (altar panel) 60 45
1962 51 e. "View of Lisbon" (painting) 70 50
1963 66 e. "Head of Youth" (Domingos Sequeira) . . . 1·10 65

400 Fencing

1984. Olympic Games, Los Angeles, and 75th Anniv of Portuguese Olympic Committee. Multicoloured.

1965 35 e. Type 400 . . . . 45 20
1966 40 e. Gymnastics 50 30
1967 51 e. Running 60 40
1968 80 e. Pole vaulting 75 60

1984. Tiles (14th issue). As T **361**. Multicoloured.

1970 16 e. Pictorial tile from Pombal Palace, Lisbon (late 18th century) 30 10

1984. Tiles (15th issue). As T **361**. Multicoloured.

1972 16 e. Four art nouveau tiles (late 19th century) 30 10

401 Gil Eanes

1984. Anniversaries. Multicoloured.

1974 16 e. Type **401** (550th anniv of rounding of Cape Bojador) 30 15
1975 51 e. King Pedro IV of Portugal and I of Brazil (150th death anniv) 90 60

1984. Tiles (16th issue). As T **361**. Multicoloured.

1976 16 e. Grasshoppers and wheat (R. Bordallo Pinheiro, 19th century) 30 10

402 Infantry Grenadier, 1740, and Regiment in Formation

1985. Army Uniforms. Multicoloured.

1979 20 e. Type **402** 35 15
1980 46 e. Officer, Fifth Cavalry, 1810 and cavalry charge . . 60 30
1981 60 e. Artillery corporal, 1891, and Krupp 9 mm gun and crew 80 45
1982 100 e. Engineer in chemical protection suit, 1985, and bridge-laying armoured car 1·40 80

1985. Tiles (17th issue). As T **361**. Multicoloured.

1983 20 e. Detail of panel by Jorge Barrados in Lisbon Faculty of Letters (20th century) . . . 35 10

403 Calcada R. dos Santos Kiosk

1985. Lisbon Kiosks. Multicoloured.

1985 20 e. Type **403** 55 25
1986 20 e. Tivoli kiosk, Avenida da Liberdade 55 25
1987 20 e. Porto de Lisboa kiosk . 55 25
1988 20 e. Rua de Artilharia Um kiosk 55 25

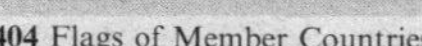

404 Flags of Member Countries

1985. 25th Anniv of European Free Trade Assn.

1989 **404** 46 e. multicoloured . . 70 40

405 Profiles

1985. International Youth Year.

1990 **405** 60 e. multicoloured . . 85 50

406 Woman holding Adufe (tambourine)

1985. Europa.

1991 **406** 60 e. multicoloured . . 1·25 60

1985. Tiles (18th issue). As T **361**. Multicoloured.

1993 20 e. Detail of panel by Maria Keil on Avenue Infante Santo (20th century) 35 10

407 Knight on Horseback

1985. Anniversaries. Multicoloured.

1995 20 e. Type **407** (600th anniv of Battle of Aljubarrota) . . 30 15
1996 46 e. Queen Leonor and hospital (500th anniv of Caldas da Rainha thermal hospital) 60 35
1997 60 e. Pedro Reinel (500th anniversary of first Portuguese sea-chart) . . 90 55

408 Farmhouse, Minho

409 Aquilino Ribeiro (writer)

1985. Architecture.

1998 – 50 c. black, bistre & blue 10 10
1999 – 1 e. black, yellow & grn 10 10
2000 – 1 e. 50 black, green and emerald 10 10
2001 – 2 e. 50 brown, orge & bl 10 10
2002 – 10 e. black, pur & pink . 10 10
2003 **408** 20 e. brown, yellow and deep yellow 15 10
2004 – 22 e. 50 brown, blue and ochre 20 10
2005 – 25 e. brown, yellow & grn 20 10
2006 – 27 e. black, yellow and light yellow 20 10
2007 – 29 e. black, yellow & orge 20 10
2008 – 30 e. black, blue & brown 25 10
2009 – 40 e. black, yellow & grn 30 10
2010 – 50 e. black, blue & ochre 40 10
2011 – 55 e. black, yellow & grn 40 15
2012 – 60 e. black, orange & bl 45 15
2013 – 70 e. black, yellow & orge 55 20
2014 – 80 e. brown, green & red 60 35
2015 – 90 e. brown, yellow & grn 70 35
2016 – 100 e. brown, yellow & bl 80 35
2017 – 500 e. black, grey & blue 3·75 1·90

DESIGNS: 50 e. Saloia house, Estremadura; 1 e. Beria inland house; 1 e. 50, Ribatejo house; 2 e. 50, Tras-os-montes houses; 10 e. Minho and Douro coast house; 22 e. 50, Alentejo houses; 25 e. Sitio house, Algarve; 27 e. Beira inland house (different); 29 e. Tras-os-montes house; 30 e. Algarve house; 40 e. Beira inland house (different); 50 e. Beira coast house; 55 e. Tras-os-montes house (different); 60 e. Beira coast house (different); 70 e. South Estramadura and Alentejo house; 80 e. Estremadura house; 90 e. Minho house; 100 e. Monte house, Alentejo; 500 e. Terraced houses, East Algarve.

1985. Tiles (19th series). As T **361**. Multicoloured.

2020 20 e. Head of woman by Querubim Lapa (20th century) 35 10

1985. Anniversaries. Multicoloured.

2022 20 e. Type **409** (birth centenary) 35 15
2023 46 e. Fernando Pessoa (poet 50th death anniv) 95 40

410 Berlenga National Reserve

1985. "Italia '85" International Stamp Exhibition Rome. National Parks and Reserves. Multicoloured.

2024 20 e. Type **410** 35 15
2025 40 e. Estrela Mountains National Park 55 30
2026 46 e. Boquilobo Marsh National Reserve 70 30
2027 80 e. Formosa Lagoon National Reserve . . . . 1·25 65

411 "Nativity"

412 Post Rider

1985. Christmas. Illustrations from "Book of Hours of King Manoel I". Multicoloured.

2029 20 e. Type **411** 30 10
2030 46 e. "Adoration of the Three Wise Men" 80 35

1985. Tiles (20th issue). As T **361**. Multicoloured.

2031 20 e. Detail of panel by Manuel Cargaleiro (20th century) 35 10

1985. No value expressed.

2034 **412** (–) green and deep green . 30 10

413 Map and Flags of Member Countries

1985. Admission of Porgual and Spain to European Economic Community. Multicoloured.

2035 20 e. Flags of Portugal and Spain joining flags of other members 35 10
2036 57 e. 50 Type **413** 90 60

414 Feira Castle

1986. Castles (1st series). Multicoloured.

2037 22 e. 50 Type **414** 35 15
2038 22 e. 50 Beja Castle 35 15

See also Nos. 2040/1, 2054/5, 2065/6, 2073/4, 2086/7 2093/4, 2102/3 and 2108/9.

415 Globe and Dove

1986. International Peace Year.

2039 **415** 75 e. multicoloured . . . 1·25 65

1986. Castles (2nd series). As T **414**. Multicoloured.

2040 22 e. 50 Braganca Castle . . 35 15
2041 22 e. 50 Guimaraes Castle . . 35 15

416 Benz Motor Tricycle, 1886

1986. Centenary of Motor Car. Multicoloured.

2042 22 e. 50 Type **416** 45 20
2043 22 e. 50 Daimler motor car, 1886 . . . . 45 20

417 Shad

1986. Europa.

2044 **417** 68 e. 50 multicoloured . 90 40

418 Alter

1986. "Ameripex '86" International Stamp Exhibition, Chicago. Thoroughbred Horses. Multicoloured.

2046 22 e. 50 Type **418** 40 15
2047 47 e. 50 Lusitano 70 45
2048 52 e. 50 Garrano 80 45
2049 68 e. 50 Sorraia . . . . . . 1·25 55

420 Diogo Cao (navigator) and Monument

421 Hand writing on Postcard

1986. Anniversaries. Multicoloured.

2051 22 e. 50 Type **420** (500th anniv of 2nd expedition to Africa) 30 10
2052 52 e. 50 Passos Manuel (Director) and capital (150th anniv of National Academy of Fine Arts, Lisbon) . . . 80 45
2053 52 e. 50 Joao Baptista Ribeiro (painter and Oporto Academy Director) and drawing (150th anniv of Portuguese Academy of Fine Arts, Oporto) 80 45

1986. Castles (3rd series). As T **414**. Multicoloured.

2054 22 e. 50 Belmonte Castle . . 35 15
2055 22 e. 50 Montemor-o-Velho Castle 35 15

1986. Anniversaries. Multicoloured.

2057 22 e. 50 Type **421** (centenary of first Portuguese postcard) . 30 15
2058 47 e. 50 Guardsman and houses (75th anniv of National Republican Guard) 75 40
2059 52 e. 50 Calipers, globe and banner (50th anniv of Order of Engineers) 80 40

422 Seasonal Mill, Douro

1986. "Luprapex '86" Portuguese–Brazilian Stamp Exhibition, Rio de Janeiro. Multicoloured.

2060 22 e. 50 Type **422** 35 15
2061 47 e. 50 Seasonal mill, Coimbra 70 40
2062 52 e. 50 Overshot bucket water mill, Gerez 80 40
2063 90 e. Permanent stream mill, Braga . . . . 1·25 55

1987. Castles (4th series). As T **414**. Mult.

2065 25 e. Silves Castle 35 15
2066 25 e. Evora-Monte Castle . . 35 15

423 Houses on Stilts, Tocha

1987. 75th Anniv (1986) of Organized Tourism. Multicoloured.

2067 25 e. Type **423** 35 15
2068 57 e. Fishing boats, Espinho 75 45
2069 98 e. Fountain, Arraiolos . . 1·10 70

424 Hand, Sun and Trees

1987. European Environment Year. Multicoloured.
2070 25 e. Type **424** 35 15
2071 57 e. Hands and flower on map of Europe 75 30
2072 74 e. 50 Hand, sea, shell, moon and rainbow . . . . 1·25 55

1987. Castles (5th series). As T **414**. Multicoloured.
2073 25 e. Leiria Castle 25 10
2074 25 e. Trancoso Castle 25 10

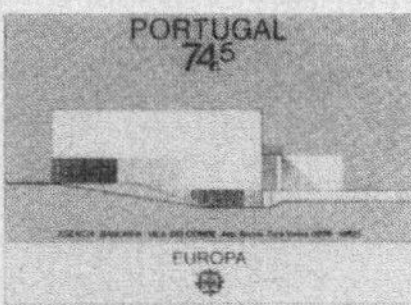

425 Bank Borges and Irmao Agency, Vila do Conde (Alvaro Siza)

1987. Europa. Architecture.
2075 **425** 74 e. 50 multicoloured . 90 40

426 Cape Mondego **427** Souza-Cardoso (self-portrait)

1987. "Capex '87" International Stamp Exhibition Toronto. Portuguese Lighthouses. Multicoloured.
2077 25 e. Type **426** 40 15
2078 25 e. Berlenga 40 15
2079 25 e. Aveiro 40 15
2080 25 e. Cape St. Vincent 40 15

1987. Birth Centenary of Amadeo de Souza-Cardoso (painter)
2081 **427** 74 e. 50 multicoloured . 85 40

428 Clipped 400 Reis Silver Coin

1987. 300th Anniv of Portuguese Paper Currency.
2082 **428** 100 e. multicoloured . . 1·00 55

429 Dias's Fleet leaving Lisbon

1987. 500th Anniv of Bartolomeu Dias's Voyages (1st issue). Multicoloured.
2083 25 e. Type **429** 35 20
2084 25 e. Ships off coast of Africa 35 20
Nos. 2083/4 were printed together, se-tenant, each pair forming a composite design.
See also Nos. 2099/2100

430 Library

1987. 150th Anniv of Portuguese Royal Library, Rio de Janeiro.
2085 **430** 125 e. multicoloured . . 1·10 70

1987. Castles (6th series). As T **414** Multicoloured.
2086 25 e. Marvao Castle 25 10
1087 25 e. St. George's Castle, Lisbon 25 10

432 Angels around Baby Jesus, Tree and Kings (Jose Manuel Coutinho)

1987. Christmas. Children's Paintings. Mult.
2089 25 e. Type **432** 25 10
2090 57 e. Children dancing around sunburst (Rosa J Leitao) . 50 30
2091 74 e. 50 Santa Claus flying on dove (Sonya Alexandra Hilario) 75 55

1988. Castles (7th series). As T **414**. Multicoloured.
2093 27 e. Fernandine Walls, Oporto 25 10
2094 27 e. Almourol Castle . . . 25 10

433 Lynx

1988. Iberian Lynx. Multicoloured.
2095 27 e. Type **433** 50 20
2096 27 e. Lynx carrying rabbit . 50 20
2097 27 e. Pair of lynxes 50 20
2098 27 e. Mother with young . . 50 20

434 King Joao II sending Pero da Covilha on Expedition

1988. 500th Anniv of Voyages of Bartolomeu Dias (2nd issue) (2099/2100) and Pero da Covilha (2101). Multicoloured.
2099 27 e. Dias's ships in storm off Cape of Good Hope . . . 30 10
2100 27 e. Contemporary map . . 25 10
2101 105 e. Type **434** 95 50
Nos. 2099/2100 are as T **429**.

1988. Castles (8th series). As T **414**. Multicoloured.
2102 27 e. Palmela Castle 25 10
2103 27 e. Vila Nova da Cerveira Castle 25 10

435 19th-century Mail Coach

1988. Europa. Transport and Communications.
2104 **435** 80 e. multicoloured . . 75 35

436 Map of Europe and Monnet

1988. Birth Centenary of Jean Monnet (statesman). "Europex 88" Stamp Exhibition.
2106 **436** 60 e. multicoloured . . 50 20

1988. Castles (9th series). As T **414**. Multicoloured.
2108 27 e. Chaves Castle 25 10
2109 27 e. Penedono Castle . . . 25 10

438 "Part of a Viola" (Amadeo de Souza-Cardoso)

1988. 20th-century Portuguese Paintings (1st series). Multicoloured.
2110 27 e. Type **438** 25 10
2111 60 e. "Acrobats" (Almada Negreiros) 50 20
2112 80 e. "Still Life with Viola" (Eduardo Viana) 70 30
See also Nos. 2121/3, 2131/3, 2148/50, 2166/8 and 2206/8

439 Archery

1988. Olympic Games, Seoul (1st issue). Mult.
2114 27 e. Type **439** 25 10
2115 55 e. Weightlifting 45 20
2116 60 e. Judo 50 20
2117 80 e. Tennis 75 30
See also Nos. 2295/8.

440 "Winter" (House of the Fountains, Coimbra)

1988. Roman Mosaics of 3rd Century. Mult.
2119 27 e. Type **440** 25 10
2120 80 e. "Fish" (Baths, Faro) . . 80 30

1988. 20th Century Portuguese Paintings (2nd series). As T **438**. Multicoloured.
2121 27 e. "Internment" (Mario Eloy) 25 10
2122 60 e. "Lisbon Houses" (Carlos Botelho) 50 20
2123 80 e. "Avejao Lirico" (Antonoi Pedro) 70 30

441 Braga Cathedral **442** "Greetings"

1989. Anniversaries. Multicoloured.
2126 30 e. Type **441** (900th anniv) . 25 10
2127 55 e. Caravel, parrot and Castle of Jorge da Mina (505th anniv) 60 20
2128 60 e. Sailor using astrolabe (500th anniv of South Atlantic voyages) 45 20
Nos. 2127/8 are inscribed for "India 89" Stamp Exhibition, New Delhi.

1989. Greetings Stamps. Multicoloured.
2129 29 e. Type **442** 25 10
2130 60 e. Airplane distributing envelopes inscribed "with Love" 45 20

1989. 20th-Century Portuguese Paintings (3rd series). As T **438**. Multicoloured.
2131 29 e. "Antithesis of Calm" (Antonio Dacosta) 25 10
2132 60 e. "Unskilled Mason's Lunch" (Julio Pomar) . . . 45 20
2133 87 e. "Simumis" (Vespeira) . 75 35

443 Flags in Ballot Box **444** Boy with Spinning Top

1989. 3rd Direct Elections to European Parliament.
2135 **443** 60 e. multicoloured . . . 45 20

1989. Europa. Children's Games and Toys.
2136 **444** 80 e. multicoloured . . . 65 30

INDEX

Countries can be quickly located by referring to the index at the end of this volume.

445 Cable Railway

1989. Lisbon Transport, Multicoloured.
2138 29 e. Type **445** 25 10
2139 65 e. Electric tram-car . . . 55 30
2140 87 e. Santa Justa lift 70 30
2141 100 e. Bus 80 35

446 Gyratory Mill, Ansiao

1989. Windmills. Multicoloured.
2143 29 e. Type **446** 25 10
2144 60 e. Stone mill, Santiago do Cacem 45 20
2145 87 e. Post mill, Afife 65 30
2146 100 e. Wooden mill, Caldas da Rainha 80 35

1989. 20th-Century Portuguese Paintings (4th series). As T **438**.
2148 29 e. blue, green and black . 25 10
2149 60 e. multicoloured 45 20
2150 87 e. multicoloured 65 30
DESIGNS: 29 e. "046-72" (Fernando Lanhas); 60 e. "Spirals" (Nadir Afonso); 87 e. "Sim" (Carlos Calvet).

448 Luis I (death centenary) and Ajuda Palace, Lisbon **449** "Armeria pseudarmeria"

1989. National Palaces (1st series). Multicoloured.
2153 29 e. Type **448** 20 10
2154 60 e. Queluz Palace 45 20
See also Nos. 2211/14

1989. Wild Flowers. Multicoloured.
2155 29 e. Type **449** 20 10
2156 60 e. "Santolina impressa" . 45 20
2157 87 e. "Linaria lamarckii" . . 65 30
2158 100 e. "Limonium multi-florum" 80 35

450 Blue and White Plate

1990. Portuguese Faience (1st series). Mult.
2159 33 e. Type **450** 25 10
2160 33 e. Blue and white plate with man in centre 25 10
2161 35 e. Vase decorated with flowers 25 10
2162 60 e. Fish-shaped jug 45 20
2163 60 e. Blue and white plate with arms in centre 45 20
2164 60 e. Blue and white dish with lid 45 20
See also Nos. 2221/6 and 2262/7.

1990. 20th-Century Portuguese Paintings (5th series). As T **438**. Multicoloured.
2166 32 e. "Aluenda-Tordesillas" (Joaquim Rodrigo) 25 10
2167 60 e. "Painting" (Noronha da Costa) 45 35
2168 95 e. "Painting" (Vasco Costa) 75 35

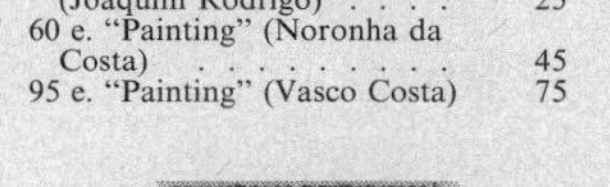

451 Joao Goncalves Zarco

1990. Portuguese Navigators.

2172 **451** 2 e. red, pink & black . . . 10 10
2173 – 3 e. green, blue and black . . . 10 10
2174 – 4 e. purple, red & black . . . 10 10
2175 – 5 e. brown, grey & blk . . . 10 10
2176 – 6 e. deep green, green and black . . . 10 10
2178 – 10 e. red, orange and black . . . 10 10
2180 – 32 e. green brn & blk . . . 25 10
2181 – 35 e. pink, red & black . . . 25 10
2182 – 38 e. blue, lt blue & blk . . . 35 15
2182a – 42 e. green, grey & blk . . . 30 15
2182b – 45 e. green, lt grn & blk
2183 – 60 e. yellow, pur & blk . . . 45 20
2184 – 65 e. brown, grn & blk . . . 60 30
2184a – 70 e. violet, mve & blk . . . 55 25
2184b – 75 e. green, yell & blk . . . 65 30
2185 – 80 e. orange, brn & blk . . . 60 30
2186 – 100 e. orange, red & blk . . . 85 35
2187 – 200 e. green, yell & blk . . . 1·60 80
2188 – 250 e. green blue & blk . . . 1·90 95
2189 – 350 e. red, pink & black . . . 3·25 1·60

DESIGNS: 3 e. Pedro Lopes de Sousa; 4 e. Duarto Pacheco Pereira; 5 e. Tristao Vaz Teixeira; 6 e. Pedro Alvares Cabral; 10 e. Joao de Castro; 32 e. Bartolomeu Perestrelo; 35 e. Gil Eanes: 38 e. Vasco da Gama; 42 e. Joao de Lisboa; 45 e. Joao Rodrigues Cabrilho; 60 e. Nuno Tristao; 65 e. Joao da Nova; 70 e. E. Fernao de Magalhaes (Magellan); 75 e. Pedro Fernandes de Queiros; 80 e. Diogo Gomes; 100 e. Diogo de Silves; 200 e. Estevao Gomes; 250 e. Diogo Cao; 350 e. Bartolomeu Dias.

452 Score and Singers

1990. Anniversaries. Multicoloured.

2191 32 e. Type **452** (centenary of "A Portuguesa" (national anthem)) . . . 25 10
2192 70 e. Students and teacher (700th anniv of granting of charter to Lisbon University) (vert) . . . 55 30

453 Santo Tirso Post Office

1990. Europa. Post Office Buildings. Mult.

2193 **453** 80 e. multicoloured . . . 60 30

455 Street with Chairs under Trees

1990. Greetings Stamps. Multicoloured.

2196 60 e. Type **455** . . . 45 20
2197 60 e. Hand holding bouquet out of car window . . . 45 20
2198 60 e. Man with bouquet crossing street . . . 45 20
2199 60 e. Women with bouquet behind pillar box . . . 45 20

456 Camilo Castelo Branco (writer)

1990. Death Anniversaries. Multicoloured.

2200 65 e. Type **456** (centenary) . . . 50 25
2201 70 e. Brother Bartolomeu dos Martires (Bishop of Braga, 400th anniv) . . . 55 30

457 Barketta

1990. 15th-Century Explorers' Ships. Mult.

2202 32 e. Type **457** . . . 30 10
2203 60 e. Carvel-built fishing boat . . . 55 25
2204 70 e. Nau . . . 70 40
2205 95 e. Caravel . . . 95 45

1990. 20th-Century Portuguese Paintings (6th series). As T **438**. Multicoloured.

2206 32 e. "Dom Sebastiao" (Costa Pinheiro) . . . 25 10
2207 60 e. "Domestic Scene with Green Dog" (Paula Rego) . . . 45 20
2208 95 e. "Homage to Magritte" (Jose de Guimaraes) . . . 75 35

458 Pena Palace

1990. National Palaces (2nd series). Mult.

2211 32 e. Type **458** . . . 25 10
2212 60 e. Vila Palace . . . 45 20
2213 70 e. Mafra Palace . . . 55 30
2214 120 e. Guimaraes Palace . . . 95 45

459 Carneiro

1990. 10th Death Anniv of Francisco Sa Carneiro (founder of Popular Democratic Party and Prime Minister, 1980).

2215 **459** 32 e. black and brown . . . 25 10

460 Steam Locomotive No. 02, 1887

1990. Centenary of Rossio Railway Station, Lisbon, Multicoloured.

2216 32 e. Type **460** . . . 25 10
2217 60 e. Steam locomotive No. 010, 1891 . . . 45 20
2218 70 e. Steam locomotive No. 071, 1916 . . . 55 30
2219 95 e. Electric locomotive, 1956 . . . 75 35

1991. Portuguese Faience (2nd series). As T **450**. Multicoloured.

2221 35 e. Barrel of fish and plate (Rato factory Lisbon) . . . 25 10
2222 35 e. Floral vase (Bica do Sapato factory) . . . 25 10
2223 35 e. Gargoyle (Costa Briozo factory, Coimbra) . . . 25 10
2224 60 e. Dish with leaf pattern (Juncal factory) . . . 45 20
2225 60 e. Coffee pot (Cavaquinho factory, Oporto) . . . 45 20
2226 60 e. Mug (Massarelos factory, Oporto) . . . 45 20

461 Greater Flamingos

1991. European Tourism Year. Multicoloured.

2228 60 e. Type **461** . . . 45 20
2229 110 e. European chameleon . . . 85 40

462 "Eutelsat II" Satellite

1991. Europa. Europe in Space. Multicoloured.

2231 **462** 80 e. multicoloured . . . 65 30

463 Caravel

1991. 16th-Century Explorers' Ships. Mult.

2233 35 e. Type **463** . . . 25 15
2234 75 e. Port view of nau . . . 45 35
2235 80 e. Stern view of nau . . . 50 35
2236 110 e. Galleon . . . 70 50

465 Emerald and Diamond Bow

1991. "Royal Treasures" Exhibition, Ajuda Palace (1st issue). Multicoloured.

2238 35 e. Type **465** . . . 30 15
2239 60 e. Royal sceptre . . . 50 25
2240 70 e. Sash of the Grand Cross . . . 55 25
2241 80 e. Hilt of sabre . . . 65 30
2242 140 e. Crown . . . 1·10 55

See also Nos. 2270/4.

466 Antero de Quental (writer)

1991. Anniversaries. Multicoloured.

2243 35 e. Type **466** (death centenary) . . . 30 15
2244 110 e. Arrival of expedition and baptism of Sonyo prince (500th anniv of first Portuguese missionary expedition to the Congo) . . . 1·10 45

467 Faculty of Architecture, Oporto University (Siza Vieira)

1991. Architecture. Multicoloured.

2245 35 e. Type **467** . . . 30 15
2246 60 e. Torre do Tombo (Arsenio Cordeiro Associates) . . . 50 25
2247 80 e. River Douro railway bridge (Edgar Cardoso) and Donna Maria bridge . . . 65 30
2248 110 e. Setubal-Braga highway . . . 90 45

468 King Manuel I creating Public Post, 1520

1991. History of Communications in Portugal. Mult.

2249 35 e. Type **468** . . . 30 15
2250 60 e. Woman posting letter and telegraph operator (merging of posts and telegraph operations, 1881) . . . 50 25
2251 80 e. Postman, mail van and switchboard operator (creation of Posts and Telecommunications administration, 1911) . . . 65 30

469 Show Jumping

1991. Olympic Games, Barcelona (1992) (1st issue). Multicoloured.

2253 35 e. Type **469** . . . 30 15
2254 60 e. Fencing . . . 50 25
2255 80 e. Shooting . . . 65 30
2256 110 e. Yachting . . . 1·10 45

See also Nos. 2300/3.

470 Peugeot "19", 1899

1991. Caramulo Automobile Museum. Mult.

2257 35 e. Type **470** . . . 30 15
2258 60 e. Rolls Royce "Silver Ghost", 1911 . . . 50 25
2259 80 e. Bugatti "35B" 1930 . . . 65 30
2260 110 e. Ferrari "1965 Inter". 1950 . . . 90 45

See also Nos. 2275/8.

1992. Portuguese Faience (3rd series). As T **450**. Multicoloured.

2262 40 e. Jug (Viana do Castelo factory) . . . 30 15
2263 40 e. Plate with flower design ("Ratinho" faience, Coimbra) . . . 30 15
2264 40 e. Dish with lid (Estremoz factory) . . . 30 15
2265 65 e. Decorated violin by Wescislau Cifka (Constancia factory, Lisbon) . . . 30 15
2266 65 e. Figure of man seated on barrel (Calvaquinho factory, Oporto) . . . 30 15
2267 65 e. Figure of woman (Fervenca factory, Oporto) . . . 30 15

471 Astrolabe (Presidency emblem)

1992. Portuguese Presidency of European Community.

2269 **471** 65 e. multicoloured . . . 50 20

1992. "Royal Treasures" Exhibition, Ajuda Palace (2nd issue). As T **465**. Multicoloured.

2270 38 e. Coral diadem . . . 30 15
2271 65 e. Faberge clock . . . 50 20
2272 70 e. Gold tobacco box studded with diamonds and emeralds by Jacqumin . . . 50 25
2273 85 e. Royal sceptre with dragon supporting crown . . . 70 35
2274 125 e. Necklace of diamond stars by Estevao de Sousa . . . 90 45

1992. Oeiras Automobile Museum. As T **470**. Multicoloured.

2275 38 e. Citroen "Torpedo", 1922 . . . 35 15
2276 65 e. Robert Schneider 12 H.P. 1914 . . . 60 30
2277 85 e. Austin "Seven", 1933 . . . 80 40
2278 120 e. Mercedes Benz "770", 1938 . . . 1·10 55

472 Portuguese Traders

1992. 450th Anniv of First Portuguese Contacts with Japan. Details of painting attributed to Kano Domi. Multicoloured.

2280 38 e. Type **472** . . . 45 15
2281 120 e. Portuguese visitors with gifts . . . 1·10 55

473 Portuguese Pavilion

474 Cross-staff

1992. "Expo '92" World's Fair, Seville.

2282 **473** 65 e. multicoloured . . . 60 30

1992. Nautical Instruments (1st series). Mult.

2283 60 e. Type **474** . . . 55 25
2284 70 e. Quadrant . . . 65 30
2285 100 e. Astrolabe . . . 90 45
2286 120 e. Compass . . . 1·10 55

See also Nos. 2318/21.

475 Royal All Saints Hospital, Lisbon

1992. Anniversaries. Multicoloured.

2288 38 e. Type **475** (500th anniv of foundation) . . . 35 15
2289 70 e. Lucia, Francisco and Jacinta (children) (75th anniv of apparition of Our Lady at Fatima) . . . 65 30
2290 120 e. Crane and docks (centenary of Port of Leixoes) . . . 1·10 55

476 Columbus with King Joao II

1992. Europa. 500th Anniv of Discovery of America by Columbus.
2291 **476** 85 e. multicoloured . . . 80 40

478 Tern flying over Contaminated River **479** Running

1992. 2nd United Nations Conference on Environment and Development, Rio de Janeiro. Multicoloured.
2293 70 e. Type **478** 65 30
2294 120 e. Kingfisher and butterfly beside clean river . . . . . 1·10 55
Nos. 2293/4 were issued together, se-tenant, forming a composite design.

1992. Olympic Games, Barcelona (2nd issue). Multicoloured.
2295 38 e. Type **479** 35 15
2296 70 e. Football 65 30
2297 85 e. Hurdling 80 40
2298 120 e. Roller hockey . . . . 1·10 55

480 Bullfighter on Horse

1992. Centenary of Campo Pequeno Bull Ring, Lisbon. Multicoloured.
2300 38 e. Type **480** 35 15
2301 65 e. Bull charging at horse . 60 30
2302 70 e. Bullfighter attacking bull 65 30
2303 155 e. Bullfighter flourishing hat 1·40 70

482 Star

1992. European Single Market.
2313 **482** 65 e. multicoloured . . . 60 30

483 Industrial Safety Equipment

1992. European Year of Health, Hygiene and Safety in the Workplace.
2314 **483** 120 e. multicoloured . . 1·10 55

484 Post Office Emblem **485** Graphic Poem

1993. No value expressed.
2315 **484** (–) red and black 35 15
No. 2315 was sold at the current first class inland letter rate. This was 42 e. at time of issue.

1993. Birth Centenary of Jose de Almada Negreiros (artist and poet). Multicoloured.
2316 40 e. Type **485** 30 15
2317 65 e. Ships (paintings) . . . 50 25

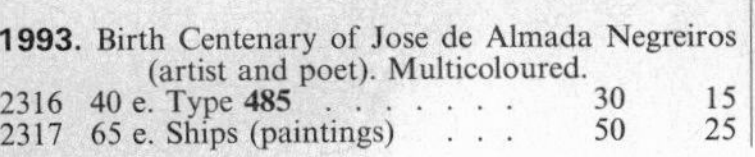

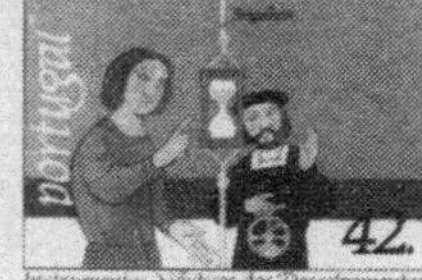

486 Sand Clock

1993. Nautical Instruments (2nd series). Mult.
2318 42 e. Type **486** 30 15
2319 70 e. Nocturiable 55 25
2320 90 e. Kamal 70 35
2321 130 e. Back-staff . . . . . . 1·00 50

487 View from Window

1993. Europa. Contemporary Art. Untitled painting by Jose Escada.
2322 **487** 90 e. multicoloured . . 70 35

488 Rossini and "The Barber of Seville"

1993. Bicentenary of San Carlos National Theatre, Lisbon. Multicoloured.
2324 42 e. Type **488** 30 15
2325 70 e. Verdi and "Rigoletto" 55 25
2326 90 e. Wagner and "Trisan and Isolde" 70 35
2327 130 e. Mozart and "The Magic Flute" . . . . 1·00 50

489 Fireman's Helmet

1993. 125th Anniv of Association of Volunteer Firemen of Lisbon.
2329 **489** 70 e. multicoloured . . 55 25

490 Santos-o-Velho, Lisbon **491** "Angel of the Annunciation"

1993. Union of Portuguese-speaking Capital Cities.
2330 **490** 130 e. multicoloured . . 1·00 50

1993. Sculptures (1st series). Multicoloured.
2332 42 e. Type **491** 30 15
2333 70 e. "St Mark" (Cornelius de Holanda) (horiz) 55 25
2334 75 e. "Madonna and Child" 60 30
2335 90 e. "Archangel St. Michael" 70 35
2336 130 e. "Earl of Ferreira" (Soares dos Reis) . . . . 1·00 50
2337 170 e. "Construction" (Heldar Batista) . . . . 1·40 70
See also Nos. 2580/5.

492 Road Tanker and Freight Train

1993. International Railways Congress, Lisbon. Multicoloured.
2339 90 e. Type **492** 70 35
2340 130 e. Train and traffic jam 1·00 50

493 Japanese Man with Musket

1993. 450th Anniv of First Portuguese Visit to Japan. Multicoloured.
2342 42 e. Type **493** 30 15
2343 130 e. Portuguese missionaries 1·00 50
2344 350 e. Traders carrying goods 2·75 1·25

494 Peniche Trawler **495** Rural Post Bag, 1800

1993. Trawlers (1st series). Multicoloured.
2345 42 e. Type **494** 30 15
2346 70 e. Peniche type trawler . . 55 25
2347 90 e. Germano 3o steam trawler 70 35
2348 130 e. Estrela 1o steam trawler 1·00 50
See also Nos. 2592/5.

1993. Post Boxes. Multicoloured.
2349 42 e. Type **495** 30 15
2350 70 e. 19th-century wall-mounted box for railway travelling post office 55 25
2351 90 e. 19th-century pillar box . 70 35
2352 130 e. Modern multi-function post box . . . . 1·00 50

496 Imperial Eagle

1993. Endangered Birds of Prey. Multicoloured.
2354 42 e. Type **496** 30 15
2355 70 e. Eagle owl 55 25
2356 130 e. Peregrine falcon . . . 1·00 50
2357 350 e. Hen harrier . . . . . 2·75 1·25

497 Knot

1993. 40th Anniv of Brazil–Portugal Consultation and Friendship Treaty.
2358 **497** 130 e. multicoloured . . . 1·00 50

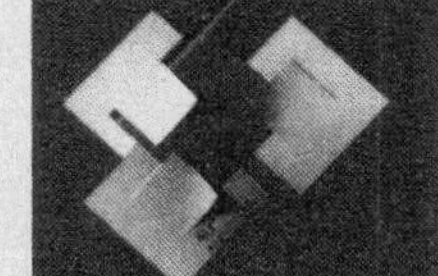

499 Stylized Map of Member Nations

1994. 40th Anniv of Western European Union.
2360 **499** 85 e. multicoloured . . . 65 30

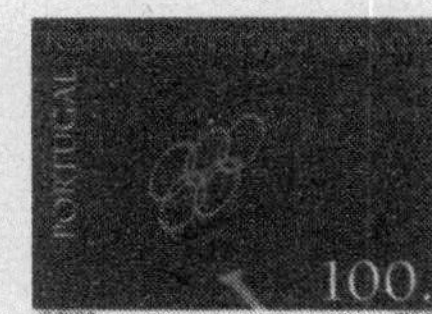

500 Olympic Rings as Torch Flame

1993. Centenary of International Olympic Committee. Multicoloured.
2361 100 e. Type **500** 80 40
2362 100 e. "100" and rings . . . 80 40

501 Oliveira Martins (historian)

1994. Centenaries. Multicoloured.
2363 45 e. Type **501** (death) . . . 35 15
2364 100 e. Florbela Espanca (poet, birth) 80 40

502 Map and Prince Henry (½-size illustration)

1994. 600th Birth Anniv of Prince Henry the Navigator.
2365 **502** 140 e. multicoloured . . 1·10 55

503 Dove

1994. 20th Anniv of Revolution.
2366 **503** 70 e. multicoloured . . . 60 30

504 Mounted Knight and Explorer with Model Caravel

1994. Europa. Discoveries.
2367 **504** 100 e. multicoloured . . 85 40

505 Emblem

1994. International Year of the Family.
2369 **505** 45 e. red, black and lake 40 20
2370 140 e. red, black and green 1·25 60

506 Footballer kicking Ball and World Map

1994. World Cup Football Championship, U.S.A. Multicoloured.
2371 100 e. Type **506** 85 40
2372 140 e. Ball and footballers' legs 1·25 60

507 King Joao II of Portugal and King Fernando of Spain (½-size illustration)

1994. 500th Anniv of Treaty of Tordesillas (defining Portuguese and Spanish spheres of influence).
2373 **507** 140 e. multicoloured . . 1·25 60

508 Music

1994. Lisbon, European Capital of Culture. Multicoloured.

2374	45 e. Type **508**	40	20
2375	75 e. Photography and cinema	65	30
2376	100 e. Theatre and dance	85	40
2377	140 e. Art	1·25	60

45 PORTUGAL
94 ANO PORTUGUÊS DA SEGURANÇA RODOVIÁRIA

509 Emblem

1994. Portuguese Road Safety Year.

2379	**509** 45 e. red, green and black	40	20

1994. Sculptures (2nd series). As T **491.** Mult.

2380	45 e. Carved stonework from Citania de Briteiros (horiz)	40	20
2381	75 e. Visigothic pilaster (7th century)	65	30
2382	80 e. Capital from Amorim Church (horiz)	75	30
2383	100 e. Laying Christ's body in tomb (attr Joao de Ruao) (Monastery Church of Santa Cruz de Coimbra) (horiz)	85	40
2384	140 e. Carved wood reliquary (Santa Maria Monastery, Alcobaca) (horiz)	1·25	60
2385	180 e. Relief of Writers (Leopoldo de Almeida) (Lisbon National Library) (horiz)	1·50	75

510 Falconer, Peregrine Falcon and Dog

1994. Falconry. Designs showing a peregrine falcon in various hunting scenes. Multicoloured.

2387	45 e. Type **510**	40	20
2388	75 e. Falcon chasing duck	65	30
2389	100 e. Falconer approaching falcon with dead duck	85	40
2390	140 e. Falcons	1·25	60

511 "Maria Arminda"

1994. Trawlers (2nd series). Multicoloured.

2392	45 e. Type **511**	40	20
2393	75 e. "Bom Pastor"	65	30
2394	100 e. "Aladores"	85	40
2395	140 e. "Sueste"	1·25	60

512 19th-century Horse-drawn Wagon

1994. Postal Transport. Multicoloured.

2396	45 e. Type **512**	40	20
2397	75 e. Travelling Post Office sorting carriage No. C7, 1910	65	30
2398	100 e. Mercedes mail van, 1910	85	40
2399	140 e. Volkswagen mail van, 1950	1·25	60

513 Multiple Car Unit, Sintra Suburban Railway (½-size illustration)

1994. Modern Electric Locomotives. Multicoloured.

2401	45 e. Type **513**	40	20
2402	75 e. Locomotive Series "5600" (national network)	65	30
2403	140 e. Lisbon Underground train	1·25	60

514 Medal

1994. 150th Anniv of Montepio Geral Savings Bank (45 e.) and World Savings Day (100 e.). Multicoloured.

2404	45 e. Type **514**	40	20
2405	100 e. Coins and bee	85	40

515 St. Philip's Fort, Setubal

1994. Pousadas (hotels) in Historic Buildings. Multicoloured.

2406	45 e. Type **515**	40	20
2407	75 e. Obidos Castle	65	30
2408	100 e. Convent of Loios, Evora	85	40
2409	140 e. Sta. Marinha Monastery, Guimaraes	1·25	60

516 Businessman and Tourist

1994. American Society of Travel Agents World Congress, Lisbon.

2410	**516** 140 e. multicoloured	1·25	60

517 Statuette of Missionary, Mozambique

1994. Evangelization by Portuguese Missionaries. Multicoloured.

2411	45 e. Type **517**	40	20
2412	75 e. "Child Jesus the Good Shepherd" (carving), India	65	30
2413	100 e. Chalice, Macao	85	40
2414	140 e. Carving of man in frame, Angola (horiz)	1·25	60

518 Africans greeting Portuguese

1994. 550th Anniv of First Portuguese Landing in Senegal.

2415	**518** 140 e. multicoloured	1·25	60

CHARITY TAX STAMPS

Used on certain days of the year as an additional postal tax on internal letters. Other values in some of the types were for use on telegrams only. The proceeds were devoted to public charities. If one was not affixed in addition to the ordinary postage, postage due stamps were used to collect the deficiency and the fine.

1911. Optd **ASSISTENCIA**.

C455	**48**	10 r. green (No. 406)	1·75	75
C484	**79**	1 c. green (No. 486)	1·00	50

C **57** "Lisbon" C **58** "Charity"

1913. Lisbon Fetes.

C485	C **57**	1 c. green	25	20

1915. For Poor People.

C486	C **58**	1 c. red	15	15
C669		15 c. red	15	15

1924. Surch **15 ctvs.**

C594	C **58**	15 c. on 1 c. red	30	20

C **71** Muse of History C **81** Hurdler

C **73** Monument to De Pombal C **75** Marquis de Pombal

1925. Portuguese Army in Flanders, 1484 and 1918.

C662	C **71**	10 c. red	30	25
C663		10 c. green	30	25
C664		10 c. blue	30	25
C665		10 c. brown	30	25

1925. Marquis de Pombal Commemoration.

C666	C **73**	15 c. blue and black	35	25
C667	–	15 c. blue and black	35	25
C668	C **75**	15 c. blue and black	15	10

DESIGN: No. C677, Planning reconstruction of Lisbon.

1928. Olympic Games.

C741	C **81**	15 c. black and red	3·00	2·25

NEWSPAPER STAMPS

N **16** N **17**

1876.

N180	N **16**	2 r. black	4·50	3·50
N178	N **17**	$2\frac{1}{2}$ r. olive	2·50	45
N187		$2\frac{1}{2}$ r. bistre	3·50	15

OFFICIAL STAMPS

1938. Optd **OFICIAL**.

O900	**99**	40 c. brown	10	10

O **144**

1952. No value.

O1069	O **144**	1 e. black & stone	10	10
O1070		1 e. black & ochre	30	10

On No. O1069 "CORREIO DE PORTUGAL" is in stone on a black background, on No. O1070 it is in black on the ochre background.

PARCEL POST STAMPS

P **59**

1920.

P578	P **59**	1 c. brown	10	10
P579		2 c. orange	10	10
P580		5 c. brown	10	10
P581		10 c. brown	10	10
P582		20 c. blue	10	10
P583		40 c. red	20	10
P584		50 c. black	25	10
P585		60 c. blue	30	10
P586		70 c. brown	1·00	50
P587		80 c. blue	1·25	50
P588		90 c. violet	1·25	50
P589		1 e. green	1·40	35
P591		2 e. lilac	3·00	35
P592		3 e. olive	3·50	60
P593		4 e. blue	6·50	1·00
P594		5 e. lilac	8·00	80
P595		10 e. brown	25·00	2·25

P **101**

1936.

P891	P **101**	50 c. grey	25	10
P892		1 e. brown	25	10
P893		1 e. 50 violet	30	10
P894		2 e. red	65	10
P895		2 e. 50 olive	75	10
P896		4 e. 50 purple	1·90	10
P897		5 e. violet	2·25	20
P898		10 e. orange	3·75	40

POSTAGE DUE STAMPS

D **48** Da Gama received by the Zamorin of Calicut D **49**

1898.

D386	D **48**	5 r. black	1·25	85
D387		10 r. mauve	1·75	1·10
D388		20 r. orange	3·50	1·75
D389		50 r. grey	10·00	4·00
D390		100 r. red	30·00	12·00
D391		200 r. brown	35·00	20·00

1904.

D392	D **49**	5 r. brown	20	10
D393		10 r. orange	1·00	40
D394		20 r. mauve	3·25	1·50
D395		30 r. green	1·00	1·00
D396		40 r. lilac	1·10	1·00
D397		50 r. red	20·00	2·25
D398		100 r. blue	2·25	1·50

1911. Optd **REPUBLICA**.

D418	D **49**	5 r. brown	20	15
D419		10 r. orange	20	15
D420		20 r. mauve	40	15
D421		30 r. green	20	15
D422		40 r. lilac	20	15
D423		50 r. red	2·25	1·25
D424		100 r. blue	2·50	1·50

1915. As Type D **49** but value in centavos.

D491	D **49**	$\frac{1}{2}$ c. brown	10	10
D498		1 c. orange	10	15
D493		2 c. red	15	15
D499		3 c. green	30	30
D500		4 c. lilac	30	35
D501		5 c. red	35	35
D497		10 c. blue	30	30

1921.

D578	D **49**	$\frac{1}{2}$ c. green	10	10
D579		4 c. green	10	10
D580		8 c. green	15	10
D581		10 c. green	15	10
D582		12 c. green	15	15
D583		16 c. green	10	10
D584		20 c. green	10	15
D585		24 c. green	10	10
D586		32 c. green	20	10
D587		36 c. green	20	15
D588	D **49**	40 c. green	25	15
D589		48 c. green	25	15
D590		50 c. green	25	20
D591		60 c. green	25	20
D592		72 c. green	25	20
D593		80 c. green	2·25	1·25
D594		1 e. 20 green	1·25	1·00

D **72** D **82**

1925. Great War Commemorative.

D662	D **72**	20 e. brown	20	15

1925. De Pombal types optd **MULTA**.

D663	C **73**	30 e. blue	25	25
D664	–	30 e. blue	25	25
D665	C **75**	30 e. blue	25	25

1928. Olympic Games.

D741	D **82**	30 e. black and red	2·00	1·60

D **91** D **108** D **218**

1932.

D865	D **91**	5 e. buff	10	10
D866		10 e. blue	10	10
D867		20 e. pink	30	20
D868		30 e. blue	30	25
D869		40 e. green	35	30
D870		50 e. grey	40	40
D871		60 e. pink	85	75
D872		80 e. red	3·25	1·10
D873		1 e. 20 green	3·00	3·75

1940.

D912	D **108**	5 e. brown	10	10
D913		10 e. lilac	10	10
D914		20 e. red	10	10
D925		30 e. violet	10	10
D916		40 e. mauve	10	10
D917		50 e. blue	10	10
D928		60 e. green	10	10
D929		80 e. red	10	10
D930		1 e. brown	25	10
D921		2 e. mauve	45	10
D922		5 e. orange	1·00	20

1967.

D1312	D **218**	10 c. brown, yellow and orange	10	10
D1313		20 e. purple, yellow and ochre	10	10
D1314		30 e. brown, yellow and orange	10	10
D1315		40 e. purple, yellow and bistre	10	10
D1316		50 e. indigo, blue and light blue	10	10
D1317		60 e. olive, blue and turquoise	10	10
D1318		80 e. indigo, blue and light blue	10	10
D1319		1 e. indigo, bl & ultram	10	10
D1320		2 e. olive, light green and green	10	10
D1321		3 e. grey, green and yellow	10	10
D1322		4 e. grey, green and yellow	10	10
D1323		5 e. brown, mve & red	10	10
D1324		9 e. grey, violet and mauve	10	10
D1325		10 e. grey, violet and lilac	10	10
D1326		20 e. brown, red and lilac	20	10
D1327		40 e. purple, lilac and mauve	35	25
D1328		50 e. red, lilac and purple	55	45

D **481**

1992.

D2305	D **481**	1 e. blue, deep blue and black	10	10
D2306		2 e. light green, green and black	10	10
D2307		5 e. yellow, brown and black	10	10
D2308		10 e. red, orange and black	10	10
D2309		20 e. green, violet and black	15	10
D2310		50 e. yellow, green and black	40	20
D2311		100 e. orange, red and black	80	40
D2312		200 e. mauve, violet and black	1·60	80

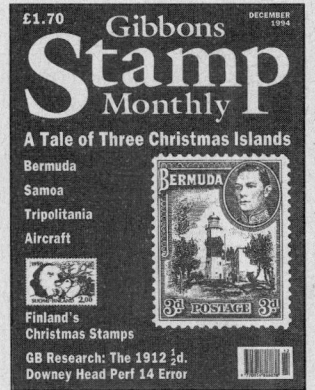

PORTUGUESE COLONIES Pt.9

General issues for the Portuguese possessions in Africa; Angola, Cape Verde Islands, Guinea, Lourenco Marques, Mozambique, Congo, St. Thomas and Prince Islands, and Zambezia.

1898 1000 reis = 1 milreis
1919 100 centavos = 1 escudo

1898. 400th Anniv of Vasco da Gama's Discovery of Route to India. As Nos. 378/85 of Portugal but inscr "AFRICA".

1 $2\frac{1}{2}$ r. green . . . 40 30
2 5 r. red . . . 40 30
3 10 r. purple . . . 40 30
4 25 r. green . . . 35 30
5 50 r. blue . . . 40 40
6 75 r. brown . . . 2·00 1·25
7 100 r. brown . . . 1·50 1·00
8 150 r. bistre . . . 2·50 1·25

CHARITY TAX STAMP

C 1

1919. Fiscal stamps optd **TAXA DE GUERRA**.

C1 C 1 1 c. black and green . . . 30 30
C2 5 c. green . . . 30 30

POSTAGE DUE STAMPS

D 1

1945. Value in black.

D1 D 1 10 c. red . . . 10 10
D2 20 c. purple . . . 10 10
D3 30 c. blue . . . 10 10
D4 40 c. brown . . . 15 15
D5 50 c. lilac . . . 15 15
D6 1 e. brown . . . 35 30
D7 2 e. green . . . 75 75
D8 3 e. red . . . 1·00 90
D9 5 e. yellow . . . 1·90 1·60

PORTUGUESE CONGO Pt.9

The area known as Portuguese Congo, now called Cabinda, was the part of Angola north of the River Congo. It issued its own stamps from 1894 until 1920

1894. 1000 reis = 1 milreis
1913. 100 centavos = 1 escudo

1894. "Figures" key-type inscr " CONGO".

8 R 5 r. orange . . . 40 40
9 10 r. mauve . . . 75 45
10 15 r. brown . . . 1·25 95
12 20 r. lilac . . . 1·25 85
13 25 r. green . . . 60 30
22 50 r. blue . . . 1·25 75
5 75 r. red . . . 1·90 1·75
6 80 r. green . . . 3·00 2·75
7 100 r. brown on yellow . . . 2·25 1·75
17 150 r. red on rose . . . 4·00 3·75
18 200 r. blue on blue . . . 4·00 3·75
19 300 r. blue on brown . . . 5·00 4·25

1898. "King Carlos" key-type inscr "CONGO".

24 S $2\frac{1}{2}$ r. grey . . . 10 15
25 5 r. orange . . . 15 15
26 10 r. green . . . 25 15
27 15 r. brown . . . 60 45
66 15 r. green . . . 45 30
28 20 r. lilac . . . 40 30
29 25 r. green . . . 55 30
67 25 r. red . . . 45 25
30 50 r. blue . . . 60 45
68 50 r. brown . . . 1·10 70
69 65 r. blue . . . 3·00 2·50
31 75 r. red . . . 1·25 90
70 75 r. purple . . . 1·25 1·00
32 80 r. mauve . . . 1·25 90
33 100 r. blue on blue . . . 90 80
71 115 r. brown on pink . . . 2·75 2·25
72 130 r. brown on yellow . . . 3·25 3·25
34 150 r. brown on yellow . . . 1·40 1·25
35 200 r. purple on pink . . . 1·75 1·50
36 300 r. blue on pink . . . 1·60 1·25
73 400 r. blue on yellow . . . 3·50 3·00
37 500 r. black on blue . . . 5·00 3·25
38 700 r. mauve on yellow . . . 8·00 5·50

1902. Surch.

74 S 50 r. on 65 r. blue . . . 1·75 1·25
40 R 65 r. on 15 r. brown . . . 1·60 1·00
41 65 r. on 20 r. lilac . . . 1·60 1·00
44 65 r. on 25 r. green . . . 1·50 1·25
46 65 r. on 300 r. blue on brn . . . 2·00 2·00
50 V 115 r. on $2\frac{1}{2}$ r. brown . . . 1·50 1·00
47 R 115 r. on 10 r. mauve . . . 1·50 1·00
48 115 r. on 50 r. blue . . . 1·50 1·00
53 130 r. on 5 r. orange . . . 1·50 1·00
54 130 r. on 75 r. red . . . 1·50 1·00
57 130 r. on 100 r. brn on yell . . . 1·50 1·00
58 400 r. on 80 r. green . . . 55 45
60 400 r. on 150 r. red on rose . . . 70 50
61 400 r. on 200 r. blue on blue . . . 70 50

1902. "King Carlos" key-type of Portuguese Congo optd **PROVISORIO**.

62 S 15 r. brown . . . 80 60
63 25 r. green . . . 80 60
64 50 r. blue . . . 80 60
65 75 r. red . . . 1·75 1·25

1911. "King Carlos" key-type of Angola, optd **REPUBLICA** and **CONGO** with bar (200 r. also surch).

75 S $2\frac{1}{2}$ r. grey . . . 50 40
76 5 r. orange . . . 70 55
77 10 r. green . . . 70 50
78 15 r. green . . . 70 55
79 25 r. on 200 r purple on pink . . . 1·10 90

1911. "King Carlos" key-type of Portuguese Congo optd **REPUBLICA**.

80 S $2\frac{1}{2}$ r. grey . . . 10 15
81 5 r. orange . . . 15 15
82 10 r. green . . . 15 15
83 15 r. green . . . 20 15
84 20 r. lilac . . . 20 15
85 25 r. red . . . 20 15
86 50 r. brown . . . 20 15
87 75 r. purple . . . 25 15
88 100 r. blue on blue . . . 25 15
89 115 r. brown on pink . . . 45 40
90 130 r. brown on yellow . . . 45 40
143 200 r. purple on pink . . . 60 55
92 400 r. blue on yellow . . . 1·00 75
93 500 r. black on blue . . . 1·60 80
94 700 r. mauve on yellow . . . 1·60 80

1913. Surch **REPUBLICA CONGO** and value on "Vasco da Gama" stamps of (a) Portuguese Colonies.

95 $\frac{1}{4}$ c. on $2\frac{1}{2}$ r. green . . . 50 45
96 $\frac{1}{2}$ c. on 5 r. red . . . 50 45
97 1 c. on 10 r. purple . . . 35 35
98 $2\frac{1}{2}$ c. on 25 r. green . . . 35 35
99 5 c. on 50 r. blue . . . 50 45
100 $7\frac{1}{2}$ c. on 75 r. brown . . . 80 65
101 10 c. on 100 r. brown . . . 50 45
102 15 c. on 150 r. bistre . . . 50 45

(b) Macao.

103 $\frac{1}{4}$ c. on $\frac{1}{2}$ a. green . . . 60 50
104 $\frac{1}{2}$ c. on 1 a. red . . . 60 50
105 1 c. on 2 a. purple . . . 45 40
106 $2\frac{1}{2}$ c. on 4 a. green . . . 45 40
107 5 c. on 8 a. blue . . . 60 50
108 $7\frac{1}{2}$ c. on 12 a. brown . . . 90 80
109 10 c. on 16 a. brown . . . 85 65
110 15 c. on 24 a. bistre . . . 65 45

(c) Timor.

111 $\frac{1}{4}$ c. on $\frac{1}{2}$ a. green . . . 70 60
112 $\frac{1}{2}$ c. on 1 a. red . . . 70 60
113 1 c. on 2 a. purple . . . 45 40
114 $2\frac{1}{2}$ c. on 4 a. green . . . 45 40
115 5 c. on 8 a. blue . . . 70 60
116 $7\frac{1}{2}$ c. on 12 a. brown . . . 90 80
117 10 c. on 16 a. brown . . . 90 60
118 15 c. on 24 a. bistre . . . 65 45

1914. "Ceres" key-type inscr "CONGO".

135 U $\frac{1}{4}$ c. olive . . . 20 15
120 $\frac{1}{2}$ c. black . . . 30 20
121 1 c. green . . . 80 50
122 $1\frac{1}{2}$ c. brown . . . 70 35
136 2 c. red . . . 20 15
124 $2\frac{1}{2}$ c. violet . . . 20 15
125 5 c. blue . . . 30 20
126 $7\frac{1}{2}$ c. brown . . . 50 40
127 8 c. black . . . 50 40
128 10 c. brown . . . 50 40
129 15 c. red . . . 65 40
130 20 c. green . . . 65 50
131 30 c. brown on green . . . 1·00 80
132 40 c. brown on rose . . . 1·00 90
133 50 c. orange on pink . . . 1·25 90
134 1 c. green on blue . . . 1·90 1·10

1914. "King Carlos" key-type of Portuguese Congo optd **PROVISORIO** and **REPUBLICA**.

146 S 15 r. brown (No. 62) . . . 25 25
147 50 r. blue (No. 64) . . . 25 25
140 75 r. red (No. 65) . . . 60 40

1914. Provisional stamps of 1902 optd **REPUBLICA**.

148 S 50 r. on 65 r. blue . . . 25 25
150 V 115 r. on $2\frac{1}{2}$ r. brown . . . 25 15
151 R 115 r. on 10 r. mauve . . . 20 15
154 115 r. on 50 r. blue . . . 20 15
156 130 r. on 5 r. orange . . . 20 15
157 130 r. on 75 r. red . . . 60 30
160 130 r. on 100 r. brown on yellow . . . 30 20

NEWSPAPER STAMP

1894. "Newspaper" key-type inscr "CONGO".

N24 V $2\frac{1}{2}$ r. brown . . . 40 35

PORTUGUESE GUINEA Pt.9

A former Portuguese territory, W. coast of Africa, with adjacent islands. Used stamps of Cape Verde from 1877 until 1881. In Sept. 1974 the territory became independent and was renamed Guinea-Bissau.

1881. 1000 reis = 1 milreis
1913. 100 centavos = 1 escudo

1881. "Crown" key-type inscr "CABO VERDE" and optd **GUINE**.

19 P 5 r. black . . . 1·60 1·50
20 10 r. yellow . . . 50·00 45·00
31 10 r. green . . . 3·00 2·10
21 20 r. olive . . . 1·40 90
32 20 r. red . . . 3·00 2·10
13 25 r. red . . . 90 65
28 25 r. lilac . . . 1·50 65
23 40 r. blue . . . 50·00 38·00
29 P 40 r. yellow . . . 80 65
24 50 r. green . . . 60·00 38·00
30 50 r. blue . . . 2·25 1·00
16 100 r. lilac . . . 2·75 2·00
17 200 r. orange . . . 4·00 3·00
18 300 r. brown . . . 5·50 4·50

1886. As T **19** of Portugal but inscr "GUINE PORTUGUEZA".

35 5 r. black . . . 1·75 1·10
36 10 r. green . . . 2·50 1·60
37 20 r. red . . . 3·50 2·25
38 25 r. mauve . . . 3·50 2·50
46 40 r. brown . . . 2·50 2·25
40 50 r. blue . . . 6·00 2·00
47 80 r. grey . . . 5·00 4·00
48 100 r. brown . . . 5·00 4·00
43 200 r. lilac . . . 13·00 8·00
44 300 r. orange . . . 15·00 12·00

1893. "Figures" key-type inscr 'GUINE'.

50 R 5 r. yellow . . . 60 50
51 10 r. mauve . . . 60 55
52 15 r. brown . . . 80 60
53 20 r. lilac . . . 80 60
54 25 r. green . . . 80 60
55 50 r. blue . . . 1·40 80
57 75 r. red . . . 3·50 3·00
58 80 r. green . . . 3·50 3·00
59 100 r. brown on buff . . . 3·75 3·00
60 150 r. red on rose . . . 4·50 4·00
61 200 r. blue on blue . . . 4·50 3·75
62 300 r. blue on brown . . . 6·00 5·50

1898. "King Carlos" key-type inscr "GUINE".

65 S $2\frac{1}{2}$ r. grey . . . 15 15
66 5 r. orange . . . 20 15
67 10 r. green . . . 20 15
68 15 r. brown . . . 1·10 90
114 15 r. green . . . 65 50
69 20 r. lilac . . . 30 20
70 25 r. green . . . 75 40
115 25 r. red . . . 40 25
71 50 r. blue . . . 1·10 50
116 50 r. brown . . . 75 60
117 65 r. blue . . . 3·00 2·50
72 75 r. red . . . 5·00 3·25
118 75 r. purple . . . 1·25 80
73 80 r. mauve . . . 1·10 75
74 100 r. blue on blue . . . 1·10 60
119 115 r. brown on pink . . . 3·00 2·25
120 130 r. brown on yellow . . . 3·00 3·25
75 150 r. brown on yellow . . . 3·00 1·50
76 200 r. purple on pink . . . 3·00 1·50
77 300 r. blue on pink . . . 2·75 1·75
121 400 r. blue on yellow . . . 3·00 2·25
78 500 r. black on blue . . . 4·00 3·00
79 700 r. mauve on yellow . . . 6·00 4·00

1902. Surch.

122 S 50 r. on 65 r. blue . . . 1·50 90
81 – 65 r. on 10 r. grn (No.36) . . . 2·50 1·50
84 R 65 r. on 10 r. mauve . . . 2·50 1·40
85 65 r. on 15 r. brown . . . 2·00 1·40
82 – 65 r. on 20 r. red (No.37) . . . 2·50 1·50
86 R 65 r. on 20 r. lilac . . . 2·00 1·40
83 – 65 r. on 25 r. mve. (No. 38) . . . 2·50 1·50
88 R 65 r. on 50 r. blue . . . 1·10 90
97 V 115 r. on $2\frac{1}{2}$ r. brown . . . 1·75 1·25
93 R 115 r. on 5 r. yellow . . . 1·75 1·25
95 115 r. on 25 r. green . . . 2·00 1·25
89 – 115 r. on 40 r. brn. (No. 46) . . . 2·00 1·50
91 – 115 r. on 50 r. blue (No. 40) . . . 2·00 1·50
92 – 115 r. on 300 r. orange (No. 44) . . . 2·75 2·25
98 – 130 r. on 80 r. grey (No. 47) . . . 2·75 2·25
100 – 130 r. on 100 r. brown (No. 48) . . . 2·75 2·25
102 R 130 r. on 150 r. red on rose . . . 2·25 1·25
103 130 r. on 200 r. blue on blue . . . 2·50 1·50
104 130 r. on 300 r. bl on brn . . . 2·50 1·50
105 – 400 r. on 5 r. blk (No. 35) . . . 10·00 7·50
107 R 400 r. on 75 r. red . . . 1·50 1·25
108 400 r. on 80 r. green . . . 1·00 75
109 400 r. on 100 r. brn on buff . . . 1·00 75
106 400 r. on 200 r. lilac (No. 43) . . . 4·50 3·25

1902. "King Carlos" key-type of Portuguese Guinea optd **PROVISORIO**.

110 S 15 r. brown . . . 1·00 60
111 25 r. green . . . 1·00 60
112 50 r. blue . . . 1·25 80
113 75 r. red . . . 1·75 1·60

1911. "King Carlos" key-type of Portuguese Guinea optd **REPUBLICA**.

123 S $2\frac{1}{2}$ r. grey . . . 15 20
124 5 r. orange . . . 20 20
125 10 r. green . . . 20 20
126 15 r. green . . . 20 20
127 20 r. lilac . . . 20 20
128 25 r. red . . . 20 20
129 50 r. brown . . . 20 25
130 75 r. purple . . . 25 25
131 100 r. blue on blue . . . 25 30
132 115 r. brown on pink . . . 55 30
133 130 r. brown on yellow . . . 55 30
134 200 r. purple on pink . . . 3·00 1·50
135 400 r. blue on yellow . . . 90 55
136 500 r. black on blue . . . 90 55
137 700 r. mauve on yellow . . . 1·50 90

1913. Surch **REPUBLICA GUINE** and value on "Vasco da Gama" stamps of (a) Portuguese Colonies.

138 $\frac{1}{4}$ c. on $2\frac{1}{2}$ r. green . . . 70 70
139 $\frac{1}{2}$ c. on 5 r. red . . . 70 70
140 1 c. on 10 r. purple . . . 40 40
141 $2\frac{1}{2}$ c. on 25 r. green . . . 40 40
142 5 c. on 50 r. blue . . . 70 70
143 $7\frac{1}{2}$ c. on 75 r. brown . . . 1·50 1·40
144 10 c. on 100 r. brown . . . 70 50
145 15 c. on 150 r. bistre . . . 1·60 1·60

(b) Macao.

146 $\frac{1}{4}$ c. on $\frac{1}{2}$ a. green . . . 80 70
147 $\frac{1}{2}$ c. on 1 a. red . . . 80 70
148 1 c. on 2 a. purple . . . 50 50
149 $2\frac{1}{2}$ c. on 4 a. green . . . 50 50
150 5 c. on 8 a. blue . . . 80 70
151 $7\frac{1}{2}$ c. on 12 a. brown . . . 1·40 1·10
152 10 c. on 16 a. brown . . . 1·25 1·10
153 15 c. on 24 a. bistre . . . 1·40 1·10

(c) Timor.

154 $\frac{1}{4}$ c. on $\frac{1}{2}$ a. green . . . 80 70
155 $\frac{1}{2}$ c. on 1 a. red . . . 80 70
156 1 c. on 2 a. purple . . . 50 50
157 $2\frac{1}{2}$ c. on 4 a. green . . . 50 50
158 5 c. on 8 a. blue . . . 80 70
159 $7\frac{1}{2}$ c. on 12 a. brown . . . 1·40 1·00
160 10 c. on 16 a. brown . . . 1·25 1·00
161 15 c. on 24 a. bistre . . . 1·40 1·00

1913. "King Carlos" key-type of Portuguese Guinea optd **PROVISORIO** and **REPUBLICA**.

184 S 15 r. brown . . . 35 30
185 50 r. blue . . . 35 30
164 75 r. red . . . 3·00 2·50

1914. "Ceres" key-type inscr "GUINE".

204 U $\frac{1}{4}$ c. olive . . . 10 10
209 $\frac{1}{2}$ c. black . . . 15 10
210 1 c. green . . . 10 10
211 $1\frac{1}{2}$ c. brown . . . 15 10
212 2 c. red . . . 15 10
213 2 c. grey . . . 10 10
214 $2\frac{1}{2}$ c. violet . . . 15 10
215 3 c. orange . . . 10 10
216 4 c. red . . . 10 10
217 $4\frac{1}{2}$ c. grey . . . 10 10
218 5 c. blue . . . 10 10
219 6 c. mauve . . . 10 10
220 7 c. blue . . . 15 10
221 $7\frac{1}{2}$ c. brown . . . 15 15
222 8 c. black . . . 15 15
223 10 c. brown . . . 15 10
224 12 c. green . . . 25 15
225 15 c. red . . . 25 10
226 20 c. green . . . 15 10
227 24 c. blue . . . 70 50
228 25 c. brown . . . 70 50
180 30 c. brown on green . . . 2·50 2·00
229 30 c. green . . . 30 15
181 40 c. brown on rose . . . 1·50 70
230 40 c. blue . . . 30 15
182 50 c. orange on pink . . . 1·50 70
231 50 c. mauve . . . 70 35
232 60 c. blue . . . 70 35
233 60 c. red . . . 70 35
234 80 c. red . . . 70 35
183 1 e. green on blue . . . 1·75 90
236 1 e. pink . . . 1·00 65
235 1 e. blue . . . 1·00 65
237 2 e. purple . . . 1·10 70
238 5 e. brown . . . 5·50 4·00
239 10 e. pink . . . 9·50 6·50
240 20 e. green . . . 22·00 17·00

1915. Provisional stamps of 1902 optd **REPUBLICA**.

186 S 50 r. on 65 r. blue . . . 35 30
187 V 115 r. on $2\frac{1}{2}$ r. brown . . . 50 45
190 R 115 r. on 5 r. yellow . . . 35 30
191 115 r. on 25 r. green . . . 35 30
192 – 115 r. on 40 r. brown (No. 89) . . . 35 30
194 – 115 r. on 50 r. bl (No. 91) . . . 35 30
196 – 130 r. on 80 r. grey (No. 98) . . . 1·25 90
197 – 130 r. on 100 r. brn (No. 100) . . . 80 65
200 R 130 r. on 200 r. blue on bl . . . 35 35
201 130 r. on 300 r. bl on brn . . . 35 35

1920. Surch.

241 U 4 c. on $\frac{1}{4}$ c. olive . . . 1·50 1·10
242 6 c. on $\frac{1}{2}$ c. black . . . 1·50 1·10
243 S 12 c. on 115 r. brown on pink (No. 132) . . . 2·25 1·60

1925. Stamps of 1902 optd **Republica** and surch.

244 R 40 c. on 400 r. on 75 r. red . . . 40 35
245 40 c. on 400 r. on 80 r. grn . . . 40 35
246 40 c. on 400 r. on 100 r. brown on buff . . . 40 35

1931. "Ceres" key-type of Portuguese Guinea surch.

247 U 50 c. on 60 c. red . . . 80 60
248 70 c. on 80 c. red . . . 90 75
249 1 e. 40 on 2 e. purple . . . 2·00 1·75

24 Ceres

31 Cacheu Castle

1933.

251 **24** 1 c. brown . . . 10 10
252 5 c. brown . . . 10 10
253 10 c. mauve . . . 10 10
254 15 c. black . . . 15 10
255 20 c. grey . . . 15 10
256 30 c. green . . . 15 10
257 40 c. red . . . 15 10
258 45 c. blue . . . 35 20
259 50 c. brown . . . 35 20
260 60 c. olive . . . 35 20
261 70 c. brown . . . 35 20
262 80 c. green . . . 40 30
263 85 c. red . . . 90 45
264 1 e. red . . . 45 30
265 1 e. 40 blue . . . 2·00 1·25
266 2 e. mauve . . . 90 60
267 5 e. green . . . 3·50 2·25
268 10 e. bistre . . . 6·00 4·25
269 20 e. orange . . . 20·00 12·00

1938. As T **54** and **56** of Macao but inscr "GUINE".

270 **54** 1 c. olive (postage) . . . 10 10
271 5 c. brown . . . 10 10
272 10 c. red . . . 10 10
273 15 c. purple . . . 10 10
274 20 c. grey . . . 15 10
275 – 30 c. purple . . . 20 10
276 – 35 c. green . . . 20 15
277 – 40 c. brown . . . 20 15
278 – 50 c. mauve . . . 20 15

279 – 60 c. black 25 20
280 – 70 c. violet 25 20
281 – 80 c. orange 35 25
282 – 1 e. red 35 25
283 – 1 e. 75 blue 60 30
284 – 2 e. red . . . . 1·50 45
285 – 5 e. olive . . . . 2·25 90
286 – 10 e. blue . . . . 4·00 1·00
287 – 20 e. brown . . . . 12·00 2·40

288 **56** 10 c. red (air) 15 10
289 20 c. violet 15 10
290 50 c. orange 15 10
291 1 e. blue 30 20
292 2 e. red . . . . 3·00 1·60
293 3 e. green 60 35
294 5 e. brown . . . . 1·75 50
295 9 e. red . . . . 2·00 90
296 10 e. mauve . . . . 4·00 1·25

DESIGNS (postage): 30 c. to 50 c. Mousinho de Albuquerque; 60 c. to 1 e. Dam; 1 e. 75, to 5 e. Prince Henry the Navigator; 10, 20 e. Afonso de Albuquerque.

1946. 500th Anniv of Discovery of Portuguese Guinea.
297 **31** 30 c. black 40 30
298 – 50 c. green 20 20
299 – 50 c. purple 20 20
300 – 1 e. 75 blue . . . . 1·25 1·50
301 – 3 e. 50 red . . . . 2·00 80
302 – 5 e. brown . . . . 4·00 2·00
303 – 20 e. violet . . . . 6·50 3·00

DESIGNS—VERT: 50 c. Nuno Tristao; 1 e. 75, President Grant; 3 e. 50, Teixeira Pinto; 5 e. Honorio Barreto. HORIZ: 20 e. Church at Bissau.

32 Native Huts

34 Letter and Globe

1948.
304 **32** 5 c. brown 10 10
305 – 10 c. purple . . . . 4·50 2·50
306 – 20 c. mauve 20 10
307 – 35 c. green 20 10
308 – 50 c. red 20 10
309 – 70 c. blue 20 15
310 – 80 c. green 25 15
311 – 1 e. red 40 15
312 – 1 e. 75 blue . . . . 5·00 90
313 – 2 e. blue . . . . 5·50 35
314 – 3 e. 50 brown . . . . . . 1·50 35
315 – 5 e. grey . . . . 2·50 60
316 – 20 e. violet . . . . 9·00 3·00

DESIGNS: 10 c. Crowned crane; 20 c., 3 e. 50, Youth; 35 c., 5 e. Woman; 50 c. Musician; 70 c. Man; 80 c., 20 e. Girl; 1 c., 2 e. Drummer; 1 e. 75, Bushbuck.

1948. Statue of Our Lady of Fatima. As T **62** of Macao.
317 50 c. olive . . . . 1·25 1·00

1949. 75th Anniv of U.P.U.
318 **34** 2 e. orange . . . . 1·50 1·00

1950. Holy Year As Nos 425/6 of Macao.
319 1 e. red 75 60
320 3 e. green . . . . 1·10 80

1951. Termination of Holy Year. As T **69** of Macao.
321 1 e. brown and buff 35 35

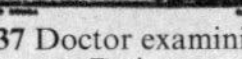
37 Doctor examining Patient

39 Exhibition Entrance

1952. 1st Tropical Medicine Congress, Lisbon.
322 **37** 50 c. brown and purple . . 25 20

1953. Missionary Art Exhibition.
323 **39** 10 c. lake and olive 10 10
324 50 c. blue and ochre . . . 35 20
325 3 e. black and salmon . . . 90 55

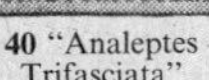
40 "Analeptes Trifasciata"

43 Arms of Cape Verde Islands and Portuguese Guinea

1953. Insects. Multicoloured.
326 5 c. Type **40** 10 10
327 10 c. "Callidea panaethiopica kirk" 10 10
328 30 c. "Craspedophorus brevicollis" 10 10
329 50 c. "Anthia nimrod" 10 10
330 70 c. "Platypria luctuosa" . . 20 10
331 1 e. "Acanthophorus maculatus" 20 10
332 2 e. "Cordylomera nitidipennis" 40 10
333 3 e. "Lycus latissimus" . . . 75 15
334 5 e. "Cicindeia Brunet" . . . 1·40 35
335 10 e. "Colluris dimidiata" . . 2·00 80

1953. Portuguese Stamp Cent. As T **75** of Macao.
336 50 c. grey and yellow 35 15

1954. 4th Cent of Sao Paulo. As T **76** of Macao.
337 1 e. black, mauve & lavender 15 15

1955. Presidential Visit.
338 **43** 1 e. multicoloured 20 15
339 2 e. 50 mulitcoloured . . . 30 20

44 Exhibition Emblem Globe and Arms

46 Statue of Barreto at Bissau

1958. Brussels International Exhibition.
340 **44** 2 e. 50 multicoloured 30 20

1958. 6th International Congress of Tropical Medicine. As T **79** of Macao.
341 5 e. multicoloured . . . . . 1·25 70
DESIGN: 5 e. "Maytenus senegalensis" (plant).

1959. Death Centenary of H. Barreto (statesman).
342 **46** 2 e. 50 multicoloured . . . 15 10

47 Astrolabe

48 "Medical Services"

1960. 500th Death Anniv of Prince Henry the Navigator.
343 **47** 2 e. 50 multicoloured 20 10

1960. 10th Anniv of African Technical Co-operation Commission.
344 **48** 1 e. 50 multicoloured . . . 20 10

1962. Sports. As T **82** of Macao. Multicolour.
345 50 c. Motor racing 10 10
346 1 e. Tennis 50 15
347 1 e. 50 Putting the shot . . . 20 15
348 2 e. 50 Wrestling 30 20
349 3 e. 50 Shooting 30 20
350 15 e. Volleyball . . . . 1·25 80

1962. Malaria Eradication. Mosquito design as T **83** of Macao. Multicoloured.
351 2 e. 50 "A gambiae" 25 20

51 Common Spitting Cobra

52 Map of Africa, Boeing 707 and Lockheed Super Constellation

1963. Snakes. Multicoloured.
352 20 c. Type **51** 15 10
353 35 c. African rock python . . 15 10
354 70 c. Boomslang 40 10
355 80 c. West African mamba . . 30 10
356 1 e. 50 Symthe's water snake . 40 10
357 2 e. Common night adder . . 20 10
358 2 e. 50 Green swamp-snake . 1·10 10
359 3 e. 50 Brown house snake . . 30 15
360 4 e. Spotted wolf snake . . . 40 20
361 5 e. Common puff adder . . 50 20
362 15 e. Striped beauty snake . . 1·25 35
363 20 e. African egg-eating snake 1·75 50
The 2 e. and 20 e. are horiz.

1963. 10th Anniv of T.A.P. Airline.
364 **52** 2 e. 50 multicoloured . . . 35 20

1964. National Overseas Bank Centenary. As T **84** of Macao, but portrait of J. de A. Corvo.
365 2 e. 50 multicoloured 30 20

1965. Centenary of I.T.U. As T **85** of Macao.
366 2 e. 50 multicoloured 70 35

55 Soldier, 1548

63 Pres. Tomas

1966. Portuguese Military Uniforms. Multicoloured.
367 25 c. Type **55** 10 10
368 40 c. Arquebusier, 1578 . . . 15 10
369 60 c. Arquebusier, 1640 . . . 20 10
370 1 e. Grenadier, 1721 . . . . . 20 10
371 2 e. 50 Captain of Fusiliers, 1740 45 10
372 4 e. 50 Infantryman, 1740 . . 1·00 40
373 7 e. 50 Sergeant-major, 1762 . 1·40 55
374 10 e. Engineers' officer, 1806 . 1·60 70

1966. 40th Anniv of Portuguese National Revolution. As T **86** of Macao, but showing different buildings. Multicoloured.
375 2 e. 50 B.C. Lopes School and Bissau Hospital 25 20

1967. Cent of Military Naval Assn. As T **88** of Macao. Multicoloured.
376 50 e. O. Muzanty and cruiser "Republica" 15 10
377 1 e. A. de Cerqueira and destroyer "Guadiana" . . . 40 20

1967. 50th Anniv of Fatima Apparitions. As T **89** of Macao.
378 50 c. multicoloured 10 10
DESIGN: 50 c. Chapel of the Apparitions and Monument of the Holy Spirit.

1968. Visit of President Tomas of Portugal.
396 **63** 1 e. multicoloured 10 10

1968. 500th Birth Anniv of Pedro Cabral (explorer). As T **90** of Macao. Multicoloured.
397 2 e. 50 Cabral's arms (vert) . . 25 15

1969. Birth Centenary of Admiral Gago Coutinho. As T **91** of Macao. Multicoloured.
409 1 e. Admiral Coutinho's astrolabe (horiz) 15 10

1969. 500th Birth Anniv of Vasco da Gama (explorer). As T **92** of Macao. Multicoloured.
410 2 e. 50 Arms of Vasco da Gama (vert) 15 10

1969. Centenary of Overseas Administrative Reforms. As T **93** of Macao.
411 50 c. multicoloured 10 10

1969. 500th Birth Anniv of Manoel I. As T **95** of Macao. Multicoloured.
412 2 e. Arms of Manoel I 15 10

70 Ulysses Grant and Square, Bolama

73 Camoens

1970. Centenary of Arbitral Judgment on Sovereignty of Bolama.
413 **70** 2 e. 50 multicoloured . . . 20 15

1970. Birth Centenary of Marshal Carmona. As T **96** of Macao.
414 1 e. 50 Portrait wearing cap and cloak 10 10

1972. 400th Anniv of Camoens' "The Lusiads" (epic poem).
422 **73** 50 c. multicoloured 15 10

74 Weightlifting and Hammer-throwing

1972. Olympic Games, Munich.
423 **74** 2 e. 50 multicoloured . . . 15 10

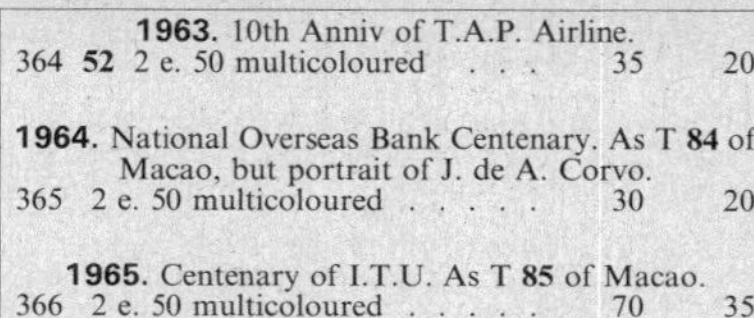

75 Seaplane "Lusitania" taking-off from Lisbon

1972. 50th Anniv of 1st Lisbon–Rio de Janeiro Flight.
424 **75** 1 e. multicoloured 15 10

1973. Centenary of I.M.O./W.M.O. As T **102** of Macao.
425 2 e. multicoloured 15 10

CHARITY TAX STAMPS

The notes under this heading in Portugal also apply here.

C 16

1919. Fiscal stamp optd **REPUBLICA** and **TAXA DE GUERRA**.
C241 C **16** 10 r. brown, buff & blk 11·00 9·00

1925. Marquis de Pombal Commem stamps of Portugal but inscr "GUINE".
C247 C **73** 15 c. black and red . . 30 25
C248 – 15 c. black and red . . 30 25
C249 C **75** 15 c. black and red . . 30 25

C 26

1934.
C270 C **26** 50 c. brown and grn . 3·00 1·75

C 29a

C 59

C 60

1938.
C299 C **29a** 30 c. black & purple . 10 10
C297 50 c. yellow . . . . . 3·00 2·00
C298 50 c. brown & green . 3·00 2·00
C300 50 c. black & yellow . 80 40
C301 50 c. brown & yellow 90 75
C302 2 e. 50 black & blue . 20 20
C303 5 e. black and green . 45 25
C304 10 e. black and blue . 90 45

Nos. C302/4 were used at several small post offices as ordinary postage stamps during a temporary shortage. Nos. C297, 300/304 are smaller ($20\frac{1}{2} \times 25$ mm).

1967. National Defence. No gum.
C379 C **59** 50 c. red and black . . 30 20
C380 1 e. red, green & blk . 35 25
C381 5 e. red, grey & black . 65 55
C382 10 e. red, blue & blk . 1·75 1·75
50 e. in the same design was for fiscal use only.

1967. National Defence. No gum.
C383 C **60** 50 c. verm, red & blk . 15 10
C384 1 e. red, green & blk . 15 10
C385 5 e. red, grey & black . 40 30
C386 10 e. red, blue & blk . 80 60

C **61.** Carved Statuette of Woman

C **65.** Hands grasping Sword

1967. Guinean Artifacts from Bissau Museum. Multicoloured.

C387 50 c. Type C **61** 15 15
C388 1 e. "Tree of life" (carving) 15 15
C389 2 e. Cow-headed statuette 15 15
C390 2 e. 50 "The Magistrate" (statuette) 15 15
C391 5 e. "Kneeling Servant" (statuette) 30 30
C392 10 e. Stylized pelican (carving) 60 60
The 1 e. is horiz.

1968. No. C389 but inscr "TOCADOR DE BOMBOLON" surch.

C394 50 c. on 2 e. multicoloured 10 10
C395 1 e. on 2 e. multicoloured 15 15

1969. National Defence.

C398 C **65** 50 c. multicoloured 10 10
C399 1 e. multicoloured 10 10
C400 2 e. multicoloured 10 10
C401 2 e. 50 multicoloured 15 15
C402 3 e. multicoloured 15 15
C403 4 e. multicoloured 20 20
C404 5 e. multicoloured 25 25
C405 8 e. multicoloured 40 40
C406 9 e. multicoloured 45 45
C407 10 e. multicoloured 50 50
C408 15 e. multicoloured 80 80
NOTE—30, 50 and 100 e. stamps in the same design were for fiscal use only.

C 72 Mother and Children

1971.

C415 C **72** 50 c. multicoloured 10 10
C416 1 e. multicoloured 10 10
C417 2 e. multicoloured 15 15
C418 3 e. multicoloured 15 15
C419 4 e. multicoloured 20 15
C420 5 e. multicoloured 30 15
C421 10 e. multicoloured 50 50
Higher values were intended for fiscal use.

NEWSPAPER STAMP

1983. "Newspaper" key-type inscr "GUINE".

N50 V 2½ r. brown 35 30

POSTAGE DUE STAMPS

1904. "Due" key-type inscr "GUINE".

D122 W 5 r. green 30 25
D123 10 r. grey 30 25
D124 20 r. brown 30 25
D125 30 r. orange 50 30
D126 50 r. brown 50 30
D127 60 r. brown 1·25 1·00
D128 100 r. mauve 1·25 1·00
D129 130 r. blue 1·25 1·00
D130 200 r. red 1·75 1·60
D131 500 r. lilac 4·50 2·50

1911. "Due" key-type of Portuguese Guinea optd **REPUBLICA**.

D138 W 5 r. green 10 10
D139 10 r. grey 10 10
D140 20 r. brown 20 10
D141 30 r. orange 20 10
D142 50 r. brown 15 10
D143 60 r. brown 50 35
D208 100 r. mauve 65 55
D145 130 r. blue 85 70
D146 200 r. red 85 70
D147 500 r. lilac 60 55

1921. "Due" key-type of Portuguese Guinea. Currency changed.

D244 W ½ c. green 15 15
D245 1 c. grey 15 15
D246 2 c. brown 15 15
D247 3 c. orange 15 15
D248 5 c. brown 15 15
D249 6 c. brown 15 15
D250 10 c. mauve 20 20
D251 13 c. blue 20 20
D252 20 c. red 20 20
D253 50 c. grey 20 20

1925. Marquis de Pombal stamps, as Nos. C247/9 optd **MULTA**.

D254 C **73** 30 c. red 30 35
D255 – 30 c. red 30 25
D256 C **75** 30 c. red 30 25

1952. As Type D **70** of Macao, but inscr "GUINE PORTUGUESA". Numerals in red, name in black (except 2 e. in blue).

D323 10 c. green and pink 10 10
D324 30 c. violet and grey 10 10
D325 50 c. green and lemon 10 10
D326 1 e. blue and grey 10 10
D327 2 e. black and olive 20 20
D328 5 e. brown and orange 25 25

MINIMUM PRICE

The minimum price quoted is 10p which represents a handling charge rather than a basis for valuing common stamps. For further notes about prices, see introductory pages.

PORTUGUESE INDIA Pt.9

Portuguese territories on the W. coast of India, consisting of Goa, Damao and Diu. Became part of India in December 1961.

1871. 1,000 reis = 1 milreis
1882. 12 reis = 1 tanga, 16 tangas = 1 rupia
1959. 100 centavos = 1 escudo

1

9

1871. Perf.

35 **1** 10 r. black 3·00 2·50
33a 15 r. pink 5·00 4·50
26 20 r. red 5·00 4·00
21 40 r. blue 30·00 25·00
22 100 r. green 40·00 32·00
23 200 r. yellow £110 90·00
27 300 r. purple 60·00 50·00
28 600 r. purple 70·00 60·00
29 900 r. purple 70·00 65·00

1877. Star above value. Perf or imperf.

241 **9** 1½ r. black 60 45
242 4½ r. olive 6·00 4·75
243 6 r. green 6·00 4·50
46 10 r. black 11·00 10·00
49 15 r. red 16·00 15·00
50 20 r. red 5·00 4·50
51 40 r. blue 9·00 6·50
52 100 r. green 40·00 35·00
53 200 r. yellow 45·00 38·00
54 300 r. purple 60·00 55·00
55 600 r. purple 60·00 55·00
56 900 r. purple 70·00 60·00

1877. "Crown" key-type inscr "INDIA PORTUGUEZA". Perf.

65 P 5 r. black 2·00 1·60
58 10 r. yellow 5·00 4·00
78 10 r. green 5·50 4·00
67 20 r. bistre 3·25 2·25
60 25 r. pink 5·00 4·00
79 25 r. grey 22·00 16·00
80 25 c. purple 15·00 12·00
69 40 r. blue 7·00 5·00
81 40 r. yellow 22·00 16·00
70 50 r. green 15·00 10·00
82 50 r. blue 10·00 8·50
71 100 r. lilac 6·00 5·00
64 200 r. orange 11·00 11·00
73 300 r. brown 12·00 12·00
See also Nos. 204/10.

1881. Surch in figures.

213 **1** 1½ on 10 r. black — £140
89 1½ on 20 r. red 38·00 30·00
91 **9** 1½ on 20 r. red 70·00 50·00
219 **1** 4½ on 40 r. blue 10·00 10·00
223 4½ on 100 r. green 20·00 18·00
96 5 on 10 r. black 3·00 2·50
98 **9** 5 on 10 r. black 19·00 15·00
101 **1** 5 on 15 r. pink 1·00 1·00
106 5 on 20 r. red 1·00 1·00
108 **9** 5 on 20 r. red 2·50 2·50
224 **1** 6 on 20 r. red
228 6 on 100 r. green 85·00 70·00
231 6 on 200 r. yellow — 65·00
233 **9** 6 on 200 r. yellow £250

1881. "Crown" key-type of Portuguese India surch in figures.

109 P 1½ on 5 r. black 60 50
110 1½ on 10 r. green 70 50
111 1½ on 20 r. olive 5·50 4·00
157 1½ on 25 r. grey 16·00 12·00
158 1½ on 100 r. lilac 27·00 20·00
114 4½ on 5 r. black 3·75 3·00
115 4½ on 10 r. green 70·00 60·00
116 4½ on 20 r. olive 1·40 1·25
162 4½ on 25 r. purple 4·50 4·00
118 4½ on 100 r. lilac 50·00 40·00
164 6 on 10 r. yellow 22·00 17·00
120 6 on 10 r. green 3·75 3·00
121 6 on 20 r. olive 7·00 5·00
167 6 on 25 r. grey 13·00 9·50
168 6 on 25 r. purple 1·40 1·00
169 6 on 40 r. blue 45·00 35·00
170 6 on 40 r. yellow 17·00 14·00
171 6 on 50 r. green 23·00 18·00
127 6 on 50 r. blue 25·00 22·00
128 1 t. on 10 r. green 70·00 60·00
129 1 t. on 20 r. olive 21·00 19·00
175 1 t. on 25 r. grey 14·00 13·00
176 1 t. on 25 r. purple 4·50 3·25
132 1 t. on 40 r. blue 8·00 6·00
178 1 t. on 50 r. green 20·00 16·00
134 1 t. on 50 r. blue 10·00 8·50
136 1 t. on 100 r. lilac 8·00 6·00
137 1 t. on 200 r. orange 18·00 15·00
139 2 t. on 25 r. purple 6·00 4·50
182 2 t. on 25 r. grey 14·00 12·00
184 2 t. on 40 r. blue 17·00 15·00
141 2 t. on 40 r. yellow 18·00 16·00
186 2 t. on 50 r. green 7·50 5·00
187 2 t. on 50 r. blue 40·00 32·00
144 2 t. on 100 r. lilac 5·00 4·00
188 2 t. on 200 r. orange 14·00 12·00
189 2 t. on 300 r. brown 14·00 12·00
190 4 t. on 10 r. green 5·50 4·50
191 4 t. on 50 r. green 4·50 5·00
192 4 t. on 200 r. orange 18·00 15·00
193 8 t. on 20 r. olive 15·00 11·00
194 8 t. on 25 r. red 75·00 65·00
151 8 t. on 40 r. blue 20·00 15·00
196 8 t. on 100 r. lilac 20·00 16·00
197 P 8 t. on 200 r. orange 14·00 11·00
198 8 t. on 300 r. brown 17·00 15·00

1882. "Crown" key-type of Portuguese India.

204II P 1½ r. black 25 20
205I 4½ r. olive 25 20
206I 6 r. green 25 20
207I 1 t. red 30 20
208I 2 t. blue 30 20
209I 4 t. purple 1·40 1·25
210I 8 t. orange 1·40 1·25

1886. "Embossed" key-type inscr "INDIA PORTUGUEZA".

244 Q 1½ r. black 90 65
245 4½ r. olive 1·00 75
246 6 r. green 1·25 85
247 1 t. red 1·75 1·25
248 2 t. blue 3·50 2·00
249 4 t. lilac 3·50 2·00
250 8 t. orange 3·25 2·00

1895. "Figures" key-type inscr "INDIA".

271 R 1½ r. black 30 20
259 4½ r. orange 45 25
273 6 r. green 50 25
274 9 r. lilac 1·75 1·50
260 1 t. blue 70 45
261 2 t. red 65 35
262 4 t. blue 80 50
270 8 t. lilac 1·60 80

1898. As Vasco da Gama stamps of Portugal T **40** etc, but inscr "INDIA".

275 1½ r. green 35 25
276 4½ r. red 35 25
277 6 r. purple 45 30
278 9 r. green 60 40
279 1 t. blue 75 55
280 2 t. brown 80 70
281 4 t. brown 1·00 75
282 8 t. bistre 1·60 1·10

1898. "King Carlos" key-type inscr "INDIA".

323 S 1 r. grey 15 15
283 1½ r. orange 15 15
324 1½ r. grey 20 10
325 2 r. orange 15 15
326 2½ r. brown 20 15
327 3 r. blue 20 15
384 4½ r. green 50 30
385 6 r. brown 50 30
328 6 r. green 20 15
286 9 r. lilac 50 30
287 1 t. green 50 20
329 1 t. red 20 15
288 2 t. blue 50 20
330 2 t. brown 80 40
331 2½ t. blue 2·75 2·00
289 4 t. blue on blue 1·25 55
332 5 t. brown on yellow 1·00 60
290 8 t. purple on pink 1·00 70
291 12 t. blue on pink 1·40 1·00
334 12 t. green on pink 2·25 1·25
292 1 rp. black on blue 2·50 1·75
335 1 rp. blue on yellow 5·00 2·25
293 2 rp. mauve on yellow 4·50 2·50
336 2 rp. black on yellow 7·50 8·00

1900. No. 288 surch **1½ Reis**.

295 S 1½ r. on 2 t. blue 80 50

1902. Surch.

299 R 1 r. on 6 r. green 25 15
298 Q 1 r. on 2 t. blue 30 20
300 2 r. on 4½ r. olive 20 15
301 R 2 r. on 8 t. lilac 25 15
302 Q 2½ r. on 6 r. green 25 15
303 R 2½ r. on 9 r. lilac 25 15
305 3 r. on 4½ r. orange 60 40
304 Q 3 r. on 1 t. red 20 15
306 R 3 r. on 1 t. blue 50 50
337 S 2 t. on 2½ t. blue 80 70
307 Q 2½ t. on 1½ r. black 70 60
312 R 2½ t. on 1½ r. black 70 40
309 Q 2½ t. on 4 t. lilac 70 50
315 R 5 t. on 2 t. red 70 50
317 5 t. on 4 t. blue 70 50
314 Q 5 t. on 8 t. orange 40 30

1902. Optd **PROVISORIO**.

319 S 6 r. brown (No. 285) 80 60
320 1 t. green (No. 287) 80 60
321 2 t. blue (No. 288) 80 60

1911. "King Carlos" key-type of Portuguese India. optd **REPUBLICA**.

338 S 1 r. grey 15 15
339 1½ r. grey 15 15
340 2 r. orange 15 15
341 2½ r. brown 20 15
342 3 r. blue 20 15
343 4½ r. green 20 15
344 6 r. green 15 15
345 9 r. lilac 20 15
346 1 t. red 30 15
347 2 t. brown 30 15
348 4 t. blue on blue 60 50
349 5 t. brown on yellow 70 50
350 8 t. purple on pink 2·00 1·10
402 12 t. green on rose 1·25 1·25
352 1 rp. blue on yellow 2·75 2·00
353 2 rp. black on yellow 3·75 3·00
404 2 rp. mauve on yellow 4·00 3·00

Both unused and used prices for the following three issues (Nos. 371 to 386) are for entire stamps showing both halves.

1911. "King Carlos" key-type of Portuguese India bisected by perforation, and each half surch.

371 S 1 r. on 2 r. orange 15 15
372 1 r. on 1 t. red 15 15
378 1 r. on 5 t. brown on yell 1·00 90
374 1½ r. on 2½ r. brown 30 25
354 1½ r. on 4½ r. green 6·00 3·00
355 1½ r. on 9 r. lilac 25 20
356 S 1½ r. on 4 t. blue on blue 25 20
375 2 r. on 2½ r. brown 25 20
357 2 r. on 4 t. blue on blue 40 25
376 3 r. on 2½ r. brown 25 20
377 3 r. on 2 t. brown 30 25
358 6 r. on 4½ r. green 35 30
359d 6 r. on 9 r. lilac 25 20
379 6 r. on 8 t. purple on pink 60 45

1912. Stamps of 1902 bisected by perf, and each half surch.

360 S 1 r. on 5 t. on 2 t. red 3·25 3·00
361 1 r. on 5 t. on 4 t. blue 3·00 2·25
363 Q 1 r. on 5 t. on 8 t. orange 1·00 75
364 2 r. on 2½ r. on 6 r. green 1·25 1·00
365 R 2 r. on 2½ r. on 9 r. lilac 7·00 7·00
366 3 r. on 5 t. on 2 t. red 3·00 2·25
367 3 r. on 5 t. on 4 t. blue 2·00 2·25
370 Q 3 r. on 5 t. on 8 t. orange 80 60

1912. "King Carlos" key-type of Portuguese India, optd **REPUBLICA**, bisected by perf and each half surch.

380 S 1 r. on 1 r. grey 15 15
381 1 r. on 2 r. orange 15 15
382 1 r. on 1 t. red 15 15
383 1 r. on 5 t. brown on yellow 15 15
384 1½ r. on 4½ r. green 20 15
419 3 r. on 2 t. brown 1·10 90
420 6 r. on 4½ r. green 40 25
386 6 r. on 9 r. lilac 20 20
422 6 r. on 8 t. purple on pink 65 55

1913. Nos. 275/82 optd **REPUBLICA**.

389 1½ r. green 25 15
390 4½ r. red 25 25
391 6 r. purple 25 20
392 9 r. green 25 20
393 1 t. blue 40 20
394 2 t. brown 80 15
395 4 t. brown 50 25
396 8 t. bistre 85 40

1914. Stamps of 1902 optd **REPUBLICA**.

406 R 2 r. on 8 t. lilac 2·75 2·25
407 Q 2½ r. on 6 r. green 40 30
459 S 2 t. on 2½ t. blue 80 45
408 R 5 t. on 2 t. red 1·25 1·00
410 5 t. on 4 t. blue 1·25 1·00
460 Q 5 t. on 8 t. orange 85 70

1914. Nos. 320/1 optd **REPUBLICA**.

415 S 1 t. green 3·00 2·25
458 2 t. blue 55 55

1914. "King Carlos" key-type of Portuguese India optd **REPUBLICA** and surch.

423 S 1½ r. on 4½ r. green 20 20
424 1½ r. on 9 r. lilac 30 20
425 1½ r. on 12 t. grn on pink 40 25
426 3 r. on 1 t. red 25 20
427 3 r. on 2 t. brown 1·00 90
428 3 r. on 8 t. purple on pink 70 60
429 3 r. on 1 rp. blue on yellow 30 20
430 3 r. on 2 rp. blk on yellow 40 30

1914. Nos. 390 and 392/6 surch.

433 1½ on 4½ r. red 20 20
434 1½ r. on 9 r. green 25 20
435 3 r. on 1 t. blue 25 20
436 3 r. on 2 t. brown 40 30
437 3 r. on 4 t. brown 20 15
438 3 r. on 8 t. bistre 80 60

1914. "Ceres" key-type inscr "INDIA".

439 U 1 r. olive 25 20
440 1½ r. green 25 20
441 2 r. black 25 20
442 2½ r. green 35 20
443 3 r. lilac 35 20
474 4 r. blue 70 60
444 4½ r. brown 35 20
445 5 r. green 35 20
446 6 r. brown 35 20
447 9 r. blue 35 20
448 10 r. red 45 25
468 1 t. violet 35 35
481 1½ t. green 70 40
469 2 t. blue 80 45
483 2½ t. blue 70 40
451 3 t. brown 1·25 35
484 3 t. 4 brown 2·25 2·00
452 4 t. grey 85 55
453 8 t. red 2·00 1·50
454 12 t. brown on green 2·00 1·50
455 1 rp. brown on red 7·00 6·50
487 1 rp. brown 9·00 7·00
456 2 rp. orange on pink 5·50 4·50
488 2 rp. yellow 9·00 7·00
457 3 rp. green on blue 6·00 4·00
489 3 rp. green 13·00 12·00
490 5 rp. red 14·00 13·00

1922. "Ceres" key-type of Portuguese India surch with new value.

496 U 1½ r. on 8 t. red 50 30
492 1½ r. on 2 r. black 25 20
497 2½ t. on 3 t. 4 brown 6·50 5·00

34 Vasco da Gama and Flagship "Sao Gabriel"

1925. 400th Death Anniv of Vasco da Gama. No gum.

493 **34** 6 r. brown 1·75 1·25
494 1 t. purple 2·25 1·25

36 The Signature of Francis
40 "Portugal" and "Galeasse"

1931. St. Francis Xavier Exhibition.
498 – 1 r. green 40 35
499 **36** 2 r. brown 40 35
500 – 6 r. purple 70 40
501 – 1½ t. brown 2·00 1·00
502 – 2 t. blue 3·50 2·25
503 – 2½ t. red 5·50 2·50
DESIGNS—VERT: 1 r. Monument to St. Francis; 6 r. St. Francis; 1½ t. St. Francis and Cross; 2½ t. St. Francis' Tomb. HORIZ: 2 t. Bom Jesus Church, Goa.

1933.
504 **40** 1 r. brown 15 10
505 2 r. brown 15 10
506 4 r. mauve 15 10
507 6 r. green 15 10
508 8 r. black 20 15
509 1 t. grey 20 20
510 1½ t. red 20 20
511 2 t. brown 20 25
512 2½ t. blue 90 25
513 3 t. blue 95 25
514 5 t. orange 1·10 25
515 1 rp. olive 2·75 1·10
516 2 rp. red 5·25 2·50
517 3 rp. orange 6·75 4·25
518 5 rp. green 13·50 12·00

1938. As T **54** and **56** of Macao, but inscr "ESTADO DA INDIA".
519 **54** 1 r. olive (postage) 15 15
520 2 r. brown 15 15
521 3 r. violet 15 15
522 6 r. green 15 15
523 – 10 r. red 20 20
524 – 1 t. mauve 20 20
525 – 1½ t. red 20 20
526 – 2 t. orange 20 20
527 – 2½ t. blue 20 20
528 – 3 t. grey 40 20
529 – 5 t. purple 70 20
530 – 1 rp. red 1·60 35
531 – 2 rp. olive 3·00 1·40
532 – 3 rp. blue 5·00 2·75
533 – 5 rp. brown 11·00 3·50
DESIGNS: 2 t. to 3 t. Prince Henry the Navigator; 5 t. to 2 rp. Dam; 3, 5 rp. Alfonso de Albuquerque.

534 **56** 1 t. red (air) 20 15
535 2½ t. violet 30 15
536 3½ t. orange 30 15
537 4½ t. blue 45 30
538 7 t. red 45 30
359 7½ t. green 80 35
540 9 t. brown 2·00 85
541 11 t. mauve 2·25 85

1942. Surch.
549 **40** 1 r. on 8 r. black 40 40
546 1 r. on 5 t. orange 40 40
550 2 r. on 8 r. black 40 30
547 3 r. on 1½ t. red 40 30
551 3 r. on 2 t. brown 40 80
552 3 r. on 3 rp. orange 1·00 90
553 6 r. on 2½ t. blue 1·25 1·00
554 6 r. on 3 t. blue 1·25 1·00
542 1 t. on 1½ t. red 1·40 1·25
548 1 t. on 2 t. brown 1·40 1·25
543 1 t. on 1 rp. olive 1·40 1·25
544 1 t. on 2 rp. red 1·40 1·25
545 1 t. on 5 rp. green 1·40 1·25

48 St. Francis Xavier
50 D. Joao de Castro

1946. Portraits and View.
555 **48** 1 r. black 15 15
556 – 2 r. red 15 15
557 – 6 r. bistre 15 15
558 – 7 r. violet 20 20
559 – 9 r. brown 50 20
560 – 1 t. green 50 20
561 – 3½ t. blue 60 45
562 – 1 rp. brown 1·50 50
DESIGNS: 2 r. Luis de Camoens; 6 r. Garcia de Orta; 7 r. Beato Joao Brito; 9 r. Vice-regal Archway; 1 t. Afonso de Albuquerque; 3½ t. Vasco da Gama; 1 rp. D. Francisco de Almeida.

1948. Portraits.
564 **50** 3 r. blue 50 30
565 – 1 t. green 50 40
566 – 1½ t. violet 80 45
567 – 2½ t. red 1·25 90
568 – 7½ t. brown 1·75 1·40
PORTRAITS: 1 t. St. Francis Xavier; 1½ t. P. Jose Vaz; 2½ t. D. Luis de Ataide; 7½ t. Duarte Pacheco Pereira.

1948. Statue of Our Lady of Fatima. As T **62** of Macao.
570 1 t. green 1·75 1·40

53 Our Lady of Fatima
59 Father Jose Vaz

1949. Statue of Our Lady of Fatima.
571 **53** 1 r. blue 50 30
572 3 r. yellow 50 30
573 9 r. pink 1·75 30
574 2 t. green 2·50 30
575 9 t. orange 2·25 90
576 2 rp. brown 4·00 1·40
577 5 rp. olive and black 7·50 2·00
578 8 rp. violet and blue 16·00 6·50

1949. 75th Anniv of U.P.U. As T **64** of Macao.
579 2½ t. red 1·50 1·10

1950. Holy Year. As Nos. 425/6 of Macao.
580 **65** 1 r. bistre 40 20
588 1 r. red 10 10
589 2 r. green 20 15
590 – 3 r. brown 20 15
591 **65** 6 r. grey 20 15
592 – 9 r. mauve 40 30
593 **65** 1 t. blue 40 30
581 – 2 t. green 55 35
594 – 2 t. yellow 40 30
595 **65** 4 t. brown 40 30

1950. Nos. 523 and 527 surch.
582 1 real on 10 r. red 15 10
583 1 real on 2½ t. blue 15 15
584 2 reis on 10 r. red 15 10
585 3 reis on 2½ t. blue 15 15
586 6 reis on 2½ t. blue 15 15
587 1 tanga on 2½ t. blue 15 15

1951. Termination of Holy Year. As T **69** of Macao.
596 1 rp. blue and lavender 80 60

1951. 300th Birth Anniv of Jose Vaz.
597 **59** 1 r. grey 10 10
598 – 2 r. orange and brown 10 10
599 **59** 3 r. black 25 15
600 – 1 t. blue and indigo 10 10
601 **59** 2 t. red 10 10
602 – 3 t. olive and black 20 10
603 **59** 9 t. blue and indigo 30 20
604 – 10 t. mauve 40 30
605 – 12 t. sepia and black 60 50
DESIGNS—Inscr "1651, 1951": 1, 3, 10 t. Sancoale Church Ruins; 12 t. Veneravel Altar.

60 Goa Medical School

1952. 1st Tropical Medicine Congress, Lisbon.
606 **60** 4½ t. blue and black 1·40 1·25

1952. 4th Death Cent of St. Francis Xavier. As Nos. 452/4 of Macao but without lined background.
607 6 r. multicoloured 15 10
608 2 t. multicoloured 75 30
609 5 t. olive, silver and mauve 1·40 50

62 St. Francis Xavier
63 Stamp of 1871
64 The Virgin

1952. Philatelic Exhibition, Goa.
612 **63** 3 t. black 4·00 4·00
613 **62** 5 t. black and lilac 4·00 4·00

1953. Missionary Art Exhibition.
614 **64** 6 r. black and blue 10 10
615 1 t. brown and buff 35 20
616 3 t. lilac and olive 1·00 80

1953. Portuguese Postage Stamp Centenary. As T **75** of Macao.
617 1 t. multicoloured 35 30

66 Dr. Gama Pinto
67 Academy Buildings

1954. Birth Centenary of Dr. Gama Pinto.
618 **66** 3 r. green and grey 10 10
619 2 t. black and blue 15 15

1954. 4th Cent of Sao Paulo. As T **76** of Macao.
620 2 t. multicoloured 20 20

1954. Centenary of Afonso de Albuquerque National Academy.
621 **67** 9 t. multicoloured 45 30

68 Mgr. Dalgado
71 M. A. de Sousa

73 Map of Bacaim
72 F. de Almeida

1955. Birth Centenary of Mgr. Dalgado.
622 **68** 1 r. multicoloured 10 10
623 1 t. multicoloured 20 10

1956 450th Anniv of Portuguese Settlements in India. Multicoloured. (a) Famous Men. As T **71**.
624 6 r. M. A. de Sousa 15 15
625 1½ t. F. N. Xavier 15 15
626 4 t. A. V. Lourenco 15 15
627 8 t. Father Jose Vaz 20 15
628 9 t. M. G. de Heredia 25 15
629 2 rp. A. C. Pacheco 75 60

(b) Viceroys. As T **72**.
630 3 r. F. de Almeida 10 10
631 9 r. A. de Albuquerque 15 15
632 1 t. Vasco da Gama 15 15
633 3 t. N. da Cunha 20 15
634 10 t. J. de Castro 20 15
635 3 rp. C. de Braganca 90 60

(c) Settlements. As T **73**.
636 2 t. Bacaim 1·40 1·00
637 2½ t. Mombaim 90 60
638 3½ t. Damao 90 60
639 5 t. Diu 35 25
640 12 t. Cochim 50 45
641 1 rp. Goa 1·25 1·00

74 Map of Damao. Dadra and Nagar Aveli Districts
75 Arms of Vasco da Gama

1957. Centres multicoloured.
642 **74** 3 r. grey 10 10
643 6 r. green 10 10
644 3 t. pink 15 15
645 6 t. blue 15 15
646 11 t. bistre 35 25
647 2 rp. lilac 65 50
648 3 rp. yellow 90 75
649 5 rp. red 1·40 1·00

1958. Heraldic Arms of Famous Men. Multicoloured designs.
650 2 r. Type **75** 10 10
651 6 r. Lopo Soares de Albergaria 10 10
652 9 r. D. Francisco de Almeida 10 10
653 1 t. Garcia de Noronha 10 10
654 4 t. D. Afonso de Albuquerque 15 15
655 5 t. D. Joao de Castro 20 15
656 11 t. D. Luis de Ataide 30 30
657 1 rp. Nuno da Cunha 35 30

1958. 6th International Congress of Tropical Medicine. As T **79** of Macao.
658 5 t. multicoloured 40 30
DESIGN: 5 t. "Holarrhena antidysenterica" (plant).

1958. Brussels Int Exn. As T **78** of Macao.
659 1 rp. multicoloured 20 20

1959. Surch in new currency.
660 – 5 c. on 2 r. (No. 650) 10 10
661 **74** 10 c. on 3 r. grey 10 10
662 – 15 c. on 6 r. (No. 651) 10 10
663 – 20 c. on 9 r. (No. 652) 10 10
664 – 30 c. on 1 t. (No. 653) 10 10
681 – 40 c. on 1½ t. (No. 566) 10 10
682 – 40 c. on 1½ t. (No. 625) 10 10
683 – 40 c. on 2 t. (No. 620) 25 15
665 – 40 c. on 2 t. (No. 636) 10 10
666 – 40 c. on 2½ t. (No. 637) 25 20
667 – 40 c. on 3½ t. (No. 638) 15 15
668 **74** 50 c. on 3 t. pink 15 15
684 **64** 80 c. on 3 t. lilac and olive 15 15
669 – 80 c. on 3 t. (No. 633) 15 15
685 – 80 c. on 3½ t. (No. 561) 15 15
686 – 80 c. on 5 t. (No. 658) 35 15
670 – 80 c. on 10 t. (No. 634) 20 20
687 – 80 c. on 1 rp. (No. 659) 85 40
671 – 80 c. on 3 rp. (No. 635) 35 20
672 – 1 e. on 4 t. (No. 654) 15 15
673 – 1 e. 50 on 5 t. (No. 655) 15 15
674 **74** 2 e. on 6 t. blue 15 15
675 2 e. 50 on 11 t. bistre 20 10
676 – 4 e. on 11 t. (No. 656) 25 25
677 – 4 e. 50 on 1 rp. (No. 657) 35 30
678 **74** 5 e. on 2 rp. lilac 35 40
679 10 e. on 3 rp. yellow 50 45
680 30 e. on 5 rp. red 1·75 45

78 Coin of Manoel I
79 Prince Henry's Arms

1959. Portuguese Indian Coins. Designs showing both sides of coins of various rulers. Multicoloured.
688 5 c. Type **78** 10 10
689 10 c. Joao III 10 10
690 15 c. Sebastiao 10 10
691 30 c. Filipe I 15 15
692 40 c. Filipe II 15 15
693 50 c. Filipe III 10 10
694 60 c. Joao IV 10 10
695 80 c. Afonso VI 10 10
696 1 e. Pedro II 10 10
697 1 e. 50 Joao V 10 10
698 2 e. Jose I 20 10
699 2 e. 50 Maria I 20 10
700 3 e. Prince Regent Joao 20 15
701 4 e. Pedro IV 25 20
702 4 e. 40 Miguel 25 20
703 5 e. Maria II 25 20
704 10 e. Pedro V 45 40
705 20 e. Luis 1·40 1·25
706 30 e. Carlos 1·75 1·60
707 50 e. Portuguese Republic 3·00 2·25

1960. 500th Death Anniv of Prince Henry the Navigator.
708 **79** 3 e. multicoloured 25 25

The 1962 sports set and malaria eradication stamp similar to those for the other territories were ready for issue when Portuguese India was occupied, but they were not put on sale there.

CHARITY TAX STAMPS.

The notes under this heading in Portugal also apply here.

1919. Fiscal stamp. Type C **1** of Portuguese Africa optd **TAXA DE GUERRA**.
C491 Rps. 0:00:05, 48 green 1·25 1·00
C492 Rps. 0:02:03, 43 green 2·25 1·75

1925. Marquis de Pombal Commem stamps of Portugal, but inscr "INDIA".
C495 C **73** 6 r. red 20 20
C496 – 6 r. red 20 20
C497 C **75** 6 r. red 20 20

C 52 Mother and Child
C 69 Mother and Child

1948. (a) Inscr "ASSISTENCIA PUBLICA".
C571 C **52** 6 r. green 1·25 75
C572 6 r. yellow 1·00 60
C573 1 t. red 1·25 75
C574 1 t. orange 1·10 60
C575 1 t. green 1·50 1·00

(b) Inscr "PROVEDORIA DE ASSISTENCIA PUBLICA".
C607 C **52** 1 t. grey 1·25 75

1951. Surch **1 tanga**.
C606 C **52** 1 t. on 6 r. red 1·00 70

1953. Optd **"Revalidado" P.A.P.** and dotted line.
C617 C **52** 1 t. red 3·00 1·75

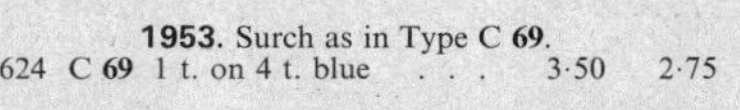

1953. Surch as in Type C **69**.
C624 C **69** 1 t. on 4 t. blue 3·50 2·75

C 70 Mother and Child
C 80 Arms and People

1956.
C625 C 70 1 t. black, green & red . . . 30 20
C626 1 t. blue, salmon & grn . . . 30 20

1957. Surch.
C650 C 70 6 r. on 1 t. black, green and red . . . 30 20

1959. Surch.
C688 C 70 20 c. on 1 t. blue, salmon and green . . . 15 15
C689 40 c. on 1 t. blue, salmon and green . . . 15 15

1960.
C709 C 80 20 e. brown and red . . . 15 15

POSTAGE DUE STAMPS

1904. "Due" key-type inscr "INDIA"
D337 W 2 r. green . . . 25 25
D338 3 r. green . . . 25 25
D339 4 r. orange . . . 25 25
D340 5 r. black . . . 25 25
D341 6 r. grey . . . 25 25
D342 9 r. brown . . . 25 25
D343 1 t. orange . . . 30 25
D344 2 t. brown . . . 65 45
D345 5 t. blue . . . 1·40 1·25
D346 10 t. red . . . 1·40 1·25
D347 1 rp. lilac . . . 4·50 3·25

1911. Nos. D337/47 optd **REPUBLICA**.
D354 W 2 r. green . . . 15 15
D355 3 r. green . . . 15 15
D356 4 r. orange . . . 15 15
D357 5 r. black . . . 15 15
D358 6 r. grey . . . 15 15
D359 9 r. brown . . . 15 15
D360 1 t. orange . . . 15 15
D361 2 t. brown . . . 40 30
D362 5 t. blue . . . 80 60
D363 10 t. red . . . 1·25 1·10
D364 1 rp. lilac . . . 3·50 1·50

1925. Marquis de Pombal stamps, as Nos. C 495/7 optd **MULTA**.
D495 C 73 1 t. red . . . 20 20
D496 – 1 t. red . . . 20 20
D497 C 75 1 t. red . . . 20 20

1943. Stamps of 1933 surch. **Porteado** and new value.
D549 40 3 r. on 2½ t. blue . . . 20 20
D550 6 r. on 3 t. blue . . . 30 30
D551 1 t. on 5 t. orange . . . 45 45

1945. As Type D 1 of Portuguese Colonies, but opt **ESTADO DA INDIA**.
D555 2 r. red . . . 40 40
D556 3 r. blue . . . 40 40
D557 4 r. yellow . . . 40 40
D558 6 r. green . . . 40 40
D559 1 t. brown . . . 40 40
D560 2 t. brown . . . 40 40

1951. Surch **Porteado** and new value and bar.
D588 2 rs. on 7 r. (No. 558) . . . 20 20
D589 3 rs. on 7 r. (No. 558) . . . 20 20
D590 1 t. on 1 rp. (No. 562) . . . 20 20
D591 2 t. on 1 rp. (No. 562) . . . 20 20

1952. As Type D 70 of Macao, but inscr "INDIA PORTUGUESA". Numerals in red, name in black.
D606 2 r. olive and brown . . . 10 10
D607 3 r. black and green . . . 10 10
D608 6 r. blue and turquoise . . . 10 10
D609 1 t. red and grey . . . 15 15
D610 2 t. orange, green and grey . . . 25 25
D611 10 t. blue, green and yellow . . . 85 85

1959. Nos. D606/8 and D610/11 surch in new currency.
D688 5 e. on 2 r. olive and brown . . . 10 10
D689 10 e. on 3 r. black & green . . . 10 10
D690 15 e. on 6 r. blue & turq . . . 15 15
D691 60 e. on 2 t. orange, green and grey . . . 55 55
D692 60 e. on 10 t. blue, grn & yell . . . 1·10 1·10

PRUSSIA Pt.7

Formerly a kingdom in the N. of Germany. In 1867 it became part of the North German Confederation.

1850. 12 pfenige = 1 silbergroschen
30 silbergroschen = 1 thaler
1867. 60 kreuzer = 1 gulden

1 Friedrich Wilhelm IV 3 4

1850. Imperf.
14 1 4 pf. green . . . 65·00 24·00
4 6 pf. red . . . 70·00 38·00
5 1 sgr. black on red . . . 80·00 4·75
16 1 sgr. red . . . 35·00 1·50
6 2 sgr. black on blue . . . 85·00 10·00
18 2 sgr. blue . . . 90·00 11·00
8 3 sgr. black on yellow . . . 85·00 8·00
21 3 sgr. yellow . . . 70·00 11·00

1861. Roul.
24 3 3 pf. lilac . . . 17·00 30·00
26 4 pf. green . . . 8·00 5·50
28 6 pf. orange . . . 6·50 12·00
31 4 1 sgr. red . . . 3·25 30
35 2 sgr. blue . . . 7·00 80
36 3 sgr. brown . . . 7·00 1·25

5 7

1866. Printed in reverse on back of specially treated transparent paper. Roul.
38 5 10 sgr. red . . . 50·00 65·00
39 30 sgr. blue . . . 70·00 £170
The 30 sgr. has the value in a square.

1867. Roul.
40 7 1 k. green . . . 17·00 38·00
42 2 k. orange . . . 38·00 85·00
43 3 k. red . . . 16·00 18·00
45 6 k. blue . . . 16·00 40·00
46 9 k. bistre . . . 20·00 45·00

PUERTO RICO Pt.9; Pt.22

A W. Indian island ceded by Spain to the United States after the war of 1898. Until 1873 stamps of Cuba were in use. Now uses stamps of the U.S.A.

1873. 100 centimos = 1 peseta
1881. 1000 milesimas = 100 centavos = 1 peso
1898. 100 cents = 1 dollar

A. SPANISH OCCUPATION

(2)

1873. Nos. 53/5 of Cuba optd with T **2**.
1 25 c. de p. lilac . . . 25·00 1·25
3 50 c. de p. brown . . . 60·00 5·00
4 1 p. brown . . . £110 12·00

1874. No. 57 of Cuba with opt similar to T **2**. (Two separate characters).
5 25 c. de p. blue . . . 20·00 2·00

1875. Nos. 61/3 of Cuba with opt similar to T **2**. (Two separate characters).
6 25 c. de p. blue . . . 13·00 1·75
7 50 c. de p. green . . . 20·00 2·50
8 1 p. brown . . . 75·00 8·00

1876. Nos. 65a and 67 of Cuba with opt similar to T **2**. (Two separate characters).
9 25 c. de p. lilac . . . 2·75 1·25
10 50 c. de p. blue . . . 7·50 2·25
11 1 p. black . . . 25·00 6·00

1876. Nos. 65a and 67 of Cuba with optd as last, but characters joined.
12 25 c. de p. lilac . . . 8·00 1·10
13 1 p. black . . . 27·00 6·00

1877. As T **45** of Spain, but inscr "PTO-RICO 1877".
14 5 c. brown . . . 3·50 1·50
15 10 c. red . . . 12·00 1·75
16 15 c. green . . . 18·00 7·50
17 25 c. blue . . . 7·00 1·10
18 50 c. brown . . . 12·00 2·50

1878. As T **45** of Spain, but inscr "PTO-RICO 1878".
19 5 c. olive . . . 10·00 10·00
20 10 c. brown . . . £110 45·00
21 25 c. green . . . 1·00 80
22 50 c. blue . . . 4·00 1·25
23a 1 p. brown . . . 7·00 3·75

1879. As T **45** of Spain, but inscr "PTO-RICO 1879".
24 5 c. red . . . 6·50 2·75
25 10 c. brown . . . 6·50 2·50
26 15 c. black . . . 6·50 2·75
27 25 c. blue . . . 2·00 95
28 50 c. green . . . 6·00 2·25
29 1 p. grey . . . 25·00 10·00

1880. "Alfonso XII" key-type inscr "PUERTO-RICO 1880".
30 X ¼ c. green . . . 15·00 8·00
31 ½ c. red . . . 4·00 1·25
32 1 c. red . . . 6·00 4·00
33 2 c. grey . . . 4·00 2·00
34 3 c. orange . . . 4·00 2·00
35 4 c. black . . . 4·00 2·00
36 5 c. green . . . 2·00 90
37 10 c. red . . . 2·50 1·25
38 15 c. brown . . . 4·00 1·60
39 25 c. lilac . . . 2·00 70
40 40 c. grey . . . 6·00 85
41 50 c. brown . . . 12·00 6·50
42 1 p. olive . . . 38·00 8·00

1881. "Alfonso XIII" key-type inscr "PUERTO-RICO 1881".
43 X ½ m. red . . . 20 10
45 1 m. violet . . . 25 10
46 2 m. red . . . 35 25
47 4 m. green . . . 60 20
48 6 m. red . . . 60 30
49 8 m. blue . . . 1·40 60
50 1 c. green . . . 2·25 1·10
51 2 c. red . . . 2·75 1·75
52 3 c. brown . . . 6·50 2·75
53 5 c. lilac . . . 2·25 20
54 8 c. brown . . . 3·50 60
55 10 c. lilac . . . 15·00 4·50
56 20 c. olive . . . 22·00 6·00

1882. "Alfonso XII" key-type inscr "PUERTO-RICO".
57 X ½ m. red . . . 15 10
74 1 m. red . . . 15 10
75 1 m. orange . . . 15 10
59 2 m. mauve . . . 20 15
60 4 m. purple . . . 20 15
61 6 m. brown . . . 25 15
62 8 m. green . . . 25 15
63 1 c. green . . . 15 15
64 2 c. red . . . 80 15
65 3 c. yellow . . . 2·25 1·00
76 3 c. brown . . . 2·25 30
77 5 c. lilac . . . 8·00 1·00
67 8 c. brown . . . 2·75 10
68 10 c. green . . . 2·75 20
69 20 c. grey . . . 3·25 20
70 40 c. blue . . . 22·00 7·00
71 80 c. brown . . . 32·00 8·00

1890. "Baby" key-type inscr "PUERTO-RICO".
95 Y ½ m. black . . . 10 10
111 ½ m. brown . . . 10 10
124 ½ m. purple . . . 10 10
81 1 m. green . . . 25 10
96 1 m. purple . . . 10 10
112 1 m. blue . . . 10 10
125 1 m. brown . . . 10 10
113 2 m. red . . . 10 10
97 2 m. purple . . . 10 10
126 2 m. green . . . 10 10
83 4 m. black . . . 8·00 4·00
98 4 m. blue . . . 10 10
114 4 m. brown . . . 10 10
127 4 m. green . . . 60 25
84 6 m. brown . . . 25·00 9·00
99 6 m. red . . . 10 10
85 8 m. bistre . . . 25·00 18·00
100 8 m. green . . . 10 10
86 1 c. brown . . . 20 10
101 1 c. green . . . 40 10
115 1 c. purple . . . 2·75 15
128 1 c. red . . . 30 10
87 2 c. purple . . . 1·00 50
102 2 c. pink . . . 70 10
116 2 c. lilac . . . 1·00 15
129 2 c. brown . . . 30 10
88 3 c. blue . . . 6·00 40
103 3 c. orange . . . 70 10
117 3 c. grey . . . 2·50 15
131 3 c. brown . . . 20 10
89 5 c. purple . . . 8·00 30
104 5 c. green . . . 60 10
133 5 c. blue . . . 20 10
120 6 c. orange . . . 25 10
134 6 c. lilac . . . 20 10
90 8 c. blue . . . 11·00 1·25
105 8 c. brown . . . 15 10
121 8 c. purple . . . 5·50 1·50
135 8 c. red . . . 1·25 50
106 10 c. red . . . 70 10
122 20 c. red . . . 75 15
107 20 c. lilac . . . 1·00 20
136 20 c. grey . . . 3·25 50
93 40 c. orange . . . 65·00 22·00
108 40 c. blue . . . 2·75 1·10
137 40 c. red . . . 3·25 1·25
94 80 c. green . . . £200 90·00
109 80 c. red . . . 6·50 3·00
138 80 c. black . . . 17·00 8·50

13 Landing of Columbus

1893. 400th Anniv of Discovery of America by Columbus.
110 13 3 c. green . . . £100 28·00

1898. "Curly Head" key-type inscr "PTO RICO 1898 y 99".
139 Z 1 m. brown . . . 10 10
140 2 m. brown . . . 10 10
141 3 m. brown . . . 10 10
142 4 m. brown . . . 1·10 50
143 5 m. brown . . . 10 10
144 1 c. violet . . . 10 10
145 2 c. green . . . 10 10
146 3 c. brown . . . 10 10
147 4 c. orange . . . 1·10 60
148 5 c. red . . . 10 10
149 6 c. blue . . . 15 10
150 8 c. brown . . . 15 10
151 10 c. red . . . 15 10
152 15 c. olive . . . 15 10
153 20 c. red . . . 1·25 40
154 40 c. lilac . . . 90 90
155 60 c. black . . . 90 90
156 80 c. brown . . . 3·00 3·00
157 1 p. green . . . 5·50 5·00
158 2 p. blue . . . 12·00 6·00

1898. "Baby" key-type inscr "PUERTO RICO" and optd **Habilitado PARA 1898 y '99**.
159 Y ½ m. purple . . . 9·00 4·25
160 1 m. brown . . . 30 15
161 2 m. green . . . 30 15
162 4 m. green . . . 30 15
163 1 c. red . . . 30 15
164 2 c. brown . . . 30 15
165 3 c. blue . . . 10·00 6·00
166 3 c. brown . . . 35 10
167 4 c. grey . . . 35 25
168 4 c. blue . . . 9·00 5·00
169 5 c. blue . . . 30 25
171 5 c. green . . . 7·50 5·00
172 6 c. lilac . . . 30 20
173a 8 c. red . . . 30 30
174 20 c. grey . . . 75 40
175 40 c. red . . . 2·00 50
176 80 c. black . . . 15·00 12·00

WAR TAX STAMPS

1898. "Baby" key-type inscr "PUERTO RICO" and "Curly Head" key-type inscr "PTO. RICO 1898 y 99", optd **IMPUESTO DE GUERRA** or surch also.
W177 Y 1 m. blue . . . 2·25 1·25
W178 1 m. brown . . . 6·00 3·75
W179 2 m. red . . . 10·00 6·00
W180 2 m. green . . . 5·50 4·00
W181 4 m. green . . . 8·00 7·00
W182a 1 c. brown . . . 4·75 2·75
W183 1 c. red . . . 9·00 7·00
W184 2 c. purple . . . 30 20
W185 2 c. red . . . 30 20
W186 2 c. lilac . . . 60 60
W187 2 c. brown . . . 35 20
W192 2 c. on 2 m. red . . . 25 15
W193c 2 c. on 5 c. green . . . 1·75 1·60
W188 3 c. orange . . . 10·00 8·00
W194 3 c. on 10 c. red . . . 10·00 7·00
W195 4 c. on 20 c. red . . . 10·00 7·00
W189 5 c. green . . . 25 15
W196a 5 c. on ½ m. brown . . . 5·00 3·00
W197 5 c. on 1 m. purple . . . 40 40
W198 5 c. on 1 m. blue . . . 30 30
W199 Z 5 c. on 1 m. brown . . . 6·50 3·50
W200 Y 5 c. on 5 c. green . . . 3·25 2·50
W191 8 c. purple . . . 15·00 12·00

B. UNITED STATES OCCUPATION

1899. 1894 stamps of United States (No. 267 etc) optd **PORTO RICO**.
202 1 c. green . . . 6·00 1·25
203 2 c. red . . . 5·50 1·00
204 5 c. blue . . . 8·50 1·75
205 8 c. brown . . . 25·00 12·00
206 10 c. brown . . . 18·00 3·75

1900. 1894 stamps of United States (No. 267 etc) optd **PUERTO RICO**.
210 1 c. green . . . 5·00 1·25
212 2 c. red . . . 4·50 90

POSTAGE DUE STAMPS

1899. Postage Due stamps of United States of 1894 optd **PORTO RICO**.
D207 D 87 1 c. red . . . 18·00 6·00
D208 2 c. red . . . 14·00 4·50
D209 10 c. red . . . £130 42·00

QATAR Pt.19

An independent Arab Shaikhdom with British postal administration until May 23, 1963, issues for which are listed in Volume 3. Later issues by the Qatar Post Department.

1964. 100 naye paise = 1 rupee
1966. 100 dirhams = 1 riyal

1964. Olympic Games Tokyo. Optd **1964** Olympic Rings and Arabic inscr or surch also.
38 9 50 n.p. brown . . . 1·75 1·25
39 – 75 n.p. blue (No. 33) . . . 2·50 1·75
40 – 1 r. on 10 r. black (No. 37) . . . 3·50 2·50
41 11 2 r. blue . . . 5·00 2·75
42 5 r. green (No. 36) . . . 9·00 7·50

1964. Pres. Kennedy Commem. Optd **John F Kennedy 1917–1963** in English and Arabic or surch also.
43 9 50 n.p. brown . . . 1·75 1·25
44 – 75 n.p. blue (No. 33) . . . 2·50 1·75
45 – 1 r. on 10 r. black (No. 37) . . . 3·50 2·50
46 11 2 r. blue . . . 5·00 3·75
47 – 5 r. green (No. 36) . . . 9·00 7·50

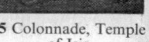

15 Colonnade, Temple of Isis

16 Scouts on Parade

1965. Nubian Monuments Preservation. Mult.
48 1 n.p. Type **15** 10 10
49 2 n.p. Temple of Isis, Philac . . 10 10
50 3 n.p. Trajan's Kiosk, Philac . 10 10
51 1 r. As 3 n.p. 40 60
52 1 r. 50 As 2 n.p. . . . . 2·50 1·25
53 2 r. Type **15** . . . . 3·00 2·00

1965. Qatar Scouts.
54 – 1 n.p. brown and green . . 10 10
55 – 2 n.p. blue and brown . . . 10 10
56 – 3 n.p. blue and green . . . 10 10
57 – 4 n.p. brown and blue . . . 10 10
58 – 5 n.p. blue and turquoise . . 10 10
59 **16** 30 n.p. multicoloured . . . 75 30
60 40 n.p. multicoloured . . . 1·25 45
61 1 r. multicoloured . . . . . 2·25 1·00
DESIGNS—TRIANGULAR (60 × 30 mm): 1., 4 n.p. Qatar Scout badge; 2, 3, 5 n.p. Ruler, badge, palms and camp.

17 "Telstar" and Eiffel Tower

1965. I.T.U. Centenary.
62 **17** 1 n.p. brown and blue . . . 10 10
63 – 2 n.p. brown and blue . . . 10 10
64 – 3 n.p. violet and green . . . 10 10
65 – 4 n.p. blue and brown . . . 10 10
66 **17** 5 n.p. ochre and violet . . . 10 10
67 – 40 n.p. black and red . . . 1·50 70
68 – 50 n.p. ochre and green . . 1·50 70
69 – 1 r. red and green . . . . . 2·50 1·25
DESIGNS: 2 n.p., 1 r. "Syncom 3" and pagoda; 3, 40 n.p. "Relay" and radar scanner; 4, 50 n.p. Post Office Tower (London), globe and satellites.

18 Triggerfish

1965. Fish of the Arabian Gulf. Multicoloured.
70 1 n.p. Type **18** 10 10
71 2 n.p. Butterfly sweetlip 10 10
72 3 n.p. Saddle-spot butterfly fish 10 10
73 4 n.p. Threadfin butterfly fish . 10 10
74 5 n.p. Mahomet's lancet fish . . 10 10
75 15 n.p. Paradise fish 30 10
76 20 n.p. Sailfin tang 35 10
77 30 n.p. Thousand-spotted grouper 45 10
78 40 n.p. Regal angelfish 60 15
79 50 n.p. As 2 n.p. 90 30
80 75 n.p. Type **18** . . . . 1·50 35
81 1 r. As 30 n.p. . . . . 2·25 35
82 2 r. As 20 n.p. . . . . 4·50 90
83 3 r. As 15 n.p. . . . . 6·50 1·75
84 4 r. As 5 n.p. . . . . 8·00 2·25
85 5 r. As 4 n.p. . . . . 8·50 2·50
86 10 r. As 3 n.p. . . . . 14·00 3·00

19 Basketball

1966. Pan-Arab Games, Cairo (1965).
87 **19** 1 r. black, grey and red . . 1·25 80
88 – 1 r. brown and green . . . . 1·25 80
89 – 1 r. red and blue . . . . . . 1·25 80
90 – 1 r. green and blue . . . . . 1·25 80
91 – 1 r. blue and brown . . . . 1·25 80
SPORTS: No. 88, Horse-jumping; No. 89, Running; No. 90, Football; No. 91, Weightlifting.

1966. Space Rendezvous. Nos. 62/9 optd **SPACE RENDEZVOUS 15th DECEMBER 1965** in English and Arabic and two space capsules.
92 **17** 1 n.p. brown and blue . . . 10 10
93 – 2 n.p. brown and blue . . . 10 10
94 – 3 n.p. violet and green . . . 10 10
95 – 4 n.p. blue and brown . . . 10 10
96 **17** 5 n.p. ochre and violet . . . 10 10
97 – 40 n.p. black and red . . . 75 30
98 – 50 n.p. ochre and green . . 1·25 35
99 – 1 r. red and green . . . . . 2·75 1·25

21 Shaikh Ahmed

1966. Gold and Silver Coinage. Circular designs embossed on gold (G) or silver (S) foil, backed with "Walsall Security Paper" inscr in English and Arabic. Imperf. (a) Diameter 1$\frac{11}{16}$in.
101 **21** 1 n.p. bistre and purple (S) 10 10
102 – 3 n.p. black and orange (S) 10 10
103 **21** 4 n.p. violet and red (G) . 10 10
104 – 5 n.p. green and red (G) . 10 10

(b) Diameter 2$\frac{3}{16}$in.
105 **21** 10 n.p. brown & violet (S) 20 10
106 – 40 n.p. red and blue (S) . 1·00 20
107 **21** 70 n.p. blue & ultram (G) 1·75 40
108 – 80 n.p. red and green (G) . 2·00 50

(c) Diameter 2$\frac{9}{16}$in.
109 **21** 1 r. mauve and black (S) . 2·25 50
110 – 2 r. green and purple (S) . 6·00 1·50
111 **21** 5 r. purple and orange (G) 11·00 3·25
112 – 10 r. blue and red (G) . . 17·00 6·50
The 1, 4, 10, 70 n.p. and 1 and 5 r. each show the obverse side of the coins as Type **21**. The remainder show the reverse side of the coins (Shaikh's seal).

22 I.C.Y. and U.N. Emblem

1966. International Co-operation Year.
113 **22** 40 n.p. brn, violet & blue 1·50 70
114 A 40 n.p. violet, brn & turq 1·50 70
115 B 40 n.p. blue, brn & violet 1·50 70
116 C 40 n.p. turq, violet & bl 1·50 70
DESIGNS: A, Pres. Kennedy, I.C.Y. emblem and U.N. Headquarters; B, Dag Hammarskjold and U.N. General Assembly; C, Nehru and dove.
Nos. 113/16 were issued together in blocks of four, each sheet containing four blocks separated by gutter margins. Subsequently the sheets were reissued perf and imperf with the opt **U.N. 20TH ANNIVERSARY** on the stamps. The gutter margins were also printed in various designs, face values and overprints.

23 Pres. Kennedy and New York Skyline

1966. Pres. Kennedy Commem. Multicoloured.
118 10 n.p. Type **23** 25 10
119 30 n.p. Pres. Kennedy and Cape Kennedy 50 15
120 60 n.p. Pres. Kennedy and Statue of Liberty . . . . 1·00 35
121 70 n.p. Type **23** . . . . . . 1·25 40
122 80 n.p. As 30 n.p. . . . . . 1·40 50
123 1 r. As 60 n.p. . . . . . . 1·60 60

24 Horse-jumping

1966. Olympic Games Preparation (Mexico). Multicoloured.
125 1 n.p. Type **24** 10 10
126 4 n.p. Running 10 10
127 5 n.p. Throwing the javelin . 10 10
128 70 n.p. Type **24** 75 40
129 80 n.p. Running 90 55
130 90 n.p. Throwing the javelin . 1·10 80

25 J. A. Lovell and Capsule

1966. American Astronauts. Each design showing space-craft and Astronaut. Multicoloured.
132 5 n.p. Type **25** 10 10
133 10 n.p. T. P. Stafford 15 10
134 15 n.p. A. B. Shepard 25 10
135 20 n.p. J. H. Glenn 25 10
136 30 n.p. M. Scott Carpenter . . 40 20
137 40 n.p. W. M. Schirra 55 20
138 50 n.p. V. I. Grissom 70 35
139 60 n.p. L. G. Cooper 90 45
Nos. 132/4 are diamond-shaped as Type **25**, the remainder are horiz designs (56 × 25 mm).

1966. Various stamps with currency names changed to dirhams and riyals by overprinting in English and Arabic.
(i) Nos. 27/37 (Definitives).
141 5 d. on 5 n.p. 10 10
142 15 d. on 15 n.p. 25 10
143 20 d. on 20 n.p. 25 10
144 30 d. on 30 n.p. 45 15
145 40 d. on 40 n.p. . . . . . . 1·00 20
146 50 d. on 50 n.p. . . . . . . 1·25 30
147 75 d. on 75 n.p. . . . . . . 1·50 45
148 1 r. on 1 r. . . . . 1·75 40
149 2 r. on 2 r. . . . . 3·75 1·50
150 5 r. on 5 r. . . . . 8·50 5·00
151 10 r. on 10 r. . . . . 14·00 7·50

(ii) Nos. 70/86 (Fish).
152 1 d. on 1 n.p. 10 10
153 2 d. on 2 n.p. 10 10
154 3 d. on 3 n.p. 10 10
155 4 d. on 4 n.p. 10 10
156 5 d. on 5 n.p. 10 10
157 15 d. on 15 n.p. 25 10
158 20 d. on 20 n.p. 30 10
159 30 d. on 30 n.p. 45 15
160 40 d. on 40 n.p. 60 15
161 50 d. on 50 n.p. 75 20
162 75 d. on 75 n.p. . . . . . . 1·25 40
163 1 r. on 1 r. . . . . 1·50 50
164 2 r. on 2 r. . . . . 3·25 1·50
165 3 r. on 3 r. . . . . 5·00 2·75
166 4 r. on 4 r. . . . . 7·00 4·00
167 5 r. on 5 r. . . . . 9·00 4·75
168 10 r. on 10 r. . . . . 15·00 9·00

27 National Library, Doha

1966. Education Day. Multicoloured.
169 2 n.p. Type **27** 10 10
170 3 n.p. School and playing field 10 10
171 5 n.p. School and gardens . . 10 10
172 1 r. Type **27** . . . . 1·50 65
173 2 r. As 3 n.p. . . . . 2·50 1·25
174 3 r. As 5 n.p. . . . . 3·50 1·75

28 Palace, Doha

29 Hands holding Jules Rimet Trophy

1966. Currency expressed in naye paise and rupees. Multicoloured.
175 2 n.p. Type **28** 10 10
176 3 n.p. Gulf Street, Shahra Al-Khalij 10 10
177 10 n.p. Doha airport 30 10
178 15 n.p. Garden, Rayan 35 10
179 20 n.p. Head Post Office, Doha 45 10
180 30 n.p. Mosque Doha (vert) . 50 10
181 40 n.p. Shaikh Ahmad 85 15
182 50 n.p. Type **28** 95 20
183 60 n.p. As 3 n.p. . . . . . . 1·25 40
184 70 n.p. As 10 n.p. . . . . . 2·00 50
185 80 n.p. As 15 n.p. . . . . . 1·75 60
186 90 n.p. As 20 n.p. . . . . . 2·00 90
187 1 r. As 30 n.p. (vert) . . . 2·25 70
188 2 r. As 40 n.p. . . . . 4·00 2·25

1966. World Football Cup Championships, England.
189 **29** 60 n.p. mult (postage) . . . 80 65
190 – 70 n.p. multicoloured . . . 1·00 80
191 – 80 n.p. multicoloured . . . 1·25 1·00
192 – 90 n.p. multicoloured . . . 1·40 1·10
193 – 1 n.p. blue (air) 15 15
194 – 2 n.p. blue 15 15
195 – 3 n.p. blue 20 20
196 – 4 n.p. blue 20 30
DESIGNS: No. 190, Jules Rimet Trophy and "football" globe; No. 191, Footballers and globe; No. 192, Wembley stadium; Nos. 193/6, Jules Rimet Trophy.

30 A.P.U. Emblem

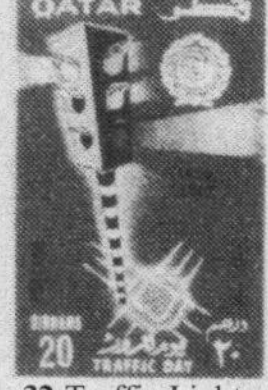
32 Traffic Lights

31 Astronauts on Moon

1967. Admission of Qatar to Arab Postal Union.
198 **30** 70 d. brown and violet . . 1·25 60
199 80 d. brown and blue . . . 1·50 80

1967. U.S. "Apollo" Space Missions. Mult.
200 5 d. Type **31** 15 10
201 10 d. "Apollo" spacecraft . . 20 10
202 20 d. Landing module on Moon 30 10
203 30 d. Blast-off from Moon . . 35 15
204 40 d. "Saturn 5" rocket . . . 40 20
205 70 d. Type **31** 65 40
206 80 d. As 10 d. 80 50
207 1 r. As 20 d. 95 60
208 1 r. 20 As 30 d. . . . . . . 1·40 85
209 2 r. As 40 d. . . . . 2·25 1·25

1967. Traffic Day.
211 **32** 20 d. multicoloured 55 10
212 30 d. multicoloured 95 25
213 50 d. multicoloured . . . . 1·60 55
214 1 r. multicoloured . . . . 3·50 1·50

33 Brownsea Island and Jamboree Camp, Idaho

1967. Diamond Jubilee of Scout Movement and World Scout Jamboree, Idaho. Multicoloured.
215 1 d. Type **33** 10 10
216 2 d. Lord Baden-Powell . . . 10 10
217 3 d. Pony-trekking 10 10
218 5 d. Canoeing 15 10
219 15 d. Swimming 55 20
220 75 d. Rock-climbing . . . . . 1·75 80
221 2 r. World Jamboree emblem 5·00 2·50

34 Norman Ship (from Bayeux Tapestry)

1967. Famous Navigators' Ships. Multicoloured.
222 1 d. Type **34** 10 10
223 2 d. "Santa Maria" (Columbus) 10 10
224 3 d. "Sao Gabriel" (Vasco da Gama) 10 10
225 75 d. "Vitoria" (Magellan) . . 1·90 80
226 1 r. "Golden Hind" (Drake) . 2·25 1·00
227 2 r. "Gipsy Moth IV" (Chichester) . . . . 5·50 2·25

35 Arab Scribe

1968. 10th Anniv of Qatar Postage Stamps. Multicoloured.
228 1 d. Type **35** 10 10
229 2 d. Pigeon post (vert) 10 10
230 3 d. Mounted postman . . . 10 10
231 60 d. Rowing boat postman (vert) . . . . 1·25 55
232 1 r. 25 Camel postman . . . 2·50 1·50
233 2 r. Letter-writing and Qatar 1 n.p. stamp of 1957 . . . 3·75 1·50

36 Human Rights Emblem and Barbed Wire

1968. Human Rights Year. Multicoloured designs embodying Human Rights emblem.

234 1 d. Type **36** 10 10
235 2 d. Arab refugees 10 10
236 3 d. Scales of justice 10 10
237 60 d. Opening doors 1·00 45
238 1 r. 25 Family (vert) 1·75 85
239 2 r. Human figures 2·50 1·50

37 Shaikh Ahmed **39**

39 Dhow

1968.

240 **37** 5 d. green and blue 15 10
241 10 d. brown and blue 15 10
242 20 d. red and black 30 10
243 25 d. green and purple 40 10
244 **38** 35 d. green, blue and pink 1·00 20
245 – 40 d. purple, blue & orange 75 15
246 – 60 d. brown, blue & violet 2·25 30
247 – 70 d. black, blue and green 1·25 40
248 – 1 r. blue, yellow and green 1·50 40
249 – 1 r. 25 blue and flesh 2·75 65
250 – 1 r. 50 green, blue & purple 4·50 85
251 **39** 2 r. blue, brown & lt brown 4·25 1·00
252 5 r. purple and green 9·00 3·00
253 10 r. brown, ultram & blue 16·00 6·00

DESIGNS—As Type **38**: 40 d. Water purification plant; 60 d. Oil jetty; 70 d. Qatar mosque; 1 r. Palace Doha; 1 r. 25, Doha fort; 1 r. 50, Peregrine falcon.

41 Maternity Ward

1968. 20th Anniv of W.H.O. Multicoloured.

258 1 d. Type **41** 10 10
259 2 d. Operating theatre 10 10
260 3 d. Dental surgery 10 10
261 60 d. X-ray examination table 1·50 60
262 1 r. 25 Laboratory 2·75 1·40
263 2 r. State Hospital Qatar 4·00 2·50

42 Throwing the Discus

1968. Olympic Games, Mexico. Multicoloured.

264 1 d. Type **42** 10 10
265 2 d. Olympic Flame and runner 10 10
266 3 d. "68", Rings and gymnast 10 10
267 60 d. Weightlifting and Flame 65 40
268 1 r. 25 "Flame" in mosaic pattern (vert) 1·40 80
269 2 r. "Cock" emblem 2·00 1·50

43 U.N. Emblem and Flags

1968. United Nations Day. Multicoloured.

270 1 d. Type **43** 10 10
271 4 d. Dove of Peace and world map 10 10
272 5 d. U. N. Headquarters and flags 10 10
273 60 d. Teacher and class 85 50
274 1 r. 50 Agricultural workers 1·75 95
275 2 r. U. Thant and U.N. Assembly 2·75 1·50

44 Trawler "Ross Rayyan"

1969. Progress in Qatar. Multicoloured.

276 1 d. Type **44** 10 10
277 4 d. Primary school 10 10
278 5 d. Doha International Airport
279 60 d. Cement factory and road-making 1·25 60
280 1 r. 50 Power station and pylon 2·75 1·40
281 2 r. Housing estate 3·25 2·00

45 Armoured Cars

1969. Qatar Security Forces. Multicoloured.

282 1 d. Type **45** 10 10
283 2 d. Traffic control 10 10
284 3 d. Military helicopter 10 10
285 60 d. Section of military band 1·75 65
286 1 r. 25 Field gun 3·25 1·25
287 2 r. Mounted police 5·50 2·25

46 Tanker "Sivella" at Mooring

1969. Qatar's Oil Industry. Multicoloured.

288 1 d. Type **46** 10 10
289 2 d. Training school 10 10
290 3 d. "Sea Shell" (oil rig) and "Shell Dolphin" (supply vessel) 10 10
291 60 d. Storage tanks, Halul 1·75 65
292 1 r. 50 Topping plant 4·00 1·50
293 2 r. Various tankers 1890-1968 6·00 2·25

47 "Guest-house" and Dhow-building

1969. 10th Scout Jamboree, Qatar. Multicoloured.

294 1 d. Type **47** 10 10
295 2 d. Scouts at work 10 10
296 3 d. Review and March Past 10 10
297 60 d. Interior gateway 1·50 65
298 1 r. 25 Camp entrance 2·75 1·40
299 2 r. Hoisting flag, and Shaikh Ahmed 4·00 2·25

48 Neil Armstrong

1969. 1st Man on the Moon. Multicoloured.

301 1 d. Type **48** 10 10
302 2 d. Edward Aldrin 10 10
303 3 d. Michael Collins 10 10
304 60 d. Astronaut on Moon 1·25 55
305 1 r. 25 Take-off from Moon 2·50 1·25
306 2 r. Splashdown (horiz) 3·75 2·00

49 Douglas DC-8 and Mail Van

1970. Admission to U.P.U. Multicoloured.

307 1 d. Type **49** 10 10
308 2 d. Liner "Oriental Empress" 10 10
309 3 d. Loading mail-van 10 10
310 60 d. G.P.O., Doha 1·00 60
311 1 r. 25 U.P.U. Building Berne 2·25 1·40
312 2 r. U.P.U. Monument Berne (detail) 3·75 2·00

50 League Emblem, Flag and Map

1970. Silver Jubilee of Arab League.

313 **50** 35 d. multicoloured 40 20
314 60 d. multicoloured 60 35
315 1 r. 25 multicoloured 1·40 75
316 1 r. 50 multicoloured 1·75 1·00

51 VC-10 on Runway

1970. 1st Gulf Aviation Vickers VC-10 Flight, Doha–London. Multicoloured.

317 1 d. Type **51** 10 10
318 2 d. Peregrine falcon and VC-10 65 10
319 3 d. Tall view of VC-10 10 10
320 60 d. Gulf Aviation emblem on map 1·25 60
321 1 r. 25 VC-10 over Doha 3·50 1·60
322 2 r. Tail assembly of VC-10 4·50 2·25

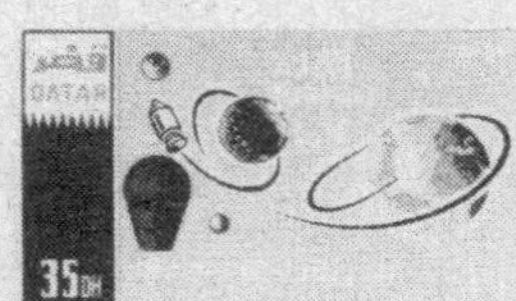

52 "Space Achievements"

1970. International Education Year.

323 **52** 35 d. multicoloured 55 25
324 60 d. multicoloured 1·10 50

53 Freesias

55 Globe, '25' and U.N. Emblem

54 Toyahama Fishermen with Giant "Fish"

1970. Qatar Flowers. Multicoloured.

325 1 d. Type **53** 10 10
326 2 d. Azalieas 10 10
327 3 d. Ixias 10 10
328 60 d. Amaryllises 1·25 60
329 1 r. 25 Cinerarias 2·75 1·40
330 2 r. Roses 4·00 2·00

1970. "EXPO 70" World Fair, Osaka. Multicoloured.

331 1 d. Type **54** 10 10
332 2 d. Expo emblem and map of Japan 10 10
333 3 d. Fisherman on Shikoku beach 10 10
334 60 d. Expo emblem and Mt. Fuji 80 45
335 1 r. 50 Gateway to Shinto Shrine 1·75 85
336 2 r. Expo Tower and Mt. Fuji 2·50 2·00

Nos. 333, 334 and 336 are vert.

1970. 25th Anniv of U.N.O. Multicoloured.

337 1 d. Type **55** 10 10
338 2 d. Flowers in gun-barrel 10 10
339 3 d. Anniversary cake 10 10
340 35 d. "The U.N. Agencies" 40 25
341 1 r. 50 "Trumpet fanfare" 1·50 90
342 2 r. "World friendship" 2·00 1·25

56 Al Jahiz (philosopher), and Ancient Globe

1971. Famous Men of Islam. Multicoloured.

343 1 d. Type **56** 10 10
344 2 d. Saladin (soldier), palace and weapons 10 10
345 3 d. Al Farabi (philosopher and musician), felucca and instruments 10 10
346 35 d. Ibn Al Haithum (scientist), palace and emblems 70 35
347 1 r. 50 Al Motanabbi (poet), symbols and desert 3·00 1·75
348 2 r. Ibn Sina (Avicenna) (physician and philosopher), medical instruments and ancient globe 3·75 2·00

57 Common Cormorant and Water Plants

1971. Qatar Fauna and Flora. Multicoloured.

349 1 d. Type **57** 40 10
350 2 d. Lizard and prickly pear 5 5
351 3 d. Greater flamingos and palms 40 10
352 60 d. Arabian oryx and yucca 1·25 65
353 1 r. 25 Mountain gazelle and desert dandelion 2·25 1·25
354 2 r. Dromedary, palm and bronzed chenopod 3·50 1·50

58 Satellite Earth Station, Goonhilly

1971. World Telecommunications Day. Mult.

355 1 d. Type **58** 10 10
356 2 d. Cable ship "Ariel" 10 10
357 3 d. Post Office Tower and T.V. control-room 10 10
358 4 d. Modern telephones 10 10
359 5 d. Video-phone equipment 10 10
360 35 d. As 3 d. 55 30
361 75 d. As 5 d. 1·25 80
362 3 r. Telex machine 5·00 2·50

59 Arab Child reading Book

60 A.P.U. Emblem

1971. 10th Anniv of Education Day.

363 **59** 35 d. multicoloured 40 20
364 55 d. multicoloured 65 30
365 75 d. multicoloured 90 45

1971. 25th Anniv of Arab Postal Union.

366 **60** 35 d. multicoloured 40 15
367 55 d. multicoloured 60 30
368 75 d. multicoloured 95 55
369 1 r. 25 multicoloured 1·40 1·00

61 "Hammering Racism"

1971. Racial Equality Year. Multicoloured.
370 1 d. Type **61** 10 10
371 2 d. "Pushing back racism" . 10 10
372 3 d. War-wounded 10 10
373 4 d. Working together (vert) . 10 10
374 5 d. Playing together (vert) . . 10 10
375 35 d. Racial "tidal-wave" . . 40 25
376 75 d. Type **61** . . . . 1·00 65
377 3 r. As 2 d. . . . . 3·25 2·25

62 Nurse and Child

1971. 25th Anniv of U.N.I.C.E.F. Multicoloured.
378 1 d. Mother and child (vert) . 10 10
379 2 d. Child's face 10 10
380 3 d. Child with book (vert) . . 10 10
381 4 d. Type **62** 10 10
382 5 d. Mother and baby 10 10
383 35 d. Child with daffodil (vert) 40 25
384 75 d. As 3 d. . . . . 1·00 65
385 3 r. As 1 d. . . . . 3·25 2·25

63 Shaikh Ahmad, and Flags of Arab League and Qatar

1971. Independence.
386 **63** 35 d. multicoloured 40 15
387 – 75 d. multicoloured 90 45
388 – 1 r. 25 black, pink & brown 1·40 85
389 – 3 r. multicoloured . . . . 3·00 2·00
DESIGNS—HORIZ: 75 d. As Type **63**, but with U.N. flag in place of Arab League flag. VERT: 1 r. 25, Shaikh Ahmad; 3 r. Handclasp.

64 Common Roller
66 Shaikh Khalifa bin Hamad al-Thani

1972. Birds. Multicoloured.
391 1 d. Type **64** 10 10
392 2 d. Common kingfisher . . . 10 10
393 3 d. Rock thrush 10 10
394 4 d. Caspian tern 15 10
395 5 d. Hoopoe 15 10
396 35 d. European bee eater . . . 70 25
397 75 d. Golden oriole . . . . . 1·75 70
398 3 r. Peregrine falcon . . . . . 6·00 2·50

1972. Provisionals. Nos. 328/30 surch with value in English and Arabic.
399 10 d. on 60 d. multicoloured . 1·00 15
400 1 r. on 1 r. 25 multicoloured . 4·00 70
401 5 r. on 2 r. multicoloured . . 8·00 3·50

1972.
402 **66** 5 d. blue and violet 15 10
403 10 d. red and brown . . . 15 10
404 35 d. green and orange . . 55 10
405 55 d. purple and green . . 90 20
406 75 d. purple and blue . . . 1·40 30
407 – 1 r. black and brown . . . 1·75 35
408 – 1 r. 25 black and green . . 2·75 55
409 – 5 r. black and blue . . . . 10·00 2·75
410 – 10 r. black and red . . . . 17·00 5·00
The rupee values are larger, 27 × 32 mm.

67 Book Year Emblem

1972. International Book Year.
411 **67** 35 d. black and blue . . . 30 20
412 55 d. black and brown . . 55 30
413 75 d. black and green . . 75 85
414 1 r. 25 black and lilac . . 1·25 85

68 Football

1972. Olympic Games. Munich. Depicting sportmen's hands or feet. Multicoloured.
415 1 d. Type **68** 10 10
416 2 d. Running (foot on starting block) 10 10
417 3 d. Cycling (hand) 10 10
418 4 d. Gymnastics (hand) . . . 10 10
419 5 d. Basketball (hand) 10 10
420 35 d. Discus (hand) 35 20
421 75 d. Type **68** 85 60
422 3 r. As 2 d. . . . . 2·75 2·25

69 Underwater Pipeline Construction

1972. "Oil from the Sea". Multicoloured.
424 1 d. Drilling (vert) 10 10
425 4 d. Type **69** 10 10
426 5 d. Offshore rig "Sea Shell" 10 10
427 35 d. Underwater "prospecting" for oil 80 30
428 75 d. As 1 d. . . . . 1·75 80
429 3 r. As 5 d. . . . . 7·50 3·75

70 Administrative Building

1972. Independence Day. Multicoloured.
430 10 d. Type **70** 20 10
431 35 d. Handclasp and Arab League flag 50 20
432 75 d. Handclasp and U.N. flag 90 50
433 1 r. 25 Shaikh Khalifa . . . 1·40 90

71 Dish Aerial Satellite and Telephone (I.T.U.)

1972. United Nations Day. Multicoloured.
435 1 d. Type **71** 10 10
436 2 d. Archaeological team (U.N.E.S.C.O.) 10 10
437 3 d. Tractor, produce and helicopter (F.A.O.) 10 10
438 4 d. Children with books (U.N.I.C.E.F.) 10 10
439 5 d. Weather satellite (W.M.O.) 10 10
440 25 d. Construction workers (I.L.O.) 40 25
441 55 d. Child care (W.H.O.) . . 1·00 60
442 1 r. Airliner and van (U.P.U.) 2·25 90

72 Emblem and Flags
72a Shaikh Khalifa

1972. 10th Session of Arab States Civil Aviation Council, Qatar.
443 **72** 25 d. multicoloured . . . 60 30
444 30 d. multicoloured . . . 80 45

1972. Coil Stamps.
444a **72a** 10 d. red and brown . . . 60 50
444b 25 d. green and purple . . 1·50 1·25

73 Shaikh Khalifa
74 Clock Tower, Doha

1973.
445 **73** 5 d. multicoloured 15 10
446 10 d. multicoloured 15 10
447 20 d. multicoloured 30 10
448 25 d. multicoloured 25 10
449 35 d. multicoloured 55 10
450 55 d. multicoloured 90 20
451 **74** 75 d. multicoloured . . . . 2·00 40
452 – 1 r. multicoloured . . . . . 2·00 30
453 – 5 r. multicoloured . . . . . 7·50 2·00
454 – 10 r. multicoloured . . . . 14·00 3·75
Nos. 452/4 are as Type **73**, but size 27 × 32 mm.

75 Housing Development

1973. 1st Anniv of Shaikh Khalifa's Accession. Multicoloured.
455 2 d. Road construction 10 10
456 3 d. Type **75** 10 10
457 4 d. Hospital operating theatre 10 10
458 5 d. Telephone exchange . . . 10 10
459 15 d. School classroom 20 10
460 20 d. Television studio 25 10
461 35 d. Shaikh Khalifa 45 15
462 55 d. Gulf Hotel, Doha . . . 90 40
463 1 r. Industrial plant . . . . . 1·40 70
464 1 r. 35 Flour mills . . . . . . 2·00 1·25

76 De Havilland Beaver crop-spraying

1973. 25th Anniv of W.H.O. Multicoloured.
465 2 d. Type **76** 10 10
466 3 d. Drugs and syringe 10 10
467 4 d. Woman in wheelchair (Prevention of polio) 10 10
468 5 d. Mosquito (Malaria control) 10 10
469 55 d. Mental patient (Mental Health Research) . . . . . 1·50 70
470 1 r. Dead trees (Anti-pollution) 2·75 1·40

77 Weather Ship

1973. Centenary of World Meteorological Organization. Multicoloured.
471 2 d. Type **77** 10 10
472 3 d. Launching radio-sonde balloon 10 10
473 4 d. Weather plane 10 10
474 5 d. Meteorological station . . 10 10
475 10 d. Met aircraft taking-off . 20 10
476 1 r. "Nimbus 1" . . . . 1·75 85
477 1 r. 55 Rocket on launch-pad 3·00 1·50

78 Handclasp

1973. 2nd Anniv of Independence Day. Mult.
478 15 d. Type **78** 10 10
479 35 d. Agriculture 20 10
480 55 d. Government building . . 55 20
481 1 r. 35 View of Doha . . . . 1·25 65
482 1 r. 55 Illuminated fountain . . 1·50 1·00

79 Child planting Sapling (U.N.E.S.C.O.)

1973. United Nations Day. Multicoloured.
483 2 d. Type **79** 10 10
484 4 d. U.N. H.Q., New York and flags 10 10
485 5 d. Building construction (I.L.O.) 10 10
486 35 d. Nurses in dispensary (W.H.O.) 30 10
487 1 r. 35 Radar control (I.T.U.) 1·50 85
488 3 r. Inspection of wheat and cattle (F.A.O.) . . . . . . 3·50 2·25

80 "Open Gates"

1973. 25th Anniv of Declaration of Human Rights. Multicoloured.
489 2 d. Type **80** 10 10
490 4 d. Freedom marchers . . . 10 10
491 5 d. "Equality of Man" . . . 10 10
492 35 d. Primary education . . . 25 10
493 1 r. 35 General Assembly, U.N. 1·50 55
494 3 r. Flame emblem (vert) . . 3·50 2·00

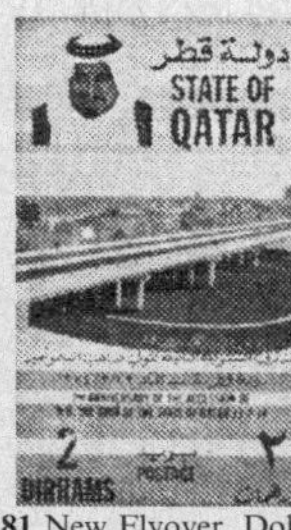

81 New Flyover, Doha

1974. 2nd Anniv of Shaikh Khalifa's Accession. Mult.
495 2 d. Type **81** 10 10
496 3 d. Education symbol 10 10
497 5 d. Gas plant 10 10
498 35 d. Gulf Hotel, Doha . . . 35 15
499 1 r. 55 Space communications station . . . . 1·75 90
500 2 r. 25 Shaikh Khalifa . . . . 2·75 1·60

82 Camel Caravan and Articulated Mail-van

1974. Centenary of U.P.U. Multicoloured.
501 2 d. Type **82** 10 10
502 3 d. Early mail wagon and modern express train . . . 10 20
503 10 d. "Hindoostan" (paddle-steamer) and "Iberia" (liner) 35 10
504 35 d. Handley Page H.P.42 and Vickers VC-10 mail planes . 50 20
505 75 d. Manual and mechanised mail-sorting 95 55
506 1 r. 25 Early and modern P.O. sales counters . . . . 1·40 1·00

83 Doha Hospital

1974. World Population Year. Multicoloured.
507 5 d. Type **83** 10 10
508 10 d. W.P.Y. emblem 15 10
509 15 d. Emblem within wreath . 15 10
510 35 d. World population map . 35 15
511 1 r. 75 New-born infants and clock ("a birth every minute") 1·75 85
512 2 r. 25 "Ideal Family" group 2·25 1·40

HAVE YOU READ THE NOTES AT THE BEGINNING OF THIS CATALOGUE?
These often provide the answers to the enquiries we receive.

84 Television Station

1974. Independence Day. Multicoloured.

513 5 d. Type **84** 10 10
514 10 d. Doha palace 15 10
515 15 d. Teachers' College 20 10
516 75 d. Clock tower and Mosque 80 35
517 1 r. 55 Roundabout and surroundings 1·50 90
518 2 r. Shaikh Khalifa 2·25 1·40

85 Operating Theatre (W.H.O.)

1974. United Nations Day.

519 **85** 5 d. orange, mauve & black 10 10
520 – 10 d. orange, red & black 15 10
521 – 20 d. blue, green & black 20 10
522 – 25 d. blue, brown & black 25 10
523 – 1 r. 75 blue, red & black 1·50 90
524 – 2 r. blue, orange & black 2·00 1·25

DESIGNS: 10 d. Satellite earth station (I.T.U.); 20 d. Tractor (F.A.O.); 25 d. Classroom (U.N.E.S.C.O.); 1 r. 75, African open-air court (Human Rights); 2 r. U.P.U. and U.N. emblems (U.P.U.).

86 Vickers VC-10 Airliner

1974. Arab Civil Aviation Day.

525 **86** 20 d. multicoloured 35 15
526 – 25 d. blue, green & yellow 35 15
527 – 30 d. multicoloured 45 20
528 – 50 d. red, green & purple 75 45

DESIGNS: 25 d. Doha airport; 30, 50 d. Flags of Qatar and the Arab League.

87 Clock-tower, Qatar

1974. Tourism. Multicoloured.

529 5 d. Type **87** 15 10
530 10 d. White-cheeked terns, hoopoes and Shara'o Island (horiz) 1·40 20
531 15 d. Fort Zubara (horiz) 25 10
532 35 d. Yachts and Gulf Hotel (horiz) 45 15
533 55 d. Qatar by night (horiz) 75 20
534 75 d. Arabian oryx (horiz) 1·50 45
535 1 r. 25 Khor-al-Udeid (horiz) 1·75 90
536 1 r. 75 Ruins Wakrah (horiz) 2·00 1·40

88 Traffic Roundabout, Doha

1975. 3rd Anniv of Shaikh Khalifa's Accession. Multicoloured.

537 10 d. Type **88** 20 10
538 35 d. Oil pipelines 55 10
539 55 d. Laying offshore pipelines 85 20
540 1 r. Oil refinery 1·50 60
541 1 r. 35 Shaikh Khalifa (vert) 2·25 1·00
542 1 r. 55 As 1 r. 35 2·75 1·50

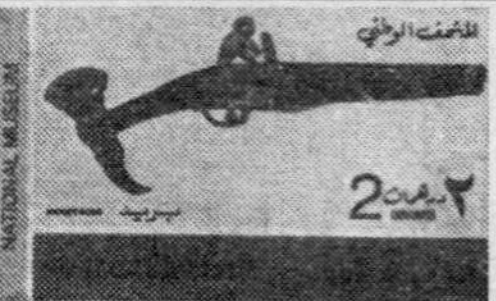

89 Flintlock Pistol

1975. National Museum Opening Multicoloured.

543 2 d. Type **89** 10 10
544 3 d. Arabesque-pattern mosaic 10 10
545 35 d. Museum buildings 35 15
546 75 d. Museum archway (vert) 1·40 60
547 1 r. 25 Flint tools 2·00 1·00
548 3 r. Gold necklace and pendant (vert) 4·25 2·50

90 Policeman and Road Signs

1975. Traffic Week. Multicoloured.

549 5 d. Type **90** 20 10
550 15 d. Traffic arrows and signal lights 50 15
551 35 d. Type **90** 1·25 35
552 55 d. As 15 d. 1·75 90

91 Flag and Emblem

1975. 10th Anniv of Arab Labour Charter.

553 **91** 10 d. multicoloured 15 10
554 35 d. multicoloured 45 15
555 1 r. multicoloured 1·25 80

92 Government Building, Doha

1975. 4th Anniv of Independence. Multicoloured.

556 5 d. Type **92** 10 10
557 15 d. Museum and clock tower, Doha 25 10
558 35 d. Constitution – Arabic text (vert) 40 10
559 55 d. Ruler and flag (vert) 60 25
560 75 d. Constitution – English text (vert) 80 50
561 1 r. 25 As 55 d. 1·40 85

93 Telecommunications Satellite (I.T.U.)

1975. 30th Anniv of U.N.O. Multicoloured.

562 5 d. Type **93** 10 10
563 15 d. U.N. Headquarters, New York 15 10
564 35 d. U.P.U. emblem and map 35 10
565 1 r. Doctors tending child (U.N.I.C.E.F.) 95 50
566 1 r. 25 Bulldozer (I.L.O.) 1·50 90
567 2 r. Students in class (U.N.E.S.C.O.) 2·50 1·50

94 Fertilizer Plant

1975. Qatar Industry. Multicoloured.

568 5 d. Type **94** 15 10
569 10 d. Flour mills (vert) 20 10
570 35 d. Natural gas plant 60 15
571 75 d. Oil refinery 1·50 70
572 1 r. 25 Cement works 1·90 1·25
573 1 r. 55 Steel mills 2·25 1·50

95 Modern Building, Doha

1976. 4th Anniv of Shaikh Khalifa's Accession.

574 **95** 5 d. multicoloured 10 10
575 – 10 d. multicoloured 10 10
576 – 35 d. multicoloured 35 10
577 – 55 d. multicoloured 55 20
578 – 75 d. multicoloured 75 35
579 – 1 r. 55 multicoloured 1·50 1·00

DESIGNS: Nos. 575/6 and 579 show public buildings etc. Nos. 577/8 show Shaikh Khalifa with flag.

96 Tracking Aerial **97** Early and Modern Telephones

1976. Opening of Satellite Earth Station. Mult.

580 35 d. Type **96** 60 15
581 55 d. "Intelsat" satellite 85 25
582 75 d. Type **96** 1·40 60
583 1 r. As 55 d. 1·75 80

1976. Telephone Centenary.

584 **97** 1 r. multicoloured 1·25 75
585 1 r. 35 multicoloured 1·75 1·00

98 Tournament Emblem **100** Football

99 Qatar Dhows

1976. 4th Arabian Gulf Football Cup Tournament. Multicoloured.

586 5 d. Type **98** 10 10
587 10 d. Qatar Stadium 10 10
588 35 d. Type **98** 40 15
589 55 d. Two players with ball 75 30
590 75 d. Player with ball 1·00 50
591 1 r. 25 As 10 d. 1·60 1·10

1976. Arab Dhows.

592 **99** 10 d. multicoloured 15 10
593 – 35 d. multicoloured 40 10
594 – 80 d. multicoloured 90 35
595 – 1 r. 25 multicoloured 1·40 30
596 – 1 r. 50 multicoloured 1·75 90
597 – 2 r. multicoloured 2·25 1·25

DESIGNS: As Type **99** showing local craft.

1976. Olympic Games, Montreal, Multicoloured.

598 5 d. Type **100** 10 10
599 10 d. Sailing 15 10
600 35 d. Show jumping 30 10
601 80 d. Boxing 75 45
602 1 r. 25 Weightlifting 1·25 80
603 1 r. 50 Basketball 1·50 1·00

101 Urban Housing Development

1976. U.N. Conference on Human Settlements. Multicoloured.

604 10 d. Type **101** 10 10
605 35 d. U.N. and conference emblems 25 10
606 80 d. Communal housing development 70 45
607 1 r. 25 Shaikh Khalifa 1·25 90

102 Kentish Plover

1976. Birds. Multicoloured.

608 5 d. Type **102** 20 10
609 10 d. Common cormorant 20 10
610 35 d. Osprey 95 25
611 80 d. Greater flamingo (vert) 2·00 55
612 1 r. 25 Rock thrush (vert) 2·75 80
613 2 r. Saker falcon (vert) 3·75 1·25

103 Shaikh Khalifa and Flag **105** Shaikh Khalifa

104 U.N. Emblem

1976. 5th Anniv of Independence. Multicoloured.

614 5 d. Type **103** 10 10
615 10 d. Type **103** 15 10
616 40 d. Doha buildings (horiz) 25 10
617 80 d. As 40 d 45 20
618 1 r. 25 "Dana" (oil rig) (horiz) 1·25 65
619 1 r. 50 U.N. and Qatar emblems (horiz) 1·25 85

1976. United Nations Day.

620 **104** 2 r. multicoloured 1·75 1·25
621 3 r. multicoloured 2·25 1·75

1977. 5th Anniv of Amir's Accession.

622 **105** 20 d. multicoloured 20 10
623 1 r. 80 multicoloured 1·90 1·40

106 Shaikh Khalifa **107** Envelope and A.P.U. Emblem

1977.

624 **106** 5 d. multicoloured 15 10
625 10 d. multicoloured 20 10
626 35 d. multicoloured 50 10
627 80 d. multicoloured 90 20
628 1 r. multicoloured 1·10 25
629 5 r. multicoloured 5·00 2·25
630 10 r. multicoloured 10·00 3·75

Nos. 628/30 are larger, size 25 × 31 mm.

1977. 25th Anniv of Arab Postal Union.

631 **107** 35 d. multicoloured 25 10
632 1 r. 35 multicoloured 1·25 90

108 Shaikh Khalifa and Sound Waves

1977. International Telecommunications Day.

633 **108** 35 d. multicoloured 25 10
634 1 r. 80 multicoloured 1·50 1·40

108a Shaikh Khalifa

109 Parliament Building, Doha

1977. Booklet Stamps.

634a	**108a**	5 d. multicoloured	15	15
634c		10 d. multicoloured	20	20
634d		35 d. multicoloured	50	50
634e		80 d. multicoloured	1·50	1·50

1977. 6th Anniv of Independence. Multicoloured.

635	80 d. Type **109**	85	60
636	80 d. Main business district, Doha	85	60
637	80 d. Motorway, Doha	85	60

110 U.N. Emblem

1977. United Nations Day.

638	**110**	20 d. multicoloured	15	10
639		1 r. multicoloured	70	65

111 Steel Mill

1978. 6th Anniv of Amir's Accession. Mult.

640	20 d. Type **111**	15	10
641	80 d. Operating theatre	60	20
642	1 r. Children's classroom	65	40
643	5 r. Shaikh Khalifa	2·25	2·00

112 Oil Refinery

1978. 7th Anniv of Independence. Multicoloured.

644	35 d. Type **112**	30	10
645	80 d. Apartment buildings	55	20
646	1 r. 35 Town centre, Doha	85	65
647	1 r. 80 Shaikh Khalifa	1·25	1·00

113 Man reading Alphabet

1978. International Literacy Day.

648	**113**	35 d. multicoloured	25	10
649		80 d. multicoloured	75	55

114 U.N. Emblem and Qatar Flag

1978. United Nations Day.

650	**114**	35 d. multicoloured	25	10
651		80 d. multicoloured	75	55

115 "Human Rights Flame"

116 I.Y.C. Emblem

1978. 30th Anniv of Declaration of Human Rights. Multicoloured.

652	35 d. Type **115**	20	10
653	80 d. Type **115**	40	25
654	1 r. 25 Emblem and balance	70	60
655	1 r. 80 As 1 r. 25	70	85

1979. International Year of the Child.

656	**116**	35 d. blue, mauve and black	25	10
657		1 r. 80 blue, green and black	85	80

117 Shaikh Khalifa

118 Shaikh Khalifa and Laurel Wreath

1979.

658	**117**	5 d. multicoloured	10	10
659		10 d. multicoloured	10	10
660		20 d. multicoloured	25	10
661		25 d. multicoloured	25	10
662		35 d. multicoloured	40	10
663		60 d. multicoloured	70	10
664		80 d. multicoloured	90	15
665		1 r. multicoloured	1·00	15
666		1 r. 25 multicoloured	1·25	25
667		1 r. 35 multicoloured	1·50	30
668		1 r. 80 multicoloured	1·75	45
669		5 r. multicoloured	4·00	1·50
670		10 r. multicoloured	7·00	2·25

Nos. 665/70 are larger, size 27 × 32½ mm.

1979. 7th Anniv of Amir's Accession.

671	**118**	35 d. multicoloured	25	10
672		80 d. multicoloured	40	20
673		1 r. multicoloured	60	45
674		1 r. 25 multicoloured	80	70

119 Wave Pattern and Television Screen

1979. World Telecommunications Day.

675	**119**	2 r. multicoloured	1·00	80
676		2 r. 80 multicoloured	1·25	1·10

120 Two Children supporting Globe

1979. 50th Anniv of Int Bureau of Education.

677	**120**	35 d. multicoloured	25	10
678		80 d. multicoloured	55	30

121 Rolling Mill

122 U.N. Emblem and Flag of Qatar

1979. 8th Anniv of Independence. Multicoloured.

679	5 d. Type **121**	10	10
680	10 d. Aerial view of Doha	10	10
681	1 r. 25 Qatar flag	70	50
682	2 r. Shaikh Khalifa	1·00	90

1979. United Nations Day.

683	**122**	1 r. 25 multicoloured	75	45
684		2 r. multicoloured	1·00	95

123 Mosque Minaret and Crescent Moon

1979. Third World Conference on the Prophet's Seera and Sunna.

685	**123**	35 d. multicoloured	25	10
686		1 r. 80 multicoloured	1·00	90

124 Shaikh Khalifa

1980. 8th Anniv of Amir's Accession.

687	**124**	20 d. multicoloured	15	10
688		60 d. multicoloured	35	15
689		1 r. 25 multicoloured	65	45
690		2 r. multicoloured	90	90

125 Emblem

1980. 6th Congress of Arab Towns, Organization, Doha.

691	**125**	2 r. 35 multicoloured	1·40	1·00
692		2 r. 80 multicoloured	1·60	1·25

126 Oil Refinery

1980. 9th Anniv of Independence. Multicoloured.

693	10 d. Type **126**	15	10
694	35 d. Doha	30	15
695	2 r. Oil Rig	1·75	90
696	2 r. 35 Hospital	2·25	1·40

127 Figures supporting O.P.E.C. Emblem

1980. 20th Anniv of Organisation of Petroleum Exporting Countries.

697	**127**	1 r. 35 multicoloured	75	45
698		2 r. multicoloured	1·25	80

128 U.N.Emblem

129 Mosque and Kaaba, Mecca

1980. United Nations Day.

699	**128**	1 r. 35 light blue, blue and mauve	65	45
700		1 r. 80 green, blue and blk	1·10	70

1980. 1400th Anniv of Hegira.

701	**129**	10 d. multicoloured	10	10
702		35 d. multicoloured	30	15
703		1 r. 25 multicoloured	75	55
704		2 r. 80 multicoloured	1·40	1·25

130 I.Y.D.P. Emblem

1981. International Year of Disabled Persons.

705	**130**	2 r. multicoloured	1·60	1·10
706		3 r. multicoloured	2·25	1·60

131 Student

132 Shaikh Khalifa

1981. 20th Anniv of Education Day.

707	**131**	2 r. multicoloured	1·50	1·00
708		3 r. multicoloured	2·25	1·60

1981. 9th Anniv of Amir's Accession.

709	**132**	10 d. multicoloured	10	10
710		35 d. multicoloured	35	20
711		80 d. multicoloured	55	35
712		5 r. multicoloured	2·75	2·00

133 I.T.U. and W.H.O. Emblems and Ribbons forming Caduceus

134 Torch

1981. World Telecommunications Day.

713	**133**	2 r. multicoloured	1·50	1·00
714		2 r. 80 multicoloured	2·00	1·50

1981. 30th International Military Football Championship.

715	**134**	1 r. 25 multicoloured	1·50	75
716		2 r. 80 multicoloured	3·00	2·00

135 Qatar Flag

1981. 10th Anniv of Independence.

717	**135**	5 d. multicoloured	10	10
718		60 d. multicoloured	60	25
719		80 d. multicoloured	85	40
720		5 r. multicoloured	4·00	2·75

136 Tractor gathering Crops

1981. World Food Day.

721	**136**	2 r. multicoloured	1·75	1·00
722		2 r. 80 multicoloured	2·50	1·50

137 Red Crescent

1982. Qatar Red Crescent.
723 **137** 20 d. multicoloured . . . 30 10
724 2 r. 80 multicoloured . . . 3·50 2·00

138 Shaikh Khalifa

1982. 10th Anniv of Amir's Accession.
725 **138** 10 d. multicoloured . . . 10 10
726 20 d. multicoloured . . . 20 10
727 1 r. 25 multicoloured . . . 1·00 60
728 2 r. 80 multicoloured . . . 2·50 1·50

139 Hamad General Hospital

140 Shaikh Khalifa

1982. Hamad General Hospital.
729 **139** 10 d. multicoloured . . . 10 10
730 2 r. 35 multicoloured . . . 2·00 1·50

1982.
731 **140** 5 d. multicoloured 10 10
732 10 d. multicoloured . . . 10 10
733 15 d. multicoloured . . . 25 10
734 20 d. multicoloured . . . 10 10
735 25 d. multicoloured . . . 15 10
736 35 d. multicoloured . . . 25 10
737 60 d. multicoloured . . . 35 10
738 80 d. multicoloured . . . 45 10
739 – 1 r. multicoloured 75 15
740 – 1 r. 25 multicoloured . . . 75 20
741 – 2 r. multicoloured . . . . 1·00 50
742 – 5 r. multicoloured . . . . 3·00 1·25
743 – 10 r. multicoloured . . . 6·00 2·50
744 – 15 r. multicoloured . . . 8·00 3·50
DESIGNS—25×32 mm: 1 r. to 2 r. Oil refinery; 5 r. to 15 r. Doha clock tower.

142 Container Ship

1982. 6th Anniv of United Arab Shipping Company.
745 **142** 20 d. multicoloured . . . 25 15
746 2 r. 35 multicoloured . . . 2·50 1·75

143 A.P.U. Emblem

144 National Flag

1982. 30th Anniv of Arab Postal Union.
747 **143** 35 d. multicoloured . . . 40 10
748 2 r. 80 multicoloured . . . 2·25 1·75

1982. 11th Anniv of Independence.
749 **144** 10 d. multicoloured . . . 10 10
750 80 d. multicoloured . . . 70 25
751 1 r. 25 multicoloured . . . 1·00 65
752 2 r. 80 multicoloured . . . 2·25 1·50

145 W.C.Y. Emblem

147 Arabic Script

146 Conference Emblem

1983. World Communications Year.
753 **145** 35 d. multicoloured . . . 45 10
754 2 r. 80 multicoloured . . 2·50 1·75

1983. 2nd Gulf Postal Organization Conference.
755 **146** 1 r. multicoloured . . . . 1·00 35
756 1 r. 35 multicoloured . . 1·50 65

1983. 12th Anniv of Independence.
757 **147** 10 d. multicoloured . . . 10 10
758 35 d. multicoloured . . . 30 15
759 80 d. multicoloured . . . 65 30
760 2 r. 80 multicoloured . . 2·25 1·75

148 Council Emblem

1983. 4th Session of Gulf Co-operation Supreme Council.
761 **148** 35 d. multicoloured . . . 35 15
762 2 r. 80 multicoloured . . 2·00 1·50

149 Globe and Human Rights Emblem

1983. 35th Anniv of Declaration of Human Rights. Multicoloured.
763 1 r. 25 Type **149** . . . . . . 1·40 60
764 2 r. 80 Globe and emblem in balance . . . . 3·00 1·75

150 Harbour

151 Shaikh Khalifa

1984.
765 **150** 15 d. multicoloured . . 10 10
765a **151** 25 d. mult (22×27 mm) 15 10
766 **150** 40 d. multicoloured . . 25 15
767 50 d. multicoloured . . 25 15
767a **151** 75 d. mult (22×27 mm) 40 25
768 1 r. multicoloured . . . 55 25
769 1 r. 50 multicoloured . . 75 40
769a 2 r. multicoloured . . . 1·10 80
770 2 r. 50 multicoloured . . 1·40 65
771 3 r. multicoloured . . . 1·60 80
772 5 r. multicoloured . . . 2·75 1·40
773 10 r. multicoloured . . . 5·50 3·00

152 Flag and Shaikh Khalifa

1984. 13th Anniv of Independence.
774 **152** 15 d. multicoloured . . . 10 10
775 1 r. multicoloured 70 25
776 2 r. 50 multicoloured . . 1·60 90
777 3 r. 50 multicoloured . . 2·25 1·50

153 Teacher and Blackboard

154 I.C.A.O. Emblem

1984. International Literacy Day. Multicoloured. Background colour behind board given.
778 **153** 1 r. mauve 65 35
779 1 r. orange 65 35

1984. 40th Anniv of I.C.A.O.
780 **154** 20 d. multicoloured . . . 25 10
781 3 r. 50 multicoloured . . . 2·75 1·75

155 I.Y.Y. Emblem

156 Crossing the Road

1985. International Youth Year.
782 **155** 50 d. multicoloured . . . 50 25
783 1 r. multicoloured . . . . 1·10 40

1985. Traffic Week. Multicoloured, frame colour given.
784 **156** 1 r. red 90 35
785 1 r. blue 90 35

157 Emblem

1985. 40th Anniv of League of Arab States.
786 **157** 50 d. multicoloured . . . 30 15
787 4 r. multicoloured . . . . 2·75 2·00

158 Doha

1985. 14th Anniv of Independence. Multicoloured.
788 40 d. Type **158** 25 15
789 50 d. Dish aerials and microwave tower 30 15
790 1 r. 50 Oil refinery 95 60
791 4 r. Cement works . . . . . . 2·75 2·00

159 O.P.E.C. Emblem in "25"

1985. 25th Anniv of Organization of Petroleum Exporting Countries. Multicoloured, background colours given.
792 **159** 1 r. red 65 35
793 1 r. green 65 35

160 U.N. Emblem

1985. 40th Anniv of U.N.O.
794 **160** 1 r. multicoloured 55 30
795 3 r. multicoloured . . . . 1·50 1·25

161 Emblem

1986. Population and Housing Census.
796 **161** 1 r. multicoloured 55 30
797 3 r. multicoloured . . . . 1·50 1·25

162 "Qatari ibn al-Fuja'a" (container ship)

1986. 10th Anniv of United Arab Shipping Company. Multicoloured.
798 1 r. 50 Type **162** 90 50
799 4 r. "Al-Wajda" (container ship) 2·40 1·75

163 Flag and Shaikh Khalifa

1986. 15th Anniv of Independence.
800 **163** 40 d. multicoloured . . . 20 15
801 50 d. multicoloured . . . 30 15
802 1 r. multicoloured 55 25
803 4 r. multicoloured . . . . 2·25 2·00

164 Shaikh Khalifa

165 Palace

1987.
804 **164** 15 r. multicoloured . . . 6·00 4·50
805 20 r. multicoloured . . . 8·00 6·50
806 30 r. multicoloured . . . 11·50 10·00

1987. 15th Anniv of Amir's Accession.
807 **165** 50 d. multicoloured . . . 30 15
808 1 r. multicoloured 55 25
809 1 r. 50 multicoloured . . 75 60
810 4 r. multicoloured . . . . 2·00 1·75

166 Emblem

167 Emblem

1987. 35th Anniv of Arab Postal Union.
811 **166** 1 r. yellow, green and black 45 25
812 1 r. 50 multicoloured . . 65 30

1987. Gulf Environment Day.
813 **167** 1 r. multicoloured 55 40
814 4 r. multicoloured . . . . 1·75 1·75

168 Modern Complex

1987. 16th Anniv of Independence.
815 25 d. Type **168** 15 10
816 75 d. Aerial view of city . . . 40 25
817 2 r. Modern building . . . . 1·10 80
818 4 r. Oil refinery . . . . 1·90 1·75

169 Pens in Fist

170 Anniversary Emblem

1987. International Literacy Day.
819 **169** 1 r. 50 multicoloured . . . 80 70
820 4 r. multicoloured . . . . 1·90 1·50

1988. 40th Anniv of W.H.O.
821 **170** 1 r. 50 yellow, black & bl . 80 70
822 2 r. yellow, black & red . 1·10 80

171 State Arms, Shaikh Khalifa and Flag

1988. 17th Anniv of Independence.
823 **171** 50 d. multicoloured . . . 20 15
824 75 d. multicoloured . . . 30 20
825 1 r. 50 multicoloured . . . 60 50
826 2 r. multicoloured 75 60

172 Post Office

1988. Opening of New Doha General Post Office.
827 **172** 1 r. 50 multicoloured . . . 60 50
828 4 r. multicoloured . . . . 1·50 1·25

173 Housing Development

1988. Arab Housing Day.
829 **173** 1 r. 50 multicoloured . . . 60 50
830 4 r. multicoloured . . . . 1·50 1·25

174 Hands shielding Flame

175 Dish Aerials and Arrows

1988. 40th Anniv of Declaration of Human Rights.
831 **174** 1 r. 50 multicoloured . . . 60 50
832 2 r. multicoloured 75 60

1989. World Telecommunications Day.
833 **175** 2 r. multicoloured 75 60
834 4 r. multicoloured . . . . 1·50 1·25

176 Headquarters

1989. 10th Anniv of Qatar Red Cresent Society.
835 **176** 4 r. multicoloured . . . . 1·50 1·25

177 Palace

1989. 18th Anniv of Independence.
836 **177** 75 d. multicoloured . . . 30 20
837 1 r. multicoloured 50 40
838 1 r. 50 multicoloured . . 60 50
839 2 r. multicoloured 75 60

178 Anniversary Emblem

1990. 40th Anniv of Gulf Air.
840 **178** 50 d. multicoloured . . . 15 10
841 75 d. multicoloured . . . 20 20
842 4 r. multicoloured . . . . 1·25 1·00

179 Map and Rising Sun

1990. 19th Anniv of Independence Multicoloured.
843 50 d. Type **179** 15 10
844 75 d. Map and sunburst . . . 25 20
845 1 r. 50 Musicians and sword dancer 50 40
846 2 r. As No. 845 . . . . 65 50

180 Anniversary Emblem

181 Emblem and Dhow

1990. 30th Anniv of Organization of Petroleum Exporting Countries. Multicoloured.
847 50 d. Type **180** 15 10
848 1 r. 50 Flags of member nations 50 40

1990. 11th Session of Supreme Council of Gulf Co-operation Council. Multicoloured.
849 50 d. Type **181** 20 15
850 1 r. Council heads of state and emblem 35 30
851 1 r. 50 State flag and Council emblem 55 45
852 2 r. State and Council emblems 75 60

182 "Glossonema edule"

183 Emblem

1991. Plants. Multicoloured.
853 10 d. Type **182** 10 10
854 25 d. "Lycium shawii" . . . 10 10
855 50 d. "Acacia tortilis" . . . 20 15
856 75 d. "Acacia ehrenbergiana" 30 25
857 1 r. "Capparis spinosa" . . . 35 30
858 4 r. "Cymbopogon parkeri" . . 1·50 1·25

1991. 20th Anniv of Independence. Multicoloured.
859 25 d. Type **183** 10 10
860 75 d. Type **183** 30 25
861 1 r. View of Doha (35 × 32 mm) 35 30
862 1 r. 50 Palace (35 × 32 mm) . 55 45

184 Fish

185 Shaikh Khalifa

1991. Fishes.
863 **184** 10 d. multicoloured . . . 10 10
864 – 15 d. multicoloured . . . 10 10
865 – 25 d. multicoloured . . . 10 10
866 – 50 d. multicoloured . . . 20 15
867 – 75 d. multicoloured . . . 30 25
868 – 1 r. multicoloured 35 30
869 – 1 r. 50 multicoloured . . . 55 45
870 – 2 r. multicoloured 75 60
DESIGNS: 15 d. to 2 r. Different fishes.

1992. Multicoloured. (a) Size 22 × 27 mm.
871 10 d. Type **185** 10 10
872 25 d. North Field gas project . 10 10
873 50 d. Map of Qatar 20 15
874 75 d. Petrochemical factory . . 30 25
875 1 r. Petrol refinery 35 30

(b) Size 25 × 32 mm.
876 1 r. 50 As No. 872 . . . . . . 55 45
877 2 r. As No. 873 . . . . 75 60
878 3 r. As No. 874 . . . . 1·10 90
879 4 r. As No. 875 . . . . 1·50 1·25
880 5 r. As No. 873 . . . . 1·90 1·50
881 10 r. As No. 875 . . . . 3·75 3·00
882 15 r. Shaikh Khalifa (different frame) . . . . 5·50 4·50
883 20 r. As No. 882 . . . . 7·50 6·00
884 30 r. As No. 882 . . . . 11·50 9·25

186 Shaikh Khalifa and Gateway

187 Heart in Centre of Flower

1992. 20th Anniv of Shaikh Khalifa's Accession. Multicoloured.
885 25 d. Type **186** 10 10
886 50 d. Type **186** 20 15
887 75 d. Archway and "20" . . . 30 25
888 1 r. 50 As No 887 . . . . . . 55 45

1992. World Health Day. "Heartbeat, the Rhythm of Health". Multicoloured.
889 50 d. Type **187** 20 15
890 1 r. 50 Heart on clockface and cardiograph (horiz) 55 45

188 Women dancing

1992. Children's Paintings. Multicoloured.
891 25 d. Type **188** 10 10
892 50 d. Children's playground . . 20 15
893 75 d. Boat race 30 25
894 1 r. 50 Fishing fleet 55 45

189 Runner and Emblems

1992. Olympic Games, Barcelona. Multicoloured.
896 50 d. Type **189** 20 15
897 1 r. 50 Footballer and emblems 55 45

190 Shaikh Khalifa and Script

1992. 21st Anniv of Independence. Multicoloured.
898 50 d. Type **190** 20 15
899 50 d. Shaikh Kalifa and "21" in English and Arabic 20 15
900 1 r. Oil well, pen and dhow (42 × 42 mm) 35 30
901 1 r. Dhow in harbour (42 × 42 mm) 35 30

191 Ball, Flag and Emblem

1992. 11th Arabian Gulf Football Championship. Multicoloured.
902 50 d. Type **191** 20 15
903 1 r. Ball bursting goal net (vert) 35 30

192 Emblems and Globe

193 Mosque

1992. International Nutrition Conference, Rome. Multicoloured.
904 50 d. Type **192** 20 15
905 1 r. Cornucopia (horiz) . . . 35 30

1993. Old Mosques. Each sepia, yellow and brown.
906 1 r. Type **193** 35 30
907 1 r. Mosque (minaret without balcony) 35 30
908 1 r. Mosque (minaret with wide balcony) 35 30
909 1 r. Mosque (minaret with narrow balcony) 35 30

194 Presenter and Dish Aerial

1993. 25th Anniv of Qatar Broadcasting. Mult.
910 25 d. Type **194** 10 10
911 50 d. Rocket and satellite . . 20 15
912 75 d. Broadcasting House . . 30 25
913 1 r. Journalists 35 30

195 Oil Refinery and Sea

196 Scroll, Quill and Paper

1993. 22nd Anniv of Independence. Multicoloured.
915 25 d. Type **195** 10 10
916 50 d. Flag and clock tower, Doha 20 15
917 75 d. "22" in English and Arabic 30 25
918 1 r. 50 Flag and fort 55 45

1993. International Literacy Day. Multicoloured.
919 25 d. Type **196** 10 10
920 50 d. Fountain pen and flags spelling "Qatar" 20 15
921 75 d. Fountain pen and Arabic characters 30 25
922 1 r. 50 Arabic text on scroll and fountain pen 55 45

197 Girls playing

1993. Children's Games. Multicoloured.
923 25 d. Type **197** 10 10
924 50 d. Boys playing with propeller (vert) 20 15
925 75 d. Wheel and stick race (vert) 30 25
926 1 r. 50 Skipping 55 45

198 Lanner Falcon **199** Headquarters

1993. Falcons. Multicoloured.

928 25 d. Type **198** 10 10
929 50 d. Saker falcon 20 15
930 75 d. Barbary falcon 20 25
931 1 r. 50 Peregrine falcon . . . 55 45

1994. 30th Anniv of Qatar Insurance Company. Multicoloured.

933 50 d. Type **199** 15 10
934 1 r. 50 Company emblem and international landmarks . . 50 40

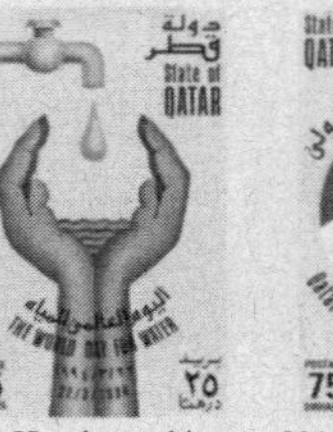

200 Hands catching Drops from Tap **201** Gavel, Scales and National Flag

1994. World Water Day. Mulicoloured.

935 25 d. Type **200** 10 10
936 1 r. Hands catching raindrop, water tower, crops and United Nations emblem 35 30

1994. Qatar International Law Conference. Multicoloured.

937 75 d. Type **201** 25 20
938 2 r. Gavel and scales suspended from flag 70 55

202 Society Emblem **203** Anniversary Emblem

1994. Qatar Society for Welfare and Rehabilitation of the Handicapped. Multicoloured.

939 25 d. Type **202** 10 10
940 75 d. Handicapped symbol and hands 25 20

1994. 75th Anniv of International Labour Organization. Multicoloured.

941 25 d. Type **203** 10 10
942 2 r. Anniversary emblem and cogwheel 70 55

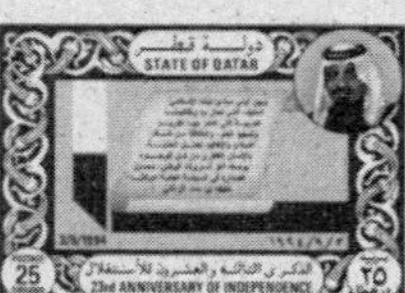

204 Family and Emblem **205** Scroll

1994. International Year of the Family.

943 **204** 25 d. blue and black . . . 10 10
944 – 1 r. multicoloured 35 30

DESIGN: 1 r. I.Y.F. emblem and stylized family standing on U.N. emblem.

1994. 23rd Anniv of Independence. Multicoloured.

945 25 d. Type **205** 10 10
946 75 d. Oasis 25 20
947 1 r. Industry 35 30
948 2 r. Scroll (different) 70 55

POSTAGE DUE STAMPS

D 40

1968.

D254 D 40 5 d. blue . . . . . . 12·00 10·00
D255 10 d. red . . . . . . 15·00 12·00
D256 20 d. green . . . . . . 17·00 15·00
D257 30 d. lilac . . . . . . 18·00 17·00

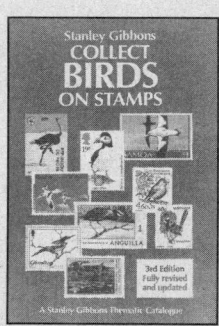

QUELIMANE Pt.9

A district of Portuguese E. Africa, now part of Mozambique, whose stamps it now uses.

100 centavos = 1 escudo

1913. Surch **REPUBLICA QUELIMANE** and new value on "Vasco da Gama" stamps of (a) Portuguese Colonies.

1		¼ c. on 2½ r. green	40	30
2		½ c. on 5 r. red	40	30
3		1 c. on 10 r. purple	40	30
4		2½ c. on 25 r. green	40	30
5		5 c. on 50 r. blue	40	30
6		7½ c. on 75 r. brown	80	70
7		10 c. on 100 r. brown	45	35
8		15 c. on 150 r. bistre	45	35

(b) Macao.

9		¼ c. on ½ a. green	40	30
10		½ c. on 1 a. red	40	30
11		1 c. on 2 a. purple	40	30
12		2½ c. on 4 a. green	40	30
13		5 c. on 8 a. blue	40	30
14		7½ c. on 12 a. brown	80	70
15		10 c. on 16 a. brown	45	35
16		15 c. on 24 a. bistre	45	35

(c) Timor.

17		¼ c. on ½ a. green	40	30
18		½ c. on 1 a. red	40	30
19		1 c. on 2 a. purple	40	30
20		2½ c. on 2 a. green	40	30
21		5 c. on 8 a. blue	40	30
22		7½ c. on 12 a. brown	80	70
23		10 c. on 16 a. brown	40	35
24		15 c. on 24 a. bistre	45	35

1914. "Ceres" key-type inscr "QUELIMANE".

25	U	¼ c. olive	20	20
26		½ c. black	60	40
42		1 c. green	50	45
28		1½ c. brown	70	50
29		2 c. red	70	60
30		2¼ c. violet	25	20
31		5 c. blue	50	40
43		7½ c. brown	50	45
33		8 c. black	60	50
44		10 c. brown	50	45
35		15 c. red	95	70
45		20 c. green	50	45
37		30 c. brown on green	1·25	90
38		40 c. brown on red	1·25	90
39		50 c. orange on pink	1·25	90
40		1 e. green on blue	1·25	90

RAS AL KHAIMA Pt.19

Arab Shaikhdom in the Arabian Gulf.

Ras al Khaima joined the United Arab Emirates in February, 1972, U.A.E. stamps were used in the shaikhdom from 1st January, 1973.

1964. 100 naye paise = 1 rupee
1966. 100 dirhams = 1 riyal

1 Shaikh Saqr bin Mohamed al-Qasimi

3 Dhow

1964.

1	1	5 n.p. brown and black	10	10
2		15 n.p. blue and black	15	10
3	–	30 n.p. yellow and black	40	10
4	–	40 n.p. blue and black	60	15
5	–	75 n.p. red and black	1·00	30
6	3	1 r. brown and green	1·50	45
7		2 r. brown and violet	2·50	1·25
8		5 r. brown and slate	5·50	3·00

DESIGNS: As Type **1**—VERT: 30 n.p. to 75 n.p. Seven palms.

3a Pres. Kennedy inspecting "Friendship 7"

1965. Pres. Kennedy Commemoration.

9	3a	2 r. blue and ochre	1·00	60
10	–	3 r. blue and ochre	1·25	80
11	–	4 r. blue and ochre	1·75	1·25

DESIGNS—HORIZ: 3 r. Kennedy and wife. VERT: 4 r. Kennedy and flame of remembrance.

MORE DETAILED LISTS are given in the Stanley Gibbons Catalogues referred to in the country headings. For lists of current volumes see introduction

4 Sir Winston Churchill and Houses of Parliament

1965. Churchill Commemoration.

12	4	2 r. blue and ochre	1·25	60
13	–	3 r. blue and ochre	1·40	80
14	–	4 r. blue and ochre	2·25	1·25

DESIGNS—HORIZ: 3 r. Churchill and Pres. Roosevelt; 4 r. Churchill, and Heads of State at his funeral.

1965. Olympic Games, Tokyo (1964). Optd **OLYMPIC TOKYO 1964** in English and Arabic and Olympic "rings".

15	3	1 r. brown and green	50	35
16		2 r. brown and violet	1·00	80
17		5 r. brown and grey	2·50	2·25

1965. Death Centenary of Abraham Lincoln. Optd **ABRAHAM LINCOLN 1809–1865** in English and Arabic.

18	3	1 r. brown and green	50	35
19		2 r. brown and violet	1·00	80
20		5 r. brown and slate	2·50	2·25

1965. 20th Death Anniv of Pres. Roosevelt. Optd **FRANKLIN D. ROOSEVELT 1882–1945** in English and Arabic.

21	3	1 r. brown and green	50	35
22		2 r. brown and violet	1·00	80
23		5 r. brown and grey	2·50	2·25

8 Satellite and Tracking Station

1966. I.T.U. Centenary. Multicoloured.

24	15 n.p. Type **8**	20	10
25	50 n.p. Post Office Tower, London, "Telstar" and tracking gantry	55	30
26	85 n.p. Rocket on launching pad and "Relay"	1·00	50
27	1 r. Type **8**	1·25	60
28	2 r. As 50 n.p.	2·00	90
29	3 r. As 85 n.p.	2·50	1·10

9 Swimming

10 Carpenter

1966. Pan-Arab Games, Cairo (1965).

31	A	1 n.p. brown, pink & green	10	10
32	B	2 n.p. black, grey & green	10	10
33	C	3 n.p. brown, pink & green	10	10
34	D	4 n.p. brown, pink & purple	10	10
35	A	5 n.p. black, grey & orange	10	10
36	9	10 n.p. brown, pink & blue	10	10
37	B	25 n.p. brown, pink & lt brn	10	10
38	C	50 n.p. black, grey & violet	20	15
39	D	75 n.p. black, grey & blue	35	15
40	9	1 r. black, grey & turquoise	45	25

DESIGNS: A, Running; B, Boxing; C, Football; D, Fencing.

1966. American Astronauts.

42	10	25 n.p. black, gold & purple	15	10
43	–	50 n.p. black, silver & brown	25	10
44	–	75 n.p. black, silver & turq	30	15
45	–	1 r. black, silver & bistre	45	20
46	–	2 r. black, silver & mauve	75	40
47	–	3 r. black, gold and green	1·25	60
48	–	4 r. black, gold and red	1·50	80
49	–	5 r. black, gold and blue	1·90	95

ASTRONAUTS: 50 n.p. Glenn; 75 n.p. Shepard; 1 r. Cooper; 2 r. Grissom; 3 r. Schirra; 4 r. Stafford; 5 r. Lovell.

11 Shaikh Sabah of Kuwait and Shaikh Saqr of Ras al Khaima

1966. International Co-operation Year.

51	11	1 r. black and brown	80	30
52	A	1 r. black and lilac	80	30
53	B	1 r. black and red	80	30
54	C	1 r. black and turquoise	80	30
55	D	1 r. black and olive	80	30
56	E	1 r. black and yellow	80	30
57	F	1 r. black and orange	80	30
58	G	1 r. black and blue	80	30

SHAIKH SAQR AND WORLD LEADERS: A, Shaikh Ahmad of Qatar; B, Pres. Nasser; C, King Hussein; D, Pres. Johnson; E, Pres. De Gaulle; F, Pope Paul VI; G, Prime Minister Harold Wilson.

NEW CURRENCY SURCHARGES. During the latter half of 1966 various issues appeared surcharged in dirhams and riyals. The 1964 definitives with this surcharge are listed below as there is considerable evidence of their postal use. Nos. 24/58 also exist with these surcharges.

In August 1966 Nos. 1/14, 24/9 and 51/8 appeared surcharged in fils and rupees. As Ras Al Khaima did not adopt this currency their status is uncertain.

1966. Nos. 1/8 with currency names changed to dirhams and riyals by overprinting in English and Arabic

60	1	5 d. on 5 n.p. black and brown	15	10
60a	–	5 d. on 75 n.p. red & black	15	10
64b	3	5 d. on 5 r. brown & grey	15	10
61	1	15 d. on 15 n.p. blue & black	25	10
62	–	30 d. on 30 n.p. black and yellow	40	15
63	–	40 d. on 40 n.p. blue & blk	55	20
64	–	75 d. on 75 n.p. red & blk	65	25
65	3	1 r. on 1 r. brown & green	75	30
66		2 r. on 2 r. brown & violet	1·50	1·25
67		5 r. on 5 r. brown & grey	3·50	2·25

15 W.H.O. Building and Flowers

1966. Inauguration of W.H.O. Headquarters, Geneva.

68	15	15 d. multicoloured (postage)	20	10
69	–	35 d. multicoloured	60	20
70	15	50 d. multicoloured (air)	75	30
71	–	3 r. multicoloured	2·00	70

DESIGN: 35 d., 3 r. As Type **15** but with red instead of yellow flowers at left.

16 Queen Elizabeth II presenting Jules Rimet Cup to Bobby Moore, Captain of England Team

1966. Air. England's Victory in World Cup Football Championships. Multicoloured.

73	1 r. Wembley Stadium	70	25
74	2 r. Goalkeeper saving ball	1·25	45
75	3 r. Footballers with ball	1·75	70
76	4 r. Type **16**	2·25	1·25

For later issues see **UNITED ARAB EMIRATES**.

APPENDIX

The following stamps have either been issued in excess of postal needs or have not been available to the public in reasonable quantities at face value. Such stamps may later be given full listing if there is evidence of regular postal use.

1967.

"The Arabian Nights". Paintings. Air 30, 70 d., 1, 2, 3 r.
Cats. Postage 1, 2, 3, 4, 5 d.: Air 3 r.
Arab Paintings. 1, 2, 3, 4, 10, 20, 30 d.
European Paintings. Air 60, 70 d., 1, 2, 3, 5, 10 r.
50th Birth Anniv of Pres. John F. Kennedy. Optd on 1965 Pres. Kennedy Commem. 2, 3, 4 r.
World Scout Jamboree, Idaho. Postage 1, 2, 3, 4 d.; Air 35, 75 d., 1 r.
U.S. "Apollo" Disaster. Optd on 1968 American Astronauts issue. 25 d. on 25 n.p., 50 d. on 50 n.p., 75 d. on 75 n.p., 1, 2, 3, 4, 5 r.
Summer Olympics Preparation, Mexico 1968. Postage 10, 20, 30, 40 d.; Air 1, 2 r.
Winter Olympics Preparation, Grenoble 1968. Postage 1, 2, 3, 4, 5, d.; Air 85 d., 2, 3 r.

1968.

Mothers' Day. Paintings. Postage 20, 30, 40, 50 d.; Air 1, 2, 3, 4 r.
Int Human Rights Year. 2 r. × 3
Int Museum Campaign. Paintings. 15, 15, 20, 25, 35, 40, 45, 60, 70, 80, 90 d.; 1, 1 r. 25, 1 r. 50, 2 r. 50, 2 r. 75.
Winter Olympic Medal Winners, Grenoble. 50 d., 1, 1 r. 50, 2, 2 r. 50, 3r.
Olympic Games, Mexico. Air 1, 2, 2, 3, 3, 4 r.
5th Death Anniv of Pres. John F. Kennedy. Air. 2, 3 r.
Christmas. Religious Paintings. Postage 20, 30, 40, 50, 60 d., 1 r.; Air 2, 3, 4 r.

1969.

Famous Composers (1st series). Paintings. 25, 50, 75 d., 1 r. 50, 2 r. 50.
Famous Operas 20, 40, 60, 80 d., 1, 2 r.
Famous Men. Postage 20, 30, 50 d.; Air 1 r. 50, 2, 3, 4, 5 r.
Int Philatelic Exhib., Mexico 1968 (EFIMEX). Postage 10, 10, 25, 35, 40, 50, 60, 70 d.; Air 1, 2, 3, 5, 5 r.
Int Co-operation in Olympics. 1, 2, 3, 4 r.
Int Co-operation in Space. Air 1 r. 50, 2 r. 50, 3 r. 50, 4 r. 50
Birth Bicentenary of Napoleon. Paintings. Postage 1 r. 75, 2 r. 75, 3 r. 75; Air 75 d.
"Apollo" Moon Missions. Air 2, 2 r. 50, 3, 3 r. 50, 4, 4 r. 50, 5, 5 r. 50
"Apollo 11" Astronauts. Air 2 r. 25, 3 r. 25, 4 r. 25, 5 r. 25.
"Apollo 12" Astronauts. Air 60 d., 2 r. 60, 3 r. 60, 4 r. 60, 5 r. 60.

1970.

Christmas 1969. Religious Paintings. Postage 50 d.; Air 3, 3 r. 50
World Cup, Mexico. Air 1, 2, 3, 4, 5, 6 r.
Easter. Religious Paintings. Postage 50 d.; Air 3, 3 r. 50
Paintings by Titian and Tiepolo. Postage 50, 50 d.; Air 3, 3, 3 r. 50, 3 r. 50.
Winter Olympics, Sapporo 1972. Air 1, 2, 3, 4, 5, 6 r.
Olympic Games, Munich 1972. Air 1, 2, 3, 4, 5, 6 r.
Paul Gauguin's Paintings. Postage 50 d.; Air 3, 3 r. 50
Christmas. Religious Paintings. Postage 50 d.; Air 3, 3 r. 50
"World Cup Champions, Brazil". Optd on Mexico World Cup issue. Air 1, 2, 3, 4, 5, 6 r.
"EXPO 70" World Fair Osaka Japan (1st issue). Postage 40, 45, 50, 55, 60, 65, 70, 75 d.; Air 80, 85, 90, 95 d., 1 r. 60, 1 r. 65, 1 r. 85, 2 r.
"EXPO 70" World Fair, Osaka, Japan (2nd issue). Postage 55, 65, 75 d.; Air 25, 85, 95 d., 1 r. 50, 1 r. 75.
Space Programmes. Air 1 r. × 6, 2 r. × 6, 4 r. × 6.
Famous Frenchmen. Air 1 r × 4, 2 r. × 4, 2 r. 50 × 2, 3 r. × 2, 4 r. × 4, 5 r. 50 × 2.
Int Philatelic Exhib (Philympia '70). Air 1 r. × 4, 1 r. 50 × 4, 2 r. 50 × 4, 3 r. × 4, 4 r. × 4.
Events in the Life of Christ. Religious Paintings. 5, 10, 25, 50 d., 1, 2, 5 r.
"Stages of the Cross". Religious Paintings. 10, 20, 30, 40, 50, 60, 70, 80 d., 1, 1 r. 50, 2, 2 r. 50, 3, 3 r. 50.
The Life of Mary. Religious Paintings. 10, 15, 30, 60, 75 d., 3, 4 r.

1971.

Easter. "Stages of the Cross" (1970) but with additional inscr "EASTER". 10, 20, 30, 40, 50, 60, 70, 80 d., 1, 1 r. 50, 2, 2 r. 50, 3, 3 r. 50.
Charles de Gaulle Memorial. Postage 50 d.; Air 1, 1 r. 50, 2, 3, 4 r.
Safe Return of "Apollo 14". Postage 50 d.; Air 1, 1 r. 50, 2, 3, 4 r.
U.S.A.–Japan Baseball Friendship. Postage 10, 25, 30, 80 d.; Air 50, 70 d., 1, 1r. 50
Munich Olympics, 1972. Postage 50 d.; Air 1, 1 r. 50, 2, 3, 4 r.
Cats. 35, 60, 65, 110, 120, 160 d.
13th World Jamboree Japan. Postage 30, 50, 60, 75 d.; Air 1, 1 r. 50, 3, 4 r.
Sapporo Olympic Gold Medal Winners. Optd on 1970 Winter Olympics, Sapporo 1972, issue, Air 1, 2, 3, 4, 5, 6 r.
Munich Olympic Medal Winners, Optd on 1970 Summer Olympics, Munich 1972 issue. Air. 1, 2, 3, 4, 5, 6r.
Japanese Locomotives. Postage 30, 35, 75 d.; Air 90 d., 1, 1 r. 50, 2, 3, 4 r.
"Soyuz 11" Russian Cosmonauts Memorial. Air 1, 2, 3, 4 r.
"Apollo 15". Postage 50 d.; Air 1, 1 r. 50, 2, 3, 4 r.
Dogs. 5, 20, 75, 85, 185, 200 d.
Durer's Paintings. Postage 50 d.; Air 1, 1 r. 50 2, 3, 4 r.
Famous Composers (2nd series). Postage 50 d.; Air 1, 1 r. 50, 2, 3, 4 r.
"Soyuz 11" and "Salyut" Space Projects. Postage 50 d,; Air 1, 1 r. 50, 2, 3, 4 r.
Butterflies. Postage 15, 20, 70 d.; Air 1 r. 25, 1 r. 50, 1 r. 70.
Wild Animals. 10, 40, 80 d,; 1 r. 15, 1 r. 30, 1 r. 65.
Fishes. 30, 50, 60, 90 d., 1 r. 45, 1 r. 55.
Ludwig van Beethoven. Portraits. Postage 50 d.; Air 1, 1 r. 50, 2, 3, 4 r.

1972.

Birds. 50, 55, 80, 100, 105, 190 d.
Winter Olympics, Sapporo (1st issue). Postage 20, 30, 50 d., Air 70, 90 d., 2 r. 50
Winter Olympics, Sapporo (2nd issue). Postage 5, 60, 80, 90 d.; Air 1 r. 10, 1 r. 75
Mozart. Portraits. Postage 50 d.; Air 1, 1 r. 50, 2, 3, 4 r.
Olympic Games, Munich. Postage 50 d.; Air 1, 1 r. 50, 2, 3, 4 r.

"In Memory of Charles de Gaulle". Optd on 1971 Charles de Gaulle memorial issue. Postage 50 d.; Air 1, 1 r. 50, 2, 3, 4 r.
Winter Olympics, Sapporo (3rd issue). Postage 15, 45 d.; Air 65, 75 d., 1 r. 20, 1 r. 25.
Horses. Postage 10, 25, 30 d.; Air 1 r. 40, 1 r. 80, 1 r. 95.
Parrots. 40, 45, 70, 95 d., 1 r. 35, 1 r. 75.
"Apollo 16". Postage 50 d.; Air 1, 1 r. 50, 2, 3, 4 r.
European Footballers. Postage 50 d.; Air 1, 1 r. 50, 2, 3, 4 r.

A number of issues on gold or silver foil also exist, but it is understood that these were mainly for presentation purposes, although valid for postage.

In common with the other states of the United Arab Emirates the Ras al Khaima stamp contract was terminated on 1st August 1972, and any further new issues released after that date were unauthorised.

REUNION Pt. 6

An island in the Indian Ocean, E. of Madagascar, now an overseas department of France.

100 centimes = 1 franc

1

1852. Imperf. No gum.

1	1	15 c. black on blue	£20000	£11000
2		30 c. black on blue	£20000	£11000

1885. Stamps of French Colonies surch **R** and value in figures. Imperf.

5	D	5 c. on 30 c. brown	30·00	28·00
7	H	5 c. on 30 c. brown	3·50	4·50
3	A	5 c. on 40 c. orange	£225	£200
6	F	5 c. on 40 c. orange	26·00	18·00
8	H	5 c. on 40 c. red on yellow	65·00	55·00
9		10 c. on 40 c. red on yellow	6·50	4·50
10		20 c. on 30 c. brown	42·00	35·00
4	A	25 c. on 40 c. orange	30·00	25·00

1891. Stamps of French Colonies optd **REUNION**. Imperf (Types F and H) or perf (Type J).

17	J	1 c. black on blue	1·40	1·60
18		2 c. brown on buff	2·25	1·00
19		4 c. brown on grey	3·00	3·00
20		5 c. green on green	4·50	2·25
21		10 c. black on lilac	19·00	1·75
22		15 c. blue on blue	28·00	1·75
23		20 c. red on green	18·00	2·50
24		25 c. black on pink	20·00	2·50
13	H	30 c. brown	23·00	21·00
25	J	35 c. black on yellow	16·00	11·50
11	F	40 c. orange	£300	£290
14	H	40 c. red on yellow	17·00	14·00
26	J	40 c. red on buff	45·00	35·00
15	H	75 c. red	£225	£225
27	J	75 c. red on pink	£400	£325
12	F	80 c. pink	35·00	30·00
16	H	1 f. green	25·00	23·00
28	J	1 f. green	£300	£300

1891. Stamps of French Colonies surch **REUNION** and new value.

29	J	02 c. on 20 c. red on green	4·50	3·75
31		2 on 20 c. red on green	1·75	1·75
30		15 c. on 20 c. red on green	5·50	5·00

1892. "Tablet" key-type inscr "REUNION"

34	D	1 c. black and red on blue	50	50
35		2 c. brown & blue on buff	50	45
36		4 c. brown & blue on grey	1·10	60
50		5 c. green and red	70	40
38		10 c. black & blue on lilac	4·00	1·00
51		10 c. red and blue	80	35
39		15 c. blue and red	11·50	75
52		15 c. grey and red	2·75	35
40		20 c. red & blue on green	4·50	5·00
41		25 c. black & red on pink	8·25	1·00
53		25 c. blue and red	9·75	9·50
42		30 c. brown & bl on drab	9·25	4·75
43		40 c. red & blue on yellow	14·00	9·00
44		50 c. red and blue on pink	42·00	21·00
54		50 c. brown & red on blue	23·00	21·00
55		50 c. brown & blue on blue	30·00	26·00
45		75 c. brown & red on orge	38·00	24·00
46		1 f. green and red	28·00	15·00

1893. Stamp of French Colonies, "Commerce" type, surch **2 c.**

47	J	2 c. on 20 c. red on green	1·00	95

1901. "Tablet" key-type surch in figures.

56	D	5 c. on 40 c. red and blue on yellow	1·25	2·25
57		5 c. on 50 c. red and blue on pink	2·75	2·75
58		15 c. on 75 c. brown and red on orange	8·00	8·00
59		15 c. on 1 f. green and red	7·00	7·00

16 Map of Reunion

17 View of Saint-Denis and Arms of the Colony

18 View of St. Pierre and Crater Dolomieu

1907.

60	16	1 c. red and lilac	10	10
61		2 c. blue and brown	10	10
62		4 c. red and green	10	10
63		5 c. red and green	25	10
92		5 c. violet and yellow	20	15
64		10 c. green and red	90	10
93		10 c. turquoise and green	20	15
94		10 c. red and lake on blue	35	15
65		15 c. blue and black	30	10
95		15 c. turquoise and green	20	25
96		15 c. red and blue	25	35
66	17	20 c. green and olive	25	25
67		25 c. brown and blue	1·40	50
97		25 c. blue and brown	20	10
68		30 c. green and brown	35	55
98		30 c. pink and red	30	50
99		30 c. red and grey	15	25
100		30 c. light green and green	55	70
69		35 c. blue and brown	35	35
101		40 c. brown and green	35	15
70		45 c. pink and violet	55	70
102		45 c. red and purple	35	50
103		45 c. red and mauve	90	1·25
71		50 c. blue and brown	1·40	75
104		50 c. ultramarine and blue	25	25
105		50 c. violet and yellow	20	15
106		60 c. brown and blue	15	30
107		65 c. blue and violet	55	70
72		75 c. pink and red	45	35
108		75 c. purple and brown	1·00	1·00
109		90 c. pink and red	3·50	3·50
78	18	1 f. blue and brown	40	45
110		1 f. blue	50	65
111		1 f. lilac and brown	50	50
112		1 f. 10 mauve and brown	55	60
113		1 f. 50 lt blue & blue on bl	6·00	4·50
74		2 f. green and red	2·25	1·60
114		3 f. mauve on pink	6·25	4·75
75		5 f. brown and pink	3·50	3·00

1912. "Tablet" key-type surch.

76	D	05 on 2 c. brown and red on buff	20	25
77		05 on 15 c. grey and red	40	50
78		05 on 20 c. red and blue on green	65	75
79		05 on 25 c. black and red on pink	35	60
80		05 on 30 c. brown and blue on drab	35	55
81		10 on 40 c. red and blue on yellow	30	50
82		10 on 50 c. brown and blue on blue	75	1·60
83		10 on 75 c. brown and red on orange	2·50	5·00

1915. Red Cross Surch **5c** and red cross.

90	16	10 c. + 5 c. green and red	50	80

1917. Surch in figures.

91	16	0.01 on 4 c. red and green	70	70
124	18	25 c. on 5 f. brown & red	40	60
115	17	40 on 20 c. yellow & green	30	40
116		50 on 45 c. red and purple	50	65
117		50 on 45 c. red and mauve	£160	£160
118		50 on 65 c. blue and violet	45	60
119		60 on 75 c. carmine and red	25	25
120	16	65 on 15 c. blue and black	65	75
121		85 on 15 c. blue and black	60	75
122	17	85 on 75 c. pink and red	70	85
123		90 on 75 c. pink and red	85	90
125	18	1 f. 25 on 1 f. blue	35	45
126		1 f. 50 on 1 f. light blue and blue on blue	35	35
127		3 f. on 5 f. blue and red	1·25	1·25
128		10 f. on 5 f. red & green	8·75	7·25
129		20 f. on 5 f. pink & brown	11·00	9·00

1931. "Colonial Exhibition" key-types inscr "REUNION".

130	E	40 c. green and black	1·50	1·60
131	F	50 c. mauve and black	1·90	2·00
132	G	90 c. red and black	2·00	2·00
133	H	1 f. 50 blue and black	2·00	2·00

MINIMUM PRICE

The minimum price quoted is 10p which represents a handling charge rather than a basis for valuing common stamps. For further notes about prices, see introductory pages.

30 Cascade, Salazie

31 Anchain Peak, Salazie

32 Leon Dierx Museum

34 Caudron C-600 "Aiglon"

1933.

134	30	1 c. purple	10	30
135		2 c. brown	10	20
136		3 c. mauve	10	25
137		4 c. olive	10	30
138		5 c. orange	10	20
139		10 c. blue	10	25
140		15 c. black	10	15
141		20 c. blue	20	25
142		25 c. brown	15	25
143		30 c. green	15	20
144	31	35 c. green	30	40
145		40 c. blue	25	35
146		40 c. brown	20	35
147		45 c. mauve	45	55
148		45 c. green	25	35
149		50 c. red	25	15
150		55 c. orange	55	55
151		60 c. blue	20	35
152		65 c. olive	70	65
153		70 c. olive	35	40
154		75 c. brown	2·50	2·25
155		80 c. black	35	50
156		90 c. red	1·25	1·00
157		90 c. purple	50	45
158		1 f. green	1·00	65
159		1 f. red	65	60
160		1 f. black	25	35
161	32	1 f. 25 brown	35	50
162		1 f. 25 red	50	50
163	30	1 f. 40 blue	50	45
164	32	1 f. 50 blue	15	15
165	30	1 f. 60 red	45	45
166	32	1 f. 75 olive	35	35
167	30	1 f. 75 blue	45	55
168	32	2 f. red	25	40
169	30	2 f. 25 blue	85	80
170		2 f. 50 brown	55	55
171	32	3 f. violet	30	30
172		5 f. mauve	30	35
173		10 f. blue	40	45
174		20 f. brown	70	75

1937. Air. Pioneer Flight from Reunion to France by Laurent, Lenier and Touge. Optd **REUNION – FRANCE par avion "ROLAND GARROS"**.

174a	31	50 c. red	£170	£160

1937. International Exhibition, Paris. As Nos. 168/73 of St.-Pierre et Miquelon.

175		20 c. violet	85	95
176		30 c. green	95	1·10
177		40 c. red	90	1·10
178		50 c. brown and agate	90	1·10
179		90 c. red	95	1·10
180		1 f. 50 blue	95	1·25

1938. Air.

181	34	3 f. 65 blue and red	60	85
182		6 f. 65 brown and red	60	85
183		9 f. 65 red and blue	60	85
184		12 f. 65 brown and green	1·00	1·40

1938. Int Anti-Cancer Fund. As T **22** of Mauritania.

185		1 f. 75 + 50 c. blue	5·50	7·50

1939. New York World's Fair. As T **28** of Mauritania.

186		1 f. 25 red	50	60
187		2 f. 25 blue	55	60

1939. 150th Anniv of French Revolution. As T **29** of Mauritania.

188		45 c. + 25 c. green and black (postage)	4·75	5·00
189		70 c. + 30 c. brown & black	4·75	5·00
190		90 c. + 35 c. orange & black	4·50	5·00
191		1 f. 25 + 1 f. red and black	4·75	5·00
192		2 f. 25 + 2 f. blue and black	4·75	5·00
193		3 f. 65 + 4 f. blk & orge (air)	9·50	11·50

1943. Surch **1f.**

194	31	1 f. on 65 c. green	55	55

1943. Optd **France Libre**.

198	30	1 c. purple (postage)	50	55
199		2 c. brown	40	55
200		3 c. purple	40	55
195	16	4 c. red and green	1·25	1·90
201	30	4 c. green	40	55
202		5 c. red	40	55
203		10 c. blue	40	55
204		15 c. black	40	55
205		20 c. blue	40	55
206		25 c. brown	40	55
207		30 c. green	40	55
208	31	35 c. green	35	55
209		40 c. blue	40	55
210	31	40 c. brown	40	55
211		45 c. mauve	40	55
212		45 c. green	40	55
213		50 c. red	45	65
214		55 c. orange	40	55
215		60 c. blue	1·40	1·40
216		65 c. green	40	55
217		70 c. green	85	90
196	17	75 c. pink and red	65	70
218	31	75 c. brown	1·50	1·60
219		80 c. black	40	55
220		90 c. purple	40	55
221		1 f. green	40	55
222		1 f. red	40	55
223		1 f. black	95	1·00
240		1 f. on 65 c. green (No. 194)	65	75
224	32	1 f. 25 brown	40	55
225		1 f. 25 red	85	90
238	–	1 f. 25 red (No. 186)	1·25	1·40
226	30	1 f. 40 blue	75	90
227	32	1 f. 50 blue	35	55
228	30	1 f. 60 red	85	1·00
229	32	1 f. 75 green	40	55
230	30	1 f. 75 blue	2·00	2·25
231	32	2 f. red	35	55
239	–	2 f. 25 blue (No. 187)	1·40	1·40
232	30	2 f. 25 blue	85	90
233		2 f. 50 brown	3·00	3·00
234	32	3 f. violet	45	55
197	18	5 f. brown and pink	27·00	27·00
235	32	5 f. mauve	85	90
236		10 f. blue	3·50	3·75
237		20 f. brown	5·75	5·75
241	34	3 f. 65 blue and red (air)	2·00	2·00
242		6 f. 65 brown and red	2·00	2·00
243		9 f. 65 red and blue	2·00	2·00
244		12 f. 65 brown and green	2·00	2·00

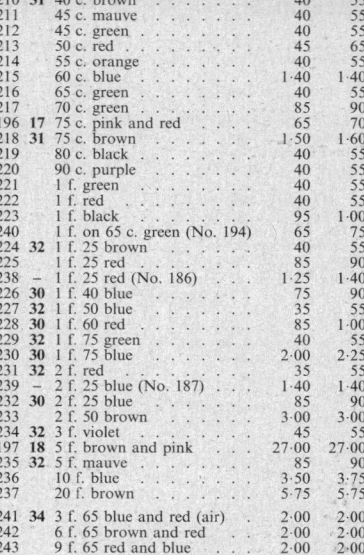

37 Chief Products

1943. Free French Issue.

245	37	5 c. brown	10	25
246a		10 c. blue	20	25
247		25 c. green	10	25
248		30 c. red	10	25
249		40 c. green	10	25
250		80 c. mauve	10	30
251		1 f. purple	15	30
252		1 f. 50 red	15	35
253		2 f. black	20	35
254		2 f. 50 blue	25	40
255		4 f. violet	15	30
256		5 f. yellow	20	30
257		10 f. brown	25	70
258		20 f. green	30	80

1944. Air. Free French Administration. As T **30** of New Caledonia.

259		1 f. orange	20	30
260		1 f. 50 red	30	35
261		5 f. purple	30	35
262		10 f. black	40	45
263		25 f. blue	40	45
264		50 f. green	40	50
265		100 f. red	60	70

1944. Mutual Air and Red Cross Funds. As T **31** of New Caledonia.

266		5 f. + 20 f. black	55	55

1945. Eboue. As T **32** of New Caledonia.

267		2 f. black	45	45
268		25 f. green	55	55

1945. Surch.

269	37	50 c. on 5 c. brown	25	35
270		60 c. on 5 c. brown	25	35
271		70 c. on 5 c. brown	25	35
272		1 f. 20 on 5 c. brown	35	50
273		2 f. 40 on 25 c. green	35	50
274		3 f. on 25 c. green	35	50
275		4 f. 50 on 25 c. green	45	60
276		15 f. on 2 f. 50 blue	45	65

1946. Air. Victory. As T **34** of New Caledonia.

277		8 f. grey	40	55

1946. Air. From Chad to the Rhine. As Nos. 300/305 of New Caledonia.

278		5 f. red	60	85
279		10 f. violet	60	85
280		15 f. black	60	80
281		20 f. red	70	90
282		25 f. blue	70	85
283		50 f. green	70	90

39 Cliffs

40 Banana Tree and Cliff

41 Mountain Landscape

42 Shadow of Airplane over Coast

1947.

284 **39** 10 c. orange & grn (postage) 10 30
285 30 c. orange and blue 10 30
286 40 c. orange and brown 10 30
287 – 50 c. brown and green 15 30
288 – 60 c. brown and blue 15 10
289 – 80 c. green and brown 15 40
290 – 1 f. purple and blue 30 20
291 – 1 f. 20 grey and green 35 50
292 – 1 f. 50 purple and orange 35 50
293 **40** 2 f. blue and green 25 30
294 3 f. purple and green 35 55
295 3 f. 60 pink and red 35 55
296 4 f. blue and brown 35 55
297 **41** 5 f. mauve and brown 35 50
298 6 f. blue and brown 50 60
299 10 f. orange and blue 80 85
300 – 15 f. purple and blue 1·75 1·90
301 – 20 f. blue and orange 2·25 2·25
302 – 25 f. brown and mauve 2·75 2·75
303 **42** 50 f. green and grey (air) 3·75 3·75
304 – 100 f. orange and brown 5·75 5·75
305 – 200 f. blue and orange 7·50 7·75

DESIGNS—20 × 37 mm: 50 c. to 80 c. Cutting sugar cane; 1 f. to 1 f. 50, Cascade. 28 × 50 mm: 100 f. Douglas DC-4 airplane over Reunion. 37 × 20 mm: 15 f. to 25 f. "Ville de Strasbourg" (liner) approaching Reunion. 50 × 28 mm: 200 f. Reunion from the air.

1949. Stamps of France surch **CFA** and value. (a) Postage. (i) Ceres.

306 **218** 50 c. on 1 f. red 15 30
307 60 c. on 2 f. green 2·25 1·40

(ii) Nos. 972/3 (Arms).

308 10 c. on 30 c. black, red and yellow (Alsace) 10 30
309 30 c. on 50 c. brown, yellow and red (Lorraine) 25 40

(iii) Nos. 981, 979 and 982/a (Views).

310 5 f. on 20 f. blue (Finistere) 1·75 50
311 7 f. on 12 f. red (Luxembourg Palace) 2·50 1·25
312 8 f. on 25 f. blue (Nancy) 6·00 1·90
313 10 f. on 25 f. brn (Nancy) 1·00 70

(iv) Marianne.

314 **219** 1 f. on 3 f. mauve 40 30
315 2 f. on 4 f. green 75 50
316 2 f. on 5 f. green 3·25 3·25
317 2 f. on 5 f. violet 60 50
318 2 f. 50 on 5 f. blue 7·50 6·75
319 3 f. on 6 f. red 90 30
320 3 f. on 6 f. green 1·60 1·40
321 4 f. on 10 f. violet 85 40
322 6 f. on 12 f. blue 2·25 75
323 6 f. on 12 f. orange 1·90 1·25
324 9 f. on 18 f. red 2·75 2·75

(v) Conques Abbey.

325 **263** 11 f. on 18 f. blue 2·00 1·90

(b) Air. (i) Nos. 967/70 (Mythology).

326 – 20 f. on 40 f. green 1·50 1·00
327 **236** 25 f. on 50 f. pink 1·75 80
328 **237** 50 f. on 100 f. blue 3·75 2·50
329 – 100 f. on 200 f. red 25·00 12·50

(ii) Nos. 1056 and 1058/9 (Cities).

330 100 f. on 200 f. green (Bordeaux) 65·00 28·00
331 200 f. on 500 f. red (Marseilles) 24·00 16·00
332 500 f. on 1000 f. purple and black on blue (Paris) £170 £130

1950. Stamps of France surch **CFA** and value.

(a) Nos. 1050 and 1052 (Arms)

342 10 c. on 50 c. yellow, red and blue (Guyenne) 15 30
343 1 f. on 2 f. red, yellow & green (Auvergne) 3·00 2·50

(b) On Nos. 1067/8 and 1068b (Views).

344 – 5 f. on 20 f. red (Comminges) 2·75 50
345 **284** 8 f. on 25 f. blue (Wandrille) 1·60 50
346 – 15 f. on 30 f. blue (Arbois) 85 60

1951. Nos. 1123/4 of France (Arms) surch **CFA** and value.

347 50 c. on 1 f. red, yellow and blue (Bearn) 30 35
348 1 f. on 2 f. yellow, blue and red (Touraine) 35 35

1952. Nos. 1138 and 1144 of France surch **CFA** and value.

349 **323** 5 f. on 20 f. violet (Chambord) 60 50
350 **317** 8 f. on 40 f. violet (Bigorre) 2·75 35

1953. Stamps of France surch **CFA** and value. (a) Nos. 1162, 1168 and 1170 (Literary Figures and National Industries).

351 3 f. on 6 f. lake and red (Gargantua) 40 35
352 8 f. on 40 f. brown and chocolate (Porcelain) 1·50 25
353 20 f. on 75 f. red and carmine (Flowers) 1·50 50

(b) Nos. 1181/2 (Arms).

354 50 c. on 1 f. yellow, red and black (Poitou) 45 60
355 1 f. on 2 f. yellow, blue and brown (Champagne) 60 55

1954. Stamps of France surch **CFA** and value. (a) Postage. (i) Nos. 1188 and 1190 (Sports).

356 8 f. on 40 f. blue and brown (Canoeing) 10·00 5·00
357 20 f. on 75 f. red and orange (Horse jumping) 35·00 23·00

(ii) Nos. 1205/8 and 1210/11 (Views).

358 2 f. on 6 f. indigo, blue and green (Lourdes) 45 45
359 3 f. on 8 f. green and blue (Andelys) 50 55
360 4 f. on 10 f. brown and blue (Royan) 65 70
361 6 f. on 12 f. lilac and violet (Quimper) 90 80
362 9 f. on 18 f. indigo, blue and green (Cheverny) 2·25 2·75
363 10 f. on 20 f. brown, chestnut & blue (Ajaccio) 1·60 90

(iii) No. 1229 (Arms).

364 1 f. on 2 f. yellow, red and black (Angoumois) 30 30

(b) Air. Nos. 1194/7 (Aircraft).

365 50 f. on 100 f. brown and blue (Mystere IV) 1·00 75
366 100 f. on 200 f. purple and blue (Noratlas) 2·00 1·25
367 200 f. on 500 f. red and orange (Magister) 10·00 9·25
368 500 f. on 1000 f. indigo, purple and blue (Provence) 11·00 8·25

1955. Stamps of France surch **CFA** and value. (a) Nos. 1262/5, 1266, 1268 and 1268b (Views).

369 2 f. on 6 f. red (Bordeaux) 70 65
370 3 f. on 8 f. blue (Marseilles) 80 80
371 4 f. on 10 f. blue (Nice) 55 50
372 5 f. on 12 f. brown and grey (Cahors) 60 50
373 6 f. on 18 f. blue and green (Uzerche) 60 50
374 10 f. on 25 f. brown and chestnut (Brouage) 65 50
375 17 f. on 70 f. black and green (Cahors) 2·75 2·00

(b) No. 1273 (Arms).

376 50 c. on 1 f. yellow, red and blue (Comtat Venaissin) 20 25

1956. Nos. 1297/1300 of France (Sports) surch **CFA** and value.

377 8 f. on 30 f. black and grey (Basketball) 1·25 45
378 9 f. on 40 f. purple and brown (Pelota) 1·90 1·10
379 15 f. on 50 f. violet and purple (Rugby) 2·75 1·25
380 20 f. on 75 f. green, black and blue (Climbing) 1·90 1·25

1957. Stamps of France surch **CFA** and value. (a) Postage. (i) Harvester.

381 **344** 2 f. on 6 f. brown 25 15
382 4 f. on 12 f. purple 1·75 65
383 5 f. on 10 f. green 1·25 55

(ii) France.

384 **362** 10 f. on 20 f. blue 55 15
385 12 f. on 25 f. red 2·00 30

(iii) No. 1335 (Le Quesnoy).

386 7 f. on 15 f. black and green 80 40

(iv) Nos. 1351, 1352/3, 1354/5 and 1356a (Tourist Publicity).

387 3 f. on 10 f. chocolate and brown (Elysee) 55 20
388 6 f. on 18 f. brown and blue (Beynac) 65 55
389 9 f. on 25 f. brown and grey (Valencay) 70 60
390 17 f. on 35 f. mauve and red (Rouen) 1·60 1·00
391 20 f. on 50 f. brown and green (St. Remy) 80 40
392 25 f. on 85 f. purple (Evian-les-Bains) 2·25 1·00

(b) Air. Nos. 1319/20 (Aircraft).

393 200 f. on 500 f. black and blue (Caravelle) 10·50 6·00
394 500 f. on 1000 f. black, violet and brown (Alouette II) 15·00 8·75

1960. Nos. 1461, 1464 and 1467 of France (Tourist Publicity) surch **CFA** and value.

395 7 f. on 15 c. indigo and blue (Laon) 65 45
396 20 f. on 50 c. purple and green (Tlemcen) 12·00 3·25
397 50 f. on 1 f. violet, green and blue (Cilaos) 1·60 55

1961. Harvester and Sower stamps of France (in new currency) surch **CFA** and value.

398 **344** 5 f. on 10 c. green 30 20
400 **453** 10 f. on 20 c. red and turquoise 20 10

1961. "Marianne" stamp of France surch **12 f. CFA**.

401 **463** 12 f. on 25 c. grey & purple 20 10

1961. Nos. 1457, 1457b and 1459/60 of France (Aircraft) surch **CFA** and value.

402 100 f. on 2 f. purple and blue (Noratlas) 3·50 1·00
403 100 f. on 2 f. indigo and blue (Mystere Falcon 20) 1·25 50
404 200 f. on 5 f. black and blue (Caravelle) 4·50 2·00
405 500 f. on 10 f. black, violet and brown (Alouette II) 11·50 4·00

1962. Red Cross stamps of France (Nos. 1593/4) surch **CFA** and value.

409 10 f. + 5 f. on 20 c. + 10 c. 1·75 1·50
410 12 f. + 5 f. on 25 c. + 10 c. 1·75 1·50

1962. Satellite Link stamps of France surch **CFA** and value.

411 12 f. on 25 c. (No. 1587) 60 50
412 25 f. on 50 c. (No. 1588) 60 50

1963. Nos. 1541 and 1545 of France (Tourist Publicity) surch **CFA** and value.

413 7 f. on 15 c. grey, purple and blue (St. Paul) 20 15
414 20 f. on 45 c. brown, green and blue (Sully) 80 30

1963. Nos. 1498b/9b and 1499e/f of France (Arms) surch **CFA** and value.

415 1 f. on 2 c. yellow, green and blue (Gueret) 10 10
416 2 f. on 5 c. mult (Oran) 10 10
417 2 f. on 5 c. red, yellow and blue (Armiens) 10 10
418 5 f. on 10 c. blue, yellow and red (Troyes) 10 10
419 6 f. on 18 c. multicoloured (St. Denis) 15 15
420 15 f. on 30 c. red and blue (Paris) 20 10

1963. Red Cross stamps of France. (Nos. 1627/8) surch **CFA** and value.

421 10 f. + 5 f. on 20 c. + 10 c. 2·50 2·25
422 12 f. + 5 f. on 25 c. + 10 c. 2·50 2·25

1964. 'PHILATEC 1964' International Stamp Exhibition stamp of France surch **CFA** and value.

423 12 f. on 25 c. (No. 1629) 85 60

1964. Nos. 1654/5 of France (Tourist Publicity) surch **CFA** and value.

431 20 f. on 40 c. chocolate, green and brown (Ronchamp) 60 45
432 35 f. on 70 c. purple, green and blue (Provins) 80 65

1964. Red Cross stamps of France. (Nos. 1665/6) surch **CFA** and value.

433 10 f. + 5 f. on 20 c. + 10 c. 1·10 1·00
434 12 f. + 5 f. on 25 c. + 10 c. 1·10 1·00

1965. No. 1621 of France (Saint Flour) surch **3F CFA**.

435 30 f. on 60 c. red, green & bl 80 65

1965. Nos 1684/5 and 1688 of France (Tourist Publicity) surch **CFA** and value.

436 25 f. on 50 c. blue, green and bistre (St. Marie) 50 25
437 30 f. on 60 c. brown and blue (Aix les Bains) 65 45
438 50 f. on 1 f. grey, green and brown (Carnac) 1·10 90

1965. Tercent of Colonisation of Reunion. As No. 1692 of France, but additionally inscr 'CFA'.

439 15 f. blue and red 45 30

1965. Red Cross stamps of France (Nos. 1698/9) surch **CFA** and value.

440 12 f. + 5 f. on 25 c. + 10 c. 1·00 1·00
441 15 f. + 5 f. on 30 c. + 10 c. 1·00 1·00

1966. "Marianne" stamp of France surch **10f CFA**.

442 **476** 10 f. on 20 c. red & blue 1·00 50

1966. Launching of 1st French Satellite. Nos. 1696/7 (plus se-tenant label) of France surch. **CFA** and value.

443 15 f. on 30 c. blue, turquoise and light blue 60 50
444 30 f. on 60 c. blue, turquoise and light blue 80 70

1966. Red Cross stamps of France (Nos. 1733/4) surch **CFA** and value.

445 12 f. + 5 f. on 25 c. + 10 c. 90 70
446 15 f. + 5 f. on 30 c. + 10 c. 90 70

1967. World Fair Montreal. No. 1747 of France surch **CFA** and value.

447 30 f. on 60 c. 90 65

1967. No. 1700 of France (Arms of Auch) surch **2fCFA**.

448 2 f. on 5 c. red and blue 15 10

1967. 50th Anniv of Lions Int. No. 1766 of France surch **CFA** and value.

449 20 f. on 40 c. 1·10 90

1967. Red Cross. Nos. 1772/3 of France surch **CFA** and value.

450 12 f. + 5 f. on 25 c. + 10 c. 2·50 2·50
451 15 f. + 5 f. on 30 c. + 10 c. 2·50 2·50

1968. French Polar Exploration. No. 1806 of France surch **CFA** and value.

452 20 f. on 40 c. 75 65

1968. Red Cross stamps of France (Nos. 1812/13) surch **CFA** and value.

453 12 f. + 5 f. on 25 c. + 10 c. 1·25 1·10
454 15 f. + 5 f. on 30 c. + 10 c. 1·25 1·10

1969. Stamp Day. No. 1824 of France, surch **CFA** and value.

455 15 f. + 5 f. on 30 c. + 10 c. 80 80

1969. "Republique" stamps of France surch **CFA** and value.

456 **604** 15 f. on 30 c. green 45 35
457 20 f. on 40 c. mauve 45 25

1969. No. 1735 of France (Arms of Saint-Lo) surch **10F CFA**.

458 10 f. on 20 c. multicoloured 25 25

1969. Birth Bicent of Napoleon Bonaparte. No. 1845 of France surch **CFA** and value.

459 35 f. on 70 c. green, violet & bl 1·10 90

1969. Red Cross stamps of France (Nos. 1853/4) surch **CFA** and value.

460 20 f. + 7 f. on 40 c. + 15 c. 1·00 1·00
461 20 f. + 7 f. on 40 c. + 15 c. 1·00 1·00

1970. Stamp Day. No. 1866 of France surch **CFA** and value.

462 20 f. + 5 f. on 40 c. + 10 c. 90 65

1970. Red Cross. Nos. 1902/3 of France surch **CFA** and value.

463 20 f. + 7 f. on 40 c. + 15 c. 2·25 1·75
464 20 f. + 7 f. on 40 c. + 15 c. 2·25 1·75

1971. "Marianne" stamp of France surch **25f CFA**.

465 **668** 25 f. on 50 c. mauve 45 10

1971. Stamp Day No. 1919 of France surch **CFA** and value.

466 25 f. + 5 f. on 50 c. + 10 c. 90 35

1971. "Antoinette". No. 1920 of France surch **CFA** and value.

467 40 f. on 80 c. 1·10 90

1971. No. 1928 of France (Rural Aid) surch **CFA** and value.

468 **678** 15 f. on 40 c. 55 45

1971. Nos. 1931/2 of France (Tourist Publicity) surch **CFA** and value.

469 45 f. on 90 c. brown, green and ochre (Riquewihr) 65 45
470 50 f. on 1 f. 10 brown, blue and green (Sedan) 90 55

1971. 40th Anniv of 1st Meeting of Crafts Guilds Association No. 1935 of France surch **CFA** and value.

471 **680** 45 c. on 90 c. purple & red 80 60

63 Reunion Chameleon

65 King Penguin, Map and Exploration Ships

1971. Nature Protection.

472 **63** 25 f. green, brn & yellow 80 55

1971. De Gaulle Commem. As T **92** of New Caledonia but with face value in CFA francs.

473 25 f. black 1·10 1·10
474 25 f. blue 1·10 1·00
475 25 f. red 1·10 1·10
476 25 f. black 1·10 1·10

DESIGNS: No. 473, De Gaulle in uniform (June, 1940); No. 474, De Gaulle at Brazzaville, 1944; No. 475, De Gaulle in Paris, 1944; No. 476, De Gaulle as President of the French Republic, 1970 (T **92**).

1971. Nos. 1942/3 of France (Red Cross Fund) surch **CFA** and value.

477 15 f. + 5 f. on 30 c. + 10 c. 90 90
478 25 f. + 5 f. on 50 c. + 10 c. 90 90

1972. Bicentenary of Discovery of Crozet Islands and Kerguelen (French Southern and Antarctic Territories).

479 **65** 45 f. black, blue & brown 1·75 1·50

1972. No. 1956 of France surch **CFA** and value.

480 **688** 25 f. + 5 f. on 50 c. + 10 c. blue, drab and yellow 65 65

1972. No. 1966 of France (Blood Donors) surch **CFA** and value.

481 **692** 15 f. on 40 c. red 45 30

1972. Air. No 1890 of France (Daurat and Vanier) surch **CFA** and value.

482 **662** 200 f. on 5 f. brn, grn and bl 3·50 1·50

1972. Postal Codes. Nos. 1969/70 of France surch **CFA** and value.

483 **695** 15 f. on 30 c. red, black and green 40 25
484 25 f. on 50 c. yellow, blk & red 40 25

1972. Red Cross Fund. Nos. 1979/80 of France surch **CFA** and value.

485 **701** 15 f. + 5 f. on 30 c. + 10 c. 75 75
486 25 f. + 5 f. on 50 c. + 10 c. 90 90

1973. Stamp Day. No. 1996 of France surch **CFA** and value.

487 **707** 25 f. + 5 f. on 50 c. + 10 c. 1·10 90

1973. No. 2011 of France surch **CFA** and value.

488 **714** 45 f. on 90 c. green, violet and blue 1·25 1·00

1973. No. 2008 of France surch **CFA** and value.

489 50 f. on 1 f. green, brown & bl 75 55

1973. No. 1960 of France surch **CFA** and value.

490 100 f. on 2 f. purple & green 1·50 90

1973. No. 2021/2 of France surch **CFA** and value.

491 **721** 15 f. + 5 f. on 30 c. + 10 c. green and red 1·00 1·00
492 25 f. + 5 f. on 50 c. + 10 c. red and black 1·10 1·10

1973. No. 2026 of France surch **CFA** and value.
494 **725** 25 f. on 50 c. brown, blue and purple 55 35

1974. Stamp Day. No. 2031 surch **FCFA** and value.
495 **727** 25 f. + 5 f. on 50 c. + 10 c. 55 55

1974. French Art. No. 2033/6 surch **FCFA** and value.
496 100 f. on 2 f. multicoloured . 1·75 1·50
497 100 f. on 2 f. multicoloured . 1·75 1·50
498 100 f. on 2 f. brown and blue . 2·00 1·50
499 100 f. on 2 f. multicoloured . 2·00 1·50

1974. French Lifeboat Service. No. 2040 surch **FCFA** and value.
500 **731** 45 f. on 90 c. blue, red and brown . . . . 1·10 90

1974. Centenary of Universal Postal Union. No. 2057 surch **FCFA** and value.
501 **741** 60 f. on 1 f. 20 green, red and blue . . . . 1·10 1·00

1974. "Marianne" stamps of France surch **FCFA** and value.
502 **668** 30 f. on 60 c. green . . . 1·40 1·25
503 40 f. on 80 c. red . . . . 1·60 1·40

1974. Red Cross Fund. "The Seasons". Nos. 2059/60 surch **FCFA** and value.
504 **743** 30 f. + 7 f. on 60 c. + 15 c. 1·00 1·00
505 – 40 f. + 7 f. on 80 c. + 15 c. 1·10 1·10

From 1st January 1975 the CFA franc was replaced by the French Metropolitan franc, and Reunion subsequently used unsurcharged stamps of France.

PARCEL POST STAMPS

P 5 P 20

1890.
P11 **P 5** 10 c. black on yellow (black frame) £200 £120
P13 10 c. black on yellow (blue frame) . . . . 14·50 12·50

1907. Receipt stamps surch as in Type **P 20**.
P76 **P 20** 10 c. brown and black . . 9·00 6·50
P77 10 c. brown and red . . 9·00 10·00

POSTAGE DUE STAMPS

D 4

D 19

1889. Imperf.
D11 **D 4** 5 c. black . . . . 11·50 5·50
D12 10 c. black . . . . 14·50 4·75
D13 15 c. black . . . . 29·00 17·00
D14 20 c. black . . . . 25·00 9·00
D15 30 c. black . . . . 23·00 9·00

1907.
D76 **D 19** 5 c. red on yellow . . . 10 20
D77 10 c. blue on blue . . . 15 25
D78 15 c. black on grey . . 15 40
D79 20 c. pink 15 35
D80 30 c. green on green . . 20 65
D81 50 c. red on green . . . 20 75
D82 60 c. pink on blue . . . 25 75
D83 1 f. lilac . . . . 75 1·40

1927. Surch.
D130 **D 19** 2 f. on 1 f. red . . . . 3·25 5·00
D131 3 f. on 1 f. brown . . 3·25 5·00

D 33 Arms of Reunion

D 43

1933.
D175 **D 33** 5 c. purple 10 25
D176 10 c. green 10 25
D177 15 c. brown 10 25
D178 20 c. orange 15 25
D179 30 c. olive 15 30
D180 50 c. blue 20 45
D181 60 c. brown 25 45
D182 1 f. violet 20 40
D183 2 f. blue 25 40
D184 3 f. red 25 45

1947.
D306 **D 43** 10 c. mauve 10 30
D307 30 c. brown 10 25
D308 50 c. green 10 30
D309 1 f. brown 15 30
D310 2 f. red 20 30
D311 3 f. brown 20 30
D312 4 f. blue 20 60
D313 5 f. red 20 60
D314 10 f. green 25 60
D315 20 f. blue 30 75

1949. As Type D **250** of France, but inscr "TIMBRE TAXE" surch **CFA** and value.
D333 10 c. on 1 f. blue 10 30
D334 50 c. on 2 f. blue 10 30
D335 1 f. on 3 f. red 30 50
D336 2 f. on 4 f. violet 60 80
D337 3 f. on 5 f. pink . . . . . 1·50 1·75
D338 5 f. on 10 f. red . . . . . 85 1·00
D339 10 f. on 20 f. brown . . . 1·25 1·50
D340 20 f. on 50 f. green . . . 3·25 2·75
D341 50 f. on 100 f. green . . . 11·00 9·50

1962. Wheat Sheaves Type of France surch **CFA** and value.
D406 **D 457** 1 f. on 5 c. mauve . . 1·00 75
D407 10 f. on 20 c. brown . 2·50 1·50
D408 20 f. on 50 c. green . 15·00 10·00

1964. Nos. D1650/4 and D1656/7 of France surch **CFA** and value.
D424 – 1 f. on 5 c. 10 10
D425 – 5 f. on 10 c. 10 10
D426 **D 539** 7 f. on 15 c. 20 20
D427 – 10 f. on 20 c. . . . . 1·25 60
D428 – 15 f. on 30 c. 35 30
D429 – 20 f. on 50 c. 45 40
D430 – 50 f. on 1 f. . . . . . 1·25 1·00

RIAU-LINGGA ARCHIPELAGO Pt.21

A group of islands E of Sumatra and S of Singapore. Part of Indonesia.

100 cents or sen = 1 rupiah

1954. Optd **RIAU**. (a) On stamps of Indonesia.
1 **96** 5 s. red . . . . 28·00 19·00
2 7½ s. green 20 35
3 10 s. blue . . . . 32·00 40·00
4 15 s. violet 80 80
5 20 s. red . . . . 95 1·10
6 25 s. green . . . . . . 65·00 22·00
7 **97** 30 s. red . . . . 2·40 1·60
8 35 s. violet 20 35
9 40 s. green 20 35
10 45 s. purple 25 35
11 50 s. brown . . . . . . £190 32·00
12 **98** 60 s. brown 20 35
13 70 s. grey 60 65
14 75 s. blue . . . . 3·25 1·60
15 80 s. purple . . . . . . 50 1·90
16 90 s. green . . . . . . 50 1·10

(b) On Netherlands Indies Nos. 566/71.
17 – 1 r. violet . . . . 6·25 1·60
18 – 2 r. green . . . . 65 1·90
19 – 3 r. purple . . . . . . 95 1·90
20 – 5 r. brown . . . . . . 95 1·90
21 – 10 r. black . . . . . . 1·25 2·40
22 – 25 r. brown . . . . . . 1·25 2·40

1958. Stamps of Indonesia optd **RIAU**.
26 **115** 5 s. blue 40 35
27 10 s. brown (No. 714) . . 40 35
28 15 s. purple (No. 715) . . 40 1·50
29 – 20 s. green (No. 716) . . 40 35
30 – 25 s. purple (No. 717) . . 40 35
31 – 30 s. orange (No. 718) . . 40 35
32 – 50 s. bistre (No. 722) . . 40 35

1960. Stamps of Indonesia optd **RIAU**.
33 **99** 1 r. 25 orange . . . . . 95 3·25
34 1 r. 50 brown . . . . . 95 3·25
35 2 r. 50 lake . . . . . . 1·25 4·75
36 4 r. olive . . . . 25 4·75
37 6 r. purple . . . . . . 25 4·75
38 15 r. yellow . . . . . . 25 4·75
39 20 r. grey . . . . 25 6·25
40 40 r. green . . . . . . 25 7·00
41 50 r. violet . . . . . . 35 7·50

RIO DE ORO Pt.9

A Spanish territory on the W. Coast of N. Africa, renamed Spanish Sahara in 1924.

100 centimos = 1 peseta

1905. "Curly Head" key-type inscr "COLONIA DE RIO DE ORO".
1 Z 1 c. green . . . . 2·50 1·25
2 2 c. red . . . . 2·50 1·25
3 3 c. black . . . . 2·50 1·25
4 4 c. brown . . . . 2·50 1·25
5 5 c. red . . . . 2·50 1·25
6 10 c. grey . . . . 2·50 1·25
7 15 c. brown . . . . . . 2·50 1·25
8 25 c. blue . . . . 48·00 15·00
9 50 c. green . . . . . . 25·00 6·00
10 75 c. violet . . . . . . 25·00 9·00
11 1 p. brown . . . . 18·00 3·75
12 2 p. orange . . . . . . 50·00 20·00
13 3 p. lilac . . . . 35·00 9·00
14 4 p. green . . . . 35·00 8·50
15 5 p. blue . . . . 50·00 17·00
16 10 p. red . . . . £110 42·00

1906. "Curly Head" key-type surch **HABILITADO PARA 15 CENTS** in circle.
17 Z 15 c. on 25 c. blue . . . . . £130 38·00

3 7 11

1907.
18 **3** 1 c. red . . . . 2·25 1·25
19 2 c. black . . . . 2·25 1·25
20 3 c. brown . . . . 2·25 1·25
21 4 c. red . . . . 2·25 1·25
22 5 c. brown . . . . 2·25 1·25
23 10 c. brown . . . . . . 2·25 1·25
24 15 c. blue . . . . 2·25 1·25
25 25 c. green . . . . . . 6·00 1·50
26 50 c. purple . . . . . . 6·00 1·50
27 75 c. brown . . . . . . 6·00 1·50
28 1 p. orange . . . . . . 10·00 1·50
29 2 p. lilac . . . . 4·25 1·50
30 3 p. green . . . . 4·25 1·50
31 4 p. blue . . . . 7·50 3·25
32 5 p. red . . . . 7·50 3·25
33 10 p. green . . . . . . 7·50 8·00

1907. Nos. 9/10 surch **1907 10 Cens**.
34 Z 10 c. on 50 c. green . . . . 40·00 13·00
35 10 c. on 75 c. violet . . . . 40·00 13·00

1908. Nos. 12 and 26 surch **1908** and value.
36 Z 2 c. on 2 p. orange . . . . . 35·00 12·00
37 **3** 10 c. on 50 c. purple . . . . 25·00 6·50

1908. Surch **HABILITADO PARA 15 CENTS** in circle.
38 **3** 15 c. on 25 c. green . . . . 25·00 5·00
39 15 c. on 75 c. brown . . . . 30·00 6·50
40 15 c. on 1 p. orange . . . . 30·00 6·00
71 15 c. on 3 p. green . . . . 85·00 8·00
72 15 c. on 5 p. red . . . . . 7·50 3·50

1908. Large Fiscal stamp inscr "TERRITORIOS ESPANOLES DEL AFRICA OCCIDENTAL" surch **HABILITADO PARA CORREOS RIO DE ORO 5 CENS**. Imperf.
45 5 c. on 50 c. green . . . . . . 65·00 25·00

1909.
47 **7** 1 c. red 40 30
48 2 c. orange 40 30
49 5 c. green 40 30
50 10 c. red 40 30
51 15 c. green 40 30
52 20 c. purple . . . . . . 1·00 40
53 25 c. blue . . . . 1·00 40
54 30 c. red . . . . 1·00 40
55 40 c. brown . . . . . . 1·00 40
56 50 c. purple . . . . . . 2·00 75
57 1 p. brown . . . . 2·75 2·50
58 4 p. red . . . . 3·50 3·00
59 10 p. purple . . . . . . 6·50 4·50

1910. Nos. 13/16 surch **1910** and value.
60 Z 10 c. on 5 p. blue . . . . . 10·00 9·00
62 10 c. on 10 p. red . . . . . 10·00 8·50
65 15 c. on 3 p. lilac . . . . . 11·00 8·50
66 15 c. on 4 p. green . . . . . 11·00 8·50

1911. Surch with value in figures and words.
67 **3** 2 c. on 4 p. blue . . . . . 8·50 2·75
68 5 c. on 10 p. green . . . . 18·00 2·75
69 10 c. on 2 p. lilac . . . . . 9·00 2·75
70 10 c. on 3 p. green . . . . 95·00 12·00

1912.
73 **11** 1 c. red 20 10
74 2 c. lilac 20 10
75 5 c. green 20 10
76 10 c. red 20 10
77 15 c. brown 20 10
78 20 c. brown 20 10
79 25 c. blue 20 10
80 30 c. lilac 20 10
81 40 c. green 20 10
82 50 c. red 20 10
83 1 p. red . . . . 1·75 40
84 4 p. red . . . . 4·00 2·00
85 10 p. brown . . . . . . 5·50 2·75

12

14

15

1914.
86 **12** 1 c. brown 20 10
87 2 c. purple 20 10
88 5 c. green 20 10
89 10 c. red 20 10
90 15 c. orange 20 10
91 20 c. red 20 10
92 25 c. blue 20 10
93 30 c. green 20 10
94 40 c. orange 20 10
95 50 c. brown 20 10
96 1 p. lilac . . . . 1·75 1·75
97 4 p. red . . . . 4·25 1·75
98 10 p. violet . . . . . . 5·50 4·50

1917. Nos. 73/85 optd **1917**.
99 **11** 1 c. red . . . . 6·50 1·00
100 2 c. lilac . . . . 6·50 1·00
101 5 c. green . . . . 2·50 50
102 10 c. red . . . . 2·50 50
103 **11** 15 c. brown . . . . . . 2·50 50
104 20 c. brown . . . . . . 2·50 50
105 25 c. blue . . . . 2·50 50
106 30 c. lilac . . . . 2·50 50
107 40 c. green . . . . . . 2·50 50
108 50 c. red . . . . 2·50 50
109 1 p. red . . . . 10·00 2·75
110 4 p. red . . . . 15·00 3·75
111 10 p. brown . . . . . . 28·00 8·00

1919.
112 **14** 1 c. brown 55 35
113 2 c. purple 55 35
114 5 c. green 55 35
115 10 c. red 55 35
116 15 c. orange 55 35
117 20 c. orange 55 35
118 25 c. blue 55 35
119 30 c. green 55 35
120 40 c. orange 55 35
121 50 c. brown 55 35
122 1 p. lilac . . . . 4·75 2·50
123 4 p. red . . . . 8·00 4·50
124 10 p. violet . . . . . . 12·00 5·00

1920.
125 **15** 1 c. purple 55 35
126 2 c. red 55 35
127 5 c. red 55 35
128 10 c. purple 55 35
129 15 c. brown 55 35
130 20 c. green 55 35
131 25 c. orange 55 35
132 30 c. blue . . . . 3·25 2·50
133 40 c. orange . . . . . . 2·50 1·10
134 50 c. purple . . . . . . 2·75 1·25
135 1 p. green . . . . 2·75 1·40
136 4 p. red . . . . 4·50 2·75
137 10 p. brown . . . . . . 11·00 5·50

1921. As T **2** of La Aguera but inscr "RIO DE ORO".
138 1 c. yellow 55 35
139 2 c. brown 55 35
140 5 c. green 55 35
141 10 c. red 55 35
142 15 c. green 55 35
143 20 c. blue 55 35
144 25 c. blue 55 35
145 30 c. red . . . . 1·40 1·10
146 40 c. violet . . . . . . 1·40 1·10
147 50 c. orange . . . . . . 1·40 1·10
148 1 p. mauve . . . . 3·75 2·25
149 4 p. red . . . . 6·50 3·75
150 10 p. brown . . . . . . 11·00 6·50

For later issues see **SPANISH SAHARA**.

RIO MUNI Pt.9

A coastal settlement between Cameroun and Gabon, formerly using the stamps of Spanish Guinea. On 12 October 1968 it became independent and joined Fernando Poo to become Equatorial Guinea.

100 centimos = 1 peseta

1 Native Boy reading Book

2 Cactus

1960.
1 **1** 25 c. grey 10 10
2 50 c. brown 10 10
3 75 c. purple 10 10
4 1 p. red 10 10
5 1 p. 50 green 10 10
6 2 p. purple 15 10
7 3 p. blue 30 10
8 5 p. brown 80 10
9 10 p. green . . . . . . 1·50 20

1960. Child Welfare Fund.
10 **2** 10 c. + 5 c. purple 10 10
11 – 15 c. + 5 c. brown 10 10
12 – 35 c. green 10 10
13 **2** 80 c. green 10 10
DESIGNS: 15 c. Sprig with berries; 35 c. Star-shaped flowers.

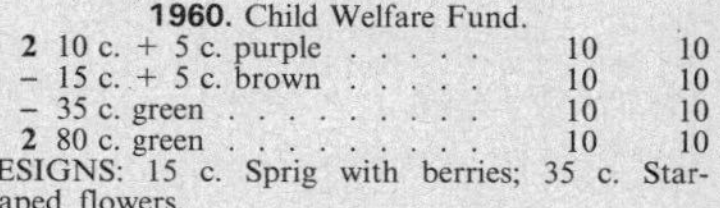

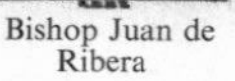
3 Bishop Juan de Ribera

4 Mandrill with Banana

1960. Stamp Day.

14 3 10 c. + 5 c. red 10 10
15 – 20 c. + 5 c. green 10 10
16 – 30 c. + 10 c. brown 10 10
17 3 50 c. + 20 c. brown 10 10

DESIGNS: 20 c. Portrait of man (after Velazquez); 30 c. Statue.

1961. Child Welfare. Inscr "PRO-INFANCIA 1961".

18 4 10 c. + 5 c. lake 15 10
19 – 25 c. + 10 c. violet 25 10
20 4 80 c. + 20 c. green 15 10

DESIGN—VERT: 25 c. African elephant.

5

6 Statuette

1961. 25th Anniv of Gen. Franco as Head of State.

21 – 25 c. grey 30 10
22 5 50 c. brown 10 10
23 – 70 c. green 10 10
24 5 1 p. orange 10 10

DESIGNS: 25 c. Map; 70 c. Govt building.

1961. Stamp Day. Inscr "DIA DEL SELLO 1961".

25 6 10 c. + 5 c. lake 5 5
26 – 25 c. + 10 c. purple 5 5
27 6 30 c. + 10 c. brown 5 5
28 – 1 p. + 10 c. orange 8 5

DESIGN: 25 c., 1 p. Figure holding offering.

7 Girl wearing Headdress

8 African Buffalo

1962. Child Welfare. Inscr "PRO-INFANCIA 1962".

29 7 25 c. violet 10 10
30 – 50 c. green 10 10
31 7 1 p. brown 15 10

DESIGN: 50 c. Native mask.

1962. Stamp Day. Inscr "DIA DEL-SELLO 1962".

32 8 15 c. olive 10 10
33 – 35 c. purple 10 10
34 8 1 p. red 15 10

DESIGN—VERT: 35 c. Gorilla.

9 Statuette

10 "Blessing"

1963. Seville Flood Relief.

35 9 50 c. green 10 10
36 1 p. brown 10 10

1963. Child Welfare. Inscr "PRO-INFANCIA 1963".

37 – 25 c. violet 10 10
38 10 50 c. olive 10 10
39 – 1 p. red 10 10

DESIGN: 25 c., 1 p. Priest.

11 Chid at Prayer

12 Copal Flower

1963. "For Barcelona".

40 11 50 c. turquoise 10 10
41 1 p. brown 10 10

1964. Stamp Day. Inscr "DIA DEL SELLO 1963".

42 12 25 c. violet 10 10
43 – 50 c. turquoise 10 10
44 12 1 p. red 10 10

FLOWER—HORIZ: 50 c. Cinchona blossom.

13 Giant Ground Pangolin

1964. Child Welfare. Inscr "PRO-INFANCIA 1964".

45 13 25 c. violet 10 10
46 – 50 c. olive (chameleon) . . 15 10
47 13 1 p. brown 20 10

1964. Wild Life. As T 13 but without "PRO INFANCIA" inscription.

48 15 c. bistre 10 10
49 25 c. violet 10 10
50 50 c. olive 10 10
51 70 c. green 15 10
52 1 p. brown 65 10
53 1 p. 50 turquoise 65 10
54 3 p. blue . . . . 1·10 10
55 5 p. brown . . . . 2·75 40
56 10 p. green . . . . 6·00 85

ANIMALS: 15, 70 c., 3 p. Crocodile; 25 c., 1, 5 p. Leopard; 50 c., 1 p. 50, 10 p. Black rhinoceros.

14 "Goliath" Frog

15 Woman

1964. Stamp Day.

57 14 50 c. bronze 20 10
58 – 1 p. lake 45 10
59 14 1 p. 50 green 25 10

DESIGN—VERT: 1 p. Helmet guineafowl.

1965. 25th Anniv of End of Spanish Civil War.

60 15 50 c. green 10 10
61 – 1 p. red 10 10
62 – 1 p. 50 turquoise 10 10

DESIGNS: 1 p. Nurse; 1 p. 50, Logging.

16 "Goliathus goliathus"

1965. Child Welfare Insects.

63 16 50 c. green 15 10
64 – 1 p. brown 15 10
65 16 1 p. 50 black 15 10

DESIGN: 1 p. "Acridoxena hewaniana".

17 Leopard and Arms of Rio Muni

1965. Stamp Day.

66 – 50 c. grey 50 10
67 17 1 p. brown 55 10
68 – 2 p. 50 violet . . . . 2·50 50

DESIGN—VERT: 50 c., 2 p. 50, Ring-necked pheasant.

18 African Elephant and Grey Parrot

1966. Child Welfare.

69 18 50 c. brown 30 10
70 1 p. lilac 30 10
71 – 1 p. 50 blue 25 10

DESIGN: 1 p. 50, African and lion.

19 Water Chevrotain

20 Floss Flowers

1966. Stamp Day.

72 19 10 c. brown and ochre . . 10 10
73 – 40 c. brown and yellow . . 15 10
74 19 1 p. 50 violet and red . . 15 10
75 – 4 p. blue and green . . . 30 10

DESIGN—VERT: 40 c., 4 p. Giant ground pangolin.

1967. Child Welfare. Similar Floral designs.

76 20 10 c. yellow, olive & green . 15 10
77 – 40 c. green, black & mve . . 15 10
78 20 1 p. 50 red and blue 25 10
79 – 4 p. black and green . . . 35 10

DESIGNS: 40 c., 4 p. Ylang-ylang.

21 Bush Pig

1967. Stamp Day.

80 21 1 p. chestnut and brown . . 25 10
81 – 1 p. 50 brown and green . . 35 10
82 – 3 p. 50 brown and green . . 40 15

DESIGNS — VERT: 1 p. 50, Potto. HORIZ: 3 p. 50, African golden cat.

1968. Child Welfare. Signs of the Zodiac. As T **56a** of Spanish Sahara.

83 1 p. mauve on yellow 30 10
84 1 p. 50 brown on pink . . . 40 10
85 2 p. 50 violet on yellow . . . 45 10

DESIGNS: 1 p. Cancer (crab); 1 p. 50, Taurus (bull); 2 p. 50, Gemini (twins).

ROMAGNA Pt.8

One of the Papal states, now part of Italy. Stamps issued prior to the annexation by Sardinia.

100 bajocchi = 1 scudo

1

1859. Imperf.

2 1 ½ b. black on yellow . . . . 10·00 £275
3 1 b. black on grey . . . . . 10·00 £110
4 2 b. black on buff . . . . . 16·00 £110
5 3 b. black on green . . . . 21·00 £275
6 4 b. black on brown £475 £110
7 5 b. black on lilac . . . . . 26·00 £325
8 6 b. black on green £250 £7500
9 8 b. black on pink £200 £1700
10 20 b. black on green £160 £2500

ROUAD ISLAND (ARWAD) Pt.6

An island in the E. Mediterranean off the coast of Syria. A French P.O. was established there during 1916.

25 centimes = 1 piastre

1916. "Blanc" and "Mouchon" key-types inscr "LEVANT" and optd **ILE ROUAD** (vert).

1 A 5 c. green £300 £130
2 B 10 c. red £300 £130
3 1 pi. on 25 c. blue £300 £130

1916. "Blanc" "Mouchon" and "Merson" key-types inscr "LEVANT" and optd **ILE ROUAD** horiz.

4 A 1 c. grey 30 30
5 2 c. purple 30 35
6 3 c. red 30 35
7 5 c. green 35 40
8 B 10 c. red 40 40
9 15 c. red 60 70
10 20 c. brown . . . . 1·00 1·00
11 1 p. on 25 c. blue . . . . . 1·00 1·00
12 30 c. lilac . . . . 1·00 1·00
13 C 40 c. red and blue . . . . . 2·00 2·00
14 2 p. on 50 c. brown & lav . 3·25 3·25
15 4 p. on 1 f. red and yellow . 4·75 5·50
16 30 p. on 5 f. blue & yellow . 17·00 20·00

RUANDA-URUNDI Pt. 4

Part of German E. Africa, including Ruanda and Urundi, occupied by Belgian forces during the war of 1914-18 and a Trust Territory administered by Belgium until 1 July 1962. The territory then became two separate independent states, named Rwanda and Burundi.

100 centimes = 1 franc

1916. Nos. 70/77 of Belgian Congo optd.

(a) **RUANDA**.

1 32 5 c. black and green . . . . 15·00
2 33 10 c. black and red . . . . 15·00
3 13 15 c. black and green . . . . 26·00
4 34 25 c. black and blue . . . . 15·00
5 14 40 c. black and red . . . . 15·00
6 – 50 c. black and red . . . . 18·00
7 – 1 f. black and brown . . . 55·00
7a – 5 f. black and orange . . . £2000

(b) **URUNDI**.

8 32 5 c. black and green . . . 15·00
9 33 10 c. black and red . . . 15·00
10 13 15 c. black and green . . . 26·00
11 34 25 c. black and blue . . . 15·00
12 14 40 c. black and red . . . 15·00
13 – 50 c. black and red . . . 18·00
14 – 1 f. black and brown . . . 55·00
14a – 5 f. black and orange . . . £2000

1916. Stamps of Belgian Congo of 1915 optd **EST AFRICAIN ALLEMAND OCCUPATION BELGE. DUITSCH OOST AFRIKA BELGISCHE BEZETTING.**

15 32 5 c. black and green 25 20
16 33 10 c. black and red 40 30
17 13 15 c. black and green 30 20
18 34 25 c. black and blue . . . . 1·75 95
19 14 40 c. black and lake . . . . 5·00 4·00
20 – 50 c. black and lake . . . . 5·50 4·00
21 – 1 f. black and olive 60 40
22 – 5 f. black and orange . . . 85 75

1918. Belgian Congo Red Cross stamps of 1918 optd **A. O.**.

23 32 5 c. + 10 c. blue & green . 20 20
24 33 10 c. + 15 c. blue and red . 20 20
25 13 15 c. + 20 c. blue & green . 20 20
26 34 25 c. + 25 c. blue 20 20
27 14 40 c. + 40 c. blue and lake . 25 25
28 – 50 c. + 50 c. blue and lake . 50 1·50
29 – 1 f. + 1 f. blue and olive . 1·25 1·25
30 – 5 f. + 5 f. blue and orange . 6·00 6·00
31 – 10 f. + 10 f. blue & green . 50·00 60·00

1922. Stamps of 1916 surch.

32 – 5 c. on 50 c. black & lake . 35 1·50
33 32 10 c. on 5 c. black & green . 30 20
34a 14 25 c. on 40 c. black & lake . 2·00 90
35 33 30 c. on 10 c. black & red . 30 20
36 34 50 c. on 25 c. black & blue . 30 20

1924. Belgian Congo stamps of 1923 optd **RUANDA URUNDI**.

37 A 5 c. yellow 15 15
38 B 10 c. green 15 15
39 C 15 c. brown 15 15
40 D 20 c. green 15 15
41 E 20 c. green 15 15
42 F 25 c. brown 25 15
43 46 30 c. pink 20 20
44 30 c. green 15 15
66 35 c. green 20 15
45 D 40 c. purple 25 25
46 G 50 c. blue 25 20
47 50 c. orange 25 20
48 E 75 c. orange 25 25
49 75 c. blue 35 25
67 46 75 c. pink 30 25
50 H 1 f. brown 40 50
51 1 f. blue 45 20
68 1 f. pink 45 30
69 D 1 f. 50 blue 50 35
71 1 f. 75 blue 95 60
52 I 3 f. brown . . . . 2·50 1·90
53 J 5 f. grey . . . . 5·00 4·00
54 K 10 f. black . . . . 19·00 10·00

1925. Stamp of Belgian Congo optd **RUANDA-URUNDI**. Inscriptions in French or in Flemish.

61 55 25 c. + 25 c. black and red . 20 30

1925. Native cattle type of Belgian Congo optd **RUANDA-URUNDI**.

62 56 45 c. purple 30 30
63 60 c. red 35 30

1927. Belgian Congo stamps of 1923 optd **RUANDA URUNDI** in two lines, wide apart.

64 B 10 c. green 20 20
65 C 15 c. brown 80 60
66 46 35 c. green 20 15
67 75 c. red 30 25
68 H 1 f. red 45 30
69 D 1 f. 25 blue 50 40
70 1 f. 50 blue 50 35
71 1 f. 75 blue 95 60

1927. No. 144 of Belgian Congo optd **RUANDA URUNDI**.

72 1 f. 75 on 1 f. 50 blue 50 35

1930. Native Fund stamps of Belgian Congo (Nos. 160/8), optd **RUANDA URUNDI**.

73 10 c. + 5 c. red 30 30
74 20 c. + 10 c. brown 65 65
75 35 c. + 15 c. green . . . . . 1·25 1·25
76 60 c. + 30 c. purple . . . . . 1·50 1·50
77 1 f. + 50 c. red . . . . 2·10 2·10
78 1 f. 75 + 75 c. blue . . . . . 2·50 2·50
79 3 f. 50 + 1 f. 50 lake . . . . 5·00 5·00
80 5 f. + 2 f. 50 brown . . . . 4·00 4·00
81 10 f. + 5 f. black . . . . . . 4·75 4·75

1931. Nos. 68 and 71 surch.

82 H 1 f. 25 on 1 f. red . . . . . 2·25 1·25
83 D 2 f. on 1 f. 75 blue . . . . 3·00 1·75

10 Mountain Scenery

11 King Albert I

1931.

84 – 5 c. red 10 10
85 10 10 c. grey 10 10
86 – 15 c. red 15 15
87 – 25 c. purple 10 10
88 – 40 c. green 30 30

89 – 50 c. violet 15 10
90 – 60 c. red 10 10
91 – 75 c. black 10 10
92 – 1 f. red 10 10
93 – 1 f. 25 brown 15 10
94 – 1 f. 50 purple 20 15
95 – 2 f. blue 20 15
96 – 2 f. 50 blue 20 20
97 – 3 f. 25 purple 20 15
98 – 4 f. red 30 30
99 – 5 f. grey 35 35
100 – 10 f. purple 70 45
101 – 20 f. brown 2·00 1·75

DESIGNS—HORIZ: 15 c. Warrior; 25 c. Chieftain's kraal; 50 c. Head of African buffalo; 1 f. Wives of Urundi chiefs; 1 f. 50, 2 f. Wooden pot hewer; 2 f. 50, 3 f. 25, Workers making tissues from ficus bark; 4 f. Hutu Potter. VERT: 5, 60 c., Native porter; 40 c. Two cowherds; 75 c. Native greeting; 1 f. 25, Mother and child; 5 f. Ruanda dancer; 10 f. Warriors; 20 f. Native prince of Urundi

1934. King Albert Mourning stamp.
102 **11** 1 f. 50 black 50 50

11a Queen Astrid and Children
14a "Belgium shall rise Again"

1936. Charity. Queen Astrid Fund.
103 **11a** 1 f. 25 + 5 c. brown 50 50
104 1 f. 50 + 10 c. red 50 50
105 2 f. 50 + 25 c. blue 70 70

1941. Stamps of Belgian Congo optd **RUANDA URUNDI**.
106 **78** 10 c. grey 5·50 5·50
107 1 f. 75 orange 3·75 3·75
108 2 f. 75 blue 3·75 3·75

1941. Ruanda-Urundi stamps of 1931 surch.
109 – 5 c. on 40 c. green 3·00 3·00
110 – 60 c. on 50 c. violet 2·00 2·00
111 – 2 f. 50 on 1 f. 50 purple 2·00 2·00
112 – 3 f. 25 on 2 f. blue 9·00 9·00

1941. Stamps of Belgian Congo optd **RUANDA URUNDI** and surch also.
113 – 5 c. on 1 f. 50 black and brown (No. 222) 10 10
114 – 75 c. on 90 c. brown and red (No. 221) 90 75
115 **78** 2 f. 50 on 10 f. red 1·50 1·25

1942. War Relief.
116 **14a** 10 f. + 40 f. red 1·75 1·75
117 10 f. + 40 f. blue 1·75 1·75

On No. 116 the French slogan is above the Flemish, on No. 117 vice versa.

1942. Nos. 107/8 of Ruanda-Urundi surch.
118 **78** 75 c. on 1 f. 75 orange 85 85
119 2 f. 50 on 2 f. 75 blue 3·25 3·25

15a Head of Warrior
17 Seated Figure

1942.
120 A 5 c. red 10 10
121 10 c. green 10 10
122 15 c. brown 10 10
123 20 c. blue 10 10
124 25 c. purple 10 10
125 30 c. blue 10 10
126 50 c. green 10 10
127 60 c. brown 10 10
128 **15a** 75 c. black and lilac 15 10
129 1 f. black and brown 10 10
130 1 f. 25 black and red 20 15
131 B 1 f. 75 brown 75 45
132 2 f. orange 75 30
133 2 f. 50 red 75 15
134 C 3 f. 50 green 40 25
135 5 f. orange 40 25
136 6 f. blue 40 25
137 7 f. black 40 30
138 10 f. brown 65 40
139 – 20 f. black and brown 1·50 95
140 – 50 f. black and red 1·75 1·10
141 – 100 f. black and green 3·50 2·75

DESIGNS—As Type **15a** (various frames): A, Oil palms; C, Askari sentry; 20 f. Head of zebra. 35 × 24 mm: B, Leopard. 29 × 34 mm: 50 f. Askari sentry; 100 f. Head of warrior.

1944. Red Cross Fund. Nos. 126, 130, 131 and 134 surch **Au profit de la Croix Rouge Ten voordeele van het Roode Kruis** (50 c., 1 f. 75) or with Flemish and French reversed (others) and premium.
147 50 c. + 50 f. green 75 90
148 1 f. 25 + 100 f. black & red 1·10 1·40
149 1 f. 75 + 100 f. brown 75 90
150 3 f. 50 + 100 f. green 1·10 1·40

1948. Native Carvings.
151 **17** 10 c. orange 10 10
152 A 15 c. blue 10 10
153 B 20 c. blue 20 10
154 C 25 c. red 40 15
155 D 40 c. purple 20 10
156 **17** 50 c. brown 20 10
157 A 70 c. green 20 10
158 B 75 c. purple 25 15
159 C 1 f. purple and orange 25 10
160 D 1 f. 25 red and blue 25 15
161 E 1 f. 50 red and green 90 40
162 **17** 2 f. red and vermilion 30 10
163 A 2 f. 50 green and brown 30 10
164 B 3 f. 50 green and blue 40 20
165 C 5 f. red and bistre 85 20
166 D 6 f. green and orange 85 15
167 E 10 f. brown and violet 1·25 20
168 F 20 f. brown and red 1·90 35
169 E 50 f. black and brown 3·75 1·00
170 F 100 f. black and red 6·00 2·50

DESIGNS: A, Seated figure (different); B, Kneeling figure; C, Double mask; D, Mask; E, Mask with tassels; F, Mask with horns.

1949. Surch.
171 3 f. on 2 f. 50 (No. 163) 40 15
172 4 f. on 6 f. (No. 166) 40 15
173 6 f. 50 on 6 f. (No. 166) 40 25

18a St. Francis Xavier
19 "Dissotis"

1953. 400th Death Anniv of St. Francis Xavier.
174 **18a** 1 f. 50 black and blue 40 40

1953. Flowers Multicoloured.
175 10 c. Type 19 15 10
176 15 c. "Protea" 15 10
177 20 c. "Vellozia" 15 10
178 25 c. "Littonia" 15 10
179 40 c. "Ipomoea" 15 10
180 50 c. "Angraecum" 15 10
181 60 c. "Euphorbia" 15 10
182 75 c. "Ochna" 15 10
183 1 f. "Hibiscus" 25 10
184 1 f. 25 "Protea" 90 40
185 1 f. 50 "Schizoglossum" 20 10
186 2 f. "Ansellia" 2·25 20
187 3 f. "Costus" 55 10
188 4 f. "Nymphaea" 55 15
189 5 f. "Thunbergia" 80 15
190 7 f. "Gerbera" 95 30
191 8 f. "Gloriosa" 1·40 45
192 10 f. "Silene" 2·50 35
193 20 f. "Aristolochia" 5·00 60

20 King Baudouin and Mountains
20a Mozart when a Child

1955.
194 **20** 1 f. 50 black and red 50 15
195 – 3 f. black and green 40 15
196 – 4 f. 50 black and blue 50 20
197 – 6 f. 50 black and purple 60 30

DESIGNS: 3 f. Forest; 4 f. 50, River; 6 f. 50, Grassland.

1956. Birth Bicentenary of Mozart.
198 **20a** 4 f. 50 + 1 f. 50 violet 1·50 1·00
199 – 6 f. 50 + 2 f. 50 purple 4·50 2·00

DESIGN—52 × 36 mm: 6 f. 50, Queen Elizabeth and Mozart sonata.

20b Nurse with Children
21 Gorilla

1957. Red Cross Fund.
200 **20b** 3 f. + 50 c. blue 55 20
201 – 4 f. 50 + 50 c. green 70 30
202 – 6 f. 50 + 50 c. brown 95 50

DESIGNS: 4 f. 50, Doctor inoculating patient; 6 f. 50, Nurse in tropical kit bandaging patient.

1959. Fauna.
203 10 c. black, red and brown 10 10
204 20 c. black and green 10 10
205 40 c. black, olive & mauve 10 10
206 50 c. brown, yellow & green 10 10
207 1 f. black, blue and brown 10 10
208 1 f. 50 black and orange 15 10
209 2 f. black, brown & turquoise 20 10
210 3 f. black, red and brown 40 10
211 5 f. multicoloured 40 15
212 6 f. 50 brown, yell & red 25 10
213 8 f. black, mauve & blue 70 30
214 10 f. multicoloured 70 20

DESIGNS—VERT: 10 c., 1 f. Type **21**: 40 c., 2 f. Eastern black and white colobus. HORIZ: 20 c. 1 f. 50, African buffaloes; 50 c., 6 f. 50, Impala; 3, 8 f. African elephants; 5, 10 f. Eland and common zebras.

22 African Resources

1960. 10th Anniv of African Technical Co-operation Commission. Inscr in French or Flemish.
222 **22** 3 f. salmon and blue 20 15

23 High Jumping

1960. Child Welfare Fund. Olympic Games, Rome.
223 50 c. + 25 c. blue and red 10 10
224 1 f. 50 + 50 c. lake & black 15 15
225 2 f. + 2 f. black and red 15 15
226 3 f. + 1 f. 25 red and green 95 85
227 6 f. 50 + 3 f. 50 green and red 95 85

DESIGNS: 50 c. Type **23**: 1 f. 50, Hurdling; 2 f. Football; 3 f. Throwing the javelin; 6 f. 50, Throwing the discus.

1960. No. 210 surch.
228 3 f. 50 on 3 f. black, red and brown 30 10

25 Leopard

1961.
229 **25** 20 f. multicoloured 85 35
230 – 50 f. multicoloured 1·90 85

DESIGN: 50 f. Lion and lioness.

26 Usumbura Cathedral

1961. Usumbura Cathedral Fund.
231 **26** 50 c. + 25 c. brown & buff 10 10
232 – 1 f. + 50 c. dp green & grn 10 10
233 – 1 f. 50 + 75 c. multicoloured 10 10
234 **26** 3 f. 50 + 1 f. 50 bl & lt bl 10 10
235 – 5 f. + 2 f. red and orange 20 20
236 – 6 f. 50 + 3 f. multicoloured 40 30

DESIGNS: 1, 5 f. Side view of Cathedral; 1 f. 50, 6 f. 50, Stained glass windows.

POSTAGE DUE STAMPS

1924. Postage Due stamps of Belgian Congo optd **RUANDA URUNDI**.
D55 **D 54** 5 c. brown 15 15
D56 10 c. red 15 15
D57 15 c. violet 20 20
D58 30 c. green 30 30
D59 50 c. blue 40 35
D60 1 f. grey 45 50

1943. Postage Due stamps of Belgian Congo optd **RUANDA URUNDI**.
D142 **D 86** 10 c. olive 10 10
D143 20 c. blue 10 10
D144 50 c. green 10 10
D145 1 f. brown 20 20
D146 2 f. orange 25 25

1959. Postage Due stamps of Belgian Congo optd **RUANDA URUNDI**.
D215 **D 99** 10 c. brown 10 10
D216 20 c. purple 10 10
D217 50 c. green 10 10
D218 1 f. blue 15 15
D219 2 f. red 20 20
D220 4 f. violet 50 40
D221 6 f. blue 60 50

For later issues see **BURUNDI** and **RWANDA**.

RUMANIA Pt.3

A republic in S.E. Europe bordering on the Black Sea originally a kingdom formed by the union of Moldavia and Wallachia.

1858. 40 parale = 1 piastre
1867. 100 bani = 1 leu

MOLDAVIA

1
2

1858. Imperf.
1 **1** 27 p. black on red £13000 £5000
2 54 p. blue on green £5000 £2250
3 81 p. blue on blue £13000 £15000
4 108 p. blue on pink £9000 £5000

1858. Imperf.
15 **2** 5 p. black £120
13 40 p. blue £120 £130
14 80 p. red £350 £200

RUMANIA

4

1862. Imperf.
29 **4** 3 p. yellow 55·00 £170
30 6 p. red 50·00 £130
31 30 p. blue 40·00 40·00

5 Prince Alexander Cuza
6 Prince Carol **7**

1865. Imperf.
49a **5** 2 p. orange 40·00 £160
46 5 p. blue 30·00 £190
48 20 p. red 18·00 26·00

1866. Imperf.
60 **6** 2 p. black on yellow 16·00 65·00
61 5 p. black on blue 40·00 £400
62 20 p. black on red 18·00 15·00

1868. Imperf.
71 **7** 2 b. orange 30·00 21·00
72 3 b. mauve 32·00 28·00
66c 4 b. blue 40·00 26·00
67 18 b. red £160 20·00

8
9
10

1869. Without beard. Imperf.
74 **8** 5 b. orange 55·00 32·00
75 10 b. blue 30·00 26·00
76d 15 b. red 27·00 23·00
77c 25 b. blue and orange 32·00 23·00
78 50 b. red and blue £130 35·00

1871. With beard. Imperf.
83 **9** 5 b. red 27·00 23·00
84 10 b. orange 45·00 27·00
99 10 b. blue 35·00 40·00
86 15 b. red £130 £130
87 25 b. brown 30·00 28·00
100 50 b. red and blue £140 £160

1872. Perf.
93 **9** 5 b. red 50·00 35·00
94 10 b. blue 42·00 35·00
95 25 b. brown 32·00 35·00

1872. Perf.
112 **10** 1½ b. green 5·00 2·10
124 1½ b. black 5·00 1·40
105 3 b. green 21·00 3·00
125 3 b. olive 10·00 7·50
106 5 b. bistre 3·00 2·00
126 5 b. green 4·00 1·60
107 10 b. blue 11·50 3·25
127c 10 b. red 10·50 1·60
115 15 b. brown 50·00 7·50

128a **10** 15 b. red 32·00 10·00
110 25 b. orange 75·00 15·00
116 25 b. blue £110 15·00
121 30 b. red £130 42·00
111 50 b. red 80·00 30·00
131 50 b. bistre 75·00 16·00

11 King Carol 12 14

1880.

146a **11** 15 b. brown 10·00 1·40
147 25 b. blue 16·00 2·00

1885. On white or coloured papers.

161 **12** 1½ b. black 2·75 1·40
163 3 b. green 4·00 1·40
165a 3 b. violet 4·00 1·40
166 5 b. green 4·00 1·40
168 10 b. red 4·00 1·40
169 15 b. brown 11·50 1·75
171 25 b. blue 11·50 3·25
186 50 b. brown 55·00 15·00

1890.

271 **14** 1½ b. lake 1·40 65
272a 3 b. mauve 1·00 1·00
273 5 b. green 2·00 1·00
254 10 b. red 8·25 1·00
255 15 b. brown 10·00 85
306 25 b. blue 6·50 95
307 50 b. orange 21·00 10·00

15 17 19

1891. 25th Anniv of Reign.

300 **15** 1½ b. lake 4·00 4·25
293 3 b. mauve 4·00 4·25
294 5 b. green 5·25 5·00
295 10 b. red 5·25 5·00
303 15 b. brown 5·25 5·00

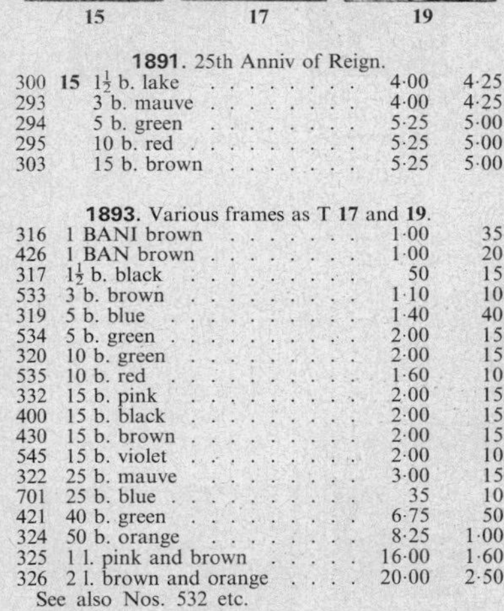

1893. Various frames as T **17** and **19**.

316 1 BANI brown 1·00 35
426 1 BAN brown 1·00 20
317 1½ b. black 50 15
533 3 b. brown 1·10 10
319 5 b. blue 1·40 40
534 5 b. green 2·00 15
320 10 b. green 2·00 15
535 10 b. red 1·60 10
332 15 b. pink 2·00 15
400 15 b. black 2·00 15
430 15 b. brown 2·00 15
545 15 b. violet 2·00 10
322 25 b. mauve 3·00 15
701 25 b. blue 35 10
421 40 b. green 6·75 50
324 50 b. orange 8·25 1·00
325 1 l. pink and brown 16·00 1·60
326 2 l. brown and orange 20·00 2·50
See also Nos. 532 etc.

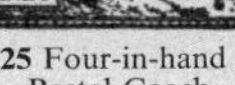

25 Four-in-hand Postal Coach
26 New Post Office, Bucharest

1903. Opening of New Post Office in 1901.

464 **25** 1 b. brown 1·40 80
465 3 b. red 2·50 75
466 5 b. green 5·00 1·60
467 10 b. red 4·00 1·60
468 15 b. black 4·00 2·00
472 **26** 15 b. black 3·25 2·50
469 **25** 25 b. blue 14·00 7·25
473 **26** 25 b. blue 8·25 5·00
470 **25** 40 b. green 20·00 8·25
474 **26** 40 b. green 11·50 6·50
471 **25** 50 b. orange 25·00 1·50
475 **26** 50 b. orange 11·50 6·50
476 1 l. brown 11·50 6·50
477 2 l. red 90·00 50·00
478 5 l. lilac £110 70·00
See also No. 1275.

1905. Various frames as T **17** and **19**.

532 1 ban black 1·00 10
625b 1½ b. yellow 1·60 1·10
703 40 b. brown 1·00 50
705 50 b. pink 1·00 45
432 1 l. black and green 20·00 2·40
706 1 l. green 1·60 30
433 2 l. black and brown 16·00 2·25
707 2 l. orange 1·75 45

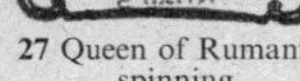

27 Queen of Rumania spinning
28 Queen of Rumania weaving

1906. Welfare Fund.

481 **27** 3 b. (+7) brown 5·00 3·25
482 5 b. (+10) green 5·00 3·25
483 10 b. (+10) red 26·00 13·00
484 15 b. (+10) purple 16·00 6·50

1906. Welfare Fund.

485 **28** 3 b. (+7) brown 5·00 3·25
486 5 b. (+10) green 5·00 3·25
487 10 b. (+10) red 26·00 13·00
488 15 b. (+10) lilac 16·00 6·50

29 Queen of Rumania nursing wounded Soldier
30

1906. Welfare Fund.

489 **29** 3 b. (+7) brown 5·00 3·25
490 5 b. (+10) green 5·00 3·25
491 10 b. (+10) red 26·00 13·00
492 15 b. (+10) purple 16·00 6·50

1906. 25th Anniv of Kingdom.

493 **30** 1 b. black and bistre 65 25
494 3 b. black and brown 1·60 65
495 5 b. black and green 1·00 50
496 10 b. black and red 1·00 50
497 15 b. black and violet 1·00 50
498 25 b. black and blue 9·50 5·00
499 40 b. black and brown 2·75 80
500 50 b. black and brown 2·75 1·00
501 1 l. black and red 2·75 80
502 2 l. black and orange 1·50 80

31 Prince Carol at Battle of Calafat
32

1906. 40 Years' Rule of Prince and King. Dated "1906".

503 – 1 b. black and bistre 20 25
504 – 3 b. black and brown 65 30
505 **31** 5 b. black and green 75 25
506 – 10 b. black and red 30 15
507 – 15 b. black and violet 30 15
508 – 25 b. black and blue 4·00 3·25
508a – 25 b. black and green 4·00 6·50
509 – 40 b. black and brown 1·00 70
510 – 50 b. black and brown 1·10 70
511 – 1 l. black and red 1·00 75
512 – 2 l. black and orange 1·40 1·40

DESIGNS—HORIZ: 1 b. Prince Carol taking oath of allegiance in 1866; 3 b. Prince in carriage; 10 b. Meeting of Prince and Osman Pasha, 1878; 15 b. Carol when Prince in 1866 and King in 1906; 25 b. Rumanian Army crossing Danube, 1877; 40 b. Triumphal entry into Bucharest, 1878; 50 b. Prince at head of Army in 1877; 1 l. King Carol at Cathedral in 1896; 2 l. King at shrine of S. Nicholas, 1904.

1906. Charity.

513 **32** 3 b. (+7) brown, bistre and blue 2·50 1·60
514 5 b. (+10) green, red and bistre 1·50 1·60
515 10 b. (+10) red, bistre and blue 5·00 3·25
516 15 b. (+10) violet, bistre and blue 13·00 5·00

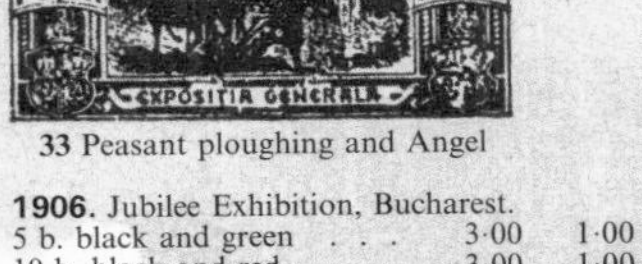

33 Peasant ploughing and Angel

1906. Jubilee Exhibition, Bucharest.

517 **33** 5 b. black and green 3·00 1·00
518 10 b. black and red 3·00 1·00
519 – 15 b. black and violet 5·00 1·60
520 – 25 b. black and blue 5·00 1·65
521 – 30 b. brown and red 6·00 1·50
522 – 40 b. brown and green 7·25 1·75
523 – 50 b. black and orange 6·00 2·40
524 – 75 b. sepia and brown 6·00 2·40
525 – 1 l. 50 brown and mauve 65·00 32·00
526 – 2 l. 50 brown and yellow 25·00 20·00
527 – 3 l. brown and orange 16·00 20·00

DESIGNS—HORIZ: 15, 25 b. Exhibition Building. VERT: 30, 40 b. Farmhouse; 50, 75 b. (different), Royal Family pavilion; 1 l. 50, 2 l. 50, King Carol on horseback; 3 l. Queen Elizabeth (Carmen Sylva).

34 Princess Maria and her Children receiving Poor Family conducted by an Angel

1907. Welfare Fund.

528 **34** 3 b. (+7) brown 6·50 3·25
529 5 b. (+10) brown & green 3·25 1·60
530 10 b. (+10) brown & red 3·25 1·60
531 15 b. (+10) brown & blue 3·25 2·00

35 37

1908.

575 **35** 5 b. green 1·25 20
562 10 b. red 30 10
577 15 b. violet 7·25 2·00
564 25 b. blue 75 10
579 40 b. green 40 15
702 40 b. brown 3·25 2·00
566 50 b. orange 40 15
705 50 b. red 1·25 45
581 1 l. brown 1·10 25
582 2 l. red 6·50 2·00

1908.

583 **37** 1 b. black 15 10
590 3 b. brown 50 10
585 5 b. green 20 10
592 10 b. red 35 10
599 15 b. violet 10·00 8·25
594 15 b. olive 45 10
692 15 b. brown 50 30

38
39 Troops crossing Danube

1913. Acquisition of Southern Dobruja.

626 – 1 b. black 65 25
627 **38** 3 b. brown and grey 1·60 50
628 **39** 5 b. black and green 1·40 15
629 – 10 b. black and orange 55 15
630 – 15 b. violet and brown 1·60 65
631 – 25 b. brown and blue 2·25 1·00
632 **39** 40 b. red and brown 3·25 1·75
633 **38** 50 b. blue and yellow 4·25 3·25
634 1 l. brown and blue 11·50 8·25
635 2 l. red and red 15·00 10·00

DESIGNS—VERT: (As Type **38**): 1 b. "Dobruja" holding flag. HORIZ: (As Type **39**): 10 b. Town of Constanza; 25 b. Church and School in Dobruja (24×16 mm); 15 b. "Mircea the Great and King Carol".

1918. Surch **25. BANI**.

657 **37** 25 b. on 1 b. black 35 30

1918. Optd **1918**.

662 **37** 5 b. green 40 25
663 10 b. red 45 25

TRANSYLVANIA

The Eastern portion of Hungary. Union with Rumania proclaimed in December 1918 and the final frontiers settled by the Treaty of Trianon 4th June, 1920.

The following issues for Transylvania (Nos. 747/858) were valid throughout Rumania.

(42)

(43)

(The "F" stands for King Ferdinand and "P.T.T." for Posts Telegraphs and Telephones).

The values "BANI", "LEU" or "LEI" appear above or below the monogram.

A. Issues for Cluj (Kolozsvar or Klausenburg).

1919. Various stamps of Hungary optd as T **42**. (a) Flood Relief Charity stamps of 1913.

747 **7** 1 l. on 1 f. grey 11·50 11·50
748 1 l. on 2 f. yellow 50·00 50·00
749 1 l. on 3 f. orange 26·00 26·00
750 1 l. on 5 f. green 1·00 1·00
751 1 l. on 10 f. red 1·00 1·00
752 1 l. on 12 f. lilac on yellow 3·75 3·75
753 1 l. on 16 f. green 2·00 2·00
754 1 l. on 25 f. blue 26·00 26·00
755 1 l. on 35 f. purple 2·00 2·00
756 **8** 1 l. on 1 k. red 32·00 32·00

(b) War Charity stamps of 1916.

757 **20** 10 (+2) b. red 15 15
758 – 15 (+2) b. violet 15 15
759 **22** 40 (+2) b. lake 15 15

(c) Harvesters and Parliament Types.

760 **18** 2 b. brown 15 15
761 3 b. red 15 15
762 5 b. green 15 15
763 6 b. blue 15 15
764 10 b. red 65·00 65·00
765 15 b. violet (No. 244) 2·50 2·50
766 15 b. violet 15 15
767 25 b. blue 15 15
768 35 b. brown 15 15
769 40 b. olive 15 15
770 **19** 50 b. purple 15 15
771 75 b. blue 15 15
772 80 b. green 15 15
773 1 l. lake 15 15
774 2 l. brown 20 20
775 3 l. grey and violet 1·75 1·75
776 5 l. brown 1·40 1·40
777 10 l. lilac and brown 1·75 1·75

(d) Karl and Zita stamps.

778 **27** 10 b. red 13·50 13·50
779 15 b. violet 5·00 5·00
780 20 b. brown 15 15
781 25 b. blue 30 30
782 **28** 40 b. olive 15 15

B. Issues for Oradea (Nagyvarad, Grosswardein).

1919. Various stamps of Hungary optd as T **43** (a) "Turul" Type.

794 **7** 2 b. yellow 2·75 2·75
795 3 b. orange 4·75 4·75
796 6 b. drab 25 25
797 16 b. green 8·50 8·50
798 50 b. lake on blue 40 40
799 70 b. brown and green 10·00 10·00

(b) Flood Relief Charity stamps of 1913.

800 **7** 1 l. on 1 f. grey 40 40
801 1 l. on 2 f. yellow 2·00 2·00
802 1 l. on 3 f. orange 45 45
803 1 l. on 5 l. green 15 15
804 1 l. on 6 f. drab 40 40
805 1 l. on 10 f. red 15 15
806 1 l. on 12 f. lilac on yellow 23·00 23·00
807 1 l. on 16 f. green 50 50
808 1 l. on 20 f. brown 3·00 3·00
809 1 l. on 25 f. blue 2·00 2·00
810 1 l. on 35 f. purple 2·00 2·00

(c) War Charity stamp of 1915.

811 **7** 5 + 2 b. green (No. 173) 5·00 5·00

(d) War Charity stamps of 1916.

812 **20** 10 (+2) b. red 20 20
813 – 15 (+2) b. violet 15 15
814 **22** 40 (+2) b. lake 15 15

(e) Harvesters and Parliament Types.

815 **18** 2 b. brown 15 15
816 3 b. red 15 15
817 5 b. green 15 15
818 6 b. blue 35 35
819 10 b. red 65 65
820 15 b. violet (No. 244) 65·00 65·00
821 15 b. violet 15 15
822 20 b. brown 6·00 6·00
823 25 b. blue 15 15
824 35 b. brown 15 15
825 40 b. olive 15 15
826 **19** 50 b. purple 15 15
827 75 b. blue 15 15
828 80 b. green 15 15
829 1 l. lake 20 20
830 2 l. brown 15 15
831 3 l. grey and violet 2·50 2·50
832 5 l. brown 1·75 1·75
833 10 l. lilac and brown 1·00 1·00

(f) Charles and Zita stamps.

834 **27** 10 b. red 1·40 1·40
835 20 b. brown 15 15
836 25 b. blue 20 20
837 40 b. olive 25 25

The following (Nos. 838/58) are also optd **KOZTARSASAG**.

(g) Harvesters and Parliament Types.

838 **18** 2 b. brown 75 75
839 3 b. red 15 15
840 4 b. grey 15 15
841 5 b. green 15 15
842 6 b. blue 1·00 1·00
843 10 b. red 8·25 8·25
844 20 b. brown 85 85
845 40 b. olive 15 15
846 **19** 1 l. lake 15 15
847 3 l. grey and violet 35 35
848 5 l. brown 2·40 2·40

(h) Charles and Zita stamps.

849 **27** 10 b. red 80·00 80·00
850 20 b. brown 1·40 1·40
851 25 b. blue 20 20
852 **28** 50 b. purple 15 15

(k) Harvesters and Parliament Types inscr "MAGYAR POSTA".

853 **18** 5 b. green 15 15
854 20 b. red 15 15
855 20 b. brown 15 15
856 25 b. blue 25 25
857 40 b. olive 40 40
858 **19** 5 l. brown 4·00 4·00

(44) King Ferdinand's Monogram
45 King Ferdinand 46

1919. Recovery of Transylvania and Return of King of Rumania to Bucharest. Optd with T **44**.

873 **37** 1 b. black 20 15
874 5 b. green 30 20
878a 10 b. red 10 10

1920.

891 **45** 1 b. black 10 10
892 5 b. green 10 10
893 10 b. red 10 10
882 15 b. brown 30 15
895 25 b. blue 20 10
896 25 b. brown 20 10
910 40 b. brown 45 20
898 50 b. pink 20 10
887 1 l. green 40 10
900 1 l. red 30 10
889 2 l. orange 45 25
902 2 l. blue 45 10
903 2 l. red 1·75 1·40

1922.

923 **46** 3 b. black 15 10
924 5 b. black 10 10
925 10 b. green 10 10
926 25 b. brown 10 10
927 25 b. red 15 10
928 30 b. violet 15 10
929 50 b. yellow 10 10
930 60 b. green 75 40
931 1 l. violet 15 10
932 2 l. red 55 10
933a 2 l. green 20 10
934 3 l. blue 1·00 65
935a 3 l. brown 1·00 65
937 3 l. red 35 10
936a 3 l. pink 25 10
938 5 l. green 1·50 65
939b 5 l. brown 20 10
940 6 l. blue 1·75 1·00
941 6 l. red 4·25 2·40
942 6 l. olive 1·75 45
943 7 l. 50 blue 1·50 25
944 10 l. blue 1·50 20

47 Cathedral of Alba Julia — 48 King Ferdinand — 49 State Arms

51 Michael the Brave and King Ferdinand

1922. Coronation.

1032 **47** 5 b. black 15 15
1033 **48** 25 b. brown 75 20
1034 **49** 50 b. green 75 50
1035 – 1 l. olive 90 60
1036 **51** 2 l. red 90 60
1037 – 3 l. blue 1·75 1·00
1050 – 6 l. violet 6·50 6·00

DESIGNS—As Type **48**: 1 l. Queen Marie as a nurse; 3 l. Portrait of King but rectangular frame. Larger (21 × 33 mm): 6 l. Queen Marie in coronation robes.

54 King Ferdinand — 55 Map of Rumania

1926. King's 60th Birthday. Imperf or perf.

1051 **54** 10 b. green 20 20
1052 25 b. orange 15 15
1053 50 b. brown 15 15
1054 1 l. violet 15 15
1055 2 l. green 15 15
1056 3 l. red 15 15
1057 5 l. brown 15 15
1058 6 l. olive 15 15
1059 9 l. grey 15 15
1060 10 l. blue 15 15

1927. 50th Anniv of Rumanian Geographical Society.

1061 **55** 1 + 9 l. violet 2·25 1·40
1062 – 2 + 8 l. green 2·25 1·40
1063 – 3 + 7 l. red 2·25 1·40
1064 – 5 + 5 l. blue 2·25 1·40
1065 – 6 + 4 l. olive 4·75 2·00

DESIGNS: 2 l. Stephen the Great; 3 l. Michael the Brave; 5 l. Carol and Ferdinand; 6 l. Adam Clisi Monument.

60 King Carol and King Ferdinand

1927. 50th Anniv of Independence.

1066 **60** 25 b. red 25 15
1067 – 30 b. black 20 15
1068 – 50 b. green 25 15
1069 **60** 1 l. blue 20 15
1070 – 2 l. green 20 20
1071 – 3 l. purple 20 25
1072 – 4 l. brown 45 30
1073 – 4 l. 50 brown 1·60 1·25
1074 – 5 l. brown 23 25
1075 – 6 l. red 80 80
1076 **60** 7 l. 50 blue 30 25
1077 10 l. blue 1·60 50

DESIGNS—HORIZ: 30 b., 2, 3, 5 l. King Ferdinand. VERT: 50 b., 4 l, 4 l. 50, 6 l. King Ferdinand as in Type **60**.

63 King Michael 64

1928.

1080 **63** 25 b. black 20 10
1081 30 b. pink 50 10
1082 50 b. olive 20 10

(a) Size 19 × 25 mm.

1083 **64** 1 l. purple 20 10
1084 2 l. green 40 10
1085 3 l. red 50 10
1086 5 l. brown 1·00 10
1087 7 l. 50 blue 6·00 45
1088 10 l. blue 5·00 15

(b) Size 18 × 23 mm.

1129 **64** 1 l. purple 25 10
1130 2 l. green 60 15
1131 3 l. red 1·40 10
1132 7 l. 50 blue 2·50 1·00
1133 10 l. blue 7·50 6·75

65 Bessarabian Parliament House

1928. 10th Anniv of Annexation of Bessarabia.

1092 **65** 1 l. green 1·10 65
1093 2 l. brown 1·10 65
1094 – 3 l. sepia 1·10 65
1095 – 5 l. lake 1·50 85
1096 – 7 l. 50 blue 1·50 85
1097 – 10 l. blue 3·50 2·00
1098 – 20 l. violet 4·75 2·75

DESIGNS: 3, 5, 20 l. Hotin Fortress; 7 l. 50, 10 l. Alba Fortress.

66 Bleriot SPAD 33 Biplane

1928. Air.

1099 **66** 1 l. brown 5·50 3·25
1100 2 l. blue 5·50 3·25
1101 5 l. red 5·50 3·25

67 King Carol and King Michael

1928. 50th Anniv of Acquisition of Northern Dobruja.

1102 **67** 1 l. green 75 30
1103 – 2 l. brown 75 30
1104 **67** 3 l. grey 90 30
1105 – 5 l. mauve 1·25 35
1106 – 7 l. 50 blue 1·50 50
1107 – 10 l. blue 3·25 1·40
1108 – 20 l. red 4·50 1·75

DESIGNS: 2 l. Constanza Harbour and Carol Lighthouse; 5 l., 7 l. 50, Adam Clisi Monument; 10, 20 l. Cernavoda Bridge over the Danube.

68 — 69 The Union

1929. 10th Anniv of Union of Rumania and Transylvania.

1109 **68** 1 l. purple 1·75 1·40
1110 **69** 2 l. green 1·75 1·40
1111 – 3 l. brown 2·50 1·40
1112 – 4 l. red 2·50 1·60
1113 – 5 l. orange 2·75 1·75
1114 – 10 l. blue 3·75 3·50

DESIGNS—HORIZ: 1 l. Ferdinand I, Stephen the Great, Michael the Brave, Hunyadi and Brancoveanu; 10 l. Ferdinand I. VERT: 2 l. Union; 3 l. Avram Jancu; 4 l. King Michael the Brave; 5 l. Bran Castle.

1930. Stamps of King Michael optd **8 IUNIE 1930** (Accession of Carol II).

1134 **63** 25 b. black (postage) 30 10
1135 30 b. pink 50 10
1136 50 b. olive 45 10
1142 **64** 1 l. purple (No. 1129) 50 10
1143 2 l. green (No. 1130) 50 10
1144 3 l. red (No. 1131) 70 10
1137 5 l. brown 70 10
1140 7 l. 50 blue (No. 1087) 2·75 1·25
1145 7 l. 50 blue (No. 1132) 2·10 55
1138 10 l. blue (No. 1088) 4·50 1·40
1146 10 l. blue (No. 1133) 1·75 65

1147 **66** 1 l. brown (air) 12·00 6·50
1148 2 l. blue 12·00 6·50
1149 5 l. red 12·00 6·50

72 — 73 King Carol II — 76

1930.

1172 **72** 25 b. black 25 10
1173 50 b. brown 60 30
1174 1 l. violet 30 10
1175 2 l. green 50 10
1176 **73** 3 l. red 1·10 10
1177 4 l. orange 1·25 10
1178 6 l. red 1·40 10
1179 7 l. 50 blue 1·60 15
1180 – 10 l. blue 4·00 10
1181 – 16 l. green 9·00 15
1182 – 20 l. yellow 12·00 40

DESIGN: 10 l. to 20 l. Portrait as Type **72**, but in plain circle, with "ROMANIA" at top.

1930. Air.

1183 **76** 1 l. violet on blue 2·50 2·00
1184 2 l. green on blue 3·00 2·00
1185 5 l. brown on blue 6·00 2·75
1186 10 l. blue on blue 12·00 6·00

77 Map of Rumania — 78 Woman with Census Paper — 79 King Carol II

1930. National Census.

1187 **77** 1 l. violet 1·25 30
1188 **78** 2 l. green 2·25 35
1189 4 l. orange 2·50 30
1190 6 l. red 5·50 35

1931.

1191 **79** 30 l. blue and olive 1·10 50
1192 50 l. blue and red 2·40 1·25
1193 100 l. blue and green 4·50 2·40

80 King Carol II

81 King Carol I — 82 Kings Carol II, Ferdinand I & Carol I

1931. 50th Anniv of Rumanian Monarchy.

1200 **80** 1 l. violet 2·25 1·75
1201 **81** 2 l. green 4·00 1·75
1202 – 6 l. red 9·00 2·75
1203 **82** 10 l. blue 13·50 5·00
1204 – 20 l. orange 15·00 6·75

DESIGNS—As Type **80**: 6 l. King Carol II, facing right. As Type **81**: 20 l. King Ferdinand I.

83 Naval Cadet Ship "Mircea"

1931. 50th Anniv of Rumanian Navy.

1205 **83** 6 l. red 5·50 3·25
1206 – 10 l. blue 7·25 3·75
1207 – 12 l. green 27·00 4·00
1208 – 20 l. orange 10·50 7·50

DESIGNS: 10 l. Monitors "Lascar Catargiu" and "Mihail Kogalniceaunu"; 16 l. Monitor "Ardeal"; 20 l. Destroyer "Regele Ferdinand".

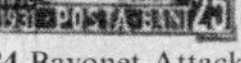

84 Bayonet Attack — 87 King Carol I

88 Infantry Attack — 89 King Ferdinand I

1931. Centenary of Rumanian Army.

1209 **84** 25 b. black 1·75 1·00
1210 – 50 b. brown 2·25 1·40
1211 – 1 l. violet 2·75 1·75
1212 **87** 2 l. green 4·50 2·00
1213 **88** 3 l. red 10·00 6·00
1214 **89** 7 l. 50 blue 12·00 13·50
1215 – 16 l. green 15·00 6·00

DESIGNS: 50 b. Infantryman, 1870, 20 × 33 mm: 1 l. Infantry and drummer, 1830, 23 × 36 mm: 16 l. King Carol II in uniform with plumed helmet, 21 × 34 mm.

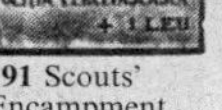

91 Scouts' Encampment — 92a Farman F.121 Jaribu

1931. Rumanian Boy Scouts' Exhibition Fund.

1221 **91** 1 l. + 1 l. red 4·00 3·25
1222 – 2 l. + 2 l. green 4·75 4·00
1223 – 3 l. + 3 l. blue 6·50 5·00
1224 – 4 l. + 4 l. brown 8·50 6·50
1225 – 6 l. + 6 l. brown 11·00 6·75

DESIGNS—VERT: As Type **91**: 3 l. Recruiting, 22 × 37½ mm; 2 l. Rescue work, 22 × 41½ mm; 4 l. Prince Nicholas; 6 l. King Carol II in scoutmaster's uniform.

1931. Air.

1226 **92a** 2 l. green 1·05 90
1227 – 3 l. red 2·00 1·25
1228 – 5 l. brown 3·00 1·50
1229 – 10 l. blue 7·50 3·25
1230 – 20 l. violet 17·00 5·00

DESIGNS—As T **92a**: 3 l. Farman F.300; 5 l. Farman F.60 Goliath; 10 l. Fokker F.XII. 34 × 20 mm: 20 l. Three aircraft flying in formation.

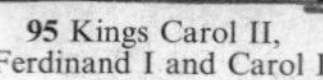

95 Kings Carol II, Ferdinand I and Carol I — 96 Alexander the Good

1931.

1231 **95** 16 l. green 13·00 50

1932. 500th Death Centenary of Alexander I, Prince of Moldavia.

1232 **96** 6 l. red 12·00 10·00

97 King Carol II

98 Semaphore Signaller

1932.
1248 **97** 10 l. blue 13·00 30

1932. Boy Scouts' Jamboree Fund.
1256 – 25 b. + 25 b. green 3·50 1·75
1257 **98** 50 b. + 50 b. blue 4·00 3·50
1258 – 1 l. + 1 l. green 5·50 5·00
1259 – 2 l. + 2 l. red 9·00 6·75
1260 – 3 l. + 3 l. blue 22·00 13·50
1261 – 6 l. + 6 l. brown 24·00 17·00
DESIGNS—VERT: As Type **98**: 25 b. Scouts in camp; 1 l. On the trail; 3 l. King Carol II; 6 l. King Carol and King Michael when a Prince. HORIZ: 20 × 15 mm: 2 l. Camp fire.

99 Cantacuzino and Gregory Chika

1932. 9th Int Medical Congress.
1262 **99** 1 l. red 7·50 6·75
1263 – 6 l. orange 21·00 10·00
1264 – 10 l. blue 35·00 17·00
DESIGNS: 6 l. Congress in session; 10 l. Hygeia and Aesculapius.

100 Tuberculosis Sanatorium

1932. Postal Employees' Fund.
1265 **100** 4 l. + 1 l. green 5·50 3·25
1266 – 6 l. + 1 l. brown 6·75 4·00
1267 – 10 l. + 1 l. blue 12·00 6·75
DESIGNS—VERT: 6 l. War Memorial tablet. HORIZ: 10 l. Convalescent home.

102 "Bull's head"

103 Dolphins

104 Arms

1932. 75th Anniv of First Moldavian Stamps. Imperf.
1268 **102** 25 b. black 1·25 20
1269 – 1 l. purple 2·00 65
1270 **103** 2 l. green 2·50 80
1271 – 3 l. red 2·50 1·00
1272 **104** 6 l. red 3·25 1·10
1273 – 7 l. 50 blue 4·00 1·75
1274 – 10 l. blue 6·00 2·75
DESIGNS—As Type **103**: 1 l.: Lion rampant and bridge; 3 l. Eagle and castles; 7 l. 50, Eagle; 10 l. Bull's head.

1932. 30th Anniv of Opening of G.P.O. Bucharest. As T **25** but smaller.
1275 16 l. green 11·50 6·75

105 Ruins of Trajan's Bridge, Arms of Turnu-Severin and Towers of Severus

1933. Centenary of Founding of Turnu-Severin.
1279 **105** 25 b. green 65 20
1280 – 50 b. blue 1·00 30
1281 – 1 l. brown 1·75 45
1282 – 2 l. green 2·50 1·00
DESIGNS: 50 b. Trajan at the completion of bridge over the Danube; 1 l. Arrival of Prince Carol at Turnu-Severin; 2 l. Trajan's Bridge.

107 Carmen Sylva and Carol I

1933. 50th Anniv of Construction of Pelesch Castle, Sinaia.
1283 **107** 1 l. violet 2·10 1·75
1284 – 3 l. brown 2·40 2·00
1285 – 6 l. red 3·25 2·40
DESIGNS: 3 l. Eagle and medallion portraits of Kings Carol I, Ferdinand I and Carol II; 6 l. Pelesch Castle.

108 Wayside Shrine

110 King Carol II

1934. Rumanian Women's Exhibition. Inscr "L.N.F.R. MUNCA NOASTRA ROMANEASC".
1286 **108** 1 l. + 1 l. brown 2·00 1·75
1287 – 2 l. + 1 l. blue 2·50 2·00
1288 – 3 l. + 1 l. green 3·75 3·00
DESIGNS—HORIZ: 2 l. Weaver. VERT: 3 l. Spinner.

1934. Mamaia Jamboree Fund. Nos. 1256/61 optd **MAMAIA 1934** and Arms of Constanza.
1289 – 26 b. + 25 b. green 4·00 3·25
1290 **98** 50 b. + 50 b. blue 5·75 4·00
1291 – 1 l. + 1 l. green 7·75 6·25
1292 – 2 l. + 2 l. red 8·75 7·75
1293 – 3 l. + 3 l. blue 19·00 12·50
1294 – 6 l. + 6 l. brown 22·00 16·00

1934.
1295 – 50 b. brown 1·00 30
1296 **110** 2 l. green 2·00 30
1297 4 l. orange 2·75 45
1298 – 6 l. lake 6·25 30
DESIGNS: 50 b. Profile portrait of King Carol II in civilian clothes; 6 l. King Carol in plumed helmet.

112 "Grapes for Health"

113 Crisan, Horia and Closca

1934. Bucharest Fruit Exhibition.
1299 **112** 1 l. green 4·00 2·75
1300 – 2 l. brown 4·00 2·75
DESIGN: 2 l. Woman with fruit.

1935. 150th Anniv of Death of Three Rumanian Martyrs. Portraits inscr "MARTIR AL NEAMULUI 1785".
1301 **113** 1 l. violet 50 30
1302 – 2 l. green (Crisan) 1·00 45
1303 – 6 l. brown (Closca) 2·75 1·25
1304 – 10 l. blue (Horia) 4·50 2·40

114 Boy Scouts

1935. 5th Anniv of Accession of Carol II.
1305 – 25 b. black 3·25 2·75
1306 – 1 l. violet 6·00 4·75
1307 **114** 2 l. green 6·75 6·75
1308 – 6 l. + 1 l. brown 8·50 8·50
1309 – 10 l. + 2 l. blue 20·00 20·00
DESIGNS—VERT: 25 b. Scout saluting; 1 l. Bugler; 6 l. King Carol II. HORIZ: 10 l. Colour party.

1935. Portraits as T **110** but additionally inscr "POSTA".
1310 – 25 b. black 10 10
1311 – 50 b. brown 10 10
1312 – 1 l. violet 15 10
1313 **110** 2 l. green 35 10
1315 – 3 l. red 70 15
1316 – 3 l. blue 1·25 15
1317 **110** 4 l. orange 1·50 10
1318 – 5 l. red 1·25 55
1319 – 6 l. lake 1·75 10
1320 – 7 l. 50 blue 1·90 35
1321 – 8 l. purple 1·90 35
1322 **110** 9 l. blue 2·75 65
1323 – 10 l. blue 1·25 20
1324 – 12 l. blue 1·75 85
1325 – 15 l. brown 1·75 50
1326 – 16 l. green 2·25 30
1327 – 20 l. orange 1·50 40
1328 – 24 l. red 2·25 50
PORTRAITS—IN PROFILE: 25 b., 15 l. In naval uniform; 50 b., 3, 8, 10 l. In civilian clothes. THREE-QUARTER FACE: 1, 5, 7 l. 50, In civilian clothes. FULL FACE: 6, 12, 16, 20, 24 l. In plumed helmet.

118 King Carol II

119 Oltenia Peasant Girl

1936. Bucharest Exhibition and 70th Anniv of Hohenzollern–Sigmaringen Dynasty.
1329 **118** 6 l. + 1 l. red 1·40 80

1936. 6th Anniv of Accession of Carol II Inscr "O.E.T.R. 8 IUNIE 1936".
1330 **119** 50 b. + 50 b. brown 1·25 50
1331 – 1 l. + 1 l. violet 75 55
1332 – 2 l. + 1 l. green 95 85
1333 – 3 l. + 1 l. red 1·40 1·00
1334 – 4 l. + 2 l. red 1·75 80
1335 – 6 l. + 3 l. grey 2·25 1·40
1336 – 10 l. + 5 l. blue 3·50 2·75
DESIGNS (costumes of following districts)—VERT: 1 l. Banat; 4 l. Gori; 6 l. Neamz. HORIZ: 2 l. Saliste; 3 l. Hateg; 10 l. Suceava (Bukovina).

120 Brasov Jamboree Badge

121 Liner "Transylvania"

1936. National Scout Jamboree, Brasov.
1337 – 1 l. + 1 l. blue 6·00 5·75
1338 – 3 l. + 3 l. grey 7·50 5·75
1339 **120** 6 l. + 6 l. red 9·50 5·75
DESIGNS: 1 l. National Scout Badge; 3 l. Tenderfoot Badge.

1936. 1st Marine Exhibition, Bucharest.
1343 – 1 l. + 1 l. violet 5·25 3·75
1344 – 3 l. + 2 l. blue 5·25 4·00
1345 **121** 6 l. + 3 l. red 6·75 5·75
DESIGNS: 1 l. Submarine "Delfinul"; 3 l. Naval cadet ship "Mircea".

1936. 18th Anniv of Annexation of Transylvania and 16th Anniv of Foundation of "Little Entente". Nos. 1320 and 1323 optd **CEHOSLOVACIA YUGOSLAVIA 1920-1936.**
1346 7 l. 50 blue 4·00 4·00
1347 10 l. blue 4·00 4·00

123 Creanga's Birthplace

1937. Birth Centenary of Ion Creanga (poet).
1348 **123** 2 l. green 1·10 50
1349 – 3 l. red 1·40 55
1350 **123** 4 l. violet 1·75 95
1351 – 6 l. brown 4·00 2·00
DESIGN: 3, 6 l. Portrait of Creanga, 37 × 22 mm.

124 Footballers

1937. 7th Anniv of Accession of Carol II.
1352 **124** 25 b. + 25 b. olive 1·00 20
1353 – 50 b. + 50 b. brown 1·00 25
1354 – 1 l. + 50 b. violet 1·25 40
1355 – 2 l. + 1 l. green 1·40 45
1356 – 3 l. + 1 l. red 2·50 50
1357 – 4 l. + 1 l. red 4·00 60
1358 – 6 l. + 2 l. brown 6·00 1·10
1359 – 10 l. + 4 l. blue 6·50 1·75
DESIGNS—HORIZ: 50 b. Swimmer; 3 l. King Carol II hunting; 10 l. U.F.S.R. Inaugural Meeting. VERT: 1 l. Javelin thrower; 2 l. Skier; 4 l. Rowing; 6 l. Steeplechaser.
Premium in aid of the Federation of Rumanian Sports Clubs (U.F.S.R.).

127 Curtea de Arges Cathedral

128 Hurdling

1937. "Little Entente".
1360 **127** 7 l. 50 blue 1·75 80
1361 10 l. blue 2·40 45

1937 8th Balkan Games, Bucharest. Inscr as in T **115**.
1362 – 1 l. + 1 l. violet 1·10 65
1363 – 2 l. + 1 l. green 1·50 90
1364 **128** 4 l. + 1 l. red 1·75 1·50
1365 – 6 l. + 1 l. brown 2·10 1·75
1366 – 10 l. + 1 l. blue 6·50 3·00
DESIGNS: 1 l. Sprinting; 2 l. Throwing the javelin; 6 l. Breasting the tape; 10 l. High jumping.

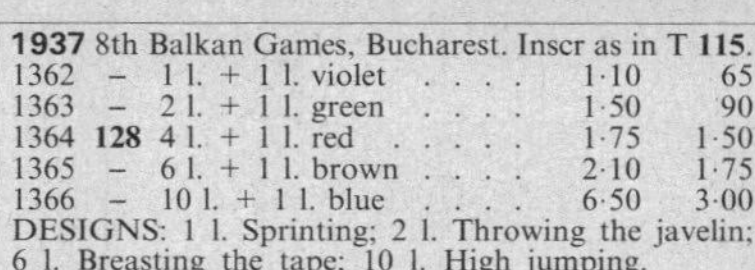

129 Arms of Rumania, Greece, Turkey and Yugoslavia

130 King Carol II

1938. Balkan Entente.
1368 **129** 7 l. 50 blue 1·50 90
1369 10 l. blue 2·00 75

1938. New Constitution. Profile portraits of King inscr "27 FEBRUARIE 1938". 6 l. shows Arms also.
1370 **130** 3 l. red 80 50
1371 – 6 l. brown 1·25 50
1372 – 10 l. blue 1·90 1·00

131 King Carol II and Provincial Arms

132 Dimitrie Cantemir

1938. Fund for Bucharest Exhibition celebrating 20th Anniv of Union of Provinces.
1373 **131** 6 l. + 1 l. mauve 1·00 35

1938. Boy Scouts' Fund. 8th Anniv of Accession of Carol II. Inscr "STRAJA TARII 8 IUNIE 1938".
1374 **132** 25 b. + 25 b. olive 35 20
1375 – 50 b. + 50 b. brown 80 20
1376 – 1 l. + 1 l. violet 90 25
1377 – 2 l. + 2 l. green 80 25
1378 – 3 l. + 2 l. mauve 85 30
1379 – 4 l. + 2 l. red 90 35
1380 – 6 l. + 2 l. brown 1·10 40
1381 – 7 l. 50 blue 1·50 40
1382 – 10 l. blue 1·60 50
1383 – 16 l. green 2·40 2·00
1384 – 20 l. red 3·50 2·00
PORTRAITS: 50 b. Maria Doamna; 1 l. Mircea the Great; 2 l. Constantin Brancoveanu; 3 l. Stephen the Great; 4 l. Prince Cuza; 6 l. Michael the Brave; 7 l. 50, Queen Elisabeth; 10 l. King Carol II; 16 l. King Ferdinand I; 20 l. King Carol I.

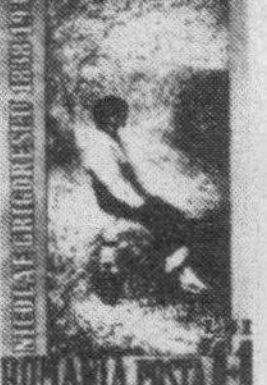
134 "The Spring"

135 Prince Carol in Royal Carriage

1938. Birth Centenary of Nicholas Grigorescu (painter).
1385 **134** 1 l. + 1 l. blue 1·25 50
1386 – 2 l. + 1 l. green 1·75 1·10
1387 – 4 l. + 1 l. red 1·75 1·25
1388 – 6 l. + 1 l. red 1·90 1·60
1389 – 10 l. + 1 l. blue 2·75 2·10
DESIGNS—HORIZ: 2 l. "Escorting Prisoners" (Russo-Turkish War 1877–78); 4 l. "Returning from Market". VERT: 6 l. "Rodica, the Water Carrier"; 10 l. Self-portrait.

1939. Birth Centenary of King Carol I.
1390 **135** 25 b. black 10 10
1391 – 50 b. brown 10 10
1392 – 1 l. violet 20 10
1393 – 1 l. 50 green 10 10
1394 – 2 l. blue 10 10
1395 – 3 l. red 10 10
1396 – 4 l. red 10 10
1397 – 5 l. black 10 10
1398 – 7 l. black 10 10
1399 – 8 l. blue 25 15
1400 – 10 l. mauve 30 15
1401 – 12 l. blue 30 20
1402 – 15 l. blue 35 15
1403 – 16 l. green 1·00 60
DESIGNS—HORIZ 50 b. Prince Carol at Battle of Calafat; 1 l. 50, Sigmaringen and Pelesch Castles; 5 l. Carol I, Queen Elizabeth and Arms of Rumania. VERT: 1 l. Examining plans for restoring Curtea de Arges Monastery; 2 l. Carol I and Queen Elizabeth; 3 l. Carol I at age of 8; 4 l. In 1866; 5 l. In 1877; 7 l. Equestrian statue; 8 l. Leading troops in 1878; 10 l. In General's uniform; 12 l. Bust; 16 l. Restored Monastery of Curtea de Arges.

136 Rumanian Pavilion N.Y. World's Fair
137 Michael Eminescu, after painting by Joano Basarab

1939. New York World's Fair.
1407 **136** 6 l. lake 80 30
1408 – 12 l. blue 80 30
DESIGN: 12 l. Another view of Pavilion.

1939. 50th Death Anniv of Michael Eminescu (poet).
1409 **137** 5 l. black 80 40
1410 – 7 l. red 80 40
DESIGN: 7 l. Eminescu in later years.

138 St. George and Dragon
139 Railway Locomotives of 1869 and 1939

1939. 9th Anniv of Accession of Carol II and Boy Scouts' Fund.
1411 **138** 25 b. + 25 b. grey . . . 60 35
1412 50 b. + 50 b. brown . . 60 35
1413 1 l. + 1 l. blue 65 35
1414 2 l. + 2 l. green 75 35
1415 3 l. + 2 l. purple . . . 90 35
1416 4 l. + 2 l. orange . . . 1·40 45
1417 6 l. + 2 l. red . . . . 1·50 45
1418 8 l. grey . . . . 1·50 50
1419 10 l. blue . . . . . . 1·60 50
1420 12 l. blue . . . . . . 2·00 1·40
1421 16 l. green . . . . . . 2·40 1·50

1939. 70th Anniv of Rumanian Railways.
1422 **139** 1 l. violet . . . . 1·25 55
1423 – 4 l. red . . . . 1·25 65
1424 – 5 l. grey . . . . 1·10 85
1425 – 7 l. mauve . . . . 1·40 90
1426 – 12 l. blue . . . . 2·25 1·25
1427 – 15 l. green . . . . 2·50 2·00
DESIGNS—HORIZ: 4 l. Steam train crossing railway-bridge; 15 l. Railway Headquarters, Budapest. VERT: 5 l., 7 l. Steam train leaving station; 12 l. Diesel train crossing railway bridge.

1940. Balkan Entente. As T **103** of Yugoslavia, but with Arms rearranged.
1428 12 l. blue 90 70
1429 16 l. blue 90 70

141 King Carol II
142 King Carol II

1940. Aviation Fund.
1430 **141** 1 l. + 50 b. green . . . 20 15
1431 2 l. 50 + 50 b. green . . 25 20
1432 3 l. + 1 l. red 35 25
1433 3 l. 50 + 50 b. brown . . 35 30
1434 4 l. + 1 l. orange . . . 45 35
1435 6 l. + 1 l. blue 95 20
1436 9 l. + 1 l. blue . . . . 1·10 95
1437 14 l. + 1 l. green . . . 1·25 1·10

1940. 10th Anniv of Carol II and Aviation Fund. Royal portraits.
1438 **142** 1 l. + 50 b. purple . . . 75 25
1439 4 l. + 1 l. brown . . . 75 35
1440 – 6 l. + 1 l. blue 75 45
1441 – 8 l. red . . . . 1·00 85
1442 – 16 l. blue . . . . . . 1·25 1·00
1443 – 32 l. brown . . . . . . 2·40 1·75
PORTRAITS: 6, 16 l. In steel helmet; 8 l. In military uniform; 32 l. In flying helmet.

144 The Iron Gates of the Danube

1940. Charity. 10th Anniv of Accession of Carol II and Boy Scouts' Fund. Inscr "STRAJA TARII 8 IUNIE 1940".
1444 **144** 1 l. + 1 l. violet 60 40
1445 – 2 l. + 1 l. brown 60 45
1446 – 3 l. + 1 l. green 65 50
1447 – 4 l. + 1 l. black 75 55
1448 – 5 l. + 1 l. orange 85 65
1449 – 8 l. + 1 l. red . . . . . 1·00 70
1450 – 12 l. + 2 l. blue . . . . 1·25 1·00
1451 – 16 l. + 2 l. grey . . . . 2·50 2·00
DESIGNS—HORIZ: 3 l. Hotin Fortress; 4 l. Hurez Monastery. VERT: 2 l. Greco-Roman ruins; 5 l. Church in Suceava; 8 l. Alba Julia Cathedral; 12 l. Village Church, Transylvania; 16 l. Triumphal Arch, Bucharest.

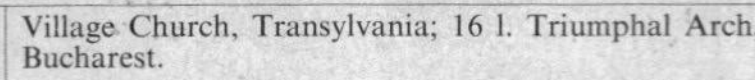

145 King Michael **146**

1940.
1455 **145** 25 b. green 10 10
1456 50 b. olive 10 10
1457 1 l. violet 10 10
1458 2 l. orange 10 10
1608 3 l. brown 10 10
1609 3 l. 50 brown 10 10
1459 4 l. grey 10 10
1611 4 l. 50 brown 10 10
1460 5 l. pink 10 10
1613 6 l. 50 violet 10 10
1461 7 l. blue 10 10
1615 10 l. mauve 10 10
1616 11 l. blue 10 10
1463 12 l. blue 10 10
1464 13 l. purple 10 10
1618 15 l. blue 10 10
1619 16 l. blue 10 10
1620 20 l. brown 10 10
1621 29 l. blue 85 70
1467 30 l. green 15 10
1468 50 l. brown 15 10
1469 100 l. brown 30 10

1940. Aviation Fund.
1470 **146** 1 l. + 50 b. green . . . 10 10
1471 2 l. + 50 b. green . . . 10 10
1472 2 l. 50 + 50 b. green . . 10 10
1473 3 l. + 1 l. violet 10 10
1474 3 l. 50 + 50 b. pink . . 15 15
1475 4 l. + 50 b. red 10 10
1476 4 l. + 1 l. brown 10 10
1477 5 l. + 1 l. red 80 25
1478 6 l. + 1 l. blue 10 10
1479 7 l. + 1 l. green 20 10
1480 8 l. + 1 l. violet 15 10
1481 12 l. + 1 l. brown . . . 20 10
1482 14 l. + 1 l. blue 25 15
1483 19 l. + 1 l. mauve . . . 75 20

147 Codreanu (founder) **148**

1940. "Iron Guard" Fund.
1484 **147** 7 l. + 30 l. grn (postage) 4·50 4·00
1485 **148** 20 l. + 5 l. green (air) . 2·00 2·50

149 Ion Mota
150 Library

1941. Marin and Mota (legionaries killed in Spain).
1486 – 7 l. + 7 l. red . . . . 2·25 3·25
1487 **149** 15 l. + 15 l. blue . . . 3·75 5·00
PORTRAIT: 7 l. Vasile Marin.

1941. Carol I Endowment Fund. Inscr "1891 1941".
1488 – 1 l. 50 + 43 l. 50 violet 1·50 1·75
1489 **150** 2 l. + 43 l. red . . . . 1·50 1·75
1490 – 7 l. + 38 l. red . . . . 1·50 1·75
1491 – 10 l. + 35 l. green . . . 1·50 1·75
1492 – 16 l. + 29 l. brown . . . 1·50 1·75
DESIGNS: 1 l. 50, Ex-libris; 7 l. Foundation building and equestrian statue; 10 l. Foundation stone; 16 l. King Michael and Carol I.

1941. Occupation of Cernauti. Nos. 1488/92 optd **CERNAUTI 5 Iulie 1941.**
1493 – 1 l. 50 + 43 l. 50 violet 2·50 3·25
1494 **150** 2 l. + 43 l. red . . . . 2·50 3·25
1495 – 7 l. + 38 l. red . . . . 2·50 3·25
1496 – 10 l. + 35 l. green . . . 2·50 3·25
1497 – 16 l. + 29 l. brown . . . 2·50 3·25

1941. Occupation of Chisinau. Nos. 1488/92 optd **CHISINAU 16 Iulie 1941.**
1498 – 1 l. 50 + 43 l. 1.50 violet 2·50 3·25
1499 **150** 2 l. + 43 l. red . . . . 2·50 3·25
1500 – 7 l. + 38 l. red . . . . 2·50 3·25
1501 – 10 l. + 35 l. green . . . 2·50 3·25
1502 – 16 l. + 29 l. brown . . . 2·50 3·25

153 "Charity"
154 Prince Voda

1941. Red Cross Fund. Cross in red.
1503 **153** 1 l. 50 + 38 l. 50 violet . 1·00 75
1504 2 l. + 38 l. red . . . . 1·00 75
1505 5 l. + 35 l. olive . . . . 1·00 75
1506 7 l. + 33 l. brown . . . 1·00 75
1507 10 l. + 30 l. blue . . . . 1·25 1·40

1941. Conquest of Transdniestria.
1572 **154** 3 l. orange 30 65
1509 6 l. brown 30 35
1510 12 l. violet 50 60
1511 24 l. blue . . . . 70 1·00

155 King Michael and Stephen the Great

1941. Anti-Bolshevik Crusade. Inscr "RAZBOIUL SFANT CONTRA BOLSE-VISMULUI".
1512 **155** 10 l. + 30 l. blue . . . . 1·50 3·25
1513 – 12 l. + 28 l. red . . . . 1·50 3·25
1514 – 16 l. + 24 l. brown . . . 2·10 3·25
1515 – 20 l. + 20 l. violet . . . 2·10 3·25
DESIGNS: 12 l. Hotin and Akkerman Fortresses; 16 l. Arms and helmeted soldiers; 20 l. Bayonet charge and Arms of Rumania.

1941. Fall of Odessa. Nos. 1512/15 optd **ODESA/16 Oct. 1941.**
1517 **155** 10 l. + 30 l. blue . . . . 1·50 3·25
1518 – 12 l. + 28 l. red . . . . 1·50 3·25
1519 – 16 l. + 24 l. brown . . . 2·10 3·25
1520 – 20 l. + 20 l. violet . . . 2·10 3·25

157 Hotin

1941. Restoration of Bessarabia and Bukovina (Suceava). Inscr "BASARABIA" or "BUCOVINA".
1522 – 25 b. red 10 10
1523 **157** 50 b. brown 10 10
1524 – 1 l. violet 10 10
1525 – 1 l. 50 green 10 10
1526 – 2 l. brown 10 10
1527 – 3 l. olive 15 10
1528 – 5 l. olive 20 10
1529 – 5 l. 50 brown 20 15
1530 – 6 l. 50 mauve 50 40
1531 **157** 9 l. 50 grey 50 50
1532 – 10 l. purple 35 15
1533 – 13 l. blue 50 20
1534 – 17 l. brown 60 15
1535 – 26 l. green 95 30
1536 – 39 l. blue . . . . 1·40 40
1537 – 130 l. yellow . . . . . . 5·00 3·50
VIEWS—VERT: 25 b., 5 l. Paraclis Hotin; 3 l. Dragomirna; 13 l. Milisauti. HORIZ: 1, 17 l. Sucevita; 1 l. 50, Soroca; 2, 5 l. 50, Tighina; 6 l. 50, Cetatea Alba; 10, 130 l. Putna; 26 l. St. Nicolae, Suceava; 39 l. Monastery, Rughi.

1941. Winter Relief Fund. Inscr "BASARABIA" or "BUCOVINA".
1538 – 3 l. + 50 b. red 20 20
1539 – 5 l. 50 + 50 b. orange . . 55 30
1540 – 5 l. 50 + 1 l. black . . . 55 30
1541 – 6 l. 50 + 1 l. brown . . . 60 40
1542 – 8 l. + 1 l. blue 60 25
1543 – 9 l. 50 + 1 l. blue . . . 75 45
1544 – 10 l. 50 + 1 l. blue . . . 75 25
1545 – 16 l. + 1 l. mauve . . . 85 55
1546 **157** 25 l. + 1 l. grey . . . . 1·10 60
VIEWS—HORIZ: 3 l. Sucevita; 5 l. 50, (1539), Monastery, Rughi; 5 l. 50, (1540), Tighina; 6 l. 50, Soroca; 8 l. St. Nicolae, Suceava; 10 l. 50, Putna; 16 l. Cetatea Alba. VERT: 8 l. 50, Milisauti.

158 Titu Maiorescu
159 Coat-of-Arms of Bukovina

1942. Prisoners of War Relief Fund through International Education Office, Geneva.
1549 **158** 9 l. + 11 l. violet 50 65
1550 20 l. + 20 l. brown . . . 1·90 1·90
1551 20 l. + 30 l. blue . . . . 2·00 2·00

1942. 1st Anniv of Liberation of Bukovina.
1553 **159** 9 l. + 4 l. red . . . . . . 2·25 3·25
1554 – 18 l. + 32 l. blue . . . . 2·25 3·25
1555 – 20 l. + 30 l. red . . . . 2·25 3·25
ARMORIAL DESIGNS: 18 l. Castle; 20 l. Mounds and crosses.

INDEX

Countries can be quickly located by referring to the index at the end of this volume.

160 Map of Bessarabia, King Michael, Antonescu, Hitler and Mussolini
161 Statue of Miron Costin

1942. 1st Anniv of Liberation of Bessarabia.
1556 **160** 9 l. + 41 l. brown . . . 2·00 3·25
1557 – 18 l. + 32 l. olive . . . 2·00 3·25
1558 – 20 l. + 30 l. blue . . . . 2·00 3·25
DESIGNS—VERT: 18 l. King Michael and Marshall Antonescu below miniature of King Stephen. HORIZ: 20 l. Marching soldiers and miniature of Marshal Antonescu.

1942. 1st Anniv of Incorporation of Transdniestria.
1559 **161** 6 l. + 44 l. brown . . . 1·50 2·50
1560 12 l. + 38 l. violet . . . 1·50 2·50
1561 24 l. + 26 l. blue . . . . 1·50 2·50

162 Andrei Muresanu
163 Statue of Avram Iancu

1942. 80th Death Anniv of A. Muresanu (novelist).
1562 **162** 5 l. + 5 l. violet 90 90

1943. Fund for Statue of Iancu (national hero).
1563 **163** 16 l. + 4 l. brown . . . 90 1·25

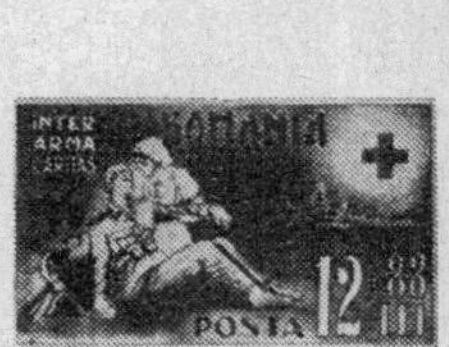

164 Nurse and wounded Soldier
165 Sword and Shield

1943. Red Cross Charity. Cross in red.
1564 **164** 12 l. + 88 l. red 75 75
1565 16 l. + 84 l. blue . . . 75 75
1566 20 l. + 80 l. olive . . . 75 75

1943. Charity. 2nd Year of War. Inscr "22 JUNIE 1941 22 JUNIE 1943".
1568 **165** 36 l. + 164 l. brown . . 2·10 2·40
1569 – 62 l. + 138 l. blue . . . 2·10 2·40
1570 – 76 l. + 124 l. red . . . 2·10 2·40
DESIGNS: 62 l. Sword severing chain; 76 l. Angel protecting soldier and family.

167 P. Maior
169 King Michael and Marshal Antonescu

1943. Transylvanian Refugees' Fund (1st issue).
1576 **167** 16 l. + 134 l. red . . . 40 65
1577 – 32 l. + 118 l. blue . . . 40 65
1578 – 36 l. + 114 l. purple . . 40 65
1579 – 62 l. + 138 l. red . . . 40 65
1580 – 91 l. + 109 l. brown . . 40 65
PORTRAITS—VERT: 32 l. G. Sincai; 36 l. T. Cipariu; 91 l. G. Cosbuc. HORIZ: 62 l. Horia, Closca and Crisan.
See also Nos. 1584/8.

1943. 3rd Anniv of King Michael's Reign.
1581 **169** 16 l. + 24 l. blue . . . . 1·50 2·50

170 Sports Shield
171 Calafat, 1877

1943. Charity. Sports Week.
1582 **170** 16 l. + 24 l. blue . . . 45 45
1583 16 l. + 24 l. brown . . . 45 45

1943. Transylvanian Refugees' Fund (2nd issue) Portraits as T **167**.

1584 16 l. + 134 l. mauve 40 65
1585 51 l. + 99 l. orange 40 65
1586 56 l. + 144 l. red 40 65
1587 76 l. + 124 l. blue 40 65
1588 77 l. + 123 l. brown 40 65

PORTRAITS—VERT: 16 l. S. Micu; 51 l. G. Lazar; 56 l. O. Goga; 76 l. S. Barnutiu; 77 l. A. Saguna.

1943. Centenary of National Artillery.

1596 **171** 1 l. + 1 l. brown 30 30
1597 – 2 l. + 2 l. violet 30 30
1598 – 3 l. 50 + 3 l. 50 blue . . 30 30
1599 – 4 l. + 4 l. mauve 30 30
1600 – 5 l. + 5 l. orange 50 50
1601 – 6l. 50 + 6 l. 50 blue . . 50 50
1602 – 7 l. + 7 l. purple . . . . 75 1·00
1603 – 20 l. + 20 l. red . . . . 1·25 1·75

DESIGNS—HORIZ: (1 l. to 7 l. inscr battle scenes): 2 l. "1916–1918"; 3 l. 50, Stalingrad; 4 l. Crossing R. Tisza; 5 l. Odessa; 6 l. 50, Caucasus; 7 l. Sevastopol; 20 l. Bibescu and King Michael.

172 Association Insignia

1943. 25th Anniv of National Engineers' Assn.

1624 **172** 21 l. + 29 l. brown . . . 1·00 85

173 Motor-cycle and Delivery Van

1944. Postal Employees' Relief Fund and Bicent of National Postal Service. (a) Without opt.

1625 **173** 1 l. + 49 l. red . . . . 2·00 2·00
1626 – 2 l. + 48 l. mauve . . . 2·00 2·00
1627 – 4 l. + 46 l. blue . . . . 2·00 2·00
1628 – 10 l. + 40 l. purple . . . 2·00 2·00

(b) Optd **1744 1944**.

1631 **173** 1l + 49 l. red . . . . 3·75 4·25
1632 – 2 l. + 48 l. mauve . . . 3·75 4·25
1633 – 4 l. + 46 l. blue . . . . 3·75 4·25
1634 – 10 l. + 40 l. purple . . . 3·75 4·25

DESIGNS—HORIZ: 2 l. Mail van and eight horses; 4 l. Chariot. VERT: 10 l. Horseman and Globe.

174 Dr. Cretzulescu 175 Rugby Player

1944. Cent of Medical Teaching in Rumania.

1637 **174** 35 l. + 65 l. blue 90 90

1944. 30th Anniv of Foundation of National Rugby Football Association.

1638 **175** 16 l. + 184 l. red . . . . 3·25 4·25

176 Stefan Tomsa Church, Radaseni 177 Fruit Pickers

1944. Cultural Fund. Town of Radaseni. Inscr "RADASENI".

1639 **176** 5 l. + 145 l. blue 60 85
1640 – 12 l. + 138 l. red 60 85
1641 **177** 15 l. + 135 l. orange . . 60 85
1642 – 32 l. + 118 l. brown . . . 60 85

DESIGNS—HORIZ: 12 l. Agricultural Institution; 32 l. School.

178 Queen Helen 179 King Michael and Carol I Foundation, Bucharest

1945. Red Cross Relief Fund. Portrait in black on yellow and Cross in red.

1643 **178** 4 l. 50 + 5 l. 50 violet . 15 20
1644 10 l. + 40 l. brown . . 25 30
1645 15 l. + 75 l. blue . . . 40 50
1646 20 l. + 80 l. red 95 75

1945. King Carol I Foundation Fund.

1647 **179** 20 l. + 180 l. orange . . 25 30
1648 25 l. + 175 l. slate . . . 25 30
1649 35 l. + 165 l. brown . . 25 30
1650 76 l. + 125 l. violet . . 25 30

180 A. Saguna 181 A Muresanu

1945. Liberation of Northern Transylvania. Inscr "1944".

1652 **180** 25 b. red 50 50
1653 **181** 50 b. orange 15 15
1654 – 4 l. 50 brown 20 20
1655 – 11 l. blue 20 20
1656 – 15 l. green 20 20
1657 – 31 l. violet 20 20
1658 – 35 l. grey 20 20
1659 – 41 l. olive . . . . . . 1·00 1·00
1660 – 55 l. brown 20 20
1661 – 61 l. mauve 20 20
1662 – 75 l. + 75 l. brown . . 40 40

DESIGNS—HORIZ: 4 l. 50, Samuel Micu; 31 l. George Lazar; 55 l. Three Heroes; 61 l. Petru Maior; 75 l. King Ferdinand and King Michael. VERT: 11 l. George Sincai; 15 l. Michael the Brave; 35 l. Avram Iancu; 41 l. Simeon Barnutiu.

182 King Michael 183

184 King Michael 185

1945.

1663 **182** 50 b. grey 10 10
1664 **183** 1 l. brown 10 10
1665 2 l. violet 10 10
1666 **182** 2 l. brown 10 10
1667 **183** 4 l. green 10 10
1668 **184** 5 l. mauve 10 10
1669 **182** 10 l. blue 10 10
1670 10 l. brown 10 10
1671 **183** 10 l. brown 10 10
1672 **182** 15 l. mauve 10 10
1673 20 l. blue 10 10
1674 20 l. lilac 10 10
1675 **184** 20 l. purple 10 10
1676 25 l. red 10 10
1677 35 l. brown 10 10
1678 40 l. red 10 10
1679 **183** 50 l. blue 10 10
1680 55 l. red 10 10
1681 **184** 75 l. green 10 10
1682 **185** 80 l. orange 10 10
1683 80 l. blue 10 10
1684 **182** 80 l. blue 10 10
1685 **185** 100 l. brown 10 10
1686 **182** 137 l. green 15 10
1687 **185** 160 l. green 10 10
1688 160 l. violet 10 10
1689 200 l. green 20 15
1690 200 l. red 10 10
1691 **183** 200 l. red 10 10
1692 **185** 300 l. blue 10 10
1693 360 l. brown 15 10
1694 400 l. violet 10 10
1695 **183** 400 l. red 10 10
1696 **185** 480 l. brown 15 10
1697 **182** 500 l. mauve 15 10
1698 **185** 600 l. green 10 10
1699 **184** 860 l. brown 20 15
1700 **185** 1000 l. green 10 10
1701 **182** 1500 l. green 10 10
1702 **185** 2400 l. lilac 25 10
1703 **183** 1500 l. blue 15 10
1704 **185** 3700 l. blue 25 10
1705 **182** 5000 l. grey 10 10
1706 8000 l. green 25 10
1707 **185** 10000 l. brown 40 20

186 N. Jorga 187 Books and Torch

1945. War Victims' Relief Fund.

1708 – 12 l. + 188 l. blue . . . 65 65
1709 – 16 l. + 184 l. brown . . 65 65
1710 **186** 20 l. + 180 l. brown . . 65 65
1711 – 32 l. + 168 l. red 65 65
1712 – 35 l. + 165 l. blue . . . 65 65
1713 – 36 l. + 164 l. violet . . . 70 80

PORTRAITS: 12 l. I. G. Duca; 16 l. Virgil Madgearu; 32 l. Ilie Pintilie; 35 l. Bernath Andrei; 36 l. Filimon Sarbu.

1945. Charity. 1st Rumanian–Soviet Congress Fund. Inscr "ARLUS".

1715 **187** 20 l. + 80 l. olive 30 30
1716 – 35 l. + 165 l. red 30 30
1717 – 75 l. + 225 l. blue . . . 30 30
1718 – 80 l. + 420 l. brown . . . 30 30

DESIGNS: 35 l. Soviet and Rumanian flags; 75 l. Drawn curtain revealing Kremlin; 80 l. T. Vladimirescu and A. Nevsky.

188 Karl Marx 189 Postman

1945. Trade Union Congress, Bucharest. Perf or imperf.

1720 **188** 75 l. + 425 l. red . . . . 3·00 3·00
1723 75 l. + 425 l. blue . . . 8·50 8·50
1721 – 120 l. + 380 l. blue . . . 3·00 3·00
1724 – 120 l. + 380 l. brown . . 8·50 8·50
1722 – 155 l. + 445 l. brown . . 3·00 3·00
1725 – 155 l. + 445 l. red . . . 8·50 8·50

PORTRAITS: 120 l. Engels; 155 l. Lenin.

1945. Postal Employees. Inscr "MUNCA P.T.T.".

1726 **189** 100 l. brown 50 50
1727 100 l. olive 50 50
1728 – 150 l. brown . . . . . . 1·00 1·00
1729 – 150 l. red . . . . . . 1·00 1·00
1730 – 250 l. olive . . . . . . 1·60 1·60
1731 – 250 l. blue . . . . . . 1·60 1·60
1732 – 500 l. mauve . . . . . . 13·50 13·50

DESIGNS: 150 l. Telegraphist; 250 l. Lineman; 500 l. Post Office, Bucharest.

190 Discus Throwing 192 Agricultural and Industrial Workers

1945. Charity. With shield inscr "O.S.P." Perf or imperf.

1733 **190** 12 l. + 188 l. olive (post) 2·50 2·40
1738 – 12 l. + 188 l. orange . . 2·50 2·40
1734 – 16 l. + 184 l. blue . . . 2·50 2·40
1739 – 16 l. + 184 l. purple . . 2·50 2·40
1735 – 20 l. + 180 l. green . . . 2·50 2·40
1740 – 20 l. + 180 l. violet . . . 2·50 2·40
1736 – 32 l. + 168 l. mauve . . 2·50 2·40
1741 – 32 l. + 168 l. green . . . 2·50 2·40
1737 – 35 l. + 165 l. blue . . . 2·50 2·40
1742 – 35 l. + 165 l. olive . . . 2·50 2·40

1743 – 200 l. + 1000 l. bl (air) . 13·00 15·00

DESIGNS—As T **190**: 16 l. Diving; 20 l. Skiing; 32 l. Volleyball; 35 l. "Sport and work". 36 × 50 mm: 200 l. Airplane and bird.

1945. 1st Anniv of Rumanian Armistice with Russia.

1744 **192** 100 l. + 400 l. red . . . 75 60
1745 – 200 l. + 800 l. blue . . . 75 60

DESIGN: 200 l. King Michael, "Agriculture" and "Industry".

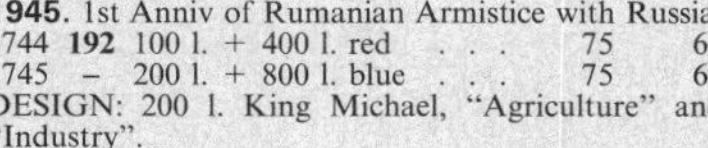

193 T. Vladimirescu 194 Destitute Children

1945. Charity. Patriotic Defence Fund. Inscr "APARAREA PATRIOTICA".

1746 – 20 l. + 580 l. brown . . 10·00 12·50
1747 – 20 l. + 580 l. mauve . . 10·00 12·50
1748 – 40 l. + 560 l. blue . . . 10·00 12·50
1749 – 40 l. + 560 l. green . . . 10·00 12·50
1750 – 55 l. + 545 l. red . . . 10·00 12·50
1751 – 55 l. + 545 l. brown . . 10·00 12·50
1752 **193** 60 l. + 540 l. blue . . . 10·00 12·50
1753 60 l. + 540 l. brown . . 10·00 12·50
1754 – 80 l. + 520 l. red . . . 10·00 12·50
1755 – 80 l. + 520 l. mauve . . 10·00 12·50
1756 – 100 l. + 500 l. green . . 10·00 12·50
1757 – 100 l. + 500 l. brown . . 10·00 12·50

DESIGNS—HORIZ: 20 l. "Political Amnesty"; 40 l. "Military Amnesty"; 55 l. "Agrarian Amnesty"; 100 l. King Michael and "Recontruction". VERT: 80 l. Nicholas Horia.

1945. Child Welfare Fund.

1758 **194** 40 l. blue 20 15

195 I. Ionescu, G. Titeica, A. G. Idachimescu and V. Cristescu

1945. 50th Anniv of Founding of Journal of Mathematics.

1759 **195** 2 l. brown 10 10
1760 – 80 l. grey 60 60

DESIGN: 80 l. Allegory of Learning.

196 Cernavoda Bridge

1945. 50th Anniv of Cernavoda Bridge

1761 **196** 80 l. black 35 25

197 German Electric Train

198

1945. Charity. 16th Congress of Rumanian Engineers. Perf or imperf. (a) Postage.

1762 **197** 10 l. + 490 l. olive . . . 1·40 1·50
1763 10 l. + 490 l. blue . . . 1·40 1·50
1764 – 20 l. + 480 l. brown . . 65 65
1765 – 20 l. + 480 l. violet . . 65 65
1766 – 25 l. + 475 l. purple . . 65 65
1767 – 25 l. + 475 l. green . . 90 1·25
1768 – 55 l. + 445 l. blue . . 65 65
1769 – 55 l. + 445 l. grey . . . 65 65
1770 – 100 l. + 400 l. brown . . 65 65
1771 – 100 l. + 400 l. mauve . . 65 65

(b) Air. Symbolical design as T **198**. Imperf.

1772 **198** 80 l. + 420 l. grey . . . 1·50 1·50
1773 200 l. + 800 l. blue . . 1·50 1·50

DESIGNS—As Type **197**: 20 l. Coats of Arms; 25 l. Arterial road; 55 l. Oil wells; 100 l. "Agriculture".

199 Globe and Clasped Hands

1945. Charity. World Trade Union Congress, Paris. Symbolical designs inscr "CONFERINTA MONDIAL LA SINDICALA DIN-PARIS 25 SEPTEMVRE 1945".

1776 **199** 80 l. + 920 l. mauve . . 17·00 17·00
1777 – 160 l. + 1840 l. brown . 17·00 17·00
1778 – 320 l. + 1680 l. violet . 17·00 17·00
1779 – 440 l. + 2560 l. green . 17·00 17·00

DESIGNS: 160 l. Globe and Dove of Peace; 320 l. Hand and hammer; 440 l. Scaffolding and flags.

1946. Nos 1444/5 surch in figures.

1780 10 l. + 90 l. on 100 l. + 400 l. 95 1·90
1781 10 l. + 90 l. on 200 l. + 800 l. 95 1·90
1782 20 l. + 80 l. on 100 l. + 400 l. 95 1·90
1783 20 l. + 80 l. on 200 l. + 800 l. 95 1·90
1784 80 l. + 120 l. on 100 l. + 400 l. 95 1·90

1785 80 l. + 120 l. on 200 l. + 800 l. 95 1·90
1786 100 l. + 150 l. on 100 l. + 400 l. 95 1·90
1787 100 l. + 150 l. on 200 l. + 800 l. 95 1·90

200 Sower

201 Distribution of Title Deeds

1946. Agrarian Reform. Inscr "REFORMA AGRARA".
1788 – 80 l. blue 20 20
1789 **200** 50 l. + 450 l. red 20 20
1790 **201** 100 l. + 900 l. purple . . 20 20
1791 – 200 l. + 800 l. orange . . 20 20
1792 – 400 l. + 1600 l. green . . 25 25
DESIGNS—VERT: 80 l. Blacksmith and ploughman. HORIZ: 200 l. Ox-drawn farm wagon; 400 l. Plough and tractor.

202

1946. 25th Anniv of Philharmonic Orchestra.
1794 **202** 10 l. blue 10 10
1795 – 20 l. brown 10 10
1796 – 55 l. green 10 10
1797 – 80 l. violet 20 15
1798 – 160 l. orange 10 10
1799 **202** 200 l. + 800 l. red . . . 1·00 1·00
1800 – 350 l. + 1650 l. blue . . 1·25 1·25
DESIGNS: 20 l., 55 l., 160 l. "XXV" and musical score; 80 l., 350 l. G. Enescu.

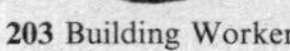

203 Building Worker **205** Sower

1946. Labour Day. Designs of workers inscr "ZIUA MUNCII".
1803 **203** 10 l. red 10 10
1804 10 l. green 40 50
1805 20 l. blue 40 50
1806 20 l. brown 10 10
1807 200 l. red 15 15

1946. Youth Issue.
1809 **205** 10 l. + 100 l. red & brn . 10 10
1810 – 10 l. + 200 l. pur & blue 1·50 1·50
1811 – 80 l. + 200 l. brn & pur 10 10
1812 – 80 l. + 300 l. mve & brn 10 10
1813 – 200 l. + 400 l. red & grn 15 15
DESIGNS: No. 1810, Hurdling; No. 1811, Student; No. 1812, Worker and factory; No. 1813, Marching with flag.

206 Aviator and Aeroplanes **207** Football

1946. Air. Youth Issue.
1814 – 200 l. blue and green . . 3·00 3·00
1815 **206** 500 l. blue and orange . . 3·00 3·00
DESIGN: 200 l. Aeroplane grounded.

1946. Sports, designs inscr "O.S.P." Perf or imperf.
1816 **207** 10 l. blue (postage) . . . 30 30
1817 – 20 l. red 30 30
1818 – 50 l. violet 30 30
1819 – 80 l. brown 30 30
1820 – 160 l. + 1340 l. green . . 30 30
1821 – 300 l. red (air) . . . . . 90 1·50
1822 – 300 l. + 1200 l. blue . . 90 1·50
DESIGNS: 20 l. Diving; 50 l. Running; 80 l. Mountaineering; 160 l. Ski-jumping; 300 l., 300 l. + 1200 l. Flying.

208 "Traditional Ties" **209** Banat Girl holding Distaff

1946. Rumanian–Soviet Friendship Pact.
1824 **208** 80 l. brown 10 10
1825 – 100 l. blue 10 10
1826 – 300 l. grey 10 10
1827 – 300 l. + 1200 l. red . . 60 60
DESIGNS: 100 l. "Cultural ties"; 300 l. "Economic ties"; 300 l. + 1200 l. Dove.
No. 1827 also exists imperf.

1946. Charity. Women's Democratic Federation.
1829 – 80 l. olive 10 10
1830 **209** 80 l. + 320 l. red . . . 15 15
1831 – 140 l. + 360 l. orange . 15 15
1832 – 300 l. + 450 l. green . . 20 20
1833 – 600 l. + 900 l. blue . . 35 30
DESIGNS: 80 l. Girl and handloom; 140 l. Wallachian girl and wheatsheaf; 300 l. Transylvanian horsewoman; 600 l. Moldavian girl carrying water.

211 King Michael and Food Transport

1947. Social Relief Fund.
1845 – 300 l. olive 15 15
1846 **211** 600 l. mauve 20 20
1847 – 1500 l. + 3500 l. orange 20 20
1848 – 3700 l. + 5300 l. violet . 20 20
DESIGNS—VERT: 300 l. Loaf of bread and hungry child; 1500 l. Angel bringing food and clothing to destitute people; 3700 l. Loaf of bread and starving family.

213 King Michael and Chariot **214** Symbols of Labour and Clasped Hands

1947. Peace.
1850 **213** 300 l. purple 20 20
1851 – 600 l. brown 20 20
1852 – 3000 l. blue 20 20
1853 – 7200 l. green 20 20
DESIGNS—VERT: 600 l. Winged figure of Peace; 300 l. Flags of four Allied Nations; 7200 l. Dove of Peace.

1947. Trades Union Congress.
1854 **214** 200 l. blue (postage) . . 45 45
1855 300 l. orange 45 45
1856 600 l. red 45 45
1857 – 1100 l. blue (air) 85 85
DESIGN—22 × 37mm: 1100 l. As Type **214** with Lockheed Super Electra airplane at top.

216 Worker and Torch **219** King Michael

1947. Air. Trades Union Congress. Imperf.
1858 **216** 300 l. + 7000 l. brown . 85 85

1947.
1865 **219** 1000 l. blue 15 10
1869 3000 l. blue 20 10
1866 5500 l. green 25 10
1870 7200 l. mauve 20 10
1871 15000 l. blue 30 10
1867 20000 l. brown 40 20
1872 21000 l. mauve 30 20
1873 36000 l. violet 60 25
1868 50000 l. orange 70 25
Nos. 1865/8 are size $18 \times 21\frac{1}{2}$ mm and Nos. 1869/73 are 25 × 30mm.

218 Symbolical of "Learning"

1947. Charity. People's Culture.
1859 – 200 l. + 200 l. blue . . . 10 15
1860 – 300 l. + 300 l. brown . . 10 15
1861 – 600 l. + 600 l. green . . 10 15
1862 – 1200 l. + 1200 l. blue . . 10 15
1863 **218** 1500 l. + 1500 l. red . . 10 15
DESIGNS—HORIZ: 200 l. Boys' reading class; 300 l. Girls' school; 600 l. Engineering classroom; 1200 l. School building.

220 N. Grigorescu **221** Lisunov Li-2 over Land

1947. Charity. Institute of Rumanian–Soviet Studies.
1874 – 1500 l. + 1500 l. purple (postage) 20 20
1875 – 1500 l. + 1500 l. orange . 20 20
1876 – 1500 l. + 1500 l. green . . 20 20
1877 **220** 1500 l. + 1500 l. blue . . 20 20
1878 – 1500 l. + 1500 l. blue . . 20 20
1879 – 1500 l. + 1500 l. lake . . 20 20
1880 – 1500 l. + 1500 l. red . . 20 20
1881 – 1500 l. + 1500 l. brown . 20 20
1882 **221** 15000 l. + 15000 l. green (air) 60 75
PORTRAITS: No. 1874, Petru Movila; No. 1875, V. Babes; No. 1876, M. Eminescu; No. 1878, P. Tchaikovsky; No. 1879, M. Lomonosov; No. 1880, A. Pushkin; No. 1881, I. Y. Repin.
No. 1882 is imperf.

222 Miner **224** Lockheed Super Electra over Black Sea

1947. Charity. Labour Day.
1883 **222** 1000 l. + 1000 l. olive . . 25 30
1884 – 1500 l. + 1500 l. brown . 20 25
1885 – 2000 l. + 2000 l. blue . . 20 25
1886 – 2500 l. + 2500 l. mauve . 20 25
1887 – 3000 l. + 3000 l. red . . 25 30
DESIGNS: 1500 l. Peasant; 2000 l. Peasant woman; 2500 l. Intellectual; 3000 l. Factory worker.

1947. Air. Labour Day.
1888 – 3000 l. red 30 25
1889 – 3000 l. green 30 25
1890 – 3000 l. brown 30 25
1891 **224** 3000 l. + 12,000 l. bl . . 30 25
DESIGNS—$24\frac{1}{2} \times 30$ mm: No. 1888, Four parachutes; No. 1889, Air Force Monument; No. 1890, Douglas DC-4 over landscape.

(New currency 1 (new) leu = 100 (old) lei.)

225 King Michael and Timber Barges **227**

1947. Designs with medallion portrait of King Michael.
1892 – 50 b. orange 10 10
1893 **225** 1 l. brown 10 10
1894 – 2 l. blue 10 10
1895 – 3 l. red 20 10
1896 – 5 l. blue 20 10
1897 – 10 l. blue 40 10
1898 – 12 l. violet 60 20
1899 – 15 l. blue . . . . . . 1·00 20
1900 – 20 l. brown . . . . . 1·60 25
1901 – 32 l. brown . . . . . 4·75 2·25
1902 – 36 l. lake . . . . . . 4·00 1·60
DESIGNS: 50 b. Harvesting; 2 l. River Danube; 3 l. Reshitza Industries; 5 l. Curtea de Arges Cathedral; 10 l. Royal Palace, Bucharest; 12, 36 l. Cernavoda Bridge; 15, 32 l. Port of Constantza; 20 l. Oil Wells, Prahova.

1947. Balkan Games. Surch **2 + 3 LEI C.B.A. 1947** and bar.
1903 **219** 2 + 3 l. on 36,000 l. vio 90 90

1947. 17th Congress of General Assn of Rumanian Engineers. With monogram as in T **227**.
1904 **227** 1 l. + 1 l. red (post) . . 10 10
1905 – 2 l. + 2 l. brown 10 10
1906 – 3 l. + 3 l. violet 20 20
1907 – 4 l. + 4 l. olive 20 20
1908 – 5 l. + 5 l. blue (air) . . 55 55
DESIGNS: 2 l. Sawmill; 3 l. Refinery; 4 l. Steel mill; 5 l. Gliders over mountains.

1947. Charity, Soviet–Rumanian Amity. As No. 1896 surch **ARLUS 1-7 XI 1947 + 5**. Imperf.
1909 **5** l. + 5 l. blue 85 50

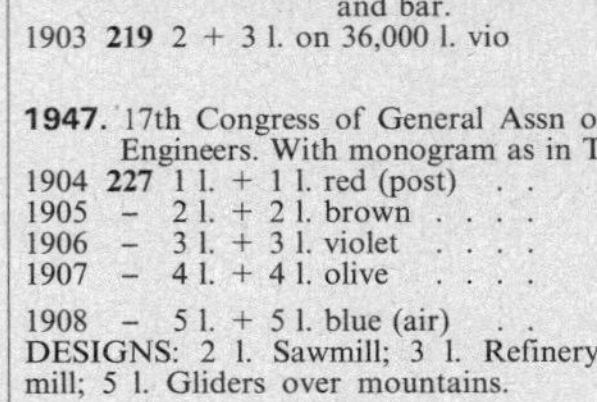

229 Beehive **230** Food Convoy

1947. Savings Day.
1910 **229** 12 l. red 15 15

1947. Patriotic Defence.
1911 **230** 1 l. + 1 l. blue 15 15
1912 – 2 l. + 2 l. brown 15 15
1913 – 3 l. + 3 l. red 15 15
1914 – 4 l. + 4 l. blue 20 20
1915 – 5 l. + 5 l. red 35 35
SYMBOLIC DESIGNS—HORIZ: 2 l. Soldiers' parcels; 3 l. Modern hospital; 4 l. Hungry children. VERT: 5 l. Manacled wrist and flag.

231 Allegory of work

1947. Charity. Trades Union Congress, Bucharest. Inscr "C.G.M. 1947".
1916 – 2 l. + 10 l. red (post) . . 15 15
1917 **231** 7 l. + 10 l. black 20 20
1918 – 11 l. red and blue (air) . . 40 40
DESIGNS—As T **231**: 2 l. Industrial and agricultural workers. 23 × 18 mm: 11 l. Lisunov Li-2 airplane over demonstration.

233 Map of Rumania

1948. Census of 1948.
1925 **233** 12 l. blue 25 15

234 Printing Works and Press **235** Discus Thrower

1948. 75th Anniv of Rumanian State Stamp Printing Works.
1926 **234** 6 l. violet . . . . 1·25 75
1927 7 l. 50 green 65 10

1948. Balkan Games, 1947. Inscr as in T **235**. Imperf or perf.
1928 **235** 1 l. + 1 l. brown (post) . 50 50
1929 – 2 l. + 2 l. red 65 65
1930 – 5 l. + 5 l. blue . . . . . 1·00 1·00
1931 – 7 l. + 7 l. violet (air) . . 1·00 75
1932 – 10 l. + 10 l. green . . . . 1·50 1·00
DESIGNS: 2 l. Runner; 5 l. Heads of two young athletes; 7, 10 l. Airplane over running track.

1948. Nos. 1892/1902 optd **RPR** (Republica Populara Romana).
1933 50 b. orange 25 20
1934 1 l. brown 15 10
1935 2 l. blue 70 15
1936 3 l. red 85 15
1937 5 l. blue . . . . 1·40 15
1938 10 l. blue . . . . 1·60 15
1939 12 l. violet . . . . 2·00 30
1940 15 l. blue . . . . 2·00 40
1941 20 l. brown . . . . 1·75 30
1942 32 l. brown . . . . 8·50 3·75
1943 36 l. lake . . . . 6·50 2·50

237 Industrial Worker

1948. Young Workers' Union. Imperf or perf.
1954 **237** 2 l. + 2 l. blue (post) . . 40 40
1955 – 3 l. + 3 l. green 35 25
1956 – 5 l. + 5 l. brown 40 30
1957 – 8 l. + 8 l. red 45 40

1958 – 12 l. + 12 l. blue (air) . 1·40 90
DESIGNS—As Type **237**: 3 l. Peasant girl and wheatsheaf; 5 l. Student and book. TRIANGULAR: 8 l. Youths bearing Filimon Sarbu banner. 36×23 mm: 12 l. Airplane and swallows.

240 "Friendship"

241 "New Constitution"

1948. Rumanian–Bulgarian Amity.
1959 **240** 32 l. brown . . . . . . 1·00 20

1948. New Constitution.
1960 **241** 1 l. red 30 20
1961 2 l. orange 65 50
1962 12 l. blue . . . . 2·00 80

242 Globe and Banner

243 Aviator and Heinkel He 116A

1948. Labour Day.
1963 **242** 8 l. + 8 l. red (postage) . 1·50 2·50
1964 – 10 l. + 10 l. green . . . 2·50 3·25
1965 – 12 l. + 12 l. brown . . . 3·25 4·25

1966 **243** 20 l. + 20 l. blue (air) . 5·25 5·75
DESIGNS—HORIZ: 10 l. Peasants and mountains. VERT: 12 l. Worker and factory.

244 Barbed Wire Entanglement

1948. Army Day.
1967 – 1 l. 50 + 1 l. 50 red (postage) 35 35
1968 **244** 2 l. + 2 l. purple 35 35
1969 – 4 l. + 4 l. brown 70 70
1970 – 7 l. 50 + 7 l. 50 black . 1·40 1·40
1971 – 8 l. + 8 l. violet . . . . 1·50 1·50

1972 – 3 l. + 3 l. blue (air) . . . 5·50 5·50
1973 – 5 l. + 5 l. blue . . . . 8·00 8·00
DESIGNS—VERT: 1 l. 50, Infantry; 3 l. Ilyushin Stormovik fighter; 5 l. Petlyakov Pe-2 dive bomber. HORIZ: 4 l. Artillery; 7 l. 50, Tank; 8 l. Destroyer.

245 Five Portraits

246 Proclamation of Islaz

1948. Cent of 1848 Revolution. Dated "1848 1948".
1974 – 2 l. + 2 l. purple 35 30
1975 **245** 5 l. + 5 l. violet 45 40
1976 **246** 11 l. red 60 15
1977 – 10 l. + 10 l. green . . . 60 60
1978 – 36 l. + 18 l. blue . . . . 1·90 1·50
DESIGS—22×38 mm. HORIZ: 10 l. Balcescu, Petofi, Iancu, Barnutiu Baritiu and Murcu. VERT: 2 l. Nicolas Balcescu; 36 l. Balcescu, Kogalniceanu, Alecsandri and Cuza.

247 Emblem of Republic

1948.
2023 **247** 50 b. red 50 50
1980 0.50 l. red 40 40
1981 1 l. brown 15 10
1982 2 l. green 20 10
1983 3 l. grey 35 10
1984 4 l. brown 30 10
1985 5 l. blue 30 10
2028 5 l. violet 60 10
1986 10 l. blue . . . . 1·40 15
No. 2023 is inscribed "BANI 0.50" (=½ bani) and in No. 1980 this was corrected to "LEI 0.50".

248 Monimoa Gliders

249 Yachts

1948. Air Force and Navy Day. (a) Air Force (vert).
1987 **248** 2 l. + 2 l. blue . . . . 1·25 1·25
1988 – 5 l. + 5 l. violet . . . . 1·25 1·25
1989 – 8 l. + 8 l. red . . . . 1·90 1·90
1990 – 10 l. + 10 l. brown . . . 2·50 2·50

(b) Navy (horiz).
1991 **249** 2 l. + 2 l. green . . . . 1·25 1·25
1992 – 5 l. + 5 l. grey . . . . 1·25 1·25
1993 – 8 l. + 8 l. blue . . . . 1·90 1·90
1994 – 10 l. + 10 l. red . . . . 2·50 2·50
DESIGNS—AIR FORCE. 5 l. Vlaicu's No. 1 "Crazy Fly"; 8 l. Lisunov Li-2 airplane and tractor; 10 l. Lisunov Li 2 airplane. NAVY. 5 l. "Mircea" (cadet ship) 1882; 8 l. "Romana Mare" (Danube river steamer); 10 l. "Transylvania" (liner).

1948. Surch.
1995 **240** 31 l. on 32 l. brown . . 60 20

251 Newspapers and Torch

252 Soviet Soldiers' Monument

1948. Press Week. Imperf or perf.
1996 **251** 5 l. + 5 l. red 20 10
1997 10 l. brown 65 65
1998 – 10 l. + 10 l. violet . . . 1·00 1·00
1999 – 15 l. + 15 l. blue . . . 1·40 1·40
DESIGNS—HORIZ: 10 l. (No. 1998), Flag, torch and ink-well. VERT: 15 l. Alexander Sahia (journalist).

1948. Rumanian–Russian Amity.
2000 **252** 10 l. red (postage) . . . 65 65
2001 – 10 l. + 10 l. green . . . 2·75 2·75
2002 – 15 l. + 15 l. blue . . . 3·25 3·25

2003 – 20 l. + 20 l. blue (air) . . 9·75 6·00
DESIGNS—VERT: 10 l. (No. 2001), Badge of Arlus; 15 l. Kremlin. HORIZ: 20 l. Twin-engined aircraft.

255 Emblem of Republic

1948. Air. Designs showing aircraft.
2004 **255** 30 l. red 50 10
2005 – 50 l. green 75 25
2006 – 100 l. blue . . . . . . 4·00 3·25
DESIGNS: 50 l. Workers in a field; 100 l. Forms of transport (steam train, liner, etc.).

256 Lorry

1948. Work on Communications.
2007 – 1 l. + 1 l. black & green 60 60
2008 **256** 3 l. + 3 l. black & brown 70 60
2009 – 11 l. + 11 l. black & blue 2·75 2·10
2010 – 15 l. + 15 l. black & red 5·50 3·75
DESIGNS: 1 l. Dockers loading freighter; 11 l. Lisunov Li-2 airplane; 15 l. Steam train.

257 Nicolas Balcescu

258 Hands breaking Chain

1948.
2012 **257** 20 l. red 65 15

1948. 1st Anniv of People's Republic.
2013 **258** 5 l. red 25 15

259 Runners

260 Lenin

1948. National Sports Organization. Imperf or perf.
2014 **259** 5 l. + 5 l. green (postage) 3·25 3·25
2017 5 l. + 5 l. brown . . . 3·25 3·25
2015 – 10 l. + 10 l. violet . . . 5·00 5·00
2018 – 10 l. + 10 l. red . . . 5·00 5·00

2016 – 20 l. + 20 l. blue (air) . . 17·00 17·00
2019 – 20 l. + 20 l. green . . . 17·00 17·00
DESIGNS—HORIZ: 10 l. Parade of athletes with flags. VERT: 20 l. Boy flying model airplane.

1949. 25th Death Anniv of Lenin. Perf or imperf.
2020 **260** 20 l. black 30 15

261 Dancers

1949. 90th Anniv of Union of Rumanian Principalities.
2021 **261** 10 l. blue 40 15

262 I. C. Frimu and Revolutionaries

263 Pushkin

1949. 30th Death Anniv of I. C. Frimu. Perf or imperf.
2022 **262** 20 l. red 30 15

1949. 150th Birth Anniv of A. S. Pushkin (Russian poet).
2030 **263** 11 l. red 75 15
2031 30 l. green 90 25

264 Globe and Posthorn

265 Forms of Transport

1949. 75th Anniv of U.P.U.
2032 **264** 20 l. brown . . . . 1·75 1·75
2033 **265** 30 l. blue . . . . 3·25 3·25

266 Russians entering Bucharest

1949. 5th Anniv of Russian Army's Entry into Bucharest. Perf or imperf.
2034 **266** 50 l. brown on green . . 85 60

267 "Rumanian–Soviet Amity"

1949. Rumanian–Soviet Friendship Week. Perf or imperf.
2035 **267** 20 l. red 65 40

268 Forms of Transport

269 Joseph Stalin

1949. International Congress of Transport Unions. Perf or imperf.
2036 **268** 11 l. blue . . . . 1·10 1·00
2037 20 l. red . . . . 1·40 1·25

1949. Stalin's 70th Birthday. Perf or imperf.
2038 **269** 31 l. black 35 15

270 "The Third Letter"

271 Michael Eminescu

1950. Birth Centenary of Eminescu (poet).
2040 **270** 11 l. green . . . . 1·00 20
2041 – 11 l. brown . . . . 1·75 45
2042 – 11 l. red . . . . 1·00 20
2043 – 11 l. violet . . . . 1·00 20
2044 **271** 11 l. blue . . . . 1·00 25
DESIGNS (Scenes representing poems): No. 2041, "Angel and Demon"; No. 2042, "Ruler and Proletariat"; No. 2043, "Life".

272 "Dragaica Fair"

1950. Birth Centenary of Andreescu (painter).

(a) Perf.
2045 **272** 5 l. olive . . . . 1·00 50
2047 – 20 l. brown . . . . . . 1·75 90

(b) Perf or imperf.
2046 – 11 l. blue . . . . 1·50 65
DESIGNS—VERT: 11 l. I. Andreescu. HORIZ: 20 l. "The Village Well".

273 Factory and Graph

274 Worker and Flag

1950. State Plan, 1950. Inscr "PLANUL DU STAT 1950".
2048 **273** 11 l. red 30 15
2049 – 31 l. violet . . . . 1·00 50
DESIGN: 31 l. Tractor and factories.
No. 2048 exists imperf.

1950. Labour Day. Perf or imperf.
2050 **274** 31 l. orange 35 10

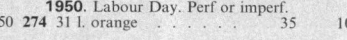

275 Emblem of Republic

276 Trumpeter and Drummer

1950.
2051 **275** 50 b. black 20 15
2052 1 l. red 10 10
2053 2 l. grey 10 10
2054 3 l. purple 15 10
2055 4 l. mauve 10 10

2056 **275** 5 l. red 15 10
2057 6 l. green 15 10
2058 7 l. brown 20 10
2059 7 l. 50 blue 25 10
2060 10 l. brown 65 10
2061 11 l. red 65 10
2062 15 l. blue 35 10
2063 20 l. green 35 10
2064 31 l. green 50 10
2065 36 l. brown . . . . . . 1·40 45

For stamps as Type **275** but with inscriptions in white, see Nos. 2240, etc., and Nos. 2277/8.

1950. 1st Anniv of Rumanian Pioneers Organization.
2074 **276** 8 l. blue . . . . 1·40 45
2075 – 11 l. purple . . . . . . 1·75 1·00
2076 – 31 l. red . . . . 3·00 2·00
DESIGNS: 11 l. Children reading; 31 l. Youth parade.

277 Engineer

278 A. Vlaicu and No. 1 "Crazy Fly"

1950. Industrial Nationalization.
2077 **277** 11 l. red 35 25
2078 11 l. blue 80 15
2079 11 l. brown 80 25
2080 11 l. olive 35 10

1950. 40th Anniv of 1st Flight by Aurel Vlaicu.
2081 **278** 3 l. green 45 10
2082 6 l. blue 50 15
2083 8 l. blue 60 20

279 Mother and Child

1950. Peace Congress, Bucharest.
2084 **279** 11 l. red 20 15
2085 – 20 l. brown 25 15
DESIGN: 20 l. Lathe operator.

280 Statue and Flags

282 Young People and Badge

1950. Rumanian–Soviet Amity.
2086 **280** 30 l. brown 65 15

1950. Rumanian–Hungarian Amity. Optd **TRAIASCA PRIETENIA ROMANO-MAGHIARA!**.
2087 **275** 15 l. blue 85 20

1950. G. M. A. Complex Sports Facilities. Designs incorporating badge.
2088 – 3 l. red . . . . 1·40 1·40
2089 **282** 5 l. brown . . . . 1·00 1·00
2090 5 l. blue . . . . 1·00 1·00
2091 – 11 l. green . . . . 1·00 1·00
2092 – 31 l. olive . . . . 2·40 2·40
DESIGNS: 3 l. Agriculture and Industry; 11 l. Runners; 31 l. Gymnasts.

283

284 Ski-jumper

1950. 3rd Congress of "ARLUS".
2093 **283** 11 l. red 30 20
2094 11 l. blue 30 20

1951. Winter Sports.
2095 **284** 4 l. brown . . . . 1·00 15
2096 – 5 l. red . . . . 1·40 25
2097 – 11 l. blue . . . . 2·00 25
2098 – 20 l. brown . . . . . . 2·00 1·40
2099 – 31 l. green . . . . 3·25 1·50
DESIGNS: 5 l. Skater; 11 l. Skier; 20 l. Ice-hockey; 31 l. Tobogganing.

286 Peasant and Tractor

1951. Agricultural and Industrial Exhibition.
2100 – 11 l. brown 20 10
2101 **286** 31 l. blue 65 20
DESIGN—VERT: 11 l. Engineer and machine.

287 Star of the Republic

288 Youth Camp

1951. Orders and Medals. Perf or imperf.
2102 – 2 l. grey 20 15
2103 – 4 l. blue 25 20
2104 – 11 l. red 40 30
2105 **287** 35 l. brown 60 45
DESIGNS: 2 l. Medal of Work; 4 l. As Type **287** but with different centre to star and with ribbon at top; 11 l. Order of Work.

1951. 2nd Anniv of Rumanian Pioneer Organization.
2106 **288** 1 l. green . . . . 1·00 65
2107 – 11 l. blue . . . . 1·00 65
2108 – 35 l. red . . . . 1·40 1·00
DESIGNS—VERT: 11 l. Children meeting Stalin. HORIZ: 35 l. Decorating boy on parade.

289 Woman and Flags

290 Ion Negulici

1951. International Women's Day. Perf or imperf.
2109 **289** 11 l. brown 25 10

1951. Death Centenary of Negulici (painter).
2110 **290** 35 l. red . . . . 3·00 2·40

291 Cyclists

292 F. Sarbu

1951. Rumanian Cycle Race.
2111 **291** 11 l. brown . . . . 1·90 75

1951. 10th Death Anniv of Sarbu (patriot).
2112 **292** 11 l. brown 30 15

293 "Revolutionary Rumania"

294 Students

1951. Death Centenary of Rosenthal (painter).
2113 **293** 11 l. green . . . . . . 1·60 50
2114 11 l. orange . . . . . . 1·60 65
2115 – 11 l. brown . . . . . . 1·60 50
2116 – 11 l. violet . . . . . . 1·60 65
DESIGN—VERT: Nos 2115/16, Portrait of a woman.

1951. 3rd World Youth Festival, Berlin.
2117 **294** 1 l. red 35 20
2118 – 5 l. blue 65 20
2119 – 11 l. purple 95 45
DESIGNS: 5 l. Girl, boy and flag; 11 l. Young people around globe.

295 "Scanteia" Building

296 Soldier and Pithead

1951. 20th Anniv of "Scanteia" (Communist newspaper).
2120 **295** 11 l. blue 65 20

1951. Miners' Day.
2121 **96** 5 l. blue 40 20
2122 – 11 l. mauve 75 15
DESIGN: 11 l. Miner and pithead.

297 Order of Defence

298 Oil Refinery

1951. Liberation Day.
2123 **297** 10 l. red 35 20

1951. Five-Year Plan. Dated "1951 1955".
2124 **295** 1 l. olive (postage) . . . 20 10
2125 – 2 l. red 30 15
2126 – 3 l. red 55 25
2127 – 4 l. brown 35 15
2128 – 5 l. green 55 10
2129 – 6 l. blue . . . . 1·60 1·00
2130 – 7 l. green . . . . 1·00 35
2131 – 8 l. brown 65 25
2132 – 11 l. blue 75 10
2133 – 35 l. violet 80 45
2134 – 30 l. green (air) . . . . . 3·25 2·75
2135 – 50 l. brown . . . . 5·00 3·50
DESIGNS: 2 l. Miner and pithead; 3 l. Soldier and pylons; 4 l. Steel furnace; 5 l. Combine-harvester; 6 l. Canal construction; 7 l. Threshing machine; 8 l. Sanatorium; 11 l. Dam and pylons; 30 l. Potato planting; 35 l. Factory; 50 l. Liner, locomotive and Lisunov Li-2 airplane.

299 Orchestra and Dancers

300 Soldier and Arms

1951. Music Festival.
2136 **299** 11 l. brown 45 20
2137 – 11 l. blue (Mixed choir) . 60 40
2138 – 11 l. mauve (Lyre and dove) (vert) 45 25

1951. Army Day.
2139 **300** 11 l. blue 40 10

301 Arms of U.S.S.R. and Rumania

302 P. Tcancenco

1951. Rumanian–Soviet Friendship.
2140 **301** 4 l. brown on buff . . . 20 20
2141 35 l. orange 65 65

1951. 25th Death Anniv of Tcancenco (revolutionary).
2142 **302** 10 l. olive 65 15

303 Open Book "1907"

304 I. L. Caragiale

1952. Birth Centenary of Caragiale (writer). (a) Unissued values surch.
2143 **303** 20 b. on 11 l. red . . . . 1·10 60
2144 – 55 b. on 11 l. green . . . 1·50 75
2145 **304** 75 b. on 11 l. blue . . . 2·50 90

(b) Without surch.
2146 **303** 55 b. red . . . . 2·75 40
2147 – 55 b. green . . . . 2·75 40
2148 **304** 55 b. blue . . . . 2·75 40
2149 – 1 l. brown . . . . 4·00 1·60
DESIGNS—HORIZ: Nos. 2144, 2147, Profile of Caragiale; 1 l. Caragiale addressing assembly.

1952. Currency revalued. Surch.
2174 **275** 3 b. on 1 l. red . . . . 1·50 75
2175 3 b. on 2 l. grey . . . . 1·25 65
2176 3 b. on 4 l. mauve . . . 1·50 75
2177 3 b. on 5 l. red . . . . 1·25 65
2178 3 b. on 7 l. 50 blue . . 1·25 75
2179 3 b. on 10 l. brown . . 1·25 65
2157a **255** 3 b. on 30 l. red . . . . 3·75 2·75
2158 – 3 b. on 50 l. (No. 2005) 1·50 75
2159 – 3 b. on 100 l. (No. 2006) 4·00 3·00
2191 **278** 10 b. on 3 l. green . . . 2·40 75
2218 **301** 10 b. on 4 l. brown on buff 2·10 1·10
2192 **278** 10 b. on 6 l. blue . . . 2·40 75
2193 10 b. on 8 l. blue . . . 2·40 75
2220 **302** 10 b. on 10 l. olive . . 2·10 75
2160 **263** 10 b. on 11 l. red . . . 3·75 1·50
2164 **270** 10 b. on 11 l. green . . 3·75 1·50
2165 – 10 b. on 11 l. (No. 2041) 2·75 1·90
2166 – 10 b. on 11 l. (No. 2042) 2·75 1·90
2167 – 10 b. on 11 l. (No. 2043) 2·75 1·90
2168 **271** 10 b. on 11 l. blue . . . 2·75 1·90
2161 **263** 10 b. on 30 l. green . . 3·75 1·50
2219 **301** 10 b. on 35 l. orange . . 2·10 1·10
2199 – 20 b. on 2 l. (No. 2102) 4·25 2·10
2200 – 20 b. on 4 l. (No. 2103) 4·25 2·10
2171 **273** 20 b. on 11 l. red . . . 4·25 2·10
2201 – 20 b. on 11 l. (No. 2104) 4·25 2·10
2194 – 20 b. on 20 l. (No. 2085) 3·00 1·50
2172 – 20 b. on 31 l. (No. 2049) 3·25 1·25
2202 **287** 20 b. on 35 l. brown . . 2·75 1·50
2206 **298** 35 b. on 1 l. olive . . . 1·90 65
2207 – 35 b. on 2 l. (No. 2125) 3·00 3·00
2208 – 35 b. on 3 l. (No. 2126) 3·75 1·90
2209 – 35 b. on 4 l. (No. 2127) 3·00 1·50
2210 – 35 b. on 5 l. (No. 2128) 3·75 3·75
2151 **241** 50 b. on 12 l. blue . . . 1·90 1·25
2180 **275** 55 b. on 50 b. black . . 5·00 1·25
2181 55 b. on 3 l. purple . . 5·00 1·25
2195 – 55 b. on 3 l. (No. 2088) 17·00 11·00
2169 **272** 55 b. on 5 l. olive . . . 9·25 3·00
2204 **295** 55 b. on 5 l. blue . . . 3·00 2·50
2182 **275** 55 b. on 6 l. green . . . 5·00 1·25
2183 55 b. on 7 l. brown . . 5·00 1·25
2188 **276** 55 b. on 8 l. blue . . . 7·50 3·75
2205 **297** 55 b. on 10 l. red . . . 5·00 2·50
2170 – 55 b. on 11 l. (No. 2046) 9·25 3·00
2189 – 55 b. on 11 l. (No. 2075) 5·00 2·50
2150 **233** 55 b. on 12 l. blue . . . 3·75 1·25
2184 **275** 55 b. on 15 l. blue . . . 7·50 1·25
2185 55 b. on 20 l. green . . 5·00 1·25
2196 – 55 b. on 20 l. (No. 2098) 30·00 13·50
2186 **275** 55 b. on 31 l. green . . 5·00 1·25
2173 **274** 55 b. on 31 l. orange . . 4·50 3·00
2190 – 55 b. on 31 l. (No. 2076) 5·00 3·25
2197 – 55 b. on 31 l. (No. 2099) 30·00 13·50
2198 **286** 55 b. on 31 l. blue . . . 5·00 3·25
2203 – 55 b. on 35 l. (No. 2108) 7·50 4·25
2187 **275** 55 b. on 36 l. brown . . 7·50 1·25
2211 – 1 l. on 6 l. (No. 2129) 5·50 2·10
2212 – 1 l. on 7 l. (No. 2130) 5·50 5·50
2213 – 1 l. on 8 l. (No. 2131) 5·50 4·25
2214 – 1 l. on 11 l. (No. 2132) 5·50 2·75
2216 – 1 l. on 30 l. (No. 2134) 9·25 2·10
2215 – 1 l. on 35 l. (No. 2133) 7·50 2·10
2217 – 1 l. on 50 l. (No. 2135) 8·50 4·50
2152 – 1 l. 75 on 2 l. + 2 l. purple (No. 1974) . . . . 13·50 4·50
2153 **245** 1 l. 75 on 5 l. + 5 l. violet 13·50 4·50
2154 **246** 1 l. 75 on 11 l. red . . . 13·50 4·50
2155 – 1 l. 75 on 10 l. + 10 l. (No. 1977) . . . . 13·50 4·50
2156 – 1 l. 75 on 36 l. + 18 l. (No. 1978) . . . . 13·50 4·50

1952. Air. Surch with airplane, **AERIANA** and value.
2162 **264** 3 l. on 20 l. brown . . . 25·00 18·00
2163 **265** 5 l. on 30 l. blue . . . . 32·00 23·00

307 Railwayman

308 Gogol and character from "Taras Bulba"

1952. Railway Day.
2229 **307** 55 b. brown . . . . . . 2·40 30

1952. Death Centenary of Gogol (Russian writer).
2230 **308** 55 b. blue . . . . . . 1·75 15
2231 – 1 l. 75 green . . . . . 3·00 40
DESIGN—VERT: 1 l. 75, Gogol and open book.

309 Maternity Medal

310 I. P. Pavlov

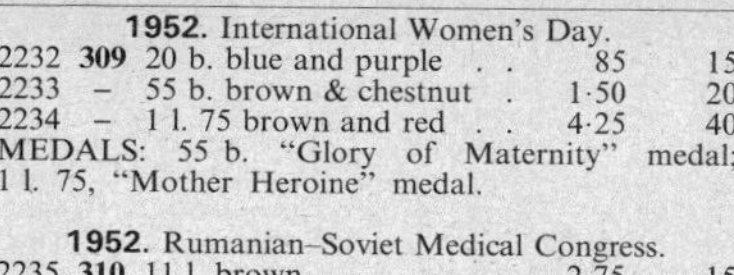

1952. International Women's Day.
2232 **309** 20 b. blue and purple . . 85 15
2233 – 55 b. brown & chestnut . 1·50 20
2234 – 1 l. 75 brown and red . . 4·25 40
MEDALS: 55 b. "Glory of Maternity" medal; 1 l. 75, "Mother Heroine" medal.

1952. Rumanian–Soviet Medical Congress.
2235 **310** 11 l. brown . . . . . . 2·75 15

311 Hammer and Sickle Medal

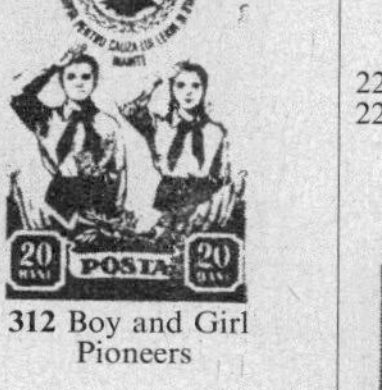

312 Boy and Girl Pioneers

1952. Labour Day.
2236 **311** 55 b. brown . . . . . . 2·40 15

1952. 3rd Anniv of Rumanian Pioneers Organization.
2237 **312** 20 b. brown . . . . . . 1·40 10
2238 – 55 b. green . . . . . . 3·25 15
2239 – 1 l. 75 blue . . . . . . 6·75 30
DESIGNS—VERT: 55 b. Pioneer nature-study group. HORIZ: 1 l. 75, Worker and pioneers.

1952. As T **275** but with figures and inscriptions in white. Bani values size $20\frac{1}{4} \times 24\frac{1}{4}$ mm, lei values size $24\frac{1}{2} \times 29\frac{1}{2}$ mm.
2240 **275** 3 b. orange 40 20
2241 5 b. red 60 10
2242 7 b. green 65 25
2243 10 b. brown 85 10
2244 20 b. blue . . . . . . 1·25 10
2245 35 b. brown . . . . . . 2·40 10
2246 50 b. green . . . . . . 2·50 10
2247 55 b. violet . . . . . . 6·00 10
2248 1 l. 10 brown . . . . . . 5·00 20
2249 1 l. 75 violet . . . . . . 22·00 35
2250 2 l. olive . . . . . . 5·75 25
2251 2 l. 35 brown . . . . . . 6·75 35
2252 2 l. 55 orange . . . . . . 8·25 40
2253 3 l. green . . . . . . 8·75 35
2254 5 l. red . . . . . . 11·00 85
For similar stamps with star added at top of emblem, see Nos. 2277/8.

314 "Smirdan" (after Grigorescu)

315 Leonardo da Vinci

1952. 75th Anniv of Independence.
2255 **314** 50 b. lake . . . . . . 1·00 10
2256 – 1 l. 10 b. blue . . . . . . 1·40 30
DESIGN—HORIZ: 1 l. 10, Rumanian and Russian soldiers.

1952. 500th Anniv of Birth of Leonardo da Vinci.
2257 **315** 55 b. violet . . . . . . 4·75 25

316 Miner

317 Students' Union Badge

1952. Miners' Day.
2258 **316** 20 b. red . . . . . . 2·00 25
2259 55 b. violet . . . . . . 2·00 20

1952. Int Students' Union Council. Bucharest.
2260 **317** 10 b. blue 25 10
2261 – 20 b. orange . . . . . . 2·75 20
2262 – 55 b. green . . . . . . 2·75 15
2263 – 1 l. 75 red . . . . . . 5·00 1·00
DESIGNS—HORIZ: 20 b. Student in laboratory ($35\frac{1}{2} \times 22$ mm). 1 l. 75, Six students dancing, (30×24 mm). VERT: 55 b. Students playing football, (24×30 mm).

318 Soldier, Sailor and Airman

1952. Army Day.
2264 **318** 55 b. blue . . . . . . 1·60 15

319 Statue and Flags

320 Workers and Views of Russia and Rumania (after N. Parlius)

1952. Rumanian-Soviet Friendship.
2265 **319** 55 b. red . . . . . . 1·10 10
2266 **320** 1 l. 75 brown . . . . . . 3·00 30

321 Rowing

322 N. Balcescu (after C. Tattarescu)

1952. Physical Culture.
2267 **321** 20 b. blue . . . . . . 4·00 20
2268 – 1 l. 75 red (Athletes) . . 9·25 90

1952. Death Centenary of Balcescu (revolutionary).
2269 **322** 55 b. grey . . . . . . 3·25 10
2270 1 l. 75 olive . . . . . . 8·25 90

323 Emblem and Flags

324

1952. New Constitution.
2271 **323** 55 b. green . . . . . . 1·60 15

1952. 5th Anniv of People's Republic.
2272 **324** 55 b. multicoloured . . 3·00 30

325 Millo, Caragiale and Mme. Romanescu

326 Foundry Worker

1953. Centenary of Caragiale National Theatre.
2273 **325** 55 b. blue . . . . . . 3·25 15

1953. 3rd Industrial and Agricultural Congress.
2274 **326** 55 b. green . . . . . . 1·00 15
2275 – 55 b. orange 90 30
2276 – 55 b. brown . . . . . . 1·40 15
DESIGNS—HORIZ: No. 2275, Farm workers and tractor; No. 2276, Workman, refinery and oil wells.

1953. As Nos. 2240 etc., but with star added at top of emblem.
2277 **275** 5 b. red 70 10
2278 55 b. purple . . . . . . 1·40 10

327 "The Strikers of Grivitsa" (after Nazarev)

1953. 20th Anniv of Grivitsa Strike.
2279 **327** 55 b. brown . . . . . . 2·75 15

328

1953. 5th Anniv of Treaty of Friendship with Russia.
2280 **328** 55 b. brown on blue . . 2·75 20

329 Table Tennis Badge

330 Oltenian Carpet

1953. 20th World Table Tennis Championship, Bucharest.
2281 **329** 55 b. green . . . . . . 6·75 1·00
2282 55 b. brown . . . . . . 6·75 1·00

1953. Rumanian Art.
2283 – 10 b. green . . . . . . 1·40 10
2284 – 20 b. brown . . . . . . 2·00 10
2285 – 35 b. violet . . . . . . 2·40 15
2286 – 55 b. blue . . . . . . 4·25 10
2287 **330** 1 l. purple . . . . . . 8·25 25
DESIGNS—VERT: 10 b. Pottery; 20 b. Campulung peasant girl; 55 b. Apuseni Mountains peasant girl. HORIZ: 35 b. National dance.

331 Karl Marx

332 Pioneers planting Tree

1953. 70th Death Anniv of Karl Marx.
2288 **331** 1 l. 55 brown . . . . . . 3·25 25

1953. 4th Anniv of Rumanian Pioneer Organization.
2289 **332** 35 b. green . . . . . . 1·60 15
2290 – 55 b. blue . . . . . . 2·00 15
2291 – 1 l. 75 brown . . . . . . 4·75 40
DESIGNS—VERT: 55 b. Boy and girl flying model gliders. HORIZ: 1 l. 75, Pioneers and instructor.

333 Women and Flags

1953. 3rd World Congress of Women.
2292 **333** 55 b. brown . . . . . . 2·00 15

334

335 Cornfield and Forest

1953. 4th World Youth Festival.
2293 **334** 20 b. orange . . . . . . 1·00 10
2294 – 55 b. blue . . . . . . 1·60 10
2295 – 65 b. red . . . . . . 2·40 30
2296 – 1 l. 75 purple . . . . . . 6·75 45
DESIGNS—VERT: 55 b. Students releasing dove over globe. HORIZ: 65 b. Girl presenting bouquet; 1 l. 75, Folk dancers.

1953. Forestry Month.
2297 – 20 b. blue . . . . . . 1·00 15
2298 **335** 38 b. green . . . . . . 3·25 90
2299 – 55 b. brown . . . . . . 4·00 15
DESIGNS—VERT: 20 b. Waterfall and trees; 55 b. Forestry worker.

336 V.V. Mayakovsky

337 Miner

1953. 60th Birth Anniv of Mayakovsky (Russian poet).
2300 **336** 55 b. brown . . . . . . 2·40 20

1953. Miners' Day.
2301 **337** 1 l. 55 black . . . . . . 3·75 20

338 Telephonist, G.P.O. and P.O. Worker

339

1953. 50th Anniv of Construction of G.P.O.
2302 **338** 20 b. brown 25 10
2303 – 55 b. olive 45 10
2304 – 1 l. blue . . . . . . 1·60 15
2305 – 1 l. 55 lake . . . . . . 2·40 35
DESIGNS: 55 b. Postwoman and G.P.O.; 1 l. G.P.O. radio-transmitter and map; 1 l. 55, Telegraphist, G.P.O. and teletypist.

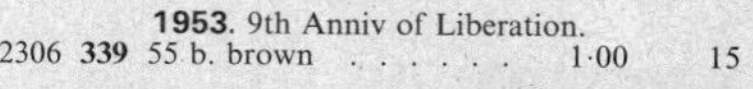

1953. 9th Anniv of Liberation.
2306 **339** 55 b. brown . . . . . . 1·00 15

340 Soldier and Flag

1953. Army Day.
2307 **340** 55 b. olive . . . . . . 1·60 15

341 Girl and Model Glider

1953. Aerial Sports.
2308 **341** 10 b. green and orange . 2·75 25
2309 – 20 b. olive and brown . 5·50 15
2310 – 55 b. purple and red . . 10·00 35
2311 – 1 l. 75 brown & purple . 12·00 75
DESIGNS: 20 b. Parachutists; 55 b. Glider and pilot; 1 l. 75, Monoplane.

342 Workman, Girl and Flags

1953. Rumanian-Soviet Friendship.
2312 **342** 55 b. brown 70 15
2313 – 1 l. 55 lake . . . . . . 2·00 25
DESIGN: 1 l. 55, Spasski Tower and Volga-Don canal.

343 "Unity"

1953. 3rd World Trades' Union Congress.
2314 **343** 55 b. olive 85 15
2315 – 1 l. 25 red . . . . . . 2·00 30
DESIGN—VERT: 1 l. 25, Workers, flags and globe.

344 C. Porumbescu

345 Agricultural Machinery

1953. Birth Centenary of Porumbescu (composer).
2316 **344** 55 b. lilac . . . . . . 8·25 20

1953. Agricultural designs.
2317 **345** 10 b. olive 25 10
2318 – 35 b. green 40 10
2319 – 2 l. 55 brown . . . . . . 4·00 70
DESIGNS: 35 b. Tractor drawing disc harrows; 2 l. 55, Cows grazing

346 A. Vlaicu **347** Lenin

1953. 40th Death Anniv of Vlaicu (pioneer aviator).
2320 **346** 50 b. blue . . . . 1·75 20

1954. 30th Death Anniv of Lenin.
2321 **347** 55 b. brown . . . . . . 2·00 15

348 Red Deer **349** Calimanesti

1954. Forestry Month.
2322 **348** 20 b. brown on yellow . . 3·25 45
2323 – 55 b. violet on yellow . . 2·75 45
2324 – 1 l. 75 blue on yellow . . 4·00 85
DESIGNS: 55 b. Pioneers planting tree; 1 l. 75, Forest.

1954. Workers' Rest Homes.
2325 **349** 5 b. black on yellow . . 40 10
2326 – 1 l. 55 black on blue . . 2·00 15
2327 – 2 l. green on pink . . . . 3·25 20
2328 – 2 l. 35 brown on green . . 3·00 1·00
2329 – 2 l. 55 brown on green . . 4·25 1·40
DESIGNS: 1 l. 55, Siniai; 2 l. Predeal; 2 l. 35, Tusnad; 2 l. 55, Govora.

350 O. Bancila **351** Child and Dove of Peace

1954. 10th Death Anniv of Bancila (painter).
2330 **350** 55 b. green and brown . . 4·00 2·00

1954. International Children's Day.
2331 **351** 55 b. brown . . . . . . 1·60 15

352 Girl Pioneer feeding Calf **353** Stephen the Great

1954. 5th Anniv of Rumanian Pioneer Organization.
2332 **352** 20 b. black 30 15
2333 – 55 b. blue 85 15
2334 – 1 l. 75 red . . . . 2·75 65
DESIGNS: 55 b. Girl Pioneers harvesting; 1 l. 75, Young Pioneers examining globe.

1954. 450th Death Anniv of Stephen the Great.
2335 **353** 55 b. brown . . . . . . 2·75 20

354 Miner operating Coal-cutter **355** Dr. V. Babes

1954. Miners' Day.
2336 **354** 1 l. 75 black . . . . . . 2·75 40

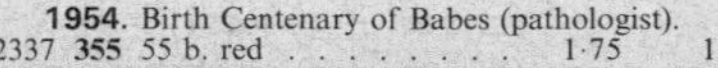

1954. Birth Centenary of Babes (pathologist).
2337 **355** 55 b. red . . . . 1·75 15

356 Sailor and Flag **357** Dedication Tablet

1954. Navy Day.
2338 **356** 55 b. blue . . . . 1·75 20

1954. 5th Anniv of Mutual Aid Organization.
2339 – 20 b. violet 35 15
2340 **357** 55 b. brown 85 15
DESIGN: 20 b. Man receiving money from counter clerk.

358 Liberation Monument **359** Recreation Centre

1954. 10th Anniv of Liberation.
2341 **358** 55 b. lilac and red . . . 1·40 15

1954. Liberation Anniv Celebrations.
2342 **359** 20 b. blue 30 10
2343 – 38 b. violet 90 25
2344 – 55 b. purple . . . . . . 1·00 10
2345 – 1 l. 55 brown . . . . . . 2·40 30
DESIGNS—38 × 22 mm: 55 b. "Scanteia" offices. 24½ × 29½ mm: 38 b. Opera House, Bucharest; 1 l. 55, Radio Station.

360 Airman **361** Chemical Plant and Oil Derricks

1954. Aviation Day.
2346 **360** 55 b. blue . . . . 2·00 15

1954. International Chemical and Petroleum Workers Conference, Bucharest.
2347 **361** 55 b. black . . . . . . 2·40 30

362 Dragon Pillar, Peking **363** T. Neculuta

1954. Chinese Culture Week.
2348 **362** 55 b. black on yellow . . 2·40 30

1954. 50th Death Anniv of Neculuta (poet).
2349 **363** 55 b. violet . . . . . . 2·00 15

364 ARLUS Badge **365** Friendship

1954. 10th Anniv of "ARLUS" and Rumanian-Russian Friendship.
2350 **364** 55 b. red 65 15
2351 **365** 65 b. purple . . . . . . 1·00 20

366 G. Tattarescu **367** B. Iscovescu

1954. 60th Death Anniv of Tattarescu (painter).
2352 **366** 55 b. red . . . . 2·50 15

1954. Death Centenary of Iscovescu (painter).
2353 **367** 1 l. 75 brown . . . . . . 3·25 45

368 Teleprinter **369** Wild Boar

1954. Cent of Telecommunications in Rumania.
2354 **368** 50 b. lilac . . . . 1·50 20

1955. Forestry Month. Inscr "LUNA PADURII 1955".
2355 **369** 35 b. brown . . . . . . 1·60 20
2356 – 65 b. blue . . . . 2·10 25
2357 – 1 l. 20 red . . . . 4·75 50
DESIGNS: 65 b. Tree planting; 1 l. 20, Logging.

370 Airman **371** Clasped Hands

1955. Occupations.
2358 – 3 b. blue 25 10
2359 – 5 b. violet 15 10
2360 **370** 10 b. brown 30 10
2361 – 20 b. mauve 40 10
2362 – 30 b. blue . . . . 1·00 10
2363 – 35 b. turquoise 60 10
2364 – 40 b. blue . . . . 1·40 15
2365 – 55 b. olive . . . . 1·40 10
2366 – 1 l. violet . . . . 2·00 10
2367 – 1 l. 55 lake . . . . . . 3·25 10
2368 – 2 l. 35 buff . . . . . . 4·75 60
2369 – 2 l. 55 green . . . . . . 6·75 40
DESIGNS: 3 b. Scientist; 5 b. Foundryman; 20 b. Miner; 30 b. Tractor driver; 35 b. Schoolboy; 40 b. Girl student; 55 b. Bricklayer; 1 l. Sailor; 1 l. 55, Millgirl; 2 l. 35, Soldier; 2 l. 55, Telegraph linesman.

1955. International Conference of Postal Municipal Workers, Vienna.
2370 **371** 25 b. red 65 20

372 Lenin **373** Dove and Globe

1955. 85th Birth Anniv of Lenin. Portraits of Lenin.
2371 **372** 20 b. brown and bistre . . 65 15
2372 – 55 b. brown (full face) . . 1·40 20
2373 – 1 l. lake and red (half length) . . . . 2·00 25

1955. Peace Congress, Helsinki.
2374 **373** 55 b. blue . . . . 1·60 15

374 War Memorial, Berlin **375** Children and Dove

1955. 10th Anniv of Victory over Germany.
2375 **374** 55 b. blue . . . . 1·40 15

1955. International Children's Day.
2376 **375** 55 b. brown . . . . . . 1·50 15

376 "Service" **377** People's Art Museum

1955. European Volley-ball Championships.
2377 – 55 b. purple on pink . . 5·00 1·00
2378 **376** 1 l. 75 red on yellow . . 11·50 1·00
DESIGN: 55 b. Volley-ball players.

1955. Bucharest Museums.
2379 – 20 b. mauve 25 15
2380 – 55 b. brown 50 15
2381 **377** 1 l. 20 black . . . . . . 1·60 50
2382 – 1 l. 75 green . . . . . . 2·75 50
2383 – 2 l. 55 purple . . . . . . 4·75 65
MUSEUMS—30 × 24½ mm: 20 b. Theodor Aman; 2 l. 55, Simu 34 × 23 mm: 55 b. Lenin-Stalin; 1 l. 75, Republican Art.

378 Mother and Child **379** "Nature Study"

1955. 1st World Mothers' Congress, Lausanne.
2384 **378** 55 b. blue . . . . 1·60 20

1955. 5th Anniv of Pioneer Headquarters, Bucharest.
2385 – 10 b. blue 60 10
2386 **379** 20 b. green . . . . . . 1·40 10
2387 – 55 b. purple . . . . . . 3·00 20
DESIGNS: 10 b. Model railway; 55 b. Headquarters building.

380 Coxed Four **381** A. Pann

1955. Women's European Rowing Championships, Snagov.
2388 **380** 55 b. green . . . . . . 8·25 1·00
2389 – 1 l. blue (Woman sculler) 13·00 1·00

1955. Rumanian Writers.
2390 – 55 b. blue . . . . 1·40 25
2391 – 55 b. grey . . . . 1·40 25
2392 **381** 55 b. olive . . . . . . 1·40 25
2393 – 55 b. violet . . . . . . 1·40 25
2394 – 55 b. purple . . . . . . 1·40 25
PORTRAITS—No. 2390 D. Cantemir; No. 2391 M. Dosoftei; No. 2393 S. C. Cantacuzino; No. 2394 E Vacarescu.

382 Marksman **383** Fire Engine

1955. European Sharpshooting Championships, Bucharest.
2395 **382** 1 l. brown & lt brown . . 6·00 65

1955. Firemen's Day.
2396 **383** 55 b. red . . . . 1·90 25

384 **385** Spraying Fruit Trees

1955. 10th Anniv of W.F.T.U.
2397 **384** 55 b. olive 50 10
2398 – 1 l. blue 85 25
DESIGN: 1 l. Workers and flag.

1955. Fruit and Vegetable Cultivation.
2399 **385** 10 b. green 40 15
2400 – 20 b. red 50 35
2401 – 55 b. blue . . . . 1·60 45
2402 – 1 l. lake . . . . 3·75 1·10
DESIGNS: 20 b. Fruit picking; 55 b. Harvesting grapes; 1 l. Gathering vegetables.

386 **387** Michurin

1955. 4th ARLUS Congress.
2403 **386** 20 b. blue and buff . . . 1·00 15

1955. Birth Cent of Michurin (Russian botanist).
2404 **387** 55 b. blue . . . . 1·60 20

388 Cotton

389 Sheep and Shepherd blowing Bucium

1955.

2405 – 10 b. pur (Sugar beet) . . 45 15
2406 **388** 20 b. grey 85 15
2407 – 55 b. blue (Linseed) . . . 2·10 60
2408 – 1 l. 55 brown (Sunflower) 4·25 1·10

1955.

2409 **389** 5 b. brown and green . . 1·00 15
2410 – 10 b. violet and bistre . . 1·40 15
2411 – 35 b. brown and salmon . 2·75 45
2412 – 55 b. brown and bistre . . 5·00 75
DESIGNS: 10 b. Pigs and farm girl; 35 b. Cows and dairy maid; 55 b. Horses and groom.

390 Schiller

391 Bank and Book

1955. Famous Writers.

2413 – 20 b. blue 25 10
2414 – 55 b. blue . . . . 1·10 15
2415 **390** 1 l. grey . . . . 2·00 20
2416 – 1 l. 55 brown . . . . . 4·00 1·00
2417 – 1 l. 75 violet . . . . . 5·00 1·00
2418 – 2 l. lake . . . . 5·75 1·60
PORTRAITS: 20 b. Hans Andersen; 55 b. Mickiewicz; 1 l. 55, Montesquieu; 1 l. 75, Walt Whitman; 2 l. Cervantes.

1955. Savings Bank.

2419 **391** 55 b. blue . . . . 2·00 25
2420 55 b. violet . . . . 6·75 4·00

392 Family

393 Brown Hare

1956. National Census.

2421 – 55 b. orange 30 10
2422 **392** 1 l. 75 brown and green . 2·00 65
DESIGNS: 55 b. "21 FEBRUARIE 1956" in circle.

1956. Wild Life.

2423 **393** 20 b. black and green . . 2·00 2·00
2424 – 20 b. black and olive . . 2·00 2·00
2425 – 35 b. black and blue . . 2·00 2·00
2426 – 50 b. brown and blue . . 2·00 2·00
2427 – 55 b. green and bistre . . 2·50 2·00
2428 – 55 b. brown & turquoise . 2·50 2·00
2429 – 1 l. lake and green . . . 4·00 4·00
2430 – 1 l. 55 lake and blue . . 4·50 4·50
2431 – 1 l. 75 brown and green . 5·00 5·00
2432 – 2 l. brown and blue . . . 20·00 20·00
2433 – 3 l. 25 black and green . 20·00 20·00
2434 – 4 l. 25 brown & salmon . 20·00 20·00
DESIGNS—VERT: No. 2424, Great bustard; 35 b. Trout; 1 l. 55, Eurasian red squirrel; 1 l. 75, Capercaillie; 4 l. 25, Red deer. HORIZ: 50 b. Wild boar; No. 2427, Ringed-necked pheasant; No. 2428, Brown bear; 1 l. Lynx; 2 l. Chamois; 3 l. 25, Pintail.

See also Nos. 2474/85

394 Insurgents

395 Boy and Globe

1956. 85th Anniv of Paris Commune.

2435 **394** 55 b. red . . . . 1·60 50

1956. International Children's Day.

2436 **395** 55 b. violet . . . . 1·90 20

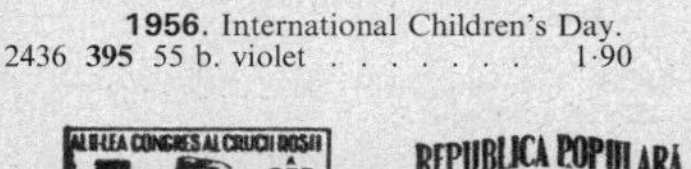

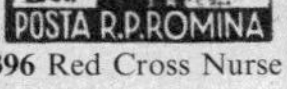
396 Red Cross Nurse

397 Tree

1956. 2nd Rumanian Red Cross Congress.

2437 **396** 55 b. olive and red . . . 2·75 20

1956. Forestry Month.

2438 **397** 20 b. grey on green . . 1·40 20
2439 – 55 b. black on green . . 4·00 30
DESIGN: 55 b. Lumber train.

398 Woman Speaking

399 Academy Buildings

1956. International Women's Congress, Bucharest.

2440 **398** 55 b. green . . . . . . 1·60 20

1956. 90th Anniv of Rumanian People's Academy.

2441 **399** 55 b. green and buff . . 1·60 20

400 Vuia, Vuia No. 1 Biplane and Yakovlev Yak-25 Fighters

1956. 50th Anniv of 1st Flight by Traian Vuia (pioneer airman).

2442 **400** 55 b. brown and olive . 2·00 35

401 Georgescu and Statues

402 Farm Girl

1956. Birth Centenary of Georgescu (sculptor).

2443 **401** 55 b. green & brown . . 2·75 20

1956. Collective Farming (a) Inscr "1951–1956".

2444 **402** 55 b. plum . . . . . . 10·00 10·00

(b) Inscr "1949-1956".

2445 **402** 55 b. plum . . . . . . 1·50 20

403 "Aporia crataegi"

404 Striker

1956. Insect Pests.

2446 **403** 10 b. cream, black and violet . . . . 3·25 30
2447 – 55 b. orange & brown . 5·00 60
2448 – 1 l. 75 lake and olive . . 13·50 10·00
2449 – 1 l. 75 brown and olive . 10·50 1·10
PESTS: 55 b. "Leptinotarsa decemlineata"; 1 l. 75, (2) "Melontha melontha".

1956. 50th Anniv of Dockers Strike at Galatz.

2450 **404** 55 b. brown on pink . . 1·60 20

405

406 Maxim Gorky

1956. 25th Anniv of Newspaper "Scanteia".

2451 **405** 55 b. blue . . . . 1·40 20

1956. 20th Death Anniv of Maxim Gorky.

2452 **406** 55 b. brown . . . . . . 1·40 20

407 T. Aman

408 Snowdrops and Polyanthus

1956. 125th Birth Anniv of Aman (painter).

2453 **407** 55 b. grey . . . . 2·75 65

1956. Flowers. Designs multicoloured. Colours of backgrounds given.

2454 **408** 5 b. blue 55 15
2455 – 55 b. black . . . . . . 2·75 60
2456 – 1 l. 75 blue . . . . . . 6·75 85
2457 – 3 l. green . . . . 10·00 1·25
FLOWERS: 55 b. Daffodil and violets; 1 l. 75, Antirrhinums and campanulas; 3 l. Poppies and lilies of the valley.

409 Janos Hunyadi

410 Olympic Flame

1956. 500th Death Anniv of Hunyadi.

2458 **409** 55 b. violet . . . . . . 2·00 25

1956. Olympic Games.

2459 **410** 20 b. red 65 15
2460 – 55 b. blue . . . . 1·00 20
2461 – 1 l. mauve . . . . . . 2·40 25
2462 – 1 l. 55 turquoise . . . 3·25 30
2463 – 1 l. 75 violet . . . . . 4·25 65
DESIGNS: 55 b. Water-polo; 1 l. Ice-skating; 1 l. 55, Canoeing; 1 l. 75, High-jumping.

411 George Bernard Shaw

412 Ilyushin Il-18 over City

1956. Cultural Anniversaries.

2464 – 20 b. blue (Franklin) . . 30 10
2465 – 35 b. red (Toyo Oda) . . 40 15
2466 **411** 40 b. brown 45 15
2467 – 50 b. brown (I. Franko) . 55 10
2468 – 55 b. olive (Curie) 95 10
2469 – 1 l. turquoise (Ibsen) . . 1·50 15
2470 – 1 l. 55 violet (Dostoevsky) 2·10 15
2471 – 1 l. 75 blue (Heine) . . . 2·75 15
2472 – 2 l. 55 pur (Mozart) . . 3·75 25
2473 – 3 l. 25 blue (Rembrandt) . 4·00 65

1956. Wild Life. As Nos. 2423/34 but colours changed. Imperf.

2474 20 b. brown and green . . . 5·00 5·00
2475 20 b. black and blue . . . . 5·00 5·00
2476 35 b. black and blue . . . . 5·00 5·00
2477 50 b. black and brown . . . 5·00 5·00
2478 55 b. black and violet . . . 5·00 5·00
2479 55 b. brown and green . . . 5·00 5·00
2480 1 l. brown and blue . . . . 5·00 5·00
2481 1 l. 55 brown and bistre . . 5·00 5·00
2482 1 l. 75 purple and green . . 5·00 5·00
2483 2 l. black and blue . . . . 5·00 5·00
2484 3 l. 25 brown and green . . 8·00 8·00
2485 4 l. 25 brown and violet . . 10·00 10·00

1956. Air. Multicoloured designs embodying airplanes and views.

2486 20 b. Type **412** 45 20
2487 55 b. Mountains 95 15
2488 1 l. 75 Cornfield . . . . . 3·00 25
2489 2 l. 55 Seashore . . . . . . 4·00 75

413 Georgi Enescu

414 "Rebels" (after O. Bancila)

1956. 75th Birth Anniv of Enescu (musician).

2490 – 55 b. blue . . . . 1·25 20
2491 **413** 1 l. 75 purple . . . . . 2·75 30
DESIGN: 55 b. Enescu when a child, holding violin.

1957. 50th Anniv of Peasant Revolt.

2492 **414** 55 b. slate . . . . 1·60 20

415 Stephen the Great

416 Dr. G. Marinescu and Institute of Medicine

1957. 500th Anniv of Accession of Stephen the Great.

2493 **415** 55 b. brown . . . . . . 1·40 25
2494 55 b. olive . . . . 1·40 25

1957. National Congress of Medical Sciences, Bucharest and Centenary of Medical and Pharmaceutical Teaching in Bucharest (11.75).

2495 **416** 20 b. green 40 15
2496 – 35 b. brown 50 20
2497 – 55 b. purple . . . . . . 1·00 50
2498 – 1 l. 75 red and blue . . . 4·25 1·60
DESIGNS: 35 b. Dr. I. Cantacuzino and Cantacuzino Institute; 55 b. Dr. V. Babes and Babes Institute; 1 l. 75, (66×23 mm) Drs. N. Kretzulescu and C. Dairla, and Faculty of Medicine, Bucharest.

417 Gymnast and Spectator

418 Emblems of Atomic Energy

1957. 1st European Women's Gymnastic Championships, Bucharest.

2499 **417** 20 b. green 65 15
2500 – 35 b. red . . . . 1·00 15
2501 – 55 b. blue . . . . 2·00 50
3502 – 1 l. 75 purple . . . . . 5·75 85
DESIGNS—HORIZ: 35 b. On asymmetric bars; 55 b. Vaulting over horse. VERT: 1 l. 75, On beam.

1957. 2nd A.S.I.T. Congress.

2503 **418** 55 b. brown . . . . . . 1·40 15
2504 55 b. blue . . . . 1·60 20

419 Dove and Handlebars

420 Rhododendron

1957. 10th International Cycle Race.

2505 **419** 20 b. blue 50 15
2506 – 55 b. brown . . . . . . 1·40 20
DESIGN: 55 b. Racing cyclist.

1957. Flowers of the Carpathian Mountains.

2513 **420** 5 b. red and grey 35 10
2514 – 10 b. green and grey . . 50 10
2515 – 20 b. orange and grey . . 60 10
2516 – 35 b. olive and grey . . . 90 15
2517 – 55 b. blue and grey . . . 1·25 15
2518 – 1 l. red and grey . . . . 3·75 30
2519 – 1 l. 55 yellow and grey . 3·75 35
2520 – 1 l. 75 violet and grey . 6·75 35
FLOWERS: 10 b. Daphne; 20 b. Lily; 35 b. Edelweiss; 55 b. Gentian; 1 l. Dianthus; 1 l. 55, Primula; 1 l. 75, Anemone.

421 N. Grigorescu

1957. 50th Death Anniv of Grigorescu (painter).

2521 – 20 b. green . . . . . . 1·00 10
2522 **421** 55 b. brown . . . . . . 2·40 20
2523 – 1 l. 75 blue . . . . . . 6·75 85
DESIGNS—HORIZ: 20 b. Country scene; 1 l. 75, Battle scene.

422 Festival Visitors 423 Festival Emblem

1957. 6th World Youth Festival, Moscow.
2524 **422** 20 b. purple 15 10
2525 – 55 b. green 45 10
2526 **423** 1 l. orange . . . . 1·10 40
2527 – 1 l. 75 blue . . . . 2·00 20
DESIGNS: 55 b. Girl with flags; (22 × 38 mm) 1 l. 75, Dancers (49 × 20 mm).

424 Destroyer "Stalingrad" 425 "The Trumpeter" (after N. Grigorescu)

1957. Navy Day.
2528 **424** 1 l. 75 blue . . . . 1·75 20

1957. 80th Anniv of War of Independence.
2529 **425** 20 b. violet . . . . 1·60 15

426 Soldiers Advancing 427 Child with Dove

1957. 40th Anniv of Battle of Marasesti.
2530 **426** 1 l. 75 brown . . . . . . 2·00 20

1957. Red Cross.
2531 **427** 55 b. green and red . . . 1·60 20

428 Sprinter and Bird 429 Ovid

1957. Int Athletic Championships, Bucharest.
2532 **428** 20 b. black and blue . . 65 10
2533 – 55 b. black and yellow . 1·40 15
2534 – 1 l. 75 black and red . . 4·75 60
DESIGNS: 55 b. Javelin-thrower and bull; 1 l. 75, Runner and stag.

1957. Birth Bimillenary of Ovid (Latin poet).
2535 **429** 1 l. 75 blue . . . . 3·25 65

430 Congress Emblem 431 Oil Refinery, 1957

1957. 4th W.F.T.U. Congress, Leipzig.
2536 **430** 55 b. blue 90 15

1957. Centenary of Rumanian Petroleum Industry.
2537 **431** 20 b. brown 35 10
2538 20 b. blue 35 10
2539 – 55 b. purple 85 30
DESIGN: 55 b. Oil production, 1857: horse-operated borer.

432 Lenin, Youth and Girl 433 Artificial Satellite encircling Globe

1957. 40th Anniv of Russian Revolution.
2540 **432** 10 b. red 20 10
2541 – 35 b. purple 65 10
2542 – 55 b. brown . . . . . . 1·00 20
DESIGNS—HORIZ: 35 b. Lenin and flags; 55 b. Statue of Lenin.

1957. Air. Launching of Artificial Satellite by Russia. Inscr "SATELITII ARTIFICIALI".
2543 **433** 25 b. green 35 15
2545 25 b. blue 35 15
2544 – 3 l. 75 green . . . . . . 3·25 35
2546 – 3 l. 75 blue . . . . . . 3·25 35
DESIGN: 3 l. 75 (2), Satellite's orbit around Globe. See also Nos. 2593/6.

434 Peasant Soldiers 435 Endre Ady

1957. 520th Anniv of Bobilna Revolution.
2547 **434** 50 b. purple 35 15
2548 – 55 b. grey 45 20
DESIGN—VERT: 55 b. Bobilna Memorial.

1957. 80th Birth Anniv of Endre Ady (Hungarian poet).
2549 **435** 55 b. olive . . . . 1·40 15

436 "Laika" and Satellite 437 Black-winged Stilt

1957. Launching of Dog "Laika" in artificial satellite.
2550 **436** 1 l. 20 brown and green 4·75 85
2551 1 l. 20 brown and blue . 4·75 85

1957. Fauna of the Danube Delta
2552 **437** 5 b. grey & brn (postage) 40 10
2553 – 10 b. orange and green 50 10
2554 – 20 b. orange and red . . 75 15
2555 – 50 b. orange and green . 65 10
2556 – 55 b. blue and purple . 1·00 10
2557 – 1 l. 30 orange and violet 2·50 20
2558 – 3 l. 30 grey & blue (air) 4·75 90
2559 – 5 l. orange and red . . . 6·00 1·40
DESIGNS—VERT: 10 b. Great egret; 20 b. White spoonbill; 50 b. Fish. HORIZ: 55 b. Stoat; 1 l. 30, Eastern white pelican; 3 l. 30, Black-headed gull; 5 l. White-tailed sea eagle.

438 Emblem of Republic and Flags

1957. 10th Anniv of People's Republic.
2560 **438** 25 b. buff, red and blue 20 10
2561 – 55 b. yellow 75 25
2562 – 1 l. 20 red . . . . 1·40 35
DESIGNS: 55 b. Emblem, Industry and Agriculture; 1 l. 20, Emblem, the Arts and Sports.

439 Republican Flag

1958. 25th Anniv of Strike at Grivitsa.
2563 **439** 1 l. red & brown on buff 1·00 20
2564 1 l. red & blue on buff . 1·00 20

440 "Telecommunications"

1958. Communist Postal Conference, Moscow.
2565 **440** 55 b. violet 35 20
2566 – 1 l. 75 purple . . . . . 1·10 15
DESIGN: 1 l. 75, Telegraph pole and pylons carrying lines.

441 N. Balcescu 442 Fencer

1958. Rumanian Writers.
2567 **441** 5 b. blue 30 15
2568 – 10 b. black (Ion Creanga) 35 15
2569 – 35 b. blue (Vlahuta) . . . 40 15
2570 – 55 b. brown (Eminescu) 75 15
2571 – 1 l. 75 brown (Alecsandri) 1·10 30
2572 – 2 l. myrtle (Delavrancea) 2·75 30

1958. World Youth Fencing Championships, Bucharest.
2573 **442** 1 l. 75 mauve . . . . . . 2·00 20

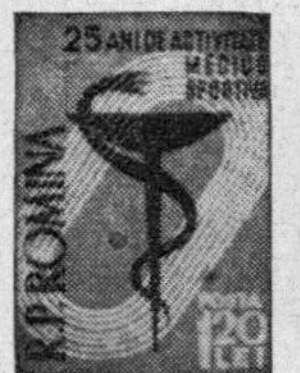

443 Symbols of Medicine and Sport 444

1958. 25th Anniv of Sports Doctors' Service.
2574 **443** 1 l. 20 red and green . . 2·00 20

1958. 4th Int Congress of Democratic Women.
2575 **444** 55 b. blue . . . . 1·10 15

445 Linnaeus 446 "Lepiota procera"

1958. Cultural Celebrities. Inscr "MARILE ANIVERSARI CULTURALE 1957".
2576 **445** 10 b. green 20 10
2577 – 20 b. brown (Comte) . . 35 10
2578 – 40 b. purple (Blake) . . 50 15
2579 – 55 b. blue (Glinka) . . . 1·25 10
2580 – 1 l. plum (Longfellow) . 1·50 20
2581 – 1 l. 75 bl (Goldoni) . . . 2·25 25
2582 – 2 l. brown (Comenius) . . 4·00 30

1958. Mushrooms. As T **446**.
2583 **446** 5 b. brn, light brn & blue 10 10
2584 – 10 b. brown,buff and bronze 15 10
2585 – 20 b. red yellow & grey . 35 10
2586 – 30 b. brown, orge and green 45 20
2587 – 35 b. brown, lt brn & bl . 50 10
2588 – 55 b. brown, red & green 85 10
2589 – 1 l. brn, buff & turquoise 1·50 15
2590 – 1 l. 55 pink, drab & grey 2·50 25
2591 – 1 l. 75 brown, buff and green . . . . 3·75 35
2592 – 2 l. yellow, brown and turquoise . . . . . . 4·50 40
MUSHROOMS: 10 b. "Clavaria aurea"; 20 b. "Amanita caesarea"; 30 b. "Lactarius deliciosus"; 35 b. "Armillaria mellea"; 55 b. "Coprinus comatus"; 1 l. "Morchella conica"; 1 l. 55, "Psalliota campestris"; 1 l. 75, "Boletus edulis"; 2 l. "Cantharellus cibarins".

1958. Brussels International Exhib. Nos. 2543/4 and 2545/6 optd **EXPOZITIA BRUXELLES 1958** and star or with star only.
2593 **433** 25 b. green . . . . . . 3·25 2·00
2594 25 b. blue . . . . . . 20·00 11·50
2595 – 3 l. 75 green . . . . . 3·25 2·00
2596 – 3 l. 75 blue . . . . . . 20·00 11·50

448 Emil Racovita (scientist), Antarctic Map and "Belgica"

1958. Racovita Commem. Inscr "1868 1947".
2597 **448** 55 b. indigo and blue . . 3·25 40
2598 – 1 l. 20 violet and olive . . 2·75 30
DESIGN: 1 l. 20, Racovita and grotto.

449 Sputnik encircling Globe 450 Servicemen's Statue

1958. Air. Launching of Third Artificial Satellite by Russia.
2599 **449** 3 l. 25 buff and blue . . 5·00 1·40

1958. Army Day.
2600 **450** 55 b. brown (postage) . 25 10
2601 – 75 b. purple 45 15
2602 – 1 l. 75 blue . . . . . . 1·10 20
2603 – 3 l. 30 violet (air) . . . . 2·00 65
DESIGNS: 75 b. Soldier guarding industrial plant; 1 l. 75, Sailor hoisting flag; 3 l. 30, Pilot and Mikoyan Gurevich MiG-17 jet fighters.

451 Costumes of Oltenia 452

1958. Provincial Costumes. Female and male costumes as T **451/2**.
2604 **451** 35 b. red and black on yellow 30 15
2605 **452** 35 b. red and black on yellow 30 15
2606 – 40 b. red and brown on grey 40 20
2607 – 40 b. red and brown on grey 40 20
2608 – 50 b. red and brown on lilac 45 15
2609 – 50 b. red and brown on lilac 45 15
2610 – 55 b. red and brown on grey 55 15
2611 – 55 b. red and brown on grey 55 15
2612 – 1 l. red & brown on pink 1·50 20
2613 – 1 l. red & brown on pink 1·50 20
2614 – 1 l. 75 red and brown on blue . . . . 2·00 35
2615 – 1 l. 75 red and brown on blue . . . . 2·00 35
PROVINCES: Nos. 2606/7, Tara Oasului; Nos. 2608/9, Transylvania; Nos. 2610/11, Muntenia; Nos. 2612/3, Banat; Nos. 2614/5, Moldova.

453 Stamp Printer 454 Runner

1958. Rumanian Stamp Centenary. Inscr "1858 1958".
2617 **453** 35 b. blue 35 10
2618 – 55 b. brown 45 10
2619 – 1 l. 20 blue . . . . . . 1·40 25
2620 – 1 l. 30 plum . . . . . . 1·50 40
2621 – 1 l. 55 brown . . . . . 2·00 20
2622 – 1 l. 75 red . . . . . . 2·40 25
2623 – 2 l. violet . . . . 3·00 65
2624 – 3 l. 30 brown . . . . . 5·00 1·00
DESIGNS: 55 b. Scissors and Moldavian stamps of 1858; 1 l. 20, Driver with whip and mail coach; 1 l. 30, Postman with horn and mounted courier; 1 l. 55, to 3 l. 30, Moldavian stamps of 1858 (Nos. 1/4).

1958. 3rd Youth Spartacist Games.
2627 **454** 1 l. brown . . . . 1·40 20

455 Revolutionary Emblem 456 Boy Bugler

1958. 40th Anniv of Workers' Revolution.
2628 **455** 55 b. red 85 15

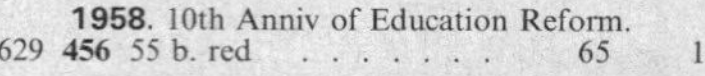
1958. 10th Anniv of Education Reform.
2629 **456** 55 b. red 65 15

457 Alexander Cuza 458 First Cosmic Rocket

1959. Centenary of Union of Rumanian Provinces.
2630 **457** 1 l. 75 b. blue . . . . . 1·60 15

1959. Air. Launching of 1st Cosmic Rocket.
2631 **458** 3 l. 25 b. blue on salmon 13·50 1·50

459 Charles Darwin

460 Maize

1959. Cultural Anniversaries.
2633 **459** 55 b. black (postage) . . 55 10
2634 – 55 b. blue (Robert Burns) 55 15
2635 – 55 b. red (Popov) 55 10
2636 – 55 b. purple (Sholem Aleichem) 55 10
2637 – 55 b. brown (Handel) . . 55 15
2638 – 3 l. 25 b. blue (Joliot-Curie) (air) . . . . 4·75 50

1959. 10th Anniv of Collective Farming in Rumania.
2639 **460** 55 b. green 35 10
2640 – 55 b. orange 35 20
2641 – 55 b. purple 35 20
2642 – 55 b. olive 35 20
2643 – 55 b. brown 35 20
2644 – 55 b. bistre 35 20
2645 – 55 b. blue 35 20
2646 – 55 b. bistre 35 20
2647 – 5 l. red . . . . . . 5·00 75
DESIGNS—VERT: No. 2640, Sunflower with bee; No. 2641, Sugar beet. HORIZ: No. 2642, Sheep; No. 2643, Cattle; No. 2644, Rooster and hens; No. 2645, Farm tractor; No. 2646, Farm wagon and horses; No. 2647, (38 × 26½ mm), Farmer and wife, and wheatfield within figure "10".

461 Rock Thrush

462

1959. Air. Birds in natural colours. Inscriptions in grey. Colours of value tablets and backgrounds given.
2648 **461** 10 b. grey on buff . . . 20 15
2649 – 20 b. grey on grey . . . 20 15
2650 – 35 b. grey on deep grey . 25 15
2651 – 40 b. red on pink . . . 40 40
2652 – 55 b. grey on green . . . 50 15
2653 – 55 b. grey on cream . . . 50 15
2654 – 55 b. green on azure . . . 50 15
2655 – 1 l. red on yellow . . . 1·60 35
2656 – 1 l. 55 red on pink . . . 2·10 35
2657 – 5 l. grey on green . . . 8·25 2·00
BIRDS—HORIZ: No. 2649, Golden oriole; No. 2656, Long-tailed tit; No. 2657, Wallcreeper. VERT: No. 2650, Lapwing; No. 2651, Barn swallow; No. 2652, Great spotted woodpecker; No. 2653, Goldfinch; No. 2654, Great tit; No. 2655, Bullfinch.

1959. 7th World Youth Festival, Vienna. Inscr "26 VII-4 VIII 1959".
2658 **462** 1 l. blue 85 20
2659 – 1 l. 60 red 90 20
DESIGN: 1 l. 60, Folk-dancer in national costume.

463 Workers and Banners

(466)

1959. 15th Anniv of Liberation.
2660 **463** 55 b. multicoloured . . . 45 15

1959. Air. Landing of Russian Rocket on the Moon. Surch **h. 00.02'.24" 14-IX-1959 PRIMA RACHETA COSMICA IN LUNA 5 LEI** in red.
2662 **458** 5 l. on 3 l. 25 blue on salmon . . . . . . 17·00 4·00

1959. 8th Balkan Games. Optd with T **466** in silver.
2663 **454** 1 l. brown . . . . 17·00 17·00

467 Prince Vlad Tepes and Charter

1959. 500th Anniv of Bucharest.
2664 **467** 20 b. black and blue . . 1·00 20
2665 – 40 b. black and brown . 1·75 25
2666 – 55 b. black and bistre . 2·40 25
2667 – 55 b. black and purple . 2·75 25
2668 – 1 l. 55 black and lilac . 6·00 1·10
2669 – 1 l. 75 black & turquoise 6·75 1·40
DESIGNS—HORIZ: 40 b. Peace Buildings, Bucharest; 55 b. (No. 2666), Atheneum; 55 b. (No 2667), "Scanteia" Printing House; 1 l. 55, Opera House; 1 l. 75, "23 August" Stadium.

468 Football

469 Atomic Icebreaker "Lenin"

1959. International Sport. Multicoloured.
2671 20 b. Type **468** (postage) . . 25 15
2672 35 b. Motor-cycle racing . . 35 10
2673 40 b. Ice-hockey 45 15
2674 55 b. Handball 50 10
2675 1 l. Horse-jumping . . . . 1·00 10
2676 1 l. 50 Boxing . . . . . 2·00 15
2677 1 l. 55 Rugby football . . . 2·10 10
2678 1 l. 60 Tennis . . . . . 2·50 25
2679 2 l. 80 Hydroplaning (air) . . 3·00 90
The 35, 40 b., 1 l. 55, 1 l. 60, and 2 l. 80, are horiz.

1959. Launching of Atomic Icebreaker "Lenin".
2680 **469** 1 l. 75 violet . . . . . 2·50 30

470 Stamp Album and Magnifier

1959. Stamp Day.
2681 **470** 1 l. 60 (+40 b.) blue . . 1·60 1·00

471 Foxglove

472 Cuza University

1959. Medicinal Flowers. Multicoloured.
2682 20 b. Type **471** 25 10
2683 40 b. Peppermint 40 20
2684 55 b. Camomile 55 10
2685 55 b. Cornflower 65 15
2686 1 l. Autumn crocus 85 15
2687 1 l. 20 Monk's-hood . . . . 1·10 20
2688 1 l. 55 Red poppy . . . . 1·40 25
2689 1 l. 60 Linden . . . . . 1·90 30
2690 1 l. 75 Wild rose . . . . 2·00 35
2691 3 l. 20 Adonis . . . . . 4·00 45

1959. Centenary of Cuza University, Jassy.
2692 **472** 55 b. brown 65 20

473 Rocket, Dog and Rabbit

474 G. Cosbuc

1959. Air. Cosmic Rocket Flight.
2693 **473** 1 l. 55 blue . . . . . 4·00 30
2694 – 1 l. 60 blue on cream . . 5·00 40
2695 – 1 l. 75 blue . . . . . 5·00 45
DESIGNS—HORIZ: (52 × 29½ mm): 1 l. 60, Picture of "invisible" side of the Moon, with lists of place-names in Rumanian and Russian. VERT—(As Type **473**): 1 l. 75, Lunik 3's trajectory around the Moon.

1960. Rumanian Authors.
2696 **474** 20 b. blue 20 15
2697 – 40 b. purple 65 20
2698 – 50 b. brown 85 15
2699 – 55 b. purple 85 15
2700 – 1 l. violet . . . . . 1·50 20
2701 – 1 l. 55 blue . . . . . 2·50 35
PORTRAITS: 40 b. I. L. Caragiale; 50 b. G. Alexandrescu; 55 b. A. Donici; 1 l. C. Negruzzi; 1 l. 55, D. Bolintineanu.

475 Huchen (Danube salmon)

476

1960. Rumanian Fauna.
2702 **475** 20 b. blue (postage) . . . 30 10
2703 – 55 b. brn (Tortoise) . . . 55 10
2704 – 1 l. 20 lilac (Common shelduck) . . . . . . 2·00 35
2705 – 1 l. 30 blue (Golden eagle) (air) . . . . 2·50 35
2706 – 1 l. 75 grn (Black grouse) 2·75 35
2707 – 2 l. red (Lammergeier) . . 3·00 50

1960. 50th Anniv of International Women's Day.
2708 **476** 55 b. blue . . . . . . 1·00 50

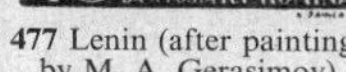

477 Lenin (after painting by M. A. Gerasimov)

478 "Victory"

1960. 90th Birth Anniv of Lenin.
2709 **477** 40 b. purple 45 15
2710 – 55 b. blue (Statue of Lenin by Boris Carogea) . . . 60 15

1960. 15th Anniv of Victory.
2712 **478** 40 b. blue 50 10
2714 40 b. purple . . . . . . 3·75 4·00
2713 – 55 b. blue 50 10
2715 – 55 b. purple . . . . . 3·75 4·00
DESIGN: 55 b. Statue of soldier with flag.

479 Rocket Flight

1960. Air. Launching of Soviet Rocket.
2716 **479** 55 b. blue . . . . . . 3·75 25

480 Diving

481 Gymnastics

1960. Olympic Games, Rome (1st issue). Multicoloured.
2717 40 b. Type **480** . . . . . 2·00 2·00
2718 55 b. Gymnastics . . . . . 2·00 2·00
2719 1 l. 20 High-jumping . . . . 2·00 2·00
2720 1 l. 60 Boxing . . . . . 3·25 3·25
2721 2 l. 45 Canoeing . . . . . 3·25 3·25
2722 3 l. 70 Canoeing . . . . . 6·75 4·00
Nos. 2717/9 and 2720/1 are arranged together in 'brickwork' fashion, se tenant in sheets forming complete overall patterns of the Olympic rings.
No. 2722 is imperf.

1960. Olympic Games, Rome (2nd issue).
2723 – 20 b. blue 20 15
2724 **481** 40 b. purple 65 15
2725 – 55 b. blue . . . . . . 1·00 15
2726 – 1 l. red . . . . 1·40 10
2727 – 1 l. 60 purple . . . . . 2·00 30
2728 – 2 l. lilac . . . . . . 3·00 65
DESIGNS: 20 b. Diving; 55 b. High-jumping; 1 l. Boxing; 1 l. 60, Canoeing; 2 l. Football.

482 Industrial Scholars

483 Vlaicu and No. 1 "Crazy Fly"

484 I.A.R. 817 Flying Ambulance

485 Pilot and Mikoyan Gurevich MiG-17 Jet Fighters

1960.
2731 **482** 3 b. mauve (postage) . . 10 10
2732 – 5 b. brown 25 10
2733 – 10 b. purple 10 10
2734 – 20 b. blue 15 10
2735 – 30 b. red 20 10
2736 – 35 b. red 20 10
2737 – 40 b. bistre 25 10
2738 – 50 b. violet 25 10
2739 – 55 b. blue 30 10
2740 – 60 b. green 30 10
2741 – 75 b. olive 50 10
2742 – 1 l. red 50 10
2743 – 1 l. 20 black 55 10
2744 – 1 l. 50 purple 75 10
2745 – 1 l. 55 turquoise . . . 90 10
2746 – 1 l. 60 blue 80 10
2747 – 1 l. 75 brown . . . . 1·00 10
2748 – 2 l. brown . . . . . 1·40 20
2749 – 2 l. 40 violet . . . . 1·50 15
2750 – 3 l. blue . . . . . . 1·50 15
2751 – 3 l. 20 blue (air) . . . 3·25 10
DESIGNS—VERT: 5 b. Diesel train; 10 b. Dam; 20 b. Miner; 30 b. Doctor; 35 b. Textile worker; 50 b. Children at play; 55 b. Timber tractor; 1 l. Atomic reactor; 1 l. 20, Petroleum refinery; 1 l. 50, Iron-works; 1 l. 75, Mason; 2 l. Road-roller; 2 l. 40, Chemist; 3 l. Radio communications and television. HORIZ: 40 b. Grand piano and books; 60 b. Combine harvester; 75 b. Cattle-shed; 1 l. 55, Dock scene; 1 l. 60, Runner; 3 l. 20, Baneasa Airport, Bucharest.

1960. 50th Anniv of 1st Flight by A. Vlaicu and Aviation Day.
2752 **483** 10 b. brown and yellow . 20 10
2753 – 20 b. brown and orange 30 10
2754 **484** 35 b. red 35 10
2755 – 40 b. violet 55 10
2756 **485** 55 b. blue 70 10
2757 – 1 l. 60 multicoloured . . 1·75 50
2758 – 1 l. 75 multicoloured . . 2·25 55
DESIGNS—As T **483**: 20 b. Vlaicu in flying helmet and his No. 2 airplane; 40 b. Antonov An-2 biplane spraying crops. 59 × 22 mm: 1 l. 60, Ilyushin Il-18 airliner and airport control tower; 1 l. 75, Parachute descents.

486 Worker and Emblem

1960. 3rd Workers' Party Congress.
2759 **486** 55 b. orange and red . . 1·00 15

487 Tolstoy

488 Tomis (Constantza)

1960. Cultural Anniversaries.
2760 10 b. purple (T **487**) . . . 10 10
2761 20 b. olive (Mark Twain) . . 15 10
2762 35 b. blue (K. Hokusai) . . 20 10
2763 40 b. green (De Musset) . . 25 15
2764 55 b. brown (Defoe) 45 10
2765 1 l. turquoise (J. Bolyai) . . 1·40 20
2766 1 l. 20 red (Chekhov) . . . . 1·50 10
2767 1 l. 55 grey (R. Koch) . . . 2·00 15
2768 1 l. 75 brown (Chopin) . . . 2·75 30

1960. Black Sea Resorts. Multicoloured.
2769 20 b. Type **488** (postage) . . 20 10
2770 35 b. Constantza 40 10
2771 40 b. Vasile Roaita 45 10
2772 55 b. Mangalia 85 10
2773 1 l. Eforie . . . . 1·40 25
2774 1 l. 60 Eforie (different) . . . 1·50 20
2775 2 l. Mamaia (air) . . . . . 2·75 65

INDEX

Countries can be quickly located by referring to the index at the end of this volume.

489 Globe and Flags 490 "Saturnia pyri" (moth)

1960. Int Puppet Theatre Festival, Bucharest. Designs (24×28½ mm, except 20 b.) show puppets. Multicoloured.

2776 20 b. Type **489** 25 10
2777 40 b. Petrushka 30 10
2778 55 b. Punch 40 10
2779 1 l. Kaspar 60 15
2780 1 l. 20 Tindarica 80 20
2781 1 l. 75 Vasilache . . . . . . 1·25 15

1960. Air. Butterflies and Moths. Multicoloured.

2782 10 b. Type **490** 30 10
2783 20 b. "Limenitus populi" . . 35 10
2784 40 b "Chrisophanus virgaureae" 40 10
2785 55 b. "Papilio machaon" . . 70 15
2786 1 l. 60 "Acherontia atropus" . 2·10 30
2787 1 l. 75 "Apatura iris" . . . 2·75 30

SIZES: TRIANGULAR—36½×21½ mm: 20, 40 b. VERT—23½×34 mm: 55 b., 1 l. 60. HORIZ—34×23½ mm: 1 l. 75.

491 Children tobagganing

1960. Village Children's Games. Multicoloured.

2788 20 b. Type **491** 15 10
2789 35 b. "Oina" (ball-game) . . 20 10
2790 55 b. Ice-skating 30 10
2791 1 l. Running 65 15
2792 1 l. 75 Swimming . . . . . . 1·75 20

The 20 b. and 1 l. are vert and the rest horiz.

492 Striker and Flag

1960. 40th Anniv of General Strike.

2793 **492** 55 b. red and lake . . . 65 25

493 Compass Points and Ilyushin Il-18 Airliner

1960 Air. Stamp Day.

2794 **493** 55 b. (+ 45 b.) blue . . 85 25

494 "XV" Globe and "Peace" Riband 496 Woman tending Vine (Cotnari)

495 Herrings

1960. 15th Anniv of World Democratic Youth Federation.

2795 **494** 55 b. yellow and blue . . 65 10

1960. Fish Culture. Fish in actual colours. Background colours given.

2796 – 10 b. turquoise 15 10
2797 – 20 b. blue 25 10
2798 – 40 b. yellow 45 10
2799 **495** 55 b. grey 85 10
2800 – 1 l. red . . . . 1·50 15
2801 – 1 l. 20 blue . . . . . 2·00 20
2802 – 1 l. 60 olive . . . . . 2·75 25

FISHES: 10 b. Carp; 20 b. Coal-fish; 40 b. Turbot; 1 l. Silurus; 1 l. 20, Sturgeon; 1 l. 60, Cod.

1960. Rumanian Vineyards. Multicoloured.

2803 20 b. Dragasani 15 10
2804 30 b. Dealul Mare (horiz) . . 25 10
2805 40 b. Odobesti (horiz) . . . 40 10
2806 55 b. Type **496** 65 10
2807 75 b. Tirnave . . . . 1·40 15
2808 1 l. Minis . . . . 2·10 25
2809 1 l. 20 Murfatlar . . . . . 2·75 40

497 "Furnaceman" (after I. Irimescu) 498 Slalom Racer

1961. Rumanian Sculptures.

2811 **497** 5 b. red 10 10
2812 – 10 b. violet 15 10
2813 – 20 b. black 20 10
2814 – 40 b. bistre 25 10
2815 – 50 b. brown 40 10
2816 – 55 b. red 75 10
2817 – 1 l. purple . . . . . . 1·10 15
2818 – 1 l. 55 blue . . . . . 1·75 15
2819 – 1 l. 75 green . . . . . 2·40 20

SCULPTURES—VERT: 10 b. "Gh. Doja" (I. Vlad); 20 b. "Reunion" (B. Caragea); 40 b. "Enescu" (G. Anghel); 50 b. "Eminescu" (C. Baraschi); 1 l. "Peace" (I. Jalea); 1 l. 55, "Constructive Socialism" (C. Medrea); 1 l. 75, "Birth of an idea" (A. Szobotka). HORIZ: 55 b. "Peasant Uprising, 1907" (M. Constantinescu).

1961. Air. 50th Anniv of Rumanian Winter Sports. (a) Perf.

2820 – 10 b. olive and grey . . 20 10
2821 **498** 20 b. red and grey . . . 25 10
2822 – 25 b. turquoise and grey 40 10
2823 – 40 b. violet and grey . . 50 10
2824 – 55 b. blue and grey . . 65 10
2825 – 1 l. red and grey . . . 1·25 15
2826 – 1 l. 55 brown and grey . 2·25 20

(b) Imperf.

2827 – 10 b. blue and grey . . 10 10
2828 **498** 20 b. brown and grey . . 20 10
2829 – 25 b. olive and grey . . 30 15
2830 – 40 b. red and grey . . . 65 25
2831 – 55 b. turquoise & grey . 90 70
2832 – 1 l. violet and grey . . 1·40 1·25
2833 – 1 l. 55 red and grey . . 2·40 2·25

DESIGNS—HORIZ: Skier: racing (10 b.), jumping (55 b.), walking (1 l. 55). VERT: 25 b. Skiers climbing slope; 40 b. Toboggan; 1 l. Rock-climber.

499 P. Poni (chemist) 500 Yuri Gagarin in Capsule

1961. Rumanian Scientists. Inscr "1961". Portraits in sepia.

2834 **499** 10 b. brown and pink . 10 10
2835 – 20 b. purple and yellow 25 10
2836 – 55 b. red and blue . . 40 10
2837 – 1 l. 55 violet & orange . 1·60 30

PORTRAITS: 20 b. A. Saligny (engineer); 55 b. C. Budeanu (electrical engineer); 1 l. 55, G. Titeica (mathematician).

1961. Air. World's First Manned Space Flight. Inscr "12 IV 1961". (a) Perf.

2838 – 1 l. 35 blue . . . . . 1·00 20
2839 **500** 3 l. 20 blue . . . . . 2·40 70

(b) Imperf.

2840 **500** 3 l. 20 red . . . . . 8·50 2·75

DESIGN—VERT: 1 l. 35, Yuri Gagarin.

501 Freighter "Galati"

1961. Merchant Navy. Multicoloured.

2841 20 b. Type **501** 35 10
2842 40 b. Liner "Oltenita" . . . 60 10
2843 55 b. Water-bus "Tomis" . . 60 10
2844 1 l. Freighter "Arad" . . . 1·00 15
2845 1 l. 55 Tug "N. Cristea" . . 1·60 15
2846 1 l. 75 Freighter "Dobrogea" 1·90 25

502 Red Flag with Marx, Engels and Lenin

1961. 40th Anniv of Rumanian Communist Party.

2847 **502** 35 b. multicoloured . . . 65 10
2848 – 55 b. multicoloured . . . 1·00 10

DESIGN: 55 b. Two bill-posters.

503 Eclipse over Scanteia Building and Observatory 504 Roe Deer

1961. Air. Solar Eclipse.

2850 – 1 l. 60 blue . . . . . . 1·50 15
2851 **503** 1 l. 75 blue . . . . . 1·75 15

DESIGN: 1 l. 60, Eclipse over Palace Square, Bucharest.

1961. Forest Animals. Inscr "1961" Multicoloured.

2852 10 b. Type **504** 15 15
2853 20 b. Lynx (horiz) 20 15
2854 35 b. Wild boar (horiz) . . . 40 15
2855 40 b. Brown bear (horiz) . . 70 25
2856 55 b. Red deer 90 25
2857 75 b. Red fox (horiz) . . . . 1·10 20
2858 1 l. Chamois . . . . 1·50 25
2859 1 l. 55 Brown hare . . . . . 2·10 35
2860 1 l. 75 Eurasian badger . . . 2·50 45
2861 2 l. Roe deer . . . . 3·75 70

505 George Enescu

1961. 2nd International George Enescu Festival.

2862 **505** 3 l. lavender and brown . 2·40 35

506 Gagarin and Titov 507 Iris

1961. Air. 2nd Soviet Space Flight.

2863 – 55 b. blue 50 10
2864 – 1 l. 35 violet 90 25
2865 **506** 1 l. 75 red . . . . . . 1·75 30

DESIGNS—VERT: 55 b. "Vostock-2" in flight; 1 l. 35, G. S. Titov.

1961. Centenary of Bucharest Botanical Gardens. Flowers in natural colours. Background and inscription colours given. Perf or imperf.

2866 – 10 b. yellow and brown . 15 10
2867 – 20 b. green and red . . . 15 10
2869 – 35 b. lilac and grey . . . 30 10
2870 **507** 40 b. yellow and violet . 40 10
2871 – 55 b. blue & ultramarine . 60 10
2872 – 1 l. orange and blue . . . 1·40 10
2873 – 1 l. 20 blue and brown . . 1·50 10
2874 – 1 l. 55 brown and lake . . 2·00 15

FLOWERS—HORIZ: 10 b. Primula; 35 b. Opuntia; 1 l. Hepatica. VERT: 20 b. Dianthus; 25 b. Peony; 55 b. Ranunculus; 1 l. 20, Poppy; 1 l. 55, Gentian.

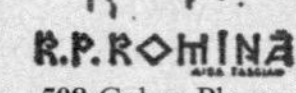

508 Cobza Player 509 Heraclides

1961. Musicians. Multicoloured.

2876 10 b. Pan piper 10 10
2877 20 b. Alpenhorn player . . . 15 10
2878 40 b. Flautist 40 10
2879 55 b. Type **508** 60 10
2880 60 b. Bagpiper 80 10
2881 1 l. Cembalo player . . . . 1·40 20

The 20 b. is horiz and the rest vert.

1961. Cultural Anniversaries.

2882 10 b. purple (T **509**) 30 25
2883 20 b. brown (Sir Francis Bacon) 30 25
2884 40 b. green (Tagore) 35 25
2885 55 b. red (Sarmiento) 55 25
2886 1 l. 35 blue (Von Kleist) . . 85 25
2887 1 l. 75 vio (Lomonosov) . . 1·40 25

510 Olympic Flame 512 Tower Building, Republic Palace Square, Bucharest

511 "Stamps Round the World"

1961. Olympic Games 1960. Gold Medal Awards. Inscr "MELBOURNE 1956" or "ROMA 1960". Perf or imperf.

2888 – 10 b. turq and ochre . . 20 10
2889 **510** 20 b. red 25 10
2890 – 20 b. grey 25 10
2891 – 35 b. brown and ochre . 35 10
2892 – 40 b. purple and ochre . 40 10
2893 – 55 b. blue 50 15
2894 – 55 b. blue 50 15
2895 – 55 b. red and ochre . . . 50 15
2896 – 1 l. 35 blue and ochre . 1·90 15
2897 1 l. 75 red and ochre . . . 2·75 20

DESIGNS (Medals)—DIAMOND: 10 b. Boxing; 35 b. Pistol-shooting; 40 b. Rifle-shooting; 55 b. (No. 2895), Wrestling; 1 l. 35, High-jumping. VERT: as Type **510**: 20 b. (No. 2890), Diving; 55 b. (No. 2893), Water-polo; 55 b. (No. 2894), Women's high-jumping. HORIZ—45×33 mm: 1 l. 75, Canoeing.

1961. Air. Stamp Day.

2899 **511** 55 b. (+ 45 b.) blue, brown and red . . . . . . 1·60 65

1961. Air. Modern Rumanian Architecture. Mult.

2900 20 b. Type **512** 30 10
2901 40 b. Constantza Railway Station . . . . 1·00 15
2902 55 b. Congress Hall, Republic Palace, Bucharest . . . 50 10
2903 75 b. Rolling mill, Hunedoara 55 10
2904 1 l. Apartment blocks, Bucharest 75 15
2905 1 l. 20 Circus Building, Bucharest 80 30
2906 1 l. 75 Workers' Club, Mangalia 1·50 20

The 40 b. to 1 l. 75 are horiz.

513 U.N. Emblem 514 Workers with Flags

1961. 15th Anniv of U.N.O. Perf or imperf.

2907 – 20 b. multicoloured . . . 20 10
2908 – 40 b. multicoloured . . . 65 15
2909 **513** 55 b. multicoloured . . . 1·00 20

DESIGNS (bearing U.N. emblem): 20 b. Peace dove over Eastern Europe; 40 b. Peace dove and youths of three races.

1961. 5th W.F.T.U. Congress, Moscow.

2910 **514** 55 b. red . . . . 1·00 15

515 Cock and Savings Book 516 Footballer

1962. Savings Day. Inscr "1962". Multicoloured.

2911 40 b. Type **515** 25 10
2912 55 b. Savings Bank book, bee and honeycombs 65 15

1962. European Junior Football Competition, Bucharest.
2913 **516** 55 b. brown and green 1·40 20

517 Ear of Corn, Map and Tractor
518 Handball Player

1962. Completion of Agricultural Collectivisation Project. Inscr "1962".
2914 **517** 40 b. red and orange 20 10
2915 – 55 b. lake and yellow 25 10
2916 – 1 l. 55 yellow, red & blue 65 20
DESIGNS: 55 b. Commemorative medal. 1 l. 55, Wheatsheaf, and hammer and sickle emblem.

1962. Women's World Handball Championships Bucharest
2917 **518** 55 b. violet and yellow 1·40 20

519 Canoe Race
520 J. J. Rousseau

1962. Boating and Sailing. Inscr "1962". (a) Perf.
2918 **519** 10 b. blue and mauve 20 10
2919 – 20 b. blue and olive 25 10
2920 – 40 b. blue and brown 30 10
2921 – 55 b. blue & ultramarine 40 15
2922 – 1 l. blue and red 1·00 15
2923 – 1 l. 20 blue and purple 1·25 15
2924 – 1 l. 55 blue and orange 1·50 15
2925 – 3 l. blue and violet 2·50 30

(b) Imperf. Colours changed.
2926 **519** 10 b. blue & ultramarine 25 15
2927 – 20 b. blue and mauve 30 20
2928 – 40 b. blue and orange 50 30
2929 – 55 b. blue and olive 65 45
2930 – 1 l. blue and brown 1·40 60
2931 – 1 l. 20 blue and violet 1·50 1·00
2932 – 1 l. 55 blue and red 1·90 1·10
2933 – 3 l. blue and purple 4·00 1·90
DESIGNS: 20 b. Kayak; 40 b. Racing "eight"; 55 b. Sculling; 1 l. Yachting; 1 l. 20, Motor-boats; 1 l. 55, Sailing; 3 l. Canoe slalom.

1962. Cultural Anniversaries (writers).
2934 **520** 40 b. olive 20 10
2935 – 55 b. lake 25 15
2936 – 1 l. 75 blue 95 15
WRITERS: 55 b. I. L. Caragiale; 1 l. 75 A. I. Herzen.

521 Flags and Globes
522 T. Vuia (aviator)

1962. World Youth Festival. Helsinki.
2938 **521** 55 b. multicoloured 1·00 15

1962. Rumanian Celebrities.
2939 **522** 15 b. brown 15 10
2940 – 20 b. red 20 10
2941 – 35 b. purple 25 10
2942 – 40 b. blue 35 15
2943 – 55 b. blue 40 10
2944 – 1 l. blue 1·00 10
2945 – 1 l. 20 red 1·25 20
2946 – 1 l. 35 turquoise 1·40 20
2947 – 1 l. 55 violet 1·50 15
PORTRAITS: 20 b. A. Davila (writer); 35 b. V. Pirvan (archaeologist); 40 b. I. Negullei (painter); 55 b. G. Cobilcescu (geologist); 1 l. Dr. G. Marinescu; 1 l. 20, Dr. I. Cantacuzino; 1 l. 35, Dr. V. Babes; 1 l. 55, Dr. C. Levaditi.

523 Anglers by Pond

1962. Fishing Sport. Multicoloured.
2948 10 b. Rod-fishing in fishing punts 10 10
2949 25 b. Line-fishing in mountain pool 15 10
2950 40 b. Type **523** 25 10
2951 55 b. Anglers on beach 35 10
2952 75 b. Line-fishing in mountain stream 50 10
2953 1 l. Shore-fishing 60 20
2954 1 l. 75 Freshwater-fishing 1·25 15
2955 3 l. 25 Fishing in Danube delta 2·10 20

524 Dove and "Space" Stamps of 1957/58
527 "Vostok 3" and "4" in Orbit

1962. Air. Cosmic Flights.
2956 **524** 35 b. brown 20 10
2957 – 55 b. green 30 10
2958 – 1 l. 35 blue 90 10
2959 – 1 l. 75 red 1·40 25
DESIGNS—Dove and: 55 b. "Space" stamps of 1959; 1 l. 35, "Space" stamps of 1957 ("Laika"), 1959 and 1960; 1 l. 75, "Spacemen" stamps of 1961.

1962. Rumanian Victory in European Junior Football Competition, Bucharest. Surch **1962. Campioana Europeana 2 lei**.
2961 **516** 2 l. on 55 b. brown & grn 2·00 2·25

1962. Rumanian Victory in Women's World Handball Championships, Bucharest. Surch **Campioana Mondiala 5 lei**.
2962 **518** 5 l. on 55 b. violet and yellow 7·50 5·00

1962. Air. 1st "Team" Manned Space Flight.
2963 – 55 b. violet 50 10
2964 **527** 1 l. 60 blue 1·50 25
2965 – 1 l. 75 purple 1·90 30
DESIGNS: 55 b. Cosmonaut Nikolaev; 1 l. 75, Cosmonaut Popovich.

528 Child and Butterfly
529 Pottery

1962. Children.
2966 **528** 20 b. blue, brown & red 20 10
2967 – 30 b. yellow, blue & red 25 10
2968 – 40 b. blue, red & turq 30 10
2969 – 55 b. olive, blue and red 60 10
2970 – 1 l. 20 red, brown & blue 1·25 20
2971 – 1 l. 55 ochre, blue & red 2·10 20
DESIGNS—VERT: 30 b. Girl feeding dove; 40 b. Boy with model yacht; 1 l. 20, Boy violinist and girl pianist. HORIZ: 55 b. Girl teaching boy to write; 1 l. 55, Pioneers around camp-fire.

1962. 4th Sample Fair. Bucharest. Inscr "AL IV — LEA PAVILION DE MOSTRE — BUCURESTI 1962". Multicoloured.
2972 5 b. Type **529** (postage) 35 15
2973 10 b. Preserved foodstuffs 40 15
2974 20 b. Chemical products 40 15
2975 40 b. Ceramics 50 10
2976 55 b. Leather goods 70 10
2977 75 b. Textiles 85 10
2978 1 l. Furniture and fabrics 1·40 10
2979 1 l. 20 Office equipment 1·75 10
2980 1 l. 55 Needlework 2·10 10
2981 1 l. 60 Fair pavillion (air) 2·75 15
The 1 l. 60 is horiz, the rest vert.

530 Lenin and Red Flag

1962. 45th Anniv of Russian Revolution.
2982 **530** 55 b. brown, red & blue 1·00 15

531 "The Coachmen" (after Szatmay)

1962. Air. Stamp Day and Centenary of 1st Rumanian Stamps.
2983 **531** 55 b. (+ 45 b.) black and blue 1·50 35

532 Lamb

1962. Prime Farm Stock.
2984 **532** 20 b. black and blue 15 10
2985 – 40 b. brown, yell & blue 15 10
2986 – 55 b. green, buff and orange 30 10
2987 – 1 l. brown, buff & grey 40 10
2988 – 1 l. 35 brown, blk & grn 60 15
2989 – 1 l. 55 brown, blk & red 70 20
2990 – 1 l. 75 brown, cream & blue 1·40 35
DESIGNS—HORIZ: 40 b. Ram; 1 l. 55, Heifer; 1 l. 75, Sows. VERT: 55 b. Bull; 1 l. Pig; 1 l. 35, Cow.

533 Arms, Industry and Agriculture

1962. 15th Anniv of People's Republic.
2991 **533** 1 l. 55 multicoloured 1·60 20

534 Strikers

1963. 30th Anniv of Grivitsa Strike.
2992 **534** 1 l. 75 multicoloured 1·75 30

535 Tractor-driver

1963. Freedom from Hunger.
2993 **535** 40 b. blue 20 10
2994 – 55 b. brown 35 10
2995 – 1 l. 55 red 1·00 15
2996 – 1 l. 75 green 1·25 20
DESIGNS (each with F.A.O. emblem): 55 b. Girl harvester; 1 l. 55, Child with beaker of milk; 1 l. 75, Girl vintager.

1963. Air. Rumanian Philatelists' Conference, Bucharest. No. 2983, optd **A.F.R.** surrounded by **CONFERINTA PE TARA BUCURESTI 30-III-1963** in diamond shape.
2997 **531** 55 b. (+ 45 b.) black and blue 5·00 4·00
The opt is applied in the middle of the se-tenant pair—stamp and 45 b. label.

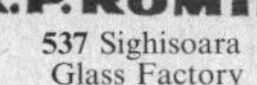

537 Sighisoara Glass Factory
538 Tomatoes

1963. Air. "Socialist Achievements".
2998 **537** 30 b. blue and red 30 10
2999 – 40 b. green and violet 40 15
3000 – 55 b. red and blue 65 15
3001 – 1 l. violet and brown 95 15
3002 – 1 l. 55 red and blue 1·25 15
3003 – 1 l. 75 blue and purple 1·25 15
DESIGNS: 40 b. Govora soda works; 55 b. Tirgul-Jiu wood factory; 1 l. Savinesti chemical works; 1 l. 55, Hunedoara metal works; 1 l. 75, Brazi thermic power station.

1963. Vegetable Culture. Multicoloured.
3004 35 b. Type **538** 20 10
3005 40 b. Hot peppers 35 10
3006 55 b. Radishes 40 10
3007 75 b. Aubergines 60 15
3008 1 l. 20 Mild peppers 85 15
3009 3 l. 25 Cucumbers (horiz) 2·00 25

539 Moon Rocket "Luna 4"
540 Chick

1963. Air. Launching of Soviet Moon Rocket "Luna 4". The 1 l. 75 is imperf.
3010 **539** 55 b. red and blue 35 15
3011 1 l. 75 red and violet 1·40 10

1963. Domestic Poultry.
3012 **540** 20 b. yellow and blue 20 10
3013 – 30 b. red, blue & brown 25 10
3014 – 40 b. blue, orge & brn 35 10
3015 – 55 b. multicoloured 40 10
3016 – 70 b. blue, red & purple 45 10
3017 – 1 l. red, grey and blue 50 10
3018 – 1 l. 35 red, blue & ochre 60 10
3019 – 3 l. 20 multicoloured 1·50 25
POULTRY: 30 b. Cockerel; 40 b. Duck; 55 b. White Leghorn; 70 b. Goose; 1 l. Rooster; 1 l. 35, Turkey (cock); 3 l. 20, Turkey (hen).

541 Diving
542 Congress Emblem

1963. Swimming. Bodies in drab.
3020 **541** 25 b. green and brown 15 10
3021 – 30 b. yellow and olive 20 10
3022 – 55 b. red and turquoise 25 10
3023 – 1 l. red and green 45 10
3024 – 1 l. 35 mauve and blue 55 10
3025 – 1 l. 55 orange and violet 1·25 10
3026 – 2 l. yellow and mauve 1·25 15
DESIGNS—HORIZ: 30 b. Crawl; 55 b. Butterfly; 1 l. Back stroke; 1 l. 35, Breast stroke. VERT: 1 l. 55, Swallow diving; 2 l. Water polo.

1963. International Women's Congress, Moscow.
3027 **542** 55 b. blue 65 15

543 Bykovsky and Globe

1963. Air. 2nd "Team" Manned Space Flights.
3028 **543** 55 b. blue 35 15
3029 – 1 l. 75 red 1·60 25
DESIGN: 1 l. 75, Tereshkova and globe.

544 Steam Locomotive

1963. Air. Transport. Multicoloured.
3031 40 b. Type **544** 65 15
3032 55 b. Diesel freight locomotive 65 15
3033 75 b. Trolley bus 65 25
3034 1 l. 35 "Oltenita" (Danube passenger vessel) 1·90 30
3035 1 l. 75 Ilyushin Il-18 airplane 1·75 20

545 W. M. Thackeray (writer)

1963. Cultural Anniversaries. Inscr "MARILE ANNIVERSARI CULTURALE 1963".
3036 **545** 40 b. black and lilac 20 15
3037 – 50 b. black and brown 35 15
3038 – 55 b. black and olive 50 15
3039 – 1 l. 55 black and red 1·10 15
3040 – 1 l. 75 black and blue 1·25 20
PORTRAITS: 50 b. E. Delacroix (painter); 55 b. G. Marinescu (physician); 1 l. 55, G. Verdi (composer); 1 l. 75, K. Stanislavsky (theatrical producer).

546 Walnuts

548 Volleyball

1963. Fruits and Nuts. Multicoloured.
3041 10 b. Type **546** 30 15
3042 20 b. Plums 30 10
3043 40 b. Peaches 60 10
3044 55 b. Strawberries 70 10
3045 1 l. Grapes 80 10
3046 1 l. 55 Apples 1·40 15
3047 1 l. 60 Cherries 1·40 15
3048 1 l. 75 Pears 2·00 20

1963. Air. 50th Death Anniv of Aurel Vlaicu (aviation pioneer). No. 2752 surch **1913-1963. 50 ani de la moarte 1,75 lei**.
3049 **483** 1 l. 75 on 10 b. brown and yellow 3·00 1·10

1963. European Volleyball Championships.
3050 **548** 5 b. mauve and grey 20 10
3051 – 40 b. blue and grey 20 10
3052 – 55 b. turquoise and grey 65 10
3053 – 1 l. 75 brown and grey 1·40 15
3054 – 3 l. 20 violet and grey 2·00 25
DESIGNS: 40 b. to 1 l. 75, Various scenes of play at net; 3 l. 20, European Cup.

549 Rumanian 1l. 55 "Centenary" Stamp of 1958

1963. Air. Stamp Day and 15th U.P.U. Congress. Inscr "AL XV-LEA CONGRESS", etc.
3055 **549** 20 b. brown & light blue 15 10
3056 – 40 b. blue and mauve 20 10
3057 – 55 b. lake and blue 25 10
3058 – 1 l. 20 violet and buff 50 15
3059 – 1 l. 55 olive and red 70 15
3060 – 1 l. 60 + 50 b. mult 1·60 40
DESIGNS (Rumanian stamps): 40 b. (1 l. 20) "Laika", 1957 (blue); 55 b. (3 l. 20) "Gagarin", 1961; 1 l. 20, (55 b.) "Nikolaev" and (1 l. 75) "Popovich", 1962; 1 l. 55, (55 b.) "Postwoman", 1953; 1 l. 60, U.P.U. Monument, Berne, globe, map of Rumania and aircraft (76 × 27 mm).

551 Ski–jumping

1963. Winter Olympic Games, Innsbruck, 1964. (a) Perf.
3061 **551** 10 b. blue and red 50 15
3062 – 20 b. brown and blue 65 15
3063 – 40 b. brown and green 85 10
3064 – 55 b. brown and violet 1·00 10
3065 – 60 b. blue and brown 1·40 15
3066 – 75 b. blue and mauve 1·50 20
3067 – 1 l. blue and ochre 2·00 20
3068 – 1 l. 20 blue & turquoise 2·75 35

(b) Imperf. Colours changed.
3069 **551** 10 b. brown and green 1·50 1·25
3070 – 20 b. brown and violet 1·50 1·25
3071 – 40 b. blue and red 1·50 1·25
3072 – 55 b. brown and blue 1·50 1·25
3073 – 60 b. blue & turquoise 1·50 1·25
3074 – 75 b. blue and ochre 1·50 1·25
3075 – 1 l. blue and mauve 1·50 1·25
3076 – 1 l. 20 blue & brown 1·50 1·25
DESIGNS: 20 b. Ice skating; 40 b. Ice hockey; 55 b. Figure skating; 60 b. Slalom; 75 b. Rifle shooting on skis; 1 l. Bobsleigh; 1 l. 20, Skiing.

552 Cone, Fern and Conifer

553 Silkworm Moth

1963. 18th Anniv of Reafforestation Campaign.
3078 **552** 55 b. green 20 10
3079 – 1 l. 75 blue 65 15
DESIGN: 1 l. 75, Chestnut trees.

1963. Bee-keeping and Silkworm–breeding. Multicoloured.
3080 10 b. Type **553** 25 10
3081 20 b. Moth emerging from chrysalis 35 10
3082 40 b. Silkworm 45 10
3083 55 b. Bee 60 10
3084 60 b. Bee extracting nectar from various flowers 1·00 20
3085 1 l. 20 As No. 3084 (different) 1·40 25
3086 1 l. 35 As No. 3084 (different) 1·60 35
3087 1 l. 60 As No. 3084 (different) 2·00 40
The 55 b. to 1 l. 60, are horiz.

554 Carved Pillar

556 G. Stephanescu

555 Gagarin

1963. Village Museum, Bucharest.
3088 **554** 20 b. purple 25 10
3089 – 40 b. blue 30 10
3090 – 55 b. violet 40 10
3091 – 75 b. green 50 10
3092 – 1 l. red and brown 1·00 10
3093 – 1 l. 20 green 1·25 10
3094 – 1 l. 75 blue and brown 2·00 10
DESIGNS: Various Rumanian peasant houses. The 40 b. and 55 b. are horiz, the rest vert.

1964. Air. "Space Navigation". Soviet flag, red and yellow; U.S. flag, red and blue; backgrounds, light blue; portrait and inscription colours below.

(a) Perf.
3095 **555** 5 b. blue 25 10
3096 – 10 b. violet 35 10
3097 – 20 b. bronze 40 10
3098 – 35 b. grey 45 10
3099 – 40 b. violet 50 15
3100 – 55 b. violet 65 15
3101 – 60 b. brown 65 20
3102 – 75 b. blue 75 20
3103 – 1 l. purple 1·00 25
3104 – 1 l. 40 purple 1·50 50

(b) Imperf. Colours changed.
3105 **555** 5 b. violet 10 10
3106 – 10 b. blue 15 10
3107 – 20 b. grey 30 15
3108 – 35 b. bronze 60 35
3109 – 40 b. purple 85 40
3110 – 55 b. purple 1·10 50
3111 – 60 b. blue 1·10 75
3112 – 75 b. brown 1·50 1·00
3113 – 1 l. violet 1·75 1·25
3114 – 1 l. 40 violet 2·40 1·90
PORTRAITS (with flags of their countries)—As Type **555**: 10 b. G. Titov; 20 b. J. Glenn; 35 b. S. Carpenter; 60 b. W. Schirra; 75 b. G. Cooper. SQUARE (35 × 34 mm): 40 b. A. Nikolaev; 55 b. P. Popovich; 1 l. V. Bykovsky; 1 l. 40, V. Tereshkova.

1964. Rumanian Opera Singers and their stage roles. Portraits in brown.
3116 **556** 10 b. olive 35 10
3117 – 20 b. blue 45 10
3118 – 35 b. green 50 10
3119 – 40 b. light blue 55 10
3120 – 55 b. mauve 65 10
3121 – 75 b. violet 70 10
3122 – 1 l. blue 80 10
3123 – 1 l. 35 violet 90 15
3124 – 1 l. 55 red 1·40 20
SINGERS: 20 b. Elena Teodorini; 35 b. I. Bajenaru; 40 b. D. Popovici; 55 b. Hariclea Darclee; 75 b. G. Folescu; 1 l. J. Athanasiu; 1 l. 35, T. Grosavescu; 1 l. 55, N. Leonard.

557 Prof. G. M. Murgoci

558 "Ascalaphus macaronius" (moth)

1964. 80th International Soil Congress, Bucharest.
3125 **557** 1 l. 60 indigo, ochre and blue 1·00 20

1964. Rumanian Insects. Multicoloured.
3126 5 b. Type **558** 20 10
3127 10 b. "Ammophila sabulosa" (flying ant) 25 10
3128 35 b. "Scolia maculata" (wasp) 30 10
3129 40 b. "Rhyparioides metelkana" (moth) 45 10
3130 55 b. "Lymantria dispar" (moth) 60 10
3131 1 l. 20 "Kanetisa circe" (butterfly) 85 15
3132 1 l. 55 "C. Fabricii malachiticus" (beetle) 90 20
3133 1 l. 75 "Procerus gigas" (horned beetle) 1·50 20

559 "Nicotiana alata"

560 Cross Country

1964. Rumanian Flowers. Multicoloured.
3134 10 b. Type **559** 25 10
3135 20 b. "Pelargonium" 25 10
3136 40 b. "Fuchsia gracilis" 35 15
3137 55 b. "Chrysanthemum indicum" 40 10
3138 75 b. "Dahlia hybrida" 45 10
3139 1 l. "Lilium croceum" 75 10
3140 1 l. 25 "Hosta ovata" 90 20
3141 1 l. 55 "Tagetes erectus" 1·40 15

1964. Horsemanship.
3142 – 40 b. multicoloured 30 10
3143 **560** 55 b. brown, red & lilac 40 10
3144 – 1 l. 35 brown, red & grn 1·00 15
3145 – 1 l. 55 mauve, blue & bis 1·60 20
DESIGNS—HORIZ: 40 b. Dressage; 1 l. 55, Horse race. VERT: 1 l. 35, Show jumping.

561 Scorpionfish

562 M. Eminescu (poet)

1964. Constantza Aquarium. Fish designs. Mult.
3146 5 b. Type **561** 10 10
3147 10 b. Blenny 10 10
3148 20 b. Mackerel 15 10
3149 40 b. Nisetru sturgeon 30 10
3150 50 b. Seahorse 40 10
3151 55 b. Gurnard 50 10
3152 1 l. Bekuga sturgeon 70 10
3153 3 l. 20 Sting ray 2·75 25

1964. Cultural Anniversaries. Portraits in brown.
3154 5 b. green (Type **562**) 10 10
3155 20 b. lake (I. Creanga) 15 10
3156 35 b. red (E. Girleanu) 25 10
3157 55 b. bistre (Michelangelo) 30 10
3158 1 l. 20 blue (Galileo) 85 15
3159 1 l. 75 violet (Shakespeare) 1·40 20
Nos. 3154/5 commemorate 75th anniv of death; No. 3156, 50th anniv of death; No. 3157, 400th anniv of death; Nos. 3158/9, 400th anniv of birth. Creanga and Girleanu were writers.

563 Cheile Bicazului (gorge)

564 High–jumping

1964. Mountain Resorts.
3160 **563** 40 b. lake 25 10
3161 – 55 b. blue 40 10
3162 – 1 l. purple 55 10
3163 – 1 l. 35 brown 65 10
3164 – 1 l. 75 green 1·40 10
DESIGNS—VERT: 55 b. Cabin on Lake Bilea; 1 l. Poiana Brasov ski–lift; 1 l. 75, Alpine Hotel. HORIZ: 1 l. 35, Lake Bicaz.

1964. Balkan Games. Multicoloured.
3165 30 b. Type **564** 15 10
3166 40 b. Throwing the javelin 15 10
3167 55 b. Running 30 10
3168 1 l. Throwing the discus 60 10
3169 1 l. 20 Hurdling 60 10
3170 1 l. 55 Flags of competing countries (24 × 44 mm) 70 15

565 Arms and Flag

1964. 20th Anniv of Liberation. Multicoloured.
3171 55 b. Type **565** 25 10
3172 60 b. Industrial plant 25 10
3173 75 b. Harvest scene 35 15
3174 1 l. 20 Apartment houses 60 15
Nos. 3172/4 are horiz.

566 High–jumping

1964. Olympic Games, Tokyo. Multicoloured. (a) Perf.
3176 20 b. Type **566** 25 10
3177 30 b. Wrestling 40 15
3178 35 b. Volley ball 45 20
3179 40 b. Canoeing 50 25
3180 55 b. Fencing 1·00 15
3181 1 l. 20 Gymnastics 1·40 25
3182 1 l. 35 Football 1·60 40
3183 1 l. 55 Rifle–shooting 2·00 75

(b) Imperf. Colours changed and new values.
3184 20 b. Type **566** 45 10
3185 30 b. Wrestling 50 20
3186 35 b. Volleyball 85 20
3187 40 b. Canoeing 85 20
3188 55 b. Fencing 1·40 50
3189 1 l. 60 Gymnastics 3·00 1·25
3190 2 l. Football 3·50 1·75
3191 2 l. 40 Rifle–shooting 4·25 2·50

567 George Enescu

568 Python

1964. 3rd International George Enescu Festival.
3193 **567** 10 b. green 25 10
3194 – 55 b. purple 40 10
3195 – 1 l. 60 purple 1·00 35
3196 – 1 l. 75 blue 1·60 20
DESIGNS (Portraits of Enescu): 55 b. At piano; 1 l. 60, Medallion; 1 l. 75, When an old man.

1964. Bucharest Zoo. Multicoloured.
3197 5 b. Type **568** 10 10
3198 10 b. Black swans 45 10
3199 35 b. Ostriches 60 10
3200 40 b. Crowned cranes 75 15
3201 55 b. Tigers 75 10
3202 1 l. Lions 1·10 20
3203 1 l. 55 Grevy's zebras 1·60 20
3204 2 l. Bactrian camels 2·40 30

569 Brincoveanu, Cantacuzino, Lazar and Academy

570 Soldier

1964. Anniversaries. Multicoloured.

3205 20 b. Type **569** 10 10
3206 40 b. Cuza and seal 15 10
3207 55 b. Emblems and the Arts (vert) 25 10
3208 75 b. Laboratory workers and class 30 10
3209 1 l. Savings Bank building . . 50 25

EVENTS, etc: 20 b. 270th Anniv of Domneasca Academy; 40 b. and 75 b. Bucharest University centenary; 55 b. "Fine Arts" centenary (emblems are masks, curtain, piano keyboard, harp, palette and brushes); 1 l. Savings Bank centenary.

1964. Centenary of Army Day.

3210 **570** 55 b. blue and lt blue . . 45 15

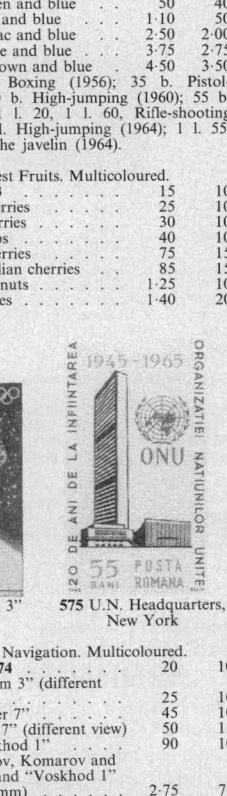

571 Post Office of 19th and 20th Centuries

1964. Air. Stamp Day.

3211 **571** 1 l. 60 + 40 b. blue, red and yellow . . . . 1·60 25

No. 3211 is a two-part design, the two parts being arranged vert imperf between.

572 Canoeing Medal (1956) **573** Strawberries

1964. Olympic Games-Rumanian Gold Medal Awards. Medals in brown and bistre (Nos. 3218/19 and 3226/7 in sepia and gold). (a) Perf.

3212 **572** 20 b. red and blue . . . 50 15
3213 – 30 b. green and blue . . 50 15
3214 – 35 b. turquoise and blue . 75 25
3215 – 40 b. lilac and blue . . . 90 35
3216 – 55 b. orange and blue . . 1·10 20
3217 – 1 l. 20 green and blue . . 1·40 35
3218 – 1 l. 35 brown and blue . . 2·00 45
3219 – 1 l. 55 mauve and blue . . 2·40 50

(b) Imperf. Colours changed and new values.

3220 **572** 20 b. orange and blue . . 15 20
3221 – 30 b. turquoise and blue . 40 30
3222 – 35 b. green and blue . . 40 30
3223 – 40 b. green and blue . . 50 40
3224 – 55 b. red and blue . . . 1·10 50
3225 – 1 l. 60 lilac and blue . . 2·50 2·00
3226 – 2 l. mauve and blue . . . 3·75 2·75
3227 – 2 l. 40 brown and blue . . 4·50 3·50

MEDALS: 30 b. Boxing (1956); 35 b. Pistol-shooting (1956); 40 b. High-jumping (1960); 55 b. Wrestling (1960); 1 l. 20, 1 l. 60, Rifle-shooting (1960); 1 l. 35, 2 l. High-jumping (1964); 1 l. 55, 2 l. 40, Throwing the javelin (1964).

1964. Forest Fruits. Multicoloured.

3229 5 b. Type **573** 15 10
3230 35 b. Blackberries 25 10
3231 40 b. Raspberries 30 10
3232 55 b. Rosehips 40 10
3233 1 l. 20 Blueberries 75 15
3234 1 l. 35 Cornelian cherries . . 85 15
3235 1 l. 55 Hazel nuts . . . . . 1·25 10
3236 2 l. 55 Cherries . . . . 1·40 20

574 "Syncom 3" **575** U.N. Headquarters, New York

1965. Space Navigation. Multicoloured.

3237 30 b. Type **574** 20 10
3238 40 b. "Syncom 3" (different view) 25 10
3239 55 b. "Ranger 7" 45 10
3240 1 l. "Ranger 7" (different view) 50 15
3241 1 l. 20 "Voskhod 1" 90 10
3242 5 l. Feoktistov, Komarov and Yegorov, and "Voskhod 1" (52½ × 29½ mm) . . . . . . 2·75 75

Nos. 3239/42 are horiz.

1965. 20th Anniv of U.N.O.

3243 **575** 55 b. gold, blue & red . . 30 10
3244 – 1 l. 60 multicoloured . . 1·00 20

DESIGN: 1 l. 60, Arms and U.N. emblem on Rumanian flag.

576 Tortoise ("Testudo graeca")

1965. Reptiles. Multicoloured.

3245 5 b. Type **576** 15 10
3246 10 b. "Lacerta taurica" . . . 15 10
3247 20 b. "Lacerta trilineata" . . 20 10
3248 40 b. "Alepharus kitaibelii" . 25 10
3249 55 b. "Anguis fragilis" . . . 30 10
3250 60 b. "Vipera ammodytes" . 45 10
3251 1 l. "Eremias arguta" . . . 55 10
3252 1 l. 20 "Vipera ursinii" . . . 65 10
3253 1 l. 35 "Coluber jugularis" . 85 15
3254 3 l. 25 "Elaphe quatuorlineata" 2·75 40

577 Tabby Cat **579** Ion Bianu (philologist)

1965. Domestic Cats. Multicoloured.

3255 5 b. Type **577** 10 10
3256 10 b. Ginger tomcat 15 10
3257 40 b. White Persians 25 10
3258 55 b. Kittens with shoe . . . 40 10
3259 60 b. Kitten with ball of wool 60 10
3260 75 b. Cat and two kittens . 75 10
3261 1 l. 35 Siamese . . . . . . 1·40 15
3262 3 l. 25 Heads of three cats (62 × 29 mm) . . . . . . 3·00 40

Nos. 3257/61 are vert.

1965. Space Flight of "Ranger 9" (24.3.65). No. 3240 surch **RANGER 9 24-3-1965 5 Lei** and floral emblem over old value.

3263 5 l. on 1 l. multicoloured . . 29·00 29·00

1965. Cultural Anniversaries. Portraits in sepia.

3264 **579** 40 l. blue 15 10
3265 – 55 b. ochre 20 10
3266 – 60 b. purple 25 10
3267 – 1 l. red 60 15
3268 – 1 l. 35 olive 50 20
3269 – 1 l. 75 red 80 25

PORTRAITS, etc: 40 b. (30th death anniv); 55 b. A. Bacalbasa (writer: birth cent); 60 b. V. Conta (philosopher: 120th birth anniv); 1 l. Jean Sibelius (composer: birth cent); 1 l. 35, Horace (poet: birth bimillenary); 1 l. 75, Dante (poet: 700th birth anniv).

580 I.T.U. Emblem and Symbols

1965. Centenary of I.T.U.

3270 **580** 1 l. 75 blue . . . . . . 1·25 20

581 Derdap Gorge (The Iron Gate)

1965. Inaug of Derdap Hydro Electric Project.

3271 **581** 30 b. (25 d.) green and grey 15 10
3272 – 55 b. (50 d.) red and grey 30 10

DESIGN: 55 b. Derdap Dam.

Nos. 3271/72 were issued simultaneously in Yugoslavia.

582 Rifleman **583** "Fat-Frumos and the Beast"

1965. European Shooting Championships, Bucharest. Multicoloured. (a) Perf.

3274 20 b. Type **582** 15 10
3275 40 b. Prone rifleman 25 10
3276 55 b. Pistol shooting 30 10
3277 1 l. "Free" pistol shooting . . 60 10
3278 1 l. 60 Standing rifleman . . 85 15
3279 2 l. Various marksmen . . . 1·40 35

(b) Imperf. Colours changed and new values.

3280 40 b. Prone rifleman 20 10
3281 55 b. Pistol shooting 25 15
3282 1 l. "Free" pistol shooting . . 45 25
3283 1 l. 60 Standing rifleman . . 65 50
3284 3 l. 25 Type **582** . . . . . 1·60 90
3285 5 l. Various marksmen . . . 2·75 1·00

Apart from Type **582** the designs are horiz, the 2 l. and 5 l. being larger 51½ × 28½ mm.

1965. Rumanian Fairy Tales. Multicoloured.

3286 20 b. Type **583** 25 10
3287 40 b. "Fat-Frumos and Ileana Cosinzeana" 25 10
3288 55 b. "Harap Alb" (horseman and bear) 30 10
3289 1 l. "The Moralist Wolf" . . 60 10
3290 1 l. 35 "The Ox and the Calf" 90 10
3291 2 l. "The Bear and the Wolf" (drawing a sledge) . . . . 1·25 25

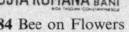

584 Bee on Flowers **585** Beliaiev, Leonov, "Voskhod 2" and Leonov in Space

1965. 20th International Bee-keeping Association Federation ("Apimondia") Congress, Bucharest.

3292 **584** 55 b. black, red & yellow 35 10
3293 – 1 l. 60 multicoloured . . 1·25 15

DESIGN—HORIZ: 1 l. 60, Congress Hall.

1965. Space Achievements. Multicoloured.

3294 5 b. "Proton 1" 15 10
3295 10 b. "Sonda 3" (horiz) . . . 20 15
3296 15 b. "Molnia 1" 25 20
3297 1 l. 75 Type **585** . . . . . 1·10 15
3298 2 l. 40 "Early Bird" satellite . 1·60 20
3299 3 l. 20 "Gemini 3" and astonauts in capsule . . . . 3·00 25
3300 3 l. 25 "Mariner 4" . . . . . 3·75 40
3301 5 l. "Gemini 5" (horiz) . . . 5·75 1·40

586 Marx and Lenin **588** V. Alecsandri

587 Common Quail

1965. Postal Ministers' Congress, Peking.

3302 **586** 55 b. multicoloured . . . 50 15

1965. Migratory Birds. Multicoloured.

3303 5 b. Type **587** 15 10
3304 10 b. Woodcock 25 10
3305 20 b. Common snipe 35 10
3306 40 b. Turtle dove 35 15
3307 55 b. Mallard 45 15
3308 60 b. White fronted goose . . 55 15
3309 1 l. Common crane 75 20
3310 1 l. 20 Glossy ibis . . . . . 1·00 20
3311 1 l. 25 Mute swan . . . . . 1·25 20
3312 3 l. 25 Eastern white pelican 3·75 60

The 3 l. 25, is vert 32 × 73 mm.

1965. 75th Death Anniv of Vasile Alecsandri (poet).

3313 **588** 55 b. multicoloured . . . 50 15

589 "Nymphaea zanzibariensis"

1965. Cluj Botanical Gardens. Multicoloured.

3314 5 b. "Strelitzia reginae" (crane flower) 10 10
3315 10 b. "Stanhopea tigrina" (orchid) 15 10
3316 20 b. "Paphiopedilum insigne" (orchid) 15 10
3317 30 b. Type **589** 30 10
3318 40 b. "Ferocactus glaucescens" (cactus) 40 10
3319 55 b. "Gossypium arboreum" 35 10
3320 1 l. "Hibiscus rosa sinensis" . 50 15
3321 1 l. 35 "Gloxinia hibrida" . . 1·00 15
3322 1 l. 75 "Victoria amazonica" (Victoria Regis lily) . . . 1·60 15
3323 2 l. 30 Hibiscus, crane flower, water lily and botanical building (52 × 29½ mm) . . 2·00 40

The 5, 10, 20 b. and 1 l. 35, are vert.

590 Running **592** Pigeon on TV Aerial

591 Pigeon and Horseman

1965. Spartacist Games. Multicoloured.

3324 55 b. Type **590** 25 15
3325 1 l. 55 Football . . . . . . 1·00 20
3326 1 l. 75 Diving . . . . 1·00 20
3327 2 l. Mountaineering (inscr "TURISM") . . . . 1·40 25
3328 5 l. Canoeing (inscr "CAMPIONATELLE EUROPENE 1965") (horiz) 3·00 50

1965. Stamp Day.

3329 **591** 55 b. + 45 b. blue and mauve 40 10
3330 **592** 1 l. brown and green . . 40 20
3331 – 1 l. 75 brown and green . 1·40 25

DESIGN: As Type **592**. 1 l. 75, Pigeon in flight.

593 Chamois

1965. "Hunting Trophies".

3332 **593** 55 b. brown, yell & mve 50 15
3333 – 1 l. brown, green & red . 90 15
3334 – 1 l. 60 brown, bl & orge 1·75 30
3335 – 1 l. 75 brown, red & grn 2·25 35
3336 – 3 l. 20 multicoloured . . 3·00 75

DESIGNS—37 × 23 mm: 1 l. Brown bear; 1 l. 60, Roe deer; 1 l. 75, Wild boar. 49 × 37½ mm: 3 l. 20, Trophy and antlers.

594 Dachshund

1965. Hunting Dogs. Multicoloured.
3337 5 b. Type **594** 10 10
3338 10 b. Spaniel 10 10
3339 40 b. Retriever with wood cock 60 10
3340 55 b. Fox terrier 40 10
3341 60 b. Red setter 55 10
3342 75 b. White setter . . . . . 1·00 15
3343 1 l. 55 Pointers . . . . 2·00 20
3344 3 l. 25 Duck–shooting with retriever . . . . 3·75 1·50
SIZES—DIAMOND. $47\frac{1}{2} \times 47\frac{1}{2}$ mm: 10 b. to 75 b. HORIZ—$43\frac{1}{2} \times 29$ mm: 1 l. 55, 3 l. 25.

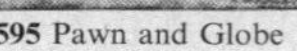
595 Pawn and Globe **596** Tractor, Corn and Sun

1966. 17th Chess Olympiad, Havana. Mult.
3345 20 b. Type **595** 35 10
3346 40 b. Jester and bishop (chess piece) 45 10
3347 55 b. Knight on horseback and rook (chess piece) 70 10
3348 1 l. As No. 3347 . . . . . . 95 10
3349 1 l. 60 Type **595** . . . . . 2·00 20
3350 3 l. 25 As No. 3346 . . . . . 4·00 1·50

1966. Co-operative Farming Union Congress.
3351 **596** 55 b. green and yellow . 45 15

597 G. Gheorghiu-Dej **598** Congress Emblem

1966. Death Anniv of G. Gheorghiu-Dej (Head of State).
3352 **597** 55 b. black and gold . . 40 15

1966. Communist Youth Union Congress.
3354 **598** 55 b. red and yellow . . 40 15

599 Dance of Moldova

1966. Rumanian Folk-dancing.
3355 **599** 30 b. black and purple . 30 10
3356 – 40 b. black and red . . . 50 20
3357 – 55 b. black & turquoise . 65 10
3358 – 1 l. black and lake . . . 85 10
3359 – 1 l. 60 black and blue . . 1·25 15
3360 – 2 l. black and green . . . 3·00 1·60
DANCES OF: 40 b. Oltenia; 55 b. Maramures; 1 l. Muntenia; 1 l. 60, Banat; 2 l. Transylvania.

600 Footballers **601** "Agriculture and Industry"

1966. World Cup Football Championships.
3361 **600** 5 b. multicoloured . . . 15 10
3362 – 10 b. multicoloured . . . 25 10
3363 – 15 b. multicoloured . . . 35 10
3364 – 55 b. multicoloured . . . 95 10
3365 – 1 l. 75 multicoloured . . 2·25 25
3366 – 4 l. multicoloured . . . 5·00 3·25
DESIGNS: 10 b. to 1 l. 75, Various footballers as Type **600**; 4 l. Jules Rimet Cup.

1966. Trade Union Congress, Bucharest.
3368 **601** 55 b. multicoloured . . . 35 15
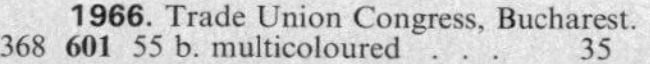

602 Red–breasted Flycatcher **603** "Venue 3"

1966. Song Birds. Multicoloured.
3369 5 b. Type **602** 25 10
3370 10 b. Red cross bill 35 10
3371 15 b. Great reed warbler . . 60 10
3372 20 b. Redstart 65 10
3373 55 b. European robin . . . 1·00 10
3374 1 l. 20 Blue throat . . . . . 1·40 15
3375 1 l. 55 Yellow wagtail . . . 2·25 20
3375 3 l. 20 Penduline tit . . . . 3·50 2·00

1966. Space Achievements. Multicoloured.
3377 10 b. Type **603** 25 10
3378 20 b. "FR 1" satellite . . . 30 10
3379 1 l. 60 "Luna 9" . . . . . . 2·00 20
3380 5 l. "Gemini 6" and "7" . . 4·75 1·60

604 U. Nestor (birth cent) **606** "Hottonia palustris"

605 "House" (after Petrascu)

1966. Cultural Anniversaries.
3381 – 5 b. blue, black & green 10 10
3382 – 10 b. green, black & red 15 10
3383 **604** 20 b. purple, black & grn 10 10
3384 – 40 b. brown, black & bl 15 10
3385 – 55 b. green, black & brn 20 10
3386 – 1 l. violet, black & bistre 45 15
3387 – 1 l. 35 olive, black & bl 70 20
3388 – 1 l. 60 purple, blk & grn 1·50 45
3389 – 1 l. 75 purple, blk & orge 95 20
3390 – 3 l. 25 lake, black & bl . 1·60 40
PORTRAITS: 5 b. G. Cosbuc (birth cent); 10 b. G. Sincai (150th death anniv); 40 b. A. Pumnul (death cent); 55 b. S. Luchian (50th death anniv); 1 l. Sun Yat-sen (birth cent); 1 l. 35, G. W. Leibnitz (250th death anniv); 1 l. 60, R. Rolland (birth cent); 1 l. 75, I. Ghica (150th birth anniv); 3 l. 25, S. C. Cantacuzino (250th death anniv).

1966. Paintings in National Gallery, Bucharest. Multicoloured.
3391 5 b. Type **605** 20 10
3392 10 b. "Peasant Girl" (Grigorescu) 25 10
3393 20 b. "Midday Rest" (Rescu) 40 15
3394 55 b. "Portrait of a Man" (Van Eyck) . . . . 1·40 25
3395 1 l. 55 "The 2nd Class Compartment" (Daumier) 5·25 60
3396 3 l. 25 "The Blessing" (El Greco) . . . . 7·50 5·25
The 10, 55 b. and 3 l. 25, are vert.

1966. Aquatic Flora. Multicoloured.
3397 5 b. Type **606** 15 10
3398 10 b. "Ceratophyllum submersum" 20 10
3399 20 b. "Aldrovanda vesiculosa" 25 10
3400 40 b. "Callitriche verna" . . 45 10
3401 55 b. "Vallisneria spiralis" . 45 10
3402 1 l. "Elodea canadensis" . . 1·25 15
3403 1 l. 55 "Hippuris vulgaris" . 1·50 20
3404 3 l. 25 "Myriophyllum spicatum" ($28 \times 49\frac{1}{2}$ mm) . 3·50 1·60

607 Diagram showing one metre in relation to quadrant of Earth **608** Putna Monastery

1966. Centenary of Metric System in Rumania.
3405 **607** 55 b. blue and brown . . 30 10
3406 – 1 l. violet and green . . . 50 20
DESIGN: 1 l. Metric abbreviations and globe.

1966. 500th Anniv of Putna Monastery.
3407 **608** 2 l. multicoloured . . . . 1·40 30

609 "Medicine"

1966. Centenary of Rumanian Academy.
3408 **609** 40 b. multicoloured . . . 20 10
3409 – 55 b. multicoloured . . . 25 10
3410 – 1 l. brown, gold & blue . 40 10
3411 – 3 l. brown, gold & yellow 1·75 1·00
DESIGNS—As Type **609**: 55 b. "Science" (formula). $22\frac{1}{2} \times 33\frac{1}{2}$ mm: 1 l. Gold medal. 67×27 mm: 3 l. I. Radulescu, M. Kogalniceanu and T. Savulescu.

610 Crayfish

1966. Crustaceans and Molluscs. Mult.
3412 5 b. Type **610** 15 10
3413 10 b. Netted dog whelk (vert) 20 10
3414 20 b. Marbled rock crab . . . 25 10
3415 40 b. Lapidary snail 40 10
3416 55 b. Brown lipped snail . . . 60 10
3417 1 l. 35 Mediterranean mussel . 1·50 15
3418 1 l. 75 Pond snail . . . . . . 1·75 20
3419 3 l. 25 Swan mussel . . . . . 3·75 1·60

611 Bucharest and Mail coach

1966. Stamp Day.
3420 **611** 55 b. + 45 b. mult. . . . 1·00 25
No. 3420 is a two-part design arranged horiz imperf between.

612 "Ursus spelaeus"

1966. Prehistoric Animals.
3421 **612** 5 b. blue, brown & green 20 10
3422 – 10 b. violet, bistre & grn . 20 10
3423 – 15 b. brown, purple & grn 25 10
3424 – 55 b. violet, bistre & grn . 70 10
3425 – 1 l. 55 blue, brown & grn 2·00 15
3426 – 4 l. mauve, bistre & green 3·75 1·75
ANIMALS: 10 b. "Mamuthus trogontherii"; 15 b. "Bison priscus"; 55 b. "Archidiscodon"; 1 l. 55, "Megaceros eurycerus". (43×27 mm): 4 l. "Deinotherium gigantissimum".

613 "Sputnik 1" orbiting Globe

1967. 10 Years of Space Achievements. Mult.
3427 10 b. Type **613** (postage) . . 15 10
3428 20 b. Gagarin and "Vostok 1" 15 10
3429 25 b. Tereshkova ("Vostok 6") 20 10
3430 40 b. Nikolaiev and Popovich ("Vostok 3" and "4") . . . 35 10
3431 55 b. Leonov in space ("Voskhod 2") 45 10
3432 1 l. 20 "Early Bird" (air) . . 1·25 15
3433 1 l. 55 Photo transmission ("Mariner 4") . . . . 1·60 20
3434 3 l. 25 Space rendezvous ("Gemini 6" and "7") . . . 2·25 40
3435 5 l. Space link up ("Gemini 8") 3·25 2·75

614 Barn Owl

1967. Birds of Prey. Multicoloured.
3442 10 b. Type **614** 45 10
3443 20 b. Eagle owl 70 10
3444 40 b. Saker falcon 65 10
3445 55 b. Egyptian vulture . . . 1·40 15
3446 75 b. Osprey 95 15
3447 1 l. Griffon vulture . . . . . 1·40 15
3448 1 l. 20 Lammergeier . . . . 2·40 25
3449 1 l. 75 European black vulture 2·75 1·90

615 "Washerwoman" (after I. Steriadi)

1967. Paintings.
3450 – 10 b. blue, gold and red . 20 10
3451 **615** 20 b. green, gold & ochre 25 15
3452 – 40 b. red, gold and blue . 40 20
3453 – 1 l. 55 purple, gold & blue 95 30
3454 – 3 l. 20 brown, gold & brn 3·25 40
3455 – 5 l. brown, gold & orge . 4·75 2·75
PAINTINGS—VERT: 10 b. "Model in Fancy Dress" (I. Andreescu); 40 b. "Peasants Weaving" (S. Dimitrescu); 1 l. 55, "Venus and Cupid" (L. Cranach); 5 l. "Haman beseeching Esther" (Rembrandt). HORIZ: 3 l. 20, "Hercules and the Lion" (Rubens).

616 Woman's Head **618** "Infantryman" (after Grigorescu)

617 Copper and Silver Coins of 1867

1967. 10th Anniv of C. Brancusi (sculptor). Sculptures.
3456 **616** 5 b. brown, yellow & red 15 10
3457 – 10 b. black, grn & violet 20 10
3458 – 20 b. black, green & red 20 10
3459 – 40 b. black, red & green 25 10
3460 – 55 b. black, olive & blue 50 20
3461 – 1 l. 20 brown, violet and orange . . . . 1·75 20
3462 – 3 l. 25 black, green and mauve . . . . 3·25 1·75
DESIGNS—HORIZ: 10 b. Sleeping muse; 40 b. "The Kiss"; 3 l. 25, Gate of Kisses, Targujiu. VERT: 20 b. "The Endless Column"; 55 b. Seated woman; 1 l. 20, "Miss Pogany".

1967. Centenary of Rumanian Monetary System.
3463 **617** 55 b. multicoloured . . . 30 15
3464 – 1 l. 20 multicoloured . . 60 55
DESIGN: 1 l. 20 Obverse and reverse of modern silver coin (1966).

1967. 90th Anniv of Independence.
3465 **618** 55 b. multicoloured . . . 1·60 1·60

MINIMUM PRICE

The minimum price quoted is 10p which represents a handling charge rather than a basis for valuing common stamps.
For further notes about prices, see introductory pages.

619 Peasants attacking (after O. Bancila)

620 "Centaurca pinnatifida"

1967. 60th Anniv of Peasant Rising.

3466	619	40 b. multicoloured	50	70
3467	–	1 l. 55 multicoloured	1·40	1·40

DESIGN—HORIZ: 1 l. 55, Peasants marching (after S. Luchian).

1967. Carpathian Flora. Multicoloured.

3468	20 b. Type **620**	15	10
3469	40 b. "Erysimum transsilvanicum"	20	10
3470	55 b. "Aquilegia transsilvanica"	25	10
3471	1 l. 20 "Viola alpina"	1·00	10
3472	1 l. 75 "Campanula carpatica"	1·10	10
3473	4 l. "Dryas octopetala" (horiz)	3·25	1·60

621 Towers, Sibiu

1967. Historic Monuments and International Tourist Year. Multicoloured.

3474	20 b. Type **621**	20	10
3475	40 b. Castle at Cris	25	10
3476	55 b. Wooden church, Plopis	50	10
3477	1 l. 60 Ruins, Neamtului	85	20
3478	1 l. 75. Mogosoaia Palace, Bucharest	1·40	20
3479	2 l. 25 Church, Voronet	2·00	1·40

No. 3479 is horiz, 48½ × 36 mm.

623 "The Marasesti Attack" (from painting by E. Stoica)

1967. 50th Anniv of Battles of Marasesti, Marasti and Oituz.

3481	623	55 b. brown, blue & grey	70	25

624 D. Lipatti (composer and pianist: 50th birth anniv)

625 Wrestling

1967. Cultural Anniversaries.

3482	624	10 b. violet, blue & black	15	10
3483	–	20 b. blue, brown & black	15	10
3484	–	40 b. brown, turq & blk	15	10
3485	–	55 b. brown, red & black	25	10
3486	–	1 l. 20 bowrn, olive & blk	40	15
3487	–	1 l. 75 green, blue & blk	1·00	1·00

DESIGNS: 20 b. A. Orascu (architect: 150th birth anniv); 40 b. G. Antipa (zoologist: birth cent); 55 b. M. Kogalniceanu (politician: 150th birth anniv); 1 l. 20, Jonathan Swift (300th birth anniv); 1 l. 75, Marie Curie (birth cent).

1967. World Wrestling Championships, Bucharest. Designs showing wrestlers and globes.

3488	625	10 b. multicoloured	10	10
3489	–	20 b. mult (horiz)	15	10
3490	–	55 b. multicoloured	25	10
3491	–	1 l. 20 multicoloured	1·00	15
3492	–	2 l. mult (horiz)	1·60	80

INDEX

Countries can be quickly located by referring to the index at the end of this volume.

626 Inscription on Globe

1967. International Linguists' Congress, Bucharest.

3493	626	1 l. 60 ultramarine, red and blue	1·40	20

627 Academy

1967. Centenary of Book Academy, Bucharest.

3494	627	55 b. grey, brown & blue	1·00	20

628 Dancing on Ice

629 Curtea de Arges Monastery

1967. Winter Olympic Games, Grenoble. Mult.

3495	20 b. Type **628**	10	10
3496	40 b. Skiing	15	10
3497	55 b. Bobsleighing	25	10
3498	1 l. Downhill skiing	45	15
3499	1 l. 55 Ice hockey	70	15
3500	2 l. Games emblem	90	25
3501	2 l. 30 Ski–jumping	1·60	1·00

1967. 450th Anniv of Curtea de Arges Monastery.

3503	629	55 b. multicoloured	65	20

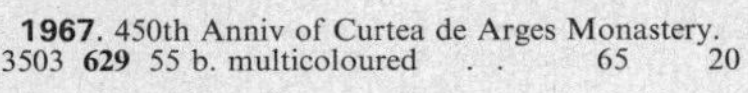

630 Karl Marx and Title Page

631 Lenin

1967. Centenary of Karl Marx's "Das Kapital".

3504	630	40 b. black, yell & red	30	15

1967. 50th Anniv of October Revolution.

3505	631	1 l. 20 black, gold & red	60	15

632 Arms of Rumania

633 Telephone Dial and Map

1967. (a) T **632**.

3506	632	40 b. blue	30	10
3506		55 b. yellow	40	10
3507		1 l. 60 red	1·00	10

(b) T **633** and similar designs.

3509	–	5 b. green	10	10
3510	–	10 b. red	10	10
3511	–	20 b. grey	40	10
3512	–	35 b. blue	20	10
3513	–	40 b. blue	20	10
3514	–	50 b. orange	25	10
3515	–	55 b. red	40	10
3516	–	60 b. brown	40	10
3517	–	1 l. green	40	10
3518	–	1 l. 20 violet	45	10
3519	–	1 l. 35 blue	75	10
3520	–	1 l. 50 red	70	10
3521	–	1 l. 55 brown	75	10
3522	–	1 l. 75 green	85	10
3523	–	2 l. yellow	90	10
3524	–	2 l. 40 blue	95	10
3525	633	3 l. turquoise	1·10	10
3526	–	3 l. 20 ochre	1·50	10
3527	–	3 l. 25 blue	1·75	10
3528	–	4 l. mauve	2·50	15
3529	–	5 l. violet	2·00	15

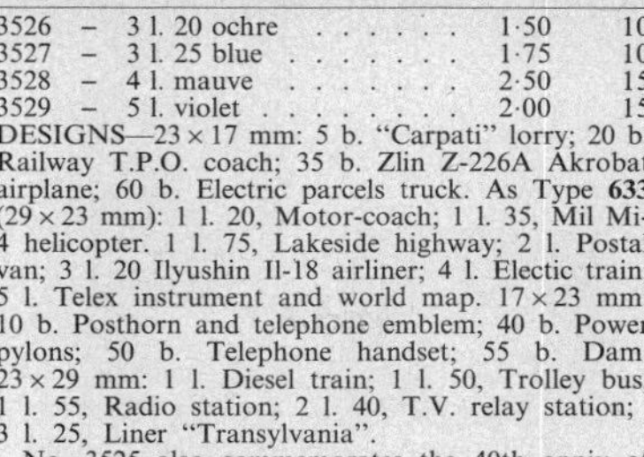

DESIGNS—23 × 17 mm: 5 b. "Carpati" lorry; 20 b. Railway T.P.O. coach; 35 b. Zlin Z-226A Akrobat airplane; 60 b. Electric parcels truck. As Type **633** (29 × 23 mm): 1 l. 20, Motor-coach; 1 l. 35, Mil Mi-4 helicopter. 1 l. 75, Lakeside highway; 2 l. Postal van; 3 l. 20 Ilyushin Il-18 airliner; 4 l. Electic train; 5 l. Telex instrument and world map. 17 × 23 mm: 10 b. Posthorn and telephone emblem; 40 b. Power pylons; 50 b. Telephone handset; 55 b. Dam. 23 × 29 mm: 1 l. Diesel train; 1 l. 50, Trolley bus; 1 l. 55, Radio station; 2 l. 40, T.V. relay station; 3 l. 25, Liner "Transylvania".

No. 3525 also commemorates the 40th anniv of the automatic telephone service.

For Nos. 3517/29 in smaller format see Nos. 3842/57.

634 "Crossing the River Buzau" (lithograph by Raffet) (½-size illustration)

1967. Stamp Day.

3530	634	55 b. + 45 b. blue and ochre	1·00	30

635 Monorail Train and Globe

636 Arms and Industrial Scene

1967. World Fair, Montreal. Multicoloured.

3531	55 b. Type **635**	30	10
3532	1 l. Expo emblem within atomic symbol	35	10
3533	1 l. 60 Gold cup and world map	70	15
3534	2 l. Expo emblem	1·10	75

1967. 20th Anniv of Republic. Multicoloured.

3535	40 b. Type **636**	15	10
3536	55 b. Arms of Rumania	15	10
3537	1 l. 60 Rumanian flag	40	15
3538	1 l. 75 Arms and cultural emblems	1·40	75

The 1 l. 60 is 34 × 48 mm.

637 I.A.R. 817 Flying Ambulance

1968. Air. Rumanian Aviation.

3539	–	40 b. multicoloured	15	10
3540	637	55 b. multicoloured	35	10
3541	–	1 l. multicoloured	40	10
3542	–	2 l. 40 multicoloured	1·10	55

DESIGNS—VERT: 40 b. Antonov An-2 biplane spraying crops; 1 l. "Aviasan" emblem and airliner; 2 l. 40, Mircea Zorileanu (pioneer aviator) and biplane.

638 "Angelica and Medor" (S. Ricci)

1968. Paintings in Rumanian Galleries. Mult.

3543	40 b. "Young Woman" (Misu Pop)	40	20
3544	55 b. "Little Girl in Red Scarf" (N. Grigorescu)	55	25
3545	1 l. "Old Nicholas, the Cobza-player" (S. Luchian)	1·25	30
3546	1 l. 60 "Man with Skull" (Dierick Bouts)	1·60	35
3547	2 l. 40 Type **638**	2·10	50
3548	3 l. 20 "Ecce Homo" (Titian)	6·75	6·00

Nos. 3543/6 and 3548 are vert.

See also Nos. 3583/8, 3631/6, 3658/63, 3756/61 and 3779/84.

640 Human Rights Emblem

641 W.H.O. Emblem

1968. Human Rights Year.

3551	640	1 l. multicoloured	1·00	15

1968. 20th Anniv of W.H.O.

3552	641	1 l. 60 multicoloured	1·40	15

642 "The Hunter"(after N. Grigorescu)

1968. Hunting Congress, Mamaia.

3553	642	1 l. 60 multicoloured	1·60	25

643 Pioneers and Liberation Monument

1968. Young Pioneers. Multicoloured.

3554	5 b. Type **643**	10	10
3555	40 b. Receiving scarves	15	10
3556	55 b. With models	25	10
3557	1 l. Operating radio sets	40	10
3558	1 l. 60 Folk-dancing	70	15
3559	2 l. 40 In camp	1·10	45

644 Prince Mircea

645 Ion Ionescu de la Brad (scholar)

1968. 550th Death Anniv of Prince Mircea (the Old).

3560	644	1 l. 60 multicoloured	1·40	25

1968. Cultural Anniversaries.

3561	645	40 b. multicoloured	15	15
3562	–	55 b. multicoloured	30	15

PORTRAITS AND ANNIVS: 40 b. Type **645** (150th birth anniv); 55 b. Emil Racovita (scientist: birth cent).

646 "Pelargonium zonale, Ait"

648 Throwing the Javelin

647 "Nicolae Balcescu" (G. Tattarescu)

1968. Garden Geraniums. Multicoloured.

3563	10 b. Type **646**	15	10
3564	20 b. "Pelargonium zonale Ait"	15	10
3565	40 b. "Pelargonium zonale Ait"	20	10
3566	55 b. "Pelargonium zonale Ait"	20	10
3567	60 b. "Pelargonium grandi–florum Hort"	35	10
3568	1 l. 20 "Pelargonium peltatum Hort"	40	10

3569 1 l. 35 "Pelargonium peltatum Hort" 50 15
3570 1 l. 60 "Pelargonium grandiflorum Hort" . . . 1·00 50

Nos. 3563/6, 3567 and 3570, 3568/9 respectively are different varieties of the same species.

1968. 120th Anniv of 1848 Revolution. Paintings. Multicoloured.
3571 55 b. Type **647** 30 10
3572 1 l. 20 "Avram Iancu" (B. Iscovescu) 35 15
3573 1 l. 60 "Vasile Alecsandri" (N. Livaditti) . . . . 1·60 85

1968. Olympic Games, Mexico. Multicoloured.
3574 10 b. Type **648** 10 10
3575 20 b. Diving 15 10
3576 40 b. Volleyball 15 10
3577 55 b. Boxing 25 10
3578 60 b. Wrestling 25 10
3579 1 l. 20 Fencing 65 15
3580 1 l. 35 Punting 85 15
3581 1 l. 60 Football . . . . . . 1·40 1·00

1968. Paintings in the Fine Arts Museum, Bucarest. Multicoloured.
3583 10 b. "The Awakening of Rumania" (G. Tattarescu) (28 × 49 mm) . . . 10 10
3584 20 b. "Composition" (Teodorescu Sionion) . . . 15 10
3585 35 b. "The Judgement of Paris" (H. van Balen) 20 10
3586 60 b. "The Mystical Betrothal of St. Catherine" (L. Sustris) 35 15
3587 1 l.75 "Mary with the Child Jesus" (J. van Bylert) . . . 1·40 25
3588 3 l. "The Summer" (J. Jordaens) 3·25 1·60

649 F.I.A.P. Emblem within "Lens"

650 Academy and Harp

1968. 20th Anniv of International Federation of Photographic Art (F.I.A.P.).
3589 **649** 1 l. 60 multicoloured . . 1·40 20

1968. Centenary of Georgi Enescu Philharmonic Academy.
3590 **650** 55 b. multicoloured . . . 70 15

651 Triumph of Trajan (Roman metope)

1968. Historic Monuments.
3591 **651** 10 b. green, blue & red . 10 10
3592 – 40 b. blue, brown & red . 20 10
3593 – 55 b. violet, brown & grn 25 10
3594 – 1 l. 20 purple, grey and ochre 45 15
3595 – 1 l. 55 blue, green & pur 1·00 20
3596 – 1 l. 75 brown, bistre and orange . . . . 1·40 50

DESIGNS—HORIZ: 40 b. Monastery Church, Moldovita; 55 b. Mon. Church, Cozia; 1 l. 20, Tower and Church, Tirgoviste; 1 l. 55, Palace of Culture, Jassy; 1 l. 75, Corvinus Castle, Hunedoara.

652 Old Bucharest (18th-cent painting)
(Illustration reduced. Actual size 76 × 28mm)

1968. Stamp Day.
3597 **652** 55 b. + 45 b. multicoloured 1·40 70

653 Mute Swan

655 Neamtz Costume (female)

654 "Entry of Michael the Brave into Alba Julia" (E. Stoica)

1968. Fauna of Nature Reservations. Multicoloured.
3598 10 b. Type **653** 40 10
3599 20 b. Black-winged stilt . . 50 10
3600 40 b. Common shelduck . . 60 10
3601 55 b. Great egret . . . . . 1·00 30
3602 60 b. Golden eagle 80 15
3603 1 l. 20 Great bustard . . . . 1·00 30
3604 1 l. 35 Chamois 80 25
3605 1 l. 60 European bison . . . 1·00 1·40

1968. 50th Anniv of Union of Transylvania with Rumania. Multicoloured.
3606 55 b. Type **654** 25 10
3607 1 l. "Union Dance" (T. Aman) 40 10
3608 1 l. 75 "Alba Julia Assembly" 1·00 30

1968. Provincial Costumes (1st series). Multicoloured.
3610 5 b. Type **655** 10 10
3611 40 b. Neamtz (male) 20 10
3612 55 b. Hunedoara (female) . . 30 10
3613 1 l. Hunedoara (male) . . . 50 10
3614 1 l. 60 Brasov (female) . . . 80 20
3615 2 l. 40 Brasov (male) . . . . 1·25 1·00

See also Nos. 3617/22.

656 Earth, Moon and Orbital Track of "Apollo 8"

657 Fencing

1969. Air. Flight of "Apollo 8" around the Moon.
3616 **656** 3 l. 30 black, sil & bl 2.75 2.75

1969. Provincial Costumes (2nd series). As T **655**. Multicoloured.
3617 5 b. Doli (female) 10 10
3618 40 b. Doli (male) 20 10
3619 55 b. Arges (female) 30 10
3620 1 l. Arges (male) 50 20
3621 1 l. 60 Timisoara (female) . 80 25
3622 2 l. 40 Timisoara (male) . . 1·25 1·00

1969. Sports.
3623 **657** 10 b. grey, black & brn . 10 10
3624 – 20 b. grey, black & vio . 10 10
3625 – 40 b. grey, black & blue 10 10
3626 – 55 b. grey, black & red . 20 10
3627 – 1 l. grey, black & green . 30 10
3628 – 1 l. 20 grey, black & bl . 35 10
3629 – 1 l. 60 grey, black & red 1·40 20
3630 – 2 l. 40 grey, black & grn 1·00 50

DESIGNS: 20 b. Throwing the javelin; 40 b. Canoeing; 55 b. Boxing; 1 l. Volleyball; 1 l. 20, Swimming; 1 l. 60, Wrestling; 2 l. 40, Football.

1969. Nude Paintings in the National Gallery. As T **638**. Multicoloured.
3631 10 b. "Nude" (C. Tattarescu) 10 10
3632 20 b. "Nude" (T. Pallady) . 10 10
3633 35 b. "Nude" (N. Tonitza) . 15 10
3634 60 b. "Venus and Cupid" (Flemish School) 40 10
3635 1 l. 75 "Diana and Endymion" (M. Liberi) . . . . . 1·60 65
3636 3 l. "The Three Graces" (J. H. von Achen) . . . . . . 3·25 1·60

SIZES—36 × 49 mm: 10 b., 35 b., 60 b., 1 l. 75. 27 × 49 mm: 3 l. 49 × 36 mm: 20 b.

658 "Soyuz 4" and "Soyuz 5"

659 I.L.O. Emblem

1969. Air. Space Link-up of "Soyuz 4" and "Soyuz 5".
3638 **658** 3 l. 30 multicoloured . . 2·75 2·75

1969. 50th Anniv of International Labour Office.
3639 **659** 55 b. multicoloured . . . 65 15

660 Stylised Head

662 Referee introducing Boxers

661 Posthorn

1969. Inter-European Cultural Economic Co-operation.
3640 **660** 55 b. multicoloured . . . 65 65
3641 1 l. 50 multicoloured . . 1·40 1·40

1969. Postal Ministers' Conference, Bucharest.
3642 **661** 55 b. dp blue and blue . . 35 15

1969. European Boxing Championships, Bucharest. Multicoloured.
3643 35 b. Type **662** 15 10
3644 40 b. Sparring 20 10
3645 55 b. Leading with punch . . 30 10
3646 1 l. 75 Declaring the winner . 1·40 50

663 "Apollo 9" and Module over Earth

1969. Air. "Apollo" Moon Flights. Multicoloured.
3647 60 b. Type **663** 15 10
3648 2 l. 40 "Apollo 10" and module approaching Moon (vert) . 1·40 15

664 "Apatura ilia"

665 Astronaut and Module on Moon

1969. Butterflies. Multicoloured.
3649 5 b. Type **664** 10 10
3650 10 b. "Prosperpinus prosperina" 10 10
3651 20 b. "Colias erate" 15 10
3652 40 b. "Pericallia matronula" . 20 10
3653 55 b. "Argynnis laodice" . . 30 10
3654 1 l. "Callimorpha quadripunctaria" 65 10
3655 1 l. 20 "Anthocaris cardamines" 85 20
3656 2 l. 40 "Meleageria daphnis" . 1·75 1·00

1969. Air. First Man on the Moon.
3657 **665** 3 l. 30 multicoloured . . 2·00 2·00

1969. Paintings in the National Gallery, Bucharest. Multicoloured. As T **638**.
3658 10 b. "Venetian Senator" (School of Tintoretto) . . . 10 10
3659 20 b. "Sofia Kretzulescu" (G. Tattarescu) 10 10
3660 35 b. "Philip IV" (Velasquez) 20 10
3661 35 b. "Man Reading" (Memling) 40 10
3662 1 l. 75 "Lady D'Aguesseau" (Vigee-Lebrun) . . . . . 1·00 20
3663 3 l. "Portrait of a Woman" (Rembrandt) . . . . . . 2·40 1·40

666 Communist Flag

667 Symbols of Learning

1969. 10th Rumanian Communist Party Congress.
3665 **666** 55 b. multicoloured . . . 60 15

1969. National "Economic Achievements" Exhibition, Bucharest. Multicoloured.
3666 35 b. Type **667** 10 10
3667 40 b. Symbols of Agriculture and Science 15 10
3668 1 l. 75 Symbols of Industry . 1·00 15

668 Liberation Emblem

669 Juggling on Trick-cycle

1969. 25th Anniv of Liberation. Multicoloured.
3669 10 b. Type **688** 10 10
3670 55 b. Crane and trowel . . 15 10
3671 60 b. Flags on scaffolding . . 25 10

1969. Rumanian State Circus. Multicoloured.
3672 10 b. Type **669** 10 10
3673 20 b. Clown 10 10
3574 35 b. Trapeze artists 25 10
3575 60 b. Equestrian act 35 10
3576 1 l. 75 High-wire act 65 10
3677 3 l. Performing tiger . . . . 1·60 60

670 Forces' Memorial

1969. "Army Day" and 25th Anniv of People's Army.
3678 **670** 55 b. black, gold & red . 40 15

671 Trains of 1869 and 1969

1969. Centenary of Rumanian Railways.
3679 **671** 55 b. multicoloured . . . 60 15

672 "Courtyard" (M. Bouquet)

1969. Stamp Day.
3680 **672** 55 b. + 45 b. multicoloured 75 65

673 Branesti Mask

674 "Apollo 12" above Moon

1969. Folklore Masks. Multicoloured.
3681 40 b. Type **673** 15 10
3682 55 b. Tudora mask 20 10
3683 1 l. 55 Birsesti mask 50 10
3684 1 l. 75 Rudaria mask 65 40

1969. Moon Landing of "Apollo 12".
3685 **674** 1 l. 50 multicoloured . . 1·10 75

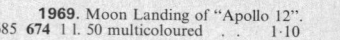

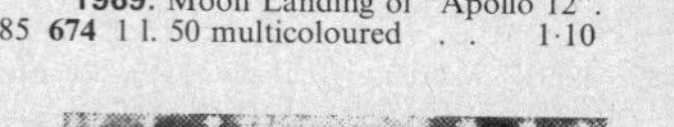

675 "Three Kings" (Voronet Monastery)

1969. Frescoes from Northern Moldavian Monasteries (1st series). Multicoloured.

3686 10 b. Type **675** 10 10
3687 20 b. "Three Kings" (Sucevita) 15 10
3688 35 b. "Holy Child in Manger" (Voronet) 20 10
3689 60 b. "Ship" (Sucevita) . . . 35 10
3690 1 l. 75 "Walled City" (Moldovita) . . . . 1·25 20
3691 3 l. "Pastoral Scene" (Voronet) 2·40 1·40

The 60 b. and 3 l. are vert.
See also Nos. 3736/42 and 3872/8.

676 "Old Mother Goose", Capra

1969. New Year. Children's Celebrations. Multicoloured.

3692 40 b. Type **676** 15 10
3693 55 b. Decorated tree, Sorcova 20 10
3694 1 l. 50 Drummers, Buhaiul . 75 10
3695 2 l. 40 Singer and bellringer, Plugusurol . . . . 1·00 45

677 Hockey players and Emblem

678 "Pulsatilla pratensis"

1970. World Ice Hockey Championships. Mult.

3696 20 b. Type **677** 10 10
3697 55 b. Goalkeeper 15 10
3698 1 l. 20 Two players 45 10
3699 2 l. 40 Goal mouth melee . . 1·00 40

1970. Flowers. Multicoloured.

3700 5 b. Type **678** 10 10
3701 10 b. "Adonis vernalis" . . . 10 10
3702 20 b. "Carduus nutans" . . . 10 10
3703 40 b. "Amygdalus nana" . . 10 10
3704 55 b. "Iris pumilla" 10 10
3705 1 l. "Linum hirsutum" . . . 25 10
3706 1 l. 20 "Salvia aethiopis" . . 40 10
3707 2 l. 40 "Paeonia tenuifolia" . 3·00 80

679 Japanese Woodcut

681 Lenin

680 B.A.C One Eleven 475

1970. World Fair, Osaka, Japan. Expo 70. Mult.

3714 20 b. Type **679** 20 10
3715 1 l. Japanese pagoda (29 × 92 mm) . . . . 1·00 65

1970. 50th Anniv of Rumanian Civil Aviation. Multicoloured.

3717 60 b. Type **680** 25 10
3718 2 l. Tail of B.A.C. One Eleven 475 . . . . 75 25

1970. Birth Centenary of Lenin.

3719 **681** 40 b. multicoloured . . . 40 10

682 "Camille" (Monet) and Maximum Card

683 "Prince Alexander Cuza" (Szathmary)

1970. Maximafila Franco–Rumanian Philatelic Exn, Bucharest.

3720 **682** 1 l. 50 multicoloured . . 1·40 30

1970. 150th Birth Anniv of Prince Alexander Cuza.

3721 **683** 55 b. multicoloured . . 55 15

684 "Co-operation" Map

685 Victory Monument, Bucharest

1970. Inter-European Cultural and Economic Co-operation.

3722 **684** 40 b. green, brn & blk . 45 45
3723 1 l. 50 blue, brown & blk . 1·40 1·40

1970. 25th Anniv of Liberation.

3724 **685** 55 b. multicoloured . . 65 15

686 Greek Silver Drachma. 5th cent B.C.

1970. Ancient Coins.

3725 **686** 10 b. black and blue . . 15 10
3726 – 20 b. black and red . . 20 10
3727 – 35 b. bronze and green . 25 10
3728 – 60 b. black and brown . 35 10
3729 – 1 l. 75 black and blue . 85 10
3730 – 3 l. black and red . . . 2·00 1·00

DESIGNS—HORIZ: 20 b. Getic-Dacian silver didrachm, 2nd–1st-cent B.C.; 35 b. Copper sestertius of Trajan, 106 A.D.; 60 b. Mircea ducat, 1400; 1 l. 75, Silver groschen of Stephen the Great, 1460. VERT: 3 l. Brasov klippe-thaler, 1601.

687 Footballers and Ball

1970. World Cup Football Championships, Mexico.

3731 **687** 40 b. multicoloured . . 15 10
3732 – 55 b. multicoloured . . 20 10
3733 – 1 l. 75 multicoloured . . 70 15
3734 – 3 l. 30 multicoloured . . 1·60 50

DESIGNS: Nos. 3732/4, various football scenes as Type **687**.

1970. Frescoes from Northern Moldavian Monasteries (2nd series). As T **675**. Multicoloured.

3736 10 b. "Prince Petru Rares and Family" (Moldovita) . . . 10 10
3737 20 b. "Metropolitan Grigore Rosca" (Voronet) 15 10
3738 40 b. "Alexander the Good and Family" (Sucevita) . . . 20 10
3739 55 b. "The Last Judgement" (Voronet) (vert) 35 10
3740 1 l. 75 "The Last Judgement" (Voronet) (different) . . 90 20
3741 3 l. "St. Anthony" (Voronet) 2·50 1·40

The 20 b. is smaller, 28 × 48 mm.

688 "Apollo 13" Spashdown

689 Engels

1970. Air. Space Flight of "Apollo 13".

3743 **688** 1 l. 50 multicoloured . . 65 65

1970. 150th Birth Anniv of Friedrich Engels.

3744 **689** 1 l. 50 multicoloured . . 1·00 15

690 Exhibition Hall

1970. National Events. Multicoloured.

3745 35 b. "Iron Gates" Dam . . 15 10
3746 55 b. Freighter and flag . . 45 10
3747 1 l. 50 Type **690** 85 15

EVENTS: 35 b. Danube navigation projects; 55 b. 75th anniv of Rumanian Merchant Marine; 1 l. 50, 1st International Fair, Bucharest.

691 New Headquarters Building

1970. New U.P.U. Headquarters Building, Berne.

3748 **691** 1 l. 50 green and blue . . 1·10 15

Iceberg
20
POSTA ROMANA

692 Education Year Emblem

693 "Iceberg"

1970. International Education Year.

3749 **692** 55 b. plum, black & red . 65 15

1970. Roses. Multicoloured.

3750 20 b. Type **693** 10 10
3751 35 b. "Wiener Charme" . . . 10 10
3752 55 b. "Pink Lustre" 20 10
3753 1 l. "Piccadilly" 60 10
3754 1 l. 50 "Orange Delbard" . . 75 10
3755 2 l. 40 "Sibelius" . . . . . . 1·50 55

0.55
POSTA ROMANA

694 "Spaniel and Pheasant" (J. B. Oudry)

695 Refugee Woman and Child

1970. Paintings in Rumanian Galleries. Multicoloured. Sizes in millimetres.

3756 10 b. "The Hunt" (D. Brandi) (38 × 50) 10 10
3757 20 b. Type **694** 10 10
3758 35 b. "The Hunt" (Jan Fyt) (38 × 50) 15 10
3759 60 b. "After the Chase" (Jordaens) (As T **694**) . . . 40 10
3760 1 l. 75 "The Game Dealer" (F. Snyders) (50 × 38) 90 20
3761 3 l. "The Hunt" (A. de Gryeff) (As T **694**) . . . . . . 2·40 1·40

1970. Danube Flood Victims (1st issue).

3763 **695** 55 b. black, blue and green (postage) 25 10
3764 – 1 l. 50 multicoloured . . 60 15
3765 – 1 l. 75 multicoloured . . 90 65
3766 – 60 b. black, drab and blue (air) 50 10

DESIGNS: 60 b. Helicopter rescue; 1 l. 50, Red Cross post; 1 l. 75, Building reconstruction.
See also No. 3777.

696 U.N. Emblem

698 Beethoven

697 Arab Horse

1970. 25th Anniv of United Nations.

3767 **696** 1 l. 50 multicoloured . . 1·10 15

1970. Horses. Multicoloured.

3768 20 b. Type **697** 10 10
3769 35 b. American trotter . . . 10 10
3770 55 b. Ghidran 15 10
3771 1 l. Hutul 50 10
3772 1 l. 50 Thoroughbred 75 15
3773 2 l. 40 Lippizaner . . . . . 2·25 1·40

1970. Birth Bicentenary of Beethoven.

3774 **698** 55 b. multicoloured . . . 1·25 15

699 "Mail–cart in the Snow" (E. Volkers). (Illustration reduced. Actual size 75 × 33 mm)

1970. Stamp Day.

3775 **699** 55 b. + 45 b. mult . . . 1·40 1·00

700 Henri Coanda's Turbine-powered Model Airplane

1970. Air. 60th Anniv of First Experimental Rocket-powered Flight.

3776 **700** 60 b. multicoloured . . . 75 15

701 "The Flood" (abstract, Joan Miro)

1970. Danube Flood Victims (2nd issue).

3777 **701** 3 l. multicoloured . . . 3·25 3·25

702 "Sight" (G. Coques)

1970. Paintings from the Bruckenthal Museum, Sibiu. Multicoloured.

3779 10 b. Type **702** 10 10
3780 20 b. "Hearing" 10 10
3781 35 b. "Smell" 15 10
3782 60 b. "Taste" 25 10
3783 1 l. 75 "Touch" 50 10
3784 3 l. Bruckenthal Museum . . 1·60 85

Nos. 3779/84 show a series of pictures by Coques entitled "The Five Senses".

703 T. Vladimirescu (T. Aman) **705** Alsatian

704 "Three Races"

1971. 150th Death Anniv of Tudor Vladimirescu (Wallachian revolutionary).

3786 **703** 1 l. 50 multicoloured . . 90 15

1971. Racial Equality Year.

3787 **704** 1 l. 50 multicoloured . . 1·10 15

1971. Dogs. Multicoloured.

3788 20 b. Type **705** 10 10
3789 35 b. Bulldog 15 10
3790 55 b. Fox terrier 20 10
3791 1 l. Setter 50 10
3792 1 l. 50 Cocker spaniel 75 20
3793 2 l. 40 Poodle . . . . 3·25 1·60

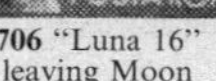

706 "Luna 16" leaving Moon **707** Proclamation of the Commune

1971. Air. Moon Missions of "Luna 16" and "Luna 17". Multicoloured.

3794 3 l. 30 Type **706** . . . . . 1·60 1·60
3795 3 l. 30 "Lunokhod 1" on Moon 1·60 1·60

1971. Centenary of Paris Commune.

3796 **707** 40 b. multicoloured . . . 50 15

708 Astonaut and Moon Trolley

1971. Air. Moon Mission of "Apollo 14".

3797 **708** 3 l. 30 multicoloured . . 1·60 1·60

709 "Three Fists" Emblem and Flags **710** "Toadstool" Rocks, Babele

1971. Trade Union Congress, Bucharest.

3798 **709** 55 b. multicoloured . . . 65 15

1971. Tourism. Multicoloured.

3799 10 b. Gorge, Cheile Bicazului (vert) 10 10
3800 40 b. Type **710** 10 10
3801 55 b. Winter resort, Poiana Brasov 15 10
3802 1 l. Holiday scene, Danube delta 45 10
3803 1 l. 50 Hotel, Baile Sovata . . 85 15
3804 2 l. 40 Venus, Jupiter and Neptune Hotels, Black Sea (77 × 29 mm) . . . . 1·25 85

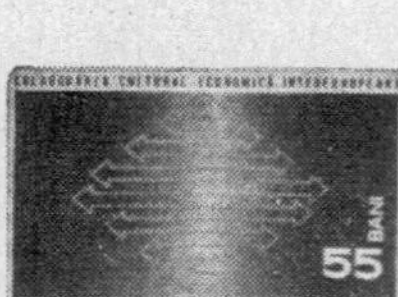

711 "Arrows" **712** Museum Building

1971. Inter-European Cultural Economic Co-operation. Multicoloured.

3805 55 b. Type **711** . . . . . . 1·50 1·50
3806 1 l. 75 Stylised map of Europe 2·75 2·40

1971. Historical Museum, Bucharest.

3807 **712** 55 b. multicoloured . . 40 10

713 "The Secret Printing–press" (S. Szonyi) **714** "Motra Tone" (K. Idromeno)

1971. 50th Anniv of Rumanian Communist Party. Multicoloured.

3808 35 b. Type **713** 10 10
3809 40 b. Emblem and red flags (horiz) 15 10
3810 55 b. "The Builders" (A. Anastasiu) 25 15

1971. "Balkanfila III". International Stamp Exhibition, Bucharest. Multicoloured.

3811 1 l. 20 + 60 b. Type **714** . . 1·25 1·25
3812 1 l. 20 + 60 b. "Maid" (V. Dimitrov-Maystora) . . . 1·25 1·25
3813 1 l. 20 + 60 b. "Rosa Botzaris" (J. Stieler) . . . . 1·25 1·25
3814 1 l. 20 + 60 b. "Portrait of a Lady" (K. Ivanovic) . . . 1·25 1·25
3815 1 l. 20 + 60 b. "Agreseanca" (C. Popp de Szathmary) . 1·25 1·25
3816 1 l. 20 + 60 b. "Woman in Modern Dress" (C. Ibrahim) 1·25 1·25

Each stamp has a premium carrying "tab" as shown in Type **714**.

715 "Punica granatum"

1971. Flowers. Multicoloured.

3818 20 b. Type **715** 10 10
3819 35 b. "Calceolus speciosum" 10 10
3820 55 b. "Life jagra" 10 10
3821 1 l. "Mimulus luteus" . . . 40 10
3822 1 l. 50 "Convolvulus tricolor" 60 20
3823 2 l. 40 "Phyllocactus phyllanthoides" (horiz) . . 1·75 20

716 "Nude" (J. Iser)

1971. Paintings of Nudes. Multicoloured.

3824 10 b. Type **716** 10 10
3825 20 b. "Nude" (C. Ressu) . . . 10 10
3826 35 b. "Nude" (N. Grigorescu) 10 10
3827 60 b. "Odalisque" (Delacroix) (horiz) 10 10
3828 1 l. 75 "Nude in a Landscape" (Renoir) . . . . 1·00 20
3829 3 l. "Venus and Cupid" (Il Vecchio) (horiz) . . . . 2·00 1·00

The 20 b. is smaller, 29 × 50 mm.

718 Astronauts and Lunar Rover on Moon

1971. Air. Moon Flight of "Apollo 15".

3833 **718** 1 l. 50 multicoloured (blue background) . . . . . 2·40 2·40

No. 3833 also exists imperforate, with background colour changed to green, from a restricted printing.

719 "Fishing Boats" (M. W. Arnold)

1971. Marine Paintings. Multicoloured.

3835 10 b. "Coastal Storm" (B. Peters) 10 10
3836 20 b. "Seascape" (I. Backhuysen) 10 10
3837 35 b. "Boat in Stormy Seas" (A. van de Eertvelt) 15 10
3838 60 b. Type **719** 25 10
3839 1 l. 75 "Seascape" (I. K. Aivazovsky) 65 20
3840 3 l. "Fishing boats, Braila" (J. A. Steriadi) . . . . . 1·75 40

1971. As Nos. 3517/29 and three new designs but in smaller format, 17 × 23 or 23 × 17 mm.

3842 1 l. green 45 10
3843 1 l. 20 violet 40 10
3844 1 l. 35 blue 75 10
3845 1 l. 50 red 50 10
3846 1 l. 55 brown 50 10
3847 1 l. 75 green 55 10
3848 2 l. green 65 10
3849 2 l. 40 blue 75 10
3850 3 l. blue 95 10
3851 3 l. 20 brown . . . . 1·50 10
3852 3 l. 25 blue . . . . 1·50 10
3853 3 l. 60 blue . . . . 1·25 10
3854 4 l. mauve . . . . 1·50 10
3855 4 l. 80 blue . . . . 1·50 10
3856 5 l. violet . . . . 1·75 10
3857 6 l. mauve . . . . 1·90 10

NEW DESIGNS—VERT: 3 l. 60, Clearing letter box; 4 l. 80, Postman on round; 6 l. Postal Ministry, Bucharest.

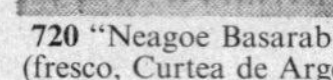

720 "Neagoe Basarab" (fresco, Curtea de Arges) **721** "T. Pallady" (self portrait)

1971. 450th Death Anniv of Prince Neagoe Basarab, Regent of Wallachia.

3858 **720** 60 b. multicoloured . . . 45 15

1971. Artists Anniversaries.

3859 **721** 40 b. multicoloured . . . 10 10
3860 – 55 b. black, stone & gold 15 10
3861 – 1 l. 50 black, stone & gold 40 10
3862 – 2 l. 40 multicoloured . . 1·10 25

DESIGNS: 40 b. (birth centenary); 55 b. "B. Cellini" (400th death anniv); 1 l. 50, "Watteau" (self-portrait) (250th death anniv); 2 l. 40, "Durer" (self-portrait) (500th birth anniv).

722 Persian Text and Seal **723** Figure–skating

1971. 2500th Anniv of Persian Empire.

3863 **722** 55 b. multicoloured . . . 50 10

1971. Winter Olympic Games, Sapporo, Japan (1972). Multicoloured.

3864 10 b. Type **723** 10 10
3865 20 b. Ice–hockey 10 10
3866 40 b. Biathlon 10 10
3887 55 b. Bobsleighing 10 10
3888 1 l. 75 Downhill skiing . . . 65 20
3869 3 l. Games emblem . . . . . 1·60 1·00

724 "Lady with Letter" (Sava Hentia)

1971. Stamp Day.

3871 **724** 1 l. 10 + 90 b. mult . . 1·50 1·00

1971. Frescoes from Northern Moldavian Monasteries (3rd series). As T **675**. Multicoloured.

3872 10 b. "St. George and The Dragon" (Moldovita) (vert) 10 10
3873 20 b. "Three Kings and Angel" (Moldovita) (vert) 10 10
3874 40 b. "The Crucifixion" (Moldovita) (vert) 10 10
3875 55 b. "Trial" (Voronet) (vert) 15 10
3876 1 l. 75 "Death of a Martyr" (Voronet) (vert) . . . . . 1·00 20
3877 3 l. "King and Court" (Arborea) . . . . 2·00 1·40

725 Matei Millo (dramatist, 75th death anniv) **726** Magellan and Ships (450th Death Anniv)

1971. Famous Rumanians. Multicoloured.

3879 55 b. Type **725** 20 10
3880 1 l. Nicolae Iorga (historian, birth cent) 35 15

1971. Scientific Anniversaries.

3881 **726** 40 b. mauve, blue & grn 40 10
3882 – 55 b. blue, green & lilac . 20 10
3883 – 1 l. multicoloured . . . 50 10
3884 – 1 l. 50 green, bl & brn . 65 20

DESIGNS AND ANNIVERSARIES: 55 b. Kepler and observatory (400th birth anniv); 1 l. Gagarin, rocket and Globe (10th anniv of first manned space flight); 1 l. 50, Lord Rutherford and atomic symbol (Birth cent).

727 Lynx Cubs

1972. Young Wild Animals. Multicoloured.

3885		20 b. Type **727**	10	10
3886		35 b. Red fox cubs	10	10
3887		55 b. Roe deer fawns	20	10
3888		1 l. Wild piglets	50	20
3889		1 l. 50 Wolf cubs	85	20
3890		2 l. 40 Brown bear cubs	2·75	1·00

728 U.T.C. Emblem

730 Stylised Map of Europe

729 Wrestling

1972. 50th Anniv of Communist Youth Union (U.T.C.).

3891	**728**	55 b. multicoloured	30	15

1972. Olympic Games, Munich (1st issue). Multicoloured.

3892		10 b. Type **729**	10	10
3893		20 b. Canoeing	10	10
3894		55 b. Football	15	10
3895		1 l. 55 High-jumping	45	10
3896		2 l. 90 Boxing	1·10	15
3897		6 l. 70 Volleyball	2·75	1·50

See also Nos. 3914/19 and 3926.

1972. Inter-European Cultural and Economic Co-operation.

3899	**730**	1 l. 75 gold, black & pur	1·40	1·40
3900	–	2 l. 90 gold, black & grn	2·50	2·00

DESIGN: 2 l. 90, "Crossed arrows" symbol.

731 Astronauts in Lunar Rover

732 Modern Trains and Symbols

1972. Air. Moon Flight of "Apollo 16".

3901	**731**	3 l. blue, green & pink	2·00	2·00

1972. 50th Anniv of Int Railway Union.

3902	**732**	55 b. multicoloured	70	15

734 "Paeonia romanica"

1972. Scarce Rumanian Flowers.

3904	**734**	20 b. multicoloured	10	10
3905	–	40 b. purple, grn & brn	15	10
3906	–	55 b. brown and blue	25	10
3907	–	60 b. red, green and light green	30	10
3908	–	1 l. 35 multicoloured	65	15
3909	–	2 l. 90 multicoloured	1·50	35

DESIGNS: 40 b. "Dianthus callizonus"; 55 b. Leontopodium alpinum"; 60 b. "Nigritella rubra"; 1 l. 35, "Narcissus stellaris"; 2 l. 90, "Cypripedium calceolus".

735 Saligny Bridge, Cernavoda

1972. Danube Bridges. Multicoloured.

3910		1 l. 35 Type **735**	80	10
3911		1 l. 75 Giurgeni Bridge, Vadul Oii	85	20
3912		2 l. 75 Prieteniel Bridge, Giurgiu–Ruse	2·75	60

736 North Railway Station, Bucharest, 1872

1972. Cent of North Railway Station, Bucharest.

3913	**736**	55 b. multicoloured	70	15

737 Water-polo

1972. Olympic Games, Munich (2nd issue). Multicoloured.

3914		10 b. Type **737**	10	10
3915		20 b. Pistol-shooting	15	10
3916		55 b. Throwing the discus	15	10
3917		1 l. 55 Gymnastics	45	10
3918		2 l. 75 Canoeing	1·40	15
3919		6 l. 40 Fencing	2·75	1·40

738 Rotary Stamp–printing Press

739 "E. Stoenescu" (S. Popescu)

1972. Centenary of State Stamp–printing Works.

3921	**738**	55 b. multicoloured	50	10

1972. Rumanian Art. Portraits and Self-portraits. Multicoloured.

3922		55 b. Type **739**	10	10
3923		1 l. 75 "O. Bancila" (self-portrait)	30	10
3924		2 l. 90 "Gh. Petrascu" (self-portrait)	60	10
3925		6 l. 50 "I. Andreescu" (self-portrait)	2·00	35

740 Runner with Torch

1972. Olympic Games, Munich (3rd issue). Olympic Flame.

3926	**740**	55 b. pur & blue on silver	1·00	45

741 Aurel Vlaicu and No. 1 "Crazy Fly"

1972. Air. Rumanian Aviation Pioneers. Mult.

3927		60 b. Type **741**	20	10
3928		3 l. Traian Vuja and Vuia No. 1 machine	1·25	45

742 Cluj Cathedral

743 Satu Mare

1972.

3929	**742**	1 l. 85 violet (postage)	35	10
3930	–	2 l. 75 grey	45	10
3931	–	3 l. 35 red	55	10
3932	–	3 l. 45 green	65	10
3933	–	5 l. 15 blue	90	10
3934	–	5 l. 60 blue	95	10
3935	–	6 l. 20 mauve	1·00	10
3936	–	6 l. 40 brown	1·25	10
3937	–	6 l. 80 red	1·25	10
3938	–	7 l. 05 black	1·10	10
3939	–	8 l. 45 red	1·50	10
3940	–	9 l. 05 green	1·40	10
3941	–	9 l. 10 blue	1·40	15
3942	–	9 l. 85 green	1·40	15
3943	–	10 l. brown	1·50	20
3944	–	11 l. 90 blue	2·00	20
3945	–	12 l. 75 violet	1·90	25
3946	–	13 l. 30 red	2·00	25
3947	–	16 l. 20 green	2·40	25
3948	–	14 l. 60 blue (air)	3·50	25

DESIGNS—HORIZ: (As Type **742**): 2 l. 75, Sphinx Rock, Mt. Bucegi; 3 l. 45, Sinaia Castle; 5 l. 15, Hydro–electric power station, Arges; 6 l. 40, Hunidoara Castle; 6 l. 80, Bucharest Polytechnic complex; 9 l. 05, Coliseum, Sarmisegtetuza; 9 l. 10, Hydro–electric power station, Iron Gates. (29 × 21 mm). 11 l. 90, Palace of the Republic, Bucharest; 13 l. 30, City Gate, Alba Julia; 14 l. 60, Otopeni Airport, Bucharest. VERT: (As Type **742**): 3 l. 35, Heroes' Monument, Bucharest; 5 l. 60, Iasi-Biserica; 6 l. 20, Bran Castle; 7 l. 05, Black Church, Brasova; 8 l. 45, Atheneum, Bucharest; 9 l. 85, Decebal's statue, Cetatea Deva. (20 × 30 mm): 10 l. City Hall Tower, Sibiu; 12 l. 75, T.V. Building, Bucharest; 16 l. 20, Clock Tower, Sighisoara.

1972. Millenium of Satu Mare.

3949	**743**	55 b. multicoloured	50	10

744 Davis Cup on Racquet

1972. Final of Davis Cup Championships 1972, Bucharest.

3950	**744**	2 l. 75 multicoloured	1·50	40

745 "Venice" (G. Petrascu)

1972. Paintings of Venice. Multicoloured.

3951		10 b. Type **745**	10	10
3952		20 b. "Marina" (Darascu)	10	10
3953		55 b. "Moliberi Palace" (Petrascu)	15	10
3954		1 l. 55 "Venice" (Bunescu)	45	10
3955		2 l. 75 "Venetian Palace" (Darascu)	1·10	15
3956		6 l. 40 "Venice" (Bunesca) (different)	2·75	1·40

746 Fencing and Bronze Medal

748 Flags and "25"

747 "Travelling Romanies" (E. Volkers)

1972. Munich Olympic Games, Medals.

3958	**746**	10 b. multicoloured	10	10
3959	–	20 b. multicoloured	15	10
3960	–	35 b. multicoloured	20	10
3961	–	1 l. 45 grey, purple & pink	50	10
3962	–	2 l. 75 grey, brn & ochre	1·25	15
3963	–	6 l. 20 multicoloured	3·75	1·50

DESIGNS: 20 b. Handball and bronze medal; 35 b. Boxing and silver medal; 1 l. 45, Hurdling and silver medal; 2 l. 75, Pistol shooting, silver and bronze medals; 6 l. 20, Wrestling and two gold medals.

1972. Stamp Day.

3965	**747**	1 l. 10 + 90 b. mult	1·60	1·00

1972. 25th Anniv of Proclamation of Republic. Multicoloured.

3966		55 b. Type **748**	20	10
3967		1 l. 20 Arms and "25"	30	10
3968		1 l. 75 Industrial scene and "25"	75	20

749 "Apollo 1, 2, 3"

750 European Bee Eater

1972. "Apollo" Moon Flights. Multicoloured.

3969		10 b. Type **749**	10	10
3970		35 b. Grissom, Chaffee and White	10	10
3971		40 b. "Apollo 4, 5, 6"	15	10
3972		55 b. "Apollo 7, 8"	20	10
3973		1 l. "Apollo 9, 10"	30	10
3974		1 l. 20 "Apollo 11, 12"	40	10
3975		1 l. 85 "Apollo 13, 14"	50	15
3976		2 l. 75 "Apollo 15, 16"	90	15
3977		3 l. 60 "Apollo 17"	2·00	1·40

1973. Protection of Nature. Multicoloured. (a) Birds.

3979		1 l. 40 Type **750**	75	15
3980		1 l. 85 Red breasted goose	1·00	20
3981		2 l. 75 Peduline tit	1·75	40

(b) Flowers.

3982		1 l. 40 Marsh marigold	40	10
3983		1 l. 85 Martagon lily	50	15
3984		2 l. 75 Gentian	75	25

751 Copernicus

752 Suceava Costume (female)

1973. 500th Birth Anniv of Copernicus.

3985	**751**	2 l. 75 multicoloured	1·40	35

1973. Regional Costumes. Multicoloured.

3986		10 b. Type **752**	10	10
3987		40 b. Suceava (male)	10	10
3988		55 b. Harghila (female)	15	10
3989		1 l. 75 Harghila (male)	45	10
3990		2 l. 75 Gorj (female)	75	15
3991		6 l. 40 Gorj (male)	1·50	1·00

253 D. Paciurea (sculptor)

254 Map of Europe

1973. Cultural Celebrities. Multicoloured.

3992		10 b. Type **753**	10	10
3993		40 b. I. Slavici (writer)	10	10
3994		55 b. G. Lazar (writer)	15	10
3995		6 l. 40 A. Flechtenmacher (composer)	2·00	1·00

1973. Inter-European Cultural and Economic Co-operation.
3996 **754** 3 l. 35 gold, blue & purple 1·40 1·40
3997 – 3 l. 60 gold and purple . 2·50 2·00
DESIGN: 3 l. 60, Symbol of collaboration.

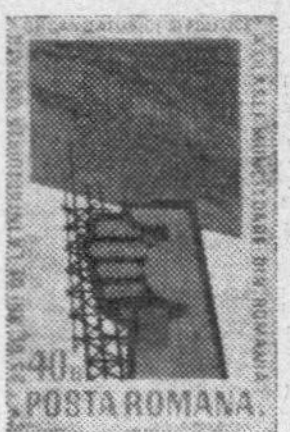

756 Hand with Hammer and Sickle

757 W.M.O. Emblem and Weather Satellite

1973. Anniversaries. Multicoloured.
3999 40 b. Type **756** 30 10
4000 55 b. Flags and bayonets . . 40 10
4001 1 l. 75 Prince Cuza . . . . 1·00 15
EVENTS: 40 b. 25th anniv of Rumanian Workers and Peasant Party; 55 b. 40th anniv of National Anti-Fascist Committee; 1 l. 75, Death cent of Prince Alexander Cuza.

1973. Centenary of I.M.O./W.M.O.
4002 **757** 2 l. multicoloured 90 20

758 "Dimitri Ralet" (anon)

759 Prince Dimitri Cantemir

1973. "Socfilex III" Stamp Exhibition, Bucharest. Portrait Paintings. Multicoloured.
4003 40 b. Type **758** 10 10
4004 60 b. "Enacheta Vacarescu" (A. Chladek) 15 10
4005 1 l. 55 "Dimitri Aman" (C. Lecca) 30 10
4006 4 l. + 2l. "Barbat at his Desk" (B. Iscovescu) . . . . . 2·00 1·00

1973. 300th Birth Anniv of Dimitri Cantemir, Prince of Moldavia (writer). Multicoloured.
4008 **759** 1 l. 75 multicoloured . . 1·00 20

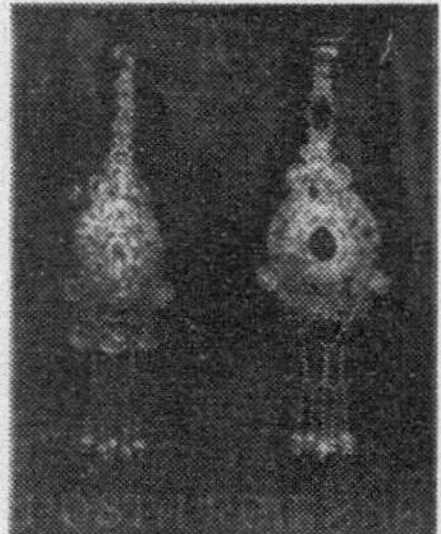
760 Fibular Brooches

1973. Treasures of Pietroasa. Multicoloured.
4010 10 b. Type **760** 10 10
4011 20 b. Golden figurine and bowl (horiz) 10 10
4012 55 b. Gold oil flask 15 10
4013 1 l. 55 Brooch and bracelets (horiz) 60 10
4014 2 l. 75 Gold platter 90 10
4015 6 l. 80 Filgree cup holder (horiz) 2·40 1·00

762 Oboga Jar

763 "Postilion" (A. Verona)

1973. Rumanian Ceramics. Multicoloured.
4018 10 b. Type **762** 10 10
4019 20 b. Vama dish and jug . . 10 10
4020 55 b. Maginea bowl 10 10
4021 1 l. 55 Sibiu Saschiz jug and dish 60 10
4022 2 l. 75 Pisc pot and dish . . 85 15
4023 6 l. 80 Oboga "bird" vessel . 2·10 45

1973. Stamp Day.
4024 **763** 1 l. 10 + 90 b. mult . . 1·10 1·10

764 "Textile Workers" (G. Saru)

765 Town Hall, Craiova

1973. Paintings showing Workers. Multicoloured.
4025 10 b. Type **764** 10 10
4026 20 b. "Construction Site" (M. Bunescu) (horiz) . . . 10 10
4027 55 b. "Shipyard Workers" (H. Catargi) (horiz) . . . 15 10
4028 1 l. 55 "Working Man" (H. Catargi) 40 10
4029 2 l. 75 "Miners" (A. Phoebus) 1·00 15
4030 6 l. 80 "The Spinner" (N. Grigorescu) . . . . . 2·00 85

1974. (a) Buidings.
4032 **765** 5 b. red 10 10
4033 – 10 b. blue 10 10
4034 – 20 b. orange 10 10
4035 – 35 b. green 10 10
4036 – 40 b. violet 10 10
4037 – 50 b. blue 10 10
4038 – 55 b. brown 10 10
4039 – 60 b. red 10 10
4040 – 1 l. blue 15 10
4041 – 1 l. 20 green 20 10

(b) Ships.
4042 – 1 l. 35 black 30 10
4043 – 1 l. 45 blue 30 10
4044 – 1 l. 50 red 30 10
4045 – 1 l. 55 blue 40 10
4046 – 1 l. 75 green 50 10
4047 – 2 l. 20 blue 55 10
4048 – 3 l. 65 lilac 80 10
4049 – 4 l. 70 purple . . . . . . 1·25 15
DESIGNS—VERT: 10 b. "Column of Infinity", Tirgu Jiu; 40 b. Romanesque church, Densus; 50 b. Reformed Church, Dej; 1 l. Curtea de Arges Monastery. HORIZ: 20 b. Heroes' Monument, Marasesti; 35 b. Citadel, Risnov; 55 b. Castle, Maldarasti; 60 b. National Theatre, Jassy; 1 l. 20, Fortress and church, Tirgu Mures; 1 l. 35, Danube Tug "Impingator"; 1 l. 45, Freighter "Dimbovita"; 1 l. 50, Danube passenger vessel "Muntenia"; 1 l. 55, Cadet barque "Mircea"; 1 l. 75, Liner "Transylvania"; 2 l. 20, Bulk carrier "Oltul"; 3 l. 65, Trawler "Mures"; 4 l. 70, Tanker "Arges".

767 "Boats at Honfleur" (Monet)

1974. Impressionist Paintings. Multicoloured.
4056 20 b. Type **767** 10 10
4057 40 b. "Moret Church" (Sisley) (vert) 10 10
4058 55 b. "Orchard in Blossom" (Pissarro) 15 10
4059 1 l. 75 "Jeanne" (Pissarro) (vert) 35 10
4060 2 l. 75 "Landscape" (Renoir) 60 15
4061 3 l. 60 "Portrait of a Girl" (Cezanne) (vert) . . . . . 1·60 35

768 Trotting with Sulky

769 Nicolas Titulescu (Rumanian League of Nations Delegate)

1974. Cent of Horse-racing in Rumania. Mult.
4063 40 b. Type **768** 10 10
4064 55 b. Three horses racing . . 15 10
4065 60 b. Horse galloping . . . 20 10
4066 1 l. 55 Two trotters racing . . 40 10
4067 2 l. 75 Three trotters racing . . 75 10
4068 3 l. 45 Two horses racing . . 1·25 35

1974. Interparliamentary Congress Session, Bucharest.
4069 **769** 1 l. 75 multicoloured . . 50 20

771 "Anniversary Parade" (Pepene Cornelia)

1974. 25th Anniv of Young Pioneers Organization.
4071 **771** 55 b. multicoloured . . . 50 10

772 "Europe"

1974. Inter-European Cultural and Economic Co-operation. Multicoloured.
4072 2 l. 20 Type **772** . . . . . . 1·50 1·50
4073 3 l. 45 Satellite over Europe . . 2·40 2·00

1974. Rumania's Victory in World Handball Championships. No. 3959 surch **ROMANIA CAMPIOANA MONDIALA 1974** and value.
4074 1 l. 75 on 20 b. multicoloured 3·25 2·25

774 Postal Motor Boat

1974. U.P.U. Centenary. Multicoloured.
4075 20 b. Type **774** 10 10
4076 40 b. Loading mail train . . . 40 10
4077 55 b. Loading Ilyushin Il-62M mail plane 10 10
4078 1 l. 75 Rural postman delivering letter 45 10
4079 2 l. 75 Town postman delivering letter 50 15
4080 3 l. 60 Young stamp collectors 90 25

775 Footballers

776 Anniversary Emblem

1974. World Cup Football Championships, West Germany.
4082 **775** 20 b. multicoloured . . . 10 10
4083 – 40 b. multicoloured . . . 10 10
4084 – 55 b. multicoloured . . . 10 10
4085 – 1 l. 75 multicoloured . . 30 10
4086 – 2 l. 75 multicoloured . . 65 15
4087 – 3 l. 60 multicoloured . . 90 20
DESIGNS: Nos. 4083/7, Football scenes similar to Type **775**.

1974. 25th Anniv of Council for Mutual Economic Aid.
4089 **776** 55 b. multicoloured . . . 45 15

777 U.N. and World Population Emblems

778 Emblem on Map of Europe

1974. World Population Year Conference, Bucharest.
4091 **778** 4 l. + 3 l. yell, bl & red . 2·40 35

779 Hand drawing Peace Dove

780 Prince John of Wallachia (400th birth anniv)

1974. 25th Anniv of World Peace Movement.
4092 **779** 2 l. multicoloured . . . 50 10

1974. Anniversaries.
4093 **780** 20 b. blue 10 10
4094 – 55 b. red 10 10
4095 – 1 l. blue 25 10
4096 – 1 l. 10 brown 20 10
4097 – 1 l. 30 purple 35 10
4098 – 1 l. 40 violet 40 10
DESIGNS AND ANNIVERSARIES—VERT: 1 l. Iron and Steel Works, Hunedoara (220th anniv); 1 l. 10, Avram Iancu (150th anniv); 1 l. 30, Dr. C. I. Parhon (birth cent); 1 l. 40, Dosoftel (savant) (350th birth anniv). HORIZ: 55 b. Soldier and Installations (Rumanian Army Day. 30th anniv).

781 Rumanian and Soviet Flags as "XXX"

783 "Centaurea nervosa"

1974. 30th Anniv of Liberation. Multicoloured.
4099 40 b. Type **781** 15 10
4100 55 b. Citizens and flags (horiz) 15 10

1974. "Save Nature". Wild Flowers. Multicoloured.
4102 20 b. Type **783** 10 10
4103 40 b. "Fritillaria montana" . 10 10
4104 55 b. "Taxus baccata" . . . 20 10
4105 1 l. 75 "Rhododendron kotschyi" 40 10
4106 2 l. 75 "Eritrichium nanum" 55 20
4107 3 l. 60 "Dianthus spiculifolius" 85 25

784 Bust of Isis

1974. Rumanian Archaeological Finds. Sculpture. Multicoloured.
4108 20 b. Type **784** 10 10
4109 40 b. Glykon serpent 15 10
4110 55 b. Head of Emperor Decius 15 10
4111 1 l. 75 Rumanian Woman . 30 10
4112 2 l. 75 Mithras 50 15
4113 3 l. 60 Roman senator . . . 1·10 25

785 Sibiu Market Place

1974. Stamp Day.
4114 **785** 2 l. 10 + 1 l. 90 mult . . 1·50 35

1974. "Nationala 74" Stamp Exhibition. No. 4114 optd **EXPOZITIA FILATELICA "NATIONALA '74" 15-24 noiembrie Bucuresti**.
4115 **786** 2 l. 10 + 1 l. 90 mult . . 2·75 2·75

MINIMUM PRICE

The minimum price quoted is 10p which represents a handling charge rather than a basis for valuing common stamps. For further notes about prices, see introductory pages.

787 Party Emblem

1974. 11th Rumanian Communist Party Congress, Bucharest.
4116 **787** 55 b. multicoloured . . . 10 10
4117 – 1 l. multicoloured 15 10
DESIGN: 1 l. Similar to Type **787**, showing party emblem and curtain.

788 "The Discus thrower" (Myron)

1974. 60th Anniv of Rumanian Olympic Committee.
4118 **788** 2 l. multicoloured . . . . 1·00 25

789 "Skylab" **790** Dr. Albert Schweitzer

1974. "Skylab" Space Laboratory.
4119 **789** 2 l. 50 multicoloured . . 1·25 1·10

1974. Birth Centenary of Dr. Albert Schweitzer.
4120 **790** 40 b. brown 25 10

791 Handball **793** Torch and Inscription

792 "Rocks and Birches"

1975. World Universities Handball Championships, Rumania.
4121 **791** 55 b. multicoloured . . . 15 10
4122 – 1 l. 75 multicoloured (vert) 30 10
4123 – 2 l. 20 multicoloured . . 55 20
DESIGNS: 1 l. 75, 2 l. 20, similar designs to Type **791**.

1975. Paintings by Ion Andreescu. Multicoloured.
4124 20 b. Type **792** 10 10
4125 40 b. "Peasant Woman with Green Kerchief" 10 10
4126 55 b. "Winter in the Forest" . . 15 10
4127 1 l. 75 "Winter in Barbizon" (horiz) 35 10
4128 2 l. 75 Self-portrait 60 20
4129 3 l. 50 "Main Road" (horiz) . 1·40 35

1975. 10th Anniv of Socialist Republic.
4130 **793** 40 b. multicoloured . . . 25 10

794 "Battle of the High Bridge" (O. Obedeanu)

1975. 500th Anniv of Victory over the Ottomans at High Bridge.
4131 **794** 55 b. multicoloured . . 40 10

795 "Peasant Woman Spinning" (N. Grigorescu) **796** "Self-portrait"

1975. International Women's Year.
4132 **795** 55 b. multicoloured . . 30 10

1975. 500th Birth Anniv of Michelangelo.
4133 **796** 5 l. multicoloured . . . 1·60 25

798 Mitsui Children's Science Pavilion, Okinawa

1975. International Exposition, Okinawa.
4135 **798** 4 l. multicoloured . . . 1·50 30

799 "Peonies" (N. Tonitza)

1975. Inter-European Cultural and Economic Co-operation. Multicoloured.
4136 2 l. 20 Type **799** . . . . . . 1·50 1·50
4137 3 l. 45 "Chrysanthemums" (St. Luchian) . . . . 2·00 2·00

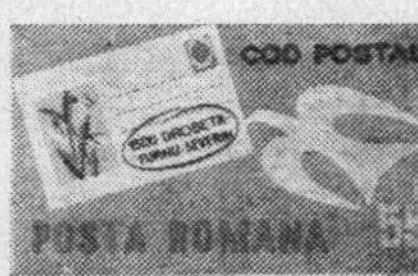

800 Dove with Coded Letter

1975. Introduction of Postal Coding.
4138 **800** 55 b. multicoloured . . 30 10

801 Convention Emblem on "Globe"

1975. Centenary of International Metre Convention.
4139 **801** 1 l. 85 multicoloured . . . 85 20

802 Mihail Eminescu and Museum

1975. 125th Birth Anniv of Mihail Eminescu (poet).
4140 **802** 55 b. multicoloured . . 30 10

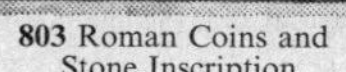

803 Roman Coins and Stone Inscription **805** Ana Ipatescu

1975. Bimillenary of Alba Julia.
4141 **803** 55 b. multicoloured . . . 30 10

1975. Death Centenary of Ana Ipatescu (revolutionary).
4143 **805** 55 b. mauve 30 10

806 Turnu-Severin

1975. European Architectural Heritage Year. Roman Antiquities.
4144 – 55 b. black and brown . . 10 10
4145 – 1 l. 20 black, light blue and blue 25 15
4146 – 1 l. 55 black and green . 50 15
4147 – 1 l. 75 black and red . . 60 20
4148 **806** 2 l. black and ochre . . . 70 25
4149 – 2 l. 25 black and blue . . 90 55
DESIGNS—VERT: 55 b. Emperor Trajan; 1 l. 20, Trajan's Column, Rome; 1 l. 55, Decebalus (sculpture); 10 l. Roman remains, Gradiste. HORIZ: 1 l. 75, Imperial monument, Adam Clissi; 2 l. 25, Trajan's Bridge.

807 "Apollo" and "Soyuz" Spacecraft

1975. Air. "Apollo-Soyuz" Space Link. Mult.
4151 1 l. 75 Type **807** . . . . . 1·40 1·40
4152 3 l. 25 "Apollo" and "Soyuz" linked together . . . . . . 1·60 1·60

808 "Michael the Brave" (A. Sadeler)

1975. 375th Anniv of First Political Union of Rumanian States. Multicoloured.
4153 55 b. Type **808** 10 10
4154 1 l. 20 "Ottoman Envoys bringing gifts to Michael the Brave" (T. Aman) (horiz) . 25 10
4155 2 l. 75 "Michael the Brave at Calugareni" (T. Aman) . . 55 20

810 "Delphinium consolida" **812** Policeman using Walkie–talkie

1975. Flowers. Multicoloured.
4157 20 b. Type **810** 10 10
4158 40 b. "Papaver dubium" . . . 10 10
4159 55 b. "Xeranthemum annuum" 15 10
4160 1 l. 75 "Helianthemum nummularium" 35 10
4161 2 l. 75 "Salvia pratensis" . . 65 15
4162 3 l. 60 "Cichorium intybus" . . 85 25

1975. International Philatelic Fair, Riccione (Italy). Optd **Tîrg international de mârci postale Riccione — Italia 23-25 August 1975**.
4163 **796** 5 l. multicoloured . . . . 5·00 5·00

1975. Road Safety.
4164 **812** 55 b. blue 40 10

813 Text on Map of Pelendava

1975. 1750th Anniv of First Documentary Attestations of Daco-Getian Settlements of Pelendava and 500th Anniv of Craiova. Multicoloured.
4165 20 b. Type **813** 10 10
4166 55 b. Map showing location of Pelendava and Craiova (horiz) 15 10
4167 1 l. Text on map of Pelendava 25 10

814 Muntenia Carpet

1975. Rumanian Carpets. Multicoloured.
4168 20 b. Type **814** 10 10
4169 40 b. Banat 10 10
4170 55 b. Oltenia 15 10
4171 1 l. 75 Moldova 50 10
4172 2 l. 75 Oltenia (different) . . 65 20
4173 3 l. 60 Maramures 80 30

815 T.V. "12M" Minibus

1975. Rumanian Motor Vehicles. Multicoloured.
4174 20 b. Type **815** 10 10
4175 40 b. L.K.W. "19 A.L.P." Oil tanker 15 10
4176 55 b. A.R.O. "240" Field car 15 10
4177 1 l. 75 L.K.W. "R 8135 F" Truck 50 10
4178 2 l. 75 P.K.W. "Dacia 1300" Saloon car 65 20
4179 3 l. 60 L.K.W. "R 19215 D.F.K." Tipper truck . . 85 35

816 Postal Transit Centre, Bucharest

1975. Stamp Day. Multicoloured.
4180 1 l. 50 + 1 l. 50 Type **816** . 1·40 60
4181 2 l. 10 + 1 l. 90 Aerial view of P.T.C. . . . . 2·40 85

818 Toboganning

1976. Winter Olympics Games, Innsbruck. Multicoloured.
4183 20 b. Type **818** 10 10
4184 40 b. Rifle-shooting (biathlon) (vert) 15 10
4185 55 b. Downhill skiing (slalom) 25 10
4186 1 l. 75 Ski-jumping 45 20
4187 2 l. 75 Figure-skating (women's) 70 30
4188 3 l. 60 Ice-hockey . . . . . 1·25 60

819 "Washington at Valley Forge" (W. Trego)

1976. Bicent of American Revolution. Mult.

4190 20 b. Type **819** 10 10
4191 40 b. "Washington at Trenton" (Trumbull) (vert) 10 10
4192 55 b. "Washington crossing the Delaware" (Leutze) 25 10
4193 1 l. 75 "Capture of the Hessians" (Trumbull) . . . 55 20
4194 2 l. 75 "Jefferson" (Sully) (vert) 85 25
4195 3 l. 60 "Surrender of Cornwallis at Yorktown" (Trumbull) 1·25 40

820 "Prayer"

1976. Birth Centenary of C. Brancusi (sculptor). Multicoloured.

4197 55 b. Type **820** 15 10
4198 1 l. 75 Architectural Assembly, Tg. Jiu 35 15
4199 3 l. 60 C. Brancusi 90 35

821 Anton Davidoglu (mathematician) (birth cent) **823** Dr. Carol Davila

822 Inscribed Tablets, Tibiscum (Banat)

1976. Anniversaries. Multicoloured.

4200 40 b. Type **821** 10 10
4201 55 b. Prince Vlad Tepes (500th death anniv) 15 10
4202 1 l. 20 Costache Negri (patriot-death centenary) 25 10
4203 1 l. 75 Gallery, Archives Museum (50th anniv) . . . 30 20

1976. Daco-Roman Archaeological Finds. Mult.

4204 20 b. Type **822** 10 10
4205 40 b. Roman sculptures 15 10
4206 55 b. Dacian coins and pottery 25 10
4207 1 l. 75 Dacian pottery 50 10
4208 2 l. 75 Roman altar and spears 65 15
4209 3 l. 60 Vase and spears . . . 95 35

1976. Centenary of Rumanian Red Cross. Mult.

4211 55 b. Type **823** (postage) . . 10 10
4212 1 l. 75 Nurse and patient . . 30 10
4213 2 l. 20 First aid 40 10
4214 3 l. 35 Blood donors (air) . . 75 25

824 King Decebalus Vase **825** Rumanian Arms

1976. Inter-European Cultural and Economic Collaboration. Multicoloured.

4215 2 l. 20 Type **824** 65 75
4216 3 l. 45 Vase with portrait of King Michael the Brave . . 2·00 2·00

1976.

4217 **825** 1 l. 75 multicoloured . . 65 10

826 De Havilland D.H.9C

1976. 50th Anniv of TAROM (State airline).

4218 20 b. Type **826** 10 10
4219 40 b. I.C.A.R. Comercial . . 20 10
4220 60 b. Douglas DC-3 . . . . 30 10
4221 1 l. 75 Antonov An-24 . . . 70 10
4222 2 l. 75 Ilyushin Il-62 . . . . 90 15
4223 3 l. 60 Boeing 707 . . . . . 1·40 45

827 Gymnastics **828** Spiru Haret

1976. Olympic Games, Montreal. Multicoloured.

4224 20 b. Type **827** 10 10
4225 40 b. Boxing 15 10
4226 55 b. Handball 30 10
4227 1 l. 75 Rowing (horiz) . . . 45 15
4228 2 l. 75 Gymnastics (different) (horiz) 70 20
4229 3 l. 60 Canoeing (horiz) . . 1·25 30

1976. 125th Birth Anniv of Spiru Haret (mathematician).

4231 **828** 20 b. brown, orge & blue 25 10

829 Daco-Getian Sculpture on Map of Buzau

1976. 1600th Anniv of Buzau State.

4232 **829** 55 b. multicoloured . . 30 10

1976. Philatelic Exhibition, Bucharest. No. 4199 surch **+1.80 EXPOZITIA FILATELICA BUCURESTI. 12-19 IX 1976.**

4233 3 l. 60 + 1 l. 80 multicoloured 8·25 8·25

831 Red Deer

1976. Endangered Animals. Multicoloured.

4234 20 b. Type **831** 10 10
4235 40 b. Brown bear 20 10
4236 55 b. Chamois 35 10
4237 1 l. 75 Wild boar 50 10
4238 2 l. 75 Red fox 95 25
4239 3 l. 60 Lynx . . . . 1·25 35

832 Cathedral, Milan

1976. "Italia '76" International Philatelic Exhibition, Milan.

4240 **832** 4 l. 75 multicoloured . . 1·50 35

833 D. Grecu (gymnast) and Bronze Medal

1976. Olympic Games, Montreal. Rumanian Medal Winners. Multicoloured.

4241 20 b. Type **833** 10 10
4242 40 b. Fencing (Bronze Medal) 15 10
4243 55 b. Javelin (Bronze Medal) . 20 10
4244 1 l. 75 Handball (Silver Medal) 35 10
4245 2 l. 75 Boxing (Silver and Bronze Medals) (horiz) . . 60 20
4246 3 l. 60 Wrestling (Silver and Bronze Medals) (horiz) . . 1·10 30
4247 5 l. 70 Nadia Comaneci (gymnastics – 3 Gold, 1 Silver and 1 Bronze Medals) (27 × 42 mm) . . . . 3·25 1·50

834 "Carnations and Oranges"

1976. Floral Paintings by Stefan Luchian. Multicoloured.

4249 20 b. Type **834** 10 10
4250 40 b. "Flower Arrangement" . 10 10
4251 55 b. "Immortelles" 10 10
4252 1 l. 75 "Roses in Vase" . . . 35 15
4253 2 l. 75 "Cornflowers" 45 15
4254 3 l. 60 "Carnations in Vase" . 90 35

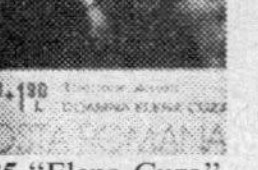
835 "Elena Cuza" (T. Aman) **836** Arms of Alba

1976. Stamp Day.

4255 **835** 2 l. 10 + 1 l. 90 mult . . 1·90 1·50

1976. Rumanian Districts' Coats of Arms (1st series). Multicoloured.

4256 55 b. Type **836** 15 10
4257 55 b. Arad 15 10
4258 55 b. Arges 15 10
4259 55 b. Bacau 15 10
4260 55 b. Bihor 15 10
4261 55 b. Bistrita Nasaud 15 10
4262 55 b. Botosani 15 10
4263 55 b. Brasov 15 10
4264 55 b. Braila 15 10
4265 55 b. Buzau 15 10
4266 55 b. Caras-Severin 15 10
4267 55 b. Cluj 15 10
4268 55 b. Constanta 15 10
4269 55 b. Covasna 15 10
4270 55 b. Dimbovita 15 10

See also Nos. 4307/31, 4496/520 and 4542/63.

837 "Ox Cart"

1977. Paintings by Nicola Grigorescu. Multicoloured.

4271 55 b. Type **837** 15 10
4272 1 l. "Self-portrait" (vert) . . . 20 10
4273 1 l. 50 "Shepherdess" 30 10
4274 2 l. 15 "Girl with Distaff" . . 40 15
4275 3 l. 40 "Shepherd" (vert) . . 50 25
4276 4 l. 80 "Halt at the Well" . . 1·00 40

838 Telecommunications Station, Cheia

1977.

4277 **838** 55 b. multicoloured . . . 20 10

839 I.C.A.R.1

1977. Air. Rumanian Gliders. Multicoloured.

4278 20 b. Type **839** 10 10
4279 40 b. IS-3d 15 10
4280 55 b. RG-5 . . . . 20 10
4281 1 l. 50 IS-11 . . . . 40 10
4282 3 l. IS-29D 65 15
4283 3 l. 40 IS-28B . . . . 1·10 40

840 Red Deer

1977. Protected Animals. Multicoloured.

4284 55 b. Type **840** 20 10
4285 1 l. 50 Mute swan 40 15
4286 1 l. 50 Egyptian vulture . . . 70 25
4287 2 l. 15 European bison . . . 60 10
4288 3 l. 40 White-headed duck . 1·40 35
4289 4 l. 80 Common kingfisher . 1·60 50

841 "The Infantryman" (O. Obedeanu)

1977. Cent of Independence. Paintings. Mult.

4290 55 b. Type **841** 15 10
4291 1 l. "Artillery Battery at Calafat" (S. Hentia) (horiz) 20 10
4292 1 l. 50 "Soldiers Attacking" (S. Luchian) 30 10
4293 2 l. 15 "Battle of Plevna" (N. Grigorescu) (horiz) . . 45 10
4294 3 l. 40 "The Artillerymen" (N. Grigorescu) (horiz) . . 65 20
4295 4 l. 80 + 2l. "Battle of Rahova" (horiz) . . . . . . 1·75 65

842 Sinaia, Carpathians **843** Petro Rares (monarch) (450th birth anniv)

1977. Inter-European Cultural and Economic Co-operation. Multicoloured.

4297 2 l. Type **842** 50 50
4298 2 l. 40 Auroa, Black Sea . . 65 65

1977. Anniversaries. Multicoloured.

4299 40 b. Type **843** 15 10
4300 55 b. I. L. Caragiale (author, 125th birth anniv) 25 10

844 Nurse with Children and Emblems

1977. 23rd Int Red Cross Conference, Bucharest.

4301 **844** 1 l. 50 multicoloured . . 40 15

845 Triumphal Arch, Bucharest

1977. 60th Anniv of Battles of Marasti, Marasesti and Oituz.
4302 **845** 2 l. 15 multicoloured . . 70 30

847 Postwoman and Letters

1977. Air.
4304 20 l. Type **847** . . . . 5·00 1·40
4305 30 l. Douglas DC-10 airliner and mail . . . . 7·50 2·00

848 Mount Titano Castle, San Marino

1977. Centenary of San Marino Postage Stamps.
4306 **848** 4 l. multicoloured . . . . 1·40 25

1977. Rumanian District Coats of Arms (2nd series). As T **836**. Multicoloured.
4307 55 b. Dolj 15 10
4308 55 b. Galati 15 10
4309 55 b. Gorj 15 10
4310 55 b. Harghita 15 10
4311 55 b. Hunedoara 15 10
4312 55 b. Ialomita 15 10
4313 55 b. Iasi 15 10
4314 55 b. Ilfov 15 10
4315 55 b. Maramures 15 10
4316 55 b. Mehedinti 15 10
4317 55 b. Mures 15 10
4318 55 b. Neamt 15 10
4319 55 b. Olt 15 10
4320 55 b. Prahova 15 10
4321 55 b. Salaj 15 10
4322 55 b. Satu Mare 15 10
4323 55 b. Sibiu 15 10
4324 55 b. Suceava 15 10
4325 55 b. Teleorman 15 10
4326 55 b. Timis 15 10
4327 55 b. Tulcea 15 10
4328 55 b. Vaslui 15 10
4329 55 b. Vilcea 15 10
4330 55 b. Vrancea 15 10
4331 55 b. Rumanian postal emblem 15 10

849 Gymnast on Vaulting Horse
850 Dispatch Rider and Army Officer

1977. Gymnastics. Multicoloured.
4332 20 b. Type **849** 10 10
4333 40 b. Floor exercise 10 10
4334 55 b. Gymnast on parallel bars 15 10
4335 1 l. Somersault on bar . . . 25 10
4336 2 l. 15 Gymnast on rings . . 40 15
4337 4 l. 80 Gymnastic exercise . . 1·60 55

1977. Stamp Day.
4338 **850** 2 l. 10 + 1 l. 90 mult . . 1·40 1·25

MORE DETAILED LISTS
are given in the Stanley Gibbons Catalogues referred to in the country headings. For lists of current volumes see introduction

851 Two Dancers with Sticks

1977. Calusarii Folk Dance. Multicoloured.
4339 20 b. Type **851** 10 10
4340 40 b. Leaping dancer with stick 10 10
4341 55 b. Two dancers 20 10
4342 1 l. Dancer with stick . . . 30 10
4343 2 l. 15 Leaping dancers . . . 50 15
4344 4 l. 80 Leaping dancer . . . 1·60 1·10

852 "Carpati" at Cazane

1977. European Navigation on the Danube. Multicoloured.
4346 55 b. Type **852** 30 10
4347 1 l. Passenger vessel "Mircesti" near Orsova 40 10
4348 1 l. 50 Passenger vessel "Oltenita" near Calafat . . 60 15
4349 2 l. 15 Hydrofoil at Giurgiu port 65 25
4350 3 l. Passenger vessel "Herculani" at Tulcea . . 80 30
4351 3 l. 40 Passenger vessel "Muntenia" at Sulina . . 95 35
4352 4 l. 80 Map of Danube delta 2·00 80

853 Arms and Flag of Rumania

1977. 30th Anniv of Rumanian Republic. Multicoloured.
4354 55 b. Type **853** 10 10
4355 1 l. 20 Rumanian-built computers 20 10
4356 1 l. 75 National Theatre, Craiova 35 20

854 Firiza Dam

1978. Rumanian Dams and Hydro-electric Installations. Multicoloured.
4357 20 b. Type **854** 10 10
4358 40 b. Negovanu dam 15 10
4359 55 b. Piatra Neamt power station 25 10
4360 1 l. Izvorul Montelui Bicaz dam 30 10
4361 2 l. 15 Vidraru dam 45 15
4362 4 l. 80 Danube barrage and navigation system, Iron Gates 90 40

855 LZ-1 over Lake Constance

1978. Air. Airships. Multicoloured.
4363 60 b. Type **855** 15 10
4364 1 l. Santos Dumont's "Ballon No. 6" over Paris 25 10
4365 1 l. 50 Beardmore R-34 over Manhattan Island 35 10
4366 2 l. 15 N.4 "Italia" at North Pole 50 10
4367 3 l. 40 "Graf Zeppelin" over Brasov 70 15
4368 4 l. 80 "Graf Zeppelin" over Sibiu . . . . 1·40 45

856 Footballers and Emblem

1978. World Cup Football Championship, Argentina.
4370 **856** 55 b. blue 10 10
4371 – 1 l. orange 15 10
4372 – 1 l. 50 yellow 25 10
4373 – 2 l. 15 red 40 10
4374 – 3 l. 40 green 65 15
4375 – 4 l. 80 mauve . . . . . 1·40 25
DESIGNS: Nos. 4371/5, Footballers and emblem, similar to Type **856**.

857 King Decebalus of Dacia
858 Worker and Factory

1978. Inter-European Cultural and Economic Co-operation. Multicoloured.
4377 1 l. 30 Type **857** 65 75
4378 3 l. 40 Prince Mircea the Elder 2·75 2·75

1978. 30th Anniv of Nationalization of Industry.
4379 **858** 55 b. multicoloured . . . 20 10

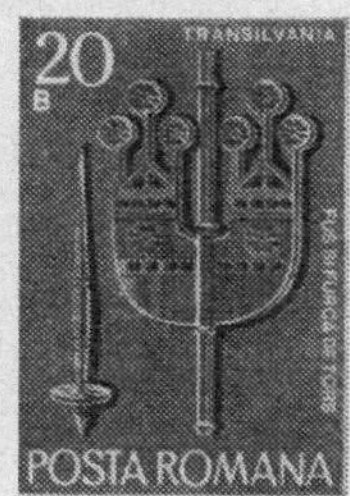

859 Spindle and Fork Handle, Transylvania

1978. Wood-carving. Multicoloured.
4380 20 b. Type **859** 10 10
4381 40 b. Cheese mould, Muntenia 15 10
4382 55 b. Spoons, Oltenia 20 10
4383 1 l. Barrel, Moldavia 25 10
4384 2 l. 15 Ladle and mug, Transylvania 40 10
4385 4 l. 80 Water bucket, Oltenia . 80 35

860 Danube Delta

1978. Tourism. Multicoloured.
4386 55 b. Type **860** 60 15
4387 1 l. Bran Castle (vert) 20 10
4388 1 l. 50 Moldavian village . . 25 10
4389 2 l. 15 Muierii caves 45 10
4390 3 l. 40 Cable car at Boiana Brasov 60 15
4391 4 l. 80 Mangalia (Black Sea resort) 90 30

861 MC-6 Electron Microscope
862 Polovraci Cave

1978. Rumanian Industry. Multicoloured.
4393 20 b. Type **861** 10 10
4394 40 b. Hydraulic excavator . . 10 10
4395 55 b. Power station control room 15 10

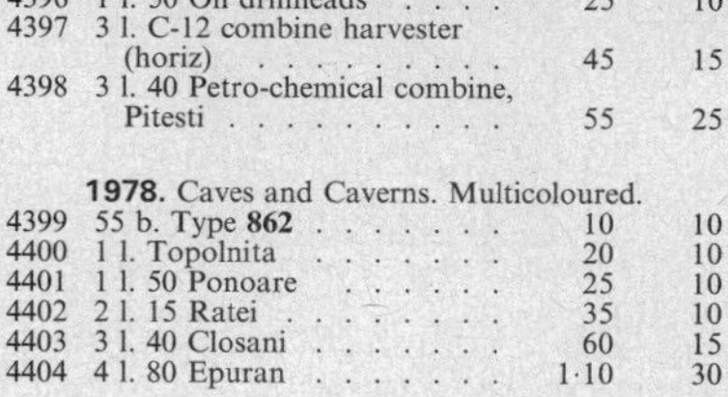
4396 1 l. 50 Oil drillheads 25 10
4397 3 l. C-12 combine harvester (horiz) 45 15
4398 3 l. 40 Petro-chemical combine, Pitesti 55 25

1978. Caves and Caverns. Multicoloured.
4399 55 b. Type **862** 10 10
4400 1 l. Topolnita 20 10
4401 1 l. 50 Ponoare 25 10
4402 2 l. 15 Ratei 35 10
4403 3 l. 40 Closani 60 15
4404 4 l. 80 Epuran . . . . 1·10 30

863 Gymnastics
865 Symbols of Equality

864 Zoomorphic Gold Plate

1978. "Daciada" Rumanian Games. Multicoloured.
4405 55 b. Type **863** 10 10
4406 1 l. Running 15 10
4407 1 l. 50 Skiing 20 10
4408 2 l. 15 Horse jumping . . . 30 10
4409 3 l. 40 Football 55 15
4410 4 l. 80 Handball . . . . . . 1·10 25

1978. Daco-Roman Archaeology. Multicoloured.
4411 20 b. Type **864** 10 10
4412 40 b. Gold torque 10 10
4413 55 b. Gold cameo ring . . . 15 10
4414 1 l. Silver bowl 25 10
4415 2 l. 15 Bronze eagle (vert) . . 45 15
4416 4 l. 80 Silver bracelet 55 30

1978. International Anti-Apartheid Year.
4418 **865** 3 l. 40 black, yell & red . 65 60

867 Ptolemaic Map of Dacia (2000th anniv of first record of Ziridava)

1978. Anniversaries in the History of Arad. Multicoloured.
4420 40 b. Type **867** 10 10
4421 55 b. Meeting place of National Council (60th anniv of unified Rumania) 10 10
4422 1 l. 75 Ceramic pots (950th anniv of first documentary evidence of Arad) 25 15

868 Dacian Warrior

1978. Stamp Day.
4423 **868** 6 l. + 3 l. multicoloured 2·00 1·40
No. 4423 was issued se-tenant with a premium carrying tab as shown in Type **868**.

869 Assembly at Alba Julia
871 Dacian Warrior

870 Wright Brothers and Wright Type A

1979. 60th Anniv of National Unity. Mult.
4424 55 b. Type **869** 10 10
4425 1 l. Open book, flag and sculpture 20 10

1979. Air. Pioneers of Aviation. Multicoloured.
4426 55 b. Type **870** 15 10
4427 1 l. Louis Bleriot and Bleriot XI 25 10
4428 1 l. 50 Anthony Fokker and "Josephine Ford" 30 10
4429 2 l. 15 A. N. Tupolev and Tupolev ANT-25 . . . . . 50 10
4430 3 l. Otto Lilienthal and Lilienthal monoplane glider 55 15
4431 3 l. 40 Traian Vuia and Vuia No. 1 . . . . 70 15
4432 4 l. 80 Aurel Vlaicu and No. 1 "Crazy Fly" 90 30

1979. 2050th Anniv of Independent Centralised Dacian State. Multicoloured.
4434 5 b. Type **871** 15 10
4435 1 l. 50 Decian warrior on horseback 25 20

872 "The Heroes from Vaslui" **873** Championship Emblem

1979. International Year of the Child (1st issue). Children's Paintings. Multicoloured.
4436 55 b. Type **872** 10 10
4437 1 l. "Tica's Folk Music Band" 15 10
4438 1 l. 50 "Buildingsite" 20 10
4439 2 l. 15 "Industrial Landscape" (horiz) 30 10
4440 3 l. 40 "Winter Holiday" (horiz) 45 15
4441 4 l. 80 "Pioneers' Celebration" (horiz) 65 25
See also Nos. 4453/6.

1979. European Junior Ice Hockey Championship, Miercurea-Ciuc, and World Championship, Galati. Multicoloured.
4442 1 l. 30 Type **873** 25 10
4443 3 l. 40 Championship emblem (different) 45 15

874 "Erythronium dens-canis" **876** Oil Derrick

875 Street with Mail-coach and Post-rider

1979. Protected Flowers. Multicoloured.
4444 55 b. Type **874** 10 10
4445 1 l. "Viola alpina" 15 10
4446 1 l. 50 "Linum borzaeanum" 20 10
4447 2 l. 15 "Convolvulus persicus" 30 10
4448 3 l. 40 "Primula auricula serratifolia" 45 15
4449 4 l. 80 "Aquilegia transsylvanica" 65 25

1979. Inter-European Cultural and Economic Co-operation.
4450 1 l. 30 Type **875** (postage) . . 45 45
4451 3 l. 40 Boeing 707 and motorcycle postman (air) . 55 55

1979. International Petroleum Congress, Bucharest.
4452 **876** 3 l. 40 multicoloured . . 50 15

877 Children with Flowers **878** Young Pioneer

1979. International Year of the Child (2nd issue). Multicoloured.
4453 40 b. Type **877** 10 10
4454 1 l. Children at creative play 20 10
4455 2 l. Children with hare . . . 35 10
4456 4 l. 60 Young pioneers . . . 70 20

1979. 30th Anniv of Young Pioneers.
4457 **878** 55 b. multicoloured . . 10 10

879 "Woman in Garden" **881** Stefan Gheorghiu

880 Brasov University

1979. Paintings by G. Tattarescu. Multicoloured.
4458 20 b. Type **879** 10 10
4459 40 b. 'Muntenian Woman" . 10 10
4460 55 b. "Muntenian Man" . . 10 10
4461 1 l. "General G. Magheru" . 20 10
4462 2 l. 15 "The Artist's Daughter" 40 10
4463 4 l. 80 "Self-portrait" . . . 1·00 20

1979. Contemporary Architecture. Multicoloured.
4464 20 b. State Theatre, Tirgu Mures 10 10
4465 40 b. Type **880** 10 10
4466 55 b. Administration Centre, Baia Mare 10 10
4467 1 l. Stefan Gheorghiu Academy, Bucharest 15 10
4468 2 l. 15 Adminstration Centre, Botosani 30 10
4469 4 l. 80 House of Culture, Tirgoviste 70 20

1979. Anniversaries and Events. Multicoloured.
4470 40 b. Type **881** (birth cent) . . 10 10
4471 55 b. Statue of Gheorghe Lazar (poet) (birth bicent) . . 10 10
4472 2 l. 15 Fallen Workers monument (Strike at Lupeni. 50th anniv) 30 10

882 Moldavian and Wallachian Women and Monuments to Union **883** Party and National Flags

1979. 120th Anniv of Union of Moldavia and Wallachia.
4473 **882** 4 l. 60 multicoloured . . 1·00 25

1979. 25th Anniv of Liberation. Multicoloured.
4474 55 b. Type **883** 10 10
4475 1 l. "Workers' Militia" (L. Suhar) (horiz) 20 10

884 Freighter "Galati" **885** "Snapdragons"

1979. Ships. Multicoloured.
4476 55 b. Type **884** 15 10
4477 1 l. Freighter "Bucuresti" . . 20 10
4478 1 l. 50 Bulk carrier "Resita" . 30 10
4479 2 l. 15 Bulk carrier "Tomis" . 35 15
4480 3 l. 40 Tanker "Dacia" . . . 55 20
4481 4 l. 80 Tanker "Independenta" 75 40

1979. "Socfilex 79" Stamp Exhibition, Bucharest. Flower Paintings by Stefan Luchian. Multicoloured.
4482 40 b. Type **885** 10 10
4483 60 b. "Carnations" 10 10
4484 1 l. 55 "Flowers on a Stairway" 25 10
4485 4 l. + 2 l. "Flowers of the Field" . . . . 1·10 1·10

888 Olympic Stadium, Melbourne (1956 Games)

1979. Olympic Games, Moscow (1980). Olympic Stadia. Multicoloured.
4489 55 b. Type **888** 10 10
4490 1 l. Rome (1960) 15 10
4491 1 l. 50 Tokyo (1964) 25 10
4492 2 l. 15 Mexico City (1968) . . 30 10
4493 3 l. 40 Munich (1972) 45 10
4494 4 l. 80 Montreal (1978) . . . 70 25

1979. Municipal Coats of Arms. As T **836**. Mult.
4496 1 l. 20 Alba Julia 20 10
4497 1 l. 20 Arad 20 10
4498 1 l. 20 Bacau 20 10
4499 1 l. 20 Baia Mare 20 10
4500 1 l. 20 Birlad 20 10
4501 1 l. 20 Botosani 20 10
4502 1 l. 20 Brasov 20 10
4503 1 l. 20 Braila 20 10
4504 1 l. 20 Buzau 20 10
4505 1 l. 20 Calarasi 20 10
4506 1 l. 20 Cluj 20 10
4507 1 l. 20 Constanta 20 10
4508 1 l. 20 Craiova 20 10
4509 1 l. 20 Dej 20 10
4510 1 l. 20 Deva 20 10
4511 1 l. 20 Drobeta Turnu Severin 20 10
4512 1 l. 20 Focsani 20 10
4513 1 l. 20 Galati 20 10
4514 1 l. 20 Gheorghe Gheorghiu Dej 20 10
4515 1 l. 20 Giurgiu 20 10
4516 1 l. 20 Hunedoara 20 10
4517 1 l. 20 Iasi 20 10
4518 1 l. 20 Lugoj 20 10
4519 1 l. 20 Medias 20 10
4520 1 l. 20 Odorheiu Secuiesc . . 20 10

889 Costumes of Maramures (female) **891** Figure Skating

890 Post Coding Desks

1979. National Costumes. Multicoloured.
4521 20 b. Type **889** 10 10
4522 40 b. Maramures (male) . . . 15 10
4523 55 b. Vrancea (female) . . . 15 10
4524 1 l. 50 Vrancea (male) . . . 30 10
4525 3 l. Padureni (female) . . . 55 15
4526 3 l. 40 Padureni (male) . . . 60 30

1979. Stamp Day.
4527 **890** 2 l. 10 + 1 l. 90 mult . . 75 30

1979. Winter Olympic Games, Lake Placid (1980). Multicoloured.
4528 55 b. Type **891** 10 10
4529 1 l. Downhill skiing 10 10
4530 1 l. 50 Biathlon 15 10
4531 2 l. 15 Bobsleighing 30 10
4532 3 l. 40 Speed skaing 50 10
4533 4 l. 80 Ice hockey 70 20

892 Locomotive No. 43 "Calugareni" **893** Dacian Warrior

1979. International Transport Exhibition, Hamburg. Multicoloured.
4535 55 b. Type **892** 15 10
4536 1 l. Locomotive No. 458 "Orleans" 35 10
4537 1 l. 50 Locomotive No. 1059 40 10
4538 2 l. 15 Locomotive No. 15021 55 15
4539 3 l. 40 Locomotive No. 231085 "Pacific" type 90 15
4550 4 l. 80 Electric locomotive "060-EA" . . . . 1·90 25

1980. Arms (4th series). As T **836**. Multicoloured.
4542 1 l. 20 Oradea 20 10
4543 1 l. 20 Petrosani 20 10
4544 1 l. 20 Piatra Neamt 20 10
4545 1 l. 20 Pitesti 20 10
4546 1 l. 20 Ploiesti 20 10
4547 1 l. 20 Resita 20 10
4548 1 l. 20 Rimnicu Vilcea . . . 20 10
4549 1 l. 20 Roman 20 10
4550 1 l. 20 Satu Mare 20 10
4551 1 l. 20 Sibiu 20 10
4552 1 l. 20 Sighetu Marmatiei . . 20 10
4553 1 l. 20 Sighisoara 20 10
4554 1 l. 20 Suceava 20 10
4555 1 l. 20 Tecuci 20 10
4556 1 l. 20 Timisoara 20 10
4557 1 l. 20 Tirgoviste 20 10
4558 1 l. 20 Tirgu Jiu 20 10
4559 1 l. 20 Tirgu–Mures 20 10
4560 1 l. 20 Tulcea 20 10
4561 1 l. 20 Turda 20 10
4562 1 l. 20 Turnu Magurele . . . 20 10
4563 1 l. 20 Bucharest 20 10

1980. 2050th Anniv of Independent Centralised Dacian State under Burebista.
4564 55 b. Type **893** 10 10
4565 1 l. 50 Dacian fighters with flag 20 10

894 Common Kingfisher

1980. European Nature Protection Year. Multicoloured.
4566 55 b. Type **894** 45 15
4567 1 l. Great egret (vert) 60 15
4568 1 l. 50 Red-breasted goose . 75 25
4569 2 l. 15 Red deer (vert) . . . 45 15
4570 3 l. 40 Roe deer fawn 70 20
4571 4 l. 80 European bison (vert) 1·10 30

895 "Vallota purpurea" **896** Tudor Vladimirescu

1980. Exotic Flowers from Bucharest Botanical Gardens. Multicoloured.
4573 55 b. Type **895** 10 10
4574 1 l. "Eichhornia crasipes" . . 20 10
4575 1 l. 50 "Sprekelia formosissima" 25 10
4576 2 l. 15 "Hypericum calycinum" 35 10
4577 3 l. 40 "Camellia japonica" . 45 25
4578 4 l. 80 "Nelumbo nucifera" . 70 25

1980. Anniversaries. Multicoloured.
4579 40 b. Type **896** (revolutionary leader)–(birth bicent) . . 10 10
4580 55 b. Mihail Sadoveanu (writer)–(birth cent) . . . 10 10
4581 1 l. 50 Battle of Posada (650th anniv) 25 10
4582 2 l. 15 Tudor Arghezi (poet)–(birth cent) 35 10
4583 3 l. Horea (leader, Transylvanian uprising)–(250th birth anniv) . . . 50 15

898 Dacian Fruit Dish **899** Throwing the Javelin

1980. Bimillenary of Dacian Fortress, Petrodava (now Piatra Neamt).
4585 **898** 1 l. multicoloured 15 10

1980. Olympic Games, Moscow. Multicoloured.
4586 55 b. Type **899** 10 10
4587 1 l. Fencing 15 10
4588 1 l. 50 Pistol shooting 20 10
4589 2 l. 15 Single kayak 30 10
4590 3 l. 40 Wrestling 45 10
4591 4 l. 80 Single skiff 90 15

901 Congress Emblem **902** Fireman carrying Child

1980. 15th International Congress of Historical Sciences.
4594 **901** 55 b. deep blue & blue . 10 10

1980. Firemen's Day.
4595 **902** 55 b. multicoloured . . . 10 10

903 Chinese and Rumanian Stamp Collectors **906** Dacian Warrior

905 Rooks and Chessboard

1980. Rumanian–Chinese Stamp Exhibition, Bucharest.
4596 **903** 1 l. multicoloured 15 10

1980. 24th Chess Olympiad, Malta. Multicoloured.
4598 55 b. Knights and chessboard 15 10
4599 1 l. Type **905** 25 10
4600 2 l. 15 Male head and chessboard 50 15
4601 4 l. 80 Female head and chessboard 95 35

1980. Military Uniforms. Multicoloured.
4602 20 b. Type **906** 10 10
4603 40 b. Moldavian soldier (15th century) 10 10
4604 55 b. Wallachian horseman (17th century) 15 10
4605 1 l. Standard bearer (19th century) 20 10
4606 1 l. 50 Infantryman (19th century) 25 10
4607 2 l. 15 Lancer (19th century) 35 15
4608 4 l. 80 Hussar (19th century) 90 20

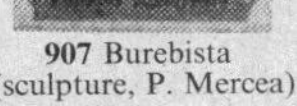

907 Burebista (sculpture, P. Mercea) **908** George Oprescu

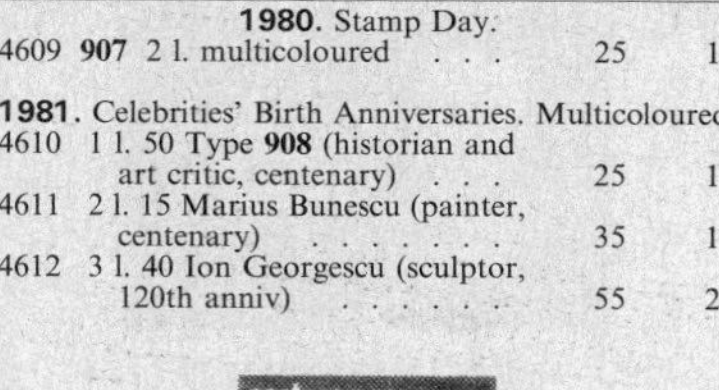

1980. Stamp Day.
4609 **907** 2 l. multicoloured . . . 25 10

1981. Celebrities' Birth Anniversaries. Multicoloured.
4610 1 l. 50 Type **908** (historian and art critic, centenary) . . . 25 10
4611 2 l. 15 Marius Bunescu (painter, centenary) 35 10
4612 3 l. 40 Ion Georgescu (sculptor, 120th anniv) 55 25

909 St. Bernard

1981. Dogs. Multicoloured.
4613 40 b. Mountain sheepdog (horiz) 10 10
4614 55 b. Type **909** 15 10
4615 1 l. Fox terrier (horiz) . . . 20 10
4616 1 l. 50 Alsatian (horiz) . . . 30 10
4617 2 l. 15 Boxer (horiz) 45 10
4618 3 l. 40 Dalmatian (horiz) . . 65 15
4619 4 l. 80 Poodle 85 30

910 Paddle-steamer "Stefan cel Mare"

1981. 125th Anniv of European Danube Committee. Multicoloured.
4620 55 b. Type **910** 20 10
4621 1 l. Danube Commission steam launch 30 15
4622 1 l. 50 Paddle-steamer "Tudor Vladimirescu" 45 15
4623 2 l. 15 Dredger "Sulina" . . 55 25
4624 3 l. 40 Paddle-steamer "Republica Populara Romana" 80 30
4625 4 l. 80 Freighter in Sulina Channel . . . . 1·00 40

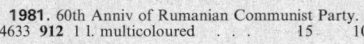

911 Bare-neck Pigeon **912** Party Flag and Oak Leaves

1981. Pigeons. Multicoloured.
4627 40 b. Type **911** 15 10
4628 55 b. Orbetan pigeon . . . 10 10
4629 1 l. Craiova chestnut pigeon 20 10
4630 1 l. 50 Timisoara pigeon . . 30 10
4631 2 l. 15 Homing pigeon . . . 45 15
4632 3 l. 40 Salonta giant pigeon . 70 40

1981. 60th Anniv of Rumanian Communist Party.
4633 **912** 1 l. multicoloured . . . 15 10

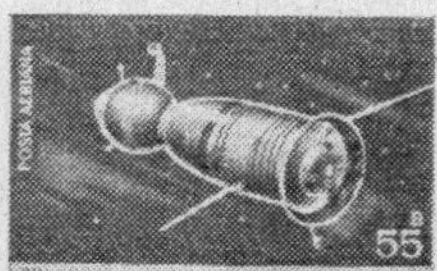

914 "Soyuz 40"

1981. Air. Soviet–Rumanian Space Flight. Mult.
4635 55 b. Type **914** 15 10
4636 3 l. 40 "Soyuz"–"Salyut" link-up 55 15

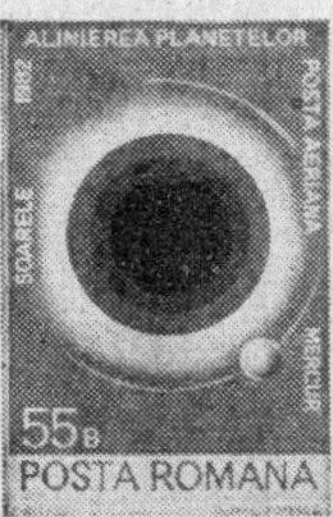

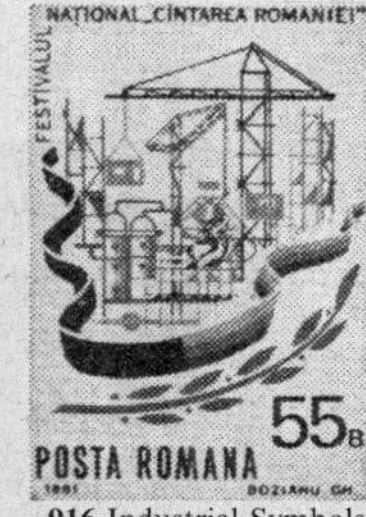

915 Sun and Mercury **916** Industrial Symbols

1981. The Planets. Multicoloured.
4638 55 b. Type **915** 15 10
4639 1 l. Venus, Earth and Mars . 25 15
4640 1 l. 50 Jupiter 35 20
4641 2 l. 15 Saturn 50 25
4642 3 l. 40 Uranus 75 30
4643 4 l. 80 Neptune and Pluto . . 1·10 45

1981. "Singing Rumania" National Festival. Multicoloured.
4645 55 b. Type **916** 15 10
4646 1 l. 50 Science 30 10
4647 2 l. 15 Agriculture 40 15
4648 3 l. 40 Culture 65 30

917 Book and Flag **918** "Woman in an Interior"

1981. "Universiada" Games, Bucharest. Multicoloured.
4649 1 l. Type **917** 20 10
4650 2 l. 15 Games emblem 40 20
4651 4 l. 80 Stadium (horiz) . . . 1·00 1·00

1981. 150th Birth Anniv of Theodor Aman (painter). Multicoloured.
4652 40 b. "Self-portrait" 10 10
4653 55 b. "Battle of Giurgiu" (horiz) 15 10
4654 1 l. "Family Picnic" (horiz) . 20 10
4655 1 l. 50 "The Painter's Studio' (horiz) 30 10
4656 2 l. 15 Type **918** 40 15
4657 3 l. 10 Aman Museum, Bucharest (horiz) 60 35

919 "The Thinker of Cernavoda" (polished stone sculpture) **920** Blood Donation

1981. 16th Science History Congress, Bucharest.
4658 **919** 3 l. 40 multicoloured . . 65 65

1981. Blood Donor Publicity.
4659 **920** 55 b. multicoloured . . . 20 15

921 Central Military Hospital

1981. 150th Anniv of Central Military Hospital, Bucharest.
4660 **849** 55 b. multicoloured . . . 15 10

922 Paul Constantinescu **923** Children at Stamp Exhibition

1981. Rumanian Musicians. Multicoloured.
4661 40 b. George Enescu 15 10
4662 55 b. Type **922** 15 10
4663 1 l. Dinu Lipatti 25 10
4664 1 l. 50 Ionel Perlea 35 10
4665 2 l. 15 Ciprian Porumbescu . 45 15
4666 3 l. 40 Mihail Jora 70 40

1981. Stamp Day.
4667 **923** 2 l. multicoloured 35 15

924 Hopscotch **925** Football Players

1981. Children's Games and Activities. Multicoloured.
4668 40 b. Type **924** (postage) . . 10 10
4669 55 b. Football 15 10
4670 1 l. Children with balloons and hobby horse 20 15
4671 1 l. 50 Fishing 30 15
4672 2 l. 15 Dog looking through school window at child . . 45 15
4673 3 l. Child on stilts 55 20
4674 4 l. Child tending sick dog . 75 25
4675 4 l. 80 Children with model gliders (air) . . . . 1·00 75

Nos. 4671/15 are from illustrations by Norman Rockwell.

1981. World Cup Football Championship, Spain (1982). Multicoloured.
4676 55 b. Type **925** 15 10
4677 1 l. Goalkeeper saving ball . 20 10
4678 1 l. 50 Player heading ball . 30 15
4679 2 l. 15 Player kicking ball over head 40 20
4680 3 l. 40 Goalkeeper catching ball 65 65
4681 4 l. 80 Player kicking ball . . 90 90

926 Alexander the Good, Prince of Moldavia **927** Entrance to Union Square Station

1982. Anniversaries. Multicoloured.
4683 1 l. Type **926** (550th death anniv) 20 10
4684 1 l.50 Bodgan P. Hasdeu (historian, 75th death anniv) 30 10
4685 2 l. 15 Nicolae Titulescu (diplomat and politician, birth centenary) 50 25

1982. Inauguration of Bucharest Underground Railway. Multicoloured.
4686 60 b. Type **927** 15 10
4687 2 l. 40 Platforms and train at Heroes' Square station . . 75 25

928 Dog rescuing Child from Sea

1982. Dog, Friend of Mankind. Multicoloured.
4688 55 b. Type **928** 15 10
4689 1 l. Shepherd and sheepdog (vert) 20 10
4690 3 l. Gundog (vert) 55 15
4691 3 l. 40 Huskies 65 20
4692 4 l. Dog carrying woman's basket (vert) 75 20
4693 4 l. 80 Dog guiding blind person (vert) 85 35
4694 5 l. Dalmatian and child with doll 90 40
4695 6 l. St. Bernard . . . . . . 1·10 55

929 Dove, Banner and Crowd

1982. 60th Anniv of Communist Youth Union. Multicoloured.
4696 1 l. Type **929** 20 10
4697 1 l. 20 Construction worker . 25 10
4698 1 l. 50 Farm workers 30 15
4699 2 l. Laboratory worker and students 40 15
4700 2 l. 50 Labourers 55 20
4601 3 l. Choir, musicians and dancers 65 25

932 Harvesting Wheat

1982. 20th Anniv of Agricultural Co-operatives. Multicoloured.

4704 50 b. Type **932** (postage) . . 15 10
4705 1 l. Cows and milking equipment 25 10
4706 1 l. 50 Watering apple trees . 30 15
4707 2 l. 50 Cultivator in vineyard 55 20
4708 3 l. Watering vegetables . . . 65 25
4709 4 l. Helicopter spraying cereal crop (air) . . . . 1·00 40

933 Vladimir Nicolae's Standard 1 Hang-glider

1982. Air. Hang-gliders. Multicoloured.

4711 50 b. Type **933** 15 10
4712 1 l. Excelsior D 35 10
4713 1 l. 50 Dedal-1 . . . . 40 15
4714 2 l. 50 Entuziast 75 25
4715 4 l. AK-22 . . . . 1·10 50
4716 5 l. Grifrom . . . . 1·40 50

934 Baile Felix

936 Vlaicu Monument, Banesti-Prahova

935 "Legend"

1982. Spas and Health Resorts. Multicoloured.

4717 50 b. Type **934** 15 10
4718 1 l. Predeal (horiz) 25 10
4719 1 l. 50 Baile Herculane . . . 30 15
4720 2 l. 50 Eforie Nord (horiz) . . 55 20
4721 3 l. Olimp (horiz) 65 20
4722 5 l. Neptun (horiz) . . . . . 1·00 40

1982. Paintings by Sabin Balasa. Multicoloured.

4723 1 l. Type **935** 25 10
4724 1 l. 50 "Contrasts" 35 15
4725 2 l. 50 "Peace Relay" 75 30
4726 4 l. "Genesis of the Rumanian People" (vert) 85 35

1982. Air. Birth Centenary of Aurel Vlaicu (aviation pioneer). Multicoloured.

4727 50 b. Vlaicu's glider, 1909 (horiz) 15 10
4728 1 l. Type **936** 30 10
4729 2 l. 50 Air Heroes' Monument 70 25
4730 3 l. Vlaicu's No. 1 "Crazy Fly", 1910 (horiz) 80 30

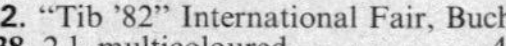

938 Central Exhibition Pavilion

1982. "Tib '82" International Fair, Bucharest.

4732 **938** 2 l. multicoloured 45 10

MINIMUM PRICE

The minimum price quoted is 10p which represents a handling charge rather than a basis for valuing common stamps. For further notes about prices, see introductory pages.

939 Young Pioneer with Savings Book and Books

940 Postwoman delivering Letters

1982. Savings Week. Multicoloured.

4733 1 l. Type **939** 25 10
4734 2 l. Savings Bank advertisement (Calin Popovici) 45 10

1982. Stamp Day. Multicoloured.

4735 1 l. Type **940** 25 10
4736 2 l. Postman 40 15

941 "Brave Young Man and the Golden Apples" (Petre Ispirescu)

942 Symbols of Industry, Party Emblem and Programme

1982. Fairy Tales. Multicoloured.

4737 50 b. Type **941** 15 10
4738 1 l. "Bear tricked by the Fox" (Ion Creanga) 25 10
4739 1 l. 50 Warrior fighting bird ("Prince of Tears" (Mihai Eminescu)) 35 10
4740 2 l. 50 Hen with bag ("Bag with Two Coins" (Ion Creanga)) 55 20
4741 3 l. Rider fighting three-headed dragon ("Ileana Simziana" (Petre Ispirescu)) 65 25
4742 5 l. Man riding devil ("Danila Prepeleac" (Ion Creanga)) 1·10 35

1982. Rumanian Communist Party National Conference, Bucharest. Multicoloured.

4743 1 l. Type **942** 30 25
4744 2 l. Wheat symbols of industry and Party emblem and open programme 60 55

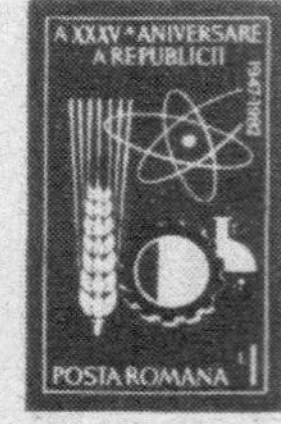

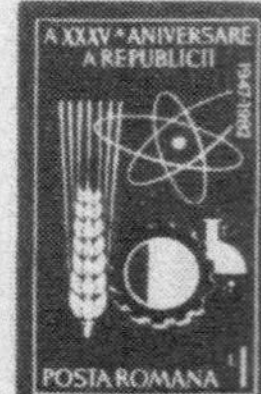

943 Wooden Canteen from Suceava

944 Wheat, Cogwheel, Flask and Electricity Emblem

1982. Household Utensils.

4745 **943** 50 b. red 10 10
4746 – 1 l. blue 20 10
4747 – 1 l. 50 orange 35 10
4748 – 2 l. blue 45 10
4749 – 3 l. green 65 10
4750 – 3 l. 50 green 75 10
4751 – 4 l. brown 90 10
4752 – 5 l. blue . . . . 1·10 10
4753 – 6 l. blue . . . . 1·40 10
4754 – 7 l. purple . . . . . . 1·50 10
4755 – 7 l. 50 mauve . . . . 1·60 10
4756 – 8 l. green . . . . . . 1·75 10
4757 – 10 l. red . . . . 2·10 10
4758 – 20 l. violet . . . . . 4·25 15
4759 – 30 l. blue . . . . . . 6·50 15
4760 – 50 l. brown . . . . . 10·50 15

DESIGNS: As T **943**—VERT: 1 l. Ceramic plates from Radauti; 2 l. Jug and plate from Vama-Maramures; 3 l. Wooden churn and pail from North Moldavia; 4 l. Wooden spoons and ceramic plate from Cluj; 5 l. Ceramic bowl and pot from Marginea-Suceava. HORIZ: 1 l. 50, Wooden dipper from Valea Mare; 3 l. 50, Ceramic plates from Leheceni-Crisana. 29 × 23 mm: 10 l. Wooden tubs from Hunedoara and Suceava; 30 l. Wooden spoons from Alba. 23 × 29 mm: 6 l. Ceramic pot and jug from Bihor; 7 l. Distaff and spindle from Transylvania; 7 l. 50, Double wooden pail from Suceava; 8 l. Pitcher and ceramic plate from Oboga and Horezu; 20 l. Wooden canteen and six glasses from Horezu; 50 l. Ceramic plates from Horezu.

1982. 35th Anniv of People's Republic. Mult.

4767 1 l. Type **944** 25 10
4768 2 l. National flag and oakleaves 45 15

945 H. Coanda and Diagram of Jet Engine

1983. Air. 25 Years of Space Exploration. Mult.

4769 50 b. Type **945** 15 10
4770 1 l. H. Oberth and diagram of rocket 25 10
4771 1 l. 50 "Sputnik 1", 1957 (first artificial satellite) 40 15
4772 2 l. 50 "Vostok 1", (first manned flight) 70 15
4773 4 l. "Apollo 11, 1969 (first Moon landing) . . . . . . 1·10 30
4774 5 l. Space shuttle "Columbia" 1·40 50

946 Rombac One Eleven

947 Matei Millo in "The Discontented" by Vasile Alecsandri

1983. Air. First Rumanian-built Jet Airliner.

4776 **946** 11 l. blue . . . . 3·50 15

1983. Rumanian Actors.

4777 **947** 50 b. red and black . . . 15 10
4778 – 1 l. green and black . . . 30 10
4779 – 1 l. 50 violet and black . 40 10
4780 – 2 l. brown and black . . 55 15
4781 – 2 l. 50 green & black . . 70 20
4782 – 3 l. blue and black . . . 80 25
4783 – 4 l. green and black . . 1·10 30
4784 – 5 l. lilac and black . . . 1·40 35

DESIGNS: 1 l. Mihail Pascaly in "Director Millo", by Vasile Alecsandri; 1 l. 50, Aristizza Romanescu in "The Dogs" by H. Lecca; 2 l. C. I. Nottara in "Blizzard" by B. S. Delavrancea; 2 l. 50, Grigore Manolescu in "Hamlet" by William Shakespeare; 3 l. Agatha Birsescu in "Medea" by Lebouvet; 4 l. Ion Brezeanu in "The Lost Letter" by I. L. Caragiale. 5 l. Aristide Demetriad in "The Despotic Prince" by Vasile Alecsandri.

948 Hugo Grotius

949 Aro "10"

1983. 400th Birth Anniv of Hugo Grotius (Dutch jurist).

4785 **948** 2 l. brown 55 15

1983. Rumanian-built Vehicles. Multicoloured.

4786 50 b. Type **949** 15 10
4787 1 l. Dacia "1300" Break . . . 30 10
4788 1 l. 50 Aro "242" 45 10
4789 2 l. 50 Aro "244" 70 20
4790 4 l. Dacia "1310" . . . . . . 1·10 30
4791 5 l. Oltcit "Club" . . . . . . 1·40 35

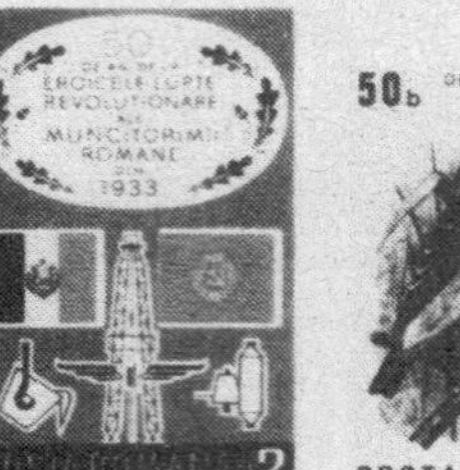

951 National and Communist Party Flags

953 Bluethroat

952 Loading Mail

1983. 50th Anniv of 1933 Workers' Revolution.

4793 **951** 2 l. multicoloured 55 15

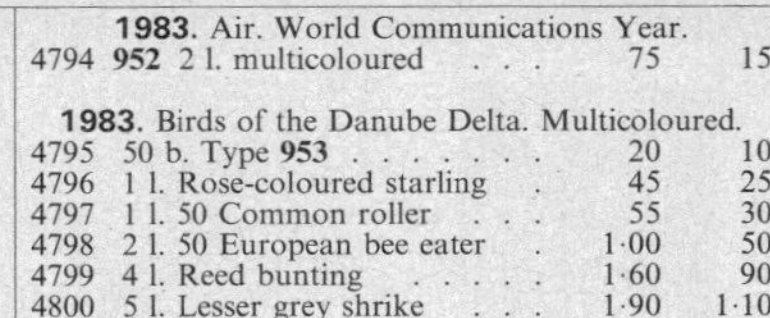

1983. Air. World Communications Year.

4794 **952** 2 l. multicoloured . . . 75 15

1983. Birds of the Danube Delta. Multicoloured.

4795 50 b. Type **953** 20 10
4796 1 l. Rose-coloured starling . 45 25
4797 1 l. 50 Common roller . . . 55 30
4798 2 l. 50 European bee eater . 1·00 50
4799 4 l. Reed bunting . . . . . 1·60 90
4800 5 l. Lesser grey shrike . . . 1·90 1·10

954 Kayak

1983. Water Sports. Multicoloured.

4801 50 b. Type **954** 15 10
4802 1 l. Water polo 30 10
4803 1 l. 50 Canoeing 40 15
4804 2 l. 50 Diving 70 20
4805 4 l. Rowing . . . . 1·10 35
4806 5 l. Swimming (start of race) 1·40 90

955 Postman on Bicycle

1983. Stamp Day. Multicoloured.

4807 1 l. Type **955** 30 10
4808 3 l. 50 (+ 3 l.) National flag as stamp . . . . 1·75 1·75

No. 4808 was issued with premium carrying label attached.

956 "Geum reptans"

1983. European Flora and Fauna. Multicoloured.

4810 1 l. Type **956** 40 25
4811 1 l. "Papaver dubium" . . . 40 25
4812 1 l. "Carlina acaulis" 40 25
4813 1 l. "Paeonia peregrina" . . . 40 25
4814 1 l. "Gentiana excisa" . . . 40 25
4815 1 l. Eurasian red squirrel . . 40 25
4816 1 l. "Grammia quenselii" (butterfly) 60 30
4817 1 l. Middle-spotted woodpecker 90 30
4818 1 l. Lynx 40 25
4819 1 l. Wallcreeper 90 30

957 "Girl with Feather"

958 Flag and Oak Leaves

1983. Paintings by C. Baba. Multicoloured.

4820 1 l. Type **957** 30 10
4821 2 l. "Congregation" 55 15
4822 3 l. "Farm Workers" 80 25
4823 4 l. "Rest in the Fields" (horiz) 1·10 35

1983. 65th Anniv of Union of Transylvania and Rumania. Multicoloured.

4824 1 l. Type **958** 30 10
4825 2 l. National and Communist Party Flags and Parliament building, Bucharest 55 15

959 Postman and Post Office

961 Cross-country Skiing

1983. "Balkanfila IX '83" Stamp Exhibition, Bucharest. Multicoloured.
4826 1 l. Type **959** 30 10
4827 2 l. Postwoman and Athenaeum Concert Hall 55 15

1984. Winter Olympic Games, Sarajevo. Multicoloured.
4830 50 b. Type **961** 15 10
4831 1 l. Biathlon 25 20
4832 1 l. 50 Ice skating 40 30
4833 2 l. Speed skating 50 40
4834 3 l. Ice hockey 75 65
4835 3 l. 50 Bobsleighing 90 80
4836 4 l. Luge . . . . 1·00 90
4837 5 l. Downhill skiing . . . . 1·25 1·10

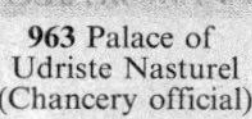

963 Palace of Udriste Nasturel (Chancery official)

967 Flowering Rush

966 Sunflower

1984. Anniversaries.
4839 50 b. green, pink and silver . 15 10
4840 1 l. violet, green and silver . 30 10
4841 1 l. 50 multicoloured 40 15
4842 2 l. brown, blue and silver . . 65 15
4843 3 l. 50 multicoloured 95 30
4844 4 l. multicoloured . . . . 1·10 35
DESIGNS: 50 b. Type **963** (325th death anniv); 1 l. Miron Costin (poet, 350th birth anniv); 1 l. 50, Crisan (Giurgiu Marcu) (leader of peasant revolt, 250th birth anniv); 2 l. Simion Barnutiu (scientist, 175th birth anniv); 3 l. 50, Diuliu Zamfirescu (writer, 125th birth anniv); 4 l. Nicolae Milescu at Great Wall of China (explorer, 275th death anniv).

1984. Protection of Environment. Multicoloured.
4847 1 l. Type **966** 30 10
4848 2 l. Red deer 55 20
4849 3 l. Fish 80 25
4850 4 l. Jay . . . . 1·90 45

1984. Flowers of the Danube. Multicoloured.
4851 50 b. Arrowhead 15 10
4852 1 l. Yellow iris 30 10
4853 1 l. 50 Type **967** 40 15
4854 3 l. White water lily 80 25
4855 4 l. Fringed water lily (horiz) . 1·10 35
4856 5 l. Yellow water lily (horiz) . 1·40 50

968 Crowd with Banners

970 Congress Emblem

969 High Jumping

1984. 45th Anniv of Anti-Fascist Demonstration.
4857 **968** 2 l. multicoloured 55 15

1984. Olympic Games, Los Angeles (1st issue). Multicoloured.
4858 50 b. Type **969** 15 10
4859 1 l. Swimming 25 20
4860 1 l. 50 Running 40 30
4861 3 l. Handball 75 65
4862 4 l. Rowing . . . . 1·00 90
4863 5 l. Canoeing . . . . 1·25 1·10
See also Nos. 4866/73.

1984. 25th Ear, Nose and Throat Association Congress, Bucharest.
4864 **970** 2 l. multicoloured 55 15

1984. Olympic Games, Los Angeles (2nd issue). As T **969**. Multicoloured.
4866 50 b. Boxing 15 10
4867 1 l. Rowing 25 20
4868 1 l. Handball 40 30
4869 2 l. Judo 50 40
4870 3 l. Wrestling 75 65
4871 3 l. 50 Fencing 90 80
4872 4 l. Kayak . . . . 1·00 90
4873 5 l. Swimming . . . . 1·25 1·10

972 Mihai Ciuca (bacteriologist, cent)

974 Flags, Flame and Power Station

973 Lockhead Super Electra

1984. Birth Anniversaries. Dated "1983".
4874 **972** 1 l. purple, blue and silver . 30 10
4875 – 2 l. brown and silver . . 55 15
4876 – 3 l. green, brown and silver . 80 25
4877 – 4 l. violet, green and silver . 1·10 35
DESIGNS: 2 l. Petre S. Aurelian (agronomist, 150th anniv); 3 l. Alexandru Vlahuta (writer, 125th anniv); 4 l. Dimitrie Leonida (engineer, centenary).

1984. Air. 40th Anniv of International Civil Aviation Organization. Multicoloured.
4878 50 b. Type **973** 15 10
4879 1 l. 50 Britten Norman Islander . 50 15
4880 3 l. Rombac One Eleven . . 1·00 35
4881 6 l. Boeing 707 . . . . 2·00 80

1984. 40th Anniv of Liberation.
4882 **974** 2 l. multicoloured . . . 55 15

975 Lippizaner

1984. Horses. Multicoloured.
4883 50 b. Type **975** 15 10
4884 1 l. Hutul 30 10
4885 1 l. 50 Bukovina 40 15
4886 2 l. 50 Nonius 70 20
4887 4 l. Arab . . . . 1·10 35
4888 5 l. Rumanian half-breed . 1·40 50

977 Memorial, Alba Julia

978 "Portrait of a Child" (Th. Aman)

1984. Bicentenary of Horea, Closa and Crisan Uprisings.
4890 **977** 2 l. multicoloured . . . 55 15

1984. Paintings of Children. Multicoloured.
4891 50 b. Type **978** 15 10
4892 1 l. "The Little Shepherd" (N. Grigorescu) 30 15
4893 2 l. "Lica with an Orange" (St. Luchian) 55 15
4894 3 l. "Portrait of a Child" (N. Tonitza) 80 25
4895 4 l. "Portrait of a Boy" (S. Popp) . . . . 1·10 35
4896 5 l. "Portrait of Young Girl" (I. Tuculescu) . . . . 1·40 50

979 Stage Coach and Rumanian Philatelic Association Emblem

1984. Stamp Day.
4897 **979** 2 l. (+ 1 l.) multicoloured 80 65
No. 4897 was issued with premium carrying label attached.

981 Dalmatian Pelicans

982 Dr. Petru Groza (former President)

1984. Protected Animals. Dalmatian Pelicans. Multicoloured.
4899 50 b. Type **981** 25 15
4900 1 l. Pelican on nest 55 25
4901 1 l. Pelicans on lake 55 25
4902 2 l. Pelicans roosting 95 65

1984. Anniversaries. Multicoloured.
4903 50 b. Type **982** (birth centenary) 15 10
4904 1 l. Alexandru Odobescu (writer) (150th birth anniv) 30 10
4905 2 l. Dr. Carol Davila (physician) (death centenary) 55 15
4906 3 l. Dr. Nicolae Gh. Lupu (physician) (birth centenary) 80 25
4907 4 l. Dr. Daniel Danielopolu (physician) (birth centenary) 1·10 35
4908 5 l. Panait Istrati (writer) (birth centenary) . . . . 1·40 50

983 Generator

985 August Treboniu Laurian (linguist and historian)

1984. Centenary of Power Station and Electric Street Lighting in Timisoara. Multicoloured.
4909 1 l. Type **983** 30 10
4910 2 l. Street lamp 55 15

1985. Anniversaries. Multicoloured.
4912 50 b. Type **985** (175th birth anniv) 15 10
4913 1 l. Grigore Alexandrescu (writer) (death centenary) . 30 10
4914 1 l. 50 Gheorghe Pop de Basesti (politician) (150th birth anniv) 40 15
4915 2 l. Mateiu Caragiale (writer) (birth centenary) . . 55 15
4916 3 l. Gheorghe Ionescu-Sisesti (scientist) (birth centenary) . 80 25
4917 4 l. Liviu Rebreanu (writer) (birth centenary) . . . . 1·10 35

986 Students in Science Laboratory

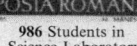

987 Racoon Dog

1985. International Youth Year. Multicoloured.
4918 1 l. Type **986** 30 10
4919 2 l. Students on construction site 55 15

1985. Protected Animals. Multicoloured.
4921 50 b. Type **987** 15 10
4922 1 l. Grey partridge 80 10
4923 1 l. 50 Snowy owl . . . . 1·40 30
4924 2 l. Pine marten 55 15
4925 3 l. Eurasian badger 80 25
4926 3 l. 50 Eurasian otter 90 30
4927 4 l. Capercaillie . . . . 3·00 65
4928 5 l. Great bustard . . . . 3·25 80

988 Flags and Victory Monument, Bucharest

989 Union Emblem

1985. 40th Anniv of Victory in Europe Day.
4929 **988** 2 l. multicoloured . . . 55 15

1985. Communist Youth Union Congress.
4930 **989** 2 l. multicoloured . . . 55 15

990 Route Map and Canal

1985. Danube–Black Sea Canal. Multicoloured.
4931 1 l. Type **990** 30 10
4932 2 l. Canal and bridge, Cernavoda 70 25
4933 3 l. Road over Canal, Medgidia 90 25
4934 4 l. Canal control tower, Agigea 1·25 35

991 Brown Pelican

992 "Fire"

1985. Birth Bicentenary of John J. Audubon (ornithologist). Multicoloured.
4936 50 b. American robin (horiz) 20 10
4937 1 l. Type **991** 40 15
4938 1 l. 50 Yellow-crowned night heron 70 30
4939 2 l. Northern oriole 90 35
4940 3 l. Red-necked grebe . . . 1·40 50
4941 4 l. Mallard (horiz) . . . 1·90 65

1985. Paintings by Ion Tuculescu. Multicoloured.
4942 1 l. Type **992** 30 10
4943 2 l. "Circulation" 55 15
4944 3 l. "Interior of Peasant's Home" (horiz) 80 25
4945 4 l. "Sunset" (horiz) . . . . 1·10 35

993 "Inachis io"

1985. Butterflies and Moths. Multicoloured.
4946 50 b. Type **933** 20 10
4947 1 l. "Papilio machaon" . . . 45 10
4948 2 l. "Vanessa atalanta" . . . 70 20
4949 3 l. "Saturnia pavonia" . . . 1·00 30
4950 4 l. "Ammobiota festiva" . . . 1·40 45
4951 5 l. "Smerinthus ocellata" . . 1·75 60

994 Transfagarasan Mountain Road

1985. 20th Anniv of Election of General Secretary Nicolae Ceausescu and 9th Communist Party Congress. Multicoloured.
4952 1 l. Type **994** 30 10
4953 2 l. Danube–Black Sea Canal 55 15
4954 3 l. Bucharest underground railway 80 25
4955 4 l. Irrigating fields . . . . 1·10 35

995 Rumanian Crest, Symbols of Agriculture and "XX"

996 "Senecio glaberrimus"

1985. 20th Anniv of Rumanian Socialist Republic. Multicoloured.

4956 1 l. Type **995** 30 10
4957 2 l. Crest, symbols of industry and "XX" 55 15

1985. 50th Anniv of Retezat National Park. Multicoloured.

4959 50 b. Type **997** 15 15
4960 1 l. Chamois 30 10
4961 2 l. "Centaurea retezatensis" 55 15
4962 3 l. Violet 80 25
4963 4 l. Alpine marmot . . . . . 1·10 35
4964 5 l. Golden eagle . . . . . . 3·00 75

998 Universal "530 DTC"

1985. Rumanian Tractors. Multicoloured.

4966 50 b. Type **998** 15 10
4967 1 l. Universal "550 M HC" . . 30 10
4968 1 l. 50 Universal "650 Super" 40 15
4969 2 l. Universal "850" 55 15
4970 3 l. Universal "S 1801 IF" tracked front loader . . . 80 25
4971 4 l. Universal "A 3602 IF" front loader . . . . 1·10 35

999 Costume of Muscel (female)

1985. Costumes (1st series). Multicoloured.

4972 50 b. Type **999** 15 10
4973 50 b. Muscel (male) 15 10
4974 1 l. 50 Bistrita-Nasaud (female) 40 15
4975 1 l. 50 Bistrita-Nasaud (male) 40 15
4976 2 l. Vrancea (female) 55 15
4977 2 l. Vrancea (male) 55 15
4978 3 l. Vilcea (female) 80 25
4979 3 l. Vilcea (male) 80 25

See also Nos. 5143/5150.

1000 Footballer attacking Goal

1985. World Cup Football Championship, Mexico (1986) (1st issue). Multicoloured.

4980 50 b. Type **1000** 15 10
4981 1 l. Player capturing ball . . 30 10
4982 1 l. 50 Player heading ball . . 40 15
4983 2 l. Player about to tackle . . 55 15
4984 3 l. Player heading ball and goal keeper 80 25
4985 4 l. Player kicking ball over head . . . . 1·10 35

See also Nos. 5038/43.

1001 U.N. Emblem and "40"

1002 Copper

1985. 40th Anniv of U.N.O. (4986) and 30th Anniv of Rumanian Membership (4987).

4986 2 l. Type **1001** 55 15
4987 2 l. U.N. building, New York, U.N. emblem and Rumanian crest 55 15

1985. Minerals. Multicoloured.

4988 50 b. Quartz and calcite . . 15 10
4989 1 l. Type **1002** 30 10
4990 2 l. Gypsum 55 15
4991 3 l. Quartz 80 25
4992 4 l. Stibium . . . . 1·10 35
4993 5 l. Tetrahedrite . . . . . . 1·40 50

1003 Posthorn

1985. Stamp Day.

4994 **1003** 2 l. (+ 1 l.) multicoloured 80 70

1004 Goofy as Hank waking to find himself at Camelot

1985. 150th Birth of Mark Twain (writer). Scenes from "A Connecticut Yankee in King Arthur's Court" (film). Multicoloured.

4995 50 b. Type **1004** . . . . . .
4996 50 b. Hank at the stake and Merlin (Mickey Mouse) . 2·00 2·00
4997 50 b. Hank being hoisted onto horseback in full armour . 2·00 2·00
4998 50 b. Pete as Sir Sagramoor on horseback . . . . 2·00 2·00

1985. Birth Bicentenaries of Grimm Brothers (folklorists). Scenes from "The Three Brothers". As T **1004**. Multicoloured.

5000 1 l. Father (Donald Duck) bidding farewell to the brothers (Huey, Louie and Dewey) . . . . 4·25 4·25
5001 1 l. Louie as fencing master brother . . . . 4·25 4·25
5002 1 l. Louie keeping rain off his father with sword . . . 4·25 4·25
5003 1 l. Huey as blacksmith brother shoeing galloping horse . 4·25 4·25
5004 1l. Dewey as barber brother shaving Brer Rabbit on the run . . . . 4·25 4·25

1005 Wright Brothers (aviation pioneers)

1985. Explorers and Pioneers. Multicoloured.

5006 1 l. Type **1005** 35 10
5007 1 l. 50 Jacques Yves Cousteau (undersea explorer) . . . 60 15
5008 2 l. Amelia Earhart Putnam (first woman trans-Atlantic flyer) 70 15
5009 3 l. Charles Lindbergh (first solo trans-Atlantic flyer) . . . 90 25
5010 3 l. 50 Sir Edmund Hillary (first man to reach summit of Everest) 90 30
5011 4 l. Robert Edwin Peary and Emil Racovita (polar explorers) . . . . 1·10 35
5012 5 l. Richard Evelyn Byrd (polar explorer and aviator) . . . 2·00 55
5013 6 l. Neil A. Armstrong (first man on Moon) . . . . . 1·40 50

1006 Edmond Halley and Comet

1986. Air. Appearance of Halley's Comet.

5014 2 l. Type **1006** 55 15
5015 4 l. Comet, orbit and space probes . . . . 1·10 35

No. 5014 is wrongly inscr "Edmund".

1007 "Nina in Green"

1010 Hotel Diana, Baile Herculane

1009 Goofy playing Clarinet

1986. Paintings by Nicolae Tonitza. Multicoloured.

5016 1 l. Type **1007** 25 10
5017 2 l. "Irina" 55 20
5018 3 l. "Forester's Daughter" . . 80 35
5019 4 l. "Woman on Veranda" . . 1·10 55

1986. 50th Anniv of Colour Animation. Scenes from "Band Concert" (cartoon film). Multicoloured.

5021 50 b. Type **1009** . . . . . . 2·00 2·00
5022 50 b. Clarabelle playing flute . 2·00 2·00
5023 50 b. Mickey Mouse conducting 2·00 2·00
5024 50 b. Paddy and Peter Pig playing euphonium and trumpet . . . . 2·00 2·00
5025 1 l. Conductor Mickey and flautist Donald Duck . . . 4·25 4·25
5026 1 l. Donald caught in trombone slide . . . . 4·25 4·25
5027 1 l. Horace playing drums . . 4·25 4·25
5028 1 l. Donald selling ice cream . 4·25 4·25
5029 1 l. Mickey and euphonium caught in tornado . . . . . 4·25 4·25

1986. Spa Hotels. Multicoloured.

5031 50 b. Type **1010** 15 10
5032 1 l. Hotel Termal, Baile Felix 25 10
5033 2 l. Hotels Delfin, Meduza and Steaua de Mare, North Eforie 55 15
5034 3 l. Hotel Caciulata, Calimanesti-Caciulata . . . 80 25
5035 4 l. Villa Palas, Slanic Moldova 1·10 35
5036 5 l. Hotel Bradet, Sovata . . . 1·25 45

1011 Ceausescu and Red Flag

1986. 65th Anniv of Rumanian Communist Party

5037 **1011** 2 l. multicoloured . . . 55 15

1012 Italy v. Bulgaria

1986. World Cup Football Championship, Mexico (2nd issue). Multicoloured.

5038 50 b. Type **1012** 15 10
5039 1 l. Mexico v. Belgium . . . 25 10
5040 2 l. Canada v. France 55 15
5041 3 l. Brazil v. Spain 80 25
5042 4 l. Uruguay v. W. Germany . 1·10 35
5043 5 l. Morocco v. Poland . . . 1·25 45

HAVE YOU READ THE NOTES AT THE BEGINNING OF THIS CATALOGUE?

These often provide the answers to the enquiries we receive.

1014 "Tulipa gesneriana"

1986. Flowers. Multicoloured.

5045 50 b. Type **1014** 15 10
5046 1 l. "Iris hispanica" 25 10
5047 2 l. "Rosa hybrida" 55 15
5048 3 l. "Anemone coronaria" . . 80 25
5049 4 l. "Freesia refracta" . . . 1·10 35
5050 5 l. "Chrysanthemum indicum" 1·25 45

1015 Mircea the Great and Horsemen

1986. 600th Anniv of Mircea the Great's Accession.

5051 **1015** 2 l. multicoloured . . . 55 15

1016 Thatched House with Veranda, Alba

1986. 50th Anniv of Museum of Historic Dwellings, Bucharest. Multicoloured.

5052 50 b. Type **1016** 15 10
5053 1 l. Stone-built house, Arges 25 10
5054 2 l. House with veranda, Constanta 55 15
5055 3 l. House with tiled roof and steps, Timis 80 25
5056 4 l. House with ramp to veranda, Neamt . . . . . 1·10 35
5057 5 l. Two storey house with first floor veranda, Gorj . . . 1·25 45

1017 Julius Popper (Tierra del Fuego, 1886 –93)

1986. Polar Research. Multicoloured.

5058 50 b. Type **1017** 15 10
5059 1 l. Bazil Gh. Assan (Spitzbergen, 1896) 40 10
5060 2 l. Emil Racovita (Antarctic, 1897–99) 75 15
5061 3 l. Constantin Dumbrava (Greenland, 1927–28) . . . 80 25
5062 4 l. Rumanian participation in 17th Soviet Antarctic Expedition, 1971–72 . . . 1·75 40
5063 5 l. 1977 "Sinoe" and 1979–80 "Tirnava" krill fishing expeditions . . . . 1·50 45

1019 The Blusher

1020 Group of Cyclists

1986. Fungi. Multicoloured.

5065 50 b. Type **1019** 25 10
5066 1 l. "Boletus luridus" 35 10
5067 2 l. "Lactarius piperatus" . . 70 20
5068 3 l. "Lepiota clypeolaria" . . 95 30
5069 4 l. "Russula cyanoxantha" . 1·50 40
5070 5 l. "Tremiscus helvelloides" 1·75 55

1986. Cycle Tour of Rumania. Multicoloured.

5071 1 l. Type **1020** 25 10
5072 2 l. Motor cycle following cyclist 55 15
5073 3 l. Jeep following cyclists . . 80 25
5074 4 l. Winner . . . . 1·10 35

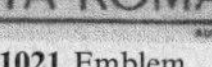

1021 Emblem

1022 Petru Maior (historian) (225th birth anniv)

1986. 40th Anniv of U.N. and 30th Anniv of Rumanian Membership.

5076 **1021** 4 l. multicoloured . . . 1·10 35

1986. Birth Anniversaries.

5077 **1022** 50 b. purple, gold and green 15 10
5078 – 1 b. green, gold and mauve 25 10
5079 – 2 l. red, gold and blue . 55 15
5080 – 3 l. blue, gold and brown 80 25

DESIGNS: 1 l. George Topirceanu (writer, centenary); 2 l. Henri Coanda (engineer, centenary); 3 l. Constantin Budeanu (engineer, centenary).

1023 Coach and Horses

1024 F 300 Oil Drilling Rigs

1986. Stamp Day.

5081 **1023** 2 l. (+ 1 l.) multicoloured 80 25

No. 5081 was issued se-tenant with premium-carrying tab.

1986. Industry. Multicoloured.

5082 50 b. Type **1024** 15 10
5083 1 l. "Promex" excavator (horiz) 25 10
5084 2 l. Petrochemical refinery, Pitesti 55 15
5085 3 l. Tipper "110 t" (horiz) . . 80 25
5086 4 l. "Coral" computer . . . 1·10 35
5087 5 l. 350 m.w. turbine (horiz) . 1·25 45

1025 "Goat"

1026 Tin Can and Motor Car ("re-cycle metals")

1986. Folk Customs. Multicoloured.

5088 50 b. Type **1025** 15 10
5089 1 l. Sorcova 25 10
5090 2 l. Plugusorul 55 15
5091 3 l. Buhaiul 80 25
5092 4 l. Caiutii . . . . 1·10 35
5093 5 l. Uratorii . . . . 1·25 45

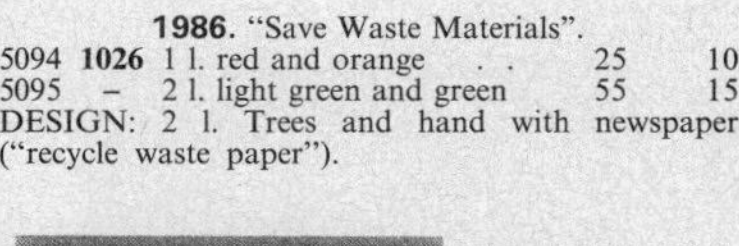

1986. "Save Waste Materials".

5094 **1026** 1 l. red and orange . . 25 10
5095 – 2 l. light green and green 55 15

DESIGN: 2 l. Trees and hand with newspaper ("recycle waste paper").

1027 Flags and Young People

1028 Anniversary Emblem

1987. 65th Anniv of Communist Youth Union. Multicoloured.

5096 1 l. Type **1027** 15 10
5097 2 l. Anniversary emblem . . 20 10
5098 3 l. Flags and young people (different) 40 10

1987. 25th Anniv of Agricultural Co-operatives.

5099 **1028** 2 l. multicoloured . . . 20 10

1030 "Birch Trees by Lake" (I. Andreescu)

1987. Paintings. Multicoloured.

5101 50 b. Type **1030** 10 10
5102 1 l. "Young Peasant Girls spinning" (N. Grigorescu) 25 10
5103 2 l. "Washerwoman" (St. Luchian) 55 10
5104 3 l. "Interior" (St. Dimitrescu) 80 10
5105 4 l. "Winter Landscape" (Al. Ciucurencu) . . . . . . 1·10 15
5106 5 l. "Winter in Bucharest" (N. Tonitza) (vert) . . . . . . 1·40 20

1031 "1907" and Peasants

1987. 80th Anniv of Peasant Uprising.

5107 **1031** 2 l. multicoloured . . . 55 10

1032 Players

1033 1 Leu Coin

1987. 10th Men's World Handball Championship. Various match scenes.

5108 **1032** 50 b. multicoloured . . 10 10
5109 – 1 l. multicoloured (horiz) 10 10
5110 – 2 l. multicoloured . . . 55 10
5111 – 3 l. multicoloured (horiz) 80 10
5112 – 4 l. multicoloured . . . 1·10 15
5113 – 5 l. multicoloured (horiz) 1·40 20

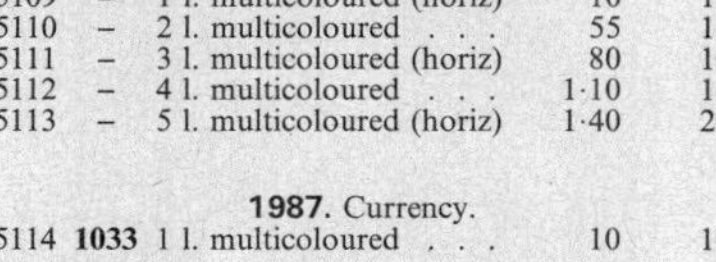

1987. Currency.

5114 **1033** 1 l. multicoloured . . . 10 10

1034 Pelicans in the Danube Delta

1987. Tourism. Multicoloured.

5116 50 b. Type **1034** 10 10
5117 1 l. Cable car above Transfagarasan mountain road 30 10
5118 2 l. Cheile Bicazului 55 10
5119 3 l. Ceahlau mountains . . . 80 10
5120 4 l. Lake Capra, Fagaras, mountains . . . . 1·10 15
5121 5 l. Borsa orchards . . . . 1·40 20

1035 Henri August's Glider, 1909

1987. Air. Aircraft. Multicoloured.

5122 50 b. Type **1035** 15 10
5123 1 l. Sky-diver jumping from IS-28 B2 glider 20 10
5124 2 l. IS-29 D2 glider 35 10
5125 3 l. IS-32 glider 65 15
5126 4 l. I.A.R.35 light airplane . . 90 25
5127 5 l. IS-28 M2 aircraft . . . . 1·10 30

1036 Youth on Winged Horse

1987. Fairy Tales by Petre Ispirescu. Multicoloured.

5128 50 b. Type **1036** 10 10
5129 1 l. King and princesses ("Salt in the Food") 30 10
5130 2 l. Girl on horse fighting lion ("Ileana Simziana") 20 10
5131 3 l. Youth with bow and arrow aiming at bird ("The Youth and the Golden Apples") . 80 10
5132 4 l. "George the Brave" . . . 1·10 15
5133 5 l. Girl looking at sleeping youth ("The Enchanted Pig") 1·40 20

1037 Class "L 45H" Diesel Shunter

1987. Railway Locomotives. Multicoloured.

5135 50 b. Type **1037** 15 10
5136 1 l. Class "LDE 125" 20 10
5137 2 l. Class "LDH 70" 30 10
5138 3 l. Class "LDE 2100" . . . 65 10
5139 4 l. Class "LDE 3000" . . . 90 15
5140 5 l. Class "LE 5100" . . . . 1·10 20

The 5 l. is an electric locomotives the rest are diesel.

1987. Costumes (2nd series). As T **999**. Multicoloured.

5143 1 l. Tirnave (female) 30 10
5144 1 l. Tirnave (male) 30 10
5145 2 l. Buzau (female) 50 10
5146 2 l. Buzau (male) 50 10
5147 3 l. Dobrogea (female) . . . 70 10
5148 3 l. Dobrogea (male) 70 10
5149 4 l. Ilfov (female) 95 15
5150 4 l. Ilfov (male) 95 15

1040 Postal Services (Illustration reduced. Actual size 78 × 23 mm)

1987. Stamp Day.

5151 **1040** 2 l. (+ 1 l.) multicoloured 75 10

No. 5151 was issued se-tenant with premium carrying tab.

1041 Bee on Flower

1987. Bee-keeping. Multicoloured.

5152 1 l. Type **1041** 15 10
5153 2 l. Bee, sunflowers and hives 60 10
5154 3 l. Hives in Danube delta . . 70 10
5155 4 l. Apiculture Complex, Bucharest 95 15

1042 Car behind Boy on Bicycle

1987. Road Safety. Multicoloured.

5156 50 b. Type **1042** 10 10
5157 1 l. Children using school crossing 10 10
5158 2 l. Driver carelessly opening car door 25 10
5159 3 l. Hand holding crossing sign and children using zebra crossing 70 10
5160 4 l. Speedometer and crashed car 95 15
5161 5 l. Child's face and speeding car . . . . 1·10 25

1043 Red Flag and Lenin

1987. 70th Anniv of Russian Revolution.

5162 **1043** 2 l. multicoloured . . . 55 10

1044 Biathlon

1045 Crest and National Colours

1987. Winter Olympic Games, Calgary (1988). Multicoloured.

5163 50 b. Type **1044** 10 10
5164 1 l. Slalom 25 10
5165 1 l. 50 Ice hockey 20 10
5166 2 l. Luge 25 10
5167 3 l. Speed skating 40 10
5168 3 l. 50 Figure skating 80 10
5169 4 l. Downhill skiing 90 15
5170 5 l. Two-man bobsleigh . . . 1·10 25

1987. 40th Anniv of People's Republic.

5171 **1045** 2 l. multicoloured . . . 55 10

1046 Pres. Ceausescu and Flags

1988. 70th Birthday and 55 Years of Revolutionary Activity of Pres. Ceausescu.

5172 **1046** 2 l. multicoloured . . . 55 10

1047 Wide-necked Pot, Marginea

1988. Pottery. Multicoloured.

5173 50 b. Type **1047** 10 10
5174 1 l. Flask, Oboga 15 10
5175 2 l. Jug and saucer, Horezu . 25 10

5176 3 l. Narrow-necked pot, Curtea de Arges 70 10
5177 4 l. Jug, Birsa 95 15
5178 5 l. Jug and plate, Vama . . 1·10 25

1049 Ceramic Clock

1051 Constantin Brincoveanu

1988. Clocks in Ploiesti Museum. Multicoloured.
5180 50 b. Type **1049** 10 10
5181 1 l. 50 Gilt clock with sun at base 20 10
5182 2 l. Clock with pastoral figure 25 10
5183 3 l. Gilt clock surmounted by figure 70 10
5184 4 l. Vase-shaped clock . . . 95 15
5185 5 l. Clock surmounted by porcelain figures . . . . . 1·10 25

1988. 300th Anniv of Election of Constantin Brincoveanu as Ruler of Wallachia.
5187 **1051** 2 l. multicoloured . . . 55 10

1052 Gymnastics

1988. Olympic Games, Seoul (1st issue). Mult.
5188 50 b. Type **1052** 10 10
5189 1 l. 50 Boxing 20 10
5190 2 l. Lawn tennis 25 10
5191 3 l. Judo 70 10
5192 4 l. Running 95 15
5193 5 l. Rowing . . . . 1·10 25
See also Nos. 5197/5204.

1053 Emblems and Roses

1988. Rumanian–Chinese Stamp Exhibition.
5194 **1053** 2 l. multicoloured . . . 55 10

1056 Running

1988. Olympic Games, Seoul (2nd issue). Mult.
5197 50 b. Type **1056** 10 10
5198 1 l. Canoeing 25 10
5199 1 l. 50 Gymnastics 20 10
5200 2 l. Double kayak 25 10
5201 3 l. Weightlifting 70 10
5202 3 l. 50 Swimming 80 10
5203 4 l. Fencing 90 15
5204 5 l. Rowing . . . . 1·10 25

1058 Past and Present Postal Services
(Illustration reduced, actual size 79 × 23 mm).

1988. Stamp Day.
5206 **1058** 2 l. (+ 1 l.) multicoloured 70 10
No. 5206 was issued with se-tenant premium-carrying label, as shown in T **1058**.

1060 State Arms

1988. 70th Anniv of Union of Transylvania and Rumania.
5208 **1060** 2 l. multicoloured . . . 55 10

1061 Athenaeum Concert Hall, Bucharest (centenary)

1988. Rumanian History. Multicoloured.
5209 50 b. Type **1061** 15 10
5210 1 l. 50 Roman coin showing Drobeta Bridge 20 10
5211 2 l. Ruins (600th anniv of Suceava as capital of Moldavian feudal state) . 25 10
5212 3 l. Scroll, arms and town (600th anniv of first documentary reference to Pitesti) . . . 70 10
5213 4 l. Dacian warriors from Trajan's Column 95 15
5214 5 l. Thracian gold helmet from Cotofenesti-Prahova . . . 1·10 25

1062 Zapodeni, 17th century

1989. Traditional House Architecture. Mult.
5215 50 b. Type **1062** 15 10
5216 1 l. 50 Berbesti, 18th century 20 10
5217 2 l. Voitinel, 18th century . 30 10
5218 3 l. Chiojdu Mic, 18th century 70 10
5219 4 l. Cimpanii de Sus, 19th century 95 15
5220 5 l. Naruja, 19th century . . 1·10 25

1063 Red Cross Worker

1989. Life-saving Services. Multicoloured.
5221 50 b. Type **1063** 15 10
5222 1 l. Red Cross orderlies giving first aid to girl (horiz) . . 15 10
5223 1 l. 50 Fireman carrying child 20 10
5224 2 l. Rescuing child from earthquake damaged building 30 10
5225 3 l. Mountain rescue team transporting casualty on sledge (horiz) 70 10
5226 3 l. 50 Rescuing climber from cliff face 85 15
5227 4 l. Rescuing child from river 95 15
5228 5 l. Life-guard in boat and children playing in sea (horiz) 1·10 25

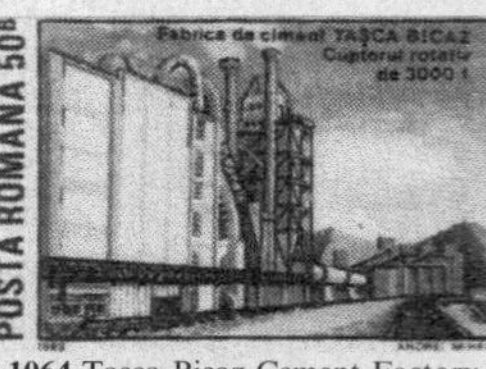

1064 Tasca Bicaz Cement Factory

1989. Industrial Achievements. Multicoloured.
5229 50 b. Type **1064** 15 10
5230 1 l. 50 Railway bridge, Cernavoda 20 10
5231 2 l. Synchronous motor, Resita 30 10
5232 3 l. Bucharest underground . 40 10
5233 4 l. Mangalia-Constanta ferry 95 15
5234 5 l. "Gloria" oil drilling platform . . . . 1·10 25

1065 Flags and Symbols of Industry and Agriculture

1989. 50th Anniv of Anti-Fascist Demonstration.
5235 **1065** 2 l. multicoloured . . . 55 10

1068 Ion Creanga (writer, death centenary)

1989. Anniversaries. Multicoloured.
5239 1 l. Type **1068** 15 10
5240 2 l. Mihai Eminescu (poet, death centenary) 30 10
5241 3 l. Nicolae Teclu (150th birth anniv) 75 10

1069 Flags and Symbols of Industry and Agriculture

1989. 45th Anniv of Liberation.
5242 **1069** 2 l. multicoloured . . . 55 10

1070 "Pin-Pin"

1989. Rumanian Cartoon Films. Multicoloured.
5243 50 b. Type **1070** 10 10
5244 1 l. "Maria" 15 10
5245 1 l. 50 "Gore and Grigore" . 20 10
5246 2 l. "Pisoiul Balanel, Manole, Monk 30 10
5247 3 l. "Gruia lui Novac" . . . 75 10
5248 3 l. 50 "Mihaela" 901 5
5249 4 l. "Harap Alb" . . . . . . 1·00 15
5250 5 l. "Homo Sapiens" . . . . 1·25 25

1071 Globe, Letter and Houses (½-size illustration)

1989. Stamp Day.
5251 **1071** 2 l. (+ 1.) multicoloured 75 10
No. 521 was issued se-tenant with premium-carrying tab as illustrated in T **1071**.

1072 Storming of the Bastille

1989. Bicentenary of French Revolution. Mult.
5252 50 b. Type **1072** 15 10
5253 1 l. 50 Street boy and Marianne 20 10
5254 2 l. Robespierre 30 10
5255 3 l. Rouget de Lisle singing "Marseillaise" 75 10
5256 4 l. Diderot (writer) . . . . 1·00 15
5257 5 l. Crowd . . . . 1·25 25

1073 Conrad Haas and Diagram

1989. Air. Space Pioneers. Multicoloured.
5259 50 b. Type **1073** 10 10
5260 1 l. 50 K. Tsiolkovski and diagram 40 10
5261 2 l. Hermann Oberth and equation 55 10
5262 3 l. Robert Goddard and diagram 80 10
5263 4 l. Sergei Pavlovich Korolev, Earth and satellite . . . . 1·10 10
5264 5 l. Wernher von Braun and landing module . . . . . 1·40 10

1075 Flags and Emblem

1076 Date, Flag, Victory Sign and Candles

1989. 14th Communist Party Congress.
5266 **1075** 2 l. multicoloured . . . 55 10

1990. Popular Uprising (1st issue).
5268 **1076** 2 l. multicoloured . . . 55 10
See also Nos. 594/5301.

1077 Flags and Footballers

1990. World Cup Football Championship, Italy (1st issue). Designs showing flags and footballers.
5269 **1077** 50 b. multicoloured . . 15 10
5270 – 1 l. 50 multicoloured . 40 10
5271 – 2 l. multicoloured . . . 55 10
5272 – 3 l. multicoloured . . . 80 15
5273 – 4 l. multicoloured . . . 1·10 25
5274 – 5 l. multicoloured . . . 1·40 25
See also Nos. 5276/83.

1079 Footballers

1990. World Cup Football Championship, Italy (2nd issue).
5276 **1079** 50 b. multicoloured . . 15 10
5277 – 1 l. multicoloured . . 25 10
5378 – 1 l. 50 multicoloured . 40 10
5379 – 2 l. multicoloured . . 55 10
5380 – 3 l. multicoloured . . . 80 15
5381 – 3 l. 50 multicoloured . 95 20
5382 – 4 l. multicoloured . . . 1·10 25
5383 – 5 l. multicoloured . . . 1·40 25
DESIGNS: 1 to 5 l. Different football scenes.

1080 German Shepherds

1990. International Dog Show, Brno. Multicoloured.
5284 50 b. Type **1080** 10 10
5285 1 l. English setter 25 10
5286 1 l. 50 Boxers 35 10
5287 2 l. Beagles 45 10
5288 3 l. Dobermann pinschers . . 70 15
5289 3 l. 50 Great danes 80 15
5290 4 l. Afghan hounds 90 15
5291 5 l. Yorkshire terriers . . . . 1·10 20

1081 Fountain

1990. "Riccione 90" International Stamp Fair.
5292 **1081** 2 l. multicoloured . . . 45 10

1082 Bucharest Athenaeum and Chinese Temple

1990. Rumanian–Chinese Stamp Exhibition, Bucharest.
5293 **1082** 2 l. multicoloured . . . 45 10

1083 Republic Palace ablaze, Bucharest

1990. Popular Uprising (2nd issue). Multicoloured.
5294 50 b. + 50 b. Type **1083** . . 25 10
5295 1 l. + 1 l. Crowd in Opera Square, Timisoara 45 10
5296 1 l. 50 + 1 l. Soldiers joining crowd in Town Hall Square, Tirgu Mures 60 10
5297 2 l. + 1 l. Soldiers and crowd before television headquarters, Bucharest (vert) 70 10
5298 3 l. + 1 l. Mourners at funeral, Timisoara 90 10
5299 3 l. 50 + 1 l. Crowd celebrating, Brasov (vert) . . . . 1·00 15
5300 4 l. + 1 l. Crowd, Sibiu . . . . 1·00 15
5301 5 l. + 2 l. Cemetery, Bucharest 1·60 20

1084 "Nicolae Cobzarul" (St. Luchian)

1990. Paintings. Multicoloured.
5303 50 b. Type **1084** 10 10
5304 1 l. 50 "Woman in White" (I. Andreescu) 35 10
5305 2 l. "Florist" (St. Luchian) . . 45 10
5306 3 l. "Vase of Flowers" (Jan Brueghel, the elder) 70 15
5307 4 l. "Spring" (Pieter Brueghel, the elder) (horiz) 95 15
5308 5 l. "Madonna and Child" (G. B. Paggi) . . . . 1·10 20

1085 Flag Stamps encircling Globe

1990. Stamp Day.
5309 **1085** 2 l. (+ 1 l.) multicoloured 70 30
No. 5309 was issued with se-tenant premium-carrying label.

1086 Prince Constantin Cantacuzino (350th birth anniv)

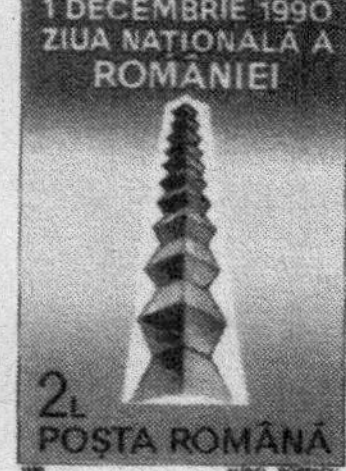

1087 Column of Infinity

1990. Anniversaries.
5310 **1086** 50 b. brown and blue . . 10 10
5311 – 1 l. 50 green and mauve 35 10
5312 – 2 l. red and blue . . . 45 10
5313 – 3 l. blue and brown . . 65 10
5314 – 4 l. brown and blue . . 90 15
5315 – 5 l. violet and green . . 1·10 20
DESIGNS: 1 l. 50, Ienachita Vacarescu (annalist, 250th birth anniv); 2 l. Titu Maiorescu (writer, 150th birth anniv); 3 l. Nicolae Iorga (historian, 50th death anniv); 4 l. Martha Bibescu (birth centenary); 5 l. Stefan Procupiu (scientist, birth centenary).

1990. National Day.
5316 **1087** 2 l. multicoloured . . . 45 10

1990. 1st Anniv of Popular Uprising. No. 5268 surch **L4 UN AN DE LA VICTORIA REVOLUTIEI.**
5317 **1076** 4 l. on 2 l. multicoloured 90 10

1089 "Irises"

1991. Death Centenary of Vincent van Gogh (painter). Multicoloured.
5318 50 b. Type **1089** 10 10
5319 2 l. "The Artist's Room" . . 10 10
5320 3 l. "Illuminated Coffee Terrace" (vert) 25 10
5321 3 l. 50 "Ochard in Blossom" 30 10
5322 5 l. "Sunflowers" (vert) . . 40 10

1090 Great Black-backed Gull

1091 Crucifixion

1991. Water Birds.
5323 **1090** 50 b. blue 10 10
5324 – 1 l. green 10 10
5325 – 1 l. 50 bistre 10 10
5326 – 2 l. blue 10 10
5327 – 3 l. green 10 10
5328 – 3 l. 50 green 10 10
5329 – 4 l. violet 20 10
5330 – 5 l. brown 25 10
5331 – 6 l. brown 25 10
5332 – 7 l. blue 35 10
DESIGNS: 1 l. Common tern; 1 l. 50, Avocet; 2 l. Pomarine skua; 3 l. Lapwings; 3 l. 50, Red-breasted merganser; 4 l. Little egret; 5 l. Dunlin; 6 l. Black-tailed godwit; 7 l. Whiskered tern.

1991. Easter.
5333 **1091** 4 l. multicoloured . . . 30 10

1092 "Eutelsat 1" Communications Satellite

1093 Posthorn

1991. Europa. Europe in Space.
5334 **1092** 4 l. 50 multicoloured . . 35 10

1991.
5335 **1093** 4 l. 50 blue 35 10

1094 Rings Exercise

1095 Curtea de Arges Monastery

1991. Gymnastics. Multicoloured.
5336 1 l. Type **1094** 10 10
5337 1 l. Parallel bars 10 10
5338 4 l. 50 Vaulting 40 10
5339 4 l. 50 Asymmetric bars . . . 40 10
5340 8 l. Floor exercises 65 10
5341 9 l. Beam 75 10

1991. Monasteries. Multicoloured.
5342 1 l. Type **1095** 10 10
5343 1 l. Putna 10 10
5344 4 l. 50 Varatec 40 10
5345 4 l. 50 Agapia (horiz) 40 10
5346 8 l. Golia (horiz) 65 10
5347 9 l. Sucevita (horiz) 75 10

1096 Hotel Continental, Timisoara

1097 Gull and Sea Shore

1991. Hotels.
5349 **1096** 1 l. blue 10 10
5450 – 2 l. green 15 10
5452 – 4 l. red 25 10
5453 – 5 l. violet 40 10
5454 – 6 l. brown 35 10
5456 – 8 l. brown 45 10
5457 – 9 l. red 75 10
5458 – 10 l. green 85 10
5460 – 18 l. red . . . . 1·00 10
5461 – 20 l. orange . . . . . . 1·10 10
5462 – 25 l. blue . . . . 1·40 10
5463 – 30 l. purple . . . . . . 1·60 10
5465 – 45 l. blue . . . . 2·50 10
5467 – 60 l. green . . . . . . 3·25 10
5469 – 80 l. violet . . . . . . 4·50 10
5471 – 120 l. blue and grey . . 2·75 10
5472 – 160 l. red and pink . . 3·75 10
5474 – 250 l. blue and grey . . 5·50 10
5476 – 400 l. brown and ochre . 9·00 10
5477 – 500 l. dp green & green . 11·00 10
5479 – 800 l. mauve and pink . 18·00 10
DESIGNS—As T **1096**: HORIZ: 2 l. Valea Caprei Chalet, Mt. Fagaras; 5 l. Hotel Lebada, Crisan; 6 l. Muntele Rosu Chalet, Mt. Ciucas; 8 l. Transsilvania Hotel, Cluj-Napoca; 9 l. Hotel Orizont, Predeal; 20 l. Alpin Hotel, Poiana Bra, Psov; 25 l. Constanta Casino; 30 l. Miorita Chalet, Mt. Bucegi; 45 l. Sura Dacilor Chalet, Poiana Brasov; 60 l. Valea Draganului Tourist Complex; 80 l. Hotel Florica, Venus. VERT: 4 l. Intercontinental Hotel, Bucharest; 10 l. Hotel Roman, Baile Herculcane; 18 l. Rarau Chalet, Mt. Rarau. 26×40 mm: 120 l. International Complex, Baile Felix; 160 l. Hotel Egreta, Tulcea. 40×26 mm: 250 l. Valea de Pesti Motel, Jiului Valley; 400 l. Baisoara Tourist Complex; 500 l. Bradul Hotel, Covasna; 800 l. Gorj Hotel, Jiu.
Nos. 5367/79 have no frame.

1991. "Riccione 91" Stamp Exhibition, Italy.
5381 **1097** 4 l. multicoloured . . . 10 10

1098 Vase

1099 Emblem

1991. Rumanian–Chinese Stamp Exhibition. Mult.
5382 5 l. Type **1098** 40 10
5383 5 l. Vase with peony decoration 40 10

1991. 125th Anniv of Rumanian Academy.
5384 **1099** 1 l. blue 10 10

1100 "Flowers" (Nicu Enea)

1102 Map with House and People

1991. "Balcanfila '91" Stamp Exhibition, Bacau. Multicoloured.
5385 4 l. Type **1100** 35 10
5386 5 l. (+ 2 l.) "Peasant Girl of Vlasca" (Georghe Tattarescu) 60 15

1991. Population and Housing Census.
5389 **1102** 5 l. multicoloured . . . 40 20

1103 Bridge

1991. "Phila Nippon '91" International Stamp Exhibition, Tokyo.
5390 **1103** 10 l. ochre, brown & red 10 10
5391 – 10 l. multicoloured . . 10 10
DESIGN: No. 5391, Junk.

1105 Running

1991. World Athletics Championships, Tokyo. Multicoloured.
5393 1 l. Type **1105** 10 10
5394 4 l. Long jumping 35 10
5395 5 l. High jumping 45 10
5396 5 l. Athlete in starting blocks 45 10
5397 9 l. Hurdling 75 10
5398 10 l. Throwing the javelin . . 85 10

1106 Mihail Kogalniceanu (policitian, death cent)

1991. Anniversaries.
5399 **1106** 1 l. brown, blue & dp bl 10 10
5400 – 4 l. green, lilac & violet 35 10
5401 – 5 l. brown, dp blue & bl 45 10
5402 – 5 l. blue, brown & red . 45 10
5403 – 9 l. red, blue & dp blue 75 10
5404 – 10 l. black, lt brn & brn 85 10
DESIGNS: No. 5400, Nicolae Titulescu (politician, 50th death anniv); 5401, Andrei Mureseanu (writer, 175th birth anniv); 5402, Aron Pumnul (writer, 125th death anniv); 5403, George Bacovia (writer, 110th birth anniv); 5404, Perpessicius (literature critic, birth centenary).

1107 Library Building

1991. Centenary of Central University Library.
5405 1107 8 l. brown 65 10

1108 Coach and Horses

1991. Stamp Day.
5406 1108 8 l. (+ 2 l.) multicoloured 85 15
No. 5406 was issued se-tenant with premium-carrying label as illustrated in Type **1108**.

1109 "Nativity" (17th-century icon)
1110 Shooting (biathlon)

1991. Christmas.
5407 1109 8 l. multicoloured . . . 65 10

1992. Winter Olympic Games, Albertville. Mult.
5408 4 l. Type **1110** 10 10
5409 5 l. Downhill skiing 15 10
5410 8 l. Cross-country skiing . . 25 10
5411 10 l. Two-man luge 30 10
5412 20 l. Speed skating 55 10
5413 25 l. Ski-jumping 70 10
5414 30 l. Ice hockey 85 10
5415 45 l. Men's figure skating . . 1·25 10

1112 Jug, Plate, Tray and Bowl

1992. Rumanian Porcelain. Multicoloured.
5419 4 l. Type **1112** 10 10
5420 5 l. Tea set 10 10
5421 8 l. Jug and goblet (vert) . . 10 10
5422 30 l. Tea set (different) . . . 65 10
5423 45 l. Vase (vert) . . . . . . 1·00 10

1113 Mackerels

1992. Fishes. Multicoloured.
5424 4 l. Type **1113** 10 10
5425 5 l. Tench 10 10
5426 8 l. Speckled trout 10 10
5427 10 l. Riffle perch 10 10
5428 30 l. Undermouth 65 10
5429 45 l. Blunt-snouted mullet . . 1·25 10

1114 Vase
1115 Gymnast on Beam

1992. Apollo Art Gallery. Unissued stamp surch.
5430 1114 90 l. on 5 l. multicoloured 2·10 10

1992. Individual Gymnastic Championships, Paris. Unissued stamp surch.
5431 1115 90 l. on 5 l. multicoloured 2·10 10

1116 Dressage
1117 "Descent into Hell" (icon)

1992. Horses. Multicoloured.
5432 6 l. Type **1116** 15 10
5433 7 l. Racing (horiz) 15 10
5434 10 l. Rearing 20 10
5435 25 l. Jumping gate 55 10
5436 30 l. Stamping foot (horiz) . 65 10
5437 50 l. Winged horse . . . . . 1·10 10

1992. Easter.
5440 1118 10 l. multicoloured . . 25 10

1120 "Tower and Hand Pump"

1992. Centenary of Bucharest Fire Tower.
5441 1120 10 l. multicoloured . . 25 10

1121 Filipino Vinta and Rook

1992. 30th Chess Olympiad, Manila. Mult.
5442 10 l. Type **1121** 25 10
5443 10 l. Exterior of venue and chessmen 25 10

1122 Post Rider approaching Town

1992. Stamp Day.
5445 1122 10 l. + 4 l. pink, violet and blue 15 10

1123 Pistol shooting
1124 Ion Bratianu

1992. Olympic Games, Barcelona. Multicoloured.
5446 6 l. Type **1123** 10 10
5447 7 l. Weightlifting 10 10
5448 9 l. Two-man kayak racing (horiz) 10 10
5449 10 l. Handball 10 10
5450 25 l. Wrestling (horiz) . . . 30 10
5451 30 l. Fencing (horiz) 35 10
5452 50 l. Running 60 10
5453 55 l. Boxing (horiz) 65 10

1992. 130th Anniv of Foreign Ministry. Designs showing former Ministers.
5455 1124 10 l. violet, green and deep green 10 10
5456 – 25 l. purple, bl & dp bl 20 10
5457 – 30 l. blue, purple & brn 25 10
DESIGNS: 25 l. Ion Duca; 30 l. Grigore Gafencu.

1125 Sculpture

1992. "Expo 92" World's Fair, Seville. "Era of Discovery". Multicoloured.
5458 6 l. Type **1125** 10 10
5459 7 l. Roman bridge, Turnu-Severin 10 10
5460 10 l. House on stilts 10 10
5461 25 l. Railway bridge, Cernavoda 10 10
5462 30 l. Vuia No. 1 (airplane) . . 20 10
5463 55 l. Rocket 35 15

1126 Doves posting Letters in Globe

1992. World Post Day.
5465 1126 10 l. multicoloured . . . 10 10

1127 "Santa Maria" and Bust of Columbus

1992. 500th Anniv of Discovery of America by Columbus. Multicoloured.
5466 6 l. Type **1127** 10 10
5467 10 l. "Nina" 10 10
5468 25 l. "Pinta" 20 10
5469 55 l. Columbus claiming New World 40 10

1128 Post Office Emblem

1992. 1st Anniv of Establishment of R.A. Posta Romana (postal organization).
5471 1128 10 l. multicoloured . . . 10 10

1129 Jacob Negruzzi (writer, 150th birth anniv)
1130 American Bald Eagle

1992. Anniversaries.
5472 1129 6 l. green and violet . . 10 10
5473 – 7 l. mauve, purple and green 10 10
5474 – 9 l. blue and mauve . . 10 10
5475 – 10 l. lt brown, brown and ultramarine 10 10
5476 – 25 l. blue and brown . . 15 10
5477 – 30 l. green and lbue . . 20 10
DESIGNS: 7 l. Grigore Antipa (zoologist, 125th birth anniv); 9 l. Alexe Mateevici (poet, 75th death anniv); 10 l. Cezar Petrescu (writer, birth centenary); 25 l. Octav Onicescu (mathematician, birth centenary); 30 l. Ecaterina Teodoroiu (first world war fighter, 75th death anniv).

1992. Animals. Multicoloured.
5478 6 l. Type **1130** 10 10
5479 7 l. Spotted owl 10 10
5480 9 l. Brown bear 10 10
5481 10 l. American black oystercatcher (horiz) . . . 10 10
5482 25 l. Wolf (horiz) 20 10
5483 30 l. White-tailed deer (horiz) 20 10
5484 55 l. Elk (horiz) 40 10

1131 Arms
1133 Nativity

7L
Posta Română

1132 Buildings and Street, Galea Victoriei

1992. New State Arms.
5486 1131 15 l. multicoloured . . 10 10

1992. Anniversaries. Multicoloured.
5487 7 l. Type **1132** (300th anniv) 10 10
5488 9 l. College building and statue, Roman (600th anniv) . . . 10 10
5489 10 l. Prince Basaral, monastery and Princess Despina (475th anniv of Curtea de Arges monastery) 10 10
5490 25 l. Bucharest School of Architecture (80th anniv) . 10 10

1992. Christmas.
5491 1133 15 l. multicoloured . . 10 10

1134 Globe and Key-pad on Telephone

1992. New Telephone Number System.
5492 1134 15 l. black, red & blue . 10 10

1136 Mihai Voda Monastery

1993. Bucharest Buildings. Multicoloured.
5494 10 l. Type **1136** 10 10
5495 15 l. Vacaresti Monastery . . 10 10
5496 25 l. Unirii Hall 15 10
5497 30 l. Mina Minovici Medico-legal Institute 20 10

1137 Parseval Sigsfeld Kite-type Observation Balloon

1993. Air. Balloons. Multicoloured.
5498 30 l. Type **1137** 20 10
5499 90 l. Caquot observation balloon 55 10

1138 Crucifixion
1139 Hawthorn

1993. Easter.
5500 1138 15 l. multicoloured . . 10 10

1993. Medicinal Plants. Multicoloured.
5501 10 l. Type **1139** 10 10
5502 15 l. Gentian 10 10

5503 25 l. Sea buckthorn 15 10
5504 30 l. Billberry 20 10
5505 50 l. Arnica 30 10
5506 90 l. Dog rose 55 15

1140 Stanescu **1141** Mounted Courier

1993. 60th Birth Anniv of Nichita Stanescu (poet).
5507 **1140** 15 l. multicoloured . . . 10 10

1993. Stamp Day.
5508 **1141** 15 l. + 10 l. multicoloured 10 10

1143 Magpie

1993. Birds.
5510 **1143** 5 l. black and green . . 10 10
5511 – 10 l. black and red . . . 10 10
5512 – 15 l. black and red . . . 10 10
5513 – 20 l. black and brown . . 10 10
5514 – 25 l. black and red . . . 15 10
5515 – 50 l. black and yellow . 30 10
5516 – 65 l. black and red . . . 40 10
5517 – 90 l. black and red . . . 55 15
5518 – 160 l. black and blue . . 95 30
5519 – 250 l. black & mauve . 1·50 50
DESIGNS—HORIZ: 10 l. Golden eagle. VERT: 15 l. Bullfinch; 20 l. Hoopoe; 25 l. Great spotted woodpecker; 50 l. Golden oriole; 65 l. White winged crossbill; 90 l. Barn swallows; 160 l. Azure tit; 250 l. Rose-coloured starling.

1144 Long-hair **1147** Pine Marten

1146 Adder

1993. Cats. Multicoloured.
5520 10 l. Type **1144** 10 10
5521 15 l. Tabby-point long-hair . 10 10
5522 30 l. Red long-hair 15 10
5523 90 l. Blue persian 40 10
5524 135 l. Tabby 60 20
5525 160 l. Long-haired white Persian 70 20

1993. Protected Animals. Multicoloured.
5527 10 l. Type **1146** 10 10
5528 15 l. Lynx (vert) 10 10
5529 25 l. Common shelduck . . . 10 10
5530 75 l. Danube salmon 25 10
5531 105 l. Poplar admiral 35 10
5532 280 l. Alpine longthorn beetle 1·00 30

1993. Mammals.
5533 **1147** 10 l. black and yellow . 10 10
5534 – 15 l. black and brown . 10 10
5535 – 20 l. red and black . . . 10 10
5536 – 25 l. black and brown . 10 10
5537 – 30 l. black and red . . . 10 10
5538 – 40 l. black and red . . . 15 10
5539 – 75 l. black and yellow . 25 10
5540 – 105 l. black & brown . 35 10
5541 – 150 l. black & orange . 50 15
5542 – 280 l. black & yellow . 95 30
DESIGNS—HORIZ: 15 l. Common rabbit; 30 l. Red fox; 150 l. Stoat; 280 l. Egyptian mongoose. VERT: 20 l. Eurasian red squirrel; 25 l. Chamois; 40 l. Argali; 75 l. Small spotted genet; 105 l. Garden dormouse.

1148 Brontosaurus

1993. Prehistoric Animals. Multicoloured.
5543 29 l. Type **1148** 10 10
5544 46 l. Plesiosaurus 15 10
5545 85 l. Triceratops 30 10
5546 171 l. Stegosaurus 60 20
5547 216 l. Tyannosaurus 75 20
5548 319 l. Archaeopteryx . . . . 1·10 35

1150 Stefan the Great, Prince of Moldavia **1151** Mounted Officers

1993. Icons. Multicoloured.
5550 75 l. Type **1150** 10 10
5551 171 l. Prince Costantin Brancoveanu of Wallachia with his sons Constantin, Stefan, Radu and Matei and Adviser Ianache Vacarescu 30 10
5552 216 l. St. Antim Ivireanul, Metropolitan of Wallachia 70 20

1993. Centenary of Rural Gendarmerie Law.
5553 **1151** 29 l. multicoloured . . 10 10

1993. "Riccione 93" International Stamp Fair. No. 5292 surch **Riccione '93 3-5 septembrie 171 L.**
5554 **1081** 171 l. on 2 l. multicoloured 70 20

1154 George Baritiu

1993. Anniversaries.
5556 **1154** 29 l. flesh, black & lilac 10 10
5557 – 46 l. flesh, black & blue 15 10
5558 – 85 l. flesh, black & grn 30 10
5559 – 171 l. flesh, black & pur 60 20
5560 – 216 l. flesh, black & bl 75 25
5561 – 319 l. flesh, black and grey 1·10 35
DESIGNS: 29 l. Type **1154** (politician and journalist, death centenary); 46 l. Horia Creanga (architect, 50th death anniv); 85 l. Armand Calinescu (leader of Peasant National Party, birth centenary); 171 l. Dr. Dumitru Bagdasar (neuro-surgeon, birth centenary); 216 l. Constantin Brailoiu (musician, birth centenary); 319 l. Iuliu Maniu (politician, 40th death anniv).

1993. 35th Annivs of Rumanian Philatelic Association and Rumanian Philatelic Federation. No. 5445 surch **35 ANI DE ACTIVITATE AFR-FFR 1958–1993 70L+45L.**
5562 **1122** 70 l. + 45 l. on 10 l. + 4 l. pink, violet and blue 40 10

75 ANI DE LA MAREA UNIRE
115L
POȘTA ROMÂNĂ
1157 Iancu Flondor (Bukovinan politician)

1993. 75th Anniv of Union of Bessarabia, Bukovina and Transylvania with Rumania.
5564 **1157** 115 l. brown, blue and black 30 10
5565 – 245 l. violet, yellow and green 55 15
5566 – 255 l. multicoloured . . 65 20
5567 – 325 l. brown, pink and deep brown 95 30
DESIGNS: 245 l. Ionel Bratianu (Prime Minister 1918–19, 1922–26 and 1927); 255 l. Iuliu Maniu (Prime Minister, 1927–30 and 1932–33); 325 l. Panteleimon Halippa (Bessarabian politician).

1158 Emblem

1993. Anniversaries. Multicoloured.
5569 115 l. Type **1158** (75th anniv of General Association of Rumanian Engineers) . . . 30 10
5570 245 l. Statue of Johannes Honterus (450th anniv of Rumanian Humanist School) 55 15
5571 255 l. Bridge, arms on book spine and seal (625th anniv of first documentary reference to Slatina) 65 20
5572 325 l. Map and town arms (625th anniv of first documentary reference to Braila) 95 30

1159 "Nativity" (17th-century icon)

1993. Christmas.
5573 **1159** 45 l. multicoloured . . . 30 10

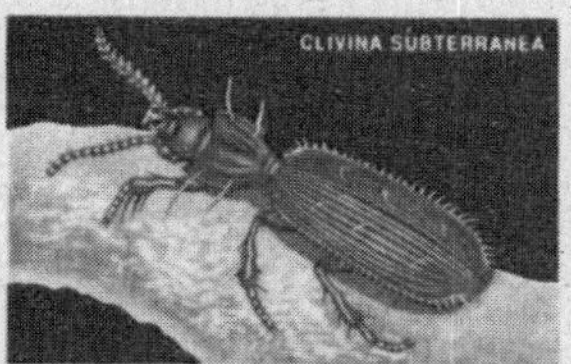

1160 "Clivina subterranea"

1993. Movile Cave Animals. Multicoloured.
5574 29 l. Type **1160** 10 10
5575 46 l. "Nepa anophthalma" . . 25 10
5576 85 l. "Haemopis caeca" . . . 45 15
5577 171 l. "Lascona cristiani" . . 65 20
5578 216 l. "Semisalsa dobrogica" . 75 25
5579 319 l. "Armadilidium tabacarui" . . . . 1·40 45

1161 Prince Alexandru Ioan Cuza and Seal

1994. 130th Anniv of Court of Accounts.
5581 **1161** 45 l. multicoloured . . . 20 10

1162 Opera House

1994. Destroyed Buildings of Bucharest. Mult.
5582 115 l. Type **1162** 25 10
5583 245 l. Vacaresti Church (vert) 55 15
5584 255 l. St. Vineri's Church . . 65 20
5585 325 l. Vacaresti Monastery . 90 30

Lillehammer '94
L70
POȘTA ROMÂNĂ
SARICHIOI - TULCEA
70L
POȘTA ROMÂNĂ
1164 Speed Skating **1165** Sarichioi Windmill, Tulcea

1994. Winter Olympic Games, Lillehammer, Norway. Multicoloured.
5588 70 l. Type **1164** 10 10
5589 115 l. Downhill skiing . . . 15 10
5590 125 l. Bobsleighing 20 10
5591 245 l. Cross-country skiing . 45 15
5592 255 l. Ski jumping 55 15
5593 325 l. Figure skating 70 20

1994. Mills. Multicoloured.
5595 70 l. Type **1165** 10 10
5596 115 l. Nucarilor Valley windmill, Tulcea 10 10
5597 125 l. Caraorman windmill, Tulcea 25 10
5598 245 l. Romanii de Jos watermill, Valcea 50 15
5599 255 l. Enisala windmill, Tulcea (horiz) 60 20
5600 325 l. Nistoresti watermill, Vrancea 75 25

1166 Calin the Backward **1167** "Resurrection of Christ" (17th-century icon)

1994. Fairy Tales. Multicoloured.
5601 70 l. Type **1166** 10 10
5602 115 l. Ileana Cosanzeana flying 15 10
5603 125 l. Ileana Cosanzeana seated 25 10
5604 245 l. Ileana Cosanzeana and castle 50 15
5605 255 l. Agheran the Brave . . 60 20
5606 325 l. The Enchanted Wolf carrying Ileana Cosanzeana 75 25

1994. Easter.
5607 **1167** 60 l. multicoloured . . 40 10

1168 "Struthiosaurus transylvanicus"

1994. Dinosaurs. Multicoloured.
5608 90 l. Type **1168** 15 10
5609 130 l. Megalosaurus 25 10
5610 150 l. Parasaurolophus . . . 50 10
5611 280 l. Stenonychosaurus . . 45 15
5612 500 l. Camarasaurus 85 25
5613 635 l. Gallimimus . . . . . 1·10 35

1170 Silver Fir **1171** Players and Flags of U.S.A., Switzerland, Colombia and Rumania

1994. Trees. Each green and black.
5615 15 l. Type **1170** 10 10
5616 35 l. Scots pine 10 10
5617 45 l. White poplar 10 10
5618 60 l. Pedunculate oak 15 10
5619 70 l. European larch 20 10
5620 125 l. Beech 25 10
5621 350 l. Sycamore 40 10

5622 940 l. Ash . . . . 1·25 40
5623 1440 l. Norway spruce . . . 1·75 55
5624 3095 l. Large-leaved lime . . 3·25 1·00

1994. World Cup Football Championship, U.S.A. Designs showing various footballing scenes and flags of participating countries. Multicoloured.
5625 90 l. Type **1171** 10 10
5626 130 l. Brazil, Russia, Cameroun and Sweden 15 10
5627 150 l. Germany, Bolivia, Spain and South Korea 20 10
5628 280 l. Argentina, Greece, Nigeria and Bulgaria . . . 35 10
5629 500 l. Italy, Ireland, Norway and Mexico 75 25
5630 635 l. Belgium, Morocco, Netherlands and Saudi Arabia 95 30

1172 Torch-bearer and Centenary Emblem

1994. Centenary of International Olympic Committee. Multicoloured.
5632 150 l. Type **1172** 20 10
5633 280 l. Athlete and International Sports Year emblem . . . 35 10
5634 500 l. Wrestlers and Olympic Peace emblem 75 25
5635 635 l. Athlete and "Paris 1994" centenary congress emblem 95 30

1173 National History Museum
1176 Tuning Fork

1175 Traian Vuia's Airplane No. 1, 1906

1994. Stamp Day.
5637 **1173** 90 l. + 60 l. multicoloured 40 10

1994. Air. 50th Anniv of I.C.A.O.
5639 **1175** 110 l. brown, black & bl 25 10
5640 – 350 l. multicoloured . . 65 20
5641 – 500 l. multicoloured . . 95 30
5642 – 635 l. black, ultramarine and blue . . . . . . 1·25 40
DESIGNS: 350 l. ROMBAC One Eleven; 500 l. Boeing 737-300; 635 l. Airbus Industrie A310.

1994. "Philakorea 1994" International Stamp Exhibition, Seoul.
5643 **1176** 60 l. multicoloured . . . 45 15

1177 Great Sturgeon

1994. Environmental Protection of Danube Delta. Multicoloured.
5645 150 l. Type **1177** 20 10
5646 280 l. Orsini's viper 25 10
5647 500 l. White-tailed sea eagle . 75 25
5648 635 l. European mink 95 30

EXPRESS LETTER STAMPS

1919. Transylvania. Cluj Issue. No. E245 of Hungary optd as T **42**.
E784 E **18** 2 b. olive and red . . 15 15

1919. Transylvania. Oradea Issue. No. E245 of Hungary optd as T **42**.
E860 E **18** 2 b. olive and red . . 15 15

NEWSPAPER STAMPS

1919. Transylvania. Cluj Issue. No. N136 of Hungary optd as T **42**.
N783 N **9** 2 b. orange 15 15

1919. Transylvania. Oradea Issue. No. 136 of Hungary optd as T **43**.
N859 N **9** 2 b. orange 15 15

OFFICIAL STAMPS

O **71** Rumanian Eagle and National Flag
O **80**

1929.
O1115 O **71** 25 b. orange 10 10
O1116 50 b. brown 10 15
O1117 1 l. violet 10 10
O1118 2 l. green 10 10
O1119 3 l. red 30 10
O1120 4 l. olive 25 15
O1221 6 l. blue 35 25
O1222 10 l. blue 35 25
O1223 25 l. red . . . . . 1·50 90
O1224 50 l. violet . . . . 4·50 2·40

1930. Optd **8 IUNIE 1930**.
O1150 O **71** 25 b. orange 15 10
O1151 50 b. brown 15 10
O1152 1 l. violet 10 10
O1153 2 l. green 10 10
O1165 3 l. red 40 15
O1154 4 l. olive 40 15
O1160 6 l. blue 30 20
O1161 10 l. blue 50 15
O1156 25 l. red . . . . . 2·10 1·10
O1157 50 l. violet . . . . 3·50 2·50

1931.
O1194 O **80** 25 b. black 15 10
O1195 1 l. purple 20 15
O1196 2 l. green 30 20
O1197 3 l. red 35 25
O1247 6 l. red 75 40

PARCEL POST STAMPS

1895. As Type D **12** but inscr at top "TAXA DE FACTAGIU".
P353 25 b. brown . . . . 10·00 1·75
P479 25 b. red . . . . 7·50 1·00

1928. Surch **FACTAJ 5 LEI**.
P1078 **46** 5 l. on 10 b. green . . . . 1·40 25

POSTAGE DUE STAMPS

A. Ordinary Postage Due Stamps

D **12**
D **38**

1881.
D152 D **12** 2 b. brown . . . . . 3·25 1·75
D153 5 b. brown . . . . . 16·00 2·75
D200 10 b. brown . . . . 6·50 65
D201 30 b. brown . . . . 6·50 65
D156 50 b. brown . . . . 13·00 3·25
D157 60 b. brown . . . . 16·00 4·00

1887.
D448 D **12** 2 b. green 50 20
D449 5 b. green 35 10
D450 10 b. green 25 10
D451 30 b. green 35 10
D452 50 b. green . . . . 1·50 65
D453 60 b. green . . . . 3·25 1·75

1911.
D617 D **38** 2 b. blue on yellow . 15 10
D618 5 b. blue on yellow . 15 10
D619 10 b. blue on yellow . 15 10
D604 15 b. blue on yellow . 20 10
D621 20 b. blue on yellow . 15 10
D622 30 b. blue on yellow . 50 15
D623 50 b. blue on yellow . 50 15
D624 60 b. blue on yellow . 55 15
D609 2 l. blue on yellow . . 1·00 50

1918. Optd **TAXA DE PLATA**.
D675 **37** 5 b. green . . . . 1·10 65
D676 10 b. red . . . . 1·10 65

1918. Re-issue of Type D **38**. On greenish or white paper.
D1001 D **38** 5 b. black 10 10
D 722 10 b. black 10 10
D 734a 20 b. black 15 10
D 735 30 b. black 15 15
D 736 50 b. black 25 35
D 998 60 b. black 15 10
D1007 D **38** 1 l. black 25 10
D1010 2 l. black 30 10
D 991 3 l. black 15 10
D 992 6 l. black 25 10
D1547 50 l. black 20 15
D1548 100 l. black 30 20

1919. Transylvania. Cluj Issue. No. D190 etc. of Hungary optd as T **42**.
D786 D **9** 1 b. red and green . . . £160 £160
D787 2 b. red and green . . 15 15
D788 5 b. red and green . . . 30·00 30·00
D789 10 b. red and green . . 15 15
D790 15 b. red and green . . 6·00 6·00
D791 20 b. red and green . . 15 15
D792 30 b. red and green . . 10·00 10·00
D793 50 b. red and green . . 10·00 10·00

1919. Transylvania. Oradea Issue. No. D190, etc. of Hungary optd as T **43**.
D861 D **9** 1 b. red and green . . . 17·00 17·00
D862 2 b. red and green . . 10 10
D863 5 b. red and green . . . 2·50 2·50
D865 10 b. red and green . . 15 15
D866 12 b. red and green . . 20 20
D867 15 b. red and green . . 20 20
D868 20 b. red and green . . 10 10
D869 30 b. red and green . . 25 25

1930. Optd **8 IUNIE 1930**.
D1168 D **38** 1 l. black 15 10
D1169 2 l. black 20 10
D1170 3 l. black 25 15
D1171 6 l. black 65 25

D **98**
D **233**

1932.
D1249 D **98** 1 l. black 10 10
D1250 2 l. black 10 10
D1251 3 l. black 10 10
D1252 6 l. black 15 10
D1835 20 l. black 10 10
D1839 50 l. black 15 10
D1840 80 l. black 25 15
D1841 100 l. black 35 20
D1842 200 l. black 55 35
D1843 500 l. black 80 50
D1844 5000 l. black . . . . 1·75 1·00

1947. Type D **233** (without opts) perforated down centre.
Un. pair
D1919 2 l. red 25
D1920 4 l. blue 65
D1921 5 l. black . . . . 1·00
D1922 10 l. brown . . . . 1·60
The left half of Nos. D1919/22, showing Crown, served as a receipt and was stuck in the postman's book and so does not come postally used.

1948. Nos. D1919/22, optd as in Type D **233**.
Un. pair Us. pair
D1944 2 l. red 20 15
D1945 4 l. blue 30 20
D1946 5 l. black 50 30
D1947 10 l. brown . . . . . . 1·40 45

D **276**
Badge Postwoman

1950.
Un. pair Us. pair
D2066 D **276** 2 l. red 40 40
D2067 4 l. blue 50 50
D2068 5 l. green . . . . 1·00 1·00
D2069 10 l. brown . . . . 1·40 1·40

1952. Currency revalued. Nos. D2066/9 surch thus: **4 Bani** on each half.
Un. pair Us. pair
D2221 D **276** 4 b. on 2 l. red . . . 35 35
D2222 10 b. on 4 l. blue . . 35 35
D2223 20 b. on 5 l. green . 1·00 1·00
D2224 50 b. on 10 l. brown 1·10 1·10

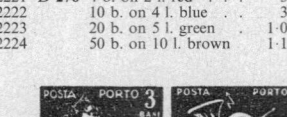

D **420**
G.P.O. Bucharest Posthorn

1957.
Un. pair Us. pair
D2507 D **420** 3 b. black 15 10
D2508 5 b. orange 15 10
D2509 10 b. purple 15 10
D2510 20 b. red 15 10
D2511 40 b. green 40 20
D2512 1 l. blue . . . . . 1·75 25

D **614**

1967.
Un. pair Us. pair
D3436 D **614** 3 b. green 10 10
D3437 5 b. blue 10 10
D3438 10 b. mauve 10 10
D3439 20 b. red 15 10
D3440 40 b. brown 20 10
D3441 1 l. violet 40 15

D **766** Postal Emblems and Postman

1974.
Un. pair Us. pair
D4050 D **766** 5 b. blue 10 10
D4051 10 b. green 10 10
D4052 – 20 b. red 10 10
D4053 – 40 b. violet 15 10
D4054 – 50 b. brown 30 10
D4055 – 1 l. orange 40 10
DESIGNS: 20 b., 40 b. Dove with letter and Hermes with posthorn. 50 b., 1 l. G.P.O., Bucharest and emblem with mail van.

1982. As Type D **766**.
D4761 – 25 b. violet 10 10
D4762 D **766** 50 b. yellow 15 10
D4763 – 1 l. red 25 10
D4764 – 2 l. green 45 10
D4765 D **766** 3 l. brown 65 15
D4766 – 4 l. blue 90 15
DESIGN: 25 b., 1 l. Dove with letter and Hermes with posthorn; 2, 4 l. G.P.O., Bucharest and emblem with mail van.

D **1111**

1992.
D5417 D **1111** 4 l. red 10 10
D5418 8 l. blue 10 10

D **1163**

1994.
D5586 D **1163** 10 l. brown 10 10
D5587 45 l. orange . . . 10 10

B. Postal Tax Due Stamps

1915. Optd **TIMBRU DE AJUTOR**.
TD643 D **38** 5 b. blue on yellow . . 35 15
TD644 10 b. blue on yellow . 30 15

TD **42**
TD **106**

1917. Green or white paper.
TD655 TD **42** 5 b. brown 55 25
TD743 5 b. red 15 15
TD654 10 b. red 35 25
TD741 10 b. brown 25 30

1918. Optd **TAXA DE PLATA**.
TD680 T **41** 5 b. black 65 25
TD681 10 b. brown . . . . 1·00 65

1922. As Type **TD 42** but inscr "ASSISTENTA SOCIALA". On green or white paper.
TD1028 10 b. brown 10 10
TD1029 20 b. brown 10 10
TD1030 25 b. brown 10 10
TD1031 50 b. brown 10 10

1931. Aviation Fund. Optd **TIMBRUL AVIATIEI**.
TD1219 D **38** 1 l. black 10 10
TD1220 2 l. black 10 10

1932.
TD1278 TD **106** 3 l. black . . . . 1·10 60

POSTAL TAX STAMPS

The following stamps were for compulsory use at certain times on inland mail to raise money for various funds. In some instances where the stamps were not applied the appropriate Postal Tax Postage Due stamps were applied.

Other demominations exist but these were purely for revenue purposes and were not applied to postal matter.

Soldiers Families Fund

1915. Optd **TIMBRU DE AJUTOR**.

T638	**37**	5 b. green	20	15
T639		10 b. red	30	15

T 41 The Queen Weaving — **T 47** "Charity"

1916.

T649	**T 41**	5 b. black	20	15
T710		5 b. green	50	15
T650		10 b. brown	25	15
T711		10 b. black	50	15

The 50 b. and 1, 2, 5 and 50 l. in similar designs were only used fiscally.

1918. Optd **1918**.

T671	**37**	5 b. green (No. T638)	30·00	30·00
T667	**T 41**	5 b. black	50	35
T672	**37**	10 b. red (No. T639)	30·00	30·00
T668	**T 41**	10 b. brown	1·00	30

1921. Social Welfare.

T978	**T 47**	10 b. green	10	10
T979		25 b. black	10	10

Aviation Fund

T 91 — T 98

1931.

T1216	**T 91**	50 b. green	30	10
T1217		1 l. brown	85	10
T1218		2 l. blue	1·00	20

1932.

T1253	**T 98**	50 b. green	15	10
T1254		1 l. purple	50	10
T1255		2 l. blue	65	10

Stamps as Type **98** but inscr "FONDUL AVIATIEI" were only for fiscal use. Nos. **T 1252/4** could only be used fiscally after 1937.

T 105 — T 121 "Aviation"

1932. Cultural Fund.

T1276	**T 105**	2 l. blue	80	40
T1277		2 l. brown	70	30

These were for compulsory use on postcards.

1936.

T1340	**T 121**	50 b. green	15	10
T1341		1 l. brown	15	10
T1342		2 l. blue	25	10

Other stamps inscr "FONDUL AVIATIEI" were only for fiscal use.

T 171 King Michael

1943.

T1589	**T 171**	50 b. orange	10	10
T1590		1 l. lilac	10	10
T1591		2 l. brown	10	10
T1592		4 l. blue	10	10
T1593		5 l. violet	10	10
T1594		8 l. green	10	10
T1595		10 l. brown	10	10

1947. Fiscal stamps (22 × 18½ mm), perf vert through centre surch **IOVR** and value.

T1923	1 l. on 2 l. red	15	15
T1924	5 l. on 1 l. green	50	45

1948. Vert designs (approx 18½ × 22 mm). Inscr "I.O.V.R.".

T1948	1 l. red	15	20
T1949	1 l. violet	40	30
T1950	2 l. blue	60	40
T1951	5 l. yellow	3·25	2·00

SAVINGS BANK STAMPS

1919. Transylvania. Cluj Issue. No. B199 of Hungary optd as T **42**.

B785	**B 17**	10 b. purple	15	15

1919. Transylvania. Oradea Issue. No. B199 of Hungary optd as T **43**.

B861	**B 17**	10 b. purple	15	15

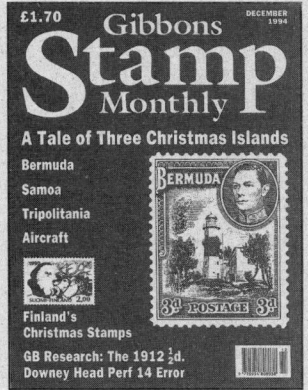

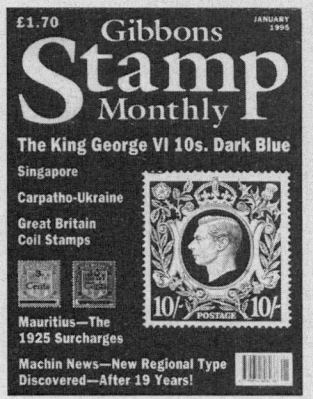

RUMANIAN OCCUPATION OF HUNGARY Pt. 2

A. BANAT BACSKA

The following stamps were issued by the Temesvar postal authorities between the period of the Serbian evacuation and the Rumanian occupation. This area was later divided, the Western part going to Yugoslavia and the Eastern part going to Rumania.

100 filler = 1 korona

1919. Stamps of Hungary optd **Banat Bacska 1919**. (a) "Turul" Type.
1 7 50 f. red on blue . . . 10·00 10·00

(b) War Charity stamps of 1916.
2 20 10 f. (+ 2 f.) red . . . 40 40
3 – 15 f. (+ 2 f.) violet . . . 40 40
4 22 40 f. (+ 2 f.) red . . . 40 40

(c) Harvesters and Parliament Types.
5 18 2 f. brown . . . 40 40
6 3 f. purple . . . 40 40
7 5 f. green . . . 40 40
8 6 f. blue . . . 40 40
9 15 f. purple . . . 40 40
10 35 f. brown . . . 11·00 11·00
11 19 50 f. purple . . . 10·00 10·00
12 75 f. blue . . . 40 40
13 80 f. green . . . 40 40
14 1 k. red . . . 40 40
15 2 k. brown . . . 40 40
16 2 k. grey and violet . . . 15·00 15·00
17 5 k. light brown and brown . . 75 75
18 10 k. mauve and brown . . 2·25 2·25

(d) Charles and Zita stamps.
19 27 10 f. pink . . . 40 40
20 20 f. brown . . . 40 40
21 25 f. blue . . . 40 40
22 28 40 f. green . . . 40 40
23 50 f. violet . . . 40 40

(e) Harvesters Type inscr "MAGYAR POSTA".
24 18 10 f. red . . . 10·00 10·00
25 20 f. brown . . . 10·00 10·00
26 25 f. blue . . . 12·00 12·00

(f) Various Types optd **KOZTARSASAG**.
(i) Harvesters and Parliament Types.
27 18 4 f. grey . . . 40 40
28 5 f. green . . . 40 40
29 6 f. blue . . . 40 40
30 10 f. red . . . 9·00 9·00
31 20 f. brown . . . 7·00 7·00
32 40 f. green . . . 40 40
33 19 1 k. red . . . 40 40
34 2 k. brown . . . 7·50 7·50
35 3 k. grey and violet . . . 7·50 7·50
36 5 k. light brown and brown . 7·50 7·50
37 10 k. mauve and brown . . 7·50 7·50

(iii) Charles portrait stamps.
38 27 15 f. purple . . . 2·50 2·50
39 25 f. blue . . . 1·90 1·90

(g) Serbian Occupation of Temesvar stamps.
40 18 10 f. on 2 f. brown . . . 50 50
41 20 45 f. on 10 f. (+ 2 f.) red . 50 50
42 18 1 k. 50 on 15 f. purple . . 1·25 1·25

EXPRESS LETTER STAMP

1919. No. E245 of Hungary optd **Banat Bacska 30 FILLER 1919**.
E44 E 18 30 f. on 2 f. green and red 1·40 1·40

NEWSPAPER STAMPS

1919. No. N136 of Hungary optd **Banat Bacska 1919**.
N43 N 9 (2 f.) orange . . . 40 40

POSTAGE DUE STAMPS

1919. Nos. D191 etc. optd as above.
D46 D 9 2 f. red and green . . . 40 40
D47 10 f. red and green . . . 40 40
D48 15 f. red and green . . . 11·00 11·00
D49 20 f. red and green . . . 40 40
D50 30 f. red and green . . . 10·00 10·00
D51 50 f. black and green . . 12·00 12·00

SAVINGS BANK STAMP

1919. No. B199 of Hungary surch **Banat Bacska 50 FILLER 1919**.
B45 B 17 50 f. on 10 f. purple . . 1·40 1·40

B. DEBRECEN

This area was later returned to Hungary.

100 filler = 1 korona

1

1919. Stamps of Hungary optd with T 1 or surch in addition. (a) "Turul" Type.
1 7 2 f. yellow . . . 25·00 25·00
2 3 f. orange . . . 35·00 35·00
3 6 f. brown . . . 7·50 7·50

(b) War Charity stamps of 1915.
4 7 2 f. + 2 f. yellow (No. 171) . 40·00 40·00
5 3 f. + 2 f. orange (No. 172) . 40·00 40·00

(c) War Charity stamps of 1916.
6 20 10 f. (+ 2 f.) red . . . 40 40
7 – 15 f. (+ 2 f.) lilac . . . 3·00 3·00
8 22 40 f. (+ 2 f.) red . . . 1·40 1·40

(d) Harvesters and Parliament Types.
9 18 2 f. brown . . . 30 10
10 3 f. purple . . . 10 10
11 18 5 f. green . . . 60 60
12 6 f. blue . . . 30 30
13 10 f. red (No. 243) . . . 30·00 30·00
14 15 f. violet (No. 244) . . . 20·00 20·00
15 15 f. purple . . . 10 15
16 20 f. brown . . . 22·00 22·00
17 25 f. blue . . . 60 60
18 35 f. brown . . . 7·00 7·00
19 35 f. on 3 f. purple . . . 65 65
20 40 f. green . . . 50 50
21 45 f. on 2 f. brown . . . 30 30
22 19 50 f. purple . . . 65 65
23 75 f. blue . . . 35 35
24 80 f. green . . . 60 60
25 1 k. red . . . 75 75
26 2 k. brown . . . 30 30
27 3 k. grey and violet . . . 6·50 6·50
28 3 k. on 75 f. blue . . . 1·40 1·40
29 5 k. light brown and brown . 6·00 6·00
30 5 k. on 75 f. blue . . . 65 65
31 10 k. mauve and brown . . 45·00 45·00
32 10 k. on 80 f. green . . . 1·10 1·10

(e) Charles and Zita stamps.
33 27 10 f. pink . . . 8·00 8·00
34 15 f. purple . . . 20·00 20·00
35 20 f. brown . . . 55 55
36 25 f. blue . . . 1·00 1·00
37 28 40 f. green . . . 60 60
38 50 f. purple . . . 5·50 5·50

(f) Harvesters and Parliament Types inscr "MAGAR POSTA".
39 18 5 f. green . . . 10 10
40 6 f. blue . . . 3·75 3·75
41 10 f. red . . . 10 10
42 20 f. brown . . . 10 10
43 25 f. blue . . . 20 20
44 45 f. orange . . . 3·50 3·50
45 19 5 k. brown . . . £325

(g) Various Types optd **KOZTARSASAG**.
(i) Harvesters and Parliament Types.
46 18 2 f. brown . . . 60 60
47 3 f. purple . . . 7·00 7·00
48 4 f. grey . . . 30 30
49 5 f. green . . . 10 10
50 10 f. red . . . 6·00 6·00
51 20 f. brown . . . 50 50
52 40 f. green . . . 30 30
53 19 1 k. red . . . 35 35
54 2 k. brown . . . 10·00 10·00
55 3 k. grey and violet . . . 1·00 1·00
56 5 k. light brown and brown . 70·00 70·00

(ii) War Charity stamps of 1916.
57 20 10 f. (+ 2 f.) red . . . 7·00 7·00
58 – 15 f. (+ 2 f.) lilac . . . 30·00 30·00
59 22 40 f. (+ 2 f.) red . . . 6·50 6·50

(iii) Charles and Zita stamps.
60 27 10 f. pink . . . 5·00 5·00
61 15 f. purple . . . 8·00 8·00
62 20 f. brown . . . 1·75 1·75
63 25 f. blue . . . 45 45
64 28 50 f. purple . . . 60 60

2 4

1920. Types 2 and 4 and similar design, optd with inscr as T 1 but in circle.
65 2 2 f. brown . . . 40 40
66 3 f. brown . . . 60 60
67 4 f. violet . . . 40 40
68 5 f. green . . . 10 10
69 6 f. grey . . . 40 40
70 10 f. red . . . 10 10
71 15 f. violet . . . 50 50
72 20 f. brown . . . 10 10
73 – 25 f. blue . . . 40 40
74 – 30 f. brown . . . 10 10
75 – 35 f. purple . . . 30 30
76 – 40 f. green . . . 30 30
77 – 45 f. red . . . 30 30
78 – 50 f. mauve . . . 30 30
79 – 60 f. green . . . 30 30
80 – 75 f. blue . . . 30 30
81 4 80 f. green . . . 30 30
82 1 k. red . . . 1·00 1·00
83 1 k. 20 orange . . . 5·50 5·50
84 2 k. brown . . . 50 50
85 3 k. brown . . . 65 65
86 5 k. brown . . . 65 65
87 10 k. purple . . . 65 65
DESIGN: Nos. 73/80, Horseman using lasso.

5

1920. War Charity. Type 5 with circular opt, and "Segely belyeg" at top.
88 5 20 f. green . . . 40 40
89 20 f. green on blue . . . 1·25 1·25
90 50 f. brown . . . 60 60
91 50 f. brown on mauve . . . 70 70
92 1 k. green . . . 60 60
93 1 k. green on green . . . 70 70
94 2 k. green . . . 60 60

EXPRESS LETTER STAMP

1919. No. E245 of Hungary optd with T 1.
E66 E 18 2 f. green and red . . . 40 40

NEWSPAPER STAMP

1919. No. N136 of Hungary optd with T 1.
N65 N 9 2 f. orange . . . 25 25

POSTAGE DUE STAMPS

1919. (a) Nos. D190 etc. of Hungary optd with T 1.
D68 D 9 1 f. red and green . . . 9·00 9·00
D69 2 f. red and green . . . 30 30
D70 5 f. red and green . . . 60·00 60·00
D71 6 f. red and green . . . 15·00 15·00
D72 10 f. red and green . . . 10 10
D73 12 f. red and green . . . 26·00 26·00
D74 15 f. red and green . . . 3·00 3·00
D75 20 f. red and green . . . 85 85
D76 30 f. red and green . . . 2·50 2·50

(b) With **KOZTARSASAG** opt.
D77 D 9 2 f. red and green . . . 6·00 6·00
D78 3 f. red and green . . . 6·00 6·00
D79 10 f. red and green . . . 6·00 6·00
D80 20 f. red and green . . . 6·00 6·00
D81 40 f. red and green . . . 6·00 6·00
D82 50 f. red and green . . . 6·00 6·00

D 6

1920.
D95 D 6 5 f. green . . . 30 30
D96 10 f. green . . . 30 30
D97 20 f. green . . . 30 30
D98 30 f. green . . . 30 30
D99 40 f. green . . . 30 30

SAVINGS BANK STAMP

1919. No. B199 of Hungary optd with T 1.
B67 B 17 10 f. purple . . . 8·00 8·00

C. TEMESVAR

After being occupied by Serbia this area was then occupied by Rumania. It later became part of Rumania and was renamed Timisoara.

100 filler = 1 korona

1919. Stamps of Hungary surch.
(a) Harvesters Type.
6 18 30 on 2 f. brown . . . 10 10
7 1 k. on 4 f. grey (optd **KOZTARSASAG** . . . 10 10
8 150 on 3 f. purple . . . 10 10
9 150 on 5 f. green . . . 15 15

(b) Express Letter Stamp.
10 E 18 3 KORONA on 2 f. green and red . . . 20 20

POSTAGE DUE STAMPS

1919. Charity stamp of Hungary surch **PORTO 40**.
D11 40 on 15 + (2 f.) lilac (No. 265) 35 35

(D 8)

1919. Postage Due stamps of Hungary surch with Type D 8.
D12 D 9 60 on 2 f. red and green . 1·00 1·00
D13 60 on 10 f. red and green 30 30

RUMANIAN POST OFFICES ABROAD Pt. 16

Rumanian P.O.s in the Turkish Empire including Constantinople. Now closed.

I. IN TURKISH EMPIRE

40 paras = 1 piastre

1896. Stamps of Rumania of 1893 surch in "PARAS".
9 10 pa. on 5 b. blue (No. 319) . 10·00 10·00
10 20 pa. on 10 b. grn (No. 320) . 10·00 10·00
11 1 pi. on 25 b. mauve (No. 322) . 10·00 10·00

II. IN CONSTANTINOPLE

100 bani = 1 leu

1

1919. Stamps of Rumania of 1893–1908 optd with T 1.
10 37 5 b. green . . . 30 35
6 10 b. red . . . 40 50
7 37 15 b. brown . . . 50 55
13 – 25 b. blue (No. 701) . . . 55 75
14 – 40 b. brown (No. 703) . . . 1·75 1·75

1919. 1916 Postal Tax stamp of Rumania optd with T 1.
16 T 41 5 b. green . . . 1·00 1·00

RUSSIA Pt.10

A country in the E. of Europe and N. Asia.
An empire until 1917 when the Russian Socialist Federal Soviet Republic was formed. In 1923 this became the Union of Soviet Socialist Republics (U.S.S.R.), eventually comprising 15 constituent republics.
In 1991 the U.S.S.R. was dissolved and subsequent issues were used in the Russian Federation only.

100 kopeks = 1 rouble

1 5 8

9 10 11

1858. Imperf.
1 1 10 k. blue and brown . . . £4000 £400

1858. Perf.
21 1 10 k. blue and brown . . . 32·00 25
22 20 k. orange and blue . . . 55·00 5·50
23 30 k. green and red . . . 75·00 25·00

1863.
8 5 5 k. black and blue . . . 20·00 80·00
No. 8 was first issued as a local but was later authorised for general use.

1864.
18 9 1 k. black and yellow . . . 3·00 35
30 2 k. black and red . . . 5·00 40
19b 3 k. black and green . . . 4·00 45
20 5 k. black and lilac . . . 7·50 25

1875.
31 8 7 k. red and grey . . . 4·50 15
32 8 k. red and grey . . . 7·50 25
33 10 k. blue and brown . . . 25·00 2·00
34 20 k. orange and blue . . . 30·00 1·75

12 No thunderbolts

1883. Posthorns in design without thunderbolts, as T 12.
38 9 1 k. orange . . . 2·50 35
40 2 k. green . . . 3·00 30
41 3 k. red . . . 3·50 20
42b 5 k. purple . . . 2·75 15
43c 7 k. blue . . . 3·00 15
44b 10 14 k. red and blue . . . 7·00 25
45 35 k. green and purple . . 12·00 1·75
46 70 k. orange and brown . . 22·00 1·75
47 11 3 r. 50 k. grey and black . . £300 £250
48 7 r. yellow and black . . £300 £300

14 15

13 With thunderbolts

1889. Posthorns in design with thunderbolts as T 13. Perf.
50 9 1 k. orange . . . 20 10
51a 2 k. green . . . 20 10
52 3 k. red . . . 20 10
53 14 4 k. red . . . 30 10
54 9 5 k. purple . . . 60 10
55 7 k. blue . . . 30 10
56 14 10 k. blue . . . 60 10
114 10 14 k. red and blue . . . 10 10
100 15 k. blue and purple . . . 10 10
116 14 20 k. red and blue . . . 10 10
102 10 25 k. violet and green . . 10 10
103 35 k. green and purple . . 10 10

119 **14** 50 k. green and purple . 10 10
120 **10** 70 k. orange and brown . 10 10
121A **15** 1 r. orange and brown . 10 10
79 **11** 3 r. 50 grey and black . . 8·00 2·00
122A 3 r. 50 green and red . . 20 30
80 7 r. yellow and black . . 6·50 3·50
124bA 7 r. pink and green . . . 20 50
For imperf stamps, see Nos. 107B/125aB.

16 Monument to Admiral Kornilov at Sevastopol

1905. War Orphans Fund (Russo-Japanese War).
88 **16** 3 (6) k. brown, red & green . 2·00 2·00
82 – 5 (8) k. purple and yellow . 2·50 2·50
83 – 7 (10) k. blue, lt blue & pink 3·00 3·00
87 – 10 (13) k. blue & lt bl & yell 3·50 3·50
DESIGNS: 5 (8) k. Monument to Minin and Pozharsky, Moscow; 7 (10) k. Statue of Peter the Great, St. Petersburg; 10 (13) k. Moscow Kremlin.

22 **23** **20**

1906.
107 **22** 1 k. orange 10 10
93 2 k. green 10 10
94 3 k. red 10 10
95 **23** 4 k. red 10 10
96 **22** 5 k. red 10 10
97 7 k. blue 10 10
98a **23** 10 k. blue 10 10
123aA **20** 5 r. blue and green . . . 30 30
125aA 10 r. grey, red & yellow . 60 65
For imperf stamps, see Nos. 107B/125aB.

25 Nicholas II

26 Elizabeth

27 The Kremlin

1913. Tercentenary of Romanov Dynasty. Views as T **27** and portraits as T **25/26**.
126 1 k. orange (Peter I) 30 15
127 2 k. green (Alexander II) . . . 40 15
128 3 k. red (Alexander III) . . . 40 15
129 4 k. red (Peter I) 40 15
130 7 k. brown (Type **25**) . . . 40 15
131 10 k. blue (Nicholas II) . . . 50 15
132 14 k. green (Katherine II) . . 50 15
133 15 k. brown (Nicholas I) . . . 75 25
134 20 k. olive (Alexander I) . . . 1·00 25
135 25 k. red (Alexei Michaelovich) . 1·50 40
136 35 k. green & violet (Paul I) . 1·50 40
137 50 k. grey and brown (T **26**) . 3·00 50
138 70 k. brown and green (Michael Feodorovich) . . . . 3·00 1·00
139 1 r. green (Type **27**) . . . . 7·50 2·00
140 2 r. brown . . . . 8·50 3·00
141 3 r. violet . . . . 20·00 6·00
142 5 r. brown . . . . 25·00 12·00
DESIGNS—As T **27**: 2 r. Winter Palace; 3 r. Castle Romanov. 23 × 29 mm: 5 r. Nicholas II.

31 Russian hero, Ilya Murometz

1914. War Charity.
143 **31** 1 (2) k. green & red on yell 25 1·00
144 – 3 (4) k. green & red on red 25 1·00
145 – 7 (8) k. green and brown on buff . . . . 25 2·00
161 – 10 (11) k. brown and blue on blue . . . . 85 3·75
DESIGNS: 3 k. Cossack shaking girl's hand; 7 k. Symbolical of Russia surrounded by her children; 10 k. St. George and Dragon.

1915. As last. Colours changed.
155 **31** 1 (2) k. grey and brown . 45 2·00
156 – 3 (4) k. black and red . . 40 2·50
158 – 10 (11) k. brown and blue 40 2·00

35

39

41

45 Cutting the fetters

1915. Nos. 131, 133 and 134 printed on card with inscriptions on back as T **35**.
165 10 k. blue . . . . 75 5·00
166 15 k. brown . . . . 75 5·00
167 20 k. olive . . . . 75 5·00

1916. Various types surch.
168 – 10 k. on 7 k. brown (No. 130) 30 15
170 **22** 10 k. on 7 k. blue 30 15
169 – 20 k. on 14 k. green (No. 132) 30 20
171 **10** 20 k. on 14 k. red and blue 30 15

1917. Various earlier types, but imperf.
107B **22** 1 k. orange 10 10
108bB 2 k. green 10 10
109B 3 k. red 10 10
110B **23** 4 k. red 15 25
111B **22** 5 k. lilac 10 10
113B **23** 10 k. blue . . . . . . 10·00 27·00
115dB **10** 15 k. blue & pur (No. 100) 10 10
116B **14** 20 k. red and blue . . . 15 30
117dB **10** 25 k. vio & grn (No. 102) 50 1·00
118B 35 k. grn & pur (No. 103) 15 25
119B **14** 50 k. green and purple . 15 25
120B **10** 70 k. orange and brown (No. 120) 10 30
121B **15** 1 r. orange and brown . 10 10
122B **11** 3 r. 50k. green and red . 20 30
123aB **20** 5 r. blue and green . . . 30 60
124aB **11** 7 r. pink and green . . . 50 1·40
125aB **20** 10 r. grey, red & yellow 22·00 30·00

1916. Types of 1913 printed on card with surch on back as T **39** or **41**, or optd with figure "I" or "2" in addition on front.
172 **39** 1 k. orange (No. 126) . . 20·00 35·00
175 1 on 1 k. orange (No. 126) 1·00 5·00
177 **41** 1 on 1 k. orange (No. 126) 75 4·50
175 **39** 2 k. green (No. 127) . . . 40·00 45·00
176 2 on 2 k. green (No. 127) . 1·00 5·00
178 **41** 2 on 2 k. green (No. 127) . 75 4·75
174 **39** 3 k. red (No. 128) . . . . 1·00 4·00
179 **41** 3 k. red (No. 128) . . . . 75 4·50

1917.
187 **45** 35 k. blue . . . . 80 1·00
188 70 k. brown . . . . 80 1·50

46 Agriculture and Industry

47 Triumph of Revolution

MINIMUM PRICE

The minimum price quoted is 10p which represents a handling charge rather than a basis for valuing common stamps. For further notes about prices, see introductory pages.

48 Agriculture

49 Industry

55 Science and Arts

56

64 Industry

1921. Imperf.
195 **48** 1 r. orange . . . . . . 75 6·00
196 2 r. brown . . . . . . 75 6·00
197 **49** 5 r. blue . . . . . . 75 6·00
198 **46** 20 r. blue . . . . . . 1·75 4·00
199a **47** 40 r. blue . . . . . . 1·50 3·25
214 **48** 100 r. yellow 10 10
215 200 r. brown 10 25
216 **55** 250 r. lilac 10 10
217 **48** 300 r. green 15 40
218 **49** 500 r. blue 15 45
219 1000 r. red 10 10
256 **64** 5000 r. violet 40 85
257 **46** 7500 r. blue 20 30
259 7500 r. blue on buff . . . 20 35
258 **64** 10,000 r. blue . . . . . . 4·00 10·00
260 22,500 r. purple on buff . . 35 50

1921. 4th Anniv of October Revolution. Imperf.
227 **56** 100 r. yellow . . . . . . 50 2·00
228 250 r. violet . . . . . . 50 2·00
229 1000 r. red . . . . . . 50 2·00

57 Famine Relief Work

58

Р. С. Ф. С. Р.
ГОЛОДЛЮЩИМ
250 р.+250 р.
(**62**)

1921. Charity. Volga Famine. Imperf.
230 **57** 2250 r. green . . . . . . 3·00 6·50
231 2250 r. red . . . . . . 2·50 8·00
232 2250 r. brown . . . . . . 3·50 11·00
235 **58** 2250 r. blue . . . . . . 10·00 15·00

1922. Surch. Imperf.
234 **48** 5000 r. on 1 r. orange . . . 75 2·00
240 5000 r. on 2 r. brown . . . 70 2·00
236 **49** 5000 r. on 5 r. blue . . . 60 2·00
242 **46** 5000 r. on 20 r. blue . . . 1·25 2·50
243 **47** 10,000 r on 40 r. blue . . . 1·00 2·50

1922. Famine Relief. Surch as T **62**. Perf.
245 **45** 100 r. + 100 r. on 70 k. brown 35 1·25
247 250 r. + 250 r. on 25 k. bl . 35 1·25

7500 РУБ.
(**63**)

1922. Surch as T **63**. Imperf.
250 **55** 7500 r. on 250 r. lilac . . . 10 10
251 100,000 r. on 250 r. lilac . . 10 20

65

1922. Obligatory Tax. Rostov-on-Don issue. Famine Relief. Various sizes. Without gum. Imperf.
261 **65** 2 T. (2000 r.) green . . . . 15·00 £120
262 – 2 T. (2000 r.) red . . . . 18·00 £120
263 – 4 T. (4000 r.) red . . . . 27·00 £130
264 – 6 T. (6000 r.) green . . . . 18·00 £120
DESIGNS: 2 T. red, Worker and family (35 × 42 mm); 4 T. Clasped hands (triangular, 57 mm each side); 6 T. Sower (29 × 59 mm).

РСФСР
Филателия
– детям
19 - 8 - 22

(**70** "Philately for the children")

1922. Optd with T **70**. Perf or imperf.
278 **22** 1 k. orange £140 £250
274 2 k. green . . . . 7·50 15·00
275 3 k. red . . . . 5·00 12·00
276 5 k. red . . . . 5·00 12·00
277 **23** 10 k. blue . . . . 5·00 15·00

71

73

1922. 5th Anniv of October Revolution. Imperf.
729 **71** 5 r. black and yellow . . . 50 45
280 10 r. black and brown . . 50 45
281 25 r. black and purple . . 2·00 1·75
282 27 r. black and red . . . 5·00 5·50
283 45 r. black and blue . . . 3·75 5·00

1922. Air. Optd with airplane. Imperf.
284 **71** 45 r. black and green . . . 18·00 45·00

1922. Famine Relief. Imperf.
285 **73** 20 r. + 5 r. mauve . . . . 30 2·00
286 – 20 r. + 5 r. violet . . . . 40 2·00
287 – 20 r. + 5 r. blue . . . . 50 2·00
288 – 20 r. + 5 r. blue . . . . 3·00 15·00
DESIGNS—HORIZ: No. 286, Freighter; No. 287, Steam train. VERT: No. 288, Airplane.

(**77**)

78 Worker

79 Soldier

1922. Surch as T **77**. Imperf or perf.
289 **14** 5 r. on 20 k. red & blue . 1·75 8·00
290 **10** 20 r. on 15 k. blue & purple 2·00 4·00
291 20 r. on 70 k. orange and brown 15 30
292a **14** 30 r. on 50 k. green & pur 35 35
293 **10** 40 r. on 15 k. blue & pur 15 15
294 100 r. on 15 k. blue & pur 15 20
295 200 r. on 15 k. blue & pur 15 20

1922. Imperf or perf.
303 **78** 10 r. blue 10 10
304 **79** 50 r. brown 10 10
305 70 r. purple 10 10
310 100 r. red 15 15

1 мая
1923 г. Филателия —
Трудящимся,
1 р.+1 р.
(**80**)

1923. Charity. Surch as T **80**. Imperf.
315 **71** 1 r. + 1 r. on 10 r. black and brown . . . . 17·00 25·00
317b **55** 2 r. + 2 r. on 250 r. violet 16·00 25·00
318 **64** 4 r. + 4 r. on 5000 r. vio 25·00 30·00

83 Worker

84 Peasant

85 Soldier

1923. Perf.

No.	Type	Description	Unused	Used
320	**85**	3 r. red	10	10
321	**83**	4 r. brown	10	10
322	**84**	5 r. blue	10	10
323	**85**	10 r. grey	15	15
324		20 r. purple	25	25

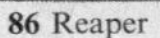
86 Reaper

88 Tractor

1923. Agricultural Exn, Moscow. Imperf or perf.

No.	Type	Description	Unused	Used
325	**86**	1 r. brown	90	3·75
326	–	2 r. green	90	3·75
327	**88**	5 r. blue	1·60	3·75
328	–	7 r. red	1·60	3·75

DESIGNS: As Type **86**: 2 r. Sower; 7 r. Exhibition buildings.

90 Worker

91 Peasant

92 Soldier

93

94

95

1923. Perf (some values also imperf).

No.	Type	Description	Unused	Used
335	**90**	1 k. yellow	30	15
359	**91**	2 k. green	30	15
360	**92**	3 k. brown	35	15
361	**90**	4 k. red	35	15
434		5 k. purple	55	15
363	**91**	6 k. blue	55	15
364	**92**	7 k. brown	55	15
437	**90**	8 k. olive	90	15
366	**91**	9 k. red	70	40
341	**92**	10 k. blue	55	15
385	**90**	14 k. grey	1·00	20
386	**91**	15 k. yellow	1·25	90
442	**92**	18 k. violet	1·75	55
443	**90**	20 k. green	2·00	30
444	**91**	30 k. violet	2·75	40
445	**92**	40 k. grey	4·00	60
343	**91**	50 k. brown	4·50	60
447	**92**	1 r. red and brown	4·75	80
375	**93**	2 r. green and red	5·50	2·00
449	**94**	3 r. green and brown	14·00	4·00
450	**95**	5 r. brown and blue	17·00	5·00

96 Lenin

97

1924. Lenin Mourning. Imperf or perf.

No.	Type	Description	Unused	Used
413	**96**	3 k. black and red	1·75	1·10
414		6 k. black and red	1·75	1·10
411		12 k. black and red	2·25	75
412		20 k. black and red	2·25	85

1924. Air. Surch. Imperf.

No.	Type	Description	Unused	Used
417	**97**	5 k. on 3 r. blue	2·00	1·50
418		10 k. on 5 r. green	2·00	1·50
419		15 k. on 1 r. brown	1·75	1·25
420		20 k. on 10 r. red	1·75	1·10

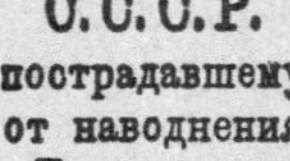

(**99** Trans "For the victims of the flood in Leningrad")

102 Lenin Mausoleum, Moscow

1924. Leningrad Flood Relief. Surch as T **99**. Imperf.

No.	Type	Description	Unused	Used
421	**48**	3 + 10 k. on 100 r. yellow	80	1·40
422		7 + 20 k. on 200 r. brown	90	1·75
423		14 + 30 k. on 300 r. green	1·10	2·00
424	**49**	12 + 40 k. on 500 r. blue	1·90	2·75
425		20 + 50 k. on 1000 r. red	1·75	2·75

1925. 1st Death Anniv of Lenin. Imperf or perf.

No.	Type	Description	Unused	Used
426	**102**	7 k. blue	3·00	2·50
427		14 k. olive	3·75	3·50
428		20 k. red	3·75	3·50
429		40 k. brown	3·75	3·50

104 Lenin

106 Prof. Lomonosov and Academy of Sciences, Leningrad

1925.

No.	Type	Description	Unused	Used
451	**104**	1 r. brown	5·50	2·00
452		2 r. brown	6·50	2·00
850		3 r. green	1·90	75
851		5 r. brown	2·50	1·50
825		10 r. blue	5·00	3·50

1925. Bicentenary of Academy of Sciences.

No.	Type	Description	Unused	Used
456b	**106**	3 k. brown	3·00	2·00
457		15 k. olive	5·00	3·00

107 A. S. Popov

110 Moscow Barricade

1925. 30th Anniv of Popov's Radio Discoveries.

No.	Type	Description	Unused	Used
458	**107**	7 k. blue	2·25	1·40
459		14 k. olive	3·00	2·25

1925. 20th Anniv of 1905 Rebellion. Imperf or perf.

No.	Type	Description	Unused	Used
463b	–	3 k. green	2·00	1·75
464c	–	7 k. brown	2·75	1·75
465a	**110**	14 k. red	2·25	2·25

DESIGNS—VERT: 3 k. Postal rioters; 7 k. Orator and mob.

111 Decembrist Exiles

112 Senate Square, St. Petersburg, 1825

1925. Centenary of Decembrist Rebellion. Imperf or perf.

No.	Type	Description	Unused	Used
466	**111**	3 k. green	2·00	2·25
467	**112**	7 k. brown	2·75	3·25
468	–	14 k. red	2·75	3·50

DESIGN—VERT: 14 k. Medallion with heads of Pestel, Ryleev, Bestuzhev-Ryumin, Muravev-Apostol and Kakhovsky.

114

1926. 6th International Proletarian Esperanto Congress.

No.	Type	Description	Unused	Used
471	**114**	7 k. red and green	3·50	3·00
472		14 k. violet and green	4·50	1·75

115 Waifs

116 Lenin when a Child

1926. Child Welfare.

No.	Type	Description	Unused	Used
473	**115**	10 k. brown	75	45
474	**116**	20 k. blue	1·75	95

1927. Same type with new inscriptions.

No.	Type	Description	Unused	Used
475	**115**	8 k. + 2 k. green	40	35
476	**116**	18 k. + 2 k. red	90	65

ПОЧТОВАЯ
МАРКА
КОП. 8 КОП.
(117)

1927. Postage Due stamps surch with T **117**.

No.	Type	Description	Unused	Used
491	D **104**	8 k. on 1 k. red	1·00	2·25
492		8 k. on 2 k. violet	1·00	2·25
493		8 k. on 3 k. blue	1·00	2·25
494		8 k. on 7 k. yellow	1·00	2·25
494b		8 k. on 8 k. green	1·00	2·25
494d		8 k. on 10 k. blue	1·00	2·25
494f		8 k. on 14 k. brown	1·00	2·25

1927. Various types of 7 k. surch (some values imperf or perf).

No.	Type	Description	Unused	Used
495	**92**	8 k. on 7 k. brown	6·00	6·00
523	**107**	8 k. on 7 k. blue	2·50	3·25
524	–	8 k. on 7 k. brown (No. 464c)	3·75	5·00
527	**112**	8 k. on 7 k. brown	3·75	6·50
526	**114**	8 k. on 7 k. red & green	11·00	14·00

119 Dr. Zamenhof

1927. 40th Anniv of Publication of Zamenhof's "Langue Internationale" (Esperanto).

No.	Type	Description	Unused	Used
498	**119**	14 k. green and brown	3·00	1·75

120

1927. 1st Int Air Post Congress, The Hague.

No.	Type	Description	Unused	Used
499	**120**	10 k. blue and brown	12·00	4·75
500		15 k. red and olive	13·00	6·00

121 Worker, Soldier and Peasant

124 Sailor and Worker

122 Allegory of Revolution

1927. 10th Anniv of October Revolution.

No.	Type	Description	Unused	Used
501	**121**	3 k. red	2·25	75
502	**122**	5 k. brown	6·00	2·00
503	–	7 k. green	8·00	2·50
504	**124**	8 k. black and brown	4·00	85
505	–	14 k. red and blue	6·00	1·25
506	–	18 k. blue	4·00	1·00
507	–	28 k. brown	13·00	8·00

DESIGNS—HORIZ: (As Type **122**): HORIZ: 7 k. Smolny Institute; 14 k. Map of Russia inscr "C.C.C.P."; 18 k. Various Russian races; 28 k. Worker, soldier and peasant.

128 Worker

129 Peasant

130 Lenin

1927.

No.	Type	Description	Unused	Used
508	**128**	1 k. orange	90	50
509	**129**	2 k. green	90	20
510	**128**	4 k. blue	90	20
511	**129**	5 k. brown	90	20
512		7 k. red	4·50	1·00
513	**128**	8 k. green	2·50	20
514	**128**	10 k. brown	2·00	20
515	**130**	14 k. green	2·25	45
516		18 k. olive	3·00	40
517		18 k. blue	4·50	70
518	**129**	20 k. olive	2·50	35
519	**128**	40 k. red	5·00	60
520	**129**	50 k. blue	7·00	1·00
521	**228**	70 k. olive	11·00	1·40
522	**129**	80 k. orange	22·00	5·00

131 Infantryman, Lenin Mausoleum and Kremlin

1928. 10th Anniv of Red Army.

No.	Type	Description	Unused	Used
529	**131**	8 k. brown	1·40	45
530	–	14 k. blue	2·25	50
531	–	18 k. red	2·50	1·25
532	–	28 k. green	4·00	4·00

DESIGNS: 14 k. Sailor and cruiser "Aurora"; 18 k. Cavalryman; 28 k. Airman.

135 Young Factory Workers

137 Trumpeter sounding the Assembly

1929. Child Welfare.

No.	Type	Description	Unused	Used
536	**135**	10 k. + 2 k. brn & sepia	1·50	1·10
537	–	20 k. + 2 k. blue & brown	1·50	1·25

DESIGN: 20 k. Children in harvest field.
See also Nos. 567/8.

1929. 1st All-Union Gathering of Pioneers.

No.	Type	Description	Unused	Used
538	**137**	10 k. brown	8·00	6·50
539		14 k. blue	6·00	4·00

138 Worker

139 Factory Girl

140 Peasant

141 Farm Girl

142 Guardsman

143 Worker, Soldier and Peasant

144 Lenin

242a Miner

242b Steel foundryman

242c Infantryman

242d Airman

242e Arms of U.S.S.R

149 Central Telegraph Office, Moscow

150 Lenin Hydro-electric Power Station

743a Farm Girl **743b** Architect **744** Furnaceman

1929. Perf, but some values exist imperf.

541 **138** 1 k. yellow 40 15
542 **139** 2 k. green 60 10
543 **140** 3 k. blue 60 10
544 **141** 4 k. mauve 85 15
545 **142** 5 k. brown 90 10
847a **242a** 5 k. red 20 10
546 **143** 7 k. red 1·75 50
547 **138** 10 k. grey 1·40 10
727f **139** 10 k. blue 60 15
1214b 10 k. black 80 15
554 **144** 14 k. blue 1·40 55
548 **143** 15 k. blue 1·50 30
847b **242b** 15 k. blue 1·50 30
847c **242c** 15 k. green 50 15
549 **140** 20 k. green and blue 2·25 20
727h **141** 20 k. green 70 25
2252a **743a** 20 k. olive 80 30
2252b **743b** 25 k. brown 1·10 45
550 **139** 30 k. violet and lilac 3·50 50
847d **242d** 30 k. blue 90 20
727l **144** 40 k. blue 1·10 40
727m **141** 50 k. brown and buff 1·25 40
847f **242e** 60 k. red 1·25 30
2253 **744** 60 k. red 1·00 20
2253a 60 k. blue 2·25 40
552 **142** 70 k. red and pink 6·00 1·40
553 **140** 80 k. brown & yellow 6·00 1·25
561 **149** 1 r. blue 1·60 40
562 **150** 3 r. brown and green 18·00 6·00

Nos. 727f, 1214b and 550 show the factory girl without factory in background. Nos. 549, 727m, 552, 553 have designs like those shown but with unshaded background.

151 Industry **153** "More metal more machines"

1929. Industrial Loan Propaganda.

563 **151** 5 k. brown 1·60 1·25
564 – 10 k. olive 2·00 2·00
565 **153** 20 k. green 6·00 3·25
566 – 28 k. violet 4·00 3·25

DESIGNS—HORIZ: 10 k. Tractors. VERT: 28 k. Blast furnace and graph of pig-iron output.

1930. Child Welfare.

567 **135** 10 k. + 2 k. olive 80 1·00
568 – 20 k. + 2 k. green (as No. 537) 1·10 1·50

155

1930. 10th Anniv of 1st Red Cavalry.

569 **155** 2 k. green 2·50 1·40
570 – 5 k. brown 2·50 1·40
571 – 10 k. olive 5·00 3·00
572 – 14 k. blue and red 2·50 2·50

DESIGNS: 5 k. Cavalry charge; 10 k. Cavalry charging; 14 k. Cavalry and map.

159 Group of Soviet Pupils

1930. Educational Exhibition, Leningrad.

573 **159** 10 k. olive 1·40 1·00

160

1930. Air. "Graf-Zeppelin" Flight to Moscow.

574 **160** 40 k. blue 24·00 18·00
575 80 k. red 18·00 13·00

162 "Potemkin"

1930. 25th Anniv of 1905 Rebellion. Imperf or perf.

576 **162** 3 k. red 1·75 50
577 – 5 k. blue 1·50 60
578 – 10 k. red and green 2·75 1·10

DESIGNS—HORIZ: 5 k. Barricade and rebels. VERT: 10 k. Red flag at Presnya barricade.

165 From the Tundra (reindeer) to the Steppes (camel)

166 Above Dnieprostroi Dam

1931. Airship Construction Fund. Imperf or perf.

579 **165** 10 k. violet 7·00 3·50
580 **166** 15 k. blue 17·00 12·00
581a – 20 k. red 8·00 3·00
582b – 50 k. brown 7·00 7·00
583 – 1 r. green 7·50 5·50

DESIGNS—As Type **166**. VERT: 20 k. Above Lenin's Mausoleum. HORIZ: 1 r. Airship construction. As Type **166**: 50 k. Above the North Pole.

See also No. E592.

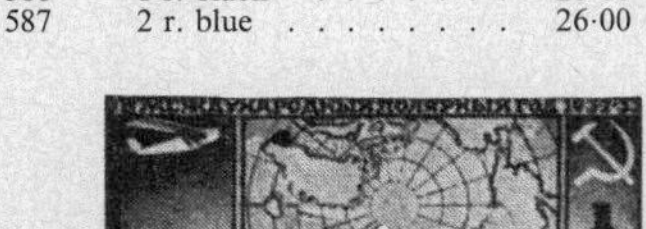

170 Ice breaker "Malygin"

1931. Air. "Graf Zeppelin" North Pole Flight. Imperf or perf.

584 **170** 30 k. purple 24·00 13·00
585 35 k. green 24·00 13·00
586 1 r. black 26·00 13·00
587 2 r. blue 26·00 13·00

171 Polar Region and Ice-breaker "Sibiriakov"

1932. Air. 2nd Int Polar Year and Franz Joseph's Land to Archangel Flight.

588 **171** 50 k. red 38·00 15·00
589a 1 r. green 38·00 20·00

172 Maksim Gorky **173** Storming the Winter Palace

1932. 40th Anniv of Publication of "Makar Chadra".

590 **172** 15 k. brown 4·00 2·50
591 35 k. blue 14·00 8·00

1932. 15th Anniv of October Revolution.

593 – 3 k. violet 90 50
594 **173** 5 k. brown 90 50
595 – 10 k. blue 2·75 1·25
596 – 15 k. green 1·60 1·25
597 – 20 k. red 5·50 1·75
598 – 30 k. grey 6·00 1·90
599 – 35 k. brown 60·00 45·00

DESIGNS—HORIZ: 10 k. Dnieper Dam; 15 k. Harvesting with combines; 20 k. Industrial Works, Magnitogorsk; 30 k. Siberians listening to Moscow broadcast. VERT: 3 k. Lenin's arrival in Petrograd; 35 k. People of the World hailing Lenin.

INDEX

Countries can be quickly located by referring to the index at the end of this volume.

175 "Liberation"

1932. 10th Anniv of International Revolutionaries' Relief Organization.

600 **175** 50 k. red 10·00 5·00

176 Museum of Fine Arts

1932. 1st All-Union Philatelic Exn, Moscow.

601 **176** 15 k. brown 18·00 13·00
602 35 k. blue 35·00 20·00

177 Trier, Marx's Birthplace

1933. 50th Death Anniv of Marx.

603 **177** 3 k. green 3·50 90
604 – 10 k. brown 6·00 1·40
605 – 35 k. purple 9·50 8·50

DESIGNS—VERT: 10 k. Marx's grave, Highgate Cemetery; 35 k. Marx.

1933. Leningrad Philatelic Exhibition. Surch **LENINGRAD 1933** in Russian characters and premium.

606 **176** 15 k. + 30 k. blk & brn 65·00 30·00
607 35 k. + 70 k. blue 85·00 40·00

182 **183**

1933. Ethnographical Issue. Racial types.

608 – 1 k. brown (Kazakhs) 1·50 40
609 **183** 2 k. blue (Lesgins) 1·50 40
610 – 3 k. green (Crimean Tatars) 1·25 40
611 – 4 k. brown (Jews of Birobidzhan) 90 60
612 – 5 k. red (Tungusians) 1·00 40
613 – 6 k. blue (Buryats) 90 40
614 – 7 k. brown (Chechens) 90 40
615 – 8 k. red (Abkhazians) 1·25 55
616 – 9 k. blue (Georgians) 2·50 60
617 – 10 k. brn (Samoyedes) 4·00 1·50
618 – 14 k. green (Yakuts) 2·50 40
619 – 15 k. purple (Ukrainians) 4·00 1·25
620 – 15 k. black (Uzbeks) 3·50 80
621 – 15 k. blue (Tadzhiks) 3·50 75
622 – 15 k. brown (Transcaucasians) 2·50 75
623 – 15 k. green (Byelorussians) 2·50 60
624 – 15 k. orange (Great Russians) 2·50 80
625 – 15 k. red (Turkmens) 3·00 1·00
626 – 20 k. blue (Koryaks) 6·00 1·60
627 – 30 k. red (Bashkirs) 7·00 1·75
628 **182** 35 k. brown (Chuvashes) 11·00 2·25

SIZES: Nos. 608, 610/11, 614/17, 626/7, As T **182**: Nos. 612/13, 618. As T **183**: Nos. 619/24, 48 × 22 mm. No. 625, 22 × 48 mm.

186 V. V. Vorovsky

1933. Communist Party Activists. Dated "1933", "1934" or "1935".

629 **186** 1 k. green 65 50
718 – 2 k. violet 4·00 25
630 – 3 k. blue 1·25 60
719 – 4 k. purple 3·25 2·00
631 – 5 k. brown 2·50 1·90
632 – 10 k. blue 12·00 5·00
633 – 15 k. red 30·00 20·00
720 – 40 k. brown 7·00 4·00

DESIGNS: 2 k. M. Frunze; 3 k. V. M. Volodarsky; 4 k. N. E. Bauman; 5 k. M. S. Uritsky; 10 k. Iacov M. Sverdlov; 15 k. Viktor P. Nogin; 40 k. S. M. Kirov.

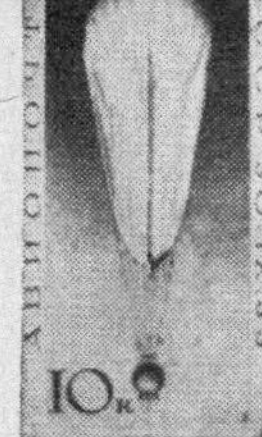

187 Stratosphere Balloon "U.S.S.R.–1" over Moscow **188** Massed Standard Bearers

1933. Air. Stratosphere record (19,000 metres).

634 **187** 5 k. blue 75·00 19·00
635 10 k. red 48·00 9·00
636 20 k. violet 23·00 5·00

1933. 15th Anniv of Order of Red Banner.

637 **188** 20 k. red, yellow & black 2·25 1·50

189 Commissar Shaumyan **190** Tupolev ANT-9 PS9 over Oilfield

1934. 15th Death Anniv of 26 Baku Commissars.

688 **189** 4 k. brown 3·50 1·25
639 – 5 k. black 3·50 1·25
640 – 20 k. violet 2·50 85
641 – 35 k. blue 18·00 4·00
642 – 40 k. red 12·00 4·00

DESIGNS: 5 k. Commissar Dzhaparidze. HORIZ: 20 k. The 26 condemned commissars; 35 k. Monument in Baku; 40 k. Workman, peasant and soldier dipping flags in salute.

1934. Air. 10th Anniv of Soviet Civil Aviation and U.S.S.R. Airmail Service.

643 – 5 k. blue 7·0 2·25
644 **190** 10 k. green 7·00 2·25
645 – 20 k. red 15·00 3·75
646 – 50 k. blue 25·00 9·25
647 – 80 k. violet 13·00 4·75

DESIGNS: Tupolev ANT-9 PS9 airplane over: 5 k. Furnaces at Kuznetsk; 20 k. Harvesters; 50 k. Volga-Moscow Canal; 80 k. Ice breaker "OB" in the Arctic.

191 New Lenin Mausoleum

1934. 10th Death Anniv of Lenin.

648 **191** 5 k. brown 1·60 50
649 10 k. blue 5·00 2·00
650 15 k. red 4·50 2·00
651 20 k. green 1·75 50
652 35 k. brown 5·00 2·25

192 Fedorov Monument, Moscow, between Hand and Rotary Presses

1934. 350th Death Anniv of Ivan Fedorov (first Russian printer).

653 **192** 20 k. red 8·00 3·75
654 40 k. blue 8·00 3·00

194 Dmitri Mendeleev **195** A. V. Vasenko and Stratosphere Balloon "Osoaviachim"

1934. Birth Centenary of Dmitri Mendeleev (chemist).

655 – 5 k. green 3·25 1·10
656 **194** 10 k. brown 12·00 4·50
657 15 k. red 13·00 4·50
658 – 20 k. blue 5·00 2·25

DESIGN—VERT: 5 k., 20 k. Mendeleev seated.

1934. Air. Stratosphere Disaster Victims.
659 – 5 k. purple . . . . 19·00 4·00
660 **195** 10 k. brown . . . . . . 45·00 4·00
661 – 20 k. violet . . . . 50·00 4·00
1042 – 1 r. green . . . . 8·50 1·75
1043 **195** 1 r. green . . . . 8·50 1·75
1044 – 1 r. blue . . . . 8·50 1·75
DESIGNS: 5 k., 1 r. (No. 1042). I. D. Usyskin; 20 k., 1 r. (No. 1044), P. F. Fedoseenko.
The 1 r. values issued in 1944, commemorated the 10th anniv of the disaster.

196 Airship "Pravda"

1934. Air. Airship Travel Propaganda.
662 **196** 5 k. red . . . . 13·00 2·25
663 – 10 k. lake . . . . 13·00 2·75
664 – 15 k. brown . . . . 17·00 8·00
665 – 20 k. black . . . . 18·00 5·50
666 – 30 k. blue . . . . 50·00 23·00
DESIGNS—HORIZ: 10 k. Airship landing; 15 k. Airship "Voroshilov"; 30 k. Airship "Lenin" and route map. VERT: 20 k. Airship's gondolas and mooring mast.

199 Stalin and Marchers inspired by Lenin **200** "War Clouds"

1934. "Ten years without Lenin". Portraits inscr "1924–1934".
667 – 1 k. black and blue . . . 1·50 75
668 – 3 k. black and blue . . . 1·50 80
669 – 5 k. black and blue . . . 3·50 1·40
670 – 10 k. black and blue . . . 2·25 2·00
671 – 20 k. blue and orange . . 6·00 3·25
672 **199** 30 k. red and orange . . 24·00 6·00
DESIGN—VERT: 1 k. Lenin aged 3; 3 k. Lenin as student; 5 k. Lenin as man; 10 k. Lenin as orator. HORIZ: 20 k. Red demonstration, Lenin Mausoleum.

1935. Anti-War. Inscr "1914–1934".
673 **200** 5 k. black . . . . 4·50 90
674 – 10 k. blue . . . . 7·50 3·75
675 – 15 k. green . . . . 13·00 5·00
676 – 20 k. brown . . . . 10·0 2·75
677 – 35 k. red . . . . 22·00 13·00
DESIGNS: 10 k. "Flight from a burning village"; 15 k. "Before war and afterwards"; 20 k. "Ploughing with the sword"; 35 k. "Fraternisation".

202 Capt. Voronin and "Chelyuskin"

1935. Air. Rescue of "Chelyuskin" Expedition.
678 **202** 1 k. orange . . . . . . 4·25 1·00
679 – 3 k. red . . . . 5·00 1·40
680 – 5 k. green . . . . 4·75 1·40
681 – 10 k. brown . . . . . . 6·75 1·75
682 – 15 k. black . . . . . . 8·50 2·50
683 – 20 k. purple . . . . . . 13·50 2·50
684 – 25 k. blue . . . . 40·00 11·00
685 – 30 k. green . . . . . . 50·00 13·00
686 – 40 k. violet . . . . . . 28·00 3·75
687 **202** 50 k. blue . . . . 40·00 9·00
DESIGNS—HORIZ: 3 k. Prof. Schmidt and Schmidt Camp; 50 k. Schmidt Camp deserted. VERT: 5 k. A. V. Lyapidevsky; 10 k. S. A. Levanevsky; 15 k. M. G. Slepnev; 20 k. I. V. Doronin; 25 k. M. V. Vodopyanov; 30 k. V. S. Molokov; 40 k. N. P. Kamanin.

205 Underground Station

1935. Opening of Moscow Underground.
688 – 5 k. orange . . . . 8·00 3·25
689 – 10 k. blue . . . . 9·00 3·25
690 **205** 15 k. red . . . . 70·00 24·00
691 – 20 k. green . . . . 15·00 9·00
DESIGNS—As Type **205**: 5 k. Excavating tunnel; 10 k. Section of roadway, escalator and station. 48½×23 mm: 20 k. Train in station.

207 Rowing

1935. Spartacist Games.
692 – 1 k. blue and orange . . 2·50 80
693 – 2 k. blue and black . . . 2·50 80
694 **207** 3 k. brown and green . . 4·50 1·50
695 – 4 k. blue and red . . . . 2·75 90
697 – 10 k. purple and red . . 14·00 3·00
698 – 15 k. brown and black . . 26·00 8·00
699 – 20 k. blue and brown . . 15·00 3·25
700 – 35 k. brown and blue . . 27·00 13·00
701 – 40 k. red and brown . . 22·00 6·00
DESIGNS: 1 k. Running; 2 k. Diving; 4 k. Football; 5 k. Skiing; 10 k. Cycling; 15 k. Lawn tennis; 20 k. Skating; 35 k. Hurdling; 40 k. Parade of athletes.

208 Friedrich Engels **210** A "Lion Hunt" from a Sassanian Silver Plate

1935. 40th Death Anniv of F. Engels.
702 **208** 5 k. red . . . . 4·50 45
703 10 k. green . . . . 8·00 2·00
704 15 k. blue . . . . 7·00 2·75
705 20 k. black . . . . 3·25 2·50

1935. Air. Moscow–San Francisco via North Pole Flight. Surch in Russian characters.
706 1 r. on 10 k. brown (No. 681) £200 £350

1935. 3rd International Congress of Persian Art and Archaeology, Leningrad.
707 **210** 5 k. orange . . . . . . 5·00 1·00
708 10 k. green . . . . . . 5·00 1·75
709 15 k. purple . . . . . . 6·50 3·00
710 35 k. brown . . . . . . 13·00 5·50

211 M. I. Kalinin **212** Tolstoi

1935. Pres. Kalinin's 60th Birthday. Autographed portraits inscr "1875–1935".
711 – 3 k. purple 75 20
712 – 5 k. green . . . . . . 1·25 25
713 – 10 k. blue . . . . 1·25 60
714 **211** 20 k. brown . . . . . . 1·60 70
DESIGNS: 3 k. Kalinin as machine worker; 5 k. Harvester; 10 k. Orator.
See also No. 1189.

1935. 25th Death Anniv of Tolstoi (writer).
715 – 3 k. violet and black . . 65 25
716 **212** 10 k. brown and blue . . 1·40 45
717 – 20 k. brown and green . . 3·00 1·75
DESIGNS: 3 k. Tolstoi in 1860; 20 k. Monument in Moscow.

213 Pioneers securing Letter-box

1936. Pioneer Movement.
721 **213** 1 k. green . . . . 1·10 30
722 2 k. red . . . . 1·00 70
723 – 3 k. blue . . . . 1·25 1·60
724 – 5 k. red . . . . 1·25 55
725 – 10 k. blue . . . . 2·00 2·50
726 – 15 k. brown . . . . 6·50 3·00
DESIGNS: 3, 5 k. Pioneer preventing another from throwing stones; 10 k. Pioneers disentangling kite line from telegraph wires; 15 k. Girl pioneer saluting.

214 N. A. Dobrolyubov **215** A. S. Pushkin

1936. Birth Cent of Dobrolyubov (author and critic).
727 **214** 10 k. purple . . . . 3·25 80

1937. Death Centenary of A. S. Pushkin (poet).
728 **215** 10 k. brown 55 30
729 20 k. green 60 30
730 40 k. red . . . . 1·25 50
731 – 50 k. blue . . . . 2·00 35
732a – 80 k. red . . . . 2·25 1·00
733a – 1 r. green . . . . 3·25 1·00
DESIGN: 50 k. to 1 r. Pushkin's Monument.

217 Meyerhold Theatre **218** F. E. Dzerzhinsky

1937. 1st Soviet Architectural Congress.
734 **217** 3 k. red . . . . 1·00 20
735 – 5 k. lake . . . . 1·00 20
736 **217** 10 k. brown . . . . 1·40 25
737 – 15 k. black . . . . 1·75 25
738 – 20 k. olive . . . . 1·10 40
739 – 30 k. black . . . . 1·50 70
740 – 40 k. violet . . . . 2·00 ·25
741 – 50 k. brown . . . . 3·50 1·50
DESIGNS—As T **217**: 5, 15 k. G.P.O.; 20, 50 k. Red Army Theatre. 45×27 mm: 30 k. Hotel Moscow; 40 k. Palace of Soviets.

1937. 10th Death Anniv of F. E. Dzerzhinsky.
742 **218** 10 k. brown 40 20
743 20 k. green 55 55
744 40 k. red . . . . 1·50 55
745 80 k. red . . . . 2·00 70

219 Yakovlev Ya-7 Air 7

1937. Air. Air Force Exhibition.
746 **173** 10 k. black and brown . . 1·50 30
747 – 20 k. black and green . . 1·50 30
748 – 30 k. black and brown . . 2·50 30
749 – 40 k. black and purple . . 3·75 80
750 – 50 k. black and violet . . 5·50 1·00
751 – 80 k. brown and blue . . 6·50 1·75
752 – 1 r. black, orange & brn . 10·00 2·25
DESIGNS—As T **173**: 20 k. Tupolev ANT-9; 30 k. Tupolev ANT-6; 40 k. O.S.G.A. 101 flying boat; 50 k. Tupolev ANT-4 TB-1. 60×26 mm: 80 k. Tupolev ANT-20 "Maksim Gorki"; 1 r. Tupolev ANT-14 "Pravda".

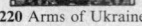

220 Arms of Ukraine **221** Arms of U.S.S.R

1937. New U.S.S.R. Constitution. Arms of Constituent Republics.
753 – 20 k. blue (Armenia) . . . 1·25 40
754 – 20 k. purple (Azerbaijan) . 1·25 40
755 – 20 k. brown (Byelorussia) . 1·25 40
756 – 20 k. red (Georgia) . . . . 1·25 40
757 – 20 k. grn (Kazakhstan) . . 1·25 40
758 – 20 k. red (Kirghizia) . . . 1·25 40
759 – 20 k. red (Tadzhikistan) . . 1·25 40
760 – 20 k. red (Turkmenistan) . . 1·25 40
761 **220** 20 k. red (Ukraine) . . . . 1·25 40
762 – 20 k. orge (Uzbekistan) . . 1·25 40
763 – 20 k. blue (R.S.F.S.R.) . . 1·25 40
764 **221** 40 k. red . . . . 3·00 1·25

222 Sculptured group on Pavilion **223** Russian Pavilion, Paris Exhibition

1938. Paris International Exhibition.
765 **222** 5 k. red . . . . 1·00 40
766 **223** 20 k. red . . . . 1·10 40
767 **222** 50 k. blue . . . . 2·75 1·00

224 Shota Rustaveli

1938. 750th Anniv of Poem "Knight in Tiger Skin".
768 **224** 20 k. green . . . . 1·10 30

225 Route of North Pole Flight **227** Infantryman

1938. North Pole Flight.
769 **225** 10 k. black and brown . . 2·75 30
770 20 k. black and grey . . 3·75 30
771 – 40 k. red and green . . . 7·50 1·25
772 – 80 k. red and deep red . . 2·75 90
DESIGN: 40 k., 80 k. Soviet Flag at North Pole.

1938. 20th Anniv of Red Army.
773 **227** 10 k. black and red . . . 50 20
774 – 20 k. black and red . . . 85 25
775 – 30 k. black, red and blue 1·25 25
776 – 40 k. black, red and blue 1·75 75
777 – 50 k. black and red . . . 2·25 75
778a – 80 k. black and red . . . 4·75 75
779 – 1 r. black and red . . . 2·75 75
DESIGNS—VERT: 20 k. Tank driver; 30 k. Sailor; 40 k. Airman; 50 k. Artilleryman. HORIZ: 80 k. Stalin reviewing cavalry; 1 r. Machine gunners.

229 Polar Flight Heroes **230**

1938. 1st Polar Flight.
780 **229** 10 k. red and black . . . 2·10 50
781 20 k. red and black . . . 2·25 70
782 40 k. red and brown . . . 4·00 1·10
783 50 k. red and purple . . . 7·25 1·50

1938. 2nd Polar Flight.
784 **230** 10 k. purple . . . . . . 3·50 45
785 20 k. black . . . . . . 4·50 90
786 50 k. purple . . . . . . 7·50 1·25

231 Ice-breaker "Murman" approaching Survivors

1938. Rescue of Papanin's North Pole Meteorological Party.
787 **231** 10 k. purple . . . . . . 4·00 50
788 20 k. blue . . . . 4·00 70
789 – 30 k. brown . . . . . . 7·00 1·25
790 – 50 k. blue . . . . 8·00 1·50
DESIGNS—VERT: 30, 50 k. Papanin survivors.

233 Nurse weighing Baby — 234 Children visiting Statue of Lenin

1938. Soviet Union Children.

791	233	10 k. blue	1·25	30
792	234	15 k. blue	1·25	35
793	–	20 k. purple	1·50	35
794	–	30 k. red	1·90	45
795	–	40 k. brown	2·40	55
796	–	50 k. blue	4·50	85
797	–	80 k. green	5·50	1·00

DESIGNS—HORIZ: 20, 40 k. Biology class; 30 k. Health camp; 50, 80 k. Young inventors at play.

235 Crimean landscape

1938. Views of Crimea and Caucasus.

798	235	5 k. black	80	40
799	A	5 k. brown	80	40
800	B	10 k. green	1·60	45
801	C	10 k. brown	1·60	45
802	D	15 k. black	2·50	50
803	A	15 k. black	2·50	50
804	E	20 k. brown	3·00	50
805	C	30 k. black	3·00	60
806	F	40 k. brown	3·75	80
807	G	50 k. green	3·75	1·25
808	H	80 k. brown	5·00	1·50
809	I	1 r. green	7·50	4·50

DESIGNS—HORIZ: A, Yalta (two views); B, Georgian military road; E, Crimean resthouse; F, Alupka; H, Crimea; I, Swallows' Nest Castle. VERT: C, Crimea (two views); D, Swallows' Nest Castle; G, Gurzuf Park.

236 Schoolchildren and Model Tupolev ANT-6

1938. Aviation.

810	236	5 k. purple	1·75	60
811	–	10 k. brown	1·75	60
812	–	15 k. red	2·00	60
813	–	20 k. blue	2·00	60
814	–	30 k. red	3·50	90
815	–	40 k. blue	6·00	90
816	–	50 k. green	11·00	1·40
817	–	80 k. brown	7·50	3·25
818	–	1 r. green	13·00	2·50

DESIGNS—HORIZ: 10 k. Glider in flight; 40 k. Yakovlev VT-2 seaplane landing; 1 r. Tupolev ANT-6 airplane. VERT: 15 k. Captive observation balloon; 20 k. Airship "Osoaviachim" over Kremlin; 30 k. Parachutists; 30 k. Balloon in flight; 80 k. Stratosphere balloon.

237 Underground Railway

1938. Moscow Underground Railway Extension.

819	–	10 k. violet	2·00	60
820	–	15 k. brown	2·50	60
821	–	20 k. black	3·00	50
822	–	30 k. violet	3·25	1·00
823	237	40 k. black	3·50	1·10
824	–	50 k. brown	4·50	1·90

DESIGNS—VERT: 10 k. Mayakovsky Square station; 15 k. Sokol Terminus station; 20 k. Kiev station. HORIZ: 30 k. Dynamo Stadium station; 50 k. Revolution Square station.

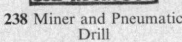

238 Miner and Pneumatic Drill — 239 Diving

1936. 20th Anniv of Federation of Young Lenin Communists.

825	–	20 k. blue	80	30
826	238	30 k. purple	1·50	30
827	–	40 k. purple	1·25	30
828	–	50 k. red	1·50	90
829	–	80 k. blue	5·50	1·25

DESIGNS—VERT: 20 k. Girl parachutist; 50 k. Students and University. HORIZ: 40 k. Harvesting; 80 k. Airman, sailor and battleship "Marat".

1938. Soviet Sports.

830	239	5 k. red	1·75	30
831	–	10 k. black	2·00	50
832	–	15 k. brown	3·50	85
833	–	20 k. green	3·50	80
834	–	30 k. purple	7·50	1·25
835	–	40 k. green	7·50	80
836	–	50 k. blue	7·00	2·25
837	–	80 k. blue	6·50	3·50

DESIGNS: 10 k. Discus throwing; 15 k. Tennis; 20 k. Motor cycling; 30 k. Skiing; 40 k. Sprinting; 50 k. Football; 80 k. Athletic parade.

241 Council of People's Commissars Headquarters and Hotel Moscow

1939. New Moscow. Architectural designs as T **241**.

838	–	10 k. brown	60	40
839	241	20 k. green	75	35
840	–	30 k. purple	1·00	60
841	–	40 k. blue	2·75	80
842	–	50 k. red	3·50	1·25
843	–	80 k. olive	4·50	1·75
844	–	1 r. blue	9·50	2·25

DESIGNS—HORIZ: 10 k. Gorky Avenue; 30 k. Lenin Library; 40 k. Suspension and 50 k. Arched Bridges over River Moskva; 80 k. Khimki River Station. VERT: 1 r. Dynamo Underground Station.

242 Paulina Osipenko — 243 Russian Pavilion, N.Y. World's Fair

1939. Women's Moscow–Far East Flight.

845	242	15 k. green	2·10	80
846	–	30 k. purple	2·10	1·00
847	–	60 k. red	3·50	1·50

PORTRAITS: 30 k. Marina Raskova; 60 k. Valentina Grisodubova.

1939. New York World's Fair.

848	–	30 k. red and black	1·00	50
849	243	50 k. brown and blue	1·60	85

DESIGN—VERT: (26×41½ mm): 30 k. Statue over Russian pavilion.

244 T. G. Shevchenko in early Manhood — 245 Milkmaid

1939. 125th Birth Anniv of Shevchenko (Ukrainian poet and painter).

853	244	15 k. black and brown	1·40	50
854	–	30 k. black and red	2·00	70
855	–	60 k. brown and green	3·25	1·50

DESIGNS: 30 k. Last portrait of Shevchenko; 60 k. Monument to Shevchenko, Kharkov.

1939. All Union Agricultural Fair.

856	245	10 k. red	60	25
857	–	15 k. red	60	15
858a	–	20 k. grey	70	15
859	–	20 k. orange	65	25
860	–	30 k. violet	65	25
861	–	45 k. green	1·40	35
862	–	50 k. brown	2·25	40
863a	–	60 k. violet	2·50	60
864	–	80 k. violet	2·50	60
865	–	1 r. blue	4·75	1·25

DESIGNS—HORIZ: 15 k. Harvesting; 20 k. Sheep farming; 30 k. (No. 860) Agricultural Fair Pavilion. VERT: 30 k. (No. 859) Agricultural Fair Emblem; 45 k. Gathering cotton; 50 k. Thoroughbred horses; 60 k. "Agricultural Wealth"; 80 k. Girl with sugar beet; 1 r. Trapper.

18 АВГУСТА
ДЕНЬ АВИАЦИИ СССР
(247)

1939. Aviation Day. As Nos. 811, 814/16 and 818 (colours changed) optd with T **247**.

866	10 k. red	2·00	55
867	30 k. blue	2·00	55
868	40 k. green	3·25	55
869	50 k. violet	4·25	1·25
870	1 r. brown	8·00	4·00

1939. Surch.

871	141	30 k. on 4 k. mauve	13·00	10·00

249 Saltykov-Shchedrin — 250 Kislovodsk Sanatorium

1939. 50th Death Anniv of M. E. Saltykov-Shchedrin (writer and satirist).

872	249	15 k. red	60	15
873	–	30 k. green	80	20
874	249	45 k. brown	1·00	35
874	–	60 k. blue	1·50	70

DESIGN: 30, 60 k. Saltykov-Shchedrin in later years.

1939. Caucasian Health Resorts.

876	250	5 k. brown	40	15
877	–	10 k. red	45	20
878	–	15 k. green	50	30
879	–	20 k. green	85	30
880	–	30 k. blue	90	30
881	–	50 k. black	1·75	35
882	–	60 k. purple	1·75	90
883	–	80 k. red	2·75	1·10

DESIGNS: 10, 15, 30, 50, 80 k. Sochi Convalescent Homes; 20 k. Abkhazia Sanatorium; 60 k. Sukumi Rest Home.

251 M. I. Lermontov — 252 N. G. Chernyshevsky

1939. 125th Birth Anniv of Lermontov (poet and novelist).

884	251	15 k. brown and blue	1·10	30
885	–	30 k. black and green	2·75	55
886	–	45 k. blue and red	2·50	95

1939. 50th Death Anniv of N. G. Chernyshevsky (writer and politician).

887	252	15 k. green	50	30
888		30 k. violet	90	40
889		60 k. green	2·00	50

253 A. P. Chekhov — 254 Welcoming Soviet Troops

1940. 80th Birth Anniv of Chekhov (writer).

890	253	10 k. green	30	15
891		15 k. blue	30	15
892	–	20 k. violet	60	30
893	–	30 k. brown	1·40	55

DESIGN: 20, 30 k. Chekhov with hat on.

1940. Occupation of Eastern Poland.

893a	254	10 k. red	80	35
894	–	30 k. green	80	35
895	–	50 k. black	1·25	55
896	–	60 k. blue	1·50	1·00
897	–	1 r. red	4·00	1·75

DESIGNS: 30 k. Villagers welcoming tank crew; 50, 60 k. Soldier distributing newspapers to crowd; 1 r. People waving to column of tanks.

255 Ice-breaker "Georgy Sedov" and Badigin and Trofimov

1940. Polar Research.

898	–	15 k. green	2·25	40
899	255	30 k. violet	3·00	70
900	–	50 k. brown	4·00	1·75
901	–	1 r. blue	8·50	2·25

DESIGNS: 15 k. Ice-breaker "Iosif Stalin" and portraits of Papanin and Belousov; 50 k. Badgin and Papanin meeting. LARGER. (46×26 mm): 1 r. Route of drift of "Georgy Sedov".

256 V. Mayakovsky

1940. 10th Death Anniv of Mayakovsky (poet).

902	256	15 k. red	30	15
903		30 k. brown	55	20
904	–	60 k. violet	1·0	45
905	–	80 k. blue	80	45

DESIGN—VERT: 60, 80 k. Mayakovsky in profile wearing a cap.

257 Timiryazev — 258 Relay Runner

1940. 20th Death Anniv of K. A. Timiryazev (scientist).

906	–	10 k. blue	45	20
907	–	15 k. violet	45	25
908	267	30 k. brown	70	30
909	–	60 k. green	1·75	1·10

DESIGNS—HORIZ: 10 k. Miniature of Timiryazev and Academy of Agricultural Sciences, Moscow; 15 k. Timiryazev in laboratory. VERT: 60 k. Timiryazev's statue (by S. Merkurov), Moscow.

1940. 2nd All Union Physical Culture Festival.

910	258	15 k. red	90	35
911a	–	30 k. purple	1·60	30
912a	–	50 k. blue	2·50	55
913	–	60 k. blue	4·00	60
914	–	1 r. green	5·50	1·40

DESIGNS—HORIZ: 30 k. Girls parade; 60 k. Skiing; 1 r. Grenade throwing. VERT: 50 k. Children and sports badges.

259 Tchaikovsky and Passage from his "Fourth Symphony" — 260 Central Regions Pavilion

1940. Birth Cent of Tchaikovsky (composer).

915	–	15 k. green	1·10	20
916	259	20 k. brown	1·25	20
917	–	50 k. red	2·00	60
919	–	60 k. red	2·50	85

DESIGNS: 15, 50 k. Tchaikovsky's house at Klin; 60 k. Tchaikovsky and excerpt from "Eugene Onegin".

920 ПАВИЛЬОН «ПОВОЛЖЬЕ»
921 ПАВИЛЬОН «ДАЛЬНИЙ ВОСТОК»
922 ПОРТАЛ ПАВИЛЬОНА „ЛЕНИНГРАД И СЕВЕРО-ВОСТОК РСФСР"
923 ПАВИЛЬОН МОСКОВСКОЙ, РЯЗАНСКОЙ И ТУЛЬСКОЙ ОБЛ.
924 ПАВИЛЬОН УКРАИНСКОЙ ССР
925 ПАВИЛЬОН БЕЛОРУССКОЙ ССР
926 ПАВИЛЬОН АЗЕРБАЙДЖАНСКОЙ ССР
927 ПАВИЛЬОН ГРУЗИНСКОЙ ССР
928 ПАВИЛЬОН АРМЯНСКОЙ ССР
929 У ВХОДА В ПАВИЛЬОН УЗБЕКСКОЙ ССР
930 ПАВИЛЬОН ТУРКМЕНСКОЙ ССР
931 ПАВИЛЬОН ТАДЖИКСКОЙ ССР
932 ПАВИЛЬОН КИРГИЗСКОЙ ССР
933 ПАВИЛЬОН КАРЕЛО-ФИНСКОЙ ССР
934 ПАВИЛЬОН КАЗАХСКОЙ ССР
935 ГЛАВНЫЙ ПАВИЛЬОН
936 ПАВИЛЬОН МЕХАНИЗАЦИИ

(211a)

1940. All Union Agricultural Fair, Coloured reproductions of Soviet Pavilions in green frames as T **260**. Inscriptions at foot as illustrated.

920	10 k. Volga provinces (RSFSR) (horiz)	1·40	70
921	15 k. Far East	1·40	70
922	30 k. Leningrad and North East RSFSR	1·40	75
923	30 k. Three Central Regions (RSFSR)	1·40	80
924	30 k. Ukrainian SSR	1·40	80
925	30 k. Byelorussian SSR	1·40	80
926	30 k. Azerbaijan SSR	1·40	80
927	30 k. Georgian SSR (horiz)	1·40	80
928	30 k. Armenian SSR	1·40	80
929	30 k. Uzbek SSR	1·40	80
930	30 k. Turkmen SSR (horiz)	1·40	80
931	30 k. Tadzhik SSR	1·40	80
932	30 k. Kirgiz SSR	1·40	80

No.	Type	Description	Mint	Used
933		30 k. Karelo-Finnish SSR	2·75	80
934		30 k. Kazakh SSR	1·40	80
935		50 k. Main Pavilion	2·25	1·75
936		60 k. Mechanization Pavilion and the statue of Stalin	8·00	1·90

261 Grenade Thrower — 262 Railway Bridge and Moscow–Volga Canal

1940. 20th Anniv of Wrangel's Defeat at Perekop (Crimea). Perf or imperf.

No.	Type	Description	Mint	Used
937	–	10 k. green	85	30
938	**261**	15 k. red	45	15
939	–	30 k. brown and red	45	30
940	–	50 k. purple	50	50
941	–	60 k. blue	1·40	65
942	–	1 r. black	2·25	1·40

DESIGNS—VERT: 10 k. Red Army Heroes Monument; 30 k. Map of Perekop and portrait of M. V. Frunze; 1 r. Victorious soldier. HORIZ: 50 k. Soldiers crossing R. Sivash; 60 k. Army H.Q. at Stroganovka.

1941. Industrial and Agricultural Records.

No.	Type	Description	Mint	Used
943	–	10 k. blue	30	15
944a	–	15 k. mauve	30	15
945a	**262**	20 k. blue	1·75	70
946	–	30 k. brown	1·75	70
947	–	50 k. brown	60	15
948	–	60 k. brown	1·25	55
949	–	1 r. green	1·60	80

DESIGNS—VERT: 10 k. Coal-miners and pithead; 15 k. Blast furnace; 1 r. Derricks and petroleum refinery. HORIZ: 30 k. Locomotives; 50 k. Harvesting; 60 k. Ball-bearing vehicles.

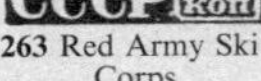

263 Red Army Ski Corps — 264 N. E. Zhukovsky and Air Force Academy

1941. 23rd Anniv of Red Army. Designs with Hammer, Sickle and Star Symbol.

No.	Type	Description	Mint	Used
950a	**263**	5 k. violet	1·60	15
951	–	10 k. blue	1·25	15
952	–	15 k. green	45	15
953a	–	20 k. red	45	15
954a	–	30 k. brown	45	15
955a	–	45 k. green	1·90	70
956	–	50 k. blue	70	75
957	–	1 r. green	1·0	80
957b	–	3 r. green	6·50	3·00

DESIGNS—VERT: 10 k. Sailor; 20 k. Cavalry; 30 k. Automatic Rifle Squad; 50 k. Airman; 1, 3 r. Marshal's star. HORIZ: 15 k. Artillery; 45 k. Clearing a hurdle.

1941. 20th Death Anniv of Zhukovsky (scientist).

No.	Type	Description	Mint	Used
958	–	15 k. blue	50	20
959	**264**	30 k. red	1·10	30
960	–	50 k. red	1·25	55

DESIGNS—VERT: 15 k. Zhukovsky; 50 k. Zhukovsky lecturing.

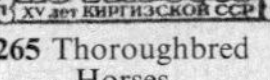

265 Thoroughbred Horses — 266 Arms of Karelo-Finnish S.S.R

1941. 15th Anniv of Kirghiz S.S.R.

No.	Type	Description	Mint	Used
961	**265**	15 k. brown	3·00	50
962a	–	30 k. violet	4·00	75

DESIGN: 30 k. Coal miner and colliery.

1941. 1st Anniv of Karelo-Finnish Republic.

No.	Type	Description	Mint	Used
963	**266**	30 k. red	70	35
964		45 k. green	85	60

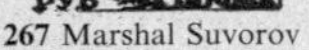

267 Marshal Suvorov — 268 Spassky Tower, Kremlin

1941. 150th Anniv of Battle of Izmail.

No.	Type	Description	Mint	Used
965	–	10 k. green	75	30
966	–	15 k. red	75	40
967	**267**	30 k. blue	1·75	35
968		1 r. brown	2·25	1·10

DESIGN: 10, 15 k. Storming of Izmail.

1941.

No.	Type	Description	Mint	Used
970	**268**	1 r. red	1·60	55
971	–	2 r. orange	3·25	1·10

DESIGN—HORIZ: 2 r. Kremlin Palace.

269 "Razin on the Volga"

1941. 25th Death Anniv of Surikov (artist).

No.	Type	Description	Mint	Used
972	–	20 k. black	1·25	80
973	**269**	30 k. red	2·75	70
974	–	50 k. purple	4·00	1·75
975	**269**	1 r. green	8·00	2·50
976	–	2 r. brown	14·00	3·00

DESIGNS—VERT: 20, 50 k. "Suvorov's march through Alps, 1799"; 2 r. Surikov.

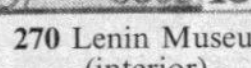

270 Lenin Museum (interior) — 271 Lermontov

1941. 5th Anniv of Lenin Museum.

No.	Type	Description	Mint	Used
977	**270**	15 k. red	2·50	1·25
978	–	30 k. violet on mauve	22·00	11·00
979	**270**	45 k. green	3·25	1·25
980	–	1 r. red on rose	8·00	5·00

DESIGN: 30 k., 1 r. Exterior of Lenin Museum.

1941. Death Centenary of M. Yu. Lermontov (poet and novelist).

No.	Type	Description	Mint	Used
981	**271**	15 k. grey	3·50	2·50
982		30 k. violet	5·00	3·00

272 Reproduction of Poster — 273 Mass Enlistment

1941. Mobilization.

No.	Type	Description	Mint	Used
983a	**272**	30 k. red	15·00	20·00

1941. National Defence.

No.	Type	Description	Mint	Used
984	**273**	30 k. blue	48·00	45·00

274 Alishir Navoi — 275 Lt. Talalikhin ramming Enemy Airplane

289a Five Heroes

1942. 5th Centenary of Uzbek poet Mir Ali Shir (Alishir Navoi).

No.	Type	Description	Mint	Used
985	**274**	30 k. brown	8·00	6·00
986		1 r. purple	13·00	15·00

1942. Russian Heroes (1st issue).

No.	Type	Description	Mint	Used
987	**275**	20 k. blue	50	15
988	A	30 k. grey	60	25
989	B	30 k. black	60	15
990	C	30 k. black	60	15
991	D	30 k. black	60	30
1048c	**275**	30 k. grey	1·00	30
1048d	A	30 k. blue	1·00	30
1048e	C	30 k. green	1·00	30
1048f	D	30 k. purple	1·00	30
1048g	**289a**	30 k. blue	1·00	30
992	C	1 r. green	4·00	2·75
993	D	2 r. green	7·50	3·50

DESIGNS: A, Capt. Gastello and burning airplane diving into enemy petrol tanks; B, Maj-Gen. Dovator and Cossack cavalry in action; C, Shura Chekalin guerilla fighting; D, Zoya Kosmodemyanskaya being led to death.

See also Nos. 1072/6.

276 Anti-tank Gun

1942. War Episodes (1st series).

No.	Type	Description	Mint	Used
994	**276**	20 k. brown	1·25	50
995	–	30 k. blue	1·25	50
996	–	30 k. green	1·25	50
997	–	30 k. red	1·25	50
998	–	60 k. grey	1·75	1·50
999	–	1 r. brown	3·75	3·75

DESIGNS—HORIZ: 30 k. (No. 996), Guerrillas attacking train; 30 k. (No. 997), Munition worker; 1 r. Machine gunners. VERT: 30 k. (No. 995), Signallers; 60 k. Defenders of Leningrad.

277 Distributing Gifts to Soldiers

1942. War Episodes (2nd series).

No.	Type	Description	Mint	Used
1000	**277**	20 k. blue	1·50	50
1001	–	20 k. purple	1·75	50
1002	–	30 k. purple	1·75	45
1003	–	45 k. red	3·75	2·25
1004	–	45 k. blue	4·00	2·75

DESIGNS—VERT: No. 1001, Bomber destroying tank; No. 1002, Food packers; No. 1003, Woman sewing; No. 1004, Anti-aircraft gun.

See also Nos. 1013/17.

278 Munition Worker

1943. 25th Anniv of Russian Revolution.

No.	Type	Description	Mint	Used
1005	**278**	5 k. brown	55	25
1006	–	10 k. brown	80	15
1007	–	15 k. blue	65	20
1008	–	20 k. blue	65	20
1009	–	30 k. brown	85	20
1010	–	60 k. brown	1·40	45
1011	–	1 r. red	2·00	1·25
1012	–	2 r. brown	3·25	1·50

DESIGNS: 10 k. Lorry convoy; 15 k. Troops supporting Lenin's banner; 20 k. Leningrad seen through an archway; 30 k. Spassky Tower, Lenin and Stalin; 60 k. Tank parade; 1 r. Lenin speaking; 2 r. Star of Order of Lenin.

279 Nurses and Wounded Soldier

1943. War Episodes (3rd series).

No.	Type	Description	Mint	Used
1013	**279**	30 k. green	1·25	65
1014	–	30 k. green (Scouts)	1·25	65
1015	–	30 k. brown (Mine-thrower)	1·25	65
1016	–	60 k. green (Anti-tank troops)	2·25	65
1017	–	60 k. blue (Sniper)	2·25	65

280 Routes of Bering's Voyages

1943. Death Bicent of Vitus Bering (explorer).

No.	Type	Description	Mint	Used
1018	–	30 k. blue	1·60	15
1019	**280**	60 k. grey	3·25	30
1020	–	1 r. green	4·50	75
1021	**280**	2 r. brown	7·50	1·00

DESIGN: 30 k., 1 r. Mt. St. Ilya.

281 Gorky

1943. 75th Birth Anniv of Maksim Gorky (novelist).

No.	Type	Description	Mint	Used
1022	**281**	30 k. green	75	15
1023		60 k. blue	1·00	15

282 Order of the Great Patriotic War — (a) Order of Suvorov

1943. War Orders and Medals (1st series). Medals with ribbon attached.

No.	Type	Description	Mint	Used
1024	**282**	1 r. black	1·25	1·00
1025	**a**	10 r. olive	6·00	4·50

See also Nos. 1051/8, 1089/94, 1097/99a, 1172/86, 1197/1204 and 1776/80a.

283 Karl Marx — 284 Naval Landing Party

1943. 125th Birth Anniv of Marx.

No.	Type	Description	Mint	Used
1026	**283**	30 k. blue	85	20
1027		60 k. green	1·40	35

1943. 25th Anniv of Red Army and Navy.

No.	Type	Description	Mint	Used
1028	**284**	20 k. brown	30	20
1029	–	30 k. green	35	15
1030	–	60 k. green	1·25	40
1031	**284**	3 r. blue	2·75	90

DESIGNS: 30 k. Sailors and anti-aircraft gun; 60 k. Tanks and infantry.

285 Ivan Turgenev — 286 Loading a Gun

1943. 125th Birth Anniv of Ivan Turgenev (novelist).

No.	Type	Description	Mint	Used
1032	**285**	30 k. green	8·00	7·00
1032a		60 k. violet	12·00	11·00

1943. 25th Anniv of Young Communist League.

No.	Type	Description	Mint	Used
1033	**286**	15 k. blue	55	15
1034	–	20 k. orange	55	15
1035	–	30 k. brown and red	70	15
1036	–	1 r. green	1·00	35
1037	–	2 r. green	2·25	75

DESIGNS—As T **286**: 20 k. Tank and banner; 1 r. Infantrymen; 2 r. Grenade thrower. $22\frac{1}{2}\times28\frac{1}{2}$ mm: 30 k. Bayonet fighter and flag.

287 V. V. Mayakovsky — 288 Memorial Tablet and Allied Flags

1943. 50th Birth Anniv of Mayakovsky (poet).

No.	Type	Description	Mint	Used
1038	**287**	30 k. orange	65	10
1039		60 k. blue	95	20

1943. Teheran Three Power Conference and 26th Anniv of Revolution.

No.	Type	Description	Mint	Used
1040	**288**	30 k. black	80	50
1041		3 r. blue	3·00	1·25

289 Defence of Odessa

АВИАПОЧТА
1944 г.
1 РУБЛЬ
(290)

1944. Liberation of Russian Towns.

No.	Type	Description	Mint	Used
1045	–	30 k. brown and red	65	25
1046	–	30 k. blue	65	25
1047	–	30 k. green	65	25
1048	**289**	30 k. green	65	25

DESIGNS: No. 1045, Stalingrad; No. 1046, Sevastopol; No. 1047, Leningrad.

1944. Air. Surch with T **290**.
1049 **275** 1 r. on 30 k. grey . . . . 1·25 30
1050 A 1 r. on 30 k. blue (No. 1048d) 1·25 30

291 Order of Kutusov

(**b**) Order of Patriotic War

(**c**) Order of Alexandr Nevsky

(**d**) Order of Suvorov

(**e**) Order of Kutusov

1944. War Orders and Medals (2nd series). Various Stars without ribbons showing as Types **b** to **e**. Perf or imperf. (a) Frames as T **291**.
1051 **b** 15 k. red 50 15
1052 **c** 20 k. blue 50 15
1053 **d** 30 k. green . . . . 1·00 25
1054 **e** 60 k. red . . . . 1·50 40
(b) Frames as T **282**.
1055 **b** 1 r. black 80 30
1056 **c** 3 r. blue . . . . 3·25 1·60
1057 **e** 5 r. green . . . . 4·00 1·00
1058 **d** 10 r. red . . . . 4·00 1·50

293 Lenin Mausoleum and Red Square, Moscow

1944. "Twenty Years without Lenin". As Nos. 667/72, but inscr "1924–1944", and T **293**.
1059 – 30 k. black and blue . . 40 10
1060 **199** 30 k. red and orange . . 40 10
1061 – 45 k. black and blue . . 60 15
1062 – 50 k. black and blue . . 70 15
1063 – 60 k. black and blue . . 1·40 20
1064 **293** 1 r. brown and blue . . . 1·75 45
1065 **199** 3 r. black and orange . . 3·50 1·40
DESIGNS—VERT: Lenin at 3 years of age (No. 1059): at school (45 k.); as man (50 k.); as orator (60 k.).

294 Allied Flags

295 Rimsky-Korsakov and Bolshoi Theatre

1944. 14 June (Allied Nations' Day).
1066 **294** 60 k. black, red & blue . 1·00 35
1067 3 r. blue and red . . . . 5·00 1·40

1944. Birth Centenary of Rimsky-Korsakov (composer). Imperf or perf.
1068 **295** 30 k. grey 40 10
1069 60 k. green 60 10
1070 1 r. green . . . . 1·25 20
1071 3 r. violet . . . . 2·50 50

296 Nuradilov and Machine-gun
297 Polivanova and Kovshova

1944. War Heroes (3rd issue).
1072 **296** 30 k. green 45 15
1073 – 60 k. violet 85 15
1074 – 60 k. blue 85 15
1075 **297** 60 k. green . . . . 1·50 45
1076 – 60 k. black . . . . 1·75 45
DESIGNS—HORIZ: No. 1073, Matrosov defending a snow-trench; No. 1074, Luzak hurling a hand grenade. VERT: No. 1076, B. Safonev, medals and aerial battle over the sea.

298 S. A. Chaplygin

299 V. I. Chapaev

1944. 75th Birth Anniv of S. A. Chaplygin (scientist).
1077 **298** 30 k. grey 30 10
1078 1 r. brown 80 30

1944. Heroes of 1918 Civil War.
1079 **299** 30 k. green . . . . . . 1·00 25
1080 – 30 k. black (N. Shchors) 1·00 25
1081 – 30 k. green (S. Lazo) . . 1·00 25
For 40 k. stamp as Type **299**, see No. 1531.
See also Nos. 1349/51.

300 Ilya Yefimovich Repin

301 "Reply of the Cossacks to Sultan Mahmoud IV"

1944. Birth Centenary of I. Y. Repin (artist). Imperf or perf.
1082 **300** 30 k. green 75 20
1083 **301** 50 k. green 75 20
1084 60 k. blue 75 20
1085 **300** 1 r. brown . . . . . . 1·00 40
1086 **301** 2 r. violet . . . . . . 2·00 80

302 I. A. Krylov

1944. Death Centenary of Krylov (fabulist).
1087 **302** 30 k. brown 25 10
1088 1 r. blue 65 25

(**f**) Partisans' Medal

(**g**) Medal for Bravery

(**h**) Order of Bogdan Chmielnitsky

(**j**) Order of Victory

(**k**) Order of Ushakov

(**l**) Order of Nakhimov

1945. War Orders and Medals (3rd series). Frame as T **291** with various centres as Types **f** to **l**. Perf or imperf.
1089 **f** 15 k. black 75 15
1090 **g** 30 k. blue . . . . . . 1·50 20
1091 **h** 45 k. blue . . . . . . 1·50 40
1092 **j** 60 k. red . . . . . . 1·75 45
1093 **k** 1 r. blue . . . . . . 2·25 1·00
1094 **l** 1 r. green . . . . . . 2·25 1·00

303 Griboedov (after P. Karatygin)

305 Soldier

1945. 150th Birth Anniv of Aleksander S. Griboedov (author).
1095 **303** 30 k. green . . . . . . 1·50 35
1096 60 k. brown . . . . . . 2·00 50

1945. War Orders and Medals (4th series). Frames as T **282**. Various centres.
1097 **g** 1 r. black . . . . . . 1·40 65
1098 **h** 2 r. black . . . . . . 3·00 1·75
1098a 2 r. purple . . . . . . 40·00 15·00
1098b **h** 2 r. olive . . . . . . 6·00 2·00
1099 **j** 3 r. red . . . . . . 4·75 1·40
1099a 3 r. purple . . . . . . 6·75 3·25

1945. Relief of Stalingrad.
1100 **305** 60 k. black and red . . . 1·40 1·10
1101 3 r. black and red . . . . 3·75 2·10

306 Standard Bearer

308 Attack

1945. Red Army Victories.
1102 **306** 20 k. green, red & black . 40 15
1103 – 30 k. black and red . . . 40 40
1104 – 1 r. green and red . . . . 2·10 2·10
DESIGN—HORIZ: 30 k. Infantry v. Tank; 1 r. Infantry charge.

1945. Liberation of Russian Soil.
1105 **308** 30 k. blue 40 60
1106 – 60 k. red . . . . . . 1·00 1·00
1107 – 1 r. green . . . . . . 2·10 2·10
DESIGNS: 60 k. Welcoming troops; 1 r. Grenade thrower.

309 Badge and Guns

310 Barricade

1945. Red Guards Commemoration.
1108 **309** 60 k. red . . . . . . 2·75 1·00

1945. Battle of Moscow.
1109 – 30 k. blue 40 50
1110 **310** 60 k. black 80 50
1111 – 1 r. black . . . . . . 1·50 1·00
DESIGNS: 30 k. Tanks in Red Square, Moscow. 1 r. Aerial battle and searchlights.

311 Prof. Lomonosov and Academy of Sciences, Leningrad

312 Popov

1945. 220th Anniv of Academy of Sciences.
1112 – 30 k. blue . . . . . . 1·00 50
1113 **311** 2 r. black . . . . . . 3·00 80
DESIGN—VERT: 30 k. Moscow Academy, inscr "1725–1945".

1945. 50th Anniv of Popov's Radio Discoveries.
1114 **312** 30 k. blue 35 40
1115 60 k. red . . . . . . 1·40 60
1116 – 1 r. brown (Popov) . . . 2·40 1·10

314 Motherhood Medal **315**

1945. Orders and Medals of Motherhood. Imperf or perf.
1117 **314** 20 k. brown on blue . . . 30 20
1118 – 30 k. brown on green . . 45 20
1119 – 60 k. red . . . . . . 1·50 70
1120 **315** 1 r. black on green . . . 1·00 20
1121 – 2 r. blue . . . . . . 2·40 30
1122 – 3 r. red on blue . . . . 3·25 1·40
DESIGNS: 30 k., 2 r. Order of Motherhood Glory; 60 k., 3 r. Order of Heroine-Mother.

316 Petlyakov Pe-2 Dive Bombers

317 Ilyushin Il-2M3 Stormovik Fighters

318 Petlyakov Pe-8 TB-7 Bomber

1945. Air. Aviation Day.
1123 **316** 1 r. brown . . . . . . 3·00 75
1124 **317** 1 r. brown . . . . . . 3·00 75
1125 – 1 r. red . . . . . . 3·00 75
1126 – 1 r. black . . . . . . 3·00 75
1127 – 1 r. blue . . . . . . 3·00 75
1128 – 1 r. green . . . . . . 3·00 75
1129 **318** 1 r. grey . . . . . . 3·00 75
1130 – 1 r. brown . . . . . . 3·00 75
1131 – 1 r. red . . . . . . 3·00 75
DESIGNS—As Type **317**: No. 1125, Lavochkin-La7 fighter shooting tail off Focke Wulf Fw 190 plane; 1126, Ilyushin Il-4 DB-3 bombers dropping bombs; 1127, Tupolev ANT-60 Tu-2 bombers in flight; 1128, Polikarpov Po-2 biplane. As Type **318**: No. 1130, Yakovlev-3 fighter destroying enemy fighter; 1131, Yakovlev Yak-9 fighter destroying Henschel Hs 129B plane.
See also Nos. 1163/71.

ПРАЗДНИК
ПОБЕДЫ

9 мая
1945 года
(**319**)

1945. VE Day. No. 1099 optd with T **319**.
1132 – 3 r. red . . . . . . 4·25 1·50

320 Lenin

321

1945. 75th Birth Anniv of Lenin.
1133 **320** 30 k. blue 50 20
1134 – 50 k. brown 85 20
1135 – 60 k. red 85 30
1136 **321** 1 r. black . . . . . . 1·40 60
1137 – 3 r. brown . . . . . . 3·25 1·75
DESIGNS—VERT: (inscr "1870–1945"). 50 k. Lenin at desk; 60 k. Lenin making a speech; 3 r. Portrait of Lenin.

322 Kutuzov (after R. Volkov)

323 A. I. Herzen

1945. Birth Bicentenary of Mikhail Kutuzov (military leader).
1138 **322** 30 k. blue 80 40
1139 60 k. brown . . . . . . 1·50 60

1945. 75th Death Anniv of Herzen (author and critic).
1140 **323** 30 k. brown . . . . . . 1·00 15
1141 2 r. black . . . . . . 1·90 65

324 I. I. Mechnikov

325 Friedrich Engels

1945. Birth Centenary of Mechnikov (biologist).
1142 **324** 30 k. brown 85 15
1143 1 r. black . . . . . . 1·60 30

1945. 125th Birth Anniv of Engels.

No.	Type	Description	Mint	Used
1144	325	30 k. brown	80	15
1145		60 k. green	1·25	60

326 Observer and Guns 327 Heavy Guns

1945. Artillery Day.

No.	Type	Description	Mint	Used
1146	326	30 k. brown	1·10	1·00
1147	327	60 k. black	3·25	3·25

328 Tank Production

1945. Home Front.

No.	Type	Description	Mint	Used
1148	328	20 k. blue and brown	1·75	35
1149	–	30 k. black and brown	1·50	40
1150	–	60 k. brown and green	2·50	1·40
1151	–	1 r. blue and brown	3·25	1·60

DESIGNS: 30 k. Harvesting; 60 k. Aircraft designing; 1 r. Firework display.

329 Victory Medal 330 Soldier with Victory Flag

1946. Victory Issue.

No.	Type	Description	Mint	Used
1152	329	30 k. violet	30	15
1153		30 k. brown	30	15
1154		60 k. black	55	20
1155		60 k. brown	55	20
1156	330	60 k. black and red	1·75	85

331 Arms of U.S.S.R 332 Kremlin, Moscow

1946. Supreme Soviet Elections.

No.	Type	Description	Mint	Used
1157	331	30 k. red	30	10
1158	332	45 k. red	50	30
1159	331	60 k. green	2·75	1·00

333 Tank Parade

334 Infantry Parade

1946. 28th Anniv of Red Army and Navy.

No.	Type	Description	Mint	Used
1160	333	60 k. brown	1·00	15
1161		2 r. violet	2·00	50
1162	334	3 r. black and red	5·00	1·40

1946. Air. As Nos. 1123/31.

No.	Type	Description	Mint	Used
1163	–	5 k. violet (as No. 1130)	40	60
1164	316	10 k. red	40	60
1165	317	15 k. red	40	60
1166	318	15 k. green	40	60
1167	–	20 k. black (as No. 1127)	40	60
1168	–	30 k. vio (as No. 1127)	85	50
1169	–	30 k. brown (as No. 1128)	90	50
1170	–	50 k. blue (as No. 1125)	1·40	65
1171	–	60 k. blue (as No. 1131)	2·75	85

A B C D E F G H J K L M N O P

1946. War Orders with Medals (5th series). Frames as T **291** with various centres as Types A to P.

No.	Type	Description	Mint	Used
1172	A	60 k. red	1·00	1·40
1173	B	60 k. red	1·00	1·40
1174	C	60 k. green	1·00	1·40
1175	D	60 k. green	1·00	1·40
1176	E	60 k. green	1·00	1·40
1177	F	60 k. blue	1·00	1·40
1178	G	60 k. blue	1·00	1·40
1179	H	60 k. violet	1·00	1·40
1180	J	60 k. purple	1·00	1·40
1181	K	60 k. brown	1·00	1·40
1182	L	60 k. brown	1·00	1·40
1183	M	60 k. purple	1·00	1·40
1184	N	60 k. red	1·00	1·40
1185	O	60 k. blue	1·00	1·40
1186	P	60 k. purple	1·00	1·40

336 P. L. Chebyshev 337 Gorky

1946. 125th Birth Anniv of Chebyshev (mathematician).

No.	Type	Description	Mint	Used
1187	336	30 k. brown	50	20
1188		60 k. black	1·00	30

1946. Death of President Kalinin. As T **211**, but inscr "3-VI-1946".

No.	Type	Description	Mint	Used
1189	20	k. black	1·90	1·00

1946. 10th Death Anniv of Maksim Gorky (novelist).

No.	Type	Description	Mint	Used
1190	337	30 k. brown	40	10
1191	–	60 k. green	70	20

DESIGN: 60 k. Gorky and laurel leaves.

338 Gagy

1946. Health Resorts.

No.	Type	Description	Mint	Used
1192	–	15 k. brown	40	15
1193	338	30 k. green	60	15
1194	–	30 k. green	70	15
1195	–	45 k. brown	1·10	35

DESIGNS—HORIZ: 15 k. Sukumi; 45 k. Novy Afon. VERT: 30 k. (No. 1194) Sochi.

339 Stalin and Parade of Athletes R

1946. Sports Festival.

No.	Type	Description	Mint	Used
1196	339	30 k. green	6·75	4·75

1946. War Medals (6th series). Frames as T **282** with various centres.

No.	Type	Description	Mint	Used
1197	R	1 r. red	1·90	1·10
1198	B	1 r. green	1·90	1·10
1199	C	1 r. brown	1·90	1·10
1200	D	1 r. blue	1·90	1·10
1201	G	1 r. grey	1·90	1·10
1202	H	1 r. red	1·90	1·10
1203	K	1 r. purple	1·90	1·10
1204	L	1 r. red	1·90	1·10

341 Moscow Opera House 342 Tanks in Red Square

1946. Moscow Buildings.

No.	Type	Description	Mint	Used
1205	–	5 k. brown	30	15
1206	341	10 k. grey	35	15
1207	–	15 k. brown	30	15
1208	–	20 k. brown	60	20
1209	–	45 k. green	70	30
1210	–	50 k. brown	80	85
1211	–	60 k. violet	1·40	1·10
1212	–	1 r. brown	2·00	1·60

DESIGNS—VERT: 5 k. Church of Ivan the Great and Kremlin; 1 r. Spassky Tower (larger). HORIZ: 15 k. Hotel Moscow; 20 k. Theatre and Sverdlov Square; 45 k. As 5 k. but horiz; 50 k. Lenin Museum; 60 k. St. Basil's Cathedral and Spassky Tower (larger).

1946. Heroes of Tank Engagements.

No.	Type	Description	Mint	Used
1213	342	30 k. green	2·00	2·00
1214		60 k. brown	3·00	3·00

343 "Iron" 345 Lenin and Stalin

344 Soviet Postage Stamps

1946. 4th Stalin "Five-Year Reconstruction Plan". Agriculture and Industry.

No.	Type	Description	Mint	Used
1215	–	5 k. olive	30	10
1216	–	10 k. green	30	10
1217	–	15 k. brown	50	10
1218	–	20 k. violet	80	10
1219	343	30 k. brown	1·40	25

DESIGNS—HORIZ: 5 k. "Agriculture"; 15 k. "Coal". VERT: 10 k. "Oil"; 20 k. "Steel".

1946. 25th Anniv of Soviet Postal Services.

No.	Type	Description	Mint	Used
1220	–	15 k. black and red	1·50	40
1221	–	30 k. brown and green	2·40	1·40
1222	344	60 k. black and green	3·75	1·60

DESIGNS: 15 k. ($48\frac{1}{2}\times23$ mm). Stamps on map of U.S.S.R.; 30 k. ($33\times22\frac{1}{2}$ mm). Reproduction of Type **47**.

1946. 29th Anniv of Russian Revolution. Imperf or Perf.

No.	Type	Description	Mint	Used
1223	345	30 k. orange	2·75	2·75
1224		30 k. green	2·75	2·75

346 N. A. Nekrasov 347 Stalin Prize Medal

1946. 125th Birth Anniv of Nekrasov (poet).

No.	Type	Description	Mint	Used
1225	346	30 k. black	85	10
1226		60 k. brown	1·40	60

1946. Stalin Prize.

No.	Type	Description	Mint	Used
1227	347	30 k. brown	2·75	1·00

348 Dnieperprostroi Dam

1946. Restoration of Dnieperprostroi Hydro-electric Power Station.

No.	Type	Description	Mint	Used
1228	348	30 k. black	1·50	65
1229		60 k. blue	2·75	1·00

349 A. Karpinsky 350 N. E. Zhukovsky

1947. Birth Centenary of Karpinsky (geologist).

No.	Type	Description	Mint	Used
1230	349	30 k. green	80	85
1231		50 k. black	3·00	90

1947. Birth Centenary of Zhukovsky (scientist).

No.	Type	Description	Mint	Used
1232	350	30 k. black	1·50	85
1233		60 k. blue	2·50	1·25

351 Lenin Mausoleum 352 Lenin

1947. 23rd Death Anniv of Lenin.

No.	Type	Description	Mint	Used
1234	351	30 k. green	65	50
1235		30 k. blue	65	50
1236	352	50 k. brown	3·25	1·00

For similar designs inscr "1924/1948" see Nos. 1334/6.

353 Nikolai M. Przhevalsky 354 Arms of R.S.F.S.R

356 Arms of U.S.S.R

1947. Centenary of Soviet Geographical Society.

No.	Type	Description	Mint	Used
1237	–	20 k. brown	2·00	50
1238	–	20 k. blue	2·00	50
1239	353	60 k. olive	3·50	1·40
1240	–	60 k. brown	3·50	1·40

DESIGN: 20 k. Miniature portrait of F. P. Litke and full rigged ship "Senyavin".

1947. Supreme Soviet Elections. Arms of Constituent Republics. As T **354**.

No.	Type	Description	Mint	Used
1241	354	30 k. red (Russian Federation)	75	65
1242	–	30 k. brown (Armenia)	75	65
1243	–	30 k. bistre (Azerbaijan)	75	65
1244	–	30 k. green (Byelorussia)	75	65
1245	–	30 k. grey (Estonia)	75	65
1246	–	30 k. brown (Georgia)	75	65
1247	–	30 k. purple (Karelo-Finnish S.S.R.)	75	65
1248	–	30 k. orange (Kazakhstan)	75	65
1249	–	30 k. purple (Kirgizia)	75	65
1250	–	30 k. brown (Latvia)	75	65
1251	–	30 k. green (Lithuania)	75	65
1252	–	30 k. purple (Moldavia)	75	65
1253	–	30 k. green (Tadzhikistan)	75	65
1254	–	30 k. black (Turkmenistan)	75	65
1255	–	30 k. blue (Ukraine)	75	65
1256	–	30 k. brown (Uzbekistan)	75	65
1257	356	1r. multicoloured	2·75	85

A Hammer and Sickle in the centre of No. 1247 and at the base of No. 1249 should assist identification.

357 Russian Soldier · 359 A. S. Pushkin

1947. 29th Anniv of Soviet Army. Perf or imperf.

No.	Type	Description	Unused	Used
1258	357	20 k. black	45	10
1259	–	30 k. blue	50	15
1260	–	30 k. brown	55	15

DESIGNS—VERT: No. 1259, Military cadet. HORIZ: No. 1260, Soldier, sailor and airman.

1947. 110th Death Anniv of Pushkin (poet).

No.	Type	Description	Unused	Used
1261	359	30 k. black	65	30
1262		50 k. green	1·00	1·10

360 Schoolroom

1947. International Women's Day.

No.	Type	Description	Unused	Used
1263	360	15 k. blue	3·25	1·60
1264	–	30 k. red	5·00	3·00

DESIGN—$26\frac{1}{2} \times 39\frac{1}{2}$ mm: 30 k. Women students and banner.

362 Moscow Council Building · 364 Soviet Yakovlev Yak-9 Aircraft and Flag

363 May Day Procession

1947. 30th Anniv of Moscow Soviet. Perf or imperf.

No.	Type	Description	Unused	Used
1265	362	30 k. red, blue & blk	2·00	1·60

1947. May Day.

No.	Type	Description	Unused	Used
1266	363	30 k. red	1·75	1·60
1267		1r. green	3·75	3·75

1947. Air Force Day.

No.	Type	Description	Unused	Used
1268	364	30 k. violet	80	15
1269		1r. blue	2·00	85

365 Yakhromsky Lock

1947. 10th Anniv of Volga-Moscow Canal.

No.	Type	Description	Unused	Used
1270	–	30 k. black	70	10
1271	365	30 k. lake	70	10
1272	–	45 k. red	65	25
1273	–	50 k. blue	1·25	30
1274	–	60 k. red	1·25	85
1275	–	1r. violet	2·75	1·10

DESIGNS—HORIZ: 30 k. (No. 1270), Karamyshevsky Dam; 45 k. Yakhromsky Pumping Station; 50 k. Khimki Pier; 1 r. Lock No. 8. VERT: 60 k. Map of Volga-Moscow Canal.

800 лет Москвы
1147—1947 гг.
(366)

367 Izmailovsky Station

1947. 800th Anniv of Moscow (1st issue). Optd as T **366**.

No.	Type	Description	Unused	Used
1276		20 k. brown (No. 1208)	55	15
1277		50 k. brown (No. 1210)	90	35
1278		60 k. violet (No. 1211)	1·40	60
1279		1 r. brown (No. 1212)	3·75	1·75

See also Nos. 1286/1300.

1947. Opening of New Moscow Underground Stations. Inscr "M".

No.	Type	Description	Unused	Used
1280	367	30 k. blue	60	15
1281	–	30 k. brown	60	15
1282	–	45 k. brown	85	35
1283	–	45 k. violet	85	35
1284	–	60 k. green	2·00	50
1285	–	60 k. red	2·00	50

DESIGNS—HORIZ: No. 1281, Power House; No. 1282, Falcon Station; No. 1283, Stalinsky Station; No. 1284, Kiev Station. VERT: No. 1285, Mayakovsky Station.

368 Crimea Bridge, Moscow

1947. 800th Anniv of Moscow (2nd issue).

No.	Type	Description	Unused	Used
1286	368	5 k. brown and blue	50	10
1287	–	10 k. black and brown	30	10
1288	–	30 k. grey	1·25	25
1289	–	30 k. blue	1·25	25
1290	–	30 k. brown	55	25
1291	–	30 k. green	55	25
1292	–	30 k. green	55	25
1293	–	50 k. green	1·25	70
1294	–	60 k. blue	2·00	55
1295	–	60 k. black and brown	2·00	55
1296	–	1 r. purple	3·25	80
		Centre in yellow, red and blue.		
1297	–	1 r. blue	5·00	85
1298	–	2 r. red	6·75	2·00
1299	–	3 r. blue	11·00	2·75
1300	–	5 r. blue	18·00	6·00

DESIGNS—VERT: 10 k. Gorky Street, Moscow; 30 k. (No. 1292), Pushkin Place; 60 k. (No. 1294), 2 r. Kremlin; 1 r. (No. 1296), "Old Moscow" after A. M. Vasnetsov; 1 r. (No. 1279), St. Basil Cathedral. HORIZ: 30 k. (No. 1288), Kiev railway station; 30 k. (No. 1289), Kazan railway station; 30 k. (No. 1290), Central Telegraph Offices; 30 k. (No. 1291), Kaluga Street; 50 k. Kremlin; 3 r. Kremlin; 5 r. Government Buildings. ($54\frac{1}{2} \times 24\frac{1}{2}$ mm): 60 k. (No. 1295), Bridge and Kremlin.

369 "Ritz", Gagry · 370 "Zapadugol", Sochi

1947. U.S.S.R. Health Resorts. (a) Vertical.

No.	Type	Description	Unused	Used
1301	369	30 k. green	55	15
1302	–	30 k. green (Sukhumi)	55	15
		(b) Horizontal.		
1303	370	30 k. black	55	15
1304	–	30 k. brown ("New Riveria", Sochi)	55	15
1305	–	30 k. purple ("Voroshilov", Sochi)	55	15
1306	–	30 k. violet ("Gulripsh", Sukhumi)	55	15
1307	–	30 k. blue ("Kemeri", Riga)	55	15
1308	–	30 k. brown ("Abkhazia", Novy Afon)	55	15
1309	–	30 k. bistre ("Krestyansky", Livadia)	55	15
1310	–	30 k. blue ("Kirov", Kislovodsk)	55	15

371 1917 Revolution

1947. 30th Anniv of Revolution. Perf or imperf.

No.	Type	Description	Unused	Used
1311	371	30 k. black and red	30	15
1312	–	50 k. blue and red	1·25	20
1313	371	60 k. black and red	1·00	30
1314	–	60 k. brown and red	1·00	30
1315	–	1 r. black and red	2·25	50
1316	–	2 r. green and red	3·75	1·00

DESIGNS: 50 k., 1 r. "Industry"; 60 k. (No. 1314), 2 r. "Agriculture".

372 Metallurgical Works · 373 Spassky Tower, Kremlin

1947. Post-War Five Year Plan. Horiz industrial designs. All dated "1947" except No. 1324. Perf or imperf.

No.	Type	Description	Unused	Used
1317	372	15 k. brown	40	20
1318	–	20 k. brown (Foundry)	50	30
1319	372	30 k. purple	1·00	30
1320	–	30 k. green (Harvesting machines)	75	50
1321	–	30 k. brown (Tractor)	1·00	30
1322	–	30 k. brown (Tractors)	75	30
1323	–	60 k. bistre (Harvesting machines)	1·50	1·00
1324	–	60 k. purple (Builders)	1·50	1·00
1325	–	1 r. orange (Foundry)	3·00	2·00
1326	–	1 r. red (Tractor)	3·00	2·00
1327	–	1 r. violet (Tractors)	3·00	2·00

1947.

No.	Type	Description	Unused	Used
1328	373	60 k. red	10·00	8·25
1329a		1 r. red	1·10	35

374 Peter I Monument · 376 Government Building, Kiev

1948. 4th Anniv of Relief of Leningrad.

No.	Type	Description	Unused	Used
1330	–	30 k. violet	50	15
1331	374	50 k. green	1·10	30
1332	–	60 k. black	1·60	50
1333	–	1 r. violet	2·10	1·10

DESIGNS—HORIZ: 30 k. Winter Palace; 60 k. Peter and Paul Fortress; 1 r. Smolny Institute.

1948. 24th Death Anniv of Lenin. As Issue of 1947, but dated "1924–1948".

No.	Type	Description	Unused	Used
1334	351	30 k. red	65	50
1355		60 k. blue	1·40	85
1336	352	60 k. green	3·00	1·40

1948. 30th Anniversary of Ukrainian S.S.R. Various designs inscr "XXX" and "1917–1947".

No.	Type	Description	Unused	Used
1337	376	30 k. blue	55	15
1338	–	50 k. violet	1·10	75
1339	–	60 k. brown	1·50	75
1340	–	1 r. brown	2·40	1·90

DESIGNS: 50 k. Dnieper hydro-electric power station; 60 k. Wheatfield and granary; 1 r. Metallurgical works and colliery.

377 Vasily I. Surikov · 378 Skiing

1948. Birth Centenary of Surikov (artist).

No.	Type	Description	Unused	Used
1341	377	30 k. brown	1·40	65
1342		60 k. green	2·40	1·40

1948. R.S.F.S.R. Games.

No.	Type	Description	Unused	Used
1343	378	15 k. blue	2·00	25
1344	–	20 k. blue	3·25	50

DESIGN—VERT: 20 k. Motor cyclist crossing stream.

379 Artillery · 381 Karl Marx and Friedrich Engels

380 Bulganin and Military School

1948. 30th Anniv of Founding of Soviet Defence Forces and of Civil War. (a) Various designs with arms and inscr "1918 XXX 1948".

No.	Type	Description	Unused	Used
1345	379	30 k. brown	1·25	60
1346	–	30 k. grey	1·25	60
1347	–	30 k. blue	1·10	60
1348	380	60 k. brown	2·75	1·10

DESIGNS—VERT: No. 1346, Navy. HORIZ: No. 1347, Air Force.

(b) Portraits of Civil War Heroes as Nos. 1079/81.

No.	Type	Description	Unused	Used
1349	299	60 k. brown (Chapaev)	1·60	1·60
1350	–	60 k. green (Shchors)	1·60	1·60
1351	–	60 k. blue (Lazo)	1·60	1·60

1948. Centenary of Publication of "Communist Manifesto".

No.	Type	Description	Unused	Used
1352	381	30 k. black	40	25
1353		50 k. brown	85	25

382 Miner · 348b Arms of U.S.S.R · 348d Spassky Tower, Kremlin

1948.

No.	Type	Description	Unused	Used
1354	382	5 k. black	1·90	80
1355	–	10 k. violet (Sailor)	1·90	80
1356	–	15 k. blue (Airman)	3·75	2·50
1361i	382	15 k. black	1·10	65
1357	–	20 k. brown (Farm girl)	4·25	2·40
1361j	–	20 k. green (Farm girl)	1·25	65
1361ka	–	25 k. bl (Airman)	1·40	65
1358	384b	30 k. brown	6·75	3·75
1361l	–	30 k. brown (Scientist)	1·40	65
1361n	384b	40 k. red	2·10	50
1359	–	45 k. violet (Scientist)	7·50	5·75
1361f	384d	50 k. blue	9·25	3·25
1361	–	60 k. grn (Soldier)	15·00	12·50

385 Parade of Workers

1948. May Day.

No.	Type	Description	Unused	Used
1362	385	30 k. red	1·10	1·00
1363		60 k. blue	2·50	1·10

386 Belinsky (after K. Gorbunov)

1948. Death Centenary of Vissarion Grigorievich Belinsky (literary critic and journalist).

No.	Type	Description	Unused	Used
1364	386	30 k. brown	1·00	40
1365		50 k. green	1·50	90
1366		60 k. violet	2·00	1·90

387 A. N. Ostrovsky · 388

1948. 125th Birth Anniv of Ostrovsky (dramatist).

No.	Type	Description	Unused	Used
1367	387	30 k. green	75	60
1368	388	60 k. brown	1·40	1·10
1369		1 r. violet	3·25	2·50

389 I. I. Shishkin (after I. Kramskoi) · 391 Factories

390 "Rye Field"

1948. 50th Death Anniv of Shishkin (landscape painter).

No.	Type	Description	Unused	Used
1370	389	30 k. brown and green	1·60	20
1371	390	50 k. yellow, red & blue	2·75	35
1372	–	60 k. multicoloured	4·00	1·00
1373	389	1 r. blue and brown	5·00	1·50

DESIGN—HORIZ: 60 k. "Morning in the Forest".

1948. Leningrad Workers' Four-Year Plan.
1374 **391** 15 k. brown and red . . 2·50 1·00
1375 – 30 k. black and red . . . 2·00 2·00
1376 **391** 60 k. brown and red . . 6·50 3·75
DESIGN—HORIZ (40 × 22 mm): 30 k. Proclamation to Leningrad workers.

392 Arms and People of the U.S.S.R
393 Caterpillar drawing Seed Drills

1948. 25th Anniv of U.S.S.R.
1377 **392** 30 k. black and red . . . 1·10 1·00
1378 60 k. olive and red . . . 3·25 3·00

1948. Five-Year Agricultural Plan.
1379 **393** 30 k. red 55 50
1380 30 k. green 65 50
1381 – 45 k. brown . . . . . . 1·40 1·10
1382 **393** 50 k. black . . . . . . 2·10 1·10
1383 – 60 k. green . . . . . . 1·60 1·40
1384 – 60 k. green . . . . . . 1·60 1·40
1385 – 1 r. violet . . . . . . 5·25 2·25
DESIGNS: 30 k. (No. 1380), 1 r. Harvesting sugar beet; 45, 60 k. (No. 1383), Gathering cotton; 60 k. (No. 1384), Harvesting machine.

(394) **395** Miners **396** A. Zhdanov

1948. Air Force Day. Optd with T **394**.
1386 **364** 30 k. violet . . . . . . 4·25 2·40
1387 1 r. blue . . . . . . 4·25 2·40

1948. Miners' Day.
1388 **395** 30 k. blue 70 40
1389 – 60 k. violet . . . . . . 1·75 1·00
1390 – 1 r. green . . . . . . 3·25 1·90
DESIGNS: 60 k. Inside a coal mine; 1 r. Miner's emblem.

1948. Death of A. A. Zhdanov (statesman).
1391 **396** 40 k. blue . . . . . . 2·50 1·50

397 Sailor **398** Football

1948. Navy Day.
1392 **397** 30 k. green . . . . . . 1·60 1·40
1393 60 k. blue . . . . . . 2·75 2·00

1948. Sports.
1394 – 15 k. violet . . . . . . 1·00 15
1395 **398** 30 k. brown . . . . . . 2·00 15
1396 – 45 k. brown . . . . . . 2·00 35
1397a – 50 k. blue . . . . . . 3·75 35
DESIGNS—VERT: 15 k. Running; 50 k. Diving. HORIZ: 45 k. Power boat racing.

399 Tank and Drivers

1948. Tank Drivers' Day.
1398 **399** 30 k. black . . . . . . 2·00 1·60
1399 – 1 r. red . . . . . . 4·75 3·00
DESIGN: 1 r. Parade of tanks.

400 Horses and Groom

1948. Five-Year Livestock Development Plan.
1400 **400** 30 k. black . . . . . . 1·50 70
1401 – 60 k. green . . . . . . 3·75 2·10
1402 **400** 1 r. brown . . . . . . 5·75 5·25
DESIGN: 60 k. Dairy farming.

401 Steam and Electric Locomotives

1948. Five-Year Transport Plan.
1403 **401** 30 k. brown . . . . . . 3·00 60
1404 50 k. green . . . . . . 3·50 1·50
1405 – 60 k. blue . . . . . . 3·25 2·00
1406 – 1 r. violet . . . . . . 7·25 5·75
DESIGNS: 60 k. Road traffic; 1 r. Liner "Vyacheslav Molotov".

402 Iron Pipe Manufacture

1948. Five-Year Rolled Iron, Steel and Machine-building Plan.
1407 – 30 k. violet . . . . . . 1·75 90
1408 – 30 k. purple . . . . . . 1·75 90
1409 – 50 k. brown . . . . . . 2·75 1·40
1410 – 50 k. black . . . . . . 2·75 1·40
1411 – 60 k. brown . . . . . . 3·75 2·50
1412 **402** 60 k. red . . . . . . 3·75 2·50
1413 1 r. blue . . . . . . 5·75 3·25
DESIGNS—HORIZ: Nos. 1407, 1410, Foundry; No. 1408/9, Pouring molten metal; No. 1411, Group of machines.

403 Abovyan **404** Miner

1948. Death Centenary of Khachatur Abovyan (writer).
1414 **403** 40 k. purple . . . . . . 2·40 2·40
1415 50 k. green . . . . . . 3·75 3·25

1948. Five-Year Coal mining and Oil Extraction Plan.
1416 **404** 30 k. black . . . . . . 3·00 1·10
1417 60 k. brown . . . . . . 7·25 2·25
1418 – 60 k. brown . . . . . . 7·25 2·40
1419 – 1 r. green . . . . . . 9·00 4·25
DESIGN: Nos. 1418/19, Oil wells and tanker train.

405 Farkhadsk Power Station **406** Flying Model Aircraft

1948. Five-Year Electrification Plan.
1420 **405** 30 k. green . . . . . . 1·25 1·00
1421 – 60 k. red . . . . . . 4·25 3·00
1422 **405** 1 r. red . . . . . . 4·25 3·00
DESIGN: 60 k. Zuevsk Power Station.

1948. Government Care of School Children's Summer Vacation.
1423 **406** 30 k. green . . . . . . 3·75 1·60
1424 – 45 k. red . . . . . . 5·75 3·20
1425 – 45 k. violet . . . . . . 3·75 3·25
1426 – 60 k. blue . . . . . . 9·00 6·00
1427 – 1 r. blue . . . . . . 20·00 6·00
DESIGNS—VERT: No. 1424, Boy and girl saluting; 60 k. Boy trumpeter. HORIZ: No. 1425, Children marching; 1 r. Children round camp fire.

407 Children in School **408** Flag of U.S.S.R

1948. 30th Anniv of Lenin's Young Communist League.
1428 – 20 k. purple . . . . . . 3·00 1·10
1429 – 25 k. red . . . . . . 2·00 1·10
1430 – 40 k. brown and red . . . 3·25 2·25
1431 **407** 50 k. green . . . . . . 6·25 3·75
1432 **408** 1 r. multicoloured . . . 10·50 4·50
1433 – 2 r. violet . . . . . . 22·00 17·00
DESIGNS—HORIZ: 20 k. Youth parade. VERT: 25 k. Peasant girl; 40 k. Young people and flag; 2 r. Industrial worker.

409 Interior of Theatre **410** Searchlights over Moscow

1948. 50th Anniv of Moscow Arts Theatre.
1434 **409** 50 k. blue . . . . . . 1·60 3·25
1435 – 1 r. purple . . . . . . 3·75 5·75
DESIGN: 1 r. Stanislavsky and Dantchenko.

1948. 31st Anniv of October Revolution.
1436 **410** 40 k. red . . . . . . 1·60 3·25
1437 1 r. green . . . . . . 6·00 5·75

411 Artillery Barrage

1948. Artillery Day.
1438 **411** 30 k. blue . . . . . . 1·60 3·25
1439 1 r. red . . . . . . 3·25 5·00

412 Trade Union Building (venue)

1948. 16th World Chess Championship, Moscow.
1440 **412** 30 k. blue . . . . . . 4·00 1·00
1441 – 40 k. violet . . . . . . 9·00 55
1442 **412** 50 k. brown . . . . . . 9·00 1·75
DESIGN—VERT: 40 k. Players badge showing chessboard and rook

413 Stasov and Building

1948. Death Centenary of Stasov (architect).
1443 – 40 k. brown . . . . . . 1·40 1·25
1444 **413** 1 r. black . . . . . . 3·25 3·25
DESIGN—VERT: 40 k. Portrait of Stasov.

414 Yakovlev Yak-9 Fighters and Flag **415** Statue of Ya. M. Sverdlov

1948. Air Force Day.
1445 **414** 1 r. blue . . . . . . 6·75 2·75

1948. 225th Anniv of Sverdlovsk City. Imperf or perf.
1446 **415** 30 k. blue 60 40
1447 – 40 k. purple . . . . . . 1·00 40
1448 **415** 1 r. green . . . . . . 1·75 60
DESIGN: 40 k. View of Sverdlovsk.

416 Sukhumi **417** State Emblem

1948. Views of Crimea and Caucasus.
1449 **416** 40 k. green . . . . . . 1·00 30
1450 – 40 k. violet . . . . . . 1·00 30
1451 – 40 k. mauve . . . . . . 1·00 30
1452 – 40 k. brown . . . . . . 1·00 30
1453 – 40 k. purple . . . . . . 1·00 30
1454 – 40 k. green . . . . . . 1·00 30
1455 – 40 k. blue . . . . . . 1·00 30
1456 – 40 k. green . . . . . . 1·00 30
DESIGNS—VERT: No. 1450, Gardens, Sochi; No. 1451, Eagle-topped monument, Pyatigorsk; No. 1452, Cliffs, Crimea. HORIZ: No. 1453, Terraced gardens, Sochi; No. 1454, Roadside garden, Sochi; No. 1455, Colonnade, Kislovodsk; No. 1456, Sea and palms, Gagry.

1949. 30th Anniv of Byelorussian Soviet Republic.
1457 **417** 40 k. red . . . . . . 1·60 1·60
1458 1 r. green . . . . . . 2·50 2·50

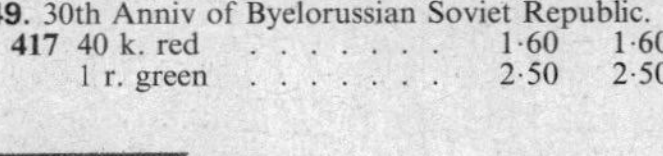

418 M. V. Lomonosov **419** Lenin Mausoleum

1949. Establishment of Lomonosov Museum of Academy of Sciences.
1459 **418** 40 k. brown . . . . . . 1·50 1·40
1460 50 k. green . . . . . . 2·00 1·40
1461 – 1 r. blue . . . . . . 4·75 2·75
DESIGN—HORIZ: 1 r. Museum.

1949. 25th Death Anniv of Lenin.
1462 **419** 40 k. brown and green . 6·00 6·00
1463 1 r. brown & dp brown . 10·50 10·50

420 Dezhnev's Ship

1949. Tercentenary of Dezhnev's Exploration of Bering Strait.
1464 – 40 k. olive . . . . . . 10·00 10·00
1465 **420** 1 r. black . . . . . . 20·00 15·00
DESIGN: 40 k. Cape Dezhnev.

421 "Women in Industry" **422** Admiral S. O. Makarov

1949. International Women's Day.
1466 **421** 20 k. violet 30 10
1467 – 25 k. blue 35 10
1468 – 40 k. red 50 10
1469 – 50 k. grey . . . . . . 1·10 30
1470 – 50 k. brown . . . . . . 1·10 30
1471 – 1 r. green . . . . . . 3·25 40
1472 – 2 r. red . . . . . . 4·75 1·10
DESIGNS—HORIZ: 25 k. Kindergarten; 50 k. grey, Woman teacher; 50 k. brown, Women in field; 1 r. Women sports champions. VERT: 40 k., 2 r. Woman broadcasting.

1949. Birth Centenary of Admiral S. O. Makarov (naval scientist).
1473 **422** 40 k. blue . . . . . . 2·00 1·00
1474 1 r. red . . . . . . 3·75 3·25

423 Soldier

1949. 31st Anniv of Soviet Army.
1475 **423** 40 k. red . . . . . . 11·50 10·00

424 Kirov Military Medical Academy

1949. 150th Anniv of Kirov Military Medical Academy.
1476 **424** 40 k. red . . . . . . 1·25 1·60
1477 – 50 k. blue . . . . . . 2·00 2·50
1478 **424** 1 r. green . . . . . . 4·75 5·00
DESIGN: 50 k. Professors Botkin, Pirogov and Sechenov and Kirov Academy.

425 V. R. Williams **425a** Three Russians with Flag

1949. Agricultural Reform.
1479 **425** 25 k. green . . . . 4·25 4·25
1480 50 k. brown . . . . 5·75 5·75

1949. Labour Day.
1481 **425a** 40 k. red . . . . 1·00 80
1482 1 r. green . . . . 3·25 2·00

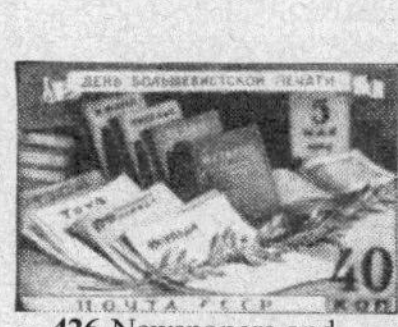
426 Newspapers and Books

427 A. S. Popov and Radio Equipment

1949. Press Day. Inscr "5 MAR 1949".
1483 **426** 40 k. red . . . . 3·25 4·75
1484 – 1 r. violet . . . . 6·75 8·25
DESIGN: 1 r. Man and boy reading newspaper.

1949. Radio Day.
1485 **427** 40 k. violet . . . . 1·90 1·90
1486 – 50 k. brown . . . . 3·25 3·25
1487 **427** 1 r. green . . . . 6·75 6·75
DESIGN—HORIZ: 50 k. Popov demonstrating receiver to Admiral Makarov.

428 A. S. Pushkin

429 Pushkin reading "Epistle to Decembrists"

1949. 150th Birth Anniv of Pushkin (poet).
1488 **428** 25 k. black and grey . . 1·00 75
1489 – 40 k. black and brown . 1·90 2·10
1490 **429** 40 k. purple and red . . 3·75 3·75
1491 – 1 r. grey and brown . . 4·50 5·25
1492 **429** 2 r. blue and brown . . 7·50 6·75
DESIGNS—VERT: No. 1489, Pushkin portrait after Kiprensky. HORIZ: 1 r. Pushkin museum, Boldino.

430 Tug "Boksirni Typlokod"

431 I. V. Michurin

1949. Centenary of Krasnoe Sormovo Machine-building and Ship-building Plant, Gorky.
1493 **430** 40 k. blue . . . . 6·75 5·25
1494 – 1 r. brown . . . . 9·25 9·25
DESIGN: 1 r. Tanker "Bolshaya Volga".

1949. Agricultural Reform.
1495 **431** 40 k. blue . . . . 1·50 1·40
1496 1 r. green . . . . 2·75 2·75

432 Yachting

1949. National Sports.
1497 **432** 20 k. blue . . . . 1·25 10
1498 – 25 k. green 85 15
1499 – 30 k. violet . . . . 1·50 15
1500 – 40 k. brown . . . . 1·40 25
1501 – 40 k. green . . . . 1·40 25
1502 – 50 k. grey . . . . 1·75 40
1503 – 1 r. red . . . . 4·00 85
1504 – 2 r. black . . . . 8·25 1·90
DESIGNS: 25 k. Canoeing; 30 k. Swimming; 40 k. (No. 1500), Cycling; 40 k. (No. 1501), Football; 50 k. Mountaineering; 1 r. Parachuting; 2 r. High jumping.

433 V. V. Dokuchaev

1949. Soil Research.
1505 **433** 40 k. brown . . . . 1·50 20
1506 1 r. green . . . . 2·50 50

434 V. I. Bazhenov

435 A. N. Radischev

1949. 150th Death Anniv of V. I. Bazhenov (architect).
1507 **434** 40 k. violet . . . . 1·40 30
1508 1 r. brown . . . . 2·00 70

1949. Birth Bicent of A. N. Radischev (writer).
1509 **435** 40 k. green . . . . 1·50 1·60
1510 1 r. black . . . . 2·75 2·75

436 Green Cape Sanatorium, Makhindzhauri

1949. State Sanatoria. Designs showing various buildings.
1511 **436** 40 k. green 75 15
1512 – 40 k. green 75 15
1513 – 40 k. blue 75 15
1514 – 40 k. violet 75 15
1515 – 40 k. red 75 15
1516 – 40 k. orange 75 15
1517 – 40 k. brown 75 15
1518 – 40 k. brown 75 15
1519 – 40 k. black 75 15
1520 – 40 k. black 75 15
DESIGNS—HORIZ: No. 1512, VTsSPS No. 41, Zheleznovodsk; No. 1513, Energetics, Hosta; No. 1514, VTsSPS No. 3, Kislovodsk; No. 1515, VTs SPS No. 3, Hosta; No. 1516, State Theatre, Sochi; No. 1517, Clinical, Tskhaltubo; No. 1518, Frunze, Sochi; No. 1519, VTsSPS No. 1, Kislovodsk; No. 1520, Communication, Hosta.

437 I. P. Pavlov

1949. Birth Centenary of I. P. Pavlov (scientist).
1521 **437** 40 k. brown . . . . 1·00 20
1522 1 r. black . . . . 2·25 85

438 Globe and Letters

1949. 75th Anniv of U.P.U. Perf or imperf.
1523 **438** 40 k. blue and brown . 2·25 25
1524 50 k. violet and blue . . 2·25 75

439 Tree Planting Machines

440 Map of S. W. Russia

1949. Forestry and Field Conservancy.
1525 **439** 25 k. green 75 50
1526 – 40 k. violet 90 85
1527 **440** 40 k. green and black . . 90 85
1528 – 50 k. blue . . . . 1·40 1·40
1529 **439** 1 r. black . . . . 2·75 2·40
1530 – 2 r. brown . . . . 6·75 5·75
DESIGNS—33 × 22½ mm: 40 k. violet, Harvesters; 50 k. River scene. 33 × 19½ mm: 2 r. Old man and children.

1949. 30th Death of V. I. Chapaev (military strategist).
1531 **299** 40 k. orange . . . . . . 9·25 10·00

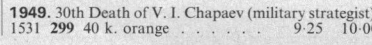

442 I. S. Nikitin

443 Malyi Theatre, Moscow

1949. 125th Birth Anniv of Nikitin (poet).
1532 **442** 40 k. brown . . . . 1·10 20
1533 1 r. blue . . . . 2·00 60

1949. 125th Anniv of Malyi Theatre, Moscow.
1534 **443** 40 k. green . . . . 1·50 20
1535 50 k. orange . . . . 2·10 65
1536 – 1 r. brown . . . . 4·25 1·25
DESIGN: 1 r. Five portraits and theatre.

444 Crowd with Banner

1949. 32nd Anniv of October Revolution.
1537 **444** 40 k. red . . . . 2·50 2·50
1538 1 r. green . . . . 4·25 4·25

445 Sheep and Cows

446 Lenin Hydro-electric Station, Caucasus

447 Ilyushin Il–12 Airliners and Map

1949. Cattle-breeding Collective Farm.
1539 **445** 40 k. brown . . . . 1·50 50
1540 1 r. violet . . . . 2·40 80

1949. Air. Aerial views and map.
1541 **446** 50 k. brown on yellow . 1·90 1·00
1542 – 60 k. brown on buff . . 2·00 1·50
1543 – 1 r. orange on yellow . 6·00 1·90
1544 – 1 r. brown on buff . . 5·50 1·90
1545 – 1 r. blue on blue . . . 5·50 1·90
1546 **447** 1 r. blue, red and grey . 10·00 5·50
1547 – 2 r. red on blue . . . 12·00 5·50
1548 – 3 r. green on blue . . 23·00 13·50
DESIGNS—Ilyushin Il–12 airliner over: HORIZ: No. 1542, Farm; 1543, Sochi. VERT: 1544, Leningrad; 1545, Aleppo; 1547, Moscow; 1548, Arctic.

448 Ski Jumping

449 Diesel Train

1949. National Sports.
1549 **448** 20 k. green 80 15
1550 – 40 k. orange . . . . 1·40 20
1551 – 50 k. blue . . . . 2·10 45
1552 – 1 r. red . . . . 5·25 45
1553 – 2 r. violet . . . . 9·00 1·90
DESIGNS: 40 k. Girl gymnast; 50 k. Ice hockey; 1 r. Weightlifting; 2 r. Shooting wolves.

1949. Modern Railway Development.
1554 – 25 k. red . . . . 2·00 35
1555 **449** 40 k. violet . . . . 2·50 1·10
1556 – 50 k. brown . . . . 3·50 1·25
1557 **449** 1 r. green . . . . 9·00 3·25
DESIGNS: 25 k. Electric tram; 50 k. Steam train.

MINIMUM PRICE

The minimum price quoted is 10p which represents a handling charge rather than a basis for valuing common stamps. For further notes about prices, see introductory pages.

450 Arms of U.S.S.R

451 Government Buildings, Dushanbe

1949. Constitution Day.
1558 **450** 40 k. red . . . . 7·50 5·00

1949. 20th Anniv of Republic of Tadzhikstan.
1559 – 20 k. blue 75 10
1560 – 25 k. green 70 10
1561 **451** 40 k. red . . . . 1·25 20
1562 – 50 k. violet . . . . 1·75 20
1563 **451** 1 r. black . . . . 3·00 75
DESIGNS: 20 k. Textile mills; 25 k. Irrigation canal; 50 k. Medical University.

452 People with Flag

453 Worker and Globe

1949. 10th Anniv of Incorporation of West Ukraine and West Byelorussia in U.S.S.R.
1564 **452** 40 k. red . . . . 9·25 9·25
1565 – 40 k. orange . . . . 9·25 9·25
DESIGN—VERT: No. 1565, Ukrainians and flag.

1949. Peace Propaganda.
1566 **453** 40 k. red 80 20
1567 50 k. blue . . . . 1·25 30

454 Government Buildings, Tashkent

1950. 25th Anniv of Uzbek S.S.R.
1568 – 20 k. blue 60 20
1569 – 25 k. black 60 20
1570 **454** 40 k. red . . . . 1·10 20
1571 – 40 k. violet 90 30
1572 – 1 r. green . . . . 3·00 70
1573 – 2 r. brown . . . . 5·50 1·40
DESIGNS: 20 k. Teachers' College; 25 k. Opera and Ballet House, Tashkent; 40 k. (violet) Navotz Street, Tashkent; 1 r. Map of Fergana Canal; 2 r. Lock, Fergana Canal.

455 Dam

456 Statue of Lenin

1950. 25th Anniv of Turkmen S.S.R.
1574 – 25 k. black . . . . 3·25 3·25
1575 **455** 40 k. brown . . . . 2·00 2·00
1576 – 50 k. green . . . . 3·75 3·75
1577 **455** 1 r. violet . . . . 6·00 6·00
DESIGNS: 25 k. Textile factory, Ashkhabad; 50 k. Carpet-making.

1950. 26th Death Anniv of Lenin.
1578 **456** 40 k. brown and grey . . 65 15
1579 – 50 k. red, brown & grn . 1·50 60
1580 – 1 r. buff, green & brown . 3·25 75
DESIGNS—HORIZ: 50 k. Lenin's Office, Kremlin; 1 r. Lenin Museum.

457 Film Show

458 Voter

1950. 30th Anniv of Soviet Film Industry.
1581 **457** 25 k. brown . . . . . . 13·50 12·50

1950. Supreme Soviet Elections. Inscr "12 МАРТА 1950".
1582 **458** 40 k. green on yellow . . 4·75 4·75
1583 – 1 r. red . . . . 6·75 6·75
DESIGN: 1 r. Kremlin and flags.

459 Statue of Morozov

460 Lenin Central Museum

1950. Unveiling of Monument to Pavlik Morozov (model Soviet youth).
1584 **459** 40 k. black and red . . . 4·00 3·25
1585 1 r. green and red . . . 6·75 5·25

1950. Moscow Museums. Buildings inscr "MOCKBA 1949".
1586 **460** 40 k. olive . . . . 1·25 25
1587 – 40 k. red . . . . 1·25 25
1588 – 40 k. turquoise . . . . . 1·25 25
1589 – 40 k. brown . . . . . . 1·25 25
1590 – 40 k. mauve . . . . . . 1·25 25
1591 – 40 k. blue (no tree) . . . 1·25 25
1592 – 40 k. brown . . . . . . 1·25 25
1593 – 40 k. blue (with tree) . . 1·25 25
1594 – 40 k. red . . . . 1·25 25
DESIGNS—HORIZ: (33½ × 23½ mm): No. 1587, Revolution Museum; No. 1588, Tretyakov Gallery; No. 1589, Timiryazev Biological Museum; No. 1591, Polytechnic Museum; No. 1593, Oriental Museum. (39½ × 26½ mm): No. 1590, Pushkin Pictorial Arts Museum. VERT: (22½ × 33½ mm); No. 1592, Historical Museum; No. 1594, Zoological Museum.

461 Hemispheres and Wireless Mast

1950. International Congress of P.T.T. and Radio Trade Unions, London.
1595 **461** 40 k. green on blue . . . 4·25 4·25
1596 50 k. blue on blue . . . 5·00 5·00

462 Three Workers

463 A. S. Shcherbakov

1950. Labour Day.
1597 **462** 40 k. red and black . . . 3·75 3·00
1598 – 1 r. red and black . . . 5·25 5·25
DESIGN—HORIZ: 1 r. Four Russians and banner.

1950. 5th Death Anniv of Shcherbakov (statesman).
1599 **463** 40 k. black . . . . . . 1·60 1·40
1600 1 r. green on pink . . . 3·25 2·75

464 Marshal Suvorov

465 Statue

1950. 150th Death Anniv of Suvorov.
1601 **464** 40 k. blue on pink . . . 3·25 2·75
1602 – 50 k. brown on pink . . . 4·25 3·25
1603 – 60 k. black on blue . . . 4·25 3·25
1604 **464** 1 r. brown on blue . . . 5·25 4·25
1605 – 2 r. green . . . . . . 10·00 8·25
DESIGNS—VERT: 50 k. Battle (32½ × 47 mm); 60 k. Order of Suvorov and military parade (24½ × 39½ mm); 2 r. Suvorov in cloak (19½ × 33½ mm).

1950. 5th Anniv of Victory over Germany.
1606 **465** 40 k. red and brown . . 3·25 3·25
1607 – 1 r. red . . . . 6·75 3·25
DESIGN—22½ × 33 mm: 1 r. Order of Stalin.

466 Sowing on Collective Farm

1950. Agricultural Workers.
1608 – 40 k. green on blue . . 3·25 2·00
1609 **466** 40 k. brown on buff . . 3·25 2·00
1610 1 r. blue on yellow . . . 5·00 4·25
DESIGNS: No. 1608, Collective farmers studying.

467 G. M. Dimitrov

468 Baku Opera House

1950. 1st Death Anniv of Bulgarian Premier, Dimitrov.
1611 **467** 40 k. black on yellow . . 2·00 2·00
1612 1 r. black on red . . . . 4·75 4·75

1950. 30th Anniv of Azerbaijan S.S.R.
1613 **468** 25 k. green on yellow . . 1·40 1·40
1614 – 40 k. brown on red . . 3·25 3·25
1615 – 1 r. black on buff . . . 5·00 5·00
DESIGNS: 40 k. Science Academy; 1 r. Stalin Avenue, Baku.

469 Lenin Street, Stalingrad

1950. Stalingrad Reconstruction.
1616 – 20 k. blue . . . . 1·25 1·25
1617 **469** 40 k. green . . . . . . 2·10 2·10
1618 – 50 k. orange . . . . . 4·25 4·25
1619 – 1 r. black . . . . . . 5·00 5·00
DESIGNS—VERT: 20 k. Pobeda Cinema. HORIZ: 50 k. Gorky Theatre; 1 r. Pavlov House and Tank Memorial.

470 Kaluzhskaya Station

1950. Underground Railway Stations.
1620 **470** 40 k. green on buff . . 1·00 35
1621 A 40 k. red . . . . 1·00 35
1622 B 40 k. blue on buff . . . 1·00 35
1623 C 1 r. brown on yellow . . 3·00 1·10
1624 D 1 r. violet on blue . . . 3·00 1·10
1625 A 1 r. green on yellow . . 3·00 1·10
1626 E 1 r. black on buff . . . 3·00 1·10
DESIGNS—HORIZ: (34 × 22½ mm): A, Culture Park; B, Taganskaya; C, Kurskaya; D, Paveletskaya. (34 × 18½ mm): E, Taganskaya.

471 National Flags and Civilians

1950. Unconquerable Democracy. Flags in red, blue and yellow.
1627 **471** 40 k. black . . . . . . 1·00 15
1628 50 k. brown . . . . . 2·10 25
1629 1 r. green . . . . . . 2·50 30

472 Trade Union Building

473 Marite Melnikaite

1950. 10th Anniv of Latvian S.S.R.
1630 **472** 25 k. brown 70 85
1631 – 40 k. red . . . . 1·25 1·25
1632 – 50 k. green . . . . . . 2·10 2·10
1633 – 60 k. blue . . . . . . 2·50 2·50
1634 – 1 r. violet . . . . . . 3·75 3·75
1635 – 2 r. brown . . . . . . 6·25 6·25
DESIGNS—VERT: 40 k. Cabinet Council Offices; 50 k. Monument to Jan Rainis (poet); 2 r. Academy of Sciences. HORIZ: 60 k. Theatre, Riga; 1 r. State University, Riga.

1950. 10th Anniv of Lithuanian S.S.R.
1636 – 25 k. blue . . . . 1·00 85
1637 **473** 40 k. brown . . . . . . 2·00 1·60
1638 – 1 r. red . . . . 7·00 5·75
DESIGNS—HORIZ: 25 k. Academy of Sciences; 1 r. Cabinet Council Offices.

474 Stalingrad Square, Tallinn

475 Signing Peace Appeal

1950. 10th Anniv of Estonian S.S.R.
1639 **474** 25 k. green 85 45
1640 – 40 k. red . . . . 1·25 1·00
1641 – 50 k. blue on yellow . . . 2·10 1·90
1642 – 1 r. brown on blue . . . 6·00 6·75
DESIGNS—HORIZ: 40 k. Government building; 50 k. Opera and Ballet Theatre, Tallin. VERT: 1 r. Victor Kingisepp (revolutionary).

1950. Peace Conference.
1643 **475** 40 k. red on buff . . . . 1·60 1·00
1644 – 40 k. black . . . . . . 1·60 80
1645 – 50 k. red . . . . 3·25 2·00
1646 **475** 1 r. brown on buff . . . 5·00 6·75
DESIGNS—VERT: 40 k. black, Children and teacher; 50 k. Young people with banner.

476 Bellingshausan Lazarev and Globe

477 M. V. Frunze

1950. 130th Anniv of 1st Antarctic Expedition.
1647 **476** 40 k. red on blue . . . . 15·00 11·50
1648 – 1 r. violet on blue . . . . 32·00 15·00
DESIGN—VERT: 1 r. "Mirnyi" and "Vostok" (ships) and map of Antarctica.

1950. 25th Death Anniv of Frunze (military strategist).
1649 **477** 40 k. blue on buff . . . 4·00 3·00
1650 1 r. brown on blue . . . 9·25 7·00

478 M. I. Kalinin

479 Picking Grapes

1950. 75th Birth Anniv of Kalinin (statesman).
1651 **478** 40 k. green . . . . . . 1·25 85
1652 1 r. brown . . . . . . 3·00 2·00
1653 5 r. violet . . . . . . 8·25 7·50

1950. 30th Anniv of Armenian S.S.R.
1654 **479** 20 k. blue on buff . . . . 1·40 1·40
1655 – 40 k. orange on blue . . 2·75 2·75
1656 – 1 r. black on yellow . . . 6·00 6·00
DESIGNS—HORIZ: (33 × 16 mm): 40 k. Government Offices. VERT: (21½ × 33 mm): 1 r. G. M. Sundukian (dramatist).

480 Kotelnicheskaya Quay

481 Spassky Tower, Kremlin

1950. Moscow Building Projects.
1657 **480** 1 r. brown on buff . . . 38·00 32·00
1658 – 1 r. black on buff . . . 38·00 32·00
1659 – 1 r. brown on blue . . . 38·00 32·00
1660 – 1 r. green on yellow . . . 38·00 32·00
1661 – 1 r. lilac on buff . . . . 38·00 32·00
1662 – 1 r. black . . . . . . 38·00 32·00
1663 – 1 r. orange . . . . . . 38·00 32·00
1664 – 1 r. green on blue . . . 38·00 32·00
DESIGNS—HORIZ: No. 1659, Vosstaniya Square; No. 1660, Moscow University; No. 1662, Dorogomilovskaya Quay; No. 1664, Smolenskaya Square. VERT: No. 1658, Krasnye Vorota; No. 1661, Komsomolskaya Square; No. 1663, Zariadie.

1950. 33rd Anniv of October Revolution.
1665 **481** 1 r. red, yellow & green . 15·00 10·00

482 "Golden Autumn"

1950. 50th Death Anniv of Levitan (painter).
1666 **482** 40 k. multicoloured . . . 4·25 65
1667 – 50 k. brown . . . . . . 5·75 1·10
PORTRAIT: 50 k. Levitan seated.

483 Aivazovsky (after A. Tyranov)

484 Newspapers "Iskra" and "Pravda"

1950. 50th Death Anniv of Aivazovsky (painter). Multicoloured centres.
1668 – 40 k. brown . . . . . . 3·75 65
1669 – 50 k. brown . . . . . . 5·25 70
1670 **482** 1 r. blue . . . . 7·75 1·90
PAINTINGS—HORIZ: 40 k. "Black Sea"; 50 k. "Ninth Wave".

1950. 50th Anniv of Newspaper "Iskra".
1671 – 40 k. red and black . . . 9·25 9·25
1672 **484** 1 r. red and black . . . 13·50 13·50
DESIGN: 40 k. Newspapers and banners.

485 Government Offices

1950. 30th Anniv of Kazakh S.S.R.
1673 **485** 40 k. black on blue . . . 4·25 2·50
1674 – 1 r. brown on yellow . . 5·00 3·25
DESIGN: 1 r. Opera House, Alma-Ata.

486 Decembrists and Senate Square, St. Petersburg

1950. 125th Anniv of Decembrist Rising.
1675 **486** 1 r. brown on yellow . . 7·25 7·00

487 Govt Offices, Tirana

1951. Friendship with Albania.
1676 **487** 40 k. green on blue . . . 17·00 13·50

488 Greeting Soviet Troops

1951. Friendship with Bulgaria.
1677 **488** 25 k. black on blue . . . 2·25 2·10
1678 – 40 k. orange on pink . . 4·50 4·50
1679 – 60 k. brown on pink . . 6·75 6·75
DESIGNS: 40 k. Lenin Square, Sofia; 60 k. Monument to Soviet fighters, Kolarovgrad.

489 Lenin at Razliv

1951. 27th Death Anniv of Lenin. Multicoloured centres.

1680 **489** 40 k. green . . . . 2·75 65
1681 – 1 r. blue . . . . 5·25 1·10

DESIGN: 1 r. Lenin talking to young Communists.

490 Horses

1951. 25th Anniv of Kirghiz S.S.R.

1682 **490** 25 k. brown on blue . . 4·00 5·00
1683 – 40 k. green on blue . . . 7·75 7·25

DESIGN—33 × 22½ mm: 40 k. Government Offices, Frunze.

490a Gathering Lemons

1951. 30th Anniv of Georgia S.S.R.

1683a – 20 k. green on yellow . 1·50 1·40
1683b **490a** 25 k. orange & purple . 2·50 2·25
1683c – 40 k. brown on blue . 4·25 3·75
1683d – 1 r. green & brown . . 10·00 6·75

DESIGNS—VERT: 20 k. Theatre, Tiflis. HORIZ: 40 k. Main thoroughfare, Tiflis; 1 r. Plucking tea.

491 University, Ulan Bator

1951. Friendship with Mongolia.

1684 **491** 25 k. violet on pink . . . 2·00 1·00
1685 – 40 k. orange on yellow . 2·75 1·25
1686 – 1 r. multicoloured . . . 7·00 4·25

DESIGNS—HORIZ: (37 × 25 mm): 40 k. State Theatre, Ulan Bator. VERT: (22 × 33 mm): 1 r. State Emblem and Mongolian Flag.

492 D. A. Furmanov **493** Soviet Soldiers Memorial, Berlin

1951. 25th Death Anniv of D. A. Furmanov (writer).

1687 **492** 40 k. brown on blue . . 1·90 1·90
1688 – 1 r. black on pink . . . 4·25 3·75

DESIGN—HORIZ: 1 r. Furmanov writing.

1951. Stockholm Peace Appeal.

1689 **493** 40 k. green and red . . . 4·25 3·25
1690 1 r. black and red . . . 9·00 8·00

494 Factories

1951. 150th Anniv of Kirov Machine-building Factory, Leningrad.

1691 **494** 40 k. brown on yellow . 6·75 5·00

495 Bolshoi State Theatre

1951. 175th Anniv of State Theatre.

1692 **495** 40 k. multicoloured . . . 4·75 45
1693 – 1 r. multicoloured . . . 7·00 1·40

DESIGN: 1 r. Medallion portraits of Glinka, Tchaikovsky, Moussorgsky, Rimsky-Korsakov, Borodin and theatre.

496 National Museum, Budapest **497** Harvesting

1951. Hungarian Peoples' Republic. Buildings in Budapest.

1694 – 25 k. green . . . . . . 1·10 1·10
1695 – 40 k. blue . . . . 1·50 1·40
1696 **496** 60 k. black . . . . . . 2·00 2·00
1697 – 1 r. black on pink . . . 5·25 4·50

DESIGNS—HORIZ: 25 k. Liberty Bridge; 40 k. Parliament buildings. VERT: 1 r. Liberation Monument.

1951. Agricultural Scenes.

1698 **497** 25 k. green 85 40
1699 – 40 k. green on blue . . 1·60 85
1700 – 1 r. brown on yellow . . 2·75 2·40
1701 – 2 r. green on pink . . . 4·75 4·75

DESIGNS: 40 k. Apiary; 1 r. Gathering citrus fruit; 2 r. Harvesting cotton.

498 M. I. Kalinin **499** F. E. Dzerzhinsky

1951. 5th Death Anniv of Pres. Kalinin.

1702 – 20 k. sepia and brown . 55 20
1703 **498** 40 k. brown and green . 1·75 35
1704 – 1 r. black and blue . . . 3·25 1·10

DESIGNS—HORIZ: 20 k. Kalinin Museum. VERT: 1 r. Kalinin Statue.

1951. 25th Death Anniv of Dzerzhinsky (founder of Cheka).

1705 **499** 40 k. red . . . . 2·40 75
1706 – 1 r. black (portrait in uniform) . . . . . . 4·25 1·60

500 P. K. Kozlov **501** Kalinnikov

1951. Russian Scientists.

1707 **500** 40 k. orange . . . . . . 1·25 25
1708 – 40 k. orange on pink . . 1·25 25
1709 – 40 k. orange on blue . . 4·00 1·50
1710 – 40 k. brown . . . . . . 1·25 25
1711 – 40 k. brown on pink (facing left) . . . . 1·25 25
1712 – 40 k. brown on pink (facing right) . . . . 1·25 25
1713 – 40 k. grey . . . . 1·25 25
1714 – 40 k. grey on pink . . . 1·25 25
1715 – 40 k. grey on blue . . . 4·00 1·50
1716 – 40 k. green . . . . . . 1·25 25
1717 – 40 k. green on pink . . 1·25 25
1718 – 40 k. blue . . . . 1·25 25
1719 – 40 k. deep blue on pink . 1·25 25
1720 – 40 k. blue on blue . . . 1·25 25
1721 – 40 k. violet . . . . . . 1·25 25
1722 – 40 k. violet on pink . . 1·25 25

PORTRAITS: No. 1708, N. N. Miklukho-Makai; No. 1709, A. M. Butlerov; No. 1710, N. I. Lobachevsky; No. 1711, K. A. Timiryazev; No. 1712, N. S. Kurnakov; No. 1713, P. N. Yablochkov; No. 1714, A. N. Severtsov; No. 1715, K. E. Tsiolkovsky; No. 1716, A. N. Lodygin; No. 1717, A. G. Stoletov; No. 1718, P. N. Lebedev; No. 1719, A. O. Kovalesky; No. 1720, D. I. Mendeleev; No. 1721, S. P. Krasheninnikov; No. 1722, S. V. Kovalevskaya.

1951. Russian Composers.

1723 **501** 40 k. grey on pink . . . 10·00 8·25
1724 – 40 k. brown on pink . . 10·00 8·25

PORTRAIT: No. 1724, Aliabiev and bar of music.

502 Aviation Society Badge **503** V. M. Vasnetsov

1951. Aviation Developement.

1725 **502** 40 k. multicoloured . . . 1·00 15
1726 – 60 k. multicoloured . . . 2·00 20
1727 – 1 r. multicoloured . . . . 3·00 85
1728 – 2 r. multicoloured . . . . 5·75 1·50

DESIGNS—VERT: 60 k. Boys and model gliders; 1 r. Parachutists descending. HORIZ: (45 × 25 mm): 2 r. Flight of Yakovlev Yak-18U trainers.

1951. 25th Death Anniv of Vasnetsov (painter).

1729 **503** 40 k. brown and blue . . 4·00 60
1730 – 1 r. multicolour . . . . 6·00 1·40

DESIGN (47 × 33 mm): 1 r. "Three Heroes".

504 Lenin, Stalin and Dnieperprostroi Dam

1951. 34th Anniv of October Revolution.

1731 **504** 40 k. blue and red . . . . 5·75 2·75
1732 – 1 r. brown and red . . . 7·75 5·25

DESIGN: 1 r. Lenin, Stalin and Spassky Tower.

505 Volga–Don Canal

1951. Construction of Hydro-electric Power Stations.

1733 – 20 k. multicoloured . . . 3·50 2·75
1734 **505** 30 k. multicoloured . . . 4·00 3·50
1735 – 40 k. multicoloured . . . 4·75 4·25
1736 – 60 k. multicoloured . . . 7·25 6·75
1737 – 1 r. multicoloured . . . . 11·50 10·00

DESIGNS—VERT: (32 × 47 mm): 20 k. Khakhovsky power station. HORIZ: (47 × 32 mm); 40 k. Stalingrad dam; 60 k. Excavator and map of Turkmen canal; 1 r. Kuibyshev power station.

506 Signing Peace Petition **507** M. V. Ostrogradsky

1951. 3rd U.S.S.R. Peace Conference.

1738 **506** 40 k. red and brown . . . 9·25 9·25

1951. 150th Birth Anniv of Ostrogradsky (mathematician).

1739 **507** 40 k. brown on pink . . 7·25 4·00

508 Zhizka Monument, Prague **509** Volkhovsky Hydro-electric Station and Lenin Monument

1951. Friendship with Czechoslovakia.

1740 **508** 20 k. blue on pink . . . 2·00 2·00
1741 – 25 k. red on lemon . . . 4·00 4·00
1742 – 40 k. orange on orange . 2·00 2·00
1733 – 60 k. grey . . . . 4·00 4·00
1744 – 1 r. grey . . . . 5·00 5·00

DESIGNS—VERT: 25 k. Soviet Army Monument, Ostrava; 40 k. J. Fucik; 60 k. Smetana Museum, Prague. HORIZ: 1 r. Soviet Soldiers Monument, Prague.

1951. 25th Anniv of Lenin Volkhovsky Hydro-electric Station.

1745a **509** 40 k. yellow and blue . . 85 25
1746 1 r. yellow and violet . . 2·40 35

510 Lenin when a Student **511** P. P. Semenov-Tian-Shansky

1952. 28th Death Anniv of Lenin. Multicoloured centres.

1747 **510** 40 k. green . . . . 2·50 1·10
1748 – 60 k. blue . . . . 2·75 1·10
1749 – 1 r. brown . . . . 2·75 1·60

DESIGNS—HORIZ: 60 k. Lenin and children; 1 r. Lenin talking to peasants.

1952. 125th Birth Anniv of Semenov-Tian-Shansky (scientist).

1750 **511** 1 r. brown on blue . . . 4·00 4·00

512 Skaters **513** V. O. Kovalevsky

1952. Winter Sports.

1751 **512** 40 k. multicoloured . . . 2·75 35
1752 – 60 k. multicoloured (Skiers) 3·25 75

1952. Birth Centenary of Kovalevsky (scientist).

1753 **513** 40 k. brown on yellow . . 5·25 3·00

514 Gogol and Character from "Taras Bulba"

1952. Death Centenary of Nikolai Gogol (writer).

1754 **514** 40 k. black on blue . . . 1·00 20
1755 – 60 k. orange and black . 1·40 30
1756 – 1 r. multicoloured . . . 2·75 1·40

DESIGNS: 60 k. Gogol and Belinsky; 1 r. Gogol and Ukrainian peasants.

515 G. K. Ordzhonikidze **516** Workers and Flag

1952. 15th Death Anniv of Ordzhonikidze (statesman).

1757 **515** 40 k. green on pink . . . 2·75 7·25
1758 1 r. black on blue . . . 4·00 7·25

1952. 15th Anniv of Stalin Constitution.

1759 **516** 40 k. red and black on cream . . . . 4·75 5·00
1760 – 40 k. red and green on green 4·75 5·00
1761 – 40 k. red and brown on blue 4·75 5·00
1762 – 40 k. red and black . . . 4·75 5·00

DESIGNS—HORIZ: No. 1760, Recreation centre; No. 1761, Old people and banners. VERT: No. 1762, Schoolgirl and Spassky Tower Kremlin.

517 Novikov-Priboy and Battleship "Orel" **518** Victor Hugo

1952. 75th Birth Anniv of Novikov-Priboy (writer).

1763 **517** 40 k. grey, yellow & grn . 3·25 80

1952. 150th Birth Anniv of Victor Hugo (French writer).

1764 **518** 40 k. black, blue & brn . 1·10 30

519 Salavat Yulaev **520** G. Ya. Sedov

1952. Birth Bicent of Yulaev (Bashkirian hero).
1765 **519** 40 k. red on pink . . . . 1·40 65

1952. 75th Birth Anniv of Sedov (Arctic explorer).
1766 **520** 40 k. brown, blue & grn . 9·25 8·00

521 Arms and Flag of Rumania **522** V. A. Zhukovsky

1952. Friendship with Rumania.
1767 **521** 40 k. multicoloured . . . 1·40 1·40
1768 – 60 k. green on pink . . . 2·00 2·00
1769 – 1 r. blue . . . . . . 2·75 2·75
DESIGNS—VERT: 60 k. Soviet Soldiers' Monument, Bucharest. HORIZ: 1 r. University Square, Bucharest.

1952. Death Centenary of Zhukovsky (poet).
1770 **522** 40 k. black on blue . . . 1·00 30

523 K. P. Bryullov

1952. Death Centenary of Bryullov (artist).
1771 **523** 40 k. green on blue . . . 1·00 30

524 N. P. Ogarev **525** G. I. Uspensky

1952. 75th Death Anniv of Ogarev (revolutionary writer).
1772 **524** 40 k. green 70 20

1952. 50th Death Anniv of Uspensky (writer).
1773 **525** 40 k. brown and blue . . 1·60 1·00

526 Admiral Nakhimov and "Rotislav" **527** Tartu University

1952. 150th Birth Anniv of Admiral Nakhimov.
1774 **526** 40 k. multicoloured . . . 3·25 2·75

1952. 150th Anniv of Extension of Tartu University.
1775 **527** 40 k. black on salmon . . 2·75 1·60

1952. War Orders and Medals (7th series). Frame as T **282** with various centres.
1776 F 1 r. brown . . . . 11·50 11·50
1777 P 2 r. red 85 65
1778 J 3 r. violet 85 65
1779a A 5 r. lake . . . . 1·00 1·00
1780 E 10 r. red . . . . 1·00 1·00

528 Kayum Nasyri **529** A. N. Radishchev

1952. 50th Death Anniv of Nasyri (educationist).
1781 **528** 40 k. brown on yellow . 2·75 2·50

1952. 150th Death Anniv of Radishchev (writer).
1782 **529** 40 k. black and red . . 2·40 1·00

530 Entrance to Volga–Don Canal **531** P. A. Fedotov

1952. 35th Anniv of Russian Revolution.
1783 **530** 40 k. multicoloured . . 3·25 3·25
1784 – 1 r. yellow, red & brown 6·75 6·75
DESIGN: 1 r. Lenin, Stalin, Spassky Tower and flags.

1952. Death Centenary of Fedotov (painter).
1785 **531** 40 k. brown and lake . . 2·00 85

532 V. D. Polenov **534** Odoevsky (after N. Bestuzhev)

533 "Moscow Courtyard" (painting)

1952. 25th Death Anniv of Polenov (painter).
1786 **532** 40 k. lake and buff . . . 1·50 85
1787 **533** 1 r. blue and grey . . . 3·75 1·60

1952. 150th Birth Anniv of A. I. Odoevsky (poet).
1788 **534** 40 k. black and red . . 1·40 30

535 Mamin-Sibiryak **536** V. M. Bekhterev

1952. Birth Centenary of D. N. Mamin-Sibiryak (writer).
1789 **535** 40 k. green on yellow . . 1·10 50

1952. 25th Death Anniv of Bekhterev (psychiatrist).
1790 **536** 40 k. black, grey & blue 1·50 65

537 Komsomolskaya Koltsevaya Station

1952. Underground Stations. Multicoloured centres.
1791 – 40 k. violet . . . . . . 1·75 55
1792 – 40 k. blue . . . . 1·75 55
1793 – 40 k. grey . . . . 1·75 55
1794 **537** 40 k. green . . . . . . 1·75 55
STATIONS: No. 1791, Byelorussia Koltsevaya; No. 1792, Botanical Gardens; No. 1793, Novoslobodskaya.

538 U.S.S.R. Arms and Flags

1952. 30th Anniv of U.S.S.R.
1795 **538** 1 r. brown, red & grn . . 4·75 3·75

539 Lenin and Flags

1953. 29th Death Anniv of Lenin.
1796 **539** 40 k. multicoloured . . . 5·00 4·25

540 Peace Prize Medal **541** V. V. Kuibyshev

1953. Stalin Peace Prize.
1797 **540** 40 k. yellow, blue & brn . 5·00 5·00

1953. 65th Birth Anniv of Kuibyshev (statesman).
1798 **541** 40 k. black and lake . . . 1·60 1·00

542 V. V. Mayakovsky **543** N. G. Chernyshevsky

1953. 60th Birth Anniv of Mayakovsky (poet).
1799 **542** 40 k. black and red . . . 2·75 2·75

1953. 125th Birth Anniv of Chernyshevsky (writer).
1800 **543** 40 k. brown and buff . . 2·75 2·75

544 R. Volga Lighthouse

1953. Views of Volga–Don Canal. Multicoloured.
1801 40 k. Type **544** . . . . . . 1·50 60
1802 40 k. Lock No. 9 . . . . . 1·50 60
1803 40 k. Lock No. 13 . . . . . 1·50 60
1804 40 k. Lock No. 15 . . . . . 1·50 60
1805 40 k. Tsimlyanskaya hydro-electric station . . . . . 1·50 60
1806 1 r. "Iosif Stalin" (river vessel) 2·50 1·40

545 V. G. Korolenko **546** Tolstoi (after N. Ge)

1953. Birth Centenary of Korolenko (writer).
1807 **545** 40 k. brown . . . . . . 1·10 20

1953. 125th Birth Anniv of Leo Tolstoi (writer).
1808 **546** 1 r. brown . . . . 6·75 5·00

547 Lomonosov University and Students **548** Peoples of the U.S.S.R

1953. 35th Anniv of "Komsomol" (Russian Youth Organization). Multicoloured.
1809 40 k. Type **547** . . . . 2·00 1·90
1810 1 r. Four medals and "Komsomol" badge . . . 5·00 4·75

1953. 36th Anniv of Russian Revolution. Mult.
1811 40 k. Type **548** . . . . 7·25 7·25
1812 60 k. Lenin and Stalin in Smolny Institute, 1917 . . 12·50 12·50

549 Lenin Medallion **550** Lenin Statue

551 Peter I Monument

1953. 50th Anniv of Communist Party.
1813 **549** 40 k. multicoloured . . . 3·75 3·25

1953. Views of Leningrad as T **550/1**.
1814 **550** 40 k. black on yellow . . 1·75 1·50
1815 40 k. brown on pink . . 1·75 80
1816 – 40 k. brown on yellow . 1·60 1·50
1817 – 40 k. black on buff . . . 90 85
1818 **551** 1 r. brown on blue . . . 3·25 3·00
1819 1 r. violet on yellow . . 2·50 2·10
1820 – 1 r. green on pink . . . 3·25 3·00
1821 – 1 r. brown on blue . . . 2·50 2·10
DESIGNS: As Type **550**: Nos. 1816/17, Admiralty. As Type **551**: 1820/1, Smolny Institute.

552 Lenin and Book "What is to be Done?" **553** Pioneers and Moscow University Model

1953. 50th Anniv of 2nd Social Democratic Workers' Party Congress.
1822 **552** 1 r. brown and red . . . 7·25 6·75

1953. Peace Propaganda.
1823 **553** 40 k. black, olive and grey 4·25 4·25

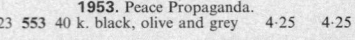

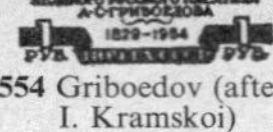

554 Griboedov (after I. Kramskoi) **555** Kremlin

1954. 125th Death Anniv of A. S. Griboedov (author).
1824 **554** 40 k. purple on buff . . 1·50 30
1825a 1 r. black on green . . 1·90 1·00

1954. General Election.
1826 **555** 40 k. grey and red . . . 2·75 2·50

556 V. P. Chkalov

557 Lenin in Smolny Institute

1954. 50th Birthday of Chkalov (aviator).
1827 **556** 1 r. brown, blue and grey . . 3·25 1·10

1954. 30th Death Anniv of Lenin. Multicoloured.
1828 40 k. Lenin (vert) . . . . . . 2·40 1·40
1829 40 k. Type **557** . . . . 2·40 1·40
1830 40 k. Cottage Museum, Ulyanovsk . . . . 2·40 1·40
1831 40 k. Lenin addressing revolutionaries . . . . . . 2·40 1·40
1832 40 k. Lenin at Kazan University 2·40 1·40
Nos. 1829/30 are 38 × 26 mm and 1831/2 48 × 35 mm.

558 Stalin

559 Supreme Soviet Buildings in Kiev and Moscow

1954. 1st Death Anniv of Stalin.
1833 **558** 40 k. brown . . . . . . 3·25 1·40

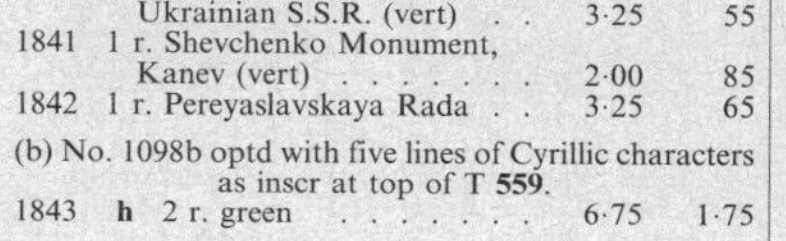

1954. Tercentenary of Reunion of Ukraine with Russia. Multicoloured. (a) Designs as T **559** inscr "1654–1954".
1834 40 k. Type **559** 80 40
1835 40 k. Shevchenko Memorial, Kharkhov (vert) 80 25
1836 40 k. State Opera House, Kiev 80 25
1837 40 k. Shevchenko University, Kiev 80 25
1838 40 k. Academy of Sciences, Kiev 1·50 25
1839 60 k. Bogdan Chmielnitsky Memorial, Kiev (vert) . . . 1·60 25
1840 1 r. Flags of R.S.F.S.R. and Ukrainian S.S.R. (vert) . . 3·25 55
1841 1 r. Shevchenko Monument, Kanev (vert) . . . . 2·00 85
1842 1 r. Pereyaslavskaya Rada . . 3·25 65

(b) No. 1098b optd with five lines of Cyrillic characters as inscr at top of T **559**.
1843 **h** 2 r. green . . . . 6·75 1·75

561 Running

1954. Sports. Frames in brown.
1844 **561** 40 k. black and stone . . 1·00 20
1845 – 40 k. black and blue . . 1·25 20
1846 – 40 k. brown and buff . . 1·00 20
1847 – 40 k. black and blue . . 1·00 20
1848 – 40 k. black . . . . 1·00 20
1849 – 1 r. grey and blue . . . . 4·00 1·50
1850 – 1 r. black and blue . . . 4·00 1·50
1851 – 1 r. brown and drab . . . 4·00 1·50
DESIGNS—HORIZ: No. 1845, Yachting; No. 1846, Cycling; No. 1847, Swimming; No. 1848, Hurdling; No. 1849, Mountaineering; No. 1850, Skiing. VERT: No. 1851, Basketball.

562 Cattle

563 A. P. Chekhov

1954. Agriculture.
1852 **562** 40 k. blue, brown & cream 2·40 35
1853 – 40 k. green, brn & buff . 2·40 35
1854 – 40 k. black, blue and green 2·40 35
DESIGNS: No. 1853, Potato cultivation; No. 1854, Collective farm hydro-electric station.

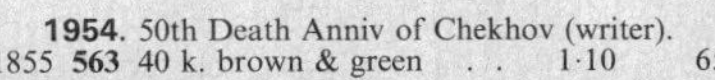

1954. 50th Death Anniv of Chekhov (writer).
1855 **563** 40 k. brown & green . . 1·10 65

564 Bredikhin, Struve, Belopolsky and Observatory

565 M. I. Glinka

1954. Rebuilding of Pulkov Observatory.
1856 **564** 40 k. black, blue & vio . 6·75 1·60

1954. 150th Birth Anniv of Glinka (composer).
1857 **565** 40 k. brown, pink & red 1·90 35
1858 – 60 k. multicoloured . . 2·10 65
DESIGN—HORIZ: (38 × 25½ mm): 60 k. "Glinka playing piano for Pushkin and Zhukovsky" (V. Artamonov).

566 Exhibition Emblem

567 N. A. Ostrovsky

1954. Agricultural Exhibition. Multicoloured.
1859 40 k. Type **566** 55 30
1860 40 k. Agricultural Pavilion . 55 30
1861 40 k. Cattle breeding Pavilion 55 30
1862 40 k. Mechanization Pavilion 55 30
1863 1 r. Exhibition Entrance . . 3·00 1·40
1864 1 r. Main Pavilion . . . . . 3·00 1·40
Nos. 1860/3 are horiz, 1860/1 being 41 × 30½ mm, 1862, 40 × 30 mm and 1863 41 × 33 mm. No. 1864 is vert 29 × 41 mm.

1954. 50th Birth Anniv of Ostrovsky (writer).
1865 **567** 40 k. multicoloured . . 1·90 40

568 Monument

569 Marx, Engels, Lenin and Stalin

1954. Centenary of Defence of Sevastopol.
1866 **568** 40 k. black, brown & grn 1·40 30
1867 – 60 k. black, brn & buff . 1·50 50
1868 – 1 r. multicoloured . . . 3·75 90
DESIGNS—HORIZ: 60 k. Defenders of Sevastopol. VERT: 1 r. Admiral Nakhimov.

1954. 37th Anniv of October Revolution.
1869 **569** 1 r. brown, red & orange 5·00 3·25

570 Kazan University

1954. 150th Anniv of Kazan University.
1870 **570** 40 k. blue on blue . . . 80 30
1871 60 k. red . . . . 2·00 55

571 Salomea Neris

1954. 50th Birth Anniv of Salomea Neris (poetess).
1872 **571** 40 k. multicoloured . . 1·00 25

572 Cultivating Vegetables

573 Stalin

1954. Agriculture. Multicoloured.
1873 40 k. Type **572** . . . . 1·50 30
1874 40 k. Tractor and plough . . 1·50 30
1875 40 k. Harvesting flax (49 × 25½ mm) . . . . 1·50 30
1876 60 k. Harvesting sunflowers (49 × 25½ mm) . . . . . . 2·00 65

1954. 75th Birth Anniv of Stalin.
1877 **573** 40 k. purple . . . . . . 1·00 50
1878 1 r. blue . . . . 2·75 1·40

574 Rubinstein

1954. 125th Birth Anniv of Rubinstein (composer).
1879 **574** 40 k. black and purple . . 1·60 40

575 V. M. Garshin

576 Ilyushin Il-12 over Landscape

1955. Birth Centenary of Garshin (writer).
1880 **575** 40 k. black, brown & grn 1·10 60

1955. Air.
1881 – 1 r. multicoloured . . . . 1·75 60
1882 **576** 2 r. black and green . . . 3·75 75
DESIGN: 1 r. Ilyushin Il-12 over coastline.

577 K. A. Savitsky and "Construction of Railway"

1955. 50th Death Anniv of Savitsky (painter).
1883 **577** 40 k. brown . . . . . . 1·50 20

578 Clasped Hands

579 Pushkin and Mickiewicz

1955. International Conference of Postal and Municipal Workers, Vienna.
1884 **578** 50 k. multicoloured . . . 80 20

1955. 10th Anniv of Russo-Polish Friendship Agreement.
1885 **579** 40 k. multicoloured . . . 2·10 30
1886 – 40 k. black . . . . 2·10 30
1887 – 1 r. multicoloured . . . . 4·75 1·00
1888 – 1 r. multicoloured . . . . 4·75 1·00
DESIGNS: No. 1886, "Brotherhood in Arms" Monument, Warsaw (26½ × 39 mm); No. 1887, Palace of Science, Warsaw (37½ × 25½ mm); No. 1888, Copernicus and Matejko (39 × 26½ mm).

580 Lenin at Shushenskoe

1955. 85th Birth Anniv of Lenin. Multicoloured centres.
1889 **580** 60 k. red . . . . 2·00 30
1890 – 1 r. red . . . . 4·00 60
1891 – 1 r. red . . . . 4·00 60
DESIGNS: No. 1890, Lenin in secret printing house (26½ × 39 mm). As Type **580**: No. 1891, Lenin and Krupskaya at Gorky.

581 Schiller

582 Ilyushin Il-12 over Globe

1955. 150th Death Anniv of Schiller (poet).
1892 **581** 40 k. brown . . . . . . 1·10 85

1955. Air.
1893 **582** 2 r. brown . . . . 4·50 80
1894 2 r. blue . . . . 3·50 95

583 V. Mayakovsky

1955. 25th Death Anniv of Mayakovsky (poet).
1895 **583** 40 k. multicoloured . . . 1·40 30

584 Tadzhik S.S.R. Pavilion

1955. Agricultural Exhibition. Soviet Pavilion. Multicoloured designs with green frames.
1896 40 k. R.S.F.S.R. 65 30
1897 40 k. Byelorussian S.S.R. . . 65 30
1898 40 k. Type **584** 65 30
1899 40 k. Azerbaijan S.S.R. . . . 65 30
1900 40 k. Latvian S.S.R. 65 30
1901 40 k. Lithuanian S.S.R. . . . 65 30
1902 40 k. Karelo-Finnish S.S.R. . 65 30
1903 40 k. Estonian S.S.R. 65 30
1904 40 k. Armenian S.S.R. . . . 65 30
1905 40 k. Ukrainian S.S.R. . . . 65 30
1906 40 k. Georgian S.S.R. . . . 65 30
1907 40 k. Kazakh S.S.R. 65 30
1908 40 k. Turkmen S.S.R. . . . 65 30
1909 40 k. Kirgiz S.S.R. 65 30
1910 40 k. Uzbek S.S.R. 65 30
1911 40 k. Moldavian S.S.R. . . . 65 30

585 M. V. Lomonosov and Building

1955. Bicentenary of Lomonosov University. Multicoloured.
1912 40 k. Type **585** 85 30
1913 1 r. Lomonosov University . 1·60 55

586 A. G. Venetsianov and "The Labours of Spring"

1955. 175th Birth Anniv of Venetsianov (painter). Multicoloured centre.
1914 **586** 1 r. black . . . . 2·75 55

587 A. Lyadov

1955. Birth Centenary of Lyadov (composer).
1915 **587** 40 k. multicoloured . . . 1·50 30

588 A. S. Popov

589 Lenin

590 Revolution Scene

1955. 60th Anniv of Popov's Radio Discoveries. Multicoloured centres.
1916 **588** 40 k. blue . . . . 1·50 20
1917 1 r. brown . . . . 2·75 65

1955. 38th Anniv of Russian Revolution.
1918 **589** 40 k. multicoloured . . . 2·50 1·90
1919 **590** 40 k. multicoloured . . . 1·50 1·90
1920 – 1 r. multicoloured . . . 5·00 3·00
DESIGN: As T **590**: 1 r. Lenin speaking to revolutionaries.

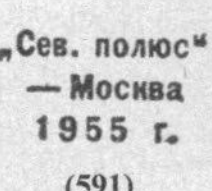

(591)

592 Magnitogorsk

1955. Air. Opening of North Pole Scientific Stations. Nos. 1881/2 optd with T **591**.
1921 – 1 r. multicoloured . . . 8·25 5·00
1922 **576** 2 r. black and green . . . 13·50 5·00

1955. 25th Anniv of Magnitogorsk.
1923 **592** 40 k. multicoloured . . . 1·50 20

593 Mil Mi-4 Helicopter over Station

594 F. I. Shubin

1955. North Pole Scientific Stations.
1924 **593** 40 k. multicoloured . . . 3·25 30
1925 60 k. multicoloured . . . 3·50 65
1926 – 1 r. multicoloured . . . 5·50 1·00
DESIGN: 1 r. Meteorologist taking observations.

1955. 150th Death Anniv of Shubin (sculptor)
1927 **594** 40 k. multicoloured . . . 80 20
1928 1 r. multicoloured . . . 1·50 30

595 A. N. Krylov

596 Racing

1956. 10th Death Anniv of Krylov (scientist).
1929 **595** 40 k. multicoloured . . . 1·10 20

1956. International Horse Racing.
1930 **596** 40 k. sepia and brown . . 75 25
1931 60 k. blue and green . . 1·10 30
1932 – 1 r. purple and blue . . . 2·75 1·10
DESIGN—HORIZ: 1 r. Trotting.

597 Badge and Stadium

598 Atomic Power Station

1956. 5th Spartacist Games.
1933 **597** 1 r. green and purple . . 1·50 35

1956. Foundation of Atomic Power Station of Russian Academy of Sciences.
1934 **598** 25 k. multicoloured . . 1·10 15
1935 – 60 k. yellow, turq & brn 2·00 25
1936 **598** 1 r. yellow, red and blue 2·75 85
DESIGN: 60 k. Top of atomic reactor.

599 Statue of Lenin

1956. 20th Communist Party Congress.
1937 **599** 40 k. multicoloured . . 75 20
1938 1 r. multicoloured . . . 1·90 40

600 Kh. Abovyan

601 Revolutionaries

1956. 150th Birth Anniv of Khatchatur Abovyan (Armenian writer).
1939 **600** 40 k. black on blue . . 85 20

1956. 50th Anniv of 1905 Revolution.
1940 **601** 40 k. multicoloured . . 3·75 1·40

602

1941 ПАВИЛЬОН «УРАЛ»
1942 ПАВИЛЬОН СЕВЕРО-ВОСТОЧНЫХ ОБЛАСТЕЙ
1943 ПАВИЛЬОН ЦЕНТРАЛЬНЫХ ЧЕРНОЗЕМНЫХ ОБЛАСТЕЙ
1944 ПАВИЛЬОН «ЛЕНИНГРАД • СЕВЕРО-ЗАПАД»
1945 ПАВИЛЬОН МОСКОВСКОЙ, ТУЛЬСКОЙ, КАЛУЖСКОЙ, РЯЗАНСКОЙ И БРЯНСКОЙ ОБЛАСТЕЙ
1946 ПАВИЛЬОН БАШКИРСКОЙ АССР
1947 ПАВИЛЬОН ДАЛЬНЕГО ВОСТОКА
1948 ПАВИЛЬОН ТАТАРСКОЙ АССР
1949 ПАВИЛЬОН ЦЕНТРАЛЬНЫХ ОБЛАСТЕЙ
1950 ПАВИЛЬОН ЮНЫХ НАТУРАЛИСТОВ
1951 ПАВИЛЬОН СЕВЕРНОГО КАВКАЗА
1952 ПАВИЛЬОН «СИБИРЬ»
1953 ПАВИЛЬОН «ПОВОЛЖЬЕ»

Inscr at foot as shown above.

1956. Agricultural Exhibition. Multicoloured. Views of Pavilions of U.S.S.R. regions as T **602**. Inscr "ВСХВ".
1941 1 r. Ural . . . . 1·50 40
1942 1 r. North East . . . . . . 1·50 40
1943 1 r. Central Black Soil Region 1·50 40
1944 1 r. Leningrad . . . . . . 1·50 40
1945 1 r. Moscow-Tula-Kaluga-Ryazan-Bryansk . . . . 1·50 40
1946 1 r. Bashkir . . . . 1·50 40
1947 1 r. Far East . . . . 1·50 40
1948 1 r. Tatar . . . . 1·50 40
1949 1 r. Central Regions . . . . 1·50 40
1950 1 r. Young Naturalists . . . 1·50 40
1951 1 r. North Caucasus . . . . 1·50 40
1952 1 r. Siberia . . . . 1·50 40
1953 1 r. Volga . . . . 1·50 40

603 N. A. Kasatkin (painter)

1956. Kasatkin Commemoration.
1954 **603** 40 k. red 70 15

604 A. E. Arkhipov and painting "On the Oka River"

1956. Arkhipov Commemoration.
1955 **604** 40 k. multicoloured . . . 1·40 20
1956 1 r. multicoloured . . . . 2·75 45

605 I. P. Kulibin

606 "Fowler" (after Perov)

1956. 220th Birth Anniv of Kulibin (inventor).
1957 **605** 40 k. multicoloured . . . 1·40 30

1956. Perov Commemoration. Inscr "1956". Multicoloured centres.
1958 – 40 k. green . . . . 1·60 25
1959 **606** 1 r. brown . . . . 3·25 85
1960 – 1 r. brown . . . . 3·25 85
DESIGNS—VERT: No. 1958, V. G. Perov. HORIZ: No. 1960, "Hunters Resting" (after Perov).

607 Lenin speaking

608 N. I. Lobachevsky

1956. 86th Birth Anniv of Lenin.
1961 **607** 40 k. multicoloured . . . 8·25 5·00

1956. Death Cent of Lobachevsky (mathematician).
1962 **608** 40 k. brown 80 15

609 Student Nurses

1956. Red Cross.
1963 **609** 40 k. red, blue & brown . 1·00 30
1964 – 40 k. red, olive & turquoise 1·00 30
DESIGN—$37\frac{1}{2} \times 25\frac{1}{2}$ mm: No. 1964, Nurse and textile factory.

610

611 I. M. Sechenov (scientist)

1956. Air. Opening of North Pole Scientific Station No. 6.
1965 **610** 1 r. multicoloured . . . . 2·50 1·40

1956. Sechenov Commemoration.
1966 **611** 40 k. multicoloured . . . 1·90 65

612 Arsenev

613 I. V. Michurin

1956. V. K. Arsenev (writer).
1967 **612** 40 k. black, violet & pink 2·00 55

1956. Birth Centenary of Michurin (naturalist). Multicoloured centres.
1968 **613** 25 k. brown 45 15
1969 – 60 k. green . . . . . . 1·10 25
1970 **613** 1 r. blue . . . . 2·00 45
DESIGN—$47\frac{1}{2} \times 26\frac{1}{2}$ mm: 60 k. Michurin and children.

614 A. K. Savrasov (painter)

615 N. K. Krupskaya (Lenin's wife)

1956. Savrasov Commemoration.
1971 **614** 1 r. brown and yellow . 1·40 50

1956. Krupskaya Commemoration.
1972 **615** 40 k. brown, black & bl . 1·60 20
For similar stamps see Nos. 2005, 2027, 2115 and 2169.

616 S. M. Kirov

617 A. A. Blok

1956. 70th Birth Anniv of Kirov (statesman).
1973 **616** 40 k. multicoloured . . . 65 15

1956. Blok (poet) Commemoration.
1974 **617** 40 k. brown, blk & olive 80 15

618 N. S. Leskov

619 Factory Building

1956. 125th Birth Anniv of Leskov (writer).
1975 **618** 40 k. multicoloured . . . 65 15
1976 1 r. multicoloured . . . 1·75 40

1956. 25th Anniv of Rostov Agricultural Machinery Works.
1977 **619** 40 k. multicoloured . . . 75 2

620 G. N. Fedotova (actress)

1956. Fedotova Commemoration.
1978 **620** 40 k. multicoloured . . . 65 20
For similar stamp see No. 2159.

621 P. M. Tretyakov and Art Gallery

1956. Centenary of Tretyakov Art Gallery.
1979 **621** 40 k. multicoloured . . . 1·75 45
1980 – 40 k. multicoloured . . . 1·75 45
DESIGN—VERT: No. 1980, "Rooks have arrived" (painting by Savrasov).

622 Relay-race

1956. Spartacist Games.
1981 **622** 10 k. red 30 10
1982 – 25 k. brown 40 10
1983 – 25 k. multicoloured . . . 40 15
1984 – 25 k. blue 40 15
1985 – 40 k. blue 65 15
1986 – 40 k. green 65 15
1987 – 40 k. brown and green . 65 15
1988 – 40 k. deep brown, brown and green 65 15
1989 – 40 k. red, green and light green 65 15
1990 – 40 k. brown 65 15
1991 – 40 k. multicoloured . . . 65 15
1992 – 60 k. violet . . . . . . 1·60 25
1993 – 60 k. violet . . . . . . 1·60 25
1994 – 1 r. brown . . . . 2·75 1·00
DESIGNS—VERT: No. 1982, Volleyball; 1983, Swimming; 1984, Rowing; 1985, Diving; 1989, Flag and stadium; 1990, Tennis; 1991, Medal; 1993, Boxing. HORIZ: No. 1986, Cycle racing; 1987, Fencing; 1988, Football; 1992, Gymnastics; 1994, Netball.

623 Parachutist Landing

624 Construction Work

1956. 3rd World Parachute-jumping Competition.
1995 **623** 40 k. multicoloured . . . 75 25

1956. Builders' Day.
1996a **624** 40 k. orange 65 25
1997 – 60 k. brown 80 30
1998 – 1 r. blue . . . . 2·50 50
DESIGNS: 60 k. Plant construction; 1 r. Dam construction.

625 I. E. Repin and "Volga River Boatmen"

626 "Reply of the Cossacks to Sultan Mahmoud IV"

1956. Repin (painter) Commemoration.
1999 **625** 40 k. multicoloured . . . 3·75 45
2000 **626** 1 r. multicoloured . . . 7·25 1·00

627 Robert Burns

628 Ivan Franko

1956. 160th Death Anniv of Burns (Scots poet).
2001 **627** 40 k. brown . . . . . . 7·25 5·25
2002 40 k. brown and blue . . 4·75 3·25

1956. Birth Cent of Franko (writer) (1st issue).
2003 **628** 40 k. purple 65 50
2004 1 r. blue . . . . 1·25 65
See also No. 2037.

1956. Lesya Ukrainka Commemoration. As T **615** but portrait of Ukrainka (author).
2005 40k. black, brown & green 65 40

629 M. Aivazov (farmer)

630 Statue of Nestor

1956. 148th Birthday of Aivazov. (a) Wrongly inscr "Muhamed" (7 characters).
2006 **629** 40 k. green . . . . . . 23·00 23·00
(b) Corrected to "Makmud" (6 characters).
2006a **629** 40 k. green . . . . . . 8·25 8·25

1956. 900th Birth Anniv of Nestor (historian).
2007 **630** 40 k. multicoloured . . 1·00 20
2008 1 r. multicoloured . . . 2·10 40

631 A. A. Ivanov

632 Feeding Poultry

1956. 150th Birth Anniv of Ivanov (painter).
2009 **631** 40 k. brown and grey . . 65 20

1956. Agriculture. Multicoloured.
2010 10 k. Type **632** 35 10
2011 10 k. Harvesting 35 10
2012 25 k. Gathering maize . . . 75 20
2013 40 k. Maize field . . . . . 1·10 20
2014 40 k. Tractor station . . . . 1·10 20
2015 40 k. Cattle grazing . . . . 1·10 20
2016 40 k. "Agriculture and Industry" . . . . 1·10 20
SIZES: Nos. 2010, 2014/5, 37 × 25½ mm. Nos. 2011/3, 37 × 28 mm. No. 2016, 37 × 21 mm.

633 Mozart

634 Mirnyi Base and Supply Ship "Lena"

1956. Cultural Anniversaries.
2017 40 k. blue (Type **633**) . . . 1·90 40
2018 40 k. green (Curie) . . . . . 1·90 40
2019 40 k. lilac (Heine) . . . . . 1·90 40
2020 40 k. brown (Ibsen) . . . . 1·90 40
2021 40 k. green (Dostoevsky) . . 1·90 40
2022 40 k. brown (Franklin) . . . 1·90 40
2023 40 k. black (Shaw) . . . . . 2·00 40
2024 40 k. orange (Sessku-Toyo Oda) 1·90 40
2025 40 k. black (Rembrandt) . . 1·90 40
Nos. 2022/5 are larger 25 × 38 mm.

1956. Soviet Scientific Antarctic Expedition.
2026 **634** 40 k. turquoise, red & grey 5·50 80

1956. Julia Zhemaite Commemoration. As T **615** but portrait of Zhemaite (author).
2027 40 k. green, brown & sepia . . 80 20

635 F. A. Bredikhin

636 G. I. Kotovsky

1956. 125th Birth Anniv of Bredikhin (astronomer).
2028 **635** 40 k. multicoloured . . 5·00 1·40

1956. 75th Birth Anniv of Kotovsky (military leader).
2029 **636** 40 k. mauve . . . . . . 1·40 65

MINIMUM PRICE

The minimum price quoted is 10p which represents a handling charge rather than a basis for valuing common stamps. For further notes about prices, see introductory pages.

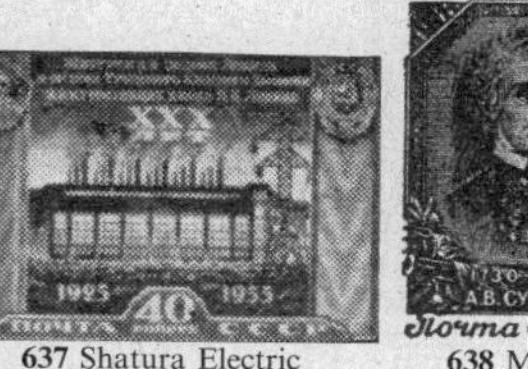
637 Shatura Electric Power Station

638 Marshal Suvorov

1956. 30th Anniv of Shatura Electric Power Station.
2030 **637** 40 k. multicoloured . . . 75 20

1956. 225th Birth Anniv of Marshal Suvorov.
2031 **638** 40 k. lake and orange . . 60 20
2032 1 r. brown and olive . . . 2·00 45
2033 3 r. black and brown . . 4·50 1·40

639 Kryakutni's Ascent

1956. 225th Anniv of First Balloon Flight by Kryakutni.
2034 **639** 40 k. multicoloured . . . 1·75 40

640 "Dawn at the Voskresenski Gate"

1956. 30th Death Anniv of A. M. Vasnetsov (artist).
2035 **640** 40 k. multicoloured . . . 1·40 55

641 Y. M. Shokalsky

642 Ivan Franko

1956. Birth Cent of Shokalsky (oceanographer).
2036 **641** 40 k. brown and blue . . 1·60 50

1956. Birth Centenary of Franko (writer) (2nd issue).
2037 **642** 40 k. green 55 20

643 Indian Temple and Books

644 F. G. Vokov (actor) and State Theatre

1956. Kalidasa (Indian poet) Commemoration
2038 **643** 40 k. red 55 20

1956. Bicentenary of Leningrad State Theatre.
2039 **644** 40 k. black, red & yellow 60 20

645 Lomonosov at St. Petersburg University

1956. Russian Writers.
2040 **645** 40 k. multicoloured . . . 80 25
2041 – 40 k. multicoloured . . . 80 25
2042 – 40 k. brown and blue . . 80 25
2043 – 40 k. olive, brown & blk . 80 25
2044 – 40 k. brown and turquoise 80 25
2045 – 40 k. purple and brown . 80 25
2046 – 40 k. olive and blue . . 80 25
DESIGNS: No. 2041, Gorky and scene from "Mother" (novel); No. 2042, Pushkin and "Bronze Horseman" (statue); No. 2043, Rustavely and episode from "The Knight in the Tiger Skin" (poem); No. 2044, Tolstoy and scene from "War and Peace" (novel); No. 2045, V. G. Belinsky and titles of literary works; No. 2046, M. Y. Lermontov and Daryal Pass.
See also Nos. 2076, 2089/90, 2256, 2316/22 and 2458.

646 Vitus Bering and Routes of his Voyages

647 Mendeleev

1956. 275th Birth Anniv of Bering (explorer).
2047 **646** 40 k. multicoloured . . . 3·00 35

1957. 50th Death Anniv of Dmitri Mendeleev (chemist).
2048 **647** 40 k. brown, grey & blk 1·60 65

648 M. I. Glinka

649 Youth Festival Emblem

1957. Death Centenary of Glinka (composer). Mult.
2049a 40 k. Type **648** . . . . . 1·10 20
2050a 1 r. Scene from "Ivan Susanin" 2·10 55

1957. All Union Festival of Soviet Youth.
2051 **649** 40 k. multicoloured . . . 40 15

650 Ice Hockey Player

651 Youth Festival Emblem and Pigeon

1957. 23rd World and 35th European Ice Hockey Championships, Moscow.
2052 – 25 k. violet 90 15
2053 **650** 40 k. blue 65 15
2054 – 60 k. green . . . . . . 1·00 30
DESIGNS: 25 k. Championship emblem; 60 k. Goal-keeper.

1957. 6th World Youth Festival, Moscow. (1st issue). Perf or imperf.
2055 **651** 40 k. multicoloured . . . 70 15
2056 60 k. multicoloured . . . 1·10 20
See also Nos. 2084/7 and 2108/11.

652 Factory Plant

653 Sika Deer

1957. Cent of "Red Proletariat" Plant. Moscow.
2057 **652** 40 k. multicoloured . . . 1·00 25

1957. Russian Wildlife. Multicoloured.
2057a 10 k. Grey partridge . . . . 1·00 30
2058 15 k. Black grouse . . . . 1·00 15
2058a 15 k. Polar bear 70 40
2059 20 k. Type **653** 75 15
2059a 20 k. Brown hare 60 25
2059b 25 k. Tiger 75 25
2059c 25 k. Wild horse 75 25
2060 30 k. Mallard . . . . . . 1·25 25
2061 30 k. European bison . . . 75 20
2062 40 k. Elk . . . . 1·90 35
2063 40 k. Sable . . . . 1·90 35
2063a 40 k. Eurasian red squirrel . 80 30
2063b 40 k. Yellow-throated marten 80 30
2063c 60 k. Hazel grouse . . . . 2·75 55
2063d 1 r. Mute swan . . . . . 3·75 1·00
Nos. 2058/a, 2059a/62, 2063a/b and 2063d are horiz.
See also Nos. 2534/6.

654 Vologda Lace-making

655 G. V. Plekhanov

1957. Regional Handicrafts. Multicoloured.
2064 40 k. Moscow wood-carving . . 1·50 25
2065 40 k. Woman engraving vase . . 1·50 25
2066 40 k. Type **654** . . . . . . 1·50 25
2067 40 k. Northern bone-carving . . 1·50 25
2067a 40 k. Wood-block engraving . . 1·00 50
2067b 40 k. Turkmen carpet-weaving . 1·00 50

1957. Birth Centenary of Plekhanov (politician).
2068 **655** 40 k. plum . . . . 1·00 20

656 A. N. Bakh

657 L. Euler

1957. Birth Centenary of Bakh (biochemist).
2069 **656** 40 k. multicoloured . . . 1·10 25

1957. 250th Birth Anniv of Euler (mathematician).
2070 **657** 40 k. black and purple . . 1·40 30

658 Lenin in Meditation

659 Dr. William Harvey

1957. 87th Birth Anniv of Lenin. Multicoloured.
2071 40 k. Type **658** 80 20
2072 40 k. Lenin carrying pole . . . 80 20
2073 40 k. Talking with soldier and sailor 80 20

1957. 300th Death Anniv of Dr. William Harvey (discoverer of circulation of blood).
2074 **659** 40 k. brown 75 15

660 M. A. Balakirev

661 12th-century Narrator

1957. 120th Birth Anniv of Balakirev (composer).
2075 **660** 40 k. black 75 20

1957. "The Tale of the Host of Igor".
2076 **661** 40 k. multicoloured . . . 80 20

662 Agricultural Medal

663 A. I. Herzen and N. P. Ogarev (writers)

1957. Cultivation of Virgin Soil.
2077 **662** 40 k. multicoloured . . . 1·10 25

1957. Centenary of Publication of Magazine "Kolokol".
2078 **663** 40 k. brown, blk & blue . . 80 25

664 Monument

250 лет
Ленинграда
(665)

1957. 250th Anniv of Leningrad. Vert designs as T **664** and stamps as Nos. 1818 and 1820 optd as T **665**.
2079 **664** 40 k. green 50 15
2080 – 40 k. violet 50 15
2081 – 40 k. brown 50 15
2082 **551** 1 r. brown on green . . 1·00 25
2083 – 1 r. green on salmon . . 1·00 25
DESIGNS: No. 2080, Nevsky Prospect, Leningrad; No. 2081, Lenin Statue.

666 Youths with Banner

1957. 6th World Youth Festival, Moscow (2nd issue). Multicoloured. Perf or imperf.
2084 10 k. Type **666** 25 10
2084a 20 k. Sculptor with statue . . 40 15
2085 25 k. Type **666** 80 15
2086 40 k. Dancers 85 15
2087 1 r. Festival emblem and fireworks over Moscow State University . . . . 1·10 30

667 A. M. Lyapunov

668 T. G. Shevchenko (after I. Repin) and Scene from "Katharina"

1957. Birth Centenary of Lyapunov (mathematician).
2088 **667** 40 k. brown . . . . . . 5·75 4·00

1957. 19th-Century Writers. Multicoloured.
2089 40 k. Type **668** 65 20
2090 40 k. N. G. Chernyshevsky and scene from "What is to be Done?" 65 20

669 Henry Fielding

670 Racing Cyclists

1957. 250th Birth Anniv of Fielding (novelist).
2091 **669** 40 k. multicoloured . . . 45 15

1957. 10th International Cycle Race.
2092 **670** 40 k. multicoloured . . . 1·00 25

671 Interior of Observatory

1957. International Geophysical Year (1st issue).
2093 **671** 40 k. brown, yellow and blue 65 40
2094 – 40 k. indigo, yellow and blue . . . . 2·00 40
2095 – 40 k. violet & lavender . 1·60 1·00
2095a – 40 k. blue . . . . . . 2·00 30
2095b – 40 k. green . . . . . . 2·50 40
2095c – 40 k. yellow and blue . 2·00 30
DESIGNS—As T **671**: No. 2094, Meteor in sky; 2095a, Malakhit radar scanner and balloon (meteorology); 2095b, "Zarya" (non-magnetic research schooner) (geo-magnetism); 2095c, Northern Lights and C-180 camera. 15×21 mm: No. 2095, Rocket.
See also Nos. 2371/3a.

672 Gymnast

1957. 3rd International Youth Games.
2096 **672** 20 k. brown and blue . . 20 10
2097 – 25 k. red and green . . . 25 10
2098 – 40 k. violet and red . . . 60 20
2099 – 40 k. olive, red and green 60 20
2100 – 60 k. brown and blue . . 1·10 40
DESIGNS—As Type **672**: No. 2097, Wrestlers; No. 2098, Young athletes; No. 2099, Moscow Stadium; No. 2100, Javelin thrower.

673 Football

674 Yanka Kupala

1957. Russian Successes at Olympic Games, Melbourne.
2101 – 20 k. brown, blue & blk . 30 10
2102 – 20 k. red and green . . . 30 10
2103 – 25 k. blue and orange . . 30 15
2104 **673** 40 k. multicoloured . . . 50 15
2105 – 40 k. brown and purple . 50 15
2106 – 60 k. brown and violet . 80 40
DESIGNS—VERT: No. 2101, Throwing the javelin; No. 2102, Running; No. 2103, Gymnastics; No. 2105, Boxing; No. 2106, Weightlifting.

1957. 75th Birth Anniv of Kupala (poet).
2107 **674** 40 k. brown . . . . . . 4·00 2·00

675 Moscow State University

676 Lenin Library

1957. 6th World Youth Festival (3rd issue). Moscow Views.
2108 – 40 k. black and brown . . 55 15
2109 – 40 k. black and purple . . 55 15
2110 – 1 r. black and blue . . . 1·10 30
2111 **675** 1 r. black and red . . . . 1·10 30
DESIGNS—HORIZ: No. 2108, Kremlin; No. 2109, Stadium; No. 2110, Bolshoi State Theatre.

1957. Int Philatelic Exn, Moscow. Perf or imperf.
2112 **676** 40 k. turquoise 45 20

677 Dove of Peace encircling Globe

678 P. Beranger

1957. "Defence of Peace".
2113 **677** 40 k. multicoloured . . . 1·10 40
2114 1 r. multicoloured . . . . 2·50 1·25

1957. Birth Centenary of Clara Zetkin (German revolutionary). As T **615** but portrait of Zetkin.
2115 40 k. multicoloured . . . . . 1·00 20

1957. Death Centenary of Beranger (French poet).
2116 **678** 40 k. green . . . . 1·10 20

679 Krengholm Factory, Narva

680 Factory Plant and Statue of Lenin

1957. Centenary of Krengholm Textile Factory, Narva, Estonia.
2117 **679** 40 k. brown . . . . . . 1·00 20

1957. Centenary of Krasny Vyborzhetz Plant, Leningrad.
2118 **680** 40 k. blue 50 25

681 V. V. Stasov

682 Pigeon with Letter

1957. 50th Death Anniv of Stasov (art critic).
2119 **681** 40 k. brown 55 15
2120 1 r. blue . . . . 1·40 20

1957. International Correspondence Week.
2121 **682** 40 k. blue 35 20
2122 60 k. purple 85 25

683 K. E. Tsiolkovsky

684 Congress Emblem

1957. Birth Centenary of Tsiolkovsky (scientist).
2123 **683** 40 k. multicoloured . . . 6·75 1·40

1957. 4th World T.U.C., Leipzig.
2124 **684** 40 k. blue on blue . . . 45 20

685 Students

686 Workers and Emblem (Ukrane)

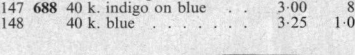

687 Lenin

688 Satellite encircling Globe

1957. 40th Anniv of Russian Revolution. (a) 1st issue. As T **685**. Multicoloured. Perf or imperf.
2125 10 k. Type **685** 20 10
2126 40 k. Railway worker (horiz) 50 30
2127 40 k. Portrait of Lenin on banner 30 10
2128 40 k. Lenin and workers with banners 40 25
2129 60 k. Harvester (horiz) . . . 1·10 60
(b) 2nd issue. As T **686**, designs representing the Soviet Republics. Multicoloured.
2130 **686** 40 k. Ukraine 55 30
2131 – 40 k. Estonia 55 30
2132 – 40 k. Uzbekistan 55 30
2133 – 40 k. R.S.F.S.R. 75 30
2134 – 40 k. Byelorussia 55 30
2135 – 40 k. Lithuania 55 30
2136 – 40 k. Armenia 55 30
2137 – 40 k. Azerbaijan 55 30
2138 – 40 k. Georgia 55 30
2139 – 40 k. Kirghizia 55 30
2140 – 40 k. Turkmenistan . . . 55 30
2141 – 40 k. Tadzhikistan . . . 55 30
2142 – 40 k. Kazakhstan . . . 55 30
2143 – 40 k. Latvia 55 30
2144 – 40 k. Moldavia 55 30
(c) 3rd Issue. As T **687**.
2145 **687** 40 k. blue . . . . . . 1·90 85
2146 – 60 k. red . . . . . . 1·90 80
DESIGN—HORIZ: 60 k. Lenin at desk.

1957. Launching of 1st Artifical Satellite.
2147 **688** 40 k. indigo on blue . . 3·00 85
2148 40 k. blue . . . . 3·25 1·00

689 Meteor Falling

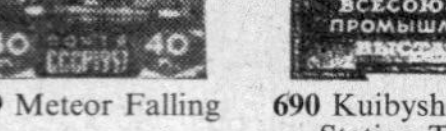
690 Kuibyshev Power Station Turbine

1957. Sikhote-Alin Meteor.
2149 **689** 40 k. multicoloured . . . 2·40 1·10

1957. All Union Industrial Exhibition (1st issue).
2150 **690** 40 k. brown 85 20
See also Nos. 2168.

4/X-57 г. Первый в мире искусств. спутник Земли
(691)

692 Soviet War Memorial, Berlin

1957. First Artificial Satellite of the World. Optd with T **691**.
2151 **683** 40 k. multicoloured . . . 30·00 22·00

1957. Bicentenary of Academy of Arts, Moscow.
2152 – 40 k. black on salmon . . 25 10
2153 **692** 60 k. black 80 15
2154 – 1 r. black on pink . . . 1·60 30
DESIGNS—$25\frac{1}{2}\times37\frac{1}{2}$ mm: 40 k. Academy and portraits of Bryullov, Repin and Surikov. $21\frac{1}{2}\times32$ mm: 1 r. Worker and Peasant Memorial, Moscow.

693 Arms of Ukraine

694 Garibaldi

1957. 40th Anniv of Ukraine S.S.R.
2155 **693** 40 k. multicoloured . . . 85 15

1957. 150th Birth Anniv of Garibaldi.
2156 **694** 40 k. purple, maroon and green 65 15

695 Edvard Grieg

696 Borovikovsky

1957. 50th Death Anniv of Grieg (composer).
2157 **695** 40 k. black on salmon . . 1·00 20

1957. Birth Bicent of Borovikovsky (painter).
2158 **696** 40 k. brown 65 15

1967. M. N. Ermolova (actress). Commemoration. As T **620** but portrait of Ermolova.
2159 40 k. brown and violet . . . 1·00 15

698 Y. Kolas

699 V. M. Kapsukas

700 G. Z. Bashindzhagian

1957. 75th Birth Anniv of Kolas (poet).
2160 **698** 40 k. black . . . . 2·40 1·50

1957. Kapsukas (Communist Party leader) Commem.
2161 **699** 40 k. brown . . . . . . 2·40 1·50

1957. Bashindzhagian (artist) Commemoration.
2162 **700** 40 k. brown . . . . . . 2·40 1·50

701 Kuibyshev Hydro-electric Station

702 Allegory of Progress

1957. 40th Anniv of Kuibyshev Hydro-electric Station.
2163 **701** 40 k. blue on flesh . . . 90 20

1957. Launching of 2nd Artificial Satellite.
2164 **702** 20 k. red and black . . . 1·00 10
2165 40 k. green and black . . . 1·40 15
2166 60 k. brown and black . . . 1·90 15
2167 1 r. blue and black . . . 2·50 45

703 Allegory of Industry

704 Tsi Bai–shi

1958. All Union Industrial Exn (2nd issue).
2168 **703** 60 k. red, black & lav . . 1·00 20

1958. Rosa Luxemburg Commemoration. As T **615** but portrait of Luxemburg (German revolutionary).
2169 40 k. brown and blue . . . 1·00 20

1958. Tsi Bai-shi (Chinese artist) Commem.
2170 **704** 40 k. violet 75 20

705 Linnaeus (Carl von Linne)

706 Tolstoi

1958. 250th Birth Anniv of Linnaeus.
2171 **705** 40 k. brown . . . . . . 3·25 75

1958. 75th Birth Anniv of A. N. Tolstoi (writer).
2172 **706** 40 k. bistre 65 20

707 Soldier, Sailor and Airman

708 E. Charents

1958. 40th Anniv of Red Army. Multicoloured.
2173 25 k. Battle of Narva, 1918 . 40 15
2174 40 k. Type **707** 60 20
2175 40 k. Soldier and blast-furnaceman (vert) 60 20
2176 40 k. Soldier and sailor (vert) 60 20
2177 60 k. Storming the Reichstag, 1945 . . . . 1·50 55

1958. Charents (Armenian poet) Commemoration.
2178 **708** 40 k. brown . . . . . . 2·40 2·00

709 Henry W. Longfellow

710 Blake

1958. 150th Birth Anniv of Longfellow.
2179 **709** 40 k. black . . . . . . 2·40 2·00

1958. Birth Bicentenary of William Blake (poet).
2180 **710** 40 k. black . . . . . . 2·40 2·40

711 Tchaikovsky

712 Admiral Rudnev and Cruiser "Varyag"

1958. Tchaikovsky International Music Competition, Moscow.
2181 **711** 40 k. multicoloured . . 85 30
2181 – 40 k. multicoloured . . 85 30
2183a – 1 r. purple and green . 3·25 1·00
DESIGNS—HORIZ: No. 2182, Scene from "Swan Lake" ballet. VERT: No. 2183, Pianist, violinist and inset portrait of Tchaikovsky.

1958. 45th Death Anniv of Admiral Rudnev.
2184 **712** 40 k. multicoloured . . 1·90 45

713 Gorky (writer)

714 Congress Emblem and Spassky Tower, Kremlin

1958. Gorky Commemoration.
2185 **713** 40 k. multicoloured . . . 1·00 20

1958. 13th Young Communists' League Congress, Moscow.
2186 **714** 40 k. violet on pink . . . 55 15
2187 60 k. red on flesh 80 20

715 Russian Pavilion

716 J. A. Komensky ("Comenius")

1958. Brussels Int Exhibition. Perf or imperf.
2188 **715** 10 k. multicoloured . . . 15 10
2189 40 k. multicoloured . . . 65 15

1958. Komensky Commem.
2190 **716** 40 k. green . . . . 3·25 1·40

717 Lenin

200 лет Академии художеств СССР. 1957
(718)

1958. Lenin Commemoration.
2191 **717** 40 k. blue 45 10
2192 60 k. red 55 25
2193 1 r. brown . . . . 1·50 45

1958. Bicentenary of Russian Academy of Artists. Optd with T **718**.
2194 **557** 40 k. multicoloured . . . 6·00 2·00

719 C. Goldoni

720 Lenin Prize Medal

1958. 250th Birth Anniv of C. Goldoni (Italian dramatist).
2195 **719** 40 k. brown and blue . . 1·00 15

1958. Lenin Prize Medal.
2196 **720** 40 k. red, yellow & brown 65 15

721 Karl Marx

1958. Karl Marx Commemoration.
2197 **721** 40 k. brown 65 15
2198 60 k. blue 80 25
2199 1 r. red . . . . 2·10 35

722 Federation Emblem

723 Radio Beacon, Airliner and Freighter

1958. 4th International Women's Federation Congress.
2200 **722** 40 k. blue and black . . . 45 15
2201 60 k. blue and black . . . 1·00 20

1958. Radio Day.
2202 **723** 40 k. green and red . . . 2·25 30

724 Chavchavadze

725 Flags of Communist Countries

1958. Chavchavadze (Georgian poet) Commem.
2203 **724** 40 k. black and blue . . 65 15

1958. Socialist Countries' Postal Ministers Conference, Moscow.
2204 **725** 40 k. multicoloured (A) . 17·00 6·75
2205 40 k. multicoloured (B) . 10·00 6·75
Central flag to left of inscription is in red, white and mauve. (A) has red at top and white at foot, (B) is vice versa.

726 Camp Bugler

727 Negro, European and Chinese Children

1958. "Pioneers" Day. Inscr "1958".
2206 **726** 10 k. multicoloured . . . 20 10
2207 – 25 k. multicoloured . . . 50 20
DESIGN: 25 k. Pioneer with model airplane.

1958. International Children's Day. Inscr "1958".
2208 **727** 40 k. multicoloured . . . 65 20
2209 – 40 k. multicoloured . . . 65 20
DESIGN: No. 2209, Child with toys, and atomic bomb.

728 Fooballers and Globe

729 Rimsky-Korsakov

1958. World Cup Football Championship, Sweden. Perf or imperf.
2210 **728** 40 k. multicoloured . . . 85 20
2211 60 k. multicoloured . . . 1·40 40

1958. Rimsky-Korsakov (composer) Commem.
2212 **729** 40 k. brown and blue . . 1·10 20

730 Athlete

1958. 14th World Gymnastic Championships, Moscow. Inscr "XIV". Multicoloured.
2213 40 k. Type **730** 60 15
2214 40 k. Gymnast 60 15

731 Young Construction Workers

1958. Russian Youth Day.
2215 **731** 40 k. orange and blue . 50 15
2216 60 k. orange and green . 60 20

732 Atomic Bomb, Globe, Sputniks, Atomic Symbol and "Lenin" (atomic ice-breaker)

733 Rifleman and Gun Crew

1958. International Disarmament Conf, Stockholm.
2217 **732** 60 k. black, orge & bl . 3·75 65

1958. 40th Anniv of Ukrainian Communist Party.
2218 **733** 40 k. violet and red . . . 1·00 30

734 Silhouette of Moscow State University

735 Sadruddin Aini

1958. 5th Int Architects Union Congress, Moscow.
2219 **734** 40 k. blue and red . . . 1·00 15
2220 – 60 k. multicoloured . . . 1·40 25
DESIGN—VERT: 60 k. "U.I.A. Moscow 1958" in square panel of bricks and "V" in background.

1958. 80th Birth Anniv of Sadruddin Aini (Tadzhik writer).
2221 **735** 40 k. red, black & buff . 55 15

736 Third Artificial Satellite

737 Conference Emblem

1958. Launching of 3rd Artificial Satellite.
2222 **736** 40 k. red, blue & green . 1·60 50

1958. 1st World T.U. Young Workers' Conf, Prague.
2223 **737** 40 k. blue and purple . . 30 20

738 Tupolev Tu-110

1958. Civil Aviation. Perf or imperf.
2224 – 20 k. black, red & blue . 50 10
2225 – 40 k. black, red & green . 65 15
2226 – 40 k. black, red & blue . 65 15
2227 – 60 k. red, buff & blue . 65 20
2228 **738** 60 k. black and red . . . 65 20
2229 – 1 r. black, red & orange . 1·50 30
2230 – 2 r. black, red & purple . 2·75 45
DESIGNS—Russian aircraft flying across globe: No. 2224, Ilyushin Il-14M; 2225, Tupolev Tu-104; 2226, Tupolev Tu-114; 2229, Antonov An-10; 2230, Ilyushin Il-18B. No. 2227, Global air routes.

739 L. A. Kulik (scientist)

1958. 50th Anniv of Tunguz Meteor.
2231 **739** 40 k. multicoloured . . . 1·90 40

740 Crimea Observatory

741 15th-century Scribe

1958. 10th International Astronomical Union Congress, Moscow.
2232 **740** 40 k. turquoise & brown 1·25 30
2233 – 60 k. yellow, violet & bl . 1·60 30
2234 – 1 r. brown and blue . . 2·00 50
DESIGNS—HORIZ: 60 k. Moscow University. VERT: 1 r. Telescope of Moscow Observatory.

1958. Centenary of 1st Russian Postage Stamp.
2235 **741** 10 k. multicoloured . . . 15 10
2236 – 10 k. multicoloured . . . 15 10
2237 – 25 k. blue, black & green 30 10
2238 – 25 k. black and blue . . 30 10
2239 – 40 k. brown, pur & sep 40 15
2240 – 40 k. lake and brown . . 40 15
2241 – 40 k. black, orange and red 40 15
2242 – 60 k. turquoise, blk & vio 1·50 25
2243 – 60 k. black, turquoise and purple . . . . 1·10 25
2244 – 1 r. multicoloured . . . 1·90 85
2245 – 1 r. purple, black and orange . . . . . . 1·90 85
DESIGNS—HORIZ: No. 2236, 16th-century courier; 2237, Ordin-Nastchokin (17th-century postal administrator) and postal sleigh coach; 2238, 18th-century mail coach; 2239, Reproduction of Lenin portrait stamp of 1947; 2240, 19th-century postal troika (three-horse sleigh); 2241, Russian Tupolev Tu-104 jet airliner; 2242, Parcel post train; 2243, V. N. Podbielsky (postal administrator, 1918-20) and postal scenes; 2244, Parcel post Tupolev Tu-104 aircraft; 2245, Globe and modern forms of mail transport.

741a Facade of Exhibition Building

742 Vladimir Gateway

1958. Stamp Cent Philatelic Exhibition, Leningrad.
2246 **741a** 40 k. brown & lt brn . 40 20

1956. 850th Anniv of Town of Vladimir. Mult.
2247 40 k. Type **742** 60 15
2248 60 k. Street scene in Vladimir 1·00 20

743 M. Chigorin

745 Red Cross Nurse and Patient

1958. 50th Death Anniv of Chigorin (chess player).
2249 **743** 40 k. green and black . 1·75 20

1958. 40th Anniv of Red Cross and Crescent Societies.
2254 **745** 40 k. multicoloured . . 85 20
2255 – 40 k. red, yellow and bistre 85 20
DESIGN: No. 2255, Convalescent home.

746 Saltykov-Shchedrin (after I. Kramskoi) and Scene from his Works

747 V. Kapnist

1958. 69th Death Anniv of Mikhail Saltykov-Shchedrin (writer).
2256 **746** 40 k. black and purple . 75 15
For similar stamps see Nos. 2316/22 and 2458.

1958. Birth Bicentenary of V. Kapnist (poet).
2257 **747** 40 k. black and blue . . 1·10 15

748 Yerevan, Armenia

1958. Republican Capitals.
2258 40 k. brown (T **748**) 55 20
2259 40 k. violet (Baku, Azerbaijan) 55 20
2260 40 k. brown (Minsk, Byelorussia) 55 20
2261 40 k. blue (Tbilisi, Georgia) 55 20
2262 40 k. green (Tallin, Estonia) 55 20
2263 40 k. green (Alma-Ata, Kazakhstan) 55 20
2264 40 k. blue (Frunze, Kirgizia) 55 20
2265 40 k. brown (Riga, Latvia) . 55 20
2266 40 k. red (Vilnius, Lithuania) 55 20
2267 40 k. bistre (Kishinev, Moldavia) 55 20
2268 40 k. violet (Moscow, R.S.F.S.R.) 55 20
2269 40 k. blue (Stalinabad, Tadzhikistan) 55 20
2270 40 k. green (Ashkhabad, Turkmenistan) 55 20
2271 40 k. mauve (Kiev, Ukraine) 55 20
2272 40 k. black (Tashkent, Uzbekistan) 55 20
See also No. 2940.

749 Open Book, Torch, Lyre and Flowers

750 Rudaki

1958. Asian-African Writers' Conference, Tashkent.
2273 **749** 40 k. orange, black and olive . . . . 1·00 15

1958. 1100th Birth Anniv of Rudaki (Tadzhik poet and musician).
2274 **750** 40 k. multicoloured . . 60 15

751 Mounted Georgian (statue)

1958. 1500th Anniv of Founding of Tblisi (Georgian capital).
2275 **751** 40 k. multicoloured . . . 1·00 20

752 Chelyabinsk Tractor Plant

1958. 25th Anniv of Industrial Plants.
2276 **752** 40 k. green and yellow . . 80 20
2277 – 40 k. blue & light blue . . 55 20
2278 – 40 k. lake & light orge . . 80 20
DESIGNS: No. 2277, Ural machine construction plant; No. 2278, Zaporozhe foundry plant.

753 Young Revolutionary

754 Marx and Lenin (bas-relief)

1958. 40th Anniv of Young Communists League. Multicoloured.
2279 10 k. Type **753** 15 10
2280 20 k. Riveters 30 10
2281 25 k. Soldier 35 15
2282 40 k. Harvester 50 15
2283 60 k. Builder 80 20
2284 1 r. Students . . . . . . 2·00 75

1958. 41st Anniv of October Revolution.
2285 **754** 40 k. black, yell & red . . 65 20
2286 – 1 r. multicoloured . . . . 1·10 50
DESIGN—HORIZ: 1 r. Lenin with student, peasant and miner.

755 "Human Rights"

756 Yesenin

1958. 10th Anniv of Declaration of Human Rights.
2287 **755** 60 k. blue, black & buff . 65 15

1958. 30th Death Anniv of Sergei Yesenin (poet).
2288 **756** 40 k. multicoloured . . . 30 15

757 Kuan Han-ching

758 G. K. Ordzhonikidze

1958. Kuan Han-ching (Chinese playwright) Commemoration.
2289 **757** 40 k. black and blue . . . 35 15

1958. 21st Death Anniv of Ordzhonikidze (statesman).
2290 **758** 40 k. multicoloured . . . 65 15

759 John Milton

760 Lenin's Statue, Minsk

1958. 350th Birth Anniv of John Milton (poet).
2291 **759** 40 k. brown . . . . . 1·00 15

1958. 40th Anniv of Byelorussian Republic.
2292 **760** 40 k. brown, grey & red . . 50 15

761 Fuzuli

762 Census Emblem

1958. Fuzuli (Azerbaijan poet). Commemoration.
2293 **761** 40 k. bistre & turquoise . 1·00 15

1958. All Union Census, 1959. Multicoloured.
2294 40 k. Type **762** 25 15
2295 40 k. Census official with workers family 25 15

763 Eleonora Duse

764 Rule

1958. Birth Centenary of Eleonora Duse (Italian actress).
2296 **763** 40 k. black, grey & grn . 1·00 20

1958. Death Centenary of K. F. Rule (naturalist).
2297 **764** 40 k. black and blue . . 1·10 20

765 Atomic Ice-breaker "Lenin"

766 Moon Rocket and Sputniks

1958. All-Union Industrial Exhibition. Mult.
2298 40 k. Type **765** . . . . . . 2·50 65
2299 60 k. "TE 3" diesel loco . . 5·50 1·50

1959. 21st Communist Party Congress, Moscow.
2300 – 40 k. multicoloured . . . 55 25
2301 – 60 k. multicoloured . . . 65 40
2302 **766** 1 r. multicoloured . . . 2·75 1·40
DESIGNS: 40 k. Lenin, Red Banner and Kremlin view; 60 k. Workers beside Lenin hydro-electric plant, Volga River.

767 E. Torricelli

768 Ice Skater

1959. 350th Birth Anniv of Torricelli (physicist).
2303 **767** 40 k. black and green . . 80 20

1959. Women's World Ice Skating Championships, Sverdlovsk.
2304 **768** 25 k. multicoloured . . . 40 10
2305 40 k. black, blue & grey 60 20

769 Charles Darwin

770 N. Gamaleya

1959. 150th Birth Anniv of Charles Darwin (naturalist).
2306 **769** 40 k. brown and blue . . 75 15

1959. Birth Centenary of Gamaleya (microbiologist).
2307 **770** 40 k. black and red . . . 1·10 50

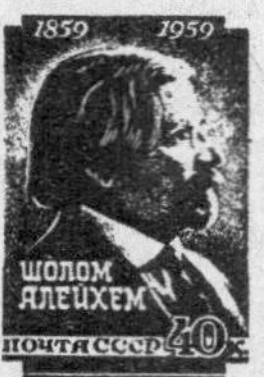

771 Sholem Aleichem

Победа
баскетбольной
команды СССР.
Чили 1959 г.
(772)

1959. Birth Centenary of Aleichem (Jewish writer).
2308 **771** 40 k. brown . . . . 1·00 15

1959. Russian (Unofficial) Victory in World Basketball Championships, Chile. No. 1851 optd with T **772**.
2309 – 1 r. brown and drab . . . 8·25 5·75

1959. Birth Bicent of Robert Burns. Optd **1759 1959.**
2310 **627** 40 k. brown and blue . . 15·00 15·00

774 Selma Lagerlof **775** P. Cvirka

1959. Birth Centenary of Selma Lagerlof (Swedish writer).
2311 **774** 40 k. black, brown and cream . . . . 1·10 50

1959. 50th Birth Anniv of Cvirka (Lithuanian poet).
2312 **775** 40 k. black and red on yellow 45 15

776 F. Joliot-Curie (scientist) **777** Popov and Polar Rescue by "Ermak"

1959. Joliot-Curie Commemoration.
2313 **776** 40 k. black and turquoise 1·25 30

1959. Birth Centenary of A. S. Popov (radio pioneer).
2314 **777** 40 k. brown, blk & blue . 1·00 30
2315 – 60 k. multicoloured . . . 1·50 55
DESIGN: 60 k. Popov and radio tower.

1959. Writers as T **746**. Inscr "1959".
2316 40 k. grey, black and red . . 90 20
2317 40 k. brown, sepia & yellow . 90 20
2318 40 k. brown and violet . . . 90 20
2319 40 k. multicoloured 90 20
2320 40 k. black, olive & yellow . 90 20
2321 40 k. multicoloured 90 20
2322 40 k. slate and violet 90 20
PORTRAITS (with scene from works): No. 2316, Anton Chekhov; 2317, Ivan Krylov (after K. Bryullov); 2318, Aleksandr Ostrovsky; 2319, Aleksandr Griboedov (after I. Kramskoi); 2320, Nikolai Gogol (after F. Moller); 2321, Sergei Aksakov (after I. Kramskoi); 2322, Aleksei Koltsov (after K. Gorbunov).

778 Saadi (Persian poet)

1959. Saadi Commemoration.
2323 **778** 40 k. black and blue . . 45 15

779 Orbeliani (Georgian writer) **780** Ogata Korin

1959. Orbeliani Commemoration.
2324 **779** 40 k. black and red . . . 45 15

1959. Birth Tercentenary of Ogata Korin (Japanese artist).
2325 **780** 40 k. multicoloured . . . 2·50 2·00

781 "Rossiya" on Odessa-Batum Service

1959. Russian Liners. Multicoloured.
2326 10 k. "Sovetsky Soyuz" on Vladivostok–Kamchatka service 30 15
2327 20 k. "Feliks Dzerzhinsky" on Odessa–Latakia service . . 45 15
2328 40 k. Type **781** 70 15
2329 40 k. "Kooperatsiya" on Murmansk–Tyksi service . 70 15
2330 60 k. "Mikhail Kalinin" leaving Leningrad 90 15
2331 1 r. "Baltika" on Leningrad–London service . . . . . 1·25 30

782 Trajectory of Moon Rocket **783** Lenin

1959. Launching of Moon Rocket. Inscr "2-1-1959".
2332 **782** 40 k. brown and pink . 1·00 20
2333 – 40 k. blue & light blue . 1·00 20
DESIGN: No. 2333, Preliminary route of moon rocket after launching.

1959. 89th Birth Anniv of Lenin.
2334 **783** 40 k. brown . . . . . . 1·00 50

784 M. Cachin **785** Youths with Banner

1959. 90th Birth Anniv of Marcel Cachin (French communist leader).
2335 **784** 60 k. brown 85 20

1959. 10th Anniv of World Peace Movement.
2336 **785** 40 k. multicoloured . . 55 20

786 A. von Humboldt

1959. Death Centenary of Alexander von Humboldt (German naturalist).
2337 **786** 40 k. brown and violet . 1·00 15

787 Haydn **788** Mountain Climbing

1959. 150th Death Anniv of Haydn (Austrian composer).
2338 **787** 40 k. brown and blue . 85 20

1959. Tourist Publicity. Multicoloured.
2339 40 k. Type **788** 65 20
2340 40 k. Map reading 65 20
2341 40 k. Cross country skiing . . 65 20
2342 40 k. Canoeing (horiz) . . . 65 20

789 Exhibition Emblem and New York Coliseum **790** Statue of Repin (painter)

1959. Russian Scientific, Technological and Cultural Exhibition, New York.
2343 **789** 20 k. multicoloured . . . 30 15
2344 40 k. multicoloured . . . 50 15

1959. Cultural Celebrities. Inscr "1959". Statues in black.
2345 **790** 10 k. ochre 15 10
2346 – 10 k. red 15 10
2347 – 20 k. lilac 25 10
2348 – 25 k. turquoise 60 10
2349 – 60 k. green 85 10
2350 – 1 r. blue . . . . 1·25 55
STATUES: 10 k. (No. 2346), Lenin; 20 k. V. Mayakovsky (poet); 25 k. Pushkin; 60 k. Gorky; 1 r. Tchaikovsky.

791 Sturgeon **792** Louis Braille

1959. Fisheries Protection.
2350a – 20 k. black and blue . . 30 10
2350b – 25 k. brown and lilac . . 50 10
2351 **791** 40 k. black & turquoise . 55 15
2351a – 40 k. purple and mauve . 70 15
2352 – 60 k. black and blue . . 85 30
DESIGNS: 20 k. Perch; 25 k. Northern fur seals; 40 k. (No. 2351a), Salmon; 60 k. Salmon and map.

1959. 150th Birth Anniv of Braille (inventor of Braille).
2353 **792** 60 k. brown, yell & turq . 65 20

793 Musa Djalil (Tatar poet) **794** Vaulting

1959. Djalil Commemoration.
2354 **793** 40 k. black and violet . . 65 15

1959. 2nd Russian Spartakiad. Inscr "1959".
2355 **794** 15 k. grey and purple . . 20 10
2356 – 25 k. grey, brown & grn . 30 10
2357 – 30 k. olive and red . . . 30 10
2358 – 60 k. grey, blue & yellow 85 15
DESIGNS—HORIZ: 25 k. Running; 60 k. Water polo. VERT: 30 k. Athletes supporting Spartakiad emblem.

795 **796** Steel Worker

1959. 2nd International T. U. Conference, Leipzig.
2359 **795** 40 k. red, blue & yellow . 65 15

1959. Seven Year Plan.
2360 – 10 k. red, blue & violet . 10 10
2361 – 10 k. light red, deep red and yellow 10 10
2362 – 15 k. red, yellow & brn . 10 10
2363 – 15 k. brn, grn & bistre . 10 10
2364 – 20 k. red, yellow & grn . 15 10
2365 – 20 k. multicoloured . . 15 10
2366 – 30 k. red, flesh & purple 30 10
2366a – 30 k. multicoloured . . 30 10
2367 **796** 40 k. orange, yell & bl . 35 10
2368 – 40 k. red, pink and blue 35 10
2369 – 60 k. red, blue & yellow 80 25
2370 – 60 k. red, buff and blue . 80 25
DESIGNS: No. 2360, Chemist; No. 2361, Spassky Tower, hammer and sickle; No. 2362, Builder's labourer; No. 2363, Farm girl; No. 2364, Machine minder; No. 2365, Tractor driver; No. 2366, Oil technician; No. 2366a, Cloth production; No. 2368, Coal miner; No. 2369, Iron moulder; No. 2370, Power station.

797 Glaciologist **798** Novgorod

1959. International Geophysical Year (2nd issue).
2371 **797** 10 k. turquoise 60 15
2372 – 25 k. red and blue . . . 1·25 15
2373 – 40 k. red and blue . . . 2·75 30
2373a – 1 r. blue and yellow . . 2·50 75
DESIGNS: 25 k. Oceanographic survey ship 'Vityaz'; 40 k. Antarctic map, camp and emperor penguin; 1 r. Observatory and rocket.

1959. 11th Centenary of Novgorod.
2374 **798** 40 k. red, brown & blue . 40 15

799 Schoolboys in Workshop **800** Exhibition Emblem

1959. Industrial Training Scheme for School-leavers. Inscr "1959".
2375 **799** 40 k. violet 30 10
2376 – 1 r. blue . . . . 1·00 30
DESIGN: 1 r. Children at night-school.

1959. All Union Exhibition.
2377 **800** 40 k. multicoloured . . . 55 20

801 Russian and Chinese Students

1959. 10th Anniv of Chinese Peoples' Republic.
2378 **801** 20 k. multicoloured . . . 20 15
2379 – 40 k. multicoloured . . . 50 20
DESIGN: 40 k. Russian miner and Chinese foundryman.

802 Postwoman **803** Mahtumkuli

1959. International Correspondence Week.
2380 **802** 40 k. multicoloured . . . 40 15
2381 60 k. multicoloured . . . 70 20

1959. 225th Birth Anniv of Mahtumkuli (Turkestan writer).
2382 **803** 40 k. brown 65 15

804 Arms and Workers of the German Democratic Republic **805** Lunik 3's Trajectory around the Moon

1959. 10th Anniv of German Democratic Republic.
2383 **804** 40 k. multicoloured . . . 35 10
2384 – 60 k. purple and cream . 65 15
DESIGN—VERT: 60 k. Town Hall, East Berlin.

1959. Launching of "Lunik 3" Rocket.
2385 **805** 40 k. violet . . . . . . 1·90 20

806 Republican Arms and Emblem **807** Red Square, Moscow

1959. 30th Anniv of Tadzhikistan Republic.
2386 **806** 40 k. multicoloured . . . 85 15

1959. 42nd Anniv of October Revolution.
2387 **807** 40 k. red 65 15

808 Capitol, Washington and Kremlin, Moscow

1959. Visit of Russian Prime Minister to U.S.A.
2388 **808** 60 k. blue and yellow . . 1·00 25

809 Mil Mi-1 Helicopter

1959. Military Sports.

2389	**809**	10 k. red and violet	30	10
2390	–	25 k. brown and blue	40	10
2391	–	40 k. blue and brown	60	15
2392	–	60 k. bistre and blue	90	25

DESIGNS: 25 k. Skin diver; 40 k. Racing motor cyclist; 60 k. Parachutist.

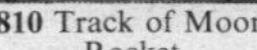

810 Track of Moon Rocket

811 Statue and aerial view of Budapest

1959. Landing of Russian Rocket on Moon. Inscr "14.IX.1959". Multicoloured.

2393	40 k. Type **810**	1·00	20
2394	40 k. Diagram of flight trajectory	1·00	20

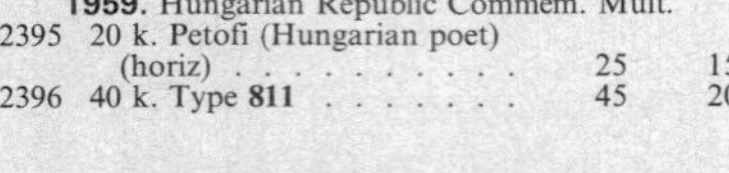

1959. Hungarian Republic Commem. Mult.

2395	20 k. Petofi (Hungarian poet) (horiz)	25	15
2396	40 k. Type **811**	45	20

812 Manolis Glezos (Greek Communist)

1959. Glezos Commemoration.

2397	**812**	40 k. brown and blue	15·00	11·50

813 A. Voskresensky (chemist)

814 River Chusovaya

1959. Voskresensky Commemoration.

2398	**813**	40 k. brown and blue	85	20

1959. Tourist Publicity. Inscr "1959".

2399	**814**	10 k. violet	15	10
2400	–	10 k. mauve	15	10
2401	–	25 k. blue	30	10
2402	–	25 k. red	30	10
2403	–	25 k. olive	30	10
2404	–	40 k. red	50	10
2405	–	60 k. turquoise	65	15
2406	–	1 r. green	2·25	60
2407	–	1 r. orange	1·10	60

DESIGNS: No. 2400, Riza Lake, Caucasus; No. 2401, River Lena; No. 2402, Iskanderkuly Lake; No. 2403, Coastal region; No. 2404, Lake Baikal; No. 2405, Beluha Mountains, Altay; No. 2406, Hibinsky Mountain; No. 2407, Gursuff region, Crimea.

815 "The Trumpeters of the First Horse Army" (after Grekov)

1959. 40th Anniv of Russian Cavalry.

2408	**815**	40 k. multicoloured	85	20

816 A. P. Chekhov and Moscow Residence

817 M. V. Frunze

1960. Birth Centenary of Chekhov (writer).

2409	**816**	20 k. red, brown and violet	25	10
2410	–	40 k. brown, bl & sepia	75	15

DESIGN: 40 k. Chekhov and Yalta residence.

1960. 75th Birth Anniv of M. V. Frunze (military leader).

2411	**817**	40 k. brown	55	15

818 G. N. Gabrichevsky

819 Vera Komissarzhevskaya

1960. Birth Centenary of G. N. Gabrichevsky (microbiologist).

2412	**818**	40 k. brown and violet	1·00	50

1960. 50th Death Anniv of V. F. Komissarzhevskaya (actress).

2413	**819**	40 k. brown	50	15

820 Free-skating

1960. Winter Olympic Games.

2414	–	10 k. blue and orange	50	10
2415	–	25 k. multicoloured	65	10
2416	–	40 k. orange, blue & pur	85	10
2417	**820**	60 k. violet, brown & grn	1·40	20
2418	–	1 r. blue, red and green	2·10	35

DESIGNS: 10 k. Ice hockey; 25 k. Ice skating; 40 k. Skiing; 1 r. Ski jumping.

821 Timur Frunze (fighter pilot) and Air Battle

822 Mil Mi-4 Helicopter over Kremlin

1960. War Heroes. Multicoloured.

2419	40 k. Type **821**	1·25	20
2420	1 r. Gen. Cherniakovksy and battle scene	1·10	40

1960. Air.

2421	**822**	60 k. blue	1·25	20

823 Women of Various Races

824 "Swords into Ploughshares"

1960. 50th Anniv of International Women's Day.

2422	**823**	40 k. multicoloured	85	20

1960. Presentation of Statue by Russia to U.N.

2423	**824**	40 k. yellow, bistre and blue	65	15

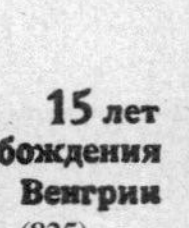

(825)

826 Lenin when a Child

1960. 15th Anniv of Liberation of Hungary. Optd with T **825**.

2424	**811**	40 k. multicoloured	4·25	3·25

1960. 90th Birth Anniv of Lenin. Portraits of Lenin. Multicoloured.

2425	**826**	10 k. multicoloured	10	10
2426	–	20 k. multicoloured	15	10
2427	–	30 k. multicoloured	25	15
2428	–	40 k. multicoloured	30	15
2429	–	60 k. multicoloured	1·40	25
2430	–	1 r. brown, blue & red	1·40	40

DESIGNS: Lenin: 20 k. holding child; 30 k. and revolutionary scenes; 40 k. with party banners; 60 k. and industrial scenes; 1 r. with globe and rejoicing people.

827 Lunik 3 photographing Moon

828 Government House, Baku

1960. Flight of Lunik 3. Inscr "7.X.1959".

2431	**827**	40 k. yellow and blue	90	50
2432	–	60 k. yellow, blue & ind	90	50

DESIGN: 60 k. Lunar map.

1960. 40th Anniv of Azerbaijan Republic.

2433	**828**	40 k. brown, bis & yell	50	15

829 "Fraternization" (after Pokorny)

830 Furnaceman

1960. 15th Anniv of Czechoslovak Republic.

2434	**829**	40 k. black and blue	30	10
2435	–	60 k. brown and yellow	85	15

DESIGN: 60 k. Charles Bridge, Prague.

1960. Completion of First Year of Seven Year Plan.

2436	**830**	40 k. brown and red	30	15

831 Popov Museum, Leningrad

1960. Radio Day.

2437	**831**	40 k. multicoloured	1·00	15

832 Robert Schumann

833 Sverdlov

1960. 150th Birth Anniv of Schumann (composer).

2438	**832**	40 k. black and blue	85	15

1960. 75th Birth Anniv of Ya. M. Sverdlov (statesman).

2439	**833**	40 k. sepia and brown	85	10

834 Magnifier and Stamp

1960. Philatelists' Day.

2440	**834**	60 k. multicoloured	1·00	15

835 Petrozavodsk (Karelian Republic)

1960. Capitals of Autonomous Republic (1st issue).

2441	**835**	40 k. turquoise	85	20
2442	–	40 k. blue	85	20
2443	–	40 k. green	85	20
2444	–	40 k. purple	85	20
2445	–	40 k. red	85	20
2446	–	40 k. blue	60	20
2447	–	40 k. brown	90	20
2448	–	40 k. brown	60	20
2449	–	40 k. red	60	20
2450	–	40 k. brown	60	20

CAPITALS: Nos. 2442, Batumi (Adzharian); No. 2443, Izhevsk (Udmurt); No. 2444, Grozny (Chechen-Ingush); No. 2445, Cheboksary (Chuvash); No. 2446, Yakutsk (Yakut); No. 2447, Ordzhonikidze (North Ossetian); No. 2448, Nukus (Kara-Kalpak); No. 2449, Makhachkala (Daghestan); No. 2450, Yoshkar-Ola (Mari).

See also Nos. 2586/92 and 2703/5.

836 Children of Different Races

838 Rocket

1960. International Children's Day. Multicoloured.

2451	10 k. Type **836**	15	10
2452	20 k. Children on farm (vert)	25	15
2453	25 k. Children with snowman	40	15
2454	40 k. Children in zoo gardens	65	20

1960. 40th Anniv of Karelian Autonomous Republic. Optd **40 лет КАССР 8.VI.1960.**

2455	**835**	40 k. turquoise	1·60	90

1960. Launching of Cosmic Rocket "Spacecraft 1" (first "Vostok" type spacecraft).

2456	**838**	40 k. red and blue	1·90	60

839 I.F.A.C. Emblem

1960. 1st International Automation Control Federation Congress, Moscow.

2457	**839**	60 k. brown and yellow	1·60	30

1960. Kosta Hetagurov Commem. As T **746**. Inscr "1960".

2458	40 k. brown and blue	85	15

DESIGN: 40 k. Portrait of Hetagurov and scene from his works.

840 Cement Works, Belgorod

1960. 1st Plant Construction of Seven Year Plan.

2459	**840**	25 k. black and blue	25	10
2460	–	40 k. black and red	40	10

DESIGN. 40 k. Metal works, Novokrivorog.

841 Capstans and Cogwheel

1960. Industrial Mass-Production Plant.

2461	**841**	40 k. turquoise	65	10
2462	–	40 k. purple (Factory plant)	65	10

842 Vilnius (Lithuania)

1960. 20th Anniv of Soviet Baltic Republics. Multicoloured.

2463	40 k. Type **842**	45	10
2464	40 k. Riga (Latvia)	45	10
2465	40 k. Tallin (Estonia)	45	10

843 Running

Международная ярмарка в Риччоне

(844)

1960. Olympic Games. Inscr "1960". Multicoloured.

2466	5 k. Type **843**	15	10
2467	10 k. Wrestling	20	10
2468	15 k. Basketball	35	10
2469	20 k. Weightlifting	35	10
2470	25 k. Boxing	35	10
2471	40 k. High diving	50	15
2472	40 k. Fencing	50	15
2473	40 k. Gymnastics	50	15
2474	60 k. Canoeing	80	20
2475	1 r. Horse jumping	2·00	45

1960. 20th Anniv of Moldavian Republic. As T **842**.
2476 40 k. multicoloured . . . 45 10
DESIGN: 40 k. Kishinev (capital).

1960. International Exhibition, Riccione. No. 2471 optd with T **844**.
2477 40 k. multicoloured . . . . . 15·00 10·00

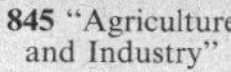
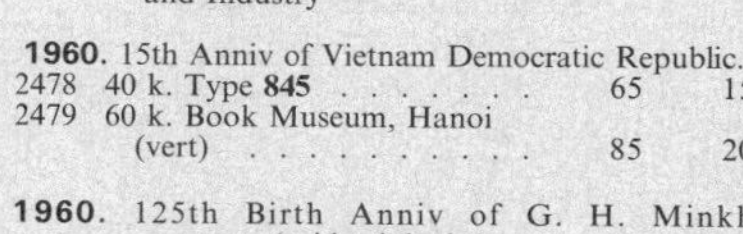

845 "Agriculture and Industry" **846** G. H. Minkh

1960. 15th Anniv of Vietnam Democratic Republic.
2478 40 k. Type **845** 65 15
2479 60 k. Book Museum, Hanoi (vert) 85 20

1960. 125th Birth Anniv of G. H. Minkh (epidemiologist).
2480 **846** 60 k. brown and bistre . 70 15

847 "March" (after I. Levitan)

1960. Birth Centenary of I. Levitan (painter).
2481 **847** 40 k. black and olive . . 80 15

848 "Forest" (after Shishkin)

1960. 5th World Forestry Congress, Seattle.
2482 **848** 1 r. brown . . . . 2·50 75

849 Addressing Letter

1960. International Correspondence Week.
2483 **349** 40 k. multicoloured . . . 40 10
2484 60 k. multicoloured . . . 70 20

850 Kremlin, Dogs "Belka" and "Strelka" and Rocket Trajectory

1960. 2nd Cosmic Rocket Flight.
2485 **850** 40 k. purple and yellow . 80 15
2486 1 r. blue and orange . . 1·90 25

851 Globes **852** People of Kazakhstan

1960. 15th Anniv of W.F.T.U.
2487 **851** 60 k. bl, drab & lilac . . 80 15

1960. 40th Anniv of Kazakh Soviet Republic.
2488 **852** 40 k. multicoloured . . . 50 10

853 "Karl Marx" **854** A. N. Voronikhin and Leningrad Cathedral

1960. River Boats. Multicoloured.
2489 25 k. Type **853** 45 10
2490 40 k. "Lenin" 65 15
2491 60 k. "Raketa" (hydro foil) . 1·10 25

1960. Birth Bicentenary of A. N. Voronikhin (architect)
2492 **854** 40 k. black and grey . . 45 10

855 Motor Coach **856** J. S. Gogebashvily

1960. Russian Motor Industry.
2493 – 25 k. black and blue . . 40 10
2494 – 40 k. blue and olive . . 55 15
2495 – 60 k. red and turquoise . 85 20
2496 **855** 1 r. multicoloured . . . 1·75 35
DESIGNS: 25 k. Lorry; 40 k. "Volga" car; 60 k. "Moskvich" car.

1960. 120th Birth Anniv of J. S. Gogebashvily (Georgian teacher).
2497 **856** 40 k. black and lake . . 45 10

857 Industrial Plant and Power Plant **858** Federation Emblem

1960. 43rd Anniv of October Revolution.
2498 **857** 40 k. multicoloured . . 55 15

1960. 15th Anniv of International Federation of Democratic Women.
2499 **858** 60 k. red and grey . . . 55 15

859 Youth of Three Races

40 лет Удмуртской АССР
4/XI 1960.
(**860**)

1960. 15th Anniv of World Democratic Youth Federation.
2500 **859** 60 k. multicoloured . . 80 15

1960. 40th Anniv of Udmurt Autonomous Republic. No. 2443 optd with T **860**.
2501 40 k. green . . . . 2·00 90

861 Tolstoi and his Moscow Residence **862** Government House, Yerevan

1960. 50th Death Anniv of Leo Tolstoi (writer).
2502 **861** 20 k. multicoloured . . 25 15
2503 – 40 k. brown, sepia & bl 40 15
2504 – 60 k. multicoloured . 1·00 25
DESIGNS—HORIZ: 40 k. Tolstoi and his country estate. VERT: 60 k. Full face portrait.

1960. 40th Anniv of Armenian Republic.
2205 **862** 40 k. multicoloured . . 45 10

863 Students and University **864** Tulip

1960. Opening of Friendship University, Moscow.
2506 **863** 40 k. purple 45 10

1960. Russian Flowers. Multicoloured.
2507 20 k. Type **864** 30 10
2508 20 k. Autumn crocus . . . 30 10
2509 25 k. Marsh marigold . . . 30 10
2510 40 k. Tulip 40 10
2511 40 k. Panax 40 10
2512 60 k. Hypericum 75 25
2513 60 k. Iris 75 25
2514 1 r. Wild rose . . . . 1·50 40

865 Engels **866** Mark Twain

1960. 140th Birth Anniv of Engels.
2515 **865** 60 k. grey . . . . . . 1·40 20

1960. 125th Birth Anniv of Mark Twain.
2516 **866** 40 k. bistre and orange . 3·00 1·90

867 N. Pirogov **868** Chopin

1960. 150th Birth Anniv of N. Pirogov (surgeon).
2517 **867** 40 k. brown and green . . 65 10

1960. 150th Birth Anniv of Chopin.
2518 **868** 40 k. bistre and buff . . . 1·10 20

869 North Korean Flag and Emblem **870** Lithuanian Costumes

1960. 15th Anniv of Korean Liberation.
2519 **869** 40 k. multicoloured . . . 70 15

1960. Provincial Costumes (1st issue). Inscr "1960". Multicoloured.
2520 10 k. Type 870 . . . . . 35 15
2521 60 k. Uzbek costumes . . . 1·10 25
See also Nos. 2537/45, 2796 and 2835/8.

871 A. Tseretely

1960. 120th Birth Anniv of A. Tseretely (Georgian poet).
2522 **871** 40 k. purple and lilac . . 1·00 10

Currency Revalued.
10 (old) Kopeks = 1 (new) Kopek

872 Worker **873** "Ruslan and Lyudmila"

1961. Inscr "1961".
2531 **872** 1 k. bistre 65 10
2524 – 2 k. green 25 10
2525 – 3 k. violet . . . . . . 1·60 10
2526 – 4 k. red 45 10
2526a – 4 k. brown . . . . . 4·00 4·00
2527 – 6 k. red . . . . 2·00 30
2528 – 6 k. claret . . . . . . 1·40 10
2529 – 10 k. orange . . . . . 1·00 10
2533 – 12 k. purple . . . . . 1·40 10
2530 – 16 k. blue . . . . . . 2·75 15
DESIGNS: 2 k. Combine harvester; 3 k. Cosmic rocket; 4 k. Soviet Arms and Flag; 6 k. Spassky Tower and Kremlin; 10 k. Workers statue; 12 k. Monument and Spassky Tower; 16 k. Airliner over power station.

1961. Russian Wild Life. As T **653** but inscr "1961". Centres in natural colours. Frame colours given.
2534 1 k. sepia (Brown bear) . . 25 15
2535 6 k. black (Eurasian beaver) . 1·00 20
2536 10 k. black (Roe deer) . . . 1·25 55
The 1 k. is vert and the rest horiz.

1961. Provincial Costumes (2nd issue). As T **870** but inscr "1961".
2537 2 k. red, brown & stone . . 40 10
2538 2 k. multicoloured 20 10
2539 3 k. multicoloured 25 15
2540 3 k. multicoloured 30 15
2541 3 k. multicoloured 40 15
2542 4 k. multicoloured 35 15
2543 6 k. multicoloured 50 15
2544 10 k. multicoloured . . . 75 15
2545 12 k. multicoloured . . . 1·10 45
COSTUMES: No. 2337, Moldavia; No. 2538, Georgia; No. 2539, Ukraine; No. 2540, Byelorussia; No. 2541, Kazakhs; No. 2542, Koryaks; No. 2543, Russia; No. 2544, Armenia; No. 2545, Estonia.

1961. Scenes from Russian Fairy Tales. Mult.
2546 1 k. "Geese Swans" . . . 35 10
2547 3 k. "The Fox, the Hare and the Cock" 55 15
2548 4 k. "The Little Humpbacked Horse" 35 15
2549 6 k. "The Muzhik and the Bear" 60 20
2550 10 k. Type **873** 95 40

874 Lenin, Map and Power Station

1961. 40th Anniv of State Electricity Plan.
2551 **874** 4 k. brown, yell & blue . 60 15
2552 10 k. black, purple and salmon . . . . . . 1·00 25

875 Tractor **876** N. A. Dobrolyubov

1961. Soviet Agricultural Achievements. Inscr "1961".
2553 – 3 k. mauve and blue . . 30 15
2554 **875** 4 k. black and green . . 30 10
2555 – 6 k. brown and blue . . 45 25
2556 – 10 k. purple and olive . 1·00 15
DESIGNS: 3 k. Dairy herd; 6 k. Agricultural machinery; 10 k. Fruit picking.

1961. 125th Birth Anniv of N. A. Dobrolyubov (writer).
2557 **876** 4 k. buff, black & blue . 45 15

877 N. D. Zelinsky

1961. Birth Centenary of N. D. Zelinsky (chemist).
2558 **877** 4 k. purple and mauve . 45 15

878 Georgian Republic Flag

1961. 40th Anniv of Georgian Republic.
2559 **878** 4 k. multicoloured . . . 30 10

879 Sgt. Miroshnichenko and Battle

1961. War Hero.
2560 **879** 4 k. blue & purple . . . 55 10
See also Nos. 2664/5.

880 T. G. Shevchenko and Birthplace **881** A. Rublev

1961. Death Centenary of T. G. Shevchenko (Ukrainian poet and painter).
2561 **880** 3 k. brown and violet . . 20 10
2562 – 6 k. purple and green . . 55 15
DESIGN: 6 k. Portrait of Shevchenko in old age, pen, book and candle.
See also Nos. 2956/62.

1961. 600th Birth Anniv of Rublev (painter).
2563 **881** 4 k. multicoloured . . . 60 20

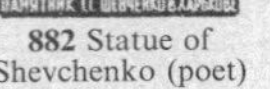

882 Statue of Shevchenko (poet) **883** N. V. Sklifosovsky

1961. Cultural Celebrities.
2564 – 2 k. brown and blue . . 25 10
2565 **882** 4 k. brown and black . . 20 15
2566 – 4 k. brown and purple . . 30 15
DESIGNS: 2 k. Shchors Monument, Kiev; 4 k. (No. 2566), Kotovsky Monument, Kishinev.

1961. 125th Birth Anniv of N. Y. Sklifosovsky (surgeon).
2567 **883** 4 k. black and blue . . . 45 10

884 Robert Koch **885** Zither-player and Folk Dancers

1961. 50th Death Anniv of Robert Koch (German microbiologist).
2568 **884** 6 k. brown 70 20

1961. 50th Anniv of Russian National Choir.
2569 **885** 4 k. multicoloured . . . 45 10

886 "Popular Science"

1961. Cent of "Vokrug Sveta" (science magazine).
2570 **886** 6 k. brown, blue and deep blue 90 75

887 Venus Rocket

1961. Launching of Venus Rocket.
2571 **887** 6 k. orange and blue . . 1·00 20
2572 – 10 k. blue and yellow . . 1·75 40
DESIGN: 10 k. Capsule and flight route.

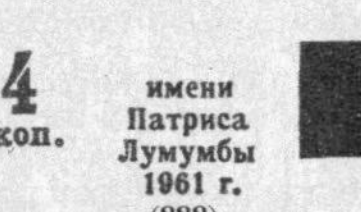

1961. Patrice Lumumba (Congolese politician) Commemoration (1st issue). Surch with T **888**.
2573 **863** 4 k. on 40 k. purple . . . 1·25 1·25
See also No. 2593.

889 African breaking Chains

1961. Africa Freedom Day. Inscr "1961".
2574 **889** 4 k. multicoloured . . . 20 10
2575 – 6 k. purple, orange & bl . . 35 20
DESIGN: 6 k. Hands clasping torch of freedom, and map.

891 Yuri Gagarin **892** Lenin

1961. World's First Manned Space Flight. Inscr 12-IV-1961". Perf or imperf.
2576 **891** 3 k. blue 45 10
2577 – 6 k. blue, violet and red . . 55 20
2578 – 10 k. red, green and brn . 1·25 60
DESIGNS—37×26 mm: 6 k. Rocket and Spassky Tower; 10 k. Rocket, Gagarin and Kremlin.

1961. 91st Birth Anniv of Lenin.
2579 **892** 4 k. blk, salmon and red . . 30 10

893 Rabindranath Tagore **894** Garibaldi

1961. Birth Centenary of Tagore (Indian writer).
2580 **893** 6 k. black, bistre & red . . 40 15

1961. International Labour Exhibition, Turin.
2581 – 4 k. salmon and red . . 40 10
2582 **894** 6 k. salmon and lilac . . 55 15
DESIGN: 4 k. Statue.

895 Lenin **896** Patrice Lumumba

1961.
2583 **895** 20 k. green and brown . 1·40 1·10
2584 – 30 k. blue and brown . 2·50 2·00
2585 – 50 k. red and brown . . 4·00 4·00
PORTRAITS (Lenin): 30 k. In cap; 50 k. Profile.

1961. Capitals of Autonomous Republics (2nd issue). As T **835**.
2586 4 k. deep violet 30 15
2587 4 k. blue 30 15
2588 4 k. orange 30 15
2589 4 k. black 30 15
2590 4 k. lake 55 15
2591 4 k. green 55 15
2592 4 k. deep purple 55 15
CAPITALS: No. 2586, Nalchik (Kabardino-Balkar); No. 2587, Ulan-Ude (Buryat); No. 2588, Sukhumi (Abkhazia); No. 2589, Syktyvkar (Komi); No. 2590, Nakhichevan (Nakhichevan); No. 2591, Rodina Cinema, Elista (Kalmyk); No. 2592, Ufa (Bashkir).

1961. Lumumba Commemoration (2nd issue).
2593 **896** 2 k. multicoloured . . . 15 10

897 Kindergarten **898** Chernushka and Rocket

1961. International Children's Day.
2594 **897** 2 k. blue and orange . . 15 10
2595 – 3 k. violet and ochre . . 25 10
2596 – 4 k. drab and red . . . 40 15
DESIGNS—HORIZ: 3 k. Children in Pioneer camp. VERT: 4 k. Children with toys and pets.

1961. 4th and 5th "Spacecraft" Flights.
2597 – 2 k. black, blue & violet 35 15
2598 **898** 4 k. turquoise and blue . 65 15
DESIGN—HORIZ: 2 k. Dog "Zvezdochka", rocket and Controller (inscr "25.III.1961").

899 Belinsky (after I. Astafev) **900**

1961. 150th Birth Anniv of Vissarion Grigorievich Belinsky (literary critic and journalist).
2599 **899** 4 k. black and red 30 15

1961. 40th Anniv of Soviet Hydro-meteorological Service.
2600 **900** 6 k. multicoloured . . . 90 25

901 D. M. Karbyshev **902** Glider

1961. Lieut-Gen. Karbyshev (war hero).
2601 **901** 4 k. black, red & yellow . 30 10

1961. Soviet Spartakiad.
2602 **902** 4 k. red and grey 30 10
2603 – 6 k. red and grey 45 15
2604 – 10 k. red and grey 85 35
DESIGNS: 6 k. Inflatable motor boat; 10 k. Motor cyclists.

903 Sukhe Bator Monument and Govt. Buildings, Ulan Bator **904** S. I. Vavilov

1961. 40th Anniv of Revolution in Mongolia.
2605 **903** 4 k. multicoloured . . . 50 15

1961. 70th Birthday of Vavilov (scientist).
2606 **904** 4 k. brown, bistre & grn . 30 15

905 V. Pshavela **906** "Youth Activities"

1961. Birth Cent of Pshavela (Georgian poet).
2607 **905** 4 k. brown and cream . . 25 10

1961. World Youth Forum.
2608 – 2 k. brown and orange . 20 10
2609 – 4 k. green and lilac . . 65 10
2610 **906** 6 k. blue and ochre . . . 70 25
DESIGNS—HORIZ: 2 k. Youths pushing tank into river. VERT: 4 k. "Youths and progress".

907 **908**

1961. 5th Int Biochemical Congress, Moscow.
2611 **907** 6 k. multicoloured . . . 65 15

1961. Centenary of "Kalevipoeg" (Estonian Saga).
2612 **908** 4 k. yellow, turq & blk . 25 10

909 Javelin Thrower

1961. 7th Soviet Trade Union Sports.
2613 **6** k. red 40 15

910 A. D. Zakharov

1961. Birth Bicentenary of Zakharov (architect).
2614 **910** buff, brown & blue . . . 40 15

911 Counter-attack

1961. War of 1941–45 (1st issue). Inscr "1961".
2615 **911** 4 k. multicoloured . . . 30 15
2616 – 4 k. multicoloured . . . 65 15
2617 – 4 k. indigo and brown . . 65 15
DESIGNS: No. 2616, Sailor with bayonet; No. 2617, Soldier with tommy gun.
See also Nos. 2717 and 2851/5.

912 Union Emblem

1961. 15th Anniv of International Union of Students.
2617a **912** 6 k. violet and red . . . 35 10

913 Stamps commemorating Industry

1961. 40th Anniv of First Soviet Stamp. Centres multicoloured.
2618 **913** 2 k. ochre and brown . . 30 15
2619 – 4 k. blue and indigo . . 45 15
2620 – 6 k. green and olive . . 70 15
2621 – 10 k. buff and brown . . 1·10 45
DESIGNS (stamps commemorating): 4 k. Electrification; 8 k. Peace; 10 k. Atomic energy.

914 Titov and "Vostok 2"

1961. 2nd Manned Space Flight. Perf or imperf.
2622 – 4 k. blue and purple . . 30 10
2623 **914** 6 k. orange, grn & brn . 55 20
DESIGN: 4 k. Space pilot and globe.

915 Angara River Bridge

1961. Tercentenary of Irkutsk, Siberia.
2624 **915** 4 k. black, lilac & bistre . 40 10

916 Letters and Mail Transport

1961. International Correspondence Week.
2625 **916** 4 k. black and mauve . . 55 10

917 Workers and Banners

1961. 22nd Communist Party Congress (1st issue).
2626 **917** 2 k. brown, yell & red . . 15 10
2627 – 3 k. blue and orange . . 60 15

2628 – 4 k. red, buff & purple . 25 10
2629 – 4 k. orange, blk & pur . 40 10
2630 – 4 k. sepia, brown & red . 25 15
DESIGNS: No. 2627, Moscow University and obelisk; No. 2628, Combine harvester; No. 2629, Workmen and machinery; No. 2630, Worker and slogan.
See also No. 2636.

918 Soviet Monument, Berlin **919** Adult Education

1961. 10th Anniv of International Federation of Resistance Fighters.
2631 **918** 4 k. grey and red 25 10

1961. Communist Labour Teams.
2632 – 2 k. purple & red on buff 35 15
2633 **919** 3 k. brown & red on buff 15 15
2634 – 4 k. blue & red on cream 35 25
DESIGNS: 2 k. Worker at machine; 4 k. Workers around piano.

920 Rocket and Globes

1961. Cosmic Flights. Aluminium-surfaced paper.
2635 **920** 1 r. red & black on silver 23·00 23·00

XXII съезд
КПСС
(921)

1961. 22nd Communist Party Congress (2nd issue). Optd with T **921**.
2636 **920** 1 r. red & black on silver 20·00 20·00

922 A. Imanov (Kazakh leader) **923** Liszt, Piano and Music

1961. Imanov Commemoration.
2637 **922** 4 k. sepia, brown & green 20 10

1961. 150th Birth Anniv of Liszt.
2638 **923** 4 k. brown, purple & yell 50 15

924 Flags, Rocket and Skyline

1961. 44th Anniv of October Revolution.
2639 **924** 4 k. red, purple and yell . 50 15

925 Congress Emblem **926** M. V. Lomonosov and Lomonosov University

1961. 5th W.F.T.U. Congress, Moscow. Inscr "MOCKBA 1961".
2640 **925** 2 k. red and bistre . . . 25 10
2641 – 2 k. violet and grey . . . 25 10
2642 – 4 k. brown, purple & bl . 45 10
2643 – 4 k. red, blue and violet . 45 10
2644 **925** 6 k. red, bistre & green . 40 15
2645 – 6 k. blue, purple & bistre 40 15
DESIGNS—HORIZ: Nos. 2641, 2645, Negro breaking chains. VERT: No. 2642, Hand holding hammer; No. 2643, Hands holding globe.

1961. 250th Birth Anniv of Lomonosov (scientist).
2646 **926** 4 k. brown, green & blue 30 15
2647 – 6 k. blue, buff & green . 50 20
2648 – 10 k. brown, blue & pur 1·00 40
DESIGNS—VERT: 6 k. Lomonosov at desk. HORIZ: 10 k. Lomonosov, his birthplace, and Leningrad Academy of Science.

927 Power Workers **928** Scene from "Romeo and Juliet"

1961. Young Builders of Seven Year Plan. Inscr "1961".
2649 **927** 3 k. grey, brown & red . 35 15
2650 – 4 k. brown, blue & red . 45 15
2651 – 6 k. grey, brown & red . 75 20
DESIGNS: 4 k. Welders; 6 k. Engineer with theodolite.

1961. Russian Ballet (1st issue). Inscr "1961". Multicoloured.
2652 6 k. Type 928 . . . . . . 45 15
2653 10 k. Scene from "Swan Lake" 80 25
See also Nos. 2666/7.

929 Hammer and Sickle **930** A. Pumpur

1961. 25th Anniv of Soviet Constitution.
2654 **929** 4 k. lake, yellow and red 30 10

1961. 120th Birth Anniv of Pumpur (Lettish poet).
2655 **930** 4 k. purple and grey . . 25 10

1961. Air. Surch **1961 r.6 kon** and bars.
2656 **822** 6 k. on 60 k. blue . . . 90 20

932 "Bulgarian Achievements"

1961. 15th Anniv of Bulgarian Republic.
2657 **932** 4 k. multicoloured . . . 25 10

933 Nansen and "Fram"

1961. Birth Centenary of Nansen (explorer).
2658 **933** 6 k. brown, blue & black 1·75 15

934 M. Dolivo-Dobrovolsky **935** A. S. Pushkin

1962. Birth Centenary of Dolivo-Dobrovolsky (electrical engineer).
2659 **934** 4 k. blue and bistre . . . 25 10

1962. 125th Death Anniv of Pushkin (poet).
2660 **935** 4 k. black, red and buff 20 10

936 Soviet Woman

1962. Soviet Women.
2661 **936** 4 k. black, bistre & orge 25 10

937 People's Dancers

1962. 25th Anniv of Soviet People's Dance Ensemble.
2662 **937** 4 k. brown and red . . . 35 10

938 Skaters

1962. Ice Skating Championships, Moscow.
2663 **938** 4 k. blue and orange . . 40 10

1962. War Heroes. As T **879** but inscr "1962".
2664 4 k. brown and blue 75 15
2665 6 k. turquoise and brown . . 1·00 20
DESIGNS: 4 k. Lieut. Shalandin, tanks and Yakovlev Yak-9T fighter planes; 6 k. Capt. Gadzhiev, "K-3" submarine and sinking ship.

1962. Russian Ballet (2nd issue). As T **928** but inscr "1962".
2666 2 k. multicoloured 25 15
2667 3 k. multicoloured 35 15
DESIGNS: Scenes from—2 k. "Red Flower" (Glier); 3 k. "Paris Flame" (Prokofiev).

СОВЕТСКИЕ КОНЬКОБЕЖЦЫ—
ЧЕМПИОНЫ
МИРА
(939)

1962. Soviet Victory in Ice Skating Championships. Optd with T **939**.
2668 **938** 4 k. blue and orange . . 2·75 1·50

940 Skiing

1962. 1st People's Winter Games, Sverdlovsk.
2669 **940** 4 k. violet and red . . . 45 15
2670 – 6 k. turquoise & purple . 55 20
2671 – 10 k. red, black & blue . 95 30
DESIGN: 6 k. Ice Hockey; 10 k. Figure skating.

941 A. I. Herzen **942** Lenin on Banner

1962. 150th Birth Anniv of A. I. Herzen (writer).
2672 **941** 4 k. flesh, black & blue . 25 10

1962. 14th Leninist Young Communist League Congress. Inscr "1962".
2673 **942** 4 k. red, yellow & purple 20 10
2674 – 6 k. purple, orange & blue 25 10
DESIGN—HORIZ: 6 k. Lenin on flag.

943 Rocket and Globe **944** Tchaikovsky (after sculpture by Z. M. Vilensky)

1962. 1st Anniv of World's First Manned Space Flight. Perf or imperf.
2675 **943** 10 k. multicoloured . . . 1·10 50

1962. 2nd Int Tchaikovsky Music Competition.
2676 **944** 4 k. drab, black & blue . . 40 10

MORE DETAILED LISTS
are given in the Stanley Gibbons Catalogues referred to in the country headings. For lists of current volumes see introduction

945 Youth of Three Races **946** The Ulyanov (Lenin's) Family

1962. International Day of "Solidarity of Youth against Colonialism".
2677 **945** 6 k. multicoloured . . . 30 10

1962. 92nd Birth Anniv of Lenin.
2678 **946** 4 k. brown, grey and red 25 15
2679 – 10 k. purple, red & black 1·00 30
DESIGN: 10 k. Lenin.

947 "Cosmos 3"

1962. Cosmic Research.
2680 **947** 6 k. black, violet & blue 50 15

948 Charles Dickens

1962. 150th Birth Anniv of Charles Dickens.
2681 **948** 6 k. purple, turq & ol . . 50 15

949 J. J. Rousseau **950** Karl Marx Monument, Moscow

1962. 250th Birth Anniv of Rousseau.
2682 **949** 6 k. bistre, grey & purple 50 15

1962. Karl Marx Commemoration.
2683 **950** 4 k. grey and blue . . . 20 10

951 Lenin reading "Pravda" **952** Mosquito and Campaign Emblem

1962. 50th Anniv of "Pravda" Newspaper.
2684 **951** 4 k. purple, red & buff . 25 15
2685 – 4 k. multicoloured . . . 25 15
2686 – 4 k. multicoloured . . . 25 15
DESIGNS—25×38 mm: No. 2685, Statuary and front page of first issue of "Pravda"; No. 2686, Lenin and modern front page of "Pravda".

1962. Malaria Eradication. Perf (6 k. also imperf).
2687 **952** 4 k. black, turquoise & red 20 10
2688 6 k. black, green & red . 65 35

953 Model Rocket Construction

1962. 40th Anniv of All Union Lenin Pioneer Organization. Designs embody Pioneer badge. Multicoloured.

2689 2 k. Lenin and Pioneers giving Oath 25 10
2690 3 k. L. Golikov and V. Kotik (pioneer heroes) 25 10
2691 4 k. Type **953** 35 10
2692 4 k. Hygiene education . . . 40 20
2693 6 k. Pioneers marching . . . 70 25

954 M. Mashtotz **955** Ski Jumping

1962. 1600th Birth Anniv of Mesrop Mashtotz (author of Armenian Alphabet).

2694 **954** 4 k. brown and yellow . 25 10

1962. F.I.S. International Ski Championships, Zakopane (Poland).

2695 **955** 2 k. red, brown & blue . 20 10
2696 – 10 k. blue, black & red . 80 35

DESIGN—VERT: 10 k. Skier.

956 I. Goncharov **957** Cycle Racing

1962. 150th Birth Anniv of I. Goncharov (writer).

2697 **956** 4 k. brown and grey . . 35 10

1962. Summer Sports Championships.

2698 **957** 2 k. black, red & brown . 40 10
2699 – 4 k. black, yellow & brn . 35 20
2700 – 10 k. black, lemon & blue 80 30
2701 – 12 k. brown, yell & blue . 95 40
2702 – 16 k. multicoloured . . . 1·25 50

DESIGN—VERT: 4 k. Volleyball; 10 k. Rowing; 16 k. Horse jumping. HORIZ: 12 k. Football (goal keeper).

1962. Capitals of Autonomous Republics. 3rd issue. As T **835**.

2703 4 k. black 50 15
2704 4 k. purple 50 15
2705 4 k. green 50 15

CAPITALS: No. 2703, Kazan (Tatar); No. 2704, Kyzyl (Tuva); No.2705, Saransk (Mordovian).

958 Lenin Library, 1862

1962. Centenary of Lenin Library.

2706 **958** 4 k. black and grey . . . 35 15
2707 – 4 k. black and grey . . . 35 15

DESIGN: No. 2707, Modern library building.

959 Fur Bourse, Leningrad and Ermine

1962. Fur Bourse Commemoration.

2708 **959** 6 k. multicoloured . . . 55 20

960 Pasteur **961** Youth and Girl with Book

1982. Centenary of Pasteur's Sterilisation Process.

2709 **960** 6 k. brown and black . . 60 15

1962. Communist Party Programme. Mult.

2710 2 k. Type **961** 15 10
2711 4 k. Workers of three races and dove 25 10

962 Hands breaking Bomb

1962. World Peace Congress, Moscow.

2712 **962** 6 k. bistre, black & blue 30 15

963 Y. Kupala and Y. Kolas

1962. Byelorussian Poets Commemoration.

2713 **963** 4 k. brown and yellow . 25 10

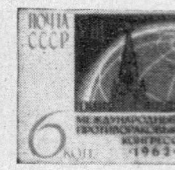

964 Sabir **965** Congress Emblem

1962. Birth Centenary of Sabir (Azerbaijan poet).

2714 **964** 4 k. brown, buff & blue 45 15

1962. 8th Anti-Cancer Congress, Moscow.

2715 **965** 6 k. red, black & blue . 45 15

966 N. N. Zinin **967** M. V. Nesterov (painter)

1962. 150th Birth Anniv of N. N. Zinin (chemist).

2716 **966** 4 k. brown and violet . 25 10

1962. War of 1941–45 (2nd issue). As T **911** inscr "1962".

2717 4 k. multicoloured 55 15

DESIGN: Sailor throwing petrol bomb.

1962. Russian Artists Commemoration.

2718 **967** 4 k. multicoloured . . . 30 15
2719 – 4 k. brown, pur & grey . 30 15
2720 – 4 k. black and brown . 30 15

PORTRAITS—VERT: No. 2719, I. N. Kramskoi (painter). HORIZ: No. 2220, I. D. Shadr (sculptor).

968 "Vostok-2" **969** Nikolaev and "Vostok 3"

1962. 1st Anniv of Titov's Space Flight. Perf or imperf.

2721 **968** 10 k. purple, black & bl 1·00 50
2722 10 k. orange, black & bl 1·00 50

1962. 1st "Team" Manned Space Flight. Perf or imperf.

2723 **969** 4 k. brown, red and blue 90 15
2724 – 4 k. brown, red and blue 90 15
2725 – 6 k. multicoloured . . . 1·50 20

DESIGNS: No. 2724, As Type **969** but with Popovich and "Vostok-4"; No. 2725 (47 × 28½ mm), Cosmonauts in flight.

970 House of Friendship

1962. People's House of Friendship, Moscow.

2726 **970** 6 k. grey and blue . . . 30 10

971 Lomonosov University and Atomic Symbols

1962. "Atoms for Peace".

2727 **971** 4 k. multicoloured . . . 35 10
2728 – 6 k. multicoloured . . . 50 20

DESIGN: 6 k. Map of Russia, Atomic symbol and "Peace" in ten languages.

972 Sazan and Bream **973** F. E. Dzerzhinsky

1962. Fish Preservation Campaign.

2729 **972** 4 k. yellow, vio & blue . 30 10
2730 – 6 k. blue, black & orge . 50 20

DESIGN: 6 k. Freshwater salmon.

1962. Birth Anniv of Feliks Dzerzhinsky (founder of Cheka).

2731 **973** 4 k. blue and green . . . 25 10

974 O. Henry

1962. Birth Cent of O. Henry (American writer).

2732 **974** 6 k. black, brown & yell . 35 10

975 Field Marshals Barclay de Tolly, Kutuzov and Bagration

1962. 150th Anniv of Patriotic War of 1812.

2733 **975** 3 k. brown 30 10
2734 – 4 k. blue 35 15
2735 – 6 k. slate 75 20
2736 – 10 k. violet 75 25

DESIGNS: 4 k. Davidov and partisans; 6 k. Battle of Borodino; 10 k. Partisans escorting French prisoners of war.

976 Vinnitsa

1962. 600th Anniv of Vinnitsa.

2737 **976** 4 k. black and bistre . . 30 10

977 Transport, "Stamp" and "Postmark" **978** Cedar

1962. International Correspondene Week.

2738 **977** 4 k. black, pur & turq . . 30 10

1962. 150th Anniv of Nikitsky Botanical Gardens. Multicoloured.

2739 3 k. Type **978** 35 10
2740 4 k. "Vostok-2" canna (plant) 55 10
2741 6 k. Strawberry tree (arbutus) 70 15
2742 10 k. "Road to the Stars" (chrysanthemum) 95 25

979 Builder **980** "Sputnik 1"

1962. "The Russian People". Multicoloured.

2743 4 k. Type **979** 30 15
2744 4 k. Textile worker 30 15
2745 4 k. Surgeon 30 15
2746 4 k. Farm girl 30 15
2747 4 k. P. T. instructor 30 15
2748 4 k. Housewife 30 15
2749 4 k. Rambler 30 15

1962. 5th Anniv of Launching of "Sputnik 1".

2750 **980** 10 k. multicoloured . . . 1·10 30

981 Akhundov **982** Harvester

1962. 150th Birth Anniv of M. F. Akhundov (poet).

2751 **981** 4 k. brown and green . . 20 10

1962. "Settlers on Virgin Lands". Multicoloured.

2752 4 k. Type **982** 50 20
2753 4 k. Surveyors, tractors and map 50 20
2754 4 k. Pioneers with flag . . . 50 20

983 N. N. Burdenko

1962. Soviet Scientists. Inscr "1962". Multicoloured.

2755 4 k. Type **983** 25 10
2756 4 k. V. P. Filatov (wearing beret) 25 10

984 Lenin Mausoleum

1962. 92nd Birth Anniv of Lenin.

2757 **984** 4 k. multicoloured . . . 25 10

985 Worker with Banner **986** "Towards the Stars"

1962. 45th Anniv of October Revolution.

2758 **985** 4 k. multicoloured . . . 20 10

1962. Space Flights Commem. Perf or imperf.

2759 **986** 6 k. black, brown & blue 65 35
2760 10 k. ultram, bis & vio 1·00 20

1.XI. ЗЕМЛЯ—МАРС

(987)

988 T. Moldo (Kirghiz poet)

1962. Launching of Rocket to Mars (1st issue). Optd with T **987**.

2761 **986** 10 k. blue, bistre & vio . 3·00 2·40

See also No. 2765.

1962. Poets' Anniversaries.
2762 **988** 4 k. black and red . . . 30 10
2763 – 4 k. black and blue . . . 30 10
DESIGN: No. 2763, Sayat-Nova (Armenian poet) with musical instrument.

989 Hammer and Sickle

1962. 40th Anniv of U.S.S.R.
2764 **989** 4 k. yellow, red and crimson 20 10

990 Mars Rocket in Space
(⅔-size illustration)

1962. Launching of Rocket to Mars (2nd issue).
2765 **990** 10 k. violet and red . . . 90 30

991 Chemical Industry and Statistics

1962. 22nd Communist Party Congress. "Achievements of the People". Multicoloured.
2766 4 k. Type **991** 55 20
2767 4 k. Engineering (machinery and atomic symbol) 55 20
2768 4 k. Hydro-electric power . . 55 20
2769 4 k. Agriculture (harvester) . 55 20
2770 4 k. Engineering (surveyor and welder) 55 20
2771 4 k. Communications (telephone installation) . . 55 20
2772 4 k. Heavy industry (furnace) 55 20
2773 4 k. Transport (signalman etc) 65 20
2774 4 k. Dairy farming (milkmaid, etc) 55 20
All the designs show production targets relating to 1980.

992 Chessmen

994 V. K. Blucher (military commander)

993 Four Soviet Cosmonauts
(⅓ size illustration)

1962. 30th Soviet Chess Championships, Yerevan.
2775 **992** 4 k. black and ochre . . 75 20

1962. Soviet Cosmonauts Commem. Perf or imperf.
2776 **993** 1 r. black and blue . . . 6·75 6·75

1962. V. K. Blucher Commemoration.
2777 **994** 4 k. multicoloured . . . 30 10

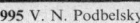

995 V. N. Podbelsky

996 A. Gaidar

1962. 75th Birth Anniv of V. N. Podbelsky (politician).
2778 **995** 4 k. violet and brown . . 20 10

1962. Soviet Writers.
2779 **996** 4 k. buff, black & blue . 20 10
2780 – 4 k. multicoloured . . . 20 10
DESIGN: No. 2780, A. S. Makharenko.

997 Dove and Christmas Tree

1962. New Year. Perf or imperf.
2781 **997** 4 k. multicoloured . . . 20 10

998 D. N. Pryanishnikov (agricultural chemist)

999 Rose-coloured Starlings

1962. D. N. Pryanishnikov Commemoration.
2782 **999** 4 k. multicoloured . . . 20 10

1962. Birds.
2783 **999** 3 k. black, red & green . 45 10
2784 – 4 k. black, brown & orge 55 10
2785 – 6 k. blue, black and red 65 15
2786 – 10 k. blue, black & red 1·10 30
2787 – 16 k. red, blue & black 1·60 50
BIRDS: 4 k. Red-breasted geese; 6 k. Snow geese; 10 k. Great white cranes; 16 k. Greater flamingoes.

1000 F.I.R. Emblem and Handclasp

1001 Badge and Yakovlev Yak-9 Fighters

1962. 4th International Federation of Resistance Heroes Congress.
2788 **1000** 4 k. violet and red . . 20 10
2789 6 k. turquoise and red . 50 15

1962. 20th Anniv of French Air Force "Normandy-Niemen" Unit.
2790 **1001** 6 k. red, green & buff . 45 15

1002 Map and Savings Book

1962. 40th Anniv of Soviet Banks.
2791 **1002** 4 k. multicoloured . . 20 10
2792 – 6 k. multicoloured . . 35 15
DESIGN: 6 k. As Type **1002** but with people and figure "53" in place of symbols and "70" within map.

1003 Fertilizer Plant, Rustavi, Georgia

1962. Heavy Industries.
2793 **1003** 4 k. black, lt blue & bl 30 15
2794 – 4 k. black, turquoise & grn 30 15
2795 – 4 k. black, blue & grey 30 15
DESIGNS: No. 2794, Construction of Bratsk hydro-electric station; No. 2795, Volzhskaya hydro-electric station, Volgograd.

1962. Provincial Costumes (3rd issue). As T **870**. Inscr "1962".
2796 3 k. red, brown and drab . . 40 15
COSTUME: 3 k. Latvia.

1004 K. S. Stanislavsky

1005 A. S. Serafimovich

1963. Russian Stage Celebrities.
2797 **1004** 4 k. green on pale grn . 30 10
2798 – 4 k. brown 30 10
2799 – 4 k. brown 30 10

PORTRAITS AND ANNIVERSARIES: No. 2797, Type **1004** (actor, birth cent); No. 2798, M. S. Shchepkin (actor, death cent); No. 2799, V. D. Durov (animal trainer and circus artiste, birth cent).

1963. Russian Writers and Poets.
2800 **1005** 4 k. brown, sepia & mve 30 10
2801 – 4 k. brown and purple . 30 10
2802 – 4 k. brown, red & buff . 30 10
2803 – 4 k. brown and green . . 30 10
2804 – 4 k. brown, sepia & mve 30 10
2805 – 4 k. multicoloured . . . 30 10
PORTRAITS AND ANNIVERSARIES: No. 2800, (birth cent); No. 2801, D. Bednii (60th birth anniv); No. 2802, G. I. Uspensky (120th birth anniv); No. 2803, N. P. Ogarev (150th birth anniv); No. 2804, V. J. Bryusov (90th birth anniv); No. 2805, F. V. Gladkov (80th birth anniv).

1006 Children in Nursery

1007 Dolls and Toys

1963. Child Welfare.
2806 **1006** 4 k. black and orange . 25 10
2807 – 4 k. purple, blue & orge 25 10
2808 – 4 k. bistre, red & green . 25 10
2809 – 4 k. purple, red & orge . 25 10
DESIGNS: No. 2807, Children with nurse; No. 2808, Young pioneers; No. 2809, Students at desk and trainee at lathe.

1963. Decorative Arts. Multicoloured.
2810 4 k. Type **1007** 25 10
2811 6 k. Pottery 35 15
2812 10 k. Books 85 20
2813 12 k. Porcelain . . . . 1·10 30

1008 Ilyushin Il-62 Airliner

1962. 40th Anniv of "Aeroflot" Airline.
2814 **1008** 10 k. black, brn & red . 80 15
2815 – 12 k. multicoloured . . 1·00 30
2816 – 16 k. red, black & blue . 1·40 90
DESIGNS: 12 k. "Aeroflot" emblem; 16 k. Tupolev Tu-124 airliner.

1009 M. N. Tukhachevsky

1010 M. A. Pavlov (scientist)

1963. 45th Anniv of Red Army and War Heroes.
2817 **1009** 4 k. green & turquoise . 30 10
2818 – 4 k. black and brown . . 30 10
2819 – 4 k. brown and blue . . 30 10
2820 – 4 k. black and red . . . 30 10
2821 – 4 k. violet and mauve . 30 10
DESIGNS (Army heroes and battle scenes): No. 2817, Type **1009** (70th birth anniv); No. 2818, U. M. Avetisyan; No. 2819, A. M. Matrosov; No. 2820, I. V. Panfilov; No. 2821, Ya. F. Fabricius.

1963. Academy of Sciences Members.
2822 **1010** 4 k. blue, grey & brown 25 10
2823 – 4 k. brown and green . . 25 10
2824 – 4 k. multicoloured . . . 25 10
2825 – 4 k. brown, red & blue . 25 10
2826 – 4 k. multicoloured . . . 25 10
PORTRAITS: No. 2823, I. V. Kurchatov; No. 2824, V. I. Vernadsky. LARGER ($23\frac{1}{2} \times 30$ mm): No. 2825, A. Krylov; No. 2826, V. Obroutchev. All commemorate birth centenaries except No. 2823 (60th anniv of birth).

1011 Games Emblem

Советские
хоккеисты-
чемпионы
мира
и Европы.
Стокгольм.
1963 г.
(**1012**)

1963. 5th Soviet T.U. Winter Sports.
2827 **1011** 4 k. orge, blk & blue . . 30 10

1963. Soviet Victory in Swedish Ice Hockey Championships. No. 2670 optd with T **1012**.
2828 6 k. turquoise and purple . . 1·60 60

1013 V. Kingisepp

1014 R. M. Blauman

1963. 75th Birth Anniv of Victor Kingisepp (Estonian Communist Party Leader).
2829 **1013** 4 k. brown and blue . . 25 10

1963. Birth Centenary of Rudolf Blauman (Latvian writer).
2830 **1014** 4 k. purple and blue . . 25 10

1015 Globe and Flowers

1016 Lenin

1963. "World without Arms and Wars". Perf or imperf.
2831 **1015** 4 k. green, blue and red 25 10
2832 – 6 k. lilac, green and red 30 10
2833 – 10 k. violet, blue & red 1·00 25
DESIGNS: 6 k. Atomic emblem and pylon; 10 k. Sun and rocket.

1963. 93rd Birth Anniv of Lenin.
2834 **1016** 4 k. brown and red . . 2·50 85

1963. Provincial Costumes (4th issue). As T **870**. Inscr "1963". Multicoloured.
2835 3 k. Tadzhikistan 40 15
2836 4 k. Azerbaijan 55 15
2837 4 k. Kirgizia 55 15
2838 4 k. Turkmenistan 55 15

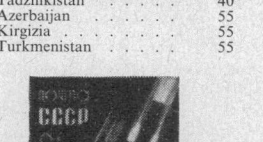

1017 "Luna 4" Rocket

1963. Launching of "Luna 4" Space Rocket. Perf or imperf.
2839 **1017** 6 k. red, black and blue 65 15
See also No. 3250.

1018 Woman and Lido

1963. 5th Anniv of World Health Day. Mult.
2840 2 k. Type **1018** 15 10
2841 4 k. Man and stadium . . . 25 20
2842 10 k. Child and school . . . 85 20

1019 Sputniks and Globe

1963. "Cosmonautics Day".
2843 **1019** 10 k. blue, black & pur 75 15
2844 – 10 k. purple, black & bl 75 15
2845 – 10 k. red, black & yellow 75 15
DESIGNS: No. 2844, "Vostok 1" and Moon; No. 2845, Space rocket and Sun.

1021 Cuban Horsemen with Flag

1963. Cuban-Soviet Friendship.
2846 **1021** 4 k. black, red and blue . . 40 10
2847 – 6 k. black, blue and red . . 50 10
2848 – 10 k. blue, red & black . . 65 20
DESIGNS: 6 k. Hands, weapon, book and flag; 10 k. Crane, hoisting tractor and flags.

1022 J. Hasek

1023 Karl Marx

1963. 40th Death Anniv of Jaroslav Hasek (writer).
2849 **1022** 4 k. black 20 10

1963. 80th Death Anniv of Karl Marx.
2850 **1023** 4 k. black and brown . . 20 10

1963. War of 1941–45 (3rd issue). As T **911** inscr "1963".
2851 4 k. multicoloured 45 15
2852 4 k. multicoloured 45 15
2853 4 k. multicoloured 45 15
2854 4 k. sepia and red 45 15
2855 6 k. olive, black and red . . 75 20
DESIGNS: No. 2851, Woman making shells (Defence of Leningrad, 1942); No. 2852, Soldier in winter kit with tommy gun (20th anniv of Battle of the Volga); No. 2853, Soldiers attacking (Liberation of Kiev, 1943); No. 2854, Tanks and map indicating Battle of Kursk, 1943; No. 2855, Tank commander and tanks.

1024 International P.O. Building

1963. Opening of Int Post Office, Moscow.
2856 **1024** 6 k. brown and blue . . 65 10

1025 Medal and Chessmen

1963. World Chess Champion, Moscow. Perf or imperf.
2857 **1025** 4 k. multicoloured . . . 65 15
2858 – 6 k. blue, mauve and ultramarine 70 20
2859 – 16 k. black, mve & pur . 1·50 50
DESIGNS: 6 k. Chessboard and pieces; 16 k. Venue and pieces.

1026 Wagner

1027 Boxers on "Glove"

1963. 150th Birth Anniv of Wagner and Verdi (composers).
2860 **1026** 4 k. black and red . . . 50 15
2861 – 4 k. purple and red . . . 50 15
DESIGN: No. 2861, Verdi.

1963. 15th European Boxing Championships, Moscow. Multicoloured.
2862 4 k. Type **1027** 20 10
2863 6 k. Referee and winning boxer on "glove" 50 15

1028 Bykovsky and "Vostok 5"

Всемирный конгресс женщин.
(1029)

1963. Second "Team" Manned Space Flights (1st issue). Perf or imperf.
2864 **1028** 6 k. brown and purple . 55 20
2865 – 6 k. red and green . . . 55 20
2866 – 10 k. red and blue . . 1·00 30
DESIGNS: No. 2865, Tereshkova and "Vostok 6"; No. 2866, Allegory—"Man and Woman in Space".
See also Nos. 2875/7.

1963. International Women's Congress, Moscow. Optd with T **1029**.
2867 **1015** 4 k. green, blue & red . . 40 25

1030 Cycling

1031 Globe, Film and Camera

1963. 3rd People's Spartakiad. Multicoloured. Perf or imperf.
2868 3 k. Type **1030** 25 10
2869 4 k. Athletics 30 10
2870 6 k. Swimming (horiz) . . . 35 15
2871 12 k. Basketball 75 30
2872 16 k. Football . . . . . . 1·00 40

1963. International Film Festival, Moscow.
2873 **1031** 4 k. blue, black & brown . 30 10

1032 V. V. Mayakovsky

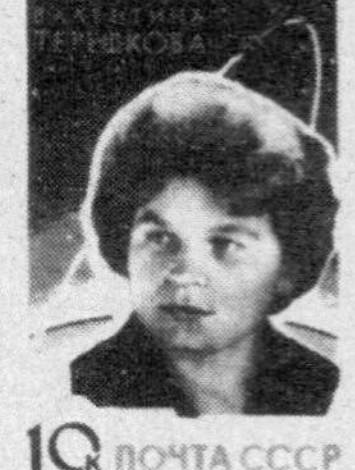

1033 Tereshkova

1963. 70th Birth Anniv of Mayakovsky (poet).
2874 **1032** 4 k. brown 25 15

1963. 2nd "Team" Manned Space Flights (2nd issue). Multicoloured.
2875 4 k. Bykovsky (horiz) . . . 30 20
2876 4 k. Tereshkova (horiz) . . 30 20
2877 10 k. Type **1033** . . . . . . 1·60 35

1034 Ice Hockey Player

1035 Lenin

1963. Russian Ice Hockey Championships.
2878 **1034** 6 k. blue and red . . . 75 20

1963. 60th Anniv of 1st Socialist Party Congress.
2879 **1035** 4 k. black and red . . . 30 10

1036 Freighter and Crate

1963. Red Cross Centenary.
2880 **1036** 6 k. red and green . . . 60 15
2881 – 12 k. red and blue . . 90 30
DESIGN: 12 k. Centenary emblem.

1037 Guibozo (polo)

1963. Regional Sports.
2882 – 3 k. multicoloured . . . 25 10
2883 **1037** 4 k. black, red & ochre . 30 10
2884 – 6 k. red, brown & yell . 55 15
2885 – 10 k. black, brn & olive . 75 25
DESIGNS—HORIZ: 3 k. Lapp reindeer racing; 6 k. Buryat archery. VERT: 10 k. Armenian wrestling.

1038 Aleksandr Mozhaisky and Model Monoplane

1963. Aviation Celebrities.
2886 **1038** 6 k. black and blue . . . 50 10
2887 – 10 k. black and blue . . 75 40
2888 – 16 k. black and blue . . 1·25 35
DESIGNS: 10 k. Pyotr Nesterov and "looping the loop"; 16 k. N. E. Zhukovsky and "aerodynamics".

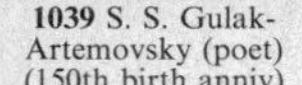

1039 S. S. Gulak-Artemovsky (poet) (150th birth anniv)

1040 Olga Kobilyanska (writer) (birth centenary)

1963. Celebrities.
2889 **1039** 4 k. black and red . . . 45 15
2890 – 4 k. brown and purple . . 45 15
2891 – 4 k. brown and violet . . 45 15
2892 **1040** 4 k. mauve and brown . . 45 15
2893 – 4 k. mauve and green . . 45 15
DESIGNS AND ANNIVERSARIES: As Type **1039**: No. 2983, M. I. Petraskas (Lithuanian composer) and scene from one of his works (90th birth anniv). As Type **1040**: No. 2890, G. D. Eristavi (writer, death cent, 1964); No. 2891, A. S. Dargomizhsky (composer, 150th birth anniv).

1041 Antactic Map and Supply Ship "Ob"

1043 E. O. Paton

1042 Letters and Transport

1963. Arctic and Antarctic Research. Mult.
2894 3 k. Type **1041** . . . . 2·00 30
2895 4 k. Convoy of snow tractors and map . . . . 1·00 30
2896 6 k. Globe and aircraft at polar base . . . . 1·75 30
2897 12 k. "Sovetskaya Ukraina" (whale factory ship), whale catcher and whale . . . . . 4·00 50

1963. International Correspondence Week.
2898 **1042** 4 k. violet, orge & blk . . 35 10

1963. 10th Death Anniv of Paton (engineer).
2899 **1043** 4 k. black, red & blue . . 20 10

1045 D. Diderot

1046 "Peace and Progess"

1963. 250th Birth Anniv of Denis Diderot (French philosopher).
2900 **1045** 4 k. brown, blue & bistre . 45 10

1963. "Peace—Brotherhood—Liberty—Labour". All black, red and lake.
2901 4 k. Type **1046** 20 15
2902 4 k. "The Plan" 20 15
2903 4 k. "Intellectual Work" 20 15
2904 4 k. "People's Union" 20 15
2905 4 k. "Nation's Elite" 20 15
2906 4 k. "The Family" 20 15

1047 Academy of Sciences, Frunze

1963. Centenary of Union of Kirgizia and Russia.
2907 **1047** 4 k. blue, yellow & red . . 20 10

1049 Lenin and Congress Building

1050 Menchnikov

1963. 13th Soviet Trade Unions' Congress, Moscow.
2908 **1049** 4 k. red and black . . . 15 10
2909 – 4 k. red and black . . . 15 10
DESIGN: No. 2909, Lenin with man and woman workers.

1963. 75th Anniv of Pasteur Institute, Paris.
2910 **1050** 4 k. green and bistre . . 25 10
2911 – 6 k. violet and bistre . . 45 15
2912 – 12 k. blue and bistre . . 1·10 30
PORTRAITS: 6 k. Pasteur; 12 k. Calmette.

1051 Cruiser "Aurora" and Rockets

1052 Gur Emi Mausoleum

1963. 46th Anniv of October Revolution.
2913 **1051** 4 k. black, orge & lake . 30 10
2914 4 k. black, red & lake . . 50 30

1963. Ancient Samarkand Buildings. Mult.
2915 4 k. Type **1052** 40 10
2916 4 k. Shachi-Zinda Mosque . . 40 10
2917 6 k. Registan Square (55 × 28½ mm) 55 20

1053 Inscription, Globe and Kremlin

1054 Pushkin Monument, Kiev

1963. Signing of Nuclear Test-ban Treaty, Moscow.
2918 **1053** 6 k. violet and pale blue . 45 15

1963.
2919 **1054** 4 k. brown 20 10

1057 Y. M. Steklov and "Izvestia"

1056 V. G. Shukhov, and Tower

1963. 110th Birth Anniv of Shukhov (engineer).
2920 **1056** 4 k. black and green . . 20 10

1963. 90th Birth Anniv of Steklov (first editor of "Izvestia")
2921 **1057** 4 k. black and mauve . . 20 10

1058 Buildings and Emblems of Moscow (and U.S.S.R.) and Prague (and Czechoslovakia)

1963. 20th Anniv of Soviet-Czech Friendship Treaty.
2922 **1058** 6 k. red, bistre & blue . 35 10

1059 F. A. Poletaev (soldier) and Medals

1963. Poletaev Commemoration.
2923 **1059** 4 k. multicoloured . . . 30 10

1062 J. Grimau (Spanish Communist)

1063 Rockets

1963. Grimau Commemoration.
2924 **1062** 6 k. violet, red and cream 45 10

1963. New Year (1st issue).
2925 **1063** 6 k. multicoloured . . . 50 10

1064 "Happy New Year"

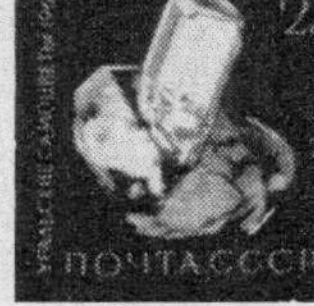
1067 Topaz

1963. New Year (2nd issue).
2926 **1064** 4 k. red, blue and green 30 10
2927 6 k. red, blue and green 60 10

1963. "Precious Stones of the Urals". Multicoloured.
2928 2 k. Type **1067** 25 10
2929 4 k. Jasper 50 10
2030 6 k. Amethyst 70 15
2931 10 k. Emerald 75 25
2932 12 k. Ruby . . . . 1·00 45
2933 16 k. Malachite . . . . . . 1·25 55

1068 Sputnik 7

1071 Flame and Rainbow

1069 Dushanbe (formerly "Stalinabad" 1929–62), Tadzhikistan

1963. "First in Space". Gold, vermilion and grey.
2934 10 k. Type **1068** 85 30
2935 10 k. Moon landing 85 30
2936 10 k. Back of Moon 85 30
2937 10 k. Vostok 7 . . . . 85 30
2938 10 k. Twin flight 85 30
2939 10 k. Seagull (first woman in space) 85 30

1963. Dushanbe Commemoration.
2940 **1069** 4 k. blue . . . 30 10

1963. 15th Anniv of Declaration of Human Rights.
2941 **1071** 6 k. multicoloured . . . 30 10

1072 F. A, Sergeev ("Artyem")

1963. 80th Birth Anniv of Sergeev (revolutionary).
2942 **1072** 4 k. brown and red . . 20 10

1073 Sun and Globe

1074 K. Donelaitis

1964. International Quiet Sun Year.
2943 – 4 k. black, orge & mve 30 10
2944 **1073** 6 k. blue, yellow & red 35 10
2945 – 10 k. violet, red & blue 40 20
DESIGNS—HORIZ: 4 k. Giant telescope and sun; 10 k. Globe and Sun.

1964. 250th Birth Anniv of K. Donelaitis (Lithuanian poet).
2946 **1074** 4 k. black and myrtle . 20 10

1075 Speed Skating

1964. Winter Olympic Games, Innsbruck.
2947 **1075** 2 k. black, mauve & bl 20 10
2948 – 4 k. black, blue & mve 35 10
2949 – 6 k. red, black & blue . 65 15
2950 – 10 k. black, mve & grn 70 25
2951 – 12 k. black, grn & mve 95 35
DESIGNS: 4 k. Skiing; 6 k. Games emblem; 10 k. Rifle shooting (biathlon); 12 k. Figure skating (pairs).
See also Nos. 2969/73.

1076 A. S. Golubkina and Statue

1077 "Agriculture"

1984. Birth Cent of A. Golubkina (sculptress).
2952 **1076** 4 k. sepia and grey . . 20 10

1964. Heavy Chemical Industries. Multicoloured.
2953 4 k. Type **1077** 50 10
2954 4 k. "Textiles" 50 10
2955 4 k. "Tyre Production" . . 50 10

150 років з дня народження. 1964 р.
(**1078**)

1079 Shevchenko's Statue, Kiev (M. Manizer)

1964. 150th Birth Anniv of T. G. Shevchenko (Ukrainian poet and painter). No. 2561 optd with T **1078** and designs as T **1079**.
2956 **880** 3 k. brown and violet . 1·60 1·60
2959 **1079** 4 k. green 25 10
2960 4 k. red 25 10
2961 – 6 k. blue 30 10
2962 – 6 k. brown 30 10
2957 – 10 k. violet and brown 85 30
2958 – 10 k. brown and bistre 85 30
DESIGNS: Nos. 2957/8, Portrait of Shevchenko by I. Repin; Nos. 2961/2, Self-portrait.

1080 K. S. Zaslonov

1964. War Heroes.
2963 **1080** 4 k. sepia and brown . 40 15
2964 – 4 k. purple and blue . 40 15
2965 – 4 k. blue and red . . 40 15
2966 – 4 k. brown and blue . 40 15
PORTRAITS: No. 2964, N. A. Vilkov; No. 2965, Yu. V. Smirnov; No. 2966, V. Z. Khoruzhaya.

1081 Federov printing the first Russian book, "Apostle"

1964. 400th Anniv of First Russian Printed Book. Multicoloured.
2967 4 k. Type **1081** 20 10
2968 6 k. Federov statue, books and newspapers 30 20

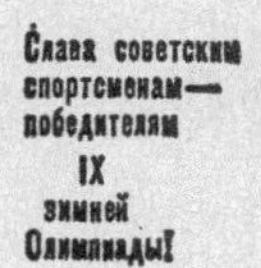

(**1082**)

1083 Ice Hockey Player

1964. Winter Olympic Games, Soviet Medal Winners.
(a) Nos. 2947/51 optd with T **1082** or similarly.
2969 2 k. black, mauve and blue . 20 10
2970 4 k. black, blue and mauve . 30 10
2971 6 k. red, black and blue . . 30 15
2972 10 k. black, mauve & green . 85 25
2973 12 k. black, green & mauve . 1·00 30
(b) New designs.
2974 **1083** 3 k. red, black & turquoise 30 10
2975 – 16 k. orange and brown 1·40 80
DESIGN: 16 k. Gold medal and inscr "Triumph of Soviet Sport–11 Gold, 8 Silver, 6 Bronze medals".

1084 Militiaman and Factory Guard

1964. "Public Security".
2976 **1084** 4 k. blue, red and black 20 10

1085 Lighthouse, Odessa and Sailor

1964. 20th Anniv of Liberation of Odessa and Leningrad. Multicoloured.
2977 4 k. Type **1085** 50 10
2978 4 k. Lenin Statue, Leningrad . 25 10

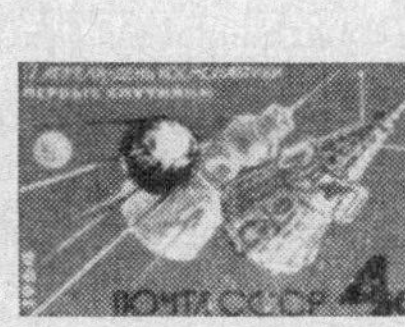
1086 Sputniks

1087 N. I. Kibalchich

1964. "The Way to the Stars". Imperf or perf. (a) Cosmonautics. As T **1086**.
2979 4 k. green, black and red . . 30 10
2980 6 k. black, blue and red . . 70 10
2981 12 k. turq, brown & black . . 1·40 30
DESIGNS: 6 k. "Mars 1" space station; 12 k. Gagarin and space capsule.
(b) Rocket Construction Pioneers. As T **1087**.
2982 10 k. black, green & violet . . 1·10 45
2983 10 k. black, turquoise and red 1·10 45
2984 10 k. black, turquoise and red 1·10 45
2985 10 k. black and blue . . . 1·00 25
DESIGNS: No. 2982, Type **1087**; No. 2983, F. A. Zander; No. 2984, K. E. Tsiolkovsky; No. 2985, Pioneers' medallion and Saransk memorial.

1088 Lenin

1964. 94th Birth Anniv of Lenin.
2986a **1088** 4 k. black, blue & mve 3·25 3·25

1089 Shakespeare (400th Birth Anniv)

1964. Cultural Anniversaries.
2987 – 6 k. yellow, brn & sepia 60 15
2988 **1089** 10 k. brown and olive . 1·00 25
2989 – 12 k. green and brown . 1·25 35
DESIGNS AND ANNIVERSARIES: 6 k. Michelangelo (400th death anniv); 12 k. Galileo (400th birth anniv).

1090 Crop-watering Machine and Produce

1964. "Irrigation".
2990 **1090** 4 k. multicoloured . . . 20 10

1091 Gamarnik

1964. 70th Birth Anniv of Ya. B. Gamarnik (Soviet Army commander).
2991 **1091** 4 k. brown, blue & blk 20 10

1092 D. I. Gulia (Abhazian poet)

1964. Cultural Anniversaries.
2992 **1092** 4 k. black, green and light green 30 15
2993 – 4 k. black, verm & red . 30 15
2994 – 4 k. black, brn & bistre 30 15
2995 – 4 k. black, yell & brn . 30 15
2996 – 4 k. multicoloured . . . 30 15
2997 – 4 k. black, yell & brn . 30 15
DESIGNS: No. 2993, Nijazi (Uzbek writer, composer and painter); No. 2994, S. Seifullin (Kazakh poet); No. 2995, M. M. Kotsyubinsky (writer); No. 2996, S. Nazaryan (Armenian writer); No. 2997, T. Satylganov (Kirghiz poet).

1093 A. Gaidar

1964. 60th Birth Annivs of Writers A. P. Gaidar and N. A. Ostrovsky.
2998 **1093** 4 k. red and blue . . . 25 10
2999 – 4 k. green and red . . . 35 10
DESIGN: No. 2999, N. Ostrovsky and battle scene.

1094 Indian Elephant

150 лет вхождения
в состав России
1964
4
коп.
(**1095**)

1964. Centenary of Moscow Zoo. Multicoloured. Imperf or perf.
3000 1 k. Type **1094** 10 10
3001 2 k. Giant panda 15 10
3002 4 k. Polar bear 35 10
3003 6 k. Elk 45 10
3004 10 k. Eastern white pelican . 1·25 25
3005 12 k. Tiger . . . . 1·25 30
3006 16 k. Lammergeier . . . . . 2·25 50
The 2 k. and 12 k. are horiz; the 4 k. and 10 k. are "square", approx $26\frac{1}{2} \times 28$ mm.

1964. 150th Anniv of Union of Azerbaijan and Russia. Surch with T **1095**.
3007 **328** 4 k. on 40 k. brown, bistre and yellow . . . . . . 2·10 1·60

1096 Rumanian Woman and Emblems on Map

1097 Maize

1964. 20th. Anniv of Rumanian–Soviet Friendship Treaty.
3008 **1096** 6 k. multicoloured . . . 40 15

1964. Agricultural Crops. Multicoloured. Imperf or perf.
3009 2 k. Type **1097** 15 10
3010 3 k. Wheat 20 10
3011 4 k. Potatoes 30 10
3012 6 k. Peas 25 20
3013 10 k. Sugar beet 55 25
3014 12 k. Cotton 75 30
3015 16 k. Flax . . . . 1·40 40

1098 Flag and Obelisk

1099 Leningrad G.P.O

1964. 20th Anniv of Liberation of Byelorussia.
3016 **1098** 4 k. multicoloured . . . 20 10

1964. 250th Anniv of Leningrad's Postal Service.
3017 **1099** 4 k. black, bistre & red . 20 10

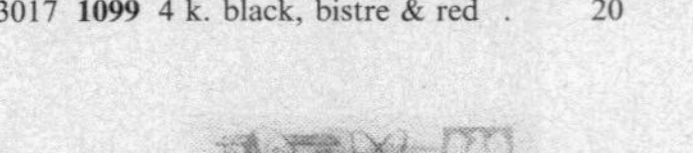

1100 Map of Poland and Emblems

1964. 20th Anniv of Polish People's Republic.
3018 **1100** 6 k. multicoloured . . . 35 10

1101 Horse-jumping

1102 M. Thorez (French Communist leader)

1964. Olympic Games, Tokyo. Imperf or perf.
3019 **1101** 3 k. multicoloured . . . 10 10
3020 – 4 k. red, black & yellow 15 10
3021 – 6 k. red, black and blue 25 10
3022 – 10 k. red, black & turq . 65 15
3023 – 12 k. black and grey . . 80 20
3024 – 16 k. violet, red and blue 1·40 50
DESIGNS: 4 k. Weightlifting; 6 k. Pole vaulting; 10 k. Canoeing; 12 k. Gymnastics; 16 k. Fencing.

1964. Maurice Thorez Commemoration.
3025 **1102** 4 k. black and red . . . 1·10 20

1103 Three Races

1104 Jawaharlal Nehru

1964. International Anthropologists and Ethnographers Congress, Moscow.
3026 **1103** 6 k. black and yellow . 35 10

1964. Nehru Commemoration.
3027 **1104** 4 k. brown and grey . . 35 10

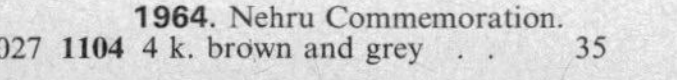

1105 Globe and Banner

1106 A. V. Vishnevsky (surgeon)

1964. Centenary of "First International".
3028 **1105** 4 k. red, bistre and blue 20 10
3029 – 4 k. red, olive and black 20 10
3030 – 4 k. drab, red and lake 20 10
3031 – 4 k. red, black and blue 20 10
3032 – 4 k. multicoloured . . 20 10
DESIGNS: No. 3029, Communist Party manifesto; No. 3030, Marx and Engels; No. 3031, Chain breaker; No. 3032, Lenin.

1964. "Outstanding Soviet Physicians".
3033 **1106** 4 k. brown and pur . . 40 15
3034 – 4 k. brown, red & yellow 40 15
3035 – 4 k. brown, blue & bistre 40 15
DESIGNS: No. 3034, N. A. Semashko (public health pioneer). Both are 90th birth anniversaries. No. 3035, D. I. Ivanovsky and siphon (25 × 32 mm).

1107 Bulgarian Flag, Rose and Emblems

1108 P. Togliatti (Italian Communist leader)

1964. 20th Anniv of Bulgarian People's Republic.
3036 **1107** 6 k. red, green & drab . 30 15

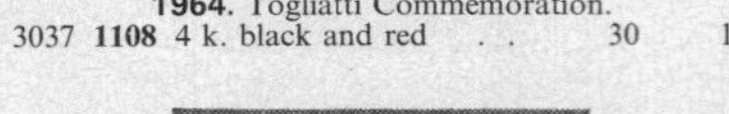

1964. Togliatti Commemoration.
3037 **1108** 4 k. black and red . . 30 10

1110 Globe and Letters

1964. International Correspondence Week.
3038 **1110** 4 k. mauve, blue & brn 30 10

1111 Soviet and Yugoslav Soldiers

1112 East German Arms, Industrial Plants, Freighter "Havel" and Goods Train

1964. 20th Anniv of Liberation of Belgrade.
3039 **1111** 6 k. multicoloured . . 45 15

1964. 15th Anniv of German Democratic Republic.
3040 **1112** 6 k. multicoloured . . 45 15

1113 Woman holding Bowl of Produce (Moldavian Republic)

40 лет Советскому Таджикистану

(1115)

1964. 40th Anniv of Soviet Republic. (a) As T **1113**.
3041 **1113** 4 k. brown, green & red 20 10
3042 – 4 k. multicoloured . . 30 10
3043 – 4 k. red, purple & yell . 30 10

(b) Optd with T **1115**.
3044 **1069** 4 k. blue . . . . . . 1·10 60
DESIGNS—VERT: No. 3042, Woman holding Arms (Turkmenistan); No. 3043, Man and woman holding produce (Uzbekistan); No. 3044, commemorates the Tadzhikistan Republic.

1116 Yegorov

1964. Three-manned Space Flight. (a) Portraits in black, orange and turquoise.
3045 4 k. Type **1116** 30 10
3046 4 k. Feoktistov 30 10
3047 4 k. Komarov 30 10
These can be identified by the close proximation of the Russian names on the stamps to the English versions.

(b) Designs $73\frac{1}{2} \times 22\frac{1}{2}$ mm.
3058 6 k. purple and violet . . . 45 15
3049 10 k. violet and blue . . . 1·10 30
DESIGNS: 6 k. The three cosmonauts; 10 k. Space ship "Voskhod 1".

1117 Soldier and Flags

1964. 20th Anniv of Liberation of Ukraine.
3050 **1117** 4 k. multicoloured . . . 20 10

1119 Lermontov's Birthplace

1121 N. K. Krupskaya (Lenin's wife)

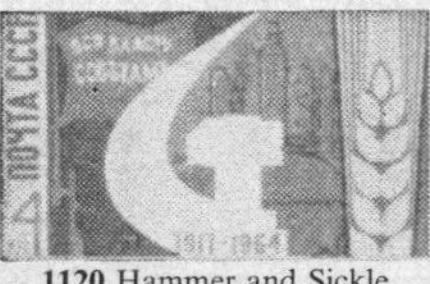

1120 Hammer and Sickle

1964. 150th Birth Anniv of M. Lermontov (poet).
3051 **1119** 4 k. violet 20 10
3052 – 6 k. black 30 10
3053 – 10 k. brown and flesh . 85 25
DESIGNS: 6 k. Lermontov; 10 k. Lermontov talking with Belinsky.

1964. 47th Anniv of October Revolution.
3054 **1120** 4 k. multicoloured . . . 20 10

1964. Birth Anniversaries.
3055 **1121** 4 k. multicoloured . . . 20 10
3056 – 4 k. multicoloured . . . 20 10
DESIGNS: No. 3055 (95th anniv); No. 3056, A. I. Yelizarova-Ulianova (Lenin's sister) (cent).

1122 Mongoilan Woman and Lamb

1124 "Suillus luteus"

1964. 40th Anniv of Mongolian People's Republic.
3057 **1122** 4 k. multicoloured . . . 30 15

1964. Mushrooms. Multicoloured.
3058 2 k. Type **1124** 30 10
3059 4 k. "Cantharellus cibarius" . 50 10
3060 6 k. "Boletus edulis" . . . 65 15
3061 10 k. "Leccinum aurantiacum" 1·00 30
3062 12 k. "Lactarius deliciosus" 1·25 40

1125 A. P. Dovzhenko

1126 Christmas Tree, Star and Globe

1964. 70th Birth Anniv of Dovzhenko (film producer).
3063 **1125** 4 k. blue and grey . . . 30 10

1964. New Year.
3064 **1126** 4 k. multicoloured . . . 40 15

1127 Struve

1128 S. V. Ivanov and Skiers

1964. Death Centenary of V. Ya. Struve (scientist).
3065 **1127** 4 k. brown and blue . . 60 15

1964. Birth Centenary of S. V. Ivanov (painter).
3066 **1128** 4 k. brown and black . 65 15

1129 Scene from Film

1964. 30th Anniv of Film "Chapaev".
3067 **1129** 6 k. black and green . . 35 15

1130 Test-tubes, Jar and Agricultural Scenes

1964. Chemistry for the National Economy.
3068 **1130** 4 k. purple and olive . 20 15
3069 – 6 k. black and blue . . 35 10
DESIGN: 6 k. Chemical plant.

1131 Cranberries

1132 Library

1964. Woodland Fruits. Multicoloured.
3070 1 k. Type **1131** 10 10
3071 3 k. Bilberries 15 10
3072 4 k. Rowanberries 20 10
3073 10 k. Blackberries 55 20
3074 16 k. Red bilberries 85 40

1964. 250th Anniv of Academy of Sciences Library, Leningrad.
3075 **1132** 4 k. black, green & red 20 10

1133 Congress Palace and Spassky Tower

1134 Mt Khan-Tengri

1964.
3076 **1133** 1 r. blue . . . . . . 7·50 1·25

1964. Mountaineering. Multicoloured.
3077 4 k. Type **1134** 20 10
3978 6 k. Mt Kazbek (horiz) . . . 40 15
3079 12 k. Mt Ushba 80 30

1136 Bowl

1964. Kremlin Treasures. Multicoloured.
3080 4 k. Helmet 70 15
3081 6 k. Quiver 90 20
3082 10 k. Coronation headgear . 1·10 35
3083 12 k. Ladle . . . . 1·25 45
3084 16 k. Type **1136** . . . . 1·50 80

1137 I. M. Sivko **1138** Dante

1965. War Heroes.
3085 **1137** 4 k. black and violet . . 40 15
3086 – 4 k. brown and blue . . 40 15
DESIGN: No. 3086, General I. S. Polbin.

1965. 700th Birth Anniv of Dante.
3038 **4** k. black, bistre and purple . 45 10

1139 Blood Donor **1140** N. P. Kravkov

1965. Blood Donors. Multicoloured.
3088 4 k. Type **1139** 35 15
3089 4 k. Hand holding red carnation 35 15

1965. Birth Cent of N. Kravkov (pharmacologist).
3090 **1140** 4 k. multicoloured . . . 25 10

1141 Figure Skaters **1142** Alsatian

1965. European Figure Skating Championships, Moscow.
3091 **1141** 6 k. red, black & green . 40 15
See also No. 3108.

1965. World Ice Hockey Championships, Moscow. Designs similar to T **1141** but depicting ice hockey players.
3092 4 k. red, blue and bistre . . . 30 15

1965. Hunting and Service Dogs.
3093 – 1 k. black, yellow & red 15 10
3097 – 2 k. brown, blue & blk . 20 10
3098 **1142** 3 k. black, red & yellow 20 10
3099 – 4 k. black, brown & grn 30 10
3100 – 4 k. black, orange & grn 30 10
3101 – 6 k. black, brown & bl . 40 15
3102 – 6 k. black, red & blue . 40 15
3104 – 10 k. multicoloured . . 65 20
3095 – 12 k. black, brn & vio . 85 30
3096 – 16 k. multicoloured . . 1·25 35
DESIGNS—HORIZ: 1 k. Hound; 2 k. Setter; 4 k. (3099) (value in green) Fox terrier; 4 k. (3100) (value in orange) Pointer; 6 k. (3101) Borzoi; 12 k. Husky. VERT: 6 k. (3102) Sheepdog; 10 k. Collie; 16 k. Caucasion sheepdog.

1143 R. Sorge

1965. Richard Sorge (Soviet secret agent) Commem.
3103 **1143** 4 k. black and red . . . 55 15

1144 I.T.U. Emblem and Telecommunications Symbol

1965. Centenary of I.T.U.
3104 **1144** 6 k. violet and blue . . 55 15

1145 Leonov in Space

1965. Space Flight of "Voskhod 2" (1st issue). Imperf or perf.
3105 **1145** 10 k. orange, blk & bl . 1·00 30
See also Nos. 3138/9.

1965. Ice Hockey Championships. Optd **ТАМПЕРЕ 1965 г.**
3107 **1034** 6 k. blue and red . . . 1·00 40

Советские
фигуристы—
чемпионы мира
в парном катании

(1147)

1148 Soldier and Woman

1965. Soviet Victory in European Figure Skating Championships. Optd with T **1147**.
3108 **1141** 6 k. red, black & green 1·00 40

1965. 20th Anniversaries.
3109 **1148** 6 k. multicoloured . . 40 15
3110 – 6 k. multicoloured . . 40 15
3111 – 6 k. ochre and red . . 40 15
3112 – 6 k. multicoloured . . 40 15
3113 – 6 k. multicoloured . . 40 15
DESIGNS: No. 3109, Type **1148** (Czech Liberation); No. 3110, Statue and emblems of development (Friendship with Hungary); No. 3111, Polish and Soviet arms (Polish–Soviet Friendship Treaty); No. 3112, Viennese buildings and Russian soldier (Freeing of Vienna); No. 3113, Liberation medal, Polish flag and building reconstruction (Freeing of Warsaw).
See also Nos. 3182 and 3232.

1149 Statue Rockets and Globe **1150** Rockets and Radio-telescope

1965. National Cosmonautics Day. Nos. 3117/18 on aluminium-surfaced paper.
3114 **1149** 4 k. green, black & red 25 10
3115 – 12 k. purple, red & blue 85 40
3116 – 16 k. multicoloured . . 1·10 60
3117 **1150** 20 k. red, black and green on silver . . . . . . 6·75 5·00
3118 – 20 k. red, black and blue on silver . . . . . . 6·75 5·00
DESIGNS: 12 k. Statue and Globe; 16 k. Rockets and Globe; No. 3118, Globe, satellite and cosomonauts.

1151 Lenin

1965. Lenin's 95th Birth Anniv.
3119 **1151** 10 k. blue, black & brn 55 50

1152 Poppies **1153** Red Flag, Reichstag Building and Broken Swastika

1965. Flowers.
3120 **1152** 1 k. red, lake & green . 10 10
3121 – 3 k. yellow, brn & grn . 20 10
3122 – 4 k. lilac, black & grn . 30 10
3123 – 6 k. red, deep green and green 40 10
3124 – 10 k. yellow, pur & grn 1·00 25
FLOWERS: 3 k. Marguerite; 4 k. Peony; 6 k. Carnation; 10 k. Tulips.

1965. 20th Anniv of Victory.
3125 **1153** 1 k. black, gold & red . 20 10
3126 – 2 k. red, black & gold . 25 15
3127 – 3 k. blue and gold . . 40 15
3128 – 4 k. violet and gold . . 55 15
3129 – 4 k. green and gold . . 60 15
3130 – 6 k. purple, grn & gold 1·00 20
3131 – 10 k. purple, brn & gold 1·75 25
3132 – 12 k. black, red & gold 2·00 30
3133 – 16 k. red and gold . . . 2·50 40
3134 – 20 k. black, red & gold . 3·25 75
DESIGNS: 2 k. Soviet mother holding manifesto (poster by I. Toidze); 3 k. "The Battle for Moscow" (V. Bogatkin); 4 k. (No. 3128), "Partisan Mother" (from S. Gerasimov's film); 4 k. (No. 3129), "Red Army Soldiers and Partisans" (from Yu. Neprintsev's film); 6 k. Soldiers and flag (poster by V. Ivanov); 10 k. "Mourning the Fallen Hero" (from F. Bogorodsky's film); 12 k. Soldier and worker holding bomb (poster by V. Korestsky); 16 k. Victory celebrations, Red Square, Moscow (from K. Yuon's film); 20 k. Soldier and machines of war.

1154 Marx and Lenin

1965. Marxism and Leninism.
3136 **1154** 6 k. black and red . . . 30 10
No. 3136 is similar in design to those issued by China and Hungary for the Postal Ministers' Congress, Peking, but this event is not mentioned on the stamp or in the Soviet philatelic bulletins.

1155 Bolshoi Theatre

1965. International Theatre Day.
3137 **1155** 6 k. ochre, blk & turq . 35 15

1156 Leonov **1157** Yakov Sverdlov (revolutionary)

1965. "Voskhod 2" Space Flight (2nd issue).
3138 **1156** 6 k. violet and silver . . 30 15
3139 – 6 k. purple and silver . . 30 15
DESIGN: No. 3139, Belyaev.

1965. 80th Birth Anniversaries.
3140 **1157** 4 k. black and brown . . 20 10
3141 – 4 k. black and violet . . 20 10
PORTRAIT: No. 3141, J. Akhunbabaev (statesman).

1158 Otto Grotewohl (1st death anniv) **1159** Telecommunications Satellite

1965. Annivs of Grotewohl and Thorez (Communist leaders).
3142 **1158** 4 k. black and purple . . 20 10
3143 – 6 k. brown and red . . 40 15
DESIGN: 6 k. Maurice Thorez (65th birth anniv).

1965. International Co-operation Year. Multi.
3144 3 k. Type **1159** 20 10
3145 6 k. Star and sputnik 40 15
3146 6 k. Foundry ladle, iron works and map of India 40 15
No. 3145 signifies peaceful uses of atomic energy and No. 3146 co-operation with India.

1160 Congress Emblem, Chemical Plant and Symbols

1965. 20th International Congress of Pure and Applied Chemistry, Moscow.
3147 **1160** 4 k. red, black & blue . 25 10

1161 V. A. Serov

1965. Birth Centenary of V. A. Serov (painter).
3148 **1161** 4 k. black, brn & stone 80 20
3149 – 6 k. black and drab . . 1·50 25
DESIGN: 6 k. Full length portrait of Chaliapin (singer) by Serov.

1162 V. Ivanov and Armoured Train

1965. Famous Writers.
3150 **1162** 4 k. black and purple . . 40 15
3151 – 4 k. black and violet . . 40 15
3152 – 4 k. black and blue . . 40 15
3153 – 4 k. black and grey . . 40 15
3154 – 4 k. blk, red and green . 40 15
3155 – 4 k. black and brown . . 40 15
WRITERS AND ANNIVERSARIES: No. 3150, (70th birth anniv); No. 3151, A. Kunanbaev and military parade; No. 3152, J. Rainis (Lettish poet: 90th birth anniv); No. 3153, E. J. Vilde (Estonian author): 90th birth anniv); No. 3154, M. Ch. Abegjan (Armenian writer and critic: 90th birth anniv); No. 3155, M. L. Kropivnitsky and scene from play (Ukrainian playwright).

1163 Festival Emblem

1965. Film Festival, Moscow.
3156 **1163** 6 k. black, gold & blue 30 10

1164 Concert Arena, Tallin **1165** Hand holding "Peace Flower"

1965. 25th Anniv of Incorporation of Estonia, Lithuania and Latvia in the U.S.S.R.
3157 **1164** 4 k. multicoloured . . . 30 10
3158 – 4 k. brown and red . . 30 10
3159 – 4 k. brn, red and blue . 30 10
DESIGNS—VERT: No. 3158, Lithuanian girl and Arms. HORIZ: No. 3159, Latvian Flag and Arms.

1965. Peace Issue.
3160 **1165** 6 k. yellow, blk & blue . 30 10

1167 "Potemkin" Sailors Monument, Odessa

1965. 60th Anniv of 1905 Rebellion.
3161 **1167** 4 k. blue and red . . . 20 15
3162 – 4 k. green, blk & red . 20 15
3163 – 4 k. green, blk & red . 20 15
3164 – 4 k. brown, blk & red . 20 15
DESIGNS: No. 3162, Demonstrator up lamp post; No. 3163, Defeated rebels; No. 3164, Troops at street barricade.

1168 G. Gheorgi-Dej (Rumanian Communist) **1169** Power Station

1965. G. Gheorgi-Dej Commemoration.
3165 **1168** 4 k. black and red . . . 25 10

1965. Industrial Progress.
3166 **1169** 1 k. multicoloured . . . 10 10
3167 – 2 k. black, orge & yell . 10 10
3168 – 3 k. vio, yell and ochre . 15 10
3169 – 4 k. deep blue, blue and red 20 10
3170 – 6 k. blue and bistre . . 30 10
3171 – 10 k. brown, yellow and orange 60 20
3172 – 12 k. turquoise and red 90 20
3173 – 16 k. purple, blue & blk 1·40 40
DESIGNS: 2 k. Steel works; 3 k. Chemical works and formula; 4 k. Machine tools production; 6 k. Building construction; 10 k. Agriculture; 12 k. Communications and transport; 16 k. Scientific research.

1170 Relay Racing **1171** Gymnastics

1965. Trade Unions Spartakiad. Multicoloured.
3174 4 k. Type **1170** 25 15
3175 4 k. Gymnastics 25 15
3176 4 k. Cycling 25 15

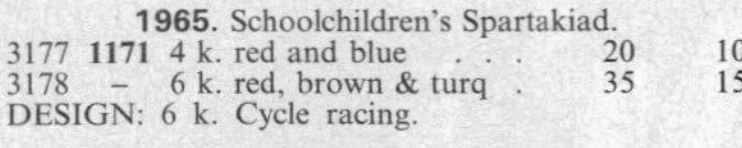

1965. Schoolchildren's Spartakiad.
3177 **1171** 4 k. red and blue . . . 20 10
3178 – 6 k. red, brown & turq . 35 15
DESIGN: 6 k. Cycle racing.

1172 Throwing the Javelin and Running **1173** Star, Palms and Lotus

1965. American–Soviet Athletic Meeting, Kiev.
3179 **1172** 4 k. red, brown & lilac . 15 10
3180 – 6 k. red, brown & green 25 10
3181 – 10 k. red, brown & grey 65 15
DESIGNS: 6 k. High jumping and putting the shot; 10 k. Throwing the hammer and hurdling.

1965. 20th Anniv of North Vietnamese People's Republic.
3182 **1173** 6 k. multicoloured . . . 30 15

1174 Worker with Hammer (World T.U. Federation) **1176** P. K. Sternberg (astonomer: birth cent)

1965. 20th Anniv of International Organizations.
3183 **1174** 6 k. drab and plum . . 20 15
3184 – 6 k. brown, red & blue . 20 15
3185 – 6 k. lt brown & turq, 20 15
DESIGNS: No. 3184, Torch and heads of three races (World Democratic Youth Federation); No. 3185, Woman holding dove (International Democratic Women's Federation).

1965. Scientists' Anniversaries.
3186 **1176** 4 k. brown and blue . . 60 15
3187 – 4 k. black and purple . 60 15
3188 – 4 k. black, pur & yell . 35 15
PORTRAITS: No. 3187, Ch. Valikhanov (scientific writer: death cent); No. 3188, V. A. Kistyakovsky (scientist: birth cent).

1177 "Battleship 'Potemkin'"

1965. "Soviet Cinema Art". Designs showing scenes from films. Multicoloured.
3189 4 k. Type **1177** 30 10
3190 6 k. "Young Guard" 40 15
3191 12 k. "A Soldier's Ballad" . 85 25

1178 Mounted Postman and Map

1965. History of the Russian Post Office.
3192 **1178** 1 k. green, brown & vio 20 10
3193 – 1 k. brown, ochre & grey 20 10
3194 – 2 k. brown, blue & lilac 20 10
3195 – 4 k. black, ochre & pur 45 10
3196 – 6 k. black, green & brn 65 15
3197 – 12 k. sepia, brown & bl 1·00 25
3198 – 16 k. plum, red & grey 1·25 45
DESIGNS: No. 3193, Mail coach and map; 2 k. Early steam train and medieval kogge; 4 k. Mail lorry and map; 6 k. Diesel train and various transport; 12 k. Moscow Post Office electronic facing sorting and cancelling machines; 16 k. Airports and Lenin.

1179 "Vostok" and "Mirnyi" (Antarctic exploration vessels)

1965. Polar Research Annivs.
3199 – 4 k. black, orange & bl 90 15
3200 – 4 k. black, orange & bl 90 15
3201 – 6 k. sepia and violet . . 1·00 25
3202 **1179** 10 k. black, drab & red 1·25 35
3203 – 16 k. black, vio & brn . 1·75 65
DESIGNS—HORIZ: $37\frac{1}{2}\times25\frac{1}{2}$ mm: No. 3199, Ice breakers "Taimyr" and "Vaigach" in Arctic (50th anniv); No. 3200, Atomic ice breaker "Lenin"; No. 3201, Dikson settlement (50th anniv); No. 3203, Vostok Antarctic station. SQUARE. No. 3202, (145th anniv of Lazarev–Bellingshausen Expedition).
Nos. 3199/200 were issued together, se-tenant, forming a composite design.

1181 Agricultural Academy

1965. Centenary of Academy of Agricultural Sciences, Moscow.
3205 **1181** 4 k. violet, red & drab . 30 15

1183 N. Poussin (self-portrait) **1184** Kremlin

1965. 300th Death Anniv of Nicolas Poussin (French painter).
3207 **1183** 4 k. multicoloured . . 50 10

1965. New Year.
3208 **1184** 4 k. red, silver & black 25 10

1185 M. I. Kalinin

1966. 90th Birth Anniv of Kalinin (statesman).
3209 **1185** 4 k. lake and red 15 10

1186 Klyuchevski Volcano

1965. Soviet Volcanoes. Multicoloured.
3210 4 k. Type **1186** 40 15
3211 12 k. Karumski Volcano (vert) 1·00 30
3212 16 k. Koryaski Volcano . . . 1·10 45

1187 Oktyabrskaya Station, Moscow

1965. Soviet Metro Stations.
3213 **1187** 6 k. blue 40 15
3214 – 6 k. brown 40 15
3215 – 6 k. brown 40 15
3216 – 6 k. green 40 15
STATIONS: No. 3214, Leninksy Prospekt, Moscow; No. 3215, Moskovian Gate, Leningrad; No. 3216, Bolshevik Factory, Kiev.

1188 Common Buzzard **1189** "Red Star" (medal) and Scenes of Odessa

1965. Birds of Prey. Birds in black.
3217 **1188** 1 k. grey 35 10
3218 – 2 k. brown 45 10
3219 – 3 k. olive 55 10
3220 – 4 k. drab 65 10
3221 – 10 k. brown . . . . . 1·25 20
3222 – 12 k. blue . . . . . . 1·50 35
3223 – 14 k. blue . . . . . . 1·75 40
3224 – 16 k. purple . . . . . 2·00 50
BIRDS—VERT: 2 k. Common kestrel; 3 k. Tawny eagle; 4 k. Red kite; 10 k. Peregrine falcon; 16 k. Gyrfalcon. HORIZ: 12 k. Golden eagle; 14 k. Lammergeier.

1965. Heroic Soviet Towns. Multicoloured.
3225 10 k. Type 1189 . . . . . . 40 25
3226 10 k. Leningrad 40 25
3227 10 k. Kiev 40 25
3228 10 k. Moscow 40 25
3229 10 k. Brest-Litovsk 40 25
3230 10 k. Volgograd 40 25
3231 10 k. Sevastopol 40 25

1190 Flag, Map and Parliament Building, Belgrade

1965. 20th Anniv of Yugoslavia Republic.
3232 **1190** 6 k. multicoloured . . . 50 10

1191 Tupolev Tu-134

1965. Soviet Civil Aviation. Multicoloured.
3233 6 k. Type **1191** 50 10
3234 10 k. Antonov An-24 . . . . 70 15
3235 12 k. Mil Mi-10 helicopter . . 80 25
3236 16 k. Beriv Be-10 flying boat . 1·10 40
3237 20 k. Antonov An-22 Anteus 1·75 45

1192 "The Proposal of Marriage", after P. Fedotov (150th birth anniv)

1965. Soviet Painters' Annivs.
3238 – 12 k. black and red . . 1·50 35
3239 **1192** 16 k. blue and red . . . 2·40 60
DESIGN—VERT: 12 k. "A Collective Farm Watchman" (after S. Gerasimov: 80th birth anniv).

1193 Crystallography Congress Emblem

1966. International Congresses, Moscow.
3240 **1193** 6 k. black, bl & bistre . 25 15
3241 – 6 k. black, red & blue . 25 15
3242 – 6 k. purple, grey & blk 25 15
3243 – 6 k. black and blue . . 50 15
3244 – 6 k. black, red & yellow 25 15
CONGRESS EMBLEMS: No. 3241, Microbiology; No. 3242, Poultry-raising; No. 3243, Oceanography; No. 3244, Mathematics.

1194 19th-cent Statuettes

1966. Bicentenary of Dmitrov Ceramic Works. Multicoloured.
3245 6 k. Type **1194** 30 15
3246 10 k. Modern tea set 65 25

1195 Rolland and Scene from Novel

1966. Birth Centenary of Romain Rolland (French writer) and 150th Birth Anniv of Eugene Potier (French poet).
3247 **1195** 4 k. brown and blue . . 30 15
3248 – 4 k. brn, red and black 30 15
DESIGN: No. 3248, Potier and revolutionary scene.

1196 Mongol Horseman

1966. 20th Anniv of Soviet–Mongolian Treaty.
3249 **1196** 4 k. multicoloured . . . 25 10

„ЛУНА-9" — НА ЛУНЕ!
3.2.1966
(1197)

1966. Landing of "Luna 9" Rocket on Moon. Optd with T **1197**.
3250 **1017** 6 k. red, black & blue . 4·25 4·25

1198 Supply Ship "Ob"

1966. 10th Anniv of Soviet Antarctic Expedition.

3251	**1198**	10 k. lake and silver	2·00	50
3252	–	10 k. lake, silver & blue	2·00	50
3253	–	10 k. lake, silver & blue	2·00	50

DESIGNS—TRIANGULAR: No. 3252, Snow vehicle. DIAMOND: No. 3253, Antarctic map.
This stamp is partly perf across the centre.

1199 Mussa Dyalil and Scene from Poem

1966. Writers.

3254	**1199**	4 k. black and brown	30	10
3255	–	4 k. black and green	30	10
3256	–	4 k. black and green	30	10

WRITERS: No. 3254 (Azerbaijan writer: 60th birth anniv); No. 3255, Akob Akopyan (Armenian poet: birth cent); No. 3256, Djalil Mamedkulizade (Azerbaijan writer: birth cent).

1200 Lenin (after bust by Kibalnikov)

1966. Lenin's 96th Birth Anniv

3257	**1200**	10 k. gold and green	1·25	65
3258		10 k. silver and red	80	25

1201 N. Ilin

1202 Scene from "Alive and Dead"

1966. War Heroes.

3259	**1201**	4 k. violet and red	30	15
3260	–	4 k. lilac and blue	30	15
3261	–	4 k. brown and green	30	15

PORTRAITS: No. 3260, G. P. Kravchenko; No. 3261, A. Uglovsky.

1966. Soviet Cinema Art.

3262	**1202**	4 k. black, grn & red	25	10
3263	–	10 k. black and blue	60	20

DESIGN: 10 k. Scene from "Hamlet".

1203 Kremlin and Inscription

Учредительная конференция
Всесоюзного общества
филателистов. 1966

(**1204**)

1966. 23rd Soviet Comunist Party Congress, Moscow (1st issue).

3264	**1203**	4 k. gold, red & blue	20	10

See also Nos. 3337/41.

1966. Philatelists All-Union Society Conference. No. 3198 optd with T **1204**.

3265		16 k. plum, red and grey	2·75	1·60

1205 Ice Skating

1966. 2nd People's Winter Spartakiad.

3266	**1205**	4 k. blue, red and olive	25	15
3267	–	6 k. red, lake and lilac	35	20
3268	–	10 k. lake, red and blue	60	30

DESIGNS: Inscription emblem and 6 k. Ice hockey; 10 k. Skiing.
Nos. 3266/8 are each perf across the centre.

1206 Liner "Aleksandr Pushkin"

1207 Government Building, Frunze

1966. Soviet Transport.

3269	–	4 k. multicoloured	55	10
3270	–	6 k. multicoloured	45	10
3271	–	10 k. multicoloured	65	20
3272	**1206**	12 k. multicoloured	1·00	20
3273	–	16 k. multicoloured	1·00	25

DESIGNS—HORIZ: 4 k. Electric train; 6 k. Map of Lenin Volga–Baltic canal system; 16 k. Silhouette of liner on Globe. VERT: 10 k. Canal lock.
Nos. 3271/3 commemorate the inaug of Leningrad–Montreal Sea Service.

1966. 40th Anniv of Kirgizia.

3274	**1207**	4 k. red	20	10

1208 S. M. Kirov (80th Birth Anniv)

1210 A. Fersman (mineralogist)

1966. Soviet Personalities.

3275	**1208**	4 k. brown	20	10
3276	–	4 k. green	20	10
3277	–	4 k. violet	20	10

PORTRAITS: No. 3276, G. I. Ordzhonikidze (80th birth anniv); No. 3277, Ion Yakir (military commander, 70th birth anniv).

1966. Soviet Scientists. Multicoloured. Colours of name panels below.

3279	**1210**	4 k. blue	25	15
3280	–	4 k. brown	25	15
3281	–	4 k. violet	25	15
3282	–	4 k. brown and blue	35	15

PORTRAITS: No. 3280, D. K. Zabolotnyi (microbiologist); No. 3281, M. A. Shatelen (electrical engineer); No. 3282, O. Yu. Shmidt (arctic explorer).

„Луна-10"—XXIII съезду КПСС

(**1211**)

1966. Launching of "Luna 10". As No. 3284, but imperf, optd with T **1211**.

3283	**1212**	10 k. multicoloured	2·40	1·40

1212 Arrowheads, "Luna 9" and Orbit

1966. Cosmonautics Day. Multicoloured.

3284	10 k. Type **1212**	60	25
3285	12 k. Rocket launching and different orbit	65	30

1213 "Molniya I" in Orbit

1214 Ernst Thalmann (80th birth anniv)

1966. Launching of "Molniya I" Telecommunications Satellite.

3286	**1213**	10 k. multicoloured	55	20

1966. Prominent Leaders.

3287	**1214**	6 k. red	30	10
3288	–	6 k. violet	30	10
3289	–	6 k. brown	30	10

PORTRAITS: No. 3288, W. Pieck (90th birth anniv); No. 3289, Sun Yat-sen (birth cent).

1216 Spaceman and Soldier

1966. 15th Young Communist League Congress.

3290	**1216**	4 k. black and red	15	10

1217 Ice Hockey Player

1966. Soviet Victory in World Ice Hockey Championships.

3291	**1217**	10 k. multicoloured	60	25

1218 N. I. Kuznetsov

1219 Tchaikovsky

1966. War Heroes. Guerilla Fighters.

3292	**1218**	4 k. black and green	20	10
3293	–	4 k. black and yellow	20	10
3294	–	4 k. black and blue	20	10
3295	–	4 k. black and purple	20	10
3296	–	4 k. black and violet	20	10

PORTRAITS: No. 3293, I. Y. Sudmalis; No. 3294, A. A. Morozova; No. 3295, F. E. Strelets; No. 3296, T. P. Bumazhkov.

1966. 3rd International Tchaikovsky Music Competition, Moscow.

3297	–	4 k. black, red & yellow	35	10
3298	**1219**	6 k. black, red & yellow	55	10
3299	–	16 k. black, red & blue	1·10	35

DESIGNS: 4 k. Moscow State Conservatoire of Music; 16 k. Tchaikovsky's house and museum, Klin.

1220 Running

1966. Sports Events.

3300	**1220**	4 k. brown, olive & grn	15	15
3301	–	6 k. black, bis & orge	30	15
3302	–	12 k. black, bistre & bl	45	25

DESIGNS: 6 k. Weightlifting; 12 k. Wrestling.

1222 Gold Medal and Chess Pieces

1966. World Chess Championship, Moscow.

3303	**1222**	6 k. multicoloured	75	20

1223 Jules Rimet Cup and Football

1966. World Cup Football Championships and World Fencing Championships.

3304	**1223**	4 k. black, gold & red	20	10
3305	–	6 k. multicoloured	30	10
3306	–	12 k. multicoloured	60	20
3307	–	16 k. multicoloured	90	40

DESIGNS: 6 k. Footballers; 12 k. Fencers; 16 k. Fencer and fencing emblems.

1224 Sable, Lake Baikal and Animals (Illustration reduced. Actual size 80 × 26 mm)

1966. Barguzin Nature Reserve.

3308	**1224**	4 k. black and blue	50	15
3309	–	6 k. black and purple	75	25

DESIGN: 6 k. Map of reserve, and brown bear.

1225 Lotus Plants

1226 "Venus 3" Medal, Globe and Flight Trajectory

1966. 125th Anniv of Sukhumi Botanical Gardens.

3310	**1225**	3 k. red, yellow & grn	15	10
3311	–	6 k. bistre, brown & bl	30	10
3312	–	12 k. red, green & turq	50	30

DESIGNS: 6 k. Palms and cypresses; 12 k. Water lilies.

1966. Space Achievements.

3313	**1226**	6 k. black, silver & red	40	15
3314	–	6 k. deep blue, blue and brown	40	15
3315	–	6 k. ochre and blue	40	15
3316	–	6 k. multicoloured	45	15
3317	–	6 k. pink, mauve & blk	45	15

DESIGNS: No. 3314, Spacedogs, Ugolek and Veterok; No. 3315, "Luna 10"; No. 3316, "Molniya I"; No. 3317, "Luna 2's" pennant, Earth and Moon.

1227 Itkol

1966. Tourist Resorts. Multicoloured.

3318	1 k. Type **1227**	10	10
3319	4 k. Cruise ship on the Volga	30	10
3320	6 k. Archway, Leningrad	25	10
3321	10 k. Kislovodsk	45	20
3322	12 k. Ismail Samani Mausoleum Bokhara	1·00	15
3323	16 k. Sochi (Black Sea)	1·25	30

The 6 k. is $27\frac{1}{2} \times 28$ mm.

1230 Congress Emblem

1231 Peace Dove and Japanese Crane

1966. 7th Consumers' Co-operative Societies Congress, Moscow.

3325 **1230** 4 k. yellow and brown . . . 40 10

1966. Soviet-Japanese Meeting, Khabarovsk.

3326 **1231** 6 k. black and red . . . 30 15

1232 "Avtandil at a Mountain Spring", after engraving by S. Kabulazde

1966. 800th Birth Anniv of Shota Rustaveli (Georgian poet).

3327 – 3 k. black on green . . . 25 10
3328 – 4 k. brown on yellow . . . 30 10
3329 **1232** 6 k. black on blue . . . 40 15

DESIGNS: 3 k. Scene from poem "The Knight in the Tiger's Skin", after I. Toidze; 4 k. Rustaveli, after bas-relief by Y. Nikoladze.

1234 Arms, Moscow Skyline and Fireworks

1235 Trawler, Net and Map of Lake Baikal

1966. 49th Anniv of October Revolution.

3331 **1234** 4 k. multicoloured . . . 15 10

1966. Fish Resources of Lake Baikal. Mult.

3332 2 k. Grayling . . . 15 10
3333 4 k. Sturgeon . . . 20 10
3334 6 k. Type **1235** . . . 30 10
3335 10 k. "Omul" . . . 50 20
3336 12 k. "Sig" (salmon) . . . 65 25

The 2, 4, 10 and 12 k. are horiz.

1236 "Agriculture and Industry"

1966. 23rd Soviet Communist Party Congress, Moscow (3rd issue).

3337 **1236** 4 k. silver and brown . . . 20 10
3338 – 4 k. silver and blue . . . 20 10
3339 – 4 k. silver and red . . . 20 10
3340 – 4 k. silver and red . . . 20 10
3341 – 4 k. silver and green . . . 20 10

DESIGN (Map as Type **1236** with symbols of): No. 3338, "Communications and Transport"; No. 3339, "Education and Technology"; No. 3340, "Increased Productivity"; No. 3341, "Power Resources".

1237 Government Buildings, Kishinev

1966. 500th Anniv of Kishinev (Moldavian Republic).

3342 **1237** 4 k. multicoloured . . . 15 10

1238 Clouds, Rain and Decade Emblem

1239 Nikitin Monument, Map and Ships

1966. International Hydrological Decade.

3343 **1238** 6 k. multicoloured . . . 30 10

1966. Nikitin's Voyage to India.

3344 **1239** 4 k. black, green & yell . . 20 10

1240 Scene from "Nargiz" (Muslim Magomaev)

1966. Azerbaijan Operas.

3345 **1240** 4 k. ochre and black . . . 35 15
3346 – 4 k. green and black . . . 35 15

DESIGN: No. 3346, Scene from "Kehzoglu" (Uzeir Gadzhibekov).

1241 "Luna 9" and Moon

1242 Agricultural and Chemical Symbols

1966.

3347 – 1 k. brown . . . 10 10
3348 **1241** 2 k. violet . . . 10 10
3349 – 3 k. purple . . . 20 10
3350 – 4 k. red . . . 20 10
3351 – 6 k. blue . . . 60 10
3563 – 10 k. olive . . . 90 35
3353 – 12 k. brown . . . 70 10
3354 – 16 k. blue . . . 90 15
3355 – 20 k. red, blue & drab . 1·10 50
3566 – 20 k. red . . . 1·40 40
3356 **1242** 30 k. green . . . 1·75 40
3357 – 50 k. ultram, blue & grey 3·50 50
3568 – 50 k. blue . . . 5·00 1·00
3358 – 1 r. brown and red . . 5·25 2·00
3569 – 1 r. brown and black . . 8·25 2·00

DESIGNS—As Type **1241**: 1 k. Palace of Congresses, Kremlin; 3 k. Youth, girl and Lenin emblem; 4 k. Arms and hammer and sickle emblem; 6 k. "Communications" (Antonov An-10A Ukrainia airliner and sputnik); 10 k. Soldier and star emblem; 12 k. Furnaceman; 16 k. Girl with dove. As Type **1242**: 20 k. Workers' demonstration and flower; 50 k. "Postal communications"; 1 r. Lenin and industrial emblems.

1243 "Presenting Arms"

1245 Campaign Meeting

1966. 25th Anniv of People's Voluntary Corps.

3359 **1243** 4 k. brown and red . . . 15 10

1966. "Hands off Vietnam".

3360 **1245** 6 k. multicoloured . . . 20 10

1246 Servicemen

1966. 30th Anniv of Spanish Civil War.

3361 **1246** 6 k. black, red & ochre . . 20 10

1247 Ostankino TV Tower, "Molniya I" (satellite) and "1967"

1249 Statue, Tank and Medal

1248 Flight Diagram

1966. New Year and "50th Year of October Revolution".

3362 **1247** 4 k. multicoloured . . . 30 10

1966. Space Flight and Moon Landing of "Luna 9".

3363 **1248** 10 k. black and silver . . 55 25
3364 – 10 k. red and silver . . 55 25
3365 – 10 k. black and silver . . 55 25

DESIGNS—SQUARE (25 × 25 mm): No. 3364, Arms of Russia and lunar pennant. HORIZ: No. 3365, "Lunar 9" on Moon's surface.

1966. 25th Anniv of Battle of Moscow.

3366 – 4 k. brown . . . 30 10
3367 **1249** 6 k. ochre and sepia . . 30 15
3368 – 10 k. yellow & brown . . 60 20

DESIGNS—HORIZ: (60 × 28 mm): 4 k. Soviet troops advancing; 10 k. "Moscow at peace"–Kremlin, Sun and "Defence of Moscow" medal.

1250 Cervantes and Don Quixote

1966. 350th Death Anniv of Cervantes.

3369 **1250** 6 k. brown, green and deep green . . . 30 10

1252 Bering's Ship "Sv. Pyotr" and Map of Komandor Islands

1966. Soviet Far Eastern Territories. Mult.

3370 1 k. Type **1252** . . . 40 10
3371 2 k. Medny Island and map . 45 10
3372 4 k. Petropavlovsk Harbour, Kamchatka . . . 65 10
3373 6 k. Geyser, Kamchatka (vert) 80 10
3374 10 k. Avatchinskaya Bay, Kamchatka . . . 1·00 15
3375 12 k. Northern fur seals, Bering Is. . . . 1·00 35
3376 16 k. Common guillemot colony, Kurile Islands . . . 2·50 65

1254 "The Lute Player" (Caravaggio)

1966. Art Treasures of the Hermitage Museum, Leningrad.

3377 – 4 k. black on yellow . . 20 10
3378 – 6 k. black on grey . . 40 10
3379 – 10 k. black on lilac . . 65 15
3380 – 12 k. black on green . . 85 20
3381 **1254** 16 k. black on buff . . 1·10 35

DESIGNS—HORIZ: 4 k. "Golden Stag" (from Scythian battle shield (6th cent B.C.). VERT: 6 k. Persian silver jug (5th cent A.D.); 10 k. Statue of Voltaire (Houdon, 1781); 12 k. Malachite vase (Urals, 1840).

1255 Sea-water Distilling Apparatus

1967. World Fair, Montreal.

3382 **1255** 4 k. black, silver & grn . . 15 10
3383 – 6 k. multicoloured . . . 25 15
3384 – 10 k. multicoloured . . 45 20

DESIGNS—VERT: 6 k. "Atomic Energy" (explosion and symbol). HORIZ: 10 k. Space station "Proton 1".

1256 Lieut. B. I. Sizov

1967. War Heroes.

3386 **1256** 4 k. brown on yellow . . 20 10
3387 – 4 k. brown on drab . . 20 10

DESIGN: No. 3387, Private V. V. Khodyrev.

1257 Woman's Face and Pavlov Shawl

1967. International Women's Day.

3388 **1257** 4 k. red, violet & green . . 20 10

1258 Cine-camera and Film "Flower"

1967. 5th International Film Festival, Moscow.

3389 **1258** 6 k. multicoloured . . . 30 10

1259 Factory Ship "Cheryashevsky"

1967. Soviet Fishing Industry. Multicoloured.

3390 6 k. Type **1259** . . . 45 15
3391 6 k. Refrigerated trawler . . 45 15
3392 6 k. Crab canning ship . . 45 15
3393 6 k. Trawler . . . 45 15
3394 6 k. Seine-fishing boat, Black Sea . . . 45 15

1260 Newspaper Cuttings, Hammer and Sickle

1261 I.S.O. Congress Emblem

1967. 50th Anniv of Newspaper "Izvestiya".

3395 **1260** 4 k. multicoloured . . . 15 10

1967. Moscow Congresses.

3396 6 k. turquoise, black & blue . 20 10
3397 6 k. red, black and blue . . 20 10

DESIGNS: No. 3396, Type **1261** (7th Congress of Int Standards Assn "I.S.O."; No. 3397, "V" emblem of 5th Int Mining Congress.

1262 I.T.Y. Emblem

1967. International Tourist Year.
3398 1262 4 k. blk, silver & blue . 15 10

Вена - 1967
(1263)

1265 "Lenin as Schoolboy" (V. Tsigal)

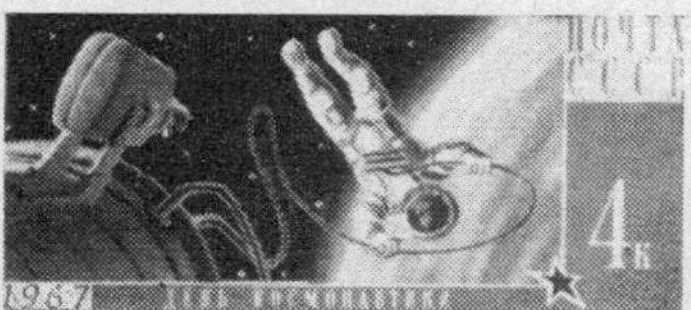

1264 A. A. Leonov in Space

1967. Victory in World Ice Hockey Championship. No. 3291 optd with T 1263.
3399 1217 10 k. multicoloured . . 2·40 1·40

1967. Cosmonautics Day. Multicoloured.
3400 4 k. Type 1284 . . . . 20 10
3401 10 k. Rocket and Earth . . . 80 15
3402 16 k. "Luna 10" over Moon . 1·00 60

1967. Lenin's 97th Birth Anniv.
3403 1265 2 k. brown, yell & grn . . 20 10
3404 – 3 k. brown and lake . . . 35 10
3405 – 4 k. green, yellow and olive 45 40
3406 – 6 k. silver, black & bl . . 95 40
3407 – 10 k. blue, blk & silver . 2·10 30
3408 – 10 k. black and gold . . 65 30
SCULPTURES—VERT: 3 k. Lenin's monument, Ulyanovsk; 6 k. Bust of Lenin (G. and Yu. Neroda); 10 k. (both) "Lenin as Leader" (Andreev). HORIZ: 4 k. "Lenin at Razliv" (Pinchuk).

1266 M. F. Shmyrev

1268 Marshal Biryuzov

1267 Transport crossing Ice on Lake Ladoga

1967. War Heroes.
3409 1266 4 k. sepia and brown . . 20 10
3410 – 4 k. brown and blue . . 20 10
3411 – 4 k. brown and violet . 20 10
DESIGNS: No. 3410, Major-General S. V. Rudnev; 3411, First Lieut. M. S. Kharchenko.

1967. Siege of Leningrad, 1941–42.
3412 1267 4 k. grey, red & cream . 20 10

1967. Biryuzov Commemoration.
3413 1268 4 k. green and yellow . 15 10

1269 Minsk Old and New

1270 Red Cross and Tulip

1967. 900th Anniv of Minsk.
3414 1269 4 k. green and black . 15 10

1967. Centenary of Russian Red Cross.
3415 1270 4 k. red and ochre . . 15 10

1271 Russian Stamps of 1918 and 1967

1967. 50th Anniv of U.S.S.R.. Philatelic Exn, Moscow.
3416 1271 20 k. green and blue . 1·50 65

1272 Komsomolsk-on-Amur and Map

1967. 35th Anniv of Komsomolsk-on-Amur.
3418 1272 4 k. brown and red . . 50 10

1273 Motor Cyclist (International Motor Rally, Moscow)

1967. Sports and Pastimes. International Events.
3419 – 1 k. brown, bistre & grn 20 10
3420 – 2 k. brown 20 10
3421 – 3 k. blue 20 10
3422 – 4 k. turquoise 20 10
3423 – 6 k. purple and bistre . 30 10
3424 1273 10 k. purple and lilac . 75 30
DESIGNS AND EVENTS: 1 k. Draughts board and players (World Draughts Championships); 2 k. Throwing the javelin; 3 k. Running; 4 k. Long jumping (all preliminary events for Europa Cup Games); 6 k. Gymnast (World Gymnastics Championships).

1275 G. D. Gai (soldier)

1276 Games Emblem and Cup

1967. Commander G. D. Gai Commemoration.
3426 1275 4 k. black and red . . 35 10

1967. All Union Schoolchildren's Spartakiad.
3427 1276 4 k. red, black & silver 10 10

1277 Spartakiad Emblem and Cup

1967. 4th People's Spartakiad.
3428 4 k. black, red and silver . . 15 10
3429 4 k. black, red and silver . . 15 10
3430 4 k. black, red and silver . . 15 10
3431 4 k. black, red and silver . . 15 10
DESIGNS: Each with Cup. No. 3428, Type 1277; No. 3429, Gymnastics; No. 3430, Diving; No. 3431, Cycling.

1278 V. G. Klochkov (Soviet hero)

1967. Klochkov Commemoration.
3432 1278 4 k. black and red . . . 15 10

1279 Crest, Flag and Capital of Moldavia

3433 АРМЯНСКАЯ ССР / ՀԱՅԿԱԿԱՆ ՍՍՀ
3434 АЗЕРБАЙДЖАНСКАЯ ССР / АЗӘРБАЈЧАН ССР
3435 БЕЛОРУССКАЯ ССР / БЕЛАРУСКАЯ ССР
3436 ЭСТОНСКАЯ ССР / EESTI NSV
3437 ГРУЗИНСКАЯ ССР / საქართველოს სსრ
3438 КАЗАХСКАЯ ССР / ҚАЗАҚ ССР
3439 КИРГИЗСКАЯ ССР / КЫРГЫЗ ССР
3440 ЛАТВИЙСКАЯ ССР / LATVIJAS PSR
3441 ЛИТОВСКАЯ ССР / LIETUVOS TSR
3442 МОЛДАВСКАЯ ССР / РСС МОЛДОВЕНЯСКЭ
3443 РОССИЙСКАЯ СОВЕТСКАЯ ФЕДЕРАТИВНАЯ СОЦИАЛИСТИЧЕСКАЯ РЕСПУБЛИКА
3444 ТАДЖИКСКАЯ ССР / РСС ТОЧИКИСТОН
3445 ТУРКМЕНСКАЯ ССР / ТУРКМЕНИСТАН ССР
3446 УКРАИНСКАЯ ССР / УКРАЇНСЬКА РСР
3447 УЗБЕКСКАЯ ССР / ЎЗБЕКИСТОН ССР

Inscr at foot as shown above

1967. 50th Anniv of October Revolution (1st issue). Designs showing crests, flags and capitals of the Soviet Republics. Multicoloured.
3433 4 k. Armenia 15 10
3434 4 k. Azerbaijan 15 10
3435 4 k. Byelorussia 15 10
3436 4 k. Estonia 15 10
3437 4 k. Georgia 15 10
3438 4 k. Kazakhstan 15 10
3439 4 k. Kirghizia 15 10
3440 4 k. Latvia 15 10
3441 4 k. Lithuania 15 10
3442 4 k. Type 1279 . . . . . . 15 10
3443 4 k. Russia 15 10
3444 4 k. Tadzhikistan 15 10
3445 4 k. Turkmenistan 15 10
3446 4 k. Ukraine 15 10
3447 4 k. Uzbekistan 15 10
3448 4 k. Soviet Arms 15 10
No. 3448 is size 47 × 32 mm.
See also Nos. 3473/82.

HAVE YOU READ THE NOTES AT THE BEGINNING OF THIS CATALOGUE?
These often provide the answers to the enquiries we receive.

1280 Telecommunications Symbols

1967. "Progress of Communism".
3449 1280 4 k. red, purple & silver 2·50 1·40

1281 Manchurian Crane and Dove

1967. Soviet–Japanese Friendship.
3450 1281 16 k. brown, blk & red 1·00 35

1282 Karl Marx and Title Page

1967. Centenary of Karl Marx's "Das Kapital".
3451 1282 4 k. brown and red . . 25 10

1283 Arctic Fox

1285 Krasnodon Memorial

1284 Ice Skating

1967. Fur-bearing Animals.
3452 1283 2 k. blue, black & brn . 15 10
3453 – 4 k. blue, black & drab 20 10
3454 – 6 k. ochre, black & grn 35 10
3455 – 10 k. brown, blk & grn 50 15
3456 – 12 k. black, ochre & vio 55 25
3457 – 16 k. brown, blk & yell 70 35
3458 – 20 k. brown, black & turq 90 50
DESIGNS—VERT: 4 k. Red fox; 12 k. Stoat; 16 k. Sable. HORIZ: 6 k. Red fox; 10 k. Muskrat; 20 k. European mink.

1967. Winter Olympic Games, Grenoble (1968). Multicoloured.
3459 2 k. Type 1284 . . . . . . 10 10
3460 3 k. Ski jumping 15 10
3461 4 k. Games emblem (vert) . . 15 10
3462 10 k. Ice hockey 55 15
3463 12 k. Skiing 90 30

1967. 25th Anniv of Krasnodon Defence.
3464 1285 4 k. black, yell & pur . 15 10

1285a Map and Snow Leopard (Illustration reduced. Actual size 80 × 26 mm)

1967. Cedar Valley Nature Reserve.
3465 1285a 10 k. black and bistre . 75 30

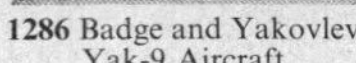

1286 Badge and Yakovlev Yak-9 Aircraft

1288 Cosmonauts in Space

1287 Militiaman and Soviet Crest

1967. 25th Anniv of French "Normandie-Niemen" Fighter Squadron.

3466 **1286** 6 k. red, blue & gold . . 35 15

1967. 50th Anniv of Soviet Militia.

3467 **1287** 4 k. red and blue . . . 20 10

1967. Space Fantasies. Multicoloured.

3468 4 k. Type **1288** 15 10
3469 6 k. Men on the Moon (horiz) 20 10
3470 10 k. Cosmic vehicle 45 15
3471 12 k. Planetary landscape (horiz) 75 20
3472 16 k. Imaginary spacecraft . 85 55

1289 Red Star and Soviet Crest

1967. 50th Anniv of October Revolution (2nd issue). "50 Heroic Years". Designs showing paintings and Soviet Arms. Multicoloured.

3473 4 k. Type **1289** 25 15
3474 4 k. "Lenin addressing Congress" (Serov—1955) . 25 15
3475 4 k. "Lenin explaining the GOELRO map" (Schmatko—1957) 25 15
3476 4 k. "The First Cavalry" (Grekov—1924) 25 15
3477 4 k. "Students" (Yoganson—1928) 25 15
3478 4 k. "People's Friendship" (Karpov—1924) 25 15
3479 4 k. "Dawn of the Five Year Plan" (construction work, Romas—1934) 35 15
3480 4 k. "Farmers' Holiday" (Gerasimov—1937) 25 15
3481 4 k. "Victory in World War II" (Korolev—1965) 25 15
3482 4 k. "Builders of Communism" (Merpert and Skripkov—1965) 25 15

1290 S. Katayama

1292 T. V. Tower, Moscow

1967. Katayama (founder of Japanese Communist Party) Commemoration.

3484 **1290** 6 k. green 15 10

1967. Opening of Ostankino T.V. Tower, Moscow.

3486 **1292** 16 k. black, sil & orge . 1·00 20

1293 Narva-Joesuu (Estonia)

1967. Baltic Health Resorts. Multicoloured.

3487 4 k. Yurmala (Latvia) 10 10
3488 6 k. Type **1293** 45 10
3489 10 k. Druskininkai (Lithuania) 55 15
3490 12 k. Zelenogradsk (Kaliningrad) (vert) 70 20
3491 16 k. Svetlogorsk (Kaliningrad) (vert) 90 25

1294 K.G.B. Emblem

1295 Moscow View

1967. 50th Anniv of State Security Commission (K.G.B.).

3492 **1294** 4 k. red, silver & blue . 15 10

1967. New Year.

3493 **1295** 4 k. brown, pink and silver 20 10

1296 Revolutionaries at Kharkov, and Monument

1967. 50th Anniv of Ukraine Republic.

3494 **1296** 4 k. multicoloured . . 15 10
3495 – 6 k. multicoloured . . 30 10
3496 – 10 k. multicoloured . . 55 15

DESIGNS: 6 k. Hammer and sickle and industrial and agricultural scenes; 10 k. Unknown Soldier's monument, Kiev, and young Ukrainians with welcoming bread and salt.

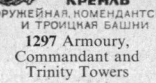

1297 Armoury, Commandant and Trinity Towers

1299 Unknown Soldiers' Tomb, Kremlin

1298 Moscow Badge, Lenin's Tomb and Rockets

1967. Kremlin Buildings.

3497 **1297** 4 k. brown, pur & grn . 15 10
3498 – 6 k. brown, grn & yell . 25 10
3499 – 10 k. brown and grey . 60 15
3500 – 12 k. green, violet and cream 75 30
3501 – 16 k. brown, red and light brown 85 30

DESIGNS—HORIZ: 6 k. Cathedral of the Annunciation. VERT: 10 k. Konstantino-Yelenin, Alarm and Spassky Towers; 12 k. Ivan the Great's bell tower; 16 k. Kutafya and Trinity Towers.

1967. "50 Years of Communist Development".

3502 **1298** 4 k. lake 20 10
3503 – 4 k. brown 20 10
3504 – 4 k. green 20 10
3505 – 4 k. blue 20 10
3506 – 4 k. blue 20 10

DESIGNS—HORIZ: No. 3503, Computer-tape cogwheel and industrial scene; 3504, Ear of wheat and grain silo; 3505, Microscope, radar antennae and Moscow University. VERT: No. 3506, T.V. Tower, liner, railway bridge and jet airliner.

1967. "Unknown Soldier" Commemoration.

3507 **1299** 4 k. red 15 10

1300 "The Interrogation of Communists" (Yoganson)

1967. Paintings in the Tretyakov Gallery, Moscow. Multicoloured.

3508 3 k. Type **1300** 15 10
3509 4 k. "The Sea-shore" (Aivazovsky) 25 10
3510 4 k. "The Lace Maker" (Tropinin) (vert) 25 10
3511 6 k. "The Bakery" (Yablonskaya) 30 10
3512 6 k. "Alexander Nevsky" (part of triptych by Korin) (vert) 30 10
3513 6 k. "Boyarynya Morozova" (Surikov) 30 10
3514 10 k. "The Swan Maiden" (Vroubel) (vert) 75 20
3515 10 k. "The Arrest of a Propagandist" (Repin) . . 75 20
3516 16 k. "Moscow Suburb in February" (Nissky) . . . 1·50 45

Nos. 3511/13 are larger 60 × 34 mm or 34 × 60 mm.

1301 Congress Emblem

1302 Lieut. S. G. Baikov

1968. 14th Soviet Trade Unions Congress, Moscow.

3517 **1301** 6 k. red and green . . . 40 10

1968. War Heroes.

3518 **1302** 4 k. black and blue . . . 20 10
3519 – 4 k. blue and green . . . 20 10
3520 – 4 k. black and red . . . 20 10

PORTRAITS: No. 3519, Lieut. P. L. Guchenko; No. 3520, A. A. Pokaltchuk.

1303 Racehorses

1304 M. Ulyanova

1968. Soviet Horse Breeding.

3521 **1303** 4 k. black, pur & blue . 25 10
3522 – 6 k. black, blue and red 35 10
3523 – 10 k. black, brn & turq . 60 15
3524 – 12 k. black, grn & brn . 65 20
3525 – 16 k. black, red & grn . 90 30

DESIGNS (each with horse's head and horses "in the field"). VERT: 6 k. Show horses; 12 k. Show jumpers. HORIZ: 10 k. Trotters; 16 k. Hunters.

1968. 90th Birth Anniv of M. I. Ulyanova (Lenin's sister).

3526 **1304** 4 k. blue and green . . . 35 10

1305 Red Star and Forces' Flags

1968. 50th Anniv of Soviet Armed Forces. Multicoloured.

3527 4 k. Type **1305** 30 15
3528 4 k. Lenin addressing recruits 30 15
3529 4 k. Recruiting poster and volunteers 30 15
3530 4 k. Red Army entering Vladivostok, 1922, and monument 30 15
3531 4 k. Dnieper Dam and statue "On Guard" 30 15
3532 4 k. "Liberators" poster and tanks in the Ukraine . . . 30 15
3533 4 k. "To the East" poster and retreating Germans fording river 30 15
3534 4 k. Stalingrad battle monument and German prisoners-of-war 30 15
3535 4 k. Victory parade, Red Square, Moscow, and monument, Treptow (Berlin) 30 15
3536 4k. Rockets, tank, warships and Red Flag 30 15

Nos. 3527 and 3536 are vert. The rest are horiz.

HAVE YOU READ THE NOTES AT THE BEGINNING OF THIS CATALOGUE?

These often provide the answers to the enquiries we receive.

1306 Gorky (after Serov)

1307 Fireman and Appliances

1968. Birth Centenary of Maksim Gorky (writer).

3538 **1306** 4 k. brown and drab . . 15 10

1968. 50th Anniv of Soviet Fire Services.

3539 **1307** 4 k. black and red . . . 20 10

1308 Linked Satellites

1309 N. N. Popudrenko

1968. Space Link of "Cosmos" Satellites.

3540 **1308** 6 k. black, gold & pur . 20 10

1968. War Heroes.

3541 **1309** 4 k. black and green . . 20 10
3542 – 4 k. black and lilac . . 20 10

DESIGN: No. 3542, P. P. Vershigora.

1310 Protective Hand

1968. "Solidarity with Vietnam".

3543 **1310** 6 k. multicoloured . . . 15 10

1311 Leonov filming in Space

1968. Cosmonautics Day. Multicoloured.

3544 4 k. Type **1311** 25 15
3545 6 k. "Kosmos 186" and "Kosmos 188" linking in space 35 15
3546 10 k. "Venera 4" space probe 1·00 15

1312 Lenin

1968. Lenin's 98th Birth Anniv.

3547 **1312** 4 k. multicoloured . . . 85 15
3548 – 4 k. black, red & gold . 85 15
3549 – 4 k. brown, red & gold 85 15

DESIGNS: No. 3548, Lenin speaking in Red Square; No. 3549, Lenin in peaked cap speaking from lorry during parade.

1313 A. Navoi

1314 Karl Marx

1968. 525th Birth Anniv of Alisher Navoi (Uzbek poet).
3550 **1313** 4 k. brown 35 10

1968. 150th Birth Anniv of Karl Marx.
3551 **1314** 4 k. black and red . . . 15 10

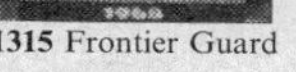
1315 Frontier Guard

1316 Gem and Congress Emblem

1968. 50th Anniv of Soviet Frontier Guards. Multicoloured.
3552 4 k. Type **1315** 15 10
3553 6 k. Jubilee badge 20 10

1968. "International Congresses and Assemblies".
3554 **1249** 6 k. deep blue, blue and green 25 15
3555 – 6 k. gold, orange & brn 25 15
3556 – 6 k. gold, black & red . 25 15
3557 – 6 k. orange, blk & mve . 25 15
DESIGNS: No. 3554, Type **1316** (8th Enriched Minerals Congress); No. 3555, Power stations, pylon and emblem (7th World Power Conference); No. 3556, Beetle and emblem (13th Entomological Congress); No. 3557, Roses and emblem (4th Congress on Volatile Oils).

1317 S. Aini

1319 "Kiev Uprising" (after V. Boroday)

1318 Congress Emblem and Postrider

1968. 90th Birth Anniv of Sadriddin Aini (Tadzhik writer).
3570 **1317** 4 k. purple and bistre . 35 10

1968. Meeting of U.P.U. Consultative Commission, Moscow.
3571 **1318** 6 k. red and grey . . . 20 10
3572 – 6 k. red and yellow . . . 30 10
DESIGN: No. 3572, Emblem and transport.

1968. 50th Anniv of Ukraine Communist Party.
3573 **1319** 4 k. red, purple & gold . 10 10

1320 Athletes and "50"

1321 Handball

1968. Young Communist League's 50th Anniv Games.
3574 **1320** 4 k. red, drab & yellow . 10 10

1968. Various Sports Events.
3575 **1321** 2 k. multicoloured . . . 15 10
3576 – 4 k. multicoloured . . . 25 10
3577 – 6 k. multicoloured . . . 30 10
3578 – 10 k. red, black & bistre 55 20
3579 – 12 k. multicoloured . . 65 25
DESIGNS AND EVENTS—VERT: Type **1321** (World Handball Games, Moscow); 6 k. Yachting (20th Baltic Regatta); 10 k. Football (70th anniv of Russian soccer). HORIZ: 4 k. Table tennis (All European Juvenile Competitions); 12 k. Underwater swimming (European Underwater Sports Championships, Alushta, Ukraine).

HAVE YOU READ THE NOTES AT THE BEGINNING OF THIS CATALOGUE?
These often provide the answers to the enquiries we receive.

1322 Girl Gymnasts

1323 Gediminas Tower, Vilnius (Vilna)

1968. Olympic Games, Mexico. Backgrounds in gold.
3580 **1322** 4 k. turquoise and blue 15 10
3581 – 6 k. violet and red . . 15 10
3582 – 10 k. green and turquoise 55 10
3583 – 12 k. brown & orange . 65 15
3584 – 16 k. blue and pink . . 85 30
DESIGNS: 6 k. Weightlifting; 10 k. Rowing; 12 k. Women's Hurdles; 16 k. Fencing match.

1968. 50th Anniv of Soviet Lithuania.
3586 **1323** 4 k. red, drab & purple 35 10

1324 Tbilisi University

1325 "Death of Laocoon and his sons" (from sculpture by Agesandre, Polidor and Asinodor)

1968. 50th Anniv of Tbilisi University.
3587 **1324** 4 k. beige and green . . 35 10

1968. "Promote Solidarity with the Greek Democrats".
3588 **1325** 6 k. drab, purple & brn 3·75 3·75

1326 Cavalryman

1968. 50th Anniv of Leninist Young Communist League (Komsomol) (1st issue). Multicoloured.
3589 2 k. Type **1326** 10 10
3590 3 k. Young workers 10 10
3591 4 k. Army officer 10 10
3592 6 k. Construction workers . 15 10
3593 10 k. Agricultural workers . 20 20
See also No. 3654.

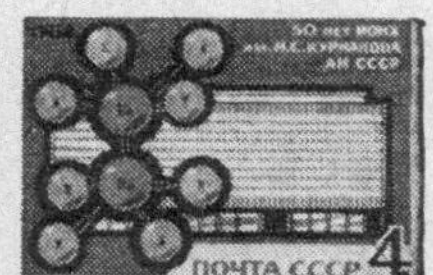
1327 Institute and Molecular Structure

1968. 50th Anniv of N. S. Kurnakov Institute of Chemistry.
3595 **1327** 4 k. purple, black and blue 10 10

1328 Letter

1968. Int Correspondence Week and Stamp Day.
3596 **1328** 4 k. brown, red & lake 15 10
3597 – 4 k. blue, ochre and deep blue 15 10
DESIGN: No. 3597, Russian stamps.

1329 "The 26 Baku Commissars" (statue by Makarov)

1330 T. Antikainen

1968. 50th Anniv of Execution of 26 Baku Commissars.
3598 **1329** 4 k. multicoloured . . 10 10

1968. 70th Birthday of T. Antikainen (Finnish Communist leader).
3599 **1330** 6 k. brown and grey . 15 10

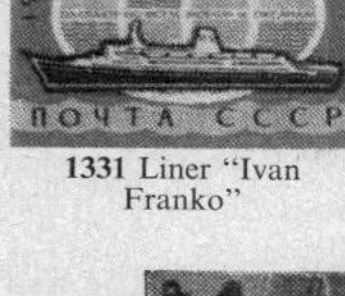

1331 Liner "Ivan Franko"

1333 P. P. Postyshev (1887–1940)

1332 Order of the October Revolution

1968. Soviet Merchant Marine.
3600 **1331** 6 k. red, dp blue & bl . 25 10

1968. 51st Anniv of October Revolution.
3601 **1332** 4 k. multicoloured . . . 10 10

1968. Soviet Personalities.
3602 **1333** 4 k. black 15 10
3603 – 4 k. black 15 10
3604 – 4 k. black 15 10
DESIGNS: No. 3603, S. G. Shaumian (1878–1918); No. 3604, A. Ikramov (1898–1938).

1334 Statuette of Warrior and Ararat Mountains

1335 I. S. Turgenev

1968. 2,750th Anniv of Yerevan (Armenian capital).
3605 **1334** 4 k. black and brown on grey 15 10
3606 – 12 k. brown & sepia on yellow 45 25
DESIGN: 12 k. Sasunsky Monument.

1968. 150th Birth Anniv of Ivan Turgenev (writer).
3607 **1335** 4 k. green 15 10

1336 American Bison and Common Zebra

1968. Fauna. Soviet Wildlife Reservations. Mult.
3608 4 k. Type **1336** 25 10
3609 4 k. Purple swamphen and lotus 30 10
3610 6 k. Great egrets (vert) . . 40 15
3611 6 k. Ostrich and golden pheasant (vert) 40 15
3612 10 k. Eland and guanaco . . 50 25
3613 10 k. Glossy ibis and white spoonbill 60 30

1337 Building and Equipment

1968. 50th Anniv of Lenin Radio-laboratory, Gorky.
3614 **1337** 4 k. blue and ochre . . . 15 10

1338 Prospecting for Minerals

1339 Djety-Oguz Kirgizia

1968. Geology Day. Multicoloured.
3615 4 k. Type **1338** 30 10
3616 6 k. "Tracking down" metals 30 20
3617 10 k. Oil derrick 85 20

1968. Central Asian Spas. Multicoloured.
3618 4 k. Type **1339** 15 10
3619 4 k. Borovoe, Kazakhstan (horiz) 15 10
3620 6 k. Issyk-kul, Kirgizia (horiz) 25 15
3621 6 k. Borovoe, Kazakhstan . 25 15

1340 Silver Medal, "Philatec", Paris 1964

1968. Awards to Soviet Post Office at Foreign Stamp Exhibitions.
3622 4 k. black, silver and purple . 20 10
3623 6 k. black, gold and blue . . 25 10
3624 10 k. black, gold and blue . 55 15
3625 12 k. black, silver & turq . . 45 15
3626 16 k. black, gold and red . . 75 30
3627 20 k. black, gold and blue . 90 40
3628 30 k. black, gold & brown . 1·40 85
DESIGNS: 4 k. Type **1340**; 6 k. Plaque, "Debria", Berlin, 1959; 10 k. Cup and medals, Riccione, 1952, 1968; 12 k. Diploma and medal, "Thematic Biennale", Buenos Aires, 1965; 16 k. Trophies and medals, Rome, 1952, 1954; 20 k. Medals and plaques, "Wipa", Vienna, 1966; 30 k. Glass trophies, Prague, 1950, 1955, 1962.

1341 V. K. Lebedinsky

1342 Soldier with Flag

1968. Birth Centenary of Lebedinsky (physicist).
3629 **1341** 4 k. multicoloured . . . 35 10

1968. 50th Anniv of Estonian Workers' Commune.
3630 **1342** 4 k. black and red . . . 10 10

1344 Moscow Buildings and Fir Branch

1968. New Year.
3632 **1344** 4 k. multicoloured . . . 35 10

1345 G. Beregovoi (cosmonaut)

1346 Electric Train, Map and Emblem

1968. Flight of "Soyuz 3".
3633 **1345** 10 k. black, red & blue 60 10

1968. Soviet Railways.
3634 **1346** 4 k. orange and mauve 25 15
3635 – 10 k. brown and green . 65 25
DESIGN: 10 k. Track-laying train.

1347 Red Flag, Newspapers and Monument

1348 "The Reapers" (Venetsianov)

1968. 50th Anniv of Byelorussian Communist Party.
3636 **1347** 4 k. black, brown & red 15 10

1968. Paintings in State Museum, Leningrad. Mult.
3637 1 k. Type **1348** 15 10
3638 2 k. "The Last Days of Pompeii" (Bryullov) . . . 20 10
3639 3 k. "A Knight at the Crossroads" (Vaznetzov) . 25 10
3640 4 k. "Conquering a Town in Winter" (Surikov) 30 10
3641 6 k. "The Lake" (Levitan) . . 70 10
3642 10 k. "The Year 1919: Alarm" (Petrov-Vodkin) 80 15
3643 16 k. "The Defence of Sevastopol" (Deineka) . . 95 20
3644 20 k. "Homer's Bust (Korzhev) 1·10 25
3645 30 k. "The Celebration in Uritsky Square" (Kustodiev) 1·40 55
3646 50 k. "The Duel between Peresvet and Chelumbey" (Avilov) . . . . 2·10 1·10
Nos. 3638/41, 3643, 3645/6 are horiz designs, size 61 × 28 mm.

1349 House, Onega Region

1968. Soviet Architecture.
3647 **1349** 3 k. brown on buff . . 20 10
3648 – 4 k. green on yellow . . 30 10
3649 – 6 k. violet on grey . . 60 10
3650 – 10 k. blue on green . . 85 25
3651 – 12 k. red on drab . . . 1·00 65
3652 – 16 k. black on yellow . 1·40 85
DESIGNS: 4 k. Farmhouse door, Gorky region; 6 k. Wooden church, Kishi; 10 k. Citadel, Rostov-Yaroslavl; 12 k. Entrance gate, Tsaritzino; 16 k. Master-builder Rossi's Street, Leningrad.

1968. 50th Death Anniv of N. G. Markin (1893–1918) (revolutionary). As T **1333**.
3653 4 k. black 15 10

1350 Flags and Order of October Revolution

1968. 50th Anniv of Leninist Young Communist League (Komsomol) (2nd issue).
3654 **1350** 12 k. multicoloured . . 60 15

1351 "Declaration of Republic"

1969. 50th Anniv of Byelorussian Republic. Mult.
3655 2 k. Type **1351** 10 10
3656 4 k. Partisans at war, 1941–45 10 10
3657 6 k. Reconstruction workers . 15 10

1352 Red Guard in Riga (statue)

1354 University Buildings

1969. 50th Anniv of Soviet Revolution in Latvia.
3658 **1352** 4 k. red and orange . . 10 10

1969. 150th Anniv of Leningrad University.
3660 **1354** 10 k. black and lake . . 50 10

1355 I. A. Krylov **1356** N. D. Filchenkov

1969. Birth Bicent of Ivan Krylov (fabulist).
3661 **1355** 4 k. multicoloured . . . 10 10

1969. War Heroes.
3662 **1356** 4 k. brown and red . . 15 10
3663 – 4 k. brown and green . . 15 10
DESIGN: No. 3663, A. A. Kosmodemiansky.

1357 "The Wheel Turns Round Again" (sculpture, Z. Kisfaludi-Strobl)

1969. 50th Anniv of 1st Hungarian Soviet Republic.
3664 **1357** 6 k. black, red & green 15 10

1358 Crest and Symbols of Petro-chemical Industry

1969. 50th Anniv of Bashkir Autonomous Soviet Socialist Republic.
3665 **1358** 4 k. multicoloured . . 15 10

1359 "Vostok 1" on Launching-pad

1969. Cosmonautics Day. Multicoloured.
3666 10 k. Type **1359** 40 15
3667 10 k. "Zond 5" in Lunar orbit (horiz) 40 15
3668 10 k. Sergei Pavlovich Korolev (space scientist) (horiz) . . 40 15

1360 Lenin University, Kazan

1969. Buildings connected with Lenin. Mult.
3670 4 k. Type **1360** 15 10
3671 4 k. Lenin Museum, Kuibyshev 15 10
3672 4 k. Lenin Museum, Pskov . 15 10
3673 4 k. Lenin Museum, Shushenskaya 15 10
3674 4 k. "Hay Hut", Razliv . . 15 10
3675 4 k. Lenin Museum, Gorky Park, Leningrad 15 10
3676 4 k. Smolny Institute, Leningrad 15 10
3677 4 k. Lenin's Office, Kremlin 15 10
3678 4 k. Library, Ulyanovsk (wrongly inscr "Lenin Museum") 15 10
3679 4 k. Lenin Museum, Ulyanovsk 15 10

1361 Telephone and Radio Set

1969. 50th Anniv of VEF Electrical Works, Riga.
3680 **1361** 10 k. brown and red . 60 15

1362 I.L.O. Emblem

1969. 50th Anniv of Int Labour Organization.
3681 **1362** 6 k. gold and red . . . 15 10

1363 Otakar Jaros **1364** P. E. Dybenko

1969. Otakar Jaros (Czech war hero) Commem.
3682 **1363** 4 k. black and blue . . . 15 10

1969. Soviet Personalities. (80th Birth Annivs).
3683 **1364** 4 k. red 15 10
3684 – 4 k. blue 15 10
DESIGN: No. 3684, S. V. Kosior (1889–1939).

1365 Suleiman Stalsky

1969. Birth Centenary of Suleiman Stalsky (Dagestan poet).
3685 **1365** 4 k. green and brown . . 15 10

1366 "Clear Glade" Rose

1969. Academy of Sciences Botanical Gardens, Moscow. Multicoloured.
3686 2 k. Type **1366** 10 10
3687 4 k. "Slender lily" 15 10
3688 10 k. "Cattleya hybr" orchid . 35 10
3689 12 k. "Leaves Fall" dahlia . . 40 15
3690 14 k. "Ural Girl" gladiolus . 60 30

1367 Scientific Centre

1969. 50th Anniv of Ukraine Academy of Sciences, Kiev.
3691 **1367** 4 k. purple & yellow . . 15 10

1368 Gold Medal within Film "Flower" **1369** Congress Emblem

1969. Cine and Ballet Events, Moscow. Mult.
3692 6 k. Type **1368** (6th Int Cinema Festival) 30 15
3693 6 k. Ballet dancers (1st Int Ballet Competitions) 30 15

1969. 3rd Int Protozoologists Congress, Leningrad.
3694 **1369** 6 k. multicoloured . . . 50 15

1370 Estonian Singer

1969. Centenary of Estonian Choir Festival.
3695 **1370** 4 k. red and ochre . . . 20 10

1371 Mendeleev and Formula

1969. Centenary of Mendeleev's Periodic Law of Elements.
3696 **1371** 6 k. brown and red . . 40 20

1372 Peace Banner and World Landmarks **1373** Rocket on Laser Beam, and Moon

1969. 20th Anniv of World Peace Movement.
3698 **1372** 10 k. multicoloured . . 20 15

1969. "50 Years of Soviet Inventions".
3699 **1373** 4 k. red, black & silver . 10 10

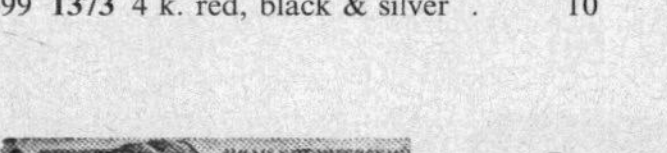

1374 Kotlyarevsky

Стокгольм. 1969
(**1375**)

1969. Birth Bicentenary of Ivan Kotlyarevsky (Ukrainian writer).
3700 **1374** 4 k. black, brown & grn 10 10

1969. Soviet Ice Hockey Victory in World Championships, Stockholm. No. 2828 further optd with **1375**.
3701 6 k. turquoise and purple . . 3·25 2·00

1376 Monument and Campaign Map

1377 Hands holding Torch, and Bulgarian Arms

1969. 25th Anniv of Byelorussian Liberation.
3702 **1376** 4 k. red, purple & olive 15 10

1969. 25th Anniv of Bulgarian and Polish Peoples' Republics.
3703 **1377** 6 k. multicoloured . . . 20 10
3704 – 6 k. red and ochre . . . 20 10
DESIGN: No. 3704, Polish map, flag and arms.

1378 Registan Square, Samarkand

1969. 2,500th Anniv of Samarkand. Mult.
3705 4 k. Type **1378** 15 10
3706 6 k. Intourist Hotel, Samarkand 20 15

1379 Liberation Monument, Nikolaev

1380 Volleyball (European Junior Championships)

1969. 25th Anniv of Liberation of Nikolaev.
3707 **1379** 4 k. red, violet & black . 15 10

1969. International Sporting Events.
3708 **1380** 4 k. red, brown & orge . 20 10
3709 – 6 k. multicoloured . . 30 10
DESIGN: 6 k. Canoeing (European Championships).

1381 M. Munkacsy and detail of painting, "Peasant Woman churning Butter"

1382 Miners' Statue, Donetsk

1969. 125th Birth Anniv of Mihaly Munkacsy (Hungarian painter).
3710 **1381** 6 k. black, orge & brn . 15 10

1969. Centenary of Donetsk.
3711 **1382** 4 k. mauve and grey . . 10 10

1383 "Horse-drawn Machine-guns" (M. Grekov)

1969. 50th Anniv of 1st Cavalry Army.
3712 **1383** 4 k. brown and red . . 25 10

1384 Ilya Repin (self-portrait)

1385 Running

1969. 125th Birth Anniv of Ilya Repin (painter). Multicoloured.
3713 4 k. "Barge-haulers on the Volga" 20 10
3714 6 k. "Unexpected" 25 15
3715 10 k. Type **1384** 30 15
3716 12 k. "The Refusal of Confession" 40 20
3717 16 k. "Dnieper Cossacks" . . 75 30

1969. 9th Trade Unions' Games, Moscow.
3718 **1385** 4 k. black, grn & red . . 10 10
3719 – 10 k. black, blue & grn . 25 10
DESIGN: 10 k. Gymnastics.

1386 V. L. Komarov

1387 O. Tumanyan and Landscape

1969. Birth Cent of V. L. Komarov (botanist).
3721 **1386** 4 k. brown and olive . . 15 10

1969. Birth Cent of O. Tumanyan (Armenian poet).
3722 **1387** 10 k. black and blue . . 50 15

1388 Turkoman Drinking-horn (2nd-cent B.C.)

1389 Mahatma Gandhi

1969. Oriental Art Treasures, State Museum of Oriental Art, Moscow. Multicoloured.
3723 4 k. Type **1388** 15 10
3724 6 k. Simurg vessel, Persia (13th-century) 20 10
3725 12 k. Statuette, Korea (8th-century) 35 15
3726 16 k. Bodhisatva statuette, Tibet (7th-century) 45 20
3727 20 k. Ebisu statuette, Japan (17th-century) 60 45

1969. Birth Centenary of Mahatma Gandhi.
3728 **1389** 6 k. brown 45 15

1390 Black Stork at Nest

1969. Belovezhaskaya Pushcha Nature Reserve. Multicoloured.
3729 4 k. Type **1390** 35 10
3730 6 k. Red deer and fawn . . 40 15
3731 10 k. European bison fighting 65 20
3732 12 k. Lynx and cubs 75 20
3733 16 k. Wild boar and young . 90 35
No. 3731 is larger, 76×24 mm.

1391 "Komitas" and Rural Scene

1969. Birth Cent of "Komitas" (S. Sogomonyan, Armenian composer).
3734 **1391** 6 k. black, flesh & grey 25 10

1392 Sergei Gritsevets (fighter-pilot)

1393 I. Pavlov (after portrait by A. Yar-Kravchenko)

1969. Soviet War Heroes.
3735 **1392** 4 k. black and green . 30 10
3736 – 4 k. brown, red & yell . 20 10
3737 – 4 k. brown and green . 20 10
DESIGNS: As Type **1392**. No. 3737, Lisa Chaikina (partisan). (35½×24 mm); No. 3736, A. Cheponis, Y. Alexonis and G. Boris (Kaunas resistance fighters).

1969. 120th Birth Anniv of Ivan P. Pavlov (physiologist).
3738 **1393** 4 k. multicoloured . . 20 10

1394 D.D.R. Arms and Berlin Landmarks

1395 A. V. Koltsov (from portrait by A. Yar-Kravchenko)

1969. 20th Anniv of German Democratic Republic.
3739 **1394** 6 k. multicoloured . . 15 10

1969. 160th Birth Anniv of A. V. Koltsov (poet).
3740 **1395** 4 k. brown and blue . . 10 10

1396 Arms of Ukraine and Memorial

1397 Kremlin, and Hammer and Sickle

1969. 25th Anniv of Ukraine Liberation.
3741 **1396** 4 k. red and gold . . . 15 10

1969. 52nd Anniv of October Revolution.
3742 **1397** 4 k. multicoloured . . . 10 10

1398 G. Shonin and V. Kubasov ("Soyuz 6")

1969. Triple Space Flights.
3744 **1398** 10 k. green and gold . . 55 15
3745 – 10 k. green and gold . . 55 15
3746 – 10 k. green and gold . . 55 15
DESIGNS: No. 3745, A. Filipchenko, V. Volkov and V. Gorbatko ("Soyuz 7"); No. 3746, V. Shatalov and A. Yeliseev ("Soyuz 8").

1399 Lenin when a Youth, and Emblems

1400 Corps Emblem on Red Star

1969. U.S.S.R. Youth Philatelic Exhibition to commemorate Lenin's Birth Centenary, Kiev.
3747 **1399** 4 k. lake and pink . . . 10 10

1969. 50th Anniv of Red Army Communications Corps.
3748 **1400** 4 k. red, brown & bistre 10 10

1401 "Male and Female Farmworkers" (sculptured group, V. Mukhina), and Title-page

1969. 3rd Soviet Collective Farmers' Congress, Moscow.
3749 **1401** 4 k. brown and gold . . 10 10

1402 "Vasilisa, the Beauty" (folk tale)

1969. Russian Fairy Tales. Multicoloured.
3750 4 k. Type **1402** 30 25
3751 10 k. "Maria Morevna" (folk tale) 75 45
3752 16 k. "The Golden Cockerel" (Pushkin) (horiz) . . . . 1·25 60
3753 20 k. "Finist, the Fine Fellow" (folk tale) . . . . . 1·50 1·10
3754 50 k. "Tale of the Tsar Saltan" (Pushkin) . . . . . . 2·75 2·40

1403 Venus Plaque and Radio-telescope

1969. Space Exploration.
3755 **1403** 4 k. red, brown & blk . 20 10
3756 – 6 k. purple, grey & blk 30 15
3757 – 10 k. multicoloured . . 55 20
DESIGNS: 6 k. Space station and capsule in orbit; 10 k. Photograph of the Earth taken by "Zond 7".

1404 Soviet and Afghan Flags

1405 Red Star and Arms

1969. 50th Anniv of U.S.S.R.–Afghanistan Diplomatic Relations.
3759 **1404** 6 k. red, black & green 35 10

1969. Coil Stamp.
3760 **1405** 4 k. red . . . . 2·00 1·60

1406 Mikoyan Gurevich MiG-3 and MiG-23 Fighters

1969. "30 Years of MiG Aircraft".
3761 **1406** 6 k. black, grey & red . 70 15

1407 Lenin

1969. New Year.
3762 **1407** 4 k. multicoloured . . . 10 10

1408 Tupolev ANT-2

1969. Development of Soviet Civil Aviation.
3763 **1408** 2 k. multicoloured . . . 20 10
3764 – 3 k. multicoloured . . . 25 10
3765 – 4 k. multicoloured . . . 25 10
3766 – 6 k. black, red & pur . 25 10
3767 – 10 k. multicoloured . . 55 15
3768 – 12 k. multicoloured . . 60 15
3769 – 16 k. multicoloured . . 80 20
3770 – 20 k. multicoloured . . 95 30
AIRCRAFT: 3 k. Polikarpov Po-2; 4 k. Tupolev ANT-9; 6 k. TsAGI 1-EA helicopter; 10 k. Tupolev ANT-20 "Maksim Gorky"; 12 k. Tupolev Tu-104; 16 k. Mil Mi-10 helicopter; 20 k. Ilyushin Il-62.

1409 Model Gliders

1969. Technical Sports.
3772 **1409** 3 k. purple 15 10
3773 – 4 k. green 15 10
3774 – 6 k. brown 25 10
DESIGNS: 4 k. Speed boat racing; 6 k. Parachuting.

1410 Rumanian Arms and Soviet Memorial, Bucharest

1411 TV Tower, Ostankino

1969. 25th Anniv of Rumanian Liberation.
3775 **1410** 6 k. red and brown . . 15 10

1969. Television Tower, Ostankino, Moscow.
3776 **1411** 10 k. multicoloured . . 20 15

1412 "Lenin" (after sculpture by N. Andreiev)

1970. Birth Centenary of V. I. Lenin (1st issue). Multicoloured.
3777 4 k. Type **1412** 15 10
3778 4 k. "Marxist Meeting, Petrograd" (A. Moravov) . 15 10
3779 4 k. "Second RSDRP Congress" (Y. Vinogradov) 15 10
3780 4 k. "First Day of Soviet Power" (F. Modorov) . . 15 10
3781 4 k. "Visiting Lenin" (F. Modorov) 15 10
3782 4 k. "Conversation with Ilyich" (A. Shirokov) 15 10
3783 4 k. "May Day 1920" (I. Brodsky) 15 10
3784 4 k. "With Lenin" (V. Serov) 15 10
3785 4 k. "Conquerors of the Cosmos" (A. Deyneka) . . 15 10
3786 4 k. "Communism Builders" (A. Korentsov, J. Merkoulov, V. Bourakov) 15 10

See also Nos. 3812/21.

1413 F. V. Sychkov and painting "Tobogganing"

1970. Birth Centenary of F. V. Sychkov (artist).
3787 **1413** 4 k. blue and brown . . 20 10

1414 "Vostok", "Mirnyi" and Antarctic Map

1415 V. I. Peshekhonov

1970. 150th Anniv of Antarctic Expedition by Bellinghausen and Lazarev.
3788 **1414** 4 k. turquoise, mve & blue 2·00 25
3789 – 16 k. red, green & pur . 2·50 55
DESIGN: 16 k. Modern polar-station and map.

1970. Soviet War Heroes.
3790 **1415** 4 k. purple and black . 15 10
3791 – 4 k. brown and olive . 15 10
DESIGN: No. 3791, V. B. Borshoev (1906–1945).

1416 Geographical Society Emblem

1417 "The Torch of Peace" (A. Dumpe)

1970. 125th Anniv of Russian Geographical Society.
3792 **1416** 6 k. multicoloured . . 15 10

1970. 60th Anniv of Int Women's Solidarity Day.
3793 **1417** 6 k. drab & turquoise . 35 10

1418 Ivan Bazhov (folk hero) and Crafts

1419 Lenin

1970. World Fair "Expo 70", Osaka, Japan.
3794 **1418** 4 k. black, red and grn 15 10
3795 – 6 k. silver, red & black 20 10
3796 – 10 k. multicoloured . . 25 15
DESIGNS: 6 k. U.S.S.R. Pavilion; 10 k. Boy and model toys.

1970. Lenin Birth Centenary. All-Union Philatelic Exhibition, Moscow.
3798 **1419** 4 k. black, gold & red . 10 10

1420 Friendship Tree

1970. Friendship Tree, Sochi.
3800 **1420** 10 k. multicoloured . . 30 15

1421 Ice Hockey Players

1970. World Ice Hockey Championships, Stockholm, Sweden.
3801 **1421** 6 k. green and blue . . 65 15

1422 Hammer, Sickle and Azerbaijan Emblems

1970. 50th Anniv of Soviet Republics.
3802 **1422** 4 k. red and gold . . . 15 10
3803 – 4 k. brown and silver . 15 10
3804 – 4 k. purple and gold . 15 10
DESIGNS: No. 3803, Woman and motifs of Armenia; No. 3804, Woman and emblem of Kazakh Republic.

1423 Worker and Book

1424 D. N. Medvedev

1970. U.N.E.S.C.O. "Lenin Centenary" Symposium.
3805 **1423** 6 k. ochre and lake . . 10 10

1970. War Heroes.
3806 **1424** 4 k. brown 15 10
3807 – 4 k. brown 15 10
PORTRAIT: No. 3807, K. P. Orlovsky.

(1425)

1426 Hungarian Arms and Budapest View

1970. Russian Victory in World Ice Hockey Championships, Stockholm. No. 3801 optd with T **1425**.
3808 **1421** 6 k. green and blue . . . 50 15

1970. 25th Anniv of Hungarian and Czech Liberation. Multicoloured.
3809 6 k. Type **1426** 15 10
3810 6 k. Czech Arms and Prague view 40 10

1427 Cosmonauts' Emblem

1428 Lenin, 1890

1970. Cosmonautics Day.
3811 **1427** 6 k. multicoloured . . . 10 10

1970. Birth Centenary of Lenin (2nd issue).
3812 **1428** 2 k. green 10 10
3813 – 2 k. olive 10 10
3814 – 4 k. blue 10 10
3815 – 4 k. lake 10 10
3816 – 6 k. brown 15 10
3817 – 6 k. lake 15 10
3818 – 10 k. purple 25 15
3819 – 10 k. brown 25 15
3820 – 12 k. black and silver . . 55 20
3821 – 12 k. red and gold . . . 55 20
PORTRAITS OF LENIN: No. 3813, Period, 1893–1900; No. 3814, Period, 1900–03; No. 3815, in 1916; No. 3816, in 1917; No. 3817, Period of Revolution; No. 3818, in 1918; No. 3819, in 1920; No. 3820, Sculptured head by J. Kolesnikov; No. 3821, Sculptured head by N. Andreiev.

1429 Order of Victory

1430 Komsomol Badge

1970. 25th Anniv of Victory in Second World War.
3823 **1429** 1 k. gold, grey & pur . . 10 10
3824 – 2 k. purple, brn & gold . 10 10
3825 – 3 k. red, black & gold . 10 10
3826 – 4 k. red, brown & gold . 15 10
3827 – 10 k. gold, red & purple 55 20
DESIGNS: 2 k. Eternal Flame; 3 k. Treptow Monument, Berlin; 4 k. Home Defence Order; 10 k. Hero of the Soviet Union and Hero of Socialist Labour medals.

1970. 16th Congress of Leninist Young Communist League (Komsomol).
3829 **1430** 4 k. multicoloured . . . 10 10

1431 Sculptured Head of Lenin

1970. World Youth Meeting for Lenin Birth Centenary.
3830 **1431** 6 k. red 10 10

1432 "Young Workers" and Federation Emblem

1970. 25th Anniv of World Democratic Youth Federation.
3831 **1432** 6 k. black and blue . . . 35 10

1433 Arms and Government Building, Kazan

1970. 50th Anniv of Russian Federation Autonomous Soviet Socialist Republics.
3832 **1433** 4 k. blue 15 10
3833 – 4 k. green 15 10
3834 – 4 k. red 15 10
3835 – 4 k. brown 15 10
3836 – 4 k. green 15 10
3837 – 4 k. brown 15 10
DESIGNS: Arms and Government Buildings. No. 3832, (Tatar Republic); No. 3833, Petrozavodzk (Karelian Republic); No. 3834, Cheboksary (Chuvash Republic); No. 3835, Elista (Kalmyk Republic); No. 3836, Izhevsk (Udmurt Republic); No. 3837, Ioshkar-Ola (Mari Republic).

See also Nos. 3903/7, 4052/3, 4175, 4253, 4298, 4367 and 4955.

1434 Gymnast on Bar (World Championships, Yugoslavia)

1435 "Swords into Ploughshares" (sculpture by E. Vuchetich)

1970. International Sporting Events.
3838 **1434** 10 k. red and drab . . 50 15
3839 – 16 k. brown and green . 85 50
DESIGN: 16 k. Three footballers (World Cup Championships, Mexico).

1970. 25th Anniv of United Nations.
3840 **1435** 12 k. purple and green . 50 10

1436 Cosmonauts and "Soyuz 9"

1970. Space Flight by "Soyuz 9".
3841 **1436** 10 k. black, red & purple 50 10

1437 Engels

1970. 150th Birth Anniv of Friedrich Engels.
3842 **1437** 4 k. brown and red . . 15 10

1438 Cruiser "Aurora"

1970. Soviet Warships.
3843 **1438** 3 k. pink, lilac & black 30 10
3844 – 4 k. black and yellow . 35 10

3845 – 10 k. blue and mauve . . 80 15
3846 – 12 k. brown and buff . . 90 20
3847 – 20 k. purple, blue & turq 1·40 40
DESIGNS: 4 k. Missile cruiser "Groznyi"; 10 k. Cruiser "Oktyabrskaya Revolyutsiya"; 12 k. Missile cruiser "Varyag"; 20 k. Nuclear submarine "Leninsky Komsomol".

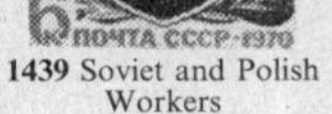

1439 Soviet and Polish Workers **1440** Allegory of the Sciences

1970. 25th Anniv of Soviet-Polish Friendship Treaty.
3848 **1439** 6 k. red and blue . . . 10 10

1970. 13th Int Historical Sciences Congress, Moscow.
3849 **1440** 4 k. multicoloured . . . 10 10

1441 Mandarins **1442** Magnifying Glass, "Stamp" and Covers

1970. Fauna of Sikhote-Alin Nature Reserve. Multicoloured.
3850 4 k. Type **1441** 40 10
3851 6 k. Yellow-throated marten . 45 15
3852 10 k. Asiatic black bear (vert) 60 15
3853 16 k. Red deer 70 25
3854 20 k. Tiger . . . . 1·00 35

1970. 2nd U.S.S.R. Philatelic Society Congress, Moscow.
3855 **1442** 4 k. silver and red . . . 15 10

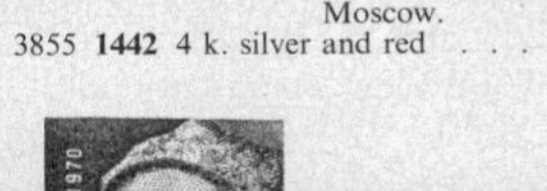

1443 V. I. Kikvidze **1444** University Building

1970. 75th Birth Anniv of V. J. Kikvidze (Civil War hero).
3856 **1443** 4 k. brown 10 10

1970. 50th Anniv of Yerevan University.
3857 **1444** 4 k. red and blue . . . 10 10

1445 Lenin Badge **1446** Library Book-plate

1970. Pioneer Organization.
3858 **1445** 1 k. gold, red and grey . . 10 10
3859 – 2 k. grey and brown . . 10 10
3860 – 4 k. multicoloured . . 10 10
DESIGNS: 2 k. "Lenin with Children" (sculpture); 4 k. Red Star, Pioneer emblem.

1970. 400th Anniv of Vilnius (Vilna) University Library (Lithuania).
3861 **1446** 4 k. black, grey & silver 10 10

1447 Woman with Bouquet

1970. 25th Anniv of International Democratic Women's Federation.
3862 **1447** 6 k. brown and blue . . 10 10

1448 Milkmaid and Cows ("Livestock")

1970. Soviet Agriculture. Multicoloured.
3863 4 k. Type **1448** 10 10
3864 4 k. Driver, tractor and harvester ("Mechanization") 10 10
3865 4 k. Lock-operator and canal ("Irrigation and Chemical Research") 10 10

1449 Lenin addressing Meeting

1970. 53rd Anniv of October Revolution.
3866 **1449** 4 k. gold and red . . . 10 10

50 лет
ленинскому плану
ГОЭЛРО • 1970
(1450)

1970. 50th Anniv of GOELRO Electrification Plan. No. 3475 optd with T **1450**.
3868 4 k. multicoloured 85 30

1451 Spassky Tower, Kremlin **1452** A. A. Baikov

1970. New Year.
3869 **1451** 6 k. multicoloured . . 10 10

1970. Birth Centenary of A. A. Baikov (metallurgic scientist).
3870 **1452** 4 k. black and brown . 10 10

1453 A. D. Tsyurupa **1454** St. Basil's Cathedral, Red Square, Moscow

1970. Birth Centenary of A. D. Tsyurupa (Vice-Chairman of Soviet People's Commissars).
3871 **1453** 4 k. brown and yellow . 10 10

1970. Tourism.
3872 **1454** 4 k. multicoloured . . 15 10
3873 – 6 k. blue, indigo & brown 30 10
3874 – 10 k. brown and green 35 15
3875 – 12 k. multicoloured . . 40 15
3876 – 14 k. blue, red & brown 45 20
3877 – 16 k. multicoloured . . 60 25
DESIGNS: 6 k. Scene from "Swan Lake"; 10 k. Sika deer; 12 k. Souvenir handicrafts; 14 k. "Swords into Ploughshares" (sculpture by E. Vuchetich); 16 k. Tourist and camera.

1455 Camomile

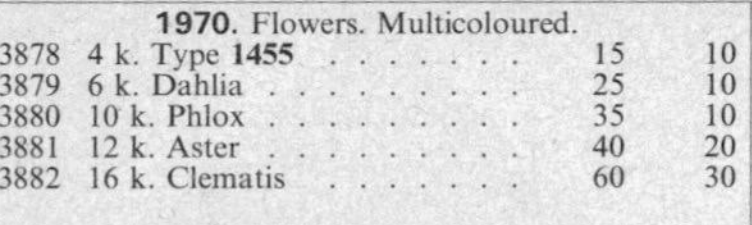

1970. Flowers. Multicoloured.
3878 4 k. Type **1455** 15 10
3879 6 k. Dahlia 25 10
3880 10 k. Phlox 35 10
3881 12 k. Aster 40 20
3882 16 k. Clematis 60 30

1456 African Woman and Child **1457** Beethoven

1970. 10th Anniv of U.N. Declaration on Colonial Independence.
3883 **1456** 10 k. brown and blue . . 20 10

1970. Birth Bicentenary of Beethoven (composer).
3884 **1457** 10 k. purple and pink . .75 20

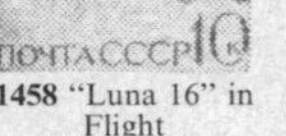

1458 "Luna 16" in Flight **1459** Speed Skating

1970. Flight of "Luna 16".
3885 **1458** 10 k. green 35 15
3886 – 10 k. purple 35 15
3887 – 10 k. green 35 15
DESIGNS: No. 3886, "Luna 16" on Moon's surface; No. 3887, Parachute descent.

1970. Trade Unions' Winter Games (1971).
3889 **1459** 4 k. blue, red & grey . . 15 10
3890 – 10 k. green, brn & grey . 45 15
DESIGN: 10 k. Cross-country skiing.

1460 "The Conestabile Madonna" (Raphael)

1970. Foreign Paintings in Soviet Galleries. Mult.
3891 3 k. Type **1460** 15 10
3892 4 k. "Saints Peter and Paul" (El Greco) 20 10
3893 10 k. "Perseus and Andromeda" (Rubens) (horiz) 35 15
3894 12 k. "The Return of the Prodigal Son" (Rembrandt) 35 15
3895 16 k. "Family Portrait" (Van Dyck) 80 25
3896 20 k. "The Actress Jeanne Samary" (Renoir) . . . . 1·10 35
3897 30 k. "Woman with Fruit" (Gauguin) . . . . 1·50 85

1461 Harry Pollitt and Freighter "Jolly George" **1462** "75" Emblem

1970. 80th Birth Anniv of H. Pollitt (British Communist).
3899 **1461** 10 k. brown & purple . . 35 15

1970. 75th Anniv of Int Co-operative Alliance.
3900 **1462** 12 k. red and green . . 60 10

1463 Sculptured Head of Lenin

1971. 24th Soviet Union Communist Party Congress.
3901 **1463** 4 k. red and gold . . . 10 10

1464 "50", State Emblem and Flag **1465** Genua Fortress and Cranes

1971. 50th Anniv of Georgian Soviet Republic.
3902 **1464** 4 k. multicoloured . . . 15 10

1971. 50th Anniv of Soviet Republics. Similar designs to T **1433**, but dated "1971".
3903 4 k. turquoise 15 10
3904 4 k. red 15 10
3905 4 k. red 15 10
3906 4 k. blue 15 10
3907 4 k. green 15 10
DESIGNS: No. 3903, Russian Federation Arms and Supreme Soviet building (Dagestan Republic); No. 3904, National emblem and symbols of agriculture and industry (Abkhazian Republic); No. 3905, Arms, produce and industry (Adjarian Republic); No. 3906, Arms and State building (Kabardino-Balkar Republic); No. 3907, Arms, industrial products and Government building (Komi Republic).

1971. 2500th Anniv of Feodosia (Crimean city).
3908 **1465** 10 k. multicoloured . . 50 15

1466 Palace of Culture, Kiev **1467** "Features of National Economy"

1971. 24th Ukraine Communist Party Congress, Kiev.
3909 **1466** 4 k. multicoloured . . . 10 10

1971. 50th Anniv of Soviet State Planning Organization.
3910 **1467** 6 k. red and brown . . 35 10

1468 N. Gubin, I. Chernykh and S. Kosinov (dive-bomber crew)

1971. Soviet Air Force Heroes.
3911 **1468** 4 k. brown and green . 15 10

1469 Gipsy Dance

1971. State Folk Dance Ensemble. Multicoloured.
3912 10 k. Type **1469** 40 15
3913 10 k. Russian "Summer" dance (women in circle) 40 15
3914 10 k. Ukraine "Gopak" dance (dancer leaping) 40 15
3915 10 k. Adjar "Khorumi" dance (with drummer) 40 15
3916 10 k. "On the Ice" (ballet) . 40 15

1470 L. Ukrainka **1472** Fighting at the Barricades

1471 "Luna 17" Module on Moon

1971. Birth Centenary of Lesya Ukrainka (Ukrainian writer).
3917 **1470** 4 k. red and brown . . 10 10

1971. Soviet Moon Exploration.
3918 **1471** 10 k. brown and violet . 35 15
3919 – 12 k. brown and blue . 65 20
3920 – 12 k. brown and blue . 65 20
3921 – 16 k. brown and violet . 65 30
DESIGNS: No. 3919, Control room and radio telescope; No. 3920, Moon trench; No. 3921, "Lunokhod 1" Moon-vehicle.

1971. Centenary of Paris Commune.
3923 **1472** 6 k. black, brn & red . 10 10

1473 Hammer, Sickle and Development Emblems
1475 E. Birznieks-Upitis

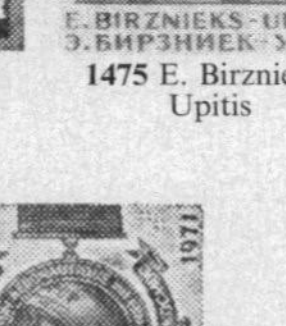

1474 Gagarin Medal, Spaceships and Planets

1971. 24th Soviet Communist Party Congress, Moscow.
3924 **1473** 6 k. red, bistre & brown . 10 10

1971. 10th Anniv of First Manned Space Flight (1st issue) and Cosmonauts' Day.
3925 **1474** 10 k. olive, yell & brn . 35 15
3926 – 12 k. purple, bl & grey . 45 20
DESIGN: 12 k. Spaceship over Globe and economic symbols.
See also No. 3974.

1971. Birth Centenary of E. Birznieks-Upitis (Lithuanian writer).
3927 **1475** 4 k. red and green . . . 10 10

1476 Bee on Flower

1971. 23rd Int Bee-keeping Congress, Moscow.
3928 **1476** 6 k. multicoloured . . . 30 15

1478 Memorial Building

1971. Lenin Memorial Building, Ulyanovsk.
3930 **1478** 4 k. olive and red . . . 10 10

1479 Lieut-Col. N. I. Vlasov
1480 Khafiz Shirazi

1971. 26th Anniv of Victory in 2nd World War.
3931 **1479** 4 k. brown and green . 10 10

1971. 650th Birth Anniv of Khafiz Shirazi (Tadzhik writer).
3932 **1480** 4 k. multicoloured . . . 10 10

1481 "GAZ-66" Truck

1971. Soviet Motor Vehicles.
3933 **1481** 2 k. multicoloured . . 15 10
3934 – 3 k. multicoloured . . 15 10
3935 – 4 k. blue, black & lilac 20 10
3936 – 4 k. grn, purple & drab 20 10
3937 – 10 k. red, black & lilac 55 15
DESIGNS: 3 k. "BelAZ-540" tipper truck; 4 k. (3935) "Moskvitch-412" 4-door saloon; 4 k. (3936) "Zaporozhets ZAZ-968" 2-door saloon; 10 k. "Volga GAZ-24" saloon.

1482 A. A. Bogomolets
1483 Commemorative Scroll

1971. 90th Birth Anniv of A. A. Bogomolets (medical scientist).
3938 **1482** 4 k. black, pink & orge 15 10

1971. International Moscow Congresses.
3939 **1483** 6 k. brown and green . 25 15
3940 – 6 k. multicoloured . . 25 15
3941 – 6 k. multicoloured . . 25 15
DESIGNS AND EVENTS—HORIZ: No. 3939, (13th Science History Congress); No. 3940, Oil derrick and symbols (8th World Oil Congress). VERT: No. 3941, Satellite over globe (15th General Assembly of Geodesics and Geophysics Union).

1484 Sukhe Bator Statue, Ulan Bator

1971. 50th Anniv of Revolution in Mongolia.
3942 **1484** 6 k. grey, gold and red 20 10

1485 Defence Monument
1486 Treaty Emblem

1971. 30th Anniv of Defence of Liepaja.
3943 **1485** 4 k. brown, blk & grey 10 10

1971. 10th Anniv of Antarctic Treaty and 50th Anniv of Soviet Hydrometeorological Service.
3944 **1486** 6 k. deep blue, black and blue 60 30
3945 – 10 k. violet, black & red 1·00 35
DESIGN: 10 k. Hydrometeorological map.

1487 "Motherland" (sculpture by E. Vuchetich)
1488 Throwing the Discus

1971. 20th Anniv of "Federation Internationale des Resistants".
3946 **1487** 6 k. green and red . . 15 10

1971. 5th Summer Spartakiad.
3947 **1488** 3 k. blue on pink . . . 10 10
3948 – 4 k. green on flesh . . 15 10
3949 – 6 k. brown on green . 30 10
3950 – 10 k. purple on blue . 55 20
3951 – 12 k. brown on yellow . 60 20
DESIGNS: 4 k. Archery; 6 k. Horse-riding (dressage); 10 k. Basketball; 12 k. Wrestling.

1489 "Benois Madonna" (Leonardo da Vinci)

1971. Foreign Paintings in Russian Museums. Multicoloured.
3952 2 k. Type **1489** 10 10
3953 4 k. "Mary Magdalene confesses her Sins" (Titian) 15 10
3954 10 k. "The Washerwoman" (Chardin) (horiz) 35 15
3955 12 k. "Young Man with Glove" (Hals) 45 20
3956 14 k. "Tancred and Erminia" (Poussin) (horiz) 50 45
3957 16 k. "Girl Fruit-seller" (Murillo) 55 50
3958 20 k. "Child on Ball" (Picasso) 90 60

1490 Lenin Badge and Kazakh Flag

1971. 50th Anniv of Kazakh Communist Youth Assn.
3959 **1490** 4 k. brown, red & blue . 10 10

1491 Posthorn within Star

1971. International Correspondence Week.
3960 **1491** 4 k. black, blue & green 15 10

1492 A. Spendiarov (Armenian composer) (after M. Saryan)

1971. Birth Anniversaries. Multicoloured.
3961 4 k. Type **1492** (cent) 20 10
3962 4 k. Nikolai Nekrasov (after I. Kramskoi) (poet, 150th anniv) 20 10
3963 10 k. Fyodor Dostoevsky (after V. Perov) (writer, 150th anniv) 50 25

1493 Z. Paliashvili
1494 Emblem, Gorky Kremlin and Hydrofoil

1971. Birth Centenary of Z. Paliashvili (Georgian composer).
3964 **1493** 4 k. brown 20 10

1971. 750th Anniv of Gorky (formerly Nizhni-Novgorod) (1st issue).
3965 **1494** 16 k. multicoloured . . 50 20
See also No. 3974.

1495 Students and Globe

1971. 25th Anniv of Int Students Federation.
3966 **1495** 6 k. blue, red and brn . 10 10

1496 Atlantic White-sided Dolphins
1497 Star and Miners' Order

1971. Marine Fauna. Multicoloured.
3967 4 k. Type **1496** 25 10
3968 6 k. Sea otter 35 10
3969 10 k. Narwhals 45 15
3970 12 k. Walrus 60 20
3971 14 k. Ribbon seals 65 45

1971. 250th Anniv of Coal Discovery in Donetz Basin.
3972 **1497** 4 k. red, brown & black 20 10

1498 Lord Rutherford and Atomic Formula
1499 Maksim Gorky Statue and View

1971. Birth Cent of Lord Rutherford (physicist).
3973 **1498** 6 k. brown & purple . . 30 15

1971. 750th Anniv of Gorky (formerly Nizhni-Novgorod) (2nd issue).
3974 **1499** 4 k. multicoloured . . . 15 10

1500 Santa Claus in Troika

1971. New Year.
3975 **1500** 10 k. red, gold & black 25 10

1501 Workers and Marx Books ("International Socialist Solidarity") (½-size illustration)

1971. 24th Soviet Union Communist Party Congress Resolutions.
3976 **1501** 4 k. blue, ultram & red 15 10
3977 – 4 k. red, yellow & brn . 15 10
3978 – 4 k. lilac, black & red . 15 10
3979 – 4 k. bistre, brown & red 15 10
3980 – 4 k. red, green & yellow 15 10
DESIGNS: No. 3977, Farmworkers and wheatfield ("Agricultural Production"); No. 3978, Factory production line ("Increased Productivity"); No. 3979, Heavy industry ("Industrial Expansion"); No. 3980, Family in department store ("National Welfare").

1502 "Meeting" (V. Makovsky)
1503 V. V. Vorovsky

1971. Russian Paintings. Multicoloured.
3982 2 k. Type **1502** 15 10
3983 4 k. "Girl Student" (N. Yaroshenko) 20 10
3984 6 k. "Woman Miner" (N. Kasatkin) 30 10
3985 10 k. "Harvesters" (G. Myasoyedov) (horiz) . 50 15
3986 16 k. "Country Road" (A. Savrasov) 70 30
3987 20 k. "Pine Forest" (I. Shishkin) (horiz) 95 40
See also Nos. 4064/70.

1971. Birth Centenary of V. V. Vorovsky (diplomat).
3989 **1503** 4 k. brown 10 10

1504 Dobrovolsky, Volkov and Patsaev

1971. "Soyuz II" Cosmonauts Commemoration.
3990 **1504** 4 k. black, purple & orge 20 10

1505 Order of the Revolution and Building Construction

1971. 54th Anniv of October Revolution.
3991 **1505** 4 k. multicoloured . . . 10 10

1506 E. Vakhtangov (founder) and characters from "Princess Turandot"
1507 "Dzhambul Dzhabaiev" (A. Yar-Kravchenko)

1971. 50th Anniv of Vakhtangov Theatre, Moscow.
3992 **1506** 10 k. red and lake . . . 30 15
3993 – 10 k. yellow & brown . 30 15
3994 – 10 k. orange & brown . 30 15
DESIGNS—HORIZ: No. 3993, B. Shchukin (actor) and scene from "The Man with the Rifle"; No. 3994, R. Simonov (director) and scene from "Cyrano de Bergerac".

1971. 125th Anniv of Dzhambul Dzhabaiev (Kazakh poet).
3995 **1507** 4 k. brown, yell & orge . 10 10

1508 Pskov Kremlin

1971. Historical Buildings. Multicoloured.
3996 3 k. Type **1508** 15 10
3997 4 k. Novgorod kremlin . . . 15 10
3998 6 k. Smolensk fortress and Liberation Monument . . 20 10
3999 10 k. Kolomna kremlin . . . 35 15

1509 William Foster

1971. 90th Birth Anniv of Foster (American communist).
4001 **1509** 10 k. black and brown . 17·00 17·00
4002 10 k. black and brown . 60 15
No. 4001 shows the incorrect date of death "1964"; No. 4002 shows the correct date, "1961".

1510 Fadeev and Scene from "The Rout" (novel)

1971. 70th Birth Anniv of Aleksandr Fadeev (writer).
4003 **1510** 4 k. orange and blue . 15 10

1511 Sapphire Brooch

1971. Diamonds and Jewels. Multicoloured.
4004 10 k. Type **1511** 60 15
4005 10 k. "Shah" diamond . . . 60 15
4006 10 k. "Narcissi" diamond brooch 60 15
4007 20 k. Amethyst pendant . . 90 40
4008 20 k. "Rose" platinum and diamond brooch 90 40
4009 30 k. Pearl and diamond pendant . . . . 1·40 60

1512 Vanda Orchid
1514 Ice Hockey Players

1513 Peter the Great's Imperial Barge, 1723

1971. Tropical Flowers. Multicoloured.
4010 1 k. Type **1512** 20 10
4011 2 k. "Anthurium scherzerium" 20 10
4012 4 k. "Cactus epiphyllum" . 30 10
4013 12 k. Amaryllis 60 20
4014 14 k. "Medinilla magnifica" 75 30

1971. History of the Russian Navy (1st series). Multicoloured.
4016 1 k. Type **1513** 15 10
4017 4 k. Galleon "Orel", 1668 (vert) 30 10
4018 10 k. Ship of the line "Poltava", 1712 (vert) 75 15
4019 12 k. Ship of the line "Ingermanland", 1715 (vert) 90 25
4020 16 k. Steam frigate "Vladimir", 1848 . . . . 1·25 40
See also Nos. 4117/21, 4209/13 and 4303/6.

1971. 25th Anniv of Soviet Ice Hockey.
4021 **1514** 6 k. multicoloured . . 50 10

1515 Baku Oil Installations
1516 G. M. Krzhizhanovsky

1971. Baku Oil Industry.
4022 **1515** 4 k. black, red and blue 25 10

1972. Birth Centenary of G. M. Krzhizhanovsky (scientist).
4023 **1516** 4 k. brown 15 10

1517 Alexander Scriabin
1518 Red-faced Cormorant

1972. Birth Centenary of Alexander Scriabin (composer).
4024 **1517** 4 k. blue and green . . . 30 10

1972. Sea Birds. Multicoloured.
4025 4 k. Type **1518** 45 10
4026 6 k. Ross's gull (horiz) . . . 65 10
4027 10 k. Pair of Barnacle geese . 80 15
4028 12 k. Pair of Spectacled eiders (horiz) . . . . 1·10 25
4029 16 k. Mediterranean gull . . 1·50 30

1519 Speed Skating
1520 Heart Emblem

1972. Winter Olympic Games, Sapporo, Japan. Multicoloured.
4030 4 k. Type **1519** 15 10
4031 6 k. Figure skating 20 10
4032 10 k. Ice Hockey 50 15
4033 12 k. Ski jumping 65 20
4034 16 k. Cross-country skiing . 75 30

1972. World Heart Month.
4036 **1520** 4 k. red and green . . . 15 10

1521 Fair Emblem
1522 Labour Emblems

1973. 50th Anniv of Soviet Participation in Leipzig Fair.
4037 **1521** 16 k. gold and red . . . 85 30

1972. 15th Soviet Trade Unions Congress, Moscow.
4038 **1522** 4 k. brown, red & pink . 15 10

1523 "Aloe arborescens"
1524 Alexandra Kollontai (diplomat) (birth cent)

1972. Medicinal Plants. Multicoloured.
4039 1 k. Type **1523** 10 10
4040 2 k. Yellow horned poppy . . 10 10
4041 4 k. Groundsel 20 10
4042 6 k. Nephrite tea 30 10
4043 10 k. Kangaroo apple 55 15

1972. Birth Anniversaries.
4044 **1524** 4 k. brown 15 10
4045 – 4 k. lake 15 10
4046 – 4 k. bistre 15 10
CELEBRITIES: No. 4045, G. Chicherin (Foreign Affairs Commissar) (birth cent); No. 4046, "Kamo" (S. A. Ter-Petrosyan—revolutionary) (90th birth anniv).

1526 "Salyut" Space-station and "Soyuz" Spacecraft

1972. Cosmonautics Day. Multicoloured.
4048 6 k. Type **1526** 30 20
4049 6 k. "Mars 2" approaching Mars 30 20
4050 16 k. Capsule, "Mars 3" . . 75 30

1527 Factory and Products

1972. 250th Anniv of Izhora Factory.
4051 **1527** 4 k. purple and silver . 20 10

1972. 50th Anniv of Russian Federation Autonomous Soviet Socalist Republics. Designs similar to T **1433**, but dated "1972".
4052 4 k. blue 25 10
4053 4 k. mauve 25 10
DESIGNS: No. 4052, Arms, natural resources and industry (Yakut Republic); No. 4053, Arms, agriculture and industry (Checheno-Ingush Republic).

1528 L. Sobinov and scene from "Eugene Onegin"

1972. Birth Centenary of L. Sobinov (singer).
4054 **1528** 10 k. brown 50 15

1529 Symbol of Knowledge and Children reading Books

1972. International Book Year.
4055 **1529** 6 k. multicoloured . . . 25 15

1530 P. Morosov (pioneer) and Pioneers Saluting

1972. 50th Anniv of Pioneer Organization.
4056 **1530** 1 k. multicoloured . . . 10 10
4057 – 2 k. purple, red & grn . 10 10
4058 – 3 k. blue, red & brown 15 10
4059 – 4 k. red, blue & green . 15 10
DESIGNS: 2 k. Girl laboratory worker and Pioneers with book; 3 k. Pioneer Place, Chukotka, and Pioneers at work; 4 k. Pioneer parade.

1531 Pioneer Trumpeter

1972. "50th Anniv of Pioneer Organization" Youth Philatelic Exhibition, Minsk.
4061 **1531** 4 k. purple, red & yellow 15 10

1532 "World Security"

1972. European Security Conference, Brussels.
4062 **1532** 6 k. blue, turquoise & gold 75 55

1533 M. S. Ordubady
1534 G. Dimitrov

1972. Birth Centenary of M. S. Ordubady (Azerbaijan writer).
4063 **1533** 4 k. purple & orange . . 15 10

1972. Russian Paintings. As T **1502**, but dated "1972". Multicoloured.
4064 2 k. "Cossack Hetman" (I. Nikitin) 10 10
4065 4 k. "F. Volkov" (A. Lossenko) 15 10
4066 6 k. "V. Majkov" (F. Rokotov) 20 10
4067 10 k. "N. Novikov" (D. Levitsky) 35 10
4068 12 k. "G. Derzhavin" (V. Borovikovsky) 40 15
4069 16 k. "Peasants' Dinner" (M. Shibanov) (horiz) . . . 55 25
4070 20 k. "Moscow View" (F. Alexeiev) (horiz) . . . 1·10 45

1972. 90th Birth Anniv of Georgi Dimitrov (Bulgarian statesman).
4071 **1534** 6 k. brown and bistre . 20 10

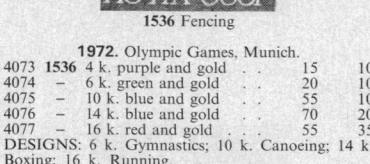

1535 Congress Building and Emblem

1972. 9th Int Gerontology Congress, Kiev.
4072 **1535** 6 k. brown and blue . . 20 10

1536 Fencing

1972. Olympic Games, Munich.
4073 **1536** 4 k. purple and gold . . 15 10
4074 – 6 k. green and gold . . 20 10
4075 – 10 k. blue and gold . . 55 10
4076 – 14 k. blue and gold . . 70 20
4077 – 16 k. red and gold . . . 55 35
DESIGNS: 6 k. Gymnastics; 10 k. Canoeing; 14 k. Boxing; 16 k. Running.

1537 Amundsen, Airship N.1 "Norge" and Northern Lights

1538 Market-place, Lvov (Lemberg)

1972. Birth Centenary of Roald Amundsen (Polar explorer).
4079 **1537** 6 k. blue and brown . . 1·50 30

1972. Ukraine's Architectural Monuments. Mult.
4080 4 k. Type **1538** 15 10
4081 6 k. 17th-century house, Tchernigov (horiz) 20 15
4082 10 k. Kovnirovsky building, Kiev (horiz) 35 20
4083 16 k. Kamenetz-Podolsk Castle 50 30

1539 Indian Flag and Asokan Capital

1540 Liberation Monument, Vladivostok, and Cavalry

1972. 25th Anniv of India's Independence.
4084 **1539** 6 k. red, blue and green 20 10

1972. 50th Anniv of Liberation of Far Eastern Territories.
4085 **1540** 3 k. grey, orange & red 15 10
4086 – 4 k. grey, yellow & ochre 15 10
4087 – 6 k. grey, pink and red . 30 15
DESIGNS: 4 k. Labour Heroes Monument, Khabarovsk, and industrial scene; 6 k. Naval statue, Vladivostok, cruiser and jet fighters.

1541 Miners' Day Emblem

1972. 25th Anniv of Miners' Day.
4088 **1541** 4 k. red, black & violet 20 10

1542 "Boy with Dog" (Murillo)

1972. Paintings by Foreign Artists in Hermitage Gallery, Leningrad. Multicoloured.
4089 4 k. "Breakfast" (Velasquez) (horiz) 20 10
4090 6 k. "The Milk Seller's Family" (Le Nain) (horiz) 25 10
4091 10 k. Type **1542** 45 20
4092 10 k. "The Capricious Girl" (Watteau) 70 35
4093 20 k. "Moroccan with Horse" (Delacroix) . . . . 1·10 45

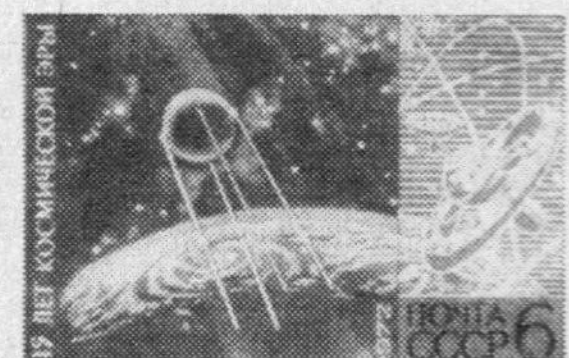
1543 "Sputnik I"

1972. 15th Anniv of "Cosmic Era". Multicoloured.
4095 6 k. Type **1543** 35 15
4096 6 k. Launch of "Vostok I" . . 35 15
4097 6 k. "Lunokhod" vehicle on Moon 35 15
4098 6 k. Man in space 35 15
4099 6 k. "Mars 3" module on Mars 35 15
4100 6 k. Touch down of "Venera 7" on Venus 35 15

1544 Konstantin Mardzhanishvili

1545 Museum Emblem

1972. Birth Centenary of K. Mardzhanishvili (Georgian actor).
4101 **1544** 4 k. green 15 10

1972. Centenary of Popov Central Communications Museum.
4102 **1545** 4 k. blue, purple & grn 15 10

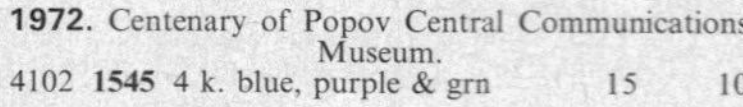

1546 Exhibition Labels

1972. "50th Anniv of U.S.S.R." Philatelic Exhibition.
4103 **1546** 4 k. red & black on yell 15 10

1547 Lenin

1972. 55th Anniv of October Revolution.
4104 **1547** 4 k. red and gold . . . 15 10

1548 Militia Badge and Soviet Flag

1549 Arms of U.S.S.R

1972. 55th Anniv of Soviet Militia.
4105 **1548** 4 k. gold, red & brown . 15 10

1972. 50th Anniv of U.S.S.R.
4106 **1549** 4 k. gold, purple & red . 15 10
4107 – 4 k. gold, red & brown . 15 10
4108 – 4 k. gold, purple & green 15 10
4109 – 4 k. gold, purple & grey 15 10
4110 – 4 k. gold, purple & grey 15 10
DESIGNS: No. 4107, Lenin and banner; No. 4108, Arms and Kremlin; No. 4109, Arms and industrial scenes; No. 4110, Arms, worker and open book "U.S.S.R. Constitutions".

1550 Emblem of U.S.S.R

1552 Savings Book

1972. U.S.S.R. Victories in Olympic Games, Munich. Multicoloured.
4112 20 k. Type **1550** . . . . . 1·00 30
4113 30 k. Olympic medals . . . . 1·50 55

1972. "50 Years of Soviet Savings Bank".
4115 **1552** 4 k. blue and purple . . 15 10

1553 Kremlin and Snowflakes

1555 "G. Skovoroda" (P. Mesheryakov)

1554 Battleship "Pyotr Veliky"

1972. New Year.
4116 **1553** 6 k. multicoloured . . . 20 10

1972. History of the Russian Navy (2nd series). Multicoloured.
4117 2 k. Type **1554** 25 10
4118 3 k. Cruiser "Varyag" 25 10
4119 4 k. Battleship "Potemkin" . . 45 10
4120 6 k. Cruiser "Ochakov" . . . 55 10
4121 10 k. Minelayer "Amur" . . 1·10 25

1972. 250th Birth Anniv of Grigory S. Skovoroda.
4122 **1555** 4 k. blue 15 10

1556 "Pioneer Girl with Books" (N. A. Kasatkin)

1972. "History of Russian Painting". Mult.
4123 2 k. "Meeting of Village Party Members" (E. M. Cheptsov) (horiz) 10 10
4124 4 k. Type **1556** 15 15
4125 6 k. "Party Delegate" (G. G. Ryazhsky) 25 15
4126 10 k. "End of Winter—Midday" (K. F. Yuon) (horiz) . . . 35 20
4127 16 k. "Partisan Lunev" (N. I. Strunnikov) 55 35
4128 20 k. "Self-portrait in Fur Coat" (I. E. Grabar) . . . 75 50

1557 Child reading Safety Code

1558 Emblem of Technology

1972. Road Safety Campaign.
4130 **1557** 4 k. black, blue and red 30 10

1972. Cent of Polytechnic Museum, Moscow.
4131 **1558** 4 k. red, yellow and green 15 10

1559 "Venus 8" and Parachute

1972. Space Research.
4132 **1559** 6 k. blue, black & pur . 20 10

1560 Solidarity Emblem

1973. 15th Anniv of Asian and African People's Solidarity Organization.
4134 **1560** 10 k. blue, red & brown 25 15

1561 Town and Gediminas Tower

1562 I. V. Babushkin

1973. 650th Anniv of Vilnius (Vilna).
4135 **1561** 10 k. red, black & green 25 15

1973. Birth Cent of I. V. Babushkin (revolutionary).
4136 **1562** 4 k. black 15 10

1563 Tupolev Tu-154 and Soviet Aircraft

1973. 50th Anniv of Soviet Civil Aviation.
4137 **1563** 6 k. multicoloured . . . 40 15

1564 "30" and Admiralty Spire, Leningrad

1565 Portrait and Masks (Mayakovsky Theatre)

1973. 30th Anniv of Relief of Leningrad.
4138 **1564** 4 k. black, orange & brn 20 10

1973. 50th Anniv of Moscow Theatres.
4139 **1565** 10 k. multicoloured . . 25 10
4140 – 10 k. red and blue . . . 25 10
DESIGN: No. 4140, Commemorative panel (Mossoviet Theatre).

1566 M. Prishvin

1973. Birth Centenary of Mikhail Prishvin (writer).

4141 **1566** 4 k. multicoloured . . . 35 10

1567 Heroes' Square, Volgograd

1973. 30th Anniv of Stalingrad Victory. Detail from Heroes' Memorial.

4142 – 3 k. black, yell & orge . 20 10

4143 **1567** 4 k. yellow and black . 20 10

4144 – 10 k. multicoloured . . 40 15

4145 – 12 k. black, light red and red 60 20

DESIGNS—VERT: 3 k. Soldier and Allegory; 12 k. Hand with torch. HORIZ: 10 k. Mother mourning for child.

1568 Copernicus and Planetary Chart

1973. 500th Birth Anniv of Copernicus.

4147 **1568** 10 k. brown and blue . 55 15

1569 "Chaliapin" (K. Korovin)

1973. Birth Centenary of F. Chaliapin (opera singer).

4148 **1569** 10 k. multicoloured . . 60 15

1570 Ice Hockey Players **1571** Athletes

1973. World Ice Hockey Championships, Moscow.

4149 **1570** 10 k. brown, bl & gold . 60 15

1973. 50th Anniv of Central Red Army Sports Club.

4151 **1571** 4 k. multicoloured . . . 15 10

1572 Red Star, Tank, and Map **1573** N. E. Bauman

1973. 30th Anniv of Battle of Kursk.

4152 **1572** 4 k. black, red and grey 20 10

1973. Birth Centenary of Nikolai Bauman (revolutionary).

4153 **1573** 4 k. brown 15 10

1574 Red Cross and Red Crescent

1973. International Co-operation.

4154 **1574** 4 k. red, black & green 15 10

4155 – 6 k. light blue, red and blue 20 10

4156 – 16 k. green, red and mauve 65 25

DESIGNS AND EVENTS: 4 k. (50th anniv of Soviet Red Cross and Red Crescent Societies Union); 6 k. Mask, emblem and theatre curtain (15th Int Theatre Institution Congress); 16 k. Floral emblem (10th World Festival of Youth, Berlin).

1575 "A. N. Ostrovsky" (V. Perov) **1576** Satellites

1973. 150th Birth Anniv of Aleksandr Ostrovsky (writer).

4157 **1575** 4 k. multicoloured . . 15 10

1973. Cosmonautics Day. Multicoloured.

4158 6 k. Type **1576** 20 15

4159 6 k. "Lunokhod 2" 20 15

1577 "Guitarist" (Tropinin) **1578** Athlete and Emblems

1973. "History of Russian Painting". Mult.

4162 2 k. Type **1577** 15 10

4163 4 k. "The Young Widow" (Fedotov) 20 10

4164 6 k. "Self-portrait" (Kiprensky) 25 10

4165 10 k. "An Afternoon in Italy" (Brullov) 30 20

4166 12 k. "That's My Father's Dinner!" (boy with dog) (Venetsianov) 40 30

4167 16 k. "Lower Gallery of Albano" (A. A. Ivanov) (horiz) 55 35

4168 20 k. "Ermak conquering Siberia" (Surikov) (horiz) . 1·00 50

1973. 50th Anniv of Dynamo Sports Club.

4169 **1578** 4 k. multicoloured . . 15 10

1580 Liner "Mikhail Lermontov" **1582** Sports

1581 E. T. Krenkel and Polar Scences

1973. Inauguration of Leningrad–New York Trans-Atlantic Service.

4171 **1580** 16 k. multicoloured . . 70 30

1973. 70th Birth Anniv of E. T. Krenkel (Polar explorer).

4172 **1581** 4 k. brown and blue . . 55 10

1973. "Sport for Everyone".

4173 **1582** 4 k. multicoloured . . . 15 10

1583 Girls' Choir

1973. Centenary of Latvian Singing Festival.

4174 **1583** 10 k. multicoloured . . . 35 10

1973. 50th Anniv of Russian Federation Autonomous Soviet Socialist Republics. Design similar to T **1433**, but dated "1973".

4175 4 k. blue 20 10

DESIGN: No. 4175, Arms and industries of Buryat Republic.

1584 Throwing the Hammer

1973. Universiade Games, Moscow. Mult.

4176 2 k. Type **1584** 10 10

4177 3 k. Gymnastics 10 10

4178 4 k. Swimming 15 10

4179 16 k. Fencing 65 25

1586 European Bison

1973. Caucasus and Voronezh Nature Reserves. Multicoloured.

4182 1 k. Type **1586** 10 10

4183 3 k. Ibex 15 10

4184 4 k. Caucasian snowcocks . . 50 15

4185 6 k. Eurasian beaver with young 35 10

4186 10 k. Red deer with fawns . . 55 20

1587 Lenin, Banner and Membership Card

1973. 70th Anniv of 2nd Soviet Social Democratic Workers Party Congress.

4187 **1587** 4 k. multicoloured . . . 15 10

1588 A. R. al-Biruni **1590** "The Sculptor" (P. D. Korin)

1589 Schaumberg Palace, Bonn, and Spassky Tower, Moscow

1973. Millennium of Abu Reihan al-Biruni (astronomer and mathematician).

4188 **1588** 6 k. brown 30 15

1973. General Secretary Leonid Brezhnev's Visits to West Germany, France and U.S.A. Multicoloured.

4189 **1589** 10 k. mauve, brn & buff 30 15

4190 – 10 k. brown, ochre and yellow 30 15

4191 – 10 k. red, grey & brown 30 15

DESIGNS: No. 4190, Eiffel Tower, Paris, and Spassky Tower; No. 4191, White House, Washington, and Spassky Tower.

See also Nos. 4245 and 4257.

1973. "History of Russian Paintings". Mult.

4193 2 k. Type **1590** 15 10

4194 4 k. "Farm-workers' Supper" (A. A. Plastov) 15 10

4195 6 k. "Letter from the Battle-front" (A. Laktionov) . . 25 15

4196 10 k. "Mountain Landscape" (M. S. Saryan) 40 25

4197 16 k. "Wedding on Tomorrow's Street" (Y. Pimenov) . . . 55 35

4198 20 k. "Ice Hockey" (A. Deineka) 80 45

1591 Lenin Museum **1592** Y. Steklov

1973. Inaug of Lenin Museum, Tashkent.

4200 **1591** 4 k. multicoloured . . . 10 10

1973. Birth Centenary of Y. Steklov (statesman).

4201 **1592** 4 k. brown, red & pink 10 10

1593 "The Eternal Pen" **1594** "Oplopanax elatum"

1973. Afro-Asian Writers' Conference, Alma-Ata.

4202 **1593** 6 k. multicoloured . . . 15 10

1973. Medicinal Plants. Multicoloured.

4203 1 k. Type **1594** 20 10

4204 2 k. Ginseng 25 10

4205 4 k. Spotted orchid 30 10

4206 10 k. Arnica 35 25

4207 12 k. Lily of the valley . . . 50 35

1595 I. Nasimi

1973. 600th Birth Anniv of Imadeddin Nasimi (Azerbaijan poet).

4208 **1595** 4 k. brown 10 10

1596 Cruiser "Kirov"

1973. History of Russian Navy (3rd series). Multicoloured.
4209 3 k. Type **1596** 20 10
4210 4 k. Battleship "Oktyabrskaya Revolyutsiya" 25 10
4211 6 k. Submarine "Krasnogvardeets" 30 10
4212 10 k. Destroyer "Soobrazitelnyi" 60 25
4213 16 k. Cruiser "Krasnyi Kavkas" 1·10 35

1597 Pugachev and Battle Scene

1973. Bicentenary of Peasant War.
4214 **1597** 4 k. multicoloured 15 10

1598 Red Flag encircling Globe

1973. 15th Anniv of Magazine "Problems of Peace and Socialism".
4215 **1598** 6 k. red, gold and green 15 10

1599 Leningrad Mining Institute

1973. Bicentenary of Leningrad Mining Institute.
4216 **1599** 4 k. multicoloured 15 10

1600 Laurel and Hemispheres

1601 Elena Stasova

1973. World Congress of "Peaceful Forces", Moscow.
4217 **1600** 6 k. multicoloured 15 10

1973. Birth Centenary of Elena Stasova (party official).
4218 **1601** 4 k. mauve 10 10

1602 Order of People's Friendship

1603 Marshal Malinovsky

1973. Foundation of Order of People's Friendship.
4219 **1602** 4 k. multicoloured 10 10

1973. 75th Birth Anniv of Marshal R. Malinovsky.
4220 **1603** 4 k. grey 15 10

1604 Workers and Red Guard

1605 D. Cantemir

1973. 250th Anniv of Sverdlovsk.
4221 **1604** 4 k. black, gold & red 10 10

1973. 300th Birth Anniv of Dmitri Cantemir (Moldavian scientist and encyclopaedist).
4222 **1605** 4 k. red 10 10

1606 Pres. Allende of Chile

1973. Allende Commemoration.
4223 **1606** 6 k. black and brown 30 10

1607 Kremlin

1608 N. Narimanov

1973. New Year.
4224 **1607** 6 k. multicoloured 15 10

1973. Birth Centenary (1970) of Nariman Narimanov (Azerbaijan politician).
4225 **1608** 4 k. green 10 10

1609 "Russobalt" Touring Car (1909)

1973. History of Soviet Motor Industry (1st series). Multicoloured.
4226 2 k. Type **1609** 15 10
4227 3 k. "AMO-F15" lorry (1924) 15 10
4228 4 k. Spartak "NAMI-1" tourer (1927) 20 10
4229 12 k. Yaroslavsky "Ya-6" bus (1929) 55 20
4230 16 k. Gorkovsky "GAZ-A" tourer (1932) 75 40
See also Nos. 4293/7, 4397/401 and 4512/16.

1610 "Game and Lobster" (Sneiders)

1973. Foreign Paintings in Soviet Galleries. Multicoloured.
4231 4 k. Type **1610** 15 10
4232 6 k. "Young Woman with Ear-rings" (Rembrandt) (vert) 20 10
4233 10 k. "Sick Woman and Physician" (Steen) (vert) 35 15
4234 12 k. "Attributes of Art" (Chardin) 45 20
4235 14 k. "Lady in a Garden" (Monet) 50 25
4236 16 k. "Village Lovers" (Bastien-Lepage) (vert) 60 30
4237 20 k. "Girl with Fan" (Renoir) (vert) 75 40

1611 Great Sea Gate, Tallin

1612 Picasso

1973. Historical Buildings of Estonia, Latvia and Lithuania.
4239 **1611** 4 k. black, red & green 10 10
4240 – 4 k. brown, red & green 10 10
4241 – 4 k. multicoloured 10 10
4242 – 10 k. multicoloured 35 15
DESIGNS: No. 4240, Organ pipes and Dome Cathedral, Riga; No. 4241, Traku Castle, Lithuania; No. 4242, Town Hall and weather-vane, Tallin.

1973. Pablo Picasso Commemoration.
4243 **1612** 6 k. green, red & gold 25 10

1613 I. G. Petrovsky (mathematician and Rector of Moscow University)

1973. Petrovsky Commemoration.
4244 **1613** 4 k. multicoloured 15 10

1973. Brezhnev's Visit to India. As T **1589**, but showing Kremlin, Red Fort, Delhi and flags.
4245 4 k. multicoloured 10 10

1614 Soviet Soldier and Title Page

1616 Oil Workers

1615 Siege Monument and Peter the Great Statue, Leningrad

1974. 50th Anniv of "Red Star" Newspaper.
4246 **1614** 4 k. black, red & gold 15 10

1974. 30th Anniv of Soviet Victory in Battle for Leningrad.
4247 **1615** 4 k. multicoloured 25 10

1974. 10th Anniv of Tyumen Oil fields.
4248 **1616** 4 k. black, red & blue 30 10

1617 "Comecon" Headquarters, Moscow

1618 Skaters and Stadium

1974. 25th Anniv of Council for Mutual Economic Aid.
4249 **1617** 16 k. green, red & brown 45 20

1974. European Women's Ice Skating Championships, Medeo, Alma-Ata.
4250 **1618** 6 k. red, blue & slate 20 10

1619 Kunstkammer Museum, Leningrad, Text and Academy

1620 L. A. Artsimovich

1974. 250th Anniv of Russian Academy of Sciences.
4251 **1619** 10 k. multicoloured 25 10

1974. 1st Death Anniv of Academician L. A. Artsimovich (physicist).
4252 **1620** 4 k. brown and green 15 10

1974. 50th Anniv of Autonomous Soviet Socialist Republics. Design similar to T **1433**, but dated "1974".
4253 4 k. brown 15 10
DESIGN: No. 4253, Arms and industries of Nakhichevan ASSR (Azerbaijan).

1621 K. D. Ushinsky

1622 M. D. Millionshchikov

1974. 150th Birth Anniv of K. D. Ushinsky (educationalist).
4254 **1621** 4 k. brown and grn 10 10

1974. 1st Death Anniv of M. D. Millionshchikov (scientist).
4255 **1622** 4 k. brown, pink & green 10 10

1623 Spartakiad Emblem

1624 Young Workers and Emblem

1974. 3rd Winter Spartakiad Games.
4256 **1623** 10 k. multicoloured 15 15

1974. General Secretary Leonid Brezhnev's Visit to Cuba. As T **1589** but showing Kremlin, Revolution Square, Havana and Flags.
4257 4 k. multicoloured 10 10

1974. Scientific and Technical Youth Work Review.
4258 **1624** 4 k. multicoloured 10 10

1625 Theatre Facade

1626 Globe and Meteorological Activities

1974. Cent of Azerbaijan Drama Theatre, Baku.
4259 **1625** 6 k. brown, red & orge 15 10

1974. Cosmonautics Day.
4260 **1626** 6 k. blue, red & violet 20 10
4261 – 10 k. brown, red & blue 35 15
4262 – 10 k. black, red & yell 35 15
DESIGNS: No. 4261, V. G. Lazarev and O. G. Makarov, and launch of "Soyuz 12"; No. 4262, P. I. Klimuk and V. V. Lebedev, and "Soyuz 13".

1627 "Odessa by Moonlight" (Aivazovsky)

1974. Marine Paintings by Ivan Aivazovsky. Multicoloured.
4263 2 k. Type **1627** 10 10
4264 4 k. "Battle of Chesma" (vert) 15 10
4265 6 k. "St. George's Monastery" 20 10
4266 10 k. "Storm at Sea" 35 15
4267 12 k. "Rainbow" 40 20
4268 16 k. "Shipwreck" 55 30

1628 Young Communists

1974. 17th Leninist Young Communist League (Komsomol) Congress (4270) and 50th Anniv of Naming League after Lenin (4271). Multicoloured.
4270 4 k. Type **1628** 10 10
4271 4 k. "Lenin" (from sculpture by V. Tsigal) 10 10

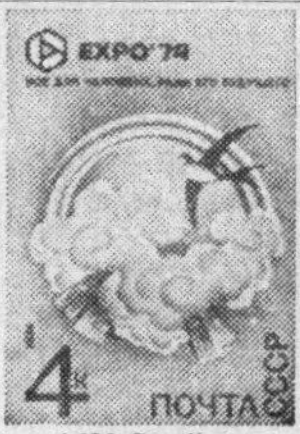

1630 Swallow ("Atmosphere")   **1631** "Cobble-stone" (sculpture, I. D. Shadr)

1974. "EXPO 74" World Fair, Spokane, U.S.A. "Preserve the Environment".
4273 **1630** 4 k. black, red & lilac . . 15 10
4274 – 6 k. yellow, blk & blue . . 20 10
4275 – 10 k. black, vio & red . . 40 15
4276 – 16 k. blue, green & blk . . 55 20
4277 – 20 k. black, brn & orge . . 75 40
DESIGNS: 6 k. Fish and globe ("The Sea"); 10 k. Crystals ("The Earth"); 16 k. Rose bush ("Flora"); 20 k. Young red deer ("Fauna").

1974. 50th Anniv of Central Museum of the Revolution.
4279 **1631** 4 k. green, red & gold . 10 10

1632 Congress Emblem within Lucerne Grass   **1634** Tchaikovsky and Competition Emblem

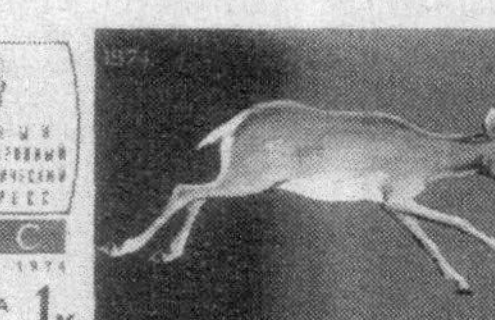

1633 Saiga

1974. 12th International Congress of Meadow Cultivation, Moscow.
4280 **1632** 4 k. red, green & dp grn . 10 10

1974. 1st International Theriological Congress, Moscow. Fauna. Multicoloured.
4281 1 k. Type **1633** 10 10
4282 3 k. Asiatic wild ass 15 10
4283 4 k. Russian desman 20 10
4284 6 k. Northern fur seal 25 10
4285 10 k. Bowhead whale 60 20

1974. 5th Int Tchaikovsky Music Competition.
4286 **1634** 6 k. black, vio & grn . . 30 10

1636 Marshal F. I. Tolbukhin   **1638** Runner and Emblem

1637 K. Stanislavsky, V. Nemirovich-Danchenko and Theatre Curtain

1974. 80th Birth Anniv of Marshal F. I. Tolbukhin.
4288 **1636** 4 k. green 15 10

1974. 75th Anniv of Moscow Arts Festival.
4289 **1637** 10 k. multicoloured . . 25 15

1974. 13th Soviet Schools Spartakiad, Alma Ata.
4290 **1638** 4 k. multicoloured . . . 15 10

1639 Modern Passenger Coach   **1640** Shield and Monument on Battle Map

1974. Centenary of Egorov Railway Wagon Works, Leningrad.
4291 **1639** 4 k. multicoloured . . 30 10

1974. 30th Anniv of Liberation of Byelorussia.
4292 **1640** 4 k. multicoloured . . 10 10
See also No. 4301.

1974. History of Soviet Motor Industry (2nd series). As T **1609**. Multicoloured.
4293 2 k. Gorkovsky "GAZ-AA" lorry (1932) 15 10
4294 3 k. Gorkovsky "GAZ-03-30" bus (1933) 15 10
4295 4 k. Moscow Auto Works "ZIS-5" lorry (1933) 15 10
4296 14 k. Moscow Auto Works "ZIS-8" bus (1934) . . . 55 15
4297 16 k. Moscow Auto Works "ZIS-101" saloon car (1936) 65 25

1974. 50th Anniv of Soviet Republics. As T **1433**, dated "1974".
4298 4 k. red 15 10
DESIGN: 4 k. Arms and industries of North Ossetian Republic.
No. 4298 also commemorates the 200th anniv of Ossetia's merger with Russia.

1641 Liberation Monument and Skyline   **1644** Admiral Isakov

1642 Warsaw Monument and Flag

1974. 800th Anniv of Poltava.
4299 **1641** 4 k. red and brown . . 10 10

1974. 30th Anniv of Polish People's Republic.
4300 **1642** 6 k. brown and red . . 15 10

1974. 30th Anniv of Liberation of Ukraine. As T **1640**, but background details and colours changed.
4301 4 k. multicoloured 15 10

1974. 80th Birth Anniv of Admiral I. S. Isakov.
4302 **1644** 4 k. blue 15 10

1645 Minesweeper

1974. History of the Russian Navy (4th series). Modern Warships. Multicoloured.
4303 3 k. Type **1645** 25 10
4304 4 k. Landing ship 25 10
4305 6 k. Helicopter carrier . . . 45 15
4306 16 k. Destroyer "Otvazhny" 1·00 25

1646 Pentathlon Sports   **1647** D. Ulyanov

1974. World Modern Pentathlon Championships, Moscow.
4307 **1646** 16 k. brown, gold & blue 60 20

1974. Birth Centenary of D. Ulyanov (Lenin's brother).
4308 **1647** 4 k. green 15 10

1648 V. Menzhinsky   **1650** S. M. Budennyi

1649 "Lilac" (P. P. Konchalovsky)

1974. Birth Cent of V. Menzhinsky (statesman).
4309 **1648** 4 k. maroon 10 10

1974. Soviet Paintings. Multicoloured.
4310 4 k. Type **1649** 15 10
4311 6 k. "Towards the Wind" (sailing) (E. Kalnins) . . 20 15
4312 10 k. "Spring" (young woman) (O. Zardarjan) 40 20
4313 16 k. "Northern Harbour" (G. Nissky) 65 30
4314 20 k. "Daughter of the Soviet Kirghiz" (S. Tchnikov) (vert) 75 35

1974. Marshal S. M. Budennyi Commem.
4315 **1650** 4 k. green 15 10

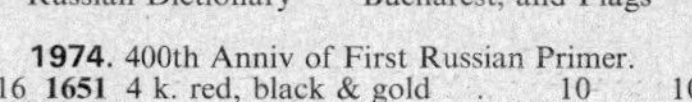

1651 Page of First Russian Dictionary   **1652** Soviet War Memorial, Bucharest, and Flags

1974. 400th Anniv of First Russian Primer.
4316 **1651** 4 k. red, black & gold . 10 10

1974. 30th Anniv of Rumanian Liberation.
4317 **1652** 6 k. blue, yellow & red . 15 10

1653 Vitebsk

1974. Millenary of Vitebsk.
4318 **1653** 4 k. red and green . . . 15 10

1654 Kirgizia   **1655** Bulgarian Crest and Flags

1974. 50th Anniv of Soviet Republics. Flags, Agricultural and Industrial Emblems. Mult. Background colours given.
4319 **1654** 4 k. blue 15 10
4320 – 4 k. purple 15 10
4321 – 4 k. blue 15 10
4322 – 4 k. yellow 15 10
4323 – 4 k. green 15 10
DESIGNS: No. 4320, Moldavia; No. 4321, Tadzhikistan; No. 4322, Turkmenistan; No. 4323, Uzbekistan.

1974. 30th Anniv of Bulgarian Revolution.
4324 **1655** 6 k. multicoloured . . . 15 10

1656 G.D.R. Crest and Soviet War Memorial, Treptow, Berlin   **1658** Theatre and Laurel Wreath

1974. 25th Anniv of German Democratic Republic.
4325 **1656** 6 k. multicoloured . . . 15 10

1974. 150th Anniv of Maly State Theatre, Moscow.
4327 **1658** 4 k. gold, red & black . 10 10

1659 "Guests from Overseas"

1974. Birth Centenary of Nikolai K. Rorich (painter).
4328 **1659** 6 k. multicoloured . . . 20 10

1660 Soviet Crest and U.P.U. Monument, Berne

1974. Centenary of U.P.U. Multicoloured.
4329 10 k. Type **1660** 30 15
4330 10 k. Ukraine crest, U.P.U. Emblem and U.P.U. H.Q., Berne 30 15
4331 10 k. Byelorussia crest, U.P.U. emblem and mail transport 30 15

1661 Order of Labour Glory

1974. 57th Anniv of October Revolution. Multicoloured.
4333 4 k. Type **1661** 15 10
4334 4 k. Kamaz truck (vert) . . . 15 10
4335 4 k. Hydro-electric power station, Nurek (vert) . . . 15 10

1662 Soviet "Space Stations" over Mars

1974. Soviet Space Exploration. Multicoloured.
4336 6 k. Type **1662** 20 10
4337 10 k. P. R. Popovich and Y. P. Artchunin ("Soyuz 14" cosomonuts) 30 15
4338 10 k. I. V. Sarafanov and L. S. Demin ("Soyuz 15" cosmonauts) 30 15
SIZES—VERT: No. 4337, 28 × 40 mm. HORIZ: No. 4338, 40 × 28 mm.

1663 Mongolian Crest Flag   **1664** Commemorative Inscription

1974. 50th Anniv of Mongolian People's Republic.
4339 **1663** 6 k. multicoloured . . . 20 10

1974. 30th Anniv of Estonian Liberation.
4340 **1664** 4 k. multicoloured . . . 15 10

1665 Liner "Aleksandr Pushkin", Freighter and Tanker

1974. 50th Anniv of Soviet Merchant Navy.
4341 **1665** 4 k. multicoloured . . . 25 10

1666 Spassky Clock-tower, Kremlin, Moscow

1974. New Year.
4342 **1666** 4 k. multicoloured . . . 15 10

1667 "The Market Place" (Beuckelaar)

1974. Foreign Paintings in Soviet Galleries. Multicoloured.
4343 4 k. Type **1667** 15 10
4344 6 k. "Woman selling Fish" (Pieters) 25 10
4345 10 k. "A Goblet of Lemonade" (Terborsh) 35 15
4346 14 k. "Girl at Work" (Metsu) 50 20
4347 16 k. "Saying Grace" (Chardin) 55 30
4348 20 k. "The Spoilt Child" (Greuze) 80 35
Nos. 4344/8 are vert.

1668 "Ostrowskia magnifica" **1669** I. S. Nikitin

1974. Flowers. Multicoloured.
4350 1 k. Type **1668** 10 10
4351 2 k. "Paeonia intermedia" . . 10 10
4352 4 k. "Roemeria refracta" . . 20 10
4353 10 k. "Tulipia dasystemon" . 40 15
4354 12 k. "Dianthus versicolor" . 45 20

1974. 150th Birth Anniv of I. S. Nikitin (poet).
4355 **1669** 4 k. black, green & ol 15 10

1670 Leningrad Mint Building

1974. 250th Anniv of Leningrad Mint.
4356 **1670** 6 k. multicoloured . . . 20 10

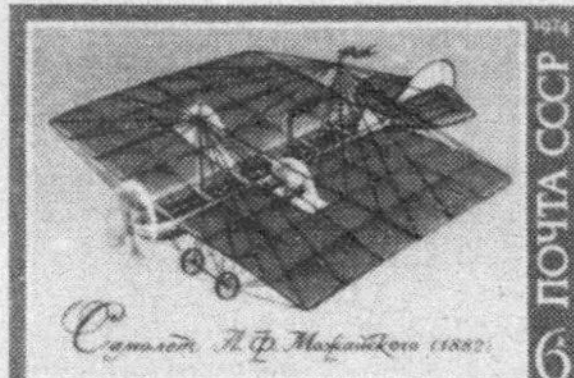
1671 Mozhaisky's Monoplane, 1884

1974. Early Russian Aircraft (1st series). Mult.
4357 6 k. Type **1671** 30 15
4358 6 k. Grizidubov No. 2 biplane, 1910 . . . . 30 15
4359 6 k. Sikorsky "Russia A", 1910 30 15
4360 6 k. Sikorsky "Russkiy Vitjaz", 1913 . . . . 30 15
4361 6 k. Grigorovich M-5 flying boat, 1914 . . . . 30 15
See also Nos. 4580/4, 4661/6 and 4791/6.

1673 Komsomol Emblem and Rotary Press ("Komsomolskaya Pravda")

1975. 50th Anniv of Children's Newspapers.
4363 **1673** 4 k. red, black & blue . 10 10
4364 – 4 k. red, black & silver 10 10
DESIGN—VERT: No. 4364, Pioneer emblem and newspaper sheet ("Pioneerskaya Pravda").

1674 Emblem and Skiers (8th Trade Unions' Games)

1975. Winter Spartakiads.
4365 **1674** 4 k. orange, black & bl 10 10
4366 – 16 k. bistre, black & bl 55 20
DESIGN—HORIZ: 16 k. Emblem, ice hockey player and skier (5th Friendly Forces Military Games).

1975. "50th Anniv of Automomous Soviet Socialist Republics. Designs similar to T **1433**, but dated "1975".
4367 4 k. green 15 10
DESIGN: No. 4367, Arms, industries and produce of Karakalpak ASSR (Uzbekistan).

1675 "David"

1975. 500th Birth Anniv of Michelangelo.
4368 **1675** 4 k. deep green & green 20 15
4369 – 6 k. brown and ochre . 25 15
4370 – 10 k. dp green & green 35 15
4371 – 14 k. brown and ochre 55 30
4372 – 20 k. dp green & green 1·00 30
4373 – 30 k. brown and ochre 1·50 65
DESIGNS: 6 k. "Crouching Boy"; 10 k. "Rebellious Slave"; 14 k. "Creation of Adam" (detail, Sistine Chapel ceiling); 20 k. Staircase of Laurentiana Library, Florence; 30 k. Christ and the Virgins (detail of "The Last Judgement", Sistine Chapel).

1676 Mozhaisky, Monoplane and Tupolev Tu-144 Jet Airliner

1975. 150th Birth Anniv of Aleksandr Mozhaisky (aircraft designer).
4375 **1676** 6 k. brown and blue 40 10

1677 Convention Emblem

1975. Cent of International Metre Convention.
4376 **1677** 6 k. multicoloured . . 15 10

1678 Games Emblem

1975. 6th Summer Spartakiad.
4377 **1678** 6 k. multicoloured . . 15 10

1679 Towers of Charles Bridge, Prague (Czechoslovakia)

1975. 30th Anniv of Liberation. Multicoloured.
4378 6 k. Type **1679** 15 10
4379 6 k. Liberation Monument and Parliament Buildings, Budapest (Hungary) 15 10

1680 French and Soviet Flags **1681** Yuri Gagarin

1975. 50th Anniv of Franco-Soviet Diplomatic Relations.
4380 **1680** 6 k. multicoloured . . . 15 10

1975. Cosmonautics Day.
4381 **1681** 6 k. red, silver and blue . 15 10
4382 – 10 k. red, black & blue . 30 15
4383 – 16 k. multicoloured . . 50 20
DESIGNS—HORIZ: 10 k. A. A. Gubarev, G. M. Grechko ("Soyuz 17") and "Salyut 4"; 16 k. A. V. Filipchenko, N. N. Rukavishnikov and "Soyuz 16".

1682 Treaty Emblem **1684** Lenin

1683 Emblem and Exhibition Hall, Sokolniki, Moscow

1975. 20th Anniv of Warsaw Treaty.
4384 **1682** 6 k. multicoloured . . . 15 10

1975. "Communication 75" International Exhibition, Moscow.
4385 **1683** 6 k. red, silver and blue . 15 10

1975. 30th Anniv of Victory in Second World War. Multicoloured.
4386 4 k. Type **1684** 15 10
4387 4 k. Eternal flame and Guard of Honour 15 10
4388 4 k. Woman in ammunition factory 15 10
4389 4 k. Partisans 15 10
4390 4 k. "Destruction of the enemy" 15 10
4391 4 k. Soviet forces 15 10

1685 "Lenin" (V. G. Tsiplakov) **1686** Victory Emblems

1975. 105th Birth Anniv of Lenin.
4393 **1685** 4 k. multicoloured . . . 15 10

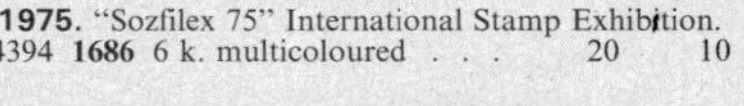
1975. "Sozfilex 75" International Stamp Exhibition.
4394 **1686** 6 k. multicoloured . . . 20 10

1687 "Apollo–Soyuz" Space Link

1975. "Apollo–Soyuz" Space Project.
4396 **1687** 20 k. multicoloured . . . 75 25

1975. History of Soviet Motor Industry (3rd series). As T **1609**.
4397 2 k. black, orange & blue . . 15 10
4398 3 k. black, brown & green . 15 10
4399 4 k. black, blue and green . 15 10
4400 12 k. black, buff and purple . 45 20
4401 16 k. black, green and olive . 60 25
DESIGNS: 2 k. Gorkovsky "GAZ-M1" saloon, 1936; 3 k. Yaroslavsky "YAG-6" truck, 1936; 4 k. Moscow Auto Works "ZIS-16" bus, 1938; 12 k. Moscow KIM Works "KIM-10" saloon, 1940; 16 k. Gorkovsky "GAZ-67B" field car, 1943.

1688 Irrigation Canal and Emblem **1689** Flags and Crests of Poland and Soviet Union

1975. 9th Int Irrigation Congress, Moscow.
4402 **1688** 6 k. multicoloured . . . 15 10

1975. 30th Anniv of Soviet–Polish Friendship.
4403 **1689** 6 k. multicoloured . . . 15 10

1690 A. A. Leonov in Space **1691** Ya. M. Sverdlov

1975. 10th Anniv of First Space Walk by A. A. Leonov.
4404 **1690** 6 k. multicoloured . . . 20 10

1975. 90th Birth Anniv of Ya. M. Sverdlov (statesman).
4405 **1691** 4 k. brown, buff & silver 10 10

1692 Congress Emblem

1975. 8th Int Plant Conservation Congress, Moscow.
4406 **1692** 6 k. multicoloured . . . 15 10

1693 Emblem and Flowers

1975. 12th Int Botanical Congress, Leningrad.

4407 **1693** 6 k. multicoloured . . . 30 10

1695 Festival Emblem

1975. 9th International Film Festival, Moscow.

4409 **1695** 6 k. multicoloured . . . 15 10

1696 Crews of "Apollo" and "Soyuz"

1975. "Apollo"–"Soyuz" Space Link. Mult.

4410 10 k. Type **1696** 30 10

4411 12 k. "Apollo" and "Soyuz 19" in docking procedure . . . 35 20

4412 12 k. "Apollo" and "Soyuz 19" linked together 35 20

4413 16 k. Launch of "Soyuz 19" (vert) 45 20

1697 Sturgeon

1975. Int Exposition, Okinawa. Marine Life.

4415 **1697** 3 k. bistre, black & bl . 15 10

4416 – 4 k. lilac, black & blue . 20 10

4417 – 6 k. purple, black & grn 25 10

4418 – 10 k. brown, black & bl 90 15

4419 – 16 k. green, blk & pur . 60 25

4420 – 20 k. blue, pur & stone . 65 30

DESIGNS: 4 k. Shell fish; 6 k. Eel; 10 k. Long tailed duck; 16 k. Crab; 20 k. Chrisipther.

1698 "Parade in Red Square, Moscow" (K. F. Yuon)

1975. Birth Centenaries of Soviet Painters. Multicoloured.

4422 1 k. Type **1698** 10 10

4423 2 k. "Winter Morning in Industrial Moscow" (K. P. Yuon) 10 10

4424 6 k. "Soldiers with Captured Guns" (E. E. Lansere) . . 25 10

4425 10 k. "Excavating the Metro Tunnel" (E. E. Lansere) . . 60 20

4426 16 k. "A. A. Pushkin and N. N. Pushkina at Palace Ball" (N. P. Ulyanov) (vert) 60 30

4427 20 k. "Lauriston at Kutuzov's Headquarters" (N. P. Ulyanov) 80 40

1699 Conference Emblem **1700** A. Isaakjan

1975. European Security and Co-operation Conference, Helsinki.

4428 **1699** 6 k. black, gold & blue 15 10

1975. Birth Centenary of Avetic Isaakjan (Armenian poet).

4429 **1700** 4 k. multicoloured . . 10 10

1701 M. K. Ciurlionis **1702** J. Duclos

1975. Birth Centenary of M. K. Ciurlionis (Lithuanian composer).

4430 **1701** 4 k. gold, green & yellow 15 10

1975. Jacques Duclos (French communist leader) Commemoration.

4431 **1702** 6 k. purple and silver . 15 10

1703 Al Farabi **1704** Ruffs

1975. 1100th Birth Anniv of Al Farabi (Persian philosopher).

4432 **1703** 6 k. multicoloured . . 15 10

1975. 50th Anniv of Berezinsky and Stolby Nature Reserves. Multicoloured.

4433 1 k. Type **1704** 30 10

4434 4 k. Siberian musk deer . . 30 10

4435 6 k. Sable 30 10

4436 10 k. Capercaillie 55 20

4437 16 k. Eurasian badger . . . 60 55

1705 Korean Crest with Soviet and Korean Flags (Korean Liberation) **1707** S. A. Esenin

1706 Cosmonauts, "Soyuz 18" and "Salyut 4" Linked

1975. 30th Anniversaries. Multicoloured.

4438 6 k. Type **1705** 15 10

4439 6 k. Vietnamese crest, Soviet and Vietnamese flags (Vietnam Democratic Republic) 15 10

1975. Space Flight of "Soyuz 18—Salyut 4" by Cosmonauts P. Klimuk and V. Sevastyanov.

4440 **1706** 10 k. black, red & blue 25 10

1975. 80th Birth Anniv of S. A. Esenin (poet).

4441 **1707** 6 k. brown, yell & grey 15 10

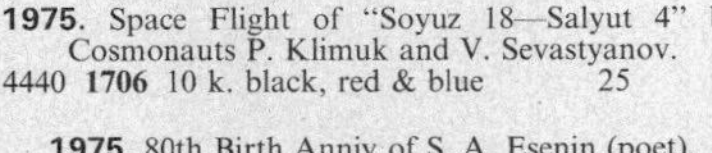

1708 Standardisation Emblems

1975. 50th Anniv of Soviet Communications Standardisation Committee.

4442 **1708** 4 k. multicoloured . . 10 10

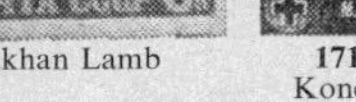

1709 Astrakhan Lamb **1710** M. P. Konchalovsky

1975. 3rd International Astrakhan Lamb Breeding Symposium, Samarkand.

4443 **1709** 6 k. black, grn & stone . 20 10

1975. Birth Centenary of M. P. Konchalovsky (therapeutist).

4444 **1710** 4 k. brown and red . . . 15 10

1711 Exhibition Emblem **1712** I.W.Y. Emblem and Rose

1975. 3rd All-Union Philatelic Exhibition, Yerevan.

4445 **1711** 4 k. red, brown & blue . 10 10

1975. International Women's Year.

4446 **1712** 6 k. red, blue & turquoise 20 10

1713 Parliament Buildings, Belgrade **1714** Title-page of 1938 Edition

1975. 30th Anniv of Yugoslav Republic.

4447 **1713** 6 k. blue, red and gold . 15 10

1975. 175th Anniv of Publication of "Tale of the Host of Igor".

4448 **1714** 4 k. red, grey and bistre 10 10

1715 M. I. Kalinin (statesman)

1975. Celebrities' Birth Centenaries.

4449 **1715** 4 k. brown 10 10

4450 – 4 k. brown 10 10

DESIGN: No. 4450, A. V. Lunacharsky (politician).

1716 Torch and Inscription

1975. 70th Anniv of Russian 1905 Revolution.

4451 **1716** 4 k. red and brown . . . 10 10

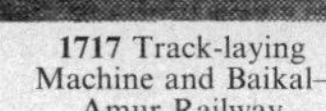

1717 Track-laying Machine and Baikal–Amur Railway **1719** Star of Spassky Tower

1718 "Decembrists in Senate Square" (D. N. Kardovsky) (Illustration reduced. Actual size 70×33 mm).

1975. 58th Anniv of October Revolution. Mult.

4452 4 k. Type **1717** 35 10

4453 4 k. Rolling mill, Novolipetsk steel plant (vert) 35 10

4454 4 k. Formula and ammonia plant, Nevynomyssk chemical works (vert) 35 10

1975. 150th Anniv of Decembrist Rising.

4455 **1718** 4 k. multicoloured . . . 20 10

1975. New Year.

4456 **1719** 4 k. multicoloured . . . 10 10

1720 "Village Street"

1975. 125th Birth Anniv of F. A. Vasilev (painter). Multicoloured.

4457 2 k. Type **1720** 10 10

4458 5 k. "Forest Path" 15 10

4459 6 k. "After the Thunderstorm" 20 10

4460 10 k. "Forest Marsh" (horiz) 35 15

4461 12 k. "In the Crimean Mountains" 45 20

4462 16 k. "Wet Meadow" (horiz) 60 30

1721 "Venus" Spacecraft

1975. Space Flights of "Venus 9" and "Venus 10".

4464 **1721** 10 k. multicoloured . . 30 30

1722 G. Sundukyan

1975. 150th Birth Anniv of G. Sundukyan (Armenian playwright).

4465 **1722** 4 k. multicoloured . . . 10 10

1723 Iceland Poppy **1724** A. L. Mints

1975. Flowers (1st series). Multicoloured.

4466 4 k. Type **1723** 30 10

4467 6 k. Globe flower 25 10

4468 10 k. Yellow anemone . . . 35 15

4469 12 k. Snowdrop windflower . 40 20

4470 16 k. "Eminium lehemannii" 50 30

See also Nos. 4585/9.

1975. A. L. Mints (scientist) Commemoration.

4471 **1724** 4 k. brown and gold . . 10 10

1725 "Demon" (A. Kochupalov) **1726** Pieck

1975. Miniatures from Palekh Art Museum (1st series). Multicoloured.

4472 4 k. Type **1725** 20 10

4473 6 k. "Vasilisa the Beautiful" (I. Vakurov) 30 10

4474 10 k. "The Snow Maiden" (T. Zubkova) 40 15

4475 16 k. "Summer" (K. Kukulieva) 55 25

4476 20 k. "Fisherman and Goldfish" (I. Vakurov) (horiz) . . . 90 30

See also Nos. 4561/5.

1975. Birth Centenary of Wilhelm Pieck (President of German Democratic Republic).
4477 **1726** 6 k. black 15 10

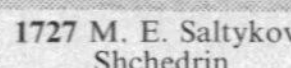

1727 M. E. Saltykov-Shchedrin **1728** Congress Emblem

1976. 150th Birth Anniv of M. Saltykov-Shchedrin (writer).
4478 **1727** 4 k. multicoloured . . . 15 10

1976. 25th Communist Party Congress, Moscow (1st issue).
4479 **1728** 4 k. gold, brown & red . 10 10
See also Nos. 4489 and 4556/60.

1729 Lenin (statue), Kiev **1730** Ice Hockey

1976. 25th Ukraine Communist Party Congress, Kiev.
4481 **1729** 4 k. black, red and blue 10 10

1976. Winter Olympic Games, Innsbruck (1st series). Multicoloured.
4482 2 k. Type **1730** 15 10
4483 4 k. Skiing 20 10
4484 6 k. Figure skating 25 10
4485 10 k. Speed skating 35 15
4486 20 k. Tobogganing 75 35

1731 Marshal C. E. Voroshilov **1732** Congress Hall and Red Banner

1976. 95th Birth Anniv of Marshal C. E. Voroshilov.
4488 **1731** 4 k. green 15 10

1976. 25th Communist Party Congress, Moscow (2nd issue).
4489 **1732** 20 k. orange, red & grn 3·75 2·50

1733 "Lenin on Red Square" (P. Vasiliev)

1976. 106th Birth Anniv of Lenin.
4490 **1733** 4 k. multicoloured . . . 15 10

1734 Atomic Symbol and Institute Emblem

1976. 20th Anniv of Joint Institute of Nuclear Research, Dubna.
4491 **1734** 6 k. multicoloured . . . 20 10

1736 Bolshoi Theatre

1976. Bicentenary of Bolshoi Theatre.
4493 **1736** 10 k. blue, brn & ochre 30 20

1737 "Back from the Fair"

1976. Birth Centenary of P. P. Konchalovsky (painter). Multicoloured.
4494 1 k. Type **1737** 10 10
4495 2 k. "The Green Glass" . . 10 10
4496 6 k. "Peaches" 20 10
4497 16 k. "Meat, Game and Vegetables by the Window" 55 30
4498 20 k. Self-portrait (vert) . . 75 35

1738 "Vostok", "Salyut" and "Soyuz" Spacecraft

1976. 15th Anniv of First Manned Space Flight by Yury Gagarin.
4499 4 k. Type **1738** 15 10
4500 6 k. "Meteor" and "Molniya" satellites 20 10
4501 10 k. Cosmonauts on board "Salyut" space-station . . 35 15
4502 12 k. "Interkosmos" satellite and "Apollo"–"Soyuz" space link 45 20

1739 I. A. Dzhavakhishvili **1740** S. Vurgun

1976. Birth Centenary of I. A. Dzhavakhishvili (scientist).
4504 **1739** 4 k. black, stone and green 10 10

1976. 70th Birth Anniv of Samed Vurgun (Azerbaijan poet).
4505 **1740** 4 k. black, brown & grn 10 10

1741 Festival Emblem **1742** F. I. P. Emblem

1976. 1st All-Union Amateur Art Festival.
4506 **1741** 4 k. multicoloured . . 10 10

1976. 50th Anniv of International Philatelic Federation.
4507 **1742** 6 k. red and blue . . . 15 10

1744 Dnepropetrovsk Crest **1745** N. N. Burdenko

1976. Bicentenary of Dnepropetrovsk.
4509 **1744** 4 k. multicoloured . . . 15 10

1976. Birth Centenary of N. N. Burdenko (neurologist).
4510 **1745** 4 k. brown and red . . . 15 10

1746 K. A. Trenev **1748** Electric Railway Train

1747 Canoeing

1976. Birth Centenary of K. A. Trenev (playwright).
4511 **1746** 4 k. multicoloured . . . 10 10

1976. History of Soviet Motor Industry (4th series). As T **1609**.
4512 2 k. black, red and green . . 10 10
4513 3 k. black, orange and bistre . 15 10
4514 4 k. black, buff and blue . . 15 10
4515 12 k. black, green & brown . 45 15
4516 16 k. black, red and yellow . 65 25

DESIGNS: 2 k. Moscow Auto Works "ZIS-110" saloon, 1945; 3 k. Gorkovsky "GAZ-51" truck, 1946; 4 k. Gorkovsky "GAZ-M20 (Pobeda)" saloon, 1946; 12 k. Moscow Auto Works "ZIS-150" truck, 1947; 16 k. Moscow Auto Works "ZIS-154" bus, 1947.

1976. Olympic Games, Montreal. Multicoloured.
4517 4 k. Type **1747** 10 10
4518 6 k. Basketball (vert) 20 10
4519 10 k. Graeco-Roman wrestling 25 15
4520 14 k. Discus throwing (vert) . . 30 15
4521 16 k. Rifle-shooting 35 20

1976. 50th Anniv of Soviet Railway Electrification.
4523 **1748** 4 k. black, red and green 30 10

1749 L. M. Pavlichenko **1750** L. E. Rekabarren

1976. 60th Birth Anniv of L. M. Pavlichenko (war heroine).
4524 **1749** 4 k. brown, yellow and silver 15 10

1976. Birth Centenary of Luis Rekabarren (founder of Chilean Communist Party).
4525 **1750** 6 k. black, red & gold . 15 10

1751 "Fresh Partner"

1976. Russian Art. Paintings by P. A. Fedotov. Mult.
4526 2 k. Type **1751** 10 10
4527 4 k. "Fastidious Fiancee" (horiz) 15 10
4528 6 k. "Aristocrat's Breakfast" . 20 10
4529 10 k. "The Gamblers" (horiz) 35 20
4530 16 k. "The Outing" 50 30

1752 S. S. Nemetkin **1753** Soviet Armed Forces Order

1754 Marx and Lenin (sculpture, Ye Belostotsky and E. Fridman)

1976. Birth Centenary of Sergei S. Nemetkin (chemist).
4532 **1752** 4 k. black, yellow & blue 15 10

1976. (a) As T **1753**.
4533 1 k. olive 10 10
4670 2 k. mauve 10 10
4671 3 k. red 10 10
4672 4 k. red 10 10
4673 6 k. blue 15 10
4674 10 k. green 25 10
4675 12 k. blue 25 10
4676 15 k. blue 50 35
4677 16 k. green 35 15

(b) As T **1754**.
4678 20 k. red 50 10
4679 30 k. red 70 20
4680 32 k. blue . . . . 1·60 65
4681 50 k. brown . . . . 1·40 40
4682 1 r. blue . . . . 3·00 1·00

DESIGNS: 2 k. Gold Star (military) and Hammer and Sickle (labour) decorations; 3 k. "Worker and Farmer" (sculpture); 4 k. Soviet crest; 6 k. Globe and Tupolev Tu-154 airplane (Soviet postal communications); 10 k. Soviet Reputation for Work Order; 23 k. Yuri Gagarin and rocket (space exploration); 15 k. Ostankino T.V. tower and globe; 16 k. International Lenin Prize medal (international peace and security); 30 k. Council for Mutual Economic Aid building; 32 k. Ilyushin Il-76 airplane and compass rose; 50 k. Lenin (after P. Zhukov); 1 r. Satellites orbiting globe.
The 6 and 32 k. are airmail stamps.

1755 Cattle Egret **1756** Peace Dove with Laurel

1976. Water Birds. Multicoloured.
4545 1 k. Type **1755** 20 15
4546 3 k. Black-throated diver . . 25 15
4547 4 k. Common coot 40 15
4548 6 k. Atlantic puffin 65 20
4549 10 k. Slender-billed gull . . . 1·10 30

1976. 2nd Stockholm World Peace Appeal.
4550 **1756** 4 k. blue, yellow & gold 10 10

1757 Federation Emblem

1976. 25th Anniv of International Resistance Movement Federation.
4551 **1757** 6 k. black, gold & blue 15 10

1759 Soviet and Indian Flags **1761** UNESCO Emblem

1760 B. V. Volynov and V. M. Zholobov

1976. Soviet–Indian Friendship.
4553 **1759** 4 k. multicoloured . . . 10 10

1976. Space Flight of "Soyuz 21".
4554 **1760** 10 k. black, blue & brn 30 15

1976. 30th Anniv of UNESCO.
4555 1761 16 k. brown, bistre & bl 40 20

1762 "Industry"

1976. 25th Communist Party Congress (3rd issue).
4556 1762 4 k. brown, red & yell . 15 10
4557 – 4 k. green, red & orange 15 10
4558 – 4 k. violet, red & pink . 15 10
4559 – 4 k. deep red, red and grey 15 10
4560 – 4 k. violet, red & blue . 15 10
DESIGNS: No. 4557, "Agriculture"; No. 4558, "Science and Technology"; No. 4559, "Transport and Communications"; No. 4560, "International Co-operation".

1763 "The Ploughman" (I. Golikov)

1976. Minatures from Palekh Art Museum (2nd series). Multicoloured.
4561 2 k. Type 1763 . . . . 10 10
4562 4 k. "The Search" (I. Markichev) (vert) . . . 15 10
4563 12 k. "The Firebird" (A. Kotuchin) 40 20
4564 14 k. "Folk Festival" (A. Vatagin) (vert) 45 25
4565 20 k. "Victory" (I. Vakurov) (vert) 70 35

1764 Shostakovich and Part of 7th Symphony
1765 G. K. Zhukov

1976. 70th Birth Anniv of Dmitri Shostakovich (composer).
4566 1764 6 k. blue 30 10

1976. 80th Birth Anniversaries of Soviet Marshals.
4567 1765 4 k. green 15 10
4568 – 4 k. brown 15 10
DESIGN: No. 4568, K. K. Rokossovsky.

1766 "Interkosmos 14" Satellite
1767 V. I. Dal

1976. International Co-operation in Space Research.
4569 1766 6 k. blue, gold & black . 20 10
4570 – 10 k. violet, gold & blk . 25 10
4571 – 12 k. purple, gold & blk 35 15
4572 – 16 k. green, gold & blk . 40 15
4573 – 20 k. mauve, gold & blk 50 20
DESIGNS: 10 k. "Aryabhata" (Indian satellite); 12 k. "Apollo"–"Soyuz" space link; 16 k. "Aureole" (French satellite); 20 k. Globe and spacecraft.

1976. 175th Birth Anniv of V. I. Dal (scholar).
4574 1787 4 k. green 15 10

1768 Electric Power Station

1976. 59th Anniv of October Revolution. Mult.
4575 4 k. Type 1768 . . . . 15 10
4576 4 k. Balashovo fabrics factory 15 10
4577 4 k. Irrigation ditch construction 15 10

1769 Medicine Emblem
1770 M. A. Novinsky (oncologist)

1976. 50th Anniv of Petrov Institute of Cancer Research.
4578 1769 4 k. lilac, gold and blue 20 10

1976. Centenary of Cancer Research.
4579 1770 4 k. brown, blue & buff 20 10

1771 Hakkel VII Biplane, 1911

1976. Early Russian Aircraft (2nd series). Multicoloured.
4580 3 k. Type 1771 . . . . . . 10 10
4581 6 k. Hakkel IX monoplane, 1912 . . . . 20 10
4582 12 k. Steglau No. 2, 1912 35 15
4583 14 k. Dybovsky Dolphin, 1913 50 15
4584 16 k. Sikorsky Ilya Mourometz, 1914 . . . . 55 25
See also Nos. 4661/6 and 4791/6.

1976. Flowers (2nd series). As T 1723. Mult.
4585 1 k. Safflower 10 10
4586 2 k. Anemone 10 10
4587 3 k. Gentian 10 10
4588 4 k. Columbine 15 10
4589 6 k. Fitillaria 20 10

1772 New Year Greeting

1976. New Year.
4590 1772 4 k. multicoloured . . 10 10

1773 "Parable of the Vineyard"

1976. 370th Birth Anniv of Rembrandt. Mult.
4591 4 k. Type 1773 . . . . . . 15 10
4592 6 k. "Danae" 20 10
4593 10 k. "David and Jonathan" (vert) 30 10
4594 14 k. "The Holy Family" (vert) 45 15
4595 20 k. "Andrian" (vert) . . . 65 25

1774 "Luna 24" and Emblem

1976. "Luna 24" Unmanned Space Flight to Moon.
4597 1774 10 k. brown, yell & bl . 30 15

1775 "Pailot"

1976. Russian Ice-breakers (1st series). Mult.
4598 4 k. Type 1775 . . . . 40 10
4599 6 k. "Ermak" (vert) 50 10
4600 10 k. "Fedor Litke" 70 15
4601 16 k. "Vladmir Ilich" (vert) . . 95 25
4602 20 k. "Krassin" . . . . 1·25 45
See also Nos. 4654/60, 4843/8 and 5147.

1776 "Raduga" Experiment and Cosmonauts

1976. "Soyuz 22" Space Flight by V. F. Bykovsky and V. V. Aksenov.
4603 1776 10 k. green, blue & red . 30 15

1777 Olympic Torch

1976. Olympic Games, Moscow (1980).
4604 1777 4 k. + 2 k. black, red and blue 15 10
4605 – 10 k. + 5 k. black, blue and red 75 25
4606 – 16 k. + 6 k. black, mauve and yellow . . . . . 1·10 40
DESIGNS: 10, 16 k. Games emblem.

1778 Society Emblem and "Red Star"
1779 S. P. Korolev Memorial Medallion

1977. 50th Anniv of Red Banner Forces Voluntary Society.
4608 1778 4 k. multicoloured . . . 15 10

1977. 70th Birth Anniv of S. P. Korolev (scientist and rocket pioneer).
4609 1779 4 k. gold, black & blue . 15 10

1780 Congress Emblem

1977. World Peace Congress, Moscow.
4610 1780 4 k. gold, ultramarine & bl 10 10

1781 Sedov and "Sv. Foka"

1977. Birth Cent of G. Y. Sedov (polar explorer).
4611 1781 4 k. multicoloured . . . 1·10 20

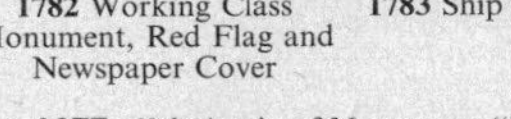
1782 Working Class Monument, Red Flag and Newspaper Cover
1783 Ship on Globe

1977. 60th Anniv of Newspaper "Izvestiya".
4612 1782 4 k. black, red & silver . 10 10

1977. 24th International Navigation Congress, Leningrad.
4613 1783 6 k. blue, black & gold . 20 10

1784 Kremlin Palace of Congresses, Moscow
1785 L. A. Govorov

1977. 16th Soviet Trade Unions Congress.
4614 1784 4 k. gold, black & red . 10 10

1977. 80th Birth Anniv of Marshal L. A. Govorov.
4615 1785 4 k. brown 15 10

1786 Academy Emblem, Text and Building

1977. 150th Anniv of Grechko Naval Academy, Leningrad.
4616 1786 6 k. multicoloured . . . 15 10

1787 J. Labourbe
1788 Chess Pieces

1977. Birth Centenary of Jeanne Labourbe (French communist).
4617 1787 4 k. black, blue & red . 10 10

1977. 6th European Chess Team Championship, Moscow.
4618 1788 6 k. multicoloured . . . 50 10

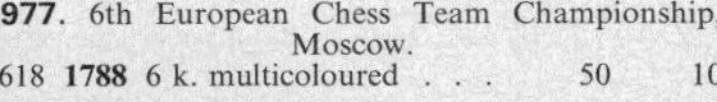

1789 "Soyuz 23" and Cosmonauts

1977. "Soyuz 23" Space Flight by V. D. Zudov and V. I. Rozhdestvensky.
4619 1789 10 k. red, black & brn . 30 15

1790 Novikov-Priboi
1791 "Welcome" (N. M. Soloninkin)

1977. Birth Centenary of Aleksei Novikov-Priboi (writer).
4620 1790 4 k. black, orange & bl 10 10

1977. Folk Paintings from Fedoskino Village. Multicoloured.
4621 4 k. Type 1791 . . . . 15 10
4622 6 k. "Along the Street" (V. D. Antonov) (horiz) . 20 10
4623 10 k. "Northern Song" (J. V. Karapaev) 30 15
4624 12 k. "Fairy Tale about Tzar Sultan" (A. I. Kozlov) . . 30 15
4625 14 k. "Summer Troika" (V. A. Nalimov) (horiz) . . 40 20
4626 16 k. "Red Flower" (V. D. Lipitsky) 45 25

1792 Congress Emblem

1977. World Electronics Congress, Moscow.
4627 1792 6 k. red, grey and blue . 15 10

1793 "In Red Square" (K. V. Filatov)

1977. 107th Birth Anniv of Lenin.
4628 **1793** 4 k. multicoloured . . . 15 10

1794 Yuri Gagarin and Spacecraft

1977. Cosmonautics Day.
4629 **1794** 6 k. blue, lilac and purple 25 15

1795 N. I. Vavilov **1796** F. E. Dzerzhinsky

1977. 90th Birth Anniv of N. I. Vavilov (biologist).
4630 **1795** 4 k. black and brown . 10 10

1977. Birth Centenary of Feliks Dzerzhinsky (founder of Cheka).
4631 **1796** 4 k. black 10 10

1797 Mountain Saxifrage **1798** V. V. Gorbatko and Yu. N. Glazkov (cosmonauts)

1977. Flowers. Multicoloured.
4632 2 k. Type **1797** 10 10
4633 3 k. Pinks 10 10
4634 4 k. "Novosieversia glacialis" 15 10
4635 6 k. "Cerastium maximum" . 20 10
4636 16 k. "Rhododendron aureum" 60 25

1977. "Soyuz 24–Salyut 5" Space Project.
4637 **1798** 10 k. black, red & blue . 50 15

1799 I. S. Konev **1800** Festival Emblem

1977. 80th Birth Anniv of Soviet Marshals.
4638 **1799** 4 k. green 15 10
4639 – 4 k. black 15 10
4640 – 4 k. brown 15 10
DESIGNS: No. 4639, V. D. Sokolovsky; No. 4640, K. A. Meretskov.

1977. 10th International Film Festival, Moscow.
4641 **1800** 6 k. gold, red and lake . 15 10

1801 Greco-Roman Wrestling

1977. Olympic Sports (1st series).
4642 **1801** 4 k. + 2 k. black, ochre and gold 15 10
4643 – 6 k. + 3 k. black, green and gold 20 10
4644 – 10 k. + 5 k. black, mauve and gold 65 20
4645 – 16 k. + 6 k. black, blue and gold 90 30
4646 – 20 k. + 10 k. black, brown and gold . . . . . 1·25 65
DESIGNS: 6 k. Free-style wrestling; 10 k. Judo; 16 k. Boxing; 29 k. Weightlifting.
See also Nos. 4684/9, 4749/53, 4820/4, 4870/4, 4896/4900, 4962/6 and 4973/7.

1802 "Portrait of a Chambermaid" **1804** Stamps and Emblem

1977. 400th Birth Anniv of Rubens. Multicoloured.
4647 4 k. Type **1802** 15 10
4648 6 k. "The Lion Hunt" (horiz) 20 10
4649 10 k. "Stone Carriers" (horiz) 25 10
4650 12 k. "Water and Earth Alliance" 40 15
4651 20 k. "Landscape with Rainbow" (horiz) 95 35

1977. Soviet Ice-breakers (2nd series). As T **1775**. Multicoloured.
4654 4 k. "Aleksandr Sibiryakov" 25 10
4655 6 k. "Georgy Sedov" . . . 30 10
4656 10 k. "Sadko" 55 10
4657 12 k. "Dezhnev" 65 15
4658 14 k. "Sibur" 75 20
4659 16 k. "Lena" 90 30
4660 20 k. "Amguema" . . . . . 1·10 40

1977. Air. Early Soviet Aircraft (3rd series). As T **1771** but dated 1977.
4661 4 k. black, brown and blue . 15 10
4662 6 k. black, orange and green 25 10
4663 10 k. black, mauve and blue 30 10
4664 12 k. black, blue and red . . 35 15
4665 16 k. multicoloured 50 15
4666 20 k. black, green and blue . 70 20
DESIGNS: 4 k. R-IV bis biplane trainer, 1917; 6 k. Kalinin AK-1, 1924; 10 k. Tupolev ANT-3 R-3, 1925; 12 k. Tupolev ANT-4 TB-1 bomber, 1929; 16 k. Polikarpov R-5 biplane, 1929; 20 k. Shvarov Sh-2 flying boat, 1930

1977. "60th Anniv of October Revolution" Philatelic Exhibition, Moscow.
4667 **1804** 4 k. red, blue and brown 10 10

1805 Buildings and Arms, Stavropol **1807** Yuri Gargarin and "Vostok" Spacecraft

1977. Bicentenary of Stavropol.
4668 **1805** 6 k. gold, red & green . 15 10

1977. Olympic Sports (2nd series). As T **1801**.
4684 4 k. + 2 k. black, gold & red 20 10
4685 6 k. + 3 k. black, gold & blue 45 15
4686 10 k. + 5 k. black, gold & grn 70 20
4687 16 k. + 6 k. black, gold & olive 95 30
4688 20 k. + 10 k. black, gold & pur 1·40 65
DESIGNS—HORIZ: 4 k. Cycling; 10 k. Rifle shooting; 16 k. Horse-jumping; 20 k. Fencing. VERT: 6 k. Archery.

1977. 20th Anniv of Space Exploration.
4690 **1807** 10 k. red, blue & brown 30 15
4691 – 10 k. brown, blue & vio 30 15
4692 – 10 k. red, purple & grn 30 15
4693 – 20 k. green, brn & red . 55 25
4694 – 20 k. purple, red & blue 55 25
4695 – 20 k. red, blue & green 55 25
DESIGNS: No. 4691, Space walking; No. 4692, "Soyuz" spacecraft and "Salyut" space station linked; No. 4693, "Proton 4" satellite; No. 4694, "Luna Venus" and "Mars" space stations; No. 4695, "Intercosmos 10" satellite and "Apollo" and "Soyuz" spacecraft linked

1808 Carving from St. Dmitri Cathedral, Vladimir (12th-cent)

1977. Russian Art. Multicoloured.
4697 4 k. Type **1808** 15 10
4698 6 k. Bracelet, Ryazan (12th cent). 20 15
4699 10 k. Detail of Golden Gate from Nativity Cathedral, Suzdal (13th-cent) 30 15
4700 12 k. Detail from "Arch-angel Michael" (icon) (A. Rublev) (15th-cent) 30 15
4701 16 k. Gold and marble chalice made by I. Fomin (15th-cent) 45 20
4702 20 k. St. Basil's Cathedral, Moscow (16th-cent) 55 20

1809 "Snowflake and Fir Twig" **1810** Cruiser "Aurora"

1977. New Year.
4703 **1809** 4 k. multicoloured . . . 10 10

1977. 60th Anniv of October Revolution.
4704 **1810** 4 k. multicoloured . . . 15 10
4705 – 4 k. black, red & gold . 15 10
4706 – 4 k. black, red & gold . 15 10
4707 – 4 k. multicoloured . . . 15 10
DESIGNS: No. 4705, Statue of Lenin; No. 4706, Page of "Izvestiya", book by Brezhnev and crowd; No. 4707, Kremlin spire, star and fireworks.

1811 First Clause of U.S.S.R. Constitution

1977. New Constitution.
4709 **1811** 4 k. yellow, red & brn . 10 10
4710 – 4 k. multicoloured . . . 10 10
DESIGN: No. 4710, People of the U.S.S.R. welcoming new constitution.

1813 Postwoman and Post Code

1977. Postal Communications. Multicoloured.
4713 4 k. Type **1813** 15 10
4714 4 k. Letter collection 15 10
4715 4 k. "Map-O" automatic sorting machine 15 10
4716 4 k. Mail transport 15 10
4717 4 k. Delivering the mail . . . 15 10

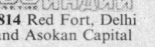

1814 Red Fort, Delhi and Asokan Capital **1815** Monument, Kharkov

1977. 30th Anniv of Indian Independence.
4718 **1814** 6 k. gold, purple & red . 20 10

1977. 60th Anniv of Establishment of Soviet Power in the Ukraine.
4719 **1815** 6 k. multicoloured . . . 15 10

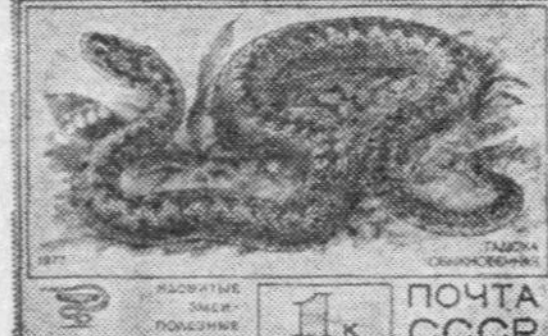

1816 Adder

1977. Snakes and Protected Animals. Mult.
4720 1 k. Type **1816** 10 10
4721 4 k. Levantine viper 15 10
4722 6 k. Saw-scaled viper 20 10
4723 10 k. Central Asian viper . . 30 15
4724 12 k. Central Asian cobra . . 30 15
4725 16 k. Polar bear and cub . . 40 25
4726 20 k. Walrus and young . . 55 25
4727 30 k. Tiger and cub 60 30

1817 Olympic Emblem and Arms of Vladimir

1977. 1980 Olympics. "Tourism around the Golden Ring" (1st issue). Multicoloured.
4728 1 r. + 50 k. Type **1817** . . . 4·50 2·75
4729 1 r. + 50 k. Vladimir Hotel . 4·50 2·75
4730 1 r. + 50 k. Arms of Suzdal 4·50 2·75
4731 1 r. + 50 k. Pozharsky monument . . . . 4·50 2·75
4732 1 r. + 50 k. Arms of Ivanovo and Frunze monument . . 4·50 2·75
4733 1 r. + 50 k. Monument to Revolutionary Fighters . . 4·50 2·75
See also Nos. 4828/31, 4850/3, 4914/17, 4928/9, 4968/9, 4981/2 and 4990/5.

1818 Combine Harvester **1819** Kremlin Palace of Congresses

1978. 50th Anniv of "Gigant" Collective Farm, Rostov.
4734 **1818** 4 k. brown, red & yellow 10 10

1978. 18th Leninist Young Communist League (Komsomol) Congress.
4735 **1819** 4 k. multicoloured . . . 10 10

1820 Globe, Obelisk and Emblem

1978. 8th International Federation of Resistance Fighters Congress, Minsk.
4736 **1820** 6 k. red, blue & black . 15 10

1821 Red Army Detachment and Modern Sailor, Airman and Soldier

1978. 60th Anniv of Soviet Military Forces. Multicoloured.
4737 4 k. Type **18321** 15 10
4738 4 k. Defenders of Moscow monument (detail), Lenin banner and Order of Patriotic War 15 10
4739 4 k. Soviet soldier 15 10

1822 "Celebration in a Village" (½-size illustration)

1978. Birth Centenary of Boris M. Kustodiev (artist). Multicoloured.

4740 4 k. Type **1822** 15 10
4741 6 k. "Shrovetide" 20 10
4742 10 k. "Morning" (50 × 36 mm) 30 15
4743 12 k. "Merchant's Wife drinking Tea" (50 × 36 mm) 40 15
4744 20 k. "Bolshevik" (50 × 36 mm) 55 25

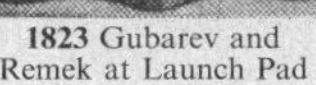

1823 Gubarev and Remek at Launch Pad

1824 "Soyuz" Capsules linked to "Salyut" Space Station

1978. Soviet–Czech Space Flight. Multicoloured.

4746 6 k. Type **1823** 15 10
4747 15 k. "Soyuz-28" docking with "Salyut-6" space station . . 35 15
4748 32 k. Splashdown . . . . . . 1·00 35

1978. Olympic Sports (3rd series). As T **1801**. Multicoloured.

4749 4 k. + 2 k. Swimmer at start 15 10
4750 6 k. + 3 k. Diving (vert) . . 20 10
4751 10 k. + 5 k. Water polo . . 65 15
4752 10 k. + 6 k. Canoeist . . . . 1·00 20
4753 20 k. + 10 k. Single sculls . 1·40 70

1978. Cosmonautics Day.

4755 **1824** 6 k. gold, blue and deep blue 15 10

1825 Shield and Laurel Wreath

1826 First Russian Locomotive and Designers

1978. 9th World Congress of Trade Unions.

4756 **1825** 6 k. multicoloured . . . 15 10

1978. Russian Locomotives (1st series). Mult.

4757 1 k. Type **1826** 20 10
4758 2 k. "D series" freight train, 1845 . . . . 20 10
4759 3 k. First passenger locomotive, 1845 . . . . 20 10
4760 16 k. "Gv series" locomotive, 1863–7 . . . . 90 20
4761 20 k. "Bv series" passenger locomotive, 1863–7 . . . . 1·10 30

Nos. 4758/61 are horizontal designs.
See also Nos. 4861/5.

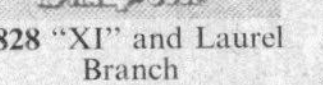

1828 "XI" and Laurel Branch

1830 I.M.C.O. Emblem

1829 Tulip "Bolshoi Theatre"

1978. 11th World Youth and Students Festival, Havana.

4763 **1828** 4 k. multicoloured . . . 10 10

1978. Moscow Flowers. Multicoloured.

4764 1 k. Type **1829** 10 10
4765 2 k. Rose "Moscow Morning" 10 10
4766 4 k. Dahlia "Red Star" . . 10 10
4767 10 k. Gladiolus "Moscovite" 35 15
4768 12 k. Iris "To Il'ich's Anniversary" 45 15

1978. 20th Anniv of Intergovernment Maritime Consultative Organization, and World Maritime Day.

4769 **1830** 6 k. multicoloured . . 10 10

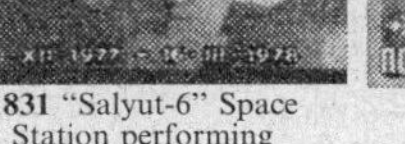

1831 "Salyut-6" Space Station performing Survey Work

1832 "Space Meteorology"

1978. "Salyut-6" Space Station. Multicoloured.

4770 15 k. Type **1831** 40 30
4771 15 k. Yu. V. Romanenko and G. M. Grechko 40 30

Nos. 4770/1 were issued in se-tenant pairs forming a composite design.

1978. Space Research. Multicoloured.

4772 10 k. Type **1832** 30 15
4773 10 k. "Soyuz" orbiting globe ("Natural resources") . . 30 15
4774 10 k. Radio waves, ground station and "Molniya" satellite ("Communication") 30 15
4775 10 k. Human figure, "Vostok" orbiting Earth ("Medicine and biology") 30 15

1833 Transporting Rocket to Launch Site

1978. Soviet–Polish Space Flight. Multicoloured.

4777 6 k. Type **1833** 15 10
4778 15 k. Crystal (Sirena experiment) 40 15
4779 32 k. Space station, map and scientific research ship "Cosmonaut Vladimir Komarov" 95 35

1834 Komsomol Awards

1835 M. V. Zakharov

1978. 60th Anniv of Leninist Young Communist League (Komsomol). Multicoloured.

4780 4 k. Type **1834** 10 10
4781 4 k. Products of agriculture and industry 20 10

1978. 80th Birth Anniv of Marshal M. V. Zakharov.

4782 **1835** 4 k. brown 15 10

1836 N. G. Chernyshevsky

1978. 150th Birth Anniv of Nikolai G. Chernyshevsky (revolutionary).

4783 **1836** 4 k. brown and yellow . 10 10

1837 Snow Petrel

1978. Antarctic Fauna. Multicoloured.

4784 1 k. Snares Island penguin (horiz) 50 15
4785 3 k. Type **1837** 65 15
4786 4 k. Emperor penguin 80 15
4787 6 k. White-blood pikes . . . 70 10
4788 10 k. Southern elephant-seal (horiz) . . . . 1·25 15

1838 Torch and Flags

1839 William Harvey

1978. Construction of Orenburg–U.S.S.R. Western Frontier Gas Pipe-line.

4789 **1838** 4 k. multicoloured . . . 10 10

1978. 400th Birth Anniv of William Harvey (discoverer of blood circulation).

4790 **1839** 6 k. green, blk & blue . 15 10

1978. Air. Early Russian Aircraft (3rd series). As T **1771**.

4791 4 k. green, brown & black . . 15 10
4792 6 k. multicoloured 20 10
4793 10 k. yellow, blue & black . . 35 15
4794 12 k. orange, blue & black . . 40 15
4795 16 k. blue, dp blue & black . . 50 15
4796 20 k. multicoloured 65 20

DESIGNS: 4 k. Polikarpov Po-2 biplane, 1928; 6 k. Kalinin K-5, 1929; 10 k. Tupolev ANT-6 TB-3, 1930; 12 k. Putilov Stal-2, 1931; 16 k. Beriev Be-2 MBR-2 reconnaissance seaplane, 1932; 20 k. Polikarpov I-16, 1934.

1840 "Bathing of Red Horse"

1978. Birth Centenary of K. S. Petrov-Vodkin (painter). Multicoloured.

4797 4 k. Type **1840** 10 10
4798 6 k. "Petrograd, 1918" . . . 15 10
4799 10 k. "Commissar's Death" . 25 15
4800 12 k. "Rose Still Life" . . . 30 15
4801 16 k. "Morning Still Life" . . 40 15

1841 Assembling "Soyuz 31"

1978. Soviet-East German Space Flight. Multicoloured.

4803 6 k. Type **1841** 15 10
4804 15 k. Space photograph of Pamir mountains 35 15
4805 32 k. Undocking from space station . . . . 1·10 35

1842 "Molniya 1" Satellite, "Orbita" Ground Station and Tupolev Tu-134 Airplane

1978. "PRAGA 78" International Stamp Exhibition.

4806 **1842** 6 k. multicoloured . . . 15 10

1843 Tolstoi

1978. 150th Birth Anniv of Leo Tolstoi (novelist).

4807 **1843** 4 k. green . . . . . . 1·60 1·00

1844 Union Emblem

1845 Bronze Figure, Erebuni Fortress

1978. 14th General Assembly of International Union for the Protection of Nature and Natural Resources, Ashkhabad.

4808 **1844** 4 k. multicoloured . . 15 10

1978. Armenian Architecture. Multicoloured.

4809 4 k. Type **1845** 10 10
4810 6 k. Echmiadzin Cathedral . 15 10
4811 10 k. Khachkary (carved stones) 25 15
4812 12 k. Matenadaran building (repository of manuscripts) (horiz) 35 15
4813 16 k. Lenin Square, Yerevan (horiz) 45 20

1846 Monument (P. Kufferge)

1847 Emblem, Ostankino TV Tower and Hammer and Sickle

1978. 70th Anniv of Russian Aid to Messina Earthquake Victims.

4814 **1846** 6 k. multicoloured . . . 20 10

1978. 20th Anniv of Organization for Communications Co-operation.

4815 **1847** 4 k. multicoloured . . . 10 10

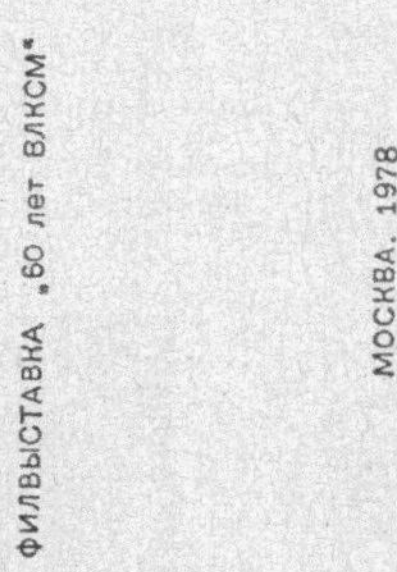

(1848)

1978. "60th Anniv of Komsomol" Philatelic Exhibition. Optd with T **1848**.

4816 **1834** 4 k. multicoloured . . . 1·00 50

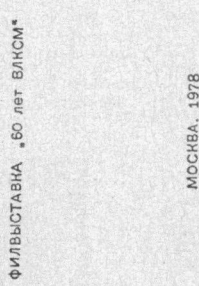

1851 Stepan Georgievich Shaumyan

1852 "Star" Class Yacht

1978. Birth Cent of S. G. Shaumyan (Commissar).
4819 **1851** 4 k. green 10 10

1978. Olympic Sports (4th series). Sailing Regatta, Tallin. Multicoloured.
4820 4 k. + 2 k. Type **1852** 20 10
4821 6 k. + 3 k. "Soling" class yacht 30 10
4822 10 k. + 5 k. "470" class yacht 40 15
4823 16 k. + 6 k. "Finn" class yacht 60 25
4824 20 k. + 10 k. "Flying Dutchman" class yacht . . 1·10 50

1853 Industrial Structures and Flags

1854 Black Sea Ferry

1978. 61st Anniv of October Revolution.
4826 **1853** 4 k. multicoloured . . . 15 10

1978. Inauguration of Il'ichevsk–Varna, Bulgaria, Ferry Service.
4827 **1854** 6 k. multicoloured . . . 15 10

1855 Zagorsk

1978. 1980 Olympics. "Tourism around the Golden Ring" (2nd issue). Multicoloured.
4828 1 r. + 50 k. Type **1855** . . . 4·75 2·75
4829 1 r. + 50 k. Palace of Culture, Zagorsk . . . . 4·75 2·75
4830 1 r. + 50 k. Kremlin, Rostov-Veliki . . . . 4·75 2·75
4831 1 r. + 50 k. View of Rostov-Veliki . . . . 4·75 2·75

1856 Church of the Intercession on River Nerl

1978. "Masterpieces of Old Russian Culture". Multicoloured.
4832 6 k. Golden crater (horiz) . . 15 10
4833 10 k. Type **1856** 25 15
4834 12 k. "St. George and the Dragon" (15th-century icon) 30 15
4835 16 k. Tsar Cannon (horiz) . . 35 20

1857 Cup with Snake and Institute

1859 Spassky Tower, Kremlin

1858 Nestor Pechersky and "Chronicle of Past Days"

1978. 75th Anniv of Herzen Oncology Research Institute, Moscow.
4836 **1857** 4 k. gold, purple & blk 15 10

1978. History of the Russian Posts. Multicoloured.
4837 4 k. Type **1858** 10 10
4838 6 k. Birch-bark letter 15 10
4839 10 k. Messenger with trumpet 25 15
4840 12 k. Mail sledges 30 15
4841 16 k. Interior of Prikaz Post Office 35 20

1978. New Year.
4842 **1859** 4 k. multicoloured . . 10 10

1978. Soviet Ice breakers (3rd series). As T **1775**. Multicoloured.
4843 4 k. "Vasily Pronchishchev" 20 10
4844 6 k. "Kapitan Belousov" (vert) 25 10
4845 10 k. "Moskva" 30 15
4846 12 k. "Admiral Makarov" . 45 15
4847 16 k. "Lenin" atomic ice-breaker (vert) 65 20
4848 20 k. "Arktika" atomic ice-breaker 80 25

1860 V. Kovalenok and A. Ivanchenkov

1978. "140 Days in Space".
4849 **1860** 10 k. multicoloured . . 20 15

1978. 1980 Olympics "Tourism around the Golden Ring" (3rd issue). As T **1855**. Multicoloured.
4850 1 r. + 50 k. Alexander Nevsky Monument, Pereslavl-Zalessky . . . . 4·00 2·75
4851 1 r. + 50 k. Peter I Monument, Pereslavl-Zalessky . . . . 4·00 2·75
4852 1 r. + 50 k. Monastery of the Transfiguration, Yaroslavl 4·00 2·75
4853 1 r. + 50 k. Ferry terminal and Eternal Glory Monument, Yaroslavl . . . . 4·00 2·75

1862 Cuban Flags

1863 Government Building, Minsk

1979. 20th Anniv of Cuban Revolution.
4855 **1862** 6 k. multicoloured . . 15 10

1979. 60th Anniv of Byelorussian Soviet Socialist Republic and Communist Party.
4856 **1863** 4 k. multicoloured . . 10 10

1864 Flags and Reunion Monument

1865 Old and New University Buildings

1979. 325th Anniv of Reunion of Ukraine with Russia.
4857 **1864** 4 k. multicoloured . . 10 10

1979. 400th Anniv of Vilnius Univeristy.
4858 **1865** 4 k. black and pink . . 10 10

1866 Exhibition Hall and First Bulgarian Stamp

1979. "Philaserdica 79" International Stamp Exhibition, Sofia.
4859 **1866** 15 k. multicoloured . . 30 15

INDEX
Countries can be quickly located by referring to the index at the end of this volume.

1867 Satellites "Radio 1" and "Radio 2"

1979. Launching of "Radio" Satellites.
4860 **1867** 4 k. multicoloured . . . 35 10

1868 "A" Series Passenger Locomotive

1979. Railway Locomotives (2nd series). Mult.
4861 2 k. Type **1868** 15 10
4862 3 k. "Shch" series locomotive 15 10
4863 4 k. "L-Putilov" series locomotive 20 10
4864 6 k. "Su" series locomotive . 35 15
4865 15 k. "L" series locomotive . 1·00 35

1870 "Venera 12" over Venus

1871 Albert Einstein

1979. "Venera" Flights to Venus.
4867 **1870** 10 k. red, lilac and purple 30 10

1979. Birth Centenary of Albert Einstein (physicist).
4868 **1871** 6 k. multicoloured . . . 20 10

1872 Congress Emblem
1873 Free Exercise

1979. 21st World Veterinary Congress, Moscow.
4869 **1872** 6 k. multicoloured . . . 15 10

1979. Olympic Sports (5th series). Gymnastics.
4870 **1873** 4 k. + 2 k. brown, stone and orange 15 10
4871 – 6 k. + 3 k. blue, grey and violet 20 10
4872 – 10 k. + 5 k. red, stone and brown 30 15
4873 – 16 k. + 6 k. mauve, grey and purple 75 40
4874 – 20 k. + 10 k. red, stone and brown . . . . . 1·00 65
DESIGNS: 6 k. Parallel bars; 10 k. Horizontal bar; 16 k. Beam; 20 k. Asymmetric bars.

1874 "To Arms" (poster by R. Beren)
1875 Cosmonauts at Yuri Gagarin Training Centre

1979. 60th Anniv of First Hungarian Socialist Republic.
4876 **1874** 4 k. multicoloured . . . 10 10

1979. Soviet–Bulgarian Space Flight. Multicoloured.
4877 6 k. Type **1875** 20 10
4878 32 k. Landing of cosmonauts 75 35

1876 "Intercosmos"

1979. Cosmonautics Day.
4879 **1876** 15 k. multicoloured . . 30 15

1878 Exhibition Emblem

1979. U.S.S.R. Exhibition, London.
4881 **1878** 15 k. multicoloured . . 25 15

1880 Antonov An-28

1979. Air. Soviet Aircraft. Multicoloured.
4883 2 k. Type **1880** 10 10
4884 3 k. Yakovlev Yak-42 . . . 15 10
4885 10 k. Tupolev Tu-154 . . . 35 15
4886 15 k. Ilyushin Il-76 . . . . 50 20
4887 32 k. Ilyushin Il-86 . . . . 85 35

1882 "Tent" Monument, Mining Institute, Pushkin Theatre and Blast Furnace

1883 Child and Apple Blossom

1979. 50th Anniv of Magnitogorsk City.
4889 **1882** 4 k. multicoloured . . . 15 10

1979. International Year of the Child (1st issue).
4890 **1883** 4 k. multicoloured . . . 15 10
See also Nos. 4918/21.

1884 Bogorodsk Wood-carvings

1979. Folk Crafts. Multicoloured.
4891 2 k. Type **1884** 10 10
4892 3 k. Khokhloma painted dish and jars 10 10
4893 4 k. Zhostovo painted tray . . 15 10
4894 6 k. Kholmogory bone-carvings 25 10
4895 15 k. Vologda lace 45 35

1885 Football

1979. Olympic Sports (6th series). Multicoloured.
4896 **1885** 4 k. + 2 k. blue, grey and orange 30 10
4897 – 6 k. + 3 k. yellow, orange and blue 40 10
4898 – 10 k. + 5 k. green, red and mauve 50 15

4899 – 16 k. + 6 k. purple, blue and green 60 25
4900 – 20 k. + 10 k. yellow, red and green . . . . . . 1·00 60
DESIGNS—VERT: 6 k. Basketball; 10 k. Volleyball. HORIZ: 16 k. Handball; 20 k. Hockey.

1886 Lenin Square Underground Station

1979. Tashkent Underground Railway.
4901 **1886** 4 k. multicoloured . . . 20 10

1887 V. A. Dzhanibekov and O. G. Makarov

1888 Council Building and Flags of Member Countries

1979. "Soyuz 27–Salyut 6–Soyuz 26" Orbital Complex.
4902 **1887** 4 k. multicoloured . . . 20 10

1979. 30th Anniv of Council of Mutual Economic Aid.
4903 **1888** 16 k. multicoloured . . 30 15

1889 Scene from "Battleship Potemkin"

1892 Exhibition Hall and Film Still

1979. 60th Anniv of Soviet Films (1st issue) and 11th International Film Festival, Moscow.
4904 **1889** 15 k. multicoloured . . 35 15
See also No. 4907.

1979. 60th Anniv of Soviet Films (2nd issue).
4907 **1892** 4 k. multicoloured . . . 15 10

1893 "Lilac" (K. A. Korovin)

1894 John McClean

1979. Flower Paintings. Multicoloured.
4908 1 k. "Flowers and Fruits" (I. F. Khrutsky) (horiz) 10 10
4909 2 k. "Phloxes" (I. N. Kramskoi) 15 10
4910 3 k. Type **1893** 15 10
4911 15 k. "Bluebells" (S. V. Gerasimov) 40 20
4912 32 k. "Roses" (P. P. Konchalovsky) (horiz) . . 85 40

1979. Birth Centenary of John McClean (first Soviet consul for Scotland).
4913 **1894** 4 k. black and red . . . 15 10

1979. 1980 Olympics. "Tourism around the Golden Ring" (4th issue). As T **1855**. Multicoloured.
4914 1 r. + 50 k. Narikaly Fortress, Tbilisi . . . . 4·00 2·75
4915 1 r. + 50 k. Georgian Philharmonic Society Concert Hall and "Muse" (sculpture), Tbilisi . . . . 4·00 2·75
4916 1 r. + 50 k. Chir-Dor Mosque, Samarkand . . . . 4·00 2·75
4917 1 r. + 50 k. People's Friendship Museum and "Courage" monument, Tashkent . . . 4·00 2·75

1895 "Friendship" (Liberda Lena)

1979. International Year of the Child (2nd issue). Children's Paintings. Multicoloured.
4918 2 k. Type **1895** 10 10
4919 3 k. "After Rain" (Akhmetshina Dania) 10 10
4920 4 k. "Dance of Friendship" (Elistratova Lilia) 15 10
4921 15 k. "On the Excursion" (Smalyuk Vika) 35 20

1896 Golden Oriole

1979. Birds. Multicoloured.
4922 2 k. Type **1896** 25 10
4923 3 k. Lesser spotted woodpecker 30 10
4924 4 k. Crested tit 35 10
4925 10 k. Barn owl 80 25
4926 15 k. European nightjar . . 1·10 40

1897 Soviet Circus Emblem

1898 Marx, Engels, Lenin and View of Berlin

1979. 60th Anniv of Soviet Circus.
4927 **1897** 4 k. multicoloured . . 20 10

1979. 1980 Olympics. "Tourism around the Golden Ring" (5th issue). As T **1855**. Multicoloured.
4928 1 r. + 50 k. Relics of Yerevan's origin . . . . 3·00 2·10
4929 1 r. + 50 k. Armenian State Opera and Ballet Theatre, Yerevan . . . . 3·00 2·10

1979. 30th Anniv of German Democratic Republic.
4930 **1898** 6 k. multicoloured . . 20 10

1899 V. A. Lyakhov, V. V. Ryumin and "Salyut 6"

1979. Lyakhov and Ryumin's 175 Days in Space. Multicoloured.
4931 15 k. Type **1899** 30 20
4932 15 k. Radio telescope mounted on "Salyut 6" 30 20
Nos. 4931/2 were issued together, se-tenant, forming a composite design.

1900 Hammer and Sickle

1901 Communications Equipment and Signal Corps Emblem

1979. 62nd Anniv of October Revolution.
4933 **1900** 4 k. multicoloured . . 15 10

1979. 60th Anniv of Signal Corps.
4934 **1901** 4 k. multicoloured . . 20 10

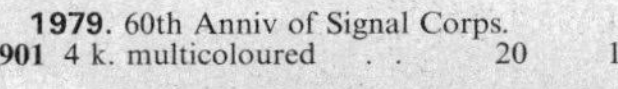

1902 "Katherine" (T. G. Shevchenko)

1903 Shabolovka Radio Mast, Moscow

1979. Ukrainian Paintings. Multicoloured.
4935 2 k. Type **1902** 10 10
4936 3 k. "Into Service" (K. K. Kostandi) 15 10
4937 4 k. "To Petrograd" (A. M. Lopukhov) 30 10
4938 10 k. "Return" (V. N. Kostetsky) 30 15
4939 15 k. "Working Morning" (M. G. Belsky) 40 20

1979. 50th Anniv of Radio Moscow.
4940 **1903** 32 k. multicoloured . . 1·00 30

1904 Misha (Olympic mascot)

1905 "Peace" and Hammer and Sickle

1979. New Year.
4941 **1904** 4 k. multicoloured . . . 15 10

1979. "Peace Programme in Action". Multicoloured.
4942 4 k. Type **1905** 15 10
4943 4 k. Hand holding demand for peace 15 10
4944 4 k. Hands supporting emblem of peace 15 10

1906 Traffic Policeman

1909 Industrial Landscape

1907 "Vulkanolog"

1979. Road Safety. Multicoloured.
4945 3 k. Type **1906** 20 10
4946 4 k. Child playing in road . . 20 10
4947 6 k. Speeding car out of control 35 10

1979. Soviet Scientific Research Ships. Multicoloured.
4948 1 k. Type **1907** 10 10
4949 2 k. "Professor Bogorov" . . 10 10
4950 4 k. "Ernst Krenkel" 15 10
4951 6 k. "Kosmonavt Vladislav Volkov" 30 10
4952 10 k. "Kosmonavt Yury Gagarin" 60 20
4953 15 k. "Akademik Kurchatov" 85 35

1980. 50th Anniv of Mordovian ASSR of Russian Federation.
4955 **1909** 4 k. red 15 10

MINIMUM PRICE
The minimum price quoted is 10p which represents a handling charge rather than a basis for valuing common stamps. For further notes about prices, see introductory pages.

1910 Speed Skating

1912 N. I. Podvoisky

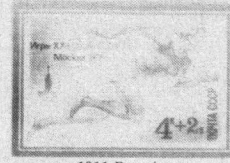

1911 Running

1980. Winter Olympic Games, Lake Placid.
4956 **1910** 4 k. blue, lt bl & orge . 15 10
4957 – 6 k. violet, blue & orge 15 10
4958 – 10 k. red, blue & gold . 40 15
4959 – 15 k. brown, bl & turq . 50 15
4960 – 20 k. turquoise, bl & red 60 25
DESIGNS—HORIZ: 6 k. Figure skating (pairs); 10 k. Ice hockey; 15 k. Downhill skiing. VERT: 20 k. Luge.

1980. Olympic Sports (7th series). Athletics. Mult.
4962 4 k. + 2 k. Type **1911** . . . 20 10
4963 6 k. + 3 k. Hurdling 20 10
4964 10 k. + 5 k. Walking (vert) . 30 20
4965 16 k. + 6 k. High jumping . 70 50
4966 20 k. + 10 k. Long jumping 80 60

1980. Birth Centenary of Nikolai Ilyich Podvoisky (revolutionary).
4967 **1912** 4 k. brown 15 10

1980. 1980 Olympics. "Tourism around the Golden Ring" (6th issue). Moscow. As T **1855**. Mult
4968 1 r. + 50 k. Kremlin . . . . 5·00 3·25
4969 1 r. + 50 k. Kalinin Prospect. 5·00 3·25

1913 "Rainbow" (A. K. Savrasov)
(Illustration reduced. Actual size 74×38 mm)

1980. Birth Annivs of Soviet Artists. Mult
4970 6 k. "Harvest Summer" (A. G. Venetsianov (bicent) (vert) 15 10
4971 6 k. Type **1913** (150th anniv) 15 10
4972 6 k. "Old Yerevan" (M. S. Saryan) (centenary) . . . 15 10

1980. Olympic Sports (8th series). Athletics. As T **1911**. Multicoloured.
4973 4 k. + 2 k. Pole vaulting . . 20 10
4974 6 k. + 3 k. Discus throwing 20 10
4975 10 k. + 5 k. Javelin throwing 30 35
4976 16 k. + 6 k. Hammer throwing 75 55
4977 20 k. + 10 k. Putting the shot 80 70

1915 Georg Ots

1916 Order of Lenin

1980. 60th Birth Anniv of Georg K. Ots (artist).
4980 **1915** 4 k. blue 10 10

1980. 1980 Olympics. "Tourism around the Golden Ring" (7th issue). As T **1855**. Multicoloured.
4981 1 r. + 50 k. St. Isaac's Cathedral, Leningrad . . . 5·00 3·25
4982 1 r. + 50 k. Monument to the Defenders of Leningrad . . 5·00 3·25

1980. 50th Anniv of Order of Lenin.
4983 **1916** 4 k. multicoloured . . . 10 10

1919 "Motherland" (detail of Heroes Monument, Volgograd)

1920 Government House, Arms and Flag of Azerbaijan

1980. 35th Anniv of World War II Victory. Multicoloured.
4986 4 k. Type **1919** 15 10
4987 4 k. Victory Monument, Treptow Park, Berlin . . . 15 10
4988 4 k. Victory Parade, Red Square, Moscow 15 10

1980. 60th Anniv of Azerbaijan Soviet Republic.
4989 **1920** 4 k. multicoloured . . . 10 10

1980. 1980 Olympics. "Tourism around the Golden Ring" (8th issue). As T **1855**. Multicoloured.
4990 1 r. + 50 k. Bogdan Khmelnitsky Monument and St, Sophia Monastery, Kiev 5·00 3·25
4991 1 r. + 50 k. Metro bridge over Dnieper, Kiev . . . . . . 5·00 3·25
4992 1 r. + 50 k. Sports Palace and War Memorial, Minsk . . 5·00 3·25
4993 1 r. + 50 k. House of Cinematograhy, Minsk . . 5·00 3·25
4994 1 r. + 50 k. Old City, Tallin 5·00 3·25
4995 1 r. + 50 k. Hotel Viru, Tallin 5·00 3·25

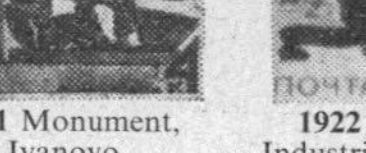

1921 Monument, Ivanovo
1922 Shield and Industrial Complexes

1980. 75th Anniv of First Soviet of Workers Deputies, Ivanovo.
4996 **1921** 4 k. multicoloured . . . 10 10

1980. 25th Anniv of Warsaw Treaty.
4997 **1922** 32 k. multicoloured . . 1·00 65

1923 Yakovlev Yak-24 Helicopter, 1953

1980. Helicopters. Multicoloured.
4998 1 k. Type **1923** 10 10
4999 2 k. Mil Mi-8, 1962 . . . . . 10 10
5000 3 k. Kamov Ka-26, 1965 . . 20 10
5001 6 k. Mil Mi-6, 1957 . . . . 30 10
5002 15 k. Mil Mi-10K, 1965 . . . 80 20
5003 32 k. Mil Mi-V12, 1969 . . 1·90 40

1924 Title Page of Book
1925 Medical Check-up of Cosmonauts

1980. 1500th Birth Anniv of David Anacht (Armenian philosopher).
5004 **1924** 4 k. multicoloured . . . 10 10

1980. Soviet–Hungarian Space Flight. Multicoloured.
5005 6 k. Type **1925** 15 10
5006 15 k. Crew meeting on "Salyut-6" space station 35 15
5007 32 k. Press conference . . . 95 80

1926 Red Fox
1927 Kazan

1980. Fur-bearing Animals. Multicoloured.
5008 2 k. Type **1926** 10 10
5009 4 k. Artic fox (horiz) 15 10
5010 6 k. European mink 20 10
5011 10 k. Coypu 30 15
5012 15 k. Sable (horiz) 50 50

1980. 60th Anniv of Tatar Republic.
5013 **1927** 4 k. multicoloured . . 10 10

1928 College and Emblem
1929 Ho Chi Minh

1980. 150th Anniv of Bauman Technical College, Moscow.
5014 **1928** 4 k. multicoloured . . 10 10

1980. 90th Birth Anniv of Ho Chi Minh (Vietnamese leader).
5015 **1929** 6 k. multicoloured . . 20 10

1930 Arms, Monument and Modern Buildings

1980. 40th Anniv of Soviet Socialist Republics of Lithuania, Latvia and Estonia. Multicoloured.
5016 **1930** 4 k. Lithuania 10 10
5017 – 4 k. Latvia 10 10
5018 – 4 k. Estonia 10 10

1933 Crew of "Soyuz 27" at Launching Site
1934 Avicenna

1980. Soviet–Vietnamese Space Flight. Multicoloured.
5019 6 k. Type **1933** 15 10
5020 15 k. Cosmonauts at work in space 40 20
5021 32 k. Cosmonauts returning to Earth . . . . 1·75 1·40

1980. Birth Millenary of Avicenna (Arab philosopher and physician).
5022 **1934** 4 k. multicoloured . . 10 10

1935 "Khadi-7" Gas turbine Car

1980. Racing cars designed by Kharkov Automobile and Road-building Institute. Multicoloured.
5023 2 k. Type **1935** 10 10
5024 6 k. "Khadi-10" piston engined car 20 10
5025 15 k. "Khadi-11 E" electric car 55 20
5026 32 k. "Khadi-13 E" electric car 1·00 85

1936 Arms, Flags, Government House and Industrial Complex

1980. 60th Anniv of Kazakh Soviet Socialist Republic.
5027 **1936** 4 k. multicoloured . . 15 10

1937 "Self-portrait" and "The Spring"

1980. Birth Bicentenary of Jean Ingres (French painter).
5028 **1937** 32 k. multicoloured . . 1·00 65

1938 "Morning on Kulikovo Field" (A. Bubnov)

1980. 600th Anniv of Battle of Kulikovo.
5029 **1938** 4 k. multicoloured . . . 15 10

1939 Town Hall
1940 Yuri V. Malyshev and Valdimir V. Aksenov

1980. 950th Anniv of Tartu, Estonia.
5030 **1939** 4 k. multicoloured . . . 10 10

1980. "Soyuz T-2" Space Flight.
5031 **1940** 10 k. multicoloured . . 25 15

1941 Theoretical Training
1942 Crew Training

1980. 20th Anniv of Gagarin Cosmonaut Training Centre. Multicoloured.
5032 6 k. Type **1941** 15 10
5033 15 k. Practical training . . . 35 15
5034 32 k. Physical endurance tests 95 65

1980. Soviet–Cuban Space Flight. Multicoloured.
5035 6 k. Type **1942** 15 10
5036 15 k. Physical exercise on board space complex 30 15
5037 32 k. Returned cosmonauts and space capsule 95 65

1943 "Bargaining" (Nevrev) (Reduced-size illustration. Acutal size 77 x 34 mm)

1980. 150th Birth Anniv of N. V. Nevrev and K. D. Flavitsky (painters). Multicoloured.
5038 6 k. Type **1943** 20 10
5039 6 k. "Princess Tarakanova" (Flavitsky) 20 10

1944 Vasilevsky
1945 Banner

1980. 85th Birth Anniv of Marshal A. M. Vasilevsky.
5040 **1944** 4 k. green 15 10

1980. 63rd Anniv of October Revolution.
5041 **1945** 4 k. red, gold & purple 10 10

1946 Guramishvili
1947 Ioffe

1980. 275th Birth Anniv of David Guramishvili (Georgian poet).
5042 **1946** 4 k. green, silver and black 10 10

1980. Birth Centenary of A. F. Ioffe (physicist).
5043 **1947** 4 k. brown and buff . . 15 10

1948 Siberian Cedar

1980. Trees. Multicoloured.
5044 2 k. Type **1948** 10 10
5045 4 k. Pedunculate oak 10 10
5046 6 k. Lime (vert) 10 10
5047 10 k. Sea buckthorn 25 15
5048 15 k. Ash 40 20

1950 Suvorov

1980. 250th Birth Anniv of Field Marshal A. V. Suvorov.
5050 **1950** 4 k. blue 15 10

1951 State Emblem and Republican Government House
1952 Blok (after K. Somov)

1980. 60th Anniv of Armenian Soviet Socialist Republic.
5051 **1951** 4 k. multicoloured . . . 10 10

1980. Birth Centenary of Aleksandr Aleksandrovich Blok (poet).
5052 **1952** 4 k. multicoloured . . . 10 10

1980. Soviet Scientific Research Ships (2nd series). As T **1907**. Multicoloured.
5053 2 k. "Ayu-Dag" 10 10
5054 3 k. "Valerian Uryvaev" . . 10 10
5055 4 k. "Mikhail Somov" . . . 25 10
5056 6 k. "Akademik Sergei Korolev" 25 10
5057 10 k. "Otto Schmidt" . . . 40 15
5058 15 k. "Akademik Mstislav Keldysh" 60 45

1953 Spassky Tower and Kremlin Palace of Congresses

1955 Sable in Cedar

1980. New Year.
5059 **1953** 4 k. multicoloured . . . 10 10

1980. Perf or imperf (2 r.), perf (others).
5060 – 3 k. orange 10 10
5061 – 5 k. blue 15 10
5063 **1955** 35 k. olive . . . . . . 1·00 35
5064 – 45 k. brown . . . . . 1·40 60
5066 – 50 k. green . . . . . . 2·00 70
5067 – 2 r. black . . . . . . 5·50 2·00
5068 – 3 r. black . . . . . . 7·50 4·00
5068a – 3 r. green . . . . . . 2·00 1·00
5069 – 5 r. blue . . . . . . 3·25 1·60
DESIGNS—14×22 mm: 3 k. State flag; 5 k. Forms of transport. 22×33 mm: 45 k. Spassky Tower; 50 k. Vodovzodny Tower and Grand Palace, Moscow Kremlin; 2 r. Atomic ice-breaker; 3 r. Globe, child and olive branch; 5 r. Globe and feather ("Peace").

1957 Institute Building

1980. 50th Anniv of Institute for Advanced Training of Doctors.
5075 **1957** 4 k. multicoloured . . . 15 10

1958 Lenin Monument, Leningrad, and Dneproges Hydro-electric Station

1959 Nesmeyanov

1980. 60th Anniv of GOELRO (electrification plan).
5076 **1958** 4 k. multicoloured . . . 10 10

1980. Academician A. N. Nesmeyanov (organic chemist) Commemoration.
5077 **1959** 4 k. multicoloured . . . 10 10

1960 Nagatinsky Bridge

1980. Moscow Bridges. Multicoloured.
5078 4 k. Type **1960** 15 10
5079 6 k. Luzhniki underground railway bridge 25 10
5080 15 k. Kalininsky bridge . . . 45 20

1961 Timoshenko

1962 Indian and Russian Flags with Government House, New Delhi

1980. 10th Death Anniv of Marshal S. K. Timoshenko.
5081 **1961** 4 k. purple 10 10

1980. President Brezhnev's Visit to India.
5082 **1962** 4 k. multicoloured . . . 10 10

1963 Antarctic Research Station

1964 Arms and Symbols of Agriculture and Industry

1981. Antarctic Exploration. Multicoloured.
5083 4 k. Type **1963** 25 10
5084 6 k. Antennae, rocket, weather balloon and tracked vehicle (Meteorological research) . 15 10
5085 15 k. Map of Soviet bases and supply ship . . . . 2·25 40

1981. 60th Anniv of Dagestan Autonomous Soviet Socialist Republic.
5086 **1964** 4 k. multicoloured . . 10 10

1965 Hockey Players and Emblem

1981. 12th World Hockey Championships, Khabarovsk.
5087 **1965** 6 k. multicoloured . . 15 10

1966 Banner and Star

1981. 26th Soviet Communist Party Congress. Multicoloured.
5088 4 k. Type **1966** 10 10
5089 20 k. Kremlin Palace of Congresses and Lenin (51×36 mm) . . . . . . 1·40 1·00

1967 Lenin and Congress Building

1968 Keldysh

1981. 26th Ukraine Communist Party Congress.
5090 **1967** 4 k. multicoloured . . 10 10

1981. 70th Birth Anniv of Academician Mtislav Vsevolodovich Keldysh (mathematician).
5091 **1966** 4 k. multicoloured . . 10 10

1970 Baikal–Amur Railway

1981. Construction Projects of the 10th Five Year Plan. Multicoloured.
5093 4 k. Type **1970** 20 10
5094 4 k. Urengoi gas field . . . 20 10
5095 4 k. Sayano-Shushenakaya hydro-electric dam 20 10
5096 4 k. Atommash Volga–Don atomic reactor 20 10
5097 4 k. Syktyvkar paper mill . . 20 10
5098 4 k. Giant excavator, Ekibastuz 20 10

1971 Freighter and Russian and Indian Flags

1981. 25th Anniv of Soviet–Indian Shipping Line.
5099 **1971** 15 k. multicoloured . . 40 20

1972 Arms, Monument and Building

1981. 60th Anniv of Georgian Soviet Socialist Republic.
5100 **1972** 4 k. multicoloured . . . 10 10

1973 Arms and Abkhazian Scenes

1974 Institute Building

1981. 60th Anniv of Abkhazian Autonomous Soviet Socialist Republic.
5101 **1973** 4 k. multicoloured . . . 10 10

1981. 60th Anniv of Moscow Electrotechnical Institute of Communications.
5102 **1974** 4 k. multicoloured . . . 10 10

1975 Communications Equipment and Satellite

1976 L. I. Popov and V. V. Ryumin

1981. 30th All-Union Amateur Radio Exhibition.
5103 **1975** 4 k. multicoloured . . . 10 10

1981. 185 Days in Space of Cosmonauts Popov and Ryumin. Multicoloured.
5104 15 k. Type **1976** 35 20
5105 15 k. "Salyut 6" – "Soyuz" complex 35 20

1977 O. G. Makarov, L. D. Kizim and G. M. Strekalov

1961. "Soyuz T-3" Space Flight.
5106 **1977** 10 k. multicoloured . . . 30 15

1978 Rocket Launch

1981. Soviet–Mongolian Space Flight. Multicoloured.
5107 6 k. Type **1978** 20 10
5108 15 k. Mongolians watching space flight on television . . 40 15
5109 32 k. Re-entry stages . . . . 1·00 65

1979 Bering

1980 Yuri Gagarin and Globe

1981. 300th Birth Anniv of Vitus Bering (navigator).
5110 **1979** 4 k. blue 25 10

1981. 20th Anniv of First Manned Space Flight. Multicoloured.
5111 6 k. Type **1989** 15 10
5112 15 k. S. P. Korolev (spaceship designer) 40 15
5113 32 k. Statue of Gagarin and "Interkosmos" emblem . . 1·00 65

1981 "Salyut" Orbital Space Station

1983 Prokofiev

1981. 10th Anniv of First Manned Space Station.
5115 **1981** 32 k. multicoloured . . 1·25 65

1981. 90th Birth Anniv of S. S. Prokofiev (composer).
5117 **1983** 4 k. lilac 30 10

1984 New Hofburg Palace, Vienna

1985 Arms, Industrial Complex and Docks

1981. "WIPA 1981" International Stamp Exhibition, Vienna.
5118 **1984** 15 k. multicoloured . . 30 20

1981. 60th Anniv of Adzharskian Autonomous Soviet Socialist Republic.
5119 **1985** 4 k. multicoloured . . . 10 10

1986 N. N. Benardos

1987 Congress Emblem

1981. Centenary of Invention of Welding.
5120 **1986** 6 k. multicoloured . . . 15 10

1981. 14th Congress of International Union of Architects, Warsaw.
5121 **1987** 15 k. multicoloured . . 30 20

1988 "Albanian Girl in Doorway" (A. A. Ivanov)

1981. Paintings. Multicoloured.
5122 10 k. Type **1988** 30 15
5123 10 k. "Sunset over Sea at Livorno" (N. N. Ge) (horiz) 30 15
5124 10 k. "Demon" (M. A. Vrubel) (horiz) 30 15
5125 10 k. "Horseman" (F. A. Rubo) 30 15

MINIMUM PRICE

The minimum price quoted is 10p which represents a handling charge rather than a basis for valuing common stamps. For further notes about prices, see introductory pages.

1989 Flight Simulator

1981. Soviet–Rumanian Space Flight. Multicoloured.
5126 6 k. Type **1989** 15 10
5127 15 k. "Salyut" - "Soyuz" space complex 35 20
5128 32 k. Cosmonauts greeting journalists after return . . 80 65

1990 "Primula minima"

1981. Flowers of the Carpathians. Multicoloured.
5129 4 k. Type **1990** 15 10
5130 6 k. "Carlina acaulis" 20 10
5131 10 k. "Parageum montanum" . . 35 15
5132 15 k. "Atragene alpina" 50 20
5133 32 k. "Rhododendron kotschyi" 1·00 50

1991 Gyandzhevi 1992 Longo

1981. 840th Birth Anniv of Nizami Gyandzhevi (poet and philosopher).
5134 **1991** 4 k. brown, yell & grn . 10 10

1981. Luigi Longo (Italian politician). Commem.
5135 **1992** 6 k. multicoloured . . . 15 10

1993 Running 1994 Flag and Arms of Mongolia

1981. Sports. Multicoloured.
5136 4 k. Type **1993** 15 10
5137 6 k. Football 15 10
5138 10 k. Throwing the discus . . 25 15
5139 15 k. Boxing 40 20
5140 32 k. Swimmer on block . . . 85 65

1981. 60th Anniv of Revolution in Mongolia.
5141 **1994** 6 k. multicoloured . . . 15 10

1995 Spassky Tower and Film encircling Globe 1996 "Lenin"

1981. 12th International Film Festival, Moscow.
5142 **1995** 15 k. multicoloured . . . 35 15

1981. River Ships. Multicoloured.
5143 4 k. Type **1996** 20 10
5144 6 k. "Kosmonavt Gagarin" (tourist ship) 25 10
5145 15 k. "Valerian Kuibyshev" (tourist ship) 60 45
5146 32 k. "Baltysky" (tanker) . . 1·40 55

1981. Russian Ice-breakers (4th issue). As T **1775**. Multicoloured.
5147 15 k. "Malygin" 65 15

1997 Industry

1981. Resolutions of the 26th Party Congress. Multicoloured.
5148 4 k. Type **1997** 15 10
5149 4 k. Agriculture 15 10
5150 4 k. Energy 15 10
5151 4 k. Transport and communications 15 10
5152 4 k. Arts and science 15 10
5153 4 k. International co-operation 15 10

1998 Ulyanov 2000 Brushes, Palette and Gerasimov

1999 Facade of Theatre

1981. 150th Birth Anniv of I. N. Ulyanov (Lenin's father).
5154 **1998** 4 k. brown, blk & grn . 10 10

1981. 225th Anniv of Pushkin Drama Theatre, Leningrad.
5155 **1999** 6 k. multicoloured . . 15 10

1981. Birth Centenary of A. M. Gerasimov (artist).
5156 **2000** 4 k. multicoloured . . 10 10

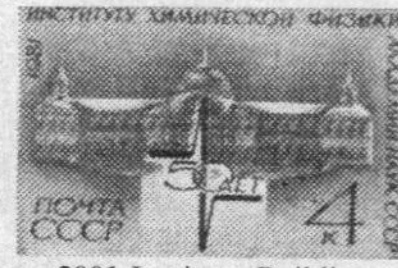

2001 Institute Building

1981. 50th Anniv of Institute of Physical Chemistry, Academy of Sciences, Moscow.
5157 **2001** 4 k. multicoloured . . 10 10

2002 Severtzov's Tit Warbler

1981. Song Birds. Multicoloured.
5158 6 k. Type **2002** 25 10
5159 10 k. Asiatic paradise flycatcher (vert) 25 15
5160 15 k. Jankowski's bunting . . 60 30
5161 20 k. Vinous-throated parrotbill (vert) 75 40
5162 32 k. Hodgson's bushchat (vert) 1·40 60

2003 Arms and Industrial Scenes

1981. 60th Anniv of Komi A.S.S.R.
5163 **2003** 4 k. multicoloured . . 30 10

2004 Orbiting Satellite and Exhibition Emblem

1981. "Svyaz 81" Communications Exhibition.
5164 **2004** 4 k. multicoloured . . 15 10

2005 Buildings, Arms and Monument 2006 Soviet Soldier (monument, Treptow Park, Berlin)

1981. 60th Anniv of Kabardino-Balkar A.S.S.R.
5165 **2005** 4 k. multicoloured . . . 10 10

1981. 25th Anniv of Soviet War Veterans Committee.
5166 **2006** 4 k. multicoloured . . . 10 10

2007 Four-masted Barque "Tovarishch"

1981. Cadet Sailing Ships. Multicoloured.
5167 4 k. Type **2007** 15 10
5168 6 k. Barquentine "Vega" . . 25 10
5169 10 k. Schooner "Kodor" (vert) 35 15
5170 15 k. Three-masted barque "Tovarishch" 50 20
5171 20 k. Four-masted barque "Kruzenshtern" 75 55
5172 32 k. Four-masted barque "Sedov" (vert) . . . . . . 1·10 85

2008 Russian and Kazakh Citizens with Flags 2009 Lavrentev

1981. 250th Anniv of Unification of Russia and Kazakhstan.
5173 **2008** 4 k. multicoloured . . . 10 10

1981. Academician Mikhail Alekseevich Lavrentev (mathematician) Commemoration.
5174 **2009** 4 k. multicoloured . . . 10 10

2010 Kremlin Palace of Congresses, Moscow, and Arch of the General Staff, Leningrad

1981. 64th Anniv of October Revolution.
5175 **2010** 4 k. multicoloured . . . 10 10

2011 Transmitter, Dish Aerial and "Ekran" Satellite

1981. "Ekran" Television Satellite.
5176 **2011** 4 k. multicoloured . . . 10 10

2012 V. V. Kovalyonok and V. P. Savinykh 2014 Merkurov

1981. "Soyuz T-4"–"Salyut 6" Space Complex. Multicoloured.
5177 10 k. Type **2012** 25 15
5178 10 k. Microscope slide, crystal and text 25 15

1981. Birth Centenary of Sergei Dmitrievich Merkurov (sculpture).
5180 **2012** 4 k. brown, grn & bis . 10 10

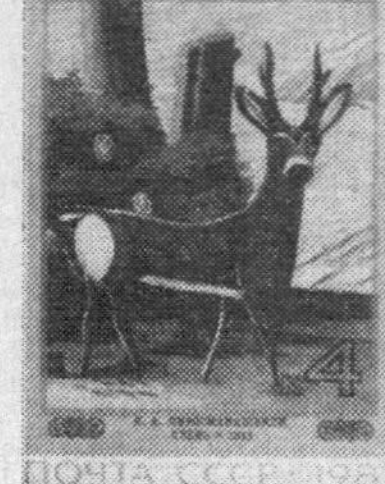

2015 "Autumn" (Nino A. Piromanashvili) 2016 Arms and Saviour Tower, Moscow

1981. Paintings by Georgian Artists. Multicoloured.
5181 4 k. Type **2015** 15 10
5182 6 k. "Gurian Woman" (Sh. G. Kikodze) 15 10
5183 10 k. "Travelling Companions" (U. M. Dzhaparidze) (horiz) 25 15
5184 15 k. "Shota Rustaveli" (S. S. Kobuladze) 45 25
5185 32 k. "Tea Pickers" (V. D. Gudiashvili" (horiz) . . . 90 45

1981. New Year.
5186 **2016** 4 k. multicoloured . . . 10 10

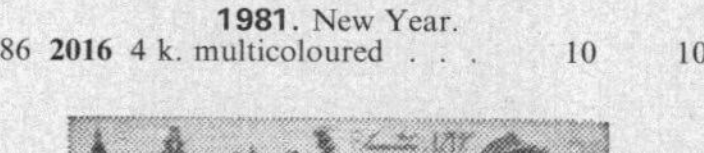

2017 Horse-drawn Sleigh (19th century)

1981. Moscow Municipal Transport.
5187 **2017** 4 k. brown and silver . 15 10
5188 – 6 k. green and silver . . 20 10
5189 – 10 k. lilac and silver . . 30 15
5190 – 15 k. black and silver . 45 20
5191 – 20 k. brown and silver . 60 30
5192 – 32 k. red and silver . . 90 50

DESIGNS: 6 k. Horse-drawn tram (19th century); 10 k. Horse-drawn cab (19th century); 15 k. Taxi, 1926; 20 k. British Leyland bus, 1926; 32 k. Electric tram, 1912.

2019 Modern Kiev

1982. 1500th Anniv of Kiev.
5194 **2019** 10 k. multicoloured . . . 35 15

2020 S. P. Korolev 2021 Arms and Industrial Complex

1982. 75th Birth Anniv of Academician S. P. Korolev (spaceship designer).
5195 **2020** 4 k. multicoloured . . . 15 10

1982. 60th Anniv of Checheno-Ingush A.S.S.R.
5196 **2021** 4 k. multicoloured . . . 15 10

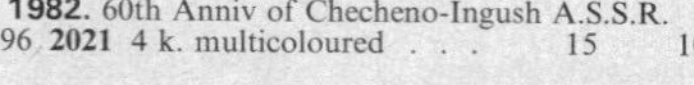

2022 Arms and Construction Sites 2023 Hikmet

1982. 60th Anniv of Yakut A.S.S.R.
5197 **2022** 4 k. multicoloured . . . 15 10

1982. 80th Birth Anniv of Nazim Hikmet (Turkish poet).
5198 **2023** 6 k. multicoloured . . . 25 10

2024 "The Oaks"

1982. 150th Birth Anniv of I. I. Shishkin (artist).
5199 **2024** 6 k. multicoloured . . . 25 10

2025 Trade Unionists and World Map

1982. 10th World Trade Unions Congress, Havana
5200 **2025** 15 k. multicoloured . . 40 20

2026 Kremlin Palace of Congresses and Flag

2027 "Self-portrait"

1982. 17th Soviet Trade Unions Congress.
5201 **2026** 4 k. multicoloured . . . 10 10

1982. 150th Birth Anniv of Edouard Manet (artist).
5202 **2027** 32 k. multicoloured . . 80 40

2028 Show Jumping

2029 Tito

1982. Soviet Horse breeding. Multicoloured.
5203 4 k. Type **2028** 30 10
5204 6 k. Dressage 30 10
5205 15 k. Racing 60 25

1982. President Tito of Yugoslavia Commemoration.
5206 **2029** 6 k. brown and black . 15 10

2030 University, Book and Monument

1982. 350th Anniv of University of Tartu.
5207 **2030** 4 k. multicoloured . . . 10 10

2031 Heart on Globe

1982. 9th International Cardiologists Conference, Moscow.
5208 **2031** 15 k. multicoloured . . 45 20

2033 Blackberry

1982. Wild Berries. Multicoloured.
5210 4 k. Type **2033** 15 10
5211 6 k. Blueberries 20 10
5212 10 k. Cranberry 30 15
5213 15 k. Cherry 45 25
5214 32 k. Strawberry . . . . . . 1·10 55

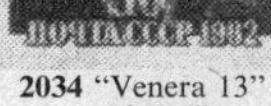

2034 "Venera 13" and "14"

2035 "M. I. Lopukhina" (V. L. Borovikovsky)

1982. "Venera" Space Flights to Venus.
5215 **2034** 10 k. multicoloured . . 30 15

1982. Paintings. Multicoloured.
5216 6 k. Type **2035** 20 10
5217 6 k. "E. V. Davydov" (O. A. Kiprensky) 20 10
5218 6 k. "The Unequal Marriage" (V. V. Pukirev) 20 10

2036 Chukovsky

2039 Solovev-Sedoi

2037 Rocket, "Soyuz" Spaceship, Globe and Space Station

1982. Birth Cent of K. I. Chukovsky (author).
5219 **2036** 4 k. black and grey . . 15 10

1982. Cosmonautics Day.
5220 **2037** 6 k. multicoloured . . 20 10

1982. 75th Birth Anniv of V. P. Solovev-Sedoi (composer).
5222 **2039** 4 k. brown 20 10

2040 Dimitrov

2041 Masthead

1982. Birth Centenary of Georgi Dimitrov (Bulgarian statesman).
5223 **2040** 6 k. green 15 10

1982. 70th Anniv of "Pravda" (Communist Party Newspaper).
5224 **2041** 4 k. multicoloured . . 15 10

INDEX

Countries can be quickly located by referring to the index at the end of this volume.

2042 Congress Emblem and Ribbons

2043 Globe and Hands holding Seeding

1982. 19th Congress of Leninist Young Communist League (Komsomol).
5225 **2042** 4 k. multicoloured . . . 15 10

1982. 10th Anniv of U.N. Environment Programme.
5226 **2043** 6 k. multicoloured . . . 15 10

2044 Pioneers

2045 I.T.U. Emblem, Satellite and Receiving Station

1982. 60th Anniv of Pioneer Organization.
5227 **2044** 4 k. multicoloured . . . 10 10

1982. I.T.U. Delegates' Conference, Nairobi.
5228 **2045** 15 k. multicoloured . . 40 20

2046 "VL80T" Electric Locomotive

1982. Locomotives. Multicoloured.
5229 4 k. Type **2046** 20 10
5230 6 k. "TEP-75" diesel 25 10
5231 10 k. "TEM-7" diesel 50 20
5232 15 k. "VL82M" electric . . . 75 30
5233 32 k. "EP200" electric . . . . 1·75 60

2047 Players with Trophy and Football

1982. World Cup Football Championship, Spain.
5234 **2047** 20 k. lilac, yellow and brown 65 30

2048 Hooded Crane

1982. 18th International Ornithological Congress, Moscow. Multicoloured.
5235 2 k. Type **2048** 15 15
5236 4 k. Steller's sea eagle 30 15
5237 6 k. Spoon-billed sandpiper . 35 15
5238 10 k. Bar-headed goose . . . 60 20
5239 15 k. Sociable plover 90 35
5240 32 k. White stork . . . . . . 2·10 75

2049 Buildings and Workers with Picks

2051 U.N. Flag

2050 "The Cart"

1982. 50th Anniv of Komsomolsk-on-Amur.
5241 **2049** 4 k. multicoloured . . . 15 10

1982. Birth Centenary of M. B. Grekov (artist).
5242 **2050** 6 k. multicoloured . . . 20 10

1982. Second U.N. Conference on the Exploration and Peaceful Uses of Outer Space, Vienna.
5243 **2051** 15 k. multicoloured . . 40 20

2052 Scientific Research in Space

1982. Soviet–French Space Flight. Multicoloured.
5244 6 k. Type **2052** 15 10
5245 20 k. Rocket and trajectory . 60 30
5246 45 k. Satellites and globe . . 1·40 75

2053 "Legend of the Golden Cockerel" (P. I. Sosin)

1982. Lacquerware Paintings. Multicoloured.
5248 6 k. Type **2053** 20 10
5249 10 k. "Minin's Appeal to Count Pozharsky" (I. A. Fomichev) 30 20
5250 15 k. "Two Peasants" (A. F. Kotyagin) 45 25
5251 20 k. "The Fisherman" (N. P. Klykov) 60 35
5252 32 k. "Arrest of the Propagandists" (N. I. Shishakov) 90 55

2054 Early Telephone Moscow, Leningrad, Odessa and Riga

2055 P. Schilling (inventor)

1982. Telephone Centenary.
5253 **2054** 4 k. multicoloured . . . 15 10

1982. 150th Anniv of Electro-magnetic Telegraph in Russia.
5254 **2055** 6 k. multicoloured . . . 20 10

2056 Gymnast and Television Screen

1982. Intervision Cup Gymnastics Contest.
5255 **2056** 15 k. multicoloured . . 40 20

2057 Mastyazhart Glider

2058 Garibaldi

1982. Gliders (1st series). Multicoloured.

5256	4 k. Type **2057**	20	10
5257	6 k. Red Star, 1930	20	10
5258	10 k. TsAGI-2, 1934	40	15
5259	20 k. Stakhanovets, 1939 (60 × 27 mm)	65	65
5260	32 k. GR-29, 1941 (60 × 27 mm)	1·10	1·10

See Nos. 5301/5.

1982. 175th Birth Anniv of Giuseppe Garibaldi.

5261 **2058** 6 k. multicoloured . . . 15 10

2059 Emblem

2060 F.I.D.E. Emblem, Chess Symbol for Queen and Equestrian Statue

1982. 25th Anniv of International Atomic Energy Agency.

5262 **2059** 20 k. multicoloured . . 50 30

1982. World Chess Championship Interzone Tournaments for Women (Tbilisi) and Men (Moscow). Multicoloured.

5263	6 k. Type **2060**	35	15
5264	6 k. F.I.D.E. emblem, chess symbol for King and Kremlin tower	35	15

2061 Shaposhnikov

2062 Clenched Fist

1982. Birth Cent of Marshal B. M. Shaposhnikov.

5265 **2061** 4 k. brown 15 10

1982. 70th Anniv of African National Congress.

5266 **2062** 6 k. multicoloured . . . 20 10

2063 Botkin

А. КАРПОВ — обладатель восьми „Шахматных Оскаров"

(2065)

1982. 150th Birth Anniv of S. P. Botkin (therapeutist).

5267 **2063** 4 k. green 15 10

1982. A. Karpov's Victory in World Chess Championship. No. 5264 optd with T **2065**.

5269 6 k. multicoloured 50 35

2066 Submarine "S-56"

1982. Soviet Naval Ships. Multicoloured.

5270	4 k. Type **2066**	20	10
5271	6 k. Minelayer "Gremyashchy"	20	10
5272	15 k. Minesweeper "Gafel"	65	25
5273	20 k. Cruiser "Krasnyi Krim"	90	40
5274	45 k. Battleship "Sevastopol"	1·90	1·25

2067 Flag and Arms

1982. 65th Anniv of October Revolution.

5275 **2067** 4 k. multicoloured . . . 15 10

2068 House of the Soviets, Moscow

1982. 60th Anniv of U.S.S.R. Multicoloured.

5276	10 k. Type **2068**	30	20
5277	10 k. Dneiper Dam and statue	30	20
5278	10 k. Soviet war memorial and resistance poster	30	20
5279	10 k. Newspaper, worker holding peace text, and sun illuminating city	30	20
5280	10 k. Workers' Monument, Moscow, rocket, Ilyushin Il-86 jet and factories	30	20
5281	10 k. Soviet arms and Kremlin tower	30	20

Всесоюзная филателистическая выставка

(2069)

1982. All-Union Stamp Exhibition, Moscow. No. 5280 optd with T **2069**.

5282 10 k. multicoloured 40 30

2070 "Portrait of an Actor" (Domenico Fetti)

2072 Hammer and Sickle, Clock and Date

1982. Italian Paintings in the Hermitage Museum, Leningrad. Multicoloured.

5283	4 k. Type **2070**	15	10
5284	10 k. "St. Sebastian" (Pietro Perugino)	30	15
5285	20 k. "Danae" (Titian) (horiz)	60	30
5286	45 k. "Portrait of a Woman" (Correggio)	1·25	75
5287	50 k. "Portrait of a Young Man" (Capriolo)	1·40	85

1982. New Year.

5289 **2072** 4 k. multicoloured . . 10 10

2075 Kherson Lighthouse, Black Sea

2076 F. P. Tolstoi

1982. Lighthouses (1st series). Multicoloured.

5292	6 k. Type **2075**	40	15
5293	6 k. Vorontsov lighthouse, Odessa, Black Sea	40	15
5294	6 k. Temryuk lighthouse, Sea of Azov	40	15
5295	6 k. Novorossiisk lighthouse, Black Sea	40	15
5296	6 k. Dneiper harbour light	40	15

See also Nos. 5362/6 and 5449/53.

1983. Birth Bicentenary of Fyodor Petrovich Tolstoi (artist).

5297 **2076** 4 k. multicoloured . . 15 10

2077 Masthead of "Iskra"

2078 Army Star and Flag

1983. 80th Anniv of 2nd Social Democratic Workers' Congress.

5298 **2077** 4 k. multicoloured . . 15 10

1983. 65th Anniv of U.S.S.R. Armed Forces.

5299 **2078** 4 k. multicoloured . . . 15 10

1983. Gliders (2nd series). As T **2057**. Multicoloured.

5301	2 k. A-9, 1948	10	10
5302	4 k. KAU-12, 1957	15	10
5303	6 k. A-15, 1960	20	10
5304	20 k. SA-7, 1970	70	35
5305	45 k. LAK-12, 1979	1·50	75

2080 "The Holy Family"

2081 B. N. Petrov

1983. 500th Birth Anniv of Raphael (artist).

5306 **2080** 50 k. multicoloured . . 1·40 1·00

1983. 70th Birth Anniv of Academician B. N. Petrov (chairman of Interkosmos).

5307 **2081** 4 k. multicoloured . . . 15 10

2082 Tashkent Buildings

1983. 2000th Anniv of Tashkent.

5308 **2082** 4 k. multicoloured . . . 15 10

2083 Popov, Serebrov and Savitskaya

1983. "Soyuz T-7" – "Salyut 7" – "Soyuz T-5" Space Flight.

5309 **2083** 10 k. multicoloured . . 30 15

2085 Aleksandrov and Bars of Music

1983. Birth Centenary of A. V. Aleksandrov (composer).

5311 **2085** 4 k. multicoloured . . . 30 10

2086 "Portrait of an Old Woman"

1983. Rembrandt Paintings in Hermitage Museum, Leningrad. Multicoloured.

5312	4 k. Type **2086**	15	10
5313	10 k. "Portrait of a Learned Man"	30	15
5314	20 k. "Old Warrior"	65	30
5315	45 k. "Portrait of Mrs B. Martens Doomer"	1·00	75
5316	50 k. "Sacrifice of Abraham"	1·40	1·10

2089 A. N. Berezovoi and V. V. Lebedev

1983. 211 Days in Space of Berezovoi and Lebedev. Multicoloured.

5320	10 k. Type **2089**	30	20
5321	10 k. "Salyut 7"–"Soyuz T" space complex	30	20

2090 Marx

1983. Death Centenary of Karl Marx.

5322 **2090** 4 k. multicoloured . . . 15 10

2091 Memorial, Building and Hydrofoil

1983. Rostov-on-Don.

5323 **2091** 4 k. multicoloured . . . 15 10

2092 Kirov Theatre

1983. Bicentenary of Kirov Opera and Ballet Theatre, Leningrad.

5324 **2092** 4 k. black, blue & gold 30 10

2093 Arms, Communications and Industrial Complex

1983. 60th Anniv of Buryat A.S.S.R.

5325 **2093** 4 k. multicoloured . . . 20 10

2094 Sports Vignettes

1983. Eight Summer Spartakiad.

5326 **2094** 6 k. multicoloured . . . 15 10

2095 Khachaturyan

1983. 80th Birth Anniv of Aram I. Khachaturyan (composer).

5327 **2095** 4 k. brown 30 10

2096 Tractor and Factory

1983. 50th Anniv of Lenin Tractor Factory, Chelyabinsk.
5328 **2096** 4 k. multicoloured . . . 15 10

2097 Simon Bolivar

1983. Birth Bicentenary of Simon Bolivar.
5329 **2097** 6 k. deep brown, brown and black 15 10

2098 18th-century Warship and modern Missile Cruiser

1983. Bicentenary of Sevastopol.
5330 **2098** 5 k. multicoloured . . . 40 15

2099 Snowdrops 2101 P. N. Pospelov

2100 "Vostok 6" and Tereshkova

1983. Spring Flowers. Multicoloured.
5331 4 k. Type **2099** 15 10
5332 6 k. Siberian squills 20 10
5333 10 k. "Anemone hepatica" . . 35 15
5334 15 k. Cyclamen 50 25
5335 20 k. Yellow star of Bethlehem 90 45

1983. 20th Anniv of First Woman Cosmonaut Valentina V. Tereshkova's Space Flight.
5336 **2100** 10 k. multicoloured . . 30 15

1983. 85th Birth Anniv of Pyotr Nicolaievich Pospelov (scientist).
5337 **2101** 4 k. multicoloured . . . 15 10

2102 Congress Emblem 2103 Film around Globe and Festival Emblem

1983. 10th European Rheumatologists' Congress, Moscow.
5338 **2102** 4 k. multicoloured . . . 20 10

1983. 13th International Film Festival, Moscow.
5339 **2103** 20 k. multicoloured . . 70 30

2104 Vakhtangov

1983. Birth Centenary of Ye. B. Vakhtangov (producer and actor).
5340 **2104** 5 k. multicoloured . . 20 10

2105 Coastal Trawlers

1983. Fishing Vessels. Multicoloured.
5341 4 k. Type **2105** 20 10
5342 6 k. Refrigerated trawler . . 25 10
5343 10 k. "Pulkovsky Meridian" (deep-sea trawler) 45 15
5344 15 k. Refrigerated freighter . . 60 25
5345 20 k. "50 let SSR" (factory ship) 1·00 50

2106 "U.S.S.R.-1" 2107 Red Salmon

1983. 50th Anniv of Stratosphere Balloon's Record Altitude Flight.
5346 **2106** 20 k. multicoloured . . 85 65

1983. Fishes. Multicoloured.
5347 4 k. Type **2107** 15 10
5348 6 k. Smarida 20 10
5349 15 k. Spotted perch 50 20
5350 20 k. Goby 65 30
5351 45 k. Starry flounder . . . . 1·40 1·00

2108 Exhibition Emblem 2110 S.W.A.P.O. Flag and Emblem

1983. "Sozphilex 83" Stamp Exhibition, Moscow.
5352 **2108** 6 k. multicoloured . . 15 10

1983. Namibia Day.
5355 **2110** 5 k. multicoloured . . 20 10

2111 Palestinian with Flag 2112 Emblem and Ostankino TV Tower, Moscow

1983. Palestinian Solidarity.
5356 **2111** 5 k. multicoloured . . . 30 10

1983. 1st European Radio-telegraphy Championship, Moscow.
5357 **2112** 6 k. multicoloured . . 20 10

2113 Council Session Emblem 2114 Mohammed al-Khorezmi

1983. 4th U.N.E.S.C.O. International Communications Development Programme Council Session, Tashkent.
5358 **2113** 10 k. blue, mauve & black 30 15

1983. 1200th Birth Anniv of Mohammed al-Khorezmi (astonomer and mathematician).
5359 **2114** 4 k. multicoloured . . . 20 10

2115 Yegorov 2116 Treaty

1983. Birth Centenary of Marshal A. I. Yegorov.
5360 **2115** 4 k. purple 15 10

1983. Bicentenary of First Russian–Georgian Friendship Treaty.
5361 **2116** 6 k. multicoloured . . . 15 10

1983. Lighthouse (2nd series). As Type **2075**. Multicoloured.
5362 1 k. Kipu lighthouse, Baltic Sea 10 10
5363 5 k. Keri lighthouse, Gulf of Finland 25 10
5364 10 k. Stirsudden lighthouse, Gulf of Finland 40 15
5365 12 k. Takhkun lighthouse, Baltic Sea 55 30
5366 20 k. Tallin lighthouse, Gulf of Finland 75 45

2117 "Wife's Portrait with Flowers" (I. F. Khrutsky)

1983. Byelorussian Paintings. Multicoloured.
5367 4 k. Type **2117** 15 10
5368 6 k. "Early spring" (V. K. Byalynitsky-Birulya) . . . 20 10
5369 15 k. "Young Partisan" (E. A. Zaitsev) (vert) 45 20
5370 20 k. "Partisan Madonna" (M. A. Savitsky) (vert) . . 60 30
5371 45 k. "Corn Harvest" (V. K. Tsvirko) . . . . 1·40 1·00

2118 Steel Mill

1983. Centenary of Hammer and Sickle Steel Mill.
5372 **2118** 4 k. multicoloured . . . 15 10

2119 Grain Production 2120 Banner and Symbols of Economic Growth

1983. Food Programme. Multicoloured.
5373 5 k. Type **2119** 15 10
5374 5 k. Cattle breeding 15 10
5375 5 k. Fruit and vegetable production 15 10

1983. 66th Anniv of October Revolution.
5376 **2120** 4 k. multicoloured . . . 15 10

2121 Ivan Fyodorov

1983. 400th Death Anniv of Ivan Fyodorov (printer) and 420th Anniv of Publication of "The Apostle" (first Russian printed book).
5377 **2121** 4 k. black 15 10

2122 Pipeline Construction

1983. Inaug of Urengoi–Uzhgorod Gas Pipeline.
5378 **2122** 5 k. multicoloured . . . 25 10

2123 Sidorenko 2124 Marchers pushing Nuclear Weapons off Globe

1983. Academician A. V. Sidorenko (geologist) Commemoration.
5379 **2123** 4 k. multicoloured . . . 20 10

1983. Nuclear Disarmament.
5380 **2124** 5 k. multicoloured . . . 20 10

2125 Makhtumkuli 2126 "Madonna and Child under Apple Tree" (Cranach the Elder)

1983. 250th Birth Anniv of Makhtumkuli (Turkmen poet).
5381 **2125** 5 k. multicoloured . . . 20 10

1983. German Paintings in the Hermitage Museum. Multicoloured.
5382 4 k. Type **2126** 15 10
5383 10 k. "Self-portrait" (Anton Raphael Mengs) 30 15
5384 20 k. "Self-portrait" (Jurgens Ovens) 60 30
5385 45 k. "On Board a Sailing Vessel" (Caspar David Friedrich) . . . . 1·25 60
5386 50 k. "Rape of the Sabine Women" (Johann Schonfeld) (horiz) . . . . 1·40 80

2127 Sukhe Bator 2128 Globe and Hand holding Baby

1983. 90th Birth Anniv of Sukhe Bator (Mongolian statesman).
5388 **2127** 5 k. multicoloured . . . 15 10

1983. International Association of Physicians against Nuclear War.
5389 **2128** 5 k. multicoloured . . . 15 10

2129 Moscow Kremlin Tower Star

1983. New Year.
5390 **2129** 5 k. multicoloured . . . 15 10

2130 Children's Music Theatre

1983. New Buildings in Moscow.
5391 **2130** 3 k. green 10 10
5392 – 4 k. blue 15 10
5393 – 6 k. brown 15 10
5394 – 20 k. green 60 30
5395 – 45 k. green . . . . . . 1·40 65
DESIGNS—VERT: 4 k. Hotel and Tourist Centre. HORIZ: 6 k. Russian Federation parliament building; 20 k. Hotel Izmailovo; 45 k. Novosti News and Press Agency.

2132 Cuban Flag

2133 Broadcasting Station

1984. 25th Anniv of Cuban Revolution.
5397 **2132** 5 k. multicoloured . . . 15 10

1984. 50th Anniv of Moscow Broadcasting Network.
5398 **2133** 4 k. multicoloured . . . 15 10

2134 Speed Skating

1984. Women's European Skating Championship, Alma-Ata.
5399 **2134** 5 k. multicoloured . . . 15 10

2135 "T-34" Medium Tank

1984. World War II Armoured Vehicles. Mult.
5400 10 k. Type **2135** 40 20
5401 10 k. "KV" heavy tank . . . 40 20
5402 10 k. "IS-2" heavy tank . . . 40 20
5403 10 k. "SU-100" self-propelled gun 40 20
5404 10 k. "ISU-152" heavy self-propelled gun 40 20

2136 Biathlon

1984. Winter Olympic Games, Sarajevo. Mult.
5405 5 k. Type **2136** 15 10
5406 10 k. Speed skating 35 15
5407 20 k. Ice hockey 65 30
5408 45 k. Figure skating . . . . 1·25 85

2137 Mandrill

1984. 120th Anniv of Moscow Zoo. Multicoloured.
5409 2 k. Type **2137** 10 10
5410 3 k. Blesbok 10 10
5411 4 k. Snow leopard 15 10
5412 5 k. South African crowned crane 30 10
5413 20 k. Blue and yellow macaw 70 50

2138 Yury Gagarin

1984. 50th Birth Anniv of Yury Alekseevich Gagarin (first man in Space)
5414 **2138** 15 k. blue 40 20

2140 "E. K. Vorontsova" (George Hayter)

2141 Ilyushin

1984. English Paintings in Hermitage Museum, Leningrad. Multicoloured.
5416 4 k. Type **2140** 15 10
5417 10 k. "Portrait of Mrs. Harriet Greer" (George Romney) 30 15
5418 20 k. "Approaching Storm" (George Morland) (horiz) 60 25
5419 45 k. "Portrait of an Unknown Man" (Marcus Gheeraerts, the younger) . . . . . . 1·25 85
5420 50 k. "Cupid untying the Robe of Venus" (Joshua Reynolds) 1·40 1·00

1984. 90th Birth Anniv of Academician S. V. Ilyushin (aircraft designer).
5422 **2134** 5 k. light brown, brown and black 15 10

2142 Bubnov

2143 Launching Site of "M-100" Meteorological Station

1984. Birth Centenary of Andrei Sergeevich Bubnov (Communist Party Leader).
5423 **2142** 5 k. light brown, brown and black 15 10

1984. Soviet–Indian Space Co-operation. Multicoloured.
5424 5 k. Type **2143** 15 10
5425 20 k. Satellite and observatory (space geodesy) 60 30
5426 45 k. Rocket, satellites and dish aerials (Soviet–Indian space flight) . . . . 1·40 65

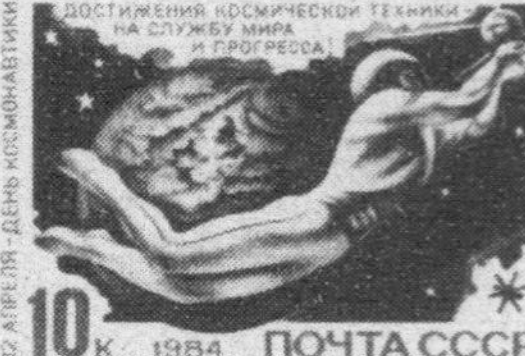

2144 Globe and Cosmonaut

1984. Cosmonautics Day.
5428 **2144** 10 k. multicoloured . . 30 15

2145 "Chelyuskin" (ice-breaker) and Route Map

1984. 50th Anniv of Murmansk–Vladivostok Voyage of "Chelyuskin". Multicoloured.
5429 6 k. Type **2145** 25 10
5430 15 k. Evacuation of sinking ship 60 25
5431 45 k. Air rescue of crew . . . 1·75 75

2148 Lotus

2149 Globe and Peace March (left)

1984. Aquatic Flowers. Multicoloured.
5434 1 k. Type **2148** 10 10
5435 2 k. Euriala 10 10
5436 3 k. Yellow water lilies (horiz) 15 10
5437 10 k. White water lilies (horiz) 35 20
5438 20 k. Marshflowers (horiz) . . 70 30

1984. Peace.
5439 **2149** 5 k. multicoloured . . . 15 10
5440 – 5 k. red, gold and black 15 10
5441 – 5 k. multicoloured . . . 15 10
DESIGNS: No. 5440, Hammer and sickle and text; No. 5441, Globe and peace march (right).

2150 Welder

2151 Communications Emblem

1984. 50th Anniv of E. O. Paton Institute of Electric Welding, Kiev.
5442 **2150** 10 k. multicoloured . . 25 15

1984. 25th Conference of Community for Mutual Economic Aid Electrical and Postal Communications Standing Committee, Cracow.
5443 **2151** 10 k. multicoloured . . 25 15

2152 Emblem and Symbols of Match Venues

2153 Maurice Bishop

1984. European Youth Football Championship.
5444 **2152** 15 k. multicoloured . . 45 20

1984. 40th Birth Anniv of Maurice Bishop (former Prime Minister of Grenada).
5445 **2153** 5 k. brown 20 10

2154 Lenin and Museum

2155 Freighter, Monument and Aurora Borealis

1984. 60th Anniv of Lenin Central Museum, Moscow.
5446 **2154** 5 k. multicoloured . . . 15 10

1984. 400th Anniv of Archangel.
5447 **2155** 5 k. multicoloured . . . 15 10

2156 Headquarters and Spassky Tower, Moscow

2158 Liner

2157 Vladimir A. Lyakhov and Aleksandr Aleksandrov

1984. Council of Mutal Economic Aid Conferene, Moscow.
5448 **2156** 5 k. blue, red and black 15 10

1984. Lighthouses (3rd series). As T **2075**. Multicoloured.
5449 1 k. Petropavlovsk lighthouse, Kamchatka 10 10
5450 2 k. Tokarev lighthouse, Sea of Japan 10 10
5451 4 k. Basargin lighthouse, Sea of Japan 20 10
5452 5 k. Kronotsky lighthouse, Kamchatka 20 10
5443 10 k. Marekan lighthouse, Sea of Okhotsk 35 15

1984. 150 Days in Space of "Salyut 7" – "Soyuz T-9" Cosmonauts.
5454 **2157** 15 k. multicoloured . . 40 20

1984. 60th Anniv of Morflot (Soviet merchant fleet).
5455 **2158** 10 k. multicoloured . . 35 15

2159 Komsomol Badge and Banner

1984. 60th Anniv of Naming of Young Communist League (Komsomol) after Lenin.
5456 **2159** 5 k. multicoloured . . . 15 10

2160 Memorial, Minsk

1984. 40th Anniv of Byelorussian Liberation.
5457 **2160** 5 k. multicoloured . . . 15 10

2161 Congress Emblem **2162** Polish Arms and Flag

1984. 27th International Geological Congress, Moscow.
5458 **2161** 5 k. blue, gold and deep blue 20 10

1984. 40th Anniv of Republic of Poland.
5459 **2162** 5 k. multicoloured . . . 15 10

2163 Asafev

1984. Birth Centenary of Boris Vladimirovich Asafev (composer).
5460 **2163** 5 k. green 20 10

2164 Russian and Mexican Flags and Scroll

1984. 60th Anniv of U.S.S.R.–Mexico Diplomatic Relations.
5461 **2164** 5 k. multicoloured . . . 15 10

2165 Title Page of "The Princess-Frog"

1984. Folk Tales. Illustration by I. Bilibin. Multicoloured.

5462	5 k. Type **2165**	20	15
5463	5 k. Hunter and frog in marshland	20	15
5464	5 k. Old man and hunter in forest	20	15
5465	5 k. Crowd and mute swans .	20	15
5466	5 k. Title page of "Ivan the Tsarevich, the Fire-bird and the Grey Wolf"	20	15
5467	5 k. Ivan and the fire-bird . .	20	15
5468	5 k. Grave and Ivan on horse .	20	15
5469	5 k. Ivan and princess . . .	20	15
5470	5 k. Title page of "Vasilisa the Beautiful"	20	15
5471	5 k. Knight on horse	20	15
5472	5 k. Tree-man in forest . . .	20	15
5473	5 k. Vasilisa and skulls . . .	20	15

2166 Basketball

1984. "Friendship 84" Sports Meetings. Mult.

5474	1 k. Type **2166**	10	10
5475	5 k. Gymnastics (vert) . . .	15	10
5476	10 k. Weightlifting	30	10
5477	15 k. Wrestling	45	20
5478	20 k. High jumping	60	30

2167 Flag and Soviet Soldiers' Monument, Bucharest **2168** Emblem, Chess Symbol for Queen and Motherland Statue

1984. 40th Anniv of Rumania's Liberation.
5479 **2167** 5k. multicoloured . . . 15 10

1984. World Chess Championship Finals for Women (Volgograd) and Men (Moscow).
5480 **2168** 15 k. gold, red and black 70 25
5481 – 15 k. multicoloured . . 70 25
DESIGN: No. 5481, Emblem, chess symbol for king and Spassky tower, Moscow Kremlin

2169 Party House and Soviet Army Monument, Sofia, and State Emblem **2170** Arms and Flag

1984. 40th Anniv of Bulgarian Revolution.
5482 **2169** 5 k. multicoloured . . 15 10

1984. 10th Anniv of Ethiopian Revolution.
5483 **2170** 5 k. multicoloured . . 15 10

2171 Excavator

1984. 50th Anniv of Lenin Machine-building Plant, Novokramatorsk.
5484 **2171** 5 k. multicoloured . . 15 10

2172 Arms and Symbols of Industry and Agriculture

1984. 60th Anniv of Nakhichevan A.S.S.R.
5485 **2172** 5 k. multicoloured . . 15 10

2174 "Luna 3" photographing Moon

1984. 25th Anniv of Photography in Space. Multicoloured.
5487 5 k. Type **2174** 15 10
5488 20 k. "Venera-9" and control centre 60 25
5489 45 k. "Meteor" meteorological satellite and Earth . . . . 1·40 85

2175 Arms and Flag

1984. 35th Anniv of German Democratic Republic.
5491 **2175** 5 k. multicoloured . . 15 10

2176 Arms and Motherland Statue, Kiev

1984. 40th Anniv of Liberation of the Ukraine.
5492 **2176** 5 k. multicoloured . . . 15 10

2177 Town, Arms and Countryside

1984. 60th Anniv of Moldavian Soviet Socialist Republic.
5493 **2177** 5 k. multicoloured . . . 15 10

2178 Arms, Power Station and Mountains

1984. 60th Anniv of Kirgizia Soviet Socialist Republic.
5494 **2178** 5 k. multicoloured . . . 15 10

2179 Arms and Symbols of Industry and Agriculture **2180** Flags and Spassky Tower

1984. 60th Anniv of Tadzhikistan Soviet Socialist Republic.
5495 **2179** 5 k. multicoloured . . . 15 10

1984. 67th Anniv of October Revolution.
5496 **2180** 5 k. multicoloured . . . 15 10

2181 Arms, State Building and Dam

1984. 60th Anniv of Uzbekistan Soviet Socialist Republic.
5497 **2181** 5 k. multicoloured . . . 15 10

2182 Arms, Flag and State Building

1984. 60th Anniv of Turkmenistan Soviet Socialist Republic.
5498 **2182** 5 k. multicoloured . . . 15 10

2183 Medal, Workers, Diesel Train and Map of Route **2184** Ilyushin Il-86 Airplane, Rocket, "Soyuz" - "Salyut" Complex and Museum

1984. Completion of Baikal–Amur Railway.
5499 **2183** 5 k. multicoloured . . . 30 10

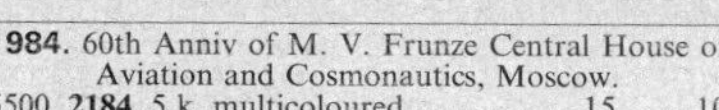

1984. 60th Anniv of M. V. Frunze Central House of Aviation and Cosmonautics, Moscow.
5500 **2184** 5 k. multicoloured . . . 15 10

2185 "Girl in Hat" (Jean-Louis Voile) **2186** Mongolian Arms and Flag

1984. French Paintings in Hermitage Museum, Leningrad. Multicoloured.

5501	4 k. Type **2185**	15	10
5502	10 k. "The Stolen Kiss" (Jean-Honore Fragonard) (horiz)	30	15
5503	20 k. "Woman at her Toilette" (Edgar Degas)	60	30
5504	45 k. "Pygmalion and Galatea" (Francois Boucher) (horiz)	1·25	60
5505	50k. "Landscape with Polyphemus" (Nicolas Poussin) (horiz)	1·40	85

1984. 60th Anniv of Mongolian People's Republic.
5507 **2186** 5 k. multicoloured . . . 15 10

2187 Spassky Tower and Snowflakes

1984. New Year.
5508 **2187** 5 k. multicoloured . . . 15 10

2189 Horse-drawn Crew Wagon (19th century)

1984. Fire Engines (1st series). Multicoloured.

5510	3 k. Type **2189**	15	10
5511	5 k. 19th-century horse-drawn steam pump	25	10
5512	10 k. "Freze" fire engine, 1904	45	15
5513	15 k. "Lessner" fire engine, 1904	45	25
5514	20 k. "Russo-Balt" fire engine, 1913	55	30

See also Nos. 5608/12.

2190 Space Observatory and Flight Trajectory

1984. International Venus–Halley's Comet Space Project. (1st issue).
5515 **2190** 15 k. multicoloured . . 45 20
See also Nos. 5562 and 5630.

2191 Indira Gandhi **2192** Heroes of December Revolution Monument, Moscow

1984. Indira Gandhi (Indian Prime Minister) Commemoration.
5516 **2191** 5 k. lt brown & brn . . 30 10

1985. 80th Anniv of 1905 Revolution.
5517 **2192** 5 k. multicoloured . . . 15 10

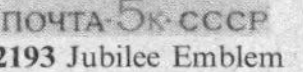

2193 Jubilee Emblem

2194 Frunze

1985. 25th Anniv of Patrice Lumumba University, Moscow.
5518 **2193** 5 k. multicoloured . . . 15 10

1985. Birth Centenary of Mikhail Vasilievich Frunze (military strategist).
5519 **2194** 5 k. stone, black and blue 15 10

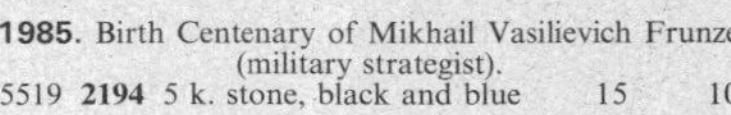

2195 Arms and Industrial Landscape

2196 Ice Hockey Player

1985. 60th Anniv of Karakalpak A.S.S.R.
5520 **2195** 5 k. multicoloured . . . 15 10

1985. 10th Friendly Armies Winter Spartakiad.
5521 **2196** 5 k. multicoloured . . . 15 10

2197 Dulcimer Player and Title Page

2198 Pioneer Badge

1985. 150th Anniv of "Kalevala" (Karelian poems collected by Elino Lonnrot).
5522 **2197** 5 k. brown, blue & blk . . 20 10

1985. 60th Anniv of "Pionerskaya Pravda" (children's newspaper).
5523 **2198** 5 k. multicoloured . . . 20 10

2199 Maria Aleksandrovna Ulyanova

2200 "Young Madonna Praying" (Francisco de Zurbaran)

1985. 150th Birth Anniv of Maria Aleksandrovna Ulyanova (Lenin's mother).
5524 **2199** 5 k. black 20 10

1985. Spanish Paintings in Hermitage Museum, Leningrad. Multicoloured.
5525 4 k. Type **2200** 15 10
5526 10 k. "Still Life" (Antonio Pereda) (horiz) 30 15
5527 20 k. "The Immaculate Conception" (Bartolome Esteban Murillo) 65 30
5528 45 k. "The Grinder" (Antonio Puga) (horiz) . . . . 1·25 70
5529 50 k. "Count Olivares" (Diego Velazquez) . . . . 1·40 85

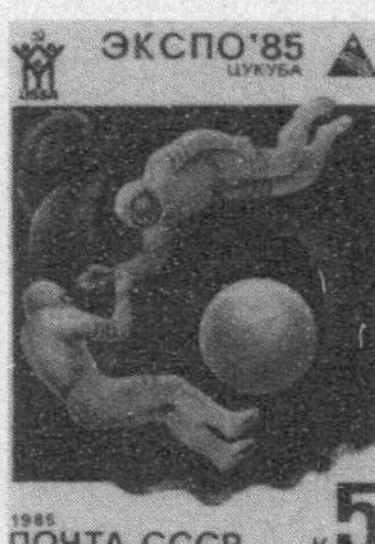

2201 Cosmonauts and Globe

2202 Hungarian Arms and Budapest

1985. "Expo 85" World's Fair, Tsukuba, Japan. Multicoloured.
5531 5 k. Type **2201** 15 10
5532 10 k. "Molniya-I" communications satellite . 30 15
5533 20 k. Energy sources of the future 65 30
5534 45 k. Futuristic city . . . . 1·40 85

1985. 40th Anniv of Hungary's Liberation.
5537 **2203** 5 k. multicoloured . . 20 10

2204 Emblem and Text

2206 Young People of Different Races

2205 Cosmonauts, "Soyuz T" Training Model and Gagarin

1985. 60th Anniv of Union of Soviet Societies of Friendship and Cultural Relations with Foreign Countries.
5538 **2204** 15 k. multicoloured . . 45 30

1985. Cosmonautics Day. 25th Anniv of Yury A. Gagarin Cosmonauts Training Centre.
5539 **2205** 15 k. multicoloured . . 45 30

1985. 12th World Youth and Students' Festival, Moscow. Multicoloured.
5540 1 k. Type **2206** 10 10
5541 3 k. Girl with festival emblem in hair 10 10
5542 5 k. Rainbow and girl . . . 15 10
5543 20 k. Youth holding camera 60 25
5544 45 k. Festival emblem . . . 1·25 85

2207 Soviet Memorial, Berlin-Treptow

Всесоюзная филателистическая выставка
„40 лет Великой Победы"
(2209)

2208 Lenin and Paris Flat

1985. 40th Anniv of Victory in Second World War (1st issue). Multicoloured.
5545 5 k. Type **2207** 20 15
5546 5 k. Partisans 20 15
5547 5 k. Lenin, soldier and Moscow Kremlin 20 15
5548 5 k. Soldiers and military equipment 20 15
5549 5 k. Woman worker, tank, tractor and aircraft assembly 20 15
See also No. 5555.

1985. 115th Birth Anniv of Lenin. Multicoloured.
5551 5 k. Type **2208** 20 15
5552 5 k. Lenin and Lenin Museum, Tampere, Finland 20 15

1985. "Second World War Victory" Philatelic Exhibition. No. 5545 optd with T **2209**.
5554 **2207** 5 k. multicoloured . . 20 20

2210 Victory Order (½-size illustration)

1985. 40th Anniv of Victory in Second World War (2nd issue).
5555 **2210** 20 k. multicoloured . . 65 45

2211 Czechoslovakian Arms and Prague Buildings

2212 Members' Flags on Shield

1985. 40th Anniv of Czechoslovakia's Liberation.
5556 **2211** 5 k. multicoloured . . . 20 10

1985. 30th Anniv of Warsaw Pact Organization.
5557 **2212** 5 k. multicoloured . . . 20 10

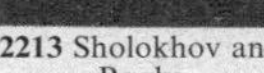

2213 Sholokhov and Books

2214 Sverdlov

1985. 80th Birth Anniv of Mikhail Aleksandrovich Sholokhov (writer).
5558 **2213** 5 k. multicoloured . . . 20 15
5559 – 5 k. multicoloured . . . 20 15
5560 – 5 k. black, gold and brown 20 15
DESIGNS—As T **2213**. No. 5559, Sholokhov and books (different); 36 × 51 mm. No. 5560, Sholokhov.

1985. Birth Centenary of Ya. M. Sverdlov (Communist Party Leader).
5561 **2214** 5 k. brown and red . . . 20 10

1985. International Venus–Halley's Comet Space Project (2nd issue). As T **2190**. Multicoloured.
5562 15 k. "Vega" space probe and Venus 55 30

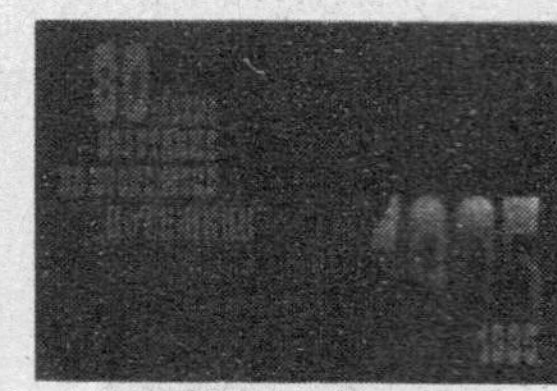

2215 Battleship "Potemkin"

1985. 80th Anniv of Mutiny on Battleship "Potemkin".
5563 **2215** 5 k. black, red and gold 20 10

2216 "VL80R" Electric Stock

1985. Locomotives and Rolling Stock.
5564 **2216** 10 k. green 45 25
5565 – 10 k. brown 45 25
5566 – 10 k. blue 45 25
5567 – 10 k. brown 45 25
5568 – 10 k. blue 45 25
5569 – 10 k. blue 45 25
5570 – 10 k. brown 45 25
5571 – 10 k. green 45 25
DESIGNS: No. 5565, Coal wagon; No. 5566, Oil tanker wagon; No. 5567, Goods wagon; No. 5568, Refrigerated wagon; No. 5569, "TEM 2" diesel locomotive; No. 5570, "Sv" passenger carriage; No. 5571, Mail van.

2217 Camp and Pioneer Badge

1985. 60th Anniv of Artek Pioneer Camp.
5572 **2217** 4 k. multicoloured . . . 20 10

2218 Leonid Kizim, Vladimir Solovyov and Oleg Atkov

1985. "237 Days in Space".
5573 **2218** 15 k. multicoloured . . 50 20

2219 Youths of different Races

2220 "Beating Swords into Ploughshares" (sculpture) and U.N. Emblem

1985. International Youth Year.
5574 **2219** 10 k. multicoloured . . 30 15

1985. 40th Anniv of U.N.O. (1st issue).
5575 **2220** 45 k. blue and gold . . 1·25 1·00
See also No. 5601.

2222 Larkspur

2224 Cecilienhof Palace and Flags

2223 V. A. Dzhanibekov, S. E. Savitskaya and I. P. Volk

1985. Plants of Siberia. Multicoloured.
5577 2 k. Type **2222** 10 10
5578 3 k. "Thermopsis lanceolata" 10 10
5579 5 k. "Rose" 20 10
5580 20 k. Cornflower 70 30
5581 45 k. Bergenia . . . . . . 1·40 65

1985. 1st Anniv of First Space-walk by Woman Cosmonaut.
5582 **2223** 10 k. multicoloured . . 30 15

1985. 40th Anniv of Potsdam Conference.
5583 **2224** 15 k. multicoloured . . 40 20

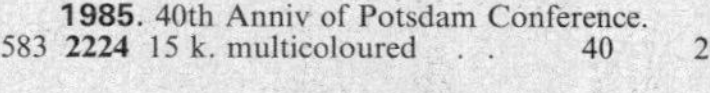

2225 Finland Palace

2226 Russian and N. Korean Flags and Monument

1985. 10th Anniv of European Security and Co-operation Conference, Helsinki.
5584 **2225** 20 k. multicoloured . . 75 35

1985. 40th Anniv of Liberation of Korea.
5585 **2226** 5 k. multicoloured . . . 20 10

2227 Pamir Shrew **2228** A. G. Stakhanov and Industrial Scenes

1985. Protected Animals. Multicoloured.

5586 2 k. Type **2227** 10 10
5587 3 k. Satunin's jerboa (horiz) . 10 10
5588 5 k. Desert dormouse 15 10
5589 20 k. Caracal (47 × 32 mm) . 60 30
5590 45 k. Goitred gazelle (47 × 32 mm) . . . . 1·40 65

1985. 50th Anniv of Stakhanov Movement (for high labour productivity).

5592 **2228** 5 k. yellow, red and black 15 10

2229 Cup, Football, F.I.F.A. Emblem and Kremlin Tower **2230** Chess Pieces

1985. World Junior Football Championship, Moscow.

5593 **2229** 5 k. multicoloured . . . 20 10

1985. World Chess Championship Final between Anatoly Karpov and Gary Kasparov.

5594 **2230** 10 k. multicoloured . . 55 20

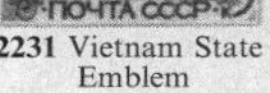

2231 Vietnam State Emblem **2232** Immortality Monument and Buildings

1985. 40th Anniv of Vietnamese Independence.

5595 **2231** 5 k. multicoloured . . . 20 10

1985. Millenary of Bryansk.

5596 **2232** 5 k. multicoloured . . . 20 10

2233 Title Page

1985. 800th Anniv of "Song of Igor's Campaigns".

5597 **2233** 10 k. multicoloured . . 35 20

2234 Lutsk Castle **2235** Gerasimov

1985. 900th Anniv of Lutsk.

5598 **2234** 5 k. multicoloured . . . 20 10

1985. Birth Centenary of Sergei Vasilievich Gerasimov (artist).

5599 **2235** 5 k. multicoloured . . . 20 10

2236 Globe, "Aurora" and 1917 **2237** Headquarters, New York, and Flag

1985. 68th Anniv of October Revolution.

5600 **2236** 5 k. multicoloured . . 20 10

1985. 40th Anniv of U.N.O. (2nd issue).

5601 **2237** 15 k. green, blue and black 45 20

2238 Krishjanis Baron

1985. 150th Birth Anniv of Krishjanis Baron (writer).

5602 **2238** 5 k. black and brown . 20 10

2239 Lenin and Worker breaking Chains

1985. 90th Anniv of Petersburg Union of Struggle for Liberating the Working Class.

5603 **2239** 5 k. multicoloured . . 20 10

2240 Telescope

1985. 10th Anniv of World's Largest Telescope.

5604 **2240** 10 k. blue 30 20

2241 Angolan Arms and Flag **2242** Yugoslav Arms, Flag and Parliament Building

1985. 10th Anniv of Independence of Angola.

5605 **2241** 5 k. multicoloured . . 20 10

1985. 40th Anniv of Federal People's Republic of Yugoslavia.

5606 **2242** 5 k. multicoloured . . 20 10

2243 Troitsky Tower and Palace of Congresses **2244** Samantha Smith

1985. New Year.

5607 **2243** 5 k. multicoloured . . 15 10

1985. Fire Engines (2nd series). As T **2189**. Multicoloured.

5608 3 k. "AMO-F15", 1926 . . 15 10
5609 5 k. "PMZ-1", 1933 . . . . 25 10
5610 10 k. "ATs-40", 1977 . . . 45 15
5611 20 k. "AL-30" with automatic ladder, 1970 . . . . 55 30
5612 45 k. "AA-60", 1978 . . . . 1·25 85

1985. Samantha Smith (American schoolgirl peace campaigner) Commemoration.

5613 **2244** 5 k. brown, blue and red 40 10

2245 N. M. Emanuel **2246** Family and Places of Entertainment

1985. Academician N. M. Emanuel (chemist) Commemoration.

5614 **2245** 5 k. multicoloured . . . 20 10

1985. Anti-alcoholism Campaign. Multicoloured.

5615 5 k. Type **2246** 25 10
5616 5 k. Sports centre and family 25 10

2247 Emblem **2248** Banners and Kremlin Palace of Congresses

1986. International Peace Year.

5617 **2247** 20 k. blue, green & sil . 60 30

1986. 27th Soviet Communist Party Congress.

5618 **2248** 5 k. multicoloured . . . 15 10
5619 – 20 k. multicoloured . . . 60 30

DESIGNS—36 × 51 mm. 20 k. Palace of Congresses, Spassky Tower and Lenin.

2249 1896 Olympics Medal **2250** Tulips

1986. 90th Anniv of First Modern Olympic Games.

5621 **2249** 15 k. multicoloured . . 45 20

1986. Plants of Russian Steppes. Multicoloured.

5622 4 k. Type **2250** 15 10
5623 5 k. Grass (horiz) 20 10
5624 10 k. Iris 35 15
5625 15 k. Violets 55 25
5626 20 k. Cornflower 70 30

2251 Voronezh and Arms **2252** Bela Kun

1986. 400th Anniv of Voronezh.

5627 **2251** 5 k. multicoloured . . . 20 10

1986. Birth Centenary of Bela Kun (Hungarian Communist Party leader).

5628 **2252** 10 k. blue 30 15

2253 Pozela **2255** "Utetheisa pulchella"

1986. 90th Birth Anniv of Karolis Pozela (founder of Lithuanian Communist Party).

5629 **2253** 5 k. grey 20 10

1986. International Venus–Halley's Comet Space Project (3rd issue). As T **2190**. Multicoloured.

5630 15 k. "Vega 1" and Halley's Comet 55 30

1986. Butterflies listed in U.S.S.R. Red Book. (1st series). Multicoloured.

5632 4 k. Type **2255** 15 10
5633 5 k. "Allancastria caucasica" 20 10
5634 10 k. "Zegris eupheme" . . 45 15
5635 15 k. "Catocala sponsa" . . 75 25
5636 20 k. "Satyrus bischoffi" . . 95 35

See also Nos. 5726/30.

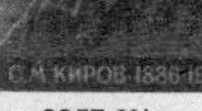

2256 Globe and Model of Space Complex **2257** Kirov

1986. "Expo '86" World's Fair, Vancouver.

5637 **2256** 20 k. multicoloured . . 60 30

1986. Birth Centenary of S. M. Kirov (Communist Party Secretary).

5638 **2257** 5 k. black 20 10

2258 Tsiolkovsky

1986. Cosmonautics Day. Multicoloured.

5639 5 k. Type **2258** 15 10
5640 10 k. Sergei Pavlovich Korolev (rocket designer) and "Vostok" rocket (vert) . . 30 15
5641 15 k. Yuri Gagarin, "Vega", sputnik and globe (25th anniv of first man in space) . . . 55 25

2259 Ice Hockey Player **2260** Thalmann

1986. World Ice Hockey Championship, Moscow.

5642 **2259** 15 k. multicoloured . . 60 20

1986. Birth Centenary of Ernst Thalmann (German politician).

5643 **2260** 10 k. brown 30 15

2261 Lenin Museum, Leipzig

1986. 116th Birth Anniv of Lenin.

5645 **2261** 5 k. multicoloured . . . 20 10
5646 – 5 k. olive, brown & blk 20 10
5647 – 5 k. multicoloured . . . 20 10

DESIGNS: No. 5646, Lenin Museum, Prague; No. 5647, Lenin Museum, Poronine, Poland.

2262 Tambov and Arms

1986. 350th Anniv of Tambov.

5648 **2262** 5 k. multicoloured . . . 20 10

2263 Dove with Olive Branch and Globe

2264 Emblem and Cyclists

1986. 25th Anniv of Soviet Peace Fund.
5649 **2263** 10 k. multicoloured . . 35 20

1986. 39th Peace Cycle Race.
5650 **2264** 10 k. multicoloured . . 45 20

2265 "Amanita phalloides"

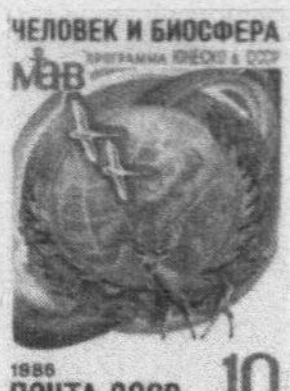

2266 Globe and Wildlife

1986. Fungi. Multicoloured.
5651 4 k. Type **2256** 15 10
5652 5 k. "Amanita muscaria" . . 25 10
5653 10 k. "Amanita pantherina" . . 45 15
5654 15 k. "Tylopilus felleus" . . 75 25
5655 20 k. "Hypholoma fasciculare" 95 40

1986. U.N.E.S.C.O. Man and Biosphere Programme.
5656 **2266** 10 k. multicoloured . . 40 15

2267 Torch and Runner

2268 Kuibyshev

1986. 9th People's Spartakiad.
5657 **2267** 10 k. multicoloured . . 35 15

1986. 400th Anniv of Kuibyshev (formerly Samara).
5658 **2268** 5 k. multicoloured . . . 20 10
No. 5658 depicts the Lenin Museum, Eternal Glory and V. I. Chapaev monuments and Gorky State Theatre.

2269 Ostankino T.V. Tower

2270 Footballers

1986. "Communication 86" International Exhibition, Moscow.
5659 **2269** 5 k. multicoloured . . . 20 10

1986. World Cup Football Championship, Mexico. Multicoloured.
5660 5 k. Type **2270** 20 10
5661 10 k. Footballers (different) . 40 15
5662 15 k. Championship medal . 50 25

2271 "Lane in Albano" (M. I. Lebedev)

2272 Arms and City

1986. Russian Paintings in Tretyakov Gallery, Moscow. Multicoloured.
5663 4 k. Type **2271** 15 10
5664 5 k. "View of the Kremlin in foul Weather" (A. K. Savrasov) (horiz) 20 10
5665 10 k. "Sunlit Pine Trees" (I. I. Shishkin) 30 15
5666 15 k. "Journey Back" (A. E. Arkhipov) (69 × 33 mm) . 50 25
5667 45 k. "Wedding Procession in Moscow" (A. P. Ryabushkin) (69 × 33 mm) . . . . . . 1·25 40

1986. 300th Anniv of Irkutsk City Status.
5668 **2272** 5 k. multicoloured . . 20 10

2273 World Map Stadium and Runners

2274 Globe, Punched Tape and Keyboard

1986. International Goodwill Games, Moscow.
5669 **2273** 10 k. blue, brown & blk 30 15

1986. U.N.E.S.C.O. Programmes in U.S.S.R. Multicoloured.
5671 5 k. Type **2274** 20 10
5672 10 k. Landscape and geological section (geological correlation) 35 15
5673 15 k. Oceanographic research vessel, albatross and ocean (Inter-governmental Oceanographic Commission) 55 30
5674 35 k. Fluvial drainage (International Hydrological Programme) . . . . 1·00 60

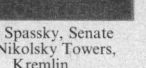

2275 Arms and Town Buildings

1986. 400th Anniv of Tyumen, Siberia.
5675 **2275** 5 k. multicoloured . . 20 10

2276 Olof Palme

2277 Hands, Ball and Basket

1986. Olof Palme (Swedish Prime Minister) Commemoration.
5676 **2276** 10 k. blue, black & brn 35 15

1986. 10th Women's Basketball Championship.
5677 **2277** 15 k. brown, blk & red 60 25

2278 "Ural-375D"

1986. Lorries. Multicoloured.
5678 4 k. Type **2278** 15 10
5679 5 k. "GAZ-53A" 20 10
5680 10 k. "KrAZ-256B" 35 15
5681 15 k. "MAZ-515B" 55 25
5682 20 k. "ZIL-133GYa" . . . 70 30

2279 Lenin Peak

1986. U.S.S.R. Sports Committee's International Mountaineers' Camps (1st series). Multicoloured.
5683 4 k. Type **2279** 15 10
5684 5 k. E. Korzhenevskaya Peak 20 10
5685 10 k. Belukha Peak 30 15
5686 15 k. Communism Peak . . 55 25
5687 30 k. Elbrus Peak 95 50
See also Nos. 5732/5.

2281 Lenin Monument and Drama Theatre

2282 Ferry, Maps and Flags

1986. 250th Anniv of Chelyabinsk City.
5689 **2281** 5 k. multicoloured . . . 20 10

1986. Opening of Mukran (East Germany)–Klaipeda (U.S.S.R.) Railway Ferry.
5690 **2282** 15 k. multicoloured . . 75 25

2283 Victory Monument and Buildings

2284 Lenin Monument and Moscow Kremlin

1986. 750th Anniv of Siauliai, Lithuania.
5691 **2283** 5 k. buff, brown & red . 20 10

1986. 69th Anniv of October Revolution.
5692 **2284** 5 k. multicoloured . . . 25 35

2285 Ice-breaker "Vladivostok", Mil Mi-4 Helicopter, Satellite and Map

15.III–26.VII.1985
Дрейф во льдах Антарктики
(2286)

1986. Antarctic Drift of "Mikhail Somov" (ice-breaker). (a) As Type **2285**.
5693 5 k. blue, black and red . . . 25 10
5694 10 k. multicoloured 50 20

(b) No. 5055 optd with T **2286**.
5696 4 k. multicoloured 20 10
DESIGN: As T **2285**. 10 k. Map and "Mikhail Somov".
Nos. 5693/4 were printed together, se-tenant, forming a composite design.

2287 Class "3u" No. EU 684–37, Slavyansk

1986. Steam Locomotive as Monuments. Mult.
5697 4 k. Type **2287** 20 10
5698 5 k. Class "FD" No. 21–3000, Novosibirsk 20 10
5699 10 k. Class "Ov" No. 5109, Volgograd 40 15
5700 20 k. Class "SO" No. 17–1613, Dnepropetrovsk 75 30
5701 30 k. Class "FDp" No. 20–578, Kiev . . . . 1·00 50

2288 G. K. Ordzhonikidze

2289 Novikov and Score

1986. Birth Centenary of Grigory Konstantinovich Ordzhonikidze (revolutionary).
5702 **2288** 5 k. grey 20 10

1986. 90th Birth Anniv of Anatoli Novikov (composer).
5703 **2289** 5 k. brown 30 10

2290 U.N. and U.N.E.S.C.O. Emblem

2291 Sun Yat-sen

1986. 40th Anniv of U.N.E.S.C.O.
5704 **2290** 10 k. silver and blue . . 40 15

1986. 120th Birth Anniv of Sun Yat-sen (first President of Chinese Republic).
5705 **2291** 5 k. black and grey . . 25 10

2292 Lomonosov

1986. 275th Birth Anniv of Mikhail Vasilievich Lomonosov (scientist).
5706 **2292** 5 k. brown 20 10

2293 Ya-1, 1927

1986. Sports Aircraft designed by Aleksandr Yakovlev. Multicoloured.
5707 4 k. Type **2293** 15 10
5708 5 k. VT-2 trainer, 1935 . . . 15 10
5709 10 k. Yak-18, 1946 . . . . . 30 15
5710 20 k. Yak-50, 1972 . . . . . 60 30
5711 30 k. Yak-55, 1981 . . . . . 95 50

2294 Spassky, Senate and Nikolsky Towers, Kremlin

2295 Computer and Terminal

1986. New Year.
5712 **2294** 5 k. multicoloured . . . 20 10

1986. Resolutions of 27th Communist Party Congress. Multicoloured.
5713 5 k. Type **2295** (scientific and technical progress) 20 10
5714 5 k. Construction engineer and building project 20 10
5715 5 k. City (welfare of people) 20 10
5716 5 k. Peace demonstration at Council for Mutual Economic Aid building (peace) . . . 20 10
5717 5 k. Spassky Tower and Kremlin Palace, Moscow Kremlin (unity of party and people) 20 10

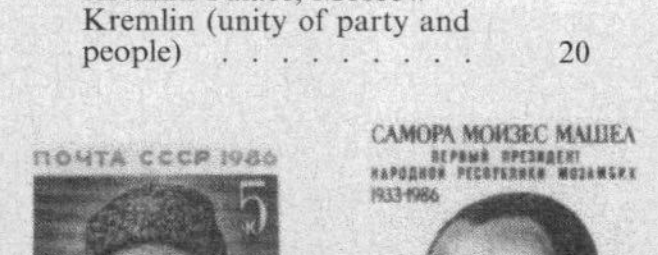

2296 Parkhomenko

2297 Machel

1986. Birth Centenary of Aleksandr Parkhomenko (revolutionary).
5718 **2296** 5 k. black 20 10

1986. Samora Moizes Machel (President of Mozambique) Commemoration.
5719 **2297** 5 k. brown & black . . 25 10

2298 Russian State Museum (Mikhailovsky Palace)

1986. Palace Museums of Leningrad.
5720 **2298** 5 k. brown and green . 20 15
5721 – 10 k. green and blue . . 30 15
5722 – 15 k. blue and green . . 50 20
5723 – 20 k. green & brown . . 60 30
5724 – 50 k. brown and blue . 1·50 70
DESIGNS: 10 k. Hermitage Museum (Winter Palace); 15 k. Grand Palace Museum (Petrodvorets); 20 k. Catherine Palace Museum (Pushkin); 50 k. Palace Museum (Pavlovsk).

2299 Couple and Industrial Landscape 2300 "Atrophaneura alcinous"

1987. 18th Soviet Trades Union Congress, Moscow.
5725 **2299** 5 k. multicoloured . . . 20 10

1987. Butterflies listed in U.S.S.R. Red Book (2nd series). Multicoloured.
5726 4 k. Type **2300** 20 10
5727 5 k. "Papilio machaon" . . . 20 10
5728 10 k. "Papilio alexanor" . . 35 15
5729 15 k. "Papilio maackii" . . . 60 25
5730 30 k. "Iphiclides podalirius" . 95 50

2301 Karlis Miesnieks 2302 Stasys Simkus

1987. Birth Centenary of Karlis Miesnieks (Latvian artist).
5731 **2301** 5 k. multicoloured . . . 20 10

1987. U.S.S.R. Sports Committee's International Mountaineers' Camps (2nd series). As T **2279**. Multicoloured.
5732 4 k. Chimbulak Gorge . . . 15 10
5733 10 k. Shavla Gorge 30 15
5734 20 k. Donguz-Orun and Nakra-Tau, Caucasus 70 30
5735 35 k. Kazbek, Caucasus . . . 1·00 60

1987. Birth Centenary of Stasys Simkus (Lithuanian composer).
5736 **2302** 5 k. purple and yellow . 30 10

2303 V. I. Chapaev

2304 Lenin

1987. Birth Centenary of Vasily Ivanovich Chapaev (revolutionary).
5737 **2303** 5 k. brown 20 10

1987. 20th Leninist Young Communist League (Komsomol) Congress, Moscow.
5738 **2304** 5 k. multicoloured . . . 20 10

2305 Heino Eller

2306 Orbeli

1987. Birth Centenary of Heino Eller (Estonian composer).
5740 **2305** 5 k. lt brown & brown 30 10

1987. Birth Centenary of Academician Iosif Abgarovich Orbeli (first President of Armenian Academy of Sciences).
5741 **2306** 5 k. brown and pink . 20 10

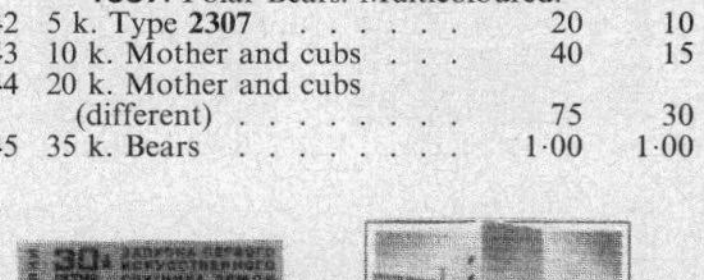

2307 Bears in and out of Water

1987. Polar Bears. Multicoloured.
5742 5 k. Type **2307** 20 10
5743 10 k. Mother and cubs . . . 40 15
5744 20 k. Mother and cubs (different) 75 30
5745 35 k. Bears . . . . 1·00 1·00

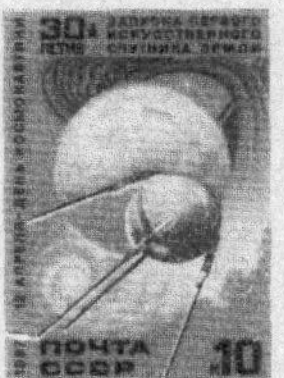

2308 "Sputnik 1" and Globe 2309 Emblem and Headquarters, Bangkok

1987. Cosmonautics Day. Multicoloured.
5746 10 k. Type **2308** (30th anniv of launching of first artificial satellite) 35 15
5747 10 k. "Vostok-3", Vostok-4" and globe (25th anniv of first group space flight) 35 15
5748 10 k. "Mars-1" and globe (25th anniv of launching of automatic interplanetary station) 35 15

1987. 40th Anniv of U.N. Economic and Social Commission for Asia and the Pacific Ocean.
5749 **2309** 10 k. multicoloured . . 35 15

2310 "Birthday" (N. A. Sysoev)

1987. 117th Birth Anniv of Lenin. Multicoloured.
5750 5 k. Type **2310** 20 10
5751 5 k. "V. I. Lenin with Delegates to the Third Congress of the Young Communist League" (P. P. Belousov) 20 10

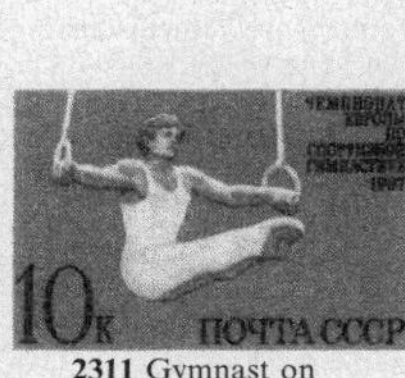

2311 Gymnast on Rings

2312 Cyclists and "40"

1987. European Gymnastics Championships, Moscow.
5753 **2311** 10 k. multicoloured . . 40 15

1987. 40th Peace Cycle Race.
5754 **2312** 10 k. multicoloured . . 50 15

2313 Menzbir's Marmot

2315 "Portrait of a Woman" (Lucas Cranach the Elder)

2314 "Maksim Gorky"

1987. Mammals listed in U.S.S.R. Red Book. Multicoloured.
5755 5 k. Type **2313** 20 10
5756 10 k. Ratel (horiz) 35 15
5757 15 k. Snow leopard (32 × 47 mm) 70 25

1987. River Tourist Ships. Multicoloured.
5758 5 k. Type **2314** 25 10
5759 10 k. "Aleksandr Pushkin" . . 40 15
5760 30 k. "Sovetsky Soyuz" . . . 1·00 45

1987. West European Art in Hermitage Museum, Leningrad. Multicoloured.
5761 4 k. Type **2315** 15 10
5762 5 k. "St. Sebastian" (Titian) . 15 10
5763 10 k. "Justice" (drawing, Albrecht Durer) 30 15
5764 30 k. "Adoration of the Magi" (Peter Breughel the younger) (horiz) 90 45
5765 50 k. "Statue of Ceres" (Peter Paul Rubens) . . . . . . 1·50 1·00

2316 Car Production Line and Lenin Hydro-electric Power Station

2317 Pushkin (after T. Rait)

1987. 250th Anniv of Togliatti (formerly Stavropol).
5766 **2316** 5 k. multicoloured . . . 25 10

1987. 150th Death Anniv of Aleksandr S. Pushkin (poet).
5767 **2317** 5 k. deep brown, yellow and brown 20 10

2318 Kovpak

2319 Congress Emblem

1987. Birth Centenary of Major-General Sidor Artemevich Kovpak.
5768 **2318** 5 k. black 20 10

1987. World Women's Congress, Moscow.
5769 **2319** 10 k. multicoloured . . 30 15

2320 Arms, Kremlin, Docks, Drama Theatre and Yermak Monument

2321 Party Flag and Mozambican

1987. 400th Anniv of Tobolsk, Siberia.
5770 **2320** 5 k. multicoloured . . . 20 10

1987. 25th Anniv of Mozambique Liberation Front (FRELIMO) (5771) and 10th Anniv of U.S.S.R.–Mozambique Friendship and Co-operation Treaty (5772). Multicoloured.
5771 5 k. Type **2321** 20 10
5772 5 k. Mozambique and U.S.S.R. flags 20 10

2322 "Scolopendrium vulgare"

2323 Moscow Kremlin and Indian Coin

1987. Ferns. Multicoloured.
5773 4 k. Type **2322** 15 10
5774 5 k. "Ceterach officinarum" . 20 10
5775 10 k. "Salvinia natans" (horiz) 35 15
5776 15 k. "Matteuccia struthiopteris" 55 25
5777 50 k. "Adiantum pedatum" . 1·50 70

1987. Indian Festival in U.S.S.R. (5778) and U.S.S.R. Festival in India (5779). Multicoloured.
5778 5 k. Type **2323** 20 15
5779 5 k. Hammer, sickle, open book, satellite and Red Fort, Delhi 20 15

2324 Rossiya Hotel (venue), Globe and Film

2325 Cosmonauts training

1987. 15th International Film Festival, Moscow.
5780 **2324** 10 k. multicoloured . . 35 15

1987. Soviet–Syrian Space Flight. Multicoloured.
5781 5 k. Type **2325** 20 10
5782 10 k. Moscow–Damascus satellite link and cosmonauts watching television screen . . 35 15
5783 15 k. Cosmonauts at Gagarin monument, Zvezdny . . . 55 25

2326 Emblem and Vienna Headquarters

1987. 30th Anniv of Int Atomic Energy Agency.
5785 **2326** 20 k. multicoloured . . 60 30

2327 14th–16th Century Messenger

1987. Russian Postal History.
5786 **2327** 4 k. black and brown . 15 10
5787 – 5 k. black and brown . 20 10
5788 – 10 k. black and brown . 35 15
5789 – 30 k. black and brown . 1·00 45
5790 – 35 k. black and brown . 1·00 50
DESIGNS: 5 k. 17th–19th century horse-drawn sledge and 17th-century postman; 10 k. 16th-century and 18th-century sailing packets; 30 k. 19th-century railway mail vans; 35 k. 1905 post car and 1926 "AMO-F-15" van.

2328 "V. I. Lenin" (P. V. Vasilev)

1987. 70th Anniv of October Revolution. Mult.
5792 5 k. Type **2328** 20 15
5793 5 k. "V. I. Lenin proclaims Soviet Power" (V. A. Serov) 20 15
5794 5 k. "Long Live the Socialist Revolution!" (V. V. Kuznetsov) 20 15
5795 5 k. "Storming the Winter Palace" (V. A. Serov) (69 × 32 mm) 20 15
5796 5 k. "On the Eve of the Storm" (portraying Lenin, Sverdlov and Podvoisky) (V. V. Pimenov) (69 × 32 mm) . . 20 15

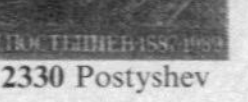

2330 Postyshev 2331 Yuri Dolgoruky (founder) Monument

1987. Birth Centenary of Pavel Petrovich Postyshev (revolutionary).
5799 **2330** 5 k. blue 20 10

1987. 840th Anniv of Moscow.
5800 **2331** 5 k. brown, yell & orge . 20 10

2332 Ulugh Beg (astronomer and mathematician)

1987. Scientists.
5801 **2332** 5 k. multicoloured . . . 25 15
5802 – 5 k. black, green and blue 25 15
5803 – 5 k. deep brown, brown and blue 25 15
DESIGNS: No. 5801, Type **2332** (550th anniv of "New Astronomical Tables"); No. 5802, Isaac Newton (300th anniv of "Principia Mathematica"); No. 5803, Marie Curie (120th birth anniv).

Всесоюзная
филателистическая выставка
„70 лет Великого Октября"
(2334)

1987. "70th Anniv of October Revolution" All-Union Stamp Exhibition. No. 5795 optd with T **2334**.
5805 5 k. multicoloured 25 20

2335 "There will be Cities in the Taiga" (A. A. Yakovlev) 2336 Reed

1987. Soviet Paintings of the 1980s. Multicoloured.
5806 4 k. Type **2335** 15 10
5807 5 k. "Mother" (V. V. Shcherbakov) 15 10
5808 10 k. "My Quiet Homeland" (V. M. Sidorov) (horiz) 30 15
5809 30 k. "In Yakutsk, Land of Pyotr Alekseev" (A. N. Osipov) (horiz) 90 45
5810 35 k. "Ivan's Return" (V. I. Yerofeev) (horiz) . . . . . 1·00 55

1987. Birth Centenary of John Reed (American journalist and founder of U. S. Communist Party).
5812 **2336** 10 k. brown, yell & blk . 35 15

2337 Marshak

1987. Birth Centenary of Samuil Yakovlevich Marshak (poet).
5813 **2337** 5 k. brown 20 10

2338 Chavchavadze

1987. 150th Anniv of Ilya Grigoryevich Chavchavadze (writer).
5814 **2338** 5 k. blue 20 10

2339 Indira Gandhi 2340 Vadim N. Podbelsky (revolutionary)

1987. 70th Birth Anniv of Indira Gandhi (former Indian Minister, 1966–77 and 1980–84).
5815 **2339** 5 k. brown and black . . 30 10

1987. Birth Centenaries.
5816 **2340** 5 k. black 20 10
5817 – 5 k. blue 20 10
DESIGN: No. 5817, Academician Nikolai Ivanovich Vavilov (geneticist).

2341 Tokamak Thermonuclear System 2342 Bagramyan

1987. Science.
5818 **2341** 5 k. brown and grey . 20 10
5819 – 10 k. green, blue and black 35 15
5820 – 20 k. black, stone and drab 60 30
DESIGNS: 10 k. Kola borehole; 20 k. "Ratan-600" radio telescope.

1987. 90th Birth Anniv of Marshal Ivan Khristoforovich Bagramyan.
5821 **2342** 5 k. brown 20 10

2343 Moscow Kremlin 2344 Flags, Spassky Tower, Moscow, and Capitol, Washington

1987. New Year.
5822 **2343** 5 k. multicoloured . . . 15 10

1987. Soviet–American Intermediate and Short-range Nuclear Weapons Treaty.
5823 **2344** 10 k. multicoloured . . 35 15

2345 Grigori Andreevich Spiridov and "Tri Svyatitelya"

1987. Russian Naval Commanders (1st series).
5824 **2345** 4 k. blue and deep blue 15 10
5825 – 5 k. purple and blue . 20 10
5826 – 10 k. purple and blue . 35 15
5827 – 25 k. blue and deep blue 85 60
5828 – 30 k. blue and deep blue 95 65
DESIGNS: 5 k. Fyodor Fyodorovich Ushakov and "Sv. Pavel"; 10 k. Dmitri Nikolaevich Senyavin and Battle of Afon; 25 k. Mikhail Petrovich Lazarev and "Azov"; 30 k. Pavel Stepanovich Nakhimov and "Imperatritsa Maria".
See also Nos. 6091/6.

2346 Torch 2347 Biathlon

1987. 30th Anniv of Asia–Africa Solidarity Organization.
5829 **2346** 10 k. multicoloured . . 30 15

1988. Winter Olympic Games, Calgary. Mult.
5830 5 k. Type **2847** 20 10
5831 10 k. Cross-country skiing . . 35 15
5832 15 k. Slalom 45 25
5833 20 k. Figure skating (pairs) . 60 30
5834 30 k. Ski jumping 95 45

2348 1918 Stamps 2349 Emblem

1988. 70th Anniv of First Soviet Postage Stamps.
5836 **2348** 10 k. blue, brown and gold 35 15
5837 10 k. brown, blue and gold 35 15
On No. 5836 the lower stamp depicted is the 35 k. in blue, on No. 5837 the lower stamp is the 70 k. in brown.

1988. 40th Anniv of W.H.O.
5838 **2349** 35 k. gold, blue and black 1·25 55

2550 Byron

1988. Birth Bicentenary of Lord Byron (English poet).
5839 **2350** 15 k. black, green and blue 45 25

2351 Exchange Activities and National Flags 352 Lomov-Oppokov

1988. 30th Anniv of Agreement on Cultural, Technical and Educational Exchanges with U.S.A.
5840 **2351** 20 k. multicoloured . . 60 30

1988. Birth Centenary of Georgy Ippolitovich Lomov-Oppokov (Communist party official).
5841 **2352** 5 k. black and brown . . 10 10

2353 "Little Humpbacked Horse" (dir. I. Ivanov-Vano, animated L. Milchin)

1988. Soviet Cartoon Films. Multicoloured.
5842 1 k. Type **2353** 10 10
5843 3 k. "Winnie the Pooh" (dir. F. Khitruk, animated V. Zuikov and E. Nazarov) 10 10
5844 4 k. "Gena the Crocodile" (dir. R. Kachanov, animated L. Shartsmann) 15 10
5845 5 k. "Just You Wait!" (dir. V. Kotyonochkin, animated S. Rusakov) 20 10
5846 10 k. "Hedgehog in a Mist" (dir. Yu. Norshtein, animated F. Yarbusova) 30 15

2354 Bonch-Bruevich 2355 Nurse and Emblems

1988. Birth Centenary of Mikhail Alexandrovich Bonch-Bruevich (radio engineer).
5848 **2354** 10 k. black and brown . 30 15

1988. 125th Anniv of International Red Cross and Red Crescent.
5849 **2355** 15 k. black, blue and red 45 25

2356 Skater

1988. World Speed Skating Championships, Alma-Ata.
5850 **2356** 15 k. blue, violet and black 45 25

2357 Makarenko

1988. Birth Centenary of Anton Semenovich Makarenko (educationist and writer).
5851 **2357** 10 k. green 30 15

2358 Skorina 2359 Banners and Globe

1988. 500th Birth Anniv of Frantsisk Skorina (printer).
5852 **2358** 5 k. black 20 10

1988. Labour Day.
5853 **2359** 5 k. multicoloured . . . 20 10

2360 Kingisepp 2361 Track and Athlete

1988. Birth Centenary of Victor Eduardovich Kingisepp (revolutionary).
5854 **2360** 5 k. green 20 10

1988. Centenary of Russian Athletics.
5855 **2361** 15 k. multicoloured . . 45 25

2362 M. S. Shaginyan

1988. Birth Centenary of Marietta Sergeevna Shaginyan (writer).
5856 **2362** 10 k. brown 30 10

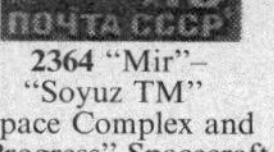

2363 Palace of Congresses, Moscow, Finlandia Hall, Helsinki, and National Flags

2364 "Mir"–"Soyuz TM" Space Complex and "Progress" Spacecraft

1988. 40th Anniv of U.S.S.R.–Finland Friendship Treaty.

5857 **2363** 15 k. multicoloured . . 45 25

1988. Cosmonautics Day.

5858 **2364** 15 k. multicoloured . . 45 25

2365 Sochi

1988. 150th Anniv of Sochi.

5859 **2365** 5 k. multicoloured . . . 20 10

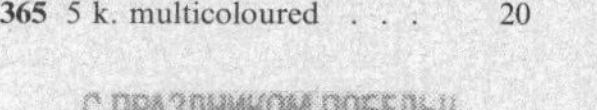

2366 "Victory" (P. A. Krivonogov)

1988. V. E. Day (8 May).

5860 **2366** 5 k. multicoloured . . . 20 10

2367 Lenin Museum, Moscow

1988. 118th Birth Anniv of Lenin. Designs showing branches of Lenin Central Museum.

5861 **2367** 5 k. brown, deep brown and gold 20 10
5862 – 5 k. red, purple & gold . 20 10
5863 – 5 k. ochre, brown & gold 20 10
5864 – 5 k. yell, grn & gold . . 20 10

DESIGNS: No. 5862, Kiev; No. 5863, Leningrad; No. 5864, Krasnoyarsk.

See also Nos. 5990/2 and 6131/3.

2368 Akulov

2369 Soviet Display Emblem

1988. Birth Centenary of Ivan Alekseevich Akulov (Communist Party official).

5865 **2368** 5 k. blue 20 10

1988. "Expo 88" World's Fair, Brisbane.

5866 **2369** 20 k. multicoloured . . 60 30

2370 Marx

2373 Shvernik

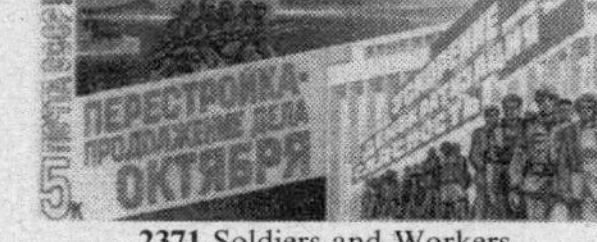

2371 Soldiers and Workers

1988. 170th Birth Anniv of Karl Marx.

5867 **2370** 5 k. brown 20 10

1988. Perestroika (Reformation).

5868 **2371** 5 k. multicoloured . . 20 10
5869 – 5 k. brown, red & orange 20 10

DESIGN: No. 5869, Banner, industrial scenes and worker.

1988. Birth Centenary of Nikolai Mikhailovich Shvernik (politician).

5871 **2373** 5 k. black 20 10

2374 Russian Borzoi

1988. Hunting Dogs. Multicoloured.

5872 5 k. Type **2374** 20 10
5873 10 k. Kirgiz borzoi 30 15
5874 15 k. Russian hound 45 25
5875 20 k. Russian spaniel . . . 60 30
5876 35 k. East Siberian husky . 1·00 50

2375 Flags, Spassky Tower and Handshake

2376 Kuibyshev

1988. Soviet–American Summit, Moscow.

5877 **2375** 5 k. multicoloured . . 20 10

1988. Birth Centenary of Valerian Vladimirovich Kuibyshev (politician).

5878 **2376** 5 k. brown 20 10

2377 Flags, "Mir" Space Station and "Soyuz TM" Spacecraft

2378 Crowd and Peace Banners

1988. Soviet–Bulgarian Space Flight.

5879 **2377** 15 k. multicoloured . . 45 25

1988. "For a Nuclear-free World".

5880 **2378** 5 k. multicoloured . . 20 10

2379 Red Flag, Hammer and Sickle and Laurel Branch

2380 Flags, Skis and Globe

1988. 19th Soviet Communist Party Conference, Moscow (1st issue). Multicoloured.

5881 5 k. Type **2379** 20 10
5882 5 k. Lenin on red flag and interior of Palace of Congresses (35 × 23 mm) . 20 10

See also Nos. 5960/2.

1988. Soviet–Canadian Transarctic Ski Expedition.

5884 **2380** 35 k. multicoloured . . 1·00 50

2381 Hurdling

2382 Giant Bellflower

1988. Olympic Games, Seoul. Multicoloured.

5885 5 k. Type **2381** 20 10
5886 10 k. Long jumping 30 15
5887 15 k. Basketball 45 25
5888 20 k. Gymnastics 60 30
5889 30 k. Swimming 90 45

1988. Deciduous Forest Flowers. Multicoloured.

5891 5 k. Type **2382** 20 10
5892 10 k. Spring pea (horiz) . . . 30 15
5893 15 k. Lungwort 45 25
5894 20 k. Turk's cap lily 60 30
5895 35 k. "Ficaria verna" . . . . 1·00 50

2383 Phobos and "Phobos" Space Probe

2384 Komsomol Badge

1988. Phobos (Mars Moon) International Space Project.

5896 **2383** 10 k. multicoloured . . 30 15

1988. 70th Anniv of Leninist Young Communist League (Komsomol).

5897 **2384** 5 k. multicoloured . . . 20 10

2385 Mandela

Филвыставка. Москва

(2387)

2386 "Obeyan Serebryanyi, Light Grey Arab Stallion" (N. E. Sverchkov)

1988. 70th Birthday of Nelson Mandela (African nationalist).

5898 **2385** 10 k. multicoloured . . 30 15

1988. Paintings in Moscow Horse Breeding Museum. Multicoloured.

5899 5 k. Type **2386** 20 10
5900 10 k. "Konvoets" (Kabardin breed) (M. A. Vrubel) (vert) 35 15
5901 15 k. "Horsewoman on Orlov-Rastopchin Horse" (N. E. Sverchkov) 45 25
5902 20 k. "Letuchy, Grey Stallion of Orlov Trotter Breed" (V. A. Serov) (vert) 60 30
5903 30 k. "Sardar, an Akhaltekin Stallion" (A. B. Villevalde) 95 75

1988. Stamp Exhibition, Moscow. No. 5897 optd with T **2387**.

5904 **2384** 5 k. multicoloured . . . 20 10

2388 Voikov

2389 "Portrait of O. K. Lansere" (Z. E. Serebryakova)

1988. Birth Centenary of Pyotr Lazarevich Voikov (diplomat).

5905 **2388** 5 k. black 20 10

1988. Soviet Culture Fund. Multicoloured.

5906 10 k. + 5 k. Type **2389** . . . 45 25
5907 15 k. + 7 k. "Boyarynya (noblewoman) looking at Embroidery Design" (K. V. Lebedev) (horiz) . . . 65 35
5908 30 k. + 15 k. "Talent" (N. P. Bogdanov-Belsky) . . . . 1·40 70

2390 Envelopes and U.P.U. Emblem

2391 "Mir" Space Station and "Soyuz-TM" Spacecraft

1988. International Correspondence Week.

5910 **2390** 5 k. turquoise, blue & blk 20 10

1988. Soviet–Afghan Space Flight.

5911 **2391** 15 k. green, red & blk . 45 25

2392 Emblem and Open Book

2393 Kviring

1988. 30th Anniv of "Problems of Peace and Socialism" (magazine).

5912 **2392** 10 k. multicoloured . . 30 15

1988. Birth Centenary of Emmanuil Ionovich Kviring (politician).

5913 **2393** 5 k. black 20 10

2394 "Ilya Muromets" (Russia) (R. Smirnova)

2395 "Appeal of the Leader" (detail, I. M. Toidze)

1988. Epic Poems of Soviet Union (1st series). Illustrations by artists named. Multicoloured.

5914 10 k. Type **2394** 30 15
5915 10 k. "Cossack Golota" (Ukraine) (M. Deregus) (horiz) 30 15
5916 10 k. "Musician-Magician" (Byelorussia) (N. Poplavskaya) 30 15
5917 10 k. "Koblandy Batyr" (Kazakhstan) (I. Isabaev) (horiz) 30 15
5918 10 k. "Alpamysh" (Uzbekistan) (R. Khalilov) 30 15

See also Nos. 6017/21 and 6139/43.

1988. 71st Anniv of October Revolution.

5919 **2395** 5 k. multicoloured . . . 20 10

2396 Bolotov

2397 Tupolev

1988. 250th Birth Anniv of Andrei Timofeevich Bolotov (agriculturalist).
5920 **2396** 10 k. brown 30 15

1988. Birth Centenary of Academician Andrei Nikolaevich Tupolev (aircraft designer).
5921 **2397** 10 k. blue 30 15

2398 Bear

2399 "Sibir" (atomic ice-breaker)

1988. Zoo Relief Fund. Multicoloured.
5922 10 k. + 5 k. Type **2398** . . . 45 25
5923 10 k. + 5 k. Wolf 45 25
5924 10 k. + 10 k. Fox 95 45
5925 20 k. + 10 k. Wild boar . . 95 45
5926 20 k. + 10 k. Lynx 95 45

1988. Soviet Arctic Expedition.
5927 **2399** 20 k. multicoloured . . 60 60

2400 Ustinov

2401 National Initials

1988. 80th Birth Anniv of Marshal Dmitri Fyodorovich Ustinov.
5928 **2400** 5 k. brown 20 10

1988. 10th Anniv of U.S.S.R.–Vietnam Friendship Treaty.
5929 **2401** 10 k. multicoloured . . 30 15

2402 Building Facade

1988. 50th Anniv of State House of Broadcasting and Sound Recording.
5930 **2402** 10 k. multicoloured . . 30 15

2403 Emblem

1988. 40th Anniv of Declaration of Human Rights.
5931 **2403** 10 k. multicoloured . . 30 15

2404 Life Guard of Preobrazhensky Regt. with Peter I's New Year Decree

1988. New Year.
5932 **2404** 5 k. multicoloured . . 20 10

2405 Flags and Cosmonauts

1988. Soviet–French Space Flight.
5933 **2405** 15 k. multicoloured . . 45 25

2406 "Skating Rink" (Olya Krutova)

2407 Lacis

1988. Lenin Soviet Children's Fund. Children's Paintings. Multicoloured.
5934 5 k. + 2 k. Type **2406** . . . 25 15
5935 5 k. + 2 k. "Cock" (Nasta Shcheglova) 25 15
5936 5 k. + 2 k. "May is flying over the Meadows, May is flying over the Fields" (Larisa Gaidash) 25 15

1988. Birth Cent of Martins Lacis (revolutionary).
5937 **2407** 5 k. green 20 10

(2408)

2410 Post Messenger

1988. "Space Post". No. 4682 optd with T **2408**.
5938 **1** r. blue . . . . 2·75 2·75

1988.
5940 **2410** 1 k. brown 10 10
6073 – 2 k. brown 10 10
5941 – 3 k. green 10 10
6075 – 4 k. blue 10 10
6076 – 5 k. red 15 10
6077 – 7 k. blue 15 10
6078 – 10 k. brown 25 15
6079 – 12 k. purple 30 20
6080 – 13 k. violet 30 20
6081 – 15 k. blue 35 20
6082 – 20 k. brown 45 25
6083 – 25 k. green 85 30
6084 – 30 k. blue 90 35
6085 – 35 k. brown . . . . . 1·00 40
6086 – 50 k. blue . . . . . . 1·50 50
6087 – 1 r. blue . . . . . . 3·00 1·40
DESIGNS: 2 k. Old mail transport (sailing packet, steam train and mail coach); 3 k. "Aurora" (cruiser); 4 k. Spassky Tower and Lenin's Tomb, Red Square, Moscow; 5 k. State emblem and flag; 7 k. Modern mail transport (aircraft, liner, train and mail van); 10 k. "The Worker and the Collective Farmer" (statue V. I. Mukhina); 12 k. Rocket on launch pad; 13 k. Satellite; 15 k. "Orbit" dish aerial; 20 k. Symbols of art and literature; 25 k. "The Discus-thrower" (5th-century Greek statue by Miron); 30 k. Map of Antarctica and penguins; 35 k. "Mercury" (statue Giovanni da Bologna); 50 k. White cranes; 1 r. Universal Postal Union emblem.

2411 Great Cascade and Samson Fountain

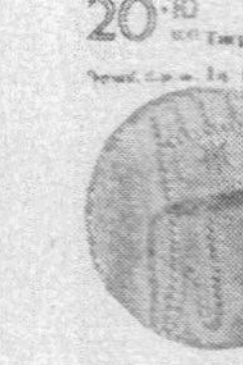
2412 1st-cent B. C. Gold Coin of Tigran the Great

1988. Petrodvorets Fountains. Each green and grey.
5952 5 k. Type **2411** 20 10
5953 10 k. Adam fountain (D. Bonazza) 30 15
5954 15 k. Golden Mountain cascade (Niccolo Michetti and Mikhail Zemtsov) 45 25
5955 30 k. Roman fountains (Bartolomeo Rastrelli) . . 95 45
5965 50 k. Oaklet trick fountain (Rastrelli) . . . . . . 1·50 1·00

1988. Armenian Earthquake Relief. Armenian History. Multicoloured.
5957 20 k. + 10 k. Type **2412** . . 95 45
5958 30 k. + 15 k. Rispsime Church 1·25 65
5959 50 k. + 25 k. "Madonna and Child" (18th-century fresco, Ovnat Ovnatanyan) . . . 2·25 1·25

2413 Hammer and Sickle

1988. 19th Soviet Communist Party Conference, Moscow (2nd issue). Multicoloured.
5960 5 k. Type **2413** 20 10
5961 5 k. Hammer and sickle and building girders 20 10
5962 5 k. Hammer and sickle and wheat 20 10

2415 "Vostok" Rocket, "Lunar 1", Earth and Moon

2416 Virtanen

1989. 30th Anniv of First Russian Moon Flight.
5964 **2415** 15 k. multicoloured . . 45 25

1989. Birth Centenary of Jalmari Virtanen (poet).
5965 **2416** 5 k. brown and bistre . . 20 10

2417 Headquarters Building, Moscow

1989. 40th Anniv of Council for Mutual Economic Aid.
5966 **2417** 10 k. multicoloured . . 30 15

2418 Forest Protection

2419 18th-century Samovar

1989. Nature Conservation. Multicoloured.
5967 5 k. Type **2418** 30 20
5968 10 k. Arctic preservation . . 30 15
5969 15 k. Anti-desertification campaign 40 20

1989. Russian Samovars in State Museum, Leningrad. Multicoloured.
5970 5 k. Type **2419** 20 10
5971 10 k. 19th-century barrel samovar by Ivan Lisitsin of Tula 30 15
5972 20 k. 1830s Kabachok travelling samovar by Sokolov Brothers factory, Tula 55 30
5973 30 k. 1840s samovar by Nikolai Malikov factory, Tula . . . 85 45

2420 Mussorgsky and Scene from "Boris Godunov"

2421 Dybenko

1989. 150th Birth Anniv of Modest Petrovich Mussorgsky (composer).
5974 **2420** 10 k. purple and brown . . 30 15

1989. Birth Centenary of Pavel Dybenko (military leader).
5975 **2421** 5 k. black 20 10

2422 Shevchenko

2423 "Lilium speciosum"

1989. 175th Birth Anniv of Taras Shevchenko (Ukrainian poet and painter).
5976 **2422** 5 k. brown, green & blk 20 10

1989. Lilies. Multicoloured.
5977 5 k. Type **2423** 20 10
5978 10 k. "African Queen" . . . 30 15
5979 15 k. "Eclat du Soir" 40 20
5980 30 k. "White Tiger" 85 45

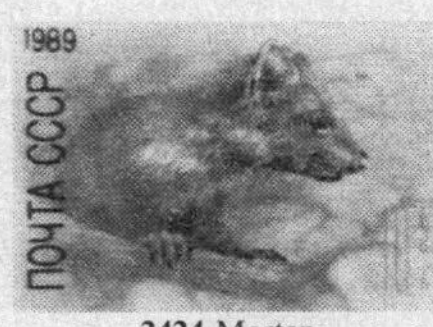
2424 Marten

1989. Zoo Relief Fund. Multicoloured.
5981 10 k. + 5 k. Type **2424** . . . 40 20
5982 10 k. + 5 k. Squirrel 40 20
5983 20 k. + 10 k. Hare 85 45
5984 20 k. + 10 k. Hedgehog . . 85 45
5985 20 k. + 10 k. Badger 85 45

2426 "Victory Banner" (P. Loginov and V. Pamfilov)

1989. Victory Day.
5987 **2426** 5 k. multicoloured . . . 20 10

2427 "Mir" Space Station

1989. Cosmonautics Day.
5988 **2427** 15 k. multicoloured . . 40 20

2428 Emblem and Flags

2430 Statue

1989. U.S.–Soviet Bering Bridge Expedition.
5989 **2428** 10 k. multicoloured . . 30 15

1989. 119th Birth Anniv of Lenin. As T **2367**. Branches of Lenin Central Museum.
5990 5 k. brown, ochre and gold . 20 10
5991 5 k. deep brown, brn & gold 20 10
5992 5 k. multicoloured 20 10
DESIGNS: No. 5990, Frunze; No. 5991, Kazan; No. 5992, Kuibyshev.

1989. 70th Anniv of First Hungarian Soviet Republic.
5994 **2430** 5 k. multicoloured . . . 20 10

2431 "Motherland Statue" **2432** Drone

1989. 400th Anniv of Volgograd (formerly Tsaritsyn).
5995 **2431** 5 k. multicoloured . . . 20 10

1989. Bees. Multicoloured.
5996 5 k. Type **2432** 20 10
5997 10 k. Bees, flowers and hive . 30 15
5998 20 k. Bee on flower 55 30
5999 35 k. Feeding queen bee . . 90 45

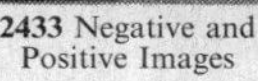

2433 Negative and Positive Images **2434** Map above Dove as Galley

1989. 150th Anniv of Photography.
6000 **2433** 5 k. multicoloured . . . 20 10

1989. "Europe—Our Common Home". Mult.
6001 5 k. Type **2434** 20 10
6002 10 k. Laying foundations of Peace 30 15
6003 15 k. Storks' nest 40 20

2435 Mukhina modelling "God of Northern Wind" (after M. Nesterov) **2436** Racine

1989. Birth Centenary of Vera I. Mukhina (sculptress).
6004 **2435** 5 k. blue 20 10

1989. 150th Birth Anniv of Jean Racine (dramatist).
6005 **2436** 15 k. multicoloured . . 40 20

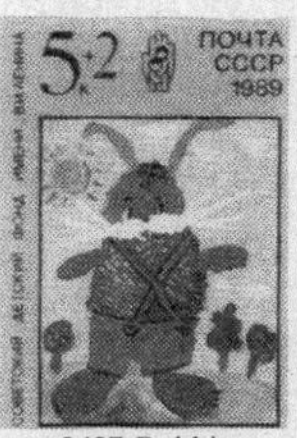

2437 Rabbit

1989. Lenin Soviet Children's Fund. Children's Paintings. Multicoloured.
6006 **5** k. + 2 k. Type **2437** . . . 25 10
6007 **5** k. + 2 k. Cat 25 10
6008 **5** k. + 2 k. Nurse 25 10
See also Nos. 6162/4.

2438 Kuratov

1989. 150th Birth Anniv of Ivan Kuratov (writer).
6009 **2438** 5 k. deep brown & brown 20 10

2439 Emblem **2440** Common Shelduck

1989. 13th World Youth and Students' Festival, Pyongyang.
6010 **2439** 10 k. multicoloured . . 30 15

1989. Ducks (1st series). Multicoloured.
6011 5 k. Type **2440** 20 10
6012 15 k. Green-winged teal . . 40 20
6013 20 k. Ruddy shelduck . . . 55 30
See also Nos. 6159/61, 6264/6, 6368/70, 6420/2 and 6487/9.

2441 "Storming of Bastille" (Gelman after Monnet)

1989. Bicentenary of French Revolution.
6014 **2441** 5 k. multicoloured . . 20 10
6015 – 15 k. blue, black & red 40 20
6016 – 20 k. blue, black & red 50 25
DESIGNS: 15 k. Jean-Paul Marat, Georges Danton and Maximilien Robespierre; 20 k. "Marseillaise" (relief by F. Rude from Arc de Triomphe).

1989. Epic Poems of Soviet Union (2nd series). Illustrations by named artists. As T **2394**. Mult.
6017 10 k. "Amirani" (Georgia) (V. Oniani) 30 15
6018 10 k. "Koroglu" (Azerbaijan) (A. Gadzhiev) 30 15
6019 10 k. "Fir, Queen of Grass Snakes" (Lithuania) (A. Makunaite) 30 15
6020 10 k. "Mioritsa" (Moldavia) (I. Bogdesko) 30 15
6021 10 k. "Lachplesis" (Lettish) (G. Wilks) 30 15

2442 Observatory **2443** Hemispheres, Roses in Envelope and Posthorn

1989. 150th Anniv of Pulkovo Observatory.
6022 **2442** 10 k. multicoloured . . 35 15

1989. International Letter Week.
6023 **2443** 5 k. multicoloured . . 20 10

2444 Lynx **2446** Buildings, Container Ship and Bicentenary Emblem

1989. 50th Anniv of Tallin Zoo.
6024 **2444** 10 k. multicoloured . . 30 15

1989. Bicentenary of Nikolaev.
6026 **2446** 5 k. multicoloured . . 20 10

2447 Nkrumah **2448** 1921 40 r. Stamp

1989. 80th Birth Anniv of Kwame Nkrumah (first Prime Minister and President of Ghana).
6027 **2447** 10 k. multicoloured . . 30 15

1989. 6th All-Union Philatelic Society Congress, Moscow.
6028 **2448** 10 k. multicoloured . . 30 15

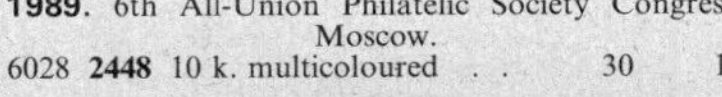

2449 Cooper

1989. Birth Bicentenary of James Fenimore Cooper (writer) (1st issue).
6029 **2449** 15 k. multicoloured . . 40 20
See also Nos. 6055/9.

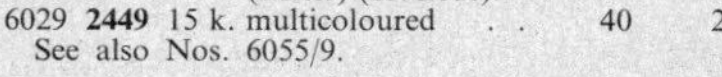

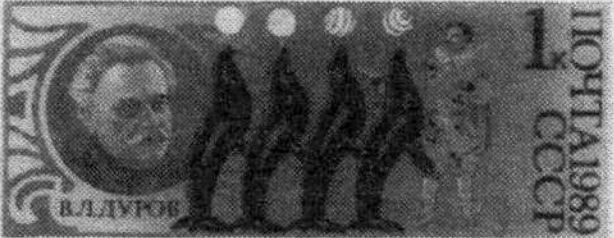

2450 V. L. Durov (trainer) and Sealions

1989. 70th Anniv of Soviet Circus. Multicoloured.
6030 1 k. Type **2450** 10 10
6031 3 k. M. N. Rumyantsev (clown "Karandash") with donkey 10 10
6032 4 k. V. I. Filatov (founder of Bear Circus) and bears on motor cycles 15 10
6033 5 k. E. T. Kio (illusionist) and act 20 10
6034 10 k. V. E. Lazarenko (clown and acrobat) and act . . . 30 15

2451 Emblem on Glove **2452** Li Dazhao

1989. International Amateur Boxing Association Championship, Moscow.
6036 **2451** 15 k. multicoloured . . 40 20

1989. Birth Centenary of Li Dazhao (co-founder of Chinese Communist Party).
6037 **2452** 5 k. brown, stone & blk 20 10

2453 Khetagurov

1989. 130th Birth Anniv of Kosta Khetagurov (Ossetian writer).
6038 **2453** 5 k. brown 20 10

2454 "October Guardsmen" (M. M. Chepik)

1989. 72nd Anniv of October Revolution.
6039 **2454** 5 k. multicoloured . . . 20 10

2455 Russian Spoons, Psaltery, Balalaika, Zhaleika and Accordion

1989. Traditional Musical Instruments (1st series). Multicoloured.
6040 10 k. Type **2455** 30 15
6041 10 k. Ukrainian bandura, trembita, drymba, svyril (pipes) and dulcimer . . . 30 15
6042 10 k. Byelorussian tambourine, bastlya (fiddle), lera and dudka (pipe) 30 15
6043 10 k. Uzbek nagors (drums), rubab, zang, karnai and gidzhak 30 15
See also Nos. 6183/6 and 6303/5.

2456 "Demonstration of First Radio Receiver, 1895" (N. A. Sysoev) **2457** National Flag and Provincial Arms

1989. 130th Birth Anniv of Aleksandr Stepanovich Popov (radio pioneer).
6044 **2456** 10 k. multicoloured . . 30 15

1989. 40th Anniv of German Democratic Republic.
6045 **2457** 5 k. multicoloured . . . 20 10

2458 Polish National Colours forming "45" **2459** Kosior

1989. 45th Anniv of Liberation of Poland.
6046 **2458** 5 k. multicoloured . . . 20 10

1989. Birth Centenary of Stanislav Vikentievich Kosior (vice-chairman of Council of People's Commissars).
6047 **2459** 5 k. black 20 10

2460 Nehru **2461** "Village Market" (A. V. Makovsky)

1989. Birth Centenary of Jawaharlal Nehru (Indian statesman).
6048 **2460** 15 k. brown 40 20

1989. Soviet Culture Fund. Multicoloured.
6049 4 k. + 2 k. Type **2461** . . . 20 10
6050 5 k. + 2 k. "Lady in Hat" (E. L. Zelenin) 25 15
6051 10 k. + 5 k. "Portrait of the Actress Bazhenova" (A. F. Sofronova) 40 20
6052 20 k. + 10 k. "Two Women" (Hugo Shaiber) 75 65
6053 30 k. + 15 k. 19th-century teapot and plates from Popov porcelain works . . . . . 1·40 85

2462 Berzin **2463** "The Hunter"

1989. Birth Centenary of Yan Karlovich Berzin (head of Red Army Intelligence).
6054 **2462** 5 k. black 20 10

1989. Birth Bicentenary of James Fenimore Cooper (writer) (2nd issue). Illustrations of his novels. Multicoloured.
6055 20 k. Type **2463** 50 25
6056 20 k. "Last of the Mohicans" 50 25
6057 20 k. "The Pathfinder" . . . 50 25
6058 20 k. "The Pioneers" 50 25
6059 20 k. "The Prairie" 50 25
Nos. 6055/9 were printed together, se-tenant, forming a composite design.

2464 St. Basil's Cathedral and Minin and Pozharsky Statue, Moscow

2465 Dymkovo Toy

1989. Historical Monuments (1st series). Mult.
6060 15 k. Type **2464** 40 20
6061 15 k. Sts. Peter and Paul Cathedral and statue of Peter I, Leningrad 40 20
6062 15 k. St. Sophia's Cathedral and statue of Bogdan Chmielnitsky, Kiev 40 20
6063 15 k. Khodzha Ahmed Yasavi mausoleum, Turkestan . . . 40 20
6064 15 k. Khazret Khyzr Mosque, Samarkand 40 20
See also Nos. 6165/72 and 6231/3.

1989. New Year.
6065 **2465** 5 k. multicoloured . . . 20 10

2466 Soviet Lunar Vehicle

2468 Acid Rain destroying Rose

1989. "Expo 89" International Stamp Exhibition, Washington D.C. Multicoloured.
6066 25 k. Type **2466** 90 65
6067 25 k. Astronaut and landing module on Moon 90 65
6068 25 k. Cosmonauts on Mars . 90 65
6069 25 k. Flag and shield on Mars 90 65

1989. Russian Naval Commanders (2nd series). As T **2345**.
6091 5 k. blue and brown 10 15
6092 10 k. blue and brown 25 15
6093 15 k. blue and deep blue . . 35 20
6094 20 k. blue and deep blue . . 45 25
6095 30 k. blue and brown 90 60
6096 35 k. blue and brown . . . . 1·10 65
DESIGNS: 5 k. V. A. Kornilov and "Pervaz Bati"; 10 k. V. I. Istomin and "Parizh"; 15 k. G. I. Nevelskoi and "Baikal"; 20 k. G. I. Butakov and iron-clad squadron; 30 k. A. A. Popov, "Pyotr Veliky" and "Vitze Admirial Popov"; 35 k. S. O. Makarov, "Intibah" (Turkish warship) and "Veliky Khyaz Konstantin".

1990. Nature Conservation. Multicoloured.
6097 10 k. Type **2468** 25 15
6098 15 k. Oil-smeared bird perching on globe 35 20
6099 20 k. Blade sawing down tree 45 25

2469 Ladya Monument and Golden Gates, Kiev (Ukraine)

2470 Flag and Hanoi Monument

1990. Republic Capitals. Multicoloured.
6100 5 k. Lenin Palace of Culture, Government House and Academy of Sciences, Alma-Ata (Kazakhstan) 15 10
6101 5 k. Library, Mollanepes Theatre and War Heroes Monument, Ashkhabad (Turkmenistan) 15 10
6102 5 k. Maiden's Tower and Divan-Khane Palace, Baku (Azerbaijan) 15 10
6103 5 k. Sadriddin Aini Theatre and Avicenna Monument, Dushanbe (Tadzhikistan) . 15 10
6104 4 k. Spendyarov Theatre and David Sasunsky Monument, Yerevan (Armenia) 15 10
6105 5 k. Satylganov Philharmonic Society building and Manas Memorial, Frunze (Kirgizia) 15 10
6106 5 k. Type **2469** 15 10
6107 5 k. Cathedral and Victory Arch, Kishinev (Moldavia) 15 10
6108 5 k. Government House and Liberation Monument, Minsk (Byelorussia) 15 10
6109 5 k. Konstantino-Yeleninsky Tower and Ivan the Great Bell Tower, Moscow (Russian Federation) 15 10
6110 5 k. Cathedral, "Three Brothers" building and Freedom Monument, Riga (Latvia) 15 10
6111 5 k. Herman the Long, Oliviste Church, Cathedral and Town hall towers and wall turret, Tallin (Estonia) 15 10
6112 5 k. Kukeldash Medrese and University, Tashkent (Uzbekistan) 15 10
6113 5 k. Metekh Temple and Vakhtang Gorgasal Monument, Tbilisi (Georgia) 15 10
6114 5 k. Gediminas Tower and St. Anne's Church, Vilnius (Lithuania) 15 10

1990. 60th Anniv of Vietnamese Communist Party.
6115 **2470** 5 k. multicoloured . . 15 10

2471 Ho Chi Minh

2472 Snowy Owl

1990. Birth Centenary of Ho Chi Minh (Vietnamese leader).
6116 **2471** 10 k. brown and black 25 15

1990. Owls. Multicoloured.
6117 10 k. Type **2472** 25 15
6118 20 k. Eagle owl (vert) . . . 45 20
6119 55 k. Long-earred owl . . . 1·10 55

2473 Sailing Ship, Posthorn and Penny Black

1990. 150th Anniv of the Penny Black.
6120 **2473** 10 k. multicoloured . . 25 15
6121 – 20 k. black and gold . . 45 25
6122 – 20 k. black and gold . . 45 25
6123 – 35 k. multicoloured . . 1·10 65
6124 – 35 k. multicoloured . . 1·10 65
DESIGNS: No. 6121, Anniversary emblem and Penny Black (lettered "TP"); No. 6122, as No. 6121 but stamp lettered "TF"; No. 6123, "Stamp World London 90" International Stamp Exhibition emblem and Penny Black (lettered "V K"); No. 6124, as No. 6123 but stamp lettered "AH".

2474 Electric Cables

1990. 125th Anniv of I.T.U.
6126 **2474** 20 k. multicoloured . . 45 25

2475 Flowers

1990. Labour Day.
6127 **2475** 5 k. multicoloured . . 15 10

2476 "Victory, 1945" (A. Lysenko)

1990. 45th Anniv of Victory in Second World War.
6128 **2476** 5 k. multicoloured . . 15 10

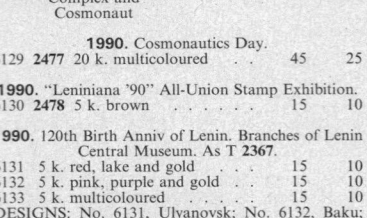

2477 "Mir" Space Complex and Cosmonaut

2478 Lenin

1990. Cosmonautics Day.
6129 **2477** 20 k. multicoloured . . 45 25

1990. "Leniniana '90" All-Union Stamp Exhibition.
6130 **2478** 5 k. brown 15 10

1990. 120th Birth Anniv of Lenin. Branches of Lenin Central Museum. As T **2367**.
6131 5 k. red, lake and gold . . . 15 10
6132 5 k. pink, purple and gold . . 15 10
6133 5 k. multicoloured 15 10
DESIGNS: No. 6131, Ulyanovsk; No. 6132, Baku; No. 6133, Tashkent.

2479 Scene from "Iolanta" (opera) and Tchaikovsky

1990. 150th Birth Anniv of Pyotr Ilich Tchaikovsky (composer).
6134 **2479** 15 k. black 90 60

2480 Golden Eagle

1990. Zoo Relief Fund. Multicoloured.
6135 10 k. + 5 k. Type **2480** . . . 35 20
6136 20 k. + 10 k. Saker falcon ("Falco cherrug") 90 60
6137 20 k. + 10 k. Raven ("Corvus corax") 90 60

2481 Etching by G. A. Echeistov

2482 Goalkeeper and Players

1990. 550th Anniv of "Dzhangar" (Kalmuk folk epic).
6138 **2481** 10 k. ochre, brn & blk . 25 15

1990. Epic Poems of Soviet Union (3rd series). Illustrations by named artists. As T **2394**. Mult.
6139 10 k. "Manas" (Kirgizia) (T. Gertsen) (horiz) . . . 25 15
6140 10 k. "Gurugli" (Tadzhikistan) (I. Martynov) (horiz) . . . 25 15
6141 10 k. "David Sasunsky" (Armenia) (M. Abegyan) . 25 15
6142 10 k. "Gerogly" (Turkmenistan) (I. Klychev) 25 15
6143 10 k. "Kalevipoeg" (Estonia) (O. Kallis) 25 15

1990. World Cup Football Championship, Italy. Multicoloured.
6144 5 k. Type **2482** 15 10
6145 10 k. Players 25 15
6146 15 k. Attempted tackle . . . 35 20
6147 25 k. Referee and players . . 55 30
6148 35 k. Goalkeeper saving ball . 1·10 65

2483 Globe and Finlandia Hall, Helsinki

2484 Competitors and Target

1990. 15th Anniv of European Security and Co-operation Conference, Helsinki.
6149 **2483** 15 k. multicoloured . . 35 20

1990. 45th World Shooting Championships, Moscow.
6150 **2484** 15 k. multicoloured . . 35 20

2485 Glaciology Research

1990. Soviet–Australian Scientific Co-operation in Antarctica. Multicoloured.
6151 5 k. Type **2485** 15 10
6152 50 k. Krill (marine biology research) . . . . 1·50 1·00

2486 Emblem and Sports Pictograms

1990. Goodwill Games, Seattle.
6154 **2486** 10 k. multicoloured . . 25 15

2488 Greylag Geese

1990. Poultry. Multicoloured.
6156 5 k. Type **2488** 15 10
6157 10 k. Adlers (chickens) . . . 25 15
6158 15 k. Bronze North Caucasian turkeys 35 20

2489 Mallards

1990. Ducks (2nd series). Multicoloured.
6159 5 k. Type **2489** 15 10
6160 15 k. Goldeneyes 35 20
6161 20 k. Red-crested pochards . . 45 25

1990. Lenin Soviet Children's Fund. Children's Paintings. As T **2437**. Multicoloured.
6162 5 k. + 2 k. Clown 20 10
6163 5 k. + 2 k. Ladies in crinolines 20 10
6164 5 k. + 2 k. Children with banner 20 10

1990. Historical Monuments (2nd series). As T **2464**. Multicoloured.
6165 15 k. St. Nshan's Church, Akhpat (Armenia) 35 20
6166 15 k. Shirvanshah Palace, Baku (Azerbaijan) 35 20
6167 15 k. Soroki Fortress and statue of Stefan III, Kishinev (Moldavia) 35 20
6168 15 k. Spaso-Efrosinevsky Cathedral, Polotsk (Byelorussia) 35 20
6169 15 k. St. Peter's Church and 16th-century Riga (Latvia) 35 20
6170 15 k. St. Nicholas's Church and carving of city arms, Tallin (Estonia) 35 20
6171 15 k. Mtatsminda Pantheon and statue of Nikoloz Baratashvili, Tbilisi (Georgia) 35 20
6172 15 k. Cathedral and bell tower, Vilnius (Lithuania) 35 20

2490 Sordes

1990. Prehistoric Animals. Multicoloured.
6173 1 k. Type **2490** 10 10
6174 3 k. Chalicotherium (vert) . . 10 10
6175 5 k. Indricotherium (vert) . . 15 10
6176 10 k. Saurolophus (vert) . . 25 15
6177 20 k. Thyestes 45 25

2491 "St. Basil's Cathedral and Kremlin, Moscow" (Sanjay Adhikari)

2492 Pigeon Post

1990. Indo–Soviet Friendship. Children's Paintings. Multicoloured.
6178 10 k. Type **2491** 25 10
6179 10 k. "Life in India" (Tanya Vorontsova) 25 10

1990. Letter Writing Week.
6180 **2492** 5 k. blue 15 10

2493 Traffic on Urban Roads

2495 Killer Whales

1990. Traffic Safety Week.
6181 **2493** 5 k. multicoloured . . . 15 10

1990. Traditional Musical Instruments (2nd series). As T **2455**. Multicoloured.
6183 10 k. Azerbaijani balalian, shar and caz (stringed instruments), zurna and drum 25 15
6184 10 k. Georgian bagpipes, tambourine, flute, pipes and chonguri (stringed instrument) 25 15
6185 10 k. Kazakh flute, rattle, daubra and kobyz (stringed instruments) 25 15
6186 10 k. Lithuanian bagpipes, horns and kankles . . . 25 15

1990. Marine Mammals.
6187 25 k. Type **2495** 55 30
6188 25 k. Northern sealions . . . 55 30
6189 25 k. Sea otter 55 30
6190 25 k. Common dolphin . . . 55 30

2496 "Lenin among Delegates to Second Congress of Soviets" (S. V. Gerasimov)

2497 Ivan Bunin (1933)

1990. 73rd Anniv of October Revolution.
6191 **2496** 5 k. multicoloured . . . 15 10

1990. Nobel Prize Winners for Literature.
6192 **2497** 15 k. brown 35 20
6193 – 15 k. brown 35 20
6194 – 15 k. black 35 20
DESIGNS: No. 6193, Mikhail Sholokhov (1965); No. 6194, Boris Pasternak.

2498 "Sever-2"

1990. Research Submarines. Multicoloured.
6195 5 k. Type **2498** 15 10
6196 10 k. "Tinro-2" 25 15
6197 15 k. "Argus" 35 20
6198 25 k. "Paisis" 55 30
6199 35 k. "Mir" . . . . 1·10 65

2499 "Motherland" Statue (E. Kocher), Screen and Emblem

Филателистическая выставка „Армения-90" (2500)

Восстановление, милосердие, помощь (2501)

1990. "Armenia '90" Stamp Exhibition, Yerevan. (a) Type **2499**.
6200 **2499** 10 k. multicoloured . . 25 15
(b) Nos. 5957/9 optd with T **2500** or as T **2501**.
6201 **2500** 20 k. + 10 k. mult . . 30 35
6202 **2501** 30 k. + 15 k. mult . . 45 50
6203 50 k. + 25 k. mult . . 75 50

2502 S. A. Vaupshasov

2503 Soviet and Japanese Flags above Earth

1990. Intelligence Agents.
6204 **2502** 5 k. deep green, green and black 15 10
6205 – 5 k. deep brown, brown and black 15 10
6206 – 5 k. deep blue, blue and black 15 10
6207 – 5 k. brown, buff & blk 15 10
6208 – 5 k. brown, bistre and black 15 10
DESIGNS: No. 6205, R. I. Abel; No. 6206, Kim Philby; No. 6207, I. D. Kudrya; No. 6208, K. T. Molodyi.

1990. Soviet–Japanese Space Flight.
6209 **2503** 20 k. multicoloured . . 20 25

2504 Grandfather Frost and Toys

1990. New Year.
6210 **2504** 5 k. multicoloured . . 15 10

2505 "Unkrada"

1990. Soviet Culture Fund. Paintings by N. K. Rerikh. Multicoloured.
6211 10 k. + 5 k. Type **2505** . . 35 20
6212 20 k. + 10 k. "Pskovo-Pechorsky Monastery" . . 30 35

2507 Globe, Eiffel Tower and Flags

1990. "Charter for New Europe". Signing of European Conventional Arms Treaty, Paris.
6214 **2507** 30 k. multicoloured . . 30 35

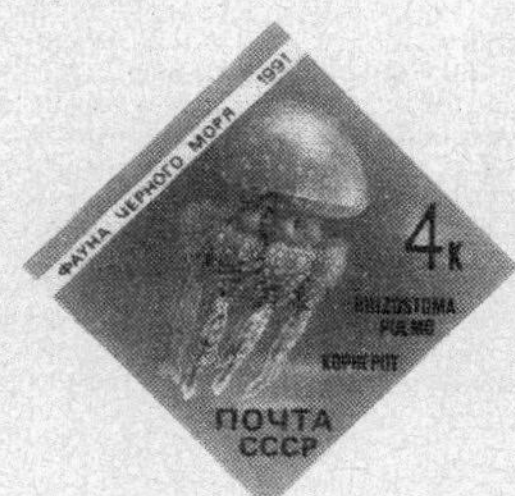

2508 Jellyfish

1991. Marine Animals. Multicoloured.
6215 4 k. Type **2508** 15 10
6216 5 k. Anemone 15 10
6217 10 k. Atlantic spiny dogfish . 25 15
6218 15 k. European anchovy . . 30 20
6219 20 k. Bottle-nosed dolphin . . 45 25

2509 Keres

1991. 75th Birth Anniv of Paul Keres (chess player).
6220 **2509** 15 k. brown 35 20

2510 Radioactive Particles killing Vegetation

1991. 5th Anniv of Chernobyl Nuclear Power Station Disaster.
6221 **2510** 15 k. multicoloured . . 35 20

2511 "Sorrento Coast with View of Capri" (Shchedrin)

1991. Birth Bicentenary of Silvestr Shchedrin and 150th Birth Anniv of Arkhip Kuindzhi (painters). Multicoloured.
6222 10 k. Type **2511** 25 15
6223 10 k. "New Rome. View of St. Angelo's Castle" (Shchedrin) 25 15
6224 10 k. "Evening in the Ukraine" (Kuindzhi) 25 15
6225 10 k. "Birch Grove" (Kuindzhi) 25 15

2512 White Stork

1991. Zoo Relief Fund.
6226 **2512** 10 k. + 5 k. mult . . . 35 20

2513 Fish and Bell Tower, Volga

1991. Environmental Protection. Multicoloured.
6227 10 k. Type **2513** 25 15
6228 15 k. Sable and Lake Baikal . 35 20
6229 20 k. Saiga and dried bed of Aral Sea 45 25

1991. Historical Monuments (3rd series). As T **2464**. Multicoloured.
6231 15 k. Minaret, Uzgen, Kirgizia 35 20
6232 15 k. Mohammed Bashar Mausoleum, Tadzhikistan . 35 20
6233 15 k. Talkhatan-baba Mosque, Turkmenistan 35 20

2515 G. Shelikhov and Kodiak, 1784

1991. 500th Anniv of Discovery of America by Columbus. Russian Settlements.
6234 **2515** 20 k. blue and black . . 45 25
6235 – 30 k. bistre, brown and black 65 35
6236 – 50 k. orange, brown and black . . . . 1·00 50
DESIGNS: 30 k. Aleksandr Baranov and Sitka, 1804; 50 k. I. Kuskov and Fort Ross, California, 1812.

2516 Satellite and Liner

2517 Yuri Gagarin in Uniform

1991. 10th Anniv of United Nations Transport and Communications in Asia and the Pacific Programme.
6237 **2516** 10 k. multicoloured . . . 20 10

1991. Cosmonautics Day. 30th Anniv of First Man in Space. Each brown.
6238 25 k. Type **2517** 15 25
6239 25 k. Gagarin wearing space suit 15 25
6240 25 k. Gagarin in uniform with cap 15 25
6241 25 k. Gagarin in civilian dress 15 25

2519 "May 1945" (A. and S. Tkachev)

1991. Victory Day.
6244 **2519** 5 k. multicoloured . . . 10 10

2520 "Lenin working on Book 'Materialism and Empirical Criticism' in Geneva Library" (P. Belousov)

1991. 121st Birth Anniv of Lenin.
6245 **2520** 5 k. multicoloured . . . 10 10

2521 Prokofiev

1991. Birth Centenary of Sergei Prokofiev (composer).
6246 **2521** 15 k. brown 30 15

2522 "Cypripedium calceolus"

2523 Ilya I. Mechnikov (medicine, 1908)

1991. Orchids. Multicoloured.
6247 3 k. Type **2522** 10 10
6248 5 k. "Orchis purpurea" . . . 10 10
6249 10 k. "Ophrys apifera" . . . 15 10
6250 20 k. "Calypso bulbosa" . . 15 20
6251 25 k. "Epipactis palustris" . . 15 25

1991. Nobel Prize Winners. Each black.
6252 15 k. Type **2523** 30 15
6253 15 k. Ivan P. Pavlov (medicine, 1904) 30 15
6254 15 k. A. D. Sakharov (physics, 1975) 30 15

2524 Soviet and British Flags in Space

1991. Soviet–British Space Flight.
6255 **2524** 20 k. multicoloured . . 15 20

2525 Saroyan

1991. 10th Death Anniv of William Saroyan (writer).
6256 **2525** 1 r. multicoloured . . . 65 40

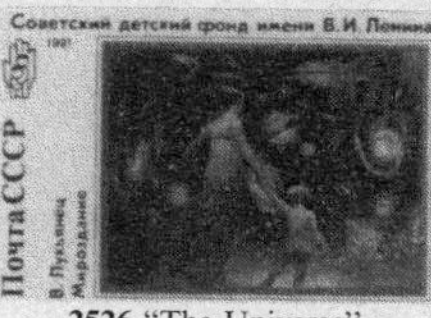

2526 "The Universe"

1991. Lenin Soviet Children's Fund. Paintings by V. Lukyanets. Multicoloured.
6257 10 k. Type **2526** 20 10
6258 10 k. "Another Planet" . . . 20 10

INDEX

Countries can be quickly located by referring to the index at the end of this volume.

2527 Miniature from "Ostromirov Gospel" (first book written in Cyrillic), 1056–57

1991. Culture of Medieval Russia. Multicoloured.
6259 10 k. Type **2527** 15 10
6260 15 k. Page from "Russian Truth" (code of laws), 11th-13th century 15 10
6261 20 k. Portrait of Sergy Radonezhsky (embroidered book cover), 1424 . . . . 15 20
6262 25 k. "The Trinity" (icon, Andrei Rublev), 1411 . . . 15 25
6263 30 k. Illustration from "Book of the Apostles", 1564 . . . . 20 30

2528 Pintails 2529 Emblem

1991. Ducks (3rd series). Multicoloured.
6264 5 k. Type **2528** 10 10
6265 15 k. Greater scaups 30 15
6266 20 k. White-headed ducks . . 40 20

1991. European Conference on Security and Co-operation Session, Moscow.
6267 **2529** 10 k. multicoloured . . 20 10

2530 Patroness 2531 Woman in Traditional Costume

1991. Soviet Charity and Health Fund.
6268 **2530** 20 k. + 10 k. mult . . 20 30

1991. 1st Anniv of Declaration of Ukrainian Sovereignty.
6269 **2531** 30 k. multicoloured . . 20 30

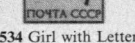

2532 "Albatross" 2534 Girl with Letter

2533 "Sv. Pyotr" and Route Map

1991. Airships. Multicoloured.
6270 1 k. Type **2532** 10 10
6271 3 k. GA-42 . . . . 15 10
6272 4 k. N.1 "Norge" (horiz) . . 15 10
6273 5 k. "Pobeda" (horiz) 15 10
6274 20 k. "Graf Zeppelin" (horiz) 55 20

1991. 250th Anniv of Bering's and Chirkov's Expedition. Multicoloured.
6275 30 k. Type **2533** 60 30
6276 30 k. Sighting land 60 30

1991. Letter Writing Week.
6277 **2534** 7 k. brown 15 10

2535 Bell and Bell Towers 2536 Kayak Race and "Santa Maria"

1991. Soviet Culture Fund.
6278 **2535** 20 k. + 10 k. mult . . 20 30

1991. Olympic Games, Barcelona (1992) (1st issue). Multicoloured.
6279 10 k. Type **2536** 10 10
6280 20 k. Running and Barcelona Cathedral 15 20
6281 30 k. Football and stadium . 20 30
See also Nos. 6358/61.

2537 Rainbow, Globe and Flags 2538 Ascension Day (Armenia)

1991. Soviet–Austrian Space Flight.
6282 **2537** 20 k. multicoloured . . 15 20

1991. Folk Festivals. Multicoloured.
6283 15 k. Type **2538** 30 15
6284 15 k. Women carrying dishes of wheat (Novruz holiday, Azerbaijan) 30 15
6285 15 k. Throwing garlands in water (Ivan Kupala summer holiday, Byelorussia) . . . 30 15
6286 15 k. Stick wrestling and dancing round decorated tree (New Year, Estonia) (horiz) 30 15
6287 15 k. Masked dancers (Berikaoba spring holiday, Georgia) 30 15
6288 15 k. Riders with goat skin (Kazakhstan) (horiz) . . . 30 15
6289 15 k. Couple on horses (Kirgizia) (horiz) 30 15
6290 15 k. Couple leaping over flames (Ligo (Ivan Kupala) holiday, Latvia) (horiz) . . 30 15
6291 15 k. Family on way to church (Palm Sunday, Lithuania) (horiz) 30 15
6292 15 k. Man in beribboned hat and musicians (Plugusorul (New Year) holiday, Moldova) 30 15
6293 15 k. Sledge ride (Shrovetide, Russia) 30 15
6294 15 k. Musicians on carpet and stilt-walkers (Novruz holiday, Tadzikistan) 30 15
6295 15 k. Wrestlers (Harvest holiday, Turkmenistan) (horiz) 30 15
6296 15 k. Dancers and couple with lute and tambourine (Christmas, Ukraine) (horiz) 30 15
6297 15 k. Girls with tulips (Tulip holiday, Uzbekistan) . . . 30 15

2539 Dimitry Komar 2540 Federation Government House and Flag

1991. Defeat of Attempted Coup. Multicoloured.
6298 7 k. Type **2539** 15 10
6299 7 k. Ilya Krichevsky 15 10
6300 7 k. Vladimir Usov 15 10
Nos. 6298/6300 depict victims killed in opposing the attempted coup.

1991. Election of Boris Yeltsin as President of the Russian Federation.
6302 **2540** 7 k. blue, gold and red 15 10

1991. Traditional Musical Instruments (3rd series). As T **2455**. Multicoloured.
6303 10 k. Kirgiz flutes, komuzes and kyyak (string instruments) 20 10
6304 10 k. Latvian ganurags and stabule (wind), tambourine, duga and kokle (string instruments) 20 10
6305 10 k. Moldavian flute, bagpipes, nai (pipes), kobza and tsambal (string instruments) 20 10

2541 Decorations and Gifts 2542 Nikolai Mikhailovich Karamzin

1991. New Year.
6306 **2541** 7 k. multicoloured . . . 15 10

1991. Historians' Birth Anniversaries. Mult.
6307 10 k. Type **2542** (225th anniv) 20 10
6308 10 k. V. O. Klyuchevsky (150th anniv) 20 10
6309 10 k. S. M. Solovev (171st anniv) 20 10
6310 10 k. V. N. Tatishchev (after A. Osipov) (305th anniv) . 20 10

2543 Cross-country Skiing and Ski Jumping 2546 Golden Gate, Vladimir

1992. Winter Olympic Games, Albertville. Mult.
6311 14 k. Type **2543** 10 15
6312 1 r. Aerobatic skiing 35 35
6313 2 r. Two and four-man bobsleighs 65 65

1992.

6317	**2546**	10 k. orange	10	10
6318	–	15 k. brown	10	10
6319	–	20 k. red	10	10
6320	–	25 k. red	10	10
6321	–	30 k. black	10	10
6322	–	50 k. black	10	10
6323	–	55 k. turquoise	10	10
6324	–	60 k. green	10	10
6324a	–	80 k. purple	15	10
6325	–	1 r. brown	20	10
6326	–	1 r. 50 green	30	15
6327	–	2 r. blue	40	20
6328	–	3 r. red	15	10
6328a	–	4 r. brown	10	10
6329	–	5 r. brown	45	20
6329a	–	6 r. blue	10	10
6330	–	10 r. blue	45	45
6330a	–	15 r. brown	30	15
6331	–	25 r. red	1·10	1·10
6332	–	45 r. blue	80	40
6341	–	50 r. violet	15	15
6333	–	75 r. brown	1·60	80
6334	–	100 r. green	2·00	1·00
6334a	**2546**	150 r. blue	10	10
6342	–	250 r. green	35	15
6334c	–	300 r. red	10	10
6347	–	500 r. red	65	35

DESIGNS: 15 k. Pskov Kremlin; 20, 50 k. St. George killing dragon; 25, 55 k. Victory Arch, Moscow; 30, 80 k. "Millenium of Russia" monument (M. Mikeshin), Novgorod; 60 k., 300 r. Minin and Pozharsky Statue, Moscow; 1, 4 r. Church, Kizki; 1 r. 50, 6 r. Statue of Peter I, St. Petersburg; 2 r. St. Basil's Cathedral, Moscow; 3 r. Tretyakov Gallery, Moscow; 5 r. Morosov House, Moscow; 10 r. St. Isaac's Cathedral, St. Petersburg; 15, 45 r. "The Horse Tamer", St. Petersburg; 25, 75 r. Yuri Dolgoruky Monument, Moscow; 50 r. Rostov Kremlin; 100 r. Moscow Kremlin; 250 r. Church, Bogulyubov; 500 r. Lomonosov University, Moscow.

2547 "Victory" (N. N. Baskakov) 2548 Wood Grouse, Oak and Pine

1992. 47th Anniv of Victory in Second World War.
6350 **2547** 5 k. multicoloured . . . 10 10

1992. Prioksko–Terrasnyi Nature Reserve.
6351 **2548** 50 k. multicoloured . . . 10 10

2549 "Mir" Space Station, Flags and Cosmonauts 2551 Pinocchio

1992. Russian–German Joint Space Flight.
6352 **2549** 5 r. multicoloured . . . 40 30

1992. Characters from Children's Books (1st series). Multicoloured.
6354 25 k. Type **2551** 10 10
6355 30 k. Cipollino 10 10
6356 35 k. Dunno 10 10
6357 50 k. Karlson 10 10
See also Nos. 6391/5.

2552 Russian Cosmonaut and Space Shuttle 2553 Handball

1992. International Space Year. Multicoloured.
6358 25 r. Type **2552** 65 35
6359 25 r. American astonaut and "Mir" space station . . . 65 35
6360 25 r. "Apollo" and "Vostok" spacecraft and sputnik . . 65 35
6361 25 r. "Soyuz", "Mercury" and "Gemini" spacecraft . . . 65 35
Nos. 6344/47 were issued together, se-tenant, forming a composite design.

1992. Olympic Games, Barcelona (2nd issue).
6362 **2553** 1 r. multicoloured . . . 20 10
6363 – 2 r. red, blue & black . 40 20
6364 – 3 r. red, green & black . 35 35
DESIGNS—HORIZ: 2 r. Fencing; 3 r. Judo.

2554 L. A. Zagoskin and Yukon River, Alaska, 1842–44

1992. Expeditions. Multicoloured.
6365 55 k. Type **2554** 10 10
6366 70 k. N. N. Miklukho-Maklai in New Guinea, 1871–74 . . . 15 10
6367 1 r. G. I. Langsdorf and route map of expedition to Brazil, 1822–28 . . . . 20 10

2555 Garganeys

1992. Ducks (4th series). Multicoloured.
6368 1 r. Type **2555** 15 10
6369 2 r. European pochards . . . 20 10
6370 3 r. Falcated teals 30 35

2556 "Taj Mahal Mausoleum in Agra"

1992. 150th Birth Anniv of Vasily Vasilevich Vereshchagin (painter).
6371 1 r. 50 Type **2556** 30 15
6372 1 r. 50 "Don't Touch, Let Me Approach!" 30 15

HAVE YOU READ THE NOTES AT THE BEGINNING OF THIS CATALOGUE?
These often provide the answers to the enquiries we receive.

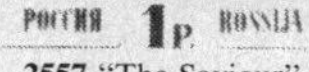

2557 "The Saviour" (icon, Andrei Rublev)   2558 Cathedral of the Assumption

1992.
6373 **2557** 1 r. multicoloured . . . 20 10

1992. Moscow Kremlin Cathedrals. Multicoloured.
6374 1 r. Type **2558** 20 10
6375 1 r. Cathedral of the Annunciation (15th century) 20 10
6376 1 r. Archangel Cathedral (16th century) 20 10
See also Nos. 6415/17 and 6440/2.

2559 Russian "Nutcracker" Puppets   2560 "Meeting of Joachim and Anne"

1992. Centenary of First Production of Tchaikovsky's "Nutcracker" Ballet. Multicoloured.
6377 10 r. Type **2559** 35 15
6378 10 r. German "Nutcracker" puppets 35 15
6379 25 r. Pas de deux from ballet 85 40
6380 25 r. Dance of the toys . . . 85 40

1992. Icons. Multicoloured.
6381 10 r. Type **2560** 50 45
6382 10 r. "Madonna and Child" . 50 45
6383 10 r. "Archangel Gabriel" (head) 50 45
6384 10 r. "Saint Nicolas" (½-length portrait) 50 45

2561 Clockface and Festive Symbols   2562 "Discovery of America" Monument (Z. Tsereteli)

1992. New Year.
6385 **2561** 50 k. multicoloured . . 10 10

1992. 500th Anniv of Discovery of America by Columbus.
6386 **2562** 15 r. multicoloured . . 70 70

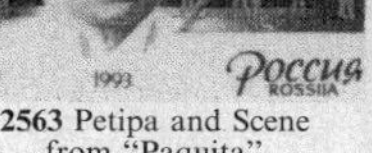

2563 Petipa and Scene from "Paquita"   2564 Scrub 'n' Rub

1993. 175th Birth Anniv of Marius Petipa (choreographer). Multicoloured.
6387 25 r. Type **2563** 20 10
6388 25 r. "Sleeping Beauty", 1890 20 10
6389 25 r. "Swan Lake", 1895 . . 20 10
6390 25 r. "Raimunda", 1898 . . 20 10

1993. Characters from Children's Books (2nd series). Illustrations by Kornei Chukovsky. Mult.
6391 2 r. Type **2564** 10 10
6392 3 r. Big Cockroach 15 10
6393 10 r. The Buzzer Fly 20 10
6394 15 r. Doctor Doolittle . . . 30 15
6395 25 r. Barmalei 55 30
Nos. 6391/5 were issued together, se-tenant, forming a composite design.

2565 Castle   2566 Part of Diorama in Belgorod Museum

1993. 700th Anniv of Vyborg.
6396 **2565** 10 r. multicoloured . . 35 25

1993. Victory Day. 50th Anniv of Battle of Kursk.
6397 **2566** 10 r. multicoloured . . 35 20

2567 African Violet   2568 "Molniya 3"

1993. Pot Plants. Multicoloured.
6398 10 r. Type **2567** 20 10
6399 15 r. "Hibiscus rosa-sinensis" 25 15
6400 25 r. "Cyclamen persicum" . 55 30
6401 50 r. "Fuchsia hybrida" . . 1·10 55
6402 100 r. "Begonia semperflorens" 1·90 1·10

1993. Communications Satellites. Multicoloured.
6403 25 r. Type **2568** 20 10
6404 45 r. "Ekran M" 35 15
6405 50 r. "Gorizont" 85 25
6406 75 r. "Luch" . . . . 1·25 35
6407 100 r. "Ekspress" . . . . . 1·60 75

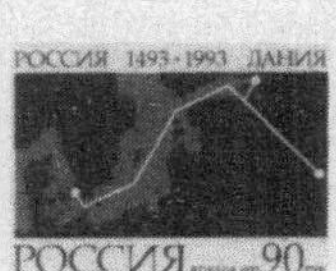

2569 Snuff Box (Dmitry Kolesnikov and Tankard)   2570 Map

1993. Silverware. Multicoloured.
6409 15 r. Type **2569** 10 10
6410 25 r. Teapot 40 10
6411 45 r. Vase 75 35
6412 75 r. Tray and candlestick . 1·25 55
6413 100 r. Cream jug, coffee pot and sugar basin (Aleksandr Kordes) . . . . 1·60 75

1993. Novgorod Kremlin. As T **2558**. Mult.
6415 25 r. Kukui and Knyazhaya Towers (14th–17th century) 20 10
6416 25 r. St. Sophia's Cathedral (11th century) 20 10
6417 25 r. St. Sophia belfry (15th–18th century) 20 10

1993. Inauguration of Denmark–Russia Submarine Cable and 500th Anniv of Friendship Treaty.
6419 **2570** 90 r. green & dp green 50 25

2571 Steller's Eider

1993. Ducks (5th series). Multicoloured.
6420 90 r. Type **2571** 55 25
6421 100 r. Eider 35 30
6422 250 r. King eider 90 45

2572 Ringed Seal

1993. Sea Animals. Multicoloured.
6423 50 r. Type **2572** 25 15
6424 60 r. "Paralithodes brevipes" (crab) 30 15
6425 90 r. "Todarodes pacificus" (squid) 50 25
6426 100 r. Salmon trout 50 30
6427 250 r. Fulmar 90 45

2573 Ceramic Candlestick, Skopino   2574 Banknotes and Coins

1993. Traditional Art. Multicoloured.
6428 50 r. Type **2573** 30 15
6429 50 r. Painted tray with picture "Summer Troika", Zhostovo (horiz) 30 15
6430 100 r. Painted box, lid and distaff, Gorodets 55 30
6431 100 r. Enamel icon of St. Dmitry of Solun, Rostov . 55 30
6432 250 r. "The Resurrection" (lacquer miniature), Fedoskino . . . . 1·00 50

1993. 175th Anniv of Goznak (State printing works and mint).
6433 **2574** 100 r. multicoloured . . 25 35

2575 Peter I and "Goto Predestinatsiya"

1993. 300th Anniv of Russian Navy (1st issue). Mult.
6434 100 r. Type **2575** 15 10
6435 100 r. K. A. Shilder and first all-metal submarine 15 10
6436 100 r. I. A. Amosov and "Arkhimed" (frigate) . . . 15 10
6437 100 r. I. G. Bubnov and "Bars" (submarine) 15 10
6438 100 r. B. M. Malinin and "Dekabrist" (submarine) . 15 10
6439 100 r. A. I. Maslov and "Kirov" (cruiser) 15 10
See also Nos. 6502/5.

1993. Moscow Kremlin. As T **2558**. Mult.
6440 100 r. Faceted Hall (15th century) 20 10
6441 100 r. Church of the Deposition of the Virgin's Robe (15th century) 20 10
6442 100 r. Grand Palace (17th century) 20 10

2576 Tiger   2577 Splash of Blood on Figure

1993. The Tiger. Multicoloured.
6443 50 r. Type **2576** 10 10
6444 100 r. Tiger in undergrowth . 20 10
6445 250 r. Two tigers 45 25
6446 500 r. Tiger in snow 65 45

1993. Anti-AIDS Campaign.
6447 **2577** 90 r. multicoloured . . . 20 10

2578 Seasonal Decorations

1993. New Year.
6448 **2578** 25 r. multicoloured . . . 10 10

2579 Indian Elephant

1993. Animals. Multicoloured.
6449 250 r. Type **2579** 40 20
6450 250 r. Japanese white-necked crane 40 20
6451 250 r. Giant panda 40 20
6452 250 r. American bald eagle . 40 20
6453 250 r. Dall's porpoise 40 20
6454 250 r. Koala 40 20
6455 250 r. Hawaiian monk seal . 40 20
6456 250 r. Grey whale 40 20

2580 Rimsky-Korsakov and Scene from "Sadko"

1994. 150th Birth Anniv of Nikolai Rimsky-Korsakov (composer). Scenes from his operas. Multicoloured.
6457 250 r. Type **2580** 40 20
6458 250 r. "The Golden Cockerel" 40 20
6459 250 r. "The Tsar's Bride" . . 40 20
6460 250 r. "The Snow Maiden" . 40 20

2581 "Epiphyllum peacockii"   2582 York Minster, Great Britain

1994. Cacti. Multicoloured.
6461 50 r. Type **2581** 10 10
6462 100 r. "Mammillaria swinglei" 20 10
6463 100 r. "Lophophora williamsii" 20 10
6464 250 r. "Opuntia basilaris" . . 40 20
6465 250 r. "Selenicereus grandiflorus" 40 20

1994. Churches. Multicoloured.
6466 150 r. Type **2582** 30 15
6467 150 r. Church, Athens . . . 30 15
6468 150 r. Roskilde Cathedral, Denmark 30 15
6469 150 r. Notre Dame Cathedral, Paris 30 15
6470 150 r. St. Peter's, Vatican City 30 15
6471 150 r. Cologne Cathedral, Germany 30 15
6472 150 r. Seville Cathedral, Spain 30 15
6473 150 r. St. Basil's Cathedral, Moscow 30 15
6474 150 r. St. Patrick's Cathedral, New York 30 15

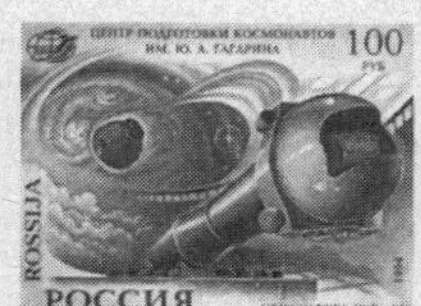

2583 "Soyuz" entering Earth's Atmosphere and "TsF-18" Centrifuge

1994. Yuri Gagarin Cosmonaut Training Centre. Multicoloured.
6475 100 r. Type **2583** 10 10
6476 250 r. "Soyuz"–"Mir" space complex and "Mir" simulator 30 15
6477 500 r. Cosmonaut on space walk and hydrolaboratory . . . 60 30

2584 Map and Rocket Launchers (Liberation of Russia)

1994. 50th Anniv of Liberation. Multicoloured.
6478 100 r. Type **2584** 20 10
6479 100 r. Map and airplanes (Ukraine) 20 10
6480 100 r. Map, tank and soldiers (Byelorussia) 20 10

2585 Red Gate, Moscow

1994. Architects' Anniversaries.

6481 **2585** 50 r. sepia, black and brown 10 15
6482 – 100 r. brown, black and flesh 15 10
6483 – 150 r. green, black and olive 20 10
6483 – 300 r. violet, black and grey 45 25

DESIGNS: 50 r. Type **2585** (D. V. Ukhtomsky, death centenary); 100 r. Academy of Sciences, St. Petersburg (Giacomo Quarenghi, 250th birth anniv); 150 r. Trinity Cathedral, St. Petersburg (V. P. Stasov, 225th birth anniv); 300 r. Church of Christ the Saviour, Moscow (K. A. Ton, birth bicentenary).

2586 "Christ and the Sinner"

1994. 150th Birth Anniv of Vasily Dmitrievich Polenev (painter). Multicoloured.

6485 150 r. Type **2586** 25 15
6486 150 r. "Golden Autumn" . . 25 15

2587 European Wigeon

2588 Games Emblem and Runners

1994. Ducks (6th series). Multicoloured.

6487 150 r. Type **2587** 20 10
6488 250 r. Tufted duck 30 15
6489 300 r. Baikal teal 50 25

1994. 3rd Goodwill Games, St. Petersburg.

6490 **2588** 100 r. multicoloured . . 15 10

2589 Pyotr Leonidovich Kapitsa

2591 Design Motifs of First Russian Stamp

2590 Olympic Flag

1994. Physics Nobel Prize Winners' Birth Anniversaries. Each sepia.

6491 150 r. Type **2589** (centenary) 30 15
6492 150 r. Pavel Alekseevich Cherenkov (90th) 30 15

1994. Centenary of International Olympic Committee.

6493 **2590** 250 r. multicoloured . . 30 15

1994. Russian Stamp Day.

6494 **2591** 125 r. multicoloured . . 20 10

2592 Snuff Box (D. Vinogradov)

2593 Centre of Asia Obelisk

1994. 250th Anniv of Imperial (now M. Lomonosov) Porcelain Factory, St. Petersburg. Multicoloured.

6495 50 r. Type **2592** 10 10
6496 100 r. Candlestick 15 10
6497 150 r. "Water-Carrier" (statuette, after S. Pimenov) 20 10
6498 250 r. Sphinx vase 35 20
6499 300 r. "Lady with Mask" (statuette, after K. Somov) 40 20

1994. 50th Anniv of Accession of Tuva to Soviet Union.

6501 **2593** 125 r. mulitcoloured . . 15 10

2594 Vice-Admiral V. M. Golovnin (Kurile Islands, 1811)

1994. 300th Anniv (1993) of Russian Navy (2nd issue). Explorations. Multicoloured.

6502 250 r. Type **2594** 20 10
6503 250 r. Admiral I. F. Kruzenshtern (first Russain round-the-world expedition, 1803–06) 20 10
6504 250 r. Admiral F. P. Vrangel (Alaska, 1829–35) 20 10
6505 250 r. Admiral F. P. Litke (Novaya Zemlya, 1821–24) 20 10

EXPRESS STAMPS

E 171

1932. Inscr "EXPRES".

E588 **E 171** 5 k. sepia . . . . . . 4·00 2·25
E589 – 10 k. purple . . . . 6·00 3·50
E590 – 80 k. green . . . . . 30·00 12·00

DESIGNS—HORIZ: 10 k. Express motor van; 80 k. Steam locomotive.

1932. Air. Airship Construction Fund. Imperf or perf.

E592 **166** 15 k. black . . . . . . 2·75 1·50

POSTAGE DUE STAMPS

Доплата
1 коп.
золотом.
(D 96)

ДОПЛАТА
1 коп.
(D 99)

1924. Surch as Type **D 96**.

D401 **45** 1 k. on 35 k. blue . . . 20 30
D402 3 k. on 35 k. blue . . . 20 30
D403 5 k. on 35 k. blue . . . 20 30
D404 8 k. on 35 k. blue . . . 50 50
D405 10 k. on 35 k. blue . . . 30 60
D406 12 k. on 70 k. brown . . 20 40
D407 14 k. on 35 k. blue . . . 20 40
D408 32 k. on 35 k. blue . . . 90 90
D409 40 k. on 35 k. blue . . . 1·00 90

1924. Surch with Type **D 99**.

D421 **48** 1 k. on 100 r. yellow . . 4·50 10·00

D 104

1925.

D464 **D 104** 1 k. red 25 30
D465 2 k. violet 25 30
D466 3 k. blue 25 30
D467 7 k. yellow 35 30
D468 8 k. green 35 30
D469 10 k. blue 40 50
D470 14 k. brown 60 70

RUSSIAN POST OFFICES IN CHINA Pt.7

Russian Post Offices were opened in various towns in Manchuria and China from 1870 onwards.

1899. 100 kopeks = 1 rouble
1917. 100 cents = 1 dollar (Chinese)

(1)

1899. Arms types (with thunderbolts) of Russia optd with T **1**.

1 **9** 1 k. orange 30 40
2 2 k. green 40 40
3 3 k. red 40 35
9 **14** 4 k. red . . . . 1·25 1·25
4 **9** 5 k. purple 50 50
5 7 k. blue 60 50
6 **14** 10 k. blue 60 50
30 **10** 14 k. red and blue . . . . . 75 1·25
31 15 k. blue and brown . . . . 45 1·00
32 **14** 20 k. red and blue . . . . . 40 1·25
33 **10** 25 k. violet and green . . . 65 1·75
34 35 k. green and purple . . . 70 1·25
35 **14** 50 k. green and purple . . . 85 1·25
36 **10** 70 k. orange and brown . . . 60 1·50
37 **15** 1 r. orange and brown . . . 1·25 1·50
20 **11** 3 r. 50 grey and black . . . 7·50 8·50
21 **20** 5 r. blue and green on grn . . 4·50 5·50
22 **11** 7 r. yellow and black . . . . 8·00 9·00
23 **20** 10 r. grey and red on yellow . 32·00 45·00

1910. Arms types of Russia optd with T **1**.

24 **22** 1 k. orange 35 60
25 2 k. green 40 60
26 3 k. red 30 35
27 **23** 4 k. red 25 50
28 **22** 7 k. blue 35 65
29 **23** 10 k. blue 35 50

1917. Arms types of Russia surch in "cents" and "dollars" diagonally in one line.

42 **22** 1 c. on 1 k. orange . . . . 40 1·50
43 2 c. on 2 k. green . . . . 40 1·50
44 3 c. on 3 k. red . . . . . 50 1·50
45 **23** 4 c. on 4 k. red . . . . . 40 1·50
46 **22** 5 c. on 5 k. lilac . . . . . 75 2·25
47 **23** 10 c. on 10 k. blue . . . . 50 2·25
48 **10** 14 c. on 14 k. red & blue . . 1·00 3·75
49 15 c. on 15 k. blue and pur . 1·00 3·00
50 **14** 20 c. on 20 k. red & blue . . 1·25 2·75
51 **10** 25 c. on 25 k. violet & grn . 1·25 3·00
52 35 c. on 35 k. green & pur . 1·25 3·25
53 **14** 50 c. on 50 k. green & pur . 1·10 3·00
54 **10** 70 c. on 70 k. orange & brn . 1·25 4·50
55 **15** 1 d. on 1 r. orange & brown on brown . . . . 1·25 5·50
39 **10** 3 d. 50 on 3 r. 50 grey and black . . . . 7·00 12·00
40 **20** 5 d. on 5 r. blue and green . 4·50 15·00
41 **11** 7 d. on 7 r. yellow & black . 2·50 10·00
57 **20** 10 d. on 10 r. grey, red and yellow . . . . 20·00 45·00

1920. Arms types of Russia surch in "cents" in two lines. Perf or imperf.

65 **22** 1 c. on 1 k. orange . . . . 7·50 12·00
59 2 c. on 2 k. green . . . . 2·50 10·00
60 3 c. on 3 k. red . . . . . 2·50 10·00
61 **23** 4 c. on 4 k. red . . . . . 7·50 12·00
62 **22** 5 c. on 5 k. lilac . . . . . 8·00 15·00
63 **23** 10 c. on 10 k. blue . . . . 30·00 45·00
64 **22** 10 c. on 10 k. on 7 k. blue . 28·00 45·00

RUSSIAN POST OFFICES IN CRETE Pt.3

(RETHYMNON PROVINCE)

The Russian Postal Service operated from 1 May to 29 July 1899.

4 metallik = 1 grosion (Turkish piastre)

These issues were optd with circular control marks as shown on T **3/4**. Prices are for stamps with these marks, but unused examples without them are known.

1

2

1899. Imperf.

1 **1** 1 m. blue . . . . 38·00 14·00
2 **2** 1 m. green . . . . 10·00 7·50
3 2 m. red £275 £170
4 2 m. green . . . . 10·00 7·50

3

4

1899. Without stars in oval.

5 **3** 1 m. pink . . . . 35·00 28·00
6 2 m. pink . . . . 35·00 28·00
7 1 g. pink . . . . 35·00 28·00
8 1 m. blue . . . . 35·00 28·00
9 2 m. blue . . . . 35·00 28·00
10 1 g. blue . . . . 35·00 28·00
11 1 m. green . . . . 35·00 28·00
12 2 m. green . . . . 35·00 28·00
13 1 g. green . . . . 35·00 28·00
14 1 m. red . . . . 35·00 28·00
15 2 m. red . . . . 35·00 28·00
16 1 g. red . . . . 35·00 28·00
17 1 m. orange . . . . 35·00 28·00
18 2 m. orange . . . . 35·00 28·00
19 1 g. orange . . . . 35·00 28·00
20 1 m. yellow . . . . 35·00 28·00
21 2 m. yellow . . . . 35·00 28·00
22 1 g. yellow . . . . 35·00 28·00
23 1 m. black £550 £550
24 2 m. black £550 £550
25 1 g. black £475 £475

1899. Starred at each side.

26 **4** 1 m. pink . . . . 28·00 18·00
27 2 m. pink . . . . 11·00 5·50
28 1 g. pink . . . . 6·50 4·50
29 1 m. blue . . . . 16·00 9·00
30 2 m. blue . . . . 11·00 5·50
31 1 g. blue . . . . 6·50 4·50
32 1 m. green . . . . 16·00 9·00
33 2 m. green . . . . 11·00 5·50
34 1 g. green . . . . 6·50 4·50
35 1 m. red . . . . 16·00 9·00
36 2 m. red . . . . 11·00 5·50
37 1 g. red . . . . 6·50 4·50

RUSSIAN POST OFFICES IN TURKEY Pt.16

General issues for Russian P.O.s in the Turkish Empire and stamps specially overprinted for use at particular offices.

1863. 100 kopeks = 1 rouble
1900. 40 paras = 1 piastre

1 Inscription = "Dispatch under Wrapper to the East"

1863. Imperf.

2a **1** 6 k. blue £190 £800

2

3

1865. Imperf.

4 **2** (10 pa.) brown and blue . . . £600 £400
5 **3** (2 pi.) blue and red £800 £450

4

5

1865. Imperf.

6 **4** (10 pa.) red and blue . . . . 20·00 35·00
7 **5** (2 pi.) blue and red . . . . . 35·00 42·00

The values of 4/7 were 10 pa. (or 2 k.) and 2 pi. (or 20 k.).

INDEX

Countries can be quickly located by referring to the index at the end of this volume.

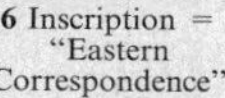
6 Inscription = "Eastern Correspondence"

12

1868. Perf.
14 **6** 1 k. brown . . . . 8·00 4·50
11 3 k. green . . . . 22·00 13·00
16 5 k. blue . . . . 5·50 3·25
17a 10 k. red and green . . . . 4·00 3·25
See also Nos. 26/35.

1876. Surch with large figures of value.
24 **6** 7 k. on 10 k. red and green . 55·00 42·00
22 8 k. on 10 k. red and green . 60·00 55·00

1879.
26 **6** 1 k. black and yellow . . . . 2·25 1·25
32 1 k. orange 50 35
27 2 k. black and red . . . . . 3·00 1·75
33 2 k. green 50 35
34 5 k. purple . . . . 1·25 1·00
28 7 k. red and grey . . . . . . 4·50 1·10
35 7 k. blue 85 35

1900. Arms types of Russia surch in "PARA" or "PIASTRES".
37 **9** 4 pa. on 1 k. orange . . . 15 10
50 **22** 5 pa. on 1 k. orange . . . 10 15
38 **9** 10 pa. on 2 k. green . . . 40 25
51 **22** 10 pa. on 2 k. green . . . 10 15
201 15 pa. on 3 k. red . . . . 20 5·00
41 **14** 20 pa. on 4 k. red 40 40
52 **23** 20 pa. on 4 k. red 10 15
42 **9** 20 pa. on 5 k. purple . . . 40 40
181 **22** 20 pa. on 5 k. purple . . . 10 15
43 **14** 1 pi. on 10 k. blue 20 20
53 **23** 1 pi. on 10 k. blue 10 15
182 **10** 1½ pi. on 15 k. blue & pur . 15 20
183 **14** 2 pi. on 20 k. red and blue 15 20
184 **10** 2½ pi. on 25 k. violet & grn 15 20
185 3½ pi. on 35 k. green & pur 20 30
54 **14** 5 pi. on 50 k. green & lilac 50 75
55 **10** 7 pi. on 70 k. orange & brn 70 90
56 **15** 10 pi. on 1 r. orange and brown on brown . . . . 80 1·10
48 **11** 35 pi. on 3 r. 50 grey and black . . . . 6·00 6·00
202 **20** 50 pi. on 5 r. blue on green 3·25 80·00
49 **11** 70 pi. on 7 r. yellow & blk 9·00 9·00
203 **20** 100 pi. on 10 r. grey and red on yellow . . . . 14·00 £275

1909. As T **14**, **15**, and **11** of Russia, but ship and date in centre as T **12**, and surch in "paras" or "piastres".
57 **14** 5 pa. on 1 k. orange 20 30
58 10 pa. on 2 k. green 30 40
59 20 pa. on 4 k. red 60 75
60 1 pi. on 10 k. blue . . . . . 60 1·10
61 5 pi. on 50 k. green & pur . 1·25 2·50
62 7 pi. on 70 k. orange & brn . 2·50 3·75
63 **15** 10 pi. on 1 r. orange & brn . 3·75 6·50
64 **11** 35 pi. on 3 r. 50 green and purple . . . . 9·00 35·00
65 70 pi. on 7 r. pink & grn . . 22·00 55·00
The above stamps exist overprinted for Constantinople, Jaffa, Jerusalem, Kerassunde, Mount Athos, Salonika, Smyrna, Trebizonde, Beyrouth, Dardanelles, Mytilene and Rizeh. For full list see Part 10 (Russia) of the Stanley Gibbons Catalogue.

1913. Nos. 126/42 (Romanov types) of Russia surch.
186 5 pa. on 1 k. orange 40 40
187 10 pa. on 3 k. green 40 40
188 15 pa. on 3 k. red 40 40
189 20 pa. on 4 k. red 40 40
190 1 pi. on 10 k. blue 40 40
191 1½ pi. on 15 k. brown 60 60
192 2 pi. on 20 k. green 70 70
193 2½ pi. on 25 k. purple . . . . 1·00 1·00
194 3½ pi. on 35 k. green & violet . 2·00 2·00
195 5 pi. on 50 k. grey & brown . 2·25 2·25
196 7 pi. on 70 k. brown & green . 7·00 17·00
197 10 pi. on 1 r. green . . . . . 8·00 17·00
198 20 pi. on 2 r. brown . . . . . 3·25 5·50
199 30 pi. on 3 r. violet . . . . . 4·50 £170
200 50 pi. on 5 r. brown . . . . . 90·00 £475

RWANDA Pt. 14

An independent republic established in July 1962, formerly part of Ruanda-Urundi.

100 centimes = 1 franc

1 Pres. Kayibanda and Map

1962. Independence.
1 **1** 10 c. sepia and green 10 10
2 – 40 c. sepia and purple 10 10
3 **1** 1 f. sepia and blue 70 35
4 – 1 f. 50 sepia and brown . . . 10 10
5 **1** 3 f. 50 sepia and orange . . . 10 10
6 – 6 f. 50 sepia and blue 15 10
7 **1** 10 f. sepia and olive 30 15
8 – 20 f. sepia and red 60 30
DESIGN: Nos. 2, 4, 6, 8, are as Type **1** but with halo around Rwanda on map in place of "R".

1963. Admission to U.N. No. 204 of Ruanda-Urundi with coloured frame obliterating old inscr (colours below), and surch **Admission a l.O.N.U. 18-9-1962 REPUBLIQUE RWANDAISE** and new value.
9 3 f. 50 on 3 f. grey 10 10
10 6 f. 50 on 3 f. pink . . . . . 1·10 90
11 10 f. on 3 f. blue 25 25
12 20 f. on 3 f. silver 40 40

1963. Flowers issue of Ruanda-Urundi (Nos. 178 etc) optd **REPUBLIQUE RWANDAISE** or surch also in various coloured panels over old inscription and values. Flowers in natural colours.
13 25 c. orange and green 20 20
14 40 c. salmon and green 20 20
15 60 c. purple and green 20 20
16 1 f. 25 blue and green 90 90
17 1 f. 50 green and violet 65 65
18 2 f. on 1 f. 50 green and violet 1·40 1·10
19 4 f. on 1 f. 50 green and violet 1·40 1·10
20 5 f. green and purple . . . . . 1·40 1·10
21 7 f. brown and green . . . . . 1·40 1·10
22 10 f. olive and purple . . . . 1·40 1·10
The coloured panels are in various shades of silver except No. 19 which is in blue.

4 Ears of Wheat and Native Implements

1963. Freedom from Hunger.
23 **4** 2 f. brown and green 10 10
24 4 f. mauve and blue 10 10
25 7 f. red and grey 20 10
26 10 f. green and yellow . . . 75 55

5 Coffee

6 Postal Services Emblem

1963. 1st Anniv of Independence.
27 **5** 10 c. brown and blue 10 10
28 – 20 c. yellow and blue 10 10
29 – 30 c. green and orange . . . 10 10
30 **5** 40 c. brown and turquoise . 10 10
31 – 1 f. yellow and purple . . . 10 10
32 – 2 f. green and blue 80 45
33 **5** 4 f. brown and red 10 10
34 – 7 f. yellow and green 20 15
35 – 10 f. green and violet 35 30
DESIGNS: 20 c., 1, 7 f. Bananas; 30 c., 2, 10 f. Tea.

1963. 2nd Anniv of African and Malagasy Posts and Telcommunications Union. As T **56** of Mauritania, but with "AERIENNE" omitted.
36 14 f. multicoloured . . . . . 1·10 90

1963. Admission of Rwanda to U.P.U.
37 **6** 50 c. blue and pink 10 10
38 1 f. 50 brown and blue . . . 65 45
39 3 f. purple and grey 10 10
40 20 f. green and yellow . . . 45 20

7 Emblem

8 Child Care

1963. 15th Anniv of Declaration of Human Rights.
41 **7** 5 f. red 15 10
42 6 f. violet 50 35
43 10 f. blue 35 15

1963. Red Cross Centenary.
44 **8** 10 c. multicoloured 10 10
45 – 20 c. multicoloured 10 10
46 – 30 c. multicoloured 10 10
47 – 40 c. brown, red and violet . 10 10
48 **8** 2 f. multicoloured 80 60
49 – 7 f. multicoloured 15 10
50 – 10 f. brown, red and brown . 20 15
51 – 20 f. brown, red and orange 60 35
DESIGNS—HORIZ: 20 c., 7 f. Patient having blood test; 40, 20 c. Stretcher party. VERT: 30 c., 10 f. Doctor examining child.

9 Map and Hydraulic Pump

10 Boy with Crutch

1964. World Meteorological Day.
52 **9** 3 f. sepia, blue and green . . 10 10
53 7 f. sepia, blue and red . . . 35 20
54 10 f. sepia, blue and orange . 50 35

1964. Stamps of Ruanda-Urundi optd **REPUBLIQUE RWANDAISE** or surch also in black over coloured metallic panels obliterating old inscription or value.
55 10 c. on 20 c. (No. 204) 10 10
56 20 c. (No. 204) 10 10
57 30 c. on 1 f. 50 (No. 208) . . . 10 10
58 40 c. (No. 205) 10 10
59 50 c. (No. 206) 10 10
60 1 f. (No. 207) 10 10
61 2 f. (No. 209) 10 10
62 3 f. (No. 210) 10 10
63 4 f. on 3 f. 50 on 3 f. (No. 228) 20 10
64 5 f. (No. 211) 20 10
65 7 f. 50 on 6 f. 50 (No. 212) . . 45 15
66 8 f. (No. 213) . . . . 4·50 2·25
67 10 f. (No. 214) 65 20
68 20 f. (No. 229) . . . . 1·10 45
69 50 f. (No. 230) . . . . 2·10 85

1964. Gatagara Re-education Centre.
70 **10** 10 c. sepia and violet 10 10
71 – 40 c. sepia and blue 10 10
72 – 4 f. sepia and brown 10 10
73 **10** 7 f. 50 sepia and green . . . 35 15
74 – 8 f. sepia and bistre . . . . 1·40 95
75 – 10 f. sepia and purple . . . 45 20
DESIGNS—HORIZ: 40 c., 8 f. Children operating sewing machines. VERT: 4, 10 f. Crippled child on crutches.

11 Running

1964. Olympic Games, Tokyo. Sportsmen in slate.
76 **11** 10 c. blue 10 10
77 – 20 c. red 10 10
78 – 30 c. turquoise 10 10
79 – 40 c. brown 10 10
80 **11** 4 f. blue 10 10
81 – 5 f. green . . . . 1·40 1·25
82 – 20 f. purple 35 35
83 – 50 f. grey . . . . 1·10 90
DESIGNS—VERT: 20 c., 5 f. Basketball; 40 c., 50 f. Football. HORIZ: 20 f. High-jumping.

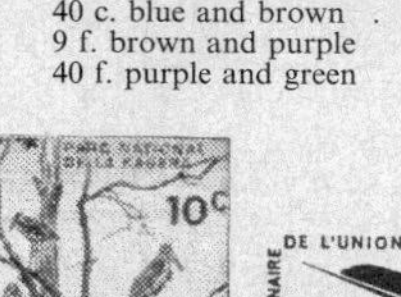

12 Faculties of "Letters" and "Sciences"

13 Abraham Lincoln

1965. National University. Multicoloured.
84 10 c. Type **12** 10 10
85 20 c. Student with microscope and building ("Medicine") 10 10
86 30 c. Scales of Justice, Hand of Law ("Social Sciences" and "Normal High School") . . . 10 10
87 40 c. University buildings . . . 10 10
88 5 f. Type **12** 10 10
89 7 f. As 20 c. 15 10
90 10 f. As 30 c. . . . . 1·00 85
91 12 f. As 40 c. 30 15
The 20 c., 40 c., 7 f. and 12 f. are horiz.

1965. Death Centenary of Abraham Lincoln.
92 **13** 10 c. green and red 10 10
93 20 c. brown and blue 10 10
94 30 c. violet and red 10 10
95 40 c. blue and brown 10 10
96 9 f. brown and purple . . . 20 15
97 40 f. purple and green . . . 1·90 70

14 Marabou Storks

15 "Telstar" Satellite

1965. Kagera National Park. Multicoloured.
98 10 c. Type **14** 10 10
99 20 c. Common zebras 10 10
100 30 c. Impalas 10 10
101 40 c. Crowned cranes, hippopotami and cattle egrets 10 10
102 1 f. African buffaloes 10 10
103 3 f. Hunting dogs 10 10
104 5 f. Yellow baboons . . . . . 4·25 1·10
105 10 f. African elephant and map 20 15
106 40 f. Reed cormorants and African darters 95 35
107 100 f. Lions . . . . 2·25 50
SIZES—As Type **14**: VERT: 30 c., 2, 5 f. HORIZ: 20, 40 c., 3, 10 f. LARGER (45 × 25½ mm); 40, 100 f.

1965. Centenary of I.T.U. Multicoloured.
108 10 c. Type 15 . . . . 10 10
109 40 c. "Syncom" satellite . . . 10 10
110 4 f. 50 Type **15** . . . . 1·40 50
111 50 f. "Syncom" satellite . . . 90 35

16 "Colotis aurigineus"

17 Cattle and I.C.Y. Emblem

1965. Rwanda Butterflies. Multicoloured.
112 10 c. "Papilio bromius" . . . 10 10
113 15 c. "Papilio hesperus" . . . 10 10
114 20 c. Type **16** 10 10
115 30 c. "Amphicallia pactolicus" 10 10
116 35 c. "Lobobunaea phaedusa" 10 10
117 40 c. "Papilio jacksoni ruandana" 10 10
118 1 f. 50 "Papilio dardanus" . . 10 10
119 3 f. "Amaurina elliotti" . . . 2·75 65
120 4 f. "Colias electo pseudohecate" 1·75 55
121 10 f. "Bunaea alcinoe" . . . 35 15
122 50 f. "Athletes gigas" . . . . 1·10 45
123 100 f. "Charaxes ansorgei R" 2·25 65
The 10, 30, 35 c., 3, 4 and 100 f. are vert.

1965. International Co-operation Year.
124 **17** 10 c. green and yellow . . 10 10
125 – 40 c. brown, blue & green . 10 10
126 – 4 f. 50 green, brown & yell 1·10 50
127 – 45 f. purple and brown . . 90 40
DESIGNS: 40 c. Crater lake and giant plants; 4 f. 50, Gazelle and candelabra tree; 45 f. Mt. Ruwenzori. Each with I.C.Y. emblem.

18 Pres. Kennedy, Globe and Satellites

19 Madonna and Child

1965. 2nd Anniv of Pres. Kennedy's Death.
128 **18** 10 c. brown and green . . 10 10
129 40 c. brown and red . . . 10 10
130 50 c. brown and blue . . . 10 10
131 1 f. brown and olive . . . 10 10
132 8 f. brown and violet . . . 1·75 1·10
133 50 f. brown and grey . . . 1·10 90

1965. Christmas.
134 **19** 10 c. green and gold . . . 10 10
135 40 c. brown and gold . . . 10 10
136 50 c. blue and gold 10 10
137 4 f. black and gold 70 65
138 6 f. violet and gold 15 10
139 30 f. brown and gold . . . 65 45

20 Father Damien

1966. World Leprosy Day.
140 **20** 10 c. blue and brown . . . 10 10
141 – 40 c. red and blue 10 10
142 **20** 4 f. 50 slate and green . . 20 15
143 – 45 f. brown and red . . . 1·75 1·25
DESIGNS: 40 c., 45 f. Dr. Schweitzer.

21 Pope Paul, Rome and New York

1966. Pope Paul's Visit to U.N. Organization.

144 **21** 10 c. blue and brown . . . 10 10
145 – 40 c. indigo and blue . . . 10 10
146 **21** 4 f. 50 blue and purple . . 1·60 1·00
147 – 50 f. blue and green . . . . 1·00 55

DESIGNS: 40 c., 50 f. Pope Paul, Arms and U.N. emblem.

22 "Echinops amplexicaulis" and "E. bequaertii"

1966. Flowers. Multicoloured.

148 10 c. Type **22** 10 10
149 20 c. "Haemanthus multiflorus" 10 10
150 30 c. "Helichrysum erici-rosenii" 10 10
151 40 c. "Carissa edulis" 10 10
152 1 f. "Spathodea campanulata" 10 10
153 3 f. "Habenaria praestans" . . 10 10
154 5 f. "Aloe lateritia" . . . . . 3·50 1·90
155 10 f. "Ammocharis tinneana" . 30 20
156 40 f. "Erythrina abyssinica" . 85 50
157 100 f. "Capparis tomentosa" . 1·90 1·10

The 20, 40 c., 1, 3, 5 and 10 f. are vert.

23 W.H.O. Building

1966. Inaug of W.H.O. Headquarters, Geneva.

159 **23** 2 f. olive 10 10
160 3 f. red 20 20
161 5 f. blue 10 10

24 Football

25 Mother and Child within Flames

1966. "Youth and Sports".

162 **24** 10 c. black, blue & green . 10 10
163 – 20 c. black, green & red . . 10 10
164 – 30 c. black, purple & blue . 10 10
165 **24** 40 c. black, green & bistre . 10 10
166 – 9 f. black, purple & grey . 20 10
167 – 50 f. black, blue & purple . 1·10 1·00

DESIGNS: 20 c., 9 f. Basketball; 30 c., 50 f. Volleyball.

1966. Nuclear Disarmament.

168 **25** 20 c. brown, red & mauve . 10 10
169 30 c. brown, red & green . 10 10
170 50 c. brown, red & blue . . 10 10
171 6 f. brown, red & yellow . 10 10
172 15 f. brown, red & turq . . 65 30
173 18 f. brown, red & lavender 65 40

26 Football

27 Yellow-crested Helmet Shrike and Mikeno Volcano

1966. World Cup Football Championships.

174 **26** 20 c. blue and turquoise . . 10 10
175 30 c. blue and violet . . 10 10
176 50 c. blue and green . . 10 10
177 6 f. blue and mauve . . 20 10
178 12 f. blue and brown . . 1·10 35
179 25 f. indigo and blue . . 2·25 60

1966. Rwanda Scenery.

180 **27** 10 c. green 10 10
181 – 40 c. lake 10 10
182 – 4 f. 50 blue 50 40
183 – 55 f. purple 60 45

DESIGNS—VERT: 40 c. Nyamiranga Falls (inscr "Nyamilanga"); 55 f. Rusumo Falls (inscr "Rusumu"). HORIZ: 4 f. 50, Gahinga and Mahubura Volcanoes, and giant plants.

28 U.N.E.S.C.O. and Cultural Emblems

1966. 20th Anniv of U.N.E.S.C.O.

184 **28** 20 c. mauve and blue . . . 10 10
185 – 30 c. turquoise and black . 10 10
186 – 50 c. brown and black . . 10 10
187 – 1 f. violet and black . . . 10 10
188 **28** 5 f. green and brown . . . 10 10
189 – 10 f. brown and black . . 15 10
190 – 15 f. purple and blue . . . 55 35
191 – 50 f. blue and black . . . 65 50

DESIGNS: 30 c., 10 f. "Animal" primer; 50 c., 15 f. Atomic symbol and drill operator; 1, 50 f. Nubian monument partly submerged in the Nile.

29 "Bitis gabonica"

1967. Snakes. Multicoloured.

192 20 c. Head of mamba 10 10
193 30 c. Python 10 10
194 50 c. Type **29** 10 10
195 1 f. "Naja melanoleuca" . . . 10 10
196 3 f. Head of python 10 10
197 5 f. "Psammophis sibilans" . 20 10
198 20 f. "Dendroaspis jamesoni kaimosae" 55 35
199 70 f. "Dasypeltis scabra" . . 65 45

The 30 c., 1, 5, and 70 f. are vert.

30 Girders and Tea Flower

1967. Ntaruka Hydro-electric Project.

200 **30** 20 c. blue and purple . . . 10 10
201 – 30 c. brown and black . . 10 10
202 – 50 c. violet and brown . . 10 10
203 **30** 4 f. purple and green . . 10 10
204 – 25 f. green and violet . . . 50 50
205 – 50 f. brown and blue . . . 1·00 1·00

DESIGNS: 30 c., 25 f. Power conductors and pyrethrum flower; 50 c., 50 f. Barrage and coffee beans.

33 "St. Martin" (Van Dyck)

1967. Paintings.

208 **33** 20 c. black, gold & violet . 10 10
209 – 40 c. black, gold & green . 10 10
210 – 60 c. black, gold and red . 10 10
211 – 80 c. black, gold and blue 10 10
212 **33** 9 f. black, gold and brown 90 50
213 – 15 f. black, gold and red . 35 20
214 – 18 f. black, gold & bronze 35 20
215 – 26 f. black, gold and lake . 45 45

PAINTINGS—HORIZ: 40 c., 15 f. "Rebecca and Eliezer" (Murillo); 80 c., 26 f. "Job and his Friends" (attributed to Il Calabrese). VERT: 60 c., 18 f. "St. Christopher" (D. Bouts).

34 Rwanda "Round Table" Emblem and Common Zebra's Head

1967. Rwanda "Round Table" Fund for Charitable Works. Each with "Round Table" Emblem. Multicoloured.

216 20 c. Type **34** 10 10
217 40 c. African elephant's head . 10 10
218 60 c. African buffalo's head . 10 10
219 80 c. Impala's head 10 10
220 18 f. Ear of wheat 35 15
221 100 f. Palm . . . . 1·60 90

35 "Africa Place" and Dancers

1967. World Fair, Montreal.

222 **35** 20 c. blue and sepia 10 10
223 – 30 c. purple and sepia . . . 10 10
224 – 50 c. orange and sepia . . . 10 10
225 – 1 f. green and sepia 10 10
226 – 3 f. violet and sepia 10 10
227 **35** 15 f. green and sepia . . . 15 15
228 – 34 f. red and sepia 50 40
229 – 40 f. turquoise and sepia . . 70 55

DESIGNS: "Africa Place" (two different views used alternately in order of value); 30 c., 3 f. Drum and handicrafts; 50 c., 40 f. Dancers leaping; 1 f., 34 f. Spears, shields and weapons.

1967. Air. 5th Anniv of U.A.M.P.T. As T **101** of Mauritania.

230 6 f. slate, brown and lake . . . 20 10
231 18 f. purple and brown 65 35
232 30 f. red, green and blue . . . 1·10 65

36 Common Zebra's Head and Lion's Emblem

37 Red Bishop

1967. 50th Anniv of Lions International.

233 **36** 20 c. black, blue and violet . 10 10
234 80 c. black, blue and green . 10 10
235 1 f. black, blue and red . . 10 10
236 8 f. black, blue and brown 20 10
237 10 f. black, blue and ultramarine 30 20
238 50 f. black, blue & green . . 1·10 70

1967. Birds of Rwanda. Multicoloured.

239 20 c. Type **37** 10 10
240 40 c. Woodland kingfisher . . 10 10
241 60 c. Red-billed quelea 10 10
242 80 c. Double-toothed barbet . 10 10
243 2 f. Pin-tailed whydah 15 10
244 3 f. Red-chested cuckoo . . . 20 10
245 18 f. Green wood hoopoe . . . 90 15
246 25 f. Cinnamon-chested bee eater 1·25 25
247 80 f. Regal sunbird . . . . . 3·00 80
248 100 f. Fan-tailed whydah . . . 4·00 95

The 40, 80 c., 3, 25 f. and 100 f. are horiz.

39 Running, and Mexican Antiquites

1968. Olympic Games, Mexico (1st issue). Multicoloured.

250 20 c. Type **39** 10 10
251 40 c. Hammer-throwing . . . 10 10
252 60 c. Hurdling 10 10
253 80 c. Javelin-throwing 10 10
254 8 f. Football (vert) 20 10
255 10 f. Mexican horseman and cacti (vert) 20 10
256 12 f. Hockey (vert) 30 10
257 18 f. Cathedral (vert) 45 15
258 20 f. Boxing (vert) 65 30
259 30 f. Mexico City (vert) . . . 80 35

The 20 c. to 80 c. include Mexican Antiquities in their designs.

41 "Diaphananthe fragrantissima"

1968. Flowers. Multicoloured.

261 20 c. Type **41** 10 10
262 40 c. "Phaeomeria speciosa" . 10 10
263 60 c. "Ravenala madagascariensis" 10 10
264 80 c. "Costus afer" 10 10
265 2 f. Banana flowers 10 10
266 3 f. Flowers and young fruit of pawpaw 10 10
267 18 f. "Clerodendron sp." . . . 35 15
268 25 f. Sweet potato flowers . . 45 30
269 80 f. Baobab flower . . . . . 1·60 80
270 100 f. Passion flower . . . . 1·90 90

42 Horse-jumping

43 Tuareg (Algeria)

1966. Olympic Games, Mexico (2nd issue).

271 **42** 20 c. brown and orange . . 10 10
272 – 40 c. brown and turquoise . 10 10
273 – 60 c. brown and purple . . 10 10
274 – 80 c. brown and blue . . . 10 10
275 – 38 f. brown and red . . . 50 40
276 – 60 f. brown and green . . 1·10 65

SPORTS: 40 c. Judo; 60 c. Fencing; 80 c. High-jumping; 38 f. High-diving; 60 f. Weightlifting. Each design also represents the location of previous Olympics as at left in Type **42**.

1968. African National Costumes (1st series). Multicoloured.

277 30 c. Type 43 . . . . 10 10
278 40 c. Upper Volta 10 10
279 60 c. Senegal 10 10
280 70 c. Rwanda 10 10
281 8 f. Morocco 10 10
282 20 f. Nigeria 35 20
283 40 f. Zambia 80 35
284 50 f. Kenya . . . . 1·10 55

See also Nos. 345/52.

1968. Air. "Philexafrique" Stamp Exhibition, Abidjan (Ivory Coast, 1969) (1st issue). As T **113a** of Mauritania.

286 100 f. "Alexandre Lenoir" (J. L. David) . . . . 3·25 1·60

45 Rwanda Scene and Stamp of Ruanda-Urundi (1953)

1969. Air. "Philexafrique" Stamp Exn (2nd issue).

287 **45** 50 f. multicoloured . . . . 1·90 1·25

46 "The Musical Angels" (Van Eyck)

47 Tuareg Tribesmen

1969. "Paintings and Music". Multicoloured.

288 20 c. Type **46** (postage) . . . 10 10
289 40 c. "The Angels' Concert" (M. Grunewald) 10 10
290 60 c. "The Singing Boy" (Frans Hals) 10 10

291 80 c. "The Lute player" (G. Terborch) 10 10
292 2 f. "The Fifer" (Manet) 10 10
293 6 f. "Young Girls at the Piano" (Renoir) 15 10
294 50 f. "The Music Lesson" (Fragonard) (air) 1·40 85
295 100 f. "Angels playing their Musical Instruments" (Memling) (horiz) 2·75 1·60

1969. African Headdresses (1st series). Multicoloured.
297 20 c. Type **47** 10 10
298 40 c. Young Ovambo woman 10 10
299 60 c. Ancient Guinean and Middle Congo festival headdresses 10 10
300 80 c. Guinean "Dagger" dancer 10 10
301 8 f. Nigerian Muslims 10 10
302 20 f. Luba dancer, Kabondo (Congo) 40 20
303 40 f. Senegalese and Gambian women 85 45
304 80 f. Rwanda dancer 1·90 1·00
See also Nos. 408/15.

48 "The Moneylender and his Wife" (Quentin Metsys)

1969. 5th Anniv of African Development Bank.
305 **48** 30 f. multicoloured on silver 55 50
306 – 70 f. multicoloured on gold 1·60 1·40
DESIGN: 70 f. "The Moneylender and his Wife" (Van Reymerswaele).

50 Pyrethrum
51 Revolutionary

1969. Medicinal Plants. Multicoloured.
308 20 c. Type **50** 10 10
309 40 c. Aloes 10 10
310 60 c. Cola 10 10
311 80 c. Coca 10 10
312 3 f. Hagenia 10 10
313 75 f. Cassia 1·40 80
314 80 f. Cinchona 1·90 90
315 100 f. Tephrosia 2·25 1·10

1969. 10th Anniv of Revolution.
316 **51** 6 f. multicoloured 15 10
317 18 f. multicoloured 50 45
318 40 f. multicoloured 1·00 95

53 "Napoleon on Horseback" (David)

1969. Birth Bicent of Napoleon Bonaparte. Mult. Portraits of Napoleon. Artists name given.
320 20 c. Type **53** 10 10
321 40 c. Debret 10 10
322 60 c. Gautherot 10 10
323 80 c. Ingres 10 10
324 8 f. Pajou 20 15
325 20 f. Gros 55 40
326 40 f. Gros 1·00 55
327 80 f. David 2·25 1·25

54 "The Quarryman" (O. Bonnevalle)

1969. 50th Anniv of I.L.O. Multicoloured.
328 20 c. Type **54** 10 10
329 40 c. "Ploughing" (detail Brueghel's "Descent of Icarus") 10 10
330 60 c. "The Fisherman" (C. Meunier) 10 10
331 80 c. "Ostend Slipway" (J. van Noten) 10 10
332 8 f. "The Cook" (P. Aertsen) 20 10
333 10 f. "Vulcan's Blacksmiths" (Velazquez) 35 15
334 50 f. "Hiercheuse" (C. Meunier) 1·25 60
335 70 f. "The Miner" (P. Paulus) 1·60 80
Nos. 330, 332 and 334/5 are vert.

55 "The Derby at Epsom" (Gericault)

1970. Paintings of Horses. Multicoloured.
336 20 c. Type **55** 10 10
337 40 c. "Horses leaving the Sea" (Delacroix) 10 10
338 60 c. "Charles V at Muhlberg" (Titian) (vert) 10 10
339 80 c. "To the Races, Amateur Jockeys" (Degas) 10 10
340 8 f. "Horsemen at Rest" (Wouwermans) 20 10
341 20 f. "Officer of the Imperial Guard" (Gericault) (vert) 60 30
342 40 f. "Horse and Dromedary" (Bonnevalle) 1·25 45
343 80 f. "The Prodigal Child" (Rubens) 1·60 80

1970. African National Costumes (2nd series). As T **43**. Multicoloured.
345 20 c. Tharaka Meru woman 10 10
346 30 c. Niger flautist 10 10
347 50 c. Tunisian water-carrier 10 10
348 1 f. Kano ceremonial (Nigeria) 10 10
349 3 f. Mali troubador 10 10
350 5 f. Quipongo, Angola women 10 10
351 50 f. Mauritanian at prayer 95 55
352 90 f. Sinehatiali dancers, Ivory Coast 1·75 1·00

58 Footballer attacking Goal

1970. World Cup Football Championships, Mexico.
353 **58** 20 c. multicoloured 10 10
354 – 30 c. multicoloured 10 10
355 – 50 c. multicoloured 10 10
356 – 1 f. multicoloured 10 10
357 – 6 f. multicoloured 10 10
358 – 18 f. multicoloured 45 30
359 – 30 f. multicoloured 60 45
360 – 90 f. multicoloured 1·75 95
Nos. 354/60 show footballers in various positions, similar to Type **58**.

59 Flowers and Green Peafowl

1970. "EXPO 70", World Fair, Osaka, Japan. Multicoloured.
361 20 c. Type **59** 10 10
362 30 c. Torii gate and "Hibiscus" (Yashuda) 10 10
363 50 c. Dancer and "Musician" (Katayama) 10 10
364 1 f. Sun Tower and "Warrior" 10 10
365 3 f. House and "Seated Buddha" 10 10
366 5 f. Pagoda and "Head of Girl" (Yamakawa) 10 10
367 20 f. Greeting and "Imperial Palace" 55 35
368 70 f. Expo emblem and "Horseman" 1·60 90

INDEX

Countries can be quickly located by referring to the index at the end of this volume.

60 Two Young Gorillas

1970. Gorillas of the Mountains.
369 **60** 20 c. black and green 10 10
370 – 40 c. black, brown & pur 10 10
371 – 60 c. black, blue & brown 10 10
372 – 80 c. black, orange & brn 10 10
373 – 1 f. black and mauve 10 10
374 – 2 f. multicoloured 10 10
375 – 15 f. black and sepia 45 20
376 – 100 f. black, brown & bl 2·75 1·60
GORILLA—VERT: 40 c. Squatting; 80 c. Beating chest; 2 f. Eating banana; 100 f. With young. HORIZ: 60 c. Walking; 1 f. With family; 15 f. Heads.

61 Cinchona Bark

1970. 150th Anniv of Discovery of Quinine. Mult.
377 20 c. Type **61** 10 10
378 80 c. Pharmaceutical equipment 10 10
379 1 f. Anopheles mosquito 10 10
380 3 f. Malaria patient and nurse 10 10
381 25 f. "Attack" on mosquito 55 35
382 70 f. Pelletier and Caventou (discoverers of quinine) 1·50 80

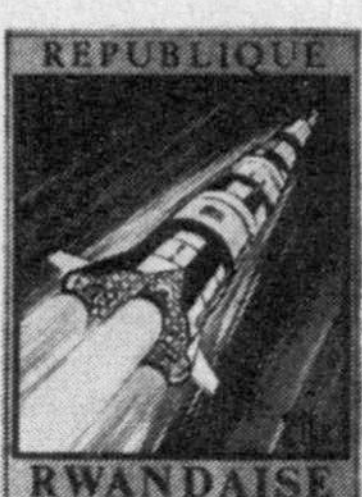

62 Rocket in Flight

1970. Moon Missions. Multicoloured.
383 20 c. Type **62** 10 10
384 30 c. Separation during orbit 10 10
385 50 c. Spaceship above the moon 10 10
386 1 f. Module and astonauts on moon 10 10
387 3 f. Take-off from the moon 10 10
388 5 f. Return journey to earth 15 10
389 10 f. Final separation before landing 30 15
390 80 f. Splashdown 1·75 1·40

63 F. D. Roosevelt and "Brasscattleya olympia alba"
65 Pope Paul VI

1970. 25th Death Anniv of F. D. Roosevelt. Portraits and Orchids.
391 **63** 20 c. brown, blue & black 10 10
392 – 30 c. brown, red and black 10 10
393 – 50 c. brown, orge and blk 10 10
394 – 1 f. brown, green & black 10 10
395 – 2 f. green, brown and black 10 10
396 – 6 f. green, purple and black 20 15
397 – 30 f. green, blue and black 90 40
398 – 60 f. green, red and black 1·60 70
ORCHIDS: 30 c. "Laeliocattleya callistoglossa"; 50 c. "Chondrorrhyncha chestertoni"; 1 f. "Paphiopedilum"; 2 f. "Cymbidium hybride"; 6 f. "Cattleya labiata"; 30 f. "Dendrobium nobile"; 60 f. "Laelia gouldiana".

1970. Centenary of 1st Vatican Council.
400 **65** 10 c. brown and gold 10 10
401 – 20 c. green and gold 10 10
402 – 30 c. lake and gold 10 10
403 – 40 c. blue and gold 10 10
404 – 1 f. violet and gold 10 10
405 – 18 f. purple and gold 50 20
406 – 20 f. orange and gold 60 20
407 – 60 f. brown and gold 1·60 70
POPES: 20 c. John XXIII; 30 c. Pius XII; 40 c. Pius XI; 1 f. Benedict XV; 18 f. Pius X; 20 f. Leo XIII; 60 f. Pius IX.

1971. African Headdresses (2nd series). Multicoloured. As T **47**.
408 20 c. Rendille woman 10 10
409 30 c. Chad woman 10 10
410 50 c. Bororo man (Niger) 10 10
411 1 f. Masai man (Kenya) 10 10
412 5 f. Air girl (Niger) 10 10
413 18 f. Rwanda woman 35 20
414 25 f. Mauritania man 65 35
415 50 f. Rwanda girls 1·25 65

68 "Beethoven" (C. Horneman)
72 "Durer" (self-portrait)

69 Horse-jumping

1971. Birth Cent (1970) of Beethoven. Portraits and funeral scene by various artists. Multicoloured.
418 20 c. Type **68** 10 10
419 30 c. K. Stieler 10 10
420 50 c. F. Schimon 10 10
421 3 f. H. Best 10 10
422 6 f. W. Fassbender 30 10
423 90 f. "Beethoven's Burial" (Stober) 2·10 1·25

1971. Olympic Games, Munich (1972). (1st issue).
424 **69** 20 c. gold and black 10 10
425 – 30 c. gold and purple 10 10
426 – 50 c. gold and violet 10 10
427 – 1 f. gold and green 10 10
428 – 8 f. gold and red 20 10
429 – 10 f. gold and violet 30 15
430 – 20 f. gold and brown 50 30
431 – 60 f. gold and green 1·40 65
DESIGNS: 30 c. Running (start); 50 c. Basketball; 1 f. High-jumping; 8 f. Boxing; 10 f. Pole-vaulting; 20 f. Wrestling; 60 f. Gymnastics.
See also Nos. 490/7.

1971. Air. 10th Anniv of U.A.M.P.T. As T **139a** of Mauritania. Multicoloured.
432 100 f. U.A.M.P.T. H.Q. and Rwandaise woman and child 2·75 1·60

1971. 500th Birth Anniv of Durer. Paintings. Multicoloured.
434 20 c. "Adam" 10 10
435 30 c. "Eve" 10 10
436 50 c. "Portrait of H. Holzschuher" 10 10
437 1 f. "Mourning the Dead Christ" 10 10
438 3 f. "Madonna and Child" 10 10
439 5 f. "St. Eustace" 10 10
440 20 f. "St. Paul and St. Mark" 45 30
441 70 f. Type **72** 1·60 1·00

73 Astonauts in Moon Rover

1972. Moon Mission of "Apollo 15".
442 **73** 600 f. gold 65·00

74 Participation in Sport

1972. National Guard. Multicoloured.
443 4 f. Type **74** 10 10
444 6 f. Transport of emergency supplies 15 10
445 15 f. Helicopter transport for the sick 40 20
446 25 f. Participation in health service 65 35
447 50 f. Guard, map and emblem (vert) 1·25 1·10

75 Ice-hockey

1972. Winter Olympic Games, Sapporo, Japan. Multicoloured.
448 20 c. Type **75** 10 10
449 30 c. Speed-skating 10 10
450 50 c. Ski-jumping 10 10
451 1 f. Figure Skating 10 10
452 6 f. Cross-country skiing . . . 10 10
453 12 f. Slalom 15 15
454 20 f. Tobogganing 45 20
455 60 f. Downhill skiing . . . . 1·40 1·10

76 Savanna Monkey and Impala

1972. Akagera National Park. Multicoloured.
456 20 c. Type **76** 10 10
457 30 c. African buffalo 10 10
458 50 c. Common zebra 10 10
459 1 f. White rhinoceros 10 10
460 2 f. Warthogs 10 10
461 6 f. Hippopotamus 15 10
462 18 f. Spotted hyenas 30 20
463 32 f. Helmet guineafowl . . . 2·00 60
464 60 f. Waterbucks . . . . 1·60 1·10
465 80 f. Lion and lioness . . . . 2·25 1·60

77 Family supporting Flag

78 Variable Sunbirds

1972. 10th Anniv of Referendum.
466 **77** 6 f. multicoloured 10 10
467 18 f. multicoloured 45 35
468 60 f. multicoloured . . . . 1·25 1·10

1972. Rwanda Birds. Multicoloured.
469 20 c. Common waxbills . . . 15 10
470 30 c. Collared sunbird 15 10
471 50 c. Type **78** 15 10
472 1 f. Greater double-collared sunbird 15 10
473 4 f. Ruwenzori puff-back flycatcher 15 10
474 6 f. Red-billed fire finch . . . 20 15
475 10 f. Scarlet-chested sunbird . . . 50 15
476 18 f. Red-headed quelea . . . 85 30
477 60 f. Black-headed gonolek . . 3·00 1·25
478 100 f. African golden oriole . . 4·25 2·10

79 King Baudouin and Queen Fabiola with President and Mrs. Kayibanda in Rwanda

1972. "Belgica 72" Stamp Exhibition, Brussels.
479 – 18 f. multicoloured 45 45
480 – 22 f. multicoloured 65 55
481 **79** 40 f. blue, black & gold . . 1·10 95
DESIGNS: 18 f. Rwanda village; 22 f. View of Bruges.
Nos. 479/80 are smaller, size 39 × 36 mm.

80 Announcement of Independence

1972. 10th Anniv of Independence.
482 **80** 20 c. green and gold . . . 10 10
483 – 30 c. purple and gold . . . 10 10
484 – 50 c. sepia and gold . . . 10 10
485 – 6 f. blue and gold . . . 10 10
486 – 10 f. purple and gold . . . 15 10
487 – 15 f. blue and gold . . . 35 20
488 – 18 f. brown and gold . . . 45 30
489 – 50 f. green and gold . . . 1·10 70
DESIGNS—HORIZ: 30 c. Promotion ceremony, officers of the National Guard; 50 c. Pres. Kayibanda, wife and family; 6 f. Pres. Kayibanda casting vote in legislative elections; 10 f. Pres. and Mrs. Kayibanda at "Festival of Justice"; 15 f. President and members of National Assembly; 18 f. Investiture of Pres. Kayibanda. VERT: 50 f. President Kayibanda.

81 Horse-jumping

1972. Olympic Games, Munich (2nd issue).
490 **81** 20 c. green and gold . . . 10 10
491 – 30 c. violet and gold . . . 10 10
492 – 50 c. green and gold . . . 10 10
493 – 1 f. purple and gold . . . 10 10
494 – 6 f. black and gold . . . 10 10
495 – 18 f. brown and gold . . . 35 30
496 – 30 f. violet and gold . . . 80 55
497 – 44 f. blue and gold . . . 1·10 65
DESIGNS: 30 c. Hockey; 50 c. Football; 1 f. Long-jumping; 6 f. Cycling; 18 f. Yachting; 30 f. Hurdling; 44 f. Gymnastics.

82 Runners

1972. Racial Equality Year. "Working Together". Multicoloured.
498 20 c. Type **82** 10 10
499 30 c. Musicians 10 10
500 50 c. Ballet dancers 10 10
501 1 f. Medical team in operating theatre 10 10
502 6 f. Weaver and painter . . . 10 10
503 18 f. Children in class . . . 35 20
504 24 f. Laboratory technicians . . . 55 35
505 50 f. U.N. emblem and hands of four races . . . . 1·00 65

84 "Phymateus brunneri"

1973. Rwanda Insects. Multicoloured.
507 20 c. Type **84** 10 10
508 30 c. "Diopsis fumipennis" (vert) . 10 10
509 50 c. "Kitoko alberti" . . . 10 10
510 1 f. "Archibracon fasciatus" (vert) 10 10
511 2 f. "Ornithacris cyanea imperialis" 10 10
512 6 f. "Clitodaca fenestralis" (vert) . 15 10
513 18 f. "Senaspis oesacus" . . . 40 20
514 22 f. "Phonoctonus grandis" (vert) 55 35
515 70 f. "Loba leopardina" . . . 1·90 1·25
516 100 f. "Ceratocoris distortus" (vert) . . . . 3·50 2·00

85 "Emile Zola" (Manet)

86 Longombe

1973. International Book Year. "Readers and Writers". Paintings and portraits. Multicoloured.
518 20 c. Type **85** 10 10
519 30 c. "Rembrandt's Mother" (Rembrandt) 10 10
520 50 c. "St. Jerome removing Thorn from Lion's paw" (Colantonio) 10 10
521 1 f. "St. Peter and St. Paul" (El Greco) 10 10
522 2 f. "Virgin and Child" (Van der Weyden) 10 10
523 6 f. "St. Jerome in his Cell" (Antonella de Messina) . . . 15 10
524 40 f. "St. Barbara" (Master of Flemalle) . . . . 1·00 60
525 100 f. "Don Quixote" (O. Bonnevalle) . . . . 2·10 1·60

1973. Musical Instruments. Multicoloured.
527 20 c. Type **86** 10 10
528 30 c. Horn 10 10
529 50 c. "Xylophone" 10 10
530 1 f. "Harp" 10 10
531 4 f. Alur horns 10 10
532 6 f. Horn, bells and drum . . . 10 10
533 18 f. Drums 40 40
534 90 f. Gourds . . . . 2·00 1·40

87 "Rubens and Isabelle Brandt" (Rubens)

88 Map of Africa and Doves

1973. "IBRA" Stamp Exhibition, Munich. Famous Paintings. Multicoloured.
535 20 c. Type **87** 10 10
536 30 c. "Portrait of a Lady" (Cranach the Younger) . . . 10 10
537 50 c. "Woman peeling Turnips" (Chardin) 10 10
538 1 f. "Abduction of the Daughters of Leucippe" (Rubens) . . . 10 10
539 2 f. "Virgin and Child" (Lippi) . 10 10
540 6 f. "Boys eating Fruit" (Murillo) . 20 10
541 40 f. "The Sickness of Love" (Steen) 90 45
542 100 f. "Jesus divested of His Garments" (El Greco) . . . 2·25 1·40

1973. 10th Anniv of O.A.U. Multicoloured.
544 6 f. Type **88** 20 10
545 94 f. Map of Africa and hands . 2·25 1·90

1973. Pan-African Drought Relief. Nos. 308/13 and 315 optd **SECHERESSE SOLIDARITE AFRICAINE** and No. 315 additionally surch.
546 **50** 20 c. multicoloured 10 10
547 – 40 c. multicoloured 10 10
548 – 60 c. multicoloured 10 10
549 – 80 c. multicoloured 10 10
550 – 3 f. multicoloured 10 10
551 – 75 f. multicoloured . . . . 1·60 1·40
552 – 100 f. + 50f. mult . . . . 4·50 4·00

90 "Distichodus sexfasciatus"

1973. Fishes. Multicoloured.
553 20 c. Type **90** 10 10
554 30 c. "Hydrocyon forskalii" . . 10 10
555 50 c. "Synodontis angelicus" . . 10 10
556 1 f. "Tilapia nilotica" . . . 10 10
557 2 f. "Protopterus aethiopicus" . . 10 10
558 6 f. "Pareutropius mandevillei" . 20 10
559 40 f. "Phenacogrammus interruptus" 90 65
560 150 f. "Julidochromis ornatus" . 3·50 2·50

1973. 12th Anniv of U.A.M.P.T. As T **155a** of Mauritania.
562 100 f. blue, brown and mauve . 3·25 3·25

1973. African Fortnight, Brussels. Nos. 408/15 optd **QUINZAINE AFRICAINE BRUXELLES 15/30 SEPT. 1973** and globe.
563 20 c. multicoloured 10 10
564 30 c. multicoloured 10 10
565 50 c. multicoloured 10 10
566 1 f. multicoloured 10 10
567 5 f. multicoloured 10 10
568 18 f. multicoloured 40 20
569 25 f. multicoloured 50 45
570 50 f. multicoloured . . . . 1·40 85

1973. Air. Congress of French-speaking Nations, Liege. No. 432 optd **LIEGE ACCUEILLE LES PAYS DE LANGUE FRANCAISE 1973** (No. 562) or congress emblem (No. 563).
571 100 f. multicoloured . . . . 4·00 2·75
572 100 f. multicoloured . . . . 4·00 2·75

1973. 25th Anniv of Declaration of Human Rights. Nos. 443/7 optd with Human Rights emblem.
574 **74** 4 f. multicoloured 10 10
575 – 6 f. multicoloured 10 10
576 – 15 f. multicoloured 30 15
577 – 25 f. multicoloured 60 40
578 – 50 f. multicoloured . . . . 1·10 70

96 Copernicus and Astrolabe

97 Pres. Habyarimana

1973. 500th Birth Anniv of Copernicus. Mult.
580 20 c. Type **96** 10 10
581 30 c. Copernicus 10 10
582 50 c. Copernicus and heliocentric system 10 10
583 1 f. Type **96** 10 10
584 18 f. As 30 c. 40 30
585 80 f. As 50 c. . . . . 1·60 1·10

1974. "New Regime".
587 **97** 1 f. brown, black and buff . . 10 10
588 2 f. brown, black and blue . . 10 10
589 5 f. brown, black and red . . 10 10
590 6 f. brown, black and blue . . 10 10
591 26 f. brown, black and lilac . . 55 45
592 60 f. brown, black & green . . 1·25 1·00

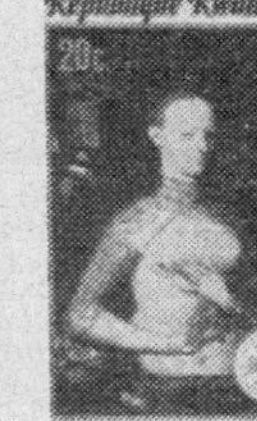

99 Yugoslavia v Zaire

101 "Diane de Poiters" (Fontainebleau School)

100 Marconi's Steam Yacht "Elettra"

1974. World Cup Football Championships, West Germany. Players represent specified teams. Multicoloured.
594 20 c. Type **99** 10 10
595 40 c. Netherlands v Sweden . . 10 10
596 60 c. West Germany v Australia . 10 10
597 80 c. Haiti v Argentina . . . 10 10
598 2 f. Brazil v Scotland . . . 10 10
599 6 f. Bulgaria v Uruguay . . . 10 10
600 40 f. Italy v Poland . . . 80 65
601 50 f. Chile v East Germany . . 1·40 1·00

1974. Birth Centenary of Guglielmo Marconi (radio pioneer). Multicoloured.
602 20 c. Type **100** 20 10
603 30 c. Cruiser "Carlo Alberto" . . 20 10
604 50 c. Marconi's telegraph equipment 10 15
605 4 f. "Global Telecommunications" . . . 10 10
606 35 f. Early radio receiver . . . 85 45
607 60 f. Marconi and Poldhu radio station . . . . 1·50 1·10

1974. International Stamp Exhibitions "Stockholmia" and "Internaba". Paintings from Stockholm and Basle. Multicoloured.
609 20 c. Type **101** 10 10
610 30 c. "The Flute-player" (J. Leyster) 10 10
611 50 c. "Virgin Mary and Child" (G. David) 10 10
612 1 f. "The Triumph of Venus" (F. Boucher) 10 10
613 10 f. "Harlequin Seated" (P. Picasso) 15 10
614 18 f. "Virgin and Child" (15th-century) 35 15
615 20 f. "The Beheading of St. John" (H. Fries) 45 35
616 50 f. "The Daughter of Andersdotter" (J. Hockert) . . 1·40 1·00

102 Monastic Messenger

105 Head of Uganda Kob

1974. Centenary of U.P.U. Multicoloured.

619 20 c. Type **102** 10 10
620 30 c. Inca messenger 10 10
621 50 c. Moroccan postman . . . 10 10
622 1 f. Indian postman 10 10
623 18 f. Polynesian postman . . . 55 40
624 80 f. Early Rwanda messenger with horn and drum . . . . . 1·75 1·40

1974. 15th Anniv of Revolution. Nos. 316/18 optd **1974 15e ANNIVERSAIRE.**

625 **51** 6 f. multicoloured . . . . .
626 18 f. multicoloured . . . .
627 40 f. multicoloured . . . .
Set of 3 11·00 9·50

1974. 10th Anniv of African Development Bank. Nos. 305/6 optd **1974 10e ANNIVERSAIRE.**

629 **48** 30 f. multicoloured 85 65
630 – 70 f. multicoloured . . . . 1·90 1·40

1975. Antelopes. Multicoloured.

631 20 c. Type **105** 10 10
632 30 c. Bongo with calf (horiz) . 10 10
633 50 c. Roan antelope and Sable antelope heads 10 10
634 1 f. Young sitatungas (horiz) . 10 10
635 4 f. Great kudu 10 10
636 10 f. Impala family (horiz) . . 30 10
637 34 f. Waterbuck head 90 45
638 100 f. Giant eland (horiz) . . 2·75 2·25

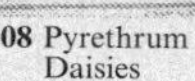

108 Pyrethrum Daisies

111 Globe and Emblem

110 Eastern White Pelicans

1975. Agricultural Labour Year. Multicoloured.

642 20 c. Type **108** 10 10
643 30 c. Tea plant 10 10
644 50 c. Coffee berries 10 10
645 4 f. Bananas 10 10
646 10 f. Maize 20 10
647 12 f. Sorghum 35 15
648 26 f. Rice 80 45
649 47 f. Coffee cultivation . . . . 1·60 90

1975. Holy Year. Nos. 400/7 optd **1975 ANNEE SAINTE.**

652 **65** 10 c. brown and gold . . . 10 10
653 – 20 c. green and gold . . . 10 10
654 – 30 c. lake and gold 10 10
655 – 40 c. blue and gold 10 10
656 – 1 f. violet and gold 10 10
657 – 18 f. purple and gold . . . 40 20
658 – 20 f. orange and gold . . . 45 20
659 – 60 f. brown and gold . . . 1·90 1·25

1975. Aquatic Birds. Multicoloured.

660 20 c. Type **110** 20 10
661 30 c. Malachite kingfisher . . 20 10
662 50 c. Goliath herons 20 10
663 1 f. Saddle-bill stork 20 10
664 4 f. African jacana 40 15
665 10 f. African darter 70 35
666 34 f. Sacred ibis . . . . . . 1·75 95
667 80 f. Hartlaub's duck (vert) . . 4·75 2·50

1975. World Population Year (1974). Mult.

669 20 f. Type **111** 45 30
670 26 f. Population graph 65 35
671 34 f. Symbolic doorway . . . 95 50

112 "La Toilette" (M. Cassatt)

113 "Arts"

1975. International Women's Year. Multicoloured.

672 20 c. Type **112** 10 10
673 30 c. "Mother and Child" (G. Melchers) 10 10
674 50 c. "The Milk Jug" (Vermeer) 10 10
675 1 f. "The Water-carrier" (Goya) 10 10
676 8 f. Coffee picking 20 10
677 12 f. Laboratory technician . . 35 20
678 18 f. Rwandaise mother and child 55 20
679 60 f. Woman carrying water jug 1·50 1·25

1975. 10th Anniv of National University. The Faculties. Multicoloured.

681 20 c. Type **113** 10 10
682 30 c. "Medicine" 10 10
683 1 f. 50 "Jurisprudence" . . . 10 10
684 18 f. "Science" 40 20
685 26 f. "Commerce" 45 30
686 34 f. University Building, Kigali 85 55

114 Cattle at Pool, and "Impatiens stuhlmannii"

1975. Protection of Nature. Multicoloured.

688 20 c. Type **114** 10 10
689 30 c. Euphorbis "candelabra" and savannah bush 10 10
690 50 c. Bush fire and "Tapinanthus prunifolius" 10 10
691 5 f. Lake Bulera and "Nymphaea lotus" 10 10
692 8 f. Soil erosion and "Protea madiensis" 15 10
693 10 f. Protected marshland and "Melanthera brownei" . . 20 15
694 26 f. Giant lobelias and groundsel 55 40
695 100 f. Sabyinyo volcano and "Polystachya kermesina" . . 2·25 1·60

1975. Pan-African Drought Relief. Nos. 345/52 optd or surch **SECHERESSE SOLIDARITE 1975.** (Both words share same capital letter).

696 20 c. multicoloured 10 10
697 30 c. multicoloured 10 10
698 50 c. multicoloured 10 10
699 1 f. multicoloured 10 10
700 3 f. multicoloured 10 10
701 5 f. multicoloured 15 10
702 50 f. + 25 f. multicoloured . 1·60 1·25
703 90 f. + 25 f. multicoloured . 2·40 2·00

116 Loading Douglas DC-8F Jet Trader

1975. Year of Increased Production. Multicoloured.

704 20 c. Type **116** 10 10
705 30 c. Coffee-picking plant . . 10 10
706 50 c. Lathe operator 10 10
707 10 f. Farmer with hoe (vert) . 15 10
708 35 f. Coffee-picking (vert) . . 60 55
709 54 f. Mechanical plough . . . 1·10 95

117 African Woman with Basket on Head

1975. "Themabelga" Stamp Exhibition, Brussels. African Costumes.

710 **117** 20 c. multicoloured . . . 10 10
711 – 30 c. multicoloured . . . 10 10
712 – 50 c. multicoloured . . . 10 10
713 – 1 f. multicoloured 10 10
714 – 5 f. multicoloured 10 10
715 – 7 f. multicoloured 15 10
716 – 35 f. multicoloured 70 60
717 – 51 f. multicoloured . . . 1·40 95

DESIGNS: 30 c. to 51 f. Various Rwanda costumes.

118 Dr. Schweitzer, Organ Pipes and Music Score

1976. World Leprosy Day.

719 – 20 c. lilac, brown & black 10 10
720 – 30 c. lilac, green & black 10 10
721 **118** 50 c. lilac, brown & black 10 10
722 – 1 f. lilac, purple & black . 10 10
723 – 3 f. lilac, blue and black . 10 10
724 – 5 f. lilac, brown and black 10 10
725 **118** 10 f. lilac, blue and black . 30 10
726 – 80 f. lilac, red and black . 1·90 1·40

DESIGNS: Dr. Schweitzer and; 20 c. Piano keyboard and music; 30 c. Lambarene Hospital; 1 f. Lambarene residence; 3 f. as 20 c.; 5 f. as 30 c; 80 f. as 1 f.

119 "Surrender at Yorktown"

1976. Bicentenary of American Revolution. Mult.

727 20 c. Type **119** 10 10
728 30 c. "The Sergeant-Instructor at Valley Forge" 10 10
729 50 c. "Presentation of Captured Yorktown Flags to Congress" 10 10
730 1 f. "Washington at Fort Lee" 10 10
731 18 f. "Washington boarding a British warship" 45 30
732 26 f. "Washington studying Battle plans" 55 40
733 34 f. "Washington firing a Cannon" 90 55
734 40 f. "Crossing the Delaware" 1·00 85

120 Sister Yohana

121 Yachting

1976. 75th Anniv of Catholic Church in Rwanda. Multicoloured.

736 20 c. Type **120** 10 10
737 30 c. Abdon Sabakati 10 10
738 50 c. Father Alphonse Brard . 10 10
739 4 f. Abbe Balthazar Gafuku . 10 10
740 10 f. Monseigneur Bigirumwami 20 10
741 25 f. Save Catholic Church (horiz) 60 45
742 60 f. Kabgayi Catholic Cathedral (horiz) . . . . 1·25 80

1976. Olympic Games, Montreal (1st issue).

743 **121** 20 c. brown and green . . 10 10
744 – 30 c. blue and green . . . 10 10
745 – 50 c. black and green . . . 10 10
746 – 1 f. violet and green . . . 10 10
747 – 10 f. blue and green . . . 20 10
748 – 18 f. brown and green . . 35 30
749 – 29 f. purple and green . . 80 60
750 – 51 f. deep green & green . 1·00 80

DESIGNS: 30 c. Horse-jumping; 50 c. Long jumping; 1 f. Hockey; 10 f. Swimming; 18 f. Football; 29 f. Boxing; 51 f. Gymnastics.

See also Nos. 767/74.

122 Bell's Experimental Telephone and Manual Switchboard

1976. Telephone Centenary.

751 **122** 20 c. brown and blue . . . 10 10
752 – 30 c. blue and violet . . . 10 10
753 – 50 c. brown and blue . . . 10 10
754 – 1 f. orange and blue . . . 10 10
755 – 4 f. mauve and blue . . . 10 10
756 – 8 f. green and blue 15 10
757 – 26 f. red and blue 70 55
758 – 60 f. lilac and blue . . . . 1·40 1·00

DESIGNS: 30 c. Early telephone and man making call; 50 c. Early telephone and woman making call; 1 f. Early telephone and exchange building; 4 f. Alexander Graham Bell and "candlestick" telephone; 26 f. Dish aerial, satellite and modern hand set; 60 f. Rwanda, PTT building, operator and push-button telephones.

1976. Bicentenary of Declaration of American Independence. Nos. 727/34 optd **INDEPENDENCE DAY** and Bicentennial Emblem.

759 **119** 20 c. multicoloured 10 10
760 – 30 c. multicoloured 10 10
761 – 50 c. multicoloured 10 10
762 – 1 f. multicoloured 10 10
763 – 18 f. multicoloured 35 20
764 – 26 f. multicoloured 65 45
765 – 34 f. multicoloured 80 55
766 – 40 f. multicoloured . . . . 1·10 80

124 Football

125 "Apollo" and "Soyuz" Launches and ASTP Badge

1976. Olympic Games, Montreal (2nd issue). Multicoloured.

767 20 c. Type **124** 10 10
768 30 c. Rifle-shooting 10 10
769 50 c. Canoeing 10 10
770 1 f. Gymnastics 10 10
771 10 f. Weightlifting 15 10
772 12 f. Diving 30 20
773 26 f. Horse-riding 55 40
774 50 f. Throwing the hammer . 1·40 90

1976. "Apollo" – "Soyuz" Test Project. Mult.

776 20 c. Type **125** 10 10
777 30 c. "Soyuz" rocket 10 10
778 50 c. "Apollo" rocket 10 10
779 1 f. "Apollo" after separation 10 10
780 2 f. Approach to link-up . . . 10 10
781 12 f. Spacecraft docked . . . 35 15
782 30 f. Sectional view of interiors 85 55
783 54 f. "Apollo" splashdown . . 1·40 95

126 "Eulophia cucullata"

128 Hands embracing. "Cultural Collaboration"

1976. Rwandaise Orchids. Multicoloured.

784 20 c. Type 126 . . . . 10 10
785 30 c. "Eulophia streptopetala" 10 10
786 50 c. "Disa stairsii" 10 10
787 1 f. "Aerangis kotschyana" . 10 10
788 10 f. "Eulophia abyssinica" . 20 10
789 12 f. "Bonatea steudneri" . . 30 15
790 26 f. "Ansellia gigantea" . . . 80 45
791 50 f. "Eulophia angolensis" . 1·60 90

1977. World Leprosy Day. Nos. 719/26 optd with **JOURNEE MONDIALE 1977.**

793 – 20 c. lilac, brown & black 10 10
794 – 30 c. lilac, green & black . 10 10
795 **118** 50 c. lilac, brown & black 10 10
796 – 1 f. lilac, purple & black 10 10
797 – 3 f. lilac, blue and black . 10 10
798 – 5 f. lilac, brown & black . 20 10
799 **118** 10 f. lilac, brown & black 35 20
800 – 80 f. lilac, red and black . 1·60 1·60

1977. 10th OCAM Summit Meeting, Kigali. Mult.

801 10 f. Type **128** 30 10
802 26 f. Hands embracing "Technical Collaboration" . 70 40
803 64 f. Hands embracing "Economic Collaboration" . 1·25 90

1977. World Water Conference. Nos. 688/95 optd **CONFERENCE MONDIALE DE L'EAU.**

805 **114** 20 c. multicoloured . . . 10 10
806 – 30 c. multicoloured . . . 10 10
807 – 50 c. multicoloured . . . 10 10
808 – 5 f. multicoloured 15 10
809 – 8 f. multicoloured 20 10
810 – 10 f. multicoloured 40 15
811 – 26 f. multicoloured . . . 1·10 50
812 – 100 f. multicoloured . . . 3·25 2·50

131 Roman Signal Post and African Tam-Tam

132 "The Ascent to Calvary" (detail)

1977. World Telecommunications Day. Mult.

813 20 c. Type **131** 10 10
814 30 c. Chappe's semaphore and post-rider 10 10
815 50 c. Morse code 10 10
816 1 f. "Goliath" laying Channel cable 10 10
817 4 f. Telephone, radio and television 10 10
818 18 f. "Kingsport" and maritime communications satellite . . 65 40
819 26 f. Telecommunications satellite and aerial 50 40
820 50 f. "Mariner 2" satellite . . 1·40 90

1977. 400th Birth Anniv of Peter Paul Rubens. Multicoloured.

823 20 c. Type **132** 10 10
824 30 c. "The Judgement of Paris" (horiz) 10 10
825 50 c. "Marie de Medici, Queen of France" 10 10
826 1 f. "Heads of Negroes" (horiz) 10 10
827 4 f. "St. Idelfonse Triptych" (detail) 10 10
828 8 f. "Helene Fourment with her Children" (horiz) 15 10
829 26 f. "St. Idelfonse Triptych" (different detail) 55 40
830 60 f. "Helene Fourment" . . . 1·50 1·00

1977. Air. 10th Anniv of International French Language Council. As T **236a** of Mali.

831 50 f. multicoloured . . . . . 1·60 1·10

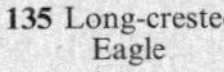

135 Long-crested Eagle

138 Scout playing Whistle

1977. Birds of Prey. Multicoloured.

833 20 c. Type **136** 10 10
834 30 c. African harrier hawk . . 10 10
835 50 c. African fish eagle 10 10
836 1 f. Hooded vulture 10 10
837 3 f. Augur buzzard 15 10
838 5 f. Black kite 20 10
839 20 f. Black-shouldered kite . . 90 55
840 100 f. Bateleur . . . . 4·25 2·75

1977. Dr. Wernher von Braun Commemoration. Nos. 776/83 optd with **in memoriam WERNHER VON BRAUN 1912–1977.**

841 20 c. Type **125** 10 10
842 30 c. "Soyuz" rocket 10 10
843 50 c. "Apollo" rocket 10 10
844 1 f. "Apollo" after separation 10 10
845 2 f. Approach to link up . . . 10 10
846 12 f. Spacecraft docked . . . 40 20
847 30 f. Sectional view of interiors 1·00 50
848 54 f. "Apollo" after splashdown 2·25 1·25

1978. 10th Anniv of Rwanda Scout Association. Multicoloured.

851 20 c. Type **138** 10 10
852 30 c. Camp fire 10 10
853 50 c. Scouts constructing a platform 10 10
854 1 f. Two scouts 10 10
855 10 f. Scouts on look-out . . . 20 10
856 18 f. Scouts in canoe 45 35
857 26 f. Cooking at camp fire . . 55 35
858 44 f. Lord Baden-Powell . . . 1·10 70

139 Chimpanzees

1978. Apes. Multicoloured.

859 20 c. Type **139** 10 10
860 30 c. Gorilla 10 10
861 50 c. Eastern black-and-white colobus 10 10
862 3 f. Eastern needle-clawed bushbaby 10 10
863 10 f. Mona monkey 30 10
864 26 f. Potto 65 40
865 60 f. Savanna monkey . . . . 1·60 90
866 150 f. Olive baboon . . . . . 3·50 2·10

140 "Euporus strangulatus"

1978. Beetles. Multicoloured.

867 20 c. Type **140** 10 10
868 30 c. "Rhina afzelii" (vert) . . 10 10
869 50 c. "Pentalobus palini" . . . 10 10
870 3 f. "Corynodes dejeani" (vert) 10 10
871 10 f. "Mecynorhina torquata" 20 10
872 15 f. "Mecocerus rhombeus" (vert) 30 10
873 20 f. "Macrotoma serripes" . . 50 20
874 25 f. "Neptunides stanleyi" (vert) 65 40
875 26 f. "Petrognatha gigas" . . 65 40
876 100 f. "Eudicella gralli" (vert) 2·75 1·90

141 Poling Boat across River of Poverty

1978. National Revolutionary Development Movement. Multicoloured.

877 4 f. Type **141** 10 10
878 10 f. Poling boat to right . . 15 10
879 26 f. Type **141** 60 40
880 60 f. As 10 f. . . . . 1·10 85

142 Footballers, Cup and Flags of Netherlands and Peru

1978. World Cup Football Championship, Argentina. Multicoloured.

881 20 c. Type **142** 10 10
882 30 c. Flags of FIFA, Sweden and Spain 10 10
883 50 c. Mascot and flags of Scotland and Iran 10 10
884 2 f. Emblem and flags of West Germany and Tunisia . . . 10 10
885 3 f. Cup and flags of Italy and Hungary 10 10
886 10 f. Flags of FIFA, Brazil and Austria 20 10
887 34 f. Mascot and flags of Poland and Mexico 60 45
888 100 f. Emblem and flags of Argentina and France . . . 2·25 1·40

No. 883 shows the Union Jack.

143 Wright Brothers and Wright Flyer I, 1903

1978. Aviation History. Multicoloured.

889 20 c. Type **143** 10 10
890 30 c. Alberto Santos-Dumont and biplane "14 bis", 1906 10 10
891 50 c. Henri Farman and Farman Voisin No. 1 bis, 1908 . . 10 10
892 1 f. Jan Olieslagers and Bleriot XI 10 10
893 3 f. General Italo Balbo and Savoia S-17 flying boat, 1919 10 10
894 10 f. Charles Lindbergh and "Spirit of St. Louis", 1927 . 15 10
895 55 f. Hugo Junkers and Junkers Ju 52/3m, 1932 . . . . . 1·10 55
896 60 f. Igor Sikorsky and Vought-Sikorsky VS-300 helicopter prototype . . . . 1·60 85

1978. Air. "Philexafrique" Stamp Exhibition, Libreville, Gabon and Int Stamp Fair, Essen, West Germany. As T **262** of Niger. Mult.

898 30 f. Great spotted woodpecker and Oldenburg 1852 ⅓ sgr. stamp . . . . 1·75 95
899 30 f. Greater kudu and Rwanda 1967 20 c. stamp . . . . . 1·75 95

1978. 15th Anniv of Organization for African Unity. Nos. 544/5 optd **1963 1978.**

901 **88** 6 f. multicoloured 30 10
902 – 94 f. multicoloured . . . . 1·90 1·10

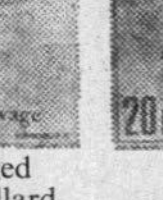

146 Spur-winged Goose and Mallard

147 "Papilio demodocus"

1978. Stock Rearing Year. Multicoloured.

903 20 c. Type **146** 10 10
904 30 c. Goats (horiz) 10 10
905 50 c. Chickens 10 10
906 4 f. Rabbits (horiz) 15 10
907 5 f. Pigs 15 10
908 15 f. Common turkey (horiz) . 80 45
909 50 f. Sheep and cattle . . . . 1·25 50
910 75 f. Bull (horiz) . . . . . . 1·60 70

1979. Butterflies. Multicoloured.

911 20 c. Type **147** 10 10
912 30 c. "Precis octavia" 10 10
913 50 c. "Charaxes smaragdalis caerulea" 10 10
914 4 f. "Charaxes guderiana" . . 15 10
915 15 f. "Colotis evippe" 20 10
916 30 f. "Danaus limniace petiverana" 55 30
917 50 f. "Byblia acheloia" . . . . 1·25 55
918 150 f. "Utetheisa pulchella" . . 3·50 1·40

148 "Euphorbia grantii" and Women weaving

1979. "Philexafrique" Exhibition, Libreville. Mult.

919 40 f. Type **148** . . . . 1·40 85
920 60 f. Drummers and "Intelsat" satellite . . . . 2·25 1·10

149 "Polyscias fulva"

150 European Girl

1979. Trees. Multicoloured.

921 20 c. Type **149** 10 10
922 30 c. "Entandrophragma excelsum" (horiz) 10 10
923 50 c. "Ilex mitis" 10 10
924 4 f. "Kigelia africana" (horiz) 15 10
925 15 f. "Ficus thonningi" 35 10
926 20 f. "Acacia senegal" (horiz) . 50 20
927 50 f. "Symphonia globulifera" 1·25 45
928 110 f. "Acacia sieberana" (horiz) 2·50 1·25

1979. International Year of the Child. Each brown, gold and stone.

929 26 f. Type **150** 65 35
930 26 f. Asian 65 35
931 26 f. Eskimo 65 35
932 26 f. Asian boy 65 35
933 26 f. African 65 35
934 26 f. South American Indian . 65 35
935 26 f. Polynesian 65 35
936 26 f. European girl (different) . 65 35
937 42 f. European and African (horiz) . . . . 1·40 65

151 Basket Weaving

1979. Handicrafts. Multicoloured.

939 50 c. Type **151** 10 10
940 1 f. 50 Wood-carving (vert) . . 10 10
941 2 f. Metal working 10 10
942 10 f. Basket work (vert) . . . 35 10
943 20 f. Basket weaving (different) 50 20
944 26 f. Mural painting (vert) . . 65 30
945 40 f. Pottery 95 40
946 100 f. Smelting (vert) . . . . . 2·25 1·10

153 Rowland Hill and 40 c. Ruanda Stamp of 1916

1979. Death Centenary of Sir Rowland Hill. Multicoloured.

948 20 c. Type **153** 10 10
949 30 c. 1916 Occupation stamp . 10 10
950 50 c. 1918 "A.O" overprint . . 10 10
951 3 f. 1925 overprinted 60 c. stamp 10 10
952 10 f. 1931 50 c. African buffalo stamp 30 10
953 26 f. 1942 20 f. Common zebra stamp 65 15
954 60 f. 1953 25 f. Protea stamp . 1·40 60
955 100 f. 1960 Olympic stamp . . 2·75 1·10

154 Strange Weaver

156 Butare Rotary Club Banner, Globe and Chicago Club Emblem of 1905

155 Armstrong's first Step on Moon

1980. Birds. Multicoloured.

956 20 c. Type **154** 15 10
957 30 c. Regal sunbird (vert) . . 15 10
958 50 c. White-spotted crake . . 15 10
959 3 f. Crowned hornbill 20 10
960 10 f. Barred owlet (vert) . . . 45 25
961 26 f. African emerald cuckoo . 1·00 60
962 60 f. Black-crowned waxbill (vert) . . . . 2·10 1·25
963 100 f. Crowned eagle (vert) . 3·75 2·25

1980. 10th Anniv of "Apollo 11" Moon Landing. Multicoloured.

964 50 c. Type **155** 10 10
965 1 f. 50 Aldrin descending to Moon's surface 10 10
966 8 f. Planting the American flag 30 10
967 30 f. Placing seisometer . . . 65 35
968 50 f. Taking samples . . . . 1·10 45
969 60 f. Setting-up experiment . 1·40 65

1980. 75th Anniv of Rotary International. Mult.

971 20 c. Type **156** 10 10
972 30 c. Kigali Rotary Club banner 10 10
973 50 c. Type **156** 10 10
974 4 f. As No. 972 . . . . 15 10
975 15 f. Type **156** 35 10
976 20 f. As No. 972 . . . . . . 45 20
977 50 f. Type **156** 95 45
978 60 f. As No. 972 . . . . . . 1·10 65

157 Gymnastics

1980. Olympic Games, Moscow.

979 **157** 20 c. yellow and black . . 10 10
980 – 30 c. green and black . . 10 10
981 – 50 c. red and black . . . 10 10
982 – 3 f. blue and black . . . 15 10
983 – 20 f. orange and black . . 45 20
984 – 26 f. purple and black . . 50 25
985 – 50 f. turquoise and black . 1·10 45
986 – 100 f. brown and black . . 2·50 1·10

DESIGNS: 30 c. Basketball; 50 c. Cycling; 3 f. Boxing; 20 f. Archery; 26 f. Weightlifting; 50 f. Javelin; 100 f. Fencing.

159 "Geaster"

1980. Mushrooms. Multicoloured.

988 20 c. Type **159** 10 10
989 30 c. "Lentinus atrobrunneus" 10 10
990 50 c. "Gomphus stereoides" . 10 10
991 4 f. "Cantharellus cibarius" . 20 10
992 10 f. "Stilbothamnium dybowskii" 45 20
993 15 f. "Xeromphalina tenuipes" 65 20
994 70 f. "Podoscypha elegans" . 2·75 80
995 100 f. "Mycena" . . . . . . 5·50 1·60

160 "At the Theatre" (Toulouse-Lautrec)

1980. Impressionist Paintings. Multicoloured.

996 20 c. "Still Life" (horiz) (Renoir) . . . 10 10
997 30 c. Type **160** . . . 10 10
998 50 c. "Seaside Garden" (Monet) (horiz) . . . 10 10
999 4 f. "Mother and Child" (Mary Cassatt) . . . 10 10
1000 5 f. "Starry Night" (Van Gogh) (horiz) . . . 20 10
1001 10 f. "Three Dancers at their Toilette" (Degas) . . . 35 10
1002 50 f. "The Card Players" (Cezanne) (horiz) . . . 1·10 45
1003 70 f. "Tahitian Girls" (Gauguin) . . . 1·75 65
1004 100 f. "La Grande Jatte" (Seurat) (horiz) . . . 2·75 90

162 Revolutionary Scene

1980. 150th Anniv of Belgian Independence. Scenes of the Independence War from contemporary engravings.

1007 **162** 20 c. green and brown . . 10 10
1008 – 30 c. buff and brown . . 10 10
1009 – 50 c. blue and brown . . 10 10
1010 – 9 f. orange and brown . . 20 10
1011 – 10 f. mauve and brown . . 30 10
1012 – 20 f. green and brown . . 45 20
1013 – 70 f. pink and brown . . 1·50 65
1014 – 90 f. yellow and brown . . 1·90 1·00

163 Draining the Marshes

1980. Soil Protection and Conservation Year. Multicoloured.

1015 20 c. Type **163** . . . 10 10
1016 30 c. Bullock in pen (mixed farming and land fertilization) . . . 10 10
1017 1 f. 50 Land irrigation and rice . . 10 10
1018 8 f. Soil erosion and planting trees . . . 20 10
1019 10 f. Terrace . . . 30 15
1020 40 f. Crop fields . . . 1·00 40
1021 90 f. Bean crop . . . 2·10 85
1022 100 f. Picking tea . . . 2·25 1·10

164 "Pavetta rwandensis"

1981. Flowers. Multicoloured.

1023 20 c. Type **164** . . . 10 10
1024 30 c. "Cyrtorchis praetermissa" . . 10 10
1025 50 c. "Pavonia urens" . . . 10 10
1026 4 f. "Cynorkis kassnerana" . . 10 10
1027 5 f. "Gardenia ternifolia" . . 15 10
1028 10 f. "Leptactina platyphylla" . . 20 10
1029 20 f. "Lobelia petiolata" . . 50 15
1030 40 f. "Tapinanthus brunneus" . . 90 45
1031 70 f. "Impatiens niamniamensis" . . . 1·60 65
1032 150 f. "Dissotis rwandensis" . . 4·00 1·60

165 Mother and Child 166 Carol Singers

1981. SOS Children's Village. Multicoloured.

1033 20 c. Type **165** . . . 10 10
1034 30 c. Child with pots . . . 10 10
1035 50 c. Children drawing . . . 10 10
1036 1 f. Girl sewing . . . 10 10
1037 8 f. Children playing . . . 20 10
1038 10 f. Girl knitting . . . 20 10
1039 70 f. Children making models . . 1·50 70
1040 150 f. Mother and children . . 3·25 1·60

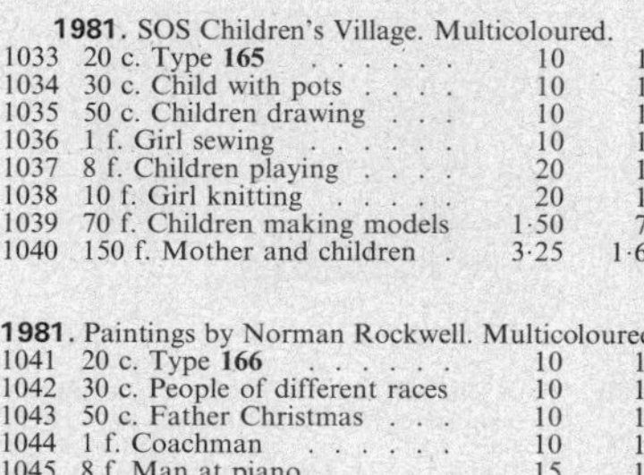

1981. Paintings by Norman Rockwell. Multicoloured.

1041 20 c. Type **166** . . . 10 10
1042 30 c. People of different races . . 10 10
1043 50 c. Father Christmas . . . 10 10
1044 1 f. Coachman . . . 10 10
1045 8 f. Man at piano . . . 15 10
1046 20 f. "Springtime" . . . 50 20
1047 50 f. Man making donation to girl "nurse" . . . 1·00 45
1048 70 f. Clown . . . 1·50 70

167 Serval

1981. Carnivorous Animals. Multicoloured.

1049 20 c. Type **167** . . . 10 10
1050 30 c. Black-backed jackal . . 10 10
1051 2 f. Servaline genet . . . 10 10
1052 2 f. 50 Banded mongoose . . 10 10
1053 10 f. Zorilla . . . 20 10
1054 15 f. Zaire clawless otter . . 35 10
1055 70 f. African golden cat . . 1·50 70
1056 200 f. Hunting dog (vert) . . 5·25 2·25

168 Drummer

1981. Telecommunications and Health. Mult.

1057 20 c. Type **168** . . . 10 10
1058 30 c. Telephone receiver and world map . . . 10 10
1059 2 f. Airliner and radar screen . . 10 10
1060 2 f. 50 Satellite and computer tape . . . 10 10
1061 10 f. Satellite orbit and dish aerial . . . 20 10
1062 15 f. Tanker and radar equipment . . . 35 25
1063 70 f. Red Cross helicopter . . 1·90 70
1064 200 f. Satellite . . . 4·25 2·25

169 "St. Benedict leaving His Parents"

1981. 1500th Birth Anniv of St. Benedict. Mult.

1065 20 c. Type **169** . . . 10 10
1066 30 c. Portrait (10th century) (vert) . . . 10 10
1067 50 c. Portrait (detail from "The Virgin of the Misericord" polyptich) (vert) . . . 10 10
1068 4 f. "St. Benedict presenting the Rules of His Order" . . . 10 10
1069 5 f. "St. Benedict and His Monks at their Meal" . . 15 10
1070 20 f. Portrait (13th century) (vert) . . . 45 15
1071 70 f. St. Benedict at prayer (detail from "Our Lady in Glory with Sts. Gregory and Benedict") (vert) . . . 1·50 85
1072 100 f. "Priest bringing the Easter Meal to St. Benedict" (Jan van Coninxlo) . . . 2·40 95

170 Disabled Child painting with Mouth

1981. International Year of Disabled Persons. Multicoloured.

1073 20 c. Type **170** . . . 10 10
1074 30 c. Boys on crutches playing football . . . 10 10
1075 4 f. 50 Disabled girl knitting . 10 10
1076 5 f. Disabled child painting pot 15 10
1077 10 f. Boy in wheelchair using saw . . . 20 10
1078 60 f. Child using sign language 1·25 60
1079 70 f. Child in wheelchair playing with puzzle . . . 1·60 70
1080 100 f. Disabled child . . . 2·25 1·10

172 Kob drinking at Pool

1981. Rural Water Supplies. Multicoloured.

1082 20 c. Type **172** . . . 10 10
1083 30 c. Women collecting water (vert) . . . 10 10
1084 50 c. Constructing a pipeline . 10 10
1085 10 f. Woman collecting water from pipe (vert) . . . 20 10
1086 10 f. Man drinking . . . 45 20
1087 70 f. Woman collecting water (vert) . . . 1·50 70
1088 100 f. Floating pump (vert) . 2·50 1·10

173 Cattle

1982. World Food Day. Multicoloured.

1089 20 c. Type **173** . . . 10 10
1090 30 c. Bee keeping . . . 10 10
1091 50 c. Fish . . . 10 10
1092 1 f. Avocado . . . 10 10
1093 8 f. Boy eating banana . . . 10 10
1094 20 f. Sorghum . . . 45 15
1095 70 f. Vegetables . . . 1·50 65
1096 100 f. Three generations and balanced diet . . . 2·50 1·10

174 "Hibiscus berberidfolius"

1982. Flowers. Multicoloured.

1097 20 c. type **174** . . . 10 10
1098 30 c. "Hypericum lanceolatum" (vert) . . . 10 10
1099 50 c. "Canarina eminii" . . 10 10
1100 4 r. "Polygala ruwenzoriensis" 10 10
1101 10 f. "Kniphofia grantii" (vert) 15 10
1102 35 f. "Euphorbia candelabrum" (vert) . . . 65 35
1103 70 f. "Disa erubescens" (vert) 1·50 55
1104 80 f. "Gloriosa simplex" . . 1·90 80

175 Pres. Habyarimana and Flags

1982. 20th Anniv of Independence. Multicoloured.

1105 10 f. Type **175** . . . 20 10
1106 20 f. Hands releasing doves (Peace) . . . 35 20
1107 30 f. Clasped hands and flag (Unity) . . . 65 35
1108 50 f. Building (Development) . 1·00 50

176 Football

1982. World Cup Football Championship, Spain.

1109 **176** 20 c. multicoloured . . . 10 10
1110 – 30 c. multicoloured . . . 10 10
1111 – 1 f. 50 multicoloured . . 10 10
1112 – 8 f. multicoloured . . . 15 10
1113 – 10 f. multicoloured . . . 20 10
1114 – 20 f. multicoloured . . . 40 15
1115 – 70 f. multicoloured . . . 1·60 65
1116 – 90 f. multicoloured . . . 2·25 85

DESIGNS: 30 c. to 90 f. Designs show different players.

177 Microscope and Slide

1982. Centenary of Discovery of Tubercle Bacillus. Multicoloured.

1117 10 f. Type **177** . . . 15 10
1118 20 f. Hand with test tube and slide . . . 40 15
1119 70 f. Lungs and slide . . . 1·60 65
1120 100 f. Dr. Robert Koch . . . 2·25 95

180 African Elephants

1982. 10th Anniv of United Nations Environment Programme. Multicoloured.

1123 20 c. Type **180** . . . 10 10
1124 30 c. Lion hunting impala . . 10 10
1125 50 c. Flower . . . 10 10
1126 4 f. African buffalo . . . 10 10
1127 5 f. Impala . . . 10 10
1128 10 f. Flower (different) . . . 20 10
1129 20 f. Common zebra . . . 45 15
1130 40 f. Crowned cranes . . . 90 35
1131 50 f. African fish eagle . . . 1·25 55
1132 70 f. Woman with basket of fruit . . . 1·60 80

181 Scout tending Injured Kob

1982. 75th Anniv of Scout Movement. Mult.

1133 20 c. Type **181** . . . 10 10
1134 30 c. Tents and northern doubled-collared sunbird . 45 15
1135 1 r. 50 Campfire . . . 10 10
1136 8 f. Scout . . . 15 10
1137 10 f. Knot . . . 20 10
1138 20 f. Tent and campfire . . . 40 15
1139 70 f. Scout cutting stake . . 1·60 80
1140 90 f. Scout salute . . . 2·25 1·00

RWANDA 20c

182 Northern Double-collared Sunbird 183 Driving Cattle

1983. Nectar-sucking Birds. Multicoloured.

1141 20 c. Type **182** . . . 10 10
1142 30 c. Regal sunbird (horiz) . . 10 10
1143 50 c. Red-tufted malachite sunbird . . . 10 10
1144 4 f. Bronze sunbird (horiz) . . 10 10
1145 5 f. Collared sunbird . . . 20 10
1146 10 f. Blue-headed sunbird (horiz) . . . 45 20
1147 20 f. Purple-breasted sunbird 90 45

1148 40 f. Coppery sunbird (horiz) 1·75 85
1149 50 f. Olive-bellied sunbird 2·10 1·10
1150 70 f. Red-chested sunbird (horiz) 2·75 1·60

1983. Campaign Against Soil Erosion. Mult.

1151 20 c. Type **183** 10 10
1152 30 c. Pineapple plantation 10 10
1153 50 c. Interrupted ditches 10 10
1154 9 f. Hedged terraces 20 10
1155 10 f. Re-afforestation 20 10
1156 20 f. Anti-erosion barriers 40 15
1157 30 f. Contour planting 65 30
1158 50 f. Terraces 1·00 40
1159 60 f. River bank protection 1·40 60
1160 70 f. Alternate fallow and planted strips 1·60 80

184 Feeding Ducks **185** Young Gorillas

1983. Birth Cent of Cardinal Cardijan (founder of Young Catholic Workers Movement). Mult.

1161 20 c. Type **184** 10 10
1162 30 c. Harvesting bananas 10 10
1163 50 c. Carrying melons 10 10
1164 10 f. Wood-carving 20 10
1165 19 f. Making shoes 35 15
1166 20 f. Children in field of millet 45 15
1167 70 f. Embroidering 1·40 60
1168 80 f. Cardinal Cardijan 1·60 65

1983. Mountain Gorillas. Multicoloured.

1169 20 c. Type **185** 10 10
1170 30 c. Gorilla family 10 10
1171 9 f. 50 Young and adult 20 10
1172 10 f. Mother with young 20 10
1173 20 f. Heads 40 15
1174 30 f. Adult and head 65 20
1175 60 f. Adult (vert) 1·50 55
1176 70 f. Close-up of adult (vert) 1·75 60

187 "Hagenia abyssinica"

1984. Trees. Multicoloured.

1178 20 c. Type **187** 10 10
1179 30 c. "Dracaena steudneri" 10 10
1180 50 c. "Phoenix reclinata" 10 10
1181 10 f. "Podocarpus milanjianus" 15 10
1182 19 f. "Entada abyssinica" 40 15
1183 70 f. "Parinari excelsa" 1·60 65
1184 100 f. "Newtonia buchananii" 2·00 95
1185 200 f. "Acacia gerrardi" (vert) 4·50 1·60

188 Diesel Train **189** "Le Martial", 1783

1984. World Communications Year. Multicoloured.

1186 20 c. Type **188** 10 10
1187 30 c. Liner and radar 15 10
1188 4 f. 50 Radio and transmitter 15 10
1189 10 f. Telephone dial and cable 20 10
1190 15 f. Letters and newspaper 35 10
1191 50 f. Airliner and control tower 1·10 45
1192 70 f. Television and antenna 1·60 65
1193 100 f. Satellite and computer tape 2·50 90

1984. Bicentenary of Manned Flight. Mult.

1194 20 c. Type **189** 10 10
1195 30 c. De Rozier and Marquis d'Arlandes flight, 1783 10 10
1196 50 c. Charles and Robert (1783) and Blanchard (1784) flights 10 10
1197 9 f. M. and Mme. Blanchard 20 10
1198 10 f. Blanchard and Jeffries, 1785 20 10
1199 50 f. Demuyter (1937) and Piccard and Kipfer (1931) flights 1·10 40
1200 80 f. Modern hot-air balloons 2·50 1·00
1201 200 f. Trans-Atlantic flight, 1978 3·00 1·60

190 Equestrian

1984. Olympic Games, Los Angeles. Multicoloured.

1202 20 c. Type **190** 10 10
1203 30 c. Windsurfing 15 10
1204 50 c. Football 10 10
1205 9 f. Swimming 20 10
1206 10 f. Hockey 20 10
1207 40 f. Fencing 90 35
1208 80 f. Running 1·60 65
1209 200 f. Boxing 4·50 1·75

191 Mare and Foal

1984. Common Zebras and African Buffaloes. Multicoloured.

1210 20 c. Type **191** 10 10
1211 30 c. Buffalo and calf (vert) 10 10
1212 50 c. Pair of zebras (vert) 10 10
1213 9 f. Zebras fighting 20 10
1214 10 f. Close-up of buffalo (vert) 30 10
1215 80 f. Herd of zebras 1·90 80
1216 100 f. Close-up of zebras (vert) 2·25 90
1217 200 f. Buffalo charging 4·50 1·90

193 Gorillas at Water-hole

1985. Gorillas. Multicoloured.

1219 10 f. Type **193** 30 15
1220 15 f. Two gorillas in tree 45 15
1221 25 f. Gorilla family 65 30
1222 30 f. Three adults 85 50

194 Man feeding Fowl

1985. Food Production Year. Multicoloured.

1224 20 c. Type **194** 10 10
1225 30 c. Men carrying pineapples 15 10
1226 50 c. Farm animals 10 10
1227 9 f. Men filling sacks with produce 20 10
1228 10 f. Agricultural instruction 30 10
1229 50 f. Sowing seeds 1·00 45
1230 80 f. Storing produce 1·60 65
1231 100 f. Working in banana plantation 2·10 80

195 Emblem

1985. 10th Anniv of National Revolutionary Redevelopment Movement.

1232 **195** 10 f. multicoloured 20 10
1233 30 f. multicoloured 65 30
1234 70 f. multicoloured 1·60 70

196 U.N. Emblem within "40"

1985. 40th Anniv of U.N.O.

1235 **196** 50 f. multicoloured 1·10 55
1236 100 f. multicoloured 2·25 1·10

197 Barn Owls

1985. Birth Bicentenary of John J. Audubon (ornithologist). Multicoloured.

1237 10 f. Type **197** 40 25
1238 20 f. White-faced scops owls 85 50
1239 40 f. Ruby-throated humming birds 1·60 1·00
1240 80 f. Eastern meadow larks 3·75 2·25

198 "Participation, Development and Peace"

1985. International Youth Year. Multicoloured.

1241 7 f. Type **198** 15 10
1242 9 f. Cycling 30 10
1243 44 f. Youths carrying articles on head (teamwork) 1·10 45
1244 80 f. Education 1·75 80

1985. 75th Anniv of Girl Guide Movement. Nos. 1133/40 optd **1910/1985** and guide emblem.

1245 20 c. Type **181** 10 10
1246 30 c. Tents 10 10
1247 1 f. 50 Campfire 10 10
1248 8 f. Scout 20 10
1249 10 f. Knot 20 10
1250 20 f. Tent and campfire 45 10
1251 70 f. Scout cutting stake 1·60 65
1252 90 f. Scout salute 2·25 90

201 Container Lorry (Transport)

1986. Transport and Communications. Mult.

1254 10 f. Type **201** 35 10
1255 30 f. Handstamping cover (posts) 80 35
1256 40 f. Kigali Earth Station (telecommunication) 1·10 45
1257 80 f. Kigali airport (aviation) (48 × 31 mm) 1·75 1·25

1986. Intensified Agriculture Year. Nos. 1152/60 optd **ANNEE 1986 INTENSIFICATION AGRICOLE** or surch also.

1258 9 f. Hedged terraces 20 10
1259 10 f. Re-afforestation 20 10
1260 10 f. on 30c. Pineapple plantation 20 10
1261 10 f. on 50c. Interrupted ditches 20 10
1262 20 f. Anti-erosion barriers 45 20
1263 30 f. Contour planning 65 35
1264 50 f. Terraces 1·10 50
1265 60 f. River bank protection 1·40 55
1266 70 f. Alternate fallow and planted strips 1·60 70

203 Morocco v England

1986. World Cup Football Championship, Mexico. Multicoloured.

1267 2 f. Type **203** 10 10
1268 4 f. Paraguay v Iraq 10 10
1269 5 f. Brazil v Spain 10 10
1270 10 f. Italy v Argentina 30 10
1271 40 f. Mexico v Belgium 1·00 40
1272 45 f. France v Russia 1·10 45

204 Roan Antelopes

1986. Akagera National Park. Multicoloured.

1273 4 f. Type **204** 10 10
1274 7 f. Whale-headed storks 50 10
1275 9 f. Cape eland 15 10
1276 10 f. Giraffe 30 10
1277 80 f. African elephant 1·90 85
1278 90 f. Crocodile 2·25 1·00
1279 100 f. Heuglin's masked weavers 4·50 3·00
1280 100 f. Zebras and eastern white pelican 4·50 3·00

205 People of Different Races on Globe

1986. Christmas. International Peace Year. Mult.

1281 10 f. Type **205** 35 15
1282 15 f. Dove and globe 45 15
1283 30 f. Type **205** 80 35
1284 70 f. As No. 1282 1·75 1·00

206 Mother breast-feeding Baby

1987. U.N.I.C.E.F. Child Survival Campaign. Multicoloured.

1285 4 f. Type **206** 15 15
1286 6 f. Mother giving oral rehydration therapy to baby 20 15
1287 10 f. Nurse immunising baby 35 25
1288 70 f. Nurse weighing baby and graph 1·75 1·60

207 Couple packing Baskets with Food

1987. Food Self-sufficiency Year. Multicoloured.

1289 5 f. Type **207** 10 10
1290 7 f. Woman and baskets of food 15 10
1291 40 f. Man with baskets of fish and fruits 1·25 45
1292 60 f. Fruits and vegetables 1·90 80

208 Pres. Habyarimana and Soldiers

1987. 25th Anniv of Independence. Multicoloured.

1293 10 f. Type **208** 20 10
1294 40 f. President at meeting 90 45
1295 70 f. President with Pope John Paul II 2·25 85
1296 100 f. Pres. Habyarimana (vert) 2·25 1·10

209 Bananas

1987. Fruits. Multicoloured.

1297	10 f. Type **209**	20	10
1298	40 f. Pineapples (horiz)	90	45
1299	80 f. Papaya (horiz)	2·25	90
1300	90 f. Avocados (horiz)	2·50	1·00
1301	100 f. Strawberries	2·50	1·10

210 Mother carrying cub

1987. The Leopard. Multicoloured.

1302	50 f. Type **210**	1·40	55
1303	50 f. Leopards fighting	1·40	55
1304	50 f. Leopards with prey	1·40	55
1305	50 f. Leopard with prey in tree	1·40	55
1306	50 f. Leopard leaping from tree	1·40	55

211 Village Activities

1987. International Volunteers Day. Mult.

1307	5 f. Type **211**	10	10
1308	12 f. Pupils in schoolroom	35	10
1309	20 f. View of village	55	30
1310	60 f. Woman tending oxen	1·75	85

213 Carpenter's Shop

1988. Rural Incomes Protection Year. Mult.

1312	10 f. Type **213**	20	10
1313	40 f. Dairy farm	95	95
1314	60 f. Workers in field	1·50	30
1315	80 f. Selling baskets of eggs	2·10	95

214 Chimpanzees

1988. Primates of Nyungwe Forest. Multicoloured.

1316	2 f. Type **214**	15	10
1317	3 f. Black and white colobus	15	10
1318	10 f. Lesser bushbabies	30	15
1319	90 f. Monkeys	2·40	95

215 Boxing

1988. Olympic Games, Seoul. Multicoloured.

1320	5 f. Type **215**	10	10
1321	7 f. Relay race	15	10
1322	8 f. Table tennis	20	10
1323	10 f. Running	35	15
1324	90 f. Hurdling	2·25	1·00

216 "25" on Map of Africa

219 "Plectranthus barbatus"

218 Newspaper Fragment and Refugees in Boat

1988. 25th Anniv of Organization of African Unity. Multicoloured.

1325	5 f. Type **216**	15	10
1326	7 f. Hands clasped across map	20	10
1327	8 f. Building on map	20	10
1328	90 f. Words forming map	2·40	1·00

1988. 125th Anniv of Red Cross Movement. Mult.

1330	10 f. Type **218**	20	10
1331	30 f. Red Cross workers and patient	80	35
1332	40 f. Red Cross worker and elderly lady (vert)	95	40
1333	100 f. Red Cross worker and family (vert)	2·75	1·25

1989. Plants. Multicoloured.

1334	5 f. Type **219**	10	10
1335	10 f. "Tetradenia riparia"	30	10
1336	20 f. "Hygrophila auriculata	60	20
1337	40 f. "Datura stramonium	1·25	45
1338	50 f. "Pavetta ternifolia"	1·60	60

220 Emblem, Dates and Sunburst

1989. Centenary of Interparliamentary Union. Mult.

1339	10 f. Type **220**	30	10
1340	30 f. Lake	85	35
1341	70 f. River	1·60	80
1342	90 f. Sun's rays	2·25	1·00

222 Throwing Clay and Finished Pots

1989. Rural Self-help Year. Multicoloured.

1344	10 f. Type **222**	30	10
1345	70 f. Carrying baskets of produce (vert)	1·60	80
1346	90 f. Firing clay pots	2·50	90
1347	200 f. Clearing roadway	5·00	1·60

223 "Triumph of Marat" (Boilly)

1990. Bicentenary of French Revolution. Mult.

1348	10 f. Type **223**	30	10
1349	60 f. "Rouget de Lisle singing La Marseillaise" (Pils)	1·60	65
1350	70 f. "Oath of the Tennis Court" (Jacques Louis David)	1·75	90
1351	100 f. "Trial of Louis XVI" (Joseph Court)	2·75	1·10

224 Old and New Lifestyles

1990. 30th Anniv of Revolution. Multicoloured.

1352	10 f. Type **224**	30	10
1353	60 f. Couple holding farming implements (vert)	1·60	55
1354	70 f. Modernisation	1·75	55
1355	100 f. Flag, map and warrior	2·50	90

225 Construction

1990. 25th Anniv (1989) of African Development Bank. Multicoloured.

1356	10 f. Type **225**	30	10
1357	20 f. Tea picking	55	35
1358	40 f. Road building	1·10	45
1359	90 f. Tea pickers and modern housing	2·50	80

1990. World Cup Football Championship, Italy. Nos. 1267/72 optd **ITALIA 90**.

1361	**203**	2 f. multicoloured	10	10
1362	–	4 f. multicoloured	10	10
1363	–	5 f. multicoloured	15	10
1364	–	10 f. multicoloured	30	20
1365	–	40 f. multicoloured	1·00	55
1366	–	45 f. multicoloured	1·10	85

228 Pope John Paul II

1990. Papal Visits. Multicoloured.

1367	10 f. Type **228**	30	10
1368	70 f. Pope giving blessing	2·25	1·00

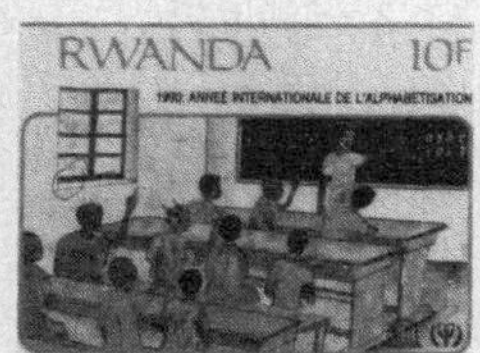

229 Adults learning Alphabet at School

1991. International Literacy Year (1990). Mult.

1370	10 f. Type **229**	15	10
1371	20 f. Children reading at school	35	20
1372	50 f. Lowland villagers learning alphabet in field	90	55
1373	90 f. Highland villagers learning alphabet outdoors	1·40	80

230 Tool-making

1991. Self-help Organizations. Multicoloured.

1374	10 f. Type **230**	15	10
1375	20 f. Rearing livestock	35	20
1376	50 f. Textile manufacture	90	55
1377	90 f. Construction	1·40	80

RYUKYU ISLANDS Pt.18

Group of islands between Japan and Formosa formerly Japanese until occupied by U.S. forces in 1945. After a period of military rule they became semi-autonomous under U.S. administration. The Amami Oshima group reverted to Japan in December 1953. The remaining islands were returned to Japan on 15 May 1972. Japanese stamps are now in use.

1948. 100 sen = 1 yen
1958. 100 cents = 1 dollar (U.S.)

1 Cycad Palm

3 Junk

1948.

1	**1**	5 s. purple	2·75	1·75
2	–	10 s. green	3·00	2·25
3	**1**	20 s. green	2·25	2·25
4	**3**	30 s. red	3·25	2·00
5	–	40 s. purple	2·75	1·75
6	**3**	50 s. blue	3·50	2·50
7	–	1 y. blue	3·50	2·50

DESIGNS: 10 s., 40 s. Easter lily; 1 y. Farmer with hoe.

6 Shi-Shi Roof Tiles

12 Dove over Map of Ryukyus

1950.

6	**6**	50 s. red	25	25
10	–	1 y. blue	2·25	1·25
11	–	2 y. purple	8·50	3·00
12	–	3 y. red	18·00	8·00
13	–	4 y. slate	5·00	3·00
14	–	5 y. green	8·00	4·50

DESIGNS: 1 y. Shuri woman; 2 y. Former Okinawa Palace, Shuri; 3 y. Dragon's head; 4 y. Okinawa women; 5 y. Sea shells.

1950. Air.

15	**12**	8 y. blue	45·00	16·00
16		12 y. green	30·00	13·00
17		16 y. red	15·00	12·00

14 University and Shuri Castle

15 Pine Tree

1951. Inauguration of Ryukyu University.

19	**14**	3 y. brown	35·00	18·00

1951. Afforestation Week.

20	**15**	3 y. green	35·00	18·00

16 Flying Goddess (17)

1951. Air.

21	**16**	13 y. blue	1·50	30
22		18 y. green	2·00	3·00
23		30 y. mauve	3·25	1·25
24		40 y. purple	5·00	2·25
25		50 y. orange	6·50	3·25

1952. Surch as T **17**.

27	**6**	10 y. on 50 s. red	7·00	5·50
29	–	100 y. on 2 y. pur (No. 11)	£1500	£750

18 Dove and Bean Seedling

19 Madanbashi Bridge

1952. Establishment of Ryukyuan Government.

30	**18**	3 y. lake	70·00	20·00

1952.

31	**19**	1 y. red	25	35
32	–	2 y. green	30	25
33	–	3 y. blue	40	25

34 – 6 y. blue . . . . 3·25 3·00
35 – 10 y. red . . . . 1·25 50
36 – 30 y. olive . . . . 4·75 2·50
37 – 50 y. purple . . . . 5·25 2·00
38 – 100 y. red . . . . 11·00 1·25
DESIGNS: 2 y. Presence Chamber, Shuri Palace; 3 y. Shuri Gate; 6 y. Sogenji Temple Wall; 10 y. Bensaitendo Temple; 30 y. Sonohyamutake Gate; 50 y. Tamaudum Mausoleum, Shuri; 100 y. Hoshochai Bridge.

27 Reception at Shuri Castle

28 Perry and American Fleet at Naha Harbour

29 Chofu Ota and Matrix

1953. Centenary of Commodore Perry's Visit to Okinawa.
39 **27** 3 y. purple . . . . 7·50 3·25
40 **28** 6 y. blue . . . . 1·00 2·40

1953. 3rd Press Week.
41 **29** 4 y. brown . . . . 8·50 5·00

30 Wine Flask to fit around Waist

33 Shigo Toma and Pen-nib

1954.
42 **30** 4 y. brown 50 35
43 – 15 y. red . . . . 2·25 1·75
44 – 20 y. orange . . . . 3·25 2·25
DESIGNS: 15 y. Tung Dar Bon (lacquer bowl); 20 y. Kasuri (textile pattern).

1954. 4th Press Week.
45 **33** 4 y. blue . . . . 5·50 3·25

34 Noguni Shrine and Sweet Potatoes

35 Stylised Trees

1955. 350th Anniv of Introduction of Sweet Potato Plant.
46 **34** 4 y. blue . . . . 9·00 4·00

1956. Afforestation Week.
47 **35** 4 y. green . . . . 5·50 3·00

38 Nidotekito Dance

39 Telephone and Dial

1956. National Dances.
48 – 5 y. purple . . . . 1·10 60
49 – 8 y. violet . . . . 1·40 1·25
50 **38** 14 y. brown . . . . 2·25 2·25
DESIGNS: 5 y. Willow dance; 8 y. Straw-hat dance.

1956. Inauguration of Telephone Dialling System.
51 **39** 4 y. violet . . . . 8·00 7·00

40 Floral Garland

41 Flying Goddess

1956. New Year.
52 **40** 2 y. multicoloured . . . . 1·40 1·40

1957. Air.
53 **41** 15 y. green . . . . 1·50 25
54 20 y. red . . . . 3·75 2·75
55 35 y. green . . . . 7·50 3·50
56 45 y. brown . . . . 12·00 5·00
57 60 y. grey . . . . 16·00 7·25

42 Rocket "Pencils"

43 Phoenix

1957. 7th Press Week.
58 **42** 4 y. blue 55 55

1957. New Year.
59 **43** 2 y. multicoloured 20 20

44 Various Ryukyuan Postage Stamps

1958. 10th Anniv of First Postage Stamps of Ryukyu Islands.
60 **44** 4 y. multicoloured 60 40

45 Stylized Dollar Sign over Yen Symbol

1958. With or without gum (Nos. 68/69), no gum (others).
61 **45** ½ c. yellow 25 20
62 1 c. green 25 20
63 2 c. blue 25 20
64 3 c. red 20 15
65 4 c. green 60 40
66 5 c. brown . . . . 2·00 40
67 10 c. turquoise . . . . . . 3·25 40
68 25 c. lavender . . . . . . 3·25 60
69 50 c. grey . . . . 6·50 75
70 $1 purple . . . . 8·00 1·00

46 Gateway of Courtesy

1958. Restoration of Shuri Gateway.
71 **46** 3 c. multicoloured 60 40

47 Lion Dance

48 Trees

1958. New Year.
72 **47** 1½ c. multicoloured 20 25

1959. Afforestation Week.
73 **48** 3 c. multicoloured 60 60

49 Atlas Moth

50 Hibiscus

1959. Japanese Biological Teachers' Conf, Okinawa.
74 **49** 3 c. multicoloured . . . . . 1·50 1·25

1959. Multicoloured. (a) Inscr as in T **50**.
75 ½ c. Type **50** 30 20
76 3 c. Tropical fish . . . . 1·10 25
77 8 c. Sea shells . . . . 6·50 2·00
78 13 c. Leaf butterfly (value at left) 2·00 1·50
79 17 c. Jellyfish . . . . 17·00 5·50

(b) Inscr smaller and 13 c. with value at right.
87 ½ c. Type **50** 20 15
88 3 c. As No. 76 . . . . 2·00 20
89 8 c. As No. 77 . . . . 1·00 1·00
90 13 c. As No. 78 . . . . 1·50 1·00
91 17 c. As No. 79 . . . . 5·50 3·25

55 Yakazi (Ryukyuan toy)

改訂 9¢

(56)

1959. New Year.
80 **55** 1½ c. multicoloured 50 40

1959. Air. Surch as T **56**.
81 **41** 9 c. on 15 y. turquoise . . . 2·00 35
82 14 c. on 20 y. lake . . . . . 2·25 2·25
83 19 c. on 35 y. green . . . . 4·00 2·50
84 27 c. on 45 y. brown . . . . 8·00 5·50
85 35 c. on 60 y. grey . . . . . 10·00 7·00

57 University Badge

60 "Munjuru"

1960. 10th Anniv of University of the Ryukyus.
86 **57** 3 c. multicoloured 75 60

1960. Air. Surch.
92 **30** 9 c. on 4 y. brown . . . . . 4·00 60
93 – 14 c. on 5 y. pur (No. 48) . . 2·00 2·00
94 – 19 c. on 15 y. red (No. 43) . . 3·25 2·75
95 **38** 27 c. on 14 y. brown . . . . 5·00 4·25
96 – 35 c. on 20 y. orge (No. 44) . . 5·50 5·25

1960. Ryukyuan Dances. Mult. (a) Inscr as in T **60**.
97 1 c. Type **60** . . . . 1·25 75
98 2½ c. "Inohabushi" . . . . . . 1·25 75
99 5 c. "Hatomabushi" 70 75
100 10 c. "Hanafu" 95 75

(b) As T **60** but additionally inscr "RYUKYUS".
107 1 c. Type **60** 15 15
108 2½ c. As No. 98 . . . . 25 15
109 4 c. As No. 98 . . . . 15 15
110 5 c. As No. 99 . . . . 20 25
111 10 c. As No. 100 . . . . . . 40 15
112 20 c. "Shudun" . . . . 1·00 35
113 25 c. "Haodori" . . . . 1·00 60
114 50 c. "Nobori Kuduchi" . . . 1·50 60
115 $ 1 "Koteibushi" . . . . 2·00 70

65 Start of Race

1960. 8th Kyushu Athletic Meeting.
101 – 3 c. red, green and blue . . 4·75 1·50
102 **65** 8 c. green and orange . . . 75 1·00
DESIGN: 3 c. Torch and coastal scene.

66 Little Egret and Rising Sun

1960. National Census.
103 **66** 3 c. brown . . . . 4·00 1·00

67 Bull Fight

1960. New Year.
104 **67** 1½ c. brown, buff & blue . . 40 60

68 Native Pine Tree

1961. Afforestation Week.
105 **68** 3 c. dp green, red & green . 1·25 60

69 Naha, Junk, Liner and City Seal

1961. 40th Anniv of Naha City.
106 **69** 3 c. turquoise . . . . . . 1·75 1·25

74 Flying Goddess

79 White Silver Temple

1961. Air.
116 **74** 9 c. multicoloured 40 15
117 – 14 c. multicoloured 60 60
118 – 19 c. multicoloured . . . . 1·10 75
119 – 27 c. multicoloured . . . . 1·25 75
120 – 35 c. multicoloured . . . . 1·60 75
DESIGNS: 14 c. Flying goddess playing flute; 19, 27 c. Wind gods; 35 c. Flying goddess over trees.

1961. Unification of Itoman District and Takamine, Kanegushiku and Miwa Villages.
121 **79** 3 c. brown 75 50

80 Books and Bird

81 Sunrise and Eagles

1961. 10th Anniv of Ryukyu Book Week.
122 **80** 3 c. multicoloured . . . . 1·00 75

1961. New Year.
123 **81** 1½ c. red, black and gold . 2·25 1·00

82 Govt Building, Steps and Trees

85 Shuri Gate and Campaign Emblem

1962. 10th Anniv of Ryukyu Government.
124 **82** 1½ c. multicoloured 50 60
125 – 3 c. grey, green and red . . 75 75
DESIGN: 3 c. Government Building.

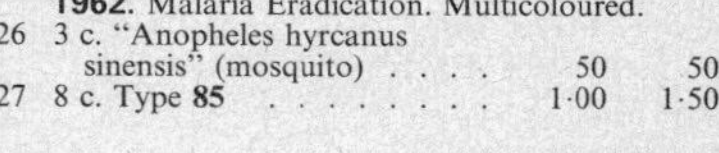

1962. Malaria Eradication. Multicoloured.
126 3 c. "Anopheles hyrcanus sinensis" (mosquito) 50 50
127 8 c. Type **85** . . . . 1·00 1·50

86 Windmill, Dolls and Horse

87 "Hibiscus liliaceus"

1962. Children's Day.
128 **86** 3 c. multicoloured . . . . 1·25 1·25

1962. Ryukyu Flowers. Multicoloured.
129 ½ c. Type **87** 15 15
142 1½ c. "Etithyllum strictum" . . 30 20
130 2 c. "Ixora chinensis" 15 25

131 3 c. "Erythrina indica" 25 20
132 3 c. "Caesalpinia pulcherrima" 20 20
133 8 c. "Schima mertensiana" . . 45 25
134 13 c. "Impatiens balsamina" . 70 50
135 15 c. "Hamaomoto" (herb) . . 85 55
136 17 c. "Alpinia speciosa" . . . 1·00 30

No. 142 is smaller, $18\frac{3}{4}\times22\frac{1}{2}$ mm.

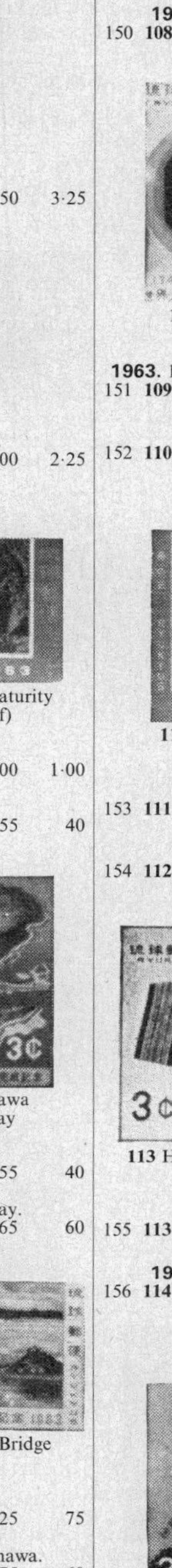

95 Akaeware Bowl

1962. Philatelic Week.
137 **95** 3 c. multicoloured . . . . 3·50 3·25

96 Kendo (Japanese Fencing)

1962. All-Japan Kendo Meeting.
138 **96** 3 c. multicoloured . . . . 4·00 2·25

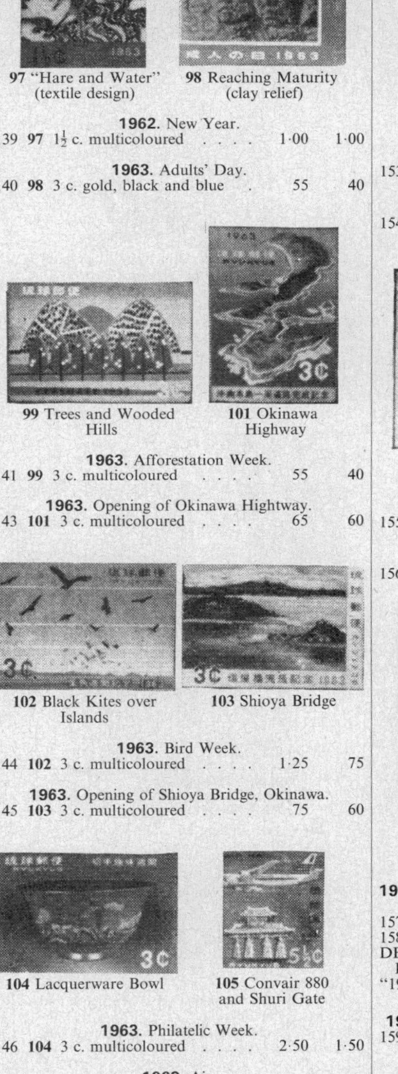

97 "Hare and Water" (textile design) 98 Reaching Maturity (clay relief)

1962. New Year.
139 **97** $1\frac{1}{2}$ c. multicoloured . . . . 1·00 1·00

1963. Adults' Day.
140 **98** 3 c. gold, black and blue . 55 40

99 Trees and Wooded Hills 101 Okinawa Highway

1963. Afforestation Week.
141 **99** 3 c. multicoloured 55 40

1963. Opening of Okinawa Hightway.
143 **101** 3 c. multicoloured 65 60

102 Black Kites over Islands 103 Shioya Bridge

1963. Bird Week.
144 **102** 3 c. multicoloured . . . . 1·25 75

1963. Opening of Shioya Bridge, Okinawa.
145 **103** 3 c. multicoloured 75 60

104 Lacquerware Bowl 105 Convair 880 and Shuri Gate

1963. Philatelic Week.
146 **104** 3 c. multicoloured . . . . 2·50 1·50

1963. Air.
147 **105** $5\frac{1}{2}$ c. multicoloured 15 25
148 – 7 c. black, red and blue . 25 25

DESIGN: 7 c. Convair 880 over sea.

107 Map and Emblem

1963. Meeting of Junior Int Chamber, Naha.
149 **107** 3 c. multicoloured 50 40

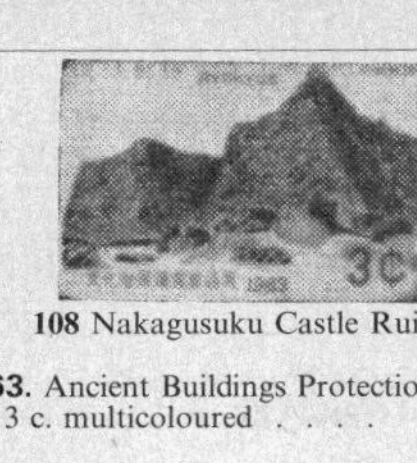

108 Nakagusuku Castle Ruins

1963. Ancient Buildings Protection Week.
150 **108** 3 c. multicoloured 60 50

109 Flame

110 Bingata "dragon" (textile design)

1963. 15th Anniv of Declaration of Human Rights.
151 **109** 3 c. multicoloured 40 25

1963. New Year.
152 **110** $1\frac{1}{2}$ c. multicoloured . . . 25 25

111 Carnation

112 Pineapples and Sugar-cane

1964. Mothers' Day.
153 **111** 3 c. multicoloured 25 25

1964. Agricultural Census.
154 **112** 3 c. multicoloured 35 25

113 Hand-woven Sash

114 Girl Scout and Emblem

1964. Philatelic Week.
155 **113** 3 c. ochre, blue and pink 40 20

1964. 10th Anniv of Ryukyu Girl Scouts.
156 **114** 3 c. multicoloured 25 25

115 Transmitting Tower

117 Shuri Gate and Olympic Torch

1964. Inauguration of Ryukyu–Japan Microwave Link.
157 **115** 3 c. green and black . . . 60 75
158 – 8 c. blue and black . . . 90 75

DESIGN: 8 c. "Bowl" receiving aerial.

Both stamps have "1963" cancelled by bars and "1964" inserted in black.

1964. Passage of Olympic Torch through Okinawa.
159 **117** 3 c. multicoloured 20 20

118 "Naihanchi" (Karate stance)

121 "Miyara Dunchi" (old Ryukyuan Residence)

1964. Karate ("self-defence"). Multicoloured.
160 3 c. Type **118** 55 40
161 3 c. "Makiwara" (karate training) 45 50
162 3 c. "Kumite" exercise . . . 45 50

1964. Ancient Buildings Protection Week.
163 **121** 3 c. multicoloured 25 25

122 Bingata "snake" (textile design) 123 Boy Scouts, Badge and Shuri Gate

1964. New Year.
164 **122** $1\frac{1}{2}$ c. multicoloured 25 25

1965. 10th Anniv of Ryukyuan Boy Scouts.
165 **123** 3 c. multicoloured 25 25

124 "Samisen" (musical instrument)

1965. Philatelic Week.
166 **124** 3 c. multicoloured 25 25

125 Stadium

1965. Completion of Onoyama Sports Ground.
167 **125** 3 c. multicoloured 25 25

126 Kin Power Station

127 I.C.Y. Emblem and "Globe"

1965. Completion of Kin Power Plant.
168 **126** 3 c. multicoloured 20 20

1965. International Co-operation Year and 20th Anniv of United Nations.
169 **127** 3 c. multicoloured 15 25

128 City Hall, Naha

129 Semaruhakogame Turtle

1965. Completion of Naha City Hall.
170 **128** 3 c. multicoloured 20 25

1965. Ryukyuan Turtles. Multicoloured.
171 3 c. Type **129** 30 25
172 3 c. Taimai or hawksbill turtle 25 25
173 3 c. Yamagame or hill tortoise 25 25

132 Bingata "horse" (textile design)

133 Pryer's Woodpecker

1965. New Year.
174 **132** $1\frac{1}{2}$ c. multicoloured 15 25

1966. "Natural Monument" (Wildlife). Mult.
175 3 c. Type **133** 25 25
176 3 c. Sika deer 25 25
177 3 c. Dugong 25 25

MORE DETAILED LISTS
are given in the Stanley Gibbons Catalogues referred to in the country headings. For lists of current volumes see introduction

136 Pacific Swallow

137 Lilies and Ruins

1966. Bird Week.
178 **136** 3 c. multicoloured 45 35

1966. Memorial Day (Battle of Okinawa).
179 **137** 3 c. multicoloured 15 25

138 University of the Ryukyus

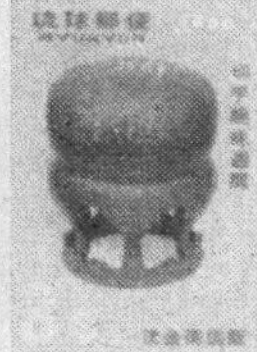

139 Lacquer Box

1966. Transfer of University of the Ryukyus to Government Administration.
180 **138** 3 c. multicoloured 15 25

1966. Philatelic Week.
181 **139** 3 c. multicoloured 20 25

140 Ryukyuan Tiled House

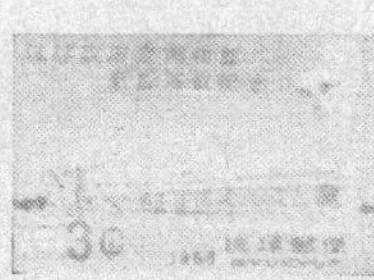

141 "GRI" Museum, Shuri

1966. 20th Anniv of U.N.E.S.C.O.
182 **140** 3 c. multicoloured 15 25

1966. Completion of Government Museum, Shuri.
183 **141** 3 c. multicoloured 15 25

142 Nakasone-Tuimya Tomb

143 Bingata "ram" (textile design)

1966. Ancient Building Protection Week.
184 **142** 3 c. multicoloured 15 25

1966. New Year.
185 **143** $1\frac{1}{2}$ c. multicoloured 15 25

144 Clown Fish

149 Tsuboya Urn

1966. Tropical Fish. Multicoloured.
186 3 c. Type **144** 25 25
187 3 c. Box fish 25 25
188 3 c. Forceps fish 25 25
189 3 c. Spotted triggerfish . . . 25 25
190 3 c. Saddleback butterfly . . . 25 25

1967. Philatelic Week.
191 **149** 3 c. multicoloured 20 20

150 Episcopal Mitre

155 Roof Tiles and Emblem

1967. Sea Shells. Multicoloured.
192 3 c. Type **150** 25 25
193 3 c. Venus comb murex . . . 25 25
194 3 c. Chiragra spider conch . . 30 25
195 3 c. Green turban 30 25
196 3 c. Bubble conch 50 25

1967. International Tourist Year.
197 **155** 3 c. multicoloured 20 25

156 Mobile Clinic

1967. 15th Anniv of Anti-T.B. Association.
198 **156** 3 c. multicoloured 20 20

157 Hojo Bridge, Enkaku

1967. Ancient Buildings Protection Week.
199 **157** 3 c. multicoloured 15 25

158 Bingata "monkey" (textile design)

159 T.V. Tower and Map

1967. New Year.
200 **158** 1½ c. multicoloured 15 25

1967. Opening of T.V. Broadcasting Stations in Miyako and Yaeyama.
201 **159** 3 c. multicoloured 15 25

160 Dr. Nakachi and Assistant

161 Medicine Case (after Sokei Dana)

1968. 120th Anniv of 1st Ryukyu Vaccination (by Dr. Kijin Nakachi).
202 **160** 3 c. multicoloured 15 25

1968. Philatelic Week.
203 **161** 3 c. multicoloured 25 25

162 Young Man, Book, Map and Library

1968. Library Week.
204 **162** 3 c. multicoloured 25 25

163 Postmen with Ryukyu Stamp of 1948

1968. 20th Anniv of 1st Ryukyu Islands Stamps.
205 **163** 3 c. multicoloured 25 25

164 Temple Gate

165 Old Man Dancing

1968. Restoration of Enkaku Temple Gate.
206 **164** 3 c. multicoloured 25 25

1968. Old People's Day.
207 **165** 3 c. multicoloured 25 25

166 "Mictyris longicarpus"

1968. Crabs. Multicoloured.
208 3 c. Type **166** 55 60
209 3 c. "Uca dubia" 50 60
210 3 c. "Baptozius vinosus" . . 50 60
211 3 c. "Cardisoma carnifex" . . 60 60
212 3 c. "Ocypode ceratophthalma" 60 60

171 Saraswati Pavilion

172 Player

1968. Ancient Buildings Protection Week.
213 **171** 3 c. multicoloured 25 25

1968. 35th All-Japan East v West Men's Softball Tennis Tournament, Onoyama.
214 **172** 3 c. multicoloured 25 25

173 Bingata "Cock" (textile design)

174 Boxer

1968. New Year.
215 **173** 1½ c. multicoloured . . . 30 20

1969. 20th All-Japan Boxing Championships.
216 **174** 3 c. multicoloured 25 25

175 Inkwell Screen

176 U.H.F. Antennae and Map

1969. Philatelic Week.
217 **175** 3 c. multicoloured 30 25

1969. Inauguration of Okinawa–Sakishima U.H.F. Radio Service.
218 **176** 3 c. multicoloured 20 25

177 "Gate of Courtesy"

178 "Tug of War" Festival

1969. 22nd All-Japan Formative Education Study Conference, Naha.
219 **177** 3 c. multicoloured 20 25

1969. Traditional Religious Ceremonies. Mult.
220 3 c. Type **178** 50 40
221 3 c. "Hari" canoe race . . . 50 40
222 3 c. "Izaiho" religious ceremony 50 40
223 3 c. "Ushideiku" dance . . . 60 40
224 3 c. "Sea God" dance 60 40

1969. No. 131 surch.
225 ½ c. on 3 c. multicoloured . . 15 25

184 Nakamura-Ke

1969. Ancient Buildings Protection Week.
226 **184** 3 c. multicoloured 20 20

185 Kyuzo Toyama and Map

186 Bingata "dog and flowers" (textile design)

1969. 70th Anniv of Toyama's Ryukyu–Hawaii Emigration Project.
227 **185** 3 c. multicoloured 35 35
No. 227 has "1970" cancelled by bars and "1969" inserted in black.

1969. New Year.
228 **186** 1½ c. multicoloured 15 20

187 Sake Flask

1970. Philatelic Week.
229 **187** 3 c. multicoloured 30 20

188 "Shushin-Kaneiri"

189 "Chu-nusudu"

190 "Mekarushi"

191 "Nidotichiuchi"

192 "Kokonomaki"

1970. "Kumi-Odori" Ryukyu Theatre. Multicoloured.
230 **188** 3 c. multicoloured 70 55
231 **189** 3 c. multicoloured 70 55
232 **190** 3 c. multicoloured 70 55
233 **191** 3 c. multicoloured 70 55
234 **192** 3 c. multicoloured 70 55

193 Observatory

194 Noboru Jahana (politician)

1970. Completion of Underwater Observatory, Busena-Misaki, Nago.
240 **193** 3 c. multicoloured 20 25

1970. Famous Ryukyuans.
241 **194** 3 c. red 50 60
242 – 3 c. green 70 60
243 – 3 c. black 50 60
PORTRAITS: No. 242, Saion Gushichan Bunjaku (statesman); No. 243, Choho Giwan (Regent).

197 "Population

198 "Great Cycad of Une"

1970. Population Census.
244 **197** 3 c. multicoloured 20 25

1970. Ancient Buildings Protection Week.
245 **198** 3 c. multicoloured 30 25

199 Ryukyu Islands, Flag and Japan Diet

200 "Wild Boar" (Bingata textile design)

1970. Election of Ryukyu Representatives to the Japanese diet.
246 **199** 3 c. multicoloured 60 60

1970. New Year.
247 **200** 1½ c. multicoloured . . . 30 25

201 "Jibata" (hand-loom)

202 "Filature" (spinning-wheel)

203 Farm-worker wearing "Shurunnu" Coat and "Kubagasa" Hat

204 Woman using "Shiri-Ushi" (rice huller)

205 Fisherman's "Umi-Fujo" (box) and "Yutui" (bailer)

1971. Ryukyu Handicrafts.
248 **201** 3 c. multicoloured 30 30
249 **202** 3 c. multicoloured 30 30
250 **203** 3 c. multicoloured 30 30
251 **204** 3 c. multicoloured 45 30
252 **205** 3 c. multicoloured 30 30

206 "Taku" (container)

208 Restored Battlefield, Okinawa

207 Civic Emblem with Old and New City Views

1971. Philatelic Week.
253 **206** 3 c. multicoloured 25 25

1971. 50th Anniv of Naha's City Status.
254 **207** 3 c. multicoloured 30 25

1971. Government Parks. Multicoloured.
255 3 c. Type **208** 30 30
256 3 c. Haneji Inland Sea 30 30
257 4 c. Yabuchi Island 30 30

211 Deva King Torinji Temple

212 "Rat" (Bingata textile pattern)

1971. Anicent Buildings Protection Week.
258 **211** 2 c. multicoloured 30 20

1971. New Year.
259 **212** 2 c. multicoloured 30 20

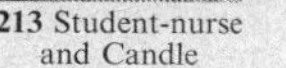

213 Student-nurse and Candle

214 Islands and Sunset

1971. 25th Anniv of Nurses' Training Scheme.
260 **213** 4 c. multicoloured 25 25

1972. Maritime Scenery. Multicoloured.
261 5 c. Type **214** 30 70
262 5 c. Coral reef 30 70
263 5 c. Islands and short-tailed albatross 80 70

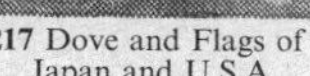
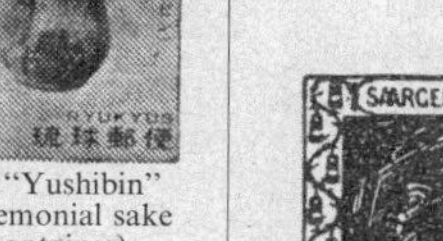

217 Dove and Flags of Japan and U.S.A

218 "Yushibin" (ceremonial sake container)

1972. Ratification of Treaty for Return of Ryukyu Islands to Japan.
264 **217** 5 c. multicoloured . . . . 40 1·00

1972. Philatelic Week.
265 **218** 5 c. multicoloured . . . . 50 1·00

SPECIAL DELIVERY STAMP

F 13 Sea Horse

1951.
E18 **F 13** 5 y. blue . . . . 17·00 15·00

SAAR Pt. 7

A German territory to the S.E. of Luxembourg. Occupied by France under League of Nations control from 1920 to 1935. Following a plebiscite, Saar returned to Germany in 1935 when German stamps were used until the Fench occupation in 1945 when Nos. F 1/13 of Germany replaced them followed by Nos. 203, etc. The territory was autonomous under French protection until it again returned to Germany at the end of 1956 following a national referendum. Issues from 1957 were authorised by the German Federal Republic pending the adoption of German currency on 6 July 1959, after which West German stamps wre used.

1920–May 1921. 100 pfennig = 1 mark
May 1921–March 1935. 100 centimes = 1 franc
1935–47. 100 pfennig = 1 reichsmark
1947. 100 pfennig = 1 saarmark
November 1947–July 1959. 100 centimes = 1 franc
From 1959. 100 pfennig = 1 Deutsche mark

LEAGUE OF NATIONS COMMISSION

1920. German stamps inscr "DEUTSCHES REICH" optd **Sarre** and bar.
1 **24** 2 pf. grey . . . . 75 2·25
2 2½ pf. grey . . . . 1·75 3·50
3 **10** 3 pf. brown . . . . 60 1·50
4 5 pf. green 15 25
5 **24** 7½ pf. orange 40 70
6 **10** 10 pf. red 15 25
7 **24** 15 pf. violet 15 25
8 **10** 20 pf. blue 15 25
9 25 pf. black & red on yell . 6·00 12·00
10 30 pf. black & orange on buff 10·00 20·00
11 **24** 35 pf. brown 25 45
12 **10** 40 pf. black and red . . . 30 45
13 50 pf. black & pur on buff . 25 45
14 60 pf. purple 35 45
15 75 pf. black and green . . . 30 45
16 80 pf. black & red on rose . £200 £225
17a **12** 1 m. red . . . . 16·00 32·00

1920. Bavarian stamps optd **Sarre** or **SARRE** and bars.
18 **15** 5 pf. green . . . . 50 1·00
19 10 pf. red . . . . 50 1·25
20a 15 pf. red . . . . 60 1·60
21 20 pf. blue . . . . 50 1·25
22 25 pf. grey . . . . 5·00 13·00
23 30 pf. orange . . . . 4·50 8·50
24 **15** 40 pf. olive . . . . 5·50 13·00
25 50 pf. brown . . . . 65 1·25
26 60 pf. green . . . . 95 3·00
27 **16** 1 m. brown . . . . 8·50 25·00
28 2 m. violet . . . . 50·00 £110
29 3 m. red . . . . 75·00 £850
30 – 5 m. blue (No. 192) . . . £800 £200
31 – 10 m. green (No. 193) . . 90·00 £200

1920. German stamps inscr "DEUTSCHES REICH" optd **SAARGEBIET**.
32 **10** 5 pf. green 20 25
33 5 pf. brown 35 45
34 10 pf. red 20 25
35 10 pf. orange 25 25
36 **24** 15 pf. violet 20 25
37 **10** 20 pf. blue 20 25
38 20 pf. green 30 45
39 30 pf. black & orge on buff . 25 25
40 30 pf. blue 40 65
41 40 pf. black and red 25 25
42 40 pf. red 55 60
43 50 pf. black & pur on buff . 30 35
44 60 pf. purple 30 35
45 75 pf. black and green . . . 30 35
46 **12** 1 m. 25 green . . . . . . 2·50 1·25
47 1 m. 50 brown . . . . . . 2·50 1·25
48 **13** 2 m. 50 red . . . . 3·00 9·50
49 **10** 4 m. red and black . . . . 5·50 19·00

1920. Stamps of Germany optd as above and surch.
50 **10** 20 on 75 pf. black & green . 30 1·00
51 **24** 5 m. on 15 pf. purple . . . 4·50 12·00
52 10 m. on 15 pf. purple . . . 5·50 15·00

9 Miner

11 Colliery Shafthead

12 Burbach Steelworks

1921.
53 – 5 pf. violet and olive . . . 20 25
54 **9** 10 pf. orange and blue . . . 20 20
55 – 20 pf. blue and green . . . 50 25
56 – 25 pf. blue and brown . . . 35 25
57 – 30 pf. brown and green . . . 30 40
58 – 40 pf. red 30 35
59 – 50 pf. black and grey . . . 1·40 2·00
60 – 60 pf. brown and red . . . 1·00 2·25
61 – 80 pf. blue 40 85
62 – 1 m. black and red 50 75
63 **11** 1 m. 25 green and brown . 60 1·25
64 – 2 m. black and orange . . 2·25 3·25
65 – 3 m. black and brown . . . 2·50 8·00
66 – 5 m. violet and yellow . . 5·00 17·00
67 – 10 m. brown and green . . 7·50 21·00
68 **12** 25 m. blue, black and red . 25·00 55·00
DESIGNS—As Type **11**: HORIZ: 5 pf. Mill above Mettlach; 20 pf. Pit head at Reden; 25 pf. River traffic, Saarbrucken; 30 pf. River Saar at Mettlach; 40 pf. Slag-heap, Volklingen; 50 pf. Signal gantry, Saarbrucken; 80 pf. "Old Bridge", Saarbrucken; 1 m. Wire-rope Railway; 2 m. Town Hall, Saarbrucken; 3 m. Pottery, Mettlach; 5 m. St. Ludwig's Church; 10 m. Chief Magistrate's and Saar Commissioner's Offices. VERT: 60 pf. Gothic Chapel, Mettlach.

1921. Nos. 55/68 surch in new currency.
70 3 c. on 20 pf. blue and green . 40 20
71 5 c. on 25 pf. blue and brown . 15 30
72 10 c. on 30 pf. brown & green 25 30
73 15 c. on 40 pf. red 35 25
74 20 c. on 50 pf. black and grey 70 15
75 25 c. on 60 pf. brown and red 35 25
76 30 c. on 80 pf. blue . . . . . 1·00 40
77 40 f. on 1 m. black and red . 1·75 40
78 50 c. on 1 m. 25 green & brown 2·75 60
79 75 c. on 2 m. black & orange . 2·75 90
80 1 f. on 3 m. black and brown . 2·75 1·50
81 2 f. on 5 m. violet and yellow . 8·50 5·00
82 3 f. on 10 m. brown and green 10·00 19·00
83 5 f. on 25 m. blue, black & red 16·00 26·00

1922. Larger designs (except 5 f.) and value in French currency.
84 3 c. green (as No. 62) 20 35
85 5 c. black & orge (as No. 54) 20 10
86 10 c. green (as No. 61) . . . 25 10
87 15 c. brown (as No. 62) . . . 25 15
98 15 c. orange (as No. 62) . . . 2·25 35
88 20 c. blue & yell (as No. 64) . 1·25 15
100 25 c. red & yellow (as No. 64) 1·50 20
90 30 c. red & yellow (as No. 58) 25 40
91 40 c. brown & yell (as No. 65) 50 10
92 50 c. blue & yellow (as No. 56) 75 10
101 75 c. green & yell (as No. 65) 15·00 1·75
94 1 f. brown (as No. 66) . . . 1·00 35
95 2 f. violet (as No. 63) . . . 3·00 2·00
96 3 f. grn & orange (as No. 60) 2·50 2·00
97 5 f. brn & chocolate (as No. 68) 35·00 60·00

14 Madonna of Blieskastel

15 Army Medical Service

1925.
102 **14** 45 c. plum . . . . 2·25 2·25
103 10 f. brown (31 × 36 mm) . 10·00 24·00

1926. Welfare Fund.
104 **15** 20 c. + 20 c. olive . . . . 6·00 13·00
105 – 40 c. + 40 c. brown . . . . 6·50 16·00
106 – 50 c. + 50 c. orange . . . 6·50 12·00
107 – 1 f. 50 + 1 f. 50 blue . . . 14·00 40·00
DESIGNS: 40 c. Hospital work (nurse and patient); 50 c. Child welfare (children at a spring); 1 f. 50, Maternity nursing service.

18 Tholey Abbey

1926.
108 – 10 c. brown 50 15
109 – 15 c. green 40 70
110 – 20 c. brown 35 15
111 **18** 25 c. blue 40 35
112 – 30 c. green 50 15
113 – 40 c. sepia 50 15
114 **18** 50 c. red 50 15
114a – 60 c. orange . . . . . . 1·25 20
115 – 75 c. purple 50 15
116 – 80 c. orange . . . . . . 2·75 6·50
116a – 90 c. red . . . . 7·00 17·00
117 – 1 f. violet . . . . 2·25 20
118 – 1 f. 50 blue . . . . . . 6·00 20
119 – 2 f. red . . . . 6·00 25
120 – 3 f. olive . . . . 14·00 75
121 – 5 f. brown . . . . 16·00 5·50
DESIGNS—VERT: 10, 30 c. Fountain, St. Johann, Saarbrucken. HORIZ: 15, 75 c. Saar Valley near Gudingen; 20, 40, 90 c. View from Saarlouis fortifications; 60, 80 c., 1 f. Colliery shafthead; 1 f. 50, 2, 3, 5 f. Burbach Steelworks.

1927. Welfare Fund. Optd **1927-28.**
122 **15** 20 c. + 20 c. olive . . . . 26·00 16·00
123 40 c. + 40 c. brown . . . . 24·00 20·00
124 50 c. + 50 c. orange . . . 20·00 16·00
125 1 f. 50 + 1 f. 50 blue . . . 29·00 42·00

19 Breguet 14 Biplane over Saarbrucken

20 "The Blind Beggar" by Dyckmanns

1928. Air.
126 **19** 50 c. red . . . . 2·50 2·50
127 1 f. violet . . . . 3·25 3·25

1928. Christmas Charity.
128 **20** 40 c. (+ 40 c.) brown . . . 7·00 22·00
129 50 c. (+ 50 c.) red . . . . 7·00 22·00
130 1 f. (+ 1 f.) violet . . . . 7·00 22·00
131 – 1 f. 50 (+ 1 f. 50) blue . . 7·00 22·00
132 – 2 f. (+ 2 f.) red . . . . . 8·00 24·00
133 – 3 f. (+ 3 f.) green . . . . 8·00 24·00
134 – 10 f. (+ 10 f.) brown . . . £400 £3000
DESIGNS: 1 f. 50, 2, 3 f. "Almsgiving" by Schiestl; 10 f. "Charity" by Raphael (picture in circle).

1929. Christmas Charity. Paintings. As T **20**.
135 40 c. (+ 15 c.) green . . . . 1·50 3·25
136 50 c. (+ 20 c.) red . . . . . 3·50 5·50
137 1 f. (+ 50 c.) purple . . . . 3·50 7·00
138 1 f. 50 (+ 75 c.) blue . . . 3·50 7·00
139 2 f. (+ 1 f.) red . . . . . . 3·50 7·00
140 3 f. (+ 2 f.) green . . . . . 5·50 16·00
141 10 f. (+ 8 f.) brown . . . . 35·00 85·00
DESIGNS: 40 c. to 1 f. "Orphaned" by H. Kaulbach; 1 f. 50, 2, 3 f. "St. Ottilia" by M. Feuerstein; 10 f. "The Little Madonna" by Ferruzzio.

1930. Nos. 114 and 116 surch.
141a **18** 40 c. on 50 c. red . . . . 85 1·10
142 – 60 c. on 80 c. orange . . . 85 1·90

1931. Christmas Charity (1930 issue). Paintings. As T **20**.
143 40 c. (+ 15 c.) brown . . . . 5·00 17·00
144 60 c. (+ 20 c.) orange . . . 5·00 17·00
145 1 f. (+ 50 c.) red . . . . . 6·50 32·00
146 1 f. 50 (+ 75 c.) blue . . . 8·00 32·00
147 2 f. (+ 1 f.) brown . . . . . 8·00 32·00
148 3 f. (+ 2 f.) green . . . . . 11·00 32·00
149 10 f. (+ 10 f.) brown . . . . 65·00 £250
DESIGNS: 40, 60 c., 1 f. 50, "The Safetyman" (miner and lamp) by F. Zolnhofer; 1, 2, 3 f. "The Good Samaritan" by J. Heinemann; 10 f. "At the Window" by F. G. Waldmuller.

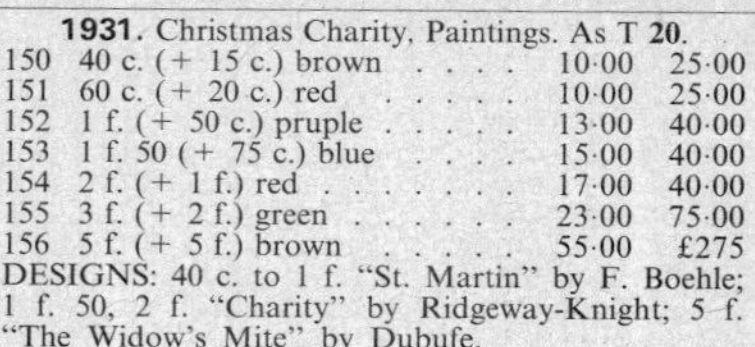

1931. Christmas Charity. Paintings. As T **20**.
150 40 c. (+ 15 c.) brown . . . . 10·00 25·00
151 60 c. (+ 20 c.) red . . . . . 10·00 25·00
152 1 f. (+ 50 c.) pruple . . . . 13·00 40·00
153 1 f. 50 (+ 75 c.) blue . . . 15·00 40·00
154 2 f. (+ 1 f.) red . . . . . . 17·00 40·00
155 3 f. (+ 2 f.) green . . . . . 23·00 75·00
156 5 f. (+ 5 f.) brown . . . . . 55·00 £275
DESIGNS: 40 c. to 1 f. "St. Martin" by F. Boehle; 1 f. 50, 2 f. "Charity" by Ridgeway-Knight; 5 f. "The Widow's Mite" by Dubufe.

29 Airport

30 Kirkel Castle Ruins

1932. Air.
157 **29** 60 c. red . . . . 5·00 2·50
158 5 f. brown . . . . 35·00 85·00

1932. Christmas Charity.
159 **30** 40 c. (+ 15 c.) brown . . 7·00 22·00
160 – 60 c. (+ 20 c.) red . . . . 7·00 22·00
161 – 1 f. (+ 50 c.) purple . . . 10·00 35·00
162 – 1 f. 50 (+ 75 c.) blue . . . 16·00 42·00
163 – 2 f. (+ 1 f.) red . . . . . 16·00 42·00
164 – 3 f. (+ 2 f.) green . . . . 40·00 £140
165 – 5 f. (+ 5 f.) brown . . . . 65·00 £225
DESIGNS—VERT: 60 c. Blieskastel Church; 1 f. Ottweiler Church; 1 f. 50, St. Michael's Church, Saarbrucken; 2 f. Cathedral and fountain, St. Wendel; 3 f. St. John's Church, Saarbrucken. HORIZ: 5 f. Kerpen Castle, Illingen.

32 Scene of the Disaster

33 "Love"

1933. Neunkirchen Explosion Disaster.
166 **32** 60 c. + 60 c. orange . . . 8·50 16·00
167 3 f. + 3 f. green . . . . . 35·00 40·00
168 5 f. + 5 f. brown . . . . . 35·00 60·00

1934. Christmas Charity.
169 **33** 40 c. (+ 15 c.) brown . . 4·25 13·00
170 – 60 c. (+ 20 c.) red . . . . 4·25 13·00
171 – 1 f. (+ 50 c.) mauve . . . 6·00 16·00
172 – 1 f. 50 (+ 75 c.) blue . . . 11·00 30·00
173 – 2 f. (+ 1 f.) red . . . . . 10·00 27·00
174 – 3 f. (+ 2 f.) green . . . . 11·00 30·00
175 – 5 f. (+ 5 f.) brown . . . . 25·00 65·00
DESIGNS: 60 c. "Solicitude". 1 f. "Peace". 1 f. 50, "Consolation". 2 f. "Welfare". 3 f. "Truth". 5 f. Countess Elizabeth von Nassau.
Nos. 169/74 show statues by C. L. Pozzi in church of St. Louis, Saarbrucken.

1934. Saar Pleblscite. Optd **VOLKSABSTIMMUNG 1935**. (a) Postage. On Nos. 108/15, 116a/21 and 103.
176 – 10 c. brown 40 55
177 – 15 c. green 40 55
178 – 20 c. orange 35 35
179 **18** 25 c. blue . . . . 55 1·25
180 – 30 c. green 35 30
181 – 40 c. sepia 35 40
182 **18** 50 c. lake . . . . 60 1·10
183 – 60 c. orange 35 30
184 – 75 c. purple . . . . 60 1·25
185 – 90 c. red . . . . 60 1·25
186 – 1 f. violet . . . . 70 1·25
187 – 1 f. 50 blue . . . . . . 3·00 3·50
188 – 2 f. red . . . . 4·50 4·75
189 – 3 f. olive . . . . 7·50 6·50
190 – 5 f. brown . . . . 32·00 32·00
191 **14** 10 f. brown . . . . 22·00 50·00

(b) Air. On Nos. 126/7 and 157/8.
192 **19** 50 c. red . . . . 3·50 8·00
193 **29** 60 c. red . . . . 2·00 2·50
194 **19** 1 r. violet . . . . 4·75 10·00
195 **29** 5 f. brown . . . . 7·50 13·00

(c) Charity. On Nos. 169/75.
196 **33** 40 c. (+ 15 c.) brown . . . 3·00 9·50
197 – 60 c. (+ 20 c.) red . . . . 3·00 9·50
198 – 1 f. (+ 50 c.) mauve . . . 7·50 22·00
199 – 1 f. 50 (+ 75 c.) blue . . . 7·50 22·00
200 – 2 f. (+ 1 f.) red . . . . . 9·50 28·00
201 – 3 f. (+ 2 f.) green . . . . 8·00 25·00
202 – 5 f. (+ 5 f.) brown . . . . 14·00 32·00

FRENCH OCCUPATION

36 Coal-miner

37 Loop of the Saar

1947. Inscr "SAAR".

203 36 2 pf. grey 10 15
204 3 pf. orange 10 50
205 6 pf. green 10 20
206 8 pf. red 10 20
207 10 pf. mauve 10 15
208 12 pf. green 10 10
209 – 15 pf. brown 10 55
210 – 16 pf. blue 10 15
211 – 20 pf. red 10 15
212 – 24 pf. brown 10 10
213 – 25 pf. mauve . . . . 40 16·00
214 – 30 pf. green 15 45
215 – 40 pf. brown 15 45
216 – 45 pf. red . . . . 45 12·00
217 – 50 pf. violet . . . . 35 15·00
218 – 60 pf. violet . . . . 35 15·00
219 – 75 pf. blue 10 30
220 – 80 pf. orange 10 30
221 – 84 pf. brown 10 30
222 37 1 m. green 10 40

DESIGNS—SMALL SIZE: 15 pf. to 24 pf. Steel workers; 25 pf. to 50 pf. Sugar Beet harvesters; 60 pf. to 80 pf. Mettlach Abbey. As T 37—VERT: 84 pf. Marshal Ney.

1947. As last surch in French currency.

223 36 10 c. on 2 pf. grey 10 50
224 60 c. on 3 pf. orange . . . 10 50
225 1 f. on 10 f. mauve 10 50
226 2 f. on 12 f. green 10 65
227 – 3 f. on 15 pf. brown . . . 10 50
228 – 4 f. on 16 pf. blue . . . . 15 5·00
229 – 5 pf. on 20 pf. red 10 80
230 – 6 f. on 24 pf. brown . . . 10 50
231 – 9 f. on 30 pf. green . . . 30 6·50
232 – 10 f. on 50 pf. violet . . . 30 10·00
233 – 14 f. on 60 pf. violet . . . 45 6·00
234 – 20 f. on 84 pf. brown . . . 30 8·00
235 37 50 pf. on 1 m. green . . . 1·10 12·00

42 Clasped Hands

43 Builders

44 Saar Valley

1948. Inscr "SAARPOST".

236 42 10 c. red (postage) . . . . 60 1·40
237 60 c. blue . . . . 60 1·40
238 1 f. black 25 15
239 – 2 f. red 25 10
240 – 3 f. brown 30 10
241 – 4 f. red 30 10
242 – 5 f. violet 30 15
243 – 6 f. red 65 15
244 – 9 f. blue . . . . 5·50 25
245 – 10 f. blue . . . . 2·50 20
246 – 14 f. purple . . . . 3·00 65
247 43 20 f. red . . . . 6·50 65
248 – 50 f. blue . . . . 16·00 2·50
249 44 25 f. red (air) . . . . . . 5·00 3·50
250 50 f. blue . . . . 2·75 1·75
251 200 f. red . . . . 24·00 28·00

DESIGNS: As Type 42: 2, 3 f. Man's head; 4, 5 f. Woman's head; 6, 9 f. Miner's head. As Type 43: 10 f. Blast furnace chimney; 14 f. Foundry; 50 f. Facade of Mettlach Abbey.

46 Floods in St. Johann, Sarbrucken

47 Map of Saarland

1948. Flood Disaster Relief Fund. Flood Scenes. Inscr as in T 46.

252 5 f. + 5 f. green (postage) . . 3·50 18·00
253 6 f. + 4 f. purple . . . . . . 3·50 18·00
254 12 f. + 8 f. red . . . . . . 3·75 24·00
255 18 f. + 12 f. blue . . . . . . 5·50 30·00
256 25 f. + 25 f. brown (air) . . . 23·00 £130

DESIGNS—VERT: 18 f. Flooded street, Saarbrucken. HORIZ: 5 f. Flooded industrial area; 12 f. Landtag building, Saarbrucken; 25 f. Floods at Ensdorf, Saarlouis.

1948. 1st Anniv of Constitution.

257 47 10 f. red . . . . 1·25 2·00
258 25 f. blue . . . . 2·00 4·50

48 Hikers and Ludweiler Hostel

1949. Youth Hostels Fund.

259 48 8 f. + 5 f. brown . . . . 1·75 4·75
260 – 10 f. + 7 f. green . . . . 2·00 3·50

DESIGN: 10 f. Hikers and Weisskirchen hostel.

49 Chemical Research

50 Mare and Foal

1949. Saar University.

261 49 15 f. red . . . . 3·50 15

1949. Horse Day.

262 50 15 f. + 5 f. red . . . . . 15·00 23·00
263 – 25 f. + 15 f. blue . . . . 17·00 27·00

DESIGN: 25 f. Two horses in steeple-chase.

51 Symbolic of Typography

52 Labourer and Foundry

1949.

264 – 10 c. purple . . . . 20 1·40
265 – 60 c. black . . . . 30 1·40
266 – 1 f. red . . . . 1·40 10
267 – 3 f. brown . . . . 8·50 30
268 – 5 f. violet . . . . 2·00 10
269 – 6 f. green . . . . 13·00 60
270 – 8 f. olive 75 35
271 51 10 f. orange . . . . 5·00 10
272 – 12 f. green . . . . 16·00 10
273 – 15 f. red . . . . 8·50 15
274 – 18 f. mauve . . . . 3·00 4·00
275 52 20 f. grey . . . . 2·00 15
276 – 25 f. blue . . . . 22·00 15
277 – 30 f. red . . . . 16·00 45
278 – 45 f. purple . . . . 5·50 35
279 – 60 f. green . . . . 5·50 1·50
280 – 100 f. sepia . . . . 12·00 1·60

DESIGNS: As Type 51: 10 c. Building trade; 60 c. Beethoven; 1 f. and 3 f. Heavy industries; 5 f. Slag heap; 6 f. and 15 f. Colliery; 8 f. Posthorn and telephone; 12 f. and 18 f. Pottery. As Type 52: VERT: 25 f. Blast furnace worker; 60 f. Landsweiler; 100 f. Wiebelskirchen. HORIZ: 30 f. St. Arnual; 45 f. "Giant's Boot", Rentrisch.

53 Detail from "Moses Striking the Rock" (Murillo)

54 A. Kolping

55 P. Wust

1949. National Relief Fund.

281 53 8 f. + 2 f. blue . . . . . 7·50 23·00
282 – 12 f. + 3 f. green . . . . 9·50 25·00
283 – 15 f. + 5 f. red . . . . . 13·00 45·00
284 – 25 f. + 10 f. blue . . . . 18·00 80·00
285 – 50 f. + 20 f. purple . . . 32·00 £120

DESIGNS—VERT: 12 f. "Our Lord healing the Paralytic" (Murillo); 15 f. "The Sick Child" (Metsu); 25 f. "St. Thomas of Villanueva" (Murillo); 50 f. "Madonna of Blieskastel".

1950. Honouring Adolf Kolping (miners' padre).

286 54 15 f. + 5 f. red . . . . . 24·00 55·00

1950. 10th Death Anniv of Peter Wust (philosopher).

287 55 15 f. red . . . . 4·25 4·25

56 Mail Coach

1950. Stamp Day.

288 56 15 f. + 5 f. brown & red . 55·00 80·00

57 "Food for the Hungry"

58 St. Peter

1950. Red Cross Fund.

289 57 25 f. + 10 f. lake & red . . 23·00 45·00

1950. Holy Year.

290 58 12 f. green . . . . 3·00 6·00
291 15 f. red . . . . 3·50 6·00
292 25 f. blue . . . . 6·50 14·00

59 Town Hall, Ottweiler

61

1950. 400th Anniv of Ottweiler.

293 59 10 f. brown . . . . 3·00 6·50

1950. Saar's Admission to Council of Europe.

294 61 25 f. blue (postage) . . . . 40·00 5·00
295 200 f. red (air) £150 £225

62 St. Lutwinus enters Monastery

1950. National Relief Fund. Inscr "VOLKSHILFE".

296 62 8 f. + 2 f. brown . . . . . 5·00 17·00
297 – 12 f. + 3 f. green . . . . 5·00 17·00
298 – 15 f. + 5 f. brown . . . . 5·50 28·00
299 – 25 f. + 10 f. blue . . . . 8·50 40·00
300 – 50 f. + 20 f. red . . . . 12·00 60·00

DESIGNS: 12 f. Lutwinus builds Mettlach Abbey; 15 f. Lutwinus as Abbot; 25 f. Bishop Lutwinus confirming children at Rheims; 50 f. Lutwinus helping needy.

63 Orphans

65 Allegory

64 Mail-carriers, 1760

1951. Red Cross Fund.

301 63 25 f. + 10 f. green & red . 20·00 40·00

1951. Stamp Day.

302 64 15 f. purple . . . . 6·00 14·00

1951. Trade Fair.

303 65 15 f. green . . . . 2·00 3·75

66 Flowers and Building

67 Calvin and Luther

1951. Horticultural Show, Bexbach.

304 66 15 f. green . . . . 2·50 65

1951. 375th Anniv of Reformation in Saar.

305 67 15 f. + 5 f. brown . . . . 1·25 5·00

68 "The Good Mother" (Lepicie)

69 Mounted Postman

1951. National Relief Fund. Inscr "VOLKSHILFE 1951".

306 68 12 f. + 3 f. green . . . . 4·50 14·00
307 – 15 f. + 5 f. violet . . . . 4·50 14·00
308 – 18 f. + 7 f. lake . . . . . 5·00 15·00
309 – 30 f. + 10 f. blue . . . . 8·00 22·00
310 – 50 f. + 20 f. brown . . . 18·00 48·00

PAINTINGS—VERT: 18 f. "Outside the Theatre" (Kampf); 18 f. "Sisters of Charity" (Browne); 30 f. "The Good Samaritan" (Bassano); 50 f. "St. Martin and the Poor" (Van Dyck).

1952. Stamp Day.

311 69 30 f. + 10 f. blue . . . . 8·00 18·00

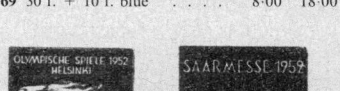

70 Athlete bearing Olympic Flame

71 Globe and Emblem

1952. 15th Olympic Games, Helsinki. Inscr "OLYMPISCHE SPIELE 1952".

312 70 15 f. + 5 f. green . . . . 2·50 6·00
313 – 30 f. + 5 f. blue . . . . . 3·00 8·50

DESIGN: 30 f. Hand, laurels and globe.

1952. Saar Fair.

314 71 15 f. red . . . . 1·50 75

72 Red Cross and Refugees

73 G.P.O., Saarbrucken

1952. Red Cross Week.

315 72 15 f. red . . . . 1·50 75

1952. (A) Without inscr in or below design. (B) With inscr.

316 – 1 f. green (B) 15 10
317 – 2 f. violet 15 10
318 – 3 f. red 15 10
319 73 5 f. turquoise (A) . . . . . 6·00 10
320 5 f. turquoise (B) 20 10
321 – 6 f. purple 35 10
322 – 10 f. olive 40 10
323 73 12 f. green (B) 40 10
324 – 15 f. sepia (A) . . . . . . 8·00 10
325 – 15 f. sepia (B) . . . . . . 5·00 10
326 – 15 f. red (B) 25 10
327 – 18 f. purple . . . . 2·75 3·25
329 – 30 f. blue 85 50
334 – 500 f. lake . . . . 17·00 50·00

DESIGNS—HORIZ: 1, 15 f. (3) Colliery shafthead; 2, 10 f. Ludwigs High School, Saarbrucken; 3, 18 f. Gersweiler Bridge; 6 f. Mettlach Bridge; 30 f. University Library, Saarbrucken. VERT: 500 f. St. Ludwig's Church, Saarbrucken.

74 "Count Stroganov as a Boy" (Greuze)

75 Fair Symbol

1952. National Relief Fund. Paintings inscr "VOLKSHILFE 1952".
335 **74** 15 f. + 5 f. sepia . . . . . 2·75 7·00
336 – 18 f. + 7 f. lake . . . . . 3·25 9·00
337 – 30 f. + 10 f. blue . . . . . 4·00 11·00
PORTRAITS: 18 f. "The Holy Shepherd" (Murillo); 30 f. "Portrait of a Boy" (Kraus).

1953. Saar Fair.
338 **75** 15 f. blue . . . . 1·50 90

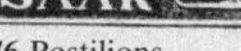

76 Postilions

77 Henri Dunant

1953. Stamp Day.
339 **76** 15 f. blue . . . . 2·50 9·00

1953. Red Cross Week and 125th Anniv of Birth of Dunant (founder).
240 **77** 15 f. + 5 f. brown and red . . 1·50 4·25

78 "Painter's Young Son" (Rubens)

79 St. Benedict blessing St. Maurus

1953. National Relief Fund. Paintings inscr "VOLKSHILFE 1953".
341 – 15 pf. + 5 f. violet . . . . 1·25 3·75
342 – 18 pf. +7 f. red . . . . . 1·40 5·00
343 **78** 30 f. + 10 f. green . . . . 2·75 7·50
DESIGNS—VERT: 15 f. "Clarice Strozzi" (Titian). HORIZ: 18 f. "Painter's Children" (Rubens).

1953. Tholey Abbey Fund.
344 **79** 30 f. + 10 f. black . . . . 1·50 5·50

80 Saar Fair

82 Red Cross and Child

81 Postal Motor Coach

1954. Saar Fair.
345 **80** 15 f. green . . . . 1·40 70

1954. Stamp Day.
346 **81** 15 f. red . . . . 2·50 9·00

1954. Red Cross Week.
347 **82** 15 f. + 5 f. brown . . . . 1·75 5·00

83 Madonna and Child (Holbein)

1954. Marian Year.
348 **83** 5 f. red . . . . 70 1·50
349 – 10 f. green . . . . 90 2·25
350 – 15 f. blue . . . . 1·40 3·25
DESIGNS: 10 f. "Sistine Madonna" (Raphael); 15 f. "Madonna and Child with Pear" (Durer).

84 "Street Urchin with a Melon" (Murillo)

85 Cyclist and Flag

86 Rotary Emblem and Industrial Plant

1954. National Relief Fund. Paintings inscr "VOLKSHILFE 1954".
351 **84** 5 f. + 3 f. red 30 75
352 – 10 f. + 5 f. green 35 95
353 – 15 f. + 7 f. violet . . . . 40 1·10
DESIGNS: 10 f. "Maria de Medici" (A. Bronzino); 15 f. "Baron Emil von Maucler" (J. F. Dietrich).

1955. World Cross Country-Cycle Race.
354 **85** 15 f. blue, red and black . 30 40

1955. 50th Anniv of Rotary International.
355 **86** 15 f. brown 25 40

87 Exhibitors' Flags

88 Nurse and Baby

1955. Saar Fair.
356 **87** 15 f. yellow, blue & green . 20 50

1955. Red Cross Week.
357 **88** 15 f. + 5 f. black and red . 30 65

89 Postman

91 "Mother" (Durer)

1955. Stamp Day.
358 **89** 15 f. purple . . . . 40 1·25

1955. Referendum. Optd **VOLKSBEFRAGUNG 1955**.
359 15 f. red (No. 326) 15 35
360 18 f. purple (No. 327) 15 40
361 30 f. blue (No. 329) 25 55

1955. National Relief Fund. Durer paintings inscr as in T **91**.
362 **91** 5 f. + 3 f. green 35 55
363 – 10 f. + 5 f. olive . . . . 60 1·40
364 – 15 f. + 7 f. bistre . . . . 70 1·25
PAINTINGS: 10 f. "The Praying Hands"; 15 f. "The Old Man from Antwerp".

92

93 Radio Tower

1956. Saar Fair.
365 **92** 15 f. green and red 15 45

1956. Stamp Day.
366 **93** 15 f. green 15 45

94 Casualty Station

95

1956. Red Cross Week.
367 **94** 15 f. + 5 f. brown 20 50

1956. Olympic Games.
368 **95** 12 f. + 3 f. blue and green . 15 35
369 15 f. + 5 f. sepia & purple . 15 35

96 Winterberg Memorial

97 "Portrait of Lucrezia Crivelli" (da Vinci)

1956. Winterberg Memorial Reconstruction Fund.
370 **96** 5 f. + 2 f. green 10 20
371 12 f. + 3 f. purple 15 30
372 15 f. + 5 f. brown 15 30

1956. National Relief Fund. Inscr as in T **97**.
373 **97** 5 f. + 3 f. blue 10 20
374 – 10 f. + 5 f. red 15 25
375 – 15 f. + 7 f. green 20 45
PAINTINGS—VERT: 10 f. "Saskia" (Rembrandt); 15 f. "Lady Playing Spinet" (Floris).

RETURN TO GERMANY

98 Arms of the Saar

99 President Heuse

1957. Return of the Saar to Germany.
376 **99** 15 f. blue and orange . . . 10 25

1957. (a) Without "F" after figure of value.
377 **99** 1 f. green 10 15
378 2 f. violet 10 15
379 3 f. brown 10 15
380 4 f. mauve 20 60
381 5 f. olive 10 10
382 6 f. red 15 40
383 10 f. grey 10 30
384 12 f. orange 10 10
385 15 f. turquoise 20 10
386 18 f. red . . . . 70 1·40
387 25 f. mauve 30 55
388 30 f. purple 35 55
389 45 f. olive . . . . 1·25 2·50
390 50 f. brown . . . . 1·25 1·00
391 60 f. red . . . . 1·60 2·75
392 70 f. salmon . . . . 3·00 4·50
393 80 f. olive . . . . 1·10 2·50
394 90 f. grey . . . . 2·75 4·50
395 100 f. red (24 × 29½ mm) . . 2·50 8·50
396 200 f. lilac (24 × 29½ mm) . 5·50 21·00

(b) With "F" after figure of value.
406 **99** 1 f. grey 10 20
407 3 f. blue 10 20
408 5 f. olive 10 10
409 6 f. brown 20 60
410 10 f. violet 20 25
411 12 f. brown 20 10
412 15 f. green 35 10
413 18 f. grey . . . . 2·00 5·00
414 20 f. olive . . . . 1·25 2·25
415 25 f. brown 55 45
416 30 f. mauve . . . . 1·10 45
417 35 f. brown . . . . 2·75 3·25
418 45 f. turquoise . . . . 2·00 3·50
419 50 f. brown . . . . 1·10 1·25
420 70 f. green . . . . 4·50 5·50
421 80 f. blue . . . . 2·75 4·50
422 90 f. red . . . . 5·50 7·50
423 100 f. red (24 × 29½ mm) . . 4·50 5·50
424 200 f. green (24 × 29½ mm) . 10·00 22·00
425 300 f. blue (24 × 29½ mm) . 13·00 26·00

100 Iron Foundry

101 Arms of Merzig and St. Pierre Church

1957. Saar Fair.
397 **100** 15 f. red and sepia . . . 10 20

1957. Centenary of Merzig.
398 **101** 15 f. blue 10 20

101a "Europa" Tree

101b Young Miner

1957. Europa.
399 **101a** 20 f. orange & yellow . . 30 70
400 35 f. violet and pink . . 50 80

1957. Humanitarian Relief Fund.
401 **101b** 6 f. + 4 f. black & brn . 10 15
402 – 12 f. + 6 f. black & grn 10 15
403 – 15 f. + 7 f. black & red 15 30
404 – 30 f. + 10 f. black & blue 45 70
DESIGNS: 12 f. Miner drilling at coalface; 15 f. Miner with coal-cutting machine; 30 f. Operator at mine lift-shaft.

101c Carrier Pigeons

101d Max and Moritz (cartoon characters)

1957. International Correspondence Week.
405 **101c** 15 f. black and red . . . 10 20

1958. 150th Death Anniv of Wilhelm Busch (writer and illustrator).
426 **101d** 12 f. olive and black . . 10 15
427 – 15 f. red and black . . . 10 30
DESIGN: 15 f. Wilhelm Busch.

101e "Prevent Forest Fires"

101g "The Fox who stole the Goose"

101f Diesel and First Oil Engine

1958. Forest Fires Prevention Campaign.
428 **101e** 15 f. black and red . . . 10 20

1958. Birth Centenary of Rudolf Diesel (engineer).
429 **101f** 12 f. turquoise 15 25

1958. Berlin Students' Fund.
430 **101g** 12 f. + 6 f. brown, black and green 10 20
431 – 15 f. + 7 f. brown, green and red 10 25
DESIGN: 15 f. "A Hunter from the Palatinate".

102 Saarbrucken Town Hall and Fair Emblem

103 Homburg

1958. Saar Fair.
432 **102** 15 f. red 10 20

1958. 400th Anniv of Homburg.
433 **103** 15 f. green 10 20

103a Emblem

103b Schulze-Delitzsch

1958. 150th Anniv of German Gymnastics.
434 **103a** 12 f. black, green and grey 10 20

1958. 150th Birth of Schulze-Delitzsch (pioneer of German Co-operative Movement).

435	103b	12 f. green	10	20

103c "Europa" **103d** Friedrich Raiffeisen (philanthropist)

1958.

436	103c	12 f. blue and green	40	70
437	–	30 f. red and blue	60	90

1958. Humanitarian Relief and Welfare Funds.

438	103d	6 f. + 4 f. brown	10	15
439	–	12 f. + 6 f. red, yellow and green	10	20
440	–	15 f. + 7 f. blue, green and red	20	35
441	–	30 f. + 10 f. yellow, green and blue	25	45

DESIGNS: Inscr "WOHLFAHRTSMARKE". 12 f. Dairymaid; 15 f. Vine-dresser 30 f. Farm labourer.

103e Fugger **104** Hands holding Crates

1959. 500th Birth Anniv of Jakob Fugger (merchant prince).

442	103e	15 f. black and red	10	20

1959. Saar Fair.

443	104	15 f. lake	10	20

105 Saarbrucken **105a** Humboldt

1959. 50th Anniv of Greater Saarbrucken.

444	105	15 f. blue	10	20

1959. Death Centenary of Alexander von Humboldt (naturalist).

445	105a	15 f. blue	10	20

OFFICIAL STAMPS

1922. Nos. 84 to 94 optd **DIENSTMARKE**.

O 98	3 c. green	85	24·00
O 99	5 c. black and orange	35	15
O100	10 c. green	35	15
O101	15 c. brown	35	15
O109	15 c. orange	2·25	30
O102	20 c. blue and yellow	35	15
O111	25 c. red and yellow	2·25	30
O104	30 c. red and yellow	35	15
O105	40 c. brown and yellow	65	15
O106	50 c. blue and yellow	70	15
O112	75 c. green and yellow	4·75	1·50
O108a	1 f. brown	8·00	1·75

1927. Nos. 108/15, 117 and 119 optd **DIENSTMARKE**.

O128	10 c. brown	1·40	1·50
O129	15 c. green	1·75	6·50
O130	20 c. brown	1·40	1·10
O131	25 c. blue	1·75	4·50
O122	30 c. green	1·75	20
O133	40 c. brown	1·25	20
O134	50 c. red	1·25	20
O135	60 c. orange	90	20
O136	75 c. purple	1·25	55
O137	1 f. violet	1·75	30
O138	2 f. red	4·00	50

O 51 Arms

1949.

O264	O 51	10 c. red	35	22·00
O265		30 c. black	25	22·00
O266		1 f. green	25	20
O267		2 f. red	1·40	1·25
O268		5 f. blue	45	20
O269		10 f. black	65	75
O270		12 f. mauve	5·50	7·00
O271		15 f. blue	65	20
O272		20 f. green	1·60	75
O273		30 f. mauve	2·00	4·00
O274		50 f. purple	2·00	3·25
O275		100 f. brown	90·00	£190

STE. MARIE DE MADAGASCAR Pt.6

An island off the East coast of Madagascar. From 1898 used the stamps of Madagascar and Dependencies.

100 centimes = 1 franc

1894. "Tablet" key-type inscr "STE MARIE DE MADAGASCAR" in red (1, 5, 15, 25, 75 c., 1 f.) or blue (others).

1	D	1 c. black on blue	65	65
2		2 c. brown on buff	90	80
3		4 c. brown on grey	2·75	2·25
4		5 c. green on green	5·50	5·00
5		10 c. black on lilac	7·75	4·75
6		15 c. blue	15·00	14·50
7		20 c. red on green	13·50	9·50
8		25 c. black on pink	7·50	6·75
9		30 c. brown on drab	6·75	6·25
10		40 c. red on yellow	8·25	6·00
11		50 c. red on pink	32·00	22·00
12		75 c. brown on orange	48·00	24·00
13		1 f. green	30·00	17·00

ST. PIERRE ET MIQUELON Pt.6

A group of French islands off the S. coast of Newfoundland. The group became an Overseas Department of France on 1 July 1976. The stamps of France were used in the islands from 1 April 1978 until 3 February 1986. Separate issues for the group were reintroduced in 1986.

100 centimes = 1 franc

1885. Stamps of French Colonies surch **S P M** and value in figures only.

1	J	5 on 2 c. brown on buff	£4250	£1600
4		5 on 4 c. brown on grey	£275	£200
8		05 on 20 c. red on green	17·00	21·00
9	H	05 on 35 c. black on yell	85·00	60·00
5		05 on 40 c. red on yellow	70·00	30·00
10		05 om 75 c. red	£200	£150
11		05 on 1 f. green	17·00	15·00
6		10 on 40 c. red on yellow	18·00	15·00
7		15 on 40 c. red on yellow	17·00	15·00
3		25 on 1 f. green	£1700	£1100

The surcharge on No. 1 is always inverted.

1891. French Colonies "Commerce" type surch **15 c. S P M**.

15	J	15 c. on 30 c. brn on drab	24·00	21·00
16		15 c. on 35 c. blk on orge	£425	£300
17		15 c. on 40 c. red on yell	60·00	48·00

1891. Stamps of French Colonies "Commerce" type, optd **ST PIERRE M-on**.

23	J	1 c. black on blue	6·75	5·00
24		2 c. brown on buff	6·75	5·50
25		4 c. brown on grey	7·50	5·50
26		5 c. green on green	7·50	5·00
22		10 c. black on lilac	11·00	11·00
28		15 c. blue on blue	17·00	9·75
29		20 c. red on green	48·00	42·00
30		25 c. black on pink	18·00	12·00
31		30 c. brown on drab	70·00	60·00
32		35 c. black on orange	£300	£225
33		40 c. red on yellow	48·00	42·00
34		75 c. red on pink	75·00	60·00
35		1 f. green	48·00	42·00

1891. Stamps of French Colonies, "Commerce" type, surch **ST-PIERRE M-on** and new value in figures and words (**cent.**) above and below opt.

36	J	1 c. on 5 c. green and green	5·00	4·25
37		1 c. on 10 c. black on lilac	6·75	5·50
38		1 c. on 25 c. black on pink	4·50	4·25
39		2 c. on 10 c. black on lilac	4·75	3·75
40		2 c. on 15 c. blue on blue	4·00	4·00
41		2 c. on 25 c. black on pink	4·00	4·00
42		4 c. on 20 c. red on green	4·00	3·75
43		4 c. on 25 c. black on pink	4·00	4·25
44		4 c. on 30 c. brn on drab	12·00	11·00
45		4 c. on 40 c. red on yellow	17·00	9·75

1892. Nos. 26 and 30 surch with figure only on top of opt.

49	J	1 on 5 c. green on green	6·50	3·75
46		1 on 25 c. black on pink	4·00	3·75
50		2 on 5 c. green on green	7·25	7·25
47		2 on 25 c. black on pink	4·00	3·75
51		4 on 5 c. green on green	7·25	6·50
48		4 on 25 c. black on pink	3·75	3·75

1892. Postage Due stamps of French Colonies optd **T ST-PIERRE M-on P.**

52	U	10 c. black	21·00	21·00
53		20 c. black	13·50	14·00
54		30 c. black	15·00	15·00
55		40 c. black	15·00	15·00
56		60 c. black	70·00	70·00
57		1 f. brown	95·00	95·00
58		2 f. brown	£160	£160
59		5 f. brown	£275	£275

1892. "Tablet" key-type inscr "ST PIERRE ET MIQUELON".

60	D	1 c. black and red on blue	50	50
61		2 c. brown & blue on buff	45	55
62		4 c. brown & blue on grey	1·00	90
63		5 c. green and red	1·50	1·25
64		10 c. black & blue on lilac	3·50	2·50
74		10 c. red and blue	2·50	95
65		15 c. blue and red	4·75	1·90
75		15 c. grey and red	60·00	30·00
66		20 c. red & blue on green	15·00	11·00
67		25 c. black & red on pink	5·50	1·25
76		25 c. blue and red	8·75	6·25
68		30 c. brown & bl on drab	5·25	2·75
77		35 c. black & red on yell	3·75	3·50
69		40 c. red & blue on yellow	4·75	2·75
70		50 c. red and blue on pink	30·00	20·00
78		50 c. brown & red on blue	20·00	18·00
71		75 c. brown & red in orge	17·00	13·50
72		1 f. green and red	14·00	8·25

17 Fisherman

18 Glaucous Gull

19 Fishing Brigantine

1909.

79	17	1 c. brown and red	20	25
80		2 c. blue and brown	20	25
81		4 c. brown and violet	20	30
82		5 c. olive and green	30	40
109		5 c. black and blue	20	30
83		10 c. red and pink	35	40
110		10 c. olive and green	30	40
111		10 c. mauve and bistre	30	40
84		15 c. red and purple	30	40
85		20 c. purple and brown	70	70
86	18	25 c. blue and deep blue	1·50	1·00
112		25 c. green and brown	45	50
87		30 c. brown and orange	75	70
113		30 c. red and carmine	45	45
114		30 c. blue and red	40	35
115		30 c. green and olive	40	45
88		35 c. brown and green	45	35
89		40 c. green and brown	1·75	1·10
90		45 c. green and violet	45	45
91		50 c. green and brown	75	70
116		50 c. light blue and blue	70	70
117		50 c. mauve and bistre	45	45
118		60 c. red and blue	45	45
119		65 c. brown and mauve	80	80
120		90 c. red and scarlet	14·00	15·00
93	19	1 f. blue and green	2·00	1·40
121		1 f. 10 red and green	2·00	2·00
122		1 f. 50 blue & ultramarine	6·25	6·25
94		2 f. brown and violet	2·25	1·50
123		3 f. mauve on pink	6·00	6·25
95		5 f. green and brown	6·25	4·25

1912. "Tablet" issue surch in figures.

96	D	05 on 2 c. brown and blue on buff	1·40	1·40
97		05 on 4 c. brown and blue on grey	25	35
98		05 on 15 c. blue and red	35	35
99		05 on 20 c. red and blue on green	25	35
100		05 on 25 c. black and red on pink	30	35
101		05 on 30 c. brown and blue on drab	35	45
102		05 on 35 c. black and red on yellow	70	70
103		10 on 40 c. red and blue on yellow	30	30
104		10 on 50 c. red and blue	40	45
105		10 on 75 c. brown and red on orange	1·10	1·25
106		10 on 1 f. green and red	1·50	1·50

1915. Red Cross. Surch **5c** and red cross.

107	17	10 c. + 5 c. red and pink	60	70
108		15 c. + 5 c. red & purple	70	85

1924. Surch with new value.

124	17	25 c. on 15 c. red & purple	30	40
125	19	25 c. on 2 f. brown & violet	30	40
126		25 c. on 5 f. green & brown	30	40
127	18	65 on 45 c. green & violet	80	90
128		85 on 75 c. green & brown	80	90
129		90 c. on 75 c. red and scarlet	1·25	1·50
130	19	1 f. 25 on 1 f. ultramarine and blue	1·25	1·50
131		1 f. 50 on 1 f. blue and light blue	2·00	2·00
132		3 f. on 5 f. mauve & brown	1·60	1·75
133		10 f. on 5 f. green and red	10·00	10·50
134		20 f. on 5 f. red and violet	15·00	15·00

1931. International Colonial Exhibition, Paris, key-types inscr "ST PIERRE ET MIQUELON".

135	E	40 c. green and black	1·75	1·75
136	F	50 c. mauve and black	1·75	1·60
137	G	90 c. red and black	1·75	1·75
138	H	1 f. 50 blue and black	1·75	1·75

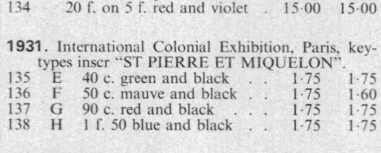

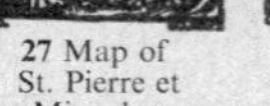

27 Map of St. Pierre et Miquelon **28** Galantry Lighthouse

29 "Jacques Coeur" (trawler)

1932.

139	27	1 c. blue and purple	15	25
140	28	2 c. green and black	25	35
141	29	4 c. brown and red	25	40
142		5 c. brown and mauve	25	40
143	28	10 c. black and purple	35	45
144		15 c. mauve and blue	65	65
145	27	20 c. red and black	65	70
146		25 c. green and mauve	65	70
147	29	30 c. green and olive	70	70
148		40 c. brown and blue	70	70
149	28	45 c. green and red	70	65
150		50 c. green and brown	70	70
151	29	65 c. red and brown	95	1·00
152	27	75 c. red and green	95	95
153		90 c. scarlet and red	95	95
154	29	1 f. scarlet and red	70	70
155	27	1 f. 25 red and blue	95	95
156		1 f. 50 blue and deep blue	95	1·00
157	29	1 f. 75 brown and black	1·25	1·25
158		2 f. green and black	5·25	5·50
159	28	3 f. brown and green	7·00	7·00
160		5 f. brown and red	17·00	17·00
161	29	10 f. mauve and green	42·00	42·00
162	27	20 f. green and red	42·00	42·00

1934. 400th Anniv of Cartier's Discovery of Canada. Optd **JACQUES CARTIER 1534-1934**.

163	28	50 c. green and brown	1·60	1·75
164	27	75 c. red and green	2·00	2·00
165		1 f. 50 blue and deep blue	2·50	2·50
166	29	1 f. 75 brown and black	2·75	2·75
167	28	5 f. brown and red	19·00	19·00

32 Commerce **39** Dog Team

1937. International Exhibition, Paris.

168	32	20 c. violet	1·10	1·10
169	–	30 c. green	1·10	1·10
170	–	40 c. red	1·10	1·10
171	–	50 c. brown and blue	1·00	1·10
172	–	90 c. red	1·00	1·10
173	–	1 f. 50 blue	1·00	1·10

DESIGNS—VERT: 50 c. Agriculture. HORIZ: 30 c. Sailing ships; 40 c. Women of three races; 90 c. France extends Torch of Civilisation; 1 f. 50, Diane de Poitiers.

1938. International Anti-Cancer Fund. As T **22** of Mauritania.

174	1 f. 75 + 50 c. blue	7·75	8·25

1938.

175	39	2 c. green	20	35
176	–	3 c. brown	20	35
177	–	4 c. purple	20	35
178	–	5 c. red	20	30
179	–	10 c. brown	25	30
180	–	15 c. purple	25	35
181	–	20 c. violet	25	35
182	–	25 c. blue	1·00	1·25
183	–	30 c. purple	25	35
184	–	35 c. green	35	45
185	–	40 c. blue	25	35
186	–	45 c. green	30	35
187	–	50 c. red	25	35
188	–	55 c. blue	1·50	1·50
189	–	60 c. violet	25	35
190	–	65 c. brown	2·25	2·50
191	–	70 c. orange	35	35
192	–	80 c. violet	60	60
193	–	90 c. blue	35	35
194	–	1 f. red	5·75	6·00
195	–	1 f. olive	35	45
196	–	1 f. 25 red	1·10	1·10
197	–	1 f. 40 brown	45	50
198	–	1 r. 50 green	40	50
199	–	1 r. 60 purple	45	45
200	–	1 r. 75 blue	85	85
201	–	2 r. purple	30	40
202	–	2 f. 25 blue	55	55
203	–	2 f. 50 orange	85	80
204	–	3 f. brown	35	45
205	–	5 f. red	55	60
206	–	10 f. blue	85	85
207	–	20 f. olive	1·10	1·10

DESIGNS: 30 to 70 c. St. Pierre harbour; 80 c. to 1 f. 75, Pointe aux Canons lighthouse (wrongly inscr "PHARE DE LA TORTUE"); 2 to 20 f. Soldiers' Cove, Langlade.

1939. New York World's Fair. As T **28** of Mauritania.

208	1 f. 25 red	80	85
209	2 f. 25 blue	80	85

1939. 150th Anniv of French Revolution. As T **29** of Mauritania.

210	45 c. + 25 c. green and black	5·50	5·50
211	70 c. + 30 c. brown and black	5·50	5·50
212	90 c. + 35 c. orange and black	5·50	5·50
213	1 f. 25 + 1 f. red and black	5·50	5·50
214	2 f. 25 + 2 f. blue and black	5·50	5·50

1941. Free French Plebiscite. Stamps of 1938 optd **Noel 1941 FRANCE LIBRE F.N.F.L.** or surch also.
215 **39** 10 c. brown 28·00 28·00
216 20 c. violet 28·00 28·00
217 25 c. blue 28·00 28·00
218 – 40 c. blue 28·00 28·00
219 – 45 c. green 28·00 28·00
220 – 65 c. brown 28·00 28·00
221 – 70 c. orange 28·00 28·00
222 – 80 c. violet 28·00 28·00
223 – 90 c. blue 28·00 28·00
224 – 1 f. green 28·00 28·00
225 – 1 f. 25 red 28·00 28·00
226 – 1 f. 40 brown 35·00 35·00
227 – 1 f. 60 purple 35·00 35·00
228 – 1 f. 75 blue 35·00 35·00
229 – 2 f. purple 35·00 35·00
230 – 2 f. 25 blue 35·00 35·00
231 – 2 f. 50 orange 35·00 35·00
232 – 3 f. brown 35·00 35·00
233 **39** 10 f. on 10 c. brown 60·00 60·00
234 – 20 f. on 90 c. blue 60·00 60·00
"F.N.F.L." = Forces Navales Francaises Libres (Free French Naval Forces).

1941. Various stamps overprinted **FRANCE LIBRE F. N. F. L.** or surch also. (a) Nos. 111 and 114.
245 **17** 10 c. mauve and bistre £750 £750
246 **18** 30 c. blue and lake £750 £750

(b) On stamps of 1932.
247 **28** 2 c. green and black £160 £160
248 **29** 4 c. brown and red 35·00 35·00
249 5 c. brown and mauve £600 £600
250 40 c. brown and blue 10·50 10·50
251 **28** 45 c. green and red £120 £120
252 50 c. green and brown 8·25 8·25
253 **29** 65 c. red and brown 24·00 24·00
254 1 f. red and brown £250 £250
255 1 f. 75 brown and black 8·25 8·25
256 2 f. green and black 11·00 11·00
257 **28** 5 f. brown and red £225 £225
258 **29** 5 f. on 1 f. 75 brn & blk 9·75 9·75

(c) On stamps of 1938.
259 **39** 2 c. green £300 £300
260 3 c. brown 90·00 90·00
261 4 c. purple 70·00 70·00
262 5 c. red £625 £625
263 10 c. brown 9·00 9·00
264 15 c. purple £1000 £1000
265 20 c. violet £140 £140
266 20 c. on 10 c. brown 7·00 7·00
267 25 c. blue 9·00 9·00
268 30 c. on 10 c. brown 4·75 4·75
269 – 35 c. green £525 £525
270 – 40 c. blue 11·00 11·00
271 – 45 c. green 11·00 11·00
272 – 55 c. blue £6000 £6000
273 – 60 c. violet £400 £400
274 – 60 c. on 90 c. blue 5·50 5·50
275 – 65 c. brown 14·00 14·00
276 – 70 c. orange 24·00 24·00
277 – 80 c. violet £300 £300
278 – 90 c. blue 12·50 12·50
279 – 1 f. green 14·00 14·00
280 – 1 f. 25 red 11·00 11·00
281 – 1 f. 40 brown 9·75 9·75
282 – 1 f. 50 green £550 £550
283 – 1 f. 50 on 90 c. blue 8·25 8·25
284 – 1 f. 60 purple 11·00 11·00
285 – 2 f. purple 42·00 42·00
286 – 2 f. 25 blue 11·00 11·00
287 – 2 f. 50 orange 14·00 14·00
288 **7** 2 f. 50 on 10 c. brown 11·00 11·00
289 – 3 f. brown £6500 £6500
290 – 5 f. red £1500 £1500
291 **7** 10 f. on 10 c. brown 38·00 38·00
292 – 20 f. olive £575 £575
293 – 20 f. on 90 c. blue 42·00 42·00

(d) On Nos. 208/9.
294 1 f. 25 red 8·25 8·25
295 2 f. 25 blue 7·25 8·25
296 2 f. 50 on 1 f. 25 red 11·00 11·00
297 3 f. on 2 f. 25 blue 11·00 11·00

1942. Stamps of 1932 overprinted **FRANCE LIBRE F. N. F. L.** or surch also.
304 **27** 20 c. red and black £250 £250
305 75 c. red and green 14·00 14·00
306 1 f. 25 red and blue 11·00 11·00
307 1 f. 50 blue & deep blue £300 £300
308 10 f. on 1 f. 25 red & blue 24·00 24·00
309 20 f. on 75 c. red & green 35·00 35·00

1942. Social Welfare Fund. Nos. 279 and 287 further surch **OEUVRES SOCIALES**, cross and premium.
320 1 f. + 50 c. green 35·00 35·00
321 2 f. 50 + 1 f. orange 35·00 35·00

47 Fishing Schooner

1942. (a) Postage.
322 **47** 5 c. blue 20 30
323 10 c. pink 15 25
324 25 c. green 15 25
325 30 c. black 15 25
326 40 c. blue 15 25
327 60 c. purple 15 25
328 1 f. violet 25 35
329 1 f. 50 red 60 70
330 2 f. brown 35 45
331 2 f. 50 blue 65 70
332 4 f. orange 35 45
333 5 f. purple 35 45
334 10 f. blue 60 70
335 20 f. green 1·00 1·10

(b) Air. As T **30** of New Caledonia.
336 1 f. orange 25 35
337 1 f. 50 red 25 35
338 5 f. purple 35 45
339 10 f. black 60 70
340 25 f. blue 75 85
341 50 f. green 85 1·00
342 100 f. red 1·25 1·40

1944. Mutual Aid and Red Cross Funds. As T **31** of New Caledonia.
343 5 f. + 20 f. blue 80 1·00

1945. Eboue. As T **32** of New Caledonia.
344 2 f. black 50 60
345 25 f. green 75 85

1945. Surch.
346 **47** 50 c. on 5 c. blue 25 35
347 70 c. on 5 c. blue 25 35
348 80 c. on 5 c. blue 30 40
349 1 f. 20 on 5 c. blue 30 40
350 2 f. 40 on 25 c. green 30 40
351 3 f. on 25 c. green 45 55
352 4 f. 50 on 25 c. green 80 90
353 15 f. on 2 f. 50 blue 1·00 1·10

1946. Air. Victory. As T **34** of New Caledonia.
354 8 f. red 75 1·00

1946. Air. From Chad to the Rhine. As Nos. 300/305 of New Caledonia.
355 5 f. red 80 85
356 10 f. lilac 80 85
357 15 f. black 90 1·00
358 20 f. violet 90 1·00
359 25 f. brown 1·60 1·75
360 50 f. black 1·60 1·75

54 Soldiers' Cove, Langlade

55 Allegory of Fishing

56 Douglas DC-4 and Wrecked Fishing Schooner

1947.
361 **54** 10 c. brown (postage) 15 25
362 30 c. violet 15 25
363 40 c. purple 15 30
364 50 c. blue 15 30
365 **55** 60 c. red 25 35
366 80 c. blue 25 40
367 1 f. green 25 35
368 – 1 f. 20 green 40 45
369 – 1 f. 50 black 40 45
370 – 2 f. red 40 35
371 – 3 f. violet 85 90
372 – 3 f. 60 red 80 85
373 – 4 f. purple 75 70
374 – 5 f. yellow 80 80
375 – 6 f. blue 80 80
376 – 8 f. sepia 1·25 1·00
377 – 10 f. green 1·10 95
378 – 15 f. green 1·25 1·25
379 – 17 f. blue 2·00 1·50
380 – 20 f. red 1·25 1·25
381 – 25 f. blue 1·50 1·50
382 – 50 f. green and red (air) 3·25 2·50
383 **56** 100 f. green 4·75 3·75
384 – 200 f. blue and red 8·75 4·75
DESIGNS—As Type **55**: 1 f. 20 to 2 f. Cross and fishermen; 3 f. to 4 f. Weighing fish; 5, 6, 10 f. Trawler "Colonel Pleven"; 8, 17 f. Red fox; 15, 20, 25 f. Windswept mountain landscape. As Type **56**: 50 f. Airplane and fishing village; 200 f. Airplane and snow-bound fishing schooner.

1949. Air. 75th Anniv of U.P.U. As T **38** of New Caledonia.
395 25 f. multicoloured 7·50 8·50

1950. Colonial Welfare Fund. As T **39** of New Caledonia.
396 10 f. + 2 f. red and brown 3·00 3·50

1952. Centenary of Military Medal. As T **40** of New Caledonia.
397 8 f. blue, yellow and green 3·50 4·25

1954. Air. 10th Anniv of Liberation. As T **42** of New Caledonia.
398 15 f. red and brown 4·50 4·75

62 Refrigeration Plant

63 Codfish

64 Dog and Coastal Scene

1955.
399 **62** 30 c. blue & dp bl (postage) 25 25
400 **63** 40 c. brown and blue 15 30
401 **62** 50 c. brown, grey & black 20 35
402 **63** 1 f. brown and green 25 35
403 2 f. indigo and blue 25 35
404 **62** 3 f. purple 40 40
405 – 4 f. purple, red and lake 50 50
406 – 10 f. brown, blue & turq 75 70
407 – 20 f. multicoloured 2·00 1·50
408 – 25 f. brown, green & blue 2·75 2·25
409 **62** 40 f. turquoise 1·60 1·60
410 **64** 50 f. multicoloured (air) 24·00 15·00
411 – 100 f. black and grey 8·50 6·50
412 – 500 f. indigo and blue 35·00 19·00
DESIGNS—As Type **62/3**: 4, 10 f. Pointe aux Canons Lighthouse and fishing dinghies; 20 f. Ice hockey players; 25 f. American minks. As Type **64**: 100 f. Sud Aviation Caravelle airliner over St. Pierre and Miquelon; 500 f. Douglas DC-3 over St. Pierre port.

65 Trawler "Galantry"

67 "Picea"

1956. Economic and Social Development Fund.
413 **65** 15 f. sepia and brown 1·25 90

1958. 10th Anniv of Declaration of Human Rights. As T **48** of New Caledonia.
414 20 f. brown and blue 1·50 1·25

1959.
415 **67** 5 f. multicoloured 1·25 90

68 Flaming Torches

1959. Air. Adoption of Constitution.
416 **68** 200 f. green, lake & violet 9·50 6·50

69 "Cypripedium acaule"

1962. Flowers.
417 **69** 25 f. purple, orange and green (postage) 3·50 3·25
418 – 50 f. red and green 5·50 3·50
419 – 100 f. orange, red and green (air) 8·50 3·50
DESIGNS—VERT: 50 f. "Calopogon pulchellus". HORIZ—48 × 27 mm: 100 f. "Sarracenia purpurae".

70 Submarine "Surcouf" and Map

1962. Air. 20th Anniv of Adherence to Free French Government.
420 **70** 500 f. black, blue and red £100 70·00

1962. Air. 1st Transatlantic TV Satellite Link. As T **50** of New Caledonia.
421 50 f. brown, green and sepia 5·50 3·50

72 Eiders

73 Dr. A. Calmette

1963. Birds.
422 **72** 50 c. bistre, black & blue 1·00 65
423 – 1 f. brown, mauve & blue 1·25 80
424 – 2 f. brown, black & blue 1·40 1·10
425 – 6 f. bistre, blue & turquoise 2·50 1·60
DESIGNS: 1 f. Rock ptarmigan; 2 f. Semi-palmated plovers; 6 f. Blue-winged teal.

1963. Birth Centenary of Dr. Albert Calmette (bacteriologist).
426 **73** 30 f. brown and blue 6·00 3·50

74 Landing of Governor from "Garonne"

1963. Air. Bicentenary of Arrival of First Governor (Dangeac) in St. Pierre and Miquelon.
427 **74** 200 f. blue, green & brn 15·00 8·00

1963. Red Cross Centenary. As T **53** of New Caledonia.
428 25 f. red, grey and blue 7·00 4·00

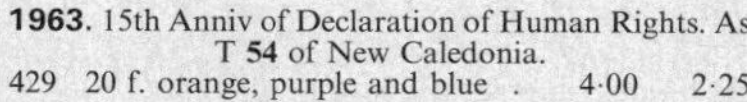

1963. 15th Anniv of Declaration of Human Rights. As T **54** of New Caledonia.
429 20 f. orange, purple and blue 4·00 2·25

1964. "PHILATEC 1964" International Stamp Exhibition, Paris. As T **54c** of New Caledonia.
430 60 f. blue, green and purple 8·00 6·00

78 Common Rabbits

1964. Fauna.
431 **78** 3 f. choc., brown & green 1·40 1·10
432 – 4 f. sepia, blue and green 2·00 1·40
433 – 5 f. brown, sepia and blue 2·50 1·90
434 – 34 f. brown, green & blue 6·00 3·50
ANIMALS: 4 f. Red fox; 5 f. Roe deer; 34 f. Charolais bull.

79 Potez 842 Airliner and Map

1964. Air. 1st St. Pierre–New York Airmail Flight.
435 **79** 100 f. brown and blue 10·00 5·30

1965. Centenary of I.T.U. As T **56** of New Caledonia.
436 40 f. blue, brown and purple 17·00 6·50

1966. Air. Launching of First French Satellite. As Nos. 398/9 of New Caledonia.
437 25 f. brown, blue and red 5·00 3·50
438 30 f. brown, blue and red 5·00 3·50

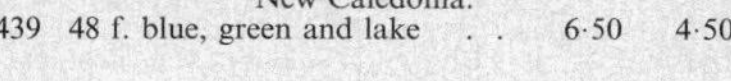

1966. Air. Launching of Satellite "D1". As T **56e** of New Caledonia.
439 48 f. blue, green and lake 6·50 4·50

83 "Revanche" and Settlers

1966. Air. 150th Anniv of Return of Islands to France.
440 **83** 100 f. multicoloured 10·00 4·50

84 "Journal Officiel" and Old and New Printing Presses
86 Trawler and Harbour Plan

85 Map and Fishing Dinghies

1966. Air. Centenary of "Journal Officiel" Printing Works.
441 **84** 60 f. plum, lake and blue . 9·00 4·00

1967. Air. Pres. De Gaulle's Visit.
442 **85** 25 f. brown, blue and red . 20·00 11·00
443 – 100 f. blue, turquoise & pur 30·00 20·00
DESIGN: 100 f. Maps and cruiser "Richelieu".

1967. Opening of St. Pierre's New Harbour.
444 **86** 48 f. brown, blue and red . 5·0 2·75

87 Map and Control Tower

1967. Opening of St. Pierre Airport.
445 **87** 30 f. multicoloured . . . . 2·25 1·40

88 T.V. Receiver, Aerial and Map

1967. Inauguration of Television Service.
446 **88** 40 f. red, green and olive . 5·00 2·75

89 Speed Skating
91 J. D. Cassini (discoverer of group), Compasses and Chart

1968. Air. Winter Olympic Games, Grenoble. Multicoloured.
447 50 f. Type **89** . . . . 6·00 3·50
448 60 f. Ice-hockey goalkeeper . . 7·50 4·50

1968. 20th Anniv of W.H.O. As T **68** of New Caledonia.
449 10 f. red, yellow and blue . . 5·50 2·75

1968. Famous Visitors to St. Pierre and Miquelon (1st series).
450 **91** 4 f. brown, yellow and lake 2·75 2·25
451 – 6 f. multicoloured . . . . . 3·50 2·50
452 – 15 f. multicoloured . . . . 4·50 3·00
453 – 25 f. multicoloured . . . . 7·00 4·50
CELEBRITIES: 6 f. Rene de Chateaubriand and warship; 15 f. Prince de Joinville, "Belle Poule" (sail frigate) and "Cassard" (survey ship); 25 f. Admiral Gauchet and flagship "Provence" (Ile aux Chiens expedition).

1968. Human Rights Year. As T **69** of New Caledonia.
454 20 f. red, blue & yellow . . . 7·00 4·00

93 War Memorial, St. Pierre

1968. Air. 50th Anniv of Armistice.
455 **93** 500 f. multicoloured . . . 18·00 14·00

1969. Air. 1st Flight of Concorde. As T **75** of New Caledonia.
456 34 f. brown and olive . . . . 20·00 10·00

95 Mountain Stream, Langlade

1969. Tourism.
457 **95** 5 f. brn, bl & grn (postage) 3·50 2·25
458 – 15 f. brown, green & blue . 4·00 3·00
459 – 50 f. purple, olive & bl (air) 10·00 5·50
460 – 100 f. brown, indigo & bl . 18·00 11·00
DESIGNS: 15 f. River bank, Debon, Langlade; 50 f. Wild horses, Miquelon; 100 f. Gathering wood, Miquelon. The 50 f. and 100 f. are larger 48×27 mm.

96 Treasury

1969. Public Buildings and Monuments.
461 **96** 10 f. black, red and blue . 2·75 1·60
462 – 25 f. red, ultramarine & blue 4·50 2·75
463 – 30 f. brown, green and blue 5·00 3·50
464 – 60 f. black, red and blue . 10·00 5·50
DESIGNS: 25 f. Maritime Fisheries Scientific and Technical Institute; 30 f. Unknown Sailor's Monument; 60 f. St. Christopher's College.

97 "L'Estoile" and Granville, 1690

1969. Maritime Links with France.
465 **97** 34 f. lake, green and emerald (postage) . . . . 7·50 3·00
466 – 40 f. green, red and bistre . 10·00 5·00
467 – 48 f. multicoloured . . . . 13·50 8·00
468 – 200 f. black, lake and green (air) . . . . 30·00 11·00
DESIGNS—As Type **97**: 40 f. "La Jolie" and St. Jean de Luz, 1750; 48 f. "La Juste" and La Rochelle, 1860; 48×27 mm. 200 f. "L'Esperance" and St. Malo, 1600.

98 Pierre Loti, Ship and Book Titles

1969. Air. Pierre Loti (explorer and writer) Commemoration.
469 **98** 300 f. multicoloured . . . 35·00 20·00

99 Ringed Seals

1969. Marine Animals.
470 **99** 1 f. brown, purple & lake . 4·00 2·25
471 – 3 f. blue, green and red . . 4·00 2·25
472 – 4 f. green, brown and red . 4·00 2·25
473 – 6 f. violet, green and red . 4·00 2·25
DESIGNS: 3 f. Sperm whales; 4 f. Long-finned pilot whale; 6 f. Common dolphins.

1969. 30th Anniv of International Labour Orangization. As T **79** of New Caledonia.
474 20 f. brown, slate and salmon 6·50 2·75

1970. New U.P.U. Headquarters Building, Berne. As T **81** of New Caledonia.
475 25 f. brown, blue and red . . . 6·50 2·75
476 34 f. slate, brown and purple . 10·00 5·50

102 Rocket and Japanese Women
104 "Rubus chamaemorus"

103 Rowing Fours

1970. Air. World Fair "EXPO 70", Osaka, Japan.
477 **102** 34 f. brown, lake & blue . 11·00 5·50
478 – 85 f. blue, red & orange . 20·00 11·00
DESIGN—HORIZ: 85 f. "Mountain Landscape" (Y. Taikan) and Expo "star".

1970. World Rowing Championships, St. Catherine, Canada.
479 **103** 20 f. brown, blue & lt bl . 6·00 3·50

1970. Fruit Plants.
480 **104** 3 f. green, purple & brn . 1·40 80
481 – 4 f. yellow, red and green . 1·60 1·00
482 – 5 f. red, green and violet . 1·75 1·40
483 – 6 f. violet, green & purple . 3·00 1·60
PLANTS: 4 f. "Fragaria vesca"; 5 f. "Rubus idaeus"; 6 f. "Vaccinium myrtillus".

105 Ewe and Lamb

1970. Livestock Breeding.
484 **105** 15 f. brown, purple & green 4·50 2·75
485 – 30 f. brown, grey and green 5·50 2·75
486 – 34 f. brown, purple & green 8·00 5·00
487 – 48 f. purple, brown & blue 8·50 4·00
DESIGNS: 30 f. Animal quarantine station; 34 f. Charolais bull; 48 f. Refrigeration plant and "Narrando" (trawler).

106 Etienne Francois, Duke of Choiseul, and Warships

1970. Air. Celebrities of St. Pierre and Miquelon.
488 **106** 25 f. brown, blue & purple 50 2·75
489 – 50 f. brown, purple & green 10·00 6·50
490 – 60 f. brown, green & purple 12·50 6·00
DESIGNS: 50 f. Jacques Cartier and "Grande Hermine"; 60 f. Sebastien Le Gonard de Sourdeval and 17th-century French galleons.

107 "St. Francis of Assisi", 1900

1971. Fisheries' Protection Vessels.
491 **107** 30 f. red, blue & turq . . . 21·00 8·50
492 – 35 f. brown, green & blue . 23·00 9·50
493 – 40 f. brown, blue & green . 23·00 9·50
494 – 80 f. black, green & blue . 27·00 18·00
DESIGNS: 35 f. "St. Jehanne", 1920; 40 f. "L'Aventure", 1950; 80 f. "Commandant Bourdais", 1970.

108 "Aconite"

1971. 30th Anniv of Allegiance to Free French Movement. British Corvettes on loan to Free French.
495 **108** 22 f. black, green & blue . 11·00 8·00
496 – 25 f. brown, turquoise & bl 11·00 8·00
497 – 50 f. black, turquoise & blue 22·00 16·00
DESIGNS: 25 f. "Alyssum"; 50 f. "Mimosa".

109 Ship's Bell
111 Haddock

1971. St. Pierre Museum. Multicoloured.
498 20 f. Type **109** . . . . 6·50 3·50
499 45 f. Navigational instruments and charts (horiz) . . . . . 10·00 4·50

1971. 1st Death Anniv of De Gaulle. As Nos. 493/4 of New Caledonia.
500 35 f. black and red . . . . . 9·00 5·50
501 45 f. black and red . . . . . 13·50 7·75

1972. Ocean Fish.
502 **111** 2 f. indigo, red and blue . 3·50 2·25
503 – 3 f. brown and green . . 3·50 2·25
504 – 5 f. red and blue . . . . 5·00 2·75
505 – 10 f. green and emerald . 8·50 4·50
DESIGNS: 3 f. Dab; 5 f. Sea perch; 10 c. Cod.

112 De Gaulle and Servicemen

1972. Air. General De Gaulle Commemoration.
506 **112** 100 f. brown, green & pur 20·00 10·00

113 Long-tailed Ducks
116 Swimming Pool

114 Montcalm and Warships

1973. Currency Revaluation.
507 **113** 6 c. brown, purple and blue (postage) . . . . 1·10 90
508 – 10 c. black, red & blue . . 1·40 1·10
509 – 20 c. bistre, ultram & bl . 1·60 1·10
510 **113** 40 c. brown, green & vio . 2·50 1·60
511 – 70 c. black, red and green 3·50 1·90
512 – 90 c. bistre, blue and pur . 9·00 6·00
513 **114** 1 f. 60 violet, indigo and blue (air) . . . . 5·00 2·75
514 – 2 f. purple, green & violet 6·50 3·50
515 – 4 f. green, mauve & brn . 11·00 5·50
DESIGNS—As Type **113**: 10, 70 c. Atlantic puffins; 20, 90 c. Snowy owls. As Type **114**: HORIZ: 4 f. La Salle, map and warships. VERT: 2 f. Frontenac and various scenes.

1973. Inauguration of St. Pierre Cultural Centre.
521 **116** 60 c. brown, blue and red 4·50 2·50
522 – 1 f. purple, orange and blue 5·50 2·75
DESIGN: 1 f. Centre building.

117 Transall C-160 in Flight

1973. Air.
523 **117** 10 f. multicoloured . . . 35·00 20·00

118 Met Balloon and Weather Ship   120 Clasped Hands on Red Cross

119 Northern Gannet with Letter

1974. World Meteorological Day.
524 **118** 1 f. 60 blue, green & red . . 9·50 5·00

1974. Centenary of Universal Postal Union.
525 **119** 70 c. ultramarine, bl & red 4·50 2·25
526 90 c. blue, red and lake . 6·00 3·50

1974. Campaign for Blood Donors.
527 **120** 1 f. 50 multicoloured . . 9·00 4·50

121 Arms and Map of Islands

1974. Air.
528 **121** 2 f. multicoloured . . . . 10·00 4·50

122 Banknotes in "Fish" Money-box   123 Copernicus and Famous Scientists

1974. Centenary of St. Pierre Savings Bank.
529 **122** 50 c. brown, blue & black 4·50 2·50

1974. Air. 500th Birth Anniv (1973) of Nicholas Copernicus (astronomer).
530 **123** 4 f. violet, red and blue . 12·00 6·00

124 St. Pierre Church and Caspian Tern, Kittiwake and Great Auk

1974. Island Churches.
531 **124** 6 c. black, brn & green . 2·75 1·10
532 – 10 c. indigo, blue & brown 2·75 1·10
533 – 20 c. multicoloured . . . 4·00 2·25
DESIGNS: 10 c. Miquelon Church and fish; 20 c. Our Lady of the Seamen Church and fishermen.

125 Red Admiral   126 Cod and St. Pierre et Miquelon Stamp of 1909

1975. Butterflies. Multicoloured.
534 1 f. Type **125** . . . . . . 6·00 2·25
535 1 f. 20 Orange tiger . . . . . 7·00 3·50

1975. Air. "Arphila 75" International Stamp Exhibition, Paris.
536 **126** 4 f. red, indigo and blue . 15·00 7·00

127 "Pottery" (Potter's wheel and products)   128 Pointe-Plate Lighthouse and Sea–birds

1975. Artisan Handicrafts.
537 **127** 50 c. purple, brown & grn 4·00 2·25
538 – 60 c. blue and yellow . . 4·00 2·25
DESIGN: 60 c. "Sculpture" (wood carving of Virgin and Child).

1975. Lighthouses.
539 **128** 6 c. black, violet & green 1·60 1·10
540 – 10 c. purple, green & slate 2·75 1·60
541 – 20 c. brown, indigo & blue 4·00 2·75
DESIGNS: 10 c. Galantry lighthouse, Atlantic puffin and pintail; 20 c. Cap Blanc lighthouse and blue whale.

129 Judo

1975. Air. "Pre-Olympic Year". Olympic Games, Montreal (1976).
542 **129** 1 f. 90 blue, red & violet . 6·50 3·50

130 Concorde in Flight

1976. Air. Concorde's 1st Commercial Flight.
543 **130** 10 f. indigo, blue and red 22·00 11·00

1976. President Pompidou Commemoration. As T **125** of New Caledonia.
544 1 f. 10 grey and purple . . . 5·50 3·50

132 Alexander Graham Bell and Early Telephone

1976. Air. Telephone Centenary.
545 **132** 5 f. blue, orange and red 7·50 4·00

133 Washington and Lafayette

1976. Bicentenary of American Revolution.
546 **133** 1 f. multicoloured . . . . 4·50 2·75

134 Basketball

1976. Olympic Games, Montreal.
547 **134** 70 c. agate, blue & brown . 3·50 2·75
548 – 2 f. 50 turquoise, grn & emerald . . . . 10·00 5·00
DESIGN—HORIZ: 2 f. 50, Swimming.

135 Vigie Dam

1976.
549 **135** 2 f. 20 brown, blue & turq 5·75 4·00

136 "Croix de Lorraine"

1976. Stern Trawlers. Multicoloured.
550 1 f. 20 Type **136** . . . . . . 5·50 3·50
551 1 f. 50 "Geolette" . . . . . . 10·00 5·50

1986. Nos. 2444 etc of France optd **ST-PIERRE ET MIQUELON**.
552 **916** 5 c. green 30 30
553 10 c. red 20 20
554 20 c. green 20 20
555 30 c. red 20 20
556 40 c. brown 20 20
557 50 c. mauve 20 20
558 1 f. green 30 30
559 1 f. 80 green 55 40
560 2 f. green 65 45
561 2 f. 20 red 80 45
562 2 f. brown . . . . 1·10 90
563 3 f. 20 blue . . . . . . 1·25 90
564 4 f. red . . . . 1·40 1·00
565 5 f. blue . . . . 1·75 1·50
566 10 f. violet . . . . . . 3·50 2·25

138 Open Book

1986. 450th Anniv of Discovery of Islands by Jacques Cartier and 1st Anniv of New Constitution.
567 **138** 2 f. 20 brown, deep brown and green . . . . 1·40 80

139 Statue and Harbour

1986. Centenary of Statue of Liberty.
568 **139** 2 f. 50 blue and red . . . 1·50 90

141 Fish and Detection Equipment   142 "Nativity" (stained glass window, L. Balmet)

1986. Fishing.
578 **141** 1 f. red 50 35
579 1 f. 10 orange 45 35
580 1 f. 30 red 55 35
581 1 f. 40 blue 70 45
582 1 f. 40 red 55 35
583 1 f. 50 blue 65 45
584 1 f. 60 green 80 45
585 1 f. 70 green 65 45

1986. Christmas.
586 **142** 2 f. 20 multicoloured . . . 1·40 80

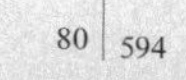

143 Buff Cap ("Hygrophorus pratensis")

1987.
587 **143** 2 f. 50 brown and ochre . 1·50 90
See also Nos. 598, 609 and 645.

144 Dunan and Hospital

1987. Dr. Francois Dunan Commemoration.
588 **144** 2 f. 20 black, brown and blue 1·00 65

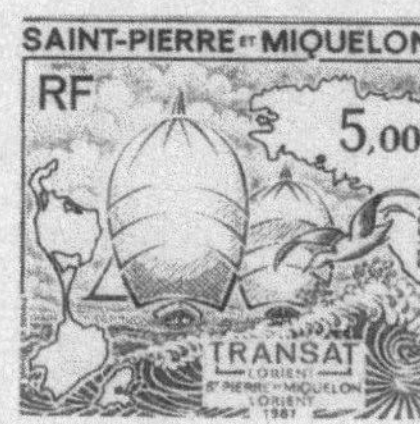

145 Ocean-racing Yachts

1987. Transatlantic Yacht Race (Lorient–St. Pierre et Miquelon–Lorient).
589 **145** 5 f. brown, dp blue & bl . 2·25 1·10

146 Maps

1987. Visit of President Francois Mitterand.
590 **146** 2 f. 20 multicoloured . . 1·40 90

147 Schooner on Slipway and Share Certificate

1987. Centenary of Marine Slipway.
591 **147** 2 f. 50 brown and light brown . . . . 1·40 90

148 Hawker Siddeley H.S. 748 (St. Pierre–Montreal first flight, 1987)

1987. Air. Airplanes named "Ville de St. Pierre".
592 **148** 5 f. blue, green & turquoise 2·25 1·10
593 – 10 f. dp blue, blue & orge 4·50 2·25
DESIGN: 10 f. Flying boat "Ville de Saint-Pierre" (first flight, 1939).

149 "La Normande" (trawler)

1987.
594 **149** 3 f. multicoloured . . . . 2·25 1·60

150 "St. Christopher carrying Christ Child" (stained glass window by L. Balmet) and Scout Emblem

1987. Christmas. 50th Anniv of Scouting.
595 **150** 2 f. 20 multicoloured . . . 1·25 80

151 Horses and Ducks

1987. Natural Heritage. Le Grand Barachois. Each orange, green and brown.
596 3 f. Type **151** 1·60 1·00
597 3 f. Canada geese, gulls and seals 1·60 1·00
Nos. 596/7 were printed together, se-tenant, with intervening half stamp size label, each strip forming a composite design.

1988. Fungi. As T **143**.
598 2 f. 50 black, orange & brown 1·00 65
DESIGN: "Russula paludosa".

152 Ice Hockey Goalkeeper

1988. Winter Olympic Games, Calgary.
599 **152** 5 f. blue and red 2·00 1·40

153 Thomas and Camera

1988. Birth Centenary of Dr. Louis Thomas (photographer).
600 **153** 2 f. 20 brown, deep brown and blue 90 55

154 Airship "Hindenburg"

1988. Air. Aircraft. Each black, blue and purple.
601 5 f. Type **154** 2·25 1·10
602 10 f. Douglas DC-3 4·50 2·25

1988. "Philexfrance 89" International Stamp Exhibition, Paris. No. 2821 of France optd **ST-PIERRE ET MIQUELON**.
603 **1073** 2 f. 20 red, black & blue 1·50 80

156 "Nellie J. Banks" and Crates

1988. 50th Anniv of End of Prohibition and Last Liquor Smuggling Run from St. Pierre to Canada.
604 **156** 2 f. 50 ultramarine, brn & bl 1·50 90

157 "Le Marmouset" (stern trawler)

1988.
605 **157** 3 f. multicoloured 1·40 90

158 Ross Cove

1988. Natural Heritage. Each brown, deep blue and blue.
606 2 f. 20 Type **158** 80 55
607 13 f. 70 Cap Perce 4·50 3·25

159 Stained Glass Window

160 Judo

1988. Christmas.
608 **159** 2 f. 20 multicoloured 80 55

1989. Fungi. As T **143**.
609 2 f. 50 brown and red 80 45
DESIGN: 2 f. 50, "Tricholoma virgatum".

1989. 25th Anniv of Judo in St. Pierre.
610 **160** 5 f. black, green & orange 1·75 1·10

161 "Liberty" (Roger Druet)

1989. Bicentenary of French Revolution and Declaration of Rights of Man. Multicoloured.
611 2 f. 20 Type **161** 90 65
612 2 f. 20 "Equality" 95 65
613 2 f. 20 "Fraternity" 95 65

162 Piper Aztec

1989. Air.
614 **162** 20 f. brown, light brown and blue 5·50 2·75

164 Fisherman in Boat

1989. Natural Heritage. Ile aux Marins. Each brown, blue and green.
616 2 f. 20 Type **164** 85 60
617 13 f. 70 Boy flying kite from boat 5·25 3·75

165 "Le Malabar" (ocean-going tug)

1989.
618 **165** 3 f. multicoloured 1·00 60

166 Georges Landry and Emblem

1989. Centenary of Islands' Bank.
619 **166** 2 f. 20 blue and brown 80 45

167 "Christmas" (Magali Olano)

1989. Christmas.
620 **167** 2 f. 20 multicoloured 65 45

1990. Stamps of France optd **ST-PIERRE ET MIQUELON**.

No.	Type	Value		Unused	Used
621	1118	10 c.	brown	10	10
622		20 c.	green	10	10
623		50 c.	violet	10	10
624		1 f.	orange	20	10
625		2 f.	green	45	25
625a		2 f.	blue	45	25
626		2 f. 10	green	45	25
627		2 f. 20	green	50	30
628		2 f. 30	red	50	30
629		2 f. 40	green	55	35
630		2 f. 50	red	55	35
631		3 f. 20	blue	70	40
632		3 f. 40	blue	75	45
633		3 f. 50	green	80	50
634		3 f. 80	mauve	85	50
635		4 f.	mauve	90	55
636		4 f. 20	mauve	95	55
637		4 f. 40	blue	1·00	60
638		5 f.	blue	1·10	65
639		10 f.	violet	2·25	1·40

The 2 f. 50, exists both perforated (ordinary gum) and imperforate (self-adhesive).

1990. Fungi. As T **143**.
645 2 f. 50 brown, black & orange 90 55
DESIGN: 2 f. 50, Hedgehog fungus ("Hydnum repandum").

168 "Pou du Ciel" and Gull

1990. Air.
646 **168** 5 f. green, blue & brown 1·40 90

169 De Gaulle and Soldiers

1990. 50th Anniv of De Gaulle's Call to Resist.
647 **169** 2 f. 30 purple, red & blue 80 45
For design as T **169** but inscr "1890–1970", see No. 653.

170 Runner and Map

1990. Miquelon 25 Km Race.
648 **170** 5 f. black, blue and brown 1·25 55

171 Moose, Micmac Canoe and Woman

1990.
649 **171** 2 f. 50 orange, brown & bl 80 45

172 "Saint-Denis" and "Saint-Pierre" at Moorings

1990. Trawlers.
650 **172** 3 f. multicoloured 90 60

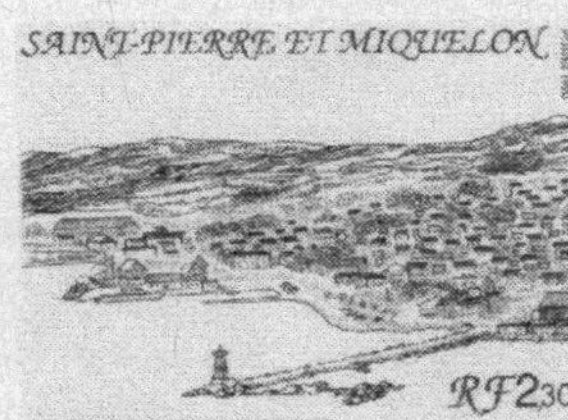

173 Entrance to Saint-Pierre Port

1990. St.-Pierre. Each brown, green and blue.
651 2 f. 30 Type **173** 75 45
652 14 f. 50 Interpeche fish factory 4·00 2·40
Nos. 651/2 were issued together, se-tenant, with intervening label, forming a composite design of part of St.-Pierre coastline.

1990. Birth Centenary of Charles de Gaulle (French statesman). As T **169** but inscr "1890–1970". Each purple, red and blue.
653 1 f. 70 Type **169** 55 35
654 2 f. 30 De Gaulle and trawler 70 45

174 Christmas Scene (Cindy Lechevallier)

1990. Christmas.
655 **174** 2 f. 30 multicoloured 65 45

175 Short-tailed Swallowtail on "Heracleum maximum"

176 Sail-makers' Tools and Sails

1991.
656 **175** 2 f. 50 multicoloured 80 45

1991.
657 **176** 1 f. 40 green and yellow 45 20
658 1 f. 70 red and yellow 50 35

177 Ile aux Marins

1991. Old Views.

659	**177**	1 f. 70 blue	50	35
660	–	1 f. 70 blue	50	35
661	–	1 f. 70 blue	50	35
662	–	1 f. 70 blue	50	35
663	**177**	2 f. 50 red	70	45
664	–	2 f. 50 red	70	45
665	–	2 f. 50 red	70	45
666	–	2 f. 50 red	70	45

DESIGNS: Nos. 660, 664, Langlade; 661, 665, Miquelon; 662, 666, Saint-Pierre.

178 Piper Tomahawk

1991. Air.

667 **178** 10 f. blue, turquoise & brown 2·75 1·60

179 Musicians

1991. Centenary of Lyre Music Society.

668 **179** 2 f. 50 red, brown & orge 80 45

180 Oars

1991. St.- Pierre–Newfoundland Crossing by Rowing Boat.

669 **180** 2 f. 50 multicoloured 80 45

181 Pelota Players

1991. Basque Sports.

670 **181** 5 f. green and red 1·40 65

182 Fishermen

1991. Natural Heritage. Multicoloured.

671 2 f. 50 Type **182** 75 45
672 14 f. 50 Canada geese and shore 3·75 2·40

Nos. 671/2 were issued together, se-tenant, forming a composite design of Savoyard.

183 "Cryos" (stern trawler)

1991.

673 **183** 3 f. multicoloured 90 60

184 Free French Central Bank 100 f. Note

1991. 50th Anniv of Central Economic Co-operation Bank.

674 **184** 2 f. 50 multicoloured 80 45

185 Naval Forces and Cross of Lorraine

1991. Christmas. 50th Anniv of Adherence to Free French Government.

675 **185** 2 f. 50 multicoloured 80 45

186 Muselier and Harbour

1992. 110th Birth Anniv of Admiral E. Muselier (commander of 1941 Free French landing force).

676 **186** 2 f. 50 multicoloured 65 35

187 Ice Skating

188 "Aeshna eremita" and "Nuphar variegatum"

1992. Winter Olympic Games, Albertville.

677 **187** 5 f. blue, ultramarine & mve 1·10 70

1992.

678 **188** 3 f. 60 multicoloured 80 50

189 Boat-building Tools and Stern of Ship

1992.

679 **189** 1 f. 50 brown and blue 45 30
680 1 f. 80 blue and azure 55 40

190 Model Airplane and Remote Control

1992.

681 **190** 20 f. red, orange & brown 4·50 2·75

191 Ile aux Marins Lighthouse

1992. Lighthouses. Multicoloured.

682 2 f. 50 Type **191** 55 35
683 2 f. 50 Galantry 55 35
684 2 f. 50 Old Rouge Feu lighthouse, St. Pierre 55 35
685 2 f. 50 Pointe-Plate 55 35

192 Cones and Woodpecker

1992. Natural Heritage. Dolisie Valley, Langlade. Multicoloured.

686 2 f. 50 Type **192** 55 35
687 15 f. 10 Valley and berries 3·25 2·00

193 Columbus and Map on Sails

1992. 500th Anniv of Discovery of America by Columbus.

688 **193** 5 f. 10 multicoloured 1·10 90

194 Baron de l'Esperance, Map and Settlers

1992. 230th Anniv (1993) of Resettlement by French of Miquelon.

689 **194** 2 f. 50 brown, blue and red 55 35

195 Nativity

1992. Christmas.

690 **195** 2 f. 50 multicoloured 55 35

196 Birot and Free French Corvette

1993. 50th Death Anniv (1992) of Commander R. Birot.

691 **196** 2 f. 50 multicoloured 60 40

197 Divers and Wreck of "L'Hortense"

198 Longhorn Beetle on "Cichorium intybus"

1993. Deep Sea Diving.

692 **197** 5 f. multicoloured 1·25 75

1993.

693 **198** 3 f. 60 multicoloured 80 50

199 Cutting-up Cod

1993.

694 **199** 1 f. 50 multicoloured 35 25
695 1 f. 80 multicoloured 40 25

200 Greater Puffin

1993. Air. Migratory Birds. Multicoloured.

696 5 f. Type **200** 1·10 70
697 10 f. Golden plover 2·25 1·40

201 Fleet of Ships

1993. Bicentenary of Settlement of Madeleine Islands.

698 **201** 5 f. 10 blue, green & brown 1·10 70

1993. No. 3121 of France optd **ST-PIERRE ET MIQUELON**.

699 **1118** (–) red 60 40

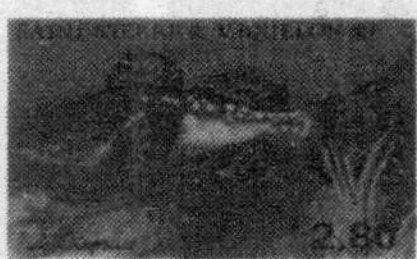

202 Frogfish

1993. Fishes. Multicoloured.

700 2 f. 80 Type **202** 65 40
701 2 f. 80 Fishermen and capelin 65 40
702 2 f. 80 Skate ("Le Raie") 65 40
703 2 f. 80 Halibut ("Le Fletan") 65 40

203 Pine Cones, Otter and Left Bank

1993. Natural Heritage. Sylvain Hills. Multicoloured.

704 2 f. 80 Type **203** 65 40
705 16 f. Otter on all fours, pine cones and right bank 3·75 2·25

Nos. 704/5 were issued together, se-tenant, with intervening ½ stamp-size label, forming a composite design of an otter pool.

204 Prefect's Residence

1993.

707 **204** 3 f. 70 blue, yellow & brn 85 50

205 Father Christmas waving to Child

1993. Christmas.

708 **205** 2 f. 80 multicoloured 65 40

206 Blaison and "Surcouf" (Free French submarine)

1994. 50th Death Anniv (1992) of Commander Louis Blaison.

709	**206**	2 f. 80 multicoloured . . .	65	40

207 Player lining up Shot

1994. 1st French Overseas Territories Petanque Championship.

710	**207**	5 f. 10 multicoloured . . .	1·25	75

208 "Cristalis tenax" on Dandelion

1994.

711	**208**	3 f. 70 multicoloured . . .	85	50

209 Drying Cod

1994.

712	**209**	1 f. 50 black and green . .	35	20
713		1 f. 80 multicoloured . . .	40	25

210 Ballot Box and Women outside Town Hall

1994. 50th Anniv of Women's Suffrage.

714	**210**	2 f. 80 multicoloured . . .	70	45

211 "Saint-Pierre" (hospital ship)

1994. Centenary of Society of Sea Works.

715	**211**	2 f. 80 multicoloured . . .	70	45

212 "Miquelon" (trawler)

1994. Ships. Multicoloured.

716	2 f. 80 Type **212**	70	45
717	2 f. 80 "Ile de St. Pierre" (trawler)	70	45
718	3 f. 70 "St. Georges XII" (pleasure cruiser)	95	60
719	3 f. 70 "St. Eugene IV" (pleasure cruiser)	95	60

MINIMUM PRICE

The minimum price quoted is 10p which represents a handling charge rather than a basis for valuing common stamps. For further notes about prices, see introductory pages.

213 Poolside

1994. Natural Heritage. Miranda Pool. Multicoloured.

720	2 f. 80 Type **213**	70	45
721	16 f. Pool	4·00	2·40

Nos. 720/1 were issued together se-tenant with intervening ½ stamp-size label, forming a composite design.

214 Parochial School

1994.

722	**214**	3 f. 70 black, blue and red	95	60

215 Envelope, Magnifying Glass and Tweezers holding "Stamp"

1994. 1st European Stamp Salon, Flower Gardens, Paris.

723	**215**	3 f. 70 blue, green and yellow	95	60

PARCEL POST STAMPS

1901. Optd **COLIS POSTAUX**.

P79	D	10 c. black on lilac . . .	55·00	55·00

1901. Optd **Colis Postaux**.

P80	D	10 c. red	9·00	9·00

1917. Nos. 83 and 85 optd **Colis Postaux**.

P109	**17**	10 c. red and pink . . .	1·25	1·40
P110		20 c. purple and brown .	1·25	1·10

1941. Free French Plebiscite. No. P110 optd **Noel 1941. FRANCE LIBRE F. N. F. L.**.

P303	**17**	20 c. purple and brown .	£550	£550

POSTAGE DUE STAMPS

1892. Postage Due stamps of French Colonies optd **ST-PIERRE M-on**.

D60	U	5 c. black	40·00	42·00
D61		10 c. black	10·00	10·00
D62		15 c. black	10·00	10·00
D63		20 c. black	10·00	10·00
D64		30 c. black	10·00	10·00
D65		40 c. black	9·25	10·50
D66		60 c. black	42·00	42·00
D67		1 f. brown	90·00	90·00
D68		2 f. brown	90·00	90·00

1925. Postage Due type of France optd **SAINT-PIERRE-ET-MIQUELON** or surch also **centimes a percevoir** and value in figures.

D135	D **11**	5 c. blue	25	40
D136		10 c. brown	30	50
D137		20 c. olive	40	50
D138		25 c. red	40	50
D139		30 c. red	55	60
D140		45 c. green	55	60
D141		50 c. red	1·10	1·25
D142		60 c. on 50 c. brown .	1·10	1·25
D143		1 f. red	1·25	1·50
D144		2 f. on 1 f. red . . .	1·75	2·00
D145		3 f. mauve	5·50	5·50

D 30 Newfoundland Dog   **D 40** Codfish

1932.

D163	D **30**	5 c. black and blue .	75	80
D164		10 c. black and green	85	80
D165		20 c. black and red .	1·10	1·10
D166		25 c. black and purple	1·10	1·10
D167		30 c. black & orange .	2·00	2·00
D168		45 c. black and blue .	2·25	2·25
D169		50 c. black and green	4·00	4·25
D170		60 c. black and red .	5·50	5·50
D171		1 f. black and brown .	14·00	14·00
D172		2 f. black and purple .	21·00	21·00
D173		3 f. black and brown .	23·00	23·00

1938.

D208	D **40**	5 c. black	25	35
D209		10 c. purple	15	30
D210		15 c. green	25	35
D211		20 c. blue	25	35
D212		30 c. red	25	35
D213	D **40**	50 c. green	30	45
D214		60 c. blue	25	45
D215		1 f. red	40	45
D216		2 f. brown	1·40	1·60
D217		3 f. violet	2·50	1·60

1941. Free French Plebiscite. Nos. D208/17 optd **NOEL 1941 F N F L**

D235	D **40**	5 c. black	15·00	15·00
D236		10 c. purple	15·00	15·00
D237		15 c. green	15·00	15·00
D238		20 c. blue	15·00	15·00
D239		30 c. red	15·00	15·00
D240		50 c. green	28·00	28·00
D241		60 c. blue	65·00	65·00
D242		1 f. red	75·00	75·00
D243		2 f. brown	80·00	80·00
D244		3 f. violet	90·00	90·00

1941. Postage Due stamps of 1932 optd **FRANCE LIBRE F. N. F. L.** or surch also.

D298	D **30**	25 c. black & purple .	£190	£190
D299		30 c. black & orange .	£190	£190
D300		50 c. black & green . .	£625	£625
D301		2 f. black & purple . .	28·00	28·00
D302		3 f. on 2 f. blk & pur .	14·00	14·00

1941. Free French Plebiscite. Nos. D208/17 optd **FRANCE LIBRE F. N. F. L.**.

D310	D **40**	5 c. black	28·00	28·00
D311		10 c. purple	5·50	5·50
D312		15 c. green	5·50	5·50
D313		20 c. blue	5·50	5·50
D314		30 c. red	5·50	5·50
D315		50 c. green	5·50	5·50
D316		60 c. blue	6·75	7·00
D317		1 f. red	14·00	14·00
D318		2 f. brown	14·00	14·00
D319		3 f. violet	£350	£350

D 57 Arms and Galleon

D 115 Newfoundland Dog and Shipwreck Scene

1947.

D385	D **57**	10 c. orange	15	25
D386		30 c. blue	15	30
D387		50 c. green	25	30
D388		1 f. red	25	35
D389		2 f. green	25	35
D390		3 f. violet	55	60
D391		4 f. brown	55	60
D392		5 f. green	55	60
D393		10 f. black	70	75
D394		20 f. red	80	90

1973.

D516	D **115**	2 c. black & brown .	60	60
D517		10 c. black and violet	90	90
D518		20 c. black and blue .	1·40	1·40
D519		30 c. black and red .	2·25	2·25
D520		1 f. black and blue . .	5·50	5·50

1986. Nos. D2493/2502 of France optd **ST-PIERRE ET MIQUELON**.

D569	10 c. brown and black . . .	20	20
D570	20 c. black	20	20
D571	30 c. red, brown & black . .	20	20
D572	40 c. blue, brown & black .	20	20
D573	50 c. red and black	20	20
D574	1 f. black	30	30
D575	2 f. yellow and black	65	65
D576	3 f. black and red	1·00	1·00
D577	4 f. brown and black	1·40	1·40
D578	5 f. blue, red and black . . .	1·75	1·75

ST. THOMAS AND PRINCE IS.

Pt. 9; Pt. 11

Two islands in the Gulf of Guinea off the west coast of Africa. A colony and then an Overseas Province of Portugal until 1975, when it became an independent republic.

1870. 1000 reis = 1 milreis
1913. 100 centavos = 1 escudo
1977. 100 cents = 1 dobra

1870. "Crown" key-type inscr "S. THOME E PRINCIPE".

17	P	5 r. black	70	65
18		10 r. orange	7·00	4·50
29		10 r. green	3·00	2·25
20		20 r. olive	1·50	1·00
30		20 r. red	1·40	1·25
21a		25 r. red	70	55
31		25 r. lilac	125	80
12		40 r. blue	2·25	1·90
32		40 r. yellow	2·00	1·75
25		50 r. green	6·00	5·00
33		50 r. blue	1·50	80
26		100 r. lilac	3·25	2·75
15		200 r. orange	3·50	2·50
16		300 r. brown	3·50	2·75

1887. "Embossed" key-type inscr "S. THOME E PRINCIPE".

38	Q	5 r. black	1·75	1·50
42		10 r. green	2·25	1·25
43		20 r. red	2·25	1·75
44		25 r. mauve	2·25	90
45		40 r. brown	2·00	1·40
40		50 r. blue	2·25	1·25
47		100 r. brown	2·25	1·25
48		200 r. lilac	6·50	5·00
49		300 r. orange	6·50	5·00

1889. Stamps of 1887 surch. No gum.

50	Q	5 r. on 10 r. green	12·00	9·50
51		5 r. on 20 r. red	12·00	9·50
52		50 r. on 40 r. brown . . .	38·00	30·00

1895. "Figures" key-type inscr "S. THOME E PRINCIPE.

60	R	5 r. yellow	55	40
61		10 r. mauve	70	60
53		15 r. brown	90	60
54		20 r. lilac	90	60
62		25 r. green	90	35
63		50 r. blue	90	35
55		75 r. red	1·90	1·60
64		80 r. green	5·00	4·00
56		100 r. brown on buff . . .	2·00	1·40
57		150 r. red on rose	2·75	2·40
58		200 r. blue on blue	3·25	2·75
59		300 r. blue on brown . . .	4·00	3·00

1898. "King Carlos" key-types inscr "S. THOME E PRINCIPE". Name and value in red (500 r.) or black (others).

66	S	2½ r. grey	15	15
67		5 r. orange	15	15
68		10 r. green	20	15
69		15 r. brown	80	65
113		15 r. green	50	35
70		20 r. lilac	40	20
71		25 r. green	30	20
114		25 r. red	50	35
72		50 r. blue	35	25
115		50 r. brown	2·00	1·40
116		65 r. blue	4·00	3·00
73		75 r. red	5·00	2·50
117		75 r. purple	1·00	70
74		80 r. mauve	2·00	1·50
75		100 r. blue on blue . . .	1·25	90
118		115 r. brown on pink . .	4·25	3·25
119		130 r. brown on yellow .	4·25	3·25
76		150 r. brown on yellow .	2·00	1·00
77		200 r. purple on pink . .	2·50	80
78		300 r. blue on pink . . .	2·75	1·75
120		400 r. blue on yellow . .	5·00	3·50
79		500 r. black on blue . .	3·50	2·00
80		700 r. mauve on yellow .	6·00	4·25

1902. Surch with new value.

121	S	50 r. on 65 r. blue . .	1·50	1·00
85	R	65 r. on 5 r. yellow . .	1·50	1·25
86		65 r. on 10 r. mauve .	1·50	1·25
87		65 r. on 15 r. brown .	1·50	1·25
81	Q	65 r. on 20 r. red . . .	3·00	2·00
88	R	65 r. on 20 r. lilac . . .	1·50	1·25
83	Q	65 r. on 25 r. mauve .	2·00	1·60
84		65 r. on 100 r. brown .	2·00	1·75
90		115 r. on 10 r. green .	2·00	1·75
92	R	115 r. on 25 r. green .	1·50	1·25
89	P	115 r. on 50 r. green .	4·50	1·50
93	R	115 r. on 150 r. red on rose	1·50	1·25
94		115 r. on 200 r. blue on bl	1·50	1·25
91	Q	115 r. on 300 r. orange	2·00	1·75
95		130 r. on 5 r. black . .	2·00	1·75
98	R	130 r. on 75 r. red . .	1·50	1·25
99		130 r. on 100 r. brown on buff	1·50	1·50
97	Q	130 r. on 200 r. lilac .	2·50	1·75
100	R	130 r. on 300 r. blue on brown	1·50	1·00
108	V	400 r. on 2½ r. brown .	50	50
101	P	400 r. on 10 r. orange .	14·00	7·50
102	Q	400 r. on 40 r. brown .	3·50	2·50
103		400 r. on 50 r. blue . .	4·00	3·50
105	R	400 r. on 50 r. blue . .	50	50
107		400 r. on 80 r. green .	90	70

1903. Stamps of 1898 optd **PROVISORIO**.

109	S	15 r. brown	90	40
110		25 r. green	90	40
111		50 r. blue	95	40
112		75 r. red	2·00	1·50

1911. Stamps of 1898 optd **REPUBLICA**.

122	S	2½ r. grey	15	15
123		5 r. orange	15	15
124		10 r. orange	15	15

125 S 15 r. green 15 15
126 20 r. lilac 15 15
127 25 r. red 15 15
128 50 r. brown 15 15
129 75 r. purple 15 15
130 100 r. blue on blue 25 20
131 115 r. brown on pink 60 40
132 130 r. brown on yellow 60 45
267 200 r. purple on pink 80 50
134 400 r. blue on yellow 75 45
268 500 r. black on blue 60 50
136 700 r. mauve on yellow 70 45

1912. "King Manoel" key type inscr "S. THOME E PRINCIPE" and optd **REPUBLICA**.
137 T 2½ r. lilac 10 10
138 5 r. black 10 10
139 10 r. green 10 10
140 20 r. red 60 40
141 25 r. brown 30 20
142 50 r. blue 30 20
143 75 r. brown 30 20
144 100 r. brown on green 50 30
145 200 r. green on pink 80 75
146 300 r. black on blue 80 75

1913. Nos. 109 and 111/2 optd **REPUBLICA**.
159 S 15 r. brown 80 75
243 50 r. blue 25 20
272 75 r. red 3·50 2·50

1913. Stamps of 1902 optd **REPUBLICA**.
244 S 50 r. on 65 r. blue 25 20
245 Q 115 r. on 10 r. green 1·00 75
246 R 115 r. on 25 r. green 20 15
164 P 115 r on 50 r. green 38·00 35·00
247 R 115r. on 150 r. red on rose 20 15
248 115 r. on 200 r. blue on blue 20 15
249 Q 115 r. on 300 r. orange 1·00 80
250 130 r. on 5 r. black 1·75 1·25
251 R 130 r. on 75 r. red 20 15
252 130 r. on 100 r. brown on buff 50 45
253 Q 130 r. on 200 r. lilac 65 50
254 R 130 r. on 300 r. blue on brown 50 30
197 V 400 r. on 2½ r. brown 1·00 90
168 Q 400 r. on 50 r. blue 22·00 20·00
200 R 400 r. on 50 r. blue 1·25 1·00
202 400 r. on 80 r. green 1·40 1·00

1913. Surch **REPUBLICA S. TOME E PRINCIPE** and new value on "Vasco da Gama" stamps of (a) **Portuguese Colonies**.
203 ¼ c. on 2½ r. green 50 40
204 ½ c. on 5 r. red 50 40
205 1 c. on 10 r. purple 50 40
206 2½ c. on 25 r. green 50 40
207 5 c. on 50 r. blue 50 40
208 7½ c. on 75 r. brown 80 65
209 10 c. on 100 r. brown 50 40
210 15 c. on 150 r. bistre 50 40

(b) **Macao**.
211 ¼ c. on ½ c. green 70 50
212 ½ c. on 1 a. red 70 50
213 1 c. on 2 a. purple 45 35
214 2½ c. on 4 a. green 45 35
215 5 c. on 8 a. blue 80 60
216 7½ c. on 12 a. brown 90 90
217 10 c. on 16 a. brown 80 60
218 15 c. on 24 a. bistre 60 50

(c) **Timor**.
219 ¼ c. on ½ a green 70 50
220 ½ c. on 1 a. red 70 50
221 1 c. on 2 a. purple 40 30
222 2½ c. on 4 a. green 40 30
223 5 c. on 8 a. blue 90 70
224 7½ c. on 12 a. brown 90 75
225 10 c. on 16 a. brown 80 60
226 15 c. on 24 a. bistre 50 45

1914. "Ceres" key-type inscr "S. TOME E PRINCIPE".
276 U ¼ c. olive 10 10
281 ½ c. black 15 15
282 1 c. green 15 15
283 1½ c. brown 15 15
284 2 c. red 15 15
285 2 c. grey 15 15
286 2½ c. violet 15 10
287 3 c. orange 15 15
288 4 c. red 15 15
289 4½ c. grey 15 15
290 5 c. blue 15 15
291 6 c. mauve 15 15
292 7 c. blue 15 15
293 7½ c. brown 15 15
294 8 c. grey 15 15
295 10 c. brown 15 10
296 12 c. green 25 20
297 15 c. red 15 15
298 20 c. green 20 15
299 24 c. blue 45 35
300 25 c. brown 45 35
239 30 c. brown on green 75 75
301 30 c. green 30 20
240 40 c. brown on red 75 75
302 40 c. blue 30 20
241 50 c. orange on pink 2·00 1·50
303 50 c. mauve 30 20
304 60 c. blue 30 20
305 60 c. pink 80 35
306 80 c. red 90 35
242 1 e. green on blue 2·00 1·50
307 1 e. pink 90 65
308 1 e. blue 75 45
309 2 e. purple 1·00 60
310 5 e. brown 7·00 2·50
311 10 e. pink 12·00 5·00
312 20 e. green 26·00 16·00

1919. "King Carlos" key-type of St. Thomas and Prince Islands surch **PROVISORIO** and **REPUBLICA** and new value.
255 S 2½ r. on 15 r. brown 35 25

1919. "King Carlos" key-type of St. Thomas and Prince Islands surch **REPUBLICA** and new value.
256 S ½ c. on 2½ r. grey 1·10 1·40
257 1 c. on 2½ r. grey 1·00 80
258 2½ c. on 2½ r. grey 45 30

1919. "Ceres" key-types of St. Thomas and Prince Islands surch.
259 U ½ c. on ¼ c. olive 80 70
260 2 c. on ¼ c. olive 80 70
261 2½ c. on 2¼ c. grey 2·75 2·50

1919. "Ceres" key-types of St. Thomas and Prince Islands surch **$04 Centavos** and with old value blocked out.
262 U 4 c. on 2½ c. violet 30 25

1923. Stamps of 1913 (optd REPUBLICA) surch **DEZ CENTAVOS** and bars.
313 R 10 c. on 115 r. on 25 r. green 25 20
314 10 c. on 115 r. on 150 r. red on rose 25 20
316 10 c. on 115 r. on 200 r. blue on blue 25 20
317 10 c. on 130 r. on 75 r. red 25 20
318 10 c. on 130 r. on 100 r. brown on buff 25 20
319 10 c. on 130 r. on 300 r. blue on brown 25 20

1925. Stamps of 1902 surch **Republica 40 c** and bars over original surcharge.
321 V 40 c. on 400 r. on 2½ r. brn 30 20
322 R 40 c. on 400 r. on 80 r. grn 30 20

1931. Nos. 307 and 309 surch.
323 U 70 c. on 1 e. pink 75 60
324 1 e. 40 on 2 e. purple 1·25 80

1934. As T **24** of Portuguese Guinea (new "Ceres" type).
325 1 c. brown 15 15
326 5 c. sepia 15 15
327 10 c. mauve 15 15
328 15 c. black 15 15
329 20 c. grey 15 15
330 30 c. green 15 15
331 40 c. red 15 15
332 45 c. blue 20 25
333 50 c. brown 15 10
334 60 c. olive 25 20
335 70 c. brown 25 20
336 80 c. green 25 20
337 85 c. red 1·00 85
338 1 e. red 40 15
339 1 e. 40 blue 1·25 70
340 2 e. mauve 1·25 80
341 5 e. green 2·75 1·75
342 10 e. brown 7·00 4·00
343 20 e. orange 24·00 14·00

1938. As T **54** and **56** of Macao, but inscr "S. TOME".
344 **54** 1 c. olive (postage) 10 10
345 5 c. brown 10 10
346 10 c. red 10 10
347 15 c. purple 10 10
348 20 c. slate 10 10
349 – 30 c. purple 15 10
350 – 35 c. green 20 15
351 – 40 c. brown 20 15
352 – 50 c. mauve 20 15
353 – 60 c. black 20 15
354 – 70 c. violet 20 15
355 – 80 c. orange 20 15
356 – 1 e. red 65 20
357 – 1 e. 75 blue 60 35
358 – 2 e. red 7·00 2·00
359 – 5 e. olive 6·00 2·00
360 – 10 e. blue 9·00 2·25
361 – 20 e. brown 15·00 3·00
362 **56** 10 c. red (air) 25·00 18·00
363 20 c. violet 10·00 8·00
364 50 c. orange 65 50
365 1 e. blue 90 75
366 2 e. red 1·50 1·25
367 3 e. green 2·50 1·90
368 5 e. brown 3·50 3·00
369 9 e. red 3·75 3·00
370 10 e. mauve 3·75 3·00
DESIGNS: 30 to 50 c. Mousinho de Albuquerque; 60 c. to 1 e. Dam; 1 e. 75 to 5 e. Prince Henry the Navigator; 10, 20 e. Afonso de Albuquerque.
See also Nos. 374/400.

37 Portuguese Colonial Column

41 Cola Nuts

1938. President's Colonial Tour.
371 **37** 80 c. green 80 50
372 1 e. 75 blue 3·00 1·75
373 20 e. brown 15·00 7·00

1939. As Nos. 344/70 but inscr "S. TOME e PRINCIPE".
374 **54** 1 c. olive (postage) 10 10
375 5 c. brown 10 10
376 10 c. red 10 10
377 15 c. purple 10 10
378 20 c. slate 20 10
379 – 30 c. purple 15 10
380 – 35 c. green 15 15
381 – 40 c. brown 20 15
382 – 50 c. mauve 20 15
383 – 60 c. black 25 15
384 – 70 c. violet 25 15
385 – 80 c. orange 25 15
386 – 1 e. red 35 20
387 – 1 e. 75 blue 60 30
388 – 2 e. red 1·00 55
389 – 5 e. olive 2·25 1·40
390 – 10 e. blue 6·00 1·75
391 – 20 e. brown 8·00 2·50
392 **56** 10 c. red (air) 10 10
393 20 c. violet 10 10
394 50 c. orange 10 10
395 1 e. blue 15 15
396 2 e. red 40 35
397 3 e. green 60 45
398 5 e. brown 1·40 85
399 9 e. red 2·00 1·25
400 10 e. mauve 2·00 1·25

1948. Fruits.
401 **41** 5 c. black and yellow 15 10
402 – 10 c. black and salmon 15 10
403 – 30 c. black and grey 1·00 50
404 – 50 c. brown and yellow 1·50 55
405 – 1 e. red and pale red 2·00 60
406 – 1 e. 75 blue and grey 3·50 2·00
407 – 2 e. black and green 3·00 60
408 – 5 e. brown and mauve 7·50 4·00
409 – 10 e. black and mauve 11·00 8·00
410 – 20 e. black and grey 25·00 13·00
DESIGNS: 10 c. Bread-fruit; 30 c. Custard-apple; 50 c. Cocoa beans; 1 e. Coffee; 1 e. 75, Dendem; 2 e. Abacate; 5 e. Pineapple; 10 e. Mango; 20 e. Coconuts.

1948. Honouring the Statue of Our Lady of Fatima. As T **62** of Macao.
411 50 c. violet 3·25 1·75

1949. 75th Anniv of U.P.U. As T **34** of Portuguese Guinea.
412 3 e. 50 black 3·00 2·25

1950. Holy Year. As Nos. 425/6 of Macao.
413 2 e. 50 blue 1·00 75
414 4 e. orange 2·25 1·75

1951. Termination of Holy Year. As T **69** of Macao.
415 4 e. indigo and blue 1·25 85

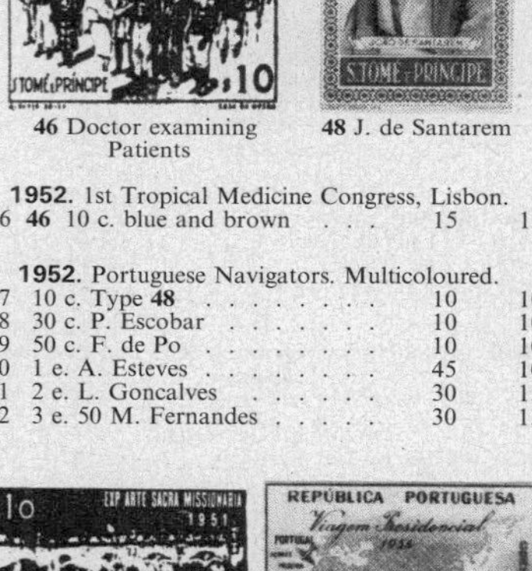

46 Doctor examining Patients

48 J. de Santarem

1952. 1st Tropical Medicine Congress, Lisbon.
416 **46** 10 c. blue and brown 15 15

1952. Portuguese Navigators. Multicoloured.
417 10 c. Type **48** 10 10
418 30 c. P. Escobar 10 10
419 50 c. F. de Po 10 10
420 1 e. A. Esteves 45 10
421 2 e. L. Goncalves 30 15
422 3 e. 50 M. Fernandes 30 15

49 Cloisters of Monastery

51 Route of President's Tour

1953. Missionary Art Exhibition.
423 **49** 10 c. sepia and green 10 10
424 50 c. brown and orange 30 20
425 3 e. indigo and blue 1·00 75

1953. Centenary of First Portuguese Postage Stamps. As T **75** of Macao.
426 50 c. multicoloured 30 25

1954. Presidential Visit.
427 **51** 15 c. multicoloured 15 10
428 5 e. multicoloured 50 40

1954. 4th Cent of Sao Paulo. As T **76** of Macao.
429 2 e. 50 multicoloured 30 20

1958. Brussels International Exhibition. As T **44** of Portuguese Guinea.
430 2 e. 50 multicoloured 35 25

1958. 6th International Congress of Tropical Medicine. As T **79** of Macao.
431 5 e. multicoloured 1·25 80
DESIGN: 5 e. "Cassia occidentalis" (plant).

55 Points of Compass

56 "Religion"

1960. 500th Death Anniv of Prince Henry the Navigator.
432 **55** 10 e. multicoloured 45 35

1960. 10th Anniv of African Technical Co-operation Commission.
433 **56** 1 e. 50 multicoloured 25 15

1962. Sports. As T **82** of Macao. Multicoloured.
434 50 c. Fishing 10 10
435 1 e. Gymnastics 30 10
436 1 e. 50 Handball 35 15
437 2 e. Yachting 40 20
438 2 e. 50 Running 50 40
439 20 e. Skin-diving 1·25 90

1962. Malaria Eradication. Mosquito design as T **83** of Macao. Multicoloured.
440 2 e. 50 "Anopheles gambiae" 35 30

1963. 10th Anniv of T.A.P. Airline. As T **52** of Portuguese Guinea.
441 2 e. 50 multicoloured 30 30

1964. Cent of National Overseas Bank. As T **84** of Macao, but portrait of F. de Oliveira Chamico.
442 2 e. 50 multicoloured 35 25

1965. Centenary of I.T.U. As T **85** of Macao.
443 2 e. 50 multicoloured 80 45

62 Infantry Officer, 1788

73 Pero Escobar and Joao de Santarem

1965. Portuguese Military Uniforms. Multicoloured.
444 20 c. Type **62** 15 10
445 35 c. Infantry sergeant, 1788 15 10
446 40 c. Infantry corporal, 1788 10 10
447 1 e. Infantryman, 1788 70 40
448 2 e. 50 Artillery officer, 1806 70 40
449 5 e. Light infantryman, 1811 1·10 80
450 7 e. 50 Infantry sapper, 1833 1·75 1·10
451 10 e. Lancers officer, 1834 2·00 1·50

1966. 40th Anniv of National Revolution. As T **86** of Macao, but showing different buildings. Multicoloured.
452 4 e. Arts and Crafts School and Anti-T.B. clinic 30 20

1967. Centenary of Military Naval Association. As T **80** of Macao. Multicoloured.
453 1 e. 50 C. Rodrigues and corvette "Vasco da Gama" 45 35
454 2 e. 50 A. Kopke, microscope and "Glossina palpalis" (insect) 75 45

1967. 50th Anniv of Fatima Apparitions. As T **89** of Macao.
455 2 e. 50 multicoloured 15 10
DESIGN: 2 e. 50 Apparition appearing to children and Valinhos Monument.

1968. 500th Birth Anniv of Pedro Cabral (explorer). As T **90** of Macao. Multicoloured.
456 1 e. 50 Medal of the Jeronimos Monastery (vert) 30 20

1969. Birth Centenary of Admiral Gago Coutinho. As T **91** of Macao. Multicoloured.
457 2 e. Island route-map and monument 40 20

1969. 500th Birth Anniv of Vasco da Gama (explorer). As T **92** of Macao. Multicoloured.
458 2 e. 50 Da Gama's fleet 15 15

1969. Centenary of Overseas Administrative Reforms. As T **92** of Macao.
459 2 e. 50 multicoloured 10 10

1969. 500th Birth Anniv of King Manoel I. As T **95** of Macao. Multicoloured.
460 4 e. Manoel Gate, Guarda See 25 15

1969. 500th Anniv of Discovery of St. Thomas and Prince Islands.
461 **73** 2 e. 50 multicoloured 15 10

74 President A. Tomas

76 Stamps on Coffee Plant

1970. Presidential Visit.
462 **74** 2 e. 50 multicoloured 20 10

1970. Birth Centenary of Marshal Carmona. Multicoloured. As T **96** of Macao.
463 5 e. Portrait in marshal's uniform 20 15

1970. Stamp Centenary. Multicoloured.
464 1 e. Type **76** 10 10
465 1 e. 50 Head Post Office, St. Thomas (horiz) 15 10
466 2 e. 50 Se Cathedral, St. Thomas 25 15

77 "Descent from the Cross" and Caravel at St. Thomas **78** Running and Throwing the Javelin

1972. 400th Anniv of Camoens' "The Lusiads" (epic poem).
467 **77** 20 e. multicoloured . . . . 3·50 1·00

1972. Olympic Games, Munich.
468 **78** 1 e. 50 multicoloured . . . 10 10

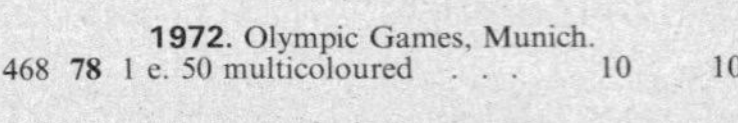

79 Seaplane "Lusitania" and Cruiser "Gladiolus" off Rock of San Pedro

1972. 50th Anniv of 1st Flight, Lisbon–Rio de Janeiro.
469 **79** 2 e. 50 multicoloured . . . 30 15

1973. Cent of World Meteorological Organization. As T **102** of Macao.
470 5 e. multicoloured 30 25

81 Flags of Portugal and St. Thomas and Prince Islands

1975. Independence.
471 **81** 3 e. multicoloured 10 10
472 10 e. multicoloured 55 20
473 20 e. multicoloured . . . . 1·00 55
474 50 e. multicoloured . . . . 2·50 1·60

82 National Flag

1975. Independence Proclamation.
475 **82** 1 e. 50 multicoloured . . . 10 10
476 4 e. multicoloured . . . 20 15
477 7 e. 50 multicoloured . . . 45 35
478 20 e. multicoloured . . . . 1·00 60
479 50 e. multicoloured . . . . 2·75 1·60

83 Diagram and Hand

1976. National Reconstruction Fund.
480 **83** 1 e. multicoloured 10 10
481 1 e. 50 multicoloured . . . 10 10
482 2 e. multicoloured 20 10

1976. Optd **Rep. Democr. 12-7-75**.
483 **48** 10 c. Joao de Santarem . .
484 **62** 20 c. Infantry officer, 1788
485 – 30 c. Pedro Escobar (No. 418)
486 – 35 c. Infantry sergeant, 1788
487 – 40 c. Infantry corporal, 1788
488 – 50 c. Fernao de Po (No. 419)
489 – 1 e. Alvaro Esteves (No. 420)
490 – 2 e. 50 Rebello da Silva (No. 459)
491 **73** 2 e. 50 Escobar and Santarem
492 – 3 e. 50 Martim Fernandes (No. 422)
493 – 4 e. Manoel Gate (No. 460)
494 – 5 e. W.M.O. emblem (No. 470)
495 – 7 e. 50 Infantry sapper, 1833 (No. 450)
496 – 10 e. Compass rose (No. 432)
Set of 14 . . . . 4·50 3·25

85 President Pinto da Costa and National Flag

1976. 1st Anniv of Independence.
497 2 e. Type **85** 20 10
498 3 e. 50 Proclamation of Independence, 12 July 1975 20 10
499 4 e. 50 As 3 e. 50 . . . . . . 45 20
500 12 e. 50 Type **85** 90 45

1977. 2nd Anniv of Independence. No. 439 optd **Rep. Democr 12-7-77**.
501 20 e. multicoloured 80 80

CHARITY TAX STAMPS

The notes under this heading in Portugal also apply here.

1925. Marquis de Pombal Commemoration. Stamps of Portugal, but inscr "S. TOME E PRINCIPE".
C323 C **73** 15 c. black and orange 20 20
C324 – 15 c. black and orange 20 20
C325 C **75** 15 c. black and orange 20 20

1946. Fiscal stamps as in Type C **1** of Portuguese Colonies surch **Assistencia** and new value.
C401 50 c. on 1 e. green . . . . 3·00
C402 50 c. on 4 e. red . . . . . 5·50
C403 1 e. on 4 e. red . . . . . . 5·50
C404 1 e. on 5 e. red . . . . . . 4·00
C405 1 e. on 6 e. green . . . . . 3·00
C406 1 e. on 7 e. green . . . . . 3·00
C409 1 e. on 10 e. red . . . . . 5·50
C410 1 e. 50 on 7 e. green . . . . 3·50
C411 1 e. 50 on 8 e. green . . . . 4·00
C412 2 e. 50 on 7 e. green . . . . 3·00
C413 2 e. 50 on 9 e. green . . . . 3·00
C414 2 e. 50 on 10 e. green . . . 3·00

40 Arms

1948. Value in black.
C415 **40** 50 c. green 30 25
C416 1 e. red 60 50
C417 1 e. green 15 15
C418 1 e. 50 brown 75 50

1965. (a) Surch **"um escudo 1 $00"** and two heavy bars.
C452 **40** 1 e. on 5 e. yellow . . . 4·00 3·00

(b) Surch **"Um escudo"**.
C453 **40** 1 e. on 1 e. green 40 40

(c) As No. C 417 but inscr "UM ESCUDO" at foot, surch **"1 $00"**.
C454 **40** 1 e. on 1 e. green 40 40

(d) Inscr "Cinco escudos 5 $00" further surch **"Um escudo 1 $00"**.
C455 **40** 1 e. on 5 e. yellow . . . 1·10 1·00

NEWSPAPER STAMPS

1982. Surch 2½ **RS**. No gum.
N53 Q 2½ r. on 5 r. black . . . 18·00 13·00
N54 2½ r. on 10 r. green . . . 21·00 15·00
N55 2½ r. on 20 r. red . . . 22·00 15·00

1893. "Newspaper" key-type inscr "S. THOME E PRINCIPE".
N59 V 2½ r. brown 40 35

1899. No. N59 optd **PROVISORIO**.
N81 V 2½ r. brown . . . . . . 10·00 4·50

POSTAGE DUE STAMPS.

1904. "Due" key-type inscr "S. THOME E PRINCIPE". Name and value in black.
D121 W 5 r. green 20 20
D122 10 r. grey 25 25
D123 20 r. brown 25 25
D124 30 r. orange 25 25
D125 50 r. brown 45 35
D126 60 r. brown 80 50
D127 100 r. mauve . . . . . 1·40 1·25
D128 130 r. blue . . . . . . 2·00 1·25
D129 200 r. red . . . . . . 2·00 1·40
D130 500 r. lilac . . . . . . 2·50 2·00

1911. As last optd **REPUBLICA**.
D137 W 5 r. green 15 15
D138 10 r. grey 15 15
D139 20 r. brown 15 15
D140 30 r. orange 15 15
D141 50 r. brown 15 15
D142 60 r. brown 30 30
D143 100 r. mauve 30 30
D144 130 r. blue 30 30
D145 200 r. red 30 30
D146 500 r. lilac 50 50

1921. "Due" key-type inscr "S. TOME E PRINCIPE" or "S. THOME E PRINCIPE". Currency changed.
D313 W ½ c. green 15 15
D314 1 c. grey 15 15
D315 2 c. brown 15 15
D316 3 c. orange 15 15
D317 5 c. brown 15 15
D318 6 c. brown 15 15
D319 10 c. mauve 15 15
D320 13 c. blue 20 20
D321 20 c. red 20 20
D322 50 c. lilac 25 25

1925. As Nos. C323/5 optd **MULTA**.
D323 C **73** 30 c. black and orange 20 20
D324 – 30 c. black and orange 20 20
D325 C **75** 30 c. black and orange 20 20

1925. As Type D **70** of Macao, but inscr "S. TOME E PRINCIPE". Numerals in red, name in black.
D417 10 c. brown and yellow . 10 10
D418 30 c. brown and blue . . 10 10
D419 50 c. blue and pink . . . 10 10
D420 1 e. blue and olive 10 10
D421 2 e. green and orange . . 15 15
D422 5 e. brown and lilac . . . 20 20

APPENDIX

The following stamps have either been issued in excess of postal needs or have not been available to the public in reasonable quantities at face value. Such stamps may later be given full listing if there is evidence of regular postal use.

1977.

400th Birth Anniv of Rubens. 1, 5, 10, 15, 20, 50 e.

150th Death Anniv of Beethoven. 20, 30, 50 e.

Centenary of U.P.U. Surch on Navigators and Military Uniforms issues of Portuguese administration. 1 e. on 10 c., 3 e. on 30 c., 3 e. 50 on 3 e. 50, 5 e. on 50 c., 10 e. on 10 c., 15 e. on 3 e. 50, 20 e. on 30 e. on 30 c., 35 e. on 35 c., 40 e. on 40 c.

Christmas. 5, 10, 25, 50, 70 d.

60th Anniv of Russian Revolution. 15, 30, 40, 50 d.

1st Death Anniv of Mao Tse-tung. 50 d.

1978.

Nobel Peace Prizes to International Organizations. Surch on Navigators and Military Uniforms issues of Portuguese administration. 3 d. on 30 c., 5 d. on 50 c., 10 d. on 10 c., 15 d. on 3 e. 50, 20 d. on 20 c., 35 d. on 35 c.

3rd Anniv of Independence. 5 d. × 3.

3rd Anniv of Admission to United Nations. Surch on Military Uniform issue. 40 d. on 40 c.

International Stamp Exhibition, Essen. 10 d. × 5.

Centenary of U.P.U. 5 d. × 4, 15 d. × 4.

1st Anniv of New Currency. 5 d. × 5, 8 d. × 5.

World Cup Football Championship, Argentina. 3 d. × 4, 25 d. × 3.

1979.

World Cup Winners. Optd on 1978 World Cup issues. 3 d. × 4, 25 d. × 3.

Butterflies. 50 c., 10 d., 11 d. × 4.

Flowers. 1 d., 8 d. × 4, 25 d.

Telecommunications Day and 50th Anniv of C.C.I.R. 1, 11, 14, 17 d.

International Year of the Child. 1, 7, 14, 17 d.

450th Death Anniv of Durer. 50 c. × 2, 1, 7, 8, 25 d.

History of Aviation. 50 c., 1, 5, 7, 8, 17 d.

History of Navigation. 50 c., 1, 3, 5, 8, 25 d.

Birds. Postage 50 c. × 2, 1, 7, 8 d.; Air 100 d.

1980.

Fishes. Postage 50 c., 1, 5, 7, 8 d.; Air 50 d.

Balloons. 50 c., 1, 3, 7, 8, 25 d.

Airships. 50 c., 1, 3, 7, 8, 17 d.

Olympic Games. 50 c., 11 d. × 4.

Death Centenary of Sir Rowland Hill. 50 c., 1, 8, 20 d.

10th Anniv of First Manned Moon Landing. 50 c., 1, 14, 17 d.

1981.

Olympic Games, Moscow. Optd on 1977 Mao Tse-tung issue. 50 d.

SAMOA Pt. 7

Islands in the W. Pacific administered jointly from 1889–99 by Gt. Britain, Germany and the U.S.A. (Stamps issued between 1897 and 1899 are listed in Volume 3). In 1899 the eastern islands were assigned to the U.S.A. and the western to Germany.

GERMAN COLONY

100 pfennig = 1 mark

1900. Stamps of Germany optd **Samoa**.
G1 **8** 3 pf. brown . . . . 7·00 10·00
G2 5 pf. green . . . . 11·00 14·00
G3 **9** 10 pf. red . . . . 7·00 14·00
G4 20 pf. blue . . . . 16·00 23·00
G5 25 pf. orange . . . . 40·00 85·00
G6 50 pf. brown . . . . 40·00 65·00

1901. "Yacht" key-type inscr "SAMOA".
G 7 N 3 pf. brown 70 75
G 8 5 pf. green 85 75
G 9 10 pf. red 85 75
G10 20 pf. blue . . . . 60 1·50
G11 25 pf. blk & red on yell . 1·00 12·00
G12 30 pf. blk & orge on buff 1·00 12·00
G13 40 pf. black and red . . . 1·00 13·00
G14 50 pf. blk & pur on buff . 1·10 13·00
G15 80 pf. black & red on rose 2·50 32·00
G16 O 1 m. red . . . . 2·75 55·00
G17 2 m. blue . . . . 3·75 85·00
G18 3 m. black . . . . 5·50 £140
G19 5 m. red and black . . . £130 £475

The colony was occupied by British forces in 1914 and a League of Nations mandate given to New Zealand in 1920. For stamps issued by New Zealand administration, see volume 3.

SAN MARINO Pt. 8

An independent republic lying near the E. coast of the Italian peninsula.

100 centesimi = 1 lira

1 2

1877.
1 **1** 2 c. green . . . . 3·25 2·00
18 2 c. blue . . . . 3·00 2·50
32 2 c. purple . . . . 2·00 1·75
2 **2** 5 c. yellow . . . . 32·00 6·00
33 5 c. green . . . . 1·50 70
3 10 c. blue . . . . 45·00 5·50
20 10 c. green . . . . 2·50 1·25
34 10 c. red . . . . 1·50 80
21 15 c. red . . . . 75·00 16·00
4 20 c. red . . . . 6·50 2·00
35 20 c. lilac . . . . 2·25 2·00
5 25 c. purple . . . . 45·00 6·50
36 25 c. blue . . . . 1·75 1·25
6 30 c. brown . . . . £325 25·00
22 30 c. yellow . . . . 3·25 2·25
7 40 c. mauve . . . . £325 25·00
23 40 c. brown . . . . 2·00 2·00
24 45 c. green . . . . 2·00 2·00
25 65 c. brown . . . . 2·00 1·75
26 1 l. red and yellow £1200 £300
37 1 l. blue £1100 £275
27 2 l. brown and buff . . . . 30·00 24·00
28 5 l. red and blue . . . . . 85·00 90·00

1892. Surch **Cmi.** and figure of value.
10c **2** 5 c. on 10 c. blue . . . . . 35·00 6·00
12 5 c. on 30 c. brown . . . . £275 35·00
16 10 c. on 20 c. red . . . . . 17·00 1·50

1892. Surch **10 10**.
17 **2** 10 c. on 20 c. red . . . . . . £150 2·50

13 Government Palace **14**

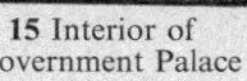

15 Interior of Government Palace **17** Statue of Liberty

1894. Opening of new Government Palace and Installation of Captains-Regent.
29 **13** 25 c. purple and blue . . . 2·00 70
30 **14** 50 c. purple and red . . . 10·00 2·00
31 **15** 1 l. purple and green . . . 10·00 2·50

1899.
38 **17** 2 c. brown 70 55
39 5 c. orange . . . . 1·10 85

See also Nos. 86/91.

18

19 Mt. Titano

1903.

40 18 2 c. lilac . . . . 4·00 1·10
73 2 c. brown 10 10
74 19 5 c. green 10 10
111 5 c. purple 10 10
42 10 c. pink . . . . 1·50 55
75 10 c. orange 10 10
112 10 c. green 10 10
76 15 c. green 15 15
113 15 c. purple 15 15
43 20 c. orange . . . . 45·00 9·00
77 20 c. brown 15 15
114 20 c. green 15 15
44 25 c. blue . . . . 5·00 1·10
78 25 c. grey 15 15
115 25 c. violet 15 15
45 30 c. red . . . . 2·00 2·50
79 30 c. mauve 25 25
116 30 c. orange . . . . 3·75 35
46 40 c. red . . . . 3·50 3·00
80 40 c. pink 25 25
117 40 c. brown 15 15
47 45 c. yellow . . . . 3·50 3·25
81 50 c. purple 35 35
118 50 c. grey 15 15
119 60 c. red 20 20
48 65 c. brown . . . . 3·50 3·25
82 80 c. blue 55 55
83 90 c. brown 55 55
49 1 l. green . . . . 10·00 5·50
120 1 l. blue 25 25
50 2 l. violet £5000 £130
85 2 l. red . . . . 7·50 7·50
121 2 l. green . . . . 1·60 1·60
122 5 l. blue . . . . 5·50 5·50

1905. Surch **1905 15.**

52 19 15 c. on 20 c. orange . . . . 2·25 1·75

22

23

26 Statue of Liberty

1907.

53a 22 1 c. brown 80 80
54 23 15 c. grey . . . . 8·00 1·75

1917. For Combatants. Surch **1917 Pro combattenti** and value.

55 18 25 c. on 2 c. lilac 80 90
56 19 50 c. on 2 l. violet . . . . . 15·00 18·00

1918. Surch **Cent 20 1918.**

57 23 20 c. on 15 c. grey . . . . . 1·25 1·10

1918. War Casualties Fund. Inscr as in T **26.**

58 26 2 c. (+ 5 c.) black & lilac . . 15 20
59 5 c. (+ 5 c.) black & green . . 15 20
60 10 c. (+ 5 c.) black & red . . 15 20
61 20 c. (+ 5 c.) black & orge . . 15 20
62 25 c. (+ 5 c.) black & blue . . 30 35
63 45 c. (+ 5 c.) black & brn . . 30 35
64 – 1 l. (+ 5 c.) black & green . . 4·00 4·50
65 – 2 l. (+ 5 c.) black & lilac . . 3·25 3·50
66 – 3 l. (+ 5 c.) black and red . . 3·25 3·50

DESIGN—HORIZ: 1, 2, 3 l. San Marino.

1918. Italian Victory over Austria and Premium for War Casualties Fund. Optd **3 Novembre 1918.**

67 26 20 c. (+ 5 c.) black & orge . . 55 70
68 25 c. (+ 5 c.) black & blue . . 55 70
69 45 c. (+ 5 c.) black & brn . . 55 70
70 – 1 l. (+ 5 c.) black & green . . 55 70
71 – 2 l. (+ 5 c.) black & lilac . . 3·25 3·50
72 – 3 l. (+ 5 c.) black and red . . 3·25 3·50

1922. Re-issue of T **17.**

86 17 2 c. purple 10 10
87 5 c. olive 10 10
88 10 c. brown 10 10
89 20 c. brown 15 15
90 25 c. blue 20 20
91 45 c. lake 60 60

30 Arbe (Rab)

31 St. Marinus

1923. Delivery to San Marino of Italian Flag flown on Arbe, after the island returned to Yugoslavia.

92 30 50 c. green 20 20

1923. San Marino Mutual Aid Society.

93 31 30 c. brown 20 20

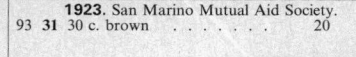

32 Mt. Titano

33 "Liberty"

34

1923. Red Cross.

94 32 5 c. + 5 c. olive 15 15
95 10 c. + 5 c. orange 15 15
96 15 c. + 5 c. green 15 15
97 25 c. + 5 c. lake 30 30
98 40 c. + 5 c. purple 60 60
99 50 c. + 5 c. grey 45 20
100 33 1 l. + 5 c. blue and black . . 1·00 1·00

1923. San Marino Volunteers in the Great War.

101 34 1 l. brown . . . . 4·00 4·00

35 Garibaldi

36

1924. 75th Anniv of Garibaldi's Refuge in San Marino.

102 35 30 c. purple 70 70
103 50 c. brown 75 75
104 60 c. lake 90 90
105 36 1 l. blue . . . . 1·60 1·60
106 2 l. green . . . . 1·90 1·90

1924. Red Cross stamps of 1918 surch.

107 26 30 c. on 45 c. black & brn . . 30 35
108 – 60 c. on 1 l. black & green . . 3·00 3·00
109 – 1 l. on 2 l. black and lilac . . 5·50 5·50
110 – 2 l. on 3 l. black and red . . 4·50 4·50

1926. Surch.

123 19 75 c. on 80 c. blue 40 40
124 1 l. 20 on 90 c. brown . . 40 40
125 1 l. 25 on 90 c. brown . . 1·00 1·00
126 2 l. 50 on 80 c. blue . . . 1·60 1·60

40 Onofri
44 San Marino War Memorial

1926. Death Centenary of Antonio Onofri, "Father of the Country".

127 40 10 c. black and blue . . . 10 10
128 20 c. black and olive . . . 55 55
129 45 c. black and violet . . . 30 30
130 65 c. black and green . . . 30 30
131 1 l. black and orange . . . 1·25 1·25
132 2 l. black and red . . . . 1·25 1·25

1926. No. E92 surch **Lire 1,85.**

133 19 1 l. 85 on 60 c. violet . . . 40 45

1927. Surch.

134 40 1 l. 25 on 1 l. black and orange 85 1·00
135 2 l. 50 on 2 l. black and red 2·25 2·50
136 5 l. on 2 l. black and red . 19·00 20·00

1927. Unissued Express stamp (No. 115 surch **EXPRESSO 50**) ruled through and surch **L. 1,75.**

137 19 1 l. 75 on 50 c. on 25 c. violet 70 75

1927. War Cenotaph Commemoration.

138 44 50 c. purple 30 30
139 1 l. 25 blue 50 60
140 10 l. black . . . . 7·50 8·50

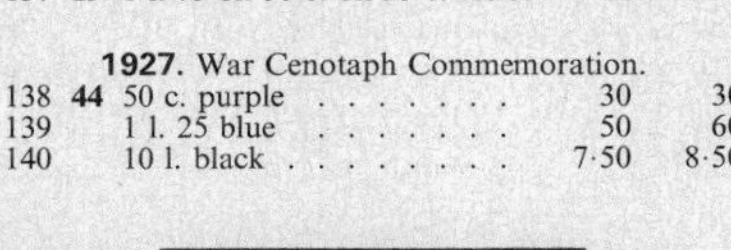

45 Franciscan Convent and Capuchin Church

1928. 700th Death Anniv of St. Francis of Assisi.

141 45 50 c. red . . . . 9·50 1·25
142 1 l. 25 blue . . . . 1·60 1·60
143 – 2 l. 50 brown . . . . . . 1·60 1·60
144 – 5 l. violet . . . . 11·00 9·50

DESIGN: 2 l. 50, 5 l. Death of St. Francis.

46 La Rocca Fortress

47 Government Palace

48 Statue of Liberty

1929.

145 46 5 c. blue and purple 10 10
146 10 c. mauve and blue . . . 30 10
147 15 c. green and orange . . . 10 10
148 20 c. red and blue 10 10
149 25 c. black and green . . . 10 10
150 30 c. red and grey 10 10
151 50 c. green and purple . . . 10 10
152 75 c. grey and red 10 10
153 47 1 l. green and brown . . . 15 10
154 1 l. 25 black and blue . . . 15 10
155 1 l. 75 orange and green . . 25 35
156 2 l. red and blue 15 15
157 2 l. 50 blue and red . . . 15 15
158 3 l. blue and orange . . . 15 15
159 3 l. 70 purple and green . . 20 35
160 48 5 l. green and violet . . . 35 40
161 10 l. blue and brown . . . 1·75 2·00
162 15 l. purple and green . . . 12·00 14·00
163 20 l. red and blue £150 £170

50 Mt Titano

51 G.P.O., San Marino

1931. Air.

164 50 50 c. green 50 50
165 80 c. red 70 70
166 1 l. brown 70 70
167 2 l. purple 75 75
168 2 l. 60 blue . . . . 9·00 11·00
169 3 l. grey . . . . 9·00 11·00
170 5 l. olive . . . . 2·00 2·00
171 7 l. 70 sepia . . . . 2·50 2·50
172 9 l. orange . . . . 2·75 2·75
173 10 l. blue £120 £140

1932. Inauguration of New G.P.O.

174 51 20 c. green . . . . 1·25 75
175 50 c. red . . . . 2·00 1·25
176 1 l. 25 blue . . . . 70·00 35·00
177 1 l. 75 brown . . . . 30·00 24·00
178 2 l. 75 violet . . . . 13·00 9·00

52 San Marino Railway Station

1932. Opening of Electric Railway between San Marino and Rimini.

179 52 20 c. green . . . . 1·25 1·25
180 50 c. red . . . . 1·50 1·50
181 1 l. 25 blue . . . . 2·25 2·25
182 5 l. brown . . . . 30·00 30·00

53 Garibaldi

1932. 50th Death Anniv of Garibaldi.

183 53 10 c. brown 45 45
184 20 c. violet 25 25
185 25 c. green 40 40
186 50 c. brown . . . . 1·25 1·25
187 – 75 c. red . . . . 1·25 1·25
188 – 1 l. 25 blue . . . . 3·00 3·00
189 – 2 l. 75 orange . . . . . . 8·00 10·00
190 – 5 l. olive £110 £130

DESIGN: 75 c. to 5 l. Garibaldi's arrival at San Marino.

1933. Air. "Graf Zeppelin". Surch **ZEPPELIN 1933** under airship and new value.

191 50 3 l. on 50 c. orange . . . . 65 48·00
192 5 l. on 80 c. olive . . . . 26·00 48·00
193 10 l. on 1 l. blue . . . . 26·00 65·00
194 12 l. on 2 l. brown . . . . 27·00 75·00
195 15 l. on 2 l. 60 red . . . . 27·00 85·00
196 20 l. on 3 l. green . . . . 27·00 £100

1933. 20th Italian Philatelic Congress. Surch **28 MAGGIO 1933 CONVEGNO FILATELICO** and new value.

197 51 25 c. on 2 l. 75 violet . . . 50 60
198 50 c. on 1 l. 75 brown . . . 2·00 2·00
199 75 c. on 2 l. 75 violet . . . 8·00 8·00
200 1 l. 25 on 1 l. 75 brown . . £170 £190

1934. Philatelic Exn. Surch **12-27 APRILE 1934 MOSTRA FILATELICA** and value with wheel.

201 51 25 c. on 1 l. 25 blue 40 40
202 50 c. on 1 l. 25 brown . . . 75 75

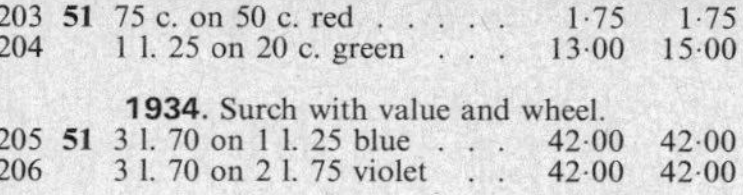

203 51 75 c. on 50 c. red . . . . . 1·75 1·75
204 1 l. 25 on 20 c. green . . . 13·00 15·00

1934. Surch with value and wheel.

205 51 3 l. 70 on 1 l. 25 blue . . . 42·00 42·00
206 3 l. 70 on 2 l. 75 violet . . 42·00 42·00

58 Ascent to Mt Titano

59 Melchiorre Delfico

1935. 12th Anniv of San Marino Fascist Party.

207 58 5 c. black and brown . . . 10 15
208 10 c. black and violet . . . 10 15
209 20 c. black and orange . . 10 15
210 25 c. black and green . . . 10 15
211 50 c. black and bistre . . . 20 35
212 75 c. black and lake . . . 80 90
213 1 l. 25 black and blue . . . 2·25 2·50

1935. Death Centenary of Delfico (historian of San Marino).

214 59 5 c. black and red 10 15
215 7½ c. black and brown . . 10 15
216 10 c. black and green . . . 10 15
217 15 c. black and red . . . . 3·25 80
218 20 c. black and orange . . 10 20
219 25 c. black and green . . . 20 20
220 – 30 c. black and violet . . . 20 20
221 – 50 c. black and green . . . 80 80
222 – 75 c. black and red . . . . 3·00 3·00
223 – 1 l. 25 black and blue . . . 80 80
224 – 1 l. 50 black and brown . . 11·00 12·00
225 – 1 l. 75 black and orange . . 14·00 15·00

DESIGN—25 × 35 mm: 30 c. to 1 l. 75, Statue of Delfico.

1936. Surch (a) Postage.

226 40 80 c. on 45 c. black & violet 1·40 1·75
227 80 c. on 65 c. black & grn . 1·40 1·75
228 45 2 l. 05 on 1 l. 25 blue . . . 3·75 3·75
229 – 2 l. 75 on 2 l. 50 brown (No. 143) . . . . 16·00 24·00

(b) Air.

230 50 75 c. on 50 c. green . . . . 1·40 1·75
231 75 c. on 80 c. red . . . . . 5·50 6·00

1941. Surch **10.**

233 19 10 c. on 15 c. purple . . . 10 10
234 10 c. on 30 c. orange . . . 45 40

1942. Air. Surch **Lire 10** and bars.

235 50 10 l. on 2 l. 60 blue . . . . 70·00 85·00
236 10 l. on 3 l. grey . . . . . 16·00 19·00

67 Gajarda Tower, Arbe, and Flags of Italy and San Marino

1942. Restoration of Italian Flag to Arbe.

237 67 10 c. red & bistre (postage) . 10 10
238 15 c. red and brown . . . 10 10
239 20 c. grey and olive . . . 10 10
240 25 c. blue and green . . . 10 10
241 50 c. brown and red . . . 10 10
242 75 c. grey and red 10 10
243 – 1 l. 25 grey and blue . . . 10 10
244 – 1 l. 75 grey and brown . . . 10 10
245 – 2 l. 75 blue and bistre . . . 25 30
246 – 5 l. brown and green . . . 2·00 3·50
247 – 25 c. grey & brown (air) . . 10 10
248 – 50 c. brown and green . . . 10 10
249 – 75 c. brown and blue . . . 10 10
250 – 1 l. brown and bistre . . . 20 20
251 – 5 l. blue and bistre . . . . 3·00 3·50

DESIGNS—As Type **67**: HORIZ: Nos. 243/6 Galleon in Arbe Harbour. VERT: Nos. 247/51, Granda Belfry, Arbe.

1942. Italian Philatelic Congress. Surch **GIORNATA FILATELICA RIMINI–SAN MARINO 3 AGOSTO 1942 (1641 d. F.R.)** and value in figures.

252 67 30 c. on 10 c. red & bistre . 10 10

1942. Surch.

253 67 30 c. on 20 c. grey & olive . . 20 20
254 – 20 l. on 75 c. black and red (No. 222) . . . . 5·50 6·50

71 Printing Press

72 Newspapers

1943. Press Propaganda.

No.	Type	Description	Mint	Used
255	71	10 c. green	10	10
256		15 c. brown	10	10
257		20 c. brown	10	10
258		30 c. purple	10	10
259		50 c. blue	10	10
260		75 c. red	10	10
261	72	1 l. 25 blue	10	10
262		1 l. 75 violet	10	10
263		5 l. blue	20	25
264		10 l. brown	2·00	2·25

1943. Philatelic Exhibition. Optd **GIORNATA FILATELICA RIMINI – SAN MARINO 5 LUGLIO 1943 (1642 d. F.R.).**

No.	Type	Description	Mint	Used
265	71	30 c. purple	10	10
266		50 c. blue	10	10

74 Gateway

75 War Memorial

1943. Fall of Fascism. Unissued series for 20th Anniv of Fascism optd **28 LVGLIO 1943 1642 d. F.R.**. (the "d." is omitted on T **74**) and bars cancelling commemorative inscription.

No.	Type	Description	Mint	Used
267	74	5 c. brown (postage)	10	10
268		10 c. orange	10	10
269		20 c. blue	10	10
270		25 c. green	10	10
271		30 c. red	10	10
272		50 c. violet	10	10
273		75 c. red	10	10
274	75	1 l. 25 blue	10	10
275		1 l. 75 orange	10	10
276		2 l. 75 brown	15	15
277		5 l. green	35	45
278		10 l. violet	55	70
279		20 l. blue	1·40	1·60
280	–	25 c. brown (air)	10	10
281	–	50 c. red	10	10
282	–	75 c. brown	10	10
283	–	1 l. purple	10	10
284	–	2 l. blue	10	10
285	–	5 l. orange	35	35
286	–	10 l. green	50	55
287	–	20 l. black	2·00	2·25

DESIGN—Air: Nos. 280/7, Map of San Marino.

1943. Provisional Govt. Optd **GOVERNO PROVVISORIO** over ornamentation.

No.	Type	Description	Mint	Used
288	74	5 c. brown (postage)	10	10
289		10 c. orange	10	10
290		20 c. blue	10	10
291		25 c. green	10	10
292		30 c. red	10	10
293		50 c. violet	10	10
294		75 c. red	10	10
295	75	1 l. 25 blue	10	10
296		1 l. 75 orange	15	15
297		5 l. green	35	40
298		20 l. blue	1·00	1·25
299	–	25 c. brown (air)	10	10
300	–	50 c. red	10	10
301	–	75 c. brown	10	10
302	–	1 l. purple	10	10
303	–	5 l. orange	35	45
304	–	20 l. black	1·50	1·75

78 St. Marinus

79 Mt Titano

1944.

No.	Type	Description	Mint	Used
305	78	20 l. + 10 l. brn (postage)	40	60
306	79	20 l. + 10 l. olive (air)	40	60

80 Govt Palace

81 Govt Palace

1945. 50th Anniv of Government Palace.

No.	Type	Description	Mint	Used
307	80	25 l. purple (postage)	7·00	2·50
308	81	25 l. brown (air)	7·00	2·50

82 Arms of Montegiardino

83 Arms of San Marino

1945. Arms Types.

No.	Type	Description	Mint	Used
309	–	10 c. blue	10	10
310	82	20 c. red	10	10
311	–	40 c. orange	10	10
312	82	60 c. slate	10	10
313	–	80 c. green	10	10
314	–	1 l. red	10	10
315	–	1 l. 20 violet	10	10
316	–	2 l. brown	20	10
317	–	3 l. blue	20	10
317a	–	4 l. orange	20	10
318	–	5 l. brown	10	10
319	–	10 l. red and brown	2·50	85
318a	–	15 l. blue	1·75	85
320	–	20 l. red and blue	5·00	1·40
321	–	20 l. brown and blue	8·50	1·40
322	82	25 l. blue and brown	7·00	1·50
323	83	50 l. blue and olive	9·50	5·50

DESIGNS (Arms of San Marino and villages in the Republic): 10 c., 1 l., 1 l. 20, 15 l. Faetano; 40 c., 5 l. San Marino; 80 c., 2, 3, 4 l. Fiorentino; 10 l. Borgomaggiore; 20 l. (2) Serravalle.

84 U.N.R.R.A. Aid for San Marino

1946. U.N.R.R.A.

No.	Type	Description	Mint	Used
324	84	100 l. red, purple and orange	3·25	3·50

85 Airplane and Mt Titano

1946. Air.

No.	Type	Description	Mint	Used
325	–	25 c. grey	10	10
326	85	75 c. red	10	10
327	–	1 l. brown	10	10
328	85	2 l. green	10	10
329		3 l. violet	10	10
330	–	5 l. blue	10	10
331	–	10 l. red	15	15
334	–	20 l. purple	1·50	1·60
332	–	35 l. red	5·50	3·50
335	–	50 l. green	11·00	5·50
333	–	100 l. brown	2·25	1·10

DESIGNS—HORIZ: 25 c., 1, 10 l. Wings over Mt Titano; 100 l. Airplane over globe. VERT: 5, 20, 35, 50 l. Four airplanes over Mt Titano.

1946. Stamp Day. Surch **L.10**.

No.	Type	Description	Mint	Used
336	83	50 l. + 10 l. blue and green	12·00	6·50

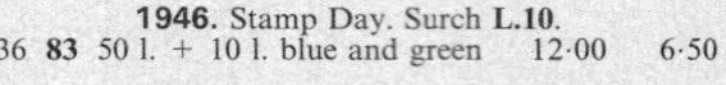
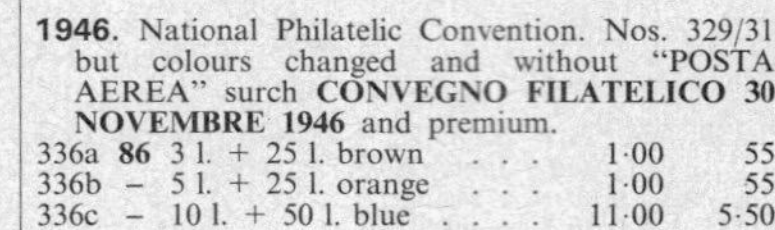

1946. National Philatelic Convention. Nos. 329/31 but colours changed and without "POSTA AEREA" surch **CONVEGNO FILATELICO 30 NOVEMBRE 1946** and premium.

No.	Type	Description	Mint	Used
336a	86	3 l. + 25 l. brown	1·00	55
336b	–	5 l. + 25 l. orange	1·00	55
336c	–	10 l. + 50 l. blue	11·00	5·50

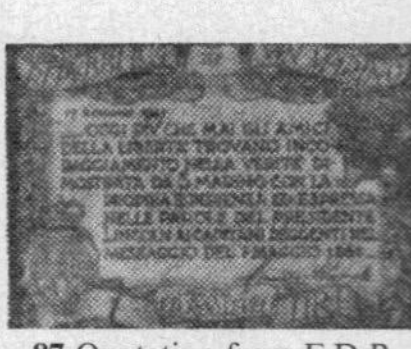
87 Quotation from F.D.R. on Liberty

88 Franklin D. Roosevelt

1947. In Memory of President Franklin D. Roosevelt.

No.	Type	Description	Mint	Used
336d	87	1 l. brn & ochre (postage)	10	10
336e	88	2 l. brown and blue	10	10
336f	–	5 l. multicoloured	10	10
336g	–	15 l. multicoloured	10	10
336h	87	50 l. brown and red	60	40
336i	88	100 l. brown and violet	1·00	65

DESIGN—HORIZ: 5 l., 15 l. Roosevelt and flags of San Marino and U.S.A.

No.	Type	Description	Mint	Used
336j	–	1 l. brown and blue (air)	10	10
336k	–	2 l. brown and red	10	10
336l	–	5 l. multicoloured	10	10
336m	–	20 l. brown and purple	20	10
336n	–	31 l. brown and orange	65	35
336o	–	50 l. brown and red	1·25	65
336p	–	100 l. brown and blue	1·75	1·00
336q	–	200 l. multicoloured	18·00	19·00

DESIGNS—HORIZ: 1, 3, 50 l. Roosevelt and eagle; 2, 20, 100 l. Roosevelt and San Marino arms. VERT: 5, 200 l. Roosevelt and flags of San Marino and U.S.A.

1947. Surch in figures.

No.	Type	Description	Mint	Used
336r	87	3 on 1 l. brown and ochre (postage)	55	35
336s	88	4 on 2 l. brown and blue	55	35
336t	–	6 on 5 l. mult. (No. 336f)	55	35
336u	–	3 on 1 l. brown and blue (No. 336j) (air)	55	35
336v	–	4 on 2 l. brown and red (No. 336k)	55	35
336w	–	6 on 5 l. mult. (No. 336l)	55	35

1947. No. 317a surch.

No.	Type	Description	Mint	Used
337		6 l. on 4 l. orange	20	10
338		21 l. on 4 l. orange	80	65

91 St. Marinus founding Republic

94 Mt Titano, Statue of Liberty and 1847 U.S.A. Stamp

95 Mt Titano and 1847 U.S.A. Stamp

1947. Reconstruction.

No.	Type	Description	Mint	Used
339	91	1 l. mve & grn (postage)	10	10
340		2 l. olive and mauve	10	10
341		4 l. green and brown	10	10
342		10 l. blue and orange	10	10
343		25 l. mauve and red	70	55
344		50 l. brown and green	18·00	9·00
345		25 l. blue & orange (air)	2·25	1·10
346		50 l. blue and brown	4·50	2·25

Nos. 343/6 are larger (24½ × 32 mm) and have two rows of ornaments forming the frame.

1947. Air. Rimini Philatelic Exhibition. No. 333 optd **Giornata Filatelica Rimini–San Marino 18 Luglio 1947**.

No.	Type	Description	Mint	Used
347		100 l. brown	1·00	70

1947. Reconstruction. Surch + and value in figures.

No.	Type	Description	Mint	Used
348	91	1 l. + 1 mauve and green	10	10
349		1 l. + 2 mauve and green	10	10
350		1 l. + 3 mauve and green	10	10
351		1 l. + 4 mauve and green	10	10
352		1 l. + 5 mauve and green	10	10
353		2 l. + 1 green and mauve	10	10
354		2 l. + 2 green and mauve	10	10
355		2 l. + 3 green and mauve	10	10
356		2 l. + 4 green and mauve	10	10
357		2 l. + 5 green and mauve	10	10
358		4 l. + 1 green and brown	3·00	1·50
359		4 l. + 2 green and brown	3·00	1·50

1947. Centenary of First U.S.A. Postage Stamp.

No.	Type	Description	Mint	Used
360	94	2 l. brown & pur (postage)	10	10
361	–	3 l. grey, red and blue	10	10
362	94	6 l. green and blue	10	10
363	–	15 l. violet, red and blue	30	20
364	–	35 l. brown, red and blue	1·00	70
365	–	50 l. green, red and blue	1·25	70
366	95	100 l. brown & vio (air)	9·00	5·00

DESIGNS: 3, 35 l. U.S.A. stamps, 5 c. and 10 c., 1847 and 90 c., 1869 and flags of U.S.A. and San Marino; 15, 50 l. Similar but differently arranged.

96 Worker and San Marino Flag

1948. Workers' Issue.

No.	Type	Description	Mint	Used
367	96	5 l. brown	10	10
368		8 l. green	10	10
369		30 l. red	25	20
370		50 l. brown and mauve	1·60	80
371		100 l. blue and violet	32·00	15·00

See also Nos. 506/7.

1948. Surch **L.100** between circular ornaments.

No.	Type	Description	Mint	Used
372	59	100 l. on 15 c. black & red	38·00	22·00

1948. Air. Surch **POSTA AEREA 200**.

No.	Type	Description	Mint	Used
373	91	200 l. on 25 l. mauve and red (No. 343)	17·00	17·00

99 Faetano

100 Mt Titano

1949.

No.	Type	Description	Mint	Used
374	–	1 l. blue and black	10	10
375	–	2 l. red and purple	10	10
376	99	3 l. blue and violet	10	10
377	–	4 l. violet and black	10	10
378	–	5 l. brown and purple	10	10
379	99	6 l. black and blue	55	20
380	100	8 l. brown & dp brown	40	20
381	–	10 l. blue and black	45	10
382	–	12 l. violet and red	1·00	40
383	–	15 l. red and violet	2·75	60
383a	99	20 l. brown and blue	5·50	65
384	–	35 l. violet and green	5·00	1·50
385	–	50 l. brown and red	2·75	65
385a	–	55 l. green and blue	30·00	12·00
386	100	100 l. green and brown	75·00	18·00
387	–	200 l. brown and blue	75·00	38·00

DESIGNS—HORIZ: 1, 5, 35 l. Guaita Tower and walls; 2, 12, 50 l. Serravalle and Mt Titano; 4, 15, 55 l. Franciscan Convent and Capuchin Church. VERT: 10, 200 l. Guaita Tower.

For similar stamps see Nos. 491/5, 522a/7a and 794/9.

1949. Stamp Day. Optd **Gionata Filatelica San Marino - Riccione 28-6-1949**.

No.	Type	Description	Mint	Used
388	91	1 l. mauve and green	15	10
389		2 l. olive and mauve	15	10

104 Garibaldi

105 Garibaldi in San Marino

1949. Centenary of Garibaldi's Retreat from Rome. (a) Postage. Portraits as T **104**. (i) Size 22 × 28 mm.

No.	Type	Description	Mint	Used
390	–	1 l. red and black	10	10
391	–	2 l. blue and brown	10	10
392	104	3 l. green and red	10	10
393	–	4 l. brown and blue	10	10
		(ii) Size 27 × 37 mm.		
394	–	5 l. brown and mauve	10	10
395	–	15 l. blue and red	1·00	55
396	–	20 l. red and violet	1·50	75
397	104	50 l. violet and purple	16·00	8·50
		(b) Air. (i) Size 28 × 22 mm.		
398	105	2 l. blue and purple	10	10
399		3 l. black and green	10	10
400		5 l. green and blue	15	15
		(ii) Size 37 × 27 mm.		
401	105	25 l. violet and green	3·50	1·75
402		65 l. black and green	11·00	5·50

PORTRAITS—VERT: 1, 20 l. Francesco Nullo; 2, 5 l. Anita Garibaldi; 4, 15 l. Ugo Bassi.

See also Nos. 538/44.

106 Mail Coach and Mt Titano

1949. 75th Anniv of U.P.U.

No.	Type	Description	Mint	Used
403	106	100 l. purple & bl (postage)	8·00	5·00
404		200 l. blue (air)	1·50	1·25
405		300 l. brown, light brown and purple	10·00	10·00

107 Mt Titano from Serravalle

108 Second and Guaita Towers

109 Guaita Tower

1950. Air. Views.
406 107 2 l. green and violet 10 10
407 – 3 l. brown and blue 10 10
408 108 5 l. red and brown (22×28 mm) 10 10
409 – 10 l. blue and green 1·10 20
410 – 15 l. violet and black 1·60 25
411 – 55 l. green and blue 18·00 9·00
412 107 100 l. black and red (37×27 mm) 10·00 2·50
413 108 250 l. brown and violet 40·00 12·00
414 109 500 l. brown and green (37×27 mm) £110 70·00
415 500 l. purple, green & bl 60·00 48·00
DESIGNS—As Type **107**: 3 l. Distant view of Domagnano; 10 l. Domagnano; 15 l. San Marino from St. Mustiola. As Type **108**: 55 l. Borgo Maggiore.

1950. Air. 28th Milan Fair. As Nos. 408, 410 and 411 but in different colours, optd **XXVIII FIERA INTERNAZIONALE DI MILANO APRILE 1950.**
416 5 l. green and blue 10 10
417 15 l. black and red 80 60
418 55 l. brown and violet 3·50 2·50

111 Government Palace

113 Flag, Douglas DC-6 and Mt Titano

1951. Red Cross.
419 111 25 l. purple, red & brown 6·50 3·00
420 – 75 l. sepia, red & brown 9·00 6·00
421 – 100 l. black, red & brown 9·50 5·00
DESIGNS—HORIZ: 75 l. Archway of Murata Nuova. VERT: 100 l. Guaita Tower.

1951. Air. Stamp Day. No. 415 surch **Giornata Filatelica San Marino–Riccione 20-8-1951** and new value.
422 109 300 l. on 500 l. purple, green and blue 35·00 28·00

1951. Air.
423 113 1000 l. blue and brown £300 £190

1951. Air. Italian Flood Relief. Surch **Pro-alluvionati italiani 1951 L. 100** and bars.
424 108 100 l. on 250 l. brown and violet 5·50 3·50

115 "Columbus at the Council of Salamanca" (after Barabino)

1952. 500th Birth Anniv (1951) of Christopher Columbus.
425 115 1 l. orange & grn (postage) 10 15
426 – 2 l. brown and violet 10 15
427 – 3 l. violet and brown 10 15
428 – 4 l. blue and brown 10 15
429 – 5 l. green and turquoise 20 20
430 – 10 l. brown and black 60 40
431 – 15 l. red and black 1·25 60
432 – 20 l. blue and green 1·75 70
433 – 25 l. purple and brown 7·00 2·50
434 115 60 l. brown and violet 9·00 4·50
435 – 80 l. grey and black 25·00 11·00
436 – 200 l. green and blue 45·00 22·00
437 – 200 l. blue & black (air) 35·00 16·00
DESIGNS—HORIZ: 2, 25 l. Columbus and fleet; 3, 10, 20 l. Landing in America; 4, 15, 80 l. Red Indians and American settlers; 5, 200 l. (No. 436) Columbus and Map of America; 200 l. (No. 437) Columbus, Statue of Liberty (New York) and skyscrapers.

1952. Trieste Fair. As Columbus issue of 1952, but colours changed, optd **FIERA DI TRIESTE 1952.**
438 1 l. violet and brown (postage) 10 15
439 2 l. red and black 10 15
440 3 l. green and turquoise 10 15
441 4 l. brown and black 10 15
442 5 l. mauve and violet 30 30
443 10 l. blue and brown 1·75 75
444 15 l. brown and blue 6·00 2·50
445 200 l. brown and black (air) 35·00 16·00

117 Rose

118 Cyclamen, Rose, San Marino and Riccione

1952. Air. Stamp Day and Philatelic Exhibition.
446 – 1 l. purple and violet 10 10
447 – 2 l. green and blue 10 10
448 117 3 l. red and sepia 10 10
449 118 5 l. brown and purple 10 10
450 25 l. green and violet 35 35
451 200 l. multicoloured 35·00 18·00
DESIGNS—As Type **117**: 1 l. Cyclamen; 2 l. San Marino and Riccione.

119 Airplane over San Marino

1952. Air. Aerial Survey of San Marino.
452 119 25 l. green 1·75 1·00
453 – 75 l. violet and brown 5·50 3·50
DESIGN: 75 l. Airplane over Mt Titano.

120 "The Discus Thrower"

21 Tennis

1953. Sports.
454 120 1 l. black & brn (postage) 10 10
455 121 2 l. brown and black 10 10
456 – 3 l. turquoise and black 10 10
457 – 4 l. blue and green 10 10
458 – 5 l. green and brown 10 10
459 – 10 l. red and blue 30 30
460 – 25 l. brown and black 2·00 90
461 – 100 l. grey and brown 7·00 3·00
462 – 200 l. turquoise & grn (air) 75·00 38·00
DESIGNS—As Type **120**: 3 l. Running. As Type **121**: HORIZ: 4 l. Cycling; 5 l. Football; 100 l. Roller skating; 200 l. Skiing. VERT: 101 l. Model glider flying; 25 l. Shooting.
See also No. 584.

1953. Stamp Day and Philatelic Exn. As No. 461 but colour changed, optd **GIORNATA FILATELICA S. MARINO-RICCIONE 24 AGOSTO 1953.**
463 100 l. green and blue 18·00 10·00

123 Narcissus

1953. Flowers.
464 123 1 l. blue, green and yellow 10 10
465 – 2 l. blue, green and yellow 10 10
466 – 3 l. blue, green and yellow 10 10
467 – 4 l. blue, green and yellow 10 10
468 – 5 l. green and red 10 10
469 – 10 l. blue, green and yellow 20 20
470 – 25 l. blue, green and red 3·50 1·40
471 – 80 l. blue, green and red 17·00 9·00
472 – 100 l. blue, green and red 26·00 13·00
FLOWERS: 2 l. Parrot tulip; 3 l. Oleander; 4 l. Cornflower; 5 l. Carnation; 10 l. Iris; 25 l. Cyclamen; 80 l. Geranium; 100 l. Rose.

124 Mt Titano and Arms

1954. Air.
473 124 1000 l. sepia and blue 65·00 50·00

125 Walking

126 Statue of Liberty

1954. Sports.
474 125 1 l. mauve and violet 10 10
475 – 2 l. violet and green 10 10
476 – 3 l. chestnut and brown 10 10
477 – 4 l. blue 10 10
478 – 5 l. sepia and green 10 10
479 – 8 l. lilac and mauve 20 10
480 – 12 l. red and black 20 10
481 – 25 l. green and blue 65 20
482 125 80 l. turquoise and blue 1·10 60
483 – 200 l. brown and lilac 5·00 2·50
484 – 250 l. multicoloured 55·00 29·00
DESIGNS—HORIZ: 2 l. Fencing; 3 l. Boxing; 5 l. Motor-cycle racing; 8 l. Throwing the javelin; 12 f. Car racing. VERT: 4, 200, 250 l. Gymnastics; 25 l. Wrestling.

1954.
485 126 20 l. blue & brn (post) 20 10
486 60 l. green and red 70 35
487 120 l. brown & blue (air) 1·25 60

127 Hurdling

128 Yacht

1955. Air. 1st Int Exhibition of Olympic Stamps.
488 127 80 l. black and red 1·10 60
489 – 120 l. red and green 1·60 1·00
DESIGN—HORIZ: 120 l. Relay racing.

1955. 7th International Philatelic Exhibition.
490 128 100 l. black and blue 3·25 1·50
See also No. 518.

1955. Views as T **99**.
491 5 l. brown and blue 10 10
492 10 l. green and orange 10 10
493 15 l. red and green 10 10
494 25 l. violet and brown 10 10
495 35 l. red and lilac 30 15
DESIGNS—HORIZ: 5, 25 l. Archway of Murata Nuova. VERT: 10, 35 l. Guaita Tower; 15 l. Government Palace.
See also Nos. 519/21 and 797/9.

129 Ice Skating

130 Pointer

1955. Winter Olympic Games, Cortina D'Ampezzo.
496 129 1 l. brown & yell (postage) 10 10
497 – 2 l. blue and red 10 10
498 – 3 l. black and brown 10 10
499 – 4 l. brown and green 10 10
500 – 5 l. blue and red 10 10
501 – 10 l. blue and pink 20 15
502 – 25 l. black and red 1·00 55
503 – 50 l. brown and blue 2·50 1·25
504 – 100 l. black and green 7·50 3·00
505 – 200 l. black & orge (air) 27·00 14·00
DESIGNS—HORIZ: 2, 25 l. Skiing; 3, 50 l. Bobsleighing; 5, 100 l. Ice hockey; 200 l. Ski jumping. VERT: 4 l. Slalom racing; 10 l. Figure skating.

1956. Winter Relief Fund. As T **96** but additionally inscr "ASSISTENZA INVERNALE".
506 50 l. green 5·00 4·50

1956. 50th Anniv of "Arengo" (San Marino Parliament). As T **96** but additionally inscr "50° ANNIVERSARIO ARENGO 25 MARZO 1906".
507 50 l. blue 5·00 4·50

1956. Dogs. 25 l. to 100 l. have multicoloured centres.
508 130 1 l. brown and blue 10 10
509 – 2 l. grey and red 10 10
510 – 3 l. brown and blue 10 10
511 – 4 l. grey and turquoise 10 10
512 – 5 l. brown and red 10 10
513 – 10 l. brown and blue 10 10
514 – 25 l. blue 30 15
515 – 60 l. red 2·00 1·25
516 – 80 l. blue 3·50 1·75
517 – 100 l. red 6·00 3·25
DOGS: 2 l. Borzoi; 3 l. Sheepdog; 4 l. Greyhound; 5 l. Boxer; 10 l. Great dane; 25 l. Irish setter; 60 l. Alsatian; 80 l. Rough collie; 100 l. Foxhound.

1956. Philatelic Exn. As T **128** but inscr "1956".
518 128 100 l. sepia & turquoise 1·75 1·25

1956. Int Philatelic Congress. Designs as Nos. 491/5 but larger and new values inscr "CONGRESSO INTERNAZ PERITI FILATELICI SAN MARINO SALSOMAGGIORE 6-8 OTTOBRE 1956".
519 20 l. brown and blue 40 20
520 80 l. red and violet 4·00 2·50
521 100 l. green and orange 1·40 1·25
SIZES—26½×37 mm: 20 l. Guaita Tower; 100 l. Government Palace. (36½×27 mm): 8 l. Archway Murata Nuova.

1956. Air. No. 504 optd with an aeroplane and **POSTA AEREA**.
522 100 l. black and green 1·40 1·25

1957. Views as T **99**.
522a 1 l. grey and deep green 10 10
523 2 l. red and green 10 10
524 3 l. brown and blue 10 10
524a 4 l. blue and brown 10 10
525 20 l. green and deep green 15 10
525a 30 l. violet and brown 55 30
526 60 l. violet and brown 85 60
526a 115 l. brown and blue 35 25
527 125 l. blue and black 45 30
527a 500 l. black and green 55·00 30·00
DESIGNS—VERT: 2 l. Borgo Maggiore Church; 3, 30 l. Town gate, San Marino; 4, 125 l. View of San Marino from southern wall; 20, 115 l. Borgo Maggiore market place. HORIZ: 1, 60 l. View of San Marino from Hospital Avenue. (37½×28 mm): 500 l. Panorama of San Marino.
See also Nos. 794/6.

132 Marguerites

134 St. Marinus Statue and Fair Entrance

1957. Flowers as T **132** in natural colours. Background colour blue (Nos. 528/32), rest multicoloured.
528 1 l. Type **182** 10 10
529 2 l. Polyanthuses 10 10
530 3 l. Lilies 10 10
531 4 l. Orchid 10 10
532 5 l. Lillies of the valley 10 10
533 10 l. Poppies 10 10
534 25 l. Pansies 10 10
535 60 l. Gladiolus 45 30
536 80 l. Wild roses 90 50
537 100 l. Anemones 1·50 85

1957. 150th Birth Anniv of Garibaldi. As T **104** but inscr "COMMEMORAZIONE 150° NASCITA G. GARIBALDI 1807 1957. (a) Size 22×28 mm.
538 – 2 l. blue and violet (as No. 391) 10 10
539 – 3 l. green and red (as No. 390) 10 10
540 104 5 l. drab and brown 10 10
(b) Size 27×37 mm.
541 – 15 l. violet and blue (as No. 395) 10 10
542 – 25 l. black and green (as No. 396) 20 20
543 – 50 l. brown and violet (as No. 394) 1·40 1·00
544 104 100 l. violet and brown 1·40 1·00

1958. 36th Milan Fair.
545 134 15 l. yell & blue (postage) 15 10
546 – 60 l. green and red 50 55
547 – 125 l. blue & brown (air) 2·25 2·00
DESIGNS—HORIZ: 60 l. Italian pavilion and giant arch. VERT: 125 l. Bristol 173 Rotocoach helicopter and airplane over fair.

135 Exhibition Emblem, Atomium and Mt Titano **137** Wheat

136 View of San Marino

1958. Brussels International Exhibition.
548 **135** 40 l. sepia and green . . . 20 15
549 60 l. lake and blue 25 30

1958. Air.
550 **136** 200 l. blue and brown . . 2·00 2·00
551 – 300 l. violet and red . . . 2·00 2·00
DESIGN: 300 l. Mt Titano.

1958. Fruit and Agricultural Products.
552 **137** 1 l. yellow and blue . . . 10 10
553 – 2 l. red and green 10 10
554 – 3 l. orange and blue . . . 10 10
555 – 4 l. red and green 10 10
556 – 5 l. yellow, green & blue . 10 10
557 **137** 15 l. yellow, brown & blue 10 10
558 – 25 l. multicoloured . . . 10 10
559 – 40 l. multicoloured 35 20
560 – 80 l. multicoloured 75 40
561 – 125 l. multicoloured . . . 3·25 1·50
DESIGNS: 2, 125 l. Maize; 3, 80 l. Grapes; 4, 25 l. Peaches; 5, 40 l. Plums.

138 Naples 10 Grana stamp of 1858 and Bay of Naples

1958. Centenary of First Naples Postage Stamps.
562 **138** 25 l. brown & bl (postage) 30 20
563 125 l. brown & bistre brown (air) . . . . 2·00 1·40
The Naples stamps on No. 563 is the 50 gr.

139 Mediterrranean Gull **140** P. de Coubertin (founder)

1959. Air. Native Birds.
564 **[139]** 5 l. black and green . . 20 10
565 – 10 l. brown, black & blue 20 10
566 – 15 l. multicoloured . . . 20 10
567 – 120 l. multicoloured . . 1·10 35
568 – 250 l. black, yellow & grn 3·25 1·00
BIRDS: 10 l. Common kestrel; 15 l. Mallard; 120 l. Rock dove; 250 l. Barn swallow.

1959. Pre-Olympic Games Issue.
569 **140** 2 l. blk, & brn (postage) . 10 10
570 – 3 l. sepia and mauve . . . 10 10
571 – 5 l. green and blue . . . 10 10
572 – 30 l. black and violet . . . 10 10
573 – 60 l. sepia and green . . . 10 10
574 – 80 l. green and lake . . . 10 10
575 – 120 l. brown (air) 80 70
PORTRAITS—As Type **140**: 3 l. A. Bonacossa; 5 l. A. Brundage; 30 l. C. Montu; 60 l. J. S. Edstrom; 80 l. De Baillet-Latour. HORIZ: (36×21½ mm): 120 l. De Coubertin and Olympic Flame. All, except the founder, De Coubertin are executives of the Olympic Games Committee.

141 Vickers Viscount 700 over Mt Titano

1959. Air. "Alitalia" Inaugural Flight, Rimini–London.
576 **141** 120 l. violet . . . . . . 1·50 1·00

142 Abraham Lincoln and Scroll

1959. Abraham Lincoln's 150th Birth Anniv. Inscr "ABRAMO LINCOLN 1809–1959".
577 **142** 5 l. brn & sepia (postage) 10 10
578 – 10 l. green and blue . . . 10 10
579 – 15 k. grey and green . . 10 10
580 – 70 k. violet 85 60
581 – 200 l. blue (air) . . . . 3·00 2·50
DESIGNS—Portraits of Lincoln with: HORIZ: 10 l. Map of San Marino; 15 l. Govt Palace, San Marino; 200 l. Mt Titano. VERT: 70 l. Mt Titano.

143 1859 Romagna ½ b. stamp and Arch of Augustus, Rimini **144** Portal of Messina Cathedral and ½ gr. Sicily stamp

1959. Romagna Stamp Centenary. Inscr "1859–1959".
582 **143** 30 l. brn, & sepia (postage) 20 15
583 – 120 l. green & black (air) 1·40 1·25
DESIGN: 120 l. 1989 Romagna 3 l. stamp and view of Bologna.

1959. World University Games, Turin. Inscr "UNIVERSITY TORINO 1959".
584 **120** 30 l. red 40 35

1959. Sicily Stamp Centenary.
585 **144** 1 l. brown & yell (postage) 10 10
586 – 2 l. red and olive 10 10
587 – 3 l. slate and blue 10 10
588 – 4 l. brown and red . . . 10 10
589 – 5 l. mauve and blue . . . 10 10
590 – 25 l. multicoloured . . . 10 10
591 – 60 l. multicoloured . . . 10 10
592 – 200 l. multicoloured (air) 75 65
DESIGNS—VERT: 2 l. Selinunte Temple (1 gr.); 3 l. Erice Church (2 gr.); 4 l. "Concordia" Temple, Agrigento (5 gr.); 5 l. "Castor and Pollux" Temple, Agrigento (10 gr.); 25 l. "St. John of the Hermits" Church, Palermo (20 gr.). HORIZ: 60 l. Taormina (50 gr.); 200 l. Bay of Palermo (50 gr.).

145 Golden Oriole **146** Putting the Shot

1960. Birds.
593 **145** 1 l. yellow, olive and blue 10 10
594 – 2 l. brown, red and green 10 10
595 – 3 l. red, brown and green 10 10
596 – 4 l. black, brown & green 10 10
597 – 5 l. red, brown and green 10 10
598 – 10 l. multicoloured . . . 10 10
599 – 25 l. multicoloured . . . 55 15
600 – 60 l. multicoloured . . . 1·90 70
601 – 80 l. multicoloured . . . 3·25 1·25
602 – 110 l. multicoloured . . . 3·75 1·75
DESIGNS—VERT: 2 l. Nightingale; 4 l. Hoopoe; 10 l. Goldfinch; 25 l. Common kingfisher; 80 l. Green woodpecker; 110 l. Red-breasted flycatcher. HORIZ: 3 l. Woodcock; 5 l. Red-legged partridge; 60 l. Ring-necked pheasant.

1960. Olympic Games.
603 **146** 1 l. violet & red (postage) 10 10
604 – 2 l. orange and black . . 10 10
605 – 3 l. violet and brown . . 10 10
606 – 4 l. brown and red . . . 10 10
607 – 5 l. blue and brown . . . 10 10
608 – 10 l. blue and brown . . 10 10
609 – 15 l. violet and green . . 10 10
610 – 25 l. orange and green . . 10 10
611 – 60 l. brown and green . . 10 10
612 – 110 l. red, black & green 10 10
613 – 20 l. violet (air) 10 10
614 – 40 l. red and brown . . . 10 10
615 – 80 l. yellow and blue . . 15 10
616 – 125 l. brown and red . . 25 20
DESIGNS—VERT: 2 l. Gymnastics; 3 l. Long-distance walking; 4 l. Boxing; 10 l. Cycling; 20 l. Handball; 40 l. Breasting the tape; 60 l. Football. HORIZ: 5 l. Fencing; 15 l. Hockey; 25 l. Rowing; 80 l. Diving; 110 l. Horse-jumping; 125 l. Rifle shooting.

147 Melvin Jones (founder) and Lions International H.Q.

1960. Lions International Commemoration.
617 – 30 l. brown and violet (postage) 10 10
618 **147** 45 l. brown and violet . . 40 40
619 – 60 l. red and blue 10 10
620 – 115 l. green and black . . 40 40
621 – 150 l. brown and violet . . 1·60 1·40
622 – 200 l. blue and green (air) . 3·25 3·25
DESIGNS—VERT: 30 l. Mt Titano; 60 l. San Marino Government Palace. HORIZ: 115 l. Pres. Clarence Sturm; 150 l. Vice-Pres. Finis E. Davis; 200 l. Globe. All designs except Type **147** bear the Lions emblem.

148 Riccione **149** "Youth with Basket of Fruit"

1960. 12th Riccione–San Marino Stamp Day. Centres multicoloured.
623 **148** 30 l. red (postage) 30 15
624 125 l. blue (air) . . . . . 1·40 1·25

1960. 350th Death Anniv of Caravaggio (painter).
625 **149** 200 l. multicoloured . . . 4·25 4·00

150 Hunting Roe Deer

1961. Hunting (1st issue). Historical Scenes.
626 **150** 1 l. blue and mauve . . . 10 10
627 – 2 l. red and brown 10 10
628 – 3 l. black and red 10 10
629 – 4 l. red and blue 10 10
630 – 5 l. brown and green . . . 10 10
631 – 10 l. violet and orange . . 10 10
632 – 30 l. blue and yellow . . . 10 10
633 – 60 l. brown, orange & blk 20 15
634 – 70 l. red, purple & green . 30 20
635 – 115 l. blue, purple & blk . 60 40
DESIGNS—VERT: 2 l. 16th-cent falconer; 10 l. 16th-cent falconer (mounted); 60 l. 17th-century hunter with rifle and dog. HORIZ: 3 l. 16th-cent wild boar hunt; 4 l. Duck-shooting with crossbow (16th-cent); 5 l. 16th-cent stag hunt with bow and arrow; 30 l. 17th-cent huntsman with horn and dogs; 70 l. 18th-cent hunter and beater; 115 l. Duck-shooting with bow and arrow (18th-cent).
See also Nos. 679/88.

151 Bell 47J Ranger Helicopter near Mt Titano

1961. Air.
636 **151** 1000 l. red . . . . 30·00 24·00

152 Guaita Tower, Mt Titano and 1858 Sardinian Stamp

1961. Centenary of Italian Independence Philatelic Exhibition, Turin.
637 **152** 30 l. multicoloured 50 40
638 70 l. multicoloured 70 55
639 200 l. multicoloured . . . 80 60

153 Mt Titano **155** King Enzo's Palace, Bologna

1961. Europe.
640 **153** 500 l. green & brown . . 4·50 5·00

1961. Bologna Stamp Exn. Inscr "BOLOGNA".
641 **155** 30 l. black and blue . . . 10 10
642 – 70 l. black and myrtle . . 15 10
643 – 100 l. black and brown . . 15 15
DESIGNS: 70 l. Gateway of Merchant's Palace; 100 l. Towers of Garisenda and Asinelli, Bologna.

156 Duryea, 1892

1962. Veteran Motor Cars.
644 **156** 1 l. blue and brown . . . 10 10
645 – 2 l. orange and blue . . . 10 10
646 – 3 l. orange and black . . 10 10
647 – 4 l. red and black 10 10
648 – 5 l. orange and violet . . 10 10
649 – 10 l. orange and black . . 10 10
650 – 15 l. red and black . . . 10 10
651 – 20 l. blue and black . . . 10 10
652 – 25 l. orange and black . . 10 10
653 – 30 l. buff and black . . . 10 10
654 – 50 l. mauve and black . . 10 10
655 – 70 l. green and black . . 20 10
656 – 100 l. red, yellow & black 25 15
657 – 115 l. green, orge & blk . 25 15
658 – 150 l. yellow, orge & blk . 50 30
MOTOR CARS—HORIZ: 2 l. Panhard and Levassor, 1895; 3 l. Peugeot "Vis-a-vis", 1895; 4 l. Daimler, 1899; 10 l. Decauville, 1900; 15 l. Wolseley, 1901; 20 l. Benz, 1902; 25 l. Napier, 1903; 50 l. Oldsmobile, 1904; 100 l. Isotta Fraschini, 1908; 115 l. Bianchi, 1910; 150 l. Alfa, 1910. VERT: 5 l. F.I.A.T., 1899; 30 l. White, 1903; 70 l. Renault, 1904.

157 Wright Type A **158** Roping Down

1962. Vintage Aircraft.
659 **157** 1 l. black and yellow . . 10 10
660 – 2 l. brown and green . . 10 10
661 – 3 l. brown and green . . 10 10
662 – 4 l. black and bistre . . 10 10
663 – 5 l. red and blue 10 10
664 – 10 l. brn and turquoise . . 10 10
665 – 30 l. bistre and blue . . . 10 10
666 – 60 l. bistre and violet . . 15 15
667 – 70 l. black and orange . . 20 15
668 – 115 l. bistre, black and grn 45 30
DESIGNS: 2 l. Archdeacon-Voisin "Boxkite" float glider; 3 l. Bonnet-Labranche biplane; 4 l. Curtiss "June Bug"; 5 l. Farman H.F.III biplane; 10 l. Bleriot XI, 30 l. Hubert Latham's Antoinette IV; 60 l. Alberto Santos-Dumont's biplane "14 bis"; 70 l. Alliott Verdon Roe's Triplane II; 115 l. Faccioli's airplane.

1962. Mountaineering.
669 **158** 1 l. bistre and black . . . 10 10
670 – 2 l. turquoise and black . 10 10
671 – 3 l. purple and black . . 10 10
672 – 4 l. blue and black . . . 10 10
673 – 5 l. orange and black . . 10 10
674 – 15 l. yellow and black . . 10 10
675 – 30 l. red and black . . . 10 10
676 – 40 l. blue and black . . . 10 10
677 – 85 l. green and black . . 20 20
678 – 115 l. blue and black . . 30 30
DESIGNS: 2 l. Sassolungo; 3 l. Mt Titano; 4 l. Three Lavaredo peaks; 5 l. The Matterhorn; 15 l. Skier; 30 l. Climber negotiating overhang; 40 l. Step-cutting in ice; 85 l. Aiguille du Geant; 115 l. Citadel on Mt Titano.

159 Hunter and Retriever

1962. Hunting (2nd issue). Modern scenes.
679 **159** 1 l. deep purple and green 10 10
680 – 2 l. blue and orange . . . 10 10

681 – 3 l. black and blue 10 10
682 – 4 l. sepia and brown . . . 10 10
683 – 5 l. brown and green . . . 10 10
684 – 15 l. black and green . . . 10 10
685 – 50 l. sepia and green . . . 15 10
686 – 70 l. turquoise and red . . 20 15
687 – 100 l. black and red . . . 50 50
688 – 150 l. green and lilac . . . 50 50
DESIGNS—HORIZ: 3 l. Marsh ducks (with decoys); 4 l. Roe deer; 5 l. Grey partridge; 15 l. Lapwing; 50 l. Partridge; 70 l. Marsh geese; 100 l. Wild boar. VERT: 2 l. Huntsman and hounds; 150 l. Hunter shooting pheasant.

160 Arrows encircling "Europa"

1962. Europa.
689 **160** 200 l. red and black . . . 1·25 1·25

161 Egyptian Merchant Ship, 2000 B.C

1963. Historical Ships.
690 **161** 1 l. blue and orange . . . 10 10
691 – 2 l. sepia and purple . . . 10 10
692 – 3 l. sepia and mauve . . . 10 10
693 – 4 l. dull purple and grey . 10 10
694 – 5 l. sepia and yellow . . . 10 10
695 – 10 l. brown and green . . 10 10
696 – 30 l. sepia and blue . . . 65 35
697 – 60 l. blue and green . . . 50 40
698 – 70 l. red and deep grey . . 70 70
699 – 115 l. brown and blue . . 1·40 1·10
DESIGNS—HORIZ: 2 l. Greek trier, 5th-cent, B.C.; 3 l. Roman trireme, 1st-cent, B.C.; 4 l. Viking longship, 10th-cent; 5 l. The "Santa Maria"; 30 l. Gallery, circa 1600; 115 l. "Duncan Dunbar" (full-rigged merchantman), 1550; VERT: 10 l. Carrack circa 1550; 60 l. "Sovereign of the Seas" (English galleon), 1637; 70 l. Danish ship of the line, circa 1750.

162 "The Fornarina" (or "The Veiled Woman")
163 Saracen Game, Arezzo

1963. Paintings by Raphael. Multicoloured.
700 30 l. Type **162** 35 35
701 70 l. Self portrait 15 15
702 100 l. Sistine Madonna (detail of woman praying) 20 20
703 200 l. "Portrait of a Young Woman" (Maddalena Strozzi) 35 35
The 200 l. is larger 27 × 44 mm.

1963. Ancient Tournaments.
704 **163** 1 l. mauve 10 10
705 – 2 l. black 10 10
706 – 3 l. black 10 10
707 – 4 l. violet 10 10
708 – 5 l. violet 10 10
709 – 10 l. green 10 10
710 – 30 l. red 10 10
711 – 60 l. blue 10 10
712 – 70 l. brown 10 10
713 – 115 l. black 20 20
TOURNAMENTS—HORIZ: 2 l. 14th-century, French cavaliers; 4 l. 15th-century, Presenting arms to an English cavalier; 30 l. Quintana game, Foligno; 70 l. 15th-century, Cavaliers (from castle mural, Malpaga). VERT: 3 l. Crossbow Championships, Gubbio; 5 l. 16th-century, Cavaliers, Florence; 10 l. Quintana game, Ascoli Piceno; 60 l. Palio (horse-race), Siena; 115 l. 13th-century, The Crusades: cavaliers' challenge.

164 Peacock
165 Corner of Government Palace, San Marino

1963. Butterflies. Multicoloured.
714 25 l. Type **164** 15 10
715 30 l. "Nessaea obrinus" 20 10
716 60 l. Large tortoiseshell . . . 30 15
717 70 l. Peacock (horiz) 35 20
718 115 l. "Papilio blumei" (horiz) 50 25

1963. San Marino–Riccione Stamp Fair.
719 **165** 100 l. black and blue . . 15 15
720 – 100 l. blue and sepia . . 15 15
DESIGN: No. 720, Fountain, Riccione.

166 Pole Vaulting
167 "E" and Flag of San Marino

1963. Olympic Games, Tokyo (1964) (1st issue).
721 – 1 l. purple and orange . . 10 10
722 **166** 2 l. sepia and green . . . 10 10
723 – 3 l. sepia and blue . . . 10 10
724 – 4 l. sepia and blue . . . 10 10
725 – 5 l. sepia and red 10 10
726 – 10 l. mauve and purple . . 10 10
727 – 30 l. purple and grey . . 10 10
728 – 60 l. sepia and yellow . . 10 10
729 – 70 l. sepia and blue . . . 10 10
730 – 115 l. sepia and green . . 15 10
SPORTS—HORIZ: 1 l. Hurdling; 3 l. Relay-racing; 4 l. High jumping (men); 5 l. Football; 10 l. High jumping (women); 60 l. Throwing the javelin; 70 l. Water polo; 115 l. Throwing the hammer. VERT: 30 l. Throwing the discus.
See also Nos. 743/52.

1963. Europa.
731 **167** 200 l. blue and brown . . 30 30

168 Tupolev Tu-104A
169 Running

1963. Air. Contemporary Aircraft.
732 **168** 5 l. purple, brown & blue 10 10
733 – 10 l. blue and red 10 10
734 – 15 l. red, mauve & violet 10 10
735 – 25 l. red, mauve & violet 10 10
736 – 50 l. red and blue 10 10
737 – 75 l. orange and green . . 10 10
738 – 120 l. red and blue . . . 20 20
739 – 200 l. black and yellow . 20 15
740 – 300 l. black and orange . 20 20
741 – 500 l. multicoloured . . 3·25 2·75
742 – 1000 l. multicoloured . . 2·00 1·60
AIRCRAFT—HORIZ: 15 l. Douglas DC-8; 25 l. Boeing 707; 50 l. Vickers Viscount 837; 120 l. Vickers VC-10; 200 l. Hawker Siddley Comet 4C; 300 l. Boeing 727-100; 1000 l. Boeing 707. VERT: 10 l. Boeing 707; 75 l. Sud Aviation SE 210 Caravelle; 500 l. Rolls Royce Dart 527 turboprop engine.

1964. Olympic Games, Tokyo (2nd issue).
743 **169** 1 l. brown and green . . . 10 10
744 – 2 l. brown and sepia . . 10 10
745 – 3 l. bown and black . . . 10 10
746 – 4 l. blue and red 10 10
747 – 5 l. brown and blue . . . 10 10
748 – 15 l. purple and orange . . 10 10
749 – 30 l. blue and light blue . 10 10
750 – 70 l. brown and green . . 15 15
751 – 120 l. brown and blue . . 15 15
752 – 150 l. purple and red . . 20 20
DESIGNS—VERT: 2 l. Gymnastics; 3 l. Basketball; 120 l. Cycling; 150 l. Fencing. HORIZ: 4 l. Pistol-shooting; 5 l. Rowing; 15 l. Long jumping; 30 l. Diving; 70 l. Sprinting.

1964. "Towards Tokyo" Sports Stamp Exn, Rimini. As Nos. 749/50, but inscr "VERSO TOKIO" and colours changed.
753 30 l. blue and violet 15 10
754 70 l. brown and turquoise . . 15 10

170 Murray Blenkinsop Locomotive (1812)

1964. "Story of the Locomotive".
755 **170** 1 l. black and buff . . . 10 10
756 – 2 l. black and green . . 10 10
757 – 3 l. black and violet . . 10 10
758 – 4 l. black and yellow . . 10 10
759 – 5 l. black and salmon . . 10 10
760 – 15 l. black and green . . 10 10
761 – 20 l. black and pink . . 10 10
762 – 50 l. black and blue . . . 10 10
763 – 90 l. black and orange . . 35 35
764 – 110 l. black and blue . . . 75 75
LOCOMOTIVES: 2 l. "Puffing Billy" (1813); 3 l. "Locomotion No. 1" (1825); 4 l. "Rocket" (1829); 5 l. "Lion" (1838); 15 l. "Bayard" (1839); 20 l. Crampton type (1849); 50 l. "Little England" (1851); 90 l. "Spitfire" (c. 1860); 110 l. "Rogers" (c. 1865).

171 Baseball Players

1964. 7th European Baseball Championships, Milan.
765 **171** 30 l. sepia and green . . . 15 10
766 – 70 l. black and red 15 15
DESIGN: 70 l. Player pitching ball.

172 "E" and Part of Globe

1964. Europa.
767 **172** 200 l. red, blue & lt blue . 30 30

173 Pres. Kennedy giving Inaugural Address
174 Cyclists at Government Palace

1964. 1st Death Anniv of John F. Kennedy (President of U.S.A.). Multicoloured.
768 70 l. Type **173** 15 15
769 130 l. Pres. Kennedy and U.S. flag (vert) 15 15

1965. Cycle Tour of Italy.
770 **174** 30 l. sepia 10 10
771 – 70 l. purple 10 10
772 – 200 l. red 15 10
DESIGNS:— Cyclists passing: 70 l. "The Rock"; 200 l. Mt Titano.

175 Brontosaurus
176 Rooks on Chessboard

1965. Prehistoric Animals.
773 **175** 1 l. purple and green . . . 10 10
774 – 2 l. black and blue . . . 10 10
775 – 3 l. yellow and green . . . 10 10
776 – 4 l. brown and blue . . . 10 10
777 – 5 l. purple and green . . . 10 10
778 – 10 l. purple and green . . 10 10
779 – 75 l. blue and turquoise . . 35 15
780 – 100 l. purple and green . . 80 25
ANIMALS—VERT: 2 l. Brachyosaurus. HORIZ: 3 l. Pteranodon; 4 l. Elasmosaurus; 5 l. Tyrannosaurus; 10 l. Stegosaurus; 75 l. Thamatosaurus Victor; 100 l. Iguanodon; 200 l. Triceratops.

1965. Europa.
782 **176** 200 l. multicoloured . . . 30 25

177 Dante

1965. 700th Anniv of Dante's Birth.
783 **177** 40 l. sepia and blue 10 10
784 – 90 l. sepia and red 10 10
785 – 130 l. sepia and brown . . 10 10
786 – 140 l. sepia and blue . . . 10 10
DESIGNS: 90 l. "Hell"; 130 l. "Purgatory"; 140 l. "Paradise".

178 Mt Titano and Flags

1965. Visit of Pres. Saragat of Italy.
787 **178** 115 l. multicoloured . . . 10 10

179 Trotting

1966. Equestrian Sports. Multicoloured.
788 10 l. Type **179** 15 10
789 20 l. Cross-country racing . . 15 10
790 40 l. Horse-jumping 15 10
791 70 l. Horse-racing 15 10
792 90 l. Steeple-chasing 20 15
793 170 l. Polo 25 15
The 20 and 170 l. are vert.

1966. New values in previous designs.
794 5 l. brown and blue (as 522a) . 10 10
795 10 l. green & black (as 524) . 10 10
796 15 l. violet & brown (as 524a) 10 10
797 40 l. red and lilac (as 491) . . 10 10
798 90 l. blue and black (as 492) . 10 10
799 140 l. orange & vio (as 493) . 10 10

180 "La Bella"

1966. Paintings by Titian. Multicoloured.
800 40 l. Type **180** 10 10
801 90 l. "The Three Graces" . . . 15 15
802 100 l. "The Three Graces" . . 15 15
803 170 l. "Sacred and Profane Love" 20 20
The 90 and 100 l. show different details from the picture.

181 Stone Bass

1966. Sea Animals. Multicoloured.
804 1 l. Type **181** 10 10
805 2 l. Cuckoo wrasse 10 10
806 3 l. Common dolphin 10 10
807 4 l. John Dory 10 10
808 5 l. Octopus 10 10
809 10 l. Orange scorpionfish . . 10 10
810 40 l. Electric ray 10 10
811 90 l. Medusa 15 10
812 115 l. Seahorse 15 10
813 130 l. Dentex 20 10
The 5, 40, 90 and 115 l. are vert.

182 Our Lady of Europe
183 Peony

1966. Europa.
814 **182** 200 l. multicoloured . . . 30 30

1967. Flowers. Multicoloured.
815 5 l. Type **183** 10 10
816 10 l. Campanula 10 10
817 15 l. Pyrenean poppy 10 10
818 20 l. Purple deadnettle 10 10
819 40 l. Hemerocallis 10 10
820 140 l. Gentian 15 10
821 170 l. Thistle 15 10
Each flower has a different background view of Mt Titano.

184 St. Marinus

185 Map of Europe

1967. Paintings by Francesco Barbieri (Guercino). Multicoloured.
822 40 l. Type **184** 10 10
823 170 l. "St. Francis" 15 15
824 190 l. "Return of the Prodigal Son" (45 × 37 mm) 15 15

1967. Europa.
825 **185** 200 l. green and orange . 30 30

186 Caesar's Mushroom

187 Salisbury Cathedral

1967. Fungi. Multicoloured.
826 5 l. Type **186** 15 10
827 15 l. The Miller 15 10
828 20 l. Parasol mushroom . . . 15 10
829 40 l. Cep 15 10
830 50 l. "Russula paludosa" . . . 15 10
831 170 l. St. George's mushroom 20 20

1967. Gothic Cathedrals.
832 – 20 l. violet on cream . . . 10 10
833 – 40 l. green on cream . . . 10 10
834 – 80 l. blue on cream . . . 10 10
835 **187** 90 l. sepia on cream . . . 10 10
836 – 170 l. red on cream . . . 15 15
DESIGNS: 20 l. Amiens; 40 l. Siena; 80 l. Toledo; 170 l. Cologne.

188 Cimabue Crucifix, Florence

1967. Christmas.
837 **188** 300 l. brown and violet . . 30 30

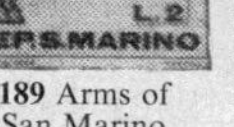
189 Arms of San Marino

190 Europa "Key"

1968. Arms of San Marino Villages. Mult.
838 2 l. Type **189** 10 10
839 3 l. Penna Rossa 10 10
840 5 l. Fiorentino 10 10
841 10 l. Montecerreto 10 10
842 25 l. Serravalle 10 10
843 35 l. Montegiardino 10 10
844 50 l. Faetano 10 10
845 90 l. Borgo Maggiore 10 10
846 180 l. Montelupo 15 10
847 500 l. State crest 35 35

1968. Europa.
848 **190** 250 l. brown 30 30

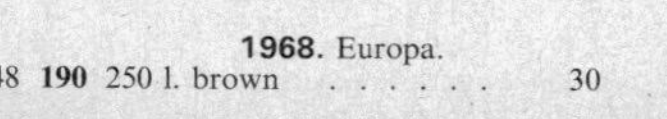

191 "The Battle of San Romano" (detail, P. Uccello)

1968. 671st Birth Anniv of Paolo Uccello (painter).
849 **191** 50 l. black on lilac . . . 10 10
850 – 90 l. black on lilac . . . 15 15
851 – 130 l. black on lilac . . . 15 15
852 – 230 l. black on pink . . . 25 25
All stamps show details of "The Battle of San Romano". The 90 l. is vert.

192 "The Nativity" (detail, Botticelli)

1968. Christmas.
853 **192** 50 l. deep blue 10 10
854 90 l. deep red 10 10
855 180 l. sepia 10 10

193 "Peace"

1969. "The Good Government" (frescoes) by Ambrogio Lorenzetti.
856 **193** 50 l. blue 10 10
857 – 80 l. sepia 10 10
858 – 90 l. violet 10 10
859 – 180 l. red 15 15
DESIGNS—VERT: 80 l. "Justice"; 90 l. "Temperance". HORIZ: 180 l. View of Siena.

194 "Young Soldier" (Bramante)

1969. 525th Birth Anniv of Donato Bramante (architect and painter). Multicoloured.
860 50 l. Type **194** 15 15
861 90 l. "Old Soldier" (Bramante) 15 15

195 Colonnade

1969. Europa.
862 **195** 50 l. green 15 15
863 180 l. purple 15 15

196 Benched Carriage ("Char-a-banc")

1969. Horses and Carriages. Multicoloured.
864 5 l. Type **196** 10 10
865 10 l. Barouche 10 10
866 25 l. Private drag 10 10
867 40 l. Hanson cab 10 10
868 50 l. Curricle 10 10
869 90 l. Wagonette 15 15
870 180 l. Spider phaeton 15 15

197 Mt Titano

1969. Paintings by R. Viola. Multicoloured.
871 20 l. Type **197** 10 10
872 180 l. "Pier at Rimini" 15 15
873 200 l. "Pier at Riccione" (horiz) 15 15

198 "Faith"

1969. Christmas. "The Theological Virtues" by Raphael.
874 **198** 20 l. violet and orange . . 10 10
875 – 180 l. violet and green . . 15 15
876 – 200 l. violet and buff . . . 15 15
DESIGNS: 180 l. "Hope"; 200 l. "Charity".

199 "Aries"

1970. Signs of the Zodiac. Multicoloured.
877 1 l. Type **199** 10 10
878 2 l. "Taurus" 10 10
879 3 l. "Gemini" 10 10
880 4 l. "Cancer" 10 10
881 5 l. "Leo" 10 10
882 10 l. "Virgo" 10 10
883 15 l. "Libra" 10 10
884 20 l. "Scorpio" 10 10
885 70 l. "Sagittarius" 10 10
886 90 l. "Capricorn" 15 10
887 100 l. "Aquarius" 20 10
888 180 l. "Pisces" 70 30

200 "Flaming Sun"

202 St. Francis' Gate

201 "The Fleet in the Bay of Naples" (Pieter Brueghel the Elder)

1970. Europa.
889 **200** 90 l. red and green 15 15
890 180 l. red and yellow . . . 15 15

1970. 10th "Europa" Stamp Exhibition, Naples.
891 **201** 230 l. multicoloured . . . 30 30

1970. 65th Anniv of Rotary International and 10th Anniv of San Marino Rotary Club. Multicoloured.
892 180 l. Type **202** 15 15
893 220 l. "Rocco" Fort, Mt Titano 15 15

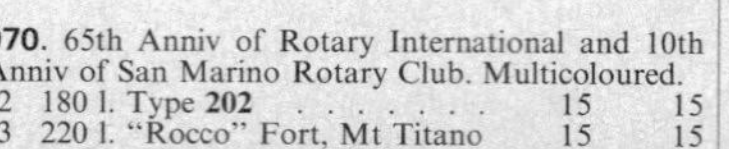

203 "Girl with Mandolin"

204 Black Pete

1970. Death Bicentenary of Giambattista Tiepolo (painter).
894 50 l. Type **203** 10 10
895 180 l. "Girl with Parrot" . . 25 15
896 220 l. "Rinaldo and Armida Surprised" 15 15
SIZES: 180 l. As Type **203**. 220 l. (57 × 37 mm).

1970. 4th Death Anniv of Walt Disney (film producer). Cartoon Characters. Multicoloured.
897 1 l. Type **204** 10 10
898 2 l. Gyro Gearloose 10 10
899 3 l. Pluto 10 10
900 4 l. Minnie Mouse 10 10
901 5 l. Donald Duck 10 10
902 10 l. Goofy 10 10
903 15 l. Scrooge McDuck 10 10
904 50 l. Hewey, Dewey and Louie 40 20
905 90 l. Mickey Mouse 65 30
906 220 l. Walt Disney and scene from "The Jungle Book" (horiz) . . . . 4·00 3·00

205 "Customs House, Venice

1971. "Save Venice" Campaign. Paintings by Canaletto. Multicoloured.
907 20 l. Type **205** 15 10
908 180 l. "Grand Canal, Balbi Palace and Rialto Bridge, Venice 30 30
909 200 l. "St. Mark's and Doge's Palace" 35 35

206 Congress Building and San Marino Flag

1971. Italian Philatelic Press Union Congress, San Marino. Multicoloured.
910 20 l. Type **206** 10 10
911 90 l. Government Palace door and emblems (vert) 10 10
912 180 l. Type **206** 15 15

207 Europa Chain

209 Day Lily

208 "Duck" Jug with "Lasa" Decoration

1971. Europa.
913 **207** 50 l. blue and yellow . . 15 15
914 90 l. orange and blue . . 15 15

1971. Etruscan Art (1st series).
915 **208** 50 l. black and orange . . 10 10
916 – 80 l. black and green . . 10 10
917 – 90 l. black and green . . 10 10
918 – 180 l. black and orange . 15 15
DESIGNS—VERT: 80 l. Head of Hermes (bust); 90 l. Man and Wife (relief on sarcophagus). HORIZ: 180 l. Chimera (bronze).
See also Nos. 1018/21.

1971. Flowers. Multicoloured.

919 1 l. Type **209** 10 10
920 2 l. "Phlox paniculata" . . . 10 10
921 3 l. Wild pink 10 10
922 4 l. Globe flower 10 10
923 5 l. "Centaurea dealbata" . . 10 10
924 10 l. Peony 10 10
925 15 l. Christmas rose 10 10
926 50 l. Pasque flower 15 10
927 90 l. "Gaillardia aristata" . . 15 15
928 220 l. "Aster dumosus" . . . 35 30

210 "Allegory of Spring" (detail, Botticelli)

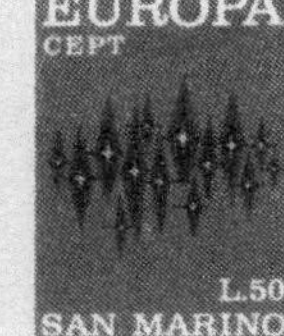

211 "Communications"

1972. "Allegory of Spring" by Sandro Botticelli. Multicoloured.

929 50 l. Type **210** 10 10
930 190 l. The Three Graces (27 × 37 mm) 20 20
931 220 l. Flora 25 25

1972. Europa.

932 **211** 50 l. multicoloured 20 15
933 90 l. multicoloured 20 15

212 "Taming the Bear"

1972. "Life of St. Marinus". 16th-century paintings from former Government Palace.

934 **212** 25 l. black and buff . . . 10 10
935 – 55 l. black and orange . . 10 10
936 – 100 l. black and blue . . . 15 10
937 – 130 l. black and yellow . . 15 15

DESIGNS: 55 l. "The Conversion of Donna Felicissima"; 100 l. "Hostile archers turned to stone"; 130 l. "Mount Titano given to St. Marinus".

213 House Sparrow

214 "Healthy Man"

1972. Birds. Multicoloured.

938 1 l. Type **213** 10 10
939 2 l. Firecrest 10 10
940 3 l. Blue tit 10 10
941 4 l. Ortulan bunting 10 10
942 5 l. Bluethroat 10 10
943 10 l. Bullfinch 20 10
944 25 l. Linnet 20 10
945 50 l. Black-eared wheatear . . 35 15
946 90 l. Sardinian warbler 45 20
947 220 l. Greenfinch . . . . . . 1·00 35

1972. World Heart Month. Multicoloured.

948 50 l. Type **214** 15 15
949 90 l. "Sick Man" (horiz) . . . 15 15

215 Veterans Emblem

216 Plane over Mt Titano

1972. "Veterans of Philately" Award of Italian Philatelic Federation.

950 **215** 25 l. gold and blue 10 10

1972. Air.

951 **216** 1000 l. multicoloured . . . 1·25 80

INDEX

Countries can be quickly located by referring to the index at the end of this volume.

217 Five-Cent Coin of 1864

1972. San Marino Coinage.

952 **217** 5 l. bronze, black & grey 10 10
953 – 10 l. bronze, black & orge 10 10
954 – 15 l. silver, black & red . 10 10
955 – 20 l. silver, black & purple 10 10
956 – 25 l. silver, black & blue . 10 10
957 – 50 l. silver, black & blue . 15 10
958 – 55 l. silver, black & ochre 15 15
959 – 220 l. gold, black & green 20 20

COINS (obverse and reverse on each stamp): 10 l. 10 c. of 1935; 15 l. 1 l. of 1906; 20 l. 5 l. of 1898; 25 l. 5 l. of 1937; 50 l. 10 l. of 1932; 55 l. 20 l. of 1938; 220 l. 20 l. of 1925.

218 New York, 1673

1973. "Interpex" Stamp Exhibition and Important Cities of the World (1st series). New York.

960 **218** 200 l. multicoloured . . . 35 35
961 – 300 l. purple, blue & black 40 40

DESIGN: 300 l. New York, 1973.

See also Nos. 1032/3, 1075/6, 1144/5, 1160/1, 1197/8, 1215/16, 1230/1, 1259/60, 1271/2, 1306/7, 1331/2 and 1358/9.

219 Printing Press

220 "Sportsmen"

1973. Tourist Press Congress.

962 **219** 50 l. multicoloured . . . 10 10

1973. Youth Games.

963 **220** 100 l. multicoloured . . . 10 10

221 Europa "Posthorn"

222 Grapes

1973. Europa

964 **221** 20 l. green, blue and flesh 10 10
965 180 l. mauve, red and blue 70 70

1973. Fruits. Multicoloured.

966 1 l. Type **222** 10 10
967 2 l. Mandarines 10 10
968 3 l. Apples 10 10
969 4 l. Plums 10 10
970 5 l. Strawberries 10 10
971 10 l. Pears 10 10
972 25 l. Cherries 10 10
973 50 l. Pomegranate 20 10
974 90 l. Apricots 25 20
975 200 l. Peaches 45 30

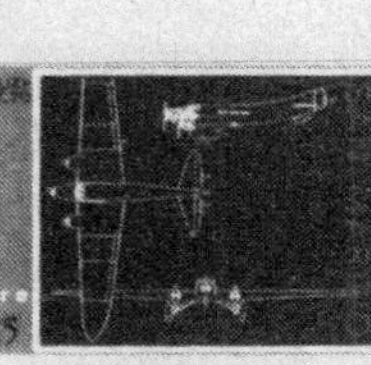
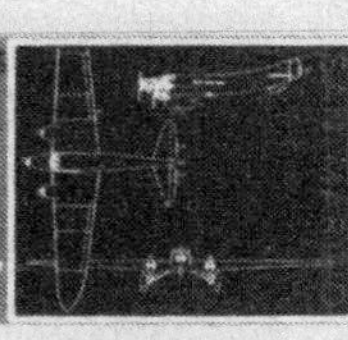

223 Couzinet 70 "Arc en Ciel"

224 Crossbowman, Serravalle Castle

1973. "Story of the Aeroplane".

976 **223** 25 l. blue, yellow & gold . 10 10
977 – 55 l. blue, grey and gold . 10 10
978 – 60 l. blue, pink and gold . 10 10
979 – 90 l. blue, bistre and gold 15 10
980 – 220 l. blue, orange & gold 25 15

DESIGNS: 55 l. Macchi Castoldi MC-72-181 seaplane; 60 l. Tupolev ANT-9; 90 l. "Spirit of St. Louis"; 220 l. Handley Page H.P.42.

1973. San Marino's Victory in Crossbow Tournament, Masa Marittima. Multicoloured.

981 5 l. Type **224** 10 10
982 10 l. Crossbowman, Pennarossa Castle 10 10
983 15 l. Drummer, Montegiardino Castle 10 10
984 20 l. Trumpeter, Fiorentino Castle 10 10
985 30 l. Crossbowman, Montecerreto Castle 10 10
986 40 l. Crossbowman, Borgo Maggiore Castle 15 10
987 50 l. Trumpeter, Guaita Castle 15 10
988 80 l. Crossbowman, Faetano Castle 20 15
989 200 l. Crossbowman, Montelupo Castle 45 20

225 "Adoration of the Magi" (detail)

226 Combat Shield (16th century)

1973. Christmas. 600th Birth Anniv of Gentile da Fabriano. Details of Gentile's altarpiece "Adoration of the Magi".

990 **225** 5 l. multicoloured 10 10
991 – 30 l. multicoloured 10 10
992 – 115 l. multicoloured . . . 10 10
993 – 250 l. multicoloured . . . 20 20

1974. Ancient Weapons from "Cesta" Museum, San Marino.

994 **226** 5 l. black brown & green 10 10
995 – 10 l. black, blue & brown 10 10
996 – 15 l. black, blue & lt blue 10 10
997 – 20 l. black, blue & brown 10 10
998 – 30 l. black, brown & blue 10 10
999 – 50 l. black, blue & pink . 10 10
1000 – 80 l. black, blue & lilac . 15 10
1001 – 250 l. black and yellow . 25 15

DESIGNS: 10 l. German armour (16th-century); 15 l. Crested morion (16th-century); 20 l. Horse head-armour (15th-16th century); 30 l. Italian morion with crest (16th-17th century); 50 l. Gauntlets and sword pommel (16th-century); 80 l. Sallet helmet (16th-century); 250 l. Sforza shield (16th-century).

227 "The Joy of Living" (Emilio Greco)

1974. Europa. Sculpture.

1002 **227** 100 l. black and brown . 15 15
1003 – 200 l. black and green . 15 15

DESIGN: 200 l. "The Joy of Living" (complete sculpture).

228 "Sea and Mountains"

229 Arms of Sansepolcro

1974. San Marino–Riccione Stamp Fair.

1004 **228** 50 l. multicoloured . . . 5 5

1974. 9th Crossbow Tournament, San Marino. Arms. Multicoloured.

1005 15 l. Type **229** 75 75
1006 20 l. Massa Marittima 75 75
1007 50 l. San Marino 75 75
1008 115 l. Gubbio 75 75
1009 300 l. Lucca 75 75

230 U.P.U. Emblem and Shadow

1974. Centenary of Universal Postal Union.

1010 **230** 50 l. multicoloured . . . 15 15
1011 90 l. multicoloured . . . 15 15

231 Glider

1974. Air. 50th Anniv of Gliding in Italy.

1012 **231** 40 l. blue, green & brown 10 10
1013 – 120 l. blue, lt blue & vio 10 10
1014 – 500 l. violet, mve & red . 30 35

DESIGNS: 120, 500 l. Gliders in "air currents" (both different).

232 Mt Titano and Verses of Hymn

233 "Madonna and Child" (4th-century painting)

1974. Death Centenary of Niccolo Tommaseo (writer).

1015 **232** 50 l. black, green & red . 15 15
1016 – 150 l. black, yellow & bl 15 15

DESIGN: 150 l. Portrait of Tommaseo.

1974. Christmas.

1017 **233** 250 l. multicoloured . . 30 30

234 "Dancing Scene", Tomb of the Leopards, Tarquinia

1975. Etruscan Art (2nd series). Tomb Paintings. Multicoloured.

1018 20 l. Type **234** 10 10
1019 30 l. "Chariot Race", Tomb of the Hill, Chiusi 10 10
1020 180 l. "Achilles and Troillus", Tomb of the Bulls, Tarquinia 30 15
1021 220 l. "Dancers", Tomb of the Triclinium, Tarquinia . . . 40 25

235 "Escape Tunnel"

236 "The Blessing"

1975. 30th Anniv of Escape of 100,000 Italian War-time Refugees to San Marino.

1022 **235** 50 l. multicoloured . . . 15 10

1975. Europa. Details from "St. Marinus" by Guercino. Multicoloured.

1023 100 l. Type **236** 15 15
1024 200 l. "St. Marinus" 25 25

237 "The Virgin Mary"

238 "Aphrodite" (sculpture)

1975. Holy Year. Details from Frescoes by Giotto from Scrovegni Chapel, Padua. Multicoloured.

1025 10 l. Type **237** 10 10
1026 40 l. "Virgin and Child" . . 10 10
1027 50 l. "Heads of Angels" . . 10 10
1028 100 l. "Mary Magdalene" (horiz) 10 10
1029 500 l. "Heads of Saints" (horiz) 35 35

1975. 15th Europa Stamp Exhibition, Naples.

1030 **238** 50 l. black, grey & violet 10 10

239 Congress Emblem

1975. "Eurocophar" International Pharmaceutical Congress, San Marino.
1031 **239** 100 l. multicoloured . . . 15 10

240 Tokyo, 1835

1975. Important Cities of the World (2nd series). Tokyo. Multicoloured.
1032 200 l. Type **240** 30 30
1033 300 l. Tokyo, 1975 . . . . . 40 40

241 "Woman on Balcony"

242 "Head of the Child" (detail)

1975. International Women's Year. Paintings by Gentilini. Multicoloured.
1034 50 l. Type **241** 10 10
1035 150 l. "Heads of Two Women" (horiz) 20 15
1036 230 l. "Profile of Girl" . . . 35 25

1975. Christmas. 500th Birth Anniv of Michelangelo. Painting "Doni Madonna" and details. Multicoloured.
1037 50 l. Type **242** 10 10
1038 100 l. "Head of Virgin" (detail) 15 15
1039 250 l. "Doni Madonna" . . . 25 25

243 "Modesty"

244 Capitol, Washington

1976. "The Civil Virtues". Sketches by Emilio Greco.
1039a – 5 l. black and lilac . . . 10 10
1040 **243** 10 l. black and stone . . 10 10
1041 – 20 l. black and lilac . . 10 10
1041a – 35 l. black and stone . . 10 10
1042 – 50 l. black and green . . 10 10
1043 – 70 l. black and pink . . 10 10
1044 – 90 l. black and pink . . 10 10
1045 – 100 l. black and pink . . 10 10
1046 – 120 l. black and blue . . 10 10
1047 – 150 l. black and lilac . . 10 10
1048 – 160 l. black and green . . 15 15
1049 – 170 l. black and flesh . . 15 15
1050 – 220 l. black and grey . . 20 15
1051 – 250 l. black and yellow . 25 20
1052 – 300 l. black and grey . . 30 20
1053 – 320 l. black and mauve . 30 20
1054 – 500 l. black and stone . 40 30
1055 – 1000 l. black and blue . 70 50
1056 – 2000 l. black & cream . 1·75 1·75

DESIGNS: 3 l. "Wisdom"; 20, 160 l. "Temperance"; 35 l. "Love"; 50, 70 l. "Fortitude"; 90, 220 l. "Prudence"; 100, 120 l. "Altruism"; 150, 170 l. "Hope"; 250 l. "Justice"; 300, 320 l. "Faith"; 500 l. "Honesty"; 1000 l. "Industry"; 2000 l. "Faithfulness".

1976. Bicentenary of American Revolution and "Interphil 1976" International Stamp Exhibition, Philadelphia. Multicoloured.
1056 70 l. Type **244** 10 10
1057 150 l. Statue of Liberty, New York 10 10
1058 180 l. Independence Hall, Philadelphia 15 15

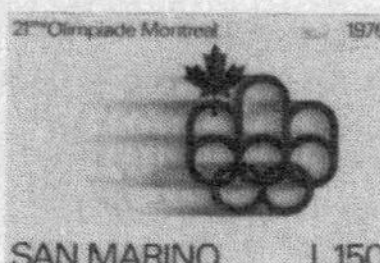

245 Emblem and Maple Leaf

1976. Olympic Games, Montreal.
1059 **245** 150 l. black and red . . 20 20

246 Polychrome Plate (U. Bruno)
247 S.U.M.S. Emblem

1976. Europa. Handicrafts. Multicoloured.
1060 150 l. Type **246** 15 15
1061 180 l. Silver plate (A. Ruscelli) 15 15

1976. Centenary of Social Welfare Union.
1062 **247** 150 l. red, yellow & lilac 15 15

248 Children of Different Races

249 "San Marino"

1976. 30th Anniv of U.N.E.S.O.
1063 **248** 180 l. brown, orange & bl 15 15
1064 220 l. brown, buff & sepia 15 15

1976. "Italia '76" International Stamp Exhibition, Milan.
1065 **249** 150 l. multicoloured . . 15 15

250 "The Annunciation"

251 Mount Titano and Emblem

1976. Christmas. 400th Death Anniv of Titian. Multicoloured.
1066 150 l. Type **250** 25 25
1067 300 l. "The Nativity" . . . 45 45

1977. "San Marino 77" International Stamp Exhibition (1st issue).
1068 **251** 80 l. red, green & olive (postage) 10 10
1069 170 l. yellow, violet & bl 10 10
1070 200 l. orange, ultramarine & blue 20 20
1071 200 l. ochre, green and blue (air) 20 20

See also No. 1082.

252 "San Marino" (Ghirlandaio)

253 Leonardo da Vinci's "Helicopter"

1977. Europa. Landscapes. Multicoloured.
1072 170 l. Type **252** 25 25
1073 200 l. "San Marino" (Guercino) 25 25

1977. Centenary of Enrico Forlanini's First Vertical Flight Experiment.
1074 **253** 120 l. multicoloured . . 15 10

254 University Square, 1877

1977. Centenary of Rumanian Independence. Important Cities of the World (3rd series). Bucharest.
1075 **254** 200 l. green and blue . . 25 25
1076 – 400 l. brown and stone . . 35 35

DESIGN: 400 l. City centre, 1977.

255 Design of First San Marino Stamp

256 "St. Marinus Blessing" (Retrosi)

1977. Centenary of San Marino Postage Stamps.
1077 **255** 40 l. green 10 10
1078 70 l. blue 10 10
1079 170 l. red 15 15
1080 500 l. brown 40 45
1081 1000 l. lilac 70 80

1977. "San Marino 1977" International Stamp Exhibition (2nd issue).
1082 **256** 1000 l. multicoloured . . 1·40 1·60

257 Medicinal Plants

259 Angel

258 Woman gripped by Octopus

1977. Italian Pharmacists' Union Congress.
1083 **257** 170 l. multicoloured . . . 30 20

1977. World Rheumatism Year.
1084 **258** 200 l. multicoloured . . . 30 25

1977. Christmas.
1085 **259** 170 l. black, grey & silver 25 25
1086 – 230 l. black, grey & silver 25 25
1087 – 300 l. black, grey & silver 35 35

DESIGNS: 230 l. Palm tree and olive; 300 l. The Virgin.

260 Baseball Player

261 San Francesco Gate

1978. World Baseball Championships.
1088 **260** 90 l. black, blue and ultramarine 15 15
1089 120 l. black, light green and green 15 15

1978. Europa. Architecture.
1090 **261** 170 l. blue & light blue . 20 20
1091 – 200 l. brown and stone . 25 25

DESIGN: 200 l. Ripa Gate.

262 Feather

263 Mt Titano and Antenna

1978. World Hypertension Month.
1092 **262** 320 l. black, red and blue 40 35

1978. San Marino's Admission to the I.T.U.
1093 **263** 10 l. yellow and red . . . 10 10
1094 200 l. blue and violet . . 20 20

264 Hawk and Slender-billed Gull

1978. 30th San Marino–Riccione Stamp Fair.
1095 **264** 120 l. multicoloured . . 40 15
1096 170 l. multicoloured . . 60 25

265 Wright Flyer I

266 Allegory of Human Rights

1978. Air. 75th Anniv of First Powered Flight.
1097 **265** 10 l. multicoloured . . . 10 10
1098 50 l. multicoloured . . . 10 10
1099 200 l. multicoloured . . 15 15

1978. 30th Anniv of Declaration of Human Rights.
1100 **266** 200 l. multicoloured . . 30 25

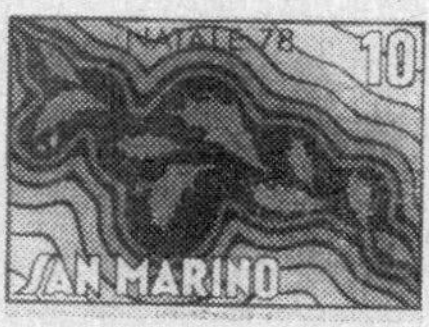

267 Holly

1978. Christmas. Multicoloured.
1101 10 l. Type **267** 10 10
1102 120 l. Star 15 10
1103 170 l. Snowflakes 15 15

268 Albert Einstein

1979. Birth Cent of Albert Einstein (physicist).
1104 **268** 120 l. brown, sepia and grey 20 15

269 Motor-coach, 1915

1979. Europa. Multicoloured.
1105 170 l. Type **269** 30 25
1106 220 l. Horse-drawn stage-coach 35 30

270 San Marino Crossbowmen Federation Emblem

271 Maigret (G. Simenon)

1979. 14th Crossbow Tournament.
1107 **270** 120 l. multicoloured . . 20 15

1979. Fictional Detectives. Multicoloured.
1108 10 l. Type **271** 10 10
1109 80 l. Perry Mason (S. Gardner) 15 10
1110 150 l. Nero Wolfe (R. Stout) 25 15
1111 170 l. Ellery Queen (F. Dannay and M. B. Lee) 30 15
1112 220 l. Sherlock Holmes (A. Conan Doyle) 50 25

272 Water Skiing

273 St. Apollonia

1979. Water Skiing Championships, Castelgandolfo.
1113 **272** 150 l. green, blue & blk . . 20 15

1979. 13th International Stomatology Congress.
1114 **273** 170 l. multicoloured . . . 30 20

274 "Knowledge"

275 Horse Chestnut and Red Deer

1979. International Year of the Child. Multicoloured.
1115 20 l. Type **274** 10 10
1116 120 l. "Friendship" 15 15
1117 170 l. "Equality" 15 15
1118 220 l. "Love" 20 20
1119 350 l. "Existence" 30 30

1979. Environment Protection. Trees and Animals. Multicoloured.
1120 5 l. Type **275** 10 10
1121 10 l. Cedar of Lebanon and golden eagle 40 10
1122 35 l. Flowering dogwood and common racoon 25 10
1123 50 l. Banyan and tiger . . . 25 10
1124 70 l. Stone pine and hoopoe . . 85 20
1125 90 l. Larch and yellow-throated marten 20 15
1126 100 l. Tasmanian blue gum and koala 20 15
1127 120 l. Date palm and dromedary 20 15
1128 150 l. Silver maple and American beaver 20 20
1129 170 l. Baobab and African elephant 45 25

276 "Disturbing Muses"

277 St. Joseph

1979. 1st Death Anniv of Giorgio de Chirico (painter). Multicoloured.
1130 40 l. Type **276** 10 10
1131 150 l. "Ancient Horses" . . . 15 10
1132 170 l. "Self-portrait" 20 10

1979. Christmas. "The Holy Family" (fresco) by Antonio Alberti or details from it.
1133 80 l. Type **277** 10 10
1134 170 l. Infant Jesus 20 20
1135 220 l. Magus 25 25
1136 320 l. "The Holy Family" . . 30 30

278 St. Benedict of Nursia

279 Cigarette Ends

1980. 1500th Birth Anniv of Saint Benedict of Nursia (founder of Benedictine Order).
1137 **278** 170 l. multicoloured . . . 30 25

1980. Anti-Smoking Campaign. Multicoloured.
1138 120 l. Type **279** 15 10
1139 220 l. Face hidden by cigarettes 30 30
1140 520 l. Face wreathed in smoke 70 50

280 Naples

1980. "Europa" Stamp Exhibition, Naples.
1141 **280** 170 l. multicoloured . . 30 20

281 Giovanbattista Belluzzi (military architect)

1980. Europa. Multicoloured.
1142 170 l. Type **281** 20 20
1143 220 l. Antonio Orafo (silver and goldsmith) 30 30

282 London, 1850

1980. "London 1980" International Stamp Exhibition and Important Cities of the World (4th series). London.
1144 **282** 200 l. brown and green . 30 30
1145 – 400 l. blue and lilac . . 40 40
DESIGN: 400 l. London, 1980.

283 Cycling

284 Stolz and Score of "Philatelic Waltz"

1980. Olympic Games, Moscow.
1146 **283** 70 l. black, emerald & grn 10 10
1147 – 90 l. black, orge & brn . 10 10
1148 – 170 l. black, red & mauve 15 15
1149 – 350 l. black, blue & dp bl 20 20
1150 – 450 l. black, violet & bl . 30 30
DESIGNS: 90 l. Basketball; 170 l. Running; 350 l. Gymnastics; 450 l. High jumping.

1980. Birth Centenary of Robert Stolz (composer).
1151 **284** 120 l. blue and black . . 30 15

285 Weightlifting

286 City Fortifications

1980. European Junior Weightlifting Championship.
1152 **285** 170 l. red, black & green 30 25

1980. World Tourism Conference, Manila.
1153 **286** 220 l. multicoloured . . 30 20

287 "The Annunciation" (detail)

288 St. Joseph's Eve Bonfire

1980. Christmas. Details of Paintings by Andrea del Sarto. Multicoloured.
1154 180 l. "Madonna of the Harpies" (detail) . . . 20 20
1155 250 l. "Annunciation" (Mary) 35 35
1156 500 l. Type **287** 55 55

1981. Europa. Multicoloured.
1157 200 l. Type **288** 25 25
1158 300 l. National Day fireworks 30 30

289 Hands holding Broken Branch

1981. International Year of Disabled Persons.
1159 **289** 300 l. brown, green & light green 30 30

290 "St. Charles' Square, 1817" (Jakob Alt)

1981. "WIPA 1981" International Stamp Exn and Important Cities of the World (5th series). Vienna. Multicoloured.
1160 200 l. Type **290** 30 30
1161 300 l. St. Charles' Square, 1981 60 60

291 Motor Cyclist

292 Girl playing Pipes

1981. San Marino Motor Cycle Grand Prix.
1162 **291** 200 l. multicoloured . . . 30 25

1981. Birth Bimillenary of Virgil (poet).
1163 **292** 300 l. grey and silver . . 35 40
1164 – 550 l. grey and silver . . 55 65
1165 – 1500 l. grey and silver . . 1·25 1·50
DESIGNS: 550 l. Soldier; 1500 l. Shepherd.

293 House

294 Judo

1981. Urban Development Scheme. Multicoloured.
1167 20 l. Type **293** 10 10
1168 80 l. Tree (provision of green belts) 15 10
1169 400 l. Gas flame (power plants) 35 35

1981. European Junior Judo Championships, San Marino.
1170 **294** 300 l. multicoloured . . . 45 35

295 "Girl with Dove" (Picasso)

296 Bread

1981. Birth Centenary of Pablo Picasso (artist). Mult.
1171 150 l. Type **295** 20 20
1172 200 l. "Homage to Picasso" (detail, Renato Guttuso) . . 30 30

1981. World Food Day.
1173 **296** 300 l. multicoloured . . . 40 35

297 King presenting Gift

298 Cancellation and "San Marino 82" Emblem

1981. Christmas. 500th Birth Anniv of Benvenuto Tisi da Garofalo (artist). Details from "Adoration of the Magi and St. Bartholomew". Multicoloured.
1174 200 l. Type **297** 20 20
1175 300 l. Kneeling King 35 35
1176 600 l. Virgin and Child . . . 65 65

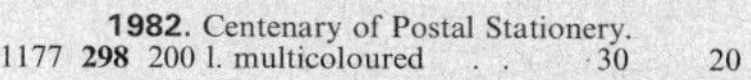
1982. Centenary of Postal Stationery.
1177 **298** 200 l. multicoloured . . 30 20

299 "The Cicada and the Ant" (Aesop fable)

1982. Centenary of Savings Bank.
1178 **299** 300 l. multicoloured . . 40 35

300 Assembly of Heads of Families, 1906

301 Archimedes

1982. Europa. Multicoloured.
1179 300 l. Type **300** 40 40
1180 450 l. Napoleon at the border of San Marino, 1797 . . . . 50 50

1982. Pioneers of Science.
1181 **301** 20 l. red and black . . . 10 10
1182 – 30 l. blue and black . . 10 10
1183 – 40 l. brown and black . . 10 10
1184 – 50 l. green and black . . 10 10
1185 – 60 l. red and black . . . 10 10
1186 – 100 l. brown and black . 15 10
1187 – 150 l. brown and black . 15 15
1188 – 200 l. brown and black . 20 15
1189 – 250 l. red and black . . 25 25
1190 – 300 l. green and black . 30 25
1191 – 350 l. green and black . 40 35
1192 – 400 l. red and black . . 45 45
1193 – 450 l. red and black . . 45 45
1194 – 1000 l. red and black . . 1·00 1·00
1195 – 1400 l. red and black . . 1·50 1·50
1196 – 5000 l. black and blue . 5·00 5·00
DESIGNS: 30 l. Copernicus; 40 l. Isaac Newton; 50 l. Antoine Lavoisier; 60 l. Marie Curie; 100 l. Robert Koch; 150 l. Alexander Fleming; 200 l. Thomas Edison; 250 l. Alessandro Volta; 300 l. Guglielmo Marconi; 350 l. Evangelista Torricelli; 400 l. Carl Linnaeus; 450 l. Hippocrates; 1000 l. Pythagoras; 1400 l. Leonardo da Vinci; 5000 l. Galileo.

302 "Notre Dame", 1806 (J. Hill)

1982. "Philexfrance 82" International Stamp Exhibition and Important Cities of the World (6th series). Paris.
1197 **302** 300 l. buff and black . . 30 30
1198 – 450 l. multicoloured . . 40 40
DESIGN: 450 l. Notre Dame and Ile de Cite, 1982.

303 Hands and Birds

304 Pope John Paul II

1982. 800th Birth Anniv of St. Francis of Assisi.
1199 **303** 200 l. multicoloured . . 30 25

1982. Visit of Pope John Paul II to San Marino.
1200 **304** 900 l. purple, deep green and green . . . . . . 1·25 1·00

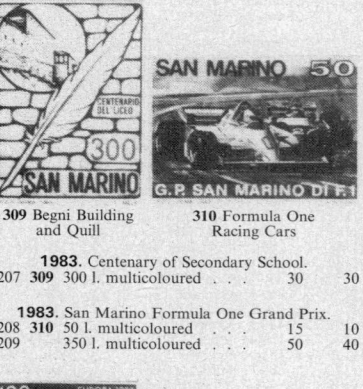

305 Globe encircled by Flag Stamps — **306** Face besplattered with Blood

1982. 5th Anniv of International Association of Stamp Catalogue Editors.
1201 **305** 300 l. multicoloured . . . 35 35

1982. 15th International Congress of Amnesty International, Rimini.
1202 **306** 700 l. red and black . . . 70 70

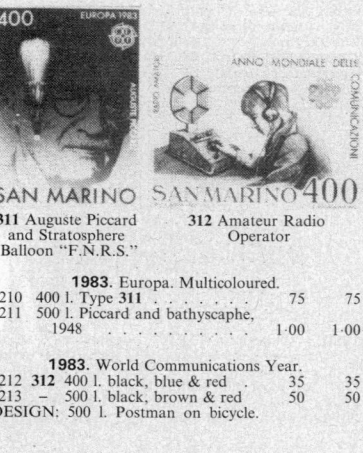

307 "Accipe Lampadam Ardentem" (detail) — **308** Refugee

1982. Christmas. Paintings by Gregorio Sciltian. Multicoloured.
1203 200 l. Type **307** 25 25
1204 300 l. "Madonna della Citta" (detail) 40 40
1205 450 l. Angel (detail, "Accipe Sal Sapientiae") 55 55

1982. "For Refugees".
1206 **308** 300 l. + 100 l. mult . . 35 35

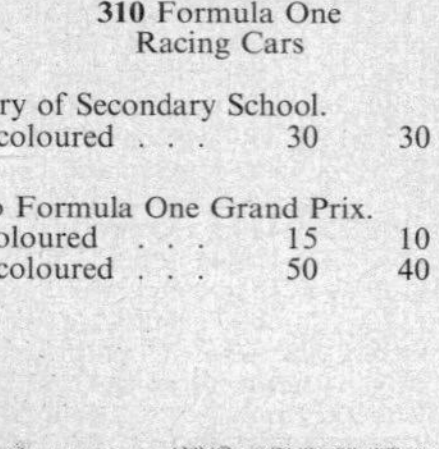

309 Begni Building and Quill — **310** Formula One Racing Cars

1983. Centenary of Secondary School.
1207 **309** 300 l. multicoloured . . . 30 30

1983. San Marino Formula One Grand Prix.
1208 **310** 50 l. multicoloured . . . 15 10
1209 350 l. multicoloured . . . 50 40

311 Auguste Piccard and Stratosphere Balloon "F.N.R.S." — **312** Amateur Radio Operator

1983. Europa. Multicoloured.
1210 400 l. Type **311** 75 75
1211 500 l. Piccard and bathyscaphe, 1948 . . . . 1·00 1·00

1983. World Communications Year.
1212 **312** 400 l. black, blue & red . 35 35
1213 – 500 l. black, brown & red 50 50
DESIGN: 500 l. Postman on bicycle.

313 Montgolfier Balloon

1983. Bicentenary of Manned Flight.
1214 **313** 500 l. multicoloured . . . 50 50

314 "Rio de Janeiro, 1845" (Richard Bate)

1983. "Brasiliana 83" International Stamp Exhibition and Important Cities of the World (7th series). Rio de Janeiro. Multicoloured.
1215 400 l. Type **314** 35 35
1216 1400 l. Rio de Janeiro, 1983 . . 1·50 1·50

315 Feeding Colt

1983. World Food Programme.
1217 **315** 500 l. multicoloured . . 60 60

316 "Madonna of the Grand Duke" — **317** Demetrius Vikelas

1983. Christmas. 500th Birth Anniv of Raphael. Multicoloured.
1218 300 l. Type **316** 40 40
1219 400 l. "Madonna of the Goldfinch" (detail) . . . 45 45
1220 500 l. "Madonna of the Chair" (detail) 60 60

1984. 90th Anniv of International Olympic Committee. I.O.C. Presidents.
1221 **317** 300 l. black and green . 25 25
1222 – 400 l. purple and blue . 35 35
1223 – 550 l. lilac and green . . 50 50
DESIGNS: 400 l. Lord Killanin; 550 l. Juan Samaranch.

318 Bridge

1984. Europa. 25th Anniv of C.E.P.T.
1224 **318** 400 l. yellow, vio & blk . 80 80
1225 550 l. yellow, red & blk . 95 95

319 Flag Waver — **321** Motorcross

1984. Flag Wavers. Multicoloured.
1226 300 l. Type **319** 30 30
1227 400 l. Waver with two flags . 40 40

1984. World Motorcross Championship.
1229 **321** 450 l. multicoloured . . 55 45

322 Collins Street, 1839

1984. "Ausipex 84" International Stamp Exhibition, and Important Cities of the World (8th series). Melbourne Multicoloured.
1230 1500 l. Type **322** . . . . . . 1·60 1·60
1231 2000 l. Collins Street, 1984 . 2·75 2·75

323 Pres. Pertini and San Marino City

1984. Visit of President Sandro Pertini of Italy.
1232 **323** 1950 l. multicoloured . . 2·10 2·10

324 "Universe" — **325** Angel with Book

1984. Youth Philately. Multicoloured.
1233 50 l. Type **324** 10 10
1234 100 l. Caveman and modern man framed by television ("The Evolution of Life") . 10 10
1235 150 l. Pipe smoker driving car ("The World in which we Live") 20 15
1236 200 l. Man with fig leaf and snake with apple ("Mankind") 25 20
1237 450 l. Scientist with H-bomb ("Science") 45 45
1238 550 l. Man in barrel with books and candle ("Philosophy") . 55 55

1984. Christmas. Designs showing details of "Madonna of San Girolamo" by Correggio. Multicoloured.
1239 400 l. Type **325** 45 45
1240 450 l. Virgin and child 55 55
1241 550 l. Attendant 65 65

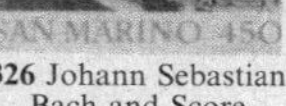

326 Johann Sebastian Bach and Score — **327** State Flags, Stadium and Swimming Pictogram

1985. Europa.
1242 **326** 450 l. black and brown . . 80 80
1243 – 600 l. black and green . . 1·25 1·25
DESIGN: 600 l. Vincenzo Bellini and score.

1985. First Small States Games. Multicoloured.
1244 50 l. Type **327** 10 10
1245 350 l. Flags, stadium and running pictogram 35 35
1246 400 l. Flags, stadium and shooting pictogram 40 40
1247 450 l. Flags, stadium and cycling pictogram 45 45
1248 600 l. Flags, stadium and handball pictogram 65 65

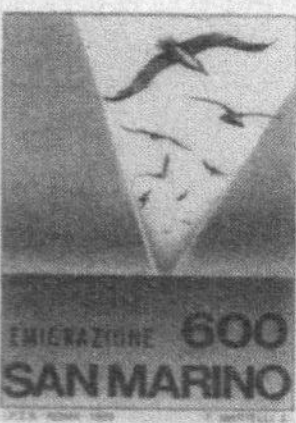

328 Sunset and Birds — **329** Face and Hand holding Dove

1985. Emigration.
1249 **328** 600 l. multicoloured . . . 60 60

1985. International Youth Year.
1250 **329** 400 l. yellow, blue and gold 40 40
1251 – 600 l. gold, blue and yellow 60 60
DESIGN: 600 l. Girl's face, dove and horse's head.

330 Camera and San Marino — **331** Sun breaking through Clouds and Sapling

1985. 18th International Federation of Photographic Art Congress.
1252 **330** 450 l. multicoloured . . 60 60

1985. 10th Anniv of Helsinki European Security and Co-operation Conference.
1253 **331** 600 l. multicoloured . . 60 60

332 Don Abbondio and Don Rodrigo's Henchmen

1985. Birth Bicentenary of Alessandro Manzoni (writer). Scenes from "I Promessi Sposi".
1254 **332** 400 l. green 35 35
1255 – 450 l. brown 40 40
1256 – 600 l. blue 55 55
DESIGNS: 450 l. Forcing curate to bless wedding; 600 l. Plague in Milan.

333 Fish caught on Hook

1985. World Angling Championships, River Arno, Florence.
1257 **333** 600 l. multicoloured . . 55 55

334 Cat (after Pompeian mosaic)

1985. International Feline Federation Congress.
1258 **334** 600 l. multicoloured . . 70 55

335 Colosseum, 85 A.D.

1985. "Italia 85" International Stamp Exhibition, and Important Cities of the World (9th series). Rome. Multicoloured.
1259 1000 l. Type **335** 90 90
1260 1500 l. Colosseum, 1985 . . 1·60 1·60

336 Flying Angel

1985. Christmas. Multicoloured.
1261 400 l. Type **336** 55 55
1262 450 l. Madonna and Child . 60 60
1263 600 l. Angel resting 75 75

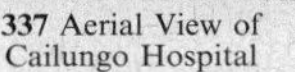
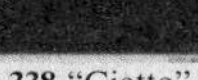

337 Aerial View of Cailungo Hospital

338 "Giotto" Space Probe

1986. 30th Anniv of Social Security Institute (450 l.) and World Health Day (650 l.). Multicoloured.

1264 450 l. Type **337** 60 60
1265 650 l. Front view of Cailungo hospital 65 65

1986. Appearance of Halley's Comet. Multicoloured.

1266 550 l. Type **338** 70 70
1267 1000 l. "Adoration of the Magi" (Giotto) . . . . 1·10 1·10

339 Player and Emblem

340 Deer

1986. World Table Tennis Championships, Rimini.

1268 **339** 450 l. blue, ultram & red 60 60

1986. Europa. Multicoloured.

1269 550 l. Type **340** . . . . 1·75 1·75
1270 650 l. Common kestrel . . . 2·00 2·00

341 Water Tower, 1870 (lithograph, Charles Shober)

1986. "Ameripex" International Stamp Exhibition, and Important Cities of the World (10th series). Chicago. Multicoloured.

1271 2000 l. Type **341** . . . . . . 2·50 2·50
1272 3000 l. Water tower, 1986 . . 3·50 3·50

342 Swallows

344 "Apollo dancing with the Muses" (detail, Giulio Romano)

1986. International Peace Year.

1273 **342** 550 l. multicoloured . . . 75 65

1986. 25th Anniv of San Marino Choral Society.

1275 **344** 450 l. multicoloured . . . 60 60

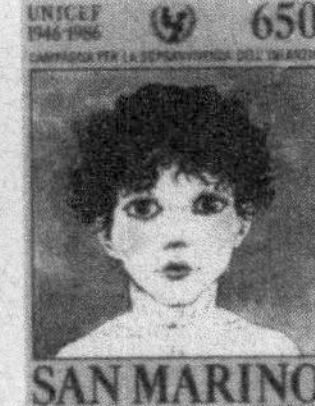

345 Boules Player

346 Boy

1986. European Boules Championships, San Marino.

1276 **345** 550 l. multicoloured . . . 70 70

1986. 40th Anniv of U.N.I.C.E.F. Child Survival Campaign.

1277 **346** 650 l. multicoloured . . . 80 80

INDEX

Countries can be quickly located by referring to the index at the end of this volume.

347 "St. John the Baptist"

1986. Christmas. Triptych by Hans Memling. Multicoloured.

1278 450 l. Type **347** 75 75
1279 550 l. "Madonna and Child" 85 85
1280 650 l. "St. John the Evangelist" 90 90

348 Motor Car and Route Map (Paris–Peking Rally, 1907)

1987. Motor Rallies. Multicoloured.

1281 500 l. Type **348** 80 80
1282 600 l. Peugeot "205" (15th San Marino Rally) 85 85
1283 700 l. Motor car and crowds (60th anniv of Mille Miglia) 95 95

349 Sketch of Church

350 Modern Sculpture (Reffi Busignani)

1987. Europa. Architecture. Our Lady of Consolation Church, Borgomaggiore (Giovanni Michelucci).

1284 **349** 600 l. black and red . . 1·25 1·25
1285 – 700 l. black and yellow . 1·50 1·50

DESIGN: 700 l. Church interior.

1987. Modern Sculptures in San Marino. Designs showing works by artists named. Multicoloured.

1286 50 l. Type **350** 10 10
1287 100 l. Bini 10 10
1288 200 l. Guguianu 20 20
1289 300 l. Berti 30 30
1290 400 l. Crocetti 40 40
1291 500 l. Berti 45 45
1292 600 l. Messina 55 55
1293 1000 l. Minguzzi 90 90
1294 2200 l. Greco . . . . 2·00 2·00
1295 10000 l. Sassu . . . . 9·00 9·00

351 "Chromatic Invention" (Corrado Cagli)

352 Baroudeur Microlight, San Marino Air Club

1987. Art Biennale.

1300 – 500 l. blue, black & red . 60 60
1301 **351** 600 l. multicoloured . . . 80 80

DESIGN: 500 l. "From My Brazilian Diary—Virgin Forest" (Emilio Vedova).

1987.

1302 **352** 600 l. multicoloured . . 80 80

353 Bust of Mahatma Gandhi in Gandhi Square, San Marino

354 Olympic Rings and Hurdler in "Stamp"

1987. "A Society based on Non-violence".

1303 **353** 500 l. multicoloured . . 75 65

1987. "Olymphilex" Olympic Stamp Exhibition and World Light Athletics Championships, Rome.

1304 **354** 600 l. multicoloured . . 70 70

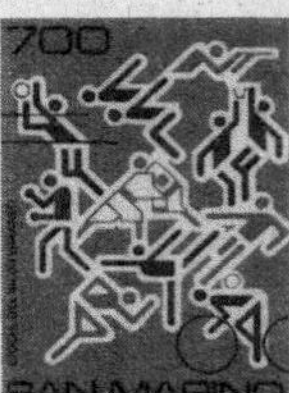

355 Sports Pictograms

357 "The Annunciation" (detail)

356 "View from Round Tower, 1836" (anon)

1987. Mediterranean Games, Syria.

1305 **355** 700 l. red, blue & black . 80 80

1987. "Hafnia 87" International Stamp Exhibition, and Important Cities of the World (11th series). Copenhagen. Multicoloured.

1306 1200 l. Type **356** . . . . . . 1·50 1·75
1307 2200 l. View from Round Tower, 1987 . . . . 2·00 2·25

1987. Christmas. 600th Birth Anniv of Fra Giovanni of Florence (Beato Angelico). Multicoloured.

1308 600 l. Type **357** 75 75
1309 600 l. Madonna and Child (detail, Triptych of Cortona) 75 75
1310 600 l. Saint (detail, "The Annunciation") 75 75

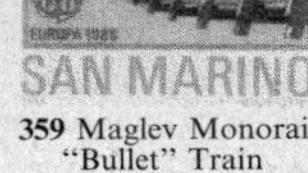

358 1923 30 c., 1944 20 l. + 10 l. and 1975 200 l. Stamps of St. Marinus

359 Maglev Monorail "Bullet" Train and Globe

1988. Thematic Collecting. Multicoloured.

1311 50 l. Type **358** 10 10
1312 150 l. Aerogramme and 1933 3 l. "Graf Zeppelin" stamp (transport) 20 20
1313 300 l. 1954 5 l. and 1981 200 l. motor cycle racing stamps and 1986 meter mark showing motor cycle (sport) 40 40
1314 350 l. 1978 200 l. human rights stamp on cover and 1982 200 l. St. Francis of Assisi stamp (art) 45 45
1315 1000 l. 1949 50 l. Garibaldi stamp, 1985 450 l. Europa stamp and 1952 1 l. Columbus stamp (famous people) . . 1·25 1·25

See also Nos. 1340/4 and 1393/7.

1988. Europa. Transport and Communications. Multicoloured.

1316 600 l. Type **359** . . . . 1·00 1·00
1317 700 l. Optical fibres and globe 1·50 1·50

360 Carlo Malagola and Palazzo della Mercanzia

361 "La Strada"

1988. 900th Anniv of Bologna University. Mult.

1318 550 l. Type **360** 60 60
1319 650 l. Pietro Ellero and Palazzo del Podesta 75 75
1320 1300 l. Giosue Carducci and Pala dei Mercanti . . . . . 1·25 1·25
1321 1700 l. Giovanni Pascoli and Atheneum . . . . 1·50 1·50

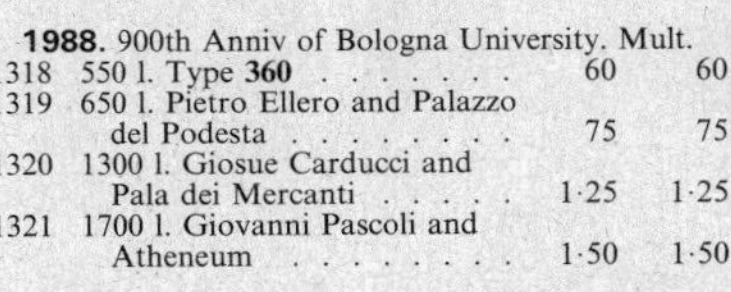

1988. Award of Celebrities of Show Business Prize to Federico Fellini (film director). Film posters. Multicoloured.

1322 300 l. Type **361** 35 35
1323 900 l. "La Dolce Vita" . . . 1·10 1·10
1324 1200 l. "Amarcord" . . . . . 1·40 1·40

362 Mt Titano from Beach

1988. 40th Riccione Stamp Fair.

1325 **362** 750 l. blue, green & mauve 80 80

363 Healthy Tree with Diseased Roots

1988. Present Day Problems. International AIDS Congress, San Marino.

1326 **363** 250 l. multicoloured . . 35 35
1327 – 350 l. red and black . . 45 45
1328 – 650 l. multicoloured . . 85 85
1329 – 1000 l. multicoloured . . 1·00 1·00

DESIGNS: 350 l. "AIDS" crumbling; 650 l. Knotted cord and emblem of virus; 1000 l. Printed information.

365 "Kurhaus, Scheveningen, 1885" (anon)

1988. "Filacept" International Stamp Exhibition, and Important Cities of the World (12th series). The Hague. Multicoloured.

1331 1600 l. Type **365** . . . . . . 1·50 1·50
1332 3000 l. Kurhaus, Scheveningen, 1988 . . . . 3·00 3·00

366 "Angel with Violin"

367 Bird in Tree (Federica Sparagna)

1988. Christmas. 550th Birth Anniv of Melozzo da Forli. Multicoloured.

1333 650 l. Type **366** 75 75
1334 650 l. "Angel of the Annunciation" (20 × 37 mm) 75 75
1335 650 l. "Angel with Mandolin" 75 75

1989. "Nature is Beautiful. Nature is Useful. Nature is ...". Multicoloured.

1336 200 l. Type **367** 25 25
1337 500 l. Birds beneath tree (Giovanni Monteduro) . . 70 70
1338 650 l. Landscape (Rosa Mannarino) 85 85

Nos. 1336/8 depict the first three winning entries in a children's drawing competition.

1989. Postal History. As T **358**. Multicoloured.

1340 100 l. "San Marino 1977" Exhibition 1000 l. stamp on cover (postal tariffs) . . . 15 15
1341 200 l. 1988 350 l. stamp on cover (cancellations) 25 25
1342 400 l. Parcel receipt (parcel post) 45 45
1343 500 l. Essay by Martin Riester, 1865 . . . . 60 60
1344 1000 l. 1862 handstamp on cover (pre-stamp period) . 1·25 1·25

369 Emblem

370 Oath of the Tennis Court

1989. Sport. Multicoloured.

1345 650 l. Type **369** (30th anniv of San Marino Olympic Committee) 85 85
1346 750 l. Emblems (admission of San Marino Football Federation to UEFA and FIFA) 95 95

1347 850 l. Tennis racquet and ball (San Marino championships) 1·00 1·00
1348 1300 l. Formula 1 racing car (San Marino Grand Prix, Imola) 1·40 1·40

1989. Bicentenary of French Revolution. Mult.
1349 700 l. Type **370** 1·00 1·00
1350 1000 l. Arrest of Louis XVI 1·50 1·50
1351 1800 l. Napoleon's army 2·25 2·25

371 "Marguerite and Armand" **372** "Angel of the Annunciation"

1989. Award of Celebrities of Show Business Prize to Rudolph Nureyev (ballet dancer). Multicoloured.
1352 1200 l. Type **371** 1·40 1·40
1353 1500 l. "Apollo Musagete" 1·75 1·75
1354 1700 l. Ken Russell's film "Valentino" 2·25 2·25

1989. Christmas. Details of the polyptych in Church of Servants of Mary. Multicoloured.
1355 650 l. Type **372** 1·00 1·00
1356 650 l. "Nativity" (50×40 mm) 1·00 1·00
1357 650 l. Mary ("Annunciation") 1·00 1·00

373 Capitol, 1850

1989. "World Stamp Expo '89" Int Stamp Exhibition, and Important Cities of the World (13th series). Washington D.C. Multicoloured.
1358 2000 l. Type **373** 2·25 2·25
1359 2500 l. Capitol, 1989 3·00 3·00

374 Old Post Office **375** "Martyrdom of St. Agatha" (Tiepolo) and Cardinal Alberoni leaving City

1990. Europa. Post Office Buildings. Multicoloured.
1360 700 l. Type **374** 1·00 1·00
1361 800 l. Dogana Post Office 1·25 1·25

1990. 250th Anniv of End of Cardinal Alberoni's Occupation of San Marino.
1362 **375** 3500 l. multicoloured 4·00 4·00

376 Map pinpointing San Marino **377** Statue, Government Palace

1990. European Tourism Year. Multicoloured.
1366 50 l. Type **377** 10 10
1367 50 l. Liberty Statue and English inscription 10 10
1368 50 l. Government Palace and German inscription 10 10
1369 50 l. Man with flag and French inscription 10 10
1363 600 l. Type **376** 80 80
1364 600 l. Aerial view showing villages 80 80
1365 600 l. First Tower 80 80
See also Nos. 1424/7.

379 Olivier in "Hamlet" **380** Mt Titano and State Flags

1990. Award of Celebrities of Show Business Prize to Laurence Olivier (actor). Multicoloured.
1374 600 l. Type **379** 90 90
1375 700 l. "Richard III" 1·10 1·10
1376 1500 l. "The Runner" 2·50 2·50
Nos. 1374/6 are wrongly inscribed "Lawrence".

1990. Visit of President Francesco Cossiga of Italy.
1377 **380** 600 l. multicoloured 75 75

381 Pinocchio

1990. Death Centenary of Carlo Collodi (writer). Characters from "Pinocchio". Multicoloured.
1378 250 l. Type **381** 30 30
1379 400 l. Geppetto 50 50
1380 450 l. Blue fairy 55 55
1381 600 l. Cat and wolf 90 90

382 Pre-Columbian Civilizations

1990. 500th Anniv (1992) of Discovery of America by Columbus (1st issue). Multicoloured.
1382 1500 l. Type **382** 2·25 2·25
1383 2000 l. Produce of the New World 2·50 2·50
See also Nos. 1401/2 and 1417/18.

383 Mary and Two Kings **384** Swallowtail on "Ephedra major"

1990. Christmas. Details of Cuciniello Crib. Multicoloured.
1384 750 l. Type **383** 1·00 1·00
1385 750 l. Baby Jesus in manger and third King 1·00 1·00
Nos. 1384/5 were issued together, se-tenant, forming a composite design.

1990. Flora and Fauna. Multicoloured.
1386 200 l. Type **384** 25 25
1387 300 l. "Apoderus coryli" (weevil) and hazelnut 35 35
1388 500 l. Garden dormouse and acorns of holm oak 60 60
1389 1000 l. Green lizard and "Ophrys bertolonii" (orchid) 1·50 1·50
1390 2000 l. Firecrest on black pine 3·25 3·25

385 Launch of "Ariane-4"

1991. Europa. Europe in Space. Multicoloured.
1391 750 l. Type **385** 3·00 3·00
1392 800 l. "E.R.S.-1." survey satellite 3·00 3·00

1991. World of Stamps. As T **358**. Multicoloured
1393 100 l. Stamp shop 15 15
1394 150 l. Stamp club 20 20
1395 200 l. Exhibition 25 25
1396 450 l. Stamp album and catalogues 50 50
1397 1500 l. Philatelic publications (25th anniv of Italian Philatelic Press Union) 1·75 1·75

386 Torch Bearer leaving Athens **387** Cat

1991. Olympic Games, Barcelona (1992). Mult.
1398 400 l. Type **386** 50 50
1399 600 l. Torch bearer passing through San Marino 70 70
1400 2000 l. Torch bearer arriving in Barcelona 2·50 2·50

1991. 500th Anniv (1992) of Discovery of America by Columbus (2nd issue). As T **382**. Multicoloured.
1401 750 l. Navigational dividers, quadrant, hour-glass, compass and route map 1·25 1·25
1402 3000 l. "Santa Maria", "Nina" and "Pinta" 4·50 4·50

1991. Pets. Multicoloured.
1403 500 l. Type **387** 70 70
1404 550 l. Hamster on wheel 75 75
1405 750 l. Great Dane and Pomeranian 1·10 1·10
1406 1000 l. Aquarium fishes 1·40 1·40
1407 1200 l. Canaries in cage 1·75 1·75

388 Players, Balls and Baskets **391** Keep

389 James Clerk-Maxwell (physicist)

1991. Centenary of Basketball. Multicoloured.
1408 650 l. Type **388** 1·25 1·25
1409 750 l. James Naismith (inventor) and players 1·50 1·50

1991. 100 Years of Radio (1st issue).
1410 **389** 750 l. multicoloured 1·00 1·00
Clerk-Maxwell formulated the theory of electromagnetic radiation.
See also Nos. 1431, 1452 and 1479.

1991. Christmas. La Rocca Fortress. Multicoloured.
1412 600 l. Type **391** (postage) 75 75
1413 750 l. Inland view of fortress 90 90
1414 1200 l. Fortress on crag (air) 1·60 1·60

392 "Bianca and Falliero" (Pesaro production)

1992. Birth Bicentenary of Gioachino Rossini (composer). Scenes from productions of his operas. Multicoloured.
1415 750 l. Type **392** 80 80
1416 1200 l. "The Barber of Seville" (La Scala Theatre, Milan) 1·25 1·25

1992. 500th Anniv of Discovery of America by Columbus (3rd issue). As T **382**. Multicoloured.
1417 1500 l. Amerindians watching fleet 1·50 1·50
1418 2000 l. Route map of the four voyages 2·00 2·00

393 Roses **394** Courting Couple

1992. Plants. Multicoloured.
1419 50 l. Type **393** 10 10
1420 200 l. Ficus as house plant 20 20
1421 300 l. Orchid in conservatory 30 30
1422 450 l. Cacti in pots 45 45
1423 5000 l. Pelargoniums in trough 5·00 5·00

1992. Tourism. Multicoloured. (a) As T **377**.
1424 50 l. Man with crossbow and Italian inscription 10 10
1425 50 l. Tennis player and English inscription 10 10
1426 50 l. Motor cycle rider and French inscription 10 10
1427 50 l. Ferrari racing car and German inscription 10 10

(b) As T **394**.
1428 600 l. Type **394** 65 65
1429 600 l. Man in restaurant 65 65
1430 600 l. Woman reading on veranda 65 65

1992. 100 Years of Radio (2nd issue). As T **389**. Multicoloured.
1431 750 l. Heinrich Rudolf Hertz (physicist) 80 80
Hertz proved Clerk-Maxwell's theory.

395 Egg-shaped Globe and Caravel **397** Inedible Mushrooms

1992. Europa. 500th Anniv of Discovery of America. Multicoloured.
1432 750 l. Type **395** 80 80
1433 850 l. Caravel and island inside broken egg 90 90

1992. 3rd Titano Mycological Exhibition, Borgo Maggiore. Multicoloured.
1435 250 l. Type **397** 25 25
1436 250 l. Inedible mushrooms (different) 25 25
1437 350 l. Edible mushrooms in bowl 35 35
1438 350 l. Edible mushrooms on cloth 35 35
Stamps of the same value were issued together, se-tenant, each pair forming a composite design.

398 View and Arms of San Marino **399** "La Sacra Conversazione"

1992. Admission of San Marino to United Nations Organization. Multicoloured.
1439 1000 l. Type **398** 1·00 1·00
1440 1000 l. View of San Marino (different) and United Nations emblem 1·00 1·00

1992. Christmas. 500th Death Anniv of Piero della Francesca (artist). Multicoloured.
1441 750 l. Type **399** 90 90
1442 750 l. Close-up of Madonna 90 90
1443 750 l. Close-up of shell decoration 90 90

400 Tennis Player **401** Stars

1993. Sporting Events. Multicoloured.
1444 300 l. Type **400** (Italian and San Marino Youth Games) 30 30
1445 400 l. Cross-country skiers (European Youth Olympic Days (winter), Aosta, Italy) 40 40
1446 550 l. Runners (European Youth Olympic Days (summer), Eindhoven, Netherlands) 50 50
1447 600 l. Fisherman (Freshwater Angling Clubs World Championship, Ostellato, Italy) 60 60
1448 700 l. Runners breasting tape (Small States Games, Malta) 70 70
1449 1300 l. Sprinters (Mediterranean Games, Rousillon, France) 1·25 1·25

1993. Europa. Contemporary Art.
1450 **401** 750 l. multicoloured . . . 65 65
1451 – 850 l. blue and orange . 70 70
DESIGN: 850 l. Silhouette.

1993. 100 Years of Radio (3rd issue). As T **389**. Multicoloured.
1452 750 l. Edouard Branly (physicist) and his "radioconductor" 65 65
Branly developed a method of revealing Hertzian waves.

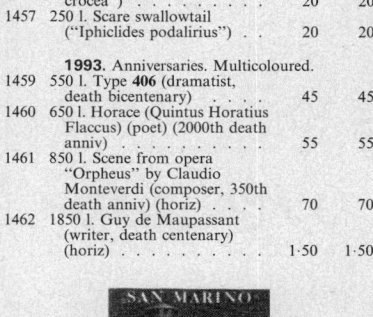

404 Mourning Cloak ("Nymphalis antiopa")

406 Carlo Goldoni

1993. Butterflies. Multicoloured.
1454 250 l. Type **404** 20 20
1455 250 l. Glanville's fritillary ("Melitaea cinxia") 20 20
1456 250 l. Clouded yellow ("Colias crocea") 20 20
1457 250 l. Scare swallowtail ("Iphiclides podalirius") . . 20 20

1993. Anniversaries. Multicoloured.
1459 550 l. Type **406** (dramatist, death bicentenary) 45 45
1460 650 l. Horace (Quintus Horatius Flaccus) (poet) (2000th death anniv) 55 55
1461 850 l. Scene from opera "Orpheus" by Claudio Monteverdi (composer, 350th death anniv) (horiz) 70 70
1462 1850 l. Guy de Maupassant (writer, death centenary) (horiz) . . . . 1·50 1·50

407 San Marino

1993. Christmas. Multicoloured.
1463 600 l. Type **407** 50 50
1464 750 l. "Adoration of the Child" (Gerrit van Honthorst) (horiz) 65 65
1465 859 l. "Adoration of the Shepherds" (Van Honthorst) 70 70

408 Long-haired Dachshund

1994. 10th International Dog Show. Multicoloured.
1466 350 l. Type **408** 30 30
1467 400 l. Afghan hound 35 35
1468 450 l. Belgian tervuren shepherd dog 40 40
1469 500 l. Boston terrier 40 40
1470 550 l. Mastiff 45 45
1471 600 l. Malamute 50 50

410 Gate

411 Olympic Flags

1994. Gardens. Multicoloured.
1473 100 l. Type **410** 10 10
1474 200 l. Pergola 15 15
1475 300 l. Well 25 25
1476 450 l. Gazebo 40 40
1477 1850 l. Pond . . . . 1·40 1·40

1994. Centenary of International Olympic Committee.
1478 **411** 600 l. multicoloured . . . 40 40

1994. 100 Years of Radio (4th issue). As T **389**. Multicoloured.
1479 750 l. Aleksandr Stepanovich Popov 55 55
Popov was the first to use a suspended wire as an aerial.

412 Players

413 Spacecraft's Route

1994. World Cup Football Championship, U.S.A. Multicoloured.
1480 600 l. Type **412** 40 40
1481 600 l. Player kicking ball . . 40 40
1482 600 l. Player heading ball . . 40 40
1483 600 l. Players tackling . . . 40 40
1484 600 l. Goalkeeper saving goal 40 40

1994. Europa. Discoveries. Exploration of Sun by "Ulysses" Spacecraft. Multicoloured.
1485 750 l. Type **413** 55 55
1486 850 l. Spacecraft approaching Sun 60 60

414 Government Palace

416 Angels playing Musical Instruments

415 St. Mark's Basilica

1994. Centenary of Government Palace. Multicoloured.
1487 150 l. Type **414** 10 10
1488 600 l. Tower and San Marino from ramparts 40 40
1489 650 l. Clock-tower 45 45
1490 1000 l. Government chamber (horiz) 70 70

1994. 900th Anniv of Dedication of St. Mark's Basilica, Venice.
1491 **415** 750 l. multicoloured . . 55 55

1994. Christmas. 500th Death Anniv of Giovanni Santi (painter). Details of "The Enthroned Madonna and Child with Saints". Multicoloured.
1493 600 l. Type **416** 40 40
1494 750 l. Madonna and child . . 55 55
1495 850 l. Angel playing harp . . 60 60

417/420 "Italy on the Road in a Sea of Flowering Greenery"

1994. Centenary of Italian Touring Club.
1496 **417** 1000 l. multicoloured . . 70 70
1497 **418** 1000 l. multicoloured . . 70 70
1498 **419** 1000 l. multicoloured . . 70 70
1499 **420** 1000 l. multicoloured . . 70 70
Nos. 1496/9 were issued together, se-tenant, forming the composite design illustrated.

EXPRESS LETTER STAMPS

E **22** Mt Titano and "Liberty"

1907.
E53 E **22** 25 c. red . . . . 5·50 3·50

1923. Optd **EXPRESSO.**
E92 **19** 60 c. violet 30 30

1923. Surch **Cent. 60.**
E93 E **22** 60 c. on 25 c. red 30 30

E **34**

1923. Red Cross.
E101 E **34** 60 c. + 5 c. red 70 80

1926. No. E92 surch **Lire 1,25.**
E134 **19** 1 l. 25 on 60 c. violet . . 55 55

1927. No. E93 surch **L. 1,25** and bars over old surch.
E138 E **22** 1 l. 25 on 60 c. on 25 c. red 45 45

E **50** Statue of Liberty and View of San Marino

1929. As Type E **50**, without "UNION POSTALE UNIVERSELLE" and inscr "ESPRESSO".
E164 E **50** 1 l. 25 green 15 15

1929. Optd **UNION POSTALLE UNIVERSELLE** as in Type E **50.**
E165 E **50** 2 l. 50 blue 55 55

E **78**

1943.
E305 E **78** 1 l. 25 green 10 10
E306 2 l. 50 orange 10 10

E **79** Mt Titano

1945.
E307 E **79** 2 l. 50 green 10 10
E308 5 l. orange 10 10
E309 5 l. red 65 65
E310 10 l. blue . . . . 1·90 1·40
E419 60 l. red . . . . 7·00 4·50

E **87** Pegasus and Mt Titano

1946.
E337 E **87** 30 l. blue . . . . 6·00 4·00
E420 80 l. blue . . . . 7·00 5·00

1947. Surch.
E339 E **79** 15 l. on 5 l. red . . . 30 25
E340 15 l. on 10 l. blue . . 30 25
E374 E **87** 35 l. on 30 l. blue . . 45·00 22·00
E341 60 l. on 30 l. blue . . 4·25 4·25
E545 E **79** 75 l. on 60 l. red . . . 2·00 1·75
E375 E **87** 80 l. on 30 l. blue . . 27·00 15·00
E546 100 l. on 80 l. blue . . 2·00 1·75
E783 E **180** 120 l. on 75 l. black and yellow 20 15
E784 135 l. on 100 l. black and orange 20 15

E **180** Crossbow and Three "Castles"

1966.
E800 E **180** 75 l. black and yellow 10 10
E801 80 l. black and purple 10 10
E802 100 l. black & orange 10 10
No. E800 has crossbow in white without "shadows".

PARCEL POST STAMPS

Unused and used prices are for complete stamps.

P **46**

1928.
P145 P **46** 5 c. purple and blue . . 10 10
P146 10 c. blue 10 10
P147 20 c. black and blue . . 10 10
P148 25 c. red and blue . . . 10 10
P149 30 c. blue 10 10
P150 30 c. orange and blue . 10 10
P151 60 c. red and blue . . . 10 10
P152 1 l. violet and red . . . 15 15
P153 2 l. green and red . . . 20 20
P154 3 l. bistre and red . . . 25 25
P155 4 l. grey and red . . . 30 30
P156 10 l. mauve and red . . 1·25 1·25
P157 12 l. lake and red . . . 3·50 3·50
P158 15 l. olive and red . . . 6·00 6·00
P159 20 l. purple and red . . 7·50 7·50

1945.
P309 P **46** 5 c. purple and red . . 10 10
P310 10 c. brown and black . 10 10
P311 20 c. red and green . . 10 10
P312 25 c. yellow and black . 10 10
P313 30 c. mauve and red . . 10 10
P314 50 c. violet and black . 10 10
P315 60 c. red and black . . 10 10
P316 1 l. brown and blue . . 10 10
P317 2 l. brown and blue . . 10 10
P318 3 l. grey and brown . . 10 10
P319 4 l. green and brown . . 10 10
P320 10 l. grey and violet . . 10 10
P770 10 l. green and red . . 10 10
P321 12 l. green and blue . . 2·25 1·25
P322 15 l. green and violet . 2·00 1·25
P323 20 l. violet and brown . 1·60 1·25
P324 25 l. red and blue . . . 35·00 20·00
P771 50 l. yellow and red . . 10 10
P455 300 l. violet and red . . £150 £100
P773 300 l. violet and brown 40 40
P526 500 l. brown and red . 2·75 2·75
P775 1000 l. green and brown 1·00 1·00

1948. Nos. P324 and P771 surch in figures and wavy lines on each half of design.
P524 P **46** 100 l. on 50 l. 70 60
P375 200 l. on 25 l. . . . . £160 70·00

POSTAGE DUE STAMPS

D **18**

D **82**

1897.
D38 D **18** 5 c. brown and green . 10 10
D39 10 c. brown and green . 10 10
D40 30 c. brown and green . 40 35
D41 50 c. brown and green . 1·00 70
D42 60 c. brown and green . 2·50 2·00
D43 1 l. brown and red . . 1·50 1·10
D44 3 l. brown and red . . 6·50 7·50
D45 5 l. brown and red . . 26·00 15·00
D46 10 l. brown and red . . 8·50 15·00

1924.
D102 D **18** 5 c. brown and red . . 10 10
D103 10 c. brown and red . . 10 10
D104 30 c. brown and red . . 15 15
D105 50 c. brown and red . . 30 30
D106 60 c. brown and red . . 1·75 1·75
D107 1 l. brown and green . 2·00 2·00
D108 3 l. brown and green . 8·00 8·00
D109 5 l. brown and green . 8·00 8·00
D110 10 l. brown and green £110 £120

1925.
D111 D **18** 5 c. brown and blue . 10 10
D113 10 c. brown and blue . 10 10
D114 15 c. brown and blue . 10 10
D115 20 c. brown and blue . 20 20
D116 25 c. brown and blue . 35 35
D117 30 c. brown and blue . 15 15
D118 40 c. brown and blue . 1·60 1·60
D119 50 c. brown and blue . 25 25
D120 60 c. brown and blue . 55 55
D121 1 l. brown and orange 1·40 45
D122 2 l. brown and orange 80 90
D123 3 l. brown and orange 24·00 15·00
D124 5 l. brown and orange 8·00 2·25
D125 10 l. brown & orange 12·00 3·75
D126 15 l. brown & orange 60 60
D127 25 l. brown & orange 18·00 12·00
D128 30 l. brown & orange 3·75 5·50
D129 50 l. brown & orange 4·75 6·00

1931. As Type **D 18** but with centre obliterated in black and new value superimposed in silver.

D164	D 18	15 c. on 5 c. blue	10	10
D165		15 c. on 10 c. blue	10	10
D166		15 c. on 30 c. blue	10	10
D167		20 c. on 5 c. blue	10	10
D168		20 c. on 10 c. blue	10	10
D169		20 c. on 30 c. blue	10	10
D170		25 c. on 5 c. blue	55	25
D171		25 c. on 10 c. blue	55	25
D172		25 c. on 30 c. blue	4·00	2·50
D173		40 c. on 10 c. blue	30	10
D174		40 c. on 10 c. blue	30	10
D175		40 c. on 30 c. blue	30	10
D176		2 l. on 5 c. blue	25·00	16·00
D177		2 l. on 10 c. blue	42·00	26·00
D178		2 l. on 30 c. blue	32·00	20·00

1936. Surch in figures and words and bars. D233/8 and D242 are brown and blue; the rest brown and orange.

D233	D 18	10 c. on 5 c.	25	25
D234		25 c. on 30 c.	5·50	5·00
D236		50 c. on 5 c.	1·60	70
D237		1 l. on 30 c.	17·00	3·25
D238		1 l. on 40 c.	5·50	3·25
D239		1 l. on 3 l.	15·00	1·00
D240		1 l. on 25 l.	40·00	6·50
D241		2 l. on 15 l.	17·00	9·00
D242		3 l. on 20 c.	20·00	14·00
D243		25 l. on 50 l.	1·25	1·75

1945.

D309	D 82	5 c. green	10	10
D310		10 c. brown	10	10
D311		15 c. red	10	10
D312		20 c. blue	10	10
D313		25 c. violet	10	10
D314		30 c. mauve	10	10
D315		40 c. yellow	10	10
D316		30 c. slate	10	10
D317		60 c. brown	10	10
D318		1 l. orange	10	10
D319		2 l. red	15	15
D320		5 l. violet	20	20
D321		10 l. blue	25	25
D322		20 l. gren	8·50	5·00
D323		25 l. brown	8·50	5·00

SANTANDER Pt. 20

One of the states of the Granadine Confederation.

A department of Colombia from 1886, now uses Colombian stamps.

100 centavos = 1 peso

1 2

1884. Imperf.

1	1	1 c. blue	15	15
2		5 c. red	30	25
3		10 c. violet	50	50

1886. Imperf.

4	2	1 c. blue	40	40
5		5 c. red	15	15
6		10 c. lilac	20	20

1887. As T **1** but inscr " REPUBLICA DE COLOMBIA". Imperf.

7		1 c. blue	15	15
8		5 c. red	45	45
9		10 c. violet	1·50	1·50

3 4

5 6 7

1890. Perf.

10	3	1 c. blue	15	15
11	4	5 c. red	60	60
12	5	10 c. violet	25	25

1895.

14	6	5 c. red on buff	35	30

1895.

15	7	5 c. brown	60	60
16		5 c. green	60	60

8 9 10

1899.

17	8	1 c. black on green	20	20
18	9	5 c. black on red	20	20
19	10	10 c. blue	35	35

F 11

1903. Fiscal stamp as Type **F 11** optd **Provisional Correos de Santander**. Imperf.

21	F 11	50 c. red	20	20

SARDINIA Pt. 8

A former Italian kingdom, including the island of Sardinia, a large part of the mainland and parts of what is now S. E. France. The Kingdom of Italy was formed by the adhesion of other Italian states to Sardinia, whose king became the first ruler of united Italy.

100 centesimi = 1 lira

1 Victor Emmanuel II 2

1851. Imperf.

1	1	5 c. black	£2750	£1600
3		20 c. blue	£3000	80·00
7		40 c. red	£3000	£3000

1853. Embossed on coloured paper. Imperf.

9	1	5 c. on green	£5000	£900
10		20 c. on blue	£5000	80·00
11		40 c. on red	£3250	£850

1854. Embossed on white paper. Imperf.

13	1	5 c. green	£24000	£425
15		20 c. blue	£7500	70·00
18		40 c. red	£65000	£2250

1855. Head embossed. Imperf.

28	2	5 c. green	3·00	9·50
40		10 c. bistre	3·00	5·00
39		10 c. brown	28·00	11·00
35		10 c. grey	70·00	55·00
48		20 c. blue	42·00	5·00
55		40 c. red	8·00	16·00
60		80 c. yellow	11·00	£130
61		3 l. bronze	£250	£2500

For Type **2** perf, see Italy Nos. 1/4.

NEWSPAPER STAMPS

N 3

1861. Numerals embossed. Imperf.

N62	N 3	1 c. black	75	2·25
N63		2 c. black	48·00	48·00

For 2 c. stamps of similar types in yellow see Italy No. N5.

SASENO Pt. 3

An island off the W. coast of Albania, temporarily occupied by Italy.

100 centesimi = 1 lira

1923. Stamps of Italy optd **SASENO**.

1	38	10 c. red	1·00	3·75
2		15 c. grey	1·00	3·75
3	41	20 c. orange	1·00	3·75
4	39	25 c. blue	1·00	3·75
5		30 c. brown	1·00	3·75
6		50 c. mauve	1·00	3·75
7		60 c. red	2·00	4·25
8	34	1 l. brown and green	2·00	4·25

SAUDI ARABIA Pt. 19

Formerly under Turkish rule, the Hejaz became an independent kingdom in 1916, but was conquered by the Sultan of Nejd in 1926 who became King of Hejaz and Nejd when combined issues of stamps were used. In 1932 the name of the state was changed to the Saudi Arabian Kingdom.

1916. 40 paras = 1 piastre
1929. 110 guerche = 10 riyal = 1 gold sovereign
1952. 440 guerche = 40 riyal = 1 gold sovereign
1960. 100 halalah = 20 guerche = 1 riyal.
1 piastre = 1 guerche
1976. 100 halalah = 1 riyal

A. HEJAZ

5 From Stucco Work over Entrance to Cairo Railway Station

1916. As T **5** (various Arabic designs). Perf or roul.

11	1 pa. purple	2·00	50
12	$\frac{1}{8}$ pi. yellow	2·75	80
13	$\frac{1}{4}$ pi. green	2·75	80
14	$\frac{1}{2}$ pi. red	3·00	1·10
15	1 pi. blue	3·00	1·10
16	2 pi. red	15·00	4·00

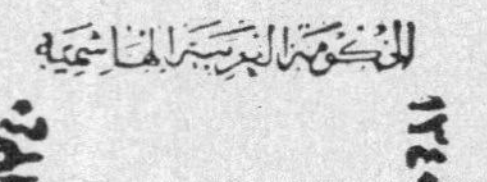

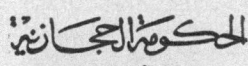

(**7** "1340 Hashemite Kingdom 1340")

1921. Optd with T **7**.

21	1 pa. purple	20·00	10·00
22	$\frac{1}{8}$ pi. yellow	30·00	15·00
23	$\frac{1}{4}$ pi. green	8·00	5·00
24	$\frac{1}{2}$ pi. red	12·00	6·00
26	1 pi. blue	10·00	5·00
28	2 pi. red	15·00	8·00

قرش واحد نصف قرش

(**8**) ($\frac{1}{2}$ pi.) (**9**) (1 pi.)

1921. No. 21 surch with T **8** or **9**.

29	$\frac{1}{2}$ pi. on 1 pa. purple	£180	60·00
30	1 pi. on 1 pa. purple	£180	60·00

(**10** "1340 Hashemite Kingdom 1340")

1922. Nos. 11 to 16 optd with T **10**.

31	1 pa. purple	3·00	1·00
32	$\frac{1}{8}$ pi. yellow	12·00	4·00
33	$\frac{1}{4}$ pi. green	2·50	1·00
34	$\frac{1}{2}$ pi. red	2·50	75
35	1 pi. blue	4·00	75
36	2 pi. red	7·50	4·00

1922. No. 31 surch with T **8** or **9**.

37	$\frac{1}{2}$ pi. on 1 pa. purple	15·00	5·00
38	1 pi. on 1 pa. purple	4·00	25

11 Meccan Sherifian Arms

1922.

39	11	$\frac{1}{8}$ pi. brown	1·00	30
57		$\frac{1}{4}$ pi. green	5·00	4·00
41		$\frac{1}{2}$ pi. red	50	20
42		1 pi. blue	1·00	20
43		$1\frac{1}{2}$ pi. violet	1·00	30
44		2 pi. orange	1·50	40
45		3 pi. brown	2·00	50
46		5 pi. olive	4·00	1·00
58		10 pi. brown and mauve	6·00	5·00

(**12**) ($\frac{1}{4}$ pi.) (**13**) (10 pi.)

1923. Surch with T **12** ($\frac{1}{4}$ pi.) or T **13** (10 pi).

47	11	$\frac{1}{4}$ pi. on $\frac{1}{8}$ pi. brown	20·00	10·00
49		10 pi. on 5 pi. olive	25·00	20·00

(**14**)

1924. Proclamation of King Hussein as Caliph. Optd with T **14**.

50	11	$\frac{1}{8}$ pi. brown	3·00	2·00
51		$\frac{1}{2}$ pi. red	2·00	1·00
52		1 pi. blue	3·00	2·00
53		$1\frac{1}{2}$ pi. violet	3·00	2·00
54		2 pi. orange	3·00	2·00
55		3 pi. brown	4·00	3·00
56		5 pi. olive	4·00	3·00

(**15** "Hejaz Government. 4th October, 1924")

1924. Optd with T **15**.

66	1 pa. purple (No. 11)	15·00	6·00
77	1 pa. purple (No. 31)	£100	50·00
59	$\frac{1}{8}$ pi. yellow (No. 12)	20·00	6·00
78	$\frac{1}{8}$ pi. yellow (No. 32)		£1500
68	$\frac{1}{4}$ pi. green (No. 13)	20·00	9·00
79	$\frac{1}{4}$ pi. green (No. 33)	50·00	30·00
71	$\frac{1}{2}$ pi. red (No. 14)	45·00	20·00
76	$\frac{1}{2}$ pi. red (No. 24)		£1650
80	$\frac{1}{2}$ pi. red (No. 34)	60·00	40·00
86	$\frac{1}{2}$ pi. red No. 41)		£950
84	$\frac{1}{2}$ pi. on 1 pa. purple (No. 37)	£120	50·00
73	1 pi. blue (No. 15)	30·00	12·00
81	1 pi. blue (No. 35)	£100	50·00
85	1 pi. on 1 pa. purple (No. 38)	£100	45·00
74	2 pi. red (No. 16)	40·00	15·00
83	2 pi. red (No. 36)	£100	50·00
87	10 pi. purple and mauve (No. 58)	£700	

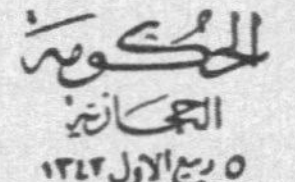

(**16** "Hejaz Government, 4th October, 1924")

1924. Nos. 13 and 39/58 optd with T **16**.

105		$\frac{1}{8}$ pi. brown	15·00	1·75
90	–	$\frac{1}{4}$ pi. green (No. 13)	45·00	12·00
96	11	$\frac{1}{4}$ pi. green	18·00	5·50
116		$\frac{1}{2}$ pi. red	4·00	2·00
98		1 pi. blue	12·00	3·25
99		$1\frac{1}{2}$ pi. violet	5·00	1·75
119		2 pi. orange	4·00	2·00
120		3 pi. brown	5·00	2·10
103		5 pi. olive	5·00	1·75
104		10 pi. brown and mauve	15·00	6·00

The overprint on No. 90 is smaller.

1925. Nos. 50/6 optd. with T **16**.

136 **11** $\frac{1}{8}$ pi. brown 50·00 6·00
137 $\frac{1}{2}$ pi. red 70·00 6·50
138 1 pi. blue 75·00 6·00
139 $1\frac{1}{2}$ pi. violet 50·00 6·50
140 2 pi. orange 75·00 10·00
141 3 pi. brown 70·00 17·00
142 5 pi. olive 70·00 6·50

١٠ قرش

(17) **(18)**

1925. Stamps of 1922 surch as Type **17**.

148 **11** $\frac{1}{4}$ pi. on $\frac{1}{8}$ pi. brown 60·00
149 $\frac{1}{4}$ pi. on $\frac{1}{2}$ pi. red 60·00
150 1 pi. on 2 pi. orange 80·00
151 1 pi. on 3 pi. brown 80·00
153 10 pi. on 5 pi. olive £100

1925. Nos. 148/53 further surch with values in larger type as Type **18**.

154 **11** $\frac{1}{4}$ pi. on $\frac{1}{4}$ pi. on $\frac{1}{8}$ pi. brown 20·00 6·00
155 $\frac{1}{4}$ pi. on $\frac{1}{4}$ pi. on $\frac{1}{2}$ pi. red 20·00 6·00
157 1 pi. on 1 pi. on 2 pi. orange 20·00 9·00
158 1 pi. on 1 pi. on 3 pi. brown 20·00 9·00
160 10 pi. on 10 pi. on 5 pi. olive 10·00 6·00

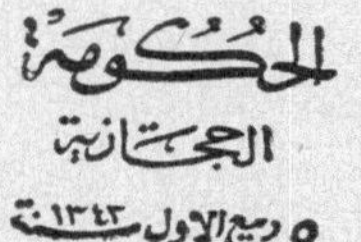

(19)

1925. Stamps of 1922 surch as T **19**.

172 **11** $\frac{1}{8}$ pi. on $\frac{1}{2}$ pi. red 5·00 3·00
173 $\frac{1}{4}$ pi. on $\frac{1}{4}$ pi. red 5·00 3·00
173b 1 pi. on $\frac{1}{4}$ pi. red 5·00 3·00
173c 1 pi. on $1\frac{1}{2}$ pi. violet 5·00 3·00
174 1 pi. on 2 pi. orange 5·00 3·00
175 1 pi. on 3 pi. brown 5·00 3·00
176 10 pi. on 5 pi. olive 5·00 3·00

20

(24)

1925. As T **20** (various Arabic designs) optd with T **24**.

177 $\frac{1}{8}$ pi. brown 1·00 1·00
178 $\frac{1}{4}$ pi. blue 1·00 1·00
179 $\frac{1}{2}$ pi. red 1·50 1·50
180 1 pi. green 1·50 1·50
181 $1\frac{1}{2}$ pi. orange 1·50 1·50
182 2 pi. blue 1·50 1·50
183 3 pi. olive 2·00 2·00
184 5 pi. brown 2·00 2·00
185 10 pi. green and red 3·00 3·00

B. NEJD

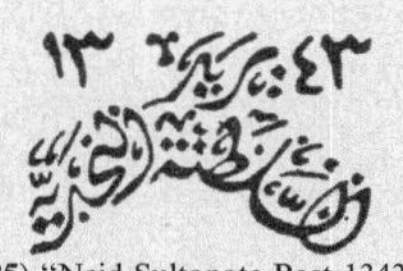

(**25**) "Nejd Sultanate Post 1343"

1925. Various stamps optd with T **25**. (a) Stamps of Turkey.

190 **30** 5 pa. orange (No. 583) 15·00 10·00
191 10 pa. green (No. 503) 15·00 11·00

26 **27**

(b) Hejaz Fiscal stamps.
(i) Notarial stamps.

192 **26** 1 pi. violet 10·00 10·00
193 1 pi. blue 10·00 10·00

(ii) Bill stamp.

194 **27** 1 pi. violet 10·00 10·00

28

(iii) Railway Tax stamps.

195 **28** 1 pi. blue 12·00 12·00
196 2 pi. orange 16·00 16·00
197 3 pi. lilac 18·00 18·00

(c) Hejaz Postage stamps (1922 issues).

198a **11** $\frac{1}{8}$ pi. brown 12·00 10·00
198c $\frac{1}{8}$ pi. red 15·00 15·00
199a $\frac{1}{2}$ pi. red 7·50 7·50
200 $1\frac{1}{2}$ pi. lilac 15·00 15·00
201 2 pi. orange 25·00 25·00
202 3 pi. red 15·00 15·00

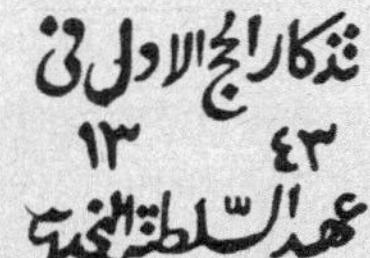

(**29**) "1343 Commemoration of First Pilgrimage under Sultan of Nejd"

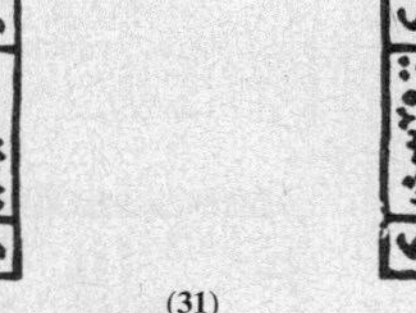

(30) "Wednesday" **(31)**

1925. Pilgrimage Commemoration. Various stamps optd with T **29** and **30** and surch as T **31**. (a) 1914 pictorial stamps of Turkey.

210 1 pi. on 10 pa. green (503) 75·00 30·00
211 5 pi. on 1 pi. blue (518) 75·00 30·00

(b) 1916 stamps of Hejaz.

212 2 pi. on 1 pa. purple £125 50·00
213 4 pi. on pi. yellow £300 £125

(c) Railway Tax stamp.

214 **28** 3 pi. lilac £175 60·00

(**32**) "Nejd Sultanate Post"

1925. Various stamps optd with **T 32**. (a) Stamps of Turkey.

215 **30** 5 pa. orange 10·00 7·50
216 – 10 pa. green (No. 503) 12·00 10·00

(b) Hejaz Fiscal stamps.
(i) Notarial stamp.

217 **26** 2 pi. blue 8·00 7·50

(ii) Railway Tax Stamps.

218b **28** 1 pi. blue 10·00 6·00
219 2 pi. orange 15·00 6·00
220 3 pi. lilac 20·00 10·00
221 5 pi. green 20·00 7·00

(c) Hejaz Postage stamps.
(i) Nos. 35/6.

222 1 pi. blue 60·00 60·00
223 2 pi. red 60·00 60·00

(ii) Stamps of 1922.

224 **11** $\frac{1}{8}$ pi. brown £2500
225 $\frac{1}{2}$ pi. red 5·00 2·00
226 1 pi. violet 12·00 10·00
227 $1\frac{1}{2}$ pi. red 12·00 10·00
228 2 pi. orange 35·00 20·00
229 2 pi. purple 25·00 20·00
230 3 pi. red 15·00 12·00
231 5 pi. red 20·00 18·00

قرشان قرش ونصف قرش واحد

(**33**) (1 pi.) (**34**) ($1\frac{1}{2}$ pi.) (**35**) (2 pi.)

1925. Stamps optd with T **32** further surch with T **33/5**.

239 **11** 1 pi. on $\frac{1}{2}$ pi. red (225) 4·00 1·50
241 $1\frac{1}{2}$ pi. on $\frac{1}{2}$ pi. red 5·00 1·50
243 2 pi. on 3 pi. red (230) 10·00 2·00

(**36**) "Postage of Nejd, 1344, Commemoration of Medina" (**37**) "Commemoration of Jeddah, 1344, Postage of Nejd"

1925. Capture of Medina. Railway Tax stamps of Hejaz optd with T **36**.

244 **28** 1 pi. on 10 pi. mauve and violet 55·00 35·00
245 2 pi. on 50 pi. red and blue 55·00 35·00
246 3 pi. on 100 pi. brown 55·00 35·00
247 4 pi. on 500 pi. red 55·00 35·00
248 5 pi. on 1000 pi. violet and red 55·00 35·00

1925. Capture of Jeddah. Optd with T **37**.

249 **28** 1 pi. on 10 pi. mauve and violet 55·00 35·00
250 2 pi. on 50 pi. red and blue 55·00 35·00
251 3 pi. on 100 pi. brown 55·00 35·00
252 4 pi. on 500 pi. red 55·00 35·00
253 5 pi. on 1000 pi. violet and red 55·00 35·00

C. HEJAZ–NEJD

38 **39**

1926.

254 **38** $\frac{1}{4}$ pi. violet 7·00 2·00
261 $\frac{1}{4}$ pi. orange 5·00 60
255 $\frac{1}{2}$ pi. grey 7·00 2·00
262 $\frac{1}{2}$ pi. green 3·00 30
263 1 pi. red 2·50 30
257 **39** 2 pi. green 7·00 2·00
264 2 pi. purple 10·00 2·50
259 3 pi. red 10·00 2·50
265 3 pi. blue 2·50 30
260 5 pi. red 8·00 2·00
266 5 pi. brown 5·00 60

(**40**) "Islamic Congress, 1 June, 1926"

1926. Pan-Islamic Congress, Cairo. Optd With **T 40**.

275 **38** $\frac{1}{4}$ pi. orange 7·00 2·00
276 $\frac{1}{2}$ pi. green 7·00 2·00
277 1 pi. red 7·00 2·00
278 **39** 2 pi. purple 7·00 2·00
279 3 pi. blue 7·00 2·00
280 5 pi. brown 7·00 2·00

41 Tougra of Ibn Saud

(**42** "25th Rajab 1345")

1926.

284 **41** $\frac{1}{8}$ pi. brown 10·00 50
285 $\frac{1}{4}$ pi. green 10·00 50
286 $\frac{1}{2}$ pi. red 10·00 20
287 1 pi. purple 10·00 50
288 $1\frac{1}{2}$ pi. blue 10·00 50
289 3 pi. olive 16·00 1·75
290 5 pi. brown 20·00 2·50
291 10 pi. brown 60·00 5·00

1927. Establishment of Kingdom. Optd with T **42**.

294 **41** $\frac{1}{8}$ pi. brown 10·00 5·00
295 $\frac{1}{4}$ pi. green 10·00 5·00
296 $\frac{1}{2}$ pi. red 10·00 5·00
297 1 pi. purple 10·00 5·00
298 $1\frac{1}{2}$ pi. blue 10·00 5·00
299 3 pi. olive 10·00 5·00
300 5 pi. brown 10·00 5·00
301 10 pi. brown 12·00 6·00

43

44

1929.

302 **43** $1\frac{3}{4}$ g. blue 10·00 70
303 20 g. violet 35·00 6·00
304 30 g. green 50·00 8·00

1930. 4th Anniv of King Ibn Saud's Accession.

305 **44** $\frac{1}{2}$ g. red 10·00 2·00
306 $1\frac{1}{2}$ g. violet 10·00 1·50
307 $1\frac{3}{4}$ g. blue 15·00 2·00
308 $3\frac{1}{2}$ g. green 15·00 2·25
309 5 g. purple 25·00 3·00

45

46

1931.

310 **45** $\frac{1}{8}$ g. yellow 8·00 1·25
311 $\frac{1}{4}$ g. green 8·00 70
312 $1\frac{3}{4}$ g. blue 25·00 80

1932.

313 **46** $\frac{1}{4}$ g. green 12·00 1·00
314 $\frac{1}{2}$ g. red 30·00 1·25
315 $2\frac{1}{4}$ g. blue 50·00 1·50

D. SAUDI ARABIA

47

1932. Proclamation of Emir Saud as Heir Apparent.

316 **47** $\frac{1}{4}$ g. green 6·00
317 $\frac{1}{2}$ g. red 6·00 2·00
318 $1\frac{1}{2}$ g. blue 12·00
319 3 g. green 15·00
320 $3\frac{1}{2}$ g. blue 18·00 3·00
321 5 g. yellow 50·00 15·00
322 10 g. orange 80·00
323 20 g. violet £110
324 30 g. violet £200
325 $\frac{1}{4}$ s. red £150
326 $\frac{1}{2}$ s. brown £400
327 1 s. purple £800

48

49

1934. Charity Tax. Fund for Wounded in War with Yemen.

328 **48** $\frac{1}{2}$ g. red £150 4·00

1934.

329 **49** $\frac{1}{8}$ g. yellow 2·50 20
330 $\frac{1}{4}$ g. green 3·25 20
331a $\frac{1}{2}$ g. red 1·00 10
332 $\frac{7}{8}$ g. blue 3·00 4·00
333a 1 g. green 1·00 10
334 2 g. olive 6·00 50
335 $2\frac{7}{8}$ g. violet 4·00 25
336b 3 g. blue 3·00 20
337 $3\frac{1}{2}$ g. blue 20·00 1·75
338a 5 g. brown 3·00 20
339b 10 g. violet 8·00 1·50
340a 20 g. purple 10·00 50
341 100 g. violet £100 8·00
342a 200 g. brown 80·00 12·00

50 General Hospital, Mecca

1936. Charity. Medical Aid. Perf or roul. (a) Three palm trees.

345 **50** $\frac{1}{8}$ g. red (37 × 20 mm) £375 7·50
346 $\frac{1}{8}$ g. red ($30\frac{1}{2}$ × 18 mm) 50·00 50

(b) One palm tree.

350 **50** $\frac{1}{8}$ g. red ($30\frac{1}{2}$ × 18 mm) 1·50 10
351 $\frac{1}{8}$ g. red ($30\frac{1}{2}$ × 18 mm) 1·00 10

53 Egyptian Royal Yacht "Fakhr el Bihar", Radhwa

54 Map of Saudi Arabia, Flags and Emblem

1945. Meeting of King Ibn Saud and King Farouk of Egypt at Radhwa.

352 **53** $\frac{1}{2}$ g. red 4·00 2·00
353 3 g. blue 8·00 5·00
354 5 g. violet 18·00 10·00
355 10 g. purple 40·00 20·00

1946. Obligatory Tax. Return of King Ibn Saud from Egypt.

356a	54	½ g. mauve	12·00	50

55 Airliner

56 Arms of Saudi Arabia and Afghanistan

1949. Air.

357	55	1 g. green	2·50	10
358		3 g. blue	3·00	10
359		4 g. orange	3·00	10
360		10 g. violet	12·00	20
361		20 g. brown	30·00	30
362		100 g. purple	90·00	7·00

1950. Visit of King Mohamed Zahir Shah of Afghanistan.

363	56	½ g. red	7·00	1·75
364		3 g. blue	9·00	2·50

57 Al-Murabba Palace, Riyadh

58 Arms of Saudi Arabia and Jordan

1950. 50th Anniv of Capture of Riyadh by King Abdulaziz Ibn Saud. Centres in purple.

365	57	½ g. purple	4·00	1·00
366		1 g. blue	6·00	1·50
367		3 g. violet	10·00	2·50
368		5 g. orange	20·00	4·00
369		10 g. green	35·00	9·00

1951. Visit of King Talal of Jordan.

370	58	½ g. red	7·00	2·00
371		3 g. blue	14·00	4·00

59 Arabs and Train

60 Arms of Saudi Arabia and Lebanon

1952. Inaug of Dammam–Riyadh Railway.

372	59	½ g. brown	7·50	2·00
373		1 g. green	10·00	2·25
374		3 g. mauve	15·00	2·00
375		10 g. red	30·00	8·50
376		20 g. blue	65·00	20·00

1953. Visit of President Chamoun of Lebanon.

377	60	½ g. red	7·50	1·75
378		3 g. blue	12·50	3·75

61

62 Arms of Saudi Arabia and Jordan

1953. Visit of Governor-General of Pakistan.

379	61	½ g. red	7·50	1·75
380		3 g. blue	12·50	2·75

1953. Visit of King Hussein of Jordan.

381	62	½ g. red	8·00	1·75
382		3 g. blue	14·00	3·75

1955. Arab Postal Union. As T **96a** of Syria but smaller, 20 × 34 mm. Inscr. "ROYAUME DE L'ARABIE SOUDITE" at top.

383		½ g. green	3·00	1·00
384		3 g. violet	8·00	2·50
385		4 g. orange	13·00	4·50

1960. Inaug of Arab League Centre, Cairo. As T **154a** of Syria, but inscr "S.A.K.".

386		2 p. black and green	1·50	60

63 Congress Building

1960. Arab Postal Union Congress, Riyadh.

387	63	2 p. blue	60	20
388		5 p. purple	1·75	50
389		10 p. green	4·00	1·50

64 Radio Mast and Globe

65 Refugee Camp

1960. Inauguration of Direct Wireless Service.

390	64	2 p. red and black	1·25	50
391		5 p. purple and red	2·00	75
392		10 p. deep blue and blue	4·00	1·50

1960. World Refugee Year.

393	65	2 p. blue	30	20
394		8 p. violet	1·00	50
395		10 p. green	1·25	70

66 Gas Oil Plant

67 Wadi Hanifa Dam, near Riyadh

68 Vickers Viscount 800

(I)

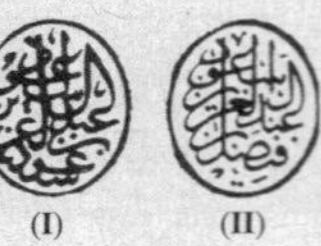

(II)

1960. Cartouche of King Saud as Type I. Size 27½ × 22 mm. (a) Postage (i) Type **66**.

396		½ p. orange and red	1·00	50
397		1 p. red and blue	1·25	15
398		2 p. blue and red	1·00	15
399		3 p. green and violet	1·00	20
400		4 p. purple and green	1·50	15
401		5 p. lake and purple	1·50	10
402		6 p. lilac and brown	1·50	15
403		7 p. myrtle and violet	1·50	10
404		8 p. black and green	2·00	10
405		9 p. brown and blue	2·25	30
406		10 p. red and blue	2·00	2·00
407		20 p. black and brown	5·00	20
408		50 p. green and brown	20·00	1·50
409		75 p. purple and red	40·00	10·00
410		100 p. brown and blue	40·00	4·50
411		200 p. bronze and black	75·00	4·50

(ii) Type **67**.

412		½ p. orange and brown	50	50
413		1 p. purple and olive	90	15
414		2 p. sepia and blue	50	15
415		3 p. blue and sepia	50	25
416		4 p. chestnut and brown	50	15
417		5 p. purple and sepia	80	10
418		6 p. red and black	2·25	10
419		7 p. olive and red	80	10
420		8 p. purple and blue	2·00	10
421		9 p. red and brown	2·25	45
422		10 p. lake and green	2·25	10
423		20 p. green and brown	3·50	1·00
424		50 p. brown and black	20·00	1·25
425		75 p. grey and brown	40·00	12·00
426		100 p. turquoise and blue	35·00	2·50
427		200 p. green and purple	65·00	3·00

(b) Air. Type **68**.

428		1 p. green and lilac	50	35
429		2 p. purple and green	50	15
430		3 p. blue and mauve	60	15
431		4 p. purple and blue	70	15
432		5 p. red and green	70	10
433		6 p. grey and brown	1·25	45
434		8 p. olive and red	1·40	15
435		9 p. brown and violet	2·00	40
436		10 p. brown and purple	3·50	50
437		15 p. brown and blue	3·50	50
438		20 p. green and brown	4·00	40
439		30 p. turquoise and bistre	15·00	25
440		50 p. blue and green	20·00	50
441		100 pa. brown and grey	42·00	4·00
442		200 pa. black and purple	65·00	11·00

See also Nos. 487/92, 529/610 and 660/744.

69 Globe, Pylon and Telegraph Pole

1960. 6th Anniv (1959) of Arab Telecommunications Union.

443	69	3 p. purple	1·25	30
444		6 p. black	3·00	30
445		8 p. brown	3·50	25

71 Damman Port

72 Campaign Emblem

1961. Opening of Damman Port Extension.

446	71	3 p. violet	1·25	20
447		6 p. blue	2·00	80
448		8 p. green	3·00	20

1962. Arab League Week. As T **76** of Libya but larger, 25 × 41 mm. Inscr "S.A.K.".

449		3 p. green	90	45
450		6 p. red	1·75	40
451		8 p. green	3·00	15

1962. Malaria Eradication.

452	72	3 p. red and blue	30	20
453		6 p. green and blue	60	30
454		8 p. black and purple	1·00	50

73 Koran

1963. 1st Anniv of Islamic Institute, Medina.

456	73	2½ p. purple and salmon	1·00	50
457		7½ p. blue and green	2·50	15
458		9½ p. green and black	3·50	2·50

74 Emblem within Hands

1963. Freedom From Hunger.

459	74	2½ p. mauve and salmon	60	50
460		7½ p. purple and pink	2·00	20
461		9 p. brown and blue	2·50	2·50

75 Boeing 707 over Airport

76 "Flame of Freedom"

1963. Opening of Dhahran Airport and Inauguration of Jet Service.

462	75	1 p. violet and brown	1·25	65
463		3½ p. blue and green	3·75	1·25
464		6 p. green and red	4·75	1·50
465		7½ p. mauve and blue	4·75	1·75
466		9½ p. red and violet	7·50	2·50

1963. As T **66/8** but redrawn in larger format (29 × 23 mm). Cartouche of King Saud as Type I. (a) Postage. (i) T **66**.

487		½ p. orange and red	15·00	2·50
488		1 p. orange and blue	10·00	1·50

(ii) T **67**.

489		1 p. orange and bistre	15·00	50

(b) Air. T **68**.

490		3 p. blue and red	7·00	1·00
491		10 p. brown and black	10·00	40
492		20 p. green and brown	18·00	10

Nos. 487/92 are widely spaced in the sheets, thus producing wide margins.

1964. 15th Anniv of Declaration of Human Rights.

493	76	3 p. blue, violet & salmon	3·00	50
494		6 p. blue, green & light blue	4·00	1·75
495		9 p. blue, brown & flesh	7·00	60

77 Arms and King Faisal

1964. Installation of King Faisal.

496	77	4 p. blue and green	4·00	30

80 Boeing 720–B

81 Kaaba, Mecca

1964. As T **66/7** but completely redrawn (Arabic inscr closer to top frame) and T **80**. Smaller size, 26½ × 21¼ mm. Cartouche of King Saud as Type I. (a) Postage. (i) Type **66**.

529		1 p. red and blue	8·50	50
530		2 p. blue and red	8·50	50
531		3 p. green and violet	7·00	20
532		4 p. purple and green	7·50	25
533		5 p. lake and purple	25·00	15
534		6 p. chocolate and brown	65·00	2·00
535		7 p. green and lilac	25·00	30
536		8 p. black and green	10·00	10
537		9 p. brown and blue	16·00	60
538		10 p. red and blue	£500	5·00
539		11 p. orange and green	8·00	3·25
540		12 p. green and ochre	8·00	1·25
541		13 p. blue and red	8·00	1·00
542		14 p. brown and lilac	9·00	1·00
543		15 p. brown and red	9·00	35
544		16 p. red and green	9·00	1·00
545		17 p. brown and cerise	9·00	2·00
546		18 p. blue and black	10·00	1·40
547		19 p. yellow and brown	10·00	35
548		20 p. black and brown	35·00	1·00
549		23 p. red and orange	11·00	1·25
550		24 p. yellow and green	12·00	2·00
551		26 p. brown and purple	13·00	1·60
552		27 p. black and red	13·00	1·60
553		31 p. red and turquoise	25·00	2·25
554		33 p. black and brown	25·00	2·75
555		50 p. green and brown	£200	6·00
555a		100 p. chocolate and blue		
556		200 p. green and slate	£250	12·00

(ii) Type **67**.

557		1 p. purple and olive	20·00	30
558		2 p. sepia and blue	7·00	30
559		3 p. blue and sepia	7·50	10
560		4 p. chestnut and brown	7·00	10
561		5 p. purple and black	7·00	10
562		6 p. red and black	7·00	30
563		7 p. black and brown	7·00	40
564		8 p. agate and blue	60·00	10
565		9 p. red and brown	60·00	2·50
566		10 p. brown and green	40·00	1·25
567		11 p. green and red	8·00	2·50
568		12 p. blue and orange	8·00	1·00
569		13 p. red and olive	8·00	1·25
570		14 p. green and brown	8·00	1·25
571		15 p. green and sepia	9·00	1·00
572		16 p. red and lilac	9·50	1·00
573		17 p. blue and purple	9·50	1·60
574		18 p. blue and green	9·50	1·60
575		19 p. ochre and black	11·00	1·60
576		20 p. green and brown	17·00	1·00
577		23 p. purple and brown	13·00	1·40
578		24 p. blue and red	13·00	1·60
579		26 p. yellow and olive	13·00	2·00
580		27 p. purple and blue	13·00	2·00
581		31 p. blue and black	15·00	2·00
582		33 p. purple and green	15·00	2·10
582a		50 p. brown and black		
583		100 p. turquoise and blue	£350	12·00
584		200 p. green and purple	£200	15·00

(b) Air. Type **80**.

585		1 p. green and purple	£100	6·00
586		2 p. purple and green	£525	22·00
587		3 p. blue and red	9·00	40
588		4 p. purple and blue	7·00	10
589		5 p. red and green	£750	35·00
590		6 p. slate and brown	75·00	4·00
591		7 p. green and mauve	7·50	60
592		8 p. olive and red	£100	1·00
593		9 p. brown and violet	7·50	4·00
594		10 p. purple and black	75·00	4·00
595		11 p. buff and green	£150	4·00
596		12 p. grey and orange	7·50	1·00
597		13 p. green and myrtle	7·50	1·00
598		14 p. orange and blue	7·50	1·00
599		15 p. brown and blue	75·00	2·50
600		16 p. blue and black	10·00	1·25
601		17 p. brown and ochre	10·00	1·25
602		18 p. green and blue	10·00	1·40
603		19 p. orange and mauve	10·00	1·40
604		20 p. green and brown	85·00	6·00
605		23 p. ochre and green	45·00	8·00
606		24 p. sepia and blue	13·00	1·60
607		26 p. green and red	13·00	1·60
608		27 p. green and sepia	13·00	1·60
609		31 p. red and mauve	15·00	2·00
610		33 p. purple and red	18·00	2·75
610a		50 p. indigo and green		
610b		100 p. brown and grey		
610c		200 p. brown and purple		

1965. Moslem League Conference, Mecca.

611	81	4 p. black and brown	1·25	60
612		6 p. black and mauve	5·50	1·40
613		10 p. black and green	13·00	60

82 Arms of Saudi Arabia and Tunisia

1965. Visit of President Bourguiba of Tunisia.

614	82	4 p. silver and mauve	1·25	75
615		8 p. silver and violet	4·75	50
616		10 p. silver and blue	6·50	50

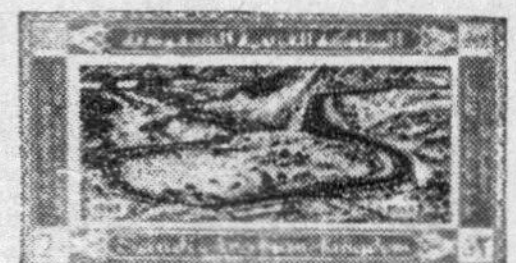

83 Highway

1965. Opening of Arafat–Taif Highway.
617 **83** 2 p. black and red . . . . 2·00 25
618 4 p. black and blue . . . . 2·50 50
619 6 p. black and violet . . . 3·50 1·00
620 8 p. black and green . . . 5·50 75

84 I.C.Y. Emblem

1965. International Co-operation Year.
621 **84** 1 p. brown and yellow . . 50 60
622 2 p. green and salmon . . . 80 70
623 3 p. olive and blue . . . . 1·00 75
624 4 p. black and olive . . . . 1·50 90
625 10 p. purple and orange . . 3·00 1·25

85 I.T.U. Symbol and Emblems

1965. Centenary of I.T.U.
626 **85** 3 p. black and violet 50 40
627 4 p. green and violet . . . 90 60
628 8 p. brown and green . . . 1·50 40
629 10 p. green and orange . . . 2·50 75

86 Lamp and Burning Library

1966. Burning of Algiers Library in 1962.
630 **86** 1 p. red . . . . 2·00 1·75
631 2 p. red . . . . 2·00 1·75
632 3 p. purple . . . . 5·00 2·50
633 4 p. violet . . . . 8·00 4·00
634 5 p. mauve . . . . 10·00 5·50
535 6 p. red . . . . 15·00 7·50

87 A.P.U. Emblem
88 Dagger on Deir Yassin, Palestine

1966. 10th Anniv (1964) of Arab Postal Union.
636 **87** 3 p. olive and plum . . . . 1·40 90
637 4 p. olive and blue . . . . 2·00 1·10
638 6 p. olive and purple . . . 2·75 20
639 7 p. olive and green . . . . 3·25 2·25

1966. Deir Yassin Massacre.
640 **88** 2 p. black and green . . . 2·50 85
641 4 p. black and brown . . . 3·75 1·00
642 6 p. black and blue . . . . 6·00 1·40
643 8 p. black and orange . . . 10·00 1·75

89 Scout Badges

1966. Arab Scout Jamboree.
644 **89** 4 p. multicoloured . . . . 5·50 2·00
645 8 p. multicoloured . . . . 5·50 1·25
646 10 p. multicoloured . . . . 7·00 1·25

90 W.H.O. Building

1966. Inaug of W.H.O. Headquarters, Geneva.
647 **90** 4 p. multicoloured . . . . 1·50 75
648 6 p. multicoloured . . . . 2·00 1·00
649 10 p. multicoloured . . . . 3·50 75

91 U.N.E.S.C.O. Emblem
92 Radio Mast, Telephone and Map

1966. 20th Anniv of U.N.E.S.C.O.
650 **91** 1 p. multicoloured 75 40
651 2 p. multicoloured . . . . 1·00 40
652 3 p. multicoloured . . . . 1·00 40
653 4 p. multicoloured . . . . 2·00 90
654 10 p. multicoloured . . . 3·00 75

1966. 8th Arab Telecommunications Union Congress, Riyadh.
655 **92** 1 p. multicoloured 75 50
656 2 p. multicoloured . . . . 1·25 70
657 4 p. multicoloured . . . . 1·75 85
658 6 p. multicoloured . . . . 4·00 1·25
659 7 p. multicoloured . . . . 5·50 1·50

1966. As 1964 issue, but with cartouche of King Faisal as Type II (see above No. 396). (a) Postage. (i) Type **66**.
755 1 p. red and blue . . . . . 5·00 1·00
661 2 p. blue and red . . . . . 5·50 25
662 3 p. green and violet . . . . 7·50 10
663 4 p. purple and green . . . 10·00 20
664 5 p. brown and purple . . . 15·00 10
760 6 p. chocolate and brown . . 15·00 50
666 7 p. green and lilac . . . . 23·00 90
667 8 p. green and turquoise . . 7·00 10
668 9 p. brown and blue . . . . 7·00 10
669 10 p. red and blue . . . . . 7·50 60
765 11 p. orange and green . . . 22·00 80
671 12 p. green and brown . . . 8·50 1·00
672 13 p. blue and red . . . . . 10·00 1·25
673 14 p. brown and lilac . . . . 10·00 1·25
674 15 p. brown and red . . . . 9·00 70
675 16 p. red and green . . . . 9·00 1·40
676 17 p. brown and red . . . . 9·00 1·00
677 18 p. blue and black . . . . 9·00 1·25
678 19 p. yellow and brown . . . 9·00 1·00
679 20 p. brown and bistre . . . 11·00 1·25
680 23 p. red and orange . . . . 18·00 2·00
681 24 p. yellow and green . . . 14·00 1·40
681a 26 p. brown and purple . . . £125 20·00
682 27 p. black and red . . . . 15·00 1·75
683 31 p. red and green . . . . 15·00 1·75
684 33 p. black and brown . . . 15·00 1·75
685 50 p. green and brown . . . £120
686 100 p. black and blue . . . £100 25·00
687 200 p. green and black . . . £325 50·00

(ii) Type **67**.
688 1 p. purple and green . . . £150 8·00
689 2 p. brown and blue . . . . 6·00 50
690 3 p. blue and brown . . . . 10·00 20
691 4 p. orange and brown . . . 6·00 20
782 5 p. purple and black . . . 22·00 1·25
783 6 p. red and black . . . . . 17·00 15
694 7 p. black and brown . . . 10·00 40
695 8 p. brown and blue . . . . 10·00 10
696 9 p. red and brown . . . . 10·00 60
697 10 p. brown and green . . . 10·00 30
698 11 p. green and red . . . . 10·00 80
699 12 p. purple and orange . . . 10·00 1·00
700 13 p. red and green . . . . 12·00 1·25
701 14 p. green and brown . . . 12·00 80
702 15 p. green and brown . . . 14·00 25
703 16 p. lilac and red . . . . . 14·00 1·25
704 17 p. blue and purple . . . . 12·00 1·00
705 18 p. blue and green . . . . 14·00 1·25
706 19 p. brown and black . . . 10·00 1·00
707 20 p. green and brown . . . 40·00 2·00
708 23 p. purple and brown . . . £125 20·00
708a 24 p. blue and red . . . . . 55·00 10·00
709 26 p. brown and green . . . 14·00 1·60
711 27 p. purple and blue . . . . 12·00 1·60
712 33 p. purple and green . . . 14·00 1·60
713 50 p. brown and black . . . 28·00 5·00
714 100 p. blue and deep blue . . £150 12·00
715 200 p. green and purple . . . £150 12·00

(b) Air. Type **80**.
716 1 p. green and purple . . . . 6·00 20
717 2 p. purple and green . . . . 6·00 20
718 3 p. blue and red . . . . . 7·00 20
719 4 p. purple and blue . . . . 7·00 20
720 5 p. red and green . . . . . £500 60·00
721 6 p. grey and brown . . . . £100 8·00
812 7 p. green and mauve . . . 15·00 1·25
813 8 p. green and red . . . . . 30·00 10
724 9 p. brown and violet . . . 8·00 50
725 10 p. brown and black . . . 10·00 50
726 11 p. brown and green . . . 9·00 50
727 12 p. grey and orange . . . 10·00 50
728 13 p. green and myrtle . . . 11·00 1·00
729 14 p. orange and blue . . . 10·00 1·25
730 15 p. brown and blue . . . . 12·00 1·25
731 16 p. blue and black . . . . 14·00 50
732 17 p. brown and yellow . . . 14·00 1·25
733 18 p. green and blue . . . . 14·00 1·25
734 19 p. orange and mauve . . . 17·00 4·00
735 20 p. green and brown . . . £100 4·00
736 23 p. brown and green . . . 11·00 1·40
737 24 p. brown and blue . . . . 17·00 1·40
741 33 p. purple and red . . . . 12·00 2·40
742 50 p. blue and green £750
743 100 p. brown and grey . . . £750
744 200 p. black and purple . . . £750 30·00

93 Moot Emblem
94 Meteorological Apparatus

1967. 2nd Rover Moot, Mecca.
745 **93** 1 p. multicoloured . . . . 2·25 85
746 2 p. multicoloured . . . . 2·75 85
747 3 p. multicoloured . . . . 2·75 85
748 4 p. multicoloured . . . . 3·75 85
749 10 p. multicoloured . . . . 9·00 2·25

1967. World Meteorological Day.
750 **94** 1 p. mauve . . . . 1·50 85
751 2 p. violet . . . . 1·50 85
752 3 p. olive . . . . 2·50 1·00
753 4 p. green . . . . 4·00 1·00
754 10 p. blue . . . . 7·50 2·50

96 Route Map and Dates
97 The Prophet's Mosque, Medina

98 Prophet's Mosque Extension
99 Ancient Wall Tomb, Madayin Saleh

100 Colonnade, Sacred Mosque, Mecca
101 Camels and Oil Derrick

102 Arab Stallion
103 Holy Ka'aba, Mecca

1968. Inauguration of Dammam–Jeddah Highway.
834 **96** 1 p. multicoloured . . . . 1·25 50
835 2 p. multicoloured . . . . 1·50 50
836 3 p. multicoloured . . . . 1·50 50
837 4 p. multicoloured . . . . 11·00 2·00
838 10 p. multicoloured . . . . 15·00 3·25

1968. (a) Type **97**.
839 **97** 1 p. green and orange . . . 3·00 20
840 2 p. green and brown . . . 3·00 20
841 3 p. green and violet . . . 3·00 30
858 4 p. green and ochre . . . 3·00 35
843 5 p. green and purple . . . 5·00 30
860 6 p. green and black . . . 6·00 2·00
861 10 p. green and brown . . . 5·00 1·25
949 20 p. green and brown . . . 10·00 1·60
864 50 p. green and purple . . . 15·00 3·00
865 100 p. green and blue . . . 10·00 5·00
866 200 p. green and red . . . 8·00 8·00

(b) Type **98**.
952 **98** 1 p. green and orange . . 2·00 20
953 2 p. green and brown . . . 2·00 30
867 3 p. green and black . . . 3·00 20
868 4 p. green and red . . . . 2·00 35
851 5 p. green and red . . . . 3·50 50
852 6 p. green and blue . . . . 5·00 80
870a 8 p. green and red . . . . 4·75 25
853 10 p. green and brown . . . 6·00 1·25
940 20 p. green and violet . . . 7·00 50

(c) Type **99**.
876 **99** 2 p. brown and blue . . . . 20·00 2·50
878 4 p. light brown and brown 5·00 30
880 7 p. brown and orange . . 40·00 5·00
881 10 p. brown and green . . . 12·00 2·00
883 20 p. brown and purple . . 10·00 1·25

(d) Type **100**.
887 **100** 3 p. grey and red . . . . £450 40·00
888 4 p. grey and green . . . . 3·00 30
891 10 p. grey and purple . . . 7·00 2·00

(e) Type **101**.
898 **101** 4 p. red and lilac . . . . 15·00 1·25
901 10 p. red and blue . . . . 12·00 2·00

(f) Type **102**.
908 **102** 4 p. brown and purple . . 5·50 30
911 10 p. brown and black . . 10·00 1·60
912 14 p. brown and blue . . . 40·00 2·50
913 20 p. brown and green . . 10·00 1·25

(g) Type **103**.
1016 **103** 4 p. black and green . . 1·50 30
923 6 p. black and purple . . 4·00 30
924 8 p. black and red . . . 4·00 15
1018 10 p. black and red . . . 3·25 80

104 Saker Falcon
105 Traffic Signals

1968. Air.
1022 **104** 1 p. brown and green . . 2·25 20
1023 4 p. orange and red . . . 80·00 7·50
1024 10 p. brown and blue . . 20·00 2·00
1025 20 p. brown and green . 40·00 2·50

1969. Traffic Day.
1026 **105** 3 p. red, green and blue . 1·00 25
1027 4 p. red, green & brown 2·50 25
1028 10 p. red, green & purple 6·00 1·25

106 Scout Emblem, Camp and Flag

1969. 3rd Arab Rover Moot, Mecca.
1029 **106** 1 p. multicoloured . . . 1·75 90
1030 4 p. multicoloured . . . 5·50 1·50
1031 10 p. multicoloured . . . 18·00 7·00

107 W.H.O. Emblem

1969. 20th Anniv (1968) of W.H.O.
1032 **107** 4 p. multicoloured . . . 6·00 50

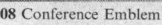

108 Conference Emblem
109 Satellite, Dish Aerial and Open Book

1970. Islamic Foreign Ministers' Conf, Jeddah.
1033 **108** 4 p. black and blue . . . 1·00 25
1034 10 p. black and ochre . . 2·00 30

1970. World Telecommunications Day.
1035 **109** 4 p. blue, mauve and ultramarine . . . . 3·50 40
1036 10 p. blue, mauve & grn 7·50 1·75

110 Steel Rolling-mill

112 Emblem and Arab Archway

1970. Inauguration (1967) of First Saudi Arabian Steel Rolling-mill.

1037 **110** 3 p. multicoloured . . . 2·25 20
1038 4 p. multicoloured . . . 3·25 25
1039 10 p. multicoloured . . . 6·00 1·25

1971. 4th Arab Rover Moot, Mecca.

1049 **112** 10 p. multicoloured . . . 6·00 1·25

113 Global Emblem

1971. World Telecommunications Day.

1050 **113** 4 p. black and blue . . . 1·00 25
1051 10 p. black and lilac . . 2·50 75

114 University "Tower" Emblem

115 I.E.Y. Emblem

1971. 4th Anniv of Inauguration of King Abdulaziz National University.

1052 **114** 3 p. black and green . . 1·00 25
1053 4 p. black and brown . . 1·50 40
1054 10 p. black and blue . . 4·00 1·25

1971. International Education Year (1970).

1055 **115** 4 p. brown and green . . 3·25 10

116 Arab League Emblem

117 O.P.E.C. Emblem

1971. Arab Propaganda Week.

1056 **116** 10 p. multicoloured . . . 3·75 1·50

1971. 10th Anniv of O.P.E.C.

1057 **117** 4 p. blue . . . . 6·50 45

O.P.E.C. = Organisation of Petroleum Exporting Countries.

118 Globe

120 Writing in Book

119 Telephone within Dial

1972. World Telecommunications Day.

1058 **118** 4 p. multicoloured . . . 4·00 45

1972. Inauguration of Automatic Telephone System (1969).

1059 **119** 1 p. black, green and red 1·00 40
1060 4 p. black, turquoise & grn 2·25 40
1061 5 p. black, grn & mauve 2·75 65
1062 10 p. black, green & brn 7·50 1·75

1973. World Literacy Day (1972).

1063 **120** 10 p. multicoloured . . 3·00 70

121 Mosque, Mecca, and Moot Emblem

1973. 5th Arab Rover Moot, Mecca. Mult.

1064 4 p. Type **121** . . . . 3·50 80
1065 6 p. Holy Ka'aba, Mecca . . 7·00 1·50
1066 10 p. Rover encampment . . 10·00 3·50

122 Globe and Map of Palestine

1973. Universal Palestine Week.

1067 **122** 4 p. red, yellow and grey 2·00 30
1068 10 p. red, yellow and blue 4·50 1·25

123 Leaf and Emblem

1973. International Hydrological Decade.

1069 **123** 4 p. multicoloured . . . 4·00 45

124 A.P.U. Emblem

1973. 25th Anniv of Founding of Arab Postal Union at Sofar Conference.

1070 **124** 4 p. multicoloured . . . 3·25 40
1071 10 p. multicoloured . . 3·25 1·75

125 Balloons

126 U.P.U. Monument and Postal Emblem

1973. Universal Childen's Day (1971).

1072 **125** 4 p. multicoloured . . . 3·25 40

1974. Centenary of U.P.U.

1073 **126** 3 p. multicoloured . . . 15·00 3·50
1074 4 p. multicoloured . . . 30·00 6·50
1075 10 p. multicoloured . . . 45·00 7·50

127 Handclasp and U.N.E.S.C.O. Emblem

1974. International Book Year (1972).

1076 **127** 4 p. multicoloured . . . 7·00 40
1077 10 p. multicoloured . . . 10·00 3·00

128 Desalination Works

1974. Inauguration of Sea-water Desalination Plant, Jeddah (1971).

1078 **128** 4 p. blue and orange . . 2·50 40
1079 6 p. lilac and green . . . 3·75 85
1080 10 p. black and red . . . 8·00 1·75

129 Interpol Emblem

130 Tower, Emblem and Hand with Letter

1974. 50th Anniv (1973) of International Criminal Police Organization (Interpol).

1081 **129** 4 p. blue and red . . . . 7·00 50
1082 10 p. blue and green . . . 13·00 2·25

1974. 3rd Session of Arab Postal Studies Consultative Council, Riyadh.

1083 **130** 4 p. multicoloured . . . 4·00 40

131 New Headquarters Building

1974. Inauguration (1970) of New U.P.U. Headquarters, Berne.

1084 **131** 3 p. multicoloured . . . 5·00 65
1085 4 p. multicoloured . . . 10·00 1·00
1086 10 p. multicoloured . . . 25·00 3·75

132 Armed Forces and Flame

1974. King Faisal Military Cantonment (1971).

1087 **132** 3 p. multicoloured . . . 2·25 40
1088 4 p. multicoloured . . . 3·75 45
1089 10 p. multicoloured . . . 11·00 2·50

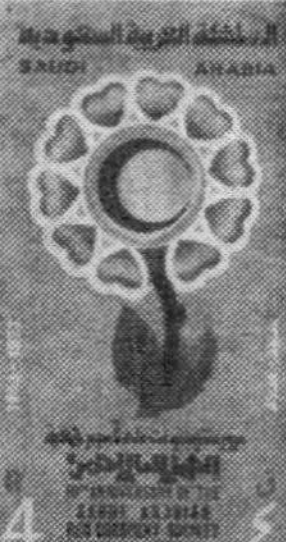

133 Red Crescent "Flower"

134 Scout Emblem and Minarets

1974. 10th Anniv (1973) of Saudi Arabian Red Crescent Society.

1090 **133** 4 p. multicoloured . . . 1·75 1·25
1091 6 p. multicoloured . . . 3·25 2·50
1092 10 p. multicoloured . . . 9·50 2·00

1974. 6th Arab Rover Moot, Mecca.

1093 **134** 4 p. multicoloured . . . 4·00 50
1094 6 p. multicoloured . . . 5·50 90
1095 10 p. multicoloured . . . 8·50 2·50

135 Reading Braille

1975. Day of the Blind.

1096 **135** 4 p. multicoloured . . . 2·75 45
1097 10 p. multicoloured . . . 5·25 75

136 Anemometer and U.N. Emblem as Weather Balloon

1975. Centenary (1973) of World Meteorological Organization.

1098 **136** 4 p. multicoloured . . . 4·00 45

137 King Faisal

138 Conference Emblem

1975. King Faisal Memorial Issue.

1099 **137** 4 p. purple and green . . 2·50 25
1100 16 p. green and violet . . 7·50 10
1101 23 p. violet and green . . 10·00 1·75

1975. 6th Islamic Conference of Foreign Ministers, Jeddah.

1103 **138** 10 p. black and brown . 2·00 2·00

139 Wheat and Sun

1975. 29th Anniv of Charity Society.

1104 **139** 4 p. multicoloured . . . 3·00 30
1105 10 p. multicoloured . . . 4·00 80

140 Kaaba, Handclasp and Globe

1975. Moslem Organizations Conference, Mecca.

1106 **140** 4 p. multicoloured . . . 1·50 15
1107 10 p. multicoloured . . . 3·00 75

141 Lockheed TriStar and Douglas DC-3 Aircraft

1975. 30th Anniv of National Airline "Saudia".
1108 **141** 4 p. multicoloured . . . 2·50 45
1109 10 p. multicoloured . . . 5·00 1·25

142 Mecca and Riyadh

1975. Conference Locations.
1110 **142** 10 p. multicoloured . . . 3·00 60

143 Friday Mosque, Medina, and Juwatha Mosque, Al-Hasa

1975. Islamic Holy Places.
1111 **143** 4 p. multicoloured . . . 2·00 25
1112 10 p. multicoloured . . . 4·50 75

144 F.A.O. Emblem

1975. 10th Anniv (1973) of World Food Programme.
1113 **144** 4 p. multicoloured . . . 1·00 20
1114 10 p. multicoloured . . . 2·50 75

145 Conference Emblem

1976. Islamic Solidarity Conference of Science and Technology, Mecca.
1115 **145** 4 p. multicoloured . . . 12·00 45

146 Map and T.V. Screen

1976. 10th Anniv (1975) of Saudi Arabian Television Service.
1116 **146** 4 p. multicoloured . . . 8·00 45

147 Ear of Wheat, Atomic Symbol and Graph

1976. 2nd Five-year Plan.
1117 **147** 20 h. multicoloured . . . 1·50 35
1118 50 h. multicoloured . . . 3·00 75

148 Quba Mosque, Medina

149 Holy Kaaba, Mecca

150 Oil Rig, Al-Khafji

1976. Size 36 × 26 mm. (a) Type **148**.
1122b 20 h. black and orange . . 85 15
1128a 50 h. violet and green . . 2·75 40

(b) Type **149**.
1137 5 h. black and lilac 10 10
1138 10 h. black and lavender . . 20 10
1139 15 h. black and pink 50 10
1140 20 h. black and blue 50 10
1141 25 h. black and yellow . . . 50 10
1142 30 h. black and green . . . 60 15
1143 35 h. black and cinnamon . . 40 10
1144 40 h. black and green . . . 1·50 25
1145 45 h. black and claret . . . 50 10
1146 50 h. black and red 50 15
1149 65 h. black and blue 70 20
1151 1 r. black and yellow . . . . 1·00 25
1152 2 r. black and green . . . . 2·00 50

(c) Type **150**.
1167 5 h. blue and orange 25 10
1168 10 h. green and orange . . . 15 10
1169a 15 h. brown and orange . . . 25 10
1170 20 h. green and orange . . . 50 10
1171 25 h. purple and orange . . . 50 10
1172a 30 h. blue and orange . . . 50 10
1173 35 h. brown and orange . . . 50 10
1174 40 h. red and orange . . . 60 10
1175 45 h. mauve and orange . . . 70 10
1176b 50 h. pink and orange . . . 60 15
1177 55 h. green and orange . . 25·00 2·50
1187 65 h. brown and orange . . 1·00 20
1188 1 r. slate and orange . . . 1·00 35
1181 2 r. purple and red . . . . 2·25 50

For Types **149/50** in smaller size, see Nos. 1283/1325 and 1435/7.

151 Globe and Telephones

1976. Telephone Centenary.
1191 **151** 50 h. multicoloured . . . 3·00 60

152 Emblem and Heads of State

153 Kaaba and Spinning Wheel

1976. Arab League Summit Conference.
1192 **152** 20 h. green and blue . . 2·75 45

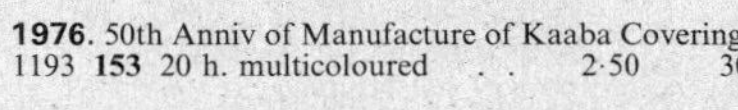

1976. 50th Anniv of Manufacture of Kaaba Covering.
1193 **153** 20 h. multicoloured . . 2·50 30

154 Eye and W.H.O. Emblem

1976. Prevention of Blindness.
1194 **154** 20 h. multicoloured . . 3·50 25

155 Emblem

1976. Islamic Jurisprudence Conference.
1195 **155** 20 h. orange, blue & brn . 2·00 25

156 Emblem

158 Diesel Train and Map

157 King Khaled

1977. 25th Anniv of Sharia Law College, Mecca.
1196 **156** 4 p. green and red . . . . 3·00 25

1977. 2nd Anniv of Installation of King Khaled.
(a) With incorrect dates at foot.
1197 **157** 20 h. brown and green . . 20·00 30·00
1198 80 h. black and green . . 20·00 25·00

(b) With corrected dates.
1199 **157** 20 h. brown and green . . 1·00 25
1200 80 h. black and green . . 3·00 60

On Nos. 1197/8 the two Arabic dates end with the same characters. On the correct version of the design, they do not.

1977. 25th Anniv (1976) of Damman–Riyadh Railway.
1201 **158** 20 h. multicoloured . . . 10·00 1·50

159/62 "The Four Imams" (Illustration reduced. Actual size 58 × 58 mm)

1977.
1202 **159** 20 h. yellow and grey . . 4·50 1·50
1203 **160** 20 h. yellow and grey . . 4·50 1·50
1204 **161** 20 h. yellow and grey . . 4·50 1·50
1205 **162** 20 h. yellow and grey . . 4·50 1·50
Nos. 1202/5 were issued se-tenant as a composite design.

163 Moenjodaro Ruins, Pakistan

164 Map by al-Idrisi

1977. "Save Moenjodaro", Campaign.
1206 **163** 50 h. multicoloured . . . 3·00 30

1977. 1st International Arab History Symposium.
1207 **164** 20 h. multicoloured . . . 1·25 25
1208 50 h. multicoloured . . . 2·25 35

165 King Faisal Hospital, Riyadh

1977. Opening of King Faisal Hospital.
1209 **165** 20 h. multicoloured . . . 1·75 30
1210 50 h. multicoloured . . . 3·50 45

166 A.P.U. Emblem

167 Kaaba, Book and Lighthouse

1977. 25th Anniv of Arab Postal Union.
1211 **166** 20 h. multicoloured . . . 75 25
1212 80 h. multicoloured . . . 3·00 50

1977. 1st World Conference on Muslim Education.
1213 **167** 20 h. blue and yellow . . 1·50 25

168 Taiz–Abha–Jizan Road and Route Map

1978. Opening of Taiz–Abha–Jizan Road.
1214 **168** 20 h. multicoloured . . . 75 20
1215 80 h. multicoloured . . . 2·00 45

169 Mount Arafat, Pilgrims and Kaaba

1978. Pilgrimage to Mecca.
1216 **169** 20 h. multicoloured . . . 75 20
1217 80 h. multicoloured . . . 2·00 45

170 Posthorn Dhow

171 5 g. Stamp of 1930

1979. 2nd Gulf Postal Organization Conference, Dubai.
1218 **170** 20 h. multicoloured . . . 40 20
1219 50 h. multicoloured . . . 1·00 35

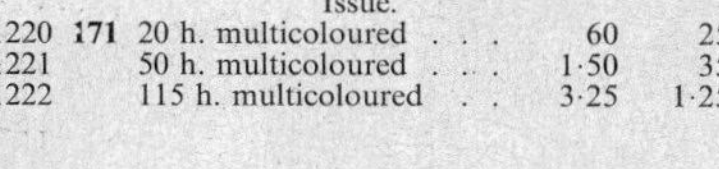

1979. 50th Anniv of First Commemorative Stamp Issue.
1220 **171** 20 h. multicoloured . . . 60 25
1221 50 h. multicoloured . . . 1·50 35
1222 115 h. multicoloured . . 3·25 1·25

172 Crown Prince Fahd

1979. Crown Prince Fahd's Birthday.
1224 **172** 20 h. multicoloured . . . 1·25 20
1225 50 h. multicoloured . . . 2·50 40

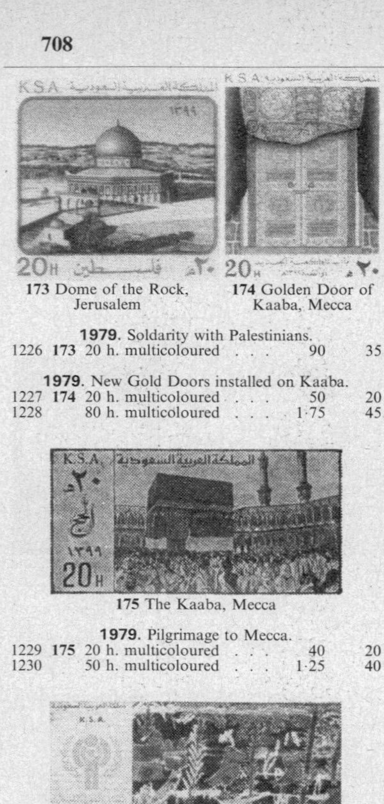

173 Dome of the Rock, Jerusalem

174 Golden Door of Kaaba, Mecca

1979. Solidarity with Palestinians.

1226 **173** 20 h. multicoloured . . . 90 35

1979. New Gold Doors installed on Kaaba.

1227 **174** 20 h. multicoloured . . . 50 20
1228 80 h. multicoloured . . . 1·75 45

175 The Kaaba, Mecca

1979. Pilgrimage to Mecca.

1229 **175** 20 h. multicoloured . . . 40 20
1230 50 h. multicoloured . . . 1·25 40

176 "Birds in a Forest"

1980. International Year of the Child. Children's Paintings. Multicoloured.

1231 20 h. Type **176** . . . . 4·00 40
1232 50 h. "Paper Lanterns" . . . 11·00 2·00

177 King Abdulaziz Ibn Saud

1980. 80th Anniv of Saudi Armed Forces.

1233 **177** 20 h. multicoloured . . . 1·00 15
1234 80 h. multicoloured . . . 4·00 60

178 Emblem

179 Globe and Books

1980. 35th Anniv of Arab League.

1235 **178** 20 h. green, black & blue 45 10

1980. 50th Anniv of International Bureau of Education.

1236 **179** 50 h. multicoloured . . . 90 20

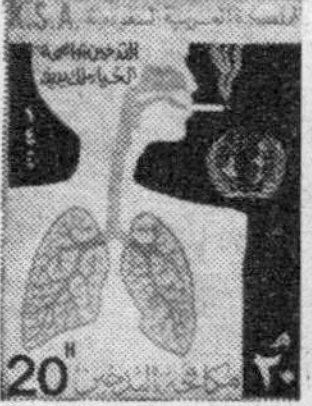

180 Polluted Air Passages and W.H.O. Emblem

181 O.P.E.C. Emblem and Globe

1980. Anti-Smoking Campaign.

1237 **180** 20 h. multicoloured . . . 75 15
1238 – 50 h. multicoloured . . . 2·50 30

DESIGN: 50 h. Cigarette crossed through and W.H.O. emblem.

1980. 20th Anniv of Organization of Petroleum Exporting Countries. Multicoloured.

1239 20 h. Type **181** 75 15
1240 50 h. Figures supporting O.P.E.C. emblem . . . . 2·50 30

182 Pilgrims leaving Airplane

1980. Pilgrimage to Mecca.

1241 **182** 20 h. multicoloured . . 50 15
1242 50 h. multicoloured . . 1·50 30

183 Kaaba, Mecca

1981. 3rd Islamic Summit Conference, Mecca. Multicoloured.

1243 20 h. Type **183** 50 20
1244 20 h. Prophet's Mosque, Medina 50 20
1245 20 h. Dome of the Rock, Jerusalem 50 20
1246 20 h. Conference emblem (36 × 36 mm) 50 20

184 Thour Cave, Mecca, and Quba Mosque, Medina, on Map

1981. 1400th Anniv of Hegira.

1247 **184** 20 h. multicoloured . . 50 20
1248 50 h. multicoloured . . 1·50 35
1249 80 h. multicoloured . . 2·50 50

185 Royal Corporation of Jubeil and Yanbou Emblem

1981. Industry Week.

1250 **185** 20 h. brown, orge & silver 40 15
1251 80 h. brown, orge & gold 1·50 35

186 Satellite Earth Station

187 Emblem of Arab Towns Organization

1981. Telecommunications Achievements.

1252 – 20 h. gold, black & blue 50 20
1253 – 80 h. multicoloured . . 1·75 30
1254 **186** 115 h. multicoloured . . 2·50 75

DESIGNS—As T **186**: 20 h. Modern telephone and graph. 36 × 36 mm: 80 h. Microwave antenna on map of Saudi Arabia.

1981. Arab Towns Day.

1255 **187** 20 h. multicoloured . . 40 10
1256 65 h. multicoloured . . 90 20
1257 80 h. multicoloured . . 1·25 35
1258 115 h. multicoloured . . 1·75 4

188 Douglas DC-9-80 over Terminal Buildings

189 Flags of participating Countries and Saudi Team Emblem

1981. Inauguration of King Abdulaziz International Airport, Jeddah. Multicoloured.

1259 20 h. Type **188** 50 20
1260 80 h. Departure halls . . . . 2·25 45

1981. World Cup Football Championship Preliminary Round, Riyadh.

1261 **189** 20 h. multicoloured . . . 50 20
1262 80 h. multicoloured . . . 2·00 35

190 Blind Person reading Braille

191 Wheat and Cogwheel on Graph

1981. Int Year of Disabled Persons. Mult.

1263 20 h. Type **190** 75 20
1264 50 h. Disabled person in wheelchair weaving on loom 2·50 40

1981. 3rd Five-year Plan.

1265 **191** 20 h. multicoloured . . . 15 10

192 King Abdulaziz Ibn Saud and Map of Saudi Arabia

1981. 50th Anniv of Unification of Saudi Arabia.

1266 **192** 5 h. multicoloured . . . 10 10
1267 10 h. multicoloured . . . 10 10
1268 15 h. multicoloured . . . 15 10
1269 20 h. multicoloured . . . 15 10
1270 50 h. multicoloured . . . 35 20
1271 65 h. multicoloured . . . 45 25
1272 80 h. multicoloured . . . 65 30
1273 115 h. multicoloured . . 1·00 45

193 Pilgrims passing through Almasa'a Arcade

1981. Pilgrimage to Mecca.

1275 **193** 20 h. multicoloured . . . 25 15
1276 65 h. multicoloured . . . 75 40

194 Tractor

1981. World Food Day.

1277 **194** 20 h. multicoloured . . . 25 10

195 Conference Emblem

1981. 2nd Session of Gulf Co-operation Council Summit Conference, Riyadh.

1278 **195** 20 h. multicoloured . . . 15 10
1279 80 h. multicoloured . . . 55 30

196 University Emblem

1982. 25th Anniv of King Saud University.

1280 **196** 20 h. multicoloured . . . 15 10
1281 50 h. multicoloured . . . 35 20

1982. As T **149/150** but in smaller size, 25 × 20 mm.

(a) Type **149**.

1283d 10 h. black and lilac 15 10
1284 15 h. black and pink 12 10
1285c 20 h. black and blue 15 10
1291c 50 h. black and red 35 20
1294c 65 h. black and blue . . . 45 25
1301c 1 r. black and green 75 40

(b) Type **150**.

1306a 5 h. blue and orange . . . 35 20
1307c 10 h. green and orange . . 25 15
1308c 15 h. brown and orange . . 20 10
1309c 20 h. green and orange . . 20 15
1310 25 h. purple and orange . . 45 10
1315c 50 h. pink and orange . . . 35 20
1318c 65 h. brown and orange . . 45 25
1325c 1 r. green and orange . . . 75 40

197 Riyadh Postal Building

198 Riyadh Television Centre

1982. New Postal Buildings. Multicoloured.

1330 20 h. Type **197** 15 10
1331 65 h. Jeddah 45 25
1332 80 h. Dammam 55 30
1333 115 h. Postal mechanised sorting 85 45

1982. Riyadh Television Centre.

1335 **198** 20 h. multicoloured . . . 25 10

199 Football and King's Cup

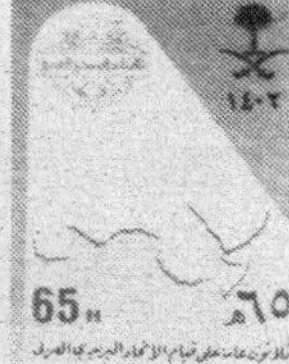

200 A.P.U. Emblem and Map

1982. 25th Anniv of King's Cup Football Championship.

1336 **199** 20 h. multicoloured . . . 15 10
1337 65 h. multicoloured . . . 45 25

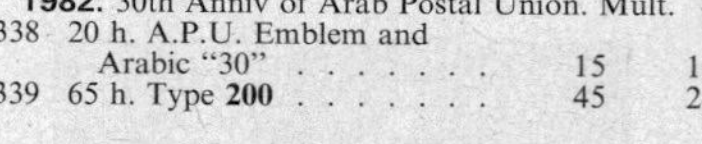

1982. 30th Anniv of Arab Postal Union. Mult.

1338 20 h. A.P.U. Emblem and Arabic "30" 15 10
1339 65 h. Type **200** 45 25

201 Pilgrims at Muzdalefa looking for Stones to stone the Devil

1982. Pilgrimage to Mecca.

1340 **201** 20 h. multicoloured . . . 20 10
1341 50 h. multicoloured

202 Saudi Arabian and World Standards Organizations Emblem

1982. World Standards Day.

1342 **202** 20 h. multicoloured . . . 20 10

203 Tractor

1982. World Food Day.

1343 **203** 20 h. multicoloured . . . 15 10

204 King Fahd

1983. Installation of King Fahd.

1344 **204** 20 h. multicoloured . . . 25 15
1345 50 h. multicoloured . . . 50 30
1346 65 h. multicoloured . . . 65 35
1347 80 h. multicoloured . . . 80 50
1348 115 h. multicoloured . . 1·25 70

205 Crown Prince Abdullah

1983. Installation of Crown Prince.

1349 **205** 20 h. multicoloured . . . 25 15
1350 50 h. multicoloured . . . 50 30
1351 65 h. multicoloured . . . 65 35
1352 80 h. multicoloured . . . 80 50
1353 115 h. multicoloured . . 1·25 70

206 Dome of the Rock, Jerusalem

1983. Solidarity with Palestinians.

1354 **206** 20 h. multicoloured . . . 45 15

207 Container Ship "Bar'zan"

1983. 6th Anniv of United Arab Shipping Company. Multicoloured.

1355 20 h. Type **207** 40 25
1356 65 h. "Al Drieya" . . . . . 1·25 60

208 Stoning the Devil

209 Saudi Arabia Post and U.P.U. Emblems

1983. Pilgrimage to Mecca.

1357 **208** 20 h. multicoloured . . . 25 15
1358 65 h. multicoloured . . . 65 40

1983. World Communications Year. Mult.

1359 20 h. Type **209** 20 15
1360 80 h. Saudi Arabia telephone and I.T.U. emblems . . . 70 35

210 Terminal Building

1983. Opening of King Khaled International Airport, Riyadh. Multicoloured.

1361 20 h. Type **210** 35 20
1362 65 h. Embarkation wing of terminal . . . . 1·25 70

211 Wheat and F.A.O. Emblem

212 Al Aqsa Mosque, Jerusalem

1983. World Food Day.

1363 **211** 20 h. multicoloured . . 30 10

1983. Solidarity with Palestinians.

1364 **212** 20 h. brown, blue & grn 40 15

213 Riyadh

214 Shobra Palace, Taif

215 Jeddah

1984. Saudi Cities. (a) Riyadh.

1365 **213** 20 h. multicoloured . . 15 10
1366 50 h. multicoloured . . 1·00 20
1370a 75 h. multicoloured . . 25 15
1371 150 h. multicoloured . . 95 30

(b) Taif.

1367 **214** 20 h. multicoloured . . 15 10
1373 50 h. multicoloured . . 35 15
1374 75 h. multicoloured . . 20 10
1375 150 h. multicoloured . . 95 30

(c) Jeddah.

1377 **215** 50 h. multicoloured . . 35 15
1378 75 h. multicoloured . . 25 10
1379 150 h. multicoloured . . 95 30

223 Family and House

1984. 10th Anniv of Estate Development Fund.

1385 **223** 20 h. multicoloured . . 25 15

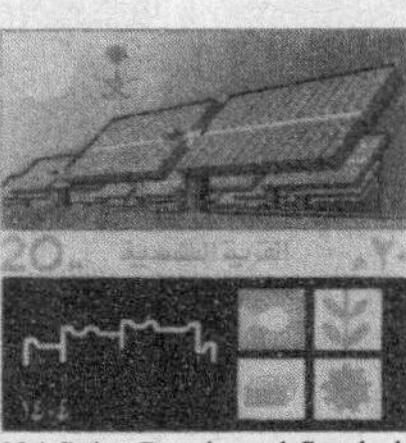
224 Solar Panels and Symbols

1984. Al-Eyenah Solar Village. Multicoloured.

1386 20 h. Type **224** 30 20
1387 80 h. Sun and solar panels . . 1·10 50

225 Al-Kheef Mosque, Mina

1984. Pilgrimage to Mecca. Multicoloured.

1389 20 h. Type **225** 30 15
1390 65 h. Al-Kheef Mosque, Mina (different) . . . . 1·10 50

226 Olympic and Saudi Football Federation Emblems

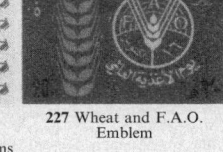

227 Wheat and F.A.O. Emblem

1984. Qualification of Saudi Football Team for Olympic Games.

1391 **226** 20 h. multicoloured . . . 30 15
1392 115 h. multicoloured . . 1·50 1·00

Nos. 1391/2 have the incorrect spellings "Gamos" and "Olympied".

1984. World Food Day.

1393 **227** 20 h. green, buff and black 30 15

228 Olympic Rings and "90"

1984. 90th Anniv of Int Olympic Committee.

1394 **228** 20 h. multicoloured . . . 40 15
1395 50 h. multicoloured . . . 1·10 40

229 "Arabsat" and Globe

1985. Launch of "Arabsat" Satellite.

1396 **229** 20 h. multicoloured . . . 30 15

230 Emblem and Koran

1985. International Koran Reading Competition.

1397 **230** 20 h. multicoloured . . . 40 20
1398 65 h. multicoloured . . . 1·40 60

231 King Fahd and Jubail Industrial Complex

1985. Five Year Plan. Multicoloured.

1399 20 h. Type **231** 50 40
1400 50 h. King Fahd, T.V. tower, dish aerial and microwave tower 85 60
1401 65 h. King Fahd and agricultural landscape . . 1·10 80
1402 80 h. King Fahd and Yanbu industrial complex . . . . 1·40 1·10

232 I.Y.Y. Emblem

1985. International Youth Year.

1403 **232** 20 h. multicoloured . . . 35 20
1404 80 h. multicoloured . . . 1·25 60

233 Map and Wheat

235 "Arabsat 2" Satellite and Launch of "Discovery" (space shuttle)

234 Loading Berth, Yanbu

1985. "Self Sufficiency in Wheat Production".

1405 **233** 20 h. multicoloured . . . 30 15

1985. Abqaiq–Yanbu Oil Pipeline. Multicoloured.

1406 20 h. Type **234** 30 20
1407 65 h. Pipeline and map . . . 1·25 65

1985. 1st Arab Astronaut, Prince Sultan Ibn Salman Al-Saud. Multicoloured.

1408 20 h. Type **235** 30 15
1409 115 h. Space shuttle and mission emblem (51 × 26 mm) . . . 1·75 85

236 "40" and U.N. Emblem

1985. 40th Anniv of U.N.O.

1410 **236** 20 h. light blue, blue and green 25 10

237 Highway and Map of Route

1985. Mecca–Medina Highway.

1411 **237** 20 h. multicoloured . . . 25 15
1412 65 h. multicoloured . . . 75 45

238 Coded Envelope and Post Emblem

1985. Post Code Publicity.

1413 **238** 20 h. multicoloured . . . 25 10

239 Trophy and Football

1985. Victory in 8th (1984) Asian Football Cup Championship.

1414 **239** 20 h. multicoloured . . . 25 15
1415 65 h. multicoloured . . . 70 40
1416 115 h. multicoloured . . 1·40 85

240 Pilgrims around Kaaba

1985. Pilgrimage to Mecca.

1417 **240** 10 h. multicoloured . . . 15 10
1418 15 h. multicoloured . . . 20 15
1419 20 h. multicoloured . . . 30 15
1420 65 h. multicoloured . . . 85 50

241 Olympic Rings and Council Emblem

1985. 1st Arabian Gulf Co-operative Council Olympic Day.

1421 **241** 20 h. multicoloured . . . 30 15
1422 115 h. multicoloured . . 1·50 80

242 Irrigation System

1985. World Food Day.

1423 **242** 20 h. multicoloured . . . 30 15
1424 65 h. multicoloured . . . 1·10 45

243 King Abdulaziz and Horsemen

1985. International Conference on King Abdulaziz.

1425 **243** 15 h. multicoloured . . . 20 15
1426 20 h. multicoloured . . . 25 15
1427 65 h. multicoloured . . . 75 50
1428 80 h. multicoloured . . . 1·10 70

244 Building within Roll of Printed Paper

1985. King Fahd Holy Koran Press Compound, Medina. Multicoloured.

1430 20 h. Type **244** 25 15
1431 65 h. Open book sculpture within roll of printed paper 75 50

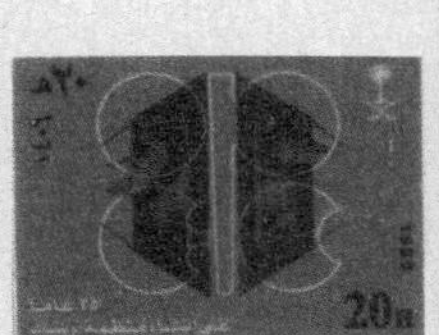

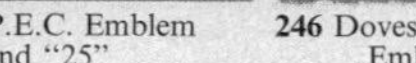

245 O.P.E.C. Emblem and "25"
246 Doves and I.P.Y. Emblem

1985. 25th Anniv of Organization of Petroleum Exporting Countries.

1432 **45** 20 h. deep brown, brown and black 25 15
1433 65 h. multicoloured . . . 75 50

1986. International Peace Year.

1434 **246** 20 h. multicoloured . . . 75 25

1986. As T **149** but size 29 × 19 mm.

1435 10 h. black and violet . . . .
1436 20 h. black and blue . . . .
1437 50 h. black and red . . . . .

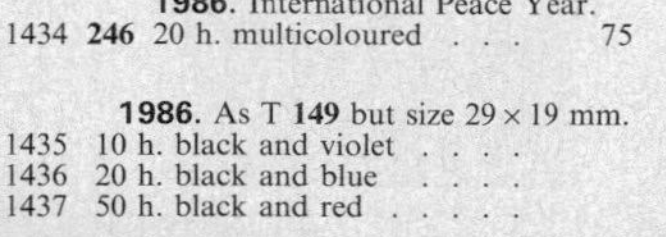

247 Riyadh
248 Child in Droplet

1986. 50th Anniv of Riyadh Municipality.

1438a **247** 20 h. multicoloured . . 25 15
1439 65 h. multicoloured . . 85 60

1986. World Health Day.

1440 **248** 20 h. multicoloured . . 30 20
1441 50 h. multicoloured . . 1·10 75

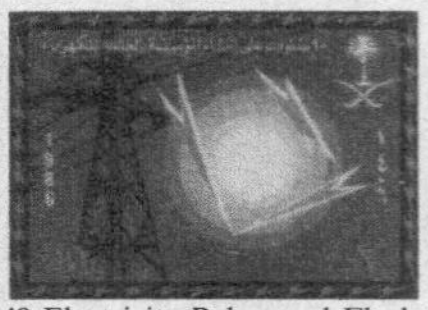

249 Electricity Pylon and Flashes

1986. 10th Anniv of General Electricity Corporation.

1442 **249** 20 h. multicoloured . . 20 15
1443 65 h. multicoloured . . 60 40

250 Route Map of Cable

1986. Inauguration of Singapore–Marseilles Communications Cable.

1444 **250** 20 h. multicoloured . . 25 15
1445 50 h. multicoloured . . 65 40

251 Houses and Soldier
252 Holy Kaaba

1986. National Guards Housing Project, Riyadh.

1446 **251** 20 h. multicoloured . . 25 20
1447 65 h. multicoloured . . 75 55

1986.

1448 **252** 30 h. black and green . 35 15
1449 40 h. black and mauve . 45 15
1450 50 h. black and green . 15 10
1452 75 h. black and blue . . 20 10
1456 150 h. black and mauve 40 20

253 Mount Arafat, Pilgrims and Kaaba

1986. Pilgrimage to Mecca. Multicoloured.

1460 20 h. Type **253** 65 50
1461 20 h. Pilgrims leaving jet airliner 80 60
1462 20 h. Stoning the Devil . . . 65 50
1463 20 h. Pilgrims at Muzdalefa looking for stones to stone the Devil 65 50
1464 20 h. Pilgrims passing through Almasa'a Arcade 65 50
1465 20 h. Kaaba, Mecca 65 50
1466 20 h. Pilgrims around Kaaba 65 50
1467 20 h. Al-Kheef Mosque, Mina 65 50

254 Refinery
255 Palm Tree and Wheat in Globe

1986. 50th Anniv of Discovery of Oil in Saudi Arabia. Multicoloured.

1468 20 h. Type **254** 25 15
1469 65 h. Oil derrick on map . . 85 60

1986. World Food Day. Multicoloured.

1470 20 h. Type **255** 25 15
1471 115 h. Corn cob and wheat in leaves of flower . . . . . . 1·40 85

256 Scroll behind Dagger and Pool of Blood

1986. 4th Anniv of Massacre of Palestinian Refugees at Sabra and Shatila Camps, Lebanon.

1472 **256** 80 h. multicoloured . . . 1·00 30
1473 115 h. multicoloured . . 1·40 95

257 258

259 260

261 262

263

1986. University Crests. (a) Imam Mohammed ibn Saud Islamic University, Riyadh.

1474 **257** 15 h. black and green . . 20 10
1475 20 h. black and blue . . 20 20
1476 50 h. black and blue . . 30 15
1477 65 h. black and blue . . 40 20
1477a 75 h. black and blue . . 25 20
1478 100 h. black and red . . 80 25
1479 150 h. black and red . . 90 40

(b) Umm al-Qura University, Mecca.

1481 **258** 50 h. black and blue . . 30 15
1482 65 h. black and blue . . 40 20
1482a 75 h. black and blue . . 20 10
1483 100 h. black and pink . . 80 25
1484 150 h. black and red . . 90 40

(c) King Saud University, Riyadh.

1487 **259** 50 h. black and blue . . . 30 15
1488 75 h. black and blue . . . 25 20
1489 100 h. black and red . . 80 25
1490 150 h. black and red . . 90 40

(d) King Abulaziz University, Jeddah.

1493 **260** 50 h. black and blue . . . 30 10
1494 75 h. black and blue . . . 25 20
1496 150 h. black and red . . 90 40

(e) King Faisal University, Al-Hasa.

1499 **261** 50 h. black and blue . . . 30 15
1500 75 h. black and blue . . . 25 20
1502 150 h. black and red . . 90 40

(f) King Fahd University of Petroleum and Minerals, Dhahran.

1505 **262** 50 h. black and blue . . . 30 15
1506 75 h. black and blue . . . 25 20
1508 150 h. black and red . . 90 40

(g) Islamic University, Medina.

1511 **263** 50 h. black and blue . . . 30 15
1512 75 h. black and blue . . . 25 20
1514 150 h. black and red . . 90 40

264 Road Bridge and Aerial View of Causeway (left)

1986. Saudi Arabia–Bahrain Causeway. Mult.

1515 20 h. Type **264** 75 60
1516 20 h. Road bridge and aerial view of causeway (right) . . 75 60

265 Olympic Torch and Rings

1986. 90th Anniv of Modern Olympic Games.

1517 **265** 20 h. multicoloured . . . 35 15
1518 100 h. multicoloured . . 1·75 1·00

266 Oil Derrick and Refinery

1987. 25th Anniv of General Petroleum and Mineral Organization.

1519 **266** 50 h. multicoloured . . . 75 30
1520 100 h. multicoloured . . 1·50 95

267 Mosque and Model of Extension

1987. Restoration and Extension of Quba Mosque, Medina.

1521 **267** 50 h. multicoloured . . . 75 30
1522 75 h. multicoloured . . . 1·10 70

268 Drill-press Operator

1987. Technical and Vocational Training. Mult.

1523 50 h. Type **268** 60 50
1524 50 h. Lathe operator 60 50
1525 50 h. Laboratory technician . 60 50
1526 50 h. Welder 60 50

Nos. 1523/6 were printed together se-tenant each block forming an overall design of a cog wheel.

269 Pyramid, Riyadh T.V. Transmitter, King Khaled International Airport and Fort
270 Dish Aerials and Satellite

1987. "Saudi Arabia—Yesterday and Today" Exhibition, Cairo.

1527 **269** 50 h. multicoloured . . . 80 40
1528 75 h. multicoloured . . . 1·25 85

1987. King Fahd Space Communications City, Umm al Salam, Jeddah. Multicoloured.

1529 50 h. Type **270** 55 30
1530 75 h. Dish aerials and buildings (51 × 26 mm) 85 70

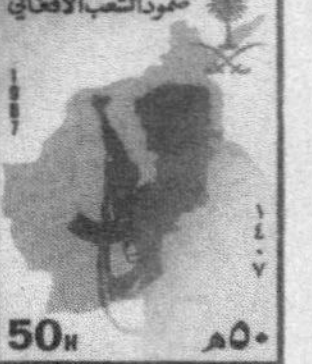

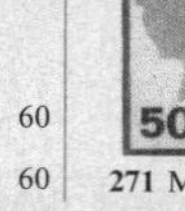

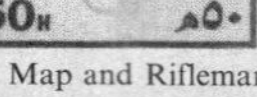

271 Map and Rifleman
273 Emblems

272 Mosque and Pilgrims

1987. Afghan Resistance to Occupation.

1531 **271** 50 h. multicoloured . . . 60 30
1532 100 h. multicoloured . . 1·00 70

1987. Pilgrimage to Mecca.

1533 **272** 50 h. multicoloured . . . 60 30
1534 75 h. multicoloured . . . 80 50
1535 100 h. multicoloured . . 1·00 70

1987. 1st Anniv of Disabled Children's Care Home.

1536 **273** 50 h. multicoloured . . . 65 30
1537 75 h. multicoloured . . . 95 70

274 Emblems and Hands writing on Airmail Envelope

1987. World Food Day.

1538 **274** 50 h. multicoloured . . . 50 30
1539 150 h. multicoloured . . 1·60 95

275 Combine Harvester within Leaf

276 Woman and Children in Hand

1987. World Food Day.

1540 **275** 50 h. multicoloured . . . 50 30
1541 75 h. multicoloured . . . 80 60

1987. 25th Anniv of First Social Welfare Society.

1542 **276** 50 h. multicoloured . . . 50 30
1543 100 h. multicoloured . . . 90 70

277 Dome of the Rock, Jerusalem

1987.

1544 **277** 75 h. multicoloured . . . 80 35
1545 150 h. multicoloured . . 1·60 90

278 Mosque

1987. Expansion of Prophet's Mosque, Medina.

1546 **278** 50 h. multicoloured . . . 60 25
1547 75 h. multicoloured . . . 80 40
1548 150 h. multicoloured . . 1·60 80

279 Dome of the Rock, Horseman and Battle Scene

280 Emblem

1987. 800th Anniv of Battle of Hattin.

1550 **279** 75 h. multicoloured . . . 80 45
1551 150 h. multicoloured . . 1·60 95

1987. 8th Supreme Council Session of Gulf Co-operation Council, Riyadh.

1552 **280** 50 h. multicoloured . . . 55 25
1553 75 h. multicoloured . . . 85 30

281 Road as "3" and Ship

282 Aerial View of Stadium and Sports Pictograms

1988. 3rd International Roads Federation (Middle East Region) Meeting, Riyadh.

1554 **261** 50 h. multicoloured . . 55 25
1555 75 h. multicoloured . . 85 50

1988. Inauguration of International King Fahd Stadium, Riyadh. Multicoloured.

1556 50 h. Type **282** 55 20
1557 150 h. Side view of stadium and sports pictograms (51 × 26 mm) . . . . 1·60 1·10

283 Anniversary Emblem and W.H.O. Building

1988. World Health Day. 40th Anniv of W.H.O.

1588 **283** 50 h. multicoloured . . 55 25
1589 75 h. multicoloured . . 85 50

284 Bottle, Arm and Blood Drop

1988. Blood Donation.

1560 **284** 50 h. multicoloured . . 55 30
1561 75 h. multicoloured . . 85 55

285 Mosque, Holy Kaaba and King Fahd

1988. Appointment of King Fahd as Custodian of Two Holy Mosques.

1562 **285** 50 h. multicoloured . . 40 25
1563 75 h. multicoloured . . 60 40
1564 150 h. multicoloured . . 1·00 70

286 Clean Air, Land and Sea

287 Palestinian Flag, Hand holding Stone and Crowd

1988. Environmental Protection.

1566 **286** 50 h. multicoloured . . 55 25
1567 75 h. multicoloured . . 85 50

1988. Palestinian "Intifida" Movement.

1568 **287** 75 h. multicoloured . . 85 40
1569 150 h. multicoloured . . 1·75 85

288 Pilgrims at al-Sail al-Kabir Migat

1988. Pilgrimage to Mecca.

1570 **288** 50 h. multicoloured . . . 55 25
1571 75 h. multicoloured . . . 85 50

289 Ear of Wheat

1988. World Food Day.

1572 **289** 50 h. multicoloured . . . 45 25
1573 75 h. multicoloured . . . 75 45

290 Mosque

1988. Expansion of Qiblatayn Mosque, Medina.

1574 **290** 50 h. multicoloured . . . 45 25
1575 75 h. multicoloured . . . 75 45

291 Footballer and Trophy on Globe

1989. World Youth Football Cup, Saudi Arabia.

1576 **291** 75 h. multicoloured . . . 65 40
1577 150 h. multicoloured . . 1·10 50

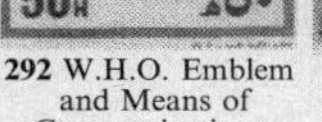

292 W.H.O. Emblem and Means of Communications

294 Palestinian Flag and Dome of the Rock, Jerusalem

293 Shuaibah Desalination Plant, Red Sea

1989. World Health Day.

1578 **292** 50 h. multicoloured . . . 35 15
1579 75 h. multicoloured . . . 65 40

1989. 1st Anniv of Sea Water Desalination and Electricity Power Station.

1580 **293** 50 h. multicoloured . . . 30 15
1581 75 h. multicoloured . . . 55 35

1989. "Freedom of Palestine".

1582 **294** 50 h. multicoloured . . . 30 15
1583 75 h. multicoloured . . . 45 25

295 Attan'eem Migat, Mecca

1989. Pilgrimage to Mecca.

1584 **295** 50 h. multicoloured . . . 30 15
1585 75 h. multicoloured . . . 45 25

296 Ears of Wheat encircling Globe

297 Hands holding Trophy aloft

1989. World Food Day.

1586 **296** 75 h. multicoloured . . . 45 25
1587 150 h. multicoloured . . 90 40

1989. 3rd World Under-16 JVC Cup Soccer Championship, Scotland.

1588 **297** 75 h. multicoloured . . . 45 25
1589 150 h. multicoloured . . 90 40

298 Mosque after Expansion

1989. Expansion of Holy Mosque, Mecca.

1590 **298** 50 h. multicoloured . . . 30 15
1591 75 h. multicoloured . . . 45 25
1592 150 h. multicoloured . . 90 40

299 Emblem and Arabic Letters

1990. International Literacy Year.

1595 **299** 50 h. multicoloured . . . 30 15
1596 75 h. multicoloured . . . 45 25

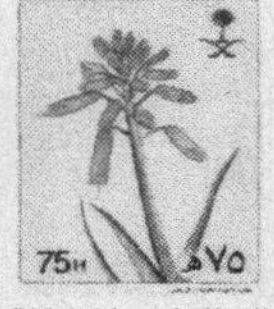

300 "Aloe sheilaa"

301 "Blopharis ciliaris"

302 "Pergularia tormentosa"

303 "Talinam cuneifolium"

304 "Echium horridum"

305 "Cleome arabica"

306 "Iris sisyrinchium"

307 "Senecio desfontaini"

308 "Cistanche phelypaea"

309 "Plumbago zeylanica"

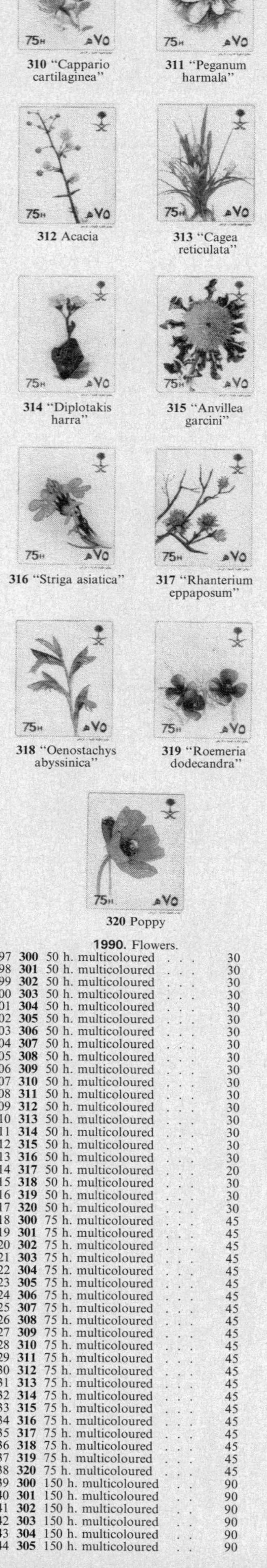

310 "Cappario cartilaginea"
311 "Peganum harmala"
312 Acacia
313 "Cagea reticulata"
314 "Diplotakis harra"
315 "Anvillea garcini"
316 "Striga asiatica"
317 "Rhanterium eppaposum"
318 "Oenostachys abyssinica"
319 "Roemeria dodecandra"
320 Poppy

1990. Flowers.

1597 **300** 50 h. multicoloured . . . 30 15
1598 **301** 50 h. multicoloured . . . 30 15
1599 **302** 50 h. multicoloured . . . 30 15
1600 **303** 50 h. multicoloured . . . 30 15
1601 **304** 50 h. multicoloured . . . 30 15
1602 **305** 50 h. multicoloured . . . 30 15
1603 **306** 50 h. multicoloured . . . 30 15
1604 **307** 50 h. multicoloured . . . 30 15
1605 **308** 50 h. multicoloured . . . 30 15
1606 **309** 50 h. multicoloured . . . 30 15
1607 **310** 50 h. multicoloured . . . 30 15
1608 **311** 50 h. multicoloured . . . 30 15
1609 **312** 50 h. multicoloured . . . 30 15
1610 **313** 50 h. multicoloured . . . 30 15
1611 **314** 50 h. multicoloured . . . 30 15
1612 **315** 50 h. multicoloured . . . 30 15
1613 **316** 50 h. multicoloured . . . 30 15
1614 **317** 50 h. multicoloured . . . 20 15
1615 **318** 50 h. multicoloured . . . 30 15
1616 **319** 50 h. multicoloured . . . 30 15
1617 **320** 50 h. multicoloured . . . 30 15
1618 **300** 75 h. multicoloured . . . 45 25
1619 **301** 75 h. multicoloured . . . 45 25
1620 **302** 75 h. multicoloured . . . 45 25
1621 **303** 75 h. multicoloured . . . 45 25
1622 **304** 75 h. multicoloured . . . 45 25
1623 **305** 75 h. multicoloured . . . 45 25
1624 **306** 75 h. multicoloured . . . 45 25
1625 **307** 75 h. multicoloured . . . 45 25
1626 **308** 75 h. multicoloured . . . 45 25
1627 **309** 75 h. multicoloured . . . 45 25
1628 **310** 75 h. multicoloured . . . 45 25
1629 **311** 75 h. multicoloured . . . 45 25
1630 **312** 75 h. multicoloured . . . 45 25
1631 **313** 75 h. multicoloured . . . 45 25
1632 **314** 75 h. multicoloured . . . 45 25
1633 **315** 75 h. multicoloured . . . 45 25
1634 **316** 75 h. multicoloured . . . 45 25
1635 **317** 75 h. multicoloured . . . 45 25
1636 **318** 75 h. multicoloured . . . 45 25
1637 **319** 75 h. multicoloured . . . 45 25
1638 **320** 75 h. multicoloured . . . 45 25
1639 **300** 150 h. multicoloured . . 90 40
1640 **301** 150 h. multicoloured . . 90 40
1641 **302** 150 h. multicoloured . . 90 40
1642 **303** 150 h. multicoloured . . 90 40
1643 **304** 150 h. multicoloured . . 90 40
1644 **305** 150 h. multicoloured . . 90 40
1645 **306** 150 h. multicoloured . . 90 40
1646 **307** 150 h. multicoloured . . 90 40
1647 **308** 150 h. multicoloured . . 90 40
1648 **309** 150 h. multicoloured . . 90 40
1649 **310** 150 h. multicoloured . . 90 40
1650 **311** 150 h. multicoloured . . 90 40
1651 **312** 150 h. multicoloured . . 90 40
1652 **313** 150 h. multicoloured . . 90 40
1653 **314** 150 h. multicoloured . . 90 40
1654 **315** 150 h. multicoloured . . 90 40
1655 **316** 150 h. multicoloured . . 90 40
1656 **317** 150 h. multicoloured . . 90 40
1657 **318** 150 h. multicoloured . . 90 40
1658 **319** 150 h. multicoloured . . 90 40
1659 **320** 150 h. multicoloured . . 90 40

321 "20" within Crescent and Circle

1990. 20th Anniv of Islamic Conference Organization.
1660 **321** 75 h. multicoloured . . 45 25
1661 150 h. multicoloured . . 90 40

322 Globe and W.H.O. Emblem

1990. World Health Day.
1662 **322** 75 h. multicoloured . . 20 10
1663 150 h. multicoloured . . 40 20

323 White Horse

1990. 25th Anniv of Horsemanship Club. Mult.

(a) Size 38 × 29 mm.
1664 50 h. Type **323** 15 10
1665 50 h. Brown horse 15 10
1666 50 h. White horse with dark muzzle 15 10
1667 50 h. Chestnut horse 15 10

(b) Size 36 × 27 mm.
1668 50 h. As No. 1667 . . . . . 15 10
1669 75 h. As No. 1665 . . . . . 20 10
1670 100 h. Type **323** 30 15
1671 150 h. As No. 1666 . . . . 40 20

324 El Johfah Migat, Rabegh

1990. Pilgrimage to Mecca.
1672 **324** 75 h. multicoloured . . . 20 10
1673 150 h. multicoloured . . 40 20

325 T.V. Tower and Centre

1990. 25th Anniv of Saudi Television.
1674 **325** 75 h. multicoloured . . . 20 10
1675 150 h. multicoloured . . 40 20

326 Ornament

1990. Islamic Heritage Year. Multicoloured.
1676 75 h. Type **326** 20 10
1677 75 h. Mosque 20 10
1678 75 h. Arabic script 20 10
1679 75 h. Decoration with stylized minarets 20 10

327 Boeing 747-300/400 and International Flights Route Map

1990. 45th Anniv of Saudi Airlines. Multicoloured.
1680 75 h. Type **327** 25 10
1681 75 h. Douglas DC-10 and domestic flight route map . 25 10
1682 150 h. Type **327** 45 25
1683 150 h. As No. 1681 . . . . . 45 25

328 Anniversary Emblem

1990. 30th Anniv of O.P.E.C.
1684 **328** 75 h. multicoloured . . . 20 10
1685 150 h. multicoloured . . 40 20

329 World Map

1990. World Food Day.
1686 **329** 75 h. multicoloured . . . 20 10
1687 150 h. multicoloured . . 40 20

330 Industrial Site, Irrigation System and Oil Refinery

1990. 5th Five Year Plan. Multicoloured.
1688 75 h. Type **330** 20 10
1689 75 h. Radio tower, road and mine 20 10
1690 75 h. Monument, sports stadium and vocational training 20 10
1691 75 h. Television tower, environmental protection and modern building 20 10

331 Arabic Script and Decoration

332 Tidal Wave, Erupting Volcano and Earthquake-damaged House

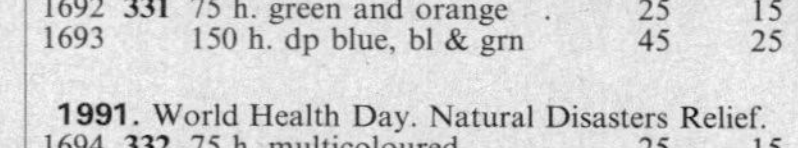

1991. Battle of Badr, 624 A.D.
1692 **331** 75 h. green and orange . 25 15
1693 150 h. dp blue, bl & grn 45 25

1991. World Health Day. Natural Disasters Relief.
1694 **332** 75 h. multicoloured . . . 25 15
1695 150 h. multicoloured . . 45 25

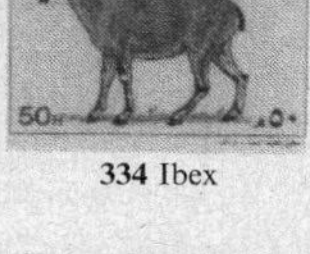

333 Mountain Gazelle
334 Ibex
335 Arabian Oryx
336 Sand Fox

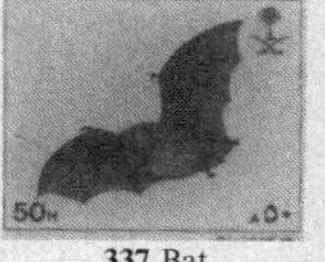

337 Bat
338 Striped Hyena

339 Sand Cat
340 Dugong

341 Arabian Leopard

1991. Animals.
1696 **333** 25 h. multicoloured . . . 10 10
1697 **334** 25 h. multicoloured . . . 10 10
1698 **335** 25 h. multicoloured . . . 10 10
1699 **336** 25 h. multicoloured . . . 10 10
1700 **337** 25 h. multicoloured . . . 10 10
1701 **338** 25 h. multicoloured . . . 10 10
1702 **339** 25 h. multicoloured . . . 10 10
1703 **340** 25 h. multicoloured . . . 10 10
1704 **341** 25 h. multicoloured . . . 10 10
1705 **333** 50 h. multicoloured . . . 15 10
1706 **334** 50 h. multicoloured . . . 15 10
1707 **335** 50 h. multicoloured . . . 15 10
1708 **336** 50 h. multicoloured . . . 15 10
1709 **337** 50 h. multicoloured . . . 15 10
1710 **338** 50 h. multicoloured . . . 15 10
1711 **339** 50 h. multicoloured . . . 15 10
1712 **340** 50 h. multicoloured . . . 15 10
1713 **341** 50 h. multicoloured . . . 15 10
1714 **333** 75 h. multicoloured . . . 25 15
1715 **334** 75 h. multicoloured . . . 25 15
1716 **335** 75 h. multicoloured . . . 25 15
1717 **336** 75 h. multicoloured . . . 25 15
1718 **337** 75 h. multicoloured . . . 25 15
1719 **338** 75 h. multicoloured . . . 25 15
1720 **339** 75 h. multicoloured . . . 25 15
1721 **340** 75 h. multicoloured . . . 25 15
1722 **341** 75 h. multicoloured . . . 25 15
1723 **333** 100 h. multicoloured . . 30 15
1724 **334** 100 h. multicoloured . . 30 15
1725 **335** 100 h. multicoloured . . 30 15
1726 **336** 100 h. multicoloured . . 30 15
1727 **337** 100 h. multicoloured . . 30 15
1728 **338** 100 h. multicoloured . . 30 15
1729 **339** 100 h. multicoloured . . 30 15
1730 **340** 100 h. multicoloured . . 30 15
1731 **341** 100 h. multicoloured . . 30 15
1732 **333** 150 h. multicoloured . . 45 25
1733 **334** 150 h. multicoloured . . 45 25
1734 **335** 150 h. multicoloured . . 45 25
1735 **336** 150 h. multicoloured . . 45 25
1736 **337** 150 h. multicoloured . . 45 25
1737 **338** 150 h. multicoloured . . 45 25
1738 **339** 150 h. multicoloured . . 45 25
1739 **340** 150 h. multicoloured . . 45 25
1740 **341** 150 h. multicoloured . . 45 25

342 Flag and Map of Kuwait

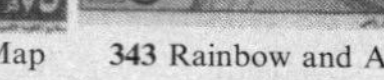

343 Rainbow and Arrows

1991. Liberation of Kuwait.
1741 **342** 75 h. multicoloured . . . 25 15
1742 150 h. multicoloured . . 45 25

1991. World Telecommunications Day.
1743 **343** 75 h. multicoloured . . . 25 15
1744 150 h. multicoloured . . 45 25

344 Thee el Halifa Migat, Medina

1991. Pilgrimmage to Mecca.
1745 **344** 75 h. multicoloured . . . 25 15
1746 150 h. multicoloured . . 45 25

345 Blackboard and I.L.Y. Emblem

346 Olive Branch and F.A.O. Emblem

1991. International Literacy Year.
1747 **345** 75 h. multicoloured . . . 25 15
1748 150 h. multicoloured . . 45 25

1991. World Food Day.
1749 **346** 75 h. multicoloured . . . 25 15
1750 150 h. multicoloured . . 45 25

347 Child's Profile and Emblem

1991. World Children's Day.
1751 **347** 75 h. multicoloured . . . 25 15
1752 150 h. multicoloured . . 45 25

348 Woodpecker

349 Arabian Bustard

350 Lark

351 Turtle Dove

352 Heron

353 Partridge

354 Hoopoe

355 Falcon

356 Houbara Bustard

1992. Birds.
1753 **348** 25 h. multicoloured . . . 10 10
1754 **349** 25 h. multicoloured . . . 10 10
1755 **350** 25 h. multicoloured . . 10 10
1756 **351** 25 h. multicoloured . . 10 10
1757 **352** 25 h. multicoloured . . 10 10
1758 **353** 25 h. multicoloured . . 10 10
1759 **354** 25 h. multicoloured . . 10 10
1760 **355** 25 h. multicoloured . . 10 10
1761 **356** 25 h. multicoloured . . 10 10
1762 **348** 50 h. multicoloured . . 15 10
1763 **349** 50 h. multicoloured . . 15 10
1764 **350** 50 h. multicoloured . . 15 10
1765 **351** 50 h. multicoloured . . 15 10
1766 **352** 50 h. multicoloured . . 15 10
1767 **353** 50 h. multicoloured . . 15 10
1768 **354** 50 h. multicoloured . . 15 10
1769 **355** 50 h. multicoloured . . 15 10
1770 **356** 50 h. multicoloured . . 15 10
1771 **348** 75 h. multicoloured . . 25 15
1772 **349** 75 h. multicoloured . . 25 15
1773 **350** 75 h. multicoloured . . 25 15
1774 **351** 75 h. multicoloured . . 25 15
1775 **352** 75 h. multicoloured . . 25 15
1776 **353** 75 h. multicoloured . . 25 15
1777 **354** 75 h. multicoloured . . 25 15
1778 **355** 75 h. multicoloured . . 25 15
1779 **356** 75 h. multicoloured . . 25 15
1780 **348** 100 h. multicoloured . . 35 20
1781 **349** 100 h. multicoloured . . 35 20
1782 **350** 100 h. multicoloured . . 35 20
1783 **351** 100 h. multicoloured . . 35 20
1784 **352** 100 h. multicoloured . . 35 20
1785 **353** 100 h. multicoloured . . 35 20
1786 **354** 100 h. multicoloured . . 35 20
1787 **355** 100 h. multicoloured . . 35 20
1788 **356** 100 h. multicoloured . . 35 20
1789 **348** 150 h. multicoloured . . 55 30
1790 **349** 150 h. multicoloured . . 55 30
1791 **350** 150 h. multicoloured . . 55 30
1792 **351** 150 h. multicoloured . . 55 30
1793 **352** 150 h. multicoloured . . 55 30
1794 **353** 150 h. multicoloured . . 55 30
1795 **354** 150 h. multicoloured . . 55 30
1796 **355** 150 h. multicoloured . . 55 30
1797 **356** 150 h. multicoloured . . 55 30

357 Heart and Cardiograph

358 Arabic Script

1992. World Health Day.
1798 **357** 75 h. multicoloured . . 25 15
1799 150 h. multicoloured . . 55 30

1992. Battle of Mt Uhod (between Mecca and Medina, 625 A.D.) Commemoration.
1800 **358** 75 h. green and orange . 25 15
1801 150 h. dp blue, bl & grn 55 30

359 Mosque, Yalamlam Miqat

1992. Pilgrimage to Mecca.
1802 **359** 75 h. multicoloured . . 25 15
1803 150 h. multicoloured . . 55 30

360 Human Pyramid inside House

1992. Population and Housing Census.
1804 **360** 75 h. multicoloured . . 25 15
1805 150 h. multicoloured . . 55 30

361 Vegetables

1992. World Food Day. Multicoloured.
1806 75 h. Type **361** 25 15
1807 150 h. Fruits 55 30

362 Regions System

363 Consultative Council System

364 Essential Governing System

1992. Declaration of Basic Law of Government.
1808 **362** 75 h. black, silver & grn . 25 15
1809 **363** 75 h. black, silver & grn . 25 15
1810 **364** 75 h. black, silver & grn . 25 15
1811 **362** 150 h. multicoloured . . 55 30
1812 **363** 150 h. multicoloured . . 55 30
1813 **364** 150 h. multicoloured . . 55 30

365 Flags, Globe and King Fahd Stadium

366 Blood Spot and W.H.O. Emblem

1993. Continental Cup Football Championship, Saudi Arabia.
1815 **365** 75 h. multicoloured . . . 25 15
1816 150 h. multicoloured . . 55 30

1993. World Health Day.
1817 **366** 75 h. multicoloured . . . 25 15
1818 150 h. multicoloured . . 55 30

367 Arabic Script

368 I.T.U. Emblem

1993. Battle of Khandaq (between Mecca and Medina, 627 A.D.) Commemoration.
1819 **367** 75 h. green and orange . 25 15
1820 150 h. dp blue, bl & grn . 55 30

1993. 25th Anniv of World Telecommunications Day.
1821 **368** 75 h. multicoloured . . . 25 15
1822 150 h. multicoloured . . 55 30

369 That Irq Migat

1993. Pilgrimage to Mecca.
1823 **369** 75 h. multicoloured . . . 25 15
1824 150 h. multicoloured . . 55 30

370 Desert, Oasis, Mountains and Sea Environments

1993. World Food Day.
1825 **370** 75 h. multicoloured . . . 25 15
1826 150 h. multicoloured . . 55 30

371 X-ray of Teeth and Cleaning Implements

1994. World Health Day.
1827 **371** 75 h. multicoloured . . . 25 15
1828 150 h. multicoloured . . 50 25

372 "100" and Olympic Rings

1994. Centenary of International Olympic Committee.
1829 **372** 75 h. multicoloured . . . 25 15
1830 150 h. multicoloured . . 50 25

373 Namirah Mosque and Tents

1994. Pilgrimage to Mecca.
1831 **373** 75 h. multicoloured . . . 25 15
1832 150 h. multicoloured . . 50 25

374 Arabic Script

1994. Battle of Khaibar Commemoration.
1833 **374** 75 h. green and gold . . 25 15
1834 150 h. blue, silver and green 50 25

375 Flag, International and Saudi Football Federation Emblems and Player

1994. Qualification of Saudi Arabian Team to Final Rounds of World Cup Football Championship, U.S.A. Multicoloured.
1835 75 h. Type **375** 25 15
1836 150 h. Maps of United States and Saudi Arabia and player (51 × 27 mm) 50 25

376 Council Building

1994. Establishment of Consultative Council (advisory body). Multicoloured.
1837 75 h. Type **376** 25 15
1838 150 h. Council building (closer view) 50 25

377 Freighters, Lighthouse and Car Park

1994. King Abdul Aziz Port, Damman.
1840 **377** 75 h. multicoloured . . . 25 15
1841 150 h. multicoloured . . 50 25

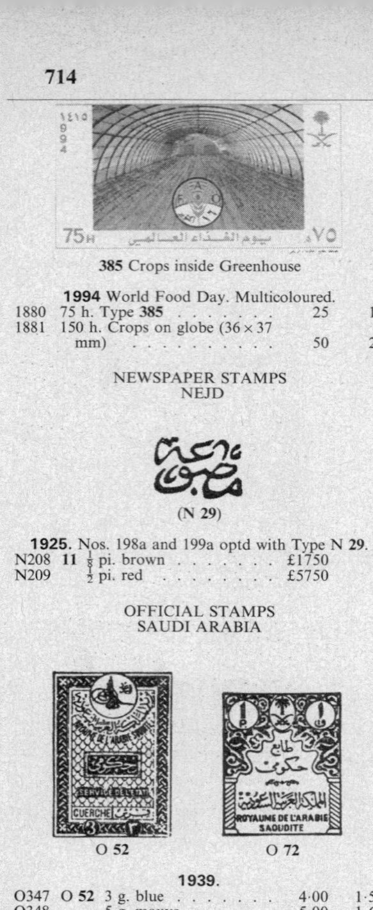

385 Crops inside Greenhouse

1994 World Food Day. Multicoloured.
1880 75 h. Type **385** 25 15
1881 150 h. Crops on globe (36 × 37 mm) 50 25

NEWSPAPER STAMPS
NEJD

(N 29)

1925. Nos. 198a and 199a optd with Type N **29**.
N208 **11** $\frac{1}{8}$ pi. brown £1750
N209 $\frac{1}{2}$ pi. red £5750

OFFICIAL STAMPS
SAUDI ARABIA

O 52 O 72

1939.
O347 **O 52** 3 g. blue 4·00 1·50
O348 5 g. mauve 5·00 1·60
O349 20 g. brown 7·00 4·00
O350 50 g. turquoise 18·00 10·00
O351 100 g. olive 70·00 40·00
O352 200 g. purple 60·00 80·00

1961. Size $18\frac{1}{2} \times 22\frac{1}{2}$ mm.
O449 **O 72** 1 p. black 1·00 50
O450 2 p. green 1·50 60
O451 3 p. bistre 2·00 90
O452 4 p. blue 2·50 1·25
O453 5 p. red 3·00 1·50
O454 10 p. purple 5·00 2·75
O455 20 p. violet 10·00 4·50
O456 50 p. brown 25·00 15·00
O457 100 p. bronze 55·00 30·00

1964. Size 21 × 26 mm.
O497 **O 72** 1 p. black 2·00 60
O498 2 p. green 4·00 1·25
O504 3 p. ochre 5·00 2·00
O505 4 p. blue 5·00 2·00
O506 5 p. red 3·00 3·00
O507 6 p. purple 5·00 3·00
O508 7 p. green 8·00 3·00
O509 8 p. red 8·00 3·00
O510 9 p. red 40·00
O511 10 p. brown 8·00 3·00
O512 11 p. turquoise 50·00
O513 12 p. violet 50·00
O514 13 p. turquoise 9·00 4·00
O515 14 p. violet 9·00 4·00
O516 15 p. orange 65·00 7·50
O517 16 p. black 65·00 7·50
O518 17 p. green 65·00
O519 18 p. yellow 65·00
O520 19 p. purple 65·00
O521 23 p. blue 80·00
O522 24 p. green 65·00
O523 26 p. bistre 65·00
O524 27 p. lilac 65·00
O525 31 p. brown £110
O526 33 p. green £110
O527 50 p. olive £650
O528 100 p. olive £550

O 111

1970.
O1040 **O 111** 1 p. brown 5·00 25
O1041 2 p. green 5·00 25
O1042 3 p. mauve 7·00 40
O1043 4 p. blue 10·00 50
O1044 5 p. red 10·00 60
O1045 6 p. orange 10·00 75
O1046 7 p. red
O1047 8 p. violet
O1048 9 p. blue
O1049 10 p. blue 7·50 1·25
O1050 11 p. green
O1050a 12 p. brown
O1051 20 p. blue 12·00 2·00
O1051b 23 p. brown
O1052 31 p. purple 14·50 3·00
O1053 50 p. brown
O1054 100 p. green

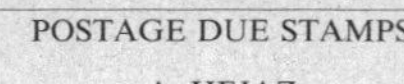

POSTAGE DUE STAMPS

A. HEJAZ

D 7 From Old Door at El Ashra Barsbai,Shari El Ashrafuga, Cairo

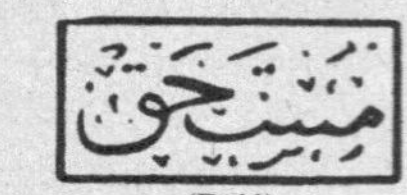

(D 11)

1917. Arabic designs as Type D **7**.
D17 20 pa. red 5·00 1·00
D18 1 pi. blue 5·00 1·00
D19 2 pi. red 5·00 1·00

1921. Nos. D17/19 optd with T **7**.
D31a 20 pa. red 20·00
D33 1 pi. blue 10·00 2·50
D34 2 pi. red 10·00 3·00

1922. Nos. D17/19 optd with T **10**.
D39 20 pa. red 25·00 12·00
D40 1 pi. blue 3·00 60
D41 2 pi. red 5·00 70

1923. Optd with Type D **11**.
D47 **11** $\frac{1}{2}$ pi. red 7·00 2·00
D48 1 pi. blue 9·00 5·00
D49 2 pi. orange 5·00 3·00

1924. Nos. D47/9 optd with T **14**.
D57 **11** $\frac{1}{2}$ pi. red £2500
D58 1 pi. blue £2500
D59 2 pi. orange £2500

1925. Nos. D17/9 optd with T **15**.
D88 20 pa. red £400 £350
D90 1 pi. blue 20·00 12·00
D92 2 pi. red 15·00 10·00

1925. Nos. D17/9 optd with T **16**.
D93 20 pa. red £750
D94 1 pi. blue 20·00
D96 2 pi. red 15·00

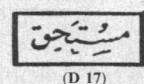

(D 17)

1925. Stamps of 1924 (optd T **16**) optd with Type D **17**.
D149 **11** $\frac{1}{2}$ pi. red 70·00
D150 $1\frac{1}{2}$ pi. violet 70·00
D151 2 pi. orange 70·00
D152 3 pi. brown 70·00
D153 5 pi. olive 70·00

(D 18)

D 25

1925. Stamps of 1922 optd with Type D **18**.
D154 **11** $\frac{1}{8}$ pi. brown 30·00
D155 $\frac{1}{2}$ pi. red 30·00
D156 1 pi. blue 30·00
D157 $1\frac{1}{2}$ pi. lilac 30·00
D158 2 pi. orange 30·00
D160 3 pi. brown 30·00
D161 5 pi. olive 40·00
D162 10 pi. brown and mauve 40·00

1925. Nos. D154/62 optd with Type D **17**.
D163 **11** $\frac{1}{8}$ pi. brown 15·00 4·50
D164 $\frac{1}{2}$ pi. red 15·00 4·50
D165 1 pi. blue 20·00 6·00
D166 $1\frac{1}{2}$ pi. lilac 15·00 4·50
D167 2 pi. orange 15·00 4·50
D169 3 pi. brown 15·00 4·50
D170 5 pi. olive 15·00 4·50
D171 10 pi. brown and mauve 20·00 9·00

1925. Optd with T **24**.
D186 **D 25** $\frac{1}{2}$ pi. blue 2·00
D187 1 pi. orange 2·00
D188 2 pi. brown 2·00
D189 3 pi. red 2·00
These stamps without overprint were not officially issued.

B. NEJD

1925. Nos. D47/9 of Hejaz optd with T **25**.
D203 **11** $\frac{1}{2}$ pi. red 20·00
D204c 1 pi. blue 35·00
D205c 2 pi. orange 35·00

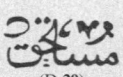

(D 29) (D 33)

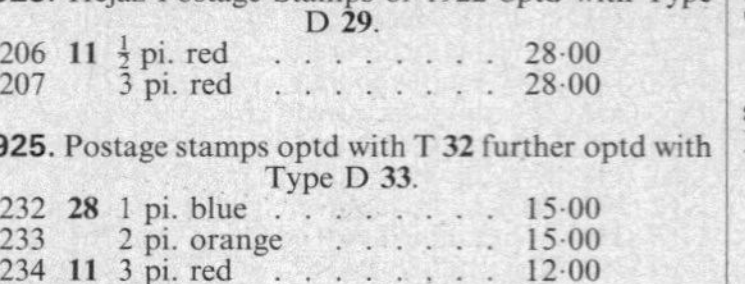

1925. Hejaz Postage Stamps of 1922 optd with Type D **29**.
D206 **11** $\frac{1}{2}$ pi. red 28·00
D207 3 pi. red 28·00

1925. Postage stamps optd with T **32** further optd with Type D **33**.
D232 **28** 1 pi. blue 15·00
D233 2 pi. orange 15·00
D234 **11** 3 pi. red 12·00
D236 **28** 5 pi. green 25·00

1925. No. D40 of Hejaz optd with T **32**.
D238 **D 7** 1 pi. blue 55·00

C. HEJAZ-NEJD

D 40

D 42 Tougra of Ibn Saud

1926.
D267 **D 40** $\frac{1}{2}$ pi. red 2·50 1·00
D270 2 pi. orange 2·50
D272 6 pi. brown 2·50

1926. Pan-Islamic Congress, Cairo. Optd with T **40**.
D281 **D 40** $\frac{1}{2}$ pi. red 6·00 2·00
D282 2 pi. orange 6·00 2·00
D283 6 pi. brown 6·00 2·00

1927.
D292 **D 42** 1 pi. grey 15·00 2·00
D293 2 pi. violet 17·00 2·00

D. SAUDI ARABIA

1935. No. 331a optd **T** in a circle.
D343 **49** $\frac{1}{2}$ g. red £200

D 52

D 72

1937.
D347 **D 52** $\frac{1}{2}$ g. brown 7·00 4·40
D348 1 g. blue 8·00 4·50
D349 2 g. purple 14·00 10·00

1961.
D449 **D 72** 1 p. violet 5·00 7·00
D450 2 p. green 7·00 9·00
D451 4 p. red 12·00 15·00

SAXONY Pt. 7

A former kingdom in S. Germany. Stamps superseded in 1868 by those of the North German Federation.

10 pfennige = 1 neugroschen
30 neugroschen = 1 thaler

1

2

3 Friedrich August II

1850. Imperf.
1 **1** 3 pf. red £4500 £4250

1851. Imperf.
7 **2** 3 pf. green 90·00 65·00

1851. Imperf.
10 **3** $\frac{1}{2}$ ngr. black on grey 48·00 7·50
12 1 ngr. black on red 48·00 7·00
13 2 ngr. black on blue £200 42·00
14 3 ngr. black on yellow £130 16·00

4 King Johann I

5

6

1855. Imperf.
16 **4** $\frac{1}{2}$ ngr. black on grey 8·00 2·25
18 1 ngr. black on red 8·00 1·50
20 2 ngr. black on blue 25·00 5·50
23 3 ngr. black on yellow 16·00 3·25
24 5 ngr. red 65·00 32·00
28 10 ngr. blue £200 £225

1863. Perf.
31 **5** 3 pf. green 75 15·00
36 $\frac{1}{2}$ ngr. orange 60 2·25
39 **6** 1 ngr. red 60 85
40 2 ngr. blue 1·00 3·25
42 3 ngr. brown 1·25 6·50
45 5 ngr. blue 6·50 32·00
46 5 ngr. purple 13·00 35·00
49 5 ngr. grey 6·50 £100

SCHLESWIG (SLESVIG) Pt. 7

Stamps issued during the plebiscite of 1920.

100 pfennig = 1 German mark
100 ore = 1 Danish krone

1 Arms

3 View of Schleswig

1920.
1 **1** $2\frac{1}{2}$ pf. grey 10 10
2 5 pf. green 10 10
3 $7\frac{1}{2}$ pf. brown 10 10
4 10 pf. red 10 10
5 15 pf. red 10 10
6 20 pf. blue 10 15
7 25 pf. orange 25 25
8 35 pf. brown 45 45
9 40 pf. violet 25 20
10 75 pf. green 40 1·00
11 **3** 1 m. brown 35 65
12 2 m. blue 70 1·75
13 5 m. green 1·00 3·00
14 10 m. red 2·00 5·00

1920. Values in Danish currency and optd **1. ZONE**.
29 **1** 1 ore grey 10 60
30 5 ore green 10 30
31 7 ore brown 10 45
32 10 ore red 15 60
33 15 ore red 15 60
34 20 ore blue 15 75
35 25 ore orange 30 2·75
36 35 ore brown 90 6·00
37 40 ore violet 40 2·00
38 75 ore green 40 4·00
39 **3** 1 k. brown 60 4·50
40 2 k. blue 5·50 27·00
41 5 k. green 3·50 27·00
42 10 k. red 8·50 50·00

OFFICIAL STAMPS

1920. Nos. 1/14 optd **C.I.S.** (= "Comission Interalliee Slesvig").
O15 **1** $2\frac{1}{2}$ pf. grey 45·00 70·00
O16 5 pf. green 45·00 80·00
O17 $7\frac{1}{2}$ pf. brown 45·00 70·00
O18 10 pf. red 45·00 80·00
O19 15 pf. red 32·00 40·00
O20 20 pf. blue 40·00 45·00

O21 1 25 pf. orange 85·00 £120
O22 35 pf. brown 85·00 £130
O23 40 pf. violet 70·00 75·00
O24 75 pf. green 75·00 £190
O25 3 1 m. brown 80·00 £190
O26 2 m. blue £130 £200
O27 5 m. green £170 £350
O28 10 m. red £350 £475

SCHLESWIG-HOLSTEIN Pt. 7

Two former grand-duchies to the S. of Denmark, annexed to Prussia in 1866. Part of Schleswig reverted to Denmark as a result of the plebiscite of 1920. The remainder is part of West Germany.

16 schilling = 1 mark

1

2

1850. Imperf.
2 1 1 s. blue £250 £4500
4 2 s. red £450 £6000

1865. Inscr "SCHLESWIG-HOLSTEIN". Roul.
6 2 ½ s. red 25·00 42·00
7 1¼ s. green 11·00 18·00
8 1⅓ s. mauve 38·00 £120
9 2 s. blue 40·00 £225
10 4 s. bistre 48·00 £1100

1864. Inscr "HERZOGTH. SCHLESWIG". Roul.
24 2 ½ s. green 26·00 48·00
21 1¼ s. green 38·00 13·00
25 1¼ s. lilac 55·00 14·00
27 1⅓ s. red 26·00 60·00
28 2 s. blue 22·00 48·00
22 4 s. red 95·00 £400
29 4 s. bistre 26·00 80·00

6

9

10

1864. Imperf or roul.
51 6 1¼ s. blue 35·00 45·00
59 9 1¼ s. blue 32·00 14·00

1865. Roul.
61 10 ½ s. green 55·00 90·00
62 1¼ s. mauve 32·00 15·00
63 1⅓ s. red 55·00 38·00
64 2 s. blue 40·00 42·00
65 4 s. bistre 45·00 70·00

On the 1⅓ s. and 4 s. the word "SCHILLING" is inside the central oval.

1868. Inscr "HERZOGTH HOLSTEIN". Roul.
66 2 1¼ s. purple 60·00 15·00
67 2 s. blue £120 £130

SENEGAL Pt. 6; Pt. 14

A French colony incorporated in French West Africa in 1944. In 1958 Senegal became an autonomous State within the French Community and in 1959 joined the Sudan to form the Mali Federation. In 1960 the Federation broke up with Mali and Senegal becoming independent republics.

100 centimes = 1 franc

1887. Stamps of French Colonies, "Commerce" type surch in figures.
1 J 5 on 20 c. red on green £120 £120
2 5 on 30 c. brown on drab £190 £190
3 10 on 4 c. brown on green 50·00 50·00
4a 10 on 20 c. red on green £375 £375
5 15 on 20 c. red on green 40·00 40·00

1892. Stamps of French Colonies, "Commerce" type, surch **SENEGAL** and new value.
6 J 75 on 15 c. blue on blue £350 £120
7 1 f. on 5 c. green on green £350 £140

1892. "Tablet" key-type inscr "SENEGAL ET DEPENDANCES".
8 D 1 c. black and red on blue 50 40
9 2 c. brown & blue on buff 1·40 1·00
10 4 c. red and blue on grey 90 90
21 5 c. green and red 85 40
12 10 c. black & blue on lilac 4·75 3·00
22 10 c. red and blue 2·25 40
13 15 c. blue and red 4·25 75
23 15 c. grey and red 2·25 80
14 20 c. red & blue on green 4·00 4·00
15 25 c. black & red on pink 6·00 2·25
24 25 c. blue and red 14·00 20·00
16 30 c. brown & bl on drab 6·75 5·00
17 40 c. red & blue on yellow 13·00 12·00
18 50 c. red and blue on pink 16·00 16·00
25 50 c. brown & red on blue 27·00 27·00
19 75 c. brown & red on orge 8·50 10·00
20 1 f. green and red 10·50 10·00

1903. Surch.
26 D 5 on 40 c. red & blue on yell 8·25 8·50
27 10 on 50 c. red and blue on pink 11·50 11·50
28 10 on 75 c. brown and red on orange 11·50 11·50
29 10 on 1 f. green and red 50·00 45·00

1906. "Faidherbe". "Palms" and "Balay" key types inscr "SENEGAL".
33 I 1 c. grey and red 70 30
34 2 c. brown and red 70 40
34a 2 c. brown and blue 2·00 2·00
35 4 c. brown & red on blue 80 25
36 5 c. green and red 1·50 35
37 10 c. pink and blue 4·75 35
38 15 c. violet and red 4·00 1·75
39 J 20 c. black & red on blue 3·00 1·75
40 25 c. blue and red 1·10 75
41 30 c. brn & red on pink 3·50 3·50
42 35 c. black & red on yell 12·00 85
43 40 c. red & blue on blue 5·25 5·00
44 45 c. brown & red on grn 11·00 8·75
45 50 c. violet and red 5·00 4·25
46 75 c. green & red on orge 3·75 2·75
47 K 1 f. black & red on blue 14·50 12·50
48 2 f. blue and red on pink 22·00 17·00
49 5 f. red & blue on yellow 40·00 35·00

1912. Surch.
58 D 05 on 15 c. grey and red 25 40
59 05 on 20 c. red and blue on green 45 70
60 05 on 30 c. brown and blue on drab 45 70
61 10 on 40 c. red and blue on yellow 50 70
62 10 on 50 c. red and blue 1·75 2·00
63 10 on 75 c. brown and red on orange 3·00 3·75

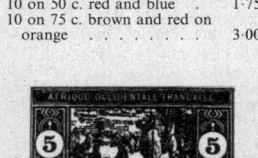

33 Market

1914.
64 33 1 c. violet and brown 10 10
65 2 c. blue and black 10 10
66 4 c. brown and grey 10 10
67 5 c. green and light green 10 10
91 5 c. red and black 15 10
68 10 c. pink and red 20 10
92 10 c. green and light green 25 20
113 10 c. blue and purple 10 10
69 15 c. purple and brown 10 10
70 20 c. grey and brown 10 15
114 20 c. green 10 25
115 20 c. blue and grey 20 30
71 25 c. blue and ultramarine 20 15
93 25 c. black and red 15 10
72 30 c. pink and black 10 10
94 30 c. carmine and red 30 45
116 30 c. blue and grey 35 20
117 30 c. green and olive 35 35
73 35 c. violet and orange 10 30
74 40 c. green and violet 45 10
75 45 c. brown and blue 70 80
95 45 c. blue and red 15 35
118 45 c. red and carmine 20 20
119 45 c. red and brown 1·90 2·00
76 50 c. blue and purple 45 60
96 50 c. blue and ultramarine 65 95
120 50 c. green and red 15 10
121 60 c. violet on pink 15 30
122 65 c. green and red 15 10
77 75 c. pink and grey 35 65
123 75 c. light blue and blue 35 50
124 75 c. blue and pink 75 75
125 90 c. carmine and red 70 65
78 1 f. black and violet 35 65
126 1 f. blue 60 50
127 1 f. blue and black 60 20
128 1 f. 10 black and green 2·00 2·00
129 1 f. 25 red and green 60 60
130 1 f. 50 light blue and blue 1·25 75
131 1 f. 75 green and brown 4·75 50
79 2 f. blue and pink 1·60 1·50
97 2 f. brown and blue 1·40 45
132 3 f. mauve on pink 2·50 75
80 5 f. violet and green 2·00 70

1915. Surch **5c** and red cross.
89 33 10 c. + 5 c. pink and red 60 85
90 15 c. + 5 c. purple & brown 50 90

1922. Surch.
102 33 0,01 on 15 c. purple & brn 15 40
103 0,02 on 15 c. purple & brn 15 40
104 0,04 on 15 c. purple & brn 15 35
105 0,05 on 15 c. purple & brn 15 35
106 25 c. on 5 f. violet on green 50 30
98 60 on 15 c. purple & pink 50 30
99 65 on 15 c. purple & brown 50 30
100 85 on 15 c. purple & brown 60 80
101 85 on 75 c. pink and grey 65 80
107 90 c. on 75 c. pink & red 35 60
108 1 f. 25 on 1 f. blue 30 40
109 1 f. 50 on 1 f. lt blue & bl 55 45
110 3 f. on 5 f. brown & purple 75 50
111 10 f. on 5 f. red and blue 3·75 2·00
112 20 f. on 5 f. brown & mauve 4·75 4·00

1931. "Colonial Exhibition" key-types.
135 E 40 c. green and black 1·40 1·40
136 F 50 c. mauve and black 1·40 1·40
137 G 90 c. red and black 1·25 1·25
138 H 1 f. 50 blue and black 1·40 1·40

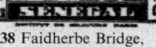

38 Faidherbe Bridge, Dakar

39 Senegalese Girl

1935.
139 38 1 c. blue (postage) 10 30
140 2 c. brown 10 25
141 3 c. violet 10 25
142 4 c. blue 10 50
143 5 c. orange 10 15
144 10 c. purple 10 20
145 15 c. black 10 15
146 20 c. red 10 20
147 25 c. brown 25 15
148 30 c. green 15 30
149 39 35 c. green 45 50
150 38 40 c. red 15 20
151 45 c. green 15 20
152 A 50 c. orange 10 20
153 39 55 c. brown 40 40
154 A 60 c. violet 20 25
155 65 c. violet 25 15
156 70 c. brown 45 50
157 75 c. brown 70 40
158 39 80 c. violet 65 50
159 A 90 c. red 85 95
160 39 90 c. violet 50 40
161 A 1 f. violet 6·00 1·25
162 39 1 f. red 1·25 60
163 1 f. brown 15 15
164 A 1 f. 25 brown 30 55
165 1 f. 25 red 30 55
166 1 f. 40 green 30 40
167 1 f. 50 blue 20 20
168 1 f. 60 blue 50 40
169 1 f. 75 green 35 20
170 39 1 f. 75 blue 55 60
171 A 2 f. blue 45 20
172 39 2 f. 25 blue 40 20
173 2 f. 50 black 65 85
174 A 3 f. green 30 20
175 5 f. brown 20 30
176 10 f. red 80 50
177 20 f. grey 65 50

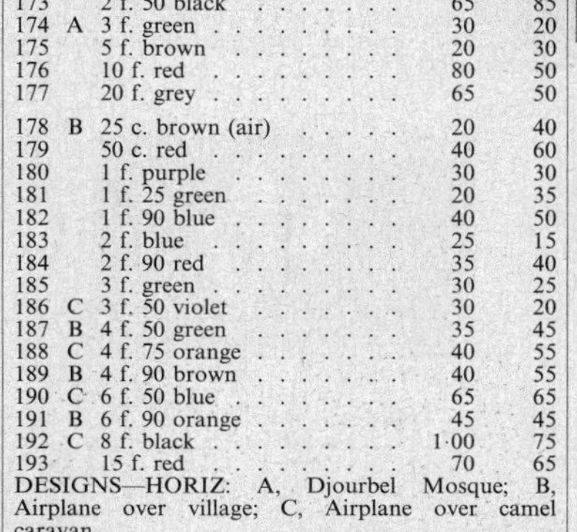

178 B 25 c. brown (air) 20 40
179 50 c. red 40 60
180 1 f. purple 30 30
181 1 f. 25 green 20 35
182 1 f. 90 blue 40 50
183 2 f. blue 25 15
184 2 f. 90 red 35 40
185 3 f. green 30 25
186 C 3 f. 50 violet 30 20
187 B 4 f. 50 green 35 45
188 C 4 f. 75 orange 40 55
189 B 4 f. 90 brown 40 55
190 C 6 f. 50 blue 65 65
191 B 6 f. 90 orange 45 45
192 C 8 f. black 1·00 75
193 15 f. red 70 65

DESIGNS—HORIZ: A, Djourbel Mosque; B, Airplane over village; C, Airplane over camel caravan.

1937. International Exhibition, Paris. As Nos. 168/73 of St.-Pierre et Miquelon.
194 20 c. violet 40 60
195 30 c. green 40 55
196 40 c. red 35 55
197 50 c. brown 35 70
198 90 c. red 35 70
199 1 f. 50 blue 50 1·40

1938. International Anti-Cancer Fund. As T **22** of Mauritania.
201 1 f. 75 + 50 c. blue 3·50 6·00

1939. Death Centenary of Rene Caillie (explorer). As T **27** of Mauritania.
202 90 c. orange 25 35
203 2 f. violet 35 50
204 2 f. 25 blue 35 50

1939. New York World's Fair. As T **28** of Mauritania.
205 1 f. 25 red 40 50
206 2 f. 25 blue 40 55

1939. 150th Anniv of French Revolution. As T **29** of Mauritania.
207 45 c. + 25 c. green and black (postage) 4·00 4·75
208 70 c. + 30 c. brown & black 4·00 4·75
209 90 c. + 35 c. orange & black 4·00 4·75
210 1 f. 25 + 1 f. red and black 4·25 4·75
211 2 f. 25 + 2 f. blue and black 4·25 4·75
212 4 f. 75 + 4 f. blk & orge (air) 6·75 6·75

1941. National Defence Fund. Surch **SECOURS NATIONAL** and value.
213 + 1 f. on 50 c. (No. 152) 2·00 2·00
214 + 2 f. on 80 c. (No. 158) 2·00 2·00
215 + 2 f. on 1 f. 50 (No. 167) 3·00 3·00
216 + 3 f. on 2 f. (No. 171) 2·75 2·75

1942. Air. Colonial Child Welfare Fund. As Nos. 98g/i of Niger.
216a 1 f. 50 + 3 f. 50 green 15
216b 2 f. + 6 f. brown 15
216c 3 f. + 9 f. red 15

1942. Air. "Imperial Fortnight". As No. 98j of Niger.
216d 1 f. 20 + 1 f. 80 blue and red 15

1942. Air. As T **32** of Mauritania, but inscr "SENEGAL" and similar design.
217 50 f. green and yellow 1·00 1·25
218 100 f. blue and red 1·50 1·50

DESIGN—48×26 mm: 100 f. Twin-engined airliner landing.

1944. Stamps of 1935 surch.
219 38 1 f. 50 on 15 c. black 40 30
220 A 1 f. 50 on 65 c. violet 30 40
221 38 4 f. 50 on 15 c. black 40 40
222 5 f. 50 on 2 c. brown 85 80
223 A 5 f. 50 on 65 c. violet 40 50
224 38 10 f. on 15 c. black 1·10 1·00
225 A 50 f. on 65 c. violet 1·25 1·25

1944. No. 202 surch.
226 20 f. on 90 c. orange 65 75
227 50 f. on 90 c. orange 1·90 2·00

42 African Buffalo

1960. Niokolo-Koba National Park.
228 – 5 f. purple, black & green 15 10
229 42 10 f. purple, black & green 35 15
230 – 15 f. purple, brown & sepia 40 30
231 – 20 f. brown, green & chest 50 30
232 – 25 f. brown, choc & green 60 40
233 – 85 f. multicoloured 1·90 1·00

ANIMALS—VERT: 5 f. Roan antelope; 15 f. Warthog; 20 f. Giant eland; 85 f. Waterbuck. HORIZ: 25 f. Bushbuck.

43 African Fish Eagle

44 Mother and Child

1960. Air.
234 – 50 f. multicoloured 3·25 1·25
235 – 100 f. multicoloured 5·50 1·75
236 – 200 f. multicoloured 11·00 5·50
237 – 250 f. multicoloured 14·00 6·75
238 43 500 f. multicoloured 28·00 9·25

BIRDS—VERT: 50 f. Carmine bee-eater; 200 f. Violet turaco; 250 f. Red bishop. HORIZ: 100 f. Abyssinian roller.

1961. Independence Commemoration.
239 44 25 f. brown, blue & green 25 20

45 Pirogue Race

1961. Sports.
240 – 50 c. brown, blue & sepia 10 10
241 45 1 f. purple, turq & green 10 10
242 – 2 f. sepia, bistre and blue 10 10
243 – 30 f. purple and red 70 25
244 – 45 f. black, blue & brown 95 35

DESIGNS: 50 c. African wrestling; 2 f. Horse race; 30 f. African dancers; 45 f. Lion game.

46 Senegal Flag, U.N. Emblem and H.Q. Building

1962. 1st Anniv of Admission of Senegal to U.N.O.
245 46 10 f. red, ochre and green 15 15
246 30 f. green, ochre and red 30 25
247 85 f. multicoloured 1·10 55

47 I.T.U. Emblems, African Map and Telephonist

48 Boxing

1962. 1st I.T.U. African Plan Sub-Committee Meeting, Dakar.
248 47 25 f. multicoloured 25 20

1962. Air. "Air Afrique" Airline. As T **42** of Mauritania.
249 25 f. purple, brown & myrtle 35 20

1962. Malaria Eradication. As T **43** of Mauritania.
250 25 f. + 5 f. turquoise 40 35

1962. 1st Anniv of Union of African and Malagasy States. As T **45** of Mauritania.
251 30 f. turquoise 40 35

1963. Freedom from Hunger. As T **51** of Mauritania.
252 25 f. + 5 f. olive, brn & vio . . 35 35

1963. Dakar Games. Inscr as in T **48**. Centres brown; inscr and frame colours given.
253 **48** 10 f. red and green 15 10
254 – 15 f. ochre and blue 20 15
255 – 20 f. red and blue 25 15
256 – 25 f. green and blue 30 20
257 – 30 f. red and green 70 25
258 – 85 f. blue . . . . 1·60 1·00
DESIGNS—HORIZ: 15 f. Diving; 20 f. High-jumping. VERT: 25 f. Football; 30 f. Basketball; 85 f. Running.

49 Main Motif of U.P.U. Monument, Berne
50 "Charaxes varanes"

1963. 2nd Anniv of Admission to U.P.U.
259 **49** 10 f. red and green 20 15
260 15 f. brown and blue . . . 20 20
261 30 f. blue and brown . . . 45 25

1963. Butterflies. Butterflies in natural colours; inscr in black; background colours given.
262 **50** 30 f. blue 90 40
263 – 45 f. orange . . . . 1·40 60
264 – 50 f. yellow . . . . 1·50 85
265 – 85 f. red . . . . 3·75 1·40
266 – 100 f. blue . . . . 4·50 2·10
267 – 500 f. green . . . . 15·00 6·75
BUTTERFLIES: 45 f. "Papilio nireus"; 10 f. "Colotis danae"; 85 f. "Epiphora bauhiniae"; 100 f. "Junonia hierta"; 500 f. "Danaus chrysippus".

1963. Air. 2nd Anniv of African and Malagasian Posts and Telecommunications Union. As T **56** of Mauritania.
268 85 f. multicoloured . . . . . 1·10 55

51 G. Berger, Owl and "Prospective" (book)

1963. 3rd Death Anniv of Prof. Gaston Berger (educationalist).
269 **51** 25 f. multicoloured 30 20

1963. Air. 1st Anniv of "Air Afrique" and "DC-8" Service Inauguration. As T **59** of Mauritania.
270 50 f. multicoloured . . . . . 1·25 55

52 Globe, Scales of Justice and Flag
53 Mother and Child

1963. 15th Anniv of Declaration of Human Rights.
271 **52** 60 f. multicoloured 65 40

1963. Senegalese Red Cross.
272 **53** 25 f. multicoloured 30 25

54 Temple Gods, Abu Simbel

1964. Air. Nubian Monument Preservation Fund.
273 **54** 25 f. + 5 f. brown, green and turquoise . . . . 1·10 70

55 Independence Monument
57 Titanium Sand Dredger

56 Allegorical Figures of Twin Towns

1964. Air.
274 **55** 300 f. multicoloured . . . 3·50 1·75

1964. Air. World Twin Towns Federation Congress, Dakar.
275 **56** 150 f. brown, black & turq 2·75 1·40

1964. Senegal Industries.
276 **57** 5 f. brown, turq & lake . . 15 15
277 – 10 f. blue, brown & green . 15 10
278 – 15 f. brown, green & blue . 20 10
279 – 20 f. purple, bistre & blue 25 10
280 – 25 f. black, ochre and blue 30 10
281 – 85 f. brown, blue and red . 1·60 1·10
DESIGNS: 10 f. Titanium sorting works; 15 f. Rufisque cement works; 20 f. Loading phosphate at Pallo; 25 f. Working phosphate at Taiba; 85 f. Mineral wharf, Dakar.

58 "Supporting the Globe"

1964. Air. "Europafrique".
282 **58** 50 f. multicoloured . . . . 1·25 55

59 Basketball
60 "Syncom 2" Satellite and Rocket

1964. Air. Olympic Games, Tokyo.
283 **59** 85 f. brown and blue . . . 1·75 70
284 – 100 f. purple and green . . 2·00 90
DESIGN: 100 f. Pole-vaulting.

1964. Air. Space Telecommunications.
285 **60** 150 f. blue, brown & grn . 2·00 1·25

1964. French, African and Malagasy Co-operation. As T **68** of Mauritania.
286 100 f. brown, red and green 1·40 90

61 Church of Ste. Therese, Dakar
62 Pres. Kennedy

1964. Religious Buildings.
287 **61** 5 f. lake, green and blue . . 10 10
288 – 10 f. brown, black and blue 15 10
289 – 15 f. slate, brown and blue . 20 15
DESIGNS—HORIZ: 10 f. Touba Mosque. VERT: 15 f. Dakar Mosque.

1964. Air. Pres. Kennedy Commemoration.
290 **62** 100 f. brown, yellow & grn . 1·75 1·00

63 Child and Microscope

1965. Anti-Leprosy Campaign.
292 **63** 20 f. black, green & brown . 25 20
293 – 65 f. multicoloured 90 45
DESIGN: 65 f. Peycouk Village.

64 Haute Casamance

1965. Senegal Landscapes.
294 **64** 25 f. green, brown and blue (postage) 25 15
295 – 30 f. blue, green & brown . 30 15
296 – 45 f. turq, green and brown 75 30
297 – 100 f. black, green and bistre (air) . . . . 1·50 70
DESIGNS: 30 f. Sangalkam; 45 f. Senegal River forest region; 100 f. Banks of Gambia River, East Senegal (48 × 27 mm).

65 A. Seck (Director of Posts, 1873–1931)
66 Berthon-Ader Telephone

1965. Postal Services Commemoration.
298 **65** 10 f. black and brown . . . 15 15
299 – 15 f. brown and green . . . 20 15
DESIGN—HORIZ: 15 f. P.T.T. Headquarters, Dakar.

1965. I.T.U. Centenary.
300 **66** 50 f. brown, bistre & grn . . 50 30
301 – 60 f. red, green and blue . . 80 50
302 – 85 f. purple, red and blue . 80 50
DESIGNS: 60 f. Cable-ship "Alsace"; 85 f. Picard's submarine telegraph cable relay apparatus.

67 Ploughing with Oxen

1965. Rural Development.
303 **67** 25 f. brown, violet and green 35 25
304 – 60 f. multicoloured 90 45
305 – 85 f. black, red and green . 1·25 55
DESIGNS—VERT: 50 f. Millet cultivation. HORIZ: 85 f. Rice cultivation, Casamance.

68 Goree Pirogue under Sail
69 Woman holding Child and U.N. Emblems

1965. Senegal Pirogues. Multicoloured.
306 10 f. Type **68** 20 15
307 20 f. Large pirogue at Seumbedioune 25 15
308 30 f. One-man pirogue at Fadiouth Island 65 20
309 45 f. One-man pirogue on Senegal River 95 65

1965. Air. International Co-operation Year.
310 **69** 50 f. brown, green & blue . 55 30

70 "Fruit of Cashew Tree"
71 "The Gentleman of Fashion"

1965. Fruits. Multicoloured.
311 10 f. Type **70** 15 10
312 15 f. Papaw 20 15
313 20 f. Mango 25 10
314 30 f. Groundnuts 30 15

1966. Goree Puppets.
315 **71** 1 f. blue, brown and red 10 10
316 – 2 f. orange, brown & blue 10 10
317 – 3 f. blue, brown and red 10 10
318 – 4 f. green, brown & violet 10 10
PUPPETS: 2 f. "The Lady of Fashion"; 3 f. "The Pedlar"; 4 f. "The Pounder".

72 Tom-tom Player

1966. World Festival of Negro Arts, Dakar ("Announcement").
319 **72** 30 f. brown, red & green . 30 15
See also Nos. 327/30.

73 Rocket "Diamant"

1966. Air. French Satellites.
320 **73** 50 f. red, blue & brown 70 40
321 – 50 f. black, brown & grn 70 40
322 – 90 f. blue, brown & slate 1·40 75
DESIGNS: No. 321, Satellite "A1"; No. 322, Rocket "Scout" and satellite "FR1".

74 Mackerel Tuna
76 Arms of Senegal

75 Satellite "D1"

1966. Senegal Fishes. Multicoloured.
323 20 f. Type **74** 25 15
324 30 f. Grouper 40 20
325 50 f. Wrasse 90 35
326 100 f. Parrot fish . . . . . . 1·75 65

1966. World Festival of Negro Arts, Dakar. As T **72**.
327 15 f. lake, orange and blue . . 15 15
328 30 f. lake, yellow and blue . . 35 20
329 75 f. black, lake and blue . . 1·25 55
330 90 f. lake, black and orange . 1·40 65
DESIGNS: 15 f. Statuette ("Sculpture"); 50 f. Musical instrument ("Music"); 75 f. Carving ("Dance"); 90 f. Ideogram.

1966. Air. Launching of Satellite "D 1".
332 **75** 100 f. blue, lake & violet . 1·50 65

1966.
333 **76** 30 f. multicoloured 25 15

1966. Air. Inauguration of DC-8F Air Services. As T **87** of Mauritania.
334 30 f. yellow, black & brown . 30 20

77 "Argemone mexicana"

79 Port of Ile de Goree

78 Couzinet 70 "Arc en Ciel"

1966. Flowers. Multicoloured.
335 45 f. Type **77** 45 20
336 55 f. "Dichrostachys glomerata" 50 25
337 60 f. "Haemanthus multiflorus" 60 35
338 90 f. "Adansonia digitata" . . 1·50 50

1966. Air. 30th Anniv of Disappearance of Jean Mermoz (aviator).
339 **78** 20 f. slate, purple and blue 30 20
340 – 35 f. slate, brown & green . 70 20
341 – 100 f. lake, emer & green . 1·25 45
342 – 150 f. lake, black and blue . 2·50 1·00
DESIGNS—HORIZ: 35 f. Latecoere 300 flying boat "Croix du Sud"; 100 f. Map of Mermoz's last flight across Atlantic Ocean. VERT: 150 f. Jean Mermoz.

1966. Tourism.
343 **79** 20 f. lake, blue and black . 20 15
344 – 25 f. sepia, green and red . 1·00 20
345 – 30 f. blue, red and green . 30 10
346 – 50 f. blue, green and red . 50 20
347 – 90 f. black, green and blue 1·10 45
DESIGNS: 25 f. Liner "France" at Dakar; 30 f. N'Gor Hotel and tourist cabins; 50 f. N'Gor Bay and Hotel; 90 f. Town Hall, Dakar.

80 Laying Water Mains

1967. International Hydrological Decade.
348 **80** 10 f. blue, green & brown . 15 15
349 – 20 f. brown, green & blue . 30 20
350 – 30 f. blue, orange & black . 35 20
351 – 50 f. lake, flesh and blue . 75 20
DESIGNS—HORIZ: 20 f. Cattle at trough. VERT: 30 f. Decade emblem; 50 f. Obtaining water from primitive well.

81 Terminal Building, Dakar-Yoff Airport

1967. Air.
352 **81** 200 f. indigo, blue & brown 2·50 1·00

82 Lions Emblem

1967. 50th Anniv of Lions International.
353 **82** 30 f. multicoloured 35 20

83 Blaise Diagne

1967. 95th Birth Anniv of Blaise Diagne (statesman).
354 **83** 30 f. brown, green & purple 30 20

84 Spiny Mimosa

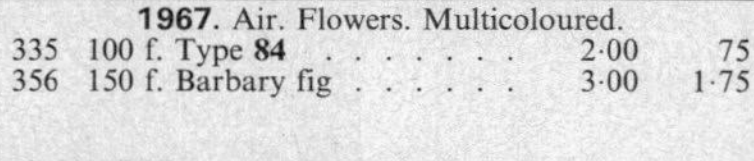
1967. Air. Flowers. Multicoloured.
335 100 f. Type **84** . . . . 2·00 75
356 150 f. Barbary fig . . . . . . 3·00 1·75

85 "Les Demoiselles d'Avignon" (Picasso)

86 Carved Eagle and Kudu's Head

1967. Air.
357 **85** 100 f. multicoloured . . . 2·25 1·10

1967. "EXPO 67" World Fair, Montreal.
358 **86** 90 f. black and red . . . . 1·25 50
359 – 150 f. multicoloured . . . 1·75 75
DESIGN: 150 f. Maple leaf and flags.

1967. Air. 5th Anniv of U.A.M.P.T. As T **101** of Mauritania.
360 100 f. red, green and violet 90 50

87 I.T.Y. Emblem

88 Currency Tokens

1967. International Tourist Year.
361 **87** 50 f. black and blue . . . 80 35
362 – 100 f. black, green & orge 2·50 1·00
DESIGN: 100 f. Tourist photographing hippopotamus.

1967. 5th Anniv of West African Monetary Union.
363 **88** 30 f. violet, purple & grey 25 15

89 "Lyre" Stone, Kaffrine

90 Nurse feeding Baby

1967. 6th Pan-American Prehistory Congress, Dakar.
364 **89** 30 f. red, blue and green . 25 15
365 – 70 f. red, brown and blue . 65 30
DESIGN: 70 f. Ancient bowl, Bandiala.

1967. Senegalese Red Cross.
366 **90** 50 f. lake, red and green . 50 25

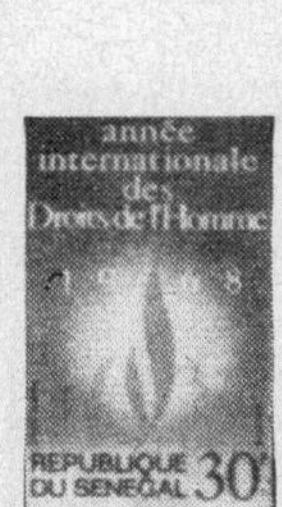

91 Human Rights Emblem

92 Chancellor Adenauer

1968. Human Rights Year.
367 **91** 30 f. gold and green . . . 35 20

1968. Air. Adenauer Commemoration.
368 **92** 100 f. sepia, red & green . 1·40 55

93 Weather Balloon, Flourishing Plants and W.M.O. Emblem

94 Parliament Building, Dakar

1968. Air. World Meteorological Day.
370 **93** 50 f. green, blue & black . . 65 40

1968. Inter-Parliamentary Union Meeting, Dakar.
371 **94** 30 f. red 30 15

95 Spiny Lobster

96 Lesser Pied Kingfisher

1968. Marine Crustacea. Multicoloured.
372 10 f. Type **95** 15 10
373 20 f. Sea crawfish 25 15
374 35 f. Prawn 75 20
375 100 f. Gooseneck barnacle . . 2·10 65

1968. Birds. Multicoloured.
376 5 f. Type **96** (postage) 50 15
377 15 f. African jacana 75 25
378 70 f. African darter . . . . . 2·50 1·50
379 250 f. Village weaver (air) . . 6·50 2·50
380 300 f. Comb duck . . . . . . 9·75 3·50
381 500 f. Bateleur . . . . 16·00 6·50
Nos. 379/81 are 45½ × 26 mm.

97 Ox and Syringe
98 Hurdling

1968. Campaign for Prevention of Cattle Plague.
382 **97** 30 f. red, green and blue . . 55 20

1968. Air. Olympic Games, Mexico.
383 **98** 20 f. brown, green & blue . 20 15
384 – 30 f. brown, ochre & pur . 25 15
385 – 50 f. lake, brown and blue . 75 35
386 – 75 f. bistre, brown & green . 1·25 60
DESIGNS: 30 f. Throwing the javelin; 50 f. Judo; 75 f. Basketball.

1968. Air. "Philexafrique". Stamp Exhibition, Abidjan (1st issue) (1969). As T **113a** of Mauritania. Multicoloured.
387 100 f. "Young Girl reading a Letter" (J. Raoux) . . . . . 2·25 2·00

99 Senegalese Boy

101 Faculty Building

1968. 20th Anniv of W.H.O.
388 **99** 30 f. black, red and green . 25 25
389 45 f. black, green & brown . 60 20

1969. Faculty of Medicine and Pharmaceutics, and Sixth "Medical Days", Dakar.
391 **101** 30 f. blue and green . . . 30 20
392 – 50 f. green, red & brown . 35 25
DESIGN—VERT: 50 f. Emblem of "Medical Days".

1969. Air. "Philexafrique". Stamp Exn, Abidjan, Ivory Coast (2nd issue). As T **114a** of Mauritania.
393 50 f. violet, slate and green . . 1·25 1·25
DESIGN: 50 f. Modern Dakar and Senegal stamp of 1935.

102 Panet, Camels and Route-map

1969. 150th Birth Anniv of Leopold Panet, first Explorer of the Mauritanian Sahara.
394 **102** 75 f. brown and blue . . 1·50 75

103 A.I.T.Y. Emblem

1969. Air. African International Tourist Year.
395 **103** 100 f. red, green and blue 75 45

104 I.L.O. Emblem
105 Pres. Lamine Gueye

1969. 50th Anniv of I.L.O.
396 **104** 30 f. black and turquoise . 25 15
397 45 f. black and red . . . 40 20

1969. Air. President Gueye Memorial.
398 **105** 30 f. black, buff & brown 25 15
399 – 45 f. black, blue & brown 35 20
DESIGN: 45 f. Pres. Lamine Gueye (different).

106 Arms of Casamance

1969. Senegal Arms. Multicoloured.
401 15 f. Type **106** 15 10
402 20 f. Arms of Ile de Goree . . 20 15

1969. 5th Anniv of African Development Bank. As T **122a** of Mauritania.
403 30 f. brown, green and slate . 25 15
404 45 f. brown and green 35 20

108 Mahatma Gandhi

109 "Transmission of Thought" (O. Faye)

1969. Birth Centenary of Mahatma Gandhi.
405 **108** 50 f. multicoloured . . . 45 25

1969. Air. Tapestries. Multicoloured.
407 25 f. Type **109** 60 20
408 30 f. "The Blue Cock" (Mamadou Niang) 35 20
409 45 f. "The Fairy" (Papa Sidi Diop) 85 50
410 50 f. "Fari" (A. N'Diaye) . . 1·25 75
411 75 f. "Lunaris" (J. Lurcat) . . 1·25 70
SIZE—VERT: 30 f., 45 f. 37 × 49 mm. HORIZ: 50 f. 49 × 37 mm.

110 Baila Bridge

1969. Air. Europafrique.
412 **110** 100 f. multicoloured . . . 1·25 45

111 Rotary Emblem and "Sailing Ship"

1969. 30th Anniv of Dakar Rotary Club.
413 **111** 30 f. yellow, blk & blue . 35 20

1969. 10th Anniv of A.S.E.C.N.A. As T **94a** of Niger.
414 100 f. slate 90 35

113 Cape Skiring, Casamance
115 Bottle-nosed Dolphins

114 Lecrivain, Latecoere 25 Airplane and Route

1969. Tourism.
415 **113** 20 f. green, lake and blue . 20 15
416 – 30 f. lake, brown and blue 25 15
417 – 35 f. black, brown & blue 1·10 30
418 – 45 f. lake and blue . . . 75 20
DESIGNS: 30 f. Tourist camp, Niokolo-Koba; 35 f. Herd of African elephants, Niokolo-Koba Park; 45 f. Millet granaries on stilts, Fadiouth Island.

1970. Air. 40th Anniv of Disappearance of Emile Lecrivain (aviator).
419 **114** 50 f. lake, slate & green . 1·00 40

1970.
420 **115** 50 f. multicoloured . . . 1·40 60

116 R. Maran (Martinique)

1970. Air. Negro Celebrities (1st series).
421 **116** 30 f. brown, green & lake 25 15
422 – 45 f. brown, blue & pink . 40 25
423 – 50 f. brown, green & yell . 45 35
PORTRAITS: 45 f. M. Garvey (Jamaica); 50 f. Dr. P. Mars (Haiti).
See also Nos. 457/60.

117 Sailing Pirogue and Obelisk
118 Lenin

1970. Air. 10th Anniv of Independence.
424 **117** 500 f. multicoloured . . . 5·00 2·75

1970. Birth Centenary of Lenin.
426 **118** 30 f. brown, stone & red . 25 15

119 Bay of Naples, and Post Office, Dakar

1970. Air. 10th "Europa" Stamp Exn, Naples.
428 **119** 100 f. multicoloured . . . 1·25 55

1970. New U.P.U. Headquarters Building, Berne. As T **81** of New Caledonia.
429 30 f. plum, blue and lake . . 25 15
430 45 f. brown, lake and green . 45 20

121 Nagakawa and Mt Fuji

1970. Air. World Fair "EXPO 70", Osaka, Japan.
431 – 25 f. red, green and lake . 20 15
432 **121** 75 f. red, blue and green . 55 30
433 – 150 f. red, brown and blue 1·60 70
DESIGNS—VERT: 25 f. "Woman playing guitar" (Hokusai) and Sun tower; 150 f. "Nanboku Beauty" (Shuncho).

122 Harbour Quayside, Dakar

1970. Air. Industrial and Urban Development.
434 **122** 30 f. blue, black and red . 25 15
435 – 100 f. brown, grn & slate 1·40 45
DESIGN: 100 f. Aerial view of city centre, Dakar.

123 Beethoven, Napoleon and "Evocation of Eroica" Symphony

1970. Air. Birth Bicentenary of Beethoven.
436 **123** 50 f. brown, orange & green 45 35
437 – 100 f. red and blue . . 1·40 75
DESIGN: 100 f. Beethoven with quillpen and scroll.

124 Heads of Four Races

1970. Air. 25th Anniv of U.N.O.
438 **124** 100 f. multicoloured . . . 1·25 55

125 Looms and Textile Works, Thies

1970. "Industrialisation".
439 **125** 30 f. red, blue and green . 30 15
440 – 45 f. blue, brown and red 40 20
DESIGN: 45 f. Fertiliser plant, Dakar.

126 Scouts in Camp
127 Three Heads and Sun

1970. 1st African Scouting Conference, Dakar. Mult.
441 30 f. Type **26** 30 20
442 100 f. Scout badge, Lord Baden-Powell and map . . . . . . 1·40 45

1970. International Education Year.
443 **127** 25 f. brown, blue & orge . 25 15
444 – 40 f. multicoloured . . . 45 20
DESIGN: 40 f. Map of Africa on Globe, and two heads.

128 Arms of Senegal
129 De Gaulle, Map, Ears of Wheat and Cogwheel

1970.
445 **128** 30 f. multicoloured . . . 35 15
446 35 f. multicoloured . . . 35 15
446a 50 f. multicoloured . . . 35 15
446b 65 f. multicoloured . . . 35 15
803 95 f. multicoloured . . . 35 30

1970. Air. "De Gaulle the De-coloniser". Mult.
447 50 f. Type **129** . . . . 1·25 60
448 100 f. De Gaulle, and map within "sun" . . . . 2·50 1·50

130 Refugees

1971. 20th Anniv of U.N. High Commissioner for Refugees. Multicoloured.
449 40 f. Type **130** (postage) . . . 35 20
450 100 f. Building house (air) . . 80 55
No. 450 is 46 × 27 mm.

131 "Mbayang" Horse

1971. Horse-breeding Improvement Campaign. Multicoloured.
451 25 f. "Madjiguene" 25 15
452 40 f. Type **131** 65 20
453 100 f. "Pass" . . . . 1·40 85
454 125 f. "Pepe" . . . . 2·00 1·10

132 European Girl and African Boy
133 Phillis Wheatley

1971. Racial Equality Year. Multicoloured.
455 30 f. Type **132** 25 15
456 50 f. People of four races (horiz) (37 × 30 mm) 40 25

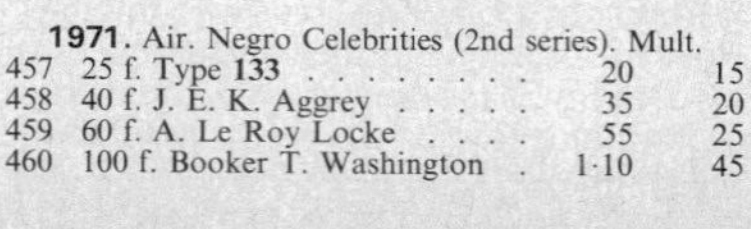

1971. Air. Negro Celebrities (2nd series). Mult.
457 25 f. Type **133** 20 15
458 40 f. J. E. K. Aggrey 35 20
459 60 f. A. Le Roy Locke . . . 55 25
460 100 f. Booker T. Washington . 1·10 45

134 "Telephones"
135 "Napoleon as First Consul" (Ingres)

1971. World Telecommunications Day.
461 **134** 30 f. brown, grn & purple 25 15
462 – 40 f. brown, red & blue . 35 20
DESIGN: 40 f. "Telecommunications" theme.

1971. Air. 150th Death Anniv of Napoleon. Mult.
463 15 f. Type **135** 30 25
464 25 f. "Napoleon in 1809" (Lefevre) 70 30
465 35 f. "Napoleon on his Death-bed" (Rouget) . . . . . . 1·00 45
466 50 f. "The Awakening to Immortality" (bronze by Rude) . . . . 1·75 80

136 Pres. Nasser
138 A. Nobel

137 Hayashida (drummer)

1971. Air. Nasser Commemoration.
467 **136** 50 f. multicoloured . . . 45 25

1971. 13th World Scout Jamboree, Asagiri, Japan. Multicoloured.
468 35 f. Type **137** 25 15
469 50 f. Japonica 40 20
470 65 f. Judo 50 25
471 75 f. Mt Fuji 60 30

1971. Air. 75th Death Anniv of Alfred Nobel (scientist and philanthropist).
472 **138** 100 f. multicoloured . . . 1·25 60

139 Persian Flag and Senegal Arms

1971. Air. 2500th Anniv of Persian Empire.
473 **139** 200 f. multicoloured . . . 2·00 1·00

140 Map and Emblem

1971. 25th Anniv of U.N.I.C.E.F. Multicoloured.
474 35 f. Type **140** 35 20
475 100 f. Nurse, children and U.N.I.C.E.F. emblem . . . 1·25 55

1971. Air. 10th Anniv of U.A.M.P.T. As T **139a** of Mauritania. Multicoloured.
476 100 f. U.A.M.P.T. H.Q., Brazzaville and arms of Senegal 80 40

INDEX

Countries can be quickly located by referring to the index at the end of this volume.

142 Louis Armstrong

143 Trying for Goal

1971. Air. Louis Armstrong Commemoration.
477 **142** 150 f. brown and gold . . 2·50 1·25

1971. 6th African Basketball Championships, Dakar. Multicoloured.
478 35 f. Type **143** 30 15
479 40 f. Players reaching for ball . 35 25
480 75 f. Championships emblem . 1·00 60

144 Ice-skating

1971. Air. Winter Olympic Games, Sapporo, Japan. Multicoloured.
481 5 f. Type **144** 15 10
482 10 f. Bob-sleighing 15 10
483 125 f. Cross-country skiing . . 1·40 60

145 "Il Fonteghetto della Farina" (detail, Canaletto)

1972. Air. U.N.E.S.C.O. "Save Venice" Campaign. Multicoloured.
484 50 f. Type **145** 50 30
485 100 f. "Giudecca e S. Giorgio Maggiore" (detail, Guardi) (vert) . . . . 1·25 70

146 "Albouri and Queen Seb Fall" (scene from "The Exile of Albouri")

1972. International Theatre Day. Multicoloured.
486 35 f. Type **146** (postage) . . . 35 20
487 40 f. Scene from "The Merchant of Venice" 65 25
488 150 f. Daniel Sorano as "Shylock" ("The Merchant of Venice") (vert) (air) . . . . 2·75 1·50

147 Human Heart

1972. World Heart Month.
489 **147** 35 f. brown and blue . . . 25 15
490 – 40 f. purple, grn & emer . 30 20
DESIGN: 40 f. Doctor and patient.

148 Vegetation in Desert

1972. U.N. Environmental Conservation Conf, Stockholm. Multicoloured.
491 35 f. Type **148** (postage) . . . 35 20
492 100 f. Oil slick on shore (air) 1·25 60

149 Tartarin of Tarascon shooting Lion

1972. 75th Death Anniv of Alphonse Daudet (writer).
493 **149** 40 f. red, green & brown 45 30
494 – 100 f. brown, lt blue & bl 1·25 50
DESIGN: 100 f. Daudet and scene from "Tartarin de Tarascon".

151 Wrestling

152 Emperor Haile Selassie and Flags

1972. Olympic Games, Munich. Multicoloured.
496 15 f. Type **151** 20 15
497 20 f. Running (100 metres) . 20 15
498 100 f. Basketball . . . . . . 1·10 45
499 125 f. Judo . . . . 1·40 55

1972. Air. Emperor Haile Selassie's 80th Birthday.
501 **152** 100 f. multicoloured . . . 95 55

153 Children reading Book

154 "Senegalese Elegance"

1972. International Book Year.
502 **153** 50 f. multicoloured . . . 45 20

1972.
502a **154** 5 f. blue 10 10
502b 10 f. red 15 10
502c 15 f. orange 15 10
502d 20 f. purple 15 10
503 25 f. black 20 10
503a 30 f. brown 15 10
504 40 f. blue 30 10
504a 45 f. orange 10 10
504b 50 f. red 10 10
504c 60 f. green 35 10
504d 75 f. purple 55 35
504e 90 f. red 65 35
504f 125 f. blue 30 20
504g 145 f. orange 35 25

155 Alexander Pushkin

157 "Amphicraspedum murrayanum"

1972. Pushkin (writer) Commemoration.
505 **155** 100 f. purple and pink . . 1·25 50

1972. 10th Anniv of West African Monetary Union. As T **149** of Mauritania.
506 40 f. brown, grey and blue . . 50 15

1972. Protozoa and Marine Life. Multicoloured.
507 5 f. Type **157** (postage) . . . 10 10
508 10 f. "Pterocanium tricolpum" 15 10
509 15 f. "Ceratospyris polygona" 15 10
510 20 f. "Cortiniscus typicus" . . 15 10
511 30 f. "Theopera cortina" . . 15 10
512 50 f. Swordfish (air) . . . . 1·00 50
513 65 f. Killer whale . . . . . 1·00 65
514 75 f. Whale shark . . . . . 1·50 80
515 125 f. Fin whale . . . . . 2·25 1·25
Nos. 512/15 are size 45 × 27 mm.

1972. No. 353 surch **1872-1972** and value.
516 **83** 100 f. on 30 f. brown, green and chestnut . . . . . 1·40 60

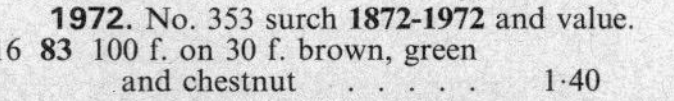

159 Melchior

160 "Sharing the Load"

1972. Christmas. Nativity Scene and Three Kings. Multicoloured.
517 10 f. Type **159** 15 15
518 15 f. Gaspard 20 15
519 40 f. Balthazar 40 20
520 60 f. Joseph 80 40
521 100 f. Mary and Baby Jesus (African representation) . . 1·50 65

1973. Europafrique.
522 **160** 65 f. black and green . . . 55 30

161 Palace of the Republic

1973. Air.
523 **161** 100 f. multicoloured . . . 1·10 60

162 Station and Aerial

1973. Inauguration of Satellite Earth Station, Gandoul.
524 **162** 40 f. multicoloured 35 20

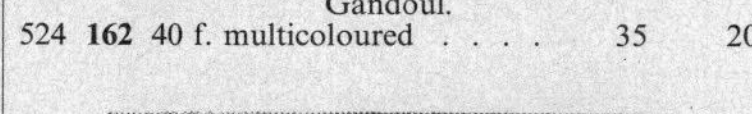

163 Hotel Teranga

1973. Air. Opening of Hotel Teranga, Dakar.
525 **163** 100 f. multicoloured . . . 1·10 60

164 "Lions" African Emblem

1973. Air. 15th Lions International District 403 Congress, Dakar.
526 **164** 150 f. multicoloured . . . 1·50 85

165 Stages of Eclipse

1973. Eclipse of the Sun. Multicoloured.
527 35 f. Type **165** 30 15
528 65 f. Eclipse in diagramatic form 50 25
529 150 f. Eclipse and "Skylab 1" . 1·60 75

166 Symbolic Torch

1973. 10th Anniv of Organization of African Unity.
530 **166** 75 f. multicoloured . . . 55 40

1973. "Drought Relief". African Solidarity. No. 451 surch **SECHERESSE SOLIDARITE AFRICAINE** and value.
531 100 f. on 25 f. multicoloured . 1·50 75

168 "Couple with Mimosa" (Chagall)

1973. Air.
532 **168** 200 f. multicoloured . . . 3·75 2·25

169 "Riccione 1973"

171 W.H.O. Emblem and Child

1973. Air. Int Stamp Exhibition, Riccione (Italy).
533 **169** 100 f. violet, green & red . 1·25 55

1973. U.A.M.P.T. As T **155a** of Mauritania.
534 100 f. violet, green and red . . 70 35

1973. Centenary of W.M.O.
535 **171** 50 f. multicoloured . . . 35 15

172 Interpol H.Q., Paris

174 Flame Emblem and People

1973. 50th Anniv of International Criminal Police Organization (Interpol).
536 **172** 75 f. brown, blue & green 1·00 40

1973. 25th Anniv of Declaration of Human Rights. Multicoloured.
538 35 f. Type **174** 30 15
539 65 f. Emblem and drummer . 70 25

175 R. Follereau (rehabilitation pioneer) and Map

1973. Air. Cent of Discovery of Leprosy Bacillus.
540 **175** 40 f. brown, green & viol 35 15
541 – 100 f. purple, red & grn . 1·25 50
DESIGN: 100 f. Dr. G. Hansen (discoverer of leprosy bacillus) and laboratory equipment.

176 "Key" Emblem

177 Amilcar Cabral and Weapons

1973. Air. World Twinned Towns Congress, Dakar. Multicoloured.

542 50 f. Type **176** 45 20
543 125 f. Arms of Dakar and meeting of citizens (horiz) . 1·25 50

1974. Amilcar Cabral (Guinea Bissau guerilla leader) Commemoration.

544 **177** 75 f. multicoloured . . . 55 40

178 Peter's Finfoot

1974. Air. Birds of Djoudj Park. Multicoloured.

545 1 f. Type **178** 10 10
546 2 f. White spoonbills 10 10
547 3 f. Crowned cranes 10 10
548 4 f. Little egret 20 10
549 250 f. Greater flamingoes (gold value) . . . . 7·00 2·00
550 250 f. Greater flamingoes (blk value) . . . . 7·00 2·00

179 "Tiger attacking Wild Horse"

1974. Air. Paintings by Delacroix. Multicoloured.

551 150 f. Type **179** . . . . . . 2·00 80
552 200 f. "Tiger-hunting" . . . . 2·40 1·25

180 Athletes on Podium — **182** U.P.U. Emblem, Letters and Transport

181 World Cup, Footballers and "Munich"

1974. National Youth Week. Multicoloured.

553 35 f. Type **180** 30 15
554 40 f. Dancer with mask . . . 35 20

1974. World Cup Football Championships. Footballers and locations.

555 25 f. Type **181** 15 10
556 40 f. "Hamburg" 30 15
557 65 f. "Hanover" 45 20
558 70 f. "Stuttgart" 45 25

1974. Centenary of U.P.U.

559 **182** 100 f. green, blue and lilac 1·25 60

183 Archway, and Africans at Work

184 Dakar, "Gateway to Africa"

1974. 1st Dakar International Fair.

560 **183** 100 f. brown, orange & blue (postage) . . . . 1·00 35
561 **184** 350 f. silver (air) . . . . 4·00
562 1500 f. gold . . . . . . 19·00
Nos. 561/2 are embossed on foil.

1975. West Germany's Victory in World Cup Football Championships, Munich. No. 566 surch **ALLEMAGNE RFA - HOLLANDE 2-1** and value.

563 200 f. on 40 f. multicoloured . 2·00 1·25

186 Pres. Senghor and King Baudouin

1975. Visit of King Baudouin of the Belgians.

564 **186** 65 f. blue and purple . . 50 25
565 100 f. green and orange . 1·25 45

187 I.L.O. Emblem

1975. Labour Day.

566 **187** 125 f. multicoloured . . . 1·10 45

188 "Apollo" and "Soyuz" Spacecraft

1975. Air. "Apollo"–"Soyuz" Space Co-operation Project.

567 **188** 125 f. green, blue and red 1·25 60

189 Spanish "Stamp", Globe and Letters

1975. "Espana 75" (Madrid) and "Arphila 75" (Paris) International Stamp Exhibitions.

568 **189** 55 f. red, blue and green . 60 30
569 – 95 f. lt brown and brown 1·75 70
DESIGN: 95 f. Head of Apollo and "Arphila" Emblem.

190 Classroom and Tractor

1975. Technical Education.

570 **190** 85 f. brown, blue & black 75 30

191 Dr. Schweitzer

1975. Birth Centenary of Dr. Albert Schweitzer.

571 **191** 85 f. lilac and green . . . 90 55

192 Soldier, Flag and Map of Sinai Desert 1973-74

1975. Senegalese Battalion with U.N.

572 **192** 100 f. multicoloured . . . 90 40

193 Stamps and Map of Italy — **194** Woman pounding Maize

1975. Air. Riccione Stamp Exhibition.

573 **193** 125 f. brown, red & lilac . 1·25 75

1975. International Women's Year. Multicoloured.

574 55 f. Type **194** 35 20
575 75 f. Mother and child with woman doctor (horiz) . . 90 25

1975. Air. "Apollo"–"Soyuz" Space Link. Optd **JONCTION 17 Juli. 1975.**

576 **188** 125 f. green, blue and red . 1·10 60

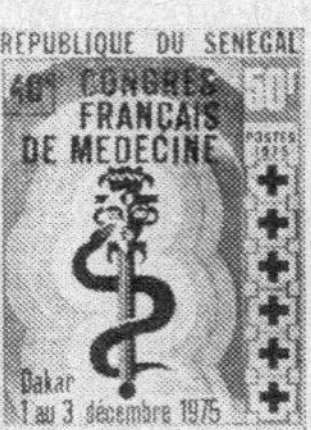

196 Stylised Caduceus

1975. French Medical Congress, Dakar.

577 **196** 50 f. multicoloured 25 15

197 "Massacre of Boston" (A. Chappel)

1975. Air. Bicentenary of American Revolution. (1st issue).

578 **197** 250 f. brown, red & blue . 2·50 1·00
579 – 500 f. red and blue . . . . 5·00 2·50
DESIGN: 500 f. Siege of Yorktown.
See also No. 593.

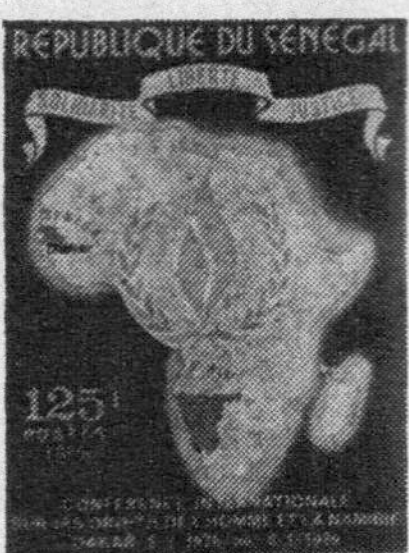

198 Emblem on Map of Africa

1976. International "Rights of Man" and Namibia Conferences, Dakar.

580 **198** 125 f. multicoloured . . . 60 30

199 Concorde and Flight Locations

1976. Air. Concorde's 1st Commercial Flight.

581 **199** 300 f. multicoloured . . . 4·50 2·25
See also No. 641.

200 Deep-sea Fishing

1976. "Expo", Okinawa. Multicoloured.

582 140 f. Type **200** . . . . 1·50 1·00
583 200 f. Yacht-racing . . . . . 2·00 1·25

201 Serval

1976. Basse Casamance National Park. Fauna. Mult.

584 2 f. Type **201** 10 10
585 3 f. Bar-tailed godwit (marsh bird) 70 30
586 4 f. Bush pig 10 10
587 5 f. African fish eagle 90 45
588 250 f. Sitatunga (males) . . . 2·75 1·50
589 250 f. Sitatunga (females) . . 2·75 1·50

202 Alexander Graham Bell

1976. Telephone Centenary.

590 **202** 175 f. multicoloured . . . 1·40 85

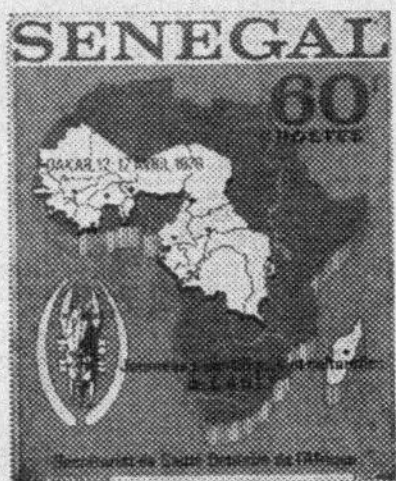

203 Map of Africa

1976. G.A.D.E.F. Scientific and Cultural Days.

591 **203** 60 f. multicoloured . . . 35 20

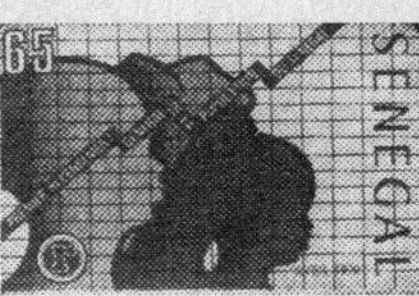

204 Heads on Graphs

1976. 1st Population Census.

592 **204** 65 f. multicoloured . . . 35 25

205 Jefferson reading Independence Declaration

1976. Bicentenary of American Revolution (2nd issue).

593 **205** 50 f. black, red and blue . 35 20

206 Plant Cultivation

1976. Operation "Sahel Vert".

594 **206** 60 f. multicoloured . . . 35 20

207 Scouts around Camp-fire

1976. 1st All African Scouts Jamboree, Jos, Nigeria. Multicoloured.

595 80 f. Type **207** 45 35
596 100 f. Emblem and map (vert) 90 45

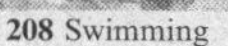

208 Swimming **210** Emblem and Map

1976. Olympic Games, Montreal. Multicoloured.

597 5 f. Type **208** (postage) . . . 10 10
598 10 f. Weightlifting 10 10
599 15 f. Hurdling (horiz) 15 10
600 20 f. Horse-jumping (horiz) . 15 10
601 25 f. Steeplechasing (horiz) . 15 10
602 50 f. Wrestling (horiz) . . . 25 15
603 60 f. Hockey 30 20
604 65 f. Running 35 20
605 70 f. Gymnastics 40 25
606 100 f. Cycling (horiz) 50 30

607 400 f. Boxing (horiz) (air) . . 3·00 40
607a 500 f. Judo . . . . 3·50 1·10
608 1000 f. Basketball (41 × 41 mm) 6·50 3·50
608a 1500 f. Running (41 × 41 mm) 10·00 5·00

1976. President Senghor's 70th Birthday. Mult.

610 40 f. Type **210** 25 20
611 60 f. Star over world map . . 35 25
612 70 f. Technicians and symbol . 45 30
613 200 f. President Senghor and extended hands . . . . . . 1·60 75

211 Harvesting Tomatoes

1976. Tomato Production.

614 **211** 180 f. multicoloured . . . 1·75 1·00

212 Concorde and Route Plan

1976. Air. Dakar International Fair.

615 **212** 500 f. silver . . . . 4·50
616 1500 f. gold . . . . 18·00

213 Black Peoples' "Charter" **214** Mohammed Ali and Joe Frazier

1977. Black Peoples' Day.

617 **213** 60 f. multicoloured . . . 35 25

1977. World Boxing Championship.

618 **214** 60 f. black and blue . . . 35 15
619 – 150 f. black and green . . 1·40 50

DESIGN—HORIZ: 150 f. Mohammed Ali landing punch.

215 Dancer and Musicians

1977. 2nd World Black and African Festival of Arts and Culture, Lagos (Nigeria). Multicoloured.

620 50 f. Type **215** 25 20
621 75 f. Statuette and masks . . 70 25
622 100 f. Statuette and dancers . 90 45

216 Cog Wheels

1977. 1st Anniv of Dakar Industrial Zone.

623 **216** 70 f. brown and green . . 40 20

217 Hauling in Net **218** Burnt Tree in "Flame"

1977. Fishing. Multicoloured.

624 25 f. Type **217** (postage) . . .
625 5 f. Fishing by trawl-line (air)
626 10 f. Harpooning . . . . . .
627 15 f. Pirogue breasting wave .
628 20 f. Displaying prize catch .

1977. Fight Against Forest Fires. Multicoloured.

629 40 f. Type **218** 20 15
630 60 f. Firefighting vehicle (horiz) 40 25

219 Industrial and Pre-Industrial Communication

1977. World Telecommunications Day. Mult.

631 80 f. Type **219** 45 35
632 100 f. Printed circuit (vert) . 70 45

220 Arms of Senegal

1977. 10th Anniv of International French Language Council. Multicoloured.

633 65 f. Type **220** 35 20
634 250 f. As T **236a** of Mali . . 1·75 1·00

221 Woman rowing on River

1977. "Amphilex 1977" International Stamp Exhibition, Amsterdam. Multicoloured.

635 50 f. Type **221** 30 25
636 125 f. Senegalese woman . . 70 45

INDEX

Countries can be quickly located by referring to the index at the end of this volume.

222 "Viking" and Control Centre **223** Class in Front of Blackboard

1977. Air. "Viking" Space Mission to Mars.

637 **222** 300 f. multicoloured . . . 2·00 1·25

1977. Literacy Week. Multicoloured.

638 60 f. Type **223** 35 25
639 65 f. Man with alphabet table . 35 25

224 "Mercury and Argus" (Rubens) **226** "Adoration of the Kings"

1977. Paintings. Multicoloured.

640 20 f. Type **224** 10 10
641 25 f. "Daniel and the Lions" (Rubens) 15 10
642 40 f. "The Empress" (Titian) . 20 15
643 60 f. "Flora" (Titian) 30 20
644 65 f. "Jo la belle Irlandaise" (Courbet) 35 20
645 100 f. "The Painter's Studio" (Courbet) . . . . 1·00 55

1977. Air. 1st Paris–New York Commercial Flight of Concorde. Optd **22.11.77 PARIS NEW-YORK**.

646 **199** 300 f. multicoloured . . . 4·25 2·25

1977. Christmas. Multicoloured.

647 20 f. Type **226** 10 10
648 25 f. Fanal (celebration) . . . 15 10
649 40 f. Family Christmas tree . . 20 15
650 100 f. "Three Wise Men" (horiz) 1·00 40

227 Wrestler **228** Dakar Cathedral and Parthenon, Athens

1978. Tourism. Multicoloured.

651 10 f. Type **227** 10 10
652 30 f. Soumbedioun Regatta (canoes) 20 15
653 65 f. Soumbedioun Regatta (race) (horiz) 45 25
654 100 f. Dancers (horiz) 95 50

1978. U.N.E.S.C.O. Campaign for Protection of Monuments.

655 **228** 75 f. multicoloured 35 25

229 Solar Pump

1978. Sources of Energy. Multicoloured.

656 50 f. Type **229** 25 15
657 95 f. Electricity power station . 75 30

230 Caspian and Royal Terns

1978. Saloum Delta National Park. Multicoloured.

658 5 f. Type **230** 10 10
659 10 f. Pink-backed pelicans . . 15 10
660 15 f. Grey Heron and warthog 25 20
661 20 f. Greater flamingoes . . . 25 20
662 150 f. Grey heron and royal terns 1·90 80
663 150 f. Abyssinian ground hornbill and warthog . . . 1·90 80

231 Dome of the Rock **232** Mahatma Gandhi

1978. Palestine Freedom-Fighters.

664 **231** 60 f. multicoloured . . . 30 20

1978. Apostles of Non-Violence. Multicoloured.

665 125 f. Type **232** 85 50
666 150 f. Martin Luther King . . 90 60

233 Jenner and Vaccination of Children **234** Players, and Flags of Group 1 Countries

1978. Global Eradication of Smallpox.

668 **233** 60 f. multicoloured . . . 30 20

1978. World Cup Football Championship, Argentina. Multicoloured.

669 25 f. Type **234** 15 10
670 40 f. Players and flags of Group 2 countries 20 15
671 65 f. Players and flags of Group 3 countries 30 20
672 100 f. Players and flags of Group 4 countries 70 30

235 Symbols of Technology, Equipment and Industrialisation

1978. 3rd International Fair, Dakar.

674 **235** 110 f. multicoloured . . . 75 30

236 Wright Brothers and Wright Type A

1978. Conquest of Space. Multicoloured.

675 75 f. Type **236** (75th anniv of first powered flight) 40 20
676 100 f. Yuri Gagarin (10th death anniv of first cosmonaut) . 55 30
677 200 f. "Apollo 8" (10th anniv of first manned moon orbit) . . 1·25 60

237 Henri Dunant and Children's Ward

1978. 150th Birth Anniv of Henri Dunant (founder of the Red Cross).

679 **237** 5 f. blue, black and red . 10 10
680 – 20 f. multicoloured . . . 15 10

DESIGN: 20 f. Henri Dunant and scenes of Red Cross aid.

1978. Air. "Philexafrique", Stamp Exhibition, Libreville, Gabon and International Stamp Fair, Essen, West Germany. As T **262** of Niger.

681 100 f. Capercaillie and Schleswig-Holstein 1850 1 s. stamp . . 1·50 1·25
682 100 f. Lion and Senegal 1960 200 f. Violet turaco . . . 1·50 1·25

238 Telecommunications

1978. Post Office Achievements. Multicoloured.
683 50 f. Type **238** 25 15
684 60 f. Social welfare 30 20
685 65 f. Travelling post offce . . 30 20

239 Doctor with Students

1979. 9th Medical Days, Dakar. Multicoloured.
686 50 f. Type **239** 25 15
687 100 f. Problems of pollution . 70 45

240 Agriculture

1979. Professional Pride. Multicoloured.
688 30 f. Type **240** 15 10
689 150 f. Symbols of progress . . 1·00 45

241 Open Air Class

1979. S.O.S. Children's Village. Multicoloured.
690 40 f. Type **241** 20 15
691 60 f. View of village 30 20

242 Young Child **243** Baobab Flower and Tree and Independence Monument

1979. International Year of the Child. Multicoloured.
692 60 f. Type **242** 30 20
693 65 f. Children with book . . . 30 20

1979. "Philexafrique" Stamp Exhibition, Libreville, Gabon. Multicoloured.
694 60 f. Type **243** 70 60
695 150 f. Drum, early telegraph apparatus and dish aerial (square, 36 × 36 mm) . . . . 1·75 1·25

244 Children ushered into Open Book

1979. 50th Anniv of International Bureau of Education.
696 **244** 250 f. multicoloured . . . 1·40 80

245 Hill and Senegal 100 f. Stamp of 1960

1979. Death Centenary of Sir Rowland Hill.
697 **245** 500 f. multicoloured . . . 3·50 2·00

246 "Black Trees" **247** Start of Race

1979. Paintings by Friedensreich Hundertwasser. Multicoloured.
698 60 f. Type **246** 75 25
699 100 f. "Head" . . . . 1·00 75
700 200 f. "Rainbow Windows" . 2·00 1·25

1980. 1st African Athletic Championships. Mult.
702 20 f. Type **247** 15 10
703 25 f. Javelin 15 10
704 50 f. Passing the relay baton . 25 10
705 100 f. Discus 45 30

248 Musicians

1980. Mudra African Arts Festival.
706 50 f. Type **248** 25 15
707 100 f. Dancers 70 25
708 200 f. Dancers and drummer . 1·25 70

249 Lions Emblem

1980. 22nd Congress of Lions' Club District 403, Dakar.
709 **249** 100 f. multicoloured . . . 45 25

250 Chimpanzees

1980. Niokolo-Koba National Park. Multicoloured.
710 40 f. Type **250** 25 10
711 60 f. African elephants . . . 35 20
712 65 f. Giant elands 60 20
713 100 f. Spotted hyenas 85 30
714 200 f. Wildlife on the savannah 1·75 70
715 200 f. Simenti Hotel . . . . 1·75 70
Nos. 714/15 were issued together, se-tenant, forming a composite deisgn.

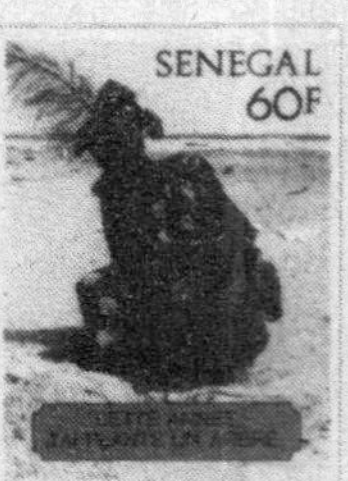

251 Watering Sapling **252** Women with Bowls of Rice Flour and Electric Mill

1980. Tree Planting Year.
717 **251** 60 f. multicoloured . . . 45 25
718 65 f. multicoloured . . . 95 30

1980. Rural Women. Multicoloured.
719 50 f. Street market (horiz) . . 25 15
720 100 f. Type **252** 45 30
721 200 f. Drawing water (horiz) . 1·25 70

253 Wrestling

1980. Olympic Games, Moscow. Multicoloured.
722 60 f. Type **253** 30 20
723 65 f. Running 30 20
724 70 f. Games emblems 35 25
725 100 f. Judo 45 30
726 200 f. Basketball . . . . . . 1·25 70

254 Dabry, Gimie, Mermoz and Seaplane "Comte de la Vaulx"

1980. Air. 50th Anniv of First South Atlantic Airmail Flight.
728 **254** 300 f. multicoloured . . . 2·00 1·00

255 Caspian Tern, Eastern White Pelicans and Grey-headed Gulls (Pointe Kalissaye Bird Sanctuary)

1981. National Parks. Multicoloured.
729 50 f. Type **255** 60 20
730 70 f. Slender-billed gulls and gull-billed tern (Langue de Barbarie) 65 30
731 85 f. Turtle and crab (Madeline Islands) 40 25
732 150 f. White-breasted cormorant and red-billed tropic bird (Madeline Islands) . . . . . 1·75 70

256 Healthy Activities **257** Fair Visitors beneath Tree

1981. Anti-Smoking Campaign. Multicoloured.
734 75 f. Type **256** 30 30
735 80 f. Cancerous mouth with pipe 35 35

1981. 4th International Fair, Dakar.
736 **257** 80 f. multicoloured 35 35

258 Lat Dior Damel Teigne **259** "Nymphaea lotus"

1982. National Heroes. Lat Dior. Multicoloured.
737 80 f. Type **258** 35 25
738 500 f. Lat Dior on horseback . 3·00 1·25

1982. Flowers. Multicoloured.
739 50 f. Type **259** 20 20
740 75 f. "Strophanthus sarmentosus" 30 30
741 200 f. "Crinum moorei" . . . 1·25 75
742 225 f. "Cochlospermum tinctorium" . . . . 1·50 1·00

260 "Euryphrene senegalensis" (male and female)

1982. Butterflies. Multicoloured.
743 45 f. Type **260** 60 35
744 55 f. "Hypolimnas salmacis, Precis octavia" and "Salamis cytora" 75 45
745 75 f. "Cymothoe caenis" and "Cyrestis camillus" 90 55
746 80 f. "Precis cebrene, Junonia terea" and "Salamis parhassus" . . . . 1·10 70

261 "Rhaguva albipunctella" **263** Black-tailed Godwit

262 Flags and Three-dimensional Map of Senegambia

1982. Harmful Insects. Multicoloured.
748 75 f. Type **261** 50 45
749 80 f. "Amsacta moloneyi, Tolyposporium penicillariae" and "Sclerospore graminicola" (horiz) . . . . 1·00 50
750 100 f. "Amsacta moloneyi" . 70 60

1982. Senegambia Confederation. Multicoloured.
751 225 f. Type **262** . . . . 1·25 60
752 350 f. Arms of Senegal and Gambia . . . . 2·00 90

1982. Birds. Multicoloured.
753 45 f. Type **263** 40 30
754 75 f. Saddle-bill stork 85 35
755 80 f. White-throated francolin 1·00 40
756 500 f. Tawny eagle . . . . . 5·00 2·75

264 Footballer and Emblem **265** Flag "Stamp" and Ribbon

1982. World Cup Football Championship, Spain. Multicoloured.
757 30 f. Type **264** 15 15
758 50 f. Footballer 20 20
759 75 f. Football 30 30
760 80 f. World Cup and emblem . 35 35

1982. "Philexfrance 82" International Stamp Exhibition, Paris. Multicoloured.
762 100 f. Type **265** 40 25
763 500 f. Arms "stamp" between circling arrows . . . . . . 3·00 1·50

266 Exhibition Poster

1983. Stamp Exhibition, Dakar. Multicoloured.
764 60 f. Type **266** 25 20
765 70 f. Butterfly stamps 25 20
766 90 f. Stamps and magnifying glass 30 25
767 95 f. Exhibition hall and Dakar arms on stamp 75 30

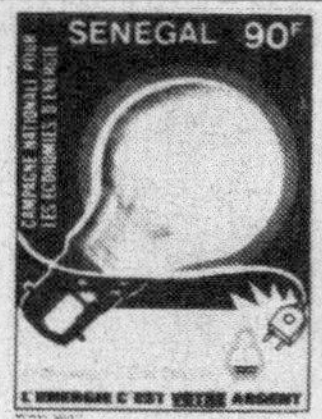

267 Light Bulb **268** Torch on Map of Africa

1983. Energy Conservation. Multicoloured.

768	90 f. Type **267**	55	30
769	95 f. Cars queueing for petrol	60	30
770	260 f. Woman cooking	1·60	85

1983. "For Namibian Independence". Multicoloured.

771	90 f. Type **268**	55	30
772	95 f. Clenched fist and broken chain on map of Africa	60	30
773	260 f. Woman with torch on map of Africa	1·90	85

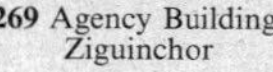

269 Agency Building, Ziguinchor **270** Dakar Rotary Banner

1983. 20th Anniv of West African Monetary Union. Multicoloured.

774	60 f. Type **269**	25	20
775	65 f. Headquarters building, Dakar (vert)	25	25

1983. 1st Anniv of Dakar Alizes Rotary Club.

776 **270**	70 f. multicoloured	50	25
777	500 f. multicoloured	3·25	1·75

271 Customs Council Headquarters **272** Anniversary Emblem

1983. 30th Anniv of Customs Co-operation Council.

778 **271**	90 f. multicoloured	30	30
779	300 f. multicoloured	2·00	1·00

1984. 25th Anniv of Economic Commission for Africa.

780 **272**	90 f. multicoloured	30	30
781	95 f. multicoloured	60	30

273 Village

1984. S.O.S. Children's Village. Multicoloured.

782	90 f. Type **273**	30	30
783	95 f. Foster-mother and child (vert)	65	30
784	115 f. Foster-family	80	40
785	260 f. House (vert)	1·75	85

274 Scout Salute **275** Javelin-throwing

1984. 75th Anniv of Boy Scout Movement. Mult.

786	60 f. Type **274**	20	15
787	70 f. Scout badge	25	20
788	90 f. Scouts of different nations	35	30
789	95 f. Lord Baden-Powell (founder)	40	35

1984. Olympic Games, Los Angeles. Multicoloured.

790	90 f. Type **275**	35	30
791	95 f. Hurdling	40	35
792	165 f. Football	1·10	70

276 Basket of Food, Fishing and Farming **278** William Ponty School

1984. World Food Day. Multicoloured. Inscr "16 OCTOBRE 1983".

794	65 f. Type **276**	25	20
795	70 f. Woman cooking and child (vert)	50	20
796	225 f. Group and food	1·60	85

1984. Drought Aid. No. 785 optd **Aide au Sahel 84**.

797	260 f. multicoloured	1·75	1·25

1984. World Heritage. Goree Island.

798 **278**	90 f. multicoloured	35	30
799 –	95 f. black and blue	40	35
800 –	250 f. multicoloured	1·75	85
801 –	500 f. multicoloured	3·50	2·00

DESIGN—HORIZ: 95 f. Map of Goree; 500 f. Slaves' House. VERT: 250 f. Goree Historical Museum.

279 Pump and Sprinkler **280** Globe, Envelopes and Map

1985. Irrigation Project. Multicoloured.

810	40 f. Type **279**	15	15
811	50 f. Tap and dam	15	15
812	90 f. Storage tanks and cattle	60	25
813	250 f. Women at water pump	1·75	85

1985. World Communication Year (1984).

814 **280**	90 f. multicoloured	30	25
815 –	95 f. blue, green & brown	35	30
816 –	350 f. multicoloured	2·25	1·10

DESIGNS: 95 f. Maps of Africa and Senegal and aerial; 350 f. Globe, dove and map of Senegal.

281 Stringed Instrument and Flute

1985. Musical Instruments. Multicoloured.

817	50 f. Type **281**	15	15
818	85 f. Drums and stringed instrument	30	25
819	125 f. Musician, stringed instruments, xylophone and drums	85	40
820	250 f. Stringed instruments	1·60	85

282 Seaplane "Comte de la Vaulx" and Map

1985. Air. 55th Anniv of 1st Airmail Flight across South Atlantic.

821 **282**	250 f. multicoloured	2·25	1·10

283 People and Broken Chain

1985. "Philexafrique" Int Stamp Exn, Lome, Togo. "Youth and Development". Mult.

822	100 f. Type **283** (political and civic education)	45	40
823	125 f. Carpenter and draughtsman (professional education)	75	45
824	150 f. Couple looking at planets (general education)	90	60
825	175 f. Farm workers (food self-sufficiency)	1·00	80

284 Laboratory and Farm Workers

1985. International Youth Year. Multicoloured.

826	40 f. Type **284**	20	15
827	50 f. Young people, forms of communication and globe	20	15
828	90 f. Youth building "Peace" monument	40	35
829	125 f. Youth, football and globe	90	45

285 Man, Woman and Boy

1985. National Costumes. Multicoloured.

830	40 f. Type **285**	20	15
831	95 f. Man in straw hat and striped gown (vert)	40	35
832	100 f. Seated gown (vert)	45	40
833	150 f. Man and woman (vert)	90	60

286 Men bringing Boat Ashore

1986. Fishing at Kayar. Multicoloured.

834	40 f. Type **286**	20	15
835	50 f. Women waiting on shore	20	15
836	100 f. Man with large fish (vert)	70	40
837	125 f. Sorting the catch (vert)	95	45
838	150 f. View of beach	1·00	60

287 Perruque and Ceeli **288** Flags and Football

1986. Hairstyles. Multicoloured.

839	90 f. Type **287**	40	30
840	125 f. Ndungu, Kearly and Rasta	50	40
841	250 f. Jamono, Kura and Kooraa	150	60
842	300 f. Mbaram and Jeere	1·175	70

1986. African Football Cup, Cairo. Multicoloured.

843	115 f. Type **288**	70	35
844	125 f. Footballer and map	75	45
845	135 f. Lion rampant with torch ascending pyramid (horiz)	80	50
846	165 f. Lions rampant beneath flag (horiz)	1·00	65

1986. 5th Convention of District 403 of Lions International. No. 818 surch **Ve CONVENTION MULTI-DISTRICT 8-10 MAI 1988**.

847	165 f. on 85 f. Drums and stringed instrument	1·00	65

290 Doe and Calf

1986. Ndama Gazelle. Multicoloured.

848	15 f. Type **290**	10	10
849	45 f. Group of gazelle resting	20	15
850	85 f. Gazelle among dead trees	35	30
851	125 f. Gazelle running	1·00	45

291 Immunising Child **294** Ostriches

292 Trophy, Footballers and Terracotta Offertory Vessel

1986. U.N.I.C.E.F. Child Survival Campaign. Multicoloured.

852	50 f. Type **291**	20	15
853	85 f. Child drinking from bowl	40	35

1986. World Cup Football Championship, Mexico. Multicoloured. (a) As T **292**.

854	125 f. Type **292**	50	45
855	135 f. Trophy, footballers and stucco Maya head from Palenque	80	50
856	165 f. Gold breastplate, footballers and trophy	1·00	65
857	340 f. Teotihuacan porcelain mask, footballers and trophy	2·00	90

(b) Nos. 854/7 optd **ARGENTINA 3 R.F.A. 2**.

858	125 f. Type **292**	50	45
859	135 f. Trophy, footballers and stucco Maya head from Palenque	80	50
860	165 f. Gold breastplate, footballers and trophy	1·00	65
861	340 f. Teotihuacan porcelain mask, footballers and trophy	2·00	90

1986. Guembeul Nature Reserve. Multicoloured

862	50 f. Type **294**	1·00	30
863	65 f. Gazelles	25	20
864	85 f. Giraffes	60	30
865	100 f. Ostrich, buffalo, gazelle and giraffe	1·75	80
866	150 f. Buffalo	1·10	60

295 Man with Puppet (Xuusmaanapaa) **296** Statue of Liberty

1986. Christmas. Customs. Multicoloured.

867	70 f. Type **295**	25	20
868	85 f. Setting up fanal (Fente) (horiz)	30	25
869	150 f. Decorating fanal (Jebele)	90	55
870	250 f. Boy praying before candle and Nativity scene (horiz)	1·50	75

1986. Centenary of Statue of Liberty.

871 **296**	225 f. multicoloured	1·50	80

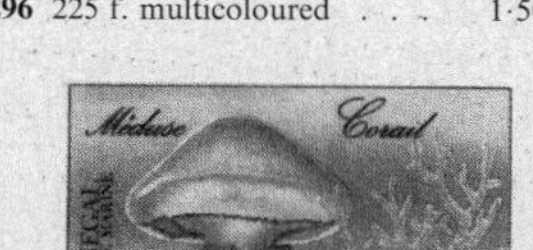

297 Jellyfish and Coral

1987. Marine Fauna. Multicoloured.

872	50 f. Type **297**	20	15
873	85 f. Sea urchin and starfish	30	25
874	100 f. Norway lobster	70	35
875	150 f. Common dolphin	1·00	55
876	200 f. Octopus	2·00	1·10

298 Motor Cyclist and Lorry — **299** Hands over Antelope

1987. Paris–Dakar Rally. Multicoloured.
877 115 f. Type **298** 80 40
878 125 f. Thierry Sabine, helicopter, motor cyclist, lorry and car (horiz) . . . . 1·50 60
879 135 f. Sabine and motor car (horiz) . . . . 1·00 45
880 340 f. Eiffel Tower, car and huts 2·40 1·10

1987. Endangered Fauna in Ferlo National Park. Multicoloured.
881 55 f. Type **299** 20 15
882 70 f. Ostriches 75 30
883 85 f. Warthog 60 25
884 90 f. Elephant 60 30

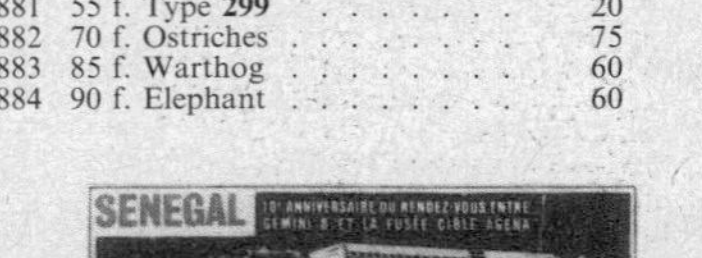

300 Spacecraft above Earth

1987. 10th Anniv of "Gemini 8" – Agena Flight.
885 **300** 320 f. multicoloured . . . 2·00 1·10

301 International Express Mail Emblem

1987. Centenary of First Senegal Stamp. Mult.
887 100 f. Type **301** 40 35
888 130 f. 1892 4 c. Senegal and Dependencies stamp 75 45
889 140 f. 1961 Senegal independence stamp 80 50
890 145 f. 1935 30 c. and 1 f. 25 Senegal stamps 85 50
891 320 f. Senegal 1887 15 c. on 20 c. stamp and cancellation . . . 2·00 1·10

302 Hand gripping Bloodied Claw above Map of South Africa

1987. Anti-Apartheid Campaign. Multicoloured.
892 130 f. Type **302** 80 45
893 140 f. Broken and bloodied chain in fist (vert) 85 50
894 145 f. Skeleton with scythe, dove and globe 85 50

303 Emblem

1987. 20th Anniv of Intelsat. Multicoloured.
895 50 f. Type **303** 20 15
896 125 f. Satellite and emblem . . 50 45
897 150 f. Emblem and globe . . . 60 55
898 200 f. Globe and satellite . . . 1·25 75

304 Emblem and Crowd — **305** Yacht and Sun

1987. West African Cities Organization. Mult.
899 40 f. Type **304** 15 15
900 125 f. Emblem and clasped hands 75 45

1987. 45th Anniv of Dakar Rotary Club.
901 **305** 500 f. multicoloured . . . 3·25 1·50

306 U.N. Building, New York — **307** Fr. Daniel Brottier (founder) and Angel

1987. 40th Anniv (1985) of U.N.O. Multicoloured.
902 85 f. Type **306** 60 25
903 95 f. Emblem 65 35
904 150 f. Hands of different races and emblem 90 55

1987. 50th Anniv of Cathedral of African Remembrance. Multicoloured.
905 130 f. Type **307** 85 45
906 140 f. Cathedral in 1936 and 1986 85 50

308 Hand pouring Grain into Globe

1987. World Food Day. Multicoloured.
907 130 f. Type **308** 80 45
908 140 f. Ear of wheat and F.A.O. emblem rising as sun (horiz) 85 50
909 145 f. Emblem 85 50

309 Servals

1987. Basse Casamance National Park. Mult.
910 115 f. Type **309** 70 40
911 135 f. Demidoff's galagos . . 90 45
912 150 f. Bush pig . . . . 1·00 55
913 250 f. Leopards . . . . 1·60 90
914 300 f. Little egrets . . . . 5·50 2·75
915 300 f. Carmine bee eaters . . 5·50 2·75

310 Wrestlers

1987. Senegalese Wrestling. Multicoloured.
916 115 f. Type **310** 70 40
917 125 f. Wrestlers and musicians 70 45
918 135 f. Wrestlers (vert) . . . 80 45
919 165 f. Referee, wrestlers and crowd (vert) . . . . 1·00 55

311 African Open-bill Stork — **312** Boy dreaming of Father Christmas's Visit

1987. Djoudj National Park. Multicoloured.
920 115 f. Type **311** 95 55
921 125 f. Greater flamingoes (horiz) 1·10 65
922 135 f. Pink-backed pelican and greater flamingoes (horiz) . . 1·40 65
923 300f. Pink-backed pelicans . . 2·75 1·25
924 350f. As No. 921 . . . . 3·00 1·75
925 350f. As No. 922 . . . . 3·00 1·75

1987. Christmas. Multicoloured.
926 145 f. Type **312** 85 50
927 150 f. Star behind Virgin gazing at Child 90 55
928 180 f. Nativity scene above people praying in church . . 1·25 65
929 200 f. Nativity scene in candle glow . . . . 1·25 75

313 Battle of Dekhele

1988. Death Centenary of Lat-Dior. Multicoloured.
930 130 f. Type **313** . . . . 1·00 45
931 160 f. Lat-Dior on his horse "Maalaw" . . . . 1·00 60

314 10th Anniv Emblem and Map

1988. Dakar International Fair.
932 **314** 125 f. multicoloured . . . 75 45

315 Catfish

1988. Fishes. Multicoloured.
933 5 f. Type **315** 10 10
934 100 f. Angel fish 40 35
935 145 f. Common barb 90 50
936 180 f. Carp . . . . 1·40 90

316 W.M.O. Emblem and Means of Conveying Information

1988. World Meteorology Day.
937 **316** 145 f. multicoloured . . . 90 30

317 Motor Cyclist

1988. 10th Anniv of Paris–Dakar Rally. Mult.
938 145 f. Type **317** 90 50
939 180 f. Rally car and emblem . . 1·00 65
940 200 f. Rally cars and man . . 1·25 70
941 410 f. Thierry Sabine and motor cyclist . . . . 2·75 1·50

318 Squid

1988. Molluscs. Multicoloured.
942 10 f. Type **318** 10 10
943 20 f. "Donax trunculus" (bivalve) 15 10
944 145 f. "Achatina fulica" (snail) (vert) . . . . 1·40 65
945 165 f. "Helix nemoralis" (snail) 1·75 75

319 Football, Cup and Map

1988. Africa Cup Football Championship, Rabat. Multicoloured.
946 80 f. Type **319** 30 25
947 100 f. Player's leg and ball (vert) 40 35
948 145 f. Match scene and map of Africa (vert) 90 50
949 180 f. Emblem and cup (vert) 1·25 65

320 Corps Member and Children — **321** "Dictyota atomaria"

1988. 25th Anniv of American Peace Corps in Senegal.
950 **320** 190 f. multicoloured . . . 1·25 65

1988. Marine Flora. Multicoloured.
951 10 f. Type **321** 10 10
952 65 f. "Agarum gmelini" . . . 25 20
953 145 f. "Saccorrhiza bulbosa" . 90 55
954 180 f. "Rhodymenia palmetta" 1·25 65

1988. Riccione Stamp Fair. No. 891 optd **RICCIONE 88 27-29-08-89.**
955 320 f. multicoloured . . . . 1·75 1·25

323 Hodori (mascot) and Stadium — **325** Thies Phosphate Mine

324 Thierno Saidou Nourou Tall Centre

1988. Olympic Games, Seoul. Multicoloured.
956 5 f. Type **323** 10 10
957 75 f. Athletics, swimming and football 30 25
958 300 f. Hodori, flame and sports pictograms . . . . 1·75 1·00
959 410 f. Emblem and athletics pictogram . . . . 2·40 1·40

1988.
960 **324** 125 f. multicoloured . . . 70 60

1988. Senegal Industries. Multicoloured.
961 5 f. Type **325** 10 10
962 20 f. Chemical industry . . . 10 10
963 145 f. Diourbel factory . . . 85 50
964 410 f. Mbao refinery . . . . 2·40 1·40

326 Children and Government Palace

1988. Postcards of 1900. Multicoloured.
965 20 f. Type **326** 10 10
966 145 f. Wrestlers and St. Louis Grand Mosque 85 50
967 180 f. Old Dakar railway station and young woman . . . 1·10 65
968 200 f. Goree Governor's residence and young woman 1·25 70

327 "Packia biglobosa" **328** Mask, Rally Car and Eiffel Tower

1988. Flowers. Multicoloured.
969 20 f. Type **327** 10 10
970 60 f. "Euphorbia pulcherrima" 20 15
971 65 f. "Cyrtosperma senegalense" 25 20
972 410 f. "Bombax costatum" . . 2·60 1·40

1989. 11th Paris–Dakar Rally. Multicoloured.
973 10 f. Type **328** 10 10
974 145 f. Crash helmet and sand dunes 60 55
975 180 f. Turban and motor cyclist 1·10 70
976 220 f. Motor cyclist and Thierry Sabine . . . . 1·40 85

329 Teranga Hotel **330** Senegal Tourism Emblem

1989. Tourism (1st series). Multicoloured.
977 10 f. Type **329** 10 10
978 80 f. Thatched hut and shades on beach 30 25
979 100 f. Saly hotel 40 35
980 350 f. Dior hotel . . . . 2·50 1·25

1989. Tourism (2nd series). Multicoloured.
981 130 f. Type **330** 75 45
982 140 f. Rural tourism (horiz) . 85 50
983 145 f. Fishing (horiz) . . . . 1·00 55
984 180 f. Water sports (horiz) . . 1·00 70

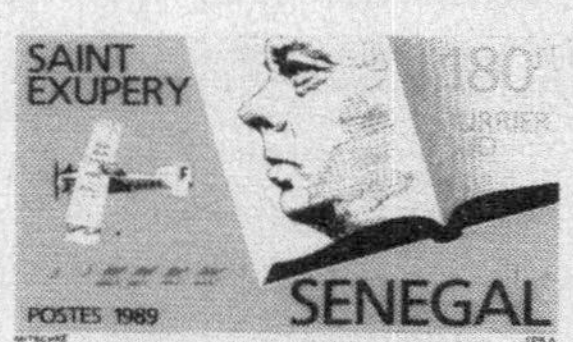

331 Saint-Exupery and Scene from "Courrier Sud"

1989. 45th Anniv of Disappearance of Antoine de Saint-Exupery (pilot and writer).
985 **331** 180 f. black, orange and grey 1·40 50
986 – 220 f. black, blue & grey . 1·75 75
987 – 410 f. multicoloured . . . 3·50 1·25
DESIGNS: 220 f. Scene from "Vol de Nuit"; 410 f. Scene from "Pilote de Guerre".

332 Presentation of Lists of Grievances by People of St. Louis

1989. Bicentenary of French Revolution. Mult.
988 180 f. Type **332** . . . . 1·25 1·00
989 220 f. Declaration of Rights of Man, quill pen in hand and phrygian cap (vert) . . . . 1·25 1·10
990 300 f. Revolutionaries and flag 2·00 1·50

333 Arts and Culture **335** Stamps

1989. 3rd Francophone Summit. Multicoloured.
991 5 f. Type **333** 10 10
992 30 f. Education (horiz) 15 10
993 100 f. Communication (horiz) . 40 35
994 200 f. Development (horiz) . . 1·25 75

1989. No. 960 surch.
995 555 f. on 125 f. multicoloured 2·75 1·00

1989. "Philexfrance 89" International Stamp Exhibition, Paris. Multicoloured.
996 10 f. Type **335** 10 10
997 25 f. Stamp on map of France (vert) 10 10
998 75 f. Couple viewing stamp on easel (vert) 30 25
999 145 f. Sticking stamp on envelope (vert) 60 55

336 "30" Dish Aerial and Envelope **337** Record Stacks and 1922 Postcard

1989. 30th Anniv Meeting of West African Post and Telecommunications Administrations Conference, Dakar. Multicoloured.
1000 25 f. Type **336** 10 10
1001 30 f. Telephone handset, punched tape and map on stamp 15 10
1002 180 f. Map of Africa, stamp and telephone earpiece . . . . 1·10 70
1003 220 f. Stamp, satellite, globe and map of Africa . . . . . . 1·25 85

1989. 75th Anniv (1988) of Senegal Archives. Multicoloured.
1004 15 f. Type **337** 10 10
1005 40 f. 1825 document 15 10
1006 145 f. 1825 document and archive building 85 55
1007 180 f. Bound volume . . . . 1·00 70

338 Jar with Lid **339** Nehru

1989. Pottery. Multicoloured.
1008 15 f. Type **338** 10 10
1009 30 f. Potter at work 15 10
1010 75 f. Stacked pots 30 25
1011 145 f. Woman carrying pots 85 55

1989. Birth Centenary of Jawaharlal Nehru (Indian statesman).
1012 **339** 220 f. multicoloured . . 1·25 85
1013 – 410 f. black, red & yell . 2·50 1·40
DESIGN—HORIZ: 410 f. Nehru (different).

340 Swimming Crab

1989. Marine Life. Multicoloured.
1014 10 f. Type **340** 10 10
1015 60 f. Seahorse (vert) 25 20
1016 145 f. Barnacles 85 55
1017 220 f. Sand-hopper . . . . 1·25 85

341 Clasped Hand and People of Different Races **342** Pilgrims

1989. World Aids Day. Multicoloured.
1018 5 f. Type **341** 10 10
1019 100 f. People under umbrella 40 35
1020 145 f. Fist smashing Aids virus 85 55
1021 180 f. Hammer smashing Aids virus . . . . 1·10 70

1989. Centenary of Pilgrimage to Our Lady of Popenguine. Multicoloured.
1022 145 f. Type **342** 60 55
1023 180 f. Our Lady of Popenguine Church . . . . 1·10 70

343 White-breasted Cormorant and African Darter, Djoudj **344** Boy looking at Christmas Tree

1989. National Parks. Multicoloured.
1024 10 f. Type **343** 10 10
1025 45 f. Grey-headed gulls, Langue de Barbarie 30 20
1026 100 f. Blue-checked bee eater and crested eagle, Basse Casamance 55 45
1027 180 f. Western reef herons, Saloum . . . . 1·75 85

1989. Christmas. Multicoloured.
1028 10 f. Type **344** 10 10
1029 25 f. Teddy bear and bauble hanging from tree 10 10
1030 30 f. Animals around Baby Jesus 15 10
1031 200 f. Madonna and Child . . 1·25 75

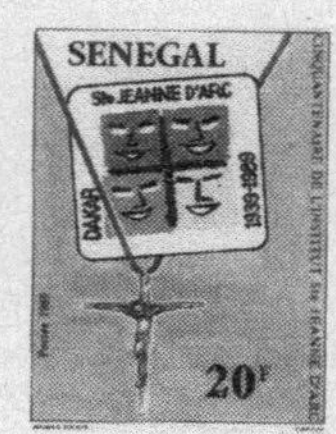

345 Crucifix and Anniversary Emblem

1989. 50th Anniv of St. Joan of Arc Institute, Dakar. Multicoloured.
1032 20 f. Type **345** 10 10
1033 500 f. Emblem and Institute building . . . . 2·75 1·40

346 "Hydravion"

1989. 79th Anniv of First Flight of Henri Fabre's Seaplane. Multicoloured.
1034 125 f. Type **346** 60 55
1035 130 f. Fabre working on engine of "Hydravion" 60 55
1036 475 f. Technical drawings and Fabre (vert) . . . . 3·25 1·00

347 Basketball

1990. Olympic Games, Barcelona (1992). Mult.
1038 10 f. Type **347** 10 10
1039 130 f. High jumping 50 45
1040 180 f. Throwing the discus . . 75 70
1041 190 f. Running 80 75
1042 315 f. Lawn tennis . . . . . 1·25 1·00
1043 475 f. Show jumping . . . . 1·90 1·75

348 Rally Car

1990. 12th Paris–Dakar Rally. Multicoloured.
1045 20 f. Type **348** 10 10
1046 25 f. Motor cycle and sidecar 10 10
1047 180 f. Crowd cheering winning driver . . . . 1·10 70
1048 200 f. Thierry Sabine and car 1·10 75

349 Piazza della Signoria, Florence, and Footballer

1990. World Cup Football Championship, Italy. Multicoloured.
1049 45 f. Type **349** 20 15
1050 140 f. Piazza Navona, Rome 55 25
1051 180 f. "Virgin with St. Anne and Infant Jesus" (Leonardo da Vinci) 75 30
1052 220 f. "Giuseppe Garibaldi" (oil painting) . . . . 1·10 30
1053 300 f. "Sistine Madonna" (Raphael) . . . . 1·50 40
1054 415 f. "Virgin and Child" (Danielle da Volterra) . . 2·10 70

350 Footballer **351** Facsimile Telegraphy

1990. African Nations Cup Football Championship, Algeria. Multicoloured.
1056 20 f. Type **350** 10 10
1057 60 f. Goalkeeper 25 20
1058 100 f. Clasped hands and pennants 40 35
1059 500 f. Trophy . . . . 3·00 1·75

1990. Postal Services. Multicoloured.
1060 5 f. Type **351** 10 10
1061 15 f. Express mail service . . 10 10
1062 100 f. Postal cheques 40 35
1063 180 f. Savings 75 40

352 Hands and Umbrella protecting Children **353** Envelopes on Map

1990. Louga S.O.S. Children's Village. Multicoloured.
1064 5 f. Type **352** 10 10
1065 500 f. Children under umbrella 2·50 1·25

1990. 20th Anniv of Multinational Postal Training School, Abidjan. Multicoloured.
1066 145 f. Type **353** 60 55
1067 180 f. Man carrying wreath containing envelope . . . 75 70

354 Excursion by Pirogue, Basse-Casamance

1990. Tourism. Multicoloured.
1068 10 f. Type **354** 10 10
1069 25 f. Hotel and beach, Goree 10 10
1070 30 f. Houses on stilts, Fadiouth 15 10
1071 40 f. Rose Lake and salt drying 15 10

355 Camp

1990. Scouting. Multicoloured.

1072 30 f. Type **355** 15 10
1073 100 f. Scouts trekking alongside lake 40 35
1074 145 f. Scouts trekking through hilly landscape 60 55
1075 200 f. Scout and emblem (vert) 80 75

356 "Cassia tora" **357** Angels and Tree

1990. Medicinal Plants. Multicoloured.

1076 95 f. Type **356** 40 35
1077 105 f. "Tamarind" 45 40
1078 125 f. "Cassia occidentalis" 50 45
1079 175 f. "Leptadenia hastata" 70 65

1990. Christmas.

1080 **357** 25 f. multicoloured 10 10
1081 – 145 f. multicoloured 60 55
1082 – 180 f. orange, red & blk 75 70
1083 – 200 f. multicoloured 80 75

DESIGNS: 145 f. Angel trumpeting stars; 180 f. Adoration of Three Kings; 200 f. Donkey and cow gazing at Child.

358 Anniversary Emblem **359** Rally Car

1991. 125th Anniv (1988) of International Red Cross and 25th Anniv of Senegal Red Cross.

1084 **358** 180 f. multicoloured 70 45

1991. 13th Paris–Dakar Rally. Multicoloured.

1085 15 f. Type **359** 10 10
1086 15 f. Car and motor cycle at night 50 35
1087 180 f. Rally car (different) 70 45
1088 220 f. Motor cycles 90 60

360 African Python

1991. Reptiles. Multicoloured.

1089 15 f. Type **360** 10 10
1090 60 f. Common green turtle 25 15
1091 100 f. Nile crocodile 40 25
1092 180 f. Senegal chameleon 70 45

361 Sphinx, House of Slaves, Frescoes, Kirdi Houses and Mohammed's Tomb **362** Nobel

1991. "Fespaco". 12th Pan-African Cinema and Television Festival. Multicoloured.

1093 30 f. Type **361** 10 10
1094 60 f. Dogon mask, B. Dioulasso Mosque, drawing of Osiris, and camel rider 25 15
1095 100 f. Rabat, "Seated Scribe" (Egyptian statue), drum and camels 40 25
1096 180 f. Pyramids of Egypt, Djenne Mosque, Guinean mask, Moroccan architecture and Moorish door decorations 70 45

1991. 95th Death Anniv of Alfred Nobel (founder of Nobel prizes). Multicoloured. Self-adhesive.

1097 145 f. Type **362** 60 40
1098 180 f. Nobel and prize presentation (horiz) 70 45

363 Oribi

1991. National Parks. Multicoloured.

1099 5 f. Type **363** 10 10
1100 10 f. Dorcas gazelle 10 10
1101 180 f. Kob 70 45
1102 555 f. Hartebeest 2·25 1·50

364 Cashew

1991. Trees and their Fruit. Multicoloured.

1103 90 f. Type **364** 35 25
1104 100 f. Mango 45 25
1105 125 f. Sugar-palm (vert) 50 35
1106 145 f. Oil palm (vert) 60 45

365 Ader, Motor Car and Telephone

1991. Air. Centenary (1990) of First Heavier than Air Powered Flight. Multicoloured.

1107 145 f. Type **365** 60 40
1108 180 f. Clement Ader and his monoplane "Eole" 90 55
1109 615 f. "Eole" and Ader (vert) 3·00 2·00

366 Columbus and Haitians

1991. 500th Anniv (1992) of Discovery of America by Columbus. Multicoloured.

1111 100 f. Type **366** 40 25
1112 145 f. Arms of Castile and Leon (vert) 60 40
1113 180 f. "Santa Maria" and Columbus 70 45
1114 200 f. Vicente Yanez Pinzon and "Nina" 80 55
1115 220 f. Martin Alonzo Pinzon and "Pinta" 90 60
1116 500 f. Details of charts 2·00 1·25
1117 625 f. Compass rose and Columbus with charts 2·50 1·75

367 Armstrong

1991. 20th Death Anniv of Louis Armstrong (musician). Multicoloured.

1118 10 f. Type **367** 10 10
1119 145 f. Armstrong singing 60 40
1120 180 f. Armstrong and trumpets 70 45
1121 220 f. Armstrong playing trumpet 90 65

368 Yuri Gagarin and "Vostok 1"

1991. 30th Anniv of First Man in Space. Mult.

1125 15 f. Type **368** 10 10
1126 145 f. "Vostok 1" and Gagarin in spacesuit 60 40
1127 180 f. Gagarin in spacesuit and "Vostok 1" (different) 70 45
1128 220 f. Globe, "Vostok 1" and Gagarin in flying kit 90 60

369 Flags and Water dripping into Bowl **370** Star and Crescents

1991. "Water, Source of Life". Senegal–Saudi Arabia Rural Water Supply Co-operation. Multicoloured.

1129 30 f. Type **369** 10 10
1130 145 f. Tap and village 60 40
1131 180 f. Tap dripping and flags 70 45
1132 220 f. Water tower and village 90 60

1991. 6th Summit Meeting of Islamic Conference Organization, Dakar. Multicoloured.

1133 15 f. Type **370** 10 10
1134 145 f. Hands 60 40
1135 180 f. Conference centre and accommodation 70 45
1136 220 f. Grand Mosque, Dakar 90 60

371 Player shooting at Basket **372** Giving Blessing

1991. Centenary of Basketball. Multicoloured.

1137 125 f. Type **371** 50 35
1138 145 f. Player approching basket 60 40
1139 180 f. King and Queen of the Basket 70 45
1140 220 f. Lion, trophies and ball 90 60

1991. Christmas. Multicoloured.

1141 5 f. Type **372** 10 10
1142 145 f. Madonna and Child 60 40
1143 160 f. Angels and star 65 45
1144 220 f. Animals and Baby Jesus 90 60

373 Bust of Mozart and Score **374** Flags on Player's Sock

1991. Death Bicentenary of Wolfgang Amadeus Mozart (composer). Multicoloured.

1145 5 f. Type **373** 10 10
1146 150 f. Mozart conducting 60 40
1147 180 f. Mozart at keyboard 70 45
1148 220 f. Mozart and score 90 60

1992. 18th African Nations Cup Football Championship. Multicoloured.

1149 10 f. Type **374** 10 10
1150 145 f. Footballs forming "92" 70 45
1151 200 f. Cup and mascot 95 65
1152 220 f. Players 1·10 75

1992. Papal Visit. No. 1143 surch **VISITE DU PAPE JEAN PAUL II AU SENEGAL 19-23/02/92 180F**.

1153 180 f. on 160 f. multicoloured 85 55

376 Saloum Delta

1992. National Parks. Multicoloured.

1154 10 f. Type **376** 10 10
1155 125 f. Djoudj 60 40
1156 145 f. Niokolo-Koba 70 45
1157 220 f. Basse Casamance 1·10 75

INDEX

Countries can be quickly located by referring to the index at the end of this volume.

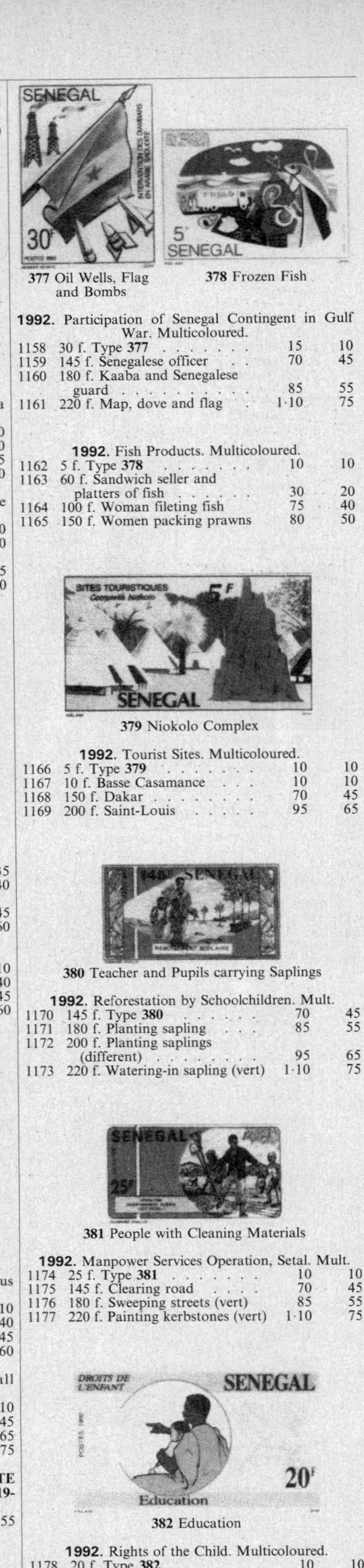

377 Oil Wells, Flag and Bombs **378** Frozen Fish

1992. Participation of Senegal Contingent in Gulf War. Multicoloured.

1158 30 f. Type **377** 15 10
1159 145 f. Senegalese officer 70 45
1160 180 f. Kaaba and Senegalese guard 85 55
1161 220 f. Map, dove and flag 1·10 75

1992. Fish Products. Multicoloured.

1162 5 f. Type **378** 10 10
1163 60 f. Sandwich seller and platters of fish 30 20
1164 100 f. Woman filleting fish 75 40
1165 150 f. Women packing prawns 80 50

379 Niokolo Complex

1992. Tourist Sites. Multicoloured.

1166 5 f. Type **379** 10 10
1167 10 f. Basse Casamance 10 10
1168 150 f. Dakar 70 45
1169 200 f. Saint-Louis 95 65

380 Teacher and Pupils carrying Saplings

1992. Reforestation by Schoolchildren. Mult.

1170 145 f. Type **380** 70 45
1171 180 f. Planting sapling 85 55
1172 200 f. Planting saplings (different) 95 65
1173 220 f. Watering-in sapling (vert) 1·10 75

381 People with Cleaning Materials

1992. Manpower Services Operation, Setal. Mult.

1174 25 f. Type **381** 10 10
1175 145 f. Clearing road 70 45
1176 180 f. Sweeping streets (vert) 85 55
1177 220 f. Painting kerbstones (vert) 1·10 75

382 Education

1992. Rights of the Child. Multicoloured.

1178 20 f. Type **382** 10 10
1179 45 f. Vocational training 20 15
1180 165 f. Instruction 80 55
1181 180 f. Health 85 55

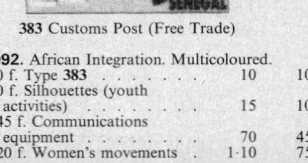

383 Customs Post (Free Trade)

1992. African Integration. Multicoloured.

1182 10 f. Type **383** 10 10
1183 30 f. Silhouettes (youth activities) 15 10
1184 145 f. Communications equipment 70 45
1185 220 f. Women's movements 1·10 75

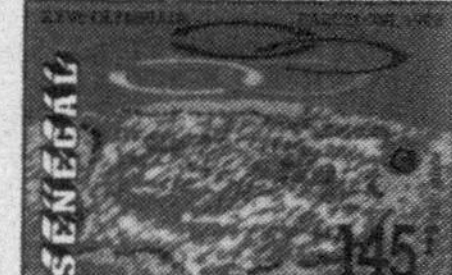

384 Rings and Map of Spain

1992. Olympic Games, Barcelona. Multicoloured.

No.	Description	Unused	Used
1186	145 f. Type **384**	70	45
1187	180 f. Runner (vert)	85	55
1188	200 f. Sprinter	95	65
1189	300 f. Athlete carrying torch (vert)	1·40	95

385 Passenger Carriages

1992. "The Blue Train". Multicoloured.

No.	Description	Unused	Used
1190	70 f. Type **385**	35	25
1191	145 f. Locomotives and carriages	70	45
1192	200 f. Train and track on map	95	65
1193	220 f. Railway station	1·10	75

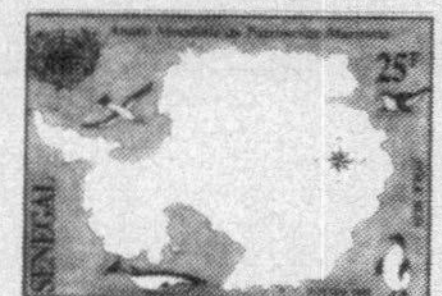

386 Sealife around Map of Antarctic

1992. International Maritime Heritage Year.

No.	Description	Unused	Used
1194	**386** 25 f. black, blue & yellow	10	10
1195	– 100 f. multicoloured	40	25
1196	– 180 f. multicoloured	85	55
1197	– 220 f. multicoloured	1·10	75

DESIGNS—VERT: 100 f. Marine life caught in sun ray; 180 f. United Nations seminar; 220 f. Fish, ship, flags and hands holding globe.

387 Coral

1992. Corals.

No.	Description	Unused	Used
1198	**387** 50 f. multicoloured	25	15
1199	– 100 f. multicoloured	40	25
1200	– 145 f. mult (vert)	70	45
1201	– 220 f. multicoloured	1·10	75

DESIGNS: 100 f. to 220 f. Different corals.

388 Adenauer   389 Crab

1992. 25th Death Anniv of Konrad Adenauer (German statesman). Multicoloured.

No.	Description	Unused	Used
1202	5 f. Type **388**	10	10
1203	145 f. Schaumburg Palace and flags (horiz)	70	45
1204	180 f. German flag and handshake (horiz)	85	55
1205	220 f. Map, flag and emblem of Germany (horiz)	1·10	75

1992. Crustaceans. Multicoloured.

No.	Description	Unused	Used
1206	20 f. Type **389**	10	10
1207	30 f. Sea spider	15	10
1208	180 f. Crayfish	85	55
1209	200 f. King prawn	95	65

MINIMUM PRICE

The minimum price quoted is 10p which represents a handling charge rather than a basis for valuing common stamps. For further notes about prices, see introductory pages.

390 "Parkia biglobosa"

1992. Flowers and their Fruits. Multicoloured.

No.	Description	Unused	Used
1210	10 f. Type **390**	10	10
1211	50 f. Desert date	25	15
1212	200 f. "Parinari macrophylla"	95	65
1213	220 f. Cactus	1·10	75

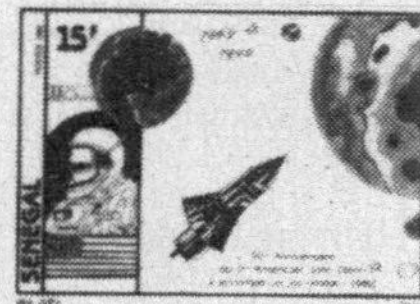

391 Rocket and Earth

1992. 30th Anniv of First American Manned Orbit of the Earth. Multicoloured.

No.	Description	Unused	Used
1214	15 f. Type **391**	10	10
1215	145 f. American flag and John Glenn	35	25
1216	180 f. Rocket launch and globe	45	30
1217	200 f. Astonaut and rocket on launch-pad (vert)	45	30

392 Bakari II and Map from 14th-century Catalan Atlas

1992. Bakari II. Multicoloured.

No.	Description	Unused	Used
1218	100 f. Type **392**	40	25
1219	145 f. Giant Mexican carved head and map from 15th-century atlas	75	45

393 Picture Frame and Obelisk   394 Children dancing round Decorated Globe

1992. Dakar Biennale. Multicoloured.

No.	Description	Unused	Used
1220	20 f. Type **393**	10	10
1221	50 f. Mask hanging from window frame	10	10
1222	145 f. Open book	35	25
1223	220 f. Traditional string instrument	50	35

1992. Christmas. Multicoloured.

No.	Description	Unused	Used
1224	15 f. Type **394**	10	10
1225	145 f. People around tree (vert)	35	25
1226	180 f. Jesus (vert)	45	30
1227	200 f. Father Christmas (vert)	45	30

1993. 15th Paris–Dakar Rally. Nos. 941 and 975 surch **Dakar le 17-01-93** and new value.

No.	Description	Unused	Used
1228	145 f. on 180 f. multicoloured	35	25
1229	220 f. on 410 f. multicoloured	50	35

396 First Aid Post

1993. Accident Prevention Campaign. Mult.

No.	Description	Unused	Used
1230	20 f. Type **396** (prevention, security and first aid)	10	10
1231	25 f. The Sonacos incident (reinforcement of preventative measures) (36×28 mm)	10	10
1232	145 f. Chemical accident (need for vigilance and security) (36×28 mm)	35	25
1233	200 f. Helicopter rescue (rapid and efficient intervention at air disasters)	45	30

397 Seck   398 Spotted Hyena

1993. 120th Birth Anniv of Abdoulaye Seck (Director of Posts and Telecommunications).

No.	Description	Unused	Used
1234	**397** 220 f. multicoloured	50	35

1993. Wild Animals. Multicoloured.

No.	Description	Unused	Used
1235	30 f. Type **398**	10	10
1236	50 f. Lioness	10	10
1237	70 f. Leopard	15	10
1238	150 f. Giraffe (vert)	35	25
1239	180 f. Stag	45	30

399 Decorated Tree, Children playing and Father Christmas

1993. Christmas. Multicoloured.

No.	Description	Unused	Used
1240	5 f. Type **399**	10	10
1241	80 f. Children decorating tree and Father Christmas	20	15
1242	145 f. Children visiting Father Christmas	35	25
1243	150 f. Girl tugging Father Christmas's beard	35	25

OFFICIAL STAMPS

O 45 Arms of Dakar   O 78 Baobab Tree

1961. Figures of value in black.

No.	Description	Unused	Used
O240	O **45** 1 f. black and blue	10	10
O241	2 f. blue and yellow	10	10
O242	5 f. lake and green	10	10
O243	10 f. red and blue	10	10
O244	25 f. blue and red	20	15
O245	50 f. red and grey	75	30
O246	85 f. purple & orange	1·40	45
O247	100 f. red and green	2·00	1·10

1966.

No.	Description	Unused	Used
O 339	O **78** 1 f. black & yellow	10	10
O 340	5 f. black & orange	10	10
O 341	10 f. black and red	10	10
O 342	20 f. black & purple	15	10
O 342a	25 f. black & mauve	15	10
O 343	30 f. black and blue	15	10
O 344	35 f. black and blue	20	10
O 344a	40 f. black and blue	20	10
O1122	50 f. black and red	20	15
O 345	55 f. black & green	35	20
O 345a	60 f. black & green	45	20
O 346	90 f. black & green	50	35
O 347	100 f. black & brown	60	40
O1123	145 f. black & green	55	35
O1124	180 f. black & orge	70	45

1969. No. O345 surch.

No.	Description	Unused	Used
O390	O **78** 60 f. on 55 f. black and green	85	10

POSTAGE DUE STAMPS

1903. Postage Due stamps of French Colonies surch.

No.	Description	Unused	Used
D30	U 10 on 50 c. purple	50·00	50·00
D31	10 on 60 c. brn on buff	50·00	50·00
D32	10 on 1 f. pink on buff	£250	£250

1906. "Natives" key-type.

No.	Description	Unused	Used
D50	L 5 c. green and red	3·00	3·00
D51	10 c. purple and blue	4·00	3·50
D52	15 c. blue & red on blue	4·50	4·25
D53	20 c. black & red on yell	5·25	3·75
D54	30 c. red & bl on cream	6·00	5·25
D55	50 c. violet and red	6·00	5·50
D56	60 c. blk & red on buff	7·50	7·25
D57	1 f. black & red on pink	12·00	13·00

1915. "Figure" key-type.

No.	Description	Unused	Used
D81	M 5 c. green	15	30
D82	10 c. red	25	20
D83	15 c. grey	25	25
D84	20 c. brown	50	40
D85	30 c. blue	75	70
D86	50 c. black	1·00	90
D87	60 c. orange	1·25	1·25
D88	1 r. violet	1·40	1·50

1927. Surch in figures.

No.	Description	Unused	Used
D133	M 2 f. on 1 f. purple	2·75	2·75
D134	3 f. on 1 f. brown	2·75	2·75

D 40

1935.

No.	Description	Unused	Used
D194	D **40** 5 c. green	10	25
D195	10 c. orange	10	25
D196	15 c. violet	10	25
D197	20 c. olive	10	25
D198	30 c. brown	10	25
D199	50 c. purple	40	65
D200	60 c. yellow	75	80
D201	1 f. black	50	50
D202	2 f. blue	55	65
D203	3 f. red	75	95

D 43   D 77 Lion's Head

1961.

No.	Description	Unused	Used
D239	D **43** 1 f. orange and red	10	10
D240	2 f. blue and red	10	10
D241	5 f. brown and red	10	10
D242	20 f. green and red	25	25
D243	25 f. purple and red	5·50	5·50

1966. Head in gold and black; value in black.

No.	Description	Unused	Used
D339	D **77** 1 f. red	15	15
D340	2 f. brown	15	15
D341	5 f. violet	20	20
D342	10 f. blue	40	40
D343	20 f. green	50	50
D344	30 f. grey	65	65
D345	60 f. blue	65	65
D346	90 f. purple	75	75

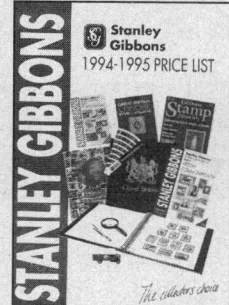

SENEGAMBIA AND NIGER Pt. 6

A French colony later re-named Upper Senegal and Niger, and later French Sudan.

100 centimes = 1 franc

1903. "Tablet" key-type inscr "SENEGAMBIE ET NIGER" in red (1, 5, 15, 25, 75 c., 1 f.) or blue (others).
22 D 1 c. black on blue 50 1·10
23 2 c. brown on buff 1·00 1·25
24 4 c. brown on grey 1·40 2·25
25 5 c. green 3·75 2·00
26 10 c. red 3·75 2·00
27 15 c. grey 6·75 5·75
28 20 c. red on green 6·50 6·75
29 25 c. blue 9·50 9·50
30 30 c. brown on drab 8·75 9·50
31 40 c. red on yellow 14·00 14·00
32 50 c. brown on blue 25·00 28·00
33 75 c. brown on orange 30·00 32·00
34 1 f. green 38·00 40·00

SERBIA Pt. 3

A kingdom in the Balkans, S. E. Europe. Part of Yugoslavia since 1918, except during the Second World War when stamps were issued by a German sponsored Government.

100 paras = 1 dinar

2 Prince Michael (Obrenovich III) 3 Prince Milan (Obrenovich IV) 5 King Milan I

1866. Perf.
12 2 10 p. orange 70·00 90·00
15 20 p. red 12·50 18·00
14 40 p. blue 42·00 32·00

1869. Perf.
42 3 10 p. brown 4·75 4·00
45 10 p. orange 1·25 3·00
31 15 p. orange 45·00 23·00
43 20 p. blue 1·10 1·25
39 25 p. red 1·90 4·75
34 35 p. green 3·50 3·50
47 40 p. mauve 1·90 1·50
36 50 p. green 6·00 4·75

1880. Perf.
54a 5 5 p. green 25 10
55 10 p. red 50 10
56 20 p. orange 35 20
57a 25 p. blue 1·25 15
58 50 p. brown 1·00 2·10
59 1 d. violet 6·75 7·50

6 7 10
King Alexander (Obrenovich V)

1890.
60 6 5 p. green 25 10
61 10 p. red 50 10
62 15 p. mauve 50 10
63 20 p. orange 45 10
64 25 p. blue 60 20
65 50 p. brown 2·40 2·40
66 1 d. lilac 8·75 7·75

1894.
75 7 1 p. red 10 10
76 5 p. green 75 10
68 10 p. red 2·00 10
69 15 p. mauve 4·00 10
79 20 p. orange 4·50 10
80 25 p. blue 4·50 15
81a 50 p. brown 9·00 80
73 1 d. green 1·25 1·60
74 1 d. red on blue 7·50 2·50

1900. Surch.
82 7 10 p. on 20 p. red 1·00 10
84 15 p. on 1 d. red on blue 3·75 75

1901.
85a 10 5 p. green 10 10
86 10 p. red 10 10
87 15 p. mauve 10 10
88 20 p. orange 10 10
89 25 p. blue 15 10
90 50 p. yellow 20 15
91 – 1 d. brown 60 1·40
92a – 3 d. pink 6·25 8·75
93a – 5 d. violet 6·25 9·50
The 1 d. to 5 d. are larger.

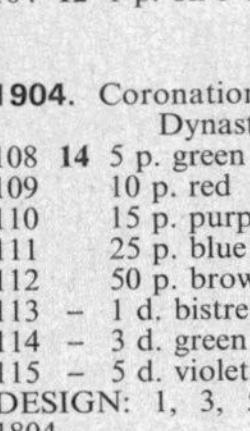

12 King Alexander I (Obrenovich V) 14 Karageorge and Peter I

1903. Optd with shield.
94 12 1 p. black and red 30 60
95 5 p. black and green 25 10
96 10 p. black and red 10 10
97 15 p. black and grey 10 10
98 20 p. black and orange 15 10
99 25 p. black and blue 20 10
100 50 p. black and grey 3·00 55
101 1 d. black and green 9·50 3·00
102 3 d. black and lilac 1·90 2·25
103 5 d. black and brown 1·90 2·50

1903. Surch **1 NAPA 1**.
104 12 1 p. on 5 d. black and brown 95 2·50

1904. Coronation. Centenary of Karageorgevich Dynasty. Dated "1804 1904".
108 14 5 p. green 10 10
109 10 p. red 10 10
110 15 p. purple 10 10
111 25 p. blue 15 15
112 50 p. brown 25 25
113 – 1 d. bistre 6 75
114 – 3 d. green 1·50 3·00
115 – 5 d. violet 1·90 3·75
DESIGN: 1, 3, 5 d. Karageorge and insurgents, 1804.

16 Peter I

17 Peter I

1905.
116 16 1 p. black and grey 15 10
117 5 p. black and green 20 10
118 10 p. black and red 1·90 10
119 15 p. black and mauve 2·10 10
120 20 p. black and yellow 3·75 10
121 25 p. black and blue 5·25 10
122 30 p. black and green 2·75 10
123 50 p. black and brown 3·75 10
135 1 d. black and bistre 80 15
136 3 d. black and green 80 86
137 5 d. black and violet 3·00 2·25

1911.
146 17 1 p. black 10 10
147 2 p. violet 10 10
169 5 p. green 10 10
170 10 p. red 10 10
150 15 p. purple 70 10
171 15 p. black 15 10
151 20 p. yellow 70 10
172 20 p. brown 35 20
173 25 p. blue 10 10
153 30 p. green 20 15
173a 30 p. bronze 10 20
154 50 p. brown 30 20
174 50 p. red 10 20
155 1 d. orange 18·00 32·00
175 1 d. green 1·00 1·75
156 3 d. lake 24·00 70·00
176 3 d. yellow 95·00 £375
177 5 d. violet 2·10 17·00

19 Peter I on the Battlefield

20 Peter I and Prince Alexander

1915.
178 19 5 p. green 15 1·00
179 10 p. red 15 1·25
179a 15 p. grey 3·00
179b 20 p. brown 40
179c 25 p. blue 6·25
179d 30 p. green 3·00
179e 50 p. brown 24·00

1918.
194 20 1 p. black 10 10
195 2 p. olive 10 10
196 5 p. green 10 10
197 10 p. red 10 10
198 15 p. sepia 10 10
199 20 p. brown 10 10
208 20 p. mauve 1·40 75
200 25 p. blue 10 10
201 30 p. olive 10 10
202 50 p. mauve 10 10
220 1 d. brown 10 10
204 3 d. slate 90 75
205 5 d. brown 1·50 90

NEWSPAPER STAMPS

1

4 King Milan

1866. Imperf.
N7 1 1 p. green on red 45·00
N4 2 p. brown on lilac 60·00

1867. Perf.
N17 2 1 p. olive 9·25 £550
N18 2 p. brown 15·00 £500

1868. Imperf.
N19 2 1 p. green 15·00
N20 2 p. brown 24·00

1869. Perf.
N49 3 1 p. yellow 1·25 £275

1872. Imperf.
N51 3 1 p. yellow 5·50 11·00
N52 4 2 p. black 1·90 9·25

POSTAGE DUE STAMPS

D 8

D 21

1895.
D87 D 8 5 p. mauve 40 25
D83 10 p. blue 2·50 20
D91 20 p. brown 15 45
D85 30 p. green 15 35
D86 50 p. red 15 45

1918.
D227 D 21 5 p. red 15 15
D232 5 p. brown 20 25
D228 10 p. green 15 15
D229 20 p. brown 15 15
D230 30 p. blue 15 15
D233 30 p. grey 30 35
D231 50 p. brown 75 35

GERMAN OCCUPATION

1941. Stamps of Yugoslavia on paper with coloured network optd **SERBIEN** reading downwards.
G 1 99 25 p. black 10 75
G 2 50 p. orange 10 20
G 3 1 d. green 10 20
G 4 1 d. 50 red 10 20
G 5 2 d. red 10 20
G 6 3 d. brown 75 4·25
G 7 4 d. blue 15 55
G 8 5 d. blue 40 1·75
G 9 5 d. 50 violet 40 1·75
G10 6 d. blue 40 1·75
G11 8 d. brown 55 2·75
G12 12 d. violet 55 2·75
G13 16 d. purple 90 7·00
G14 20 d. blue 90 8·50
G15 30 d. pink 4·50 55·00

1941. Air. Stamps of Yugoslavia on paper with coloured network, optd **SERBIEN**.
G16 80 50 p. brown 3·50 19·00
G17 – 1 d. green (No. 361) 3·50 19·00
G18 – 2 d. blue (No. 362) 3·50 19·00
G19 – 2 d. 50 red (No. 363) 3·50 19·00
G20 80 5 d. violet 3·50 19·00
G21 – 10 d. red (No. 365) 3·50 19·00
G22 – 20 d. green (No. 366) 3·50 19·00
G23 – 30 d. blue (No. 367) 4·75 21·00
G24 – 40 d. green (No. 443) 8·00 £100
G25 – 50 d. blue (No. 444) 40·00 80·00

1941. Air. As last, but without network surch **SERBIEN** and value.
G26 – 1 d. on 10 d. red (No. 365) 2·00 13·50
G27 – 3 d. on 20 d. grn (No. 366) 2·00 13·50
G28 – 6 d. on 30 d. blue (No. 367) 2·00 13·50
G29 – 8 d. on 40 d. grn (No. 443) 2·50 38·00
G30 – 12 d. on 50 d. bl (No. 444) 4·75 65·00

1941. As Nos. G1/15, but with **SERBIEN** reading upwards.
G31 99 25 p. black 10 3·00
G32 50 p. orange 10 55
G33 1 d. green 15 35
G34 1 d. 50 red 15 60
G35 2 d. red 15 35
G36 3 d. brown 25 4·00
G37 4 d. blue 20 35
G38 5 d. blue 20 1·00
G39 5 d. 50 violet 40 3·00
G40 6 d. blue 50 3·00
G41 8 d. brown 70 3·00
G42 12 d. violet 90 3·00
G43 16 d. purple 90 8·50
G44 20 d. blue 90 14·00
G45 30 d. pink 5·50 48·00

4 Smederevo Fortress

6 Christ and the Virgin Mary

1941. Smederevo Explosion Relief Fund.
G46 4 50 p. + 1 d. brown 15 70
G47 – 1 d. + 2 d. green 15 75
G48 – 1 d. 50 + 3 d. purple 30 1·25
G49 4 2 d. + 4 d. blue 40 2·00
DESIGN: 1 d., 1 d. 50, Refugees.

1941. Prisoners of War Fund.
G50 6 50 p. + 1 d. 50 brown 20 3·00
G51 1 d. + 3 d. green 20 3·00
G52 2 d. + 6 d. red 20 3·00
G53 4 d. + 12 d. blue 20 3·00
This set also exists with an optd network, both plain and incorporating a large "E", this letter being either normal or reversed.

7

8

1942. Anti-Masonic Exn. Dated "22.X.1941".
G54 7 50 p. + 50 p. brown 15 35
G55 – 1 d. + 1 d. green 15 35
G56 8 2 d. + 2 d. red 25 75
G57 – 4 d. + 4 d. blue 25 75
DESIGNS—HORIZ: 1 d. Hand grasping snake. VERT: 4 d. Peasant demolishing masonic symbols.

9 Kalenic

11 Mother and Children

1942. Monasteries.
G58 – 50 p. violet 10 15
G59 9 1 d. red 10 10
G60 – 1 d. 50 brown 70 2·50
G61 – 1 d. 50 green 10 15
G62 – 2 d. purple 10 15
G63 – 3 d. blue 70 2·50
G64 – 3 d. pink 10 15
G65 – 4 d. blue 10 15
G66 – 7 d. green 10 15
G67 – 12 d. red 15 1·00
G68 – 16 d. black 45 1·50
DESIGNS—VERT: 50 p. Lazarica; 1 d. 50, Ravanica; 12 d. Gornjak; 16 d. Studenica. HORIZ: 2 d. Manasija; 3 d. Ljubostinja; 4 d. Sopocani; 7 d. Zica.

1942. As Nos. G50/53, colours changed.
G68a 6 0.50 d. + 1.50 d. brown 50 1·40
G68b 1 d. + 3 d. green 50 1·40
G68c 2 d. + 6 d. red 50 1·40
G68d 4 d. + 12 d. blue 50 1·40

1942. Air. 1939 issue of Yugoslavia surch with airplane, "SERBIA" in cyrillic characters and new value.
G69 99 2 on 2 d. mauve 10 1·25
G70 4 on 4 d. blue 10 1·25
G71 10 on 12 d. violet 15 2·00
G72 14 on 20 d. blue 15 2·00
G73 20 on 30 d. pink 30 9·00

1942. War Orphans Fund.
G74 11 2 d. + 6 d. violet 1·00 2·50
G75 4 d. + 8 d. blue 1·00 2·50
G76 7 d. + 13 d. green 1·00 2·50
G77 20 d. + 40 d. red 1·00 2·50

12 Broken Sword

13 Post Rider

1943. War Invalids' Relief Fund.
G78 12 1 d. 50 + 1 d. 50 brown 40 90
G79 – 2 d. + 3 d. green 40 90

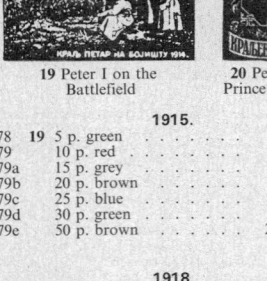

G80 – 3 d. + 5 d. mauve . . . . 60 1·60
G81 – 4 d. + 10 d. blue . . . . 90 2·50
DESIGNS—HORIZ: 2 d. Fallen standard bearer; 3 d. Wounded soldier (seated). VERT: 4 d. Nurse tending soldier.

1943. Postal Centenary. Inscr "15.X.1843-15.X.1943".
G82 **13** 3 d. red and lilac . . . 30 1·10
G83 – 8 d. mauve and grey . . . 30 1·10
G84 – 9 d. green and brown . . 75 1·00
G85 – 30 d. brown and green . . 30 1·10
G86 – 50 d. blue and red . . . . 30 1·10
DESIGNS: 8 d. Horse wagon; 9 d. Railway van; 30 d. Postal motor van; 50 d. Junkers Ju 52/3m mail plane.

1943. Bombing of Nish Relief Fund. Monasteries issue of 1942 on paper with network, surch ... **Serbian Inscr, 20-X-1943** and value.
G87 50 p. + 2 d. violet . . . . . 10 2·00
G88 1 d. + 3 d. red . . . . . . 10 2·00
G89 1 d. 50 + 4 d. green . . . . 10 2·00
G90 2 d. + 5 d. purple . . . . . 15 2·00
G91 3 d. + 7 d. pink . . . . . . 15 2·00
G92 4 d. + 9 d. blue . . . . . . 15 2·00
G93 7 d. + 15 d. green . . . . . 40 2·50
G94 12 d. + 25 d. red . . . . . 40 8·00
G95 16 d. + 33 d. black . . . . 65 13·00

OFFICIAL STAMP

O 12

1943.
GO78 **O 12** 3 d. red . . . . 30 1·00

POSTAGE DUE STAMPS

D 2 D 3 D 13

1941. Unissued Postage Due stamps optd **SERBIEN**.
GD16 **D 2** 50 p. violet . . . . . 35 2·75
GD17 1 d. red . . . . . . 35 2·75
GD18 2 d. blue . . . . . . 35 2·75
GD19 3 d. red . . . . . . 45 3·50
GD20 **D 3** 4 d. blue . . . . . . 75 7·50
GD21 5 d. orange . . . . . 75 7·50
GD22 10 d. violet . . . . . 2·00 17·00
GD23 20 d. green . . . . . 6·00 70·00

1942. Types **D 2** and **D 3** without opt. Bottom inscription on white background.
GD69 **D 2** 1 d. red and green . . 15 1·50
GD70 2 d. blue and red . . . 15 1·50
GD71 3 d. red and blue . . . 20 2·50
GD72 **D 3** 4 d. blue and red . . . 20 2·50
GD73 5 d. orange and blue . . 30 2·75
GD74 10 d. violet and red . . 35 6·50
GD75 20 d. green and red . . 95 16·00

1943.
GD82 **D 13** 50 p. black . . . . . 15 1·00
GD83 3 d. violet . . . . . 15 1·00
GD84 4 d. blue . . . . . . 15 1·00
GD85 5 d. green . . . . . 15 1·00
GD86 6 d. orange . . . . . 25 2·75
GD87 10 d. red . . . . . . 40 6·00
GD88 20 d. blue . . . . . 1·00 13·00

SERBIAN OCCUPATION OF HUNGARY Pt. 2

BARANYA

100 filler = 1 korona

1919. Stamps of Hungary optd **1919 Baranya** or surch also. (a) "Turul" Type.
1 **7** 6 f. drab 15 15
2 50 f. red on blue 10 10
3 60 f. green on red 25 25
4 70 f. brown on green 10 10
5 80 f. violet . . . . 1·75 1·75

(b) War Charity stamp of 1915.
6 **7** 50 + 2 f. red on blue . . . . 6·00 6·00

(c) War Charity stamps of 1916.
8 **20** 10 f. (+ 2 f.) red 10 10
9 – 15 f. (+ 2 f.) violet 10 10

(d) Harvesters and Parliament Types.
10 **18** 2 f. brown 10 10
11 3 f. purple 10 10
12 5 f. green 10 10
13 6 f. blue 30 30
14 15 f. purple 10 10
15 20 f. brown . . . . 10·00 10·00
16 25 f. blue . . . . 1·40 1·40
17 35 f. brown . . . . 2·50 2·50
18 40 f. green . . . . 10·00 10·00
19 45 on 2 f. brown 20 20
20 45 on 5 f. green 10 10
21 45 on 15 f. purple 10 10
22 **19** 50 f. purple 35 35
23 **19** 75 f. blue 10 10
24 80 f. green 15 15
25 1 k. red 15 15
26 2 k. brown 15 15
27 3 k. grey and violet 15 15
28 5 k. light brown and brown . . 65 65
29 60 k. mauve and brown . . . 3·00 3·00

(e) Charles and Zita stamps.
30 **27** 10 f. pink 10 10
31 20 f. brown 10 10
32 25 k. blue 55 55
33 **28** 40 f. green . . . . 6·00 6·00

(f) Stamps optd **KOZTARSASAG**. (i) Harvesters Type.
34 **18** 2 f. brown . . . . 1·50 1·50
35 45 on 2 f. brown 20 20

(ii) Zita stamp.
36 **28** 40 f. green . . . . 8·00 8·00

1919. Stamps of Hungary surch **BARANYA** and value. (a) Harvesters and Parliament Types.
42 **18** 20 on 2 f. brown . . . . . 4·00 4·00
43 50 on 5 f. green . . . . . 2·25 2·25
44 150 on 15 f. purple 80 80
45 **19** 200 on 75 f. blue 60 60

(b) Harvesters Type inscr "MAGYAR POSTA".
46 **18** 20 on 2 f. brown 10 10
47 30 on 6 f. blue 20 20
48 50 on 5 f. green 10 10
49 100 on 25 f. blue 10 10
50 100 on 40 f. green 10 10
51 100 on 45 f. orange 30 30
52 150 on 20 f. brown 55 55

(c) Charles stamp optd **KOZTARSASAG**.
53 **27** 150 on 15 f. purple 75 75

EXPRESS LETTER STAMPS

1919. No. E245 of Hungary surch **1919 Baranya 105**.
E37 **E 18** 105 on 2 f. green and red 55 55

1919. No. E245 of Hungary surch **BARANYA 10**.
E55 **E 18** 10 on 2 f. olive and red 10 10

NEWSPAPER STAMP

1919. No. N136 of Hungary surch **BARANYA 10**.
N54 **N 9** 10 on 2 (f). orange . . . 10 10

POSTAGE DUE STAMPS

1919. Nos. D191 etc of Hungary optd **1919 BARANYA** or surch also.
D38 **D 9** 2 f. red and green . . . 2·50 2·50
D39 10 f. red and green . . . 45 45
D40 20 f. red and geen . . . 45 45
D41 40 on 2 f. red and green 45 45

SAVINGS BANK STAMP

1919. No. B199 of Hungary surch **BARANYA 10**.
B56 **B 17** 10 on 10 f. purple . . . 10 10

TEMESVAR

Temesvar was later occupied by Rumania which issued stamps for this area. It was then incorporated in Rumania and renamed Timosoara.

100 filler = 1 korona

1919. Stamps of Hungary surch. (a) War Charity stamp of 1916.
1 **20** 45 f. on 10 f. (+ 2 f.) red . . 10 10

(b) Harvesters Type.
2 **18** 10 f. on 2 f. brown 10 10
3 30 f. on 2 f. brown 10 10
4 1 k. 50 on 15 f. purple . . . 15 15

(c) Charles stamp.
5 **27** 50 f. on 20 f. brown 10 10

POSTAGE DUE STAMPS

1919. No. D191 of Hungary surch.
D6 **D 9** 40 f. on 2 f. red & green 15 15
D7 60 f. on 2 f. red & green 15 15
D8 100 f. on 2 f. red & green 15 15

SHANGHAI Pt. 17

A seaport on the E. coast of China, which for a time had a separate postal system.

1865. 10 cash = 1 candareen
100 candareens = 1 tael
1890. 100 cents = 1 dollar (Chinese)

1 Dragon

1865. Value in candareens. Imperf. (a) "CANDAREEN" in singular.
28 **1** 1 ca. blue . . . . 55·00 £180
12 2 ca. black £140 £2500
29 3 ca. brown . . . . 55·00 £2500
13 4 ca. yellow £150 £2500
14 8 ca. green £100
15 16 ca. red £140

(b) "CANDAREENS" in plural.
30 **1** 2 ca. black . . . . 50·00
31 3 ca. brown . . . . 50·00 £1500
3 **1** 4 ca. yellow £140 £1800
18 6 ca. brown . . . . 85·00
20 6 ca. red £100
4 8 ca. green £150 £2500
21 12 ca. brown . . . . 90·00
22 16 ca. red . . . . 90·00

2 6

1866. Value in cents. Frames differ. Perf.
32 **2** 2 c. red . . . . 7·50 18·00
33 4 c. lilac . . . . 11·00 32·00
34 8 c. ble . . . . 15·00 32·00
35 16 c. green . . . . 22·00 48·00

1867. Value in candareens. Frames differ.
37 **6** 1 ca. brown . . . . 4·50 8·00
59 1 ca. yellow on yellow . . . 10·00 15·00
62 1 ca. yellow . . . . 6·50 9·00
73 1 ca. red £450 £850
38 3 ca. yellow . . . . 13·00 25·00
60 3 ca. pink on pink . . . . 10·00 15·00
63 3 ca. red . . . . 35·00 45·00
39 6 ca. grey . . . . 14·00 48·00
64 6 ca. green . . . . 55·00 90·00
65 9 ca. grey . . . . 70·00 £120
40 12 ca. brown . . . . 20·00 48·00

1873. Surch with value in English and Chinese.
41 **2** 1 ca. on 2 c. red . . . . . 20·00 30·00
44 1 ca. on 4 c. lilac . . . . . 9·50 10·00
46 1 ca. on 8 c. blue . . . . . 13·00 14·00
48 1 ca. on 16 c. green £950 £750
50 3 ca. on 2 c. red . . . . . 60·00 75·00
52 3 ca. on 16 c. green £1400 £1300

1873. Surch with value in English and Chinese.
53 **6** 1 ca. on 3 ca. yellow £8250 £5750
67 1 ca. on 3 ca. red . . . . . 35·00 30·00
68 1 ca. on 3 ca. pink on pink . . £160 £150
54 1 ca. on 6 ca. grey £225 £225
69 1 ca. on 6 ca. green . . . . 70·00 65·00
70 1 ca. on 9 ca. grey £140 £140
56 1 ca. on 12 ca. brown . . . £190 £180
58 3 ca. on 12 ca. brown . . . £1600 £1000

1877. Value in cash.
74 **6** 20 cash blue . . . . 3·25 3·25
75 20 cash lilac . . . . 2·75 3·00
93 20 cash green . . . . . . 3·00 3·25
114 20 cash grey . . . . 2·50 3·25
81 40 cash pink . . . . 5·50 7·50
94 40 cash brown . . . . . . 4·00 4·75
107 40 cash black . . . . . . 3·50 3·25
82 60 cash green . . . . . . 6·50 8·50
95 60 cash violet . . . . . . 5·50 5·50
108 60 cash red . . . . 5·50 6·50
83 80 cash blue . . . . 7·50 10·00
96 80 cash brown . . . . . . 4·75 2·25
109 80 cash green . . . . . . 5·50 5·50
84 100 cash brown . . . . . . 7·50 10·00
97 100 cash yellow . . . . . . 5·50 5·50
110 100 cash blue . . . . . . 7·50 8·50

1879. Surch in English and Chinese.
89 **6** 20 cash on 40 cash pink . . . 8·00 10·00
103 20 cash on 40 cash brown . . 13·00 15·00
105 20 cash on 80 cash brown . . 7·50 7·50
111 20 cash on 80 cash green . . 5·50 6·00
112 20 cash on 100 cash blue . . 5·50 6·00
100 40 cash on 80 cash brown . . 4·50 7·00
101 40 cash on 100 cash yellow . 5·50 6·50
90 60 cash on 80 cash blue . . 17·00 20·00
88 60 cash on 100 cash brown . 18·00 19·00
102 60 cash on 100 cash yellow . 6·50 7·50

1886. Surch **20 CASH** in English and Chinese in double-lined frame.
104 **6** 20 cash on 40 cash brown . . 18·00 14·00

1889. Surch **100 CASH** over **20 CASH** in English and Chinese in double-lined frame.
113 **6** 100 cash on 20 cash on 100 cash yellow . . . . 45·00 50·00

16 25 26

1890. Value in cents.
119 **16** 2 c. brown . . . . 2·25 1·50
142 2 c. green . . . . 1·50 1·50
120 5 c. pink . . . . 6·00 3·75
143 5 c. red . . . . 4·50 4·50
122 10 c. black . . . . 7·50 6·50
144 10 c. orange . . . . 13·00 16·00
123 15 c. blue . . . . 9·50 10·00
145 15 c. mauve . . . . 8·00 7·50
124 20 c. mauve . . . . 7·50 7·50
146 20 c. brown . . . . 8·50 7·50

1892. Surch **2 Cts** and in Chinese.
141 **16** 2 c. on 5 c. pink . . . . . 55·00 32·00

1893. Surch in words in English and Chinese.
147 **16** ½ c. on 15 c. mauve . . . . 6·50 6·50
148 1 c. on 20 c. brown . . . . 6·50 6·50

1893. Surch ½ **Ct** or **1 Ct.**.
149 **16** ½ c. on half of 5 c. pink . . 5·50 5·50
152 ½ c. on half of 5 c. red . . 5·00 5·00
155 1 c. on half of 2 c. brown . 2·00 2·00
156 1 c. on half of 2 c. green . 7·50 7·50

1893. Inscriptions in outer frame in black.
165 **25** ½ c. orange 20 20
166 1 c. brown 20 20
187 2 c. red 25 50
188 4 c. orange on yellow . . . 1·50 2·25
161 5 c. blue 50 75
189 6 c. red on pink . . . . . 2·25 2·75
167 10 c. green . . . . 65 1·25
163 15 c. yellow . . . . 1·00 2·50
168 20 c. mauve . . . . 95 2·00

1893. Jubilee of First Settlement.
176 **26** 2 c. red and black 75 75

1893. Optd **1843 Jubilee 1893**. Inscriptions in outer frame in black.
177 **25** ½ c. orange 20 20
178 1 c. brown 25 25
179 2 c. red 30 35
180 5 c. blue . . . . 1·75 1·75
181 10 c. green . . . . 2·25 2·75
182 15 c. yellow . . . . 3·50 3·75
183 20 c. mauve . . . . 3·50 3·75

1896. Surch in English and Chinese.
184 **25** 4 c. on 15 c. yellow . . . . 4·50 4·25
185 6 c. on 20 c. mauve . . . . 4·50 4·00

POSTAGE DUE STAMPS

1892. T **16** optd **Postage Due**.
D134 2 c. brown . . . . 2·00 1·75
D135 5 c. pink . . . . 4·50 4·50
D130 10 c. black . . . . 14·50 13·00
D138 10 c. orange . . . . 8·50 8·50
D131 15 c. blue . . . . 13·00 12·00
D139 15 c. mauve . . . . 15·00 16·00
D132 20 c. mauve . . . . 9·50 10·00
D140 20 c. brown . . . . 15·00 16·00

D 26

1893. Inscriptions in outer frame in black.
D169 **D 26** ½ c. orange 20 25
D170 1 c. brown 20 15
D171 2 c. red 20 40
D172 5 c. blue 35 65
D173 10 c. green . . . . . . 45 1·25
D174 15 c. yellow . . . . . . 50 1·75
D175 20 c. mauve . . . . . . 75 1·50

SHARJAH Pt. 19

Part of the Trucial States on the Persian Gulf. Embodies the principalities of Diba, Khor Fakkan and Kalba.

On 2nd December, 1971, Sharjah, together with six other Gulf Shaikdoms, formed the United Arab Emirates.

1963. 100 naye paise = 1 rupee
1966. 100 dirhams = 1 riyal

IMPERF STAMPS. Some sets exist also imperf in limited quantities.

1 Shaikh Saqr bin Sultan al Qasimi, Flag and Map

2 Mosquito and W.H.O. Emblem

1963. Multicoloured.
1 **1** 1 n.p. (postage) 10 10
2 2 n.p. 10 10
3 3 n.p. 10 10
4 4 n.p. 10 10
5 5 n.p. 10 10
6 6 n.p. 10 10
7 8 n.p. 10 10
8 10 n.p. 10 10
9 16 n.p. 15 10
10 20 n.p. 20 10
11 30 n.p. 25 10
12 40 n.p. 30 15
13 50 n.p. 40 20
14 75 n.p. . . . . 1·00 45
15 100 n.p. . . . . 1·50 70
16 1 r. (air) 75 30
17 2 r. . . . . 1·40 65
18 3 r. . . . . 1·75 95

19 1 4 r. 2·50 2·25
20 5 r. 2·25 2·00
21 10 r. 6·00 3·50

The air stamps are as T 1 but additionally inscr "AIR MAIL" in English and Arabic, and with a hawk in flight.

1963. Malaria Eradication.

22 2 1 n.p. turquoise 10 10
23 2 n.p. blue 10 10
24 3 n.p. violet 10 10
25 4 n.p. green 10 10
26 90 n.p. brown 1·60 1·10

3 "Red Crescent"

1963. Red Cross Centenary.

27 3 1 n.p. red and purple 10 10
28 2 n.p. red and turquoise 10 10
29 3 n.p. red and blue 10 10
30 4 n.p. red and green 10 10
31 5 n.p. red and sepia 10 10
32 85 n.p. red and green 1·40 55

4 Campaign Emblem between Hands

1963. Freedom from Hunger.

33 4 1 n.p. green 10 10
34 2 n.p. brown 10 10
35 3 n.p. olive 10 10
36 4 n.p. blue 10 10
37 90 n.p. red 1·50 55

1963. Surch.

38 4 10 n.p. on 1 n.p. green 15 15
39 20 n.p. on 2 n.p. brown 25 20
40 30 n.p. on 3 n.p. olive 40 30
41 40 n.p. on 4 n.p. blue 50 40
42 75 n.p. on 90 n.p. red 1·25 85
43 80 n.p. on 90 n.p. red 1·25 85
44 2 1 r. on 90 n.p. brown 1·50 1·25

1964. Air. Pres. Kennedy Memorial Issue (1st issue). Nos. 16/21 optd **In Memoriam John F. Kennedy 1917–1963** in English and Arabic, and emblems.

45 1 1 r. multicoloured 1·10 1·10
46 2 r. multicoloured 2·25 2·25
47 3 r. multicoloured 4·50 4·50
48 4 r. multicoloured 5·50 5·00
49 5 r. multicoloured 8·00 7·00
50 10 r. multicoloured 12·00 11·00

See also Nos. 98/100.

7 Orbiting Astronomical Observatory

1964. Scientific Space Research.

51 1 n.p. blue (Type 7) 10 10
52 2 n.p. green and brown 10 10
53 3 n.p. turquoise and black 10 10
54 4 n.p. black and bistre 10 10
55 5 n.p. bistre and violet 10 10
56 35 n.p. violet and turquoise 70 55
57 50 n.p. brown and green 1·10 70

DESIGNS: 2 n.p. "Nimbus" weather satellite; 3 n.p. "Pioneer V" space probe; 4 n.p. "Explorer XIII" satellite; 5 n.p. "Explorer XII" satellite; 35 n.p. Project "Relay" satellite; 50 n.p. Orbiting solar observatory.

8 Running

1964. Olympic Games, Tokyo (1st issue).

58 1 n.p. blue, turquoise and yellow (Type 8) 10 10
59 2 n.p. red and turquoise 10 10
60 3 n.p. brown and green 10 10
61 4 n.p. turquoise and brown 10 10
62 20 n.p. blue and brown 25 15
63 30 n.p. bistre and pink 25 15
64 40 n.p. violet and yellow 50 30
65 1 r. brown and blue 1·25 80

DESIGNS: 2 n.p. Throwing the discus; 3 n.p. Hurdling; 4 n.p. Putting the shot; 20 n.p. High jumping; 30 n.p. Weightlifting; 40 n.p. Throwing the javelin; 1 r. High diving.

See also Nos. 90/7.

9 Flame and World Map

1964. Air. Human Rights Day.

66 9 50 n.p. brown 35 20
67 1 r. violet 70 40
68 150 n.p. green 1·00 60

10 Girl Scouts Marching

1964. Sharjah Girl Scouts.

69 10 1 n.p. green 10 10
70 2 n.p. green 10 10
71 3 n.p. blue 10 10
72 4 n.p. violet 10 10
73 5 n.p. red 10 10
74 2 r. brown 2·50 1·50

11 Khor Fakkan

1964. Air. Multicoloured.

75 10 n.p. Type 11 15 15
76 20 n.p. Bedouin camp, Beni Qatab 20 15
77 30 n.p. Dhaid oasis 25 15
78 40 n.p. Kalba Castle 35 20
79 75 n.p. Street and Wind tower, Sharjah 80 40
80 100 n.p. Fortress 1·40 60

12 "Mr. Gus" (oil rig) 13 Scout at Attention

1964. Air. New York World's Fair. Multicoloured.

81 20 n.p. Type 12 30 15
82 40 n.p. Unisphere 20 15
83 1 r. New York skyline (85½×44½ mm) 55 40

1964. Sharjah Boy Scouts.

84 13 1 n.p. olive 10 10
85 – 2 n.p. green 10 10
86 – 3 n.p. blue 10 10
87 13 4 n.p. violet 10 10
88 – 5 n.p. mauve 10 10
89 – 2 r. brown 2·50 1·25

DESIGNS—HORIZ: 2, 5 n.p. Scouts marching. VERT: 3 n.p., 2 r. Boy scout.

14 Olympic Torch

1964. Olympic Games, Tokyo (2nd issue).

90 14 1 n.p. olive 10 10
91 2 n.p. blue 10 10
92 3 n.p. brown 10 10
93 4 n.p. turquoise 10 10
94 5 n.p. violet 10 10
95 40 n.p. blue 40 25
96 50 n.p. brown 55 35
97 2 r. ochre 1·75 1·25

15 Pres. Kennedy and Statue of Liberty

1964. Air. Pres. Kennedy Commem (2nd issue). Inscr in gold.

98 15 40 n.p. blue, brown & grn 65 55
99 60 n.p. brown, grn & blue 95 80
100 100 n.p. green, blue & brn 1·60 1·10

16 Rock Dove

1965. Air. Birds. Multicoloured.

101 30 n.p. Type 16 50 15
102 40 n.p. Red junglefowl 60 25
103 75 n.p. Hoopoe 1·75 50
104 150 n.p. Type 16 2·40 90
105 2 r. Red junglefowl 3·00 1·25
106 3 r. Hoopoe 5·50 2·75

17 Early Telephone

1965. "Science, Transport and Communications".

107 A 1 n.p. black and red 10 10
108 B 1 n.p. black and red 10 10
109 B 2 n.p. blue and orange 10 10
110 C 2 n.p. blue and orange 10 10
111 D 3 n.p. sepia and green 10 10
112 E 3 n.p. sepia and green 10 10
113 F 4 n.p. violet and green 10 10
114 G 4 n.p. violet and green 10 10
115 H 5 n.p. brown and green 10 10
116 I 5 n.p. brown and green 10 10
117 J 30 n.p. indigo and blue 50 25
118 K 30 n.p. indigo and blue 50 25
119 L 40 n.p. blue and yellow 50 25
120 M 40 n.p. blue and yellow 50 25
121 N 50 n.p. brown and blue 60 40
122 O 50 n.p. brown and blue 60 40
123 P 75 n.p. sepia and green 75 45
124 Q 75 n.p. sepia and green 75 45
125 R 1 r. blue and yellow 1·75 80
126 S 1 r. blue and yellow 1·75 80

DESIGNS: A, Modern teleprinter; B, 1895 Car; C, 1964 American car; D, Early X-ray apparatus; E, T.V. X-ray machine; F, Early mail coach; G, "Telstar" satellite; H, Medieval ship; I, Nuclear-powered freighter "Savannah"; J, Early astronomers; K, Jodrell Bank radio-telescope; L, Greek messengers; M, "Relay" satellite; N, "Man's early flight" (Lilienthal biplane glider); O, Sud Aviation Caravelle airliner; P, Persian waterwheel; Q, Hydro-electric dam; R, Old steam locomotive; S, Modern diesel train.

1965. Air. Churchill Commem (1st issue). Optd **In Memoriam Sir Winston Churchill 1874-1965** in English and Arabic.

127 15 40 n.p. blue, brown & grn 45 20
128 60 n.p. brown, green & bl 70 25
129 100 n.p. green, blue & brn 90 30

See also Nos. 201/4.

1965. 10th Anniv (1964) of Arab Postal Union's Permanent Office. Similar design to T 43 of Kuwait.

130 5 n.p. blue and yellow 10 10
131 30 n.p. blue and red 20 15
132 65 n.p. green and orange 55 35

1965. Various issues of Shakh Saqr with portrait obliterated with three or four horizontal bars.

(a) Postage. Nos. 5, 8/13.

150 1 5 n.p. multicoloured 10 15
151 10 n.p. multicoloured 10 15
152 16 n.p. multicoloured 20 15
153 20 n.p. multicoloured 20 15
154 30 n.p. multicoloured 25 20
155 40 n.p. multicoloured 30 15
156 50 n.p. multicoloured 35 25

(b) Air. (i) Nos. 16, 18/21.

157 1 1 r. multicoloured 60 30
158 3 r. multicoloured 1·75 1·25
159 4 r. multicoloured 2·00 1·50
160 5 r. multicoloured 2·75 2·25
161 10 r. multicoloured 5·50 4·75

(ii) Nos. 75/80.

144 11 10 n.p. multicoloured 15 15
145 – 20 n.p. multicoloured 20 15
146 – 30 n.p. multicoloured 25 15
147 – 30 n.p. multicoloured 35 15
148 – 75 n.p. multicoloured 70 40
149 – 100 n.p. multicoloured 80 45

22 Rameses II in his War Chariot 23 Cable-laying Ship "Monarch IV" and COMPAC Cable Route Map

1965. Nubian Monuments Preservation.

162 22 5 n.p. blue and yellow 10 10
163 10 n.p. green and brown 15 10
164 30 n.p. blue and orange 35 20
165 55 n.p. violet and blue 60 30

1965. I.T.U. Centenary. Country name in gold.

166 23 1 n.p. brown and blue 10 10
167 – 2 n.p. brown and blue 10 10
168 – 3 n.p. violet and green 10 10
169 – 4 n.p. brown and blue 10 10
170 23 5 n.p. ochre and violet 10 10
171 – 50 n.p. purple and black 75 20
172 – 1 r. green and ochre 1·40 45
173 – 120 n.p. red and green 2·00 65

DESIGNS: 2, 120 n.p. "Relay I" satellite and tracking station, Goonhilly Down; 3, 50 n.p. "Telstar" satellite and Atlas-Agena Rocket on launching pad; 4 n.p. "Syncom" satellite, Post Office Tower (London) and horn paraboloid reflector aerial.

24 Running

1965. Pan-American Games, Cairo.

174 24 50 n.p. turquoise and lilac 50 20
175 – 50 n.p. green and brown 50 20
176 – 50 n.p. lilac and sepia 50 20
177 – 50 n.p. sepia and green 50 20
178 – 50 n.p. brown and turquoise 50 20

SPORTS: No. 175, Pole-vaulting; No. 176, Boxing; No. 177, High-jumping; No. 178, Long-jumping.

25 Flags (reverse of 5 r. coin)

1966. Arabian Gulf Area Monetary Conf. Circular designs on silver foil, backed with paper inscr "Walsall Security Paper" in English and Arabic. Imperf. (a) Diameter 1⅝ in.

179 25 50 n.p. black 60 50
180 – 75 n.p. violet 60 50

(b) Diameter $2\frac{1}{16}$ in.

181 25 1 r. purple 75 65
182 – 3 r. blue 2·00 1·75

(c) Diameter 2½ in.

183 25 4 r. green 2·75 2·75
184 – 5 r. orange 3·00 3·00

COINS: 75 n.p., 3 r. and 5 r. show the obverse (Pres. Kennedy).

1966. Rendezvous in Space. Nos. 33/6 optd **15-12-1965 Rendezvous in SPACE**, two space capsules and four bars obliterating portrait or surch also in English and Arabic.

185	4	1 n.p. green	10	10
186		2 n.p. brown	10	10
187		3 n.p. olive	10	10
188		4 n.p. blue	10	10
189		15 n.p. on 1 n.p. green	25	15
190		30 n.p. on 2 n.p. brown	30	20
191		50 n.p. on 3 n.p. olive	70	50
192		1 r. on 4 n.p. blue	80	60

27 I.C.Y. Emblem and Prime Minister Harold Wilson

1986. International Co-operation Year.

193	27	80 n.p. sepia and violet	70	20
194	–	80 n.p. brown and green	70	20
195	–	80 n.p. olive and red	70	20
196	–	80 n.p. purple and blue	70	20
197	–	80 n.p. blue and red	70	20
198	–	80 n.p. plum and olive	70	20
199	–	80 n.p. blue and grey	70	20
200	–	80 n.p. purple and ochre	70	20

DESIGNS: I.C.Y. emblem and "World Leaders"; No. 194, Chancellor Erhard; No. 195, Pres. Nasser; No. 196, Pres. Johnson; No. 197, Pope Paul VI; No. 198, Pres. De Gaulle; No. 199, Shaikh Isa bin Sulman al-Khalifa (Bahrain); No. 200, King Faisal (Saudi Arabia).

28 Sir Winston Churchill, Pen and Ink, and Books

1966. Churchill Commem (2nd issue). Multicoloured, printed on gold foil, backed with paper.

201	2 r. Type **28**	1·00	60
202	3 r. Churchill and Houses of Parliament, pen and ink	1·50	1·10
203	4 r. Churchill and St. Paul's Cathedral	2·25	1·50
204	5 r. Churchill and "Big Ben" (clock tower, Houses of Parliament) and Tower Bridge	2·75	2·00

29 Banded Butterfly-fish

1966. Fishes. Multicoloured.

206	1 n.p. Type **29**	10	10
207	2 n.p. Striped surgeon-fish	10	10
208	3 n.p. Young imperial angel-fish	10	10
209	4 n.p. False mouthbreeder	10	10
210	5 n.p. Undulate trigger-fish	10	10
211	15 n.p. Moonfish	25	10
212	20 n.p. Clown butterfly-fish	35	10
213	30 n.p. Moorish goddess	40	10
214	40 n.p. Zebra-striped angel-fish	50	10
215	50 n.p. False mouth breeder	55	10
216	75 n.p. Undulate trigger-fish	70	20
217	1 r. Zebra-striped angel-fish	80	25
218	2 r. Moorish goddess	1·75	45
219	3 r. Clown butterfly-fish	2·50	80
220	4 r. Moonfish	2·75	95
221	5 r. Young imperial angel-fish	3·25	1·25
222	10 r. Type **29**	6·50	2·25

30 Arms of Munich and "Souvenir Sheet"

34 Pres. Kennedy

33 Greek 6th-cent Ball-player

1966. International Philatelic Federation and International Philatelic Journalists Association Congresses, Munich. Multicoloured.

223	80 n.p. Type **30**	35	15
224	120 n.p. Frauenkirche, Munich	45	20
225	2 r. Statue and Hall of Fame, Munich (horiz 81 × 41 mm)	75	35

NEW CURRENCY SURCHARGES. During the latter half of 1966 various issues appeared surcharged in dirhams and riyals. The 1966 definitives with this surcharge are listed below as there is evidence of their postal use. Nos. 102, 107/126, 135, 145, 150/61 and 174/84 also exist with these surcharges.

Earlier in 1966 Nos. 98/100, 171/3, 193/4, 196, 198, 200/5 appeared surcharged in piastres and rials. As Sharjah did not adopt this currency their status is uncertain.

1966. Nos. 206/22 with currency names changed by overprinting in English and Arabic.

226	29	1 d. multicoloured	10	10
227	–	2 d. multicoloured	10	10
228	–	3 d. multicoloured	10	10
229	–	4 d. multicoloured	10	10
230	–	5 d. multicoloured	10	10
231	–	15 d. multicoloured	25	10
232	–	20 d. multicoloured	35	10
233	–	30 d. multicoloured	40	10
234	–	40 d. multicoloured	50	10
235	–	50 d. multicoloured	55	20
236	–	75 d. multicoloured	75	30
237	–	1 r. multicoloured	85	35
238	–	2 r. multicoloured	1·40	75
239	–	3 r. multicoloured	2·00	1·50
240	–	4 r. multicoloured	2·50	1·75
241	–	5 r. multicoloured	3·25	2·00
242	29	10 r. multicoloured	6·50	3·75

1966. World Cup Football Championships. Designs printed on coloured metal foil surfaced paper. Multicoloured.

243	½ r. Type **33**	35	15
244	½ r. Tsu-chu "Kick-ball" game, China, circa 175 B.C.	35	15
245	½ r. 14th-cent ball game	35	15
246	½ r. Blowing up ball-bladder (17th-cent)	35	15
247	½ r. Football game, Barnet, England, circa 1750	35	15
248	½ r. England v. Scotland game, Kennington Oval (London), 1879	35	15
249	½ r. Victorious England team, Wembley, 1966 (56 × 55½ mm)	35	15

1966. 3rd Death Anniv of Pres. Kennedy and Inaug of Arlington Memorial.

251	50 d. Type **34**	25	15
252	2 r. Sharjah 50 n.p. Kennedy stamp of 1964	1·00	50
253	2 r. 50 Pres. Kennedy's grave (horiz 55 × 42 mm)	1·25	65

35 Shaikh Khalid bin Mohammed al Qasimi and Arms

1968. Multiocloured.

255	5 d. Type **35** (postage)	15	15
256	10 d. Flag	15	15
257	15 d. Flag and arms (vert)	20	15
258	20 d. Decorative pattern (vert)	20	15
259	35 d. Type **35** (air)	40	20
260	40 d. As 10 d.	40	15
261	60 d. As 15 d.	55	20
262	75 d. As 20 d.	70	30
363	1 r. Type **35**	85	30
264	2 r. As 10 d.	1·75	75
265	3 r. As 15 d.	2·50	1·25
266	4 r. As 20 d.	3·25	1·75
267	5 r. Type **35**	4·00	1·75
268	10 r. As 10 d.	7·50	4·50

OFFICIAL STAMPS

1966. Optd **ON STATE SERVICE** in English and Arabic.

O101	1	8 n.p.	15	15
O102		10 n.p.	15	15
O103		16 n.p.	30	15
O104		20 n.p.	30	15
O105		30 n.p.	40	20
O106		40 n.p.	60	30
O107		50 n.p.	1·00	55
O108		75 n.p.	1·75	1·25
O109		100 n.p.	2·25	1·40

For later issues see **UNITED ARAB EMIRATES**.

APPENDIX

The following stamps have either been issued in excess of postal needs or have not been available to the public in reasonable quantities at face value. Such stamps may later be given full listing if there is evidence of regular postal use.

1967.

Post Day. Japanese Paintings. 1 r. × 3.

United Nations. 22nd Anniv 10, 30, 60 d.

Olympics Preparation, Mexico 1968. Postage 1, 2, 3, 10 d; Air 30, 60 d., 2 r.

Flowers and Butterflies. Postage 1, 2, 3, 4, 5, 10, 20 d.; Air 30, 60 d., 1, 2 r.

Famous Paintings. Postage 1, 2, 3, 4, 5, 30, 40, 60, 75 d.; Air 1, 3, 4, 5 r.

1968.

Winter Olympic Games, Grenoble. Postage 1, 2, 3, 4, 5 d.; Air 1, 2, 3 r.

12th World Jamboree. Postage 1, 2, 3, 4, 5, 10 d.; Air 30, 50, 60 d., 1 r. 50.

Grenoble Olympic Medal Winners. Optd on Winter Olympics. Grenoble issue. Postage 1, 2, 3, 4, 5 d.; Air 1, 2, 3 r.

Mothers' Day. Paintings. Postage 10, 20, 30, 40 d.; Air 1, 2, 3, 4 r.

American Paintings. Postage 20, 30, 40, 50, 60 d.; Air 1, 4, 5 r.

Egyptian Art. 15, 25, 35, 45, 55, 65, 75, 95 d.

Martyrs of Liberty. Air 35 d. × 4, 60 d. × 4, 1 r. × 4.

Olympic Games Mexico. 10, 20, 30 d., 2 r., 2 r. 40, 5 r.

Previous Olympic Games. Air 25, 50, 75 d., 1 r. 50, 3, 4 r.

Sportsmen and women. Postage 20, 30, 40, 60 d., 1 r. 50, 2 r. 50; Air 25, 50 d., 1, 2 r., 3 r. 25, 4, 4 r.

Robert Kennedy Memorial. Optd on American Paintings issue. Air 4 r.

Olympic Medal Winners, Mexico. 35, 50, 60 d., 1, 2, 4 r.

1969.

Famous Men and Women. Postage 10, 20, 25, 35, 50, 60 d.; Air 1, 2, 3, 4, 5, 6 r.

"Apollo 8" Moon Mission. Postage 5 d. × 6; Air 10, 15, 20 d., 2, 3, 4 r.

"Apollo 11" Moon Mission (1st series). Postage 5 d. × 8; Air 75 d. × 8, 1 r. × 8.

Post Day. Famous Ships. Postage 5 d. × 8; Air 90 d. × 8.

"Apollo 12" Moon Mission. Optd on Famous Ships issue 5 d. × 8.

1970.

U.N.I.C.E.F. Paintings of Children. Postage 5 d. × 9; Air 20, 25, 35, 40, 50, 60, 75 d., 1, 3 r.

Animals. Postage 3 d. × 14, 10, 10, 15, 15 d.; Air 20, 20, 35, 35 d., 1, 1, 2, 2 r.

"Expo 70" World Fair, Osaka, Japan (1st series). Japanese Paintings. Postage 3 d. × 4; Air 1 r. × 4.

"Expo 70" World Fair, Osaka, Japan (2nd series). Pavilions. Postage 2, 2, 3, 3 d.; Air 40 d. × 4.

Paintings of Napoleon. Postage 3 d. 5; Air 20, 30, 40, 60 d., 2 r.

De Gaulle Commemoration. Postage 3 d. × 5; Air 20, 30, 40, 60 d., 2 r.

5th Anniv of Ruler's Accession. Postage 5 d. × 5; Air 20 d., 35 d. × 5, 40 d. × 5, 60 d. × 5; the 5 40 d. values also exist each surch 5 d.

"Mercury" and "Vostok" Moon Missions. Postage 1, 2, 3, 4, 5 d.; Air 25, 40, 85 d., 1, 2 r.

"Gemini" Space Programme. Postage 1, 2, 3, 4, 5 d.; Air 25, 40, 85 d. 1, 2 r.

"Apollo", "Voskhod" and "Soyuz" Projects. Postage 1, 2, 3, 4, 5 d.; Air 25, 40, 85 d., 1, 2 r.

Events of 1970. Postage 1 d. × 5, 5 d.; Air 75 d., 1, 2, 3 r.

200th Birth Anniv of Beethoven. Postage 3 d. × 5; Air 35, 40, 60 d., 1, 2 r.

Mozart. Postage 3 d. × 5; Air 35, 40, 60 d., 1, 2 r.

The Life of Christ (1st series). Postage 1, 2, 3, 4, 5 d.; Air 25, 40, 60 d., 1, 2 r.

1971.

"Apollo 14" Moon Mission. Optd on 1969.

"Apollo 11" issue. Postage 5 d. × 4; Air 75 d. × 4.

Post Day 1970. Cars. Postage 1, 2, 3, 4, 5 d.; Air 25, 50, 60 d., 2, 3 r.

Post Day (1st series). American Cars. Postage 1, 2, 3, 4, 5 d.; Air 35, 50 d. 1, 2, 3 r.

Post Day (2nd series). Trains. Postage 1, 2, 3, 4, 5 d.; Air 25, 50, 60 d., 1, 2 r.

Pres. Nasser Commemoration. Postage 5 d. × 5; Air 20, 35, 40, 60 d., 2 r.

Safe return of "Apollo 13". Optd on 1969 "Apollo 8" issue. Air 10, 15, 20 d., 2, 3, 4 r.

De Gaulle Memorial. Postage 3, 4, 5, 6, 7 d.; Air 40, 60, 75 d., 1, 2 r.

Olympics Preparation, Munich 1972. Postage 2, 3, 4, 5, 6 d.; Air. 35, 40, 60 d., 1, 2 r.

Miracles of Christ. Postage 1, 2, 3, 4, 5 d.; Air 25, 40, 60 d., 1, 2 r.

6th Anniv of Ruler's Accession. Postage 5 d. × 3; Air 75 d. × 4, 1 r. × 3, 2 r., 3 r. × 4, 5 r.

Proclamation of the United Arab Emirates. Air 25, 35, 65, 75 d., 1, 2 r.

Various surcharges. Postage 35 d on 5 d. (No. 255) 35 d. on 5 d. (Winter Olympics, listed above, 1968); Air 60 d. on 75 d. (No. 262) 65 d. on 75 d. (Proclamation of UAE, listed above), 65 d. on 1 r. (Proclamation of UAE, listed above) 65 d. on 2 r. (Proclamation of UAE, listed above).

1972.

Sport. Postage 2, 3, 4, 5, 6 d.; Air 35, 40, 60 d., 1, 2 r.

The Life of Christ (2nd series). Postage 1, 2, 3, 4, 5 d.; Air 25, 40, 60 d., 1, 2 r.

Winter Olympics Preparation, Sapporo. Postage 2, 3, 4, 5, 6 d.; Air 35, 40, 60 d., 1, 2 r.

Safe Return of "Apollo 14". Optd on 1969 "Apollo 11" issue. Postage 5 d. × 4; Air 1 r. × 4.

Previous World Cup Winners. Postage 5, 10, 15, 20, 25 d.; Air 35, 75 d., 1, 2, 3 r.

Sapporo Olympic Medal Winners. Paintings, Postage 5, 10, 15, 20, 25 d.; Air 35, 75 d., 1, 2, 3 r.

Famous People, Churchill, De Gaulle and John Kennedy. Postage 5 d. × 4, 10 d. × 4, 35 d. × 4; Air 75 d. × 4, 1 r. × 4, 3 r. × 4.

Olympic Games, Munich. Postage 5, 10, 15, 20, 25 d.; Air 35, 75 d., 1, 2, 3 r.

Cats. Postage 20, 25 d.; Air 75 d., 1, 2 r.

Birds (1st series). Postage 20, 25, 75 d., Air 1, 2 r.

"Apollo 11" Moon Mission (2nd series). Air 1 r. × 5.

"Apollo 16" Moon Mission. Postage 1, 1 r.; Air 1 r. × 5.

Dogs. Postage 20, 25 d.; Air 75 d., 1, 2 r.

"Apollo 17" Moon Mission. Postage 1, 1 r.; Air 1 r. × 3.

Munich Olympic Medal Winners. Air 5 r. × 20.

Horses. Postage 20, 25 d.; Air 75 d., 1, 2 r.

"Apollo 17" Astronauts. Postage 1, 1 r.; Air 1 r. × 3.

Butterflies. Postage 20, 25 d.; Air 75 d., 1, 2 r.

"Luna 9" Soviet Space Programme. Postage 1, 1 r.; Air 1 r. × 3.

Monkeys. Postage 20, 25 d.; Air 75 d., 1, 2 r.

Birds (2nd series). Air 25, 25, 35, 35, 50, 50, 65, 65 d., 1 r. × 6, 3, 3 r.

Fish. Air 25, 35, 50, 65 d., 1 r. × 5, 3 r.

Insects. Air 25, 35, 50, 65 d., 1, 3 r.

Flowers. Postage 25, 35, 50, 65 d., 1, 3 r.; Air 1 r. × 4.

Fruit. Air 1 r. × 4.

Children. Air 1 r. × 4.

Eastern Antiquities. Air 25, 35, 40, 65, 75 d., 3 r., 1 r. × 4.

Planetary Exploration. Postage 1 r. × 3; Air 1, 1 r.

13th World Jamboree. Postage 2 d. × 3, 3 d. × 3, 4 d. × 3, 5 d. × 3, 6 d. × 3; Air 35 d. × 3, 75 d. × 3, 1 r. × 3, 2 r. × 3, 3 r. × 3.

A number of issues on gold or silver foil also exist, but it is understood that these were mainly for presentation purposes, although valid for postage.

In common with the other states of the United Arab Emirates the Sharjah stamp contract was terminated on 1 August 1972, and further new issues released after that date were unauthorised.

SIBERIA — Pt. 10

Various Anti-Bolshevist governments existed in this area, culminating in Kolchak's assumption of power as "Supreme Ruler". The Kolchak Government fell in January 1920, provincial issues followed until the area was incorporated into the Soviet Union in 1922.

100 kopeks = 1 rouble

1919. Admiral Kolchak Govt. Arms types of Russia surch in figures, or in figures and words (rouble values). Imperf or perf.

5	22	35 on 2 k. green	25	1·25
6		50 on 3 k. red	25	1·40
3		70 on 1 k. orange	30	3·25
8	23	1 r. on 4 k. red	40	1·40
9	22	3 r. on 7 k. blue	70	3·50
10	10	5 r. on 14 k. red and blue	1·25	8·00

1920. Transbaikal Province. Ataman Semyonov regime. Arms types of Russia surch thus: **p. 1 p.**. Perf.

11	23	1 r. on 4 k. red	17·00	26·00
12	14	2 r. 50 on 20 k. red & blue	17·00	24·00
13	22	5 r. on 5 k. red	10·00	17·00
14	10	10 r. on 70 k. orange & brn	17·00	27·00

6

1920. Amur Province. Imperf.

15	6	2 r. red	1·60	4·50
16		3 r. green	1·60	4·50
17		5 r. blue	1·60	4·50

18 6 15 r. brown 1·60 4·50
19 30 r. mauve 1·60 4·50

FAR EASTERN REPUBLIC

1920. Vladivostok issue. Optd **D B P** in fancy letters or surch also. Imperf or perf (a) On Arms types of Russia.
32 **22** 1 k. orange 3·75 6·50
33 2 k. green 1·90 2·50
21 3 k. red 2·40 3·25
39 **10** 3 k. on 35 k. green & pur 4·00 5·00
22 **23** 4 k. red 2·00 4·75
40 **10** 4 k. on 70 k. orange & brn 2·50 3·50
41 7 k. on 15 k. blue & purple 1·25 1·75
23 **23** 10 k. blue 38·00 45·00
44 **11** 10 k. on 3 r. 50 green and brown 5·00 7·00
24 **10** 14 k. red and blue 6·50 15·00
25 15 k. blue and purple 4·25 6·00
25 **14** 20 k. red and blue 32·00 45·00
27 **10** 20 k. on 14 k. red & blue 3·00 4·75
28 25 k. mauve and green 4·00 8·00
29 35 k. green and purple 16·00 26·00
30 **14** 50 k. green and purple 3·25 6·50
35 **15** 1 r. orange and brown 8·00 17·00

(b) On Nos. 5 and 3 of Siberia.
37 **22** 35 k. on 2 k. green 2·75 4·00
38 70 k. on 1 k. orange 2·25 4·00

(c) On Postal Savings Bank stamps of Russia.
45 1 k. on 5 k. green on buff 5·00 7·00
46 2 k. on 10 k. brn on buff 7·00 10·00

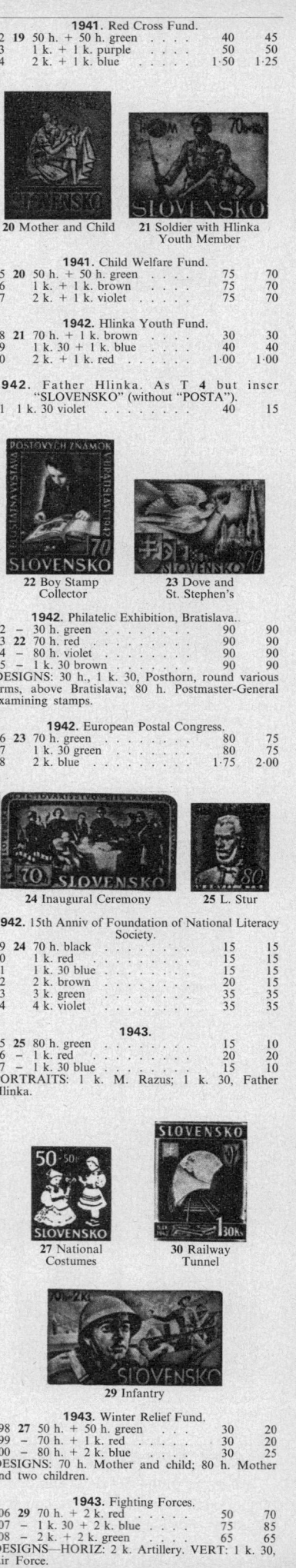

10 11 13

1921. Chita issue. Imperf.
47 **10** 1 k. orange 50 1·10
48 3 k. red 50 60
49 **11** 4 k. brown and red 20 50
50 **10** 5 k. brown 40 70
51b 7 k. blue 40 1·00
52 **11** 10 k. red and blue 30 70
53 **10** 15 k. red 40 1·00
54 **11** 20 k. red and blue 40 1·25
55 30 k. red and green 45 1·25
56 50 k. red and black 1·00 2·00

1922. Vladivostok issue. 5th Anniv of Russian October Revolution. Optd **1917 7-XI 1922**. Imperf.
57 **13** 2 k. green 8·00 10·00
58 4 k. red 8·00 10·00
59 5 k. brown 9·00 16·00
60 10 k. blue 9·00 16·00

PRIAMUR AND MARITIME PROVINCES
Anti-Bolshevist Government.

1921. Vladivostok issue. Imperf.
61 **13** 2 k. green 40 65
62 4 k. red 40 65
63 5 k. purple 50 95
64 10 k. blue 95 1·60

Приам. Земскій. Край. коп 3 коп
Д. В. коп. 1 коп. ЗОЛОТОМ

(15) (16 Trans. "Priamur Territory") (18)

1922. Anniv of Priamur Provisinal Govt. Optd. with T **15**.
89 **13** 2 k. green 13·00 17·00
90 4 k. red 13·00 17·00
91 5 k. purple 13·00 17·00
92 10 k. blue 13·00 17·00

1922. Optd or surch as T **16**.
93 **13** 1 k. on 2 k. green 1·40 3·50
94 2 k. green 1·40 3·50
95 3 k. on 4 k. red 1·40 3·50
96 4 k. red 1·40 3·50
97 5 k. purple 1·40 3·50
98 10 k. blue 1·40 3·50

1922. Optd as T **16**. Imperf or perf. (a) On Arms types of Russia.
114 **22** 1 k. orange 1·75 5·00
115 2 k. green 2·50 7·50
116 3 k. red 4·25 13·00
102 **23** 4 k. red 1·25 3·50
118 **22** 5 k. red 7·00 20·00
104 7 k. blue 13·00 28·00
105 **23** 10 k. blue 13·00 28·00
106 **10** 14 k. red and blue 30·00 60·00
107 15 k. blue and purple 2·50 6·00
108 **14** 20 k. red and blue 4·00 10·00
109 **10** 20 k. on 14 k. red & blue 38·00 80·00
110 25 k. mauve and green 11·00 24·00
111 35 k. green and purple 1·75 5·00
112 **14** 50 k. green and purple 2·25 6·00
113 **10** 70 k. orange and brown 7·00 18·00
121 **15** 1 r. orange and brown 6·00 17·00

(b) On Nos. 5 and 3 of Siberia.
122 **22** 35 k. on 2 k. green 22·00 38·00
123 70 k. on 1 k. orange 30·00 55·00

1922. Nos. 37 and 38 optd **ПЗК** and three bars. Imperf and perf.
125 **22** 35 k. on 2 k. green 2·00 4·00
126 70 k. on 1 k. orange 3·25 7·00

SOVIET UNION ISSUE FOR THE FAR EAST

1923. Stamps of Russia surch as T **18**. Imperf or perf.
131 **79** 1 k. on 100 r. red 35 60
128 2 k. on 70 r. purple 25 35
129 **78** 5 k. on 10 r. blue 25 50
130 **79** 10 k. on 50 r. brown 35 50

SICILY Pt. 8

An island to the S. of Italy, which, with Naples, formed the Kingdom of the Two Sicilies, until incorporated in the Kingdom of Italy.

100 grano = 1 ducato

1 King "Bomba"

1859. Imperf.
1 **1** ½ g. yellow £250 £650
2b 1 g. olive £100 85·00
3 2 g. blue 70·00 55·00
4 5 g. red £425 £300
5 10 g. blue £425 £200
6 20 g. grey £450 £375
7 50 g. brown £450 £3750

SLOVAKIA Pt 5

Formerly part of Hungary, Slovakia joined with Bohemia and Moravia in 1918 to form Czechoslovakia. From 1939 to 1945 they were separate states.

In 1993 the federation of Czechoslovakia was dissolved and Slovakia became an independent republic.

100 haleru = 1 koruna

A. REPUBLIC OF SLOVAKIA

1939. Stamps of Czechoslovakia optd **Slovensky stat 1939**.
2 **34** 5 h. blue 55 70
3 10 h. brown 10 15
4 20 h. red 10 10
5 25 h. green 1·00 1·25
6 30 h. purple 10 10
7 **59** 40 h. blue 10 15
8 **60a** 50 h. green 10 10
9 **66** 50 h. green 10 10
10 **60a** 60 h. violet 10 10
11 60 h. blue 6·50 7·50
12 **61** 1 k. purple 10 10
13 – 1 k. 20 purple (No. 354) 20 30
14 **64** 1 k. 50 red 20 30
15 – 1 k. 60 green (No. 355a) 1·75 2·00
16 – 2 k. green (No. 356) 1·75 2·00
17 – 2 k. 50 blue (No. 357) 35 45
18 – 3 k. brown (No. 358) 40 60
19 – 3 k. 50 violet (No. 359) 18·00 20·00
20 **65** 4 k. violet 8·00 10·00
21 – 5 k. green (No. 361) 10·00 12·50
22 – 10 k. blue (No. 362) 75·00 85·00

4 Father Hlinka 7 Krivan 8 Chamois

9 Mgr. Tiso 10 Weaving

11 Sawyer 12 Presidential Palace, Bratislava

1939. As T **4**, but inscr "CESKO-SLOVENSKO SLOVENSKA POSTA", optd **SLOVENSKY STAT**.
23 **4** 50 h. green 1·25 50
24 1 k. red 1·00 50

1939. Perf or imperf (20, 30 h.), perf (others).
25 **4** 5 h. blue 40 40
26 10 h. green 65 55
27a 20 h. red 50 65
28 30 h. violet 65 55
29 50 h. green 65 55
33 1 k. red 65 45
34a 2 k. 50 blue 50 65
35a 3 k. sepia 1·00 75
See also No. 81.

1939.
40 – 5 h. green 15 15
41 **7** 10 h. brown 10 15
42 – 20 h. grey 10 10
43 **8** 25 h. brown 40 15
44 – 30 h. brown 20 15
45 **9** 50 h. green 40 25
46 70 h. brown 25 15
47 **10** 2 k. green 4·50 40
48 **11** 4 k. brown 1·00 60
49 – 5 k. red 90 25
50 **12** 10 k. blue 75 55

DESIGNS—As Type **7**: 5 h., Zelene Pleso; 20 h. Kvety Satier (Edelweiss); 30 h. Javorina. As Type **11**: 5 k. Woman filling ewer at spring.

For 10 to 50 h. values in larger size, see Nos. 125/9.

13 Rev. J. Murgas and Wireless Masts

1939. 10th Death Anniv of Rev. J. Murgas.
53 **13** 60 h. violet 20 15
52 1 k. 20 grey 50 15

1939. Child Welfare. As No. 45 but larger (24×30 mm) and inscr "+2.50 DETOM".
54 2 k. 50 + 2 k. 50 blue 2·25 2·50

14 Heinkel He 111C over Lake Csorba 15 Heinkel He 116A over Tatra Mountains

16 Eagle and Aero A-204

1939. Air.
55 **14** 30 h. violet 25 25
56 50 h. green 25 25
57 1 k. red 30 25
58 **15** 2 k. green 45 40
59 3 k. brown 90 80
60 4 k. blue 1·50 1·50
62 **16** 5 k. purple 1·00 1·40
63 10 k. grey 1·25 1·50
64 20 k. green 1·50 2·00

17 Stiavnica Castle 18 S. M. Daxner and Bishop Moyses

1941.
65 **17** 1 k. 20 purple 20 15
66 – 1 k. 50 red (Lietava) 20 15
67 – 1 k. 60 blue (Spissky Hrad) 25 10
68 – 2 k. green (Bojnice) 20 10

1941. 80th Anniv of Presentation of Slovak Memorandum to Emperor Francis Joseph.
69 **18** 50 h. green 1·40 1·50
70 1 k. blue 6·00 6·00
71 2 k. black 6·00 6·00

19 Wounded Soldier and Red Cross Orderly

1941. Red Cross Fund.
72 **19** 50 h. + 50 h. green 40 45
73 1 k. + 1 k. purple 50 50
74 2 k. + 1 k. blue 1·50 1·25

20 Mother and Child 21 Soldier with Hlinka Youth Member

1941. Child Welfare Fund.
75 **20** 50 h. + 50 h. green 75 70
76 1 k. + 1 k. brown 75 70
77 2 k. + 1 k. violet 75 70

1942. Hlinka Youth Fund.
78 **21** 70 h. + 1 k. brown 30 30
79 1 k. 30 + 1 k. blue 40 40
80 2 k. + 1 k. red 1·00 1·00

1942. Father Hlinka. As T **4** but inscr "SLOVENSKO" (without "POSTA").
81 1 k. 30 violet 40 15

22 Boy Stamp Collector 23 Dove and St. Stephen's

1942. Philatelic Exhibition, Bratislava.
82 – 30 h. green 90 90
83 **22** 70 h. red 90 90
84 – 80 h. violet 90 90
85 – 1 k. 30 brown 90 90

DESIGNS: 30 h., 1 k. 30, Posthorn, round various arms, above Bratislava; 80 h. Postmaster-General examining stamps.

1942. European Postal Congress.
86 **23** 70 h. green 80 75
87 1 k. 30 green 80 75
88 2 k. blue 1·75 2·00

24 Inaugural Ceremony 25 L. Stur

1942. 15th Anniv of Foundation of National Literacy Society.
89 **24** 70 h. black 15 15
90 1 k. red 15 15
91 1 k. 30 blue 15 15
92 2 k. brown 20 15
93 3 k. green 35 35
94 4 k. violet 35 35

1943.
95 **25** 80 h. green 15 10
96 – 1 k. red 20 20
97 – 1 k. 30 blue 15 10

PORTRAITS: 1 k. M. Razus; 1 k. 30, Father Hlinka.

27 National Costumes 30 Railway Tunnel

29 Infantry

1943. Winter Relief Fund.
98 **27** 50 h. + 50 h. green 30 20
99 – 70 h. + 1 k. red 30 20
100 – 80 h. + 2 k. blue 30 25

DESIGNS: 70 h. Mother and child; 80 h. Mother and two children.

1943. Fighting Forces.
106 **29** 70 h. + 2 k. red 50 70
107 – 1 k. 30 + 2 k. blue 75 85
108 – 2 k. + 2 k. green 65 65

DESIGNS—HORIZ: 2 k. Artillery. VERT: 1 k. 30, Air Force.

1943. Opening of the Strazke–Presov Railway..
109 – 70 h. purple . . . . 80 1·00
110 – 80 h. blue . . . . 1·00 1·25
111 **30** 1 k. 30 black . . . . 1·00 1·40
112 – 2 k. brown . . . . 1·25 2·00
DESIGNS—HORIZ: 70 h. Presov Church; 2 k. Railway viaduct. VERT: 80 h. Railway locomotive.

32 "The Slovak Language is our Life"

33 National Museum

1943. Culture Fund.
113 **32** 30 h. + 1 k. brown 40 30
114 **33** 70 h. + 1 k. green 50 50
115 – 80 h. + 2 k. blue 40 30
116 – 1 k. 30 + 2 k. brown . . . 40 30
DESIGNS—HORIZ: 80 h. Matica Slovenska College. VERT: 1 k. 30, Agricultural student.

34 Prince Pribina Okolo

35 Footballer

1944. 5th Anniv of Declaration of Independence.
117 **34** 50 h. green 10 10
118 – 70 h. mauve 10 10
119 – 80 h. brown 10 10
120 – 1 k. 30 blue 15 10
121 – 2 k. blue 15 15
122 – 3 k. brown 35 25
123 – 5 k. violet 65 50
124 – 10 k. black . . . . 1·75 1·60
DESIGNS: 70 h. Prince Mojmir; 80 h. Prince Ratislav; 1 k. 30, King Svatopluk; 2 k. Prince Kocel; 3 k. Prince Mojmir II; 5 k. Prince Svatopluk II; 10 k. Prince Braslav.

1944. As 1939 issue but larger ($18\frac{1}{2} \times 22\frac{1}{2}$ mm).
125 **7** 10 h. red 15 25
126 – 20 h. blue 15 25
127 **8** 25 h. purple 15 25
128 – 30 h. purple 15 25
129 – 50 h. green 15 25
DESIGN: 50 h. Zelene Pleso (as No. 40).

1944. Sports.
130 **35** 70 h. + 70 h. green 55 65
131 – 1 k. + 1 k. violet 70 75
132 – 1 k. 30 + 1 k. 30 green . . 70 75
133 – 2 k. + 2 k. brown . . . . 75 1·10
DESIGNS—VERT: 1 k. Skiing; 1 k. 30, Diving. HORIZ: 2 k. Running.

36 Symbolic of "Protection"

1944. Protection Series.
134 **36** 70 h. + 4 k. blue . . . . . 80 1·10
135 1 k. 30 + 4 k. brown . . . 80 1·10
136 2 k. green 30 20
137 3 k. 80 purple 30 40

37 Children Playing

38 Mgr. Tiso

1944. Child Welfare.
138 **37** 2 k. + 4 k. blue . . . . . 3·00 3·00

1945.
139 **38** 1 k. orange 75 50
140 1 k. 50 brown 20 15
141 2 k. green 25 15
142 4 k. red 75 50
143 5 k. blue 75 50
144 10 k. purple 50 25

B. SLOVAK REPUBLIC

39 State Arms

40 Ruzomberok

1993.
145 **39** 3 k. multicoloured 20 20
146 8 k. mult (26 × 40 mm) . . 85 85

1993.
146a – 3 k. black, blue and red . 15 10
147 **40** 5 k. blue and red 25 15
148 – 10 k. lilac and orange . . 55 30
150 – 30 k. black, blue and red 1·50 75
151 – 50 k. black, orange and blue 2·75 12·40
DESIGNS—VERT: 10 k. Kosice; 50 k. Bratislava. HORIZ: 3 k. Banska Bystrica; 30 k. Suden Castle.

41 Pres. Michal Kovac

42 St. John and Charles Bridge, Prague

1993.
156 **41** 2 k. black 10 10
157 3 k. brown and mauve . . 15 10

1993. 600th Death Anniv of St. John of Nepomuk (patron saint of Bohemia).
158 **42** 8 k. multicoloured 50 25

43 Pedunculate Oak

44 Jan Levoslav Bella (composer)

1993. Trees. Multicoloured.
159 3 k. Type **43** 15 10
160 4 k. Hornbeam 20 10
161 10 k. Scots pine 55 30

1993. Anniversaries.
162 **44** 5 k. cream, brown & blue 25 15
163 – 8 k. brown, sepia and red . 45 25
164 – 20 k. buff, blue & orange 1·00 50
DESIGNS: 5 k. Type **44** (150th birth anniv); 8 k. Alexander Dubcek (statesman) (1st death anniv); 20 k. Jan Kollar (poet and scholar) (birth bicent).

45 "Woman with Jug" (Marian Cunderlik)

1993. Europa. Contemporary Art.
165 **45** 14 k. multicoloured . . . 1·00 1·00

46 Sun

47 Arms of Dubnica nad Vahom

1993. Anniversaries. Multicoloured.
166 2 k. Type **46** (150th anniv of Slovakian written language) 10 10
167 8 k. Sts. Cyril and Methodius (1130th anniv of arrival in Moravia) 45 25

1993.
168 **47** 1 k. silver, black and blue 10 10

48 "The Big Pets" (Lane Smith)

1993. 14th Biennial Exhibition of Book Illustrations for Children, Bratislava.
169 **48** 5 k. multicoloured 25 15

49 Canal Lock, Gabcikovo

1993. Rhine–Main–Danube Canal.
170 **49** 10 k. multicoloured 65 35

50 Child's Face in Blood-drop

51 "Madonna and Child" (Jozef Klemens)

1993. Red Cross.
171 **50** 3 k. + 1 k. red and blue . . 20 10

1993. Christmas.
172 **51** 2 k. multicoloured 10 10

53 "The Labourer's Spring" (Jozef Kostka)

1993. Art (1st series).
174 **53** 9 k. multicoloured 45 45
See also Nos. 198/9.

54 Ski Jumping

55 Family

1994. Winter Olympic Games, Lillehammer, Norway.
175 **54** 2 k. black, mauve and blue 10 10

1994. International Year of the Family.
176 **55** 3 k. multicoloured 15 10

56 Antoine de Saint-Exupery (writer and pilot) (50th death)

57 Jozef Murgas (radio-telegraphy pioneer)

1994. Anniversaries.
177 **56** 8 k. red and blue 45 25
178 – 9 k. multicoloured 45 25
DESIGNS: 8 k. Janos Andras Segner (mathematician and physicist) (290th birth).

1994. Europa. Inventions.
179 **57** 28 k. multicoloured . . . . 1·40 70

58 Cigarettes

59 Football Pitch as Tie

1994. World No Smoking Day.
180 **58** 3 k. multicoloured 15 10

1994. World Cup Football Championship, U.S.A.
181 **59** 2 k. multicoloured 10 10

60 Ancient Greek Runner passing Baton to Modern Athlete

1994. Centenary of International Olympic Committee.
182 **60** 3 k. multicoloured 15 10

61 Golden Eagle

63 Boat with Stamp for Sail

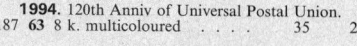

62 Prince Svatopluk

1994. Birds. Multicoloured.
183 4 k. Type **62** 20 10
184 5 k. Peregrine falcon 25 15
185 7 k. Eagle owl 30 15

1994. 1100th Death Anniv of Prince Svatopluk of Moravia.
186 **62** 12 k. brown, buff and black 50 50

1994. 120th Anniv of Universal Postal Union.
187 **63** 8 k. multicoloured 35 20

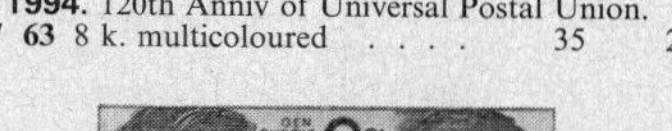

64 Generals Rudolf Viest and Jan Golian

1994. 50th Anniv of Slovak Uprising.
188 **64** 6 k. blue, pink and yellow . 25 15
189 – 8 k. multicoloured 35 20
DESIGNS: 8 k. French volunteers and their Memorial.

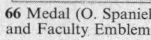

66 Medal (O. Spaniel) and Faculty Emblems

68 St. George's Church, Kostolany pod Tribecom

67 Tajar (winner of first race)

1994. 75th Anniv of Comenius University, Bratislava.
191 **66** 12 k. gold, black and red . 50 25

1994. 180th Anniv of Mojmirovce Horse Race.
192 **67** 2 k. blue and yellow . . . 10 10

1994.
193 **68** 20 k. multicoloured 85 45

69 "Nativity" (early 19th-century glass painting)

1994. Christmas.
194 **69** 2 k. multicoloured 10 10

70 Chattam Sofer, Rabbi of Bratislava

1994. Anniversaries. Multicoloured.
195 5 k. Type **70** (165th death) . . 20 10
196 6 k. Wolfgang Kempelen (conducted study into human speech) (190th death) . . . 25 15
197 10 k. Stefan Banic (inventor of parachute) (125th birth (1995)) 40 20

1994. Art (2nd series). As T **53**. Multicoloured.
198 7 k. "Girls" (Janko Alexy) (horiz) 30 30
199 14 k. "Bulls" (Vincent Hloznik) 60 60

71 Container Ship

1994. Ships. Multicoloured.
200 5 k. Type **71** 20 10
201 8 k. "Ryn" (cargo vessel) . . 35 20
202 10 k. Passenger liner 40 20

72 Samuel Jurkovic (founder)
73 "Ciminalis clusii"

1995. 150th Anniv of Landlords' Association.
203 **72** 9 k. multicoloured 40 20

1995. European Nature Protection Year. Flowers. Multicoloured.
204 2 k. Type **73** 10 10
205 3 k. "Pulsatilla slavica" . . . 15 10
206 8 k. "Onosma tornense" . . . 35 20

74 Theatre Masks

1995. 75th Anniv of Slovak National Theatre..
207 **75** 10 k. pink, black and blue . 40 20

NEWSPAPER STAMPS

1939. Nos. N364/72 of Czechoslovakia optd **1939 SLOVENSKY STAT.**
N25 2 h. brown 25 25
N26 5 h. blue 25 25
N27 7 h. red 25 25
N28 9 h. green 25 25
N29 10 h. red 25 25
N30 12 h. blue 25 25
N31 20 h. green 65 75
N32 50 h. brown . . . . 1·90 2·00
N33 1 k. green . . . . 7·00 7·50

N 7

N **29** Printer's Type

1939. Imperf.
N40 N **7** 2 h. brown 20 15
N65 5 h. blue 20 20
N42 7 h. red 20 20
N43 9 h. green 20 20
N66 10 h. red 20 15
N45 12 h. blue 20 20
N67 15 h. purple 20 15
N68 20 h. green 40 45
N69 25 h. blue 30 45
N70 40 h. red 40 45
N71 50 h. brown 65 50
N72 1 k. green 65 50
N73 2 k. green . . . . 1·25 90

1943. Imperf.
N101 N **29** 10 h. green 15 15
N102 15 h. brown 15 15
N103 20 h. blue 15 15
N104 50 h. red 20 20
N105 1 k. green 40 40
N106 2 k. blue 65 65

PERSONAL DELIVERY STAMPS

P 17

1940. Imperf.
P65 P **17** 50 h. blue . . . . 75 1·25
P66 50 h. red . . . . 75 1·25

POSTAGE DUE STAMPS

D 13
D 24

1939.
D51 D **13** 5 h. blue 25 40
D52 10 h. blue 25 25
D53 20 h. blue 40 20
D54 30 h. blue . . . . . . 1·00 65
D55 40 h. blue 50 40
D56 50 h. blue 65 75
D57 60 h. blue 75 75
D58 1 k. red . . . . 1·25 85
D59 2 k. red . . . . 7·50 6·50
D60 5 k. red . . . . 2·00 1·90
D61 10 k. red . . . . 2·50 2·40
D62 20 k. red . . . . 12·00 9·00

1942.
D 89 D **24** 10 h. brown 10 10
D 90 20 h. brown 10 15
D 91 40 h. brown 10 15
D 92 50 h. brown 70 50
D 93 60 h. brown 15 15
D 94 80 h. brown 20 15
D 95 1 k. red 20 15
D 96 1 k. 10 red 40 45
D 97 1 k. 30 red 30 15
D 98 1 k. 60 red 40 15
D 99 2 k. red 45 15
D100 2 k. 60 red 90 75
D101 3 k. 50 red . . . . . 6·25 6·25
D102 5 k. red . . . . 2·25 2·00
D103 10 k. red . . . . . . 2·75 2·50

SLOVENIA Pt. 3

Formerly part of Austria, in 1918 Slovenia was combined with other areas to form Yugoslavia. Separate stamps were issued during the Second World War whilst under Italian and German Occupation.

In 1991 Slovenia seceded and became an independent state.

1941. 100 paras = 1 dinar
1991. Tolar

ITALIAN OCCUPATION, 1941

Co. Ci.
(1)

1941. Nos. 330/1 and 414/26 of Yugoslavia optd with Type **1**.
1 **99** 25 p. black 10 15
2 50 p. orange 10 20
3 1 d. green 10 15
4 1 d. 50 red 10 20
5 2 d. red 10 15
6 3 d. brown 10 20
7 4 d. blue 10 20
8 5 d. blue 10 20
9 5 d. 50 violet 10 20
10 6 d. blue 10 30
11 8 d. brown 10 40
12 **70** 10 d. violet 15 35
13 **99** 12 d. violet 20 30
14 **70** 15 d. olive . . . . 60·00 70·00
15 **99** 16 d. purple 20 40
16 20 d. blue . . . . 1·60 2·25
17 30 d. pink . . . . 9·00 13·50

1941. Nos. 330 and 414/26 of Yugoslavia optd **R. Commissariato Civile Territori Sloveni occupati LUBIANA**, with four lines of dots at foot.
23 **99** 25 p. black 10 20
24 50 p. orange 10 20
25 1 d. green 10 20
26 1 d. 50 red 10 15
27 2 d. red 10 15
28 3 d. brown 10 30
29 4 d. blue 10 15
30 5 d. blue 25 75
31 5 d. 50 violet 15 25
32 6 d. blue 15 25
33 8 d. brown 15 25
34 **70** 10 d. violet 45 90
35 **99** 12 d. violet 20 45
36 16 d. purple 70 90
37 20 d. blue . . . . 1·60 2·50
38 30 d. pink . . . . 15·00 22·00

1941. Nos. 446/9 of Yugoslavia optd as Nos. 23/38 but with only three lines of dots at foot.
45 50 p. + 50 p. on 5 d. violet 2·25 4·25
46 1 d. + 1 d. on 10 d. lake . . 2·25 4·25
47 1 d. 50 + 1 d. 50 on 20 d. grn 2·25 4·25
48 2 d. + 2 d. on 30 d. blue . . 2·25 4·25

1941. Nos. 360/7 and 443/4 of Yugoslavia optd as Nos. 23/38, with three or four (No. 57) lines of dots at foot.
49 50 p. brown . . . . 70 1·25
50 1 d. green . . . . 70 1·25
51 2 d. blue . . . . 85 1·25
52 2 d. 50 red . . . . 85 1·25
53 5 d. violet . . . . 1·90 2·50
54 10 d. lake . . . . 1·90 2·50
55 20 d. green . . . . 10·00 15·00
56 30 d. blue . . . . 26·00 27·00
57 40 d. green . . . . 55·00 70·00
58 50 d. blue . . . . 45·00 60·00

1941. Nos. 26 and 29 surch.
59 **99** 0 d. 50 on 1 d. 50 red . . . 10 10
60 0 d. 50 on 1 d. 50 red . . . £130 £225
61 1 d. on 4 d. blue 10 15

POSTAGE DUE STAMPS

1941. Postage Due stamps of Yugoslavia, Nos. D89/93 optd with Type **1**.
D18 D **56** 50 p. violet 15 30
D19 1 d. mauve 15 30
D20 2 d. blue 15 30
D21 5 d. orange . . . . . . 1·50 2·00
D22 10 d. brown . . . . . . 1·50 2·00

Optd as Nos. 18/33, but with four lines of dots at top.
D40 D **56** 50 p. violet 10 15
D41 1 d. mauve 10 15
D42 2 d. blue 20 55
D43 5 d. orange . . . . . . 9·25 12·50
D44 10 d. brown . . . . . . 2·25 3·00

Optd as Nos. D6/10, but with narrower lettering.
D62 D **56** 50 p. violet 30 70
D63 1 d. mauve 40 80
D64 2 d. blue . . . . 7·00 11·00

GERMAN OCCUPATION, 1943–45

(3)

(4)

1944. Stamps of Italy optd with Types **3** or **4**. (a) On Postage stamps of 1929.
65 **4** 5 c. brown 10 90
66 **3** 10 c. brown 10 90
67 **4** 15 c. green 10 75
68 **3** 20 c. red 10 90
69 **4** 25 c. green 10 90
70 **3** 30 c. brown 10 90
71 **4** 35 c. blue 10 70
72 **3** 50 c. violet . . . . 10 1·10
73 **4** 75 c. red . . . . 10 2·10
74 **3** 1 l. violet . . . . 20 2·10
75 **4** 1 l. 25 blue . . . . 15 1·25
76 **3** 1 l. 75 orange . . . . 75 8·50
77 **4** 2 l. red . . . . 15 1·90
78 **3** 10 l. violet . . . . 3·75 24·00

Surch with new value.
79 – 2 l. 55 on 5 c. brown . . . . 25 4·50
80 **4** 5 l. on 25 c. green . . . . . 30 6·00
81 20 l. on 20 c. red . . . . . . 3·00 30·00
82 **3** 25 l. on 2 l. red . . . . . . 3·75 60·00
83 **4** 50 l. on 1 l. 75 orange . . . 6·75 £100

In No. 79 the overprint inscriptions are at each side of the eagle.

(b) On Air stamps, Nos. 270, etc.
84 **4** 25 c. green . . . . 1·00 1·50
85 **3** 50 c. brown . . . . 4·25 30·00
86 **4** 75 c. brown . . . . 1·50 9·00
87 **3** 1 l. violet . . . . 5·00 22·50
88 **4** 2 l. blue . . . . 2·50 13·00
89 **3** 5 l. green . . . . 2·50 19·00
90 **4** 10 l. red . . . . 2·25 15·00

(c) On Air Express stamp.
E91 **3** 2 l. black (No. E370) . . . 7·50 48·00

(d) On Express Letter stamp.
E92 **3** 1 l. 25 green (No. E350) . . 1·40 7·50

1944. Red Cross. Express Letter stamps of Italy surch as Types **3** or **4** with a red cross and new value alongside.
102 E **132** 1 l. 25 + 50 l. green . . 24·00 £300
103 2 l. 50 + 50 l. orange . 24·00 £300

1944. Homeless Relief Fund. Express Letter stamps of Italy surch as Types **3** and **4**, but in circular frame, and **BREZDOMCEM DEN OBDACHLOSEN** alongside with new value between.
104 E **132** 1 l. 25 + 50 l. green . . 24·00 £300
105 2 l. 50 + 50 l. orange . 24·00 £300

1944. Air. Orphans' Fund. Air stamps of Italy Nos. 270, etc., surch as Types **3** and **4**, but in circular frame between **DEN WAISEN SIROTAM** and new value.
106 – 25 c. + 10 l. green . . . 10·00 £180
107 **110** 50 c. + 10 l. brown . . . 10·00 £180
108 – 75 c. + 20 l. brown . . . 10·00 £180
109 – 1 l. + 20 l. violet . . . 10·00 £180
110 **113** 2 l. + 20 l. blue . . . . 10·00 £180
111 **110** 5 l. + 20 l. green . . . 10·00 £180

1944. Air. Winter Relief Fund. Air stamps of Italy Nos. 270, etc., surch as Types **3** and **4**, but between **ZIMSKA POMOC WINTERHILFE** and new value.
112 – 25 c. + 10 l. green . . . 10·00 £180
113 **110** 50 c. + 10 l. brown . . . 10·00 £180
114 – 75 c. + 20 l. brown . . . 10·00 £180
115 – 1 l. + 20 l. violet . . . 10·00 £180
116 **113** 2 l. + 20 l. blue . . . . 10·00 £180
117 **110** 5 l. + 20 l. green . . . 10·00 £180

9 Railway Viaduct, Borovnice

10 Church in Novo Mesto

1945. Inscr "PROVINZ LAIBACH".
118 – 5 c. brown . . . . 20 1·50
119 – 10 c. orange . . . . 20 1·50
120 **9** 20 c. brown . . . . 50 1·50
121 – 25 c. green . . . . 20 1·50
122 **10** 50 c. violet . . . . 20 1·50
123 – 75 c. red . . . . 20 1·50
124 – 1 l. green . . . . 20 1·75
125 – 1 l. 25 blue . . . . 20 3·25
126 – 1 l. 50 green . . . . 35 3·25
127 – 2 l. blue . . . . 30 5·25
128 – 2 l. 50 brown . . . . 30 5·25
129 – 3 l. mauve . . . . 60 9·25
130 – 5 l. brown . . . . 85 9·25
131 – 10 l. green . . . . 2·10 45·00
132 – 20 l. blue . . . . 12·50 £140
133 – 30 l. red . . . . 70·00 £600

DESIGNS—VERT: 5 c. Stalagmites, Krizna Jama; 1 l. 25, Kocevje; 1 l. 50, Borovnice Falls; 3 l. Castle, Zuzemberg; 30 l. View and Tabor Church. HORIZ: 10 c. Zirknitz Lake; 25 c. Farm near Ljubljana; 75 c. View from Ribnica; 1 l. Old Castle, Ljubljana; 2 l. Castle, Kostanjevica; 2 l. 50, Castle, Turjak; 5 l. View on River Krka; 10 l. Castle, Otocec; 20 l. Farm at Dolenjskom.

POSTAGE DUE STAMPS

(D 5)

(D 6)

1944. Postage Due stamps of Italy, Nos. D395, etc., optd as Type D **5**.

D97 D **141** 50 c. violet 15 35
D98 D **142** 1 l. orange . . . . . . 60 6·25
D99 2 l. green . . . . . . 60 6·25

Surch as Type D **6**.

D100 D **141** 30 c. on 50 c. violet . 15 35
D101 40 c. on 5 c. brown . 15 35

INDEPENDENT STATE

11 Parliament Building

12 Arms

1991. Declaration of Independence.

134 **11** 5 d. multicoloured 25 20

1991.

135 **12** 1 t. multicoloured 10 10
136 4 t. multicoloured 15 15
137 5 t. multicoloured 15 15
138 11 t. multicoloured 25 25

13 Ski Jumping

1992. Winter Olympic Games, Albertville. Multicoloured.

139 30 t. Type **13** 85 85
140 50 t. Slalom . . . . 1·40 1·40

14 Arms

15 Opera House

1992. Multicoloured, background colours given.

141 **14** 1 t. brown 10 10
142 2 t. purple 10 10
143 4 t. green 15 15
144 5 t. red 15 15
145 6 t. yellow 20 20
146 11 t. orange 25 25
147 15 t. blue 30 30
148 20 t. violet 50 50
149 50 t. green 85 85
150 100 t. grey . . . . 1·60 1·60

1992. Centenary of Ljubljana Opera House.

155 **15** 20 t. multicoloured 25 25

16 Tartini and Violins

1992. 300th Birth Anniv of Giuseppe Tartini (violinist and composer).

156 **16** 27 t. multicoloured 35 35

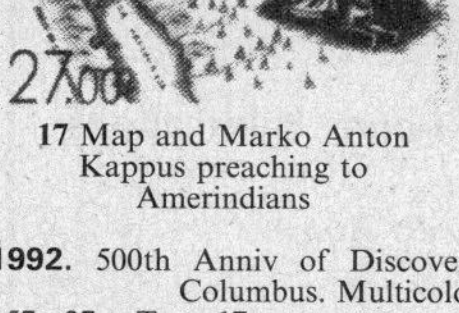

17 Map and Marko Anton Kappus preaching to Amerindians

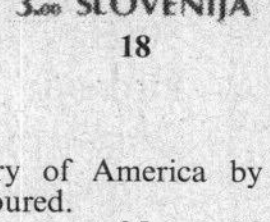

18

1992. 500th Anniv of Discovery of America by Columbus. Multicoloured.

157 27 t. Type **17** 35 35
158 47 t. Map and "Santa Maria" . . 60 60

1992. Obligatory Tax. Red Cross.

159 **18** 3 t. black, red and blue . . 10 10

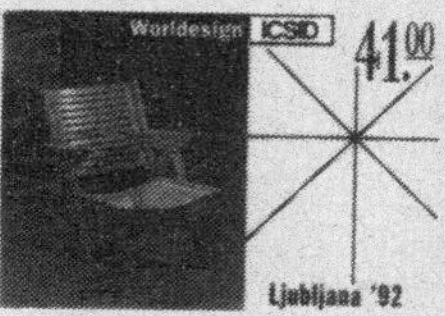

19 Collapsible Chair by Niko Kralj and Map

20 Slomsek

1992. World Industrial Design Congress, Ljubljana.

160 **19** 41 t. multicoloured 55 55

1992. 130th Death Anniv of Anton Slomsek, Bishop of Maribor.

161 **20** 41 t. multicoloured 55 55

21 Wreckage

22 Rescuing Mountaineer

1992. Obligatory Tax. Solidarity Week. Perf and imperf.

162 **21** 3 t. brown, black & red . 10 10

1992. 80th Anniv of Alpine Rescue Service.

164 **22** 41 t. multicoloured 55 55

23 River Jousting

24 Linden Leaf and Flowers

1992. 900th Anniv of River Jousting in Ljubljana.

165 **23** 6 t. multicoloured 10 10

1992. 1st Anniv of Independence.

166 **24** 41 t. multicoloured 55 55

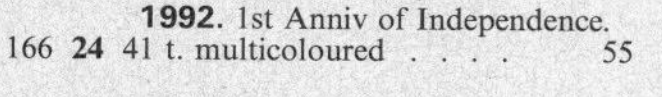

25 Leon Stukelj and Medals

1992. Olympic Games, Barcelona. Multicoloured.

167 40 t. Type **25** 50 50
168 46 t. Head of Apoxymenos repeated in three Slovene colours 60 60

26 Sheepdog

1992. "Psov '92" World Dog-training Championships, Ljubljana.

169 **26** 40 t. multicoloured 50 50

27 Hand crushing Cigarettes

28 Kogoj and scene from "Black Masks" (opera)

1992. Obligatory Tax. Red Cross. Anti-smoking Week.

170 **27** 3 t. multicoloured 10 10

1992. Birth Centenary of Marij Kogoj (composer).

171 **28** 40 t. multicoloured 50 50

29 Langus (self-portrait)

1992. Birth Bicentenary of Matevz Langus (painter).

172 **29** 40 t. multicoloured 50 50

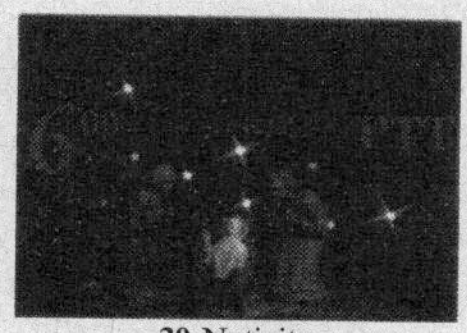
30 Nativity

1992. Christmas. Multicoloured.

173 6 t. Type **30** 10 10
174 7 t. Type **30** 10 10
175 41 t. "Madonna and Child" (stained-glass window by V. Sorli-Puc in St. Mary's Church, Bovec) (vert) . . . 55 55

31 View of Earth from Space and Satellite

1992. Birth Centenary of Herman Potocnik (space flight pioneer).

176 **31** 46 t. multicoloured 60 60

32 Illustration from "Solzice"

1993. Birth Centenary of Prezihov Voranc (writer).

177 **32** 7 t. multicoloured 10 10

33 "Underneath the Birches"

1993. 50th Death Anniv of Rihard Jakopic (painter).

178 **33** 44 t. multicoloured 45 45

34 Bust of Stefan (J. Savinsek)

35 Honey-cake from Skofja Loka

1993. Death Centenary of Jozef Stefan (physicist).

179 **34** 51 t. multicoloured 50 50

1993. Slovene Culture.

180 **35** 1 t. brown, cinnamon and deep brown 10 10
181 – 2 t. green and lt green . . . 10 10
182 – 5 t. grey and mauve 10 10
183 – 6 t. lt green, green & yellow 10 10
186 – 7 t. red, crimson and grey . 10 10
187 – 8 t. green, dp grn & olive . 10 10
188 – 9 t. red, brown and grey . . 10 10
189 – 10 t. brown and lt brown . . 10 10
190 – 11 t. green, light green and yellow 10 10
191 – 12 t. red, orange and grey . 10 10
193 – 20 t. green and grey . . . 20 20
195 – 44 t. lt blue, black & blue . 45 45
196 – 50 t. purple and mauve . . 50 50
198 – 100 t. deep brown, light brown and brown . . . 1·00 1·00
198a – 300 t. chestnut and brown . 3·25 3·25
198b – 400 t. red and brown . . . 4·25 4·25

DESIGNS: 2 t. Musical pipes; 5 t. Storage barn; 6 t. Shepherd's hut, Velika; 7 t. Zither; 8 t. Mill on the Mur; 9 t. Sledge; 10 t. Drum; 11 t. Hay basket; 12 t. Boy on horseback (statuette from Ribnica); 20 t. House, Prekmurju; 44 t. House, Karst; 50 t. Wind-propelled pump; 100 t. Cake; 300 t. Straw sculpture; 400 t. Wine press.

36 Mountains and Founder Members

1993. Centenary of Alpine Association.

199 **36** 7 t. multicoloured 10 10

37 Cop's Route up Triglav

38 Chainbreaker

1993. Birth Centenary of Joza Cop (climber and mountain rescuer).

200 **37** 44 t. multicoloured 45 45

1993. 75th Anniv of Slovenian Postal Service.

201 **38** 7 t. multicoloured 10 10

39 "St. Nicholas" (altar painting, Tintoretto)

40 "Table in Pompeii" (Marij Pregelj)

1993. 500th Anniv of College Chapter of Novo Mesto. Multicoloured.

202 7 t. Type **39** 10 10
203 44 t. Arms 45 45

1993. Europa. Contemporary Art. Multicoloured.

204 44 t. Type **40** 45 45
205 159 t. "Girl with Toy" (Gabrijel Stupica) . . . . 1·60 1·60

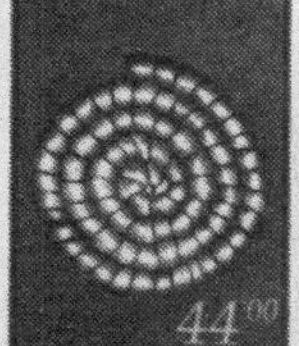

41 "Schwagerina carniolica"

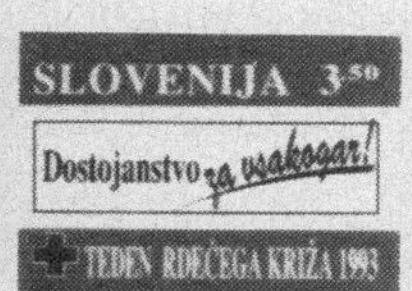

42

1993. Fossils.

206 **41** 44 t. multicoloured 45 45

1993. Obligatory Tax. Red Cross.

207 **42** 3 t. 50 black, red & blue . 10 10

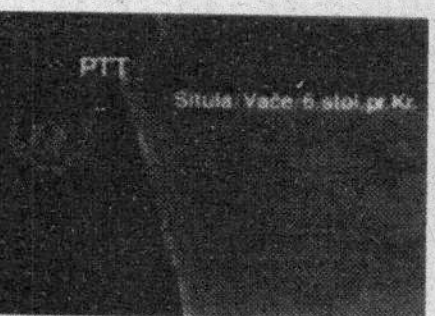

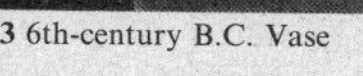
43 6th-century B.C. Vase

44 Red Cross Rescue Workers

1993. 1st Anniv of Admission to United Nations Organization.
208 **43** 62 t. multicoloured 65 65

1993. Obligatory Tax. Solidarity Week.
209 **44** 3 t. 50 multicoloured . . . 10 10

45 Basketball, Hurdling and Swimming

1993. Mediterranean Games, Roussillon (Languedoc).
210 **45** 36 t. multicoloured 35 35

46 "Battle of Sisak" (Janez Valvasor)

1993. 400th Anniv of Battle of Sisak.
211 **46** 49 t. multicoloured 50 50

47 "Monolistra spinosissima"

1993. Cave Fauna. Multicoloured.
212 7 t. Type **47** 10 10
213 40 t. "Aphaenopidius kamnikensis" (insect) . . . 40 40
214 55 t. "Proteus anguinus" . . . 55 55
215 65 t. "Zospeum spelaeum" (mollusc) 65 65

48 Horse and Diagram of Movements

49 Boy smoking and Emblem

1993. European Dressage Championships, Lipica.
216 **48** 65 t. multicoloured 65 65

1993. Obligatory Tax. Red Cross. Anti-smoking Week.
217 **49** 4 t. 50 multicoloured . . . 10 10

50 Arms (death anniv of Johnann Valvasor (historian))

1993. 300th Anniversaries.
218 **50** 9 t. black, lilac and gold . . 10 10
219 – 65 t. black, stone & gold . . 65 65
DESIGN: 65 t. Arms of Academia Operosorum.

51 Christmas Crib

1993. Christmas. Multicoloured.
220 9 t. Type **51** 10 10
221 65 t. Dr. Joze Pogacnik (archbishop) 65 65

52 Illustration from "The Vagabond"

53 Hearts

1994. 150th Anniversaries. Multicoloured.
222 8 t. Type **52** (birth anniv of Josip Juncic (writer)) 10 10
223 9 t. Nightingale and bridge over river (birth anniv of Simon Gregorcic, poet) 10 10
224 55 t. Book showing Slovenian vowels (birth anniv of Stanisla Skrabec, philologist) . . . 55 55
225 65 t. Cover of grammar book (death anniv of Jernei Kopitar, philologist) 65 65

1994. Greetings Stamp.
226 **53** 9 t. multicoloured 10 10

54 Cross-country Skiing

1994. Winter Olympic Games, Lillehammer, Norway. Multicoloured.
227 9 t. Type **54** 10 10
228 65 t. Slalom skiing 70 70

55 Ski Jumping

1994. 60th Anniv of Ski Jumping Championships, Planica.
229 **55** 70 t. multicoloured 75 75

56 Town Names

1994. 850th Anniv of First Official Record of Ljubljana.
230 **56** 9 t. multicoloured 10 10

57 Janez Puhar and Camera

1994. Europa. Discoveries and Inventions. Multicoloured.
231 70 t. Type **57** (invention of glass-plate photography) 75 75
232 215 t. Moon, natural logarithm diagram and Jurij Vega (mathematician) . . . . . 2·40 2·40

58 Balloons

1994. Obligatory Tax. Red Cross.
233 **58** 4 t. 50 multicoloured . . . 10 10

59 "Primula carniolica"

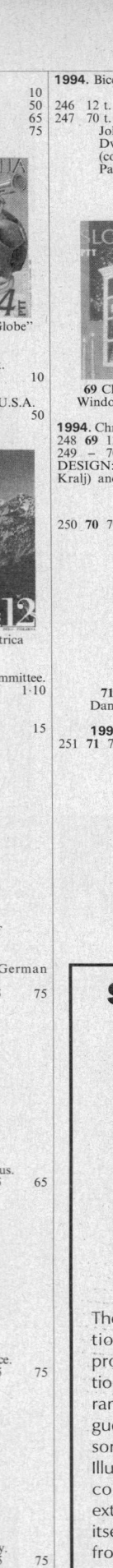

1994. Flowers. Multicoloured.
234 9 t. Type **59** 10 10
235 44 t. "Hladnikia pastinacifolia" 50 50
236 60 t. "Daphne blagayana" . . 65 65
237 70 t. "Campanula zoysii" . . . 75 75

60 Red Cross Worker with Child

61 Inflating "Globe" Football

1994. Obligatory Tax. Solidarity Week.
238 **60** 4 t. 50 multicoloured . . . 10 10

1994. World Cup Football Championship, U.S.A.
239 **61** 44 t. multicoloured 50 50

62 Globes in Olympic Colours and Flags

63 Mt. Ojstrica

1994. Centenary of International Olympic Committee.
240 **62** 100 t. multicoloured . . . . 1·10 1·10

1994.
241 **63** 12 t. multicoloured 15 15

64 Maks Pletersnik and University of Laibach Professors

1994. Centenary of First Slovenian–German Dictionary.
242 **64** 70 t. multicoloured 75 75

65 Roman Infantry

1994. 1600th Anniv of Battle of Frigidus.
243 **65** 60 t. red, black and grey . . 65 65

66 Post Office

1994. Centenary of Maribor Post Office.
244 **66** 70 t. multicoloured 75 75

67 Locomotive kkStB 5722

1994. Centenary of Ljubljana Railway.
245 **67** 70 t. multicoloured 75 75

68 Orchestra Venue and Music

1994. Bicentenary of Ljubljana Philharmonic Society. Multicoloured.
246 12 t. Type **68** 15 15
247 70 t. Ludwig van Beethoven, Johannes Brahms, Antonin Dvorak and Joseph Haydn (composers) and Niccolo Paganini (violinist) 75 75

69 Christmas Tree, Window and Candles

70 "Madonna and Child" (statue, Loreto Basilica)

1994. Christmas and International Year of the Family.
248 **69** 12 t. multicoloured 15 15
249 – 70 t. cream, black and blue 75 75
DESIGN: 70 t. "Children with Christmas Tree" (F. Kralj) and I.Y.F. emblem.

1994. 700th Anniv of Loreto.
250 **70** 70 t. multicoloured 75 75

71 Ivan Hribar, Mihajlo Rostohar and Danilo Majaron (founders) and University

1994. 75th Anniv of Ljubljana University.
251 **71** 70 t. multicoloured 75 75

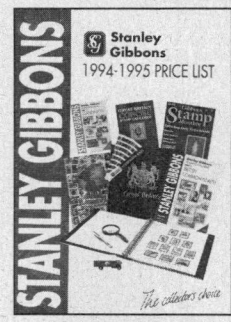

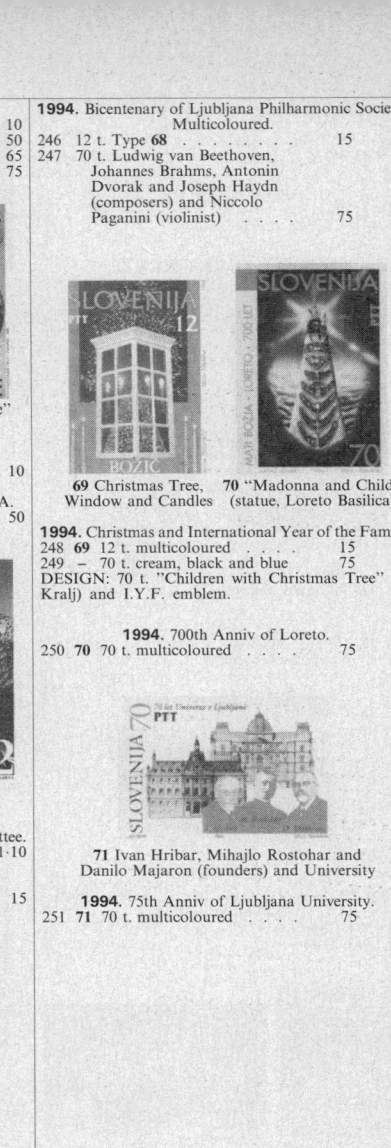

SOMALIA Pt. 8; Pt. 14

A former Italian colony in East Africa on the Gulf of Aden, including Benadir (S. Somaliland), and Jubaland. Under British Administration 1943-50 (for stamps issued during this period see volume 3). Then under United Nations control with Italian Administration. Became independent on 1st July, 1960. Following a revolution in Oct. 1969, the country was designated "Somali Democratic Republic". See also Middle East Forces.

1903. 16 annas = 1 rupia
1905. 100 centesimi = 1 lira
1922. 100 besa = 1 rupia
1926. 100 centesimi = 1 lira
1950. 100 centesimi = 1 somalo
1961. 100 cents = 1 Somali shilling

ITALIAN COLONY

1 African Elephant

2 Somali Lion

1903.
1 1 1 b. brown 19·00 2·75
2 2 b. green 2·25 1·00
3 2 1 a. red 2·50 1·90
4 2 a. orange 5·00 8·50
5 2½ a. blue 2·25 3·00
6 5 a. yellow 5·00 10·00
7 10 a. lilac 5·00 10·00

1905. Surch with new value without bars at top.
10 1 2 c. on 1 b. brown 4·50 12·00
11 5 c. on 2 b. green 4·50 8·00
12 10 c. on 1 a. red 4·50 7·00
13 15 c. on 2 a. orange 4·50 7·00
8 15 c. on 5 a. yellow £1400 £225
13a 20 c. on 2 a. orange 7·00 3·00
14 25 c. on 2½ a. blue 7·00 7·00
9 40 c. on 10 a. lilac £325 £100
15 50 c. on 5 a. yellow 9·50 14·00
16 1 l. on 10 a. lilac 9·50 16·00
For stamps with bars at top, see Nos. 68, etc.

1916. Nos. 15 and 16 re-surcharged and with bars cancelling original surcharge.
17 2 5 c. on 50 c. on 5 a. yellow 14·00 20·00
18 20 c. on 11 c. on 10 a. lilac 4·00 10·00

Nos. 19 to 160 are all, except where stated, Italian stamps, sometimes in new colours, optd. **SOMALIA ITALIANA** or **SOMALIA**.

1916. Red Cross stamps optd or surch **20** also.
19 53 10 c. + 5 c. red 1·50 3·75
20 54 15 c. + 5 c. grey 5·00 15·00
21 20 c. + 5 c. orange 5·00 15·00
22 20 on 15 c. + 5 c. grey 1·50 5·00

1922. Nos. 12, etc., again surch at top.
23 1 3 b. on 5 c. on 2 b. green 5·50 13·00
24 2 6 b. on 10 c. on 1 a. red 7·00 10·00
25 9 b. on 15 c. on 2 a. orange 7·00 10·00
26 15 b. on 25 c. on 2½ a. blue 8·50 10·00
27 30 b. on 50 c. on 5 a. yellow 9·50 24·00
28 60 b. on 1 l. on 10 a. lilac 9·50 32·00

1922. Victory stamps surch.
29 62 3 b. on 5 c. green 40 2·00
30 6 b. on 10 c. red 40 2·00
31 9 b. on 15 c. grey 40 3·25
32 15 b. on 25 c. blue 40 3·25

1923. Nos. 11 to 16 re-surcharged with new values and bars. (No. 33 is optd with bars only at bottom).
33 1 2 c. on 1 b. brown 4·25 13·00
34 2 on 2 c. on 1 b. brown 4·25 13·00
35 3 on 2 c. on 1 b. brown 4·25 13·00
36 2 5 b. on 50 c. on 5 a. yellow 4·25 10·00
37 1 6 on 5 c. on 2 b. green 5·50 7·50
38 2 18 b. on 10 c. on 1 a. red 5·50 7·50
39 20 b. on 15 c. on 2 a. orange 7·00 10·00
40 25 b. on 15 c. on 2 a. orange 8·00 10·00
41 30 b. on 25 c. on 2½ a. blue 9·50 12·00
42 60 b. on 1 l. on 10 a. lilac 10·00 27·00
43 1 r. on 1 l. on 10 a. lilac 12·00 32·00

1923. Propaganda of Faith stamps surch.
44 66 6 b. on 20 c. orange & grn 1·10 5·50
45 13 b. on 30 c. orge & red 1·10 5·50
46 20 b. on 50 c. orge & vio 75 4·75
47 30 b. on 1 l. orge & blue 75 4·75

1923. Fascisti stamps surch.
48 73 3 b. on 10 c. green 1·75 6·00
49 13 b. on 30 c. violet 1·75 6·00
50 20 b. on 50 c. red 1·75 6·00
51 74 30 b. on 1 l. blue 1·75 6·00
52 1 r. on 2 l. brown 1·75 6·00
53 75 3 l. on 5 l. black and blue 1·75 7·50

1924. Manzoni stamps surch.
54 77 6 b. on 10 c. black & red 60 12·00
55 9 b. on 15 c. black & green 60 12·00
56 13 b. on 30 c. black 60 12·00
57 20 b. on 50 c. black & brn 60 12·00
58 30 b. on 1 l. black & blue 15·00 90·00
59 3 r. on 5 l. black & purple £200 £950

1925. Holy Year stamps surch.
60 – 6 b. + 3 b. on 20 c. + 10 c. brown and green 75 4·25
61 81 13 b. + 6 b. on 30 c. + 15 c. brown and chocolate 75 4·25
62 – 15 b. + 8 b. on 50 c. + 25 c. brown and violet 75 4·25
63 – 18 b. + 9 b. on 60 c. + 30 c. brown and red 75 4·25
64 – 30 b. + 15 b. on 1 l. + 50 c. purple and blue 75 4·25
65 – 1 r. + 50 b. on 5 l. + 2 l. 50 c. purple and red 75 4·25

1925. Royal Jubilee stamps optd.
66 82 60 c. red 15 2·75
67 1 l. blue 2·25 19·00
67a 1 l. 25 c. blue 35 8·50

1926. Nos. 10/13, and 13a/16 optd with bars at top.
68 1 2 c. on 1 b. brown 9·50 25·00
69 5 c. on 2 b. green 7·00 20·00
70 2 10 c. on 1 a. red 4·25 4·75
71 15 c. on 2 a. orange 4·25 5·50
72 20 c. on 2 a. orange 5·50 7·50
73 25 c. on 2½ a. blue 5·50 8·50
74 50 c. on 5 a. yellow 7·00 17·00
75 1 l. on 10 a. lilac 9·50 20·00

1926. St. Francis of Assisi stamps optd.
76 83 20 c. green 70 4·25
77 40 c. violet 70 4·25
78 60 c. red 70 4·25
79 1 l. 25 c. blue 70 4·25
80 5 l. + 2 l. 50 c. olive 1·50 5·50

21

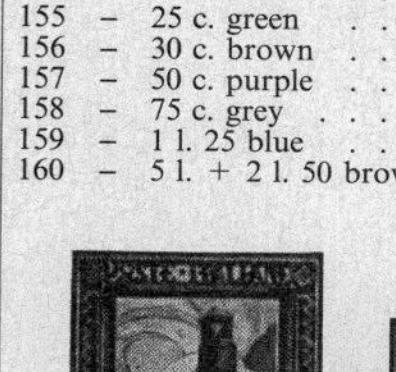

25

1926. Italian Colonial Institute.
81 21 5 c. + 5 c. brown 20 2·25
82 10 c. + 5 c. olive 20 2·25
83 20 c. + 5 c. green 20 2·25
84 40 c. + 5 c. red 20 2·25
85 60 c. + 5 c. orange 20 2·25
86 1 l. + 5 c. blue 20 2·25

1926. Italian stamps optd.
87 31 2 c. brown 1·00 2·25
88 33 5 c. green 1·40 2·25
89 92 7½ c. brown 4·75 17·00
90 37 10 c. red 85 40
91 39 20 c. purple 90 70
92 34 25 c. green 35 30
92a 39 30 c. black 4·00 6·00
93 91 50 c. grey and brown 4·00 4·25
94 92 50 c. mauve 11·00 22·00
95 39 60 c. orange 1·10 1·25
96 34 75 c. red 35·00 5·00
97 1 l. brown and green 1·10 60
98 1 l. 25 c. blue 3·50 1·00
99 91 1 l. 75 brown 18·00 7·00
100 34 2 l. green and orange 6·00 2·50
101 2 l. 50 c. green & orange 7·50 3·00
102 5 l. blue and red 17·00 12·00
103 10 l. red and olive 17·00 15·00

1927. 1st National Defence issue optd.
104 89 40 c. + 20 c. black & brn 80 4·25
105 – 60 c. + 30 c. brown & red 80 4·25
106 – 1 l. 25 + 60 c. black & blue 80 4·25
107 – 5 l. + 2 l. 50 black & green 1·25 6·50

1927. Centenary of Volta.
108 90 20 c. violet 3·00 10·00
109 50 c. orange 3·00 7·00
110 1 l. 25 blue 4·00 11·00

1928. 45th Anniv of Italian–African Society.
111 25 20 c. + 5 c. green 60 3·50
112 30 c. + 5 c. red 60 3·50
113 50 c. + 10 c. violet 60 3·50
114 1 l. 25 + 20 c. blue 60 3·50

1929. 2nd National Defence issue.
115 89 30 c. + 10 c. black & red 1·00 4·75
116 – 50 c. + 20 c. black & lilac 1·00 4·75
117 – 1 l. 25 + 50 c. blue & brn 1·40 6·00
118 – 5 l. + 2 l. black and olive 1·40 6·00

1929. Montecassino Abbey.
119 104 20 c. green 1·75 4·25
120 – 25 c. orange 1·75 4·25
121 – 50 c. + 10 c. red 1·75 8·50
122 – 75 c. + 15 c. brown 1·75 8·50
123 104 1 l. 25 + 25 c. purple 3·25 8·50
124 – 5 l. + 1 l. blue 3·25 8·50
125 – 10 l. + 2 l. brown 3·25 10·00

1930. Royal Wedding.
126 109 20 c. green 40 1·90
127 50 c. + 10 c. orange 35 2·50
128 1 l. 25 + 25 c. red 35 2·75

1930. Ferrucci.
129 114 20 c. violet 50 1·60
130 – 25 c. green (No. 283) 50 1·60
131 – 50 c. black (No. 284) 50 1·60
132 – 1 l. 25 blue (No. 285) 50 1·60
133 – 5 l. + 2 l. red (No. 286) 1·75 2·75

1930. 3rd National Defence issue.
134 89 30 c. + 10 c. green & olive 4·00 15·00
135 – 50 c. + 10 c. violet & olive 4·00 15·00
136 – 1 l. 25 + 30 c. brown 4·00 15·00
137 – 5 l. + 1 l. 50 green & blue 12·00 42·00

29 Irrigation Canal

1930. 25th Anniv (1929) of Colonial Agricultural Institute.
138 29 50 c. + 20 c. brown 75 5·00
139 1 l. 25 + 20 c. blue 75 5·00
140 1 l. 75 + 20 c. green 75 5·00
141 2 l. 55 + 50 c. violet 1·50 5·00
142 5 l. + 1 l. red 1·50 5·00

1930. Bimillenary of Virgil.
143 15 c. violet 25 1·40
144 20 c. brown 25 1·40
145 25 c. green 25 1·40
146 30 c. brown 25 1·40
147 50 c. purple 25 1·10
148 75 c. red 25 1·40
149 1 l. 25 blue 25 1·40
150 5 l. + 1 l. 50 purple 1·75 7·00
151 10 l. + 2 l. 50 brown 1·75 7·00

1931. Portraits.
152 – 25 c. green 2·25 4·25
153 103 50 c. violet 5·50 1·00

1931. St. Anthony of Padua.
154 121 20 c. brown 55 2·50
155 – 25 c. green 55 2·50
156 – 30 c. brown 55 2·50
157 – 50 c. purple 55 1·40
158 – 75 c. grey 55 2·50
159 – 1 l. 25 blue 55 2·50
160 – 5 l. + 2 l. 50 brown 2·00 11·00

32 Tower at Mnara-Ciromo

33 Hippopotamus

1932.
161a – 5 c. brown 15 10
162a – 7½ c. violet 15 1·10
163a – 10 c. black 15 10
164a – 15 c. olive 15 30
165a 32 20 c. red 15 10
166a 25 c. green 15 10
167a 30 c. brown 20 20
168a – 35 c. blue 65 1·50
169a – 50 c. violet 2·75 10
170 – 75 c. red 85 40
171 – 1 l. 25 blue 1·75 25
172 – 1 l. 75 orange 1·25 25
173 – 2 l. red 70 35
174 – 2 l. 55 slate 12·00 20·00
175a – 5 l. red 4·50 1·25
176 33 10 l. violet 7·50 4·50
177 – 20 l. green 18·00 20·00
178 – 25 l. blue 30·00 30·00
DESIGNS—HORIZ: 5, 7½, 10, 15 c. Francesco Crispi Lighthouse, Cape Guardafui; 35, 50, 75 c. Governor's Residence, Mogadishu; 25 l. Lioness. VERT: 1 l. 25, 1 l. 75, 2 l. Ant-hill; 2 l. 55, 5 l. Ostrich; 20 l. Lesser kudu.

1934. Abruzzi issue. Optd **ONORANZE AL DUCA DEGLI ABRUZZI**.
179 10 c. brown 2·50 8·00
180 25 c. green 2·50 8·00
181 50 c. mauve 1·90 8·00
182 1 l. 25 blue 1·90 8·00
183 5 l. black 3·00 8·00
184 10 l. red 2·50 8·00
185 20 l. green 2·50 8·00
186 25 l. blue 2·50 8·00
DESIGNS: As Nos. 163a to 178.

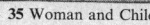

35 Woman and Child

37 King Victor Emmanuel III

36

1934. 2nd Int Colonial Exhibition, Naples.
187 35 5 c. green & brown (post) 1·50 6·00
188 10 c. brown and black 1·50 6·00
189 20 c. red and slate 1·50 6·00

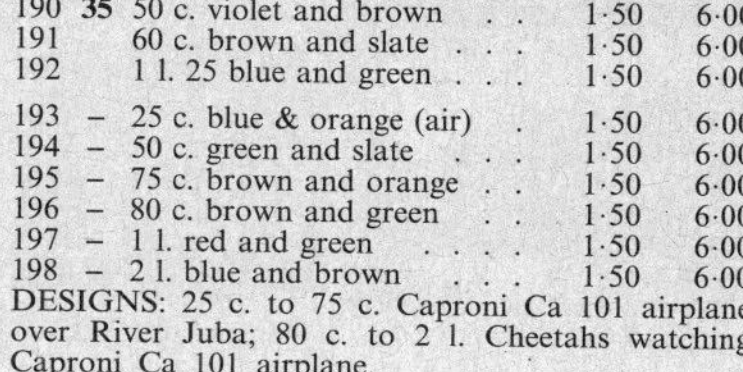

190 35 50 c. violet and brown 1·50 6·00
191 60 c. brown and slate 1·50 6·00
192 1 l. 25 blue and green 1·50 6·00
193 – 25 c. blue & orange (air) 1·50 6·00
194 – 50 c. green and slate 1·50 6·00
195 – 75 c. brown and orange 1·50 6·00
196 – 80 c. brown and green 1·50 6·00
197 – 1 l. red and green 1·50 6·00
198 – 2 l. blue and brown 1·50 6·00
DESIGNS: 25 c. to 75 c. Caproni Ca 101 airplane over River Juba; 80 c. to 2 l. Cheetahs watching Caproni Ca 101 airplane.

1934. Air. Rome–Mogadishu Flight.
199 36 25 c. + 10 c. green 1·75 5·00
200 50 c. + 10 c. brown 1·75 5·00
201 75 c. + 15 c. red 1·75 5·00
202 80 c. + 15 c. black 1·75 5·00
203 1 l. + 20 c. red 1·75 5·00
204 2 l. + 20 c. blue 1·75 5·00
205 3 l. + 25 c. violet 14·00 40·00
206 5 l. + 25 c. orange 14·00 40·00
207 10 l. + 30 c. purple 14·00 40·00
208 25 l. + 2 l. green 14·00 40·00

1934. King of Italy's Visit to Italian Somaliland.
209 37 5 c. + 5 c. black 65 3·00
210 7½ c. + 7½ c. purple 65 3·00
211 15 c. + 10 c. green 65 3·00
212 20 c. + 10 c. red 65 3·00
213 25 c. + 10 c. green 65 3·00
214 30 c. + 10 c. brown 65 3·00
215 50 c. + 10 c. violet 65 3·00
216 75 c. + 15 c. red 65 3·00
217 1 l. 25 + 15 c. blue 65 3·00
218 1 l. 75 + 25 c. orange 65 3·00
219 2 l. 75 + 25 c. slate 7·50 29·00
220 5 l. + 1 l. red 7·50 29·00
221 10 l. + 1 l. 80 red 7·50 29·00
222 – 25 l. + 2 l. 75 brn & red 55·00 95·00
DESIGN—36×44 mm: 25 l. King Victor Emmanuel III on horseback.

38a Native Girl and Macchi Castoldi MC-94 Flying Boat

1936. Air.
223 – 25 c. green 85 2·00
224 – 50 c. brown 20 15
225 – 60 c. orange 1·10 4·25
226 – 75 c. brown 70 90
227 38a 1 l. blue 15 10
228 – 1 l. 50 violet 70 35
229 – 2 l. blue 1·60 85
230 38a 3 l. red 5·00 2·25
231 – 5 l. green 5·00 2·75
232 – 10 l. red 6·00 9·00
DESIGNS: 25 c., 1 l. 50, Banana trees; 50 c., 2 l. Native woman in cotton plantation; 60 c., 5 l. Orchard; 75 c., 10 l. Native women harvesting.

ITALIAN TRUST TERRITORY

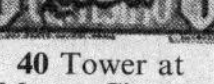
40 Tower at Mnara-Ciromo

41 Ostrich

42 Governor's Residence, Mogadishu

43 River Scene

1950.
233 40 1 c. black (postage) 10 10
234 41 5 c. red 75 25
235 42 6 c. violet 15 10
236 40 8 c. green 15 10
237 42 10 c. green 10 10
238 41 20 c. turquoise 1·25 20
239 40 35 c. red 35 20
240 42 55 c. blue 45 15
241 41 60 c. violet 1·75 35
242 40 65 c. brown 70 15
243 42 1 s. orange 85 15
244 43 30 c. brown (air) 30 30
245 45 c. red 30 30
246 65 c. slate 30 30
247 70 c. blue 30 30
248 90 c. brown 30 30
249 1 s. purple 45 30
250 1 s. 35 violet 70 70
251 1 s. 50 turquoise 85 50
252 3 s. blue 7·00 2·25
253 5 s. brown 8·00 3·00
254 10 s. orange 9·50 2·25

44 Councillors

45 Symbol of Fair

1951. 1st Territorial Council.

255 **44** 20 c. brn & grn (postage) . 2·00 20
256 55 c. violet and sepia . . . 3·75 3·50
257 – 1 s. blue and violet (air) . . 2·25 70
258 – 1 s. 50 brown and green . . 3·75 2·75

DESIGN—VERT: 1 s, 1 s. 50, Flags and Savoia Marchetti S.M.95C airplane over Mogadiscio.

1952. 1st Somali Fair, Mogadiscio.

259 **45** 25 c. brn & red (postage) 1·75 1·75
260 55 c. brown and blue . . . 1·75 1·75
261 – 1 s. 20 blue & bistre (air) 2·00 2·00

DESIGN: 1 s. 20, Palm tree, Douglas DC-4 airliner and minaret.

46 Mother and Baby

47 Somali and Entrance to Fair

1953. Anti-Tuberculosis Campaign.

262 **46** 5 c. brown & vio (postage) 10 10
263 25 c. brown and red . . . 15 10
264 50 c. brown and blue . . . 70 70
265 1 s. 20 brown & grn (air) . 85 85

1953. 2nd Somali Fair, Mogadiscio.

266 **47** 25 c. green (postage) . . . 20 20
267 60 c. blue 40 40
268 – 1 s. 20 lake (air) 40 40
269 – 1 s. 50 brown 40 40

DESIGN: 1 s. 20, 1 s. 50, Palm, airplane and entrance.

48 Stamps of 1903 and Map

1953. 50th Anniv of First Stamps of Italian Somaliland. (a) Postage.

270 **48** 25 c. brown, red & lake . . 25 25
271 35 c. brown, red & green . . 25 25
272 60 c. brown, red & orange 25 25

(b) Air. Aeroplane on Map.

273 **48** 60 c. brown, red & chestnut 45 45
274 1 s. brown, red & black . . 45 45

49 Aeroplane and Constellations

1953. Air. 75th Anniv of U.P.U.

275 **49** 1 s. 20 red and buff 35 35
276 1 s. 50 brown and buff . . 40 40
277 2 s. green and blue 45 40

50 Somali Bush Country

51 Alexander Is. and R. Juba

1954. Leprosy Convention.

278 **50** 25 c. green & blue (postage) 30 30
279 60 c. sepia and brown . . . 30 30
280 **51** 1 s. 20 brn and grn (air) . . 40 40
281 2 s. violet and red 55 65

MORE DETAILED LISTS
are given in the Stanley Gibbons Catalogues referred to in the country headings. For lists of current volumes see introduction

52 Somali Flag

52a "Adenium somalense"

1954. Institution of Somali Flag.

282 **52** 25 c. multicoloured (post) . 25 25
283 1 s. 20 multicoloured (air) 25 25

1955. Floral Designs.

290a **52a** 1 c. red, black and blue . 10 10
285 – 5 c. mauve, green & blue 10 10
290c – 10 c. yellow, grn & lilac 10 10
290d – 15 c. yellow, grn & red . 20 20
290e – 25 c. yellow, grn & brn . 15 10
290f – 50 c. multicoloured . . 30 30
288 – 60 c. red, green & black 10 15
289 – 1 s. yellow, green & pur 15 20
290 – 1 s. 20 yellow, grn & sep 20 20

FLOWERS—VERT: 5 c. "Haemanthus multiflorus martyn"; 10 c. "Grinum scabrum"; 15 c. "Adansonia digitata"; 25 c. "Poinciana elata"; 50 c. "Gloriosa virescens"; 60 c. "Calatropis procera"; 1 s. "Pancratium trainthum her"; 1 s. 20, "Sesamothamnus bussernus".

54 Oribi

54a Lesser Kudu

1955. Air. Antelopes. (a) As T **54**. Heads in black and orange.

291 **54** 35 c. green 30 20
292 – 45 c. violet . . . . 1·25 35
293 – 50 c. violet 30 20
294 – 75 c. red 65 25
295 – 1 s. 20 turquoise 65 25
296 – 1 s. 50 blue 75 45

ANTELOPES: 45 c. Salt's dik-dik; 50 c. Speke's gazelle; 75 c. Gerenuk; 1 s. 20, Soemmering's gazelle; 1 s. 50, Waterbuck.

(b) As T **54a**.

296a **54a** 3 s. purple and brown . . 1·00 85
296b – 5 s. yellow and black . . 1·00 85

DESIGN: 5 s. Hunter's hartebeest.

55 Native Weaver

56 Voters and Map

1955. 3rd Somali Fair.

297 **55** 25 c. brown (postage) . . 25 25
298 – 30 c. green 25 25
299 – 45 c. brown & orange (air) 25 25
300 – 1 s. 20, blue and pink . . 35 35

DESIGNS: 30 c. Cattle fording river; 45 c. Camels around well; 1 s. 20, Native woman at well.

1956. 1st Legislative Assembly.

301 **56** 5 c. brn & grey (postage) . 10 10
302 10 c. brown and olive . . 10 10
303 25 c. brown and red . . . 10 10
304 60 c. brown and blue (air) 15 15
305 1 s. 20 brown and orange . 20 20

57 Somali Arms

58 Falcheiro Barrage

1957. Inauguration of National Emblem. Arms in blue and ochre.

306 **57** 5 c. brown (postage) . . . 10 10
307 25 c. red 15 15
308 60 c. violet 15 15
309 45 c. blue (air) 20 20
310 1 s. 20 green 25 25

1957. 4th Somali Fair.

311 **58** 5 c. lilac & brown (postage) 10 10
312 – 10 c. green and bistre . . 10 10
313 – 25 c. blue and red . . . 15 15
314 – 60 c. sepia and blue (air) . . 25 25
315 – 1 s. 20 black and red . . . 25 25

DESIGNS—HORIZ: 10 c. Juba River bridge; 25 c. Silos at Margherita; 60 c. Irrigation canal. VERT: 1 s. 20, Oil well.

59 Somali Nurse with Baby

60 Track Running

1957. Tuberculosis Relief Campaign.

316 **59** 10 c. + 10 c. sepia and red (postage) 15 15
317 25 c. + 10 c. sepia & green 15 15
318 55 c. + 20 c. sepia and blue (air) 20 20
319 1 s. 20 c. + 20 c. sepia and violet 30 30

1958. Sports.

320 **60** 2 c. lilac (postage) 10 10
321 – 4 c. green (Football) 10 10
322 – 5 c. red (Discus) 10 10
323 – 6 c. grey (Motor-cycling) . . 10 10
324 – 8 c. blue (Fencing) 10 10
325 – 10 c. orange (Archery) . . . 10 10
326 – 25 c. green (Boxing) 10 10
327 – 60 c. brn (air) (Running) . . 10 10
328 – 1 s. 20 blue (Cycling) . . . 15 15
329 – 1 s. 50 red (Basketball) . . 20 15

The 4, 6, 10 and 25 c. are horiz.

61 The Constitution and Assembly Building, Mogadishu

62 White Stork

1959. Opening of Constituent Assembly. Inscr "ASSEMBLEA CONSTITUENTE".

330 **61** 5 c. blue & green (postage) . 10 10
331 25 c. blue and bistre 10 10
332 – 1 s. 20 blue and bistre (air) . 25 25
333 – 1 s. 50 blue and green . . . 25 25

DESIGNS—HORIZ: 1 s. 20, 1 s. 50, Police bugler.

1959. Somali Water Birds.

334 **62** 5 c. black, red & yellow (postage) 20 10
335 – 10 c. red, yellow & brown . 20 10
336 – 15 c. black and orange . . 20 10
337 – 25 c. black, orange & red 20 10
338 – 1 s. 20 black, red and violet (air) . . . . 1·10 50
339 – 2 s. red and blue . . . . 1·10 50

BIRDS—VERT: 10 c. Saddle-bill stork; 15 c. Sacred ibis; 25 c. Pink-backed pelicans. HORIZ: 1 s. 20, Marabou stork; 2 s. Great egret.

63 Incense Tree

64 Institute Badge

1959. 5th Somali Fair.

340 **63** 20 c. blk & orge (postage) . 10 10
341 – 60 c. black, red & orange 20 20
342 – 1 s. 20 black and red (air) . 25 25
343 – 2 s. black, orge & brown . . 40 40

DESIGNS—VERT: 60 c. Somali child with incense-burner. HORIZ: 1 s. 20, 15th-century B.C. incense shipment; 2 s. Incense-burner and Mogadishu Harbour.

1960. Opening of University Institute of Somalia, Mogadishu. Inscr as in T **64**.

344 **34** 5 c. red & brown (postage) . 10 10
345 – 50 c. brown and blue . . . 10 10
346 – 80 c. black and red . . . 20 20
347 – 45 c. brown, black and green (air) 20 20
348 – 1 s. 20 ultram, blk & bl . . 35 35

DESIGNS—HORIZ: 45 c., 1 s. 20, Institute buildings; 50 c. Map of Africa. VERT: 80 c. Institute emblem.

65 "The Horn of Africa"

1960. World Refugee Year.

349 **65** 10 c. green, black and brown (postage) 10 10
350 – 60 c. brown, ochre & blk . 10 10
351 – 80 c. green, black & pink 10 10
352 – 1 s. 50 red, blue and green (air) . . . . 1·00 40

DESIGNS—HORIZ: 60 c. Similar to Type **65**. VERT: 80 c. Palm; 1 s. 50, White stork.

REPUBLIC

1960. Optd **Somaliland Independence 26. June 1960**.

353 10 c. yellow, green & lilac (No. 290c) (postage) . . . . . . 12·00 12·00
354 50 c. black, orange and violet (No. 293) (air) . . . . . . 22·00 17·00
355 1 s. 20 blk, orge & turq (No. 295) 19·00 17·00

Nos. 353/5 were only issued in the former British protectorate, which united with Somalia when the latter became independent on 1st July, 1960.

67 Gazelle and Map of Africa

68 Olympic Flame and Somali Flag

1960. Proclamation of Independence.

356 **67** 5 c. brn, bl & lilac (post) . 20 20
357 – 25 c. blue 35 35
358 – 1 s. brown, red & green (air) 40 20
359 – 1 s. 80 blue and orange . . 1·10 90

DESIGNS—VERT: 25 c. U.N. Flag and Headquarters Building. HORIZ: 1 s. Chamber of Deputies, Montecitorio Palace, Rome; 1 s. 80, Somali Flag.

1960. Olympic Games. Inscr "1960".

360 **68** 5 c. blue & grn (postage) . 15 10
361 – 10 c. blue and yellow . . . 15 10
362 – 45 c. blue and lilac (air) . . 10 15
363 – 1 s. 80 blue and red . . . 1·10 95

DESIGNS: 10 c. Relay race; 45 c. Runner breasting tape; 1 s. 80, Runner.

69 Child drawing Giraffe

70 Girl harvesting Papaws

1960. Child Welfare. Inscr "PRO INFANZIA".

364 **69** 10 c. black, brown and green (postage) 10 10
365 – 15 c. black, lt green & red . 15 15
366 – 25 c. brown, black & yell . 30 30
367 – 3 s. orange, black, blue and green (air) . . . . 1·60 1·10

ANIMALS: 15 c. Common zebra; 25 c. Black rhinoceros; 3 s. Leopard.

1961. Multicoloured. Designs each show a girl harvesting.

368 5 c. Type **70** 10 10
369 10 c. Girl harvesting durra . . 10 10
370 20 c. Cotton 15 15
371 25 c. Sesame 15 15
372 40 c. Sugar cane 20 20
373 50 c. Bananas 35 35
374 75 c. Groundnuts (horiz) . . . 55 55
375 80 c. Grapefruit (horiz) . . . 1·10 1·10

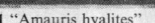

71 "Amauris hyalites"

72 Shield, Bow and Arrow, Quiver and Dagger

1961. Air. Butterflies. Multicoloured.

376		60 c. Type **71**	25	15
377		90 c. "Euryphura chalcis"	30	20
378		1 s. "Papilio lormieri"	3·25	25
379		1 s. 80 "Druryia antimachus"	75	45
380		3 s. "Danaus formosa"	90	60
381		5 s. "Papilio phorcas"	3·25	90
382		10 s. "Charaxes cynthia"	6·75	2·40

1961. 6th Somali Trade Fair.

383	**72**	25 c. yellow, black and red (postage)	10	10
384	–	45 c. yellow, blk & green	20	20
385	–	1 s. yellow, blk & bl (air)	55	45
386	–	1 s. 80 brown, blk & yell	1·10	65

DESIGNS—Handicrafts—VERT: 45 c. "Tungi" wooden vase and pottery. HORIZ: 1 s. National head-dress, support and comb; 1 s. 80, Statuettes of camel and man, and balancing novelty.

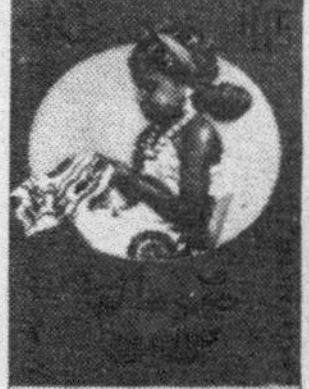
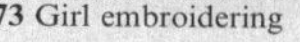

73 Girl embroidering **74** Mosquito

1962. Child Welfare. Tropical Fishes. Inscr "PRO INFANZIA". Multicoloured.

387		15 c. Type **73** (postage)	15	15
388		25 c. Blue angelfish	15	15
389		40 c. Wrasse	80	80
390		2 s. 70 Red snapper (air)	2·25	1·10

1962. Malaria Eradication. Inscr "MONDO UNITO CONTRO LA MALARIA".

391	**74**	10 c. green & red (postage)	15	15
392	–	25 c. brown and mauve	30	30
393	–	1 s. brown and black (air)	55	20
394	–	1 s. 80 green and black	1·10	90

DESIGNS—VERT: 25 c. Insecticide sprayer; 1 s., 1 s. 80, Campaign emblem and mosquitoes.

75 Auxiliaries tending Casualty **76** Wooden Spoon and Fork

1963. Women's Auxiliary Forces Formation. Multicoloured.

395		5 c. Policewoman (postage)	10	10
396		10 c. Army auxiliary	20	20
397		25 c. Policewomen with patrol car	35	35
398		75 c. Type **75**	45	45
399		1 s. Policewomen marching with flag (air)	55	35
400		1 s. 80 Army auxiliaries at attention with flag	1·40	80

The 5 c., 10 c. and 25 c. are horiz.

1963. Freedom from Hunger.

401	**76**	75 c. brn & grn (postage)	45	45
402	–	1 s. multicoloured (air)	1·10	65

DESIGN: 1 s. Sower.

77 Pres. Osman and Arms **78** Open-air Theatre

1963. 3rd Anniv of Independence. Arms in blue and yellow.

403	**77**	25 c. sepia & blue (postage)	30	15
404		1 s. sepia and red (air)	65	35
405		1 s. 80 sepia and green	1·00	55

1963. 7th Somali Fair.

406	**78**	25 c. green (postage)	20	20
407	–	55 c. red	65	45
408	–	1 s. 80 blue (air)	1·40	90

DESIGNS: 55 c. African Trade Building; 1 s. 80, Government Pavilion.

HAVE YOU READ THE NOTES AT THE BEGINNING OF THIS CATALOGUE?

These often provide the answers to the enquiries we receive.

79 Credit Bank, Mogadishu **80** Running

1964. 10th Anniv of Somali Credit Bank. Multicoloured.

409		60 c. Type **79** (postage)	45	20
410		1 s. Map of Somalia and globe (air)	90	45
411		1 s. 80 Bank emblem	1·40	90

1964. Olympic Games, Tokyo. Colours: sepia, brown and blue.

412		10 c. Type **80** (postage)	15	15
413		25 c. High-jumping	20	20
414		90 c. Diving (air)	55	45
415		1 s. 80 Footballer	1·10	65

81 Douglas DC-3 Airliner

1964. Inaug of Somali Airlines.

416	**81**	5 c. blue and red (postage)	20	35
417	–	20 c. blue and orange	65	35
418	–	1 s. ochre and green (air)	1·10	55
419	–	1 s. 80 blue and black	2·25	1·60

DESIGNS: 20 c. Passengers disembarking from DC-3; DC-3 in flight over: 1 s. African elephants; 1 s. 80, Mogadishu.

82 Refugees **83** I.T.U. Emblem on Map of Africa

1964. Somali Refugees Fund.

420	**82**	25 c. + 10 c. red and blue (postage)	55	20
421	–	75 c. + 20 c. purple, black and red (air)	45	45
422	–	1 s. 80 + 50 c. green, black and bistre	1·50	1·25

DESIGNS—HORIZ: 75 c. Ruined houses. VERT: 1 s. 80, Soldier with child refugees.

1965. I.T.U. Centenary.

423	**83**	25 c. blue & orge (postage)	45	10
424		1 s. black and green (air)	85	55
425		1 s. 80 brown and mauve	1·60	1·10

84 Tanning

1965. Somali Industries.

426	**84**	10 c. sepia and buff (postage)	15	15
427	–	25 c. sepia and pink	20	15
428	–	35 c. sepia and blue	35	15
429	–	1 s. 50 sepia and grn (air)	1·10	55
430	–	2 s. sepia and mauve	2·25	1·10

DESIGNS: 25 c. Meat processing and canning; 35 c. Fish processing and canning; 1 s. 50, Sugar-cutting cane and refining; 2 s. Dairying-milking and bottling.

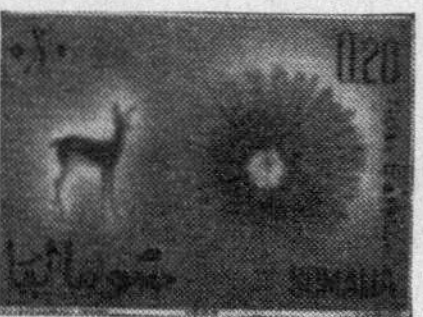

85 Hottentot Fig and Gazelle

1965. Somali Flora and Fauna. Multicoloured.

431		20 c. Type **85**	10	10
432		60 c. African tulips and giraffes	20	10
433		1 s. White lotus and greater flamingoes	45	20
434		1 s. 30 Pervincia and ostriches	90	45
435		1 s. 80 Bignonia and common zebras	2·25	80

86 Narina Trogon

1966. Somali Birds. Multicoloured.

436		25 c. Type **86**	40	10
437		35 c. Bateleur (vert)	50	10
438		50 c. Ruppell's griffon	65	25
439		1 s. 30 Common roller	1·25	35
440		2 s. Vulturine guineafowl (vert)	1·50	55

87 Globe and U.N. Emblem

1966. 21st Anniv of U.N.O. Multicoloured.

441		35 c. Type **87**	35	15
442		1 s. Map of Africa and U.N. emblem	45	20
443		1 s. 50 Map of Somalia and U.N. emblem	90	45

88 Woman sitting on Crocodile

1966. Somali Art. Showing Paintings from Garesa Museum, Mogadishu. Multicoloured.

444		25 c. Type **88**	10	10
445		1 s. Woman and warrior	20	10
446		1 s. 50 Boy leading camel	45	20
447		2 s. Women pounding grain	90	55

89 U.N.E.S.C.O. Emblem and Palm **90** Oribi

1966. 20th Anniv of U.N.E.S.C.O.

448	**89**	35 c. black, red and grey	10	10
449		1 s. black, green & yellow	15	10
450		1 s. 80 black, blue & red	85	45

1967. Antelopes.

451	**90**	35 c. ochre, black & blue	10	10
452	–	60 c. brown, black & orge	15	15
453	–	1 s. bistre, black and red	30	20
454	–	1 s. 80 ochre, black & grn	1·10	60

ANTELOPES: 60 c. Kirk's dik-dik; 1 s. Gerenuk gazelle; 1 s. 80, Soemmering's gazelle.

91 Somali Dancers **92** Badge and Scout Saluting

1967. "Popular Dances". Designs showing dancers.

455	**91**	25 c. multicoloured	10	10
456	–	50 c. multicoloured	10	10
457	–	1 s. 30 multicoloured	35	30
458	–	2 s. multicoloured	1·10	60

1967. World Scout Jamboree. Multicoloured.

459		35 c. Type **92**	10	10
460		50 c. Scouts and flags	15	10
461		1 s. Camp scene	40	20
462		1 s. 80 Jamboree emblem	1·00	65

93 Pres. Schermarche and King Faisal

1967. Visit of King Faisal of Saudi Arabia.

463	**93**	50 c. black & blue (postage)	20	10
464	–	1 s. multicoloured	45	35
465	–	1 s. 80 multicoloured (air)	90	55

DESIGNS: 1 s. Somali and Saudi Arabian flags; 1 s. 80, Kaaba, Mecca and portraits as Type **93**.

94 Sweetlips

1967. Fishes. Multicoloured.

466		35 c. Type **94**	10	10
467		50 c. Butterfly fish	20	10
468		1 s. Lunar-tailed bullseye	45	35
469		1 s. 80 Speckled grouper	90	55

95 Inoculation **96** Somali Girl with Lemons

1968. 20th Anniv of W.H.O.

470	**95**	35 c. multicoloured	10	10
471	–	1 s. black, brown & green	20	20
472	–	1 s. 80 blac brn & orge	90	55

DESIGNS: 1 s. Chest examination; 1 s. 80, Heart examination.

1968. Agricultural Produce. Multicoloured.

473		5 c. Type **96**	10	10
474		10 c. Oranges	10	10
475		25 c. Coconuts	10	10
476		35 c. Papaws	15	10
477		40 c. Mangoes	15	10
478		50 c. Grapefruit	15	10
479		1 s. Bananas	55	20
480		1 s. 30 Cotton bolls	85	45

Each design includes a Somali girl.

97 Waterbuck **98** Throwing the Javelin

1968. Somali Antelopes. Multicoloured.

481		1 s. 50 Type **97**	35	20
482		1 s. 80 Speke's gazelle	45	35
483		2 s. Lesser kudu	60	35
484		5 s. Hunter's hartebeest	1·40	80
485		10 s. Dibatag gazelle	4·50	1·60

1968. Olympic Games, Mexico.

486	**98**	35 c. black, brown & lemon	10	10
487	–	50 c. black, brown & red	10	10
488	–	80 c. black, brown & pur	20	20
489	–	1 s. 50 black, brown & grn	1·40	65

DESIGNS: 50 c. Running; 80 c. Pole-vaulting; 1 s. 50, Basketball.

99 Great Egret **100** "Pounding Meal"

1968. Air. Birds. Multicoloured.

491		35 c. Type **99**	30	20
492		1 s. Carmine bee eater	50	20
493		1 s. 30 Yellow-bellied green pigeon	80	45
494		1 s. 80 Paradise whydah	2·25	80

1968. Somali Art.

495	**100**	25 c. brown, black & lilac	15	10
496	–	35 c. brown, black & red	15	10
497	–	2 s. 80 brown, blk & grn	20	20

DESIGNS (wood-carvings): 35 c. "Preparing food"; 2 s. 80, "Rug-making".

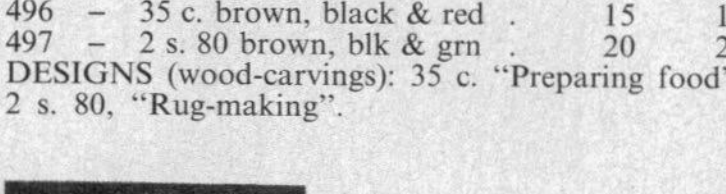

101 Cornflower **102** Workers at Anvil

1969. Flowers. Multicoloured.
498 40 c. Type **101** 10 10
499 80 c. Sunflower 20 15
500 1 s. Oleander 55 30
501 1 s. 80 Chrysanthemum . . . 1·40 85

1969. 50th Anniv of I.L.O. Multicoloured.
502 25 c. Type **102** 10 10
503 1 s. Ploughing with oxen . . . 20 20
504 1 s. 80 Drawing water for irrigation 80 45

103 Gandhi, and Hands releasing Dove

1969. Birth Centenary of Mahatma Gandhi.
505 – 35 c. purple 10 10
506 **103** 1 s. 50 orange 45 30
507 – 1 s. 80 brown . . . . . . 1·10 70
DESIGNS—VERT—(Size $25\frac{1}{2} \times 36$ mm): 35 c. Mahatma Gandhi; 1 s. 80, Gandhi seated.

SOMALI DEMOCRATIC REPUBLIC

An issue for the "Apollo 11" Moon Landing was prepared in 1970, but not issued.

104 "Charaxes varanes"

105 Lenin with Children

1970. Butterflies. Multicoloured.
508 25 c. Type **104** 15 10
509 50 c. "Cethosia lamarcki" . . 40 10
510 1 s. 50 "Troides aeacus" . . . 55 45
511 2 s. "Chrysiridia ripheus" . . 1·40 55

1970. Birth Centenary of Lenin.
512 **105** 25 c. multicoloured . . . 10 10
513 – 1 s. multicoloured 20 15
514 – 1 s. 80 black, orange and brown 80 55
DESIGNS—VERT: 1 s. Lenin making speech. HORIZ: 1 s. 80, Lenin at desk.

106 Dove feeding Young

1970. 10th Anniv of Independence.
515 25 c. Type **106** 10 10
516 35 c. Dagahtur Memorial . . 10 10
517 1 s. Somali arms (vert) 35 20
518 2 s. 80 Camel and star (vert) 1·10 90

107 Tractor and Produce

1970. 1st Anniv of 21st October Revolution.
519 **107** 35 c. multicoloured . . . 10 10
520 – 40 c. black and blue . . . 10 10
521 – 1 s. black and brown . . . 35 20
522 – 1 s. 80 multicoloured . . . 80 45
DESIGNS: 40 c. Soldier and flag; 1 s. Hand on open book; 1 s. 80, Emblems of Peace, Justice and Prosperity.

108 African within Snake's Coils

1971. Racial Equality Year.
523 **108** 1 s. 30 multicoloured . . . 45 20
524 – 1 s. 80 black, red & brn . 65 45
DESIGN: 1 s. 80, Human figures, chain and barbed wire.

INDEX

Countries can be quickly located by referring to the index at the end of this volume.

109 I.T.U. Emblem

1971. World Telecommunications Day.
525 **109** 25 c. black, ultram & bl . . 10 10
526 – 2 s. 80 black, blue & grn . 1·10 65
DESIGN: 2 s. 80, Global emblem.

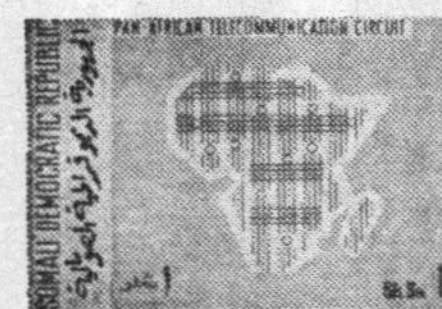
110 Telecommunications Map

1971. Pan-African Telecommunications Network.
527 **110** 1 s. green, black & blue . . 35 20
528 – 1 s. 50 black, grn & yell . . 80 35
DESIGN: 1 s. 50, similar to Type **110** but with different network pattern.

111 White Rhinoceros

1971. Wild Animals.
529 **111** 35 c. multicoloured . . . 20 20
530 – 1 s. multicoloured 35 35
531 – 1 s. 30 black, yellow and violet 90 90
532 – 1 s. 80 multicoloured . . 1·40 1·40
DESIGNS: 1 s. Cheetahs; 1 s. 30, Common zebras; 1 s. 80, Lion attacking dromedary.

112 Ancient Desert City

1971. East and Central African Summit Conference, Mogadishu.
533 **112** 1 s. 30 brown, blk & red . 55 55
534 – 1 s. 50 multicoloured . . 95 95
DESIGN: 1 s. 50, Headquarters building, Mogadishu.

113 Memorial

1971. 2nd Anniv of Revolution.
535 **113** 10 c. black, cobalt & blue . 10 10
536 – 1 s. multicoloured 30 30
537 – 1 s. 35 multicoloured . . 1·00 1·00
DESIGNS: 1 s. Agricultural workers; 1 s. 35, Building workers.

114 Inoculating Cattle

1971. Rinderpest Control Programme. Multicoloured.
538 40 c. Type **114** 55 35
539 1 s. 80 Herdsmen with cattle . 1·10 80

115 A.P.U. Emblem and Back of Airmail Envelope

1972. 10th Anniv of African Postal Union.
540 1 s. 50 A.P.U. emblem and dove with letter (postage) 80 55
541 1 s. 30 Type **115** (air) 90 65

116 Mother and Child

117 Dromedary

1972. 25th Anniv of U.N.I.C.E.F.
542 **116** 50 c. black, brown and light brown 20 10
543 – 2 s. 80 multicoloured . . . 1·40 1·00
DESIGNS—HORIZ: 2 s. 80, U.N.I.C.E.F. emblem and schoolchildren.

1972. Domestic Animals.
544 **117** 5 c. multicoloured 10 10
545 – 10 c. multicoloured 10 10
546 – 20 c. multicoloured 10 10
547 – 40 c. black, brown & red . 20 20
548 – 1 s. 70 black, green & black 1·60 1·60
DESIGNS: 10 c. Cattle on quayside; 20 c. Bull; 40 c. Black-headed sheep; 1 s. 70, Goat.

118 Child within Cupped Hands

1972. 3rd Anniv of 21st October Revolution. Multicoloured.
549 70 c. Type **118** 20 10
550 1 s. Parade of standards . . . 30 15
551 1 s. 50 Youth Camps emblem . 90 55

119 Folk Dancers

1973. Folk Dances. Multicoloured.
552 5 c. Type **119** 10 10
553 40 c. Pair of dancers (vert) . . 10 10
554 1 s. Team of dancers (vert) . . 45 20
555 2 s. Three dancers . . . . . . 1·00 55

120 Old Alphabet in Flames

121 Soldiers and Chains within O.A.U. Emblem

1973. Introduction of New Somali Script.
556 **120** 40 c. multicoloured 10 10
557 – 1 s. multicoloured 20 15
558 – 2 s. black, stone & yellow 80 55
DESIGNS—HORIZ: 1 s. Alphabet in sun's rays; 2 s. Writing new script.

1974. 10th Anniv (1973) of Organization of African Unity. Multicoloured.
559 40 c. Type **121** 20 10
560 2 s. Spiral on map of Africa . 90 65

122 Hurdling

123 Somali Youth and Girl

1974. Sports.
561 **122** 50 c. black, red & orange . 15 10
562 – 1 s. black, grey & green . . 35 20
563 – 1 s. 40 black, grey & olive 90 55
DESIGNS—HORIZ: 1 s. Running. VERT: 1 s. 40, Basketball.

1974. Guulwade Youth Movement. Multicoloured.
564 40 c. Type **123** 10 10
565 2 s. Guulwade members helping old woman . . . . 1·00 65

124 Map of League Members

1974. 30th Anniv (1975) of Arab League. Multicoloured.
566 1 s. 50 Type **124** 55 35
567 1 s. 70 Flags of Arab League countries 85 55

125 Desert Landscape

1975. 5th Anniv of 21 October Revolution. Multicoloured.
568 40 c. Type **125** 20 15
569 2 s. Somali villagers reading books (vert) 90 65

126 Doves

128

1975. Centenary of U.P.U. Multicoloured.
570 50 c. Type **126** 30 10
571 3 s. Mounted postman . . . . 2·00 1·00

1975. African Postal Union. As T **126**. Multicoloured.
572 1 s. Maps of Africa (repetitive motif) 35 20
573 1 s. 50 Dove with letter . . . 1·00 65

1975. Traditional Costumes.
574 **128** 10 c. multicoloured . . . 10 10
575 – 40 c. multicoloured . . . 10 10
576 – 50 c. multicoloured . . . 15 10
577 – 1 s. multicoloured 35 20
578 – 5 s. multicoloured . . . . 2·10 85
579 – 10 s. multicoloured . . . 4·50 2·50
DESIGNS: 40 c. to 10 s. Various costumes.

129 Independence Square, Mogadishu

130 Hassan Statue

1976. Int Women's Year. Multicoloured.
580 50 c. Type **129** 30 10
581 2 s. 30 I.W.Y. emblem (horiz) 1·40 1·00

1976. Sayed M. A. Hassan Commemoration. Multicoloured.
582 50 c. Type **130** 15 10
583 60 c. Hassan directing warriors (vert) 20 10
584 1 s. 50 Hassan inspiring warriors (vert) 55 35
585 2 s. 30 Hassan leading attack 1·60 55

131 Nurse and Child

132 "Cypraea gracilis"

1976. Famine Relief. Multicoloured.
586 75 c. + 25 c. Type **131** . . . 45 45
587 80 c. + 20 c. Devastated land (horiz) 45 45
588 2 s. 40 + 10 c. Somali family with produce 80 80
589 2 s. 90 + 10 c. Relief emblem and medical officer (horiz) 1·60 1·60

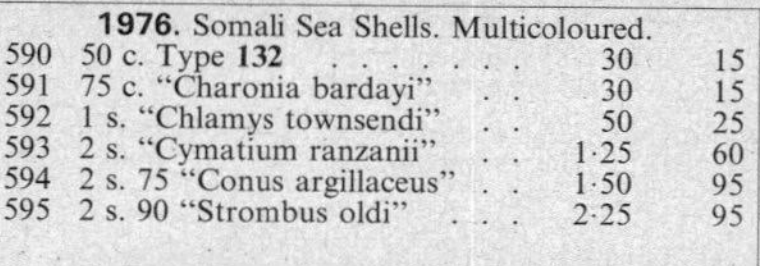

1976. Somali Sea Shells. Multicoloured.

590	50 c. Type **132**	30	15
591	75 c. "Charonia bardayi"	30	15
592	1 s. "Chlamys townsendi"	50	25
593	2 s. "Cymatium ranzanii"	1·25	60
594	2 s. 75 "Conus argillaceus"	1·50	95
595	2 s. 90 "Strombus oldi"	2·25	95

133 Benin Head and Hunters

1977. Second World Black and African Festival of Arts and Cultures, Lagos, Nigeria. Multicoloured.

597	50 c. Type **133**	20	15
598	75 c. Handicrafts	35	30
599	2 s. Dancers	85	65
600	2 s. 90 Musicians	1·60	1·10

The Benin Head appears on all designs.

134 Somali Flags

135 Hunting Dog

1977. 1st Anniv of Somali Socialist Revolutionary Party. Multicoloured.

601	75 c. Type **134**	20	10
602	1 s. Somali Arms (horiz)	35	20
603	1 s. 50 Pres. Barre and globe (horiz)	55	35
604	2 s. Arms over rising sun	85	45

1977. Protected Animals. Multicoloured.

605	50 c. Type **135**	15	10
606	75 c. Lesser bushbaby	20	10
607	1 s. African ass	45	20
608	1 s. 50 Aardwolf	55	35
609	2 s. Greater kudu	1·10	55
610	3 s. Giraffe	2·00	90

136 Leonardo da Vinci's Drawing of Helicopter

137 Dome of the Rock

1977. 30th Anniv of I.C.A.O. Multicoloured.

612	1 s. Type **136**	35	25
613	1 s. 50 Montgolfier Brothers' balloon	45	35
614	2 s. Wright Flyer I	65	45
615	2 s. 90 Boeing 720B of Somali Airlines	1·40	65

1978. Palestine Freedom-Fighters.

617	**137** 75 c. black, green & pink	20	10
618	2 s. black, red and blue	90	55

138 Stadium and Footballer

1978. World Cup Football Championship, Argentina. Multicoloured.

619	1 s. 50 Type **138**	45	35
620	4 s. 90 Stadium and goalkeeper	1·50	1·00
621	5 s. 50 Stadium and footballer (different)	2·00	1·40

139 "Acacia tortilis"

1978. Trees. Multicoloured.

623	40 c. Type **139**	15	10
624	50 c. "Ficus sycomorus" (vert)	30	20
625	75 c. "Terminalia catapa" (vert)	45	35
626	2 s. 90 "Adansonia digitata"	1·40	65

140 "Hibiscus rosa-sinensis"

142 "Child going to School" (Ahmed Dahir Mohamed)

141 Fishing from Punt and "Siganus rivulatus"

1978. Flowers. Multicoloured.

627	50 c. Type **140**	20	10
628	1 s. "Cassia baccarinii"	45	20
629	1 s. 50 "Kigelia somalensis"	80	45
630	2 s. 30 "Dichrostachys glomerata"	1·40	65

1979. Fishing. Multicoloured.

632	75 c. Type **141**	20	10
633	80 c. Fishing from felucca and "Gaterin gaterinus"	20	15
634	2 s. 30 Fishing fleet and "Hypacanthus amia"	1·00	55
635	2 s. 50 Trawler and "Scomberomorus commersoni"	1·40	85

1979. International Year of the Child. Children's Paintings. Multicoloured.

636	50 c. Type **142**	15	10
637	75 c. "Sailboat" (M. A. Mohamed)	20	15
638	1 s. 50 "House in the Country" (A. M. Ali)	45	30
639	3 s. "Bird on Blossoming Branch" (A. A. Siyad)	1·10	65

143 University Students and Open-air Class

1979. 10th Anniv of Revolution. Multicoloured.

641	20 c. Type **143**	10	10
642	50 c. Housing construction	10	10
643	75 c. Children at play	20	10
644	1 s. Health and agriculture	35	20
645	2 s. 40 Hydro-electric power	80	45
646	3 s. Telecommunications	1·25	65

144 "Barbopsis devecchii"

1979. Fish. Multicoloured.

647	50 c. Type **144**	20	10
648	90 c. "Phreatichthys andruzzi"	50	20
649	1 s. "Uegitglanis zammaranoi"	65	35
650	2 s. 50 "Pardiglanis tarabinii"	1·10	65

145 Taleh Fortress

1980. 1st International Congress of Somali Studies.

652	**145** 2 s. 25 multicoloured	85	45
653	3 s. 50 multicoloured	1·10	65

146 Marka

1980. Landscapes (1st series). Multicoloured.

654	75 c. Type **146**	20	10
655	1 s. Gandershe	35	20
656	2 s. 30 Afgooye	85	35
657	3 s. 50 Mogadishu	1·10	65

See also Nos. 673/6.

147 Pygmy Puffback Flycatcher

148 Parabolic Antenna and Shepherd

1980. Birds. Multicoloured.

658	1 s. Type **147**	40	20
659	2 s. 25 Golden-winged grosbeak	1·00	35
660	5 s. Red-crowned bush shrike	1·60	1·10

1981. World Telecommunications Day.

662	**148** 1 s. multicoloured	40	20
663	– 3 s. blue, black and red	1·00	55
664	– 4 s. 60 multicoloured	1·40	90

DESIGNS: 3 s., 4 s. 60, Ribbons forming caduceus, I.T.U. and W.H.O. emblems.

149 F.A.O. Emblem and Stylised Wheat

150 Refugee Family

1981. World Food Day. Multicoloured.

665	75 c. Type **149**	20	15
666	3 s. 25 F.A.O. emblem on stylized field (horiz)	1·10	55
667	5 s. 50 Type **149**	2·00	95

1981. Refugee Aid.

668	**150** 2 s. + 50 c. multicoloured	70	45
669	6 s. 80 + 50 c. multicoloured	2·50	1·25

151 Mosques, Mecca and Medina

153 Footballer

1981. 1500th Anniv of Hejira.

671	**151** 1 s. 50 multicoloured	45	35
672	3 s. 80 multicoloured	1·50	80

1982. Landscapes (2nd series). As T **146**. Multicoloured.

673	2 s. 25 Balcad	80	45
674	4 s. Jowhar	1·40	90
675	5 s. 50 Golaleey	1·60	1·10
676	8 s. 30 Muqdisho	2·75	2·00

1982. World Cup Football Championship, Spain. Multicoloured.

677	1 s. Type **153**	35	20
678	1 s. 50 Footballer running to right	80	45
679	3 s. 25 Footballer running to left	1·60	1·00

154 I.T.U. Emblem

1982. I.T.U. Delegates' Conference, Nairobi.

681	**154** 75 c. multicoloured	20	15
682	3 s. 25 multicoloured	1·10	65
683	5 s. 50 multicoloured	2·00	1·10

155 "Bitis arietans somalica"

1982. Snakes. Multicoloured.

684	2 s. 80 Type **155**	1·10	45
685	3 s. 20 "Psammophis punctulatus trivirgatus"	1·60	65
686	4 s. 60 "Rhamphiophis oxyrhynchis rostratus"	2·25	1·10

156 Bacillus, Microscope and Dr. Robert Koch

1982. Centenary of Discovery of Tubercle Bacillus.

688	**156** 4 s. 60 + 60 c mult	1·10	1·10
689	5 s. 80 + 60 c. mult	1·40	1·40

157 Somali Woman

158 W.C.Y. Emblem

1982.

690	**157** 1 s. multicoloured	15	10
691	5 s. 20 multicoloured	80	35
692	5 s. 80 multicoloured	1·00	45
693	6 s. 40 multicoloured	1·10	60
694	9 s. 40 multicoloured	1·60	1·00
695	25 s. multicoloured	4·25	1·60

1983. World Communications Year.

696	**158** 5 s. 20 multicoloured	45	35
697	6 s. 40 multicoloured	85	40

159 View of Hamburg

1983. 2nd International Congress of Somali Studies, Hamburg. Multicoloured.

698	5 s. 20 Type **159**	85	65
699	6 s. 40 View of Hamburg (different)	1·25	1·00

160 Air Force Uniform

1983. Military Uniforms. Multicoloured.

700	3 s. 20 Type **160**	85	55
701	3 s. 20 Women's Auxiliary Corps	85	55
702	3 s. 20 Border Police	85	55
703	3 s. 20 People's Militia	85	55
704	3 s. 20 Infantry	85	55
705	3 s. 20 Custodial Corps	85	55
706	3 s. 20 Police Force	85	55
707	3 s. 20 Navy	85	55

161 Barawe

1983. Landscapes. Multicoloured.

708	2 s. 80 Type **161**	55	35
709	3 s. 20 Bur Hakaba	65	45
710	5 s. 50 Baydhabo	1·00	60
711	8 s. 60 Dooy Nuunaay	1·60	1·10

162 "Volutocorbis rosavittoriae"

1984. Shells. Multicoloured.

712	2 s. 80 Type **162**	80	40
713	3 s. 20 "Phalium bituberculosum"	1·25	50
714	5 s. 50 "Conus milne-edwardsi"	3·00	1·00

163 Running

165 Girl holding Shell to Ear

164 North African Crested Porcupine

1984. Olympic Games, Los Angeles. Multicoloured.

716	1 s. 50 Type **163**	35	20
717	3 s. Throwing the discus	80	45
718	8 s. High jumping	2·25	1·00

1984. Mammals. Multicoloured.

720	1 s. Type **164**	20	20
721	1 s. 50 White-tailed mongoose	35	20
722	2 s. Banded mongoose	55	35
723	4 s. Ratel	1·10	65

1984. 36th International Fair, Riccione.

725	**165**	5 s. 20 multicoloured	2·00	65
726		6 s. 40 multicoloured	2·75	1·10

166 Emblem within Winged Horse

1985. 40th Anniv of International Civil Aviation Organization.

727	**166**	3 s. multicoloured	65	35
728		6 s. 40 multicoloured	1·10	80

167 Aquila

169 Woman and Posthorn

168 Ras Kiambone

1985. Constellations. Illustrations from "The Book of Stars" by Abd al-Rahman al-Sufi. Multicoloured.

730	4 s. 30 Type **167**	55	20
731	11 s. Taurus	1·40	65
732	12 s. 50 Aries	1·60	80
733	13 s. Orion	2·00	1·10

1985. Architecture (1st series). Multicoloured.

734	2 s. Type **168**	20	20
735	6 s. 60 Hannassa	90	35
736	10 s. Mnarani	1·10	65
737	18 s. 60 Ras Kiambone (different)	2·25	1·25

See also Nos. 758/61.

1985. "Italia '85" Stamp Exhibition, Rome.

738	**169**	2 s. multicoloured	55	35
739		20 s. multicoloured	2·75	1·40

170 Persian Leaf-nosed Bat

1985. Bats. Multicoloured.

741	2 s. 50 Type **170**	55	35
742	4 s. 50 Heart-nosed false vampire bat	85	55
743	16 s. Wrinkle-lipped bat	2·25	1·40
744	18 s. Mozambique sheath-tailed bat	2·50	1·60

171 Kenyan and Somali Presidents, Solar System and Industry

1986. Trade Agreement with Kenya.

746	**171**	9 s. multicoloured	65	45
747		14 s. 50 multicoloured	1·60	65

172 Flower Arrangement

173 Seated Man holding Pottery Flask

1986. "Euroflora" International Flower Exhibition, Genoa. Multicoloured.

748	10 s. Type **172**	65	55
749	15 s. Flower arrangement (different)	1·60	1·10

1986. 3rd International Somali Studies Conference, Rome.

751	**173**	11 s. 35 multicoloured	65	45
752		20 s. multicoloured	1·60	90

174 Footballers

1986. World Cup Football Championship, Mexico. Footballing Scenes.

753	**174**	3 s. 60 multicoloured	35	20
754	–	4 s. 80 multicoloured	45	20
755	–	6 s. 80 multicoloured	90	45
756	–	22 s. 60 multicoloured	1·50	1·10

1986. Architecture (2nd series). As T **168**. Multicoloured.

758	10 s. Bulaxaar ruins	55	30
759	15 s. Saylac mosque	85	45
760	20 s. Saylac mosque (different)	1·40	65
761	31 s. Jasiiradaha Jawaay tomb	2·25	1·10

175 Rehabilitation Centre, Mogadishu

176 Runner

1987. Norwegian Red Cross in Somalia.

762	**175**	56 s. multicoloured	2·75	2·25

1987. "Olymphilex '87" Olympic Stamps Exhibition, Rome. Multicoloured.

764	20 s. Type **176**	85	55
765	40 s. Javelin thrower	2·00	1·10

177 Modern and Shanty Towns

178 Western Indian Ocean 160,000,000 Years Ago

1987. International Year of Shelter for the Homeless.

767	**177**	53 s. multicoloured	1·40	65
768		72 s. multicoloured	2·00	1·10

1987. "Geosom 87" Geological Evolution of Western Indian Ocean Symposium. Multicoloured.

769	10 s. Type **178**	20	10
770	20 s. 60,000,000 years ago	55	20
771	40 s. 15,000,000 years ago	90	45
772	50 s. Today	1·60	90

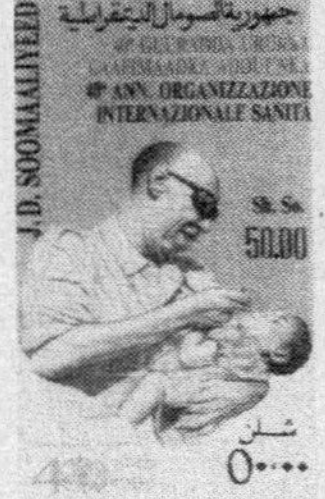

179 Baby receiving Oral Vaccination (Italian inscr)

180 Somali Hare

1988. 40th Anniv of W.H.O.

774	**179**	50 s. multicoloured	45	20
775		168 s. multicoloured (English inscr)	1·75	90

1989. Animals. Multicoloured.

776	75 s. Type **180**	45	20
777	198 s. African buffalo	1·10	35
778	200 s. Hamadryas baboon (horiz)	1·25	45
779	216 s. Hippopotamus (horiz)	1·60	65

181 Water Lily and Boys playing Football

1989. 20th Anniv of 21 October Revolution. Multicoloured.

781	70 s. Type **181**	35	20
782	100 s. Boys playing on swing	45	20
783	150 s. Girls on see-saw	90	35
784	300 s. Girl skipping and boy rolling hoop	1·60	65

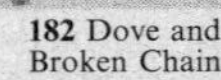

182 Dove and Broken Chain

183 Sun, Building and Scaffolding

1991. Liberation. (a) Type **182** (without opt).

785	**182**	150 s. multicoloured	85	35
786		300 s. multicoloured	1·60	80

(b) No. 785 additionally optd **"FREEDOM"**.

787	**182**	150 s. multicoloured	3·00	2·75

1991. Reconstruction.

788	**183**	70 s. multicoloured	35	20
789		100 s. multicoloured	55	35
790		150 s. multicoloured	80	45
791		300 s. multicoloured	1·60	65

AIR EXPRESS STAMP

E 61 Young Gazelles

1958.
E330 E 61 1 s. 70 c. red and black . . 85 85

EXPRESS LETTER STAMPS

1923. Express Letter stamps of Italy surch **Somalia Italiana** and value.
E44 E 12 30 b. on 60 c. red . . . 11·00 12·00
E45 E 13 60 b. on 1 l. 20 red & bl 16·00 17·00

E 17

1924.
E60 E 17 30 b. brown and red . . 5·00 6·00
E61 60 b. red and blue . . . 7·00 8·50
No. E61 is inscr "EXPRES".

1926. Nos. E60/1 surch.
E104 70 c. on 30 b. brown & red 5·50 6·00
E106 1 l. 25 on 30 b. brown & red 7·00 8·50
E105 2 l. 50 on 60 b. red & blue 5·00 7·50

E 44 Grant's Gazelle

1950.
E255 E 44 40 c. turquoise . . . . 1·25 60
E256 80 c. violet . . . . . . 1·75 1·75

E 54 "Gardenia Lutea Fresen"

1955.
E291 E 54 50 c. yellow, grn & lilac 30 30
E292 – 1 s. red, green & blue . 55 55
FLOWER: 1 s. "Eryhrina Melanocantha Taub".

PARCEL POST STAMPS

Parcel Post stamps of Italy optd or surch on each half of stamp.

1920. Optd **SOMALIA ITALIANA**.
P23 P 53 5 c. brown . . . . 1·40 30
P24 10 c. blue . . . . 1·75 30
P25 20 c. black . . . . 48·00 6·00
P26 25 c. red . . . . 4·50 50
P27 50 c. orange . . . . . . 38·00 4·50
P28 1 l. violet . . . . . . 16·00 75
P29 2 l. green . . . . 19·00 1·25
P30 3 l. yellow . . . . . . 21·00 2·25
P31 4 l. grey . . . . 23·00 6·00
P89 10 l. purple . . . . . . 10·00 4·50
P90 12 l. brown . . . . . . 10·00 4·50
P91 15 l. olive . . . . . . 10·00 4·50
P92 20 l. purple . . . . . . 10·00 4·50

1922. Optd **SOMALIA**.
P32 P 53 25 c. red . . . . 19·00 5·00
P33 50 c. orange . . . . . . 24·00 1·50
P34 1 l. violet . . . . . . 24·00 1·50
P35 2 l. green . . . . 28·00 2·00
P36 3 l. yellow . . . . . . 35·00 5·00
P37 4 l. grey . . . . 35·00 5·00

1923. Surch **SOMALIA ITALIANA** and value.
P44 P 53 3 b. on 5 c. brown . . . 1·75 40
P45 5 b. on 5 c. brown . . . 1·75 40
P46 10 b. on 10 c. blue . . . 1·75 40
P47 25 b. on 25 c. red . . . 7·00 60
P48 50 b. on 50 c. orange . . 12·00 1·10
P49 1 r. on 1 l. violet . . . . 17·00 1·50
P50 2 r. on 2 l. green . . . . 21·00 2·50
P51 3 r. on 3 l. yellow . . . 24·00 4·50
P52 4 r. on 4 l. grey . . . . 26·00 7·00

1928. Optd **SOMALIA ITALIANA**.
P111 P 92 5 c. brown 60 80
P112 10 c. blue 80 80
P126 25 c. red . . . . 45·00 6·00
P114 30 c. blue 20 40
P116 60 c. red 20 40
P127 1 l. violet . . . . . . 19·00 2·00
P128 2 l. green . . . . 21·00 2·00
P119 3 l. yellow 70 80
P120 4 l. black . . . . 70 1·00
P121 10 l. mauve . . . . . . £200 12·00
P122 20 l. purple . . . . . . £200 12·00

P 44

1950.
P255 P 44 1 c. red 45 45
P256 3 c. slate 45 45
P257 5 c. purple 45 45
P258 10 c. orange 45 45
P259 20 c. brown 45 45
P260 50 c. turquoise 70 70
P261 1 s. violet . . . . . . 3·50 3·50
P262 2 s. brown . . . . . . 4·75 4·75
P263 3 s. blue . . . . 5·00 5·00
Unused prices are for complete stamps, used prices are for half stamps except in the case of Nos. P255/63.

POSTAGE DUE STAMPS

Postage Due stamps of Italy optd or surch.

1906. Optd **Somalia Italiana Meridionale**.
D17 D 12 5 c. purple and orange 3·00 16·00
D18 10 c. purple & orange 22·00 19·00
D19 20 c. purple & orange 14·00 19·00
D20 30 c. purple & orange 11·00 19·00
D21 40 c. purple & orange 48·00 24·00
D22 50 c. purple & orange 24·00 24·00
D23 60 c. purple & orange 19·00 24·00
D24 1 l. purple and blue . . £300 80·00
D25 2 l. purple and blue . . £275 90·00
D26 5 l. purple and blue . . £275 90·00
D27 10 l. purple and blue . 65·00 £130

1909. Optd **Somalia Italiana**.
D28 D 12 5 c. purple and orange 2·00 4·50
D29 10 c. purple & orange 2·00 4·50
D30 20 c. purple & orange 3·25 9·00
D31 30 c. purple & orange 9·00 15·00
D32 40 c. purple & orange 9·00 15·00
D33 50 c. purple & orange 9·00 15·00
D34 60 c. purple & orange 14·00 24·00
D35 1 l. purple and blue . . 32·00 18·00
D36 2 l. purple and blue . . 38·00 55·00
D37 5 l. purple and blue . . 48·00 70·00
D38 10 l. purple and blue . 8·00 28·00

1923. Stamps without figures of value, surch **Somalia Italiana** and value in "besa" or "rupia" in figures and words.
D49 D 12 1 b. black and orange 75 1·75
D50 2 b. black and orange 75 1·75
D51 3 b. black and orange 75 1·75
D52 5 b. black and orange 85 1·75
D53 10 b. black and orange 85 1·75
D54 20 b. black and orange 85 1·75
D55 40 b. black and orange 85 1·75
D56 1 r. black and blue . . 1·25 2·50

1926. Optd **Somalia Italiana** and surch with figures only.
D76 5 c. black and orange . . . 9·00 4·50
D77 10 c. black and orange . . . 7·50 4·50
D78 20 c. black and orange . . . 9·00 4·50
D79 30 c. black and orange . . . 9·00 4·50
D80 40 c. black and orange . . . 9·00 4·50
D81 50 c. black and orange . . . 12·00 4·50
D82 60 c. black and orange . . . 12·00 4·50
D83 1 l. black and blue . . . . 17·00 5·50
D84 2 l. black and blue . . . . 20·00 5·50
D85 5 l. black and blue . . . . 20·00 5·50
D86 10 l. black and blue . . . . 20·00 5·50

1934. Optd **SOMALIA ITALIANA**.
D187 D 141 5 c. brown . . . . . 40 1·60
D188 10 c. blue . . . . . 40 1·60
D189 20 c. red . . . . . 2·50 2·50
D190 25 c. green . . . . 2·50 2·50
D191 30 c. orange . . . . 5·00 5·50
D192 40 c. brown . . . . 5·00 6·00
D193 50 c. violet . . . . 6·50 1·40
D194 60 c. blue . . . . . 10·00 12·00
D195 D 142 1 l. orange . . . . . 13·00 3·75
D196 2 l. green . . . . . 20·00 17·00
D197 5 l. violet . . . . . 21·00 26·00
D198 10 l. blue . . . . . 21·00 32·00
D199 20 l. red . . . . . . 24·00 38·00

D 44

1950.
D255 D 44 1 c. slate 20 20
D256 2 c. blue 20 20
D257 5 c. turquoise 20 20
D258 10 c. purple 20 20
D259 40 c. violet . . . . . 1·10 1·10
D260 1 s. brown . . . . . 2·00 2·00

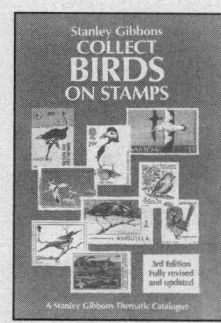

SOUTH KASAI Pt. 14

100 centimes = 1 franc

Region of Zaire around the town of Bakwanga. The area was declared autonomous in 1960, during the upheaval following independence, but returned to the control of the central government in Oct. 1962.

Various stamps of Belgian Congo were overprinted "ETAT AUTONOME DU SUD-KASAI" and some surcharged in addition with new values. These were put on sale at the Philatelic Bureau in Brussels and were also valid for use in South Kasai but no supplies were sent out.

1 Leopard's Head and "V"

2 A. D. Kalonji

1961.
1 **1** 1 f. multicoloured 10 10
2 1 f. 50 multicoloured 10 10
3 3 f. 50 multicoloured 15 15
4 8 f. multicoloured 25 25
5 10 f. multicoloured 30 30

1961.
6 **2** 6 f. 50 brown, blue and black . 20 20
7 9 f. lt brown, brown & blk . . 25 25
8 14 f. 50 brown, green & blk . . 40 40
9 20 f. multicoloured . . . . . 45 1·45

SOUTH RUSSIA Pt. 10

Stamps of various anti-Bolshevist forces and temporary governments in S. Russia after the revolution.

100 kopeks = 1 rouble

A. KUBAN TERRITORY: COSSACK GOVERNMENT

1918. Arms type of Russia surch. Imperf or perf.
8 **22** 25 k. on 1 k. orange 25 45
2 50 k. on 2 k. green 15 25
23 70 k. on 1 k. orange 30 55
10 70 k. on 5 k. red 35 60
11 1 r. on 3 k. red 20 50
13 **23** 3 r. on 4 k. red . . . . . . 7·50 11·00
14 10 r. on 4 k. red . . . . . . 4·00 5·00
15 **10** 10 r. on 15 k. blue & purple 70 1·10
16 **22** 25 r. on 3 k. red . . . . . . 4·00 3·00
17 25 r. on 7 k. blue . . . . . 30·00 60·00
18 **10** 25 r. on 14 k. red and blue . 70·00 £100
19 25 r. on 25 k. mauve & grn . 35·00 65·00

1919. Postal Savings Bank stamps of Russia surch.
20 10 r. on 1 k. red on buff . . . 30·00 70·00
21 10 r. on 5 k. green on buff . . 32·00 70·00
22 10 r. on 10 k. brown on buff . 75·00 £225

B. DON TERRITORY: COSSACK GOVERNMENT

1919. Arms type of Russia surch in figures only. Imperf or perf.
25 **22** 25 k. on 1 k. orange 20 45
29 25 k. on 2 k. green 20 40
30 25 k. on 3 k. red 25 60
31 **23** 25 k. on 4 k. red 20 45
32 **22** 50 k. on 7 k. blue . . . . . 1·75 2·75

10 T. Ermak (16th century Cossack Ataman)

13

1919. Currency stamp with arms and seven-line print on back used for postage.
33 **10** 20 k. green . . . . 16·00 £100

C. CRIMEA: REGIONAL GOVERNMENT

1919. Arms type of Russia surch **35 Kon**. Imperf.
34 **22** 35 k. on 1 k. orange 15 40

1919. Currency and postage stamp. Arms and inscription on back. Imperf.
35 **13** 50 k. brown on buff . . . . 13·00 16·00

D. SOUTH RUSSIA: GOVERNMENT OF GENERAL DENIKIN

1919. Nos. G6 and G10 of Ukraine surch in figs.
36 **G 1** 35 k. on 10 s. brown . . . 3·75 14·00
37 **G 5** 70 k. on 50 s. red . . . . 13·00 40·00

15

16

1919. Imperf or perf.
38 **15** 5 k. yellow 10 15
39 10 k. green 10 15
40 15 k. red 10 15
41 35 k. blue 10 15
42 70 k. blue 10 15
43 **16** 1 r. red and brown 15 35
44 2 r. yellow and lilac 35 55
45 3 r. green and brown 35 60
46 5 r. violet and blue . . . . 1·00 1·50
47 7 r. pink and green . . . . 80 1·75
48 10 r. grey and red . . . . . 1·50 2·00
Higher values similar to Type **16** are bogus.

E. SOUTH RUSSIA: GOVERNMENT OF GENERAL WRANGEL

5
пять
рублей.
(17)

ЮГЪ
РОССІИ.
100
рублей.
(18)

1920. Crimea issue. Surch with T **17**. (a) On Arms types of Russia. Imperf or perf.
52 **22** 5 r. on 5 k. red . . . . . . 1·00 3·75
54 **14** 5 r. on 20 k. red and blue . 1·75 3·75

(b) On No. 41 of South Russia.
55 **15** 5 r. on 35 k. blue . . . . . 4·50 12·00

1920. Arms type of Russia surch with T **18**.
56 **22** 100 r. on 1 k. orange . . . 1·75

SOUTHERN YEMEN Pt. 19

PEOPLE'S REPUBLIC

Independent Republic comprising the areas formerly known as Aden, the Aden States and the South Arabian Federation.

From 30 November, 1970, the country was renamed The Peoples Democratic Republic of Yemen.

1968. 1000 fils = 1 dinar

1968. Stamps of South Arabian Federation optd **PEOPLE'S REPUBLIC OF SOUTHERN YEMEN** in English and Arabic, in four lines (Nos. 1/10) or three lines (Nos. 11/14) and bold bar.
1 **2** 5 f. blue 10 10
2 10 f. lavender 10 10
3 15 f. green 10 10
4 20 f. green 15 10
5 25 f. brown 15 10
6 30 f. bistre 20 10
7 35 f. brown 25 20
8 50 f. red 30 25
9 65 f. green 35 30
10 75 f. red 45 35
11 **3** 100 f. multicoloured 60 40
12 250 f. multicoloured . . . . 1·40 90
13 500 f. multicoloured . . . . 2·50 1·90
14 1 d. multicoloured . . . . 6·50 4·00

3 National Flag across Globe

1968. Independence. Multicoloured.
15 10 f. Type 3 . . . . 10 10
16 15 f. Revolutionary (vert) . . . 10 10
17 50 f. Aden harbour 30 30
18 100 f. Cotton-picking 70 60

4 Girl Guides

1968. Aden Girl Guides' Movement.
19 – 10 f. brown and blue 20 10
20 – 25 f. blue and brown 35 15
21 **4** 50 f. blue, brown & yellow . 70 40
DESIGNS—HORIZ: 10 f. Guides around camp-fire. VERT: 25 f. Brownies.

5 Revolutionary Soldier

1968. Revolution Day.
22 **5** 20 f. brown and blue 20 15
23 – 30 f. brown and green . . . 25 20
24 – 100 f. red and yellow 75 60
DESIGNS—HORIZ: 30 f. Radfan Mountains ("where first martyr fell"). VERT. 100 f. Open book and torch ("Freedom, Socialism and Unity").

6 Sculptured Plaque ("Assyrian influence")

1968. Antiquities.
25 – 5 f. yellow and green 10 10
26 – 35 f. blue and purple 30 20
27 **6** 50 f. buff and blue 50 30
28 – 65 f. green and purple 60 45
DESIGNS—VERT: 5 f. King Yusdqil Far'am of Ausan (statue); 35 f. Sculptured figure ("African-inspired"). HORIZ: 65 f. Bull's head ("Moon God").

7 Martyrs' Monument, Aden

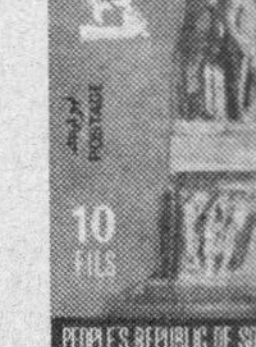

8 Albert Thomas Memorial, Geneva

1969. Martyrs' Day.
29 **7** 15 f. multicoloured 10 10
30 35 f. multicoloured 25 20
31 100 f. multicoloured 60 45

1969. 50th Anniv of I.L.O.
32 **8** 10 f. sepia, black and green . 10 10
33 25 f. sepia, black and mauve . 25 20

9 Teacher and Class

1969. International Literacy Day.
34 **9** 35 f. multicoloured 30 25
35 100 f. multicoloured 65 50

10 Mahatma Gandhi

11 Yemeni Family

1969. Birth Centenary of Mahatma Gandhi.
36 **10** 35 f. purple and blue . . . . 1·00 35

1969. Family Day.
37 **11** 25 f. multicoloured 25 15
38 75 f. multicoloured 60 45

12 U.N. Headquarters, New York

1969. United Nations Day.
39 **12** 20 f. multicoloured 15 10
40 65 f. multicoloured 50 35

13 Map and Flag

1969. 2nd Anniv of Independence. Multicoloured.
41 15 f. Type **13** 12 10
42 35 f. Type **13** 25 20
43 40 f. Bulldozers 30 25
44 50 f. As No. 43 . . . . 35 30

14 Arab League Flag, Emblem and Map

1970. 25th Anniv of Arab League.
45 **14** 35 f. multicoloured 25 25

15 Lenin

16 Palestinian Guerrilla

1970. Birth Centenary of Lenin.
46 **15** 75 f. multicoloured 70 50

1970. Palestine Day. Multicoloured.
47 15 f. Type **16** 25 10
48 35 f. Guerrilla and attack on airliner 90 30
49 50 f. Guerrillas and Palestinan flag (horiz) 85 40

17 New Headquarters Building, Berne

1970. Inauguration of New U.P.U. Headquarters Building, Berne.
50 **17** 15 f. green and orange . . . 15 10
51 65 f. red and buff 40 30

18 Girl with Pitcher

1970. National Costumes. Multicoloured.
52 10 f. Type 18 . . . . 25 10
53 15 f. Woman in veil 35 15
54 20 f. Girl in burnous 45 15
55 50 f. Three Yemeni men . . . 75 30

19 Dromedary and Calf

1970. Fauna. Multicoloured.
56 15 f. Type 19 . . . 25 20
57 25 f. Goats . . . 40 30
58 35 f. Arabian oryx and kid . . . 75 60
59 65 f. Socotran dwarf cows . . . 1·00 85

20 Torch and Flags

1970. 7th Revolution Day. Multicoloured.
60 25 f. Type 20 . . . 20 15
61 35 f. National Front H.Q. (57 × 27 mm) . . . 40 30
62 50 f. Farmer and soldier (42 × 25 mm) . . . 50 40

21 U.N. H.Q., New York, and Emblem

1970. 25th Anniv of United Nations.
63 **21** 10 f. orange and blue . . . 10 10
64 65 f. red and blue . . . 50 40

For later issues see **YEMEN PEOPLE'S DEMOCRATIC REPUBLIC**.

SPAIN Pt. 9

A kingdom in S.W. Europe; a republic between 1873 and 1874, and from 1931 until 1939.

1850. $8\frac{1}{2}$ (later 8) cuartos = 1 real
1866. 80 cuartos = 100 centimos de escudo = 1 escudo
1867. 1000 milesimas = 100 centimos de escudo = 80 cuartos = 1 escudo
1872. 100 centimos = 1 peseta

1 **2** **3**
Queen Isabella II

1850. Imperf.
2 **1** 6 c. black . . . £225 15·00
3 12 c. lilac . . . £1500 £180
4 **2** 5 r. red . . . £1200 £180
5 6 r. blue . . . £2000 £550
6 10 r. green . . . £2750 £1300

1851. Imperf.
9 **3** 6 c. black . . . £150 2·50
10 12 c. lilac . . . £2000 £130
11 2 r. red . . . £9000 £5000
12 5 r. red . . . £1500 £160
13 6 r. blue . . . £2250 £650
14 10 r. green . . . £1800 £350

4 **5** **7** Arms of Castile and Leon

1852. Imperf.
16 **4** 6 c. red . . . £200 9·00
17 12 c. purple . . . £1200 £100
18 2 r. red . . . £8000 £3000
19 5 r. green . . . £1200 95·00
20 6 r. blue . . . £2250 £350

1853. Imperf.
22 **5** 6 c. red . . . £225 1·50
23 12 c. purple . . . £1100 85·00
24 2 r. orange . . . £7500 £2500
25 5 r. green . . . £1000 85·00
26 6 r. blue . . . £1800 £300

1854. Imperf.
32 **7** 2 c. green . . . £1200 £300
33 4 c. red . . . £180 1·50
34 6 c. red . . . £180 1·40
35 1 r. blue . . . £1600 £200
36 2 r. orange . . . £750 80·00
37 5 r. green . . . £800 80·00
38 6 r. blue . . . £1200 £200

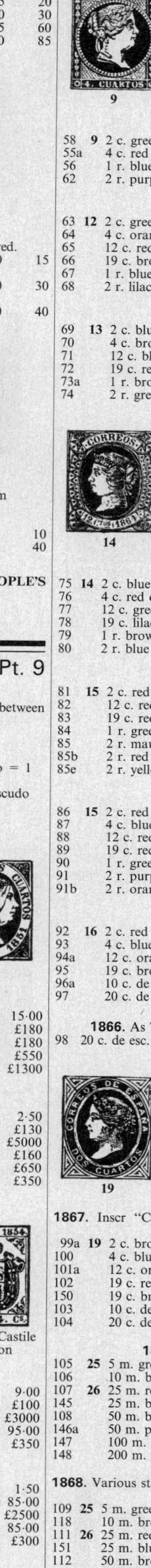

9 **12** **13**

1855. Imperf.
58 **9** 2 c. green . . . £250 25·00
55a 4 c. red . . . 3·50 30
56 1 r. blue . . . 14·00 9·00
62 2 r. purple . . . 42·00 15·00

1860. Imperf.
63 **12** 2 c. green on green . . . £200 14·00
64 4 c. orange on green . . . 25·00 60
65 12 c. red on buff . . . £200 10·00
66 19 c. brown on brown . . . £1500 £850
67 1 r. blue on green . . . £110 7·00
68 2 r. lilac on lilac . . . £180 6·50

1862. Imperf.
69 **13** 2 c. blue on yellow . . . 24·00 9·00
70 4 c. brown on brown . . . 1·50 45
71 12 c. blue on red . . . 30·00 8·00
72 19 c. red on lilac . . . £110 £130
73a 1 r. brown on yellow . . . 35·00 16·00
74 2 r. green on red . . . 23·00 10·00

14 **15** **16**

1864. Imperf.
75 **14** 2 c. blue on lilac . . . 30·00 12·00
76 4 c. red on red . . . 1·75 60
77 12 c. green on red . . . 30·00 10·00
78 19 c. lilac on lilac . . . £120 £140
79 1 r. brown on green . . . £110 60·00
80 2 r. blue on red . . . 30·00 9·00

1865. Imperf.
81 **15** 2 c. red . . . £160 19·00
82 12 c. red and blue . . . £250 17·00
83 19 c. red and brown . . . £900 £425
84 1 r. green . . . £225 45·00
85 2 r. mauve . . . £220 28·00
85b 2 r. red . . . £275 50·00
85e 2 r. yellow . . . £250 40·00

1865. Perf.
86 **15** 2 c. red . . . £275 65·00
87 4 c. blue . . . 30·00 75
88 12 c. red and blue . . . £350 40·00
89 19 c. red and brown . . . £2250 £1400
90 1 r. green . . . £1000 £275
91 2 r. purple . . . £650 £150
91b 2 r. orange . . . £650 £175

1866. Perf.
92 **16** 2 c. red . . . £140 15·00
93 4 c. blue . . . 25·00 70
94a 12 c. orange . . . £130 10·00
95 19 c. brown . . . £550 £250
96a 10 c. de esc. green . . . £175 16·00
97 20 c. de esc. lilac . . . £130 14·00

1866. As T **14**, but dated 1866, and perf.
98 20 c. de esc. lilac . . . £550 40·00

19 **25** **26**

1867. Inscr "CORREOS DE ESPANA". Various frames.
99a **19** 2 c. brown . . . £225 24·00
100 4 c. blue . . . 20·00 70
101a 12 c. orange . . . £130 5·00
102 19 c. red . . . £750 £250
150 19 c. brown . . . £1300 £400
103 10 c. de esc. green . . . £140 15·00
104 20 c. de esc. lilac . . . 65·00 6·00

1867. Various frames.
105 **25** 5 m. green . . . 26·00 9·00
106 10 m. brown . . . 26·00 7·50
107 **26** 25 m. red and blue . . . £140 15·00
145 25 m. blue . . . £190 12·00
108 50 m. brown . . . 14·00 60
146a 50 m. purple . . . 17·00 50
147 100 m. brown . . . £300 45·00
148 200 m. green . . . £120 9·00

1868. Various stamps optd **HABILITADO POR LA NACION**.
109 **25** 5 m. green . . . 16·00 5·00
118 10 m. brown . . . 12·00 5·50
111 **26** 25 m. red and blue . . . 35·00 12·00
151 25 m. blue . . . 26·00 9·00
112 50 m. brown . . . 6·50 4·50
152 50 m. purple . . . 7·00 3·50
153 100 m. brown . . . 75·00 25·00
154 200 m. green . . . 24·00 8·00
113 **19** 10 c. de esc. green . . . 24·00 10·00
114 20 c. de esc. lilac . . . 27·00 7·50
125 12 c. orange . . . 32·00 10·00
116 19 c. red . . . £350 £150
156 19 c. brown . . . £650 £170

36 **38a** **38**

1870.
172 **36** 1 m. brown on buff . . . 7·00 6·00
173 2 m. black on buff . . . 8·00 7·50
174 4 m. brown . . . 15·00 12·00
175 10 m. red . . . 18·00 5·50
176 25 m. mauve . . . 40·00 7·00
177 50 m. blue . . . 11·00 45
178 100 m. brown . . . 27·00 6·00
179 200 m. brown . . . 27·00 6·00
180 400 m. green . . . £180 22·00
181 12 c. red . . . £180 6·50
182 19 c. green . . . £275 £160
183 1 esc. 600 m. lilac . . . £800 £400
184 2 esc. blue . . . £650 £225

1872.
185 **38a** $\frac{1}{4}$ c. blue . . . 2·00 2·00
186 **38** $\frac{1}{4}$ c. green . . . 1·10 1·10
187 **38a** $\frac{1}{4}$ c. green . . . 15 10

1872. As T **25**, but currency in centavos de peseta.
192 **25** 2 c. lilac . . . 20·00 8·50
193 5 c. green . . . £110 45·00

40 King Amadeo **41** **42** Allegorical Figure of Peace

1872.
194 **40** 5 c. red . . . 20·00 6·00
195b 6 c. blue . . . £100 18·00
196 10 c. lilac . . . £225 90·00
197 10 c. blue . . . 6·50 45
199 12 c. lilac . . . 14·00 1·75
200 20 c. lilac . . . 85·00 30·00
201 25 c. brown . . . 35·00 7·00
202 40 c. brown . . . 60·00 7·00
203a 50 c. green . . . 85·00 7·00
204 **41** 1 p. lilac . . . 80·00 25·00
205 4 p. brown . . . £400 £275
206 10 p. green . . . £1200 £950

1873.
207 **42** 2 c. orange . . . 13·00 6·00
208 5 c. red . . . 32·00 6·00
209 10 c. green . . . 8·00 45
210 20 c. black . . . 75·00 20·00
211 25 c. brown . . . 28·00 7·00
212 40 c. purple . . . 32·00 7·50
213 50 c. blue . . . 12·00 7·50
214 1 p. lilac . . . 42·00 17·00
215 4 p. brown . . . £450 £275
216 10 p. purple . . . £1300 £1000

43 Allegorical Figure of Justice **44** **45** King Alfonso XII

1874.
217 **43** 2 c. yellow . . . 23·00 8·00
218a 5 c. mauve . . . 32·00 6·50
219 10 c. blue . . . 10·00 40
220 20 c. green . . . £120 35·00
221 25 c. brown . . . 35·00 7·50
222a 40 c. mauve . . . £275 9·00
223 50 c. orange . . . 80·00 9·00
224 1 p. green . . . 65·00 18·00
225 4 p. red . . . £400 £250
226 10 p. black . . . £1800 £1100

1874.
227 **44** 10 c. brown . . . 18·00 90

1875.
228 **45** 2 c. brown . . . 18·00 6·50
229 5 c. lilac . . . 45·00 8·50
230 10 c. blue . . . 8·00 45
231 20 c. orange . . . £200 60·00
232 25 c. red . . . 40·00 6·50
233 40 c. brown . . . 80·00 30·00
234 50 c. mauve . . . £110 21·00
235 1 p. black . . . £140 40·00
236 4 p. green . . . £275 £190
237 10 p. blue . . . £900 £750

46 **48** **49**

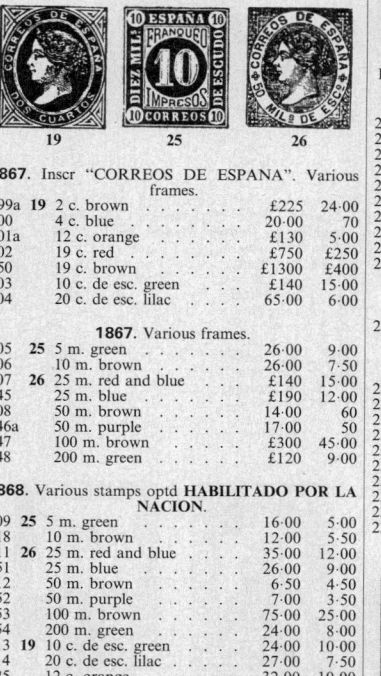

1876.
238 **46** 5 c. brown . . . 10·00 2·40
239 10 c. blue . . . 2·75 45
240 20 c. green . . . 18·00 8·50
241 25 c. brown . . . 7·00 3·00
242 40 c. brown . . . 50·00 26·00
243 50 c. green . . . 12·00 4·75
244 1 p. blue . . . 18·00 7·50
245 4 p. purple . . . 35·00 26·00
246 10 p. red . . . £100 90·00

1878.
253 **48** 2 c. mauve . . . 20·00 7·50
254 5 c. yellow . . . 32·00 7·50
255 10 c. brown . . . 7·00 40
256 20 c. black . . . £100 70·00
257 25 c. olive . . . 20·00 1·75
258 40 c. brown . . . £120 80·00
259 50 c. green . . . 70·00 7·50
260 1 p. grey . . . 60·00 18·00
261 4 p. violet . . . £120 70·00
262 10 p. blue . . . £225 £200

1879.
263 **49** 2 c. black . . . 5·00 50
264 5 c. green . . . 10·00 95
265 10 c. pink . . . 9·50 40
266 20 c. brown . . . 85·00 12·00
267 25 c. lilac . . . 11·00 40
268 40 c. brown . . . 23·00 4·25
269 50 c. yellow . . . 75·00 4·25
270 1 p. red . . . 75·00 1·90
271 4 p. grey . . . £325 23·00
272 10 p. bistre . . . £1000 £180

50 **51** **52**
King Alfonso XIII

1882.
273 **50** 15 c. pink . . . 7·50 30
273b 15 c. yellow . . . 22·00 70
274 30 c. mauve . . . £180 5·50
275 75 c. violet . . . £180 5·50

1889.
276 **51** 2 c. green . . . 4·25 30
289 2 c. black . . . 20·00 3·50
277 5 c. blue . . . 7·00 15
290 5 c. green . . . 60·00 1·00
278 10 c. brown . . . 10·00 15
291 10 c. red . . . £140 3·25
279 15 c. brown . . . 3·00 15
280 20 c. green . . . 27·00 3·00
281 25 c. blue . . . 9·00 15
282 30 c. grey . . . 45·00 2·00
283 40 c. brown . . . 42·00 1·90
284 50 c. red . . . 42·00 1·00
285 75 c. orange . . . 95·00 2·10
286 1 p. purple . . . 32·00 30
287 4 p. red . . . £375 21·00
288 10 p. red . . . £550 50·00

For 15 c. yellow see No. O289.

1900.
292a **52** 2 c. brown . . . 2·40 15
293 5 c. green . . . 5·00 15
294 10 c. red . . . 7·00 15
295 15 c. black . . . 13·00 15
296 15 c. mauve . . . 10·00 15
297 15 c. violet . . . 4·75 15
298 20 c. black . . . 24·00 85
299 25 c. blue . . . 4·50 15
300 30 c. green . . . 26·00 30
301 40 c. bistre . . . 80·00 3·00
302 40 c. pink . . . £170 1·50
303 50 c. blue . . . 27·00 30
304 1 p. purple . . . 25·00 30
305 4 p. purple . . . £170 11·00
306 10 p. orange . . . £160 45·00

54 Quixote setting out

1905. Tercentenary of Publication of Cervantes' "Don Quixote".
307 **54** 5 c. green . . . 1·00 70
308 – 10 c. red . . . 2·00 1·00
309 – 15 c. violet . . . 2·00 1·00
310 – 25 c. blue . . . 5·00 1·25
311 – 30 c. green . . . 30·00 5·50
312 – 40 c. red . . . 65·00 15·00
313 – 50 c. grey . . . 14·00 4·00
314 – 1 p. red . . . £200 55·00
315 – 4 p. violet . . . 80·00 55·00
316 – 10 p. orange . . . £130 85·00

DESIGNS: 10 c. Quixote attacking windmill; 15 c. Meeting country girls; 25 c. Sancho Panza tossed in a blanket; 30 c. Don Quixote knighted by innkeeper; 40 c. Tilting at the flock of sheep; 50 c. On the wooden horse; 1 p. Adventure with lions; 4 p. In the bullock-cart; 10 p. The enchanted lady.

64

66

67 G.P.O., Madrid

1909.

329 64 2 c. brown 40 10
330 5 c. green . . . . 1·10 10
331 10 c. red . . . . 1·40 10
332 15 c. violet . . . . 7·00 10
343 15 c. yellow . . . . 3·50 10
321 20 c. green . . . . 27·00 7·00
335 20 c. violet . . . . 27·00 10
336 25 c. blue . . . . 2·75 10
337 30 c. green . . . . 7·00 10
338 40 c. pink . . . . 11·00 20
339 50 c. blue . . . . 9·00 15
340 1 p. red . . . . 24·00 20
341 4 p. purple . . . . 65·00 6·00
342 10 p. orange . . . . 75·00 12·00

1920. Air. Optd **CORREO AEREO**.

353 64 5 c. green . . . . 1·00 50
354 10 c. red . . . . 1·50 70
355 25 c. blue . . . . 2·00 90
356 50 c. blue . . . . 10·00 3·50
357 1 p. red . . . . 30·00 14·00

1920. Imperf.

358 66 1 c. green 20 10

1920. U.P.U. Congress, Madrid.

361 67 1 c. black and blue . . . 20 10
362 2 c. black and brown . . . 20 10
363 5 c. black and green . . . 80 70
364 10 c. black and red . . . 80 60
365 15 c. black and yellow . . . 1·25 90
366 20 c. black and violet . . . 1·75 90
367 25 c. black and blue . . . 1·90 1·90
368 30 c. black and green . . . 5·00 3·00
369 40 c. black and red . . . 20·00 4·50
370 50 c. black and blue . . . 23·00 15·00
371 1 p. black and red . . . 25·00 12·00
372 4 p. black and brown . . . 75·00 50·00
373 10 p. black and orange . . . £150 £100

68

69

1922.

374 68 2 c. green 35 10
375 5 c. purple . . . . 3·25 10
376 5 c. red . . . . 1·50 10
377 10 c. red . . . . 1·50 60
378a 10 c. green . . . . 1·50 10
380 15 c. blue . . . . 6·00 10
382 20 c. violet . . . . 3·00 10
383a 25 c. red . . . . 3·00 10
387 30 c. brown . . . . 9·00 15
388 40 c. blue . . . . 3·50 10
389 50 c. orange . . . . 14·00 10
391 69 1 p. grey . . . . 13·00 10
392 4 p. red . . . . 55·00 3·00
393 10 p. brown . . . . 25·00 9·00

70 Princesses Maria Cristina and Beatriz

71 King Alfonso XIII

1926. Red Cross.

394 70 1 c. black . . . . 1·50 1·00
395 – 2 c. blue . . . . 1·50 1·00
396 – 5 c. purple . . . . 3·00 2·00
397 – 10 c. green . . . . 3·00 2·00
398 70 15 c. blue . . . . 1·00 85
399 – 20 c. violet . . . . 1·00 85
400 71 25 c. red 25 20
401 70 30 c. green . . . . 24·00 22·00
402 – 40 c. blue . . . . 15·00 12·00
403 – 50 c. orange . . . . 5·00 12·00
404 – 1 p. grey . . . . 1·00 50
405 – 4 p. red 50 50
406 71 10 p. brown 75 75

DESIGNS—VERT: 2, 50 c. Queen Victoria Eugenie as nurse; 5, 40 c., 4 p. Queen Victoria Eugenie; 10, 20 c., 1 p. Prince of Asturias.

75 Flying Boat "Plus Ultra"

76 Route Map and Gallarza and Loriga's Breguet 19A2 Biplane

1926. Air. Red Cross and Trans-Atlantic and Madrid–Manila Flights.

407 75 5 c. violet and black . . . 1·50 1·75
408 10 c. black and blue . . . 1·50 1·75
409 76 15 c. blue and orange . . . 20 15
410 20 c. red and green . . . 20 15
411 75 25 c. black and red . . . 20 15
412 76 30 c. brown and blue . . . 20 15
413 40 c. green and brown . . . 20 15
414 75 50 c. black and red . . . 20 15
415 1 p. green and black . . . 2·25 1·75
416 76 4 p. red and yellow . . . 60·00 50·00

1927. 25th Anniv of Coronation. Red Cross stamps of 1926 optd either **17-V 1902 17-V 1927 A XIII**, or same dates and **ALFONSO XIII** and laurel wreath.

417 70 1 c. black . . . . 3·50 3·00
418 – 2 c. blue . . . . 6·00 4·75
419 – 5 c. purple . . . . 1·50 1·50
420 – 10 c. green . . . . 40·00 38·00
421 70 15 c. blue . . . . 1·25 1·00
422 – 20 c. violet . . . . 2·25 1·90
423 71 25 c. red 35 30
424 70 30 c. green 70 60
425 – 40 c. blue 70 55
426 – 50 c. orange 70 55
427 – 1 p. grey . . . . 1·10 1·00
428 – 4 p. red . . . . 6·00 5·00
429 71 10 p. brown . . . . 25·00 25·00

1927. Red Cross stamps of 1926 optd **17-V-1902 17-V-1927 ALFONSO XIII** and surch also.

430 – 3 c. on 2 c. blue . . . 7·00 6·50
431 – 4 c. on 2 c. blue . . . 7·00 6·50
432 71 10 c. on 25 c. red . . . 35 15
433 – 25 c. on 25 c. red . . . 35 15
434 – 55 c. on 2 c. blue . . . 70 60
435 – 55 c. on 10 c. green . . . 45·00 42·00
436 – 55 c. on 20 c. violet . . . 45·00 42·00
437 70 75 c. on 15 c. blue . . . 25 25
438 75 c. on 30 c. green . . . £130 £125
439 – 80 c. on 5 c. purple . . . 40·00 32·00
440 – 2 p. on 40 c. blue . . . 55 45
441 – 2 p. on 1 p. grey . . . 55 45
442 – 5 p. on 50 c. orange . . . 1·40 1·00
443 – 5 p. on 4 p. red . . . 2·25 1·50
444 71 10 p. on 10 p. brown . . . 20·00 20·00

1927. Red Cross Air stamps of 1926 optd either **17-V-1902 17-V-1927 A XIII**, or **17 MAYO 17 1902 1927 ALFONSO XIII.**

445 75 5 c. violet and black . . . 1·50 1·50
446 10 c. black and blue . . . 1·50 1·50
447 76 15 c. blue and orange . . . 40 40
448 20 c. red and green . . . 40 40
449 75 25 c. black and red . . . 40 40
450 76 30 c. brown and blue . . . 40 40
451 40 c. green and brown . . . 40 40
452 75 50 c. black and red . . . 40 40
453 1 p. green and black . . . 2·00 2·25
454 76 4 p. red and yellow . . . 80·00 70·00

1927. Red Cross Air stamps optd as last and surch **75 CTS. 75.**

455 75 75 c. on 5 c. violet & black 3·50 2·50
456 75 c. on 10 c. black & blue 15·00 11·00
457 75 c. on 25 c. black & red 30·00 25·00
458 75 c. on 50 c. black & red 13·00 11·00

1927. Red Cross stamps of Spanish Morocco and Nos. 24/5 of Spanish P.Os. in Tangier optd as above or surch also.

462 – 55 c. on 4 p. brown (No. 122) 10·00 10·00
463 71 80 c. on 10 p. lilac (No. 123) 10·00 10·00
460 1 p. on 10 p. lilac (No. 25) 35·00 38·00
461 – 4 p. brown (No. 24) 15·00 12·00

1927. Red Cross stamps of Cape Juby surch and optd as above.

464 – 5 p. on 4 p. brown (No. 34) 28·00 30·00
465 71 10 p. on 10 p. lilac (No. 35) 18·00 18·00

1927. Red Cross stamps of Spanish Guinea surch and optd as above.

466 71 1 p. on 10 p. lilac (No. 232) 9·00 9·00
467 – 2 p. on 4 p. brown (No. 231) 9·00 9·00

1927. Red Cross stamps of Spanish Sahara surch and optd as above.

468 71 80 c. on 10 p. lilac (No. 24) 14·00 14·00
469 – 2 p. on 4 p. brown (No. 23) 10·00 9·00

82 Pope Pius XI and King Alfonso XIII

1928. Rome Catacombs Restoration Fund.

470 82 2 c. black and violet . . . 20 20
471 2 c. black and purple . . . 35 30
486 2 c. red and black . . . 25 20
487 2 c. red and blue . . . 35 30
472 3 c. violet and black . . . 20 20
473 3 c. violet and blue . . . 35 30
488 3 c. blue and bistre . . . 20 20
489 3 c. blue and green . . . 35 30
474 5 c. violet and green . . . 70 35
490 5 c. red and purple . . . 70 35
475 10 c. black and green . . . 1·10 85
491 10 c. blue and green . . . 1·10 85
476 15 c. violet and green . . . 4·00 3·50
492 15 c. red and blue . . . 4·00 3·50
477 25 c. violet and red . . . 4·00 3·50
493 25 c. blue and brown . . . 4·00 3·50
478 40 c. black and blue . . . 15 15
494 40 c. red and blue . . . 15 15
479 55 c. violet and brown . . . 15 15
495 55 c. blue and brown . . . 15 15
480 80 c. black and red . . . 15 15
496 80 c. red and black . . . 15 15
481 1 p. violet and grey . . . 15 15
497 1 p. red and yellow . . . 15 15
482 2 p. black and brown . . . 4·50 4·50
498 2 p. blue and grey . . . 4·50 4·50
483 3 p. violet and pink . . . 4·50 4·50
499 3 p. red and violet . . . 4·50 4·50
484 4 p. black and purple . . . 4·50 4·50
500 4 p. red and purple . . . 4·50 4·50
485 5 p. violet and black . . . 4·50 4·50
501 5 p. blue and yellow . . . 4·50 4·50

83 A Spanish Caravel, Seville in background

84 Miniature of Exhibition Poster

1929. Seville and Barcelona Exhibitions. Inscr "EXPOSICION GENERAL (or GRAL.) ESPANOLA".

502 83 1 c. blue 20 20
503 84 2 c. green 20 20
504 – 5 c. red 35 30
505 – 10 c. green 40 35
506 83 15 c. blue 30 25
507 84 20 c. violet 40 35
508 83 25 c. red 40 35
509 – 30 c. brown . . . . 3·00 3·00
510 – 40 c. blue . . . . 3·75 3·00
511 84 50 c. orange . . . . 3·00 3·00
512 – 1 p. grey . . . . 5·50 5·00
513 – 4 p. red . . . . 16·00 15·00
514 – 10 p. brown . . . . 35·00 35·00

DESIGNS—VERT: 5, 30 c., 1 p. View of exhibition. HORIZ: 10, 40 c., 4, 10 p. Alfonso XIII and Barcelona.

87 "Spirit of St. Louis" over Coast

1929. Air. Seville and Barcelona Exhibitions.

515 87 5 c. brown . . . . 5·00 4·25
516 10 c. red . . . . 5·00 4·25
517 25 c. blue . . . . 5·00 4·75
518 50 c. violet . . . . 6·00 6·25
519 1 p. green . . . . 28·00 26·00
520 4 p. black . . . . 22·00 21·00

1929. Meeting of Council of League of Nations at Madrid. Optd **Sociedad de las Naciones LV reunion del Consejo Madrid**.

521 66 1 c. green 40 35
522 68 2 c. green 40 35
523 5 c. red 40 35
524 10 c. green 40 35
525 15 c. blue 40 35
526 20 c. violet 40 35
527 25 c. red 30 25
528 30 c. brown . . . . 1·90 1·25
529 40 c. blue . . . . 1·90 1·25
530 50 c. orange . . . . 1·90 1·25
531 69 1 p. grey . . . . 8·50 7·00
532 4 p. red . . . . 8·50 7·00
533 10 p. brown . . . . 30·00 27·00

89 Steam Locomotive

90 Stinson Junior Airplane

1930. 11th Int Railway Congress, Madrid.

534 89 1 c. turquoise (postage) . . 40 40
535 2 c. green 40 40
536 5 c. red 40 40
537 10 c. green 40 40
538 15 c. blue 40 40
539 20 c. violet 40 40
540 25 c. red 40 40
541 30 c. brown . . . . 1·75 1·75
542 40 c. blue . . . . 1·75 1·75
543 50 c. orange . . . . 4·00 4·00
544 – 1 p. grey . . . . 5·50 5·50
545 – 4 p. red . . . . 60·00 60·00
546 – 10 p. brown £300 £300

DESIGN—VERT: 1 p. to 10 p. Steam locomotive at points.

547 90 5 c. brown (air) . . . . 5·50 5·50
548 10 c. red . . . . 5·50 5·50
549 25 c. blue . . . . 5·50 5·50
550 50 c. violet . . . . 14·00 14·00
551 1 p. green . . . . 27·00 27·00
552 4 p. black . . . . 27·00 27·00

91

92
Francisco Goya (after Lopez)

93 "The Naked Maja"

1930. Death Cent of Goya (painter). (a) Postage.

553 91 1 c. yellow 10 10
554 2 c. brown 10 10
555 92 2 c. olive 10 10
556 91 5 c. mauve 10 10
557 92 5 c. violet 10 10
558 91 10 c. green 20 15
559 15 c. blue 15 10
560 20 c. red 15 10
561 25 c. red 15 10
562 92 25 c. red 35 35
563 91 30 c. brown . . . . 4·50 3·75
564 40 c. blue . . . . 4·50 3·75
565 50 c. orange . . . . 4·50 3·75
566 1 p. black . . . . 6·00 4·50
567 93 1 p. purple 85 70
568 4 p. black 60 50
569 10 p. brown . . . . 12·00 10·00

94 "Flight"

97 King Alfonso XIII

(b) Air. Designs show works by Goya, all with curious flying figures.

570 94 5 c. yellow and red . . . 10 10
571 – 5 c. blue and olive . . . 10 10
572 – 10 c. green and blue . . . 15 10
573 – 15 c. orange and black . . . 15 10
574 – 20 c. red and blue . . . 15 10
575 94 25 c. red and deep red . . . 20 10
576 – 30 c. violet and brown . . . 40 30
577 – 40 c. blue and violet . . . 40 30
578 – 50 c. green and red . . . 40 30
579 – 1 p. purple and plum . . . 40 30
580 – 4 p. black and red . . . 2·50 2·00
581 – 4 p. grey and black . . . 2·50 2·00
582 – 10 p. brown and deep brn . . 10·00 10·00

The 5 c. (No. 571), 10, 20, 40 c., 1, 4 p. (No. 581) and 10 p. are vert and the 30, 50 c. and 4 p. (No. 580) are horiz.

1930.

583 97 2 c. brown 10 10
584 5 c. grey 50 10
585 10 c. green . . . . 2·75 10
586 15 c. turquoise . . . . 9·00 10
587 20 c. violet . . . . 5·00 40
588 25 c. red 50 10
589 30 c. red . . . . 11·00 90
590 40 c. blue . . . . 15·00 60
592 50 c. orange . . . . 15·00 1·25

MINIMUM PRICE

The minimum price quoted is 10p which represents a handling charge rather than a basis for valuing common stamps. For further notes about prices, see introductory pages.

98 The "Santa Maria" 99

100 "Santa Maria", "Pinta" and "Nina"

101 The Departure from Palos

1930. Columbus issue.

593	**98**	1 c. brown	15	10
594		2 c. olive	15	10
595	**99**	2 c. olive	15	10
596	**98**	5 c. red	15	10
597	**99**	5 c. red	15	10
598		10 c. green	1·00	75
599	**98**	15 c. blue	1·00	75
600	**99**	20 c. violet	1·00	1·00
601	**100**	25 c. red	1·00	1·00
602	**101**	30 c. brown and blue	5·00	5·00
603	**100**	40 c. blue	4·75	4·00
604	**101**	50 c. violet, blue & purple	5·50	5·00
605	**100**	1 p. black	5·50	5·00
606	–	4 p. black and blue	5·00	5·50
607	–	10 p. brown and purple	25·00	27·00

DESIGNS—As Type **101**: 4, 10 p. Arrival in America.

103 Monastery of La Rabida

104 Martin Pinzon

106 Columbus

1930. "Columbus" Air stamps (for Europe and Africa).

608	**103**	5 c. red	10	10
609		5 c. brown	10	10
610		10 c. green	20	15
611		15 c. violet	20	15
612		20 c. blue	20	15
613	**104**	25 c. red	20	15
614	–	30 c. brown	1·50	1·50
615	**104**	40 c. blue	1·50	1·50
616	–	50 c. orange	1·50	1·50
617	**104**	1 p. violet	1·50	1·50
618	**106**	4 p. olive	1·50	1·50
619		10 p. brown	8·50	9·00

DESIGNS—As Type **104**: 30, 50 c. Vincent Pinzon.

107 Monastery of La Rabida

108 Columbus

109 Columbus and the brothers Pinzon

1930. "Columbus" Air stamps (for America and Philippines).

620	**107**	5 c. red	10	10
621		10 c. green	15	10
622	**108**	25 c. red	15	10
623		50 c. grey	1·75	1·75
624		1 p. brown	1·75	1·75
625	**109**	4 p. blue	1·75	1·75
626		10 p. purple	7·50	8·50

110 Arms of Bolivia and Paraguay

113 Sidar (Mexico)

114 King, Queen and Columbus

1930. Spanish-American Exhibition. Views of pavilions of various countries.

627	**110**	1 c. green (postage)	10	10
628	–	2 c. brown (C. America)	10	10
629	–	5 c. brown (Venezuela)	10	10
630	–	10 c. sepia (Colombia)	25	20
631	–	15 c. blue (Dominican Republic)	25	20
632	–	20 c. violet (Uruguay)	25	20
633	–	25 c. red (Argentina)	25	20
634	–	25 c. red (Chile)	25	20
635	–	30 c. purple (Brazil)	1·00	1·10
636	–	40 c. blue (Mexico)	55	50
637	–	40 c. blue (Cuba)	55	50
638	–	50 c. orange (Peru)	1·25	1·50
639	–	1 p. blue (U.S.A.)	1·75	2·25
640	–	4 p. purple (Portugal)	12·00	15·00
641	–	10 p. brown	1·00	1·50

The 10 p. shows King Alfonso and Queen Victoria, maps of S. America and Spain, and the Giralda, Seville. The 2, 5 c., 4, 10 p. are vert.

643	–	5 c. black (air)	30	15
644	–	10 c. green	30	15
645	–	25 c. blue	30	15
646	–	50 c. blue	60	75
647	**113**	50 c. black	60	75
648	–	1 p. red	1·25	1·50
649	–	1 p. purple	35·00	32·00
650	–	1 p. green	1·25	1·50
651	**114**	4 p. blue	2·25	3·00

DESIGNS: Portraits of aviators and views as Types **113/14**—HORIZ: 5 c. Alberto Santos Dumont (Brazil); 10 c. Teodoro Fels (Argentina); 25 c. Dagoberto Godoy (Chile); 50 c. Cabral and Coutinho (Portugal) (No. 646); 1 p. Charles Lindbergh (United States) (No. 650). VERT: 1 p. Jimenez and Iglesias (Spain) (Nos. 648/9).

115

121 The Fountain of the Lions

1930.

652	**115**	5 c. black	5·00	10

1931. Optd **REPUBLICA**. (a) Postage.

660	**66**	1 c. green (imperf)	10	10
673	**97**	2 c. brown	10	10
662		5 c. brown	15	15
671	**115**	5 c. black	2·10	2·10
675	**97**	10 c. green	25	25
664		15 c. green	80	80
677		20 c. violet	50	35
678		25 c. red	50	35
667		30 c. red	5·50	5·50
668		40 c. blue	1·50	1·25
669		50 c. orange	1·50	1·25
670	**69**	1 p. grey	10·00	8·00

(b) Air. On Nos. 353/6.

683	**64**	5 c. green	9·00	8·50
684		10 c. red	9·00	8·50
685		25 c. blue	13·00	12·00
686		50 c. blue	24·00	20·00

1931. Optd **Republica Espanola** in two lines continuously.

687	**97**	2 c. brown	10	10
688		5 c. grey	25	10
689		10 c. green	25	10
690		15 c. turquoise	2·25	10
691		20 c. violet	1·10	60
692		25 c. red	35	10
693		30 c. red	3·00	60
694		40 c. blue	3·00	60
695		50 c. orange	6·50	40
696	**69**	1 p. grey	42·00	60

1931. 3rd Pan-American Postal Union Congress. (a) Postage.

697	**121**	5 c. purple	10	10
698	–	10 c. green	35	35
699	–	15 c. violet	35	35
700	–	25 c. red	35	35
701	–	30 c. olive	35	35
702	**121**	40 c. blue	75	55
703	–	50 c. red	75	55
704	–	1 p. black	1·40	1·10
705	–	4 p. purple	7·00	6·50
706	–	10 p. brown	22·00	22·00

DESIGNS—VERT: 10, 25, 50 c. Cordoba Cathedral. HORIZ: 15 c., 1 p. Alcantara Bridge, Toledo; 30 c. Dr. F. Garcia y Santos; 4, 10 p. Revolutionaries hoisting Republican flag, 14 April, 1931.

123 Royal Palace and San Francisco el Grande

(b) Air.

707	**123**	5 c. red	10	10
708		10 c. green	10	10
709		25 c. red	10	10
710	–	50 c. blue	40	35
711	–	1 p. violet	60	50
712	–	4 p. black	8·00	8·50

DESIGNS—HORIZ: 50 c., 1 p. G.P.O. and Cibeles Fountain; 4 p. The Calle de Alcala.

125a Montserrat Arms

125b Airplane above Montserrat

1931. 900th Anniv of Montserrat Monastery.

713	**125a**	1 c. green (postage)	1·50	1·50
714		2 c. brown	1·00	1·00
715		5 c. brown	1·00	1·00
716		10 c. green	1·00	1·00
717	–	15 c. green	1·50	1·50
718	–	20 c. purple	3·00	3·00
719	–	25 c. red	4·50	4·50
720	–	30 c. red	35·00	35·00
721	–	40 c. blue	25·00	25·00
722	–	50 c. orange	50·00	50·00
723	–	1 p. blue	50·00	50·00
724	–	4 p. mauve	£400	£400
725	–	10 p. brown	£300	£300

DESIGNS: 15, 50 c. Monks planning Monastery; 20, 30 c. "Black Virgin" (full length); 25 c., 1, 10 p. "Black Virgin" (profile); 40 c., 4 p. Monastery.

726	**125b**	5 c. brown (air)	50	50
727		10 c. green	2·50	2·50
728		25 c. red	10·00	10·00
729		50 c. orange	30·00	30·00
730		1 p. blue	20·00	20·00

143

144

126 Blasco Ibanez

127 Pi y Margall

128 Joaquin Costa

129 Mariana Pineda

130 Nicolas Salmeron

131 Concepcion Arenal

132 Ruiz Zorilla

133 Pablo Iglesias

134 Ramon y Cajal

135 Azcarate

136 Jovellanos

137 Pablo Iglesias

138 Emilio Castelar

139 Pablo Iglesias

140 Velazquez

141 F. Salvoechea

142 Cuenca

1931.

770	**143**	1 c. green (imperf)	10	10
738	**126**	2 c. brown	10	10
771	**143**	2 c. brown	25	10
772	**144**	2 c. brown	10	10
731	**127**	5 c. brown	2·40	20
740	**126**	5 c. brown	10	10
773	**143**	5 c. brown	10	10
741	**128**	10 c. green	4·00	10
742	**129**	10 c. green	10	10
774	**143**	10 c. green	10	10
744	**130**	15 c. green	60	10
745	**131**	15 c. green	55	10
747		15 c. black	20	10
775	**143**	15 c. green	10	10
748	**127**	20 c. violet	30	10
776a	**143**	20 c. violet	10	10
734	**133**	25 c. red	19·00	40
750	**132**	25 c. red	45	10
777a	**143**	25 c. mauve	10	10
751	**133**	30 c. red	1·60	10
752	**134**	30 c. brown	12·00	50
753	**135**	30 c. red	7·50	20
755	**136**	30 c. red	10	10
756	**137**	30 c. red	10	10
757	**139**	30 c. red	1·10	35
778	**143**	30 c. red	10	10
758	**138**	40 c. blue	20	10
759		40 c. red	1·10	35
760	**139**	45 c. red	10	10
761	**130**	50 c. orange	21·00	35
762		50 c. blue	1·00	35
763	**140**	50 c. blue	10	10
764	**138**	60 c. green	10	15
765	**141**	60 c. blue	75	70
766		60 c. orange	5·00	4·00
767c	**142**	1 p. black	15	10
768c	–	4 p. mauve	50	30
769c	–	10 p. brown	1·00	50

DESIGNS—As Type **142**: 4 p. Castle of Segovia; 10 p. Sun Gate, Toledo.

MINIMUM PRICE

The minimum price quoted is 10p which represents a handling charge rather than a basis for valuing common stamps. For further notes about prices, see introductory pages.

145 Cierva C.30A Autogyro over Seville

1935.
780 **145** 2 p. blue 65 20

146 Lope De Vega's Book-plate
148 Scene from "Peribanez"

1935. 300th Death Anniv of Lope de Vega (author).
781 **146** 15 c. green . . . . 6·00 25
782 – 30 c. red . . . . 2·40 20
783 – 50 c. blue . . . . 12·00 1·90
784 **148** 1 p. black . . . . 20·00 1·25
DESIGN—As Type **146**: 30, 50 c. Lope de Vega (after Tristan).

149 Old-time Map of the Amazon

1935. Iglesias' Amazon Expedition.
785 **149** 30 c. red . . . . 2·25 70

150 M. Moya

151 House of Nazareth and Rotary Press

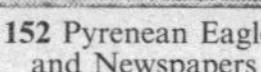
152 Pyrenean Eagle and Newspapers

153 Airplane over Press Association Building

1936. 40th Anniv of Madrid Press Association.
786 **150** 1 c. red (postage) 10 10
787 – 2 c. brown 10 10
788 – 5 c. sepia 10 10
789 – 10 c. green 10 10
790 **150** 15 c. green 15 10
791 – 20 c. violet 15 10
792 – 25 c. mauve 15 10
793 – 30 c. red 10 10
794 **150** 40 c. orange 45 10
795 – 50 c. blue 30 10
796 – 60 c. olive 50 15
797 – 1 p. black 50 15
798 **151** 2 p. blue . . . . 6·50 2·25
799 4 p. red . . . . 6·50 4·25
800 10 p. lake . . . . 16·00 10·00
PORTRAITS: 2, 20, 50 c. T. L. de Tena; 5, 25, 60 c. J. F. Rodriguez; 10, 30 c., 1 p. A. Lerroux.
SIZES: 1 c. to 10 c. 22×27 mm; 15 c. to 30 c. 24×30 mm; 40 c. to 1 p. 26×31½ mm.

801 **152** 1 c. red (air) 10 10
802 **153** 2 c. brown 15 15
803 **152** 5 c. sepia 10 10
804 **153** 10 c. green 15 15
805 – 15 c. blue 15 10
806 **152** 20 c. violet 15 10
807 **153** 25 c. mauve 15 15
808 – 30 c. red 10 10
809 **152** 40 c. orange 45 70
810 **152** 50 c. blue 30 70
811 **153** 60 c. olive 50 70
812 – 1 p. black 60 70
813 – 2 p. blue . . . . 4·00 3·00
814 – 4 p. red . . . . 4·50 4·50
815 – 10 p. lake . . . . 12·00 8·00
DESIGNS—VERT: 15, 30, 50 c., 1 p. Cierva C.30A autogyro over House of Nazareth. HORIZ: 2, 4, 10 p. Don Quixote on wooden horse.

155 Gregorio Fernandez

156

1936. 300th Birth Anniv of Gregorio Fernandez (sculptor).
816 **155** 30 c. red . . . . 1·50 70

1939. 1st National Philatelic Exhibition, Madrid. (a) Postage.
817 **156** 10 c. brown . . . . . . 40·00 45·00
818 15 c. green . . . . . . 40·00 45·00

(b) Air. Optd **CORREO AEREO**.
819 **156** 10 c. red £130 £130
320 15 c. blue £130 £130

1936. Manila–Madrid Flight of Arnaiz and Calvo. Optd **VUELO MANILA MADRID 1936 ARNAIZ CALVO**.
821 **137** 30 c. red . . . . 5·00 3·25

159

160a Republican Symbol

1937. Fiscal stamp of Austrias and Leon surch.
822 **159** 25 c. on 5 c. red . . . . 16·00 5·50
823 45 c. on 5 c. red . . . . 6·00 3·00
824 60 c. on 5 c. red 40 35
825 1 p. on 5 c. red 35 30

1938. Surch **45 centimos.**
826 **143** 45 c. on 1 c. green (imperf) . . 5·00 5·00
827 45 c. on 1 c. grn (perf) . . 30 25
830 45 c. on 2 c. brown . . . 12·00 9·50
831 **144** 45 c. on 2 c. brown . . . 10 10
832 **126** 45 c. on 2 c. brown . . . 24·00 20·00

1938.
833 **160a** 40 c. red 10 10
834 45 c. red 10 10
835 50 c. blue 10 10
836 60 c. blue 40 30

1938. 7th Anniv of Republic. Surch **14 ABRIL 1938 VII Aniversario de la Republica** and values. (a) Postage.
837 **54** 45 c. on 15 c. violet . . . 12·00 11·00

(b) Air. Optd **CORREO AEREO**.
838 **54** 2 p. 50 on 10 c. red . . . 80·00 75·00

163 Defence of Madrid

1938. Defence of Madrid Relief Fund. (a) Postage.
839 **163** 45 c. + 2 p. blue & lt bl . . 50 40

(b) Air. Surch **AEREO + 5 Pts**.
841 **163** 45 c. + 2 p. + 5 p. blue and light blue £200 £190

1938. Labour Day. Surch **FIESTA DEL TRABAJO 1 MAYO 1938** and values.
843 **54** 45 c. on 15 c. violet . . . 2·75 2·75
844 1 p. on 15 c. violet . . . 5·00 4·25

167 Statue of Liberty and Flags

1938. 150th Anniv of U.S. Constitution. (a) Postage.
845 **167** 1 p. multicoloured . . . . 12·00 12·00

(b) Air. Surch **AEREO + 5 Pts.**
847 **167** 1 p. + 5 p. multicoloured £180 £160

169

172 Steelworks

1938. Red Cross (a) Postage.
849 **169** 45 c. + 5 p. red 55 50

(b) Air. Surcharged **Aereo** and new value.
850 **169** 45 c. + 5 p. + 3 p. red . 8·00 8·00

1938. Air. No. 719 surch with two airplanes and **CORREO AEREO** repeated twice and value.
851 50 c. on 25 c. red . . . . . . 23·00 23·00
852 1 p. on 25 c. red . . . . . . 1·50 1·00
853 1 p. 25 on 25 c. red . . . . . 1·50 1·00
854 1 p. 50 on 25 c. red . . . . . 1·50 1·00
855 2 p. on 25 c. red . . . . . . 26·00 24·00

1938. Workers of Sagunto.
856 **172** 45 c. black 15 15
857 – 1 p. 25 blue 15 15
DESIGN: 1 p. 25, Blast furnace and air raid victims.

173 "Isaac Peral"

1938. Submarine Service.
857a **173** 1 p. blue . . . . 5·50 5·50
857b – 2 p. brown . . . . 10·00 10·00
857c – 4 p. orange . . . . . . 10·00 10·00
857d – 6 p. blue . . . . 15·00 18·00
857e – 10 p. red . . . . 35·00 42·00
857f – 15 p. green £375 £400
DESIGNS: 2 p., 6 p. "Narciso Monturiol". 4 p., 10 p. "B-2".

174 Troops on the Alert

176a Man and Woman in Firing Position

1938. In Honour of 43rd Division. Perf or imperf.
858 **174** 25 c. green . . . . 8·00 7·00
859 – 45 c. brown . . . . 8·00 7·00
DESIGN—VERT: 45 c. Two soldiers on guard.

1938. 2nd Anniv of Defence of Madrid. Optd **SECUNDO ANIVERSARIO DE LA HEROICA DEFENSA DE MADRID 7 NOV. 1938**.
860 **163** 45 c. + 2 p. blue . . . . 2·50 2·00

1938. No. 719 surch **2'50 PTAS** and bars and ornaments.
861 2 p. 50 on 25 c. red 15 15

1938. In honour of the Militia.
861b **176a** 5 c. brown . . . . . . 2·75 2·40
861c 10 c. purple . . . . . . 2·75 2·40
861d 25 c. green . . . . . . 2·75 2·40
861e – 45 c. red . . . . 2·75 2·40
861f – 60 c. blue . . . . 4·75 4·00
861g – 1 p. 20 black . . . . . £100 95·00
861h – 2 p. orange . . . . . . 30·00 30·00
861i – 5 p. brown £170 £140
861j – 10 p. green . . . . . . 35·00 30·00
DESIGNS—HORIZ: 45, 60 c., 1 p. 20, Militia with machine gun. VERT: 2, 5, 10 p. Grenade-thrower.

NATIONAL STATE

The Civil War began on July 17, 1936. Until it ended on April 1, 1939, the stamps listed below were current only in areas held by the forces of General Franco.

179

177 Seville Cathedral

178 Xavier Castle, Navarre

180 Cordoba Cathedral

1936.
868 **179** 1 c. green (imperf) . . . . 4·75 5·00
869 2 c. brown 55 35
862 – 5 c. brown 60 50
870 – 10 c. green 55 35
863 – 15 c. green 60 35
864 **177** 25 c. red 60 35
865 **178** 30 c. red 60 35
871 – 50 c. blue . . . . 13·00 10·00
872 **180** 60 c. green 85 70
867 – 1 p. black . . . . 5·50 2·40
873 – 4 p. lilac, red and yellow . 45·00 25·00
874 – 10 p. brown . . . . . . 48·00 25·00
DESIGNS—VERT: 5 c. Burgos Cathedral; 4 p. National flag at Malaga. HORIZ: As Type **178**: 15 c. Zaragoza Cathedral; 1 p. Alcantara Bridge and Alcazar, Toledo. As Type **180**: 10 c. Salamanca University; 50 c. Court of Lions, Granada; 10 p. Troops disembarking at Algeciras.

181

182

183 "El Cid"

184 Isabella the Catholic

1937.
875 **181** 1 c. green (imperf) 10 10
876 **182** 2 c. brown 10 10
902 **183** 5 c. brown 10 10
879 10 c. green 10 10
903 10 c. red 10 10
896 15 c. green 40 10
880 **184** 15 c. black 20 10
881 20 c. violet 30 10
882 25 c. red 25 10
883 30 c. red 40 10
885 40 c. orange . . . . 1·75 10
886 50 c. blue . . . . 1·75 10
887 60 c. yellow 30 10
897 70 c. blue 60 10
888 1 p. blue . . . . 14·00 35
889 4 p. mauve . . . . 18·00 4·25
891 **183** 10 p. blue . . . . 25·00 11·00

186 Santiago Cathedral

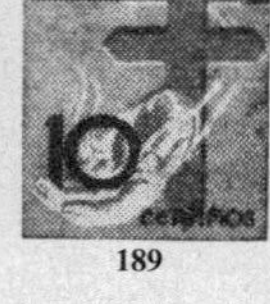
189

1937. Holy Year of Compostela.
905 – 15 c. brown . . . . 1·00 70
906 **186** 30 c. red . . . . 4·00 35
908 – 1 p. orange and blue . . . 12·00 3·50
DESIGNS—VERT: 15 c. St. James of Compostela. HORIZ: 1 p. Portico de la Gloria.

1937. Anti-Tuberculosis Fund. Cross in red.
913 **189** 10 c. blue and black . . . 4·00 1·00

190 Ferdinand the Catholic

192

1938.

917	**190**	15 c. green	1·25	10
918		20 c. violet	10·00	1·50
919		25 c. red	60	10
921		30 c. red	4·50	10

1938. Air. Optd **correo aereo**.

922	**190**	50 c. blue	85	45
923		1 p. blue	2·75	55

1938. 2nd Anniv of National Uprising.

926	**192**	15 c. green	4·50	4·00
927		25 c. red	4·50	4·00
928		30 c. blue	2·50	2·50
929		1 p. brown and yellow	75·00	65·00

193 Isabella the Catholic

194

1938.

930	**193**	20 c. violet	75	15
931		25 c. red	7·50	40
932		30 c. red	40	15
933		40 c. mauve	50	10
934		50 c. blue	25·00	1·75
935		1 p. blue	8·00	70

1938. Anti-Tuberculosis Fund. Cross in red.

940	**194**	10 c. blue and black	4·00	1·40

195 Juan de la Cierva and C.30A Autogyro

196 General Franco

1939. Air.

1010	**195**	20 c. orange	15	10
1011		25 c. red	15	10
943		35 c. mauve	50	30
1013		50 c. brown	35	10
945		1 p. blue	55	20
1015		2 p. green	2·10	10
947		4 p. blue	4·50	2·00
1017		10 p. violet	5·00	50

1939.

960	**196**	5 c. brown	35	10
961		10 c. red	1·75	45
962		15 c. green	40	10
1114		20 c. violet	20	10
1115		25 c. purple	20	10
950		30 c. red	25	10
1116		30 c. blue	25	10
1117		35 c. blue	35	10
951		40 c. green	30	10
1118		40 c. grey	35	10
952		45 c. red	2·00	1·90
1119		45 c. blue	10	10
1120		50 c. grey	25	10
1121		60 c. orange	20	10
955		70 c. blue	50	10
956		1 Pts. black	12·00	10
974		1 PTA. black	5·50	10
975		1 PTS. grey	60·00	50
957		2 Pts. brown	18·00	1·00
1124		2 PTAS. brown	7·00	10
958		4 Pts. purple	95·00	12·00
977a		4 PTAS. red	10·00	10
959		10 Pts. brown	48·00	29·00
978		10 PTS. brown	£140	2·75
1126		10 PTAS. brown	3·00	30

For 10 c. brown imperf, see No. 981.

197 "Spain" and Wreath of Peace

1939. Homage to the Army.

980	**197**	10 c. blue	15	10

1939. Anti-Tuberculosis Fund. Imperf.

981	**196**	10 c. brown	15	10

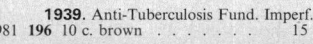

198 Ruins of Belchite

1940. Zaragoza Cathedral Restoration Fund and 19th Centenary of Apparition of Virgin of El Pilar at Zaragoza. (a) Postage.

982	**198**	10 c. + 5 c. brown & blue	10	10
983	–	15 c. + 10 c. olive & lilac	15	10
984	–	20 c. + 10 c. blue & vio	15	10
985	–	25 c. + 10 c. brown & red	15	10
986	–	40 c. + 10 c. pur & grn	10	10
987	–	45 c. + 15 c. red & blue	30	20
988	**198**	70 c. + 20 c. blk & brn	30	20
989	–	80 c. + 20 c. violet & red	35	25
990	–	1 p. + 30 c. pur & blk	35	25
991	–	1 p. 40 + 40 c. blk & pur	30·00	25·00
992	–	1 p. 50 + 50 c. pur & bl	40	35
993	–	2 p. 50 + 50 c. bl & pur	40	35
994	–	4 p. + 1 p. slate & lilac	10·00	8·00
995	–	10 p. + 4 p. brown & bl	£140	£140

DESIGNS—HORIZ: 15, 80 c. Procession of the Rosary; 20 c., 1 p. 50, El Pilar; 25 c., 1 p. Mother Rafols praying; 40 c., 2 p. 50, Sanctuary of the Virgin; 45 c., 1 p. 40, Oath of the besieged; 4 p. Miracle of Calanda; 10 p. Virgin appearing to St. James.

(b) Air.

996	25 c. + 5 c. slate & purple	25	20
997	50 c. + 5 c. violet and red	25	20
998	65 c. + 15 c. blue & violet	25	20
999	70 c. + 15 c. violet & slate	25	20
1000	90 c. + 20 c. red & brown	25	20
1001	1 p. 20 + 30 c. purple & vio	25	20
1002	1 p. 40 + 40 c. brown & bl	25	30
1003	2 p. + 50 c. violet & purple	35	30
1004	4 p. + 1 p. purple & green	8·50	6·00
1005	10 p. + 4 p. blue & brown	£190	£170

DESIGNS—VERT: 25, 70 c. Prayer during bombardment; 50 c., 1 p. 40, Caravel and Image of the Virgin; 65, 90 c. The Assumption; 1 p. 20, 2 p. Coronation of the Virgin; 4 p. "The Cave", after Goya; 10 p. Bombing of Zaragoza Cathedral.

199 Gen. Franco

200 Knight and Cross of Lorraine

1940. Anti-Tuberculosis Fund.

1006	**199**	10 c. violet & red (post)	10	10
1007		20 c. + 5 c. green & red	40	45
1008		40 c. + 10 c. blue & red	55	20
1009		10 c. pink and red (air)	50	40

1941. Anti-Tuberculosis Fund.

1018	**200**	10 c. black & red (post)	15	10
1019		20 c. + 5 c. violet & red	50	30
1020		40 c. + 10 c. slate & red	50	30
1021		10 c. blue and red (air)	25	20

201 Gen. Franco

202 St. John of the Cross

1942.

1022	**201**	40 c. brown	50	15
1023		75 c. blue	4·50	35
1024a		90 c. green	40	10
1025b		1 p. 35 violet	35	10

1942. 400th Birth Anniv of St. John of the Cross.

1026	**202**	20 c. violet	70	10
1027		40 c. orange	1·40	30
1028		75 c. blue	1·60	1·60

203 Doves and Lorraine Cross

1942. Anti-T.B. Fund. Inscr "1942–43".

1029	**203**	10 c. pink & red (post)	15	10
1030		20 c. + 5 c. brn & red	1·10	1·10
1031		40 c. + 10 c. grn & red	85	20
1032	–	10 c. pink & red (air)	75	30

DESIGN—HORIZ: No. 1032, Lorraine Cross and two doves in flight.

204 St. James of Compostela

205

1943. Holy Year. Inscr "ANO SANTO 1943".

1033	**204**	20 c. blue	20	15
1034	–	20 c. red	20	15
1035	–	20 c. lilac	20	15
1036	–	40 c. brown	60	20
1037	**205**	40 c. green	50	20
1038	–	40 c. brown	75	20
1039	–	75 c. blue	2·25	2·25
1040	–	75 c. blue	2·75	2·50
1041	–	75 c. blue	30·00	25·00

DESIGNS—VERT: Nos. 1034 and 1040. Details of pillars in Santiago Cathedral; No. 1036, St. James enthroned; No. 1038, Portal of Santiago Cathedral; No. 1039, Censer; No. 1041, Santiago Cathedral. HORIZ: No. 1035, Tomb of St. James.

206

1943. Anti-Tuberculosis Fund. Inscr "1943–1944".

1042	**206**	10 c. vio & red (postage)	30	25
1043		20 c. + 5 c. green & red	3·00	1·40
1044		40 c. + 10 c. blue & red	2·00	1·00
1045	–	10 c. violet and red (air)	55	55

DESIGN: No. 1045. Lorraine Cross and outline of bird.

207 10th-cent Tower

208 Arms of Soria

1944. Millenary of Castile. Arms designs as T **208** inscr "MILENARIO DE CASTILLA".

1046	**207**	20 c. lilac	20	20
1047	**208**	20 c. lilac	20	15
1048	–	20 c. lilac	20	20
1049	–	40 c. brown	3·00	45
1050	–	40 c. brown	3·00	45
1051	–	40 c. brown	2·75	50
1052	–	75 c. blue	3·00	2·50
1053	–	75 c. blue	2·75	2·50
1054	–	75 c. blue	2·25	2·50

DESIGNS: No. 1048, Avila (Shield at left); No. 1049, Castile (Arms in centre); No. 1050, Segovia (Shield at left); No. 1051, Burgos (Shield at right); No. 1052, Avila (Shield at left); No. 1053, Fernan Gonzalez, founder of Castile (Helmet, bow and arrows at left); No. 1054, Santander (Shield at right).

209 "Dr. Thebussem" (M. P. Figueroa, author and postal historian)

1944. Air. Stamp Day.

1055	**209**	5 p. blue	19·00	16·00

210

211 Quevedo

1944. Anti-Tuberculosis Fund. Inscr "1944 1945". (a) Postage.

1056	**210**	10 c. orange and red	15	10
1057		20 c. + 5 c. black & red	30	25
1058		40 c. + 10 c. violet & red	50	20
1059		80 c. + 10 c. blue & red	8·00	7·50

(b) Air. Inscr "CORRESPONDENCIA AEREA".

1060	–	25 c. orange and red	3·50	3·50

DESIGN—HORIZ: No. 1060, Hospital.

1945. 300th Death Anniv of Francisco de Quevedo (author).

1061	**211**	40 c. brown	70	45

212 Conde de San Luis, Mail Vehicle of 1850, and Airplane

1945. Air. Stamp Day.

1062	**212**	10 p. green	27·00	18·00

213 Carlos de Haya Gonzalez

214 J. Garcia Morato

1945. Air. Civil War Air Aces.

1063	**213**	4 p. red	15·00	6·00
1064	**214**	10 p. purple	35·00	8·00

215 St. George and Dragon

216 Lorraine Cross and Eagle

1945. Anti-T.B. Fund.

1065	**215**	10 c. orge & red (post)	20	10
1066		20 c. + 5 c. green & red	30	20
1067		40 c. + 10 c. vio & red	40	20
1068		80 c. + 10 c. blue & red	12·00	8·00
1069	**216**	25 c. red (air)	1·75	1·25

217 E. A. de Nebrija (compiler of first Spanish Grammar)

219 Statue of Fray Bartolome de las Casas and native Indian

1946. Stamp Day and Day of the Race.

1070	**217**	50 c. red (postage)	50	30
1071	–	75 c. blue	60	35
1072	**219**	5 p. 50 green (air)	3·25	2·25

DESIGN—As Type **217**: 75 c. Salamanca University and signature of F. F. de Vitoria (founder of International Law).

220 Self-portrait of Goya

221 Woman and Child

1946. Birth Bicentenary of Goya (painter).

1073	**220**	25 c. red	10	10
1074		50 c. green	15	10
1075		75 c. blue	75	60

1946. Anti-Tuberculosis Fund. Dated "1946 1947".

1076	**221**	5 c. violet and red (postage)	10	10
1077		10 c. green and red	10	10
1078	–	25 c. orange & red (air)	30	20

DESIGN—HORIZ: 25 c. Eagle.

222 B. J. Feijoo y Montenegro

1947.

1079	**222**	50 c. green	70	40

223 Don Quixote in Library

224 Don Quixote

1947. Stamp Day and 400th Birth Anniv of Cervantes.
1080 **223** 50 c. brown (postage) . . 30 20
1081 **224** 75 c. blue 60 35
1082 – 5 p. 50 violet (air) . . . 6·00 4·00
DESIGN—HORIZ: 5 p. 50, Quixote on Wooden Horse (after Gustav Dore).

226 Manuel de Falla (composer)

228 Lorraine Cross

1947. Air.
1083 **226** 25 p. purple . . . . . . 45·00 15·00
1084 – 50 p. red . . . . £160 25·00
PORTRAIT: 50 p. Ignacio Zuloaga (painter).

1947. Anti-Tuberculosis Fund. Dated. "1947 1948".
1085 **228** 5 c. brn & red (postage) . 10 10
1086 – 10 c. blue and red . . . 10 10
1087 – 25 c. mauve & red (air) . . 30 20
DESIGNS—VERT: 10 c. Deckchair in garden. HORIZ: 25 c. Santorium.

229 General Franco

230 Hernando Cortes

1948.
1088 **229** 5 c. brown 10 10
1088a 5 c. olive 45 10
1089 15 c. green 30 10
1090 50 c. brown 30 10
1091 80 c. lake . . . . . . 5·00 10

1948.
1092 **230** 35 c. black 20 15
1093 – 70 c. purple . . . . . . 2·50 2·00
PORTRAIT: 70 c. M. Aleman (writer).

232 Gen. Franco and Castillo de la Mota

233 Ferdinand III of Castile

1948.
1094 **232** 25 c. orange 10 10
1095 30 c. myrtle 10 10
1096 35 c. green 10 10
1097 40 c. brown 90 10
1098 45 c. pink 45 10
1099 45 c. red . . . . . 1·50 10
1100 50 c. purple . . . . . 1·75 10
1101 70 c. violet . . . . . 2·50 15
1102 75 c. blue . . . . . 2·25 20
1103 1 p. pink . . . . . 7·50 10

1948. 700th Anniv of Institution of Castilian Navy.
1104 **233** 25 c. violet 30 10
1105 – 30 c. red (Admiral R. de Bonifaz) 20 10

235 Marquis of Salamanca

236 Diesel Train

1948. Stamp Day and Spanish Railway Cent. Inscr "F.F.C.C. ESPANOLES 1848 1948".
1106 **235** 50 c. brown (postage) . . 75 10
1107 – 5 p. green . . . . . . 2·25 10
1108 **236** 2 p. red (air) . . . . . 3·25 1·40
DESIGN—HORIZ: 5 p. Garganta de Pancorbo Viaduct.

238 Aesculapius

240 Globe and Buildings

1948. Anti-Tuberculosis Fund. Dated "1948 1949".
1109 **238** 5 c. brn & red (postage) 10 10
1110 10 c. green and red . . . 10 10
1111 50 c. + 10 c. brn and red 1·00 75
1112 – 25 c. blue and red (air) . . 40 30
DESIGN: 25 c. Lockheed Constellation airliner over sanatorium.

1949. Relief of War Victims. As T **183**, but larger and inscr "AUXILIO A LAS VICTIMAS DE LA GUERRA 1946".
1113 5 c. violet 25 10

1949. 75th Anniv of U.P.U.
1127 **240** 50 c. brown (postage) . 85 15
1128 75 c. blue 60 35
1129 4 p. olive (air) 50 30

241 Galleon

242 San Juan de Dios and Leper

1949. Anti-Tuberculosis Fund. Inscr "1949 1950".
1130 **241** 5 c. vio & red (postage) 10 10
1131 10 c. green and red . . . 10 10
1132 50 c. + 10 c. bis & red . 40 30
1133 – 25 c. deep red and red (air) 25 15
DESIGN: 25 c. Bell.

1950. 400th Death Anniv of San Juan de Dios.
1134 **242** 1 p. violet . . . . 18·00 4·50

243 Calderon de la Barca (dramatist)

244 Isabella II

1950. Portraits.
1135 **243** 5 c. brown 20 10
1136 – 10 c. lake 20 10
1137 – 15 c. green 70 10
1138 – 20 c. violet 50 10
1139 – 2 p. blue . . . . . . 35·00 15
1140 – 4 p. 50 purple 70 50
PORTRAITS—VERT: 10 c. Lope de Vega (author); 15 c. T. de Molina (poet); 20 c. Ruiz de Alarcon (author); 2 p. Dr. Ramon y Cajal (physician); 4 p. 50, Dr. Ferran y Clua (bacteriologist).

1950. Stamp Centenary. Imperf. (a) Postage. Reproduction of T **1**.
1141 **244** 50 c. violet . . . . . . 13·00 7·50
1142 75 c. blue . . . . . . 13·00 7·50
1143 10 p. black £150 £110
1144 15 p. red £150 £110

(b) Air. Reproduction of T **2**.
1145 – 1 p. purple . . . . . . 13·00 7·50
1146 – 2 p. 50 brown . . . . . 13·00 7·50
1147 – 20 p. blue £150 £110
1148 – 25 p. green £150 £110

1950. Gen. Franco's Canary Is Visit. Nos. 1100 and 1103 surch **VISITA DEL CAUDILLO A CANARIAS OCTUBRE 1950 SOBRETASA DIEZ CTS** and No. 1083 with **Correspondencia por avion** also.
1149 **232** 10 c. on 50 c. purple (postage) . . . . . 45·00 35·00
1150 10 c. on 1 p. pink . . . 45·00 35·00
1151 **226** 10 c. on 25 p. purple (air) £450 £225

246 Candle and Conifer

247 Map

1950. Anti-T.B. Fund. Cross in red. Inscr "1950 1951".
1152 **246** 5 c. violet (postage) . . . 10 10
1153 10 c. green 10 10
1154 50 c. + 10 c. brown . . . 3·75 1·40
1155 – 25 c. blue (air) 80 70
DESIGN: 25 c. Dove and flowers.

1951. Air. 6th Conference of Spanish–American Postal Union.
1156 **247** 1 p. blue . . . . 7·50 2·00

248 Isabella the Catholic

248a St. Antonio Claret

1951. 5th Centenary of Birth of Isabella.
1157 **248** 50 c. brown . . . . . . 1·00 45
1158 75 c. blue . . . . . . 1·50 45
1159 90 c. purple . . . . . . 1·00 30
1160 1 p. 50 orange . . . . . 17·00 8·00
1161 2 p. 80 olive . . . . . 35·00 25·00

1951. Stamp Day.
1162 **248a** 50 c. blue . . . . 7·00 2·50

249 Children on Beach

250 Isabella the Catholic

1951. Anti-Tuberculosis Fund. Cross in red.
1163 **249** 5 c. red (postage) 15 10
1164 10 c. green 60 10
1165 – 25 c. brown (air) . . . . 1·00 15
DESIGN: 25 c. Nurse and child.

1951. Air. Stamp Day and 500th Birth Anniv of Isabella the Catholic.
1166 **250** 60 c. green . . . . . . 11·00 50
1167 90 c. yellow . . . . . . 1·50 70
1168 1 p. 30 red . . . . . . 10·00 5·50
1169 1 p. 90 sepia . . . . . 7·50 7·50
1170 2 p. 30 blue . . . . . 5·00 3·00

251 Ferdinand the Catholic

252 St. Maria Micaela

1952. 500th Birth Anniv of Ferdinand the Catholic.
1171 **251** 50 c. green . . . . . . 1·00 35
1172 75 c. blue . . . . . . 6·50 1·75
1173 90 c. purple . . . . . . 1·00 35
1174 1 p. 50 orange . . . . . 17·00 8·00
1175 2 p. 80 brown . . . . . 25·00 17·00

1952. 35th International Eucharistic Congress, Barcelona.
1176 **252** 60 c. red (postage) . . . 20 10
1177 – 1 p. green (air) . . . . . 6·00 40
DESIGN: 1 p. "The Eucharist" (Tiepolo).

252a St. Francis Xavier

254 Nurse and Baby

1952. Air. 400th Death Anniv of St. Francis Xavier.
1178 **252a** 2 p. blue . . . . 60·00 20·00

1952. Air. Stamp Day and 500th Anniv of Birth of Ferdinand the Catholic. As T **250** but interior scene and portrait of Ferdinand the Catholic.
1179 60 c. green 45 20
1180 90 c. orange 45 20
1181 1 p. 30 red 85 20
1182 1 p. 90 brown . . . . . . 5·50 2·75
1183 2 p. 30 blue . . . . . . 15·00 11·00

1953. Anti-Tuberculosis Fund. Cross in red.
1184 **254** 5 c. lake (postage) . . . 70 10
1185 10 c. green . . . . . . 1·60 10
1186 – 25 c. brown (air) . . . . 7·00 3·00
DESIGN: 25 c. Girl and angel.

255 J. Sorolla (painter)

1953. Air.
1229 – 25 p. black . . . . . . 30·00 70
1187 **255** 50 p. violet . . . . . . £550 18·00
1230 – 50 p. violet . . . . . . 10·00 1·25
PORTRAITS: No. 1229, Fortuny (painter); 1230, T. Quevedo (engineer and inventor).

256 Bas-relief

257 Fray Luis de Leon

1953. Stamp Day and 700th Anniv of Salamanca University. Inscr "UNIVDAD DE SALAMANCA".
1188 **256** 50 c. red 60 10
1189 **257** 90 c. green . . . . . . 3·00 2·40
1190 – 2 p. brown . . . . . . 23·00 3·00
DESIGN—As Type **185**—HORIZ: 2 p. Salamanca University.

258 M. L. de Legazpi (founder of Manila)

1953. Air. Signing of Filipino–Spanish Postal Convention.
1191 **258** 25 p. black . . . . . . £140 30·00

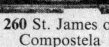

259 "St. Mary Magdalene"

260 St. James of Compostela

1954. Death Tercentenary of Ribera (painter).
1192 **259** 1 p. 25 lake 15 10

1954. Holy Year.
1193 **260** 50 c. brown 20 10
1194 – 3 p. blue . . . . . . 50·00 2·50
DESIGN: 3 p. Santiago Cathedral.

261 "Purity" (after Cano)

262 M. Menendez Pelayo (historian)

1954. Marian Year.
1195 **261** 10 c. red 10 10
1196 – 15 c. green 10 10
1197 – 25 c. violet 15 10
1198 – 30 c. brown 20 10
1199 – 50 c. green 90 10
1200 – 60 c. black 20 10
1201 – 80 c. green . . . . . . 5·00 10
1202 – 1 p. violet . . . . . . 5·00 10
1203 – 2 p. brown . . . . . . 1·25 10
1204 – 3 p. blue . . . . . . 1·25 90
DESIGNS: 15 c. Virgin of Begona, Bilbao; 25 c. Virgin of the Abandoned, Valencia Cathedral; 30 c. The "Black Virgin" of Montserrat; 50 c. El Pilar Virgin, Zaragoza; 60 c. Covadonga Virgin; 80 c. Virgin of the Kings, Seville Cathedral; 1 p. Almudena Virgin, Madrid; 2 p. Virgin of Africa; 3 p. Guadalupe Virgin.

1954. Stamp Day.
1205 **262** 80 c. green 10·00 20

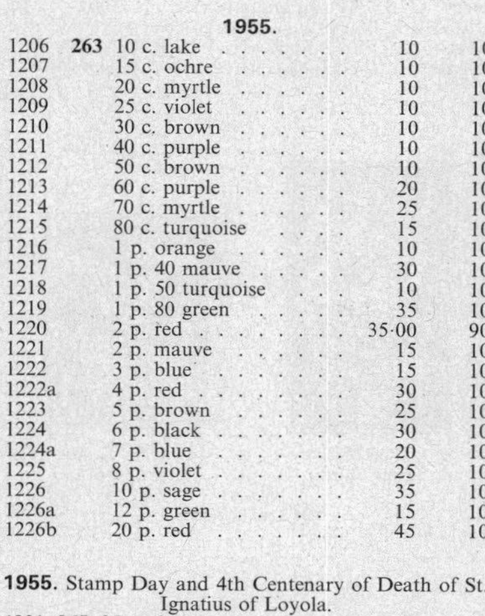
263 Gen. Franco **265** St. Ignatius of Loyola

1955.
1206 **263** 10 c. lake 10 10
1207 15 c. ochre 10 10
1208 20 c. myrtle 10 10
1209 25 c. violet 10 10
1210 30 c. brown 10 10
1211 40 c. purple 10 10
1212 50 c. brown 10 10
1213 60 c. purple 20 10
1214 70 c. myrtle 25 10
1215 80 c. turquoise 15 10
1216 1 p. orange 10 10
1217 1 p. 40 mauve 30 10
1218 1 p. 50 turquoise 10 10
1219 1 p. 80 green 35 10
1220 2 p. red 35·00 90
1221 2 p. mauve 15 10
1222 3 p. blue 15 10
1222a 4 p. red 30 10
1223 5 p. brown 25 10
1224 6 p. black 30 10
1224a 7 p. blue 20 10
1225 8 p. violet 25 10
1226 10 p. sage 35 10
1226a 12 p. green 15 10
1226b 20 p. red 45 10

1955. Stamp Day and 4th Centenary of Death of St. Ignatius of Loyola.
1231 **265** 25 c. slate 15 10
1232 – 60 c. ochre 1·10 20
1233 **265** 80 c. green 4·50 15
DESIGN—HORIZ: 60 c. St. Ignatius and Loyola Castle.

266 Lockheed L.1049 Super Constellation and Caravel

1955. Air.
1234 **266** 20 c. myrtle 10 10
1235 25 c. slate 10 10
1236 50 c. brown 15 10
1237 1 p. red 15 10
1238 1 p. 10 green 20 10
1239 1 p. 40 mauve 25 10
1240 3 p. blue 25 10
1241 4 p. 80 yellow 25 10
1242 5 p. brown 2·25 10
1243 7 p. mauve 75 20
1244 10 p. green 1·10 25

267 "Telecommunications" **269** "The Holy Family" (after El Greco)

1955. Centenary of Telegraphs in Spain.
1245 **267** 15 c. brown 55 15
1246 80 c. green 12·00 25
1247 3 p. blue 23·00 1·00

1955. 500th Anniv of Canonization of St. Vincent Ferrer. As T **259** but portrait of the Saint (after C. Vilar).
1248 15 c. ochre 70 20

1955. Christmas.
1249 **269** 80 c. myrtle 5·00 45

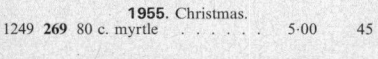

270 **272** The "Black Virgin"

271 "Ciudad de Toledo"

1956. 20th Anniv of Civil War.
1250 **270** 15 c. brown and bistre 15 10
1251 50 c. olive and green 1·00 40
1252 80 c. grey and mauve 9·00 20
1253 3 p. blue and ultramarine 10·00 1·75

1956. 1st Floating Exhibition of National Products.
1254 **271** 3 p. blue 6·00 1·75

1956. 75th Anniv of "Black Virgin" of Montserrat.
1255 **272** 15 c. brown 10 10
1256 – 60 c. purple 55 30
1257 **272** 80 c. green 75 35
DESIGN—VERT: 60 c. Montserrat Monastery.

273 Archangel Gabriel **274** "Statistics"

1956. Stamp Day.
1258 **273** 80 c. green 95 50

1956. Centenary of Statistics in Spain.
1259 **274** 15 c. ochre 40 25
1260 80 c. green 5·00 50
1261 1 p. red 5·00 50

275 Hermitage and Monument **276** Refugee Children

1956. 20th Anniv of Gen. Franco's Assumption of Office as Head of State.
1262 **275** 80 c. green 4·50 30

1956. Hungarian Children's Relief.
1263 **276** 10 c. lake 10 10
1264 15 c. brown 15 10
1265 50 c. sepia 40 20
1266 80 c. green 4·00 15
1267 1 p. red 4·00 15
1268 3 p. blue 12·00 1·75

277 Apparition of the Sacred Heart **278** "The Great Captain"

1957. Stamp Day and Centenary Feast of the Sacred Heart.
1269 **277** 15 c. olive 10 10
1270 60 c. purple 50 10
1271 80 c. green 50 10

1958. 5th Birth Cent of Gonzalves de Cordoba.
1272 **278** 1 p. 80 green 15 10

279 Francisco Goya after Lopez **280** Exhibition Emblem

1958. Stamp Day and Goya (painter) Commem. Frames in gold.
1273 – 15 c. ochre 10 10
1274 – 40 c. purple 10 10
1275 – 50 c. olive 10 10
1276 – 60 c. purple 15 10
1277 – 70 c. green 15 10
1278 **279** 80 c. myrtle 20 10
1279 – 1 p. red 20 10
1280 – 1 p. 80 green 25 10
1281 – 2 p. mauve 55 30
1282 – 3 p. blue 1·00 50
PAINTINGS—HORIZ: 15 c. "The Sunshade"; 3 p. "The Drinker". VERT: 40 c. "The Bookseller's Wife"; 50 c. "The Count of Fernan-Nunez"; 60 c. "The Crockery Vendor"; 70 c. "Dona Isabel Cobos de Porcel"; 1 p. "The Carnival Doll"; 1 p. 80, "Marianito Goya"; 2 p. "The Vintage".
For similar designs see Nos. 1301/10, 1333/42, 1391/1400, 1479/88, 1495/8, 1559/68, 1627/36, 1718/27, 1770/9, 1837/46, 1912/21, 1968/77, 2021/30, 2077/84, 2135/42 and 2204/11.

1958. Brussels International Exhibition.
1283 **280** 80 c. brown, red and deep brown 50 10
1284 3 p. blue, red & black 2·00 80

281 Emperor Charles V (after Strigell)

1958. 4th Death Cent of Emperor Charles V.
1287 **281** 15 c. brown and ochre 10 10
1288 – 50 c. olive and green 15 10
1289 – 70 c. green and drab 30 20
1290 – 80 c. green and brown 20 10
1291 **281** 1 p. red and buff 40 10
1292 – 1 p. 80 emerald & green 30 20
1293 – 2 p. purple and grey 95 60
1294 – 3 p. blue and brown 2·25 1·25
PORTRAITS of Charles V: 50 c., 1 p. 80, At Battle of Muhlberg (after Titian); 70 c., 2 p. (after Leoni); 80 c., 3 p. (after Titian).

282 Talgo Express and Escorial

1958. 17th Int Railway Congress, Madrid. Inscr "XVII CONGRESO", etc.
1295 **282** 15 c. ochre 15 50
1296 – 60 c. plum 20 10
1297 – 80 c. green 35 10
1298 **282** 1 p. orange 1·00 10
1299 – 2 p. purple 1·00 10
1300 – 3 p. blue 3·00 90
DESIGNS—VERT: 60 c., 2 p. Diesel train on viaduct, Despenaperros Gorge. HORIZ: 80 c., 3 p. Steam locomotive and Castillo de La Mota.

1959. Stamp Day and Velazquez Commem. Designs as T **279**. Frames in gold.
1301 15 c. sepia 10 10
1302 40 c. purple 10 10
1303 50 c. olive 10 10
1304 60 c. sepia 10 10
1305 70 c. green 10 10
1306 80 c. myrtle 10 10
1307 1 p. brown 15 10
1308 1 p. 80 green 10 10
1309 2 p. purple 25 20
1310 3 p. blue 45 45
PAINTINGS—HORIZ: 15 c. "The Drunkards". VERT: 40 c. "The Spinners" (detail); 50 c. "The Surrender of Breda"; 60 c. "Las Meninas"; 70 c. "Balthasar Don Carlos"; 80 c. Self-portrait; 1 p. "The Coronation of the Virgin"; 1 p. 80, "Aesop"; 2 p. "The Forge of Vulcan"; 3 p. "Menippus".

284 The Holy Cross of the Valley of the Fallen

1959. Completion of Holy Cross Monastery.
1311 **284** 80 c. green and sepia 20 10

285 Mazarin and Luis de Haro (after tapestry by Lebrun) **286** Monastery from Courtyard

1959. 300th Anniv of Treaty of the Pyrenees.
1312 **285** 1 p. brown and gold 20 10

1959. 50th Anniv of Entry of Franciscan Community into Guadeloupe Monastery.
1313 **286** 15 c. brown 10 10
1314 – 80 c. myrtle 20 10
1315 – 1 p. red 25 10
DESIGNS: 80 c. Exterior view of monastery; 1 p. Entrance doors of church.

287 "The Holy Family" (after Goya) **288** Pass with Muleta

1959. Christmas.
1316 **287** 1 p. brown 30 10

1960. Bullfighting.
1317 – 15 c. brown & ochre (postage) 10 10
1318 – 20 c. violet and blue 10 10
1319 – 25 c. black 10 10
1320 – 30 c. sepia and bistre 10 10
1321 – 50 c. violet and sepia 25 10
1322 – 70 c. turq and brown 25 10
1323 **288** 80 c. green and turq 10 10
1324 – 1 p. brown and red 55 10
1325 – 1 p. 40 red and brown 10 10
1326 – 1 p. 50 green and blue 10 10
1327 – 1 p. 80 blue and green 10 10
1328 – 5 p. lake and brown 1·10 60
1329 – 25 c. purple & mve (air) 15 10
1330 – 50 c. blue & turquoise 20 10
1331 – 1 p. red and deep red 45 10
1332 – 5 p. violet and purple 1·10 50
DESIGNS—HORIZ: No. 1317, Fighting bull; No. 1318, Rounding-up bull; No. 1327, Placing darts from horseback; No. 1330, Pass with cape; No. 1332, Bull-ring. VERT: No. 1319, Corralling bulls at Pamplona; No. 1320, Bull entering ring; No. 1321, As No. 1330 (different pass); No. 1322, Banderillero placing darts; No. 1323/6, As Type **288** (different passes with muleta); No. 1328, Old-time bull-fighter; No. 1329, Village bull-ring; No. 1331, Dedicating the bull.

1960. Stamp Day and Murillo Commemoration. (painter). Designs as T **279**. Frames in gold.
1333 25 c. violet 10 10
1334 40 c. purple 15 10
1335 50 c. olive 20 10
1336 70 c. green 20 10
1337 80 c. turquoise 20 10
1338 1 p. brown 20 10
1339 1 p. 50 turquoise 20 10
1340 2 p. 50 red 30 10
1341 3 p. blue 1·40 65
1342 5 p. brown 50 25
PAINTINGS—VERT: 25 c. "The Good Shepherd"; 40 c. "Rebecca and Elizer"; 50 c. "The Virgin of the Rosary"; 70 c. "The Immaculate Conception"; 80 c. "Children with Shells"; 1 p. Self-portrait; 2 p. 50, "The Dice Game"; 3 p. "Children Eating"; 5 p. "Children with Coins". HORIZ: 1 p. 50, "The Holy Family with Bird".

289 "Christ of Lepanto" **290** Pelota Player

1960. Int Philatelic Congress and Exhibition, Barcelona. Inscr "CIF".

1343 **289** 70 c. lake & grn (postage) 2·00 1·50
1344 – 80 c. black and sage 2·00 1·50
1345 **289** 1 p. purple and red 2·00 1·50
1346 – 2 p. 50 slate and violet 2·00 1·50
1347 **289** 5 p. sepia and bistre 2·00 1·50
1348 – 10 p. sepia and ochre 2·00 1·50

1349 **290** 1 p. black and red (air) 4·50 3·25
1350 5 p. red and brown 4·50 3·25
1351 6 p. red and purple 4·50 3·25
1352 10 p. red and green 4·50 3·25

DESIGN—VERT: Nos. 1344, 1346, 1348, Church of the Holy Family, Barcelona.

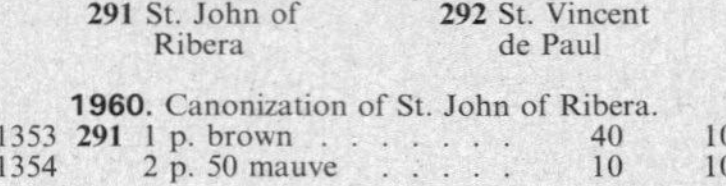

291 St. John of Ribera **292** St. Vincent de Paul

1960. Canonization of St. John of Ribera.

1353 **291** 1 p. brown 40 10
1354 2 p. 50 mauve 10 10

1960. Europa. 1st Anniv of European Postal and Telecommunications Conference. As T **129a** of Luxembourg but size 38½ × 22 mm.

1355 1 p. drab and myrtle 2·25 20
1356 5 p. red and brown 2·25 35

1960. 300th Death Anniv of St. Vincent de Paul.

1357 **292** 25 c. violet 10 10
1358 1 p. brown 30 10

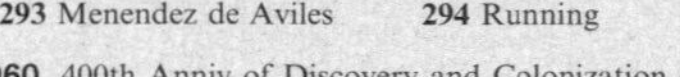

293 Menendez de Aviles **294** Running

1960. 400th Anniv of Discovery and Colonization of Florida.

1359 **293** 25 c. violet and blue 10 10
1360 – 70 c. myrtle and salmon 10 10
1361 – 80 c. green and stone 10 10
1362 – 1 p. brown and yellow 15 10
1363 **293** 2 p. red and pink 30 10
1364 – 2 p. 50 mauve & green 50 10
1365 – 3 p. blue and green 2·25 40
1366 – 5 p. sepia and bistre 1·75 75

PORTRAITS: 70 c., 2 p. 50, Hernando de Soto; 80 c., 3 p. Ponce de Leon; 1, 5 p. Cabeza de Vaca.

1960. Sports.

1367 **294** 25 c. brown and blue (postage) 10 10
1368 – 40 c. orange and violet 10 10
1369 – 70 c. red and green 30 10
1370 – 80 c. red and green 20 10
1371 – 1 p. green and red 60 10
1372 **294** 1 p. 50 sepia & turquoise 30 10
1373 – 2 p. green and purple 80 10
1374 – 2 p. 50 green & mauve 30 10
1375 – 3 p. red and blue 45 15
1376 – 5 p. blue and brown 80 30

1377 – 1 p. 25 red & brown (air) 35 10
1378 – 1 p. 50 brown & violet 35 10
1379 – 6 p. red and violet 80 45
1380 – 10 p. red and olive 95 55

DESIGNS—HORIZ: 40 c., 2 p. Cycling; 70 c., 2 p. 50, Football; 1, 5 p. Hockey; 1 p. 25, 6 p. Horse-jumping. VERT: 80 c., 3 p. Gymnastics; 1 p. 50 (air), 10 p. Pelota.

295 Albeniz **296** Cloisters

1960. Birth Cent of Isaac Albeniz (composer).

1381 **295** 25 c. violet 10 10
1382 1 p. brown 30 10

1960. Samos Monastery.

1383 **296** 80 c. turquoise and green 10 10
1384 – 1 p. lake and brown 1·50 10
1385 – 5 p. sepia and bistre 90 50

DESIGNS—VERT: 1 p. Fountain; 5 p. Portico and facade.

297 "The Nativity" (Velazquez) **298** "The Flight to Egypt" (after Bayeu)

1960. Christmas.

1386 **297** 1 p. brown 20 10

1961. World Refugee Year.

1387 **298** 1 p. brown 45 10
1388 5 p. brown 80 10

299 L. F. Moratin (after Goya) **301** Velazquez (Prado Memorial)

1961. Birth Bicentenary of Moratin (poet and dramatist).

1389 **299** 1 p. red 20 10
1390 1 p. 50 turquoise 10 10

1961. Stamp Day and El Greco (painter) Commem. Designs as T **279**. Frames in gold.

1391 25 c. purple 25 10
1392 40 c. purple 20 10
1393 70 c. green 25 20
1394 80 c. turquoise 25 10
1395 1 p. purple 2·00 10
1396 1 p. 50 turquoise 35 10
1397 2 p. 50 lake 35 10
1398 3 p. blue 1·00 70
1399 5 p. sepia 2·50 1·75
1400 10 p. violet 50 40

PAINTINGS: 25 c. "St. Peter"; 40 c. Part of "The Holy Family"; 70 c. Part of "The Agony in the Garden"; 80 c. "Man with Hand on Breast"; 1 p. Self-portrait; 1 p. 50, "The Baptism of Christ"; 2 p. 50, "The Holy Trinity"; 3 p. "Burial of the Count of Orgaz"; 5 p. "The Spoliation"; 10 p. "The Martyrdom of St. Maurice".

1961. 300th Death Anniv of Velazquez.

1401 **301** 80 c. green and blue 1·40 20
1402 – 1 p. brown and red 2·75 20
1403 – 2 p. 50 violet and blue 85 30
1404 – 10 p. green & lt green 2·25 80

PAINTINGS—VERT: 1 p. "The Duke of Olivares"; 2 p. 50, "Princess Margarita". HORIZ: Part of "The Spinners".

302 "Stamp" and "Postmark" **303** Vazquez de Mella

1961. World Stamp Day.

1409 **302** 25 c. black and red 15 10
1410 1 p. red and black 1·60 10
1411 10 p. green and purple 1·60 50

1961. Birth Centenary of Juan Vazquez de Mella (politician and writer).

1412 **303** 1 p. red 50 10
1413 2 p. 30 purple 15 15

304 Gen. Franco **305** "Portico de la Gloria" (Cathedral of Santiago de Compostela)

1961. 25th Anniv of National Uprising. Multicoloured.

1414 70 c. Angel and flag 20 10
1415 80 c. Straits of Gibraltar 20 10
1416 1 p. Knight and Alcazar, Toledo 35 10
1417 1 p. 50 Victory Arch 25 10
1418 2 p. Knight crossing River Ebro 25 10
1419 2 p. 30 Soldier, flag and troops 25 10
1420 2 p. 50 Shipbuilding 30 30
1421 3 p. Steelworks 40 30
1422 5 p. Map of Spain showing electric power stations 2·75 1·25
1423 6 p. Irrigation (woman beside dam) 1·50 1·00
1424 8 p. Mine 1·00 55
1425 10 p. Type **304** 75 55

The 5 p. is horiz and the rest vert.

1961. Council of Europe's Romanesque Art Exhibition. Inscr as in T **305**.

1426 **305** 25 c. violet and gold 45 10
1427 – 1 p. brown and gold 45 10
1428 – 2 p. purple and gold 60 10
1429 – 3 p. multicoloured 1·00 15

DESIGNS: 1 p. Courtyard of Dominican Monastery, Santo Domingo de Silos; 2 p. Madonna of Irache; 3 p. "Christos Pantocrator" (from Tahull Church fresco).

306 L. de Gongora (after Velazquez) **308** Burgos Cathedral

307 Doves and C.E.P.T. Emblem

1961. 400th Birth Anniv of De Gongora (poet).

1430 **306** 25 c. violet 10 10
1431 1 p. brown 20 10

1961. Europa.

1432 **307** 1 p. red 15 10
1433 5 p. brown 40 30

1961. 25th Anniv of Gen. Franco as Head of State.

1434 **308** 1 p. green and gold 20 10

309 S. de Belalcazar **310** Courtyard

1961. Explorers and Colonizers of America (1st series).

1435 **309** 25 c. violet and green 10 10
1436 – 70 c. green and buff 15 10
1437 – 80 c. green and pink 15 10
1438 – 1 p. blue and flesh 55 10
1439 **309** 2 p. red and blue 3·50 10
1440 – 2 p. 50 purple & mauve 80 35
1441 – 3 p. blue and grey 1·75 60
1442 – 5 p. brown and yellow 1·90 75

PORTRAITS: 70 c., 2 p. 50, B de Lezo; 80 c., 3 p. R. de Bastidas; 1, 5 p. N. de Chaves.

See also Nos. 1515/22, 1587/94, 1683/90, 1738/45, 1810/17, 1877/84, 1947/51, 1997/2001 and 2054/8.

1961. Escorial.

1443 – 70 c. green and turquoise 20 10
1444 **310** 80 c. slate and green 20 10
1445 – 1 p. red and brown 65 10
1446 – 2 p. 50 purple & violet 50 10
1447 – 5 p. sepia and ochre 1·75 55
1448 – 6 p. purple and blue 2·00 1·40

DESIGNS—VERT: 70 c. Patio of the Kings; 2 p. 50, Grand Staircase; 6 p. High Altar. HORIZ: 1 p. Monks' Garden; 5 p. View of Escorial.

311 King Alfonso XII Monument **312** Santa Maria del Naranco Church

1961. 400th Anniv of Madrid as Capital of Spain.

1449 **311** 25 c. purple and green 25 10
1450 – 1 p. brown and bistre 45 10
1451 – 2 p. purple and grey 45 10
1452 – 2 p. 50 violet and red 40 10
1453 – 3 p. black and blue 90 40
1454 – 5 p. blue and brown 2·00 55

DESIGNS—VERT: 1 p. King Philip II (after Pantoja); 5 p. Plaza, Madrid. HORIZ: 2 p. Town Hall, Madrid; 2 p. 50, Fountain of Cybele; 3 p. Portals of Alcala Palace.

1961. 1200th Anniv of Oviedo.

1455 **312** 25 c. violet and green 10 10
1456 – 1 p. brown and bistre 35 10
1457 – 2 p. sepia and purple 75 10
1458 – 2 p. 50 violet & purple 20 10
1459 – 3 p. black and blue 75 40
1460 – 5 p. brown and green 1·10 55

DESIGNS: 1 p. Fruela (portrait); 2 p. Cross of the Angels; 2 p. 50, Alfonso II; 3 p. Alfonso III; 5 p. Apostles of the Holy Hall, Oviedo Cathedral.

313 "The Nativity" (after Gines) **314** Cierva C.30A Autogyro

1961. Christmas.

1461 **313** 1 p. plum 30 10

1961. 50th Anniv of Spanish Aviation.

1462 **314** 1 p. violet and blue 20 10
1463 – 2 p. green and lilac 40 15
1464 – 3 p. black and green 2·25 40
1465 – 5 p. purple and slate 4·25 1·40
1466 – 10 p. brown and blue 1·90 50

DESIGNS—HORIZ: 2 p. CASA-built Dornier Do-J Wal flying boat "Plus Ultra"; 3 p. Breguet 19GR "Jesus del Gran Poder"; 5 p. Avro 504K biplane hunting great bustard; 10 p. Madonna of Loreto (patron saint).

315 Arms of Alava **316** "Ecstasy of St. Teresa" (Bernini)

1962. Arms of Provincial Capitals. Multicoloured.

1467 5 p. Type **315** 20 10
1468 5 p. Albacete 20 10
1469 5 p. Alicante 30 25
1470 5 p. Almeria 35 25
1471 5 p. Avila 35 25
1472 5 p. Badajoz 25 10
1473 5 p. Baleares 25 10
1474 5 p. Barcelona 25 10
1475 5 p. Burgos 1·10 30
1476 5 p. Caceres 75 20
1477 5 p. Cadiz 90 25
1478 5 p. Castellon de la Plana 6·00 1·75

See also Nos. 1542/53, 1612/23, 1692/1703 and 1756/64.

1962. Stamp Day and Zurbaran (painter) Commem. As T **279**. Frames in gold.

1479 25 c. olive 10 10
1480 40 c. purple 10 10
1481 70 c. green 15 10
1482 80 c. turquoise 15 10
1483 1 p. sepia 2·75 10
1484 1 p. 50 turquoise 40 10
1485 2 p. 50 lake 40 10
1486 3 p. blue 40 35
1487 5 p. brown 1·10 80
1488 10 p. olive 1·10 85

PAINTINGS—HORIZ: 25 c. "Martyr". VERT: 40 c. "Burial of St. Catalina"; 70 c. "St. Casilda"; 80 c. "Jesus crowning St. Joseph"; 1 p. Self-portrait; 1 p. 50, "St. Hieronymus"; 2 p. 50, "Madonna of the Grace"; 3 p. Detail from "Apotheosis of St. Thomas Aquinas"; 5 p. "Madonna as a Child"; 10 p. "The Immaculate Madonna".

1962. 4th Centenary of Teresian Reformation.

1489 – 25 c. violet 10 10
1490 **316** 1 p. brown 20 10
1491 – 3 p. blue 1·40 20

DESIGNS—As Type **316**: 25 c. St. Joseph's Monastery, Avila. (22 × 38½ mm): 3 p. "St. Teresa of Avila" (Velazquez).

317 Mercury

318 St. Benedict

1962. World Stamp Day.
1492 **317** 25 c. pink, purple & violet . . 10 10
1493 1 p. yellow, brown and bistre 20 10
1494 10 p. green & turquoise . 1·75 55

1962. Rubens Paintings. As T **279**. Frames in gold.
1495 25 c. violet 40 15
1496 1 p. brown . . . . 2·00 10
1497 3 p. turquoise . . . . 2·00 1·00
1498 10 p. green . . . . 2·00 1·25
PAINTINGS—As Type **279**: 25 c. Ferdinand of Austria; 1 p. Self-portrait; 3 p. Philip II. (26×39 mm): 10 p. Duke of Lerma.

1962. 400th Death Anniv of Alonso Berruguete (sculptor). Sculptures by Berruguete.
1499 **318** 25 c. mauve and blue . . 10 10
1500 – 80 c. green and brown . . 25 10
1501 – 1 p. red and stone . . . 50 10
1502 – 2 p. mauve and stone . . 3·00 10
1503 – 3 p. blue and mauve . . 1·25 75
1504 – 10 p. brown and pink . . 1·25 50
SCULPTURES: 80 c. "The Apostle"; 1 p. "St. Peter"; 2 p. "St. Christopher and Child Jesus"; 3 p. "Ecce Homo"; 10 p. "St. Sebastian".

319 El Cid (R. Diaz de Vivar), after statue by J. Cristobal

321 Throwing the Discus

320 Bee and Honeycomb

1962. El Cid Campeador Commem. Inscr "EL CID".
1505 **319** 1 p. drab and green . . . 15 10
1506 – 2 p. violet and sepia . . 1·25 10
1507 – 3 p. green and blue . . . 3·50 1·10
1508 – 10 p. green and yellow . 1·75 75
DESIGNS—VERT: 2 p. El Cid (equestrian statue by A. Huntington). HORIZ: 3 p. El Cid's treasure chest; 10 p. Oath-taking ceremony of Santa Gadea.

1962. Europa.
1509 **320** 1 p. red 40 10
1510 5 p. green . . . . 1·50 30

1962. 2nd Spanish–American Athletic Games, Madrid.
1511 **321** 25 c. violet and pink . . 10 10
1512 – 80 c. green and yellow . . 40 10
1513 – 1 p. sepia and salmon . . 20 10
1514 – 3 p. blue and pale blue . . 20 15
DESIGNS: 80 c. Running; 1 p. Hurdling; 3 p. Start of sprint.

1962. Explorers and Colonizers of America (2nd series). As T **309**.
1515 25 c. purple and grey . . . 10 10
1516 70 c. green and pale pink . . 70 10
1517 80 c. green and yellow . . . 55 10
1518 1 p. brown and green . . . 95 10
1519 2 p. lake and blue . . . . 2·50 10
1520 2 p. 50 violet & brown . . . 55 20
1521 3 p. blue and pink . . . . 6·00 75
1522 5 p. brown and yellow . . . 2·75 1·00
PORTRAITS: 25 c., 2 p. A. de Mendoza; 70 c., 2 p. 50, J. de Quesada; 80 c., 3 p. J. de Garay; 1 p., 5 p. P. de la Gasca.

322 U.P.A.E. Emblem

323 "The Annunciation" (after Murillo)

1962. 50th Anniv of Postal Union of the Americas and Spain.
1523 **322** 1 p. brown, grn & dp grn 20 10

1962. Mysteries of the Rosary.
1524 **323** 25 c. brn & vio (postage) 10 10
1525 – 70 c. turquoise and green 10 10
1526 – 80 c. turquoise and olive 10 10
1527 – 1 p. sepia and green . . 2·25 60
1528 – 1 p. 50 blue and green . 10 5
1529 – 2 p. sepia and violet . . 70 40
1530 – 2 p. 50 red and purple . 20 15
1531 – 3 p. black and violet . . 20 15
1532 – 5 p. lake and brown . . 35 35
1533 – 8 p. black and purple . 35 30
1534 – 10 p. green and myrtle . 50 30
1535 – 25 c. violet and slate (air) 10 5
1536 – 1 p. olive and purple . . 20 15
1537 – 5 p. lake and purple . . 35 25
1538 – 10 p. yellow, grn & grey 85 55
PAINTINGS—"Joyful Mysteries": No. 1525, "Visit of Elizabeth" (Correa); No. 1526, "The Birth of Christ" (Murillo); No. 1527, "Christ shown to the Elders" (Campana); No. 1528, "Jesus lost and found in the Temple" (unknown artist). "Sorrowful Mysteries": No. 1529, "Prayer on the Mount of Olives" (Giaquinto); No. 1530, "Scourging" (Cano); No. 1531, "The Crown of Thorns" (Tiepolo); No. 1532, "Carrying the Cross" (El Greco); No. 1533, "The Crucifixion" (Murillo). "Glorious Mysteries": No. 1534, "The Resurrection" (Murillo); No. 1535, "The Ascension" (Bayeu); No. 1536, "The Sending-forth of the Holy Ghost" (El Greco); No. 1537, "The Assumption of the Virgin" (Cerezo); No. 1538, "The Coronation of the Virgin" (El Greco).

324 "The Nativity" (after Pedro de Mena)

325 Campaign Emblem and Swamp

1962. Christmas.
1539 **324** 1 p. olive 50 10

1962. Malaria Eradication.
1540 **325** 1 p. black, yellow & grn 30 10

326 Pope John and Dome of St. Peter's

327 "St. Paul" (after El Greco)

1962. Ecumenical Council. Vatican City (1st issue).
1541 **326** 1 p. slate and purple . . 30 10
See also Nos. 1601 and 1755.

1963. Arms of Provincial Capitals. As T **315**. Multicoloured.
1542 5 p. Ciudad Real 75 25
1542 5 p. Cordoba . . . . 6·00 1·50
1543 5 p. Coruna 75 30
1544 5 p. Cuenca 75 30
1545 5 p. Fernando Poo . . . . . 1·50 90
1546 5 p. Gerona 15 10
1547 5 p. Gran Canaria 15 10
1549 5 p. Granada 30 20
1550 5 p. Guadalajara 75 25
1551 5 p. Guipuzcoa 15 10
1552 5 p. Huelva 15 10
1553 5 p. Huesca 15 10

1963. 1900th Anniv of Arrival of St. Paul in Spain.
1554 **327** 1 p. sepia, olive & brown 50 10

328 Poblet Monastery

329 Mail Coach

1963. Poblet Monastery.
1555 **328** 25 c. purple, sepia & grn 10 10
1556 – 1 p. orange and red . . 50 10
1557 – 3 p. blue and violet . . 1·00 20
1558 – 5 p. ochre and brown . 1·75 1·00
DESIGNS—VERT: 1 p. Tomb; 5 p. Arch. HORIZ: 3 p. Aerial view of monastery.

1963. Stamp Day and Ribera (painter) Commem. As T **279**. Frames in gold.
1559 25 c. violet 10 10
1560 40 c. purple 10 10
1561 70 c. green 25 10
1562 80 c. turquoise 25 10
1563 1 p. brown 25 10
1564 1 p. 50 turquoise 25 10
1565 2 p. 50 red . . . . 1·10 15
1566 3 p. blue . . . . 1·10 30
1567 5 p. brown . . . . 4·50 1·40
1568 10 p. brown and purple . . 1·10 70
PAINTINGS: 25 c. "Archimedes"; 40 c. "Jacob's Flock"; 70 c. "Triumph of Bacchus"; 80 c. "St. Christopher"; 1 p. Self-portrait; 1 p. 50, "St. Andrew"; 2 p. 50, "St. John the Baptist"; 3 p. "St. Onofrius"; 5 p. "St. Peter"; 10 p. "The Madonna".

1963. Centenary of Paris Postal Conference.
1569 **329** 1 p. multicoloured . . . 10 10

330 Globe

1963. World Stamp Day.
1570 **330** 25 c. multicoloured . . . 15 10
1571 1 p. multicoloured . . . 25 10
1572 10 p. multicoloured . . . 1·75 30

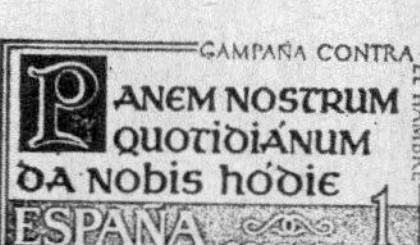

331 "Give us this day our daily bread"

332 Pillars and Globes

1963. Freedom from Hunger.
1573 **331** 1 p. multicoloured . . . 20 10

1963. Spanish Cultural Institutions Congress. Multicoloured.
1574 25 c. Type **332** 15 10
1575 80 c. "Santa Maria", "Pinta" and "Nina" 30 10
1576 1 p. Columbus 30 10

333 Civic Seals

334 "St. Maria of Europe"

1963. 150th Anniv of San Sebastian.
1577 **333** 25 c. blue and green . . . 10 10
1578 – 80 c. red and purple . . . 20 10
1579 – 1 p. green and bistre . . 20 10
DESIGNS: 80 c. City aflame; 1 p. View of San Sebastian, 1836.

1963. Europa.
1580 **334** 1 p. brown and bistre . . 30 10
1581 5 p. sepia and green . . . 80 30

335 Arms of the Order of Mercy

336 Scenes from Parable of the Good Samaritan

1963. 75th Anniv of the Order of Mercy.
1582 **335** 25 c. red, gold & black . 10 10
1583 – 80 c. sepia and green . . 10 10
1584 – 1 p. purple and blue . . . 15 15
1585 – 1 p. 50 brown and blue . 15 10
1586 – 3 p. black and violet . . 25 15
DESIGNS: 80 c. King Jaime I; 1 p. Our Lady of Mercy; 1 p. 50, St. Pedro Nolasco; 3 p. St. Raimundo de Penafort.

1963. Explorers and Colonizers of America (3rd series). As T **309**.
1587 25 c. deep blue and blue . . 25 10
1588 70 c. green and salmon . . 25 10
1589 80 c. green and cream . . . 50 10
1590 1 p. blue and salmon . . . 50 10
1591 2 p. red and blue . . . . . 2·00 10
1592 2 p. 50 violet and flesh . . 1·25 10
1593 3 p. blue and pink . . . . 2·25 10
1594 5 p. brown and cream . . . 2·50 1·40
PORTRAITS: 25 c., 2 p. Brother J. Serra; 70 c., 2 p. 50, Vasco Nunez de Balboa; 80 c., 3 p. J. de Galvez; 1 p., 5 p. D. Garcia de Paredes.

1963. Red Cross Centenary.
1595 **336** 1 p. violet, red and gold 15 10

337 "The Nativity" (after sculpture by Berruguete)

338 Fr. Raimundo Lulio

1963. Christmas.
1596 **337** 1 p. green 15 10

1963. Famous Spaniards (1st series).
1597 **338** 1 p. blk & vio (postage) . 25 10
1598 – 1 p. 50 violet and sepia . 25 10
1599 – 25 p. purple and red (air) 1·25 25
1600 – 50 p. black and green . . 1·25 40
PORTRAITS: 1 p. 50, Cardinal Belluga; 25 p. King Recaredo; 50 p. Cardinal Cisneros.
See also Nos. 1714/17.

339 Pope Paul and Dome of St. Peter's

1963. Ecumenical Council, Vatican City (2nd issue).
1601 **339** 1 p. black & turquoise . 20 10

340 Alcazar de Segovia

1964. Tourist Series.
1602 – 40 c. brown, blue & grn . 15 10
1603 – 50 c. sepia and blue . . 15 10
1604 – 70 c. blue and green . . 15 10
1605 – 70 c. brown and lilac . . 15 10
1606 – 80 c. black and blue . . 25 10
1607 **340** 1 p. lilac and violet . . . 15 10
1608 – 1 p. red and purple . . . 15 10
1609 – 1 p. black and green . . 15 10
1610 – 1 p. red and purple . . . 15 10
1611 – 1 p. 50 brown, green and blue 15 10
DESIGNS—HORIZ: No. 1602, Potes; No. 1604, Crypt of St. Isidore (Leon); No. 1608, Lion Court of the Alhambra (Granada); No. 1611, Gerona. VERT: No. 1603, Leon Cathedral; No. 1605, Costa Brava; No. 1606, "Christ of the Lanterns" (Cordoba); No. 1609, Drach Caves (Majorca); No. 1610, Mosque (Cordoba).
See also Nos. 1704/13, 1786/95, 1798/1805, 1860/6, 1867/74, 1933/42, 1985/9, 1993/6, 2035/9, 2040/5, 2311/6, 2379/84, 2466/7, 2575/8, 2696/2700, 2744/8, 2858/9, 2870/1 and 2915/18.

1964. Arms of Provincial Capitals. As T **315**. Multicoloured.
1612 5 p. Ifni 25 10
1613 5 p. Jaen 25 10
1614 5 p. Leon 25 10
1615 5 p. Lerida 25 10
1616 5 p. Logrono 25 10
1617 5 p. Lugo 25 10
1618 5 p. Madrid 25 10
1619 5 p. Malaga 25 10
1620 5 p. Murcia 25 10
1621 5 p. Navarra 25 10
1622 5 p. Orense 25 10
1623 5 p. Oviedo 25 10

341 Santa Maria Monastery

1964. Monastery of Santa Maria, Huerta.
1624 – 1 p. bronze and green . . 10 10
1625 – 2 p. sepia, black & turq . 10 10
1626 **341** 5 p. slate and violet . . 1·50 40
DESIGNS—VERT: 1 p. Great Hall; 2 p. Cloisters.

1964. Stamp Day and Sorolla (painter(Commem. As T **279**. Frames in gold.

1627 25 c. violet 10 10
1628 40 c. purple 10 10
1629 70 c. green 10 10
1630 80 c. turquoise 10 10
1631 1 p. brown 10 10
1632 1 p. 50 turquoise 10 10
1633 2 p. 50 mauve 15 10
1634 3 p. blue 40 20
1635 5 p. brown . . . . 1·00 75
1636 10 p. green 60 20

PAINTINGS—VERT: 25 c. "The Earthen Jar"; 70 c. "La Mancha Types"; 80 c. "Valencian Fisherwoman"; 1 p. Self-portrait; 5 p. "Pulling the Boat"; 10 p. "Valencian Couple on Horse". HORIZ: 40 c. "Castillan Oxherd"; 1 p. 50, "The Cattlepen"; 2 p. 50, "And people say fish is dear" (fish market); 3 p. "Children on the Beach".

342 "25 Years of Peace"

1964. 25th Anniv of End of Spanish Civil War.

1637 **342** 25 c. gold, green & blk . . 10 10
1638 – 30 c. salmon, blue and green 10 10
1639 – 40 c. black and gold . . . 10 10
1640 – 50 c. multicoloured . . . 10 10
1641 – 70 c. multicoloured . . . 10 10
1642 – 80 c. multicoloured . . . 10 10
1643 – 1 p. multicoloured . . . 35 10
1644 – 1 p. 50 olive, red & blue . 25 10
1645 – 2 p. multicoloured . . . 25 10
1646 – 2 p. 50 multicoloured . . 25 10
1647 – 3 p. multicoloured . . . 1·25 50
1648 – 5 p. red, green and gold . 50 25
1649 – 6 p. multicoloured . . . 80 40
1650 – 10 p. multicoloured . . . 80 40

DESIGNS—VERT: 30 c. Athletes ("Sport"); 50 c. Apartment-houses ("National Housing Plan"); 1 p. Graph and symbols ("Economic Development"); 1 p. 50, Rocks and tower ("Construction"); 2 p. 50, Wheatear and dam ("Irrigation"); 5 p. "Tree of Learning" ("Scientific Research"); 10 p. Gen. Franco. HORIZ: 40 c. T.V. screen and symbols ("Radio and T.V."); 70 c. Wheatears, tractor and landscape ("Agriculture"); 80 c. Tree and forests ("Reafforestation"); 2 p. Forms of transport ("Transport and Communications"); 3 p. Pylon and part of dial ("Electrification"); 6 p. Ancient buildings ("Tourism").

343 Spanish Pavilion at Fair

344 6 c. Stamp of 1850 and Globe

1964. New York World's Fair.

1651 **343** 1 p. green & turquoise . 35 10
1652 – 1 p. 50 brown and red . . 10 10
1653 – 2 p. 50 green and blue . . 15 10
1654 – 5 p. red 45 45
1655 – 50 p. blue and grey . . . 1·50 40

DESIGNS—VERT: 1 p. 50, Bullfighting; 2 p. 50, Castillo de la Mota; 5 p. Spanish dancing; 50 p. Pelota.

1964. World Stamp Day.

1656 **344** 25 c. red and purple . . 10 10
1657 1 p. green and blue . . 25 10
1658 10 p. orange and red . . 65 30

345 Macarena Virgin

346 Medieval Ship

1964. Canonical Coronation of Macarena Virgin.

1659 **345** 1 p. green and yellow . . 15 10

1964. Spanish Navy Commemoration.

1660 **346** 15 c. slate and purple . . 10 10
1661 – 25 c. green and orange . . 10 10
1662 – 40 c. grey and blue . . . 10 10
1663 – 50 c. green and slate . . 10 10
1664 – 70 c. violet and blue . . 10 10
1665 – 80 c. blue and green . . 10 10
1666 – 1 p. purple and brown . . 10 10
1667 – 1 p. 50 sepia and red . . 10 10
1668 – 2 p. black and green . . 1·00 10
1669 – 2 p. 50 red and violet . . 25 10
1670 – 3 p. blue and brown . . 25 10
1671 – 5 p. blue and green . . 1·10 55
1672 – 6 p. violet & turquoise . 70 50
1673 – 10 p. red and orange . . 70 30

SHIPS—VERT: 25 c. Carrack; 1 p. Ship of the line "Santissima Trinidad"; 1 p. 50, Corvette "Atrevida". HORIZ: 40 c. "Santa Maria"; 50 c. Galley; 70 c. Galleon; 80 c. Xebec; 2 p. Steam frigate "Isabel II"; 2 p. 50, Frigate "Numancia"; 3 p. Destroyer "Destructor"; 5 p. Isaac Peral's submarine; 6 p. Cruiser "Baleares"; 10 p. Cadet schooner "Juan Sebastian de Elcano".

347 Europa "Flower"

348 "The Virgin of the Castle"

1964. Europa.

1674 **347** 1 p. ochre, red & green . 50 10
1675 5 p. blue, purple & grn . 1·50 35

1964. 700th Anniv of Reconquest of Jerez.

1676 **348** 25 c. brown and buff . . 15 10
1677 1 p. blue and grey . . . 15 10

349 Putting the Shot

350 "Adoration of the Shepherds" (after Zurbaran)

1965. Olympic Games, Tokyo and Innsbruck. Olympic rings in gold.

1678 **349** 25 c. blue and orange . . 10 10
1679 – 80 c. blue and green . . 10 10
1680 – 1 p. blue & light blue . . 10 10
1681 – 3 p. blue and buff . . . 15 15
1682 – 5 p. blue and violet . . 15 15

DESIGNS: 80 c. Long jumping; 1 p. Skiing (slalom); 3 p. Judo; 5 p. Throwing the discus.

1964. Explorers and Colonizers of America (4th series). As T **309**. Inscr "1964" at foot.

1683 25 c. violet and blue 10 10
1684 70 c. olive and pink 10 10
1685 80 c. green and buff 30 20
1686 1 p. violet and buff 30 10
1687 2 p. olive and blue 30 10
1688 2 p. 50 purple and turquoise . 20 15
1689 3 p. blue and grey . . . . . 2·00 55
1690 5 p. brown and cream . . . 1·40 70

PORTRAITS: 25 c., 2 p. D. de Almagro; 70 c., 2 p. 50, F. de Toledo; 80 c., 3 p. T. de Mogrovejo; 1, 5 p. F. Pizarro.

1964. Christmas.

1691 **350** 1 p. brown 10 10

1965. Arms of Provincial Capitals. As T **315**. Multicoloured.

1692 5 p. Palencia 25 10
1693 5 p. Pontevedra 25 10
1694 5 p. Rio Muni 25 10
1695 5 p. Sahara 25 10
1696 5 p. Salamanca 25 10
1697 5 p. Santander 25 10
1698 5 p. Segovia 25 10
1699 5 p. Seville 25 10
1700 5 p. Soria 25 10
1701 5 p. Tarragona 25 10
1702 5 p. Tenerife 25 10
1703 5 p. Teruel 25 10

1965. Tourist Series. As T **340**.

1704 25 c. black and blue 20 10
1705 30 c. brown and turquoise . . 20 10
1706 50 c. purple and red 20 10
1707 70 c. indigo and blue 20 10
1708 80 c. purple and mauve . . . 20 10
1709 1 p. mauve, red and sepia . . 20 10
1710 2 p. 50 purple and brown . . 20 10
1711 2 p. 50 olive and blue . . . 20 10
1712 3 p. purple and purple . . . 20 10
1713 6 p. violet and slate 20 10

DESIGNS—VERT: 25 c. Columbus Monument, Barcelona; 30 c. Santa Maria Church, Burgos; 50 c. Synagogue, Toledo; 80 c. Seville Cathedral; 1 p. Cudillero Port; 2 p. 50, (No. 1710), Burgos Cathedral (interior); 3 p. Bridge at Cambados (Pontevedra); 6 p. Ceiling, Lonja (Valencia). HORIZ: 70 c. Zamora; 2 p. 50, (No. 1711), Mogrovejo (Santander).

1965. Famous Spaniards (2nd series). As T **338**.

1714 25 c. sepia and turquoise . . 10 10
1715 70 c. deep blue and blue . . 20 10
1716 2 p. 50 sepia and bronze . . 20 10
1717 5 p. bronze and green . . . 40 10

PORTRAITS: 25 c. Donoso Cortes; 70 c. King Alfonso X (the Saint); 2 p. 50, G. M. de Jovellanos; 5 p. St. Dominic de Guzman.

1965. Stamp Day and J. Romero de Torres Commem. As T **279**. Frames in gold.

1718 25 c. purple 10 10
1719 40 c. purple 10 10
1720 70 c. green 10 10
1721 80 c. turquoise 10 10
1722 1 p. brown 10 10
1723 1 p. 50 turquoise 10 10
1724 2 p. 50 mauve 10 10
1725 3 p. blue 15 10
1726 5 p. brown 25 10
1727 10 p. green 30 15

PAINTINGS (by J. Romero de Torres): 25 c. "Girl with Jar"; 40 c. "The Song"; 70 c. "The Virgin of the Lanterns"; 80 c. "Girl with Guitar"; 1 p. Self-portrait; 1 p. 50, "Poem of Cordoba"; 2 p. 50, "Marta and Maria"; 3 p. "Poem of Cordoba" (different); 5 p. "A Little Charcoal-maker"; 10 p. "Long Live the Hair!".

351 Bull and Stamps

352 I.T.U. Emblem and Symbols

1965. World Stamp Day.

1728 **351** 25 c. multicoloured . . . 10 10
1729 1 p. multicoloured . . . 20 10
1730 10 p. multicoloured . . . 80 30

1965. Centenary of I.T.U.

1731 **352** 1 p. red, black and pink . 10 10

353 Pilgrim

354 Spanish Knight and Banners

1965. Holy Year of Santiago de Compostela. Multicoloured.

1732 1 p. Type **353** 10 10
1733 2 p. Pilgrim (profile) 15 10

1965. 400th Anniv of Florida Settlement.

1734 **354** 3 p. black, red & yellow . 15 10

355 St. Benedict (after sculpture by Pereira)

356 Sports Palace, Madrid

1965. Europa.

1735 **355** 1 p. green & emerald . . 35 10
1736 5 p. violet and purple . . 1·10 10

1965. Int Olympic Committee Meeting, Madrid.

1737 **356** 1 p. brown, gold & grey . 10 10

1965. Explorers and Colonizers of America (5th series). As T **309**. Inscr "1965" at foot.

1738 25 c. violet and green 10 10
1739 70 c. brown and pink 10 10
1740 80 c. green and cream 10 10
1741 1 p. violet and buff 10 10
1742 2 p. brown and blue 15 10
1743 2 p. 50 purple and turquoise . 15 10
1744 3 p. blue and grey 75 15
1745 5 p. brown and yellow . . . 75 20

PORTRAITS: 25 c., 2 p. Don Fadrique de Toledo; 70 c., 2 p. 50, Padre Jose de Anchieta; 80 c., 3 p. Francisco de Orellana; 1 p., 5 p. St. Luis Beltran.

357 Cloisters

1965. Yuste Monastery.

1746 **357** 1 p. blue and sepia . . . 10 10
1747 – 2 p. sepia and brown . . 20 10
1748 – 5 p. green and blue . . . 25 10

DESIGNS—VERT: 2 p. Charles V room. HORIZ: 5 p. Courtyard.

358 Spanish 1 r. Stamp of 1865

360 Madonna of Antipolo

359 "The Nativity" (after Mayno)

1965. Centenary of Spanish Perforated Stamps.

1749 **358** 80 c. green and bronze . 15 10
1750 – 1 p. brown and purple . 15 10
1751 – 5 p. brown and sepia . . 20 10

DESIGNS: 1 p. 1865 19 c. stamp; 5 p. 1865 2 r. stamp.

1965. Christmas.

1752 **359** 1 p. green and blue . . . 10 10

1965. 400th Anniv of Christianity in the Philippines.

1753 **360** 1 p. brown, black & buff 25 10
1754 – 3 p. blue and grey . . . 30 10

DESIGN: 3 p. Father Urdaneta.

361 Globe

362 Admiral Alvaro de Bazan

1965. 21st Ecumenical Council, Vatican City (3rd issue).

1755 **361** 1 p. multicoloured . . . 20 10

1966. Arms of Provincial Capitals. As T **315**. Multicoloured.

1756 5 p. Toledo 25 10
1757 5 p. Valencia 25 10
1758 5 p. Valladolid 25 10
1759 5 p. Vizcaya 25 10
1760 5 p. Zamora 25 10
1761 5 p. Zaragoza 25 10
1762 5 p. Ceuta 25 10
1763 5 p. Melilla 25 10
1764 10 p. Spain ($26 \times 38\frac{1}{2}$ mm) . . 25 10

1966. Celebrities (1st series).

1765 **362** 25 c. black and blue (postage) 10 10
1766 – 2 p. violet and purple . . 15 10
1767 – 25 p. bronze & green (air) 1·50 20
1768 – 50 p. grey and blue . . . 2·25 30

PORTRAITS: 2 p. Benito Daza de Valdes (doctor); 25 p. Seneca; 50 p. St. Damaso.

See also Nos. 1849/52.

363 Exhibition Emblem

364 Luno Church

1966. Graphic Arts Exn, "Graphispack", Barcelona.

1769 **363** 1 p. green, blue and red . 15 10

1966. Stamp Day and J. M. Sert Commem. Designs as T **279**. Frames in gold.

1770 25 c. violet 10 10
1771 40 c. purple 10 10
1772 70 c. green 10 10
1773 80 c. bronze 10 10
1774 1 p. brown 10 10
1775 1 p. 50 blue 10 10
1776 2 p. 50 red 10 10
1777 3 p. blue 10 10
1778 5 p. sepia 15 10
1779 10 p. green 20 10

PAINTINGS (by J. M. Sert)—VERT: 25 c. "The Magic Ball"; 70 c. "Christ Addressing the Disciples"; 80 c. "The Balloonists"; 1 p. Self-portrait; 1 p. 50, "Audacity"; 2 p. 50, "Justice"; 3 p. "Jacob's Struggle with the Angel"; 5 p. "The Five Parts of the World"; 10 p. "St. Peter and St. Paul". HORIZ: 40 c. "Memories of Toledo".

1966. 600th Anniv of Guernica. Multicoloured.

1780 80 c. Type **364** 10 10
1781 1 p. Arms of Guernica . . . 10 10
1782 3 p. "Tree of Guernica" . . 10 10

365 Postmarked 6 cuartos Stamp of 1850

1966. World Stamp Day.
1783 365 25 c. multicoloured . . . 10 10
1784 – 1 p. multicoloured . . . 10 10
1785 – 10 p. multicoloured . . . 40 15
DESIGNS—POSTMARKED STAMPS: 1 p. 5 r. of 1850; 10 p. 10 r. of 1850.

1966. Tourist Series. As T **340**.
1786 10 c. emerald and green . . . 10 10
1787 15 c. bistre and green 10 10
1788 40 c. brown and chestnut . . 10 10
1789 50 c. purple and red 10 10
1790 80 c. purple and mauve . . . 10 10
1791 1 p. turquoise and blue . . . 10 10
1792 1 p. 50 black and blue . . . 10 10
1793 2 p. brown and blue 10 10
1794 3 p. brown and blue 10 10
1795 10 p. blue and turquoise . . . 20 10
DESIGNS—VERT: 10 c. Bohi waterfalls (Lerida); 40 c. Sigena monastery (Huesca); 50 c. Santo Domingo Church (Soria); 80 c. Golden Tower (Seville); 1 p. El Teide (Canaries); 10 p. Church of St. Gregory (Valladolid). HORIZ: 15 c. Torla (Huesca); 1 p. 50, Cathedral, Guadalupe; 2 p. University, Alcala de Henares; 3 p. La Seo Cathedral (Lerida).

366 Tree and Globe

1966. World Forestry Congress.
1796 366 1 p. green, brown and deep brown 15 10

367 Crown and Anchor

368 Butron Castle (Vizcaya)

1966. Naval Week, Barcelona.
1797 367 1 p. blue and grey . . . 15 10

1966. Spanish Castles (1st series).
1798 – 10 c. sepia and blue . . . 10 10
1799 – 25 c. purple and violet . . 10 10
1800 – 40 c. green & turquoise . . 10 10
1801 – 50 c. blue and indigo . . 15 10
1802 – 70 c. blue & ultramarine . 15 10
1803 368 80 c. green and violet . . 20 20
1804 – 1 p. olive and brown . . 20 10
1805 – 3 p. purple and red . . . 25 10
CASTLES—HORIZ: 10 c. Guadamur (Toledo); 25 c. Alcazar (Segovia); 40 c. La Mota (Medina del Campo); 50 c. Olite (Navarra); 70 c. Monteagudo (Murcia); 1 p. Manzanares (Madrid). VERT: 3 p. Almansa (Albacete).

369 Don Quixote, Dulcinea and Aldonza Lorenzo

1966. 4th World Psychiatric Congress, Madrid.
1806 369 1 p. 50 multicoloured . . 10 10

370 "Europa and the Bull"

371 Horseman in the Sky

1966. Europa.
1807 370 1 p. multicoloured . . . 35 10
1808 5 p. multicoloured . . . 75 10

1966. 17th Int Astronautics Federation Congress, Madrid.
1809 371 1 p. 50 red, blk & blue . . 10 10

1966. Explorers and Colonisers of America (6th series). As T **309**. Inscr "1966" at foot.
1810 30 c. bistre and brown . . . 10 10
1811 50 c. red and green 10 10
1812 1 p. violet and blue 10 10
1813 1 p. 20 slate and grey . . . 10 10
1814 1 p. 50 myrtle and green . . 15 10
1815 3 p. blue 15 10
1816 3 p. 50 violet and lilac . . . 15 10
1817 6 p. brown and buff 20 10
DESIGNS: 30 c. A. de Mendoza; 50 c. Title page of Dominican Fathers' "Christian Doctrine"; 1 p. J. A. Manso de Velasco; 1 p. 20, Coins of Lima Mint (1699); 1 p. 50, M. de Castro y Padilla; 3 p. Oruro Convent; 3 p. 50, M. de Amat; 6 p. Inca postal runner.

372 R. del Valle Inclan

373 Monastery Facade

1966. Spanish Writers.
1818 372 1 p. 50 green and black . . 10 10
1819 – 3 p. violet and black . . 15 10
1820 – 6 p. blue and black . . 15 10
WRITERS: 3 p. Carlos Arniches; 6 p. J. Benavente y Martinez.
See also Nos. 1888/91.

1966. St. Mary's Carthusian Monastery, Jerez.
1821 373 1 p. indigo and blue . . 10 10
1822 – 2 p. lt green and green . . 10 10
1823 – 5 p. plum and purple . . 20 10
DESIGNS—HORIZ: 2 p. Cloisters; 5 p. Gateway.

374 "The Nativity" (after P. Duque Cornejo)

375 Alava Costume

1966. Christmas.
1824 374 1 p. 50 multicoloured . 10 10

1967. Provincial Costumes. Multicoloured.
1825 6 p. Type **375** 15 10
1826 6 p. Albacete 15 10
1827 6 p. Alicante 15 10
1828 6 p. Almeria 15 10
1829 6 p. Avila 15 10
1830 6 p. Badajoz 15 10
1831 6 p. Baleares 15 10
1832 6 p. Barcelona 15 10
1833 6 p. Burgos 15 10
1834 6 p. Caceres 15 10
1835 6 p. Cadiz 15 10
1836 6 p. Castellon de la Plana . 15 10
See also Nos. 1897/1908, 1956/67, 2007/18 and 2072/6.

376 Archers

1967. Stamp Day. Cave Paintings. Multicoloured.
1837 40 c. Type **376** 10 10
1838 50 c. Boar-hunting 10 10
1839 1 p. Trees (vert) 10 10
1840 1 p. 20 Bison 10 10
1841 1 p. 50 Hands 10 10
1842 2 p. Hunter (vert) 10 10
1843 2 p. 50 Deer (vert) 10 10
1844 3 p. 50 Hunters 10 10
1845 4 p. Chamois-hunters (vert) . 10 10
1846 6 p. Deer-hunter (vert) . . . 15 10

377 Cathedral, Palma de Mallorca, and Union Emblem

1967. Interparliamentary Union Congress, Palma de Mallorca.
1847 377 1 p. 50 green 10 10

378 Wilhelm Rontgen (physicist)

1967. Radiology Congress, Barcelona.
1848 378 1 p. 50 green 40 10

1967. Celebrities (2nd series). As T **362**.
1849 1 p. 20 violet and purple . . . 15 10
1850 3 p. 50 purple 15 10
1851 4 p. sepia and brown 75 10
1852 25 p. grey and blue 35 10
PORTRAITS: 1 p. 20, Averroes (physician and philosopher); 3 p. 50, Acosta (poet); 4 p. Maimonides (physician and philosopher); 25 p. Andres Laguna (physician).

379 Cogwheels

381 Spanish 5 r. Stamp of 1850 with Numeral Postmark

380 Fair Building

1967. Europa.
1853 379 1 p. 50 green, brn & red . 35 10
1854 6 p. violet, blue & purple 30 10

1967. 50th Anniv of Valencia Int Samples Fair.
1855 380 1 p. 50 green 10 10

1967. World Stamp Day.
1856 381 40 c. brown, blue & blk . 10 10
1857 – 1 p. 50 lake, black and green 10 10
1858 – 6 p. blue, red and black . 10 10
DESIGNS: 1 p. 50, Spanish 12 c. stamp of 1850 with crowned "M" (Madrid) postmark; 6 p. Spanish 6 r. stamp of 1850 with "I.R." postmark.
See also Nos. 1927/8, 1980/1, 2032, 2091, 2150 and 2185.

382 Sleeping Vagrant and "Guardian Angel"

383 I.T.Y. Emblem

1967. National Day for Caritas Welfare Organization.
1859 382 1 p. 50 multicoloured . . 10 10

1967. Tourist Series and Int Tourist Year.
1860 – 10 c. black and blue . . . 10 10
1861 – 1 p. black and blue . . . 10 10
1862 – 1 p. 50 black and brown . 10 10
1863 – 2 p. 50 blue and turquoise . 10 10
1864 383 3 p. 50 blue and purple . . 10 10
1865 – 5 p. bronze and green . . 10 10
1866 – 6 p. purple and mauve . . 20 10
DESIGNS: 10 c. Betanzos Church (Corunna); 1 p. St. Miguel's Tower (Palencia); 1 p. 50, Castellers (acrobats); 2 p. 50, Columbus Monument (Huelva); 5 p. "Enchanted City" (Cuenca); 6 p. Church of our Lady, Sanlucar (Cadiz).

1967. Spanish Castles (2nd series). As T **368**.
1867 50 c. brown and grey 15 10
1868 1 p. violet and grey 25 10
1869 1 p. 50 green and blue . . . 25 10
1870 2 p. brown and red 25 10
1871 2 p. 50 brown and green . . 25 10
1872 5 p. blue and purple 30 10
1873 6 p. sepia and brown . . . 30 10
1874 10 p. green and blue . . . 35 10
CASTLES—HORIZ: 50 c. Balsareny (Barcelona); 1 p. Jarandilla (Caceres); 1 p. 50, Almodovar (Cordoba); 2 p. 50, Peniscola (Castellon); 5 p. Coca (Segovia); 6 p. Loarre (Huesca); 10 p. Belmonte (Cuenca). VERT: 2 p. Ponferrada (Leon).

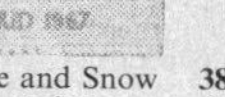

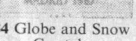

384 Globe and Snow Crystal

385 Map of the Americas, Spain and the Philippines

1967. 12th Int Refrigeration Congress, Madrid.
1875 384 1 p. 50 blue 10 10

1967. 4th Spanish, Portuguese, American and Philippine Municipalities Congress, Barcelona.
1876 385 1 p. 50 violet 15 10

1967. Explorers and Colonisers of America (7th series). As T **309**. Inscr "1967" at foot.
1877 40 c. olive and orange . . . 15 10
1878 50 c. agate and grey 15 10
1879 1 p. mauve and blue . . . 15 10
1880 1 p. 20 green and cream . . 15 10
1881 1 p. 50 green and flesh . . . 15 10
1882 3 p. violet and buff 15 10
1883 3 p. 50 blue and pink . . . 15 10
1884 6 p. brown 20 10
DESIGNS—VERT: 40 c. J. Francisco de la Bodega y Quadra; 50 c. Map of Nutka coast; 1 p. F. A. Mourelle; 1 p. 50, E. J. Martinez; 3 p. 50, Cayetano Valdes y Florez. HORIZ: 1 p. 20, View of Nutka; 3 p. Map of Californian coast; 6 p. San Elias, Alaska.

387 Ploughing with Oxen

388 Main Portal, Veruela Monastery

1967. 2000th Anniv of Caceres. Multicoloured.
1885 1 p. 50 Statue and archway . 10 10
1886 3 p. 50 Type **387** 10 10
1887 6 p. Roman coins 15 10
Nos. 1885 and 1887 are vert.

1967. Anniversaries. Portraits as T **372**.
1888 1 p. 20 brown and black . . 10 10
1889 1 p. 50 green and black . . . 10 10
1890 3 p. 50 violet and black . . 10 10
1891 6 p. blue and black 10 10
DESIGNS: 1 p. 20, P. de S. Jose Bethencourt (founder of Bethlehemite Order, 300th death anniv); 1 p. 50, Enrique Granados (composer, birth cent); 3 p. 50, Ruben Dario (poet, birth centenary); 6 p. San Ildefonso, Archbishop of Toledo (after El Greco) (1900th death anniv).

1967. Veruela Monastery.
1892 388 1 p. 50 blue & ultramarine 10 10
1893 – 3 p. 50 grey and green . . 10 10
1894 – 6 p. purple and brown . . 30 10
DESIGNS—HORIZ: 3 p. 50, Aerial view of monastery; 6 p. Cloisters.

389 "The Canonization of San Jose de Calasanz" (from painting by Goya)

390 "The Nativity" (Salzillo)

1967. Bicentenary of Canonization of San Jose de Calasanz.
1895 389 1 p. 50 multicoloured . . 15 10

1967. Christmas.
1896 390 1 p. 50 multicoloured . . 10 10

1968. Provincial Costumes. As T **375**. Multicoloured.
1897 6 p. Ciudad Real 15 10
1898 6 p. Cordoba 15 10
1899 6 p. Coruna 15 10
1900 6 p. Cuenca 15 10
1901 6 p. Fernando Poo 15 10
1902 6 p. Gerona 15 10
1903 6 p. Las Palmas (Gran Canaria) 15 10
1904 6 p. Granada 15 10
1905 6 p. Guadalajara 15 10
1906 6 p. Guipuzcoa 15 10
1907 6 p. Huelva 15 10
1908 6 p. Huesca 15 10

391 Slalom

1968. Winter Olympic Games, Grenoble. Multicoloured.
1909 1 p. 50 Type **391** 10 10
1910 3 p. 50 Bobsleighing (vert) 20 10
1911 6 p. Ice hockey 20 10

1968. Stamp Day and Fortuny Commem. As T **279**. Frames in gold.
1912 40 c. purple 10 10
1913 50 c. green 10 10
1914 1 p. brown 10 10
1915 1 p. 20 violet 10 10
1916 1 p. 50 green 10 10
1917 2 p. brown 10 10
1918 2 p. 50 red 10 10
1919 3 p. 50 brown 30 10
1920 4 p. olive 10 10
1921 6 p. blue 20 10
Fortuny Paintings—HORIZ: 40 c. "The Vicarage"; 1 p. 20, "The Print Collector"; 6 p. "Queen Christina". VERT: 50 c. "Fantasia"; 1 p. "Idyll"; 1 p. 50, Self-portrait; 2 p. "Old Man Naked to the Sun"; 2 p. 50, "Typical Calabrian"; 3 p. 50, "Portrait of Lady"; 4 p. "Battle of Tetuan".

392 Beatriz Galindo

1968. Famous Spanish Women. With background scenes.
1922 **392** 1 p. 20 brown and bistre 10 10
1923 – 1 p. 50 blue & turquoise 10 10
1924 – 3 p. 50 violet 15 10
1925 – 6 p. black and blue 20 10
WOMEN: 1 p. 50, Agustina de Aragon; 3 p. 50, Maria Pacheco; 6 p. Rosalia de Castro.

393 Europa "Key"

1968. Europa.
1926 **393** 3 p. 50 gold, brn & blue 30 10

1968. World Stamp Day. As T **381**, but stamps and postmarks changed. Inscr "1968".
1927 1 p. 50 black, brown & blue 10 10
1928 3 p. 50 blue, black & green 20 10
DESIGNS: 1 p. 50, Spanish 6 c. stamp of 1850 with Puebla (Galicia) postmark; 3 p. 50, Spanish 6 r. stamp of 1850 with Serena postmark.

394 Emperor Galba's Coin

395 Human Rights Emblem

1968. 1900th Anniv of Foundation of Leon by VIIth Roman Legion.
1929 – 1 p. brown and purple 10 10
1930 – 1 p. 50 brown & yellow 10 10
1931 **394** 3 p. 50 green and ochre 30 10
DESIGNS—VERT: 1 p. Inscribed tile and town map of Leon (26×47 mm); 1 p. 50, Legionary with standard (statue).

1968. Human Rights Year.
1932 **395** 3 p. 50 red, green & blue 15 10

1968. Tourist Series. As T **340**.
1933 50 c. brown 10 10
1934 1 p. 20 green 10 10
1935 1 p. 50 blue and green 10 10
1936 2 p. purple 20 10
1937 3 p. 50 purple 15 10
DESIGNS—VERT: 50 c. Count Benavente's Palace, Baeza; 1 p. 50, Sepulchre, St. Vincent's Church, Avila; 3 p. 50, Main portal, Church of Santa Maria, Sanguesa (Navarra). HORIZ: 1 p. 20, View of Salamanca; 2 p. "The King's Page" (statue), Siguenza Cathedral.

1968. Spanish Castles (3rd series). As T **368**.
1938 40 c. sepia and blue 15 10
1939 1 p. 20 purple 10 10
1940 1 p. 50 black and bistre 10 10
1941 2 p. 50 bronze and green 35 10
1942 6 p. turquoise and blue 50 10
DESIGNS—HORIZ: 40 c. Escalona; 1 p. 20, Fuensaldana; 1 p. 50, Penafiel; 2 p. 50, Villas and obroso. VERT: 6 p. Frias.

396 Rifle-shooting

1968. Olympic Games, Mexico. Multicoloured.
1943 1 p. Type **396** 15 10
1944 1 p. 50 Horse-jumping 15 10
1945 3 p. 50 Cycling 25 10
1946 6 p. Yachting (vert) 20 10

1968. Explorers and Colonisers of America (8th series). As T **309** but inscr "1968" at foot.
1947 40 c. blue and light blue 10 10
1948 1 p. purple and blue 10 10
1949 1 p. 50 green and flesh 10 10
1950 3 p. 50 blue and mauve 25 10
1951 6 p. brown and yellow 30 20
DESIGNS—VERT: 40 c. Map of Orinoco missions; 1 p. Diego de Losada (founder of Caracas); 1 p. 50, Arms of the Losadas; 3 p. 50, Diego de Henares (builder of Caracas). HORIZ: 6 p. Old plan of Santiago de Leon de Caracas.

397 Monastery Building

398 "The Nativity" (Barocci)

1968. Santa Maria del Parral Monastery.
1952 **397** 1 p. 50 lilac and blue 10 10
1953 – 3 p. 50 brown & chocolate 35 10
1954 – 6 p. brown and red 40 10
DESIGNS—VERT: 3 p. 50, Cloisters; 6 p. "Santa Maria del Parral".

1968. Christmas.
1955 **398** 1 p. 50 multicoloured 15 10

1969. Provincial Costumes. As T **375**. Multicoloured.
1956 6 p. Ifni 15 10
1957 6 p. Jaen 15 10
1958 6 p. Leon 15 10
1959 6 p. Lerida 15 10
1960 6 p. Logrono 15 10
1961 6 p. Lugo 15 10
1962 6 p. Madrid 15 10
1963 6 p. Malaga 15 10
1964 6 p. Murcia 15 10
1965 6 p. Navarra 15 10
1966 6 p. Orense 15 10
1967 6 p. Oviedo 15 10

1969. Stamp Day and Alonso Cano Commem. Various paintings as T **279**. Frames gold: centre colours below.
1968 40 c. red 10 10
1969 50 c. green 10 10
1970 1 p. sepia 10 10
1971 1 p. 50 green 10 10
1972 2 p. brown 20 10
1973 2 p. 50 mauve 15 10
1974 3 p. blue 15 10
1975 3 p. 50 purple 15 10
1976 4 p. purple 15 10
1977 6 p. blue 25 10
Alonso Cano paintings—VERT: 40 c. "St. Agnes"; 50 c. "St. Joseph"; 1 p. "Christ supported by an Angel"; 1 p. 50, "Alonso Cano" (Velazquez); 2 p. "The Holy Family"; 2 p. 50, "The Circumcision"; 3 p. "Jesus and the Samaritan"; 3 p. 50, "Madonna and Child"; 6 p. "The Vision of St. John the Baptist". HORIZ: 4 p. "St. John Capistrano and St. Bernardin".

399 Molecules and Diagram

1969. 6th European Biochemical Congress.
1978 **399** 1 p. 50 multicoloured 10 10

400 Colonnade

1969. Europa.
1979 **400** 3 p. 50 multicoloured 35 10

1969. World Stamp Day. As T **381**.
1980 1 p. 50 black, red and green 10 10
1981 3 p. 50 green, red and blue 15 10
DESIGNS: 1 p. 50, Spanish 6 c. stamp of 1851 with "A 3 1851" postmark; 3 p. 50, Spanish 10 r. stamp of 1851 with "CORVERA" postmark.

401 Spectrum

1969. 15th Int Spectroscopical Conf, Madrid.
1982 **401** 1 p. 50 multicoloured 10 10

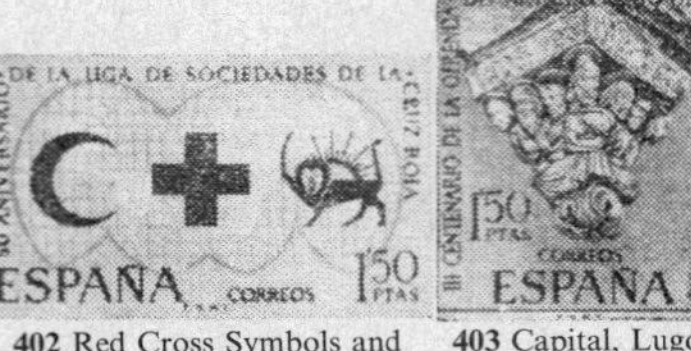

402 Red Cross Symbols and Globe

403 Capital, Lugo Cathedral

1969. 50th Anniv of League of Red Cross Societies.
1983 **402** 1 p. 50 multicoloured 25 10

1969. 300th Anniv of Dedication of Galicia to Jesus Christ.
1984 **403** 1 p. 50 brown, blk & grn 10 10

1969. Spanish Castles (4th series). As T **368**.
1985 1 p. purple and green 15 10
1986 1 p. 50 blue and violet 25 10
1987 2 p. 50 lilac and blue 20 10
1988 3 p. 50 brown and green 30 10
1989 6 p. drab and green 30 10
CASTLES—HORIZ: 1 p. Turegano; 1 p. 50, Villalonso; 2 p. 50, Velez Blanco; 3 p. 50, Castilnovo; 6 p. Torrelobaton.

404 Franciscan Friar and Child

405 Rock of Gibraltar

1969. Bicentenary of San Diego (California).
1990 **404** 1 p. 50 multicoloured 10 10

1969. Aid for Spanish "ex-Gibraltar" Workers.
1991 **405** 1 p. 50 blue 35 10
1992 – 2 p. purple 45 10
DESIGN: 2 p. Aerial view of Rock.

1969. Tourist Series. As T **340**.
1993 1 p. 50 green and turquoise 20 10
1994 3 p. turquoise and green 25 10
1995 3 p. 50 blue and green 25 10
1996 6 p. violet and green 25 10
DESIGNS—HORIZ: 1 p. 50, Alcaniz (Teruel). VERT: 3 p. Murcia Cathedral; 3 p. 50, "The Lady of Elche" (sculpture); 6 p. Church of Our Lady of the Redonda, Logrono.

1969. Explorers and Colonisers of America (9th series). Chile. As T **309**. Inscr "1969" at foot.
1997 40 c. brown on blue 10 10
1998 1 p. 50 violet on flesh 10 10
1999 2 p. green on mauve 25 10
2000 3 p. 50 green on cream 30 10
2001 6 p. brown on cream 40 10
DESIGNS—VERT: 40 c. Convent of Santo Domingo, Santiago de Chile; 2 p. Ambrosio O'Higgins; 3 p. 50, Pedro de Valdivia (founder of Santiago de Chile). HORIZ: 1 p. 50, Chilean Mint; 6 p. Cal y Canto Bridge.

406 "Adoration of the Three Kings" (Maino)

407 Las Huelgas Monastery

1969. Christmas. Multicoloured.
2002 1 p. 50 Type **406** 10 10
2003 2 p. "The Nativity" (Gerona Cathedral) 15 10

1969. Las Huelgas Monastery, Burgos.
2004 **407** 1 p. 50 slate and green 35 10
2005 – 3 p. 50 blue 30 10
2006 – 6 p. olive and green 45 10
DESIGNS—HORIZ: 3 p. 50, Tombs. VERT: 6 p. Cloisters.

1970. Provincial Costumes. As T **375**. Multicoloured.
2007 6 p. Palencia 15 10
2008 6 p. Pontevedra 15 10
2009 6 p. Sahara 15 10
2010 6 p. Salamanca 15 10
2011 6 p. Santa Cruz de Tenerife 15 10
2012 6 p. Santander 15 10
2013 6 p. Segovia 15 10
2014 6 p. Seville 15 10
2015 6 p. Soria 15 10
2016 6 p. Tarragona 15 10
2017 6 p. Teruel 15 10
2018 6 p. Toledo 15 10

408 Blessed Juan of Avila (after El Greco)

409 "St. Stephen"

1970. Spanish Celebrities.
2019 **408** 25 p. blue and lilac 3·25 10
2020 – 50 p. brown and orange 2·50 30
DESIGN: 25 p. Type **408** (400th death anniv); 50 p. Cardinal Rodrigo Ximenes de Rada (after J. de Borgena) (800th birth anniv).
See also Nos. 2129/31.

1970. Stamp Day and Luis de Morales Commem. Various paintings. Multicoloured.
2021 50 c. Type **409** 10 10
2022 1 p. "The Annunciation" 10 10
2023 1 p. 50 "Virgin and Child with St. John" 20 10
2024 2 p. "Virgin and Child" 20 10
2025 3 p. "The Presentation of the Infant Christ" 10 10
2026 3 p. 50 "St. Jerome" 10 10
2027 4 p. "St. John of Ribera" 20 10
2028 5 p. "Ecce Homo" 20 10
2029 6 p. "Pieta" 20 15
2030 10 p. "St. Francis of Assisi" 30 20
See also Nos. 2077/84, 2135/42, 2204/11, 2261/8, 2420/7, 2478/85, 2529/36 and 2585/90.

410 "Flaming Sun"

1970. Europa.
2031 **410** 3 p. 50 gold & ultram 30 10

1970. World Stamp Day. As T **381** but stamp and postmark changed.
2032 2 p. red, black and green 35 10
DESIGN: 2 p. Spanish 12 c. stamp of 1860 with railway cachet.

411 Fair Building

412 Gen. Primo de Rivera

1970. 50th Anniv of Barcelona Fair.
2033 **411** 15 p. multicoloured 45 10

1970. Birth Cent of General Primo de Rivera.
2034 **412** 2 p. green, brn & buff 15 10

1970. Spanish Castles (5th series). As T **368**.
2035 1 p. black and blue 75 10
2036 1 p. 20 blue and turquoise 50 10
2037 3 p. 50 brown and green 75 10
2038 6 p. violet and brown 75 10
2039 10 p. brown & chestnut 1·25 10
CASTLES—HORIZ: 1 p. Valencia de Don Juan; 1 p. 20, Monterrey; 3 p. 50, Mombeltran; 6 p. Sadaba; 10 p. Bellver.

1970. Tourist Series. As T **340**.
2040 50 c. lilac and blue 10 10
2041 1 p. brown and ochre 25 10
2042 1 p. 50 green and blue 20 10
2043 2 p. blue and deep blue 80 10
2044 3 p. 50 blue and violet 40 10
2045 5 p. brown and blue 1·25 10
DESIGNS—HORIZ: 50 c. Alcazaba, Almeria; 1 p. Malaga Cathedral; 2 p. St. Francis' Convent, Orense. VERT: 1 p. 50, Our Lady of the Assumption, Lequeitio; 3 p. 50, The Lonja, Zaragoza; 5 p. The Portalon, Vitoria.

413 17th-century Tailor

1970. International Tailoring Congress.
2046 **413** 2 p. violet, red and brown 10 10

414 Diver on Map

1970. 12th European Swimming, Diving and Water-polo Championships, Barcelona.
2047 **414** 2 p. brown, blue and grn 10 10

415 Concha Espina
416 Survey Map of Southern Spain and North Africa

1970. Spanish Writers.
2048 **415** 50 c. blue, brown & buff 10 10
2049 – 1 p. violet, green & drab 10 10
2050 – 1 p. 50 green, bl & drab 15 10
2051 – 2 p. olive, green & buff 25 10
2052 – 2 p. 50 pur, vio & ochre 20 10
2053 – 3 p. 50 red, brn & lilac 20 10
WRITERS: 1 p. Guillen de Castro; 1 p. 50, J. R. Jimenez; 2 p. G. A. Becquer; 2 p. 50, Miguel de Unamuno; 3 p. 50, J. M. Gabriel y Galan.

1970. Explorers and Colonizers of America (10th series). Mexico. As T **309**.
2054 40 c. green on light green 10 10
2055 1 p. 50 brown on blue 25 10
2056 2 p. violet on cream 60 10
2057 3 p. 50 green on light green 35 10
2058 6 p. blue on pink 50 10
DESIGNS—VERT: 40 c. House in Queretaro; 2 p. Vasco de Quiroga; 3 p. 50, F. Juan de Zumarraga; 6 p. Morelia Cathedral. HORIZ: 1 p. 50, Cathedral, Mexico City.

1970. Centenary of Spanish Geographical and Survey Institute.
2059 416 2 p. multicoloured 30 10

417 "The Adoration of the Shepherds" (El Greco)
418 U.N. Emblem and New York Headquarters

1970. Christmas. Multicoloured.
2060 1 p. 50 Type **417** 15 10
2061 2 p. "The Adoration of the Shepherds" (Murillo) 15 10

1970. 25th Anniv of United Nations.
2062 **418** 8 p. multicoloured 20 10

419 Ripoll Monastery
420 Pilgrims' Route Map

1970. Ripoll Monastery.
2063 – 2 p. purple and violet 90 10
2064 **419** 3 p. 50 purple & orange 45 10
2065 – 5 p. green and slate 1·50 10
DESIGNS: 2 p. Entrance; 5 p. Cloisters.

1971. Holy Year of Compostela (1st issue). "St. James in Europe".
2066 **420** 50 c. brown and blue 10 10
2067 – 1 p. black and brown 25 10
2068 – 1 p. 50 purple & green 40 10
2069 – 2 p. brown and purple 35 10
2070 – 3 p. dp blue and blue 45 10
2071 – 4 p. olive 70 10
DESIGNS—VERT: 1 p. Statue of St. Brigid, Vadstena (Sweden); 1 p. 50, St. Jacques' Church tower, Paris; 2 p. "St. James" (carving from altar, Pistoia, Italy). HORIZ: 3 p. St. David's Cathedral, Wales; 4 p. Carving from Ark of Charlemagne (Aachen, West Germany).
See also Nos. 2105/11 and 2121/8.

1971. Provincial Costumes. As T **375**. Mult.
2072 6 p. Valencia 25 10
2073 8 p. Valladolid 30 10
2074 8 p. Vizcaya 30 10
2075 8 p. Zamora 30 10
2076 8 p. Zaragoza 30 10

1971. Stamp Day and Ignacio Zuloaga Commem. Paintings as T **409**. Multicoloured.
2077 50 c. "My Uncle Daniel" 15 10
2078 1 p. "Segovia" (horiz) 15 10
2079 1 p. 50 "The Duchess of Alba" 15 10
2080 2 p. "Ignacio Zuloaga" (self-portrait) 35 10
2081 3 p. "Juan Belmonte" 40 10
2082 4 p. "The Countess of Noailles" 25 10
2083 5 p. "Pablo Uranga" 35 10
2084 8 p. "Boatmen's Houses, Lerma" (horiz) 45 15

421 Amadeo Vives (composer)

1971. Spanish Celebrities. Multicoloured.
2085 1 p. Type **421** 40 10
2086 2 p. St. Teresa of Avila (mystic) 45 10
2087 8 p. B. Perez Galdos (writer) 45 10
2088 15 p. R. Menendez Pidal (writer) 45 10

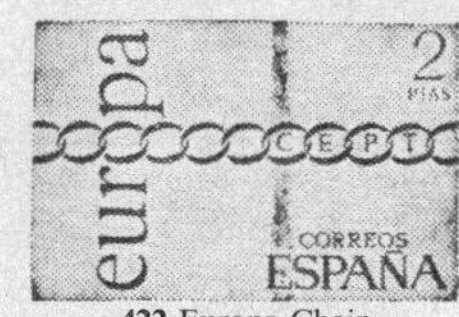

422 Europa Chain

1971. Europa.
2089 **422** 2 p. brown, violet & blue 1·50 10
2090 8 p. brown, light green and green 60 15

1971. World Stamp Day. As T **381**, but with different stamp and postmark.
2091 2 p. black, blue and green 25 10
DESIGN: 2 p. Spanish 6 c. stamp of 1850 with "A.s." postmark.

423 Gymnast on Vaulting-horse

1971. 9th European Male Gymnastics Cup Championships, Madrid. Multicoloured.
2092 1 p. Type **423** 25 10
2093 2 p. Gymnast on bar 25 10

424 Great Bustard

1971. Spanish Fauna (1st series). Mult.
2094 1 p. Type **424** 1·00 10
2095 2 p. Lynx 95 10
2096 3 p. Brown bear 95 10
2097 5 p. Red-legged partridge (vert) 2·25 20
2098 8 p. Spanish ibex (vert) 1·25 25
See also Nos. 2160/4, 2192/6, 2250/4, 2317/21, 2452/6 and 2579/83.

426 Legionaries in Battle

1971. 50th Anniv of Spanish Foreign Legion. Multicoloured.
2101 1 p. Type **426** 10 10
2102 2 p. Ceremonial parade 75 10
2103 5 p. Memorial service 75 10
2104 8 p. Officer and mobile column 60 20

1971. Holy Year of Compostela (2nd issue). "En Route to Santiago". As T **420**.
2105 50 c. purple and blue 10 10
2106 6 p. blue 35 10
2107 7 p. purple and deep purple 45 10
2108 7 p. 50 red and purple 35 20
2109 8 p. purple and green 35 10
2110 9 p. violet and green 35 20
2111 10 p. brown and green 60 10
DESIGNS—HORIZ: 50 c. Pilgrims' route map of northern Spain; 7 p. 50, Cloisters, Najera Monastery; 9 p. Eunate Monastery. VERT: 6 p. "Pilgrims" (sculpture, Royal Hospital, Burgos); 7 p. Gateway, St. Domingo de la Calzada Monastery; 8 p. Statue of Christ, Puente de la Reina; 10 p. Cross of Roncesvalles.

427 "Children of the World"
428 "Battle of Lepanto" (after L. Valdes)

1971. 25th Anniv of U.N.I.C.E.F.
2112 **427** 8 p. multicoloured 20 10

1971. 400th Anniv of Battle of Lepanto.
2113 – 2 p. green & brn (vert) 1·40 10
2114 **428** 5 p. chocolate & brown 1·50 10
2115 – 8 p. blue and red (vert) 1·75 25
DESIGNS: 2 p. "Don John of Austria" (S. Coello); 8 p. Standard of the Holy League.

429 Hockey Players
431 "The Nativity" (detail from altar, Avia)

430 De Havilland D.H.9B over Seville

1971. World Hockey Cup Championships, Barcelona.
2116 **429** 5 p. multicoloured 1·25 10

1971. 50th Anniv of Spanish Airmail Services. Multicoloured.
2117 2 p. Type **430** 60 10
2118 15 p. Boeing 747-100 over Madrid 65 10

1971. Christmas. Multicoloured.
2119 2 p. Type **431** 20 10
2120 8 p. "The Birth" (detail from altar, Saga) 20 10

1971. Holy Year of Compostela (3rd issue). As T **420**.
2121 1 p. black and green 30 10
2122 1 p. 50 violet and purple 20 10
2123 2 p. blue and green 1·10 10
2124 2 p. 50 violet and red 30 10
2125 3 p. purple and red 50 10
2126 3 p. 50 green and pink 35 10
2127 4 p. brown and blue 40 10
2128 5 p. black and green 75 10
DESIGNS—VERT: 1 p. Santiago Cathedral; 2 p. Lugo Cathedral; 3 p. Astorga Cathedral; 4 p. San Tirso, Sahagun. HORIZ: 1 p. 50, Pilgrim approaching Santiago de Compostela; 2 p. 50, Villafranca del Bierzo; 3 p. 50, San Marcos, Leon; 5 p. San Martin, Fromista.

1972. Spanish Celebrities. As T **408**.
2129 15 p. green and brown 30 10
2130 25 p. black and green 30 10
2131 50 p. brown and red 50 20
CELEBRITIES: 15 p. Emilia Pardo Bazan (novelist); 25 p. Jose de Espronceda (poet); 50 p. Fernan Gonzalez (first King of Castile).

432 Ski Jumping
433 Title-page of "Don Quixote" (1605)

1972. Winter Olympic Games, Sapporo. Japan. Multicoloured.
2132 2 p. Type **432** 55 10
2133 15 p. Figure skating (vert) 40 20

1972. International Book Year.
2134 **433** 2 p. red and brown 30 10

1972. Stamp Day and Solana Commem. Paintings by Solana. As T **409**. Multicoloured.
2135 1 p. "Clowns" (horiz) 35 10
2136 2 p. "Solana and Family" (self-portrait) 80 10
2137 3 p. "Blind Musician" 80 10
2138 4 p. "Return of the Fishermen" 70 10
2139 5 p. "Decorating Masks" 1·75 10
2140 7 p. "The Bibliophile" 60 10
2141 10 p. "Merchant Navy Captain" 80 10
2142 15 p. "Pombo Reunion" (vert) 80 10

434 "Abies pinsapo"
435 "Europeans"

1972. Flora (1st series). Multicoloured.
2143 1 p. Type **434** 50 10
2144 2 p. Strawberry tree 70 10
2145 3 p. Maritime pine 75 10
2146 5 p. Holm oak 80 10
2147 8 p. "Juniperus thurifera" 90 10
See also Nos. 2178/82, 2278/82 and 2299/303.

1972. Europa. Multicoloured.
2148 2 p. Type **435** 3·25 10
2149 8 p. "Communications" 2·00 10

436 Cordoba Pre-stamp Postmark

1972. World Stamp Day.
2150 **436** 2 p. red, blk & brown 10 10

1972. Spanish Castles (6th series). As T **368**.
2151 1 p. brown and green 1·00 10
2152 2 p. brown and green 1·40 10
2153 3 p. brown and red 1·40 10
2154 5 p. green and blue 1·50 15
2155 10 p. violet and blue 3·25 15
CASTLES—VERT: 1 p. Sajazarra. HORIZ: 2 p. Santa Catalina; 3 p. Biar; 5 p. San Servando; 10 p. Pedraza.

437 Fencing

1972. Olympic Games, Munich. Multicoloured.
2156 1 p. Type **437** 20 10
2157 2 p. Weightlifting (vert) 35 10
2158 5 p. Rowing (vert) 35 10
2159 8 p. Pole vaulting (vert) 35 15

438 Chamois

439 Brigadier M. A. de Ustariz

1972. Spanish Fauna (2nd series). Mult.

2160 1 p. Pyrenean desman 25 10
2161 2 p. Type **438** 60 10
2162 3 p. Wolf 80 10
2163 5 p. Egyptian mongoose (horiz) 1·25 10
2164 7 p. Small-spotted genet (horiz) 1·00 10

1972. "Spain in the New World" (1st series). 450th Anniv of Puerto Rico. Multicoloured.

2165 1 p. Type **439** 30 10
2166 2 p. View of San Juan, 1870 (horiz) 45 10
2167 5 p. View of San Juan, 1625 (horiz) 50 10
2168 8 p. Map of Plaza de Bahia, 1792 (horiz) 70 20
See also Nos. 2212/5, 2271/4, 2338/41 and 2430/3.

440 Facade of Monastery

441 Grand Lyceum Theatre

1972. Monastery of St.Thomas, Avila.

2169 **440** 2 p. green and blue . . . 1·25 10
2170 – 8 p. purple and brown . . 85 10
2171 – 15 p. blue and purple . . 1·40 15
DESIGNS—VERT: 8 p. Interior of monastery. HORIZ: 15 p. Cloisters.

1972. 125th Anniv of Grand Lyceum Theatre, Barcelona.

2172 **441** 8 p. brown and blue . . 50 10

442 "The Nativity"

1972. Christmas. Murals in Royal Collegiate Basilica of San Isidoro, Leon. Multicoloured.

2173 2 p. Type **442** 20 10
2174 8 p. "The Annunciation" . . 20 10

443 J. de Herrera and Escorial

1973. Spanish Architects (1st series).

2175 **443** 8 p. green and sepia . . . 1·00 10
2176 – 10 p. blue and brown . . 2·00 15
2177 – 15 p. blue and green . . 75 10
DESIGNS: 10 p. J. de Villanueva and Prado; 15 p. V. Rodriguez and Apollo Fountain, Madrid.
See also Nos. 2295/7.

444 "Apollonias canariensis"

1973. Spanish Flora (2nd series). Canary Islands. Multicoloured.

2178 1 p. Type **444** 30 10
2179 2 p. "Myrica faya" 85 10
2180 4 p. "Phoenix canariensis" . 30 10
2181 5 p. "Ilex canariensis" . . . 85 10
2182 15 p. "Dracaena draco" . . . 40 10
Nos. 2179/82 are vert.

445 Roman Mosaic

446 Iznajar Dam

1973. Europa.

2183 **445** 2 p. multicoloured . . . 1·50 10
2184 – 8 p. blue, red and black 1·00 10
DESIGN—HORIZ—(37×26 mm): 8 p. Europa "Posthorn".

1973. World Stamp Day. As T **381**, but with different stamp and postmark.

2185 2 p. red, blue and black . . 10 10
DESIGN: 2 p. Spanish 6 r. stamp of 1853 with Madrid postmark.

1973. 11th Congress of Int High Dams Commission, Madrid.

2186 **446** 8 p. multicoloured . . . 30 10

1973. Tourist Series. As T **340**.

2187 1 p. brown and green . . . 30 10
2188 2 p. green and dark green . 80 10
2189 3 p. brown and light brown . 70 10
2190 5 p. violet and blue . . . . 1·50 10
2191 8 p. red and green . . . . 1·25 20
DESIGNS—HORIZ: 1 p. Gateway, Onate University, Guipuzcoa; 2 p. Town Square, Lugo; 5 p. Columbus' House, Las Palmas; 8 p. Windmills, La Mancha. VERT: 3 p. Llerena Square, Badajoz.

447 Black-bellied Sandgrouse

448 Hermandad Standard-bearer, Castile, 1488

1973. Spanish Fauna (3rd series). Birds. Mult.

2192 1 p. Type **447** 60 15
2193 2 p. Black stork . . . . . . 1·25 15
2194 5 p. Azure-winged magpie (vert) 1·75 15
2195 7 p. Imperial eagle . . . . . 2·00 15
2196 15 p. Red-crested pochard (vert) 1·25 40

1973. Spanish Military Uniforms (1st series). Multicoloured.

2197 1 p. Type **448** 35 10
2198 2 p. Mounted knight, Castile, 1493 (horiz) . . . . 1·00 10
2199 3 p. Arquebusier, 1534 . . . 1·00 10
2200 7 p. Mounted arquebusier, 1560 . . . . 1·00 10
2201 8 p. Infantry sergeant, 1567 . 1·00 20
See also Nos. 2225/7, 2255/9, 2290/4, 2322/6, 2410/14, 2441/5, 2472/6 and 2499/503.

449 Fishes in Net

1973. World Fishing Fair and Congress, Vigo.

2202 **449** 2 p. multicoloured . . . 10 10

450 Conference Building

1973. I.T.U. Conference, Torremolinos.

2203 **450** 8 p. multicoloured . . . 15 10

1973. Stamp Day and Vicente Lopez Commem. Paintings. As T **409**. Mult.

2204 1 p. "Ferdinand VII" . . . 10 10
2205 2 p. Self-portrait 30 10
2206 3 p. "La Senora de Carvallo" 30 10
2207 4 p. "M. de Castelldosrrius" 20 10
2208 5 p. "Isabella II" 20 10
2209 7 p. "Goya" 20 10
2210 10 p. "Maria Amalia of Saxony" 20 10
2211 15 p. "The Organist, Felix Lopez" 30 15

451 Leon Cathedral, Nicaragua

452 Pope Gregory XI receiving St. Jerome's Petition

1973. "Spain in the New World" (2nd series). Nicaragua. Multicoloured.

2212 1 p. Type **451** 10 10
2213 2 p. Subtiava Church 35 10
2214 5 p. Colonial-style house (vert) 45 10
2215 8 p. Rio San Juan Castle . . 35 10

1973. 600th Anniv of Order of St. Jerome.

2216 **452** 2 p. multicoloured . . . 25 10

453 Courtyard

454 "The Nativity" (pillar capital, Silos)

1973. Monaster of Santo Domingo de Silos, Burgos.

2217 **453** 2 p. purple and brown . . 60 10
2218 – 8 p. purple and blue . . . 60 10
2219 – 15 p. blue and green . . 60 10
DESIGNS—HORIZ: 8 p. Cloisters. VERT: 15 p. "Three Saints" (statue).

1973. Christmas. Multicoloured.

2220 2 p. Type **454** 20 10
2221 8 p. "Adoration of the Kings" (bas-relief, Butrera) (horiz) . 15 10

455 Map of Spain and the Americas

1973. 500th Anniv of Spanish Printing.

2222 **455** 1 p. blue and green . . . 60 10
2223 – 7 p. violet and blue . . . 40 10
2224 – 15 p. green and purple . . 75 15
DESIGNS—VERT: 7 p. "Teacher and pupils" (ancient woodcut); 15 p. "Los Sinodales" (manuscript).

1974. Spanish Military Uniforms (2nd series). As T **448**. Multicoloured.

2225 1 p. Mounted arquebusier, 1603 35 10
2226 2 p. Arquebusier, 1632 . . . 1·00 10
2227 3 p. Mounted cuirassier, 1635 1·25 10
2228 5 p. Mounted drummer, 1677 1·50 20
2229 9 p. Musketeers, "Viejos Morados" Regiment, 1694 1·10 20

456 14th-century Nautical Chart

457 M. Biada (construction engineer) and Early Locomotive

1974. 50th Anniv of Spanish Higher Geographical Council.

2230 **456** 2 p. multicoloured . . . 25 10

1974. 125th Anniv of Barcelona–Mataro Railway.

2231 **457** 2 p. multicoloured . . . 50 10

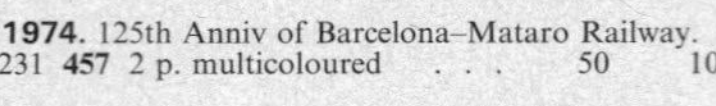

458 Stamp Collector, Album and Magnifier

459 "Woman with Offering"

1974. "ESPANA 75" Int Stamp Exhibition, Madrid.

2232 **458** 2 p. multicoloured . . . 10 10
2233 – 5 p. blue, black & brown 45 10
2234 – 8 p. multicoloured . . . 30 15
DESIGNS—DIAMOND (43×43 mm): 5 p. Exhibition emblem; 8 p. Globe and arrows.

1974. Europa. Stone Sculptures. Multicoloured.

2235 2 p. Type **459** . . . . 2·25 10
2236 8 p. "Woman from Baza" . 1·00 15

460 2 r. Stamp of 1854 with Seville Postmark

1974. World Stamp Day.

2237 **460** 2 p. multicoloured . . . 40 10

461 Jaime Balmes (philosopher) and Monastery

462 Bramante's "Little Temple", Rome

1974. Spanish Celebrities.

2238 **461** 8 p. brown and blue . . 55 10
2239 – 10 p. brown and red . . 1·50 10
2240 – 15 p. blue and brown . . 75 10
DESIGNS: 10 p. Pedro Poveda (educationalist) and mountain village; 15 p. Jorge Juan (cosmographer and mariner) and shipyard.

1974. Centenary of Spanish Fine Arts Academy, Rome.

2241 **462** 5 p. multicoloured . . . 35 10

463 Roman Aqueduct, Segovia

1974. Spain as a Province of the Roman Empire.

2242 **463** 1 p. black and brown . . 10 10
2243 – 2 p. brown and green . . 50 10
2244 – 3 p. brown & lt brown . 15 10
2245 – 4 p. blue and green . . . 15 10
2246 – 5 p. purple and blue . . 20 10
2247 – 7 p. purple and green . . 20 10
2248 – 8 p. green and red . . . 20 10
2249 – 9 p. brown and purple . . 20 15
DESIGNS—HORIZ: 2 p. Roman Bridge, Alcantara; 3 p. Martial (poet) giving public reading; 5 p. Theatre, Merida; 7 p. Ossio, 1st Bishop of Cordoba, addressing the Synod. VERT: 4 p. Triumphal Arch, Bara; 8 p. Ruins of Curia, Talavera la Vieja; 9 p. Statue of Emperor Trajan.

464 Tortoise

1974. Fauna (4th series). Reptiles. Multicoloured.

2250 1 p. Type **464** 25 10
2251 2 p. Chameleon 75 10
2252 5 p. Gecko . . . . 1·25 10
2253 7 p. Green lizard . . . . . . 1·10 15
2254 15 p. Adder . . . . 1·00 15

1974. Spanish Military Uniforms (3rd series). As T **448**. Multicoloured.

2255 1 p. Dismounted trooper, Hussars de la Muerte, 1705 15 10
2256 2 p. Officer, Royal Regiment of Artillery, 1710 . . . . . . 60 10
2257 3 p. Drummer and fifer, Granada Regiment, 1734 . 90 10
2258 7 p. Guidon-bearer, Numancia Dragoons, 1737 . . . . . 60 10
2259 8 p. Ensign with standard, Zamora Regiment, 1739 . 75 15

465 Swimmer making Rescue

1974. 18th World Life-saving Championships. Barcelona.
2260 **465** 2 p. multicoloured . . . 30 10

1974. Stamp Day and Eduardo Rosales. Commemoration. Various paintings as T **409**. Multicoloured.
2261 1 p. "Tobias and the Angel" 15 10
2262 2 p. Self-portrait 15 10
2263 3 p. "Testament of Isabella the Catholic" (horiz) 25 10
2264 4 p. "Nena" 15 10
2265 5 p. "Presentation of Don Juan of Austria" (horiz) 30 10
2266 7 p. "The First Steps" (horiz) 25 10
2267 10 p. "St. John the Evangelist" 40 10
2268 15 p. "St. Matthew the Evangelist" 40 20

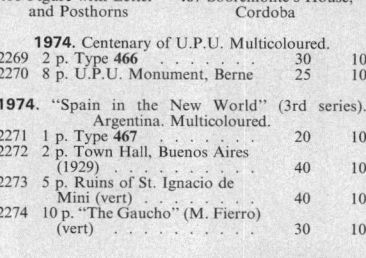

466 Figure with Letter and Posthorns **467** Sobremonte's House, Cordoba

1974. Centenary of U.P.U. Multicoloured.
2269 2 p. Type **466** 30 10
2270 8 p. U.P.U. Monument, Berne 25 10

1974. "Spain in the New World" (3rd series). Argentina. Multicoloured.
2271 1 p. Type **467** 20 10
2272 2 p. Town Hall, Buenos Aires (1929) 40 10
2273 5 p. Ruins of St. Ignacio de Mini (vert) 40 10
2274 10 p. "The Gaucho" (M. Fierro) (vert) 30 10

468 "Nativity" (detail, Valdavia Church) **469** "Teucrium lanigerum"

1974. Christmas. Church Fonts. Multicoloured.
2275 2 p. Type **468** 15 10
2276 3 p. "Adoration of the Kings", Valcobero Church (vert) . . 20 10
2277 8 p. As No. 2276 . . . . . . 20 10

1974. Flora (3rd series). Multicoloured.
2278 1 p. Type **469** 15 10
2279 2 p. "Hypericum ericoides" 35 10
2280 4 p. "Thymus longiflorus" . 20 10
2281 5 p. "Anthyllis onobrychioides" 40 10
2282 8 p. "Helianthemum paniculatum" 40 10

The 1 p. and 8 p. are wrongly inscribed "Teucriun" and "Helianthemun" respectively.

470 Leyre Monastery **471** Spanish 6 c. and 5 p. Stamps of 1850 and 1975

1974. Leyre Monastery.
2283 **470** 2 p. grey and green . . . 75 10
2284 – 8 p. red and brown . . . 25 10
2285 – 15 p. dp green & green 40 10
DESIGNS—VERT: 8 p. Pillars and bas-relief. HORIZ: 15 p. Crypt.

1975. 125th Anniv of Spanish Postage Stamps.
2286 **471** 2 p. blue 35 10
2287 – 3 p. brown and green . . 65 10
2288 – 8 p. mauve and violet . . 1·10 10
2289 – 10 p. green and purple . . 75 15
DESIGNS—HORIZ: 3 p. Mail coach, 1850; 8 p. Sail packet of West Indian service. VERT: 10 p. St. Mark's Chapel.

1975. Spanish Military Uniforms (4th series). As T **448**. Multicoloured.
2290 1 p. Toledo Regiment, 1750 . 50 10
2291 2 p. Royal Corps of Artillery, 1762 . . . . 1·00 10
2292 3 p. Queen's Regt of the Line, 1763 . . . . 2·00 10
2293 5 p. Vitoria Regt of Fusiliers, 1766 . . . . 1·00 10
2294 10 p. Dragoon of Sagunto Regt, 1775 . . . . 2·00 10

1975. Spanish Architects (2nd series). As T **443**.
2295 8 p. olive and green 50 10
2296 10 p. brown and red 50 10
2297 15 p. black and brown . . . 75 10
ARCHITECTS: 8 p. Antonio Gaudi and apartment building; 10 p. Antonio Palacios and palace; 15 p. Secundino Zuazo and block of flats.

473 Almonds

1975. Flora (4th series). Multicoloured.
2299 1 p. Type **473** 15 10
2300 2 p. Pomegranates (vert) . . 60 10
2301 3 p. Oranges (vert) 60 10
2302 4 p. Chestnuts (vert) 35 10
2303 5 p. Apples (vert) 35 10

474 Woman and Pitcher, La Aranya **475** Early Leon Postmark

1975. Europa. Primitive Cave Paintings.
2304 **474** 3 p. red, brown and stone 95 10
2305 – 12 p. mauve, black & brn 1·10 10
DESIGN—HORIZ: 12 p. Horse, Tito Bustillo.

1975. World Stamp Day.
2306 **475** 3 p. multicoloured . . . 30 10

476 Emblem and Inscription **477** Farm Scene

1975. 1st General Assembly of World Tourism Organization, Madrid.
2307 **476** 3 p. blue 25 10

1975. 25th Anniv of "Feria del Campo".
2308 **477** 3 p. multicoloured . . . 25 10

478 Heads of Different Races

1975. International Women's Year.
2309 **478** 3 p. multicoloured . . . 30 10

479 Virgin of Cabeza Sanctuary and Forces Emblems

1975. Defence of Virgin of Cabeza Sanctuary during Civil War.
2310 **479** 3 p. multicoloured . . . 25 10

1975. Tourist Series. As T **340**.
2311 1 p. black and purple . . . 10 10
2312 2 p. brown and lake 20 10
2313 3 p. black and blue 20 10
2314 4 p. mauve and red 10 10
2315 5 p. blue and green 30 10
2316 7 p. deep blue and blue . . . 60 10
DESIGNS—HORIZ: 1 p. Cervantes' cell, Argamasilla de Alba; 2 p. St. Martin's Bridge, Toledo; 3 p. St. Peter's Church, Tarrasa. VERT: 4 p. Alhambra archway, Granada; 5 p. Mijas village, Malaga; 7 p. St. Mary's Chapel, Tarrasa.

480 Salamander Lizard

1975. Spanish Fauna (5th series). Reptiles and Amphibians. Multicoloured.
2317 1 p. Type **480** 35 10
2318 2 p. Triton lizard 75 10
2319 3 p. Tree-frog 75 10
2320 6 p. Toad 55 10
2321 7 p. Frog 60 10

1975. Spanish Military Uniforms (5th series). As T **448**. Multicoloured.
2322 1 p. Montesa Regt. 1788 . . . 30 10
2323 2 p. Asturias Regt of Fusiliers, 1789 . . . . 80 10
2324 3 p. Infantry of the Line, 1802 50 10
2325 4 p. Royal Corps of Artillery, 1803 . . . . 50 10
2326 7 p. Royal Engineers Regt, 1809 60 10

481 Child

1975. Child Welfare.
2327 **481** 3 p. multicoloured . . . 25 10

482 Scroll

1975. Latin Notaries' Congress, Barcelona.
2328 **482** 3 p. multicoloured . . . 25 10

483 "Blessing the Birds"

1975. Stamp Day and Millenary of Gerona Cathedral. Beatitude Miniatures. Multicoloured.
2329 1 p. Type **483** 15 10
2330 2 p. "Angel and River of Life" (vert) 35 10
2331 3 p. "Angel at Gates of Paradise" (vert) 35 10
2332 4 p. "Fox seizing Cockerel" 30 10
2333 6 p. "Daniel with the Lions" 30 10
2334 7 p. "Blessing the Multitude" (vert) 35 10
2335 10 p. "The Four Horsemen of the Apocalypse" (vert) . . 35 10
2336 12 p. "Peacock and Snake" (vert) 40 10

484 Industry Emblems

1975. Spanish Industry.
2337 **484** 3 p. violet and purple . . 15 10

485 El Cabildo, Montevideo

1975. "Spain in the New World" (4th series). 150th Anniv of Uruguayan Independence. Multicoloured.
2338 1 p. Type **485** 15 10
2339 2 p. Ox wagon 35 10
2340 3 p. Fortress, St. Teresa . . . 35 10
2341 8 p. Cathedral, Montevideo (vert) 35 10

486 San Juan de la Pena Monastery **487** "Virgin and Child"

1975. San Juan de la Pena Monastery Commem.
2342 **486** 3 p. brown and green . . 30 10
2343 – 8 p. violet and mauve . . 15 10
2344 – 10 p. red and mauve . . 45 10
DESIGNS—HORIZ: 8 p. Cloisters. VERT: 10 p. Pillars.

1975. Christmas. Navarra Art. Multicoloured.
2345 3 p. Type **487** 40 10
2346 12 p. "The Flight into Egypt" (horiz) 40 10

488 King Juan Carlos I **489** Virgin of Pontevedra

1975. Proclamation of King Juan Carlos I. Multicoloured.
2347 3 p. Type **488** 30 10
2348 3 p. Queen Sophia 30 10
2349 3 p. King Juan Carlos and Queen Sophia (33 × 33 mm) 30 10
2350 12 p. As No. 2349 . . . . . 50 10

1975. Holy Year of Compostela.
2351 **489** 3 p. brown and orange . 35 10

490 Mountain Scene and Emblems **491** Cosme Damian Churruca

1976. Centenary of Catalunya Excursion Centre.
2352 **490** 6 p. multicoloured . . . 15 10

1976. Spanish Navigators.
2353 **491** 7 p. black and brown . . 1·40 10
2354 – 12 p. violet 75 10
2355 – 50 p. brown and green . 1·00 15
NAVIGATORS—VERT: 12 p. Luis de Requesens. HORIZ: 50 p. Juan Sebastian del Cano and "Victoria".

492 Alexander Graham Bell and Telephone Equipment

1976. Telephone Centenary.
2356 **492** 3 p. multicoloured . . . 40 10

493 Crossing the Road

1976. Road Safety. Multicoloured.
2357 1 p. Type **493** 30 10
2358 3 p. Dangerous driving (vert) 85 10
2359 5 p. Wearing of seat-belts . . 75 10

494 St. George on Horseback

1976. 700th Anniv of St. George's Guardianship of Alcoy.

2360 **494** 3 p. multicoloured . . . 30 10

495 Talavera Pottery

1976. Europa. Multicoloured.

2361 3 p. Type **495** . . . . 1·40 10
2362 12 p. Camarinas lace-making 1·90 10

496 Spanish 1851 6 r. Stamp with Coruna Postmark

1976. World Stamp Day.

2363 **496** 3 p. red, blue and black . 30 10

497 Coins

1976. Bimillenary of Zaragoza. Roman Antiquities.

2364 **497** 3 p. brown and black . . 2·75 10
2365 – 7 p. blue and black . . . 1·50 10
2366 – 25 p. brown and black . 1·50 10

DESIGNS—HORIZ: 7 p. Plan of site and coin. VERT: 25 p. Mosaic.

498 Rifle, 1757

1976. Bicentenary of American Revolution.

2367 **498** 1 p. blue and brown . . 50 10
2368 – 3 p. brown and green . . 1·75 10
2369 – 5 p. green and brown . . 80 10
2370 – 12 p. brown and green . 1·00 10

DESIGNS: 3 p. Bernado de Galvez and emblem; 5 p. Richmond $1 banknote of 1861; 12 p. Battle of Pensacola.

499 Customs-house, Cadiz

1976. Spanish Customs Buildings.

2371 **499** 1 p. brown and black . . 30 10
2372 – 3 p. brown and green . . 90 10
2373 – 7 p. purple and brown . 1·75 10

BUILDINGS: 3 p. Madrid; 7 p. Barcelona.

500 Savings Jar and "Industry"

1976. Spanish Post Office. Multicoloured.

2374 1 p. Type **500** 30 10
2375 3 p. Railway mail-sorting van 75 10
2376 6 p. Mounted postman (horiz) 30 10
2377 10 p. Automatic letter sorting equipment (horiz) 90 10

501 King Juan Carlos I, Queen Sophia and Map of the Americas

1976. Royal Visit to America (1st issue).

2378 **501** 12 p. multicoloured . . 40 10

See also No. 2434.

1976. Tourist Series. As T **340**.

2379 1 p. brown and grey 25 10
2380 2 p. blue and green 75 10
2381 3 p. brown and red 60 10
2382 4 p. blue and brown 30 10
2383 7 p. brown and blue 80 10
2384 12 p. purple and mauve . . 1·00 10

DESIGNS—HORIZ: 1 p. Cloisters, San Marcos, Leon; 2 p. Las Canadas, Tenerife; 4 p. Cruz de Tejeda, Las Palmas; 7 p. Gredos, Avila; 12 p. La Arruzafa, Cordoba. VERT: 3 p. Hospice of the Catholic Kings, Santiago de Compostela.

502 Rowing

1976. Olympic Games, Montreal. Multicoloured.

2385 1 p. Type **502** 15 10
2386 2 p. Boxing 35 10
2387 3 p. Wrestling (vert) 50 10
2388 12 p. Basketball (vert) . . . 50 10

503 King Juan Carlos I

504 "Giving Blood"

1976.

2389 **503** 10 c. orange 10 10
2390 25 c. yellow 10 10
2391 30 c. blue 10 10
2392 50 c. purple 10 10
2393 1 p. green 10 10
2394 1 p. 50 red 10 10
2395 2 p. blue 10 10
2396 3 p. green 10 10
2397 4 p. turquoise 10 10
2398 5 p. red 10 10
2399 6 p. turquoise 15 10
2400 7 p. olive 10 10
2401 8 p. blue 15 10
2402 10 p. red 15 10
2403 12 p. brown 15 10
2403a 13 p. brown 25 10
2403b 14 p. orange 15 10
2404 15 p. violet 30 10
2405 16 p. brown 30 10
2405a 17 p. blue 30 10
2406 19 p. orange 30 10
2407 20 p. red 30 10
2408 30 p. green 35 10
2409 50 p. red 55 10
2409a 60 p. blue 70 10
2409b 75 p. green 85 10
2409c 85 p. grey 95 10
2409d – 100 p. brown . . . . 1·10 10
2409e – 200 p. green . . . . 2·25 20
2409f – 500 p. blue . . . . . 5·00 40

Nos. 2409 d/f are as Type **503**, but larger, 25 x 30 mm.

1976. Spanish Military Uniforms (6th series). As T **448**. Multicoloured.

2410 1 p. Alcantara Regiment, 1815 25 10
2411 2 p. Regiment of the line, 1821 1·25 10
2412 3 p. Gala Engineers, 1825 . 55 10
2413 7 p. Artillery Regiment, 1828 35 10
2414 25 p. Light Infantry Regiment, 1830 . . . . 65 15

1976. Blood Donors Publicity.

2415 **504** 3 p. red and black . . . 15 10

505 Batitales Mosaic

506 Parliament House, Madrid

1976. Bimillenary of Lugo.

2416 **505** 1 p. purple and black . . 35 10
2417 – 3 p. brown and black . . 75 10
2418 – 7 p. red and green 75 10

DESIGNS: 3 p. Old City Wall; 7 p. Roman coins.

1976. 63rd Inter-Parliamentary Union Congress, Madrid.

2419 **506** 12 p. brown and green . . 35 10

1976. Stamp Day and Luis Menendez Commemoration. Paintings as T **409**. Mult.

2420 1 p. "Jug, Cherries, Plums and Cheese" 15 10
2421 2 p. "Jar, Melon, Oranges and Savouries" 15 10
2422 3 p. "Barrel, Pears and Melon" 35 10
2423 4 p. "Pigeons, Basket and Bowl" 20 10
2424 6 p. "Fish and Oranges" (horiz) 25 10
2425 7 p. "Melon and Bread" (horiz) 25 10
2426 10 p. "Jug, Plums and Bread" (horiz) 35 10
2427 12 p. "Pomegranates, Apples and Grapes" (horiz) 35 10

507 "The Nativity"

508 Nicoya Church

1976. Christmas. Multicoloured.

2428 3 p. Type **507** 85 10
2429 12 p. St. Christopher carrying Holy Child (vert) . . . . . 1·75 10

1976. "Spain in the New World" (5th series). Costa Rica. Multicoloured.

2430 1 p. Type **508** 15 10
2431 2 p. Juan Vazquez de Coronado 30 10
2432 3 p. Orosi Mission (horiz) . . 35 10
2433 12 p. Tomas de Acosta . . . 35 10

1976. Royal Visit to America (2nd issue). As T **501**. Multicoloured.

2434 12 p. "Santa Maria" and South America 50 10

510 San Pedro de Alcantara Monastery

1976. Monastery of San Pedro de Alcantara.

2435 **510** 3 p. brown and purple . . 35 10
2436 – 7 p. purple and blue . . . 40 10
2437 – 20 p. chocolate. and brown 55 10

DESIGNS—VERT: 7 p. High Altar; 20 p. San Pedro de Alcantara.

511 Hand releasing Doves

1976. Civil War Invalids' Association.

2438 **511** 3 p. multicoloured . . . 30 10

512 Pablo Casals and Cello

1976. Birth Centenaries.

2439 **512** 3 p. black and blue . . . 40 10
2440 – 5 p. green and red 40 10

DESIGN: 5 p. Manuel de Falla and "Fire Dance".

1977. Spanish Military Uniforms (7th series). Vert designs as T **448**. Multicoloured.

2441 1 p. Outrider, Calatrava Lancers, 1844 . . . . . . 20 10
2442 2 p. Sapper, Engineers' Regt., 1850 . . . . 40 10
2443 3 p. Corporal, Light Infantry, 1861 . . . . 40 10
2444 4 p. Drum Major, Infantry of the Line, 1861 . . . . . . 25 10
2445 20 p. Captain, Horse Artillery, 1862 . . . . 75 10

513 King James I and Arms of Aragon

1977. 700th Death Anniv of King James I.

2446 **513** 4 p. brown and violet . . 25 10

514 Jacinto Verdaguer (poet)

516 Salmon

515 King Charles III

1977. Spanish Celebrities.

2447 **514** 5 p. red and violet . . . 40 10
2448 – 7 p. green and brown . . 40 10
2449 – 12 p. turquoise and blue 45 10
2450 – 50 p. brown and green . 75 10

DESIGNS: 7 p. Miguel Servet (theologian and physician); 12 p. Pablo Sarasate (violinist); 50 p. Francisco Tarrega (guitarist).

1977. Bicentenary of Economic Society of the Friends of the Land.

2451 **515** 4 p. brown and green . . 30 10

1977. Spanish Fauna (6th series). Freshwater Fishes. Multicoloured.

2452 1 p. Type **516** 20 10
2453 2 p. Brown trout (horiz) . . 40 10
2454 3 p. Eel (horiz) 35 10
2455 4 p. Carp (horiz) 30 10
2456 6 p. Barbel (horiz) 40 10

517 Skiing

1977. World Ski Championships, Granada.

2457 **517** 5 p. multicoloured . . . 30 10

518 La Cuadra, 1902

1977. Vintage Cars. Multicoloured.

2458 2 p. Type **518** 20 10
2459 4 p. Hispano Suiza, 1916 . . 25 10
2460 5 p. Elizade, 1915 . . . . . 35 10
2461 7 p. Abadal, 1914 . . . . . 45 10

519 Donana

1977. Europa. Landscapes, National Parks. Multicoloured.

2462 3 p. Type **519** 35 10
2463 12 p. Ordesa 75 10

520 Plaza Mayor, Madrid and Stamps

1977. 50th Anniv of Philatelic Bourse on Plaza Mayor, Madrid.

2464 **520** 3 p. green, red and vio . 25 10

521 Enrique de Osso (founder)

1977. Centenary of Society of St. Theresa of Jesus.

2465 **521** 8 p. multicoloured . . . 25 10

1977. Tourist Series. As T **340**.

2466 1 p. brown and orange . . . 20 10
2467 2 p. grey and brown 20 10
2468 3 p. purple and blue 20 10
2469 4 p. green and blue 20 10
2470 7 p. grey and brown 20 10
2471 12 p. brown and violet . . . 25 10

DESIGNS—HORIZ: 1 p. Toledo Gate, Ciudad Real; 2 p. Roman Aqueduct, Almunecar; 7 p. Ampudia Castle, Palencia; 12 p. Bisagra Gate, Toledo. VERT: 3 p. Jaen Cathedral; 4 p. Bridge and Gate, Ronda Gorge, Malaga.

1977. Spanish Military Uniforms (8th series). As T **448**. Multicoloured.

2472 1 p. Administration officer, 1875 . . . . 10 10
2473 2 p. Lancer, 1883 . . . . . . 25 10
2474 3 p. General Staff commander, 1884 . . . . 25 10
2475 7 p. Trumpeter, Divisional Artillery, 1887 . . . . . . 20 10
2476 25 p. Medical Corps officer, 1895 . . . . 40 10

522 San Marino de la Cogalla (carving) and Early Castilian Manuscript

1977. Millenary of Castilian Language.

2477 **522** 5 p. brown, grn & pur . 30 10

1977. Stamp Day and F. Madrazo (painter) Commemoration. Portraits. As T **409**. Mult.

2478 1 p. "The Youth of Florez" 15 10
2479 2 p. "Duke of San Miguel" . 20 10
2480 3 p. "C. Coronado" 20 10
2481 4 p. "Campoamor" 15 10
2482 6 p. "Marquesa de Montelo" 15 10
2483 7 p. "Rivadeneyra" 15 10
2484 10 p. "Countess of Vilches" 25 10
2485 15 p. "Gomez de Avellaneda" 35 10

523 Sailing Ship and Map of Mail Routes to America

1977. Bicentenary of Mail to the Indies, and "Espamer 77" Stamp Exhibition, Barcelona.

2486 **523** 15 p. green and brown . 70 50

524 St. Francis's Church

1977. Spanish–Guatemalan Relations. Guatemala City Buildings. Multicoloured.

2487 1 p. Type **524** 15 10
2488 3 p. High-rise flats 15 10
2489 7 p. Government Palace . . 25 10
2490 12 p. Monument, Columbus Square 30 10

525 Monastery Building

1977. St. Peter's Monastery, Cardena Commem.

2491 **525** 3 p. grey and blue . . . 15 10
2492 – 7 p. red and brown . . 10 10
2493 – 20 p. grey and green . . 25 10

DESIGNS: 7 p. Cloisters; 20 p. El Cid (effigy).

526 Adoration of the Kings

1977. Christmas. Miniatures from Manuscript "Romanico de Huesca". Multicoloured.

2494 5 p. Type **526** 15 10
2495 12 p. Flight into Egypt (vert) 20 10

527 Rohrbach Ro.VII Roland, 1927, and Douglas DC-10

1977. 50th Anniv of IBERIA (State Airline).

2496 **527** 12 p. multicoloured . . 60 10

528 Crown Prince Felipe 529 Judo

1977. Felipe de Borbon, Prince of Asturias.

2497 **528** 5 p. multicoloured . . . 30 10

1977. 10th World Judo Championships.

2498 **529** 3 p. black, red and brown 40 10

1977. Spanish Military Uniforms (9th series). Multicoloured. Vert designs as T **448**.

2499 1 p. Standard bearer, Royal Infantry Regiment, 1908 . 15 10
2500 2 p. Lieutenant-colonel, Pavia Hussars', 1909 . . . . . . 15 10
2501 3 p. Lieutenant, Horse Artillery, 1912 . . . . 20 10
2502 5 p. Engineers' Captain, 1921 20 10
2503 12 p. Captain-General of the Armed Forces, 1925 . . . 20 10

530 Hilarion Eslava (composer) 531 "The Deposition of Christ" (detail Juan de Juni)

1977. Spanish Celebrities.

2504 **530** 5 p. black and purple . 15 10
2505 – 8 p. black and green . . 15 10
2506 – 25 p. black and green . 35 10
2507 – 50 p. purple and brown 60 10

DESIGNS: 8 p. Jose Clara (sculptor); 25 p. Pio Baroja (writer); 50 p. Antonio Machado (writer).

1978. Anniversaries of Artists.

2508 **531** 3 p. multicoloured . . . 10 10
2509 – 3 p. multicoloured . . . 10 10
2510 – 3 p. mauve and violet . . 10 10
2511 – 5 p. multicoloured . . . 15 10
2512 – 5 p. multicoloured . . . 15 10
2513 – 5 p. brown and black . . 15 10
2514 – 8 p. multicoloured . . . 15 10
2515 – 8 p. multicoloured . . . 15 10
2516 – 8 p. pink and green . . . 15 10

DESIGNS—As T **531**. No. 2510, Portrait of Juan de Juni (sculptor, 400th death anniv); No. 2511, Detail of "Rape of the Sabines" (Rubens); No. 2513, Artist's palette and Ruben's signature; No. 2514, Detail of "Bacchanal" (Titian); No. 2516, Artist's palette and Titian's initial. 46 × 25 mm: No. 2509, Different detail of "Deposition of Christ" and sculptor's tools; No. 2512, Different detail of "Rape of the Sabines" and portrait of Rubens (400th birth anniv); No. 2515, Different detail of "Bacchanal" and portrait of Titian (500th birth anniv).

532 Edelweiss in the Pyrenees

1978. Protection of the Environment. Mult.

2517 3 p. Type **532** 15 10
2518 5 p. Fish and red-breasted merganser 35 10
2519 7 p. Forest (fire prevention) 25 10
2520 12 p. Tanker, oil rig and industrial complex (protection of the sea) . . . 25 10
2521 20 p. Audouin's gull and Mediterranean monk seal (vert) 55 25

533 Palace of Charles V, Granada

1978. Europa.

2522 **533** 5 p. green & light green 25 10
2523 – 12 p. red and green . . . 30 10

DESIGN: 12 p. Exchange building, Seville.

534 Council Emblem and Map of Spain

1978. Membership of the Council of Europe.

2524 **534** 12 p. multicoloured . . . 20 10

535 Columbus Hermitage

1978. 500th Anniv of Las Palmas, Gran Canaria. Multicoloured.

2525 3 p. 16th-cent plan of city (horiz) 10 10
2526 5 p. Type **535** 10 10
2527 12 p. Las Palmas (16th century) (horiz) 15 10

536 Post Box, Stamp, U.P.U. Emblem and Postal Transport

1978. World Stamp Day.

2528 **536** 5 p. green & dp green 30 10

1978. Stamp Day and Picasso Commemoration. As T **409**. Multicoloured.

2529 3 p. "Portrait of Senora Canals" 15 10
2530 5 p. Self-portrait 15 10
2531 8 p. "Portrait of Jaime Sabartes" 15 10
2532 10 p. "The End of the Number" 20 10
2533 12 p. "Science and Charity" (horiz) 20 10
2534 15 p. "Las Meninas" (horiz) 25 10
2535 20 p. "The Pigeons" 25 10
2536 25 p. "The Painter and Model" (horiz) 30 10

537 Jose de San Martin

1978. Latin-American Heroes.

2537 **537** 7 p. brown and red . . . 10 10
2538 – 12 p. violet and red . . . 20 20

DESIGNS: 12 p. Simon Bolivar.

538 Flight into Egypt

1978. Christmas. Capitals from Santa Maria de Nieva. Multicoloured.

2539 5 p. Type **538** 10 10
2540 12 p. The Annunciation . . 15 10

539 Aztec Calendar 540 Philip V

1978. Royal Visits to Mexico, Peru and Argentina. Multicoloured.

2541 5 p. Type **539** 10 10
2542 5 p. Macchu Piccu, Peru . . 10 10
2543 5 p. Pre-Columbian pots, Argentina 10 10

1978. Spanish Kings and Queens of the House of Bourbon.

2544 **540** 5 p. red and blue 10 10
2545 – 5 p. deep green and green 10 10
2546 – 8 p. lake and blue . . . 20 10
2547 – 10 p. black and green . . 20 10
2548 – 12 p. lake and brown . . 25 10
2549 – 15 p. blue and green . . 25 10
2550 – 20 p. blue and olive . . 30 10
2551 – 25 p. violet and blue . . 35 10
2552 – 50 p. brown and red . . 60 15
2553 – 100 p. violet and blue . . 1·25 40

DESIGNS: 5 p. (No. 2545), Luis I; 8 p. Ferdinand VI; 10 p. Charles III; 12 p. Charles IV; 15 p. Ferdinand VII; 20 p. Isabel II; 25 p. Alfonso XII; 50 p. Alfonso XIII; 100 p. Juan Carlos I.

541 Miniatures from Bible

1978. Millenary of Consecration of Third Basilica of Santa Maria, Ripoll.

2554 **541** 5 p. multicoloured . . . 15 10

542 Flag, First Lines of Constitution and Cortes Building

1978. New Constitution.

2555 **542** 5 p. multicoloured . . . 15 10

543 Car and Oil Drop **544** St. Jean Baptiste de la Salle (founder)

1979. Energy Conservation. Multicoloured.
2556 5 p. Type **543** 10 10
2557 8 p. Insulated house and thermometer 10 10
2558 10 p. Hand removing electric plug 15 10

1979. Centenary of Brothers of the Christian Schools in Spain.
2559 **544** 5 p. brown, blue & mauve 10 10

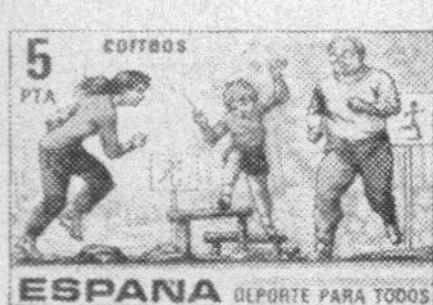

545 Jorge Manrique (poet) **546** Running and Jumping

1979. Spanish Celebrities.
2560 **545** 5 p. brown and green . . 10 10
2561 – 8 p. blue and red 10 10
2562 – 10 p. violet and brown . 10 10
2563 – 20 p. green and bistre . . 30 10
DESIGNS: 8 p. Fernan Caballero (novelist); 10 p. Francisco Villaespesa (poet); 20 p. Gregorio Maranon (writer).

1979. Sport for All.
2564 **546** 5 p. red, green & black . 10 10
2565 – 8 p. blue, ochre & black . 10 10
2566 – 10 p. brown, blue & black 10 10
DESIGNS: 8 p. Football, running, skipping and cycling; 10 p. Running.

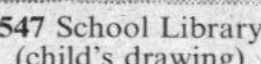

547 School Library (child's drawing) **548** Cabinet Messenger and Postilion, 1761

1979. International Year of the Child.
2567 **547** 5 p. multicoloured . . . 15 10

1979. Europa.
2568 **548** 5 p. deep brown and brown on yellow 20 10
2569 – 12 p. green and brown on yellow 25 10
DESIGN—HORIZ: 12 p. Manuel de Ysasi (postal reformer).

549 Wave Pattern and Television Screen

1979. World Telecommunications Day. Mult.
2570 5 p. Type **549** 10 10
2571 8 p. Satellite and receiving aerial (horiz) 20 10

550 First Bulgarian Stamp and Exhibition Hall

1979. "Philaserdica 79" Stamp Exhibition, Sofia.
2572 **550** 12 p. multicoloured . . 15 10

551 Tank, Destroyer "Roger de Lauria" and Hawker Siddeley Matador Jet Fighter

1979. Armed Forces Day.
2573 **551** 5 p. multicoloured . . . 60 10

552 King receiving Messenger

1979. Stamp Day.
2574 **552** 5 p. multicoloured . . . 25 10

1979. Tourist Series. As T **340**.
2575 5 p. lilac and blue 10 10
2576 8 p. brown and blue 10 10
2577 10 p. green and myrtle . . . 10 10
2578 20 p. sepia and brown . . . 15 10
DESIGNS—VERT: 5 p. Daroca Gate, Zaragoza; 8 p. Gerona Cathedral; 10 p. Interior of Carthusian Monastery Church, Granada; 20 p. Portal of Marques de Dos Aguas Palace, Valencia.

553 Turkey Sponge

1979. Spanish Fauna (7th series). Invertebrates. Multicoloured.
2579 5 p. Type **553** 10 10
2580 7 p. Crayfish 10 10
2581 8 p. Scorpion 10 10
2582 20 p. Starfish 20 10
2583 25 p. Sea anemone 30 10

554 Antonio Gutierrez **555** Cathedral and Statue of Virgin and Child, Zaragoza

1979. Defence of Tenerife, 1797.
2584 **554** 5 p. multicoloured . . . 30 10

1979. Stamp Day and J. de Juanes (painter) Commemoration. Religious Paintings as T **409**. Multicoloured.
2585 8 p. "Immaculate Conception" 15 10
2586 10 p. "Holy Family" 15 10
2587 15 p. "Ecce Homo" 25 10
2588 20 p. "St. Stephen in the Synagogue" 25 10
2589 25 p. "The Last Supper" (horiz) 30 10
2590 50 p. "Adoration of the Mystic Lamb" (horiz) 50 20

1979. 8th Mariological Congress, Zaragoza.
2591 **555** 5 p. multicoloured . . . 30 10

556 St. Bartholomew's College, Bogota

1979. Latin-American Architecture.
2592 **556** 7 p. green, blue & brown 10 10
2593 – 12 p. indigo, purple & brn 15 10
DESIGN: 12 p. University of San Marcos, Lima.

557 Hands and Governor's Palace, Barcelona **558** Autonomy Statute

1979. Catalonian Autonomy.
2594 **557** 8 p. multicoloured . . . 25 10

1979. Basque Autonomy.
2595 **558** 8 p. multicoloured . . . 30 10

559 Prince of Asturias and Hospital

1979. Centenary of Hospital of the Child Jesus, Madrid.
2596 **559** 5 p. multicoloured . . . 30 10

560 Barcelona Tax Stamp, 1929

1979. 50th Anniv of Barcelona Exhibition Tax Stamps.
2597 **560** 5 p. multicoloured . . . 25 10

561 The Nativity

1979. Christmas. Capitals from San Pedro el Viejo, Huesca. Multicoloured.
2598 8 p. Type **561** 10 10
2599 19 p. Flight into Egypt . . . 20 10

562 Charles I

1979. Spanish Kings of the House of Hapsburg.
2600 **562** 15 p. green and blue . . . 30 10
2601 – 20 p. blue and mauve . . 35 10
2602 – 25 p. violet and brown . 45 10
2603 – 50 p. brown and green . . 75 20
2604 – 100 p. mauve & brown . 1·25 35
DESIGNS: 20 p. Philip II; 25 p. Philip III; 50 p. Philip IV; 100 p. Charles II.

563 Olive Plantation and Harvester

1979. International Olive Oil Year.
2605 **536** 8 p. multicoloured . . . 30 10

564 Electric Train

1980. Public Transport.
2606 **564** 3 p. lake and brown . . . 10 10
2607 – 4 p. blue and brown . . . 10 10
2608 – 5 p. green and brown . . 15 10
DESIGNS: 4 p. Motorbus; 5 p. Underground train.

565 Steel Products

1980. Spanish Exports (1st series). Multicoloured.
2609 5 p. Type **565** 10 10
2610 8 p. Tankers 10 10
2611 13 p. Footwear 15 10
2612 19 p. Industrial machinery . 20 10
2613 25 p. Factory buildings, bridge and symbols of technology 30 10
See also Nos. 2653/5.

566 Federico Garcia Lorca

1980. Europa. Writers.
2614 **566** 8 p. violet and green . . 15 10
2615 – 19 p. brown and green . . 30 10
DESIGN: 19 p. J. Ortega y Gasset.

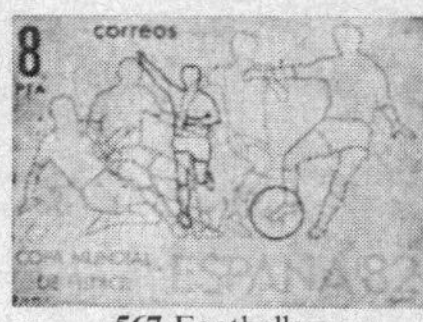

567 Footballers

1980. World Cup Football Championship, Spain (1982) (1st issue). Multicoloured.
2616 8 p. Type **567** 15 10
2617 19 p. Football and flags . . 35 10
See also Nos. 2640/1, 2668/9 and 2683/4.

568 Armed Forces

1980. Armed Forces Day.
2618 **568** 8 p. multicoloured . . . 50 10

569 Bourbon Arms, Ministry of Finance, Madrid

1980. Public Finances under the Bourbons.
2619 **569** 8 p. dp brown & brown . 15 10

570 Helen Keller

1980. Birth Centenary of Helen Keller.
2620 **570** 19 p. red and green . . . 30 10

571 Postal Courier (14th century)

1980. Stamp Day.
2621 **571** 8 p. brown, stone & red . 20 10

572 King Alfonso XIII and Count of Maceda at Exhibition

573 Altar of the Virgin, La Palma Cathedral

1980. 50th Anniv of First National Stamp Exhibition.
2622 **572** 8 p. multicoloured . . . 30 10

1980. 300th Anniv of Appearance of the Holy Virgin at La Palma.
2623 **573** 8 p. brown and black . . 25 10

574 Ramon Perez de Ayala

1980. Birth Centenary of Ramon Perez de Ayala (writer).
2624 **574** 100 p. green and brown . 95 20

576 Juan de Garay and Founding of Buenos Aires (after Moreno Carbonero)

1980. 400th Anniv of Buenos Aires.
2626 **576** 19 p. blue, green & red . 20 10

578 Palace of Congresses, Madrid

579 "Nativity" (mural from Church of Santa Maria de Cuina, Oza de los Rios)

1980. European Security and Co-operation Conference, Madrid.
2628 **578** 22 p. multicoloured . . . 25 10

1980. Christmas. Multicoloured.
2629 10 p. Type **579** 10 10
2630 22 p. "Adoration of the Kings" (doorway of Church of St. Nicholas of Cines, Oza de los Rios) (horiz) 25 10

580 Pedro Vives and Farman H.F.III Biplane

1980. Aviation Pioneers. Multicoloured.
2631 5 p. Type **580** 15 10
2632 10 p. Benito Loygorri 15 10
2633 15 p. Alfonso de Orleans . . 30 10
2634 22 p. Alfredo Kindelan . . . 40 10

581 Games Emblem and Skier

1981. Winter University Games.
2635 **581** 30 p. multicoloured . . . 30 10

582 "Homage to Picasso" (Joan Miro)

1981. Birth Centenary of Pablo Picasso (artist).
2636 **582** 100 p. multicoloured . . 1·25 20

583 Newspaper, Camera, Notepaper and Pen

1981. The Press.
2637 **583** 12 p. multicoloured . . 20 10

584 Map of Galicia, Arms and National Anthem

1981. Galician Autonomy.
2638 **584** 12 p. multicoloured . . 25 10

585 Mosaic forming Human Figure

586 Heading Ball

1981. International Year of Disabled Persons.
2639 **585** 30 p. multicoloured . . 40 10

1981. World Cup Football Championship (1982) (2nd issue). Multicoloured.
2640 12 p. Type **586** 35 10
2641 30 p. Kicking ball (horiz) . . 55 10

587 La Jota (folk dance)

588 King Juan Carlos reviewing Army

1981. Europa.
2642 **587** 12 p. black and brown . 20 10
2643 – 30 p. dp lilac and lilac . 40 10
DESIGN: 30 p. Procession of the Virgin of Rocio.

1981. Armed Forces Day.
2644 **588** 12 p. multicoloured . . 15 10

589 Gabriel Miro (writer)

590 Messenger (14th-century woodcut)

1981. Spanish Celebrities.
2645 **589** 6 p. violet and green . . 15 10
2646 – 12 p. brown and violet . 20 10
2647 – 30 p. green and brown . . 35 10
DESIGNS: 12 p. Francisco de Quevedo (writer); 30 p. St. Benedict.

1981. Stamp Day.
2648 **590** 12 p. pink, brown & grn . 30 10

591 Map of the Balearic Islands (from Atlas of Diego Homem, 1563)

1981. Spanish Islands. Multicoloured.
2649 7 p. Type **591** 15 10
2650 12 p. Map of the Canary Islands (from map of Mateo Prunes, 1563) 20 10

592 Alfonso XII, Juan Carlos and Arms

1981. Century of Public Prosecutor's Office.
2651 **592** 50 p. brown, green & bl . 85 10

593 King Sancho VI of Navarre with Foundation Charter

1981. 800th Anniv of Vitoria.
2652 **593** 12 p. multicoloured . . . 15 10

594 Citrus Fruit

1981. Spanish Exports (2nd series). Multicoloured.
2653 6 p. Type **594** 10 10
2654 12 p. Wine 15 10
2655 30 p. CASA C-212 Aviocar airplane, car and lorry . . . 45 10

595 Foodstuffs

1981. World Food Day.
2656 **595** 30 p. multicoloured . . . 30 10

597 Congress Palace, Buenos Aires

598 "Adoration of the Kings" (from Cervera de Pisuerga)

1981. "Espamer 81" International Stamp Exhibition, Buenos Aires.
2658 **597** 12 p. red and blue 15 10

1981. Christmas. Multicoloured.
2659 12 p. Type **598** 15 10
2660 30 p. "Nativity" (from Paredes de Nava) 30 10

599 Plaza de Espana, Seville

1981. Air.
2661 **599** 13 p. green and blue . . 25 10
2662 – 20 p. blue and brown . . 35 10
DESIGN: 20 p. Rande Bridge, Ria de Vigo.

600 Telegraph Operator

1981. Postal and Telecommunications Museum, Madrid.
2663 **600** 7 p. green and brown . . 10 10
2664 – 12 p. brown and violet . 15 10
DESIGN: 12 p. Post wagon.

601 Royal Mint, Seville

602 Iparraguirre

1981. Financial Administration by the Bourbons in Spain and the Indies.
2666 **601** 12 p. brown and grey . . 15 10

1981. Death Centenary of Jose Maria Iparraguirre.
2667 **602** 12 p. blue and black . . 15 10

603 Publicity Poster by Joan Miro

604 Andres Bello (author and philosopher) (birth bicent)

1982. World Cup Football Championship, Spain (3rd issue). Multicoloured.
2668 14 p. Type **603** 30 10
2669 33 p. World Cup trophy and championship emblem . . 50 15

1982. Anniversaries (1981).
2670 **604** 30 p. deep green and green 35 10
2671 – 30 p. green and blue . . 35 10
2672 – 50 p. violet and black . . 55 15
DESIGNS: No. 2671, J. R. Jimenez (author, birth centenary); No. 2672, P. Calderon (playwright, 300th death anniv).

605 St. James of Compostela (Codex illustration)

606 Manuel Fernandez Caballero

1982. Holy Year of Compostela.
2673 **605** 14 p. multicoloured . . . 15 10

1982. Masters of Operetta (1st series). As T **606** (2674, 2676, 2678) or T **625** (others). Multicoloured.
2674 3 p. Type **606** 10 10
2675 3 p. Scene from "Gigantes y Cabezudos" (horiz) 10 10
2676 6 p. Amadeo Vives Roig . . 10 10
2677 6 p. Scene from "Maruxa" (horiz) 10 10
2678 8 p. Tomas Breton y Hernandez 15 10
2679 8 p. Scene from "La Verbena de la Paloma" (horiz) 15 10
See also Nos. 2713/8 and 2772/7.

607 Arms, Seals and Signatures (Unification of Spain, 1479)

1982. Europa. Multicoloured.
2680 14 p. Type **607** 15 10
2681 33 p. Symbolic ship, Columbus map of "La Spanola" and signature (Discovery of America) 40 10

608 Swords, Arms and Flag **609** Tackling

1982. Armed Forces Day and Centenary of General Military Academy.
2682 **608** 14 p. multicoloured . . . 15 10

1982. World Cup Football Championship, Spain (4th issue). Multicoloured.
2683 14 p. Type **609** 25 10
2684 33 p. Goal 55 10

610 "St. Andrew and St. Francis" **612** "Transplants"

611 Map of Tenerife and Letter

1982. Air. Paintings by El Greco. Multicoloured.
2686 13 p. Type **610** 20 10
2687 20 p. "St. Thomas" 30 10

1982. Stamp Day.
2688 **611** 14 p. multicoloured 30 10

1982. Organ Transplants.
2689 **14** p. multicoloured 15 10

613 Storks and Modern Locomotive

1982. 23rd International Railway Congress, Malaga. Multicoloured.
2690 9 p. Type **613** 15 10
2691 14 p. Locomotive "Antigua" (37×26 mm) 50 10
2692 33 p. Locomotive "Montana" (wrongly inscr "Santa Fe") (37×26 mm) 60 10

614 La Fortaleza, San Juan

1982. "Espamer 82" Stamp Exhibition, San Juan, Puerto Rico.
2693 **614** 33 p. blue and lilac . . . 35 10

615 St. Theresa of Avila (sculpture by Gregorio Hernandez)

1982. 400th Death Anniv of St. Theresa of Avila.
2694 **615** 33 p. brown, blue and green 35 15

616 Pope John Paul II

1982. Papal Visit.
2695 **616** 14 p. blue and brown . 25 10

1982. Tourist Series. As T **340**.
2696 4 p. blue and grey 10 10
2697 6 p. grey and blue 10 10
2698 9 p. lilac and blue 10 10
2699 14 p. lilac and blue 15 10
2700 33 p. brown and red 35 10
DESIGNS—VERT: 4 p. Arab water-wheel, Alcantarilla; 9 p. Dying Christ, Seville; 14 p. St. Martin's Tower, Teruel; 33 p. St. Andrew's Gate, Villalpando. HORIZ: 6 p. Bank of Spain, Madrid.

617 "Adoration of The Kings" (sculpture, Covarrubias Collegiate Church) **618** "The Prophet"

1982. Christmas. Multicoloured.
2701 14 p. Type **617** 15 10
2702 33 p. "The Flight into Egypt" (painting) 35 10

1982. Birth Centenary of Pablo Gargallo (sculptor).
2703 **618** 14 p. green and blue . . 15 10

619 St. John Bosco (founder) and Children

1982. Centenary of Salesian Schools in Spain.
2704 **619** 14 p. multicoloured . . 15 10

620 Arms of Spain

1983.
2705 **620** 14 p. multicoloured . . . 15 10

621 Sunrise over Andalusia

1983. Andalusian Autonomy.
2706 **621** 14 p. multicoloured . . . 15 10

622 Arms of Cantabria, Mountains and Monuments

1983. Cantabrian Autonomy.
2707 **622** 14 p. multicoloured . . . 15 10

623 National Police **624** Cycling

1983. State Security Forces. Multicoloured.
2708 9 p. Type **623** 10 10
2709 14 p. Civil Guard 15 10
2710 33 p. Superior Police Corps 35 10

1983. Air. Sports. Multicoloured.
2711 13 p. Type **624** 15 10
2712 20 p. Bowling (horiz) 20 10

625 Scene from "La Parranda"

1983. Masters of Operetta (2nd series). As T **625** (2714, 2716, 2718) or T **606** (others). Multicoloured.
2713 4 p. Francisco Alonso (vert) 10 10
2714 4 p. Type **625** 10 10
2715 6 p. Jacinto Guerrero (vert) 15 10
2716 6 p. Scene from "La Rosa del Azafran" 15 10
2717 9 p. Jesus Guridi (vert) . . . 30 10
2718 9 p. Scene from "El Caserio" 30 10

626 Cervantes and Scene from "Don Quixote"

1983. Europa.
2719 **626** 16 p. red and green . . 20 10
2720 – 38 p. sepia and brown . . 40 10
DESIGN: 38 p. Torres Quevedo and Niagara cable-car.

627 Francisco Salzillo (artist) **628** W.C.Y. Emblem

1983. Spanish Celebrities.
2721 **627** 16 p. purple and green . 40 10
2722 – 38 p. blue and brown . . 50 10
2723 – 50 p. blue and brown . . 70 15
2724 – 100 p. brown and violet . 1·25 20
DESIGNS: 38 p. Antonio Soler (composer); 50 p. Joaquin Turina (composer); 100 p. St. Isidro Labrador (patron saint of Madrid).

1983. World Communications Year.
2725 **628** 38 p. multicoloured . . . 40 10

629 Leaves

1983. Riojan Autonomy.
2726 **629** 16 p. multicoloured . . . 20 10

630 Army Monument, Burgos

1983. Armed Forces Day.
2727 **630** 16 p. multicoloured . . . 20 10

631 Burgos Setter

1983. Spanish Dogs.
2728 **631** 10 p. blue, brown & red 15 10
2729 – 16 p. multicoloured . . . 25 10
2730 – 26 p. multicoloured . . . 30 10
2731 – 38 p. multicoloured . . . 40 10
DESIGNS: 16 p. Spanish mastiff; 26 p. Ibiza spaniel; 38 p. Navarrese basset.

632 Juan-Jose and Fausto Elhuyar y de Suvisa

1983. Anniversaries. Multicoloured.
2732 16 p. Type **632** (bicentenary of discovery of wolfram) . . 20 10
2733 38 p. Scout camp (75th anniv of Boy Scout Movement) . . 40 10
2734 50 p. University of Zaragoza (400th anniv) 50 15

633 Arms of Murcia

1983. Murcian Autonomy.
2735 **633** 16 p. multicoloured . . . 30 10

634 Covadonga Basilica and Victory Cross

1983. Autonomy of Asturias.
2736 **634** 14 p. multicoloured . . . 30 10

635 National Statistical Institute, Madrid

1983. 44th International Institute of Statistics Congress.
2737 **635** 38 p. multicoloured . . . 40 10

636 Roman Horse-drawn Mail Cart

1983. Stamp Day.
2738 **636** 16 p. pink and brown . . 20 10

637 Palace and Arms of Valencia

1983. Valencian Autonomy.
2739 **637** 16 p. multicoloured . . . 30 10

638 Seville (Illustration from "Floods of Guadalquivir" by Francisco Palomo)

1983. America–Spain.
2740 **638** 38 p. violet and blue . . 40 10

639 "Biblical King" (Leon Cathedral)

1983. Stained Glass Windows. Multicoloured.
2741 10 p. Type **639** 20 10
2742 16 p. "Epiphany" and Gerona Cathedral 35 10
2743 38 p. "St. James" and Santiago de Compostela Hospital . . 55 10

1983. Tourist Series. As T **340**.
2744 3 p. blue and green 10 10
2745 6 p. indigo 10 10
2746 16 p. violet and red 20 10
2747 38 p. red and brown 40 10
2748 50 p. red and brown 50 15
DESIGNS: 3 p. Church and tower, Llivia, Gerona; 6 p. Santa Maria del Mar, Barcelona; 16 p. Ceuta Cathedral; 38 p. Bridge gateway, Melilla; 50 p. Charity Hospital, Seville.

640 "Nativity" (altarpiece, Tortosa)

641 Indalecio Prieto

1983. Christmas. Multicoloured.
2749 16 p. Type **640** 20 10
2750 38 p. "Adoration of the Kings" (altarpiece, Vich) 40 10

1983. Birth Centenary of Indalecio Prieto (politician).
2751 **641** 16 p. brown and black . 20 10

642 Worker falling from Scaffolding

1984. Safety at Work. Multicoloured.
2752 7 p. Type **642** 10 10
2753 10 p. Burning factory and extinguisher 10 10
2754 16 p. Electric plug and wiring, cutters, gloved hands and warning sign 20 10

643 Tree

1984. Estremaduran Autonomy.
2755 **643** 16 p. multicoloured . . 20 10

644 Burgos Cathedral and Coat of Arms

1984. 1500th Anniv of Burgos City.
2756 **644** 16 p. brown and blue . 20 10

645 Carnival Dancer, Santa Cruz, Tenerife

1984. Festivals. Multicoloured.
2757 16 p. Type **645** 20 10
2758 16 p. Carnival figure and fireworks, Valencia . . . 20 10

646 "Man" (Leonardo da Vinci)

1984. Man and Biosphere.
2759 **646** 38 p. multicoloured . . 40 10

647 Map and Flag of Aragon and "Justice"

1984. Aragon Autonomy.
2760 **647** 16 p. multicoloured . . 20 10

649 F.I.P. Emblem

1984. 53rd International Philatelic Federation Congress, Madrid.
2762 **649** 38 p. red and violet . . . 40 10

650 Bridge

1984. Europa.
2763 **650** 16 p. red 30 10
2764 38 p. blue 50 10

651 Monument to the Alcantara Cazadores Regiment, Valladolid (Mariano Benlliure)

1984. Armed Forces Day.
2765 **651** 17 p. multicoloured . . . 40 10

652 Arms of Canary Islands

1984. Autonomy of Canary Islands.
2766 **652** 16 p. multicoloured . . . 35 10

653 Arms of Castilla-La Mancha

655 "James III confirming Grants"

654 King Alfonso X, the Wise, of Castile and Leon (700th death anniv)

1984. Autonomy of Castilla–La Mancha.
2767 **653** 17 p. multicoloured . . . 30 10

1984. Anniversaries.
2768 **654** 16 p. red, blue & black 20 10
2769 – 38 p. blue, red & black 40 10
DESIGN: 38 p. Ignacio Barraquer (opthalmologist, birth centenary).

1984. Autonomy of Balearic Islands.
2770 **655** 17 p. multicoloured . . . 30 10

656 Running before Bulls

1984. Pamplona Festival, San Fermin.
2771 **656** 17 p. multicoloured . . . 35 10

1984. Masters of Operetta (3rd series). Horiz designs as T **625** (2772, 2775/6) or vert designs as T **606** (others). Multicoloured.
2772 6 p. Scene from "El Nino Judio" 10 10
2773 6 p. Pablo Luna 10 10
2774 7 p. Ruperto Chapi 15 10
2775 7 p. Scene from "La Revoltosa" 15 10
2776 10 p. Scene from "La Reina Mora" 20 10
2777 10 p. Jose Serrano 20 10

657 Bronze of Swimmer ready to Dive

1984. Olympic Games, Los Angeles. Mult.
2778 1 p. Roman quadriga (horiz) 10 10
2779 2 p. Type **657** 10 10
2780 5 p. Bronze of two wrestlers (horiz) 10 10
2781 8 p. "The Discus-thrower" (statue, Miron) 15 10

658 Arms and Map of Navarra

1984. Autonomy of Navarra.
2782 **658** 17 p. multicoloured . . . 30 10

659 Cyclist

660 Arms (Levante Building Salamanca University)

1984. International Cycling Championship, Barcelona.
2783 **659** 17 p. multicoloured . . . 30 10

1984. Autonomy of Castilla y Leon.
2784 **660** 17 p. multicoloured . . . 30 10

661 Women gathering Grapes

1984. Vintage Festival, Jerez.
2785 **661** 17 p. multicoloured . . . 45 10

662 Egeria on Donkey and Map of Middle East

1984. 1600th Anniv of Nun Egeria's Visit to Middle East.
2786 **662** 40 p. multicoloured . . . 45 10

663 Arab Courier

1984. Stamp Day.
2787 **663** 17 p. multicoloured . . . 40 10

664 Father Junipero Serra

665 "Adoration of the Kings" (Miguel Moguer) (Campos altarpiece)

1984. Death Bicentenary of Father Junipero Serra (missionary).
2788 **664** 40 p. red and blue . . . 45 10

1984. Christmas. Multicoloured.
2789 17 p. "Nativity" (15th-century retable) (horiz) 25 10
2790 40 p. Type **665** 45 10

666 Arms, Buildings and Trees

1984. Autonomy of Madrid.
2791 **666** 17 p. multicoloured . . . 45 10

667 Flags and Andean Condor

1985. 15th Anniv (1984) of Andes Pact.
2792 **667** 17 p. multicoloured . . . 30 10

668 "Virgin of Louvain" (attr Jan Gossaert)

669 College Porch and Tympanum

1985. "Europalia 85 Espana" Festival.
2793 **668** 40 p. multicoloured . . . 55 10

1985. 500th Anniv of Santa Cruz College, Valladolid University.
2794 **669** 17 p. yellow, brn & red 35 10

670 Flames and "Olymphilex '85"

1985. "Olymphilex 85" International Olympic Stamps Exhibition, Lausanne.
2795 **670** 40 p. red, yellow & black 50 10

671 Havana Cathedral

1985. "Espamer '85" International Stamp Exhibition, Havana, Cuba.
2796 **671** 40 p. blue and purple . 50 10

672 Couple in Traditional Dress on Horseback

1985. April Fair, Seville.
2797 **672** 17 p. multicoloured . . 45 10

673 Heads as Holder for Flames

1985. International Youth Year.
2798 **673** 17 p. green, black and red 30 10

674 Moors and Christians fighting

1985. Festival of Moors and Christians, Alcoy.
2799 **674** 17 p. multicoloured . . 40 10

675 Don Antonio de Cabezon (organist)

1985. Europa.
2800 **675** 18 p. red, black and blue on yellow 50 10
2801 – 45 p. red, black and green on yellow 75 10
DESIGN: 45 p. Musicians of National Youth Orchestra.

676 Capitania General Headquarters, La Coruna

1985. Armed Forces Day.
2802 **676** 18 p. multicoloured . . 50 10

677 Carlos III's Arms, 1785 Decree and "Santissima Trinidad"

1985. Bicentenary of National Flag. Mult.
2803 18 p. Type **677** 25 10
2804 18 p. State arms, 1978 constitution and lion (detail from House of Deputies) . 25 10

678 Sunflower and Bird

1985. World Environment Day.
2805 **678** 17 p. multicoloured . . 65 10

679 Monstrance in Decorated Street

680 King Juan Carlos I

1985. Corpus Christi Festival, Toledo.
2806 **679** 18 p. multicoloured . . . 45 10

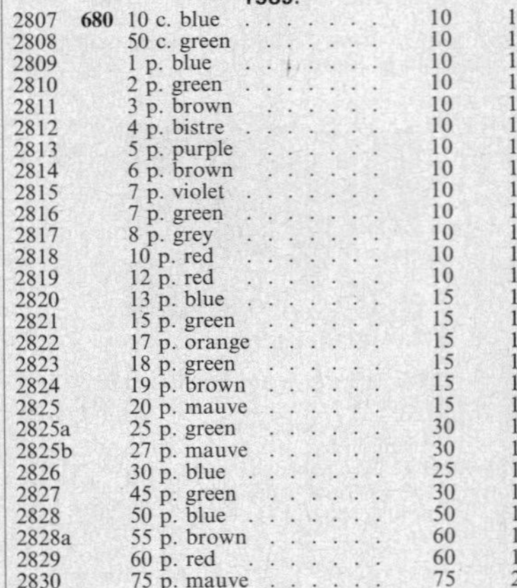

1985.
2807 **680** 10 c. blue 10 10
2808 50 c. green 10 10
2809 1 p. blue 10 10
2810 2 p. green 10 10
2811 3 p. brown 10 10
2812 4 p. bistre 10 10
2813 5 p. purple 10 10
2814 6 p. brown 10 10
2815 7 p. violet 10 10
2816 7 p. green 10 10
2817 8 p. grey 10 10
2818 10 p. red 10 10
2819 12 p. red 10 10
2820 13 p. blue 15 10
2821 15 p. green 15 10
2822 17 p. orange 15 10
2823 18 p. green 15 10
2824 19 p. brown 15 10
2825 20 p. mauve 15 10
2825a 25 p. green 30 10
2825b 27 p. mauve 30 10
2826 30 p. blue 25 10
2827 45 p. green 30 10
2828 50 p. blue 50 10
2828a 55 p. brown 60 15
2829 60 p. red 60 15
2830 75 p. mauve 75 25

681 Planetary System

1985. Inauguration of Astrophysical Observatories, Canary Islands.
2831 **681** 45 p. multicoloured . . . 50 10

682 Ataulfo Argenta (conductor)

1985. European Music Year. Multicoloured.
2832 12 p. Type **682** 35 10
2833 17 p. Tomas Luis de Victoria (composer) 45 10
2834 45 p. Fernando Sor (guitarist and composer) 65 10

683 Bernal Diaz del Castillo (conquistador)

1985. Celebrities.
2835 **683** 7 p. red, black and green on yellow 15 10
2836 – 12 p. red, black and blue on yellow 20 10
2837 – 17 p. green, red and black on yellow 25 10
2838 – 45 p. green, black and brown on yellow . . . 40 10
DESIGNS: 12 p. Esteban Terradas (mathematician); 17 p. Vicente Aleixandre (poet); 45 p. Leon Felipe Camino (poet).

684 Canoeist

1985. "Descent down the Sella" Canoe Festival, Asturias.
2839 **684** 17 p. multicoloured . . . 40 10

685 Monk returning with Rotulet to Savigni Abbey, 1122

686 Ribbon Exercise

1985. Stamp Day.
2840 **685** 17 p. multicoloured . . . 40 10

1985. 12th World Rhythmic Gymnastics Championship, Valladolid. Multicoloured.
2841 17 p. Type **686** 35 10
2842 45 p. Hoop exercise 55 10

688 "Virgin and Child" (Escalas Chapel, Seville Cathedral)

690 Subalpine Warbler

689 "Nativity" (detail of altarpiece by Ramon de Mur)

1985. Stained Glass Windows. Multicoloured.
2844 7 p. Type **688** 15 10
2845 12 p. Monk (Toledo Cathedral) 35 10
2846 17 p. King Enrique II of Castile and Leon (Alcazar of Segovia) 40 10

1985. Christmas. Multicoloured.
2847 17 p. Type **689** 35 10
2848 45 p. "Adoration of the Magi" (embroidered frontal, after Jaume Huguet) 65 10

1985. Birds. Multicoloured.
2849 6 p. Type **690** 25 10
2850 7 p. Rock thrush 45 10
2851 12 p. Spotless starling . . . 55 10
2852 17 p. Bearded reedling . . . 60 10

691 Count of Penaflorida

1985. Death Bicentenary of Count of Penaflorida (founder of Economic Society of Friends of the Land).
2853 **691** 17 p. blue 40 10

692 Royal Palace, Madrid

1986. Admission of Spain and Portugal to European Economic Community. Multicoloured.
2854 7 p. Type **692** 15 10
2855 17 p. Map and flags of member countries 25 10
2856 30 p. Hall of Columns, Royal Palace 50 10
2857 45 p. Flags of Portugal and Spain uniting with flags of other members 60 10

1986. Tourist Series. As T **340**.
2858 12 p. black and red 30 10
2859 35 p. brown and blue 55 10
DESIGNS: 12 p. Lupiana Monastery, Guadalajara; 35 p. Balcony of Europe, Nerja.

693 Merino

1986. Second World Conference on Merinos.
2860 **693** 45 p. multicoloured . . . 85 10

694 "Revellers" (detail, F. Hohenleiter)

1986. Cadiz Carnival.
2861 **694** 17 p. multicoloured . . . 40 10

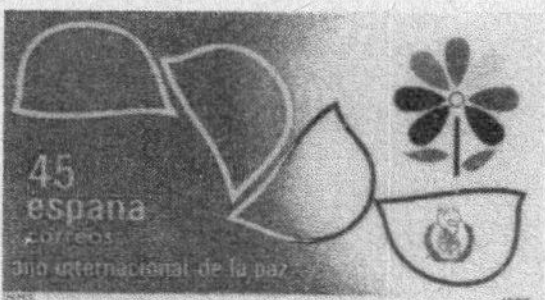

695 Helmets and Flower

1986. International Peace Year.
2862 **695** 45 p. multicoloured . . . 55 10

696 Organ Pipes

1986. Religious Music Week, Cuenca.
2863 **696** 17 p. multicoloured . . . 40 10

697 "Swearing in of Regent, Queen Maria Cristina" (detail, Joaquin Sorolla y Bastida)

1986. Centenary of Chambers of Commerce, Industry and Navigation.
2864 **697** 17 p. black and green . . 35 10

698 Man with Suitcase

1986. Emigration.
2865 **698** 45 p. multicoloured . . . 60 10

699 Boy and Birds

1986. Europa. Multicoloured.
2866 17 p. Type **699** 50 10
2867 45 p. Woman watering young tree 75 10

700 Our Lady of the Dew

1986. Our Lady of the Dew Festival, Rocio, near Almonte.
2868 **700** 17 p. multicoloured . . 40 10

701 Capitania General Building, Tenerife

1986. Armed Forces Day.
2869 **701** 17 p. multicoloured . . 40 10

1986. Tourist Series. As T **340**. Multicoloured.
2870 12 p. black and blue 30 10
2871 35 p. brown and blue . . . 65 10
DESIGNS: 12 p. Ciudad Rodrigo Cathedral, Salamanca; 35 p. Calella lighthouse, Barcelona.

702 Hands and Ball

1986. 10th World Basketball Championship.
2872 **702** 45 p. multicoloured . . 65 10

703 Francisco Loscos (botanist)
704 Apostles awaiting Angels carrying Virgin's Soul

1986. Celebrities.
2873 **703** 7 p. green and black . . 10 10
2874 – 11 p. red and black . . 20 10
2875 – 17 p. brown and black . . 25 10
2876 – 45 p. purple, orange and black 55 10
DESIGNS: 11 p. Salvador Espriu (writer); 17 p. Azorin (Jose Martinez Ruiz) (writer); 45 p. Juan Gris (artist).

1986. Elche Mystery Play.
2877 **704** 17 p. multicoloured . . 30 10

705 Swimmer

1986. 5th World Swimming, Water Polo, Leap and Synchronous Swimming Championships.
2878 **705** 45 p. multicoloured . . 65 10

706 Pelota Player

1986. 10th World Pelota Championship.
2879 **706** 17 p. multicoloured . . 40 10

707 King's Messenger with Letter summoning Nobleman to Court

1986. Stamp Day.
2880 **707** 17 p. multicoloured . . 30 10

709 Aristotle

1986. 500th Anniv (1992) of Discovery of America by Columbus (1st issue). Designs showing historic figures and prophecies of discovery of New World.
2882 **709** 7 p. black and mauve . . 10 10
2883 – 12 p. black and lilac . . . 15 10
2884 – 17 p. black and yellow . . 25 10
2885 – 30 p. black and mauve . . 40 10
2886 – 35 p. black and green . . 50 10
2887 – 45 p. black and orange . . 65 10
DESIGNS: 12 p. Seneca and quote from "Medea"; 17 p. St. Isidoro of Seville and quote from "Etymologies"; 30 p. Cardinal Pierre d'Ailly and quote from "Imago Mundi"; 35 p. Mayan and quote from "Chilam Balam" books; 45 p. Conquistador and quote from "Chilam Balam" books.
See also Nos. 2932/7, 2983/8, 3035/40, 3079/82 and 3126/9.

710 Gaspar de Portola
711 "Holy Family" (detail, Diego de Siloe)

1986. Death Bicentenary of Gaspar de Portola (first Governor of California).
2888 **710** 22 p. blue, red & black . 55 10

1986. Christmas. Wood Carvings. Multicoloured.
2889 19 p. Type **711** 30 10
2890 48 p. "Nativity" (detail, Toledo Cathedral altarpiece, Felipe de Borgona) (horiz) 65 10

712 Abd-er Rahman II and Cordoba Mosque

1986. Hispanic Islamic Culture.
2891 **712** 7 p. brown and red . . . 15 10
2892 – 12 p. brown and red . . . 25 10
2893 – 17 p. blue and black . . . 35 10
2894 – 45 p. green and black . . 80 10
DESIGNS: 12 p. Ibn Hazm (writer) and burning book; 17 p. Al-Zarqali (astronomer) and azophea (astrolabe); 45 p. King Alfonso VII of Castile and Leon and scholars of Toledo School of Translators.

713 "The Good Curate"

1986. Birth Centenary of Alfonso Castelao (artist and writer).
2895 **713** 32 p. multicoloured . . . 45 10

714 Chateau de la Muette (headquarters)

1987. 25th Anniv of Organization for Economic Co-operation and Development.
2896 **714** 48 p. multicoloured . . . 90 10

715 Abstract Shapes

1987. "Expo 92" World's Fair, Seville (1st issue). Multicoloured.
2897 19 p. Type **715** 20 10
2898 48 p. Moon surface, Earth and symbol 50 10
See also Nos. 2941/2, 2951/2, 3004/7, 3052/5, 3094/7, 3143 and 3148/71.

716 Francisco de Vitoria

1987. 500th Birth Anniv of Francisco de Vitoria (jurist).
2899 **716** 48 p. brown 70 10

717 18th-century Warship and Standard Bearer
718 University

1987. 450th Anniv of Marine Corps.
2900 **717** 19 p. multicoloured . . . 40 10

1987. Centenary of Deusto University.
2901 **718** 19 p. red, green and black 30 10

719 Breastfeeding Baby

1987. U.N.I.C.E.F. Child Survival Campaign.
2902 **719** 19 p. brown and deep brown 40 10

720 Crowd
721 15th-century Pharmacy Jar, Manises

1987. 175th Anniv of Constitution of Cadiz. Multicoloured.
2903 25 p. Type **720** 30 10
2904 25 p. Crowd and herald on steps 30 10
2905 25 p. Dignitaries on dais . . 30 10
2906 25 p. Crown and Constitution 30 10
Nos. 2903/6 were printed together, se-tenant, the first three stamps forming a composite design showing "The Promulgation of the Constitution of 1812" by Salvador Viniegra.

1987. Ceramics. Multicoloured.
2907 7 p. Type **721** 25 10
2908 14 p. 20th-century glazed figure, Sargadelos 25 10
2909 19 p. 18th-century vase, Buen Retiro 30 10
2910 32 p. 20th-century pot, Salvatierra de los Barros . 35 10
2911 40 p. 18th-century jar, Talavera 45 10
2912 48 p. 18-19th century jug, Granada 55 10

722 "Procession at Dawn, Zamora" (Gallego Marquina)
723 Bilbao Bank, Madrid (Saenz de Oiza)

1987. Holy Week Festivals. Multicoloured.
2913 19 p. Type **722** 35 10
2914 48 p. Gate of Pardon, Seville Cathedral and "Passion" (statue by Martinez Montanes) 50 10

1987. Tourist Series. As T **340**.
2915 14 p. green and blue 20 10
2916 19 p. deep green and green . 30 10
2917 40 p. brown 50 10
2918 48 p. black 55 10
DESIGNS—HORIZ: 14 p. Ifach Rock, Calpe, Alicante; 19 p. Ruins of Church of Santa Maria d'Ozo, Pontevedra; 40 p. Palace of Sonanes, Villacarriedo, Santander. VERT: 48 p. 11th-century monastery of Sant Joan de les Abadesses, Gerona.

1987. Europa. Architecture.
2919 **723** 19 p. multicoloured . . . 25 10
2920 – 48 p. brown, bistre & grn 45 10
DESIGN—HORIZ: 14 p. National Museum of Roman Art, Merida (Rafael Moneo).

724 Horse's Head and Harnessed Pair

1987. Jerez Horse Fair.
2921 **724** 19 p. multicoloured . . . 35 10

725 Carande

1987. Birth Centenary of Ramon Carande (historian and Honorary Postman).
2922 **725** 40 p. black and brown . 50 10

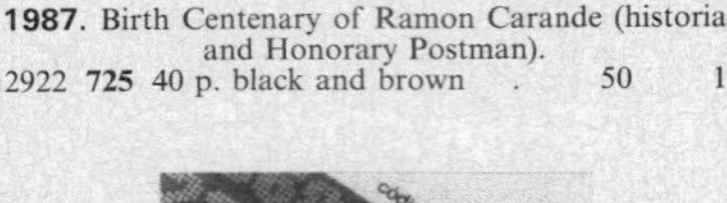

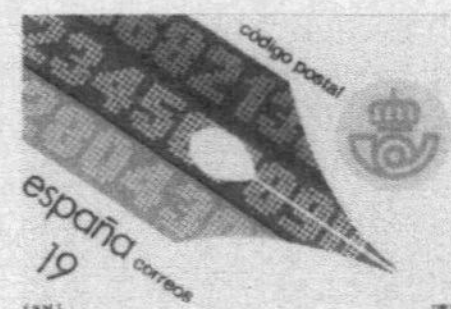

726 Numbers on Pen Nib

1987. Postal Coding.
2923 **726** 19 p. multicoloured . . . 30 10

727 Arms and School

1987. 75th Anniv of Eibar Armoury School.
2924 **727** 20 p. multicoloured . . . 30 10

728 Batllo House Chimneys (Antonio Gaudi)

1987. Nomination of Barcelona as 1992 Olympic Games Host City. Multicoloured.
2925 32 p. Type **723** 35 10
2926 65 p. Athletes 85 10

729 Festival Poster (Fabri)

1987. 25th Pyrenees Folklore Festival, Jaca.
2927 **729** 50 p. multicoloured . . . 65 10

730 Monturiol (after Marti Alsina) and Diagrams of Submarine "Ictineo"

1987. Death Cent of Narcis Monturiol (scientist).
2928 **730** 20 p. black and brown . 30 10

731 Detail from Jaime II of Majorca's Law appointing Couriers

1987. Stamp Day.
2929 **731** 20 p. multicoloured . . 30 10

734 Amerigo Vespucci

1987. 500th Anniv (1992) of Discovery of America by Columbus (2nd issue). Explorers. Multicoloured.
2932 14 p. Type **734** 20 10
2933 20 p. King Ferdinand and Queen Isabella the Catholic and arms on ships 25 10
2934 32 p. Juan Perez and departing ships 35 10
2935 40 p. Juan de la Cosa and ships 55 10
2936 50 p. Map, ship and Christopher Columbus . . 75 10
2937 65 p. Native on shore, approaching ships and Martin Alonzo and Vincente Yanez Pinzon 90 10

735 Star and Baubles

736 Macho (self-sculpture)

1987. Christmas. Multicoloured.
2938 20 p. Type **735** 35 10
2939 50 p. Zambomba and tambourine 50 10

1987. Birth Centenary of Victorio Macho (sculptor).
2940 **736** 50 p. brown and black . . 60 10

1987. "Expo '92" World's Fair, Seville (2nd issue). As Nos. 2897/8 but values changed. Multicoloured.
2941 20 p. Type **715** 35 10
2942 50 p. As No. 2898 . . . . . 75 10

737 Queen Sofia

739 Speed Skating

738 Campoamor

1988. 50th Birthdays of King Juan Carlos I and Queen Sofia. Each brown, yellow and violet.
2943 20 p. Type **737** 25 10
2944 20 p. King Juan Carlos I . . 25 10

1988. Birth Centenary of Clara Campoamor (politician and women's suffrage campaigner).
2945 **738** 20 p. multicoloured . . . 30 10

1988. Winter Olympic Games, Calgary.
2946 **739** 45 p. multicoloured . . . 55 10

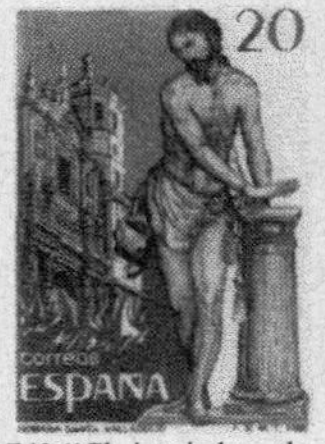

740 "Christ tied to the Pillar" (statue) and Valladolid Cathedral

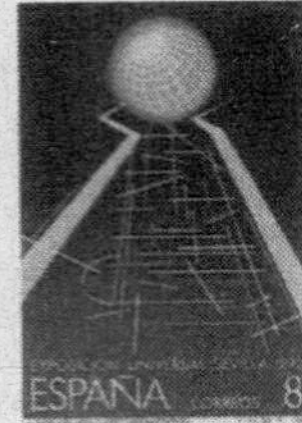

742 Globe and Stylized Roads

741 Ingredients for and Dish of Paella

1988. Holy Week Festivals. Multicoloured.
2947 20 p. Type **740** 25 10
2948 50 p. Float depicting Christ carrying the Cross, Malaga 60 10

1988. Tourist Series. Multicoloured.
2949 18 p. Type **741** 25 20
2950 45 p. Covadonga National Park (70th anniv of National Parks) 60 10

1988. "Expo '92" World's Fair, Seville (3rd issue).
2951 8 p. Type **742** 10 10
2952 45 p. Compass rose and globe (horiz) 55 10

743 18th-Century Valencian Chalice

744 Francis of Taxis (organiser of European postal service, 1505)

1988. Glassware. Multicoloured.
2953 20 p. Type **743** 25 10
2954 20 p. 18th-century pitcher, Cadalso de los Vidrios, Madrid 25 10
2955 20 p. 18th-century crystal sweet jar, La Granja de San Ildefonso 25 10
2956 20 p. 18th-century Andalusian two-handled jug, Castril . . 25 10
2957 20 p. 17th-century Catalan four-spouted jug 25 10
2958 20 p. 20th-century bottle, Balearic Islands 25 10

1988. Stamp Day.
2959 **744** 20 p. violet and brown . 25 10

745 Pablo Iglesias (first President)

1988. Centenary of General Workers' Union.
2960 **745** 20 p. multicoloured . . . 25 10

746 "La Junta" (1st Cuban railway locomotive), 1837

1988. Europa. Transport and Communications.
2961 **746** 20 p. red and black . . . 25 10
2962 – 50 p. green and black . . 60 10
DESIGN: 50 p. Light telegraph, Philippines, 1818.

747 Monnet

749 Couple in Granada

748 Emblem

1988. Birth Cent of Jean Monnet (statesman).
2963 **747** 45 p. blue 55 10

1988. Centenary of 1888 Universal Exhibition, Barcelona.
2964 **748** 50 p. multicoloured . . . 60 10

1988. International Festival of Music and Dance, Granada.
2965 **749** 50 p. multicoloured . . . 60 10

750 Bull

1988. "Expo 88" World's Fair, Brisbane.
2966 **750** 50 p. multicoloured . . . 60 10

751 "Virgin of Hope"

1988. Coronation of "Virgin of Hope", Malaga.
2967 **751** 20 p. multicoloured . . . 25 10

753 Orreo (agricultural store), Cantabria

1988. Tourist Series.
2969 **753** 18 p. green, brown & bl . 25 10
2970 – 45 p. black, brn & ochre 55 10
DESIGN: 45 p. Dulzaina (wind instrument), Castilla y Leon.

754 Players

1988. 28th World Roller Skate Hockey Championship, La Coruna.
2971 **754** 20 p. multicoloured . . . 25 10

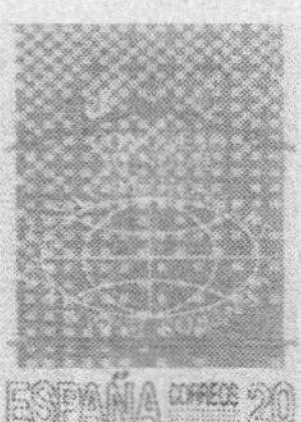

755 Congress Emblem

756 "Olympic" Class Yacht

1988. 1st Spanish Regional Homes and Centres World Congress, Madrid.
2972 **755** 20 p. multicoloured . . . 25 10

1988. Olympic Games, Seoul.
2973 **756** 50 p. multicoloured . . . 60 10

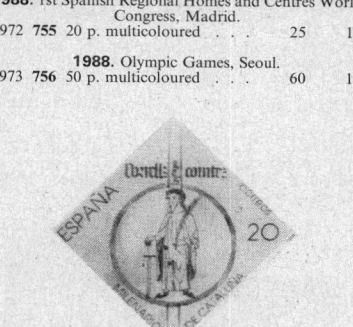

757 Borrell II, Count of Barcelona

1988. Millenary of Catalonia.
2974 **757** 20 p. multicoloured . . . 25 10

758 King Alfonso IX of Leon (detail of Codex of "Toxos Outos")

1988. 800th Anniv of 1st Leon Parliament.
2975 **758** 20 p. multicoloured . . . 25 10

759 Emblem on Band around Peace Year Stamps

1988. 25th Anniv of Spanish Philatelic Associations Federation.
2976 **759** 20 p. multicoloured . . . 25 10

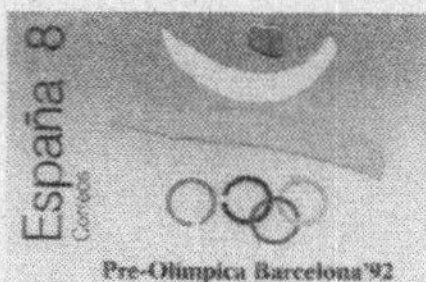

760 Games Emblem

1988. Olympic Games, Barcelona (1992) (1st issue). Designs showing stylized representations of sports. Multicoloured.
2977 8 p. Type **760** 10 10
2978 20 p. + 5 p. Athletics . . . 30 20
2979 45 p. + 5 p. Badminton . . 60 40
2980 50 p. + 5 p. Basketball . . . 65 45
See also Nos. 3008/11, 3031/3, 3056/8, 3076/8, 3098/3100, 3123/5, 3144/6, 3180/2 and 3183/5.

761 Palace of the Generality, Valencia, and Seal of Jaime I

762 Manuel Alonso Martinez (statesman)

1988. 750th Anniv of Re-conquest of Valencia by King Jaime I of Aragon.
2981 **761** 20 p. multicoloured . . . 25 10

1988. Centenary of Civil Code.
2982 **762** 20 p. multicoloured . . . 25 10

763 Hernan Cortes and Quetzalcoatl Serpent

1988. 500th Anniv (1992) of Discovery of America by Columbus (3rd issue). Each red, blue and orange.
2983 10 p. Type **763** 10 10
2984 10 p. Vasco Nunez de Balboa and waves 10 10
2985 20 p. Francisco Pizarro and guanaco 25 10
2986 20 p. Ferdinand Magellan, Juan Sebastian del Cano and globe 25 10
2987 50 p. Alvar Nunez Cabeza de Vaca and river 60 10
2988 50 p. Andres de Urdaneta and maritime currents 60 10

764 Enrique III of Castile and Leon (first Prince of Asturias)

1988. 600th Anniv of Title of Prince of Asturias.
2989 **764** 20 p. multicoloured . . 25 10

765 Snowflakes

1988. Christmas. Multicoloured.
2990 20 p. Type **765** 25 10
2991 50 p. Shepherd carrying sheep (vert) 60 10

766 Cordoba Mosque

1988. U.N.E.S.C.O. World Heritage Sites.
2992 **766** 18 p. brown 20 10
2993 – 20 p. blue 25 10
2994 – 45 p. brown 55 10
2995 – 50 p. green 60 10
DESIGNS—VERT: 20 p. Burgos Cathedral. HORIZ: 45 p. San Lorenzo Monastery, El Escorial; 50 p. Alhambra, Granada.

767 Representation of Political Parties

1988. 10th Anniv of Constitution.
2996 **767** 20 p. multicoloured . . 25 10

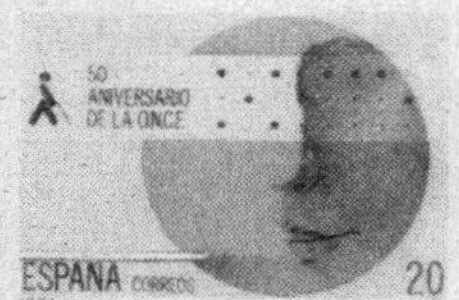

769 Blind Person

1988. 50th Anniv of National Organization for the Blind.
2998 **769** 20 p. multicoloured . . 25 10

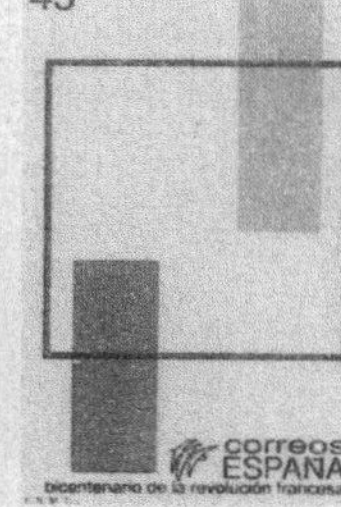

770 Luis de Granada

772 Abstract

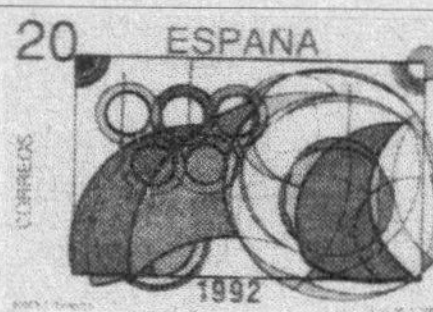

771 Olympic Rings and Sails (Natalia Barrio Fernandez)

1988. 400th Death Anniv of Brother Luis de Granada (mystic).
2999 **770** 20 p. multicoloured . . . 25 10

1989. Children's Stamp Designs. Multicoloured.
3000 20 p. Type **771** 25 10
3001 20 p. Magnifying glass on stamp (Jose Luis Villegas Lopez) (vert) 25 10

1989. Bicentenary of French Revolution.
3002 **772** 45 p. red, blue & black 55 10

773 Maria de Maeztu

774 London, 1851

1989. 107th Birth Anniv of Maria de Maeztu (educationist).
3003 **773** 20 p. multicoloured . . . 20 10

1989. "Expo '92" World's Fair, Seville (4th issue). Great Exhibitions. Multicoloured.
3004 8 p. + 5 p. Type **774** 15 10
3005 8 p. + 5 p. Paris, 1889 . . . 15 10
3006 20 p. + 5 p. Brussels, 1958 . 30 20
3007 20 p. + 5 p. Osaka, 1970 . . 30 20

1989. Olympic Games, Barcelona (1992) (2nd issue). As T **760**. Multicoloured.
3008 8 p. + 5 p. Handball 15 10
3009 18 p. + 5 p. Boxing 25 15
3010 20 p. + 5 p. Cycling 30 20
3011 45 p. + 5 p. Show jumping 60 40

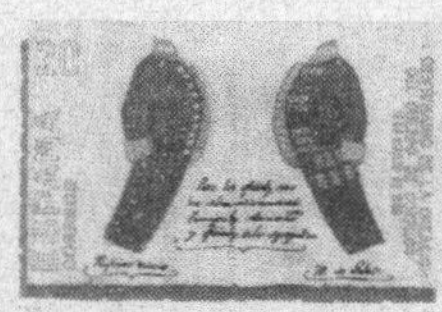

775 Uniforms, 1889

1989. Centenary of Post Office.
3012 **775** 20 p. multicoloured . . . 20 10

776 International Postal Service Treaty, 1601

777 Entrance Door

1989. Stamp Day.
3013 **776** 20 p. black 20 10

1989. Cordon House, Burgos.
3014 **777** 20 p. black 20 10

778 Skittles

781 Manuscript and Portrait

779 European Flag

1989. Europa. Children's Toys. Multicoloured.
3015 40 p. Type **778** 50 10
3016 50 p. Spinning top 60 10

1989. Spanish Presidency of European Economic Community.
3017 **779** 45 p. multicoloured . . . 55 10

1989. Birth Centenary of Gabriela Mistral (poet).
3019 **781** 50 p. multicoloured . . . 60 10

782 Flags forming Ballot Box

1989. European Parliament Elections.
3020 **782** 45 p. multicoloured . . . 55 10

783 Catalonia

1989. Lace. Typical designs from named region.
3021 **783** 20 p. blue and brown . . 20 10
3022 – 20 p. blue and brown . . 20 10
3023 – 20 p. blue 20 10
3024 – 20 p. blue 20 10
3025 – 20 p. blue and brown . . 20 10
3026 – 20 p. blue and brown . . 20 10
DESIGNS: No. 3022, Andalucia; 3023, Extremadura; 3024, Canary Islands; 3025, Castilla–La Mancha; 3026, Galicia.

784 Pope John Paul II and Youths

1989. 3rd Papal Visit.
3027 **784** 50 p. green, brown & blk 55 10

785 Foot leaving Starting Block

1989. World Cup Athletics Championships, Barcelona.
3028 **785** 50 p. multicoloured . . . 55 10

786 Chaplin

787 1 p. Stamp

1989. Birth Centenary of Charlie Chaplin (actor).
3029 **786** 50 p. multicoloured . . . 55 10

1989. Centenary of First King Alfonso XIII Stamps.
3030 **787** 50 p. brown, grey & red 55 10

1989. Olympic Games, Barcelona (1992) (3rd issue). As T **760**.
3031 18 p. + 5 p. Fencing 25 20
3032 20 p. + 5 p. Football . . . 25 20
3033 45 p. + 5 p. Gymnastics . . 55 40

788 Fr. Andres Manjon (founder)

1989. Centenary of Ave Maria Schools.
3034 **788** 20 p. multicoloured . . . 20 10

789 Maize

1989. 500th Anniv (1992) of Discovery of America by Columbus (4th issue). Multicoloured.
3035 8 p. + 5 p. Type **789** 15 10
3036 8 p. + 5 p. Cacao nut . . . 15 10
3037 20 p. + 5 p. Tomato 25 20
3038 20 p. + 5 p. Horse 25 20
3039 50 p. + 5 p. Potato 60 45
3040 50 p. + 5 p. Turkey 60 45

790 Inca irrigating Corn (from "New Chronicle" by Waman Puma)
791 "Navidad 89"

1989. America. Pre-Columbian Life.
3041 **790** 50 p. multicoloured . . . 55 10

1989. Christmas. Multicoloured.
3042 20 p. Type **791** 20 10
3043 45 p. Girl with Christmas present (horiz) 50 10

792 Altamira Caves

1989. World Heritage Sites. Multicoloured.
3044 20 p. Type **792** 20 10
3045 20 p. Segovia Aqueduct . . . 20 10
3046 20 p. Santiago de Compostela 20 10
3047 20 p. Guell Park and Palace and Mila House 20 10

794 Olympic Rings, Compass Rose, Church of Holy Family, Barcelona, and Seville
795 Getxo City Hall and Competitor

1990. Children's Stamp Design.
3049 **794** 20 p. multicoloured . . . 20 10

1990. World Cyclo-cross Championship, Getxo.
3050 **795** 20 p. multicoloured . . . 20 10

796 Victoria Kent
797 Curro (mascot) flying over Path of Discoveries

1990. 3rd Death Anniv of Victoria Kent (prison reformer).
3051 **796** 20 p. lilac 20 10

1990. "Expo '92" World's Fair, Seville (5th issue). Multicoloured.
3052 8 p. + 5 p. Type **797** . . . 15 10
3053 20 p. + 5 p. Curro and Exhibition building . . . 25 20
3054 45 p. + 5 p. Curro and view of Project Cartuja '93 . . . . 55 40
3055 50 p. + 5 p. Curro crossing bridge in Project Cartuja '93 60 45

1990. Olympic Games, Barcelona (1992) (4th issue). As T **760**. Multicoloured.
3056 18 p. + 5 p. Weightlifting . 25 20
3057 20 p. + 5 p. Hockey 25 20
3058 45 p. + 5 p. Judo 55 40

798 Rafael Alvarez Sereix (Honorary Postman)

1990. Stamp Day.
3059 **798** 20 p. flesh, brown & grn 20 10

799 Vitoria Post Office

1990. Europa. Post Office Buildings.
3060 20 p. Type **799** 20 10
3061 50 p. Malaga Post Office (vert) 55 10

800 "Hispasat" Communications Satellite

1990. 125th Anniv of I.T.U.
3062 **800** 8 p. multicoloured . . . 10 10

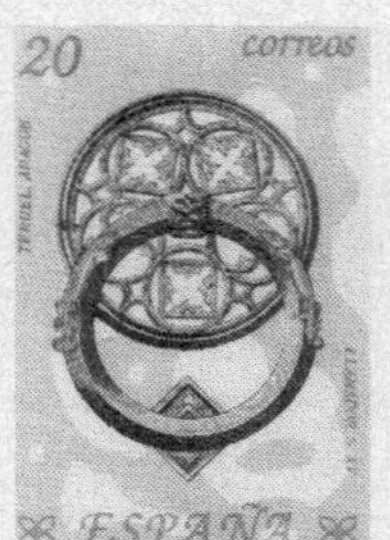

801 Door Knocker, Aragon

1990. Wrought Ironwork. Each black, brown and red.
3063 20 p. Type **801** 20 10
3064 20 p. Door knocker, Andalucia 20 10
3065 20 p. Pistol, Catalonia . . . 20 10
3066 20 p. Door knocker, Castilla-La Mancha 20 10
3067 20 p. Mirror with lock, Galicia 20 10
3068 20 p. Basque fireback . . . 20 10

803 "Charity" (Lopez Alonso)
805 Poster

1990. Anniversaries.
3070 **803** 8 p. multicoloured . . . 10 10
3071 – 20 p. multicoloured . . 20 10
3072 – 45 p. orange and brown 50 10
3073 – 50 p. red and blue . . . 55 10
DESIGNS—VERT: 8 p. Type **803** (bicent of arrival in Spain of Daughters of Charity); 50 p. Page of book (500th anniv of publication of "Tirant lo Blanch" by Joanot Martorell and Marti Joan de Galba). HORIZ: 20 p. Score of "Leilah" and Jose Padilla (composer, birth centenary (1989)); 45 p. Palace of Kings of Navarre (900th anniv of grant of privileges to Estella).

1990. 17th International Historical Sciences Congress, Madrid.
3075 **805** 50 p. multicoloured . . . 55 10

1990. Olympic Games, Barcelona (1992) (5th issue). As T **760**. Multicoloured.
3076 8 p. + 5 p. Wrestling 15 10
3077 18 p. + 5 p. Swimming . . . 25 20
3078 20 p. + 5 p. Baseball 25 20

806 Caravel and Compass Rose

1990. 500th Anniv of Discovery of America by Columbus (5th issue). Multicoloured.
3079 8 p. + 5 p. Type **806** 25 15
3080 8 p. + 5 p. Caravels 25 15
3081 20 p. + 5 p. Caravel 45 25
3082 20 p. + 5 p. Galleons 45 25

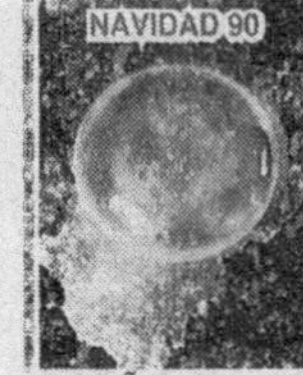

807 Todys
808 Sun

1990. America. The Natural World.
3083 **807** 50 p. multicoloured . . . 55 10

1990. Christmas. Details of "Cosmic Poem" by Jose Antonio Sistiaga. Multicoloured.
3084 25 p. Type **808** 25 10
3085 45 p. Moon (horiz) 50 10

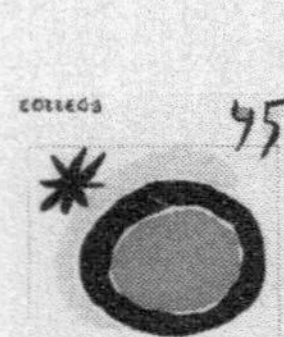

810 Tourism Logo (Joan Miro)
811 Church of St. Miguel de Lillo, Oviedo

1990. European Tourism Year.
3087 **810** 45 p. multicoloured . . . 50 10

1990. World Heritage Sites. Multicoloured.
3088 20 p. Type **811** 20 10
3089 20 p. St. Peter's Tower, Teruel 20 10
3090 20 p. Bujaco Tower, Caceres (horiz) 20 10
3091 20 p. St. Vincent's Church, Avila (horiz) 20 10

812 Conductor and Orchestra
813 Maria Moliner

1990. Spanish National Orchestra.
3092 **812** 25 p. green, turq & blk . 25 10

1991. 10th Death Anniv of Maria Moliner (philologist).
3093 **813** 25 p. multicoloured . . . 25 10

814 La Cartuja (Santa Maria de las Cuevas) Monastery

1991. "Expo 92" World's Fair, Seville (6th issue). Views of Seville. Multicoloured.
3094 15 p. + 5 p. Type **814** . . . 20 15
3095 25 p. + 5 p. The Auditorium 30 25
3096 45 p. + 5 p. La Cartuja bridge 55 45
3097 55 p. + 5 p. La Barqueta bridge 65 50

1991. Olympic Games, Barcelona (1992) (6th series). As T **760**.
3098 15 p. + 5 p. grey, black and red 20 15
3099 25 p. + 5 p. multicoloured . 30 25
3100 45 p. + 5 p. multicoloured . 55 45
DESIGNS: 15 p. Modern pentathlon; 25 p. Canoeing; 45 p. Rowing.

815 Olympic Rings and Yachts (Ana Perello Rebasa)
817 Juan de Tassis y Peralta (Chief Courier to Kings Philip III and IV)

1991. Children's Stamp Design.
3101 **815** 25 p. multicoloured . . . 30 10

1991. Stamp Day.
3103 **817** 25 p. black 30 10

819 Dish Aerials, INTA-NASA Earth Station, Robledo de Chavela

1991. Europa. Europe in Space. Multicoloured.
3105 25 p. Type **819** 30 10
3106 45 p. "Olympus I" telecommunications satellite 50 10

820 Table and Chair (400th death anniv of St. John of the Cross)

1991. Anniversaries.
3107 **820** 15 p. multicoloured . . . 15 10
3108 – 15 p. orange, red & blk . 15 10
3109 – 25 p. multicoloured . . . 30 10
3110 – 25 p. multicoloured . . . 30 10
DESIGNS—VERT: No. 3108, Brother Luis Ponce de Leon (translator and poet, 400th death anniv); 3109, Banner and cap (500th birth anniv of St. Ignatius de Loyola (founder of Society of Jesus)); 3110, Abd-er Rahman III, Emir of Cordoba (1100th birth anniv).

821 Apollo Fountain

1991. Madrid. European City of Culture (1st issue). Multicoloured.
3111 15 p. + 5 p. Type **821** . . . 20 15
3112 25 p. + 5 p. "Don Alvaro de Bazan" (statue, Mariano Benlliure) 30 25
3113 45 p. + 5 p. Bank of Spain 55 45
3114 55 p. + 5 p. Cloisters, St. Isidro Institute 65 50
See also Nos. 3195/8.

822 Choir (after mural mosaic, Palau de la Musica)
823 Basque Drug Cupboard

1991. Centenary of Orfeo Catala (Barcelona choral group).

3115 **822** 25 p. multicoloured . . . 30 10

1991. Furniture. Multicoloured.

3116 25 p. Type **823** 30 10
3117 25 p. Kitchen dresser, Castilla y Leon 30 10
3118 25 p. Chair, Murcia 30 10
3119 25 p. Cradle, Andalucia . . . 30 10
3120 25 p. Travelling chest, Castilla-La Mancha 30 10
3121 25 p. Bridal chest, Catalonia 30 10

824 Hands holding Net

1991. World Fishing Exhibition, Vigo.

3122 **824** 55 p. multicoloured . . . 60 10

1991. Olympic Games, Barcelona (1992) (7th series). As T **760**. Multicoloured.

3123 15 p. + 5 p. Tennis 20 15
3124 25 p. + 5 p. Table tennis . . 30 25
3125 55 p. + 5 p. Shooting . . . 65 50

825 Garcilaso de la Vega (Spanish-Inca poet)

1991. 500th Anniv of Discovery of America by Columbus (6th issue). Multicoloured.

3126 15 p. + 5 p. Type **825** . . . 20 15
3127 25 p. + 5 p. Pope Alexander VI 30 25
3128 45 p. + 5 p. Luis de Santangel (banker) 55 45
3129 55 p. + 5 p. Brother Toribio Motolinia (missionary) . . 65 50

826 Nocturlabe

827 "Nativity" (from "New Chronicle" by Guaman Poma de Ayala)

1991. America. Voyages of Discovery.

3130 **826** 55 p. brown and purple . . 60 10

1991. Christmas. Icons.

3131 **827** 25 p. buff and brown . . 30 10
3132 – 45 p. multicoloured . . . 50 10

DESIGN: 45 p. "Nativity" (16th-century icon).

829 Alcantara Gate, Toledo

830 Gen. Carlos Ibanez de Ibero (cartographer)

1991. World Heritage Sites.

3134 **829** 25 p. agate and brown . 40 10
3135 – 25 p. black and brown . 40 10
3136 – 25 p. brown and blue . . 40 10
3137 – 25 p. violet and green . . 40 10

DESIGNS—VERT: No. 3135, Casa de las Conchas, Salamanca. HORIZ: No. 3136, Seville Cathedral; 3137, Aeonio (flower) and Garajonay National Park, Gomera.

1991. Anniversaries and Events. Multicoloured.

3138 25 p. Type **830** (death centenary) 30 10
3139 55 p. "Las Palmas" (Antarctic survey ship) (meeting of Antarctic Treaty members, Madrid) 95 15

831 Margarita Xirgu

1992. 23rd Death Anniv of Margarita Xirgu (actress).

3140 **831** 25 p. brown and red . . 30 10

832 "Expo 92, Seville"

1992. Children's Stamp Design.

3141 **832** 25 p. multicoloured . . 30 10

833 Pedro Rodriguez, Count of Campomanes (administrator and postal consultant)

1992. Stamp Day.

3142 **833** 27 p. multicoloured . . 30 10

834 Spanish Pavilion

1992. "Expo '92" World's Fair, Seville (7th issue).

3143 **834** 27 p. grey, black & brown 30 10

1992. Olympic Games, Barcelona (8th issue). As T **760**. Multicoloured.

3144 15 p. + 5 p. Archery . . . 20 15
3145 25 p. + 5 p. Sailing 35 30
3146 55 p. + 5 p. Volleyball . . 70 55

836 Cable-cars

1992. "Expo '92" World's Fair, Seville (8th issue). Multicoloured.

3148 17 p. Exhibition World Trade Centre 20 10
3149 17 p. Type **836** 20 10
3150 17 p. Fourth Avenue 20 10
3151 17 p. Barqueta entrance . . 20 10
3152 17 p. Nature pavilion . . . 20 10
3153 17 p. Bioclimatic sphere . . 20 10
3154 17 p. Alamillo bridge . . . 20 10
3155 17 p. Press centre 20 10
3156 17 p. Pavilion of the 15th century 20 10
3157 17 p. Expo harbour 20 10
3158 17 p. Tourist train 20 10
3159 17 p. One-day entrance ticket showing bridge 20 10
3160 27 p. Santa Maria de las Cuevas Carthusian monastery . . 30 10
3161 27 p. Palisade 30 10
3162 27 p. Monorail 30 10
3163 27 p. Avenue of Europe . . . 30 10
3164 27 p. Pavilion of Discovery . 30 10
3165 27 p. Auditorium 30 10
3166 27 p. First Avenue 30 10
3167 27 p. Square of the Future . 30 10
3168 27 p. Italica entrance 30 10
3169 27 p. Last avenue 30 10
3170 27 p. Theatre 30 10
3171 27 p. Curro (official mascot) 30 10

837 Wheelchair Sports

1992. Paralympic (Physically Handicapped) Games, Barcelona.

3173 **837** 27 p. multicoloured . . 30 10

839 "Preparation before leaving Palos" (R. Espejo)

841 "Water and the Environment"

1992. Europa. 500th Anniv of Discovery of America by Columbus.

3175 **839** 17 p. multicoloured . . . 20 10
3176 – 45 p. grey and brown . . 50 10

DESIGN: 45 p. Map of the Americas, Columbus's fleet and Monastery of Santa Maria de La Rabida.

1992. World Environment Day.

3178 **841** 27 p. blue and yellow . . 30 10

842 "Albertville", Olympic Rings and "Barcelona"

1992. Winter Olympic Games, Albertville, and Summer Games, Barcelona.

3179 **842** 45 p. multicoloured . . . 50 10

843 Victorious Athlete

1992. Olympic Games, Barcelona (9th issue). Multicoloured.

3180 17 p. + 5 p. Type **843** . . . 25 20
3181 17 p. + 5 p. Cobi (official mascot) 25 20
3182 17 p. + 5 p. Olympic torch (horiz) 25 20

844 Olympic Stadium

845 Cobi holding Magnifying Glass and Stamp Album

1992. Olympic Games, Barcelona (10th issue). Multicoloured.

3183 27 p. + 5 p. Type **844** . . . 35 30
3184 27 p. + 5 p. San Jordi sports arena 35 30
3185 27 p. + 5 p. I.N.E.F. sports university 35 30

1992. "Olymphilex 92" International Stamp Exhibition, Barcelona. Multicoloured.

3186 17 p. + 5 p. Type **845** . . . 25 20
3187 17 p. + 5 p. Church of the Holy Family, Barcelona, and exhibition emblem 25 20

846 Athletes

1992. Paralympic (Mentally Handicapped) Games, Madrid.

3188 **846** 27 p. blue and red 30 10

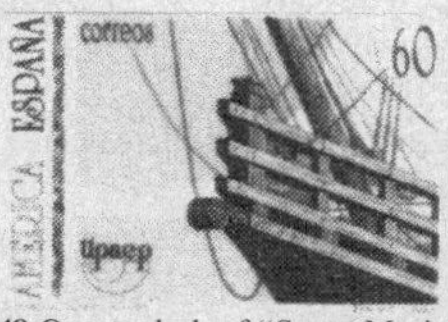

848 Quarterdeck of "Santa Maria"

1992. America. 500th Anniv of Discovery of America by Columbus.

3190 **848** 60 p. brown, cinnamon and ochre 70 10

849 Luis Vives (philosopher)

850 Helmet of Mercury and European Community Emblem

1992. Anniversaries. Multicoloured.

3191 17 p. Type **849** (500th birth anniv) 20 10
3192 27 p. Pamplona Choir (centenary) (horiz) 30 10

1992. European Single Market.

3193 **850** 45 p. blue and yellow . . 55 10

851 "Nativity" (Obdulia Acevedo)

852 Municipal Museum

1992. Christmas.

3194 **851** 27 p. multicoloured . . . 30 10

1992. Madrid, European City of Culture (2nd issue). Multicoloured.

3195 17 p. + 5 p. Type **852** . . . 25 20
3196 17 p. + 5 p. Queen Sofia Art Museum 25 20
3197 17 p. + 5 p. Prado Museum 25 20
3198 17 p. + 5 p. Royal Theatre 25 20

854 Bird, Sun, Leaves and Silhouettes

855 Maria Zambrano

1993. Public Services. Protection of the Environment.

3200 **854** 28 p. blue and green . . 30 10

1993. 2nd Death Anniv of Maria Zambrano (writer).

3201 **855** 45 p. multicoloured . . . 50 10

856 Figures and Blue Cross

857 Segovia

1993. Public Services. Health and Sanitation.

3202 **856** 65 p. blue and green . . 75 10

1993. Birth Centenary of Andres Segovia (guitarist).

3203 **857** 65 p. black and brown . . 75 10

858 Post-box, Cadiz, 1908

1993. Stamp Day.

3204 **858** 28 p. multicoloured . . . 30 10

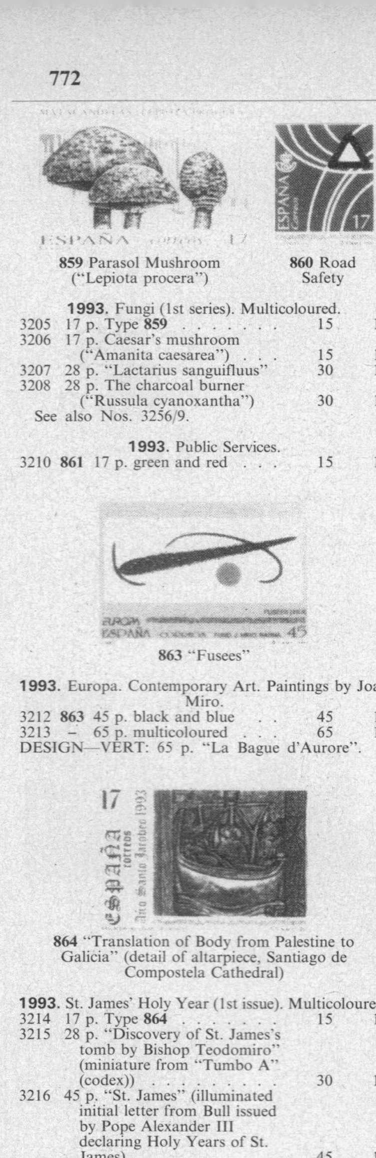

859 Parasol Mushroom ("Lepiota procera")

860 Road Safety

1993. Fungi (1st series). Multicoloured.
3205 17 p. Type **859** 15 10
3206 17 p. Caesar's mushroom ("Amanita caesarea") . . . 15 10
3207 28 p. "Lactarius sanguifluus" 30 10
3208 28 p. The charcoal burner ("Russula cyanoxantha") 30 10
See also Nos. 3256/9.

1993. Public Services.
3210 **861** 17 p. green and red . . . 15 10

863 "Fusees"

1993. Europa. Contemporary Art. Paintings by Joan Miro.
3212 **863** 45 p. black and blue . . 45 10
3213 – 65 p. multicoloured . . . 65 10
DESIGN—VERT: 65 p. "La Bague d'Aurore".

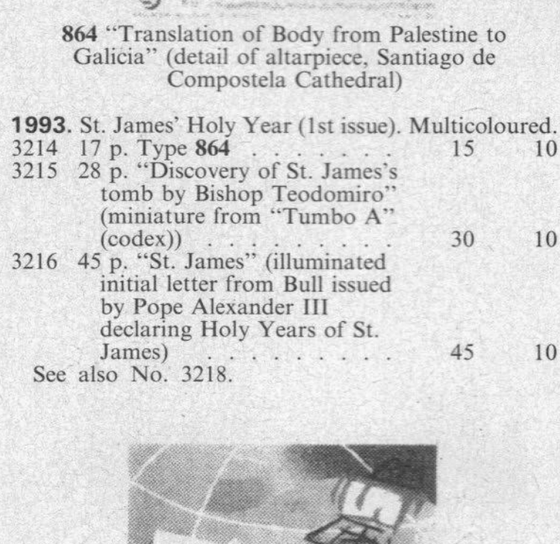

864 "Translation of Body from Palestine to Galicia" (detail of altarpiece, Santiago de Compostela Cathedral)

1993. St. James' Holy Year (1st issue). Multicoloured.
3214 17 p. Type **864** 15 10
3215 28 p. "Discovery of St. James's tomb by Bishop Teodomiro" (miniature from "Tumbo A" (codex)) 30 10
3216 45 p. "St. James" (illuminated initial letter from Bull issued by Pope Alexander III declaring Holy Years of St. James) 45 10
See also No. 3218.

865 Letters, Map and Satellite

1993. World Telecommunications Day.
3217 **865** 28 p. multicoloured . . . 30 10

866 Bagpipe Player (Isaac Diaz Pardo)

867 King Juan Carlos I

1993. St. James's Holy Year (2nd issue).
3218 **866** 28 p. multicoloured . . . 40 10

1993.
3220 **867** 1 p. blue and gold . . . 10 10
3220a 17 p. orange and gold . 15 10
3223 18 p. turquoise and gold 20 10
3225 28 p. brown and gold . 30 10
3226 29 p. green and gold . 30 10
3227 45 p. green and gold . 45 10
3228 55 p. brown and gold . 55 10
3229 65 p. orange and gold . 65 10

868 "Water and the Environment"

869 Count of Barcelona

1993. World Environment Day.
3240 **868** 28 p. multicoloured . . 30 10

1993. Juan de Borbon, Count of Barcelona (King Juan Carlos's father) Commemoration.
3241 **869** 28 p. multicoloured . . 30 10

870 Locomotive

1993. Centenary of Igualada–Martorell Railway.
3242 **870** 45 p. green and black . 45 10

871 "The Mint" (lithograph, Pic de Leopold, 1866)

1993. Cent of National Coin and Stamp Mint.
3243 **871** 65 p. blue 65 10

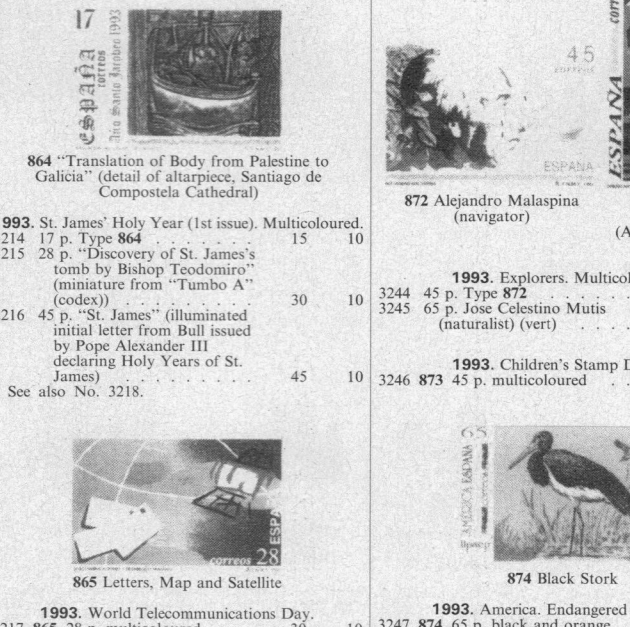

872 Alejandro Malaspina (navigator)

873 "Road to Santiago" (Alejandro Mayor Gamo)

1993. Explorers. Multicoloured.
3244 45 p. Type **872** 45 10
3245 65 p. Jose Celestino Mutis (naturalist) (vert) 65 10

1993. Children's Stamp Design.
3246 **873** 45 p. multicoloured . . 60 10

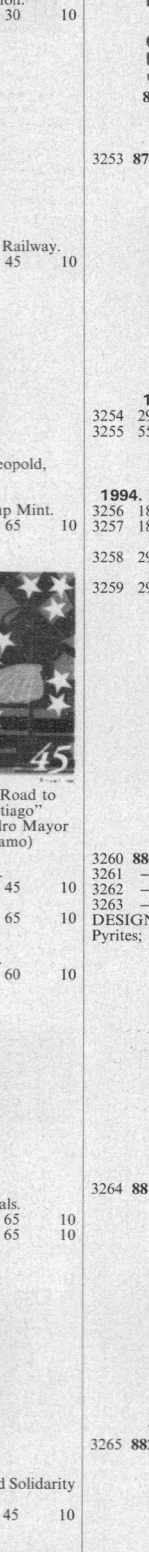

874 Black Stork

1993. America. Endangered Animals.
3247 **874** 65 p. black and orange 65 10
3248 – 65 p. black and red . . 65 10
DESIGN: No. 3248, Lammergeier.

875 Old and Young Hands

1993. European Year of Senior Citizens and Solidarity between Generations.
3249 **875** 45 p. multicoloured . . 45 10

876 Star and Three Wise Men

877 Guillen

1993. Christmas. Multicoloured.
3250 17 p. Type **876** 15 10
3251 28 p. Holy Family (vert) . . 30 10

1993. Birth Centenary of Jorge Guillen (poet).
3252 **877** 28 p. green 30 10

878 Santa Maria de Poblet Monastery, Tarragona

1993. World Heritage Sites.
3253 **878** 50 p. brown, blue & grn 50 10

879 Luis Bunuel and Camera

1994. Spanish Cinema. Multicoloured.
3254 29 p. Type **879** 30 10
3255 55 p. Segundo de Chomon and scene from "Goblin House" 55 10

1994. Fungi (2nd series). As T **859**. Multicoloured.
3256 18 p. Cep ("Boletus edulis") . 20 10
3257 18 p. Satan's mushroom ("Boletus satanas") 20 10
3258 29 p. Death cap ("Amanita phalloides") 30 10
3259 29 p. Saffron milk cap ("Lactarius deliciosus") . . 30 10

880 Cinnabar

1994. Minerals.
3260 **880** 29 p. multicoloured . . . 30 10
3261 – 29 p. multicoloured . . . 30 10
3262 – 29 p. multicoloured . . . 30 10
3263 – 29 p. black and blue . . . 30 10
DESIGNS: 3261, Blende (inscr "Esfalerita"); 3262, Pyrites; 3263, Galena.

881 Barristers' Mailbox, Barcelona

1994. Stamp Day.
3264 **881** 29 p. brown and cinnamon 30 10

882 Sculpture (detail), I.L.O

1994. 75th Anniv of I.L.O., Geneva.
3265 **882** 65 p. multicoloured . . . 65 10

883 "Poetry of America"

1994. 90th Birth Anniv of Salvador Dali (painter). Multicoloured.
3266 18 p. Type **883** 20 10
3267 18 p. "Portrait of Gala" (horiz) 20 10
3268 29 p. "Port Alguer" 30 10
3269 29 p. "The Great Masturbator" (horiz) 30 10
3270 55 p. "The Bread Basket" . . 55 10
3271 55 p. "Soft Self-portrait" . . 55 10
3272 65 p. "Galatea of the Spheres" 65 10
3273 65 p. "The Enigma without End" (horiz) 65 10

884 Pla

1994. 13th Death Anniv of Josep Pla (writer).
3274 **884** 65 p. green and red . . . 65 10

885 "Martyrdom of St. Andrew" (Peter Paul Rubens)

886 "Foundation of Santa Cruz de Tenerife" (M. Gonzalez Mendez)

1994. 400th Anniv of Carlos de Amberes Foundation.
3275 **885** 55 p. multicoloured . . . 55 10

1994. Anniversaries. Multicoloured.
3276 18 p. Type **886** (500th anniv of city) 20 10
3277 29 p. Sancho IV's Foundation Charter at Alcala, 1293 (700th anniv of Complutense University, Madrid) (horiz) 30 10

887 Severo Ochoa (biochemist)

1994. Europa. Discoveries. Multicoloured.
3278 55 p. Type **887** (research into DNA) 55 10
3279 65 p. Miguel Catalan (spectrochemist) (research into atomic structures) . . 65 10

888 "Family of Pascual Duarte"

889 Sancho I Ramirez

1994. Spanish Literature. Works of Camilo Jose Cela. Multicoloured.
3280 18 p. Type **888** 20 10
3281 29 p. Walker and horse rider ("Journey to Alcarria") . . 30 10

1994. 900th Death Anniv of King Sancho I Ramirez of Aragon (3282) and 500th Anniv of Treaty of Tordesillas (defining Portuguese and Spanish spheres of influence) (others). Multicoloured.
3282 18 p. Type **889** 20 10
3283 29 p. Compass rose and arms of Tordesillas (horiz) 30 10
3284 55 p. Building where treaty was signed (horiz) 55 10

891 "Giralda"

893 Knight of Swords (14th-century Catalan deck)

892 Forum Caryatid and Tablet bearing Roman Name of Merida

1994. Ships sailed by Count of Barcelona. Multicoloured.
3286 16 p. Type **891** 15 10
3287 29 p. "Saltillo" 30 10

1994. World Heritage Site. Merida.
3288 **892** 55 p. brn, cinnamon & red 55 10

1994. Playing Card Museum, Vitoria. Multicoloured.
3289 18 p. Type **893** 20 10
3290 29 p. Jack of Clubs (Catalan Tarot deck, 1900) 30 10
3291 55 p. King of Cups (Spanish deck by Juan Barbot, 1750) 55 10
3292 65 p. Jack of Diamonds (English deck by Stopforth, 1828) 65 10

894 Globe and Douglas DC-8

1994. America. Postal Transport.
3293 **894** 65 p. multicoloured . . . 65 10

895 Civil Guard (150th anniv)

1994. Public Services.
3294 – 18 p. red and blue . . . 20 10
3295 **895** 29 p. multicoloured . . . 30 10
DESIGN: As T **854**—18 p. Underground train (75th anniv of Madrid Metro).

896 Map of Member Countries

1994. 40th Anniv of West European Union.
3296 **896** 55 p. multicoloured . . . 55 10

897 Running

1994. Centenary of International Olympic Committee. Spanish Olympic Gold Medal Sports. Multicoloured.
3297 29 p. Type **897** 30 10
3298 29 p. Cycling 30 10
3299 29 p. Skiing 30 10
3300 29 p. Football 30 10
3301 29 p. Show jumping 30 10
3302 29 p. Hockey 30 10
3303 29 p. Judo 30 10
3304 29 p. Swimming 30 10
3305 29 p. Archery 30 10
3306 29 p. Yachting 30 10

898 "Adoration of the Kings" (detail of altarpiece, Esteve Bover)

1994. Christmas.
3307 **898** 29 p. multicoloured . . . 30 10

EXPRESS LETTER STAMPS

E **53** Pegasus and Arms

1905.
E308 E **53** 20 c. red . . . . . . 30·00 30

E **77** Spanish Royal Family

1926. Red Cross.
E417 E **77** 20 c. purple . . . . . 5·00 5·00

1927. No. E417 optd **17-V-1902 17-V-1927 ALFONSO XIII.**
E459 E **77** 20 c. purple . . . . . 4·50 4·50

E **88** Gazelle

E **89**

1929. Seville and Barcelona Exhibitions.
E521 E **88** 20 c. red . . . . . . 12·00 10·00

1929.
E522 E **89** 20 c. red . . . . . . 13·00 70

1929. Optd **Sociedad de las Naciones LV reunion del Consejo Madrid.**
E534 E **89** 20 c. red . . . . . . 9·50 9·00

1930. Optd **URGENCIA.**
E535 E **89** 20 c. red . . . . . . 11·00 50

E **91**

1930. 11th International Railway Congress.
E553 E **91** 20 c. red . . . . . . 75·00 85·00

1930. "Goya" type optd **URGENTE.**
E570 **91** 20 c. mauve 30 25

1930. Air. "Goya" type optd **URGENTE.**
E583 – 20 c. brown and grey . . 30 25

1930. "Columbus" type optd **URGENTE.**
E608 **99** 20 c. purple . . . . . . 2·00 2·00

E **113** Seville Exhibition

1930. Spanish–American Exhibition.
E643 E **113** 20 c. orange 25 20

1931. Optd **REPUBLICA.**
E660 E **89** 20 c. red (No. E535) . 5·50 6·50
E672 20 c. red (No. E522) . 5·50 5·50

1931. Optd **Republica Espanola** in two lines continuously.
E697 E **89** 29 c. red (No. E522) . 5·50 55

E **126**

E **145**

1931. 900th Anniv of Montserrat Monastery.
E731 E **126** 20 c. red . . . . . . 20·00 20·00

1934.
E779 E **145** 20 c. red 10 10

E **152** Newspaper Boy

E **185** Pegasus

1936. 40th Anniv of Madrid Press Assoc.
E801 E **152** 20 c. red 30 25

1937.
E906 E **185** 20 c. brown . . . . . 1·00 15

E **198** Pegasus

1939.
E1022 E **198** 25 c. red 20 10

E **199**

1940. 19th Centenary of Apparition of Virgin of El Pilar at Zaragoza.
E1006 E **199** 25 c. + 5 c. red & buff 30 25

E **270** "Speed"

E **271** Centaur

1956.
E1250 E **270** 2 p. red 10 10
E1251 3 p. red 10 10
E1252 E **271** 4 p. mauve & black 15 10
E1253 E **270** 5 p. red 25 10
E1254 E **271** 6 p. 50 red & violet 20 10

E **425** Roman Chariot

1971.
E2099 E **425** 10 p. grn, blk & red 10 10
E2100 – 15 p. blue, blk & red 20 10
DESIGN—VERT: 15 p. Letter encircling globe.

E **862** Arrows (communications)

1993. Public Services.
E3211 E **862** 180 p. red & yellow . 1·75 10

OFFICIAL STAMPS

O **9**

O **52**

1854.
O46 O **9** ½ onza black on orange . 2·10 1·00
O47 1 onza black on red . . 3·25 1·40
O48 4 onza black on green . 7·50 2·10
O49 1 libra black on blue . . 40·00 25·00

1855. Similar to Type **O 9**, but Arms in oval frame, inscr "CORREO OFICIAL".
O50 ½ onza black on yellow . . 1·75 1·00
O51 1 onza black on red . . . . 1·75 1·00
O52 4 onza black on green . . 3·25 1·90
O53 1 libra black on lilac . . . 14·00 7·75

1895.
O289 **51** 15 c. yellow . . . . . 6·50 65
O290 O **52** (–) red . . . . 6·00 1·10
O291 (–) blue . . . . 15·00 4·00

O **66** National Library

O **67** Cervantes

O **68**

1916. Death Tercent of Cervantes. (a) For use by Members of the Chamber of Deputies.
O353 – (–) black and violet . . 80 80
O354 O **66** (–) black and green . . 80 80
O355 O **67** (–) black and violet . . 80 80
O356 O **68** (–) black and red . . . 80 80

(b) For use by Members of the Senate.
O357 – (–) black and green . . 80 80
O358 O **66** (–) black and red . . 80 80
O359 O **67** (–) black and brown . 80 80
O360 O **68** (–) black and brown . 80 80
DESIGN—As Type **O 66**: Chamber of Deputies.

1931. 3rd Pan-American Postal Union Congress. T **121**, etc. Optd **Oficial.**
O707 5 c. brown 20 15
O708 10 c. green 20 15
O709 15 c. violet 20 15
O710 25 c. red 20 15
O711 30 c. olive 20 15
O712 40 c. blue 35 35
O713 50 c. orange 35 35
O714 1 p. grey 35 35
O715 4 p. mauve . . . . 5·50 5·50
O716 10 p. brown . . . . 14·00 16·00

Air. T **123**, etc., optd **OFICIAL.**
O717 5 c. brown 10 10
O718 10 c. green 10 10
O719 25 c. red 10 10
O720 50 c. blue 10 10
O721 1 p. lilac 10 10
O722 4 p. grey . . . . 3·75 4·50

WAR TAX STAMPS

W **42**

W **48**

W **49**

1874. The 5 c. perf or imperf.
W217 W **42** 5 c. de p. black . . 7·50 75
W218 10 c. de p. blue . . . 12·00 2·10

1875. As Type **W 42**, but large figures in bottom corners.
W228 5 c. de p. green . . . . . . 6·00 80
W229 10 c. de p. mauve . . . . . 13·00 3·00

1876.
W253 W **48** 5 c. de p. green . . . 2·40 65
W254 10 c. de p. blue . . . 2·40 65
W258 W **49** 15 c. de p. red . . . 10·00 50
W255 W **48** 25 c. de p. black . . 25·00 7·00
W259 W **49** 50 c. de p. yellow . £350 50·00
W256 W **48** 1 p. lilac . . . . . . £225 45·00
W257 5 p. red £300 £120

W **52**

W **53**

W **163**

1897. Inscr "1897–1898".
W289 W **52** 5 c. green . . . . . . 3·00 50
W290 10 c. green . . . . . . 3·00 50
W291 15 c. green £325 £120
W292 20 c. green . . . . . . 6·50 1·25

1898. Inscr "1898–99".
W293 W **52** 5 c. black . . . . . . 1·75 60
W294 10 c. black . . . . . . 1·75 60
W295 15 c. black . . . . . . 38·00 8·00
W296 20 c. black . . . . . . 3·00 1·25

1898.
W297 W **53** 5 c. black . . . . . . 6·00 25

1938.

W839	W **163**	10 c. red	30	30
W840		20 c. blue	30	30
W841		60 c. red	80	80
W842		1 p. blue	85	85
W843		2 p. green	90	90
W844		10 p. blue	95	95

Nos. W842/3 have coloured figures of value on white backgrounds.

SPANISH GUINEA Pt. 9

A Spanish colony consisting of the islands of Fernando Poo, Annobon and the Corisco Islands off the west coast of Africa and Rio Muni on the mainland. In 1959 it was divided into the two Spanish Overseas Provinces of Fernando Poo and Rio Muni.

100 centimos = 1 peseta

1902. "Curly Head" key-type inscr "GUINEA ESPANOLA 1902".

1	Z	5 c. green	10·00	1·00
2		10 c. grey	10·00	1·00
3		25 c. red	50·00	8·50
4		50 c. brown	50·00	7·50
5		75 c. lilac	50·00	7·50
6		1 p. red	80·00	7·50
7		2 p. green	90·00	11·00
8		5 p. orange	£150	45·00

1903. Fiscal stamps inscr "POSESIONES ESPANOLAS DE AFRICA OCCIDENTAL", surch **HABILITADO PARA CORREOS 10 cen de peseta**.

9	10 c. on 25 c. black	£300	£120
10	10 c. on 50 c. orange	85·00	20·00
11	10 c. on 1 p. 25 pink	£450	£200
12	10 c. on 2 p. red	£500	£300
13a	10 c. on 2 p. 50 brown	£850	£375
14a	10 c. on 5 p. black	£800	£275
15	10 c. on 10 p. brown	£650	£275
16	10 c. on 5 p. lilac	£500	£275
17	10 c. on 25 p. blue	£550	£275
18	10 c. on 50 p. brown	£600	£400
19	10 c. on 70 p. violet	£800	£400
20	10 c. on 100 p. green	£1100	£450

1903. "Curly Head" key-type inscr "GUINEA CONTIAL-ESPANOLA PARA 1903".

21	Z	¼ c. black	70	20
22		½ c. green	70	20
23		1 c. red	70	15
24		2 c. olive	70	15
25		3 c. brown	70	15
26		4 c. red	70	15
27		5 c. brown	70	15
28		10 c. brown	1·00	20
29		15 c. blue	3·75	1·50
30		25 c. orange	3·75	2·25
31		50 c. red	7·50	2·50
32		75 c. lilac	10·00	2·50
33		1 p. green	17·00	3·75
34		2 p. green	17·00	3·75
35		3 p. red	40·00	4·75
36		4 p. blue	55·00	8·00
37		5 p. purple	85·00	15·00
38		10 p. red	1·40	15·00

1905. "Curly-Head" key-type inscr as above but dated "1905".

39	Z	1 c. black	15	10
40		2 c. green	15	10
41		3 c. red	15	10
42		4 c. green	15	10
43		5 c. brown	15	10
44		10 c. red	70	35
45		15 c. brown	2·50	1·00
46		25 c. brown	2·50	1·00
47		50 c. blue	5·50	3·25
48		75 c. orange	6·00	3·25
49		1 p. red	6·00	3·25
50		2 p. lilac	12·00	5·50
51		3 p. green	29·00	12·00
52		4 p. green	29·00	15·00
53		5 p. red	50·00	15·00
54		10 p. blue	85·00	42·00

1905. No. 19/34 of Elobey optd **CONTINENTAL GUINEA CORREOS ASSOBLA**.

55	Z	1 c. pink	5·00	1·40
56		2 c. purple	5·00	1·40
57		3 c. black	5·00	1·40
58		4 c. red	5·00	1·40
59		5 c. green	5·00	1·40
60		10 c. green	8·50	4·25
61		15 c. lilac	15·00	6·50
62		25 c. red	15·00	7·00
63		50 c. orange	20·00	10·00
64		75 c. blue	25·00	12·00
65		1 p. brown	42·00	20·00
66		2 p. brown	55·00	15·00
67		3 p. red	85·00	30·00
68		4 p. brown	£300	£110
69		5 p. green	£300	£100
70		10 p. red	£1300	£600

1907. As T **3** of Rio de Oro, but inscr "GUINEA CONTIAL ESPANOLA".

71	1 c. green	40	10
72	2 c. blue	40	10
73	3 c. lilac	40	10
74	4 c. green	40	10
75	5 c. red	40	10
76	10 c. orange	2·25	45
77	15 c. brown	1·50	30
78	25 c. blue	1·50	30
79	50 c. brown	1·50	30
80	75 c. blue	1·50	30
81	1 p. orange	2·75	50
82	2 p. brown	6·00	2·00
83	3 p. black	6·00	2·00
84	4 p. red	7·00	2·00
85	5 p. green	7·50	3·00
86	10 p. purple	11·00	4·00

1908. Surch **HABILITADO PARA** and value in figures and **CTMS**.

87	**3**	05 c. on 1 c. green	2·75	2·00
88		05 c. on 2 c. blue	2·75	2·00
89		05 c. on 3 c. lilac	2·75	2·00
90		05 c. on 4 c. green	2·75	2·00
91		05 c. on 10 c. orange	2·75	2·00
92		15 c. on 10 c. orange	13·00	9·00

1909. Fiscal stamps inscr "TERRITORIOS ESPANOLES DEL AFRICA OCCIDENTAL", surch **HABILITADO PARA CORREOS 10 cen de peseta**.

93	10 c. on 50 c. green	50·00	35·00
94	10 c. on 1 p. 25	£140	45·00
95	10 c. on 2 p. brown	£375	£225
96	10 c. on 5 p. mauve	£375	£225
97	10 c. on 25 p. brown	£475	£325
98	10 c. on 50 p. red	£1600	£850
99	10 c. on 75 p. pink	£1600	£850
100	10 c. on 100 p. orange	£1600	£850

1909. As T **7** of Rio de Oro but inscr "TERRITORIOS ESPANOLES DEL GOLFO DE GUINEA".

101	1 c. brown	10	10
102	2 c. red	10	10
103	5 c. green	85	10
104	10 c. red	30	10
105	15 c. brown	30	10
106	20 c. mauve	45	20
107	25 c. blue	50	20
108	30 c. brown	50	25
109	40 c. red	35	20
110	50 c. lilac	35	20
111	1 p. green	11·00	3·50
112	4 p. orange	3·50	2·75
113	10 p. red	4·00	2·75

1911. Nos. 101/13 optd **GUINEA 1911**.

114	1 c. brown	20	15
115	2 c. red	20	15
116	5 c. green	70	15
117	10 c. red	55	20
118	15 c. brown	70	35
119	20 c. mauve	1·00	50
120	25 c. blue	1·25	85
121	30 c. brown	1·50	1·00
122	40 c. red	1·75	1·75
123	50 c. lilac	2·50	2·50
124	1 p. green	25·00	6·50
125	4 p. orange	14·00	7·00
126	10 p. orange	17·00	9·00

1912. As T **11** of Rio de Oro, but inscr "TERRS. ESPANOLES DEL GOLFO DE GUINEA".

127	1 c. black	10	10
128	2 c. brown	10	10
129	5 c. green	10	10
130	10 c. red	20	10
131	15 c. red	20	10
132	20 c. red	30	10
133	25 c. blue	20	10
134	30 c. red	1·75	80
135	40 c. red	1·25	50
136	50 c. orange	90	20
137	1 p. lilac	1·50	90
138	4 p. mauve	3·50	2·00
139	10 p. green	7·50	4·50

1914. As T **12** of Rio de Oro but inscr as 1912 issue.

140	1 c. violet	20	10
141	2 c. red	20	15
142	5 c. green	20	10
143	10 c. red	20	15
144	15 c. purple	20	15
145	20 c. brown	50	20
146	25 c. blue	25	20
147	30 c. brown	90	35
148	40 c. green	90	35
149	50 c. red	40	20
150	1 p. orange	1·10	85
151	4 p. red	4·25	2·50
152	10 p. brown	5·50	3·50

1917. Nos. 127/39 optd **1917**.

153	1 c. black	55·00	22·00
154	2 c. brown	55·00	22·00
155	5 c. green	35	20
156	10 c. red	35	20
157	15 c. purple	35	20
158	20 c. red	35	15
159	25 c. blue	15	15
160	30 c. red	35	20
161	40 c. pink	50	30
162	50 c. orange	30	20
163	1 p. lilac	50	30
164	4 p. mauve	6·00	2·75
165	10 p. green	6·00	2·75

1918. Stamps of 1912 surch **HTADO-1917**. and value in figures and words.

166	**11**	5 c. on 40 c. red	25·00	8·50
167		10 c. on 4 p. mauve	25·00	8·50
168		15 c. on 20 c. red	50·00	15·00
169		25 c. on 10 p. green	50·00	15·00

12

13

14 Nipa House

1919.

170	**12**	1 c. violet	70	20
171		2 c. red	70	20
172		5 c. red	70	20
173		10 c. purple	1·00	20
174		15 c. brown	1·00	35
175		20 c. blue	1·00	20
176		25 c. green	1·00	35
177		30 c. orange	1·00	35
178		40 c. orange	3·25	35
179		50 c. red	3·50	35
180		1 p. green	3·75	1·25
181		4 p. red	8·50	3·75
182		10 p. brown	14·00	5·50

1920. As T **15** of Rio de Oro, but inscr as T **12**.

183	1 c. brown	15	10
184	2 c. red	15	10
185	5 c. green	20	15
186	10 c. red	20	10
187	15 c. orange	20	15
188	20 c. yellow	20	15
189	25 c. blue	40	15
190	30 c. green	25·00	7·50
191	40 c. brown	35	25
192	50 c. purple	1·25	25
193	1 p. brown	1·50	35
194	4 p. red	3·75	2·25
195	10 p. violet	5·50	4·00

1922.

196	**13**	1 c. brown	35	10
197		2 c. red	35	10
198		5 c. green	35	10
199		10 c. red	2·25	35
200		15 c. orange	35	10
201		20 c. mauve	1·40	30
202		25 c. blue	2·40	35
203		30 c. violet	2·25	40
204		40 c. blue	2·00	20
205		50 c. red	2·00	20
206		1 p. green	2·00	40
207		4 p. brown	7·50	4·75
208		10 p. yellow	15·00	7·50

1925.

209	**14**	5 c. blue and brown	20	10
210		10 c. blue and green	20	10
211		15 c. black and red	20	20
212		20 c. black and violet	20	10
213		25 c. black and red	45	30
214		30 c. black and orange	45	20
215		40 c. black and blue	45	20
216		50 c. black and red	45	20
217		60 c. black and brown	50	20
218		1 p. black and violet	1·75	20
219		4 p. black and blue	4·50	1·75
220		10 p. black and green	9·00	4·50

1926. Red Cross stamps of Spain optd **GUINEA ESPANOLA**.

221	–	5 c. brown	4·00	2·50
222	–	10 c. green	4·00	2·50
223	**70**	15 c. violet	1·00	80
224	–	20 c. purple	1·00	80
225	**71**	25 c. red	1·00	80
226	**70**	30 c. green	1·00	80
227	–	40 c. blue	20	20
228	–	50 c. red	20	20
229	**71**	60 c. green	20	20
230	–	1 p. red	20	20
231	–	4 p. bistre	75	75
232	**71**	10 p. violet	2·75	2·00

1929. Seville and Barcelona Exhibition stamps of Spain (1929) optd **GUINEA**.

233	5 c. red	10	10
234	10 c. green	10	10
235	15 c. blue	10	10
236	20 c. violet	10	10
237	25 c. red	10	10
238	30 c. brown	10	10
239	40 c. blue	20	20
240	50 c. orange	20	20
241	1 p. grey	1·75	1·50
242	4 p. red	3·50	3·00
243	10 p. brown	7·00	5·50

17 Porter

24

26 Gen. Franco

1931.

244	**17**	1 c. green	10	10
245		2 c. brown	10	10
246		5 c. black	10	10
318		5 c. grey	1·50	10
247		10 c. green	10	10
248		15 c. black	20	10
290		15 c. green	2·25	10
249		20 c. violet	20	10
250	–	25 c. red	20	10
251	–	30 c. red	20	10
252	–	40 c. blue	65	45
320	–	40 c. green	65	10
253	–	50 c. orange	1·50	90
292	–	50 c. blue	6·00	50
254	–	80 c. blue	2·50	1·50
255	–	1 p. black	3·75	2·75
256	–	4 p. mauve	29·00	12·00
257	–	5 p. brown	12·00	9·00

DESIGNS: 25 c. to 50 c. Native drummers; 80 c. to 5 p. King Alfonso XIII and Queen Victoria.

1931. Optd **REPUBLICA ESPANOLA** horiz.

258	**17**	1 c. green	10	10
259		2 c. brown	10	10
260		5 c. grey	15	10
261		10 c. green	15	10
262		15 c. blue	15	10
263		20 c. violet	15	10
264	–	25 c. red	15	10
265	–	30 c. red	35	20
266	–	40 c. blue	1·00	35
267	–	50 c. orange	7·50	4·00
268	–	80 c. blue	2·50	1·25
269	–	1 p. black	8·50	2·50
270	–	4 p. red	13·00	7·50
271	–	5 p. brown	13·00	7·50

1933. Optd **Republica Espanola**.
272 **17** 1 c. green 10 10
273 2 c. brown 10 10
274 5 c. grey 15 10
275 10 c. green 15 10
276 15 c. blue 15 10
277 20 c. violet 35 10
278 – 25 c. red 30 20
279 – 30 c. red 30 20
280 – 40 c. blue . . . . 2·00 50
281 – 50 c. orange . . . . 8·00 3·00
282 – 80 c. blue . . . . 3·75 2·50
283 – 1 p. black . . . . 8·50 2·75
284 – 4 p. red . . . . 27·00 12·00
285 – 5 p. brown . . . . 29·00 12·00

1937. Surch **HABILITADO 30 Cts.**
293 – 30 c. on 40 c. (No. 252) . . 2·75 1·75
294 – 30 c. on 40 c. (No. 266) . . 11·00 2·50
295 – 30 c. on 40 c. (No. 280) . . 40·00 12·00

1939. Stamps of Spain, 1937, optd **Territorios Espanoles del Golfo de Guinea** in script type.
296 **183** 10 c. green . . . . 1·50 35
297 **184** 15 c. black . . . . 1·50 35
298 20 c. violet . . . . 3·25 1·10
299 25 c. red . . . . 3·25 1·10

1939. Surch **Habilitado 40 cts.**
300 – 40 c. on 80 c. (No. 268) . . 8·50 4·50
301 – 40 c. on 80 c. (No. 282) . . 8·50 3·00

1940. Fiscal stamps as T **24** inscr "ESPECIAL MOVIL", "TIMBRE MOVIL" or "IMPUESTO SOBRE CONTRATOS" and surch or optd **Habilitado Correos.**
302 5 c. red . . . . 8·50 2·25
304 5 c. on 35 c. green . . . . . 8·50 2·40
307 10 c. on 75 c. brown . . . . . 12·00 3·50
308 15 c. on 1 p. 50 violet . . . . 10·00 3·00
305 25 c. on 60 c. brown . . . . . 8·50 2·75
306 50 c. on 75 c. sepia . . . . . 11·00 3·25
310 1 p. bistre . . . . £120 40·00
303 1 p. on 15 c. olive . . . . . 7·00 5·50
316 1 p. on 17 p. red . . . . . 65·00 20·00
315 1 p. on 40 p. green . . . . . 17·00 5·50

1940.
311 **26** 5 c. brown . . . . 2·50 45
312 40 c. blue . . . . 3·25 45
314 50 c. green . . . . 3·75 45

1941. Air. Fiscal stamp as T **24** inscr "IMPUESTO SOBRE CONTRATOS" surch **Habilitado para Correo Aereo Intercolonial Una Peseta** and bar.
317a 1 p. on 17 p. red . . . . . . 45·00 12·00

1942. No. 249 surch **Habilitado 3 Pesetas.**
321 **17** 3 p. on 20 c. violet . . . . 9·50 1·50

1942. Stamps of Spain, 1939, optd **Golfo de Guinea.**
322 **196** 1 PTA. black 45 20
323 4 PTAS. pink . . . . . . 6·00 50

1942. Air. Air stamp of Spain optd **Golfo de Guinea.**
324 **195** 1 p. blue . . . . 1·75 20

1943. Stamp of Spain, 1939, optd **Territorios espanoles del Golfo de Guinea.**
325 **196** 2 PTAS. brown . . . . . 1·00 20

1948. Air. Ministerial Visit. No. 323 optd **CORREO AEREO Viaje Ministerial 10-19 Enero 1948.**
326 **196** 4 PTAS. pink . . . . . . 7·50 2·75

1949. Nos. 322 and 325 surch **Habilitado para** and value in words.
327 **196** 5 c. on 1 PTA. black . . . 20 10
328 15 c. on 2 PTAS. brown . 20 10

33 Natives in Pirogue

1949. 75th Anniv of U.P.U.
329 **33** 4 p. violet . . . . 1·75 50

34 Count Argalejo and San Carlos Bay

1949. Air. Colonial Stamp Day.
330 **34** 5 p. green . . . . 1·75 50

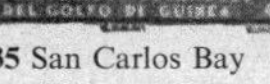

35 San Carlos Bay

36 Manuel Iradier y Bulfy

1949.
331 **35** 2 c. brown 20 10
332 – 5 c. violet 20 10
333 – 10 c. blue 20 10
334 – 15 c. black 20 10
335 **35** 25 c. purple 20 10
336 – 30 c. yellow 20 10
337 – 40 c. olive 20 10
338 – 45 c. red 20 10
339 **35** 50 c. orange 20 10
340 – 75 c. blue 20 10
341 – 90 c. green 20 10
342 – 1 p. slate . . . . 1·50 20
343 **35** 1 p. 35 violet . . . . . . 5·00 85
344 – 2 p. grey . . . . 13·00 2·00
345 – 5 p. mauve . . . . 18·00 6·00
346 **35** 10 p. brown . . . . 70·00 20·00
DESIGNS: 5, 30, 75 c., 2 p. Benito River rapids; 10, 40, 90 c., 5 p. Coast scene and Clarence Peak, Fernando Poo; 15, 45, 1 p. Niepan, Benito River.

1950. Air. Colonial Stamp Day.
347 **36** 5 p. brown . . . . 2·50 55

37 Hands and Natives

38 Mt Mioco

1951. Native Welfare.
348 **37** 50 c. + 10 c. blue 30 20
349 1 p. + 25 c. green . . . . 13·00 3·75
350 6 p. 50 + 1 p. 65 orange . 3·50 1·75

1951. Air.
351 – 25 c. yellow 10 10
352 **38** 50 c. mauve 10 10
353 – 1 p. green 15 10
354 – 2 p. blue 35 10
355 **38** 3 p. 25 violet 95 10
356 – 5 p. sepia . . . . 6·50 2·00
357 – 10 p. red . . . . 25·00 5·50
DESIGNS: 25 c., 2, 10 p. Benito Rapids; 1, 5 p. Santa Isabel Bay.

1951. Air. 500th Birth Anniv of Isabella the Catholic. As T **9a** of Spanish Sahara.
358 5 p. blue . . . . 22·00 3·25

39 Leopard

40 Native and Map

1951. Colonial Stamp Day.
359 **39** 5 c. + 5 c. brown 15 10
360 10 c. + 5 c. orange . . . 15 10
361 60 c. + 15 c. olive . . . 30 20

1951. International W. African Conference.
362 **40** 50 c. orange 30 10
363 5 p. blue . . . . 8·50 1·25

41 Native Man
42 "Crinum giganteum"

1952.
364 **41** 5 c. brown 10 10
365 50 c. olive 10 10
366 5 p. violet . . . . 2·50 10

1952. Native Welfare Fund.
367 **42** 5 c. + 5 c. brown 15 10
368 50 c. + 10 c. black . . . 20 10
369 2 p. + 30 c. blue . . . . 1·50 70

43 Ferdinand the Catholic

44 Brown-cheeked Hornbills

1952. Air. 500th Birth Anniv of Ferdinand the Catholic.
370 **43** 5 p. brown . . . . 30·00 4·75

1952. Colonial Stamp Day.
371 **44** 5 c. + 5 c. brown 35 10
372 10 c. + 5 c. purple 55 30
373 60 c. + 15 c. green 85 50

45 Native Musician
46 Native Woman and Dove

1953. Native Welfare Fund. Inscr "PRO INDIGENAS 1953".
374 **45** 5 c. + 5 c. lake 15 10
375 – 10 c. + 5 c. purple 15 10
376 **45** 15 c. olive 15 10
377 – 60 c. brown 15 10
DESIGN: 10, 60 c. Musician facing right.

1953.
378 **46** 5 c. orange 10 10
379 10 c. purple 10 10
380 60 c. brown 10 10
381 – 1 p. lilac . . . . 1·00 10
382 – 1 p. 90 green . . . . . . 2·50 30
DESIGN: 1, 1 p. 90, Native drummer.

47 "Tragocephala nobilis"
48 Hunting with Bow and Arrow

1953. Colonial Stamp Day. Inscr "DIA DEL SELLO COLONIAL 1953".
383 **47** 5 c. + 5 c. blue 10 10
384 – 10 c. + 5 c. purple 30 10
385 **47** 15 c. green 25 20
386 – 60 c. brown 50 20
DESIGN: 10, 60 c. "Papilio antimachus" (butterfly).

1954. Native Welfare Fund. Inscr "PRO-INDIGENAS 1954".
387 **48** 5 c. + 5 c. lake 10 10
388 – 10 c. + 5 c. lilac 10 10
389 **48** 15 c. green 10 10
390 – 60 c. brown 30 10
DESIGN: 10, 60 c. Native hunting elephant with spear.

49 Turtle

1954. Colonial Stamp Day. Inscr "DIA DEL SELLO COLONIAL 1954".
391 **49** 5 c. + 5 c. red 10 10
392 – 10 c. + 5 c. purple 10 10
393 **49** 15 c. green 10 10
394 – 60 c. brown 30 15
DESIGN: 10, 60 c. "Leptocharias smithi" (fish).

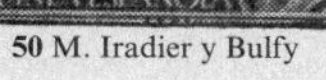

50 M. Iradier y Bulfy
51 Native Priest

1955. Birth Centenary of Iradier (explorer).
395 **50** 60 c. brown 20 10
396 1 p. violet . . . . 3·50 30

1955. Centenary of Apostolic Prefecture in Fernando Poo.
397 **51** 10 c. + 5 c. purple 10 10
398 – 25 c. + 10 c. violet 10 10
399 **51** 50 c. olive 15 10
DESIGN: 25 c. "Baptism".

52 Footballers

53 El Pardo Palace, Madrid

1955. Air.
400 **52** 25 c. grey 10 10
401 50 c. olive 10 10
402 1 p. 50 brown . . . . . . 1·25 10
403 4 p. red . . . . 3·50 20
404 10 p. green . . . . 2·50 20

1955. Treaty of Pardo, 1778.
405 **53** 5 c. brown 10 10
406 15 c. red 10 10
407 80 c. green 10 10

54 Moustached Monkeys

55 "Orquidea"

1955. Colonial Stamp Day. Inscr "DIA DEL SELLO COLONIAL 1955".
408 **54** 5 c. + 5 c. lake & brown . 20 15
409 – 15 c. + 5 c. sepia & lake . 20 15
410 **54** 70 c. blue and slate 25 20
DESIGN—HORIZ: 15 c. Talapoin and young.

1956. Native Welfare Fund. Inscr "PRO INDIGENAS 1956".
411 **55** 5 c. + 5 c. olive 10 10
412 – 15 c. + 5 c. ochre 10 10
413 **55** 20 c. turquoise 20 10
414 – 50 c. brown 25 10
DESIGN: 15, 50 c. "Strophantus kombe".

56 Arms of Santa Isabel

57 Grey Parrot

58 "Flight"

1956. Colonial Stamp Day. Inscr "DIA DEL SELLO 1956".
415 **56** 5 c. + 5 c. brown 10 10
416 – 15 c. + 5 c. violet 10 10
417 **56** 70 c. green 10 10
DESIGN—HORIZ: 15 c. Arms of Bata and natives.

1957. Native Welfare Fund. Inscr "PRO INDIGENAS 1957".
418 **57** 5 c. + 5 c. purple 15 10
419 – 15 c. + 5 c. ochre 15 10
420 **57** 70 c. green 35 15
DESIGN—HORIZ: 15 c. Parrot in flight.

1957. Air. 30th Anniv of Spain–Fernando Poo Flight by "Atlantida" Seaplane Squadron.
421 **58** 25 p. sepia and bistre . . . 8·00 85

59 African Elephant and Calf

1957. Colonial Stamp Day.
422 **59** 10 c. + 5 c. mauve 10 10
423 – 15 c. + 5 c. brown 15 10
424 **59** 20 c. turquoise 15 10
425 – 70 c. green 25 10
DESIGN—VERT: 15, 70 c. African elephant trumpeting.

60 Doves and Arms of Valencia and Santa Isabel

1958. "Aid for Valencia".
426 **60** 10 c. + 5 c. brown 10 10
427 15 c. + 10 c. ochre 10 10
428 50 c. + 10 c. brown 10 10

61 Boxing

1958. Sports.
429 **61** 5 c. brown 10 10
430 – 10 c. brown 10 10
431 – 15 c. bistre 10 10
432 – 80 c. green 10 10
433 **61** 1 p. salmon 10 10
434 – 2 p. purple 20 10
435 – 2 p. 30 violet 35 10
436 – 3 p. blue 35 10
DESIGNS—VERT: 10 c., 2 p. Basketball; 80 c., 3 p. Running. HORIZ: 15 c., 2 p. 30, Long jumping.

62 Missionary holding Cross

63 "Danaus chrysippus"

1958. Native Welfare Fund. Inscr "1883 PRO-INDIGENAS 1958".
437 **62** 10 c. + 5 c. brown 10 10
438 – 15 c. + 5 c. ochre 10 10
439 **62** 20 c. turquoise 10 10
440 – 70 c. green 10 10
DESIGN: 15, 70 c. The Crucifixion.

1958. Colonial Stamp Day. Inscr "1958".
441 **63** 10 c. + 5 c. red 15 10
442 – 25 c. + 10 c. violet 25 10
443 – 50 c. + 10 c. olive 30 10
DESIGNS: 25, 50 c. Different views of butterflies on plants.

64 Digitalis

65 Boy on "Penny-farthing" Cycle

1959. Child Welfare Fund. Floral designs as T **64**. Inscr "PRO-INFANCIA 1959".
444 **64** 10 c. + 5 c. lake 10 10
445 – 15 c. + 5 c. ochre 15 10
446 – 20 c. myrtle 15 10
447 **64** 70 c. green 15 10
DESIGN: 15, 20 c. Castor bean.

1959. Colonial Stamp Day. Inscr "1959".
448 **65** 10 c. + 5 c. lake 20 10
449 – 20 c. + 5 c. myrtle 20 10
450 – 50 c. + 20 c. olive 20 10
DESIGNS: 20 c. Racing cyclists; 50 c. Winning cyclist.

EXPRESS LETTER STAMP

E **38** Fernando Poo

1951.
E358 E **38** 25 c. red 20 15

SPANISH MOROCCO Pt. 9

100 centimos = 1 peseta

I. SPANISH POST OFFICES IN MOROCCO.

Nos. 2/150, except Nos. 93/8 and 124/37 are all stamps of Spain overprinted.

1903. Optd **CORREO ESPANOL MARRUECOS.**
2 **38a** ¼ c. green 30 10

1903. Optd **CORREO ESPANOL MARRUECOS.**
3 **52** 2 c. brown 75 30
4 5 c. green 85 20
5 10 c. red . . . . 1·00 10
6 15 c. violet . . . . 1·25 20
7 20 c. black . . . . 4·75 90
8 25 c. blue 50 20
9 30 c. green . . . . 2·75 95
10 40 c. pink . . . . 5·50 1·75
11 50 c. blue . . . . 2·75 1·10
12 1 p. purple . . . . 6·50 2·25
13 4 p. purple . . . . 15·00 3·00
14 10 p. orange . . . . 15·00 8·00

1908. Stamps of Spain handstamped **TETUAN.**
15 **38a** ¼ c. green . . . . 7·00 3·00
16 **52** 2 c. brown . . . . 32·00 12·00
17 5 c. green . . . . 45·00 32·00
18 10 c. red . . . . 42·00 22·00
19 15 c. violet . . . . 45·00 24·00
20 20 c. black £130 £110
21 25 c. blue . . . . 65·00 35·00
22 30 c. green . . . . £150 55·00
23 40 c. bistre £200 £110

1908. Nos. 2/5 and 7/8 handstamped **TETUAN.**
24 **38a** ¼ c. green . . . . 11·00 10·00
25 **52** 2 c. brown . . . . £120 55·00
26 5 c. green . . . . 95·00 30·00
27 10 c. red . . . . £100 30·00
28 20 c. grey £250 £120
29 25 c. blue . . . . 85·00 35·00

1909. Optd **CORREO ESPANOL MARRUECOS.**
30 **64** 2 c. brown 30 10
31 5 c. green . . . . 1·50 10
32 10 c. red . . . . 1·75 10
33 15 c. violet . . . . 4·25 15
34 20 c. green . . . . 10·00 25·00
35 25 c. blue . . . . 70·00
36 30 c. green . . . . 3·25 15
37 40 c. pink . . . . 3·25 15
38 50 c. blue . . . . 6·00 3·00
39 1 p. lake . . . . 12·00 6·00
40 4 p. purple . . . . 70·00
41 10 p. orange . . . . 70·00
After the appearance of Nos. 42/54 for the Spanish Protectorate in 1914, the use of Nos. 30/41 was restricted to Tangier.

II. SPANISH PROTECTORATE (excluding Tangier).

1914. Optd **MARRUECOS.**
42 **38a** ¼ c. green 10 10
43 **64** 2 c. brown 10 10
44 5 c. green 20 15
45 10 c. red 20 15
46 15 c. violet 60 45
47 20 c. green . . . . 1·50 85
48 25 c. blue . . . . 1·50 50
49 30 c. green . . . . 2·75 1·10
50 40 c. pink . . . . 6·00 2·00
51 50 c. blue . . . . 3·00 1·10
52 1 p. red . . . . 3·00 1·50
53 4 p. purple . . . . 14·00 9·50
54 10 p. orange . . . . 20·00 11·00

1915. Optd **PROTECTORADO ESPANOL EN MARRUECOS.**
55 **38a** ¼ c. green 15 10
56 **64** 2 c. brown 10 10
57 5 c. green 30 10
58 10 c. red 25 10
59 15 c. violet 30 10
60 20 c. green 85 15
61 25 c. blue 70 15
62 30 c. green 95 20
63 40 c. pink . . . . 1·50 20
64 50 c. blue . . . . 2·50 15
65 1 p. red . . . . 2·50 20
66 4 p. purple . . . . 15·00 9·00
67 10 p. orange . . . . 25·00 10·00

1916. Optd **ZONA DE PROTECTORADO ESPANOL EN MARRUECOS.**
68 **38a** ¼ c. green 30 10
69 **66** 1 c. green . . . . 1·10 10
70 **64** 2 c. brown 80 10
71 5 c. green . . . . 2·75 10
72 10 c. red . . . . 3·50 10
73 15 c. orange . . . . 4·00 10
74 20 c. violet . . . . 7·50 10
75 25 c. blue . . . . 12·00 1·10
76 30 c. green . . . . 15·00 8·00
77 40 c. red . . . . 18·00 30
78 50 c. blue . . . . 9·00 15
79 1 p. red . . . . 22·00 1·00
80 4 p. purple . . . . 30·00 13·00
81 10 p. orange . . . . 70·00 25·00

1920. Optd **PROTECTORADO ESPANOL EN MARRUECOS** perf through centre and each half surch in figures and words.
82 **64** 10 c. + 10 c. on 20 c. green 5·00 1·75
83 15 c. + 15 c. on 30 c. green 10·00 7·00

1920. No. E68 perf through centre, and each half surch **10 centimos.**
84 E **53** 10 c. + 10 c. on 20 c. red 11·00 7·50

1920. Fiscal stamps showing figure of Justice, bisected and surch **CORREOS** and value.
93 5 c. on 5 p. blue . . . . . . 9·00 1·75
94 5 c. on 10 p. green 40 10
95 10 c. on 25 p. green 40 10
96 10 c. on 50 p. grey 45 10
97 15 c. on 100 p. red 45 10
98 15 c. on 500 p. red . . . . . . 12·00 5·00

1923. Optd **ZONA DE PROTECTORADO ESPANOL EN MARRUECOS.**
101 **68** 2 c. green 45 10
102 5 c. purple 45 10
103 10 c. green . . . . 1·50 10
105 15 c. blue . . . . 1·50 10
106 20 c. violet . . . . 3·50 10
107 25 c. red . . . . 7·00 55
108 40 c. blue . . . . 7·50 2·00
109 50 c. orange . . . . 18·00 2·75
110 **69** 1 p. grey . . . . 28·00 2·00

1926. Red Cross stamps optd **ZONA PROTECTORADO ESPANOL.**
111 **70** 1 c. orange . . . . 3·25 2·25
112 – 2 c. red . . . . 3·25 2·25
113 – 5 c. brown . . . . 1·50 1·00
114 – 10 c. green . . . . 1·50 1·00
115 **70** 15 c. violet 60 50
116 – 20 c. purple 60 50
117 **71** 25 c. red 60 50
118 **70** 30 c. green 60 50
119 – 40 c. blue 20 25
120 – 50 c. red 20 25
121 – 1 p. red 35 35
122 – 4 p. bistre 35 35
123 **71** 10 p. violet . . . . 1·75 1·25

11 Mosque of Alcazarquivir

12 Moorish Gateway, Larache

1928.
124 **11** 1 c. red 10 10
126 2 c. violet 25 20
127 3 c. blue 10 10
128 10 c. green 10 10
129 15 c. brown 30 10
130 **12** 20 c. olive 30 10
131 25 c. red 30 10
132 30 c. brown 80 10
133 40 c. blue . . . . 1·25 10
134 50 c. purple . . . . 2·25 10
135 – 1 p. green . . . . 3·50 20
136 – 2 p. 50 purple . . . . 12·00 3·75
137 – 4 p. blue . . . . 8·00 1·50
DESIGNS—HORIZ: 1 p. Well at Alhucemas; 2 p. 50, Xauen; 4 p. Tetuan.

1929. Seville–Barcelona Exhibition stamps, Nos. 502/14 optd **PROTECTORADO MARRUECOS.**
138 1 c. blue 15 10
139 2 c. green 10 10
140 5 c. red 10 10
141 10 c. green 10 10
142 15 c. blue 10 10
143 20 c. violet 10 10
144 25 c. red 10 10
145 30 c. brown 25 25
146 40 c. blue 30 30
147 50 c. orange 30 30
148 1 p. grey . . . . 2·25 1·25
149 4 p. red . . . . 4·50 4·00
150 10 p. brown . . . . 8·50 6·50

14 Xauen

15 Market-place, Larache

1933.
151 **14** 1 c. red 10 10
152 – 2 c. green 10 10
153 – 5 c. mauve 10 10
154 – 10 c. green 20 10
155 – 15 c. yellow 90 10
156 **14** 20 c. green 35 10
157 – 25 c. red . . . . 10·00 20
165 – 25 c. violet 60 10
158 – 30 c. lake . . . . 2·50 10
166 – 30 c. red . . . . 8·00 10
159 **15** 40 c. blue . . . . 5·50 10
167 – 40 c. red . . . . 4·50 15
160 – 50 c. red . . . . 17·00 2·50
168 – 50 c. blue . . . . 4·50 15
169 – 60 c. green . . . . 4·25 15
161 – 1 p. grey . . . . 6·50 10
170 – 2 p. lake . . . . 22·00 3·00
162 – 2 p. 50 brown . . . . 12·00 2·50
163 – 4 p. green . . . . 12·00 2·50
164 – 5 p. black . . . . 15·00 2·50
DESIGNS—HORIZ: 2 c., 1 p. Xauen; 5 c., 2 p. 50, Arcila; 25 c. (No. 157), 5 p. Sultan and bodyguard; 30 c. (No. 166), 50 c. (No. 168), 2 p. Forest at Ketama. VERT: 10 c., 30 c. (No. 158), Tetuan; 15 c., 4 p. Alcazarquivir; 25 c. (No. 165), 40 c. (No. 167), Wayside scene at Arcila.
See also Nos. 177/83 and 213/6.

1936. Air. No. 157 surch with new value and **18-7-36.**
171 25 c. + 2 p. on 25 c. red . . . 12·00 4·00

1936. Surch.
172 – 1 c. on 4 p. blue (137) . 25 10
173 – 2 c. on 2 p. 50 pur (136) 25 10
174 **12** 5 c. on 25 c. red (131) . 15 10
175 – 10 c. on 1 p. green (135) 4·25 2·25
176 E **12** 15 c. on 20 c. black . . 3·75 1·10

1937. Pictorials as T **14/15.**
177 1 c. green 10 10
178 2 c. mauve 10 10
179 5 c. orange 15 10
180 15 c. violet 15 10
181 30 c. red 35 10
182 1 p. blue . . . . 3·50 35
183 10 p. brown . . . . 30·00 9·00
DESIGNS—VERT: 1, 15 c. Caliph and Viziers; 30 c. Tetuan; 1 p. Arcila; 10 p. Caliph on horseback. HORIZ: 2 c. Bokoia; 5 c. Alcazarquivir.

18 Legionaries

19 General Franco

1937. 1st Anniv of Civil War.
184 – 1 c. blue 10 10
185 **18** 2 c. brown 10 10
186 – 5 c. mauve 10 10
187 – 10 c. green 10 10
188 – 15 c. blue 10 10
189 – 20 c. purple 10 10
190 – 25 c. mauve 10 10
191 – 30 c. red 10 10
192 – 40 c. orange 10 10
193 – 50 c. blue 10 10
194 – 60 c. green 10 10
195 – 1 p. violet 10 10
196 – 2 p. blue . . . . 4·50 3·00
197 – 2 p. 50 black . . . . 4·50 3·25
198 – 4 p. brown . . . . 4·50 3·25
199 – 10 p. black . . . . 4·75 3·50
DESIGNS—VERT: 1 c. Sentry; 5 c. Trooper; 10 c. Volunteers; 15 c. Colour bearer; 20 c. Desert halt; 25 c. Ifni mounted riflemen; 30 c. Trumpeters; 40 c. Cape Juby Camel Corps; 50 c. Infantryman; 60 c., 1, 2, 4 p. Sherifian Guards; 2 p. 50, Cavalryman. HORIZ: 10 p. "Road to Victory".

1937. Obligatory Tax. Disabled Soldiers in N. Africa.
200 **19** 10 c. brown 40 10
201 10 c. blue 40 10

20 Yellow-billed Stork over Mosque

22 Soldier on Horseback

1938. Air.
203 – 5 c. brown 10 10
204 **20** 10 c. green 45 10
205 – 25 c. red 10 10
206 – 40 c. blue . . . . 2·00 70
207 – 50 c. mauve 10 10
208 – 75 c. blue 10 10
209 – 1 p. brown 10 10
210 – 1 p. 50 violet . . . . 2·50 30
211 – 2 p. red 40 10
212 – 3 p. black . . . . 1·50 20
DESIGNS—VERT: 5 c. Mosque de Baja, Tetuan; 25 c. Straits of Gibraltar; 40 c. Desert natives; 1 p. Mounted postman; 1 p. 50, Farmers; 2 p. Sunset; 3 p. Shadow of airplane over city. HORIZ: 50 c. Airplane over Tetuan; 75 c. Airplane over Larache.

1939. Pictorials as T **14.**
213 5 c. orange 25 10
214 10 c. green 25 10
215 15 c. brown 45 10
216 20 c. blue 45 10
DESIGNS: 5 c. "Carta de Espana"; 10 c. "Carta de Marruecos"; 15 c. Larache; 20 c. Tetuan.

1940. Pictorials as T **14**, inscr "ZONA" on back.
217 1 c. brown 10 10
218 2 c. olive 10 10
219 5 c. blue 20 10
220 10 c. lilac 15 10
221 15 c. green 15 10
222 20 c. violet 15 10
223 25 c. sepia 15 10
224 30 c. green 15 10
225 40 c. green 15 10
226 45 c. orange . . . . 1·25 10
227 50 c. brown 50 10
228 70 c. blue 50 10
229 1 p. brown and blue . . . . . 1·50 10
230 2 p. 50 green and brown . . . 7·50 2·25
231 5 p. sepia and purple . . . . 1·50 20
232 10 p. brown and olive . . . . 14·00 4·25
DESIGNS—VERT: 1 c. Postman; 2 c. Pillar-box; 5 c. Winter landscape; 10 c. Alcazar street; 15 c. Castle wall, Xauen; 20 c. Palace sentry, Tetuan; 25 c. Caliph on horseback; 30 c. Market-place, Larache; 40 c. Gateway, Tetuan; 45 c. Gateway, Xauen; 50 c. Street, Alcazarquivir; 70 c. Post Office; 1 p. Spanish War veterans.

1940. 4th Anniv of Civil War. Nos. 184/99 optd **17-VII-940 40 ANIVERSARIO.**
233 1 c. blue 50 50
234 2 c. brown 50 50
235 5 c. mauve 50 50
236 10 c. green 50 50
237 15 c. blue 50 50
238 20 c. purple 50 50
239 25 c. mauve 50 50
240 30 c. red 50 50
241 40 c. orange 1·25 1·25
242 50 c. blue 1·25 1·25
243 60 c. green 1·25 1·25
244 1 p. violet 1·25 1·25
245 2 p. blue 28·00 28·00
246 2 p. 50 black 28·00 28·00
247 4 p. brown 28·00 28·00
248 10 p. black 28·00 28·00

1941. Obligatory Tax for Disabled Soldiers.
249 **22** 10 c. green 2·00 10
250 10 c. pink 2·00 10
251 10 c. red 2·00 10
252 10 c. blue 2·00 10

23 Larache

25 General Franco

1941.
253 **23** 5 c. brown & deep brown 10 10
263 – 5 c. blue 10 10
254 – 10 c. deep red and red 15 10
255 – 15 c. yellow and green 15 10
256 – 20 c. blue and deep blue 35 10
264 – 40 c. brown 15·00 20
257 – 40 c. red and purple 95 10
DESIGNS: 5 c. blue, 10 c. Alcazarquivir; 15, 40 c. brown, Larache market; 20 c. Moorish house; 40 c. purple, Gateway, Tangier.

1942. Air. New designs as T **14**, optd **Z.**
258 5 c. blue 10 10
259 10 c. brown 10 10
260 15 c. green 10 10
261 90 c. red 10 10
262 5 p. black 95 50
DESIGNS—VERT: 5 c. Atlas mountains; 10 c. Mosque at Tangier; 15 c. Velez fortress; 90 c. Sanjurjo harbour; 5 p. Straits of Gibraltar.

1943. Obligatory Tax for Disabled Soldiers.
265 **25** 10 c. grey 3·75 10
266 10 c. blue 3·75 10
267 10 c. brown 3·75 10
268 10 c. violet 3·75 10
283 10 c. brown and mauve 3·50 10
284 10 c. green and orange 3·50 10
295 10 c. brown and blue 3·50 10
296 10 c. lilac and grey 3·50 10

26 Homeward Bound

1944. Agricultural Scenes.
269 – 1 c. blue and brown 25 10
270 – 2 c. green 10 10
271 **26** 5 c. black and brown 10 10
272 – 10 c. orange and blue 10 10
273 – 15 c. green 10 10
274 – 20 c. black and red 10 10
275 – 25 c. brown and blue 15 10
276 – 30 c. blue and green 1·00 25
277 – 40 c. purple and brown 10 10
278 **26** 50 c. brown and blue 30 10
279 – 75 c. blue and green 35 10
280 – 1 p. brown and blue 35 10
281 – 2 p. 50 blue and black 4·00 1·75
282 – 10 p. black and orange 7·00 3·50
DESIGNS—HORIZ: 1, 30 c. Ploughing; 2, 40 c. Harvesting; 10, 75 c. Threshing; 15 c., 1 p. Vegetable garden; 20 c., 2 p. 50, Gathering oranges; 25 c., 10 p. Shepherd and flock.

27 Dyers

28 Sanatorium

1946. Craftsmen.
285 – 1 c. brown and purple 10 10
286 **27** 2 c. violet and green 10 10
287 – 10 c. blue and orange 10 10
288 **27** 15 c. green and blue 10 10
289 – 25 c. blue and green 10 10
290 – 40 c. brown and blue 10 10
291 **27** 45 c. red and black 40 10
292 **27** 1 p. blue and green 50 10
293 – 2 p. 50 green and orange 1·60 50
294 – 10 p. grey and blue 2·75 1·40
DESIGNS: 1, 10, 25 c. Potters; 40 c. Blacksmiths; 1 p. Cobblers; 2 p. 50, Weavers; 10 p. Metal workers.

1946. Anti-T.B. Fund.
297 – 10 c. green and red 10 10
298 **28** 25 c. brown and red 10 10
299 – 25 c. + 5 c. violet & red 10 10
300 – 50 c. + 10 c. blue & red 35 25
301 – 90 c. + 10 c. brown & red 65 35
DESIGNS: 10 c. Emblem and arabesque ornamentation; 25 c. + 5 c. Mountain roadway; 50 c. + 10 c. Fountain; 90 c. + 10 c. Wayfarers.

29 Sanatorium

30 Steam Goods Train

1947. Anti-T.B. Fund.
302 – 10 c. blue and red 10 10
303 **29** 25 c. brn and red 10 10
304 – 25 c. + 5 c. lilac and red 10 10
305 – 50 c. + 10 c. blue & red 35 20
306 – 90 c. + 10 c. brown & red 60 40
DESIGNS: 10 c. Emblem, mosque and palm tree; 25 c. + 5 c. Hospital ward; 50 c. + 10 c. Nurse and children; 90 c. + 10 c. Arab swordsman.

1948. Transport and Commerce.
307 **30** 2 c. brown and violet 20 10
308 – 5 c. violet and red 10 10
309 – 15 c. green and blue 10 10
310 – 25 c. green and black 10 10
311 – 35 c. black and blue 10 10
312 – 50 c. violet and orange 10 10
313 – 70 c. blue and green 10 10
314 – 90 c. green and red 15 10
315 – 1 p. violet and blue 40 10
316 **30** 2 p. 50 green and purple 7·50 7·50
317 – 10 p. blue and black 1·75 1·10
DESIGNS: 5, 35 c. Road transport; 15, 70 c. Urban market; 25, 90 c. Rural market; 50 c., 1 p. Camel caravan; 10 p. "Arango" (freighter) at quay.

31 Emblem

32 Herald

1948. Anti-T.B. Fund.
318 **31** 10 c. green and red 10 10
319 – 25 c. green and red 1·25 60
320 **32** 50 c. + 10 c. purple & red 20 10
321 – 90 c. + 10 c. black & red 80 35
322 – 2 p. 50 + 50 c. brn & red 7·00 2·75
323 – 5 p. + 1 p. violet & red 10·00 4·00
DESIGNS: 25 c. Airplane over sanatorium; 90 c. Arab swordsman; 2 p. 50, Natives sitting in the sun; 5 p. Airplane over Ben Karrich.

33 Market Day

34 Caliph on Horseback

1949. Air.
324 – 5 c. green and purple 10 10
325 **33** 10 c. mauve and black 10 10
326 – 30 c. grey and blue 10 10
327 – 1 p. 75 blue and black 10 10
328 **33** 3 p. black and blue 20 10
329 – 4 p. red and black 40 25
330 – 6 p. 50 brown and green 1·10 25
331 – 8 p. blue and mauve 2·00 45
DESIGNS—VERT: 5 c., 1 p. 75, Straits of Gibraltar; 30 c., 4 p. Kebira Fortress; 6 p. 50, Arrival of mail plane; 8 p. Galloping horseman.

1949. Caliph's Wedding Celebrations.
332 **34** 50 c. + 10 c. red (postage) 20 20
333 – 1 p. + 10 c. black (air) 70 30
DESIGN: 1 p. Wedding crowds in palace grounds.

35 Emblem

36 Postman, 1890

1949. Anti-T.B. Fund.
334 **35** 5 c. green and red 10 10
335 – 10 c. blue and red 10 10
336 – 25 c. black and red 50 20
337 – 50 c. + 10 c. brown & red 30 10
338 – 90 c. + 10 c. green & red 85 20
DESIGNS: 10 c. Road to recovery; 25 c. Palm tree and tower; 50 c. Flag and followers; 90 c. Moorish horseman.

1950. 75th Anniv of U.P.U.
339 **36** 5 c. blue and brown 10 10
340 – 10 c. black and blue 10 10
341 – 15 c. green and black 10 10
342 – 35 c. black and violet 10 10
343 – 45 c. mauve and red 15 15
344 **36** 50 c. black and green 10 10
345 – 75 c. blue and deep blue 10 10
346 **36** 90 c. red and black 10 10
347 – 1 p. green and purple 10 10
348 – 1 p. 50 blue and red 25 10
349 – 5 p. purple and black 50 15
350 – 10 p. blue and violet 14·00 12·00
DESIGNS: 10, 45 c., 1 p. Mounted postman; 15 c., 1 p. 50, Mail coach; 35, 75 c., 5 p. Mail van; 10 p. Steam mail train.

37 Morabito

38 Hunting

1950. Anti-T.B. Fund.
351 – 5 c. black and red 10 10
352 – 10 c. green and red 10 10
353 – 25 c. blue and red 55 30
354 – 50 c. + 10 c. brown & red 25 10
355 **37** 90 c. + 10 c. green & red 1·25 50
DESIGNS: 5 c. Arab horseman; 10 c. Fort; 25 c. Sanatorium; 50 c. Crowd at Fountain of Life.

1950.
356 **38** 5 c. mauve and brown 10 10
357 – 10 c. grey and red 10 10
358 **38** 50 c. sepia and green 10 10
359 – 1 p. red and violet 40 10
360 – 5 p. violet and red 70 10
361 – 10 p. red and green 2·00 50
DESIGNS: 10 c., 1 p. Hunters and hounds; 5 p. Fishermen; 10 p. Carabo (fishing boat).

39 Emblem

40 Mounted Riflemen

1951. Anti-T.B. Fund.
362 **39** 5 c. green and red 10 10
363 – 10 c. blue and red 10 10
364 – 25 c. black and red 60 35
365 – 50 c. + 10 c. brown & red 10 10
366 – 90 c. + 10 c. blue and red 30 15
367 – 1 p. + 5 p. blue and red 8·00 3·50
368 – 1 p. 10 + 25 c. sepia & red 2·75 1·75
DESIGNS: 10 c. Natives and children; 25 c. Airplane over Nubes; 50 c. Moorish horsemen; 90 c. Riverside fortress; 1 p. Brig "Hernan Cortes"; 1 p. 10, Airplane over caravan.

1952.
369 **40** 5 c. brown and blue 10 10
370 – 10 c. mauve and sepia 10 10
371 – 15 c. green and black 10 10
372 – 20 c. purple and green 10 10
373 – 25 c. blue and red 10 10
374 – 35 c. orange and olive 10 10
375 – 45 c. red 10 10
376 – 50 c. green and red 10 10
377 – 75 c. blue and purple 10 10
378 – 90 c. purple and blue 10 10
379 – 1 p. brown and blue 10 10
380 – 5 p. blue and red 1·60 35
381 – 10 p. black and green 2·40 50
DESIGNS—HORIZ: 10 c. Grooms leading horses; 15 c. Parade of horsemen; 20 c. Peasants; 25 c. Monastic procession; 35 c. Native band; 45 c. Tribesmen; 50 c. Natives overlooking roof tops; 75 c. Inside a tea house; 90 c. Wedding procession; 1 p. Pilgrims on horseback; 5 p. Storyteller and audience; 10 p. Natives talking.

41 Road to Tetuan

1952. Air. Tetuan Postal Museum Fund.
382 **41** 2 p. blue and black 10 10
383 – 4 p. red and black 30 10
384 – 8 p. green and black 40 25
385 – 16 p. brown and black 2·00 80
DESIGNS: 4 p. Moors watching airplane; 8 p. Horseman and airplane; 16 p. Shadow of airplane over Tetuan.

42 Natives at Prayer

43 Sidi Saidi

1952. Anti-T.B. Fund. Frame in red.
386 **42** 5 c. green 10 10
387 – 10 c. brown 10 10
388 – 25 c. blue 30 20
389 – 50 c. + 10 c. black 10 10
390 – 60 c. + 25 c. green 60 35
391 – 90 c. + 10 c. purple 60 35
392 – 1 p. 10 + 25 c. violet 1·50 75
393 – 5 p. + 2 p. black 3·75 2·00
DESIGNS: 10 c. Beggars outside doorway; 25 c. Airplane over cactus; 50 c. Natives on horseback; 60 c. Airplane over palms; 90 c. Hilltop fortress; 1 p. 10, Airplane over agaves; 5 p. Mounted warrior.

1953. Air.
394 – 35 c. red and blue 15 10
395 **43** 60 c. green and lake 15 10
396 – 1 p. 10 black and blue 25 10
397 – 4 p. 50 brown and lake 85 20
DESIGNS: 35 c. Carabo (fishing boat); 1 p. 10, Le Yunta (ploughing); 4 p. 50, Fortress, Xauen.

1953. Air. No. 208 surch **50.**
398 50 c. on 75 c. blue 30 10

1953. Anti-T.B. Fund. As T **32** but inscr "PRO TUBERCULOSOS 1953". Frame in red.
400 5 c. green 10 10
401 10 c. purple 10 10
402 25 c. green 55 35
403 50 c. + 10 c. violet 10 10
404 60 c. + 25 c. brown 1·25 10
405 90 c. + 10 c. black 40 30
406 1 p. 10 + 25 c. brown 2·00 1·25
407 5 p. + 2 p. blue 6·50 4·00
DESIGNS: 5 c. Herald; 10 c. Moorish horseman; 25 c. Airplane over Ben Karrich; 50 c. Mounted warrior; 60 c. Airplane over sanatorium; 90 c. Moorish horseman; 1 p. 10, Airplane over sea; 5 p. Arab swordsman.

46

47 Water-carrier

1953.
408 **46** 5 c. red 10 10
409 10 c. green 10 10

1953. 25th Anniv of 1st Pictorial Stamps of Spanish Morocco.
410 – 25 c. purple and green 10 10
411 **47** 50 c. green and red 10 10
412 – 90 c. orange and blue 10 10
413 – 1 p. green and brown 10 10
414 – 1 p. 25 mauve and green 10 10
415 – 2 p. blue and purple 20 20
416 **47** 2 p. 50 orange and grey 50 20
417 – 4 p. 50 green and mauve 2·25 30
418 – 10 p. black and green 2·50 85
DESIGNS—VERT: 35 c., 1 p. 25, Mountain women; 90 c., 2 p. Mountain tribesmen; 1, 4 p. 50, Veiled Moorish women; 10 p. Arab dignitary.

1954. Anti-T.B. Fund. As T **32**, but inscr "PRO TUBERCULOSOS 1954". Frame in red.
419 5 c. turquoise 10 10
420 5 c. + 5 c. purple 50 25
421 10 c. sepia 10 10
422 25 c. blue 15 15
423 50 c. + 10 c. green 50 40
424 5 p. + 2 p. black 4·75 3·50
DESIGNS: 5 c. Convent; 5 c. + 5 c. White stork on a tower; 10 c. Moroccan family; 25 c. Airplane over Spanish coast; 50 c. Father and child; 5 p. Chapel.

48 Saida Gate

49 Celebrations

1955. Frames in black.

425 – 15 c. green 10 10
426 **48** 25 c. purple 10 10
427 – 80 c. blue 10 10
428 **48** 1 p. mauve 20 10
429 – 15 p. turquoise . . . . . . 2·40 85

DESIGNS: 15 c., 80 c. Queen's Gate; 15 p. Ceuta Gate.

1955. 30th Anniv of Caliph's Accession.

430 **49** 15 c. olive and brown . . . 10 10
431 – 25 c. lake and purple . . . 10 10
432 – 30 c. green and sepia . . . 10 10
433 **49** 70 c. green and myrtle . . 10 10
434 – 80 c. brown and olive . . . 10 10
435 – 1 p. brown and blue . . . 10 10
436 **49** 1 p. 80 violet and black . . 20 10
437 – 3 p. grey and blue 20 10
438 – 5 p. brown and myrtle . . 1·25 40
439 – 15 p. green and brown . . 2·40 1·40

DESIGNS: 25 c., 80 c., 3 p. Caliph's portrait; 30 c., 1, 5 p. Procession; 15 p. Coat of Arms.

EXPRESS LETTER STAMPS

Express Letter Stamps of Spain overprinted.

1914. Optd **MARRUECOS**.

E55 E **53** 20 c. red . . . . 2·50 1·00

1915. Optd **PROTECTORADO ESPANOL EN MARRUECOS**.

E68 E **53** 20 c. red . . . . 1·75 80

1923. Optd **ZONA DE PROTECTORADO ESPANOL EN MARRUECOS**.

E111 E **53** 20 c. red . . . . 6·00 3·25

1926. Red Cross. Optd **ZONA PROTECTORADO ESPANOL**.

E124 E **77** 20 c. black and blue . . 1·50 1·25

E **12** Moorish Courier

E **16**

1928.

E138 E **12** 20 c. black . . . . . . 2·00 1·50

1935.

E171 E **16** 20 c. red 85 10

E **19** Moorish Courier

E **21**

1937. 1st Anniv of Civil War.

E200 E **19** 20 c. red 10 10

1940.

E233 E **21** 25 c. red 30 20

1940. No. E200 optd as Nos. 233/48 and surch also.

E249 E **19** 25 c. on 20 c. red . . . 9·00 9·00

E **37** Air Mail 1935

E **41** Moorish Courier

1950. 75th Anniv of U.P.U.

E351 E **37** 25 c. black and red . . 10·00 10·00

1952.

E382 E **41** 25 c. red 10 10

E **48** Moorish Courier E **49** Tangier Gate

1953. 25th Anniv of First Pictorial Stamps of Spanish Morocco.

E419 E **48** 25 c. mauve and blue . 20 25

1955.

E430 E **49** 2 p. violet and black . 15 10

For later issues see **MOROCCO**.

SPANISH POST OFFICES IN TANGIER Pt. 9

See note below No. 41 of Spanish P.O.s in Morocco, concerning the exclusive use of Nos. 30/41 in Tangier after 1914.

Postage stamps of Spain overprinted.

1921. Optd **CORREO ESPANOL MARRUECOS**.

1 **66** 1 c. green 20 10
2 **64** 2 c. brown £225
3 15 c. yellow . . . . 1·50 10
4 20 c. violet . . . . 2·25 10

1939. Optd as 1921.

5 **68** 2 c. green . . . . 2·25 10
6 5 c. purple . . . . 2·25 10
7 5 c. red . . . . 2·25 10
8a 10 c. green . . . . 2·25 20
10 20 c. violet . . . . 4·50 10
11 50 c. orange . . . . . . 20·00 2·25
12 **69** 10 p. brown . . . . 2·50 2·50

1926. Red Cross stamps optd **CORREO ESPANOL TANGER**.

13 **70** 1 c. orange . . . . 2·75 2·50
14 – 2 c. red . . . . 2·75 2·50
15 – 5 c. grey . . . . 1·50 1·00
16 – 10 c. green . . . . 1·50 1·00
17 **70** 15 c. violet 70 50
18 – 20 c. purple 70 50
19 **71** 25 c. red 70 50
20 **70** 30 c. olive 75 50
21 – 40 c. blue 25 25
22 – 50 c. brown 25 25
23 – 1 p. red 35 30
24 – 4 p. brown 45 40
25 **71** 10 p. lilac . . . . 1·75 1·25

1929. Seville–Barcelona Exhibition stamps, Nos. 504/14 optd **TANGER**.

27 5 c. red 10 10
28 10 c. green 10 10
29 15 c. blue 25 10
30 20 c. violet 10 10
31 25 c. red 25 10
32 30 c. brown 15 10
33 40 c. blue 25 25
34 50 c. orange 25 25
35 1 p. grey . . . . 2·50 2·50
36 4 p. red . . . . 5·75 4·50
37 10 p. brown . . . . 8·50 6·50

1930. Optd as 1921.

38 **97** 10 c. green . . . . 3·50 20
39 15 c. turquoise . . . . . 80·00 50
40 20 c. violet . . . . 2·50 25
41 30 c. red . . . . 2·75 45
42 40 c. blue . . . . 10·00 2·75

1933. Optd **MARRUECOS**.

43 **143** 1 c. green (imperf) 15 10
44 2 c. brown 15 10
45 **127** 5 c. brown 15 10
46 **128** 10 c. green 15 10
47 **130** 15 c. blue 15 10
48 **127** 20 c. violet 15 10
49 **132** 25 c. red 15 10
50 **133** 30 c. red . . . . 32·00 2·50
51 **138** 40 c. blue 30 10
52 **130** 50 c. orange 70 10
53 **138** 60 c. green 70 10
54 **142** 1 p. black 70 10
55 – 4 p. mauve . . . . 2·00 1·25
56 – 10 p. brown . . . . 2·75 2·75

1937. Optd **TANGER**.

58 **143** 1 c. green (imperf) 25 10
59 2 c. brown 35 10
60 **127** 5 c. brown 35 10
61 **128** 10 c. green 35 10
62 **130** 15 c. blue 40 35
63 **127** 20 c. violet 40 35
64 **132** 25 c. red 40 10
65 **136** 30 c. red 40 35
66 **138** 40 c. blue . . . . 1·10 35
67 **130** 50 c. orange . . . . . . 2·75 35
68 **142** 1 p. black . . . . 4·75 2·00
69 – 4 p. mauve (No. 768c) . . £140
70 – 10 p. brown (No. 769c) . . £190

1938. Optd **Correo Espanol Tanger**.

71 **143** 5 c. brown . . . . 1·00 50
72 10 c. green . . . . 1·25 50
73 15 c. green . . . . 1·10 50
74 20 c. violet . . . . 1·10 35
75 25 c. mauve . . . . 1·25 35
76 30 c. red . . . . 4·40 1·75
77 **160a** 40 c. red . . . . 2·25 75
78 45 c. red . . . . 1·10 20
79 50 c. blue . . . . 1·25 20
80 60 c. blue . . . . 2·75 75
81 **145** 2 p. blue . . . . 20·00 6·00
82 – 4 p. mauve (No. 768c) . . 18·00 7·50

1938. Air. Optd **Correo Aereo TANGER**.

83 **143** 25 c. mauve 75 25
84 **160a** 50 c. blue 75 25

1938. Air. Optd **CORREO AEREO TANGER**.

86 **142** 1 p. black 85 25
85 **145** 2 p. blue . . . . 6·50 1·40
87 – 4 p. mauve (No. 768c) . . 5·50 1·75
88 – 10 p. brown (No. 769c) . . 32·00 22·00

1939. Optd Tanger.

89 **143** 5 c. brown 30 20
90 10 c. green 30 20
91 15 c. green 30 20
92 20 c. violet 30 20
93 25 c. mauve 30 20
94 30 c. red 30 20
95 **160a** 40 c. red 30 20
96 45 c. red 30 20
97 50 c. blue 90 55
98 60 c. blue 40 20
99 **142** 1 p. black 65 30
100 **145** 2 p. blue . . . . 17·00 9·00
101 – 4 p. mauve (No. 768c) . . 16·00 8·50
102 – 10 p. brown (No. 769c) . . 17·00 11·00

1939. Air. Optd **Via Aerea Tanger**.

103 **143** 5 c. brown 45 40
104 10 c. green 45 40
105 15 c. green 40 35
106 20 c. violet 40 35
107 25 c. mauve 40 35
108 30 c. red 80 50
109 **160a** 40 c. red . . . . 28·00
110 45 c. red 20 20
111 50 c. blue . . . . 55·00
112 60 c. blue . . . . 55·00 12·00
113 **142** 1 p. black . . . . 20·00
114 – 4 p. mauve (No. 768c) . . 25·00 17·00
115 – 10 p. brown (No. 769c) . . 80·00

1939. Air. Express Letter stamp optd **Via Aerea Tanger**.

116 E **145** 20 c. red . . . . 1·75 1·00

1939. Various fiscal types inscr "DERECHOS CONSULARES ESPANOLES" optd **Correo Tanger**.

117 50 c. pink . . . . 12·00 10·00
118 1 p. pink . . . . 2·75 2·25
119 2 p. pink . . . . 2·50 2·25
120 5 p. red and green . . . . . 3·50 2·75
121 10 p. red and violet . . . . 16·00 13·00

1939. Air. Various fiscal types inscr "DERECHOS CONSULARES ESPANOLES" optd **Correo Aereo Tanger**.

122 1 p. blue . . . . 32·00 30·00
123 2 p. blue . . . . 30·00 30·00
124 5 p. blue . . . . 4·50 4·50
125 10 p. blue . . . . 4·75 4·50

15 Moroccan Woman

16 Douglas DC-3

1948.

126 – 1 c. green 10 10
127 – 2 c. orange 10 10
128 – 5 c. purple 10 10
129 – 10 c. blue 10 10
130 – 20 c. sepia 15 10
131 – 25 c. green 15 10
132 – 30 c. grey 45 10
133 – 45 c. red 45 10
134 **15** 50 c. red 40 10
135 – 75 c. blue 75 10
136 – 90 c. green 55 10
137 – 1 p. 35 red . . . . 1·90 30
138 **15** 2 p. violet . . . . 3·25 35
139 – 10 p. green . . . . 3·75 55

DESIGNS: 1, 2 c. Woman's head facing right; 5, 25 c. Palm tree; 10, 20 c. Woman's head facing left; 30 c., 1 p. 35, Old map of Tangier; 45 c., 10 p. Street scene; 75, 90 c. Head of Moor.

1949. Air.

140 – 20 c. brown 45 10
141 **16** 25 c. red 45 10
142 – 35 c. green 50 10
143 – 1 p. violet . . . . 1·25 10
144 **16** 2 p. green . . . . 2·50 30
145 – 10 p. purple . . . . 3·25 1·10

DESIGNS: 20 c., 1 p. Lockheed Constellation and map; 35 c., 10 p. Boeing 377 Stratocruiser in clouds.

EXPRESS LETTER STAMPS

Express Letter Stamps of Spain overprinted.

1926. Red Cross. Optd **CORREO ESPANOL TANGER**.

E26 E **77** 20 c. black and blue . . 1·50 1·10

1933. No. E17 optd **MARRUECOS**.

E57 E **145** 20 c. red . . . . 1·25 20

E **17** Courier

1949.

E146 E **17** 25 c. red 60 20

SPANISH SAHARA Pt. 9

Former Spanish territory on the north-west coast of Africa, previously called Rio de Oro. Later divided between Morocco and Mauritania.

100 centimos = 1 peseta

1 Tuareg and Camel

1924.

1 **1** 5 c. green . . . . 1·40 30
2 10 c. green . . . . 1·40 30
3 15 c. blue . . . . 1·40 30
4 20 c. violet . . . . 1·40 35
5 25 c. red . . . . 1·40 35
6 30 c. brown . . . . 1·40 35
7 40 c. blue . . . . 1·40 35
8 50 c. orange . . . . 1·40 35
9 60 c. purple . . . . 1·40 35
10 1 p. red . . . . 6·50 1·75
11 4 p. brown . . . . 32·00 10·00
12 10 p. purple . . . . 65·00 28·00

1926. Red Cross stamps of Spain optd **SAHARA ESPANOL**.

13 – 5 c. grey . . . . 3·75 3·25
14 – 10 c. green . . . . 3·75 3·25
15 **70** 15 c. violet . . . . 1·40 1·00
16 – 20 c. purple . . . . 1·40 1·00
17 **71** 25 c. red . . . . 1·40 1·00
18 **70** 30 c. olive . . . . 1·40 1·00
19 – 40 c. blue 15 20
20 – 50 c. brown 15 20
21 **71** 60 c. green 15 20
22 – 1 p. red 15 20
23 – 4 p. brown . . . . 1·10 75
24 **71** 10 p. lilac . . . . 3·25 2·50

1929. Seville and Barcelona Exn stamps of Spain. Nos. 504/14, optd **SAHARA**.

25 5 c. red 10 15
26 10 c. green 10 15
27 15 c. blue 10 15
28 20 c. violet 10 15
29 25 c. red 10 15
30 30 c. brown 10 15
31 40 c. blue 25 25
32 50 c. orange 25 25
33 1 p. grey . . . . 1·00 1·00
34 4 p. red . . . . 6·50 4·50
35 10 p. brown . . . . 12·00 9·00

1931. Optd **Republica Espanola**.

36 **1** 5 c. green 40 35
37 10 c. green 40 35
38 15 c. blue 45 35
39 20 c. violet 45 35
40 25 c. red 45 35
41 30 c. brown 45 35
42 40 c. blue . . . . 2·75 45
43 50 c. orange . . . . 3·00 1·25
44 60 c. purple . . . . 3·25 1·10
45 1 p. red . . . . 3·00 1·00
46 4 p. brown . . . . 25·00 10·00
47 10 p. purple . . . . 45·00 15·00

1941. Stamps of Spain optd **SAHARA ESPANOL**.

47a **181** 1 c. green . . . . 1·40 1·40
47b **182** 2 c. brown . . . . 1·40 1·40
48 **183** 5 c. brown 35 35
49 10 c. red . . . . 1·40 1·40
50 15 c. green 35 35
51 **196** 20 c. violet 35 35
52 25 c. red 85 70
53 30 c. blue 85 80
54 40 c. green 35 35
55 50 c. blue . . . . 4·00 85
56 70 c. blue . . . . 3·00 1·40
57 1 PTA. black . . . . . . 13·00 2·00
58 2 PTAS. brown . . . . . . 70·00 40·00
59 4 PTAS. red . . . . £140 90·00
60 10 PTS. brown £350 £120

6 Dorcas Gazelles

7 Ostriches

1943.
61 **6** 1 c. mauve & brown (postage) 10 10
62 – 2 c. blue and green 10 10
63 – 5 c. blue and red 10 10
64 **6** 15 c. green and myrtle 15 15
65 – 20 c. brown and mauve 15 15
66 **6** 40 c. mauve and purple 15 15
67 – 45 c. red and purple 25 25
68 – 75 c. blue and indigo 35 35
69 **6** 1 p. brown and red 1·10 1·10
70 – 3 p. green and violet 2·25 2·00
71 – 10 p. black and sepia 24·00 20·00
DESIGNS—VERT: 2, 20, 45 c., 3 p. Camel caravan; 5, 75 c., 10 p. Camel troops.

72 **7** 5 c. brown and red (air) 75 30
73 – 25 c. olive and green 20 15
74 **7** 50 c. turquoise and blue 1·50 40
75 – 1 p. blue and mauve 50 25
76 **7** 1 p. 40 blue and green 2·00 45
77 – 2 p. brown and purple 85 85
78 **7** 5 p. mauve and brown 4·75 2·50
79 – 6 p. green and blue 18·00 16·00
DESIGN: 25 c., 1, 2, 6 p. Airplane and camels.

8 Boy carrying Lamb

9 Diego de Herrera

1950. Child Welfare.
80 **8** 50 c. + 10 c. brown 25 20
81 1 p. + 25 c. red 11·00 4·75
82 6 p. 50 + 1 p. 65 green 6·00 1·60

1950. Air. Colonial Stamp Day.
83 **9** 5 p. violet 2·75 1·00

9a Woman and Dove

9b General Franco

1951. Air. 500th Birth Anniv of Isabella the Catholic.
84 **9a** 5 p. green 25·00 5·50

1951. Visit of Gen. Franco.
85 **9b** 50 c. orange 10 10
86 1 p. brown 35 35
87 5 p. turquoise 38·00 12·00

10 Dromedary and Calf

11 Native Woman

1951. Colonial Stamp Day.
88 **10** 5 c. + 5 c. brown 10 10
89 10 c. + 5 c. orange 10 10
90 60 c. + 15 c. olive 30 10

1952. Child Welfare Fund.
91 **11** 5 c. + 5 c. brown 10 10
92 50 c. + 10 c. black 10 10
93 2 p. + 30 c. blue 1·75 90

12 Morion, Sword and Banner

13 Head of Ostritch

1952. Air. 500th Birth Anniv of Ferdinand the Catholic.
94 **12** 5 p. brown 30·00 6·00

1952. Colonial Stamp Day.
95 **13** 5 c. + 5 c. brown 15 10
96 10 c. + 5 c. red 25 10
97 60 c. + 15 c. green 50 20

14 "Geography"

15 Woman Musician

1953. 75th Anniv of Royal Geographical Society.
98 **14** 5 c. red 10 10
99 35 c. green 10 10
100 60 c. brown 20 10

1953. Child Welfare Fund. Inscr "PRO INFANCIA 1953".
101 **15** 5 c. + 5 c. brown 10 10
102 – 10 c. + 5 c. purple 10 10
103 **15** 15 c. olive 10 10
104 – 60 c. brown 15 10
DESIGN: 10, 60 c. Native man musician.

16

1953. Colonial Stamp Day. Inscr "DIA DEL SELLO COLONIAL 1953".
105 **16** 5 c. + 5 c. violet 10 10
106 – 10 c. + 5 c. green 15 10
107 **16** 15 c. olive 15 10
108 – 60 c. orange 15 10
DESIGN—HORIZ: 10, 60 c. Two fishes.

17 Hurdlers

1954. Child Welfare Fund. Inscr "PRO INFANCIA 1954".
109 **17** 5 c. + 5 c. brown 10 10
110 – 10 c. + 5 c. violet 10 10
111 **17** 15 c. green 10 10
112 – 60 c. brown 10 10
DESIGN—VERT: 10, 60 c. Native runner.

18 Flying Fish

1954. Colonial Stamp Day. Inscr "DIA DEL SELLO COLONIAL 1954".
113 **18** 5 c. + 5 c. red 10 10
114 – 10 c. + 5 c. purple 15 10
115 **18** 15 c. green 15 10
116 – 60 c. brown 20 10
DESIGN—HORIZ: 10, 60 c. "Sparus auratus" (fish).

19 E. Bonelli

1955. Birth Centenary of Bonelli (explorer).
117 **19** 10 c. + 5 c. purple 10 10
118 – 25 c. + 10 c. violet 10 10
119 **19** 50 c. olive 10 10
DESIGN: 25 c. Bonelli and felucca.

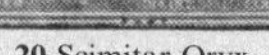
20 Scimitar Oryx

21 "Antirrhinum ramosissimum"

1955. Colonial Stamp Day. Inscr "DIA DEL SELLO COLONIAL 1955".
120 **20** 5 c. + 5 c. brown 10 10
121 – 15 c. + 5 c. bistre 15 10
122 **20** 70 c. green 25 10
DESIGN: 15 c. Scimitar oryx's head.

1956. Child Welfare Fund. Inscr "PRO-INFANCIA 1956".
123 **21** 5 c. + 5 c. olive 10 10
124 – 15 c. + 5 c. ochre 10 10
125 **21** 20 c. turquoise 15 10
126 – 50 c. brown 20 10
DESIGN: 15, 50 c. "Sesuvium portulacastrum" (wrongly inscr "Sesiviun").

22 Arms of Aaiun and Native on Camel

23 Dromedaries

1956. Colonial Stamp Day. Inscr "DIA DEL SELLO 1956".
127 **22** 5 c. + 5 c. black & violet 10 10
128 – 15 c. + 5 c. green & ochre 15 10
129 **22** 70 c. brown and green 15 10
DESIGN—VERT: 15 c. Arms of Villa Cisneros and native chief.

1957. Animals.
130 **23** 5 c. violet 10 10
131 – 15 c. ochre 50 10
132 – 50 c. brown 10 10
133 **23** 70 c. green 1·25 20
134 – 80 c. turquoise 2·50 20
135 – 1 p. 80 mauve 1·25 20
DESIGNS: 15, 80 c. Ostrich; 50 c., 1 p. 80, Dorcas gazelle.

24 Golden Eagle

25 Head of Striped Hyena

1957. Child Welfare Fund. Inscr "PRO-INFANCIA 1957".
136 **24** 5 c. + 5 c. brown 15 10
137 – 15 c. + 5 c. bistre 20 15
138 **24** 70 c. green 40 30
DESIGN: 15 c. Tawny eagle in flight.

1957. Colonial Stamp Day. Inscr "DIA DEL SELLO 1957".
139 **25** 10 c. + 5 c. purple 10 10
140 – 15 c. + 5 c. ochre 10 10
141 **25** 20 c. green 10 10
142 – 70 c. myrtle 15 10
DESIGN: 15, 70 c. Striped hyena.

26 White Stork and Arms of Valencia and Aaiun

27 Cervantes

1958. Aid for Valencia.
143 **26** 10 c. + 5 c. brown 20 10
144 15 c. + 10 c. ochre 20 10
145 50 c. + 10 c. brown 25 10

1958. Child Welfare Fund. Inscr "1958".
146 **27** 10 c. + 5 c. brown & chest 10 10
147 – 15 c. + 5 c. myrtle & orge 10 10
148 – 20 c. green and brown 10 10
149 **27** 50 c. green and yellow 10 10
DESIGNS—VERT: 15 c. Don Quixote and Sancho Panza on horseback. HORIZ: 20 c. Don Quixote and the lion.

28 Hoopoe Lark

29 Lope de Vega (author)

1958. Colonial Stamp Day. Inscr "1958".
150 **28** 10 c. + 5 c. red 25 15
151 – 25 c. + 10 c. violet 25 15
152 – 50 c. + 10 c. olive 25 15
DESIGNS—HORIZ: 25 c. Hoopoe lark feeding young. VERT: 50 c. Fulvous babbler.

1959. Child Welfare Fund. Inscr "PRO INFANCIA 1959".
153 **29** 10 c. + 5 c. olive & brown 10 10
154 – 15 c. + 5 c. brown & bis 10 10
155 – 20 c. sepia and green 10 10
156 **29** 70 c. myrtle and green 10 10
DESIGNS—Characters from the comedy "The Star of Seville": 15 c. Spanish lady; 20 c. Caballero.

30 Grey Heron

31 Sahara Postman

1959. Birds.
157 **30** 25 c. violet 15 10
158 – 50 c. green 15 10
159 – 75 c. sepia 15 10
160 **30** 1 p. red 15 10
161 – 1 p. 50 green 15 10
162 – 2 p. purple 1·75 10
163 **30** 3 p. blue 1·75 15
164 – 5 p. brown 3·25 35
165 – 10 p. olive 10·00 5·75
DESIGNS: 50 c., 1 p. 50, 5 p. European sparrow hawk; 75 c., 2, 10 p. Herring gull.

1959. Colonial Stamp Day. Inscr "1959".
166 **31** 10 c. + 5 c. brown & red 10 10
167 – 20 c. + 5 c. brown & grn 10 10
168 – 50 c. + 20 c. slate & olive 10 10
DESIGNS: 20 c. Postman tendering letters; 50 c. Camel postman.

32 F. de Quevedo (writer)

33 Leopard

1960. Child Welfare Fund. Inscr "PRO-INFANCIA 1960".
169 **32** 10 c. + 5 c. purple 10 10
170 – 15 c. + 5 c. bistre 10 10
171 – 35 c. green 10 10
172 **32** 80 c. turquoise 10 10
DESIGNS—VERT: (representing Quevedo's works): 15 c. Winged wheel and hour-glass; 25 c. Man in plumed hat wearing cloak and sword.

1960. Stamp Day. Inscr "1960".
173 **33** 10 c. + 5 c. mauve 10 10
174 – 20 c. + 5 c. myrtle 10 10
175 – 30 c. + 10 c. brown 35 15
176 – 50 c. + 20 c. brown 20 10
DESIGNS: 20 c. Fennec fox; 30 c. Golden eagle defying leopard; 50 c. Red fox.

34 Houbara Bustard

35 Cameleer and Airplane

1961.
177 **34** 25 c. violet 15 10
178 – 50 c. brown 15 10
179 **34** 75 c. dull purple 15 10
180 – 1 p. red 15 10
181 **34** 1 p. 50 green 15 15
182 – 2 p. mauve 1·40 15
183 **34** 3 p. blue 2·25 15
184 – 5 p. brown 2·50 50
185 **34** 10 p. olive 4·75 1·50
DESIGN: 50 c., 1, 2, 5 p. Rock doves.

1961. Air.
186 **35** 25 p. sepia 3·25 85

36 Dorcas Gazelle   37

1961. Child Welfare. Inscr "PRO-INFANCIA 1961".

187	36	10 c. + 5 c. red	10	10
188	–	25 c. + 10 c. violet	15	10
189	36	80 c. + 20 c. green	15	10

DESIGN: 25 c. One dorcas gazelle.

1961. 25th Anniv of Gen. Franco as Head of State.

190	–	25 c. grey	10	10
191	37	50 c. olive	10	10
192	–	70 c. green	10	10
193	37	1 p. orange	10	10

DESIGNS—VERT: 25 c. Map; 70 c. Aaiun Chapel.

38 A. Fernandez de Lugo   39 "Neurada procumbres linn"

1961. Stamp Day. Inscr "DIA DEL SELLO 1961".

194	38	10 c. + 5 c. salmon	10	10
195	–	25 c. + 10 c. plum	10	10
196	38	30 c. + 10 c. brown	10	10
197	–	1 p. + 10 c. orange	15	10

PORTRAIT: 25 c., 1 p. D. de Herrera.

1962. Flowers.

198	39	25 c. violet	10	10
199	–	50 c. sepia	10	10
200	–	70 c. green	10	10
201	39	1 p. orange	10	10
202	–	1 p. 50 turquoise	50	10
203	–	2 p. purple	1·75	10
204	39	3 p. blue	2·50	30
205	–	10 p. olive	5·00	1·40

FLOWERS: 50 c., 1 p. 50, 10 p. "Anabasis articulata moq"; 70 c., 2 p. "Euphorbia resinifera".

40 Two Barred Fishes   42 Seville Cathedral

41 Goats

1962. Child Welfare.

206	40	25 c. violet	10	10
207	–	50 c. green	15	10
208	40	1 p. brown	15	10

DESIGN—HORIZ: 50 c. Two fishes.

1962. Stamp Day.

209	41	15 c. green	10	10
210	–	35 c. purple	10	10
211	41	1 p. brown	15	10

DESIGN: 35 c. Sheep.

1963. Seville Flood Relief.

212	42	50 c. olive	15	10
213		1 p. brown	10	10

43 Cameleer and Camel   44 Dove in Hands

1963. Child Welfare. Inscr "PRO-INFANCIA 1963".

214	–	25 c. violet	10	10
215	43	50 c. grey	10	10
216	–	1 p. red	15	10

DESIGN: 25 c., 1 p. Three camels.

1963. "For Barcelona".

217	44	50 c. turquoise	10	10
218		1 p. brown	10	10

45 Fish ("Zeus faber")

1964. Stamp Day. Inscr "DIA DEL SELLO 1963".

219	45	25 c. violet	15	10
220	–	50 c. olive	20	10
221	45	1 p. brown	30	10

FISH—VERT: 50 c. "Cossus pulchra".

46 "Hyles lineata"   47 Mounted Dromedary and Microphone

1964. Child Welfare.

222	46	25 c. violet	15	10
223	–	50 c. olive	25	10
224	46	1 p. red	25	10

DESIGN—VERT: 50 c. Carpenter moths.

1964.

225	47	25 c. purple	10	10
226	–	50 c. olive	10	10
227	–	70 c. green	10	10
228	47	1 p. purple	10	10
229	–	1 p. 50 turquoise	10	10
230	–	2 p. turquoise	25	15
231	–	3 p. blue	35	15
232	–	10 p. lake	2·00	85

DESIGNS: 50 c., 1 p. 50, 3 p. Flute-player; 70 c., 2, 10 p. Women drummer.

48 Barbary Ground Squirrel

1964. Stamp Day.

233	–	50 c. olive	10	10
234	48	1 p. lake	15	10
235	–	1 p. 50 green	15	10

DESIGN—VERT: 50 c., 1 p. 50, Eurasian red squirrel eating.

49 Doctor tending Patient, and Hospital

1965. 25th Anniv of End of Spanish Civil War.

236	–	50 c. olive	10	10
237	49	1 p. red	15	10
238	–	1 p. 50 blue	15	10

DESIGNS—VERT: 50 c. Saharan woman; 1 p. 50, Desert installation and cameleer.

50 "Anthia sexmaculata"   51 Handball

1965. Child Welfare. Insects.

239	50	50 c. blue	10	10
240	–	1 p. green	10	10
241	50	1 p. 50 brown	15	10
242	–	3 p. blue	1·25	60

INSECTS—VERT: 1, 3 p. "Blepharopsis mendica".

1965. Stamp Day.

243	51	50 c. red	10	10
244	–	1 p. purple	15	10
245	51	1 p. 50 blue	20	10

DESIGN: 1 p. Arms of Spanish Sahara.

52 Bows of "Rio de Oro"

1966. Child Welfare.

246	52	50 c. olive	10	10
247		1 p. brown	10	10
248	–	1 p. 50 green	15	10

DESIGN: 1 p. 50, Freighter "Fuerta Ventura".

53 "Parathunnus obesus" (fish)   54 Fig

1966. Stamp Day.

249	53	10 c. blue and yellow	10	10
250	–	40 c. grey and salmon	15	10
251	53	1 p. 50 brown and green	25	10
252	–	4 p. purple and green	30	10

DESIGN—VERT: 40 c., 4 p. "Mola mola" (fish).

1967. Child Welfare.

253	54	10 c. yellow and blue	10	10
254	–	40 c. purple and green	10	10
255	54	1 p. 50 yellow and green	20	10
256	–	4 p. orange and blue	35	10

DESIGN: 40 c., 4 p. Lupin.

55 Quay, Aaiun

1967. Inauguration of Sahara Ports.

257	55	1 p. 50 brown and blue	10	10
258	–	4 p. ochre and blue	20	10

DESIGN: 4 p. Port of Villa Cisneros.

56 Ruddy Shelduck   56a Scorpio (scorpion)

1968. Stamp Day.

259	56	1 p. brown and green	25	10
260	–	1 p. 50 mauve and black	35	15
261	–	3 p. 50 lake and brown	45	30

DESIGNS—VERT: 1 p. 50, Greater flamingo. HORIZ: 3 p. 50, Rufous bushchat.

1968. Child Welfare. Signs of the Zodiac.

262	56a	1 p. mauve on yellow	20	10
263	–	1 p. 50 brown on pink	25	10
264	–	2 p. 50 violet on yellow	35	15

DESIGNS: 1 p. 50, Capricorn (goat); 2 p. 50, Virgo (virgin).

57 Dove, and Stamp within Posthorn   58 Head of Dorcas Gazelle

1968. Stamp Day.

265	57	1 p. blue and purple	10	10
266	–	1 p. 50 green & light green	10	10
267	–	2 p. 50 blue and orange	20	10

DESIGNS: 1 p. 50, Postal handstamp, stamps and letter; 2 p. 50, Saharan postman.

1969. Child Welfare.

268	58	1 p. brown and black	15	10
269	–	1 p. 50 brown and black	25	10
270	–	2 p. 50 brown and black	25	10
271	–	6 p. brown and black	40	20

DESIGNS: 1 p. 50, Dorcas gazelle tending young; 2 p. 50, Dorcas gazelle and camel; 6 p. Dorcas gazelle leaping.

59 Woman beating Drum   61 Dorcas Gazelle and Arms of El Aaiun

60 "Grammodes boisdeffrei"

1960. Stamp Day.

272	59	50 c. brown and bistre	15	10
273	–	1 p. 50 turquoise & green	15	10
274	–	2 p. blue and brown	15	30
275	–	25 p. brown and green	1·50	30

DESIGNS—VERT: 1 p. 50, Man playing flute. HORIZ: 2 p. Drum and mounted cameleer; 25 p. Flute.

1970. Child Welfare. As T **58**.

276	50 c. ochre and blue	20	10
277	2 p. brown and blue	25	10
278	2 p. 50 ochre and blue	35	10
279	6 p. ochre and blue	45	20

DESIGNS: 50 c. Fennec fox; 2 p. Fennec fox walking; 2 p. 50, Head of fennec fox; 6 p. Fennec fox family.

1970. Stamp Day. Butterflies. Multicoloured.

280	50 c. Type **60**	20	10
281	1 p. Type **60**	30	10
282	2 p. "Danaus chrysippus"	30	10
283	5 p. As 2 p.	45	10
284	8 p. "Celerio euphorbiae"	65	20

1971. Child Welfare.

285	61	1 p. multicoloured	10	10
286	–	2 p. green and olive	10	10
287	–	5 p. blue, brown and grey	15	10
288	–	25 p. green, grey & blue	90	20

DESIGNS—VERT: 25 p. Smara Mosque. HORIZ: 2 p. Tourist inn, Aaiun; 5 p. Assembly House, Aaiun.

63 Trumpeter Finch

1971. Stamp Day. Multicoloured.

290	1 p. 50 Type **63**	40	15
291	2 p. Type **63**	60	15
292	5 p. Cream-coloured courser	80	20
293	24 p. Lanner falcon	2·50	45

64 Seated Woman   65 Tuareg Woman

1972. Saharan Nomads.

294	64	1 p. black, pink and blue	10	10
295	–	1 p. 50 slate, lilac & brown	10	10
296	–	2 p. black, flesh & green	10	10
297	64	5 p. purple, olive & green	15	10
298	–	8 p. violet, green & black	25	10
299	–	10 p. green, grey & black	40	10
300	–	12 p. multicoloured	45	20
301	–	15 p. multicoloured	55	30
302	–	24 p. multicoloured	1·10	40

DESIGNS: 1 p. 50, 2 p. Squatting nomad; 8, 10 p. Head of nomad; 12 p. Woman with bangles; 15 p. Nomad with rifle; 24 p. Woman displaying trinkets.

1972. Child Welfare. Multicoloured.

303	8 p. Type **65**	30	10
304	12 p. Tuareg elder	40	20

66 Mother and Child **67** Sahara Desert

1972. Stamp Day. Multicoloured.
305 4 p. Type **66** 20 10
306 15 p. Nomad 50 20

1973. Child Welfare. Multicoloured.
307 2 p. Type **67** 15 10
308 7 p. City Gate, El Aaiun 20 10

68 Villa Cisneros

1973. Stamp Day. Multicoloured.
309 2 p. Type **68** 10 10
310 7 p. Tuareg (vert) 20 10

69 U.P.U. Monument, Berne **70** Archway, Smara Mosque

1974. Centenary of Universal Postal Union.
311 **69** 15 p. multicoloured 45 15

1974. Child Welfare. Multicoloured.
312 1 p. Type **70** 10 10
313 2 p. Villa Cisneros Mosque 15 10

71 Eagle Owl

1974. Stamp Day. Multicoloured.
314 2 p. Type **71** 65 10
315 5 p. Lappet-faced vulture 1·10 15

72 "Espana" Emblem and Spanish Sahara Stamp **74** Tuareg Elder

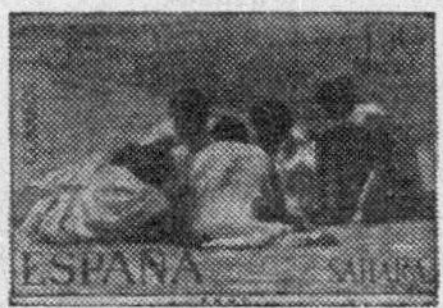

73 Desert Conference

1975. "Espana 75" International Stamp Exhibition, Madrid.
316 **72** 8 p. yellow, blue & black 30 10

1975. Child Welfare. Multicoloured.
317 1 p. 50 Type **73** 15 10
318 3 p. Desert oasis 15 10

1975.
319 **74** 3 p. purple, green & blk 15 10

EXPRESS LETTER STAMP

1943. Design as No. 63 inscr "URGENTE".
E80 25 c. red and myrtle 70 70

E **62** Despatch-rider

1971.
E289 E **62** 10 p. brown and red 65 30

SPANISH WEST AFRICA Pt. 9

100 centimos = 1 peseta

Issues for use in Ifni and Spanish Sahara.

1 Native **2** Isabella the Catholic

1949. 75th Anniv of U.P.U.
1 **1** 4 p. green 2·25 1·00

1949. Air. Colonial Stamp Day.
2 **2** 5 p. brown 1·75 80

3 Tents

1950.
3 **3** 2 c. brown 10 10
4 – 5 c. violet 10 10
5 – 10 c. blue 10 10
6 – 15 c. black 25 10
7 **3** 25 c. brown 25 10
8 – 30 c. yellow 20 10
9 – 40 c. olive 20 10
10 – 45 c. red 20 10
11 **3** 50 c. orange 20 10
12 – 75 c. blue 20 15
13 – 90 c. green 20 10
14 – 1 p. grey 20 10
15 **3** 1 p. 35 violet 85 40
16 – 2 p. sepia 1·50 1·00
17 – 5 p. mauve 12·00 2·25
18 **3** 10 p. brown 22·00 12·00
DESIGNS: 5, 30, 75 c., 2 p. Palm trees, Lake Tinzgarrentz; 10, 40, 90 c., 5 p. Camels and irrigation; 15, 45 c., 1 p. Camel transport.

8 Camel Train

1951. Air.
19 – 25 c. yellow 30 10
20 **8** 50 c. mauve 15 10
21 – 1 p. green 35 10
22 – 2 p. blue 65 10
23 **8** 3 p. 25 violet 1·25 45
24 – 5 p. sepia 11·00 1·50
25 – 10 p. red 22·00 9·00
DESIGNS: 25 c., 2, 10 p. Desert camp; 1, 5 p. Four camels.

EXPRESS LETTER STAMP

E **10** Port Tilimenzo

1951.
E26 E **10** 25 c. red 1·00 35

SUDAN Pt. 14

A territory in Africa, extending S. from Egypt towards the equator, jointly administered by Gt. Britain and Egypt until 1954 when the territory was granted a large measure of self-government. Became independent 1 Jan. 1956 (for issues before this date see volume 3).

1000 milliemes = 100 piastres = £1 Sudanese

52 "Independent Sudan"

1956. Independence Commemoration.
143 **52** 15 m. orange and purple 15 10
144 3 p. orange and blue 35 15
145 5 p. orange and green 50 35

53 Globe on Rhinoceros (Badge of Sudan) **54** Sudanese Soldier and Farmer

1958. Arab Postal Congress, Khartoum.
146 **53** 15 m. orange and purple 20 10
147 3 p. orange and blue 35 15
148 5 p. orange and green 50 35

1959. 1st Anniv of Army Revolution.
149 **54** 15 m. yellow, blue & brown 15 10
150 3 p. multicoloured 50 20
151 55 m. multicoloured 65 40

1960. Inauguration of Arab League Centre, Cairo. As T **154a** of Syria.
152 15 m. black and green 15 10

55 Refugees **56** Football

1960. World Refugee Year.
153 **55** 15 m. blue, black & brown 15 15
154 55 m. red, black and sepia 55 45

1960. Olympic Games, Rome.
155 **56** 15 m. multicoloured 20 10
156 3 p. multicoloured 45 25
157 55 m. multicoloured 65 35

57 Forest **58** King Ta'rhaqa

1960. 5th World Forestry Congress, Seattle.
158 **57** 15 m. green, brown & red 15 10
159 3 p. green, brown and deep green 35 20
160 55 m. multicoloured 60 35

1961. Sudanese Nubian Monuments Preservation Campaign.
161 **58** 15 m. brown and green 20 10
162 3 p. violet and orange 35 20
163 55 m. brown and blue 60 35

59 Girl with Book **60** "The World United against Malaria"

1961. "50 Years of Girls' Education in the Sudan".
164 **59** 15 m. mauve, purple & bl 15 10
165 3 p. blue, orange & black 40 20
166 55 m. brown, green & blk 55 40

1962. Malaria Eradication.
167 **60** 15 m. violet, blue & black 15 10
168 55 m. green, emerald & blk 50 35

1962. Arab League Week. As T **76** of Libya but larger, 24 × 41 mm.
169 15 m. orange 15 10
170 55 m. turquoise 45 35

62 Republican Palace **63** Nile Felucca

64 Camel Postman **65** Campaign Emblem and "Millet" Cobs

1962.
185 **62** 5 m. blue 10 10
186 – 10 m. purple and blue 10 10
187 – 15 m. purple, orge & bis 10 10
188 **62** 2 p. purple 10 10
189 – 3 p. brown and green 20 10
190 – 35 m. brn, dp brn & grn 55 10
191 – 4 p. mauve, red & blue 55 10
192 – 55 m. black and green 55 20
193 – 6 p. brown and blue 65 20
194 – 8 p. green 65 20
195 **63** 10 p. brown, bistre & bl 80 35
196 – 20 p. green and bronze 1·40 55
194a – 25 p. brown and green 10 10
197 – 50 p. green, blue & blk 3·50 1·25
469 **64** £S1 brown and green 7·25 4·25
198 – £S5 green and brown 45 25
199 **63** £S10 orange and green 90 40
DESIGNS: As Type **62**—HORIZ: 15 m. "Tabbaque" (food cover); 55 m., 6, 25 p. Cattle; 8 p. Date palms. VERT: 10 m., 3 p. Cotton picking; 35 m., 4 p. Wild game. As Type **63**—HORIZ: 20 p., £S5 Bohein Temple; 50 p. Sennar Dam.

1963. Freedom from Hunger.
226 **65** 15 m. green and brown 15 15
227 55 m. violet, lilac & blue 55 35

66 Centenary Emblem and Medallions **67** "Knight"

1963. Centenary of Red Cross.
228 **66** 15 m. multicoloured 35 15
229 55 m. multicoloured 65 35

1964. Nubian Monuments Preservation. Frescoes from Faras Church, Nubia. Multicoloured.
230 15 m. Type **67** 20 15
231 30 m. "Saint" (horiz) 35 20
232 55 m. "Angel" 85 55

68 Sudan Map **69** Chainbreakers and Mrs. E. Roosevelt

1964. New York World's Fair. Multicoloured.
233 15 m. Khashm el Girba Dam 10 10
234 3 p. Sudan Pavilion 20 15
235 55 m. Type **68** 50 30
Nos. 233/4 are horiz:

1964. 80th Birth Anniv of Mrs. Eleanor Roosevelt (Human Rights pioneer).
236 **69** 15 m. blue and black 10 10
237 3 p. violet and black 30 15
238 55 m. brown and black 45 30

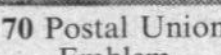

70 Postal Union Emblem

71 I.T.U. Symbol and Emblems

1964. 10th Anniv of Arab Postal Unions' Permanent Bureau.

239 **70** 15 m. black, gold and red . 10 10
240 3 p. black, gold and green . 30 15
241 55 m. black, gold and violet 45 30

1965. Centenary of I.T.U.

242 **71** 15 m. brown and gold . . . 10 10
243 3 p. black and gold 30 15
244 55 m. green and gold . . . 45 30

72 Gurashi (martyr) and Demonstrators

1965. 1st Anniv of 21 October Revolution.

245 **72** 15 m. black and brown . . 10 10
246 3 p. black and red 20 15
247 55 m. black and grey . . . 45 30

73 I.C.Y. Emblem

74 El Siddig El Mahdi

1965. International Co-operation Year.

248 **73** 15 m. lilac and black . . . 10 10
249 3 p. green and black . . . 20 15
250 55 m. red and black . . . 45 30

1966. 5th Death Anniv of Imam El Siddig El Mahdi.

251 **74** 15 m. violet and blue . . . 35 15
252 3 p. brown and orange . . 50 35
253 55 m. brown and grey . . . 1·10 60

75 M. Zaroug (politician)

1966. Mubarak Zaroug Commemoration.

254 **75** 15 m. olive and pink . . 35 15
255 3 p. green and light green . 50 35
256 55 m. brown and chestnut . 1·10 55

76 W.H.O. Building

77 Crests of Upper Nile, Blue Nile and Kassala Provinces

1966. Inaug of W.H.O. Headquarters, Geneva.

257 **76** 15 m. blue 10 10
258 3 p. purple 20 15
259 55 m. brown 45 30

1967. "The Month of the South".

260 **77** 15 m. multicoloured . . . 10 10
261 – 3 p. multicoloured 20 10
262 – 55 m. multicoloured . . . 80 40

DESIGNS (Crests of): 3 p. Equatoria, Kordofan and Khartoum Provinces; 55 m. Bahr El Gazal, Darfur and Northern Provinces.

78 Giraffe and Tourist Emblem

79 Handclasp Emblem

1967. International Tourist Year.

263 **78** 15 m. multicoloured . . . 20 10
264 3 p. multicoloured 45 25
265 55 m. multicoloured . . . 70 25

1967. Arab Summit Conference, Khartoum.

266 **79** 15 m. multicoloured . . . 10 10
267 3 p. green and orange . . 20 10
268 55 m. violet and yellow . . 45 20

80 P.L.O. Shoulder Flash

1967. Palestine Liberation Organization.

269 **80** 15 m. multicoloured . . . 10 10
270 3 p. multicoloured 20 10
271 55 m. multicoloured . . . 45 20

81 Mohamed Nur El Din

1968. Nur El Din (politician) Commemoration.

272 **81** 15 m. green and blue . . . 35 15
273 3 p. bistre and blue . . . 50 30
274 55 m. ultramarine & blue . 1·10 50

82 Abdullahi El Fadil El Mahdi

1968. Abdullahi El Fadil El Mahdi (Ansar leader) Commemoration.

275 **82** 15 m. violet and blue . . . 35 15
276 3 p. green and blue . . . 50 30
277 55 m. green and orange . 1·10 50

83 Ahmed Yousif Hashim

1968. 10th Death Anniv of Ahmed Yousif Hashim (journalist).

278 **83** 15 m. brown and green . . 35 10
279 3 p. brown and blue . . . 50 10
280 55 m. violet and blue . . . 1·10 30

84 Mohamed Ahmed El Mardi

1968. Mohamed Ahmed El Mardi (politician) Commemoration.

281 **84** 15 m. ultramarine blue 35 15
282 3 p. orange, blue pink . . 50 35
283 55 m. brown and blue . . 1·10 55

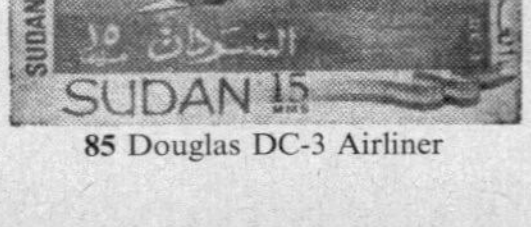

85 Douglas DC-3 Airliner

1968. 20th Anniv of Sudan Airways. Mult.

284 15 m. Type **85** 10 10
285 2 p. De Havilland Dove . . . 20 10
286 3 p. Fokker Friendship . . . 40 20
287 55 m. Hawker Siddeley Comet 4C 65 45

87 Anniversary and Bank Emblems

1969. 5th Anniv of African Development Bank.

288 **87** 2 p. black and gold 15 10
289 4 p. red and gold 30 15
290 65 m. green and gold . . . 45 20

88 I.L.O. Emblem

1969. 50th Anniv of Int Labour Organization.

291 **88** 2 p. black, red and blue . . 15 10
292 4 p. black, blue & yellow . 30 15
293 65 m. black, mauve & grn . 45 20

89 "Solidarity of the People"

1970. 1st Anniv of May 25th Revolution (1st issue).

294 **89** 2 p. multicoloured . . . .
295 4 p. multicoloured
296 65 m. multicoloured
Set of 3 . . . . 25·00

Nos. 294/6 were withdrawn on day of issue (25 May) as being unsatisfactory. They were later replaced by Nos. 297/9 and the 1st issue may be easily distinguished by the figures of value which appear on the extreme left of the design.

90 "Solidarity of the People"

1970. 1st Anniv of May 25th Revolution (2nd issue).

297 **90** 2 p. brown, green and red . 15 10
298 4 p. blue, green and red . . 35 15
299 65 m. green, blue and red . 50 25

91 Map of Egypt, Libya and Sudan

92 I.E.Y. Emblem

1971. 1st Anniv of Tripoli Charter.

300 **91** 2 p. green, black and red . 20 10

1971. International Education Year.

301 **92** 2 p. multicoloured 15 10
302 4 p. multicoloured 30 10
303 65 m. multicoloured 45 20

93 Laurel and Bayonets on Star

94 Emblems of Arab League and Sudan Republic

1971. 2nd Anniv of 25th May Revolution.

304 **93** 2 p. black, green & yell . . 15 10
305 4 p. black, green and blue . 35 15
306 10½ p. black, green & grey . 60 35

1972. 25th Anniv of Arab League.

307 **94** 2 p. black, yellow & green 15 10
308 4 p. multicoloured . . . 35 15
309 10½ p. multicoloured . . . 70 35

95 U.N. Emblem and Text

96 Cogwheel Emblem

1972. 25th Anniv of United Nations.

310 **95** 2 p. green, orange & red . 15 10
311 4 p. blue, orange & red . . 35 15
312 10½ p. black, orge & red . 70 40

1972. World Standards Day (14.10.71).

313 **96** 2 p. multicoloured 15 10
314 4 p. multicoloured 40 20
315 10½ p. multicoloured . . . 85 55

97 Sudanese Arms and Pres. Nemery

1972. Presidential Elections.

316 **97** 2 p. multicoloured 15 10
317 4 p. multicoloured 35 15
318 10½ p. multicoloured . . . 70 40

98 Arms and Emblem

1972. Socialist Union's Founding Congress (January, 1972).

319 **98** 2 p. black, yellow & blue . 10 10
320 4 p. mauve, yellow & black 20 15
321 10½ p. black, yellow & grn 65 25

99 Airmail Envelope and A.P.U. Emblem

1972. 10th Anniv of African Postal Union (1971).

322 **99** 2 p. multicoloured 10 10
323 4 p. multicoloured 20 15
324 10½ p. multicoloured . . . 80 30

100 Provincial Emblems

101 Emperor Haile Selassie of Ethiopia

1973. National Unity.

325 **100** 2 p. multicoloured 10 10
326 – 4 p. brown and black . . 20 10
327 – 10½ p. green, orange & sil 80 35

DESIGNS—HORIZ: 4 p. Revolutionary Council. VERT: 10½ p. Entwined trees.

1973. 80th Birthday of Emperor Haile Selassie.

328 **101** 2 p. multicoloured 20 15
329 4 p. multicoloured 50 20
330 10½ p. multicoloured . . . 1·10 45

102 President Nasser

104 Scout Emblem

103 Ancient Gateway

1973. 3rd Death Anniv of Pres. Nasser.

331 **102** 2 p. black 10 10
332 4 p. black and green . . . 20 10
333 $10\frac{1}{2}$ p. black and violet . . 65 35

1973. 10th Anniv of World Food Programme.

334 **103** 2 p. multicoloured 10 10
335 4 p. multicoloured 20 10
336 $10\frac{1}{2}$ p. multicoloured . . . 80 45

1973. World Scout Conference, Nairobi and Addis Ababa.

337 **104** 2 p. multicoloured 30 10
338 4 p. multicoloured 45 20
339 $10\frac{1}{2}$ p. multicoloured . . . 95 55

105 Interpol Emblem

1974. 50th Anniv of International Criminal Police Organization (Interpol).

340 **105** 2 p. multicoloured 10 10
341 4 p. multicoloured 30 15
342 $10\frac{1}{2}$ p. multicoloured . . . 70 35

106 K.S.M. Building, Khartoum University

107 African Postal Union Emblem

1974. 50th Anniv of Faculty of Medicine, Khartoum University.

343 **106** 2 p. multicoloured 15 10
344 4 p. green, brown & red . 35 10
345 $10\frac{1}{2}$ p. red, brown & grn . 70 45

1974. Centenary of Universal Postal Union. Multicoloured.

346 2 p. Type **107** 10 10
347 4 p. Arab Postal Union emblem 20 15
348 $10\frac{1}{2}$ p. Universal Postal Union emblem 80 35

108 A. A. Latif and A. F. Elmaz (revolution leaders)

1975. 50th Anniv of 1924 Revolution.

349 **108** $2\frac{1}{2}$ p. green and blue . . . 10 10
350 4 p. red and blue 20 10
351 $10\frac{1}{2}$ p. brown and blue . . 80 35

109 Bank and Commemorative Emblems

1975. 10th Anniv of African Development Bank.

352 **109** $2\frac{1}{2}$ p. multicoloured . . . 10 10
353 4 p. multicoloured 20 10
354 $10\frac{1}{2}$ p. multicoloured . . . 80 35

110 Earth Station and Camel Postman

1976. Inauguration of Satellite Earth Station.

355 **110** $2\frac{1}{2}$ p. multicoloured . . . 15 10
356 4 p. multicoloured . . . 30 15
357 $10\frac{1}{2}$ p. multicoloured . . 65 35

111 Woman, Flag and IWY Emblem

1976. International Women's Year.

358 **111** $2\frac{1}{2}$ p. multicoloured . . . 10 10
359 4 p. multicoloured . . . 30 15
360 $10\frac{1}{2}$ p. multicoloured . . 70 35

112 Arms of Sudan and "Gold Medal"

113 "Unity"

1976. Olympic Games, Montreal.

361 **112** $2\frac{1}{2}$ p. multicoloured . . . 40 10
362 4 p. multicoloured . . . 45 20
363 $10\frac{1}{2}$ p. multicoloured . . 1·10 55

1977. 5th Anniv of National Unity.

364 **113** $2\frac{1}{2}$ p. red, black and blue 10 10
365 4 p. red, black and green 20 15
366 $10\frac{1}{2}$ p. red, black & brown 65 30

114 Archbishop Capucci

1977. Archbishop Capucci's Imprisonment. Commemoration.

367 **114** $2\frac{1}{2}$ p. black 45 10
368 4 p. black and green . . 65 20
369 $10\frac{1}{2}$ p. black and red . . 1·10 45

115 Fair Emblem and Flags

1978. International Fair, Khartoum.

370 **115** 3 p. multicoloured . . . 20 10
371 4 p. multicoloured . . . 35 15
372 $10\frac{1}{2}$ p. multicoloured . . 55 25

117 Commemorative and A.P.U. Emblems

1978. Silver Jubilee of Arab Postal Union.

373 **117** 3 p. black, silver & red . 15 10
374 4 p. black, silver & green — 30 10
375 $10\frac{1}{2}$ p. black, silver & blue 65 35

118 Jinnah and Sudanese Flag

1978. Birth Cent of Mohammed Ali Jinnah (first Governor-General of Pakistan).

376 **118** 3 p. multicoloured 20 10
377 4 p. multicoloured 35 15
378 $10\frac{1}{2}$ p. multicoloured . . . 55 25

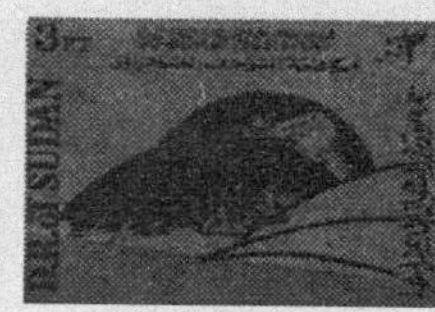

119 Desert Scene

1978. U.N. Conference on Desertification.

379 **119** 3 p. black, yellow & green 20 10
380 4 p. black, pink & green 35 15
381 $10\frac{1}{2}$ p. black, brown & grn 85 45

120 Lion God Apedemek and O.A.U. Emblem

121 Sudanese Flag

1978. 15th African Summit Conference, Khartoum.

382 **120** 3 p. black, yellow & purple 15 10
383 4 p. black, yellow & blue . 30 15
384 $10\frac{1}{2}$ p. black, yellow & grn 55 30

1979. 10th Anniv of May Revolution.

385 **121** $3\frac{1}{2}$ p. multicoloured 15 10
386 6 p. multicoloured 35 15
387 13 p. multicoloured . . . 60 30

122 I.B.E. and U.N.E.S.C.O. Emblems

123 I.Y.C. Emblem and Hands carrying Child

1980. 50th Anniv of International Bureau of Education. (1979).

388 **122** $4\frac{1}{2}$ p. black and orange . . 20 15
389 8 p. black and green . . 45 25
390 $15\frac{1}{2}$ p. black and blue . . . 90 40

1980. International Year of the Child (1979).

391 **123** $4\frac{1}{2}$ p. multicoloured 20 15
392 8 p. multicoloured 40 25
393 $15\frac{1}{2}$ p. multicoloured . . . 70 40

124 National Flag, Arms and Sudanese Warrior

1982. 25th Anniv of Independence.

396 **124** 60 m. multicoloured . . . 20 10
397 120 m. multicoloured . . . 45 20
398 250 m. multicoloured . . . 90 45

125 Hands reaching for F.A.O. Emblem on Map of Sudan

1983. World Food Day.

399 **125** 60 m. blue, green & blk . 20 10
400 – 120 m. green, black & red 45 20
401 – 250 m. green, black & red 90 45

DESIGNS: 120 m. F.A.O. emblem, crops and cattle; 250 m. Emblem, crops and cattle on map of Sudan.

126 Commission Emblem

127 Warrior on Horseback

1984. 25th Anniv of Economic Commission for Africa.

402 **126** 10 p. lilac and silver . . . 20 15
403 25 p. blue and silver . . . 55 35
404 40 p. green and silver . . 1·00 60

1984. Centenary of Shaykan Battle, Kordofan.

405 **127** 10 p. multicoloured . . . 20 15
406 25 p. multicoloured . . . 55 35
407 40 p. multicoloured . . . 90 50

128 Sudan Olympic Committee Emblem

129 Emblem and Flags

1984. First Olympic Week.

408 **128** 10 p. multicoloured . . . 20 15
409 25 p. multicoloured . . . 60 30
410 40 p. multicoloured . . . 1·10 55

1984. 2nd Anniv of Sudan–Egypt Co-operation Treaty.

411 **129** 10 p. multicoloured . . . 20 15
412 25 p. multicoloured . . . 55 35
413 40 p. multicoloured . . . 90 50

130 Institute Emblem

131 Map and Broken Chain

1985. 50th Anniv of Bakht Erruda Teacher Training Institute, Edduein Town.

414 **130** 10 p. multicoloured . . . 20 15
415 25 p. multicoloured . . . 55 35
416 40 p. multicoloured . . . 90 50

1986. 1st Anniv of 6th April Rising.

417 **131** 5 p. black, green & brn . 10 10
418 25 p. black, green & bl . 55 30
419 40 p. black, green & brn . 90 45

132 Fishermen hauling in Nets

1988. World Food Day (1986).

420 **132** 25 p. black, silver and brown 30 15
421 – 30 p. green and black . . 35 15
422 – 50 p. multicoloured . . . 55 35
423 – 75 p. black, deep blue and blue 80 45
424 – 300 p. blue, black and silver 3·00 1·40

DESIGNS—VERT: 30 p. Two fishes. HORIZ: 50 p. Plant and globe; 75 p. Outline of fish and waves; 300 p. Shoal of fish.

133 Mother breastfeeding Baby

134 Emblem

1988. Child Health Campaign.

426	133	50 p. black and mauve	55	20
427	–	75 p. multicoloured	85	35
428	–	100 p. multicoloured	1·10	45
429	–	150 p. multicoloured	1·60	65

DESIGNS—HORIZ: No. 427, Mother spoon-feeding child; 428, Child being given oral vaccination; 429, Children on scales.

1988. 30th Anniv of Sudan Red Crescent.

431	134	40 p. black, yellow & red	40	30
432	–	100 p. black, red & green	90	60
433	–	150 p. black, red & blue	1·25	80

DESIGNS: 100 p. Candle; 150 p. Figure with crescent on head.

135 Anniversary Emblem

1988. 75th Anniv of Bank of Khartoum. Mult.

434		40 p. Type **135**	40	20
435		100 p. Bubbles and medal	90	45
436		150 p. Inscription and emblem	1·25	65

136 Plough 137 Emblem

1988. World Food Day. The Small Farmer. Multicoloured.

437		40 p. Type **136**	40	20
438		100 p. Farmer ploughing	90	45
439		150 p. Farmer drawing water from river	1·25	65

1989. "Freedom of Palestine".

440	137	100 p. multicoloured	50	20
441		150 p. multicoloured	80	35
442		200 p. multicoloured	95	55

138 Crowd of Youths 139 Emblem

1989. Palestinian "Intifada" Movement.

443	138	100 p. multicoloured	50	20
444		150 p. multicoloured	80	35
445		200 p. multicoloured	95	55

1989. 25th Anniv of African Development Bank.

446	139	100 p. green, blk & silver	50	20
447		150 p. blue, black & silver	80	35
448		200 p. purple, blk & silver	95	55

140 Map 141 Leopard

1990. 34th Anniv of Independence.

449	140	50 p. blue and yellow	20	10
450		100 p. brown and yellow	50	20
451		150 p. mauve and yellow	80	35
452		200 p. mauve and yellow	1·00	55

1990. Mammals. Multicoloured.

453		25 p. Type **141**	15	10
454		50 p. African elephant	35	20
455		75 p. Giraffe (vert)	45	35
456		100 p. White rhinoceros	60	45
457		125 p. Addax (vert)	65	55

142 Zande Hornbill 146 Flag

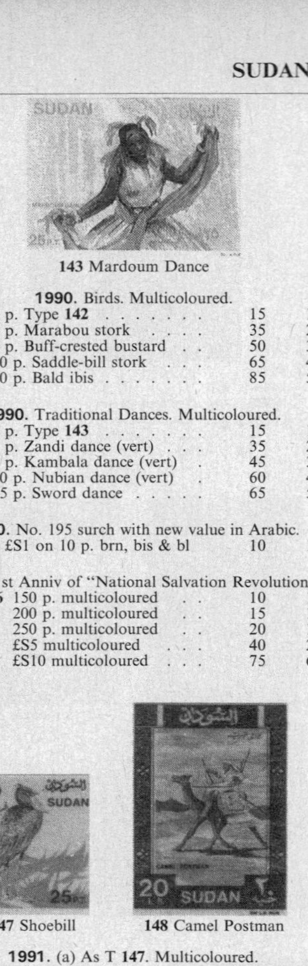

143 Mardoum Dance

1990. Birds. Multicoloured.

458		25 p. Type **142**	15	10
459		50 p. Marabou stork	35	20
460		75 p. Buff-crested bustard	50	35
461		100 p. Saddle-bill stork	65	45
462		150 p. Bald ibis	85	55

1990. Traditional Dances. Multicoloured.

463		25 p. Type **143**	15	10
464		50 p. Zandi dance (vert)	35	20
465		75 p. Kambala dance (vert)	45	35
466		100 p. Nubian dance (vert)	60	45
467		125 p. Sword dance	65	55

1990. No. 195 surch with new value in Arabic.

468	63	£S1 on 10 p. brn, bis & bl	10	10

1991. 1st Anniv of "National Salvation Revolution".

470	146	150 p. multicoloured	10	10
471		200 p. multicoloured	15	10
472		250 p. multicoloured	20	10
473		£S5 multicoloured	40	25
474		£S10 multicoloured	75	65

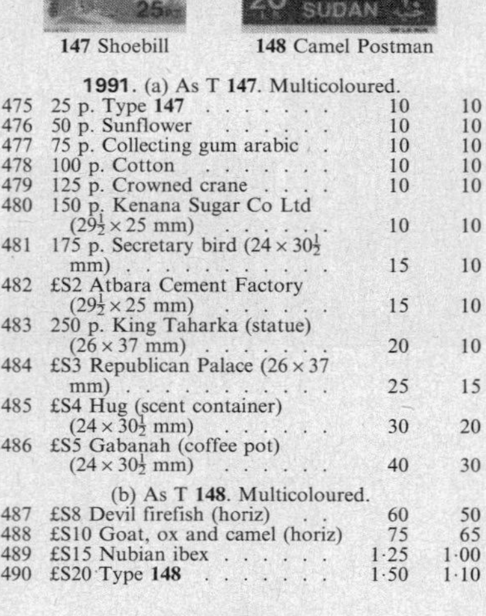

147 Shoebill 148 Camel Postman

1991. (a) As T **147**. Multicoloured.

475		25 p. Type **147**	10	10
476		50 p. Sunflower	10	10
477		75 p. Collecting gum arabic	10	10
478		100 p. Cotton	10	10
479		125 p. Crowned crane	10	10
480		150 p. Kenana Sugar Co Ltd ($29\frac{1}{2}\times25$ mm)	10	10
481		175 p. Secretary bird ($24\times30\frac{1}{2}$ mm)	15	10
482		£S2 Atbara Cement Factory ($29\frac{1}{2}\times25$ mm)	15	10
483		250 p. King Taharka (statue) (26×37 mm)	20	10
484		£S3 Republican Palace (26×37 mm)	25	15
485		£S4 Hug (scent container) ($24\times30\frac{1}{2}$ mm)	30	20
486		£S5 Gabanah (coffee pot) ($24\times30\frac{1}{2}$ mm)	40	30

(b) As T **148**. Multicoloured.

487		£S8 Devil firefish (horiz)	60	50
488		£S10 Goat, ox and camel (horiz)	75	65
489		£S15 Nubian ibex	1·25	1·00
490		£S20 Type **148**	1·50	1·10

150 Campaign Emblem

1991. Pan-African Campaign against Rinderpest.

507	150	£S1 black and green	10	10
508		£S2 violet and green	15	10
509		£S5 orange and green	40	30

OFFICIAL STAMPS

ح.س.

(O 65 "S.G.")

1962. Nos. 171/84 optd with Type O **65** (larger on 10 p. to £S10).

O185	62	5 m. blue	10	10
O186	–	10 m. purple and blue	10	10
O187	–	15 m. pur, orge & bis	10	10
O188	62	2 p. violet	10	10
O189	–	3 p. brown and green	45	10
O190	–	35 m. brown, deep brown and green	55	20
O191	–	4 p. purple, red & bl	65	20
O192	–	55 m. brown & green	90	20
O193	–	6 p. brown and blue	90	35
O194	–	8 p. green	1·10	55
O222	63	10 p. brown, blk & bl	1·10	55
O223	–	20 p. green and olive	2·75	90
O223a	–	25 p. brown and green	10	10
O224	–	50 p. green, bl & blk	4·50	2·00
O198	64	£S1 brown and green	9·00	4·50
O226	–	£S5 green and brown	65	40
O227	63	£S10 orange and blue	1·40	85

1991. Nos. 475/90 optd similarly to Type O **65**.

O491		25 p. multicoloured	10	10
O492		50 p. multicoloured	10	10
O493		75 p. multicoloured	10	10
O494		100 p. multicoloured	15	10
O495		125 p. multicoloured	15	10
O496		150 p. multicoloured	20	10
O497		175 p. multicoloured	25	15
O498		£S2 multicoloured	25	15
O499		250 p. multicoloured	35	20
O500		£S3 multicoloured	40	25
O501		£S4 multicoloured	55	35
O502		£S5 multicoloured	65	40
O503		£S8 multicoloured	1·10	65
O504		£S10 multicoloured	1·40	85
O505		£S15 multicoloured	2·00	1·25
O506		£S20 multicoloured	2·75	1·75

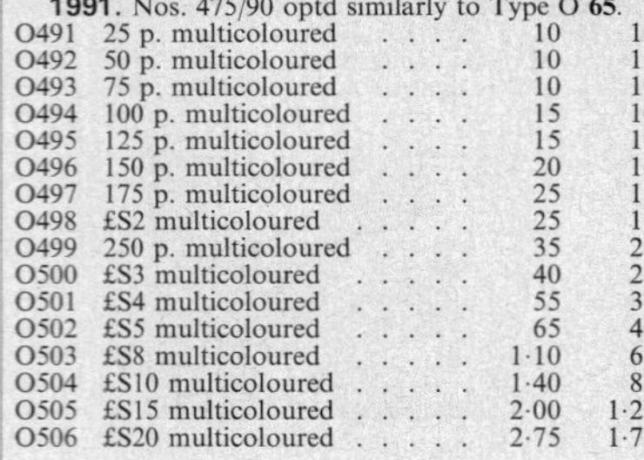

SURINAM Pt. 4; Pt. 20

A Netherlands colony on the north-east coast of South America. In December 1954 Surinam became an autonomous state within the Kingdom of the Netherlands.

Became an independent state in November 1975.

100 cents = 1 gulden

1 King William III 3

1873. No gum.

32	1	1 c. grey	1·25	1·40
33		2 c. yellow	60	55
14		$2\frac{1}{2}$ c. red	65	35
15		3 c. green	15·00	11·00
16		5 c. lilac	17·00	4·25
17		10 c. bistre	2·25	1·75
34		$12\frac{1}{2}$ c. blue	14·00	4·25
18		15 c. grey	17·00	4·50
19		20 c. green	35·00	24·00
20		25 c. blue	85·00	7·50
22		30 c. brown	29·00	25·00
23		40 c. brown	24·00	22·00
12		50 c. brown	28·00	16·00
35		1 g. grey and brown	45·00	50·00
13		$2\frac{1}{2}$ g. brown and green	60·00	55·00

The gulden values are larger.

1890.

44	3	1 c. grey	45	65
45		2 c. brown	1·10	90
46		$2\frac{1}{2}$ c. red	1·75	80
47		3 c. green	4·25	2·75
48		5 c. blue	24·00	1·40

1892. Surch **$2\frac{1}{2}$ CENT.**

53	1	$2\frac{1}{2}$ c. on 50 c. brown	£275	9·00

5 6 Queen Wilhelmina

1892. No gum.

56	5	$2\frac{1}{2}$ c. black and yellow	85	50

1892.

63	6	10 c. bistre	35·00	1·75
64		$12\frac{1}{2}$ c. mauve	45·00	4·25
65		15 c. grey	1·50	1·00
66		20 c. green	2·25	1·25
67		25 c. blue	9·00	3·25
68		30 c. brown	2·25	1·40

1898. Surch **10 CENT.**

69	1	10 c. on $12\frac{1}{2}$ c. blue	25·00	2·75
70		10 c. on 15 c. grey	60·00	50·00
71		10 c. on 20 c. green	3·00	2·75
72		10 c. on 25 c. blue	7·00	4·25
74		10 c. on 30 c. brown	3·00	3·00

1900. Stamps of Netherlands surch **SURINAME** and value.

77	13	50 c. on 50 c. red & green	24·00	6·00
78	11	1 g. on 1 g. green	18·00	12·00
79		$2\frac{1}{2}$ g. on $2\frac{1}{2}$ g. lilac	13·00	9·50

1900. Surch.

83	1	25 c. on 40 c. brown	1·75	2·25
84		25 c. on 50 c. brown	1·50	1·25
86		50 c. on 1 g. grey & brown	28·00	28·00
82		50 c. on $2\frac{1}{2}$ g. brown & green	£130	£180

11 (shaded background) 12 13

1902.

87	11	$\frac{1}{2}$ c. lilac	55	45
88		1 c. green	1·40	15
89		2 c. brown	8·50	2·50
90		$2\frac{1}{2}$ c. green	3·00	3·00
91		3 c. yellow	4·50	2·50
92		5 c. red	5·50	15
93		$7\frac{1}{2}$ c. grey	14·00	6·00
94	12	10 c. slate	10·00	70
95		$12\frac{1}{2}$ c. blue	1·40	15
96		15 c. brown	24·00	8·00
97		20 c. green	26·00	3·75
98		$22\frac{1}{2}$ c. green and brown	17·00	9·00
99		25 c. violet	18·00	1·00
100		30 c. brown	42·00	12·00
101		50 c. brown	25·00	5·50

1907.

102	13	1 g. purple	50·00	8·50
103		$2\frac{1}{2}$ g. slate	48·00	65·00

14 17

1909. Roul or perf. No gum.
104 14 5 c. red 8·50 8·00

1911. Surch with crown and value.
106 3 ½ c. on 1 c. grey 70 70
107 ½ c. on 2 c. brown 6·00 8·00
108 6 15 c. on 25 c. blue 65·00 60·00
109 20 c. on 30 c. brown 7·50 7·00
110 – 30 c. on 2½ g. on 2½ g. purple (No. 79) £130 £120

1912. No gum.
113 17 ½ c. lilac 60 60
114 2½ c. green 65 60
115 5 c. red 6·50 6·00
116 12½ c. blue 9·50 8·50

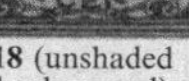

18 (unshaded background) 19

20 21

1913. With or without gum.
117 18 ½ c. lilac 20 25
118 1 c. green 20 15
119 1½ c. blue 20 15
120 2 c. brown 80 1·10
121 2½ c. green 45 10
122 3 c. yellow 50 40
123 3 c. green 2·25 2·25
125 4 c. blue 6·50 3·75
126 5 c. pink 1·00 10
127 5 c. green 1·00 75
128 5 c. violet 1·00 10
129 6 c. buff 2·25 2·25
130 6 c. red 2·00 30
131 7½ c. brown 75 15
132 7½ c. red 1·00 30
133 7½ c. yellow 7·50 7·50
134 10 c. lilac 3·25 2·75
135 10 c. red 2·75 30
136 19 10 c. red 1·25 45
137 12½ c. blue 1·50 40
138 12½ c. red 1·50 1·75
139 15 c. green 45 45
140 15 c. blue 6·00 3·75
142 20 c. blue 2·25 1·25
143 20 c. green 2·50 1·75
144 22½ c. orange 1·75 2·25
145 25 c. mauve 3·00 30
146 30 c. grey 3·75 90
147 32½ c. violet and orange 13·00 17·00
148 35 c. blue and orange 4·00 3·75
149 20 50 c. green 2·75 40
150 1 g. brown 3·75 30
151 1½ g. purple 30·00 30·00
152a 2½ g. pink 22·00 22·00

1923. Queen's Silver Jubilee.
169a 21 5 c. green 50 55
170 10 c. red 85 1·25
171 20 c. blue 2·00 2·40
172a 50 c. orange 11·00 19·00
173 1 g. purple 20·00 12·00
174 2 g. 50 grey 60·00 2·00
175 5 g. brown 75·00 £225

1925. Surch.
176 18 3 c. on 5 c. green 70 80
177 19 10 c. on 12½ c. red 1·60 1·50
180 12½ c. on 22½ c. orange 21·00 24·00
178 15 c. on 12½ c. blue 1·25 1·10
179 15 c. on 20 c. blue 1·10 1·00

1926. Postage Due stamps surch **Frankeerzegel 12½ CENT SURINAME**. (a) In three lines with bars.
181 D 6 12½ c. on 40 c. mauve and black 1·75 1·75
(b) In four lines without bars.
182 D 6 12½ c. on 40 c. lilac 25·00 25·00

28 29

1927.
183 28 10 c. red 70 30
184 12½ c. orange 1·40 1·50
185 15 c. blue 1·60 45
186 20 c. blue 1·60 40
187 21 c. brown 13·00 14·00
188 22½ c. brown 7·50 9·50
189 25 c. purple 2·50 55
190 30 c. green 2·50 90
191 35 c. sepia 2·75 3·00

1927. Green Cross Fund. Various designs incorporating green cross.
192 29 2 c. + 2 c. green & slate 1·00 1·00
193 – 5 c. + 3 c. green & purple 1·00 1·00
194 – 10 c. + 3 c. green & red 1·50 1·50

1927. Unissued Marine Insurance stamps (as Type M 22 of Netherlands but inscr "SURINAME") surch **FRANKEER ZEGEL** and value.
195 3 c. on 15 c. green 15 20
196 10 c. on 60 c. red 20 25
197 12½ c. on 75 c. brown 25 15
198 15 c. on 1 g. 50 blue 1·90 1·90
199 25 c. on 2 g. 25 brown 4·25 4·00
200 30 c. on 4½ g. black 10·00 8·50
201 50 c. on 7½ g. red 4·25 4·00

32 Indigenous Disease 33 The Good Smaritan

1928. Governor Van Heemstrastichting Medical Foundation Fund.
202 32 1½ c. + 1½ c. blue 4·25 4·25
203 2 c. + 2 c. green 4·25 4·25
204 5 c. + 3 c. violet 4·25 4·25
205 7½ c. + 2½ c. red 4·25 4·25

1929. Green Cross Fund.
206 33 1½ c. + 1½ c. green 6·00 6·00
207 2 c. + 2 c. red 6·00 6·00
208 5 c. + 3 c. blue 6·00 6·00
209 6 c. + 4 c. black 6·00 6·00

1930. No. 132 surch **6**.
210 18 6 c. on 7½ c. red 1·60 70

35 Mercury and Posthorn 37 Mother and Child

1930. Air.
276 35 10 c. red 1·40 25
212 15 c. blue 3·25 55
213 20 c. green 10 20
214 40 c. red 20 30
215 60 c. purple 40 35
216 1 g. black 1·25 1·40
217 1½ g. brown 1·40 1·50
281 2½ g. yellow 8·50 11·00
282 5 g. green £180 £275
283 10 g. bistre 22·00 56·00

1931. Air. "Dornier 10" Flight. Optd **Vlucht Do. X. 1931**.
218 35 10 c. red 18·00 15·00
219 15 c. blue 18·00 15·00
220 20 c. green 18·00 15·00
221 40 c. red 27·00 22·00
222 60 c. purple 60·00 50·00
223 1 g. black 70·00 60·00
224 1½ g. brown 70·00 65·00

1931. Child Welfare.
225 37 1½ c. + 1½ c. black 4·25 4·25
226 2 c. + 2 c. red 4·25 4·25
227 5 c. + 3 c. blue 4·25 4·25
228 6 c. + 4 c. green 4·25 4·25

37a William I (after Key) 38 "Supplication"

1933. 400th Birth Anniv of William I of Orange.
229 37a 6 c. red 4·50 1·40

1935. Bicent of Moravian Mission in Surinam.
230 38 1 c. + ½ c. brown 2·75 1·75
231 2 c. + 1 c. blue 2·40 1·75
232 – 3 c. + 1½ c. green 2·75 2·75
233 – 4 c. + 2 c. orange 2·75 2·75
234 – 5 c. + 2½ c. black 2·75 3·00
235 38 10 c. + 5 c. red 2·75 3·00
DESIGN: 3, 4, 5 c. Cross and clasped hands.

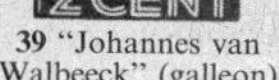

39 "Johannes van Walbeeck" (galleon) 40 Queen Wilhelmina

1936.
236 39 ½ c. brown 20 25
237 1 c. green 30 10
238 1½ c. blue 45 35
239 2 c. brown 55 25
240 2½ c. green 10 15
241 3 c. blue 50 35
242 4 c. orange 55 65
243 5 c. grey 55 20
244 6 c. red 2·25 1·60
245 7½ c. purple 10 10
246 40 10 c. red 65 10
247 12½ c. green 3·00 1·00
248 15 c. blue 1·00 5·00
249 20 c. orange 1·75 50
250 21 c. black 2·50 2·75
251 25 c. red 2·00 85
252 30 c. purple 3·00 70
253 35 c. bistre 3·50 3·25
254 50 c. green 3·50 1·40
255 1 g. blue 6·50 1·50
256 1 g. 50 brown 18·00 14·00
257 2 g. 50 red 11·00 7·00
Nos. 254/7 are larger 22 × 33 mm.

41 "Infant Support"

1936. Child Welfare.
258 41 2 c. + 1 c. green 2·50 2·50
259 3 c. + 1½ c. blue 2·50 2·50
260 5 c. + 2½ c. black 3·00 3·00
261 10 c. + 5 c. red 3·00 3·00

42 "Emancipation" 42a Surinam Girl

1938. 75th Anniv of Liberation of Slaves in Surinam and Paramaribo Girls' School Funds.
262 42 2½ c. + 2 c. green 1·60 1·40
263 42a 3 c. + 2 c. black 1·60 1·40
264 5 c. + 3 c. brown 1·75 1·60
265 7½ c. + 5 c. blue 1·75 1·60

1938. 40th Anniv of Coronation. As T **87** of Netherlands.
266 2 c. violet 35 25
267 7½ c. red 80 75
268 15 c. blue 2·25 2·00

44 Creole 44d Dutch Royal Family

1940. Social Welfare Fund.
269 44 2½ c. + 2 c. green 1·60 1·75
270 – 3 c. + 2 c. red 1·60 1·75
271 – 5 c. + 3 c. blue 1·60 1·75
272 – 7½ c. + 5 c. red 1·60 1·75
DESIGNS: 3 c. Javanese woman; 5 c. Hindu woman; 7½ c. Indian woman.

1941. Prince Bernhard and "Spitfire" Funds. As T **69** of Netherlands Indies.
273 7½ c. + 7½ c. blue and orange 2·00 2·75
274 15 c. + 15 c. blue and red 2·10 2·75
275 1 g. + 1 g. blue and grey 15·00 20·00

1941. As T **94** of Netherlands.
342 12½ c. blue 25 20
284 15 c. blue 11·00 6·00

1942. Red Cross. Surch with red cross and new values.
289 39 2 c. + 2 c. brown (post) 1·00 1·75
291 2½ c. + 2 c. green 1·00 1·75
292 7½ c. + 5 c. purple 1·00 1·75
293 35 10 c. + 5 c. red (air) 2·75 4·25

1943. Birth of Princess Margriet.
294 44d 2½ c. orange 20 40
295 7½ c. red 20 15
296 15 c. black 1·40 1·50
297 40 c. blue 1·75 1·75

1945. Surch.
298 39 ½ c. on 1 c. green 10 20
299 1½ c. on 7½ c. purple 10 20
300 2½ c. on 7½ c. purple 1·75 2·25
301 40 2½ c. on 10 c. red 85 20
302 5 c. on 10 c. red 60 45
303 7½ c. on 10 c. red 65 45

1945. Air. Surch.
304 35 22½ c. on 60 c. purple 35 60
305 1 g. on 2½ g. yellow 13·00 13·00
306 5 g. on 10 g. bistre 17·00 18·00

1945. National Welfare Fund. Surch **CENT/ VOOR HET/ NATIONAAL/ STEUNFONDS** and premium.
307 49 7½ c. + 5 c. orange 7·00 8·00
308 50 15 c. + 10 c. brown 2·00 1·75
309 20 c. + 15 c. green 2·00 1·75
310 22½ c. + 20 c. grey 2·00 1·75
311 40 c. + 35 c. red 2·00 1·75
312 60 c. + 50 c. violet 2·00 1·75

49 Sugar-cane Train

50 Queen Wilhelmina 51 53 Star

1945.
313 – 1 c. red 50 50
314 – 1½ c. red 1·00 1·00
315 – 2 c. violet 45 35
316 – 2½ c. brown 45 35
317 – 3 c. green 1·00 50
318 – 4 c. brown 95 55
319 – 5 c. blue 1·75 45
320 – 6 c. olive 1·60 1·25
321 49 7½ c. orange 2·75 75
322 50 10 c. blue 1·25 10
323 15 c. brown 1·50 20
324 20 c. green 2·50 15
325 22½ c. grey 3·00 70
326 25 c. red 8·00 3·25
327 30 c. olive 7·50 40
328 35 c. blue 13·00 6·00
329 40 c. red 7·50 25
330 50 c. red 7·50 20
331 60 c. violet 7·50 65
332 51 1 g. brown 10·00 25
333 1 g. 50 lilac 90 60
334 2 g. 50 brown 16·00 70
335 5 g. red 35·00 9·50
336 10 g. orange 60·00 15·00
DESIGNS—As Type **49**: 1 c. Bauxite mine, Moengo; 1½ c. Natives in canoes; 2 c. Native and stream; 2½ c. Road in Coronie; 3 c. River Surinam near Berg en Dal; 4 c. Government Square, Paramaribo; 5 c. Mining gold; 6 c. Street in Paramaribo.

1946. Air. Anti-tuberculosis Fund. Surch **LUCHT POST** and premium.
340 50 10 c. + 40 c. blue 1·00 1·00
341 15 c. + 60 c. brown 1·00 1·00

1947. Anti-Leprosy Fund.
343 53 7½ c. + 12½ c. orge (post) 2·50 2·25
344 12½ c. + 37½ c. blue 2·50 2·25
345 22½ c. + 27½ c. grey (air) 2·50 2·25
346 27½ c. + 47½ c. green 2·50 2·25

1948. Types of Netherlands inscr "SURINAME". (a) Numeral type as T **118**.
347 1 c. red 10 10
348 1½ c. purple 10 20
349 2 c. violet 25 10
350 2½ c. green 1·25 15
351 3 c. green 15 10
352 4 c. brown 20 15
353 5 c. blue 1·25 10
354 7½ c. orange 2·75 1·10
(b) Portrait of Queen Wilhelmina as T **119**.
355 5 c. blue 35 15
356 6 c. green 90 65
357 7½ c. red 35 20
358 10 c. blue 55 10
359 12½ c. blue 1·00 90
360 15 c. brown 1·40 30
361 17½ c. purple 1·60 1·25
362 20 c. green 1·25 15
363 22½ c. blue 1·25 65
364 25 c. red 1·25 25
365 27½ c. red 1·25 20
366 30 c. green 1·60 15
367 37½ c. brown 2·50 2·00
368 40 c. purple 1·75 25
369 50 c. orange 1·90 25
370 60 c. violet 2·00 35
371 70 c. black 2·25 50

1948. Queen Wilhelmina's Golden Jubilee. As T **125** of Netherlands.
372 7½ c. orange 65 60
373 12½ c. blue 65 60

1948. Accession of Queen Juliana. As T **126** of Netherlands.
374 7½ c. orange 2·00 2·25
375 12½ c. blue 2·00 2·25

55 Women of Netherlands and Surinam

56 Marie Curie

1949. Air. 1st K.L.M. Flight on Paramaribo–Amsterdam Service.
376 **55** 27½ c. brown . . . . 4·75 2·50

1949. 75th Anniv of U.P.U. As T **50** of Netherlands Antilles.
377 7½ c. red . . . . 4·50 2·25
378 27½ c. blue . . . . 4·50 1·75

1950. Cancer Research Fund.
379 **56** 7½ c. + 7½ c. violet . . . . 12·50 7·50
380 – 7½ c. + 22½ c. green . . . . 12·50 7·50
381 – 27½ c. + 12½ c. blue . . . . 12·50 7·50
382 **56** 27½ c. + 97½ c. brown . . . 12·50 7·50
PORTRAIT: Nos. 380/1, Wilhelm Rontgen.

1950 Surch **1 Cent** and bars.
383 **49** 1 c. on 7½ c. orange . . . . 1·00 1·60

1951. Portrait of Queen Juliana as T **129/30** of Netherlands.
395 **129** 10 c. blue 35 10
396 15 c. brown 95 25
397 20 c. turquoise . . . . . . 2·25 10
398 25 c. red . . . . 1·50 35
399 27½ c. lake . . . . 1·40 15
400 30 c. green . . . . 1·40 30
401 35 c. olive . . . . 1·60 1·00
402 40 c. mauve . . . . 1·75 35
403 50 c. orange . . . . 2·25 35
404 **130** 1 g. brown . . . . 24·00 30

1953. Netherlands Flood Relief Fund. Nos. 374/5 surch **STORMRAMP NEDERLAND 1953** and premium.
405 12½ c. + 7½ c. on 7½ c. orange . . 2·25 2·25
406 20 c. + 10 c. on 12½ c. blue . . 2·25 2·25

60 Fisherman

61 Surinam Stadium

1953.
407 – 2 c. brown 10 10
408 **60** 2½ c. green 25 20
409 – 5 c. grey 25 10
410 – 6 c. blue . . . . 1·50 1·10
411 – 7½ c. violet 15 10
412 – 10 c. red 20 10
413 – 12½ c. blue . . . . 1·60 1·25
414 – 15 c. red . . . . 1·75 30
415 – 17½ c. brown . . . . 3·00 1·75
416 – 20 c. green 45 10
417 – 25 c. green . . . . 2·25 70
DESIGNS—HORIZ: 2 c. Native shooting fish; 10 c. Woman gathering fruit. VERT: 5 c. Bauxite mine; 6 c. Log raft; 7½ c. Ploughing with buffalo; 12½ c. "Kwie kwie" fish; 15 c. Blue and yellow macaw; 17½ c. Nine-banded armadillo; 20 c. Poling pirogue; 25 c. Iguana.

1953. Sports Week.
419 **61** 10 c. + 5 c. red . . . . 8·50 7·00
420 15 c. + 7½ c. brown . . . 8·50 7·00
421 30 c. + 15 c. green . . . 8·50 7·00

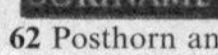

62 Posthorn and Globe

63 Native Children and Youth Centre

1954. Air. 25th Anniv of Surinam Airlines.
422 **62** 15 c. blue . . . . 1·10 1·00

1954. Child Welfare Fund.
423 **63** 7½ c. + 3 c. purple . . . . 5·50 4·50
424 10 c. + 5 c. green . . . . 5·50 4·50
425 15 c. + 7½ c. brown . . . 5·50 4·50
426 30 c. + 15 c. blue . . . . 5·50 4·50

1954. Ratification of Statute for the Kingdom. As T **158** of Netherlands.
427 7½ c. purple 50 60

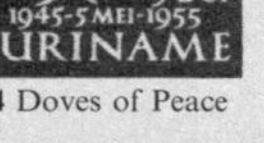

64 Doves of Peace

65 Gathering Bananas

1955. 10th Anniv of Liberation of Netherlands and War Victims Relief Fund.
428 **64** 7½ c. + 3½ c. red . . . . . 2·50 2·50
429 15 c. + 8 c. blue . . . . . 2·50 2·50

1955. 4th Caribbean Tourist Assn Meeting.
430 **65** 2 c. green . . . . 1·40 1·10
431 – 7½ c. yellow . . . . 2·00 1·75
432 – 10 c. brown . . . . 2·00 1·75
433 – 15 c. blue . . . . 2·00 1·75
DESIGNS: 7½ c. Pounding rice; 10 c. Preparing cassava; 15 c. Fishing.

66 Caduceus and Globe

67 Queen Juliana and Prince Bernhard

1955. Surinam Fair.
434 **66** 5 c. blue 35 25

1955. Royal Visit.
435 **67** 7½ c. + 2½ c. olive 50 50

68 Flags and Caribbean Map

69 Facade of 19th-century Theatre

1956. 10th Anniv of Caribbean Commission.
447 **68** 10 c. blue and red 25 25

1958. 120th Anniv of "Thalia" Amateur Dramatic Society.
448 **69** 7½ c. + 3 c. blue & black . . 40 45
449 – 10 c. + 5 c. purple & blk . . 40 45
450 – 15 c. + 7½ c. green & blk . . 40 45
451 – 20 c. + 10 c. orange & blk . . 40 45
DESIGNS: 10 c. Early 20th-century theatre; 15 c. Modern theatre; 20 c. Performance on stage.

1959. No. 399 surch **8 C.**
452 8 c. on 27½ c. red 15 15

71 Queen Juliana

72 Symbolic Plants

1959.
453 **71** 1 g. purple . . . . 1·40 10
454 1 g. 50 brown . . . . . . 2·25 45
455 2 g. 50 red . . . . 3·00 25
456 5 g. blue . . . . 6·00 25

1959. 5th Anniv of Ratification of Statute for the Kingdom.
457 **72** 20 c. multicoloured . . . 2·00 1·25

73 Wooden Utensils

74 Boeing 707

1960. Surinam Handicrafts.
458 **73** 8 c. + 4 c. multicoloured . 80 80
459 – 10 c. + 5 c. red, blue and brown 80 80
460 – 15 c. + 7 c. grn, brn & red 80 80
461 – 20 c. + 10 c. multicoloured 80 80
DESIGNS: 10 c. Indian chief's headgear; 15 c. Clay pottery; 20 c. Wooden stool.

1960. Opening of Zanderij Airport Building.
462 – 8 c. blue . . . . 1·25 1·25
463 – 10 c. green . . . . 1·75 1·50
464 – 15 c. red . . . . 1·75 1·50
465 – 20 c. lilac . . . . 1·90 1·75
466 **74** 40 c. brown . . . . 2·75 2·75
DESIGNS: 8 c. Charles Lindbergh's seaplane, 1929; 10 c. Fokker "De Snip", 1934; 15 c. Cessna 170A, 1954; 20 c. Lockheed Super Constellation 1957.

75 "Uprooted Tree"

76 Surinam Flag

1960. World Refugee Year.
467 **75** 8 c. + 4 c. green & brown . 15 20
468 10 c. + 5 c. green & blue . 15 20

1960. Freedom Day. Multicoloured.
469 10 c. Type **76** 40 40
470 15 c. Coat-of-arms (30 × 26 mm) 40 40

77 Putting the Shot

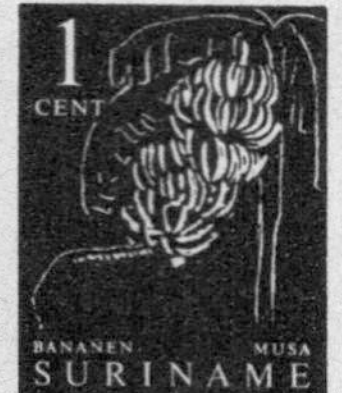

78 Bananas

1960. Olympic Games, Rome.
471 **77** 8 c. + 4 c. brown, black and grey 60 60
472 – 10 c. + 5 c. brown, black and orange 75 75
473 – 15 c. + 7 c. brown, black and violet 80 80
474 – 20 c. + 10 c. brown, black and blue 80 80
475 – 40 c. + 20 c. brown, black and green 80 80
DESIGNS: 10 c. Basketball; 15 c. Running; 20 c. Swimming; 40 c. Football.

1961. Local Produce.
476 **78** 1 c. yellow, black & green 10 10
477 – 2 c. green, black & yellow 10 10
478 – 3 c. brown, black & choc 10 10
479 – 4 c. yellow, black and blue . 10 10
480 – 5 c. red, black and brown 10 10
481 – 6 c. yellow, black & grn . . 10 10
482 – 8 c. yellow, black and blue 10 10
DESIGNS: 2 c. Citrus fruit; 3 c. Cocoa; 4 c. Sugar-cane; 5 c. Coffee; 6 c. Coconuts; 8 c. Rice.

79 Treasury

80 Commander Shepard, Rocket and Globe

1961. Surinam Buildings. Multicoloured.
483 10 c. Type **79** 15 10
484 15 c. Court of Justice 20 10
485 20 c. Concordia Masonic Lodge 25 15
486 25 c. Neve Shalom Synagogue 65 30
487 30 c. Lock Gate, Nieuw Amsterdam . . . . 1·40 1·25
488 35 c. Government Building . . 1·40 1·40
489 40 c. Governor's House . . . 65 50
490 50 c. Legislative Assembly . . 70 25
491 60 c. Old Dutch Reform Church 80 75
492 70 c. Fort Zeelandia (1790) . . 1·00 1·00
The 10, 15, 20 and 30 c. are vert and the rest horiz.

1961. Air. "Man in Space". Multicoloured.
493 15 c. Globe and astronaut in capsule 70 75
494 20 c. Type **80** 70 75

81 Girl Scout saluting

82 Dag Hammarskjold

1961. Caribbean Girl Scout Jamborette. Mult.
495 8 c. + 2 c. Semaphoring (horiz) 45 35
496 10 c. + 3 c. Type **81** 45 35
497 15 c. + 4 c. Brownies around a "toadstool" (horiz) 45 35
498 20 c. + 5 c. Campfire sing-song 45 45
499 25 c. + 6 c. Lighting fire (horiz) 45 45

1962. Dag Hammarskjold Memorial Issue.
500 **82** 10 c. black and blue . . . 10 15
501 20 c. black and violet . . . 15 20

1962. Royal Silver Wedding. As T **187** of Netherlands.
502 20 c. green 30 25

83 "Hibiscus rosa sinensis"

84 Campaign Emblem

1962. Red Cross Fund. Flowers in natural colours. Background colours given.
503 **83** 8 c. + 4 c. olive 30 30
504 – 10 c. + 5 c. blue 30 30
505 – 15 c. + 6 c. brown 30 30
506 – 20 c. + 10 c. violet 30 30
507 – 25 c. + 12 c. turquoise . . 30 30
FLOWERS: 10 c. "Caesalpinia pulcherrima"; 15 c. "Heliconia psittacorum"; 20 c. "Lochnera rosea"; 25 c. "Ixora macrothyrsa".

1962. Malaria Eradication.
508 **84** 8 c. red 15 15
509 10 c. blue 15 20

85 Stoelmans Guesthouse

1962. Opening of New Hotels. Multicoloured.
510 10 c. Type **85** 30 30
511 15 c. Torarica Hotel 30 30

86 Sisters' Residence

87 Wildfowl

1962. Nunnery and Hospital of the Deaconesses. Multicoloured.
512 10 c. Type **86** 30 30
513 20 c. Hospital building . . . 30 30

1962. Animal Protection Fund.
514 **87** 2 c. + 1 c. red and blue . 10 10
515 – 8 c. + 2 c. red and black . 20 20
516 – 10 c. + 3 c. black & green 20 20
517 – 15 c. + 4 c. black and red 25 25
ANIMALS: 8 c. Dog; 10 c. Donkey; 15 c. Horse.

88 Emblem in Hands

1963. Freedom from Hunger.
518 **88** 10 c. red 15 15
519 – 20 c. blue 15 15
DESIGN—VERT: 20 c. Tilling the land.

89 "Freedom"

1963. Centenary of Abolition of Slavery in Dutch West Indies.
520 **89** 10 c. black and red 15 15
521 20 c. black and green . . . 15 15

90 Indian Girl

91 North American X-15

1963. Child Welfare Fund.
522 **90** 8 c. + 3 c. green 10 10
523 – 10 c. + 4 c. brown 10 10
524 – 15 c. + 10 c. blue 25 25
525 – 20 c. + 10 c. red 25 25
526 – 40 c. + 20 c. purple . . . 35 35

PORTRAITS OF CHILDREN: 10 c. Bush negro; 15 c. Hindustani; 20 c. Indonesian; 40 c. Chinese.

1963. 150th Anniv of Kingdom of the Netherlands. As T **199** of Netherlands but smaller, size 26 × 26 mm.
528 10 c. black, bistre and blue . . 10 10

1964. Aeronautical and Astronomical Foundation, Surinam.
529 3 c. + 2 c. sepia and lake . . 15 15
530 8 c. + 4 c. sepia, indigo & bl 20 20
531 10 c. + 5 c. sepia and green . 20 20
532 15 c. + 7 c. sepia and brown . 20 20
533 20 c. + 10 c. sepia & violet . 25 25
DESIGNS: 3, 15 c. Type **91**; 8 c. Foundation flag; 10, 20 c. Agena B-Ranger rocket.

92 "Camp Fire" **93** Skipping

1964. Scout Jamborette, Paramaribo, and 40th Anniv of Surinam Boy Scouts Association.
534 **92** 3 c. + 1 c. light yellow, yellow and bistre 15 15
535 8 c. + 4 c. brown, blue and deep blue 15 15
536 10 c. + 5 c. brown, red and deep red 15 15
537 20 c. + 10 c. brown, green and blue 20 20

1964. Child Welfare.
538 **93** 8 c. + 3 c. blue 10 10
539 – 10 c. + 4 c. red 10 10
540 – 15 c. + 9 c. green 10 10
541 – 20 c. + 10 c. purple . . . 15 15
DESIGNS: 10 c. Children swinging; 15 c. Child on scooter; 20 c. Child with hoop.

94 Crown and Wreath **95** Expectant Mother ("Prenatal Care")

1964. 10th Anniv of Statute of the Kingdom.
543 **94** 25 c. multicoloured 20 20

1965. 50th Anniv of "Het Groene Kruis" (The Green Cross).
544 **95** 4 c. + 2 c. green 15 15
545 – 10 c. + 5 c. brown & green 15 15
546 – 15 c. + 7 c. blue & green 15 15
547 – 25 c. + 12 c. violet & grn 20 20
DESIGNS: 10 c. Mother and baby ("Infant care"); 15 c. Young girl ("Child care"); 25 c. Old man ("Care in old age").

96 Abraham Lincoln **97** I.C.Y. Emblem

1965. Death Centenary of Abraham Lincoln.
548 **96** 25 c. purple and bistre . . 10 10

1965. International Co-operation Year.
549 **97** 10 c. orange and blue . . . 10 10
550 15 c. red and blue 10 10

98 Surinam Waterworks **99** Bauxite Mine, Moengo

1965. Air. Size 25 × 18 mm.
551 **98** 10 c. green 10 10
552 – 15 c. ochre 15 10
553 – 20 c. green 20 10
554 – 25 c. indigo 25 10
555 – 30 c. turquoise 25 15
556 – 35 c. red 35 20
557 – 40 c. orange 35 15
558 – 45 c. red 40 45
559 – 50 c. red 45 15
560 **98** 55 c. green 45 25
561 – 65 c. yellow 50 35
562 – 75 c. blue 55 35
DESIGNS: 15, 65 c. Brewery; 20 c. River scene; 25, 75 c. Timber yard; 30 c. Bauxite mine; 35, 50 c. Poelepantje Bridge; 40 c. Shipping; 45 c. Jetty.
For same designs but size 22 × 18 mm, see Nos. 843a/h.

1965. Opening of Brokopondo Power Station.
563 **99** 10 c. ochre 25 25
564 – 15 c. green 10 10
565 – 20 c. blue 10 10
566 – 25 c. red 15 15
DESIGNS: 15 c. Alum-earth works, Paranam; 20 c. Power station and dam, Afobaka; 25 c. Aluminium smeltery, Paranam.

100 Girl with Leopard **101** Red-breasted Blackbird

1965. Child Welfare.
567 **100** 4 c. + 4 c. black, turquoise and green 15 15
568 – 10 c. + 5 c. black, brown and light brown . . . 15 15
569 – 15 c. + 7 c. black, orange and red 15 15
570 – 25 c. + 10 c. black, blue and cobalt 15 15
DESIGNS: 10 c. Boy with monkey; 15 c. Girl with tortoise; 25 c. Boy with rabbit.

1966. Intergovernmental Committee for European Migration (I.C.E.M.) Fund. As T **215** of Netherlands.
572 10 c. + 5 c. green & black . 10 10
573 25 c. + 10 c. red and black . 15 15

1966. Birds. Multicoloured.
575 1 c. Type **101** 35 15
576 2 c. Great kiskadee 35 15
577 3 c. Silver-beaked tanager . . 35 15
578 4 c. Ruddy ground dove . . . 35 15
579 5 c. Blue-grey tanager 35 15
580 6 c. Straight-billed hermit . . 35 15
581 8 c. Turquoise tanager . . . 35 15
582 10 c. Pale-breasted thrush . . 35 15

102 Hospital Building **103** Father P. Donders

1966. Opening of Central Hospital, Paramaribo. Multicoloured.
583 10 c. Type **102** 10 10
584 15 c. Different view 10 10

1966. Centenary of Redemptorists Mission.
585 **103** 4 c. black and brown . . 10 10
586 – 10 c. black, brown & red 10 10
587 – 15 c. black and ochre . . 10 10
588 – 25 c. black and lilac . . . 15 15
DESIGNS: 10 c. Batavia Church, Coppename; 15 c. Mgr. J. B. Swinkels; 25 c. Paramaribo Cathedral.

104 Mary Magdalene and Disciples **105** "Century Tree"

1966. Easter Charity.
589 **104** 10 c. + 5 c. black, red and gold 15 15
590 15 c. + 8 c. black, violet and blue 15 15
591 20 c. + 10 c. black, yellow and blue 15 15
592 25 c. + 12 c. black, green and gold 20 20
593 30 c. + 15 c. black, blue and gold 20 20
On Nos. 590/3 the emblems at bottom left differ for each value. These represent various welfare organizations.

1966. Centenary of Surinam Parliament.
594 **105** 25 c. black, green & red . . 10 10
595 30 c. black, red & green . . 10 10

106 TV Mast, Eye and Globe **107** Boys with Bamboo Gun

1966. Inauguration of Surinam Television Service.
596 **106** 25 c. red and blue 10 10
597 30 c. red and brown 10 10

1966. Child Welfare. Multicoloured.
598 10 c. + 5 c. Type **107** 10 10
599 15 c. + 8 c. Boy pouring liquid on another 15 15
600 20 c. + 10 c. Children rejoicing 10 10
601 25 c. + 12 c. Children on merry-go-round 15 15
602 30 c. + 15 c. Children decorating room 20 20
The designs symbolise New Year's Eve, the End of Lent, Liberation Day, Queen's Birthday and Christmas respectively.

108 Mining Bauxite, 1916 **109** "The Good Samaritan"

1966. 50th Anniv of Surinam Bauxite Industry.
604 **108** 20 c. black, orange & yell . 25 10
605 – 25 c. black, orange & blue 25 10
DESIGN: 25 c. Modern bauxite plant.

1967. Easter Charity. Printed in black, background colours given.
606 **109** 10 c. + 5 c. yellow 10 10
607 – 15 c. + 8 c. blue 15 15
608 – 20 c. + 10 c. ochre . . . 15 15
609 – 25 c. + 12 c. pink 20 20
610 – 30 c. + 15 c. green 20 20
DESIGNS: 15 to 30 c. Various episodes illustrating the parable of "The Good Samaritan".

110 Central Bank

1967. 10th Anniv of Surinam Central Bank.
611 **110** 10 c. black and yellow . . 10 10
612 – 25 c. black and lilac . . . 10 10
DESIGN: 25 c. Aerial view of Central Bank.

111 Amelia Earhart and Lockheed 10E Electra Airplane **112** Siva Nataraja and Ballerina's Foot

1967. 30th Anniv of Visit of Amelia Earhart to Surinam.
613 **111** 20 c. red and yellow . . . 15 10
614 25 c. green and yellow . . 15 10

1967. 20th Anniv of Surinam Cultural Centre. Multicoloured.
615 10 c. Type **112** 10 10
616 25 c. "Bashi-Lele" mask and violin scroll 10 10

113 Fort Zeelandia, Paramaribo (c. 1670) **114** Stilt-walking

1967. 300th Anniv of Treaty of Breda. Multicoloured.
617 10 c. Type **113** 15 15
618 20 c. Nieuw Amsterdam (c. 1660) 20 20
619 25 c. Breda Castle (c. 1667) . . 20 20

1967. Child Welfare. Multicoloured.
620 10 c. + 5 c. Type **114** 10 10
621 15 c. + 8 c. Playing marbles . . 20 20
622 20 c. + 10 c. Playing dibs . . 20 20
623 25 c. + 12 c. Kite-flying . . . 20 20
624 30 c. + 15 c. "Cooking" game 25 25

115 "Cross of Ashes" **116** W.H.O. Emblem

1968. Easter Charity.
626 10 c. + 5 c. grey and violet . 10 10
627 15 c. + 8 c. green and red . . 15 15
628 20 c. + 10 c. green & yellow . 20 20
629 25 c. + 12 c. black and grey 20 20
630 30 c. + 15 c. brown & yellow 20 20
DESIGNS: 10 c. Type **115** (Ash Wednesday); 15 c. Palm branches (Palm Sunday); 20 c. Cup and wafer (Maundy Thursday); 25 c. Cross (Good Friday); 30 c. Symbol of Christ (Easter).

1968. 20th Anniv of W.H.O.
631 **116** 10 c. blue and purple . . 10 10
632 25 c. violet and blue . . . 20 20

117 Chandelier, Reformed Church **119** Map of Joden Savanne

118 Missionary Shop, 1768

1968. 300th Anniv of Reformed Church, Paramaribo.
633 **117** 10 c. blue 10 10
634 – 25 c. green 15 15
DESIGN: 25 c. No. 633 reversed; chandelier on left.

1968. Bicentenary of Evangelist Brothers' Missionary Store, G. Kersten and Co.
635 **118** 10 c. black and yellow . . 10 10
636 – 25 c. black and blue . . . 15 15
637 – 30 c. black and mauve . . 15 15
DESIGNS: 25 c. Paramaribo Church and Kersten's store, 1868; 30 c. Kersten's modern store, Paramaribo.

1968. Restoration of Joden Savanne Synagogue. Multicoloured.
638 20 c. Type **119** 40 40
639 25 c. Synagogue, 1685 . . . . 40 40
640 30 c. Gravestone at Joden Savanne, dated 1733 . . . . 50 50

120 Playing Hopscotch **121** Western Hemisphere illuminated by Full Moon

1968. Child Welfare.
641 **120** 10 c. + 5 c. black & brn 10 10
642 – 15 c. + 8 c. black & blue 15 15
643 – 20 c. + 10 c. black & pink 15 15
644 – 25 c. + 12 c. black & grn 25 25
645 – 30 c. + 15 c. blk & lilac 30 30
DESIGNS: 15 c. Forming "pyramids"; 20 c. Playing ball; 25 c. Handicrafts; 30 c. Tug-of-war.

1969. Easter Charity.
647 **121** 10 c. + 5 c. blue & lt blue 25 25
648 15 c. + 8 c. grey & yellow 25 25
649 20 c. + 10 c. turq & green 30 30
650 25 c. + 12 c. brown & buff 30 30
651 30 c. + 15 c. violet & grey 30 30

122 Cayman **123** Mahatma Gandhi

1969. Opening of Surinam Zoo, Paramaribo. Multicoloured.
652 10 c. Type **122** 45 35
653 20 c. Common squirrel-monkey (vert) 45 35
654 25 c. Nine-banded armadillo 45 35

1969. Birth Centenary of Mahatma Gandhi.
655 **123** 25 c. black and red . . . 40 25

124 I.L.O. Emblem

125 Pillow Fight

1969. 50th Anniv of Int Labour Organization.
656 **124** 10 c. green and black . . 15 15
657 25 c. red and black . . . 20 20

1969. Child Welfare.
658 10 c. + 5 c. purple and blue 10 10
659 15 c. + 8 c. brown & yellow 25 25
660 20 c. + 10 c. blue and grey . 20 20
661 25 c. + 12 c. blue and pink 25 25
662 30 c. + 15 c. brown & green 25 25
DESIGNS: 10 c. Type **125**; 15 c. Eating contest; 20 c. Pole-climbing; 25 c. Sack-race; 30 c. Obstacle-race.

1969. 15th Anniv of Statute for the Kingdom. As T **240** of Netherlands.
664 25 c. multicoloured 25 25

127 "Flower"

128 "1950–1970"

1970. Easter Charity. "Wonderful Nature". Multicoloured.
665 10 c. + 5 c. Type **127** 55 55
666 15 c. + 8 c. "Butterfly" . . . 55 55
667 20 c. + 10 c. "Bird" 55 55
668 25 c. + 12 c. "Sun" 55 55
669 30 c. + 15 c. "Star" 55 55

1970. 20th Anniv of Secondary Education in Surinam.
670 **128** 10 c. yellow, green & brown 10 10
671 25 c. yellow, blue & green 15 15

129 New U.P.U. Headquarters Building

130 U.N. "Diamond"

1970. New U.P.U. Headquarters Building.
672 **129** 10 c. violet, blue & turq . 15 15
673 – 25 c. black and red . . . 20 20
DESIGN: 25 c. Aerial view of H.Q. Building.

1970. 25th Anniv of United Nations.
674 **130** 10 c. multicoloured . . . 15 15
675 25 c. multicoloured . . . 20 20

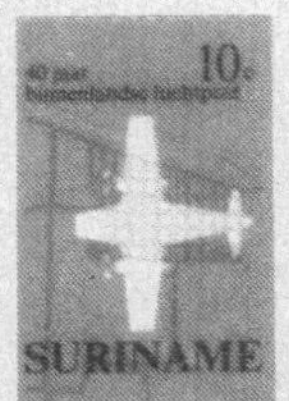
131 Aircraft over Paramaribo Town Plan

132 Football Pitch (ball in centre)

1970. "40 years of Inland Airmail Flights".
676 **131** 10 c. grey, ultram & bl . . 25 25
677 – 20 c. grey, red & yellow . 25 25
678 – 25 c. grey, red and pink . 25 25
DESIGNS: As Type **131**, but showing different background maps—20 c. Totness; 25 c. Nieuw-Nickerie.

1970. 50th Anniv of Surinam Football Association.
679 **132** 4 c. brown, yellow & black 10 10
680 – 10 c. brown, olive & black 20 20
681 – 15 c. brown, green & black 20 20
682 – 25 c. brown, green & black 30 30
DESIGNS: As Type **132**, but with ball: 10 c. in "corner"; 15 c. at side ("throw-in"); 25 c. at top ("goal").

133 Beethoven (1786)

134 Cocoi Heron

1970. Child Welfare. Birth Bicentenary of Beethoven (composer).
683 **133** 10 c. + 5 c. yellow, drab and green 75 60
684 – 15 c. + 8 c. yellow, drab and red 80 65
685 – 20 c. + 10 c. yellow, drab and blue 80 65
686 – 25 c. + 12 c. yellow, drab and orange 85 60
687 – 30 c. + 15 c. yellow, drab and violet 85 60
DESIGNS: Beethoven 15 c. 1804; 20 c. 1812; 25 c. 1814; 30 c. 1827.

1971. 25th Anniv of Netherlands–Surinam–Netherlands Antilles Air Service. Multicoloured.
689 15 c. Type **134** 65 50
690 20 c. Greater flamingo . . . 85 55
691 25 c. Scarlet macaw 95 55

135 Donkey and Palm

136 Morse Key

1971. Easter. The Bible Story. Multicoloured.
692 10 c. + 5 c. Type **135** 55 55
693 15 c. + 8 c. Cockerel 60 60
694 20 c. + 10 c. Lamb 60 60
695 25 c. + 12 c. Crown of Thorns 60 60
696 30 c. + 15 c. Sun ("The Resurrection") 60 60

1971. World Telecommunications Day. Mult.
697 15 c. Type **136** 45 45
698 20 c. Telephones 50 50
699 25 c. Lunar module and telescope 60 60
EVENTS: 15 c. First national telegraph, Washington—Baltimore, 1843; 20 c. First international telephone communication, England—Sweden, 1926; 25 c. First interplanetary television communication, Earth—Moon, 1969.

137 Prince Bernhard

138 Population Map

1971. Prince Bernhard's 60th Birthday.
700 **137** 25 c. multicoloured . . . 30 25

1971. 50th Anniv of 1st Census and Introduction of Civil Registration.
701 **138** 15 c. blue, black & red . 15 15
702 30 c. red, black & blue . 25 25
DESIGN: 30 c. "Individual" representing civil registration.

139 William Mogge's Map of Surinam

1971. 300th Anniv of First Surinam Map.
703 **139** 30 c. brown on yellow . . 65 45

140 Leap-frog

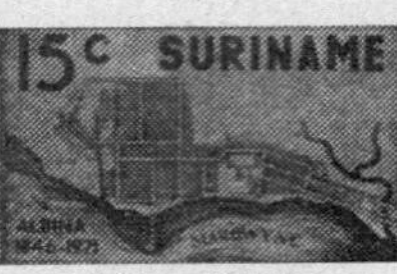
141 Plan of Albina

1971. Child Welfare. Details from Brueghel's "Children's Games". Multicoloured.
704 10 c. + 5 c. Type **140** . . . 65 65
705 15 c. + 8 c. Strewing flowers 65 65
706 20 c. + 10 c. Rolling hoop . . 65 65
707 25 c. + 12 c. Playing ball . . 70 70
708 30 c. + 15 c. Stilt-walking . . 70 70

1971. 125th Anniv of Albina Settlement.
710 **141** 15 c. black on blue . . . 30 30
711 – 20 c. black on green . . . 30 30
712 – 25 c. black on yellow . . . 30 30
DESIGNS—HORIZ: 20 c. Albina and River Marowijne. VERT: 25 c. August Kappler (naturalist and founder).

142 Drop of Water

143 Easter Candle

1972. 40th Anniv of Surinam Waterworks.
713 **142** 15 c. black and violet . . 25 25
714 – 30 c. black and blue . . 30 30
DESIGN: 30 c. Water tap.

1972. Easter Charity. Multicoloured.
715 10 c. + 5 c. Type **143** . . . 50 50
716 15 c. + 8 c. "Christ teaching the Apostles" 50 50
717 20 c. + 10 c. Hands holding cup ("Christ in Gethsemane") . . 50 50
718 25 c. + 12 c. Fishes in net ("Miracle of the Fishes") . . 50 50
719 30 c. + 15 c. Pieces of silver ("Judas's Betrayal") 50 50

144 "Eucyane bicolor"

145 Air-letter Motif

1972. Moths and Butterflies. Multicoloured.
720 15 c. Type **144** 30 15
721 20 c. Gold drop 30 15
722 25 c. Orange swallowtail . . . 40 20
723 30 c. White tailed page . . . 40 10
724 35 c. "Stalachtis calliope" . . . 60 35
725 40 c. "Stalachtis phlegia" . . . 60 25
726 45 c. Malachite 60 10
727 50 c. Spear-winged cattle heart 75 10
728 55 c. Red anartia 90 50
729 60 c. Five continent butterfly 1·00 80
730 65 c. Doris . . . . 1·00 50
731 70 c. "Nessaea obrinus" . . . 1·10 75
732 75 c. Cracker . . . . 1·00 45

1972. 50th Anniv of 1st Airmail in Surinam.
733 **145** 15 c. red and blue 20 20
734 30 c. blue and red 25 25

146 Doll and Toys (kindergarten)

147 Giant Tree

1972. Child Welfare. Multicoloured.
735 10 c. + 5 c. Type **146** 50 45
736 15 c. + 8 c. Clock and abacus (primary education) 50 45
737 20 c. + 10 c. Blocks (primary education) 50 45
738 25 c. + 12 c. Molecule complex (secondary education) . . . 55 50
739 30 c. + 15 c. Wrench and blue-print (technical education) 55 50

1972. 25th Anniv of Surinam Forestry Commission.
741 **147** 15 c. brown and yellow . . 25 25
742 – 20 c. brown, black & blue 30 30
743 – 30 c. chocolate, brn & grn 40 40
DESIGNS: 20 c. Aerial transport of logs; 30 c. Planting tree.

148 "The Storm on the Lake"

149 Hindu Peasant Woman

1973. Easter Charity. Jesus's Life and Death. Multicoloured.
744 10 c. + 5 c. Type **148** 50 50
745 15 c. + 8 c. "Washing the Disciples' Feet" 50 50
746 20 c. + 10 c. "Jesus taken to Execution" 50 50
747 25 c. + 12 c. The Cross . . . 50 50
748 30 c. + 15 c. "The Men of Emmaus" 50 50

1973. Centenary of Arrival of Indian Immigrants in Surinam.
749 **149** 15 c. violet and yellow . . 25 20
750 – 25 c. red and grey 25 20
751 – 30 c. orange and blue . . 35 30
DESIGNS: 25 c. J. F. A. Cateau van Rosevelt, Head of Department of Immigration, holding map; 30 c. Symbols of immigration.

150 Queen Juliana

1973. Silver Jubilee of Queen Juliana's Reign.
752 **150** 30 c. black, orange & sil . 50 50

151 Florence Nightingale and Red Cross

152 Interpol Emblem

1973. 30th Anniv of Surinam Red Cross.
753 **151** 30 c. + 10 c. multicoloured 70 70

1973. 50th Anniv of International Criminal Police Organization (Interpol). Multicoloured.
754 15 c. Type **152** 40 25
755 30 c. Emblem within passport stamp 40 30

153 Flower

154 Carrier-pigeons

1973. Child Welfare.
756 **153** 10 c. + 5 c. multicoloured 30 30
757 – 15 c. + 8 c. green, brown and emerald 45 45
758 – 20 c. + 10 c. violet, blue and green 35 35
759 – 25 c. + 12 c. multicoloured 55 55
760 – 30 c. + 15 c. multicoloured 55 55
DESIGNS: 15 c. Tree; 20 c. Dog; 25 c. House; 30 c. Doll.

1973. Stamp Centenary.
762 **154** 15 c. green and blue . . . 15 15
763 – 25 c. multicoloured . . . 25 25
764 – 30 c. multicoloured . . . 60 60
DESIGNS: 25 c. Postman; 30 c. Map and postal routes.

155 "Quassia amara"

156 Nurse and Blood Transfusion Equipment

1974. Easter Charity Flowers. Multicoloured.
765 10 c. + 5 c. Type **155** 45 45
766 15 c. + 8 c. "Passiflora quadrangularis" 45 45
767 20 c. + 10 c. "Combretum rotundifolium" 45 45
768 25 c. + 12 c. "Cassia alata" 50 50
769 30 c. + 15 c. "Asclepias curassavica" 50 50

1974. 75th Anniv of Surinam Medical School. Multicoloured.
770 15 c. Type **156** 20 15
771 30 c. Microscope slide and oscilloscope scanner 30 20

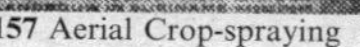
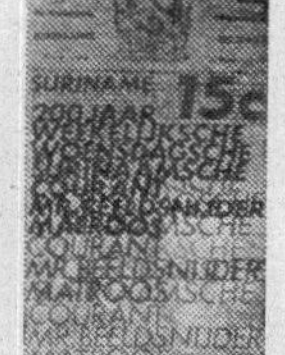

157 Aerial Crop-spraying **158** Commemorative Text superimposed on Early Newspaper

1974. 25th Anniv of Mechanised Agriculture. Multicoloured.
772 15 c. Type **157** 20 15
773 30 c. Fertiliser plant 25 20

1974. Bicentenary of Surinam's "Weekly Wednesday" Newspaper.
774 **158** 15 c. multicoloured . . . 20 15
775 30 c. multicoloured . . . 25 20

159 Scout and Tent **160** G.P.O., Paramaribo

1974. "50 Years of Scouting in Surinam". Multicoloured.
776 10 c. + 5 c. Type **159** 35 35
777 15 c. + 8 c. Jamboree emblem 35 35
778 20 c. + 10 c. Scouts and badge 40 40

1974. Centenary of Universal Postal Union.
779 **160** 15 c. black and brown . . 20 20
780 – 30 c. black and blue . . . 25 25
DESIGN: 30 c. G.P.O., Paramaribo (different view).

161 Girl with Fruit

1974. Child Welfare.
781 **161** 10 c. + 5 c. green, emerald and pink 25 25
782 – 15 c. + 8 c. brown, mauve and green 35 35
783 – 20 c. + 10 c. yellow, orange and mauve 35 35
784 – 25 c. + 12 c. brown, lilac and yellow 55 55
785 – 30 c. + 15 c. cobalt, blue and lilac 65 65
DESIGNS: 15 c. Birds and nest; 20 c. Mother and Child with flower; 25 c. Young boy in cornfield; 30 c. Children at play.

162 Panning for Gold **163** "I am the Good Shepherd"

1975. Centenary of Prospecting Concession Policy.
787 **162** 15 c. brown and bistre . . 25 20
788 – 30 c. purple and red . . . 30 25
DESIGN: 30 c. Claws of modern excavator.

1975. Easter Charity.
789 **163** 15 c. + 5 c. yellow and green 45 40
790 – 20 c. + 10 c. yellow and blue 60 60
791 – 30 c. + 15 c. yellow and red 70 65
792 – 35 c. + 20 c. blue and violet 70 65
DESIGNS—Quotations from the New Testament. 20 c. "I do not know the man"; 30 c. "He is not here; He has been raised again"; 35 c. "Because you have seen Me you have found faith. Happy are they who never saw Me and yet have found faith".

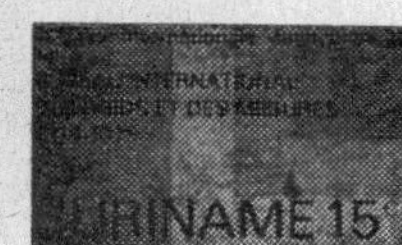

164 "Looking to Equality, Education and Peace" **165** "Weights and Measures"

1975. International Women's Year.
793 **164** 15 c. + 5 c. blue & green 60 55
794 30 c. + 15 c. vio & mauve 60 55

1975. Centenary of Metre Convention.
795 **165** 15 c. multicoloured . . 30 30
796 25 c. multicoloured . . 30 30
796a 30 c. multicoloured . . 40 30

166 Caribbean Water Jug **167** "Labour and Technology"

1975. Child Welfare. Multicoloured.
797 15 c. + 5 c. Type **166** 55 55
798 20 c. + 10 c. Indian arrowhead 85 75
799 30 c. + 15 c. "Maluana" (protection against evil spirits) 85 85
800 35 c. + 20 c. Indian arrowhead (different) . . . . 2·40 2·25

1975. Independence. "Nation in Development". Multicoloured.
802 25 c. Type **167** 20 20
803 50 c. Open book ("Education and Art") 50 50
804 75 c. Hands with ball ("Physical Training") 70 70

168 Central Bank, Paramaribo **169** "Oncidium lanceanum"

1975.
805 **168** 1 g. black, mve and pur . 90 25
806 1½ g. black, orge & brn . 1·50 25
807 2½ g. black, red and brn . 2·75 35
808 5 g. black, emer & grn . 5·50 55
809 10 g. black, bl & dp bl . 11·00 1·10

1976. Surinam Orchids. Multicoloured.
809 1 c. Type **169** 10 10
810 2 c. "Epidendrum stenopetalum" 10 10
811 3 c. "Brassia lanceana" . . . 10 10
812 4 c. "Epidendrum ibaguense" 10 10
813 5 c. "Epidendrum fragans" . 10 10

170 Surinam Flag **171** "Feeding the Hungry"

1976. Multicoloured.
814 25 c. Type **170** 30 30
815 35 c. Surinam arms 35 35

1976. Easter. Paintings in Alkmaar Church. Multicoloured.
816 20 c. + 10 c. Type **171** . . . 30 30
817 25 c. + 15 c. "Visiting the Sick" 35 35
818 30 c. + 15 c. "Clothing the Naked" 40 40
819 35 c. + 15 c. "Burying the Dead" 45 55
820 50 c. + 25 c. "Refreshing the Thirsty" 70 80

172 "Pomacanthus semicirculatus"

1976. Fishes. Multicoloured.
822 1 c. Type **172** (postage) 10 10
823 2 c. "Adioryx diadema" . . . 10 10
824 3 c. "Pogonoculius zebra" . . 10 10
825 4 c. "Balistes vetula" 10 10
826 5 c. "Myripristis jacobus" . . 10 10
827 35 c. "Chaetodon unimaculatus" (air) 40 35
828 60 c. "Centropyge loriculus" 70 60
829 95 c. "Chaetodon collare" . . 1·00 90

173 Early Telephone and Switchboard

1976. Telephone Centenary.
830 20 c. Type **173** 25 20
831 35 c. Globe, satellite and modern telephone 40 35

174 "Anansi Tori" (A. Baag)

1976. Paintings by Surinam Artists. Mult.
832 20 c. Type **174** 25 20
833 30 c. "Surinam Now" (R. Chang) 35 30
834 35 c. "Lamentation" (N. Hatterman) (vert) 45 40
835 50 c. "Chess-players" (Q. Jan Telting) 60 55

175 "Join or Die" (Franklin's "Divided Snake" poster of 1754)

1976. Bicentenary of American Revolution.
836 **175** 20 c. black, grn & cream 25 20
837 60 c. black, red and cream 75 75

176 Pekinese **177** "Ionopsis utricularioides"

1976. Child Welfare. Pet Dogs.
838 20 c. + 10 c. Type **176** 40 40
839 25 c. + 10 c. Alsatian 45 45
840 30 c. + 10 c. Dachshund . . . 55 55
841 35 c. + 15 c. Surinam breed . 60 60
842 50 c. + 25 c. Mongrel 85 85

1976. As Nos. 551/7 and new values but size 22 × 18 mm.
843a – 5 c. brown 10 10
843b **98** 10 c. green 15 10
843c – 20 c. green 25 15
843d – 25 c. blue 25 15
843e – 30 c. green 30 15
843f – 35 c. red 35 20
843g – 40 c. orange 50 25
843h – 60 c. red 75 35
NEW VALUES: 5 c. Brewery; 60 c. Jetty.

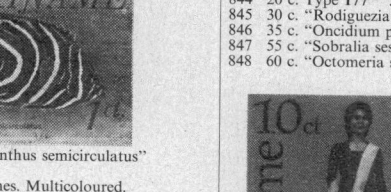

1977. Surinam Orchids. Multicoloured.
844 20 c. Type **177** 30 25
845 30 c. "Rodiguezia secunda" . 45 40
846 35 c. "Oncidium pusillum" . . 50 45
847 55 c. "Sobralia sessulis" . . . 75 65
848 60 c. "Octomeria surinamensis" 80 70

178 Javanese Costume **179** Triptych, left panel (Jan Mostaert)

1977. Surinam Costumes (1st series). Mult.
849 10 c. Type **178** 15 10
850 15 c. Forest Negro 20 15
851 35 c. Chinese 40 35
852 60 c. Creole 75 65
853 75 c. Aborigine Indian 95 85
854 1 g. Hindustani . . . . 1·25 1·25
DESIGNS: 15 c. to 1 g. Various women's festival costumes.
See also Nos. 906/11.

1977. Easter. Multicoloured.
855 20 c. + 10 c. Type **179** . . . 25 30
856 25 c. + 15 c. Right panel . . 35 40
857 30 c. + 15 c. Right panel . . 40 45
858 35 c. + 15 c. Centre panel (30 × 38 mm.) 50 55
859 50 c. + 25 c. Left panel . . . 70 80
The 20 c. and 25 c. show the triptych closed, the 30 c. and 50 c. show designs on the reverse of the doors, and the 35 c. shows the centre panel.

180 Green Honeycreeper

1977. Air. Birds. Multicoloured.
860 20 c. Red-breasted blackbird 60 35
861 25 c. Type **180** 70 40
862 30 c. Paradise tanager . . . 75 45
863 40 c. Spot-tailed nightjar . . 90 55
864 45 c. Yellow-backed tanager 95 60
865 50 c. White-tailed goldenthroat 1·00 70
866 55 c. Grey-breasted sabrewing 1·10 75
867 60 c. Caica parrot (vert) . . 1·10 80
868 65 c. Cuvier's toucan (vert) 1·25 90
869 70 c. Crimson-hooded manakin (vert) . . . . 1·40 95
870 75 c. Hawk-headed parrot (vert) 1·50 1·00
871 80 c. Spangled cotinga (vert) 1·75 1·10
872 85 c. Black-tailed trogon (vert) 1·90 1·25
872a 90 c. Orange-winged amazon (vert) . . . . 1·75 1·10
873 95 c. Black-banded owl (vert) 2·00 1·40

181 "Liopropoma carmabi"

1977. Fishes. Multicoloured.
875 1 c. Type **181** (postage) . . . 10 10
876 2 c. "Holacanthus ciliaris" . . 10 10
877 3 c. "Opistognathus aurifrons" 10 10
878 4 c. "Anisotremus virginicus" 10 10
879 5 c. "Gramma loreto" 10 10
880 60 c. "Chaetodon striatus" (air) 75 65
881 90 c. "Bodianus pulchellus" . 1·10 95
882 120 c. "Centropyge argi" . . 1·50 1·40

182 Edison's Phonograph, 1877

1977. Centenary of Sound Reproduction. Mult.
883 20 c. Type **182** 25 20
883a 60 c. Modern gramophone turntable 75 75

183 Paddle Steamer "Curacao" **185** Dog

1977. 150th Anniv of Regular Passenger Steam Service with Netherlands.

884 **183** 5 c. blue and light blue . . 15 10
885 – 15 c. red and orange . . . 30 15
886 – 30 c. black and ochre . . 40 35
887 – 35 c. black and olive . . . 50 40
888 – 60 c. black and lilac . . . 80 70
889 – 95 c. green & light green . 1·50 1·50

DESIGNS: 15 c. Hellevoetsluis port; 30 c. Chart of steamer route from Hellevoetsluis to Paramaribo; 35 c. Log of "Curacao"; 60 c. Chart of Paramaribo and 1852 postmark; 95 c. Passenger liner "Stuyvesant".

1977. Surch.

890 – 1 c. on 25 c. mult (No. 722) 10 10
891 **144** 4 c. on 15 c. multicoloured 10 10
892 – 4 c. on 30 c. mult (No. 723) 10 10
893 – 5 c. on 40 c. mult (No. 725) 10 10
894 – 10 c. on 75 c. mult (No. 732) 15 15

The word "LUCHTPOST" ("AIR-MAIL") on the original stamp is obliterated by bars.

1977. Child Welfare. Multicoloured.

895 20 c. + 10 c. Type **185** . . . 30 35
896 25 c. + 15 c. Monkey 40 45
897 30 c. + 15 c. Rabbit 45 50
898 35 c. + 15 c. Cat 50 55
899 50 c. + 25 c. Parrot 75 80

186 "Passiflora quadrangularis"

187 Javanese Costumes

1978. Flowers. Multicoloured.

901 20 c. Type **186** 25 20
902 30 c. "Centropogon surinamensis" 35 30
903 55 c. "Gloxinia perennis" . . 65 55
904 60 c. "Hydrocleys nymphoides" 70 60
905 75 c. "Clusia grandiflora" . . 85 75

1978. Surinam Costumes (2nd series). Mult.

906 10 c. Type **187** 15 10
907 20 c. Forest Negro 25 20
908 35 c. Chinese 40 35
909 60 c. Creole 75 60
910 75 c. Aborigine Indian 85 75
911 1 g. Hindustani . . . . . . 1·25 1·25

188 Cross and Halo

189 Municipal Church, 1783

1978. Easter Charity.

912 **188** 20 c. + 10 c. mult 30 35
913 – 25 c. + 15 c. brown, yellow and red 45 50
914 – 30 c. + 15 c. brown, red and yellow 50 55
915 – 35 c. + 15 c. brown, violet and red 55 60
916 – 60 c. + 30 c. brown, yellow and green . . . . . . 1·00 1·10

DESIGNS: 25 c. Serpent and cross; 30 c. Blood and lamb; 35 c. Passover dish and chalice; 60 c. Eclipse and crucifix.

1978. Bicentenary of Church of Evangelistic Brothers Community.

917 **189** 10 c. brown, black & blue 10 10
918 – 20 c. black and grey . . . 20 20
919 – 55 c. black and purple . . 55 55
920 – 60 c. black and orange . . 70 70

DESIGNS: 20 c. Brother Johannes King, 1830–1899; 55 c. Modern Municipal Church; 60 c. Brother Johannes Raillard, 1939–1954.

190 "Nannacara anomala"

192 Coconuts

1978. Tropical Fish. Multicoloured.

921 1 c. Type **190** (postage) . . . 10 10
922 2 c. "Leporinus fasciatus" . . 10 10
923 3 c. "Pristella riddlei" 10 10
924 4 c. "Nannostomus beckfordi" 10 10
925 5 c. "Rivulus agilae" 10 10
926 60 c. "Astyanax species" (air) 75 65
927 90 c. "Corydoras wotroi" . . 1·25 1·10
928 120 c. "Gasteropelecus sternicla" 1·50 1·40

1978. Fruits. Multicoloured.

930 5 c. Type **192** 10 10
931 10 c. Citrus 10 10
932 15 c. Papaya 15 15
933a 20 c. Bananas 15 15
934 25 c. Sour-sop 25 25
934b 30 c. Cacao 25 25
935 35 c. Water melons 35 35

193 Children's Heads and Kittens

194 Daedalus and Icarus

1978. Child Welfare.

936 **193** 20 c. + 10 c. multicoloured 25 30
937 – 25 c. + 15 c. multicoloured 35 40
938 – 30 c. + 15 c. multicoloured 40 45
939 – 35 c. + 15 c. multicoloured 40 45
940 – 60 c. + 30 c. multicoloured 80 90

DESIGNS: 25 c. to 60 c. Different designs showing kittens at play.

1978. 75th Anniv of First Powered Flight. Multicoloured.

942 20 c. Type **194** 25 20
943 60 c. Wright Flyer I (horiz) . 60 50
944 95 c. Douglas DC-8-63 (horiz) 85 70
945 125 c. Concorde (horiz) . . . 1·25 1·25

195 Black Curassow

196 "Rodriguezia candida"

1979. Air.

946 **195** 5 g. purple . . . . . . 7·50 6·00

1979. Orchids. Multicoloured.

947 10 c. Type **196** 15 10
948 20 c. "Stanhopea grandiflora" 25 20
949 35 c. "Scuticaria steelei" . . 40 35
950 60 c. "Bollea violacea" . . . 65 60

197 Javanese Dance

198 Church, Chalice and Cross

1979. Dancing Costumes. Multicoloured.

951 5 c. Type **197** 10 10
952 10 c. Forest Negro 10 10
953 15 c. Chinese 20 15
954 20 c. Creole 20 20
955 25 c. Aborigine Indian . . . 25 20
956 25 c. Hindustani 35 35

1979. Easter Charity.

957 **198** 20 c. + 10 c. multicoloured 25 30
958 – 30 c. + 15 c. multicoloured 35 40
959 – 35 c. + 15 c. multicoloured 40 45
960 – 40 c. + 20 c. multicoloured 45 50
961 – 60 c. + 30 c. multicoloured 70 80

DESIGNS: 30 c. to 60 c. Different churches.

199 "Equetus pulchellus"

1979. Fishes. Multicoloured.

962 1 c. Type **199** (postage) . . . 10 10
963 2 c. "Apogon binotatus" . . 10 10
964 3 c. "Anisotremus virginicus" 10 10
965 5 c. "Bodianus rufus" . . . 10 10
966 35 c. "Microspathodon chrysurus" 35 35
967 60 c. "Cantherinus macrocerus" (air) 65 65
968 90 c. "Holocentrus rufus" . . 95 95
969 120 c. "Holacanthus tricolor" 1·25 1·25

200 Javanese Wooden Head

1979. Art Objects. Multicoloured.

970 20 c. Type **200** 20 20
971 35 c. American Indian hair ornament 30 30
972 60 c. Javanese horse's head . . 55 55

201 S.O.S. Children's Village and Emblem

202 Sir Rowland Hill

1979. International Year of the Child. Multicoloured.

973 20 c. Type **201** 20 15
974 60 c. Different view of Village, and emblem 55 55

1979. Death Centenary of Sir Rowland Hill.

975 **202** 1 g. green and yellow . . . 1·00 1·00

203 Bird, Running Youth and Blood Transfusion Bottle

204 Javanese

1979. Child Welfare.

976 **203** 20 c. + 10 c. blk, vio & red 25 30
977 30 c. + 15 c. black, red and violet 40 45
978 35 c. + 15 c. multicoloured 45 50
979 40 c. + 20 c. multicoloured 50 55
980 60 c. + 30 c. multicoloured 70 80

1980. Children's Costumes. Multicoloured.

982 10 c. Type **204** 10 10
983 15 c. Forest Negro 15 15
984 25 c. Chinese 25 20
985 60 c. Creole 55 55
986 90 c. Indian 80 80
987 1 g. Hindustani 85 85

205 Handshake and Rotary Emblem

206 Church Interior

1980. 75th Anniv of Rotary International. Each blue and yellow.

988 20 c. Type **205** 20 20
989 60 c. Globe and Rotary emblem 50 50

1980. Easter Charity. Various Easter symbols.

990 **206** 20 c. + 10 c. multicoloured 25 30
991 – 30 c. + 15 c. multicoloured 40 45
992 – 40 c. + 20 c. multicoloured 50 55
993 – 50 c. + 25 c. multicoloured 60 70
994 – 60 c. + 30 c. multicoloured 70 80

207 Mail Coach

208 Weightlifting

1980. "London 1980" International Stamp Exhibition.

995 **207** 50 c. yellow, black & blue . 40 40
996 – 1 g. yellow, black & purple 80 80
997 – 2 g. pink, black & turq . . 1·60 1·60

DESIGNS: 1 g. Sir Rowland Hill; 2 g. People posting letters.

1980. Olympic Games, Moscow.

999 **208** 20 c. multicoloured . . . 20 20
1000 – 30 c. multicoloured . . . 25 25
1001 – 50 c. green, yellow & red . 40 40
1002 – 75 c. multicoloured . . . 60 60
1003 – 150 c. multicoloured . . 1·25 1·25

DESIGNS: 30 c. Diving; 50 c. Gymnastics; 75 c. Basketball; 150 c. Running.

209 "Osteoglossum bicirrhosum"

210 Anansi disguised as Spider

1980. Tropical Fishes. Multicoloured.

1005 10 c. Type **209** (postage) . . 10 10
1006 15 c. "Colossoma species" . . 15 15
1007 25 c. "Hemigrammus pulcher" 25 20
1008 30 c. "Petitella georgiae" . . 30 25
1009 45 c. "Copeina guttata" . . 45 40
1010 60 c. "Symhysodon discus" (air) 60 55
1011 75 c. "Aequidens curviceps" 70 65
1012 90 c. "Catoprion mento" . . 80 75

1980. Child Welfare. "The Story of Anansi and his Creditors".

1013 **210** 20 c. + 10 c. bistre and yellow 30 35
1014 – 25 c. + 15 c. yellow, brown and orange 35 40
1015 – 30 c. + 15 c. brown, red and orange 40 45
1016 – 35 c. + 15 c. green, light green & yellow 45 50
1017 – 60 c. + 30 c. multicoloured 80 90

DESIGNS: (Anansi in various disguises) 25 c. Bear; 30 c. Cockerel; 35 c. Hunter; 60 c. Beetle.

212 Old Woman reading

213 "Passiflora laurifolia"

1980. Welfare of the Aged. Multicoloured.

1020 25 c. + 10 c. Type **212** . . . 30 35
1021 50 c. + 15 c. Old man tending flowers 50 60
1022 75 c. + 20 c. Grandfather and grandchildren 80 90

1981. Flower Drawings by Maria Sibylle Merian. Multicoloured.

1023 20 c. Type **213** 20 20
1024 30 c. "Aphelandra pectinata" 30 25
1025 60 c. "Caesalpinia pulcherrima" 55 55
1026 75 c. "Hibiscus mutabilis" . 70 70
1027 1 g. 25 "Hippeastrum puniceum" . . . . . . 1·25 1·25

214 Justice and Text "Renewal of the Governmental and Political Order"

215 Christ with Jug

1981. The Four Renewals.

1028 – 30 c. yellow, brown and deep yellow 25 25
1029 – 60 c. orange, brn & red . . 50 50
1030 – 75 c. green, deep green and olive 60 60
1031 **214** 1 g. deep yellow, green and yellow 80 80

DESIGNS: 30 c. "Renewal of the Economic Order"; 60 c. "Renewal of the Educational Order"; 75 c. "Renewal of the Social Order".

1981. Easter Charity. Multicoloured.

1033 20 c. + 10 c. Type **215** . . . 25 30
1034 30 c. + 15 c. Christ and pointing hand 40 45
1035 50 c. + 25 c. Christ and Roman soldier 60 65
1036 60 c. + 30 c. Christ wearing crown of thorns 70 80
1037 75 c. + 35 c. Christ and Mary 80 90

218 "Phyllomedusa hypochondrialis"

1981. Frogs. Multicoloured.
1040 40 c. Type **218** (postage) . . 40 35
1041 50 c. "Leptodactylus pentadactylus" 45 40
1042 60 c. "Hyla boans" 55 50
1043 75 c. "Phyllomedusa burmeisteri" (vert) (air) . . 70 65
1044 1 g. "Dendrobates tinctorius" (vert) 90 85
1045 1 g. 25 "Bufo guttatus" (vert) 1·25 1·25

219 Deaf Child

1981. International Year of Disabled Persons.
1046 **219** 50 c. yellow and green . 40 40
1047 – 100 c. yellow and green . 80 80
1048 – 150 c. yellow and red . . 1·25 1·25
DESIGNS: 100 c. Child reading braille; 150 c. Woman in wheelchair.

220 Planter's House on the Parakreek River **221** Indian Girl

1981. Illustrations to "Journey to Surinam" by P. I. Benoit. Multicoloured.
1049 20 c. Type **220** 20 20
1050 30 c. Sarameca Street, Paramaribo 25 25
1051 75 c. Negro hamlet, Paramaribo 60 60
1052 1 g. Fish market, Paramaribo 80 80
1053 1 g. 25 Blaauwe Berg Cascade 1·00 1·00

1981. Child Welfare. Multicoloured.
1055 20 c. + 10 c. Type **221** . . . 25 30
1056 30 c. + 15 c. Negro girl . . 40 45
1057 50 c. + 25 c. Hindustani girl 60 70
1058 60 c. + 30 c. Javanese girl . 70 80
1059 75 c. + 35 c. Chinese girl . . 80 90

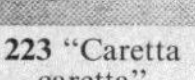

222 Satellites orbiting Earth

1982. Peaceful Uses of Outer Space. Mult.
1061 35 c. Type **222** 35 30
1062 65 c. Space shuttle 60 55
1063 1 g. U.S.–Russian space link 85 85

223 "Caretta caretta" **224** Pattern from Stained Glass Window

1982. Turtles. Multicoloured.
1064 5 c. Type **223** (postage) . . . 10 10
1065 10 c. "Chelonia mydas" . . . 10 10
1066 20 c. "Dermochelys coriacea" 20 20
1067 25 c. "Eretmochelys imbricata" 25 25
1068 35 c. "Lepidochelys olivacea" 30 30
1069 65 c. "Platemys platycephala" (air) 60 60
1070 75 c. "Phrynops gibba" . . . 75 75
1071 125 c. "Rihnoclemys punctularia" . . . . 1·10 1·10

1982. Easter. Stained-glass windows, Church of Saints Peter and Paul, Paramaribo.
1072 **224** 20 c. + 10 c. multicoloured 25 30
1073 – 35 c. + 15 c. multicoloured 40 45
1074 – 50 c. + 25 c. multicoloured 60 70
1075 – 65 c. + 30 c. multicoloured 75 85
1076 – 75 c. + 35 c. multicoloured 80 90
DESIGNS: 35 c. to 75 c. Different patterns.

225 Lions Emblem **226** Father Donders with the Sick

1982. 25th Anniv of Surinam Lions Club.
1077 **225** 35 c. multicoloured . . 30 30
1078 70 c. multicoloured . . 60 60

1982. Beatification of Father Peter Donders.
1079 **226** 35 c. multicoloured . . 30 30
1080 – 65 c. silver, black and red 50 50
DESIGN: 65 c. Portrait, birthplace, Tilburg, and map of South America.

227 Stamp Designer **228** Dr. Robert Koch

1982. "Philexfrance 82" International Stamp Exhibition, Paris. Multicoloured.
1082 50 c. Type **227** 40 40
1083 100 c. Stamp printing . . . 80 80
1084 150 c. Stamp collector . . . 1·25 1·25

1982. Cent of Discovery of Tubercle Bacillus.
1086 **228** 35 c. yellow and green . 35 30
1087 – 65 c. orange and brown 60 55
1088 – 150 c. light blue, blue and red . . . . 1·50 1·50
DESIGNS: 65 c. Dr. Koch and microscope; 150 c. Dr. Koch and Bacillus.

229 Sugar Mill **230** Cleaning Tools and Flag

1982. Cent of Marienburg Sugar Company.
1089 **229** 35 c. yellow, green and black 30 30
1090 – 65 c. orange and brown 50 50
1091 – 100 c. light blue, blue and black . . . . 1·10 1·10
1092 – 150 c. lilac and purple . 1·25 1·25
DESIGNS: 65 c. Workers in cane fields; 100 c. Sugar cane railway; 150 c. Mill machinery.

1982. Child Welfare. "Keep Surinam Tidy" (children's paintings). Multicoloured.
1093 20 c. + 10 c. Type **230** . . . 25 30
1094 35 c. + 15 c. Man with barrow 40 45
1095 50 c. + 25 c. Litter bin and cleaning tools 60 70
1096 65 c. + 30 c. Spraying weeds 75 85
1097 75 c. + 35 c. Litter bin . . 85 95

231 Municipal Church, Paramaribo

1982. 250th Anniv of Moravian Church Mission in the Caribbean.
1099 **231** 35 c. multicoloured . . 30 30
1100 – 65 c. light blue, black and blue 50 50
1101 – 150 c. multicoloured . . 1·25 1·25
DESIGNS—HORIZ: 65 c. Aerial view of St. Thomas Monastery. VERT: 150 c. Johann Leonhardt Dober (missionary).

232 "Erythrina fusca"

1983. Flower Paintings by Maria Sibylle Merian. Multicoloured.
1102 1 c. Type **232** 10 10
1103 2 c. "Ipomoea acuminata" . 10 10
1104 3 c. "Heliconia psittacorum" . 10 10
1105 5 c. "Ipomoea" 10 10
1106 10 c. "Herba non denominata" 10 10
1107 15 c. "Anacardium occidentale" 15 15
1108 20 c. "Inga edulis" (vert) . . 20 15
1109 25 c. "Abelmoschus moschatus" (vert) 25 20
1110 30 c. "Argemone mexicana" (vert) 30 25
1111 35 c. "Costus arabicus" (vert) 35 30
1112 45 c. "Muellera frutescens" (vert) 45 45
1113 65 c. "Punica granatum" (vert) 60 60

233 Scout Anniversary Emblem **234** Dove of Peace

1983. Year of the Scout.
1114 **233** 40 c. mauve, vio & grn . 45 40
1115 – 65 c. lt grey, bl & grey 70 60
1116 – 70 c. multicoloured . . 80 70
1117 – 80 c. blue, lt grn & grn . 85 80
DESIGNS: 65 c. Lord Baden-Powell; 70 c. Tent and campfire; 80 c. Axe in tree trunk.

1983. Easter. Multicoloured.
1118 10 c. + 5 c. Type **234** 15 15
1119 15 c. + 5 c. Bread 20 25
1120 25 c. + 10 c. Fish 30 35
1121 50 c. + 25 c. Eye 60 70
1122 65 c. + 30 c. Chalice 75 85

235 Drawing by Raphael

1983. 500th Birth Anniv of Raphael.
1123 **235** 5 c. multicoloured 10 10
1124 – 10 c. multicoloured . . . 10 10
1125 – 40 c. multicoloured . . . 35 35
1126 – 65 c. multicoloured . . . 60 60
1127 – 70 c. multicoloured . . . 65 65
1128 – 80 c. multicoloured . . . 70 70
DESIGNS: Drawings by Raphael.

236 1 c. Coin **237** "25" on Map of Surinam

1983. Coins and Banknotes. Multicoloured.
1129 5 c. Type **236** 10 10
1130 10 c. 5 c. coin 10 10
1131 40 c. 10 c. coin 45 40
1132 65 c. 25 c. coin 65 65
1133 70 c. 1 g. note 70 70
1134 80 c. 2½ g. note . . . . . . 1·50 90

1983. 25th Anniv of Department of Construction. Multicoloured.
1135 25 c. Type **237** 25 25
1136 50 c. Construction vehicles on map 45 45

238 "Papilio anchisiades" **239** Montgolfier Balloon "Le Martial", 1783

1983. Butterfly Paintings by Maria Sibylle Merian. Multicoloured.
1137 1 c. Type **238** 10 10
1138 2 c. "Urania leilus" 10 10
1139 3 c. "Morpho deidamia" . . 10 10
1140 5 c. "Thysania agrippina" . . 10 10
1141 10 c. "Morpho sp." 20 10
1142 15 c. "Philaethria dido" . . 30 20
1143 20 c. "Morpho menelaus" (horiz) 40 25
1144 25 c. "Protoparce rustica" (horiz) 50 30
1145 30 c. "Rothschildia aurota" (horiz) 60 40
1146 35 c. "Phoebis sennae" (horiz) 80 50
1147 45 c. "Papilio androgeos" (horiz) 90 70
1148 65 c. "Dupo vitis" (horiz) . . 1·40 1·00

1983. Bicentenary. of Manned Flight. Mult.
1149 5 c. Type **239** 10 10
1150 10 c. Montgolfier balloon (1st manned free flight by D'Arlandes and Pilatre de Rozier, 1783) 10 10
1151 40 c. Charles's hydrogen balloon, 1783 . . . . . . 40 40
1152 65 c. Balloon "Armand Barbes", 1870 . . . . . . 65 65
1153 70 c. Balloon "Double Eagle II" (transatlantic flight, 1978) 70 70
1154 80 c. Hot-air balloons at International Balloon Festival, Albuquerque, U.S.A. 75 75

240 Calabash Pitcher **241** Martin Luther

1983. Child Welfare. Caribbean Artifacts. Multicoloured.
1155 10 c. + 5 c. Type **240** . . . 15 15
1156 15 c. + 5 c. Umari (headdress) 15 20
1157 25 c. + 10 c. Maraka (medicine man's rattle) 20 35
1158 50 c. + 25 c. Manari (sieve) 60 70
1159 65 c. + 30 c. Pasuwa/pakara (basket) 70 80

1983. 500th Birth Anniv of Martin Luther (Protestant reformer).
1161 **241** 25 c. yellow, brown and black 20 20
1162 – 50 c. pink, purple & blk 40 40
DESIGN: 50 c. Selling of indulgences.

242 "Catasetum discolor" **243** "Arca zebra"

1983. Orchids. Multicoloured.
1163 5 c. Type **242** 10 10
1164 10 c. "Menadenium labiosum" 10 10
1165 40 c. "Comparettia falcata" 45 40
1166 50 c. "Rodriguezia decora" . 70 60
1167 70 c. "Oncidium papilio" . . 80 70
1168 75 c. "Epidendrum porpax" 85 75

1984. Sea Shells. Multicoloured.
1169 40 c. Type **243** 45 45
1170 65 c. "Trachycardium egmontianum" 80 80
1171 70 c. "Tellina radiata" . . . 80 80
1172 80 c. "Vermicularia knorrii" 95 95

244 Cross and Flower **245** Sikorsky S-40 Flying Boat

1984. Easter. Multicoloured.
1173 10 c. + 5 c. Type **244** . . . 15 15
1174 15 c. + 5 c. Cross and gate of cemetery 15 20
1175 25 c. + 10 c. Candle flames . 30 35
1176 50 c. + 25 c. Cross and crown of thorns 60 70
1177 65 c. + 30 c. Lamp 70 80

1984. 40th Anniv of I.C.A.O. Multicoloured.
1178 35 c. Type **245** 40 40
1179 65 c. Surinam Airways De Havilland Twin Otter 200/300 85 85

246 Running **247** Emblem of 8th Caribbean Scout Jamboree

1984. Olympic Games, Los Angeles. Multicoloured.
1180 2 c. Type **246** 10 10
1181 3 c. Javelin, discus and long jump 10 10
1182 5 c. Massage 10 10
1183 10 c. Rubbing with ointment 10 10
1184 15 c. Wrestling 15 15
1185 20 c. Boxing 20 20
1186 30 c. Horse-racing 30 30
1187 35 c. Chariot-racing 35 35
1188 45 c. Temple of Olympia . . 40 40
1189 50 c. Entrance to Stadium, Olympia 45 45
1190 65 c. Stadium, Olympia . . . 60 60
1191 75 c. Zeus 70 70

1984. 60th Anniv of Scouting in Surinam. Multicoloured.
1193 30 c. + 10 c. Type **247** . . . 40 40
1194 35 c. + 10 c. Scout saluting 50 50
1195 50 c. + 10 c. Scout camp . . 65 65
1196 90 c. + 10 c. Campfire and map 95 95

248 Ball entering Basket

249 Red Square, Moscow

1984. International Military Sports Council Basketball Championship. Multicoloured.
1197 50 c. Type **248** 50 45
1198 90 c. Ball leaving basket . . 85 75

1984. World Chess Championship, Moscow.
1199 **249** 10 c. brown 10 10
1200 – 15 c. green & light green 15 15
1201 – 30 c. lt brown and brown 30 30
1202 – 50 c. brown and purple . 50 50
1203 – 75 c. brown & lt brown . 80 80
1204 – 90 c. green and blue . . 90 90
DESIGNS: 15 c. Knight, king and pawn on board; 30 c. Gary Kasparov; 50 c. Start of game and clock; 75 c. Anatoly Karpov; 90 c. Position during Andersen–Kizeritski game.

250 Children collecting Milk from Cow

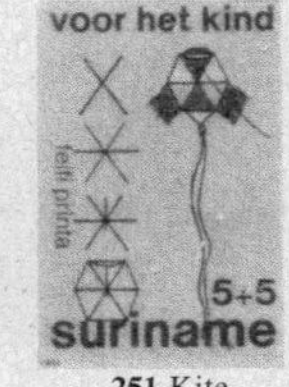

251 Kite

1984. World Food Day. Multicoloured.
1206 50 c. Type **250** 50 45
1207 90 c. Platter of food 85 75

1984. Child Welfare. Multicoloured.
1208 5 c. + 5 c. Type **251** 10 10
1209 10 c. + 5 c. Kites 15 15
1210 30 c. + 10 c. Pingi-pingi-kasi (game) 40 40
1211 50 c. + 25 c. Cricket 85 85
1212 90 c. + 30 c. Peroen, peroen (game) . . . . 1·10 1·10

252 Leaf Cactus

1985. Cacti. Multicoloured.
1215 5 c. Type **252** 10 10
1216 10 c. Melocactus 10 10
1217 30 c. Pillar cactus 25 25
1218 50 c. Fig cactus 45 45
1219 75 c. Night queen 70 70
1220 90 c. Segment cactus 80 80

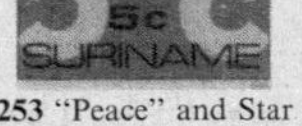

253 "Peace" and Star

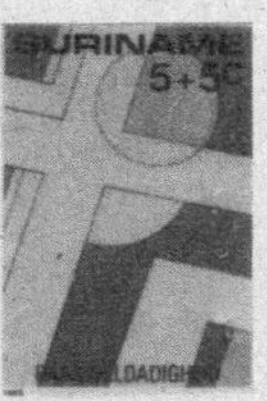

254 Crosses

1985. 5th Anniv of Revolution. Multicoloured.
1221 5 c. Type **253** 10 10
1222 30 c. "Unity in labour" and manual workers 20 20
1223 50 c. "5 years of Steadfastness" and flower 40 40
1224 75 c. "Progress" and wheat as flower 60 60
1225 90 c. "Unity", flower and dove 70 70

1985. Easter. Multicoloured.
1227 5 c. + 5 c. Type **254** 10 10
1228 10 c. + 5 c. Crosses (different) 10 10
1229 30 c. + 15 c. Sun's rays illuminating crosses . . . 30 30
1230 50 c. + 25 c. Crosses (different) 55 65
1231 90 c. + 30 c. Crosses and leaves (Resurrection) 75 85

255 Emblem

256 U.N. Emblem and State Arms

1985. 75th Anniv of Chamber of Commerce and Industry.
1232 **255** 50 c. yellow, green & red 40 40
1233 – 90 c. green, blue & yell . 70 70
DESIGN: 90 c. Chamber of Commerce building.

1985. 40th Anniv of U.N.O.
1234 **256** 50 c. multicoloured . . 40 40
1235 90 c. multicoloured . . 70 70

257 Sugar-cane Train (detail of 1945 stamp)

1985. Railway Locomotives.
1236 **257** 5 c. orange and blue . . 10 10
1237 – 5 c. green, red & blue . 10 10
1238 – 10 c. multicoloured . . 15 10
1239 – 10 c. multicoloured . . 15 10
1240 – 20 c. multicoloured . . 30 20
1241 – 20 c. multicoloured . . 30 20
1242 – 30 c. multicoloured . . 55 30
1243 – 30 c. multicoloured . . 55 30
1244 – 50 c. multicoloured . . 95 55
1245 – 50 c. multicoloured . . 95 55
1246 – 75 c. multicoloured . . 1·25 80
1247 – 75 c. multicoloured . . 1·25 80
DESIGNS: No. 1237, Monaco 3 f. Postage due train stamp; 1238, Steam locomotive "Dam"; 1239, Modern electric locomotive and carriage unit; 1240, Steam locomotive "3737"; 1241, Electric locomotive "NS-IC III"; 1242, Stephenson's "Rocket"; 1243, French "TGV" (high speed) locomotive; 1244, Stephenson's "Der Adler"; 1245, French double-decker "UB2N"; 1246, American locomotive "The General"; 1247, Japanese "Shinkansen" train.

258 Purple Gallinule

259 German Letterbox, 1900

1985. Birds. Multicoloured.
1248 1 g. Type **258** . . . . 1·10 1·00
1249 1 g. 50 Rufescent tiger heron 1·50 1·40
1250 2 g. 50 Scarlet ibis . . . . . 2·75 2·50
1251 5 g. Guianan cock of the rock 3·50 3·00
1252 10 g. Harpy eagle . . . . . 7·50 7·00

1985. Old Letterboxes. Multicoloured.
1254 15 c. Type **259** 15 15
1255 30 c. French letterbox, 1900 20 20
1256 50 c. English pillar box, 1932 35 35
1257 90 c. Dutch letterbox, 1850 55 55

260 Emblem on Map

261 Studying

1985. 25th Anniv of Evangelical Brotherhood in Surinam.
1258 **260** 30 c. + 10 c. multicoloured 30 30
1259 – 50 c. + 10 c. red, yellow and brown 45 45
1260 – 90 c. + 20 c. yellow, brown and red 75 75
DESIGNS: 50 c. Different population groups around cross and clasped hands emblem; 90 c. List of work undertaken by Brotherhood.

1985. Child Welfare. Multicoloured.
1261 5 c. + 5 c. Type **261** 10 10
1262 10 c. + 5 c. Writing alphabet on board 15 15
1263 30 c. + 10 c. Writing 30 30
1264 50 c. + 25 c. Reading 55 55
1265 90 c. + 30 c. Thinking . . . 80 80

1985. Victory of Kasparov in World Chess Championship. No. 1201 optd **КАСПАРОВ Wereldkampioen 9 nov. 1985.**
1267 30 c. light brown and brown . 30 20

263 Agriculture

264 "Epidendrum ciliare"

1985. 10th Anniv of Independence.
1268 **263** 50 c. yellow and green . . 40 40
1269 – 90 c. orange and brown . 70 70
DESIGN: 90 c. Industry.

1986. Orchids. Multicoloured.
1271 5 c. Type **264** 10 10
1272 15 c. "Cycnoches chlorochilon" 15 15
1273 30 c. "Epidendrum anceps" 25 25
1274 50 c. "Epidendrum vespa" . . 45 45

265 Bayeux Tapestry (detail)

266 Couple and Palm Leaves

1986. Appearance of Halley's Comet. Multicoloured.
1275 50 c. Type **265** 35 35
1276 110 c. Comet 75 75

1986. Easter.
1277 **266** 5 c. + 5 c. multicoloured 10 10
1278 10 c. + 5 c. multicoloured 15 15
1279 30 c. + 15 c. multicoloured 30 30
1280 50 c. + 25 c. multicoloured 55 55
1281 90 c. + 30 c. multicoloured 80 80

1986. Nos. 1244/5 surch.
1282 15 c. on 50 c. multicoloured . 45 15
1283 15 c. on 50 c. multicoloured . 45 20

268 Cathedral

270 National Forestry Emblem

1986. Centenary of St. Peter and St. Paul's Cathedral, Paramaribo.
1284 **268** 30 c. + 10 c. brown and ochre 30 30
1285 – 50 c. + 10 c. brown and red 50 50
1286 – 110 c. + 30 c. deep brown and brown . . . . . 1·10 1·10
DESIGNS: 50 c. Relief of St. Peter and St. Paul; 110 c. Font.

1986. 150th Anniv of Finance Building. No. 1133 surch **30 c 150 jaar FINANCIENGE BOUW.**
1287 30 c. on 70 . multicoloured . 30 30

1986. Centenary of Foresters' Court Charity. Multicoloured.
1288 50 c. + 20 c. Type **270** . . . 60 60
1289 110 c. + 30 c. First Court building . . . . 1·25 1·25

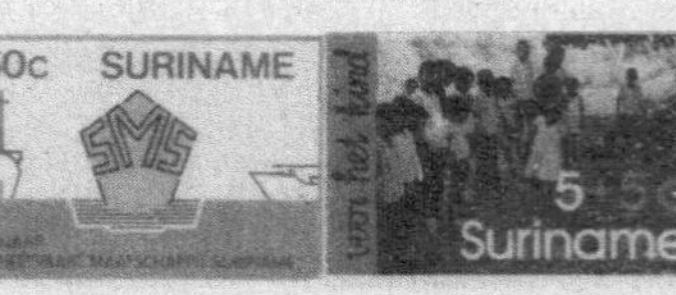

271 Emblem

273 Children playing Hopscotch

1986. 50th Anniv of Surinam Shipping Line. Multicoloured.
1290 50 c. Type **271** 40 40
1291 110 c. Container ship "Saramacca" . . . . . . 2·00 1·10

1986. No. 862 surch **15ct.**
1292 15 c. on 30 c. multicoloured . 60 25

1986. Child Welfare. Multicoloured.
1293 5 c. + 5 c. Type **273** 10 10
1294 10 c. + 5 c. Ballet class . . 15 15
1295 30 c. + 10 c. Children boarding library bus 35 35
1296 50 c. + 25 c. Boys at display of craftwork 65 65
1297 110 c. + 30 c. Children in class 1·10 1·10

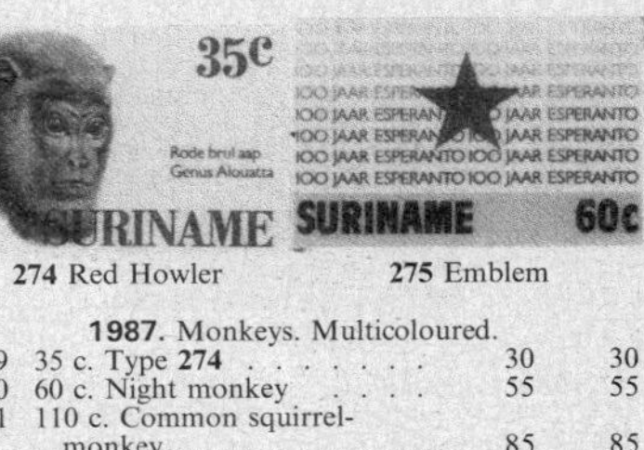

274 Red Howler 275 Emblem

1987. Monkeys. Multicoloured.
1299 35 c. Type **274** 30 30
1300 60 c. Night monkey 55 55
1301 110 c. Common squirrel-monkey 85 85
1302 120 c. Red uakari 90 90

1987. Centenary of Esperanto (invented language). Multicoloured.
1303 60 c. Type **275** 55 55
1304 110 c. Dove holding "Esperanto" banner across world map 85 85
1305 120 c. L. L. Zamenhof (inventor) 90 90

1987. Various stamps surch.
1306 – 10 c. on 85 c. multicoloured (No. 872) 50 20
1307 – 10 c. on 95 c. multicoloured (No. 873) 50 20
1308 **168** 50 c. on $1\frac{1}{2}$ g. black, orange and brown 45 45
1309 60 c. on $2\frac{1}{2}$ g. black, red and brown 55 55

277 "Crucifixion"

278 Mushroom (Brownie emblem)

1987. Easter. Etchings by Rembrandt. Each light mauve, mauve and black.
1310 5 c. + 5 c. Type **277** 10 10
1311 10 c. + 5 c. "Christ on the Cross" 15 15
1312 35 c. + 15 c. "Descent from the Cross" 35 35
1313 60 c. + 30 c. "Christ carried to His Tomb" 65 65
1314 110 c. + 50 c. "Entombment of Christ" . . . . 1·10 1·10

1987. 40th Anniv of Surinam Girl Guides.
1315 **278** 15 c. + 10 c. mult . . . 20 20
1316 – 60 c. + 10 c. mult . . . 50 50
1317 – 110 c. + 10 c. mult . . 80 80
1318 – 120 c. + 10 c. green, black and yellow 90 90
DESIGNS: 60 c. Cloverleaf and star (Guide emblem); 110 c. Campfire (Rangers emblem) on Guide trefoil; 120 c. Ivy leaves (Captain's emblem).

279 Football

280 Commission Emblem

1987. 10th Pan-American Games, Indianapolis.
1319 **279** 90 c. blue, green and brown 80 80
1320 – 110 c. blue, light blue and brown 90 90
1321 – 150 c. blue, mauve and brown . . . . 1·25 1·25
DESIGNS: 110 c. Swimming; 150 c. Basketball.

1987. 40th Anniv of Forestry Commission. Multicoloured.
1322 90 c. Type **280** 80 80
1323 120 c. Loading tree trunks for export 95 95
1324 150 c. Parrot in forest . . . 1·75 1·25

282 Boy and Tents

283 Banana

1987. International Year of Shelter for the Homeless (90, 120 c.) and Centenary of Salvation Army in the Caribbean Territory (150 c.). Multicoloured.

1331 90 c. Type **282** 70 70
1332 120 c. Shanty town and man 85 85
1333 150 c. William and Catherine Booth and emblem 1·10 1·10

1987. Fruits. Multicoloured.

1334 10 c. Type **283** 10 10
1335 15 c. Cacao bean 15 15
1336 20 c. Pineapple 15 15
1337 25 c. Papaya 20 20
1338 35 c. China orange 30 30

284 Jacob Degen's Balloon-assisted "Ornithopter", 1808

1987. Aircraft. Multicoloured.

1339 25 c. Type **284** 20 20
1340 25 c. Microlight airplane 20 20
1341 35 c. Ellehammer II, 1906 30 30
1342 35 c. Concorde 30 30
1343 60 c. Fokker F.VII (inscr "F.7"), 1924 50 50
1344 60 c. Fokker F28 Friendship 50 50
1345 90 c. Fokker monoplane "Haarlem Spin", 1910 75 75
1346 90 c. Douglas DC-10 75 75
1347 110 c. Lockheed 9 Orion, 1932 80 80
1348 110 c. Boeing 747 80 80
1349 120 c. 1967 Amelia Earhart 25 c. stamp 95 95
1350 120 c. 1978 Douglas DC-8-63 95 c. stamp 95 95

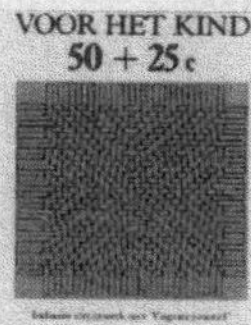
285 Herring-bone Design

287 Ganges Gavial

1987. Child Welfare. Indian Weaving.

1351 **285** 50 c. + 25 c. grn & blk 65 65
1352 – 60 c. + 30 c. orange and black 70 70
1353 – 110 c. + 50 c. red & blk 1·25 1·25

DESIGNS: 60 c. Tortoise-back design; 110 c. Concentric diamonds design.

1987. Nos. 869 and 805 surch.

1356 – 25 c. on 70 c. mult 60 40
1357 **168** 35 c. on 1 g. black, mauve and purple 60 60

1988. Reptiles. Multicoloured.

1358 50 c. Type **287** 40 40
1359 60 c. Nile crocodile 50 50
1360 90 c. Black cayman 70 70
1361 110 c. Mississippi alligator 80 80

288 Javanese Costumes

290 Cross and Chalice

1988. Wedding Costumes. Multicoloured.

1362 35 c. Type **288** 30 30
1363 60 c. Bushman 50 50
1364 80 c. Chinese 65 65
1365 110 c. Creole 80 80
1366 120 c. Amerindian 85 85
1367 130 c. Hindustan 90 90

1988. Various stamps surch.

1368 – 60 c. on 75 c. mult (No. 1246) 1·40 1·00
1369 – 60 c. on 75 c. mult (No. 1247) 1·40 1·00
1370 **168** 125 c. on 10 g. black, blue and deep blue 1·75 1·75

1988. Easter.

1371 **290** 50 c. + 25 c. mult 65 65
1372 60 c. + 30 c. mult 75 75
1373 110 c. + 50 c. mult 1·40 1·40

291 Relay

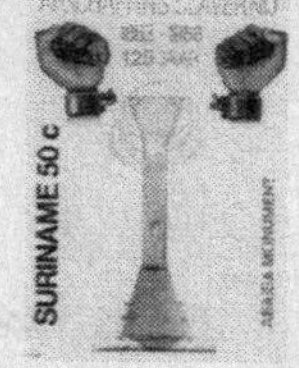
292 Abaisa Monument

1988. Olympic Games, Seoul. Multicoloured.

1374 90 c. Type **291** 80 80
1375 110 c. Football 90 90
1376 120 c. Pole vaulting 1·00 1·00
1377 250 c. Tennis 2·00 2·00

1988. 125th Anniv of Abolition of Slavery. Multicoloured.

1379 50 c. Type **292** 50 50
1380 110 c. Kwakoe monument 90 90
1381 120 c. Anton de Kom's house 1·10 1·10

293 Combine Harvester

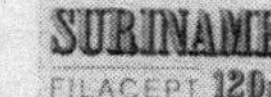
294 Egypt 1906 4 m. Stamp

1988. 10th Anniv of International Agricultural Development Fund. "For a World without Hunger". Multicoloured.

1382 105 c. Type **293** 90 90
1383 110 c. Fishing 95 95
1384 125 c. Cultivation 1·25 1·25

1988. "Filacept" International Stamp Exhibition, The Hague.

1385 **294** 120 c. red, black & orge 1·00 1·00
1386 – 150 c. green, blk & bl 1·25 1·25
1387 – 250 c. red, black & deep red 2·25 2·25

DESIGNS: No. 1386, Netherlands 1952 10 c. Stamp Centenary stamp; No. 1387, Surinam 1949 $7\frac{1}{2}$ c. U.P.U. stamp.

295 Anniversary Emblem

296 Symbolic Representation of Butterfly Stroke

1988. 125th Anniv of Red Cross. Multicoloured.

1389 60 c. + 30 c. Type **295** 85 85
1390 120 c. + 60 c. Anniversary emblem and red cross in blood drop 1·60 1·60

1988. Anthony Nesty, Seoul Olympic Gold Medal Winner for 100 m Butterfly.

1391 **296** 110 c. multicoloured 95 95

297 "Man and Animal"

1988. 25th Anniv of Child Welfare Stamps. Multicoloured.

1392 50 c. + 25 c. Type **297** 70 70
1393 60 c. + 30 c. "The Child in Nature" 85 85
1394 110 c. + 50 c. Children helping each other ("Stop Drugs") 1·50 1·50

1988. Nos. 1238/9 and 1244/5 surch.

1396 2 c. on 10 c. mult (No. 1238) 10 10
1397 2 c. on 10 c. mult (No. 1239) 10 10
1398 3 c. on 50 c. mult (No. 1244) 10 10
1399 3 c. on 50 c. mult (No. 1245) 10 10

299 Otter on Rock

300 "The Passion" (left wing)

1989. Otters. Multicoloured.

1400 10 c. Type **299** 10 10
1401 20 c. Two otters 20 10
1402 25 c. Two otters (different) 25 25
1403 30 c. Otter with fish 30 30
1404 185 c. Two otters (vert) (air) 1·60 1·60

1989. Easter. Altarpiece by Tamas of Koloszvar. Multicoloured.

1405 60 c. + 30 c. Type **300** 85 85
1406 105 c. + 50 c. "Crucifixion" (centre panel) (28 × 36 mm) 1·50 1·50
1407 110 c. + 55 c. "Resurrection" (right wing) 1·50 1·50

301 Mercedes Touring Car, 1930

1989. Motor Cars. Multicoloured.

1408 25 c. Type **301** 15 15
1409 25 c. Mercedes Benz "300 E", 1985 15 15
1410 60 c. Daimler, 1897 40 40
1411 60 c. Jaguar "Sovereign", 1986 40 40
1412 90 c. Renault "Voiturette", 1898 60 60
1413 90 c. Renault "25 TX", 1989 60 60
1414 105 c. Volvo "Jacob", 1927 70 70
1415 105 c. Volvo "440", 1989 70 70
1416 110 c. Left-half of 1961 1 f. Monaco stamp 75 75
1417 110 c. Right-half of 1961 1 f. Monaco stamp 75 75
1418 120 c. Toyota "AA", 1936 80 80
1419 120 c. Toyota "Corolla" sedan, 1988 80 80

303 Joseph Nicephore Niepce (pioneer)

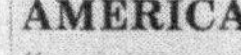
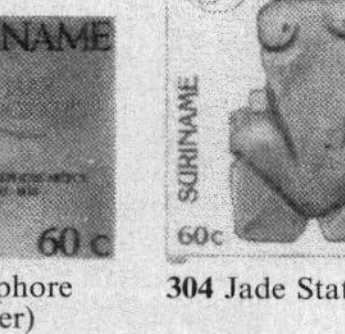
304 Jade Statuette

1989. 150th Anniv of Photography. Mult.

1421 60 c. Type **303** 40 40
1422 110 c. First camera using daguerreotype process 75 75
1423 120 c. Louis Jacques Mande Daguerre (inventor of daguerreotype process) 80 80

1989. America. Pre-Columbian Artifacts. Multicoloured.

1424 60 c. Type **304** 40 40
1425 110 c. Statuette of pregnant woman 75 75

305 1976 25 c. Surinam Stamp

306 "Children Helping Each Other" (Gianna Karg)

1989. "World Stamp Expo '89" International Stamp Exhibition, Washington, D.C. Multicoloured.

1426 110 c. Type **305** 75 75
1427 150 c. 1950 3 c. U.S.A. White House stamp 1·00 1·00
1428 250 c. 1976 60 c. Surinam "Divided Snake" stamp 1·75 1·75

1989. Child Welfare. Children's Paintings. Multicoloured.

1430 60 c. + 30 c. Type **306** 60 60
1431 105 c. + 50 c. "Child and Nature" (Tamara Busropan) 1·00 1·00
1432 110 c. + 55 c. "In the School Bus" (Cindy Kross) 1·10 1·10

307 Local Emblem

308 Temple

1990. International Literacy Year. Multicoloured.

1434 60 c. Type **307** 40 40
1435 110 c. I.L.Y. emblem 75 75
1436 120 c. Emblems and boy reading 80 80

1990. 60th Anniv of Arya Dewaker Temple.

1437 **308** 60 c. brown, red & black 40 40
1438 110 c. violet and black 75 75
1439 200 c. green and black 1·40 1·40

309 Mary and Baby Jesus

310 Surinam 1930 10 c. Air Stamp

1990. Easter. Multicoloured.

1440 60 c. + 30 c. Type **309** 55 55
1441 105 c. + 50 c. Jesus teaching 90 90
1442 110 c. + 55 c. Jesus's body taken from cross 1·00 1·00

1990. "Stamp World London 90" International Stamp Exhibition, London, and 150th Anniv of the Penny Black. Multicoloured.

1443 110 c. Type **310** 65 65
1444 200 c. Penny Black 1·25 1·25
1445 250 c. G.B. 1929 $2\frac{1}{2}$d. Postal Union Congress stamp 1·50 1·50

311 Couple carrying Goods

313 Swamp

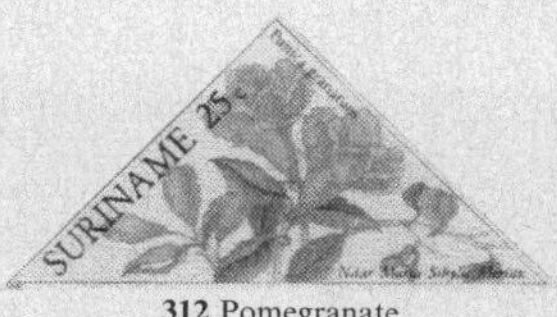
312 Pomegranate

1990. Centenary of Javanese Immigration. Mult.

1447 60 c. Type **311** 35 35
1448 110 c. Woman 65 65
1449 120 c. Man 70 70

1990. Flowers. Paintings by Maria Sibylle Merian. Multicoloured.

1450 25 c. Type **312** 15 15
1451 25 c. Passion flower 15 15
1452 35 c. "Hippeastrum puniceum" 20 20
1453 35 c. Sweet potato 20 20
1454 60 c. Rose of Sharon 35 35
1455 60 c. Jasmine 35 35
1456 105 c. Blushing hibiscus 60 60
1457 105 c. "Musa serapionis" 60 60
1458 110 c. Frangipani 65 65
1459 110 c. "Hibiscus diversifolius" 65 65
1460 120 c. Annatt ("Bixa orellana") 70 70
1461 120 c. Dwarf poinciana ("Caesalpinia pulcherima") 70 70

1990. America. Natural World.

1462 **313** 60 c. multicoloured 35 35
1463 110 c. multicoloured 65 65

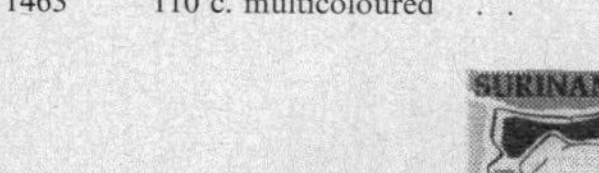
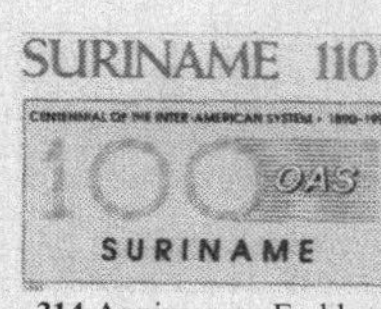
314 Anniversary Emblem

315 Fish and Flag as Map

1990. Centenary of Organization of American States.

1464 **314** 100 c. multicoloured 65 65

1990. 15th Anniv of Independence. Multicoloured.

1465 10 c. Type **315** 10 10
1466 60 c. Passion flower and flag as map 35 35
1467 110 c. Dove and flag as map 65 65

316 Painting by Janneke Fleskens

1990. Child Welfare. The Child in Nature. Paintings by children named. Multicoloured.

1468 60 c. + 30 c. Type **316** 55 55
1469 105 c. + 50 c. Tahlita Zuiverloon 90 90
1470 110 c. + 55 c. Samuel Jensen 1·00 1·00

317 Toucan

1991. Birds. Multicoloured.

1472 10 c. Type **317** 10 10
1473 15 g. Parrot . . . . 9·75 9·75

318 Christ carrying Cross 319 Shipping Company Store

1991. Easter. Multicoloured.

1474 60 c. + 30 c. Type **318** . . . 60 60
1475 105 c. + 50 c. Christ wearing crown of thorns . . . . . 1·00 1·00
1476 110 c. + 55 c. Woman cradling Christ's body . . . . . . 1·10 1·10

1991. Buildings.

1478 **319** 35 c. black, blue & lt bl . 20 20
1479 – 60 c. black, green and emerald 40 40
1480 – 75 c. blk, yell & lemon . 50 50
1481 – 105 c. black, orange and light orange 70 70
1482 – 110 c. black, pink & red . 70 70
1483 – 200 c. black, deep mauve and mauve . . . . . . 1·25 1·25

DESIGNS: 60 c. Upper class house; 75 c. House converted into Labour Inspection offices; 105 c. Plantation supervisor's house; 110 c. Ministry of Labour building; 200 c. Houses.

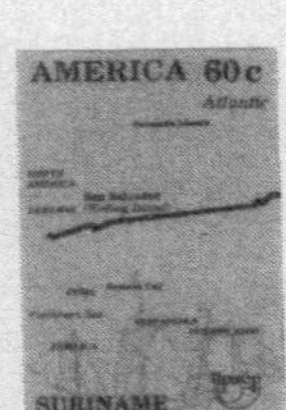

320 Puma 321 Route Map to Bahamas via San Salvador

1991. The Puma. Multicoloured.

1484 10 c. Type **320** (postage) . . 10 10
1485 20 c. Stalking 15 15
1486 25 c. Stretching 15 15
1487 30 c. Licking nose 20 20
1488 125 c. Lying down (horiz) (air) 80 80
1489 500 c. Leaping (horiz) . . . . 3·25 3·25

1991. America. Voyages of Discovery. Each red, blue and black.

1490 60 c. Type **321** 65 65
1491 110 c. Route map from Canary Islands . . . . 1·00 1·00

Nos. 1490/1 were printed together, se-tenant, forming a composite design.

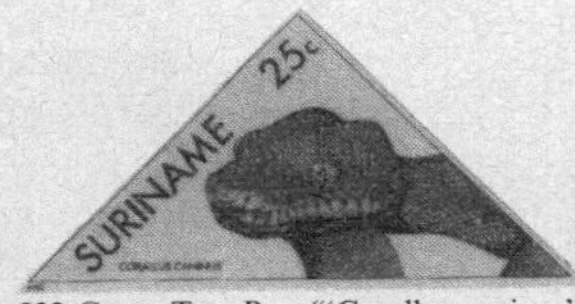

322 Green Tree Boa ("Corallus caninus")

1991. Snakes. Multicoloured.

1492 25 c. Type **322** 15 15
1493 25 c. Garden tree boa ("Corallus enydris") . . . 15 15
1494 35 c. Boa constrictor 20 20
1495 35 c. Bushmaster ("Lachesis muta") 20 20
1496 60 c. South American rattlesnake ("Crotalus durissus") 40 40
1497 60 c. Surinam coral snake ("Micrurus surinamensis") 40 40
1498 75 c. Mussurana ("Clelia cloelia") 50 50
1499 75 c. Anaconda ("Eunectes murinus") 50 50
1500 110 c. Rainbow boa ("Epicrutes cenchris") 70 70
1501 110 c. Sipo ("Chrironius carinatus") 70 70
1502 200 c. Black and yellow rat snake ("Spilotes pullatus") 1·25 1·25
1503 200 c. Vine snake ("Oxybelis argenteus") . . . . . . 1·25 1·25

INDEX

Countries can be quickly located by referring to the index at the end of this volume.

323 Child in Wheelchair 324 "Cycnoches haagii"

1991. Child Welfare. Multicoloured.

1504 60 c. + 30 c. Type **323** . . . 60 60
1505 105 c. + 50 c. Trees and girl 1·10 1·00
1506 110 c. + 55 c. Girls playing in yard . . . . 1·10 1·10

1992. Orchids. Multicoloured.

1508 50 c. Type **324** 30 30
1509 60 c. "Lycaste cristata" . . 40 40
1510 75 c. "Galeandra dives" (horiz) 50 50
1511 125 c. "Vanilla mexicana" . 80 80
1512 150 c. "Cyrtopodium glutiniferum" . . . . . 1·00 1·00
1513 250 c. "Gongora quinquenervis" . . . . . 1·60 1·60

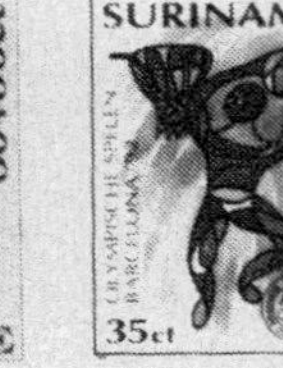

325 Crucifixion 327 Basketball

1992. Easter. Multicoloured.

1514 60 c. + 30 c. Type **325** . . . 70 70
1515 105 c. + 50 c. Women taking away Christ's body . . . 1·10 1·10
1516 110 c. + 55 c. The Resurrection 1·25 1·25

1992. Olympic Games, Barcelona. Multicoloured.

1518 35 c. Type **327** 25 25
1519 60 c. Volleyball 45 45
1520 75 c. Sprinting 55 55
1521 125 c. Football 95 95
1522 150 c. Cycling . . . . . . 1·10 1·10
1523 250 c. Swimming . . . . . 1·90 1·90

328 Emblems

1992. 50th Anniv of Young Women's Christian Association.

1525 **328** 60 c. multicoloured . . 45 45
1526 250 c. multicoloured . . 1·90 1·90

1992. Nos. 1236/7 surch **1 c.**

1527 1 c. on 5 c. orange and blue 10 10
1528 1 c. on 5 c. green, red & blue 10 10

330 Nau 331 Matzeliger and Shoe-lasting Machine

1992. 500th Anniv of Expulsion of Jews from Spain.

1529 **330** 250 c. multicoloured . . 2·25 2·25

1992. 140th Birth Anniv of Jan E Matzeliger (inventor).

1530 **331** 60 c. multicoloured . . 45 45
1531 250 c. multicoloured . . 1·90 1·90

332 Amerindian Ornament 333 Tree with Child's Face

1992. America. 500th Anniv of Discovery of America by Columbus.

1532 **332** 60 c. multicoloured . . 45 45
1533 250 c. multicoloured . . 1·90 1·90

1992. Child Welfare. Multicoloured.

1534 60 c. + 30 c. Type **333** . . . 70 70
1535 105 c. + 50 c. Tree with child's face beside flower . . . . 1·10 1·10
1536 110 c. + 55 c. Children hanging from tree . . . . 1·25 1·25

334 Star and Holly 336 "Costus arabicus"

1992. Christmas. Multicoloured.

1538 10 c. Type **334** 10 10
1539 60 c. Candle 45 45
1540 250 c. Parcels . . . . 1·90 1·90
1541 400 c. Crown . . . . 3·00 3·00

1993. Birds. (a) Postage. As T **258**. Multicoloured.

1542 25 g. Owl . . . . 19·00 19·00

(b) Air. No. 865 surch **35 ct.**

1543 35 c. on 50 c. multicoloured . . 25 25

1993. Medicinal Plants. Multicoloured.

1544 50 c. Type **336** 40 40
1545 75 c. "Quassia amara" . . . 55 55
1546 125 c. "Combretum rotundifolium" (horiz) . . . 95 95
1547 500 c. "Bixa orellana" (horiz) 3·75 3·75

337 Christ and Cross 339 90 r. "Bull's Eye" Stamp

338 Long-horned Beetle ("Macrodontia cervicornis")

1993. Easter. Multicoloured.

1548 60 c. + 30 c. Type **337** . . . 70 70
1549 110 c. + 50 c. Crucifixion . . 1·25 1·25
1550 125 c. + 60 c. Resurrection . . 1·40 1·40

1993. Insects. Multicoloured.

1551 25 c. Type **338** 20 20
1552 25 c. Locust 20 20
1553 35 c. Weevil ("Curculionidae") 25 25
1554 35 c. Grasshopper ("Acrididae") 25 25
1555 50 c. Goliath beetle ("Euchroma gigantea") 40 40
1556 50 c. Bush cricket ("Tettigonidae") 40 40
1557 100 c. "Tettigonidae" 75 75
1558 100 c. Scarab beetle ("Phanaeus festivus") 75 75
1559 175 c. Cricket ("Gryllidae") 1·25 1·25
1560 175 c. Dung beetle ("Phanaeus lancifer") . . . . 1·25 1·25
1561 220 c. "Tettigonidae" (different) 1·60 1·60
1562 220 c. Longhorn beetle ("Batus barbicornis") . . . . . 1·60 1·60

1993. 150th Anniv of First Brazilian Stamps and "Brasiliana 93" International Stamp Exhibition, Rio de Janeiro.

1563 **339** 50 c. black and violet . . 40 40
1564 – 250 c. black and blue . . 1·90 1·90
1565 – 500 c. black and green . . 3·75 3·75

DESIGNS: 250 c. 60 r. "Bull's eye" stamp; 500 c. 30 r. "Bull's eye" stamp.

340 Dwarf Cayman 341 Afro-Caribbean Angel

1993. America. Endangered Animals.

1567 **340** 50 c. multicoloured . . . 40 40
1568 100 c. multicoloured . . . 75 75

1993. Christmas. Multicoloured.

1569 25 c. Type **341** 20 20
1570 45 c. Asian angel 35 35
1571 50 c. Oriental angel 40 40
1572 150 c. Amerindian angel . . . 1·10 1·10

342 Hopscotch 344 Sambura

1993. Child Welfare. Children's Games.

1573 **342** 25 g. + 10 g. brown & grn 25 25
1574 – 35 g. + 10 g. brown & bl 35 35
1575 – 50 g. + 25 g. brown & grn 55 55
1576 – 75 g. + 25 g. brown & bl 75 75

DESIGNS: 35 g. Hopscotch (different); 50 g. Djoel (variant of hopscotch); 75 g. Djoel (different).

1993. Nos. 1252 and 1473 surch **f 5.-.**

1578 5 g. on 10 g. multicoloured . 3·75 3·75
1579 5 g. on 15 g. multicoloured . 3·75 3·75

1994. Traditional Drums. Multicoloured.

1580 25 g. Type **344** 20 20
1581 50 g. Apinti 40 40
1582 75 g. Terbangan 60 60
1583 100 g. Dhol 80 80

345 Roseate Spoonbill

1994.

1584 **345** 1300 g. multicoloured . . 10·00 10·00

1994. Air. No value expressed. Nos. 864 and 866/7 optd **Port Paye.**

1585 (–) on 45 c. multicoloured . 35 35
1586 (–) on 55 c. multicoloured . 45 45
1587 (–) on 60 c. multicoloured . 55 55

347 Smoking Chimneys

1994. Environmental Protection. Multicoloured.

1588 50 g. Type **347** 40 40
1589 350 g. Dead fish in polluted sea 2·60 2·60

POSTAGE DUE STAMPS

D 2 D 6

1885.

D36 D 2 2½ c. mauve and black . 2·00 2·00
D37 5 c. mauve and black . . 6·00 6·00
D38 10 c. mauve and black . £100 70·00
D39 20 c. mauve and black . 6·00 6·00
D40 25 c. mauve and black . 9·00 9·00
D41 30 c. mauve and black . 2·50 2·50
D42 40 c. mauve and black . 4·00 4·00
D43 50 c. mauve and black . 2·25 2·25

1892.

D57 D 6 2½ c. mauve and black . 20 20
D58 5 c. mauve and black . . 80 65
D59 10 c. mauve and black . 15·00 11·00
D60 20 c. mauve and black . 1·75 1·10
D61 25 c. mauve and black . 6·50 5·50
D62 40 c. mauve and black . 2·00 2·40

1911.

D111 D 2 10 c. on 30 c. mauve and black . . . . 65·00 65·00
D112 10 c. on 50 c. mauve and black . . . . 95·00 95·00

1913.

D153 D 6 ½ c. lilac 10 10
D154 1 c. lilac 10 15
D155 2 c. lilac 15 20
D156 2½ c. lilac 15 10
D157 5 c. lilac 10 10
D158 10 c. lilac 15 10
D159 12 c. lilac 20 20
D160 12½ c. lilac 20 10
D161 15 c. lilac 25 25
D162 20 c. lilac 60 25
D163 25 c. lilac 25 10
D164 30 c. lilac 20 35
D165 40 c. lilac . . . . 9·00 9·50
D166 50 c. lilac 75 65
D167 75 c. lilac 90 90
D168 1 g. lilac . . . . 1·10 90

D 52

D 68

1945.

No.	Type	Description	Unused	Used
D337	D 52	1 c. purple	30	35
D338		5 c. purple	3·25	1·40
D339		25 c. purple	8·50	20

1950. As Type D **121** of Netherlands.

No.	Type	Description	Unused	Used
D384		1 c. purple	1·60	1·75
D385		2 c. purple	2·25	2·00
D386		2½ c. purple	2·50	1·50
D387		5 c. purple	3·50	30
D388		10 c. purple	2·25	30
D389		15 c. purple	6·50	2·50
D390		20 c. purple	1·50	3·25
D391		25 c. purple	21·00	20
D392		50 c. purple	24·00	1·40
D393		75 c. purple	35·00	27·00
D394		1 g. purple	26·00	6·00

1956.

No.	Type	Description	Unused	Used
D436	D 68	1 c. purple	10	10
D437		2 c. purple	35	20
D438		2½ c. purple	35	30
D439		5 c. purple	25	25
D440		10 c. purple	35	30
D441		15 c. purple	60	45
D442		20 c. purple	60	50
D443		25 c. purple	65	20
D444		50 c. purple	1·60	35
D445		75 c. purple	2·25	1·00
D446		1 g. purple	3·00	10

1987. Various stamps optd **TE BETALEN**.

No.	Type	Description	Unused	Used
D1325		65 c. mult (No. 868)	1·00	50
D1326		65 c. mult (No. 1132)	50	50
D1327		80 c. mult (No. 1134)	1·00	60
D1328		90 c. mult (No. 872a)	1·10	70
D1329		95 c. mult (No. 873)	1·25	75
D1330		1 g. mult (No. 1248)	1·25	75

SWEDEN — Pt. 11

A kingdom of N. Europe, united to Norway till 1905.

1855. 48 skilling banco = 1 riksdaler
1858. 100 ore = 1 riksdaler
1875. 100 ore = 1 krona

1

2

3

1855.

No.	Type	Description	Unused	Used
1	1	3 s. green	£6000	£3000
2		4 s. blue	£1100	45·00
3		6 s. grey	£7000	£800
3b		6 s. brown	£7500	£850
4		8 s. orange	£3750	£400
5		24 s. red	£6000	£1700

1858.

No.	Type	Description	Unused	Used
6b	1	5 ore green	£120	13·00
7a		9 ore purple	£300	£170
8a		12 ore blue	£130	1·40
9		24 ore orange	£300	18·00
10		30 ore brown	£300	22·00
11b		50 ore red	£375	65·00

1862.

No.	Type	Description	Unused	Used
12c	2	3 ore brown	70·00	9·50

1866.

No.	Type	Description	Unused	Used
13	3	17 ore purple	£450	£100
14		17 ore grey	£600	£550
15b		20 ore red	£150	12·00

4

6 King Oscar II

5

1872.

No.	Type	Description	Unused	Used
29	4	2 ore orange	1·75	3·00
30		3 ore brown	7·50	9·00
31		4 ore grey	19·00	60
32		5 ore green	38·00	30
33a		6 ore purple	16·00	21·00
20		6 ore olive	£650	35·00
34	6	10 ore red	60·00	10
21	4	12 ore blue	17·00	25
35		20 ore red	75·00	30
23a		24 ore yellow	35·00	12·00
36		30 ore brown	£100	55
37a		50 ore red	£100	2·40
26	5	1 r. blue and brown	£550	40·00
38		1 k. blue and brown	60·00	1·40

On No. 26 the value is expressed as one riksdaler; on No. 38 the value is one krona.

1889. Surch with new value and Arms.

No.	Type	Description	Unused	Used
39	4	10 ore on 12 ore blue	1·60	2·50
40		10 ore on 24 ore yellow	9·00	20·00

9

10 Oscar II

11

1891.

No.	Type	Description	Unused	Used
41	9	1 ore blue and brown	1·00	20
42a		2 ore yellow and blue	3·75	10
43		3 ore orange and brown	55	80
44		4 ore blue and red	4·50	10
45c	10	5 ore green	1·75	10
46		8 ore purple	2·25	60
47		10 ore red	4·25	10
48		15 ore brown	18·00	10
49		20 ore blue	18·00	10
50		25 ore orange	21·00	10
51a		30 ore brown	40·00	10
53		50 ore grey	55·00	20
54	11	1 k. grey and red	90·00	80

13 G.P.O., Stockholm

14

15 Gustav V

1903. Opening of new Post Office.

No.	Type	Description	Unused	Used
57	13	5 k. blue	£190	20·00

1910.

No.	Type	Description	Unused	Used
65	14	1 ore black	10	10
66		2 ore orange	10	10
67		3 ore brown	10	10
68		4 ore mauve	10	10
69	15	5 ore green	1·40	10
70	15	7 ore green	15	10
71		8 ore purple	15	10
72		10 ore red	1·60	10
73		12 ore red	15	10
74		15 ore brown	4·50	10
75		20 ore blue	6·00	10
76		25 ore orange	20	10
77		27 ore blue	40	70
78		30 ore brown	17·00	10
79		35 ore violet	15·00	10
80		40 ore green	22·00	10
81		50 ore grey	42·00	10
82		55 ore blue	£1100	£3500
83		65 ore green	65	1·50
84		80 ore black	£1100	£3500
85		90 ore green	70	40
86		1 k. black on yellow	65·00	20
64		5 k. purple on yellow	2·50	2·00

1916. Clothing Fund for Mobilized Reservists ("Landstorm"). Surch **FRIMARKE LANDSTORMEN** and value in figures and words round Arms.

No.	Type	Description	Unused	Used
86a	4	5 + 5 on 2 ore orange	3·75	4·50
86b		5 + 5 on 3 ore brown	3·75	4·50
86c		5 + 5 on 4 ore grey	3·75	4·50
86d		5 + 5 on 5 ore green	3·75	4·50
86e		5 + 5 on 6 ore mauve	3·75	4·50
86f		10 + 10 on 12 ore blue	3·75	4·50
86g		10 + 10 on 20 ore red	3·75	4·50
86h		10 + 10 on 24 ore yellow	3·75	4·50
86i		10 + 10 on 30 ore brown	3·75	4·50
86j		10 + 10 on 50 ore red	3·75	4·50

1916. Clothing Fund for Mobilized Reservists. Surch **LANDSTORMEN** and **FRIMARKE SVERIGE** in frame round Arms and value in figures and words.

No.	Type	Description	Unused	Used
86k	D 6	5 + 5 on 1 ore black	9·00	7·00
86l		5 + 5 on 3 ore red	2·50	3·50
86m		5 + 5 on 5 ore brown	2·25	3·50
86n		5 + 10 on 6 ore orange	3·50	4·50
86o		5 + 15 on 12 ore red	24·00	16·00
86p		10 + 20 on 20 ore blue	8·50	12·00
86q		10 + 40 on 24 ore mauve	32·00	65·00
86r		10 + 20 on 30 ore green	2·75	4·25
86s		10 + 40 on 50 ore brown	15·00	24·00
86t		10 + 90 on 1 k. black and brown	90·00	£275
86u	13	10 ore + 4 k. 90 ore on 5 k. blue	90·00	£225

1917. Surch in figures only.

No.	Type	Description	Unused	Used
87	15	7 on 10 ore red	20	10
88		12 on 25 ore orange	1·40	25
89		12 on 65 ore green	1·00	60
90		27 on 55 ore blue	70	1·00
91		27 on 65 ore green	1·10	2·00
92		27 on 80 ore black	60	1·00
93		1.98 k. on 5 k. pur on yellow	2·00	3·50
94		2.12 k. on 5 k. pur on yellow	2·00	3·50

1918. Landstorm Fund. Charity stamps of 1916 surch.

No.	Type	Description	Unused	Used
94a	4	7 + 3 on 5 ore on 2 ore	6·50	8·00
94b		7 + 3 on 5 ore on 3 ore	1·75	1·40
94c		7 + 3 on 5 ore on 4 ore	1·75	1·40
94d		7 + 3 on 5 ore on 5 ore	1·75	1·40
94e		7 + 3 on 5 ore on 6 ore	1·75	1·40
94f		12 + 8 on 10 ore on 12 ore	1·75	1·40
94g		12 + 8 on 10 ore on 20 ore	1·75	1·40
94h		12 + 8 on 10 ore on 24 ore	1·75	1·40
94i		12 + 8 on 10 ore on 30 ore	1·75	1·40
94j		12 + 8 on 10 ore on 50 ore	1·75	1·40

19 Arms

20 Lion (after sculpture by B. Foucquet)

21 Gustav V

22 Emblem of Swedish Post

1920.

No.	Type	Description	Unused	Used
95	19	3 ore brown	60	30
96	20	5 ore green	2·50	30
97a		5 ore brown	80	2·25
98		10 ore green	1·50	40
99		10 ore violet	2·00	10
102a	21	10 ore red	8·00	3·00
103		15 ore red	15	20
104a		20 ore blue	15·00	4·00
100	20	25 ore orange	7·50	25
101		30 ore brown	20	25
105	22	35 ore yellow	22·00	20
106		40 ore olive	22·00	35
107		45 ore brown	1·00	40
108		60 ore purple	11·00	20
109		70 ore brown	45	1·10
110		80 ore green	30	20
111		85 ore green	2·00	30
112		90 ore blue	38·00	10
113		1 k. orange	4·50	10
114		110 ore blue	40	10
115		115 ore brown	4·50	30
116		120 ore black	42·00	45
117		120 ore mauve	6·50	50
118		140 ore black	75	15
119		145 ore green	5·00	70

INDEX

Countries can be quickly located by referring to the index at the end of this volume.

23 Gustavus II Adolphus

24 Gustav V (after portrait by E. Osterman)

25 Gustavus Vasa

1920. Tercentenary of Swedish Post between Stockholm and Hamburg.

No.	Type	Description	Unused	Used
120	23	20 ore blue	1·25	10

1920. Air. Official stamps surch **LUFTPOST** and value.

No.	Type	Description	Unused	Used
120a	O 17	10 on 3 ore brown	2·00	4·50
120b		20 on 2 ore yellow	4·00	6·00
120c		50 on 4 ore lilac	15·00	16·00

1921.

No.	Type	Description	Unused	Used
121	24	15 ore violet	11·00	10
122		15 ore red	12·00	15
123		15 ore brown	3·50	10
124		20 ore violet	30	10
125		20 ore red	13·00	20
126		20 ore orange	30	15
128		25 ore red	50	1·00
129		25 ore blue	10·00	10
131		25 ore orange	22·00	10
133		30 ore brown	20·00	10
134		30 ore blue	5·50	35
135		35 ore mauve	14·00	10
136		40 ore blue	40	35
137		40 ore olive	25·00	50
138		45 ore brown	3·50	30
139a		50 ore black	1·25	15
140		85 ore green	11·00	1·00
141		115 ore brown	8·00	85
142		145 ore green	6·00	1·00

1921. 400th Anniv of Liberation of Sweden.

No.	Type	Description	Unused	Used
143	25	20 ore violet	7·50	14·00
144		110 ore blue	40·00	3·50
145		140 ore black	22·00	3·75

26 Old City, Stockholm

27 Gustav V

1924. 8th Congress of U.P.U. Perf.

No.	Type	Description	Unused	Used
146	26	5 ore brown	1·40	2·00
147		10 ore green	1·40	2·00
148		15 ore violet	1·25	1·10
149		20 ore red	8·50	8·50
150		25 ore orange	11·00	14·00
151		30 ore blue	9·00	10·00
152		35 ore black	14·00	16·00
153		40 ore green	17·00	19·00
154		45 ore brown	23·00	24·00
155		50 ore grey	22·00	22·00
156		60 ore red	30·00	30·00
157		80 ore green	25·00	25·00
158	27	1 k. green	50·00	65·00
159		2 k. red	£120	£160
160		5 k. blue	£225	£325

28 Post Rider and Friedrichsafen FF-49 Seaplane

29 Carrier-pigeon

1924. 50th Anniv of U.P.U. Perf.

No.	Type	Description	Unused	Used
161	28	5 ore brown	1·75	2·25
162		10 ore green	1·75	2·00
163		15 ore violet	1·75	1·50
164		20 ore red	13·00	20·00
165		25 ore orange	15·00	21·00
166		30 ore blue	15·00	12·00
167		35 ore black	19·00	26·00
168		40 ore green	20·00	22·00
169		45 ore brown	25·00	24·00
170		50 ore grey	32·00	26·00
171		60 ore red	35·00	45·00
172		80 ore green	30·00	23·00
173	29	1 k. green	60·00	75·00
174		2 k. red	£175	65·00
175		5 k. blue	£250	£175

29a King Gustav V

29c Night Flight by Junkers F-13 over Stockholm

1928. 70th Birthday of King Gustav V and Cancer Research Fund. Perf.

No.	Type	Description	Unused	Used
175a	29a	5 + 5 ore green	2·00	3·75
175b		10 + 5 ore violet	2·00	3·75
175c		15 + 5 ore red	2·00	3·00
175d		20 + 5 ore orange	3·00	1·75
175e		25 + 5 ore blue	3·00	2·50

1930. Air.

No.	Type	Description	Unused	Used
175f	29c	10 ore blue	15	40
175g		50 ore violet	40	1·00

30 Royal Palace, Stockholm

31 Death of Gustavus Adolphus at Lutzen

1931. Perf.

No.	Type	Description	Unused	Used
176	30	5 k. green	65·00	5·50

1932. Death Tercentenary of Gustavus Adolphus.

No.	Type	Description	Unused	Used
177	31	10 ore violet	1·75	10
178		15 ore red	1·75	10
179		25 ore blue	4·25	55
180		90 ore green	17·00	1·50

32 Allegory of Thrift

33 Stockholm Cathedral

1933. 50th Anniv of Swedish Postal Savings Bank.

No.	Type	Description	Unused	Used
181	32	5 ore green	1·25	55

1935. 500th Anniv of First Swedish Parliament. Stockholm Buildings.

No.	Type	Description	Unused	Used
182	–	5 ore green	1·00	10
183	–	10 ore violet	4·00	10
184	33	15 ore red	1·60	10
185	–	25 ore blue	5·50	45
186	–	35 ore red	8·50	1·60
187	–	60 ore red	12·00	1·40

DESIGNS: 5 ore Old City Hall; 10 ore Exchange; 25 ore House of the Nobility; 35 ore Houses of Parliament; 60 ore Arms of Engelbrekt.

35 A. Oxenstierna (after D. Dumonstier)

38 Junkers W.34 over Scandinavia

1936. Tercentenary of Swedish Post.

No.	Type	Description	Unused	Used
188	35	5 ore green	1·25	10
189	–	10 ore violet	1·25	10
190	–	15 ore red	1·75	10
191	–	20 ore blue	8·00	2·50
192	–	25 ore blue	6·00	40
193	–	30 ore brown	13·00	1·75
194	–	35 ore purple	4·25	85
195	–	40 ore green	7·50	2·00
196	–	45 ore green	5·50	2·25
197	–	50 ore grey	18·00	1·75
198	–	60 ore purple	28·00	50
199	–	1 k. blue	8·00	5·00

DESIGNS: 10 ore Early courier; 15 ore Post rider; 20 ore Sailing packet "Hiorten"; 25 ore Paddle-steamer "Constitutionen"; 30 ore Mail coach; 35 ore Arms; 40 ore Steam train; 45 ore A. W. Roos (Postmaster General 1867–89); 50 ore Motor bus and trailer; 60 ore Liner "Gripsholm"; 1 k. Junkers Ju 52/3m seaplane.

For similar designs, but dated "1972" at foot, see Nos. 700/4.

1936. Inauguration of Bromma Aerodrome.

No.	Type	Description	Unused	Used
200	38	50 ore blue	5·50	6·50

39 E. Swedenborg (after P. Krafft)

40 Governor Printz and Red Indian

1938. 250th Birth Anniv of Swedenborg.

No.	Type	Description	Unused	Used
201	39	10 ore violet	70	10
202		100 ore green	3·50	90

1938. 300th Anniv of Founding of New Sweden, U.S.A.

No.	Type	Description	Unused	Used
203	40	5 ore green	45	10
204	–	15 ore brown	45	10
205	–	20 ore red	11·00	50
206	–	30 ore blue	3·50	65
207	–	60 ore purple	4·50	20

DESIGNS: 15 ore Emigrant ships "Calmare Nyckel" and "Fagel Grip"; 20 ore Swedish landing in America; 30 ore First Swedish church, Wilmington; 60 ore Queen Christina (after S. Bourdon).

41 King Gustav V 42

43 Small Arms of Sweden

1938. 80th Birthday of King Gustav V.

No.	Type	Description	Unused	Used
208	41	5 ore green	45	10
209		15 ore brown	45	10
210		30 ore blue	11·00	55

1939.

No.	Type	Description	Unused	Used
234b	42	5 ore green	10	10
299		5 ore orange	15	10
235b		10 ore violet	10	10
300		10 ore green	15	10
236b		15 ore brown	10	10
237		20 ore red	10	10
238		25 ore orange	95	10
301		25 ore violet	1·25	10
239		30 ore blue	30	10
240		35 ore purple	60	10
241		40 ore olive	60	10
242		45 ore brown	60	10
243		50 ore grey	2·75	10
301a	43	50 ore grey	3·00	10
302		55 ore brown	2·50	10
221		60 ore red	80	10
302a		65 ore green	55	10
302b		70 ore blue	3·50	1·00
302c		75 ore brown	3·50	50
303		80 ore olive	60	10
222		85 ore green	50	10
303a		85 ore brown	6·50	1·00
223		90 ore blue	65	10
224		1 k. orange	40	10
303b		1 k. 5 blue	1·40	25
304		1 k. 10 violet	8·00	10
225		1 k. 15 brown	45	10
226		1 k. 20 purple	1·40	10
304a		1 k. 20 blue	3·75	2·00
305		1 k. 40 green	1·00	10
227		1 k. 45 green	2·25	50
305a		1 k. 50 purple	1·75	1·00
305b		1 k. 50 brown	1·40	20
305c		1 k. 70 red	1·50	10
306		1 k. 75 blue	18·00	4·50
306a		1 k. 80 blue	2·00	40
306b		1 k. 85 blue	3·75	70
306c		2 k. purple	80	10
306ca		2 k. cerise	55	10
306d		2 k. 10 blue	10·00	10
306e		2 k. 15 olive	5·00	25
306f		2 k. 30 purple	6·00	10
306g		2 k. 50 green	1·25	10
306h		2 k. 55 red	3·50	1·75
306i		2 k. 80 red	1·25	10
306j		2 k. 85 orange	3·50	3·75
306k		3 k. blue	1·25	10

44 P. H. Ling (after J. G. Sandberg)

45 Carl von Linne (Linnaeus) (after A. Roslin)

47 Carl Michael Bellman

1939. Death Centenary of P. H. Ling (creator of "Swedish Drill").

No.	Type	Description	Unused	Used
228	44	5 ore green	10	10
229		25 ore brown	70	10

1939. Bicent of Swedish Academy of Sciences.

No.	Type	Description	Unused	Used
230a	–	10 ore violet	1·10	40
231	45	15 ore brown	20	10
232	–	30 ore blue	10·00	25
233	45	50 ore grey	9·00	55

PORTRAIT: 10 ore, 30 ore J. J. Berzelius (after O. J. Sodermark).

1940. Birth Bicent of C. M. Bellman (poet).

No.	Type	Description	Unused	Used
244	47	5 ore green	10	10
245		35 ore red	55	20

48 Johan Tobias Sergel (self-portrait bust)

49 Reformers presenting Bible to Gustavus Vasa

1940. Birth Bicent of Sergel (sculptor).

No.	Type	Description	Unused	Used
246	48	15 ore brown	2·00	10
247		50 ore grey	14·00	60

1941. 400th Anniv of First Authorised Version of Bible in Swedish.

No.	Type	Description	Unused	Used
248	49	15 ore brown	20	10
249		90 ore blue	15·00	60

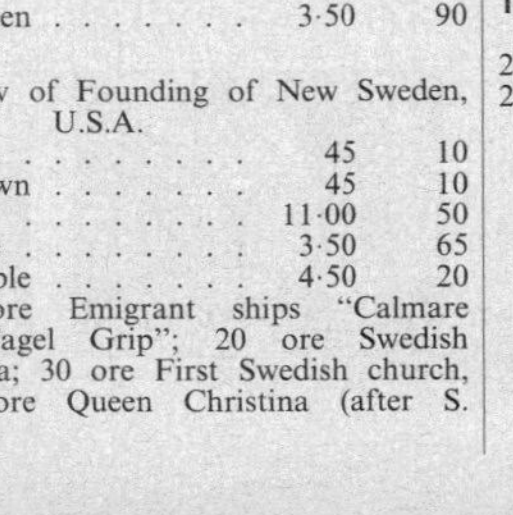

50 Hasjo Belfry

50a Royal Palace, Stockholm

1941. 50th Anniv of Foundation of Skansen Open-air Museum.

No.	Type	Description	Unused	Used
250	50	10 ore violet	1·40	10
251		60 ore red	6·50	30

1941. Perf.

No.	Type	Description	Unused	Used
252b	50a	5 k. blue	1·50	10

51 A. Hazelius

52 St. Bridget (from altar painting, Vasteras Cathedral)

1941. Artur Hazelius (founder of Skansen Museum).

No.	Type	Description	Unused	Used
253	51	5 ore green	10	10
254		1 k. orange	5·50	1·75

1941. 550th Anniv of Canonization of St. Bridget (Foundress of Brigittine Order of Our Saviour).

No.	Type	Description	Unused	Used
255	52	15 ore brown	10	10
256		120 ore purple	20·00	7·00

53 Mute Swans

54 King Gustavus III (after A. Roslin)

1942. Perf.

No.	Type	Description	Unused	Used
257a	53	20 k. blue	3·50	40

1942. 150th Anniv of National Museum, Stockholm.

No.	Type	Description	Unused	Used
258	54	20 ore red	30	10
259	–	40 ore olive	15·00	75

PORTRAIT: 40 ore Carl Gustaf Tessin (architect and chancery president) (after Gustav Lundberg).

55 Count Rudenschold and Nils Mansson

56 Carl Wilhelm Scheele

1942. Centenary of Institution of National Elementary Education.

No.	Type	Description	Unused	Used
260	55	10 ore red	30	30
261		90 ore blue	2·00	5·00

1942. Birth Bicent of C. W. Scheele (chemist).

No.	Type	Description	Unused	Used
262	56	5 ore green	10	10
263		60 ore red	5·00	25

57 King Gustav V

58 Rifle Assn Badge

1943. 85th Birthday of King Gustav V.

No.	Type	Description	Unused	Used
264	57	20 ore red	40	10
265		30 ore blue	70	2·00
266		60 ore purple	90	2·25

1943. 50th Anniv of National Voluntary Rifle Association.

No.	Type	Description	Unused	Used
267	58	10 ore purple	10	10
268		90 ore blue	2·50	25

59 O. Montelius (after E. Stenberg)

60 First Swedish Navigators' Chart

1943. Birth Centenary of Oscar Montelius (archaeologist).

No.	Type	Description	Unused	Used
269	59	5 ore green	10	10
270		120 ore purple	4·00	1·75

1944. Tercent of First Swedish Marine Chart.

No.	Type	Description	Unused	Used
271	60	5 ore green	20	10
272		60 ore red	4·25	30

61 "Smalands Lejon" (ship of the line)

1944. Swedish Fleet (Tercentenary of Battle of Femern).

No.	Type	Description	Unused	Used
273	61	10 ore violet	20	10
274	–	20 ore red	40	10
275	–	30 ore blue	55	60
276	–	40 ore olive	70	55
277	–	90 ore grey	9·00	1·40

DESIGNS—$27 \times 22\frac{1}{2}$ mm: 30 ore "Kung Karl" (ship of the line); 40 ore Stern of "Amphion" (royal yacht); 90 ore "Gustav V" (cruiser). $18\frac{1}{2} \times 20\frac{1}{2}$ mm: 20 ore Admiral C. Fleming (after L. Pasch).

See also Nos. 517/22.

62 Red Cross

63 Press Symbols

1945. 80th Anniv of Swedish Red Cross and Birthday of Prince Carl.

No.	Type	Description	Unused	Used
278	62	20 ore red	40	10

1945. Tercentenary of Swedish Press.

No.	Type	Description	Unused	Used
279	63	5 ore green	10	10
280		60 ore red	4·50	20

64 Viktor Rydberg (after A. Edelfelt)

65 Oak Tree, Savings Banks' Symbol

1945. 50th Death Anniv of Viktor Rydberg (author).

No.	Type	Description	Unused	Used
281	64	20 ore red	20	10
282		90 ore blue	4·50	25

1945. 125th Anniv of Swedish Savings Banks.

No.	Type	Description	Unused	Used
283	65	10 ore violet	10	10
284		40 ore olive	1·10	65

66 Cathedral Model

67 Lund Cathedral

1946. 800th Anniv of Lund Cathedral.

No.	Type	Description	Unused	Used
285	66	15 ore brown	60	10
286	67	20 ore red	20	10
287	66	90 ore blue	6·50	50

68 Mare and Foal

69 Tegner (after bust by J. N. Bystrom)

70 A. Nobel

1946. Centenary of Swedish Agricultural Show.

No.	Type	Description	Unused	Used
288	68	5 ore green	15	10
289		60 ore red	6·50	20

1946. Death Centenary of Esaias Tegner (poet).

No.	Type	Description	Unused	Used
290	69	10 ore violet	10	10
291		40 ore olive	1·00	25

1946. 50th Death Anniv of Alfred Nobel (scientist and creator of Nobel Foundation).

No.	Type	Description	Unused	Used
292	70	20 ore red	65	10
293		30 ore blue	1·75	45

71 E. G. Geijer (after J. G. Sandberg)

72 King Gustav V

73 Ploughman and Skyscraper

1947. Death Centenary of Erik Gustav Geijer (historian, philosopher, poet and composer).

No.	Type	Description	Unused	Used
294	71	5 ore green	10	10
295		90 ore blue	3·75	10

1947. Forty Years Reign of King Gustav V.

No.	Type	Description	Unused	Used
296	72	10 ore violet	10	10
297		20 ore red	25	10
298		60 ore purple	90	95

1948. Centenary of Swedish Pioneers in U.S.A.

No.	Type	Description	Unused	Used
307	73	15 ore brown	15	10
308		30 ore blue	40	25
309		1 k. orange	1·00	60

73a King Gustav V

74 J. A. Strindberg (after R. Bergh)

75 Gymnasts

1948. King Gustav V's 90th Birthday, and Youth Fund.
309a 73a 10 ore + 10 ore green . 30 35
309ba 20 ore + 10 ore red . . 35 55
309c 30 ore + 10 ore blue . 30 40

1949. Birth Centenary of Strindberg (dramatist).
310 74 20 ore red 20 10
311 30 ore blue 50 50
312 80 ore olive . . . . 1·75 35

1949. 2nd Lingiad, Stockholm.
313 75 5 ore blue 10 10
314 15 ore brown 10 10

76 Globe and Hand Writing 77

1949. 75th Anniv of U.P.U.
315 76 10 ore green 10 10
316 20 ore red 10 10
317 77 30 ore blue 25 25

78 King Gustav VI Adolf

79 Christopher Polhem (after G. E. Schroder)

80

1951. (a) Coloured lettering and figures.
318 78 10 ore green 15 10
318b 10 ore brown 10 10
319 15 ore brown 20 10
388 15 ore red 15 10
320 20 ore red 20 10
391 20 ore black 20 10
322a 25 ore black 40 10
323a 25 ore red 90 10
324a 25 ore blue 15 10
392 25 ore sepia 45 10
393 30 ore blue 30 10
326 30 ore sepia 40 20
326a 30 ore red . . . . 12·00 10
327 40 ore blue 55 10
394 40 ore green 70 10

(b) White lettering and figures.
429 78 15 ore red 10 10
430 20 ore black 25 10
431a 25 ore brown 10 10
432a 30 ore blue 45 10
433a 30 ore violet 45 30
433b 30 ore red 50 60
434 35 ore violet 50 10
435a 35 ore blue 20 10
436 35 ore black 50 10
437 40 ore green 70 10
438a 40 ore blue 20 10
439a 45 ore orange 50 10
439c 45 ore blue 65 10
440 50 ore olive 70 10
440a 50 ore green 40 10
440c 55 ore red 40 10
441 60 ore red 70 50
441a 65 ore blue . . . . 1·00 10
441c 70 ore mauve 60 10
441d 85 ore purple . . . . . . 1·00 20

1951. Death Bicentenary of Polhem (engineer).
329a 79 25 ore black 20 20
330 45 ore brown 30 20

1951.
383 80 5 ore red 10 10
386 10 ore blue 10 10
387a 10 ore brown 10 10
389 15 ore green 10 10
390a 15 ore brown 30 35

81 Olavus Petri Preaching

81a King Gustav VI Adolf

1952. 400th Death Anniv of Petri (reformer).
332 81 25 ore black 10 10
333 1 k. 40 brown . . . . . . 2·25 45

1952. 70th Birthday of King Gustav VI Adolf and Culture Fund.
333a 81a 10 ore + 10 ore green . 20 15
333b 25 ore + 10 ore red . . 15 30
333c 40 ore + 10 ore blue . . 25 35

82 Ski Jumping

83 Stockholm, 1650

1953. 50th Anniv of Swedish Athletic Assn.
334 82 10 ore green 30 10
335 – 15 ore brown 70 40
336 – 40 ore blue . . . . 1·00 95
337 – 1 k. 40 mauve . . . . . 2·50 70
DESIGNS—HORIZ: 1 k. 40, Wrestling. VERT: 15 ore Ice hockey; 40 ore Slingball.

1953. 700th Anniv of Stockholm.
338 83 25 ore blue 20 10
339 – 1 k. 70 red . . . . 3·00 55
DESIGN: 1 k. 70, Seal of Stockholm, 1296 (obverse and reverse).

84 "Radio"

85 Skier

1953. Cent of Telecommunications in Sweden.
340 – 25 ore blue ("Telephones") 20 10
341 84 40 ore green . . . . 1·00 1·10
342 – 60 ore red ("Telegraphs") 2·00 2·00

1954. World Skiing Championships.
343 85 20 ore grey 30 30
344 – 1 k. blue (Woman skier) . 7·00 80

86 Anna Maria Lenngren (after medallion, J. T. Sergel)

87 Rock-carvings

88

1954. Birth Bicentenary of Anna Maria Lenngren (poetess).
345 86 20 ore grey 20 10
346 65 ore brown . . . . . . 5·00 2·00

1954.
347 87 50 ore grey 30 10
348 55 ore red . . . . 1·10 10
349 60 ore red 40 10
350 65 ore green . . . . 1·40 10
351 70 ore orange 50 10
352 75 ore brown . . . . . . 2·50 10
353 80 ore green 60 10
355 90 ore blue 75 10
356 95 ore violet . . . . . . 5·00 2·75

1955. Centenary of First Swedish Postage Stamps.
362 88 25 ore blue 10 10
363 40 ore green 80 25

89 Swedish Flag

91 P. D. A. Atterbom (after Fogelberg)

1955. National Flag Day. Perf.
364 89 10 ore yellow, blue & grn . 10 10
365 15 ore yellow, blue & red . 15 10

1955. Cent of First Swedish Postage Stamps and "Stockholmia" Philatelic Exn. As T 1 but with two rules through bottom panel. Perf.
366 1 3 ore green . . . . 2·00 3·75
367 4 ore blue . . . . 2·00 3·75
368 6 ore grey . . . . 2·00 3·75
369 8 ore yellow . . . . 2·00 3·75
370 24 ore red . . . . 2·00 3·75
Nos. 366/70 were sold only at the Exhibition in single sets, at 2 k. 45 ore (45 ore face + 2 k. entrance fee).

1955. Death Centenary of Atterbom (poet).
371 91 20 ore blue 20 10
372 1 k. 40 brown . . . . . . 3·25 55

92 Greek Horseman, (from Parthenon frieze)

93 Railway Construction

1956. 16th Olympic Games Equestrian Competitions, Stockholm.
373 92 20 ore red 10 10
374 25 ore blue 25 10
375 40 ore green . . . . 1·50 1·00

1956. Northern Countries' Day. As T 101a of Norway.
376 25 ore red 75 10
377 40 ore blue . . . . 2·25 40

1956. Centenary of Swedish Railways.
378 93 10 ore green 55 15
379 – 25 ore blue 40 15
380 – 40 ore orange . . . . . . 3·00 2·50
DESIGNS: 25 ore First Swedish steam locomotive, "Fryckstad"; 40 ore Arsta Bridge, Stockholm.

94 Trawler in Distress and Lifeboat

1957. 50th Anniv of Swedish Life Saving Service.
381a 94 30 ore blue . . . . 3·00 1·10
382 1 k. 40 red . . . . 4·00 90

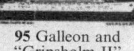

95 Galleon and "Gripsholm II"

96 Bell 47G Helicopter

1958. Postal Services Commemoration.
395 95 15 ore red 20 10
396 96 30 ore blue 15 10
397 95 40 ore green . . . . 4·25 2·10
398 96 1 k. 40 brown . . . . . . 4·50 75

97 Footballer

98 Bessemer Tilting-furnace

1958. World Football Championships.
399 97 15 ore red 10 10
400 20 ore green 20 10
401 1 k. 20 blue . . . . 1·40 65

1958. Centenary of Swedish Steel Industry.
402 98 30 ore blue 20 10
403 170 ore brown . . . . . . 3·00 65

99 Selma Lagerlof (after bust by G. Malmquist)

100 Overhead Power Lines

1958. Birth Centenary of Selma Lagerlof (writer).
404 99 20 ore red 10 10
405 30 ore blue 15 10
406 80 ore green 50 60

1959. 50th Anniv of Swedish State Power Board.
407 100 30 ore blue 25 10
408 – 90 ore red . . . . 3·25 1·75
DESIGN—HORIZ: 90 oe Dam sluice-gates.

101 Henri Dunant (founder)

102 V. von Heidenstam

1959. Red Cross Centenary.
409 101 30 ore + 10 ore red . . . 40 50

1959. Birth Centenary of Verner von Heidenstam (poet).
410 102 15 ore red 50 10
411 1 k. black . . . . 2·75 60

103 Forest Trees

104 S. Arrhenius

1959. Centenary of Crown Lands and Forests Administration.
412a 103 30 ore green 70 85
413 – 1 k. 40 brown . . . . . 2·50 50
DESIGN: 1 k. 40, Forester felling tree.

1959. Birth Centenary of Arrhenius (chemist).
414 104 15 ore brown 20 10
415 1 k. 70 blue . . . . 2·75 30

105 Anders Zorn (self-portrait)

106 "Uprooted Tree"

1960. Birth Cent of Zorn (painter and etcher).
416 105 30 ore grey 20 10
417 80 ore brown . . . . . . 1·60 90

1960. World Refugee Year.
418 106 20 ore brown 10 10
419 – 40 ore violet 20 20
DESIGN—VERT: 40 ore Refugees.

107 Target-shooting

108 G. Froding

1960. Centenary of Voluntary Shooting Organization.
420 107 15 ore red 20 10
421 – 90 ore turquoise . . . . . 1·25 90
DESIGN: 90 ore Organization members marching, 1860.

1960. Birth Centenary of Gustav Froding (poet).
422 108 30 ore brown 20 10
423 1 k. 40 green . . . . . . 2·00 25

1960. Europa. As T 113a of Norway.
424 40 ore blue 10 10
425 1 k. red 25 25

109 H. Branting

111 "Coronation of Gustav III" (after Pilo)

1960. Birth Centenary of Hjalmar Branting (statesman).
426 109 15 ore red 10 10
427 1 k. 70 blue . . . . 2·25 30

1961. 10th Anniv of Scandinavian Airlines System. As T 113b of Norway.
428 40 ore blue 20 10

1961. 250th Birth Anniv of Carl Gustav Pilo (painter).
442 111 30 ore brown 20 10
443 1 k. 40 blue . . . . 2·00 65

112 J. Alstromer (after bust by P. H. l'Archeveque)

113 Printing Works and Library

1961. Death Bicentenary of Jonas Alstromer (industrial reformer).
444 112 15 ore purple 15 10
445 90 ore blue . . . . 1·10 1·00

1961. Tercentenary of Royal Library Regulation.
446 113 20 ore red 10 10
447 1 k. blue . . . . 5·00 60

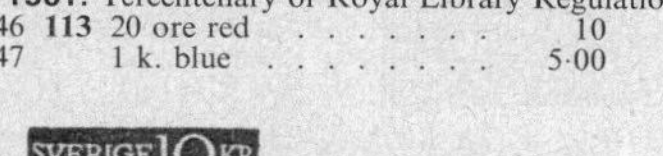

114 Motif on Runic Stone at Oland

115 Nobel Prize Winners of 1901

1961.
448 114 10 k. purple . . . . . . 15·00 30

1961. Nobel Prize Winners.
449 115 20 ore red 15 10
450 40 ore blue 25 10
451 50 ore green 25 10
See also Nos. 458/9, 471a/2, 477/8, 488/9, 523/4, 546/7 and 573/4.

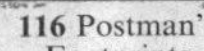

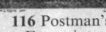

116 Postman's Footprints　117 Code, Voting Instrument and Mallet

1962. Centenary of Swedish Local Mail Delivery Service.

452 **116** 30 ore violet 10 10
453 1 k. 70 red . . . . 2·00 30

1962. Centenary of Municipal Laws.

454 **117** 30 ore blue 20 10
455 2 k. red . . . . 2·50 30

118 St. George and Dragon, Storkyrkan ("Great Church"), Stockholm　119 Ice-hockey Player

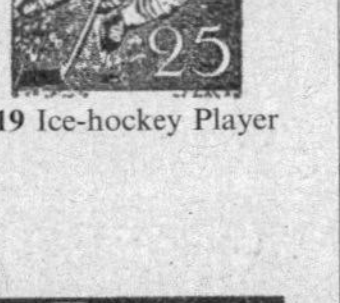

118a King Gustav VI Adolf and Cultural Themes

1962. Swedish Monuments (1st series).

456 **118** 20 ore red 15 10
457 – 50 ore green 40 10

DESIGN—HORIZ: 50 ore Skokloster Castle.
See also Nos. 469/70 and 479/80.

1962. King Gustav's 80th Birthday and Swedish Culture Fund.

457b **118a** 20 ore + 10 ore brown 15 20
457c 35 ore + 10 ore blue . . 15 20

1962. Nobel Prize Winners. As T **115** but inscr "NOBELPRIS 1902".

458 25 ore red 25 10
459 50 ore blue 35 10

PORTRAITS: Nobel Prize Winners of 1902; 25 ore Theodor Mommsen (literature) and Sir Ronald Ross (medicine); 50 ore Emily Hermann Fischer (chemistry) and Pieter Zeeman and Hendrik Lorentz (physics).

1963. World Ice Hockey Championships.

460 **119** 25 ore 10 10
461 1 k. 70 blue . . . . . . 2·25 30

120 Hands reaching for Wheat　121 Engineering and Industrial Symbols

1963. Freedom from Hunger.

462 **120** 35 ore mauve 10 10
463 50 ore violet 20 15

1963. "Engineering and Industry".

464 **121** 50 ore black 20 10
465 1 k. 05 orange . . . . . 1·50 1·50

122 Dr. G. F. Du Rietz (after D. K. Ehrenstrahl)　123 Linne's Hammarby (country house)

1963. 300th Anniv of Swedish Board of Health.

466 **122** 25 ore brown 25 10
467 35 ore blue 25 10
468 2 k. red . . . . 3·25 45

1963. Swedish Monuments (2nd series).

469 **123** 20 ore red 15 10
470 50 ore green 20 10

1963. Nobel Prize Winners. As T **115** but inscr "NOBELPRIS 1903".

471 25 ore green 50 35
472 50 ore brown 60 15

PORTRAITS: Nobel Prize winners of 1903. 25 ore Svante Arrhenius (chemistry), Niels Ryberg Finsen (medicine) and Bjornstjerne Bjornson (literature); 50 ore Antoine Henri Becquerel and Pierre and Marie Curie (physics).

124 Motif from poem "Elie Himmelsfard"　125 Seal of Archbishop Stefan

1964. Birth Centenary of E. A. Karlfeldt (poet).

473 **124** 35 ore blue 50 10
474 1 k. 05 red . . . . . . 2·75 2·50

1964. 800th Anniv of Archbishopric of Uppsala.

475 **125** 40 ore green 10 10
476a 60 ore brown 20 20

1964. Nobel Prize Winners. As T **115** but inscr "NOBELPRIS 1904".

477 30 ore blue 30 25
478 40 ore red 55 10

PORTRAITS: Nobel Prize winners of 1904. 30 ore Jose Echegaray y Eizaguirre and Frederic Mistral (literature) and J. W. Strutt (Lord Rayleigh) (physics); 40 ore Sir William Ramsay (chemistry) and Ivan Petrovich Pavlov (medicine).

126 Visby Town Wall　127 Posthorns　128 Telecommunications

1965. Swedish Monuments (3rd series).

479 **126** 30 ore red 10 10
480 2 k. blue . . . . 2·25 10

1965.

481 **127** 20 ore blue and yellow . 10 10

1965. Centenary of I.T.U.

482 **128** 60 ore violet 25 10
483 1 k. 40 blue . . . . . . 1·60 70

129 Prince Eugen (after D. Tagtstrom)　130 F. Bremer (after O. J. Sodermark)

1965. Birth Centenary of Prince Eugen (painter).

484 **129** 40 ore black 10 10
485 1 k. brown 90 15

1965. Death Centenary of Fredrika Bremer (novelist).

486 **130** 25 ore violet 10 10
487 3 k. green . . . . 4·00 30

1965. Nobel Prize Winners. As T **115** but inscr "NOBELPRIS 1905".

488 30 ore blue 30 10
489 40 ore red 30 10

PORTRAITS: Nobel Prize winners of 1905; 30 ore Philipp von Lenard (physics) and Johann von Baeyer (chemistry); 40 ore Robert Koch (medicine) and Henryk Sienkiewicz (literature).

131 N. Soderblom　132 Skating

1966. Birth Centenary of Nathan Soderblom, Archbishop of Uppsala.

490 **131** 60 ore brown 20 10
491 80 ore green 50 10

1966. World Men's Speed Skating Championships, Gothenburg.

492 **132** 5 ore red 10 10
493 25 ore green 15 15
494 40 ore blue 20 30

133 Entrance Hall, National Museum　134 Ale's Stones, Ship Grave, Kaseberga

1966. Centenary of Opening of National Museum Building.

495 **133** 30 ore violet 10 10
496 2 k. 30 green 60 70

1966.

498 – 35 ore brown and blue . . 10 10
499 **134** 3 k. 50 grey . . . . . . 1·10 10
500 – 3 k. 70 violet . . . . . . 1·25 10
501 – 4 k. 50 red . . . . 1·50 10
502 – 7 k. red and blue . . . . 2·25 30

DESIGNS—HORIZ: 35 ore Fjeld (mountains); 7 k. Gripsholm Castle. VERT: 3 k. 70, Lion Fortress, Gothenburg; 4 k. 50, Uppsala Cathedral (interior).

135 Louis de Geer (advocate of reform)

1966. Cent of Representative Assembly Reform.

510 **135** 40 ore blue 30 10
511 3 k. red . . . . 2·50 40

136 Theatre Stage　137 C. J. Almqvist (after C. P. Mazer)

1966. Bicentenary of Drottningholm Theatre.

512 **136** 5 ore red on red 10 10
513 25 ore brown on red . . . 10 10
514 40 ore purple on red . . . 25 40

1966. Death Centenary of Carl Almqvist (writer).

515 **137** 25 ore mauve 20 10
516 1 k. green . . . . 1·25 20

1966. National Cancer Fund. Swedish Ships. Designs as T **61**, but with imprint "1966" at foot.

517 10 ore red 15 20
518 15 ore red 15 20
519 20 ore green 15 20
520 25 ore blue 15 15
521 30 ore red 15 20
522 40 ore red 15 20

SHIPS—HORIZ: 10 ore "Smalands Lejon"; 15 ore "Calmare Nyckel" and "Fagel Grip"; 20 ore "Hiorten"; 25 ore "Constitutionen"; 30 ore "Kung Karl"; 40 ore Stern of "Amphion".

1966. Nobel Prize Winners. As T **115** but inscr "NOBELPRIS" 1906".

523 30 ore red 30 10
524 40 ore green 20 10

PORTRAITS: Nobel Prize winners of 1906; 30 ore Sir Joseph John Thomson (physics) and Giosue Carducci (literature); 40 ore Henri Moissan (chemistry) and Camillo Golgi and Santiago Ramon y Cajal (medicine).

138 Handball　139 "E.F.T.A."

1967. World Handball Championships.

525 **138** 45 ore blue 10 10
526 2 k. 70 mauve . . . . . 1·90 80

1967. European Free Trade Assn ("E.F.T.A.").

527 **139** 70 ore orange 30 10

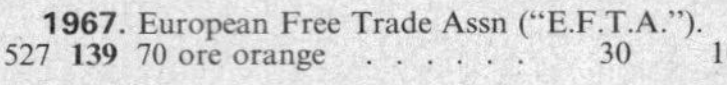

140 Table Tennis Player　141 Axeman and Beast

1967. World Table Tennis Championships, Stockholm.

528 **140** 35 ore mauve 10 10
529 90 ore blue 70 35

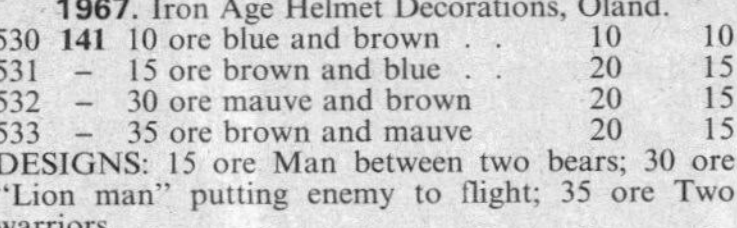

1967. Iron Age Helmet Decorations, Oland.

530 **141** 10 ore blue and brown . . 10 10
531 – 15 ore brown and blue . . 20 15
532 – 30 ore mauve and brown 20 15
533 – 35 ore brown and mauve 20 15

DESIGNS: 15 ore Man between two bears; 30 ore "Lion man" putting enemy to flight; 35 ore Two warriors.

142 "Solidarity"　144 18th-century Post-rider

143 "Keep to the Right"

1967. Finnish Settlers in Sweden.

534 **142** 10 ore multicoloured . . 10 10
535 35 ore multicoloured . . 10 10

1967. Adoption of Changed Rule of the Road.

536 **143** 35 ore black, orange & bl 10 10
537 45 ore black, orge & grn 10 10

1967.

538 **144** 5 ore black and red . . . 10 10
539 – 10 ore black and blue . . 15 10
539b – 20 ore black on flesh . . 10 10
540 – 30 ore red and blue . . . 10 10
541 – 40 ore blue, green & blk 20 10
541b – 45 ore black and blue . . 10 10
542 – 90 ore brown and blue . . 20 15
543 – 1 k. olive 30 10

DESIGNS—As T **144**: VERT: 10 ore "Svent Skepp" (warship); 20 ore "St. Stephen" (ceiling painting, Dadesjo Church, Smaland); 30 ore Angelica plant on coast. HORIZ: 40 ore Haverud Aqueduct, Dalsland Canal. $27\frac{1}{2} \times 22\frac{1}{2}$ mm: 45 ore Floating logs; 90 ore Elk; 1 k. Dancing cranes.

145 King Gustav VI Adolf　146 Berwald, Violin and Music

1967. 85th Birthday of King Gustav VI Adolf.

544 **145** 45 ore blue 10 10
545 70 ore green 15 10

1967. Nobel Prize Winners. As T **115**, but inscr "NOBELPRIS 1907".

546 35 ore red 60 30
547 45 ore blue 35 10

PORTRAITS: Nobel Prize winners of 1907; 35 ore Eduard Buchner (chemistry) and Albert Abraham Michelson (physics); 45 ore Charles Louis Alphonse Laveran (medicine) and Rudyard Kipling (literature).

1968. Death Centenary of Franz Berwald (composer).

548 **146** 35 ore black and red . . . 25 10
549 2 k. black, blue & yellow 2·75 45

147 Bank Seal　148 Butterfly Orchids

1968. 300th Anniv of Bank of Sweden.

550 **147** 45 ore blue 10 10
551 70 ore black on salmon . 15 10

1968. Wild Flowers.

552 **148** 45 ore green 70 30
553 – 45 ore green 70 30
554 – 45 ore red and green . . . 70 30
555 – 45 ore green 70 30
556 – 45 ore green 70 30

DESIGNS: No. 553, Wood anemone; 554, Wild rose; 555, Wild cherry; 556, Lily of the valley.

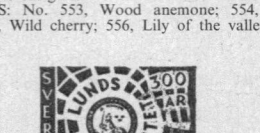

149 University Seal

1968. 300th Anniv of Lund University. Perf.
557 **149** 10 ore blue 10 10
558 35 ore red 20 20

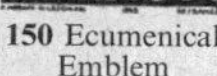

150 Ecumenical Emblem

151 "The Universe"

1968. 4th General Assembly of World Council of Churches, Uppsala.
559 **150** 70 ore purple 30 30
560 90 ore blue 80 10

1968. Centenary of the People's College.
561 **151** 45 ore red 10 10
562 2 k. blue . . . . 1·90 25

152 "Orienteer" crossing Forest

153 "The Tug of War" (wood-carving by Axel Petersson)

1968. World "Orienteering" Championships, Linkoping.
563 **152** 40 ore red and violet . . . 20 10
564 2 k. 80 violet and green . 2·75 2·25

1968. Birth Centenary of Axel Petersson ("Doderhultarn").
565 **153** 5 ore green 10 10
566 25 ore brown 65 95
567 45 ore brown and sepia . 10 10

154 Red Fox

155 "The Worker" (A. Amelin)

1968. Bruno Liljefors' Fauna Sketches. Perf.
568 – 30 ore blue 50 55
569 – 30 ore black 50 55
570 **154** 30 ore brown 50 55
571 – 30 ore brown 50 55
572 – 30 ore blue 50 55
DESIGNS: No. 568 Arctic hare; 569, Great black-backed gull; 571, Golden eagle and carrion crows; 572, Stoat.

1968. Nobel Prize Winners. As T **115**, but inscr "NOBELPRIS 1908".
573 35 ore lake 35 20
574 45 ore green 30 10
PORTRAITS: Nobel Prize winners of 1908; 35 ore Ilya Mechnikov and Paul Ehrlich (medicine) and Lord Rutherford (chemistry); 45 ore Gabriel Lippman (physics) and Rudolf Eucken (literature).

1969. 50th Anniv of Northern Countries Union. As T **161a** of Norway.
575 45 ore brown 20 10
576 70 ore blue 50 40

1969. 50th Anniv of I.L.O.
577 **155** 55 ore red 10 10
578 70 ore blue 50 25

156 Colonnade

157 A. Engstrom with Eagle Owl (self-portrait)

1969. Europa.
579 **156** 70 ore multicoloured . . . 65 10
580 1 k. multicoloured 95 10

1969. Birth Centenary of Albert Engstrom (painter and writer).
581 **157** 35 ore black 15 10
582 55 ore blue 20 10

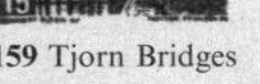

159 Tjorn Bridges

160 Helmeted Figure (carving)

1969. Tjorn Bridges.
584 **159** 15 ore blue on blue . . . 1·50 40
585 – 30 ore green and black on blue . . . . 1·50 40
586 – 55 ore black and blue on blue 1·50 40
DESIGNS: 30 ore Tjorn Bridges (different). LARGER (41 × 19 mm): 55 ore Tjorn Bridges (different).

1969. Warship "Wasa" Commemoration.
587 **160** 55 ore red 20 15
588 – 55 ore brown 20 15
589 – 55 ore blue 40 30
590 – 55 ore brown 20 15
591 – 55 ore red 20 15
592 – 55 ore blue 40 30
DESIGNS—VERT: No. 588, Crowned lion's head (carving); 590, Lion's head (carving); 591; Carved support. 46 × 28 mm: No. 589, Ship's coat-of-arms; 592, Ship of the line "Wasa", 1628.

161 H. Soderberg (writer)

163 "The Adventures of Nils" by S. Lagerlof (illus by J. Bauer)

162 Lighthouses and Lightship "Cyklop"

1969. Birth Centenaries of Hjalmar Soderberg and Bo Bergman.
593 **161** 45 ore brown on cream . 20 10
594 – 55 ore olive on green . . 20 10
DESIGN—HORIZ: 55 ore Bo Bergman (poet).

1969. 300th Anniv of Swedish Lighthouse Service.
595 **162** 30 ore black, red and grey 40 15
596 55 ore black, orge & blue 40 10

1969. Swedish Fairy Tales. Perf.
597 – 35 ore brown, red & orge 1·40 1·00
598 **163** 35 ore brown . . . . . . 1·40 1·00
599 – 35 ore brown, red & orge 1·40 1·00
600 – 35 ore brown . . . . . . 1·40 1·00
601 – 35 ore red and orange . 1·40 1·00
DESIGNS: No. 597, "Pelle's New Suit" written and illus by Elsa Beskow; 599, "Pippi Longstocking" (by A. Lindgren, illus by I. Vang Nyman); 600, "Vill-Vallareman, the Shepherd" (from "With Pucks and Elves" illus by J. Bauer); 601, "The Cat's Journey" written and illus by I. Arosenius.

164 Emil Kocher (medicine) and Wilhelm Ostwald (chemistry)

165 Weathervane, Soderala Church

1969. Nobel Prize Winners.
602 **164** 45 ore green 70 30
603 – 55 ore black on flesh . . 50 10
604 – 70 ore black 50 40
DESIGNS: Prize winners of 1909. 56 ore Selma Lagerlof (literature); 70 ore Guglielmo Marconi and Ferdinand Braun (physics).

1970. Swedish Forgings.
605 **165** 5 ore green and brown . 35 15
606 – 10 green and brown . . . 35 15
607 – 30 ore black and green . 35 15
608 – 55 ore brown and green . 35 15
DESIGNS—HORIZ: 10 ore As Type **165**, but design and country name/figures of value in reverse order; 30 ore Memorial Cross, Eksharad Churchyard. VERT: 55 ore (larger, 24 × 44 mm): 14th-century door, Bjorksta Church.

166 Seal of King Magnus Ladulas

167 River Ljungan

1970.
609 **166** 2 k. 55 blue on cream . 80 35
610a – 3 k. blue on cream . . . 50 10
611a – 5 k. green on cream . . 1·00 10
DESIGNS: 3 k. Seal of Duke Erik Magnusson; 5 k. Great Seal of Erik IX.

1970. Nature Conservation Year.
612 **167** 55 ore multicoloured . . 30 10
613 70 ore multicoloured . . 50 35

168 View of Kiruna

1970. Sweden within the Arctic Circle.
614 **168** 45 ore brown 45 60
615 – 45 ore blue 45 60
616 – 45 ore green 45 60
617 – 45 ore brown 45 60
618 – 45 ore blue 45 60
DESIGNS: No. 615, Winter landscape and skiers; 616, Lake and Lapp hut, Stora National Park; 617, Reindeer herd; 618, Rocket-launching.

170 Chinese Palace, Drottningholm

171 Lumber Trucks

1970. Historic Buildings.
619 – 55 ore green 20 10
620 **170** 2 k. multicoloured . . . 1·25 10
DESIGN—VERT: (21 × 27½ mm): 55 ore Glimmingehus (15th-century Castle).

1970. Swedish Trade and Industry. Perf (Nos. 621/6).
621 **171** 70 ore brown and blue . 2·50 2·75
622 – 70 ore blue, brn & pur . 4·25 3·75
623 – 70 ore purple and blue . 4·25 3·75
624 – 70 ore blue and purple . 5·50 3·75
625 – 70 ore blue and purple . 5·50 3·75
626 – 70 ore brown & purple . 2·50 2·75
627a – 1 k. black on cream . . . 30 10
DESIGNS—As Type **171**: No. 623, Ship's propeller; 624, Dam and electric locomotive; 626, Technician and machinery. 44 × 20 mm: No. 622, Loading freighter at quayside; 625, Mine and electric ore train. 26 × 20 mm: No. 627a, Miners at coal face.

173 Three Hearts

1970. 25th Anniv of United Nations.
628 **173** 55 ore red, yellow & black 15 10
629 – 70 ore green, yellow & blk 25 10
DESIGN: 70 ore Three four-leaved clovers.

174 Blackbird

175 Paul Heyse. (literature)

1970. Christmas. Birds. Multicoloured.
630 30 ore Type **174** 90 60
631 30 ore Great tit 90 60
632 30 ore Bullfinch 90 60
633 30 ore Greenfinch 90 60
634 30 ore Blue tit 90 60

1970. Nobel Prize Winners.
635 **175** 45 ore violet 70 45
636 – 55 ore blue 40 10
637 – 70 ore black 70 50
PORTRAITS: 55 ore Otto Wallach (chemistry) and Johannes van der Waals (physics); 70 ore Albrecht Kossel (medicine).

176 Ferry "Storskar" and Royal Palace, Stockholm

178 Kerstin Hesselgren (suffragette)

1971.
638 **176** 80 ore black and blue . . 30 10
639 – 4 k. black 90 10
639a – 6 k. blue 90 10
DESIGN: 4 k. 16th-century "Blood Money" coins; 6 k. Gustav Vasa's dollar.

1971. 50th Anniv of Swedish Women's Suffrage.
640 **178** 45 ore violet on green . . 20 10
641 1 k. brown on yellow . . . 45 10

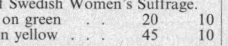

179 Arctic Terns

180 "The Prodigal Son" (painting, Sodra Rada Church)

1971. Nordic Help for Refugees Campaign.
642 **179** 40 ore red 35 25
643 55 ore blue 70 10

1971.
644 **180** 15 ore olive on green . . 10 10
645 – 25 ore blue and ochre . . 10 10
646 – 25 ore blue and ochre . . 10 10
DESIGNS—HORIZ: (Panels from Grodinge Tapestry, Swedish Natural History Museum): No. 645 Griffin; No. 646 Lion.

182 Container Port, Gothenburg

1971.
647 **182** 55 ore violet and blue . . 25 30
648 – 60 ore brown on cream . 15 10
649 – 75 ore deep green on grn . 25 10
DESIGNS—28 × 23 mm: 60 ore Timber-sledge; 75 ore Windmills, Oland.

184 Musical Score

186 "The Three Wise Men"

185 "The Mail Coach" (after E. Schwab)

1971. Bicentenary of Swedish Royal Academy of Music.
650 **184** 55 ore purple 20 10
651 85 ore green 30 20

1971.
652 **185** 1 k. 20 multicoloured . . 35 10

1971. Gotland Stone-masons Art.
653 **186** 5 ore violet and brown . . 50 30
654 – 10 ore violet and green . 50 30
655 – 55 ore green and brown . 60 20
656 – 65 ore brown and violet . 30 10
DESIGNS—VERT: 10 ore "Adam and Eve". HORIZ—40 × 21 mm: 55 ore "Winged Knight" and "Samson and the Lion"; 65 ore "The Flight to Egypt".

187 Child beside Lorry Wheel

188 State Sword of Gustavus Vasa, ca. 1500

1971. Road Safety.
657 **187** 35 ore black and red . . . 20 20
658 65 ore blue and red . . . 35 10

1971. Swedish Crown Regalia. Multicoloured.
659 65 ore Type **188** 40 40
660 65 ore Erik XIV's sceptre, 1561 40 40
661 65 ore Erik XIV's crown, 1561 40 40
662 65 ore Erik XIV's orb, 1561 . 40 40
663 65 ore Karl IX's anointing horn, 1606 . . . . 40 40

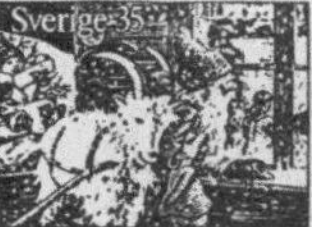

189 Santa Claus and Gifts

190 "Nils Holgersson on Goose" (from "The Wonderful Adventures of Nils" by Selma Lagerlof)

1971. Christmas. Traditional Prints.
664 **189** 35 ore red . . . . 1·10 90
665 – 35 ore blue . . . . 1·10 90
666 – 35 ore purple . . . . . . 1·10 90
667 – 35 ore blue . . . . 1·10 90
668 – 35 ore green . . . . 1·10 90
DESIGNS: No. 665, Market scene; 666, Musical evening; 667, Skating; 668, Arriving for Christmas service.

1971.
669 **190** 65 ore blue 20 10

191 Maurice Maeterlinck (literature) **192** Fencing

1971. Nobel Prize Winners.
670 **191** 55 ore orange 40 20
671 – 65 ore green 40 10
672 – 85 ore red 40 40
DESIGNS: Prize winners of 1911: 65 ore Allvar Gullstrand (medicine) and Wilhelm Wien (physics); 85 ore Marie Curie (chemistry).

1972. Sportswomen. Perf.
673 **192** 55 ore purple 60 60
674 – 55 ore blue 60 60
675 – 55 ore green 60 60
676 – 55 ore purple 60 60
677 – 55 ore blue 60 60
DESIGNS: No. 674, Diving; 675, Gymnastics; 676, Tennis; 677, Figure-skating.

193 L. J. Hierta (newspaper editor, statue by C. Eriksson) **195** Roe Deer

1972. Anniversaries of Swedish Cultural Celebrities.
678 **193** 35 ore multicoloured . . . 15 10
679 – 50 ore violet 20 10
680 – 65 ore blue 40 10
681 – 85 ore multicoloured . . . 40 20
DESIGNS AND ANNIVERSARIES—VERT: 35 ore (death cent); 85 ore G. Stiernhielm (poet 300th death anniv). HORIZ: 50 ore F. M. Franzen (poet and hymn-writer birth bicent); 65 ore Hugo Alfven (composer birth cent).

1972.
682 **195** 95 ore brown on cream . 20 10

196 Glass-blowing

1972. Swedish Glass Industry.
683 **196** 65 ore black 85 40
684 – 65 ore blue 85 40
685 – 65 ore red 85 40
686 – 65 ore black 85 40
687 – 65 ore blue 85 40
DESIGNS: No. 684, Glass-blowing (close-up); 685, Shaping glass; 686, Handling glass vase; 687, Bevelling glass vase.

197 Horses, Borgholm Castle (after N. Kreuger)

1972. Tourism in South-east Sweden.
688 **197** 55 ore brown on cream . . 45 45
689 – 55 ore blue on cream . . 45 45
690 – 55 ore brown on cream . . 45 45
691 – 55 ore green on cream . . 45 45
692 – 55 ore blue on cream . . 45 45
DESIGNS: No. 689, Oland Bridge and sailing barque "Meta"; 690, Kalmar Castle; 691, Salmon-fishing, Morrumsan; 692, Cadet schooner "Falken", Karlskrona Naval Base.

198 Conference Emblem and Motto, "Only One Earth"

1972. U.N. Environment Conservation Conference, Stockholm.
693 **198** 65 ore blue and red on cream 20 10
694 – 85 ore mult on cream . . 50 30
DESIGN—VERT: (28 × 45 mm): 85 ore "Sprint" (wooden relief by B. Hjorth).

199 Junkers F-13 **201** Early Courier

200 Reindeer and Sledge (woodcut from "Lapponia")

1972. Swedish Mailplanes.
695 **199** 5 ore lilac 10 10
696 – 15 ore blue 40 10
697 – 25 ore blue 40 10
698 – 75 ore green 30 10
DESIGNS—45 × 19 mm: 15 ore Junkers Ju-52/3m; 25 ore Friedrichshafen FF-49 seaplane; 75 ore Douglas DC-3.

1972. Centenary of "Lapponia" (book by J. Schefferus).
669 **200** 1 k. 40 red on blue . . . 35 10

1972. "Stockholmia 74" Exn (1st issue) and Birth Centenary of Olle Hjortzberg (stamp designer). Perf.
700 **201** 10 ore red 30 40
701 – 15 ore green 30 40
702 – 40 ore blue 60 60
703 – 50 ore brown 30 40
704 – 60 ore blue 40 40
DESIGNS: 15 ore Post-rider; 40 ore Steam train; 50 ore Motor bus and trailer; 60 ore Liner "Gripsholm".
See also Nos. 779/82.

202 Figurehead of Royal Yacht "Amphion" (Per Ljung) **203** Christmas Candles (J. Wikstrom)

1972. Swedish 18th-century Art.
705 – 75 ore green 25 20
706 – 75 ore brown 25 20
707 **202** 75 ore red 25 20
708 – 75 ore red 25 20
709 – 75 ore black, brn & red . 25 20
710 – 75 ore black, blue & brn . 25 20
DESIGNS—59 × 24 mm: No. 705, "Stockholm" (F. Martin); 706, "The Forge" (P. Hillestrom). As T **202**: No. 708, "Quadriga" (Sergel). 28 × 37 mm: No. 709, "Lady with a Veil" (A. Roslin); 710, "Sophia Magdalena" (C. G. Pilo).

1972. Christmas. Multicoloured.
711 45 ore Type **203** 25 10
712 45 ore Father Christmas (E. Flygh) 25 10
713 75 ore Carol singers (S. Hagg) (40 × 23 mm) 40 10

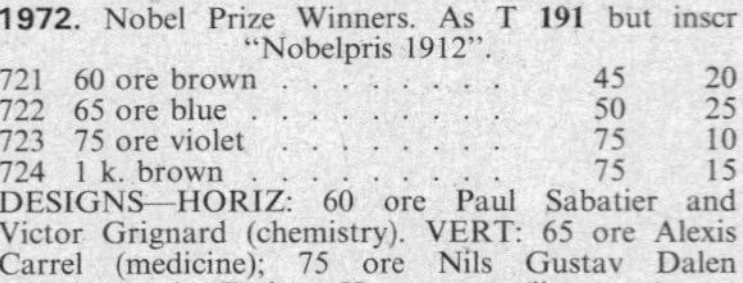
204 King Gustav VI Adolf **205** King Gustav with Book

1972.
714 **204** 75 ore blue 20 10
715 1 k. red 35 10

1972. King Gustav VI Adolf's 90th Birthday.
716 **205** 75 ore blue . . . . . . 1·40 2·25
717 – 75 ore green . . . . . . 1·40 2·25
718 – 75 ore red . . . . 1·40 2·25
719 – 75 ore blue . . . . . . 1·40 2·25
720 – 75 ore green . . . . . . 1·40 2·25
DESIGNS: No. 717, Chinese objets d'art; 718, Opening Parliament; 719, Greek objets d'art; 720, King Gustav tending flowers.

1972. Nobel Prize Winners. As T **191** but inscr "Nobelpris 1912".
721 60 ore brown 45 20
722 65 ore blue 50 25
723 75 ore violet 75 10
724 1 k. brown 75 15
DESIGNS—HORIZ: 60 ore Paul Sabatier and Victor Grignard (chemistry). VERT: 65 ore Alexis Carrel (medicine); 75 ore Nils Gustav Dalen (physics); 1 k. Gerhart Hauptmann (literature).

207 "Tintomara" Stage Set (B-R. Hedwall) **208** Modern Mail Coach, Vietas

1973. Bicentenary of Swedish Royal Theatre.
725 **207** 75 ore green 30 10
726 – 1 k. purple 30 15
DESIGN—HORIZ: (41 × 23 mm): 1 k. "Orpheus" (P. Hillestrom).

1973.
727 – 60 ore black on yellow . . 20 20
728 **208** 70 ore orange, blue & grn . 25 10
DESIGN: 60 ore Mail bus, 1923.

209 Vasa Ski Race **210** Horse (bas relief)

1973. Tourism in Dalecarlia.
729 **209** 65 ore green 30 25
730 – 65 ore green 30 25
731 – 65 ore black 30 25
732 – 65 ore green 30 25
733 – 65 ore lake 30 25
DESIGNS: No. 730, "Going to the Church in Mora" (A. Zorn); 731, Church stables in Rattvik; 732, "The Great Pit"; 733, "Mid-summer Dance" (B. Nordenberg).

1973. Gottland's Picture Stones.
734 **210** 5 ore purple 10 10
735 – 10 blue 10 10
DESIGN: 10 ore Viking longship (bas relief).

211 "Row of Willows" (P. Persson)

1973. Swedish Landscapes.
736 **211** 40 ore brown 10 10
737 – 50 ore black and brown . 10 10
738 – 55 ore green 20 10
DESIGNS—VERT: (20 × 28 mm): 50 ore "View of Trosa" (R. Ljunggren). HORIZ. (27 × 23 mm): 55 ore "Spring Birches" (O. Bergman).

212 Lumberman **213** Observer reading Thermometer

1973. 75th Anniv of Swedish Confederation of Trade Unions.
739 **212** 75 ore red 20 10
740 1 k. 40 blue 30 10

1973. Centenary of I.M.O./W.M.O. and Swedish Meteorological Organizations.
741 **213** 65 ore green . . . . . . 1·00 30
742 – 65 ore blue and black . . 1·00 30
DESIGN: No. 742, U.S. satellite weather picture.

214 Nordic House, Reykjavik

1973. Nordic Countries' Postal Co-operation.
743 **214** 75 ore multicoloured . . . 30 10
744 1 k. multicoloured 40 10

215 C. P. Thunberg, Japanese Flora and Scene

1973. Swedish Explorers.
745 **215** 1 k. brown, green & blue . 90 1·00
746 – 1 k. multicoloured . . . . 90 1·00
747 – 1 k. brown, green & blue . 90 1·00
748 – 1 k. multicoloured . . . . 90 1·00
749 – 1 k. multicoloured . . . . 90 1·00
DESIGNS: No. 746, Anders Sparrman and Tahiti; 747, Adolf Erik Nordenskiold and the "Vega"; 748, Salomon Andree and wreckage of balloon "Ornen"; 749, Sven Hedin and camels.

216 Team of Oxen **217** Grey Seal

1973. Centenary of Nordic Museum.
750 **216** 75 ore black . . . . . . 1·60 30
751 – 75 ore brown . . . . . . 1·60 30
752 – 75 ore black . . . . . . 1·60 30
753 – 75 ore purple . . . . . . 1·60 30
754 – 75 ore brown . . . . . . 1·60 30
DESIGNS: No. 751, Braking flax; 752, Potato-planting; 753, Baking bread; 754, Spring sowing.

1973. "Save Our Animals". Perf.
755 **217** 10 ore green 10 10
756 – 20 ore violet 40 10
757 – 25 ore turquoise 20 10
758 – 55 ore turquoise 30 10
759 – 65 ore violet 30 10
760 – 75 ore green 60 15
DESIGNS: 20 ore Peregrine falcon; 25 ore Lynx; 55 ore European otter; 65 ore Wolf; 75 ore White-tailed sea eagle.

218 King Gustav VI Adolf **220** "Goosegirl" (E. Josephson)

219 "Country Dance" (J. Nilsson)

1973. King Gustav VI Adolf Memorial Issue.
761 **218** 75 ore blue 20 10
762 1 k. purple 30 10

1973. Christmas. Peasant Paintings. Mult.
763 45 ore Type **219** 40 10
764 45 ore "The Three Wise Men" (A. Clemetson) 40 10
765 75 ore "Gourd Plant" (B. A. Hansson) (vert) . . . . . . 1·40 10
766 75 ore "The Rider" (K. E. Jonsson) (vert) . . . . . . 1·40 10
Nos. 765/6 are size 23 × 28 mm.

1973. Ernst Josephson Commemoration.
767 **220** 10 k. multicoloured . . . 1·75 10

221 A. Werner (chemistry) and H. Kamerlingh-Onnes (physics)

1973. Nobel Prize-winners. Inscr "NOBELPRIS 1913".
768 **221** 75 ore violet 40 10
769 – 1 k. brown 50 10
770 – 1 k. 40 green 60 10
DESIGNS: Prize winners of 1913: VERT: 1 k. Charles Robert Richet (medicine); 1 k. 40, Rabindranath Tagore (literature).

222 Ski-jumping

1974. "Winter Sports on Skis".
771 **222** 65 ore green 40 40
772 – 65 ore blue 40 40
773 – 65 ore green 40 40
774 – 65 ore red 40 40
775 – 65 ore blue 40 40
DESIGNS: No 772, Cross-country (man); 773, Relay-racing; 774, Downhill-racing; 775, Cross-country (woman).

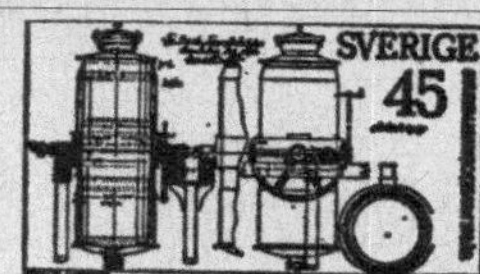

223 Ekman's Sulphite Pulping Machine

1974. Swedish Anniversaries.

776 **223** 45 ore brown on grey . . 15 10
777 – 60 ore green 20 10
778 – 75 ore red 25 10

DESIGNS AND EVENTS: 45 ore Type **223** (centenary of first sulphite pulp plant, Bergvik); 60 ore Hans Jarta and part of Government Act (birth bicent); 75 ore Samuel Owen and engineers (birth bicent).

224 U.P.U. Congress Stamp of 1924

1974. "Stockholmia '74" Stamp Exn (2nd issue).

779 **224** 20 ore green 15 20
780 25 ore blue 15 20
781 30 ore brown 15 20
782 35 ore red 15 20

225 Great Falls **226** "Figure in a Storm" (B. Marklund)

1974.

784 **225** 35 ore black and blue . . 15 10
785 – 75 ore brown 20 10

DESIGN—HORIZ: 75 ore Ystad (town).

1974. Europa. Sculptures.

786 **226** 75 ore purple 50 10
787 – 1 k. green 60 10

DESIGN: 1 k. Picasso statue, Kristinehamn.

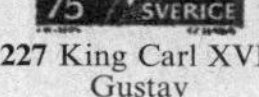

227 King Carl XVI Gustav **228** Central Post Office, Stockholm

1974.

788 **227** 75 ore green 30 10
789 90 ore blue 40 10
790 1 k. purple 30 10
791 1 k. 10 red 20 10
792 1 k. 30 green 20 10
793 1 k. 40 blue 30 15
794 1 k. 50 mauve 30 10
795 1 k. 70 orange 40 10
796 2 k. brown 40 10

1974. Centenary of Universal Postal Union.

800 **228** 75 ore purple 70 25
801 – 75 ore purple 70 25
802 – 1 k. green 35 10

DESIGNS—As Type **228**: No. 801, Interior of Central Post Office, Stockholm; 40×24 mm: No. 802, Rural postman.

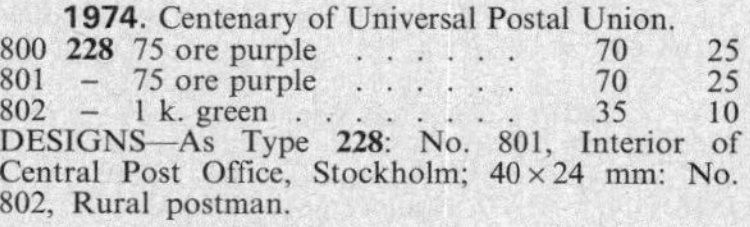

229 Regatta

1974. Tourism on Sweden's West Coast.

803 **229** 65 ore red 50 30
804 – 65 ore blue 50 30
805 – 65 ore green 50 30
806 – 65 ore green 50 30
807 – 65 ore purple 50 30

DESIGNS: No. 804, Vinga Lighthouse; 805, Varberg Fortress; 806, Seine fishing; 807, Mollosund.

230 "Mr. Simmons" (A. Fridell) **231** Thread and Spool

1974. Centenary of Publicists' Club (Swedish press, radio and television association).

808 **230** 45 ore black 15 15
809 1 k. 40 purple 35 10

1974. Swedish Textile and Clothing Industry.

810 **231** 85 ore violet 25 25
811 – 85 ore black and orange . 25 25

DESIGN: No. 811, Stylised sewing-machine.

232 Deer

1974. Christmas. Mosaic Embroideries of Mythical Creatures. Each turquoise, red and green (45 ore) or multicoloured (75 ore). Perf (Nos. 812/21).

812 45 ore Type **232** 70 70
813 45 ore Griffin 70 70
814 45 ore Lion 70 70
815 45 ore Griffin 70 70
816 45 ore Unicorn 70 70
817 45 ore Horse 70 70
818 45 ore Lion 70 70
819 45 ore Griffin 70 70
820 45 ore Lion 70 70
821 45 ore Lion-like creature . . 70 70
822 75 ore Deer-like creature . . 20 10

No. 813 is facing right and has inscr at top, No. 815 faces left with similar inscr and No. 819 has inscr at bottom.

No. 814 has the inscr at top, No. 818 has it at the foot of the design, the lion having blue claws, No. 820 has similar inscr, but white claws.

233 Tanker "Bill"

1974. Swedish Shipping. Each blue.

823 1 k. Type **233** 70 60
824 1 k. "Snow Storm" (liner) . . 70 60
825 1 k. "Tor" and "Atle" (ice-breakers) 70 60
826 1 k. "Skanes" (train ferry) . . 70 60
827 1 k. Tugs "Bill", "Bull" and "Starkodder" 70 60

234 Max von Laue (physics) **235** Sven Jerring (first announcer), Children and Microphone

1974. Nobel Prize-winners of 1914.

828 **234** 65 ore red 35 20
829 – 70 ore green 35 20
830 – 1 k. blue 65 15

DESIGNS:—70 ore Theodore William Richards (chemistry); 1 k. Richard Barany (medicine).

1974. 50th Anniv of Swedish Broadcasting Corporation.

831 **235** 75 ore blue and brown . 70 20
832 – 75 ore blue and brown . 70 20

DESIGN: No. 832, Television camera at Parliamentary debate.

236 Giro Envelope

1975. 50th Anniv of Swedish Postal Giro Office.

833 **236** 1 k. 40 black and brown . 30 10

237 Male and Female Engineers **238** Bronze Helmet Decoration, Vendel

1975. International Women's Year.

834 **237** 75 ore green 20 10
835 – 1 k. purple 35 10

DESIGN—VERT: 1 k. Jenny Lind (singer) (portrait by O. J. Sodermark).

1975. Archaeological Discoveries.

836 **238** 10 ore red 10 10
837 – 15 ore green 10 10
838 – 20 ore violet 10 10
839 – 25 ore yellow 10 10
840 – 55 ore brown 10 10

DESIGNS: 15 ore Iron sword hilt and chapel, Vendel; 20 ore Iron shield buckle, Vendel; 25 ore Embossed gold plates (Gold Men), Eketorp Fortress, Oland; 55 ore Iron helmet, Vendel.

239 "New Year's Eve at Skansen (Eric Hallstrom)

1975. Europa. Multicoloured.

841 90 ore Type **239** 25 10
842 1 k. 10 "Inferno" (August Strindberg) (vert) 30 10

240 Metric Tape-measure (centenary of Metre Convention) **241** Western European Hedgehog

1975. Anniversaries.

843 **240** 55 ore blue 15 10
844 – 70 ore sepia and brown . . 15 10
845 – 75 ore violet 15 10

DESIGNS AND EVENTS—HORIZ: (44×27 mm): 70 ore Peter Hernqvist (founder) and title-page of his book "Comprehensive Thesis on Glanders in Horses" (bicent of Swedish Veterinary Service). VERT: (24×31 mm): 75 ore "Folke Filbyter" (birth centenary of Carl Milles (sculptor)).

1975.

846 **241** 55 ore black 20 10
847 – 75 ore red 20 10
848 – 1 k. 70 blue 40 10
849 – 2 k. purple 50 10
850 – 7 k. green 90 10

DESIGNS—HORIZ: 75 ore Key-fiddler; 1 k. 70, Capercaillie ("cock of the woods"). VERT: 2 k. Rok stone (ancient inscribed rock), Ostergotland; 7 k. Ballet dancers (from "Romeo and Juliet").

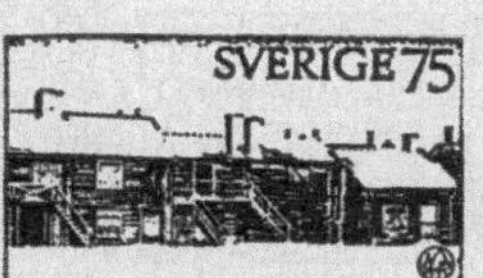

242 Village Buildings, Skelleftea

1975. European Architectural Heritage Year.

851 **242** 75 ore black 20 20
852 – 75 ore red 20 20
853 – 75 ore black 20 20
854 – 75 ore red 20 20
855 – 75 ore blue 20 20

DESIGNS: No. 852, Iron-works, Engelsberg; 853, Gunpowder tower, Visby, Gotland; 854, Iron-mine, Falun; 855, Rommehed military barracks, Dalecarlia.

243 Fire Brigade

1975. "Watch, Guard and Help". Public Services.

856 **243** 90 ore red 55 20
857 – 90 ore blue 55 20
858 – 90 ore red 55 20
859 – 90 ore blue 55 20
860 – 90 ore green 55 20

DESIGNS: No. 857, Customs service; 858, Police service; 859, Ambulance and hospital service; 860, Shipwreck of "Merkur" (Sea rescue service).

244 "Fryckstad"

1975. Swedish Steam Locomotives.

861 **244** 5 ore green 10 10
862 – 5 ore blue 10 10
863 – 90 ore green 80 15

DESIGNS—As Type **244**: No. 862, "Gotland". 49×22 mm: 90 ore "Prince August".

245 Canoeing **246** "Madonna" (sculpture), Vikiau church, Gotland

1975. Scouting. Multicoloured.

864 90 ore Type **245** 80 20
865 90 ore Camping 80 20

1975. Christmas. Religious Art.

866 **246** 55 ore multicoloured . . 20 10
867 – 55 ore multicoloured . . 20 10
868 – 55 ore multicoloured . . 20 10
869 – 90 ore brown 30 10
870 – 90 ore red 60 10
871 – 90 ore blue 60 10

DESIGNS—VERT: No. 867, "Birth of Christ" (embossed copper), Broddetorp church, Vastergotland; 868, "The Sun" (embossed copper), Broddetorp church, Vastergotland; 869, "Mourning Mary" (sculpture), Oja church, Gotland. HORIZ: 870, 871, "Jesse at Foot of Christ's genealogical tree" (retable), Lofta church, Smaland.

247 W. H. and W. L. Bragg (physics) **248** Bronze Coiled Snake Brooch, Vendel

1975. Nobel Prize Winners of 1915.

872 **247** 75 ore purple 20 20
873 – 90 ore blue 30 10
874 – 1 k. 10 green 30 20

DESIGNS: 90 ore Richard Willstatter (chemistry); 1 k. 10, Romain Rolland (literature).

1976.

875 **248** 15 ore brown 10 10
876 – 20 ore green 10 10
877 – 30 ore purple 10 10
878 – 85 ore blue 30 10
879 – 90 ore blue 20 10
880 – 1 k. purple 20 10
881 – 1 k. 90 green 40 10
882 – 9 k. green . . . . 1·50 15

DESIGNS—21×19 mm: 20 ore Pilgrim badge; 28×21 mm: 30 ore Drinking horn; 85 ore Common guillemot and razorbills. 28×23 mm: 1 k. 90, "Cave of the Winds" (sculpture) (Eric Grate). 21×28 mm: 90 ore Chimney sweep; 1 k. Bobbin lace-making; 9 k. "Girl's Head" (wood-carving) (Bror Hjorth).

249 Early and Modern Telephones **250** Wheat and Cornflower Seed

1976. Telephone Centenary.

883 **249** 1 k. 30 violet 30 15
884 3 k. 40 red 80 15

1976. Swedish Seed-testing Centenary.

885 **250** 65 ore brown 20 20
886 – 65 ore green and brown . . 20 20

DESIGN: No. 886, Viable and non-viable plants.

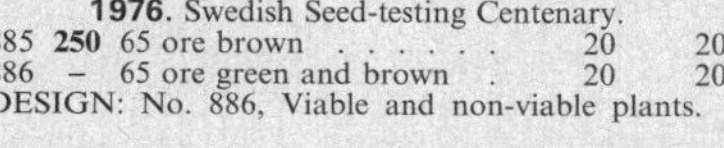

251 Lapp Spoon **253** Ship's Wheel and Cross

252 "View from Ringkallen" (H. Osslund)

1976. Europa. Handicrafts.

887 **251** 1 k. black, pink and blue . 35 10
888 – 1 k. 30 multicoloured . . 35 10

DESIGN: 1 k. 30, Tile stove (from a aquarell by C. Slania).

1976. Tourism. Angermanland.
889 **252** 85 ore green 20 20
890 – 85 ore blue 20 20
891 – 85 ore brown 20 20
892 – 85 ore blue 20 20
893 – 85 ore brown 20 20
DESIGNS: No. 890, Tug towing timber; 891, Hay-drying racks; 892, Granvagsnipan; 893, Seine-net fishing.

1976. Centenary of Swedish Seamen's Church.
894 **253** 85 ore blue 25 10

254 Torgny Segerstedt and "Goteborg Handels-och Sjofartstidning"

1976. Birth Centenary of Torgny Segerstedt (newspaper editor).
895 **254** 1 k. 90 black and brown . . 40 10

255 King Carl XVI Gustav and Queen Silvia **257** Hands and Cogwheels

256 John Ericsson (marine propeller)

1976. Royal Wedding.
896 **255** 1 k. red 20 10
897 1 k. 30 green 30 10

1976. Swedish Technological Pioneers. Mult.
898 1 k. 30 Type **256** 55 55
899 1 k. 30 Helge Palmcrantz (hay maker) 55 55
900 1 k. 30 Lars Magnus Ericsson (telephone improvements) . 55 55
901 1 k. 30 Sven Wingquist (ball bearing) 55 55
902 1 k. 30 Gustaf de Laval (milk separator and reaction turbine) 55 55

1976. Industrial Safety.
903 **257** 85 ore orange and violet . 25 10
904 1 k. green and brown . . 25 10

258 Verner von Heidenstam

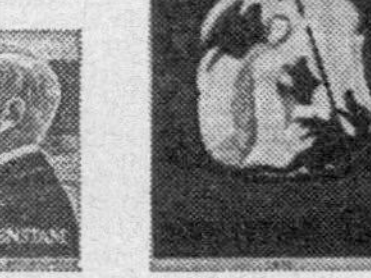

259 "Archangel Michael Destroying Lucifer" (Flemish prayer book)

1976. Literature Nobel Prize Winner of 1916.
905 **258** 1 k. green 30 10
906 1 k. 30 blue 40 20

1976. Christmas. Mediaeval Book Illustrations. Multicoloured.
907 65 ore Type **259** 20 10
908 65 ore "St. Nicholas awakening Children from Dead" (Flemish prayer book) 20 10
909 1 k. "Mary visiting Elizabeth" (Austrian prayer book) . . . 30 10
910 1 k. "Prayer to the Virgin" (Austrian prayer book) . . . 30 10
Nos. 909/10 are vertical, 26 × 44 mm.

1977. Nordic Countries Co-operation in Nature Conservation and Environment Protection. As T **222** of Norway.
911 1 k. multicoloured 30 10
912 1 k. 30 multicoloured 20 20

261 Tawny Owl

262 "Politeness"

1977.
913 **261** 45 ore green 30 20
914 – 70 ore blue 20 10
915 – 1 k. 40 brown 30 15
916 – 2 k. 10 brown 35 10
DESIGNS—23 × 29 mm: 70 ore Norwegian cast-iron stove decoration. 41 × 21 mm: 1 k. 40, Gotland ponies; 28 × 22 mm: 2 k. 10, Tailor.

1977. Birth Centenary of Oskar Andersson (cartoonist).
917 **262** 75 ore black 15 10
918 3 k. 80 red 70 20

263 Skating

1977. Keep-fit Activities.
919 **263** 95 ore blue 20 30
920 – 95 ore green 20 30
921 – 95 ore red 20 30
922 – 95 ore green 20 30
923 – 95 ore blue 20 30
DESIGNS: No. 920, Swimming; 921, Cycling; 922, Jogging; 923, Badminton.

264 Gustavianum Building

1977. 500th Anniv of Uppsala University.
924 **264** 1 k. 10 black, yellow & bl 30 10

265 Winter Forest Scene

1977. Europa. Landscapes. Multicoloured.
925 1 k. 10 Type **265** 30 10
926 1 k. 40 Rapadalen valley, Sarek 40 30

266 Calle Schewen at Breakfast **267** Blackberries

1977. Tourism.
927 **266** 95 ore green 20 30
928 – 95 ore violet 50 30
929 – 95 ore black and red . . 20 30
930 – 95 ore blue 20 30
931 – 95 ore red 20 30
DESIGNS: No. 928, Black-headed gull; 929, Calle Schewen dancing; 930, Fishing; 931, Sunset.

1977. Wild Berries. Multicoloured. Perf.
932 75 ore Type **267** 20 20
933 75 ore Cowberries 20 20
934 75 ore Cloudberries 20 20
935 75 ore Bilberries 20 20
936 75 ore Strawberries 20 20

268 Horse-drawn Tram

1977. Public Transport.
937 **268** 1 k. 10 green 60 40
938 – 1 k. 10 blue 60 40
939 – 1 k. 10 green 60 40
940 – 1 k. 10 blue 60 40
941 – 1 k. 10 green 60 40
DESIGN: No. 938, Electric tram; 939, Ferry "Djurgarden 6"; 940, Articulated bus; 941, Underground train.

269 H. Pontoppidan and K. A. Gjellerup (literature)

270 Erecting Sheaf for Birds

1977. Nobel Prize Winners of 1917.
942 **269** 1 k. 10 brown 30 10
943 – 1 k. 40 green 40 20
DESIGN: 1 k. 40, Charles Glover Barkla (physics).

1977. Christmas. Seasonal Customs.
944 **270** 75 ore violet 20 10
945 – 75 ore orange 20 10
946 – 75 ore green 20 10
947 – 1 k. 10 green 30 10
948 – 1 k. 10 red 30 10
949 – 1 k. 10 blue 30 10
DESIGNS: No. 945, Making gingersnaps; 946, Bringing in the Christmas tree; 947, Preparing the traditional fish dish; 948, Making straw goats for the pantomime; 949, Candle-making.

271 Brown Bear **272** Orebro Castle

1978.
950 **271** 1 k. 15 brown 40 10
951 – 2 k. 50 blue 40 10
DESIGN: 2 k. 50, "Space without Affiliation" (sculpture by Arne Jones).

1978. Europa.
952 **272** 1 k. 30 green 40 10
953 – 1 k. 70 brown 50 25
DESIGN—VERT: 1 k. 70, Doorway, Orebro Castle.

273 Pentecostal Meeting

1978. Independent Christian Associations. Perf.
954 **273** 90 ore purple 30 30
955 – 90 black 30 30
956 – 90 ore violet 30 30
957 – 90 ore green 30 30
958 – 90 ore purple 30 30
DESIGNS: No. 955, Minister with children (Swedish Missionary Society); 956, Communion Service, Ethopia (Evangelical National Missionary Society); 957, Baptism (Baptist Society); 958, Salvation Army band.

274 Brosarp Hills

1978. Travels of Carl Linne (botanist).
959 **274** 1 k. 30 black 50 30
960 – 1 k. 30 blue . . . . . . 1·25 30
961 – 1 k. 30 purple 50 30
962 – 1 k. 30 red 50 30
963 – 1 k. 30 blue 50 30
964 – 1 k. 30 purple 50 30
DESIGNS—HORIZ: (58 × 23 mm): No. 960, Avocets; (27 × 23 mm): No. 961, Grindstone production; No. 962, "Linnaea borealis". VERT: (27 × 36 mm): No. 963, Red limestone cliff; 964, Linnaeus wearing Lapp dress and Dutch doctor's hat, and carrying Lapp drum.

275 Glider over Alleberg Plateau

1978. Tourism. Vastergotland.
965 **275** 1 k. 15 green 40 30
966 – 1 k. 15 brown 40 30
967 – 1 k. 15 blue 40 30
968 – 1 k. 15 slate 40 30
969 – 1 k. 15 black and purple . 40 30
DESIGNS: No. 966. Common cranes; 967, Fortress on Lacko Island Skara; 968, Rock tomb, Luttra; 969, "Traders of South Vastergotland" (sculpture) (N. Sjogren).

276 Diploma and Laurel Wreath

1978. Centenary of Stockholm University.
970 **276** 2 k. 50 green on stone . . 45 10

277 "The Homecoming" (Carl Kylberg)

1978. Paintings by Swedish Artists. Multicoloured.
971 90 ore Type **277** 30 10
972 1 k. 15 "Standing Model seen from Behind" (Karl Isakson) 30 10
973 4 k. 50 "Self-portrait with a Floral Wreath" (Ivar Arosenius) 80 20

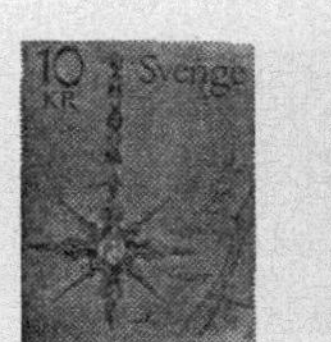

278 Northern Arrow

280 "Russula decolorans"

279 Coronation Carriage, 1699

1978.
974 **278** 10 k. mauve . . . . 1·40 10

1978.
975 **279** 1 k. 70 red on cream . . 40 30

1978. Edible Mushrooms. Multicoloured. Perf.
976 1 k. 15 Type **280** 50 40
977 1 k. 15 Common puff-ball ("Lycoperdon perlatum") 50 40
978 1 k. 15 Parasol mushroom ("Macrolepiota procera") 50 40
979 1 k. 15 Chanterelle ("Cantharellus cibarius") 50 40
980 1 k. 15 Cep ("Boletus edulis") 50 40
981 1 k. 15 Cauliflower clavaria ("Ramaria botrytis") . . . 50 40

281 Dalecarlian Horse

282 Fritz Haber (chemistry)

1978. Christmas. Old Toys.
982 **281** 90 ore multicoloured . . 30 10
983 – 90 ore multicoloured . . 30 10
984 – 90 ore green and red . . . 30 10
985 – 1 k. 30 multicoloured . . 30 10
986 – 1 k. 30 multicoloured . . 30 10
987 – 1 k. 30, blue 30 10
DESIGNS—VERT: No. 983, Swedish Court doll; No. 984, Meccano; No. 987, Teddy bear. HORIZ: No. 985, Tops; No. 986, Equipage with water barrel (metal toy).

1978. Nobel Prize Winners of 1918.
988 **282** 1 k. 30 brown 40 10
989 – 1 k. 70 blue 50 30
DESIGN: 1 k. 70, Max Planck (physics).

283 Bandy Players fighting for Ball

1979. Bandy.
990 **283** 1 k. 05 blue 20 10
991 2 k. 50 orange 50 10

284 Child in Gas-mask

285 Wall Hanging

1979. International Year of the Child.
992 **284** 1 k. 70 blue 30 20

1979.
993 **285** 4 k. blue and red 80 10

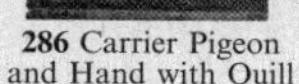

286 Carrier Pigeon and Hand with Quill

287 Sledge-boat

1979. Rebate Stamp.

994 **286** (1 k.) yellow, black & bl . 30 10

No. 994 was only issued in booklets of 20 sold at 20 k. or supplied in exchange for tokens distributed to all households in Sweden. Valid for inland postage only, they represented a rebate of 30 ore on the normal rate of 1 k. 30.

1979. Europa.

995 **287** 1 k. 30 black and turquoise 40 10
996 – 1 k. 70 black and brown . 45 30
DESIGN: 1 k. 70, Hand using telegraph key.

288 Felling Tree

1979. Farming.

997 **288** 1 k. 30 black, red & grn . 35 15
998 – 1 k. 30 green and black . 35 15
999 – 1 k. 30 green and black . 35 15
1000 – 1 k. 30 brown and green 35 15
1001 – 1 k. 30 red, black & grn . 35 15
DESIGNS: No. 998, Sowing; No. 999, Cows; No. 1000, Harvesting; No. 1001, Ploughing.

289 Tourist Launch "Juno"

1979. Tourism. Gota Canal.

1002 **289** 1 k. 15 violet 45 45
1003 – 1 k. 15 green 45 45
1004 – 1 k. 15 purple 45 45
1005 – 1 k. 15 red 45 45
1006 – 1 k. 15 violet 45 45
1007 – 1 k. 15 green 45 45
DESIGNS—As T **289**: No. 1003, Borenshult lock; $27\times23\frac{1}{2}$ mm: 1004, Hajstorp roller bridge; 1005, Opening lock gates; $27\times36\frac{1}{2}$ mm: 1006, Motor barge "Wilhelm Tham" in lock; 1007, Kayak in lock.

290 "Aeshna cyanea" (dragonfly)

291 Workers leaving Sawmills

1979. Wildlife.

1008 **290** 60 ore violet 40 10
1009 – 65 ore olive 50 10
1010 – 80 ore green 50 10
DESIGNS—41×21 mm: 65 ore Pike; 27×22 mm: 80 ore Green spotted toad.

1979. Centenary of Sundsvall Strike.

1011 **291** 90 ore brown and red . . 20 10

292 Banner

293 J. J. Berzelius

1979. Centenary of Swedish Temperance Movement.

1012 **292** 1 k. 30 multicoloured . . 30 10

1979. Birth Bicentenaries of J. J. Berzelius (chemist) and J. O. Wallin (poet and hymn-writer).

1013 **293** 1 k. 70 brown and green 30 20
1014 – 4 k. 50 blue 80 30
DESIGN: 4 k. 50, J. O. Wallin and hymn numbers.

295 Herrings and Growth Marks

296 Ljusdal Costume

1979. Marine Research.

1016 **295** 1 k. 70 green and blue . 50 40
1017 – 1 k. 70 brown 50 40
1018 – 1 k. 70 green and blue . 50 40
1019 – 1 k. 70 brown 50 40
1020 – 1 k. 70 green and blue . 50 40
DESIGNS: No. 1017, Acoustic survey of sea-bed; 1018, Plankton bloom; 1019, Echo-sounding chart of Baltic Sea, October 1978; 1020, Fishery research ship "Argos".

1979. Peasant Costumes and Jewellery.

1021 **296** 90 ore multicoloured . . 20 20
1022 – 90 ore multicoloured . . 20 20
1023 – 90 ore blue 20 10
1024 – 1 k. 30 multicoloured . 30 20
1025 – 1 k. 30 multicoloured . 30 20
1026 – 1 k. 30 red 30 10
DESIGNS: $(22\times27$ mm) No. 1022, Osteraker costume; $(21\times27$ mm) 1023, Brooch from Jamtland; 1026, Brooch from Smaland; $(23\times40$ mm) 1024, Goinge church dress; 1025. Mora church dress.

297 Jules Bordet (chemistry)

298 Wind Power

1979. Nobel Prize Winners of 1919.

1027 **297** 1 k. 30 mauve 30 10
1028 – 1 k. 70 blue 40 40
1029 – 2 k. 50 green 70 20
DESIGNS: 1 k. 70, Johannes Stark (physics); 2 k. 50, Carl Spitteler (literature).

1980. Renewable Energy Sources.

1030 **298** 1 k. 15 blue 30 40
1031 – 1 k. 15 ochre and green 30 40
1032 – 1 k. 15 orange 30 40
1033 – 1 k. 15 green 30 40
1034 – 1 k. 15 green and blue . 30 40
DESIGNS: No. 1031, Biological energy; No. 1032, Solar energy; No. 1033, Geothermal energy; No. 1034, Wave energy.

299 King Carl XVI Gustav and Princess Victoria

300 Child's Hand in Adult's

1980. New Order of Succession to Throne.

1035 **299** 1 k. 30 blue 20 10
1036 1 k. 70 red 30 20

1980. Care.

1037 **300** 1 k. 40 brown 25 10
1038 – 1 k. 60 green 25 10
DESIGN: 1 k. 60, Aged hand clasping stick.

301 Squirrel

302 Elise Ottesen-Jensen (pioneer of birth control)

1980. Rebate Stamp.

1039 **301** (1 k.) yellow, blue & blk 30 10

No. 1039 was only issued in booklets of 20 sold at 20 k. or supplied in exchange for tokens distributed to all households in Sweden.

1980. Europa.

1040 **302** 1 k. 30 green 40 10
1041 – 1 k. 70 red 30 30
DESIGN: 1 k. 70, Joe Hill (member of workers' movement).

303 Tybling Farm, Tyby

1980. Tourism. Halsingland.

1042 **303** 1 k. 15 red 30 30
1043 – 1 k. 15 blue & purple . . 30 30
1044 – 1 k. 15 green 30 30
1045 – 1 k. 15 purple 30 30
1046 – 1 k. 15 blue 30 30
DESIGNS: No. 1043, Old iron works, Iggesund; No. 1044, Blaxas ridge, Forsa; No. 1045, Banga farm, Alfta; No. 1046, Sunds Canal, Hudiksvall.

304 Chair from Scania (1831)

305 Motif from film "Diagonal Symphony"

1980. Nordic Countries Co-operation.

1047 **304** 1 k. 50 green 30 10
1048 – 2 k. brown 40 10
DESIGN: 2 k. Cradle from North Bothnia (19th century).

1980. Birth Bicentenary of Viking Eggeling (film-maker).

1049 **305** 3 k. blue 60 10

307 Bamse

308 "Necken" (Ernst Josephson)

1980. Christmas. Swedish Comic Strips.

1051 **307** 1 k. 15 blue and red . . . 25 10
1052 – 1 k. 15 multicoloured . . 25 10
1053 – 1 k. 50 black 30 10
1054 – 1 k. 50 multicoloured . . 30 10
DESIGNS—VERT: No. 1052, Karlsson; No. 1053, Adamson. HORIZ: No. 1054, Kronblom.

1980.

1055 **308** 8 k. brown, blk & grey . 1·25 15

309 Knut Hamsun (literature)

310 Angel blowing Horn

1980. Nobel Prize Winners of 1920.

1056 **309** 1 k. 40 blue 30 20
1057 – 1 k. 40 red 30 20
1058 – 2 k. green 40 25
1059 – 2 k. brown 40 25
DESIGNS: No. 1057, August Krogh (medicine); 1058, Charles-Edouard Guillaume (physics); 1059, Walther Nernst (chemistry).

1980. Christmas.

1060 **310** 1 k. 25 brown and blue . 30 10

311 Ernst Wigforss

312 Thor catching Midgard Serpent

1981. Birth Centenary of Ernst Wigforss (politician).

1061 **311** 5 k. red 90 20

1981. Norse Mythology.

1062 **312** 10 ore black 10 10
1063 – 15 ore red 10 10
1064 – 50 ore red 10 10
1065 – 75 ore green 20 10
1066 – 1 k. black 20 10
DESIGNS: 15 ore Heimdall blowing horn; 50 ore Freya riding boar; 75 ore Freya in carriage drawn by cats; 1 k. Odin on eight-footed steed.

313 Gyrfalcon

314 Troll

1981.

1067 **313** 50 k. brown and blue . . 7·50 2·75

1981. Europa.

1068 **314** 1 k. 50 blue and brown . 50 10
1069 – 2 k. red and green . . . 60 20
DESIGN: 2 k. The Lady of the Woods.

315 Blind Boy feeling Globe

316 Arms of Ostergotland

1981. International Year of Disabled Persons.

1070 **315** 1 k. 50 green 30 10
1071 3 k. 50 violet 70 10

1981. Rebate stamps. Arms of Swedish Provinces (1st series). Multicoloured.

1072 1 k. 40 Type **316** 45 10
1073 1 k. 40 Jamtland 45 10
1074 1 k. 40 Dalarna 45 10
1075 1 k. 40 Bohuslan 45 10

See also Nos. 1112/15, 1153/6, 1186/9, 1246/9 and 1302/5.

317 King Carl XVI Gustav

318 Sailing Boat from Bohuslan

1981.

1076 **317** 1 k. 65 green 30 10
1077 – 1 k. 75 blue 40 10
1077a **317** 1 k. 80 blue 30 10
1077b 1 k. 90 brown 30 10
1078 2 k. 40 purple 50 10
1078a – 2 k. 40 green 50 10
1078b **317** 2 k. 70 purple 50 10
1078c – 3 k. 20 red 60 15
DESIGN: 1 k. 75, 2 k. 40 (1078a), 3 k. 20, Queen Silvia.

1981. Provincial Sailing Boats.

1079 **318** 1 k. 65 blue 50 20
1080 – 1 k. 65 blue 50 20
1081 – 1 k. 65 blue 50 20
1082 – 1 k. 65 blue 50 20
1083 – 1 k. 65 blue 50 20
1084 – 1 k. 65 blue 50 20
DESIGNS: No. 1080, Boat from Blekinge; No. 1081, Boat from Norrbotten; No. 1082, Boat from Halsingland; No. 1083, Boat from Gotland; No. 1084, Boat from West Skane.

319 "Night and Day"

320 Par Lagerkvist riding Railway Trolley with Father (illustration from "Guest of Reality")

1981.

1085 **319** 1 k. 65 violet 30 10

1981.

1086 **320** 1 k. 50 green 30 10

321 Electric Locomotive

1981. "Sweden in the World".

1087 **321** 2 k. 40 red 65 40
1088 – 2 k. 40 red 65 40
1089 – 2 k. 40 purple 65 40
1090 – 2 k. 40 violet 65 40
1091 – 2 k. 40 blue 65 40
1092 – 2 k. 40 blue 65 40
DESIGNS—HORIZ: No. 1088, Scania trucks with rock drilling equipment; 1089, Birgit Nilsson (opera singer) and Sixten Ehrling (conductor); 1090, North Sea gas rig. VERT: 1091, Bjorn Borg (tennis player); 1092, Ingemar Stenmark (skier).

322 Baker's Sign

324 Wooden Bird

1981. Business Mail.

1093 **322** 2 k. 30 brown 55 10
1094 – 2 k. 30 brown 55 10
DESIGN: No. 1094, Pewterer's sign.

1981. Christmas.

1096	324	1 k. 40 red	30	10
1097	–	1 k. 40 green	30	10

DESIGN: No. 1097, Wooden bird (different).

325 Albert Einstein (physics)

1981. Nobel Prize Winners of 1921.

1098	325	1 k. 35 red	40	10
1099	–	1 k. 65 green	40	10
1100	–	2 k. 70 blue	60	20

DESIGNS: 1 k. 65, Anatole France (literature); 2 k. 70, Frederick Soddy (chemistry).

326 Knight on Horseback 327 Impossible Triangle

1982. Birth Centenary of John Bauer (illustrator of fairy tales).

1101	326	1 k. 65 blue, yellow & lilac	30	30
1102	–	1 k. 65 multicoloured	30	30
1103	–	1 k. 65 orange & yellow	30	30
1104	–	1 k. 65 yellow and lilac	30	30

DESIGNS: No. 1102, "What a wretched pale creature, said the Troll Woman"; No. 1103, "The Princess beside the Forest Lake"; No. 1104, "Now it is already twilight Night".

1982.

1105	327	25 ore brown	10	10
1106	–	50 ore green	10	10
1107	–	75 ore blue	20	10
1108	–	1 k. 35 blue	30	10
1109	–	5 k. maroon	85	10

DESIGNS: 50 ore, 75 ore, Impossible figures (different); 1 k. 35, Newspaper distributor; 5 k. "Graziella wonders if she could be a Model" (etching, Carl Larsson).

328 Villages before and after Land Reform

1982. Europa.

1110	328	1 k. 65 green and black	1·00	10
1111	–	2 k. 40 green	75	60

DESIGN—26 × 22 mm: 2 k. 40, Anders Celsius.

1982. Rebate Stamps. Arms of Swedish Provinces (2nd series). As T **316**. Multicoloured.

1112	1 k. 40 Dalsland	45	10
1113	1 k. 40 Oland	45	10
1114	1 k. 40 Vastmanland	45	10
1115	1 k. 40 Halsingland	45	10

329 Elin Wagner 330 Burgher House

1982. Birth Centenary of Elin Wagner (novelist).

1116	329	1 k. 35 brown	30	10

1982. Centenary of Museum of Cultural History, Lund.

1117	330	1 k. 65 brown	25	10
1118	–	2 k. 70 ochre	45	20

DESIGN: 2 k. 70, Embroidered lace.

331 Lateral Mark

1982. New International Buoyage System.

1119	331	1 k. 65 blue and green	50	20
1120	–	1 k. 65 green and blue	50	20
1121	–	1 k. 65 blue and deep blue	50	20
1122	–	1 k. 65 blue and green	50	20
1123	–	1 k. 65 blue and deep blue	50	20

DESIGNS: No. 1120, Cardinal mark and Sweden–Finland ferry "Sally"; 1121, Racing yachts and special mark; 1122, Safe-water mark; 1123, Pilot boat, isolated danger mark and lighthouse.

332 Scene from "The Emigrants" (film)

1982. Living Together.

1124	332	1 k. 65 green	50	20
1125	–	1 k. 65 purple	50	20
1126	–	1 k. 65 blue	50	20
1127	–	1 k. 65 red	50	20

DESIGNS: No. 1125, Vietnamese boat people in factory; No. 1126, Immigrants examining local election literature; No. 1127, Three girls arm-in-arm.

334 Angel

1982. Christmas. Medieval Glass Paintings from Lye Church. Multicoloured.

1129	1 k. 40 Type **334**	30	30
1130	1 k. 40 "The Child in the Temple"	30	30
1131	1 k. 40 "Adoration of the Magi"	30	30
1132	1 k. 40 "Tidings to the Shepherds"	30	30
1133	1 k. 40 "The Birth of Christ"	30	30

335 Quantum Mechanics (Niels Bohr, 1922)

1982. Nobel Prize Winners for Physics.

1134	335	2 k. 40 blue	80	60
1135	–	2 k. 40 red	80	60
1136	–	2 k. 40 green	80	60
1137	–	2 k. 40 lilac	80	60
1138	–	2 k. 40 red	80	60

DESIGNS: No. 1135, Fuse distribution (Erwin Schrodinger, 1933); No. 1136, Wave pattern (Louis de Broglie, 1929); No. 1137, Electrons (Paul Dirac, 1933); No. 1138, Atomic model (Werner Heisenberg, 1932).

336 Horse Chestnut 337 Ferlin (statue by K. Bejemark)

1983. Fruits.

1139	336	5 ore brown	10	10
1140	–	10 ore green	10	10
1141	–	15 ore red	10	10
1142	–	20 ore blue	10	10

DESIGNS: 10 ore Norway maple; 15 ore Dog rose; 20 ore Blackthorn.

1983. 85th Birth Anniv of Nils Ferlin (poet).

1143	337	6 k. green	85	20

338 Peace March 340 Family cycling in Countryside

339 Lead Type

1983. Centenary of Swedish Peace Movement.

1144	338	1 k. 35 blue	30	25

1983. 500th Anniv of Printing in Sweden.

1145	339	1 k. 65 black and brown on stone	40	20
1146	–	1 k. 65 black, green and red on stone	40	20
1147	–	1 k. 65 brown and black on stone	40	20
1148	339	1 k. 65 black and brown on stone	40	20
1149	–	1 k. 65 brown, green and black on stone	40	20

DESIGNS: No. 1146, Ox plough (illustration from "Dialogus creaturarum" by Johan Snell, 1483); No. 1147, Title page of Karl XII's Bible, 1703; No. 1148, 18th-century alphabet books; No. 1149, Laser photocomposition.

1983. Nordic Countries' Postal Co-operation. "Visit the North".

1150	340	1 k. 65 green	40	10
1151	–	2 k. 40 blue and brown	60	25

DESIGN: 2 k. 40, Yachts at Stockholm.

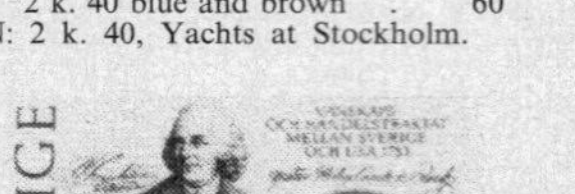

341 Benjamin Franklin and Great Seal of Sweden

1983. Bicentenary of Sweden–U.S.A. Treaty of Amity and Commerce.

1152	341	2 k. 70 blue, brown & blk	50	30

1983. Rebate Stamps. Arms of Swedish Provinces (3rd series). As T **316**. Multicoloured.

1153	1 k. 60 Vastergotland	40	10
1154	1 k. 60 Medelpad	40	10
1155	1 k. 60 Gotland	40	10
1156	1 k. 60 Gastrikland	40	10

342 Costume Sketch by Fernand Leger for "Creation du Monde" 343 Essay for Unissued Stamp, 1885

1983. Europa.

1157	1 k. 65 dp brown & brown	30	10
1158	2 k. 70 blue	50	25

DESIGNS: 1 k. 65, Type **342** (Swedish Ballet); 2 k. 70, J. P. Johansson's adjustable spanner.

1983. "Stockholmia 86" International Exhibition (1st issue). Oscar II stamp designs by Max Mirowsky.

1159	343	1 k. blue	25	25
1160	–	2 k. red	45	45
1161	–	3 k. blue	55	55
1162	–	4 k. green	75	75

DESIGNS: 2 k. Issued stamp of 1885; 3 k. Essay for unissued stamp, 1891; 4 k. Issued stamp of 1891.

See also Nos. 1199/1202, 1252/5, 1285/8 and 1310/3.

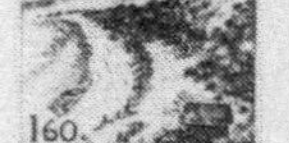

344 Greater Karlso 345 Fresh-water Snail

1983.

1163	344	1 k. 60 blue	30	10
1164	345	1 k. 80 green	35	10
1165	–	2 k. 10 green	40	10

DESIGN—22 × 27 mm: 2 k. 10, Arctic fox.

346 Bergman 347 Helgeandsholmen, 1580 (after Franz Hogenberg) and Riksdag

1983. Birth Centenary of Hjalmar Bergman (novelist and dramatist).

1166	346	1 k. 80 blue	35	10
1167	–	1 k. 80 multicoloured	35	10

DESIGN: No. 1167, Jac the Clown (novel character).

1983. Return of Riksdag (Parliament) to Helgeandsholmen Island, Stockholm.

1168	347	2 k. 70 maroon & blue	45	35

MINIMUM PRICE

The minimum price quoted is 10p which represents a handling charge rather than a basis for valuing common stamps. For further notes about prices, see introductory pages.

348 Red Cross 350 Dancing round the Christmas Tree

1983. Swedish Red Cross.

1169	348	1 k. 50 red	30	10

1983. Christmas. Early Christmas Cards. Multicoloured.

1171	1 k. 60 Type **350**	40	10
1172	1 k. 60 Straw goats	40	10
1173	1 k. 60 The Christmas table	40	10
1174	1 k. 60 Carrying Christmas presents on pole	40	10

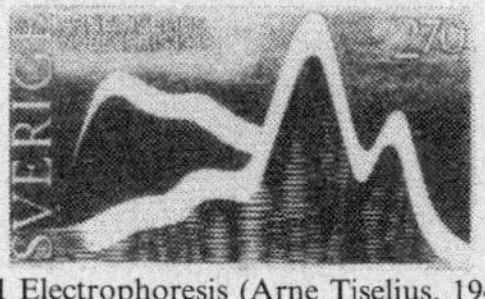

351 Electrophoresis (Arne Tiselius, 1948)

1983. Nobel Prize Winners for Chemistry.

1175	351	2 k. 70 black	60	50
1176	–	2 k. 70 violet	60	50
1177	–	2 k. 70 mauve	60	50
1178	–	2 k. 70 violet	60	50
1179	–	2 k. 70 black	60	50

DESIGNS: No. 1176, Radioactive isotopes (George de Hevesy, 1943); 1177, Electrolytic dissociation (Svante Arrhenius, 1903); 1178, Colloids (Theodor Svedberg, 1926); 1179, Fermentation of sugar (Hans von Euler-Chelpin, 1929).

352 Three Crowns (detail from Postal Savings Receipt)

1984. Centenary of Postal Savings.

1180	352	100 ore orange	20	15
1181	–	1 k. 60 violet	30	15
1182	–	1 k. 80 purple	40	10

DESIGNS: 1 k. 60, 1 k. 80, Postal Savings badge.

353 Bridge

1984. Europa. 25th Anniv of European Post and Telecommunications Conference.

1183	353	1 k. 80 red	50	10
1184		2 k. 70 blue	1·50	60

354 Norway Lemming 355 Paraffin Stove (F. W. Lindqvist)

1984. Swedish Mountain World.

1185	354	1 k. 90 brown	40	10
1186	–	1 k. 90 blue	40	10
1187	–	2 k. green	45	10
1188	–	2 k. 25 black	55	25

DESIGNS: No. 1186, Musk ox; 1187, Garden angelica; 1188, Tolpagorni mountain.

1984. Rebate Stamps. Arms of Swedish Provinces (4th series). As T **316**. Multicoloured.

1189	1 k. 60 Sodermanland	40	10
1190	1 k. 60 Blekinge	40	10
1191	1 k. 60 Vasterbotten	40	10
1192	1 k. 60 Skane	40	10

1984. "Made in Sweden". Centenary of Patent Office. Patented Swedish Inventions.

1193	355	2 k. 70 red	60	50
1194	–	2 k. 70 lilac	60	50
1195	–	2 k. 70 green	60	50
1196	–	2 k. 70 green	60	50
1197	–	2 k. 70 lilac	60	50
1198	–	2 k. 70 blue	60	50

DESIGNS: No. 1194, "ASEA IRB 6" industrial robot for arc welding; 1195, Vacuum cleaner (Axel Wennergren); 1196, "AQ 200" inboard/outboard engine; 1197, Integrated circuit; 1198, Tetrahedron container.

356 King Erik IV (after S. van der Meulen) and Letter to Queen Elizabeth I of England

358 Genetic Symbols forming "100"

357 Jonkoping

1984. "Stockholmia 86" International Stamp Exhibition (2nd issue).

1199 **356** 1 k. brown, blue and deep blue 25 25
1200 – 2 k. multicoloured . . . 45 45
1201 – 3 k. multicoloured . . . 55 55
1202 – 4 k. multicoloured . . . 75 75

DESIGNS: 2 k. Erik Dahlbergh (architect) (after J. H. Stromer) and letter to Sten Bielke (Paymaster General), 1674; 3 k. Feather letter, 1843; 4 k. Harriet Bosse and letter from her husband, August Strindberg, 1905.

1984. Old Towns. 17th-century views by M. Karl (1207) or Erik Dahlberg (others).

1203 **357** 1 k. 90 blue 40 30
1204 – 1 k. 90 brown 40 30
1205 – 1 k. 90 blue 50 30
1206 – 1 k. 90 brown 40 30
1207 – 1 k. 90 blue 40 30
1208 – 1 k. 90 brown 40 30

DESIGNS: No. 1204, Karlstad; 1205, Gavle; 1206, Sigtuna; 1207, Norrkoping; 1208. Vadstena.

1984. Centenary of Fredrika Bremer Association (for promotion of male/female equal rights).

1209 **358** 1 k. 50 purple 30 10
1210 6 k. 50 red . . . . 1·10 25

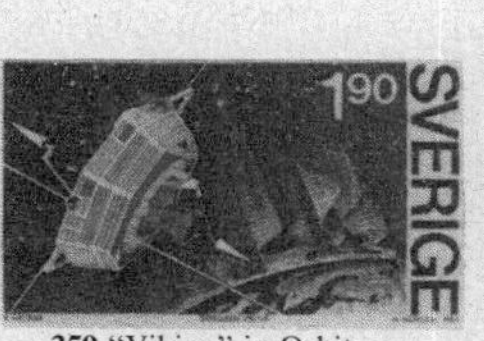

359 "Viking" in Orbit

JULPOST 1984
SVERIGE 1 60

361 Hawfinch

1984. Launch of Swedish "Viking" Satellite.

1211 **359** 1 k. 90 ultramarine, blue and deep blue 40 10
1212 – 3 k. 20 green, yellow and black 85 50

DESIGN: 3 k. 20, Dish aerial and rocket pad at Esrange space station.

1984. Christmas. Birds. Multicoloured.

1214 1 k. 60 Type **361** 60 40
1215 1 k. 60 Bohemian waxwing . 60 40
1216 1 k. 60 Great-spotted woodpecker 60 40
1217 1 k. 60 European nuthatch . 60 40

362 Inner Ear (Georg von Bekesy, 1961)

1984. Nobel Prize Winners for Medicine.

1218 **362** 2 k. 70 blue, black and red 80 70
1219 – 2 k. 70 blue and black . 80 70
1220 – 2 k. 70 red, black and blue 80 70
1221 – 2 k. 70 blue and black . 80 70
1222 – 2 k. 70 red, black and blue 80 70

DESIGNS: No. 1219, Nerve cell activation (John Eccles, Alan Hodgkin and Andrew Huxley, 1963); 1220, Nerve cell signals (Bernard Katz, Ulf von Euler and Julius Axelrod, 1970); 1221, Functions of the brain (Roger Sperry, 1981); 1222, Eye (David Hubel and Torsten Wiesel, 1981).

363 Post Office Emblem

364 King Carl XVI Gustav

1985.

1223 **363** 1 k. 60 blue 30 10
1224 1 k. 70 violet 40 10
1326 1 k. 80 mauve 35 10
1225 2 k. 50 yellow 45 10
1226 2 k. 80 green 60 10
1327 3 k. 20 brown 50 10
1227 4 k. red 70 10
1328 6 k. turquoise . . . . . 1·10 10

1985.

1228 **364** 2 k. black 35 10
1229 2 k. 10 blue 50 10
1230 2 k. 20 blue 35 10
1230a 2 k. 30 green 45 10
1230b 2 k. 50 purple 45 10
1231 2 k. 70 brown 45 10
1232 2 k. 90 green 55 10
1233 3 k. 10 brown 55 10
1234 – 3 k. 20 blue 55 10
1235 **364** 3 k. 30 purple 60 25
1236 – 3 k. 40 red 70 10
1237 – 3 k. 60 green 60 10
1238 – 3 k. 90 blue 70 35
1239 – 4 k. 60 orange 85 45

DESIGNS: 3 k. 20 and 3 k. 40 to 4 k. 60, Queen Silvia.

365 Hazel Dormouse

366 Jan-Ove Waldner

1985. Nature.

1240 **365** 2 k. brown and black . 45 15
1241 – 2 k. orange and black . 45 15
1242 – 2 k. 20 red 60 20
1243 – 3 k. 50 red and green . . 80 20

DESIGNS: No. 1241, Char; 1242, Black vanilla orchid; 1243, White water-lily.

1985. World Table Tennis Championships, Gothenburg.

1244 **366** 2 k. 70 blue 70 30
1245 – 3 k. 20 mauve 80 45

DESIGN: 3 k. 20, Cai Zhenhua (Chinese player).

1985. Rebate Stamps. Arms of Swedish Provinces (5th series). As T **316**. Multicoloured.

1246 1 k. 80 Narke 40 10
1247 1 k. 80 Angermanland . . . 40 10
1248 1 k. 80 Varmland 40 10
1249 1 k. 80 Smaland 40 10

367 Clavichord

1985. Europa. Music Year.

1250 **367** 2 k. purple on buff . . . 1·50 10
1251 – 2 k. 70 brown on buff . 90 55

DESIGN: 2 k. 70, Keyed fiddle.

368 "View of Slussen" (Sigrid Hjerten)

2KR
SVERIGE

369 Syl Hostel, 1920

1985. "Stockholmia '86" International Stamp Exhibition (3rd issue). Multicoloured.

1252 2 k. Type **368** 40 40
1253 2 k. "Skeppsholmen, Winter" (Gosta Adrian-Nilsson) . 40 40
1254 3 k. "A Summer's Night by Riddarholmen Canal" (Hilding Linnqvist) . . . 55 55
1255 4 k. "Klara Church Tower" (Otte Skold) 70 70

1985. Centenary of Swedish Touring Club.

1256 **369** 2 k. blue and black . . 50 15
1257 – 2 k. black and blue . . 60 15

DESIGN—58 × 24 mm: No. 1257, "Af Chapman" (youth hostel in Stockholm).

370 Canute and Helsingborg

371 Nilsson's Music Shop Sign

1985. 900th Anniv of Saint Canute's Deed of Gift to Lund.

1258 – 2 k. blue and black . . . 40 10
1259 **370** 2 k. red and black 40 10

DESIGN: No. 1258, Canute and Lund Cathedral.

1985. Trade Signs.

1260 **371** 10 ore blue 10 10
1261 – 20 ore brown 10 10
1262 – 20 ore brown 10 10
1263 – 50 ore blue 15 10
1264 – 2 k. green 50 10

DESIGNS: No. 1261, Erik Johansson's furrier's sign; 1262, O. L. Sjowals's coppersmith's sign; 1263, Bodecker's hatter's sign; 1264, Berggren's shoemaker's sign.

372 "Otryades" (Johan Tobias Sergel)

1985. 250th Anniv of Royal Academy of Fine Arts.

1265 **372** 2 k. blue 35 10
1266 – 7 k. brown . . . . 1·25 30

DESIGN—20 × 28 mm: 7 k. "Baron Carl Fredrik Adelcrantz" (former Academy president) (Alexander Roslin).

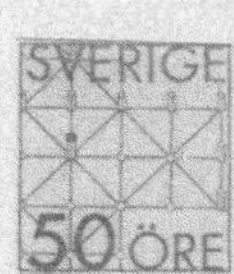

373 Fox and Geese

374 Birger Sjoberg (writer)

1985. Board Games.

1267 **373** 50 ore blue 10 10
1268 – 60 ore green 15 10
1269 – 70 ore yellow 15 10
1270 – 80 ore red 25 10
1271 – 90 ore mauve 25 10
1272 – 3 k. purple . . . . 1·10 20

DESIGNS—As T **373**: 60 ore Dominoes; 70 ore Ludo; 80 ore Chinese checkers; 90 ore Backgammon. 23 × 28 mm: 3 k. Chess.

1985. Birth Centenaries.

1273 – 1 k. 60 red and black . . 40 10
1274 **374** 4 k. green 85 25

DESIGN—40 × 24 mm: 1 k. 60, Per Albin Hansson (politician).

376 "Annunciation"

377 American Deep South Scene (William Faulkner, 1949)

1985. Christmas. Medieval Church Frescoes by Albertus Pictor.

1276 **376** 1 k. 80 blue, brown and red 35 20
1277 – 1 k. 80 brown, blue and red 35 20
1278 – 1 k. 80 brown, blue and red 35 20
1279 – 1 k. 80 blue, brown and red 35 20

DESIGNS: No. 1277, "Birth of Christ"; 1278, "Adoration of the Magi"; 1279, "Mary as the Apocalyptic Virgin".

1985. Nobel Prize Winners for Literature.

1280 **377** 2 k. 70 green 70 60
1281 – 2 k. 70 brown, blue and green 70 60
1282 – 2 k. 70 green and brown . 70 60
1283 – 2 k. 70 green and blue . . 1·25 60
1284 – 2 k. 70 brown and blue . 70 60

DESIGNS: No. 1281, Icelandic scene (Halldor Kiljan Laxness, 1955); 1282, Guatemalan scene (Miguel Angel Asturias, 1967); 1283, Japanese scene (Yasunari Kawabata, 1968); 1284, Australian scene (Patrick White, 1973).

378 1879 "20 TRETIO" Error

379 Eiders

1986. "Stockholmia 86" International Stamp Exhibition (4th issue).

1285 **378** 2 k. orange, pur & grn . . 70 60
1286 – 2 k. multicoloured . . . 70 60
1287 – 3 k. purple, blue and green 80 70
1288 – 4 k. multicoloured . . . 80 80

DESIGNS: No. 1286, Sven Ewert (engraver); 1287, Magnifying glass and United States 1938 Scandinavian Settlement 3 c. stamp; 1288, Boy soaking stamps.

1986. Water Birds.

1289 **379** 2 k. 10 blue and brown . 1·10 45
1290 – 2 k. 10 brown . . . . . 1·10 45
1291 – 2 k. 30 blue . . . . . . 1·10 55

DESIGNS: No. 1290, Whimbrel; 1291, Black-throated diver.

380 Swedish Academy Emblem

381 Jubilee Emblem

1986. Bicentenaries of Swedish Academy and Royal Swedish Academy of Letters, History and Antiquities.

1292 **380** 1 k. 70 green and red on grey 50 30
1293 – 1 k. 70 blue and purple on grey 50 30

DESIGN: No. 1293, Royal Swedish Academy Emblem.

1986. 350th Anniv of Post Office.

1294 **381** 2 k. 10 blue and yellow . 45 10

382 Palme

383 Carl Gustav Birdwatching

1986. Olof Palme (Prime Minister) Commemoration.

1295 **382** 2 k. 10 purple 50 40
1296 2 k. 90 black 75 70

1986. 40th Birthday of King Carl XVI Gustav.

1297 **383** 2 k. 10 black and green . 45 15
1298 – 2 k. 10 gold, mauve and blue 45 15
1299 – 2 k. 10 dp blue & blue . 45 15
1300 – 2 k. 10 gold, blue and deep blue 45 15
1301 – 2 k. 10 black & mauve . 45 15

DESIGNS: Nos. 1298, 1300, Crowned cypher; 1299, King presenting Nobel Prize for Literature to Czeslaw Milosz; 1301, King and family during summer holiday at Solliden Palace.

1986. Rebate Stamps. Arms of Swedish Provinces (6th series). As T **316**. Multicoloured.

1302 1 k. 90 Harjedalen 55 10
1303 1 k. 90 Uppland 55 10
1304 1 k. 90 Halland 55 10
1305 1 k. 90 Lappland 55 10

384 Uppsala

385 Forest and Car Fumes

1986. Nordic Countries' Postal Co-operation. Twinned Towns.

1306 **384** 2 k. 10 green, light brown and brown 65 10
1307 – 2 k. 90 green, red & brn 85 40

DESIGN: 2 k. 90, Eskilstuna.

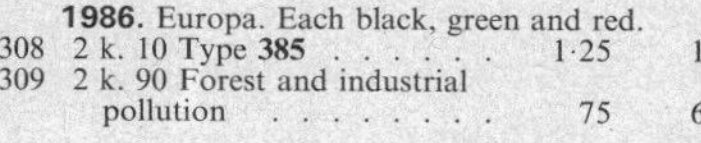

1986. Europa. Each black, green and red.

1308 2 k. 10 Type **385** . . . . . . 1·25 10
1309 2 k. 90 Forest and industrial pollution 75 60

386 Tomteboda Sorting Office (20th-century)

388 Olive branch sweeping away Weapons

1986. "Stockholmia 86" International Stamp Exhibition (5th issue). Multicoloured.
1310 2 k. 10 19th-century mail carriage . . . . 2·50 3·00
1311 2 k. 10 Type **386** . . . . . . 2·50 3·00
1312 2 k. 90 17th-century farmhand postal messenger . . . . . 2·50 3·00
1313 2 k. 90 18th-century post-office 2·50 3·00

1986. International Peace Year (1315) and 25th Anniv of Amnesty International (1316).
1315 **388** 3 k. 40 green and black . 80 40
1316 – 3 k. 40 red and black . . 80 40
DESIGN: No. 1316, Emblem above broken manacles.

389 Bertha von Suttner (founder of Austrian Society of Peace Lovers, 1905)

1986. Nobel Prize Winners for Peace.
1317 **389** 2 k. 90 black, red & blue 75 60
1318 – 2 k. 90 black and red . . 75 60
1319 – 2 k. 90 black, brown and blue 75 60
1320 – 2 k. 90 brown and black 75 60
1321 – 2 k. 90 red, black & blue 75 60
DESIGNS: No. 1318, Carl von Ossietzky (anti-Nazi fighter and concentration camp victim, 1935); 1319, Albert Luthuli (South African anti-apartheid leader, 1960); 1320, Martin Luther King (American civil rights leader, 1964); 1321, Mother Teresa (worker amongst poor of Calcutta, 1979).

390 Mail Van **391** Clouded Apollo

1986. Christmas. Designs showing village at Christmas. Multicoloured.
1322 1 k. 90 Type **390** 45 15
1323 1 k. 90 Postman on cycle delivering mail 45 15
1324 1 k. 90 Children and sledge loaded with parcels 45 15
1325 1 k. 90 Christmas tree man carrying parcel and child posting letter 45 15
Nos. 1322/5 were printed together, se-tenant, forming a composite design.

1987. Threatened Species of Meadows and Pastures.
1331 **391** 2 k. 10 black, green and purple 50 10
1332 – 2 k. 10 black, green and purple 50 10
1333 – 2 k. 50 brown 60 20
1334 – 4 k. 20 green and yellow 1·00 20
DESIGNS: 2 k. 10 (1332), Field gentian ("Gentianella campestris"); 2 k. 50, Leather beetle; 4 k. 20, Arnica.

392 SAAB-Fairchild SF-340 **393** Boys flying over Rooftops ("Karlsson")

1987. Swedish Aircraft.
1335 **392** 25 k. purple . . . . . . 4·00 25

1987. Rebate Stamps. Characters from Children's Books by Astrid Lindgren. Multicoloured.
1336 1 k. 90 Type **393** 45 15
1337 1 k. 90 Girl holding doll ("Bullerby Children") . . . 45 15
1338 1 k. 90 Girls dancing ("Madicken") 45 15
1339 1 k. 90 Boys on horse ("Mio, Min Mio") 45 15
1340 1 k. Boy doing handstand ("Nils Karlsson-Pyssling") 45 15
1341 1 k. 90 Emil picking cherries ("Emil") 45 15
1342 1 k. 90 "Ronja the Robber's Daughter" 45 15
1343 1 k. 90 "Pippi Longstocking" 45 15
1344 1 k. 90 Dragon ("Brothers Lionheart") 45 15
1345 1 k. 90 "Lotta" 45 15

394 Hans Brask, Bishop of Linkoping (sculpture, Karl-Olav Bjork)

395 Stockholm City Library (Gunnar Asplund)

1987. Town Anniversaries. Each brown, blue and black.
1346 2 k. 10 Type **394** (700th anniv) 55 20
1347 2 k. 10 Nykoping Castle (800th anniv) 55 20

1987. Europa. Architecture.
1348 **395** 2 k. 10 brown & blue . 1·00 10
1349 3 k. 10 brown & green . 70 70
1350 – 3 k. 10 purple & green . 70 70
DESIGN: No. 1350, Marcus Church (Sigurd Lewerentz).

396 "King Gustavus Vasa" (anon) **398** Clowns

397 Raoul Wallenberg (rescuer of Hungarian Jews) and Prisoners

1987. 450th Anniv of Gripsholm Castle.
1351 **396** 2 k. 10 multicoloured . 45 15
1352 – 2 k. 10 multicoloured . 45 15
1353 – 2 k. 10 multicoloured . 45 15
1354 – 2 k. 10 brown, black and blue 45 15
DESIGNS: No. 1352, "Blue Tiger" (David Klocker Ehrenstrahl); 1353, "Hedvig Charlotta Nordenflycht" (after Johan Henrik Scheffel); 1354, "Gripsholm Castle" (lithograph, Carl Johan Billmark).

1987. "In the Service of Humanity".
1355 **397** 3 k. 10 blue 70 60
1356 – 3 k. 10 green 70 60
1357 – 3 k. 10 brown 70 60
DESIGNS: No. 1356, Dag Hammarskjold (U.N. Secretary-General, 1953–1961); 1357, Folke Bernadotte (leader of "white bus" relief action to rescue prisoners, 1945).

1987. Stamp Day. Bicentenary of Circus in Sweden. Multicoloured.
1358 2 k. 10 Type **398** 80 60
1359 2 k. 10 Reino riding one-wheel cycle on wire 80 60
1360 2 k. 10 Acrobat on horseback 80 60

399 "Victoria cruziana" at Bergian Garden, Stockholm University **400** Porridge left for the Grey Christmas Elf

1987. Bicentenary of Swedish Botanical Gardens.
1361 **399** 2 k. 10 green, deep green and blue 50 25
1362 – 2 k. 10 green & brown . 50 25
1363 – 2 k. 10 deep green, green and blue 50 25
1364 – 2 k. 10 yellow, brown and green 50 25
DESIGNS: No. 1362, Uppsala University Baroque Garden plan and Carl Harleman (architect); 1363, Rock garden, Gothenburg Botanical Garden; 1364, "Liriodendron tulipifera", Lund Botanical Garden.

1987. Christmas. Folk Customs. Multicoloured.
1365 2 k. Type **400** 35 15
1366 2 k. Staffan ride (watering horses in North-running spring on Boxing Day) . . 35 15
1367 2 k. Christmas Day sledge race home from church 35 15
1368 2 k. Bullfinches on corn sheaf 35 15

401 Pulsars (Antony Hewish, 1974)

1987. Nobel Prize Winners for Physics.
1369 **401** 2 k. 90 blue 70 60
1370 – 2 k. 90 black 70 60
1371 – 2 k. 90 blue 70 60
1372 – 2 k. 90 blue 70 60
1373 – 2 k. 90 black 70 60
DESIGNS: No. 1370, Formula of maximum white dwarf star mass (S. Chandrasekhar), 1983); 1371, Heavy atom nuclei construction (William Fowler, 1983); 1372, Temperature of cosmic background radiation (A. Penzias and R. Wilson, 1978); 1373, Radio telescopes receiving radio waves from galaxy (Martin Ryle, 1974).

402 Lake Hjalmaren Skiff **404** White-tailed Sea Eagle

403 Bishop Hill and Erik Jansson (founder)

1988. Inland Boats. Each purple on buff.
1374 3 k. 10 Type **402** 60 30
1375 3 k. 10 Lake Vattern market boat 60 30
1376 3 k. 10 River Byske logging boat 60 30
1377 3 k. 10 Lake Asnen rowing boat 60 30
1378 3 k. 10 Lake Vanern ice boat 60 30
1379 3 k. 10 Lake Lockne church longboat 60 30

1988. 350th Anniv of New Sweden (settlement in America).
1380 – 3 k. 60 multicoloured . . 85 70
1381 **403** 3 k. 60 multicoloured . . 85 70
1382 – 3 k. 60 brown 85 70
1383 – 3 k. 60 blue and brown . 85 70
1384 – 3 k. 60 blue, yellow and red 85 70
1385 – 3 k. 60 black, blue and red 85 70
DESIGNS—As T **403**: No. 1380, Map, settlers, Indians, "Calmare Nyckel" and "Fagel Grip". 27 × 23 mm: 1382, Carl Sandburg (American poet) and Jenny Lind (Swedish soprano); 1383, Charles Lindbergh (aviator) and Ryan NYP Special "Spirit of St. Louis". 27 × 37 mm: 1384, Alan Bean (astronaut) on Moon with Hasselblad camera; 1385, Ice hockey.

1988. Coastal Wildlife.
1386 **404** 2 k. 20 brown and red . . 40 15
1387 – 2 k. 20 brown and blue . 40 15
1388 – 4 k. black, brown and green 80 40
DESIGNS: No. 1387, Grey seal; 1388, Eel.

405 Daisies and Bluebells **406** Detail of "Creation" Stained Glass Window (Bo Beskow), Skara Cathedral

1988. Rebate stamps. Midsummer Festival. Multicoloured.
1389 2 k. Type **405** 40 15
1390 2 k. Garlanded longboat . . . 40 15
1391 2 k. Children making garlands 40 15
1392 2 k. Raising the maypole . . 40 15
1393 2 k. Fiddlers 40 15
1394 2 k. "Norrskar" (tourist launch) 40 15
1395 2 k. Couples dancing 40 15
1396 2 k. Accordianist 40 15
1397 2 k. Archipelago with decorated landing stage 40 15
1398 2 k. Bouquet of seven wild flowers 40 15

1988. Anniversaries.
1399 **406** 2 k. 20 multicoloured . . 50 15
1400 – 4 k. 40 red on brown . . 90 40
1401 – 8 k. red, green & black . 1·90 80
DESIGNS: 2 k. 20, Type **406** (millenary of Skara); 23 × 41 mm: 4 k. 40, "Falun Copper Mine" (Pehr Hillestrom) (700th anniv of Stora Kopparberg (mining company)); 8 k. Scene from play "The Queen's Diamond Ornament" (bicentenary of Royal Dramatic Theatre, Stockholm).

407 "Self-portrait" (Nils Dardel) **408** "X2" High-speed Train

1968. Swedish Artists in Paris. Multicoloured.
1402 2 k. 20 Type **407** 40 40
1403 2 k. 20 "Autumn, Gubbhuset" (Vera Nilsson) (40 × 43 mm) 40 40
1404 2 k. 20 "Self-Portrait" (Isaac Grunewald) 40 40
1405 2 k. 20 "Visit to an Eccentric Lady" (Nils Dardel) . . . 40 40
1406 2 k. 20 "Soap Bubbles" (Vera Nilsson) (40 × 43 mm) . . 40 40
1407 2 k. 20 "The Singing Tree" (Isaac Grunewald) 40 40

1988. Europa. Transport and Communications.
1408 **408** 2 k. 20 blue, orange and brown 85 10
1409 3 k. 10 blue, black and purple 60 60
1410 – 3 k. 10 black and purple 60 60
DESIGN: No. 1410, Narrow-gauge steam locomotive.

409 Swift **410** Andersson

1988.
1411 **409** 20 k. purple and mauve . 3·75 1·60

1988. Birth Centenary of Dan Andersson (poet). Each violet, green and blue.
1412 2 k. 20 Type **410** 40 10
1413 2 k. 20 Lake, Finnmarken (58 × 24 mm) 40 10

411 Players **412** Angel and Shepherds

1988. Swedish Football. Multicoloured.
1414 2 k. 20 Type **411** 50 50
1415 2 k. 20 Three players . . . 50 50
1416 2 k. 20 Women players . . . 50 50

1988. Christmas. Multicoloured.
1417 2 k. Type **412** 35 15
1418 2 k. Horse and angel 35 15
1419 2 k. Birds singing in trees . . 35 15
1420 2 k. Three kings 35 15
1421 2 k. Holy Family 35 15
1422 2 k. Shepherds and sheep . . 35 15
Nos. 1418/22 were printed together, se-tenant, forming a composite design.

413 Archaeologist, Carbon 14 Dating Graph and Tutankhamun **414** Nidingen 1946 Concrete and 1832 Twin Lighthouses

1988. Nobel Prize Winners for Chemistry. Mult.
1423 3 k. 10 Type **413** (Willard Frank Libby, 1960) 55 55
1424 3 k. 10 Plastics molecules (Karl Ziegler and Giulio Natta, 1963) 55 55
1425 3 k. 10 Electron microscope (Aaron Klug, 1982) . . . 55 55
1426 3 k. 10 Landscape and symbols (Ilya Prigogine, 1977) . . . 55 55

1989. Lighthouses.
1427 **414** 1 k. 90 green, brown and black 35 10
1428 – 2 k. 70 blue, red and deep blue 50 25
1429 – 3 k. 80 brown, deep blue and blue 70 35
1430 – 3 k. 90 black, red & brn . 70 45
DESIGNS: 2 k. 70, Soderarm stone lighthouse; 3 k. 80, Sydostbrotten caisson lighthouse; 3 k. 90, Sandhammaren iron lighthouse.

415 Wolverine

1989. Animals in Threatened Habitats.
1431 **415** 2 k. 30 brown, orange and green 45 20
1432 – 2 k. 30 brown, green and orange 45 20
1433 – 2 k. 40 deep brown, brown and red 45 20
1434 – 2 k. 60 deep brown, brown and orange 50 25
1435 – 3 k. 30 deep green, green and brown 60 35
1436 – 4 k. 60 black, green and orange 85 50
DESIGNS: 2 k. 30 (1432), Ural owl; 2 k. 40, Lesser spotted woodpecker; 2 k. 60, Dunlin; 3 k. 30, Common tree frog; 4 k. 60, Red-breasted flycatcher.

416 Globe Arena

1989. Opening of Globe Arena, Stockholm. Mult.
1437 2 k. 30 Type **416** 45 15
1438 2 k. 30 Ice hockey 45 15
1439 2 k. 30 Gymnastics 45 15
1440 2 k. 30 Pop concert 45 15

417 Woman's Woollen Bib Front   **418** Sailing

1989. Nordic Countries' Postal Co-operation. Traditional Lapp Costumes.
1441 2 k. 30 Type **417** 45 15
1442 3 k. 30 Man's belt pouch . . 60 50

1989. Rebate stamps. Summer Activities. Mult.
1443 2 k. 10 Type **418** 50 15
1444 2 k. 10 Beach ball 50 15
1445 2 k. 10 Cycling 50 15
1446 2 k. 10 Canoeing 50 15
1447 2 k. 10 Fishing 50 15
1448 2 k. 10 Camping 50 15
1449 2 k. 10 Croquet 50 15
1450 2 k. 10 Badminton 50 15
1451 2 k. 10 Gardening 50 15
1452 2 k. 10 Sand castle, bucket and spade 50 15

419 "Protest March" (Nils Kreuger)   **420** Playing with Boats

1989. Centenary of Swedish Labour Movement.
1453 **419** 2 k. 30 black and red . . 45 15

1989. Europa. Children's Games and Toys.
1454 **420** 2 k. 30 brown 70 15
1455 – 3 k. 30 mauve 60 60
1456 – 3 k. 30 green 60 60
DESIGN: No. 1456, Girl riding kick-sled.

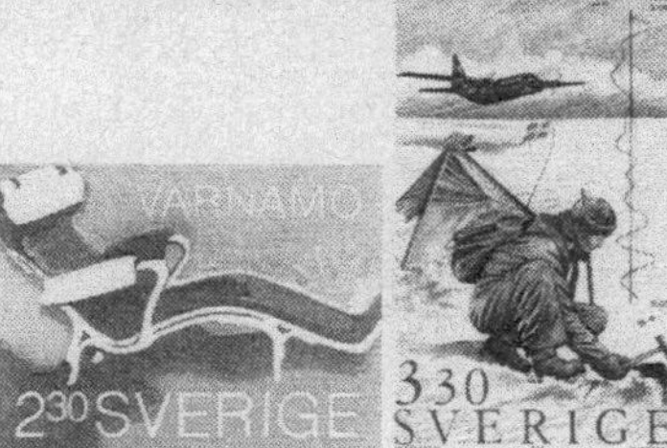

421 Lounger (Varnamo)   **422** Researcher in Greenland and Temperature Curve

1989. Industries of Smaland Towns. Each mauve, orange and red.
1457 2 k. 30 Type **421** 45 45
1458 2 k. 30 Tools for self-assembly furniture (Almhult) . . . 45 45
1459 2 k. 30 Sewing machine and embroidery (Huskvarna) . . 45 45
1460 2 k. 30 Blowing glass (Afors) . . 45 45
1461 2 k. 30 Coathanger hook and clothes-peg spring (Gnosjo) . 45 45
1462 2 k. 30 Match (Jonkoping) . . 45 45

1989. 250th Anniv of Swedish Academy of Sciences. Polar Research. Multicoloured.
1463 3 k. 30 Type **422** 75 75
1464 3 k. 30 Abisko Natural Science Station, Lapland (40 × 43 mm) 75 75
1465 3 k. 30 "Oden" (ice research ship) and researchers . . . 75 75
1466 3 k. 30 Otto Nordenskiold 1901–03 expedition's "Antarctic" and Emperor penguin with chick 75 75
1467 3 k. 30 1988 Antarctic expedition's vehicles and Hughes Model 500 helicopter (40 × 43 mm) 75 75
1468 3 k. 30 Geodimeter and McCormick's skua 75 75

423 Eagle Owl

1989.
1469 **423** 30 k. brown, blk & mve 5·75 4·25

424 Arctic Rhododendron   **425** Jamthund

1989. National Parks (1st series).
1470 **424** 2 k. 40 mauve, grn & bl 45 10
1471 – 2 k. 40 mauve & green . 45 10
1472 – 4 k. 30 red, black & blue 80 40
DESIGNS: No. 1471, Calypso ("Calypso bulbosa"); 1472, Black guillemots at Bla Jungfrun.
See also Nos. 1486/90.

1989. Centenary of Swedish Kennel Club. Mult.
1473 2 k. 40 Type **425** 60 60
1474 2 k. 40 Hamilton foxhound . 60 60
1475 2 k. 40 Vastgota sheep dog . 60 60

426 Decorated Tree   **427** Vinegar Flies (T. H. Morgan, 1933)

1989. Christmas. Multicoloured.
1476 2 k. 10 Type **426** 35 15
1477 2 k. 10 Candelabra and food 35 15
1478 2 k. 10 Star, poinsettia and tureen 35 15
1479 2 k. 10 Decorated tree and straw goat 35 15
1480 2 k. 10 Girl watching television 35 15
1481 2 k. 10 Family with present . 35 15
Nos. 1476/81 were printed together se-tenant, forming a composite design.

1989. Nobel Prize Winners for Medicine.
1482 **427** 3 k. 60 brown, yell & bl . 75 30
1483 – 3 k. 60 yellow, bl & red . 65 30
1484 – 3 k. 60 multicoloured . . 65 30
1485 – 3 k. 60 multicoloured . . 65 30
DESIGNS: No. 1483 X-ray diffractogram and D.N.A. molecule (Francis Crick, James Watson and Maurice Wilkins, 1962); 1484, D.N.A. molecule cut by restriction enzyme (W. Arber, D. Nathans and H. O. Smith, 1978); 1485, Maize kernels (Barbara McClintock, 1983).

428 Angso   **429** Lumberjack

1990. National Parks (2nd series).
1486 **428** 2 k. 50 blue, green & red 60 20
1487 – 2 k. 50 red, green & blue 45 15
1488 – 3 k. 70 blue, brown & grn 70 35
1489 – 4 k. 10 blue, green & brn 70 45
1490 – 4 k. 80 green, brown & bl 85 50
DESIGNS: No. 1487, Pieljekaise; 1488, Muddus; 1489, Padjelanta; 1490, Sanfjallet.

1990. Centenary of Industrial Safety Inspectorate.
1491 **429** 2 k. 50 blue and brown . 45 15

430 Postal Museum, Stockholm   **431** Carved Bone Head and Cast Dragon Head

1990. Europa. Post Office Buildings.
1492 **430** 2 k. 50 brown, orge & bl . 60 10
1493 – 3 k. 80 multicoloured . . 70 50
1494 – 3 k. 80 multicoloured . . 70 50
DESIGNS: No. 1493, Sollebrunn Post Office; 1494, Vasteras Post Office.

1990. Vikings. Multicoloured.
1495 2 k. 50 Type **431** 45 25
1496 2 k. 50 Returning Viking longships (34 × 29 mm) . . 60 25
1497 2 k. 50 Wooden houses (34 x 29 mm) 45 25
1498 2 k. 50 Bronze figurine of God of Fertility and silver cross 45 25
1499 2 k. 50 Crosier and gold embroidered deer 45 25
1500 2 k. 50 Vikings in roundship (34 × 29 mm) 60 25
1501 2 k. 50 Viking disembarking (34 × 29 mm) 60 25
1502 2 k. 50 Viking swords 45 25
Nos. 1496/7 and 1500/1 form a composite design.

432 Worker collecting Pollen   **433** Prow of "Wasa" and Museum

1990. Rebate stamps. Honey Bees. Multicoloured.
1503 2 k. 30 Type **432** 45 25
1504 2 k. 30 Worker on bilberry . 45 25
1505 2 k. 30 Worker flying back to hive 45 25
1506 2 k. 30 Beehive 45 25
1507 2 k. 30 Bees building honeycombs 45 25
1508 2 k. 30 Drone 45 25
1509 2 k. 30 Queen 45 25
1510 2 k. 30 Swarm on branch . . 45 25
1511 2 k. 30 Beekeeper collecting frame 45 25
1512 2 k. 30 Pot of honey 45 25

1990. Opening of New "Wasa" (17th-century ship of the line) Museum.
1513 **433** 2 k. 50 black and red . . 55 10
1514 – 4 k. 60 blue and red . . 95 50
DESIGNS: 4 k. 60, Stern of "Wasa" and museum.

434 Endurance Event

1990. World Equestrian Games, Stockholm. Mult.
1515 3 k. 80 Type **434** 70 50
1516 3 k. 80 Mark Todd on Carisma jumping wall (3-day event) 70 50
1517 3 k. 80 John Whitaker on Next Milton jumping fence (show jumping) 70 50
1518 3 k. 80 Louise Nathorst (dressage) 70 50
1519 3 k. 80 Team vaulting . . . 70 50
1520 3 k. 80 Pahlsson brothers driving four-in-hand . . . 70 50

435 Papermaking, 1600   **436** "Dearest Brothers, Sisters and Friends"

1990. Centenary of Swedish Pulp and Paper Industry. Multicoloured.
1521 2 k. 50 Type **435** 45 15
1522 2 k. 50 Crown watermark . . 45 15
1523 2 k. 50 Foreign newspapers using Swedish newsprint . 45 15
1524 2 k. 50 Rolls of paper . . . 45 15

1990. 250th Birth Anniv of Carl Michael Bellman (poet) (1525/7) and Birth Centenary of Evert Taube (poet) (1528/30). Designs showing illustrations of their poems.
1525 **436** 2 k. 50 brown and black 45 25
1526 – 2 k. 50 multicoloured . . 45 25
1527 – 2 k. 50 black, bl and red 45 25
1528 – 2 k. 50 multicoloured . . 45 25
1529 – 2 k. 50 multicoloured . . 45 25
1530 – 2 k. 50 multicoloured . . 45 25
DESIGNS—As Type **436**: No. 1527, "Fredman in the Gutter"; 1528, "Happy Baker of San Remo"; 1530, "Violava". 40 × 43 mm: 1526, "Proud City"; 1529, "At Sea".

437 Oved Castle

1990.
1531 **437** 40 k. brown, blk & red . 6·75 50

438 Moa Martinson   **439** Box Camera with Bellows

1990. Birth Centenary of Moa Martinson (novelist).
1532 **438** 2 k. 50 black and red . . 45 15
1533 – 2 k. 50 black and violet 45 15
DESIGN: No. 1533, Fredrika and Sofi bathing (from "Women and Apple Trees").

1990. 150 Years of Photography. Multicoloured.
1534 2 k. 50 Type **439** 60 60
1535 2 k. 50 August Strindberg (self-photograph) 60 60
1536 2 k. 50 Modern 35 mm camera 60 60

440 Cumulus Clouds   **441** Christmas Cactus

1990. Clouds.
1537 **440** 4 k. 50 multicoloured . . 75 20
1538 – 4 k. 70 black and blue 1·00 50
1539 – 4 k. 90 blue, grn & brn 85 50
1540 – 5 k. 20 blue & ultram . . 90 50
DESIGNS: 4 k. 70, Cumulonimbus; 4 k. 90, Cirus uncinus; 5 k. 20, Altocumulus lenticularis.

1990. Christmas. Flowers. Multicoloured.
1541 2 k. 30 Type **441** 45 15
1542 2 k. 30 Christmas rose . . . 45 15
1543 2 k. 30 Azalea 45 15
1544 2 k. 30 Amaryllis 45 15
1545 2 k. 30 Hyacinth 45 15
1546 2 k. 30 Poinsettia 45 15

INDEX

Countries can be quickly located by referring to the index at the end of this volume.

442 Par Lagerkvist (1951)

1990. Nobel Prize Winners for Literature.
1547 **442** 3 k. 80 blue 70 45
1548 – 3 k. 80 red 70 45
1549 – 3 k. 80 green 70 45
1550 – 3 k. 80 violet 70 45
DESIGNS: No. 1548, Ernest Hemingway (1954); 1549, Albert Camus (1957); 1550, Boris Pasternak (1958).

443 European Catfish
444 Carta Marina, 1572 (Olaus Magnus)

1991. Freshwater Fishes.
1551 **443** 2 k. 50 black, grn & brn . 45 10
1552 – 2 k. 50 black, grn & brn . 45 10
1553 – 5 k. black, blue & brown 85 10
1554 – 5 k. 40 black, vio & red . 95 50
1555 – 5 k. 50 black and green . 95 10
1556 – 5 k. 60 black, bl & orge . 1·00 50
DESIGNS: No. 1552, European catfish (different); 1553, Siberian spiny loach; 1554, Gudgeon; 1555, Bearded stone leach; 1556, Verkhovka.
Nos. 1551/2 form a composite design of two catfish.

1991. Maps. Multicoloured.
1557 5 k. Type **444** 85 45
1558 5 k. Sweden, Denmark and Norway, 1662 (A. Bureus and J. Blaeu) (40 × 43 mm) . . 85 45
1559 5 k. Star globe, 1759 (Anders Akerman) 85 45
1560 5 k. Relief map of Areskutan, 1938 . . . . 85 45
1561 5 k. Stockholm old town, 1989 (40 × 43 mm) 85 45
1562 5 k. Bed-rock map of Areskutan, 1984 . . . . 85 45

445 Queen Silvia
447 Seglora Church

446 Drottningholm Palace (after Erik Dahlbergh)

1991.
1564 – 2 k. 80 blue 50 10
1565 – 2 k. 90 green 50 10
1566 – 3 k. 20 violet 55 10
1568 **445** 5 k. purple 85 10
1569 6 k. red . . . . 1·00 10
1570 6 k. 50 violet . . . . . . 1·10 25
DESIGN: 2 k. 80 to 3 k. 20, King Carl XVI Gustav.

1991. 10th Anniv of Royal Residence at Drottningholm Palace.
1576 **446** 25 k. ochre, black & grn 4·25 85

1991. Rebate stamps. Centenary of Skansen Park, Stockholm. Multicoloured.
1577 2 k. 40 Type **447** 45 20
1578 2 k. 40 Celebration of Swedish Flag and National Days at Skansen 45 20
1579 2 k. 40 Wedding at Skansen . 45 20
1580 2 k. 40 Animals, Skansen Zoo 45 20

448 Park Entrance
449 Polar Bears

1991. Centenary of Public Amusement Parks. Each blue. Imperf.
1581 2 k. 50 Type **448** 45 15
1582 2 k. 50 Dancers and violinist 45 15

1991. Nordic Countries' Postal Co-operation. Tourism. Animals in Kolmarden Zoo.
1583 **449** 2 k. 50 black, brn & bl . 45 15
1584 – 4 k. red and purple . . 70 35
DESIGN: 4 k. Dolphins and trainer.

450 "Hermes" Rocket
451 Magda Julin (figure skating, Antwerp, 1920)

1991. Europa. Europe in Space. Multicoloured.
1585 4 k. Type **450** 70 35
1586 4 k. "Freja" Northern Lights research satellite 70 35
1587 4 k. "Tele-X" television satellite 70 35

1991. Olympic Games Gold Medallists (1st issue). Multicoloured.
1588 2 k. 50 Type **451** 45 25
1589 2 k. 50 Toini Gustafsson (cross-country skiing, Grenoble, 1968) 45 25
1590 2 k. 50 Agneta Andersson and Anna Olsson (canoeing, Los Angeles, 1984) 45 25
1591 2 k. 50 Ulrika Knape (high diving, Munich, 1972) . . 45 25
See also Nos. 1619/22 and 1635/8.

452 Spetal Mine, Norberg (after Carl David af Uhr)

1991. Bergslagen Iron Industry. Multicoloured.
1592 2 k. 50 Type **452** 45 25
1593 2 k. 50 Walloon smithy, Forsmark Mill (after J. Wilhem Wallender) . . . 45 25
1594 2 k. 50 Forge (27 × 24 mm) 45 25
1595 2 k. 50 Foundry (after Johann Ahlback) (27 × 24 mm) . . 45 25
1596 2 k. 50 Dannemora Mine (after Elias Martin) (27 × 37 mm) 45 25
1597 2 k. 50 Pershyttan Mill (27 × 37 mm) 45 25

453 Stromsholm Castle

1991.
1598 **453** 10 k. green and black . 1·75 25

454 Lena Philipsson
455 Close-up of Gustav III

1991. Rock and Pop Music. Multicoloured.
1599 2 k. 50 Type **454** 45 25
1600 2 k. 50 Roxette (duo) . . . 45 25
1601 2 k. 50 Jerry Williams . . . 45 25

1991. 70th Birthday of Czeslaw Slania (engraver). Designs showing "Coronation of King Gustav III" by Carl Gustav Pilo.
1602 **455** 10 k. blue . . . . 2·00 2·00
1603 – 10 k. violet . . . . . . 2·00 2·00
1604 – 10 k. black . . . . . . 2·00 2·00
DESIGNS—As T **455**: No. 1603, Close-up of lowering of crown onto King's head. 76 × 44 mm: 1604, Complete picture.

456 Mans and Mari from "Spring to Winter" (Kaj Beckman)
457 Henri Dunant (founder of Red Cross), 1901

1991. Christmas. Illustrations from children's books. Multicoloured.
1605 2 k. 30 Type **456** 45 10
1606 2 k. 30 Family dancing round Christmas tree ("Peter and Lottas's Christmas", Elsa Beskow) 45 10
1607 2 k. 30 Dressed cat by Christmas tree ("Pettersson gets a Christmas Visit", Sven Nordqvist) 45 10
1608 2 k. 30 Girl by bed ("Little Anna's Christmas Present", Lasse Sandberg) 45 10

1991. Nobel Prize Winners for Peace.
1609 **457** 4 k. red 70 35
1610 – 4 k. green 70 35
1611 – 4 k. blue 70 35
1612 – 4 k. lilac 70 35
DESIGNS: No. 1610, Albert Schweitzer (medical missionary), 1953; 1611, Alva Myrdal (disarmament negotiator), 1982; 1612, Andrei Sakharov (human rights activist), 1975.

458 Mulle, the Forest Elf, with Children
459 Roe Buck

1992. Centenary of Outdoor Life Association.
1613 **458** 2 k. 30 black, red & grn 45 10

1992. Wildlife.
1614 **459** 2 k. 80 brown, blk & grn 50 10
1615 – 2 k. 80 black, brn & grn 50 10
1617 – 6 k. brown and black . . 1·00 50
1618 – 7 k. black and green . . . 1·25 60
DESIGNS—As T **459**: No. 1615, Roe deer with fawn. 20 × 28 mm: 1617, Eurasian red squirrel; 1618, Elk.

1992. Olympic Games Gold medallists (2nd issue). As T **451**. Multicoloured.
1619 2 k. 80 Gunde Svan (cross-country skiing, Sarajevo, 1984, and Calgary, 1988) . . 50 35
1620 2 k. 80 Thomas Wassberg (cross-country skiing, Lake Placid, 1980, and Sarajevo, 1984) 50 35
1621 2 k. 80 Tomas Gustafson (speed skating, Sarajevo, 1984, and Calgary, 1988) 50 35
1622 2 k. 80 Ingemar Stenmark (slalom, Lake Placid, 1980) 50 35

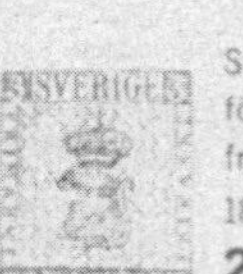

460 Gunnar Nordahl (Sweden)
461 1855 3 s. Green

1992. European Football Championships, Sweden. Each blue and green.
1623 2 k. 80 Type **460** 50 15
1624 2 k. 80 Lothar Matthaus (Germany) and Tomas Brolin (Sweden) 50 15

1992. Stamp Year.
1625 **461** 2 k. 80 green, yell & blk . 1·00 1·00
1626 4 k. 50 green, yell & blk . 1·25 1·40
1627 – 5 k. 50 yellow, grey & blk 85 60
DESIGN: 5 k. 50, 1857 3 s. yellow error.

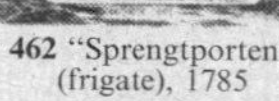

462 "Sprengtporten" (frigate), 1785
463 Rabbit (Emma Westerberg)

1992. Europa. 500th Anniv of Discovery of America by Columbus. Multicoloured.
1628 4 k. 50 Type **462** 90 45
1629 4 k. 50 "Superb" (brig), 1855 90 45
1630 4 k. 50 "Big T" (yacht) (competitor in Discovery Race) 90 45

1992. Rebate stamps. Centenary of "Kamratposten" (children's magazine). Multicoloured.
1631 2 k. 50 Type **463** 45 15
1632 2 k. 50 Horses (Helena Johansson) 45 15
1633 2 k. 50 Kitten (Sabina Ostermark) 45 15
1634 2 k. 50 Elephant (Hanna Bengtsson) 45 15

1992. Olympic Games Gold Medallists (3rd series). As T **451**. Multicoloured.
1635 5 k. 50 Gunnar Larsson (swimming, Munich, 1972) 95 60
1636 5 k. 50 Bernt Johansson (cycling, Montreal, 1976) 95 60
1637 5 k. 50 Anders Garderud (steeplechase, Montreal, 1976) 95 60
1638 5 k. 50 Gert Fredriksson (canoeing, London, 1948) 95 60

464 Karlberg Castle

1992.
1639 **464** 20 k. black, green & blue 3·50 85

465 Hand holding Flower
466 Gustaf Dalen's Sun Valve and First Automated Lighthouse, Gasfeten

1992. Greetings stamps. Multicoloured.
1640 2 k. 80 Type **465** 50 25
1641 2 k. 80 Wedge of cheese ("Lyckans ost") 50 25
1642 2 k. 80 New-born baby ("Lev val!") 50 25
1643 2 k. 80 Writing with feather "Gratulerar" 50 25

1992. Centenary of Patent and Registration Office.
1644 **466** 2 k. 80 black and blue . 50 15

467 Riksdag (Parliament), Helgeandsholmen Island

1992. 88th Interparliamentary Union Conference, Stockholm.
1645 **467** 2 k. 80 violet on buff . . 50 15

468 "Kitchen Maid" (Rembrandt)
469 Plateosaurus

1992. Bicentenary of National Museum of Fine Arts. Multicoloured.
1646 5 k. 50 Type **468** 95 60
1647 5 k. 50 "Triumph of Venus" (Francois Boucher) (40 x 44 mm) 95 60
1648 5 k. 50 "Portrait of a Girl" (Albrecht Durer) 95 60
1649 5 k. 50 Rorstrand vase decorated by Erik Wahlberg 95 60
1650 5 k. 50 "Seine Motif" (Carl Fredrik Hill) (40 × 44 mm) 95 60
1651 5 k. 50 "Sergel in his Studio" (Carl Larsson) 95 60

1992. Prehistoric Animals. Mult.

1652		2 k. 80 Type **469**	60	50
1653		2 k. 80 Crocodile ("Thoracosaurus scanicus")	60	50
1654		2 k. 80 Woolly-haired rhino ("Coelodonta antiquitatis")	60	50
1655		2 k. 80 Mammoth ("Mammuthus primigenius")	60	50

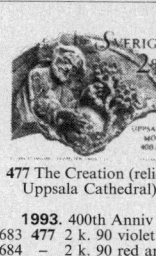

470 Volvo "PV831", 1950

471 Osprey ("Pandion haliaetus")

1992. Swedish Cars.

1656	**470**	4 k. blue	70	35
1657	–	4 k. green and blue	70	35

DESIGN: No. 1657 Saab "92", 1950.

1992. Birds of the Baltic.

1658	**471**	4 k. 50 black and blue	75	45
1659	–	4 k. 50 brown, blk & bl	75	45
1660	–	4 k. 50 deep brown, brown and blue	75	45
1661	–	4 k. 50 black, brn & bl	75	45

DESIGNS: No. 1659, Black-tailed godwit ("Limosa limosa"); 1660, Goosander ("Mergus merganser"); 1661, Common shelducks ("Tadorna tadorna").

472 "Meeting of Joachim and Anna"

473 Walcott

1992. Christmas. Icons. Multicoloured.

1662	2 k. 30 Type **472**	45	15
1663	2 k. 30 "Madonna and Child"	45	15
1664	2 k. 30 "Archangel Gabriel" (head)	45	15
1665	2 k. 30 "Saint Nicholas" (½-length portrait)	45	15

1992. Award of Nobel Literature Prize to Derek Walcott.

1666	**473**	5 k. 50 purple, bl & brn	95	45
1667	–	5 k. 50 purple, brn & bl	95	45

DESIGN: No. 1667, Palm trees, ocean and text.

474 Brown Bear Cubs

1993. Wildlife.

1668	**474**	2 k. 90 brown & black	50	15
1669	–	2 k. 90 brown & black	50	15
1671	–	3 k. multicoloured	50	15
1672	–	5 k. 80 blk, grey & brn	1·00	25
1673	–	12 k. brown, blue & red	2·10	70

DESIGNS—As T **474**: No. 1669, Brown bear. 27×21 mm: 1671, Polecat; 1672, Wolf, 21×27 mm: 1673, Lynx.

475 "Big Bird" Glider (World Gliding Championships, Borlange)

476 Gooseberries

1993. International Sports Championships in Sweden. Multicoloured.

1674	6 k. Type **475**	1·00	70
1675	6 k. Martin Kornbakk (World Wrestling Championships, Stockholm)	1·00	70
1676	6 k. Jorgen Persson (World Table Tennis Championships, Gothenburg)	1·00	70
1677	6 k. Lars Erik Andersson (European Bowling Championships, Malmo)	1·00	70
1678	6 k. Per Carlen (World Handball Championships, Gothenburg)	1·00	70
1679	6 k. Marie Helene Westin (World Cross-country Skiing Championships, Falun)	1·00	70

Nos. 1675/9 show Swedish competitors.

1993. Fruits.

1680	**476**	2 k. 40 green	40	15
1681	–	2 k. 40 green	40	15
1682	–	2 k. 40 red	40	15

DESIGNS: No. 1681, Pears; 1682, Cherries.

477 The Creation (relief, Uppsala Cathedral)

478 "Poseidon" (Carl Milles)

1993. 400th Anniv of Uppsala Convocation.

1683	**477**	2 k. 90 violet and buff	50	15
1684	–	2 k. 90 red and buff	50	15

DESIGN: No. 1684, Uppsala Cathedral before fire of 1702.

1993. Nordic Countries' Postal Co-operation. Tourism. Tourist attractions in Gothenburg.

1685	**478**	3 k. 50 green, yell & bl	60	35
1686	–	3 k. 50 indigo, yellow and blue	60	35

DESIGN: No. 1686, Liseberg Loop (fairground ride).

479 Ox-eye Daisies

480 "Oguasark" (Olle Baertling)

1993. Rebate stamps. Flowers. Multicoloured.

1687	2 k. 60 Type **479**	45	15
1688	2 k. 60 Poppies	45	15
1689	2 k. 60 Buttercups	45	15
1690	2 k. 60 Bluebells	45	15

1993. Europa. Contemporary Art. Multicoloured.

1691	5 k. Type **480**	85	50
1692	5 k. "Ade-Ledic-Nander II" (Oyvind Fahlstrom) (horiz)	85	50
1693	5 k. "The Cubist Chair" (Otto Carlsund)	85	50

481 Swallowtail ("Papilio machaon")

1993. Butterflies. Multicoloured.

1694	6 k. Type **481**	1·00	70
1695	6 k. Camberwell beauty ("Nymphalis antiopa")	1·00	70
1696	6 k. Moorland clouded yellow ("Colias palaeno")	1·00	70
1697	6 k. Scarce fritillary ("Euphydryas maturna")	1·00	70

482 Fireworks ("Hurray")

483 Red-breasted Merganser ("Mergus serrator")

1993. Greetings Stamps. Multicoloured.

1698	2 k. 90 Type **482**	50	15
1699	2 k. 90 "Hor av Dig" ("Get in touch")	50	15
1700	2 k. 90 "Tycker om Dig" ("I like you")	50	15
1701	2 k. 90 "Lycka Till" ("Good luck")	50	15

1993. Sea Birds. Multicoloured.

1702	5 k. Type **483**	85	50
1703	5 k. Velvet scoter ("Melanitta fusca")	85	50
1704	5 k. Tufted duck ("Aythya fuligula")	85	50
1705	5 k. Eider ("Somateria mollissima")	85	50

484 Surveyor, 1643 (cover of Johan Mansson's nautical book)

485 King Carl Gustav

1993. 350th Anniv of Hydrographic Service.

1706	**484**	2 k. 90 brown, blue & blk	50	15
1707	–	2 k. 90 brown, blue & blk	50	15

DESIGN: No. 1707, Survey ship "Nils Stromcrona", 1993.

1993. 20th Anniv of Accession of King Carl XVI Gustav and Queen Silvia's 50th Birthday.

1708	8 k. Type **485**	1·40	80
1709	10 k. King Carl Gustav wearing medals	1·75	1·00
1710	10 k. Queen Silvia	1·75	1·00
1711	12 k. Family group and Stockholm and Drottningholm Palaces (75×44 mm)	2·10	1·25

486 Plaited Heart

487 Stockholm City Hall

1993. Christmas.

1712	**486**	2 k. 40 green	40	10
1713	–	2 k. 40 red	40	10

DESIGN: No. 1713, Straw goat.

1993. Award of Nobel Literature Prize to Toni Morrison.

1714	**487**	6 k. red and blue	1·00	60
1715	–	6 k. brown and red	1·00	60

DESIGN: No. 1715, Toni Morrison.

488 Victoria Plums

489 North Sweden Horse's Head

1994. Fruits.

1716	**488**	2 k. 80 multicoloured	50	15
1717	–	2 k. 80 multicoloured	50	15
1718	–	2 k. 80 lt green & green	50	15

DESIGNS: No. 1717, Opal plums; 1718, "James Grieve" apples.

1994. Domestic Animals.

1719	**489**	3 k. 20 brown, agate and red	55	15
1720	–	3 k. 20 brown, agate and red	55	15
1721	–	3 k. 20 black, brn & bl	55	15
1722	–	6 k. 40 black and green	55	15

DESIGNS—VERT: No. 1720, North Sweden horses in harness. HORIZ: 1721, Gotland sheep; 1722, Mountain cow.

490 Mother Svea and European Union Emblem

491 Siamese

1994. Single European Market.

1723	**490**	5 k. blue	85	50

1994. Cats. Multicoloured.

1724	4 k. 50 Type **491**	75	45
1725	4 k. 50 Persian	75	45
1726	4 k. 50 European	75	45
1727	4 k. 50 Abyssinian	75	45

492 Illustration from "Le Roman de la Rose"

1994. Franco-Swedish Cultural Relations. Multicoloured.

1728	5 k. Type **492**	85	50
1729	5 k. Swedish and French flags	85	50
1730	5 k. Sketch by De la Vallee of Knight's House (40×43 mm)	85	50
1731	5 k. "Household Chores" (Pehr Hillestrom)	85	50
1732	5 k. "Banquet for Gustav III at the Trianon, 1784" (Niclas Lafrensen the younger) (40×43 mm)	85	50
1733	5 k. "Carl XIV Johan" (Franois Gerard)	85	50

493 Martin Dahlin during Match

1994. World Cup Football Championship, U.S.A.

1734	**493**	3 k. 20 blue and red	55	15

494 Wild Rose ("Rosa dumalis")

495 Lunar Module "Eagle" and Astronauts

1994. Roses. Multicoloured.

1735	3 k. 20 Type **494**	55	15
1736	3 k. 20 "Rosa alba maxima"	55	15
1737	3 k. 20 "Tuscany Superb"	55	15
1738	3 k. 20 "Peace"	55	15
1739	3 k. 20 "Four Seasons"	55	15

1994. 25th Anniv of First Manned Moon Landing.

1740	**495**	6 k. 50 orange, blk & blue	1·10	65

496 Iris Vase (Gunnar Wennerberg), 1897

497 Cat ("Love and Kisses")

1994. 150th Annivs of Stockholm College of Arts, Crafts and Design and of Swedish Society of Crafts and Design. Multicoloured.

1741	6 k. 50 Type **496**	1·10	65
1742	6 k. 50 Wallpaper (Uno Ahren) and Chair (Carl Malmsten), 1917	1·10	65
1743	6 k. 50 Aralia cloth, 1920, and cabinet, 1940 (Josef Frank)	1·10	65
1744	6 k. 50 Crystal bowl engraved with fireworks design (Edward Hald), 1921	1·10	65
1745	6 k. 50 Silver water jug, 1941, and sketch of coffee pot, 1970s (Wiwen Nilsson)	1·10	65
1746	6 k. 50 Linen towel (Astrid Sampe), plate (Stig Lindberg) and cutlery (Sigurd Persson), 1955	1·10	65

1994. Greetings booklet stamps. Multicoloured.

1747	3 k. 20 Type **497**	55	15
1748	3 k. 20 Snail ("You've got time")	55	15
1749	3 k. 20 Frog ("You're lovely just as you are")	55	15
1750	3 k. 20 Dog ("Hi there!")	55	15

498 Musicians (sketch, Johan Silvius) and Opening Bars of "Drottningholm Music"

499 Sepo Raty (javelin)

1994. 300th Birth Anniv of Johan Helmich Roman (composer) (1751) and Inauguration of Gothenburg Opera House (1752).

1751	**498**	3 k. 20 brown and blue	55	15
1752	–	3 k. 20 multicoloured	55	15

DESIGN: No. 1752, Opera House (designed Jan Izikowitz) and opening bars of opera "Aniara" by Karl Birger (inaugural programme).

1994. Sweden–Finland Athletics Meeting, Stockholm. Multicoloured.

1753	4 k. 50 Type **499**	75	25
1754	4 k. 50 Patrik Sjoberg (high jump)	75	25

500 Erland Nordenskiold (South America) **501** Caspian Tern

1994. Europa. Discoveries. Swedish Explorers. Multicoloured.

1755		5 k. 50 Type **500**	90	50
1756		5 k. 50 Eric von Rosen (Africa)	90	50
1757		5 k. 50 Sten Bergman (Asia and Australasia)	90	50

1994. Endangered Birds. Multicoloured.

1758		5 k. 50 Type **501**	90	50
1759		5 k. 50 White-tailed sea eagle	90	50
1760		5 k. 50 White-backed woodpecker	90	50
1761		5 k. 50 Lesser white-fronted goose	90	50

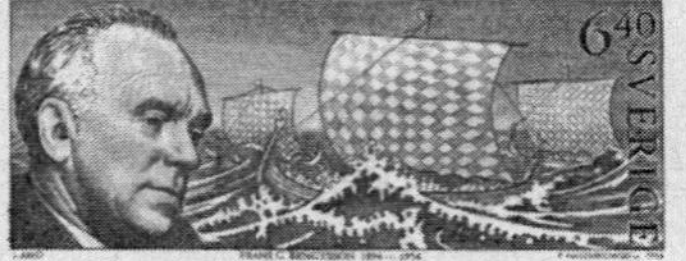

502 Bengtsson and Illustration from "The Longships" (novel)

1994. Birth Centenary of Frans Bengtsson (writer).

1762	**502**	6 k. 40 violet, red and black	1·10	65

503 "Ja" ("Yes") **504** "The Annunciation"

1994. European Union Membership Referendum. Multicoloured.

1763		3 k. 20 Type **503**	55	15
1764		3 k. 20 "Nej" ("No")	55	15

1994. Christmas. Details from Askeby altarpiece. Multicoloured.

1765		2 k. 80 Type **504**	50	15
1766		2 k. 80 "Flight into Egypt"	50	15

505 Erik Axel Karlfeldt (1931)

1994. Swedish Winners of the Nobel Literature Prize.

1767	**505**	4 k. 50 brown, dp bl & bl	75	25
1768	–	5 k. 50 deep brn, bl & brn	90	50
1769	–	6 k. 50 brn, dp grn & grn	1·10	65

DESIGNS: 5 k. 50, Eyvind Johnson (1974); 6 k. 50, Harry Martinsson (1974).

OFFICIAL STAMPS

O 6 O 17

1874.

O27	**O 6**	2 ore orange	1·10	1·50
O28		3 ore brown	1·10	2·00
O29b		4 ore grey	1·25	25
O30b		5 ore green	1·25	15
O31		6 ore lilac	15·00	20·00
O32		6 ore grey	21·00	45·00
O33b		10 ore red	1·50	10
O34		12 ore blue	30·00	9·50
O35		20 ore red	£110	1·00
O36		20 ore blue	2·75	10
O37		24 ore yellow	38·00	8·50
O38b		30 ore brown	12·00	30
O39		50 ore red	80·00	9·00
O40		50 ore grey	9·00	1·10
O41c		1 k. blue and brown	5·00	90

1889. Surch with value in ornamental scroll between two crowns.

O42	**O 6**	10 ore on 12 ore blue	7·50	10·00
O43		10 ore on 24 ore yellow	10·00	13·00

1910.

O 87	**O 17**	1 ore black	15	10
O101		2 ore yellow	20	10
O102		3 ore brown	30	35
O103		4 ore lilac	20	10
O104		5 ore green	20	10
O105		7 ore green	40	45
O 91		8 ore red	55	70
O107		10 ore red	20	10
O108		12 ore red	20	10
O109		15 ore brown	20	10
O110		20 ore blue	20	10
O111		25 ore orange	80	30
O112		30 ore brown	35	25
O113		35 ore violet	70	30
O114		50 ore grey	1·50	90
O 98		1 k. black on yellow	6·50	4·75
O 99		5 k. purple on yellow	9·00	2·50

POSTAGE DUE STAMPS

D 6

1874.

D27	**D 6**	1 ore black	1·10	2·00
D28a		3 ore red	3·00	4·00
D29a		5 ore brown	2·25	2·50
D30a		6 ore yellow	2·25	2·50
D31		12 ore red	3·75	2·75
D32		20 ore blue	3·00	1·90
D33a		24 ore lilac	12·00	13·00
D34		24 ore grey	25·00	25·00
D35		30 ore green	3·25	2·50
D36		50 ore brown	6·00	3·25
D37		1 k. blue and brown	21·00	11·00

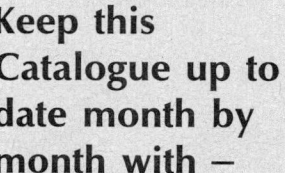

SWITZERLAND Pt. 8

A federal republic of C. Europe between France, Germany and Italy.

100 rappen = 1 franken
100 centimes = 1 franc
100 centesimi = 1 franco

These are expressions of the same currency in three languages.

For the issues under the Cantonal Administrations of Basel, Geneva and Zurich, see Stanley Gibbons' Part 8 (Italy and Switzerland) Catalogue.

1

6

1850. Inscr "ORTS-POST", Imperf.
1 1 2½ r. black and red £1500 £1000

1850. As T 1, but inscr "POSTE LOCALE". Imperf.
3 1 2½ r. black and red £1200 £900

1850. As T 1 but inscr "RAYON I, II, or III". Imperf.
6 1 5 r. red, black and blue (I) . £1000 £300
13 5 r. red and blue (I) . . . . . £350 90·00
10 10 r. red, black and yell (II) . £600 80·00
23 15 rp. red (III) . . . . . . £1400 80·00
21 15 cts. red (III) £8000 £700

1854. Imperf.
46 6 2 r. grey £150 £300
47a 5 r. brown . . . . £100 5·00
48 10 r. blue . . . . £100 4·75
49a 15 r. rose . . . . £190 25·00
50 20 r. orange . . . . £225 35·00
51 40 r. green . . . . £225 30·00
38 1 f. lilac £700 £450

7 9

10

1862. Perf.
52 7 2 c. grey . . . . 45·00 1·60
61 2 c. brown . . . . 1·00 25
61a 2 c. bistre . . . . 1·50 75
53 3 c. black . . . . 6·00 65·00
54 5 c. brown . . . . 1·60 10
55 10 c. blue £180 10
62 10 c. pink . . . . 1·60 10
63 15 c. yellow . . . . 2·00 15·00
56a 20 c. orange . . . . 1·00 1·00
64 25 c. green . . . . 1·00 75
57 30 c. red . . . . £700 15·00
65a 30 c. blue . . . . £250 2·25
58 40 c. green . . . . £700 35·00
66 40 c. grey . . . . 1·00 45·00
67 50 c. purple . . . . 35·00 10·00
59 60 c. bronze . . . . £400 85·00
60a 1 f. gold . . . . 12·00 30·00

1882.
126B 9 2 c. brown 80 15
127cB 3 c. brown . . . . 1·50 1·50
128d 5 c. purple . . . . 11·00 10
196 5 c. green . . . . 3·00 10
130e 10 c. red . . . . 1·75 10
131e 12 c. blue . . . . 3·50 10
132 15 c. yellow . . . . £110 10·00
133b 15 c. violet . . . . 25·00 70
214 10 20 c. orange . . . . . . 2·00 1·50
146cB 25 c. green . . . . 7·50 25
207 25 c. blue . . . . 5·00 50
202 30 c. brown . . . . 5·50 1·25
209 40 c. grey . . . . 28·00 5·50
150B 50 c. blue . . . . 38·00 2·50
218 50 c. green . . . . 5·00 2·50
138a 1 f. purple . . . . £200 1·50
161 1 f. red . . . . 4·50 12·00
139 3 f. brown . . . . £150 5·00

11

1900. 25th Anniv of U.P.U.
191 11 5 c. green . . . . 3·00 50
189 10 c. red . . . . 10·00 40
190 25 c. blue . . . . 15·00 7·50

INDEX

Countries can be quickly located by referring to the index at the end of this volume.

14 Tell's Son

15

17

1907.
241 14 2 c. yellow 20 20
242 3 c. brown . . . . 25 5·75
243 5 c. green . . . . 2·50 10
244 15 10 c. red . . . . 2·00 10
245 12 c. brown . . . . 30 2·00
246 15 c. mauve . . . . 3·50 5·00
248 17 20 c. yellow and red . . . 1·60 20
249 25 c. blue and deep blue . 1·60 10
250 30 c. green and brown . . 1·50 10
251 35 c. yellow and green . . 1·50 15
252 40 c. yellow and purple . 13·00 20
253a 50 c. green & deep green 6·50 30
254 70 c. yellow and brown . 55·00 2·50
255 1 f. green and purple . . 6·50 15
256 3 f. yellow and bistre . . £175 65

For further stamps in Type 17 see Nos. 314, 1910 issue.

18 Cord in front of Shaft

19

1908.
257 18 2 c. bistre 25 50
258 3 c. violet . . . . 15 5·50
259 5 c. green . . . . 2·00 10
260 19 10 c. red 60 10
261 12 c. brown 75 10
262 15 c. mauve . . . . 23·00 45

20a Cord behind Shaft

21 William Tell

1910.
266 20a 2 c. bistre 10 10
292 2½ c. purple 10 60
325b 2½ c. olive on buff . . . 40 1·00
264 3 c. violet 10 10
293 3 c. brown 10 10
325c 3 c. blue on buff . . . . 2·00 4·50
267 5 c. green 55 10
309 5 c. orange on buff . . . 10 10
326 5 c. lilac on buff 10 10
326b 5 c. purple on buff . . . 10 10
326c 5 c. green on buff . . . 25 10
294 7½ c. grey . . . . 1·00 10
326e 7½ c. green on buff . . . 30 1·75
281 21 10 c. red on buff 45 10
310 10 c. green on buff . . . 10 10
326g 10 c. violet on buff . . . 1·00 10
282 12 c. brown on buff . . . 35 3·25
295 13 c. green on buff . . . 1·40 20
283 15 c. violet on buff . . . 2·50 10
326i 15 c. red on buff . . . . 3·25 1·75
311 20 c. violet on buff . . . 2·00 10
328 20 c. red on buff 35 10
313 25 c. red on buff . . . . 1·00 35
328c 25 c. brown on buff . . . 3·25 75
329 30 c. blue on buff . . . 8·00 10
315 17 40 c. blue . . . . 1·75 10
330 40 c. green and mauve . 22·00 10
296 60 c. brown . . . . 8·50 10
331 70 c. buff and violet . . 15·00 60
297 80 c. buff and grey . . . 9·50 20

22 The Mythen

1914. Mountain Views.
284 22 3 f. green . . . . £800 3·00
298 3 f. red . . . . 90·00 35
285 – 5 f. blue . . . . 30·00 1·25
286 – 10 f. purple . . . . . . £120 1·25
331b – 10 f. green . . . . £225 20·00

DESIGNS: 5 f. The Rutli; 10 f. The Jungfrau.

1915. Surch.
287 20a 1 c. on 2 c. bistre . . . 10 15
303 2½ c. on 3 c. brown . . . 10 15
304 3 c. on 2½ c. olive on buff 10 1·00
304a 5 c. on 2 c. bistre . . . 10 1·00
305 5 c. on 7½ c. grey . . . 10 10
305c 5 c. on 7½ c. grn on buff 15 4·75
306 21 10 c. on 13 c. olive on buff 15 1·40
288 19 13 c. on 12 c. brown . . 10 4·75
289 21 13 c. on 12 c. brn on buff 20 70
307a 20 c. on 15 c. vio on buff 60 1·25
308 17 20 c. on 25 c. blue . . . 15 25
290 80 c. on 70 c. yell & brn 30·00 6·50

1919. Air. Optd with wings and propeller.
298a 17 30 c. green and brown . . £120 £1100
299 50 c. green & deep green 40·00 85·00

30

31

32

1919. Peace Celebrations
300 30 7½ c. olive and grey . . . . 65 1·10
301 31 10 c. yellow and red . . . . 1·00 3·25
302 32 15 c. yellow and violet . . . 2·00 90

34

35

36

37

1923. Air.
317 34 15 c. green and red . . . 2·75 4·25
317ab 20 c. green and dp green . 30 15
318 25 c. grey and blue . . . 7·00 11·00
319 35 35 c. cinnamon and brown 14·00 35·00
320 40 c. lilac and violet . . . 13·00 32·00
321 36 45 c. red and blue . . . . 1·50 4·50
322a 50 c. grey and red . . . . 1·25 75
323a 37 65 c. blue and light blue . 2·00 5·00
324 75 c. orange and purple . 16·00 55·00
325a 1 f. violet and purple . . 3·00 1·75

38

40 Seat of first U.P.U. Congress

1924.
332 38 90 c. red & green on grn . 14·00 20
333 1 f. 20 red and lake on pink 6·00 45
334 1 f. 50 red & blue on blue 22·00 60
335a 2 f. red & black on grey . 45·00 2·25

1924. 50th Anniv of U.P.U.
336 – 20 c. red 40 40
337 40 30 c. blue . . . . 1·00 3·50

DESIGN: 20 c. As T 40 but with different frame.

41

1929. Air.
339a 41 35 c. bistre and ochre . . 6·50 35·00
340a 40 c. blue and green . . . 35·00 30·00
341a – 2 f. chocolate and brown on cinnamon . . . . 10·00 5·50

DESIGN: 2 f. Bird with letter in beak.

43 The Mythen

1931.
342 43 3 f. brown . . . . 60·00 1·60

44 Symbol of Peace

45 "After the Darkness, Light"

46 Peace and the Air Post

1932. International Disarmament Conference.
343 44 5 c. green (postage) 10 10
344 10 c. orange 20 10
345 20 c. red 30 10
346 30 c. blue . . . . 3·00 30
347 60 c. brown . . . . 17·00 1·50
348 45 1 f. grey and blue . . . . 22·00 3·50
349 46 15 c. light green and green (air) . . . . 30 1·25
350 20 c. flesh and red . . . . 65 2·00
351 90 c. light blue and blue . 8·00 22·00

47 Louis Favre (engineer)

48 Staubbach Falls

1932. 50th Anniv of St. Gotthard Railway.
352 47 10 c. brown 10 10
353 – 20 c. red 25 20
354 – 30 c. blue . . . . 40 1·25

DESIGNS: 20 c. Alfred Escher (President of Railway); 30 c. Emil Welti (founder).

1934. Landscapes.
355 48 3 c. olive . . . . 25 1·50
356 – 5 c. green 25 10
357 – 10 c. violet 50 10
358 – 15 c. orange 55 80
359 – 20 c. red 80 10
360 – 25 c. brown . . . . 10·00 4·00
361 – 30 c. blue . . . . 30·00 40

DESIGNS: 5 c. Mt Pilatus; 10 c. Chillon Castle and Dents du Midi; 15 c. Grimsel Pass; 20 c. Landwasser Viaduct, Filisur (St. Gotthard Railway); 25 c. Viamala Gorge; 30 c. Rhine Falls near Schaffhausen.

1935. Air. Surch.
362 34 10 on 15 c. green and red 5·00 30·00
363 46 10 on 15 c. light green and green 40 40
364 10 on 20 c. flesh and red . 50 1·60
381 37 10 on 65 c. blue & lt blue 20 30
365 46 30 on 90 c. lt blue & blue . 3·50 12·00
366 40 on 20 c. flesh and red . 4·00 11·00
367 40 on 90 c. lt blue & blue 4·00 10·00

51 Freiburg Cowherd

52 Staubbach Falls

1936. National Defence Fund.
368 51 10 c. + 5 c. purple 35 40
369 20 c. + 10 c. red . . . . . 70 2·75
370 30 c. + 10 c. blue . . . . 3·50 12·00

1936. As T 48 but redrawn with figure of value lower down. Various landscapes.
371 52 3 c. olive 10 10
372 – 5 c. green 10 10
489 – 5 c. brown 20 10
373b – 10 c. purple 35 10
373d – 10 c. brown 10 10
490 – 10 c. green 30 10
374 – 15 c. orange 40 15
375b – 20 c. red (Railway) . . . 7·00 10
375d – 20 c. red (Lake) 15 10

491 **52** 20 c. brown 60 10
376 – 25 c. brown 60 30
492 – 25 c. red 1·50 1·00
377 – 30 c. blue 1·00 10
378 – 35 c. green 1·00 50
379 – 40 c. grey 7·00 10
494 – 40 c. blue 21·00 20

DESIGNS: 3 c. to 20 c. (No. 375b) As Nos. 355/9; 20 c. (Nos. 375d, 491) Lake Lugano and Mt San Salvatore; 25 c. (No. 376) Viamala Gorge; 25 c. (No. 492) National Park; 30 c. Rhine Falls; 35 c. Mt. Neufalkenstein and Klus; 40 c. Mt Santis and Lake Seealp.

53 Mobile P.O.

1937. For Mobile P.O. Mail.
380 **53** 10 c. yellow and black 30 10

55 International Labour Office

1938.
382 **55** 20 c. red and buff 20 10
383 – 30 c. blue and light blue 30 10
384 – 60 c. brown and buff 1·75 85
385 – 1 f. black and buff 8·50 8·00

DESIGNS: 30, 60 c. Palace of League of Nations (different views); 1 f. International Labour Office.

1938. Air. Special Flights. Surch **1938 "PRO AERO" 75 75** and bars.
386 **36** 75 c. on 50 c. green & red 4·50

60 William Tell's Chapel

1938. National Fete. Fund for Swiss Subjects Abroad.
387 **60** 10 c. + 10 c. violet & yellow 40 25

61 First Act of Federal Parliament

1938.
388A **61** 3 f. brown on blue 15·00 1·50
388c 3 f. brown on buff 6·00 10
389A – 5 f. blue on blue 15·00 1·50
389c – 5 f. blue on buff 6·00 10
390A – 10 f. green on blue 65·00 20·00
390c – 10 f. green on buff 8·00 35

DESIGNS: 5 f. "The Assembly at Stans"; 10 f. Polling booth.

62 Symbolical of Swiss Culture

64 Crossbow and Floral Branch

1939. National Exhibition, Zurich. Inscr in French (F.), German (G.) or Italian (I.).

			F.		G.		I.	
391	–	10 c. vio	25	10	20	10	25	10
392	**62**	20 c. red	75	10	60	10	1·40	10
393	–	30 c. blue & buff	3·60	2·00	2·75	50	3·00	4·50

DESIGNS: 10 c. Group symbolic of Swiss Industry and Agriculture; 30 c. Piz Rosegg and Tschirva Glacier.

1939. National Exhibition, Zurich. Inscr in French (F.), German (G.) or Italian (I.).

			F.		G.		I.	
394a	**64**	5 c. green	70	1·50	70	1·25	70	1·50
395a/b		10 c. brn	75	1·25	55	80	85	1·50
396a		20 c. red	1·50	1·25	1·25	1·00	1·40	2·25
397		30 c. blue	3·50	6·00	3·00	5·50	3·00	6·50

65 Laupen Castle

1939. National Fete. Fund for Destitute Mothers.
398 **65** 10 c. + 10 c. brown, grey and red 30 25

66 Geneva

1939. 75th Anniv of Geneva (Red Cross) Convention.
399 **66** 20 c. red and buff 30 10
400 30 c. blue, grey and red 45 90

67 "Les Rangiers"

68 "William Tell" (Ferdinand Hodler)

1940. National Fete and Red Cross Fund. Memorial designs inscr "FETE NATIONALE 1940" in German (5 c., 20 c.), Italian (10 c.) and French (30 c.).
401 – 5 c. + 5 c. black & green 30 90
402 – 10 c. + 5 c. black & orange 30 25
403 – 20 c. + 5 c. black & red 2·00 75
404 **67** 30 c. + 10 c. black & blue 1·60 5·00

DESIGNS—Battle Memorials: 5 c. Sempach; 10: c. Giornico; 20 c. Calven.

1941. Historical designs.
405 – 50 c. blue on green 5·00 10
406 **68** 60 c. brown on cinnamon 6·00 10
407 – 70 c. purple on mauve 3·75 30
408 – 80 c. black on grey 1·10 10
408a – 80 c. black on mauve 1·50 20
409 – 90 c. red on pink 1·10 10
409a – 90 c. red on buff 2·00 30
410 – 1 f. green on green 1·25 10
411 – 1 f. 20 purple on grey 1·25 10
411a – 1 f. 20 purple on lilac 2·00 25
412 – 1 f. 50 blue on buff 1·50 10
413 – 2 f. red on pink 2·00 10
413a – 2 f. red on cream 3·50 25

DESIGNS—(Works of Art): 50 c. "Oath of Union" (James Vibert); 70 c. "Kneeling Warrior" (Ferdinand Hodler); 80 c. "Dying Ensign" (Hodler); 90 c. "Standard Bearer" (Niklaus Deutsch). Portraits: 1 f. Col. Louis Pfyffer; 1 f. 20, George Jenatsch; 1 f. 50, Lt. Gen. Francois de Reynold; 2 f. Col. Joachim Forrer.

69 Ploughing

1941. Agricultural Development Plan.
414 **69** 10 c. brown and buff 15 10

70 The Jungfrau

71 Chemin Creux near Kussnacht

1941. Air. Landscapes.
415 **70** 30 c. blue on orange 1·00 10
415a – 30 c. grey on orange 7·50 10·00
416 – 40 c. grey on orange 1·00 10
416a – 40 c. blue on orange 42·00 1·75
417 – 50 c. green on orange 1·25 10
418 – 60 c. brown on orange 1·75 10
419 – 70 c. violet on orange 1·25 30
420 – 1 f. green on orange 2·50 35
421 – 2 f. red on orange 6·50 1·50
422 – 5 f. blue on orange 25·00 7·50

DESIGNS: 40 f. Valais; 50 c. Lac Leman; 60 c. Alpstein; 70 c. Ticino; 1 f. Lake Lucerne; 2 f. Engadin; 5 f. Churfirsten.

1941. Air. Special (Buochs-Payerne) Flights. No. 420, with "PRO AERO 28.V.1941" added.
423 – 1 f. green on buff 5·50 20·00

1941. National Fete and 650th Anniv of Swiss Confederation.
424 – 10 c. + 10 c. bl, red & yell 25 45
425 **71** 20 c. + 10 c. scarlet, red and buff 25 40

DESIGN: 10 c. Relief Map of Lake Lucerne with Arms of Uri, Schwyz and Unterwalden.

72 Arms of Berne, Masons laying Cornerstone and Knight

1941. 750th Anniv of Berne.
426 **72** 10 c. multicoloured 10 10

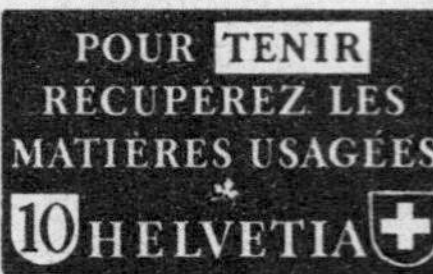

73 "To survive collect salvage"

1942. Salvage Campaign. Inscr in French (F.), German (G.) or Italian (I.).

			F.		G.		I.	
427	**73**	10 c. brn	50	15	10	10	7·00	2·00

INSCRIPTIONS: (G.) Zum Durchhalten/Altstoffe sammeln"; (I.) "PER RESISTERE/ RACCOGLIETE/LA ROBA VECCHIA".

74 View of Old Geneva

75 Soldiers' Memorial at Forch, near Zurich

1942. National Fete, National Relief Fund and Bimillenary of Geneva.
428 **74** 10 c. + 10 c. black, yellow and red 30 40
429 **75** 20 c. + 10 c. red & yellow 30 45

76

1943. Cent of Swiss Cantonal Postage Stamp.
430 **76** 10 c. (4 + 6) black 10 10

77 Intragna (Ticino)

78 Apollo of Olympia

1943. National Fete and Youth's Vocational Training Fund.
431 **77** 10 c. + 10 c. black, buff and red 30 45
432 – 20 c. + 10 c. red and buff 35 65

DESIGN: 20 c. Federal Palace, Berne.

1943. Air. Special Flights. 30th Anniv of First Flight across Alps by Oscar Bider. No. 432 optd **PRO AERO 13 VII 1943** and value.
433 – 1 f. red and buff 2·00 9·00

1944. Olympic Games Jubilee.
434 **78** 10 c. black and orange 15 50
435 20 c. black and red 35 50
436 30 c. black and blue 70 7·50

79 Heiden

1944. National Fete and Red Cross Fund.
437 **79** 5 c. + 5 c. grn, buff & red 35 1·50
438 – 10 c. + 10 c. grey, buff and red 35 35
439 – 20 c. + 10 c. red and buff 35 55
440 – 30 c. + 10 c. blue, buff and red 3·00 12·50

DESIGNS: 10 c. St. Jacques on the R. Birs; 20 c. Castle Ruins, Mesocco; 30 c. Basel.

80 Haefeli DH-3 Biplane

81 Symbolical of Faith, Hope and Charity

1944. Air. 25th Anniv of National Air Post.
441 **80** 10 c. brown and olive 15 10
442 – 20 c. red and buff 20 10
443 – 30 c. ultramarine and blue 40 45
444 – 1 f. 50 violet, pur and red 6·50 16·00

DESIGNS: 20 c. Fokker F.VIIb/3m; 30 c. Lockheed 9B Orion; 1 f. 50, Douglas DC-3.

1945. War Relief Fund.
445 **81** 10 c. + 10 c. olive, black and grey 50 40
446 20 c. + 60 c. red, black and grey 1·75 4·50

82 Trans "Peace to men of good will"

83 Olive Branch

1945. Peace. Inscr "PAX".
447 **82** 5 c. green and grey 10 15
448 10 c. brown and grey 25 10
449 20 c. red and grey 40 10
450 30 c. blue and grey 1·00 2·00
451 40 c. orange and grey 3·00 9·50
452 **83** 50 c. red and buff 3·50 15·00
453 – 60 c. grey and light grey 3·50 5·00
454 – 80 c. green and buff 8·00 60·00
455 – 1 f. blue and buff 11·00 65·00
456 – 2 f. brown and buff 38·00 £110
457 – 3 f. green on buff 50·00 38·00
458 – 5 f. brown on buff £150 £225
459 – 10 f. violet on buff £190 £100

DESIGNS—As Type **83**: 60 c. Keys; 80 c. Horn of plenty; 1 f. Dove; 2 f. Spade and flowers in ploughed field. 38 × 21 mm: 3 f. Crocuses; 5 f. Clasped hands; 10 f. Aged couple.

1945. Red Cross. As T **82**, but red cross and "5 + 10" in centre of stamp.
460 5 c. + 10 c. green 45 50

85 Silk Weaving

1945. National Fete.
461 **85** 5 c. + 5 c. green and red 75 1·50
462 – 10 c. + 10 c. brown, grey and red 60 40
463 – 20 c. + 10 c. red and buff 75 40
464 – 30 c. + 10 c. blue grey and red 9·00 24·00

DESIGNS: 10, 20 c. Jura and Emmental farmhouses; 30 c. Timbered house.

86 J. H. Pestalozzi

87 Zoglig Glider

1946. Birth Bicentenary of J. H. Pestalozzi (educational reformer).
465 **86** 10 c. purple 10 10

1946. Air. Special (Lausanne, Lucerne, Locarno) Flights.
466 **87** 1 f. 50 red and grey 20·00 25·00

88 Cheese-making

89 Chalet in Appenzell

1946. National Fete and Fund for Swiss Citizens Abroad.
467 **88** 5 c. + 5 c. green and red . 70 1·75
468 – 10 c. + 10 c. brown, buff and red 50 50
469 **89** 20 c. + 10 c. red and buff 60 50
470 – 30 c. + 10 c. blue, grey and red 6·00 7·50
DESIGNS: 10 c. Chalet in Vaud; 30 c. Chalet in Engadine.

90 Douglas DC-4, Statue of Liberty and St. Peter's Cathedral, Geneva

1947. Air. 1st Geneva–New York "Swissair" Flight.
472 **90** 2 f. 50 dp blue, blue & red 11·50 16·00

92 Rorschach Station

1947. Charity. National Fete, and Professional Education of Invalids and Anti-Cancer Funds. Inscr "I VIII 1947". Arms in red.
473 – 5 c. + 5 c. green 60 1·75
474 **92** 10 c. + 10 c. black & buff 70 60
475 – 20 c. + 10 c. red and buff 70 60
476 – 30 c. + 10 c. blue & grey 5·00 8·00
DESIGNS: 5 c. Platelayers; 20 c. Luen-Castiel station; 30 c. Fluelen station.

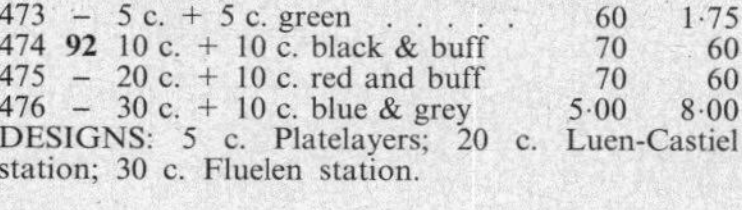

93 "Limmat" First Swiss Steam Locomotive

1947. Centenary of Swiss Federal Railways.
477 **93** 5 c. green, yellow & black 20 35
478 – 10 c. black and brown 30 10
479 – 20 c. red, buff and lake 40 10
480 – 30 c. blue, grey & light blue 1·40 1·75
DESIGNS: 10 c. Steam freight locomotive; 20 c. Electric train crossing Melide causeway; 30 c. Railway bridge.

95 Sun of St. Moritz 96 Ice Hockey

1948. Charity. 5th Winter Olympic Games.
481 **95** 5 c. + 5 c. brn, yell & grn 50 1·25
482 – 10 c. + 10 c. blue, light blue and brown 65 1·25
483 **96** 20 c. + 10 c. yellow, black and purple 75 1·50
484 – 30 c. + 10 c. black, light blue and blue 2·25 5·50
DESIGN: 10 c. Snow crystals; 30 c. Ski-runner.

97 Johann Rudolf Wettstein

1948. Tercentenary of Treaty of Westphalia and Centenaries of the Neuchatel Revolution and Swiss Federation.
485 **97** 5 c. green and deep green 10 20
486 – 10 c. black and grey 15 10
487 – 20 c. red and pink 20 10
488 – 30 c. blue, grey and brown 60 75
DESIGNS: 10 c. Neuchatel Castle; 20 c. Symbol of Helvetia; 30 c. Symbol of Federal State.

99 Frontier Guard

1948. National Fete and Anti-Tuberculosis Fund. Coat of Arms in red.
495 **99** 5 c. + 5 c. green 50 75
496 – 10 c. + 10 c. slate & grey 50 50
497 – 20 c. + 10 c. red and buff 50 60
498 – 30 c. + 10 c. blue & grey 3·50 5·75
DESIGNS: 10 c., 20 c., 30 c. Typical houses in Fribourg, Valais and Ticino respectively.

101 Glider

1949. Air. Special (La Chaux-de-Fonds–St. Gallen–Lugano) Flights.
499 **101** 1 f. 50 purple & yellow 27·00 32·00

102 Posthorn

1949. Centenary of Federal Post.
500 **102** 5 c. yellow, pink & grey 10 20
501 – 20 c. yellow, violet & grey 30 10
502 – 30 c. yellow, brn & grey 60 5·50
DESIGNS: 20 c. Mail coach drawn by five horses; 30 c. Postal motor coach and trailer.

103 Main Motif of U.P.U. Monument, Berne

1949. 75th Anniv of U.P.U.
503 **103** 10 c. green 15 10
504 – 25 c. purple 70 7·00
505 – 40 c. blue 90 1·50
DESIGNS: 25 c. Globe and ribbon; 40 c. Globe and pigeons.

104 Postman

1949. National Fete and Youth Fund. T **104** and designs as T **89**, but dated "I. VIII 1949". Arms in red.
506 **104** 5 c. + 5 c. purple 40 1·00
507 – 10 c. + 10 c. grn & buff 40 50
508 – 20 c. + 10 c. brn & buff 50 50
509 – 40 c. + 10 c. blue & lt bl 4·50 8·00
DESIGNS—Typical houses in: 10 c. Basel; 20 c. Lucerne; 40 c. Prattigau.

106 High-tension Pylons 107 Sitter Viaducts near St. Gall

1949. Landscapes.
510 **106** 3 c. black 3·50 3·50
511 **107** 5 c. orange 30 10
512 – 10 c. green 25 10
513 – 15 c. turquoise 30 10
514a – 20 c. purple 40 10
515 – 25 c. red 50 10
516 – 30 c. olive 60 10
517 – 35 c. brown 75 30
518 – 40 c. blue 3·00 10
519 – 50 c. grey 3·00 10
520 – 60 c. green 6·00 10
521 – 70 c. violet 2·25 25
DESIGNS: 10 c. Mountain cog railway, Rochers de Naye; 15 c. Rotary snowplough; 20 c. Grimsel Reservoir; 25 c. Lake Lugano and Melide railway causeway; 30 c. Verbois hydro-electric power station; 35 c. Alpine road (Val d'Anniviers); 40 c. Rhine harbour, Basel; 50 c. Suspension railway, Santis; 60 c. Railway viaduct, Landwasser; 70 c. Survey mark, Finsteraarhorn.

110 First Federal Postage Stamps

111 Putting the Weight

1950. National Fete, Red Cross Fund and Cent of First Federal Postage Stamps. T **110** and designs, as T **111**, inscr "I. VIII. 1950". Coat of arms in red.
522 **110** 5 c. + 5 c. black 40 55
523 **111** 10 c. + 10 c. grn & grey 1·10 50
524 – 20 c. + 10 c. grn & grey 1·25 65
525 – 30 c. + 10 c. mve & grey 6·50 15·00
526 – 40 c. + 10 c. blue & grey 7·00 8·50
DESIGNS: 20 c. Wrestling; 30 c. Sprinting; 40 c. Rifle shooting.

112 Arms of Zurich

113 Valaisan Polka

1951. National Fete, Mothers' Fund and 600th Anniv of Zurich. Coat of arms in red.
527 **112** 5 c. + 5 c. black 50 50
528 **113** 10 c. + 10 c. grn & grey 1·25 50
529 – 20 c. + 10 c. grn & grey 1·25 45
530 – 30 c. + 10 c. mve & grey 7·00 12·00
531 – 40 c. + 10 c. blue & grey 6·50 9·00
DESIGNS—As Type **113**: 20 c. Flag-swinging; 30 c. "Hornussen" (game); 40 c. Blowing alphorn.

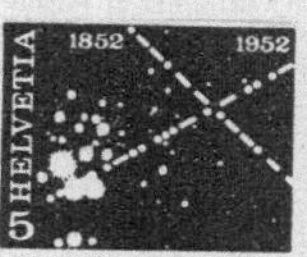

114 "Telegraph"

1952. Centenary of Swiss Telecommunications.
532 **114** 5 c. orange and yellow 40 25
533 – 10 c. green and pink 50 10
534 – 20 c. mauve and lilac 65 10
535 – 40 c. blue and light blue 3·00 2·75
DESIGNS: 10 c. "Telephone"; 20 c. "Radio"; 40 c. "Television".

115 Arms of Glarus and Zug 116 River Doubs

1952. Pro Patria. Cultural Funds and 600th Anniv of Glarus and Zug joining Confederation.
536 **115** 5 c. + 5 c. red and black 50 60
537 **116** 10 c. + 10 c. green and cream 60 40
538 – 20 c. + 10 c. pur & pink 60 40
539 – 30 c. + 10 c. brn & buff 4·25 6·00
540 – 40 c. + 10 c. blue and light blue 4·50 5·75
DESIGNS—As T **116**: 20 c. St. Gotthard Lake; 30 c. River Moesa; 40 c. Marjelen Lake.

1953. Pro Patria. Emigrants' Fund and 600th Anniv of Berne joining Confederation.
541 5 c. + 5 c. red and black 60 70
542 10 c. + 10 c. green & cream 60 40
543 20 c. + 10 c. purple and pink 60 40
544 30 c. + 10 c. brown and buff 4·25 7·00
545 40 c. + 10 c. blue & light blue 4·25 6·00
DESIGNS—As T **115**: 5 c. Arms of Berne (inscr "BERN 1353"); As T **116** (inscr "PRO PATRIA 1953"): 10 c. Rapids, R. Reuss; 20 c. Lake Sihl; 30 c. Aqueduct, Bisse; 40 c. Lac Leman.

119 Zurich Airport

1953. Inauguration of Zurich Airport.
546 **119** 40 c. blue, grey and red 4·75 7·00

120 Alpine Postal Coach and Winter Landscape

1953. For Mobile P.O. Mail.
547 **120** 10 c. yellow, grey & green 15 10
548 – 20 c. yellow, lake and red 25 10
DESIGN: 10 c. Alpine postal coach and summer landscape.

121 Ear of Wheat and Flower 122 Rhine Map and Steering Wheel

1954. Publicity Issue.
549 **121** 10 c. yellow, red and green 40 10
550 – 20 c. multicoloured 80 10
551 **122** 25 c. green, blue and red 2·00 2·50
552 – 40 c. blue, yellow & black 2·40 1·50
DESIGNS—HORIZ: 10 c. Type **121** (Agricultural Exhibition, Lucerne); 20 c. Winged spoon (Cooking Exhibition, Berne); 40 c. Football and world map (World Football Championship). VERT: 25 c. Type **122** (50th anniv of navigation of River Rhine).

123 Opening Bars of "Swiss Hymn"

1954. Pro Patria. Youth Fund and Death Centenary of Father Zwyssig (composer of "Swiss Hymn").
553 **123** 5 c. + 5 c. green 40 75
554 – 10 c. + 10 c. grn & turq 60 40
555 – 20 c. + 10 c. purple and cream 60 40
556 – 30 c. + 10 c. brn & buff 3·75 7·00
557 – 40 c. + 10 c. deep blue and blue 3·75 5·50
DESIGNS: 10 c. Lake Neuchatel; 20 c. Maggia River; 30 c. Taubenloch Gorge Waterfall; Schuss River; 40 c. Lake Sils.

124 Lausanne Cathedral 125 Alphorn Blower

1955. Publicity Issue. Inscr "1955".
558 **124** 5 c. multicoloured 40 10
559 – 10 c. multicoloured 40 10
560 **125** 20 c. sepia and red 1·00 10
561 – 40 c. red, black and blue 3·00 1·25
DESIGNS—HORIZ: 5 c. Type **124** (National Philatelic Exhibition, Lausanne); 10 c. Vaud girl's hat (Vevey Winegrowers' Festival); 40 c. Car steering-wheel (25th International Motor Show, Geneva). VERT: 20 c. Type **125** (Alpine Herdsmen and Costume Festival, Interlaken).

126 Federal Institute of Technology, Zurich

1955. Pro Patria. Mountain Population Fund and Centenary of Federal Institute of Technology.

562 126 5 c. + 5 c. grey 60 60
563 – 10 c. + 10 c. green and cream 60 40
564 – 20 c. + 10 c. red & pink 60 40
565 – 30 c. + 10 c. brn & buff 3·75 6·00
566 – 40 c. + 10 c. deep blue and blue 3·75 5·50

DESIGNS: 10 c. Grandfey railway viaduct, River Saane; 20 c. Lake Aegeri; 30 c. Lake Grappelensee; 40 c. Lake Bienne.

127 "Road Safety"

128 Fokker F.VIIb/3m and Douglas DC-6 Aircraft

1956. Publicity Issue. Inscr "1956".

567 – 5 c. yellow, black and green 40 25
568 – 10 c. black, green and red 40 10
569 127 20 c. multicoloured 80 10
570 128 40 c. blue and red 2·50 80

DESIGNS: 5 c. First postal motor coach (50th anniv of postal motor coach service); 10 c. Electric train emerging from Simplon Tunnel and Stockalper Palace (50th anniv of opening of Simplon Tunnel).
The 40 c. commemorates 25th anniv of Swissair.

129 Rose, Scissors and Tape-measure

130 Printing Machine's Inking Rollers

1956. Pro Patria. Swiss Women's Fund. T **129** and design as T **116** but inscr "PRO PATRIA 1956".

571 129 5 c. + 5 c. green 60 75
572 – 10 c. + 10 c. emerald and green 60 40
573 – 20 c. + 10 c. pur & pink 60 50
574 – 30 c. + 10 c. deep brown and brown 3·50 6·00
575 – 40 c. + 10 c. deep blue and blue 3·50 5·00

DESIGNS: 10 c. R. Rhone at St. Maurice; 20 c. Katzensee; 30 c. R. Rhine at Trin; 40 c. Walensee.

1957. Publicity Issue. Inscr "1957".

576 130 5 c. multicoloured 15 10
577 – 10 c. brown, grn & turq 1·75 10
578 – 20 c. grey and red 50 10
579 – 40 c. multicoloured 2·00 80

DESIGNS: 10 c. Electric train crossing bridge (75th anniv of St. Gotthard Railway); 20 c. Civil Defence shield and coat of arms ("Civil Defence"); 40 c. Munatius Plancus, Basel and Rhine (2000th anniv of Basel).
The 5 c. commemorates "Graphic 57" International Exhibition, Lausanne.

131 Shields of Switzerland and the Red Cross

132 "Charity"

1957. Pro Patria. Swiss Red Cross and National Cancer League Funds. Cross in red.

580 131 5 c. + 5 c. red and grey 40 60
581 132 10 c. + 10 c. pur & grn 55 20
582 20 c. + 10 c. grey & red 50 20
583 30 c. + 10 c. blue & brn 4·00 5·00
584 40 c. + 10 c. ochre & bl 4·00 3·75

133 Symbol of Unity

1957. Europa.

585 133 25 c. red 80 10
586 40 c. blue 2·75 10

134 Nyon Castle (2000th anniv of Nyon)

1958. Publicity Issue. Inscr "1958".

587 134 5 c. violet, buff and olive 20 10
588 – 10 c. myrtle, red and grn 20 10
589 – 20 c. red, lilac and deep red 40 10
590 – 40 c. deep blue, red and blue 1·50 75

DESIGNS: 10 c. Woman's head with ribbons (Saffa Exhibition, Zurich); 20 c. Crossbow (25th anniv as symbol of Swiss manufacture); 40 c. Salvation Army bonnet (75th anniv of Salvation Army in Switzerland).

135 "Needy Mother"

136 Fluorite

1958. Pro Patria. For Needy Mothers, T **135** and designs showing minerals, rocks and fossils as T **136**. Inscr "PRO PATRIA 1958".

591 5 c. + 5 c. purple 30 50
592 10 c. + 10 c. yell, grn & blk 40 30
593 20 c. + 10 c. bistre, red & blk 40 30
594 30 c. + 10 c. purple, brn & blk 3·00 4·50
595 40 c. + 10 c. turq, bl & blk 3·00 3·50

DESIGNS: 20 c. Ammonite; 30 c. Garnet; 40 c. Rock crystal.

137 Atomic Symbol

1958. 2nd U.N. Atomic Conference, Geneva.

596 137 40 c. red, blue and cream 40 35

138 Modern Transport

139 "Swiss Citizens Abroad"

1959. Publicity Issue. Inscr "1959".

597 5 c. multicoloured 25 10
598 10 c. yellow, grey and green 25 10
599 20 c. multicoloured 55 10
600 50 c. blue, violet & light blue 90 75

DESIGNS: 5 c. Type **138** (opening of "The Swiss House of Transport and Communications"); 10 c. Lictor's fasces of the Coat of Arms of St. Gall and posthorn (NABAG—National Philatelic Exhibition, St. Gall); 20 c. Owl, hare and fish (Protection of Animals); 50 c. J. Calvin, Th. de Beze and University building (4th cent of University of Geneva).

1959. Pro Patria. For Swiss Citizens Abroad. T **139** and other designs showing minerals, rocks and fossils as T **136**, and inscr "PRO PATRIA 1959".

601 5 c. + 5 c. red and grey 30 50
602 10 c. + 10 c. multicoloured 40 35
603 20 c. + 10 c. multicoloured 40 35
604 30 c. + 10 c. vio, brn & blk 2·25 2·75
605 40 c. + 10 c. blue, turquoise and black 2·25 2·25

DESIGNS: 10 c. Agate; 20 c. Tourmaline; 30 c. Amethyst; 40 c. Fossilized giant salamander.

140 "Europa"

142 "Campaign against Cancer"

1959. Europa.

606 140 30 c. red 40 10
607 50 c. blue 40 10

1959. European P.T.T. Conference, Montreux. Optd **REUNION DES PTT D'EUROPE 1959**.

608 140 30 c. red 8·50 7·00
609 50 c. blue 8·50 7·00

1960. Publicity Issue. Inscr "1460–1960" (20 c.) or "1960" (50 c., 75 c.).

610 10 c. red, light green & green 45 10
611 20 c. multicoloured 60 10
612 50 c. yellow, ultramarine & blue 75 90
613 75 c. red, black and blue 2·50 2·75

DESIGNS: 10 c. Type **142** (50th anniv of Swiss League for Cancer Control); 20 c. Charter and sceptre (500th anniv of Basel University); 50 c. "Uprooted tree" (World Refugee Year); 75 c. Douglas DC-8 jet airliner ("Swissair enters the jet age").

INDEX

Countries can be quickly located by referring to the index at the end of this volume.

143 15th-century Schwyz Cantonal Messenger

143a Lausanne Cathedral

1960. Postal History and "Architectural Monuments" (1st series).

614 – 5 c. blue 10 10
615 143 10 c. green 10 10
616 – 15 c. red 15 10
617 – 20 c. mauve 20 10
618 143a 25 c. green 25 10
619p – 30 c. red 25 10
620 – 35 c. red 50 45
621p – 40 c. purple 35 10
622 – 50 c. blue 50 10
623 – 60 c. red 60 10
624 – 70 c. orange 70 40
625 – 75 c. blue 1·00 25
626p – 80 c. purple 80 15
627p – 90 c. green 80 10
628 – 1 f. orange 1·00 10
629 – 1 f. 20 red 1·10 10
632 – 1 f. 30 brown on lilac 1·25 10
630 – 1 f. 50 green 1·40 25
633 – 1 f. 70 purple on lilac 1·50 15
631 – 2 f. blue 6·00 65
634 – 2 f. 20 green on green 2·00 40
635 – 2 f. 80 orange on orge 2·75 25

DESIGNS—HORIZ: 5 c. 17th-century Fribourg Cantonal messenger; 15 c. 17th-century muledriver; 20 c. 19th-century mounted postman; 1 f. Fribourg Town Hall; 1 f. 20, Basel Gate, Solothurn; 1 f. 50, Ital Reding's house, Schwyz; 1 f. 70, 2 f., 2 f. 20 Abbey Church, Einsiedeln. VERT: 30 c. Grossmunster, Zurich; 35 c., 1 f. 30, Woodcutters Guildhall, Bienne; 40 c. St. Peter's Cathedral, Geneva; 50 c. Spalentor (gate), Basel; 60 c. Clock Tower, Berne; 70 c. Collegiate Church of St. Peter and St. Stephen, Bellinzona; 75 c. Kapellbrucke (bridge) and Wasserturm, Lucerne; 80 c. St. Gall Cathedral; 90 c. Munot Fort, Schaffhausen; 2 f. 80, as 70 c. but redrawn without bell-tower.
See also Nos. 698/713.

144 Symbols of Occupational Trades

145 "Aid for Development"

1960. Pro Patria. For Swiss Youth. T **144** and other designs showing minerals, rocks and fossils as T **136** and inscr "PRO PATRIA 1960".

636 – 5 c. + 5 c. multicoloured 60 75
637 – 10 c. + 10 c. pink, green and black 60 25
638 – 20 c. + 10 c. yellow, purple and black 60 25
639 – 30 c. + 10 c. blue, brown and black 3·75 3·75
640 144 50 c. + 10 c. gold & blue 3·75 3·25

DESIGNS: 5 c. Smoky quartz; 10 c. Orthoclase (feldspar); 20 c. Gryphaea (fossilized shellfish); 30 c. Azurite; 50 c. Type **144** ("50 Years of National Day Collection").

1960. Europa. As T **129a** of Luxembourg, but size 33×23 mm.

642 30 c. red 40 10
643 50 c. blue 40 10

1961. Publicity Issue.

644 5 c. red, blue and grey 25 10
645 10 c. yellow and blue 25 10
646 20 c. multicoloured 70 10
647 50 c. red, green and blue 1·10 90

DESIGNS: 5 c. Type **145** ("Aid to countries in process of development"); 10 c. Circular emblem ("Hyspa" Exhibition of 20th-century Hygiene, Gymnastics and Sport, Berne); 20 c. Hockey stick (World and European Ice Hockey Championships, Geneva and Lausanne); 50 c. Map of Switzerland with telephone centres as wiring diagram (inauguration of Swiss fully automatic telephone service).

146 "Cultural Works of Eternity"

147 Doves

1961. Pro Patria. For Swiss Cultural Works, T **146** and other designs showing minerals, rocks and fossils as T **136** and inscr "PROPATRIA 1961".

648 5 c. + 5 c. blue 20 40
649 10 c. + 10 c. purple, green and black 50 30
650 20 c. + 10 c. red, blue and black 60 30
651 30 c. + 10 c. turquoise, orange and black 1·75 3·00
652 50 c. + 10 c. bistre, blue and black 2·00 3·00

DESIGNS: 10 c. Fluorite; 20 c. Petrified fish; 30 c. Lazulite; 50 c. Fossilised fern.

1961. Europa.

653 147 30 c. red 40 10
654 50 c. blue 50 10

148 St. Matthew

149 W.H.O. Emblem and Mosquito

1961. Wood Carvings from St. Oswald's Church, Zug.

655 148 3 f. mauve 3·00 10
656 – 5 f. blue 5·00 10
657 – 10 f. brown 9·00 15
658 – 20 f. red 18·00 1·75

DESIGNS: 5 f. St. Mark; 10 f. St. Luke; 20 f. St. John.

1962. Publicity Issue.

659 5 c. multicoloured 60 10
660 10 c. bistre, purple and green 50 10
661 20 c. multicoloured 65 10
662 50 c. green, mauve and blue 90 80

DESIGNS: 5 c. Electric train (Introduction of TEE Trains); 10 c. Oarsman (World Rowing Championship, Lucerne); 20 c. Jungfraujoch and Monch (50th anniv of Jungfraujoch railway station); 50 c. Type **149** (Malaria Eradication).

150 Rousseau

151 Obwalden Silver Halftaler

1962. Pro Patria. For Swiss Old People's Homes and Cultural Works.

663 150 5 c. + 5 c. blue 20 15
664 151 10 c. + 10 c. blue, black and green 40 20
665 – 20 c. + 10 c. yellow, black and red 40 20
666 – 30 c. + 10 c. green, blue and red 1·10 1·60
667 – 50 c. + 10 c. violet, black and blue 1·10 1·60

COINS—As Type **151**: 20 c. Schwyz gold ducat; 30 c. Uri batzen; 50 c. Nidwalden batzen.

152 Europa "Tree"

1962. Europa.

668 152 30 c. orange, yellow & brn 40 25
669 50 c. blue, turquoise & brn 90 40

153 Campaign Emblem (Freedom from Hunger)

1963. Publicity Issue.

670 – 5 c. brown, red and blue 80 25
671 – 10 c. red, grey and green 40 10
672 – 20 c. lake, red and grey 1·50 10
673 153 30 c. yellow, ochre & grn 1·50 1·50
674 – 50 c. red, silver and blue 75 60
675 – 50 c. multicoloured 75 60

DESIGNS: No. 670, Boy scout (50th anniv of Swiss Boy Scout League); No. 671, Badge (Swiss Alpine Club cent); No. 672, Luegelkinn Viaduct (50th anniv of Lotschberg Railway); No. 674, Jubilee Emblem (Red Cross cent); No. 675, Hotel des Postes, Paris, 1863 (Paris Postal Conference).

154 Dr. Anna Heer (nursing pioneer)

155 Roll of Bandage

1963. Pro Patria. For Swiss Medical and Refugee Aid. T **154** and other designs as T **155** showing Red Cross activities. Inscr "PRO PATRIA 1963".
676 5 c. + 5 c. blue 20 25
677 10 c. + 10 c. red, grey and green 20 20
678 20 c. + 10 c. multicoloured . 35 20
679 30 c. + 10 c. multicoloured 1·25 1·40
680 50 c. + 10 c. red, indigo & bl 1·50 1·25
DESIGNS: 20 c. Gift parcel; 30 c. Blood plasma; 50 c. Red Cross brassard.

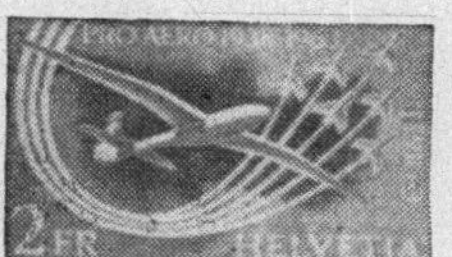

156 Glider and Jet Aircraft

1963. Air 25th Anniv of Swiss "Pro Aero" Foundation. Berne–Locarno or Langenbruck–Berne (helicopter feeder) Special Flights.
681 **156** 2 f. multicoloured . . . . 5·50 4·00

157 "Co-operation" **158** Exhibition Emblem

1963. Europa.
682 **157** 50 c. ochre and blue . . . 60 25

1963. Swiss National Exhibition, Lausanne.
683 **158** 10 c. green and sepia . . . 20 10
684 20 c. red and sepia 30 10
685 – 50 c. blue and red 40 35
686 – 75 c. violet and red . . . 60 50
DESIGNS: 50 c. "Outlook" (emblem on globe and smaller globe); 75 c. "Insight" (emblem on large globe).

159 Great St. Bernard Tunnel

1964. Publicity Issue.
687 5 c. blue, red and olive 20 10
688 10 c. turquoise and blue . . . 25 10
689 20 c. multicoloured 40 10
690 50 c. multicoloured 80 70
DESIGNS: 5 c. Type **159** (Opening of Great St. Bernard Road Tunnel); 10 c. Ancient "god of the waters" (Protection of water supplies); 20 c. Swiss soldiers of 1864 and 1964 (Centenary of Swiss Association of Non-commissioned Officers); 50 c. Standards of Geneva and Swiss Confederation (150th anniv of arrival of Swiss in Geneva).

160 J. G. Bodmer (inventor) **161** Europa "Flower"

1964. Pro Patria. For Swiss Mountain Aid and Cultural Funds. T **160** and vert designs of Swiss coins as T **151**. Inscr "PRO PATRIA 1964".
691 5 c. + 5 c. blue 10 10
692 10 c. + 10 c. drab, blk & grn 20 15
693 20 c. + 10 c. blue, blk & mve 25 20
694 30 c. + 10 c. blue, blk & orge 75 80
695 50 c. + 10 c. olive, brn & blue 80 80
COINS: 10 c. Zurich copper; 20 c. Basel "doppeldicken"; 30 c. Geneva silver thaler; 50 c. Berne half gold florin.

1964. Europa.
696 **161** 20 c. red 35 10
697 50 c. blue 65 15

1964. "Architectural monuments" (2nd series). As T **143a**.
698 5 c. mauve 10 10
699 10 c. blue 10 10
700 15 c. brown 15 10
701 20 c. green 15 10
702 30 c. red 25 10
703 50 c. blue 40 10
704 70 c. brown 60 10
705 1 f. green 85 10
706 1 f. 20 red . . . . 1·00 10
707 1 f. 30 blue . . . . 1·50 50
708 1 f. 50 green . . . . 1·25 10
709 1 f. 70 red . . . . 1·50 75
710 2 f. orange . . . . 1·75 15
711 2 f. 20 green . . . . 2·75 50
712 2 f. 50 green . . . . 2·25 25
713 3 f. 50 purple . . . . 3·00 25

DESIGNS—HORIZ: 5 c. Lenzburg Castle; 10 c. Freuler Mansion, Nafels; 15 c. Mauritius Church, Appenzell; 20 c. Planta House, Samedan; 30 c. Town Square, Gais; 50 c. Neuchatel Castle and Collegiate Church. VERT: 70 c. Lussy "Hochhus", Wolfenschiessen; 1 f. Riva San Vitale Church; 1 f. 20, Payerne Abbey Church; 1 f. 30, St. Pierre-de Clages Church; 1 f. 50, Gateway, Porrentruy; 1 f. 70, Frauenfeld Castle; 2 f. Castle Seedorf (Uri); 2 f. 20, Thomas Tower and Arch, Liestal; 2 f. 50, St. Oswald's Church, Zug; 3 f. 50, Benedictine Abbey, Engelberg.

162 Swiss 5 r. Stamp of 1854 with "Lozenge" Cancellation

1965. Publicity Issue.
714 – 5 c. black, red and blue . 10 10
715 **162** 10 c. brown, blue & green 10 10
716 – 20 c. multicoloured . . . 20 10
717 – 50 c. red, black and blue 40 35
DESIGNS, etc: 5 c. Nurse and patient ("Nursing"); 10 c. Type **162** "NABRA 1965" National Stamp Exhibition, Berne); 20 c. WAC Officer (25th anniv of Women's Army Corps); 50 c. World telecommunications map (centenary of I.T.U.).

163 Father T. Florentini **164** Fish-tailed Goose ("Evil")

1965. Pro Patria. For Swiss Abroad and Art Research. Inscr "PRO PATRIA 1965".
719 **163** 5 c. + 5 c. blue 10 10
720 **164** 10 c. + 10 c. multicoloured 10 10
721 – 20 c. + 10 c. multicoloured 15 10
722 – 30 c. + 10 c. brown & blue 30 35
723 – 50 c. + 10 c. blue & brown 50 40
DESIGNS—As Type **164**: Ceiling paintings in St. Martin's Church, Zillis (Grisons); 20 c. One of the magi journeying to Herod; 30 c. Fishermen; 50 c. The Temptation of Christ.

165 Swiss Emblem and Arms of Cantons

1965. 150th Anniv of Entry of Valais, Neuchatel and Geneva into Confederation.
724 **165** 20 c. multicoloured . . . 20 10

166 Matterhorn **167** Europa "Sprig"

1965. Mobile P.O. Issue.
725 **166** 10 c. multicoloured . . . 20 10
726 30 c. multicoloured . . . 50 50
The 30 c. is inscr "CERVIN".

1965. Europa.
727 **167** 50 c. green and blue . . . 40 20

168 I.T.U. Emblem and Satellites

1965. I.T.U. Centenary Congress, Montreux. Multicoloured.
728 10 c. Type **168** 10 10
729 30 c. Symbols of world telecommunications 35 25

169 Figure Skating

1965. World Figure Skating Championships. Davos.
730 **169** 5 c. multicoloured 10 10

170 Common Kingfisher **171** H. Federer (author)

1966. Publicity Issue. Multicoloured.
731 10 c. Type **170** 15 10
732 20 c. Mercury's helmet and laurel twig 15 10
733 50 c. Phase in nuclear fission and flags 40 35
PUBLICITY EVENTS: 10 c. Preservation of natural beauty; 20 c. 50th Swiss Industrial Fair, Bale (MUBA); 50 c. International Institute for Nuclear Research (CERN).

1966. Pro Patria. For Aid to Mothers. Inscr "PRO PATRIA 1966".
734 **171** 5 c. + 5 c. blue 10 10
735 – 10 c. + 10 c. multicoloured 10 10
736 – 20 c. + 10 c. multicoloured 20 10
737 – 30 c. + 10 c. multicoloured 30 30
738 – 50 c. + 10 c. multicoloured 50 45
DESIGNS—As Type **164**: "The Flight to Egypt"; Ceiling paintings in St. Martin's Church, Zillis (Grisons); 10 c. Joseph's dream; 20 c. Joseph on his way; 30 c. Virgin and Child; 50 c. Angel pointing the way.

172 Society Emblem **173** Europa "Ship"

1966. 50th Anniv of New Helvetic Society for Swiss Abroad.
739 **172** 20 c. red and blue 15 10

1966. Europa.
740 **173** 20 c. red 20 10
741 50 c. blue 45 15

174 Finsteraarhorn

1966. "Swiss Alps".
742 **174** 10 c. multicoloured 10 10

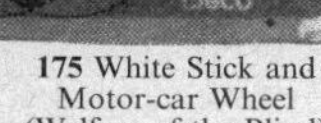

175 White Stick and Motor-car Wheel (Welfare of the Blind) **176** C.E.P.T. Emblem and Cogwheels

1967. Publicity Issue.
743 **175** 10 c. multicoloured 10 10
744 – 20 c. multicoloured 15 10
DESIGN: 20 c. Flags of E.F.T.A. countries (Abolition of E.F.T.A. tariffs).

1967. Europa.
745 **176** 30 c. blue 25 10

177 Theodor Kocher (surgeon) **178** Cogwheel and Swiss Emblem

1967. Pro Patria. For National Day Collection. Inscr "PRO PATRIA 1967".
746 **177** 5 c. + 5 c. blue 10 10
747 – 10 c. + 10 c. multicoloured 10 10
748 – 20 c. + 10 c. multicoloured 20 10
749 – 30 c. + 10 c. multicoloured 30 30
750 – 50 c. + 10 c. multicoloured 50 50
DESIGNS—As Type **164**: Ceiling paintings in St. Martin's Church, Zillis (Grisons); 10 c. Annunciation to the Shepherds; 20 c. Christ and the woman of Samaria; 30 c. Adoration of the Magi; 50 c. Joseph seated on throne.

1967. Publicity Issue. Multicoloured.
751 10 c. Type **178** 10 10
752 20 c. Hour-glass and Sun . . 15 10
753 30 c. San Bernadino tunnel . 25 10
754 50 c. "OCTI" emblem 40 35
PUBLICITY EVENTS: 10 c. 50th anniv of Swiss Week; 20 c. 50th anniv of Aged People Foundation; 30 c. Opening of San Bernardino road tunnel; 50 c. 75th anniv of Central Office for International Railway Transport (OCTI).

179 "Mountains" and Swiss Emblem

1968. Publicity Issue.
755 10 c. multicoloured 10 10
756 20 c. yellow, brown and blue . 20 10
757 30 c. blue, ochre and brown . 35 10
758 50 c. red, turquoise and blue . 45 35
DESIGNS AND EVENTS: 10 c. T **179** (50th anniv of Swiss Women's Alpine Club); 20 c. Europa "Key" (Europa); 30 c. Staunton rook and chessboard (18th Chess Olympiad, Lugano); 50 c. Dispatch "satellites" and aircraft tail-fin (inauguration of new Geneva Air Terminal).

180 "Maius" **181** Protective helmet

1968. Pro Patria. For National Day Collection. Inscr "PRO PATRIA 1968".
759 **180** 10 c. + 10 c. multicoloured 10 10
760 – 20 c. + 10 c. multicoloured 20 10
761 – 30 c. + 10 c. multicoloured 30 15
762 – 50 c. + 20 c. multicoloured 50 50
DESIGNS: Stained-glass panels in the rose window, Lausanne Cathedral; 20 c. "Leo"; 30 c. "Libra"; 50 c. "Pisces" (symbols of the months and signs of the zodiac).

1968. Publicity Issue. Multicoloured.
763 10 c. Type **181** 10 10
764 20 c. Geneva and Zurich stamps of 1843 . . . . 20 10
765 30 c. Part of Swiss man . . . 25 10
766 50 c. "Six Stars" (countries) and anchor 45 35
PUBLICITY EVENTS: 10 c. 50th anniv of Swiss Accident Insurance Company; 20 c. 125th anniv of Swiss stamps; 30 c. 25th anniv of Swiss Territorial Planning Society; 50 c. Cent of Rhine Navigation Act.

182 Guide Camp and Emblem

1969. Publicity Issue. Multicoloured.
767 10 c. Type **182** 25 10
768 20 c. Pegasus constellation . . 25 10
769 30 c. Emblem of Comptoir Suisse 25 10
770 50 c. Emblem of Gymnaestrade 40 40
771 2 f. Haefeli DH-3 biplane and Douglas DC-8 airliner . . . 1·75 1·40
EVENTS: 10 c. 50th anniv of Swiss Girl Guides' Federation; 20 c. Opening of first Swiss Planetarium, Lucerne; 30 c. 50th anniv of Comptoir Suisse, Lausanne; 50 c. 5th Gymnaestrada, Basel; 2 f. 50th anniv of Swiss Airmail Services.

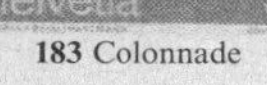

183 Colonnade **184** "St. Francis of Assisi preaching to the Birds" (Abbey-church, Konigsfelden)

1969. Europa.
772 **183** 30 c. multicoloured . . . 25 10
773 50 c. multicoloured . . . 45 35

1969. Pro Patria. For National Day Collection. Stained-glass Windows. Multicoloured.
774 10 c. + 10 c. Type **184** . . . 10 15
775 20 c. + 10 c. "The People of Israel drinking..." (Berne Cathedral) 20 15
776 30 c. + 10 c. "St. Christopher" (Laufelfingen Church, Basle) 30 20
777 50 c. + 20 c. "Madonna and Child" (St. Jacob's Chapel, Grapplang, Flums) 50 50

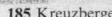

185 Kreuzberge

186 Huldrych Zwingli (Protestant reformer)

1969. Publicity and "Swiss Alps" Issues. Multicoloured.

778 20 c. Type **185** 25 10
779 30 c. Children crossing road 25 10
780 50 c. Hammersmith 45 35

EVENTS: 30 c. Road Safety campaign for children; 50 c. 50th anniv of I.L.O.

1969. Swiss Celebrities.

781 **186** 10 c. violet 10 10
782 – 20 c. green 20 10
783 – 30 c. red 25 10
784 – 50 c. blue 50 50
785 – 80 c. brown 65 60

CELEBRITIES: 20 c. General Henri Guisan; 30 c. Francesco Borromini (architect); 50 c. Othmar Schoeck (composer); 80 c. Germaine de Stael (writer).

187 Telex Tape

188 "Flaming Sun"

1970. Publicity Issue. Multicoloured.

786 20 c. Type **187** 20 10
787 30 c. Fireman saving child . . 40 10
788 30 c. "Chained wing" emblem 25 10
789 50 c. U.N. emblem 30 45
790 80 c. New U.P.U. Headquarters 80 70

EVENTS: 20 c. 75th anniv of Swiss Telegraphic Agency; 30 c. (No. 787), Centenary of Swiss Firemen's Assn; 30 c. (No. 788), 50th anniv of "Pro Infirmis" Foundation; 50 c. 25th anniv of U.N. Organization; 80 c. Inauguration of new U.P.U. headquarters, Berne.

1970. Europa.

791 **188** 30 c. red 30 10
792 50 c. blue 50 30

1970. Pro Patria. For National Day Collection. Glass paintings by contemporary artists. As T **184** but inscr "1970". Multicoloured.

793 10 c. + 10 c. "Sailor" (G. Casty) 15 15
794 20 c. + 10 c. Architectonic composition (Celestino Piatti) 20 20
795 30 c. + 10 c. "Bull" symbol of Marduk, from "The Four Elements" (Hans Stocker) 30 15
796 50 c. + 20 c. "Man and Woman" (Max Hunziker and Karl Ganz) 50 55

189 Footballer (75th Anniv of Swiss Football Association)

190 Numeral

1970. Publicity and "Swiss Alps" (30 c.) Issue. Multicoloured.

797 10 c. Type **189** 30 10
798 20 c. Census form and pencil (Federal Census) 20 10
799 30 c. Piz Palu, Grisons 30 10
800 50 c. Conservation Year Emblem (Nature Conservation Year) 45 40

1970. Coil Stamps.

801 **190** 10 c. red 10 10
802 20 c. green 20 10
803 50 c. blue 40 25

191 Female Gymnasts ("Youth and Sport")

193 Europa Chain

1971. Publicity Issue.

804 **191** 10 c. multicoloured . . . 20 20
805 – 10 c. multicoloured . . . 20 20
806 – 20 c. multicoloured . . . 20 10
807 – 30 c. multicoloured . . . 25 10
808 – 50 c. brown and blue . . . 45 35
809 – 80 c. multicoloured . . . 75 60

DESIGNS AND EVENTS: 10 c. (No. 805), Male athletes ("Youth and Sport" Constitutional Amendment); 20 c. Stylized rose (Child Welfare); 30 c. "Rayon II" stamp of 1850 and basilisk ("NABA" Philatelic Exhibition, Basel); 50 c. "Co-operation" symbol (Aid for technical development); 80 c. "Intelstat 4" (I.T.U. Space Conference).

1971. Europa.

811 **193** 30 c. yellow and mauve . . 30 10
812 50 c. yellow and blue . . 50 25

1971. Pro Patria. For National Day Collection. Contemporary Glass Paintings. As T **184**.

813 10 c. + 10 c. "Religious Abstract", (J. F. Comment) 15 15
814 20 c. + 10 c. "Cockerel", (J. Prahin) 20 20
815 30 c. + 10 c. "Fox", (K. Volk) 30 20
816 50 c. + 20 c. "Christ's Passion" (B. Schorderet) 50 55

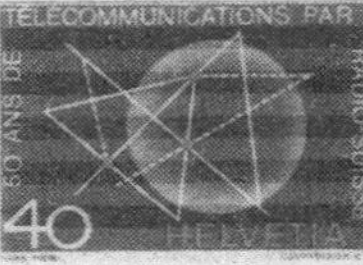

194 "Telecommunications Services" (50th anniv of Radio-Suisse)

195 Alexandre Yersin (bacteriologist)

1971. Publicity and "Swiss Alps".

817 – 30 c. purple, grey & mve 30 10
818 **194** 40 c. multicoloured . . . 40 35

DESIGN: 30 c. Les Diablerets, Vaud.

1971. Famous Physicians.

819 **195** 10 c. green 10 10
820 – 20 c. green 20 10
821 – 30 c. red 30 10
822 – 40 c. blue 60 60
823 – 80 c. purple 80 70

PHYSICIANS: 20 c. Auguste Forel (psychiatrist); 30 c. Jules Gonin (opthalmologist); 40 c. Robert Koch (German bacteriologist); 80 c. Frederick Banting (Canadian physiologist).

196 Warning Triangle and Wrench (75th Annivs of Motoring Organisations)

1972. Publicity Issue.

824 **196** 10 c. multicoloured . . . 10 10
825 – 20 c. multicoloured . . . 25 10
826 – 30 c. orge, red & carmine 25 10
827 – 40 c. violet, green & blue 40 35

DESIGNS AND EVENTS: 20 c. Signal-box switch-table (125th anniv of Swiss Railways); 30 c. Stylized radio waves and girl's face (50th anniv of Swiss Broadcasting); 40 c. Symbolic tree (50th "Swiss Citizens Abroad" Congress).

197 Swissair Boeing 747-100

198 "Communications"

1972. Air. Pro Aero Foundation and 50th Annivs of North Atlantic and Int Airmail Services.

828 **197** 2 f. + 1 f. multicoloured 2·25 2·25

1972. Europa.

829 **198** 30 c. multicoloured . . . 25 10
830 40 c. multicoloured . . . 40 20

199 Late Stone Age Harpoon Heads

200 Civil Defence Emblem

1972. Pro Patria. For National Day Collection. Archaeological Discoveries (1st series). Multicoloured.

831 10 c. + 10 c. Type **199** . . 30 15
832 20 c. + 10 c. Bronze water-vessel, c. 570 B.C. 30 10
833 30 c. + 10 c. Gold bust of Marcus Aurelius, 2nd cent A.D. 30 20
834 40 c. + 20 c. Alemannic disc. 7th-cent A.D. 80 75

See also Nos. 869/72, 887/90 and 901/4.

1972. Publicity and "Swiss Alps" Issue. Mult.

835 10 c. Type **200** 10 10
836 20 c. Spannorter 30 10
837 30 c. Rescue helicopter . . . 35 10
838 40 c. The "Four Elements" (53 × 31 mm) 50 40

SUBJECTS: 10 c. Swiss Civil Defence; 20 c. Tourism; 30 c. Swiss Air Rescue Service; 40 c. Protection of the environment.

201 Alberto Giacometti (painter)

202 Dish Aerial

1972. Swiss Celebrities.

839 **201** 10 c. black and brown . . 10 10
840 – 20 c. black and bistre . . . 15 10
841 – 30 c. black and pink . . . 25 10
842 – 40 c. black and blue . . . 50 45
843 – 80 c. black and purple . . 75 75

PORTRAITS: 20 c. Charles Ramuz (novelist); 30 c. Le Corbusier (architect); 40 c. Albert Einstein (physicist); 80 c. Arthur Honegger (composer).

1973. Publicity Issue. Multicoloured.

844 15 c. Type **202** 25 15
845 30 c. Quill pen 25 10
846 40 c. Interpol emblem 45 35

EVENTS: 15 c. Construction of Satellite Earth Station, Leuk-Brentiong; 30 c. Centenary of Swiss Association of Commercial Employees; 40 c. 50th anniv of International Criminal Police Organisation (Interpol).

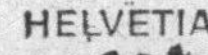

203 Sottoceneri

204 Toggenburg Inn Sign

1973.

847 **203** 5 c. blue and yellow . . . 10 10
848 – 10 c. green and purple . . 10 10
849 – 15 c. blue and orange . . 15 10
850 – 25 c. violet and green . . 20 10
851 – 30 c. violet and red . . . 25 10
852 – 35 c. violet and orange . . 35 20
853 – 40 c. grey and blue . . . 35 10
854 – 50 c. green and orange . . 45 10
855 – 60 c. brown and grey . . 55 10
856 – 70 c. green and purple . . 60 10
857 – 80 c. red and green . . . 75 10
858 – 1 f. purple 85 10
859 – 1 f. 10 blue 95 10
860 – 1 f. 20 red . . . . . . 1·00 90
861 **204** 1 f. 30 orange . . . . . 2·00 20
862 – 1 f. 50 green . . . . . . 1·25 10
863 – 1 f. 70 grey . . . . . . 1·50 25
864 – 1 f. 80 red . . . . 1·50 15
865 – 2 f. blue . . . . 1·75 10
866 – 2 f. 50 brown . . . . . . 2·00 25
866a – 3 f. red . . . . 2·50 30
866b – 3 f. 50 green . . . . . . 2·50 55

DESIGNS—As Type **203**: 10 c. Grisons; 15 c. Central Switzerland; 25 c. Jura; 30 c. Simmental; 35 c. Houses, Central Switzerland; 40 c. Vaud; 50 c. Valais; 60 c. Engadine; 70 c. Sopraceneri; 80 c. Eastern Switzerland. As Type **204**: 1 f. Rose window, Lausanne Cathedral; 1 f. 10, Gallus portal, Basel Cathedral; 1 f. 20, Romanesque capital, St.-Jean-Baptiste Church, Grandson; 1 f. 50, Medallion, St. Georgen Monastery, Stein am Rhein; 1 f. 70, Roman Capital, St.-Jean-Baptiste Church, Grandson; 1 f. 80, Gargoyle, Berne Cathedral; 2 f. Oriel, Schaffhausen; 2 f. 50, Weathercock, St. Ursus Cathedral, Solothurn; 3 f. Font, St. Maurice Church, Saanen; 3 f. 50, Astronomical clock, Berne.

205 Europa "Posthorn"

1973. Europa.

867 **205** 25 c. yellow and red . . . 25 20
868 40 c. yellow and blue . . . 40 25

1973. Pro Patria. For National Day Collection. Archaeological Discoveries (2nd series). As T **199**, but horiz Multicoloured.

869 15 c. + 5 c. Rauraric jar . . . 20 20
870 30 c. + 10 c. Head of a Gaul (bronze) 35 20
871 40 c. + 20 c. Almannic "Fish" brooches 70 65
872 60 c. + 20 c. Gold bowl . . . 90 95

206 Horological Emblem

1973. Publicity Issue. Multicoloured.

873 15 c. Type **206** 15 10
874 30 c. Skiing emblem 25 10
875 40 c. Face of child 40 30

SUBJECTS: 15 c. Inaug (1974) of Int Horological Museum, Neuchatel; 30 c. World Alpine Skiing Championships, St. Moritz (1974); 40 c. "Terre des Hommes" (Child-care organisation).

207 Global Hostels

209 "Continuity" (Max Bill)

1974. Publicity Issue. Multicoloured.

876 15 c. Type **207** 15 10
877 30 c. Gymnast and hurdlers . 30 10
878 40 c. Pistol and target 40 40

SUBJECTS: 15 c. "50 Years of Swiss Youth Hostels"; 30 c. Centenary of Swiss Workmen's Gymnastics and Sports Assn (S.A.T.U.S.); 40 c. World Shooting Championships, 1974.

1974. Europa. Swiss Sculptures.

880 **209** 30 c. black and red . . . 25 10
881 – 40 c. brown, blue & black 40 35

DESIGN: 40 c. "Amazone" (Carl Burckhardt).

210 Eugene Borel (first Director of International Bureau, U.P.U.)

211 View of Berne

1974. Centenary of U.P.U.

882 **210** 30 c. black and pink . . . 25 10
883 – 40 c. black and grey . . . 40 35
884 – 80 c. black and green . . 75 70

DESIGNS: 40 c. Heinrich von Stephan (founder of U.P.U.); 80 c. Montgomery Blair (U.S. Postmaster-General and initiator of 1863 Paris Postal Conference.

1974. 17th U.P.U. Congress, Lausanne. Mult.

885 30 c. Type **211** 30 25
886 30 c. View of Lausanne . . . 30 25

1974. Pro Patria. For National Day Collection. Archaeological Discoveries (3rd series). As T **199** but horiz. Multicoloured.

887 15 c. + 5 c. Glass bowl . . . 25 20
888 30 c. + 10 c. Bull's head (bronze) 35 15
889 40 c. + 20 c. Gold brooch . . 65 65
890 60 c. + 20 c. "Bird" vessel (clay) 80 95

212 "Oath of Allegiance" (sculpture) (W. Witschi)

1974. Publicity Issue.

891 **212** 15 c. deep green, green and lilac 15 10
892 – 30 c. multicoloured . . . 25 10
893 – 30 c. multicoloured . . . 25 10

EVENTS AND COMMEMORATIONS: No. 891, Centenary of Federal Constitution; No. 892, Foundation emblem (Aid for Swiss Sport Foundation); No. 893, Posthorn and "postal transit" arrow (125th anniv of Federal Posts).

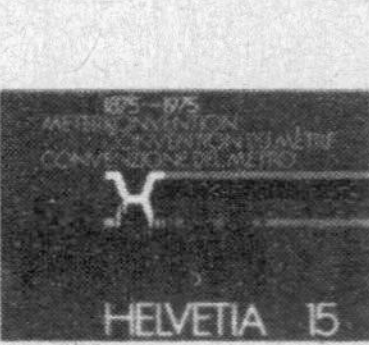

213 "Metre" and Krypton Line

214 "The Monch" (F. Hodler)

1975. Publicity Issue.

894 **213** 15 c. orange, blue & grn . 15 10
895 – 30 c. brown, purple & yell 25 10
896 – 60 c. red, black and blue . 50 45
897 – 90 c. multicoloured . . . 85 70

DESIGNS AND EVENTS: 15 c. Centenary of International Metre Convention; 30 c. Women talking (International Women's Year); 60 c. Red Cross Flag and barbed-wire (Conference on Humanitarian International Law, Geneva); 90 c. Airship "Ville de Lucerne", 1910 ("Aviation and Space Travel" Exhibition, Transport and Communications Museum, Lucerne).

1975. Europa. Paintings. Multicoloured.

No.	Type	Description	Mint	Used
898		30 c. Type **214**	30	10
899		50 c. "Still Life with Guitar" (R. Auberjonois)	50	40
900		60 c. "L'effeuilleuse" (M. Barraud)	60	50

1975. Pro Patria. Archaeological Discoveries. (4th series). As T **199**. Multicoloured.

No.	Type	Description	Mint	Used
901		15 c. + 10 c. Gold brooch, Oron-le-Chatel	25	25
902		30 c. + 20 c. Bronze head of Bacchus, Avenches	40	30
903		50 c. + 20 c. Bronze daggers, Bois-de-Vaux, Lausanne	75	75
904		60 c. + 25 c. Glass decanter, Maralto	80	80

215 "Eliminate Obstacles!" (Disabled Person in Wheelchair being dragged up steps)

1975. Publicity Issue.

No.	Type	Description	Mint	Used
905	**215**	15 c. black, green & lilac	15	10
906	–	30 c. black, pink and red	25	10
907	–	50 c. brown and bistre	50	45
908	–	60 c. multicoloured	60	45

DESIGNS: 30 c. Organization emblem (Inter-confessional Pastoral Care by Telephone Organization); 50 c. European Architectural Heritage Year emblem; 60 c. Beat Fischer von Reichenbach (founder) (300th anniv of Fischer postal service).

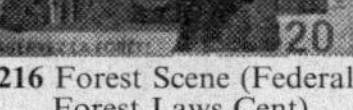

216 Forest Scene (Federal Forest Laws Cent)

217 Floral Embroidery

1976. Publicity Issue.

No.	Type	Description	Mint	Used
919	**216**	20 c. multicoloured	15	10
910	–	40 c. multicoloured	30	10
911	–	40 c. black, orange & pur	30	10
912	–	80 c. black and blue	75	60

DESIGNS: No. 910, Fruit and vegetables (campaign to promote nutriments as opposed to alcohol); No. 911, African child (fight against leprosy); No. 912, Early and modern telephones (telephone centenary).

1976. Europa. Handicrafts.

No.	Type	Description	Mint	Used
913	**217**	40 c. yellow, brn & pink	35	10
914	–	80 c. blue, red and orchre	70	55

DESIGN: 80 c. Decorated pocket watch.

218 Kyburg Castle, Zurich

219 Roe Deer, Barn Swallow and Frog (World Fed. for Protection of Animals)

1976. Pro Patria. Swiss Castles (1st series). Multicoloured.

No.	Type	Description	Mint	Used
915		20 c. + 10 c. Type **218**	30	25
916		40 c. + 20 c. Grandson, Vaud	60	25
917		40 c. + 20 c. Murten, Fribourg	60	25
918		80 c. + 40 c. Bellinzona, Ticino	1·25	1·25

See also Nos. 932/5, 955/8 and 977/80.

1976. Publicity Issue.

No.	Type	Description	Mint	Used
919	**219**	20 c. black, brown & grn	25	10
920	–	40 c. black, yellow & red	30	10
921	–	40 c. multicoloured	40	10
922	–	80 c. red, violet and blue	75	70

DESIGNS: No. 920, "Sun" and inscription ("Save Energy" campaign); No. 921, St. Gotthard mountains (Swiss Alps); No. 922, Skater (World Speed Skating Championships, Davos).

220 Oskar Bider

221 Blue Cross (society for care of alcoholics, cent)

1977. Aviation Pioneers.

No.	Type	Description	Mint	Used
923	**220**	40 c. black, mauve & red	35	10
924	–	80 c. black, pur and blue	90	80
925	–	100 c. black, grn & bistre	90	70
926	–	150 c. black, brn & turq	1·50	1·00

DESIGNS: 80 c. Eduard Spelterini; 100 c. Armand Dufaux; 150 c. Walter Mittelhalzer.

1977. Publicity Issues.

No.	Type	Description	Mint	Used
927	**221**	20 c. blue and brown	15	10
928	–	40 c. multicoloured	35	10
929	–	80 c. multicoloured	80	75

DESIGNS: 40 c. Festival emblem (Vevey vintage festival); 80 c. Balloons carrying letters ("Juphilex 1977" youth stamp exhibition, Berne).

222 St. Ursanne

1977. Europa. Landscapes. Multicoloured.

No.	Type	Description	Mint	Used
930		40 c. Type **222**	35	10
931		80 c. Sils-Baselgia	65	55

1977. Pro Patria. Swiss Castles (2nd series). As T **218**. Multicoloured.

No.	Type	Description	Mint	Used
932		20 c. + 10 c. Aigle, Vaud	25	25
933		40 c. + 20 c. Pratteln, Basel-Landschaft	40	15
934		70 c. + 30 c. Sargans, St. Gallen	1·00	1·25
935		80 c. + 40 c. Hallwil, Aargau	1·10	1·25

223 Factory Worker

1977. Publicity Issue. Multicoloured.

No.	Type	Description	Mint	Used
936		20 c. Type **223**	15	10
937		40 c. Ionic capital	35	10
938		80 c. Association emblem and butterfly	75	75

EVENTS: 20 c. Centenary of Federal Factories Act; 40 c. Protection of cultural monuments; 80 c. Swiss Footpaths Association.

224 Sternsingen, Bergun

225 Mailcoach Route Plate, Vaud Canton

1977. Regional Folk Customs.

No.	Type	Description	Mint	Used
939	**224**	5 c. green	10	10
940	–	10 c. red	10	10
941	–	20 c. orange	15	10
941b	–	25 c. brown	40	15
941c	–	30 c. green	35	10
942	–	35 c. green	35	10
943	–	40 c. red	35	10
943c	–	45 c. blue	50	35
944	–	50 c. red	45	10
944b	–	60 c. brown	70	40
945	–	70 c. lilac	65	10
946	–	80 c. blue	75	20
947	–	90 c. brown	85	25

DESIGNS: 10 c. Sechselauten, Zurich; 20 c. Silvesterklause, Herisau; 25 c. Chesstete, Solothurn; 30 c. Rollelibutzen, Alstatten; 35 c. Gansabhauet, Sursee; 40 c. Escalade, Geneva; 45 c. Klausjagen, Kussnacht; 50 c. Archetringele, Laupen; 60 c. Schnabelgeissen, Ottenbach; 70 c. Processioni storiche, Mendrisio; 80 c. Vogel Gryff, Basel; 90 c. Roitschaggata, Lotschental.

1978. Publicity Issue. Multicoloured.

No.	Type	Description	Mint	Used
948		20 c. Type **225**	15	10
949		40 c. View of Lucerne	35	10
950		70 c. Title page of book "Melusine"	60	50
951		80 c. Stylised camera and lens	70	70

EVENTS: 20 c. "Lemanex '78" National Stamp Exhibition; 40 c. 800th anniv of Lucerne; 70 c. 500th anniv of Printing at Geneva; 80 c. 2nd International Triennial Exhibition of Photography, Fribourg.

227 Stockalper Palace, Brig

228 Abbe Joseph Bovet (composer)

1978. Europa.

No.	Type	Description	Mint	Used
953	**227**	40 c. multicoloured	35	10
954	–	80 c. blue, brown & black	70	50

DESIGN: 80 c. Old Diet Hall, Berne.

1978. Pro Patria. Swiss Castles (3rd series). As T **218**.

No.	Type	Description	Mint	Used
955		20 c. + 10 c. Hagenwil, Thurgau	25	25
956		40 c. + 20 c. Burgdorf, Berne	40	20
957		70 c. + 30 c. Tarasp, Graubunden	1·00	1·25
958		80 c. + 40 c. Chillon, Vaud	1·10	1·25

1978. Celebrities.

No.	Type	Description	Mint	Used
959	**228**	20 c. green	15	10
960	–	40 c. purple	35	10
961	–	70 c. grey	1·10	1·25
962	–	80 c. blue	2·50	2·75

DESIGNS: 40 c. Henri Dunant (founder of Red Cross); 70 c. Carl Gustav Jung (psychiatrist); 80 c. Auguste Piccard (physicist).

229 Worker wearing Goggles

1978. Safety at Work. Multicoloured.

No.	Type	Description	Mint	Used
963		40 c. Type **229**	40	15
964		40 c. Worker wearing respirator	40	15
965		40 c. Worker wearing safety helmet	40	15

230 Arms of Switzerland and Jura

1978. Creation of Canton of Jura.

No.	Type	Description	Mint	Used
966	**230**	40 c. red, black & ochre	35	10

231 Rainer Maria Rilke (writer)

232 Othmar H. Ammann and Verrazano Narrows Bridge

1979. Celebrities.

No.	Type	Description	Mint	Used
967	**231**	20 c. green	15	10
968	–	40 c. red	35	10
969	–	70 c. brown	60	50
970	–	80 c. blue	70	50

DESIGNS: 40 c. Paul Klee (artist); 70 c. Herman Hesse (novelist and poet); 80 c. Thomas Mann (novelist).

1979. Publicity Issue. Multicoloured.

No.	Type	Description	Mint	Used
971		20 c. Type **232**	15	10
972		40 c. Target and marker	30	10
973		70 c. Hot-air balloon "Esperanto"	70	55
974		80 c. Aircraft tail fins	80	60

SUBJECTS: 20 c. Birth centenary of O. H. Ammann (engineer); 40 c. 50th Federal Riflemen's Festival, Lucerne; 70 c. World Esperanto Congress, Lucerne; 80 c. Basel-Mulhouse Airport.

233 Old Letter Box, Basel

234 Gold Stater

1979. Europa.

No.	Type	Description	Mint	Used
975	**233**	40 c. multicoloured	35	10
976	–	80 c. blue, lt blue & ochre	75	70

DESIGN: 80 c. Alpine relay station on the Jungfraujoch.

1979. Pro Patria. Swiss Castles (4th series). As T **218**. Multicoloured.

No.	Type	Description	Mint	Used
977		20 c. + 10 c. Oron, Vaud	25	25
978		40 c. + 20 c. Spiez, Berne	40	15
979		70 c. + 30 c. Porrentruy, Jura	90	90
980		80 c. + 40 c. Rapperswil, St. Gallen	1·10	1·10

1979. Publicity Issue. Multicoloured.

No.	Type	Description	Mint	Used
981		20 c. Type **234**	15	10
982		40 c. Child on dove (horiz)	35	10
983		70 c. Morse key and satellite (horiz)	60	50
984		80 c. "Ariane" rocket	70	50

EVENTS: 20 c. Centenary of Swiss Numismatic Society; 40 c. International Year of the Child; 70 c. 50th anniv of Swiss Radio Amateurs; 80 c. European Space Agency programme.

MINIMUM PRICE

The minimum price quoted is 10p which represents a handling charge rather than a basis for valuing common stamps. For further notes about prices, see introductory pages.

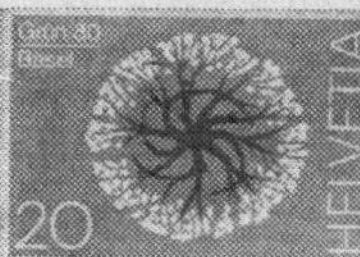

235 Tree in Blossom

236 Johann Konrad Kern (politician)

1980. Publicity Issue. Multicoloured.

No.	Type	Description	Mint	Used
985		20 c. Type **235**	15	10
986		40 c. Milk vessel	35	10
987		70 c. Winterthur Town Hall	60	50
988		80 c. "Pic-Pic" motor car	80	65

SUBJECTS: 20 c. "Grun 80" Horticultural and Landscape Gardening Exhibition, Basel; 40 c. 50th anniv of Swiss Arts and Crafts Centre; 70 c. Centenary of Society for Swiss Art History; 80 c. 50th International Motor Show, Geneva.

1980. Europa.

No.	Type	Description	Mint	Used
989	**236**	40 c. flesh, black & pink	35	10
990	–	80 c. flesh, black & blue	70	60

DESIGN: 80 c. Gustav Adolf Hasler (communications pioneer).

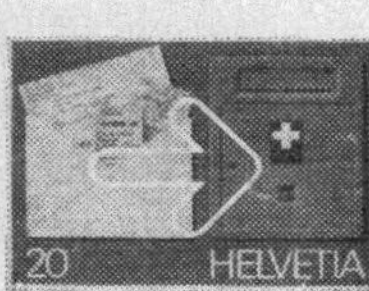

237 Mason and Carpenter

238 Girocheque and Letter Box

1980. Pro Patria. Trade and Craft Signs. Mult.

No.	Type	Description	Mint	Used
991		20 c. + 10 c. Type **237**	25	25
992		40 c. + 20 c. Barber	45	15
993		70 c. + 30 c. Hatter	90	1·00
994		80 c. + 40 c. Baker	1·10	1·10

1980. Swiss P.T.T. Services.

No.	Type	Description	Mint	Used
995	**238**	20 c. multicoloured	15	10
996	–	40 c. multicoloured	40	10
997	–	70 c. brown, blk & lilac	65	50
998	–	80 c. multicoloured	80	55

DESIGNS: 40 c. Postbus; 70 c. Transfer roller (50th anniv of P.T.T. postage stamp printing office); 80 c. Flowers and telephone (centenary of telephone in Switzerland.

239 Weather Chart

1980. Publicity. Multicoloured.

No.	Type	Description	Mint	Used
999		20 c. Type **239**	15	10
1000		40 c. Figures and cross	35	10
1001		80 c. Motorway sign	90	90

SUBJECTS: 20 c. Centenary of Swiss Meteorological Office; 40 c. Centenary of Swiss Trades Union Federation; 80 c. Opening of St. Gotthard road tunnel.

240 Granary from Kiesen

1981. Publicity Issue. Multicoloured.

No.	Type	Description	Mint	Used
1002		20 c. Type **240**	15	10
1003		40 c. Disabled figures	35	10
1004		70 c. "The Parish Clerk" (Albert Anker) (vert)	70	70
1005		80 c. Theodolite	75	55
1006		110 c. Tail of DC9-81	1·00	85

SUBJECTS: 20 c. Ballenberg Open-air Museum; 40 c. International Year of Disabled Persons; 70 c. 150th birth anniv of Albert Anker (artist); 80 c. 16th International Federation of Surveyors Congress, Montreux; 110 c. 50th anniv of Swissair.

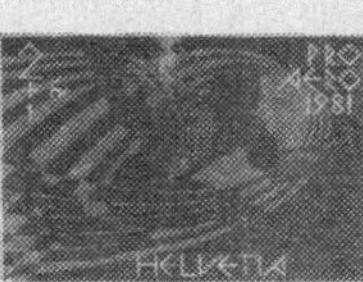

241 Figure leaping from Earth

242 Dancing Couple

1981. 50th Anniv of Swissair.

No.	Type	Description	Mint	Used
1007	**241**	2 f. + 1 f. lilac, violet and yellow	2·00	2·00

1981. Europa. Multicoloured.

No.	Type	Description	Mint	Used
1008		40 c. Type **242**	35	10
1009		80 c. Stone putter	80	70

243 Aarburg Post Office Sign, 1685

244 Seal of Fribourg

1981. Pro Patria. Postal Signs. Multicoloured.

1010 20 c. + 10 c. Type **243** . . . 30 30

1011 40 c. + 20 c. Mail coach sign of Fribourg Cantonal office 50 20

1012 70 c. + 30 c. Gordola post office sign (Ticino Cantonal Post) 90 95

1013 80 c. + 40 c. Splugen post office sign . . . . 1·10 1·10

1981. 500th Anniv of Covenant of Stans.

1014 **244** 40 c. red, black & brown 35 15

1015 – 40 c. green, black & red . 35 15

1016 – 80 c. brown, black & bl . 70 60

DESIGNS: 40 c. (No. 1015) Seal of Solothurn; 80 c. Old Town Hall, Stans.

245 Voltage Regulator from Jungfrau Railway's Power Station

1981. Publicity Issue. Multicoloured.

1017 20 c. Type **245** 20 10

1018 40 c. Crossbow quality seal . 40 10

1019 70 c. Group of youths . . . 70 60

1020 1 f. 10 Mosaic . . . . 1·00 85

SUBJECTS: 20 c. Opening of Technorama of Switzerland, Winterthur (museum of science and technology); 40 c. 50th anniv of Organization for Promotion of Swiss Products and Services; 70 c. 50th anniv of Swiss Association of Youth Organizations; 1 f. 10, Restoration of St. Peter's Cathedral, Geneva.

246 "C 4/5" Class Steam Locomotive

1982. Centenary of St. Gotthard Railway.

1021 **246** 40 c. black and purple . 35 20

1022 – 40 c. multicoloured . . . 35 20

DESIGN: No. 1022, "Re 6/6" class electric locomotive.

247 Hoteliers Association Emblem

1982. Publicity Issue. Multicoloured.

1023 20 c. Type **247** 15 10

1024 40 c. Flag formed by four 'Fs' 35 10

1025 70 c. Gas flame encircling emblem 60 50

1026 80 c. Lynx and scientific instruments 70 50

1027 110 c. Retort . . . . 1·00 75

SUBJECTS: 20 c. Centenary of Swiss Hoteliers Association; 40 c. 150th anniv of Swiss Gymnastics Association; 70 c. 50th anniv of International Gas Union; 80 c. 150th anniv of Natural History Museum, Berne; 110 c. Centenary of Swiss Society of Chemical Industries.

248 "Swearing Oath of Eternal Fealty, Rutli Meadow" (detail of mural, Heinrich Danioth)

1982. Europa. Multicoloured.

1028 40 c. Type **248** 50 10

1029 80 c. Treaty of 1291 founding Swiss Confederation . . . 85 65

249 "The Sun", Willisau

250 "Aquarius" and Old Berne

1982. Pro Patria. Inn Signs (1st series). Multicoloured.

1030 20 c. + 10 c. Type **249** . . . 30 30

1031 40 c. + 20 c. "On the Wave", St. Saphorin 55 20

1032 70 c. + 30 c. "The Three Kings", Rheinfelden . . . 90 1·00

1033 80 c. + 40 c. "The Crown", Winterhur . . . . 1·00 1·00

See also Nos. 1056/9.

1982. Signs of the Zodiac and Landscapes.

1034 **250** 1 f. multicoloured . . . 80 10

1035 – 1 f. 10 brown, bl & vio 90 10

1036 – 1 f. 20 green, bl & brn . 1·00 10

1036a – 1 f. 40 multicoloured . 1·10 75

1037 – 1 f. 50 deep blue, blue and orange . . . . 1·25 15

1038 – 1 f. 60 multicoloured . 1·60 75

1039 – 1 f. 70 blue, brown and turquoise . . . . . . 1·40 10

1040 – 1 f. 80 brown, green and deep green . . . . . 1·50 35

1041 – 2 f. blue, brown & dp bl 2·25 1·25

1042 – 2 f. blue, brown & dp bl 1·60 20

1042a – 2 f. 50, red, green and deep green . . . . . . 2·00 35

1043 – 3 f. red, green & black 2·40 15

1044 – 4 f. green, violet & pur 3·25 40

1045 – 4 f. 50 ochre, blue and brown . . . . 3·75 60

DESIGNS: 1 f. 10, "Pisces" and Nax near Sion; 1 f. 20, "Aries" and the Graustock, Obwalden; 1 f. 40, "Gemini" and Bischofszell; 1 f. 50, "Taurus" and Basel Cathedral; 1 f. 60, "Gemini" and Schonengrund; 1 f. 70, "Cancer" and Wetterhorn; 1 f. 80, "Leo" and Areuse Gorge; 2 f. (1041), "Virgo" and Aletsch Glacier; 2 f. (1042), "Virgo" and Schwarzsee above Zermatt; 2 f. 50, "Libra" and Fechy; 3 f. "Scorpio" and Corippo; 4 f. "Sagittarius" and Glarus; 4 f. 50, "Capricorn" and Schuls.

251 Articulated Tram

1982. Publicity Issue. Multicoloured.

1046 20 c. Type **251** 20 15

1047 40 c. Salvation Army singer and guitarist 40 10

1048 70 c. Dressage rider 75 55

1049 80 c. Emblem 80 50

SUBJECTS: 20 c. Centenary of Zurich trams; 40 c. Centenary of Salvation Army in Switzerland; 70 c. World Dressage Championship, Lausanne; 80 c. 14th International Water Supply Association Congress, Zurich.

252 Perch

253 Jost Burgi's Celestial Globe, 1594

1983. Publicity Issue. Multicoloured.

1050 20 c. Type **252** 20 10

1051 40 c. University of Zurich . . 40 10

1052 70 c. Teleprinter tape forming "JP" 70 50

1053 80 c. Micrometer and cycloidal computer drawing 80 50

EVENTS: 20 c. Centenary of Swiss Fishing and Pisciculture Federation; 40 c. 150th anniv of University of Zurich; 70 c. Centenary of Swiss Journalists' Federation; 80 c. Centenary of Swiss Machine Manufacturers' Association.

1983. Europa.

1054 **253** 40 c. orange, pink and brown 35 10

1055 – 80 c. green, blue & blk . 70 60

DESIGN: 80 c. Niklaus Riggenbach's rack and pinion railway, 1871.

1983. Pro Patria. Inn Sings (2nd series). As T **249**. Multicoloured.

1056 20 c. + 10 c. "The Lion", Heimiswil 30 30

1057 40 c. + 20 c. "The Cross", Sachseln 60 20

1058 70 c. + 30 c. "The Jug", Lenzburg Castle 95 95

1059 80 c. + 40 c. "The Cavalier", St. George . . . . 1·10 1·00

254 Seal, 1832–48

255 Gallo-Roman Capital, Martigny

1983. 150th Anniv of Basel-Land Canton.

1060 **254** 40 c. multicoloured . . 35 10

1983. Publicity Issue.

1061 **255** 20 c. orange and black . 25 10

1062 – 40 c. multicoloured . . . 45 10

1063 – 70 c. multicoloured . . . 75 60

1064 – 80 c. multicoloured . . . 75 60

DESIGNS: 20 c. Type **255** (Bimillenary of Octodurus/Martigny); 40 c. Bernese shepherd-dog and Schwyz hunting dog (Centenary of Swiss Kennel Club); 70 c. Cyclists (Centenary of Swiss Cyclists and Motor Cyclists Federation); 80 c. Carrier pigeon and world map (World Communications Year).

256 Pre-stamp Cover, 1839

257 Bridge

1984. Publicity Issue. Multicoloured.

1065 25 c. Type **256** 25 15

1066 50 c. Collegiate Church clock and buildings 50 10

1067 80 c. Olympic rings and Lausanne 80 50

SUBJECTS: 25 c. National Stamp Exhibition, Zurich; 50 c. 1100th anniv of Saint-Imier; 80 c. Permanent headquarters of International Olympic Committee at Lausanne.

1984. Europa. 25th Anniv of European Posts and Telecommunications Conference.

1068 **257** 50 c. purple, red and crimson 40 10

1069 80 c. ultramarine, blue and deep blue 75 55

258 Hexagonal Stove from Rosenburg Mansion, Stans

260 Burning Match

1984. Pro Patria. Tiled Stoves. Multicoloured.

1070 35 c. + 15 c. Type **258** . . . 50 30

1071 50 c. + 20 c. Winterthur stove (by Hans Heinrich Pfau) Freuler Palace, Nafels . . . 70 20

1072 70 c. + 30 c. Box-stove (by Rudolf Stern) from Plaisance, Riaz . . . . 90 1·00

1073 80 c. + 40 c. Frame-modelled stove (by Leonard Racle) . 1·25 1·10

1984. Fire Prevention.

1075 **260** 50 c. multicoloured . . . 40 10

261 Railway Conductor's Equipment

262 Ernest Ansermet (orchestral conductor)

1985. Publicity Issue. Multicoloured.

1076 35 c. Type **261** (cent of Train Staff Association) 40 15

1077 50 c. Stone with Latin inscription (200 years of Rhaeto-Romanic culture) 50 10

1078 70 c. Rescue of man (cent of International Lake Geneva Rescue Society) 70 60

1079 80 c. Grande Dixence dam (International Large Dams Congress, Lausanne) . . . 80 60

1985. Europa. Music Year. Multicoloured.

1080 50 c. Type **262** 50 10

1081 80 c. Frank Martin (composer) 85 60

263 Music Box, 1895

1985. Pro Patria. Musical Instruments. Mult.

1082 25 c. + 10 c. Type **263** . . . 35 35

1083 35 c. + 15 c. 18th - century box rattle 50 50

1084 50 c. + 20 c. Emmental necked zither (by Peter Zaugg), 1828 65 20

1085 70 c. + 30 c. Drum, 1571 . . 1·00 1·00

1086 80 c. + 40 c. 20th - century diatonic accordion . . . . 1·25 1·00

264 Baker

1985. Publicity Issue. Multicoloured.

1087 50 c. Type **264** (centenary of Swiss Master Bakers' and Confectioners' Federation) 50 10

1088 70 c. Cross on abstract background (50th anniv of Swiss Radio International) 70 60

1089 80 c. Geometric pattern and emblem (Postal, Telegraph and Telephone International World Congress, Interlaken) 80 70

265 Intertwined Ropes

1986. Publicity Issue.

1090 **265** 35 c. multicoloured . . . 35 15

1091 – 50 c. deep brown, brown and red 15 10

1092 – 80 c. orange, green and black 80 60

1093 – 90 c. multicoloured . . . 90 60

1094 – 1 f. 10 multicoloured . . 1·10 95

DESIGNS: 35 c. Type **265** (50th anniv of Swiss Workers' Relief Organization); 50 c. Battle site on 1698 map (600th anniv of Battle of Sempach); 80 c. Statuette of Mercury (2000th anniv of Roman Chur); 90 c. Gallic head (2000th anniv of Vindonissa); 1 f. 10, Roman coin of Augustus (2000th anniv of Zurich).

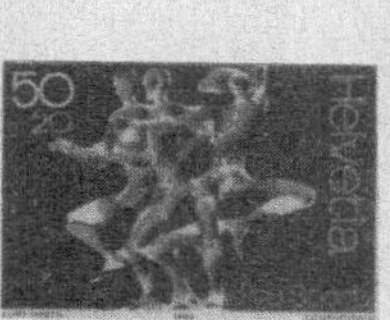

266 Sportsman

267 Woman's Head

1986. Pro Sport.

1095 **266** 50 c. + 20 c. multicoloured 70 50

1986. Europa. Multicoloured.

1096 50 c. Type **267** 50 10

1097 90 c. Man's head 90 60

268 "Bridge in the Sun" (Giovanni Giacometti)

269 Franz Mail Van

1986. Pro Patria. Paintings. Multicoloured.

1098 35 c. + 15 c. Type **268** . . . 50 30

1099 50 c. + 20 c. "The Violet Hat" (Cuno Amiet) 70 20

1100 80 c. + 40 c. "After the Funeral" (Max Buri) . . . 1·10 1·10

1101 90 c. + 40 c. "Still Life" (Felix Vallotton) . . . . 1·25 1·10

1986. The Post Past and Present.

1102 **269** 5 c. yellow, purple & red 10 10

1103 – 10 c. deep green, green and orange 10 10

1104 – 20 c. orange, brown & bl 20 15

1105 – 25 c. deep blue, blue and yellow 25 10

1106 – 30 c. grey, black & yell 25 15

1107 – 35 c. lake, red and yellow 30 15

1108 – 45 c. blue, black & brn . 40 20

1109 – 50 c. violet, green & pur 45 10

1110 – 60 c. orange, yell & brn 55 20

1111 – 75 c. grn, dp grn & red . 70 45

1112 – 80 c. indigo, blue & brn 75 25

1113 – 90 c. deep green, brown and green 80 25

DESIGNS: 10 c. Mechanized parcel sorting; 20 c. Mule post; 25 c. Letter cancelling machine; 30 c. Stagecoach; 35 c. Post Office counter clerk; 45 c. Paddle-steamer "Stadt Luzern", 1830s; 50 c. Postman; 60 c. Loading mail bags onto airplane; 75 c. 17th-century mounted courier; 80 c. Town postman, 1900s; 90 c. Interior of railway mail sorting carriage.

270 Stylized Doves (International Peace Year)

1986. Publicity Issue. Multicoloured.

1115 35 c. Type **270** 35 20
1116 50 c. Sun behind snow-covered tree (50th anniv of Swiss Winter Relief Fund) . . . 45 10
1117 80 c. Symbols of literature and art (cent of Berne Convention for protection of literary and artistic copyright) 85 70
1118 90 c. Red Cross, Red Crescent and symbols of aggression (25th Int Red Cross Conference meeting, Geneva) 95 70

271 Mobile Post Office

1987. Publicity Issue. Multicoloured.

1119 35 c. Type **271** (50th anniv of mobile post offices) 40 20
1120 50 c. Lecturers of the seven faculties (450th anniv of Lausanne University) . . . 45 10
1121 80 c. Profile, maple leaf and logarithmic spiral (150th anniv of Swiss Engineers' and Architects' Association) . . 90 80
1122 90 c. Boeing 747-300/400 airliner and electric train (Geneva Airport rail link) 1·00 80
1123 1 f. 10 Symbolic figure and water (2000th anniv of Baden thermal springs) . . . . . 1·25 1·25

272 "Scarabaeus" (Bernhard Luginbuhl)

1987. Europa. Sculpture. Multicoloured.

1124 50 c. Type **272** 50 10
1125 90 c. "Carnival Fountain", Basel (Jean Tinguely) . . . 90 85

273 Wall Cabinet, 1764

1987. Pro Patria. Rustic Furniture. Multicoloured.

1126 35 c. + 15 c. Type **273** . . . 70 50
1127 50 c. + 20 c. 16th-century chest 85 70
1128 80 c. + 40 c. Cradle, 1782 . 1·25 1·40
1129 90 c. + 40 c. Wardrobe, 1698 1·25 1·50

274 Butcher cutting Chops

277 Society Emblem

1988. Publicity Issue. Multicoloured.

1139 25 c. Type **277** (cent of Swiss Women's Benevolent Society) 35 20
1140 35 c. Brushing woman's hair (centenary of Swiss Master Hairdressers' Association) 40 25
1141 50 c. St. Fridolin banner and detail of Aegidius Tschudy's manuscript (600th anniv of Battle of Naefels) 50 10
1142 80 c. Map and farming country seen from Beromunster radio tower (European Campaign for Rural Areas) 80 80
1143 90 c. Girl playing shawm (50th anniv of Lucerne Int Music Festival) . . . . 1·00 90

278 Junkers Ju 52/3m flying past Matterhorn

279 Rudolf von Neuenburg

1988. 50th Anniv of Pro Aero Foundation.

1144 **278** 140 c. + 60 c. mult . . 2·75 2·75

1988. Pro Patria. Minnesingers. Multicoloured.

1145 35 c. + 15 c. Type **279** . . . 65 50
1146 50 c. + 20 c. Rudolf von Rotenburg 85 25
1147 80 c. + 40 c. Johannes Hadlaub 1·40 1·40
1148 90 c. + 40 c. Hardegger . . 1·60 1·40

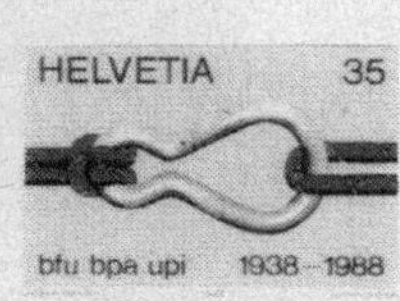

280 Arrows on Map of Europe

281 Snap Link

1988. Europa. Transport and Communications.

1149 **280** 50 c. bistre, emerald and green 50 10
1150 – 90 c. lilac, green and vio 1·00 80

DESIGN: 90 c. Computer circuit on map of Europe.

1988. Publicity Issue. Multicoloured.

1151 35 c. Type **281** (50th anniv of Swiss Accident Prevention Office) 40 25
1152 50 c. Drilling letters (cent of Swiss Metalworkers' and Watchmakers' Association) 50 10
1153 80 c. Triangulation pyramid, theodolite and map (150th anniv of Swiss Federal Office of Topography) 90 80
1154 90 c. International Red Cross Museum, Geneva (inauguration) . . . . . . 1·00 90

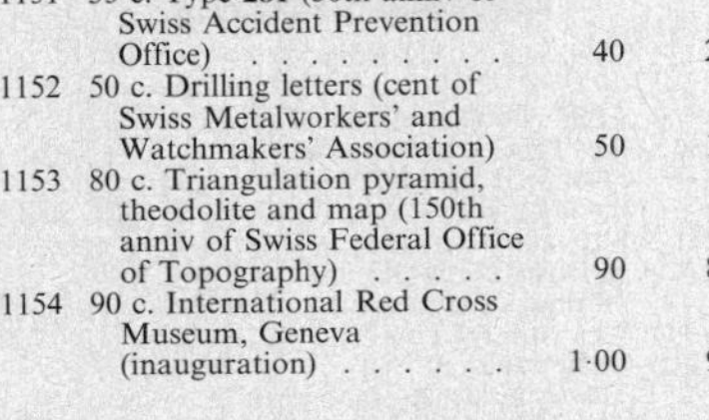

282 "Meta" (Jean Tinguely)

1988. Modern Art.

1155 **282** 90 c. multicoloured . . 4·00 4·00

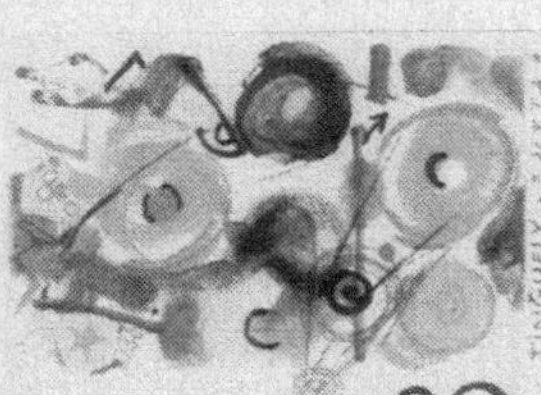

283 Army Postman

1989. Publicity Issue. Multicoloured.

1156 25 c. Type **283** (centenary of Swiss Army postal service) 30 20
1157 35 c. Fontaine du Sauvage and Porte au Loup, Delemont (700th anniv of granting of town charter) 35 30
1158 50 c. Eye and composite wheel (cent of Public Transport Association) 50 10
1159 80 c. Diesel train on viaduct (centenary of Rhaetian railway) 90 80
1160 90 c. St. Bernard dog and hospice (2000th anniv of Great St. Bernard Pass) . . 1·00 80

284 King Friedrich II presenting Berne Town Charter (Bendicht Tschachtlan Chronicle)

285 Hopscotch

1989. Pro Patria. Medieval Chronicles. Mult.

1161 35 c. + 15 c. Type **284** . . . 60 50
1162 50 c. + 20 c. Adrian von Bubenberg watching troops entering Murten (Diebold Schilling's Berne Chronicle) 80 20
1163 80 c. + 40 c. Messenger presenting missive to Council of Zurich (Gerold Edlibach Chronicle) . . . . 1·40 1·40
1164 90 c. + 40 c. Schilling presenting Chronicle to Council of Lucerne (Diebold Schilling's Lucerne Chronicle) 1·50 1·40

1989. Europa. Children's Games. Multicoloured.

1165 50 c. Type **285** 50 15
1166 90 c. Blind-man's buff 90 85

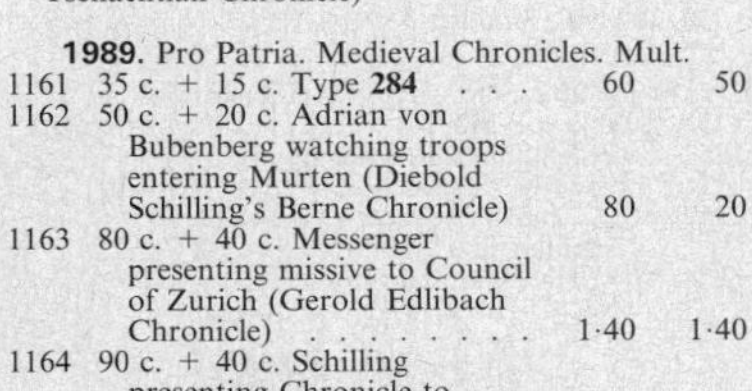

286 Bricklayer

287 Testing Device

1989. Occupations.

1168 **286** 2 f. 75 purple, blk & yell 2·50 50
1169 – 2 f. 80 yellow, brn & bl . 2·50 50
1170 – 3 f. blue, dp brn & brn . 3·00 60
1171 – 3 f. 60 orge, brn & pur . 3·25 70
1173 – 3 f. 75 deep green, green and light green . . . . 1·40 75
1173a – 4 f. multicoloured . . . 4·75 1·40
1174 – 5 f. ultram, stone & bl . 4·75 1·40
1175 – 5 f. 50 grey, red and mauve 5·00 1·00

DESIGNS: 2 f. 80, Cook; 3 f. Carpenter; 3 f. 60, Pharmacist; 3 f. 75, Fisherman; 4 f. Vine grower; 5 f. Cheesemaker; 5 f. 50, Dress-maker.

1989. Publicity Issue. Multicoloured.

1181 35 c. Type **287** (cent of Swiss Electrotechnical Association) 40 20
1182 50 c. Family on butterfly (50th anniv of Swiss Travel Fund) 55 10
1183 80 c. "Wisdom" and "Science" (bronze statues) (centenary of Fribourg University) . . . 90 75
1184 90 c. Audio tape (1st anniv of National Sound Archives) 1·00 85
1185 1 f. 40 Bands of colour forming bridge (centenary of Inter-parliamentary Union) . . . 1·60 1·50

288 Exercises

1989. Pro Sport.

1186 **288** 50 c. + 20 c. multicoloured 85 75

289 1882 5 c. and 50 c. Stamps and Emblem

290 Cats

1990. Publicity Issue. Multicoloured.

1187 25 c. Type **289** (centenary of Union of Swiss Philatelic Societies) 30 20
1188 35 c. Locomotive and control car (inauguration of Zurich Rapid Transit System) . . . 40 30
1189 50 c. Mountain farmer (50th anniv of Assistance for Mountain Communities) . . 55 10
1190 90 c. Ice hockey players (A-series World Ice Hockey Championships, Berne and Fribourg) 95 90

1990. Animals. Multicoloured.

1192 10 c. Cow 10 10
1197 50 c. Type **290** 45 10
1199 70 c. Rabbit 65 25
1200 80 c. Barn owl 85 45
1201 100 c. Horse and foal . . . 95 85
1202 120 c. Dog . . . . 1·10 1·00
1202a 150 c. Goats . . . . 1·50 50
1203 160 c. Turkey . . . . 1·50 50
1204 200 c. Chickens . . . . . . 2·00 1·75

291 Flyswats and Starch Sprinklers Seller

292 Lucerne Post Office

1990 Pro Patria. Street Criers. Engravings by David Herrliberger. Multicoloured.

1205 35 c. + 15 c. Type **291** . . . 65 50
1206 50 c. + 20 c. Clock seller . . 80 20
1207 80 c. + 40 c. Knife grinder . 1·25 1·40
1208 90 c. + 40 c. Couple selling pinewood sticks . . . . . 1·40 1·50

1990. Europa. Post Office Buildings. Mult.

1209 50 c. Type **292** 50 15
1210 90 c. Geneva Post Office . . 85 75

293 Conrad Ferdinand Meyer (writer)

294 Anniversary Emblem and Crosses

1990. Celebrities.

1211 **293** 35 c. black and green . . 40 25
1212 – 50 c. black and blue . . 50 15
1213 – 80 c. black and yellow . 80 75
1214 – 90 c. black and pink . . 80 80

DESIGNS: 50 c. Angelika Kauffmann (painter); 80 c. Blaise Cendrars (writer); 90 c. Frank Buchser (painter).

1990. 700th Anniv (1991) of Swiss Confederation (1st issue).

1215 50 c. Type **294** 50 15
1216 90 c. Emblem and crosses (different) 85 85

See also Nos. 1219/22 and 1224.

296 Figures on Jigsaw Pieces

1990. Population Census.

1218 **296** 50 c. multicoloured . . . 50 15

297 "700 JAHRE"

298 Alps and City Skyline

1991. 700th Anniv of Swiss Confederation (2nd issue). Multicoloured.

1219 50 c. Type **297** 45 15
1220 50 c. "700 ONNS" 45 15
1221 50 c. "700 ANS" 45 15
1222 50 c. "700 ANNI" 45 15

Nos. 1219/22 were printed together, se-tenant. forming a composite design of the Swiss cross in the centre.

1991. 800th Anniv of Berne.

1223 **298** 80 c. multicoloured . . . 75 40

299 Federal Palace, Berne, and Capitol, Washington

1991. 700th Anniv of Swiss Confederation (3rd issue). Swiss Emigration to U.S.A.

1224 **299** 160 c. multicoloured . . 1·50 80

275 Zug Clock Tower

1987. Publicity Issue. Multicoloured.

1130 35 c. Type **274** (centenary of Swiss Master Butchers' Federation) 40 25
1131 50 c. Profiles on stamps (50th anniv of Stamp Day) . . . 50 10
1132 90 c. Cheesemaker breaking up curds (centenary of Swiss Dairying Association) . . . 90 90

1987. Bicentenary of Tourism. Multicoloured.

1133 50 c. Type **275** 55 10
1134 80 c. St. Charles's church, Negrentino, Prugiasco/Blenio valley 85 80
1135 90 c. Witches Tower, Sion . . 95 80
1136 1 f. 40 Jorgenberg Castle, Waltensburg/Vuorz, Surselva 1·50 1·40

1987. Flood Victims Relief Fund. No. 1109 surch **7.9.87 + 50** and clasped hands.

1138 50 c. + 50 c. vio, grn & pur . 1·25 90

300 Jettison of "Ariane" Rocket Friction Protection Jacket

301 Abstract

1991. Europa. Europe in Space. Multicoloured.

1225 50 c. Type **300** 50 15
1226 90 c. Orbit of Halley's Comet, "Giotto" space probe and its trajectory 85 75

1991. Pro Patria. Modern Art. Multicoloured.

1227 50 c. + 20 c. Type **301** . . . 75 20
1228 70 c. + 30 c. Artist's monogram 1·00 1·00
1229 80 c. + 40 c. "Labyrinth" . . 1·25 1·25
1230 90 c. + 40 c. "Man and Beast" 1·40 1·50

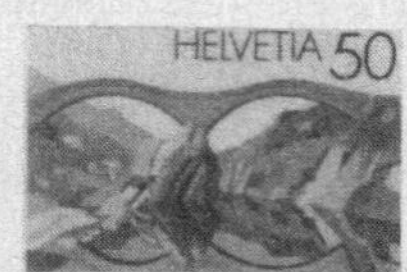

302 Stone Bridge, Lavertezzo

1991. Bridges. Multicoloured.

1231 50 c. Type **302** 50 15
1232 70 c. Wooden Neubrugg, Bremgarten 65 75
1233 80 c. Koblenz-Felsenau iron truss railway bridge 75 75
1234 90 c. Ganter concrete bridge, Simplon Pass 85 80

303 P.T.T. Employees

304 Lake Moesola

1991. Centenary of Swiss Postal, Telephone and Telegraph Officials' Union.

1235 **303** 80 c. multicoloured . . . 75 40

1991. Mountain Lakes.

1236 **304** 50 c. multicoloured . . . 45 15
1237 – 80 c. brown, red & pur 75 15

DESIGN: 80 c. Fishing boat moored at jetty on Melchsee.

305 Mouth of River Rhine

306 Map of Americas and "Santa Maria"

1992. Publicity Issue. Multicoloured.

1238 50 c. Type **305** (centenary of Treaty for International Regulation of the Rhine) 45 25
1239 80 c. Family (50th anniv of Pro Familia) 75 40
1240 90 c. Chemical formula and model of difluorobutane molecule (cent of International Chemical Nomenclature Conference, Geneva) 80 70

1992. Europa. 500th Anniv of Discovery of America by Columbus. Multicoloured.

1241 50 c. Type **306** 45 15
1242 90 c. Route map of first voyage and sketch for statue of Columbus (Vincenzo Vela) 80 70

307 Skier

308 1780s Earthenware Plate, Heimberg

1992. Sierre International Comics Festival. Multicoloured.

1243 50 c. Type **307** 45 15
1244 80 c. Mouse-artist drawing strip 75 40
1245 90 c. Love-struck man holding bunch of stamp-flowers behind back 80 70

1992. Pro Patria. Folk Art. Multicoloured.

1246 50 c. + 20 c. Type **308** . . . 65 20
1247 70 c. + 30 c. Paper cut-out by Johann Jakob Hauswirth 90 90
1248 80 c. + 40 c. Maplewood cream spoon, Gruyeres . . . . . 1·10 1·10
1249 90 c. + 40 c. Carnation from 1780 embroidered saddle cloth, Grisons . . . . . . 1·25 1·25

309 Flags and Alps

310 Clowns on Trapeze

1992. Alpine Protection Convention.

1250 **309** 90 c. multicoloured . . 80 70

1992. The Circus. Multicoloured.

1251 50 c. Type **310** 45 15
1252 70 c. Sealion with Auguste the clown 65 60
1253 80 c. Chalky the clown and elephant 75 40
1254 90 c. Harlequin and horse . 80 70

311 Sport Pictograms

1992. Pro Sport.

1255 **311** 50 c. + 20 c. black & bl 65 65

312 Train and Map

313 "A" (first class) Mail

1992. Centenary (1993) of Central Office for International Rail Carriage.

1256 **312** 90 c. multicoloured . . 80 70

1993.

1257 – 60 c. dp blue, yellow & bl 55 15
1258 **313** 80 c. red, orange and scarlet 75 40

DESIGN: 60 c. Lake Tanay.

314 Zurich and Geneva 1843 Stamps

315 Paracelsus (500th birth anniv) (after Augustin Hirschvogel)

1993. 150th Anniv of Swiss Postage Stamps. Multicoloured.

1259 60 c. Type **314** 55 15
1260 80 c. Postal cancellation (stamps for postage) 75 40
1261 100 c. Magnifying glass (stamp collecting) 95 85

1993. Publicity Issue.

1262 **315** 60 c. brown, grey & blue 55 15
1263 – 80 c. multicoloured . . 75 40
1264 – 180 c. multicoloured . . 1·75 1·60

DESIGNS—VERT: 80 c. Discus thrower (from Greek vase) (inauguration of Olympic Museum, Lausanne). HORIZ: 180 c. Worker's head (cent of International Metalworkers' Federation).

316 "Hohentwiel" (lake steamer) and Flags

317 Interior of Media House, Villeurbanne, France

1993. Lake Constance European Region.

1265 **316** 60 c. multicoloured . . 55 15

1993. Europa. Contemporary Architecture.

1266 **317** 60 c. blue, black & green 55 15
1267 – 80 c. red, black and grey 75 40

DESIGN: 80 c. House, Breganzona, Ticino.

318 Appenzell Dairyman's Earring

1993. Pro Patria. Folk Art. Multicoloured.

1268 60 c. + 30 c. Type **318** . . . 85 25
1269 60 c. + 30 c. Fluhli enamelled glass bottle, 1738 . . . . . 85 25
1270 80 c. + 40 c. Driving cows to summer pasture (detail of mural, Sylvestre Pidoux) . . 1·10 1·10
1271 100 c. + 40 c. Straw hat ornaments . . . . 1·25 1·25

319 "Work No. 095" (Emma Kunz)

320 Kapell Bridge and Water Tower, Lucerne

1993. Paintings by Swiss Women Artists. Mult.

1272 60 c. Type **319** 55 15
1273 80 c. "Great Singer Lilas Goergens" (Aloise) (33 × 33 mm) 75 40
1274 100 c. "Under the Rain Cloud" (Meret Oppenheim) (33 × 33 mm) 95 85
1275 120 c. "Four Spaces with Horizontal Bands" (Sophi Taeuber-Arp) (33 × 33 mm) 1·10 1·00

1993. Kapell Bridge Restoration Fund.

1276 **320** 80 c. + 20 c. carmine and red 95 95

321 Hieroglyphic, Cuneiform and Roman Scripts

1994. "Books and the Press" Exhibition, Geneva. Multicoloured.

1277 60 c. Type **321** 55 15
1278 80 c. Gothic letterpress script 75 40
1279 100 c. Modern electronic fonts 95 85

322 Athletes

1994. Publicity Issue. Multicoloured.,

1280 60 c. Type **322** (50th Anniv of National Sports School, Magglingen) 55 15
1281 80 c. Jakob Bernoulli (after Nicolas Bernoulli) and formula and diagram of the law of large numbers (International Mathematicians' Congress, Zurich) 75 40
1282 100 c. Heads, Unisource emblem, globe and flags (collaboration of Swiss, Dutch and Swedish telecommunications companies) 95 85
1283 180 c. Radar image, airliner and globe (50th anniv of I.C.A.O.) 1·75 1·60

323 Footballers

324 "Trieste" (bathyscaphe)

1994. World Cup Football Championship, U.S.A., and Centenary (1995) of Swiss Football Association.

1284 **323** 80 c. multicoloured . . . 75 40

1994. Europa. Discoveries and Inventions. Designs showing vehicles used by Auguste Piccard in stratospheric and deep-sea explorations. Multicoloured.

1285 60 c. Type **324** 65 15
1286 100 c. "F.N.R.S." (stratosphere balloon) . . . . 1·10 1·00

325 Neuchatel Weight-driven Clock (Jacques Matthey-Jonais)

326 Symbolic Condom

1994. Pro Patria. Folk Art. Multicoloured.

1287 60 c. + 30 c. Type **325** . . . 1·00 30
1288 60 c. + 30 c. Embroidered pomegranate on linen . . 1·00 30
1289 80 c. + 40 c. Mould for Krafli pastry . . . . 1·25 1·25
1290 100 c. + 40 c. Paper bird cradle mobile . . . . 1·50 1·50

1994. Anti-AIDS Campaign.

1291 **326** 60 c. multicoloured . . . 65 15

327 Simenon and his Home, Echandens Castle, Lausanne

1994. 5th Death Anniv of Georges Simenon (novelist).

1292 **327** 100 c. multicoloured . . 1·10 1·00

FRANK STAMPS

Issued to charity hospitals for free transmission of their mails.

F 21 — F 49 Deaconess

1911. With control figures at top.

F268 F 21 2 c. red and green . . . 10 15
F269 3 c. red and green . . . 2·00 25
F270 5 c. red and green . . . 60 10
F271 10 c. red and green . . . 80 10
F272 15 c. red and green . . 15·00 2·00
F273 20 c. red and green . . 2·75 40

1935. With or withour control figures.

F362B F 49 5 c. green . . . . . . 1·25 2·25
F363B – 10 c. violet . . . . . 1·00 2·00
F364B – 20 c. red . . . . . . 1·25 2·25

DESIGNS: 10 c. Sister of the Ingenbohl Order; 20 c. Henri Dunant (founder of Red Cross).

OFFICIAL STAMPS

1918. Optd **Industrielle Kriegswirtschaft**.

O308 20a 3 c. brown . . . . . . 4·25 15·00
O300 5 c. green . . . . . . 10·00 25·00
O310 7½ c. grey . . . . . . 5·50 14·00
O303 21 10 c. red on buff . . . 13·00 30·00
O304 15 c. violet on buff . . . 13·00 32·00
O313 17 20 c. yellow and red . . 9·00 30·00
O314 25 c. blue and dp blue . . 9·00 30·00
O315 30 c. green and brown . . 15·00 50·00

1938. Optd with Geneva Cross.

O381 52 3 c. olive 15 20
O382 – 5 c. green (No. 372) . . . 15 20
O383 – 10 c. purple (No. 373b) . . 1·00 40
O384 – 15 c. orange (No. 374) . . 35 1·25
O385 – 20 c. red (No. 375d) . . . 50 30
O386 – 25 c. brown (No. 376) . . 55 1·00
O387 – 30 c. blue (No. 377) . . . 75 75
O388 – 35 c. green (No. 378) . . 70 1·00
O389 – 40 c. grey (No. 379) . . . 70 50
O390 17 50 c. green and dp green . 80 1·00
O391 60 c. brown . . . . . . 1·25 1·50
O392 70 c. buff and violet . . . 75 3·00
O393 80 c. buff and grey . . . 1·25 2·00
O395 38 90 c. red & grn on grn . 1·60 2·50
O394 17 1 f. green and purple . . 1·50 2·25
O396 38 1 f. 20 red and lake on pink 1·75 3·00
O397 1 f. 50 red & blue on bl . 2·25 4·50
O398 – 2 f. red & black on grey . 2·40 5·00

1942. Optd **Officiel**. (a) Landscape designs of 1936.

O427 3 c. olive . . . . 30 1·25
O428 5 c. green 30 15
O430 10 c. brown 25 30
O431 15 c. orange . . . . . . 60 1·25
O432 20 c. red (Lake) 60 20
O433 25 c. brown . . . . 65 1·75
O434 30 c. blue . . . . 1·75 60
O435 35 c. green . . . . . . 1·75 2·00
O436 40 c. grey . . . . 1·10 45

(b) Historical designs of 1941.

O437 – 50 c. blue on green . . . 4·50 3·25
O438 68 60 c. brn on cinnamon . . 4·75 7·25
O439 – 70 c. purple on mauve . . 5·00 6·00
O440 – 80 c. black on grey . . . 1·25 1·10
O441 – 90 c. red on pink . . . 1·50 1·00
O442 – 1 f. green on green . . . 1·75 1·50
O443 – 1 f. 20 purple on grey . . 1·90 1·75
O444 – 1 f. 50 blue on buff . . 2·25 2·75
O445 – 2 f. red on pink . . . . 3·00 3·00

1950. Landscape designs of 1949 optd **Officiel**.

O522 107 5 c. orange 70 60
O523 – 10 c. green . . . . . . 1·25 60
O524 – 15 c. turquoise . . . . 11·00 11·00
O525 – 20 c. purple . . . . . 2·00 35
O526 – 25 c. red . . . . 5·00 6·00
O527 – 30 c. olive . . . . . . 3·00 2·00
O528 – 35 c. brown . . . . . 5·00 9·00
O529 – 40 c. blue . . . . . . 5·00 2·50
O530 – 50 c. grey . . . . . . 6·00 6·00
O531 – 60 c. green . . . . . 8·50 4·00
O532 – 70 c. violet . . . . . 22·00 16·00

For Swiss stamps overprinted for the use of officials of the League of Nations, International Labour Office and other special U.N. Agencies having their headquarters at Geneva, see subsection INTERNATIONAL ORGANIZATIONS SITUATED IN SWITZERLAND.

POSTAGE DUE STAMPS

D 10 — D 21 — D 38

1878.

D105 D 10 1 c. blue . . . . . . 1·25 75
D106 2 c. blue . . . . . . 1·25 75
D107B 3 c. blue . . . . . . 9·00 6·00
D108A 5 c. blue . . . . . . 12·00 5·00
D109B 10 c. blue . . . . . £130 5·00
D110B 20 c. blue . . . . . £150 3·00
D111B 50 c. blue . . . . . £300 9·50
D112A 100 c. blue . . . . . £400 10·00
D113A 500 c. blue . . . . . £350 15·00

The 1 c. has a rayed background behind the figure of value.

1883. Numerals in red.

D188F D 10 1 c. green 30 30
D189D 3 c. green . . . . . 2·75 2·75
D190F 5 c. green . . . . . 1·25 20
D191F 10 c. green . . . . . 2·75 25
D192F 20 c. green . . . . . 7·00 50
D193F 50 c. green . . . . . 11·00 1·90
D194F 100 c. green . . . . 12·00 1·50
D195D 500 c. green . . . . 95·00 11·00

The above were issued in a wide range of shades from pale turquoise to olive between 1883 and 1910. A detailed list of these appears in the Stanley Gibbons Part 8 (Italy and Switzerland) Catalogue.

1910.

D274 D 21 1 c. green and red . . 10 10
D275 3 c. green and red . . 10 10
D276 5 c. green and red . . 10 10
D277 10 c. green and red . . 60 10
D278 15 c. green and red . . 35 55
D279 20 c. green and red . . 11·00 10
D280 25 c. green and red . . 80 30
D281 30 c. green and red . . 65 25
D282 50 c. green and red . . 90 45

1916. Surch.

D299 D 21 5 c. on 3 c. red and green 10 20
D300 10 c. on 1 c. red and green . . . . 20 4·50
D301 10 c. on 3 c. red and green . . . . 20 1·00
D302 20 c. on 50 c. red and green . . . . 80 1·00

1924.

D332 D 38 5 c. red and olive . . 50 10
D333 10 c. red and olive . . 1·75 10
D334 15 c. red and olive . . 1·50 40
D335a 20 c. red and olive . . 3·00 80
D336 25 c. red and olive . . 1·75 35
D337 30 c. red and olive . . 1·75 40
D338 40 c. red and olive . . 2·40 40
D339 50 c. red and olive . . 2·40 50

1937. Surch.

D380 D 38 5 on 15 c. red & olive 75 3·25
D381 10 on 30 c. red & olive 75 1·00
D382 20 on 50 c. red & olive 1·50 4·00
D383 40 on 50 c. red & olive 2·50 10·00

D 54

1938.

D384 D 54 5 c. red 35 10
D385 10 c. red 65 10
D386 15 c. red . . . . 75 1·60
D387 20 c. red 85 10
D388 25 c. red . . . . 1·00 1·50
D389 30 c. red . . . . 1·25 75
D390 40 c. red . . . . 1·50 20
D391 50 c. red . . . . 2·00 1·75

"PRO JUVENTUTE" CHARITY STAMPS

PREMIUMS. All "Pro Juventute" stamps are sold at an additional premium which goes to Benevolent Societies. Until 1937 these premiums were not shown on the stamps, but were as follows: 2 c. for all 3 c. franking values; 5 c. for all 5, 7½, 10, 15 c. and 20 c. values and 10 c. for all 30 c. and 40 c. values.

From 1937, when the premium first appeared on the designs, we show it in the catalogue listing.

C 1 Helvetia and Matterhorn — C 2 Appenzell

1913. Children's Fund.

J1 C 1 5 c. green . . . . 3·00 3·75

1915. Children's Fund.

J1a C 2 5 c. green on buff . . . 4·00 4·75
J2 – 10 c. red on buff . . . . 95·00 60·00

DESIGN: 10 c. Girl of Lucerne.

C 4 Berne — C 6 Valais — C 9 Uri

1916. Children's Fund.

J3 – 3 c. violet on buff . . . . 6·00 23·00
J4 C 4 5 c. green on buff . . . . 11·00 4·50
J5 – 10 c. red on buff . . . . 35·00 40·00

DESIGNS: 3, 10 c. Girls of Freiburg and Vaud.

1917. Children's Fund.

J6 C 6 3 c. violet on buff . . . . 5·50 27·00
J7 – 5 c. green on buff . . . . 7·50 3·50
J8 – 10 c. red on buff . . . . 24·00 16·00

DESIGNS: 5 c. Man of Unterwalden; 10 c. Girl of Ticino.

1918. Children's Fund. Dated "1918".

J9 C 9 10 c. red, yellow and black on buff . . . . . . 8·50 8·00
J10 – 15 c. multicoloured on buff 10·00 5·00

ARMS: 15 c. Geneva.

1919. Children's Fund. As Type C **9** but dated "1919". Cream paper.

J11 7½ c. red, grey and black . . . 3·00 8·00
J12 10 c. green, red and black . . 3·00 8·00
J13 15 c. red, violet and black . . 4·00 4·00

ARMS: 7½ c. Nidwalden; 10 c. Vaud; 15 c. Obwalden.

1920. Children's Fund. As Type C **9** but dated "1920". Cream paper.

J14 7½ c. red, grey and black . . . 3·50 8·00
J15 10 c. blue, red and black . . 4·25 7·50
J16 15 c. red, blue, violet & blk . 3·00 2·75

ARMS: 7½ c. Schwyz; 10 c. Zurich; 15 c. Ticino.

1921. Children's Fund. As Type C **9** but dated "1921". Cream paper.

J17 10 c. red, green and black . . 75 1·75
J18 20 c. multicoloured . . . . . 2·00 1·75
J19 40 c. red, blue and black . . . 8·00 25·00

ARMS: 10 c. Valais; 20 c. Berne; 40 c. Switzerland.

1922. Children's Fund. As Type C **9** but dated "1922". Cream paper.

J20 5 c. orange, blue and black . . 75 3·75
J21 10 c. green and black . . . . 75 1·25
J22 20 c. violet, blue and black . . 75 1·25
J23 40 c. blue, red and black . . . 8·50 32·00

ARMS: 5 c. Zug; 10 c. Freiburg; 20 c. Lucerne; 40 c. Switzerland.

1923. Children's Fund. As Type C **9** but dated "1923". Cream paper.

J24 5 c. orange and black . . . . 35 1·75
J25 10 c. multicoloured . . . . . 35 1·00
J26 20 c. multicoloured . . . . . 35 1·00
J27 40 c. blue, red and black . . . 7·50 25·00

ARMS: 5 c. Basel; 10 c. Glarus; 20 c. Neuchatel; 40 c. Switzerland.

1924. Children's Fund. As Type C **9** but dated "1924".

J28 5 c. black and lilac 20 80
J29 10 c. red, green and black on cream 20 70
J30 20 c. black, yellow and red on cream 30 70
J31 30 c. red, blue and black on cream . . . . 1·40 6·00

ARMS: 5 c. Appenzell; 10 c. Solothurn; 20 c. Schaffhausen; 30 c. Switzerland.

1925. Children's Fund. As Type C **9** but dated "1925". Cream paper.

J32 5 c. green, black and violet . . 20 65
J33 10 c. black and green 20 50
J34 20 c. multicoloured 30 55
J35 30 c. red, blue and black . . . 1·10 5·50

ARMS: 5 c. St. Gall; 10 c. Appenzell-Ausser-Rhoden; 20 c. Graubunden; 30 c. Switzerland.

1926. Children's Fund. As Type C **9** but dated "1926". Cream paper.

J36 5 c. multicoloured 20 65
J37 10 c. green, black and red . . 20 55
J38 20 c. red, black and blue . . . 30 55
J39 30 c. blue, red and black . . . 1·10 5·50

ARMS: 5 c. Thurgau; 10 c. Basel; 20 c. Aargau; 30 c. Switzerland and Lion of Lucerne.

C 40 Forsaken Child — C 42 J. H. Pestalozzi

C 43 J. H. Pestalozzi

1927. Children's Fund. Dated "1927".

J40 C 40 5 c. pur & yell on grey . . 15 60
J41 – 10 c. grn & red on grn . . 15 20
J42 C 42 20 c. red 20 20
J43 C 43 30 c. blue and black . . 1·00 3·25

DESIGN—As Type C **40**: 40 c. Orphan at Pestalozzi School.

C 44 Lausanne — C 47 J. H. Dunant

1928. Children's Fund. Dated "1928".

J44 C 44 5 c. red, purple and black on buff 15 65
J45 – 10 c. red, green and black on buff 15 45
J46 – 20 c. black, yellow and red on buff 15 30
J47 C 47 30 c. blue and red . . . 1·40 3·00

DESIGNS—As Type C **44**: 10 c. Arms of Winterthur; 20 c. Arms of St. Gall.

C 48 Mt San Salvatore, Lake Lugano

1929. Children's Fund. Dated "1929".

J48 C 48 5 c. red and violet . . . 15 60
J49 – 10 c. blue and brown . . 15 25
J50 – 20 c. blue and red . . . 20 25
J51 – 30 c. blue . . . . 1·60 6·00

DESIGNS: 10 c. Mt. Titlis, Lake Engstlen; 20 c. Mt Lyskamm from Riffelberg; 30 c. Nicholas de Flue.

C 50 Freiburg — C 51 A. Bitzius—"Jeremias Gotthelf"

1930. Children's Fund. Dated "1930".

J52 C 50 5 c. blue, black and green on buff 15 70
J53 – 10 c. multicoloured on buff 15 40
J54 – 20 c. multicoloured on buff 20 40
J55 C 51 30 c. blue . . . . 1·50 3·75

ARMS—As Type C **51**: 10 c. Altdorf; 20 c. Schaffhausen.

C 52 St. Moritz and Silvaplana Lakes

1931. Children's Fund. Dated "1931".

J56 C 52 5 c. green 40 90
J57 – 10 c. violet 35 35
J58 – 20 c. lake 50 40
J59 – 30 c. blue . . . . 5·00 9·00

DESIGNS: 10 c. The Wetterhorn; 20 c. Lac Leman; 30 c. Alexandre Vinet.

C 54 Flag swinging — C 56 Vaud — C 59 A. von Haller

1932. Children's Fund. Dated "1932".

J60 C 54 5 c. red and green . . . 55 1·00
J61 – 10 c. orange . . . . . . 75 1·00
J62 – 20 c. red . . . . 75 1·00
J63 – 30 c. blue . . . . . . 2·40 4·75

DESIGNS: 10 c. Putting the weight; 20 c. Wrestlers; 30 c. Eugen Huber.

1933. Children's Fund. Dated "1933".

J64 C 56 5 c. green and buff . . . 40 80
J65 – 10 c. violet and buff . . . 40 40
J66 – 20 c. scarlet and buff . . 55 40
J67 – 30 c. blue . . . . 2·50 4·75

SWISS GIRL DESIGNS: Berne (10 c.); Ticino (20 c.); 30 c. Father Gregoire Girard.

1934. Children's Fund. Dated "1934".

J68 – 5 c. green and buff . . . 40 90
J69 – 10 c. violet and buff . . . 50 35
J70 – 20 c. red and buff . . . 50 35
J71 C 59 30 c. blue . . . . 2·40 5·00

SWISS GIRL DESIGNS—As Type C **56**: 5 c. Appenzell; 10 c. Valais; 20 c. Graubunden.

C 61 Stefano Franscini — C 62 H. G. Nageli

1935. Children's Fund. Dated "1935".

J72 – 5 c. green and buff . . . 35 1·00
J73 – 10 c. violet and buff . . . 45 40
J74 – 20 c. red and buff . . . 45 60
J75 C 61 30 c. blue . . . . 2·50 5·50

DESIGNS—As Type C **56**: Costumes of Basel (5 c.), Lucerne (10 c.) and Geneva (20 c.).

1936. Children's Fund.

J76 C 62 5 c. green 30 25
J77 – 10 c. purple and buff . . 30 35
J78 – 20 c. red and buff . . . 35 50
J79 – 30 c. blue and buff . . . 3·75 10·00

DESIGNS—As Type C **56**: Costumes of Neuchatel (10 c.), Schwyz (20 c.) and Zurich (30 c.).

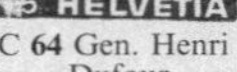

C 64 Gen. Henri Dufour — C 66 "Youth"

1937. Children's Fund.

J80 C 64 5 c. + 5 c. green 10 15
J81 – 10 c. + 5 c. purple . . . 10 15
J82 C 66 20 c. + 5 c. red, buff and silver 40 30
J83 – 30 c. + 10 c. blue, buff and silver . . . . 1·50 3·00

DESIGNS: 10 c. Nicholas de Flue; 30 c. as Type C 66, but girl's head facing other way.

C 67 Salomon Gessner — C 69 Gen. Herzog

1938. Children's Fund. Dated "1938".

J84 C 67 5 c. + 5 c. green 15 20
J85 – 10 c. + 5 c. vio & buff . 15 20
J86 – 20 c. + 5 c. red & buff 25 20
J87 – 30 c. + 10 c. blue & buff 1·60 3·00

SWISS GIRL DESIGNS as Type C 56: 10 c. St. Gall; 20 c. Uri; 30 c. Aargau.

1939. Children's Fund.

J88 C 69 5 c. + 5 c. green 15 20
J89 – 10 c. + 5 c. vio and buff 20 20
J90 – 20 c. + 5 c. red & buff . 35 30
J91 – 30 c. + 10 c. blue & buff 1·75 4·25

SWISS GIRL DESIGNS—As Type C 56: 10 c. Freiburg; 20 c. Nidwalden; 30 c. Basel.

C 71 Gottfried Keller — C 73 Johann Kasper Lavater

1940. Children's Fund. Dated "1940".

J92 C 71 5 c. + 5 c. green 10 20
J93 – 10 c. + 5 c. brn & buff 20 15
J94 – 20 c. + 5 c. red and buff 30 20
J95 – 30 c. + 10 c. blue & buff 1·50 6·00

SWISS GIRL DESIGNS—As Type C 56: 10 c. Thurgau; 20 c. Solothurn; 30 c. Zug.

1941. Children's Fund. Bicent of Birth of Lavater (philosopher) and of Death of Richard (clockmaker). Dated "1941".

J96 C 73 5 c. + 5 c. green 15 15
J97 – 10 c. + 5 c. brn & buff 25 20
J98 – 20 c. + 5 c. red & buff 30 25
J99 – 30 c. + 10 c. blue . . . 1·25 4·00

DESIGNS—Type C 56: 10 c., 20 c. Girls in costumes of Schaffhausen and Obwalden. As Type 73: 30 c. Daniel Jean Richard.

C 74 Niklaus Riggenbach (rack railway pioneer) — C 75 Emanuel von Fellenberg — C 76 Silver Thistle

1942. Children's Fund. Dated "1942".

J100 C 74 5 c. + 5 c. green . . . 20 30
J101 – 10 c. + 5 c. brn & buff 25 25
J102 – 20 c. + 5 c. red & buff 30 25
J103 – 30 c. + 10 c. blue . . . 1·50 4·00

DESIGNS: 10 c. and 20 c. Girls in costumes of Appenzell-Ausser-Rhoden and Glarus; 30 c. Conrad Escher von der Linth (statesman).

1943. Death Centenary of Philip Emanuel von Fellenberg (economist).

J104 C 75 5 c. + 5 c. green . . . 15 20
J105 C 76 10 c. + 5 c. green, buff and grey 25 15
J106 – 20 c. + 5 c. red, yellow and pink 30 15
J107 – 30 c. + 10 c. blue, light blue and black . . . 1·40 7·00

FLOWERS: As Type C 76: 20 c. Ladies slipper; 30 c. Gentian.

C 77 Numa Droz — C 78 Ludwig Forrer

1944. Birth Centenary of Droz (statesman).

J108 C 77 5 c. + 5 c. green . . . 20 15
J109 – 10 c. + 5 c. olive, yellow and green 20 15
J110 – 20 c. + 5 c. red, yellow and grey 40 15
J111 – 30 c. + 10 c. blue, grey and blue . . . . . . 1·50 6·50

DESIGNS: 10 c. Edelweiss; 20 c. Martagon lily; 30 c. "Aquilegia alpina".

1945. Children's Fund. Cent of Births of Ludwig Forrer (statesman) and Susanna Orelli (social reformer). Dated "1945".

J112 C 78 5 c. + 5 c. green . . . 30 25
J113 – 20 c. + 10 c. brown . 30 15
J114 – 20 c. + 10 c. red, pink and yellow 60 15
J115 – 30 c. + 10 c. blue, mauve and grey . . . . . . 2·50 6·50

DESIGNS: 10 c. Susanna Orelli; 20 c. Alpine dog rose; 30 c. Spring crocus.

C 79 Rudolf Toepffer — C 80 Jacob Burckhardt (historian)

1946. Death Centenary of Rudolf Toepffer (author and painter). Type C 79 and floral designs inscr "PRO JUVENTUTE 1946".

J116 C 79 5 c. + 5 c. green . . . 25 15
J117 – 10 c. + 10 c. green, grey and orange 30 15
J118 – 20 c. + 10 c. red, grey and yellow 40 15
J119 – 30 c. + 10 c. blue, grey and mauve . . . . . 2·75 6·00

DESIGNS: 10 c. Narcissus; 20 c. Houseleek; 30 c. Blue thistle.

1947. Children's Fund. Type C 80 and floral designs inscr "PRO JUVENTUTE 1947".

J120 C 80 5 c. + 5 c. green . . . 15 15
J121 – 10 c. + 10 c. black, yellow and grey 25 15
J122 – 20 c. + 10 c. brown, orange and grey . . . 35 15
J123 – 30 c. + 10 c. blue, pink and grey . . . . . . 2·00 4·75

DESIGNS: 10 c. Alpine primrose; 20 c. Orange lily; 30 c. Cyclamen.

C 81 Gen. U. Wille — C 82 Nicholas Wengi

1948. Children's Fund. Type C 81 and floral designs as Type C 76. Dated "1948".

J124 C 81 5 c. + 5 c. purple . . 25 10
J125 – 10 c. + 10 c. green, yellow and grey 40 15
J126 – 20 c. + 10 c. brown, red and buff 50 15
J127 – 40 c. + 10 c. blue, yellow and grey . . . . . . 2·50 4·75

FLOWERS: 10 c. Yellow foxglove; 20 c. Rust-leaved Alpine rose; 40 c. Lily of Paradise.

1949. Children's Fund. Type C 82 and floral designs inscr "PRO JUVENTUTRE 1949".

J128 C 82 5 c. + 5 c. red 20 10
J129 – 10 c. + 10 c. green, grey and yellow 30 15
J130 – 20 c. + 10 c. brown, blue and buff 35 15
J131 – 40 c. blue, mauve and yellow . . . . 2·75 5·00

DESIGNS: 10 c. "Pulsatilla alpina"; 20 c. Alpine clematis; 40 c. Superb pink.

C 83 General Theophil Sprecher von Bernegg — C 84 Red Admiral

1950. Children's Fund. Inscr "PRO JUVENTUTE 1950".

J132 C 83 5 c. + 5 c. brown 20 15
J133 C 84 10 c. + 10 c. mult . . . 50 20
J134 – 20 c. + 10 c. black, blue and orange 55 20
J135 – 30 c. + 10 c. brown, grey and mauve . . . . . 5·00 12·00
J136 – 40 c. + 10 c. yellow, brown and blue . . . 4·25 9·50

DESIGNS: 20 c. Clifden's nonpareil (moth); 30 c. Honey bee; 40 c. Moorland clouded yellow (butterfly).

C 85 Johanna Spyri (authoress) — C 86 "Portrait of a Boy" (Anker)

1951. Children's Fund. Type C 85 and various insects as Type C 84. Inscr "PRO JUVENTUTE 1951".

J137 C 85 5 c. + 5 c. purple . . . 20 10
J138 – 10 c. + 10 c. bl & grn 40 20
J139 – 20 c. + 10 c. black, cream and mauve 50 20
J140 – 30 c. + 10 c. black, orange and green . . . . . . 4·00 8·00
J141 – 40 c. + 10 c. brown, red and blue . . . . . . 4·00 7·50

INSECTS: 10 c. Banded agrion (dragonfly); 20 c. Scarce swallowtail (butterfly); 30 c. Orange-tip (butterfly); 40 c. Viennese emperor moth.

1952. Children's Fund. Type C 86 and insects as Type C 84. Inscr "PRO JUVENTUTE 1952".

J142 C 86 5 c. + 5 c. lake 20 15
J143 – 10 c. + 10 c. red, black and green 35 15
J144 – 20 c. + 10 c. cream, black and mauve 45 15
J145 – 30 c. + 10 c. blue, black and brown . . . . . 3·50 6·50
J146 – 40 c. + 10 c. buff, brown and blue . . . . . . 3·50 6·50

INSECTS: 10 c. Seven-spotted ladybird; 20 c. Marbled white (butterfly); 30 c. Chalk-hill blue (butterfly); 40 c. Oak eggar moth.

1953. Children's Fund. Portraits as Type C 86 and insects as Type C 84. Inscr "PRO JUVENTUTE 1953".

J147 5 c. + 5 c. red 20 10
J148 10 c. + 10 c. pink, brown and green 35 15
J149 20 c. + 10 c. black, buff and mauve 45 15
J150 30 c. + 10 c. blk, red & grn 3·50 7·50
J151 40 c. + 10 c. blue . . . . 4·25 5·50

DESIGNS: 5 c. "Portrait of a girl" (Anker); 10 c. Black arches moth; 20 c. Camberwell beauty (butterfly); 30 c. "Purpureus kaehleri" (longhorn beetle); 40 c. F. Hodler (self-portrait).

1954. Children's Fund. Portrait as Type C 85 and insects as Type C 84. Inscr "PRO JUVENTUTE 1954".

J152 5 c. + 5 c. brown 20 10
J153 10 c. + 10 c. multicoloured . 40 15
J154 20 c. + 10 c. multicoloured . 55 35
J155 30 c. + 10 c. multicoloured . 4·00 6·00
J156 40 c. + 10 c. multicoloured . 4·00 6·50

DESIGNS: 5 c. Jeremias Gotthelf (novelist, after A. Bitzius); 10 c. Garden tiger moth; 20 c. Buff-tailed bumble bee; 30 c. "Ascalaphus libelluloides" (owl-fly); 40 c. Swallowtail (butterfly).

1955. Children's Fund. Portrait as Type C 85 and insects as Type C 84. Inscr "PRO JUVENTUTE 1955".

J157 5 c. + 5 c. lake 20 15
J158 10 c. + 10 c. multicoloured 40 20
J159 20 c. + 10 c. multicoloured 45 20
J160 30 c. + 10 c. multicoloured 4·00 4·50
J161 40 c. + 10 c. black red & bl 4·00 4·50

DESIGNS: 5 c. C. Pictet-de-Rochemont; 10 c. Peacock (butterfly); 20 c. Great horntail; 30 c. Yellow tiger moth; 40 c. Apollo (butterfly).

1956. Children's Fund. Portrait as Type C 85 and insects as Type C 84. Inscr "PRO JUVENTUTE 1956".

J162 5 c. + 5 c. purple 20 10
J163 10 c. + 10 c. deep green, red and green 40 15
J164 20 c. + 10 c. multicoloured 50 20
J165 30 c. + 10 c. blue, indigo and yellow . . . . 2·40 4·25
J166 40 c. + 10 c. yell, brn & bl 2·50 4·50

DESIGNS: 5 c. Carlo Maderno (architect); 10 c. Common burnet (moth); 20 c. Lesser purple emperor (butterfly); 30 c. Blue ground beetle; 40 c. Large white (butterfly).

1957. Children's Fund. Portrait as Type C 85 and insects as Type C 84. Inscr "PRO JUVENTUTE 1957".

J167 5 c. + 5 c. purple 30 10
J168 10 c. + 10 c. multicoloured 40 15
J169 20 c. + 10 c. yellow, brown and mauve 45 15
J170 30 c. + 10 c. emerald, green and purple . . . . 2·40 4·00
J171 40 c. + 10 c. multicoloured 2·50 3·00

DESIGNS—VERT: 5 c. L. Euler (mathematician); 10 c. Clouded yellow (butterfly); 20 c. Magpie moth; 30 c. Rose chafer (beetle); 40 c. Rosy underwing (moth).

C 92 Albrecht von Haller (naturalist) — C 93 Pansy

1958. Children's Fund. Type C 92 and flowers as Type C 93. Inscr "PRO JUVENTUTE 1958".

J172 C 92 5 c. + 5 c. red 15 10
J173 C 93 10 c. + 10 c. yellow, brown and green . . 40 10
J174 – 20 c. + 10 c. mult . . 50 20
J175 – 30 c. + 10 c. mult . . 2·00 2·75
J176 – 40 c. + 10 c. mult . . 2·00 2·50

FLOWERS: 20 c. Chinese aster; 30 c. Morning Glory; 40 c. Christmas rose.

1959. Children's Fund. Portrait as Type C 92 and flowers as Type C 93. Inscr "PRO JUVENTUTE 1959".

J177 5 c. + 5 c. red 15 10
J178 10 c. + 10 c. multicoloured 30 15
J179 20 c. + 10 c. red, green and purple 40 15
J180 30 c. + 10 c. multicoloured 2·00 3·00
J181 50 c. + 10 c. multicoloured 2·00 2·75

DESIGNS: 5 c. Karl Hilty (lawyer); 10 c. Marsh marigold; 20 c. Poppy; 30 c. Nasturtium; 50 c. Sweet pea.

1960. Children's Fund. Portrait as Type C 92 and flowers as Type C 93. Inscr "PRO JUVENTUTE 1960".

J182 5 c. + 5 c. blue 20 10
J183 10 c. + 10 c. yellow, drab and green 30 10
J184 20 c. + 10 c. green, brown and mauve 40 20
J185 30 c. + 10 c. green, blue and brown . . . . 3·00 3·50
J186 50 c. + 10 c. yell, grn & bl . 3·00 3·00

DESIGNS: 5 c. Alexandre Calame (painter); 10 c. Dandelion; 20 c. Phlox; 30 c. Larkspur; 50 c. Thorn apple.

1961. Children's Fund. Portrait as Type C 92 and flowers as Type C 93. Inscr "PRO JUVENTUTE 1961".

J187 5 c. + 5 c. blue 15 10
J188 10 c. + 10 c. multicoloured . 20 10
J189 20 c. + 10 c. multicoloured . 25 15
J190 30 c. + 10 c. multicoloured . 1·50 2·25
J191 50 c. + 10 c. multicoloured . 1·75 2·25

DESIGNS: 5 c. J. Furrer (first President of Swiss Confederation); 10 c. Sunflower; 20 c. Lily-of-the-Valley; 30 c. Iris; 50 c. Silverweed.

C 97 "Child's World" — C 98 Mother and Child

1962. Children's Fund. 50th Anniv of Pro Juventute Foundation. Type C 97 and similar designs inscr "1912–1962" and Type C 98.

J192 – 5 c. + 5 c. multicoloured 15 10
J193 C 97 10 c. + 10 c. red & green 25 10
J194 C 98 20 c. + 10 c. mult . . 50 20
J195 – 30 c. + 10 c. red, mauve and yellow . . . . . 1·25 2·25
J196 – 50 c. + 10 c. yellow, brown and blue . . . 1·50 2·25

DESIGNS—As Type C 97: 5 c. Apple blossom; 30 c. "Child's World" (child in meadow); 50 c. Forsythia.

1963. Children's Fund. Portrait as Type C 86 and flowers as Type C 93. Inscr "PRO JUVENTUTE 1963".

J197 5 c. + 5 c. blue 10 35
J198 10 c. + 10 c. multicoloured 30 2·25
J199a 20 c. + 10 c. orange, green and red 90 50
J200 30 c. + 10 c. multicoloured 1·50 1·50
J201 50 c. + 10 c. purple, green and blue . . . . 1·50 1·50

DESIGNS: 5 c. "Portrait of a Boy" (Anker); 10 c. Oxeye daisy; 20 c. Geranium; 30 c. Cornflower; 50 c. Carnation.

1964. Children's Fund. Portrait as Type C 86 and flowers as Type C 93. Inscr "PRO JUVENTUTE 1964".

J202 5 c. + 5 c. blue 10 10
J203 10 c. + 10 c. orange, yellow and green 15 10
J204 20 c. + 10 c. rose, green and red 20 10
J205 30 c. + 10 c. purple, green and brown 50 50
J206 50 c. + 10 c. multicoloured . 65 60

DESIGNS: 5 c. "Portrait of a Girl" (Anker); 10 c. Daffodil; 20 c. Rose; 30 c. Red clover; 50 c. White water-lily.

C **101** Western European Hedgehogs — C **102** Roe Deer

1965. Children's Fund. Animals. Inscr "PRO JUVENTUTE 1965".
J207 C **101** 5 c. + 5 c. ochre, brown and red 10 10
J208 – 10 c. + 10 c. mult 10 10
J209 – 20 c. + 10 c. blue, brown and chestnut 30 10
J210 – 30 c. + 10 c. blue, black and yellow 35 40
J211 – 50 c. + 10 c. black brown and blue 50 50
ANIMALS: 10 c. Alpine marmots; 20 c. Red deer; 30 c. Eurasian badgers; 50 c. Arctic hares.

1966. Children's Fund. Animals. As Type C **101** but inscr "PRO JUVENTUTE 1966". Multicoloured.
J212 5 c. + 5 c. Stoat 10 10
J213 10 c. + 10 c. Eurasian red squirrel 10 10
J214 20 c. + 10 c. Red fox 30 10
J215 30 c. + 10 c. Brown hare 35 40
J216 50 c. + 10 c. Chamois 50 50

1967. Children's Fund. Animals. Inscr "PRO JUVENTUTE 1967". Multicoloured.
J217 10 c. + 10 c. Type C **102** 15 10
J218 20 c. + 10 c. Pine marten 20 10
J219 30 c. + 10 c. Ibex 30 10
J220 50 c. + 10 c. European otter 50 50

1968. Children's Fund. Birds. As Type C **102** but inscr "1968". Multicoloured.
J221 10 c. + 10 c. Capercaillie 25 10
J222 20 c. + 10 c. Bullfinch 35 10
J223 30 c. + 10 c. Woodchat shrike 50 15
J224 50 c. + 20 c. Firecrest 85 60

1969. Children's Fund. Birds. As Type C **102**. Inscr "1969". Multicoloured.
J225 10 c. + 10 c. Goldfinch 20 10
J226 20 c. + 10 c. Golden oriole 30 15
J227 30 c. + 10 c. Wallcreeper 40 15
J228 50 c. + 20 c. Jay 65 70

1970. Children's Fund. Birds. As Type C **102**. Inscr "1970". Multicoloured.
J229 10 c. + 10 c. Blue tits 15 15
J230 20 c. + 10 c. Hoopoe 25 10
J231 30 c. + 10 c. Great spotted woodpecker 35 15
J232 50 c. + 20 c. Great crested grebes 80 95

1971. Children's Fund. Birds. As Type C **102**. Inscr "1971". Multicoloured.
J233 10 c. + 10 c. Redstarts 25 20
J234 20 c. + 10 c. Bluethroats 45 10
J235 30 c. + 10 c. Peregrine falcon 60 20
J236 40 c. + 20 c. Mallards 1·40 1·10

C **104** "McGredy's Sunset" Rose — C **105** Chestnut

1972. Children's Fund. Roses. Multicoloured.
J237 10 c. + 10 c. Type C **104** 25 15
J238 20 c. + 10 c. "Miracle" 35 15
J239 30 c. + 10 c. "Papa Meilland" 60 15
J240 40 c. + 20 c. "Madame Dimitriu" 1·00 1·00
See also Nos. J258/61 and J279/82.

1973. Children's Fund. "Fruits of the Forest". Multicoloured.
J241 15 c. + 5 c. Type C **105** 15 10
J242 30 c. + 10 c. Cherries 30 10
J243 40 c. + 20 c. Blackberries 70 65
J244 60 c. + 20 c. Bilberries 90 95
See also Nos. J245/8, J249/53 and J254/7.

1974. Children's Fund. "Fruits of the Forest". Poisonous Plants. As Type C **105**. Inscr "1974". Multicoloured.
J245 15 c. + 10 c. Daphne 20 10
J246 30 c. + 20 c. Belladonna 40 10
J247 50 c. + 20 c. Laburnum 75 75
J248 60 c. + 25 c. Mistletoe 90 75

1975. Children's Fund. As Type C **105**. Inscr "1975". Multicoloured.
J249 10 c. + 5 c. "Post-Brent" (postman's hamper) 10 10
J250 15 c. + 10 c. Hepatica 20 15
J251 30 c. + 20 c. Rowan 35 10
J252 50 c. + 20 c. Yellow deadnettle 75 75
J253 60 c. + 25 c. Sycamore 80 75

1976. Children's Fund. "Fruits of the Forest". As Type C **105**. Inscr "1976". Multicoloured.
J254 20 c. + 10 c. Barberry 25 15
J255 40 c. + 20 c. Black elder 40 15
J256 40 c. + 20 c. Lime 40 15
J257 80 c. + 40 c. Lungwort 1·25 1·10

1977. Children's Fund. Roses. As Type C **104**. Inscr "1977". Multicoloured.
J258 20 c. + 10 c. "Rosa foetida bicolor" 25 10
J259 40 c. + 20 c. "Parfum de l'Hay" 45 10
J260 70 c. + 30 c. "R. foetida persiana" 1·00 1·00
J261 80 c. + 40 c. "R. centifolia muscosa" 1·10 1·10

C **106** Arms of Aarburg — C **107** Letter Balance

1978. Children's Fund. Arms of the Communes (1st series). Multicoloured.
J262 20 c. + 10 c. Type C **106** 25 10
J263 40 c. + 20 c. Gruyeres 45 10
J264 70 c. + 30 c. Castasegna 1·00 1·00
J265 80 c. + 40 c. Wangen 1·00 1·10
See also Nos. J266/9, J270/3 and J274/7.

1979. Children's Fund. Arms of the Communes (2nd series). As Type C **106**. Multicoloured.
J266 20 c. + 10 c. Cadro 20 15
J267 40 c. + 20 c. Rute 40 10
J268 70 c. + 30 c. Schwamendingen 90 95
J269 80 c. + 40 c. Perroy 1·00 95

1980. Children's Fund. Arms of the Communes. As Type C **106**. Multicoloured.
J270 20 c. + 10 c. Cortaillod 25 20
J271 40 c. + 20 c. Sierre 50 10
J272 70 c. + 30 c. Scuol 85 1·00
J273 80 c. + 40 c. Wolfenschiessen 1·00 1·00

1981. Children's Fund. Arms of the Communes. As Type C **106**. Multicoloured.
J274 20 c. + 10 c. Uffikon 30 20
J275 40 c. + 20 c. Torre 50 10
J276 70 c. + 30 c. Benken 85 1·00
J277 80 c. + 40 c. Preverenges 1·00 1·00

1982. Children's Fund. Type C **107** and roses as Type C **104**. Multicoloured.
J278 10 c. + 10 c. Type C **107** 20 20
J279 20 c. + 10 c. "La Belle Portugaise" 25 15
J280 40 c. + 20 c. "Hugh Dickson" 50 15
J281 70 c. + 30 c. "Mermaid" 90 90
J282 80 c. + 40 c. "Madame Caroline" 1·00 90

C **108** Kitchen Stove, c. 1850 — C **109** Heidi and Goat (Johanna Spyri)

1983. Children's Fund. Toys. Multicoloured.
J283 20 c. + 10 c. Type C **108** 30 20
J284 40 c. + 20 c. Rocking-horse, 1826 55 15
J285 70 c. + 30 c. Doll, c. 1870 1·00 95
J286 80 c. + 40 c. Steam locomotive, c. 1900 1·25 1·00

1984. Children's Fund. Characters from Children's Books. Multicoloured.
J287 35 c. + 15 c. Type C **109** 50 35
J288 50 c. + 20 c. Pinocchio and kite (Carlo Collodi) 75 10
J289 70 c. + 30 c. Pippi Longstocking (Astrid Lindgren) 1·00 1·00
J290 80 c. + 40 c. Max and Moritz on roof (Wilhelm Busch) 1·25 1·25

1985. Children's Fund. Characters from Children's Books. As Type C **109**. Multicoloured.
J291 35 c. + 15 c. Hansel, Gretel and Witch 50 35
J292 50 c. + 20 c. Snow White and the Seven Dwarfs 75 15
J293 80 c. + 40 c. Red Riding Hood and Wolf 1·00 1·00
J294 90 c. + 40 c. Cinderella and Prince Charming 1·25 1·25

C **110** Teddy Bear — C **111** Girl carrying Pine Branch and Candle

1986. Children's Fund. Toys. Multicoloured.
J295 35 c. + 15 c. Type C **110** 50 45
J296 50 c. + 20 c. Spinning top 65 70
J297 80 c. + 40 c. Steamroller 1·50 1·40
J298 90 c. + 40 c. Doll 1·60 1·50

1987. Children's Fund. Child Development. Preschool Age. Multicoloured.
J299 25 c. + 10 c. Type C **111** 40 30
J300 35 c. + 15 c. Mother breastfeeding baby 60 55
J301 50 c. + 20 c. Toddler playing with bricks 90 15
J302 80 c. + 40 c. Children playing in sand 1·50 1·40
J303 90 c. + 40 c. Father with child on his shoulders 1·50 1·50

C **112** Learning to Read — C **113** Community Work

1988. Children's Fund. Child Development. School Age. Multicoloured.
J304 35 c. + 15 c. Type C **112** 60 50
J305 50 c. + 20 c. Playing triangle 80 15
J306 80 c. + 40 c. Learning arithmetic 1·40 1·40
J307 90 c. + 40 c. Drawing 1·50 1·40

1989. Children's Fund. Child Development. Adolescence. Multicoloured.
J308 35 c. + 15 c. Type C **113** 60 50
J309 50 c. + 20 c. Young couple (friendship) 80 15
J310 80 c. + 40 c. Boy at computer screen (vocational training) 1·40 1·40
J311 90 c. + 40 c. Girl in laboratory (higher education and research) 1·50 1·50

C **114** Building Model Ship (hobbies) — C **115** Ramsons

1990. Child Development. Leisure Activities. Multicoloured.
J312 35 c. + 15 c. Type C **114** 60 50
J313 50 c. + 20 c. Youth group 80 15
J314 80 c. + 40 c. Sport 1·40 1·40
J315 90 c. + 40 c. Music 1·50 1·50

1991. Woodland Flowers. Multicoloured.
J316 50 c. + 25 c. Type C **115** 75 15
J317 70 c. + 30 c. Wood cranesbill 1·00 1·00
J318 80 c. + 40 c. Nettle-leaved bellflower 1·25 1·25
J319 90 c. + 40 c. Few-leaved hawkweed 1·50 1·50

C **116** Melchior (wood puppet)

1992. Christmas (J320) and Trees (others). Multicoloured.
J320 50 c. + 25 c. Type C **116** 70 15
J321 50 c. + 25 c. Beech 70 15
J322 70 c. + 30 c. Norway maple 90 90
J323 80 c. + 40 c. Pedunculate oak 1·10 1·10
J324 90 c. + 40 c. Norway spruce 1·25 1·25
Nos. J321/4 show silhouette of tree and close-up of its leaves and fruit.

C **117** Christmas Wreath — C **118** Candles

1993. Christmas (J325) and Woodland Plants (others). Multicoloured.
J325 60 c. + 30 c. Type C **117** 85 25
J326 60 c. + 30 c. Male fern 85 25
J327 80 c. + 40 c. Guelder rose 1·10 1·10
J328 100 c. + 50 c. "Mnium punctatum" 1·40 1·40

1994. Christmas (J329) and Fungi (others). Multicoloured.
J329 60 c. + 30 c. Type C **118** 1·00 20
J330 60 c. + 30 c. Wood blewit 1·00 20
J331 80 c. + 40 c. Red boletus 1·25 1·25
J332 100 c. + 50 c. Shaggy pholiota 1·60 1·60

INTERNATIONAL ORGANIZATIONS SITUATED IN SWITZERLAND

The stamps listed under this heading were issued by the Swiss Post Office primarily for the use of officials of the Organizations named, situated in Geneva.

These stamps could not be legitimately obtained unused before February 1944.

A. LEAGUE OF NATIONS.

1922. Optd **SOCIETE DES NATIONS.**
LN 1 **20a** 2½ c. green on buff — 20
LN 2 3 c. blue on buff — 5·00
LN 3 5 c. orange on buff — 3·00
LN 4 5 c. lilac on buff — 1·90
LN 5 5 c. purple on buff — 1·25
LN 5a 5 c. green on buff — 5·00
LN 6 7½ c. green on buff — 25
LN 7 **21** 10 c. green on buff — 30
LN 8 10 c. violet on buff — 85
LN 9 15 c. red on buff — 80
LN10 20 c. violet on buff — 4·00
LN11 20 c. red on buff — 1·00
LN13 25 c. red on buff — 60
LN14 25 c. brown on buff — 7·00
LN15 **17** 30 c. green and brown — 8·00
LN16 **21** 30 c. blue on buff — 3·50
LN17 **17** 35 c. yellow and green — 4·00
LN18 40 c. blue — 1·00
LN19 40 c. green and mauve — 4·00
LN20 50 c. green & dp grn — 4·00
LN21 60 c. brown 20·00 90
LN22a 70 c. buff and violet 1·00 2·00
LN23a 80 c. buff and grey 2·50 1·50
LN24a **38** 90 c. red and green on green — 3·00
LN25 **17** 1 f. green and purple — 4·00
LN26b **38** 1 f. 20 red and lake on pink 2·00 3·00
LN27a 1 f. 50 red and blue on blue 2·00 2·50
LN28a 2 f. red and black on grey 2·50 3·50
LN29 **22** 3 f. red — 20·00
LN29a **43** 3 f. brown — £140
LN30 – 5 f. blue (No. 285) — 40·00
LN32 – 10 f. pur (No. 286) — £100
LN33 – 10 f. grn (No. 331b) — £110

1932. International Disarmament Conference. Optd **SOCIETE DES NATIONS.**
LN34 **44** 5 c. green — 14·00
LN35 10 c. orange — 1·00
LN36 20 c. red — 1·00
LN37 30 c. blue — 35·00
LN38 60 c. brown — 10·00
LN39 **45** 1 f. grey and blue — 10·00

1934. Landscape designs of 1934 optd **SOCIETE DES NATIONS.**
LN40 **48** 3 c. green — 20
LN41 – 5 c. green — 25
LN43 – 15 c. orange — 75
LN45 – 25 c. brown — 12·00
LN46 – 30 c. blue — 1·10

1937. Landscape designs of 1936 optd **SOCIETE DES NATIONS.**
LN47 **52** 3 c. green 10 10
LN48 – 5 c. green 20 15
LN49aa – 10 c. purple — 80
LN49b – 10 c. brown 55 60
LN50 – 15 c. orange 40 30
LN51 – 20 c. red (railway) — 1·25
LN51a – 20 c. red (lake) 60 1·00
LN52 – 25 c. brown 60 75
LN53 – 30 c. blue 60 70
LN54 – 35 c. green 60 75
LN55 – 40 c. grey 75 90

1938. Nos. 382/5 optd **SOCIETE DES NATIONS.**
LN56 **55** 20 c. red and buff — 2·00
LN57 – 30 c. blue and light blue — 3·00
LN58 – 60 c. brown and buff — 5·00
LN59 – 1 f. black and buff — 6·00

1938. Nos. 382/5 optd **SERVICE DE LA SOCIETE DES NATIONS** in circle.
LN60 **55** 20 c. red and buff — 2·00
LN61 – 30 c. blue and light blue — 3·50
LN62 – 60 c. brown and buff — 6·00
LN63 – 1 f. black and buff — 10·00

1939. Nos. 388c/90c optd **SOCIETE DES NATIONS.**
LN64 **61** 3 f. brown on buff 3·00 7·00
LN65 – 5 f. blue on buff 4·50 10·00
LN66 – 10 f. green on buff 9·50 24·00

1944. Optd **COURRIER DE LA SOCIETE DES NATIONS.** (a) Landscape designs of 1936.
LN67 **52** 3 c. olive 15 20
LN68 – 5 c. green 15 20
LN69 – 10 c. brown 30 40
LN70 – 15 c. orange 25 30
LN71 – 20 c. red (lake) 40 45
LN72 – 25 c. brown 60 60
LN73 – 30 c. blue 70 70
LN74 – 35 c. green 75 75
LN75 – 40 c. grey 75 90

(b) Historical designs of 1941.
LN76 – 50 c. blue on green 1·00 1·50
LN77 **68** 60 c. brn on cinnamon 1·40 1·75
LN78 – 70 c. purple on mauve 1·40 2·00
LN79 – 80 c. black on grey 1·25 1·60
LN80 – 90 c. scarlet on pink 1·25 1·60
LN81 – 1 f. green on green 1·50 2·00
LN82 – 1 f. 20 purple on grey 1·60 2·40
LN83 – 1 f. 50 blue on buff 2·00 2·75
LN84 – 2 f. red on pink 3·00 3·25

(c) Parliament designs of 1938.
LN85 **61** 3 f. brown on buff 5·00 7·00
LN86 – 5 f. blue on buff 6·50 10·00
LN87 – 10 f. green on buff 12·00 22·00

B. INTERNATIONAL LABOUR OFFICE

Optd **S.d.N. Bureau International du Travail** (Nos. LB1/47).

1923.
LB 1 **20a** 2½ c. green on buff . . — 20
LB 2 3 c. blue on buff . . . — 85
LB 3 5 c. orange on buff . . — 30
LB 4 5 c. purple on buff . . — 20
LB 5 7½ c. green on buff . . — 25
LB 6 **21** 10 c. green on buff . . — 20
LB 8 15 c. red on buff . . . — 90
LB 9 20 c. violet on buff . . — 9·00
LB10 20 c. red on buff . . . — 4·00
LB11 25 c. red on buff . . . — 80
LB12 25 c. brown on buff . . — 2·25
LB13 **17** 30 c. green and brown . — 40·00
LB14 **21** 30 c. blue on buff . . . — 1·50
LB15 **17** 35 c. yellow and grn . . — 8·00
LB16 40 c. blue . . . . . — 90
LB17 40 c. green and mve . . — 11·00
LB18a 50 c. green & dp grn . 1·50 1·50
LB19 60 c. brown . . . . . 1·25 1·75
LB20a 70 c. buff and violet . 1·50 2·50
LB21 80 c. buff and grey . . 8·50 1·50
LB22 **38** 90 c. red and green on green . . . . . . — 3·25
LB23 **17** 1 f. green and purple . — 2·00
LB24b **38** 1 f. 20 red and lake on pink . . . . 10·00 3·00
LB25a 1 f. 50 red and blue on blue . . . . . . 2·25 2·50
LB26a 2 f. red and black on grey 2·75 4·50
LB27 **22** 3 f. red . . . . . . — 23·00
LB27a **43** 3 f. brown . . . . . — £160
LB28 – 5 f. blue (No. 285) . . — 30·00
LB30 – 10 f. purple (No. 286) . — £140
LB31 – 10 f. green (No. 331a) . £120

1932. International Disarmament Conference.
LB32 **44** 5 c. green . . . . . . — 90
LB33 10 c. orange . . . . . — 60
LB34 20 c. red . . . . . . — 1·10
LB35 30 c. blue . . . . . . — 7·00
LB36 60 c. sepia . . . . . — 7·50
LB37 **45** 1 f. grey and blue . . . — 7·50

1937. Landscape design of 1934.
LB38 **48** 3 c. olive . . . . — 3·50

1937. Landscape designs of 1936.
LB39 **52** 3 c. green 20 15
LB40 – 5 c. green 20 15
LB41 – 10 c. purple . . . . . — 90
LB41b – 10 c. brown 45 60
LB42 – 15 c. orange 40 30
LB43 – 20 c. red (mountain) . . — 70
LB43a – 20 c. red (lake) . . . . 45 1·00
LB44 – 25 c. brown 50 60
LB45 – 30 c. blue 55 70
LB46 – 35 c. green . . . . . 55 1·00
LB47 – 40 c. grey . . . . . . 80 1·10

1938. Nos. 382/5 optd **S.d.N. Bureau International du Travail**.
LB48 **55** 20 c. red and buff . . . — 1·50
LB49 – 30 c. blue and light blue — 2·75
LB50 – 60 c. brown and buff . — 6·00
LB51 – 1 f. black and buff . . — 6·50

1938. Nos. 382/5 optd **SERVICE DU BUREAU INTERNATIONAL DU TRAVAIL** in circle.
LB52 **55** 20 c. red and buff . . . — 4·50
LB53 – 30 c. blue and light blue — 3·50
LB54 – 60 c. brown and buff . — 6·50
LB55 – 1 f. black and buff . . — 6·50

1939. Nos. 388c/90c optd **S.d.N. Bureau International du Travail**.
LB56 **61** 3 f. brown on buff . . . 4·50 8·00
LB57 – 5 f. blue on buff . . . 5·50 11·00
LB58 – 10 f. green on buff . . . 9·50 24·00

1944. Optd **COURRIER DU BUREAU INTERNATIONAL DU TRAVAIL**. (a) Landscape designs of 1936.
LB59 **52** 3 c. olive 20 20
LB60 – 5 c. green 20 20
LB61 – 10 c. brown 30 30
LB62 – 15 c. orange 45 45
LB63 – 20 c. red (lake) 70 70
LB64 – 25 c. brown 80 80
LB65 – 30 c. blue . . . . . . 1·10 1·10
LB66 – 35 c. green . . . . . 1·25 1·25
LB67 – 40 c. grey . . . . . . 1·50 1·50

(b) Historical designs of 1941.
LB68 – 50 c. blue on green . . . 2·50 4·50
LB69 **68** 60 c. brown on cinnamon 2·50 4·50
LB70 – 70 c. purple on mauve . 2·50 4·00
LB71 – 80 c. black on grey . . . 80 1·25
LB72 – 90 c. red on pink . . . 80 1·25
LB73 – 1 f. green on green . . . 90 1·25
LB74 – 1 f. 20 purple on grey . 1·25 1·40
LB75 – 1 f. 50 blue on buff . . 1·40 1·50
LB76 – 2 f. red on pink . . . 2·25 2·25

(c) Parliament designs of 1938.
LB77 **61** 3 f. brown on buff . . . 5·00 6·00
LB78 – 5 f. blue on buff . . . 6·50 8·00
LB79 – 10 f. green on buff . . . 12·50 14·00

1950. Landscape designs of 1949 optd **BUREAU INTERNATIONAL DU TRAVAIL**.
LB80 **107** 5 c. orange . . . . . . 4·75 4·00
LB81 – 10 c. green . . . . . . 4·75 5·00
LB82 – 15 c. turquoise . . . . 6·50 5·00
LB83 – 20 c. purple . . . . . 6·50 5·00
LB84 – 25 c. red . . . . . . 7·00 6·00
LB85 – 30 c. green . . . . . 7·00 7·00
LB86 – 35 c. brown . . . . . 7·00 7·00
LB87 – 40 c. blue . . . . . . 7·00 5·50
LB88 – 50 c. grey . . . . . . 9·50 7·50
LB89 – 60 c. green . . . . . 10·00 8·50
LB90 – 70 c. violet . . . . . 14·50 14·00

LB 4 Miners (bas-relief)

1952. Inscr as in Type LB 4.
LB91 **LB 4** 5 c. purple 10 10
LB92 10 c. green 10 10
LB94 – 20 c. red 15 15
LB95 – 30 c. orange 20 20
LB96 **LB 4** 40 c. blue . . . . . 1·75 1·75
LB97 50 c. blue 30 30
LB98 – 60 c. brown 40 35
LB99 – 2 f. purple . . . . 1·25 75
DESIGN—HORIZ: 20, 30, 60 c., 2 f. Globe, flywheel and factory chimney.

1969. Pope Paul's Visit to Geneva. No. LB95 optd **Visite du Pape Paul VI Geneve 10 juin 1969**.
LB100 30 c. orange 15 15

LB 6 New Headquarters Building

1974. Inauguration of New I.L.O. Headquarters, Geneva.
LB101 **LB 6** 80 c. multicoloured . . 60 60

LB 7 Man at Lathe

1975.
LB102 **LB 7** 30 c. brown 30 30
LB103 – 60 c. blue 45 45
LB104 – 90 c. brown, red and green 80 80
LB105 – 100 c. green 80 80
LB106 – 120 c. ochre and brn 1·00 1·00
DESIGNS: 60 c. Woman at drilling machine; 90 c. Welder and laboratory assistant; 100 c. Surveyor with theodolite; 120 c. Apprentice and instructor with slide rule.

LB 8 Keys

1994. 75th Anniv of I.L.O.
LB107 **LB 8** 180 c. multicoloured 2·00 2·00

C. INTERNATIONAL EDUCATION OFFICE

1944. Optd **COURRIER DU BUREAU INTERNATIONAL D'EDUCATION**. (a) Landscape designs of 1936.
LE1 **52** 3 c. olive 20 50
LE2 – 5 c. green . . . . . . 50 1·40
LE3 – 10 c. brown . . . . . 55 1·40
LE4 – 15 c. orange . . . . . 50 1·40
LE5 – 20 c. red (lake) . . . . 50 1·40
LE6 – 25 c. brown . . . . . 50 1·40
LE7 – 30 c. blue . . . . . . 1·75 2·50
LE8 – 35 c. green . . . . . 75 2·00
LE9 – 40 c. grey . . . . . . 90 2·25

(b) Historical designs of 1941.
LE10 – 50 c. blue on green . . 4·50 9·00
LE11 **68** 60 c. brown on cinnamon 4·50 9·00
LE12 – 70 c. purple on mauve . 4·50 9·00
LE13 – 80 c. black on grey . . 60 1·40
LE14 – 90 c. red on pink . . . 70 1·75
LE15 – 1 f. green on green . . 80 2·00
LE16 – 1 f. 20 purple on grey . 1·10 2·50
LE17 – 1 f. 50 blue on buff . . 1·40 3·00
LE18 – 2 f. red on pink . . . 1·75 4·00

(c) Parliament designs of 1938.
LE19 **61** 3 f. brown on buff . . . 7·00 15·00
LE20 – 5 f. blue on buff . . . 9·50 25·00
LE21 – 10 f. green on buff . . . 14·00 35·00

1946. Optd **BIE**.
LE22 **86** 10 c. purple 15 15

Optd **BUREAU INTERNATIONAL D'EDUCATION** (Nos. LE23/39).

1948. Landscape designs of 1936.
LE23 5 c. brown . . . . 2·50 2·75
LE24 10 c. green . . . . . . 2·50 2·75
LE25 20 c. brown . . . . . . 2·50 2·75
LE26 25 c. red . . . . 2·50 2·75
LE27 30 c. blue . . . . . . 2·50 2·75
LE28 40 c. blue . . . . . . 2·50 2·75

1950. Landscape designs of 1949.
LE29 **107** 5 c. orange 60 60
LE30 – 10 c. green 80 80
LE31 – 15 c. turquoise 90 90
LE32 – 20 c. purple . . . . . 3·50 3·50
LE33 – 25 c. red . . . . . . 9·00 8·00
LE34 – 30 c. green . . . . . 9·00 8·00
LE35 – 35 c. brown . . . . . 5·50 7·00
LE36 – 40 c. blue . . . . . . 5·50 7·00
LE37 – 50 c. grey . . . . . . 6·00 7·50
LE38 – 60 c. green . . . . . 7·50 8·50
LE39 – 70 c. violet . . . . . 9·00 10·00

LE 3 Globe on Books

1958. Inscr as in Type LE 3.
LE40 **LE 3** 5 c. purple 10 10
LE41 10 c. green 10 10
LE43 – 20 c. red 15 15
LE44 – 30 c. orange 25 25
LE45 **LE 3** 40 c. blue . . . . . 2·25 2·25
LE46 50 c. blue 35 35
LE47 – 60 c. brown 50 50
LE48 – 2 f. purple . . . . 1·25 1·25
DESIGN—VERT: 20, 30, 60 c., 2 f. Pestalozzi Monument, Yverdon.

D. WORLD HEALTH ORGANIZATION

1948. Optd **ORGANISATION MONDIALE DE LA SANTE**. (a) Landscape designs of 1936.
LH1 5 c. brown (No. 489) . . . 3·50 2·00
LH2 10 c. green (No. 490) . . . 3·50 4·00
LH3 20 c. brown (No. 491) . . . 3·50 4·50
LH4 25 c. red (No. 492) . . . 3·50 5·50
LH5 40 c. blue (No. 494) . . . 3·50 4·00

(b) Landscape designs of 1949.
LH 6 **107** 5 c. orange 45 30
LH 7 – 10 c. green 90 90
LH 8 – 15 c. turquoise . . . . 1·25 1·50
LH 9 – 20 c. purple . . . . . 4·00 3·25
LH10 – 25 c. red . . . . . . 4·50 3·75
LH11 – 30 c. green . . . . . 2·00 2·00
LH12 – 35 c. brown . . . . . 2·75 4·00
LH13 – 40 c. blue . . . . . . 2·75 1·50
LH14 – 50 c. grey . . . . . . 3·00 3·75
LH15 – 60 c. green . . . . . 3·75 3·50
LH16 – 70 c. violet . . . . . 4·50 3·75

(c) Historical designs of 1941 (Nos. 408/13).
LH17 80 c. black on grey . . . 3·50 3·00
LH18 90 c. red on pink . . . . 7·00 5·50
LH19 1 f. green on green . . . 3·50 3·00
LH20 1 f. 20 purple on grey . . 8·00 9·00
LH21 1 f. 50 blue on buff . . . 18·00 10·00
LH22 2 f. red on pink . . . . 6·00 4·00

(d) Parliament designs of 1938.
LH23 **61** 3 f. brown on buff . . . 38·00 32·00
LH24 – 5 f. blue on buff . . . 15·00 8·00
LH25 – 10 f. green on buff . . . 75·00 80·00

LH 2 Staff of Aesculapius

1957.
LH26 **LH 2** 5 c. purple 10 10
LH27 10 c. green 10 10
LH29 20 c. red 15 15
LH30 30 c. orange 25 25
LH31 40 c. blue . . . . . 2·25 2·25
LH32 50 c. blue 35 30
LH33 60 c. brown 45 45
LH34 2 f. purple . . . . . 1·25 1·10

1962. Malaria Eradication. Optd **ERADICATION DU PALUDISME**.
LH35 **LH 2** 50 c. blue 25 35

LH 4 Staff of Aesculapius

1975.
LH36 **LH 4** 30 c. green, purple and pink 25 30
LH37 60 c. yellow, blue and light blue 45 45
LH38 90 c. yellow, violet and light violet 75 60
LH39 100 c. blue, brown and orange 85 75
LH40 140 c. green, turquoise and red . . . . . 1·25 1·25

E. INTERNATIONAL REFUGEES ORGANIZATION

Optd **ORGANISATION INTERNATIONALE POUR LES REFUGIES**.

1950. (a) Landscape designs of 1949.
LR1 **107** 5 c. orange . . . . . . 16·00 10·00
LR2 – 10 c. green . . . . . . 16·00 10·00
LR3 – 20 c. purple . . . . . 16·00 10·00
LR4 – 25 c. red . . . . . . 16·00 10·00
LR5 – 40 c. blue . . . . . . 16·00 10·00

(b) Historical designs of 1941 (Nos. 408/13).
LR6 80 c. black on grey . . . 16·00 10·00
LR7 1 f. green on green . . . . 16·00 10·00
LR8 2 f. red on pink . . . . . 16·00 10·00

F. WORLD METEOROLOGICAL ORGANIZATION

LM 1 "The Elements" LM 2 W.M.O. Emblem

1956. Inscr as in Type LM 1.
LM1 **LM 1** 5 c. purple 10 10
LM2 10 c. green 10 10
LM4 – 20 c. red 20 20
LM5 – 30 c. orange 25 25
LM6 **LM 1** 40 c. blue . . . . . 2·00 2·00
LM7 50 c. blue 35 30
LM8 – 60 c. brown 45 45
LM9 – 2 f. purple . . . . 1·25 1·25
DESIGN—HORIZ: 20, 30, 60 c., 2 f. Weathervane.

1973.
LM10 **LM 2** 30 c. red 25 25
LM11 40 c. blue 30 30
LM13 1 f. brown 80 80

LM 3 W.M.O. Emblem

1973. Centenary of I.M.O./W.M.O.
LM12 **LM 3** 80 c. violet and gold . 60 60

G. UNIVERSAL POSTAL UNION

LP 1 U.P.U. Monument, Berne LP 2 "Letter Post"

1957. Inscr as in Type LP 1.
LP1 **LP 1** 5 c. purple 10 10
LP2 – 10 c. green 10 10
LP4 – 20 c. red 20 20
LP5 – 30 c. orange 25 25
LP6 **LP 1** 40 c. blue . . . . . 2·00 2·00
LP7 50 c. blue 35 35
LP8 – 60 c. brown 45 45
LP9 **LP 1** 2 f. purple . . . . . 1·25 1·25
DESIGN—HORIZ: 10, 20, 30, 60 c. Pegasus (sculpture).

1976.
LP10 **LP 2** 40 c. purple, blue and claret 35 35
LP11 – 80 c. multicoloured . . 70 70
LP12 – 90 c. multicoloured . . 80 80
LP13 – 100 c. multicoloured . 85 85
LP14 – 120 c. multicoloured . 1·00 1·00
LP15 – 140 c. grey, blue and red 1·25 1·25
DESIGNS: 80 c. "Parcel Post"; 90 c. "Financial Services"; 100 c. Technical co-operation; 120 c. Carrier pigeon, international reply coupon and postal money order; 140 c. Express Mail Service.

H. UNITED NATIONS

Optd NATIONS UNIES OFFICE EUROPEEN.

1950. (a) Landscape designs of 1949.
LU 1 **107** 5 c. orange 45 90
LU 2 – 10 c. green 45 90
LU 3 – 15 c. turquoise . . . . 90 1·40
LU 4 – 20 c. purple . . . . . 1·40 1·75
LU 5 – 25 c. red . . . . . . 2·75 4·00
LU 6 – 30 c. green . . . . . 2·75 4·00
LU 7 – 35 c. brown . . . . . 2·75 8·00
LU 8 – 40 c. blue . . . . . . 4·00 3·75
LU 9 – 50 c. grey . . . . . . 4·75 6·50
LU10 – 60 c. green . . . . . 5·00 8·50
LU11 – 70 c. violet . . . . . 6·00 8·00

(b) Historical designs of 1941 (Nos. 408/13).
LU12 80 c. black on grey . . . 10·00 10·00
LU13 90 c. red on pink . . . . 10·00 10·00
LU14 1 f. green on green . . . 10·00 10·00
LU15 1 f. 20 purple on grey . . 12·50 12·50
LU16 1 f. 50 blue on buff . . . 12·50 14·00
LU17 2 f. red on pink . . . . 12·50 11·00

(c) Parliament designs of 1938.

LU18	**61**	3 f. brown on buff . . .	£120	£120
LU19	–	5 f. blue on buff . . .	£120	£120
LU20	–	10 f. green on buff . . .	£150	£150

LU 2 LU 4

1955. 10th Anniv of U.N.O.

LU21	LU **2**	40 c. blue and yellow .	3·25	4·50

1955. Nos. LU22/3 and LU27/8 are as Type LU **2** but without dates.

LU22	–	5 c. purple	10	10
LU23	–	10 c. green	10	10
LU25	LU **4**	20 c. red	20	20
LU26		30 c. orange	25	25
LU27	–	40 c. blue	4·50	4·00
LU28	–	50 c. blue	35	35
LU29	LU **4**	60 c. brown	35	35
LU30		2 f. purple	1·25	1·00

1960. World Refugee Year. Nos. LU25 and LU28 optd **ANNEE MONDIALE DU REFUGIE 1959 1960**.

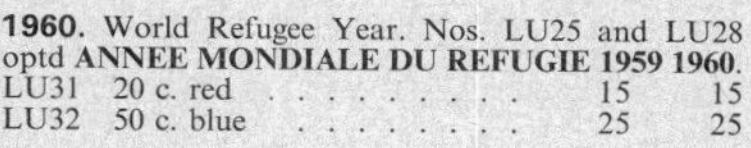

LU31	20 c. red	15	15
LU32	50 c. blue	25	25

LU **6** Palace of Nations, Geneva

1960. 15th Anniv of U.N.O.

LU33	LU **6**	5 f. blue	3·50	3·50

LU **7** LU **8** UNCSAT Emblem

1962. Opening of U.N. Philatelic Museum, Geneva.

LU34	LU **7**	10 c. green and red . .	10	10
LU35	–	30 c. red and blue . .	20	25
LU36	LU **7**	50 c. blue and red . .	30	30
LU37	–	60 c. brown and grn .	35	40

DESIGN—HORIZ: 30, 60 c. As Type LU **4** but inscr "ONU MUSEE PHILATELIQUE".

1963. U.N. Scientific and Technological Conference, Geneva.

LU38	LU **8**	50 c. red and blue . .	30	30
LU39	–	2 f. green and purple	80	1·00

DESIGN—HORIZ: 2 f. As Type LU **4**, but with emblem.

From 1969 stamps for the Geneva Headquarters were issued by the United Nations (q.v.).

I. INTERNATIONAL TELECOMMUNICATION UNION

LT **1** Transmitting Aerial LT **2** New H.Q. Building

1958. Inscr as in Type LT **1**.

LT1	LT **1**	5 c. purple	10	10
LT2		10 c. green	10	10
LT4	–	20 c. red	20	20
LT5	–	30 c. orange	25	25
LT6	LT **1**	40 c. blue	1·75	2·00
LT7		50 c. blue	35	35
LT8	–	60 c. brown	45	45
LT9	–	2 f. purple	1·25	1·25

DESIGN—VERT: 20, 30, 60 c., 2 f. Receiving aerials.

1973. Inauguration of New I.T.U. Headquarters, Geneva.

LT10	LT **2**	80 c. black and blue	55	55

LT **3** Boeing 747 and Ocean Liner

1976. World Telecommunications Network.

LT11	–	40 c. blue and red . .	35	35
LT12	LT **3**	90 c. violet, bl & yell .	75	75
LT13	–	1 f. red, green & yell .	80	80

DESIGNS: 40 c. "Sound waves"; 1 f. Face and microphone in television screen.

LT **4** Optical Fibre Cables

1988.

LT14	LT **4**	1 f. 40 multicoloured .	1·75	1·75

LT **5** Emblem emitting Radio Signals

1994. 100 Years of Radio.

LT15	LT **5**	1 f. 80 multicoloured .	2·00	2·00

J. WORLD INTELLECTUAL PROPERTY ORGANIZATION.

LV **1** WIPO Seal

1989. Multicoloured.

LV1	40 c. Type LV **1**	35	35
LV2	50 c. Face and symbolic representation of intellect	45	45
LV3	80 c. WIPO building, Geneva	70	70
LV4	100 c. Hand pressing buttons, retort and cogwheel (industrial property) . . .	1·00	1·00
LV5	120 c. Head, ballet dancer, cello and book (copyright) . .	1·25	1·25

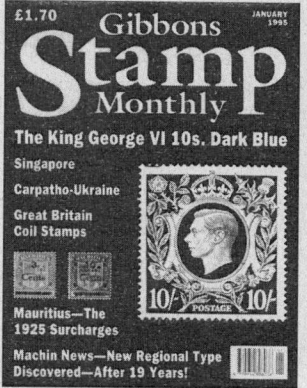

SYRIA Pt. 19

A country at the E. end of the Mediterranean Sea, formerly Turkish territory. Occupied by the Allies in 1918 and administered under French Military Occupation. An Arab kingdom was set up in the Aleppo and Damascus area during 1919, but the Emir Faisal came into conflict with the French and was defeated in July 1920. In April 1920, the Mandate was offered to France, becoming effective in September 1923. Separate governments were established for the Territories of Damascus, Aleppo, the Alaouites (including Latakia), Great Lebanon and the Jebel Druze. Syria became a republic in 1934, and the Mandate ended with full Independence in 1942. In 1958 the United Arab Republic was formed which comprised Egypt and Syria. Separate stamps were issued for each territory as they employed different currencies. In 1961 Syria left the U.A.R. and the Syrian Arab Republic was established.

1919. 40 paras = 10 milliemes = 1 piastre
1920. 100 centimes (or centiemes) = 1 piastre

A. FRENCH MILITARY OCCUPATION.

1919. Stamps of France surch **T.E.O.** and value in "Milliemes" or "Piastres".

1 **11** 1 m. on 1 c. grey £110 £110
2 2 m. on 2 c. red £325 £325
3 3 m. on 3 c. orange £120 £120
4 **15** 4 m. on 15 c.green . . . . . 20·00 20·00
5 **18** 5 m. on 5 c. green . . . . . 10·00 10·00
6 1 p. on 10 c. red . . . . . 15·00 15·00
7 2 p. on 25 c. blue . . . . . 9·00 8·00
8 **13** 5 p. on 40 c. red and blue . . 11·00 11·00
9 9 p. on 50 c. brown and lav . 25·00 25·00
10 10 p. on 1 f. red and yellow . 40·00 40·00

1919. "Blanc", "Mouchon" and "Merson" key-types of French Levant surch **T.E.O.** and value in "Milliemes" or "Piastres".

11 A 1 m. on 1 c. grey 20 20
12 2 m. on 2 c. red 20 20
13 3 m. on 3 c. orange 50 40
14 B 4 m. on 15 c. red 25 25
15 A 5 m. on 5 c. green 25 15
16 B 1 p. on 25 c. blue 25 15
17 C 2 p. on 50 c. brown & lav . . 40 40
18 4 p. on 1 f. red and yellow . . 75 50
19 8 p. on 2 f. lilac & yellow . . 2·50 2·25
20 20 p. on 5 f. blue & yellow . . £160 £110

1920. Stamps of France surch **O.M.F. Syrie** and value in "Milliemes" or "Piastres".

25 **11** 1 m. on 1 c. grey 20 20
26 2 m. on 2 c. red 40 40
27 **18** 3 m. on 5 c. green 30 30
28 5 m. on 10 c. red 20 20
29 **13** 20 p. on 5 f. blue & yellow . 40·00 40·00

1920. Stamps of France surch **O.M.F. Syrie** and value in two lines. (a) Value in "Centimes" or "Piastres".

31 **11** 25 c. on 1 c. grey 30 30
32 50 c. on 2 c. red 30 30
33 75 c. on 3 c. orange 30 30
35 **18** 1 p. on 5 c. green 15 15
36 2 p. on 10 c. red 20 20
37 2 p. on 25 c. blue 30 30
38 3 p. on 25 c. blue 30 30
39 **15** 5 p. on 15 c. green 30 30
40 **13** 10 p. on 40 c. red and blue . . 40 40
41 25 p. on 50 c. brown and lav . 75 75
42 50 p. on 1 f. red and yellow . 12·00 12·00
44 100 p. on 5 f. blue and yell . 23·00 23·00

(b) Value in "Centiemes".

45 **11** 25 c. on 1 c. grey 20 15
46 50 c. on 2 c. red 15 15
47 75 c. on 3 c. orange 30 30

1920. Air. Nos. 35, 39/40 optd **POSTE PAR AVION** in frame.

57 **18** 1 p. on 5 c. green . . . . . 90·00 25·00
58 **15** 5 p. on 15 c. green . . . . . £170 25·00
59 **13** 10 p. on 40 c. red and blue . . £250 50·00

1921. Issued at Damascus. Nos. K88/95 of Arab Kingdom surch **O.M.F. Syrie** and value in two lines in "Centiemes" or "Piastres".

60 K **3** 25 c. on $\frac{1}{10}$ m. 30 30
61 50 c. on $\frac{2}{10}$ p. green . . . 30 30
62 1 p. on $\frac{3}{10}$ p. yellow . . . 40 30
63 K **4** 1 p. on 5 m. red 50 40
64a 2 p. on 5 m. red 60 40
65 K **3** 3 p. on 1 p. blue 80 60
66 5 p. on 2 p. green . . . . 2·25 2·00
67 10 p. on 5 p. purple . . . 4·00 2·75
68 25 p. on 10 p. grey . . . 5·50 3·00

1921. Stamps of France surch **O.M.F. Syrie** and value in two lines in "Centiemes" or "Piastres".

69 **18** 25 c. on 5 c. green 15 15
70 50 c. on 10 c. red 15 15
71 **15** 75 c. on 15 c. green 20 20
72 **18** 1 p. on 20 c. brown 10 10
73 **13** 2 p. on 40 c. red and blue . . 30 20
74 3 p. on 60 c. violet & blue . . 40 30
75 5 p. on 1 f. red and yellow . . 80 60
76 10 p. on 2 f. orange & grn . . 1·50 1·40
77 25 p. on 5 f. blue and yell . 60·00 60·00

1921. Air. Nos. 72, 75/6 optd **POSTE PAR AVION** in frame.

78 **18** 1 p. on 20 c. brown . . . 45·00 23·00
79 **13** 5 p. on 1 f. red and yellow . £250 90·00
80 10 p. on 2 f. orange & grn . 25·00 90·00

1921. Stamps of France surch **O.M.F. Syrie** and value in "Piastres" in one line.

81 **13** 2 p. on 40 c. red and blue . . 20 10
82 3 p. on 60 c. violet & blue . . 40 20
83 5 p. on 1 f. red and yellow . 2·50 2·25
84 10 p. on 2 f. orange & grn . 6·00 5·50
85 25 p. on 5 f. blue & yellow . 5·50 5·00

1921. Air. Nos. 72, 75/6 optd **AVION.**

86 **18** 1 p. on 20 c. brown . . . . 35·00 9·00
87 **13** 5 p. on 1 f. red and yellow . 85·00 18·00
88 10 p. on 2 f. orange & grn . £110 28·00

1922. Air. Nos. 81/4 optd **Poste par Avion.**

89 **13** 2 p. on 40 c. red and blue . 10·00 10·00
90 3 p. on 60 c. violet & blue . 10·00 10·00
91 5 p. on 1 f. red and yellow . 10·00 10·00
92 10 p. on 2 f. orange & grn . 10·00 10·00

1922. Stamps of France surch **O.M.F. Syrie** and value in two lines in "Centiemes" or "Piastres".

93 **11** 10 c. on 2 c. red 20 20
94 **18** 10 c. on 5 c. orange 20 20
95 25 c. on 5 c. orange 20 20
96 50 c. on 10 c. green 30 20
96a 1,25 p. on 25 c. blue . . . 40 40
96b 1,50 p. on 30 c. orange . . 25 20
96c **13** 2,50 p. on 50 c. brn & lav . 30 30
96d **15** 2,50 p. on 50 c. blue . . . 40 30

B. ARAB KINGDOM.

Prior to the issues listed below, the Kingdom used stamps of Turkey variously overprinted. These are listed in Part 19 (Middle East) of the Stanley Gibbons Catalogue.

K 3

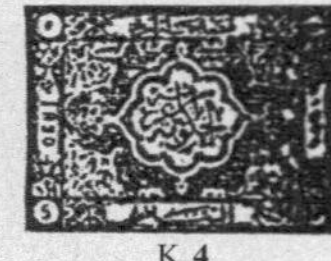
K 4

1920. As Type K **3** (various sizes) and Type K **4**.

K88 K **3** $\frac{1}{10}$ m. brown 10 10
K89 $\frac{2}{10}$ p. green 35 35
K90 $\frac{3}{10}$ p. yellow 15 15
K91 K **4** 5 m. red 15 10
K92 K **3** 1 p. blue 15 10
K93 2 p. green . . . . . . 1·50 50
K94 5 p. purple . . . . . . 10·00 2·00
K95 10 p. grey . . . . . . 10·00 2·50

For 1 p. black as Type K **3**, see No. KD96.

1920. Independence Commem. Optd with Arabic inscription.

K98 K **4** 5 m. red £130 £130

C. FRENCH MANDATED TERRITORY.
Issues for Lebanon and Syria.

Nos. 97/174 are all stamps of France surch.

1923. Surch **Syrie Grand Liban** in two lines and value in "Centiemes" or "Piastres".

97 **11** 10 c. on 2 c. red 10 10
98 **18** 25 c. on 5 c. orange 10 10
99 50 c. on 10 c. green 20 20
100 **15** 75 c. on 15 c. green 20 20
101 **18** 1 p. on 20 c. brown 15 15
102 1 p. 25 on 25 c. blue . . . 20 20
103 1 p. 50 on 30 c. orange . . 20 20
104 1 p. 50 on 30 c. red . . . 10 10
105 **15** 2 p. 50 on 50 c. blue . . . 15 15

1923. Surch **Syrie-Grand Liban** in one line and value in "Piastres".

106 **13** 2 p. on 40 c. red and blue . . 15 15
107 3 p. on 60 c. violet & blue . . 30 30
108 5 p. on 1 f. red and yellow . . 60 60
109 10 p. on 2 f. orange & grn . 3·25 3·25
110 25 p. on 5 f. blue & yellow . 11·00 11·00

1923. "Pasteur" issue surch **Syrie Grand Liban** in two lines and value in "Centiemes" or "Piastres".

111 **30** 50 c. on 10 c. green . . . 35 35
112 1 p. 50 on 30 c. red . . . 35 35
113 2 p. 50 on 50 c. blue . . . 35 35

1923. Air. Surch **Post par Avion Syrie-Grand Liban** and value in "PIASTRES".

114 **13** 2 p. on 40 c. red and blue . 16·00 16·00
115 3 p. on 60 c. violet & blue . 16·00 16·00
116 5 p. on 1 f. red & yellow . 16·00 16·00
117 10 p. on 2 f. orange and green 16·00 16·00

Issues for Syria only.

1924. Surch **SYRIE** and value in two lines.

118 **11** 10 c. on 2 c. red 10 10
119 **18** 25 c. on 5 c. orange 10 10
120 50 c. on 10 c. green 15 15
121 **15** 75 c. on 15 c. green 20 15
122 **18** 1 p. on 20 c. brown 20 15
123 1 p. 25 on 25 c. blue . . . 30 30
124 1 p. 50 on 30 c. orange . . 30 30
125 1 p. 50 on 30 c. red . . . 30 30
126 **15** 2 p. 50 on 50 c. blue . . . 30 30

1924. Surch **SYRIE** and value in one line.

127 **13** 2 p. on 40 c. red and blue . . 20 15
128 3 p. on 60 c. violet & blue . . 35 30
129 5 p. on 1 f. red and yellow . 1·10 1·10
130 10 p. on 2 f. orange & grn . 1·10 1·10
131 25 p. on 5 f. blue & yellow . 2·00 2·00

1924. "Pasteur" issue surch **SYRIE** and value in two lines.

132 **30** 50 c. on 10 c. green . . . 10 10
133 1 p. 50 on 30 c. red . . . 30 25
134 2 p. 50 on 50 c. blue . . . 20 10

1924. Air. Surch **Poste par Avion Syrie** and value.

135 **13** 2 p. on 40 c. red and blue . 1·10 1·10
136 3 p. on 60 c. violet & blue . 1·10 1·10
137 5 p. on 1 f. red and yellow . 1·10 1·10
138 10 p. on 2 f. orange & grn . 1·10 1·10

1924. Olympic Games issue (Nos. 401/4) surch **SYRIE** and value in two lines.

139 **31** 50 c. on 10 c. green . . . 25·00 25·00
140 – 1 p. 25 on 25 c. red . . . 25·00 25·00
141 – 1 p. 50 on 30 c. red & blk . 25·00 25·00
142 – 2 p. 50 on 50 c. blue . . . 25·00 25·00

1924. Surch **Syrie** and value and Arabic inscription.

143 **11** 0 p. 10 on 2 c. red 10 10
144 **18** 0 p. 25 on 5 c. orange . . . 10 10
145 0 p. 50 on 10 c. green . . . 15 15
146 **15** 0 p. 75 on 15 c. green . . . 15 15
147 **18** 1 p. on 20 c. brown 10 10
148 1 p. 25 on 25 c. blue . . . 15 15
149 1 p. 50 on 30 c. red . . . 20 20
150 1 p. 50 on 30 c. orange . . 13·00 13·00
151 2 p. on 35 c. violet 15 15
152 **13** 2 p. on 40 c. red and blue . . 15 15
153 2 p. on 45 c. green & blue . 1·60 1·60
154 3 p. on 60 c. violet & blue . . 30 30
155 **15** 3 p. on 60 c. violet 30 30
156 4 p. on 85 c. red 15 15
157 **13** 5 p. on 1 f. red and yellow . . 40 40
158 10 p. on 2 f. orange & grn . . 70 70
159 25 p. on 5 f. blue & yellow . . 70 70

1924. "Pasteur" issue surch **Syrie** and value and Arabic inscription.

160 **30** 0 p. 50 on 10 c. green . . . 20 20
161 0 p. 75 on 15 c. green . . . 40 40
162 1 p. 50 on 30 c. red . . . 30 30
163 2 p. on 45 c. red 20 20
164 2 p. 50 on 50 c. blue . . . 40 40
165 4 p. on 75 c. blue 50 50

1924. Olympic Games Issue (Nos. 401/4) surch **Syrie** and value and Arabic inscription.

166 **31** 0 p. 50 on 10 c. green . . . 25·00 25·00
167 – 1 p. 25 on 25 c. red . . . . 25·00 25·00
168 – 1 p. 50 on 30 c. red & blk . 25·00 25·00
169 – 2 p. 50 on 50 c. blue . . . 25·00 25·00

1924. Ronsard stamp surch **Syrie** and value and Arabic inscription.

170 **35** 4 p. on 75 c. blue 30 30

1924. Air Surch **Syrie Avion**, new value and Arabic inscription.

171 **13** 2 p. on 40 c. red and blue . 2·00 2·00
172 3 p. on 60 c. violet & blue . 2·00 2·00
173 5 p. on 1 f. red and yellow . 2·00 2·00
174 10 p. on 2 f. orange & grn . 2·00 2·00

16 Hama

17 Merkab

18 Damascus

1925. Views.

175 **16** 0 p. 10 violet 10 10
176 **17** 0 p. 25 black 35 25
177 – 0 p. 50 green 25 15
178 – 0 p. 75 red 20 10
179 **18** 1 p. red 20 5
180 – 1 p. 25 green 70 50
181 – 1 p. 50 red 15 10
182 – 2 p. sepia 35 10
183 – 2 p. 50 blue 45 35
184 – 3 p. brown 20 10
185 – 5 p. violet 55 10
186 – 10 p. plum 85 10
187 – 25 p. blue . . . . . . 1·25 70

DESIGNS—As Type **17**: 50 c. Alexandretta; 75 c. Hama; 1 p. 25, Latakia; 1 p. 50, Damascus; 2, 25 p. Palmyra (different views); 2 p. 50, Kalat Yamoun; 3 p. Bridge of Daphne; 5, 10 p. Aleppo (different views).

1925. Air. Nos. 182 etc. optd **AVION** and Arabic inscription.

188 2 p. sepia 85 85
189 3 p. brown 85 85
190 5 p. violet 85 85
191 10 p. plum 85 85

1926. Air. Nos. 182 etc. optd with Bleriot XI airplane.

192 2 p. sepia 40 40
193 3 p. brown 50 50
194 5 p. violet 60 60
195 10 p. plum 60 60

1926. War Refugees Fund. Nos. 176 and Nos. 192/5 etc. surch **Secours aux Refugies Afft**, value and Arabic inscr.

196 **17** 0 p. 25 on 0 p. 25 black (postage) . . . . 1·00 1·00
197 – 0 p. 25 on 0 p. 50 green . . 1·00 1·00
198 – 0 p. 25 on 0 p. 75 red . . 1·00 1·00
199 **18** 0 p. 50 on 1 p. red . . . 1·00 1·00
200 – 0 p. 50 on 1 p. 25 green . . 1·00 1·00
201 – 0 p. 50 on 1 p. 50 red . . 1·00 1·00
202 – 0 p. 75 on 2 p. sepia . . . 1·00 1·00
203 – 0 p. 75 on 2 p. 50 blue . . 1·00 1·00
204 – 1 p. on 3 p. brown . . . 1·00 1·00
205 – 1 p. on 5 p. violet . . . 1·00 1·00
206 – 2 p. on 10 p. plum . . . 1·00 1·00
207 – 5 p. on 25 p. blue . . . 1·00 1·00
208 – 1 p. on 2 p. sepia (air) . . 1·00 1·00
209 – 2 p. on 3 p. brown . . . 1·00 1·00
210 – 3 p. on 5 p. violet . . . 1·00 1·00
211 – 5 p. on 10 p. plum . . . 1·00 1·00

1926. No. 176, etc., surch with new value in English and Arabic figures and bars.

222 1 p. on 3 p. brown 35 20
223 2 p. on 1 p. 25 green 25 10
212 3 p. 50 on 75 c. red 20 10
214 4 p. on 25 c. black 20 10
215 4 p. 50 on 75 c. red 20 10
216 6 p. on 2 p. 50 blue 20 10
217 7 p. 50 on 2 p. 50 blue . . . 20 10
218 12 p. on 1 p. 25 green 20 10
219 15 p. on 25 p. blue 20 15
220 20 p. on 1 p. 25 green 30 15

1928. No. 175 surch in English and Arabic figures and single bar.

221 05 on 0 p. 10 violet 10 10

1929. Air. Nos. 177, etc., optd with Bleriot XI airplane or surch also in English and Arabic figures and bars.

225 0 p. 50 green 30 20
226 1 p. red 40 40
227 2 p. on 1 p. 25 green 70 70
228 15 p. on 25 p. blue . . . . 1·00 1·00
229 25 p. blue . . . . 1·75 2·00

1929. Damascus Industrial Exn. Nos. 177 etc. and various air stamps optd **EXPOSITION INDUSTRIELLE DAMAS 1929** and Arabic inscr.

230 0 p. 50 green (postage) . . . 1·40 1·40
231 1 p. red . . . . 1·40 1·40
232 1 p. 50 red . . . . 1·40 1·40
233 3 p. brown . . . . 1·40 1·40
234 5 p. violet . . . . 1·40 1·40
235 10 p. plum . . . . 1·40 1·40
236 25 p. blue . . . . 1·40 1·40
237 0 p. 50 green (No. 225) (air) . 1·00 1·00
238 1 p. red (No. 226) . . . . . 1·00 1·00
239 2 p. sepia (No. 192) . . . . 1·00 1·00
240 3 p. brown (No 193) . . . . 1·00 1·00
241 5 p. violet (No. 194) . . . . 1·00 1·00
242 10 p. plum (No. 195) . . . . 1·00 1·00
243 25 p. (No. 229) . . . . . 1·00 1·00

26 Hama

27 Damascus

1930. Views.

244 **26** 0 p. 10 purple 10 10
245 – 0 p. 20 blue 10 10
245a – 0 p. 20 red 10 10
246 – 0 p. 25 green 10 10
246a – 0 p. 25 violet 10 10
247 – 0 p. 50 violet 10 10
247a – 0 p. 75 red 10 10
248 – 1 p. green 10 10
248a – 1 p. brown 10 10
249 – 1 p. 50 brown . . . . . . 2·50 1·75
249a – 1 p. 50 green 25 20
250 – 2 p. violet 10 10
251 – 3 p. green 50 30
252 **27** 4 p. orange 10 10
253 – 4 p. 50 red 50 25
254 – 6 p. green 25 15
255 – 7 p. 50 blue 50 25
256 – 10 p. brown 60 10
257 – 15 p. green 80 40
258 – 25 p. red . . . . . . 1·00 55
259 – 50 p. sepia . . . . . . 3·50 2·25
260 – 100 p. red . . . . . . 8·00 6·00

DESIGNS—As Type **26**: 20 c. Aleppo; 25 c. Hama. As Type **27**: 50 c. Alexandretta; 75 c, 4 p. 50, Homs; 1 p., 7 p. 50, Aleppo; 1 p. 50., 100 p. Damascus; 2, 10 p. Antioch; 3 p. Bosra; 5 p. Sednaya; 15 p. Hama; 25 p. St. Simeon; 50 p. Palmyra.

28 River Euphrates

1931. Air. Views with Potez 29-4 biplane.

261 – 0 p. 50 yellow (Homs) . . 35 15
261a – 0 p. 50 brown (Homs) . . 40 20
262 – 1 p. brown (Damascus) . . 40 20
263 **28** 2 p. blue . . . . 1·25 60
264 – 3 p. green (Palmyra) . . . 40 20
265 – 5 p. purple (Deir-el-Zor) . . 40 20
266 – 10 p. blue (Damascus) . . . 40 20
267 – 15 p. red (Aleppo citadel) . . 80 60
268 – 25 p. orange (Hama) . . . 1·00 60
269 – 50 p. black (Zebdani) . . 1·25 80
270 – 100 p. mauve (Telebisse) . . 1·40 90

D. REPUBLIC UNDER FRENCH MANDATE.

29 Parliament House, Damascus

30 Aboulula el Maari

31 Farman F-190 Airplane over Bloudan

1934. Establishment of Republic.

271 **29** 0 p. 10 olive (postage) 60 60
272 0 p. 20 black 60 60
273 0 p. 25 red 60 60
274 0 p. 50 blue 60 60
275 0 p. 75 purple 60 60
276 **30** 1 p. red 1·50 1·50
277 1 p. 50 green 2·50 2·50
278 2 p. red 2·50 2·50
279 3 p. blue 2·50 2·50
280 4 p. violet 2·50 2·50
281 4 p. 50 red 2·50 2·50
282 5 p. blue 2·50 2·50
283 6 p. brown 2·50 2·50
284 7 p. 50 blue 2·50 2·50
285 – 10 p. brown 4·00 4·00
286 – 15 p. blue 5·50 5·50
287 – 25 p. red 8·50 8·50
288 – 50 p. brown 15·00 15·00
289 – 100 p. red 23·00 23·00

DESIGNS—As Type **30**: Nos. 285/7, President Mohammed Ali Bey el-Abed; Nos. 288/9, Sultan Saladin.

290 **31** 0 p. 50 brown (air) 1·00 1·00
291 1 p. green 1·00 1·00
292 2 p. blue 1·00 1·00
293 3 p. red 1·00 1·00
294 5 p. purple 1·25 1·25
295 10 p. violet 12·00 12·00
296 15 p. brown 13·00 13·00
297 25 p. blue 15·00 15·00
298 50 p. black 26·00 26·00
299 100 p. red 50·00 50·00

1936. Damascus Fair. Optd **FOIRE DE DAMAS 1936** in Arabic and French. (a) Postage stamps of 1930.

300 – 0 p. 50 violet 1·00 1·00
301 – 1 p. brown 1·00 1·00
302 – 2 p. violet 1·00 1·00
303 – 3 p. green 1·00 1·00
304 **27** 4 p. orange 1·00 1·00
305 – 4 p. 50 red 1·00 1·00
306 – 6 p. green 1·00 1·00
307 – 7 p. blue 1·25 1·25
308 – 10 p. brown 1·75 1·75

(b) Air stamps of 1931.

309 – 0 p. 50 sepia 2·00 2·00
310 – 1 p. brown 2·00 2·00
311 **28** 2 p. blue 2·00 2·00
312 – 3 p. green 2·00 2·00
313 – 5 p. purple 2·00 2·00

33 Exhibition Pavilion

1937. Air. Paris International Exhibition.

314 **33** ½ p. green 1·00 1·00
315 1 p. green 1·00 1·00
316 2 p. brown 1·00 1·00
317 3 p. red 1·00 1·00
318 5 p. orange 1·00 1·00
319 10 p. green 1·75 1·75
320 15 p. blue 2·00 2·00
321 25 p. violet 2·00 2·00

34 Savoia Marchetti S-73 over Aleppo

1937. Air.

322 **34** ½ p. violet 30 30
323 – 1 p. black 30 30
324 **34** 2 p. green 30 30
325 – 3 p. blue 30 30
326 **34** 5 p. mauve 80 80
327 – 10 p. brown 60 60
328 **34** 15 p. brown 2·25 2·25
329 – 25 p. blue 2·50 2·50

DESIGN: 1, 3, 10, 25 p. Potez 62 airplane over Damascus.

1938. Stamps of 1930 surch in English and Arabic figures and bars.

330 0 p. 25 on 0 p. 75 red 10 10
331 0 p. 50 on 1 p. 50 green 10 10
332 2 p. on 7 p. 50 blue 15 10
333 2 p. 50 on 4 p. orange 20 15
334 5 p. on 7 p. 50 blue 25 20
335 10 p. on 50 p. sepia 55 55
336 10 p. on 100 p. red 60 60

MINIMUM PRICE

The minimum price quoted is 10p which represents a handling charge rather than a basis for valuing common stamps. For further notes about prices, see introductory pages.

38 Maurice Nogues and 1st Flight Route

39 President Atasi

1938. Air. 10th Anniv of 1st Air Service Flight between France and Syria.

337 **38** 10 p. green 1·50 1·50

1938. Unissued stamp surch **12.50** and in Arabic figures.

338 **39** 12 p. 50 on 10 p. blue 40 30

1938.

338a **39** 10 p. blue 30 20
339 20 p. sepia 45 30

41 Palmyra

1940.

340 **41** 5 p. pink 20 15

42 Damascus Museum

45 Deir-el-Zor Bridge

1940.

341 **42** 0 p. 10 red (postage) 10 10
342 0 p. 20 blue 10 10
343 0 p. 25 brown 10 10
344 0 p. 50 blue 10 10
345 – 1 p. blue 10 10
346 – 1 p. 50 brown 10 10
347 – 2 p. 50 green 10 10
348 – 5 p. violet 20 10
349 – 7 p. 50 red 40 30
350 – 50 p. purple 90 70

DESIGNS—As Type **45**: 1 p., 1 p. 50, 2 p. 50, Hotel de Bloudan; 5, 7 p. 50, 50 p. Kasr-el-Heir Fortress.

351 **45** 0 p. 25 black (air) 10 10
352 0 p. 50 blue 10 10
353 1 p. blue 15 10
354 2 p. brown 15 15
355 5 p. green 40 40
356 10 p. red 60 60
357 50 p. violet 1·75 1·75

E. SYRIAN REPUBLIC.

46 President Taj Addin el-Husni

47

1942. National Independence. Inscr "PROCLAMATION/DE L'INDEPENDENCE/ 27 Septembre 1941".

358 **46** 0 p. 50 green (postage) 2·50 2·50
359 1 p. 50 sepia 2·50 2·50
360 6 p. red 2·50 2·50
361 15 p. blue 2·50 2·50
362 – 10 p. blue (air) 2·00 2·00
363 – 50 p. purple 2·00 2·00

DESIGN: 10, 50 p. As Type **46**, but President bareheaded and airplane inset.

1942. (a) Postage. Portrait in oval frame.

364 **47** 6 p. red and pink 1·50 1·50
365 15 p. blue 1·50 1·50

(b) Air. Portrait in rectangular frame.

366 10 p. green 2·75 2·75

48 Syria and late President's portrait

49 Shukri Bey al-Quwatli

1943. Union of Latakia and Jebel Druze with Syria.

(a) President bare-headed.

367 **48** 1 p. green (postage) 1·25 1·25
368 4 p. brown 1·25 1·25
369 8 p. violet 1·25 1·25
370 10 p. orange 1·25 1·25
371 20 p. blue 1·25 1·25

(b) President wearing turban.

372 2 p. brown (air) 1·25 1·25
373 10 p. purple 1·25 1·25
374 20 p. blue 1·25 1·25
375 50 p. pink 1·25 1·25

1943. Death of President Taj Addin-el-Husni. Nos. 367/75 optd with narrow black border.

376 **48** 1 p. green (postage) 1·25 1·25
377 4 p. brown 1·25 1·25
378 8 p. violet 1·25 1·25
379 10 p. orange 1·25 1·25
380 20 p. blue 1·25 1·25
381 – 2 p. brown (air) 1·25 1·25
382 – 10 p. purple 1·25 1·25
383 – 20 p. blue 1,25 1·25
384 – 50 p. pink 1·25 1·25

1944. Air.

385 **49** 200 p. purple 5·50 5·50
386 500 p. blue 9·00 9·00

(**50** Trans. "First Congress of Arab Lawyers, Damascus".)

(**51** Trans. "Aboulula-el-Maari. Commemoration of Millenary, 363–1363")

1944. Air. 1st Arab Lawyers' Congress. Optd with T **50**.

387 – 10 p. brown (No. 327) 1·50 1·50
388 – 15 p. red (No. 267) 1·50 1·50
389 – 25 p. orange (No. 268) 1·50 1·50
390 – 100 p. mauve (No. 270) 4·50 4·50
391 **49** 200 p. purple 6·00 6·00

1945. Millenary of Aboulula-el-Maari (Arab poet and philosopher). Optd with T **51**.

392 – 2 p. 50 green (No. 347) (postage) 2·00 2·00
393 – 7 p. 50 red (No. 349) 2·00 2·00
394 – 15 p. red (No. 267) (air) 1·50 1·50
395 – 25 p. orange (No. 268) 1·50 1·50
396 **49** 500 p. blue 12·00 12·00

52 Pres. Shukri Bey al-Quwatli

53 Pres. Shukri Bey al-Quwatli

1945. Resumption of Constitutional Govt.

397 **52** 4 p. violet (postage) 25 25
398 6 p. blue 25 25
399 10 p. red 25 25
400 15 p. brown 40 40
401 20 p. green 45 45
402 40 p. orange 85 75
403 **53** 5 p. green (air) 25 30
404 10 p. red 25 30
405 15 p. orange 25 30
406 25 p. blue 60 30
407 50 p. violet 1·00 30
408 100 p. brown 2·00 60
409 200 p. brown 5·00 2·25

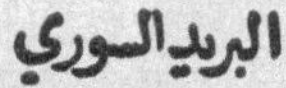

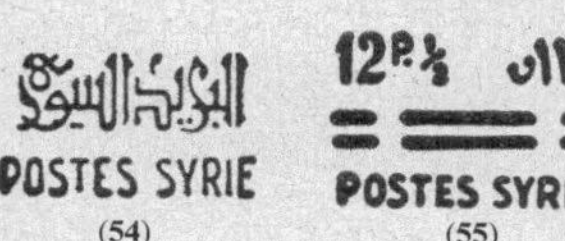

(54) (55)

1945. Fiscal stamps inscr "TIMBRE FISCAL", optd with T **54**.

410 25 p. brown 2·50 2·50
411 50 p. on 75 p. brown 3·00 3·00
412 75 p. brown 4·50 4·50
413 100 p. green 5·00 5·00

1945. Fiscal stamps surch as T **55** or optd with T **54** and additional Arabic inscription.

414 12½ p. on 15 p. green 1·40 1·40
415 25 p. on 25 s. purple 1·60 1·60
416 50 p. on 75 p. brown 1·10 1·10
417 50 p. mauve 3·00 3·00
418 100 p. green 2·00 2·00

(56)

57 Ear of Wheat

58 Pres. Shukri Bey al-Quwatli

60 Arab Horse

1946. Fiscal stamp optd with T **56**.

419 200 p. blue 15·00 8·50

1946.

420 **57** 0 p. 50 orange (postage) 15 10
421 1 p. violet 40 10
422 2 p. 50 grey 45 15
423 5 p. green 60 20
424 **58** 7 p. 50 brown 20 10
425 10 p. blue 20 10
426 12 p. 50 violet 75 15
427 – 15 p. red 30 15
428 – 20 p. violet 45 25
429 – 25 p. blue 75 25
430 **60** 50 p. brown 3·75 60
431 100 p. green 8·00 1·40
432a 200 p. purple 45·00 3·75

DESIGN—As Type **58**: 15, 20, 25 p. Pres. Shukri Bey al-Quwatli bareheaded.

433 – 3 p. brown (air) 40 10
434 – 5 p. green 40 10
435 – 6 p. orange 40 10
436 – 10 p. grey 30 10
437 – 15 p. red 30 10
438 – 25 p. blue 45 15
439 – 50 p. violet 60 15
440 – 100 p. green 1·50 35
441 – 200 p. brown 3·75 90
442 – 300 p. brown 12·00 1·50
443 – 500 p. olive 13·00 3·00

DESIGNS—HORIZ: 3, 5, 6 p. Flock of sheep; 10, 15, 25 p. Kattineh dam; 50, 100, 200 p. Temple ruins, Kanaouat; 300, 500 p. Sultan Ibrahim Mosque.

(65)

1946. Withdrawal of Allied Forces. Optd with T **65**.

444 **58** 10 p. blue (postage) 40 40
445 12 p. 50 violet 55 55
446 **60** 50 p. brown 1·50 1·50
447 – 25 p. blue (No. 438) (air) 1·25 80

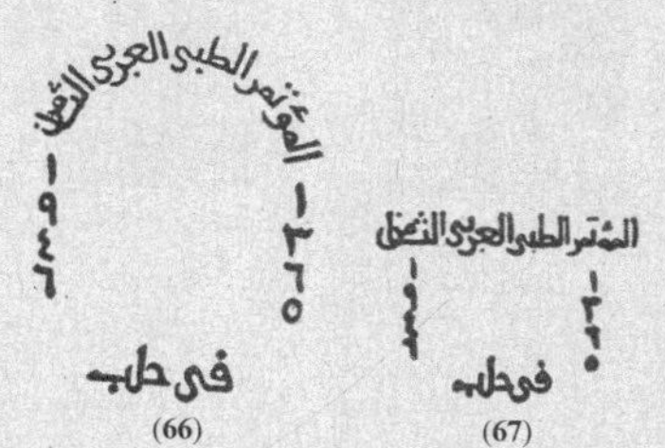

(66) (67)

1946. 8th Arab Medical Congress, Aleppo. (a) Postage. Optd with T **66**.

448 25 p. blue (No. 429) 1·00 75

(b) Air. Optd with T **67**.

449 25 p. blue (No. 438) 1·10 70
450 50 p. violet (No. 439) 1·90 1·10
451 100 p. green (No. 440) 3·50 2·00

(68)

1947. 1st Anniv of Evacuation of Allied Forces. Nos. 444/447 optd as T **68** ("1947").

452 **58** 10 p. blue (postage) 40 10
453 12 p. 50 violet 55 15
454 **60** 50 p. brown 1·50 45
455 – 25 p. blue (air) 1·25 70

69 Hercules and Lion

70 Mosaic of the Mosque of the Omayades

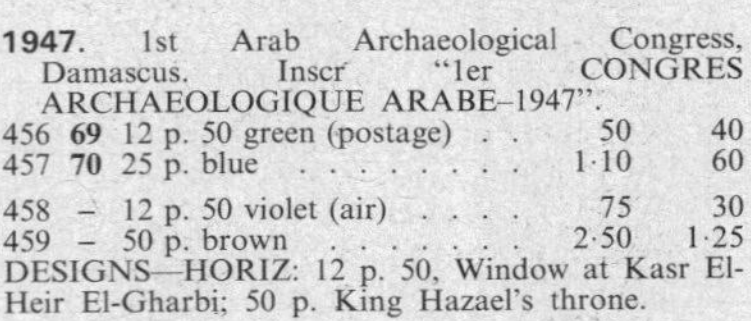

1947. 1st Arab Archaeological Congress, Damascus. Inscr "1er CONGRES ARCHAEOLOGIQUE ARABE–1947".
456 **69** 12 p. 50 green (postage) . . 50 40
457 **70** 25 p. blue . . . . 1·10 60

458 – 12 p. 50 violet (air) 75 30
459 – 50 p. brown . . . . 2·50 1·25
DESIGNS—HORIZ: 12 p. 50, Window at Kasr El-Heir El-Gharbi; 50 p. King Hazael's throne.

71 Courtyard of Azem Palace

72 Congress Symbol

1947. 3rd Arab Engineers' Congress, Damascus. Inscr "3e CONGRES DES INGENIEURS ARABES 1947".
460 **71** 12 p. 50 purple (postage) . 40 35
461 – 25 p. blue 80 45

462 – 12 p. 50 olive (air) 55 30
463 **72** 50 p. violet . . . . 1·90 1·25
DESIGNS—HORIZ: No. 461, Telephone Exchange Building; No. 462, Fortress at Kasr El-Heir El-Charqui.

73 Parliament Building

74 Pres. Shukri Bey al-Quwatli

1948. Re-election of Pres. Shukri Bey al-Quwatli.
464 **73** 12 p. 50 brown and grey (postage) 40 20
465 **74** 25 p. mauve 60 40

466 **73** 12 p. 50 blue and violet (air) 35 20
467 **74** 50 p. purple and green . . 1·60 70

75 Syrian Arms

76 Soldier and Flag

1948. Compulsory Military Service.
468 **75** 12 p. 50 brown and grey (postage) 40 25
469 **76** 25 p. multicoloured 65 35

470 **75** 12 p. 50 blue (air) 55 25
471 **76** 50 p. green, red and black . 1·90 60

1948. Surch. (a) Postage.
472 – 50 c. on 75 c. red (No. 247a) 20 10
472ab **60** 2 p. 50 on 200 p. purple . 35 10
472ab 10 p. on 100 p. green . . 45 20
473 25 p. on 200 p. purple . . 30·00 30

(b) Air
474 – 2 p. 50 on 3 p. (No. 433) 10 10
475 – 2 p. 50 on 6 p. (No. 435) . 10 10
475a – 2 p. 50 on 6 p. (No. 435) . 10 10
476 – 25 p. on 200 p. (No. 441) 75 20
477 – 50 p. on 300 p. (No. 442) . 15·00 75
478 – 50 p. on 500 p. (No. 443) 15·00 75

MORE DETAILED LISTS
are given in the Stanley Gibbons Catalogues referred to in the country headings. For lists of current volumes see introduction

78 Palmyra

79 President Husni el-Zaim and Lockheed Super Constellation over Damascus

1949. 75th Anniv of U.P.U.
479 – 12 p. 50 violet (postage) . 1·50 1·50
480 **78** 25 p. blue . . . . 2·00 2·00

481 – 12 p. 50 purple (air) . . . 4·50 4·50
482 **79** 50 p. slate . . . . 13·00 9·00
DESIGNS—HORIZ: No. 479, Ain-el-Arous; No. 481, Globe and mountains.

80 President Husni el-Zaim

81 Pres. Husni el-Zaim and Map

1949. Revolution of 30 March, 1949.
483 **80** 25 p. blue (postage) . . . 60 35

484 50 p. brown (air) . . . . 2·25 1·75

1949. Presidential Election.
485 **81** 25 p. brn & blue (postage) 2·00 1·25

486 50 p. blue and red (air) . . 2·25 1·75

82 Tel-Chehab

83 Damascus

1949.
487 **82** 5 p. grey 35 10
488 7 p. 50 brown 50 10
524 7 p. 50 green . . . . . . 2·50 15
489 **83** 12 p. 50 purple 60 15
490 25 p. blue . . . . 1·25 35

84

85 G.P.O., Damascus

1950.
491 **84** 0 p. 50 brown 15 10
492 2 p. 50 pink 20 10
493 – 10 p. violet . . . . . . 7·50 25
494 – 12 p. 50 green 70 40
495 **85** 25 p. blue . . . . 1·25 25
496 50 p. black . . . . . . 3·50 50
DESIGN—HORIZ: 10, 12 p. 50, Road to Damascus.

86 Port of Latakia

1950. Air.
497 **86** 2 p. 50 violet 60 10
498 10 p. turquoise . . . . . 1·00 10
526 10 p. blue 60 10
499 15 p. brown . . . . . . 2·00 20
500 25 p. blue . . . . 4·50 25

87 Parliament Building

88 Book and Torch

1951. New Constitution, 1950.
501 **87** 12 p. 50 black (postage) . . 25 20
502 25 p. blue 40 30

503 **88** 12 p. 50 red (air) 25 15
504 50 p. purple 80 70

89 Hama

1952.
505 **89** 0 p. 50 sepia (postage) . . . 15 10
506 2 p. 50 slate 25 10
507 5 p. green 30 10
508 10 p. red 45 10
509 – 12 p. 50 black 85 10
510 – 15 p. red . . . . 2·00 25
511 – 25 p. blue . . . . 6·50 35
512 – 100 p. bistre . . . . . . 30·00 1·75

513 – 2 p. 50 red (air) 20 10
514 – 5 p. green 40 10
515 – 15 p. violet 55 15
516 – 25 p. blue 75 25
517 – 100 p. purple . . . . . . 6·00 75
DESIGNS—Postage: 12 p. 50 to 100 p. Palace of Justice, Damascus. Air: 2 p. 50 to 15 p. Palmyra; 25, 100 p. Citadel, Aleppo.

1952. Air. United Nations Social Welfare Seminar, Damascus. Optd **U.N.S.W.S. Damascus 8-20 Dec. 1952** and curved line of Arabic.
518 **86** 10 p. turquoise . . . . . . 1·25 1·00
519 15 p. violet (No. 515) . . . 1·25 1·00
520 25 p. blue (No. 516) . . . . 2·00 1·50
521 50 p. violet (No. 439) . . . 5·50 2·00

91 Qalaat el Hasn Fortress

92 "Labour"

93 "Family"

94 "Communications"

1953.
522 **91** 0 p. 50 red (postage) . . . 10 10
523 – 2 p. 50 brown 25 10
525 **91** 12 p. 50 blue . . . . . . 7·00 15

527 – 50 p. brown (air) . . . . . 1·50 25
DESIGNS: 2 p. 50, Qalaat el Han fortress (different); 50 p. G.P.O., Aleppo.

1954.
528 **92** 1 p. olive (postage) 10 10
529 2½ p. lake 10 10
530 5 p. blue 10 10
531 **93** 7½ p. lake 20 10
532 10 p. black 30 10
533 12½ p. violet 45 10
534 – 20 p. red 70 20
535 – 25 p. violet . . . . . . 1·50 30
536 – 50 p. green . . . . . . 5·00 65

537 **94** 5 p. violet (air) 20 10
538 10 p. brown 30 10
539 15 p. green 30 10
540 – 30 p. brown 70 20
541 – 35 p. blue . . . . 1·00 20
542 – 40 p. orange . . . . . . 3·25 35
543 – 50 p. purple . . . . . . 1·50 45
544 – 70 p. violet . . . . . . 4·00 55
DESIGNS—HORIZ: (As Type **93**): Postage: 20 p. to 50 p. "Industry". Air: 30 p. to 70 p. Syrian University.

95

96a

1954. Air. Damascus Fair. Inscr as in T **95**.
545 **95** 40 p. magenta 65 35
546 – 50 p. green 80 40
DESIGN—VERT: 50 p. Mosque and Syrian flag.

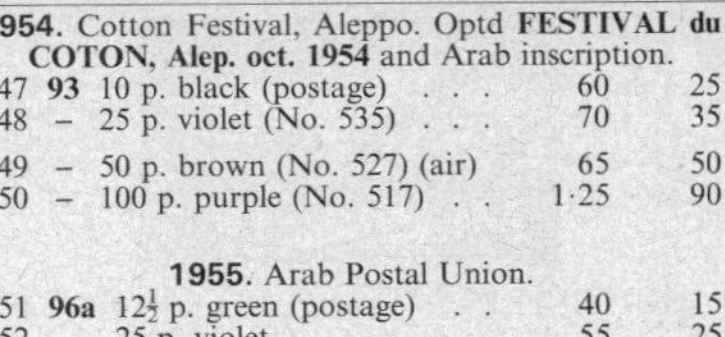

1954. Cotton Festival, Aleppo. Optd **FESTIVAL du COTON, Alep. oct. 1954** and Arab inscription.
547 **93** 10 p. black (postage) . . . 60 25
548 – 25 p. violet (No. 535) . . . 70 35

549 – 50 p. brown (No. 527) (air) 65 50
550 – 100 p. purple (No. 517) . . 1·25 90

1955. Arab Postal Union.
551 **96a** 12½ p. green (postage) . . 40 15
552 25 p. violet 55 25

553 5 p. brown (air) 25 10

97

98

1955. Air. Middle East Rotary Congress.
554 **97** 35 p. red 55 35
555 65 p. green . . . . 1·00 65

1955. Air. 50th Anniv of Rotary International.
556 **98** 25 p. violet 40 25
557 75 p. turquoise . . . . . . 1·25 80

99 "Facing the Future"

100 Mother and Child

1955. Air. 9th Anniv of Evacuation of Allied Forces.
558 **99** 40 p. mauve 40 35
559 – 60 p. blue . . . . 2·00 40
DESIGN: 60 p. Tank and infantry attack.
See also Nos. 847/9.

1955. Mothers' Day.
560 **100** 25 p. red (postage) . . . 40 25

561 35 p. violet (air) 60 40
562 40 p. black 90 45

101 Lockheed Super Constellation, Flag and Crowd

102 Syrian Pavilion

1955. Air. Emigrants' Congress.
563 **101** 5 p. mauve 35 15
564 – 15 p. blue 40 25
DESIGN: 15 p. Lockheed Super Constellation over globe.

1955. Air. International Fair, Damascus.
565 **102** 25 p. + 5 p. black 40 40
566 – 35 p. + 5 p. blue 45 45
567 – 40 p. + 10 p. mauve . . 55 55
568 – 70 p. + 10 p. green . . . 1·10 1·10
DESIGNS: 35, 40 p. "Industry and Agriculture"; 70 p. Exhibition pavilions and flags.

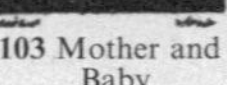

103 Mother and Baby

104 U.N. Emblem and Torch

1955. Air. International Children's Day.
569 **103** 25 p. blue 50 30
570 50 p. purple 90 45

1955. 10th Anniv of U.N.O.
571 **104** 7½ p. red (postage) 35 25
572 12½ p. slate 55 30

573 – 15 p. blue (air) 50 25
574 – 35 p. sepia 90 45
DESIGN: 15, 35 p. Globe, dove and Scales of Justice.

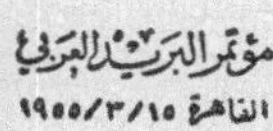
105 Saracen Gate, Aleppo Citadel (**106**)

1955. Installation of Aleppo Water Supply from River Euphrates.
575 **105** 7 p. 50 violet (postage) . . 20 10
576 12 p. 50 red 25 15
577 30 p. blue (air) . . . . . 1·50 70

1955. 2nd Arab Postal Union Congress, Cairo. Nos. 551/3 optd with T **106**.
578 12½ p. green (postage) 20 15
579 25 p. violet 60 30
580 5 p. brown (air) 30 15

(**107**) **108** Monument

1956. Visit of King Hussein of Jordan. Nos. 551/3 optd with T **107**.
581 12½ p. green (postage) 35 25
582 25 p. violet 55 55
583 5 p. brown (air) 35 20

1956. Air. 10th Anniv of Evacuation of Allied Forces.
584 **108** 35 p. sepia . . . . 1·10 60
585 – 65 p. red . . . . 2·00 1·10
586 – 75 p. grey . . . . 2·50 1·25
DESIGNS: 65 p. Winged female figure; 75 p. Pres. Shukri Bey al-Quwatli.

109 Pres. Shukri Bey al-Quwatli **110** Cotton

1956. Air.
587 **109** 100 p. black . . . . . . 1·50 85
588 200 p. violet . . . . . . 3·00 1·25
589 300 p. red . . . . 25·00 2·25
590 500 p. green . . . . . . 7·50 4·00

1956. Aleppo Cotton Festival.
591 **110** 2½ p. green 30 15

1956. Air. Nos. 565/8 with premiums obliterated by bars.
592 **102** 25 p. black . . . . . . 1·50 15
593 – 35 p. blue . . . . 1·75 20
594 – 40 p. mauve . . . . . . 2·75 35
595 – 70 p. green . . . . . . 4·00 80

111 Gate of Kasr al-Heir, Palmyra **112** Clay Alphabetical Tablet

1956. Air. 3rd International Fair, Damascus.
596 **111** 15 p. sepia 25 25
597 – 20 p. blue 35 35
598 – 30 p. green 45 45
599 – 35 p. blue 55 55
600 – 50 p. red 70 70
DESIGNS: 20 p. Cotton mill; 30 p. Tractor; 35 p. Phoenician galley and cog-wheels; 50 p. Textiles, carpets and pottery.

1956. Air. International Campaign for Museums.
601 **112** 20 p. black 55 30
602 – 30 p. red 80 35
603 – 50 p. sepia . . . . 1·40 85
DESIGNS—VERT: 30 p. Syrian legionary's helmet. HORIZ: 50 p. Lintel of Belshamine Temple, Palmyra.

1956. 11th Anniv of U.N.O. Nos. 571/4 optd **11 eme ANNIVERSAIRE de L'ONU** in French and Arabic.
604 **104** 7½ p. red (postage) . . . 40 25
605 – 12½ p. slate 45 35
606 – 15 p. blue (air) 85 35
607 – 35 p. sepia . . . . 1·50 80

114 Oaks and Mosque

1956. Air. Afforestation Day.
608 **114** 10 p. brown 30 15
609 40 p. grey 65 45

115 Azem Palace, Damascus

1957.
610 **115** 12½ p. purple 25 10
611 15 p. black 45 10

116 "Resistance"

1957. Syrian Defence Force.
612 **116** 5 p. mauve 25 10
613 20 p. slate 45 15

1957. Evacuation of Port Said. Optd **22.12.56 EVACUATION PORT SAID** in French and Arabic.
614 **116** 5 p. mauve 20 10
615 20 p. slate 35 25

118 Mother and Child **119** "Sword of Liberty"

1957. Air. Mothers' Day.
616 – 40 p. blue 50 35
617 **118** 60 p. red 80 50
DESIGN: 40 p. Mother fondling child.

1957. Air. 11th Anniv of Evacuation of Allied Forces.
618 **119** 10 p. brown 15 10
619 – 15 p. green 25 10
620 – 25 p. violet 30 15
621 – 35 p. mauve 45 35
622 **119** 40 p. grey 75 45
DESIGNS: 15, 35 p. Woman holding torch and map; 25 p. Pres. Shukri Bey al-Quwatli.

120 Freighter "Latakia" and Fair Emblem **121** "Cotton"

1957. Air. 4th Damascus Fair.
623 **120** 25 p. purple 25 15
624 – 30 p. brown 30 25
625 – 35 p. blue 50 35
626 – 40 p. green 65 40
627 **120** 70 p. olive 90 50
DESIGNS—VERT: 30, 40 p. Girls harvesting and cotton picking. HORIZ: 35 p. Interior of processing plant.

1957. Aleppo Cotton Festival.
628 **121** 12½ p. blk & grn (postage) 35 20
629 17½ p. black & orge (air) 40 25
630 40 p. black and blue . . 65 35

122 Children at Work and Play **123** Letter and Post-box

1957. International Children's Day.
631 **122** 12½ p. olive (postage) . . . 45 25
632 17½ blue (air) 80 30
633 20 p. brown 80 30

1957. International Correspondence Week.
634 **123** 5 p. mauve (postage) . . . 40 20
635 – 5 p. green (air) 35 15
DESIGN; 5 p. (air) Family writing letters.

(**124**) **125** Scales of Justice, Map and Damascus Silhouette

1957. National Defence Week. Optd with T **124**.
636 **116** 5 p. mauve 15 10
637 20 p. slate 30 25

1957. 3rd Arab Lawyers Union Congress, Damascus.
638 **125** 12½ p. green (postage) . . 20 15
639 17½ p. red (air) 35 25
640 40 p. sepia 50 35

126 Glider

1957. Air. Gliding Festival.
641 **126** 25 p. brown . . . . 1·00 25
642 35 p. green . . . . 1·40 35
643 40 p. blue . . . . 2·25 50

127 Torch and Map **128** Khaled Ibn el-Walid Mosque, Homs

1957. Afro-Asian Jurists' Congress, Damascus.
644 **127** 20 p. drab (postage) . . . 35 15
645 30 p. green (air) 40 25
646 50 p. violet 40 35

1957.
647 **128** 2½ p. brown 15 10

UNITED ARAB REPUBLIC

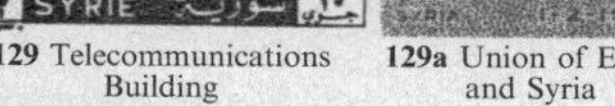
129 Telecommunications Building **129a** Union of Egypt and Syria

1958. Five Year Plan.
648 **129** 25 p. blue (postage) . . . 25 20
649 10 p. green (air) 20 10
650 – 15 p. brown 25 15
DESIGN—VERT: 15 p. Telephone, radio tower and telegraph pole.

1958. Birth of United Arab Republic.
651 **129a** 12½ p. green and yellow (postage) 20 10
652 17½ p. brown & blue (air) 35 20

130 "Eternal Flame"

1958. 12th Anniv of Evacuation of Allied Forces.
653 **130** 5 p. violet & lemon (postage) 40 20
654 15 p. red and green . . . 55 35
655 – 35 p. black and red (air) . 75 35
656 – 45 p. brown and blue . . 1·40 45
DESIGN: 35, 45 p. Broken chain, dove and olive branch.

131 Scout fixing Tent-peg

1958. Air. 3rd Pan-Arab Scout Jamboree.
657 **131** 35 p. sepia . . . . 3·00 1·50
658 40 p. blue . . . . 3·50 2·25

132 Mosque, Chimneys and Cogwheel **133** Bronze Rattle

1958. Air. 5th Int Fair, Damascus. Inscr "1.9.58".
659 – 25 p. red 50 35
660 – 30 p. green 75 50
661 **132** 45 p. violet 90 55
DESIGNS—HORIZ: 25 p. View of Fair. VERT: 30 p. Minaret, vase and emblem.

1958. Ancient Syrian Art.
662 **133** 10 p. olive 10 10
663 – 15 p. brown 15 10
664 – 20 p. purple 15 15
665 – 30 p. sepia 20 12
666 – 40 p. grey 35 20
667 – 60 p. green 60 25
668 – 75 p. blue 90 35
669 – 100 p. red . . . . 1·25 50
670 – 150 p. purple . . . . . . 2·50 70
DESIGNS: 15 p. Goddess of Spring; 20 p. "Lamgi Mari" (statue); 30 p. Mithras fighting bull; 40 p. Aspasia; 60 p. Minerva; 75 p. Ancient gourd; 100 p. Enamelled vase; 150 p. Mosaic from Omayyad Mosque, Damascus.

1958. International Children's Day. Optd **R A U** and Arabic inscription.
670a **122** 12½ p. olive (postage) . . 35·00 30·00
670b 17½ p. blue (air) . . . . 22·00 22·00
670c 20 p. brown . . . . . . 22·00 22·00

134 Cotton and Textiles **134a** Hand holding Torch, and Iraqi Flag

1958. Air. Aleppo Cotton Festival.
671 **134** 25 p. yellow and sepia . . 50 40
672 35 p. red and sepia . . . 75 55

1958. Republic of Iraq Commemoration.
673 **134a** 12½ p. red 25 10

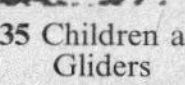

135 Children and Gliders **137** U.N. Emblem and Charter

136 Damascus

1958. Air. Gliding Festival.
674 **135** 7½ p. green 80 30
675 12½ p. olive . . . . 2·25 1·25

1958. 4th N.E. Regional Conference, Damascus.
676 **136** 12½ p. green (postage) . . 30 10
677 17½ p. violet (air) 30 15

1958. Air. 10th Anniv of Declaration of Human Rights.
678 **137** 25 p. purple 20 20
679 35 p. grey 35 25
680 40 p. brown 45 30

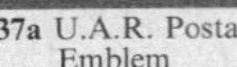
137a U.A.R. Postal Emblem
137b

1959. Post Day and Postal Employees' Social Fund.
681 **137a** 20 p. + 10 p. red, black and green 45 45

1959. 1st Anniv of United Arab Republic.
682 **137b** 12½ p. red, black and green 20 10

138 Secondary School, Damascus

1959.
683 **138** 12½ p. green 15 10

138a "Telecommunications"

1959. Air. Arab Telecommunications Union Commemoration.
684 **138a** 40 p. black and green . . 60 25

1959. No. 684 optd **2nd CONFERANCE DAMASCUS 1.3.1959** in English and Arabic.
685 **138a** 40 p. black and green . . 35 20

139a U.A.R. and Yemeni Flags

1959. 1st Anniv of Proclamation of United Arab States (U.A.R. and Yemen).
686 **139a** 12½ p. red and green . . 25 10

140 Mother with Children

142

1959. Arab Mothers' Day.
687 **140** 15 p. pink 25 10
688 25 p. green 30 20

1959. Surch **U.A.R 2½ p** and also in Arabic.
689 **92** 2½ p. on 1 p. olive 10 10

1959. Air. 13th Anniv of Evacuation of Allied Forces.
690 **142** 15 p. green and yellow . 25 10
691 – 35 p. red and grey . . . 40 25
DESIGN: 35 p. Broken chain and flame.

143
144 "Emigration"

1959. Patterns as T **143**.
692 **143** 2½ p. violet 10 10
693 – 5 p. olive 10 10
694 – 7½ p. blue 15 10
695 – 10 p. green 15 10
DESIGNS: 5 p to 10 p show different styles of ornamental scrollwork.

1959. Air. Emigrants' Congress.
696 **144** 80 p. black, red & green . 80 45

(145)

147

146 Oil Refinery

1959. Optd as T **145**.
697 **115** 15 p. black (postage) . . 35 15
698 – 50 p. green (No. 536) . . 1·00 50
690 – 5 p. green (No. 635) (air) 15 10
700 – 50 p. purple (No. 543) . . 80 25
701 – 70 p. violet (No. 544) . . 1·50 35

1959. Air. Inauguration of Oil Refinery.
702 **146** 50 p. red, black and blue 1·75 40

1959. 6th Damascus Fair.
703 **147** 35 p. green, vio & grey . 40 25

148

149 Child and Factory

1959. Air. Aleppo Cotton Festival.
704 **148** 45 p. slate 50 20
705 50 p. red 50 30

1959. Air. Children's Day.
706 **149** 25 p. red, blue and lilac . 30 15

150 Boys' College, Damascus
150a "Shield against Aggression"

1959.
707 **150** 25 p. blue 50 15
708 – 35 p. brown 60 20
DESIGN: 35 p. Girls' College, Damascus.

1959. Army Day.
709 **150a** 50 p. sepia 75 35

151 Ears of Corn, Cotton, Cogwheel and Factories

152 Mosque and Oaks

1959. Industrial and Agricultural Production Fair, Aleppo.
710 **151** 35 p. brown, blue & grey . 45 25

1959. Tree Day.
711 **152** 12½ p. brown and green . . 30 10

153 A. R. Kawakbi

153a

1960. 50th Death Anniv of A. R. Kawakbi (writer).
712 **153** 15 p. deep green 25 10

1960. 2nd Anniv of U.A.R.
713 **153a** 12½ p. green and red . . . 20 10

154 Diesel Train

1960. Latakia–Aleppo Railway Project.
714 **154** 12½ p. brown, black & bl . 1·50 65

154a Arab League Centre, Cairo

1960. Inaug of Arab League Centre, Cairo.
715 **154a** 12½ p. black and green . . 20 10

1960. Mothers' Day. Optd **ARAB MOTHERS DAY 1960** in English and Arabic.
716 **140** 15 p. pink 25 10
717 25 p. green 30 20

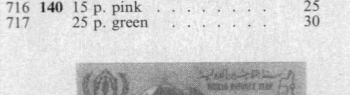

155a Refugee Children

1960. World Refugee Year.
718 **155a** 12½ p red 15 10
719 50 p. green 30 30

156 Government Building and Inscription

1960. 14th Anniv of Evacuation of Allied Forces.
720 **156** 12½ p. multicoloured . . . 35 10

157 Hittin School

1960.
721 **157** 17½ p. lilac 30 10

1960. Industrial and Agricultural Production Fair, Aleppo. Optd **1960** and in Arabic.
722 **151** 35 p. brown, blue & grey 30 20

159 Mobile Crane and Compasses

(160)

1960. Air. 7th International Damascus Fair.
723 **159** 50 p. black, bistre & red . 50 35

1960. Air. Aleppo Cotton Festival. Optd with T **160**.
724 **148** 45 p. slate 45 20
725 50 p. red 50 30

161
162 Basketball

1960. Children's Day.
726 **161** 35 p. brown and green . . 55 25

1960. Air. Olympic Games.
727 **162** 15 p. brown, black & bl . 25 10
728 – 20 p. brown, black & bl . 40 15
729 – 25 p. violet, black & yell . 40 15
730 – 40 p. violet, red & black . 70 35
DESIGNS: 20 p. Swimming; 25 p. Fencing (Arab-style); 40 p. Horse-jumping.

(163)

164 "UN" and Globe

1960. Tree Day. Optd with T **163**.
731 **152** 12½ p. brown and green . 30 15

1960. Air. 15th Anniv of U.N.O.
732 **164** 35 p. red, green & blue . 25 20
733 50 p. blue, ochre & red . 35 25

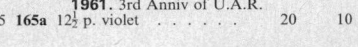

165 Hanano

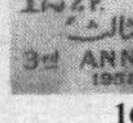
165a

1961. Air. 25th Death Anniv (1960) of Ibrahim Hanano (patriot).
734 **165** 50 p. green and drab . . 45 30

1961. 3rd Anniv of U.A.R.
735 **165a** 12½ p. violet 20 10

166 St. Simeon's Monastery

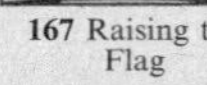
167 Raising the Flag

1961.
736 **166** 12½ p. blue (postage) . . . 20 10
746 – 200 p. blue (air) . . . . . 2·75 60
DESIGN—VERT: 200 p. Entrance to St. Simeon's Monastery.

1961. Air. 15th Anniv of Evacuation of Allied Forces.
737 **167** 40 p. green 50 25

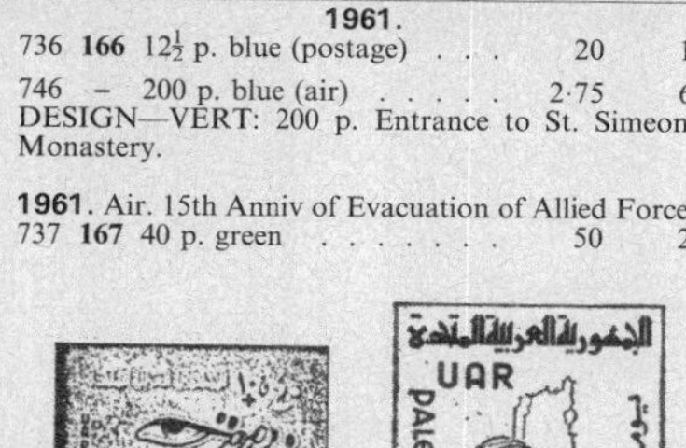

168 Eye and Hand "reading" Braille — **169** Palestinian and Map

1961. Air. U.N. Campaign for Welfare of Blind.
738 **168** 40 p. + 10 p. black and green 45 55

1961. Air. Palestine Day.
739 **169** 50 p. blue and black . . . 1·25 30

170 Cogwheel and Corn — **171** Abou Tammam (796–846)

1961. Industrial and Agricultural Production Fair, Aleppo.
740 **170** 12½ p. multicoloured . . . 25 20

1961. Air. Abou Tammam (writer) Commem.
741 **171** 50 p. brown 55 25

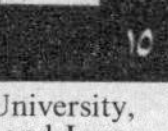

172 Damascus University, Discus-thrower and Lyre — **173** Open Window on World

1961 Air. 5th Universities Youth Festival.
742 **172** 15 p. black and red . . . 30 10
743 35 p. violet and green . . 75 25

1961 Air. 8th International Damascus Fair.
744 **173** 17½ p. violet and green . . 20 10
745 – 50 p. violet and black . . 45 25
DESIGN: 50 p. U.A.R. Pavilion.

SYRIAN ARAB REPUBLIC

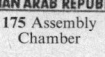

175 Assembly Chamber — **176** The Noria, Hama

177 Arch of Triumph, Latakia — **178** Arab League Emblem and Headquarters, Cairo

1961. Establishment of Syrian Arab Republic.
747 **175** 15 p. purple 20 10
748 35 p. olive 50 25

1961.
749 **176** 2½ p. red (postage) . . . 10 10
750 5 p. blue 20 10
751 – 7½ p. green 40 10
752 – 10 p. orange 60 10
753 **177** 12½ p. drab . . . . . . 1·00 10
754 – 12½ p. green 75 10
755 – 15 p. blue 75 10
756 – 17½ p. brown 85 10
757 – 22½ p. turquoise . . . . . 9·00 10
758 **177** 25 p. brown . . . . . . 1·00 10
759 – 45 p. yellow (air) 75 25
760 – 50 p. red . . . . 1·00 35
761 – 85 p. purple . . . . . . 1·50 40
762 – 100 p. purple . . . . . . 1·75 45
763 – 200 p. green . . . . . . 3·50 80
764 – 300 p. blue . . . . . . 3·75 90
764a – 500 p. purple . . . . . . 6·00 2·00
764b – 1000 p. black . . . . . . 12·00 3·50
DESIGNS: 7½ p, 10 p Khaled ibn-el-Walid Mosque, Homs; 12½ p (No. 754), 15, 17½, 22½, 45, 50 p. "The Beauty of Palmyra" (statue); 85, 100 p. Archway and columns, Palmyra; 200 p. to 1000 p. King Zahir Bibar's tomb.
See also Nos. 799/800.

1962. Air. Arab League Week.
765 **178** 17½ p. turquoise and green 15 10
766 22½ p. violet and blue . . 25 20
767 50 p. sepia and salmon . 50 25

179 Campaign Emblem — **180** Prancing Horse

1962. Air. Malaria Eradication.
768 **179** 12½ p. violet, sepia & bl . 15 10
769 50 p. green, brown & yell 35 30

1962. Air. 16th Anniv of Evacuation of Allied Forces.
770 **180** 45 p. orange and violet . 50 25
771 – 55 p. violet and blue . . 65 30
DESIGN: 55 p. Military commander.

181 Qalb Lozah Church — **182** Martyrs' Memorial, Swaida

1962.
772 **181** 17½ p. olive 40 10
773 35 p. turquoise 55 25

1962. Syrian Revolution Commemoration.
774 **182** 12½ p. brown and drab . . 15 10
775 35 p. turquoise and green 35 20

183 Jupiter Temple Gate — **184** Globe, Monument and Handclasp

1962.
776 **183** 2½ p. turquoise 15 10
777 5 p. brown 30 10
778 7½ p. sepia 70 10
779 10 p. purple 25 10

1962. Air. 9th Int Fair, Damascus.
780 **184** 17½ p. brown and purple . 15 10
781 22½ p. mauve and red . . 20 15
782 – 40 p. dull purple and pale brown 30 20
783 – 45 p. turquoise and green 45 25
DESIGN: 40, 45 p. Fair entrance.

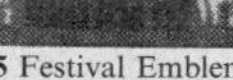

185 Festival Emblem — **186** Pres. Kudsi

1962. Air. Aleppo Cotton Festival.
784 **185** 12½ p. multicoloured . . . 25 15
785 50 p. multicoloured . . . 40 35
See also Nos. 820/1.

1962. Presidential Elections.
786 **186** 12½ p. brown and blue (postage) 20 10
787 50 p. blue and buff (air) . 40 25

187 Zenobia — **188** Saadallah el-Jabiri

1962. Air.
788 **187** 45 p. violet . . . . 1·00 15
789 50 p. red . . . . 1·00 20
790 85 p. turquoise 95 30
791 100 p. purple . . . . . 1·25 50
See also Nos. 801/4.

1962. Air. 15th Death Anniv of Saadallah el-Jabiri (revolutionary).
792 **188** 50 p. blue 40 25

189 Moharde Woman — **190** Ears of Wheat, Hand and Globe

1962. Air. Women in Regional Costumes. Multicoloured.
793 40 p. Marje Sultan 40 15
794 45 p. Kalamoun 50 20
795 50 p. Type **189** 60 20
796 55 p. Jabal al-Arab 70 30
797 60 p. Afrine 75 30
798 65 p. Hauran 90 35

1963. As Nos. 754/7 and T **187** but smaller (20×26 mm).
799 – 2½ p. violet 20 10
800 – 5 p. purple 20 10
801 **187** 7½ p. slate 75 10
802 10 p. drab . . . . . . 1·00 10
803 12½ p. blue . . . . . . 1·50 10
804 15 p. brown . . . . . . 2·00 15

1963. Freedom from Hunger.
805 **190** 12½ p. blk & bl (postage) . 20 10
806 – 50 p. black and red (air) . 60 25
DESIGN: 50 p. Bird feeding young in nest.

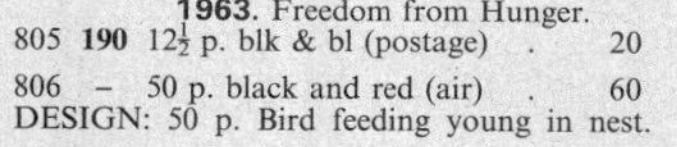

191 Faris el-Khouri (politician) — **192** S.A.R. Emblem

1963. Air. 17th Anniv of Evacuation of Allied Forces.
807 **191** 17½ p. sepia 25 15
808 **192** 22½ p. turquoise and black 25 15

193 Eagle — **194** Ala el-Ma'ari (bust)

1963. Air. Baathist Revolution Commemoration.
809 **193** 12½ p. green 10 10
810 50 p. mauve 40 30

1963. Air. 990th Birth Anniv of Ala el-Ma'ari (poet).
811 **194** 50 p. violet 45 25

195 Copper Water Jug — **196** Central Bank

1963. Air. 10th International Fair, Damascus.
812 **195** 37½ p. multicoloured . . . 40 20
813 50 p. multicoloured . . . 50 25

1963. Damascus Buildings.
814 – 17½ p. violet . . . . . . 1·00 10
815 – 22½ p. violet . . . . . . 1·50 10
816 **196** 25 p. brown 60 20
817 – 35 p. mauve . . . . . . 2·00 20
BUILDINGS: 17½ p. Hejaz Railway Station; 22½ p. Mouassat Hospital; 35 p. Post Office, Al-Jalaa.

197 "Red Crescent" and Centenary Emblem — **198** Child with Ball

1963. Air. Red Cross Centenary. Crescent in red.
818 **197** 15 p. black and blue . . . 35 20
819 – 50 p. black and green . . 65 35
DESIGN: 50 p. "Red Crescent", globe and centenary emblem.

1963. Aleppo Cotton Festival. As T **185** but inscr "POSTAGE" and "1963" in place of "AIRMAIL" and "1962".
820 **185** 17½ p. multicoloured . . . 20 10
821 22½ p. multicoloured . . . 35 15

1963. Children's Day.
822 **198** 12½ p. green and deep green 15 10
823 22½ p. green and red . . . 30 10

199 Firas el-Hamadani — **200** Flame on Head

1963. Air. Death Millenary of Abou Firas el-Hamadani (poet).
824 **199** 50 p. sepia and bistre . . 45 30

1963. Air. 15th Anniv of Declaration of Human Rights. Flame in red.
825 **200** 17½ p. black and grey . . 15 10
826 22½ p. black and green . . 20 15
827 50 p. black and violet . . 35 25

201 Emblem and Flag

1964. Air. 1st Anniv of 8th March Baathist Revolution. Emblem and flag in red, black and green; inscr in black.
828 **201** 15 p. green 10 10
829 17½ p. pink 15 10
830 22½ p. grey 25 15

202 Ugharit Princess — **203** Chahba, Thalassa, Mosaic

1964.
831 **202** 2½ p. grey (postage) . . . 10 10
832 5 p. brown 10 10
833 7½ p. purple 15 10
834 10 p. green 20 10
835 12½ p. violet 25 10
836 17½ p. blue 40 10
837 20 p. red . . . . 1·50 10
838 25 p. orange . . . . . . 2·00 15

839 **203** $27\frac{1}{2}$ p. red (air) 45 10
840 45 p. brown 70 15
841 50 p. green 75 15
842 55 p. bronze 80 25
843 60 p. blue . . . . 1·25 30

204 Kaaba, Mecca, and Mosque, Damascus

1964. Air. 1st Arab Moslem Wakf Ministers' Conference.
844 **204** $12\frac{1}{2}$ p. black and blue . . 10 10
845 $22\frac{1}{2}$ p. black and mauve . 20 15
846 50 p. black and green . . 40 25

1964. Air. 18th Anniv of Evacuation of Allied Forces. As T **99** but larger $38\frac{1}{2}\times26$ mm inscr "1964".
847 **99** 20 p. blue 15 10
848 25 p. mauve 20 15
849 60 p. green 35 25

205 Abou al Zahrawi **206** Bronze Chimes

1964. Air. 4th Arab Dental and Oral Surgery Congress, Damascus.
850 **205** 60 p. brown 70 30

1964. Air. 11th International Fair, Damascus.
851 **206** 20 p. multicoloured . . . 25 10
852 – 25 p. multicoloured . . . 25 15
DESIGN: 25 p. Fair emblem.

207 Cotton Plant and Symbols (**208**)

1964. Air. Aleppo Cotton Festival. No. 854 is optd with T **208**.
853 **207** 25 p. multicoloured . . . 25 10
854 25 p. multicoloured . . . 25 10

209 Aero Club Emblem

1964. Air. 10th Anniv of Syrian Aero Club.
855 **209** $12\frac{1}{2}$ p. black and green . . 20 10
856 $17\frac{1}{2}$ p. black and red . . . 25 15
857 20 p. black and blue . . . 45 15

210 A.U.P. Emblem **211** Book within Hands

1964. Air. 10th Anniv of Arab Postal Union.
858 **210** $12\frac{1}{2}$ p. black and orange . 10 10
859 20 p. black and green . . 15 10
860 25 p. black and mauve . . 20 15

1964. Air. Burning of Algiers Library.
861 **211** $12\frac{1}{2}$ p. black and green . . 10 10
862 $17\frac{1}{2}$ p. black and red . . . 15 10
863 20 p. black and blue . . . 20 15

212 Tennis

1965. Air. Olympic Games, Tokyo. Multicoloured.
864 $12\frac{1}{2}$ p. Type **212** 15 10
865 $17\frac{1}{2}$ p. Wrestling 25 10
866 20 p. Weightlifting 30 15

213 Flag, Map and Revolutionaries

1965. 2nd Anniv of Baathist Revolution of March 8th 1963.
867 **213** $12\frac{1}{2}$ p. multicoloured . . 10 10
868 $17\frac{1}{2}$ p. multicoloured . . 15 10
869 20 p. multicoloured . . . 20 10

214 Rameses II in War Chariot, Abu Simbel

1965. Air. Nubian Monuments Preservation.
870 **214** $22\frac{1}{2}$ p. black, blue & grn . 40 10
871 – 50 p. black, green & blue 60 25
DESIGN: 50 p. Heads of Rameses II.

215 Weather Instruments and Map

1965. World Meteorological Day.
872 **215** $12\frac{1}{2}$ p. black and purple . 10 10
873 $27\frac{1}{2}$ p. black and blue . . 20 15

216 Al-Radi **217** Evacuation Symbol

1965. Air. 950th Death Anniv of Al-Sharif al-Radi (writer).
874 **216** 50 p. black 40 25

1965. 19th Anniv of Evacuation of Allied Forces.
875 **217** $12\frac{1}{2}$ p. green and blue . . 10 10
876 $27\frac{1}{2}$ p. lilac and red . . . 25 15

218 Hippocrates and Avicenna

1965. Air. "Medical Days of the Near and Middle East".
877 **218** 60 p. black and green . . 75 45

219 Dagger on Deir Yassin, Palestine **220** I.T.U. Emblem and Symbols

1965. Air. Deir Yassin Massacre on 9 April 1948.
878 **219** $12\frac{1}{2}$ p. multicoloured . . . 40 10
879 60 p. multicoloured . . . 1·00 30

1965. Air. Centenary of I.T.U.
880 **220** $12\frac{1}{2}$ p. multicoloured . . . 25 10
881 $27\frac{1}{2}$ p. multicoloured . . . 40 15
882 60 p. multicoloured . . . 70 45

221 Arab Family, Flags and Map **222** Hands holding Hoe and Pick

1965. Palestine Week.
883 **221** $12\frac{1}{2}$ p. + 5 p. multicoloured 40 25
884 25 p. + 5 p. multicoloured 50 40

1965. Peasants' Union.
885 **222** $2\frac{1}{2}$ p. green 10 10
886 $12\frac{1}{2}$ p. violet 10 10
887 15 p. purple 10 10
The above stamps are inscr "RERUBLIC" for "REPUBLIC".

223 Welcoming Emigrant **224** Fair Entrance

1965. Air. "Welcome Arab Emigrants".
888 **223** 25 p. multicoloured . . . 25 10
889 100 p. multicoloured . . . 65 30

1965. Air. 12th Int Fair, Damascus. Multicoloured.
890 $12\frac{1}{2}$ p. Type **224** 10 10
891 $27\frac{1}{2}$ p. Globe and compasses . 20 10
892 60 p. Syrian brassware . . . 35 25

226 Cotton Boll and Shuttles

1965. Air. Aleppo Industrial and Agricultural Production Fair. Optd **INDUSTRIAL & AGRICULTURAL PRODUCTION FAIR—ALEPPO 1965** in English and Arabic.
893 **226** 25 p. multicoloured . . . 20 10

1965. Air. Aleppo Cotton Festival.
894 **226** 25 p. multicoloured . . . 20 10

227 I.C.Y. Emblem and View of Damascus

1965. Air. International Co-operation Year.
895 **227** 25 p. multicoloured . . . 40 15

228 Arabs, Torch and Map **229** Industrial Workers

1965. National Revolution Council.
896 **228** $12\frac{1}{2}$ p. multicoloured . . . 10 10
897 25 p. multicoloured . . . 20 10

1966. Labour Unions.
898 **229** $12\frac{1}{2}$ p. blue 10 10
899 15 p. red 10 10
900 20 p. lilac 20 10
901 25 p. drab 30 15

230 Radio Aerial, Globe and Flag **231** Dove-shaped Hand holding Flower

1966. Air. Arab Information Ministers' Conf, Damascus.
902 **230** 25 p. multicoloured . . . 20 10
903 60 p. multicoloured . . . 40 25

1966. Air. 3rd Anniv of March 8th Revolution. Multicoloured.
904 $12\frac{1}{2}$ p. Type **231** 10 10
905 $17\frac{1}{2}$ p. Revolutionaries (horiz) 10 10
906 50 p. Type **231** 60 25

232 Colossi, Abu Simbel **233** Roman Lamp

1966. Air. Nubian Monuments Preservation Week.
907 **232** 25 p. blue 35 10
908 60 p. grey 75 25

1966.
909 **233** $2\frac{1}{2}$ p. green 10 10
910 5 p. purple 30 10
911 – $7\frac{1}{2}$ p. brown 15 10
912 – 10 p. violet 25 10
DESIGN: $7\frac{1}{2}$, 10 p. 12th-century Islamic vessel.

234 U.N. Emblem and Headquarters

1966. Air. 20th Anniv of U.N.
913 **234** 25 p. black and grey . . . 15 10
914 50 p. black and green . . 30 20

236 "Evacuation" (abstract)

1966. 20th Anniv of Evacuation of Allied Forces.
916 **236** $12\frac{1}{2}$ p. multicoloured . . . 10 10
917 $27\frac{1}{2}$ p. multicoloured . . . 20 15

237 Workers marching across Globe

1966. Air. Labour Day.
918 **237** 60 p. multicoloured . . . 35 25

238 W.H.O. Building **239** Traffic Signals and Map on Hand

1966. Air. Inauguration of W.H.O. Headquarters, Geneva.

919	238	60 p. black, blue & yellow	60	25

1966. Air. Traffic Day.

920	239	25 p. multicoloured	50	10

240 Astarte and Tyche (wrongly inscr "ASTRATE") 241 Fair Emblem

1966. Air.

921	240	50 p. brown	1·00	20
922		60 p. grey	1·25	25

1966. Air. 13th International Fair, Damascus.

923	241	12½ p. multicoloured	10	10
924		60 p. multicoloured	35	30

242 Shuttle (stylised) 243 Decade Emblem

1966. Air. Aleppo Cotton Festival.

925	242	50 p. black, red and grey	35	25

1966. Air. International Hydrological Decade.

926	243	12½ p. black, orange & grn	15	10
927		60 p. black, orange & blue	50	30

244 Emir Abd-el-Kader 245 U.N.R.W.A. Emblem

1966. Air. Return of Emir Abd-el-Kader's Remains to Algiers.

928	244	12½ p. black and green	20	10
929		50 p. brown and green	35	25

1966. Air. 21st Anniv of U.N. Day and Refugee Week.

930	245	12½ p. + 2½ p. black and blue	10	10
931		50 p. + 5 p. black and green	25	35

246 Handclasp and Map 247 Doves and Oil Pipelines

1967. Air. Solidarity Congress, Damascus.

932	246	20 p. multicoloured	15	10
933		25 p. multicoloured	20	15

1967. Air. 4th Anniv of Baathist Revolution of 8 March 1963.

934	247	17½ p. multicoloured	20	10
935		25 p. multicoloured	25	15
936		27½ p. multicoloured	30	15

248 Soldier and Citizens with Banner 249 Workers' Monument, Damascus

1967. Air. 21st Anniv of Evacuation.

937	248	17½ p. green	20	10
938		25 p. purple	25	15
939		27½ p. blue	30	15

1967. Air. Labour Day.

940	249	12½ p. turquoise	10	10
941		50 p. mauve	35	25

250 Core Bust 251 "African Woman" (vase)

252 Head of a Young Man from Amrith 253 Flags and Fair Entrance

1967.

942	250	2½ p. green (postage)	10	10
943		5 p. red	10	10
944		10 p. blue	15	10
945		12½ p. brown	20	10
946	251	15 p. purple	20	10
947		20 p. blue	30	10
948		25 p. green	40	10
949		27½ p. blue	60	10
950	252	45 p. red (air)	70	20
951		50 p. red	80	20
952		60 p. turquoise	1·25	35
953	–	100 p. green	1·40	45
954	–	500 p. red	6·00	2·25

DESIGN—VERT: 100, 500 p. Bust of Princess (2nd-century bronze).

1967. Air. 14th International Damascus Fair.

955	253	12½ p. multicoloured	10	10
956		60 p. multicoloured	35	25

254 Statue of Ur-Nina and Tourist Emblem 255 Cotton Boll and Cogwheel

1967. Air. International Tourist Year.

957	254	12½ p. purple, black & bl	10	10
958		25 p. red, black and blue	15	10
959		27½ p. blue, black & lt bl	25	15

1967. Air. Aleppo Cotton Festival.

961	255	12½ p. black, brown and yellow	10	10
962		60 p. black, brown and yellow	30	25

1967. Air. Industrial and Agricultural Production Fair, Aleppo. Optd **INDUSTRIAL AND AGRICULTURAL PRODUCTION FAIR ALEPPO 1967** in English and Arabic.

963	255	12½ p. black, brown & yell	10	10
964		60 p. black, brown & yell	30	25

257 Ibn el-Naphis (scientist) 258 Acclaiming Human Rights

1967. Air. Sciences Week.

965	257	12½ p. red and green	10	10
966		27½ p. mauve and blue	15	10

1968. Air. Human Rights Year.

967	258	12½ p. black, turquoise and blue	10	10
968		60 p. black, red and pink	30	25

259 Learning to Read 260 "The Arab Revolutionary" (Damascus statue)

1968. Air. Literacy Campaign.

970	259	12½ p. multicoloured	10	10
971	–	17½ p. multicoloured	10	10
972	259	25 p. multicoloured	20	10
973	–	45 p. multicoloured	25	20

DESIGN: 17½, 45 p. Flaming torch and open book.

1968. 5th Anniv of March 8th Baathist Revolution.

974	260	12½ p. brown, yell & blk	10	10
975		25 p. mauve, pink & blk	20	10
976		27½ p. green, light green and black	20	15

261 Map of North Africa and Arabia 263 Hands holding Spanner, Rifle and Torch

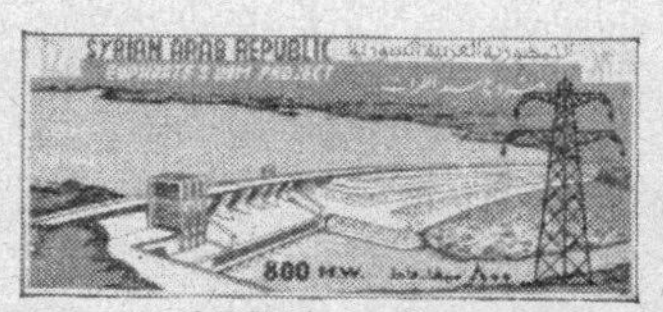

262 Euphrates Dam

1968. 21st Anniv of Baath Arab Socialist Party.

977	261	12½ p. multicoloured	10	10
978		60 p. multicoloured	35	25

1968. Air. Euphrates Dam Project.

979	262	12½ p. multicoloured	20	10
980		17½ p. multicoloured	25	15
981		25 p. multicoloured	50	20

1968. "Mobilisation Efforts".

982	263	12½ p. multicoloured	10	10
983		17½ p. multicoloured	15	10
984		25 p. multicoloured	25	15

264 Railway Track and Sun 266 Torch, Map and Laurel

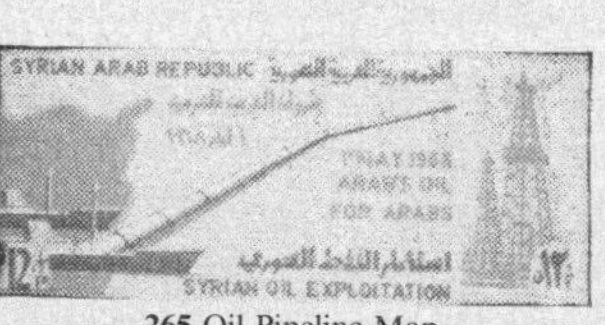

265 Oil Pipeline Map

1968. 22nd Anniv of Evacuation of Allied Forces.

985	264	12½ p. multicoloured	75	60
986		27½ p. multicoloured	1·75	1·40

1968. Syrian Oil Exploration.

987	265	12½ p. blue, green and yellow	25	10
988		17½ p. blue, brown & pink	50	20

1968. Palestine Day.

989	266	12½ p. multicoloured	20	10
990		25 p. multicoloured	40	15
991		27½ p. multicoloured	65	20

267 Refugee Family

1968. Red Crescent Refugees Fund.

992	267	12½ p. + 2½ p. black, purple and blue	20	25
993		27½ p. + 7½ p. black, red and violet	20	25

268 Avenzoar (physician) and W.H.O. Emblem 269 Ear of Corn, Cogwheel and Saracen Gate, Aleppo Citadel

1968. Air. 20th Anniv of W.H.O.

994	268	12½ p. multicoloured	15	10
995	–	25 p. multicoloured	25	10
996	–	60 p. multicoloured	45	25

DESIGNS—As Type **268**, but with different portraits of Arab physicians: 25 p. Razi; 60 p. Jabir.

1968. Industrial and Agricultural Production Fair, Aleppo.

997	269	12½ p. multicoloured	10	10
998		27½ p. multicoloured	15	10

270 Emblems of Fair, Agriculture and Industry 271 Gathering Cotton

1968. 15th International Damascus Fair.

999	270	12½ p. black, grn & brn	10	10
1000	–	27½ p. multicoloured	20	10
1001	270	60 p. black, orge & blue	30	25

DESIGN—HORIZ: 27½ p. Flag, hand with torch and emblems.

1968. Aleppo Cotton Festival.

1002	271	12½ p. multicoloured	10	10
1003		27½ p. multicoloured	15	10

272 Monastery of St. Simeon the Stylite 273 Oil Derrick

1968. Air. Ancient Monuments (1st series).

1004	272	15 p. multicoloured	15	10
1005	–	17½ p. purple, brown and chocolate	20	10
1006	–	22½ p. multicoloured	25	15
1007	–	45 p. multicoloured	40	20
1008	–	50 p. brown, sepia and blue	45	25

DESIGNS—VERT: 17½ p. El Tekkieh Mosque, Damascus; 22½ p. Temple columns, Palmyra. HORIZ: 45 p. Chapel of St. Paul, Bab Kisan; 50 p. Amphitheatre, Bosra.

See also Nos. 1026/30.

1968.

1009	273	2½ p. green and blue	15	10
1010		5 p. blue and green	15	10
1011		7½ p. blue and green	20	10
1012		10 p. green and yellow	20	10
1013		12½ p. red and yellow	30	10
1014		15 p. brown and bistre	35	10
1015		27½ p. brown & orange	55	15

274 Al-Jahez (scientist) 275 Throwing the Hammer

1968. 9th Science Week.
1016 **274** 12½ p. black and olive . . 10 10
1017 27½ p. black and grey . . 15 15

1968. Air. Olympic Games, Mexico.
1018 **275** 12½ p. black, mauve and green 10 10
1019 – 25 p. black, red & green . 15 10
1020 – 27½ p. black, grey and green 20 15
1021 – 60 p. multicoloured . . . 30 25
DESIGNS—VERT: 25 p. Throwing the discus; 27½ p. Running; 60 p. Basketball. HORIZ (53×36 mm): 50 p. Polo.

276 Aerial View of Airport

1969. Air. Construction of Damascus Int Airport.
1023 **276** 12½ p. green, blue & yell . 25 10
1024 17½ p. violet, red and green 30 10
1025 60 p. black, mauve and yellow 85 30

277 Baal-Shamin Temple, Palmyra

1969. Air. Ancient Monuments (2nd series). Multicoloured.
1026 25 p. Type **277** 25 10
1027 45 p. Omayyad Mosque, Damascus (vert) 35 15
1028 50 p. Amphitheatre, Palmyra 40 20
1029 60 p. Khaled ibn el-Walid Mosque, Homs (vert) . . . 45 20
1030 100 p. St. Simeon's Column, Jebel Samaan 70 35

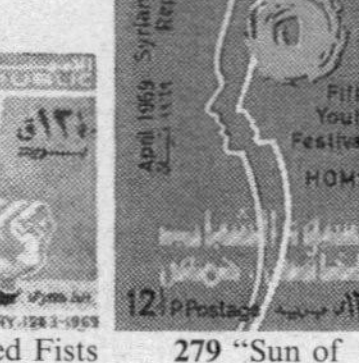

278 "Sun" and Clenched Fists in Broken Handcuffs 279 "Sun of Freedom"

1969. 6th Anniv of March 8th Baathist Revolution.
1031 **278** 12½ p. multicoloured . . 10 10
1032 25 p. multicoloured . . . 20 10
1033 27½ p. multicoloured . . . 20 10

1969. 5th Youth Week.
1034 **279** 12½ p. red, yellow and blue 10 10
1035 25 p. red, yellow and green 15 10

280 Symbols of Progress 281 "Workers", Cogwheel and I.L.O. Emblem

1969. 23rd Anniv of Evacuation of Allied Forces.
1036 **280** 12½ p. multicoloured . . 10 10
1037 27½ p. multicoloured . . 15 10

1969. Air. 50th Anniv of I.L.O.
1038 **281** 12½ p. multicoloured . . 10 10
1039 27½ p. multicoloured . . 20 10

282 Russian Dancers 283 "Fortune" (statue)

1969. Air. 16th Int Damascus Fair. Mult.
1041 12½ p. Type **282** 25 20
1042 27½ p. Ballet dancers 40 25
1043 45 p. Lebanese dancers . . . 40 35
1044 55 p. Egyptian dancers . . . 50 35
1045 60 p. Bulgarian dancers . . 55 35

1969. Air. 9th Int Archaeological Congress, Damascus. Multicoloured.
1046 17½ p. Type **283** 20 10
1047 25 p. "Lady from Palmyra" (statue) 25 15
1048 60 p. "Motherhood" (statue) 55 25

284 Children dancing 285 Mahatma Gandhi

1969. Air. Children's Day.
1049 **284** 12½ p. green, blue and turquoise 15 10
1050 25 p. violet, blue & red . 20 10
1051 27½ p. grey, dp blue & blue 25 15

1969. Birth Centenary of Mahatma Gandhi.
1052 **285** 12½ p. brown and buff . 25 15
1053 27½ p. green and yellow . 65 25

286 Cotton 287 "Arab World" (6th Arab Science Congress)

1969. Aleppo Cotton Festival.
1054 **286** 12½ p. multicoloured . . 10 10
1055 17½ p. multicoloured . . 10 10
1056 25 p. multicoloured . . 15 10

1969. 10th Science Week.
1057 **287** 12½ p. blue and green . . 10 10
1058 – 25 p. violet and pink . . 20 15
1059 – 27½ p. ochre and green . 25 15
DESIGNS: 25 p. Arab Academy (50th anniv); 27½ p. Damascus University (50th anniv of Faculty of Medicine.).

288 Cockerel

1969. Air. Damascus Agricultural Museum. Multicoloured.
1060 12½ p. Type **288** 20 15
1061 17½ p. Cow 20 15
1062 20 p. Maize 25 20
1063 50 p. Olives 30 25

289 Rising Sun, Hand and Book

1970. 7th Anniv of March 8th Baathist Revolution.
1064 **289** 17½ p. black, brn & blue 10 10
1065 25 p. black, blue & red . 15 10
1066 27½ p. black, brn & grn . 20 15

290 Map of Arab World, League Emblem and Flag

1970. Silver Jubilee of Arab League.
1067 **290** 12½ p. multicoloured . . . 10 10
1068 25 p. multicoloured . . . 15 10
1069 27½ p. multicoloured . . . 20 15

291 Dish Aerial and Hand on Book

1970. Air. World Meteorological Day.
1070 **291** 25 p. black, yellow & grn 40 15
1071 60 p. black, yellow & blue 60 30

292 Lenin

1970. Air. Birth Centenary of Lenin.
1072 **292** 15 p. brown and red . . . 15 10
1073 60 p. green and red . . . 45 30

293 Battle of Hattin

1970. 24th Anniv of Evacuation of Allied Forces.
1074 **293** 15 p. brown and cream . . 25 15
1075 35 p. violet and cream . . 40 25

294 Emblem of Workers' Syndicate

1970. Air. Labour Day.
1076 **294** 15 p. brown and green . . 10 10
1077 60 p. brown and orange . 35 30

295 Young Syrians and Map

1970. Revolution's Youth Union, 1st Youth Week.
1078 **295** 15 p. green and ochre . . 15 10
1079 25 p. brown and ochre . . 20 15
This issue is inscr "YOUTH'S FIRST WEAK" in error.

296 Refugee Family

1970. World Arab Refugee Week.
1080 **296** 15 p. multicoloured . . . 10 10
1081 25 p. multicoloured . . . 15 10
1082 35 p. multicoloured . . . 20 15

297 Dish Aerial and Open Book

1970. Air. World Telecommunications Day.
1083 **297** 15 p. black and lilac . . 15 10
1084 60 p. black and blue . . 55 30

298 New U.P.U. Headquarters Building

1970. New U.P.U. Headquarters Building.
1085 **298** 15 p. multicoloured . . . 10 10
1086 60 p. multicoloured . . . 40 30

299 "Industry" and Graph 300 Khaled ibn el-Walid

1970.
1087 **299** 2½ p. red and brown (postage) 15 10
1088 5 p. blue and orange . . 40 10
1089 7½ p. black and purple . 20 10
1090 10 p. bistre and brown . 20 10
1091 12½ p. red and blue . . . 20 10
1092 15 p. purple and green . 30 10
1093 20 p. red and blue . . . 45 10
1094 22½ p. black and brown . 50 10
1095 25 p. blue and grey . . . 50 10
1096 27½ p. brown and green . . 75 10
1097 35 p. green and red . . . 80 15
1098 **300** 45 p. mauve (air) 80 15
1099 50 p. green 85 20
1100 60 p. purple 90 30
1101 100 p. blue . . . . . . 1·00 25
1102 200 p. green . . . . . . 3·00 75
1103 300 p. violet . . . . . . 4·00 1·50
1104 500 p. black . . . . . . 5·50 2·75

301 Medieval Warriors

1970. Air. Folk Tales and Legends.
1105 **301** 5 p. multicoloured . . . 20 20
1106 – 10 p. multicoloured . . . 20 20
1107 – 15 p. multicoloured . . . 20 20
1108 – 20 p. multicoloured . . . 25 25
1109 – 60 p. multicoloured . . . 45 45
Nos. 1106/9 show horsemen similar to Type **301**.

302 Cotton

1970. Aleppo Agricultural and Industrial Fair. Multicoloured.
1110 5 p. Type **302** 15 15
1111 10 p. Tomatoes 15 15
1112 15 p. Tobacco 15 15
1113 20 p. Sugar beet 20 20
1114 35 p. Wheat 30 30

303 Mosque in Flames

1970. Air. 1st Anniv of Burning of Al-Aqsa Mosque, Jerusalem.
1115 **303** 15 p. multicoloured . . . 40 15
1116 60 p. multicoloured . . . 1·00 40

304 Wood-carving

1970. Air. 17th Damascus Int Fair. Mult.
1117 15 p. Type **304** 20 20
1118 20 p. Jewellery 20 20
1119 25 p. Glass-making 25 25
1120 30 p. Copper-engraving . . . 35 35
1121 60 p. Shell-work 40 40

305 Scout, Encampment and Badge

1970. Pan-Arab Scout Jamboree, Damascus.
1122 **305** 15 p. grey-green 50 15

306 Olive Tree and Emblem 307 I.E.Y. Emblem

1970. World Year of Olive-oil Production.
1123 **306** 15 p. multicoloured . . . 20 10
1124 25 p. multicoloured . . . 30 15

1970. Air. International Education Year.
1125 **307** 15 p. brown, green & blk 10 10
1126 60 p. brown, blue & blk . 40 30

308 U.N. Emblems

1970. Air. 25th Anniv of U.N.O.
1127 **308** 15 p. multicoloured . . . 10 10
1128 60 p. multicoloured . . . 35 30

309 Protective Shield 310 Girl holding Garland

1971. 8th Anniv of March 8th Baathist Revolution.
1129 **309** 15 p. blue, yellow & grn . 10 10
1130 22½ p. green, yellow & brn 15 10
1131 27½ p. brown, yellow & bl 20 15

1971. Air. 25th Anniv of Evacuation of Allied Forces.
1132 **310** 15 p. multicoloured . . . 15 10
1133 60 p. multicoloured . . . 50 30

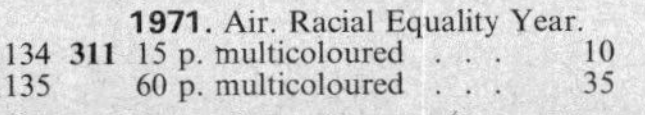
311 Globe and World Races

1971. Air. Racial Equality Year.
1134 **311** 15 p. multicoloured . . . 10 10
1135 60 p. multicoloured . . . 35 25

312 Soldier, Worker and Labour Emblems

1971. Labour Day.
1136 **312** 15 p. purple, blue & yell 10 10
1137 25 p. deep blue, blue and yellow 20 15

313 Hailing Traffic

1971. World Traffic Day.
1138 **313** 15 p. red, blue & black . 40 10
1139 – 25 p. multicoloured . . 60 15
1140 **313** 45 p. red, yellow & blk 1·00 40
DESIGN—VERT: 25 p. Traffic signs and signal lights.

314 Cotton, Cogwheel and Factories

1971. Aleppo Agricultural and Industrial Fair.
1141 **314** 15 p. black, blue & grn . 15 10
1142 30 p. black, red & pink . 25 15

315 A.P.U. Emblem 317 Flag and Federation Map

316 Peppers and Fertiliser Plant

1971. 25th Anniv of Sofar Conference and Founding of Arab Postal Union.
1143 **315** 15 p. multicoloured . . 12 10
1144 20 p. multicoloured . . 20 10

1971. 18th Damascus International Fair. Industries. Multicoloured.
1145 5 p. Type **316** 10 10
1146 15 p. TV set and telephone ("Electronics") 15 10
1147 35 p. Oil lamp and dish ("Glassware") 45 15
1148 50 p. Part of carpet ("Carpets") 65 30

1971. Arab Federation Referendum.
1149 **317** 15 p. black, red & green 15 10

318 Pres. Hafez al-Assad and People's Council Chamber

1971. Air. People's Council and Presidential Election.
1150 **318** 15 p. multicoloured . . 15 10
1151 65 p. multicoloured . . 45 25

319 Pres. Nasser

320 "Telstar" and Dish Aerial

1971. Air. 1st Death Anniv of Pres. Nasser of Egypt.
1152 **319** 15 p. brown and green . . 20 10
1153 20 p. brown and grey . . 30 10

1971. 25th Anniv of U.N.E.S.C.O.
1154 **320** 15 pp. multicoloured . . 20 10
1155 50 p. multicoloured . . . 60 25

321 Flaming Torch 322 Quill-pen and Open Book

1971. "Movement of 16 November 1970".
1156 **321** 15 p. multicoloured . . . 10 10
1157 20 p. multicoloured . . . 20 15

1971. 8th Writers' Congress.
1158 **322** 15 p. brown, orange and turquoise 15 10

323 Children with Ball 324 Book Year Emblem

1971. 25th Anniv of U.N.I.C.E.F.
1159 **323** 15 p. red, blue and deep blue 15 10
1160 25 p. ochre, green & bl . 25 15

1972. International Book Year.
1161 **324** 15 p. lilac, blue & brown 15 10
1162 20 p. green, light green and brown 25 15

325 Emblems of Reconstruction 326 Baath Party Emblem

1972. 9th Anniv of March 8th Baathist Revolution.
1163 **325** 15 p. violet and green . . 15 10
1164 20 p. lake and brown . . 20 10

1972. 25th Anniv of Baath Party.
1165 **326** 15 p. multicoloured . . . 15 10
1166 20 p. multicoloured . . . 20 10

327 Eagle, Factory Chimneys and Rifles 328 Flowers and Broken Chain

1972. 1st Anniv of Arab Republics Federation.
1167 **327** 15 p. gold, black & red . 15 10

1972. 26th Anniv of Evacuation of Allied Forces.
1168 **328** 15 p. grey and red 20 10
1169 50 p. grey and green . . . 60 35

329 Hand with Spanner 331 Environment Emblem

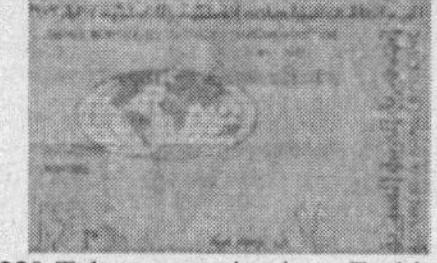
330 Telecommunications Emblem

1972. Labour Day.
1170 **329** 15 p. multicoloured . . . 15 10
1171 50 p. multicoloured . . . 40 30

1972. Air. World Telecommunications Day.
1172 **330** 15 p. multicoloured . . . 25 10
1173 50 p. multicoloured . . . 75 30

1972. U.N. Environmental Conservation Conf, Stockholm.
1174 **331** 15 p. blue, azure & pink 25 10
1175 50 p. purple, orge & yell 75 35

332 Discus, Football and Swimming

1972. Olympic Games, Munich.
1176 **332** 15 p. violet, black & brn 15 10
1177 – 60 p. orange, black & bl 55 40
DESIGN: 60 p. Running, gymnastics and fencing.

334 Dove and Factory

335 President Hafez al-Assad

1972. Aleppo Agricultural and Industrial Fair.
1179 **334** 15 p. multicoloured . . . 20 10
1180 20 p. multicoloured . . . 25 10

1972. Air.
1181 **335** 100 p. green . . . . . . 1·50 40
1182 500 p. brown . . . . . 5·00 1·60

336 Women's Dance

1972. 19th Damascus International Fair. Mult.
1183 15 p. Type **336** 25 10
1184 20 p. Tambourine dance . . 35 15
1185 50 p. Men's drum dance . . 80 45

337 Airline Emblem

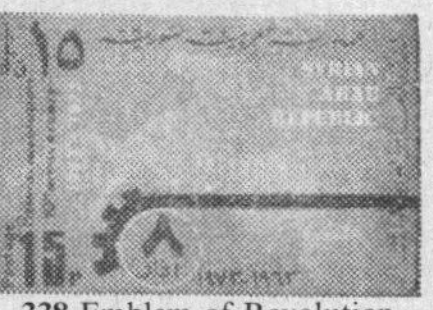
338 Emblem of Revolution

1972. Air. 25th Anniv of "Syrianair" Airline.
1186 **337** 15 p. blue, light blue and black 30 10
1187 50 p. blue, grey & black 95 25

1973. 10th Anniv of March 8th Baathist Revolution.
1188 **338** 15 p. green, red & black 10 10
1189 20 p. orange, red & blk . 15 10
1190 25 p. blue, red & black . 20 10

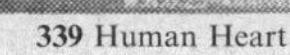
339 Human Heart

340 Emblems of Agriculture and Industry

1973. 25th Anniv of W.H.O.
1191 **339** 15 p. blue, purple & grey . . 30 10
1192 20 p. blue, purple & brn . . 80 25

1973. 27th Anniv of Evacuation of Allied Forces.
1193 **340** 15 p. multicoloured . . . 15 10
1194 20 p. multicoloured . . . 15 10

341 Globe and Workers

1973. Labour Day.
1195 **341** 15 p. black, pink & yell . 10 10
1196 50 p. black, blue & buff . 40 25

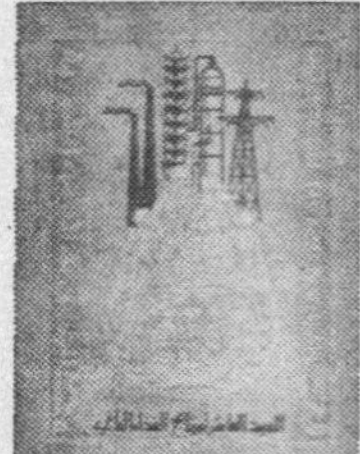

342 Family and Emblems **343** Three Heads

1973. 10th Anniv of World Food Programme.
1197 **342** 15 p. brown and green . 20 10
1198 50 p. blue and purple . . 55 20

1973.
1199 **343** $2\frac{1}{2}$ p. green 10 10
1200 5 p. orange 10 10
1201 – $7\frac{1}{2}$ p. brown 15 10
1202 – 10 p. red 15 10
1203 **343** 15 p. blue 25 10
1204 – 25 p. blue 30 10
1205 – 35 p. blue 45 10
1206 – 55 p. green 75 15
1207 – 70 p. purple . . . . . . 1·25 20
DESIGNS—HORIZ: $7\frac{1}{2}$, 10, 55 p. As Type **343**, but with one head above the other two. VERT: 25, 35, 70 p. Similar to Type **343**, but with heads in vertical arrangement.

344 Stock

1973. Int Flower Show, Damascus. Mult.
1208 5 p. Type **344** 25 25
1209 10 p. Gardenia 25 25
1210 15 p. Jasmine 30 30
1211 20 p. Rose 35 35
1212 25 p. Narcissus 40 40

345 Cogs and Flowers

1973. Aleppo Agricultural and Industrial Fair.
1213 **345** 15 p. multicoloured . . . 15 10

346 Euphrates Dam

1973. Euphrates Dam Project. Diversion of the River.
1214 **346** 15 p. multicoloured . . . 50 20
1215 50 p. multicoloured . . . 1·25 45

347 Deir Ezzor Costume **348** Anniversary Emblem

1973. 20th Damascus International Fair. Costumes. Multicoloured.
1216 5 p. Type **347** 25 25
1217 10 p. Hassake 30 30
1218 20 p. As Sahel 40 40
1219 25 p. Zakie 40 40
1220 50 p. Sarakeb 45 45

1973. 25th Anniv of Declaration of Human Rights.
1221 **348** 15 p. black, red & green . 10 10
1222 50 p. black, red & blue . 30 15

349 Citadel of Ja'abar

1973. "Save the Euphrates Monuments" Campaign. Multicoloured.
1223 10 p. Type **349** 15 10
1224 15 p. Meskeneh Minaret (vert) . 25 10
1225 25 p. Psyche, Anab al-Safinah (vert) 45 20

350 W.M.O. Emblem

1973. Centenary of W.M.O.
1226 **350** 70 p. multicoloured . . 60 25

351 Ancient City of Maalula

1973. Arab Emigrants' Congress, Buenos Aires.
1227 **351** 15 p. black and blue . . 15 10
1228 – 50 p. black and brown . 45 20
DESIGN: 50 p. Ruins of Afamia.

352 Soldier and Workers **353** Copernicus

1973. 3rd Anniv of November 16th Revolution.
1229 **352** 15 p. blue and brown . 10 10
1230 25 p. violet and red . . 20 10

1973. 14th Science Week.
1231 **353** 15 p. black and gold . . 25 10
1232 – 25 p. black and gold . . 40 15
DESIGN: 25 p. Al-Biruni.

354 National Symbols **355** U.P.U. Monument, Berne

1973. 11th Anniv of March 8th Baathist Revolution.
1233 **354** 10 p. blue and green . . 10 10
1234 25 p. blue and green . . 10 10

1974. Centenary of U.P.U. Multicoloured.
1235 15 p. Type **355** 10 10
1236 20 p. Emblem on airmail letter (horiz) 15 10
1237 70 p. Type **355** 40 35

356 Postal Institute

1974. Inauguration of Higher Arab Postal Institute, Damascus.
1238 **356** 15 p. multicoloured . . . 15 10

357 Sun and Monument **358** Machine Fitter

1974. 28th Anniv of Evacuation of Allied Forces.
1239 **357** 15 p. multicoloured . . . 10 10
1240 20 p. multicoloured . . . 15 10

1974. Labour Day.
1241 **358** 15 p. multicoloured . . . 10 10
1242 50 p. multicoloured . . . 30 20

359 Abul Fida (historian) **360** Diamond and Part of Cogwheel

1974. Famous Arabs.
1243 **359** 100 p. green . . . . . . 1·00 35
1244 – 100 p. brown . . . . . . 2·00 70
DESIGN: 200 p. Al-Farabi (philosopher and encyclopedist).

1974. 21st Damascus International Fair. Mult.
1245 15 p. Type **360** 10 10
1246 25 p. "Sun" within cogwheel . 15 10

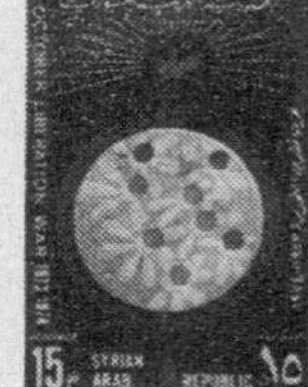

361 Figs **362** Flowers within Drop of Blood

1974. Aleppo Agricultural and Industrial Fair. Fruits. Multicoloured.
1247 5 p. Type **361** 25 25
1248 15 p. Grapes 25 25
1249 20 p. Pomegranates 30 30
1250 25 p. Cherries 30 30
1251 35 p. Rose-hips 35 35

1974. 1st Anniv of October Liberation War. Multicoloured.
1252 15 p. Type **362** 20 10
1253 20 p. Flower and stars . . . 30 10

363 Knight and Rook **364** Symbolic Figure, Globe and Emblem

1974. 50th Anniv of International Chess Federation.
1254 **363** 15 p. blue, lt blue & blk . 60 15
1255 – 50 p. multicoloured . . . 2·25 1·25
DESIGN: 50 p. Knight on chessboard.

1974. World Population Year.
1256 **364** 50 p. multicoloured . . . 35 20

365 Ishtup-ilum **366** Oil Rig and Crowd

1974. Statuettes.
1257 **365** 20 p. green 20 10
1258 – 55 p. brown 35 15
1259 – 70 p. blue 55 20
DESIGNS: 55 p. Woman with vase; 70 p. Ur-nina.

1975. 12th Anniv of Baathist Revolution of 8 March 1963.
1260 **366** 15 p. multicoloured . . . 20 10

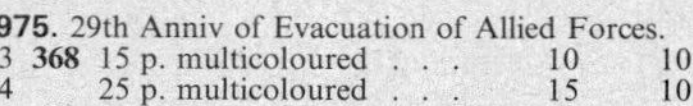

367 Savings Emblem and Family ("Savings Certificates") **368** Dove Emblem

1975. Savings Campaign.
1261 **367** 15 p. black, orge & grn . . 10 10
1262 – 20 p. brown, blk & pink . 20 10
DESIGN: 20 p. Family with savings box and letter ("Postal Savings Bank").

1975. 29th Anniv of Evacuation of Allied Forces.
1263 **368** 15 p. multicoloured . . . 10 10
1264 25 p. multicoloured . . . 15 10

369 Worker supporting Cog **370** Camomile

1975. Labour Day.
1265 **369** 15 p. multicoloured . . . 10 10
1266 25 p. multicoloured . . . 15 10

1975. International Flower Show, Damascus. Multicoloured.
1267 5 p. Type **370** 20 20
1268 10 p. Chincherinchi 25 25
1269 15 p. Carnations 25 25
1270 20 p. Poppy 30 30
1271 25 p. Honeysuckle 30 30

371 "Destruction and Reconstruction"

1975. Reoccupation of Qneitra.
1272 **371** 50 p. multicoloured . . . 45 20

372 Apples **373** Arabesque Pattern

1975. Aleppo Agricultural and Industrial Fair. Fruits. Multicoloured.
1273 5 p. Type **372** 20 20
1274 10 p. Quinces 25 25
1275 15 p. Apricots 25 25
1276 20 p. Grapes 30 30
1277 25 p. Figs 30 30

1975. 22nd International Damascus Fair.
1278 **373** 15 p. multicoloured . . . 10 10
1279 35 p. multicoloured . . . 30 15

374 Pres. Hafez al-Assad

1975. 5th Anniv of "Movement of 16 November 1970".
1280 **374** 15 p. multicoloured . . . 10 10
1281 50 p. multicoloured . . . 30 20

375 Symbolic Woman
376 Bronze "Horse" Lamp

1976. International Women's Year. Multicoloured.
1282 10 p. Type **375** 10 10
1283 15 p. "Motherhood" 10 10
1284 25 p. "Education" 15 15
1285 50 p. "Science" 35 20

1976.
1286 – 5 p. green 10 10
1287 **376** 10 p. green 15 10
1288 – 10 p. blue 15 10
1289 – 15 p. brown 15 10
1290 **376** 20 p. red 20 10
1291 25 p. blue 20 10
1292 – 30 p. brown 25 10
1293 – 35 p. green 25 10
1294 – 40 p. orange 25 10
1295 – 50 p. blue 60 10
1296 – 55 p. mauve 35 10
1297 – 60 p. violet . . . . 1·75 15
1298 – 70 p. red 45 10
1299 – 75 p. orange 75 25
1300 – 80 p. green . . . . 1·50 15
1301 – 100 p. mauve 70 25
1302 – 200 p. blue . . . . 1·25 45
1303 – 300 p. mauve . . . . 2·00 55
1304 – 500 p. grey . . . . 6·50 1·75
1305 – 1000 p. green . . . . . . 8·00 2·50
DESIGNS—VERT: 5 p. Wall-painting showing figure of a man; 10 p. (No. 1288) Flying goddess with wreath; 30, 35, 40 p. Man's head inkstand; 50, 55, 60 p. Nike; 70, 75, 80 p. Hera; 100 p. Imdugub-Mari (bird goddess); 200 p. Arab astrolabe; 500 p. Palmyrean coin of Valabathus; 1000 p. Abraxas stone. HORIZ: 15 p. Wall-painting showing figures; 300 p. Herodian coin from Palmyra.

377 National Theatre, Damascus

1976. 13th Anniv of March 8th Baathist Revolution.
1306 **377** 25 p. green, blk & silver . 15 10
1307 35 p. olive, blk & silver . 20 15

378 Nurse and Emblem
380 Eagle and Stars

379 Syrian 5 m. Stamp of 1920

1976. 8th Arab Red Crescent and Red Cross Societies' Conference, Damascus.
1308 **378** 25 p. blue, black & red . 20 10
1309 100 p. violet, blk & red . 75 50

1976. Post Day.
1310 **379** 25 p. multicoloured . . . 20 10
1311 35 p. multicoloured . . . 30 15

1976. 30th Anniv of Evacuation of Allied Forces.
1312 **380** 25 p. multicoloured . . 15 10
1313 35 p. multicoloured . . 20 15

381 Hand gripping Spanner
382 Cotton Boll

1976. Labour Day.
1314 **381** 25 p. blue and black . . 15 10
1315 – 60 p. multicoloured . . 45 25
DESIGN: 60 p. Hand supporting globe.

1976. Aleppo Agricultural and Industrial Fair.
1316 **382** 25 p. multicoloured . . 15 10
1317 35 p. multicoloured . . 30 15

383 Tulips

1976. International Flower Show, Damascus. Multicoloured.
1318 5 p. Type **383** 20 20
1319 15 p. Yellow daisies 25 25
1320 20 p. Turk's-cap lilies . . . 25 25
1321 25 p. Irises 30 30
1322 35 p. Honeysuckle 35 35

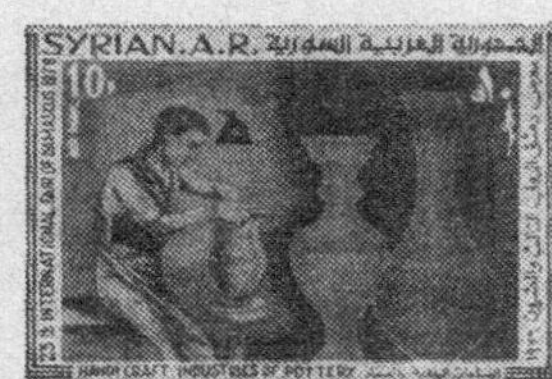
384 Pottery

1976. Air. 23rd International Damascus Fair. Handicraft Industries. Multicoloured.
1323 10 p. Type **384** 25 25
1324 25 p. Rug-making 35 35
1325 30 p. Metalware 35 35
1326 35 p. Wickerware 35 35
1327 100 p. Wood-carving 55 55

385 People supporting Olive Branch

1976. Non-aligned Countries Summit Conference, Colombo. Multicoloured.
1328 40 p. Type **385** 25 20
1329 60 p. Symbolic arrow penetrating "grey curtain" 35 25

386 Football
387 Construction Emblems

1976. 5th Pan-Arab Games. Multicoloured.
1330 5 p. Type **386** 25 25
1331 10 p. Swimming 30 30
1332 25 p. Running 35 35
1333 35 p. Basketball 40 40
1334 50 p. Throwing the javelin . 45 45

1976. 6th Anniv of Movement of 16 November.
1336 **387** 35 p. multicoloured . . 20 10

388 "The Fox and the Crow"
389 Muhammad Kurd-Ali (philosopher)

1976. Fairy Tales. Multicoloured.
1337 10 p. Type **388** 25 25
1338 15 p. "The Hare and the Tortoise" (horiz) 25 25
1339 20 p. "Little Red Riding Hood" 30 30
1340 25 p. "The Wolf and the Goats" (horiz) 30 30
1341 35 p. "The Wolf and the Lamb" 35 35

1976. Birth Centenary of Muhammad Kurd-Ali.
1342 **389** 25 p. multicoloured . . . 20 10

390 Boeing 747SP

1977. Civil Aviation Day.
1343 **390** 35 p. multicoloured . . . 75 20

391 Woman hoisting Flag
392 A.P.U. Emblem

1977. 14th Anniv of 8th March Baathist Revolution.
1344 **391** 35 p. multicoloured . . . 25 15

1977. 25th Anniv of Arab Postal Union.
1345 **392** 35 p. multicoloured . . . 25 10

393 Mounted Horseman

1977. 31st Anniv of Evacuation of Foreign Troops from Syria.
1346 **393** 100 p. multicoloured . . 75 50

394 Industrial Scene and Tools

1977. Labour Day.
1347 **394** 60 p. multicoloured . . . 35 20

395 I.C.A.O. Emblem, Boeing 747SP and Globe

1977. 30th Anniv of I.C.A.O.
1348 **395** 100 p. multicoloured . . 1·00 75

396 Lemon
397 Mallows

1977. International Agricultural Fair, Aleppo. Multicoloured.
1349 10 p. Type **396** 25 25
1350 20 p. Lime 30 30
1351 25 p. Grapefruit 30 30
1352 35 p. Oranges 35 35
1353 60 p. Tangerines 40 40

1977. International Flower Show. Multicoloured.
1354 10 p. Type **397** 20 20
1355 20 p. Cockscomb 25 25
1356 25 p. Convolvulus 25 25
1357 35 p. Balsam 30 30
1358 60 p. Lilac 40 40

398 Young Pioneers and Emblem

1977. Al Baath Pioneers Organization.
1359 **398** 35 p. multicoloured . . . 25 15

399 Arabesque Pattern and Coffee Pot
400 Globe and Measures

1977. 24th International Damascus Fair.
1360 **399** 25 p. red, blue & black . 15 10
1361 60 p. brown, grn & blk . 35 25

1977. World Standards Day.
1362 **400** 15 p. multicoloured . . . 10 10

401 Microscope, Book and Lyre

1977. 30th Anniv of U.N.E.S.C.O.
1363 **401** 25 p. multicoloured . . . 15 10

402 Shield, Surgeon and Crab
403 Archbishop Capucci and Map of Palestine

1977. Fighting Cancer Week.
1364 **402** 100 p. multicoloured . . 70 35

1977. 3rd Anniv of Archbishop Capucci's Arrest.
1365 **403** 60 p. multicoloured . . . 65 20

404 Blind Man, Eye and Globe
405 Dome of the Rock, Jerusalem

1977. World Blind Week.

1366 **404** 55 p. multicoloured . . . 40 20
1367 70 p. multicoloured . . . 60 25

1977. Palestinian Welfare.

1368 **405** 5 p. multicoloured . . . 40 15
1369 10 p. multicoloured . . . 60 15

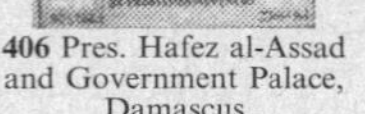

406 Pres. Hafez al-Assad and Government Palace, Damascus

408 Arrow and Blood Circulation

407 Goldfinch

1977. 7th Anniv of Movement of 16 November.

1370 **406** 50 p. multicoloured . . . 20 10

1978. Birds. Multicoloured.

1371 10 p. Type **407** . . . . . . 1·50 90
1372 20 p. Peregrine falcon . . . . 1·75 1·25
1373 25 p. Rock dove . . . . . . 1·75 1·25
1374 35 p. Hoopoe . . . . 3·25 1·50
1375 60 p. Chukar partridge . . . 4·00 2·00

1978. World Health Day. "Fighting Blood Pressure".

1376 **408** 100 p. multicoloured . . 70 30

409 Factory, Moon and Stars

410 Geometric Design

1978. 32nd Anniv of Evacuation of Foreign Troops.

1377 **409** 35 p. green, orge & blk . . 20 10

1978. 14th Arab Engineering Conference, Damascus.

1378 **410** 25 p. green and black . . 20 10

411 Map of Arab Countries, Flag, Eye and Police

412 Trout

1978. 6th Arab Conference of Police Commanders.

1379 **411** 35 p. multicoloured . . . 45 15

1978. Fishes. Multicoloured.

1380 10 p. Type **412** 25 25
1381 20 p. Sea-bream 30 30
1382 25 p. Grouper 30 30
1383 35 p. Goatfish 35 35
1384 60 p. Catfish 45 45

413 President Assad

1978. Air. Re-election of President Hafez al-Assad.

1385 **413** 25 p. multicoloured . . . 15 10
1386 35 p. multicoloured . . . 20 15
1387 60 p. multicoloured . . . 30 15

414 "Lobivia sp."

415 President Hafez al-Assad

1978. International Flower Show, Damascus. Mult.

1389 25 p. Type **414** 25 25
1390 30 p. "Mamillaria sp." . . . 30 30
1391 35 p. "Opuntia sp." 30 30
1392 50 p. "Chamaecereus sp." . 35 35
1393 60 p. "Mamillaria sp." (different) 35 35

1978. 8th Anniv of Movement of November 16.

1394 **415** 60 p. multicoloured . . 25 15

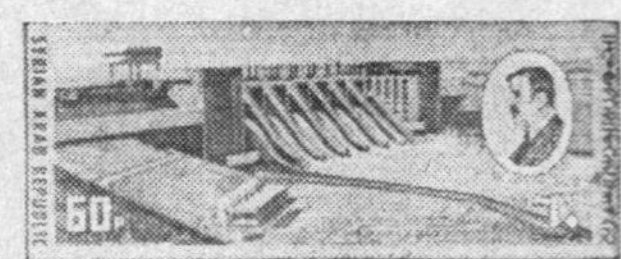

416 Euphrates Dam

1978. Inauguration of Euphrates Dam.

1395 **416** 60 p. multicoloured . . 55 25

417 Fair Emblem

418 Averroes (philosopher)

1979. 25th International Damascus Fair.

1396 **417** 25 p. multicoloured . . 15 10
1397 35 p. multicoloured . . 20 10

1979. Averroes Commemoration.

1399 **418** 100 p. multicoloured . . 70 50

419 Standing Figures within Globe

420 Pyramid and Flower

1979. International Year to Combat Racism.

1400 **419** 35 p. multicoloured . . 20 10

1979. 16th Anniv of Baathist 8th March Revolution.

1401 **420** 100 p. multicoloured . . 60 25

421 Hands supporting Globe

422 Helmet of Homs

1979. 30th Anniv of Declaration of Human Rights.

1402 **421** 60 p. multicoloured . . 30 10

1979. Exhibits from National Museum, Damascus.

1403 – 5 p. red 10 10
1404 – 10 p. green 10 10
1405 – 15 p. mauve 10 10
1406 **422** 20 p. green 10 10
1407 – 25 p. red 10 10
1408 – 35 p. brown 10 10
1409 – 75 p. blue 35 20
1410 – 160 p. green 70 40
1411 – 500 p. brown . . . . . 4·00 1·10

DESIGNS—VERT: 5, 160 p. Umayyad window; 10 p. Figurine; 15 p. Rakka horseman (Abbeid ceramic); 25 p. Head of Clipeata (Cleopatra); 35 p. Seated statue of Ishtar (Astarte). HORIZ: 75 p. Abdul Malik gold coin; 500 p. Umar B. Abdul Aziz gold coin.

423 Geometric Design and Flame

424 Ibn Assaker

1979. 33rd Anniv of Evacuation of Foreign Troops from Syria.

1416 **423** 35 p. multicoloured . . . 20 10

1979. 900th Anniv of Ibn Assaker (historian and biographer).

1417 **424** 75 p. brown, blue & grn . 35 20

425 Tooth, Emblem and Mosque

426 Welder working on Power Pylon

1979. International Middle East Dental Congress.

1418 **425** 35 p. multicoloured . . . 30 10

1979. Labour Day.

1419 **426** 50 p. multicoloured . . . 25 15
1420 75 p. multicoloured . . . 30 20

427 Girl holding Emblem with Flowers

428 Wright Type A

1979. International Year of the Child. Multicoloured.

1421 10 p. Type **427** 10 10
1422 15 p. Boy and globe 20 10

1979. 75th Anniv of First Powered Flight. Multicoloured.

1423 50 p. Type **428** 35 20
1424 75 p. Bleriot XI crossing English Channel 50 25
1425 100 p. Lindbergh's "Spirit of St. Louis" 75 40

429 Power Station

430 Flags and Pavilion

1979.

1426 **429** 5 p. blue 10 10
1427 10 p. mauve 10 10
1428 15 p. green 15 10

1979. 26th International Damascus Fair. Mult.

1429 60 p. Type **430** 25 15
1430 75 p. Lamp post and flags . . 30 20

431 Running

1979. 8th Mediterranean Games, Split. Mult.

1431 25 p. Type **431** 15 10
1432 35 p. Swimmer on starting-block 20 10
1433 50 p. Football 25 15

432 President Assad with Symbols of Agriculture and Industry

1979. 9th Anniv of Movement of 16 November.

1434 **432** 100 p. multicoloured . . 1·25 20

433 "Papilio machaon"

434 Astrolabe

1979. Butterflies. Multicoloured.

1435 20 p. Type **433** 40 20
1436 25 p. "Inachis io" 45 20
1437 30 p. "Limenitis camilla" . . 55 20
1438 35 p. "Morpho cypris" . . . 60 20
1439 50 p. "Parnassius apollo" . . 75 30

1979. International Flower Show, Damascus. Designs similar to T **414** showing various roses.

1440 5 p. multicoloured 10 10
1441 10 p. multicoloured 15 10
1442 15 p. multicoloured 20 10
1443 50 p. multicoloured 40 20
1444 75 p. multicoloured 65 30
1445 100 p. multicoloured 90 45

1980. 2nd International Symposium. on History of Arab Science

1446 **434** 50 p. violet 25 10
1447 100 p. brown 50 25
1448 1000 p. green . . . . . 4·00 2·50

435 "8" over Buildings

436 Smoker

1980. 17th Anniv of Baathist Revolution of 8 March 1963.

1449 **435** 40 p. multicoloured . . . 20 10

1980. World Health Day. Anti-smoking Campaign.

1450 **436** 60 p. brown, grn & blk . . 60 25
1451 – 100 p. multicoloured . . 90 40

DESIGN: 100 p. Skull and cigarette.

437 Monument

1980. 34th Anniv of Evacuation of Foreign Troops from Syria.

1452 **437** 40 p. multicoloured . . . 25 10
1453 60 p. multicoloured . . . 30 15

438 Wrestling

1980. Olympic Games, Moscow. Multicoloured.

1454 15 p. Type **438** 10 10
1455 25 p. Fencing 15 10
1456 35 p. Weightlifting 20 10
1457 50 p. Judo 25 10
1458 75 p. Boxing 35 20

439 "Savings"

1980. Savings Certificates.

1460 **439** 25 p. violet, red & blue . 15 10

440 "Aladdin and the Magic Lamp"

1980. Popular Stories. Multicoloured.

1461 15 p. "Sinbad the Sailor" . . 20 20
1462 20 p. "Shahrazad and Shahrayar" 30 30
1463 35 p. "Ali Baba and the Forty Thieves" 35 35
1464 50 p. "Hassan the Clever" . . 40 40
1465 100 p. Type **440** 55 55

441 Kaaba and Mosque, Mecca

1980. 1400th Anniv of Hegira.

1466 **441** 35 p. multicoloured . . . 25 15

442 Daffodils

443 "Industry"

1980. International Flower Show, Damascus. Multicoloured.

1467 20 p. Type **442** 25 25
1468 30 p. Dahlias 30 30
1469 40 p. Bergamot 35 35
1470 60 p. Globe flowers 40 40
1471 100 p. Cornflowers 55 55

1980. 10th Anniv of Movement of 16 November.

1472 **443** 100 p. multicoloured . . 55 25

444 Construction Worker

445 Children encircling Globe

1980. Labour Day.

1473 **444** 35 p. multicoloured . . . 20 15

1980. International Children's Day.

1474 **445** 25 p. green, black & yell 20 10

446 Steam-powered Passenger Wagon, 1830

447 Mother's Arms around Child

1980. Cars. Multicoloured.

1475 25 p. Type **446** 30 30
1476 35 p. Benz, 1899 . . . . . . 35 35
1477 40 p. Rolls-Royce, 1903 . . . 35 35
1478 50 p. Mercedes, 1906 . . . . 40 40
1479 60 p. Austin, 1915 . . . . . 50 50

1980. Mothers' Day. Multicoloured.

1480 40 p. Type **447** 25 10
1481 100 p. Faces of mother and child 45 25

448 Fair Emblem

1980. 27th International Damascus Fair. Mult.

1482 50 p. Type **448** 30 15
1483 100 p. As T **448** but with different motif on right . . 60 30

449 Armed Forces

1980. Army Day.

1484 **449** 50 p. multicoloured . . 1·00 30

450 Arabesque Pattern

451 Geometric Design, Laurel and Hand holding Torch

1981. 18th Anniv of Baathist Revolution of 8 March 1963.

1485 **450** 50p. multicoloured . . . 35 15

1981. 35th Anniv of Evacuation of Foreign Troops from Syria.

1486 **451** 50 p. multicoloured . . 35 15

452 Mosque and Script

1981. History of Arab-Islamic Civilisation World Conference, Damascus.

1487 **452** 100 p. light green, green and black 80 50

453 Marching Workers and Emblem

454 Human Figure and House on Graph

1981. May Day.

1488 **453** 100 p. multicoloured . . 60 35

1981. Housing and Population Census.

1489 **454** 50 p. multicoloured . . 35 15

455 Family and Savings Emblem

456 Dove and Map on Globe

1981. Savings Certificates.

1490 **455** 50 p. black and brown . 35 15

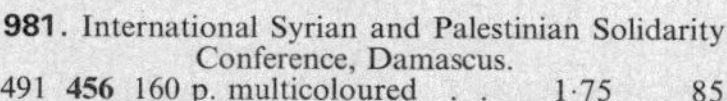

1981. International Syrian and Palestinian Solidarity Conference, Damascus.

1491 **456** 160 p. multicoloured . . 1·75 85

457 Avicenna

459 Festival Emblem

458 Glass Lamp

1981. Birth Millenary of Avicenna (philosopher and physician).

1492 **457** 100 p. multicoloured . . 80 50

1981. Damascus Museum Exhibits.

1493 **458** 50 p. red 50 20
1494 – 180 p. multicoloured . . 1·50 80
1495 – 180 p. multicoloured . . 1·50 80

DESIGNS: No. 1494, "Grand Mosque, Damascus" (painting); No. 1495, Hunting scene (tapestry).

1981. Youth Festival.

1496 **459** 60 p. multicoloured . . . 45 20

460 Decorative Pattern

461 Palestinians and Dome of the Rock

1981. 28th International Damascus Fair.

1497 **460** 50 p. mauve, blue & grn . 40 15
1498 – 160 p. brown, yell & lilac 1·00 50

DESIGN: 160 p. Globe encircled by wheat and cogwheel.

1981. Palestinian Solidarity.

1499 **461** 100 p. multicoloured . . 1·25 55

462 F.A.O. Emblem

463 Tobacco Flowers

1981. World Food Day.

1500 **462** 180 p. blue, green and black 1·50 80

1981. International Flower Show, Damascus. Multicoloured.

1501 25 p. Type **463** 45 45
1502 40 p. Mimosa 60 60
1503 50 p. Ixias 70 70
1504 60 p. Passion flower 70 70
1505 100 p. Dendrobium 95 95

464 Hands releasing Dove and Horseman

1981. 1300th Anniv of Bulgarian State.

1506 **464** 380 p. multicoloured . . 2·50 1·75

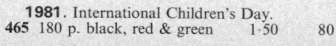

465 Classroom

1981. International Children's Day.

1507 **465** 180 p. black, red & green 1·50 80

467 President Assad and Diesel Train

468 Symbols of Development

1981. 11th Anniv of Movement of 16 November.

1509 **467** 60 p. blue, black and brown 1·50 35

1982. 19th Anniv of Baathist Revolution of 8 March 1963.

1510 **468** 50 p. grey, red and black 45 15

469 Robert Koch and Microscope

470 Pattern and Hand holding Rifle

1982. Cent of Discovery of Tubercle Bacillus.

1511 **469** 180 p. blue, brown and black . . . . 2·25 1·00

1982. 36th Anniv of Evacuation of Foreign Troops from Syria.

1512 **470** 70 p. red and blue . . . 65 35

471 Disabled People and Emblem

472 A.P.U. Emblem

1982 International Year of Disabled Persons (1981).

1513 **471** 90 p. black, blue and yellow 1·25 55

1982. 30th Anniv of Arab Postal Union.

1514 **472** 60 p. red, green and yellow 60 30

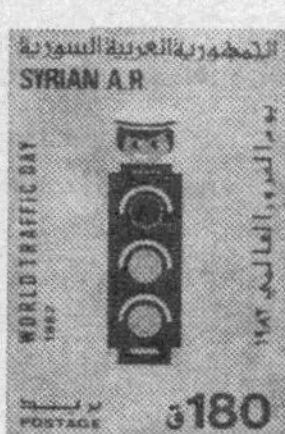

473 Traffic Lights

475 Oil Rig, Factory Chimneys and Hand holding Torch

474 Geometric Pattern

1982. World Traffic Day.

1515 **473** 180 p. black, red and blue 2·75 1·50

1982. World Telecommunications Day.

1516 **474** 180 p. light yellow, brown and yellow . . . . . 1·75 1·25

1982. Labour Day.

1517 **475** 180 p. red, blue and light blue . . . . 1·75 1·25

476 Mother and Children

477 Olives

1982. Mothers' Day.

1518 **476** 40 p. green 30 15
1519 75 p. brown 50 35

1982.

1520 **477** 50 p. green 40 15
1521 60 p. grey 25 15
1522 – 100 p. mauve . . . . . . 1·00 25
1523 – 150 p. blue . . . . . . 1·50 30
1524 – 180 p. red 75 45

DESIGNS: 100, 180 p. Harbour; 150 p. President Assad.

479 Footballer

1982. World Cup Football Championship, Spain. Multicoloured.

1525 40 p. Type **479** 40 20
1526 60 p. Two footballers 55 30
1527 100 p. Two footballers (different) 90 70

480 Policeman

481 Government Building

1982. Police Day.

1529 **480** 50 p. black, red and green 1·25 40

1982.

1530 **481** 30 p. brown 25 10
1531 – 70 p. green 35 20
1532 – 200 p. red . . . . . . 2·50 85

DESIGNS—HORIZ: 200 p. Ruins. VERT: 70 p. Arched wall.

482 Communications Emblem and Map

1982. Arab Telecommunication Day.

1533 **482** 50 p. light blue, blue and red 75 30

483 Scout pitching Tent

1982. 75th Anniv of Boy Scout Movement.

1534 **483** 160 p. green . . . . . . 2·50 1·25

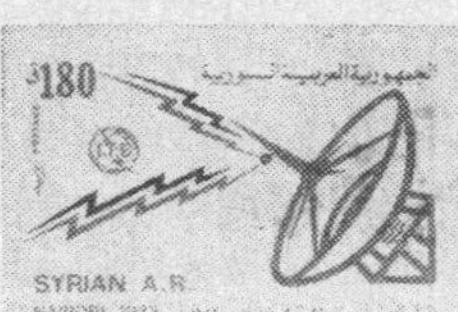

484 Dish Aerial and World Map

1982. I.T.U. Delegates' Conference, Nairobi.

1535 **484** 180 p. light blue, blue and red . . . . 2·25 1·25

485 President Assad

1982. 12th Anniv of Movement of 16 November.

1536 **485** 50 p. blue and grey . . . 70 30

486 Water-wheel, Hama

487 Dragonfly

1982.

1537 **486** 5 p. brown 10 10
1538 10 p. violet 10 10
1539 20 p. red 20 10
1540 50 p. blue 50 20

1982. Insects. Multicoloured.

1541 5 p. Type **487** 30 30
1542 10 p. "Lucanus cervus" . . 30 30
1543 20 p. "Coccinella septempunctata" 45 45
1544 40 p. "Schistocerca gregaria" 90 90
1545 50 p. "Apis mellifera" . . . 1·10 1·10

488 Honeysuckle

489 Satellites within Dove

1982. International Flower Show, Damascus. Multicoloured.

1546 50 p. Type **488** 85 40
1547 60 p. Geranium . . . . . . 1·00 60

1982. U.N. Conference on Exploration and Peaceful Uses of Outer Space, Vienna.

1548 **489** 50 p. multicoloured . . 90 30

490 Dove on Gun

1982. International Palestine Day.

1549 **490** 50 p. multicoloured . . 1·25 40

491 Damascus International Airport

1983. 20th Anniv of Baathist Revolution of 8 March.

1550 **491** 60 p. multicoloured . . 1·25 50

492 I.T.U., U.P.U. and W.C.Y. Emblems

1983. World Communications Year.

1551 **492** 180 p. multicoloured . . 2·25 1·50

493 Figurine

1983.

1552 **493** 380 p. brown and green 3·00 1·40

494 Pharmacist

1983. Arab Pharmacists' Day.

1553 **494** 100 p. multicoloured . . 1·75 75

495 Liberation Monument, Qneitra

496 Wave within Ship's Wheel

1983. 9th Anniv of Liberation of Qneitra.

1554 **495** 50 p. green 70 30
1555 – 100 p. brown . . . . . . 1·25 70

DESIGN: 100 p. Ruined buildings.

1983. 25th Anniv of I.M.O.

1556 **496** 180 p. multicoloured . . 2·25 1·25

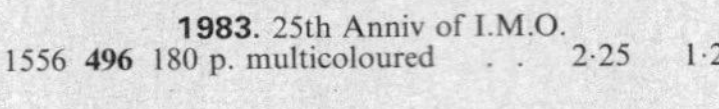

497 Flame on Map

1983. Namibia Day.

1557 **497** 180 p. blue, mauve and black . . . . 2·25 1·25

498 I.S.O. Emblem and Factory

499 Gateway, Bosra

1983. World Standards Day.

1558 **498** 50 p. multicoloured . . . 65 30
1559 – 100 p. violet, green & blk 1·40 70

DESIGN: 100 p. I.S.O. emblem and measuring equipment.

1983. 10th Anniv of World Heritage Agreement.

1560 **499** 60 p. brown 80 40

500 Flowers

501 Farmland

1983. International Flower Show, Damascus. Multicoloured.

1561 50 p. Type **500** 80 35
1562 60 p. Hibiscus 95 45

1983. World Food Day.

1563 **501** 180 p. green, cream and deep green . . . . . . 2·25 1·25

502 Factory **503** Statuette

1983.

1564 **502** 50 p. green 40 20

1984. International Deir Ez-Zor History and Archaeology Symposium.

1565 **503** 225 p. brown . . . . . . 2·25 1·25

504 Aleppo

505 Alassad Library

1984. International Symposium for the Conservation of Aleppo.

1566 **504** 245 p. multicoloured . . 2·25 1·25

1984. 21st Anniv of Baathist Revolution of 8 March.

1567 **505** 60 p. multicoloured . . . 70 40

506 Bodies and mourning Woman with Child

1984. Sabra and Shatila (refugee camps in Lebanon) Massacres.

1568 **506** 225 p. multicoloured . . 2·00 1·10

507 Mother and Child

509 Swimming

508 Dam, Emblem and Pioneers

1984. Mothers' Day.

1569 **507** 245 p. brown & green . 2·00 1·25

1984. 9th Regional Festival of Al Baath Pioneers. Multicoloured.

1570 50 p. Type **508** 60 35
1571 60 p. Pioneers, ruins and emblems 80 50

1984. Olympic Games, Los Angeles. Multicoloured.

1572 30 p. Type **509** 30 30
1573 50 p. Wrestling 45 45
1574 60 p. Running 50 50
1575 70 p. Boxing 60 60
1576 90 p. Football 75 75

510 Flowers

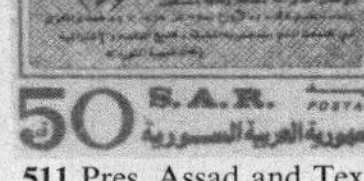

511 Pres. Assad and Text

1984. International Flower Show, Damascus. Multicoloured.

1578 245 p. Type **510** . . . . . . 2·00 1·25
1579 285 p. Flowers (different) . . 2·25 1·75

1984. 4th Revolutionary Youth Union Congress.

1580 **511** 50 p. brown, deep brown and green 60 30
1581 – 60 p. multicoloured . . . 80 50

DESIGN—37×25 mm: 60 p. Pres. Assad and saluting youth.

512 Emblem and Administration Building, Damascus

1984. Arab Postal Union Day.

1582 **512** 60 p. multicoloured . . . 75 40

513 Globe, Dish Aerial and Telephone

514 Arabesque Pattern

1984. World Telecommunications Day.
1583 **513** 245 p. multicoloured . . 2·25 1·40

1984. 31st International Damascus Fair. Mult.
1584 45 p. Type **514** 55 30
1585 100 p. Ornate gold decoration 1·00 60

515 Stylized Aircraft and Emblem

1984. 40th Anniv of I.C.A.O.
1586 **515** 45 p. lt blue and blue . . 60 30
1587 – 245 p. light blue, blue and deep blue . . . . 2·25 1·25
DESIGN: 245 p. Emblem and stylized building.

516 Text, Flag and Pres. Assad

1984. 14th Anniv of Movement of 16 Nov.
1588 **516** 65 p. orange, black and brown 65 35

517 Palmyra Roman Arch and Colonnades

1984. International Tourism Day.
1589 **517** 100 p. brown, black and blue . . . . 1·00 45

518 Wooded Landscape

1985. Woodland Conservation.
1590 **518** 45 p. multicoloured . . . 70 35

519 University and Students

1985. 26th Anniv (1984) of Aleppo University.
1591 **519** 45 p. black, blue and brown 60 35

520 Oil Lamp

1985. 26th Anniv (1984) of Supreme Council of Science.
1592 **520** 65 p. green, red and black 90 45

521 Soldier holding Flag

1985. Army Day.
1593 **521** 65 p. deep brown and brown . . . . 1·00 45

522 Pres. Assad

1985. Re-election of President Assad
1594 **522** 200 p. multicoloured . . 1·25 75
1595 300 p. multicoloured . . 2·00 1·25
1596 500 p. multicoloured . . 3·50 1·90

523 Flag and Party Emblem

524 Torch and "22"

1985. 8th Baath Arab Socialist Party Congress.
1598 **523** 50 p. multicoloured . . . 65 35

1985. 22nd Anniv of Baathist Revolution of 8 March 1963.
1599 **524** 60 p. multicoloured . . 70 35

525 Tractor and Cow

1985. Aleppo Industrial and Agricultural Fair (1984). Multicoloured.
1600 65 p. Type **525** 70 45
1601 150 p. Fort and carrots (vert) 1·60 1·25

526 Liberation Movement, Qneitra

1985. 10th Anniv (1984) of Liberation of Qneitra.
1602 **526** 70 p. multicoloured . . 75 40

527 Parliament Building

1985. 10th Anniv of Arab Parliamentary Union.
1603 **527** 245 p. multicoloured . . 2·25 1·50

528 U.P.U. Emblem and Pigeon with Letter

529 A.P.U. Emblem

1985. World Post Day.
1604 **528** 285 p. multicoloured . . 2·25 1·50

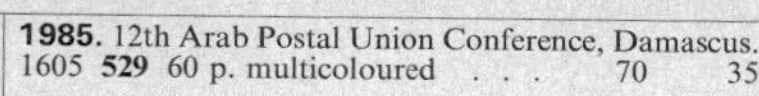

1985. 12th Arab Postal Union Conference, Damascus.
1605 **529** 60 p. multicoloured . . . 70 35

530 Medal

1985. Labour Day.
1606 **530** 60 p. multicoloured . . . 70 35

531 Old and New Locomotives

1985. 2nd Scientific Symposium.
1607 **531** 60 p. blue . . . . 1·25 45

532 Emblem and Child with empty Bowl

1985. U.N. Child Survival Campaign.
1608 **532** 60 p. black, green & pink 75 35

533 Pres. Assad and Road

1985. 15th Anniv of Movement of 16 Nov.
1609 **533** 60 p. multicoloured . . . 70 35

534 Emblem and "40"

535 Lily-flowered Tulip

1985. 40th Anniv of U.N.O.
1610 **534** 245 p. multicoloured . . 2·00 1·40

1986. International Flower Show, Damascus (1985). Multicoloured.
1611 30 p. Type **535** 50 25
1612 60 p. Tulip 90 65

536 Flask

1986. 32nd International Damascus Fair (1985).
1613 **536** 60 p. multicoloured . . . 75 35

INDEX

Countries can be quickly located by referring to the index at the end of this volume.

537 Abd-er-Rahman I

538 Pres. Hafez al-Assad

1986. 1200th Anniv of Abd-er-Rahman I ad Dakhel, Emir of Cordoba.
1614 **537** 60 p. brown, pink and brown 75 35

1988.
1615 **538** 10 p. red 10 10
1616 30 p. blue 20 10
1616a 50 p. lilac 10 10
1617 100 p. blue 65 20
1618 150 p. brown 90 25
1619 175 p. violet . . . . . 1·10 30
1620 200 p. brown . . . . . 1·25 35
1621 300 p. mauve . . . . . 1·90 50
1622 500 p. orange . . . . . 3·00 90
1623 550 p. red . . . . . . 3·50 1·25
1624 600 p. green . . . . . 4·00 1·50
1625 1000 p. mauve . . . . 5·50 2·00
1626 2000 p. green . . . . . 10·00 4·75

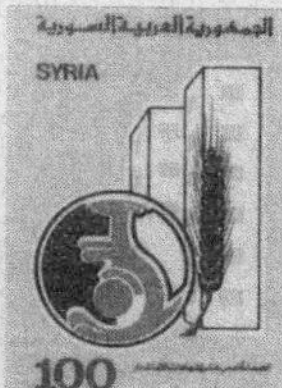

539 Tooth and Map

540 Tower Blocks, Ear of Wheat and Kangaroo

1986. 19th Arab Dentists' Union Congress, Damascus.
1627 **539** 110 p. multicoloured . . 2·00 1·25

1986. 15th Anniv of Syrian Investment Certificates.
1628 **540** 100 p. multicoloured . . 1·40 70

541 Traffic Policewoman, Globe and Traffic Lights

542 Policeman and Building in Laurel Wreath

1986. World Traffic Day.
1629 **541** 330 p. multicoloured . . 3·25 2·00

1986. Police Day.
1630 **542** 110 p. multicoloured . . 2·25 1·40

1986. Labour Day.
1631 **543** 330 p. red, black & blue 2·50 1·90

1986. 12th Anniv of Liberation of Qneitra.
1632 **544** 110 p. multicoloured . . 2·00 1·40

545 Pictogram and Ball

546 Mother and Children

1986. World Cup Football Championship, Mexico.
1633 **545** 330 p. multicoloured . . 2·50 1·50
1634 370 p. multicoloured . . 2·50 1·75

1986. Mothers' Day.
1636 **546** 100 p. multicoloured . . 1·50 75

547 Pres. Assad and Train

1986. 23rd Anniv of Baathist Revolution of 8 March 1963.
1637 **547** 110 p. multicoloured . . 1·50 80

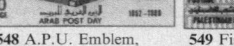

548 A.P.U. Emblem, Post Office and Box

549 Fists, Map and Globe

1986. Arab Post Day.
1638 **548** 110 p. multicoloured . . 1·75 85

1986. International Palestine Day.
1639 **549** 110 p. multicoloured . . 2·50 1·40

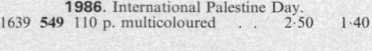

550 Tulips

1986. International Flower Show, Damascus. Multicoloured.
1640 10 p. Type **550** 25 25
1641 50 p. Mauve flowers 60 60
1642 100 p. Yellow flowers . . . . 1·00 1·00
1643 110 p. Pink flowers . . . . . 1·00 1·00
1644 330 p. Yellow flowers (different) 2·50 2·50

551 Pres. Assad and Tishreen Palace

1986. 16th Anniv of Movement of 16 Nov.
1645 **551** 110 p. multicoloured . . 1·60 80

552 Rocket and Flags

553 Jug and Star

1986. 1st Anniv of Announcement of Syrian–Soviet Space Flight.
1646 **552** 330 p. multicoloured . . 2·75 1·75

1986. 33rd International Damascus Fair.
1647 **553** 110 p. multicoloured . . 1·25 80
1648 – 330 p. black, green and brown . . . . 3·00 1·75
DESIGN: 330 p. Coffee pot.

554 Girls and National Flag

1987. International Children's Art Exhibition.
1649 **554** 330 p. multicoloured . . 2·75 1·50

555 U.P.U. Emblem and Airmail Envelope

556 Children in Balloon over Town

1987. World Post Day.
1650 **555** 330 p. multicoloured . . 2·25 1·25

1987. International Children's Day.
1651 **556** 330 p. multicoloured . . 2·50 1·25

557 Citadel, Aleppo

1987. International Tourism Day.
1652 330 p. Type **557** . . . . . . 2·50 1·25
1653 370 p. Water-wheel, Hama . 2·75 1·50

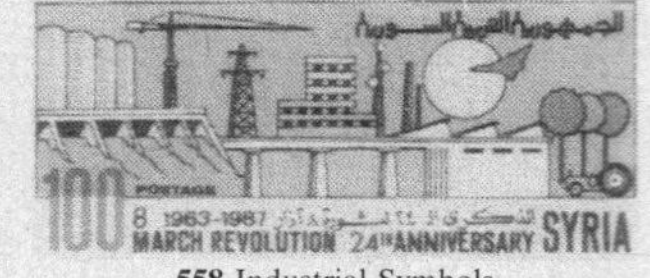

558 Industrial Symbols

1987. 24th Anniv of Baathist Revolution of 8 March 1963.
1654 **558** 100 p. multicoloured . . 1·00 60

559 Doves flying from Globe

560 Party Emblem

1987. International Peace Year.
1655 **559** 370 p. multicoloured . . 2·50 1·40

1987. 40th Anniv of Baath Arab Socialist Party.
1656 **560** 100 p. multicoloured . . 1·00 55

561 Stars

1987. 41st Anniv of Evacuation of Foreign Troops from Syria.
1657 **561** 100 p. multicoloured . . 1·00 55

562 Draughtsman

1987. 6th Arab Ministers of Culture Conference.
1658 **562** 330 p. blue, green & blk 2·50 1·40

563 Map of Arab Postal Union Members

564 Couple within Cogwheel

1987. Arab Post Day.
1659 **563** 110 p. multicoloured . . 1·25 65

1987. Labour Day.
1660 **564** 330 p. multicoloured . . 2·50 1·40

565 Statue

566 Pres. Assad with Children and Nurse

1987. 13th Anniv of Liberation of Qneitra.
1661 **565** 100 p. multicoloured . . 1·00 55

1987. Child Vaccination Campaign.
1662 **566** 100 p. multicoloured . . 1·00 60
1663 330 p. multicoloured . . 2·75 1·50

567 Dome of the Rock, Battle Scene and Saladin

1987. 800th Anniv of Battle of Hattin.
1664 **567** 110 p. multicoloured . . 1·25 65

568 Rocket Launch and National Flags

1987. Syrian–Soviet Space Flight. Multicoloured.
1665 330 p. Type **568** . . . . . . 2·50 1·75
1666 330 p. Spacecraft docking with "Mir" space station (37 × 25 mm) . . . . 2·50 1·75
1667 330 p. Space capsule re-entering Earth's atmosphere and group of cosmonauts (25 × 37 mm) . . . . 2·50 1·75

569 Flags, Cosmonauts and Pres. Assad

1987. President's Space Conversation with Lt-Col. Mohammed Faris (Syrian cosmonaut).
1669 **569** 500 p. multicoloured . . 3·75 2·75

570 Stylized Flowers

571 Sports Pictograms

1987. 34th International Damascus Fair.
1670 **570** 330 p. multicoloured . . 2·00 1·40

1987. 10th Mediterranean Games, Latakia.
1671 **571** 100 p. purple & black . . 65 35
1672 – 110 p. multicoloured . . 70 55
1673 – 330 p. multicoloured . . 2·00 1·50
1674 – 370 p. multicoloured . . 2·25 1·75
DESIGNS—As Type **571**. HORIZ: 110 p. Swimming bird and emblem. 52 × 23 mm—330 p. Phoenician galley (Games emblem); 370 p. Flags forming "SYRIA".

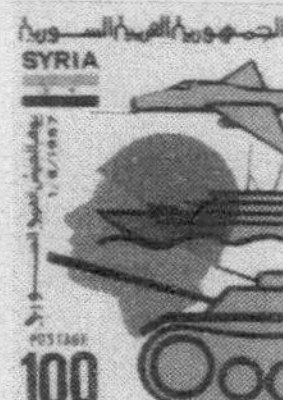

572 Soldier, Mikoyan Gurevich MiG-21D Fighter, Ship and Tank

573 Trees, Sun and Birds

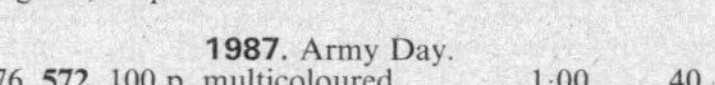

1987. Army Day.
1676 **572** 100 p. multicoloured . . 1·00 40

1987. Tree Day.
1677 **573** 330 p. multicoloured . . 2·00 1·40

574 Poppies

576 Barbed Wire around Map of Israel

575 Pres. Assad acknowledging Applause

1987. International Flower Show, Damascus.
1678 330 p. Type **574** . . . . . 2·00 1·40
1679 370 p. Mauve flower . . . . 2·25 1·75

1987. 17th Anniv of Movement of 16 November.
1680 **575** 150 p. multicoloured . . 1·00 70

1987. International Palestine Day.
1681 **576** 500 p. multicoloured . . 2·75 1·90

577 U.P.U. and U.N. Emblems

1988. World Post Day.
1682 **577** 500 p. multicoloured . . 2·75 1·90

578 Bosra Amphitheatre

1988. International Tourism Day. Multicoloured.
1683 500 p. Type **578** . . . . . 2·50 1·60
1684 500 p. Palmyra ruins . . . . 2·50 1·60

579 Children as Astronauts

1988. International Children's Day.
1685 **579** 500 p. multicoloured . . 2·50 1·60

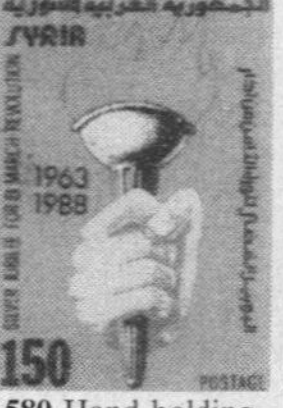

580 Hand holding Torch

581 Woman cradling Baby, Children and Adults

1988. 25th Anniv of Baathist Revolution of 8 March 1963.

1686 **580** 150 p. multicoloured . . 90 60

1988. Mothers' Day.

1688 **581** 500 p. multicoloured . . 2·50 1·60

582 Arms, Cogwheel, Laurel Branch and Book

583 Dove, Airmail Envelope and Map

1988. 42nd Anniv of Evacuation of Foreign Troops from Syria.

1689 **582** 150 p. multicoloured . . 75 55

1988. Arab Post Day.

1690 **583** 150 p. multicoloured . . 75 55

584 Spanner, Chimney, Cogwheel and Scroll

585 Modern Buildings

1988. Labour Day.

1691 **584** 550 p. multicoloured . . 2·25 1·50

1988. Arab Engineers' Union.

1692 **585** 150 p. multicoloured . . 75 55

586 Lily

1988. International Flower Show, Damascus. Multicoloured.

1693 550 p. Type **586** . . . . . . 2·25 1·50

1694 600 p. Carnations . . . . . 2·25 1·50

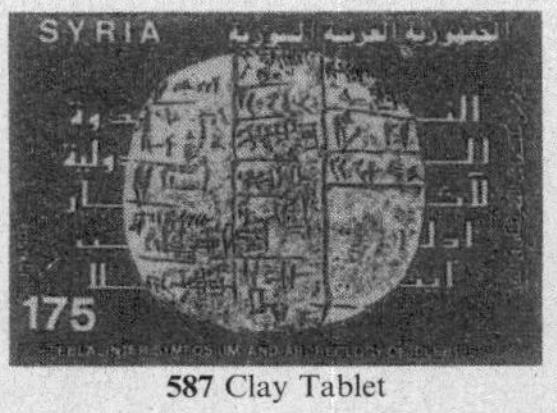

587 Clay Tablet

1988. International Symposium on Archaeology of Ebla.

1695 **587** 175 p. black and brown . 55 40

1696 – 550 p. brown, blue & blk 1·40 90

1697 – 600 p. multicoloured . . 1·50 1·00

DESIGNS: 550 p. King making offering (carving from stone votive basin); 600 p. Golden statue of goddess Ishtar.

588 Old City

589 Emblem

1988. Preservation of Sana'a, Yemen.

1698 **588** 550 p. multicoloured . . 1·40 90

1988. Children's Day.

1699 **589** 600 p. black, yellow & grn 1·50 1·00

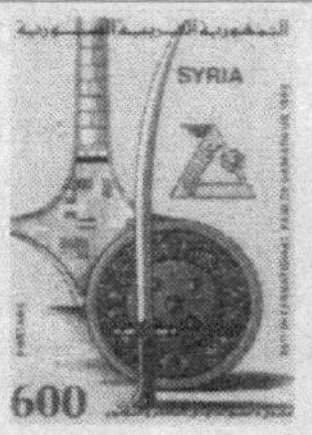

590 Sword, Shield and Emblems

591 Emblem and People

1988. 35th International Damascus Fair.

1700 **590** 600 p. multicoloured . . 1·50 1·00

1988. 40th Anniv of W.H.O.

1701 **591** 600 p. multicoloured . . 1·50 1·00

592 Emblems and Map

1988. 50th Anniv of Arab Scout Movement.

1702 **592** 150 p. mutlicoloured . . 50 35

593 Cycling

1988. Olympic Games, Seoul. Multicoloured.

1703 550 p. Type **593** . . . . . . 1·40 90

1704 600 p. Football . . . . . . 1·50 1·00

594 Old Houses and Modern Flats

1988. Housing. Multicoloured.

1706 150 p. Type **594** (Arab Housing Day) 50 35

1707 175 p. House and makeshift shelter (International Year of Shelter for the Homeless (1987)) 55 40

1708 550 p. Types of housing (World Housing Day) . . . . . . 1·40 90

1709 600 p. As No. 1707 but inscr for International Day for Housing the Homeless . . 1·50 1·00

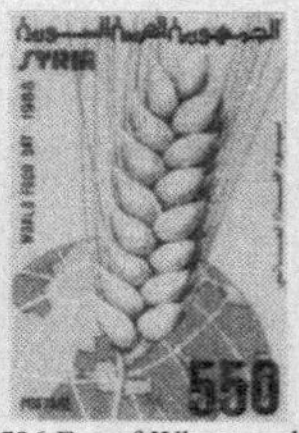

595 Euphrates Bridge, Deir el Zor

596 Ear of Wheat and Globe

1988. International Tourism Day. Multicoloured.

1710 550 p. Type **595** . . . . . . 1·40 90

1711 600 p. Tetrapylon of Latakia 1·50 1·00

1988. World Food Day.

1712 **596** 550 p. multicoloured . . 1·40 90

597 Al-Assad University Hospital

1988. 18th Anniv of Corrective Movement of 16 November 1970.

1713 **597** 150 p. multicoloured . . 50 35

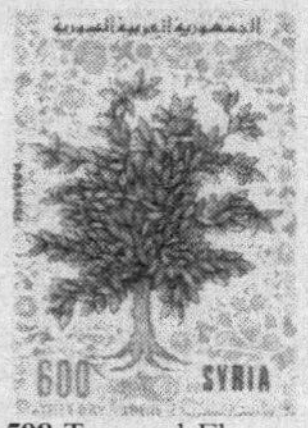

598 Tree and Flowers

599 Dove with Envelope over Globe

1988. Tree Day.

1714 **598** 600 p. multicoloured . . 1·50 1·00

1988. World Post Day.

1715 **599** 600 p. multicoloured . . 1·50 1·00

600 Emblem and Doctor within Stethoscope

602 Pres. Assad and Women

601 Symbols of Agriculture and Industry

1989. 10th Anniv of Arab Board for Medical Specializations.

1716 **600** 175 p. multicoloured . . 35 25

1989. 26th Anniv of Baathist Revolution of 8 March 1963.

1717 **601** 150 p. multicoloured . . 30 20

1989. 5th General Congress of Union of Women.

1718 **602** 150 p. multicoloured . . 30 20

603 Candle and Books

1989. Arab Teachers' Day.

1719 **603** 175 p. multicoloured . . 35 25

604 Nehru

605 Mother and Children

1989. Birth Centenary of Jarwaharlal Nehru (Indian statesman).

1720 **604** 550 p. brown & lt brown 80 55

1989. Mothers' Day.

1721 **605** 550 p. multicoloured . . 80 55

606 Goldfinch

1989. Birds. Multicoloured.

1722 600 p. Type **606** . . . . . . 1·00 75

1723 600 p. European bee eater . . 1·00 75

1724 600 p. Turtle dove . . . . 1·00 75

607 State Arms on Map

608 Workers

1989. 43rd Anniv of Evacuation of Foreign Troops from Syria.

1725 **607** 150 p. multicoloured . . 30 20

1989. Labour Day.

1726 **608** 850 p. green and black . 1·25 85

609 Snapdragons

610 Girl and Envelope

1989. International Flower Show, Damascus. Multicoloured.

1727 150 p. Type **609** 30 20

1728 150 p. "Canaria" 30 20

1729 450 p. Cornflowers 70 50

1730 850 p. "Clematis sackmani" . 1·25 85

1731 900 p. "Gesneriaceae" . . . 1·25 85

1989. Arab Post Day.

1732 **610** 175 p. multicoloured . . 35 25

611 Emblem and Map

612 "Cynthia cardui"

1989. 13th Arab Teachers' Union General Congress.

1733 **611** 175 p. multicoloured . . 35 25

1989. Butterflies. Multicoloured.

1734 550 p. Type **612** . . . . . . 1·25 85

1735 550 p. "Colias crocea" . . . 1·25 85

1736 550 p. "Pieris brassicae" . . 1·25 85

613 Symbols of International Co-operation

1989. World Telecommunications Day.

1737 **613** 550 p. multicoloured . . 80 55

614 Emblem and Map

615 Monument and Al-Baath Pioneers

1989. 17th Arab Lawyers' Union Congress.

1738 **614** 175 p. multicoloured . . 35 25

1989. 15th Anniv of Liberation of Qneitra.

1739 **615** 450 p. multicoloured . . 70 50

616 Globe and Envelopes

1989. World Post Day.

1740 **616** 550 p. multicoloured . . 80 55

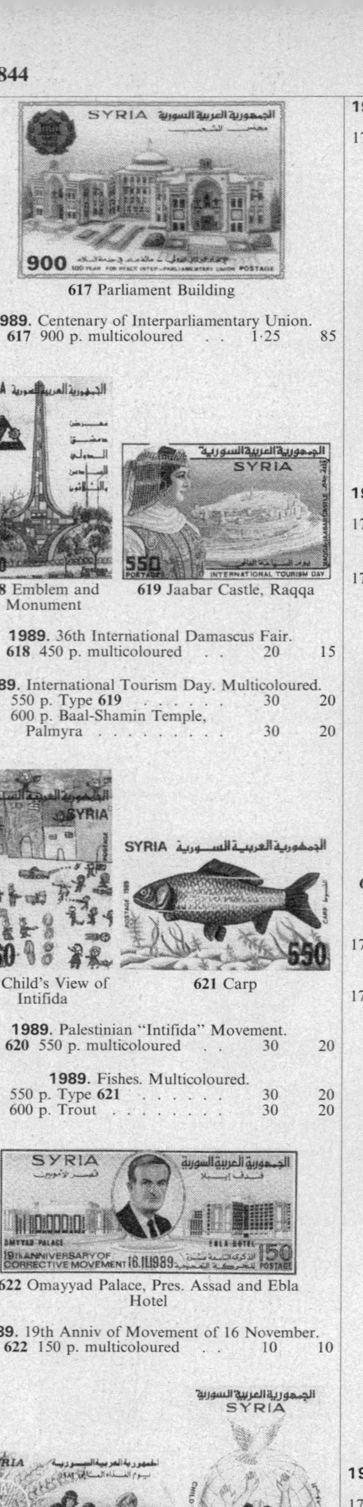

617 Parliament Building

1989. Centenary of Interparliamentary Union.
1741 **617** 900 p. multicoloured . . 1·25 85

618 Emblem and Monument
619 Jaabar Castle, Raqqa

1989. 36th International Damascus Fair.
1742 **618** 450 p. multicoloured . . 20 15

1989. International Tourism Day. Multicoloured.
1743 550 p. Type **619** 30 20
1744 600 p. Baal-Shamin Temple, Palmyra 30 20

620 Child's View of Intifida
621 Carp

1989. Palestinian "Intifida" Movement.
1745 **620** 550 p. multicoloured . . 30 20

1989. Fishes. Multicoloured.
1746 550 p. Type **621** 30 20
1747 600 p. Trout 30 20

622 Omayyad Palace, Pres. Assad and Ebla Hotel

1989. 19th Anniv of Movement of 16 November.
1748 **622** 150 p. multicoloured . . 10 10

623 Children of Different Races taking Food from Large Bowl
624 Dove, Globe and Children of Different Races

1990. World Food Day (1989).
1749 **623** 850 p. multicoloured . . 40 30

1990. International Children's Day.
1750 **624** 850 p. multicoloured . . 40 30

625 Flag, Emblem and Ear of Wheat
626 Tree-lined Road

1990. 5th Revolutionary Youth Union Congress.
1751 **625** 150 p. multicoloured . . 10 10

1990. 27th Anniv of Baathist Revolution of 8 March 1963.
1752 **626** 600 p. multicoloured . . 30 20

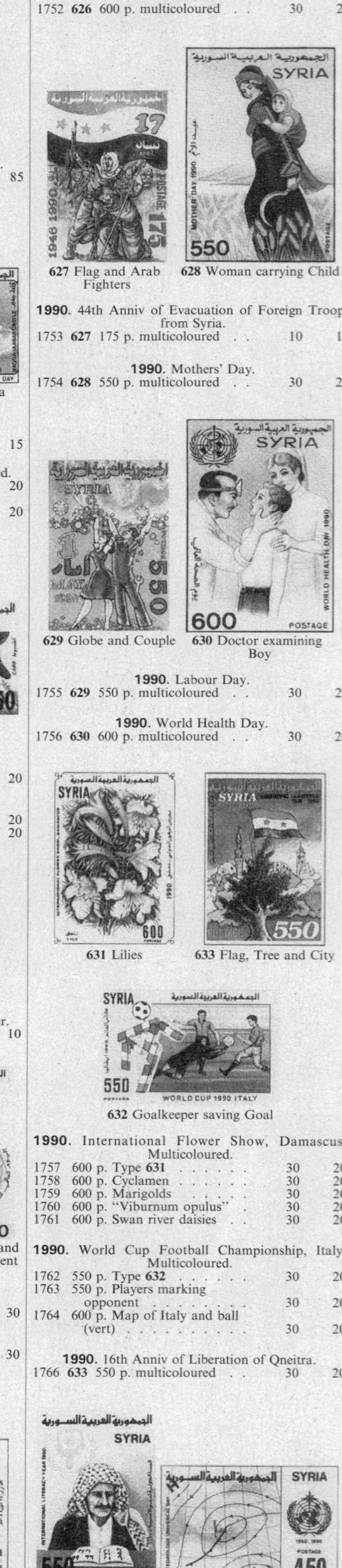

627 Flag and Arab Fighters
628 Woman carrying Child

1990. 44th Anniv of Evacuation of Foreign Troops from Syria.
1753 **627** 175 p. multicoloured . . 10 10

1990. Mothers' Day.
1754 **628** 550 p. multicoloured . . 30 20

629 Globe and Couple
630 Doctor examining Boy

1990. Labour Day.
1755 **629** 550 p. multicoloured . . 30 20

1990. World Health Day.
1756 **630** 600 p. multicoloured . . 30 20

631 Lilies
633 Flag, Tree and City

632 Goalkeeper saving Goal

1990. International Flower Show, Damascus. Multicoloured.
1757 600 p. Type **631** 30 20
1758 600 p. Cyclamen 30 20
1759 600 p. Marigolds 30 20
1760 600 p. "Viburnum opulus" . . 30 20
1761 600 p. Swan river daisies . . 30 20

1990. World Cup Football Championship, Italy. Multicoloured.
1762 550 p. Type **632** 30 20
1763 550 p. Players marking opponent 30 20
1764 600 p. Map of Italy and ball (vert) 30 20

1990. 16th Anniv of Liberation of Qneitra.
1766 **633** 550 p. multicoloured . . 30 20

634 Man and Book
635 Weather Map

1990. International Literacy Year.
1767 **634** 550 p. multicoloured . . 30 20

1990. World Meteorology Day.
1768 **635** 450 p. multicoloured . . 20 15

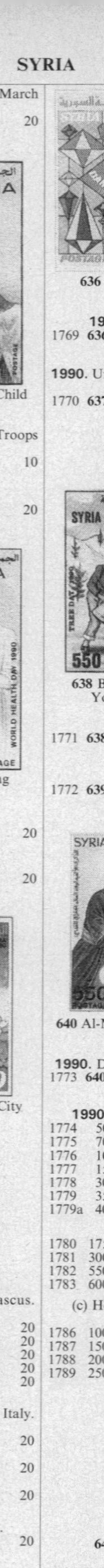

636 Emblem
637 Old and Modern Methods of Ploughing

1990. 37th International Damascus Fair.
1769 **636** 550 p. multicoloured . . 30 20

1990. United Nations Conference on Least Developed Countries.
1770 **637** 600 p. multicoloured . . 30 20

638 Boy watering Young Tree
639 Children with Bread and Water in Wheat Field

1990. Tree Day.
1771 **638** 550 p. multicoloured . . 30 20

1990. World Food Day.
1772 **639** 850 p. multicoloured . . 40 30

640 Al-Maqdisi and Map
641 Pres. Hafez al-Assad

1990. Death Millenary of Al-Maqdisi (geographer).
1773 **640** 550 p. multicoloured . . 30 20

1990. (a) As T **538** but with full-face portrait.
1774 50 p. lilac 10 10
1775 70 p. grey 10 10
1776 100 p. blue 10 10
1777 150 p. brown 10 10
1778 300 p. mauve 20 15
1779 350 p. grey 20 15
1779a 400 p. red 25 20

(b) Type **641**.
1780 175 p. multicoloured 10 10
1781 300 p. multicoloured 15 10
1782 550 p. multicoloured 30 20
1783 600 p. multicoloured 30 20

(c) Horiz design with portrait as T **641** within decorative frame.
1786 1000 p. multicoloured 50 35
1787 1500 p. multicoloured 75 50
1788 2000 p. multicoloured . . . . 1·00 70
1789 2500 p. multicoloured . . . . 1·25 85

643 Control Tower, Douglas DC-9-80 and Emblem

1990. Arab Civil Aviation Day.
1796 **643** 175 p. multicoloured . . 10 10

644 Emblem, Open Book, Cogwheel and Ear of Wheat
645 U.P.U. Emblem and Girl posting Letter

1990. 40th Anniv of United Nations Development Programme.
1797 **644** 550 p. multicoloured . . 30 20

1990. World Post Day.
1798 **645** 550 p. multicoloured . . 30 20

646 Leapfrog
647 Emblem, Flames and Open Book

1990. World Children's Day.
1799 **646** 550 p. multicoloured . . 30 20

1990. Arab–Spanish Cultural Symposium.
1800 **647** 550 p. multicoloured . . 30 20

648 Paths to and away from Aids
649 Modern Roads and Buildings

1990. World AIDS Day.
1801 **648** 550 p. multicoloured . . 30 20

1991. 28th Anniv of Baathist Revolution of 8 March 1963.
1802 **649** 150 p. multicoloured . . 10 10

650 Changefull Great Mars
651 Golden Orioles

1991. Butterflies. Multicoloured.
1803 550 p. Type **650** 30 20
1804 550 p. Small Tortoiseshell . . 30 20
1805 550 p. "Machaon sp." . . . 30 20

1991. Birds. Multicoloured.
1806 600 p. Type **651** 55 45
1807 600 p. House sparrows . . . 55 45
1808 600 p. European roller . . . 55 45

652 Three Generations
653 Statue

1991. Mothers' Day.
1809 **652** 550 p. multicoloured . . 30 20

1991. 45th Anniv of Evacuation of Foreign Troops from Syria.
1810 **653** 150 p. multicoloured . . 10 10

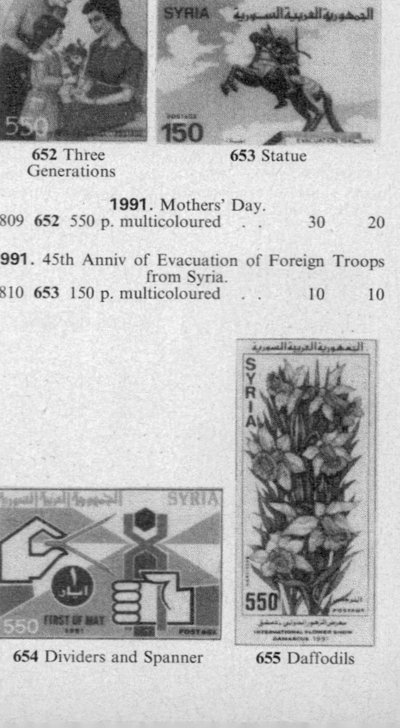

654 Dividers and Spanner
655 Daffodils

1991. Labour Day.
1811 **654** 550 p. multicoloured . . 30 20

1991. International Flower Show, Damascus. Mult.
1812 550 p. Type **655** 30 20
1813 600 p. Bee balm 30 20

656 City and Ruins

1991. 17th Anniv of Liberation of Qneitra.
1814 **656** 550 p. multicoloured . . 30 20

657 Running **658** Hall

1991. 11th Mediterranean Games, Athens. Mult.
1815 550 p. Type **657** 30 20
1816 550 p. Football 30 20
1817 600 p. Show jumping 30 20

1991. 38th International Damascus Fair.
1819 **658** 550 p. multicoloured . . 30 20

659 Courtyard, Azem Palace, Damascus **660** People encircling Block of Flats

1991. International Tourism Day. Multicoloured.
1820 450 p. Type **659** 25 20
1821 550 p. Castle, Arwad Island . 30 20

1991. Housing Day.
1822 **660** 175 p. multicoloured . . 10 10

661 Roller Skating **662** Rhazes treating Patient

1991. International Children's Day.
1823 **661** 600 p. multicoloured . . 30 20

1991. Science Week.
1824 **662** 550 p. multicoloured . . 35 25

663 Envelopes and Globe

1991. World Post Day.
1825 **663** 550 p. multicoloured . . 35 25

664 Globe, Produce and Livestock

1991. World Food Day.
1826 **664** 550 p. multicoloured . . 35 25

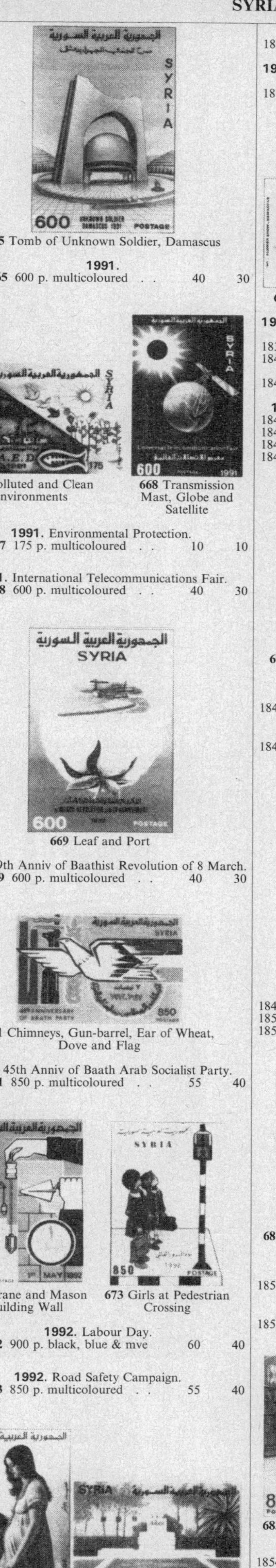

665 Tomb of Unknown Soldier, Damascus

1991.
1827 **665** 600 p. multicoloured . . 40 30

667 Polluted and Clean Environments **668** Transmission Mast, Globe and Satellite

1991. Environmental Protection.
1830 **667** 175 p. multicoloured . . 10 10

1991. International Telecommunications Fair.
1831 **668** 600 p. multicoloured . . 40 30

669 Leaf and Port

1992. 29th Anniv of Baathist Revolution of 8 March.
1832 **669** 600 p. multicoloured . . 40 30

671 Chimneys, Gun-barrel, Ear of Wheat, Dove and Flag

1992. 45th Anniv of Baath Arab Socialist Party.
1834 **671** 850 p. multicoloured . . 55 40

672 Crane and Mason building Wall **673** Girls at Pedestrian Crossing

1992. Labour Day.
1835 **672** 900 p. black, blue & mve 60 40

1992. Road Safety Campaign.
1836 **673** 850 p. multicoloured . . 55 40

674 Girl listening to Mother's Stomach **675** Memorial

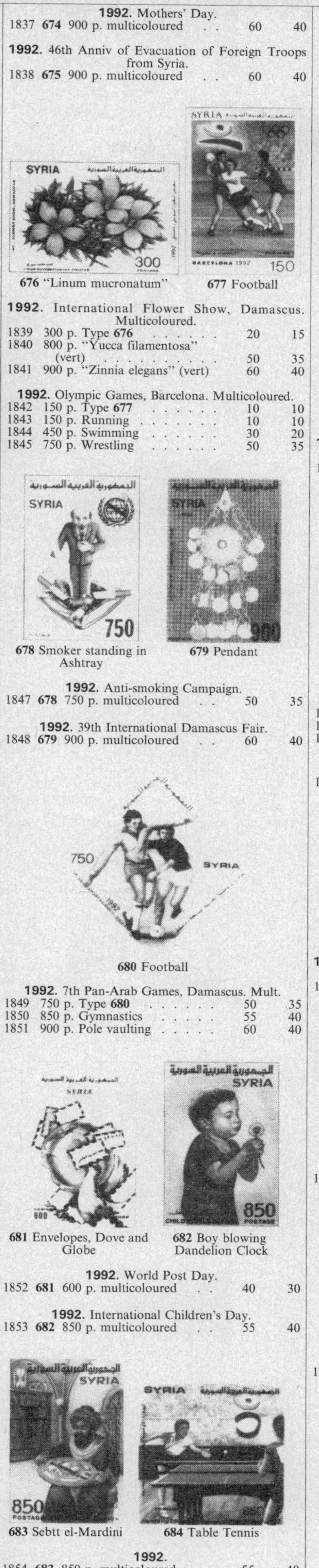

1992. Mothers' Day.
1837 **674** 900 p. multicoloured . . 60 40

1992. 46th Anniv of Evacuation of Foreign Troops from Syria.
1838 **675** 900 p. multicoloured . . 60 40

676 "Linum mucronatum" **677** Football

1992. International Flower Show, Damascus. Multicoloured.
1839 300 p. Type **676** 20 15
1840 800 p. "Yucca filamentosa" (vert) 50 35
1841 900 p. "Zinnia elegans" (vert) 60 40

1992. Olympic Games, Barcelona. Multicoloured.
1842 150 p. Type **677** 10 10
1843 150 p. Running 10 10
1844 450 p. Swimming 30 20
1845 750 p. Wrestling 50 35

678 Smoker standing in Ashtray **679** Pendant

1992. Anti-smoking Campaign.
1847 **678** 750 p. multicoloured . . 50 35

1992. 39th International Damascus Fair.
1848 **679** 900 p. multicoloured . . 60 40

680 Football

1992. 7th Pan-Arab Games, Damascus. Mult.
1849 750 p. Type **680** 50 35
1850 850 p. Gymnastics 55 40
1851 900 p. Pole vaulting 60 40

681 Envelopes, Dove and Globe **682** Boy blowing Dandelion Clock

1992. World Post Day.
1852 **681** 600 p. multicoloured . . 40 30

1992. International Children's Day.
1853 **682** 850 p. multicoloured . . 55 40

683 Sebtt el-Mardini **684** Table Tennis

1992.
1854 **683** 850 p. multicoloured . . 55 40

1992. Paralympic Games for Mentally Handicapped, Madrid.
1855 **684** 850 p. multicoloured . . 55 40

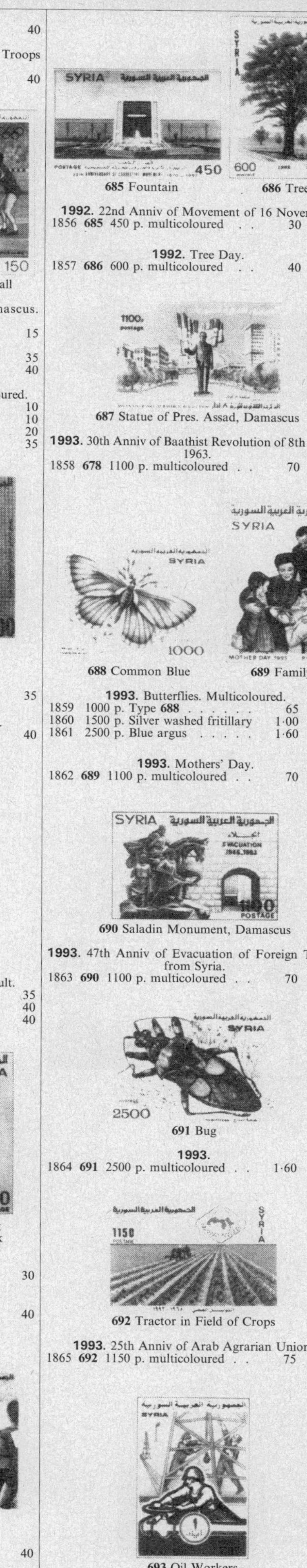

685 Fountain **686** Tree

1992. 22nd Anniv of Movement of 16 November.
1856 **685** 450 p. multicoloured . . 30 20

1992. Tree Day.
1857 **686** 600 p. multicoloured . . 40 30

687 Statue of Pres. Assad, Damascus

1993. 30th Anniv of Baathist Revolution of 8th March 1963.
1858 **678** 1100 p. multicoloured . . 70 50

688 Common Blue **689** Family

1993. Butterflies. Multicoloured.
1859 1000 p. Type **688** 65 45
1860 1500 p. Silver washed fritillary 1·00 70
1861 2500 p. Blue argus . . . . . 1·60 1·10

1993. Mothers' Day.
1862 **689** 1100 p. multicoloured . . 70 50

690 Saladin Monument, Damascus

1993. 47th Anniv of Evacuation of Foreign Troops from Syria.
1863 **690** 1100 p. multicoloured . . 70 50

691 Bug

1993.
1864 **691** 2500 p. multicoloured . . 1·60 1·10

692 Tractor in Field of Crops

1993. 25th Anniv of Arab Agrarian Union.
1865 **692** 1150 p. multicoloured . . 75 50

693 Oil Workers

1993. Labour Day.
1866 **693** 1100 p. multicoloured . . 70 50

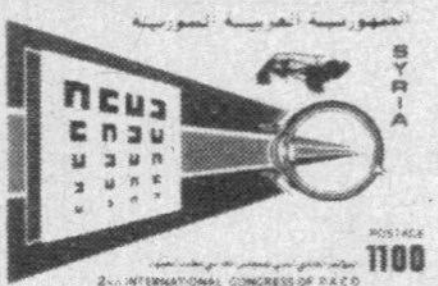

694 Eye and Eye-chart

1993. 2nd Pan-Arab Ophthalmology International Council Congress.
1867 **694** 1100 p. multicoloured . . 70 50

695 Landscapes and Eye **696** "Alcea setosa"

1993. 25th Anniv of National Ophthalmological Association.
1868 **695** 1150 p. multicoloured . . 75 50

1993. 21st International Flower Show, Damascus. Multicoloured.
1869 1000 p. Type **696** 65 45
1870 1100 p. Primulas 70 50
1871 1150 p. Gesnerias 75 50

697 Prism Tomb

1993. International Tourism Day.
1872 **697** 1000 p. multicoloured . . 65 45

698 Hand posting Letter and Globe

1993. World Post Day.
1873 **698** 1000 p. multicoloured . . 65 45

699 Boys playing Football **700** Ibn al-Bittar (chemist)

1993. International Children's Day.
1874 **699** 1150 p. multicoloured . . 70 50

1993. Science Week.
1875 **700** 1150 p. multicoloured . . 70 50

702 White Horse

1993. Arabic Horses. Multicoloured.
1877 1000 p. Type **702** 65 45
1878 1000 p. Horse with white feet 65 45
1879 1500 p. Black horse 95 65
1880 1500 p. White horse with brown mane 95 65

703 Orchard in Blossom

1993. Tree Day.
1881 **703** 1100 p. multicoloured . . 70 45

704 Flags outside Venue

1993. 40th International Damascus Fair.
1882 **704** 1100 p. multicoloured . 70 45

705 Basel al-Assad

1994. Basel al-Assad (President's son) Commem.
1883 **705** 2500 p. multicoloured . 1·60 1·10

706 Oranges

1994. 31st Anniv of Baathist Revolution of 8th March 1963. Multicoloured.
1884 1500 p. Type **706** 95 65
1885 1500 p. Mandarins 95 65
1886 1500 p. Lemons 95 65

707 Flags, Flame, Laurel and Dates

1994. 48th Anniv of Evacuation of Foreign Troops from Syria.
1887 **707** 1800 p. multicoloured . 1·10 75

708 Mechanical Digger loading Truck

1994. Labour Day.
1888 **708** 1700 p. multicoloured . 1·10 75

709 Mother and Child at Different Ages

1994. Mothers' Day.
1889 **709** 1800 p. multicoloured . 1·10 75

710 Emblem, "50" and "75"

1994. 75th Anniv of I.L.O. and 50th Anniv of Philadelphia Declaration (social charter).
1890 **710** 1700 p. multicoloured . 1·10 75

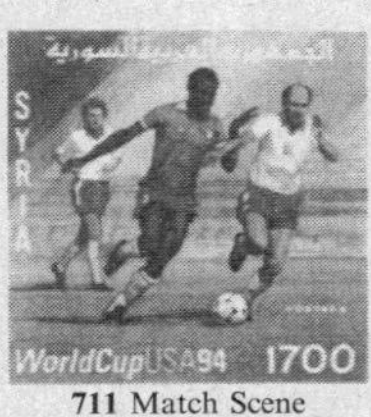

711 Match Scene

1994. World Cup Football Championship, U.S.A. Multicoloured.
1891 1700 p. Type **710** . . . . . . 1·10 75
1892 1700 p. Match scene (different) 1·10 75

712 Olympic Flag, Greek Temple and "100"

1994. Centenary of International Olympic Committee.
1894 **712** 1700 p. multicoloured . . 1·10 75

713 Flags, Lanterns and Fountain **714** Camomile

1994. 41st International Damascus Fair.
1895 **713** 1800 p. multicoloured . . 1·10 75

1994. International Flower Show, Damascus. Multicoloured.
1896 1800 p. Type **714** . . . . . . 1·10 75
1897 1800 p. Gloxinia . . . . . . 1·10 75
1898 1800 p. Mimosa . . . . . . 1·10 75

715 Apollo

1994. Butterflies. Multicoloured.
1899 1700 p. Type **715** . . . . . . 1·10 75
1900 1700 p. Purple emperor (value at right) . . . . . . 1·10 75
1901 1700 p. Birdwing (value at left) 1·10 75

716 Symbols and Map

1994. 4th Population Census.
1902 **716** 1000 p. multicoloured . . 65 45

OBLIGATORY TAX STAMPS

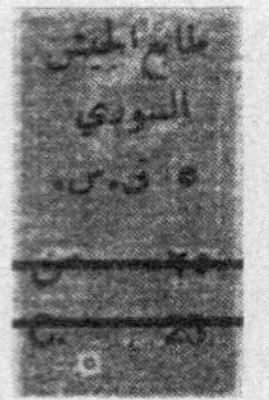
T 57 T 58

T 59 T 60

T 61

1945. Syrian Army Fund. Revenue Stamps surch or optd.
T419 T **57** 5 p. on 25 p. on 40 p. . 60·00 2·00
T420 – 5 p. on 25 p. on 40 p. pink 60·00 2·00
T421 T **58** 5 p. on 25 p. on 40 p. pink 60·00 1·00
T422 T **59** 5 p. blue . . . . 85·00 60
T423 T **60** 5 p. blue . . . . 60·00 75
T424 – 5 p. blue . . . . 70·00 20
T425 T **61** 5 p. blue . . . . 70·00 70
T426 – 5 p. blue . . . . 60·00 1·25

No. T420 is as Type **57** but with additional overprint as top line of Type **61**.

No. T424 has top line of overprint as Type **59** and other lines as Type **60**.

No. T426 has top line overprinted as Type **61** and other lines as Type **60**.

POSTAGE DUE STAMPS

A. FRENCH MILITARY OCCUPATION

1920. "Mouchon" and "Merson" key-types of French Levant surch **O.M.F. Syrie Ch taxe** and value.
D48 B 1 p. on 10 c. red . . . . 90·00 90·00
D49 2 p. on 20 c. red . . . . 90·00 90·00
D50 3 p. on 30 c. mauve . . 90·00 90·00
D51 C 4 p. on 40 c. red & blue 90·00 90·00

1920. Postage Due stamps of France surch **O.M.F. Syrie** and value.
D60 D **11** 50 c. on 10 c. brown . 30 30
D52 1 p. on 10 c. brown . . 70 70
D61 1 p. on 20 c. olive . . . 30 30
D53 2 p. on 20 c. olive . . . 70 70
D62 2 p. on 30 c. red . . . 1·00 1·00
D54 3 p. on 30 c. red . . . 70 70
D63 3 p. on 50 c. purple . . 1·25 1·50
D55 4 p. on 50 c. red . . . 2·50 3·00
D64 5 p. on 1 f. red on yellow 2·50 3·00

1921. Issued at Damascus. No. KD96 of Arab Kingdom surch **O.M.F. Syrie Chiffre Taxe** and value.
D69 K **3** 50 c. on 1 p. black . . . 1·40 1·40
D70 1 p. on 1 p. black . . . 1·00 1·00

1921. Issued at Damascus. No. 64a/5 of Syria optd **TAXE.**
D89 K **4** 2 p. on 5 m. red . . . . 2·25 2·25
D90 K **3** 3 p. on 1 p. blue . . . . 5·00 5·00

B. ARAB KINGDOM

1920. As Type K **3** but colour changed.
KD96 K **3** 1 p. black . . . . . . 1·00 1·00

C. FRENCH MANDATED TERRITORY

1923. Postage Due stamps of France surch **Syrie Grand Liban** in two lines and value.
D118 D **11** 50 c. on 10 c. brown . 40 40
D119 1 p. on 20 c. olive . . 70 70
D120 2 p. on 30 c. red . . . 55 55
D121 3 p. on 50 c. purple . 60 60
D122 5 p. on 1 f. red on yellow 1·75 2·00

1924. Postage Due stamps of France surch **SYRIE** and value.
D139 D **11** 50 c. on 10 c. brown . 30 30
D140 1 p. on 20 c. olive . . 35 35
D141 2 p. on 30 c. red . . . 50 50
D142 3 p. on 50 c. purple . 50 50
D143 5 p. on 1 f. red on yellow 65 65

1924. Postage Due stamps of France surch **Syrie** and value and also in Arabic.
D175 D **11** 0 p. 50 on 10 c. brown 25 25
D176 1 p. on 20 c. olive . . 30 30
D177 2 p. on 30 c. red . . . 40 40
D178 3 p. on 50 c. purple . 40 40
D179 5 p. on 1 f. red on yellow 80 80

D **20** Hama

1925.
D192 D **20** 0 p. 50 brown on yell 15 15
D193 – 1 p. black on red . . 15 15
D194 – 2 p. black on blue . . 20 20
D195 – 3 p. black on orange . 45 45
D196 – 5 p. black on green . 60 60
D197 – 8 p. black on blue . . 2·00 2·00
D198 – 15 p. black on red . . 3·50 3·50

DESIGNS—VERT: 1 p. Antioch. HORIZ: 2 p. Tarsus; 3 p. Banias; 5 p. Castle; 8 p. Ornamental design; 15 p. Lion.

E. SYRIAN REPUBLIC

D **221**

1965.
D883 D **221** $2\frac{1}{2}$ p. blue 25 15
D884 5 p. sepia 30 15
D885 10 p. green 35 15
D886 $17\frac{1}{2}$ p. red 75 80
D887 25 p. blue . . . . . 1·00 1·10

TAHITI Pt. 6

The largest of the Society Islands in the S. Pacific Ocean. Later renamed Oceanic Settlements.

100 centimes = 1 franc

1882. Stamps of French Colonies. "Peace and Commerce" type, surch **25 c.**

1 H 25 c. on 35 c. black on orange . . . £170 £160
3a 25 c. on 40 c. red on yellow . . . £2500 £3000

1884. Stamps of French Colonies, "Commerce" (perf) and "Peace and Commerce" (imperf) types, surch **TAHITI** and value.

4 J 5 c. on 20 c. red on green . . £120 £190
5 10 c. on 20 c. red on green . . £160 £150
2 H 25 c. on 35 c. black on orge . . £3000 £3000
6 25 c. on 1 f. green £375 £300

1893. Stamps of French Colonies, "Commerce" type, optd **TAHITI**.

7 J 1 c. black on blue £425 £375
8 2 c. brown on buff £2000 £1500
9 4 c. brown on grey £700 £550
10 5 c. green on green . . . . . 20·00 20·00
11 10 c. black on lilac . . . . . 20·00 20·00
12 15 c. blue . . . . 20·00 20·00
13 20 c. red on green . . . . . 27·00 27·00
14 25 c. brown £4250 £4250
15 25 c. black on pink . . . . . 20·00 20·00
16 35 c. black on orange . . . £1400 £1200
17 75 c. red on pink . . . . . 35·00 35·00
18 1 f. green . . . . 38·00 38·00

1893. Stamps of French Colonies, "Commerce" type, optd **1893 TAHITI**.

32 J 1 c. black on blue £425 £400
33 2 c. brown on buff £2250 £1700
34 4 c. brown on grey £1000 £800
35 5 c. green on green £575 £500
36 10 c. black on lilac £190 £190
37 15 c. blue . . . . 20·00 20·00
38 20 c. red on green . . . . . 20·00 20·00
39 25 c. brown £17000 £15000
40 25 c. black on pink . . . . . 20·00 20·00
41 35 c. black on orange . . . £1400 £1200
42 75 c. red on pink . . . . . 20·00 20·00
43 1 f. green . . . . 20·00 20·00

1903. Stamps of Oceanic Settlements, "Tablet" key-type, surch **TAHITI 10 centimes**.

57 D 10 c. on 15 c. blue and red . . 4·00 4·00
58 10 c. on 25 c. black and red on pink . . . . 4·00 4·00
59 10 c. on 40 c. red and blue on yellow . . . . 4·75 4·75

1915. Stamps of Oceanic Settlements, "Tablet" key-type, optd **TAHITI** and red cross.

60 D 15 c. blue and red £110 £110
61 15 c. grey and red . . . . . 13·50 13·50

POSTAGE DUE STAMPS

1893. Postage Due stamps of French Colonies optd **TAHITI**.

D19 U 1 c. black £250 £250
D20 2 c. black £250 £250
D21 3 c. black £300 £300
D22 4 c. black £300 £300
D23 5 c. black £300 £300
D24 10 c. black £300 £300
D25 15 c. black £300 £300
D26 20 c. black £250 £250
D27 30 c. black £300 £300
D28 40 c. black £300 £300
D29 60 c. black £300 £300
D30 1 f. brown £575 £575
D31 2 f. brown $575 £575

1893. Postage Due stamps of French Colonies optd **1893 TAHITI**.

D44 U 1 c. black £1500 £1500
D45 2 c. black £400 £400
D46 3 c. black £400 £400
D47 4 c. black £400 £400
D48 5 c. black £400 £400
D49 10 c. black £400 £400
D50 15 c. black £400 £400
D51 20 c. black £250 £250
D52 30 c. black £400 £400
D53 40 c. black £400 £400
D54 60 c. black £400 £400
D55 1 f. brown £400 £400
D56 2 f. brown £400 £400

For later issues see **OCEANIC SETTLEMENTS**.

TAJIKISTAN Pt.10

Formerly a constituent republic of the Soviet Union, Tajikistan became independent in 1991.

100 kopeks = 1 rouble

1 Hunter (gold relief)

2 Sheikh Muslihiddin Mosque

1992.

1 1 50 k. multicoloured . . . . . 2·90 2·90

1992.

2 2 50 k. multicoloured . . . . . 2·90 2·90

3 Traditional Musical Instruments

1992.

3 3 35 k. multicoloured 55 55

4 Argali

1992.

4 4 30 k. multicoloured 55 55

Точикистон 3.00
5.00
1992
1992
Тадж.
(5) (7)

1992. No. 2 surch as T **5**.

5 2 5 r. on 50 k. multicoloured . . 1·60 1·60
6 25 r. on 50 k. multicoloured . . 2·75 2·75

1992. No. 3 surch.

7 3 15 r. on 35 k. multicoloured . . 2·75 2·75
8 50 r. on 35 k. multicoloured . . 2·75 2·75

1993. No. 6072 of Russia surch as T **7**.

9 2410 3 r. on 1 k. brown . . . . 4·75 4·75
10 100 r. on 1 k. brown . . . . 4·75 4·75

60. 00
Точикистон
10.00
(8) (9)

1993. No. 6073 of Russia surch as T **8**.

11 10 r. on 2 k. brown 70 70
12 15 r. on 2 k. brown 70 70

On No. 12 the surcharge is in smaller letters.

1993. No. 1 surch with T **9**.

13 1 60 r. on 50 k. multicoloured . . 1·25 1·25

10 Mountain Landscape

1993. Multicoloured.

16 1 r. Statue of Abuabdullokhi Rudaki, Dushanbe (vert) . . 10 10
17 5 r. Type **10** 25 25
18 15 r. Mausoleum of Sadriddin Aini (poet), Dushanbe (vert) . . 75 75
19 20 r. State flag and map . . . 95 95
20 25 r. Gissar Fort . . . . . . 1·00 1·00
21 50 r. Aini Opera and Ballet House, Dushanbe . . . . 2·25 2·25
22 100 r. State flag and map (different) . . . . 4·25 4·25

11 Brown Bear

1993. Mammals. Multicoloured.

23 3 r. Type **11** 15 15
24 10 r. Red deer 20 20
25 15 r. Markhor 35 35
26 25 r. Porcupine 45 45
27 100 r. Snow leopard . . . . . 2·25 2·25

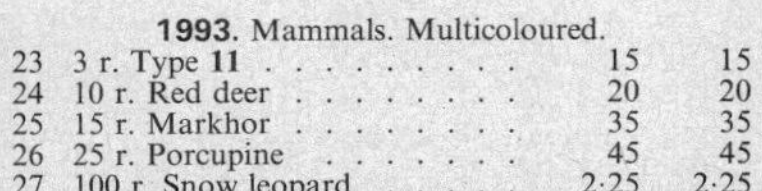

12 Geb and Talkhand in Battle

1993. Millenary of "Book of Kings" by Abu-I Kasim Mansur, Firdausi (poet). Multicoloured.

28 5 r. Type **12** 60 60
29 20 r. Rustam and Sukhrov in combat . . . . 2·00 2·00
30 30 r. Eagle Simurg brings Zola to his father Som (vert) . . . . 3·00 3·00

14 Ceiling Decoration

1993.

33 14 1 r. 50 multicoloured . . . . 1·00 1·00

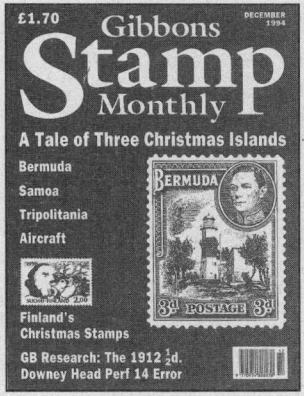

TCHONGKING (CHUNGKING) Pt.17

An Indo-Chinese Post Office was opened at Chungking in February 1902 and operated until it closed in December 1922.

1903. 100 centimes = 1 franc
1919. 100 cents = 1 piastre

Stamps of Indo-China surch.

1903. "Tablet" key-type surch with value in Chinese and **TCHONGKING**.
1 D 1 c. black and red on blue . 1·60 1·60
2 2 c. brown and blue on buff 1·60 1·60
3 4 c. brown and blue on grey 1·60 1·60
4 5 c. green and red 1·60 1·60
5 10 c. red and blue 1·60 1·60
6 15 c. grey and red 1·50 1·50
7 20 c. red and blue on green 1·60 1·60
8 25 c. blue and red 24·00 24·00
9 25 c. black and red on pink 3·25 3·25
10 30 c. brown and blue on drab 5·50 5·25
11 40 c. red and blue on yellow 25·00 25·00
12 50 c. red and blue on pink £120 £120
13 50 c. brown and red on blue 75·00 75·00
14 75 c. brown and red on orange 24·00 24·00
15 1 f. green and red 30·00 30·00
16 5 f. mauve and blue on lilac 55·00 55·00

1906. Surch with value in Chinese and **Tch'ong K'ing**.
17 8 1 c. green 95 95
18 2 c. purple on yellow 95 95
19 4 c. mauve on blue 95 95
20 5 c. green 95 95
21 10 c. pink 95 95
22 15 c. brown on blue 3·25 3·25
23 20 c. red on green 95 95
24 25 c. blue 2·00 2·00
25 30 c. brown on cream 1·50 1·50
26 35 c. black on yellow 1·50 1·50
27 40 c. black on grey 3·25 3·25
28 50 c. brown on cream 3·25 3·25
29 D 75 c. brown and red on orange 20·00 20·00
30 8 1 f. green 13·50 13·50
31 2 f. brown on yellow 13·50 13·50
32 D 5 f. mauve and blue on lilac 60·00 60·00
33 8 10 f. red on green 75·00 75·00

1908. Native types surch with value in Chinese and **TCHONGKING**.
34 10 1 c. black and brown 15 25
35 2 c. black and brown 30 35
36 4 c. black and blue 35 40
37 5 c. black and green 55 55
38 10 c. black and red 65 75
39 15 c. black and violet 90 90
40 11 20 c. black and violet 1·50 1·50
41 25 c. black and blue 1·50 1·50
42 30 c. black and brown 1·60 1·60
43 35 c. black and green 3·00 3·00
44 40 c. black and brown 7·25 7·25
45 50 c. black and red 4·75 4·75
46 12 75 c. black and orange 4·75 4·75
47 – 1 f. black and red 6·00 6·25
48 – 2 f. black and green 50·00 50·00
49 – 5 f. black and blue 17·00 17·00
50 – 10 f. black and violet £150 £150

1919. As last, but surch in addition in figures and words.
51 10 ⅖ c. on 1 c. black & brown 45 45
52 ⅘ c. on 2 c. black & brown 50 55
53 1⅗ c. on 4 c. black and blue 65 65
54 2 c. on 5 c. black & green 50 45
55 4 c. on 10 c. black and red 50 45
56 6 c. on 15 c. black & violet 50 45
57 11 8 c. on 20 c. black & violet 50 45
58 10 c. on 25 c. black & blue 70 60
59 12 c. on 30 c. blk & brown 90 60
60 14 c. on 35 c. black & green 90 55
61 16 c. on 40 c. black & brown 1·00 90
62 20 c. on 50 c. black & red 5·00 5·00
63 12 30 c. on 75 c. black & orge 1·10 1·00
64 – 40 c. on 1 f. black and red 1·60 1·00
65 – 80 c. on 2 f. black & green 2·75 2·25
66 – 2 p. on 5 f. black & blue 3·75 3·25
67 – 4 p. on 10 f. black & violet 5·75 4·00

TETE Pt. 9

Formerly using the stamps of Mozambique, this district of Mozambique was permitted to issue its own stamps from 1913 to 1920 when Mozambique stamps were again used.

100 centavos = 1 escudo

1913. Surch **REPUBLICA TETE** and new value on "Vasco da Gama" issues of (a) **Portugese Colonies**.
1 ¼ c. on 2½ r. green 40 30
2 ½ c. on 5 r. red 40 30
3 1 c. on 10 r. purple 40 30
4 2½ c. on 25 r. green 40 30
5 5 c. on 50 r. blue 40 30
6 7½ c. on 75 r. brown 80 65
7 10 c. on 100 r. brown 45 40
8 15 c. on 150 r. bistre 45 40

(b) **Macao**.
9 ¼ c. on ½ a. green 40 30
10 ½ c. on 1 a. red 40 30
11 1 c. on 2 a. purple 40 30
12 2½ c. on 4 a. green 40 30
13 5 c. on 8 a. blue 40 30
14 7½ c. on 12 a. brown 80 65
15 10 c. on 16 a. brown 45 40
16 15 c. on 24 a. yellow 45 40

(c) **Timor**.
17 ¼ c. on ½ c. green 40 30
18 ½ c. on 1 a. red 40 30
19 1 c. on 2 a. purple 40 30
20 2½ c. on 4 a. green 40 30
21 5 c. on 8 a. blue 40 30
22 7½ c. on 12 a. brown 80 65
23 10 c. on 16 a. brown 45 40
24 15 c. on 24 a. bistre 45 40

1914. "Ceres" key-type inscr "TETE".
25 U ¼ c. olive 40 30
26 ½ c. black 40 30
27 1 c. green 40 30
28 1½ c. brown 40 30
29 2 c. red 40 30
30 2½ c. violet 40 30
31 5 c. blue 40 30
32 7½ c. brown 60 60
33 8 c. grey 60 60
34 10 c. brown 70 70
35 15 c. red 90 70
36 20 c. green 90 70
37 30 c. brown on green 90 70
38 40 c. brown on red 1·10 80
39 50 c. orange on pink 1·10 1·00
40 1 e. green on blue 1·40 1·25

THAILAND Pt.21

An independent kingdom in S.E. Asia, previously known as Siam.

1883. 32 solot = 16 atts = 8 peinung (sio) = 4 songpy (sik) = 2 fuang = 1 salung. 4 salungs = 1 tical
1909. 100 satangs = 1 tical
1912. 100 satangs = 1 baht

1 King Chulalongkorn 2

3 King Chulalongkorn 9

1883.
1 1 1 solot blue 4·25 5·75
2 1 att red 7·00 8·50
3 1 sio red 17·00 21·00
4 2 1 sik yellow 7·00 8·50
5 3 1 salung orange 25·00 28·00

1885. Surch **1 Tical**.
7 1 1 t. on 1 solot blue £275 £200

1887.
11 9 1 a. green 1·25 85
12 2 a. green and red 1·25 85
13 3 a. green and blue 2·00 1·00
14 4 a. green and brown 5·75 2·75
15 8 a. green and yellow 4·25 2·00
16 12 a. purple and red 11·50 1·25
17 24 a. purple and blue 14·50 1·40
18 64 a. purple and brown 55·00 14·00

(11) (12)

1889. Surch with T **11**.
19 1 1 a. on 1 sio red 5·75 5·75

1889. Surch as T **12**.
20 9 1 a. on 2 a. green and red 1·40 1·40
24 1 a. on 3 a. green and blue 4·25 3·50
26 2 a. on 3 a. green and blue 15·00 15·00

1 Att.

(23) (42)

1892. Surch with T **23**.
32 9 4 a. on 24 a. purple and blue 22·00 22·00

1892. Surch as T **42**.
63 9 1 a. on 12 a. purple and red 5·75 1·75
46 1 a. on 64 a. purple & brown 85 85
44 2 a. on 64 a. purple & brown 85 85
58 3 a. on 12 a. purple and red 4·25 1·75
60 4 a. on 12 a. purple and red 4·25 1·40
33 4 a. on 24 a. purple and blue 4·25 3·00
50 10 a. on 24 a. purple & blue 2·25 85

49 50 53 Wat Cheng "Temple of Light"

1899.
67 49 1 a. green 85 45
68 2 a. green 1·10 45
69 2 a. red and blue 1·40 55
70 3 a. red and blue 3·25 1·10
71 3 a. green 8·50 5·50
72 4 a. red 1·40 55
73 4 a. brown and pink 4·50 1·10
74 6 a. red 12·00 7·00
75 8 a. green and orange 2·75 60
76 10 a. blue 4·25 1·40
77 12 a. purple and red 17·00 1·40
78 14 a. blue 11·50 8·50
79 24 a. purple and blue 85·00 5·50
80 28 a. brown and blue 13·00 10·00
81 64 a. purple and brown 28·00 2·75

1899.
82 50 1 a. green £150 75·00
83 2 a. green and red £200 £120
84 3 a. red and blue £250 £160
85 4 a. black and green £2250 £550
86 10 a. red and green £2500 £750

1905. Surch in English and Siamese.
90 49 1 a. on 14 a. blue 4·25 3·25
91 2 a. on 28 a. brown & blue 4·75 3·75

1905.
92 53 1 a. green and yellow 70 30
93 2 a. grey and violet 1·25 55
94 2 a. green 4·25 2·10
95 3 a. green 1·90 55
96 3 a. grey and violet 6·75 2·75
97 4 a. red and sepia 2·00 60
98 4 a. red 3·50 60
99 5 a. red 4·00 1·40
100 8 a. olive and black 3·50 55
101 9 a. blue 12·50 4·50
102 12 a. blue 9·50 1·50
103 18 a. brown 35·00 8·75
104 24 a. brown 16·00 3·00
105 1 t. yellow and blue 27·00 4·25

1907. Tall Fiscal stamp with portrait and scales surch **Siam Postage** and new value.
106 10 t. green £450 70·00
107 20 t. green £4250 £200
108 40 t. green £3500 £450

1907. Surch **1 att** and thin line.
109 9 1 a. on 24 s. purple & blue 85 55

1908. Surch in English and Siamese.
110 9 2 a. on 24 a. purple & blue 85 55
111 53 4 a. on 5 a. red 5·00 2·25
112 49 9 a. on 10 a. blue 5·75 3·00

1908. 40th Anniv of Reign of King Chulalongkorn. Optd **Jubilee 1868–1908** in English and Siamese.
113 53 1 a. green and yellow 85 60
114 3 a. green 1·40 1·25
115 4 a. on 5 a. (No. 111) 2·00 1·75
116 8 a. olive and black 13·00 13·00
117 18 a. brown 18·00 12·50

61 Statue of King Chulalongkorn, Bangkok

64 King Chulalongkorn

1908.
118 61 1 t. violet and green 22·00 1·40
119 2 t. orange and purple 45·00 5·75
120 3 t. blue and olive 55·00 8·75
121 5 t. green and lilac 80·00 17·00
122 10 t. red and olive £950 60·00
123 20 t. brown and grey £190 50·00
124 40 t. black and blue £325 £140

1909. Surch in satangs in English and Siamese.
125 53 2 s. on 1 a. green & yellow 55 30
127a 2 s. on 2 a. green 60 30
164 2 s. on 2 a. grey & violet 1·40 1·25
129 3 s. on 3 a. green 1·40 1·40
130 3 s. on 3 a. grey & violet 1·25 30
131 6 s. on 4 a. red and sepia 35·00 32·00
132a 6 s. on 4 a. red 1·25 55
134 6 s. on 5 a. red 1·40 1·40
138 49 6 s. on 6 a. red 1·10 1·10
135 53 12 s. on 8 a. olive & black 2·25 30
136 14 s. on 9 a. blue 3·00 85
137 14 s. on 12 a. blue 11·50 11·50
139 9 14 s. on 12 a. purple & red 42·00 42·00
140 49 14 s. on 14 a. blue 10·00 10·50

1910.
141 64 2 s. green and orange 60 30
142 3 s. green 90 30
143 6 s. red 1·40 30
144 12 s. brown and black 3·00 60
145 14 s. blue 8·75 85
146 28 s. brown 20·00 4·00

65 King Vajiravudh 66

1912.
166 65 2 s. brown 45 15
167 3 s. green 70 30
168 5 s. red 60 15
149 6 s. red 1·60 30
169 10 s. brown and black 85 20
150 12 s. sepia and black 2·40 35
151 14 s. blue 3·75 45
170 15 s. blue 1·75 45
152 28 s. brown 12·00 3·75
153 66 1 b. sepia and blue 11·50 75
154 2 b. sepia and red 17·00 1·40
155 3 b. black and green 23·00 2·40
156 5 b. black and violet 30·00 2·25
157 10 b. purple and olive £160 38·00
158 20 b. brown and blue £275 35·00

1914. Surch in English and Siamese.
165 64 2 s. on 14 s. blue 85 45
159 65 2 s. on 14 s. blue 60 15
160 5 s. on 6 s. red 1·25 15
161 10 s. on 12 s. sepia & blk 1·10 30
162 15 s. on 28 s. brown 2·40 45

1918. Red Cross Fund. Optd with small cross in circle.
177 65 2 s. (+ 3 s.) brown 60 60
178 3 s. (+ 2 s.) green 60 60
179 5 s. (+ 5 s.) red 1·25 90
180 10 s. (+ 5 s.) brown and black 3·00 1·75
181 15 s. (+ 5 s.) blue 3·25 1·75
182 66 1 b. (+ 25 s.) sepia and blue 14·00 8·00
183 2 b.(+ 30 s.) brown and red 22·00 12·00
184 3 b. (+ 35 s.) black and green 30·00 20·00
185 5 b. (+ 40 s.) black and violet 90·00 42·00
186 10 b.(+ 1 b.) purple and olive £275 £110
187 20 b. (+ 1 b.) brown & grn £1400 £800

1918. Optd **VICTORY** in English and Siamese.
188 65 2 s. brown 55 50
189 3 s. green 75 50
190 5 s. red 1·25 1·10
191 10 s. brown and black 1·40 1·25
192 15 s. blue 2·50 2·00
193 66 1 b. sepia and blue 18·00 15·00
194 2 b. brown and red 35·00 30·00
195 3 b. black and green 80·00 45·00
196 5 b. black and violet £180 £150

1919. Surch in English and Siamese figures.
197 65 5 s. on 6 s. red 75 15
198 10 s. on 12 s. sepia & black 1·75 15

(72a) (72b)

1920. Scouts' Fund. Various stamps hand-stamped.

(a) With Type **72a**.
199 65 2 s. (+3 s.) brown 25·00 25·00
200 3 s. (+2 s.) green 25·00 25·00
201 5 s. on 6 s. (+20 s.) red (No. 160) 35·00 35·00
202 10 s. on 12 s. (+5 s.) brown and black (No. 161) 35·00 35·00
203 15 s. (+5 s.) blue 70·00 70·00
204 53 1 t. (+25 s.) yellow & blue £275 £275

(b) With Type **72b**.
205 65 2 s. (+3 s.) brown 10·00 10·00
206 3 s. (+2 s.) green 10·00 10·00
207 73 5 s. (+20 s.) red on pink 75·00 75·00
208 65 10 s. on 12 s. (+5 s.) brown and black (No. 161) 15·00 15·00
209 15 s. (+5 s.) blue 15·00 15·00
210 53 1 t. (+25 s.) yellow & blue £250 £250

These stamps were sold in aid of the "Wild Tiger" Scouts organisation at the premium stated.

73 SCOUT'S FUND (73a)

1920.
211 73 2 s. brown on yellow 75 15
212 3 s. green on green 1·00 25
213 3 s. brown 1·00 15
214 5 s. red on pink 1·25 15
215 5 s. green 12·00 1·60
216 5 s. violet on mauve 2·50 25
217 10 s. brown and black 2·50 15
218 15 s. blue on blue 3·75 20
219 15 s. red 20·00 2·25
220 25 s. brown 10·00 1·25
221 25 s. blue 16·00 45
222 50 s. black and brown 24·00 75

1920. Scouts' Fund. Optd with T **73a**.
223 **73** 2 s. (+ 3 s.) brown on yellow 7·00 7·00
224 3 s. (+ 2 s.) green on green 7·00 7·00
225 5 s. (+ 5 s.) red on pink 7·00 7·00
226 10 s. (+ 5 s.) brown and black 7·00 7·00
227 15 s. (+ 5 s.) blue on blue 14·00 14·00
228 25 s. (+ 25 s.) brown 38·00 38·00
229 50 s. (+ 30 s.) black & brn £180 £180

74 "Garuda" Bird **75** Coronation Stone

1925. Air.
230 **74** 2 s. purple on yellow 60 15
231 3 s. brown 60 15
239 5 s. green 60 15
240 10 s. orange and black 60 15
234 15 s. red 2·50 50
242 25 s. blue 1·25 75
243 50 s. black and brown 1·25 75
237 1 b. sepia and blue 23·00 6·50

1926.
244 **75** 1 t. green and lilac 7·50 1·25
245 2 t. red 18·00 3·75
246 3 t. blue and olive 38·00 16·00
247 5 t. olive and violet 38·00 12·00
248 10 t. brown and red £100 15·00
249 10 t. brown and blue £100 48·00

1928. Surch in English and Siamese.
250 **73** 5 s. on 15 s. red 2·50 1·25
251 **65** 10 s. on 28 s. brown 7·50 1·00

76 King Prajadhipok **77**

1928.
252 **76** 2 s. brown 50 15
253 3 s. green 50 25
254 5 s. violet 50 15
255 10 s. red 50 15
256 15 s. blue 55 25
257 25 s. orange and black 2·50 50
258 50 s. black and orange 1·25 75
259 80 s. black and blue 2·50 50
260 **77** 1 b. black and blue 3·75 75
261 2 b. brown and red 5·00 1·50
262 3 b. black and green 7·50 2·00
263 5 b. brown and violet 12·00 3·00
264 10 b. purple and olive 25·00 5·00
265 20 b. brown and green 50·00 10·00
266 40 b. sepia and green 90·00 38·00

1930. Surch in English and Siamese.
267 **64** 10 s. on 12 s. brown & blk 2·50 50
268 25 s. on 28 s. brown 12·00 75

79 Kings Prajadhipok and Chao Phya Chakri **81** Chao Phya Chakri

80 Kings Prajadhipok and Chao Phya Chakri

1932. 150th Anniv of Chakri Dynasty and of Bangkok as Capital and Opening of Memorial Bridge over Menam.
269 **79** 2 s. red 1·00 15
270 3 s. green 1·50 25
271 5 s. violet 1·00 15
272 **80** 10 s. black and red 1·50 15
273 15 s. black and blue 5·00 50
274 25 s. black and mauve 7·50 75
275 50 s. black and red 32·00 1·90
276 **81** 1 b. blue 50·00 8·50

(82)

1939. Red Cross Fund. 75th Anniv of Membership of the International Red Cross. Surch. as T **82**.
277 **66** 5 + 5 s. on 1 b. (193) 8·50 8·50
278 10 + 5 s. on 2 b. (194) 20·00 20·00
279 15 + 5 s. on 3 b. (195) 16·00 16·00

83 National Assembly Hall **84** Chakri Palace and "Garuda" Bird

1939. 7th Anniv of Constitution and National Day (1st issue).
280 **83** 2 s. brown 2·50 35
281 3 s. green 5·00 1·25
282 5 s. mauve 2·50 15
283 10 s. red 7·50 15
284 15 s. blue 20·00 65

1940. National Day (2nd issue).
285 **84** 2 s. brown 1·25 35
286 3 s. green 3·75 1·25
287 5 s. mauve 2·50 15
288 10 s. red 12·00 15
289 15 s. blue 25·00 65

85 King Ananda Mahidol **86** Ploughing Rice Field

87 Ban Pa'im Palace, Ayuthia **88** Monument of Democracy, Bangkok

1941.
290 **85** 2 s. brown 50 15
291 3 s. green 75 25
292 5 s. violet 50 15
293 10 s. red 75 15
294 **86** 15 s. grey and blue 75 25
295 25 s. orange and slate 75 25
296 50 s. grey and orange 1·00 25
297 **87** 1 b. grey and blue 2·75 65
298 2 b. grey and red 5·00 1·25
299 3 b. grey and green 13·00 4·00
300 5 b. red and black 32·00 12·00
301 10 b. yellow and black 48·00 30·00

1942. Air.
302 **88** 2 s. brown 1·25 1·00
303 3 s. green 20·00 22·00
304 5 s. purple 1·25 50
305 10 s. red 12·00 75
306 15 s. blue 2·75 1·40

89 King Ananda Mahidol **90** Indo-China War Monument, Bangkok **91** Bangkaen Monument and Ears of Rice

1943.
307 **89** 1 b. blue 10·00 1·00

1943.
311 **91** 2 s. orange 1·25 1·00
310 **90** 3 s. green 1·25 75
312 **91** 10 s. red 2·50 25

92 King Bhumibol **93**

1947.
313 **92** 5 s. violet 15 15
314 10 s. red 75 15
315 20 s. brown 50 15
316 50 s. green 75 15
317 1 b. blue and violet 5·00 15
318 2 b. green and blue 13·00 90
319 3 b. black and red 20·00 2·00
320 5 b. red and green 45·00 3·00
321 10 b. violet and sepia £180 1·00
322 20 b. lilac and black £225 3·75
The baht values are larger, size $21\frac{1}{2} \times 27$ mm.

1947. Coming of Age of King Bhumibol.
323 **93** 5 s. orange 1·00 1·00
324 10 s. brown 38·00 40·00
325 10 s. green 1·00 1·00
326 20 s. blue 3·00 1·00
327 50 s. green 7·50 2·00

94 King and Palace **95** King Bhumibol

1950. King's Coronation.
328 **94** 5 s. purple 25 15
329 10 s. red 50 15
330 15 s. violet 1·75 1·75
331 20 s. brown 50 15
332 80 s. green 5·50 2·50
333 1 b. blue 2·00 15
334 2 b. yellow 8·00 1·00
335 3 b. grey 35·00 6·00

1951.
336 **95** 5 s. purple 25 10
337 10 s. green 25 10
338 15 s. brown 75 15
339 20 s. brown 75 10
340 25 s. red 25 10
341 50 s. olive 75 10
342 1 b. blue 1·00 15
343 1 b. 15 blue 25 15
344 1 b. 25 lake 3·75 25
345 2 b. green 4·50 25
346 3 b. grey 7·50 40
347 5 b. red and blue 30·00 50
348 10 b. violet and sepia £180 90
349 20 b. olive and black £160 9·00

96 U.N. Emblem **97** "Garuda" Bird

1951. United Nations Day.
350 **96** 25 s. blue 2·50 2·50

1952. Air.
351 **97** 1 b. purple 1·25 25
352 2 b. blue 7·50 1·50
353 3 b. grey 10·00 75

1952. United Nations Day. Optd **1952**.
354 **96** 25 s. blue 1·50 1·50

1952. 20th Anniv of Constitution. Surch with emblem and value.
355 **76** 80 s. + 20 s. black & blue 12·00 11·00

99 Dancer over Cross **103** Processional Elephant

1953. 60th Anniv of Thai Red Cross Society. Cross in red, figures in blue and red.
356 **99** 25 s. + 25 s. cream & green 3·75 3·75
357 50 s. + 50 s. cream & red 13·00 13·00
358 1 b. + 1 b. cream & blue 15·00 15·00

1953. United Nations Day. Optd **1953**.
359 **96** 25 s. blue 1·00 1·00

1954. United Nations Day. Optd **1954** vert.
360 **96** 25 s. blue 2·50 2·50

1955. Optd **THAILAND** in English and Siamese.
361 **76** 5 s. violet 3·75 5·00
362 10 s. red 3·75 5·00

1955. Surch.
363 **92** 5 s. on 20 s. brown 1·00 35
364 10 s. on 20 s. brown 1·00 35

1955. 400th Birth Anniv of King Naresuan.
365 **103** 25 s. red 75 15
366 80 s. purple 13·00 4·00
367 1 b. 25 green 30·00 75
368 2 b. blue 7·00 1·10
369 3 b. lake 26·00 60

1955. Red Cross Fair. Optd **24 98**.
370 **99** 25 s. + 25 s. cream & grn 13·00 13·00
371 50 s. + 50 s. cream & red 75·00 75·00
372 1 b. + 1 b. cream & blue £100 £100

105 Tao Suranari **106** Equestrian Statue

1955. Tao Suranari Commemoration.
373 **105** 10 s. lilac 75 25
374 25 s. green 50 15
375 1 b. brown 24·00 1·60

1955. King Taksin Commemoration.
376 **106** 5 s. blue 75 25
377 25 s. green 5·50 10
378 1 b. 25 red 21·00 1·75

1955. U.N. Day. Optd **1955** vert.
379 **96** 25 s. blue 2·50 2·50

107 Don Chedi Pagoda **108** Dharmachakra and Sambar

1956.
380 **107** 10 s. green 1·25 1·10
381 50 s. brown 13·00 1·00
382 75 s. violet 3·75 75
383 1 b. 50 brown 13·00 75

1956. U.N. Day. Optd **1956** vert.
384 **96** 25 s. blue 1·25 1·25

1957. 2500th Anniv of Buddhist Era.
385 **108** 5 s. sepia 50 15
386 10 s. red 50 15
387 15 s. green 1·25 1·00
388 – 20 s. orange 1·25 1·00
389 – 25 s. brown 25 10
390 – 50 s. mauve 1·00 30
391 – 1 b. bistre 1·50 40
392 – 1 b. 25 blue 20·00 2·75
393 – 2 b. purple 3·75 50
DESIGNS: 20 s. to 50 s. Hand of Peace and Dharmachakra; 1 b. to 2 b. Nakon Phatom pagoda.

110 U.N. Emblem and Laurel Sprays **111** Gateway to Grand Palace

1957. United Nations Day.
394 **110** 25 s. olive 60 25
395 25 s. brown (1958) 60 25
400 25 s. blue (1959) 75 25

1959. 1st South East Asia Peninsula Games (S.E.A.P.).
396 **111** 10 s. orange 25 15
397 – 25 s. lake 40 15
398 – 1 b. 25 green 1·90 1·00
399 – 2 b. blue 2·00 50
DESIGNS: 25 s. Royal parasols; 1 b. 25, Bowman; 2 b. Wat Arun (temple) and prow of royal barge.

112 Pagoda **113** Wat Arun Temple

1960. World Refugee Year.
401 **112** 50 s. brown 25 10
402 2 b. green 75 40

1960. Leprosy Relief Campaign.
403 **113** 50 s. red 25 10
404 2 b. blue 1·75 45

114 Indian Elephant
115 S.E.A.T.O. Emblem

1960. 5th World Forestry Congress, Seattle.
405 **114** 25 s. green 50 15

1960. S.E.A.T.O. Day.
406 **115** 50 s. brown 60 15

116 Siamese Child
117 Letter-writing

1960. Children's Day.
407 **116** 50 s. mauve 35 10
408 1 b. brown . . . . 2·10 55

1960. International Correspondence Week.
409 **117** 50 s. mauve 25 10
410 2 b. blue . . . . 1·75 45

118 U.N. Emblem and Globe
119 King Bhumibol

1960. U.N. Day.
411 **118** 50 s. violet 50 15
446 50 s. lake (1961) 35 15
467 50 s. red (1962) 35 15

1961.
422 **119** 5 s. purple 15 10
423 10 s. turquoise 15 10
424 15 s. brown 25 10
425 20 s. brown 15 10
426 25 s. red 25 10
427 50 s. olive 25 10
428 80 s. orange . . . . 1·25 65
429 1 b. brown and blue . . . 90 15
430 1 b. 25 olive and red . . . 2·50 50
431 1 b. 50 green and violet . . 80 15
432 2 b. violet and red . . . 1·10 10
433 3 b. blue and brown . . . 2·75 25
434 4 b. black and bistre . . . 3·00 1·00
435 5 b. green and blue . . . 9·00 30
436 10 b. black and red . . . 45·00 40
437 20 b. blue and green . . . 40·00 2·00
438 25 b. blue and green . . . 15·00 1·25
439 40 b. black and yellow . . 32·00 3·00

120 Children in Garden

1961. Children's Day.
440 **120** 10 s. blue 50 15
441 2 b. violet . . . . 1·50 50

121 Pen, Letters and Globe
122 Thai Scout Badge and Saluting Hand

1961. International Correspondence Week.
442 – 25 s. myrtle 25 15
443 – 50 s. purple 15 10
444 **121** 1 b. red 80 35
445 2 b. blue 90 40
DESIGN: 25 s., 50 s. Pen, and world map on envelope.

1961. 50th Anniv of Thai Scout Movement.
447 **122** 50 s. mauve 25 15
448 – 1 b. green 50 40
449 – 2 b. blue 75 50
DESIGNS—VERT: 1 b. Scout camp and scout saluting flag; 2 b. King Vajiravudh in uniform, and scout, cub and guide marching.

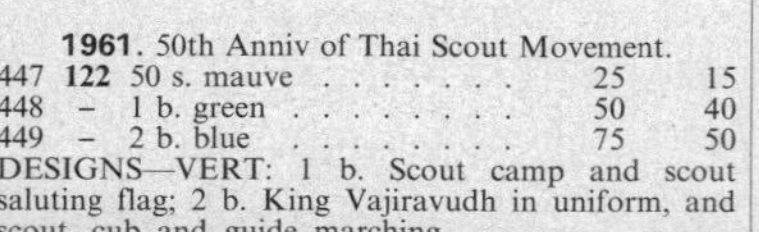

123 Campaign Emblem and Temple
124 Bangkok

1962. Malaria Eradication.
450 **123** 5 s. brown 15 10
451 10 s. brown 15 10
452 20 s. blue 15 10
453 50 s. red 15 10
454 – 1 b. green 75 15
455 – 1 b. 50 purple . . . . . 1·75 50
456 – 2 b. blue . . . . 1·00 25
457 – 3 b. violet . . . . 3·25 1·75
DESIGN: 1 b. to 3 b. Hanuman fighting mosquitoes.

1962. "Century 21" Exhibition, Seattle.
458 **124** 50 s. purple 50 15
459 2 b. blue . . . . 3·25 50

125 Thai Child with Doll
126 Correspondence Symbols
127 Exhibition Emblem

1962. Children's Day.
460 **125** 25 s. turquoise 40 15
461 50 s. buff 50 10
462 2 b. mauve . . . . 3·75 55

1962. International Correspondence Week.
463 **126** 25 s. violet 25 15
464 50 s. red 25 10
465 – 1 b. yellow . . . . 2·00 30
466 – 2 b. green . . . . 3·75 50
DESIGN: 1, 2 b. Quill pen.

1962. Students' Exhibition, Bangkok.
468 **127** 50 s. bistre 60 15

128 Harvesting

1963. Freedom from Hunger.
469 **128** 20 s. green 60 25
470 50 s. brown 50 15

129 "Temple Guardian"
130 Centenary Emblem

1963. 1st Anniv of Asian-Oceanic Postal Union.
471 **129** 50 s. green and brown . . 50 10

1963. Red Cross Centenary.
472 **130** 50 s. + 10 s. red & grey . 20 15
473 – 50 s. + 10 s. red & grey . 20 15
DESIGN: No. 473, As Type **130**, but with positions of emblem and inscr reversed.

131 G.P.O. Bangkok and (inset) old P.O

1963. 80th Anniv of Post and Telegraph Department.
474 **131** 50 s. green, orange and violet 75 15
475 3 b. sepia, green and red . 3·00 1·10

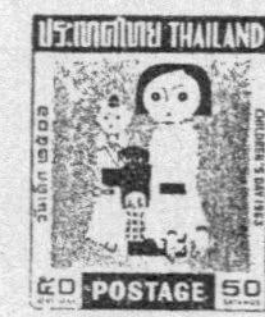

132 King Bhumibol
133 Children with Dolls

1963.
476 **132** 5 s. mauve 10 10
477 10 s. green 10 10
478 15 s. brown 10 10
479 20 s. brown 10 10
480 25 s. red 10 10
481 50 s. drab 15 10
482 75 s. lilac 25 10
483 80 s. orange 75 30
484 1 b. brown and blue . . . 75 15
485 1 b. 25 bistre and brown . 3·75 75
486 1 b. 50 green and violet . . 75 15
487 2 b. violet and red . . . 60 10
488 3 b. blue and brown . . . 1·25 20
489 4 b. black and bistre . . . 1·50 25
490 5 b. green and blue . . . 5·50 25
491 10 b. black and red . . . 10·00 55
492 20 b. blue and green . . . 85·00 3·25
493 25 b. blue and bronze . . . 7·75 50
494 40 b. black and yellow . . 70·00 3·75

1963. Children's Day.
505 **133** 50 s. red 25 10
506 2 b. blue . . . . 3·50 45

134 "Garuda" Bird with Scroll in Beak

1963. International Correspondence Week.
507 **134** 50 s. purple & turquoise . 50 15
508 1 b. purple and green . . 2·00 40
509 – 2 b. blue and bistre . . . 20·00 50
510 – 3 b. green and brown . . . 7·50 2·00
DESIGN: 2 b., 3 b. Thai women writing letters.

135 U.N. Emblem
137 Mother and Child

136 King Bhumibol

1963. U.N. Day.
511 **135** 50 s. blue 35 10

1963. King Bhumibol's 36th Birthday.
512 **136** 1 b. 50 indigo, yellow & bl 1·25 25
513 5 b. blue, yellow & mauve 10·00 1·50

1964. 17th Anniv of U.N.I.C.E.F.
514 **137** 50 s. blue 25 10
515 2 b. olive . . . . 2·25 35

138 "Hand" of Flags, Pigeon and Globe

1964. International Correspondence Week.
516 **138** 50 s. mauve and green . . 25 10
517 – 1 b. brown and green . . 2·25 30
518 – 2 b. violet and yellow . . 7·50 35
519 – 3 b. olive and blue . . . 2·50 1·25
DESIGNS: 1 b. Thai girls and map; 2 b. Map, pen and pencil; 3 b. Hand with quill pen, and globe.

139 Globe and U.N. Emblem
140 King Bhumibol and Queen Sirikit

1964. United Nations Day.
520 **139** 50 s. grey 75 10

1965. 15th Royal Wedding Anniv.
521 **140** 2 b. multicoloured . . . 3·75 25
522 5 b. multicoloured . . . 9·00 1·50

141 I.T.U. Emblem and Symbols

1965. I.T.U. Centenary
523 **141** 1 b. green . . . . 2·50 35

142 Goddess, Letters and Globes

1965. International Correspondence Week. Mult.
524 50 s. Type **142** 25 10
525 1 b. Type **142** . . . . . . 2·25 30
526 2 b. Handclasp, letters and world map . . . . 8·00 40
527 3 b. As 2 b. . . . . . . 12·00 1·75

143 Grand Palace, Bangkok
145 U.P.U. Monument, Berne, and Map of Thailand

1965. International Co-operation Year.
528 **143** 50 s. slate, yellow & blue . 1·00 10

1965. 80th Anniv of Thailand's Admission to the U.P.U.
529 **145** 20 s. blue and mauve . . 25 10
530 50 s. black and turquoise 50 15
531 1 b. orange and blue . . . 3·00 30
532 3 b. green and ochre . . . 8·00 1·50

146 Child and Lotus

1965. Children's Day.
533 **146** 50 s. brown and black . . 35 10
534 – 1 b. green and black . . . 1·50 15
DESIGN: 1 b. Child mounting stairs.

147 Cycling

1966. Publicity for 5th Asian Games, Bangkok.
535 20 s. lake (Type **147**) . . . 25 10
536 25 s. violet (Tennis) 50 15
537 50 s. red (Running) 25 10
538 1 b. blue (Weightlifting) . . 1·50 25
539 1 b. 25 black (Boxing) . . . 2·50 1·50
540 2 b. blue (Swimming) . . . 5·00 25
541 3 b. brown (Basketball) . . 11·00 2·40
542 5 b. purple (Football) . . . 32·00 8·00
See also Nos. 553/6.

148 Emblem and Fair Buildings
149 "Reading and Writing"

1966. 1st International Trade Fair, Bangkok.
543 **148** 50 s. purple 75 25
544 1 b. brown . . . . 1·25 50

1966. International Correspondence Week.
545 – 50 s. red 25 10
546 – 1 b. brown . . . . 1·00 20
547 **149** 2 b. violet . . . . 7·50 25
548 3 b. turquoise . . . . . . 2·50 1·50
DESIGN: 50 s., 1 b. "Map" envelope representing the five continents and pen.

150 U.N. Emblem

151 Pra Buddha Bata (monastery)

1966. United Nations Day.

549	**150**	50 s. blue	50	10

1966. 20th Anniv of U.N.E.S.C.O.

550	**151**	50 s. olive and black	35	10

152 "Goddess of Rice"

1966. International Rice Year.

551	**152**	50 s. blue and green	1·25	25
552		3 b. red and purple	7·50	2·25

153 Thai Boxing

1966. 5th Asian Games Bangkok. Each black, red and brown.

553	50 s. Type **153**	50	15
554	1 b. Takraw (ball game)	2·00	90
555	2 b. "Kite fighting"	16·00	1·50
556	3 b. "Cudgel play"	12·50	6·50

154 "Channa striatus"

1967. Fishes. Multicoloured.

557	1 b. Type **154**	2·50	75
558	2 b. "Rastrelliger brachysomus"	17·00	1·25
559	3 b. "Puntius gonionotus"	7·50	3·00
560	5 b. "Betta splendens"	10·00	3·75

DESIGNS—HORIZ: 2, 3 b., 45×26 mm.

155 Djarmachakra and Globe

1967. Establishment of Buddhist World Fellowship Headquarters in Thailand.

561	**155**	2 b. black and yellow	2·50	50

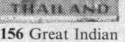

156 Great Indian Hornbill

157 "Vandopsis parishii"

1967. Birds. Multicoloured.

562	20 s. Type **156**	50	25
563	25 s. Hill myna	75	50
564	50 s. White-rumped shama	1·25	15
565	1 b. Siamese fireback pheasant	2·50	75
566	1 b. 50 Spotted dove	2·50	85
567	2 b. Sarus crane	15·00	1·25
568	3 b. White-breasted kingfisher	7·50	3·75
569	5 b. Asian open-bill stork	16·00	5·00

1967. Thai Orchids. Multicoloured.

570	20 s. Type **157**	50	25
571	50 s. "Ascocentrum curvifolium"	75	15
572	80 s. "Rhynchostylis retusa"	1·25	85
573	1 b. "Rhynchostylis gigantea	2·50	75
574	1 b. 50 "Dendrobium alconeri"	2·50	75
575	2 b. "Paphiopedilum callosum"	12·50	1·00
576	3 b. "Dendrobium formosum"	7·50	3·75
577	5 b. "Dendrobium primulinum"	14·50	5·00

158 Thai House

1967. Thai Architecture.

578	**158**	50 s. violet and blue	80	25
579	–	1 b. 50 chestnut & brown	1·75	1·00
580	–	2 b. blue and turquoise	11·00	1·25
581	–	3 b. sepia and yellow	7·75	5·00

BUILDINGS: 1 b. 50, Pagodas; 2 b. Temple bell-tower; 3 b. Temple.

159 "Sri Suphanahong" (royal barge) and Palace

1967. International Tourist Year.

582	**159**	2 b. sepia and blue	3·00	50

160, Dove, Globe, People and Letters

1967. International Correspondence Week.

583	**160**	50 s. multicoloured	25	10
584		1 b. multicoloured	1·00	30
585	–	2 b. black and green	3·75	40
586	–	3 b. black and brown	5·00	1·75

DESIGNS: 2, 3 b. Handclasp, globe and doves.

161 U.N. Emblem

1967. U.N. Day.

587	**161**	50 s. multicoloured	35	10

162 National Flag

1967. 50th Anniv of Thai National Flag.

588	**162**	50 s. red, blue & turquoise	35	10
589		2 b. red, blue and green	3·50	90

163 Elephant carrying Teak Log

1968. Export Promotion.

590	**163**	2 b. brown and red	2·50	25

See also Nos. 630, 655 and 673.

164 Satellite and Thai Tracking Station

1968. "Satellite Communications".

591	**164**	50 s. multicoloured	25	10
592		3 b. multicoloured	1·75	80

165 "Goddess of the Earth"

1968. International Hydrological Decade.

593	**165**	50 s. multicoloured	40	10

166 Snakeskin Gourami

1968. Thai Fishes (1st issue). Mult.

594	10 s. Type **166**	25	10
595	20 s. Red-tailed black shark	25	15
596	25 s. Barb	50	15
597	50 s. Giant catfish	75	15
598	80 s. Thai catfish	1·25	1·00
599	1 b. 25 Goby	3·75	2·00
600	1 b. 50 Thai carp	11·50	1·50
601	4 b. Knife fish	28·00	8·75

See also Nos. 955/8.

167 "Papilio arcturus"

1968. Thai Butterflies (1st issue). Mult.

602	50 s. Type **167**	70	15
603	1 b. "Papilio aecus"	3·75	60
604	3 b. "Papilio memnon"	12·00	3·00
605	4 b. "Papilio palinurus"	19·00	6·50

See also Nos. 967/70.

168 Queen Sirikit

1968. Queen Sirikit's "Third Cycle" Anniversary. Designs showing Queen Sirikit in different Thai costumes.

606	**168**	50 s. multicoloured	15	10
607	–	2 b. multicoloured	1·25	45
608	–	3 b. multicoloured	2·75	1·40
609	–	5 b. multicoloured	6·50	1·40

169 W.H.O. Emblem and Medical Equipment

1968. 20th Anniv of W.H.O.

610	**169**	50 s. black and olive	40	10

170 Globe, Letter and Pen

1968. International Correspondence Week. Mult.

611	50 s. Type **170**	25	10
612	1 b. Globe on pen nib	80	20
613	2 b. Type **170**	1·50	30
614	3 b. Globe on pen nib	4·00	1·40

171 U.N. Emblem and Flags

173 King Rama II

172 Human Rights Emblem and Sculpture

1968. United Nations Day.

615	**171**	50 s. multicoloured	40	10

1968. 20th Anniv of Human Rights Year.

616	**172**	50 s. violet, red and green	50	10

1968. Birth Bicentenary of King Rama II.

617	**173**	50 s. yellow and brown	25	10

174 National Assembly Building

1969. First Election Day under New Constitution.

618	**174**	50 s. multicoloured	25	10
619		2 b. multicoloured	1·75	45

175 I.L.O. Emblem within Cogwheels

1969. 50th Anniv of I.L.O.

620	**175**	50 s. blue, black & violet	25	10

176 Ramwong Dance

1969. Thai Classical Dances. Multicoloured.

621	50 s. Type **176**	25	10
622	1 b. Candle dance	80	30
623	2 b. Krathop Mai dance	1·60	25
624	3 b. Nohra dance	2·75	1·60

177 "Letters by Post"

1969. International Correspondence Week. Mult.

625	50 s. Type **177**	15	10
626	1 b. Type **177**	40	20
627	2 b. Writing and posting a letter	1·00	30
628	3 b. As 2 b.	1·60	80

178 Globe in Hand

1969. United Nations Day.

629	**178**	50 s. multicoloured	25	10

179 Tin Mine

1969. Export Promotion and 2nd Technical Conference of the International Tin Council, Bangkok.

630	**179**	2 b. blue, purple and brown	2·00	25

180 Loy Krathong Festival

1969. Thai Ceremonies and Festivals. Multicoloured.
631 50 s. Type **180** 15 10
632 1 b. Marriage ceremony . . . 65 20
633 2 b. Khwan ceremony 80 25
634 5 b. Songkran festival . . . . 2·40 90

181 Breguet 14 Mail Plane

1969. 50th Anniv of Thai Airmail Services.
635 **181** 1 b. brown, green & blue . 65 15

182 "Phra Rama"

1969. Nang Yai Shadow Theatre. Multicoloured.
636 50 s. Type **182** 25 10
637 2 b. "Ramasura" . . . . . . 2·00 20
638 3 b. "Mekhala" . . . . 1·60 75
639 5 b. "Ongkhot" . . . . 2·75 75

183 "Improvement of Productivity"

1969. Productivity Year.
640 **183** 50 s. multicoloured . . . 25 10

184 Thai Temples within I.C.W. Emblem

1970. 19th Triennial Conference of International Council of Women, Bangkok.
641 **184** 50 s. black and blue . . . 40 10

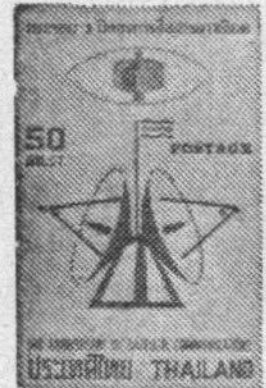

185 Dish Aerials

1970. 3rd Anniv of Thai Satellite Communications.
642 **185** 50 s. multicoloured . . . 25 10

186 Households and Data

1970. 7th Population Census.
643 **186** 1 b. multicoloured 25 10

187 New Headquarters Building

1970. Inauguration of New U.P.U. Headquarters Building, Berne.
644 **187** 50 s. black, green & blue 25 10

188 Khun Ram Kamhang as Teacher

1970. International Education Year.
645 **188** 50 s. multicoloured . . . 25 10

189 Swimming Stadium

1970. 6th Asian Games, Bangkok.
646 **189** 50 s. lilac, red & yellow . 25 15
647 – 1 b. 50 green, red & blue 55 20
648 – 3 b. black, red & bronze . 1·25 30
649 – 5 b. blue, red and green . 1·40 80
STADIUMS: 1 b. 50, Velodrome; 3 b. Subhajalasaya Stadium; 5 b. Kittikachorn Indoor Stadium.
See also No. 660.

190 Boy and Girl writing Letter

1970. International Correspondence Week. Mult.
650 50 s. Type **190** 15 10
651 1 b. Woman writing letter . . 55 20
652 2 b. Women reading letters 1·25 30
653 3 b. Man reading letter . . . 1·40 80
See also Nos. 683/6.

191 U.N. Emblem and Royal Palace, Bangkok

194 King Bhumibol lighting Flame

193 The Heroes of Bangrachan

1970. 25th Anniv of United Nations.
654 **191** 50 s. multicoloured . . . 55 10

1970. Export Promotion.
655 2 b. brn, red and green . . 1·25 20
DESIGN: 2 b. As Type **163**, but showing rubber plantation.

1970. Heroes and Heroines of Thai History.
656 **193** 50 s. violet and red . . . 25 10
657 – 1 b. purple and violet . . 65 30
658 – 2 b. brown and red . . . 1·25 50
659 – 3 b. green and blue . . . 1·10 65
DESIGNS: 1 b. Heroines Thao Thepkrasatri and Thao Srisunthorn on ramparts; 2 b. Queen Suriyothai riding elephant; 3 b. Phraya Phichaidaphak and battle scene.

1970. Inaug of 6th Asian Games, Bangkok.
660 **194** 1 b. multicoloured . . . 25 10

195 Woman playing So Sam Sai

1970. Thai Musicians and Instruments. Mult
661 50 s. Type **195** 25 10
662 2 b. Khlui phiang-o (flute) . . 80 20
663 3 b. Krachappi (guitar) . . . . 1·60 40
664 5 b. Thon rammana (drums) 2·75 80

196 Chocolate-pointed Siamese

1971. Siamese Cats. Multicoloured.
665 50 s. Type **196** 15 10
666 1 b. Blue-pointed cat 90 35
667 2 b. Seal-pointed cat . . . . 1·60 30
668 3 b. Pure white cat and kittens 2·75 1·40

197 Pagoda, Nakhon Si Thammarat

1971. Buddhist Holy Places in Thailand. Pagodas.
669 **197** 50 s. black, brown & pink 25 10
670 – 1 b. brown, violet & grn . 50 20
671 – 3 b. sepia, orange & brn . 1·40 30
672 – 4 b. brown, sepia & blue . 1·90 1·60
DESIGNS: 1 b. Nakhon Phanom; 3 b. Nakhon Pathom; 4 b. Chiang Mai.

1971. Export Promotion.
673 2 b. multicoloured . . . . . . 1·00 20
DESIGN: 2 b. As Type **163**, but showing corncob with cornfield.

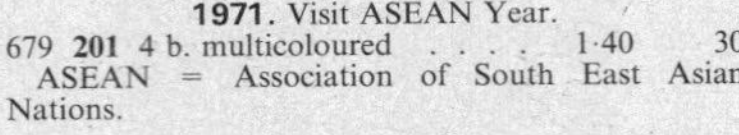

199 Buddha's Birthplace, Lumbini, Nepal

1971. 20th Anniv of World Fellowship of Buddhists.
674 **199** 50 s. black and blue . . . 15 10
675 – 1 b. black and green . . . 55 20
676 – 2 b. black and yellow . . . 1·25 25
677 – 3 b. black and red . . . . 1·10 80
DESIGNS: 1 b. "Place of Enlightenment", Buddha Gaya, Bihar; 2 b. "Place of First Sermon", Sarnath, Banaras; 3 b. "Place of Final Passing Away", Kusinara.

200 King Bhumibol and Thai People

201 Floating Market, Wat Sai

1971. 25th Anniv of Coronation.
678 **200** 50 s. multicoloured 20 10

1971. Visit ASEAN Year.
679 **201** 4 b. multicoloured . . . . 1·40 30
ASEAN = Association of South East Asian Nations.

202 King and Queen in Scout Uniform

1971. 60th Anniv of Thai Boy Scout Movement.
680 **202** 50 c. black, red & yellow . 25 10

1971. "THAILANDAPEX 71" National Stamp Exhibition, Bangkok. Optd **THAILANDAPEX '71** and **4–8 AUG. '71** in English and Thai, with map within "perforations", covering four stamps.
681 **119** 80 s. orange (No. 428) . . 2·00 2·00
682 **132** 80 s. orange (No. 483) . . 2·00 2·00
Prices are for blocks of four stamps showing the entire overprint. The overprint on No. 682 is smaller—size 23×26 mm.

1971. International Correspondence Week. As T **190**. Multicoloured.
683 1 b. Two girls writing a letter . 15 10
684 1 b. Two girls reading letters 40 20
685 2 b. Women with letter on veranda . . . . 1·10 25
686 3 b. Man handing letter to woman . . . . 1·60 60

205 Marble Temple, Bangkok

1971. United Nations Day.
687 **205** 50 s. multicoloured . . . 25 10

206 Raising Ducks

1971. Rural Life. Multicoloured.
688 50 s. Type **206** 15 10
689 1 b. Growing tobacco seedlings 40 30
690 2 b. Cooping fish 80 20
691 3 b. Cleaning rice-seed . . . . 1·40 65

207 Mother and Child

1971. 25th Anniv of U.N.I.C.E.F.
692 **207** 50 s. multicoloured . . . 25 10

208 Costumes from Chiang Saen Period (17th-century)

1972. Historical Costumes. Multicoloured.
693 50 s. Type **208** 15 10
694 1 b. Sukhothai period (13th-14th centuries) 40 20
695 1 b. 50 Ayudhya period (14th-17th centuries) 80 25
696 2 b. Bangkok period (18th-19th centuries) . . . . 1·90 50

209 Globe and A.O.P.U. Emblem

1972. 10th Anniv of Asian–Oceanic Postal Union.
697 **209** 75 s. blue 25 10

210 King Bhumibol

1972.
698 **210** 10 s. green 10 10
699 20 s. blue 15 10
700 25 s. red 15 10
701 50 s. olive 20 10
702 75 s. lilac 15 10
703 1 b. 25 pink, green and light green 55 15
704 2 b. violet and red . . . 25 10
705 2 b. 75 green and red . . . 55 10
706 3 b. blue and sepia . . 2·10 15
707 4 b. brown and blue . . . 80 15
708 5 b. brown and violet . . 80 10
709 6 b. violet and green . . 2·10 20
710 10 b. black and red . . . 90 15
711 20 b. green, orange and light orange . . . . 3·00 75
898d 40 b. violet and brown . . 2·75 65
712a 50 b. green and lilac . . 20·00 1·75
713 100 b. blue and orange . . 40·00 4·00

211 Two Women, Iko Tribe

1972. Hill Tribes of Thailand. Multicoloured.

714 50 s. Type **211** 15 10
715 2 b. Musician and children, Musoe tribe 90 20
716 4 b. Woman embroidering, Yao tribe . . . . 4·25 2·40
717 5 b. Woman with chickens, Maeo tribe . . . . 5·50 60

212 Ruby

1972. Precious Stones.

718 **212** 75 s. multicoloured . . . 25 10
719 – 2 b. multicoloured . . . . 3·75 35
720 – 4 b. black and green . . . 5·25 2·50
721 – 6 b. brown, black and red 11·00 2·00

DESIGNS: 2 b. Yellow sapphire; 4 b. Zircon; 6 b. Star sapphire.

213 Prince Vajiralongkorn

214 Thai Ruan-ton Costume

1972. Prince Vajiralongkorn's 20th Birthday.

722 **213** 75 s. multicoloured . . . 25 10

1972. Thai Women's National Costumes. Mult.

723 75 s. Type **214** 15 10
724 2 b. Thai Chitrlada 65 20
725 4 b. Thai Chakri . . . . . . 1·90 1·25
726 5 b. Thai Borompimarn . . . 2·75 55

215 Rambutan

1972. Thai Fruits. Multicoloured.

728 75 s. Type **215** 15 10
729 1 b. Mangosteen 90 30
730 3 b. Durian . . . . 2·00 75
731 5 b. Mango . . . . 7·50 1·40

216 Princess-Mother with Old People

1972. Princess-Mother Sisangwan's 72nd Birthday.

732 **216** 75 s. green and orange . . 25 10

217 Lod Cave, Phangnga

1972. International Correspondence Week. Mult.

733 75 s. Type **217** 15 10
734 1 b. 25 Kang Kracharn Reservoir, Phetchaburi . . . 40 20
735 2 b. 75 Erawan Waterfall, Kanchanaburi . . . . 3·25 15
736 3 b. Nok-kaw Mountain, Loei 2·10 90

218 Globe on U.N. Emblem

220 Crown Prince Vajiralongkorn

219 Watphrajetubon Vimolmanklaram Rajvaramahaviharn (ancient university)

1972. 25th Anniv of E.C.A.F.E.

737 **218** 75 s. multicoloured . . . 25 10

1972. International Book Year.

738 **219** 75 s. multicoloured . . . 25 10

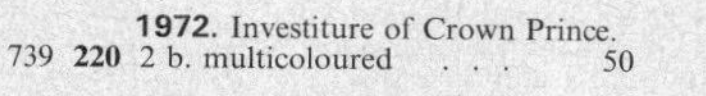

1972. Investiture of Crown Prince.

739 **220** 2 b. multicoloured . . . 50 15

221 Servicemen and Flag

1973. 25th Anniv of Veterans' Day.

740 **221** 75 s. multicoloured . . . 25 10

1973. Red Cross Fair (1972). Nos. 472/3 surch.

741 **130** 75 s. + 25 s. on 50 s. + 10 s. 50 50
742 – 75 s. + 25 s. on 50 s. + 10 s. 50 50

223 Emblem, Bank and Coin-box

1973. 60th Anniv of Government Savings Bank.

743 **223** 75 s. multicoloured . . . 25 10

224 "Celestial Being" and Emblem

1973. 25th Anniv of W.H.O.

744 **224** 75 s. multicoloured . . . 25 10

225 "Nymphaea pubescens"

1973. Lotus Flowers. Multicoloured.

745 75 s. Type **225** 25 10
746 1 b. 50 "Nymphaea pubescens" (different) 50 30
747 2 b. "Nelumbo nucifera" . . 1·75 25
748 4 b. "Nelumbo nucifera" (different) . . . . 4·75 1·25

227 King Bhumibol

1973.

749 **227** 5 s. purple 15 10
1031 20 s. blue 15 10
1031a 25 s. red 15 10
1032 50 s. green 50 10
1032a 75 s. violet 15 10
753 5 b. brown and violet . . 2·25 50
754 6 b. violet and green . . 1·40 50
755 10 b. brown and red . . 4·00 75
755a 20 b. green and orange . 55·00 5·50

228 Silverware

1973. Thai Handicrafts. Multicoloured.

756 75 s. Type **228** 25 10
757 2 b. 75 Lacquerware . . . . . 1·00 20
758 4 b. Pottery . . . . 3·25 1·50
759 5 b. Paper umbrellas . . . . . 3·00 50

229 King Janaka's Procession

1973. "Ramayana" Mural, Temple of Emerald Buddha, Bangkok.

760 **229** 25 s. multicoloured 25 15
761 – 75 s. multicoloured 15 10
762 – 1 b. 50 multicoloured . . . 1·50 1·00
763 – 2 b. multicoloured . . . . 2·75 90
764 – 2 b. 75 multicoloured . . . 1·25 20
765 – 3 b. multicoloured . . . . 5·50 1·40
766 – 5 b. multicoloured . . . . 6·75 3·00
767 – 6 b. multicoloured . . . . 2·25 1·10

DESIGNS: Nos. 761/7, different details from the mural.

230 "Postal Services"

1973. 90th Anniv of Thai Post and Telegraph Department. Multicoloured.

768 75 s. Type **230** 30 10
769 2 b. "Telecommunication Services" 90 40

231 1 Solot Stamp of 1883

1973. "THAIPEX 73" National Stamp Exn.

770 **231** 75 s. blue and red 25 10
771 – 1 b. 25 red and blue . . . 1·00 30
772 – 1 b. 50 violet and green . . 1·25 50
773 – 2 b. green and orange . . 1·25 70

DESIGNS: 1 b. 25, 6 s. stamp of 1912; 1 b. 50, 5 s. stamp of 1928; 2 b. 3 s. stamp of 1941.

232 Interpol Emblem

1973. 50th Anniv of International Criminal Police Organization (Interpol).

775 **232** 75 s. multicoloured 25 10

233 "Lilid Pralaw"

1973. Int Correspondence Week. Characters from Thai Literature. Multicoloured.

776 75 s. Type **233** 15 10
777 1 b. 50 "Khun Chang Khun Phan" 65 30
778 2 b. "Sang Thong" . . . . . 1·25 55
779 5 b. "Pha Apai Manee" . . . 3·25 90

234 Wat Suan Dok Temple, Chiangmai

1973. United Nations Day.

781 **234** 75 s. multicoloured . . . 25 10

235 Schomburgk's Deer

1973. Protected Wild Animals. Multicoloured.

782 20 s. Type **235** 25 10
783 25 s. Kouprey 25 10
784 75 r. Common gorals 50 10
785 1 b. 25 Water buffaloes . . . 50 25
786 1 b. 50 Javan rhinoceros . . . 2·75 1·50
787 2 b. Thamin . . . . 5·50 1·60
788 2 b. 75 Sumatran rhinoceros 2·75 40
789 4 b. Mainland serows . . . . 4·25 3·75

236 Flame Emblem

1973. 25th Anniv of Declaration of Human Rights.

790 **236** 75 s. multicoloured . . . 50 10

238 Children within Flowers

241 "Pha la Phiang Lai"

240 Statue of Krom Luang Songkia Nakarin

1973. Children's Day.

791 **238** 75 s. multicoloured . . . 40 10

1974. Red Cross Fair. Nos. 472/3 surch **75** + **25** and date.

792 **130** 75 s. + 25 s. on 50 s. + 10 s. 30 30
793 – 75 s. + 25 s. on 50 s. + 10 s. 30 30

1974. 84th Anniv of Siriraj Hospital.

794 **240** 75 s. multicoloured . . . 25 10

1974. Thai Classical Dance. Multicoloured.

795 75 s. Type **241** 25 10
796 2 b. 75 "Phra Lak Phlaeng Rit" 1·00 20
797 4 b. "Chin Sao Sai" . . . . 2·50 1·40
798 5 b. "Charot Phra Sumen" . . 2·50 50

242 World's Largest Teak, Amphur Nam-Pad

1974. 15th Anniv of Arbor Day.
799 **242** 75 s. multicoloured 25 10

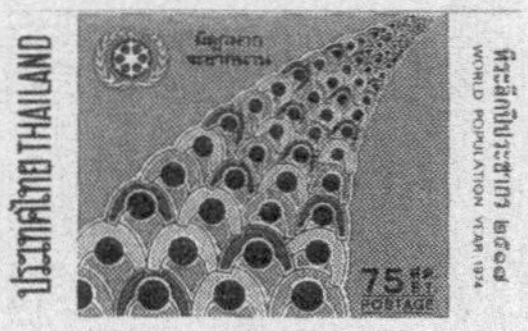

243 "Increasing Population"

1974. World Population Year.
800 **243** 75 s. multicoloured 25 10

244 Royal Chariot

1974. Centenary of National Museum. Mult.
801 75 s. Type **244** 15 10
802 2 b. Ban Chiang painted pottery vase 50 30
803 2 b. 75 Avalokitesavara Bodhisattva statue 1·10 25
804 3 b. King Mongkut Rama IV 1·60 50

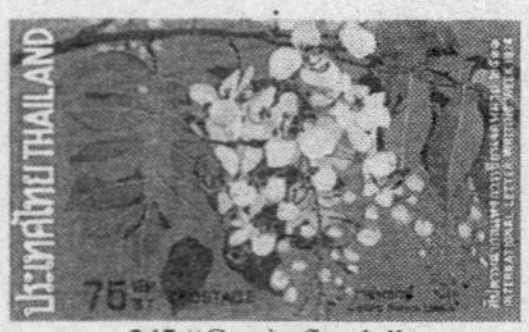

245 "Cassia fistula"

1974. International Correspondence Week. Tropical Plants. Multicoloured.
805 75 s. Type **245** 15 10
806 2 b. 75 "Butea superba" 65 20
807 3 b. "Jasminum sambac" 1·75 25
808 4 b. "Lagerstroemia speciosa" 1·40 1·10

246 "UPU 100"

1974. Centenary of U.P.U.
810 **246** 75 s. multicoloured 25 10

247 Wat Suthat Thepvararam

1974. United Nations Day.
811 **247** 75 s. multicoloured 25 10

248 Elephant Round-up

1974. Tourism.
812 **248** 4 b. multicoloured 1·50 75

249 "Vanda coerulea"

1974. Thai Orchids (1st series). Multicoloured.
813 75 s. Type **249** 15 10
814 2 b. 75 "Dendrobium aggregatum" 65 20
815 3 b. "Dendrobium scabrilingue" 1·75 40
816 4 b. "Aerides falcata" var "houlletiana" 1·25 90
See also Nos. 847/50.

250 Boy riding Toy Horse

1974. Children's Day.
818 **250** 75 c. multicoloured 40 10

252 Democracy Monument

1975. Democratic Institutions Campaign. Mult.
819 75 s. Type **252** 15 10
820 2 b. "Rights and Liberties" 65 25
821 2 b. 75 "Freedom to choose work" 1·00 20
822 5 b. Top of Monument and text 1·75 65

1975. Red Cross Fair 1974. Nos. 472/3 surch **1974** and new value in English and Thai.
823 **130** 75 s. + 25 s. on 50 s. + 10 s. red and grey 50 50
824 – 75 s. + 25 s. on 50 s. + 10 s. red and grey 50 50

254 Marbled Cat

1975. Protected Wild Animals (1st series). Mult.
825 20 s. Type **254** 25 15
826 75 s. Gaur 50 10
827 2 b. 75 Indian elephant 3·75 55
828 3 b. Clouded leopard 2·50 1·25
See Nos. 913/16.

255 White-eyed River Martin

1975. Thailand Birds. Multicoloured.
829 75 s. Type **255** 30 15
830 2 b. Asiatic paradise fly catcher 1·25 70
831 2 b. 75 Long-tailed broad bill 1·50 40
832 5 b. Sultan tit 3·00 1·25

256 King Bhumibol and Queen Sirikit

1975. Silver Wedding of King Bhumibol and Queen Sirikit. Multicoloured.
833 75 s. Type **256** 25 10
834 3 b. As Type **256**, but different background 50 20

257 "Roundhouse Kick"

1975. Thai Boxing. Multicoloured.
835 75 s. Type **257** 25 15
836 2 b. 75 "Reverse elbow" 1·00 25
837 3 b. "Flying knee" 1·75 90
838 5 b. "Ritual homage" 5·25 1·40

258 Toskanth

1975. Thai Culture. Masks. Multicoloured.
839 75 s. Type **258** 25 10
840 2 b. Kumbhakarn 1·50 20
841 3 b. Rama 2·00 55
842 4 b. Hanuman 5·75 2·40

259 "Thaipex 75" Emblem

1975. "Thaipex 75" National Stamp Exhibition, Bangkok. Multicoloured.
843 75 s. Type **259** 25 10
844 2 b. 75 Stamp designer 1·50 20
845 4 b. Stamp printing works 2·00 55
846 5 b. "Stamp collecting" 5·75 2·40

1975. Thai Orchids (2nd series). As T **249**. Multicoloured.
847 75 s. "Dendrobium cruentum" 25 10
848 2 b. "Dendrobium parishii" 80 30
849 2 b. 75 "Vanda teres" 1·10 25
850 5 b. "Vanda denisoniana" 2·75 80

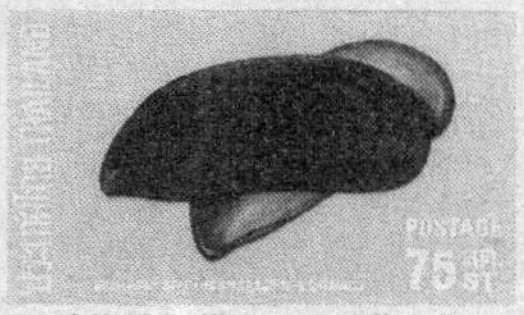

260 "Mytillus smaragdinus"

1975. Seashells. Multicoloured.
852 75 s. Type **260** 45 30
853 1 b. "Turbo marmoratus" 30 10
854 2 b. 75 "Oliva mustelina" 70 15
855 5 b. "Cypraea moneta" 1·90 80

261 Yachting

1975. 8th SEAP Games, Bangkok (1st issue).
856 **261** 75 s. black and blue 15 10
857 – 1 b. 25 black and mauve 40 20
858 – 1 b. 50 black and red 1·10 65
859 – 2 b. black and green 1·60 65
DESIGNS: 1 b. 25, Badminton; 1 b. 50, Volleyball; 2 b. Rifle and pistol shooting.
See also Nos. 878/81.

262 Pataya Beach

1975. International Correspondence Week. Mult.
861 75 s. Type **262** 25 10
862 2 b. Samila Beach 80 30
863 3 b. Prachuap Bay 1·50 25
864 5 b. Laem Singha Bay 2·25 90

263 Children within Letters "U N"

1975. United Nations Day.
865 **263** 75 s. multicoloured 25 10

264 Early Telegraphs

1975. Centenary of Telegraph Service. Mult.
866 75 s. Type **264** 40 25
867 2 b. 75 Teleprinter and dish aerial 75 25

265 "Sukhrip Khrong Muang"

1975. Thai Ceremonial Barges. Multicoloured.
868 75 s. Type **265** 25 10
869 1 b. Royal barge "Anekchat Phuchong" 1·00 40
870 2 b. Royal barge "Anantana Karat" 1·50 50
871 2 b. 75 "Krabi Ran Ron Rap" 1·75 50
872 3 b. "Asura Wayuphak" 2·75 80
873 4 b. "Asura Paksi" 2·10 1·50
874 5 b. Royal barge "Sri Suphanahong" 5·50 4·00
875 6 b. "Phali Rang Thawip" 3·50 2·00

266 King's Cipher and Thai Crown

1975. King Bhumibol's 48th Birthday. Multicoloured.
876 75 s. Type **26**⁄ 15 10
877 5 b. King Bhumibol in uniform 90 30

267 Putting the Shot

1975. 8th SEAP Games, Bangkok (2nd issue).
878 **267** 1 b. black and orange 25 10
879 – 2 b. black and green 75 50
880 – 3 b. black and yellow 90 35
881 – 4 b. black and violet 1·25 65
DESIGNS: 2 b. Table-tennis; 3 b. Cycle-racing; 4 b. Relay-running.

268 I.W.Y. Emblem on Globe

1975. International Women's Year.
883 **268** 75 s. blue, orange & black 25 10

269 Children writing

1976. Children's Day.
884 **269** 75 s. multicoloured 25 10

270 "Macrobrachium rosenbergii"

1976. Thai Lobsters and Shrimps. Multicoloured.

885 75 s. Type **270** 25 10
886 2 b. "Penaeus merguiensis" . . 2·25 55
887 2 b. 75 "Panulirus ornatus" . 2·00 25
888 5 b. "Penaeus monodon" . 5·00 1·50

1976. Red Cross Fair 1975. Nos. 472/3 surch **1975** and value.

889 **130** 75 s. + 25 s. on 50 s. + 10 s. red and grey . . . 25 25
890 – 75 s. + 25 s. on 50 s. + 10 s. red and grey 25 25

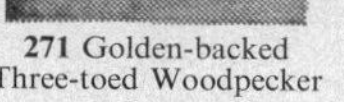

271 Golden-backed Three-toed Woodpecker

272 Ben Chiang Pot

1976. Thailand Birds (2nd series). Multicoloured.

891 1 b. Type **271** 30 20
892 1 b. 50 Greater green-billed malcoha 50 40
893 3 b. Long-billed scimitar babbler 4·25 1·50
894 4 b. Green magpie . . . . . . 1·60 80

1976. Ben Chiang Pottery.

895 **272** 1 b. multicoloured 25 10
896 – 2 b. miltcoloured . . . . 3·00 30
897 – 3 b. multicoloured . . . . 1·75 25
898 – 4 b. multicoloured . . . . 2·25 1·60

DESIGNS: 2 b. to 4 b. Various items of pottery.

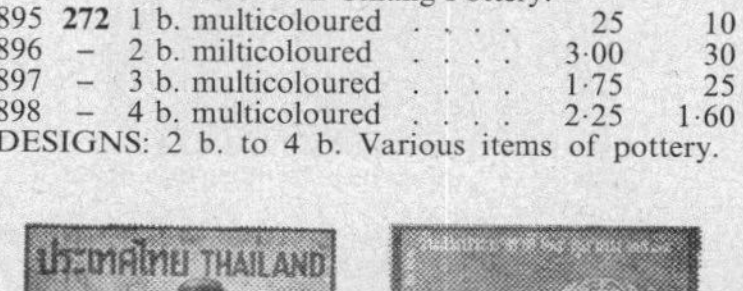

273 Postman of 1883

275 "Drug Addictions"

274 Kinnari

1976. Postmen's Uniforms. Multicoloured.

899 1 b. Type **273** 25 10
900 3 b. Postman of 1935 . . . . 1·00 20
901 4 b. Postman of 1950 . . . . 1·75 1·25
902 5 b. Postman of 1974 . . . . 3·25 50

1976. International Correspondence Week. Deities. Multicoloured.

903 1 b. Type **274** . . . . 2·50 65
904 2 b. Suphan-Mat-Cha 25 15
905 4 b. Garuda 75 25
906 5 b. Naga . . . . 1·00 20

1976. United Nations Day.

907 **275** 1 b. multicoloured 25 10

276 Early and Modern Telephones

1976. Telephone Centenary.

908 **276** 1 b. multicoloured 25 10

277 Sivalaya

1976. Thai Royal Halls. Multicoloured.

909 1 b. Type **277** 15 10
910 2 b. Cakri . . . . 3·75 30
911 4 b. Mahisra . . . . 1·75 1·00
912 5 b. Dusit . . . . 2·00 65

1976. Protected Wild Animals (2nd series). As T **254**. Multicoloured.

913 1 b. Bangteng . . . . 1·25 50
914 2 b. Malayan tapir . . . . . 1·75 75
915 4 b. Sambar 65 25
916 5 b. Hog-deer 90 25

278 "From Child to Adult"

1977. Children's Day.

917 **278** 1 b. multicoloured . . . 25 10

279 Alsthom Electric Locomotive

1977. 80th Anniv of Thai State Railway. Multicoloured.

918 1 b. Type **279** 50 10
919 2 b. Davenport electric locomotive . . . . 2·25 30
920 4 b. Pacific steam locomotive 5·75 2·50
921 5 b. George Egestoff's steam locomotive . . . . 9·50 2·10

280 University Building

1977. 60th Anniv of Chulalongkorn University.

922 **280** 1 b. multicoloured . . . 40 10

281 Flags of A.O.P.U. Countries

1977. 15th Anniv of Asian-Oceanic Postal Union.

923 **281** 1 b. multicoloured . . . 40 10

282 Crippled Ex-Serviceman

1977. Sai-Jai-Thai Foundation Day.

924 **282** 5 b. multicoloured . . . 75 15

1977. Red Cross Fair. Nos. 472/3 surch **75 + 25 2520—1977.**

925 **130** 75 s. + 25 s. on 50 s. + 10 s. red and grey 25 25
926 – 75 s. + 25 s. on 50 s. + 10 s. red and grey 25 25

284 Phra Aphai Mani and Phisua Samut

1977. Puppet Shows. Multicoloured.

927 2 b. Type **284** 25 10
928 3 b. Rusi and Sutsakhon . . 1·00 20
929 4 b. Nang Vali and Usren . . 50 25
930 5 b. Phra Aphai Mani and Nang Laweng's portrait 75 40

285 Drum Dance

1977. Thai Folk Dances. Multicoloured.

931 2 b. Type **285** 25 10
932 3 b. Dance of Dip-nets . . . . 1·00 15
933 4 b. Harvesting dance 40 20
934 5 b. Kan dance 65 25

286 1 b. Stamp of 1972

1977. "THAIPEX 77" National Stamp Exhibition.

935 **286** 75 s. multicoloured 40 10

287 "Pla Bu Thong"

1977. International Correspondence Week, Scenes from Thai Literature. Multicoloured.

936 75 s. Type **287** 50 10
937 2 b. "Krai Thong" 75 40
938 5 b. "Nang Kaew Na Ma" . . 1·25 25
939 6 b. "Pra Rot Mali . . . . . 1·25 30

288 U.N. Building, Bangkok

1977. United Nations Day.

940 **288** 75 s. multicoloured 50 10

289 King Bhumibol in Scout Uniform, and Camp Fire

1977. 9th National Scout Jamboree.

941 **289** 75 s. multicoloured 75 10

290 Map of A.S.E.A.N. Countries

1977. 10th Anniv of Association of South East Asian Nations.

942 **290** 5 b. multicoloured . . . . 1·00 20

291 Elbow and Wrist Joints

1977. World Rheumatism Year.

943 **291** 75 s. multicoloured 40 10

292 Children with Thai Flag

1978. Children's Day.

944 **292** 75 s. multicoloured . . . 50 10

293 "Dendrobium heterocarpum"

1978. 9th World Orchid Conference. Mult.

945 75 s. Type **293** 50 25
946 1 b. "Dendrobium pulchellum" 75 25
947 1 b. 50 "Doritis pulcherrima var buyssoniana" . . . . 1·25 75
948 2 b. "Dendrobium hercoglossum" 25 15
949 2 b. 75 "Aerides odorata" . . 2·50 10
950 3 b. "Trichoglottis fasciata" . 25 10
951 5 b. "Dendrobium wardianum" 40 20
952 6 b. "Dendrobium senile" . . 40 35

294 Agricultural Scenes and Rice Production Graph

1978. Agricultural Census.

953 **294** 75 s. multicoloured . . . 20 10

295 Blood Donation and Red Cross

1978. Red Cross Fair.

954 **295** 2 b. 75 + 25 s. multicoloured 75 75

296 "Anabas testudineus"

1978. Fishes. Multicoloured.

955 1 b. Type **296** . . . . 1·25 65
956 2 b. "Datnioides microlepis" 15 10
957 3 b. "Kryptopterus apogon" 40 15
958 4 b. "Probarbus jullieni" . . . 50 30

297 "Birth of Prince Siddhartha"

1978. "Buddha's Story" Mural; Puthi Savan Hall, National Museum. Multicoloured.

959 2 b. Type **297** 50 15
960 3 b. "Prince Siddhartha cuts his hair" . . . . 1·00 25
961 5 b. "Buddha descends from Tavatimsa Heaven" . . . . 4·00 90
962 6 b. "Buddha enters Nirvana" 2·00 1·00

298 Bhumibol Dam

1978. Dams. Multicoloured.

963 75 s. Type **298** 50 10
964 2 b. Sirikit Dam 50 15
965 2 b. 75 Vajiralongkorn Dam 1·25 20
966 6 b. Ubolratana Dam . . . . 1·50 1·25

299 "Idea lynceus"

1978. Butterflies. Multicoloured.

967 2 b. Type **299** 50 15
968 3 b. "Sephisa chandra" . . . 75 15
969 5 b. "Charaxes durnfordi" . . 2·75 15
970 6 b. "Cethosia penthesilea" . . 1·50 1·00

300 Phra Chedi Chai Mongkhon, Ayutthaya **301** Mother and Children

1978. International Correspondence Week. Mult.

971 75 s. Type **300** 25 10
972 2 b. Phra That Hariphunchai, Lamphun 40 15
973 2 b. 75 Phra Borom That Chaiya, Surat Thani . . . . . . 1·50 20
974 5 b. Phra That Choeng Chum, Sakon Nakhon 90 65

1978. United Nations Day.

975 **301** 75 s. multicoloured . . . 25 10

302 Basketball, Hockey and Boxing

1978. 8th Asian Games, Bangkok. Multicoloured.

976 25 s. Silhouettes of boxers, footballer & pole-vaulter . . 15 10
977 2 b. Javelin, weightlifting and running 25 15
978 3 b. Yacht and sports equipment 65 20
979 5 b. Type **302** . . . . 1·50 75

303 World Map and Different Races holding Hands

1978. International Anti-Apartheid Year.

980 **303** 75 s. multicoloured . . . 25 10

304 Children and S.O.S. Village, Tambol Bangpu

1979. International Year of the Child. Mult.

981 75 s. Children painting Thai flag (horiz) 75 20
982 75 s. Type **304** 25 10

305 "Matuta lunaris"

1979. Crabs. Multicoloured.

983 2 b. Type **305** 40 15
984 2 b. 75 "Matuta planipes" . . 1·75 15
985 3 b. "Portunus pelagicus" . . 65 15
986 5 b. "Scylla serrata" . . . . . 1·75 75

306 Eye and Blind People **307** Sugar Apples

1979. Thai Red Cross Fair.

987 **306** 75 s. + 25 s. multicoloured 40 30

1979. Thai Fruits. Multicoloured.

988 1 b. Type **307** 75 15
989 2 b. Pineapple 50 15
990 5 b. Bananas . . . . 1·50 65
991 6 b. Longans . . . . 1·00 90

308 Planting Sapling

1979. 20th Arbor Day.

992 **308** 75 s. multicoloured . . . 25 10

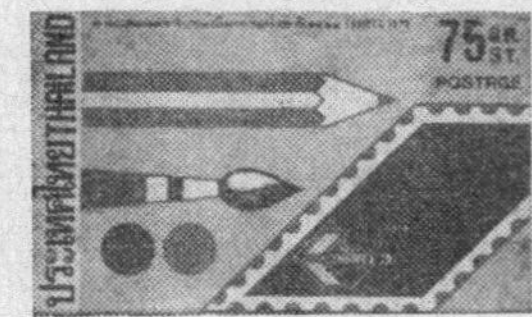

309 Pencil, Brush and Colours

1979. "Thaipex '79" National Stamp Exhibition, Bangkok. Multicoloured.

993 75 s. Type **309** 15 10
994 2 b. Envelopes 25 15
995 2 b. 75 Stamp stockbook . . . 50 15
996 5 b. Tweezers and magnifying glass . . . . 1·60 70

310 Baisi Pak Cham **311** U.N.O. Emblem, Farmer, Cattle and Wheat

1979. International Correspondence Week. Traditional Flower Arrangements. Mult.

997 75 s. Kruai upatcha 15 10
998 2 b. Type **310** 25 15
999 2 b. 75 Krathong dokmai . . 50 15
1000 5 b. Phum dokmai . . . . . 1·60 70

1979. United Nations Day.

1001 **311** 75 s. multicoloured . . . 25 10

312 "Makutrajakumarn" (frigate)

1979. Ships of the Royal Thai Navy. Mult.

1002 2 b. Type **312** 40 15
1003 3 b. "Tapi" (frigate) 40 15
1004 5 b. "Prabparapak" (missile craft) . . . . 2·50 75
1005 6 b. "T 91" patrol boat . . 3·00 1·00

313 Order of the Rajamitrabhorn **314** Transplanting Rice

1979. Royal Orders and Decorations. Mult.

1006 1 b. Type **313** 50 25
1007 1 b. Rajamitrabhorn ribbon 50 25
1008 2 b. Order of the Royal House of Chakri 50 15
1009 2 b. Royal House of Chakri ribbon 50 15
1010 5 b. Order of the Nine Gems 1·00 40
1011 5 b. Nine Gems ribbon . . . 1·00 40
1012 6 b. Knight Grand Cross of the Order of Chula Chom Klao 1·25 50
1013 6 b. Chula Chom Klao ribbon 1·25 50

1980. Children's Day. Multicoloured.

1014 75 s. Type **314** 40 15
1015 75 s. Family in rice field . . . 40 15

315 Family House and Map of Thailand **316** Golden-fronted Leafbird

1980. Population and Housing Census.

1016 **315** 75 s. multicoloured . . . 20 10

1980. 9th Conference of International Commission for Bird Preservation, Asian Section. Multicoloured.

1017 75 s. Type **316** 25 20
1018 2 b. Chinese yellow tit 45 25
1019 3 b. Chestnut-tailed minla . . 1·10 35
1020 5 b. Scarlet minivet . . . . . 1·75 1·10

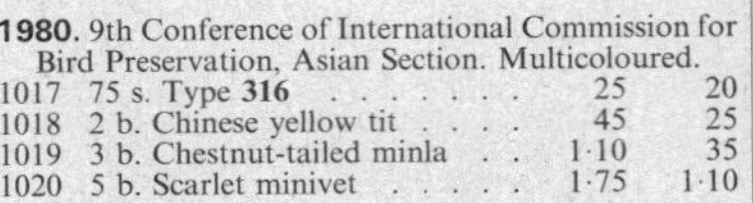

317 Extracting Snake Venom

1980. Red Cross Fair.

1021 **317** 75 s. + 25 s. mult 40 30

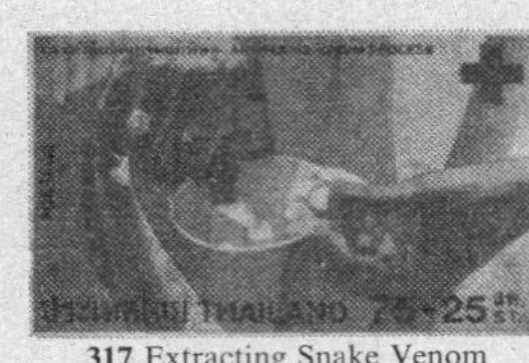

318 Smokers and Diagram of Lungs

1980. World Health Day. Anti-smoking Campaign.

1022 **318** 75 s. multicoloured . . . 20 10

319 Garuda and Rotary Emblem

1980. 75th Anniv of Rotary International.

1023 **319** 5 b. multicoloured . . . 75 20

320 Sai Yok Falls, Kanchanaburi

1980. Waterfalls. Multicoloured.

1024 1 b. Type **320** 15 10
1025 2 b. Punyaban Falls, Ranong 25 15
1026 5 b. Heo Suwat Falls, Nakhon Ratchasima . . . . 1·00 45
1027 6 b. Siriphum Falls, Chiang Mai 90 65

321 Family and Reverse of F.A.O. Medal

1980. Queen Sirikit's 48th Birthday. Mult.

1028 75 s. Queen Sirikit (vert) . . 15 10
1029 5 b. Type **321** 75 25
1030 5 b. Thai family and Ceres medal (obverse) 75 25

322 Khao Phanomrung Temple, Buri Ram

1980. International Correspondence Week. Temples. Multicoloured.

1033 75 s. Type **322** 15 10
1034 2 b. Prang Ku Temple, Chaiyaphum 25 15
1035 2 b. 75 Phimai Temple, Nakhon Ratchasima 40 15
1036 5 b. Srikhoraphum temple, Surin . . . . 1·00 55

323 Princess Mother **324** Golden Mount Temple, Bangkok

1980. The Princess Mother's 80th Birthday.

1037 **323** 75 s. multicoloured . . . 20 10

1980. United Nations Day.

1038 **324** 75 s. multicoloured . . . 20 10

325 King Bhumibol **326** King Rama VII signing Constitutional Document

1980.

1039 **325** 25 s. red 50 10
1179 50 s. green . . . . . . 1·25 10
1040 75 s. violet 15 10
1041 1 b. blue 10 10
1040a 1 b. 25 green 15 10
1180a 1 b. 50 orange . . . . 1·00 85
1080b 2 b. purple and red . . 40 10
1180c 2 b. brown 10 10
1042a 3 b. blue and brown . . 15 10
1042b 4 b. brown and blue . . 25 10
1043a 5 b. brown and lilac . . 25 10
1044a 6 b. lilac and green . . 25 10
1044b 6 b. 50 olive & green . 50 15
1044c 7 b. dp brown & brn . . 50 10
1044d 7 b. 50 blue and red . . 40 20
1044e 8 b. green and brown . . 40 15
1045 8 b. 50 brown & green . 50 20
1045a 9 b. brown and blue . . 45 15
1046 9 b. 50 green & olive . 50 20
1047 10 b. green and red . . 50 10
1048 20 b. green & orange . . 1·00 20
1049 50 b. green and lilac . . 3·50 40
1050 100 b. blue & orange . . 5·00 90

1980. King Rama VII Monument.
1051 326 75 s. multicoloured . . . 20 10

327 Bowl

1980. Bencharong Ware. Multicoloured.
1052 2 b. Type 327 . . . . 40 15
1053 2 b. 75 Covered bowls . . . 40 15
1054 3 b. Jar 75 25
1055 5 b. Stem-plates 75 50

328 King Vajiravudh 329 "Youth in Electronics Age" (Veth Maichun)

1981. Birth Centenary of King Vajiravudh.
1056 328 75 s. multicoloured . . . 20 10

1981. Children's Day.
1057 329 75 s. multicoloured . . . 30 10

330 Mosque, Pattani Province

1981. 1400th Anniv of Hegira.
1058 330 5 b. multicoloured . . . 1·25 40

331 Palm Leaf Fish Mobile

1981. International Handicraft Exhibition. Multicoloured.
1059 75 s. Type 331 . . . . 15 10
1060 75 s. Carved teakwood elephant 15 10
1061 2 b. 75 Basketwork 50 30
1062 2 b. 75 Thai folk dolls . . . 50 30

332 Scout aiding Cripple 334 Ongkhot

333 Red Cross Volunteer aiding Refugee

1981. International Year of Disabled People. Multicoloured.
1063 75 s. Type 332 . . . . 15 10
1064 5 b. Disabled person cutting gem-stones 65 20

1981. Red Cross.
1065 333 75 s.+25 s. green and red 75 75

1981. Khon (Thai classical dance). Masks. Mult.
1066 75 s. Type 334 . . . . 15 10
1067 2 b. Maiyarab 25 15
1068 3 b. Sukrip 55 20
1069 5 b. Indrajit 75 50

336 8 a. Stamp 1899

1981. "Thaipex '81" National Stamp Exhibition. Multicoloured.
1070 75 s. Type 336 . . . . 15 10
1071 75 s. 28 s. stamp, 1910 . . . 15 10
1072 2 b. 75 50 s. stamp, 1919 . . 50 25
1073 2 b. 75 3 s. stamp, 1932 . . 50 25

337 Luang Praditphairo 338 Mai Hok-Hian

1981. Birth Centenary of Luang Praditphairo (musician).
1074 337 1 b. 25 multicoloured . 25 10

1981. International Correspondence Week. Dwarf Trees. Multicoloured.
1075 75 s. Type 337 . . . . 15 10
1076 2 b. Mai Kam-Mao-Lo . . 25 15
1077 2 b. 75 Mai Khen 50 15
1078 5 b. Mai Khabuan . . . . . 1·25 55

339 Food Produce

1981. World Food Day.
1079 339 75 s. multicoloured . . . 25 10

340 Samran Mukhamat Pavilion, Bangkok

1981. United Nations Day.
1080 340 1 b. 25 multicoloured . 25 10

341 Expressway at Klongtoey

1981. Inauguration of First Thai Expressway. Multicoloured.
1081 1 b. Type 341 . . . . . . 15 10
1082 5 b. Expressway interchange 1·00 30

342 King Cobra

1981. Snakes. Multicoloured.
1083 75 s. Type 342 . . . . 15 10
1084 2 b. Banded krait 50 30
1085 2 b. 75 Thai cobra 50 15
1086 5 b. Malayan pit viper . . . 1·25 50

343 Girl carrying Child 344 Scouts reaching for Peace

1982. Children's Day.
1087 343 1 b. 25 multicoloured . . 25 10

1982. 75th Anniv of Boy Scout Movement.
1088 344 1 b. 25 multicoloured . . 25 10

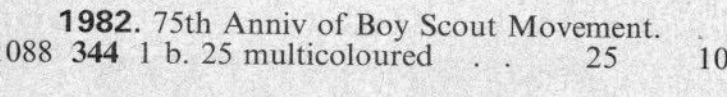

345 King Buddha Yod-Fa (Rama I)

1982. Bicentenary of Chakri Dynasty and of Bangkok. Multicoloured.
1089 1 b. Type 345 . . . . 15 10
1090 1 b. 25 Aerial view of Bangkok 15 10
1091 2 b. King Buddha Lert La Naphalai (Rama II) 25 10
1092 3 b. King Nang Klao (Rama III) 75 15
1093 4 b. King Mongkut (Rama IV) 50 15
1094 5 b. King Chulalongkorn (Rama V) . . . . 1·00 25
1095 6 b. King Vajiravudh (Rama VI) . . . . 1·00 30
1096 7 b. King Prajadhipok (Rama VII) . . . . 1·25 50
1097 8 b. King Ananda Mahidol (Rama VIII) 65 25
1098 9 b. King Bhumipol Adulyadej (Rama IX) 65 30

346 Dr. Robert Koch and Cross of Lorraine

1982. Cent of Discovery of Tubercle Bacillus.
1100 346 1 b. 25 multicoloured . . 20 10

347 "Quisqualis indica"

1982. Flowers. Multicoloured.
1101 1 b. 25 Type 347 . . . . . . 15 10
1102 1 b. 50 "Murraya paniculata" 25 15
1103 6 b. 50 "Mesua ferrea" . . . 75 40
1104 7 b. "Desmos chinensis" . . . 65 30

348 Wat Bowon Sathan Sutthawat

1982. "Bangkok 1983" International Stamp Exhibition (1st issue). Multicoloured.
1105 1 b. 25 Type 348 . . . . . . 15 10
1106 4 b. 25 Wat Phra Chetuphon Wimon Mang Khalaram . . . 40 20
1107 6 b. 50 Wat Mahathat Yuwarat Rangsarit 65 40
1108 7 b. Wat Phar Sri Rattana Satsadaram 90 25

See also Nos. 1133/4 and 1142/5.

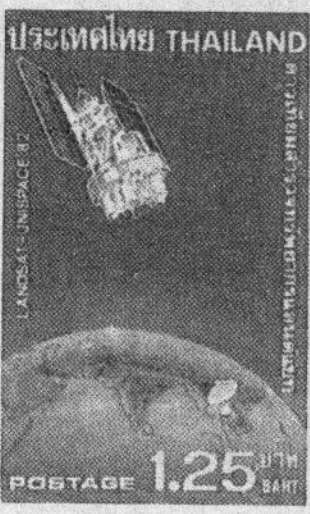

349 "Landsat" Satellite 350 Prince Purachatra

1982. Second U.N. Conference on the Exploration and Peaceful Uses of Outer Space, Vienna.
1110 349 1 b. 25 multicoloured . . 20 10

1982. Birth Centenary of Prince Purachatra.
1111 350 1 b. 25 multicoloured . . 20 10

351 Covered Jar

1982. International Correspondence Week. Sangalok Pottery. Multicoloured.
1112 1 b. 25 Type 351 . . . . . . 15 10
1113 3 b. Small jar 65 15
1114 4 b. Celadon plate 50 30
1115 7 b. Plate with fish design . . 75 50

352 Loha Prasat, Bangkok

1982. United Nations Day.
1116 352 1 b. 25 multicoloured . . 20 10

353 Chap and Ching

1982. Thai Musical Instruments. Multicoloured.
1117 50 s. Type 353 . . . . 10 10
1118 1 b. Pi nok and pi nai (pipes) 30 10
1119 1 b. 25 Klong that and taphon (drums) 15 10
1120 1 b. 50 Khong mong (gong) and krap (wooden sticks) . . . 15 15
1121 6 b. Khong wong yai (glockenspiel) . . . . . . 2·00 65
1122 7 b. Khong wong lek (glockenspiel) 90 25
1123 8 b. Ranat ek (xylophone) . . 75 40
1124 9 b. Ranat thum (xylophone) 75 40

354 Pileated Gibbon 355 Emblem and Flag of Member Countries

1982. National Wild Animal Preservation Day. Monkeys. Multicoloured.
1125 1 b. 25 Type 634 . . . . . . 15 10
1126 3 b. Pigtail macaque 90 20
1127 5 b. Slow loris 50 40
1128 7 b. Silvered leaf monkey . . 75 40

1982. 15th Anniv of Association of South-East Asian Nations.
1129 355 6 b. 50 multicoloured . . 75 25

356 Child sweeping

1983. Children's Day.
1130 **356** 1 b. 25 multicoloured . . 20 10

357 Postcodes

1983. 1st Anniv of Postcodes. Multicoloured.
1131 1 b. 25 Type **357** 25 10
1132 1 b. 25 Postcoded envelope 25 10

358 Old General Post Office

1983. "Bangkok 1983" International Stamp Exhibition (2nd issue).
1133 **358** 7 b. multicoloured . . . 75 20
1134 10 b. multicoloured . . . 1·25 30

359 Junks

1983. 25th Anniv of International Maritime Organization.
1136 **359** 1 b. 25 multicoloured . . 20 10

360 Civil Servant's Shoulder Strap

362 Prince Sithiporn Kridakara

361 Giving and receiving Aid and Red Cross

1983. Civil Servants' Day.
1137 **360** 1 b. 25 multicoloured . . 20 10

1983. Red Cross.
1138 **361** 1 b. 25+25 s. multicoloured 50 50

1983. Birth Centenary of Prince Sithiporn Kridakara (agriculturalist).
1139 **362** 1 b. 25 multicoloured . . 20 10

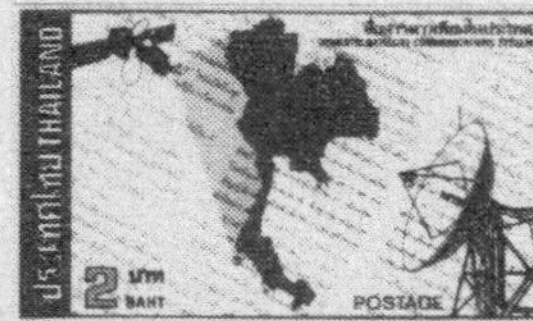

363 Satellite, Map and Dish Aerial

1983. Domestic Satellite Communications System.
1140 **363** 2 b. multicoloured . . . 25 10

364 Prince Bhanurangsi

366 Cable Map of A.S.E.A.N. Countries and Cable Ship

365 Post Box Clearance

1983. Prince Bhanurangsi (founder of Thai postal service) Commemoration.
1141 **364** 1 b. 25 multicoloured . 25 10

1983. "Bangkok 1983" International Stamp Exhibition (3rd issue). Multicoloured.
1142 1 b. 25 Type **365** 15 10
1143 7 b. 50 Post office counter . 75 30
1144 8 b. 50 Mail transportation 1·00 65
1145 9 b. 50 Mail delivery 50 25

1983. Inauguration of Malaysia–Singapore–Thailand Submarine Cable. Multicoloured.
1147 1 b. 25 Type **366** 40 15
1148 7 b. Map of new cable . . . 65 30

367 Flower Coral ("Acropora asper")

1983. International Correspondence Week. Corals. Multicoloured.
1149 2 b. Type **367** 25 15
1150 3 b. Lesser valley coral . . . 75 15
1151 4 b. Mushroom coral . . . 25 25
1152 7 b. Common lettuce coral . 1·00 30

368 Satellite and Submarine Cable Communications Equipment

1983. World Communications Year. Mult.
1153 2 b. Type **368** 60 10
1154 3 b. Telegraph and telephone service equipment 25 10

369 Fishing for Skipjack

1983. United Nations Day.
1155 **369** 1 b. 25 multicoloured . 25 10

370 Sangkhalok Pottery

1983. 700th Anniv of Thai Alphabet.
1156 **370** 3 b. multicoloured . . . 50 15
1157 – 7 b. black and brown . 75 25
1158 – 8 b. multicoloured . . . 40 25
1159 – 9 b. multicoloured . . . 40 25
DESIGNS—HORIZ: 7 b. Thai characters. VERT: 8 b. Buddha (sculpture); 9 b. Mahathat Temple.

371 Prince Mahidol of Songkhla

1983. Co-operation between Siriraj Hospital and Rockefeller Foundation.
1160 **371** 9 b. 50 multicoloured . . 75 50

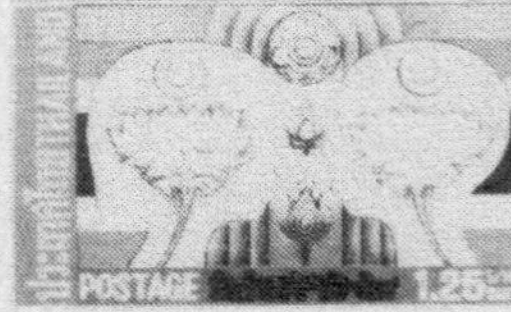

372 Lotus Blossoms within Heads

1984. Children's Day.
1161 **372** 1 b. 25 multicoloured . . 20 10

373 Running

1984. 17th National Games, Phitsanulok Province. Multicoloured.
1162 1 b. 25 Type **373** 30 10
1163 3 b. Football 25 15

374 Skeletal Joints, Globe and Emblem

1984. 5th S.E.A.P.A.L. Rheumatology Congress.
1164 **374** 1 b. 25 multicoloured . . 20 10

375 Statue of King Naresuan and Modern Armed Forces

376 Royal Institute Emblem in Door Arch

1984. Armed Forces Day.
1165 **375** 1 b. 25 multicoloured . . 30 10

1984. 50th Anniv of Royal Institute.
1166 **376** 1 b. 25 multicoloured . . 20 10

1984. Red Cross. No. 954 surch.
1167 **295** 3 b. 25+25 s. on 2 b. 75+25 s. mult . . 1·00 60

378 King and Queen examining Development Project

1984. Royal Initiated Projects. Multicoloured.
1168 1 b. 25 Type **378** 25 10
1169 1 b. 25 Improving barren area 25 10
1170 1 b. 25 Dam, terrace farming and agricultural aircraft . . 25 10
1171 1 b. 25 Crops, fish and farm animals 25 10
1172 1 b. 25 King and Queen of Thailand 25 10

379 Dome Building and University Emblem

1984. 50th Anniv of Thammasat University.
1173 **379** 1 b. 25 multicoloured . . 20 10

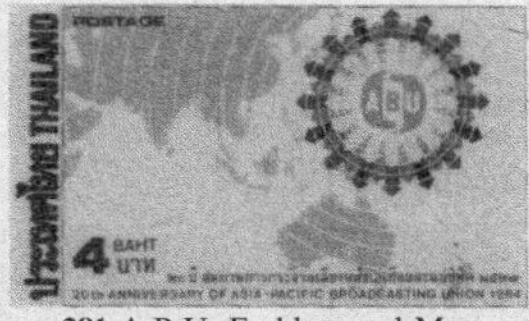

381 A.B.U. Emblem and Map

1984. 20th Anniv of Asia-Pacific Broadcasting Union.
1174 **381** 4 b. multicoloured . . . 50 20

382 Chiang Saen Style Buddha

384 "Alocasia indica var. metallica"

1984. Thai Sculptures of Buddhas. Multicoloured
1175 1 b. 25 Type **382** 15 10
1176 7 b. Sukhothai style 75 30
1177 8 b. 50 Thong style 40 40
1178 9 b. 50 Ayutthaya style . . . 40 40

1984. International Correspondence Week. Medicinal Plants. Multicoloured.
1181 1 b. 50 Type **384** 15 10
1182 2 b. "Aloe barbadensis" . . 20 10
1183 4 b. "Gynura pseudo-china" 35 15
1184 10 b. "Rhoeo spathacea" . . 1·25 70

385 Princess Mother

386 Threshing Rice

1984. 84th Birthday of Princess Mother.
1185 **385** 1 b. 50 multicoloured . . 15 10

1984. United Nations Day.
1186 **386** 1 b. 50 multicoloured . . 15 10

387 "Bhutanitis lidderdalei"

1984. Butterflies. Multicoloured.
1187 2 b. Type **387** 40 20
1188 3 b. "Stichophthalma louisa" 60 25
1189 5 b. "Parthenos sylvia" . . . 1·00 55
1190 7 b. "Stichophthalma godfreyi" 1·25 65

388 "Crossing the Road by Flyover" (U-Tai Raksorn)

390 Monument to Tao-Thep-Krasattri and Tao-Sri-Sundhorn

389 Bangkok Mail Centre

1985. Children's Day. Multicoloured.
1191 1 b. 50 Type **388** 15 10
1192 1 b. 50 "Crossing the Road by Flyover" (Sravudh Charoennawee) (horiz) . . 15 10

1985. Inauguration of Bangkok Mail-sorting Centre.
1193 **389** 1 b. 50 multicoloured . . 25 10

1985. Heroines of Phuket. Bicentennial Ceremony.
1194 **390** 2 b. multicoloured . . . 20 10

1985. Red Cross. No. 987 surch.
1195 **306** 2 b. + 25 s. on 75 s. + 25 s. multicoloured 75 75

392 Bank Headquarters, Bangkok, and King Vajiravudh (Rama VII)

1985. 72nd Anniv of Government Savings Bank.
1196 **392** 1 b. 50 multicoloured . . 15 10

393 Satellite over Thai Buildings

1985. 20th Anniv of International Telecommunications Satellite Organization.
1197 **393** 2 b. multicoloured . . . 25 10

394 Douglas DC-6 and DC-8 and Loi-Krathong Festival

1985. 25th Anniv of Thai Airways. Mult.
1198 2 b. Type **394** 15 10
1199 7 b. 50 Douglas DC-10-30 and Thai classical dancing . . . 1·00 55
1200 8 b. 50 Airbus Industrie A300 and Thai buildings . . . . 1·10 80
1201 9 b. 50 Boeing 747-200 and world landmarks . . . . . 1·10 80

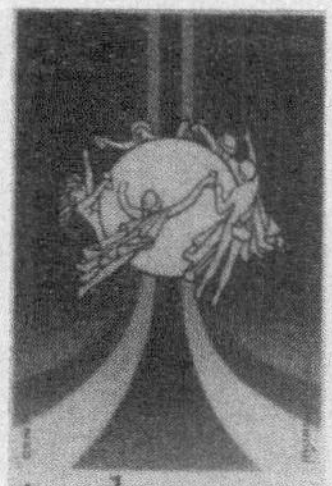

395 U.P.U.Emblem

397 Aisvarya Pavillion

396 Pigeon

1985. Centenary of Membership of U.P.U. and I.T.U. Multicoloured.
1202 2 b. Type **395** 15 10
1203 10 b. I.T.U. Emblem 55 20

1985. National Communications Day.
1204 **396** 2 b. blue, red and deep blue 20 10

1985. "Thaipex '85" Stamp Exhibition. Multicoloured.
1205 2 b. Type **397** 15 10
1206 3 b. Varopas Piman Pavilion (horiz) 25 15
1207 7 b. Vehas Camrun Pavilion (horiz) 50 20
1208 10 b. Vitoon Tassana Tower 60 50

398 King Mongkut, Eclipsed Sun and Telescope

1985. National Science Day.
1210 **398** 2 b. multicoloured . . . 20 10

399 Department Seals, 1885 and 1985

1985. Centenary of Royal Thai Survey Department.
1211 **399** 2 b. multicoloured . . . 20 10

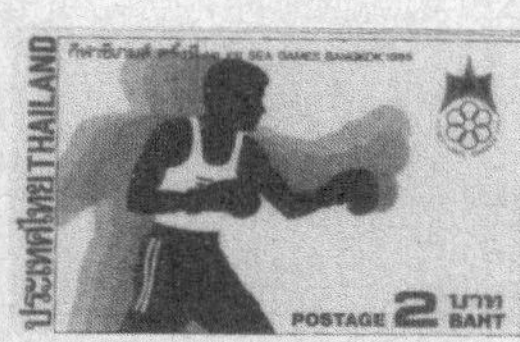

400 Boxing

1985. 13th South-East Asia Games, Bangkok (1st issue). Multicoloured.
1212 2 b. Type **400** 20 10
1213 2 b. Putting the shot 20 10
1214 2 b. Badminton 20 10
1215 2 b. Javelin-throwing 20 10
1216 2 b. Weightlifting 20 10
See also Nos. 1229/32.

401 "Allemanda cathartica"
402 Mothers and Children at Clinic

1985. International Correspondence Week. Climbing Plants. Multicoloured.
1218 2 b. Type **401** 25 15
1219 3 b. "Jasminum auriculatum" 35 15
1220 7 b. Passion flower 50 25
1221 10 b. "Antigonon leptopus" 60 35

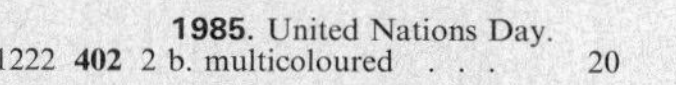

1985. United Nations Day.
1222 **402** 2 b. multicoloured . . . 20 10

403 Prince Dhani Nivat
404 Prince of Jainad

1985. Birth Centenary of Prince Dhani Nivat.
1223 **403** 2 b. multicoloured . . . 15 10

1985. Birth Centenary of Rangsit, Prince of Jainad (Minister of Health).
1224 **404** 1 b. 50 multicoloured . 15 10

405 Emblem and Buildings

1985. 5th Asian-Pacific Postal Union Congress.
1225 **405** 2 b. multicoloured . . . 15 10
1226 – 10 b. multicoloured . . . 55 25
DESIGN: 10 b. As Type **405** but different buildings.

406 Emblem

1985. International Youth Year.
1227 **406** 2 b. multicoloured . . . 25 10

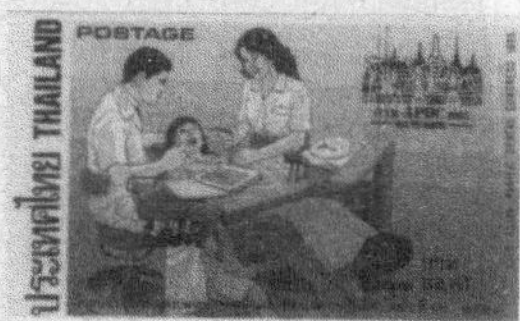

407 Dentist and Nurse tending Patient

1085. 12th Asian-Pacific Dental Congress.
1228 **407** 2 b. multicoloured . . . 20 10

408 Volleyball
409 Chevalier de Chaumont presenting Message from Louis XIV to King Narai the Great, 1685

1985. 12th South-East Asia Games, Bangkok (2nd issue). Multicoloured.
1229 1 b. Type **408** 20 15
1230 2 b. Sepak-takraw 20 10
1231 3 b. Gymnastics 25 15
1232 4 b. Bowling 25 20

1985. 300th Anniv of Franco–Thai Relations. Multicoloured.
1234 2 b. Type **409** 15 10
1235 8 b. 50 Siamese emissaries carrying reply from King Narai to Louis XIV 50 40

410 Emblem

1986. 3rd Anniv of International and Inauguration of Domestic Express Mail Services.
1236 **410** 2 b. multicoloured . . . 15 10

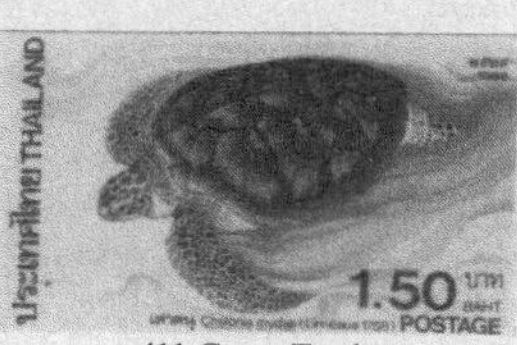

411 Green Turtle

1986. Turtles. Multicoloured.
1237 1 b. 50 Type **411** 15 10
1238 3 b. Hawksbill turtle 35 10
1239 5 b. Leatherback turtle . . . 1·00 20
1240 10 b. Olive turtle 75 25

412 Family picking Lotus
414 Statue of Sunthon Phu

1986. Children's Day.
1241 **412** 2 b. multicoloured . . . 20 10

1986. No. 1021 surch.
1242 **317** 2 b. + 25 s. on 75 s. + 25 s. multicoloured 75 75

1986. Birth Bicentenary of Sunthon Phu (poet).
1243 **414** 2 b. multicoloured . . . 20 10

415 Watermelon

1986. Fruit. Multicoloured.
1244 2 b. Type **415** 50 15
1245 2 b. Malay apple ("Eugenia malaccensis") 15 15
1246 6 b. Pomelo ("Citrus maxima") 50 20
1247 6 b. Papaya ("Carica papaya") 50 20

416 Trees on Grid and Water Line

1986. National Tree Year.
1248 **416** 2 b. multicoloured . . . 15 10

417 Pigeon flying from Man's Head to Transmission Masts

1986. National Communications Day.
1249 **417** 2 b. multicoloured . . . 15 10

418 Chalom

1986. International Correspondence Week. Bamboo Baskets. Multicoloured.
1250 2 b. Type **418** 15 10
1251 2 b. Krabung 15 10
1252 6 b. Kratib 35 15
1253 6 b. Kaleb 35 15

1986. No. 1031 surch **1 BAHT**.
1254 **227** 1 b. on 20 s. blue 20 10

419 Emblem and War Scenes

1986. International Peace Year.
1255 **419** 2 b. blue, dp blue & red 20 15

420 Industrial and Agricultural Scenes within Emblem

1986. Productivity Year.
1256 **420** 2 b. multicoloured . . . 20 10

421 Scouts saluting and Scout helping Blind Man across Road

1986. 75th Anniv of Thai Scouting. Mult.
1257 2 b. + 50 s. Type **421** . . . 15 15
1258 2 b. + 50 s. Scouting activities 15 15
1259 2 b. + 50 s. King and Queen making presentations to scouts 15 15
1260 2 b. + 50 s. 15th Asia-Pacific Scout Conference, Thailand 15 15

422 "Vanda Varavuth"

1986. 6th ASEAN Orchid Congress, Thailand. Multicoloured.
1261 2 b. Type **422** 20 10
1262 3 b. "Ascocenda Emma" . . 20 15
1263 4 b. "Dendrobium Sri-Siam" (horiz) 35 30
1264 5 b. "Dendrobium Ekapol Panda" (horiz) 35 25

423 "Volvariella volvacea"

1986. Edible Fungi. Multicoloured.
1266 2 b. Type **423** 25 10
1267 2 b. "Pleurotus ostreatus" . . 25 10
1268 6 b. "Auricularia polytricha" 85 25
1269 6 b. "Pleurotus cystidiosus" . 85 25

424 "Morulius chrysophekadion"

1986. 60th Anniv of Fisheries Department. Multicoloured.
1270 2 b. Type **424** 15 10
1271 2 b. "Notopterus blanci" . . 15 10
1272 7 b. "Scleropages formosus" . 35 15
1273 7 b. "Pangasianodon gigas" . 35 15

426 Children in Playground

1987. National Children's Day. Multicoloured.
1274 2 b. Type **426** 20 10
1275 2 b. Children in and around swimming pool 20 10

Nos. 1274/5 were printed together, se-tenant, forming a composite design showing "Our School" by Lawan Maneenetr.

427 Norlthrop F-5 Tiger II and General Dynamics Fighting Falcon Aircraft and Pilot

1987. 72nd Anniv of Royal Thai Air Force.
1276 **427** 2 b. multicoloured . . . 25 10

428 King Rama III and Temples

1987. Birth Bicentenary of King Rama III.
1277 **428** 2 b. multicoloured . . . 20 10

429 Communications and Transport Systems

1987. 75th Anniv of Ministry of Communications.
1278 **429** 2 b. multicoloured . . . 25 10

1987. Red Cross. No. 1065 surch **2 + 0.50 BAHT.**
1279 **333** 2 b. + 50 s. on 75 s. + 25 s. green and red 75 75

431 Tree-lined Street

1987. National Tree Year.
1280 **431** 2 b. multicoloured . . . 15 10

432 Gold Peacock

1987. "Thaipex '87" National Stamp Exhibition. Handicrafts. Multicoloured.
1281 2 b. Type **432** 15 10
1282 2 b. Gold mirrors 15 10
1283 6 b. Gold lustre water urn and finger bowls with trays . . 30 15
1284 6 b. Gold swan vase 30 15

433 Flying Bird and Animal Horn (Somsak Junthavorn)

1987. National Communications Day.
1286 **433** 2 b. multicoloured . . . 15 10

434 King Rama IX at Presentation Ceremony, King Rama V and Emblem

1987. Centenary of Chulachomklao Royal Military Academy, Khao Cha-Ngok.
1287 **434** 2 b. multicoloured . . . 15 10

435 Spiral Ropes leading to Member Countries' Flags

1987. 20th Anniv of Association of South-East Asian Nations.
1288 **435** 2 b. multicoloured . . . 10 10
1289 3 b. multicoloured . . . 15 10
1290 4 b. multicoloured . . . 20 15
1291 5 b. multicoloured . . . 25 15

436 People and Open Book

437 Flower-offering Ceremony, Saraburi

1987. International Literacy Day.
1292 **436** 2 b. multicoloured . . . 15 10

1987. Visit Thailand Year.
1293 2 b. Type **437** 10 10
1294 3 b. Duan Sib Festival, Nakhon Si Thammarat 15 10
1295 5 b. Bang Fai Festival, Yasothon 25 15
1296 7 b. Loi Krathong, Sukhothai 35 20

438 Ministry Building

1987. 72nd Anniv of Auditor General's Office.
1297 **438** 2 b. multicoloured . . . 15 10

439 Temple of Dawn, "Sri Suphanahong" (royal barge) and Mt Fuji within "100"

1987. Centenary of Japan–Thailand Friendship Treaty.
1298 **439** 2 b. multicoloured . . . 15 10

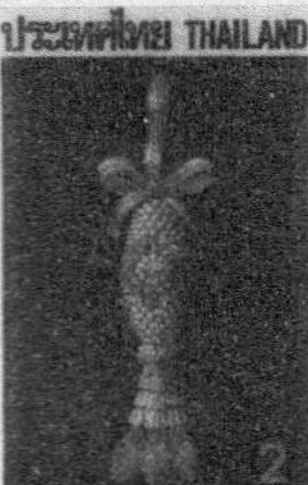

440 Floral Tassel

1987 International Correspondence Week. Ceremonial Floral Garlands. Multicoloured.
1299 2 b. Type **440** 15 10
1300 3 b. Tasselled garland 25 10
1301 5 b. Wrist garland 30 20
1302 7 b. Double-ended garland . . 35 25

1987. No. 1180a surch. **2 BAHT.**
1303 **325** 2 b. on 1 b. 50 orange . . 15 10

442 Thai Pavilion

1987. Inauguration of Social Education and Cultural Centre.
1304 **442** 2 b. multicoloured . . . 15 10

443 King Bhumibol Adulyadej as a Boy

1987. King Bhumibol Adulyadej's 60th Birthday. Multicoloured.
1305 2 b. Type **443** 15 10
1306 2 b. Wedding photograph of King Bhumibol Adulyadej and Queen Sirikit, 1950 . . 15 10
1307 2 b. King on throne during Accession ceremony at Paisan Hall, 1950 . . . . 15 10
1308 2 b. King as monk on alms round 15 10
1309 2 b. Elderly woman greeting King 15 10
1310 2 b. King demonstrating to hill tribes how to take medicine 15 10
1311 2 b. King and Queen visiting wounded servicemen . . . 15 10
1312 2 b. King examining new system for small farms 15 10
1314 2 b. Princess Mother Somdej Phra Sri Nakarindra Boromrajjonnani 15 10
1315 2 b. Crown Prince Maha Vajiralongkorn 15 10
1316 2 b. Princess Maha Chakri Sirindhorn 15 10
1317 2 b. Princess Chulabhorn . . 15 10
1318 2 b. King Bhumibol Adulyadej and Queen Sirikit 15 10
1319 2 b. King and family (48 × 33 mm) 15 10
1320 100 b. gold and blue (King Bhumibol Adulyadej) (48 × 33 mm) . . . . 38·00 38·00

444 "Teacher's Day" (Nutchaliya Suddhiprasit)

445 Prince Kromamun Bridhyalongkorn (founder)

1988. National Children's Day.
1321 **444** 2 b. multicoloured . . . 15 10

1988. 72nd Anniv of Thai Co-operatives.
1322 **445** 2 b. multicoloured . . . 15 10

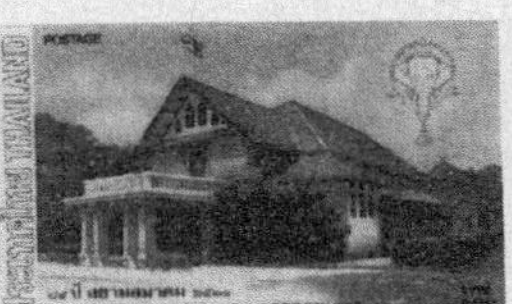

446 Society Building

1988. 84th Anniv of Siam Society (for promotion of arts and sciences).
1323 **446** 2 b. multicoloured . . . 15 10

447 Phra Phai Luang Monastery

1988. Sukhothai Historical Park. Multicoloured.
1324 2 b. Type **447** 15 10
1325 3 b. Traphang Thonglang Monastery 20 10
1326 4 b. Maha That Monastery . 30 15
1327 6 b. Thewalai Maha Kaset . 45 25

1988. No. 1040a surch. **1 BAHT.**
1328 **325** 1 b. on 1 b. 25 green . . 15 10

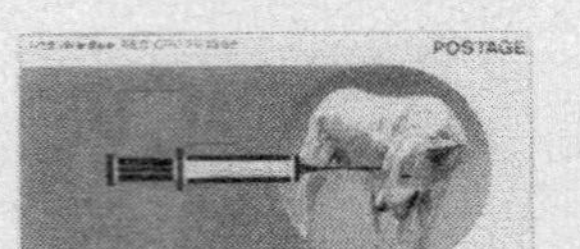

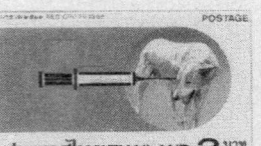

449 Syringe between Red Cross and Dog

1988. Red Cross Anti-rabies Campaign.
1329 **449** 2 b. multicoloured . . . 15 10

450 King Rama V (founder)

452 Hand holding Coloured Ribbons

451 Crested Fireback Pheasant

1988. Centenary of Siriraj Hospital.
1330 **450** 5 b. multicoloured . . . 50 15

1988. Pheasants. Multicoloured.
1331 2 b. Type **451** 20 15
1332 3 b. Kalij pheasant 25 15
1333 6 b. Silver pheasant 45 25
1334 7 b. Mrs. Hume's pheasant . 50 25

1988. Centenary of International Women's Council.
1335 **452** 2 b. multicoloured . . . 15 10

453 King Rama IX in King's Own Bodyguard Uniform

454 King Rama IX in Full Robes

1988.
1631 **453** 25 s. brown 10 10
1336 50 s. green 10 10
1337 1 b. blue 10 10
1753 2 b. red 10 10
1339 3 b. blue and brown . . 15 10
1340 4 b. brown and blue . . 20 10
1341 5 b. brown and lilac . . 25 10
1342 6 b. purple and green . . 30 10
1343 7 b. deep brown & brown 35 15
1344 8 b. green and red . . . 40 20
1345 9 b. brown and blue . . 45 15
1346 10 b. green and brown . . 50 15
1348 20 b. green and orange . 1·00 40
1350 25 b. blue and green . . 1·25 50
1352 50 b. green and lilac . . 2·50 70
1354 100 b. blue and orange . 5·00 3·75

1988. 42nd Anniv of Accession to Throne of King Rama IX. (a) As T **454**. Multicoloured.
1356 2 b. Type **454** 15 10

(b) Royal Regalia.
1357 2 b. Great Crown of Victory 15 10
1358 2 b. Sword of Victory and scabbard (horiz) 15 10
1359 2 b. Sceptre (horiz) 15 10
1360 2 b. Royal Fan and Fly Whisk (horiz) 15 10
1361 2 b. Slippers (horiz) 15 10

(c) Thrones.
1362 2 b. Atthathit Uthumphon Ratchaat throne (octagonal base) 15 10
1363 2 b. Phatthrabit throne (rectangular base) 15 10
1364 2 b. Phuttan Kanchanasinghat throne (gold throne on angular steps) 15 10
1365 2 b. Butsabokmala Mahachakkraphatphiman throne (ship shape) 15 10
1366 2 b. Throne inlaid with mother-of-pearl (blue throne on angular steps) 15 10
1367 2 b. Peony design niello throne (circular steps) 15 10

No. 1357 is 33 × 48 mm and Nos. 1358/61 48 × 33 mm in size.

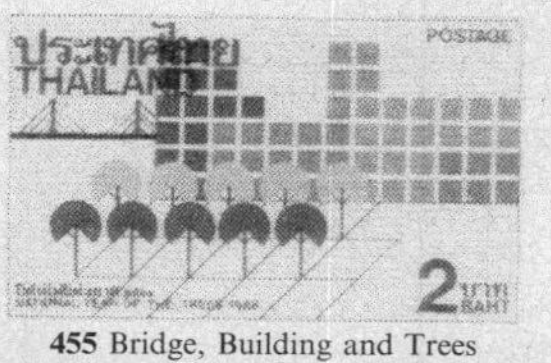
455 Bridge, Building and Trees

1988. National Tree Year.
1369 **455** 2 b. multicoloured . . . 15 10

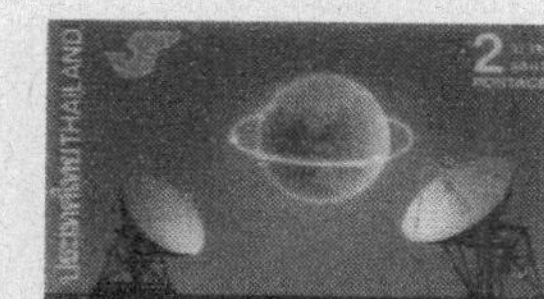
456 Globe and Dish Aerials

1988. National Communications Day.
1370 **456** 2 b. multicoloured . . . 15 10

458 Grasshopper

1988. International Correspondence Week. Woven Coconut-leaf Folk Toys. Multicoloured.
1371 2 b. Type **458** 15 10
1372 2 b. Carp 15 10
1373 6 b. Bird 30 15
1374 6 b. Takro 30 15

459 Flats and Construction Workers

1988. Housing Development.
1375 **459** 2 b. multicoloured . . . 15 10

460 King Rama V in Full Uniform

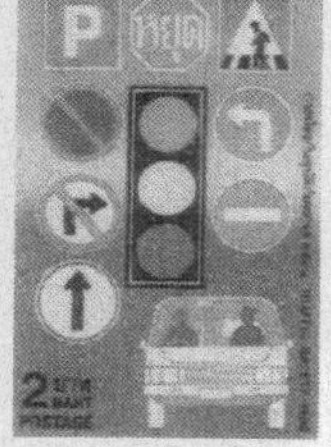
461 Road Signs

1988. 120th Anniv of King's Own Bodyguard.
1376 **460** 2 b. multicoloured . . . 20 10

1988. Road Safety Campaign.
1377 **461** 2 b. multicoloured . . . 15 10

462 "Crotalaria sessiliflora"

464 Knight Grand Commander of Honourable Order of Rama

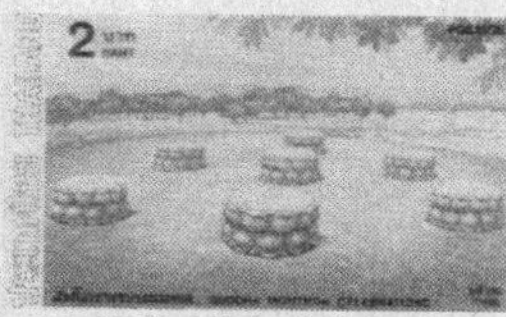
463 Buddha's Birthplace

1988. New Year. Multicoloured.
1378 1 b. Type **462** 10 10
1379 1 b. "Uvaria grandiflora" . . 10 10
1380 1 b. "Reinwardtia trigyna" . . 10 10
1381 1 b. "Impatiens griffithii" . . 10 10

1988. Buddha Monthon Celebrations. Mult.
1382 2 b. Type **463** 15 10
1383 3 b. Buddha's place of enlightenment 15 10
1384 4 b. Site of Buddha's first sermon 20 15
1385 5 b. Buddha's Place of Nirvana 30 15
1386 6 b. Buddha (vert) 35 20

1988. Insignia of Orders. Multicoloured.
1387 2 b. Type **464** 15 10
1388 2 b. Close-up of badge . . . 15 10
1389 3 b. Knight Grand Cordon of Most Exalted Order of White Elephant 20 15
1390 3 b. Close-up of badge . . . 20 15
1391 5 b. Knight Grand Cordon of Most Noble Order of Crown of Thailand 25 15
1392 5 b. Close-up of badge . . . 25 15
1393 7 b. Close-up of Rarana Varabhorn Order of Merit . 35 20
1394 7 b. Badge on chain of office 35 20

Stamps of the same value were issued together, se-tenant, each pair forming a composite design.

465 "Floating Market" (Thongbai Siyam)

1989. National Children's Day. Designs showing plasticine paintings by blind people. Multicoloured.
1395 2 b. Type **465** 20 10
1396 2 b. "Flying Birds" (Kwanchai Kerd-Daeng) 20 10
1397 2 b. "Little Mermaid" (Chalermpol Jiengmai) . . 20 10
1398 2 b. "Golden Fish" (Natetip Korsantirak) 20 10

466 Emblem and Symbols of Communication

1989. 12th Anniv of Thai Communications Authority.
1399 **466** 2 b. multicoloured . . . 15 10

467 Statue of Kings Rama V and VI and Auditorium

1989. 72nd Anniv of Chulalongkorn University.
1400 **467** 2 b. multicoloured . . . 15 10

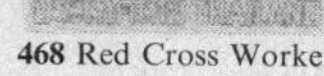
468 Red Cross Worker

469 Phra Kaeo Monastery

1989. 96th Anniv of Thai Red Cross (1401) and 125th Anniv of International Red Cross (1402). Multicoloured.
1401 2 b. Type **468** 15 10
1402 10 b. Red Cross and pillar . . 50 30

1989. Phra Nakhon Khiri Historical Park. Multicoloured.
1403 2 b. Type **469** 15 10
1404 3 b. Chatchawan Wiangchai Observatory 25 15
1405 5 b. Phra That Chom Phet stupa 35 25
1406 6 b. Wetchayan Wichian Phrasat Throne Hall . . . 50 35

470 Lottery Office Building and Profit Recipients

1989. 50th Anniv of Government Lottery Office.
1407 **470** 2 b. multicoloured . . . 15 10

471 Campaign Emblem and Figures

472 Gold Nielloware Figures

1989. International Anti-drugs Day.
1408 **471** 2 b. multicoloured . . . 15 10

1989. National Arts and Crafts Year. Mult.
1409 2 b. Type **472** 15 10
1410 2 b. Ceramics 15 10
1411 6 b. Ornament inlaid with gemstones (horiz) 30 15
1412 6 b. Triangular cushion (horiz) 30 15

473 Cone Shell

1989. Shells. Multicoloured.
1413 2 b. Type **473** 15 10
1414 3 b. Thorny oyster 25 15
1415 6 b. Great spotted cowrie . . 45 25
1416 10 b. Emperor nautilus . . . 80 45

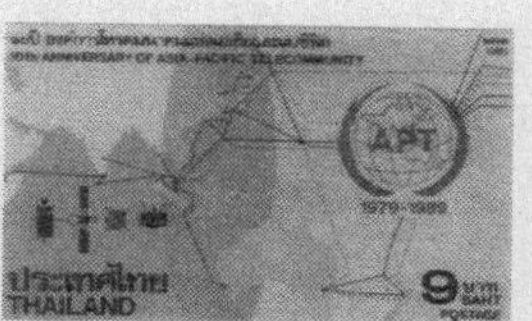
474 Satellites, Submarine Cable Network and Emblem

1989. 10th Anniv of Asia–Pacific Telecommunity.
1417 **474** 9 b. multicoloured . . . 45 20

475 Phya Anuman Rajadhon

1989. Birth Centenary (1988) of Phya Anuman Rajadhon (writer).
1418 **475** 2 b. multicoloured . . . 15 10

476 Emblem and School

1989. Centenary of Post and Telecommunications School.
1419 **476** 2 b. multicoloured . . . 15 10

477 Communications Symbols

478 Post Box

1989. National Communications Day.
1420 **477** 2 b. multicoloured . . . 20 10

1989. "Thaipex '89" National Stamp Exhibition. Post Boxes. Multicoloured.
1421 2 b. Type **478** 15 10
1422 3 b. Provincial box 20 10
1423 4 b. City box 25 15
1424 5 b. Imported English box . . 30 15
1425 6 b. West German box sent as a gift on introduction of Thai Postal Service 30 15

479 Dragonfly

1989. International Correspondence Week. Multicoloured.
1426 2 b. Type **479** 20 10
1427 5 b. Dragonfly (different) . . 30 15
1428 6 b. Dragonfly (different) . . 45 20
1429 10 b. Damselfly 60 40

480 Means of Transport and Communications

1989. Asia–Pacific Transport and Communications Decade.
1431 **480** 2 b. multicoloured . . . 20 10

481 Figure and "Thoughts"

482 "Hypericum uralum"

1989. Centenary of Mental Health Care.
1432 **481** 2 b. multicoloured . . . 15 10

1989. New Year. Flowers. Multicoloured.
1433 1 b. Type **482** 10 10
1434 1 b. "Uraria rufescens" . . . 10 10
1435 1 b. "Manglietia garrettii" . . 10 10
1436 1 b. "Aeschynanthus macranthus" 10 10

483 "Catacanthus incarnatus" (shieldbug)

1989. Beetles. Multicoloured.
1438 2 b. Type **483** 20 10
1439 3 b. "Aristobia approximator" 25 10
1440 6 b. "Chrysochroa chinensis" 60 20
1441 10 b. "Enoplotrupes sharpi" . 60 50

484 Medallists on Rostrum

1989. Sports Welfare Fund. Multicoloured.
1442 2 b.+1 b. Type **484** 15 15
1443 2 b.+1 b. Nurse attending fallen cyclist 15 15
1444 2 b.+1 b. Boxing 15 15
1445 2 b.+1 b. Football 15 15

485 Official, Family and Graph

1990. Population and Housing Census.
1446 **485** 2 b. multicoloured . . . 15 10

486 Skipping (Phethai Setharangsi)

1990. National Children's Day. Multicoloured.
1447 2 b. Type **486** 15 10
1448 2 b. Various sports activities (Chalermpol Wongpim) (vert) 15 10

487 Skull splitting Heart

488 Tiap

1990. Red Cross. Anti-AIDS Campaign.
1449 **487** 2 b. blue, red & black . 15 10

1990. Heritage Conservation Day. Mother-of-Pearl Inlaid Containers. Multicoloured.
1450 2 b. Type **488** 15 10
1451 2 b. Phan waenfa 15 10
1452 8 b. Lung (horiz) 40 25
1453 8 b. Chiat klom (horiz) . . . 40 25

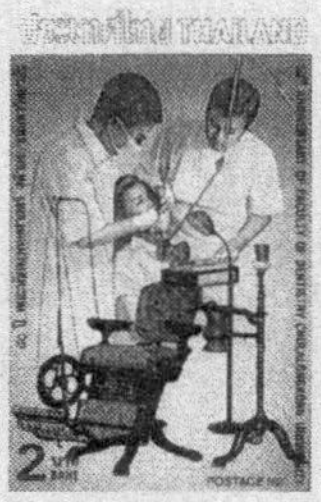

489 Dental Students and Old Chair

490 Tin

1990. 50th Anniv of Chulalongkorn University Dentistry Faculty.
1454 **489** 2 b. multicoloured . . . 15 10

1990. Minerals. Multicoloured.
1460 2 b. Type **490** 15 10
1461 3 b. Zinc 15 10
1462 5 b. Lead 25 15
1463 6 b. Fluorite 30 20

491 Pigeon

1990. National Communications Day.
1465 **491** 2 b. blue, dp blue & pur 15 10

492 Pigeons and Envelopes

1990. 20th Anniv of Asian–Pacific Postal Training Centre, Bangkok.
1466 **492** 2 b. green, blue & black 15 10
1467 8 b. blue, green & black 40 30

493 Jaipur Foot Project

1990. 60th Anniv of Rotary International in Thailand. Multicoloured.
1468 2 b. Type **493** 15 10
1469 3 b. Child anti-polio vaccination campaign 15 10
1470 6 b. Literacy campaign . . . 30 15
1471 8 b. King Chulalongkorn and his engraved cypher (Thai Museum, Nordkapp, Norway 60 30

494 Account and Staff at Computer Terminals

1990. Centenary of Comptroller-General's Department.
1472 **494** 2 b. multicoloured . . . 15 10

495 Flowers in Dish (Cho Muang)

1990. International Correspondence Week. Designs showing winning paintings in design competition. Multicoloured.
1473 2 b. Type **495** 15 10
1474 3 b. Flowers on tray (Cha Mongkut) 20 15
1475 5 b. Sweetmeats on tray with leaf design (Sane Chan) . . 25 20
1476 6 b. Fruit in bowl (Luk Chup) 35 25

496 Princess Mother with Flower

497 "Cyrtandromoea grandiflora"

1990. 90th Birthday of Princess Mother.
1478 **496** 2 b. multicoloured . . . 20 10

1990. New Year. Flowers. Multicoloured.
1479 1 b. Type **497** 15 10
1480 1 b. "Rhododendron arboreum sp. delavayi" 15 10
1481 1 b. "Merremia vitifolia" . . 15 10
1482 1 b. "Afgekia mahidolae" . . 15 10

498 Wiman Mek Royal Hall

1990. Dusit Palace. Multicoloured.
1484 2 b. Type **498** 15 10
1485 3 b. Ratcharit Rungrot Royal House 15 10
1486 4 b. Aphisek Dusit Royal Hall 20 15
1487 5 b. Amphon Sathan Palace . 25 15
1488 6 b. Udon Phak Royal Hall . 30 20
1489 8 b. Anantasamakhom Throne Hall 40 30

499 Phrachetuphon Wimolmangkalaram Temple and Supreme Patriarch

1990. Birth Bicentenary of Supreme Patriarch Somdet Phra Maha Samanachao Kromphra Paramanuchitchinorot.
1490 **499** 2 b. multicoloured . . . 15 10

500 Judo

1990. Sports Welfare Fund. Multicoloured.
1491 2 b.+1 b. Type **500** 20 20
1492 2 b.+1 b. Archery 20 20
1493 2 b.+1 b. High jumping . . 20 20
1494 2 b.+1 b. Windsurfing . . . 20 20

501 Aspects of Petroleum Industry

1990. 12th Anniv of Thai Petroleum Authority.
1495 **501** 2 b. multicoloured . . . 15 10

502 Mae Klong Railway Locomotive No. 6

1990. Steam Locomotives. Multicoloured.
1496 2 b. Type **502** 15 10
1497 3 b. "Sung Noen" locomotive No. 32 . . . . 25 15
1498 5 b. "C 56" locomotive No. 715 40 30
1499 6 b. "Mikado" locomotive No. 953 . . . . 40 30

503 Luk Khang (tops)

1991. Children's Day. Games. Multicoloured.
1501 2 b. Type **503** 15 10
1502 3 b. Pid Ta Ti Mo (blindfolded child smashing vase) . . . 15 10
1503 5 b. Doen Kala (walking on stones) 25 20
1504 6 b. Phong Phang (blind man's bluff) 30 20

504 Map, Surveyor and Cartographer

505 Princess (patron) wearing Red Cross Uniform

1991. Land Deeds Project.
1505 **504** 2 b. multicoloured . . . 15 10

1991. Red Cross Fair. Princess Maha Chaki Sirindhorn's "Third Cycle" Birthday.
1506 **505** 2 b. multicoloured . . . 15 10

506 "Indra's Heavenly Abode"

507 Goddess riding Goat

1991. Heritage Conservation Day. Floral Hanging Decorations. Multicoloured.
1508 2 b. Type **506** 15 10
1509 3 b. "Celestial Couch" . . . 15 10
1510 4 b. "Crystal Ladder" . . . 20 15
1511 5 b. "Crocodile" 25 20

1991. Songkran (New Year) Day. Year of the Goat.
1513 **507** 2 b. multicoloured . . . 1·25 35

508 Prince Narisranuvattivongs

1991. 44th Death Anniv of Prince Narisranuvattivongs.
1515 **508** 2 b. brown, deep brown and yellow 15 10

509 Pink Lotus (Sutthiporn Wiset) 511 Yok

510 World Map, Communication Systems and Healthy Tree

1991. Runners-up in International Correspondence Week Competition. Multicoloured.
1516 2 b. Type **509** 10 10
1517 3 b. Pink lotuses (Mathayom Suksa group, Khonkaen-vityayon School) 15 10
1518 5 b. White lotus (Rattanaporn Sukhasem) (horiz) 25 20
1519 6 b. Red lotuses (Phanupongs Sayasombat and Kanokwan Cholaphum) (horiz) 30 20

1991. National Communications Day. "Communications and Preservation of the Environment".
1520 **510** 2 b. multicoloured . . . 10 10

1991. "Thaipex '91" National Stamp Exhibition. Textile patterns. Multicoloured.
1521 2 b. Type **511** 10 10
1522 4 b. Mudmee 20 10
1523 6 b. Khit 30 15
1524 8 b. Chok 40 30

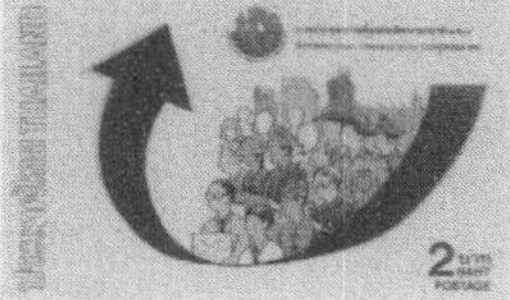

512 Workers and Productivity Arrow

1991. International Productivity Congress.
1526 **512** 2 b. multicoloured . . . 15 10

513 "Co-operation of Women around the World"

1991. 26th Int Council of Women Triennial.
1527 **513** 2 b. multicoloured . . . 15 10

514 Black

1991. International Correspondence Week. Japanese Bantams. Multicoloured.
1528 2 b. Type **514** 10 10
1529 3 b. Black-tailed buff . . . 20 10
1530 6 b. Buff 30 15
1531 8 b. White 40 30

515 Silver Coin of King Rama IV and Wat Phra Sri Rattana Satsadaram

1991. World Bank and International Monetary Fund Annual Meetings. Multicoloured.
1533 2 b. Type **515** 10 10
1534 4 b. Pod Duang money, Wat Mahathat Sukhothai and Wat Aroonrachawararam . . . 20 10
1535 8 b. Chieng and Hoi money and Wat Phrathat Doi Suthep 40 25
1536 10 b. Funan, Dvaravati and Srivijaya money, Phra Pathom Chedi and Phra Borommathat Chaiya . . 50 35

516 1908 1 t. Stamp 518 "Dillenia obovata"

517 Adult and Calves

1991. "Bangkok 1993" International Stamp Exhibition (1st series). Stamps from the 1908 King Chulalongkorn issue. Multicoloured.
1538 2 b. Type **516** 10 10
1539 3 b. 2 t. stamp 15 10
1540 4 b. 3 t. stamp 20 15
1541 5 b. 5 t. stamp 25 15
1542 6 b. 10 t. stamp 30 15
1543 7 b. 20 t. stamp 35 20
1544 8 b. 40 t. stamp 40 25
See also Nos. 1618/22, 1666/9 and 1700/3.

1991. The Indian Elephant. Multicoloured.
1546 2 b. Type **517** 10 10
1547 4 b. Elephants pulling log . 20 15
1548 6 b. Adult male resting . . . 30 15
1549 8 b. Adults bathing 40 25

1991. New Year. Flowers. Multicoloured.
1551 1 b. Type **518** 10 10
1552 1 b. "Melastoma sanguineum" 10 10
1553 1 b. "Commelina diffusa" . 10 10
1554 1 b. "Plumbago indica" . . 10 10

520 Jogging 522 Prince Mahidol

521 Large Indian Civet

1991. Sports Welfare Fund. Multicoloured.
1558 2 b.+1 b. Type **520** 15 15
1559 2 b.+1 b. Cycling 15 15
1560 2 b.+1 b. Skipping 15 15
1561 2 b.+1 b. Swimming 15 15

1991. Mammals. Multicoloured.
1562 2 b. Type **521** 10 10
1563 3 b. Banded linsang 15 10
1564 6 b. Asiatic golden cat . . 30 15
1565 8 b. Black giant squirrel . . 40 30

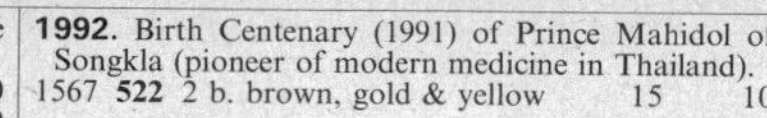

1992. Birth Centenary (1991) of Prince Mahidol of Songkla (pioneer of modern medicine in Thailand).
1567 **522** 2 b. brown, gold & yellow 15 10

523 Archaeologists and Dinosaur Skeletons

1992. Centenary of Department of Mineral Resources. Multicoloured.
1568 2 b. Type **523** 10 10
1569 2 b. Mining excavation . . . 10 10
1570 2 b. Extracting natural gas and oil 10 10
1571 2 b. Digging artesian wells . . 10 10

524 Drawing by Nachadong Bunprasoet

1992. Children's Day. "World under the Sea". Children's Drawings. Multicoloured.
1572 2 b. Type **524** 15 10
1573 3 b. Fishes and seaweed (Varaporn Phadkhan) . . . 15 10
1574 5 b. Mermaid (Phannipha Ngoenkon) (vert) 35 20

525 Battle Scene (mural, Chan Chittrakon)

1992. 400th Anniv of Duel between King Naresuan the Great of Thailand and Phra Maha Upparacha of Burma.
1575 **525** 2 b. multicoloured . . . 15 10

526 "Paphiopedilum bellatulum"

1992. 4th Asia-Pacific Orchid Conference. Multicoloured.
1576 2 b. Type **526** 10 10
1577 2 b. "Paphiopedilum exul" . . 10 10
1578 3 b. "Paphiopedilum godefroyae" 15 10
1579 3 b. "Paphiopedilum concolor" 15 10
1580 6 b. "Paphiopedilum niveum" 30 15
1581 6 b. "Paphiopedilum villosum" 30 15
1582 10 b. "Paphiopedilum parishii" 50 35
1583 10 b. "Paphiopedilum sukhahulii" 50 35

527 Sugar Cane 528 Prince Rabi Badhanasakdi (founder of School of Law)

1992. 21st International Sugar Cane Technologists Society Congress.
1585 **527** 2 b. multicoloured . . . 15 10

1992. Centenary of Ministry of Justice. Legal Reformers. Multicoloured.
1586 3 b. Type **528** 15 10
1587 5 b. King Rama V (reformer of Courts system) 25 15

529 "Innocent" (Kamolporn Tapsuang)

1992. Red Cross.
1588 **529** 2 b. multicoloured . . . 15 10

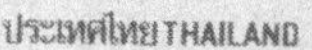

530 Container Ships and Lorry 531 Prince Damrong Rajanubharb (first Minister)

1992. 80th Anniv of Ministry of Transport and Communications. Multicoloured.
1589 2 b. Type **530** 10 10
1590 3 b. Train and bus 15 10
1591 5 b. Boeing 747-200 airliner and control tower 25 15
1592 6 b. Lorry, satellites and aerials 30 20

1992. Centenary of Ministry of the Interior. Multicoloured.
1593 2 b. Type **531** 10 10
1594 2 b. Polling station 10 10
1595 2 b. Emergency services and army 10 10
1596 2 b. Child fetching water . . 10 10

532 Royal Ceremony of First Ploughing

1992. Centenary of Ministry of Agriculture and Co-operatives.
1597 **532** 2 b. multicoloured . . . 10 10
1598 3 b. multicoloured . . . 15 10
1599 4 b. multicoloured . . . 20 15
1600 5 b. multicoloured . . . 25 20

533 Ministry

1992. Centenary of Ministry of Education.
1601 **533** 2 b. multicoloured . . . 10 10

534 Western Region

1992. Thai Heritage Conservation Day. Traditional Carts. Multicoloured.
1602 2 b. Type **534** 10 10
1603 3 b. Northern region 15 10
1604 5 b. North-eastern region . . 25 15
1605 10 b. Eastern region 50 35

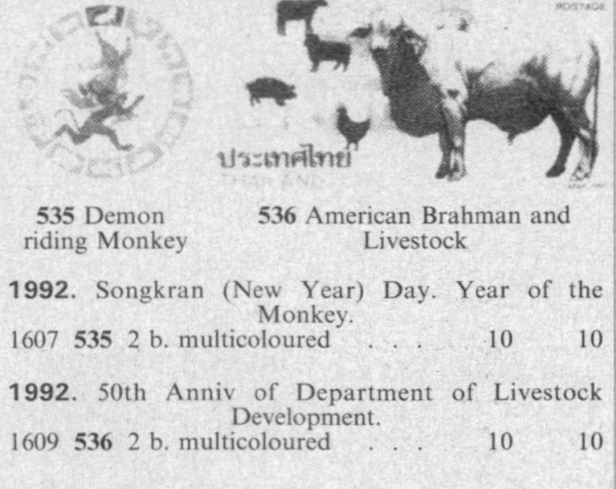

535 Demon riding Monkey — 536 American Brahman and Livestock

1992. Songkran (New Year) Day. Year of the Monkey.
1607 535 2 b. multicoloured . . . 10 10

1992. 50th Anniv of Department of Livestock Development.
1609 536 2 b. multicoloured . . . 10 10

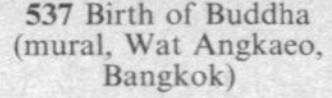

537 Birth of Buddha (mural, Wat Angkaeo, Bangkok) — 538 Weather Balloon, Dish Aerial, Satellite and Map

1992. Wisakhabucha Day. Multicoloured.
1610 2 b. Type 537 . . . . 10 10
1611 3 b. "Enlightenment of Buddha" (illustration by Phraya Thewaphinimmit from biography) 20 15
1612 5 b. Death of Buddha (mural, Wat Kanmatuyaram, Bangkok) 25 20

1992. 50th Anniv of Meteorological Department.
1613 538 2 b. multicoloured . . . 10 10

539 Bua Tong Field, Mae Hong Son Province — 540 1887 64 a. stamp

1992. Association of South-East Asian Nations Tourism Year. Multicoloured.
1614 2 b. Type 539 . . . . 10 10
1615 3 b. Klong Larn Waterfall, Kamphaeng Phet Province . . 15 10
1616 4 b. Coral, Chumphon Province . . 20 15
1617 5 b. Khao Ta-Poo, Phangnga Province 30 20

1992. "Bangkok 1993" International Stamp Exhibition (2nd series). Multicoloured.
1618 2 b. Type 540 . . . . 10 10
1619 3 b. 1916 20 b. stamp 15 10
1620 5 b. 1928 40 b. stamp 25 15
1621 7 b. 1943 1 b. stamp 35 20
1622 8 b. 1947 20 b. stamp 40 25

541 Prince Chudadhuj Dharadilok — 543 Culture and Sports

542 "Communications"

1992. Birth Centenary of Prince Chudadhuj Dharadilok of Bejraburna.
1624 541 2 b. multicoloured . . . 10 10

1992. National Communications Day.
1625 542 2 b. multicoloured . . . 10 10

1992. 25th Anniv of Association of South-East Asian Nations. Multicoloured.
1626 2 b. Type 543 . . . . 10 10
1627 3 b. Tourist sites 15 10
1628 5 b. Transport and communications 35 15
1629 7 b. Agriculture 35 20

544 Sirikit Medical Centre

1992. Inauguration of Sirikit Medical Centre.
1630 544 2 b. multicoloured . . . 10 10

545 Wedding Ceremony

546 Queen Sirikit and Cipher

1992. 60th Birthday of Queen Sirikit. (a) As T 545. Multicoloured.
1635 2 b. Type 545 . . . . 10 10
1636 2 b. Royal couple seated at Coronation ceremony . . 10 10
1637 2 b. Anointment as Queen . . 10 10
1638 2 b. Seated on chair 10 10
1639 2 b. Visiting hospital patient 10 10
1640 2 b. Talking to subjects . . 10 10

(b) Royal Regalia. Enamelled gold objects. As T 546. Multicoloured.
1642 2 b. Bowls on footed tray (betel and areca nut set) 10 10
1643 2 b. Kettle 10 10
1644 2 b. Water holder within bowl 10 10
1645 2 b. Box on footed tray (betel and areca nut set) 10 10
1646 2 b. Vase 10 10

(c) Type 546.
1647 100 b. blue and gold . . . . 5·00 5·00

547 Prince Wan Waithayakon — 548 Bhirasri

1992. Birth Centenary (1991) of Prince Wan Waithayakon (diplomat).
1648 547 2 b. multicoloured . . . 10 10

1992. Birth Centenary of Silpa Bhirasri (sculptor).
1649 548 2 b. multicoloured . . . 10 10

549 "Catalaphyllia jardinei"

1992. International Correspondence Week. Corals. Multicoloured.
1650 2 b. Type 549 . . . . 10 10
1651 3 b. "Porites lutea" 15 10
1652 6 b. "Tubastraea coccinea" . 30 20
1653 8 b. "Favia pallida" 40 30

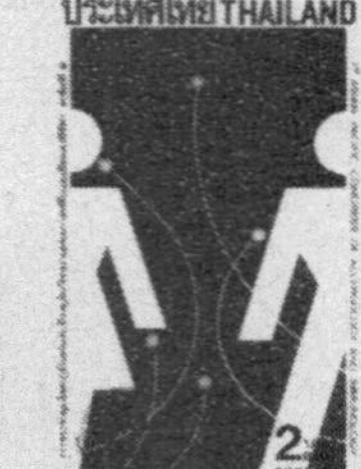

550 "Rhododendron simsii" — 551 Figures of Man and Woman

1992. New Year. Flowers. Multicoloured.
1655 1 b. Type 550 . . . . 10 10
1656 1 b. "Cynoglossum lanceolatum" 10 10
1657 1 b. "Tithonia diversifolia" . . 10 10
1658 1 b. "Agapetes parishii" . . . 10 10

1992. 1st Asian–Pacific Allergy and Immunology Congress, Bangkok.
1660 551 2 b. multicoloured . . . 10 10

552 Anantasamakhom Throne Hall, National Assembly Building and King Prajadhipok's Monument

1992. 60th Anniv of National Assembly.
1661 552 2 b. multicoloured . . . 10 10

553 Bank's Emblem and Bang Khun Phrom Palace (old headquarters)

1992. 50th Anniv of Bank of Thailand.
1662 553 2 b. multicoloured . . . 10 10

554 "River and Life" (Prathinthip Mensin)

1993. Children's Day. Drawings. Mult.
1663 2 b. Type 554 . . . . 15 10
1664 2 b. "Lovely Wild Animals and Beautiful Forest" (Pratsani Thammaprasert) 15 10
1665 2 b. "Communications in the Next Decade" (Natchaliya Sutiprasit) 15 10

555 Kendi, Water Dropper and Bottle

1993. "Bangkok 1993" International Stamp Exn (3rd series). Traditional Pottery. Multicoloured.
1666 3 b. Type 555 . . . . 15 10
1667 6 b. Vase and bottles 30 20
1668 7 b. Bowls 35 20
1669 8 b. Jars 40 25

556 Anniversary Emblem

1993. Centenary of Thai Teacher Training Institute.
1671 556 2 b. multicoloured . . . 10 10

557 Agricultural Produce

1993. 50th Anniv of Kasetsart University.
1672 557 2 b. multicoloured . . . 10 10

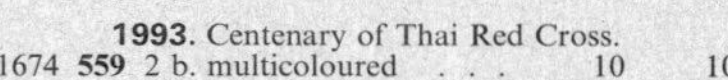

558 Buddha preaching (mural, Kanmatuyaram Temple, Bangkok) — 559 Queen Sri Bajarindra (first royal patron)

1993. Maghapuja Day.
1673 558 2 b. multicoloured . . . 10 10

1993. Centenary of Thai Red Cross.
1674 559 2 b. multicoloured . . . 10 10

560 Clock, Emblem and Attorney General

1993. Centenary of Attorney General's Office.
1675 560 2 b. multicoloured . . . 15 10

561 Wat Chedi Chet Thaeo

1993. Thai Heritage Conservation Day. Si Satchanalai Historical Park, Sukhothai Province. Multicoloured.
1676 3 b. Type 561 . . . . 15 10
1677 4 b. Wat Chang Lom 20 15
1678 6 b. Wat Phra Si Rattanamahathat 30 20
1679 7 b. Wat Suan Kaeo Utthayan Noi 40 20

562 Demon riding Cock

1993. Songkran (New Year) Day. Year of the Cock.
1681 562 2 b. multicoloured . . . 10 10

563 "Marasmius sp."

1993. Fungi. Multicoloured.
1683 2 b. Type 563 . . . . 10 10
1684 4 b. "Coprinus sp." 20 15
1685 6 b. "Mycena sp." 30 20
1686 8 b. "Cyathus sp." 40 25

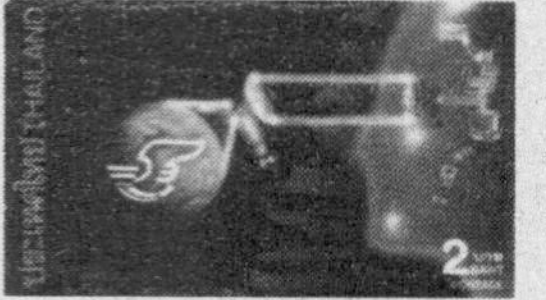

564 "Communications in the Next Decade"

1993. National Communications Day.
1688 564 2 b. multicoloured . . . 10 10

565 Emblem, Morse Key and Satellite

1993. 110th Anniv of Post and Telegraph Department.
1689 **565** 2 b. multicoloured . . . 10 10

566 Monument, Park and Reservoir

1993. Unveiling of Queen Suriyothai's Monument.
1690 **566** 2 b. multicoloured . . . 10 10

567 Fawn Ridgeback

1993. International Correspondence Week. The Thai Ridgeback. Multicoloured.
1691 2 b. Type **567** 10 10
1692 3 b. Black 15 10
1693 5 b. Tan 25 15
1694 10 b. Grey 50 30

568 Tangerine 569 Bencharong Cosmetic Jar

1993. Fruits. Multicoloured.
1696 2 b. Type **568** 10 10
1697 3 b. Bananas 15 10
1698 6 b. Star gooseberry 30 15
1699 8 b. Marian plum 40 25

1993. "Bangkok 1993" International Stamp Exhibition (4th issue). Multicoloured.
1700 3 b. Type **569** 15 10
1701 5 b. Bencharong round cosmetic jar 25 15
1702 6 b. Lai Nam Thong tall cosmetic jar 30 20
1703 7 b. Lai Nam Thong cosmetic jar 35 20

570 Emblem and Oil Rigs

1993. 5th Association of South East Asian Nations Council on Petroleum Conference and Exhibition.
1706 **570** 2 b. multicoloured . . . 10 10

571 King Prajadhipok 572 "Ipomea cairica"

1993. Birth Centenary of King Prajadhipok (Rama VII).
1707 **571** 2 b. brown and gold . . 15 10

1993. New Year. Flowers. Multicoloured.
1708 1 b. Type **572** 10 10
1709 1 b. "Decaschistia parviflora" . . 10 10
1710 1 b. "Hibiscus tiliaceus" . . . 10 10
1711 1 b. "Passiflora foetida" . . . 10 10

1993. No. 1031a surch **1 BAHT**.
1713 **227** 1 b. on 25 s. red 10 10

574 "Thaicom-1" Satellite, "Ariane 4" Rocket and Map of Thailand

1993. Launch of "Thaicom-1" (1st Thai communications satellite).
1714 **574** 2 b. multicoloured . . . 10 10

575 "Play Land" (Piyathida Chapirom)

1994. Children's Day.
1715 **575** 2 b. multicoloured . . . 10 10

576 Hospital Administrative Building

1994. Red Cross. 80th Anniv of Chulalongkorn Hospital.
1716 **576** 2 b. multicoloured . . . 10 10

577 Emblem and Book

1994. 60th Anniv of Royal Institute.
1717 **577** 2 b. multicoloured . . . 10 10

578 Wat Ratchaburana

1994. Thai Heritage Conservation Day. Phra Nakhon Si Ayutthaya Historical Park. Multicoloured.
1718 2 b. Type **578** 10 10
1719 3 b. Wat Maha That 15 10
1720 6 b. Wat Maheyong 30 20
1721 9 b. Wat Phra Si Sanphet . . 45 30

579 Friendship Bridge

1994. Inauguration of Friendship Bridge (between Thailand and Laos).
1723 **579** 9 b. multicoloured . . . 45 30

580 Demon riding Dog

1994. Songkran (New Year) Day. Year of the Dog.
1724 **580** 2 b. multicoloured . . . 10 10

582 Football

1994. Centenary of International Olympic Committee. Multicoloured.
1727 2 b. Type **582** 10 10
1728 3 b. Running 15 10
1729 5 b. Swimming 25 15
1730 6 b. Weightlifting 30 20
1731 9 b. Boxing 45 30

583 Dome Building

1994. 60th Anniv of Thammasat University.
1732 **583** 2 b. multicoloured . . . 10 10

584 "Buddha giving First Sermon" (mural from Wat Thong Thammachat)

1994. Asalhapuja Day.
1733 **584** 2 b. multicoloured . . . 10 10

585 Communications orbiting Thailand

1994. National Communications Day.
1734 **585** 2 b. multicoloured . . . 10 10

586 "Phricotelphusa limula"

1994. Crabs. Multicoloured.
1735 3 b. Type **586** 15 10
1736 5 b. "Thaipotamon chulabhorn" 25 15
1737 6 b. "Phricotelphusa sirindhorn" 30 20
1738 10 b. "Thaiphusa sirikit" . . 50 30

587 Gold Niello Betel Nut Set

1994. International Correspondence Week. Betel Nut Sets.
1740 2 b. Type **587** 10 10
1741 6 b. Gold-plated silver niello set 30 20
1742 8 b. Silver niello set 40 25
1743 9 b. Gold niello set 45 25

588 Emblem and Workers

1994. 75th Anniv of I.L.O.
1745 **588** 2 b. multicoloured . . . 10 10

589 "Eriocaulon odoratum"

1994. New Year. Flowers. Multicoloured.
1746 1 b. Type **589** 10 10
1747 1 b. "Utricularia bifida" . . 10 10
1748 1 b. "Utricularia delphinioides" 10 10
1749 1 b. "Utricularia minutissima" 10 10

590 Making Garland

1994. 60th Anniv of Suan Dusit Teachers' College.
1751 **590** 2 b. multicoloured . . . 10 10

591 Chakri Mahaprasart Throne Hall and Kings Chulalongkorn and Bhumibol

1994. 120th Anniv of Council of State.
1754 **591** 2 b. stone, blue and green 10 10

592 Emblem and Airplane

1994. 50th Anniv of I.C.A.O.
1755 **592** 2 b. multicoloured . . . 10 10

593 Dvaravati Grinding Stone (7–11th century)

1994. 80th Anniv of Pharmacy in Thailand.
1756 2 b. Type **593** 10 10
1757 6 b. Lopburi grinding stone (11–13th century) 30 20
1758 9 b. Bangkok period grinding stone (18–20th century) . . 45 30

OFFICIAL STAMPS

O 133 (Trans "For Government Service Statistical Research")

1963. No gum.
O495 **O 133** 10 s. red and pink . . 10 10
O496 20 s. red and green . 15 10
O500 20 s. green 25 20
O497 25 s. red and blue . . 25 25
O501 25 s. blue 25 25
O502 50 s. red 60 75
O498 1 b. red and silver . . 75 110
O503 1 b. silver 45 45
O499 2 b. red and bronze . 1·25 1·10
O504 2 b. bistre . . . . . 1·40 1·60

The above were used compulsorily by Government Departments between 1st October 1963 and 31st January 1964, to determine the amount of mail sent out by the different departments for the purpose of charging them in the future. They were postmarked in the usual way.

THESSALY Pt. 16

Special stamps issued during the Turkish occupation in the Graeco-Turkish War of 1898.

40 paras = 1 piastre

20

1898.

M162 **20** 10 pa. green . . . . . . 2·75 2·75
M163 20 pa. red . . . . . . 2·75 2·75
M164 1 pi. blue . . . . . . 2·75 2·75
M165 2 pi. orange . . . . . . 2·75 2·75
M166 5 pi. violet . . . . . . 2·75 2·75

THRACE Pt. 3

A portion of Greece to the N. of the Aegean Sea for which stamps were issued by the Allies in 1919 and by the Greek Government in 1920. Now uses Greek stamps.

1919. 100 stotinki = 1 leva
1920. 100 lepta = 1 drachma

1920. Stamps of Bulgaria optd **THRACE INTERALLIEE** in two lines.

28 **49** 1 s. black 10 15
29 2 s. grey 10 15
30 **50** 5 s. green 10 15
31 10 s. red 10 15
32 15 s. violet 15 15
33 – 25 s. black & blue (No. 165) . . 10 15
34 – 1 l. brown (No. 168) . . . . 65 1·00
35 – 2 l. brown (No. 191) . . . . 1·25 1·50
36 – 3 l. red (No. 192) . . . . 1·75 2·50

1920. Stamps of Bulgaria optd **THRACE INTERALLIEE** in one line.

40 **49** 1 s. black 30 45
41 2 s. grey 30 45
42 **50** 5 s. green 20 15
43 10 s. red 20 15
44 15 s. violet 35 35
45 – 25 s. black & blue (No. 165) . . 35 35

1920. Stamps of Bulgaria optd **THRACE Interalliee** in two lines vertically.

46 **50** 5 s. green 10 10
47 10 s. red 10 10
48 15 s. violet 10 10
49 50 s. brown 25 25

1920. Stamps of Bulgaria optd **THRACE OCCIDENTALE**.

50 **50** 5 s. green 10 10
51 10 s. red 10 10
52 15 s. violet 10 10
53 25 s. blue 10 10
54 30 s. brown (imperf) 15 15
55 50 s. brown 10 10

Διοίκησις
Δυτικῆς
Θράκης
(8)

1920. 1911 stamps of Greece optd with T **8**.

69 **29** 1 l. green 20 20
70 **30** 2 l. red 20 20
71 **29** 3 l. red 20 20
72 **31** 5 l. green 20 20
73 **29** 10 l. red 20 20
74 **30** 15 l. blue 20 20
75 25 l. blue 45 45
76 **31** 30 l. red . . . . . . 14·00 14·00
77 **30** 40 l. blue 90 90
78 **31** 50 l. purple . . . . . . 1·00 1·00
79 **32** 1 d. blue . . . . . . 5·50 5·50
80 2 d. red . . . . . . 12·00 12·00
65 3 d. red . . . . . . 32·00 32·00
66 5 d. blue . . . . . . 11·00 11·00
67 10 d. blue . . . . . . 7·00 7·00
68 – 25 d. blue (No. 212) . . . . 26·00 26·00

The opt on the 25 d. is in capital letters.

1920. 1916 stamps of Greece, with opt Greece T **38**, optd with T **8**.

81 **29** 1 l. green (No. 269) 20 20
82 **30** 2 l. red 20 20
83 **29** 10 l. red 25 25
84 **30** 20 l. purple 55 55
85 **31** 30 l. red 70 70
86 **32** 2 d. red . . . . . . 14·00 14·00
87 3 d. red . . . . . . 4·50 4·50
88 5 d. blue . . . . . . 17·00 17·00
89 10 d. blue . . . . . . 12·00 12·00

Διοίκησις
Θράκης
(10)

Ὑπάτη Ἀρμοστεία
Θράκης
5 Λεπτὰ 5
(11)

1920. Issue for E. Thrace. 1911 stamps of Greece optd with T **10**.

93 **29** 1 l. green 20 20
94 **30** 2 l. red 20 20
95 **29** 3 l. red 20 20
96 **31** 5 l. green 20 20
97 **29** 10 l. red 55 55
98 **30** 20 l. lilac 55 55
99 25 l. blue 80 80
100 40 l. blue . . . . . . 1·50 1·50
101 **31** 50 l. purple . . . . . . 1·75 1·75
102 **32** 1 d. blue . . . . . . 5·50 5·50
103 2 d. red . . . . . . 13·00 13·00
92 – 25 d. blue (No. 212) . . . . 40·00 40·00

1920. 1916 stamps of Greece with opt T **38** of Greece, optd with T **10**.

104 **30** 2 l. red (No. 270) 25 25
105 **31** 5 l. green . . . . . . 1·40 1·40
106 **30** 20 l. purple 50 50
107 **31** 30 l. red 50 50
108 **32** 3 d. red . . . . . . 5·00 5·00
109 5 d. blue . . . . . . 9·50 9·50
110 10 d. blue . . . . . . 19·00 19·00

1920. Occupation of Adrianople. Stamps of Turkey surch as T **11**.

111 **72** 1 l. on 5 pa. orange . . . 45 60
112 – 5 l. on 3 pi. blue (No. 965) . . 45 55
113 – 20 l. on 1 pi. grn (No. 964) . . 60 60
114 **69** 25 l. on 5 pi. on 2 pa. blue . . 70 70
115 **78** 50 l. on 5 pi. black & grn . . 2·25 2·25
116 **74** 1 d. on 20 pa. red . . . . 1·75 1·75
117 **30** 2 d. on 10 pa. on 2 pa. olive . 2·25 2·25
118 **85** 3 d. on 1 pi. blue . . . . 6·00 6·00
119 **31** 5 d. on 20 pa. red . . . . 7·50 7·50

POSTAGE DUE STAMPS

1919. Postage Due stamps of Bulgaria optd **THRACE INTERALLIEE**. Perf.

D37 **D 37** 5 s. green 15 15
D38 10 s. violet 25 25
D39 50 s. blue 40 50

1920. Postage Due stamps of Bulgaria optd **THRACE OCCIDENTALE**. Imperf or perf (10 s.).

D56 **D 37** 5 s. green 10 10
D57 10 s. violet 60 60
D58 20 s. orange 10 10
D59 50 s. blue 30 30

THURN AND TAXIS Pt. 7

The Counts of Thurn and Taxis had a postal monopoly in parts of Germany and issued special stamps.

N. District. 30 silbergroschen = 1 thaler
S. District. 60 kreuzer = 1 gulden

NORTHERN DISTRICT

1

1852. Imperf.

1 **1** $\frac{1}{4}$ s. black on brown . . . . £130 32·00
2 $\frac{1}{3}$ s. black on pink . . . . 50·00 £250
3 $\frac{1}{2}$ s. black on green . . . . £200 17·00
5 1 s. black on blue . . . . £350 50·00
8 2 s. black on rose . . . . £325 15·00
10 3 s. black on yellow . . . . £300 9·00

1859. Imperf.

12 **1** $\frac{1}{4}$ s. red . . . . . . 30·00 42·00
20 $\frac{1}{4}$ s. black . . . . . . 12·00 38·00
21 $\frac{1}{3}$ s. green . . . . . . 15·00 £300
13 $\frac{1}{2}$ s. green . . . . . . £150 55·00
23 $\frac{1}{2}$ s. orange . . . . . . 48·00 26·00
14 1 s. blue . . . . . . £150 17·00
25 1 s. red . . . . . . 30·00 13·00
15 2 s. red . . . . . . 80·00 42·00
27 2 s. blue . . . . . . 22·00 60·00
17 3 s. red . . . . . . 80·00 60·00
29 3 s. brown . . . . . . 10·00 27·00
18 5 s. mauve . . . . . . 1·00 £275
19 10 s. orange . . . . . . 1·00 £550

1865. Rouletted.

31 **1** $\frac{1}{4}$ s. black . . . . . . 8·50 £550
32 $\frac{1}{3}$ s. green . . . . . . 10·00 £300
33 $\frac{1}{2}$ s. yellow . . . . . . 20·00 32·00
34 1 s. red . . . . . . 22·00 16·00
35 2 s. blue . . . . . . 1·25 65·00
36 3 s. brown . . . . . . 1·75 28·00

SOUTHERN DISTRICT

3

1852. Imperf.

51 **3** 1 k. black on green . . . . 85·00 9·50
53 3 k. black on blue . . . . £375 22·00
57 6 k. black on red . . . . £400 16·00
58 9 k. black on yellow . . . . £325 8·50

1859. Imperf.

60 **3** 1 k. green . . . . . . 12·00 6·00
62 3 k. blue . . . . . . £300 12·00
68 3 k. red . . . . . . 27·00 10·00
63 6 k. red . . . . . . £300 38·00
70 6 k. blue . . . . . . 5·00 18·00
65 9 k. yellow . . . . . . £300 50·00
73 9 k. brown . . . . . . 5·00 18·00
66 15 k. purple . . . . . . 1·00 £150
67 30 k. orange . . . . . . 1·00 £425

1865. Roul.

74 **3** 1 k. green . . . . . . 11·00 12·00
81 3 k. red . . . . . . 1·00 17·00
76 6 k. blue . . . . . . 1·25 20·00
77 9 k. brown . . . . . . 1·25 23·00

TIBET Pt. 17

Former independent state in the Himalayas, now part of China.

A. CHINESE POST OFFICES

12 pies = 1 anna
16 annas = 1 Indian rupee

分 貳
One Anna
(C 1)

1911. Stamps of China of 1898 surch as Type C **1**.

C 1 **32** 3 p. on 1 c. buff . . . . 2·25 6·00
C 2 $\frac{1}{2}$ a. on 2 c. green . . . . 3·25 6·50
C 3 1 a. on 4 c. red . . . . 3·50 6·50
C 4 2 a. on 7 c. lake . . . . 3·50 8·00
C 5 $2\frac{1}{2}$ a. on 10 c. blue . . . . 3·50 8·00
C 6 **33** 3 a. on 16 c. olive . . . . 10·00 12·00
C 7 4 a. on 20 c. red . . . . 8·50 12·00
C 8 6 a. on 30 c. red . . . . 14·00 18·00
C 9 12 a. on 50 c. green . . . . 25·00 30·00
C10 **34** 1 r. on $1 red and salmon . . £150 £150
C11 2 r. on $2 red and yellow . . £500 £500

These stamps were used in Post Offices set up by the Chinese army sent to Tibet in 1910. Following a revolt by the Tibetans these troops were withdrawn during 1912.

B. INDEPENDENT STATE

$6\frac{2}{3}$ trangka = 1 sang

1 ($\frac{1}{6}$ t.) $\frac{1}{3}$ t. $\frac{1}{2}$ t. $\frac{2}{3}$ t. 1 t. 1 s.

1912. Imperf.

1 **1** $\frac{1}{6}$ t. green . . . . . . 10·00 15·00
2 $\frac{1}{3}$ t. blue . . . . . . 14·00 15·00
3 $\frac{1}{2}$ t. purple . . . . . . 15·00 15·00
4 $\frac{2}{3}$ t. red . . . . . . 19·00 18·00
5 1 t. red . . . . . . 22·00 40·00
6 1 s. green . . . . . . 45·00 45·00

2 (4 t.)

1914. Imperf.

7b **2** 4 t. blue £225 £225
8b 8 t. red £140 £140

In the 8 t. the rays from the circles in the corners of the stamp point outwards towards the corner.

3 (1 t.) Tibetan Lion

$\frac{1}{2}$ t. $\frac{2}{3}$ t. 2 t. 4 t.

1933. Perf or Imperf.

9a **3** $\frac{1}{2}$ t. yellow to orange . . . 8·50 15·00
10b $\frac{2}{3}$ t. blue . . . . . . 10·00 12·00
11a 1 t. red . . . . . . 8·00 8·50
11b 1 t. orange . . . . . . 8·00 9·00
12a 2 t. red . . . . . . 9·00 8·00
12c 2 t. orange . . . . . . 9·50 9·00
13d 4 t. green . . . . . . 8·50 5·50

TIERRA DEL FUEGO Pt. 20

An island at the extreme S. of S. America. Stamp issued for use on correspondence to the mainland. Currency is expressed in centigrammes of gold dust.

1 Gold-digger's Pick and Hammer

1891.

1 **1** 10 c. red . . . . . . 12·00

TIMOR Pt. 9

The eastern part of Timor in the Indonesian Archipelago. Administered as part of Macao until 1896, then as a separate Portuguese Overseas Province until 1975.

Following a civil war and the intervention of Indonesian forces the territory was incorporated into Indonesia on 17th July, 1976.

1885. 1000 reis = 1 milreis
1894 100 avos = 1 pataca
1960. 100 centavos = 1 escudo

1885. "Crown" key-type inscr "MACAU" optd **TIMOR**.

1 P 5 r. black 80 70
2 10 r. green . . . . . . 1·75 1·50
3 20 r. red . . . . . . 3·00 1·75
4 25 r. lilac 60 40
5 40 r. yellow . . . . . . 1·75 1·25
6 50 r. blue 80 50
7 80 r. grey . . . . . . 1·75 1·25
8 100 r. purple 60 60
19 200 r. orange . . . . . . 1·25 1·10
20 300 r. brown . . . . . . 1·25 1·10

1887. "Embossed" key-type inscr "CORREIO DE TIMOR".

21 Q 5 r. black . . . . . . 1·25 80
22 10 r. green . . . . . . 1·60 1·25
23 20 r. red . . . . . . 1·60 1·25
24 25 r. purple . . . . . . 2·50 1·50
25 40 r. brown . . . . . . 3·25 1·75
26 50 r. blue . . . . . . 3·25 1·75
27 80 r. grey . . . . . . 4·00 1·90
28 100 r. brown . . . . . . 3·75 2·10
29 200 r. lilac . . . . . . 6·50 5·00
30 300 r. orange . . . . . . 8·00 5·00

1892. "Embossed" key-type inscr "PROVINCIA DE MACAU" surch **TIMOR 30 30**. No gum.

32 Q 30 on 300 r. orange . . . 1·90 1·25

1894. "Figures" key-type inscr "TIMOR".

33 R 5 r. orange 60 45
34 10 r. mauve 75 60
35 15 r. brown 80 60
36 20 r. lilac 80 60
37 25 r. green 80 60
38 50 r. blue . . . . . . 1·90 1·50
39 75 r. red . . . . . . 2·25 1·90
40 80 r. green . . . . . . 2·25 1·90
41 100 r. brown on buff . . . 2·25 1·90
42 150 r. red on rose . . . 4·75 3·00
43 200 r. blue on blue . . . 4·75 3·75
44 300 r. blue on brown . . . 6·00 4·25

1894. "Embossed" key-type of Timor surch **PROVISORIO** and value in European and Chinese. No gum.

46 Q 1 a. on 5 r. black 45 35
47 2 a. on 10 r. green 60 50
48 3 a. on 20 r. red 80 60
49 4 a. on 25 r. purple 80 50
50 6 a. on 40 r. brown . . . . 1·75 1·00
51 8 a. on 50 r. blue . . . . 2·00 1·25
52 13 a. on 80 r. grey . . . . 2·50 3·00
53 16 a. on 100 r. brown . . . 3·50 3·00
54 31 a. on 200 r. lilac . . . 7·50 6·00
55 47 a. on 300 r. orange . . . 9·00 8·00

1895. No. 32 further surch **5 avos PROVISORIO** and Chinese characters with bars over the original surch.

56 Q 5 a. on 30 on 300 r. orange . . 2·00 1·75

1898. Vasco da Gama stamps of Portugal as T **40, 43** and **44**, but inscr "TIMOR" and value in local currency.

58 $\frac{1}{2}$ a. green 90 60
59 1 a. red 90 60
60 2 a. purple 70 40
61 4 a. green 70 40
62 8 a. blue . . . . . . 1·25 75
63 12 a. brown . . . . . . 1·00 75
64 16 a. brown . . . . . . 1·75 1·50
65 24 a. brown . . . . . . 2·00 1·00

1898. "King Carlos" key-type inscr "TIMOR". Name and value in red (78 a.) or black (others). With or without gum.

68 S $\frac{1}{2}$ a. grey 25 25
69 1 a. orange 25 25
70 2 a. green 25 25
71 $2\frac{1}{2}$ a. brown 70 60
72 3 a. lilac 70 60
112 3 a. green 90 75
73 4 a. green 70 60
113 5 a. red 90 75
114 6 a. brown 90 75
74 8 a. blue 70 60

No.	Type	Description	Unused	Used
115	S	9 a. brown	90	75
75		10 a. blue	70	60
116		10 a. brown	90	75
76		12 a. red	1·50	1·40
117		12 a. blue	4·50	3·75
118		13 a. purple	1·25	1·10
119		15 a. lilac	2·10	1·50
78		16 a. blue on blue	1·50	1·40
79		20 a. brown on yellow	1·50	1·40
120		22 a. brown on pink	2·10	1·90
80		24 a. brown on buff	1·50	1·40
81		31 a. purple on pink	1·50	1·40
121		31 a. brown on yellow	2·10	1·75
82		47 a. blue on pink	2·50	2·25
122		47 a. purple on pink	2·40	1·75
83		78 a. black on blue	3·25	2·25
123		78 a. blue on yellow	4·50	3·00

1899. "King Carlos" key-type of Timor surch **PROVISORIO** and value in figures and bars.

84	S	10 on 16 a. blue on blue	1·25	1·00
85		20 on 31 a. purple on pink	1·25	1·00

1902. Surch.

88	R	5 a. on 5 r. orange	60	50
86	Q	5 a. on 25 r. purple	80	70
89	R	5 a. on 25 r. green	60	50
90		5 a. on 50 r. blue	70	60
87	Q	5 a. on 200 r. lilac	1·25	90
95	V	6 a. on 2½ r. brown	40	30
92	Q	6 a. on 10 r. green	35·00	32·00
94	R	6 a. on 20 r. lilac	60	40
93	Q	6 a. on 300 r. orange	1·00	75
100	R	9 a. on 15 r. brown	70	55
98	Q	9 a. on 40 r. brown	1·00	80
101	R	9 a. on 75 r. red	70	55
99	Q	9 a. on 100 r. brown	1·00	80
124	S	10 a. on 12 a. blue	80	65
104	R	15 a. on 10 r. mauve	75	60
102	Q	15 a. on 20 r. red	1·50	1·00
103		15 a. on 50 r. blue	35·00	32·00
105	R	15 a. on 100 r. brn on buff	75	60
106		15 a. on 300 r. bl on brn	75	60
107	Q	22 a. on 80 r. green	3·00	2·75
108	R	22 a. on 80 r. green	1·50	1·25
109		22 a. on 200 r. blue on bl	1·50	1·25

1902. Nos. 72 and 76 optd **PROVISORIO**.

110	S	3 a. lilac	80	60
111		12 a. red	2·00	1·60

1911. Nos. 68, etc, optd **REPUBLICA**.

125	S	½ a. grey	20	15
126		1 a. orange	15	15
127		2 a. green	20	15
128		3 a. green	20	15
129		5 a. red	30	20
130		6 a. brown	30	20
131		9 a. brown	30	20
132		10 a. brown	30	20
133		13 a. purple	30	20
134		15 a. lilac	60	45
135		22 a. brown on pink	65	45
136		31 a. brown on yellow	65	50
163		31 a. purple on pink	1·00	85
137		47 a. purple on pink	1·25	90
165		47 a. blue on pink	1·40	1·25
167		78 a. blue on yelow	1·75	1·50
168		78 a. black on blue	1·50	1·25

1911. No. 112 and provisional of 1902 optd **Republica**.

139	S	3 a. green	80	75
140	R	5 a. on 5 r. orange	40	40
141		5 a. on 25 r. green	40	40
142		5 a. on 50 r. blue	1·00	1·00
144	V	6 a. on 2½ r. brown	90	70
146	R	6 a. on 20 r. lilac	60	40
147		9 a. on 15 r. brown	60	40
148	S	10 a. on 12 r. blue	60	40
149	R	15 a. on 100 r. brown on buff	80	65
150		22 a. on 80 r. green	1·25	90
151		22 a. on 200 r. blue on bl	1·25	90

1913. Provisional stamps of 1902 optd **REPUBLICA**.

192	S	3 a. lilac (No. 110)	15	15
194	R	5 a. on 5 r. orange	15	15
195		5 a. on 25 r. green	15	15
196		5 a. on 50 r. blue	15	15
200	V	6 a. on 2½ r. brown	15	15
201	R	6 a. on 20 r. lilac	25	20
202		9 a. on 15 r. brown	25	20
203		9 a. on 75 r. red	30	20
193	S	10 a. on 10 r. blue	25	20
204	R	15 a. on 10 r. mauve	30	20
205		15 a. on 100 r. brown on buff	30	20
206		15 a. on 300 r. bl on brn	30	20
207		22 a. on 80 r. green	85	60
151		22 a. on 200 r. blue on bl	1·25	90

1913. Vasco da Gama stamps of Timor optd **REPUBLICA** or surch also.

169		½ a. green	30	20
170		1 a. red	30	20
171		2 a. purple	30	20
172		4 a. green	30	20
173		8 a. blue	50	30
174		10 a. on 12 a. brown	80	70
175		16 a. brown	60	50
176		24 a. bistre	90	70

1914. "Ceres" key-type inscr "TIMOR". Name and value in black.

177	U	½ a. olive	20	20
178		1 a. black	20	20
213		1½ a. green	30	30
179		2 a. green	20	20
180		3 a. brown	35	30
181		4 a. red	35	30
182		6 a. violet	40	30
216		7 a. green	50	45
217		7½ a. blue	60	45
218		9 a. blue	80	50
183		10 a. blue	40	30
219		11 a. grey	90	85
184		12 a. brown	75	50
221		15 a. mauve	2·50	2·00
185		16 a. grey	75	50
222		18 a. blue	2·50	2·00
223	U	19 a. green	2·50	2·00
186		20 a. brown	5·50	2·00
224		36 a. blue	2·50	2·00
187		40 a. red	2·50	1·25
225		54 a. brown	2·50	2·00
188		58 a. brown on green	2·50	1·50
226		72 a. red	5·00	3·75
189		76 a. brown on red	2·75	2·25
190		1 p. orange on pink	5·00	3·75
191		3 p. green on blue	11·00	8·00
227		5 p. red	24·00	13·00

1920. No. 196 surch ½ **Avo P.P. n°. 68 19-3-1920** and bars.

229	R	½ a. on 5 a. on 50 r. blue	2·00	1·90

1932. "Ceres" key-type of Timor surch with new value and bars.

230	U	6 a. on 72 a. red	35	30
231		12 a. on 15 a. mauve	35	30

1935. As T **40** of Portuguese India ("Portugal" and San Gabriel), but inscr "TIMOR".

232	**40**	½ a. brown	15	15
233		1 a. sepia	15	15
234		2 a. green	15	15
235		3 a. mauve	15	15
236		4 a. black	20	15
237		5 a. grey	20	20
238		6 a. brown	20	20
239		7 a. red	20	20
240		8 a. blue	50	20
241		10 a. red	30	20
242		12 a. blue	30	20
243		14 a. olive	40	20
244		15 a. red	40	20
245		20 a. orange	40	20
246		30 a. green	40	20
247		40 a. violet	1·60	80
248		50 a. brown	1·60	80
249		1 p. blue	3·25	2·25
250		2 p. brown	8·50	3·75
251		3 p. green	11·50	4·00
252		5 p. mauve	19·00	8·00

1938. As T **54** and **56** of Macao. Name and value in black.

253	**54**	1 a. olive (postage)	15	15
254		2 a. brown	15	15
255		3 a. violet	15	15
256		4 a. green	15	15
257	–	5 a. red	15	15
258	–	6 a. slate	15	15
259	–	8 a. purple	15	15
260	–	10 a. mauve	15	15
261	–	12 a. red	20	15
262	–	15 a. orange	35	25
263	–	20 a. blue	35	25
264	–	40 a. black	60	35
265	–	50 a. brown	75	50
266	–	1 p. red	2·25	1·60
267	–	2 p. olive	5·00	1·60
268	–	3 p. blue	6·50	3·75
269	–	5 p. brown	17·00	7·00
270	**56**	1 a. red (air)	15	15
271		2 a. violet	15	15
272		3 a. orange	15	15
273		5 a. blue	15	15
274		10 a. red	40	30
275		20 a. green	80	60
276		50 a. brown	1·50	90
277		70 a. red	2·25	1·75
278		1 p. mauve	3·50	2·25

DESIGNS—POSTAGE: 5 a. to 8 a. Mousinho de Albuquerque; 10 a. to 15 a. Prince Henry the Navigator; 20 a. to 50 a. Dam; 1 p. to 5 p. Afonso de Albuquerque.

1946. Stamps as above but inscr "MOCAMBIQUE" surch **TIMOR** and new value.

279	**54**	1 a. on 15 c. purple (post)	2·00	1·50
280	–	4 a. on 35 c. green	2·00	1·50
281	–	8 a. on 50 c. mauve	2·00	1·50
282	–	10 a. on 70 c. violet	2·00	1·50
283	–	12 a. on 1 e. red	2·00	1·50
284	–	20 a. on 1 e. 75 blue	2·00	1·50
285	**56**	8 a. on 50 c. orange (air)	1·50	1·25
286		12 a. on 1 e. blue	1·50	1·25
287		40 a. on 3 e. green	1·50	1·25
288		50 a. on 5 e. brown	2·00	1·50
289		1 p. on 10 e. mauve	2·00	1·50

1947. Nos. 253/64 and 270/78 optd **"LIBERTACAO"**.

290	**22**	1 a. olive (postage)	6·00	3·75
291		2 a. brown	10·00	6·00
292		3 a. violet	4·00	2·25
293		4 a. green	4·00	2·25
294	–	5 a. red	1·75	70
295	–	8 a. purple	40	30
296	–	10 a. mauve	2·00	85
297	–	12 a. red	2·00	85
298	–	15 a. orange	2·00	85
299	–	20 a. blue	18·00	12·00
300	–	40 a. black	4·25	3·00
301	**27**	1 a. red (air)	5·50	2·50
302		2 a. violet	5·50	2·50
303		3 a. orange	5·50	2·50
304		5 a. blue	5·50	2·50
305		10 a. red	1·50	80
306		20 a. green	1·50	80
307		50 a. brown	1·50	80
308		70 a. red	5·50	2·10
309		1 p. mauve	2·75	80

30 Girl with Gong

31 Pottery-making

1948. Natives.

310	–	1 a. brown and green	25	20
311	**30**	3 a. brown and grey	80	40
312	–	4 a. green and pink	1·10	90
313	–	8 a. slate and red	60	20
314	–	10 a. green and orange	60	20
315	–	20 a. blue and light blue	60	30
316	–	1 p. blue and orange	9·00	1·75
317	–	3 p. brown and violet	12·00	4·00

DESIGNS: 1 a. Native woman; 4 a. Girl with baskets; 8 a. Chief of Aleixo de Ainaro; 10 a. Timor chief; 20 a. Warrior and horse; 1, 3 p. Tribal chieftains.

1948. Honouring the Statue of Our Lady of Fatima. As T **62** of Macao.

318		8 a. grey	1·75	1·75

1949. 75th Anniv of U.P.U. As T **64** of Macao.

319		16 a. brown	3·00	2·25

1950.

320	**31**	20 a. blue	40	30
321	–	50 a. brown (Young girl)	80	40

1950. Holy Year. As Nos. 425/6 of Macao.

322		40 a. green	50	50
323		70 a. brown	90	90

32 "Belamcanda chinensis"

34 Statue of The Virgin

1950.

324	**32**	1 a. red, green and grey	15	15
325	–	3 a. yellow, green & brown	1·40	60
326	–	10 a. red, green and blue	1·50	40
327	–	16 a. multicoloured	3·25	90
328	–	20 a. yellow, green & grey	1·50	50
329	–	30 a. yellow, green & blue	1·50	45
330	–	70 a. red, green & purple	2·00	90
331	–	1 p. red, yellow and green	3·50	1·25
332	–	2 p. green, yellow and red	5·50	3·50
333	–	5 p. pink, green and black	9·50	5·50

FLOWERS: 3 a. "Caesalpinia pulcherrima"; 10 a. "Calotropis gigantea"; 16 a. "Delonix regia"; 20 a. "Plumeria rubra"; 30 a. "Allamanda cathartica"; 70 a. "Haemanthus multiflorus"; 1 p. "Bauhinia"; 2 p. "Eurycles amboiniensis"; 5 p. "Crinum longiflorum".

1951. Termination of Holy Year. As T **69** of Macao.

334		86 a. blue	85	85

1952. 1st Tropical Medicine Congress, Lisbon. As T **46** of St. Thomas and Prince Islands.

335		10 a. brown and green	60	50

DESIGN: Nurse weighing baby.

1952. 400th Death Anniv of St. Francis Xavier. Designs as No. 452/4 of Macao.

336		1 a. black and grey	10	10
337		16 a. brown and buff	40	35
338		1 p. red and slate	1·50	75

1953. Missionary Art Exhibition.

339	**34**	3 a. brown and stone	10	10
340		16 a. brown and bistre	35	30
341		50 a. blue and stone	70	70

1954. Portuguese Stamp Cent. As T **75** of Macao.

342		10 a. multicoloured	35	30

1954. 400th Anniv of Sao Paulo. As T **76** of Macao.

343		16 a. multicoloured	35	30

35 Map of Timor

37 Elephant Jar

1956.

344	**35**	1 a. multicoloured	10	10
345		3 a. multicoloured	10	10
346		8 a. multicoloured	15	10
347		24 a. multicoloured	20	10
348		32 a. multicoloured	30	15
349		40 a. multicoloured	35	15
350		1 p. multicoloured	1·25	35
351		3 p. multicoloured	3·75	80

1958. 6th Int Congress of Tropical Medicine. As T **79** of Macao.

352		32 a. multicoloured	1·50	1·25

DESIGN: 32 a. "Calophyllum inophyllum" (plant).

1958. Brussels Int Exn. As T **78** of Macao.

353		40 a. multicoloured	30	20

1960. New currency. Nos. 344/51 surch thus: **$05** and bars.

354	**35**	5 c. on 1 a. multicoloured	10	10
355		10 c. on 3 a. multicoloured	10	10
356		20 c. on 8 a. multicoloured	10	10
357		30 c. on 24 a. multicoloured	10	10
358		50 c. on 32 s. multicoloured	10	10
359		1 e. on 40 c. multicoloured	15	10
360		2 e. on 40 c. multicoloured	20	10
361		5 e. on 1 p. multicoloured	40	15
362		10 e. on 3 p. multicoloured	1·50	50
363		15 e. on 3 p. multicoloured	1·50	65

1960. 500th Death Anniv of Prince Henry the Navigator. As T **55** of St. Thomas and Prince Islands.

364		4 e. 50 multicoloured	25	20

1962. Timor Art. Multicoloured.

365		5 c. Type **37**	10	10
366		10 c. House on stilts	10	10
367		20 c. Idol	10	10
368		30 c. Rosary	20	15
369		50 c. Model of outrigger canoe (horiz)	15	15
370		1 e. Casket	45	15
371		2 e. 50 Archer	30	15
372		4 e. Elephant	30	15
373		5 e. Native climbing palm tree	45	15
374		10 e. Statuette of woman	75	15
375		20 e. Model of cockfight (horiz)	1·75	65
376		50 e. House, bird and cat	4·00	1·40

1962. Sports. As T **82** of Macao. Multicoloured.

377		50 c. Game shooting	10	10
378		1 e. Horse-riding	30	15
379		1 e. 50 Swimming	35	25
380		2 e. Athletes	35	25
381		2 e. 50 Football	40	30
382		15 e. Big-game hunting	1·00	90

1962. Malaria Eradication. Mosquito design as T **83** of Macao. Multicoloured.

382		2 e. 50 "Anopheles sundaicus"	30	30

1964. Centenary of National Overseas Bank. As T **84** of Macao but portrait of M. P. Chagas.

384		2 e. 50 multicoloured	30	30

1965. I.T.U. Centenary. As T **85** of Macao.

385		1 e. 50 multicoloured	60	40

1966. 40th Anniv of National Revolution. As T **86** of Macao but showing different buildings. Multicoloured.

386		4 e. 50 Dr. V. Machado's College and Health Centre, Dili	50	35

1967. Centenary of Military Naval Assn. As T **88** of Macao. Multicoloured.

387		10 c. G. Coutinho and gunboat "Patria"	15	15
388		4 e. 50 S. Cabral and Fairey IIID seaplane "Lusitania"	95	65

39 Sepoy Officer, 1792

40 Pictorial Map of 1834, and Arms

1967. Portuguese Military Uniforms. Mult.

389		35 c. Type **39**	15	10
390		1 e. Infantry officer, 1815	70	15
391		1 e. 50 Infantryman 1879	15	10
392		2 e. Infantryman, 1890	15	10
393		2 e. 50 Infantry officer, 1903	20	10
394		3 e. Sapper, 1918	35	20
395		4 e. 50 Commando, 1964	75	20
396		10 e. Parachutist, 1964	85	70

1967. 50th Anniv of Fatima Apparitions. As T **89** of Macao.

397		3 e. Virgin of the Pilgrims	15	10

1968. 500th Birth Anniv of Pedro Cabral (explorer). As T **90** of Macao. Multicoloured.

398		4 e. 50 Lopo Homen-Reineis' map, 1519 (horiz)	40	25

1969. Birth Centenary of Admiral Gago Coutinho. As T **91** of Macao. Multicoloured.

399		4 e. 50 Frigate "Almirante Gago Coutinho" (horiz)	1·75	70

1969. Bicentenary of Dili (capital of Timor).

400	**40**	1 e. multicoloured	15	15

1969. 500th Anniv of Vasco da Gama (explorer). Multicoloured. As T **92** of Macao.

401		5 e. Convent Medallion	20	15

1969. Centenary of Overseas Administrative Reforms. As T **93** of Macao.

402		5 e. multicolured	15	15

1969. 500th Birth Anniv of King Manoel I. As T **95** of Macao. Multicoloured.

403		4 e. Emblem of Manoel I in Jeronimos Monastery	25	15

41 Map, Sir Ross Smith, and Arms of Britain, Timor and Australia

1969. 50th Anniv of 1st England–Australia Flight.
404 **41** 2 e. multicoloured 25 20

1970. Birth Centenary of Marshal Carmona. As T **96** of Macao.
414 1 e. Portrait in civilian dress . 10 10

1972. 400th Anniv of Camoens' "The Lusiads" (epic poem). As T **77** of St. Thomas and Prince Islands. Multicoloured.
415 1 e. Missionaries, natives and galleon 15 15

1972. Olympic Games, Munich. As T **78** of St. Thomas and Prince Islands. Multicoloured.
416 4 e. 50 Football 20 20

1972. 50th Anniv of 1st Flight, Lisbon–Rio de Janeiro. As T **79** of St. Thomas and Prince Islands. Multicoloured.
417 1 e. Aviators G. Coutinho and S. Cabral in Fairey IIID seaplane 30 20

1973. W.M.O. Centenary. As T **102** of Macao.
418 20 e. multicoloured 85 80

CHARITY TAX STAMPS

The notes under this heading in Portugal also apply here.

1919. "Ceres" key-type of Timor surch **2 AVOS TAXA DA GUERRA**. With or without gum.
C228 U 2 a. on ½ a. olive . . . 2·00 1·00

1919. No. 196 surch **2 TAXA DE GUERRA** and bars.
C230 R 2 on 5 a. on 50 r. blue . 28·00 16·00

1925. Marquis de Pombal Commem. Stamps of Portugal, but inscr "TIMOR".
C231 C **4** 2 a. red 20 20
C232 – 2 a. red 20 20
C233 C **5** 2 a. red 20 20

1934. Educational Tax. Fiscal stamps with values in black optd **Instrucao D.L.n.° 7 de 3-2-1934** or surch also. With or without gum.
C234 2 a. green . . . . 1·00 90
C235 5 a. green . . . . 2·00 1·25
C236 7 a. on ½ a. red . . . . . . 2·00 1·40

1936. Fiscal stamps with value in black optd **Assistencia D.L.n.°72**. With or without gum.
C253 10 a. red . . . . 1·40 1·10
C254 10 a. green . . . . 1·00 1·00

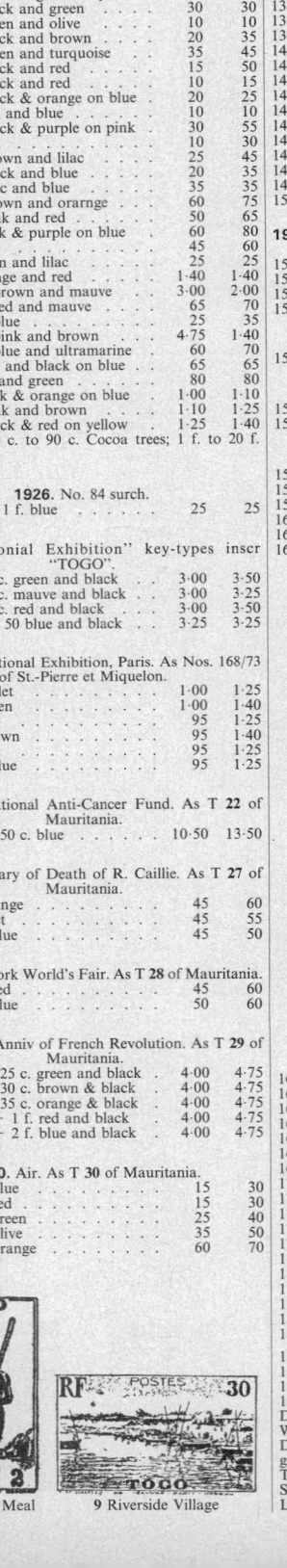

C 29 C 42 Woman and Star

1948. No gum.
C405 C **29** 10 a. blue 1.28 80
C311 20 a. green 1.50 1.00
The 20 a. has a different emblem.

1960. Similar design. New currency. No gum.
C366 70 c. blue 40 40
C367 1 e. 30 green 70 70

1969.
C405 C **42** 30 c. blue 10 10
C406 50 c. purple & orange . . 10 10
C407 1 e. brown & yellow . . . 15 15

1970. Nos. C366/7 surch **D.L. no.776** and value.
C408 30 c. on 70 c. blue . . . . 2·75 2·25
C409 30 c. on 1 e. 30 green . . . 2·75 2·25
C410 50 c. on 70 c. blue . . . . 4·50 2·50
C411 50 c. on 1 e. 30 green . . . 2·00 1·75
C412 1 e. on 70 c. blue . . . . 2·50 2·25
C413 1 e. on 1 e. 30 green . . . 2·00 1·75

NEWSPAPER STAMPS

1892. "Embossed" key-type inscr "PROVINCIA DE MACAU" surch **JORNAES TIMOR 2½ 2½**. No gum.
N31 Q 2½ on 20 r. red 75 40
N32 2½ on 40 r. brown 75 40
N33 2½ on 80 r. grey 75 40

1893. "Newspaper" key-type inscr "TIMOR".
N36 V 2½ r. brown 30 25

1894. No. N36 surch **½ avo PROVISORIO**.
N58 V ½ a. on 2½ r. brown 20 20

POSTAGE DUE STAMPS

1904. "Due" key-type inscr "TIMOR". Name and value in black with or without gum (1, 2 a.), no gum (others).
D124 W 1 a. green 20 20
D125 2 a. grey 20 20
D126 5 a. brown 45 40
D127 6 a. orange 45 40
D128 10 a. brown 50 45
D129 15 a. brown 90 85
D130 24 a. blue . . . . 2·25 1·50
D131 40 a. red . . . . 2·25 1·75
D132 50 a. orange . . . . 3·00 4·00
D133 1 p. lilac . . . . 5·00 4·00

1911. "Due" key-type of Timor optd **REPUBLICA**.
D139 W 1 a. green 15 15
D140 2 a. grey 15 15
D141 5 a. brown 15 15
D142 6 a. orange 20 20
D143 10 a. brown 30 25
D144 15 a. brown 40 30
D145 24 a. blue 80 70
D146 40 a. red . . . . 1·00 90
D147 50 a. orange . . . . 1·25 90
D148 1 p. lilac . . . . 3·50 2·25

1925. Marquis de Pombal tax stamps, as Nos. C231/3 of Timor, optd **MULTA**.
D231 C **73** 4 a. red 20 20
D232 – 4 a. red 20 20
D233 C **75** 4 a. red 20 20

1952. As Type D **70** of Macao, but inscr "TIMOR PORTUGUES". Numerals in red; name in black.
D336 1 a. sepia and brown . . . 10 10
D337 3 a. brown and orange . . 10 10
D338 5 a. green and turquoise . . 10 10
D339 10 a. green and light green . 10 10
D340 30 a. violet & light violet . 20 15
D341 1 p. red and orange 40 30

TOGO Pt. 7; Pt. 6; Pt. 14

A territory in W. Africa, formerly a German Colony. Divided between France and Gt. Britain in 1919, the British portion being attached to the Gold Coast for administration and using the stamps of that country. In 1956 the French portion became an autonomous republic within the French Union. Full independence was achieved in April 1960.

GERMAN ISSUES

100 pfenning = 1 mark

1897. Stamps of Germany optd **TOGO**.
G1a **8** 3 pf. brown . . . . . . 3·75 6·50
G2 5 pf. green . . . . . . 3·50 2·25
G3 **9** 10 pf. red . . . . . . 3·50 2·25
G4 20 pf. blue . . . . . . 4·50 12·00
G5 25 pf. orange . . . . . 32·00 60·00
G6 50 pf. brown . . . . . 32·00 60·00

1900. "Yacht" key-types inscr "TOGO".
G 7 N 3 pf. brown 65 75
G21 5 pf. green . . . . . . 1·00 1·60
G 9 10 pf. red . . . . . . 35·00 55
G10 20 pf. blue . . . . . . 85 1·25
G11 25 pf. blk & red on buff 85 1·25
G12 30 pf. blk & orge on buff 1·25 10·00
G13 40 pf. black and red . . 85 10·00
G14 50 pf. black and purple on buff . . . . 1·25 8·50
G15 80 pf. black & red on rose 2·00 22·00
G16 O 1 m. red . . . . 2·75 55·00
G17 2 m. blue . . . . 4·25 85·00
G18 3 m. black . . . . . . 6·00 £150
G19 5 m. red and black . . £100 £475

FRENCH OCCUPATION

1914. Stamps of German Colonies, "Yacht" key-type, optd **Togo Occupation franco-anglaise** or surch also.
1 N 05 on 3 pf. brown . . . 35·00 35·00
9 5 pf. green £750 £325
2 10 on 5 pf. green . . . . 14·00 12·50
10 10 pf. red £875 £350
3 20 pf. blue . . . . 35·00 35·00
4 25 pf. black & red on yell 38·00 35·00
5 30 pf. blk & orge on orge 65·00 60·00
6 40 pf. black and red . . £450 £400
15 50 pf. black & pur on buff £7500 £6500
7 80 pf. black & red on pink £450 £400
16 O 1 m. red . . . . — £14000
17 2 m. blue . . . . — £14000
18 3 m. black . . . . . . — £14000
19 5 m. red and black

1916. Stamps of Dahomey optd **TOGO Occupation franco-anglaise**.
20 **6** 1 c. black and violet 15 30
21 2 c. pink and brown 20 25
22 4 c. brown and black 20 25
23 5 c. green and light green . . 40 45
24 10 c. pink and orange 30 30
25 15 c. purple and red 60 60
26 20 c. brown and grey 45 45
27 25 c. blue and ultramarine . . 45 45
28 30 c. violet and brown . . . 45 70
29 35 c. black and brown . . . 60 90
30 40 c. orange and black . . . 55 80
31 45 c. blue and grey 45 65
32 50 c. brown and chocolate . . 45 60
33 75 c. violet and blue . . . . 3·25 4·00
34 1 f. black and green . . . . 4·50 5·00
35 2 f. brown and yellow . . . 6·00 6·75
36 5 f. blue and violet . . . . 7·25 5·50

FRENCH MANDATE

1921. Stamps of Dahomey optd **TOGO**.
37 **6** 1 c. green and grey 10 30
38 2 c. orange and blue 10 20
39 4 c. orange and green . . . 20 30
40 5 c. black and red 20 30
41 10 c. green and turquoise . . 10 30
42 15 c. red and brown 40 60
43 20 c. orange and green . . . 55 60
44 25 c. orange and grey . . . 35 35
45 30 c. red and carmine . . . 40 60
46 35 c. green and purple . . . 55 75
47 40 c. grey and green . . . . 90 1·25
48 45 c. grey and purple . . . 90 1·25
49 50 c. blue 45 50
50 75 c. blue and brown . . . . 95 1·25
51 1 f. blue and grey . . . . . 1·10 1·25
52 2 f. red and green . . . . . 3·25 3·50
53 5 f. black and yellow . . . 4·75 4·75

1922. Stamps of 1921 (No. 57 colour changed) surch.
54 **6** 25 c. on 15 c. red and brown . 20 25
55 25 c. on 2 f. red and green . . 25 40
56 25 c. on 5 f. black & orange . 25 40
57 60 on 75 c. violet on pink . . 55 75
58 65 on 45 c. grey and purple . 80 1·00
59 85 on 75 c. blue and brown . . 95 1·25

5 Coconut Palms

1924.
60 **5** 1 c. black and yellow 10 15
61 2 c. black and red 10 20
62 4 c. black and blue 10 25
63 5 c. black and orange . . . 10 10
64 10 c. black and mauve . . . 10 10
65 15 c. black and green . . . 10 10
66 – 20 c. black and grey 10 10
67 – 25 c. black & green on yellow 10 10
68 – 30 c. black and green . . . 30 30
69 – 30 c. green and olive . . . 10 10
70 – 35 c. black and brown . . . 20 35
71 – 35 c. green and turquoise . . 35 45
72 – 40 c. black and red 15 50
73 – 45 c. black and red 10 15
74 – 50 c. black & orange on blue . 20 25
75 – 55 c. red and blue 10 10
76 – 60 c. black & purple on pink . 30 55
77 – 60 c. red 10 30
78 – 65 c. brown and lilac . . . 25 45
79 – 75 c. black and blue 20 35
80 – 80 c. lilac and blue 35 35
81 – 85 c. brown and orarnge . . . 60 75
82 – 90 c. pink and red 50 65
83 – 1 f. black & purple on blue . 60 80
84 – 1 f. blue 45 60
85 – 1 f. green and lilac 25 25
86 – 1 f. orange and red . . . . 1·40 1·40
87 – 1 f. 10 brown and mauve . . 3·00 2·00
88 – 1 f. 25 red and mauve . . . 65 70
89 – 1 f. 50 blue 25 35
90 – 1 f. 75 pink and brown . . . 4·75 1·40
91 – 1 f. 75 blue and ultramarine . 60 70
92 – 2 f. grey and black on blue . 65 65
93 – 3 f. red and green 80 80
94 – 5 f. black & orange on blue . 1·00 1·10
95 – 10 f. pink and brown . . . . 1·10 1·25
96 – 20 f. black & red on yellow . 1·25 1·40
DESIGNS: 20 c. to 90 c. Cocoa trees; 1 f. to 20 f. Palm trees.

1926. No. 84 surch.
98 1 f. 25 on 1 f. blue 25 25

1931. "Colonial Exhibition" key-types inscr "TOGO".
99 E 40 c. green and black . . 3·00 3·50
100 F 50 c. mauve and black . . 3·00 3·25
101 G 90 c. red and black . . . 3·00 3·50
102 H 1 f. 50 blue and black . . 3·25 3·25

1937. International Exhibition, Paris. As Nos. 168/73 of St.-Pierre et Miquelon.
103 20 c. violet . . . . 1·00 1·25
104 30 c. green . . . . 1·00 1·40
105 40 c. red . . . . 95 1·25
106 50 c. brown . . . . 95 1·40
107 90 c. red . . . . 95 1·25
108 1 f. 50 blue . . . . 95 1·25

1938. International Anti-Cancer Fund. As T **22** of Mauritania.
109 1 f. 75+50 c. blue . . . . . . 10·50 13·50

1939. Centenary of Death of R. Caillie. As T **27** of Mauritania.
110 90 c. orange 45 60
111 2 f. violet 45 55
112 2 f. 25 blue 45 50

1939. New York World's Fair. As T **28** of Mauritania.
113 1 f. 25 red 45 60
114 2 f. 25 blue 50 60

1939. 150th Anniv of French Revolution. As T **29** of Mauritania.
115 45 c. + 25 c. green and black . 4·00 4·75
116 70 c. + 30 c. brown & black . 4·00 4·75
117 90 c. + 35 c. orange & black . 4·00 4·75
118 1 f. 25 + 1 f. red and black . 4·00 4·75
119 2 f. 25 + 2 f. blue and black . 4·00 4·75

1940. Air. As T **30** of Mauritania.
120 1 f. 90 blue 15 30
121 2 f. 90 red 15 30
122 4 f. 50 green 25 40
123 4 f. 90 olive 35 50
124 6 f. 90 orange 60 70

8 Pounding Meal

9 Riverside Village

10 Hunting

11 Young Girl

1940.
125 **8** 2 c. violet 10 30
126 3 c. green 10 30
127 4 c. black 10 25
128 5 c. red 10 25
129 10 c. blue 10 25
130 15 c. brown 10 30
131 **9** 20 c. plum 10 25
132 25 c. blue 10 20
133 30 c. black 15 20
134 40 c. red 20 30
135 45 c. green 10 30
136 50 c. brown 20 40
137 60 c. violet 25 30
138 **10** 70 c. black 40 55
139 90 c. violet 65 85
140 1 f. green 25 45
141 1 f. 25 red 60 85
142 1 f. 40 brown 30 55
143 1 f. 60 orange 40 55
144 2 f. blue 40 65
145 **11** 2 f. 25 blue 70 90
146 2 f. 50 red 65 75
147 3 f. violet 50 75
148 5 f. red 60 60
149 10 f. violet 80 95
150 20 f. black . . . . 1·50 10

1941. National Defence Fund. Surch **SECOURS NATIONAL** and value.
151 + 1 f. on 50 c. (No. 136) . . 2·00 2·00
152 + 2 f. on 80 c. (No. 80) . . 2·75 3·00
153 + 2 f. on 1 f. 50 (No. 89) . . 2·75 3·00
154 + 3 f. on 2 f. (No. 144) . . . 3·00 3·00

1942. Air. As T **32** of Mauritania.
154a 50 f. violet and yellow . . . 70 80

1944. Nos. 75 and 82 surch **1 f. 50**.
155 1 f. 50 on 55 c. red and blue . 45 60
156 1 f. 50 on 90 c. pink and red . 45 60

1944. No. 139 surch in figures and ornament.
157 **10** 3 f. 50 on 90 c. violet . . . 45 60
158 4 f. on 90 c. violet . . . 45 60
159 5 f. on 90 c. violet . . . 70 90
160 5 f. 50 on 90 c. violet . . . 90 1·10
161 10 f. on 90 c. violet . . . 90 1·10
162 20 f. on 90 c. violet . . . . 1·40 1·60

18 Oil Extraction Process

19 Archer

20 Postal Runner and Lockheed Constellation

1947.
163 **18** 10 c. red (postage) 15 25
164 30 c. blue 15 30
165 50 c. green 15 30
166 **19** 60 c. pink 15 30
167 1 f. brown 20 20
168 1 f. 20 green 20 40
169 – 1 f. 50 orange 35 60
170 – 2 f. bistre 35 35
171 – 2 f. 50 black . . . . 80 1·00
172 – 3 f. blue 40 65
173 – 3 f. 60 red 60 75
174 – 4 f. blue 40 45
175 – 5 f. brown . . . . 1·00 60
176 – 6 f. blue . . . . 1·00 1·25
177 – 10 f. red . . . . 1·25 40
178 – 15 f. green . . . . 1·40 50
179 – 20 f. green . . . . 1·25 70
180 – 25 f. pink . . . . 1·40 60
181 – 40 f. blue (air) . . . . . . 4·00 2·50
182 – 50 f. mauve and violet . . . 1·90 1·10
183 – 100 f. brown and green . . . 3·00 2·00
184 **20** 200 f. pink . . . . 5·00 4·00
DESIGNS—As Type **18**: VERT: 1 f. 50, to 2 f. 50, Women hand-spinning cotton. HORIZ: 3 f. to 4 f. Drummer and village; 5 f. to 10 f. Red-fronted gazelles; 15 f. to 25 f. Trees and village. As Type **20**: 40 f. African elephants and Sud Ouest SO.95 Corse II airplane; 50 f. Airplane; 100 f. Lockheed Constellation.

1949. Air. 75th Anniv of U.P.U. As T **38** of New Caledonia.
185 25 f. multicoloured . . . . . 3·25 4·00

1950. Colonial Welfare Fund. As T **39** of New Caledonia.
186 10 f. +2 f. blue and indigo . . 2·00 2·25

1952. Centenary of Military Medal. As T **40** of New Caledonia.
187 15 f. brown, yellow & green . 3·00 3·25

1954. Air. 10th Anniv of Liberation. As T **42** of New Caledonia.
188 15 f. violet and blue . . . . . 2·50 2·75

22 Gathering Palm Nuts **23** Roadway through Forest

1954.
189 **22** 8 f. purple, lake and violet (postage) 70 60
190 15 f. brown, grey & blue . 95 40
191 **23** 500 f. blue & green (air) . . 35·00 28·00

AUTONOMOUS REPUBLIC

24 Goliath Beetle **25** Rural School

1955. Nature Protection.
192 **24** 8 f. black and green . . . . 1·90 1·10

1956 Economic and Social Fund Development Fund.
193 **25** 15 f. brown and chestnut . 3·00 1·40

26 Togolese Woman and Flag

1957. New National Flag.
194 **26** 15 f. brown, red & turquoise 60 30

27 Togolese Woman and "Liberty" releasing Dove

1957. Air. 1st Anniv of Autonomous Republic.
195 **27** 25 f. sepia, red and blue . . 55 45

28 Konkomba Helmet **29** Kob

30 Torch and Flags

1957. Inscr "REPUBLIQUE AUTONOME DU TOGO".
196 **28** 30 c. lilac and red (postage) 10 25
197 50 c. indigo and blue . . . 10 25
198 1 f. lilac and purple . . . 10 25
199 2 f. brown and green . . . 10 25
200 3 f. black and green . . . 15 25
201 **29** 4 f. black and blue 55 30
202 5 f. purple and grey . . . 55 30
203 6 f. grey and red 70 35
204 8 f. violet and grey 70 35
205 10 f. brown and green . . . 70 35
206 – 15 f. multicoloured 45 30
207 – 20 f. multicoloured 50 30
208 – 25 f. multicoloured 70 35
209 – 40 f. multicoloured . . . . 1·10 50
210 **30** 50 f. multicoloured (air) . 1·10 50
211 100 f. multicoloured . . . 2·00 1·10
212 200 f. multicoloured . . . 3·75 1·90
213 – 500 f. indigo, green & blue 27·00 11·00
DESIGNS—HORIZ: 15 f. to 40 f. Teak forest; 48 × 27 mm: 500 f. Great egret.
See also Nos. 217/35.

31 "Human Rights" **32** "Bombax"

1958. 10th Anniv of Human Rights Declaration.
214 **31** 20 f. red and green 65 35

1959. Tropical Flora.
215 **32** 5 f. multicoloured 40 30
216 – 20 f. yellow, green & blk . 75 35
DESIGN—HORIZ: 20 f. "Tectona".

1959. As Nos. 196/213 but colours changed and inscr "REPUBLIQUE DU TOGO".
217 **28** 30 c. blue & black (post) 10 25
218 50 c. green and green . . 20 25
219 1 f. purple and green . . 20 10
220 2 f. brown and green . . 20 10
221 3 f. violet and purple . . 20 25
222 **29** 4 f. violet and purple . . 45 30
223 5 f. brown and green . . 45 30
224 6 f. blue and ultramarine 45 40
225 8 f. bistre and green . . . 45 35
226 10 f. brown and violet . . 45 30
227 – 15 f. multicoloured . . . 50 30
228 – 20 f. multicoloured . . . 60 50
229 – 25 f. multicoloured . . . 80 45
230 – 40 f. multicoloured . . . 1·00 45
231 – 25 f. brown, green and blue (air) 45 30
232 **30** 50 f. multicoloured . . . 90 45
233 100 f. multicoloured . . . 1·90 85
235 – 500 f. sepia, green & purple 4·25 1·75
DESIGN—VERT: 25 f. (No. 231) Togo flag and shadow of airliner over Africa.

32a Patient on Stretcher **33** "The Five Continents"

1959. Red Cross Commemoration.
236 **32a** 20 f. +5 f. red, orange and slate 80 80
237 – 30 f. +5 f. red, brown and blue 80 80
238 – 50 f. +10 f. red, brown and green 80 80
DESIGNS: 30 f. Mother feeding child; 50 f. Nurse superintending blood transfusion.

1959. United Nations Day.
239 **33** 15 f. blue and brown . . . 30 30
240 20 f. blue and violet . . . 35 30
241 25 f. blue and brown . . . 45 35
242 40 f. blue and green . . . 55 45
243 60 f. blue and red 75 50

34 Skiing **35** "Uprooted Tree"

1960. Olympic Games, California and Rome.
244 **34** 30 c. turquoise, red & green 15 25
245 – 50 c. purple, red and black . 35 30
246 – 1 f. green, red and black . . 35 30
247 – 10 f. brown, blue & indigo . 40 10
248 – 15 f. purple and green . . . 45 40
249 – 20 f. chocolate, green & brn 55 40
250 – 25 f. brown, red & orange . 85 45
DESIGNS—HORIZ: 50 c. Ice hockey; 1 f. Tobogganing; 10 f. Cycling; 25 f. Running. VERT: 125 f. Throwing the discus; 20 f. Boxing.

1960. World Refugee Year.
251 **35** 25 f. +5 f. green, brown and blue 55 75
252 – 45 f. +5 f. olive, black and blue 75 75
DESIGN: 45 f. As Type **35** but "TOGO" at foot.

INDEPENDENT REPUBLIC

36 Prime Minister S. Olympio and Flag **37** Benin Hotel

1960. Independence Commemoration. (a) Postage. Centres mult; backgrounds cream; inscription and frame colours given.
253 **36** 30 c. sepia 10 10
254 50 c. brown 10 10
255 1 f. purple 10 10
256 10 f. blue 15 10
257 20 f. red 40 15
258 25 f. green 50 20

(b) Air.
259 **37** 100 f. red, yellow & green . 1·60 50
260 200 f. multicoloured . . . . 2·75 90
261 – 500 f. brown and green . . 10·00 2·75
DESIGN—As Type **37**: VERT: 500 f. Palm-nut vulture and map of Togo.

38 Union Jack and Flags

1960. Four-Power "Summit" Conf, Paris. Flags and inscr in red and blue.
262 **38** 50 c. buff 10 10
263 – 1 f. turquoise 10 10
264 – 20 f. grey 35 20
265 – 25 f. blue 40 20
DESIGNS—As Type **38** but flags of: 1 f. Soviet Union; 20 f. France; 25 f. U.S.A. The Conference did not take place.

39 Togo Flag **40** South African Crowned Cranes

1961. Admission of Togo into U.N.O. Flag in red, yellow and green.
266 **39** 30 c. red 10 10
267 50 c. brown 10 10
268 1 f. blue 10 10
269 10 f. purple 20 10
270 25 f. black 40 15
271 30 f. violet 45 20

1961.
272 **40** 1 f. multicoloured 50 10
273 10 f. multicoloured 70 15
274 25 f. multicoloured . . . . 1·10 40
275 30 f. multicoloured . . . . 1·25 50

41 Augustino de Souza (statesman) **42** Daniel Beard (founder of American Boy Scout Movement) and Scout Badge

1961. 1st Anniv of Independence.
276 **41** 50 c. black, red and yellow . 10 10
277 1 f. black, brown and green 10 10
278 10 f. black, violet and blue . 20 15
279 25 f. black, green & salmon 40 10
280 30 f. black, blue and mauve 50 20

1961. Boy Scout Movement Commemoration.
281 **42** 50 c. lake, green and red . 10 10
282 – 1 f. violet and red 10 10
283 – 10 f. black and brown . . 20 10
284 – 25 f. multicoloured 55 15
285 – 30 f. red, brown & green . 65 20
286 – 100 f. mauve and blue . . 1·60 60
DESIGNS—HORIZ: 1 f. Lord Baden Powell; 10 f. Daniel Mensah ("Rover" Scout Chief); 100 f. Scout salute. VERT: 25 f. Chief Daniel Wilson (Togolese Scout); 30 f. Campfire on triangular emblem.

43 Jet Airliner and Motor Launch **44** U.N.I.C.E.F. Emblem

1961. U.N. Economic Commission on Africa. Multicoloured.
287 20 f. Type **43** 30 15
288 25 f. Electric train and gantry 70 15
289 30 f. Excavator and pylons . . 65 30
290 85 f. Microscope and atomic symbol . . . . 1·25 50
The designs are superimposed on a map of Africa spread over the four stamps when the 30 and 85 f. are mounted below the 20 and 25 f.

1961. 15th Anniv of U.N.I.C.E.F.
291 **44** 1 f. blue, green and black . 10 10
292 – 10 f. multicoloured 15 10
293 – 20 f. multicoloured 20 10
294 – 25 f. multicoloured 45 20
295 – 30 f. multicoloured 80 20
296 – 85 f. multicoloured . . . . 1·25 60
DESIGNS: 10 f. to 85 f. Children dancing round the globe. The six stamps, arranged in the following order, form a composite picture: Upper row, 1, 25 and 20 f. Lower row, 10, 85 and 30 f.

45 Alan Shepard **47** Togolese Girl

1962. Space Flights Commemoration.
297 **45** 50 c. green 10 10
298 – 1 f. mauve 15 10
299 **45** 25 f. blue 35 20
300 – 30 f. violet 50 30
DESIGN: 1, 30 f. As Type **45** but portrait of Yuri Gagarin.

1962. Col. Glenn's Space Flight. Surch **100 F COL. JOHN H. GLENN U S A VOL ORBITAL 20 FEVRIER 1962.**
301 **45** 100 f. on 50 c. green . . . 2·00 2·00

1962. 2nd Anniv of Independence.
303 – 50 c. multicoloured 10 10
304 **47** 1 f. green and pink 10 10
305 – 5 f. multicoloured 20 15
306 **47** 20 f. violet and yellow . . 30 15
307 – 25 f. multicoloured 35 15
308 **47** 30 f. red and yellow . . . 35 15
DESIGN: 50 c., 5, 25 f. Independence Monument.

48 Arrows piercing Mosquito

1962. Malaria Eradication.
309 **48** 10 f. multicoloured 30 10
310 25 f. multicoloured 45 20
311 30 f. multicoloured 50 35
312 85 f. multicoloured . . . . 1·00 55

49 Presidents Kennedy and Olympio, and Capitol, Washington

1962. Visit of President Olympio to U.S.A.
313 49 50 c. slate and ochre . . . 10 10
314 1 f. slate and blue 10 10
315 2 f. slate and red 10 10
316 5 f. slate and mauve 10 10
317 25 f. slate and lilac 40 15
318 100 f. slate and green . . . 1·60 70

50 Stamps of 1897 and Mail-coach

1963 65th Anniv of Togolese Postal Services.
319 50 30 c. multicoloured (post) . . 10 10
320 – 50 c. multicoloured 10 10
321 – 1 f. multicoloured 10 10
322 – 10 f. multicoloured 45 15
323 – 25 f. multicoloured 60 20
324 – 30 f. multicoloured 85 40
325 – 100 f. multicoloured (air) . . 2·25 80
DESIGNS (Togo stamps of): 50 c. 1900 and German imperial yacht "Hohenzollern"; 1 f. 1915 and steam mail train; 10 f. 1924 and motor-cycle mail carrier; 25 f. 1940 and mail-van; 30 f. 1947 and Douglas DC-3 airplane; 100 f. 1960 and Boeing 707 airplane.

51 Hands reaching for F.A.O. Emblem

1963. Freedom from Hunger.
326 51 50 c. multicoloured 10 10
327 1 f. multicoloured 10 10
328 25 f. multicoloured 60 20
329 30 f. multicoloured 85 30

52 Lome Port and Togolese Flag
53 Centenary Emblem

1963. 3rd Anniv of Independence. Flag in red, yellow and green.
330 52 50 c. black and brown . . 10 10
331 1 f. black and red 15 10
332 25 f. black and blue 35 20
333 50 f. black and ochre . . . 70 35

1963. Red Cross Centenary. Flag red, yellow and green; cross red.
334 53 25 f. blue and black 85 30
335 30 f. green and black . . . 1·10 40

54 Broken Shackles and Abraham Lincoln

55 Flame and U.N. Emblem

1963. Cent of American Slaves' Emancipation. Centre in grey and green.
336 54 50 c. black & brown (post) 10 10
337 1 f. black and blue 10 10
338 25 f. black and red 45 15
339 100 f. black & orange (air) 1·40 60

1963. 15th Anniv of Declaration of Human Rights. Flame in red.
340 55 50 c. blue & ultramarine . . 10 10
341 1 f. green and black 15 10
342 25 f. lilac and blue 40 15
343 85 f. gold and blue . . . . 1·10 60

56 Hibiscus

58 Temple and Isis

1964. Multicoloured.
344 50 c. "Odontoglossum grande" (orchid) (postage) 10 10
345 1 f. Type 56 . . . . 10 10
346 2 f. "Papilio dardanus" (butterfly) 35 10
347 3 f. "Morpho aega" (butterfly) 55 10
348 4 f. "Pandinus imperator" (scorpion) 40 10
349 5 f. Tortoise 20 15
350 6 f. Strelitzia (flower) 55 15
351 8 f. Python 45 15
352 10 f. "Bunaea alcinde" (butterfly) 85 15
353 15 f. Chameleon . . . . . . 1·25 15
354 20 f. Octopus . . . . 1·50 20
355 25 f. "Zeus faber" (fish) . . . 1·25 20
356 30 f. "Pomacanthus arcuatus" (fish) . . . . 1·50 35
357 40 f. Pygmy hippopotamus . . 2·00 35
358 45 f. African palm civet . . . 3·25 60
359 60 f. Bohar reedbuck . . . . 4·50 90
360 85 f. Olive baboon . . . . . 5·50 1·00
361 50 f. Black-bellied seed-cracker (air) . . . . 3·75 80
362 100 f. Black and white mannikin 6·00 1·25
363 200 f. Red-faced lovebird . . 14·00 3·00
364 250 f. Grey parrot . . . . . 32·00 6·50
365 500 f. Yellow-breasted barbet 45·00 11·00

1964. President Kennedy Memorial Issue. Optd **En Memoire de JOHN F. KENNEDY 1917-1963.** Centre in grey and green.
366 54 50 c. blk & brn (postage) . 15 10
367 1 f. black and blue 15 10
368 25 f. black and red 50 20
369 100 f. black & orge (air) . 1·60 80

1964. Nubian Monuments Preservation.
370 58 20 f. multicoloured 30 10
371 – 25 f. mauve and black . . 35 20
372 – 30 f. olive, black & yellow 50 30
DESIGNS: 25 f. Head of Rameses II, Abu Simbel; 30 f. Temple of Philae.

59 Phosphate Mine, Kpeme

1964. 4th Anniv of Independence.
373 59 5 f. ochre, bistre & brown 10 10
374 – 25 f. lake, brown & violet . 35 15
375 – 60 f. yellow, olive & green 60 35
376 – 85 f. blue, slate & violet . 1·25 50
DESIGNS: 25 f. Mine installations; 60 f. Phosphate train; 85 f. Loading phosphate onto "Panama Maru" bulk carrier.

60 Togolese breaking Chain

61 Pres. Grunitzky and "Papilio memnon"

1964. 1st Anniv of African Heads of State Conf, Addis Ababa.
377 60 5 f. sepia & orge (postage) 15 10
378 25 f. sepia and green . . . 35 15
379 85 f. sepia and red 95 45
380 100 f. sepia & turq (air) . . 1·25 65

1964. "National Union and Reconciliation".
381 61 1 f. violet and mauve . . . 20 10
382 – 5 f. sepia and ochre . . . 10 10
383 – 25 f. violet and blue . . . 45 15
384 61 45 f. purple and red . . . 1·75 50
385 – 85 f. bronze and green . . 1·90 60
DESIGNS—President and: 5 f. Dove; 25, 85 f. Flowers.

62 Football

1964. Olympic Games, Tokyo.
386 62 1 f. green (postage) . . . 10 10
387 – 5 f. blue (Running) 15 15
388 – 25 f. red (Throwing the discus) 50 15
389 62 45 f. turquoise 80 40
390 – 100 f. brown (Tennis) (air) 1·50 55

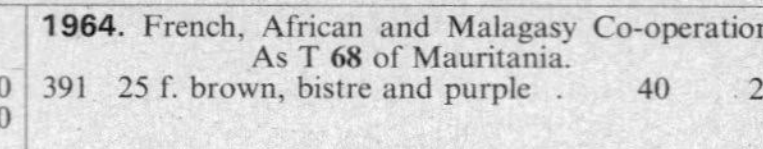
1964. French, African and Malagasy Co-operation. As T 68 of Mauritania.
391 25 f. brown, bistre and purple . 40 20

63 Charles's Hydrogen Balloon, Giffard's Steam-powered Dirigible Airship and Airship LZ-5

1964. Inaug of "Air Togo" (National Airline).
392 63 5 f. multicoloured (postage) 10 10
393 10 f. blue, lake and green . 30 10
394 – 25 f. ultramarine, orge & bl 50 15
395 – 45 f. mauve, green & blue . 1·10 35
396 – 100 f. multicoloured (air) . 1·90 80
DESIGNS: 25, 45 f. Farman H.F. III biplane, Lilienthal biplane glider and Boeing 707; 100 f. Boeing 707 and Togolese flag.

64 Sun, Globe and Satellites "Ogo" and "Mariner"

1964. International Quiet Sun Years. Sun yellow.
397 64 10 f. blue and red 15 10
398 – 15 f. blue, brown & mauve . 20 10
399 – 20 f. green and violet . . . 30 10
400 – 25 f. purple, green & blue . 35 15
401 64 45 f. blue and green 70 35
402 – 50 f. green and red 80 40
SATELLITES: 15, 25 f. "Tiros", "Telstar" and orbiting solar observatory; 20, 50 f. "Nimbus", "Syncom" and "Relay".

65 Pres. Grunitzky and the Mount of the Beatitudes Church

1965. Israel–Togo Friendship. Inscr "AMITIE ISRAEL–TOGO 1964".
403 – 5 f. purple 10 10
404 65 20 f. blue and purple . . . 20 10
405 – 25 f. turquoise and red . . 35 15
406 – 45 f. olive, bistre & purple . 70 35
407 – 85 f. turquoise and purple . 1·10 50
DESIGNS—VERT: 5 f. Togolese stamps being printed on Israel press. HORIZ: 25, 85 f. Arms of Israel and Togo; 45 f. As Type 65 but showing old synagogue, Capernaum.

66 "Syncom 3", Dish Aerial and I.T.U. Emblem

1965. I.T.U. Centenary.
408 66 10 f. turquoise and green . 15 10
409 20 f. olive and black . . . 35 15
410 25 f. blue and ultramarine . 40 15
411 45 f. rose and red 70 35
412 50 f. green and black . . . 90 45

67 Abraham Lincoln
68 Throwing the Discus

1965. Death Centenary of Lincoln.
413 67 1 f. purple (postage) 10 10
414 5 f. greeen 10 10
415 20 f. brown 35 10
416 25 f. blue 45 20
417 100 f. olive (air) . . . . . 1·60 70

1965. 1st African Games, Brazzaville. Flags in red, yellow and green.
418 68 5 f. purple (postage) . . . 10 10
419 – 10 f. blue 15 10
420 – 15 f. brown 35 10
421 – 25 f. purple 90 20
422 – 100 f. green (air) . . . . . 1·50 65
SPORTS: 10 f. Throwing the javelin; 15 f. Handball; 25 f. Running; 100 f. Football.

69 Sir Winston Churchill

1965. Churchill Commemoration.
423 69 5 f. green (postage) 10 10
424 – 10 f. violet and blue . . . 15 10
425 69 20 f. brown 40 15
426 – 45 f. blue 65 35
427 69 85 f. red (air) . . . . . . 1·50 65
DESIGNS—HORIZ: 10, 45 f. Stalin, Roosevelt and Churchill at Teheran Conference, 1943.

70 Unisphere

1965. New York World's Fair.
428 70 5 f. plum and blue 15 10
429 – 10 f. sepia and green . . . 20 10
430 70 25 f. myrtle and brown . . 35 20
431 – 50 f. myrtle and violet . . 65 40
432 70 85 f. brown and red . . . 1·10 50
DESIGNS: 10 f. Native dancers and drummer; 50 f. Michelangelo's "Pieta".

71 "Laying Bricks of Peace"

1965. International Co-operation Year.
433 71 5 f. multicoloured 10 10
434 15 f. multicoloured 15 15
435 – 25 f. multicoloured 30 15
436 – 40 f. multicoloured 60 30
437 – 85 f. multicoloured . . . . 1·00 50
DESIGNS: 25, 40 f. Hands suppporting globe; 85 f. I.C.Y. emblem.

72 Leonov with Camera

1965. Astronauts in Space.
438 72 25 f. mauve and blue . . . 50 20
439 – 50 f. brown and green . . 90 40
DESIGN: 50 f. White with rocket-gun.

73 "ONU" and Doves

1966. 20th Anniv of U.N.O.
440 73 5 f. brown, yellow and blue (postage) 10 10
441 – 10 f. blue, turquoise and orange 20 10
442 – 20 f. orange, green and light green 35 15
443 – 25 f. blue, turquoise & yell 45 20
444 – 100 f. ochre, blue and light blue (air) 1·60 55
DESIGNS: 10 f. U.N. Headquarters and emblem; 20 f. "ONU" and orchids; 25 f. U.N. Headquarters and Adlai Stevenson; 100 f. "ONU", fruit and ears of wheat.

74 Pope Paul, Boeing 707 and U.N. Emblem

1966. Pope Paul's Visit to U.N. Organization. Multicoloured.
445 5 f. Type **74** (postage) 10 10
446 15 f. Pope before microphones at U.N. (vert) 20 10
477 20 f. Pope and U.N. Headquarters 35 15
448 30 f. As 15 f. 45 20
449 45 f. Pope before microphones at U.N., and map (air) 80 30
450 90 f. Type **74** 1·60 80

75 W.H.O. Building and Roses

1966. Inaug of W.H.O Headquarters, Geneva. Multicoloured designs showing W.H.O. Building and flower as given.
451 5 f. Type **75** (postage) 20 10
452 10 f. Alstroemerias 35 10
453 15 f. Asters 45 20
454 20 f. Freesias 55 35
455 30 f. Geraniums 65 35
456 50 f. Asters (air) 95 35
457 50 f. Type **75** 1·50 55

76 Surgical Operation

1966. 7th Anniv of Togolese Red Cross. Mult.
459 5 f. Type **76** (postage) 10 10
460 10 f. Blood transfusion 15 10
461 15 f. Type **76** 30 15
462 30 f. Blood transfusion 40 15
463 45 f. African man and woman 70 45
464 100 f. J. H. Dunant (air) 1·75 90

1966. Space Achievements. Nos. 438/9 optd as below or surch also.
465 50 f. (**ENVOLEE SURVEYOR 1**) 85 40
466 50 f. (**ENVOLEE GEMINI 9**) 85 40
467 100 f. on 25 f. (**ENVOLEE LUNA 9**) 1·60 70
468 100 f. on 25 f. (**ENVOLEE VENUS 3**) 1·60 70

78 Wood-carving

79 Togolese Man

1966. Togolese Arts and Crafts.
469 78 5 f. brn, yell & bl (postage) 10 10
470 – 10 f. brown, salmon & grn 15 10
471 – 15 f. brown, yellow & red 30 15
472 – 30 f. brown, bistre & violet 55 20
473 – 60 f. brown, salmon and blue (air) 1·40 60
474 78 90 f. brown, yellow & red 1·40 60
DESIGNS: 10, 60 f. Basket-making; 15 f. Weaving; 30 f. Pottery.

1966. Air. Inauguration of Douglas DC-8F Air Services. As T **87** of Mauritania.
475 30 f. black, green & yellow 65 25

1966. Togolese Costumes and Dances. Multicoloured.
476 5 f. Type **79** (postage) 10 10
477 10 f. Togolese woman 10 10
478 20 f. Female dancer 40 10
479 25 f. Male dancer 50 15
480 30 f. Dancer in horned helmet 65 20
481 45 f. Drummer 1·00 50
482 50 f. Female dancer (air) 85 45
483 60 f. Dancer in horned helmet 1·40 60

80 Footballers and Jules Rimet Cup

1966. World Cup Football Championships, England. Showing football scenes and Jules Rimet Cup.
484 80 5 f. mult (postage) 10 10
485 – 10 f. multicoloured 20 10
486 – 20 f. multicoloured 40 10
487 – 25 f. multicoloured 40 15
488 – 30 f. multicoloured 55 20
489 – 45 f. multicoloured 85 40
490 – 50 f. multicoloured (air) 85 30
491 – 60 f. multicoloured 1·25 40

81 African Mouthbreeder

1967. Fishes. Multicoloured designs showing fishes with fishing craft in the background.
493 5 f. Type **81** (postage) 20 10
494 10 f. Golden cavally 35 10
495 15 f. Six banded distichodus 40 10
496 25 f. Spotted cichlid 60 20
497 30 f. Type **81** 80 35
498 45 f. As 10 f. (air) 1·25 45
499 90 f. As 15 f. 1·75 65

82 African Boy and Greyhound

1967. 20th Anniv (1966) of U.N.I.C.E.F.
500 82 5 f. multicoloured (postage) 20 10
501 – 10 f. brown, grn, & lt grn 30 15
502 82 15 f. blk, brown & mauve 45 20
503 – 20 f. black, ultram & blue 60 30
504 82 30 f. black, blue & olive 95 35
505 – 45 f. bronze, brown and yellow (air) 1·00 40
506 82 90 c.. black, bronze & bl 1·50 55
DESIGNS: 10 f. Boy and Irish setter; 20 f. Girl and doberman; 45 f. Girl and miniature poodle.

83 Launching "Diamant" Rocket

1967. French Space Achievements. Multicoloured.
508 5 f. Type **83** (postage) 10 10
509 10 f. Satellite "A-1" (horiz) 20 10
510 15 f. Satellite "FR-1" 30 10
511 20 f. Satellite "D-1" (horiz) 40 15
512 25 f. 25 f. As 10 f. 50 30
513 40 f. As 20 f. 70 35
514 50 f. Type **83** (air) 95 40
515 90 f. As 15 f. 1·50 55

84 Bach and Organ

1967. 20th Anniv (1966) of U.N.E.S.C.O.
517 84 5 f. mult (postage) 10 10
518 – 10 f. multicoloured 20 10
519 – 15 f. multicoloured 45 20
520 – 20 f. multicoloured 55 20
521 – 30 f. multicoloured 90 45
522 84 45 f. multicoloured (air) 1·10 40
523 – 90 f. multicoloured 1·60 55
DESIGNS: 10, 90 f. Beethoven, violin and clarinet; 15, 30 f. Duke Ellington, saxophone, trumpet and drums; 20 f. Debussy, grand piano and harp.

85 British Pavilion and Lilies

1967. World Fair, Montreal. Multicoloured.
525 5 f. Type **85** (postage) 15 10
526 10 f. French Pavilion and roses 20 10
527 30 f. "Africa Place" and strelitzia 55 15
528 45 f. As 10 f. (air) 85 35
529 60 f. Type **85** 95 45
530 90 f. As 30 f. 1·50 60
531 105 f. U.S. Pavilion and daisies 1·60 65

86 "Peace"

1967. Air. Disarmament. Designs showing sections of the "Peace" mural by J. Zanetti at the U.N. Headquarters Building Conference Room.
533 86 5 f. multicoloured 15 10
534 A 15 f. multicoloured 20 10
535 B 30 f. multicoloured 40 10
536 86 45 f. multicoloured 70 35
537 A 60 f. multicoloured 1·25 45
538 B 90 f. multicoloured 1·60 55

MINIMUM PRICE

The minimum price quoted is 10p which represents a handling charge rather than a basis for valuing common stamps. For further notes about prices, see introductory pages.

87 Lions Emblem with Supporters

1967. 50th Anniv of Lions International Mult.
540 10 f. Type **87** 20 10
541 20 f. Flowers and Lions emblem 35 15
542 30 f. Type **87** 45 20
543 45 f. As 20 f. 1·25 45

88 Bohar Reedbuck

1967. Wildlife.
544 88 5 f. brown & pur (postage) 10 10
545 – 10 f. blue, red and yellow 75 20
546 – 15 f. black, lilac & green 45 15
547 – 20 f. blue, sepia & yellow 1·25 30
548 – 25 f. brown, yellow & olive 85 35
549 – 30 f. blue, violet & yellow 1·75 55
550 – 45 f. brown & blue (air) 90 35
551 – 60 f. black, brown and green 1·25 50
DESIGNS: 10, 20, 30 f. Montagu's harriers (birds of prey); 15 f. Common zebra; 25 f. Leopard; 45 f. Lion; 60 f. African elephants.

1967. Air. 5th Anniv of U.A.M.P.T. As T **101** of Mauritania.
552 100 f. brown, blue and green 1·60 1·10

89 Stamp Auction and Togo Stamps—1 m. (German) of 1900 and 100 f. Conference of 1964

1967. 70th Anniv of 1st Togolese Stamps. Mult.
553 5 f. Type **89** (postage) 15 10
554 10 f. Exhibition and 1d. (British) of 1915 and 50 f. I.T.U. of 1965 15 10
555 15 f. Stamp shop and 50 c. (French) of 1924 40 10
556 20 f. Stamp-packet vending machine and 5 f. U.N. of 1965 40 10
557 30 f. As 15 f. 60 30
558 45 f. As 10 f. 85 40
559 90 f. Type **89** (air) 1·50 60
560 105 f. Father and son with album and 1 f. Kennedy of 1964 1·75 80

1967. 5th Anniv of West African Monetary Union. As T **103** of Mauritania.
562 30 f. blue and green 55 30

90 Long-jumping

1967. Olympic Games. Mexico and Grenoble (1968). Multicoloured.
563 5 f. Type **90** (postage) 10 10
564 15 f. Ski-jumping 20 10
565 30 f. Relay runners 55 20
566 45 f. Bob-sleighing 90 35
567 60 f. As 30 f. (air) 1·10 40
568 90 f. Type **90** 1·00 55

1967. National Day (29 Sept). Nos. 525/31 optd **JOURNEE NATIONALE DU TOGO 29 SEPTEMBRE 1967**.
570 5 f. multicoloured (postage) 35 20
571 10 f. multicoloured 35 20
572 30 f. multicoloured 1·00 40
573 45 f. multicoloured (air) 40 20
574 60 f. multicoloured 80 35
575 90 f. multicoloured 1·25 45
576 105 f. multicoloured 1·40 65

92 "The Gleaners" (Millet) and Benin Phosphate Mine

1968. Paintings and Local Industries.
577 92 10 f. multicoloured . . . 10 10
578 – 20 f. multicoloured . . . 30 10
579 92 30 f. multicoloured . . . 45 15
580 – 45 f. multicoloured . . . 70 20
581 92 60 f. multicoloured . . . 95 45
582 – 90 f. multicoloured . . . 1·40 70
DESIGN: 20, 45, 90 f. "The Weaver at the Loom" (Van Gogh) and textile plant, Dadia.

93 Brewing Beer

1968. Benin Brewery. Multicoloured.
583 20 f. Type 93 . . . . 35 10
584 30 f. "Drinking at a Bar" (detail from painting by Manet) . . 60 30
585 45 f. Bottling-washing machine and bottle of Benin beer . . 70 40
The 30 f. is a vert design.

94 Decade Emblem and Sunflowers
96 Dr. Adenauer and Europa "Key"

95 Viking Longship and Portuguese Galleon

1968. International Hydrological Decade.
586 94 30 f. mult (postage) 60 30
587 60 f. multicoloured (air) . . 85 40

1968. Inaug of Lome Port. Multicoloured.
588 5 f. Type 95 (postage) 15 10
589 10 f. Paddle-steamer "Clermont" and Liner "Athlone Castle" 20 10
590 20 f. Quayside, Lome Port . . 60 20
591 30 f. Type 95 . . . . 85 35
592 45 f. As 10 f. (air) 95 35
593 90 f. Nuclear-powered freighter "Savannah" . . . . 1·60 55

1968. Adenauer (German statesman) Commem.
595 95 90 f. multicoloured . . . . 1·60 80

97 "Dr. Turp's Anatomy Lesson" (Rembrandt)

1968. 20th Anniv of World Health Organization. Paintings. Multicoloured.
596 15 f. "Expulsion from the Garden of Eden" (Michelangelo) (postage) . . 30 10
597 20 f. Type 97 . . . . 40 15
598 30 f. "Johann Deyman's Anatomy Lesson" (Rembrandt) 55 20
599 45 f. "Christ healing the sick" (Raphael) 85 35
600 60 f. As 30 f. (air) 85 40
601 90 f. As 45 f. . . . . 1·10 55

98 Wrestling

1968. Olympic Games, Mexico. Multicoloured.
603 15 f. Type 98 (postage) . . . 20 15
604 20 f. Boxing 45 15
606 45 f. Running 80 35
607 60 f. Type 98 (air) 90 40
608 90 f. As 45 f. . . . . 1·25 55

99 "Try Your Luck"
100 Scout and Tent

1968. 2nd Anniv of National Lottery. Mult.
610 30 f. Type 99 . . . . 55 25
611 45 f. Lottery ticket, horse-shoe and cloverleaf 80 30

1968. Air. "Philexafrique" Stamp Exn, Abidjan (Ivory Coast 1969) (1st issue). As T **113a** of Mauritania. Multicoloured.
612 100 f. "The Letter" (J. A. Franquelin) . . . . 2·75 1·90

1968. Togolese Scouts. Multicoloured.
613 5 f. Type 100 (postage) . . . 10 10
614 10 f. Scoutmaster with cubs . 30 10
615 20 f. Giving first aid 40 15
616 30 f. Scout game 50 20
617 45 f. As 10 f. 65 35
618 60 f. As 20 f. (air) 90 45
619 90 f. As 30 f. . . . . 1·25 65
The 10, 20, 45 and 60 f. are horiz.

101 "The Adoration of the Shepherds" (Giorgione)

1968. Christmas. Paintings. Multicoloured.
621 15 f. Type 101 (postage) . . . 35 10
622 20 f. "The Adoration of the Kings" (Brueghel) 45 10
623 30 f. "The Adoration" (Botticelli) 55 15
624 45 f. "The Adoration" (Durer) 90 35
625 60 f. As 20 f. (air) . . . . . 1·00 40
626 90 f. As 45 f. . . . . 1·50 55

102 Martin Luther King
104 Module landing on Moon

103 Football

1969. Human Rights Year.
628 102 15 f. grn & brn (postage) . 20 10
629 – 20 f. violet & turquoise . . 35 15
630 102 30 f. blue and red 55 20
631 – 45 f. red and olive . . . 1·10 45
632 – 60 f. blue & purple (air) . . 90 45
633 102 90 f. brown and green . . 1·25 55
PORTRAITS: 20 f. Prof. Rene Cassin (Nobel Peace Prize-winner); 45 f. Pope John XXIII; 60 f. Robert E. Kennedy.

1969. Air. "Philexafrique" Stamp Exn, Abidjan, Ivory Coast (2nd issue). As T **114a** of Mauritania.
635 50 f. red, brown and green . . 80 80
DESIGN: 50 f. Aledjo Rock and stamp of 1900.

1969. Inaug of Sports Stadium, Lome.
636 103 10 f. brown, red and green (postage) 10 10
637 – 15 f. brown, blue and orange 30 10
638 – 20 f. brown, green and yellow 40 15
639 – 30 f. brown, blue and green 50 20
640 – 45 f. brown, violet and orange 65 30
641 – 60 f. brown, red and blue (air) 90 35
642 – 90 f. brown, mauve and blue 1·25 55
DESIGNS: 15 f. Handball; 20 f. Volleyball; 30 f. Basketball; 45 f. Tennis; 60 f. Boxing; 90 f. Cycling.

1969. 1st Man on the Moon. Multicoloured.
644 1 f. Type 104 (postage) 10 10
645 20 f. Astronaut and module on Moon 20 10
646 30 f. As Type 104 . . . . . . 40 15
647 45 f. As 20 f. 65 35
648 60 f. Astronaut exploring lunar surface (air) 85 40
649 100 f. Astronaut gathering Moon rock . . . . 1·40 70

105 "The Last Supper" (Tintoretto)

1969. Religious Paintings. Multicoloured.
651 5 f. Type 105 (postage) 15 10
652 10 f. "Christ's Vision at Emmaus" (Velazquez) . . . 30 10
653 20 f. "Pentecost" (El Greco) . 50 20
654 30 f. "The Annunciation" (Botticelli) 70 20
655 45 f. As 10 f. . . . . 1·10 45
656 90 f. As 20 f. (air) . . . . . 1·90 65

1969. Eisenhower Commem. Nos. 628/33 optd with Eisenhower's silhouette and **EN MEMOIRE DWIGHT D. EISENHOWER 1890-1968.**
658 102 15 f. grn & brn (postage) . 25 15
659 – 20 f. violet and turquoise . 45 15
660 102 30 f. blue and red 55 20
661 – 45 f. red and olive 95 30
662 – 60 f. blue & purple (air) . . 90 45
663 102 90 f. brown and green . . 1·25 65

107 Bank in Hand and Emblem

1969. 5th Anniv of African Development Bank. Multicoloured.
665 30 f. Type 107 (postage) . . . 85 20
666 45 f. Diesel locomotive in hand, and emblem . . . . 1·10 35
667 100 f. Farmer and cattle in hand, and emblem (air) . . . . 1·25 55

108 Dunant and Red Cross Workers

1969. 50th Anniv of League of Red Cross Societies. Multicoloured.
668 15 f. Type 108 (postage) . . . 35 10
669 20 f. Pasteur and help for flood victims 40 10
670 30 f. Fleming and flood control 55 15
671 45 f. Rontgen and Red Cross post 95 30
672 60 f. As 45 f. (air) 90 45
673 90 f. Type 108 . . . . 1·25 65

109 Weeding Corn

1969. Young Pioneers Agricultural Organization. Multicoloured.
675 1 f. Type 109 (postage) . . . 10 10
676 2 f. Glidji Agricultural Centre 10 10
677 3 f. Founding meeting 10 10
678 4 f. Glidji class 15 10
679 5 f. Student "pyramid" . . . 15 10
680 7 f. Students threshing 15 10
681 8 f. Gardening instruction . . 15 10
682 10 f. Co-op village 15 10
683 15 f. Students gardening . . . 30 15
684 20 f. Cattle-breeding 35 15
685 25 f. Poultry-farming 45 15
686 30 f. Independence parade . . 45 20
687 40 f. Boys on high-wire . . . 65 35
688 45 f. Tractor and trailer . . . 80 35
689 50 f. Co-op village 85 35
690 60 f. Tractor-driving tuition . 90 45
691 90 f. Harvesting manioc (air) . 1·10 45
692 100 f. Gardening instruction . 1·40 55
693 200 f. Thinning-out corn . . . 2·25 1·10
694 250 f. Drummers marching . . 4·25 1·50
695 500 f. Young pioneers marching 9·50 3·00

111 Books and Map
113 George Washington

1969. 12th Anniv of International African Library Development Association.
700 111 30 f. multicoloured . . . 45 30

1969. Christmas. No. 644/5 and 647/9 optd **JOYEUX NOEL.**
701 1 f. Type 104 (postage) . . . 35 20
702 20 f. Astronaut and module on Moon . . . . 1·10 45
703 45 f. As 20 f. . . . . 1·50 1·00
704 60 f. Astronaut exploring lunar surface (air) . . . . . . 1·90 65
705 100 f. Astronaut gathering Moon rock . . . . 3·00 1·00

1969. "Leaders of World Peace". Multicoloured.
707 15 f. Type 113 (postage) . . . 30 10
708 20 f. Albert Luthule 35 10
709 30 f. Mahatma Gandhi . . . 55 15
710 45 f. Simon Boliver 90 20
711 60 f. Friedrich Ebert (air) . . 90 35
712 90 f. As 30 f. . . . . 1·25 50

114 "Ploughing" (Klodt)

1970. 50th Anniv of I.L.O. Paintings. Multicoloured.
713 5 f. Type 114 (postage) . . . 10 10
714 10 f. "Gardening" (Pissarro) . 20 10
715 20 f. "Harvesting Fruit" (Rivera) 35 10
716 30 f. "Seeds of Spring" (Van Gogh) 80 35
717 45 f. "Workers of the Fields" (Rivera) 80 35
718 60 f. As 30 f. (air) . . . . . 1·00 35
719 90 f. As 45 f. . . . . 1·50 50

115 Model Coiffures

1970. Togolese Hair-styles. Multicoloured.

721 5 f. Type **115** (postage) 15 10
722 10 f. As T **115**, but different styles . . 35 10
723 20 f. Fefe style 50 15
724 30 f. Danmlongbedji style . . 1·25 20

725 45 f. Blom style (air) 90 30
726 90 f. Aklui and Danmlongbedji styles . . . . 1·60 65

Nos. 723/5 are vert.

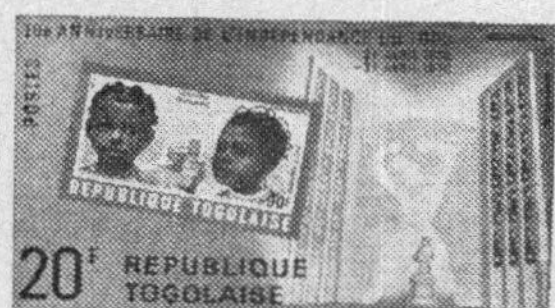

116 Togo Stamp and Independence Monument, Lome

1970. 10th Anniv of Independence. Multicoloured.

727 20 f. Type **116** (postage) . . . 45 15
728 30 f. Pres. Eyademe and Palace 65 20
729 50 f. Map, dove and monument (vert) . . . . 1·10 35

730 60 f. Togo stamp and monument (air) 80 30

117 New U.P.U. Headquarters Building

1970. New U.P.U. Headquarters Building.

731 **117** 30 f. violet and orange (postage) . . . . 1·00 35
732 50 f. red and blue (air) . . 80 35

118 Italy and Uruguay

1970. World Cup Football Championships, Mexico. Multicoloured.

733 5 f. Type **118** (postage) 10 10
734 10 f. England and Brazil . . . 20 10
735 15 f. Russia and Mexico . . . 35 10
736 20 f. Germany and Morocco . . 45 10
737 30 f. Rumania and Czecho-slovakia 85 20

738 50 f. Sweden and Israel (air) . 55 30
739 60 f. Bulgaria and Peru . . . 65 35
740 90 f. Belgium and El Salvador 1·25 50

119 Lenin

1970. Birth Centenary of Lenin. Multicoloured.

742 30 f. Type **119** (postage) . . . 1·00 45

743 50 f. "Peasant messengers with Lenin" (Serov) (air) . . . . 1·10 35

120 British Pavilion

1970. "Expo 70", Osaka, Japan. Multicoloured.

744 2 f. Pennants, Sanyo Pavilion (57×36 mm) 15 10
745 20 f. Type **120** 20 10
746 30 f. French Pavilion 45 15
747 50 f. Soviet Pavilion 85 30
748 60 f. Japanese Pavilion . . . . 1·10 45

121 Armstrong, Collins and Aldrin

1970. "Apollo" Moon Flights. Multicoloured.

750 1 f. Type **121** (postage) . . . 10 10
751 2 f. U.S. flag and moon-rock 10 10
752 20 f. Astronaut and module on Moon 35 10
753 30 f. Conrad, Gordon and Bean 65 20
754 50 f. As 2 f. . . . . 1·00 35

755 200 f. Lovell, Haise and Swigert ("Apollo 13") (air) . . . . 2·50 1·40

1970. Safe Return of "Apollo 13". As Nos. 750/5, but additionally inscr "FELICITATIONS BON RETOUR APOLLO XIII".

757 **121** 1 f. multicoloured (postage) 10 10
758 – 2 f. multicoloured 10 10
759 – 20 f. multicoloured . . . 35 10
760 – 30 f. multicoloured . . . 65 20
761 – 50 f. multicoloured . . . 1·00 35

762 – 200 f. multicoloured (air) 2·50 1·60

123 "Euchloron megaera"

1970. Butterflies and Moths. Multicoloured.

764 1 f. Type **123** (postage) . . . 15 10
765 2 f. "Cymothoe sangaris" . . 30 10
766 30 f. "Danaus chrysippus" . . 1·50 35
767 50 f. "Morpho sp." . . . . . 2·75 65

768 60 f. Type **123** (air) . . . . . 3·00 70
769 90 f. "Pseudacraea boisiduvali" 4·25 95

124 Painting by Velasquez (I.L.O.)

1970. 25th Anniv of U.N.O. Multicoloured.

770 1 f. Type **124** (postage) . . . 10 10
771 15 f. Painting by Delacroix (F.A.O.) 10 10
772 20 f. Painting by Holbein (U.N.E.S.C.O.) 20 15
773 30 f. Painting of U.N. H.Q., New York 60 15
774 50 f. Painting by Renoir (U.N.I.C.E.F.) 90 35

775 60 f. Painting by Van Gogh (U.P.U.) (air) . . . . . . 1·00 35
776 90 f. Painting by Carpaccio (W.H.O./O.M.S.) . . . . . 1·50 50

125 "The Nativity" (Botticelli)

1970. Christmas. "Nativity" Paintings by Old Masters. Multicoloured.

778 15 f. Type **125** (postage) . . . 15 10
779 20 f. Veronese 15 10
780 30 f. El Greco 55 15
781 50 f. Fra Angelico 90 30

782 60 f. Botticelli (different) (air) 1·00 30
783 90 f. Tiepolo . . . . 1·50 45

1971. De Gaulle Commemoration (1st issue). Nos. 708/9, 711/12 optd **EN MEMOIRE Charles De Gaulle 1890-1970** or surch in addition.

785 30 f. multicoloured (postage) . 1·10 35
786 30 f. on 90 f. multicoloured . 1·10 35
787 150 f. on 20 f. multicoloured . 6·75 1·75

788 200 f. on 60 f. mult (air) . . . 5·25 2·50

127 De Gaulle and Churchill

1971. De Gaulle Commemoration (2nd issue).

789 **127** 20 f. blue & blk (postage) . 55 15
790 – 30 f. red and black 65 20
791 – 40 f. green and black . . . 1·00 40
792 – 50 f. brown and black . . 1·25 50

793 – 60 f. violet & blk (air) . . 2·25 55
794 – 90 f. blue and black . . . 3·25 80

DESIGNS. 30 f. De Gaulle with Eisenhower; 40 f. With Pres. Kennedy; 50 f. With Adenauer; 60 f. With Pope Paul VI; 90 f. General De Gaulle.

128 Shepard and Moon Exploration

1971 Moon Mission of "Apollo 14". Mult.

796 1 f. Type **128** (postage) . . . 10 10
797 10 f. Mitchell and rock-gathering 15 10
798 30 f. Roosa and module approaching Moon 50 15
799 40 f. Launch from Moon . . . 90 30

800 50 f. "Apollo 14" emblem (air) 60 20
801 100 f. As 40 f. . . . . 1·25 40
802 200 f. As 50 f. . . . . 2·10 80

129 "The Resurrection" (after Raphael)

1971. Easter. Paintings of "The Resurrection" by various artists. Multicoloured.

804 1 f. Type **129** (postage) . . . 15 10
805 30 f. Master of Trebon . . . 55 15
806 40 f. Type **129** 95 30

807 50 f. M. Grunewald (air) . . . 80 30
808 60 f. As 30 f. . . . . 1·00 40
809 90 f. El Greco . . . . 1·50 55

130 Cocoa Tree and Pods

1971. International Cocoa Day. Multicoloured.

811 30 f. Type **130** (postage) . . . 55 15
812 40 f. Sorting beans 85 20
813 50 f. Drying beans . . . . . 1·10 35

814 60 f. Agricultural Ministry, Lome (air) 60 30
815 90 f. Type **130** . . . . . . 1·10 50
816 100 f. As 40 f. . . . . 1·25 60

131 Sud Aviation Caravelle over Control Tower

132 Napoleon

1971. 10th Anniv of A.S.E.C.N.A. (Aerial Navigation Security Agency).

817 **131** 30 f. multicoloured (postage) 90 35
818 100 f. multicoloured (air) . 1·50 65

1971. 150th Death Anniv of Napoleon. Embossed on gold foil.

819 **132** 1000 f. gold . . . . 22·00

133 Great Market, Lome

1971. Tourism. Multicoloured.

821 20 f. Type **133** (postage) . . . 35 10
822 30 f. Wooden sculpture and protea 55 15
823 40 f. Aledjo Gorge and olive baboon 80 20

824 50 f. Vale Castle and red-fronted gazelle (air) 65 20
825 60 f. Lake Togo and alligator 90 30
826 100 f. Furnace, Tokpli, and hippopotamus . . . . . . 1·25 40

134 Gbatchoume Image

1971. Togolese Religions. Multicoloured.

827 20 f. Type **134** (postage) . . . 35 15
828 30 f. High priest, Temple of Atta Sakuma 50 20
829 40 f. "Holy Stone" ceremony . 85 30

830 50 f. Moslem worshippers, Lome Mosque (air) 55 20
831 60 f. Protestants 70 30
832 90 f. Catholic ceremony, Djogbegan Monastery . . . 95 40

1971. Memorial Issue for "Soyuz 11" Astronauts. Nos. 799/802 optd **EN MEMOIRE DOBROVOLSKY - VOLKOV - PATSAYEV SOYUZ 11** or surch also.

834 40 f. multicoloured (postage) . 1·00 35

835 90 f. on 50 f. multicoloured (air) 90 35
836 100 f. multicoloured . . . . . 1·10 40
837 200 f. multicoloured . . . . . 2·00 65

136 Speed-skating

1971. Winter Games, Sapporo, Japan (1972). Multicoloured.

839 1 f. Type **136** (postage) . . . 10 10
840 10 f. Slalom skiing 10 10
841 20 f. Figure-skating 35 10
842 30 f. Bob-sleighing 55 20
843 50 f. Ice-hockey . . . . . . 1·10 35

844 200 f. Ski-jumping (air) . . . 2·25 95

1971. Air. 10th Anniv of African and Malagasy Posts and Telecommunications Union. As T **139a** of Mauritania. Multicoloured.

846 100 f. U.A.M.P.T. H.Q. and Adjogobo dancers . . . . . 1·10 55

137 Togolese Child and Mask

1971. Air. "Children of the World". Embossed on gold foil.

847 **137** 1500 f. gold 15·00

138 Wooden Crocodile

1971. 25th Anniv of U.N.I.C.E.F. Mult.

848 20 f. Type **138** (postage) 20 10
849 30 f. Toy "Bambi" and butterfly 45 15
850 50 f. Toy monkey 80 30
851 50 f. Wooden elephant on wheels 1·00 30
852 60 f. Toy turtle (air) 55 20
853 90 f. Toy parrot 85 35

139 "Virgin and Child" (Botticelli)

1971. Christmas. "Virgin and Child" Paintings by Old Masters. Multicoloured.

855 10 f. Type **139** (postage) 10 10
856 30 f. (Maitre de la Vie de Marie) 65 20
857 40 f. (Durer) 1·10 35
858 50 f. (Veronese) 1·40 45
859 60 f. (Giorgione) (air) 1·00 35
860 100 f. (Raphael) 1·75 55

140 St. Mark's Basilica, Venice

1972. U.N.E.S.C.O. "Save Venice" Campaign. Multicoloured.

862 30 f. Type **140** (postage) 90 30
863 40 f. Rialto Bridge 1·25 40
864 100 f. Doge's Palace (air) 1·40 65

141 "The Crucifixion" (unknown artist)

1972. Easter. Religious Paintings. Multicoloured.

866 25 f. Type **141** (postage) 45 15
867 30 f. "The Deposition" (Botticelli) 70 15
868 40 f. Type **141** 90 30
869 50 f. "The Resurrection" (Thomas de Coloswar) (air) 85 20
870 100 f. "The Ascension" (Mantegna) 1·60 40

142 Heart Emblem and Blacksmith **145** Woman preparing Cassava

143 Hotel de la Paix, Lome

1972. World Heart Month. Multicoloured.

872 30 f. Type **142** (postage) 45 15
873 40 f. Typist 55 20
874 60 f. Javelin-thrower 85 35
875 100 f. Type **142** (air) 1·25 45

1972. O.C.A.M. Summit Conference, Lome. Embossed on gold foil.

877 **143** 1000 f., gold, red & green 10·00

1972. Pres. Nixon's Visit to China. Nos. 823/4 optd **VISITE DU PRESIDENT NIXON EN CHINE FEVRIER 1972.** and additionally surch (No. 879).

878 300 f. on 40 f. mult (postage) 4·00 1·90
879 50 f. multicoloured (air) 1·00 35

1972. Cassava Industries. Multicoloured.

880 25 f. Collecting cassava (horiz) (postage) 45 15
881 40 f. Type **145** 65 20
882 60 f. Cassava truck and factory (horiz) (air) 90 20
883 80 f. Mother with Benin tapioca cake 1·25 45

146 Video-telephone **148** Basketball

1972. World Telecommunications Day. Multicoloured.

884 40 f. Type **146** (postage) 1·00 35
885 100 f. "Intelsat 4" and map of Africa (air) 1·50 45

1972. Air. Pres. Nixon's Visit to Russia. No. 743, surch **VISITE DU PRESIDENT NIXON EN RUSSIE MAI 1972**, and value.

886 300 f. on 50 f. multicoloured 5·00 2·75

1972. Olympic Games, Munich. Multicoloured.

887 30 f. Type **148** (postage) 50 15
888 40 f. Running 65 20
889 50 f. Throwing the discus 90 30
890 90 f. Gymnastics (air) 65 35
891 200 f. Type **148** 1·75 80

149 Pin-tailed Whydah **150** Paul Harris (founder)

1973. Exotic Birds. Multicoloured.

893 25 f. Type **149** (postage) 55 40
894 30 f. Broad-tailed paradise whydah 80 40
895 40 f. Yellow-mantled whydah 1·10 55
896 60 f. Long-tailed whydah 2·00 55
897 90 f. Rose-ringed parakeet (air) 2·75 1·10

1972. Rotary International. Multicoloured.

899 40 f. Type **150** (postage) 40 20
900 50 f. Rotary and Togo flags 50 30
901 60 f. Rotary emblem, map and laurel (air) 65 20
902 90 f. As 50 f. 90 35
903 100 f. Type **150** 1·25 45

151 "Mona Lisa" (L. da Vinci)

1972. Famous Paintings. Multicoloured.

905 25 f. Type **151** (postage) 95 30
906 40 f. "Virgin and Child" (Bellini) 1·10 30
907 60 f. "Mystical Marriage of St. Catherine" (Master P.N.'s assistant) (air) 80 30
908 80 f. "Self-portrait" (L. da Vinci) 1·10 35
909 100 f. "St. Marie and Angels" (Botticelli) 1·40 50

1972. 10th Anniv of West African Monetary Union. As T **149** of Mauritania.

911 40 f. brown, grey and red 55 40

152 Party H.Q. of R.P.T., Pres. Pompidou and Eyadama

1972. Visit of President Pompidou to Togo. Multicoloured.

912 40 f. Type **152** (postage) 1·10 45
913 100 f. Party H.Q. rear view and portraits as T **152** (air) 1·75 55

153 Goethe

1972. Air. 140th Death Anniv of Goethe (poet).

914 **153** 100 f. multicoloured 1·50 65

154 "The Annunciation" (unknown artist)

1972. Christmas. Religious Paintings. Multicoloured.

915 25 f. Type **154** (postage) 35 20
916 30 f. "The Nativity" (Master Theodor of Prague) 55 20
917 40 f. Type **154** 80 20
918 60 f. As 30 f. (air) 80 20
919 80 f. "The Adoration of the Magi" (unknown artist) 1·00 30
920 100 f. "The Flight into Egypt" (Giotto) 1·25 45

155 R. Follerau and Allegory

1973. "World Day of the Leper". (a) Postage. 20th Anniv of Follereau Foundation.

922 **155** 40 f. violet and green 1·60 55

(b) Air. Cent of Hansen's Bacillus Discovery.

923 – 100 f. blue and red 2·50 85

DESIGN: 100 f. Dr. Hansen, microscope and bacillus slide.

156 W.H.O. Emblem **157** The Crucifixion

1973. 25th Anniv of W.H.O.

924 **156** 30 f. multicoloured 45 15
925 40 f. multicoloured 55 20

1973. Easter. Multicoloured.

926 25 f. Type **157** (postage) 35 15
927 30 f. The Deposition 55 20
928 40 f. The Resurrection 80 20
929 90 f. "Christ in Majesty" (air) 1·25 45

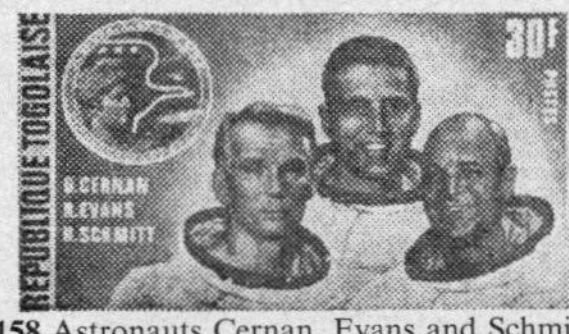

158 Astronauts Cernan, Evans and Schmitt

1973. "Apollo 17" Moon Flight. Multicoloured.

931 30 f. Type **158** (postage) 80 15
932 40 f. Moon rover 1·00 30
933 100 f. Discovery of "orange" rock (air) 1·10 40
934 200 f. Pres. Kennedy and lift-off 2·25 85

159 Erecting Tent **160** Heliocentric System

1873. Int Scout Congress. Nairobi/Addis Ababa. Multicoloured.

936 10 f. Type **159** (postage) 20 10
937 20 f. Cooking meal (horiz) 45 10
938 30 f. Rope-climbing 65 15
939 40 f. Type **159** 85 20
940 100 f. Canoeing (horiz) (air) 1·25 40
941 200 f. As 20 f. 2·50 85

1973. 500th Birth Anniv of Copernicus. Multicoloured.

943 10 f. Type **160** (postage) 15 10
944 20 f. Copernicus 30 10
945 30 f. "Astronomy" and "Astronautics" 65 15
946 40 f. Astrolabe 85 20
947 90 f. Type **160** (air) 1·25 35
948 100 f. As 20 f. 1·40 45

161 Ambulance Team

1973. Togolese Red Cross. Multicoloured.

950 40 f. Type **161** (postage) 90 35
951 100 f. Dove of peace, sun and map (air) 1·90 65

1973. "Drought Relief". African Solidarity. No. 766 surch **SECHERESSE SOLIDARITE AFRICAINE** and value.

952 100 f. on 30 f. multicoloured 1·25 85

163 Classroom

1973. Literacy Campaign. Multicoloured.
953 30 f. Type **163** (postage) . . . 35 15
954 40 f. African reading book (vert) 85 30
955 90 f. Classroom (different) (air) 85 45

1973. African and Malagasy Posts and Telecommunications Union. As T **155a** of Mauritania.
956 100 f. red, yellow and purple . 1·10 65

164 Interpol Emblem and H.Q. Paris
165 W.M.O. Emblem in Weather-vane

1973. 50th Anniv of Interpol.
957 **164** 30 f. green, brown & yell . 45 15
958 40 f. blue, mauve & grn . 65 20

1973. Centenary of W.M.O.
959 **165** 40 f. grn, brn & yell (post) 90 35
960 200 f. brn, vio & blue (air) 1·90 85

166 Togo Stamp and Diesel Locomotives

1973. 75th Anniv of Togolese Postal Services. Multicoloured.
961 25 f. Type **166** (postage) . . . 50 15
962 30 f. Togo stamp and mail coaches 60 20
963 90 f. Togo stamps and mail boats 1·60 45
964 100 f. Togo stamps and mail-planes (air) . . . . 1·90 65

167 Kennedy and A. Schaerf
168 Flame Emblem and "People"

1973. 10th Death Anniv of Pres. Kennedy.
966 **167** 20 f. violet and black on blue (postage) 35 10
967 – 30 f. brown and black on brown 50 20
968 – 40 f. green & blk on grn . 85 30
969 – 90 f. purple and black on mauve (air) . . . . . . 1·60 45
970 – 100 f. blue & black on bl . 1·60 45
971 – 200 f. brown & blk on brn 2·75 80
DESIGNS: 30 f. Kennedy and Harold Macmillan; 40 f. Kennedy and Konrad Adenauer; 90 f. Kennedy and Charles de Gaulle; 100 f. Kennedy and Nikita Kruschev; 200 f. Kennedy and "Apollo" spacecraft.

1973. Air. 25th Anniv of Declaration of Human Rights.
973 **168** 250 f. multicoloured . . . 2·75 1·40

169 "Virgin and Child" (anon)
173 "Girl Before Mirror" (Picasso)

171 Footballers

1973. Christmas. Multicoloured.
974 25 f. Type **169** (postage) . . . 50 15
975 30 f. "Adoration of the Magi" (Vivarini) 60 20
976 90 f. "Virgin and Child" (S. di Pietro) (air) . . . . . . 1·00 35
977 100 f. "Adoration of the Magi" (anon) . . . . 1·40 40

1974. Lome District Rotary International Convention. Nos. 899, 901 and 903 optd **PREMIERE CONVENTION 210eme DISTRICT FEVRIER 1974 LOME.**
979 **150** 40 f. mult (postage) . . . 55 35
980 – 60 f. multicoloured (air) . 45 20
981 **150** 100 f. multicoloured . . . 90 35

1974. World Cup Football Championships, Munich.
982 **171** 20 f. mult (postage) . . . 35 15
983 – 30 f. multicoloured . . . 45 15
984 – 40 f. multicoloured . . . 55 20
985 – 90 f. multicoloured (air) 90 35
986 – 100 f. multicoloured . . . 1·00 40
987 – 200 f. multicoloured . . . 2·00 70
DESIGNS: Nos. 983/7, similar designs to Type **171**, showing footballers in action.

1974. 10th Anniv of World Food Programme. Nos. 880/1 optd **10e ANNIVERSAIRE DU P. A. M.** or surch also.
989 **145** 40 f. multicoloured . . . 55 35
990 – 100 f. on 25 f. multicoloured 1·25 80

1974. Picasso Commemoration. Multicoloured.
991 20 f. Type **173** (postage) . . . 55 20
992 30 f. "The Turkish Shawl" . 80 35
993 40 f. "Mandoline and Guitar" 1·10 35
994 90 f. "The Muse" (air) . . . 1·00 35
995 100 f. "Les Demoiselles d'Avignon" . . . . 1·25 40
996 200 f. "Sitting Nude" . . . . 2·50 85

174 Kpeme Village
175 Togolese Postman

1974. Coastal Scenes. Multicoloured.
998 30 f. Type **174** (postage) . . 45 20
999 40 f. Tropicana tourist village 65 40
1000 90 f. Fisherman on Lake Togo (air) . . . . 1·00 35
1001 100 f. Mouth of Aneche River 1·25 40

1974. Centenary of U.P.U. Multicoloured.
1003 30 f. Type **175** (postage) . . 40 20
1004 40 f. Postman with cleft carrying-stick 50 30
1005 50 f. Type **175** (air) 60 30
1006 100 f. As 40 f. . . . . 1·25 45

1974. 15th Anniv of Council of Accord. As T **158** of Dahomey.
1007 40 f. multicoloured 50 30

177 Hauling-in Net
178 Earth Station and Probe

1974. Lagoon Fishing. Multicoloured.
1008 30 f. Type **177** (postage) . . 45 20
1009 40 f. Throwing net 65 30
1010 90 f. Fishes in net (air) . . . 1·00 30
1011 100 f. Fishing with lines . . 1·25 35
1012 200 f. Fishing with basket (vert) 2·75 70

1974. U.S. "Jupiter" Space Mission. Mult.
1014 30 f. Type **178** (postage) . . 35 15
1015 40 f. Probe transmitting to Earth (horiz) 45 20
1016 100 f. Blast-off (air) 95 40
1017 200 f. Jupiter probe (horiz) . 1·75 70

1974. "Internaba 1974" Stamp Exhibition Basel. Nos. 884/5 optd · **INTERNABA 1974** · **CENTENARIUM U P U** and emblem.
1019 **146** 40 f. mult (postage) . . 3·50 1·00
1020 – 100 f. mult (air) . . . . 4·25 1·40

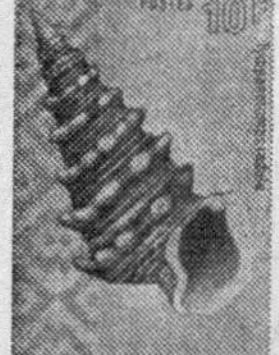

180 "Tympanotomus radula"
181 Groom with Horses

1974. Seashells. Multicoloured.
1021 10 f. Type **180** (postage) . . . 25 20
1022 20 f. "Tonna galea" 35 20
1023 30 f. "Conus mercator" . . . 55 20
1024 40 f. "Cardium costatum" . . 85 20
1025 90 f. "Alcithoe ponsonbyi" (air) 1·40 40
1026 100 f. "Casmaria iredalei" . . 1·90 40

1974. Horse-racing. Multicoloured.
1028 30 f. Type **181** (postage) . . . 45 20
1029 40 f. Exercising horses 65 30
1030 90 f. Steeple-chaser taking fence (air) . . . . 1·00 35
1031 100 f. Horses racing . . . . . 1·50 45

1974. Air. West Germany's Victory in World Cup Football Championships, Munich. Nos. 890/1 optd **COUPE DU MONDE DE FOOTBALL MUNICH 1974 VAINQUERS REPUBLIQUE FEDERALE ALLEMAGNE.**
1033 – 90 f. multicoloured . . . 90 35
1034 **148** 200 f. multicoloured . . . 1·75 80

183 Leopard

1974. Wild Animals. Multicoloured.
1036 20 f. Type **183** (postage) . . . 35 15
1037 30 f. Giraffes 45 20
1038 40 f. Two African elephants . 65 35
1039 90 f. Lion and lioness (air) . . 1·00 45
1040 100 f. Black rhinoceros and calf 1·50 45

184 Herd of Cows

1974. Pastoral Economy. Multicoloured.
1042 30 f. Type **184** (postage) . . . 45 20
1043 40 f. Milking 65 30
1044 90 f. Cattle at water-hole (air) 85 45
1045 100 f. Village cattle-pen . . . 1·10 55

185 Churchill and Frigate H.M.S. "Loch Fada"

1974. Birth Centenary of Sir Winston Churchill. Multicoloured.
1047 30 f. Type **185** (postage) . . . 50 15
1048 40 f. Churchill and Supermarine Spitfires 60 20
1049 100 f. Type **185** (air) . . . . 1·40 35
1050 200 f. As 40 f. . . . . 2·25 80

1975. Opening of Hotel de la Paix, Lome. Optd **Inauguration de la l'hotel Paix 9-1-75.**
1051a **143** 1000 f. gold, red and green 9·50

186 "Strelitzia reginae"
188 Radio Station, Kamina

1975. Flowers of Togo. Multicoloured.
1052 25 f. Type **186** (postage) . . . 35 15
1053 30 f. "Strophanthus sarmentosus" 45 15
1054 40 f. "Chlamydocarya macrocarpa" (horiz) . . . 55 20
1055 60 f. "Clerodendrum scandens" (horiz) 90 35
1056 100 f. "Clerodendrum thosonae" (horiz) (air) . . . 1·40 45
1057 200 f. "Gloriosa superba" (horiz) . . . . 2·50 65

1975. 70th Anniv of Rotary International. Optd **70e ANNIVERSAIRE 23 FEVRIER 1975.**
1059 **150** 40 f. mult (postage) . . . 30 25
1060 – 90 f. multicoloured (No. 902) (air) 85 35
1061 **150** 100 f. multicoloured . . 1·00 40

1975. Tourism. Multicoloured.
1062 25 f. Type **188** 20 10
1063 30 f. Benedictine Monastery, Zogbegan 35 20
1064 40 f. Causeway, Atchinedji . 45 30
1065 60 f. Ayome Waterfalls . . . 80 40

189 "Jesus Mocked" (El Greco)

1975. Easter. Multicoloured.
1066 25 f. Type **189** (postage) . . 20 10
1067 30 f. "The Crucifixion" (Master Janoslen) 35 10
1068 40 f. "The Descent from the Cross" (Bellini) 55 20
1069 90 f. "Pieta" (anon) 95 40
1070 100 f. "Christ rising from the Grave" (Master MS) (air) . 1·10 35
1071 200 f. "The Holy Trinity" (detail) (Durer) . . . . . 1·90 80

190 Stilt-walking

1975. 15th Anniv of Independence. Mult.
1073 25 f. Type **190** (postage) . . 30 10
1074 30 f. Dancers 35 15
1075 50 f. Independence parade (vert) (air) 40 15
1076 60 f. Dancer 60 35

191 Hunting Bush Hare with Club

1975. Hunting. Multicoloured.
1078 30 f. Type **191** (postage) . . . 45 20
1079 40 f. Hunting Eurasian beavers with bow 55 35
1080 90 f. Hunting red deer with snare (air) . . . . 1·25 45
1081 100 f. Hunting wild boar with gun . . . . 1·40 55

192 Pounding Palm Nuts

1975. Palm-oil Production. Multicoloured.
1082 30 f. Type **192** (postage) . . 35 15
1083 40 f. Extracting palm-oil (vert) 40 20
1084 85 f. Selling palm-oil (vert) (air) 80 45
1085 100 f. Oil-processing plant, Aloknegbe 90 55

193 "Apollo" and "Soyuz" in Docking Procedure

1975. "Apollo–Soyuz" Space Link. Mult.
1087 30 f. Type **193** (postage) . . 45 15
1088 50 f. "Soyuz" spacecraft (vert) (air) 40 15
1089 60 f. Slaton, Brand and Stafford ("Apollo" astronauts) . . 55 20
1090 90 f. Leonov and Kubasov ("Soyuz" cosmonauts) . . 70 30
1091 100 f. U.S., Soviet flags and "Apollo" and "Soyuz" linked 1·10 50
1092 200 f. Emblem and globe . . 2·25 65

194 "African Women"

1975. International Women's Year.

1094 **194** 30 f. multicoloured . . . 40 15
1095 40 f. multicoloured . . . 45 20

195 Dr. Schweitzer, and Children drinking Milk

1975. Birth Centenary of Dr. Albert Schweitzer. Multicoloured.

1096 40 f. Type **195** (postage) . . . 55 30
1097 80 f. Schweitzer playing organ (vert) (air) 90 30
1098 90 f. Schweitzer feeding Eastern white pelican (vert) . . . . 1·10 35
1099 100 f. Schweitzer and Lambarene Hospital . . . 1·25 35

196 "Merchant writing Letter" (V. Carpaccio)
199 "Virgin and Child" (Mantegna)

1975. International Letter-writing Week. Multicoloured.

1101 40 f. Type **196** (postage) . . . 55 30
1102 80 f. "Erasmus writing Letter" (Holbein) (air) 90 35

1975. 30th Anniv of United Nations. Nos. 851/3 optd **30eme Anniversaire des Nations-Unies**.

1103 50 f. multicoloured (postage) 55 30
1104 60 f. multicoloured (air) . . . 50 20
1105 90 f. multicoloured 60 30

1975. Air. World Scout Jamboree, Norway. Nos. 940/1 optd **14eme JAMBOREE MONDIAL DES ECLAIREURS**.

1107 100 f. multicoloured 95 45
1108 200 f. multicoloured . . . . 1·75 80

1975. Christmas. "Virgin and Child" paintings by artists named. Multicoloured.

1110 20 f. Type **199** (postage) . . . 30 20
1111 30 f. El Greco 40 20
1112 40 f. Barend van Orley 45 20
1113 90 f. Federigo Barocci (air) . 80 30
1114 100 f. Bellini 90 35
1115 200 f. Correggio . . . . . . 1·60 55

200 Crashed Airplane

1975. Pres. Eyadema's Escape in Air Crash at Sarakawa.

1117 **200** 50 f. multicoloured . . . 7·25 5·00
1118 60 f. multicoloured . . . 7·25 5·00

200a Pole Vault

1976. Olympic Games. Montreal. Multicoloured.

1118a 1000 f. Type **200a** . . . . . 10·00
1118b 1000 f. Diving . . . . . . 10·00
1118c 1000 f. Running . . . . . . 10·00
1118d 1000 f. Show-jumping . . . 10·00
1118e 1000 f. Cycling . . . . . . 10·00

201 "Frigates forcing the Hudson Passage"

1976. Bicentenary of American Revolution. Mult.

1119 35 f. Type **201** (postage) . . 40 20
1120 50 f. "George Washington" (G. Stuart) (vert) 55 30
1121 60 f. "Surrender of Burgoyne" (Trumbull) (air) 65 20
1122 70 f. "Surrender at Trenton" (Trumbull) (vert) 85 30
1123 100 f. "Signing of Declaration of Independence" (Trumbull) 90 35
1124 200 f. "Washington crossing the Delaware" (E. Leutze) . . 1·75 60

202 Cable-laying Ship
203 Blind Man and Mosquito

1976. Telephone Centenary. Multicoloured.

1126 25 f. Type **202** (postage) . . 20 15
1127 30 f. Automatic telephone and tape-recording equipment . 40 30
1128 70 f. Edison and communications equipment (air) . 55 30
1129 105 f. Alexander Graham Bell, early and modern telephones 85 40

1976. World Health Day. Multicoloured.

1131 50 f. Type **203** (postage) . . 65 30
1132 60 f. Eye examination (air) . 55 20

204 A.C.P. and C.E.E. Emblems
205 Exhibition Hall

1976. 1st Anniv of A.C.P./C.E.E. Treaty (between Togo and European Common Market). Multicoloured.

1133 10 f. Type **204** (postage) . . 15 10
1134 50 f. Map of Africa, Europe and Asia 40 30
1135 60 f. Type **204** (air) 45 20
1136 70 f. As 50 f. 55 30

1976. Anniversaries. Multicoloured.

1136a 5 f. Type **205** (postage) . . 10 10
1136b 10 f. Electricity pylon and flags 15 10
1137 50 f. Type **205** 50 30
1138 60 f. As 10 f. (air) 50 30

The 5 f. and 50 f. commemorate the 10th anniv of the Marine Exhibition and the 10 f. and 60 f. the 1st anniv of the Ghana–Togo–Dahomey Electricity Link.

1976. Air. "Interphil '76" International Stamp Exhibition, Philadelphia. Nos. 1121/4 optd **INTERPHIL MAI 29 - JUIN 6 1976**.

1139 60 f. multicoloured 40 15
1140 70 f. multicoloured 60 20
1141 10 f. multicoloured 90 30
1142 200 f. multicoloured . . . . 1·40 55

207 Running

1976. Olympic Games, Montreal. Multicoloured.

1144 25 f. Type **207** (postage) . . 20 10
1145 30 f. Canoeing 35 15
1146 50 f. High-jumping 45 20
1147 70 f. Sailing (air) 55 20
1148 105 f. Motorcycling 85 35
1149 200 f. Fencing . . . . 1·60 55

208 "Titan 3" and "Viking" Emblem

1976. "Viking" Space Mission. Multicoloured.

1151 30 f. Type **208** (postage) . . . 15 10
1152 50 f. "Viking" en route between Earth and Mars 40 20
1153 60 f. "Viking landing on Mars" (air) 55 20
1154 70 f. Nodus Gordii, Mars . . 65 20
1155 100 f. "Viking" over Mare Tyrrhenum 85 40
1156 200 f. "Viking" landing on Mars (different) . . . . . 1·50 55

209 "Young Routy"
212 Quaid-i-Azam

211 "Adoration of the Shepherds" (Pontormo)

1976. 75th Death Anniv of Toulouse-Lautrec (painter). Multicoloured.

1158 10 f. Type **209** (postage) . . . 15 10
1159 20 f. "Helene Vary" 40 15
1160 35 f. "Louis Pascal" 65 15
1161 60 f. "Carmen" (air) 80 20
1162 70 f. "Maurice at the Somme" 90 30
1163 200 f. "Messalina" . . . . . 2·25 60

1976. International Children's Day. Nos. 950/1 optd **Journee Internationale de l'Enfance**.

1165 **161** 40 f. mult (postage) . . . 45 15
1166 – 100 f. multicoloured (air) 80 45

1976. Christmas. Nativity scenes by artists named. Multicoloured.

1167 25 f. Type **211** (postage) . . . 35 15
1168 30 f. Crivelli 45 15
1169 50 f. Pontormo 80 20
1170 70 f. Lotto (air) 65 20
1171 105 f. Pontormo (different) . 1·90 35
1172 200 f. Lotto (different) . . . 1·60 55

1976. Birth Centenary of Mohammad Ali Jinnah, "Quaid-i-Azam".

1174 **212** 50 f. multicoloured . . . 55 30

1977. Gold Medal Winners, Montreal Olympic Games. Nos. 1146/7 and 1149 optd **CHAMPIONS OLYMPIQUES** with events and countries.

1175 50 f. multicoloured (postage) . 50 20
1176 70 f. multicoloured (air) . . . 60 35
1177 200 f. multicoloured . . . . 1·40 80

OPTD: 50 f. **SAUT EN HAUTEUR POLOGNE**; 70 f. **YACHTING - FLYING DUTCHMAN REPUBLIQUE FEDERALE ALLEMAGNE**; 200 f. **ESCRIME-FLEURET PAR EQUIPES REPUBLIQUE FEDERALE ALLEMAGNE**.

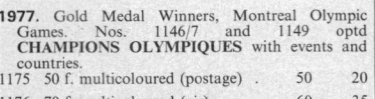

214 Queen Elizabeth II

1977. Silver Jubilee of Queen Elizabeth II.

1179 **214** 1000 f. multicoloured . . 7·75

215 Phosphate Complex, Kpeme

1977. 10th Anniv of Eyadema Regime. Multicoloured.

1181 50 f. Type **215** (postage) . . 55 20
1182 60 f. Parliament Building, Lome (air) 55 30
1183 100 f. Crowd greeting Pres. Eyadema 80 40

216 Gongophone

1977. Musical Instruments. Multicoloured.

1185 5 f. Type **216** (postage) . . . 15 10
1186 10 f. Tamtam (vert) 20 10
1187 25 f. Dondon 55 15
1188 60 f. Atopani (air) 65 20
1189 80 f. One-string fiddle (vert) . 1·00 30
1190 105 f. African flutes (vert) . 1·40 35

217 Victor Hugo and Guernsey Scene

1977. 175th Birth Anniv of Victor Hugo (writer). Multicoloured.

1192 50 f. Victor Hugo as a young man, and residence (postage) 55 15
1193 60 f. Type **217** (air) 60 30

218 Beethoven and Birthplace, Bonn

1977. 150th Death Anniv of Ludwig van Beethoven. Multicoloured.

1195 30 f. Type **218** (postage) . . 55 15
1196 50 f. Beethoven's bust and Heiligenstadt residence . . 65 20
1197 100 f. Young Beethoven and grand piano (air) . . . . 1·10 35
1198 200 f. Beethoven on death-bed and Trinity Church, Vienna 1·90 65

219 Benz, 1894

1977. Early Motor Cars. Multicoloured.

1200 35 f. Type **219** (postage) . . 65 20
1201 50 f. De Dion Bouton, 1903 . 1·00 30
1202 60 f. Cannstatt-Daimler, 1899 (air) 80 20
1203 70 f. Sunbeam, 1904 . . . . 90 20
1204 100 f. Renault, 1908 . . . . 1·10 35
1205 200 f. Rolls-Royce, 1909 . . 1·90 65

220 Lindbergh, Ground Crew and "Spirit of St. Louis"

1977. 50th Anniv of Lindbergh's Transatlantic Flight. Multicoloured.

1207 25 f. Type **220** (postage) . . 35 15
1208 50 f. Lindbergh before take-off 65 20
1209 60 f. Lindbergh with son (air) 50 15
1210 85 f. Lindbergh's home, Kent (England) 80 20
1211 90 f. "Spirit of St. Louis" over Atlantic 80 30
1212 100 f. Concorde over New York City . . . . 1·25 50

1977. 10th Anniv of International French Language Council. Nos. 1192/3 optd **10eme ANNIVERSAIRE DU CONSEIL INTERNATIONAL DE LA LANGUE FRANCAISE.**

1214 **217** 50 f. mult (postage) . . . 60 40
1215 60 f. multicoloured (air) . 55 35

222 Nile Crocodile

1977. Endangered Wildlife. Multicoloured.

1216 5 f. African crocodile (postage) 15 15
1217 15 f. Type **222** 40 20
1218 60 f. Western black-and-white colobus (air) 80 15
1219 90 f. Chimpanzee (vert) . . . 90 20
1220 100 f. Leopard . . . . 1·10 30
1221 200 f. African manatee . . . 1·90 55

223 Agricultural School, Tove

1977. Agricultural Development. Multicoloured.

1223 50 f. Type **223** (postage) . . . 50 20
1224 60 f. Corn silo (air) 55 15
1225 100 f. Hoeing and planting . 70 30
1226 200 f. Tractor . . . . 1·50 55

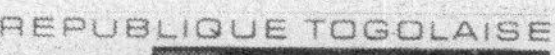

224 "Landscape at Sunset" (Rubens)

1977. 400th Birth Anniv of Rubens. Multicoloured.

1228 15 f. Type **224** (postage) . . . 35 10
1229 35 f. "Exchange of the Princesses at Hendaye" . . 80 15
1230 60 f. "Four Negro Heads" (air) 85 15
1231 100 f. "Anne of Austria" . . 1·10 40

225 Shuttle after Landing

1977. Space Shuttle. Multicoloured.

1233 20 f. Type **225** (postage) . . . 20 10
1234 30 f. Launching 35 15
1235 50 f. Ejecting propellant tanks 55 15
1236 90 f. Retrieving a satellite (air) 70 20
1237 100 f. Ejecting repaired satellite 85 30
1238 200 f. Shuttle landing . . . . 1·50 60

226 Lafayette at 19 (after Le Mire)

227 Lenin and Cruiser "Aurora"

1977. Bicentenary of Lafayette's Arrival in America.

1240 **226** 25 f. brown, yellow and purple (postage) . . . 30 10
1241 – 50 f. red, violet & pink . . 55 15
1242 – 60 f. turquoise, green and deep green (air) . . . 50 15
1243 – 105 f. blue, light blue and purple 90 35

DESIGNS—HORIZ: 50 f. Lafayette at Montpelier; 60 f. Lafayette's arrival in New York; 105 f. Lafayette with Washington at Valley Forge.

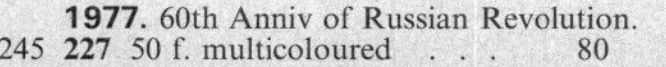

1977. 60th Anniv of Russian Revolution.

1245 **227** 50 f. multicoloured . . . 80 30

228 "Madonna and Child" (Lotto)

229 Edward Jenner

1977. Christmas. "Madonna and Child" by artists named. Multicoloured.

1246 20 f. Type **228** (postage) . . 20 15
1247 30 f. Crivelli 35 15
1248 50 f. C. Tura 55 15
1249 90 f. Crivelli (different) (air) 65 30
1250 100 f. Bellini 90 35
1251 200 f. Crivelli (different) . . 1·50 55

1978. World Eradication of Smallpox.

1253 **229** 5 f. ochre, black and lilac (postage) 10 10
1254 – 20 f. multicoloured . . . 20 10
1255 **229** 50 f. ochre, black and green (air) 35 15
1256 – 60 f. multicoloured . . . 40 15

DESIGN—HORIZ: 20, 60 f. Patients queuing for vaccination.

230 Wright Brothers

1978. 75th Anniv of 1st Flight by Wright Brothers. Multicoloured.

1258 35 f. Type **230** (postage) . . 45 20
1259 50 f. Wilbur Wright flying Glider No. III 85 35
1260 60 f. Orville Wright Flight of 7 min 31 sec (air) . . . . . 1·00 40
1261 70 f. Wreckage of Wright Type A . . . . 1·10 40
1262 200 f. Wright Brothers' cycle workshop, Dearborn, Michigan . . . . 1·40 55
1263 300 f. Wright Flyer I (1st motorised flight). . . . . 2·00 85

231 "Apollo 8" (10th anniv of first mission)

232 St. John

1978. Anniversaries and Events. Multicoloured.

1265 1000 f. Type **231** . . . . . . 8·25
1266 1000 f. High-jumping (Olympic Games, 1980) . . . . . . 8·25
1267 1000 f. Westminster Abbey (25th anniv of Queen Elizabeth II's Coronation) 8·25
1268 1000 f. "Duke of Wellington" (150th death anniv of Goya) 8·25
1269 1000 f. Footballers and Cup (World Cup Football Championship) . . . . . 8·25

1978. The Evangelists. Multicoloured.

1271 5 f. Type **232** 10 10
1272 10 f. St. Luke 10 10
1273 25 f. St. Mark 20 10
1274 30 f. St. Mathew 30 10

233 Fishing Harbour

1978. Autonomous Port of Lome. Multicoloured.

1276 25 f. Type **233** (postage) . . 45 15
1277 60 f. Industrial port (air) . . 55 20
1278 100 f. Merchant port 80 30
1279 200 f. General view . . . . 1·25 55

234 "Venera 1" Probe

235 Goalkeeper catching Ball

1978. Space Mission–Venus. Multicoloured.

1281 20 f. Type **234** (postage) . . . 15 10
1282 30 f. "Pioneer" (horiz) . . . 20 15
1283 50 f. Soviet fuel base and antenna 40 15
1284 90 f. "Venera" blast jets (horiz) (air) 40 20
1285 100 f. "Venera" antennae . . 55 30
1286 200 f. "Pioneer" in orbit . . . 1·00 55

1978. World Cup Football Championship, Argentina. Multicoloured.

1288 30 f. Type **235** (postage) . . . 30 10
1289 50 f. Two players with ball . 40 15
1290 60 f. Heading the ball (air) . . 50 15
1291 80 f. High kick 60 20
1292 200 f. Chest stop . . . . . . 1·25 55
1293 300 f. Player with ball . . . . 2·00 85

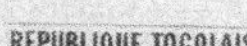

236 Thomas Edison (inventor)

237 "Celerifere" 1818

1878. Centenary of Invention of the Phonograph. Multicoloured.

1295 30 f. Type **236** (postage) . . . 20 10
1296 50 f. Couple dancing to H.M.V. "Victor", phonograph 1905 45 15
1297 60 f. Edison's original phonograph (horiz) (air) . . 40 15
1298 80 f. Berliner's first phonograph, 1888 . . . . 50 20
1299 200 f. Berliner's improved phonograph, 1894 (horiz) . 1·25 55
1300 300 f. "His Master's Voice" phonograph, c. 1900 (horiz) 2·00 85

1978. Early Bicycles. Multicoloured.

1302 25 f. Type **237** (postage) . . . 35 15
1303 50 f. First bicycle side-car (vert) 65 20
1304 60 f. Bantam bicycle (vert) (air) 55 15
1305 85 f. Military folding bicycle 65 20
1306 90 f. "La Draisienne" (vert) . 90 35
1307 100 f. Penny-farthing (vert) . 95 40

238 Dunant's Birthplace, Geneva

240 Eiffel Tower

239 "Threshing" (Raoul Dufy)

1978. 150th Birth Anniv of Henri Dunant (founder of Red Cross).

1309 **238** 5 f. blue & red (postage) . . 10 10
1310 – 10 f. brown and red . . . 15 10
1311 – 25 f. green and red . . . 30 10
1312 – 60 f. purple and red (air) . . 55 20

DESIGNS: 10 f. Dunant at 35; 25 f. Tending battle casualties, 1864; 60 f. Red Cross pavilions, Paris Exhibition, 1867.

1978. Air. "Philexafrique" Stamp Exhibition, Libreville (Gabon), and Int Stamp Fair, Essen, West Germany. As T **262** of Niger. Mult.

1314 100 f. Jay and Thurn and Taxis ¼ sgr. stamp of 1854 . . . 1·90 1·40
1315 100 f. Warthog and Togo 50 f. stamp, 1964 . . . . 1·90 1·40

1978. Artists' Anniversaries. Multicoloured.

1316 25 f. Type **239** (25th death anniv) (postage) 40 15
1317 50 f. "Horsemen on the Seashore" (Gauguin 75th death anniv) 70 15
1318 60 f. "Langlois Bridge" (Van Gogh 125th birth anniv) (air) 50 15
1319 70 f. "Sabbath of the Witches" (Goya 150th death anniv) 60 20
1320 90 f. "Christ Among the Doctors" (Durer 450th death anniv) 60 20
1321 200 f. "View of Arco" (Durer) 1·40 55

1978. Centenary of Paris U.P.U. Congress. Multicoloured.

1323 50 f. Type **240** (postage) . . 80 20
1324 60 f. Full-rigged ship "Slieve Roe" (air) 65 25
1325 105 f. Congress medallion . . 70 30
1326 200 f. 1870s locomotive . . . 1·40 55

241 "Madonna and Child" (Antonello)

242 H.M.S. "Endeavour" and Route round New Zealand

1978. Christmas. Paintings of the Virgin and Child by artists shown below. Multicoloured.

1328 20 f. Type **241** (postage) . . 20 15
1329 30 f. Crivelli 35 15
1330 50 f. Tura 55 15
1331 90 f. Crivelli (different) (air) . 65 30
1332 100 f. Tura (different) . . . 90 30
1333 200 f. Crivelli (different) . . 1·50 55

1979. Death Bicentenary of Captain James Cook. Multicoloured.

1335 25 f. Type **242** (postage) . . 50 15
1336 50 f. Careening H.M.S "Endeavour" (horiz) . . . 80 35
1337 60 f. "Freelove" at Whitby (horiz) (air) 75 35
1338 70 f. Antarctic voyage of H.M.S. "Resolution" (horiz) 1·25 45
1339 90 f. Capt. Cook . . . . . . 1·25 45
1340 200 f. Sail plan of H.M.S. "Endeavour" . . . . . . 2·50 1·10

243 Christ entering Jerusalem

1979. Easter. Multicoloured.

1342 30 f. Type **243** (postage) . . 20 10
1343 40 f. The Last Supper (horiz) 30 15
1344 50 f. Descent from the Cross (horiz) 40 15
1345 60 f. Resurrection (air) . . . 45 15
1346 100 f. Ascension 65 30
1347 200 f. Jesus appearing to Mary Magdalene . . . . 1·25 55

244 Statuette of Drummer

1979. Air. "Philexafrique 2" Stamp Exhibition, Libreville. Multicoloured.

1349 60 f. Type **244** . . . . . . 1·10 55
1350 100 f. Hands with letter . . . 1·60 1·10

245 Einstein Observatory, Potsdam

1979. Birth Centenary of Albert Einstein (physicist).

No.	Type	Description	Unused	Used
1351	245	35 f. red, yellow and black (postage)	20	10
1352	–	50 f. green, mve & blk	35	10
1353	–	60 f. multicoloured (air)	40	10
1354	–	85 f. lilac, brown & blk	60	15
1355	–	100 f. multicoloured	65	20
1356	–	200 f. green, brn & blk	1·40	40

DESIGNS—HORIZ: 50 f. Einstein and J. R. Macdonald in Berlin, 1931; 60 f. Sight and actuality diagram. VERT: 85 f. Einstein playing violin; 100 f. Atomic symbol and relativity formula; 200 f. Albert Einstein.

246 Children with Flag

247 Planting Sapling

1979. International Year of the Child. Multicoloured.

No.	Description	Unused	Used
1358	5 f. Type **246**	10	10
1359	10 f. Mother with children	10	10
1360	15 f. Children's Village symbol on map of Africa (horiz)	15	10
1361	20 f. Woman taking children to Children's Village (horiz)	15	10
1362	25 f. Children sitting round Fan palm	30	10
1363	30 f. Map of Togo showing Children's Villages	35	10

1979. Tree Day.

No.	Type	Description	Unused	Used
1365	247	50 f. green and violet (postage)	50	15
1366	–	60 f. brown and grn (air)	55	20

DESIGN: 60 f. Watering sapling.

248 Sir Rowland Hill

249 Stephenson's "Rocket", 1829

1979. Death Centenary of Sir Rowland Hill. Multicoloured.

No.	Description	Unused	Used
1367	20 f. Type **248** (postage)	15	10
1368	30 f. French mail sorting office in the reign of Louis XV (horiz)	20	10
1369	50 f. Parisian postbox, 1850	40	15
1370	90 f. Bellman collecting letters, 1820 (air)	60	20
1371	100 f. "Centre-cycles" used for mail delivery, 1880 (horiz)	65	20
1372	200 f. Post Office railway carriage, 1848 (horiz)	1·25	40

1979. Railway Locomotives. Multicoloured.

No.	Description	Unused	Used
1374	35 f. Type **249** (postage)	35	10
1375	50 f. William Norris' "Austria", 1843	45	15
1376	60 f. "The General", 1862 (air)	55	15
1377	85 f. Stephenson locomotive, 1843	75	35
1378	100 f. De Witt Clinton train, 1831	85	35
1379	200 f. D. Joy's "Jenny Lind"	1·75	55

Nos. 1375/9 are horizontal.

250 Skiing

251 Native praying

1979. Olympic Games, Lake Placid and Moscow. Multicoloured.

No.	Description	Unused	Used
1381	20 f. Type **250** (postage)	15	10
1382	30 f. Yachting	20	15
1383	50 f. Throwing the discus	40	10
1384	90 f. Ski-jumping (air)	65	20
1385	100 f. Canoeing	70	20
1386	200 f. Gymnastics (ring exercise)	1·40	40

1979. Togo Religions.

No.	Type	Description	Unused	Used
1388	251	30 f. brown, green and yellow (postage)	20	10
1389	–	50 f. blue, brown & red	35	10
1390	–	60 f. purple, blue and buff (air)	45	15
1391	–	70 f. lilac, orange & grn	50	20

DESIGNS—HORIZ: 50 f. Catholic priests; 60 f. Muslims at prayer; 70 f. Protestant preachers.

252 Astronaut on Moon

253 Dish Aerial

1979. 10th Anniv of First Moon Landing. Multicoloured.

No.	Description	Unused	Used
1393	35 f. Type **252** (postage)	30	10
1394	50 f. Capsule orbiting Moon	40	10
1395	60 f. Armstrong descending to Moon	45	10
1396	70 f. Astronaut and flag (air)	50	15
1397	200 f. Astronaut performing experiment	1·25	35
1398	300 f. Module leaving Moon	2·00	50

1979. 3rd World Telecommunications Exposition, Geneva.

No.	Type	Description	Unused	Used
1400	–	50 f. light brown, brown and green (postage)	35	10
1401	253	60 f. green, blue and deep blue (air)	50	20

DESIGN—HORIZ: 50 f. Television screen.

254 Pres. Eyadema

1979. Air. 10th Anniv of R.P.T. Multicoloured.

No.	Description	Unused	Used
1402	1000 f. Pres. Eyadema and Party badge	6·75	
1403	1000 f. Type **254**	6·75	

255 Holy Family

256 Rotary Emblem

1979. Christmas. Multicoloured.

No.	Description	Unused	Used
1404	20 f. Type **255** (postage)	15	10
1405	30 f. Madonna and Child and angels playing musical instruments	20	10
1406	50 f. Adoration of the shepherds	40	10
1407	90 f. Adoration of the Magi (air)	55	20
1408	100 f. Mother presenting Child	70	20
1409	200 f. The Flight into Egypt	1·50	40

1980. 75th Anniv of Rotary International. Multicoloured.

No.	Description	Unused	Used
1411	25 f. Type **256** postage)	15	10
1412	30 f. Anniversary emblem	30	10
1413	40 f. Paul Harris (founder)	35	10
1414	90 f. Figure exercising and sun (health) (air)	65	20
1415	100 f. Fish and grain (food)	70	20
1416	200 f. Family group (humanity)	1·40	40

257 Shooting (Biathlon)

1980. Winter Olympic Games, Lake Placid. Multicoloured.

No.	Description	Unused	Used
1418	50 f. Type **257** (postage)	50	10
1419	60 f. Downhill skiing	40	10
1420	100 f. Speed skating (air)	70	20
1421	200 f. Cross-country skiing	1·40	40

258 Swimming

1980. Olympic Games, Moscow. Multicoloured.

No.	Description	Unused	Used
1423	20 f. Type **258** (postage)	15	10
1424	30 f. Gymnastics	20	10
1425	50 f. Running	40	10
1426	100 f. Fencing (air)	65	20
1427	200 f. Pole vaulting	1·25	45
1428	300 f. Hurdles	2·00	55

259 Truck going to Market

1980. Market Scenes. Multicoloured.

No.	Description	Unused	Used
1430	1 f. Grinding savo (postage)	10	10
1431	2 f. Women preparing meat	10	10
1432	3 f. Type **259**	10	10
1433	4 f. Unloading produce	10	10
1434	5 f. Sugar-cane seller	10	10
1435	6 f. Barber doing child's hair	10	10
1436	7 f. Vegetable seller	10	10
1437	7 f. Mangoes (vert)	10	10
1438	9 f. Grain seller	10	10
1439	10 f. Fish seller	10	10
1440	15 f. Clay pot seller	10	10
1441	20 f. Straw baskets	15	10
1442	25 f. Lemon and onion seller (vert)	15	10
1443	30 f. Straw baskets (different)	20	10
1444	40 f. Shore market	30	15
1445	45 f. Selling cooked food	35	15
1446	50 f. Women carrying produce (vert)	35	15
1447	60 f. Selling oil	45	15
1448	90 f. Linen seller (air)	55	15
1449	100 f. Bananas	65	20
1450	200 f. Pottery	1·25	45
1451	250 f. Setting-up stalls	1·60	55
1452	500 f. Vegetable seller (different)	3·00	1·10
1453	1000 f. Drink seller	6·00	2·25

260 Concorde and Map of Africa

1980. 20th Anniv of African Air Safety Organization.

No.	Type	Description	Unused	Used
1458	260	50 f. mult (postage)	55	20
1459		60 f. multicoloured (air)	55	25

261 "Christ with Angels" (Mantegna)

263 Radio Waves

1980. Easter. Multicoloured.

No.	Description	Unused	Used
1460	30 f. Type **261** (postage)	30	15
1461	40 f. "Christ with Disciples" (Crivelli)	40	15
1462	50 f. "Christ borne by His Followers" (Pontormo)	45	15
1463	60 f. "The Deposition" (Lotto) (air)	50	10
1464	100 f. "The Crucifixion" (El Greco)	70	20
1465	200 f. "Christ with Angels" (Crivelli)	1·40	45

1980. "London 1980" International Stamp Exhibition. No. 1267 optd **Londres 1980**.

No.	Description	Unused	Used
1467	1000 f. Westminster Abbey	7·25	

1980. World Telecommunciations Day.

No.	Type	Description	Unused	Used
1469	–	50 f. violet and green (postage)	45	10
1470	263	60 f. pink, brown and blue (air)	50	15

DESIGN—HORIZ: 50 f. Satellite.

264 Red Cross and Globe

265 Jules Verne

1980. Togo Red Cross. Multicoloured.

No.	Description	Unused	Used
1471	50 f. Type **264** (postage)	55	10
1472	60 f. Nurses and patient (air)	45	15

1980. 75th Death Anniv of Jules Verne (writer). Multicoloured.

No.	Description	Unused	Used
1473	30 f. Type **265** (postage)	30	10
1474	50 f. "20,000 Leagues under the Sea"	40	10
1475	60 f. "From the Earth to the Moon" (air)	40	15
1476	80 f. "Around the World in Eighty Days"	55	20
1477	100 f. "From the Earth to the Moon" (different)	1·40	60
1478	200 f. "20,000 Leagues under the Sea" (different)	1·75	60

266 "Baroness James de Rothschild"

1980. Birth Bicentenary of Jean Ingres (painter). Multicoloured.

No.	Description	Unused	Used
1480	25 f. Type **266** (postage)	35	10
1481	30 f. "Napoleon I on the Imperial Throne"	55	10
1482	40 f. "Don Pedro of Toledo putting down the Sword of Henry IV"	50	10
1483	90 f. "Jupiter and Thetis" (air)	65	20
1484	100 f. "The Countess of Hassonville"	85	20
1485	200 f. "Tu Marcellus Eris"	1·50	35

267 Minnie holding Mirror for Leopard

1980. Walt Disney Characters and Wildlife.

1487 1 f. Type **267** 10 10
1488 2 f. Goofy cleaning hippo's teeth 10 10
1489 3 f. Donald clinging to crocodile 10 10
1490 4 f. Donald hanging over cliff edge from rhino's horn . . 10 10
1491 5 f. Goofy riding a water buffalo 10 10
1492 10 f. Monkey photographing Mickey 10 10
1493 100 f. Doctor Mickey examining giraffe 80 20
1494 300 f. Elephant showering Goofy . . . . 1·60 40

1980. 50th Anniv of Pluto. As T **267**.

1496 200 f. Pluto in party mood . 1·60 40

268 Wreath

1980. Famous Men of the Decade.

1498 **268** 25 f. orange and green (postage) 15 10
1499 – 40 f. dp green & green . 65 20
1500 – 90 f. dp blue & bl (air) . 60 20
1501 – 100 f. lilac and pink . . . 1·10 20

DESIGNS: 40 f. Mao Tse Tung; 90 f. Pres. Allende; 100 f. Pope Paul VI; 200 f. Pres. Kenyatta.

269 Tourist Hotel Emblem **270** Human Rights Emblem, and Map of Australia

1980. World Tourism Conference, Manila. Multicoloured.

1504 50 f. Type **269** 35 10
1505 150 f. Conference emblem . . 1·00 35

1980. 30th Anniv of Human Rights Convention.

1506 **270** 30 f. violet, purple and black (postage) 30 10
1507 – 50 f. green, light green and black 40 10
1508 – 60 f. deep blue, blue and black (air) 40 15
1509 – 150 f. brown, orge & blk 1·00 35

DESIGNS: 50 f. Map of Eurasia; 60 f. Map of the Americas; 250 f. Map of Africa.

271 Emblem

1980. Air. General Conclave of French-speaking Countries of the American Order of Rosicrucians, Lome.

1511 **271** 60 f. multicoloured . . . 50 15

271 Church at Melk, Austria

1980. Christmas. Multicoloured.

1512 20 f. Type **272** (postage) . . 15 10
1513 30 f. Tarragona Cathedral, Spain 20 10
1514 50 f. Church of St. John the Baptist, Florence 35 10
1515 100 f. Cologne Cathedral (air) 65 20
1516 150 f. Notre-Dame, Paris . . 1·00 30
1517 200 f. Canterbury Cathedral 1·40 35

1980. 5th Anniv of African Posts and Telecommunications Union. As T **292** of Niger.

1519 100 f. multicoloured 65 40

273 "February 2nd" Hotel

1981. Inauguration of "February 2nd" Hotel.

1520 **273** 50 f. mult (postage) . . 45 15
1521 60 f. multicoloured (air) 45 15

274 "Rembrandt's Father"

1981. Easter. Rembrandt Paintings. Multicoloured.

1522 30 f. Type **274** (postage) . . 30 10
1523 40 f. "Self-portrait" 35 10
1524 50 f. "Rembrandt's Father as an Old Man" 40 10
1525 60 f. "Rider on Horseback" . . 50 15
1526 100 f. "Rembrandt's Mother" (air) 70 20
1527 200 f. "Man in a Ruff" . . 1·50 45

275 Grey-necked Bald Crow

1981. Birds. Multicoloured.

1529 30 f. Type **275** (postage) . . 35 10
1530 40 f. Splendid sunbird . . . 45 10
1531 60 f. Violet starling . . . 55 15
1532 90 f. Red-collard whydah . . 90 20
1533 50 f. Violet-backed sunbird (air) 55 15
1534 100 f. Red bishop . . . . . 1·00 30

276 Dish Aerial

1981. 6th African Postal Union Council Meeting. Multicoloured.

1536 70 f. Type **276** 50 15
1537 90 f. Telecommunications control room 60 20
1538 105 f. Map of Togo and Africa (vert) 70 30

277 Blind Man with Guide Dog

1981. International Year of Disabled People. Multicoloured.

1539 70 f. Type **277** (postage) . . . 85 30
1540 90 f. One-legged carpenter (air) 60 15
1541 200 f. Wheelchair basket-ball . 1·60 55

278 "Woman with Hat"

1981. Birth Centenary of Pablo Picasso. Mult.

1543 25 f. Type **278** (postage) . . . 35 10
1544 50 f. "She-goat" 45 10
1545 60 f. "Violin" 55 15
1546 90 f. "Violin and Bottle on Table" (air) 80 20
1547 100 f. "Baboon with Young" . 90 30
1548 200 f. "Mandolin and Clarinet" 1·90 55

279 Aachen Cathedral, West Germany

1981. World Heritage Convention. Multicoloured.

1550 30 f. Type **279** (postage) . . . 20 10
1551 40 f. Yellowstone National Park, U.S.A. 30 10
1552 50 f. Nahanni National Park, Canada 35 10
1553 60 f. Cruciform rock churches, Lalibela, Ethiopia 40 15
1554 100 f. Old city centre, Cracow, Poland (air) 65 20
1555 200 f. Goree Island, Senegal . 1·25 35

280 "Vostok I", (20th anniv of first Manned Space Flight)

1981. Space Anniversaries. Multicoloured.

1557 25 f. Type **280** (postage) . . . 15 10
1558 50 f. "Freedom 7", first American in space (20th anniv) 35 10
1559 60 f. "Lunar Orbiter I" (15th anniv) 40 15
1560 90 f. "Soyuz 10" (10th anniv) (air) 60 15
1561 100 f. Astronauts on Moon ("Apollo XIV", 10th anniv) 65 20

281 "Adoration of the Magi" **282** Association Emblem and Togo Flag

1981. Christmas. Paintings by Rubens. Multicoloured.

1563 20 f. Type **281** (postage) . . 15 10
1564 30 f. "Adoration of the Shepherds" 20 10
1565 50 f. "Coronation of St. Catherine" 40 10
1566 100 f. "Adoration of the Magi" (different) (air) 60 20
1567 200 f. "Madonna and Child" 1·40 45
1568 300 f. "The Madonna giving the Robe to St. Idefonse" . . 2·25 65

1981. West African Rice Development Association.

1570 **282** 70 f. mult (postage) . . . 60 20
1571 105 f. multicoloured (air) 65 30

283 Peace Dove and National Flag

1982. 15th Anniv of National Liberation. Mult.

1572 70 f. Type **283** (postage) . . 55 20
1573 90 f. Pres. Eyadema and citizens (vert) 60 20
1574 105 f. Pres. Eyadema and citizens holding hands (vert) (air) 65 35
1575 130 f. Hotel complex 90 45

284 Scouts

1982. 75th Anniv of Boy Scout Movement. Multicoloured.

1576 70 f. Type **284** (postage) . . 50 15
1577 90 f. Signalling (air) 65 20
1578 120 f. Constructing a tower . 85 30
1579 130 f. Scouts with canoe . . 90 50
1580 135 f. Scouts and tent . . . 95 35

285 Moses and the Burning Bush **286** Togo and Italy Olympic Stamps

1982. Easter. The Ten Commandments. Multicoloured.

1582 10 f. Type **285** (postage) . . 10 10
1583 25 f. Jephtha's daughter . . 15 10
1584 30 f. St. Vincent Ferrer preaching in Verona . . . 20 10
1585 45 f. The denouncing of Noah 30 10
1586 50 f. Cain and Abel 35 10
1587 70 f. Potiphar's wife 50 20
1588 90 f. Isaac blessing Jacob . . 60 35
1589 105 f. Susannah and the elders (air) 65 30
1590 120 f. Bathsheba 85 35

1982. Air. "Romolymphil" Stamp Exhibition.

1592 **286** 105 f. multicoloured . . 70 30

287 First Stamps of France and Togo

1982. Air. "Philexfrance '82" International Stamp Exhibition.

1593 **287** 90 f. multicoloured . . . 65 40

288 Goalkeeper

1982. World Cup Football Championship, Spain. Multicoloured.

1594 25 f. Type **288** (postage) . . . 15 10
1595 45 f. Tackle 35 10
1596 105 f. Heading ball (air) . . . 65 20
1597 200 f. Fighting for possession 1·25 45
1598 300 f. Dribble . . . . 2·00 55

289 "Papilio dardanus"

1982. Butterflies. Multicoloured.

1600 15 f. Type **289** (postage) . . . 20 10
1601 20 f. "Belenois calypso" . . . 35 10
1602 25 f. "Palla decius" 40 10
1603 90 f. "Euxanthe eurinome" (air) 1·40 90
1604 105 f. "Mylothris rhodope" . 1·60 1·00

290 Infant Jesus

1982. Christmas. Details of Raphael's "Madonna del Baldacchino". Multicoloured.

1606 45 f. Type **290** 40 10
1607 70 f. Madonna 55 15
1608 105 f. Angel 70 20
1609 130 f. Angel (different) . . . 1·00 30
1610 150 f. Putti . . . . 1·10 35

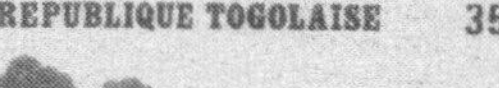

291 Building, Sokode

1983. Visit of President Mitterrand of France. Multicoloured.

1612 35 f. Type **291** (postage) . . . 20 10
1613 45 f. Children of different races and world map 35 15
1614 70 f. French and Togolese soldiers (vert) 55 20
1615 90 f. President Mitterrand (air) (vert) 70 30
1616 105 f. Presidents Mitterrand and Eyadema shaking hands (vert) 80 35
1617 130 f. Presidents Mitterrand and Eyadema and crowds . . . 1·00 40

1983. World Cup Football Championship Results. Nos. 1594/8 optd **VAINQUER COUPE DU MONDE FOOTBALL 82 "ITALIE"**. Multicoloured.

1618 25 f. Type **288** (postage) . . . 15 10
1619 45 f. Tackle 35 15
1620 105 f. Heading ball (air) . . . 65 35
1621 200 f. Fighting for possession 1·25 55
1622 300 f. Dribble . . . . 2·00 80

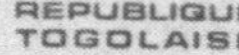

293 Map of Africa showing W.A.M.U. Members

294 Drummer

1983. 20th Anniv of West African Monetary Union. Multicoloured.

1624 70 f. Type **293** 50 15
1625 90 f. West African coin . . . 60 20

1983. World Communications Year. Multicoloured.

1626 70 f. Type **294** (postage) . . 55 15
1627 90 f. Modern post office and telecommunications system (air) 65 20

295 Boxing

1983. Air. Pre-Olympic Year. Multicoloured.

1628 70 f. Type **295** 50 15
1629 90 f. Hurdles 60 20
1630 105 f. Pole vault 65 20
1631 130 f. Sprinting . . . . . . 1·00 30

296 Kondona Dance

1983. Traditional Dances. Multicoloured.

1633 70 f. Type **296** (postage) . . 60 20
1634 90 f. Kondona dance (different) (air) 80 20
1635 105 f. Toubole dance 90 20
1636 130 f. Adjogbo dance . . . 1·10 20

297 Painting by Bellini

1983. Easter. Multicoloured.

1637 35 f. Type **297** (postage) . . 30 10
1638 70 f. Raphael (vert) 50 15
1639 90 f. Carracci (air) 65 20

298 Catholic Church, Kante

1983. Christmas. Multicoloured.

1641 70 f. Type **298** (postage) . . 50 15
1642 90 f. Altar, Dapaong Cathedral (air) 60 20
1643 105 f. Protestant church, Dapaong 70 20

299 Wrecked Airplane

1984. 10th Anniv of Sarakawa Assassination Attempt. Multicoloured.

1645 70 f. Type **299** (postage) . . . 50 25
1646 90 f. Wrecked airplane (different) 60 30
1647 120 f. Memorial Hall (air) . . 85 40
1648 270 f. Statue of President Eyadema (vert) . . . . . . 1·90 70

300 Picking Coffee Beans

1984. World Food Programme Day. Multicoloured.

1649 35 f. Type **300** 20 10
1650 70 f. Harvesting cocoa pods . 50 15
1651 90 f. Planting rice 65 20

301 Flags, Agriculture and Symbols of Unity Growth

1984. 25th Anniv of Council of Unity.

1653 **301** 70 f. multicoloured . . . 50 15
1654 90 f. multicoloured . . . 60 20

1984. Air. 19th Universal Postal Union Congress, Hamburg. Nos 1451/2 optd **19E CONGRES UPU HAMBOURG 1984**.

1655 250 f. multicoloured . . . . . 1·60 85
1656 500 f. multicoloured . . . . . 3·25 1·60

303 Tim Thorpe (gold, pentathlon and decathlon, 1912)

304 Thief on right-hand Cross

1984. Air. Olympic Games Medal Winners (1st series). Multicoloured.

1657 500 f. Type **303** . . . . 4·50 85
1658 500 f. Mathias Behr (silver, fencing, 1984) . . . . . . 4·50 85
1659 500 f. Fredy Schmidtke (gold, cycling, 1984) . . . . . . 4·50 85
1660 500 f. Dietmar Mogenburg (gold, high jumping, 1984) . 4·50 85
1661 500 f. Sabine Everts (bronze, heptathlon, 1984) . . . . . 4·50 85
1662 500 f. Jesse Owens (gold, 200 metres, 1936) . . . . . . 4·50 85
1663 500 f. Bob Beamon (gold, long jumping, 1968) . . . . . 4·50 85
1664 500 f. Muhammad Ali (gold, boxing, 1960) . . . . 22·00 85

See also Nos. 1825/32.

1984. Easter. Details from stained glass window in Norwich Cathedral. Multicoloured.

1665 70 f. Roman guard (postage) . 50 15
1666 90 f. Mary Magdalene (air) . . 55 15
1667 120 f. The Apostles comforting Mary 80 20
1668 270 f. Type **304** . . . . . . 1·60 45
1669 300 f. Thief on left-hand Cross 2·00 55

305 Baguida (site of Protectorate Treaty signature, 1884)

1984. Centenary of Proclamation of German Protectorate. Multicoloured.

1671 35 f. Type **305** 20 20
1672 35 f. Degbenou School, 1893 (horiz) 20 20
1673 35 f. Degbenou Catholic Mission, 1893 (horiz) . . . 20 20
1674 35 f. Kara suspension bridge, 1911 (horiz) 20 20
1675 35 f. Adjido state school (horiz) 20 20
1676 35 f. Administration post, Sansane Mango, 1908 (horiz) 20 20
1677 35 f. Sokode cotton market, 1910 (horiz) 20 20
1678 45 f. Main street, Lome, 1895, and 5 m. "Yacht" stamp (horiz) 35 35
1679 45 f. Governor's Palace, Lome, 1905 (horiz) 35 35
1680 45 f. Drilling police squad, 1905 (horiz) 35 35
1681 45 f. Guillaume fountain, Atakpame, 1906 . . . . . 35 35
1682 45 f. Constructing Lome–Atakpame railway (horiz) . 35 35
1683 45 f. Rue de Commerce, Lome, and 10 pf. "Yacht" stamp (horiz) 35 35
1684 70 f. 20 pf. and 2 m. "Yacht" stamps, 1900 (horiz) . . . 50 45
1685 70 f. Lome wharf, 1903 (horiz) 50 45
1686 90 f. Farming, Sansane Mango, 1908 (horiz) 60 55
1687 90 f. Chancellor Otto von Bismark 60 55
1688 90 f. Emperor Wilhelm II . . 60 55
1689 90 f. Commissoner J. von Puttkamer, 1891–93 . . . 60 55
1690 90 f. Consul-General G. Nachtigal, 1884 . . . . 60 55
1691 90 f. Governor A. Koehler, 1895–1902 . . . . 60 55
1692 90 f. Governor W. Horn, 1902–1905 . . . . 60 55
1693 90 f. Governor J. G. von Zech, 1905–10 . . . . 60 55
1694 90 f. Governor E. Bruckner, 1911–12 . . . . 60 55
1695 90 f. Governor A. F. von Mecklenberg, 1912–14 . . 60 55
1696 90 f. Governor H. G. von Doering, 1914 . . . . . . 60 55
1697 120 f. Signing of Protectorate Treaty, 1885 (horiz) . . . 90 85
1698 120 f. Postmen, 1885 . . . . . 90 85
1699 150 f. Children dancing around maps and flags . . . . . . 1·10 95
1700 270 f. German gunboat "Mowe", 1884 (horiz) . . 2·00 1·75
1701 270 f. German sail corvette "Sophie", 1884 . . . . . 2·00 1·75
1702 270 f. Steam train from Aneho railway, 1905 (horiz) . . . 2·00 1·75
1703 270 f. "Mallet" train from Kpalime, railway, 1907 (horiz) . . . . 2·00 1·75
1704 270 f. Flags and Presidents of Togo and Germany (horiz) 2·25 1·90

306 High Jumping

1984. Air. Olympic Games, Los Angeles. Mult.

1705 70 f. Type **306** 45 25
1706 90 f. Cycling 55 20
1707 120 f. Football 80 30
1708 250 f. Boxing (horiz) . . . . 1·60 50
1709 400 f. Running (horiz) . . . 2·75 80

307 Donald with Presents and Chip

1984. 50th Anniv of Donald Duck (cartoon character). Multicoloured.
1711 1 f. Type **307** (postage) . . . 10 10
1712 2 f. Donald and Chip'n'Dale 10 10
1713 3 f. Huey, Chip and Dale blowing up balloons . . . 10 10
1714 5 f. Donald and Chip holding birthday cake 10 10
1715 10 f. Daisy kissing Donald . 30 10
1716 15 f. Goofy giving Donald his present 40 10
1717 105 f. Huey, Dewey and Louie decorating cake (air) . . . 85 15
1718 500 f. Huey, Dewey, Louie and Donald with birthday cake 4·50 95
1719 1000 f. Huey, Duey and Louie startling Donald . . . . . 7·50 1·60

308 West African Manatee

1984. Endangered Wildlife. Multicoloured.
1722 45 f. Type **308** (postage) . . . 85 15
1723 70 f. Manatee (close up) . . 1·10 20
1724 90 f. Manatees in water (air) . 1·40 35
1725 105 f. Manatee with cub . . 1·40 35

309 Flame and Eleanor Roosevelt

1984. Birth Cent of Eleanor Roosevelt. Mult.
1727 70 f. Type **309** (postage) . . . 55 15
1728 90 f. Eleanor Roosevelt and Statue of Liberty (air) . . . 65 15

310 Lockheed Constellation, 1944

1984. 40th Anniv of International Civil Aviation Organization. Multicoloured.
1729 70 f. Type **310** (postage) . . . 55 30
1730 105 f. Boeing 707, 1954 (air) 60 40
1731 200 f. Douglas DC-8-61, 1966 1·25 80
1732 500 f. Concorde, 1966 . . . . 3·25 1·75

311 Bristol "400", 1947

1984. Classic Cars. Multicoloured.
1734 1 f. Type **311** (postage) . . . 10 10
1735 2 f. Frazer Nash "Standard", 1925 . . . . 10 10
1736 3 f. Healey "Silverstone", 1950 10 10
1737 4 f. Kissell "Gold Bug Speedstar", 1925 . . . . . 10 10
1738 50 f. La Salle 5 litre, 1927 . . 80 15
1739 90 f. Minerva 30 h.p., 1921 (air) 70 15
1740 500 f. Morgan "Plus 4", 1950 4·25 95
1741 1000 f. Napier 40/50 T75 Six", 1921 . . . . 7·75 2·25

313 "Connestabile Madonna"

1984. Christmas. Paintings by Raphael. Multicoloured.
1744 70 f. Type **313** (postage) . . 55 15
1745 290 f. "The Cowper Madonna" (air) . . . . 1·90 65
1746 300 f. "The Alba Madonna" 2·00 65
1747 500 f. "Madonna of the Curtain" . . . . 3·25 1·10

314 "Decapotable" Locomotive, Madeira

1984. Railway Locomotives. Multicoloured.
1749 1 f. Type **314** (postage) . . . 10 10
1750 2 f. British-made locomotive, Egyptian railway 10 10
1751 3 f. "Garratt" locomotive, Algerian railway 10 10
1752 4 f. Diesel train, Congo-Ocean railway 10 10
1753 50 f. Italian-made locomotive, Libyan railway 65 15
1754 90 f. No. "49" Northern railway locomotive (air) 55 15
1755 105 f. "Mallet" locomotive, Togo railway 65 20
1756 500 f. Steam locomotive, Rhodesian railway . . . . 3·75 70
1757 1000 f. Beyer-Garratt steam locomotive, East African railway . . . . 7·25 2·25

315 Map of Americas and Flags

316 St. Paul

1984. 3rd E.E.C.-African States Convention, Lome. Multicoloured.
1759 100 f. Type **315** 80 20
1760 130 f. Map of Europe and Africa and flags . . . . . 1·10 30
1761 270 f. Map of Asia and Australasia and flags . . . 2·00 60

Nos. 1759/61 were printed in se-tenant strips of three, forming a composite design showing map of the world.

1984. The Twelve Apostles. Multicoloured.
1763 1 f. Type **316** (postage) . . . 10 10
1764 2 f. Saint Thomas 10 10
1765 3 f. Saint Matthew 10 10
1766 4 f. Saint James, the Less . . 10 10
1767 5 f. Saint Simon, the Zealot 10 10
1768 70 f. Saint Thaddeus 85 15
1769 90 f. Saint Bartholomew (air) 55 15
1770 105 f. Saint Philip 65 15
1771 200 f. Saint John . . . . . 1·25 35
1772 270 f. Saint James, son of Zebedee . . . . 1·60 45
1773 400 f. Saint Andrew . . . . 2·50 80
1774 500 f. Saint Peter . . . . . 3·25 90

317 Allez France

1985. Racehorses. Multicoloured.
1776 1 f. Type **317** (postage) . . . 10 10
1777 2 f. Arkle (vert) 10 10
1778 3 f. Tingle Creek (vert) . . . 10 10
1779 4 f. Interco 10 10
1780 50 f. Dawn Run 95 15
1781 90 f. Seattle Slew (vert) (air) . 85 20
1782 500 f. Nijinsky . . . . 4·75 90
1783 1000 f. Politician . . . . . . 7·75 2·25

318 Map, Globe and Doves

1985. Air. Peace and Human Rights. Multicoloured.
1785 230 f. Type **318** . . . . 1·50 55
1786 270 f. Palm tree by shore and emblem . . . . 1·75 55
1787 500 f. Mining and emblem . . 3·25 1·10
1788 1000 f. Human Rights monument . . . . 6·75 2·50

319 "Christ and the Fisherman"

1985. Easter. Paintings by Raphael. Multicoloured.
1789 70 f. "Christ and the Apostles" (postage) 55 15
1790 90 f. Type **319** 60 20
1791 135 f. "Christ making Benediction" (vert) (air) . . 1·00 20
1792 150 f. "The Entombment" (vert) 1·10 30
1793 250 f. "The Resurrection" (vert) 1·75 50

320 Profiles and Emblem

1985. 15th Anniv of Cultural and Technical Co-operation Agency.
1795 **320** 70 f. multicoloured . . . 50 20
1796 90 f. multicoloured . . . 60 30

321 Adifo Dance

1985. Air. Traditional Dances. Multicoloured.
1797 120 f. Type **321** 80 30
1798 125 f. Whip dance 90 35
1799 290 f. Idjombi dance . . . . 1·90 65
1800 500 f. Moba dance . . . . . 3·25 95

322 Kabye Man **324** "Clavatula muricata"

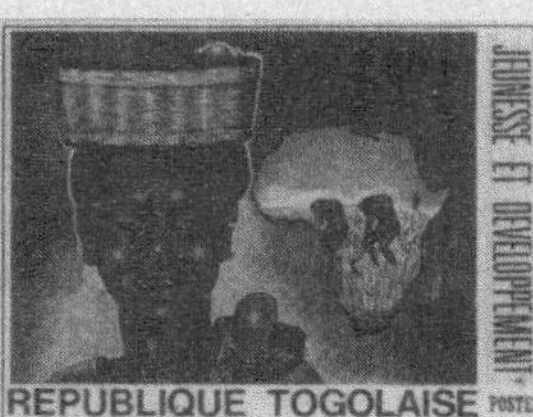

323 Woman carrying Basket on Head and Workers on Map

1985. Tribal Markings. Multicoloured.
1801 25 f. Type **322** (postage) . . . 15 10
1802 70 f. Mollah woman 50 20
1803 90 f. Moba man (air) 60 20
1804 105 f. Kabye woman 80 20
1805 270 f. Peda woman . . . . . 1·90 65

1985. "Philexafrique" Stamp Exhibition, Lome. "Youth and Development". Multicoloured.
1806 200 f. Type **323** . . . . . . 1·60 90
1807 200 f. Man ploughing field with oxen . . . . 1·60 90

1985. Sea Shells. Multicoloured.
1808 70 f. Type **324** (postage) . . . 95 20
1809 90 f. "Marginella desjardini" (air) . . . . 1·00 25
1810 120 f. "Clavatula nifat" . . . 1·25 25
1811 135 f. "Cypraea stercoraria" . 1·50 25
1812 270 f. "Conus genuanus" . . 3·00 60

1985. "Expo '85" World's Fair, Tsukuba, Japan. Nos. 1738 and 1741 optd **EXPOSITION MONDIALE 1985 TSUKUBA, JAPON.**
1814 50 f. La Salle 5 litre, 1927 (postage) 85 20
1815 1000 f. Napier "40/50 T75 Six", 1921 (air) . . . . 9·50 2·75

326 Pope giving Blessing

327 Brown Pelican

1985. Air. Visit of Pope John Paul II. Multicoloured.
1817 90 f. Pope and children . . . 85 20
1818 130 f. Type **326** . . . . . . 1·10 35
1819 500 f. Pres. Eyadema greeting Pope . . . . 4·25 2·25

1985. Birth Bicentenary of John J. Audubon (ornithologist). Multicoloured.
1820 120 f. Type **327** (postage) . . 1·40 85
1821 270 f. Golden eagle . . . . 3·00 2·00
1822 90 f. Bonaparte's gulls (air) . 1·10 65
1823 135 f. Great-tailed grackle . . 1·50 95
1824 500 f. Red-headed wood-pecker 6·25 4·00

1985. Air. Olympic Games Medal Winners (2nd series). Nos. 1657/64 optd.
1826 500 f. **"ITALIE MEDAILLE D'OR"** . . . . 4·00 85
1827 500 f. **"PHILIPPE BOISSE/ FRANCE/MEDAILLE D'OR"** . . . . 4·00 85
1828 500 f. **"ROLF GOLZ/R.F.A./ MEDAILLE D'ARGENT"** 4·00 85
1829 500 f. **"PATRIK SJOBERG/ SUEDE/MEDAILLE D'ARGENT"** . . . . . . 4·00 85
1830 500 f. **"GLYNIS NUNN/ AUSTRALIE/MEDAILLE D'OR"** . . . . 4·00 85
1831 500 f. **"KIRK BAPTISTE/ ETATS UNIS/MEDAILLE D'ARGENT"** . . . . . . 4·00 85
1832 500 f. **"CARL LEWIS/ETATS UNIS/MEDAILLE D'OR"** 4·00 85
1833 500 f. **"KEVIN BARRY/NLE ZELANDE/MEDAILLE D'ARGENT"** . . . . . . 4·00 85

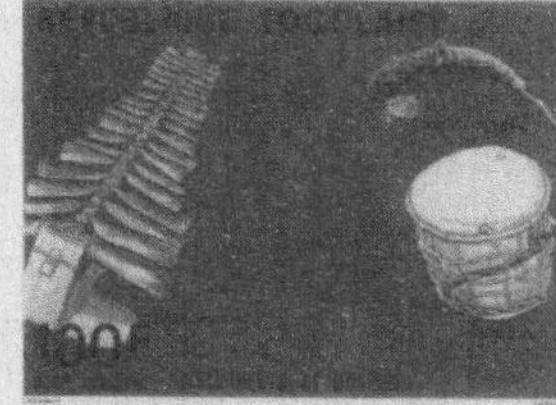
330 Gongophone, Kante Horn and Drum

1985. Air. "Philexafrique" Stamp Exhibition, Lome (2nd issue). Musical Instruments. Multicoloured.
1835 100 f. Type **330** . . . . . . 1·40 65
1836 100 f. Twin drums, Bassar horn and castanets . . . . . . 1·40 65

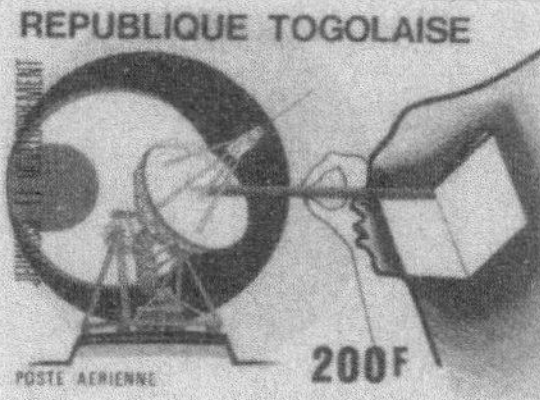

331 Open Book, Profile, Hand holding Pencil and Dish Aerial

1985. Air. "Philexafrique" Stamp Exhibition, Lome (3rd issue). "Youth and Development". Mult.
1837 200 f. Type **331** . . . . . . 1·90 1·10
1838 200 f. Profiles, factory, cogwheel and maize . . . . 1·90 1·10

332 Dove, Sun and U.N. Emblem

1985. 40th Anniv of U.N.O. Multicoloured.
1839 90 f. Type **332** (postage) . . . 60 20
1840 115 f. Hands reaching up to Emblem . . . 90 20
1841 150 f. Building new bridge on river Kara (air) . . . 1·10 35
1842 250 f. Preparing experimental field of millet at Atalote, Keran . . . 1·60 50
1843 500 f. Pres. Eyadema, U.N. Secretary-General, U.N. and national flags . . . 3·25 85

333 "Madonna of the Rose Garden" (Sandro Botticelli)
335 "The Resurrection" (Andrea Mantegna)

1985. Christmas. Multicoloured.
1844 90 f. Type **333** (postage) . . . 65 20
1845 115 f. "Madonna and Child" (11th-century Byzantine painting) (air) . . . 90 20
1846 150 f. "Rest during the flight into Egypt" (Gerard David) . . . 1·00 30
1847 160 f. "African Madonna" (16th-century statue) . . . 1·10 30
1848 250 f. "African Madonna" (statue, 1900) . . . 2·00 45

1985. Various stamps optd. (a) Nos. 1739/40 optd **10e ANNIVERSAIRE DE APOLLO-SOYUZ.**
1850 90 f. Minerva 30 h.p., 1921 . . . 85 30
1851 500 f. Morgan "Plus 4", 1950 . . . 4·75 1·40

(b) Nos. 1752, 1755 and 1757 optd **80e ANNIVERSAIRE du/ROTARY INTERNATIONAL.**
1853 4 f. Train, Congo-Ocean railway . . . 85 20
1854 105 f. "Mallet" locomotive, Togo railways . . . 65 30
1855 1000 f. Beyer-Garratt steam locomotive, East African railway . . . 8·25 2·75

(c) 150th Anniv of German Railways. Nos. 1753/4 and 1756 optd **"150e ANNIVERSAIRE/DE CHEMIN FER 'LUDWIG'"**
1857 50 f. Italian-made locomotive, Libyan railway . . . 85 20
1858 90 f. No. "49" Northern railway locomotive . . . 85 30
1859 500 f. Locomotive, Rhodesian railway . . . 4·75 1·40

(d) Nos. 1773/4 optd **"75e ANNIVERSAIRE DE LA/MORT DE HENRI DUNANT/FONDATEUR DE LA/CROIX ROUGE".**
1861 400 f. Saint Andrew . . . 3·25 1·10
1862 500 f. Saint Peter . . . 4·00 1·40

(e) Nos. 1780 and 1783 optd **"75e ANNIVERSAIRE/DU SCOUTISME FEMININ".**
1864 50 f. Dawn Run . . . 85 20
1865 1000 f. Politician . . . 8·25 2·25

1986. Easter. Multicoloured.
1867 25 f. Type **335** (postage) . . . 20 10
1868 70 f. "Calvary" (Paul Veronese) . . . 55 15
1869 90 f. "The Last Supper" (Jacopo Robusti Tintoretto) (horiz) (air) . . . 65 30
1870 200 f. "Christ in the Tomb" (Berruguette) (horiz) . . . 1·50 55

336 "Suisie" Space Probe and Kohoutek's Comet

INDEX

Countries can be quickly located by referring to the index at the end of this volume.

1986. Appearance of Halley's Comet (1st issue). Multicoloured.
1872 70 f. Type **336** (postage) . . . 55 15
1873 90 f. "Vega I" space probe and people pointing at comet (air) . . . 55 20
1874 150 f. Comet and observation equipment . . . 90 30
1875 200 f. "Giotto" space probe and comet over town . . . 1·25 40
See also Nos. 1917/20.

337 New York, Statue and Eiffel Tower
338 Cashew Nut

1986. Air. Centenary of Statue of Liberty. Multicoloured.
1877 70 f. Type **337** . . . 50 15
1878 90 f. Statue, Arc de Triomphe and Brooklyn Bridge . . . 60 20
1879 500 f. Statue, Pantheon and Empire State Building . . . 3·25 1·10

1986. Fruit. Multicoloured.
1880 70 f. Type **338** (postage) . . . 55 15
1881 90 f. Pineapple . . . 80 20
1882 120 f. Avocado (air) . . . 90 20
1883 135 f. Papaw . . . 1·10 20
1884 290 f. Mango (vert) . . . 2·25 65

339 Footballers
341 "Ramaria moelleriana"

1986. World Cup Football Championship, Mexico.
1885 **339** 70 f. mult (postage) . . . 55 15
1886 – 90 f. mult (air) . . . 55 30
1887 – 130 f. multicoloured . . . 85 35
1888 – 300 f. multicoloured . . . 1·90 70
DESIGNS: 90 f. to 300 f. Various footballing scenes.

1986. Air. "Ameripex '86" International Stamp Exhibition, Chicago. Nos. 1718/19 optd **AMERIPEX 86.**
1890 500 f. Huey, Dewey, Louie and Donald with birthday cake . . . 4·50 1·10
1891 1000 f. Huey, Dewey and Louie startling Donald . . . 8·25 2·25

1986. Fungi. Multicoloured.
1893 70 f. Type **341** . . . 50 30
1894 90 f. "Hygrocybe firma" . . . 60 40
1895 150 f. "Kalchbrennera corallocephala" . . . 1·10 75
1896 200 f. "Cookeina tricholoma" . . . 1·60 1·00

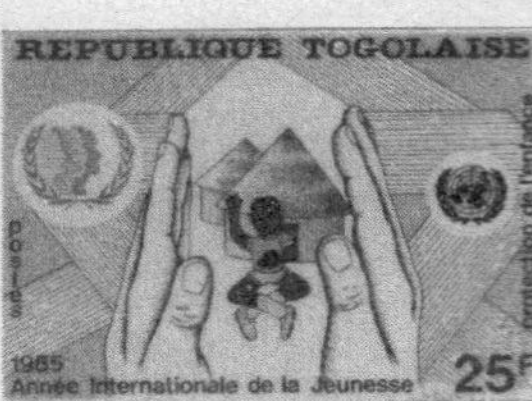

342 Hand framing Huts and Child

1986. International Youth Year (1985). Mult.
1897 25 f. Type **342** . . . 30 15
1898 90 f. Children feeding birds . . . 1·10 40

343 Wrestlers
344 Miss Sarah Ferguson

1986. Evala Wrestling Contest.
1899 **343** 15 f. mult (postage) . . . 15 10
1900 – 20 f. multicoloured . . . 30 10
1901 – 70 f. multicoloured . . . 65 15
1902 – 90 f. multicoloured (air) . . . 40 35
DESIGNS: 20 to 90 f. Wrestling scenes.

1986. Wedding of Prince Andrew. Multicoloured.
1903 10 f. Type **344** (postage) . . . 55 10
1904 1000 f. Prince Andrew (air) . . . 6·75 2·25

1986. World Cup Winners. Nos. 1886/9 optd.
1906 70 f. **DEMI-FINALE/ARGENTINE 2/BELGIQUE 0** (postage) . . . 55 35
1907 90 f. **DEMI-FINALE/ALLEMAGNE/DE L'OUEST 2/FRANCE 0** (air) . . . 55 20
1908 130 f. **3 eme et 4 eme PLACE/FRANCE 4/BELGIQUE 2** . . . 85 35
1909 300 f. **FINALE/ARGENTINE 3/ALLEMAGNE/DE L'OUEST 2** . . . 1·90 80

346 Fazao Hotel

1986. Hotels. Multicoloured.
1910 70 f. Type **346** (postage) . . . 55 15
1911 90 f. Sarakawa Hotel (air) . . . 65 30
1912 120 f. The Lake Hotel . . . 90 40

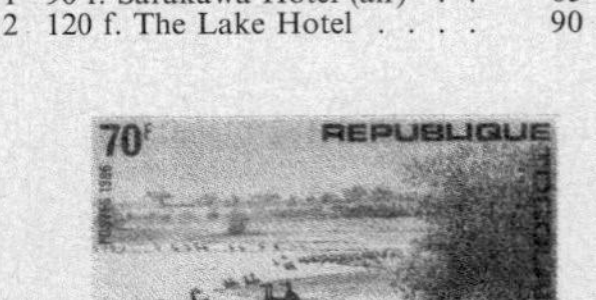

347 Spur-winged Geese

1986. Keran National Park. Multicoloured.
1913 70 f. Type **347** (postage) . . . 55 20
1914 90 f. Antelope (air) . . . 65 30
1915 100 f. African elephant . . . 80 35
1916 130 f. Kob . . . 1·00 45

1986. Appearance of Halley's Comet (2nd issue). Nos. 1872/5 optd as T **213a** of Maldive Islands.
1917 **336** 70 f. mult (postage) . . . 1·25 35
1918 – 90 f. multicoloured (air) . . . 1·00 30
1919 – 150 f. multicoloured . . . 1·50 40
1920 – 200 f. multicoloured . . . 1·90 70

349 "The Annunciation"
350 Rainbow and Douglas DC-10

1986. Christmas. Multicoloured.
1922 45 f. Type **349** (postage) . . . 45 15
1923 120 f. "Nativity" (air) . . . 90 35
1924 130 f. "Adoration of the Magi" . . . 1·10 45
1925 200 f. "Flight into Egypt" . . . 1·50 65

1986. Air. 25th Anniv of Air Afrique.
1927 **350** 90 f. multicoloured . . . 75 45

351 Pres. Eyadema and Phosphate Mine

1987. 20th Anniv of National Liberation. Multicoloured.
1928 35 f. Type **351** (postage) . . . 20 10
1929 50 f. Anie sugar refinery . . . 35 15
1930 70 f. Nangbeto Dam . . . 50 20
1931 90 f. February 2 Hotel and Posts and Telecommunications building, Lome . . . 60 20
1932 100 f. Post and Telecommunications building, Kara (air) . . . 55 15
1933 120 f. Peace monument . . . 80 30
1934 130 f. Baby being vaccinated . . . 90 35

352 "The Last Supper"

1987. Easter. Paintings from Nadoba Church, Keran. Multicoloured.
1936 90 f. Type **352** (postage) . . . 65 30
1937 130 f. "Christ on the Cross" (air) . . . 90 30
1938 300 f. "The Resurrection" . . . 2·00 65

353 Adenauer speaking in the Bundestag

1987. Air. 20th Death Anniv of Konrad Adenauer (German Chancellor). Multicoloured.
1940 120 f. Type **353** . . . 85 30
1941 500 f. Adenauer with John F. Kennedy . . . 3·25 1·10

354 Player falling with Ball

1987. World Rugby Football Cup. Multicoloured.
1943 70 f. Type **354** (postage) . . . 80 30
1944 130 f. Player running with ball (air) . . . 1·25 35
1945 300 f. Scrum . . . 2·75 1·25

355 "Adenium obesum"

1987. Flowers. Multicoloured.
1947 70 f. Type **355** (postage) . . . 60 20
1948 90 f. "Amorphophallus abyssinicus" (vert) (air) . . . 65 30
1949 100 f. "Ipomoea mauritiana" . . . 80 30
1950 120 f. "Salacia togoica" (vert) . . . 90 35

356 Wilhelm I Coin and Victory Statue

1987. Air. 750th Anniv of Berlin. Multicoloured.
1951 90 f. Friedrich III coin and Brandenburg Gate . . . 1·00 35
1953 300 f. Wilhelm II coin and Place de la Republique . . . 2·00 65

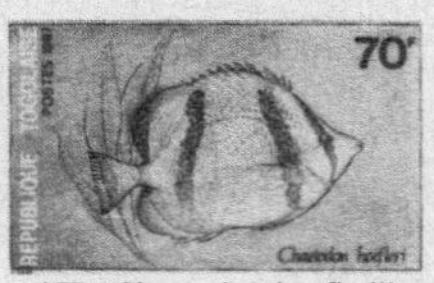

357 "Chaetodon hoefleri"

1987. Fishes. Multicoloured.
1955 70 f. Type **357** . . . 55 20
1956 90 f. "Tetraodon lineatus" . . . 65 25
1957 120 f. "Chaetodipterus goreensis" . . . 85 35
1958 130 f. "Labeo parvus" . . . 1·00 35

358 Long Jumping

1987. Olympic Games, Seoul (1988). Mult.
1959 70 f. Type **358** (postage) 60 20
1960 90 f. Relay race (air) 60 20
1961 200 f. Cycling 1·25 45
1962 250 f. Javelin throwing 1·60 55

1987. Endangered Wildlife. As Nos. 1722/5 but values changed and size 37 × 24 mm.
1964 60 f. Type **308** (postage) 80 20
1965 75 f. Manatee (close up) 90 35
1966 80 f. Manatees in water 1·10 35
1967 100 f. Manatee with cub (air) 1·40 40

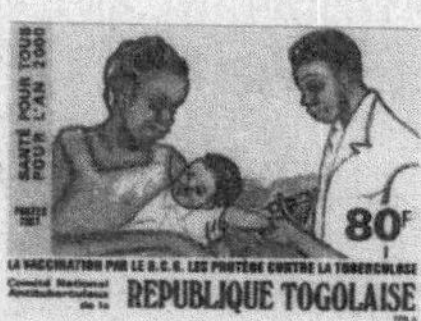

359 Doctor vaccinating Child

1987. "Health for All by Year 2000". Anti-tuberculosis Campaign. Multicoloured.
1968 80 f. Type **359** (postage) 55 30
1969 90 f. Family under umbrella (vert) (air) 60 30
1970 115 f. Faculty of Medicine building, Lome University 80 35

360 "Spring or the Earthly Paradise"

1987. Christmas. Multicoloured.
1971 40 f. Type **360** (postage) 35 10
1972 45 f. "The Creation of Adam" (Michelangelo) 35 10
1973 105 f. "Presentation in the Temple" (vert) (air) 65 20
1974 270 f. "The Original Sin" (vert) 1·75 65

361 Men ploughing and Women collecting Water

1988. 10th Anniv of Agricultural Development Fund.
1976 **361** 90 f. multicoloured 65 20

363 "The Dance"

1988. 15th Death Anniv of Pablo Picasso (painter). Multicoloured.
1978 45 f. Type **363** (postage) 45 10
1979 160 f. "Portrait of a Young Girl" 1·50 35
1980 300 f. "Gueridon" (air) 2·75 85

364 Cement

365 "Jesus and the Disciples at Emmaus"

1988. Industries. Multicoloured.
1982 125 f. Type **354** 85 30
1983 165 f. Brewery 1·10 40
1984 195 f. Phosphates 1·25 45
1985 200 f. Plastics 1·25 45
1986 300 f. Milling (vert) 2·10 65

1988. Easter. Stained Glass Windows. Mult.
1987 70 f. Type **365** (postage) 60 15
1988 90 f. "Mary at the Foot of the Cross" 80 20
1989 120 f. "Crucifixion" (air) 85 30
1990 200 f. "St. Thomas and Resurrected Jesus" 1·40 45

366 Paris Crowd welcoming Kennedy, 1961

367 Watchi Chief

1988. 25th Death Anniv of John F. Kennedy (U.S. President). Multicoloured.
1992 125 f. Type **366** 1·00 20
1993 155 f. Kennedy at Paris Town Hall (vert) 1·10 20
1994 165 f. Kennedy and De Gaulle at Elysee Palace (vert) 1·25 40
1995 180 f. John and Jacqueline Kennedy at Orly Airport 1·40 75

1988. Traditional Tribal Costumes. Multicoloured.
1997 80 f. Type **367** 55 20
1998 125 f. Watchi woman 85 20
1999 165 f. Kotokoli man 1·10 35
2000 175 f. Ewe man 1·10 35

368 Basketball

369 People with Candles

1988. Olympic Games, Seoul. Multicoloured.
2002 70 f. Type **368** (postage) 50 15
2003 90 f. Tennis 60 20
2004 120 f. Archery (air) 85 30
2005 200 f. Throwing the discus 1·40 45

1988. 40th Anniv of W.H.O. Multicoloured.
2007 80 f. Type **369** 55 15
2008 125 f. Maps, emblem and "40" 85 20

370 Plaited Style

1988. Hairstyles. Multicoloured.
2009 80 f. Type **370** 55 20
2010 125 f. Knotted style 85 20
2011 170 f. Plaited style with bow 1·00 40
2112 180 f. Style with plaits all over head (vert) 1·25 40

371 Collecting Water (B. Gossner)

372 "Adoration of the Magi" (Pieter Brueghel the Elder)

1988. "Philtogo" National Stamp Exhibition. Designs depicting winning entries of a schools drawing competition. Multicoloured.
2014 10 f. Type **371** 10 10
2015 35 f. Villagers working on farm (K. Ekoue-Kouvahey) 20 10
2016 70 f. Family (A. Abbey) 65 15
2017 90 f. Village women preparing food (T. D. Lawson) 85 30
2018 120 f. Fishermen and boats on shore (A. Tazzar) 1·10 35

1988. Christmas. Multicoloured.
2019 80 f. Type **372** (postage) 55 20
2020 150 f. "The Virgin, The Infant Jesus, Saints Jerome and Dominic" (Fra. Filippo Lippi) (air) 1·00 20
2021 175 f. "The Madonna, The Infant Jesus, St. Joseph and the Infant St. John the Baptist" (Federico Barocci) 1·25 35
2022 195 f. "The Virgin and Child" (Gentile Bellini) 1·40 45

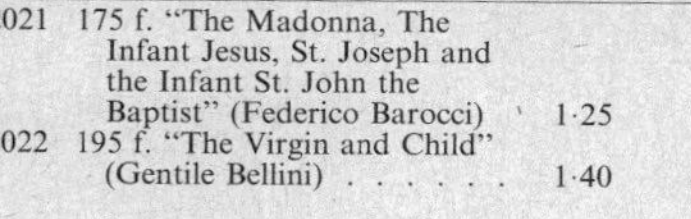

373 Wreckage of Airplane

1989. 15th Anniv of Sarakawa Assassination Attempt. Multicoloured.
2024 10 f. Type **373** 10 10
2025 80 f. Tail section (vert) 55 25
2026 125 f. Soldiers and wreckage 85 50

374 Anniversary Emblem

1989. 20th Anniv of Benin Electricity Community.
2027 **374** 80 f. multicoloured 60 20
2028 125 f. multicoloured 95 20

375 Boxing

1989. Prince Emanuel of Liechtenstein Foundation. Multicoloured.
2029 80 f. Type **375** 55 20
2030 125 f. Long jumping 55 30
2031 165 f. Running 1·10 40

376 Table Tennis

1989. Olympic Games, Barcelona (1992). Mult.
2032 80 f. Type **376** (postage) 65 20
2033 125 f. Running (horiz) 90 20
2034 165 f. Putting the shot 1·00 35
2035 175 f. Basketball 1·25 35
2036 380 f. High jumping (horiz) (air) 2·50 55
2037 425 f. Boxing (horiz) 3·00 55

377 Footballers and St. Janvier's Cathedral, Naples

1989. World Cup Football Championship, Italy. Multicoloured.
2039 80 f. Type **377** (postage) 55 20
2040 125 f. Milan Cathedral 85 20
2041 165 f. Bevilacqua Palace, Verona 1·10 35
2042 175 f. Baptistry, Florence 1·10 35
2043 380 f. Madama Palace, Turin (air) 2·75 55
2044 425 f. St. Laurent's Cathedral, Genoa 2·75 55

378 Bundestag

1989. 40th Anniv of Federal Republic of Germany. Multicoloured.
2046 90 f. Type **378** 65 20
2047 125 f. Konrad Adenauer (Chancellor, 1949–63) and Theodor Heuss (President, 1949–59) (vert) 95 30
2048 180 f. West German flag and emblem 1·25 40

379 Tractor, Map and Woman at Water-pump

1989. 30th Anniv of Council of Unity.
2049 **379** 75 f. multicoloured 55 20

380 Boys learning First Aid

1989. 125th Anniv of International Red Cross. Multicoloured.
2050 90 f. Type **380** 50 20
2051 125 f. Founding meeting 85 35

381 Storming the Bastille

383 People with Banners and Pres. Eyadema

382 Jacques Necker (statesman) and The Three Orders

1989. Bicentenary of French Revolution (1st issue). Multicoloured.
2052 90 f. Type **381** 65 20
2053 125 f. Oath of the Tennis Court (horiz) 1·00 35
2054 180 f. Abolition of Privileges (horiz) 1·40 45
See also Nos. 2056/9.

1989. Bicentenary of French Revolution (2nd issue). Multicoloured.
2056 90 f. Type **382** (postage) 65 20
2057 190 f. Guy le Chapelier and abolition of seigneurial rights 1·50 45
2058 425 f. Talleyrand-Perigord (statesman) and La Fayette's oath 2·75 55
2059 480 f. Paul Barras (revolutionary) and overthrow of Robespierre 3·25 55

1989. 20th Anniv of Kpalime Appeal. Mult.
2061 90 f. Type **383** 60 20
2062 125 f. Pres. Eyadema addressing gathering 90 35

384 "Apollo II" Launch

386 Emblem

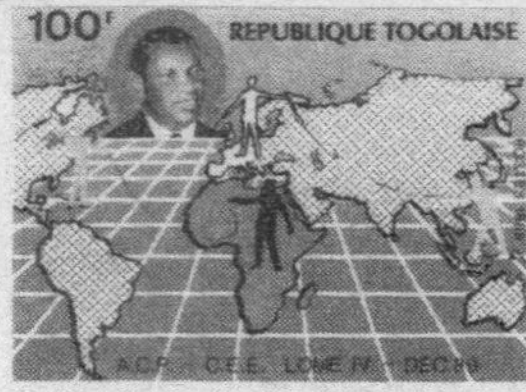

385 Figures on Map (dated "DEC.89")

1989. 20th Anniv of First Manned Landing on Moon. Multicoloured.

2063	40 f. Type **384**	30	10
2064	90 f. Space capsule in orbit	55	20
2065	150 f. Landing capsule	1·10	35
2066	250 f. Splashdown	1·60	45

1989. 4th Lome Convention (on relations between European Community and African, Caribbean and Pacific countries). Multicoloured.

2068	100 f. Type **385**	80	30
2069	100 f. As T **385** but dated "15 DEC.89"	80	30

1990. 10th Anniv of Pan-African Postal Union.

2070	**386**	125 f. gold, blue & brown	90	30

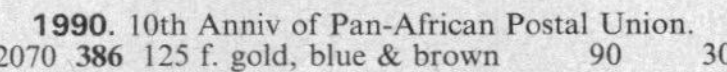

387 Party Headquarters, Kara

1990. 20th Anniv (1989) of Rally of Togolese People Party. Multicoloured.

2071	45 f. Type **387**	35	15
2072	90 f. Pres. Eyadema and anniversary emblem	60	20

388 "Myrina silenus" and Scout

389 "Danaus chrysippus"

1990. Scouts, Butterflies and Fungi. Mult.

2073	80 f. Type **388** (postage)	65	15
2074	90 f. "Phlebobus silvaticus" (fungus)	65	15
2075	125 f. "Volvariella esculenta" (fungus)	90	20
2076	165 f. "Hypolycaena antifaunus" (butterfly)	1·10	35
2077	380 f. "Termitomyces striatus" (fungus) (air)	3·00	55
2078	425 f. "Axiocerces harpax" (butterfly)	3·00	55

1990. Butterflies. Multicoloured.

2080	5 f. Type **389**	10	10
2081	10 f. "Morpho aega"	10	10
2082	15 f. "Papilio demodocus"	10	10
2083	90 f. "Papilio dardanus"	60	35

390 Emblem

391 Nile Monitor

1990. 9th Convention of Lions Club Internationals District 403, Lome.

2085	**390**	90 f. multicoloured	60	35
2086		125 f. multicoloured	85	55
2087		165 f. multicoloured	1·10	80

1990. Reptiles. Multicoloured.

2088	1 f. Type **391**	10	10
2089	25 f. Puff adder	15	10
2090	60 f. Black-lipped cobra	45	15
2091	90 f. African rock python	65	20

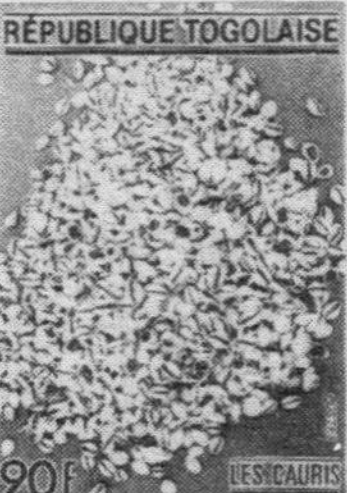

392 Pile of Cowrie Shells

393 Maps, Cogwheel and Arrows

1990. Cowrie Shells. Multicoloured.

2092	90 f. Type **392**	75	20
2093	125 f. Cowrie and bead ornament	1·25	25
2094	180 f. Headdress with cowries and animal horns	1·60	55

1990. United States–Togo Friendship. Mult.

2095	125 f. Type **393**	90	35
2096	180 f. Presidents Bush and Eyadema shaking hands (horiz)	1·25	35

394 Cinkasse Post Office

1990. Stamp Day.

2098	**394**	90 f. multicoloured	60	35

395 Addressing Crowd, Brazzaville, 1944

1990. 20th Death Anniv of Charles de Gaulle (statesman).

2099	**395**	125 f. multicoloured	85	45

396 Thatched Houses

1990. Traditional Housing. Multicoloured.

2100	90 f. Type **396**	60	35
2101	125 f. Village	85	45
2102	190 f. Tamberma house	1·25	65

397 Airport, Airliners and Airline Emblems

1990. New Lome Airport.

2103	**397**	90 f. multicoloured	60	35

398 Woman carrying Basket on Head (Sikou Dapau)

1990.

2104	**398**	90 f. multicoloured	60	35

399 Chimpanzee, Missahoue Kloto

1991. Forests. Multicoloured.

2105	90 f. Type **399**	60	35
2106	170 f. Parrot, Aledjo Forest	1·10	65
2107	185 f. Parrot, Chateau Vial Kloto Forest	1·25	65

400 Dancers

1992. Spirit Dances.

2108	**400**	90 f. multicoloured	60	35
2109	–	125 f. multicoloured	85	55
2110	–	190 f. multicoloured	1·25	80

DESIGNS: 125, 190 f. Various dances.

401 Royal Python hatching

1992. The Royal Python. Multicoloured.

2111	90 f. Type **401**	60	35
2112	125 f. Hatchlings emerging from shells	85	35
2113	190 f. Hatchlings and empty shells	1·25	65
2114	300 f. Close-up of hatchling and empty shell	1·90	90

POSTAGE DUE STAMPS

1921. Postage Due stamps of Dahomy, "figure" key-type, optd **TOGO**.

D54	M	5 c. green	40	70
D55		10 c. red	40	70
D56		15 c. grey	65	70
D57		20 c. brown	1·50	2·00
D58		30 c. blue	1·50	2·00
D59		50 c. black	1·10	1·40
D60		60 c. orange	1·40	1·60
D61		1 f. violet	2·75	3·25

D **8** Cotton Growing

1925. Centres and inscr in black.

D 97	D **8**	2 c. blue	10	30
D 98		4 c. red	10	30
D 99		5 c. greeen	10	30
D100		10 c. red	20	45
D101		15 c. yellow	20	45
D102		20 c. mauve	30	55
D103		25 c. grey	40	65
D104		30 c. yellow on blue	25	40
D105		50 c. brown	35	60
D106		60 c. green	45	70
D107		1 f. violet	50	80

1927. Surch.

D108	D **8**	2 f. on 1 f. mauve and red	2·75	2·25
D109		3 f. on 1 f. blue and brown	2·50	3·25

D **12** Native Mask

D **21**

D **31** Kon-komba Helmet

1940.

D151	D **12**	5 c. black	10	30
D152		10 c. green	15	25
D153		15 c. red	10	30
D154		20 c. blue	20	45
D155		30 c. brown	20	45
D156		50 c. olive	1·00	1·40
D157		60 c. violet	25	45
D158		1 f. blue	55	80
D159		2 f. red	30	60
D160		3 f. violet	60	85

1947.

D185	D **21**	10 c. blue	10	30
D186		30 c. red	10	30
D187		50 c. green	10	30
D188		1 f. brown	10	30
D189		2 f. red	20	40
D190		3 f. black	25	45
D191		4 f. blue	40	55
D192		5 f. brown	50	65
D193		10 f. orange	50	80
D194		20 f. blue	70	90

1957.

D214	D **31**	1 f. violet	10	25
D215		2 f. orange	10	25
D216		3 f. grey	15	30
D217		4 f. red	15	30
D218		5 f. blue	15	30
D219		10 f. green	35	45
D220		20 f. purple	50	55

1959. As Nos. D214/20 but colours changed and inscr "REPUBLIQUE DU TOGO".

D244	D **31**	1 f. brown	10	25
D245		2 f. turquoise	10	25
D246		3 f. orange	10	25
D247		4 f. blue	15	30
D248		5 f. purple	15	30
D249		10 f. violet	25	45
D250		20 f. black	55	60

D **57** "Cardium costatum"

D **110** Tomatoes

1964. Seashells. Multicoloured.

D366	1 f. "Conus papilionaceus"	10	10
D367	2 f. "Marginella faba"	10	10
D368	3 f. "Cypraea stercoraria"	10	10
D369	4 f. "Strombus latus"	20	20
D370	5 f. Type D **57**	50	50
D371	10 f. "Cancellaria cancellata"	60	60
D372	15 f. "Cymbium pepo"	1·75	1·75
D373	20 f. "Tympanotomus radula"	1·90	1·90

1969. Young Pioneers Agricultural Organization. Multicoloured.

D696	5 f. Type D **110**	10	10
D697	10 f. Corn on the cob	30	30
D698	19 f. Red pepper	40	40
D699	20 f. Peanuts	55	55

1980. As T **259**. Multicoloured.

D1454	5 f. Women examining produce (vert)	10	10
D1455	10 f. Market stall	10	10
D1456	25 f. Poultry seller	15	10
D1457	50 f. Carvings and ornaments	35	15

APPENDIX

The following stamps have either been issued in excess of postal needs or have not been available to the public in reasonable quantities at face value. Such stamps may later be given full listing if there is evidence of regular postal use.

All embossed on gold foil.

1989.

Prince Emanuel of Liechtenstein Foundation. Air. 1500 f. × 2

Bicentenary of French Revolution (2nd issue). Air. 1500 f.

Scouts, Butterflies, and Fungi. Air. 1500 f.

TOLIMA Pt. 20

One of the states of the Granadine Confederation.

A department of Colombia from 1886, now uses Colombian stamps.

100 centavos = 1 peso

1 2 3

1870. On white or coloured paper. Imperf.

6 **1** 5 c. black 25·00 20·00
13 10 c. black 30·00 18·00

1871. Various frames. Imperf.

14 **2** 5 c. brown 75 75
15 **3** 10 c. blue 2·00 2·00
16 50 c. green 3·00 3·00
17 1 p. red 6·00 6·00

6 7 8

9 10 11

1879. Imperf.

18a **6** 5 c. brown 20 20
19 **7** 10 c. blue 25 25
20a **8** 50 c. green 25 30
21a **9** 1 p. red 90 1·00

1883. Imperf.

22 **6** 5 c. orange 20 20
23 **7** 10 c. red 35 35
24 **10** 20 c. violet 50 50

1884. Imperf.

25 **11** 1 c. grey 10 10
26 2 c. red 10 10
27 2½ c. orange 10 10
28 5 c. brown 10 10
29a 10 c. blue 15 15
30 20 c. yellow 30 30
31 25 c. black 15 15
32 50 c. green 20 20
33 1 p. red 25 25
34 2 p. violet 40 35
35 5 p. orange 25 25
36 10 p. red 60 60

12 16

1886. Condor's wings touch Arms. Perf.

37 **12** 5 c. brown 50 50
38 10 c. blue 1·75 1·75
39 50 c. green 60 60
40 1 p. red 1·25 1·25

1886. Condor's wings do not touch Arms. Perf or imperf.

45 **16** 1 c. grey 2·50 2·50
46 2 c. red 3·25 3·25
47 2½ c. pink 12·00 12·00
48 5 c. brown 4·50 4·50
49 10 c. blue 6·00 6·00
50 20 c. yellow 3·25 3·25
51 25 c. black 3·00 3·00
52 50 c. green 1·40 1·10
53 1 p. red 2·25 2·25
54 2 p. violet 4·00 4·00
55 5 p. orange 7·50 7·50
56 10 p. red 3·50 3·50

20

21

1888. Perf.

67 **20** 1 c. blue on red 15 15
68 2 c. green on green 15 15
69 5 c. red 10 10
70 10 c. green 20 25
71 20 c. blue on yellow 30 30
65 50 c. blue 45 45
72 1 p. brown 75 75

1903. Imperf or perf.

85 **21** 4 c. black on green 10 10
78 10 c. green 10 10
87 20 c. orange 20 20
88 50 c. black on red 15 15
81 1 p. brown 10 10
82 2 p. grey 10 10
91 5 p. red 10 10
92 10 p. black on blue 15 15
92a 10 p. black on green 15 15

TRANSCAUCASIAN FEDERATION Pt. 10

A Federation of Armenia, Azerbaijan and Georgia, which was absorbed into the U.S.S.R. in 1923.

100 kopeks = 1 rouble

1 Mt Ararat and Oilfield

2 Mts Ararat and Elbruz and Oil-derricks

1923.

1 **1** 40,000 r. purple 1·50 3·00
2 75,000 r. green 1·50 3·00
3 100,000 r. grey 1·00 1·50
4 150,000 r. red 70 90
5 **2** 200,000 r. green 1·00 50
6 300,000 r. blue 70 1·40
7 350,000 r. brown 70 1·40
8 500,000 r. red 1·25 2·50

1923. Surch **700000 RYb**.

9 **1** 700,000 r. on 40,000 r. purple 1·50 3·00
10 700,000 r. on 75,000 r. green 1·50 3·00

1923. Values in gold kopeks.

11 **2** 1 k. orange 70 1·25
12 2 k. green 70 1·25
13 3 k. red 70 1·25
14 4 k. brown 70 1·00
15 **1** 5 k. purple 70 1·25
16 9 k. blue 70 1·25
17 18 k. grey 70 1·25

TRIESTE Pt. 8

The Free Territory of Trieste situated on the Adriatic Coast between the frontiers of Italy and Yugoslavia. In 1954 when the Territory was divided between Italy and Yugoslavia, the overprinted issues were superseded by the ordinary issues of these countries in their respective zones.

For stamps of Italy surcharged **1.V.1945. TRIESTE TRST**, five-pointed star and value, see Venezia Giulia Nos. 20/32.

ZONE A
ALLIED MILITARY GOVERNMENT

100 centesimi = 1 lira

Stamps of Italy variously overprinted **A.M.G. F.T.T.** or **AMG-FTT** (Allied Military Government — Free Territory of Trieste) except where otherwise stated.

1947. Optd in two lines. (a) Postage stamps of 1945, Nos. 647, etc.

1 25 c. turquoise 10 10
2 50 c. violet 10 10
3 1 l. green 10 10
4 2 l. brown 10 10
5 3 l. red 10 10
6 4 l. orange 10 10
7 5 l. blue 10 10
8 6 l. violet 10 10
9 8 l. green 1·00 75
10 10 l. grey 10 10
11 10 l. red 3·75 10
12 15 l. blue 25 10
13 20 l. violet 1·00 10
14 25 l. green 1·75 1·00
15 30 l. blue 60·00 90
16 50 l. purple 2·00 65
17 100 l. red (No. 669) 9·00 3·25

(b) Air stamps of 1945, Nos. 670, etc.

18 1 l. slate 10 20
19 2 l. blue 10 20
20 5 l. green 70 85
21 10 l. red 70 85
22 25 l. brown 1·00 1·00
23 50 l. violet 4·50 1·10
24 100 l. green 25·00 1·10
25 300 l. mauve 7·50 7·50
26 500 l. blue 9·50 11·00
27 1000 l. brown 75·00 85·00

1947. Air. 50th Anniv of Radio (Nos. 688/93).

59 6 l. blue 65 85
60 10 l. red 65 85
61 20 l. orange 2·00 1·00
62 25 l. blue 65 90
63 35 l. blue 65 90
64 50 l. purple 2·00 90

1948. Cent of 1848 Revolution (Nos. 706, etc.).

65 3 l. brown 10 10
66 4 l. purple 10 10
67 5 l. blue 15 10
68 6 l. green 20 15
69 8 l. brown 15 15
70 10 l. red 20 10
71 12 l. green 30 85
72 15 l. black 7·00 4·50
73 20 l. red 8·00 4·50
74 30 l. blue 1·25 1·10
75 50 l. violet 6·00 9·00
76 100 l. blue 18·00 24·00

1948. Trieste Philatelic Exn stamps of 1945 optd **A.M.G. F.T.T. 1948 TRIESTE** and posthorn.

77 8 l. green (postage) 10 10
78 10 l. red 10 10
79 30 l. blue 1·25 1·25
80 10 l. red (air) 20 20
81 25 l. brown 50 50
82 50 l. violet 50 50

1948. Rebuilding of Bassano Bridge.

84 **209** 15 l. green 75 60

1948. Donizetti.

85 **210** 15 l. brown 1·75 60

1949. 25th Biennial Art Exhibition, Venice.

86 **212** 5 l. red and flesh 70 75
87 – 15 l. green and cream 6·00 7·00
88 – 20 l. brown and buff 4·00 75
89 – 50 l. blue and yellow 8·50 5·00

1949. 27th Milan Fair.

90 **211** 20 l. sepia 4·00 90

1949. 75th Anniv of U.P.U.

91 **213** 50 l. blue 2·50 2·50

1949. Centenary of Roman Republic.

92 **214** 100 l. brown 35·00 42·00

1949. 1st Trieste Free Election.

93 **218** 20 l. lake 2·50 1·25

1949. European Recovery Plan.

94 **215** 5 l. green 3·75 3·75
95 15 l. violet 4·25 7·50
96 20 l. brown 6·00 7·00

1949. 2nd World Health Congress, Rome.

97 **219** 20 l. violet 12·00 2·50

1949. Giuseppe Mazzini.

98 **216** 20 l. black 4·50 1·75

1949. Bicentenary of Vittorio Alfieri.

99 **217** 20 l. brown 4·50 1·75

1949. 400th Anniv of Palladio's Basilica at Vicenza.

100 **220** 20 l. violet 12·00 8·00

1949. 500th Birth Anniv of Lorenzo de Medici.

101 **221** 20 l. blue 4·00 1·50

1949. 13th Bari Fair.

102 **222** 20 l. red 5·00 1·75

1949. (a) Postage.

103 **195** 1 l. green 10 10
104 – 2 l. brown (No. 656) 10 10
105 – 3 l. red (No. 657) 10 10
106 **193** 5 l. blue 10 10
107 **195** 6 l. violet 10 10
108 – 8 l. green (No. 661) 3·25 3·00
109 **193** 10 l. red 10 10
110 **195** 15 l. blue 80 10
111 – 20 l. green (No. 665) 45 10
112 **196** 25 l. green 12·00 1·10
113 50 l. purple 17·00 70
114 **197** 100 l. red 30·00 3·00

(b) Air.

115 **198** 10 l. red 10 10
116 – 25 l. brown (No. 676) 15 10
117 **198** 50 l. violet 20 20
118 – 100 l. green (No. 911) 65 20
119 – 300 l. mauve (No. 912) 6·00 6·00
120 – 500 l. blue (No. 913) 7·00 7·50
121 – 1000 l. purple (No. 914) 12·00 12·00

1949. 150th Anniv of Volta's Discovery of the Electric Cell.

135 **223** 20 l. red 2·00 1·75
136 **224** 50 l. blue 7·00 6·00

1949. Holy Trinity Bridge, Florence.

137 **225** 20 l. green 2·00 1·25

1949. Death Bimillenary of Catullus.

138 **226** 20 l. slate 2·00 1·25

1949. Birth Bicentenary of Cimarosa.

153 **227** 20 l. slate 2·00 1·25

1950. 28th Milan Fair.

154 **228** 20 l. brown 1·75 70

1950. 32nd Int Automobile Exn, Turin.

155 **229** 20 l. violet 1·25 70

1950. 5th General U.N.E.S.C.O. Conference.

156 – 20 l. green 2·00 70
157 **230** 55 l. blue (No. 754) 6·00 6·50

1950. Holy Year.

158 **231** 20 l. violet 2·00 70
159 55 l. blue 6·00 6·50

1950. Ferrari.

160 **232** 20 l. green 2·00 1·25

1950. International Radio Conference.

161 **233** 20 l. violet 5·00 3·25
162 55 l. blue 12·00 15·00

1950. Death Bicentenary of Muratori.

163 **234** 20 l. brown 2·00 1·25

1950. 900th Death Anniv of D'Arezzo. Optd in two lines.

164 **235** 20 l. green 1·75 1·25

1950. 14th Levant Fair, Bari.

165 **236** 20 l. brown 1·60 1·25

1950. 2nd Trieste Fair. Optd **AMG FTT Fiera di Trieste 1950**.

166 **195** 15 l. blue 80 1·10
167 – 20 l. purple (No. 665) 80 30

1950. Wool Industry Pioneers. Optd in two lines.

168 **237** 20 l. blue 70 70

1950. European Tobacco Conf (Nos. 755/7).

169 5 l. green and red 40 80
170 20 l. green and brown 1·50 80
171 55 l. brown and blue 12·00 15·00

1950. Bicentenary of Fine Arts Academy.

172 **239** 20 l. red and brown 1·60 85

1950. Birth Centenary of Augusto Righi.

173 **240** 20 l. black and buff 1·50 85

1950. Provincial Occupations (Nos. 760/78).

176 50 c. blue 10 15
177 1 l. violet 10 10
178 2 l. brown 10 10
179 5 l. black 10 10
180 6 l. brown 10 10
181 10 l. green 10 10
182 12 l. green 15 30
183 15 l. blue 70 10
184 20 l. violet 45 10
185 25 l. brown 1·00 10
186 30 l. purple 30 20
187 35 l. red 1·00 75
188 40 l. brown 70 30
189 50 l. violet 15 10
190 55 l. blue 15 30
191 60 l. red 3·00 1·50
192 65 l. green 15 30
193 100 l. brown 1·50 10
194 200 l. brown 1·40 2·25

1951. Centenary of Tuscan Stamp.

195 **249** 20 l. red and purple 2·00 1·25
196 55 l. blue & ultramarine 20·00 21·00

1951. 33rd International Motor Show, Turin.

197 **243** 20 l. green 1·25 1·25

1951. Consecration of Hall of Peace, Rome.

198 **244** 20 l. violet 1·25 1·25

1951. 29th Milan Fair.

199 **245** 20 l. brown 1·50 1·50
200 **246** 55 l. blue 1·50 1·75

1951. 10th International Textiles Exn, Turin.

201 **247** 20 l. violet 1·10 1·10

1951. 500th Birth Anniv of Columbus.

202 **248** 20 l. turquoise 2·00 2·00

1951. International Gymnastic Festival, Florence.

203 **249** 5 l. red and brown 3·25 5·50
204 10 l. red and green 3·25 5·50
205 15 l. red and blue 3·25 5·50

1951. Restoration of Montecassino Abbey.

206 **250** 20 l. violet 60 50
207 – 55 l. blue (No. 791) 1·25 1·40

1951. 3rd Trieste Fair, Optd **AMG-FTT FIERA di TRIESTE 1951**.

208 6 l. brown (No. 764) 30 40
209 20 l. violet (No. 768) 40 30
210 55 l. blue (No. 774) 45 65

1951. 500th Birth Anniv of Perugino. Optd in two lines.

211 **251** 20 l. brown and sepia 55 50

1951. Triennial Art Exhibition, Milan.

212 **252** 20 l. black and green 70 65
213 – 55 l. pink and blue (No. 794) 1·40 1·60

1951. World Cycling Championship.

214 **253** 25 l. grey 85 50

1951. 15th Levant Fair, Bari.

215 **254** 25 l. blue 70 55

1951. Birth Centenary of F. P. Michetti.

216 **255** 25 l. brown 65 50

1951. Sardinian Stamp Centenary.

217 **256** 10 l. black and sepia 35 50
218 – 25 l. green and red (799) 40 30
219 – 60 l. red and blue (800) 65 75

1951. 3rd Industrial and Commercial Census.

220 **257** 10 l. green 45 60

1951. 9th National Census.

221 **258** 25 l. slate 45 35

1951. Forestry Festival.

222 **260** 10 l. green and olive 50 75
223 25 l. green (No. 807) 50 40

1951. Verdi.

224 – 10 l. green & purple (803) 75 75
225 **259** 25 l. sepia and brown 45 35
226 – 60 l. blue & green (805) 85 85

1952. Bellini.
227 **261** 25 l. black 65 40

1952. Caserta Palace.
228 **262** 25 l. brown and green 50 35

1952. 1st International Sports Stamps Exn, Rome.
229 **263** 25 l. brown and black 35 25

1952. 30th Milan Fair.
230 **264** 60 l. blue 1·00 1·40

1952. Leonardo da Vinci.
231 **265** 25 l. orange 10 10
232 – 60 l. blue (813) 55 85
233 **265** 80 l. red 1·25 35

1952. Overseas Fair, Naples.
234 **268** 25 l. blue 35 30

1952. Modena and Parma Stamp Centenary.
235 **267** 25 l. black and brown 35 25
236 60 l. indigo and blue 45 75

1952. 26th Biennial Art Exhibition, Venice.
237 **269** 25 l. black and cream 35 25

1952. 30th Padua Fair.
238 **270** 25 l. red and blue 35 25

1952. 4th Trieste Fair.
239 **271** 25 l. grn, red and brown 35 25

1952. 16th Levant Fair, Bari.
240 **272** 25 l. green 40 25

1952. Savonarola.
241 **273** 25 l. violet 35 25

1952. 1st Private Aeronautics Conf, Rome.
242 **274** 60 l. blue & deep blue 1·00 1·60

1952. Alpine Troops National Exhibition.
243 **275** 25 l. grey 35 25

1952. Armed Forces Day.
244 **276** 10 l. green 10 10
245 **277** 25 l. sepia and brown 35 10
246 – 60 l. black & blue (827) 35 45

1952. Mission to Ethiopia.
247 **278** 25 l. deep brown & brown 45 30

1952. Birth Centenary of Gemito.
248 **279** 25 l. brown 35 25

1952. Birth Centenary of Mancini.
249 **280** 25 l. myrtle 35 25

1952. Martyrdom of Belfiore.
250 **281** 25 l. blue and black 35 25

1953. Antonello Exhibition, Messina.
251 **282** 25 l. red 35 25

1953. 20th "Mille Miglia" Car Race.
252 **283** 25 l. violet 40 30

1953. Labour Orders of Merit.
252 **284** 25 l. violet 35 25

1953. Birth Centenary of Corelli.
254 **285** 25 l. brown 50 30

1953. Coin type.
255 **286** 5 l. slate 10 10
256 10 l. red 10 10
257 12 l. green 10 10
258 13 l. mauve 10 10
259 20 l. brown 15 10
260 25 l. violet 15 10
261 35 l. red 35 35
262 60 l. blue 35 35
263 80 l. brown 40 40

1953. 7th Death Centenary of St. Clare.
264 **287** 25 l. chestnut and brown 35 25

1953. 5th Trieste Fair. Optd **V FIERA DI TRIESTE AMG FTT 1953**.
265 10 l. green (No. 765) 20 35
266 25 l. orange (No. 769) 25 20
267 60 l. red (No. 775) 30 40

1953. Mountains Festival.
272 **288** 25 l. green 45 25

1953. International Agricultural Exn, Rome.
273 **289** 25 l. brown 25 20
274 60 l. blue 35 40

1953. 4th Anniv of Atlantic Pact.
275 **290** 25 l. slate and yellow 45 35
276 60 l. blue and mauve 1·60 1·75

1953. 5th Birth Centenary of Signorelli.
277 **291** 25 l. green and brown 35 25

1953. 6th Int Microbiological Congress, Rome.
278 **292** 25 l. brown and slate 40 30

1953. Tourist series (Nos. 855/60).
279 10 l. brown and sepia 15 15
280 12 l. black and blue 15 20
281 20 l. brown and orange 15 15
282 25 l. green and blue 15 10
283 35 l. brown and buff 25 30
284 60 l. blue and green 30 35

1954. 25th Anniv of Lateran Treaty.
285 **294** 25 l. sepia anad brown 20 20
286 60 l. blue and light blue 30 40

1954. Television.
287 **295** 25 l. violet 20 20
288 60 l. turquoise 40 50

1954. Encouragement to Taxpayers.
289 **296** 25 l. violet 40 25

1954. Milan–Turin Helicopter Mail Flight.
290 **297** 25 l. green 35 25

1954. 10th Anniv of Resistance Movement.
291 **298** 25 l. black and brown 40 25

1954. 6th Trieste Fair. Nos. 858 and 860 of Italy optd **AMG-FTT FIERA DI TRIESTE 1954**.
292 – 25 l. green and blue 25 20
293 **293** 60 l. blue and green 35 40

1954. Birth Centenary of Catalani.
294 **299** 25 l. green 45 25

1954. 7th Birth Centenary of Marco Polo.
295 **300** 25 l. brown 20 20
296 60 l. green 35 45

1954. 60th Anniv of Italian Touring Club.
297 **301** 25 l. green and red 50 55

1954. International Police Congress, Rome.
298 **302** 25 l. red 20 15
299 60 l. blue 25 30

CONCESSIONAL LETTER POST

1947. Optd **A.M.G. F.T.T.** in two lines.
CL44 – 1 l. brown (No. CL649) 10 10
CL45 CL **201** 8 l. red 1·50 30
CL46 CL **220** 15 l. violet 12·00 2·00

1949. Optd **AMG-FTT.**
CL122 CL **220** 15 l. violet 55 10
CL123 20 l. violet 85 10

CONCESSIONAL PARCEL POST

1953.
CP268 CP **288** 40 l. orange 1·50 15
CP269 50 l. blue 1·50 15
CP270 75 l. brown 1·50 15
CP271 110 l. pink 1·50 20
Unused prices are for the complete stamp, used prices for the left half of the stamp.

EXPRESS LETTER STAMPS

1947. Express Letter stamps optd **A.M.G. F.T.T.** in two lines.
E28 – 15 l. lake (No. E681) 15 10
E29 **200** 25 l. orange 10·00 3·00
E30 30 l. violet 35 40
E31 – 60 l. red (No. E685) 6·50 5·50

1948. Centenary of Revolution. Express Letter stamp optd **A.M.G.-F.T.T.**
E83 E **209** 35 l. violet 2·00 2·75

1950. Express Letter stamps optd **AMG-FTT** in one line.
E174 E **209** 50 l. purple 95 60
E175 – 60 l. red (No. E685) 95 60

PARCEL POST STAMPS
Prices are for complete stamps.

1947. Parcel Post stamps optd **A.M.G. F.T.T.** in two lines on each half of stamp.
P32 P **201** 1 l. brown 25 25
P33 2 l. blue 40 30
P34 3 l. orange 40 35
P35 4 l. grey 45 40
P36 5 l. purple 1·25 1·00
P37 10 l. violet 2·50 2·00
P38 20 l. purple 3·75 3·00
P39 50 l. red 5·00 4·75
P40 100 l. blue 6·50 6·50
P41 200 l. green £200 £225
P42 300 l. purple £100 £120
P43 500 l. brown 50·00 75·00

1949. Parcel Post stamps optd **AMG-FTT** in one line on each half of stamp.
P139 P **201** 1 l. brown 55 70
P140 2 l. blue 10 25
P141 3 l. orange 10 25
P142 4 l. grey 10 25
P143 5 l. purple 15 25
P144 10 l. violet 25 25
P145 20 l. purple 30 25
P146 30 l. purple 30 45
P147 50 l. red 70 25
P148 100 l. blue 1·40 1·40
P149 200 l. green 13·00 15·00
P150 300 l. purple 45·00 50·00
P151 500 l. brown 26·00 35·00
P152 P **928** 1,000 l. blue £130 £150

POSTAGE DUE STAMPS

1947. Postage Due stamps optd **A.M.G. F.T.T.** in two lines.
D44 D **192** 1 l. orange 10 10
D48 D **201** 1 l. orange 10 30
D49 2 l. green 10 10
D50 3 l. red 40 65
D51 4 l. brown 3·25 4·25
D45 D **192** 5 l. violet 1·50 10
D52 D **201** 5 l. violet 30·00 6·00
D53 6 l. blue 10·00 10·00
D54 8 l. mauve 20·00 20·00
D46 D **192** 10 l. blue 2·00 35
D55 D **201** 10 l. blue 35·00 3·00
D56 12 l. brown 8·00 10·00
D47 D **192** 20 l. red 7·00 35
D57 D **201** 20 l. purple 7·00 1·50
D58 50 l. green 1·25 25

1949. Postage Due stamps optd **AMG-FTT** in one line.
D122 D **201** 1 l. orange 10 10
D123 2 l. green 10 10
D124 3 l. red 10 10
D125 5 l. violet 30 10
D126 6 l. blue 10 10
D127 8 l. mauve 10 10
D128 10 l. blue 10 10
D129 12 l. brown 45 15
D130 20 l. purple 1·10 10
D131 25 l. red 1·00 1·25
D132 50 l. green 1·50 10
D133 100 l. orange 2·50 20
D134 500 l. purple & blue 24·00 11·00

ZONE B
YUGOSLAV MILITARY GOVERNMENT

1948. 100 centesimi = 1 lira
1949. 100 paras = 1 dinar

Apart from the definitive issues illustrated below the following are stamps of Yugoslavia (sometimes in new colours), variously overprinted **STT VUJA** or **VUJA-STT** or (Nos. B65 onwards) **STT VUJNA** unless otherwise stated.

B 1  B 2

1948. Labour Day.
B1 B **1** 100 l. red and stone (A) 1·50 1·25
B2 100 l. red and stone (B) 1·50 1·25
B3 100 l. red and stone (C) 1·50 1·25
Inscr in Slovene (A) "I. MAJ 1948 V STO"; Italian (B) "I. MAGGIO 1948 NEL TLT"; or Croat (C) "I. SVIBANJ 1948 U STT".

1948. Red Cross. No. 545 optd and surch.
B3a **131** 2 l. on 50 p. brown & red 8·00 8·00

1948. Air. Economic Exhibition, Capodistria.
B4 B **2** 25 l. grey 75 55
B5 50 l. orange 75 55

B **3** Clasped Hands, Hammer and Sickle

B **4** Fishermen and Flying Boat

B **5** Man with Donkey
B **6** Mediterranean Gull over Chimney 

1949. Labour Day.
B6 B **3** 10 l. black 30 15

1949. Air.
B 7 B **4** 1 l. blue 15 15
B 8 B **5** 2 l. brown 15 15
B 9 B **4** 5 l. blue 15 15
B10 B **5** 10 l. violet 75 50
B11 B **4** 25 l. olive 90 90
B12 B **5** 50 l. green 90 90
B13 B **6** 100 l. purple 2·25 1·10

1949. Partisans issue.
B14 **119** 50 p. olive 10 10
B15 1 d. green 10 10
B16 **120** 2 d. red 10 10
B17 – 3 d. red (No. 508) 10 10
B18 **120** 4 d. blue 10 10
B19 – 5 d. blue (No. 511) 10 10
B20 – 9 d. mauve (No. 514) 25 15
B21 – 12 d. blue (No. 515) 1·50 90
B22 **119** 16 d. blue 1·10 80
B23 – 20 d. red (No. 517) 2·00 1·25

1949. 75th Anniv of U.P.U.
B24 – 5 d. blue (No. 612) 9·00 9·00
B25 **158** 12 d. brown 9·00 9·00

1949. Air. Optd **DIN** or surch also.
B26 B **4** 1 d. blue 10 10
B27 B **5** 2 d. brown 10 10
B28 B **4** 5 d. blue 15 10
B29 B **5** 10 d. violet 30 25
B30 B **4** 15 d. on 25 l. olive 6·00 4·25
B31 B **5** 20 d. on 50 l. green 1·25 90
B32 B **6** 30 d. on 100 l. purple 2·00 90

1950. Centenary of Yugoslav Railways.
B33 **116** 2 d. green 1·50 1·00
B34 – 3 d. red (No. 632) 2·25 1·40
B35 – 5 d. blue (No. 633) 3·75 2·50
B36 – 10 d. orange (No. 633a) 7·50 5·00

B **10** Girl on Donkey
B **11** Workers 

1950.
B37 B **10** 50 p. slate 10 10
B38 – 1 d. red (Cockerel) 10 10
B38a – 1 d. brown (Cockerel) 15 10
B39 – 2 d. blue (Geese) 10 10
B40 – 3 d. brown (Bees) 20 10
B40a – 3 d. red (Bees) 20 10
B41 – 5 d. green (Oxen) 35 10
B42 – 10 d. brown (Turkey) 50 10
B43 – 15 d. violet (Kids) 3·50 3·00
B44 – 20 d. olive (Silkworms) 1·60 80

1950. May Day.
B45 B **11** 3 d. violet 50 40
B46 10 d. red 75 45

1950. Red Cross.
B47 **160** 50 p. brown and red 75 60

B **12** Worker
B **13** P. P. Vergerio Jr. 

1951. May Day.
B48 B **12** 3 d. red 70 40
B49 10 d. olive 90 80

1951. Red Cross.
B49a **191** 50 p. blue and red 7·50 6·00

1951. Festival of Italian Culture.
B50 B **13** 5 d. blue 75 60
B51 10 d. red 75 60
B52 20 d. brown 75 60

1951. Cultural Anniversaries.
B53 **189** 10 d. orange 80 45
B54 – 12 d. black (As No. 699) 80 45

B **14a** Koper Square
B **15** Cyclists 

1952. Air. 75th Anniv of U.P.U.
B54a B **14a** 5 d. brown 15·00 13·00
B54b – 15 d. blue 12·00 10·00
B54c – 25 d. green 7·50 5·50
DESIGNS—VERT: 15 d. Lighthouse, Piran. HORIZ: 25 d. Hotel, Portoroz.

1952. Physical Culture Propaganda.
B55 B **15** 5 d. brown 10 10
B56 – 10 d. green 15 10
B57 – 15 d. red 15 10
B58 – 28 d. blue 45 25
B59 – 50 d. lake 80 30
B60 – 100 d. slate 4·00 3·00
DESIGNS: 10 d. Footballers; 15 d. Rowing four; 28 d. Yachts; 50 d. Netball players; 100 d. Diver.

1952. Marshal Tito's 60th Birthday Stamps of Yugoslavia inscr "STT VUJA".
B61 **196** 15 d. brown 1·10 70
B62 **197** 28 d. lake 1·10 70
B63 – 50 d. green (No. 729) 1·10 70

1952. Children's Week.
B64 **198** 15 d. red 75 30

1952. 15th Olympic Games, Helsinki. As Nos. 731/6.
B65 **199** 5 d. brown on flesh 30 10
B66 – 10 d. green on cream 30 10
B67 – 15 d. violet on mauve 30 10
B68 – 28 d. brown on buff 70 35
B69 – 50 d. brown on yellow 6·00 3·50
B70 – 100 d. blue on pink 20·00 15·00

1952. Navy Day (Nos. 737/9).
B71 – 15 d. purple 1·50 1·50
B72 **200** 28 d. brown 1·50 1·50
B73 – 50 d. black 2·00 1·50

1952. Red Cross.
B74 **201** 50 p. red, grey & black 30 30

1952. 6th Yugoslav Communist Party Congress.
B75 **202** 15 d. brown 60 50
B76 15 d. turquoise 60 50
B77 15 d. brown 60 50
B78 15 d. blue 60 50

B 17 Starfish

1952. Philatelic Exhibition, Koper.
B78a B 17 15 d. lake . . . . . . 1·50 1·10

1953. Tesla.
B79 203 15 d. red 25 20
B80 30 d. blue . . . . 1·00 80

1953. Pictorials of 1950.
B 81 1 d. grey (No. 705) . . . . . 3·00 2·50
B 86 2 d. red (No. 718) 10 10
B 82 3 d. red (No. 655) 10 10
B 87 5 d. orange (No. 719) . . . 10 10
B106 10 d. green (No. 721) 25 10
B 88 15 d. red (No. 723) 20 10
B 84 30 d. blue (No. 712) 40 15
B 85 50 d. green (No. 714) . . . 2·75 2·50

1953. United Nations (Nos. 747/9).
B89 204 15 d. green 10 10
B90 – 30 d. blue 15 10
B91 – 50 d. lake 55 35

1953. Adriatic Car Rally. As Nos. 750/3.
B92 205 15 d. brown and yellow . 25 10
B93 – 30 d. green & turquoise . 25 10
B94 – 50 d. lake and pink . . . 25 10
B95 – 70 d. indigo and blue . . 70 40

1953. Marshal Tito.
B96 206 50 d. green . . . . 1·50 90

1953. 38th Esperanto Congress, Zagreb.
B97 207 15 d. green and turquoise (postage) . . . . . . 1·25 1·25
B98 300 d. green and violet (air) £250 £275

1953. Liberation of Istria and Slovene Coast.
B99 208 15 d. blue . . . . 1·75 1·25

1953. Radicevic.
B100 210 15 d. black . . . . . . 1·10 75

1953. Red Cross.
B101 211 2 d. red and brown . . . 40 40

1953. 1st Republican Legislative Assembly. As Nos. 762/4.
B102 212 15 d. slate 75 60
B103 – 30 d. lake 75 60
B104 – 50 d. green 75 60

1954. Air. As Nos. 675 etc.
B108 1 d. lilac 10 10
B109 2 d. green 10 10
B110 3 d. red 10 10
B111 5 d. brown 10 10
B112 10 d. turquoise 10 10
B113 20 d. brown 20 10
B114 30 d. blue 20 15
B115 50 d. olive 35 20
B116 100 d. red . . . . 1·25 90
B117 200 d. violet . . . . 3·00 1·40
B118 500 d. orange . . . . . . 12·00 12·50

1954. Animals. As Nos. 765/76.
B119 2 d. grey, buff and red . . . 10 10
B120 5 d. slate, buff and grey . . 10 10
B121 10 d. brown and green . . . 15 10
B122 15 d. brown and blue . . . 20 10
B123 17 d. sepia and brown . . . 20 10
B124 25 d. yellow, blue & ochre . 40 10
B125 30 d. brown and violet . . . 50 10
B126 35 d. black and purple . . . 65 20
B127 50 d. brown and green . . . 85 30
B128 65 d. black and brown . . . 2·25 1·40
B129 70 d. brown and blue . . . 4·00 1·50
B130 100 d. black and blue . . . 7·00 8·00

1954. Serbian Insurrection. As Nos. 778/81.
B131 – 15 d. multicoloured . . . 60 30
B132 214 30 d. multicoloured . . . 60 30
B133 – 50 d. multicoloured . . . 60 30
B134 – 70 d. multicoloured . . . 1·25 75

POSTAGE DUE STAMPS

1948. Red Cross. No. D564 surch **VUJA STT** and new value.
BD4 131 2 l. on 50 p. red & grn . £150 £150

1949. On 1946 issue.
BD26 D 126 50 p. orange 30 30
BD27 1 d. orange 30 30
BD74 1 d. brown 10 10
BD28 2 d. blue 45 30
BD75 2 d. green 10 10
BD29 3 d. green 30 20
BD30 5 d. violet 60 50
BD76 5 d. blue 15 10
BD77 10 d. red 10 10
BD78 20 d. violet 20 10
BD79 30 d. orange 20 15
BD80 50 d. blue 35 20
BD81 100 d. purple . . . . 4·00 4·00
Nos. BD26/30 optd **STT VUJA** and the rest **STT VUJNA**.

1950. Red Cross. No. D617 optd **VUJA STT**.
BD48 160 50 p. purple and red . . 1·25 90

BD 12 Fish

1950.
BD49 – 0 d. 50 brown . . . 15 15
BD50 – 1 d. green 55 45
BD51 BD 12 2 d. blue . . . . . 1·25 70
BD52 3 d. blue . . . . . 1·25 70
BD53 5 d. purple . . . . . 3·00 1·50
DESIGN: 0 d. 50, 1 d. Two fishes.

1951. Red Cross. No. 703 optd **STT VUJA**.
BD54 191 50 p. green and red . . £100 90·00

The following are optd **STT VUJNA**.

1952. Red Cross. No. D741.
BD82 D 202 50 p. red and grey . 40 40

1953. Red Cross. As No. D762.
BD102 211 2 d. red and purple . 50 50

TRIPOLITANIA Pt. 8

One of the provinces into which the Italian colony of Libya was divided.

100 centesimi = 1 lira

Stamps optd **Tripoli di Barberia** formerly listed here will be found under Italian P.O.'s in the Levant Nos. 171/81.

Nos. 1/138, except where otherwise described, are Italian stamps, sometimes in new colours, overprinted **TRIPOLITANIA**.

1923. Propagation of the Faith.
1 66 20 c. orange and green . . . 1·10 5·50
2 30 c. orange and red . . . . 1·10 5·50
3 50 c. orange and violet . . . 75 4·75
4 1 l. orange and blue . . . . 75 4·75

1923. Fascisti.
5 73 10 c. green . . . . 1·40 6·00
6 30 c. violet . . . . 1·40 6·00
7 50 c. red . . . . 1·40 6·00
8 74 1 l. blue . . . . 1·40 6·00
9 2 l. brown . . . . 1·40 6·00
10 75 5 l. black and blue . . . . 1·40 7·50

1924. Manzoni.
11 77 10 c. black and purple . . . 60 12·00
12 – 15 c. black and green . . . 60 12·00
13 – 30 c. black . . . . 60 12·00
14 – 50 c. black and brown . . . 60 12·00
15 – 1 l. black and blue . . . . 15·00 90·00
16 – 5 l. black and purple . . . £200 £950

1925. Holy Year.
17 – 20 c. + 10 c. brown & grn . 75 4·25
18 81 30 c.+ 15 c. brown & choc . 75 4·25
19 – 50 c. + 25 c. brown & vio . 75 4·25
20 – 60 c. + 30 c. brown & red . 75 4·25
21 – 1 l. + 50 c. purple & blue . 75 4·25
22 – 5 l. + 2 l. 50 purple & red . 75 4·25

1925. Royal Jubilee.
23 82 60 c. red . . . . 15 2·75
24 1 l. blue . . . . 20 2·75
24c 1 l. 25 blue . . . . 45 9·00

1926. St. Francis of Assisi.
25 83 20 c. green . . . . 70 4·25
26 – 40 c. violet . . . . 70 4·25
27 – 60 c. red . . . . 70 4·25
28 – 1 l. 25 blue . . . . 70 4·25
29 – 5 l. + 2 l. 50 olive . . . . 1·50 5·50

1926. As Colonial Propaganda stamps of Somalia, T 21, but inscr "TRIPOLITANIA".
30 5 c. + 5 c. brown . . . . . . 20 2·25
31 10 c. + 5 c. olive . . . . . . 20 2·25
32 20 c. + 5 c. green . . . . . . 20 2·25
33 40 c. + 5 c. red . . . . . . 20 2·25
34 60 c. + 5 c. orange . . . . . 20 2·25
35 1 l. + 5 c. blue . . . . 20 2·25

6 Port of Tripoli

9 Palm Tree

1927. 1st Tripoli Trade Fair.
36 6 20 c. + 05 c. black & purple 1·50 2·50
37 25 c. + 05 c. black & green . 1·50 2·50
38 – 40 c. + 10 c. black & brown 1·50 2·50
39 – 60 c. + 10 c. black & brown 1·50 2·50
40 – 75 c. + 20 c. black and red . 1·50 2·50
41 – 1 l. 25 + 20 c. black & blue 5·50 8·50
DESIGNS: 40, 60 c. Arch of Marcus Aurelius; 75 c., 1 l. 25, View of Tripoli.

1927. 1st National Defence issue.
42 88 40 + 20 c. black & brown . 80 4·25
43 60 + 30 c. brown and red . 80 4·25
44 1 l. 25 + 60 c. black & blue 80 4·25
45 5 l. + 2 l. 50 black & green . 1·25 6·50

1927. Death Centenary of Volta.
46 91 20 c. violet . . . . 3·00 10·00
47 50 c. orange . . . . 3·00 7·00
48 1 l. 25 blue . . . . 4·00 10·00

1928. 2nd Tripoli Trade Fair.
49 – 30 c. + 20 c. brown & purple 1·40 4·25
50 9 50 c. + 20 c. brown & green . 1·40 4·25
51 – 1 l. 25 + 20 c. brown & red . 1·40 4·25
52 – 1 l. 75 + 20 c. brown & blue 1·40 4·25
53 – 2 l. 55 + 50 c. sepia & brown 2·00 6·00
54 – 5 l. + 1 l. brown and violet . 2·75 9·00
DESIGNS—VERT: As T 9: 30 c. Tripoli; 1 l. 25, Camel riders. 38 × 22½ mm: 1 l. 75, Arab citadel; 2 l. 55, Tripoli; 5 l. Desert outpost.

1928. 45th Anniv of Italian-African Society. As T 25 of Somalia.
55 20 c. + 5 c. green . . . . . . 60 3·50
56 30 c. + 5 c. red . . . . 60 3·50
57 50 c. + 10 c. violet . . . . . 60 3·50
58 1 l. 25 + 20 c. blue . . . . . 60 3·50

1929. 2nd National Defence issue.
59 89 30 c. + 10 c. black and red . 1·00 4·75
60 – 50 c. + 20 c. black & lilac . 1·00 4·75
61 – 1 l. 25 + 50 c. blue & brown 1·40 6·00
62 – 5 l. + 2 l. black and olive . 1·40 6·00

1929. 3rd Tripoli Trade Fair. Inscr "1929".
63 30 c. + 20 c. black and red . . 4·50 12·00
64 50 c. + 20 c. black and green . 4·50 12·00
65 1 l. 25 + 20 c. black and red . 4·50 12·00
66 1 l. 75 + 20 c. black and blue . 4·50 12·00
67 2 l. 55 + 50 c. black & brown . 4·50 12·00
68 5 l. + 1 l. black and violet . . 80·00 £170
DESIGNS—VERT: As T 9: 30 c., 1 l. 25, Different trees; 50 c. Dorcas gazelle. 38 × 22½ mm: 1 l. 75, Goats; 2 l. 55, Camel caravan; 5 l. Trees.

1929. Abbey of Montecassino.
69 104 20 c. green . . . . 1·75 4·25
70 – 25 c. orange . . . . 1·75 4·25
71 – 50 c. + 10 c. red . . . . . 1·75 8·50
72 – 75 c. + 15 c. brown . . . . 1·75 8·50
73 104 1 l. 25 + 25 c. purple . . . 3·25 8·50
74 – 5 l. + 1 l. blue . . . . . . 3·25 8·50
75 – 10 l. + 2 l. brown . . . . . 3·25 10·00

1930. 4th Tripoli Trade Fair. Inscr "1930".
76 30 c. brown . . . . 1·10 4·75
77 50 c. violet . . . . 1·10 4·75
78 1 l. 25 blue . . . . 1·10 4·75
79 1 l. 75 +20 c. red . . . . . . 1·10 7·00
80 2 l. 55 +45 c. green . . . . . 7·00 12·00
81 5 l. + 1 l. orange . . . . . . 7·00 15·00
82 10 l. + 2 l. purple . . . . . . 7·00 17·00
DESIGNS—As T 9: 30 c. Gathering bananas; 50 c. Tobacco plant; 1 l. 25, Venus of Cyrene. 38 × 22½ mm: 5 l. Motor and camel transport; 10 l. Rome pavilion.

1930. Marriage of Prince Humbert and Princess Marie Jose.
83 109 20 c. green . . . . 45 1·90
84 50 c. + 10 c. orange . . . 45 2·50
85 1 l. 25 + 25 c. red . . . . 45 2·75

1930. Ferrucci.
86 114 20 c. violet (postage) . . . 50 1·60
87 – 25 c. green (No. 283) . . . 50 1·60
88 – 50 c. black (as No. 284) . . 50 1·60
89 – 1 l. 25 blue (No. 285) . . . 50 1·60
90 – 5 l. + 2 l. red (as No. 286) 1·75 2·75
91 117 50 c. purple (air) . . . . . 80 2·25
92 1 l. blue . . . . 80 2·25
93 5 l. + 2 l. red . . . . . . 4·50 10·00

1930. 3rd National Defence issue.
94 89 30 c. + 10 c. green & olive . 4·00 15·00
95 – 50 c. + 10 c. violet & olive . 4·00 15·00
96 – 1 l. 25 + 30 c. brown . . . 4·00 15·00
97 – 5 l. + 1 l. 50 green & blue . 12·00 42·00

17 Roman Arch

18 Columns of Leptis

19

1930. 25th Anniv (1929) of Italian Colonial Agricultural Institute.
98 17 50 c. + 20 c. brown . . . . 75 5·00
99 1 l. 25 + 20 c. blue . . . . 75 5·00
100 1 l. 75 + 20 c. green . . . . 75 5·00
101 2 l. 55 + 50 c. violet . . . 1·50 5·00
102 5 l. + 1 l. red . . . . 1·50 5·00

1930. Virgil.
103 – 15 c. grey (postage) . . . 25 1·40
104 – 20 c. brown . . . . 25 1·40
105 – 25 c. green . . . . 25 1·10
106 – 30 c. brown . . . . 25 1·40
107 – 50 c. purple . . . . 25 1·10
108 – 75 c. red . . . . 25 1·40
109 – 1 l. 25 blue . . . . 25 1·40
110 – 5 l. + 1 l. 50 purple . . . 1·75 7·00
111 – 10 l. + 2 l. 50 brown . . . 1·75 7·00
112 119 50 c. green (air) . . . . . 70 2·25
113 1 l. red . . . . 70 2·25
114 7 l. 70 + 1 l. 30 brown . 2·25 10·00
115 9 l. + 2 l. blue . . . . . 2·25 10·00

1931. Air.
116 18 50 c. red 20 10
117 60 c. orange . . . . . . 1·60 6·00
117a 75 c. blue . . . . 1·60 6·00
118 80 c. purple . . . . . . 3·00 6·50
119 19 1 l. blue 45 10
120 1 l. 20 brown . . . . . . 6·50 10·00
121 1 l. 50 orange . . . . . 3·00 6·00
122 5 l. green . . . . 7·00 7·00

20 Statue of Youth

22

1931. 5th Tripoli Trade Fair.
123 20 10 c. black (postage) . . . 1·75 5·00
124 – 25 c. green . . . . 1·75 5·00
125 – 50 c. violet . . . . 1·75 5·00
126 – 1 l. 25 blue . . . . 1·75 5·00
127 – 1 l. 75 + 25 c. red . . . . 2·00 7·00
128 – 2 l. 75 + 45 c. orange . . 2·00 10·00
129 – 5 l. + 1 l. purple . . . . . 7·00 17·00
130 – 10 l. + 2 l. brown . . . . 24·00 45·00
131 – 50 c. blue (air) . . . . . . 1·10 5·00
DESIGNS—As Type 20: 25 c. Arab musician; 50 c. (postage) View of Zeughet; 1 l. 25, Snake charmer; 1 l. 75, House and windmill; 2 l. 75, Libyan "Zaptie"; 5 l. Arab horseman. As Type E 21: 10 l. Exhibition Pavilion; 50 c. (air) Airplane over desert.

1931. St. Anthony of Padua.
132 121 20 c. brown . . . . . . 55 2·50
133 – 25 c. green . . . . . . 55 2·50
134 – 30 c. brown . . . . . . 55 2·50
135 – 50 c. purple . . . . . . 55 1·40
136 – 75 c. grey . . . . 55 2·50
137 – 1 l. 25 blue . . . . . . 55 2·50
138 – 5 l. + 2 l. 50 brown . . . 2·00 11·00

1931. Air. 25th Anniv (1929) of Italian Colonial Agricultural Institute.
139 22 50 c. blue . . . . 1·10 6·00
140 80 c. violet . . . . 1·10 6·00
141 1 l. black . . . . 1·10 6·00
142 2 l. green . . . . 2·25 7·00
143 5 l. + 2 l. red . . . . . . 3·50 15·00

23 Paw-paw Tree

24 Arch of Marcus Aurelius

1932. 6th Tripoli Trade Fair. Inscr "1932".
144 23 10 c. brown (postage) . . . 2·75 6·00
145 – 20 c. red . . . . 2·75 6·00
146 – 25 c. green . . . . 2·75 6·00
147 – 30 c. black . . . . 2·75 6·00
148 – 50 c. violet . . . . 2·75 6·00
149 – 75 c. red . . . . 3·50 10·00
150 – 1 l. 25 blue . . . . 3·50 10·00
151 – 1 l. 75 + 25 c. brown . . 15·00 32·00
152 – 5 l. + 1 l. blue . . . . . 16·00 45·00
153 – 10 l. + 2 l. purple . . . . 42·00 90·00
154 – 50 c. blue (air) . . . . . . 4·50 12·00
155 – 1 l. brown . . . . 4·50 12·00
156 – 2 l. + 1 l. black . . . . . 14·00 45·00
157 – 5 l. + 2 l. red . . . . . . 42·00 90·00
DESIGNS—POSTAGE. VERT: 10 c. to 50 c. Various trees; 75 c. Roman mausoleum at Ghirza; 10 l. Dorcas gazelle. HORIZ: 1 l. 25, Mogadiscio aerodrome; 1 l. 75, Lioness; 5 l. Arab and camel. AIR. HORIZ: 50 c., 1 l. Marina Fiat MF.5 flying boat over Bedouin camp; 2, 5 l. Marina Fiat MF.5 flying boat over Tripoli.

1933. 7th Tripoli Trade Fair. Inscr "1933".
158 – 10 c. purple (postage) . . . 17·00 15·00
159 – 25 c. green . . . . 9·00 11·00
160 – 30 c. brown . . . . 9·00 15·00
161 24 50 c. violet . . . . 9·00 9·00
162 – 1 l. 25 blue . . . . 19·00 38·00
163 – 5 l. + 1 l. brown . . . . . 29·00 85·00
164 – 10 l. + 2 l. 50 red . . . . 29·00 85·00

165 24 50 c. green (air) . . . . . 4·50 12·00
166 – 75 c. red . . . . 4·50 12·00
167 – 1 l. blue . . . . 4·50 12·00
168 – 2 l. + 50 c. violet . . . . 9·00 24·00
169 – 5 l. + 1 l. brown . . . . . 12·00 32·00
170 – 10 l. + 2 l. 50 black . . . 12·00 32·00
DESIGNS—POSTAGE. VERT: 10 c. Ostrich; 25 c. Incense plant; 1 l. 25, Golden eagle; 10 l. Tripoli and Fascist emblem. HORIZ: 30 c. Arab drummer; 5 l. Leopard. AIR. HORIZ: 50 c., 2 l. Seaplane over Tripoli; 75 c., 10 l. Caproni Ca 101 airplane over Tagiura; 1, 5 l. Seaplane leaving Tripoli.

25 Mercury

1933. "Graf Zeppelin" Air stamps. Inscr "CROCIERA ZEPPELIN 1933".
171 25 3 l. brown . . . . 4·00 35·00
172 – 5 l. violet . . . . 4·00 35·00
173 – 10 l. green . . . . 4·00 55·00
174 25 12 l. blue . . . . 4·00 85·00
175 – 15 l. red . . . . 4·00 70·00
176 – 20 l. black . . . . 4·00 95·00
DESIGNS: 5, 15 l. Arch of Marcus Aurelius; 10, 20 l. "Dawn".

26 "Flight"

1933. Air. Balbo Transatlantic Flight.
177 26 19 l. 75 brown and black . 9·50 £225
178 44 l. 75 green and blue . . 9·50 £225

1934. Air. Rome–Buenos Aires Flight. Optd with Savoia Marchetti S-71 airplane and **1934 XII PRIMO VOLO DIRETTO ROMA=BUENOS-AYRES TRIMOTORE LOMBARDI-MAZZOTTI**, or surch also in Italian.
179 19 2 l. on 5 l. brown . . . . 1·50 27·00
180 3 l. on 5 l. green . . . . . 1·50 27·00
181 5 l. bistre . . . . 1·50 27·00
182 10 l. on 5 l. red . . . . . 1·50 27·00

27 Water Carriers

1934. 8th Tripoli Trade Fair.
183 27 10 c. brown (postage) . . . 2·00 5·00
184 – 20 c. red . . . . 2·00 5·00
185 – 25 c. green . . . . 2·00 5·00
186 – 30 c. brown . . . . 2·00 5·00
187 – 50 c. violet . . . . 2·00 5·00
188 – 75 c. red . . . . 2·00 5·00
189 – 1 l. 25 blue . . . . 24·00 38·00
DESIGNS—VERT: 20 c. Arab; 25 c. Minaret; 50 c. Statue of Emperor Claudius. HORIZ: 30 c., 1 l. 25, Moslem shrine; 75 c. Ruins of Ghadames.

190 50 c. blue (air) . . . . . . 4·50 12·00
191 75 c. orange . . . . 4·50 12·00
192 5 l. + 1 l. green . . . . . 38·00 95·00
193 10 l. + 2 l. purple . . . . 38·00 95·00
194 25 l. + 3 l. brown . . . . . 42·00 95·00
DESIGNS—HORIZ: 50 c., 5 l. Marina Fiat MF.5 flying boat off Tripoli; 75 c., 10 l. Airplane over mosque. VERT: 25 l. Caproni Ca 101 airplane and camel.
See also Nos. E195/6.

1934. Air. Oasis Flight. As Nos. 190/4 optd **CIRCUITO DELLE OASI TRIPOLI MAGGIO 1934 – XII.**
197 50 c. red . . . . 4·50 10·00
198 75 c. yellow . . . . 4·50 10·00
199 5 l. + 1 l. brown . . . . . 4·50 10·00
200 10 l. + 2 l. blue £140 £200
201 25 l. + 3 l. violet £140 £200
See also Nos. E202/3.

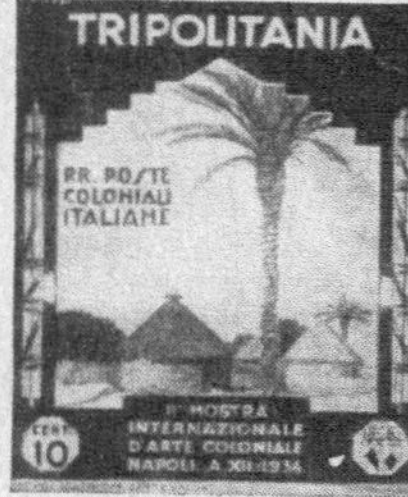

29 Native Village

1934. 2nd International Colonial Exn, Naples.
204 29 5 c. brown & green (postage.) 1·25 5·50
205 10 c. black and brown . . 1·25 5·50
206 20 c. slate and red . . . . 1·25 5·50
207 50 c. brown and violet . . 1·25 5·50
208 60 c. slate and brown . . 1·25 5·50
209 1 l. 25 green and blue . . 1·25 5·50
210 29 25 c. orange & blue (air) . 1·25 5·50
211 – 50 c. slate and green . . . 1·25 5·50
212 – 75 c. red and brown . . . 1·25 5·50
213 – 80 c. green and brown . . 1·25 5·50
214 – 1 l. green and red . . . . 1·25 5·50
215 – 2 l. brown and blue . . . 1·25 5·50
DESIGNS: 25 c. to 75 c. Shadow of airplane over desert; 80 c. to 2 l. Arab camel corps and Caproni Ca 101 airplane.

30

1934. Air. Rome–Mogadiscio Flight.
216 30 25 c. + 10 c. green . . . 1·75 5·00
217 50 c. + 10 c. brown . . . 1·75 5·00
218 75 c. + 15 c. red . . . . 1·75 5·00
219 80 c. + 15 c. black . . . 1·75 5·00
220 1 l. + 20 c. brown . . . 1·75 5·00
221 2 l. + 20 c. blue . . . . 1·75 5·00
222 3 l. + 25 c. violet . . . 14·00 40·00
223 5 l. + 25 c. orange . . . 14·00 40·00
224 10 l. + 30 c. purple . . . 14·00 40·00
225 25 l. + 2 l. green . . . . 14·00 40·00

32 Camel Transport

1935. 9th Tripoli Exhibition.
226 – 10 c. + 10 c. brown (post) 50 2·50
227 – 20 c. + 10 c. red . . . . 50 2·50
228 – 50 c. + 10 c. violet . . . 50 2·50
229 – 75 c. + 15 c. red . . . . 50 2·50
230 – 1 l. 25 + 25 c. blue . . . 50 2·50
231 – 2 l. + 50 c. green . . . . 50 2·50
232 – 25 c. + 10 c. green (air) . 70 3·00
233 32 50 c. + 10 c. slate . . . . 70 3·00
234 – 1 l. + 25 c. blue . . . . 70 3·00
235 – 2 l. + 30 c. red . . . . . 70 3·00
236 – 3 l. + 1 l. 50 brown . . . 70 3·00
237 – 10 l. + 5 l. purple . . . 6·00 15·00
DESIGNS—VERT—POSTAGE: 10, 20 c. Pomegranate tree; 50 c., 2 l. Arab flautist; 75 c., 1 l. 25, Arab in burnous. AIR: 25 c., 3 l. Watch-tower. HORIZ: 1 l., 10 l. Arab girl and Caproni Ca 101 airplane.
For issue inscr "XII FIERA CAMPIONARIA TRIPOLI" and dated "1938", see Libya Nos. 88/95.

CONCESSIONAL LETTER POST

1931. Optd **TRIPOLITANIA.**
CL23 CL 109 10 c. brown . . . . 3·50 4·50

EXPRESS LETTER STAMPS

Express stamps optd **TRIPOLI DI BARBERIA** formerly listed here will be found under Italian P.O.s in the Levant Nos. E6/7.

1927. 1st Tripoli Exhibition. Inscr "EXPRES".
E42 1 l. 25 + 30 c. black & vio . 5·00 7·00
E43 2 l. 50 + 1 l. black & orge . 5·00 7·00
DESIGN—HORIZ: As T 6 1 l. 25, 2 l. 50, Camels and palm trees.

E 21 War Memorial

1931. 5th Tripoli Exn.
E132 E 21 1 l. 25 + 20 c. red . . . 3·50 10·00

1934. Air. 8th Tripoli Trade Fair.
E195 2 l. 25 green . . . . 14·00 38·00
E196 4 l. 50 + 1 l. blue . . . . 14·00 38·00
DESIGN—As T 27. Nos. E195/6, Caproni Ca 101 airplane over Bedouins.

1934. Air. Oasis Flight. As Nos. E195/6 optd **CIRCUITO DELLE OASI TRIPOLI MAGGIO 1934. XII.**
E202 2 l. 25 red . . . . 4·50 10·00
E203 4 l. 50 + 1 l. red . . . . . 4·50 10·00

OFFICIAL STAMPS

1934. No. 225 (colour changed) optd **SERVIZIO DI STATO** and Crown.
O226 30 25 l. + 2 l. red £1300 £2750

From 1943 to 1951 Tripolitania was under British administration; stamps issued during this period are listed in Volume 3. From 1952 it was part of independent Libya.

INDEX

Countries can be quickly located by referring to the index at the end of this volume.

TUNISIA Pt. 6; Pt. 14

Formerly a French Protectorate in N. Africa, Tunisia became an independent kingdom in 1956 and a republic in 1957.

1888. 100 centimes = 1 franc
1959. 1000 milliemes = 1 dinar

1

2

1888. Arms on plain background.
1 1 1 c. black on blue . . . . . . 1·75 1·10
2 2 c. brown on buff . . . . . . 1·40 1·10
3 5 c. green on green . . . . . 12·50 7·00
4 15 c. blue on blue . . . . . . 32·00 9·00
5 25 c. black on pink . . . . . 65·00 35·00
6 40 c. red on yellow . . . . . 60·00 55·00
7 75 c. pink on pink . . . . . . 60·00 42·00
8 5 f. mauve on lilac £300 £200

1888. Arms on shaded background.
9 2 1 c. black on blue 50 20
10 2 c. brown on buff 60 30
22 5 c. green . . . . 4·00 25
12 10 c. black on lilac . . . . . 5·00 30
23 10 c. red . . . . 3·25 25
14 15 c. blue . . . . 35·00 25
24 15 c. grey . . . . 3·25 25
15 20 c. red on green . . . . . . 5·50 25
16 25 c. black on pink . . . . . 14·50 45
25 25 c. blue . . . . 8·00 40
26 35 c. brown . . . . 32·00 80
17 40 c. red on yellow . . . . . 9·00 45
18 75 c. pink on pink . . . . . . £100 55·00
19 75 c. violet on yellow . . . . 14·00 2·75
20 1 f. green . . . . 19·00 3·00
27 2 f. lilac . . . . £120 95·00
21 5 f. mauve on lilac . . . . . £120 55·00

1902. Surch **25** and bars.
28 2 25 on 15 c. blue . . . . 3·00 1·40

4 Mosque at Kairouan

6 Ruins of Hadrian's Aqueduct

5 Agriculture

7 Carthaginian Galley

1906.
30 4 1 c. black on yellow 10 10
31 2 c. brown 10 10
32 3 c. red 10 30
33 5 c. green on green 10 10
34 5 10 c. red 10 10
35 15 c. violet 40 15
36 20 c. brown 15 10
37 25 c. blue 65 10
38 6 35 c. brown and green . . . . 5·75 50
39 40 c. red and brown . . . . . 3·00 25
40 75 c. red and purple 55 25
41 7 1 f. brown and red 65 35
42 2 f. green and brown . . . . 2·75 80
43 5 f. blue and violet . . . . 6·75 3·00
See also Nos. 72/8, 105 and 107/13.

1908. Surch.
44 2 10 on 15 c. grey 50 50
45 35 on 1 f. green . . . . 60 1·60
46 40 on 2 f. lilac . . . . 2·75 4·75
47 75 on 5 f. mauve on lilac . . . 2·00 3·00

1911. Surch in figures and bar.
48 5 10 on 15 c. violet . . . . . . 1·25 20
60 15 c. on 10 c. red 30 10
79 20 c. on 15 c. violet 60 15

1915. Red Cross Fund. Optd with red cross.
49 5 15 c. violet 50 60

1916. Red Cross Fund. Optd with red cross and bars.
50 4 5 c. green on green 50 85

1916. Prisoners-of-War Fund. Surch with red cross and **10 c.**
51 5 10 c. on 15 c. brown on blue . 30 60
52 10 c. on 20 c. brown on yell . 30 60
53 10 c. on 25 c. blue on green . 1·25 2·25
54 6 10 c. on 35 c. violet & green . 2·25 4·00
55 10 c. on 40 c. black & brown . 1·25 2·25
56 10 c. on 75 c. green and red . 2·75 5·00
57 7 10 c. on 1 f. green and red . . 2·50 2·50
58 10 c. on 2 f. blue and brown . 60·00 60·00
59 10 c. on 5 f. red and violet . . 70·00 65·00

1918. Prisoners-of-War Fund. Surch **15c** and red cross.
61 5 15 c. on 20 c. black on grn . 40 95
62 15 c. on 25 c. blue 50 95
63 6 15 c. on 35 c. red and olive . 1·00 1·50
64 15 c. on 40 c. blue & brown . 2·00 2·50
65 15 c. on 75 c. black and red . 3·50 4·50
66 7 15 c. on 1 f. violet and red . 11·50 13·50
67 15 c. on 2 f. red and brown . 45·00 50·00
68 15 c. on 5 f. black and violet £100 £100

1919. Air. Optd **Poste Aerienne** and wings or surch **30 c.** and bars also.
69 6 30 c. on 35 c. brown & green . 60 85
70 30 c. blue and olive 35 40

1920. New values and colours changed.
72 4 5 c. orange 10 20
73 5 10 c. green 25 30
74 25 c. violet 25 10
75 6 30 c. violet and purple . . . 70 30
76 5 30 c. red 35 40
77 50 c. blue 30 25
78 6 60 c. violet and green 30 25

18 Ruin at Dougga

1922.
80 18 10 c. green 10 20
81 30 c. red 60 90
82 50 c. blue 25 40
See also Nos. 104 and 106.

1923. War Wounded Fund. Surch **AFFt**, medal and new value.
83 4 0 c. on 1 c. blue 30 45
84 0 c. on 2 c. brown 30 45
85 1 c. on 3 c. green 30 45
86 2 c. on 5 c. mauve 30 45
87 18 3 c. on 10 c. mauve on bl . . 30 45
88 5 5 c. on 15 c. green 30 45
89 5 c. on 20 c. blue on red . . 1·00 1·50
90 5 c. on 25 c. mauve on blue . 1·00 1·50
91 18 5 c. on 30 c. orange . . . . 1·00 1·50
92 6 5 c. on 35 c. mauve & blue . 1·00 1·50
93 5 c. on 40 c. brown & blue . 1·10 1·50
94 18 10 c. on 50 c. black on blue . 1·25 1·60
95 6 10 c. on 60 c. blue & brown . 1·25 1·40
96 10 c. on 75 c. green & mve . 2·00 2·75
97 7 25 c. on 1 f. mauve & lake . 2·25 2·75
98 25 c. on 2 f. red and blue . 9·00 10·50
99 25 c. on 5 f. brown & green . 32·00 45·00

1923. Surch.
100 4 10 on 5 c. green on green . . 30 25
101 5 20 on 15 c. violet 60 55
102 30 on 20 c. brown 15 25
103 50 on 25 c. blue 60 10

1923. New values and colours.
104 18 10 c. pink 15 25
105 5 15 c. brown on orange . . . 10 20
106 18 30 c. mauve 10 20
107 5 40 c. black on pink 40 45
108 40 c. green 10 15
109 6 60 c. carmine and red 30 30
110 75 c. scarlet and red 20 25
111 7 1 f. light blue and blue . . . 25 25
112 2 f. red & green on pink . . 35 45
113 5 f. green and lilac 55 75

1925. Parcel Post stamps surch **PROTECTION DE L'ENFANCE POSTES** and value in figures.
114 P 8 1 c. on 5 c. red and brown on rose 10 40
115 2 c. on 10 c. blue and brown on yellow 10 40
116 3 c. on 20 c. red and purple on mauve 25 55
117 5 c. on 25 c. red and green on green 50 70
118 5 c. on 40 c. green and red on yellow 50 70
119 10 c. on 50 c. green and violet on mauve . . . . 1·00 1·50
120 10 c. on 75 c. brown and green on green . . . . . 90 1·25
121 25 c. on 1 f. green and blue on blue . . . . 90 1·40
122 25 c. on 2 f. purple and red on rose . . . . 2·00 3·75
123 25 c. on 5 f. brown and red on green . . . . 17·00 28·00

21 Arab Woman

22 Grand Mosque, Tunis

23 Mosque, Place Halfaouine, Tunis

24 Amphitheatre, El Djem

1926.
124 21 1 c. red 10 15
125 2 c. green 10 15
126 3 c. blue 10 20
127 5 c. green 10 10
128 10 c. mauve 10 15

129 **22** 15 c. lilac 20 15
130 20 c. red 10 10
131 25 c. green 10 20
131a 25 c. mauve 15 15
132 30 c. mauve 15 15
133 30 c. green 15 20
134 40 c. brown 15 15
134a 45 c. green 50 60
135 **23** 50 c. black 10 10
135a 50 c. blue 45 10
135b 50 c. green 15 20
135c 60 c. red 15 30
135d 65 c. blue 35 20
135e 70 c. red 15 30
136 75 c. red 30 25
136a 75 c. mauve 30 10
137 80 c. blue 30 30
137a 80 c. brown 45 65
138 90 c. red 15 10
138a 90 c. blue 6·00 6·00
139 1 f. purple 25 10
139a 1 f. red 10 10
140 **24** 1 f. 05 pink and blue 25 25
141 1 f. 25 blue & light blue 55 65
141a 1 f. 25 red 55 65
141b 1 f. 30 violet and blue 55 65
141c 1 f. 40 purple 55 60
142 1 f. 50 blue & light blue 40 15
142a 1 f. 50 orange and red 50 65
143 2 f. brown and red 40 20
143a 2 f. red 50 15
143b 2 f. 25 blue 65 80
143c 2 f. 50 green 50 55
144 3 f. orange and blue 60 20
144a 3 f. violet 15 15
145 5 f. green & red on green 75 45
145a 5 f. brown 1·00 1·40
146 10 f. grey & red on blue 3·25 1·50
146a 10 f. pink 65 75
146b 20 f. red & mve on pink 1·00 90

For similar designs see Nos. 172/91, 220/31 and 257/286.

1927. Surch **1f 50**.

147 **24** 1 f. 50 on 1 f. 25 blue and ultramarine 30 20

1927. Air. Optd **Poste Aerienne** and airplane or surch in figures and bars also.

148 **7** 1 f. light blue and blue 40 50
152 **24** 1 f. 30 mauve and orange 1·50 1·90
169 1 f. 50 on 1 f. 30 mauve and orange 1·25 75
170 1 f. 50 on 1 f. 80 red and green 1·75 75
171 1 f. 50 on 2 f. 55 brown and mauve 4·00 1·50
149 **6** 1 f. 75 on 75 c. scarlet and red 40 70
150 **7** 1 f. 75 on 5 f. green and lilac 1·50 1·90
153 **24** 1 f. 80 red and green 2·00 2·00
151 **7** 2 f. red and green on pink 1·60 1·50
154 **24** 2 f. 55 brown and mauve 1·00 1·00

26 First Tunis–Chad Motor Service

1928. Child Welfare.

155 **26** 40 c. + 40 c. brown 60 80
156 50 c. + 50 c. purple 50 75
157 75 c. + 75 c. blue 50 80
158 1 f. + 1 f. red 50 85
159 1 f. 50 + 1 f. 50 blue 50 80
160 2 f. + 2 f. green 60 1·10
161 5 f. + 5 f. brown 60 1·10

1928. Surch.

162 **4** 3 c. on 5 c. orange 10 30
163 **5** 10 c. on 15 c. brn on orge 15 20
164 **18** 25 c. on 30 c. mauve 15 20
165 **23** 40 c. on 80 c. blue 15 30
166 **22** 50 c. on 40 c. brown 3·00 25
167 **23** 50 c. on 75 c. red 25 40

1929. Precancelled **AFFRANCHts POSTES** and surch **10**.

168 **22** 10 on 30 c. mauve 60 90

28

29

30

31

1931.

172 **28** 1 c. blue 10 25
173 2 c. brown 10 30
174 3 c. black 15 40
175 5 c. green 10 25
176 10 c. red 10 30
177 **29** 15 c. purple 35 30
178 20 c. brown 10 15
179 25 c. red 10 15
180 30 c. green 20 25
181 40 c. orange 10 15

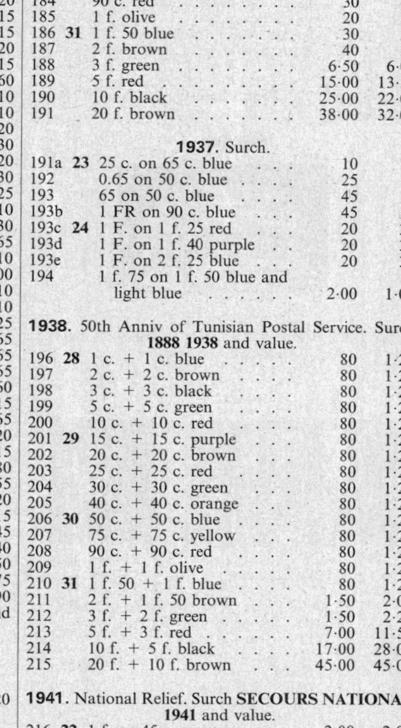

182 **30** 50 c. blue 20 10
183 75 c. yellow 85 85
184 90 c. red 30 45
185 1 f. olive 20 20
186 **31** 1 f. 50 blue 30 24
187 2 f. brown 40 30
188 3 f. green 6·50 6·00
189 5 f. red 15·00 13·50
190 10 f. black 25·00 22·00
191 20 f. brown 38·00 32·00

1937. Surch.

191a **23** 25 c. on 65 c. blue 10 10
192 0.65 on 50 c. blue 25 10
193 65 on 50 c. blue 45 10
193b 1 FR on 90 c. blue 35 15
193c **24** 1 F. on 1 f. 25 red 20 30
193d 1 F. on 1 f. 40 purple 20 30
193e 1 F. on 2 f. 25 blue 20 30
194 1 f. 75 on 1 f. 50 blue and light blue 2·00 1·00

1938. 50th Anniv of Tunisian Postal Service. Surch **1888 1938** and value.

196 **28** 1 c. + 1 c. blue 80 1·25
197 2 c. + 2 c. brown 80 1·25
198 3 c. + 3 c. black 80 1·25
199 5 c. + 5 c. green 80 1·25
200 10 c. + 10 c. red 80 1·25
201 **29** 15 c. + 15 c. purple 80 1·25
202 20 c. + 20 c. brown 80 1·25
203 25 c. + 25 c. red 80 1·25
204 30 c. + 30 c. green 80 1·25
205 40 c. + 40 c. orange 80 1·25
206 **30** 50 c. + 50 c. blue 80 1·25
207 75 c. + 75 c. yellow 80 1·25
208 90 c. + 90 c. red 80 1·25
209 1 f. + 1 f. olive 80 1·25
210 **31** 1 f. 50 + 1 f. blue 80 1·25
211 2 f. + 1 f. 50 brown 1·50 2·00
212 3 f. + 2 f. green 1·50 2·25
213 5 f. + 3 f. red 7·00 11·50
214 10 f. + 5 f. black 17·00 28·00
215 20 f. + 10 f. brown 45·00 45·00

1941. National Relief. Surch **SECOURS NATIONAL 1941** and value.

216 **22** 1 f. on 45 c. green 2·00 2·00
217 **24** 1 f. 30 on 1 f. 25 red 2·00 2·00
218 1 f. 50 on 1 f. 40 purple 2·00 2·00
219 2 f. on 2 f. 25 blue 2·00 2·00

1941. As stamps of 1926 but without monogram "RF".

220 **22** 30 c. red 55 65
221 **23** 1 f. 20 grey 15 30
222 1 f. 50 brown 25 20
223 **24** 2 f. 40 pink and red 30 45
224 2 f. 50 light blue and blue 30 40
225 3 f. violet 45 55
226 4 f. blue and black 25 25
227 4 f. 50 brown and green 30 45
228 5 f. black 30 25
229 10 f. violet and purple 30 25
230 15 f. red 2·50 2·25
231 20 f. red and lilac 1·40 85

41a "Victory"

42 Allied Soldiers

1943.

232 **41a** 1 f. 50 red 15 30

1943. Charity. Tunisian Liberation.

233 **42** 1 f. 50 + 8 f. 50 red 25 30

43 Mosque and Olive Trees

44 Sidi Mahrez Mosque

45 Ramparts of Sfax

1944.

234 **43** 30 c. yellow 25 25
235 40 c. brown 25 30
236 60 c. orange 25 35
237 70 c. red 25 35
238 80 c. green 35 40
239 90 c. violet 25 30
240 1 f. red 25 30
241 1 f. 50 blue 20 30
242 2 f. 40 red 35 45
243 **43** 2 f. 50 brown 25 35
244 3 f. violet 25 25
245 4 f. blue 30 25
246 4 f. 50 green 40 35
247 5 f. grey 35 25
248 6 f. brown 40 25
249 10 f. lake 45 35
250 15 f. brown 50 40
251 20 f. lilac 45 45

Nos. 234/41 are smaller 15½ × 19 mm.

1944. Forces Welfare Fund. Surch + **48 frcs pour nos Combattants**.

252 **43** 2 f. + 48 f. red (21¼ × 26½ mm) 60 80

1945. Forces Welfare Fund. Surch **POUR NOS COMBATTANTS** and value.

253 **44** 1 f. 50 + 8 f. 50 brown 50 75
254 **45** 3 f. + 12 f. green 60 80
255 – 4 f. + 21 f. brown 50 75
356 – 10 f. + 40 f. red 50 75

DESIGNS—HORIZ: 4 f. Camel patrol at Fort Saint; 10 f. Mosque at Sidi-bou-Said.

1945. New values and colours.

257 **23** 10 c. brown 10 25
258 30 c. olive 10 25
259 40 c. red 15 25
260 50 c. turquoise 10 15
261 60 c. blue 15 15
262 80 c. green 15 15
263 1 f. 20 brown 15 30
264 1 f. 50 lilac 10 15
265 2 f. green 10 15
267 **24** 2 f. 40 red 30 50
268 **23** 2 f. 50 brown 25 20
269 **24** 3 f. brown 10 10
270 **23** 3 f. red 15 15
271 **24** 4 f. blue 40 50
272 **23** 4 f. violet 40 25
273 **24** 4 f. violet 50 45
273a **23** 4 f. orange 25 30
274 4 f. 50 blue 25 20
275 **24** 5 f. green 20 20
275a **23** 5 f. blue 35 40
275b 5 f. green 30 10
276 **24** 6 f. blue 25 25
277 6 f. red 50 50
278 **23** 6 f. red 15 15
279 **24** 10 f. orange 20 40
280 10 f. blue 25 20
281 15 f. mauve 20 20
281a **23** 15 f. red 35 30
282 **24** 20 f. green 20 20
283 25 f. violet 40 45
284 25 f. orange 40 60
285 50 f. red 50 50
286 100 f. red 75 65

1945. Anti-Tuberculosis Fund. Type of France optd **TUNISIE**.

287 **222** 2 f. + 1 f. orange 30 35

1945. Postal Employees' War Victims' Fund. Type of France optd **TUNISIE**.

288 **223** 4 f. + 6 f. brown 30 45

1945. Stamp Day. Type of France (Louis XI) optd **TUNISIE**.

289 **228** 2 f. + 3 f. green 30 45

1945. War Veterans' Fund. Surch **ANCIENS COMBATTANTS R F** and value.

290 **21** 4 f. + 6 f. on 10 c. blue 30 45
291 **23** 10 f. + 30 f. on 80 c. green 30 45

49 Legionary

1946. Welfare Fund for French Troops in Indo-China.

292 **49** 20 f. + 30 f. black, red and green 75 1·00

1946. Red Cross Fund. Surch with cross **1946** and new values.

293 **23** 80 c. + 50 c. green 45 60
294 1 f. 50 + 1 f. 50 lilac 50 60
295 2 f. + 2 f. green 50 60
296 **24** 2 f. 40 + 2 f. red 60 75
297 4 f. + 4 f. blue 60 75

1946. Stamp Day. La Varane Type of France optd **TUNISIE**.

298 **241** 3 f. + 2 f. blue 60 65

1947. Stamp Day. Louvois Type of France optd **TUNISIE**.

299 **253** 4 f. 50 + 5 f. 50 brown 55 70

1947. Naval Charities. Type of France surch **TUNISIE** and new value.

300 **234** 10 + 15 on 2 f. + 3 f. blue 60 70

1947. Welfare Fund. Surch **SOLIDARITE 1947 + 40 F.**

301 **24** 10 f. + 40 f. black 40 70

53 Arabesque Ornamentation from Great Mosque at Kairouan

54 Neptune

1947.

302 **53** 3 f. green and turquoise 50 60
303 4 f. red and purple 35 50
304 **54** 5 f. black and green 50 65
305 **53** 6 f. red and brown 10 10
306 **54** 10 f. black and brown 25 20
306a **53** 10 f. violet 25 10
306b 12 f. brown 55 30
306c 12 f. orange and brown 40 20
306d 15 f. red and brown 65 50
307 **54** 18 f. blue and green 75 55
307a 25 f. turquoise and blue 95 40
307b **53** 30 f. blue and deep blue 50 50

55 Feeding a Fledgling

57 Triumphal Arch, Sbeitla

1947. Infant Welfare Fund.

308 **55** 4 f. 50 + 5 f. 50 green 30 75
309 6 f. + 9 f. blue 30 75
310 8 f. + 17 f. red 30 75
311 10 f. + 40 f. violet 30 75

1948. Stamp Day. Type of France (Arago) optd **TUNISIE**.

312 **253** 6 f. + 4 f. red 50 90

1948. Anti-Tuberculosis Fund. Surch **AIDEZ LES TUBERCULEUX + 10f.**

313 **53** 4 f. + 10 f. orange & green 40 65

1948. Army Welfare Fund.

315 **57** 10 f. + 40 f. green & bistre 70 85
316 18 f. + 42 f. dp blue & bl 70 85

1949. Stamp Day. Type of France (Choiseul), optd **TUNISIE**.

317 **278** 15 f. + 5 f. black 90 1·25

58 Child in Cot

1949. Child Welfare Fund.

318 **58** 25 f. + 50 f. green 1·50 1·75

59 Oued Mellegue Barrage

1949. Tunisian Development.

319 **59** 15 f. black 1·25 65

60 Bird from Antique Mosaic

61 Globe, Mounted Postman and Sud Est Languedoc Airliner

1949. Air.

320 **60** 100 f. brown and green 1·75 75
321 200 f. black & blue (A) 2·75 1·75
322 200 f. black & blue (B) 2·75 2·00

In A the Arabic inscription is in two lines and in B it is in one line.

1949. 75th Anniv of U.P.U.

323 **61** 5 f. green on bl (postage) . 90 1·10
324 15 f. brown on blue . . . . 90 1·10
325 15 f. blue on blue (air) . . 95 1·40

1949. Free French Association Fund. Surch Lorraine Cross and **FFL + 15F.**

326 **54** 10 f. + 15 f. red and blue . 65 95

1950. Stamp Day. Type of France (Postman) optd **TUNISIE.**

327 **292** 12 f. + 3 f. green . . . . 95 1·25

62 "Tunisia Thanks France"   **63** Old Soldier

1950. Franco-Tunisian Relief Fund.

328 **62** 15 f. + 35 f. red . . . . . 90 1·10
329 25 f. + 45 f. blue . . . . . 90 1·10

1950. Veterans' Relief Fund.

330 **63** 25 f. + 25 f. blue . . . . . 1·25 1·40

64 Horse (bas-relief)   **65** Hermes of Berbera

1950. (a) Size $21\frac{1}{2} \times 17\frac{1}{2}$ mm.

331 **64** 10 c. blue 15 30
332 50 c. brown 10 30
333 1 f. violet 15 30
334 2 f. grey 20 20
335 3 f. brown 30 35
336 4 f. orange 25 30
337 5 f. green 20 10
338 8 f. blue 30 30
340 12 f. red 75 20
341 15 f. red 30 25
342 15 f. blue 40 10

(b) Size $22\frac{1}{2} \times 18\frac{3}{4}$ mm.

343 **64** 15 f. red 60 50
344 15 f. blue 60 55
345 30 f. blue . . . . 1·40 65

1950.

346 **65** 15 f. red 50 50
347 25 f. blue 50 35
348 50 f. green . . . . 1·00 35

1951. Stamp Day. Type of France (Sorting Van), but colour changed optd **TUNISIE.**

349 **300** 12 f. + 3 f. grey . . . . . 2·25 2·50

66 Sleeping Child

1951. Child Welfare Fund.

350 **66** 30 f. + 15 f. blue . . . . . 1·75 1·90

67 Gammarth National Cemetery   **68** Panel from Great Mosque at Kairouan

1951. War Orphans' Fund.

351 **67** 30 f. + 10 f. blue . . . . . 1·40 1·40

1952. Stamp Day. Type of France (Mail Coach), optd **TUNISIE.**

352 **319** 12 f. + 3 f. violet 80 80

1952. Army Welfare Fund. Inscr "OEURVRES SOCIALES DE L'ARMEE"

353 – 15 f. + 1 f. indigo and blue (postage) 70 60
354 **68** 50 f. + 10 f. green and black (air) . . . . 1·90 2·00

DESIGN: 15 f. Ornamental stucco, Bardo Palace.

69 Schoolboys clasping Hands   **70** Charles Nicolle

1952. Holiday Camp Fund.

355 **69** 30 f. + 10 f. green . . . . 1·10 1·10

1952. Golden Jubilee of Tunisian Medical Sciences Society.

356 **70** 15 f. brown 70 80
357 30 f. blue 70 80

1952. Centenary of Military Medal. Type of France surch **Tunisie + 5F.**

358 **327** 15 f. + 5 f. green . . . . 75 1·25

1953. Stamp Day. Type of France (Count D'Argenson), optd **TUNISIE.**

359 **334** 12 f. + 3 f. red 65 80

71 Tower and Flags   **72** Tozeur Mosque

1953. 1st International Fair, Tunis.

360 **71** 8 f. brown & deep brown . 60 70
361 12 f. green and emerald . . 60 70
362 15 f. indigo and blue . . . 60 70
363 18 f. deep violet & violet . 60 70
364 30 f. red and carmine . . 65 70

1953. Air.

365 – 100 f. blue, turq & green . 2·50 80
366 – 200 f. sepia, purple & brn . 3·50 1·40
367 – 500 f. brown and blue . . 17·00 10·00
368 **72** 1000 f. green . . . . . . 29·00 20·00

DESIGNS: 100, 200 f. Monastir; 500 f. View of Korbous.

For similar stamps but without "R F" see Nos. 423/6.

1954. Stamp Day. Type of France (Lavallette), optd **TUNISIE.**

369 **346** 12 f. + 3 f. blue 70 80

73 Courtyard, Sousse   **74** Sidi Bou Maklouf Mosque, Le Kef

1954.

370 **73** 50 c. green 10 30
371 1 f. red 10 20
372 – 2 f. purple 25 30
373 – 4 f. turquoise 30 35
374 – 5 f. violet 20 20
375 – 8 f. brown 30 30
376 – 10 f. green 30 35
377 – 12 f. brown 25 15
378 – 15 f. blue (18 × 22 mm) . . 1·50 20
386 – 15 f. blue (17 × $21\frac{1}{2}$ mm) . 35 10
379 **74** 18 f. brown 85 70
380 – 20 f. blue 55 25
381 – 25 f. blue 70 30
382 – 30 f. purple 55 40
383 – 40 f. green 70 50
384 – 50 f. lilac . . . . 1·50 30
385 – 75 f. red . . . . 2·75 1·75

DESIGNS—As Type **73**: 2, 4 f. Takrouna ramparts; 5, 8 f. Dwellings and Mosque, Tatahouine; 10, 12 f. Cave dwellings, Matmata; 15 f. Street, Sidi-bou-said. As Type **74**: 20, 25 f. Genoese Fort, Tabarka; 30, 40 f. Bab-el-Khadra Gate, Tunis; 50, 75 f. Four-storey dwellings, Medenine.

For similar stamps but without "R F" see Nos. 406/22.

76 Bey of Tunisia   **76a** Paris Balloon Post, 1870

1954.

387 **76** 8 f. deep blue and blue . . 45 55
388 12 f. indigo and blue . . . 45 55
389 15 f. red and carmine . . . 45 55
390 18 f. deep brown & brown . 45 55
391 30 f. deep green & green . . 1·00 1·10

1955. Stamp Day.

392 **76a** 12 f. + 3 f. brown 90 90

77

1955. 50th Anniv of "L'Essor" (Tunisian Amateur Dramatic Society).

393 **77** 15 f. blue, red and orange . 45 50

78 Tunisian Buildings and Rotary Emblem   **79** Bey of Tunisia

1955. 50th Anniv of Rotary International.

394 **78** 12 f. deep brown & brown . 45 55
395 15 f. brown and grey . . . 45 55
396 18 f. lilac and violet . . . 45 55
397 25 f. deep blue and blue . . 45 55
398 30 f. indigo and blue . . . 95 1·10

1955.

399 **79** 15 f. blue 40 10

80 "Embroidery"   **81** Bey of Tunisia

80a Francis of Taxis

1955. 3rd International Fair, Tunis.

400 **80** 5 f. lake 50 60
401 12 f. blue 50 60
402 – 15 f. green 55 65
403 – 18 f. red 60 65
404 – 20 f. violet 70 80
405 – 30 f. purple 70 80

DESIGNS: 15, 18 f. "Pottery"; 20, 30 f. "Jasmin sellers".

1956. Nos. 365/6 and 368/86 re-engraved without "R F".

406 50 c. green (postage) 10 30
407 1 f. red 10 10
408 2 f. purple 15 20
409 4 f. blue 15 20
410 5 f. violet 15 15
411 8 f. brown 15 30
412 10 f. green 15 10
413 12 f. brown 15 30
414 15 f. blue (18 × 22 mm) . . . 80 40
415 15 f. blue (17 × $21\frac{1}{2}$ mm) . . . 15 15
416 18 f. brown 25 30
417 20 f. blue 30 15
418 25 f. blue 25 10
419 30 f. purple 85 25
420 40 f. green 85 25
421 50 f. lilac 60 25
422 75 f. red . . . . 1·25 80
423 100 f. blue, turquoise and green (air) . . . . 1·25 50
424 200 f. sepia, purple & brown . 2·00 1·40
425 500 f. brown and blue . . . . 4·75 4·00
426 1000 f. green . . . . 8·50 7·25

1956. Stamp Day.

427 **80a** 12 f. + 3 f. green 60 70

INDEPENDENT KINGDOM

1956. Autonomous Government.

428 **81** 5 f. blue 35 35
429 – 12 f. purple 35 35
430 **81** 15 f. red 35 35
431 – 18 f. grey 45 35
432 **81** 20 f. green 45 35
433 – 30 f. brown 90 40

DESIGN: 12, 18, 30 f. Tunisian girl releasing dove.

82 Farhat Hached   **83** Market Scene

1956. Labour Day.

434 **82** 15 f. lake 30 30
435 30 f. blue 35 35

1956. Tunisian Products.

436 – 12 f. violet, purple & mauve 60 20
437 – 15 f. green, brown & bl . . 60 20
438 – 18 f. blue 90 35
439 – 20 f. brown 90 35
440 **83** 25 f. brown . . . . 1·25 55
441 30 f. blue . . . . 1·40 55

DESIGNS—VERT: 12 f. Bunch of grapes; 15 f. Sprig of olives; 18 f. Harvesting; 20 f. Man with basket containing wedding offering.

84 Pres. Habib Bourguiba   **85** Pres. Bourguiba and Agricultural Workers

1957. 1st Anniv of Independence.

442 **84** 5 f. blue 20 20
443 **85** 12 f. pink 20 20
444 **84** 20 f. blue 30 20
445 **85** 25 f. green 35 20
446 **84** 30 f. brown 40 30
447 **85** 50 f. red 80 50

86 Dove and Handclasp

1957. 5th Int Confederation of Free Trade Unions Congress.

448 **86** 18 f. purple 35 35
449 – 20 f. red 40 40
450 **86** 25 f. green 40 40
451 – 30 f. blue 45 45

DESIGN—VERT: 20, 30 f. Handclasp and Labour Exchange.

INDEPENDENT REPUBLIC

نصف شهر الجيش ١٩٥٧
+
10f (87)

1957. Tunisian Army Fortnight. No. 417 optd with T **87**.

452 20 f. + 10 f. blue 55 55

88 Tunisian Soldiers and Flag

1957. Proclamation of Republic.

453 **88** 20 f. red . . . . 14·50 14·50
454 25 f. violet . . . . 14·50 14·50
455 30 f. brown . . . . 14·50 14·50

1957. 5th Int Fair, Tunis. As No. 404 but additionally inscr "5e FOIRE INTERNATIONALE" and Arabic inscriptions at sides, surch + **10 F.**

456 20 f. + 10 f. violet 45 45

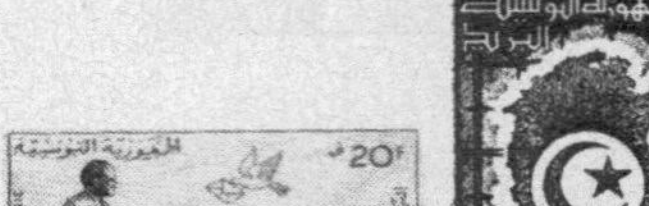

90 Pres Bourguiba on Ile de la Galite   **91** Tunisian Emblems and Map

1958. 6th Anniv of Exile of Pres. Bourguiba.
457 90 20 f. blue and brown . . . 55 35
458 25 f. blue and violet 55 35

1958. 2nd Anniv of Independence.
459 91 20 f. green and brown . . . 35 15
460 – 25 f. brown and blue . . . 35 15
461 – 30 f. brown, deep brown & red 45 20
DESIGNS: 25 f. Mother and child; 30 f. Clenched fist holding Tunisian flag.
For 20 f. brown and blue see No. 464.

92 Andreas Vesalius (scientist) and A. ibn Khaldoun 93 Planting Olives

1958. Brussels International Exhibition.
462 92 30 f. green and bistre . . . 45 20

1958. Labour Day.
463 93 20 f. multicoloured 45 45

1958. 3rd Anniv of Return of Pres. Bourguiba. As T 91 but with inscr altered.
464 91 20 f. brown and blue . . . 40 20

94 95 Pres. Bourguiba

1958. 1st Anniv of Proclamation of Tunisian Republic.
465 94 5 f. purple and bistre . . . 45 20
466 10 f. dp green & lt green . . 45 20
467 15 f. brown and orange . . 45 20
468 20 f. violet, olive & yellow . 45 20
469 25 f. purple 45 20

1958. Pres. Bourguiba's 55th Birthday.
470 95 20 f. purple and violet . . . 35 20

96 Fishermen with Catch 97 U.N.E.S.C.O. Headquarters, Paris

1958. 6th International Fair.
471 96 25 f. purple, red & green . . 55 35

1958. Inaug of U.N.E.S.C.O. Building.
427 97 25 f. myrtle 35 35

98 "Shedding the Veil" 99 Hand holding Plant

1959. Emancipation of Tunisian Women.
473 98 20 m turquoise 45 30

1959. 25th Anniv of Neo-Destour (Nationalist Party) and Victory Congress.
474 99 5 m. red, brown & purple . . 30 10
475 – 10 m. multicoloured . . . 35 15
476 – 20 m. blue 40 20
477 – 30 m. blue, turq & brown . . 65 40
DESIGNS—VERT: 10 m. Tunisians with flaming torch and flag on shield; 20 m. Pres. Bourguiba in exile at Borj le Boeuf, 1954. HORIZ: 30 m. Pres. Bourguiba and Borj le Boeuf, 1934.

100 "Tunisia"

1959. 3rd Anniv of Independence.
478 100 50 m. multicoloured . . . 65 35

101 Tunisian Horseman 102 "Freedom"

1959. Designs as T 101.
479 ½ m. brown, green & emerald 15 10
480 1 m. bistre and blue 10 10
481 2 m. brown, yellow & blue . 15 10
482 3 m. myrtle 10 10
483 4 m. brown 30 15
484 5 m. myrtle 20 10
485 6 m. violet 20 15
486 8 m. purple 65 30
487 10 m. red, green and bistre . 20 10
487a 12 m. violet and bistre . . . 65 20
488 15 m. blue 35 10
489 16 m. green 30 20
490 20 m. turquoise . . . . . . 1·00 30
491 20 m. purple, olive & myrtle 2·75 30
492 25 m. blue, brown & turq . 30 20
493 30 m. brown, green & turq . 45 10
494 40 m. green . . . . 1·60 20
495 45 m. green 70 30
496 50 m. multicoloured 90 20
497 60 m. brown and green . . . 90 35
498 70 m. multicoloured . . . . 1·40 50
499 75 m. brown . . . . 1·25 55
500 90 m. brown, green & blue . 1·25 55
501 95 m. multicoloured . . . . 1·60 1·00
502 100 m. multicoloured . . . 1·75 90
503 200 m. red, bistre and blue . 4·50 2·25
504 ½ d. brown . . . . 12·00 6·00
505 1 d. ochre and green . . . . 21·00 12·00
DESIGNS—VERT: ½ m. Ain Draham; 2 m. Camel-driver; 3 m. Saddler's shop; 5 m. Type 101; 6 m. Weavers; 8 m. Gafsa; 10 m. Woman holding pomegranates; 12 m. Turner; 20 m. (No. 491), Gabes; 40 m. Kairouan; 70 m. Carpet weaver; 75 m. Nabeul vase; 95 m. Olive-gatherer; ½ d. Sbeitla. HORIZ: 1 m. Kairouan environs; 4 m. Medenine; 15 m. Monastir; 16 m. Tunis; 20 m. (No. 490), Room in Arab house, Sidi-Bou-Said; 25 m. Sfax; 30 m. Aqueduct, Medjerda Valley; 45 m. Bizerta; 50 m. Djerba; 60 m. Le Jerid; 90 m. Le Kef; 100 m. Sidi-bou-Said highway; 200 m. Old port of Sfax; 1 d. Beja ploughman.

1959. Africa Freedom Day.
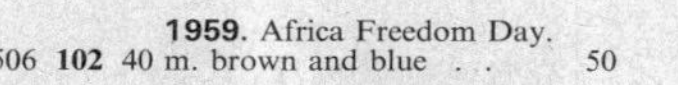
506 102 40 m. brown and blue . . 50 35

103 Postman 104 Clenched Hands

1959. Stamp Day.
507 103 20 m. + 5 m. brown & orge 45 45

1959. U.N. Day.
508 104 80 m. brown, blue & pur 65 45

105 106 Dancer and Coin

1959. Red Crescent Day.
509 105 10 m. + 5 m. multicoloured 35 35

1959. 1st Anniv of Tunisian Central Bank.
510 106 50 m. black and blue . . 50 50

107 "Uprooted Tree" 108 Camel Rider telephoning

1960. World Refugee Year. Inscr "ANNEE MONDIALE DES REFUGIES 1959–1960".
511 107 20 m. blue 40 20
512 – 40 m. black and purple . . 50 35
DESIGN—HORIZ: 40 m. Doves.

1960. Stamp Day.
513 108 60 m. + 5 m. orange, blue and olive 80 80

109 Pres. Bourguiba signing Promulgation 110 Fair Emblems

1960. Promulgation of Constitution.
514 109 20 m. red, brown & green . 40 35

1960. 5th Sousse National Fair.
515 110 100 m. black and green . . 65 45

111 President Bourguiba 112 Jamboree Emblems

1960.
516 111 20 m. black 20 10
517 30 m. black, red and blue . 35 10
518 40 m. black, red & green . 45 20

1960. 4th Arab Scout Jamboree, Tunis.
519 112 10 m. turquoise 35 35
520 – 25 m. purple, red & green . 40 35
521 – 30 m. lake, violet & green . 60 35
522 – 40 m. black, blue and red . 65 40
523 – 60 m. violet, pur & sepia . 1·25 55
DESIGNS: 25 m. Saluting hand with scouts as fingers; 30 m. Camp bugler; 40 m. Scout peacock badge; 60 m. Scout by camp fire.

113 Cyclist in Stadium 114

1960. Olympic Games.
524 113 5 m. brown and olive . . . 30 25
525 – 10 m. purple, green & bl . 35 30
526 – 15 m. carmine and red . . 35 30
527 – 25 m. slate and blue . . . 45 40
528 – 50 m. blue and green . . . 85 65
DESIGNS: 10 m. Flowers composed of Olympic rings; 15 m. Girl with racquet; 25 m. Runner; 50 m. Handball player.

1960. 5th World Forestry Congress, Seattle.
529 114 8 m. lake, green and blue . 35 15
530 – 15 m. green 40 20
531 – 25 m. red, green & violet . 65 30
532 – 50 m. turquoise, brn & grn 1·10 50
DESIGNS: 15 m. Removing bark from tree; 25 m. Tree within leaf; 50 m. Diamond pattern featuring palm.

115 U.N. Emblem and People's Arms 116 Dove of Peace

1960. U.N. Day.
533 115 40 m. blue, red and black . 65 45

1961. 5th Anniv of Independence.
534 116 20 m. blue, bistre & pur . 30 20
535 30 m. brown, violet & blue 35 20
536 40 m. ultram, bl & grn . . 55 40
537 – 75 m. blue, mauve & olive 80 45
DESIGN: 75 m. Globe and Arms of Tunisia.

117 Tunisian Animals and Map of Africa 118 Stamps and Magnifier

1961. Africa Day and 3rd Anniv of Accra Conference. Inscr "JOURNEE DE L'AFRIQUE 15.4.1961".
538 117 40 m. green, brown and bistre 35 20
539 – 60 m. black, brn & turq . 40 30
540 – 100 m. violet, emerald and grey 70 45
541 – 200 m. brown & orange . 1·40 1·00
DESIGNS (all showing outline of Africa): 50 m. Profiles of Negress and Arab woman; 100 m. Masks and "Africa Day" in Arabic; 200 m. Clasped hands.

1961. Stamp Day. Inscr "JOURNEE DU TIMBRE 1961". Multicoloured.
542 12 m. + 4 m. Kerkennah dancer and costume of stamps . . 45 45
543 15 m. + 5 m. Mobile postal delivery 60 60
544 20 m. + 6 m. Type 118 . . . 65 65
545 50 m. + 5 m. Postman in shirt depicting stamps 80 80
The 12 m. and 20 m. are vert and the rest horiz.

119 "Celebration" 120 Dag Hammarskjoeld

1961. National Day.
546 119 25 m. brown, red & violet 45 15
547 – 50 m. brown, choc & grn 45 20
548 – 95 m. mauve, brown & bl 65 40
DESIGNS: 50 m. Family celebrating in street; 95 m. Girl astride crescent moon.

1961. U.N. Day.
549 120 40 m. blue 60 35

121 Arms of Tunisia 122 Mosquito in Web

1962. 10th Anniv of Independence Campaign. Arms in red, yellow, blue and black.
550 121 1 m. yellow and black . . 10 10
551 2 m. pink and black . . . 15 15
552 3 m. blue and black . . . 15 15
553 6 m. grey and black . . . 20 20

1962. Malaria Eradication. Inscr "LE MONDE UNI CONTRE LE PALUDISME".
554 122 20 m. brown 45 30
555 – 30 m. brown, grn & choc 45 30
556 – 40 m. red, green & brown 80 35
DESIGNS—VERT: 30 m. "Horseman" attacking mosquito; 40 m. Hands destroying mosquito.

557 African

1962. Africa Day. Inscr "JOURNEE DE L'AFRIQUE 1962".
557 123 50 m. brown and buff . . 55 35
558 – 10 m. multicoloured . . . 80 45
DESIGN: 100 m. Symbolic figure clasping "Africa".

124 Dancer

125 Rejoicing Tunisians

1962. May Day. Inscr "FETE DU TRAVAIL 1962".
559 **124** 40 m. multicoloured . . . 40 20
560 – 60 m. brown 45 30
DESIGN: 60 m. Worker with pneumatic drill.

1962. National Day.
561 **125** 20 m. black and salmon . 50 35

126 Gabes Costume

127 U.N. Emblem and Tunisian Flag

1962. Republic Festival. Regional Costumes. Multicoloured.
562 5 m. Type **126** 55 20
563 10 m. Mahdia 65 35
564 15 m. Kairouan 90 45
565 20 m. Hammamet . . . . . 1·10 55
566 25 m. Djerba . . . . 1·25 55
567 30 m. As 10 m. . . . . . . 1·25 65
568 40 m. As 20 m. . . . . . . 1·40 65
569 50 m. Type **126** . . . . . 1·40 85
570 55 m. Ksar Hellal . . . . . 2·25 1·00
571 60 m. Tunis . . . . 2·75 1·40

1962. U.N. Day.
572 **127** 20 m. red, black & grey . 35 30
573 – 30 m. multicoloured . . . 40 30
574 – 40 m. blue, black & brown 65 35
DESIGNS—HORIZ: 30 m. "Plant" with three leaves and globe. VERT: 40 m. Globe and dove.

128 A. Q. Chabbi (poet)

129 Pres. Bourguiba

1962. Aboul Qasim Chabbi Commemoration.
575 **128** 15 m. violet 35 20

1962.
576 **129** 20 m. blue 15 15
577 30 m. red 15 10
578 40 m. green 20 15

130 Hached Telephone Exchange

131 Runners

1962. Modernisation of Telephone System.
579 **130** 5 m. multicoloured . . . 30 20
580 – 10 m. multicoloured . . . 35 20
581 – 15 m. multicoloured . . . 50 35
582 – 50 m. flesh, brown & blk . 80 50
583 – 100 m. blue, purple & blk 1·75 90
584 – 200 m. multicoloured . . 2·40 1·40
DESIGNS: 10 m. Carthage Telephone Exchange; 15 m. Aerial equipment; 50 m. Telephone switchboard operators; 100 m. Telephone equipment as human figure; 200 m. Belvedere Telephone Exchange.

1963. 13th International Military Sports Council Cross-country Championships.
585 **131** 30 m. brown, green & blk 60 45

MINIMUM PRICE

The minimum price quoted is 10p which represents a handling charge rather than a basis for valuing common stamps. For further notes about prices, see introductory pages.

132 Dove with Wheatear and Globe

133 Centenary Emblem

1963. Freedom from Hunger.
586 **132** 20 m. blue and brown . . 30 20
587 – 40 m. purple and brown . 40 20
DESIGN: 40 m. Child taking nourishment.

1963. Red Cross Centenary.
588 **133** 20 m. red, grey & brown 45 20

1963. U.N. Day. Nos. 542/5 optd **1963 O.N.U.** in English and Arabic.
589 12 m. +4 m. multicoloured . 30 30
590 15 m. +5 m. multicoloured . 35 35
591 20 m. +6 m. multicoloured . 40 40
592 50 m. +5 m. multicoloured . 65 65

135 "Miss World"

136 "Out of Reach"

1963. 15th Anniv of Declaration of Human Rights.
593 **135** 30 m. brown and green . 45 30

1964. Nubian Monuments Preservation.
594 **136** 50 m. ochre, brown & blue 45 30

137 "Unsettled Forecast"

138 Mohamed Ali (trade union leader)

1964. World Meteorological Day.
595 **137** 40 m. mauve, bl & brn . 45 20

1964. 70th Birth Anniv of Mohamed Ali.
596 **138** 50 m. purple 45 35

139 Africa within Flower

140 Pres. Bourguiba

1964. 1st Anniv of Addis Ababa Conference of the Organization of African Unity.
597 **139** 60 m. multicoloured . . . 50 30

1964. National Day.
598 **140** 20 m. blue 15 10
599 30 m. brown 20 10

141 "Bizerte" ("ship")

142 Fulvous Babbler

1964. Neo-Destour Congress, Bizerta.
600 **141** 50 m. green and black . . 40 30

1965. Air. Tunisian Birds. Multicoloured.
601 25 m. Type **142** . . . . . . 1·75 50
602 55 m. Great grey strike . . 2·50 75
603 55 m. Cream-coloured courser 2·75 95
604 100 m. Chaffinch . . . . . 3·25 1·10
605 150 m. Greater flamingoes . . 5·75 2·40
606 200 m. Barbary partridge . . 8·75 2·75
607 300 m. Common roller . . 13·50 5·25
608 500 m. Hourgara bustard . . 17·00 6·25
SIZES—As Type **142**: 55 m. (both). Others, 23 × 32½ mm.

143 Early Telegraphist and Aerial Mast

144 Carthaginian Coin

1965. I.T.U. Centenary.
609 **143** 55 m. blue and black . . . 50 30

1965. Festival of Popular Arts, Carthage.
610 **144** 5 m. purple and green . . 15 10
611 10 m. purple and yellow . 30 20
612 75 m. purple and blue . . 65 20

145 Girl reading Book

146 Joined Hooks

1965. Opening of Students' Home, Tunis.
613 **145** 25 m. blue, black and red . 30 20
614 40 m. black, blue and red . 40 20
615 50 m. red, black and blue . 45 30

1965. International Co-operation Year.
617 **146** 40 m. blue, purple & blk . 45 25

147 Women bathing

149 Independence

148 Pres. Bourguiba and Hands

1966. Mineral Springs. Inscr "EAUX MINERALES".
618 **147** 10 m. red, ochre & grey . 30 20
619 – 20 m. multicoloured . . . 40 30
620 – 30 m. red, blue & yellow . 45 35
621 – 100 m. olive, yellow & bl . 1·10 55
DESIGNS: 20 m. Man pouring water; 30 m. Woman pouring water; 100 m. Mountain and fronds of tree.

1966. 10th Anniv of Independence.
622 **148** 5 m. lilac and blue . . . 15 10
623 10 m. green and blue . . . 20 15
624 **149** 25 m. multicoloured . . . 20 15
625 – 40 m. multicoloured . . . 55 20
626 – 60 m. multicoloured . . . 80 35
DESIGNS—As Type **149**—HORIZ: 40 m. "Development". VERT: 60 m. "Promotion of Culture" ("man" draped in books, palette, musical instruments, etc.).

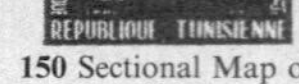
150 Sectional Map of Africa

152 "Athletics"

151 U.N.E.S.C.O. Emblem of the Muses

1966. 2nd U.N. African Regional Cartographic Conference, Tunisia.
627 **150** 15 m. multicoloured . . . 30 20
628 35 m. multicoloured . . . 35 20
629 40 m. multicoloured . . . 50 35

1966. 20th Anniv of U.N.E.S.C.O.
631 **151** 100 m. brown and black . . 85 35

1967. Publicity for Mediterranean Games (September, 1967).
632 **152** 20 m. brown, blue & red . 20 15
633 30 m. black and blue . . 40 30

153 Gabes Costume and Fair Emblem

154 Emblems of Civilisation

1967. "Expo 67" World Fair, Montreal. T **154** and earlier designs redrawn as T **153**.
634 – 50 m. mult (As No. 566) . 35 15
635 **153** 75 m. multicoloured . . . 50 30
636 **154** 100 m. green, blk & turq . 80 30
637 110 m. red, sepia & blue . 95 40
638 – 155 m. mult (As No. 605) 1·75 45

155 Tunisian Pavilion, Pres. Bourguiba and Map

1967. "National Day at World Fair, Montreal".
639 **155** 65 m. purple and red . . 40 35
640 – 105 m. brown, red & blue 50 35
641 – 120 m. blue 60 40
642 – 200 m. black, red & pur . 1·00 50
DESIGNS: 105 m. As Type **155**, but with profile bust of Pres. Bourguiba. Tunisian pavilion (different view) with: 120 m. Silhouette and 200 m. Bust of Pres. Bourguiba.

156 "Tunisia" holding Clover

158 Bas-relief from Statue of Apollo

157 Tennis Club

1967. 10th Anniv of Republic. Multicoloured.
643 25 m. Type **156** 20 15
644 40 m. Woman releasing doves (vert) 35 15

1967. Mediterranean Games, Tunis.
645 **157** 5 m. red and green . . . 20 20
646 – 10 m. multicoloured . . . 20 15
647 – 15 m. black 35 20
648 – 35 m. turq, pur & blk . . 45 20
649 – 75 m. green, violet & red . 80 40
DESIGNS—VERT: 10 m. "Spring Triumphs" (squared panel). HORIZ: 15 m. Olympic swimming pool; 35 m. Sports Palace; 75 m. Olympic stadium.

1967. Tunisian History. Punic period.
650 **158** 15 m. red, black & green . 30 20
651 – 20 m. flesh, red & blue . 35 20
652 – 25 m. brown and olive . . 45 20
653 – 30 m. red and grey . . . 45 20
654 – 40 m. lemon, yell & pur . 50 20
655 – 60 m. multicoloured . . . 50 30
DESIGNS: 20 m. Sea horseman (Kerkouane medallion); 25 m. Hannibal (bronze bust); 30 m. "The Sacrifice" (votive stele); 40 m. Hamilcar (coin); 60 m. Glass funeral pendant mask.

159 "Human Rights"

160 "Electronic Man"

1968. Human Rights Year.
656 **159** 25 m. red 40 35
657 60 m. blue 45 20

1968. Electronics in Postal Service.
658 **160** 25 m. blue, brown & pur . 35 30
659 40 m. black, brown & grn 35 30
660 60 m. purple, slate & blue 45 35

161 "Doctor and Patient" **162** Arabian Jasmine

1968. 20th Anniv of W.H.O.
661 **161** 25 m. green & turquoise . 40 35
662 60 m. red and lake 45 35

1968. Tunisian Flowers. Multicoloured.
663 5 m. Flax 20 15
664 6 m. Indian shot 20 15
665 10 m. Pomegranate 30 15
666 12 m. Type **162** 30 15
667 15 m. Raponticum 35 15
668 20 m. Geranium 40 20
669 25 m. Madonna lily 40 30
670 40 m. Almond 60 30
671 50 m. Capers 80 45
672 60 m. Ariana rose . . . . . . 1·25 70
673 100 m. Jasmine . . . . 1·60 1·10

163 Globe on "Sunflower" **164** Flautist

1968. Red Crescent Day.
674 **163** 15 m. red, green & blue . 35 30
675 – 25 m. red and purple . . 40 30
DESIGN: 25 m. Red crescent on wings of dove.

1968. Stamp Day.
676 **164** 20 m. multicoloured . . . 35 20
677 50 m. multicoloured . . . 40 35

165 Golden Jackal **166** Worker

1968. Fauna. Multicoloured.
678 5 m. Type **165** 20 15
679 8 m. North African crested porcupine 30 20
680 10 m. Dromedary 40 20
681 15 m. Dorcas gazelle 50 20
682 20 m. Fennec fox 80 45
683 25 m. Algerian hedgehog . . . 1·00 55
684 40 m. Horse . . . . 1·40 80
685 60 m. Wild boar . . . . 1·90 1·00

1969. 50th Anniv of I.L.O. Multicoloured.
686 25 m. Type **166** 35 30
687 60 m. Youth and girl holding "May 1" banner 50 35

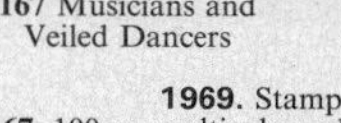
167 Musicians and Veiled Dancers **168** Tunisian Arms

1969. Stamp Day.
688 **167** 100 m. multicoloured . . 70 35

1969.
689 **168** 15 m. multicoloured . . . 20 20
690 25 m. multicoloured . . . 30 20
691 40 m. multicoloured . . . 35 20
692 60 m. multicoloured . . . 40 20

169 "Industrial Development" **170** Lute

1969. 5th Anniv of African Development Bank.
693 **169** 60 m. multicoloured . . . 40 30

1970. Musical Instruments. Multicoloured.
694 25 m. Type **170** 45 35
695 50 m. Zither 55 35
696 70 m. Rehab 80 35
697 90 m. Naghrat (drums) . . . 1·00 35
Nos. 695 and 697 are horiz, size 33 × 22 mm.

171 Nurse, Caduceus and Flags **172** New U.P.U. Headquarters Building

1970. 6th North-African Maghreb Medical Seminar, Tunis.
698 **171** 25 m. multicoloured . . . 35 20

1970. New U.P.U. Headquarters Building, Berne.
699 **172** 25 m. brown and red . . 40 20

173 Mounted Postman

1970. Stamp Day. Multicoloured.
700 25 m. Type **173** 20 20
701 35 m. "Postmen of yesterday and today" (23 × 38 mm) . . . 35 20

174 U.N. Emblem, "N" and Dove forming "O.N.U." **175** "The Flower-seller"

1970. 25th Anniv of United Nations.
702 **174** 40 m. multicoloured . . . 40 20

1970. "Tunisian Life" (1st series). Multicoloured.
703 20 m. Type **175** 20 15
704 25 m. "The husband's third day of marriage" 30 20
705 35 m. "The Perfumer" 45 35
706 40 m. "The Fish-seller" . . . 50 35
707 85 m. "The Coffee-house keeper" 80 35
See also Nos. 715/18, 757/62 and 819/23.

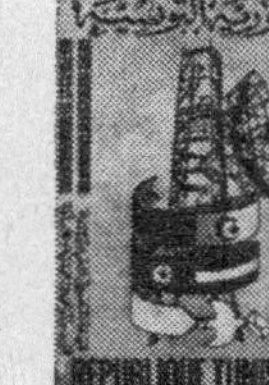
176 Lenin **177** Dish Aerial and Flags

1970. Birth Centenary of Lenin.
709 **176** 60 m. lake 65 35

1971. Maghreban Posts and Telecommunciations Co-ordination.
710 **177** 25 m. multicoloured . . . 40 35

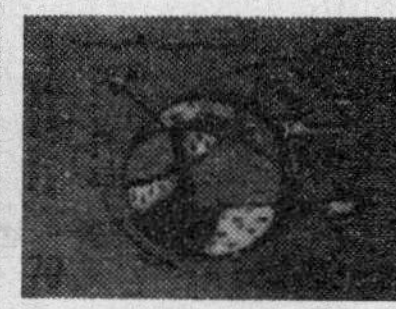
178 U.N. Building and Symbol **179** Globe and Satellites

1971. Racial Equality Year.
711 **178** 80 m. multicoloured . . . 45 30

1971. World Telecommunications Day.
712 **179** 70 m. multicoloured . . . 40 20

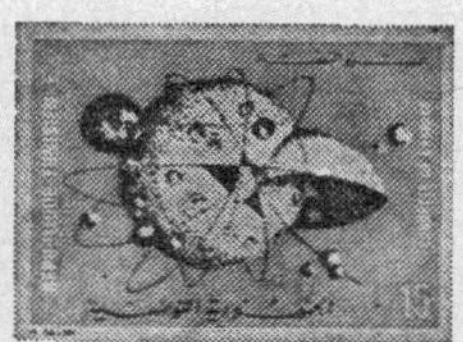
180 Moon, Earth and Satellites

1971. "Conquest of Space".
713 **180** 15 m. black and blue . . . 35 20
714 – 90 m. black and red . . . 60 30
DESIGN: 90 m. Space allegory.

181 "The Pottery Dealer" **182** Pres. Bourguiba

1971. "Tunisian Life" (2nd series). Multicoloured.
715 25 m. Type **181** 35 20
716 30 m. "The Esparto dealer" . . 35 20
717 40 m. "The Poulterer" 45 20
718 50 m. "The Dyer" 55 30

1971. 8th P.S.D. Destourian Socialist Party Congress, Tunis. Multicoloured.
720 25 m. Type **182** 20 20
721 30 m. Bourguiba in bed, 1938 (horiz) 20 20
722 50 m. Bourguiba acclaimed . . 35 30
723 80 m. Bourguiba—"Builder of the Nation" (horiz) 45 30
SIZES: 30 m., 80 m. $13\frac{1}{2} \times 14$; 50 m. As Type **182**.

183 Shah Mohammed Riza Pahlavi and Achaemenidian Effigy **184** Pimento

1971. 2500th Anniv of Persian Empire. Mult.
724 25 m. Type **183** 30 20
725 50 m. "King Bahram-Gur hunting" (14th-century) . . 35 20
726 100 m. "Coronation of Louhrasap" (Persian 11th-century miniature) 60 30

1971. "Flowers, Fruits and Folklore". Mult.
728 1 m. Type **184** 10 10
729 2 m. Mint 20 15
730 5 m. Pear 35 20
731 25 m. Laurel rose 40 30
732 60 m. Quince 80 20
733 100 m. Grapefruit . . . . . . 1·25 35
Each design includes a scene from Tunisian folklore.

185 "The Musicians of Kerkena" **186** Telephone

1971. Stamp Day.
735 **185** 50 m. multicoloured . . . 40 20

1971. Pan-African Telecommunications Network.
736 **186** 95 m. multicoloured . . . 50 45

187 U.N.I.C.E.F. Emblem **189** Olive-tree Emblem

188 Rialto Bridge, Venice

1971. 25th Anniv of U.N.I.C.E.F.
737 **187** 110 m. multicoloured . . 50 35

1971. U.N.E.S.C.O. "Save Venice" Campaign. Multicoloured.
738 25 m. Gondolier (vert) 35 20
739 30 m. De Medici and Palace (vert) 40 20
740 50 m. Prow of gondola (vert) . 45 35
741 80 m. Type **188** 80 35

1972. World Olive-oil Year.
742 **189** 60 m. multicoloured . . . 40 20

190 Tunisian reading Book **191** Heart Emblem

1972. International Book Year.
743 **190** 90 m. multicoloured . . . 50 40

1972. World Health Day. Multicoloured.
744 25 m. Type **191** 35 20
745 60 m. Heart within "hour-glass" 55 35

192 "Old Age" **193** "Only One Earth"

1972. Tunisian Red Crescent.
746 **192** 10 m. + 10 m. violet & red 35 30
747 – 75 m. + 10 m. brown & red 50 35
DESIGN: 75 m. Mother and Child ("Child Care").

1972. U.N. Environmental Conservation Conf, Stockholm.
748 **193** 60 m. green and brown . 50 20

194 Hurdling **195** Chessboard

1972. Olympic Games, Munich.
749 – 5 m. multicoloured . . . 10 10
750 **194** 15 m. multicoloured . . . 15 10
751 – 20 m. black, green & gold 15 10
752 – 25 m. multicoloured . . . 15 15
753 – 60 m. multicoloured . . . 35 20
754 – 80 m. multicoloured . . . 45 30
DESIGNS—VERT: 5 m. Handball; 20 m. Athletes saluting. HORIZ: 25 m. Football; 60 m. Swimming; 80 m. Running.

1972. 20th Chess Olympiad, Skopje, Yugoslavia.
756 **195** 60 m. multicoloured . . . 90 55

196 "The Fisherman"

1972. "Tunisian Life" (3rd series). Multicoloured.
757 5 m. Type **196** 20 15
758 10 m. "The Basket-maker" . . 20 15
759 25 m. "The Musician" 30 15
760 50 m. "The Berber Bride" . . 55 20
761 60 m. "The Flower-seller" . . 80 20
762 80 m. "The Mystic" 80 40

197 New P.T.T. H.Q., Tunis

1972. Stamp Day.
764 **197** 25 m. multicoloured . . . 30 20

198 Dome of the Rock, Jerusalem

1973. Dome of the Rock Commemoration.
765 **198** 25 m. multicoloured . . . 40 30

199 Globe and Beribboned Pen

1973. 9th Writers' Congress and 11th Poetry Festival. Multicoloured.
766 25 m. Type **199** 20 20
767 60 m. Lyre emblem 35 20

200 Heads of Family 201 Figures "10" and Bird feeding Young

1973. Family Planning. Multicoloured.
768 20 m. Type **200** 20 20
769 25 m. Family profiles and bird 35 30

1973. 10th Anniv of World Food Programme. Multicoloured.
770 25 m. Type **201** 30 20
771 60 m. Symbolic "10" 30 20

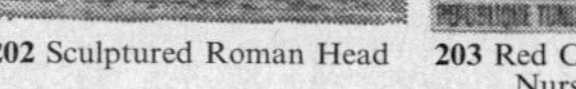
202 Sculptured Roman Head 203 Red Crescent Nurse

1973. U.N.E.S.C.O. "Save Carthage" Campaign. Multicoloured.
772 5 m. type 202 . . . . 30 20
773 25 m. Carthagian mosaics . . 45 35
774 30 m. "Cycle of mosaics" . . 45 35
775 40 m. "Goodwill" stele (vert) . 60 35
776 60 m. Preacher's hand (from Korba statue) 70 35
777 75 m. "Malga" (17th-century potsherd) (vert) 85 40

1973. Tunisian Red Crescent.
779 **203** 25 m. + 10 m. multicoloured 45 35
780 – 60 m. + 10 m. red & grey 65 35
DESIGN—HORIZ: 60 m. Arms of blood donors.

204 "World Telecommunications" 205 Smiling Youth

1973. 5th World Telecommunications Day. Multicoloured.
781 60 m. Type **204** 35 20
782 75 m. "The Universe" 40 20

1973. 1st Pan-African Festival of Youth. Multicoloured.
783 25 m. Festival Map 35 30
784 40 m. Type **205** 40 30

206 Scout Badge

1973. International Scouting.
785 **206** 25 m. multicoloured . . . 35 30

207 "Rover" in Car

1973. 2nd Pan-Arab Rover Rally.
786 **207** 60 m. multicoloured . . . 40 35

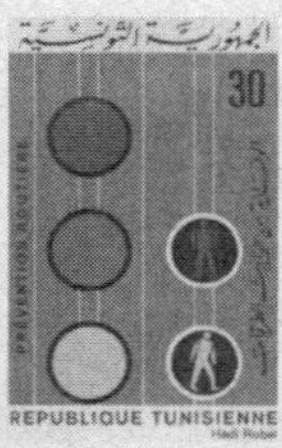

208 Traffic Lights 209 Winged Camel

1973. Road Safety. Multicoloured.
787 25 m. Motorway junction (horiz) 35 30
788 30 m. Type **208** 40 30

1973. Stamp Day. Multicoloured.
789 10 m. Peacock ("collectors pride") (horiz) 35 20
790 65 m. Type **209** 40 35

210 Copernicus 211 O.A.U. Emblems within Arms

1973. 500th Birth Anniv of Copernicus.
791 **210** 60 m. multicoloured . . . 55 35

1973. 10th Anniv of Organization of African Unity.
792 **211** 25 m. multicoloured . . . 40 20

212 Interpol Emblem and Handclasp 213 Flower Offering

1973. 50th Anniv of International Criminal Police Organization (Interpol).
793 **212** 65 m. multicoloured . . . 45 35

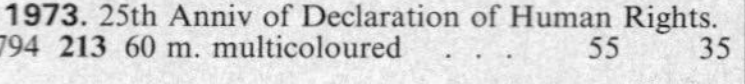

1973. 25th Anniv of Declaration of Human Rights.
794 **213** 60 m. multicoloured . . . 55 35

214 W.M.O. H.Q., Geneva

1973. W.M.O. Centenary Multicoloured.
795 25 m. Type **214** 40 20
796 60 m. Earth and emblems . . 45 30

215 President Bourguiba, 1934 216 Scientist using Microscope

1974. 40th Anniv of Neo-Destour Party.
797 **215** 15 m. purple, red & black . 20 20
798 – 25 m. brown, orge & blk . 20 20
799 – 60 m. blue, red and black . 30 20
800 – 75 m. brown, mve & blk . 35 20
801 – 100 m. green, orge & blk . 45 35
DESIGNS: Nos. 798/801, Various portraits of Pres. Bourguiba (founder), similar to Type **215**.

1974. 6th Africn Micro-Palaeontologica Conference, Tunis.
803 **216** 60 m. multicoloured . . . 1·40 60

217 "Blood Donation" 218 Telephonist holding Globe

1974. Tunisian Red Crescent. Multicoloured.
804 25 m. + 10 m. Type **217** . . . 35 35
805 75 m. + 10 m. "Blood Transfusion" 45 45

1974. Inauguration of International Automatic Telephone Service. Multicoloured.
806 15 m. Type **218** 20 20
807 60 m. Telephone dial 45 35

219 Population Emblems

1974. World Population Year.
808 **219** 110 m. multicoloured . . . 55 35

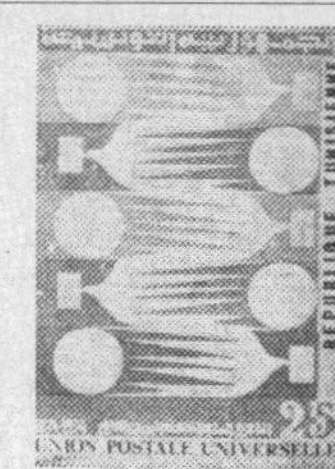
220 Pres. Bourguiba and Emblem 222 "Carrier-pigeons"

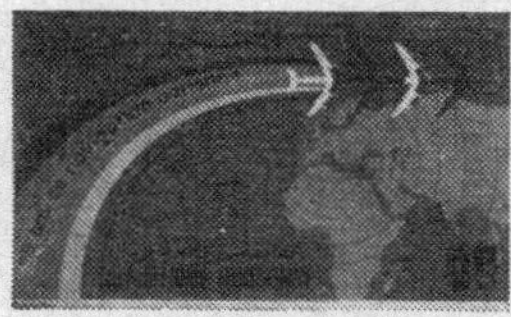
221 Aircraft crossing Globe

1974. Destourian Socialist Party Congress.
809 **220** 24 m. blue, turq & blk . . 20 20
810 – 60 m. red, yellow & black 30 25
811 – 200 m. purple, grn & blk . 90 95
DESIGNS—HORIZ: 60 m. Pres. Bourguiba and sunflower;

1974. 25th Anniv of Tunisian Aviation.
813 **221** 60 m. multicoloured . . . 45 35

1974. Centenary of U.P.U. Multicoloured.
814 25 m. Type **222** 35 25
815 60 m. Handclasp 45 30

223 Bardo Palace as "Ballot Box" 224 Postman with Parcels on Head

1974. Legislative and Presidential Elections.
816 **223** 25 m. blue, green & blk . 35 30
817 – 100 m. black and orange . 50 35
DESIGN: 100 m. Pres. Bourguiba on poll card.

1974. Stamp Day.
818 **224** 75 m. multicoloured . . . 45 20

225 "The Water-carrier" 226 Stylised Bird

1975. "Scenes from Tunisian Life" (4th series). Multicoloured.
819 5 m. Type **225** 15 15
820 15 m. "The Scent Sprinkler" . 20 20
821 25 m. "The Washer-women" . 20 20
822 60 m. "The Potter" 35 20
823 110 m. "The Fruit-seller" . . 85 50

1975. 13th Arab Engineers' Union Conference, Tunis. Multicoloured.
825 25 m. Skyscraper and scaffolding (vert) 20 20
826 65 m. Type **226** 40 30

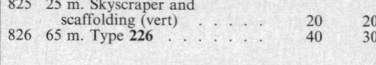

227 Gold Coffee-pot and Tray

1975. Handicrafts. Multicoloured.
827 10 m. Type **227** 20 20
828 15 m. Horseman and saddlery (embroidery) 20 20
829 25 m. Still life (painting) . . . 30 20
830 30 m. Bird-cage (fine-crafts) (vert) 35 20
831 40 m. Silver head-dress (jewellery) (vert) 35 20
832 60 m. Textile patterns 55 30

228 Man and Scales **229** "Telecommunications"

1975. Tunisian Red Crescent Campaign against Malnutrition.

833 **228** 50 m. + 10 m. mult . . . 40 35

1975. 7th World Telecommunications Day.

834 **229** 50 m. multicoloured . . . 30 20

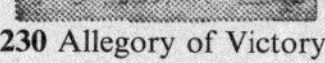

230 Allegory of Victory **231** Tunisian Woman

1975. 20th Anniv of "Victory" (Return of Bourguiba). Multicoloured.

835 25 m. Type **230** 20 20
836 65 m. Return of President Bourguiba (horiz) 35 20

1975. International Women's Year.

837 **231** 110 m. multicoloured . . 55 30

232 Children on Road Crossing

1975. Road Safety Campaign.

838 **232** 25 m. multicolured 20 20

233 Djerba

1975. "Tunisia, Yesterday and Today" (1st series). Multicoloured.

839 10 m. Type **233** 20 20
840 15 m. Tunis 20 20
841 20 m. Monastir 20 20
842 65 m. Sousse 45 30
843 500 m. Tozeur . . . . 3·25 1·25
844 1 d. Kairouan . . . . 5·50 2·25

See also Nos. 864/7.

234 Figures representing Sport **235** Bouquet of Flowers

1975. 7th Mediterranean Games, Algiers. Multicoloured.

845 25 m. Type **234** 20 20
846 50 m. "Ship of sport" (horiz) . 35 20

1975. Stamp Day.

847 **235** 100 m. multicoloured . . 45 20

236 College Building

1975. Centenary of Sadiki College.

848 **236** 25 m. multicoloured . . . 30 20

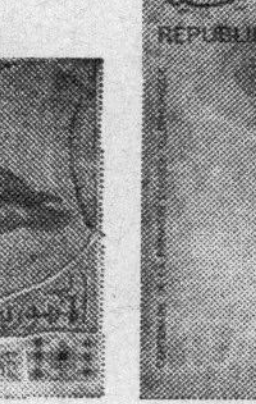

237 "Duck" **238** Early and Modern Telephones

1976. Tunisian Mosaics. Multicoloured.

849 5 m. Type **237** 30 20
850 10 m. Fish 30 20
851 25 m. Lioness (40 × 27 mm) . 55 45
852 60 m. Gorgon (40 × 27 mm) . 60 45
853 75 m. Circus spectators (27 × 40 mm) 65 45
854 100 m. Virgil (27 × 40 mm) . 95 45

1976. Telephone Centenary.

856 **238** 150 m. multicoloured . . 55 30

239 Figures "20" and Banners **240** Blind Man with Stick

1976. 20th Anniv of Independence. Mult.

857 40 m. Type **239** 20 20
858 100 m. Figures "20" and flag emblem 40 20
859 150 m. Floral allegory of "Tunisia" 60 30

1976. World Health Day.

861 **240** 100 m. black and red . . 45 20

241 Blood Donation **242** "Urban Development"

1976. Tunisian Red Crescent.

862 **241** 40 m. + 10 m. mult . . . 40 30

1976. "Habitat" Human Settlements Conference, Vancouver.

863 **242** 40 m. multicoloured . . . 30 20

243 Henna Tradition

1976. "Tunisia, Yesterday and Today" (2nd series). Multicoloured.

864 40 m. Type **243** 20 20
865 50 m. Diving for sponges . . 35 20
866 65 m. Weaving 35 20
867 110 m. Pottery 50 35

244 "Spirit of 1776" (Willard)

1976. Bicentenary of American Revolution.

868 **244** 200 m. multicoloured . . 1·40 65

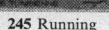

245 Running **246** Girl reading Book

1976. Olympic Games, Montreal. Multicoloured.

870 50 m. Type **245** 20 20
871 75 m. Olympic flags and rings . 35 20
872 120 m. Olympic "dove" . . . 55 30

1976. Literature for Children.

873 **246** 100 m. multicoloured . . . 45 20

247 Bird and Faces Emblem **248** Mausoleum, Tunis

1976. 15th Anniv of 1st Non-aligned Countries' Conference, Belgrade.

874 **247** 150 m. multicoloured . . . 60 20

1976. Cultural Heritage. Multicoloured.

875 85 m. Type **248** 35 20
876 100 m. Great Mosque, Kairouan 40 20
877 150 m. Ribat, Monastery, Monastir 60 20
878 200 m. Barber's Mosque, Kairouan 90 35

249 Emblem and Globe

1976. 25th Anniv of U.N. Postal Administration.

879 **249** 150 m. multicoloured . . . 65 30

250 Red Crescent on Litter

1977. Tunisian Red Crescent.

880 **250** 50 m. + 10 m. mult . . . 40 35

251 Circuit Diagram **252** "Dialogue"

1977. World Telecommunications Day.

881 **251** 150 m. multicoloured . . . 65 40

1977. 10th Anniv of International French Language Council.

882 **252** 100 m. multicoloured . . . 80 35

253 Footballers **254** Gold Coin

1977. 1st World Junior Football Tournament.

883 **253** 150 m. multicoloured . . . 90 45

1977. Cultural Patrimony. Multicoloured.

884 10 m. Type **254** 10 10
885 15 m. 13th-century stele . . . 15 15
886 20 m. 17th-century illuminated manuscript 20 15
887 30 m. Glass painting 35 20
888 40 m. Ceramic pot decor . . . 40 20
889 50 m. Gate, Sidi-Bou-Said . . 45 20

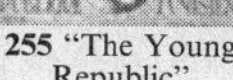

255 "The Young Republic" **257** Globe and Cogwheels

256 A.P.U. Emblem within Postmark

1977. 20th Anniv of Republic. Multicoloured.

890 40 m. Type **255** 35 20
891 100 m. "The Confident Republic" 40 20
892 150 m. "The Determined Republic" 65 30

1977. 25th Anniv of Arab Postal Union.

894 **256** 40 m. multicoloured . . . 20 20

1977. World Rheumatism Year.

895 **257** 120 m. brown, red & blk . 65 35

258 Harvester and Rural Cameos

1977. Rural Development.

896 **258** 40 m. multicoloured . . . 35 20

259 Factory Workers **260** Pres. Bourguiba and Flaming Torch within "9"

1978. Employment Priority Plan. Multicoloured.

897 20 m. Forms of transport and driver (horiz) 20 15
898 40 m. Tractor driver and farm workers (horiz) 20 20
899 100 m. Type **259** 45 30

1978. 40th Anniv of April 9th Revolution.

900 **260** 40 m. green, brn & olive . 20 20
901 – 60 m. red, brown, & blk . 20 20

DESIGN: 60 m. President Bourguiba within figure "9".

261 Policeman in Safety Helmet **262** "Blood Donors"

1978. 6th African Regional Interpol Conference.

902 **261** 150 m. multicoloured . . 80 35

1978. Tunisian Red Crescent.

903 **262** 50 m. + 10 m. mult . . . 45 30

263 Goalkeeper catching World Cup Emblem

264 Hammer and Chisel chipping away Apartheid

1978. World Cup Football Championship, Argentina. Multicoloured.
904 40 m. Type **263** 30 20
905 150 m. Footballer, map and flags 85 35

1978. International Anti-Apartheid Year. Mult.
906 50 m. Type **264** 20 20
907 100 m. Black and white doves 45 30

265 Flora, Fauna and Polluting Factory

266 Crane removing Smallpox from Globe

1978. Protection of Nature and the Environment. Multicoloured.
908 10 m. Type **265** 15 15
909 50 m. "Pollution of the oceans" 40 20
910 120 m. "Making the deserts green" 95 20

1978. Global Eradication of Smallpox.
911 **266** 150 m. multicoloured . . 65 35

267 Zlass Horseman

268 Lenin Banner

1978. Calligraphy, Art and Traditions. Multicoloured.
912 5 m. Type **267** 10 10
913 60 m. Djerba wedding 30 15
914 75 m. Women potters from the Mogods 40 15
915 100 m. Dove over cupolas of Marabout Sidi Mahrez . . 45 20
916 500 m. Opening of the ploughing season, Jenduba . . . . . . 3·00 1·00
917 1 d. Man on swing between palm trees (Spring Festival, Tozeur) 4·75 1·90

1978. 60th Anniv of Russian Revolution.
918 **268** 150 m. multicoloured . . 85 45

269 Farhat Hached

270 Family Group

1978. Farhat Hached (Trade Union leader). Commemoration.
919 **269** 50 m. multicoloured . . . 35 10

1978. 10th Anniv of Tunisian Family Planning Association.
920 **270** 50 m. multicoloured . . . 40 20

271 "The Sun"

273 Hand holding Bird

272 Boeing 747 and Flags

1978. Solar Energy.
921 **271** 100 m. multicoloured . . 60 20

1978. 20th Anniv of Tunisian Civil Aeronautics and Meteorology.
922 **272** 50 m. multicoloured . . . 30 20

1979. Tunisian Red Crescent.
923 **273** 50 m. + 10 m. mult . . 40 30

274 Pres. Bourguiba

275 Sun, Yacht and Golfer

1979. 20th Anniv of Constitution.
924 **274** 50 m. brown, yell & blk . 20 20

1979. Inauguration of El Kantaoui Port.
925 **275** 150 m. multicoloured . . 65 30

276 Korbous

277 Bow-net Making

1979. Tunisian Landscapes. Multicoloured.
926 50 m. Type **276** 15 10
927 100 m. Mides 35 15

1979. Crafts. Multicoloured.
928 10 m. Type **277** 15 10
929 50 m. Bee-keeping 35 10

278 Pres. Bourguiba and "10"

279 Dish Aerial and Satellite

1979. 10th Congress of Socialist Destourian Party.
930 **278** 50 m. multicoloured . . . 30 10

1979. 3rd World Telecommunications Exhibition, Geneva.
931 **279** 150 m. multicoloured . . 65 35

280 World Map, Koran and Symbols of Arab Achievements

281 Children crossing Road

1979. The Arabs.
932 **280** 50 m. multicoloured . . . 20 15

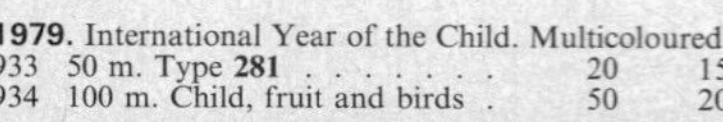
1979. International Year of the Child. Multicoloured.
933 50 m. Type **281** 20 15
934 100 m. Child, fruit and birds . 50 20

282 Dove and Olive Tree

283 Symbolic Figure

1979. 2nd World Olive-oil Year.
935 **282** 150 m. multicoloured . . . 80 35

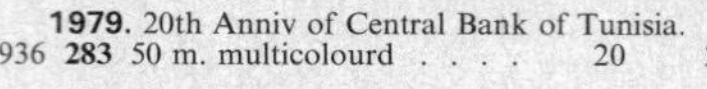
1979. 20th Anniv of Central Bank of Tunisia.
936 **283** 50 m. multicolourd 20 20

284 Children and Jujube Tree

1979. Animals and Plants. Multicoloured.
937 20 m. Type **284** 20 10
938 30 m. Common peafowl . . . 35 15
939 70 m. Goat 65 20
940 85 m. Girl and date palm . . . 70 20

285 Coded Letter

1980. Introduction of Postal Coding.
941 **285** 50 m. multicoloured . . . 30 20

286 Smoker

1980. World Health Day. Anti-smoking Campaign.
942 **286** 150 m. multicoloured . . . 65 30

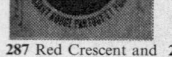

287 Red Crescent and Globe forming an Eye

288 President Bourguiba, Flower and Open Book

1980. Tunisian Red Crescent.
943 **287** 20 m. + 10 m. mult . . . 40 30

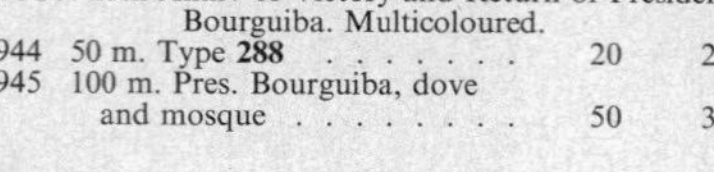
1980. 25th Anniv of Victory and Return of President Bourguiba. Multicoloured.
944 50 m. Type **288** 20 20
945 100 m. Pres. Bourguiba, dove and mosque 50 35

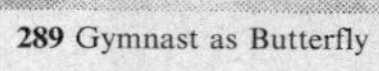
289 Gymnast as Butterfly

290 Tools

1980. Turin Gymnastic Games.
946 **289** 100 m. multicoloured . . . 45 20

1980. Handicrafts. Multicoloured.
947 30 m. Type **290** 30 20
948 75 m. Woman embroidering . 40 20

291 Ibn Khaldoun (philosopher)

292 Avicenna

1980. Ibn Khaldoun Commemoration.
949 **291** 50 m. multicoloured . . . 20 20

1980. Birth Millenary of Avicenna (philosopher).
950 **292** 100 m. sepia and brown . 65 35

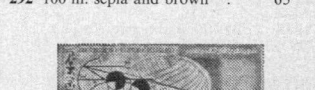

293 Al-Biruni and Scientific Diagram

1980. The Arabs' Contribution to Science.
951 **293** 50 m. multicoloured . . . 35 20

294 Yachts at Sidi Bou Said

1980. Sidi Bou Said.
952 **294** 100 m. multicoloured . . 65 35

295 "Tourists"

1980. World Tourism Conference, Manila.
953 **295** 150 m. multicoloured . . 55 20

296 "Wedding at Djerba"

1980. Yahia (painter) Commemoration.
954 **296** 50 m. multicoloured . . . 40 30

297 Aircraft over Tozeur

298 "Eye"

1980. Opening of Tozeur International Airport.
955 **297** 85 m. multicoloured . . . 35 20

1980. 7th Afro-Asian Congress on Ophthalmology.
956 **298** 100 m. multicoloured . . 55 35

299 Spider's Web

1980. 1400th Anniv of Hegira. Multicoloured.
957 50 m. Type **299** 20 20
958 80 m. Minarets 35 20

300 Face as Camera

301 "Ophrys scolopax scolopax"

1980. Carthage Cinematographic Days.
959 **300** 100 m. multicoloured . . 45 30

1980. Flora and Fauna. Multicoloured.
960 20 m. Type **301** 20 20
961 25 m. "Cyclamen europaeum" 20 20
962 50 m. Mouflon 20 20
963 100 m. Golden eagle 45 30

302 Kairouan Mosque

1980. Conservation of Kairouan.
964 **302** 85 m. multicoloured . . . 35 20

303 H. von Stephan

304 Hands holding Bottle containing Blood Drop

1981. 150th Birth Anniv of Heinrich von Stephan (founder of U.P.U.).
965 **303** 150 m. multicoloured . . 65 35

1981. 20th Anniv of Tunisian Blood Donors Association.
966 **304** 75 m. multicoloured . . . 65 45

305 Flags and Pres. Bourguiba

1981. 25th Anniv of Independence. Multicoloured.
967 50 m. Type **305** 20 20
968 60 m. Stork and ribbons forming "25" 35 20
969 85 m. Stylized birds 55 35
970 120 m. Victory riding a winged horse 55 35

306 Flower and Pres. Bourguiba

1981. Special Congress of Destourian Socialist Party. Multicoloured.
972 50 m. Type **306** 20 15
973 75 m. Arrows forming flower . 35 20

307 Mosque, Mahdia and Galley

1981. Tourism. Multicoloured.
974 50 m. Type **307** 20 20
975 85 m. Djerid bride passing Great Mosque of Tozeur (vert) . . 35 30
976 100 m. Needle rocks, Tabarka 45 30

308 Stylized Peacock hatching Egg

1981. Red Crescent.
977 **308** 50 m. + 10 m. mult . . 35 35

309 I.T.U. and W.H.O. Emblems and Ribbons forming Caduceus

310 Flowers and Youths

1981. World Telecommunications Day.
978 **309** 150 m. multicoloured . . 60 30

1981. Youth Festival.
979 **310** 100 m. multicoloured . . 45 20

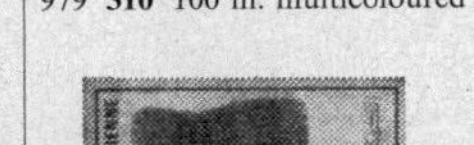

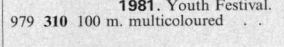

311 Kemal Ataturk

312 Skifa Khala, Mahdia

1981. Birth Centenary of Kemal Ataturk.
980 **311** 150 m. multicoloured . . 65 35

1981. Tunisian Monuments.
981 **312** 150 m. multicoloured . . 65 35

313 Cheikh Mohamed Tahar ben Achour and Minaret

1981. Cheikh Mohamed Tahar ben Achour (scholar and teacher) Commemoration.
982 **313** 200 m. multicoloured . . 1·00 45

314 Rejoicing Woman

315 Tree with Broken Branch

1981. 25th Anniv of Personal Status Code. Multicoloured.
983 50 m. Type **314** 20 20
984 100 m. Dove and head of woman 40 30

1981. International Year of Disabled People.
985 **315** 250 m. multicoloured . . 1·00 65

316 Stylized Figure and Ka'aba, Mecca

327 Food Sources

1981. Pilgrimage to Mecca.
986 **316** 50 m. multicoloured . . . 30 20

1981. World Food Day.
987 **317** 200 m. multicoloured . . . 90 50

318 Dome of the Rock

1981. Palestinian Welfare.
988 **318** 50 m. + 5 m. mult 35 20
989 150 m. + 5 m. mult . . . 60 35
990 200 m. + 5 m. mult . . . 90 50

319 Mnaguech (earring)

321 Chemist (detail from 13th-century manuscript)

320 Ship passing under Bridge

1981. Jewellery. Multicoloured.
991 150 m. Type **319** 60 30
992 180 m. Mahfdha (pendant) (horiz) 70 35
993 200 m. Essalta (hairnet) . . . 90 40

1981. Bizerta Drawbridge.
994 **320** 230 m. multicoloured . . . 80 40

1982. Arab Pharmacists' Union.
995 **321** 80 m. multicoloured . . . 55 35

322 Ring of People around Red Crescent

1982. Red Crescent.
996 **322** 80 m. + 10 m. mult . . . 40 30

323 "Ocean Research"

234 "Productive Family"

1982. International Symposium "Ocean Venture", Tunis.
997 **323** 150 m. multicoloured . . . 80 45

1982. The Productive Family.
998 **324** 80 m. multicoloured . . . 35 20

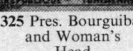

325 Pres. Bourguiba and Woman's Head

326 Scout within "50"

1982. 25th Anniv of Republic.
999 **325** 80 m. blue and black . . 30 20
1000 – 100 m. multicoloured . . 40 30
1001 – 200 m. multicoloured . . 65 35
DESIGNS: 100 m. President and woman with "XXV" headband; 200 m. President and woman with "25" in hair.

1982. 75th Anniv of Scout Movement and 50th Anniv of Tunisian Scout Movement. Multicoloured.
1003 80 m. Type **326** 35 20
1004 200 m. Scout camp (vert) . . 65 20

327 "Pseudophillipsia azzouzi"

328 Tunisian Woman

1982. Fossils. Multicoloured.
1005 80 m. Type **327** 45 35
1006 200 m. "Mediterraneotrigonia cherahilensis" . . . . . . 1·40 65
1007 280 m. "Numidiopleura enigmatica" (horiz) . . . . 1·10 80
1008 300 m. "Micreschara tunisiensis" . . . . 2·00 1·40
1009 500 m. "Mantelliceras pervinquieri" . . . . . . 3·75 2·00
1010 100 m. "Elephas africanavus" (horiz) . . . . 5·50 2·75

1982. 30th Anniv of Arab Postal Union.
1011 **328** 80 m. multicoloured . . 40 20

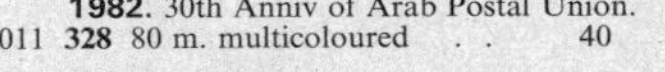

329 I.T.U. Emblem

330 Tunisian Buildings and Congress Centre

1982. I.T.U. Delegates' Conference, Nairobi.
1012 **329** 200 m. multicoloured . . 65 45

1982. "Tunisia Land of Congresses".
1013 **330** 200 m. multicoloured . . 65 30

331 "Feeding the World"

332 Tahar Haddad

1982. World Food Day.
1014 **331** 200 m. multicoloured . . 65 30

1982. Tahar Haddad (social reformer) Commemoration.
1015 **332** 200 m. brown 80 35

333 Microscope

334 Figure dancing in Rain

1982. Cent of Discovery of Tubercle Bacillus.
1016 **333** 100 m. multicoloured . . 55 30

1982. Stories and Songs from Tunisia. Multicoloured.
1017 20 m. Type **334** 15 15
1018 30 m. Woman with broom . . 15 15
1019 70 m. Boy and fisherman . . 20 15
1020 80 m. Chicken (horiz) . . . 30 20
1021 100 m. Woman admiring herself in mirror (horiz) 40 20
1022 120 m. Two girls 45 30

335 Clasped Hands and Palestine Flag

1982. Palestinian Solidarity Day.
1023 **335** 80 m. multicoloured . . 30 20

336 Farhat Hached 337 Bourguiba Sidi Saad Dam

1982. 30th Death Anniv of Farhat Hached.
1024 **336** 80 m. red 35 20

1982. Inauguration of Bourguiba Sidi Saad Dam.
1025 **337** 80 m. multicoloured . . 45 20

338 Environment Emblem on Blackboard 339 Giving Blood

1982. Opening of Environment Training Work School.
1026 **338** 80 m. multicoloured . . 35 15

1983. Red Crescent.
1027 **339** 80 m. + 10 m. mult . . 50 30

340 "Communications"

1983. World Communications Year.
1028 **340** 200 m. multicoloured . . 55 30

341 Dove and Map of Africa 342 Customs Officer, Globes and Suitcases

1983. 20th Anniv of Organization of African Unity.
1029 **341** 230 m. blue & dp blue . 65 40

1983. 20th Anniv of Customs Co-operation Council.
1030 **342** 100 m. multicoloured . . 35 20

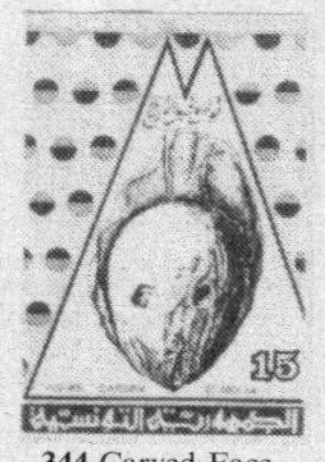

343 Aly Ben Ayed 344 Carved Face, El Mekta

1983. Aly Ben Ayed (actor) Commemoration.
1031 **343** 80 m. red, black and deep red 30 30

1983. Pre-historic Artefacts. Multicoloured.
1032 15 m. Type **244** 20 20
1033 20 m. Neolithic necklace, Kef el Agab (horiz) 30 20
1034 30 m. Neolithic grindstone, Redeyef (horiz) 30 20
1035 40 m. Animal petroglyph, Gafsa 35 20
1036 80 m. Dolmen, Mactar (horiz) 40 30
1037 100 m. Bi-face flint, El Mekta 55 30

345 Dove, Barbed Wire and Dome of the Rock

1983. Palestinian Welfare.
1038 **345** 80 m. + 5 m. mult . . . 40 40

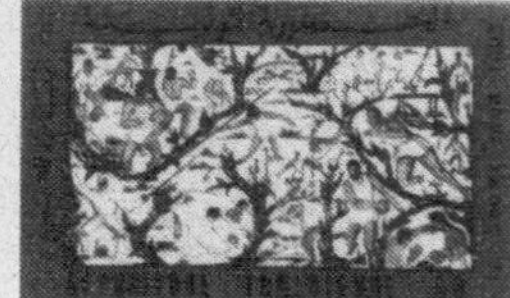
346 Sporting Activities

1983. Sport for All.
1039 **346** 40 m. multicoloured . . 15 10

347 Tunisian with Flag and French Freighter 348 Fishing Boats and Fish

1983. 20th Anniv of Evacuation of Foreign Troops.
1040 **347** 80 m. multicoloured . . 30 20

1983. World Fishing Day.
1041 **348** 200 m. multicoloured . . 1·00 25

349 "The Weaver" (Hedi Khayachi)

1983. Hedi Khayachi (painter) Commem.
1042 **349** 80 m. multicoloured . . 45 35

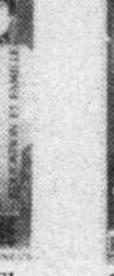
350 Saluting the Flag 351 Air Hostess and Airliner

1983. Salute to the Flag.
1043 **350** 100 m. multicoloured . . 35 20

1983. 25th Anniv of Tunisian Civil Aviation and Meteorology.
1044 **351** 150 m. multicoloured . . 55 20

352 Pres. Bourguiba and Archway 353 Map of Africa

1984. 50th Anniv of Neo-Destour Party. Multicoloured.
1045 40 m. Type **352** 15 10
1046 70 m. Bourguiba and torch . 20 10
1047 80 m. Bourguiba and flag . . 30 15
1048 150 m. Bourguiba and wall . 50 30
1049 200 m. Bourguiba and dove (horiz) 60 35
1050 230 m. Pres. Bourguiba (horiz) 70 45

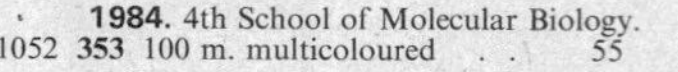

1984. 4th School of Molecular Biology.
1052 **353** 100 m. multicoloured . . 55 30

354 First Aid

1984. Red Crescent.
1053 **354** 80 m. + 10 m. mult . . . 40 30

355 Ibn el Jazzar 356 "Co-operation"

1984. Ibn el Jazzar (doctor) Commem.
1054 **355** 80 m. multicoloured . . . 40 30

1984. Economic Co-operation among Developing Countries.
1055 **356** 230 m. multicoloured . . 80 35

357 Witch, Maiden and Coquette

1984. Stories and Songs from Tunisia. Multicoloured.
1056 20 m. Type **357** 10 10
1057 80 m. Puppet, hands and mouse 30 20
1058 100 m. Boy and horse (vert) . 35 15

358 Family facing the Future

1984. 20th Anniv of Tunisian Education and Family Organization.
1059 **358** 80 m. multicoloured . . . 30 20

359 Medina, Tunis 360 Aboul Qasim Chabbi

1984. National Heritage Protection.
1060 **359** 100 m. multicoloured . . 35 30

1984. 50th Death Anniv of Aboul Qasim Chabbi (poet).
1061 **360** 100 m. sepia, light brown and brown 35 20

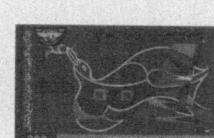

361 Emblem, Stylised Bird and Airplane

1984. 40th Anniv of International Civil Aviation Organization.
1062 **361** 200 m. multicoloured . . 65 20

362 Band and Singers

1984. Sahara Festival.
1063 **362** 20 m. multicoloured . . 45 20

363 Telephonist, Satellite and Dish Aerial

1984. 20th Anniv of "Intelsat" Communication Satellite.
1064 **363** 100 m. multicoloured . . 35 15

364 "Mediterranean Countryside"

1984. Jilani Abdulwahelb (artist) Commem.
1065 **364** 100 m. multicoloured . . 55 35

365 Profile and Exterior of House 366 Crescents and Stars within Circle

1985. "Expo 85" World's Fair, Tsukuba.
1066 **365** 200 m. multicoloured . . 65 35

1985. Red Crescent.
1067 **366** 100 m. + 10 m. mult . . 35 30

367 Hands reaching from Sea and Flames 368 Pres. Bourguiba on Horseback

1985. 3rd Civil Protection Week.
1068 **367** 100 m. multicoloured . . 30 15

1985. 30th Anniv of Independence. Mult.
1069 75 m. Type **368** 20 10
1070 100 m. Pres. Bourguiba in boat and crowd on quay (horiz) 30 10
1071 200 m. Pres. Bourguiba in sombrero 55 20
1072 230 m. Pres. Bourguiba waving to crowd from balcony (horiz) 60 20

369 Pres. Bourguiba and Ancient Sculpture

1985. Tunisian Day at "Expo '85" World's Fair, Tsukuba.
1074 **369** 250 m. multicoloured . . 80 30

370 Images within Film **372** Heart as Dove and I.Y.Y. Emblem

371 Dark Clouds, Sun and Flowers

1985. International Amateur Film Festival, Kelibia.
1075 **370** 250 m. multicoloured . . 1·50 1·10

1985. Stories and Songs from Tunisia. Multicoloured.
1076 25 m. Type **371** 10 10
1077 50 m. Man's profile and hand holding women 15 10
1078 100 m. Man and cooking pot over fire 35 15

1985. International Youth Year.
1079 **372** 250 m. multicoloured . . 80 30

373 "The Perfumiers Hall"

1985. Painting by Hedi Larnaout.
1080 **373** 100 m. multicoloured . . 45 20

374 Matmata Wedding Dress **375** Stylized People and U.N. Emblem

1985. Wedding Dresses (1st series). Mult.
1081 20 m. Type **374** 10 10
1082 50 m. Moknine dress 15 10
1083 100 m. Tunis dress 35 15
See also Nos. 1099/1101.

1985. 40th Anniv of U.N.O.
1084 **375** 250 m. multicoloured . . 80 30

376 Harvest (Makthar stele)

1985. Food Self-sufficiency.
1085 **376** 100 m. multicoloured . . 35 20

377 Emblem illuminating Globe and Flags **378** Aziza Othmana

1985. 40th Anniv of Arab League.
1086 **377** 100 m. multicoloured . . 30 15

1985. Aziza Othmana (founder of hospitals) Commemoration.
1087 **378** 100 m. brown, green and red 45 20

379 Surveying Instruments and Books forming Face **380** Dove and Pres. Bourguiba

1985. Centenary of Land Law.
1088 **379** 100 m. multicoloured . . 30 10

1986. 30th Anniv of Independence.
1089 **380** 100 m. multicoloured . . 30 10
1090 – 120 m. black, blue and deep blue 35 15
1091 – 280 m. blue, violet and black 80 35
1092 – 300 m. multicoloured . . 85 40
DESIGNS—HORIZ: 120 m. Rocket; 280 m. Horse and rider. VERT: 300 m. Balloons.

381 Hulusi Behcet (dermatologist) **382** Map and Red Crescent

1986. 3rd Mediterranean Rheumatology Days, Tunis, and Ninth International Society of Geographical Ophthalmology Congress, Monastir. Multicoloured.
1094 300 m. Type **381** . . . . . . 1·25 35
1095 380 m. Behcet and sun and eye emblems . . . . 1·60 45

1986. World Red Crescent and Red Cross Day.
1096 **382** 120 m. + 10 m. mult . 40 30

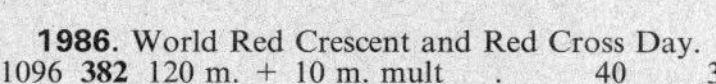

383 Pres. Bourguiba, Symbols and "12"

1986. 12th Destourian Socialist Party Congress, Tunis. Multicoloured.
1097 120 m. Type **383** 30 10
1098 300 m. Flaming torch, Pres. Bourguiba and "12" . . . 85 30

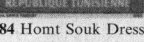

384 Homt Souk Dress **285** Hassen Husni Abdulwaheb

1986. Wedding Dresses (2nd series). Mult.
1099 40 m. Type **384** 10 10
1100 280 m. Mahdia dress 80 30
1101 300 m. Nabeul dress 90 35

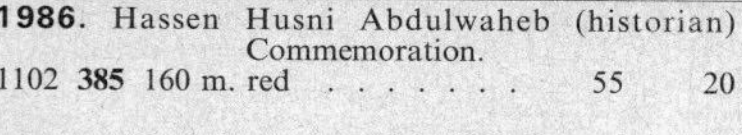

1986. Hassen Husni Abdulwaheb (historian) Commemoration.
1102 **385** 160 m. red 55 20

386 Reconstructed View of Carthage

1986. 2800th Anniv of Foundation of Carthage.
1103 **386** 2 d. purple . . . . 6·00 2·25

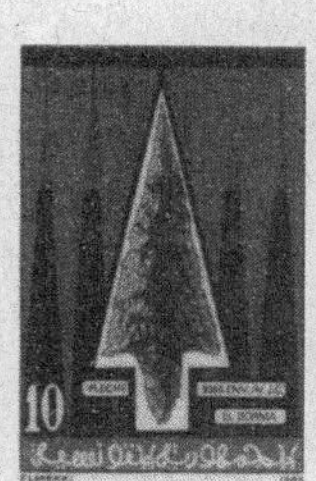

387 Arrow Head, El Borma, 3000 B.C **388** "Bedouins"

1986. Prehistoric Artefacts. Multicoloured.
1104 10 m. Type **387** 20 20
1105 20 m. Tomb, Sejnane, 1000 B.C. 20 20
1106 50 m. Bas-relief, Zaghouan, 1000 B.C. (horiz) 35 20
1107 120 m. Neolithic vase, Kesra (horiz) 55 20
1108 160 m. Painting of Phoenician ship, Kef el Blida, 800 B.C. (horiz) 65 20
1109 250 m. 7th-century decorated pottery, Sejnane . . . . . 1·40 35

1986. Painting by Ammar Farhat.
1110 **388** 250 m. multicoloured . . 90 35

389 Doves and Globe

1986. International Peace Year.
1111 **389** 300 m. multicoloured . . 85 35

390 Emblem **391** Computer Terminal

1986. 40th Anniv of F.A.O.
1112 **390** 280 m. multicoloured . . 80 30

1986. Introduction of Computers into Education.
1113 **391** 2 d. multicoloured . . . 6·00 2·25

392 Mother and Child **393** Mountain Gazelle (Chambi National Park)

1986. Child Survival.
1114 **392** 120 m. multicoloured . . 35 10

1986. National Parks. Multicoloured.
1115 60 m. Type **393** 15 10
1116 120 m. Addax (Bou Hedma National Park) 30 10
1117 350 m. Monk seal (Zembra and Zembretta National Park) . . 85 30
1118 380 m. Greylag goose (Ichkeul National Park) . . . . . . 1·50 80

394 Pres. Bourguiba and Arms

1987. Centenary of Monastir Municipality.
1119 **394** 120 m. multicoloured . . 35 15

395 Radiation and Red Crescent Symbols in Face

1987. Radiation Protection and Red Crescent.
1120 **395** 150 m. + 10 m. mult . . 55 45

396 Samuel Morse (inventor) and Morse Key

1987. 150th Anniv of Morse Telegrarph.
1121 **396** 500 m. multicoloured . . 1·40 55

397 Pres. Bourguiba and Woman's Head

1987. 30th Anniv of Republic. Designs each show Pres. Bourguiba and a different woman's head.
1122 **397** 150 m. mauve, brown and yellow 35 25
1123 – 250 m. brown, red and yellow 55 25
1124 – 350 m. blue, brown and green 80 20
1125 – 500 m. multicoloured . . 1·10 35

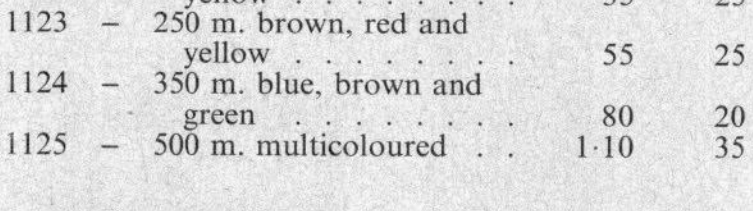

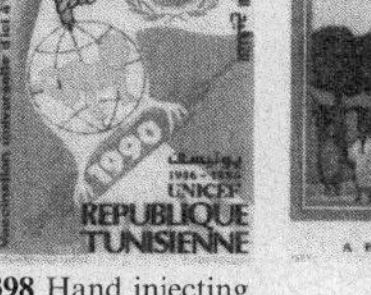

398 Hand injecting Baby in Globe and Dove holding Syringe **399** "The Road"

1987. Universal Vaccination for Everyone by 1990. 40th Anniv of United Nations Children's Fund.
1127 **398** 250 m. multicoloured . . 65 45

1987. 25th Death Anniv of Azouz Ben Rais (painter).
1128 **399** 250 m. multicoloured . . 90 45

400 Couple's Faces in House

1987. Arab Housing Day.
1129 **400** 150 m. multicoloured . . 40 30

401 Dove carrying Parcel **402** Ibn Mandhour

1987. 30th Anniv of Consultative Postal Studies Council. Multicoloured.
1130 150 m. Type **401** 35 10
1131 350 m. Postman and electronically sorted letters 80 30

1987. 675th Death Anniv of Ibn Mandhour (lexicographer).
1132 **402** 250 m. purple 80 45

403 Bunches of Grapes  **404** Player with Ball

1987. International Vine Year.
1133 **403** 250 m. multicoloured . . 80 35

1987. 6th African Nations Volleyball Championship, Tunis.
1134 **404** 350 m. multicoloured . . 1·10 45

405 Players and Ball  **406** Tunis Institute and Adrien Loir (first director)

1987. African Basketball Championships.
1135 **405** 350 m. multicoloured . . 1·10 45

1987. Centenary of Pasteur Institute, Paris.
1136 **406** 250 m. green, brown and black 80 35

407 Midoun  **408** Narcissi

1987. Costumes. Multicoloured.
1137 20 m. Type **407** 10 10
1138 30 m. Tozeur 10 10
1139 150 m. Sfax 40 15

1987. Flowers. Multicoloured.
1140 30 m. Type **408** 10 10
1141 150 m. Gladioli 40 15
1142 400 m. Iris . . . . 1·00 35
1143 500 m. Tulips . . . . 1·25 55

409 Hand holding Scales of Justice

1988. Declaration of 7 November, 1987. Multicoloured.
1144 150 m. Type **409** (Justice for all) 35 20
1145 200 m. Girl with party badges as flowers in hair (Multi-party system) (vert) 45 20
1146 350 m. Girl in cornfield wearing coat of arms (International co-operation and friendship) 80 35
1147 370 m. Maghreb states emblem (vert) 90 35

410 Couple

1988. Youth and Change. Multicoloured.
1149 75 m. Type **410** 20 15
1150 150 m. Young people 35 15

411 Crowd with Banners

1988. 50th Anniv of Martyrs' Day.
1151 **411** 150 m. orange & brown 35 15
1152 – 500 m. multicoloured . . 1·10 40
DESIGN: 500 m. Martyrs monument.

412 Roses and Banners

1988. 125th Anniv of Red Cross.
1153 **412** 150 m. + 10 m. mult . 45 35

413 Hand saving drowning Country

1988. 1st Democratic Constitutional Assembly Congress.
1154 **413** 140 m. multicoloured . . 35 15

414 Sportsmen

1988. Olympic Games, Seoul. Multicoloured.
1155 150 m. Type **414** 40 20
1156 430 m. Sportsman (different) 1·00 45

415 Beit Hussein Sari and Eye  **416** "7" and Flowers

1988. Restoration of Sana'a, Yemen.
1157 **415** 200 m. multicoloured . . 45 20

1988. 1st Anniv of Presidency of Zine el Abidine.
1158 **416** 150 m. multicoloured . . 35 15

417 "Amilcar Beach, 1942"

1988. 70th Birth Anniv of Amara Debbeche (painter).
1159 **417** 100 m. multicoloured . . 35 20

418 Boeing 747 and Globe forming "40"  **419** Man holding Book

1988. 40th Anniv of Tunis Air.
1160 **418** 500 m. multicoloured . . 1·50 70

1988. 40th Anniv of Declaration of Human Rights.
1161 **419** 370 m. black 85 45

420 Tweezers and Magnifying Glasses forming "100"

1988. Cent of First Tunisian Postage Stamps.
1162 **420** 150 m. multicoloured . . 55 30

421 18th-century Door, Rue du Tresor  **422** Ali Douagi

1988. Tunis Doorways and Fountains. Mult.
1163 50 m. Type **421** 10 10
1164 70 m. 19th-century door, Rue el Mbazaa 15 10
1165 100 m. 15th-16th century door, Rue des Fabricants de Tamis 20 10
1166 150 m. 19th-century door, Rue Bach Hamba 30 15
1167 370 m. 16th-17th century door, Rue el Ariane 70 30
1168 400 m. Fountain, Manouba, 1793 . . . . 80 35

1989. 40th Death Anniv of Ali Douagi (writer).
1169 **422** 1 d. blue . . . . 2·25 65

423 Stretcher Bearers  **424** Crippled Person and Healthy Girl

1989. Red Crescent.
1170 **423** 150 m. + 10 m. mult . . 40 30

1989. National Day for Disabled People.
1171 **424** 150 m. multicoloured . . 45 20

425 Children using Computer and Microscope

1989. Knowledge Day.
1172 **425** 180 m. multicoloured . . 40 20

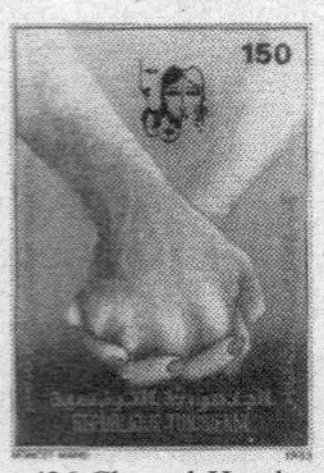

426 Clasped Hands

1989. 20th Anniv of Tunisian Family Planning Association.
1173 **426** 150 m. multicoloured . . 35 15

427 Family

1989. Family Welfare.
1174 **427** 150 m. multicoloured . . 35 15

428 Tortoise

1989. Endangered Animals. Multicoloured.
1175 250 m. Type **428** 65 35
1176 350 m. Oryx . . . . 1·00 45

429 Flags and Emblem  **430** Beyram

1989. Tunis International Fair (1990). Mult.
1177 150 m. Type **429** 35 15
1178 370 m. Fair Pavilion 80 35

1989. Death Centenary of Mohamed Beyram (writer).
1179 **430** 150 m. purple and black 35 15

431 Actors wearing Comedy Masks 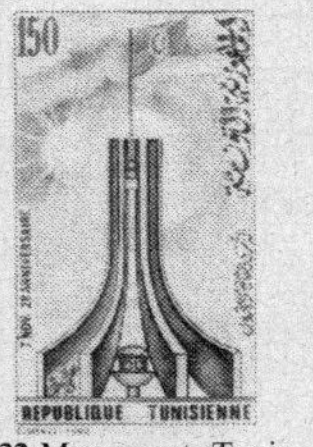 **432** Monument, Tunis

1989. Carthage Theatre Festival.
1180 **431** 300 m. multicoloured . . 65 35

1989. 2nd Anniv of Declaration of 7 November, 1987.
1181 **432** 150 m. multicoloured . . 35 20

433 Nehru  **434** Members' Flags

1989. Birth Centenary of Jawaharlal Nehru (Indian statesman).
1182 **433** 300 m. brown 65 35

1990. Maghreb Union Presidential Summit.
1183 **434** 200 m. multicoloured . . 45 30

435 Museum and Sculptures

1990. Centenary of Bardo Museum.
1184 **435** 300 m. multicoloured . . 80 45

436 Ceramic Tiles, Vases and Crockery

1990. Arts and Crafts. Multicoloured.
1185 75 m. Type **436** 15 10
1186 100 m. Copper pots and grinder 20 15

437 Ram and Ewes

1990. Ram Museum. Multicoloured.

1187 400 m. Type **437** 90 35

1188 450 m. Ram's head . . . . . 1·00 45

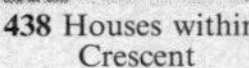

438 Houses within Crescent — 440 Child's Drawing

439 Olympic Rings and Athlete

1990. Red Crescent.

1190 **438** 150 m. + 10 m. mult . . 35 20

1990. Tunisian Olympic Movement.

1191 **439** 150 m. multicoloured . . 35 15

1990. The Child and the Environment.

1192 **440** 150 m. multicoloured . . 35 15

441 Sbiba Horseman — 442 Dougga

1990. Costumes. Multicoloured.

1193 150 m. Type **441** 45 35

1194 500 m. Bou Omrane man . . 1·40 65

1990. Tourism.

1195 **442** 300 m. multicoloured . . 65 35

443 Adults learning to Read and Write

1990. International Literacy Year.

1196 **443** 120 m. multicoloured . . 30 15

444 Figures, Tree and Fishes in Water — 445 Fireworks and Date

1990. Water.

1197 **444** 150 m. multicoloured . . 45 30

1990. 3rd Anniv of Declaration of 7 November, 1987. Multicoloured.

1198 150 m. Type **445** 35 15

1199 150 m. Clock tower 35 15

HAVE YOU READ THE NOTES AT THE BEGINNING OF THIS CATALOGUE?

These often provide the answers to the enquiries we receive.

446 Kheireddine et Tounsi — 447 Red Deer

1990. Death Centenary of Kheireddine et Tounsi (political reformer).

1200 **446** 150 m. green 45 20

1990. Flora and Fauna. Multicoloured.

1201 150 m. Type **447** 35 15

1202 200 m. Thistle 45 15

1203 300 m. Water buffalo . . . 65 20

1204 600 m. Orchid . . . . 1·40 55

448 Members' Flags forming Stars — 449 Montazah Tabarka

1991. 2nd Anniv of Maghreb Union.

1205 **448** 180 m. multicoloured . . 45 20

1991. Tourism.

1206 **449** 450 m. multicoloured . . 1·00 45

450 Doves and Emblem — 451 Sea Bream

1991. Red Crescent. Help for War Victims.

1207 **450** 180 m. + 10 m. mult . 45 35

1991. Fishes. Multicoloured.

1208 180 m. Type **451** 45 20

1209 350 m. Red mullet 85 35

1210 450 m. Mackerel . . . . . . 1·10 45

1211 550 m. Gunner bream . . . 1·40 65

452 Vase of Flowers (Taieb Khlif)

1991. Children's Rights.

1212 **452** 450 m. multicoloured . . 1·00 35

453 "Plein-Sud" (anon.)

1991.

1213 **453** 400 m. multicoloured . . 90 35

454 Bracelets and Ring — 455 Date and Profile of Woman

1991. Jewellery. Multicoloured.

1214 120 m. Type **454** 30 15

1215 180 m. Headdress and necklace (vert) 40 15

1216 220 m. Headdress, earrings and collar (vert) 45 20

1217 730 m. Key ring (vert) . . . . 1·60 80

1991. 4th Anniv of Declaration of 7 November, 1987.

1218 **455** 180 m. multicoloured . . 45 20

456 Sorting Office

1991. Tunis-Carthage Sorting Office.

1219 **456** 80 m. blue, red & green . 20 10

457 Dove and Globe — 458 Bayram Ettounsi

1991. World Human Rights Day.

1220 **457** 450 m. blue . . . . 1·00 35

1991. 31st Death Anniv of Bayram Ettounsi.

1221 **458** 200 m. blue 45 15

459 Emblem on Microchip — 460 G.P.O

1992. "Expo '92" World's Fair, Seville.

1222 **459** 180 m. multicoloured . . 45 20

1992. Centenary of General Post Office, Tunis.

1223 **460** 180 m. brown 45 20

1224 – 450 m. brown . . . . . . 1·00 35

DESIGN—VERT: 450 m. Different view of G.P.O.

461 "When the Subconscious Awakes" (Moncef ben Amor)

1992.

1225 **461** 500 m. multicoloured . . 1·10 45

462 Running — 463 European Bee Eater

1992. Olympic Games, Barcelona. Multicoloured.

1226 180 m. Type **462** 65 30

1227 450 m. Judo (vert) . . . . . 1·60 55

1992. Birds. Multicoloured.

1228 100 m. Type **463** 45 15

1229 180 m. Goldfinch 65 35

1230 200 m. Serin 85 35

1231 500 m. Greenfinch . . . . . 1·60 85

464 President and Children — 465 Women and Open Book

1992. United Nations Convention on Rights of the Child.

1233 **464** 180 m. multicoloured . . 45 30

1992. African Regional Human Rights Conference, Tunis.

1234 **465** 480 m. multicoloured . . 1·10 65

466 Ribbon forming "7" — 467 "Acacia tortilis"

1992. 5th Anniv of Declaration of 7 November, 1987. Multicoloured.

1235 180 m. Type **466** 45 20

1236 730 m. President with people and doves . . . . 1·75 90

1992. National Tree Day.

1237 **467** 180 m. multicoloured . . 45 30

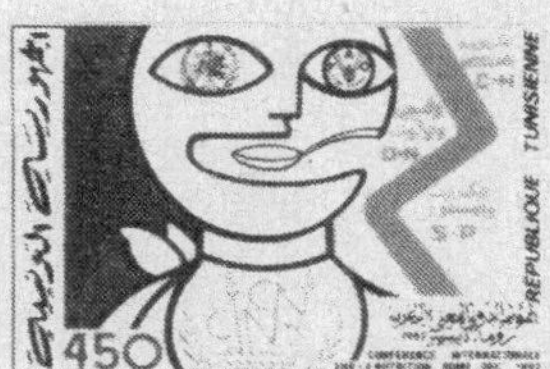

468 Stylized Figure and Emblems

1992. International Nutrition Conference, Rome.

1238 **468** 450 m. multicoloured . . 1·10 55

469 Chemesse — 470 "Billy Goat between Two Bushes" (El Jem)

1992. Traditional Costumes. Multicoloured.

1239 100 m. Type **469** 30 20

1240 350 m. Hanifites 85 45

1992. Mosaics. Multicoloured.

1241 100 m. Type **470** 30 15

1242 180 m. "Wild Duck" (El Jem) 50 35

1243 350 m. "Racehorse" (Sidi Abdallah) 90 45

1244 450 m. "Gazelle in the Grass" (El Jem) . . . . 1·10 70

471 Wolf

1992. Flora and Fauna. Multicoloured.

1245 20 m. Type **471** 10 10

1246 60 m. "Hoya carnosa" (plant) (vert) 10 10

472 Line Graph on World Map

1993. United Nations World Conference on Human Rights, Vienna.
1247 **472** 450 m. multicoloured . . 60 30

473 Publicity Poster inside Open Brief-case
474 "Relaxing on the Patio" (Ali Guermassi)

1993. Arab-African Fair, Tunis.
1248 **473** 450 m. multicoloured . . 60 30

1993.
1249 **474** 450 m. multicoloured . . 60 30

475 Conference Emblem
476 Blood Transfusion

1993. Constitutional Democratic Assembly Party Conference.
1250 **475** 180 m. red and black . . 25 15

1993. Red Crescent. "Dignity for All".
1251 **476** 120 m. + 30 m. mult . . 20 10

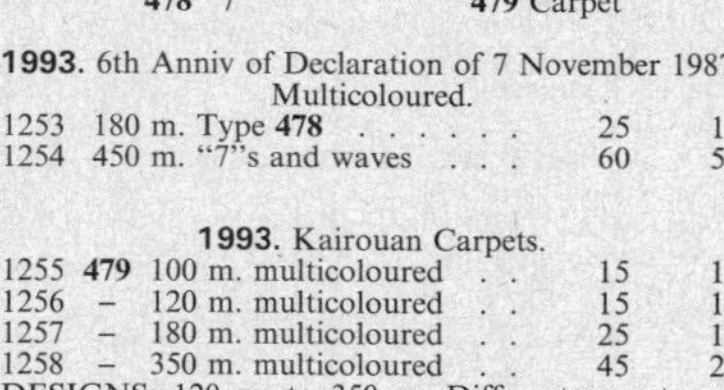

477 Louis Pasteur and Charles Nicolle (former director)

1993. Centenary of Pasteur Institute, Tunis.
1252 **477** 450 m. multicoloured . . 60 30

478 "7"
479 Carpet

1993. 6th Anniv of Declaration of 7 November 1987. Multicoloured.
1253 180 m. Type **478** 25 15
1254 450 m. "7"s and waves . . . 60 50

1993. Kairouan Carpets.
1255 **479** 100 m. multicoloured . . 15 10
1256 – 120 m. multicoloured . . 15 10
1257 – 180 m. multicoloured . . 25 15
1258 – 350 m. multicoloured . . 45 25
DESIGNS: 120 m. to 350 m. Different carpets.

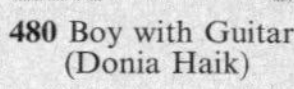

480 Boy with Guitar (Donia Haik)
481 Ballot Box, Hands and Map

1993. School Cultural Activities. Children's drawings. Multicoloured.
1259 180 m. Type **480** 25 15
1260 180 m. Painting and reading (Anissa Chatbouri) (horiz) . 25 15

1994. Presidential and Legislative Elections.
1261 **481** 180 m. multicoloured . . 25 15

482 Players, Trophy and Mascot

1994. African Nations Cup Football Championship. Multicoloured.
1262 180 m. Type **482** 25 15
1263 350 m. Trophy, goalkeeper making save and mascot . . 45 25
1264 450 m. Map of Africa, Olympic Rings, player, trophy and mascot 60 30

483 Workers, "75" and Emblem
484 Family within House

1994. 75th Anniv of I.L.O.
1265 **483** 350 m. multicoloured . . 45 25

1994. International Year of the Family.
1266 **484** 180 m. multicoloured . . 25 15

485 President Ben Ali
486 Blackthorn

1994. Re-election of President Zine el Abidine Ben Ali.
1267 **485** 180 m. multicoloured . . 25 15
1268 350 m. multicoloured . . 45 25

1994. Plants. Multicoloured.
1270 50 m. Type **486** 10 10
1271 100 m. "Xeranthemum inapertum" 15 10
1272 200 m. "Orchis simia" . . . 25 15
1273 1 d. "Scilla peruviana" . . . 1·40 70

487 Dove and Emblem

1994. 30th Organization of African Unity Summit Meeting, Tunis.
1274 **487** 480 m. multicoloured . . 65 35

488 Torch with Map as Flame and Centenary Emblem

1994. Centenary of International Olympic Committee.
1275 **488** 450 m. multicoloured . . 60 30

PARCEL POST STAMPS

P 8 Mail Carrier
P 25 Date Gathering

1906.
P44 **P 8** 5 c. purple and green . . 20 15
P45 10 c. pink and red . . 20 20
P46 20 c. red and brown . . . 65 20
P47 25 c. brown and blue . . 1·00 20
P48 40 c. red and grey . . . . 1·00 25
P49 50 c. violet and brown . . 1·00 15
P50 75 c. blue and brown . . 2·00 20
P51 1 f. red and brown . . . . 1·40 10
P52 2 f. blue and red . . . . 3·75 25
P53 5 f. brown and violet . . . 7·00 55

1926.
P147 **P 25** 5 c. blue and brown . . 15 20
P148 10 c. mauve and red . . 20 20
P149 20 c. black and green . . 25 20
P150 25 c. black & brown . . 30 25
P151 40 c. green and red . . 65 70
P152 50 c. black and violet . . 65 75
P153 60 c. red and brown . . 65 70
P154 75 c. green and lilac . . 65 65
P155 80 c. brown and red . . 65 40
P156 1 f. pink and blue . . . 60 35
P157 2 f. red and mauve . . 1·00 30
P158 4 f. black and red . . . 1·25 25
P159 5 f. violet and brown . . 1·50 30
P160 10 f. green and red on green . . . . 1·75 50
P161 20 f. violet and green on pink . . . . 10·00 1·50

POSTAGE DUE STAMPS

D 3
D 20 Carthaginian Statue
D 86 Agricultural Produce

1901.
D28 **D 3** 1 c. black 15 15
D29 2 c. orange 10 15
D30 5 c. blue 10 10
D31 10 c. brown 15 10
D32 20 c. green . . . . . . 1·90 35
D33 30 c. red 95 40
D34 50 c. lake 60 45
D35 1 f. olive 50 45
D36 2 f. red on green . . . 1·75 1·00
D37 5 f. black on yellow . . . 35·00 24·00

1914. Surch **2 FRANCS**.
D49 **D 3** 2 f. on 5 f. black on yell . 60 80

1923.
D100 **D 20** 1 c. black 10 35
D101 2 c. black on yellow . . 10 40
D102 5 c. purple 10 40
D103 10 c. blue 20 25
D104 20 c. orange on yellow 20 20
D105 30 c. brown 10 20
D106 50 c. red 40 30
D107 60 c. mauve 40 35
D108 80 c. brown 25 30
D109 90 c. red 40 40
D110 1 f. green 15 20
D111 2 f. green 20 25
D112 3 f. violet on pink . . 20 30
D113 5 f. violet 30 45

1945.
D287 **D 20** 10 c. green 10 30
D288 50 c. violet 10 30
D289 2 f. pink 15 20
D290 4 f. blue 25 45
D291 10 f. mauve 25 45
D292 20 f. brown 60 55
D293 30 f. blue 80 70
Nos. D293 is inscribed "TIMBRE TAXE".

1957.
D448 **D 86** 1 f. green 20 20
D449 2 f. brown 20 20
D450 3 f. green 20 40
D451 4 f. blue 45 45
D452 5 f. mauve 45 45
D453 10 f. red 45 45
D454 20 f. sepia . . . . . . 1·40 1·40
D455 30 f. blue . . . . . . 1·60 1·60

1960. Inscr "REPUBLIQUE TUNISIENNE" and new currency.
D534 **D 86** 1 m. green 10 10
D535 2 m. brown 10 10
D536 3 m. green 15 15
D537 4 m. blue 15 15
D538 5 m. violet 20 20
D539 10 m. red 40 40
D540 20 m. brown 60 60
D541 30 m. blue 70 70
D542 40 m. brown 15 15
D543 100 m. green 40 30

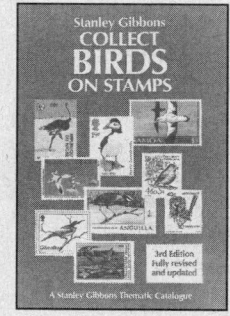

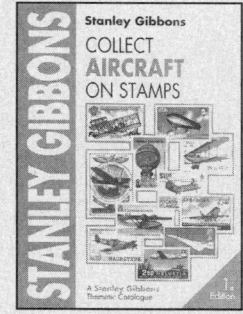

TURKEY Pt. 16

Formerly an empire, this country is now a republic, the greater part of its territory lying in Asia Minor.

1863. 40 paras = 1 piastre or grush
1942. 100 paras = 1 kurus
1947. 100 kurus = 1 lira

For designs as Types **1, 2, 9, 15, 21, 23, 25, 28** and **30** but in black or brown, see Postage Due stamps.

1 2

1863. Imperf.
1 **1** 20 pa. black on yellow 60·00 25·00
2 1 pi. black on purple 75·00 27·00
3 2 pi. black on blue 85·00 38·00
4 5 pi. black on red 95·00 55·00

1865. Perf.
11 **2** 10 pa. green 2·75 8·50
64 10 pa. mauve 15 40
35a 10 pa. brown 40·00 2·25
12 20 pa. yellow 90 1·50
65 20 pa. green 15 40
94 20 pa. grey 55 85
13 1 pi. lilac 1·75 2·00
66 1 pi. yellow 20 25
14 2 pi. blue 1·00 1·25
95 2 pi. red to brown 25 25
15 5 pi. red 50 2·25
46 5 pi. blue 20 95
39c 5 pi. grey 7·50 12·00
16 25 pi. orange 95·00 £130
48 25 pi. red 6·00 20·00

1876. Surch with value in figures and **Pres**.
77 **2** ¼ pre. on 10 pa. mauve 1·00 1·00
78 ½ pre. on 20 pa. green 2·25 2·25
79 1¼ pre. on 50 pa. red 20 2·50
80 2 pre. on 2 pi. brown 8·00 2·25
81 5 pre. on 5 pi. blue 1·00 10·00

9 15

1876.
89 **9** 5 pa. black and yellow 20 20
96 5 pa. lilac 35·00 38·00
109 5 pa. black 15 55
113 5 pa. green and yellow 15 15
82 10 pa. black and mauve 25 30
90 10 pa. black and green 20 20
97 10 pa. green 20 10
83 20 pa. purple and green 24·00 2·25
91 20 pa. black and pink 1·00 15
103 20 pa. pink 15 10
84 50 pa. blue and yellow 40 60
92 1 pi. black and grey (A) 1·50 15
93 1 pi. black and blue (B) 25·00 1·00
99 1 pi. blue 15 10
85 2 pi. black and flesh 20 35
126a 2 pi. yellow 20 20
110 2 pi. orange and blue 15 15
114 2 pi. mauve and grey 25 25
86 5 pi. pink and blue 75 1·50
115 5 pi. brown 75 2·50
111 5 pi. green 65 2·00
87 25 pi. purple and mauve 6·00 18·00
107 25 pi. black 65·00 £110
112 25 pi. brown 9·00 15·00
116 25 pi. red and yellow 9·00 22·00

1892. Various frames.
141 **15** 10 pa. green 15 10
142a 20 pa. red 25 10
143 1 pi. blue 4·50 10
144 2 pi. brown 40 15
145 5 pi. purple 1·50 2·00

1897. Surch **5 5 Cinq Paras**.
160 **15** 5 pa. on 10 pa. green 35 10

21 22 23

1901. For Internal Mail.
167 **21** 5 pa. violet 15 10
168 10 pa. green 15 10
169 20 pa. red 15 10
170 1 pi. blue 15 10
171 2 pi. orange 40 10
203 5 pi. mauve 1·00 20
173 25 pi. brown 3·75 1·50
174 50 pi. brown 6·50 2·00

1901. For Foreign Mail.
175 **22** 5 pa. brown 25 15
176 10 pa. green 15 10
177 20 pa. mauve 15 10
178 1 pi. blue 40 10
179 2 pi. blue 60 20
180 5 pi. brown 1·75 85
181 25 pi. green 13·00 8·00
182 50 pi. yellow 40·00 25·00

1905.
212 **23** 5 pa. brown 10 10
213 10 pa. green 10 10
214 20 pa. pink 10 10
215 1 pi. blue 15 10
216 2 pi. blue 25 10
217 2½ pi. purple 45 15
218 5 pi. brown 75 25
219 10 pi. orange 1·10 30
220 25 pi. green 2·75 1·75
221 50 pi. purple 12·00 4·75

ب
(24)

Type **24** is the Turkish letter "B" which stands for Behie = discount.

1906. Optd with T **24**.
230 **23** 10 pa. green 20 10
231 20 pa. pink 20 10
232 1 pi. blue 40 10
233 2 pi. blue 3·00 2·50

25 27 28

1908.
234 **25** 5 pa. brown 10 10
235 10 pa. green 20 10
236 20 pa. red 6·00 10
237 1 pi. blue 1·50 10
238 2 pi. black 1·75 15
239 2½ pi. brown 70 15
240 5 pi. purple 2·75 15
241 10 pi. red 8·00 1·75
242 25 pi. green 3·00 2·25
243 50 pi. brown 8·00 5·50

1908. Optd as T **24** but smaller.
252 **25** 10 pa. green 85 30
253 20 pa. red 1·25 40
254 1 pi. blue 1·90 70
255 2 pi. black 4·00 1·75

1908. Granting of Constitution.
256 **27** 5 pa. brown 20 15
257 10 pa. green 20 15
258 20 pa. red 45 25
259 1 pi. blue 50 25
260 2 pi. black 6·50 3·00

1909.
271 **28** 2 pa. green 10 10
261 5 pa. brown 10 10
262 10 pa. green 10 10
263 20 pa. red 15 10
264 1 pi. blue 25 10
265 2 pi. black 25 10
266 2½ pi. brown 8·50 6·00
267 5 pi. purple 1·75 20
268 10 pi. red 3·00 40
269 25 pi. green 55·00 25·00
270 50 pi. brown 22·00 22·00

1909. Optd as T **24** but smaller.
289 **28** 10 pa. green 35 10
290 20 pa. red 20 10
291 1 pi. blue 45 20
292 2 pi. black 6·00 3·25

1910. No. 261 surch **2** and Turkish inscr.
296 **28** 2 pa. on 5 pa. brown 10 10

30 G.P.O., Constantinople
31 Mosque of Selim

1913.
333 **30** 2 pa. green 10 10
334 5 pa. bistre 10 10
335 10 pa. green 10 10
336 20 pa. pink 10 10
337 1 pi. blue 10 10
338 2 pi. grey 15 10
339 5 pi. purple 35 15
340 10 pi. red 1·25 55
341 25 pi. green 4·25 2·00
342 50 pi. brown 13·00 14·00

1913. Optd as T 24 but smaller.
343 **30** 10 pa. green 10 10
344 20 pa. pink 15 10
345 1 pi. blue 40 10
346 2 pi. grey 2·50 1·00

1913. Recapture of Adrianople.
353 **31** 10 pa. green 35 20
963 20 pa. red 15 10
355 40 pa. blue 85 55

For Type **31** surcharged, see Postage Due stamps.

32 Obelisk of Theodosius
34 Leander's Tower

1914.
499 **32** 2 pa. purple 10 20
500 – 4 pa. brown 10 25
501 **34** 5 pa. purple 10 10
961 5 pa. brown 10 15
502 – 6 pa. blue 15 30
503 – 10 pa. green 15 10
504 – 20 pa. red 40 10
518 – 1 pi. blue 30 10
964 – 1 pi. green 1·75 25
506 – 1½ pi. grey and red 40 35
507 – 1¾ pi. brown and grey 25 10
508 – 2 pi. black and green 1·00 30
509 – 2½ pi. green and orange 50 15
965 – 3 pi. blue 20 20
510 – 5 pi. lilac 2·75 40
966 – 5 pi. grey 6·50 50
511 – 10 pi. brown 3·75 50
967 – 10 pi. lilac 2·25 25
512 – 25 pi. green 24·00 2·75
968 – 25 pi. purple 60 1·25
513 – 50 pi. pink 3·50 2·25
969 – 50 pi. brown 75 2·50
514 – 100 pi. blue 22·00 18·00
515 – 200 pi. black and green £225 £150

DESIGNS—VERT: 4 pa. Column of Constantine; 6 pa. Seven Towers Castle, Yedikule. HORIZ: 10 pa. Lighthouse-Garden, Constantinople; 20 pa. Castle of Europe; 1 pi. Mosque of Sultan Ahmed; 1½ pi. Monument to Martyrs of Liberty; 1¾, 3 pi. Fountains of Suleiman; 2 pi. Cruiser "Hamidiye"; 2½, 5 (966) pi. Candilli, Bosphorus; 5 pi. (510) Former Ministry of War; 10 pi. Sweet Waters of Europe; 25 pi. Suleiman Mosque; 50 pi. Bosphorus at Rumeli Hisar; 100 pi. Sultan Ahmed's Fountain; 200 pi. Sultan Mohamed V

SIZES—As Type **32**: 4, 6 pa; 31½ × 20 mm: 10 pa. to 1 pi; 26 × 21 mm: 1½ pi. to 2½ pi; 38 × 24 mm: 5 pi. to 50 pi; 40 × 25½ mm: 100, 200 pi.

1914. Stamps of 1914 optd with small star.
516 10 pa. green 20 20
517 20 pa. red 2·25 40
518 1 pi. blue 45 15
519 1¾ pi. brown and grey 35 30
520 2 pi. black and green 12·00 1·00

(49)

1914. 7th Anniv of Constitution No. 506 surch with T **49**.
521 1 pi. on 1½ pi. grey and red 75 75

(50)

1914. Abrogation of the Capitulations. Nos. 501/11 optd with T **50**.
524 5 pa. purple 25 25
526 10 pa. green 35 30
527 20 pa. red 75 35
528 1 pi. blue 1·25 70
530 2 pi. black and green 3·00 75
532 5 pi. lilac 9·00 2·40
533 10 pi. brown 20·00 14·00

(51)

1915. Nos. 514/15 surch as T **51**.
534 10 pi. on 100 pi. blue 18·00 7·50
535 25 pi. on 200 pi. black & grn 10·00 5·00

(53) ("1331" = 1915)

1915. Various issues optd with T **53**.
I. On postage stamps. (a) 1892 and 1897 issues.
536 **15** 5 pa. on 10 pa. green 15 10
537 10 pa. green 15 10
538 2 pi. brown 20 10
539 5 pi. purple 1·50 25

(b) 1901 issues (i) For Internal mail.
540 **21** 5 pa. violet 10 10
541 10 pa. green 20 10
542 20 pa. red 20 10
543 1 pi. blue 40 10
544 2 pi. orange 1·50 20
545 5 pi. mauve 40 15
546 25 pi. brown 2·75 2·00

(ii) For Foreign mail.
547 **22** 5 pa. brown 10 10
548 1 pi. blue 40 15
549 2 pi. blue 40 10
550 5 pi. brown 2·50 60
551 25 pi. green 14·00 6·00

(c) 1905 and 1906 issues.
552 **23** 5 pa. buff 10 10
553b 10 pa. green 25 10
561 10 pa. green (230) 20 10
554a 20 pa. pink 25 10
555a 1 pi. blue 60 10
556b 2 pi. grey 80 10
562 2 pi. grey (233) 75 20
557 2½ pi. purple 50 10
558a 5 pi. brown 75 10
559 10 pi. orange 3·00 60
560 25 pi. green 10·00 2·50

(d) 1908 issues.
563 **25** 5 pa. brown 40·00 30·00
564 2 pi. black 35·00 15·00
569a 2 pi. black (255) 3·25 80
565 2½ pi. brown 60 20
566a 5 pi. purple 22·00 10·00
567 10 pi. red 3·25 1·50
568 25 pi. green 8·00 2·25

(e) 1909 issues.
570 **28** 5 pa. brown 10 10
572 20 pa. red 20 10
579 20 pa. red (290) 15 10
573 1 pi. blue 40 10
581 1 pi. blue (291) 50 15
574 2 pi. black 40 10
582 2 pi. black (292) 45 15
575 2½ pi. brown 20·00 8·50
576 5 pi. purple 40 10
577 10 pi. red 2·25 20
578 25 pi. green £325 £300

(f) 1913 issues.
583 **30** 5 pa. bistre 10 10
584 10 pa. green 10 10
591 10 pa. green (343) 25 15
585 20 pa. pink 10 10
592 20 pa. pink (344) 40 10
586 1 pi. blue 20 10
593 1 pi. blue (345) 50 15
587 2 pi. grey 75 25
594 2 pi. grey (346) 3·00 85
588 5 pi. purple 1·00 60
589 10 pi. red 3·25 60
590 25 pi. green 12·00 4·50

II. On printed matter stamps (for use as postage stamps). (a) 1894 issue.
595 **15** 10 pa. green 25 10
596 2 pi. brown 1·25 30

(b) 1901 issues.
597 **21** 5 pa. violet 25 10
600 **22** 10 pa. green 20 10
598 **21** 20 pa. red 75 20
599 5 pi. mauve 6·00 1·10

(c) 1905 issues.
601b **23** 5 pa. buff 25 10
602 2 pi. grey 2·75 1·25
603 5 pi. brown 2·25 50

(d) 1908 issues.
604 **25** 2 pi. black £250 £160
605a 5 pi. purple 30·00 10·00

(e) 1909 issues.
606 **28** 5 pa. brown 20 10
608 5 pi. purple 30·00 10·00

(54) (56)

1915. Various issues optd with T **54** (star varies).
I. On postage stamps. (a) 1892 issue, also surch with T **56**.
630 **15** 10 pa. on 20 pa. red 15 10

(b) 1901 issues.
631 **21** 1 pi. blue 20 10
632a 5 pi. mauve 1·50 30

(c) 1905 and 1906 issues, Nos. 633 and 636 also surch with T **56**.
609a **23** 10 pa. green 10 10
611b 10 pa. green (230) 4·75 1·75
633 10 pa. on 20 pa. pink 25 10
636 10 pa. on 20 pa. pink (231) 20 10
634 1 pi. blue 30 10
637 1 pi. blue (232) 25 10
610 10 pi. orange 2·25 40

(d) 1908 issues.
612 **25** 10 pa. green 20 10
614a 10 pa. green (252) 35·00 22·00
638 20 pa. red 10 10
640a 20 pa. red (253) 25 15
641 1 pi. blue (254) 1·10 10
613 5 pi. purple 8·00 2·25
639 10 pi. red 60·00 40·00

(e) 1909 issues.
616 **28** 10 pa. green 20 10
620 10 pa. green (289) 15 10
643 20 pa. red 15 10
647 20 pa. red (290) 10 10
645 1 pi. blue 15 10
649 1 pi. blue (291) 25 10
619 5 pi. purple 2·00 40
646 10 pi. red 22·00 20·00

(f) 1913 issues.
623 **30** 10 pa. green 20 10
625 10 pa. green (343) 20 10
650 20 pa. pink 15 10
653 20 pa. pink (344) 15 10
624 1 pi. blue 25 10
652 10 pi. red . . . . 5·50 2·75

(g) 1916 Postal Jubilee issue.
654 **60** 10 pa. red 15 10
655 20 pa. blue 20 10
656 1 pi. black and violet . . . 15 10
657 5 pi. black and brown . . . 60 15

II. On printed matter stamps (for use as postage stamps). (a) 1894 issue, also surch with T **56**.
658 **15** 10 pa. on 20 pa. red . . . 15 10

(b) 1901 issue.
659 **22** 5 pi. brown . . . . . . 2·00 60

(c) 1908 issue.
626 **25** 10 pa. green . . . . 35·00 22·00
627 5 pi. purple . . . . . . 40·00 22·00

(d) 1909 issue.
629 **28** 10 pa. green 15 10

(57) (58) (59)
("1332" = 1916)

1916. Various issues optd with T **57**, some also surch in piastres as T **58**.

I. On postage stamps. (a) 1892 and 1897 issues.
660 **15** 5 pa. on 10 pa. green (160) 15 10
661 10 pa. green 30 10
662 20 pa. red 15 10
663 1 pi. blue . . . . 12·00 12·00
664 2 pi. brown . . . . 1·25 65
665 5 pi. purple . . . . . . 12·00 12·00

(b) 1901 issues. (i) Internal mail.
666 **21** 5 pa. violet . . . . . . 11·00 10·00
667 10 pa. green 50 35
668 20 pa. red 20 10
669 1 pi. blue 25 10
670 2 pi. orange 60 20
671a 10 pi. on 25 pi. brown . . . 2·50 95
672 10 pi. on 50 pi. brown . . . 3·25 1·25
673a 25 pi. brown . . . . . . 2·50 1·00
674 50 pi. brown . . . . . . 4·50 65

(ii) Foreign mail.
675 **22** 5 pa. brown 10 10
676 10 pa. green 60 25
677 20 pa. mauve 15 10
678 1 pi. blue 30 10
679 2 pi. blue . . . . 1·75 95
680 5 pi. on 25 pi. green . . . 15·00 14·00
681 10 pi. on 25 pi. green . . . 15·00 14·00
682 25 pi. green . . . . . . 16·00 14·00

(c) 1905 and 1906 issues.
683 **23** 5 pa. buff 15 15
692a 10 pa. green (230) 35 15
684 20 pa. pink 25 10
693 20 pa. pink (231) 35 15
685a 1 pi. blue 40 10
694a 1 pi. blue (232) 60 15
686a 2 pi. grey . . . . 1·25 40
687 2½ pi. purple . . . . . . 1·50 60
688 10 pi. on 25 pi. green . . . 3·50 1·75
689 10 pi. on 50 pi. purple . . . 3·75 1·50
690 25 pi. green . . . . . . 3·50 1·00
691 50 pi. purple . . . . . . 5·00 1·25

(d) 1908 issues.
701 **25** 2 pi. black (255) . . . . 14·00 12·00
695 2½ pi. brown . . . . . . 12·00 11·00
696 10 pi. on 25 pi. green . . . 5·50 3·25
697a 10 pi. on 50 pi. brown . . . 14·00 14·00
698 25 pi. on 50 pi. brown . . . 14·00 14·00
699 25 pi. green . . . . . . 3·50 3·25
700 50 pi. brown . . . . . . 15·00 15·00

(e) 1908 Constitution issue.
702 **27** 5 pa. brown . . . . . . 15·00 15·00

(f) 1909 issues.
703 **28** 5 pa. brown 15 10
704 10 pa. green . . . . 13·00 13·00
705 20 pa. red . . . . 14·00 13·00
707 1 pi. blue 85 15
711 1 pi. blue (291) . . . . 12·00 12·00
708 2 pi. black . . . . 1·10 45
712 2 pi. black (292) . . . . 12·00 12·00
709 2½ pi. brown . . . . . . 12·00 12·00
710 5 pi. purple . . . . . . 13·00 12·00

(g) 1913 issues.
713 **30** 5 pa. bistre 15 10
714 20 pa. pink 45 20
715 1 pi. blue 45 10
720 1 pi. blue (345) 60 10
716 2 pi. grey . . . . 1·10 40
717 10 pi. on 50 pi. brown . . . 4·00 1·90
718 25 pi. green . . . . . . 4·00 75
719 50 pi. brown . . . . . . 4·25 1·75

(h) 1913 Adrianople issue.
721 **31** 10 pa. green 15 10
722 20 pa. red 60 20
723 40 pa. blue 75 40

(i) 1914 Constitution issue with further surch.
724 60 pa. on 1 pi. on 1½ pi. grey and red . . . . 1·00 25

(j) 1916 Postal Jubilee issues.
725 **60** 5 pi. black and brown . . . 50 10

II. On printed matter stamps (for use as postage stamps). (a) 1894 issues.
726 **15** 5 pa. on 10 pa. green . . . 15 10
727 10 pa. green 35 15
728 20 pa. red 20 15
729 5 pi. purple . . . . . . 15·00 15·00

(b) 1901 issues. (i) Internal mail.
730 **21** 5 pa. violet . . . . . . 14·00 14·00
731 10 pa. green . . . . 14·00 14·00
732 20 pa. red 40 15
733 1 pi. blue 40 15
734 2 pi. orange 60 15

(ii) Foreign mail.
735 **22** 5 pa. brown 15 10
736 10 pa. green 25 10
737 20 pa. mauve 20 10
738 1 pi. blue 35 15

(c) 1905 issue.
739 **23** 5 pa. buff 15 10
740 10 pa. green . . . . 14·00 12·00
741 20 pa. pink . . . . 14·00 12·00
742a 1 pi. blue 60 15

(d) 1908 issue.
743a **25** 5 pa. brown . . . . . . 15·00 14·00

(e) 1909 issue.
744 **28** 5 pa. brown . . . . . . 15·00 14·00

III. On 1913 Adrianople postage due issues (for use as postage stamps).
745 **31** 10 on 2 pa. on 10 pa. green 18·00 12·00
746 20 on 5 pa. on 20 pa. red . 18·00 12·00
747 40 on 10 pa. on 40 pa. blue 18·00 12·00

1916. Occupation of Sinai Peninsula. Optd with T **59**.
749 **21** 5 pa. violet 45 25
750 10 pa. green 60 25
751 **28** 20 pa. red 75 45
752 1 pi. blue . . . . 1·00 45
753 **30** 5 pi. purple . . . . . . 10·00 3·75

60 Old G.P.O., Constantinople (**61**)

1916. Jubilee of Constantinople City Post.
754 **60** 5 pa. green 10 10
755 10 pa. red 10 10
756 20 pa. blue 20 10
757 1 pi. black and violet . . . 30 10
758 5 pi. black and brown . . . 7·00 85

1916. National Fete. Optd. with T **61**.
759 **15** 10 pa. green . . . . . . 85 1·00
760b **23** 20 pa. red 90 55
761a 1 pi. blue . . . . 1·25 60
762b 2 pi. grey . . . . 2·50 55
763 2½ pi. purple . . . . . . 3·25 55

62 Dolmabahce Palace

63 Sentry **64** Sultan Mohamed V

1916.
764 **62** 10 pi. violet . . . . . . 2·75 50
765 10 pi. green on grey . . . 1·50 35
766 10 pi. brown . . . . . . 3·25 25
767 **63** 25 pi. red on buff 40 30
768 **64** 50 pi. red . . . . 1·75 70
769 50 pi. green on yellow . . 4·00 3·00
770 50 pi. blue 35 35

65 Off to the Front (**66**)

1917. Charity.
771 **65** 10 pa. purple 10 10

1917. Various issues optd with T **66** or surch in addition.

A. On postage stamp issue of 1865.
782 **2** 10 pa. mauve . . . . . . 10·00 10·00
772a 20 pa. yellow . . . . . . 10·00 10·00
783 20 pa. green . . . . 10·00 10·00
785 20 pa. grey . . . . 10·00 10·00
773b 1 pi. lilac . . . . 10·00 10·00
784 1 pi. yellow . . . . 10·00 10·00
774 **2** 2 pi. blue . . . . 10·00 10·00
780 2 pi. red to brown . . . . 10·00 10·00
775 5 pi. red . . . . 10·00 10·00
778 5 pi. blue . . . . 10·00 10·00
779 25 pi. red . . . . 10·00 10·00

B. On surcharged postage stamp issue of 1876.
787 **2** ¼ pre. on 10 pa. mauve . . . 10·00 10·00
788 ½ pre. on 20 pa. green . . . 10·00 10·00
789 1¼ pre. on 50 pa. red . . . 10·00 10·00

C. On postage stamp issue of 1876.
790 **9** 5 pa. black and yellow . . . 10·00 10·00
791 5 pa. black 40 50
792 10 pa. black and green . . . 10·00 10·00
793 10 pa. green . . . . 10·00 10·00
794 50 pa. black and yellow . . . 10·00 10·00
795 2 pi. black and flesh . . . 10·00 10·00
796 2 pi. ochre . . . . 10·00 10·00
797 2 pi. orange and blue . . . 1·10 1·50
798 5 pi. brown . . . . 10·00 10·00
799 5 pi. green . . . . 10·00 10·00
801 25 pi. purple and mauve . . 10·00 10·00
802 25 pi. brown . . . . . . 10·00 10·00

D. On postage stamp issue of 1892.
803 **15** 20 pa. purple 50 50
804 2 pi. brown . . . . 1·25 1·25

E. On postage stamp issue of 1901.
805 **21** 5 pa. violet . . . . . . 10·00 10·00
806 10 pa. green . . . . 1·00 1·00
807 20 pa. red 25 20
808 1 pi. blue 25 25
809 2 pi. orange 75 75
810 5 pi. mauve . . . . 10·00 10·00
811 10 pi. on 50 pi. brown . . . 10·00 10·00
812 25 pi. brown . . . . . . 2·00 1·00

F. On postage stamp issue of 1901.
813 **22** 5 pa. brown 75 75
814 20 pa. mauve 30 30
815 1 pi. blue . . . . 1·00 1·00
816 2 pi. blue . . . . 2·00 2·00
817 5 pi. brown . . . . 10·00 10·00
818 10 pi. on 50 pi. yellow . . . 28·00 28·00
819 25 pi. green . . . . . . 15·00 15·00

G. On postage stamp issues of 1905 and 1906.
820 **23** 5 pa. buff 10 10
821 10 pa. green . . . . 11·00 11·00
830 10 pa. green (No. 230) . . . 15 15
822 20 pa. pink 15 10
831 20 pa. pink (No. 231) . . . 25 15
823 1 pi. blue 10 10
832 1 pi. blue (No. 232) . . . 60 25
824 2 pi. grey . . . . 1·00 50
833 2 pi. grey (No. 233) . . . 10·00 10·00
825 2½ pi. purple . . . . . . 1·25 65
826 5 pi. brown . . . . 10·00 10·00
827 10 pi. orange . . . . . . 12·00 10·00
828 10 pi. on 50 pi. purple . . 10·00 10·00
829 25 pi. green . . . . . . 12·00 10·00

H. On postage stamp issues of 1908.
834a **25** 5 pa. brown . . . . 1·00 1·00
835 10 pa. green . . . . 2·00 15
840 10 pa. green (No. 252) . . . 10·00 10·00
841 1 pi. blue (No. 254) . . . 10·00 10·00
836 2 pi. black . . . . 4·50 5·50
842 2 pi. black (No. 255) . . . 4·00 3·25
837a 2½ pi. brown . . . . . . 6·50 6·50
838 10 pi. on 50 pi. brown . . . 10·00 10·00
839 25 pi. green . . . . . . 10·00 10·00

I. On Constitution issue of 1908.
843 **27** 5 pa. brown 40 40

J. On postage stamp issues of 1909.
844 **28** 5 pa. brown 25 25
846 10 pa. green 20 20
854 10 pa. green (No. 289) . . . 25·00 25·00
847 20 pa. red 25 25
849 1 pi. blue 25 25
856 1 pi. blue (No. 291) . . . 50 50
850 2 pi. black . . . . 1·00 75
857 2 pi. black (No. 292) . . . 5·50 5·50
851 2½ pi. brown . . . . . . 10·00 10·00
852a 5 pi. purple . . . . . . 10·00 10·00
853 10 pi. red . . . . 10·00 10·00

K. On postage stamp issues of 1913.
858 **30** 5 pa. bistre 30 30
859 10 pa. green . . . . 10·00 10·00
865 10 pa. green (No. 343) . . . 40 40
860 20 pa. pink 30 30
861 1 pi. blue 30 30
866 1 pi. blue (No. 345) . . . 1·00 1·00
862 2 pi. grey 75 75
867 2 pi. grey (No. 346) . . . 10·00 10·00
863 5 pi. purple . . . . . . 10·00 10·00
864 10 pi. red . . . . 10·00 10·00

L. On Adrianople Commem stamps of 1913.
868 **31** 10 pa. green 50 50
869 40 pa. blue 65 65

M. On Constitution Commem of 1914 with additional surch in Turkish.
870 60 pa. on 1 pi. on 1½ pi. grey and red (No. 521) . . . . 1·00 1·00

N. On postage stamp issues of 1916.
871 **63** 25 pi. red on buff 75 75
872 **64** 50 pi. red . . . . 6·50 3·25
873 50 pi. green on yellow . . 5·50 3·50
874 50 pi. blue . . . . 7·50 5·50

O. On stamps of Eastern Roumelia of 1881 (T **9** of Turkey, but inscr "ROUMELIE ORIENTALE" at left).
876 5 pa. lilac . . . . 11·00 11·00
877 10 pa. green . . . . 11·00 11·00
875 20 pa. black and red . . . 11·00 11·00
878 20 pa. red . . . . 11·00 11·00

P. On printed matter stamps of 1893 optd with Type N **16**.
879 **15** 20 pa. red (No. N 156a) . . 1·00 1·00
880 1 pi. blue (No. N 157) . . 20 20

Q. On printed matter stamps of 1901 optd with Type N **23**.
881 **21** 5 pa. violet (No. N183) . . 50 50
882 10 pa. green (No. N184) . . 6·00 5·50
883 20 pa. red (No. N185) . . 50 25
884 1 pi. blue (No. N186) . . 60 50
885 **21** 2 pi. orange (No. N187) . . 60 50
886 5 pi. mauve (No. N188) . . 10·00 10·00

R On printed matter stamps of 1901 optd with Type N **23**.
887 **22** 5 pa. brown (No. N189) . . 75 75
888 10 pa. green (No. N190) . . 75 75
889 20 pa. mauve (No. N191) . . 75 75
890 2 pi. blue (No. N193) . . . 10·00 10·00

S. On printed matter stamps of 1905 optd with Type N **23**.
891d **23** 5 pa. brown (No. N222) . . 15 15
892 10 pa. green (No. N223) . . 60 60
893 20 pa. pink (No. N224) . . 15 10
894 1 pi. blue (No. N225) . . 25 25
895 2 pi. grey (No. N226) . . 10·00 10·00
896 5 pi. brown (No. N227) . . 10·00 10·00

T. On printed matter stamp of 1908 optd with Type N **27**.
897 **25** 5 pa. brown (No. N244) . . 10·00 10·00

U. On postage due stamps of 1865.
898 **D 4** 20 pa. brown . . . . . . 10·00 10·00
899 1 pi. brown . . . . 10·00 10·00
900 2 pi. brown . . . . 10·00 10·00
901 5 pi. brown . . . . 10·00 10·00
902 25 pi. brown . . . . . . 10·00 10·00

V. On postage due stamps of 1888.
904 **9** 1 pi. black (D118) . . . . 10·00 10·00
905 2 pi. black (D119) . . . . 10·00 10·00

W. On postage due stamps of 1892.
906 **15** 20 pa. black (D146) 50 50
907 1 pi. black (D148) 50 50
908 2 pi. black (D149) 50 25

X. On Adrianople commemoration issue of 1913 (postage due stamps surch in Arabic further surch).
909 **31** 10 on 2 pa. on 10 pa. green (D356) 10 10
910 20 on 5 pa. on 20 pa. red (D357) 15 15
911 40 on 10 pa. on 40 pa. blue (D358) 30 30
912 40 on 20 pa. on 40 pa. blue (D359) 45 35

The overprints on printed matter and postage due stamps were used for ordinary postage.

67 In the Trenches **69** Howitzer at Sedd el Bahr

1917. Surch variously in Turkish.
913 **67** 5 pa. on 1 pi. red 10 10
915 **65** 10 pa. on 20 pa. red . . . 20 10
914 **69** 5 pi. on 2 pa. blue . . . . 2·25 40

72 Mosque at Ortakoy **73** Lighthouse, Achir Kapu

74 Martyrs' Column **77** Seraglio Point

75 Map of Gallipoli **76**

1917.
916 **69** 2 pa. violet 10 20
917 **72** 5 pa. orange 10 15
918 **73** 10 pa. green 10 10
919 **74** 20 pa. red 10 10
920 **75** 1 pi. blue 25 10
921 **76** 50 pa. blue 10 45
921b **77** 2 pi. blue and brown . . . 45 15
922 – 5 pi. brown and blue . . . 7·00 1·10
DESIGNS—As T **77**. 5 pi. Pyramids.

1918. Surch **5 Piastres 5** and in Turkish.
923 **69** 5 pi. on 2 pa. blue 65 20

1918. No. 913 with additional surch.
924 **67** 2 pa. on 5 pa. on 1 pi. red 10 25

(**81**) **84** Wells at Beersheba

85 Sentry at Beersheba — **87** Turkish Column in Sinai

1918. Armistice. Optd. as T **81**.

925 **84** 20 pa. purple 15 40
926 **75** 1 pi. blue . . . . 1·75 2·75
927 **85** 1 pi. blue . . . . 50·00 50·00
937 **D 51** 1 pi. blue (No. D518) . . 50·00 60·00
928 **76** 50 pa. blue 20 60
929 **77** 2 pi. blue and brown . . 20 75
930 – 2½ pi. green and orange (No. 509) . . . . . . 50·00 50·00
931 – 5 pi. brown and blue (No. 922) 20 85
932 **62** 10 pi. green on grey . . 2·25 4·50
933 **63** 25 pi. red on buff . . . 2·25 4·50
934 **87** 25 pi. blue . . . . . . 50·00 50·00
935 – 50 pi. pink (No. 513) . . 50·00 50·00
936 **64** 50 pi. green on yellow . 2·25 4·50

1918. Stamp of 1909 optd with Sultan's toughra and surch in Turkish.

938 **28** 5 pa. on 2 pa. green . . . 10 40

86 Dome of the Rock, Jerusalem

(**88**)

1919. Accession of Sultan Mohamed VI. Optd with date as in T **88** and ornaments or inscription.

939 **84** 20 pa. purple . . . . . . 35 2·25
940 **85** 1 pi. blue . . . . 1·00 3·50
941 **86** 60 pa. on 10 pa. green . . 1·00 4·50
942 **87** 25 pi. blue . . . . . . 10·00 15·00

The illustrations Type **85** (optd with date and inscription at foot) and **86** (surch with T **88**) illustrate Nos. 940/1. Nos. 939 and 942 are overprinted with the date and the central motif only at bottom of Type **88**.

(**89**) (**91**)

(**90**)

1919. 1st Anniv of Sultan's Accession. Optd or surch as T **89, 90** or **91**.

943 **69** 2 pa. violet 40 75
944 **72** 5 pa. orange 10 45
945 **28** 5 pa. on 2 pa. green . . 10 25
946 **30** 10 pa. on 2 pa. green . . 10 30
960a **D 49** 10 pa. on 5 pa. brown . 7·50 8·50
947 **73** 10 pa. green 45 65
948 **74** 20 pa. red 15 45
960b **D 50** 20 pa. red . . . . . 7·50 8·50
949 **75** 1 pi. blue 10 40
960c **D 51** 1 pi. blue . . . . . . 7·50 8·50
950 **76** 60 pa. on 50 pa. blue . . 75 1·50
951 **77** 60 pa. on 2 pi. blue and brown . . . . 15 1·00
952 2 pi. blue and brown . . 45 1·00
960d **D 52** 2 pi. blue . . . . . . 7·50 8·50
952a – 2½ pi. green and orange (No. 509) . . . . . . 8·00 10·00
953 – 5 pi. brown and blue (No. 922) . . . . 15 1·00
954 **62** 10 pi. brown . . . . . 1·00 2·25
955 **84** 10 pi. on 20 pa. purple . 1·00 2·50
956 **63** 25 pi. red and buff . . . 1·00 2·50
957 **85** 35 pi. on 1 pi. blue . . 2·50 3·50
958 **64** 50 pi. green on yellow . . 4·50 7·00
958a 50 pi. red . . . . 8·50 10·00
959 **86** 100 pi. on 60 pa. on 10 pa. green . . . . 5·50 7·50
960 **87** 250 pi. on 25 pi. blue . . 7·50 8·50

Types **84** and **87** illustrate Nos. 955 and 960.

1921. Surch in figures and words and in Turkish characters.

970 **65** 30 pa. on 10 pa. purple . . 15 10
971 – 60 pa. on 10 pa. green (No. 503) 15 10
972 **67** 4½ pi. on 1 pi. red . . . . 1·00 75
973 – 7½ on 3 pi. blue (No. 965) . 2·25 55

Numerous fiscal and other stamps were surcharged or overprinted by the Turkish Nationalist Government at Angora during 1921, but as they are not often met with by general collectors we omit them. A full listing will be found in Part 16 (Central Asia) of the Stanley Gibbons catalogue.

Nos. A79/90 and A119/24 were the only definitive issue of the Angora Government at this period.

A **24** National Pact — A **25** Parliament House, Sivas

1921.

A79 A **24** 10 pa. purple 20 10
A80 – 20 pa. green 25 10
A81 – 1 pi. blue 40 10
A82 – 2 pi. purple 85 10
A83 – 5 pi. blue 90 10
A84 – 10 pi. brown . . . . . 3·00 10
A85 – 25 pi. red . . . . . . 4·25 10
A86 A **25** 50 pi. blue (A) . . . . 1·25 65
A87 50 pi. blue (B) . . . . 1·25 75
A88 – 100 pi. violet . . . . . 30·00 1·00
A89 – 200 pi. violet . . . . . 70·00 12·00
A90 – 500 pi. green . . . . . 40·00 8·00

DESIGNS—HORIZ: 20 pa. Izmir Harbour; 1 pi. Mosque, Adrianople; 10 pi. Legendary grey wolf, Boz Kurt; 25 pi. Castle Adana; 200 pi. Map of Anatolia. VERT: 2 pi. Mosque, Konya; 5 pi. Soldier taking oath; 100 pi. Mosque, Ourfa; 500 pi. Declaration of faith from Koran.

Type (B) of the 50 pi. as illustrated. In Type (A) the inscription at the top is similar to that of Type A **30** and the figures in the value tablets are above instead of below the Turkish inscription.

A **30** First Parliament House, Angora

1922.

A119 A **30** 5 pa. mauve 20 10
A120 10 pa. green 25 10
A121 20 pa. red 35 20
A122 1 pi. orange . . . . . 2·25 50
A123 2 pi. brown . . . . . 9·50 1·25
A124 3 pi. red . . . . . . 1·00 90

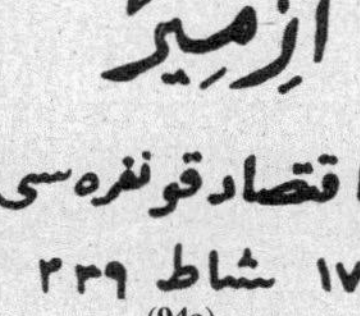

(**94a**)

1923. Izmir (Smyrna) Economic Congress. Nos. 918 and A80/4 optd with T **94a**.

973b **73** 10 pa. green . . . . . 1·75 1·25
973c – 20 pa. green . . . . . 1·75 1·25
973d – 1 pi. blue . . . . . . 2·50 1·25
973e – 2 pi. purple . . . . . 3·75 3·25
973f – 5 pi. blue . . . . . . 4·00 2·75
973g – 10 pi. brown . . . . . 7·50 6·00

95 — **96** Kemal Ataturk and Sakarya Bridge

1923.

974 **95** 10 pa. grey 25 10
975 20 pa. yellow 30 10
976 1 pi. mauve 30 10
977 1½ pi. green 35 10
978 2 pi. green 80 10
979 3 pi. brown 45 10
980 3¾ pi. brown 85 25
1001 4½ pi. red 50 10
1002 5 pi. violet . . . . . 1·50 10
1003 7½ pi. blue 90 10
1004 10 pi. grey . . . . . 3·25 25
1012a 10 pi. blue . . . . . 28·00 15
986 **95** 11¼ pi. pink . . . . . 1·10 35
1006 15 pi. brown . . . . . 3·25 25
988 18¾ pi. green . . . . . 1·75 60
989 22½ pi. orange . . . . . 2·75 80
990 25 pi. brown . . . . . 7·50 25
991 50 pi. grey . . . . . . 25·00 55
992 100 pi. purple . . . . . 32·00 70
993 500 pi. green . . . . . £160 40·00

1924. Treaty of Lausanne.

1013 **96** 1½ pi. green 55 25
1014 3 pi. violet 60 25
1015 4½ pi. pink . . . . . 1·00 95
1016 5 pi. brown . . . . . 1·50 25
1017 7½ pi. blue 80 55
1018 50 pi. orange . . . . . 13·00 7·50
1019 100 pi. purple . . . . . 30·00 15·00
1020 200 pi. olive . . . . . 40·00 27·00

97 Legendary Blacksmith and Grey Wolf, Boz Kurt — **98** Gorge and R Sakarya

99 Fortress af Ankara — **100** Kemal Ataturk

1926.

1021 **97** 10 pa. grey 10 10
1022 20 pa. orange 15 10
1023 1 gr. red 15 10
1024 **98** 2 gr. green 50 10
1025 2½ gr. black 50 10
1026 3 gr. red 60 10
1027 **99** 5 gr. violet . . . . . 1·10 10
1028 6 gr. red 60 10
1029 10 gr. blue . . . . . 1·60 10
1030 15 gr. orange . . . . . 2·00 10
1031 **100** 25 gr. black and green . . 4·50 10
1032 50 gr. black and red . . 5·50 10
1033 100 gr. black and olive . 12·00 55
1034 200 gr. black and brown . 30·00 1·25

(**101** "1927 Izmir Exhibition") — (**102** "Izmir, 9 Sept, 1928")

1927. Izmir (Smyrna) Exhibition. Optd with T **101**.

1035 **97** 1 gr. red 20 10
1036 **98** 2 gr. green . . . . . 1·60 40
1037 2½ gr. black . . . . . 1·60 40
1038 3 gr. red . . . . . . 2·25 75
1039 **99** 5 gr. violet 85 35
1040 6 gr. red 35 15
1041 10 gr. blue . . . . . 2·25 85
1042 15 gr. orange . . . . . 2·40 85
1043 **100** 25 gr. black and green . . 6·50 3·25
1044 50 gr. black and red . . 11·00 6·00
1045 100 gr. black and olive . 25·00 25·00

1928. 2nd Izmir Exhibition. T **97/9** optd with T **102** and T **100** optd **928** and 2 lines of Turkish.

1053 **97** 10 pa. grey 15 10
1054 20 pa. orange 20 10
1055 1 gr. red 20 10
1056 **98** 2 gr. green . . . . . 1·10 30
1057 2½ gr. black . . . . . 1·10 40
1058 3 gr. red . . . . . . 1·10 75
1059 **99** 5 gr. violet . . . . . 1·90 1·00
1060 6 gr. red 65 10
1061 10 gr. blue . . . . . 1·90 65
1062 15 gr. orange . . . . . 2·10 50
1063 **100** 25 gr. black and green . . 6·00 2·25
1064 50 gr. black and red . . 11·00 6·00
1065 100 gr. black and olive . 25·00 12·00
1066 200 gr. black and brown . 35·00 18·00

1929. Surch with value in "Paradir" or "Kurustur".

1067 **97** 20 par. on 1 gr. red . . . 40 10
1068 **99** 2½ kur. on 5 gr. violet . . 55 10
1069 6 kur. on 10 gr. blue . . 7·50 10

106 Bridge over Kizil-Irmak — **107** Gorge and R Sakarya

1929. T **106/7** and 1926 stamps but inscr "TURKIYE CUMHURIYETI".

1076 **97** 10 pa. green 10 10
1077 **106** 20 pa. violet 25 10
1078 1 k. green 50 10
1079 **97** 1½ k. green 15 10
1070 **106** 2 k. black . . . . . . 1·00 10
1080 2 k. violet . . . . . . 2·00 10
1081 2½ k. green 25 10
1072 3 k. purple . . . . . 1·60 10
1082 3 k. red . . . . . . 2·75 10
1083 **97** 4 k. red . . . . . . 2·50 10
1084 **99** 5 k. purple . . . . . 3·25 10
1085 **97** 6 k. blue . . . . . . 3·25 10
1086 **107** 7½ k. red 65 10
1088 **99** 12½ k. blue 45 10
1089 15 k. orange 55 10
1090 **107** 17½ k. black 65 50
1091 **99** 20 k. brown . . . . . 20·00 25
1092 **107** 25 k. brown . . . . . 1·75 15
1093 **99** 30 k. brown . . . . . 1·75 15
1094 **107** 40 k. purple . . . . . 2·00 15
1075 **100** 50 k. black and red . . . 21·00 60

109 — **112** — **113**
Kemal Ataturk

1930.

1095 **109** 50 k. black and red . . . 1·90 10
1096 100 k. black and olive . . 3·25 30
1097 200 k. black and green . . 2·25 50
1098 500 k. black and brown . 12·00 2·25

1930. Opening of the Ankara–Sivas Railway. Surch **Sivas D.Y. 30 ag. 930** and value.

1099 **97** 10 pa. on 10 pa. green . . 10 10
1100 **106** 10 pa. on 20 pa. violet . . 15 10
1101 20 pa. on 1 k. green . . 15 10
1102 **97** 1 k. on 1½ k. green . . . 20 15
1103 **106** 1½ k. on 2 k. violet . . . 35 30
1104 2 k. on 2½ k. green . . . 50 40
1105 2½ k. on 3 k. red . . . 55 50
1106 **97** 3 k. on 4 k. red 70 40
1107 **99** 4 k. on 5 k. purple . . . 1·40 1·25
1108 **97** 5 k. on 6 k. blue . . . 1·90 1·75
1109 **107** 6 k. on 7½ k. red . . . 70 65
1110 **99** 7½ k. on 12½ k. blue . . 95 85
1111 12½ k. on 15 k. orange . 2·10 1·00
1112 **107** 15 k. on 17½ k. black . . 2·75 2·50
1113 **99** 17½ k. on 20 k. brown . . 2·75 2·00
1114 **107** 20 k. on 25 k. brown . . 2·75 2·50
1115 **99** 25 k. on 30 k. brown . . 2·75 2·50
1116 **107** 30 k. on 40 k. purple . . 3·75 3·00
1117 **109** 40 k. on 50 k. black and red 4·75 2·50
1118 50 k. on 100 k. black and green . . . . 27·00 8·00
1119 100 k. on 200 k. black and green . . . . 32·00 12·00
1120 250 k. on 500 k. black and brown . . . . 32·00 10·00

1931. Surch **1 Kurus**.

1121 **97** 1 k. on 1½ k. green . . . 1·25 10

1931.

1122 **112** 10 pa. green 10 10
1444 10 pa. brown 10 10
1444a 10 pa. red 10 10
1123 10 pa. orange 10 10
1445 20 pa. green 10 10
1453b 20 pa. yellow 10 10
1123a 30 pa. violet 10 10
1124 **113** 1 k. green 10 10
1453c 1 k. orange 10 10
1124a **112** 1½ k. lilac 15 10
1125 **113** 2 k. violet 15 10
1125a 2 k. green 25 10
1447 2 k. mauve 25 10
1447a 2 k. yellow 60 10
1453d 2 k. pink 10 10
1126 **112** 2½ k. green 25 10
1126a **113** 3 k. brown 20 10
1448 3 k. orange 45 10
1448a 3 k. blue 30 10
1127 4 k. black . . . . . . 1·75 10
1453f 4 k. green 20 10
1128 5 k. red 45 10
1128a 5 k. black . . . . . . 1·00 10
1453g 5 k. blue 20 10
1449a 5 k. purple . . . . . 2·75 10
1129 6 k. blue . . . . . . 2·00 10
1129a 6 k. red 15 10
1130 **112** 7½ k. red 20 10
1130a **113** 8 k. blue 40 10
1453h 8 k. violet 10 10
1131 **112** 10 k. black . . . . . . 2·25 10
1131a 10 k. blue . . . . . . 4·00 10
1450 10 k. brown . . . . . 1·25 10
1453i 10 k. green 10 10
1132 12 k. brown 30 10
1453j 12 k. red 15 10
1133 12½ k. blue 35 10
1134 15 k. yellow 40 10
1451 15 k. violet . . . . . 1·60 10
1453k 15 k. red 20 10
1135 20 k. green 40 10
1452 20 k. blue . . . . . . 10·00 10
1453la 20 k. purple . . . . . 2·10 10
1136 25 k. blue 55 10
1137 30 k. purple 85 10
1453 30 k. pink . . . . . . 10·00 10
1453m 30 k. green 80 10
1138 100 k. brown 60 10
1139 200 k. violet . . . . . 1·25 10
1453a 200 k. brown . . . . . 4·50 45
1140 250 k. brown . . . . . 4·50 10

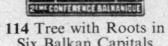

114 Tree with Roots in Six Balkan Capitals 115 "Rebirth of Turkey"

1931. 2nd Balkan Conference.
1141 **114** 2½ k. green 10 10
1142 4 k. red 15 10
1143 6 k. blue 15 10
1144 7½ k. red 20 10
1145 12 k. orange 20 10
1146 12½ k. blue 35 10
1147 30 k. violet 60 10
1148 50 k. brown . . . . . . 1·00 10
1149 100 k. purple . . . . . 2·25 25

1933. 10th Anniv of Turkish Republic.
1150 **115** 1½ k. green 45 10
1151 2 k. bistre 45 10
1152 – 3 k. red 45 10
1153 – 6 k. blue 45 10
1154 **115** 12½ k. blue . . . . . . 1·10 75
1155 25 k. brown . . . . . 2·75 2·75
1156 – 50 k. brown . . . . . 4·50 2·75
DESIGNS—HORIZ: 3, 6, 50 k. Wheat, cogwheels, factory, "X" and Kemal Ataturk.

1934. Air. Optd **1934** and airplane or surch also.
1157 **107** 7½ k. lake 40 25
1158 **99** 12½ k. on 15 k. orange . 40 20
1159 **107** 20 k. on 25 k. brown . . 70 35
1160 25 k. brown 90 55
1161 40 k. purple . . . . . . 1·50 70

1934. Izmir International Fair. Optd **Izmir 9 Eylul 934 Sergisi** or surch also.
1162 **97** 10 pa. green 25 10
1163 1 k. on 1½ k. green . . . 35 10
1164 **107** 2 k. on 25 k. brown . . . 2·50 80
1165 5 k. on 7½ k. red . . . . 3·50 80
1166 6 k. on 17½ k. black . . . 2·00 50
1167 **99** 12½ k. blue . . . . . . 4·50 1·00
1168 15 k. on 20 k. brown . . 42·00 20·00
1169 **107** 20 k. on 25 k. brown . . 32·00 32·00
1170 **109** 50 k. on 100 k. black and green . . . . 30·00 17·00

119 Alliance Badge 120 Mrs. C. Chapman Catt

1935. 12th Congress of the International Women's Alliance, Istanbul.
1171 **119** 20 pa. + 20 pa. bistre . 35 25
1172 – 1 k. + 1 k. red 40 25
1173 – 2 k. + 2 k. blue 40 25
1174 – 2½ k. + 2½ k. green . . 40 30
1175 – 4 k. + 4 k. blue 65 55
1176 – 5 k. + 5 k. purple . . . 90 75
1177 – 7½ k. + 7½ k. red . . . 1·60 1·50
1178 **120** 10 k. + 10 k. orange . . 2·75 2·00
1179 – 12½ k. + 12½ k. blue . . 4·00 4·00
1180 – 15 k. + 15 k. violet . . 4·00 3·00
1181 – 20 k. + 20 k. red . . . 8·00 6·00
1182 – 25 k. + 25 k. green . . 14·00 14·00
1183 – 30 k. + 30 k. blue . . 40·00 25·00
1184 – 50 k. + 50 k. green . . 85·00 65·00
1185 – 100 k. + 100 k. red . . 48·00 40·00
DESIGNS: 1 k. Woman teacher; 2 k. Woman farmer; 2½ k. Typist; 4 k. Woman pilot and policewoman; 5 k. Women voters; 7½ k. Yildiz Palace, Istanbul; 12½ k. Jane Addams; 15 k. Grazia Deledda; 20 k. Selma Lagerlof; 25 k. Bertha von Suttner; 30 k. Sigrid Undset; 50 k. Mme. Curie-Sklodowska; 100 k. Kemal Ataturk.

1936. Remilitarization of Dardanelles. Surch **BOGAZLAR MUKAVELESININ IMZASI 20/7/1936** and value in figures.
1186 **107** 4 k. on 17½ k. black . . . 1·25 65
1187 5 k. on 25 k. brown . . . 1·25 65
1188 **100** 6 k. on 50 k. black and red 75 20
1189 **109** 10 k. on 100 k. black and olive . . . . 1·00 20
1190 20 k. on 200 k. black and green . . . . 2·25 25
1191 50 k. on 500 k. black and brown . . . . 7·50 1·50

122 Stag 124 Arms of Turkey, Greece, Rumania and Yugoslavia

1937. 2nd Turkish Historical Congress.
1192 **122** 3 k. violet 60 25
1193 – 6 k. blue 65 25
1194 **122** 7½ k. red . . . . 1·25 60
1195 – 12½ k. blue . . . . . . 2·00 85
DESIGN: 6, 12½ k. Bust of Ataturk.

1937. Balkan Entente.
1196 **124** 8 k. red . . . . 4·50 1·25
1197 12½ k. blue . . . . 9·50 1·75

1938. Air. Surch **1937** with airplane above and value.
1198 **107** 4½ k. on 7½ k. lake . . . 2·00 1·25
1199 **99** 9 k. on 15 k. orange . . 12·00 12·00
1200 **107** 35 k. on 40 k. purple . . 3·25 9·75

127 Fig Tree 129 Railway Bridge

1938. Izmir International Fair.
1201 – 10 pa. brown 20 10
1202 – 30 pa. violet 20 10
1203 **127** 2½ k. green 30 15
1204 – 3 k. orange 20 10
1205 – 5 k. green 45 25
1206 – 6 k. brown . . . . . . 1·75 60
1207 – 7½ k. red . . . . . . 1·10 40
1208 – 8 k. red 75 45
1209 – 12 k. purple 65 45
1210 – 12½ k. blue . . . . . 2·50 2·00
DESIGNS—HORIZ: 10 pa. An Izmir boulevard; 30 pa. Izmir Fair; 6 k. Woman gathering grapes. VERT: 3 k. Clock Tower, Hukunet Square; 5 k. Olive branch; 7½ k. Woman gathering grapes; 8 k. Izmir Harbour; 12 k. Equestrian statue of Ataturk; 12½ k. Ataturk.

1938. 15th Anniv of Proclamation of Turkish Republic.
1211 – 2½ k. green 15 10
1212 – 3 k. red 15 10
1213 – 6 k. bistre 25 25
1214 **129** 7½ k. red . . . . 2·25 60
1215 – 8 k. purple 60 70
1216 – 12½ k. blue . . . . . . 60 1·00
DESIGNS—HORIZ: 2½ k. Military display; 3 k. Aerial view of Kayseri; 8 k. Scout buglers. VERT: 6 k. Ataturk driving a tractor; 12½ k. Ataturk.

130 Kemal Ataturk teaching Alphabet

1938. 10th Anniv of Introduction of Latin Alphabet into Turkey.
1217 **130** 2½ k. green 25 15
1218 3 k. orange 20 20
1219 6 k. purple 25 20
1220 7½ k. red 45 40
1221 8 k. red . . . . 1·25 1·10
1222 12½ k. blue 75 75

1938. Death of Kemal Ataturk. Mourning Issue. Optd **21-11-1938** and bar.
1223 **113** 3 k. brown 20 10
1224 5 k. red 20 10
1225 6 k. blue 35 30
1226 **112** 7½ k. red 25 10
1227 **113** 8 k. blue 50 40
1228 **112** 12½ k. blue . . . . . . 1·10 1·10

133 Presidents Inonu and Roosevelt and Map of North America

1939. 150th Anniv of U.S. Constitution.
1229 – 2½ k. green, red & blue . 15 15
1230 **133** 3 k. brown and blue . . 15 15
1231 – 6 k. violet, red & blue . 15 15
1232 – 7½ k. red and blue . . 20 10
1233 **133** 8 k. purple and blue . . 35 35
1234 – 12½ k. ultram & blue . . 1·25 75
DESIGNS—VERT: 2½, 6 k. Turkish and U.S. flags. HORIZ: 7½, 12½ k. Ataturk and George Washington.

1939. Cession of Hatay to Turkey. Surch **Hatayin Anavatana Kavusmasi 23/7/1939** and new values.
1235 **107** 3 k. on 25 k. brown . . 80 25
1236 **109** 6 k. on 200 k. black and green 10 20
1237 **107** 7½ k. on 25 k. brown . . 2·00 30
1238 **109** 12 k. on 100 k. (1096) . . 25 25
1239 12½ k. on 200 k. (1097) . . 40 40
1240 17½ k. on 500 k. (1098) . . 45 60

135 Railway Bridge 136 Kemal Ataturk

1939. Opening of Ankara–Erzurum Railway.
1241 **135** 3 k. red . . . . 3·25 4·00
1242 – 6 k. brown . . . . . . 6·00 8·50
1243 – 7½ k. red . . . . 6·75 9·50
1244 – 12½ k. blue . . . . . . 8·75 11·00
DESIGNS—VERT: 6 k. Locomotive. HORIZ: 7½ k. Railway and mountain gorge; 12½ k. Tunnel entrance at Atma-Bogazi.

1939. 1st Death Anniv of Kemal Ataturk.
1245 – 2½ k. green 15 10
1246 – 3 k. blue 20 15
1247 – 5 k. brown 25 15
1248 **136** 6 k. brown 20 20
1249 – 7½ k. red 35 40
1250 – 8 k. olive 25 30
1251 – 12½ k. blue 45 20
1252 – 17½ k. red . . . . . . 1·25 95
DESIGN: 2½ k. Ataturk's residence; 3 k. to 17½ k. Portraits of Kemal Ataturk as Type **136**.

1940. Balkan Entente. As T **103** of Yugoslavia, but with the torch and Arms of Turkey, Greece, Rumania and Yugoslavia rearranged.
1253 8 k. blue . . . . 1·25 40
1254 10 k. blue . . . . 1·50 25

137 Namik Kemal 139 Map and Census Figures

1940. Birth Centenary of Namik Kemal (poet).
1255 **137** 6 k. brown 25 15
1256 8 k. olive 45 45
1257 12 k. red 60 45
1258 12½ k. blue . . . . . . 1·50 1·00

1940. Izmir International Fair. Surch **IZMIR ENTERNASYONAL FUARI 1940** and value.
1259 **109** 6 k. on 200 k. black and green 30 25
1260 10 k. on 200 k. black and green 30 25
1261 12 k. on 500 k. black and brown 35 35

1940. National Census.
1262 **139** 10 pa. green 15 10
1263 3 k. orange 20 15
1264 6 k. red 35 30
1265 10 k. blue 90 60

140 Hurdling

1940. 11th Balkan Games.
1266 – 3 k. olive 75 65
1267 – 6 k. red . . . . 1·75 1·50
1268 **140** 8 k. brown . . . . . . 1·25 45
1269 – 10 k. blue . . . . . . 1·75 2·00
DESIGNS—VERT: 3 k. Running; 6 k. Pole vaulting; 10 k. Throwing the discus.

141 Postmen of 1840 and 1940

1940. Centenary of First Adhesive Postage Stamps.
1270 – 3 k. green 20 10
1271 **141** 6 k. red 40 30
1272 – 10 k. blue . . . . . . 1·50 65
1273 – 12 k. brown . . . . . . 1·00 60
DESIGNS—HORIZ: 3 k. Mail carriers on horseback. VERT: 10 k. Early paddle-steamer and modern mail launch; 12 k. G.P.O., Istanbul.

142 Exhibition Building

1941. Izmir International Fair.
1274 – 30 pa. green 20 10
1275 **142** 3 k. grey 10 10
1276 – 6 k. red 25 10
1277 – 10 k. blue 20 15
1278 – 12 k. purple 35 20
1279 – 17½ k. brown 65 50
DESIGNS—HORIZ: 30 pa. Freighter "Etrusk" in Izmir harbour; 6, 17½ k. Exhibition pavilions; 12 k. Girl in field. VERT: 10 k. Equestrian statue.

143 Barbarossa's Corsair Fleet

144 Barbarossa

1941. 400th Death Anniv of Barbarossa (Khair-ed-Din).
1280 – 20 pa. violet 10 10
1281 **143** 3 k. blue 20 10
1282 6 k. red 35 20
1283 10 k. blue 45 25
1284 12 k. brown . . . . . . 1·00 30
1285 **144** 17½ k. multicoloured . . 1·10 60
DESIGN—24 × 37 mm: 20 pa. Barbarossa's tomb.

1941. Air. Surch with airplane and new value.
1286 **107** 4½ k. on 25 k. brown . . 75 1·40
1287 **109** 9 k. on 200 k. blk & grn 6·00 5·00
1288 35 k. on 500 k. black and brown . . . . 3·50 3·25

146 President Inonu 147

1942.
1289 **146** 0.25 k. bistre 10 10
1290 0.50 k. green 10 10
1291 1 k. grey 10 10
1292 1½ k. mauve 10 10
1293 2 k. green 10 10
1294 4 k. brown 10 10
1295 4½ k. black 10 10
1296 5 k. blue 10 10
1297 6 k. red 10 10
1298 6¾ k. blue 45 10
1299 9 k. violet 45 10
1300 10 k. blue 15 10
1301 13½ k. purple 15 10
1302 16 k. green 20 10
1303 17½ k. red 20 10
1304 20 k. purple 35 10
1305 27½ k. orange 25 10
1306 37 k. brown 20 10
1307 50 k. violet 40 10
1308 100 k. brown . . . . . . 2·50 85
1309 **147** 200 k. brown . . . . . 8·50 15

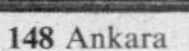

148 Ankara 150 Pres. Inonu

149 Tile-decorating

1943. Inscr "TURKIYE POSTALARI" between two crescents and stars.
1310 148 0.25 k. yellow 10 10
1311 – 0.50 k. green 25 10
1312 – 1 k. olive 10 10
1313 – 1½ k. violet 10 10
1314 – 2 k. green 20 10
1315 – 4 k. red 85 15
1316 – 4½ k. black . . . . . . 2·50 30
1317 149 5 k. blue 45 15
1318 – 6 k. red 20 10
1319 – 6¾ k. blue 15 10
1320 – 10 k. blue 20 10
1321 – 13½ k. mauve 25 10
1322 – 16 k. green . . . . . . 1·10 15
1323 – 17½ k. brown 45 10
1324 – 20 k. brown 45 10
1325 – 27½ k. orange . . . . . . 1·25 10
1326 – 27 k. brown 40 10
1327 – 50 k. purple . . . . . . 3·25 20
1328 – 100 k. olive . . . . . . 4·50 20
1329 150 200 k. brown . . . . . . 6·50 15
DESIGNS—VERT: 0.50 k. Mohair goats; 2 k. Oranges; 4 k. Merino sheep; 4½ k. Steam train entering tunnel; 6 k. Statue of Kemal Ataturk, Ankara, 6¾, 10 k. Full face portrait of Pres. Inonu; 17½ k. Republic Monument, Istanbul; 20 k. National Defence Monument, Ankara; 27½ k. P.O., Istanbul; 37 k. Monument at Afyon; 100 k. Ataturk and Inonu. HORIZ: 1 k. Antioch; 1½ k. Ankara Reservoir; 13½ k. National Assembly building; 16 k. View of Arnavutkoy; 50 k. People's House, Ankara.

152 Fair Entrance

1943. Izmir International Fair.
1330 – 4½ k. grey 20 10
1331 152 6 k. red 20 10
1332 – 6¾ k. blue 20 10
1333 152 10 k. blue 20 10
1334 – 13½ k. brown 50 20
1335 – 27½ k. grey 55 30
DESIGNS—VERT: 4½, 13½ k. Girl eating grapes. HORIZ: 6¾, 27½ k. Fair Pavilion.

153 Marching Athletes

154 Soldier guarding Flag

1943. 20th Anniv of Republic.
1336 153 4½ k. olive 40 25
1337 154 6 k. red 10 10
1338 – 6¾ k. blue 60 60
1339 – 10 k. blue 20 10
1340 – 13½ k. olive 25 15
1341 – 27½ k. brown 35 25
DESIGNS—HORIZ: 6¾ k. Bridge; 10 k. Hospital; 13½ k. Ankara. VERT: 27½ k. President Inonu.

155 Filling Census Form

157 Pres. Inonu

1945. National Census.
1342 155 4½ k. olive 45 20
1343 – 9 k. violet 45 20
1344 – 10 k. blue 45 20
1345 – 18 k. red 95 40

1945. Surch 4½ KURUS.
1346 4½ k. on 6¾ k. blue (No. 1319) 20 10

1946.
1347 157 0.25 k. red 10 10
1348 1 k. green 10 10
1349 1½ k. purple 15 10
1350 9 k. violet 35 10
1351 10 k. blue 35 10
1352 50 k. brown . . . . . . 3·25 15

158 U.S.S. "Missouri"

159 Sower

1946. Visit of U.S. Battleship "Missouri" to Istanbul.
1353 158 9 k. violet 35 10
1354 10 k. blue 50 15
1355 27½ k. grey . . . . 1·10 35

1946. Agrarian Reform.
1356 159 9 k. violet 10 10
1357 10 k. blue 10 10
1358 18 k. olive 20 15
1359 27½ k. orange 40 35

160 Dove of Peace

161 Monument at Afyon

1947. Izmir International Fair.
1360 160 15 k. purple and violet . . 10 10
1361 20 k. blue and deep blue . . 10 10
1362 30 k. brown and black . . 15 10
1363 1 l. olive and green . . . 75 25

1947. 25th Anniv of Battle of Dumlupinar.
1364 161 10 k. brown and lt brn . . 10 10
1365 – 15 k. violet and grey . . 10 10
1366 – 20 k. blue and grey . . 15 10
1367 161 30 k. green and grey . . 20 10
1368 – 60 k. green and bistre . . 35 15
1369 – 1 l. green and grey . . . 90 40
DESIGN: 15, 60 k. Ismet Inonu; 20 k., 1 l. Kemal Ataturk.

163 Istanbul, Grapes and Ribbon

1947. International Vintners' Congress.
1370 163 15 k. purple 10 10
1371 20 k. blue 10 10
1372 60 k. brown 20 15

164 Steam Express Train

165 Pres. Inonu

1947. International Railway Congress, Istanbul.
1373 164 15 k. purple 80 40
1374 20 k. blue . . . . 1·50 85
1375 60 k. olive . . . . . . 1·60 1·75

1948.
1376 165 0.25 k. red 10 10
1377 1 k. black 10 10
1378 2 k. purple 10 10
1379 3 k. orange 10 10
1380 4 k. green 10 10
1381 5 k. blue 10 10
1382 10 k. brown 15 10
1383 12 k. red 15 10
1384 15 k. violet 15 10
1385 20 k. blue 30 10
1386 30 k. brown 70 15
1387 60 k. black . . . . 1·00 15
1388 1 l. olive . . . . 1·00 20
1389 2 l. brown . . . . 15·00 45
1390 5 l. purple . . . . 8·50 3·50
The lira values are larger.

167 Signing the Treaty

168 Statue of Kemal Ataturk

1948. 25th Anniv of Treaty of Lausanne.
1391 167 15 k. purple 10 10
1392 – 20 k. blue 15 20
1393 – 40 k. green 30 20
1394 167 1 l. brown . . . . 1·00 40
DESIGN: 20, 40 k. Lausanne Palace.

1948. 25th Anniv of Proclamation of Republic.
1395 168 15 k. violet 10 10
1396 20 k. blue 15 10
1397 40 k. green 20 10
1398 1 l. brown . . . . 1·00 55

170 Douglas DC-6 over Izmir

1949. Air.
1399 170 5 k. violet and lilac . . . 25 10
1400 – 20 k. brown and lilac . . 20 10
1401 – 30 k. green and grey . . . 25 10
1402 170 40 k. blue and light blue . 85 15
1403 – 50 k. brown and mauve . 75 25
1404 – 1 l. green and blue . . . 2·25 60
AIRCRAFT: 20, 50 k. Vickers Viking 1B; 30 k., 1l. Light monoplane.

172 Wrestlers

1949. 5th European Wrestling Championships. Designs depicting wrestling holds and inscr as in T 172.
1405 – 15 k. mauve (vert) . . . . 1·75 60
1406 – 20 k. blue (vert) . . . . . 2·75 1·25
1407 172 30 k. brown . . . . . . 2·25 25
1408 – 60 k. green (horiz) . . . 4·00 2·25

173 Galley

1949. Navy Day.
1409 173 5 k. violet 25 10
1410 – 10 k. brown 60 10
1411 – 15 k. red 65 10
1412 – 20 k. blue 70 20
1413 – 30 k. slate . . . . 1·25 40
1414 – 40 k. olive 40 60
DESIGNS—HORIZ: 15 k. Cruiser "Hamidiye"; 20 k. Submarine "Sakarya"; 30 k. Battlecruiser "Yavuz". VERT: 10 k. Ship of the line "Mahmudiye"; 40 k. Statue of Barbarossa.

175 Exhibition Building

1949. Istanbul Fair.
1415 175 15 k. brown 15 10
1416 20 k. blue 15 10
1417 30 k. olive 35 20

176 U.P.U. Monument, Berne

1949. 75th Anniv of U.P.U.
1418 – 15 k. violet 10 10
1419 – 20 k. blue 15 10
1420 176 30 k. red 15 10
1421 40 k. green 40 15
DESIGN: 15, 20 k. as Type 176 but vert.

177 Sud Est Languedoc over Bogazia

1950. Air.
1422 177 2 l. 50 green and blue . . 10·00 7·50

HAVE YOU READ THE NOTES AT THE BEGINNING OF THIS CATALOGUE?
These often provide the answers to the enquiries we receive.

178 Youth, Istanbul and Ankara

180 Voting

1950. 2nd World Youth Union Meeting.
1423 178 15 k. violet 15 10
1424 20 k. blue 25 15

1950. General Election.
1425 180 15 k. brown 10 10
1426 20 k. blue 15 10
1427 – 30 k. blue and green . . 25 10
DESIGNS—HORIZ: 30 k. Kemal Ataturk and map of Turkey.

181 Hazel Nut

182 Map and Statistics

1950. Izmir Fair.
1428 181 8 k. green and yellow . . 20 10
1429 – 12 k. mauve 25 10
1430 – 15 k. brown 35 10
1431 – 20 k. blue and light blue . 45 20
1432 – 30 k. brown 55 20
DESIGN: 12 k. Acorns; 15 k. Cotton; 20 k. Fair symbol; 30 k. Tobacco.

1950. National Census.
1433 182 15 k. brown 20 10
1434 20 k. blue 20 10

183 Hezarfen Celebi's "Bird Flight" and Tower

184 Farabi (philosopher)

1950. Air. International Civil Aviation Congress, Istanbul.
1435 183 20 k. blue and green . . 50 10
1436 – 40 k. blue and brown . . 75 15
1437 – 60 k. blue and violet . . 1·75 75
DESIGNS—VERT: 40 k. Biplane over Taurus Mountains. HORIZ: 60 k. Douglas DC-3 airplane over Istanbul.

1950. 1000th Death Anniv of Farabi.
1438 184 15 k. multicoloured . . . 50 20
1439 20 k. multicoloured . . . 85 20
1440 60 k. multicoloured . . . 2·00 75
1441 1 l. multicoloured . . . 2·50 75

185 Mithat Pasha and Deposit Bank

1950. 3rd Co-operative Congress, Istanbul.
1442 185 15 k. violet 30 10
1443 – 20 k. blue 35 15
DESIGN: 20 k. Agricultural Bank.

1951. Air. Industrial Congress, Ankara. Nos. 1399, 1401 and 1403 optd **SANAYI KONGRESI 9-NISAN-1951.**
1454 170 5 k. violet and lilac . . . 50 80
1455 – 30 k. green and grey . . 50 20
1456 – 50 k. brown and mauve . 1·25 30

187 "Iskendrun" (liner)

1951. 25th Anniv of Coastal Trading Rights.

1457	–	15 k. blue	55	15
1458	187	20 k. blue	85	15
1459	–	30 k. grey	65	20
1460	–	1 l. green	75	60

DESIGNS—HORIZ: 15 k. Tug "Hora" and liner "Providence"; 30 k. Diver and launch. VERT: 1 l. Lighthouse.

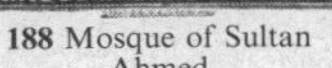

188 Mosque of Sultan Ahmed 189 Count Carton de Wiart

1951. 40th Interparliamentary Conference, Istanbul.

1461	188	15 k. green	20	10
1462	–	20 k. blue	20	10
1463	189	30 k. brown	40	10
1464	–	60 k. purple	1·60	70

DESIGNS—As Type 188: 20 k. Dolmabahce Palace; 60 k. Rumeli Tower.

190 F.A.O. Emblem and Silo 191 A. H. Tarhan

1952. U.N. Economic Conf, Ankara. Inscr "Ankara 1951".

1465	190	15 k. green	30	20
1466	–	20 k. violet	30	20
1467	–	30 k. blue	40	20
1468	–	60 k. red	75	40

DESIGNS: 20 k. Int Bank emblem and hydro-electric station; 30 k. U.N. emblem and New York headquarters; 60 k. Ankara University.

1952. Birth Centenary of Tarhan (writer).

1469	191	15 k. purple	10	10
1470		20 k. blue	10	10
1471		30 k. brown	25	15
1472		60 k. green	60	40

192 Bergama 193 Kemal Ataturk

1952. Views. Imperf or perf.

1473	192	1 k. orange	10	10
1474	–	2 k. green	10	10
1475	–	3 k. brown	10	10
1476	–	4 k. green	10	10
1477	–	5 k. brown	10	10
1478	193	10 k. brown	15	10
1479		12 k. red	20	10
1480		15 k. violet (medallion)	25	10
1481		20 k. blue (medallion)	75	10
1482	–	30 k. green	40	10
1483	–	40 k. blue	65	10
1484	–	50 k. green	65	10
1485	–	75 k. black	75	10
1486	–	1 l. violet	95	10
1487	–	2 l. blue	1·75	10
1488	–	5 l. brown	14·00	4·00

DESIGNS—VERT: 2 k. Ruins at Milas; 3 k. Karatay Gate, Konya; 4 k. Trees on Kozak Plateau; 5 k. Urgup; 30 k. Emirsultan Mosque, Bursa; 40 k. Yenicami (New Mosque), Istanbul. HORIZ: 50 k. Waterfall, Tarsus; 75 k. Rocks at Urgup; 1 l. Dolmabahce Palace, Istanbul; 2 l. Pavilion, Istanbul; 5 l. Interior of Istanbul Museum.

1952. Surch **0.50 Kurus**.

1489	192	0.50 k. on 1 k. orange	20	10

MINIMUM PRICE

The minimum price quoted is 10p which represents a handling charge rather than a basis for valuing common stamps. For further notes about prices, see introductory pages.

196 Congress Building 197 Turkish Sentry

1952. 8th Int Mechanics Congress, Istanbul.

1490	196	15 k. violet	35	15
1491		20 k. blue	35	15
1492		60 k. brown	75	25

1952. Turkish Participation in Korean War.

1493	197	15 k. slate	25	15
1494	–	20 k. blue	20	15
1495	–	30 k. brown	55	25
1496	–	60 k. red and green	80	40

DESIGNS: 20 k. Turkish soldier and flag; 30 k. Soldier and Korean child reading comic paper; 60 k. Soldiers planting Turkish flag.

198 Doves, Hand and Red Crescent 199 Bas-relief on Monument

1952. 75th Anniv of Red Crescent Society.

1497	198	15 k. red and green	50	30
1498	–	20 k. red and blue	1·00	50

DESIGN: 20 k. Red Crescent flag.

1952. 75th Anniv of Battle of Erzurum.

1499	199	15 k. violet	20	15
1500	–	20 k. blue	20	15
1501	–	40 k. grey	55	25

DESIGNS—HORIZ: 20 k. Azizye Monument, Erzurum; 40 k. View of Erzurum.

200 Pigeon carrying Newspaper 202 Sultan Mohammed II (after Gentile Bellini)

201 Rumeli Fort

1952.

1502	200	0.50 k. green	10	10
1503		0.50 k. violet	10	10
1503a		0.50 k. orange	10	10
1503b		0.50 k. brown	10	10

1953. 500th Anniv of Fall of Constantinople.

1504	201	5 k. blue & ultramarine	10	10
1505	–	8 k. grey	10	10
1506	–	10 k. blue	20	10
1507	–	12 k. purple	25	10
1508	–	15 k. brown	20	10
1509	–	20 k. red	30	15
1510	–	30 k. green	80	15
1511	–	40 k. violet	80	25
1512	–	60 k. brown	80	35
1513	–	1 l. green	1·75	60
1514	–	2 l. multicoloured	4·00	2·25
1515	202	2½ l. lt brown, yell & brn	5·00	3·25

DESIGNS—As Type 201: HORIZ: 8 k. Turkish army at Edirne; 10 k. Horsemen and fleet; 12 k. Landing of Turkish Army; 15 k. Topkapi ramparts; 40 k. Sultan Mohammed II and Patriarch Yenadios; 60 k. 15th-century map of Constantinople; 1 l. Mausoleum of Mohammed II. VERT: 20 k. Turkish army entering Constantinople; 30 k. Sultan Mohammed II Mosque. As Type 202: 2 l. Sultan Mohammed II (after miniature by Sinan).

203 Odeon Theatre, Ephesus

1953. Views of Ephesus. Inscr "EFES". Multicoloured centres.

1516	203	12 k. green	15	10
1517	–	15 k. violet	15	10
1518	–	20 k. slate	25	10
1519	–	40 k. turquoise	40	25
1520	–	60 k. blue	30	25
1521	–	1 l. red	1·25	60

DESIGNS: 15 k. St. John's Church and Acropolis; 20 k. Statue of Blessed Virgin, Panaya Kapulu; 40 k. Council Church ruins; 60 k. Grotto of the Seven Sleepers; 1 l. House of the Blessed Virgin, Panaya Kapulu.

204 Pres. Bayar, Mithat Pasha, Dr. Delitsch and Ankara Bank

1953. 5th International Public Credit Congress.

1522	204	15 k. brown	15	10
1523	–	20 k. turquoise	25	15

DESIGN: 20 k. Pres. Bayar, Mithat Pasha and Ankara University.

205 Berdan Barrage

1953. 30th Anniv of Republic.

1524	–	10 k. bistre	10	10
1525	205	15 k. slate	10	10
1526	–	20 k. red	10	10
1527	–	30 k. olive	3·50	1·75
1528	–	35 k. blue	20	10
1529	–	55 k. lilac	25	15

DESIGNS—HORIZ: 10 k. Combine-harvester; 20 k. Soldiers on parade; 30 k. Diesel-engined train; 35 k. Yesilkoy airport. VERT: 55 k. Kemal Ataturk.

206 Kemal Ataturk and Mausoleum

1953. Transfer of Ashes of Kemal Ataturk to Mausoleum.

1530	206	15 k. black	20	10
1531		20 k. purple	55	15

207 Map of World and Compass

1954. 5th Anniv of N.A.T.O.

1532	207	15 k. brown	25	25
1533	–	20 k. blue	25	25
1534	–	40 k. green	8·00	7·00

DESIGNS: 20 k. Globe and stars; 40 k. Allegory of growth of N.A.T.O.

208 "Industry, Agriculture and Construction" 209 Flying Exercise

1954. 5th Anniv of Council of Europe.

1535	208	10 k. brown	3·25	2·25
1536	–	15 k. green	2·25	2·00
1537	–	20 k. blue	2·25	2·00
1538	208	30 k. violet	12·00	7·50

DESIGN: 15, 20 k. Flag and figure of "Peace and Justice".

1954. 47th Conference of Int Aeronautical Federation. Inscr "20.IX.1954".

1539	209	20 k. black	20	10
1540	–	35 k. lilac	35	15
1541	–	45 k. blue	85	20

DESIGNS: 35 k. Baron Delagrange and glider; 45 k. Ataturk and formation of De Havilland Tiger Moth biplanes.

210 Z. Gokalp 211 Yesilkoy Airport

1954. 30th Death Anniv of Gokalp (sociologist).

1542	210	15 k. violet	10	10
1543		20 k. green	20	10
1544		30 k. red	35	15

1954. Air.

1545	211	5 k. blue and brown	15	10
1546	–	20 k. blue and brown	25	10
1547	–	35 k. blue and green	25	10
1548	211	40 k. blue and red	35	10
1549	–	45 k. blue and violet	55	20
1550	–	55 k. blue and black	1·25	25

DESIGNS: 20, 45 k. Frontal view of Yesilkoy Airport; 35, 55 k. Ankara Airport.

212 Kemal Ataturk 213 Relief Map of the Dardanelles

1955.

1551	212	15 k. red	10	10
1552		20 k. blue	15	10
1553		40 k. slate	20	10
1554		50 k. green	30	10
1555		75 k. brown	65	10

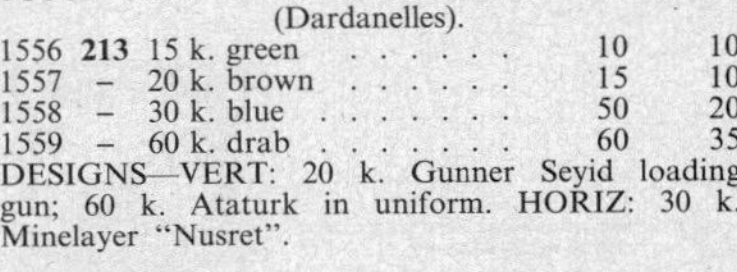

1955. 40th Anniv of Battle of Canakkale (Dardanelles).

1556	213	15 k. green	10	10
1557	–	20 k. brown	15	10
1558	–	30 k. blue	50	20
1559	–	60 k. drab	60	35

DESIGNS—VERT: 20 k. Gunner Seyid loading gun; 60 k. Ataturk in uniform. HORIZ: 30 k. Minelayer "Nusret".

214 "Reconstruction" 215 Lillies

1955. Town Planning Congress.

1560	214	15 k. grey	15	10
1561		20 k. blue	20	10
1562		50 k. brown	25	15
1563		1 l. violet	60	25

1955. Spring Flower Festival. Inscr "ISTANBUL 1955".

1564	–	10 k. red and green	30	10
1565	–	15 k. yellow and green	25	10
1566	–	20 k. red and green	35	10
1567	215	50 k. green and yellow	2·75	60

FLOWERS: 10 k. Carnations; 15 k. Tulips; 20 k. Roses.

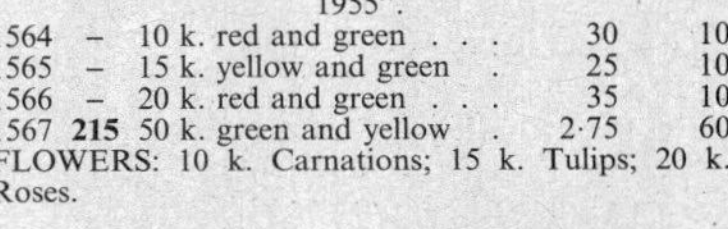

216 First-aid Centre

1955. 18th Congress of International Documentation Office of Military Medicine.

1568	216	20 k. red and grey	20	10
1569	–	30 k. green and lt green	45	15

DESIGN: 30 k. Gulhane Military Hospital, Ankara.

217 Footballers

1955. Int Military Football Championships.

1570	217	15 k. blue	55	15
1571	–	20 k. red	30	10
1572	–	1 l. green	1·60	45

DESIGNS—VERT: 20 k. Footballers' badge. HORIZ: 1 l. Championship plaque.

218 Police Monument, Ankara

1955. International Police Commission Meeting, Istanbul.
1573 **218** 15 k. green and turquoise 20 10
1574 – 20 k. violet and lilac 25 10
1575 – 30 k. black and grey 35 15
1576 – 45 k. brown and lt brn 85 25
DESIGNS: 20 k. Dolmabahce Palace, Istanbul; 30 k. Police College, Ankara; 45 k. Police Martyrs' Monument, Istanbul.

219 Radio Mast **220** Istanbul University

1955. Cent of Telecommunications in Turkey.
1577 – 15 k. olive 20 10
1578 **219** 20 k. red 20 10
1579 – 45 k. brown 25 10
1580 **219** 60 k. blue 35 15
DESIGNS—HORIZ: 15, 45 k. Telegraph table and pole.

1955. 10th Meeting of Governors of Int Reconstruction and Development Bank and Int Monetary Fund.
1581 – 15 k. orange 20 10
1582 **220** 20 k. red 20 10
1583 – 60 k. purple 25 15
1584 – 1 l. blue 30 25
DESIGNS: 15 k. Faculty of Letters, Istanbul; 60 k. Hilton Hotel; 1 l. Kiz Kulesi.

221 Ruins, Istanbul **222**

1955. 10th International Congress of Byzantine Research.
1585 **221** 15 k. green and blue 25 10
1586 – 20 k. red and orange 20 10
1587 – 30 k. brown and pink 30 10
1588 – 75 k. blue and lilac 70 25
DESIGNS—VERT: 20 k. Obelisk and Sultan Ahmed Mosque; 75 k. Map of Istanbul in 1422. HORIZ: 30 k. Church of St. Sophia.

1955. 10th International Road Planning Congress.
1589 – 20 k. mauve 20 10
1590 **222** 30 k. green 25 15
1591 – 55 k. blue 1·00 40
DESIGNS: 20 k. Congress emblem; 55 k. Bridges.

223 Population Pictograph

1955. National Census.
1592 **223** 15 k. grey and red 25 10
1593 20 k. lilac and red 20 10
1594 30 k. blue and red 20 10
1595 60 k. green and red 40 10

224 Santa Claus Church, Demre **225** Kemal Ataturk

1955. Tourism.
1596 – 18 k. green and blue 25 10
1597 – 20 k. brown and blue 25 10
1598 – 30 k. brown and green 30 10
1599 – 45 k. green and brown 1·25 25
1600 – 50 k. brown and green 35 20
1601 **224** 65 k. black and red 65 15
DESIGNS—VERT: 18 k. Waterfall near Antalya; 45 k. Theatre doorway ruins, Side; 50 k. Countryside, Antalya. HORIZ: 20 k. Alanya; 30 k. Amphitheatre, Aspendos.

1955.
1602 **225** 0.50 k. pink 10 10
1603 1 k. yellow 10 10
1604 2 k. blue 10 10
1605 3 k. red 10 10
1606 5 k. brown 10 10
1606a 6 k. green 25 10
1607 10 k. green 10 10
1607a 18 k. purple 25 10
1608 20 k. blue 10 10
1609 25 k. olive 25 10
1610 30 k. violet 25 10
1611 40 k. brown 25 10
1612 75 k. slate 1·00 15

226 Mausoleum of Hudavent Hatum **227** Zubeyde

1956. 25th Anniv of Turkish Historical Association.
1613 **226** 40 k. deep blue & blue 20 10

1956. Mothers' Day.
1614 **227** 20 k. brn & buff (perf) 10 10
1615 20 k. olive and green (imperf) 50 30

228 Shah of Iran and Queen Soraya **229** Kemal Ataturk

1956. Visit of Shah of Iran to Turkey.
1616 **228** 100 k. green and light green (perf) 60 10
1617 100 k. red and green (imperf) 5·00 5·00

1956.
1618 **229** ½ k. green 10 10
1619 1 k. orange 10 10
1620 3 k. green 10 10
1621 5 k. violet 10 10
1622 6 k. mauve 10 10
1623 10 k. purple 10 10
1624 12 k. brown 10 10
1625 15 k. blue 10 10
1626 18 k. pink 10 10
1627 20 k. brown 10 10
1628 25 k. green 15 10
1629 30 k. slate 15 10
1630 40 k. olive 15 10
1631 50 k. orange 20 10
1632 60 k. blue 25 10
1633 70 k. turquoise 60 15
1634 75 k. brown 50 10
See also Nos. 1659/78.

230 Erenkoy Sanatorium **231**

1956. Turkish Post Office Health Service.
1635 **230** 50 k. turquoise & pink 35 10

1956. 25th Izmir International Fair.
1636 **231** 45 k. green (postage) 10 10
1637 25 k. brown (air) 15 10

232 Serpent in Bottle **233** Medical Clinic, Kayseri

1956. International Anti-Alcoholism Congress.
1638 **232** 25 k. multicoloured 25 10

1956. 750th Anniv of Medical Clinic, Kayseri.
1639 **233** 60 k. violet & yellow 20 10

234 Sariyar Barrage **235** Wrestling

1956. Inaug of Sariyar Dam.
1640 **234** 20 k. red 15 10
1641 20 k. blue 15 10

1956. Olympic Games. Inscr as in T **235**.
1642 **235** 40 k. sepia on green 40 20
1643 – 65 k. red on grey 50 20
DESIGN: 65 k. Another wrestling match.

236 Mehmet Akif Ersoy **237** Vase of Troy

1956. 20th Death Anniv of Ersoy (poet).
1644 **236** 20 k. brown and green 15 10
1645 20 k. red and grey 15 10
1646 20 k. violet and pink 15 10
Each stamp is inscribed with a different line of verse from the Turkish National Anthem composed by Ersoy.

1956. Troy Commemoration. Inscr "TRUVA (TROIA)".
1647 – 15 k. green 75 25
1648 **237** 20 k. purple 50 25
1649 – 30 k. brown 90 75
DESIGNS—HORIZ: 15 k. Troy Amphitheatre; 30 k. Trojan Horse.

238 Mobile X-ray Unit **239** Pres. Heuss

1957. T.B. Relief Campaign.
1650 **238** 25 k. red and drab 15 10

1957. Visit of President of West Germany.
1651 **239** 40 k. brown and yellow (postage) 25 10
1652 40 k. purple and pink (air) 20 10

240 View of Bergama

1957. Bergama Fair.
1653 **240** 30 k. brown 15 10
1654 – 40 k. green 10 10
DESIGN: 40 k. Folk-dancing.

241

1957. Turkish–American Friendship.
1655 **241** 25 k. violet 20 10
1656 40 k. blue 25 15

242 Osman Hamdi Bey (founder) **243** Kemal Ataturk

1957. 75th Anniv of Fine Arts Academy, Istanbul.
1657 **242** 20 k. drab, buff & black 20 10
1658 – 30 k. grey, grn & lt grn 25 10
DESIGN—HORIZ: 30 k. Hittite relic of Alacahoyuk; Inscr "GUZEL SANATLAR AKADEMISI 75. YIL".

1957.
1659 **243** ½ k. brown 10 10
1660 1 k. blue 10 10
1661 2 k. violet 10 10
1662 3 k. orange 10 10
1663 5 k. green 10 10
1664 6 k. green 10 10
1665 10 k. violet 10 10
1666 12 k. green 10 10
1667 15 k. green 10 10
1668 18 k. mauve 10 10
1669 20 k. sepia 10 10
1670 25 k. brown 10 10
1671 30 k. blue 15 10
1672 40 k. slate 15 10
1673 50 k. yellow 20 10
1674 60 k. black 25 10
1675 70 k. purple 25 10
1676 75 k. olive 35 10
1677 – 100 k. red 40 15
1678 – 250 k. olive 1·00 40
Nos. 1677/8 are larger 21 × 29 mm.

244 Mohammed Zahir Shah **245** Amasya Medical Centre

1957. Visit of Mohammed Zahir Shah of Afghanistan.
1679 **244** 45 k. red and orange (postage) 15 10
1680 25 k. deep green and green (air) 15 10

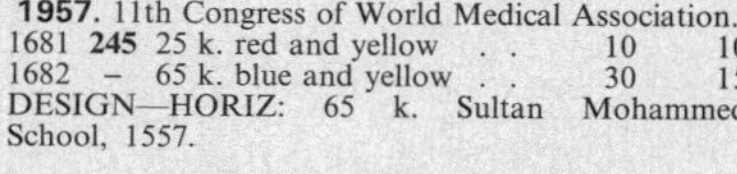

1957. 11th Congress of World Medical Association.
1681 **245** 25 k. red and yellow 10 10
1682 – 65 k. blue and yellow 30 15
DESIGN—HORIZ: 65 k. Sultan Mohammed School, 1557.

246 Sultan Mohammed II Mosque

1957. 400th Anniv of the Suleiman Mosque, Istanbul.
1683 **246** 20 k. green 10 10
1684 – 1 l. brown 35 15
DESIGN—VERT: 1 l. Mimar Koca Sinan (architect).

1957. 2nd Philatelic Exhibition, Istanbul. Surch **50 Kurus ISTANBUL Filatelik II. Sergisi 1957.**
1685 50 k. on 2 l. bl (No. 1487) 25 10

248 Forestry Map of Turkey

1957. Centenary of Forestry Teaching.
1686 **248** 20 k. green and brown 15 10
1687 – 25 k. green and blue 20 10
DESIGN—VERT: 25 k. Planting fir-tree.

249 Fuzuli (poet) **250** Franklin

1957. Fuzuli Year.
1688 **249** 50 k. multicoloured . . . 25 10

1957. 250th Birth Anniv of Benjamin Franklin.
1689 **250** 65 k. purple 25 10
1690 65 k. blue 25 10

251 Mevlana's Tomb, Konya

252 Adana

1957. 750th Birth Anniv of Mevlana (poet).
1691 **251** 50 k. violet, blue & green 20 15
1692 – 100 k. dp blue and blue . 40 25
DESIGN—HORIZ: 100 k. Konya Museum.

1958. Turkish Towns. As T **252**. (a) 26 × 21 mm.
1693 5 k. brown (Adana) 10 10
1694 5 k. mauve (Adapazari) . . . 10 10
1695 5 k. red (Adiyaman) 10 10
1696 5 k. brown (Afyon) 10 10
1697 5 k. green (Amasya) 10 10
1698 5 k. blue (Ankara) 10 10
1699 5 k. green (Antakya) 10 10
1700 5 k. green (Antalya) 10 10
1701 5 k. lilac (Artvin) 10 10
1702 5 k. orange (Aydin) 10 10
1703 5 k. violet (Balikesir) . . . 10 10
1704 5 k. green (Bilecik) 10 10
1705 5 k. purple (Bingol) 10 10
1706 5 k. blue (Bitlis) 10 10
1707 5 k. purple (Bolu) 10 10
1708 5 k. brown (Burdur) 10 10
1709 5 k. green (Bursa) 10 10
1710 5 k. blue (Canakkale) 10 10
1711 5 k. violet (Cankiri) 10 10
1712 5 k. blue (Corum) 10 10
1713 5 k. blue (Denizli) 10 10
1714 5 k. orange (Diyrbakir) . . . 10 10
1715 5 k. violet (Edirne) 10 10
1716 5 k. green (Elazig) 10 10
1717 5 k. blue (Erzincan) 10 10
1718 5 k. orange (Erzurum) . . . 10 10
1719 5 k. green (Eskisehur) . . . 10 10
1720 5 k. green (Gaziantep) . . . 10 10
1721 5 k. blue (Giresun) 10 10
1722 5 k. blue (Gumusane) . . . 10 10
1723 5 k. purple (Hakkari) 10 10
1724 5 k. mauve (Isparta) 10 10
1725 5 k. blue (Istanbul) 10 10
1726 5 k. blue (Izmir) 10 10
1727 5 k. blue (Izmit) 10 10
1728 5 k. violet (Karakose) . . . 10 10
1729 5 k. green (Kars) 10 10
1730 5 k. mauve (Kastamonu) . . 10 10
1731 5 k. green (Kayseri) 10 10
1732 5 k. brown (Kirklareli) . . . 10 10
1733 5 k. orange (Kirsehir) . . . 10 10
1734 5 k. blue (Konya) 10 10
1735 5 k. violet (Kutahya) 10 10
1736 5 k. brown (Malatya) 10 10
1737 5 k. green (Manisa) 10 10
1738 5 k. purple (Maras) 10 10
1739 5 k. red (Mardin) 10 10
1740 5 k. green (Mersin) 10 10
1741 5 k. green (Mugla) 10 10
1742 5 k. green (Mus) 10 10
1743 5 k. green (Nevsehir) 10 10
1744 5 k. red (Nigde) 10 10
1745 5 k. blue (Ordu) 10 10
1746 5 k. violet (Rize) 10 10
1747 5 k. purple (Samsun) 10 10
1748 5 k. brown (Siirt) 10 10
1749 5 k. blue(Sinop) 10 10
1750 5 k. green (Sivas) 10 10
1751 5 k. blue (Tekirdag) 10 10
1752 5 k. red (Tokat) 10 10
1753 5 k. blue (Trabzon) 10 10
1754 5 k. orange (Tunceli) 10 10
1755 5 k. brown (Urfa) 10 10
1756 5 k. green (Usak) 10 10
1757 5 k. red (Van) 10 10
1758 5 k. mauve (Yozgat) 10 10
1759 5 k. blue (Zonguldak) 10 10

(b) $32\frac{1}{2}$ × 22 mm.
1760 20 k. brown (Adana) 20 20
1761 20 k. mauve (Adapazari) . . 20 20
1762 20 k. red (Adiyaman) 20 20
1763 20 k. brown (Afyon) 20 20
1764 20 k. green (Amasya) 20 20
1765 20 k. blue (Ankara) 20 20
1766 20 k. blue (Antakya) 20 20
1767 20 k. green (Antalya) 20 20
1768 20 k. blue (Artvin) 20 20
1769 20 k. orange (Aydin) 20 20
1770 20 k. purple (Balikesir) . . . 20 20
1771 20 k. green (Bilecik) 20 20
1772 20 k. grey (Bingol) 20 20
1773 20 k. violet (Bitlis) 20 20
1774 20 k. purple (Bolu) 20 20
1775 20 k. brown (Burdur) 20 20
1776 20 k. green (Bursa) 20 20
1777 20 k. blue (Canakkale) . . . 20 20
1778 20 k. purple (Cankiri) 20 20
1779 20 k. grey (Corum) 20 20
1780 20 k. blue (Denizli) 20 20
1781 20 k. red (Diyrbakir) 20 20
1782 20 k. grey (Edirne) 20 20
1783 20 k. green (Elazig) 20 20
1784 20 k. blue (Erzincan) 20 20
1785 20 k. orange (Erzurum) . . . 20 20
1786 20 k. green (Eskisehur) . . . 20 20
1787 20 k. green (Gaziantep) . . . 20 20
1788 20 k. blue (Giresun) 20 20
1789 20 k. blue (Gumusane) . . . 20 20
1790 20 k. purple (Hakkari) . . . 20 20
1791 20 k. mauve (Isparta) . . . 20 20
1792 20 k. blue (Istanbul) 20 20
1793 20 k. blue (Izmir) 20 20
1794 20 k. green (Izmit) 20 20
1795 20 k. violet (Karakose) . . . 20 20
1796 20 k. green (Kars) 20 20
1797 20 k. mauve (Kastamonu) . . 20 20
1798 20 k. green (Kayseri) 20 20
1799 20 k. brown (Kirklareli) . . . 20 20
1800 20 k. brown (Kirsehir) . . . 20 20
1801 20 k. blue (Konya) 20 20
1802 20 k. violet (Kutahya) . . . 20 20
1803 20 k. brown (Malatya) . . . 20 20
1804 20 k. green (Manisa) 20 20
1805 20 k. purple (Maras) 20 20
1806 20 k. red (Mardin) 20 20
1807 20 k. green (Mersin) 20 20
1808 20 k. green (Mugla) 20 20
1809 20 k. green (Mus) 20 20
1810 20 k. green (Nevsehir) . . . 20 20
1811 20 k. red (Nigde) 20 20
1812 20 k. blue (Ordu) 20 20
1813 20 k. violet (Rize) 20 20
1814 20 k. purple (Samsun) . . . 20 20
1815 20 k. brown (Siirt) 20 20
1816 20 k. blue (Sinop) 20 20
1817 20 k. green (Sivas) 20 20
1818 20 k. blue (Tekirdag) 20 20
1819 20 k. red (Tokat) 20 20
1820 20 k. blue (Trabzon) 20 20
1821 20 k. red (Tunceli) 20 20
1822 20 k. brown (Urfa) 20 20
1823 20 k. grey (Usak) 20 20
1824 20 k. red (Van) 20 20
1825 20 k. red (Yozgat) 20 20
1826 20 k. blue (Zonguldak) . . . 20 20

253

254 Hierapolis at Pamukkale

1958. 75th Anniv of the Institute of Economics and Commerce, Ankara.
1827 **253** 20 k. orange, bl & bis . . 10 10
1828 25 k. blue, orge & bis . . 10 10

1958. Pamukkale Tourist Publicity. Inscr "PAMUKKALE".
1829 **254** 20 k. brown 10 10
1830 – 25 k. blue 15 10
DESIGN—HORIZ: 25 k. Travertins (rocks) near Denizli.

255 Katib Celebi

256 Letters

1958. 300th Death Anniv of Katib Celebi (author).
1831 **255** 50 k. + 10 k. black . . 20 15

1958. International Correspondence Week.
1832 **256** 20 k. orange and black . 10 10

257 Symbol of Industry

258 Symbol of "Europa"

1958. Industrial Fair, Istanbul.
1833 **257** 40 k. black and blue . . 15 10

1958. Europa.
1834 **258** 25 k. lilac and violet . . 20 10
1835 40 k. blue & ultramarine 30 10

259 Bulldozer

260 Flame of Remembrance

1958. 35th Anniv of Republic.
1836 **259** 15 k. + 5 k. orange . . 10 10
1837 – 20 k. + 5 k. brown . . . 10 10
1838 – 25 k. + 5 k. green . . . 30 10
DESIGNS—VERT: 20 k. Portrait of Kemal Ataturk. HORIZ: 25 k. Army tanks and Republic F-84G Thunderjets

1958. 20th Death Anniv of Kemal Ataturk.
1839 **260** 25 k. red 10 10
1840 – 75 k. green 20 15
DESIGN: 75 k. Sword, sprig and bust of Kemal Ataturk.

261

262 Blackboard

1959. 25th Anniv of Faculty of Agriculture, Ankara University.
1841 **261** 25 k. yellow and violet . . 10 10

1959. 75th Anniv of Boys' High School, Istanbul.
1842 **262** 75 k. black and yellow . . 25 15

263 Eagle

1959. Air. Birds.
1843 – 40 k. purple and mauve . 25 10
1844 – 65 k. myrtle & turquoise . 30 15
1845 – 85 k. blue and black . . . 40 20
1846 **263** 105 k. bistre and yellow . 40 20
1847 – 125 k. lilac and violet . . 80 25
1848 – 155 k. green & yellow . . 90 30
1849 – 195 k. blue and black . . 80 45
1850 – 245 k. brown & orange . 1·50 80
BIRDS (in flight)—HORIZ: 40 k. Barn swallows; 65 k. Cranes; 85 k. Gulls. VERT: 125 k. House martin; 155 k. Demoiselle crane; 195 k. Gulls; 245 k. Turtle dove.

264 Theatre, Ankara

1959. Centenary of Turkish Theatre.
1851 **264** 20 k. brown and green . . 10 10
1852 – 25 k. green and orange . 10 10
DESIGN: 25 k. Portrait of Sinasi and masks.

265 "Karadeniz" (liner)

266 Northern Hemisphere and Stars

1959.
1853 – 1 k. blue 10 10
1854 **245** 5 k. blue 20 10
1855 – 10 k. blue 10 10
1856 – 15 k. brown 20 10
1857 – 20 k. green 10 10
1858 – 25 k. lilac 15 10
1859a – 30 k. purple 20 10
1860 – 40 k. blue 20 10
1861 – 45 k. violet 20 10
1862 – 55 k. brown 25 10
1863 – 60 k. green 65 10
1864 – 75 k. olive . . . . . 2·75 10
1865 – 90 k. blue . . . . . . 2·75 10
1866 – 100 k. grey . . . . . 2·25 10
1867 – 120 k. purple . . . . 2·00 10
1868 – 150 k. orange . . . . 2·75 20
1869 – 200 k. green . . . . . 2·75 25
1870 – 250 k. brown . . . . 2·75 45
1871 – 500 k. blue . . . . . 6·00 60
DESIGNS—HORIZ: 1 k. Vickers Viscount 700 airliner; 10 k. Grain silo; 15 k. Steel works; 20 k. Euphrates Bridge; 25 k. Zonguldak Harbour; 30 k. Oil refinery; 40 k. Rumeli Hisari Fortress; 45 k. Sugar factory; 55 k. Coal mine; 150 k. Combine-harvester. VERT: 60 k. Telegraph pole; 75 k. Railway; 90 k. Crane loading ships; 100 k. Cement factory; 120 k. Coast road; 200 k. Electric transformer; 250, 500 k. Portrait of Ataturk.

1959. Postage Due Stamps surch **20 = 20** for ordinary postage.
1872 D **121** 20 k. on 20 pa. brown 10 10
1873 20 k. on 2 k. violet . . 10 10
1874 20 k. on 3 k. violet . . 10 10
1875 20 k. on 5 k. green . . 10 10
1876 20 k. on 12 k. red . . 10 10

1959. 10th Anniv of N.A.T.O.
1877 **267** 105 k. red 35 10
1878 195 k. green 55 25

268 Amphitheatre, Aspendos

270 Basketball Players

1959. Aspendos Festival.
1879 **268** 20 k. violet and bistre . . 10 10
1880 20 k. brown and green . 10 10

1959. 10th Anniv of Council of Europe. Surch **X. YIL** in circle of stars, **105 AVRUPA KONSEYI.**
1881 **259** 105 k. on 15 k. + 5 k. orange 40 15

1959. 11th European and Mediterranean Basketball Championships, Istanbul.
1882 **270** 25 k. red and blue . . . 25 10

271 Marine Symbols

272 Goreme

1959. 50th Anniv of Turkish Merchant Marine College.
1883 **271** 30 k. multicoloured . . . 10 10
1884 – 40 k. multicoloured . . . 15 10
DESIGN: 40 k. As 30 k. but sea-horse in place of anchor symbol.

1959. Tourist Publicity.
1885 **272** 105 k. + 10 k. orange and violet 25 25

273 Mounted Warrior

1959. 888th Anniv of Battle of Malazgirt.
1886 **273** $2\frac{1}{2}$ l. purple and blue . . 50 15

274 Istanbul

1959. 15th International T.B. Conf, Istanbul.
1887 **274** 105 k. + 10 k. blue and red 35 20

275 Ornamental Pattern

276 Kemal Ataturk

1959. 1st International Congress of Turkish Arts.
1888 **275** 30 k. red and black . . . 10 10
1889 – 40 k. blue, blk & ochre . 15 10
1890 – 75 k. blue, yellow & red 30 10
DESIGNS—HORIZ: 40 k. Sultan Mohammed II Mosque in silhouette. VERT: 75 k. Circular ornament.

1959.
1891 **276** 500 k. blue . . . . . . 1·00 25

277 Faculty Building

278 Crossed Sabres

1959. Centenary of Turkish Political Science Faculty.
1892 **277** 40 k. brown and green . . 15 10
1893 40 k. blue and brown . . 15 10
1894 – 1 l. ochre and violet . . . 25 10
DESIGN—VERT: 1 l. "S.B.F." emblem of Faculty.

1960. 125th Anniv of Territorial War College.
1895 **278** 30 k. red and yellow . . 10 10
1896 – 40 k. yellow, brown & red 20 10
DESIGN: 40 k. Bayonet in bowl of fire.

279 "Uprooted Tree" and Globe

1960. World Refugee Year.
1897 **279** 90 k. black & turquoise . . 10 10
1898 – 105 k. black and yellow . 10 10
DESIGN: 105 k. "Uprooted Tree" and houses representing refugee camp.

280 Mental Home, Manisa **281** Carnations

1960. Manisa Fair. Inscr "MANISA MESIR BAYRAMI"
1899 **280** 40 k. + 5 k. violet & mve 15 10
1900 40 k. + 5 k. green & blue 15 10
1901 – 90 k. + 5 k. purple & mve 25 10
1902 – 105 k. + 10 k. mult . . 25 10
DESIGNS—VERT: 90 k. Sultan Mosque, Manisa; $30\frac{1}{2} \times 42\frac{1}{2}$ mm: 105 k. Merkez Muslihittin Efendi (portrait).

1960. Spring Flowers Festival, Istanbul. Inscr "1960". Flowers in natural colours. Colours of inscriptions and backgrounds given.
1903 **281** 30 k. red and yellow . . 20 15
1904 – 40 k. green and grey . . 25 20
1905 – 75 k. red and blue . . . 50 25
1906 – 105 k. green and pink . . 70 25
FLOWERS: 40 k. Jasmine; 75 k. Rose; 105 k. Tulips.

282 Map of Cyprus

1960. Proclamation of Cyprus Republic. Inscr "KIBRIS CUMHURIYETI"
1907 **282** 40 k. mauve and blue . . 25 10
1908 – 105 k. yellow, blue & grn 45 20
DESIGN: 40 k. Town Centre, Nicosia.

283 Globe

1960. 16th Women's Int Council Meeting.
1909 **283** 30 k. yellow and lilac . . 10 10
1910 – 75 k. drab and blue . . . 25 10
DESIGN: 75 k. Women, "W.I.C." emblem and nest.

283a Football **285** "Population"

1960. Olympic Games.
1911 30 k. green (Type **283a**) . . . 25 20
1912 30 k. black (Basketball) . . . 25 20
1913 30 k. blue (Wrestling) 25 20
1914 30 k. purple (Hurdling) . . . 25 20
1915 30 k. brown (Show jumping) . . 25 20

1960. Europa. As T **129a** of Luxembourg but size $32\frac{1}{2} \times 22\frac{1}{2}$ mm.
1916 75 k. turquoise and green . . 50 25
1917 105 k. light and deep blue . . 75 25

1960. National Census.
1918 – 30 k. + 5 k. red and blue 20 10
1919 **285** 50 k. + 5 k. blue and turq 20 10
DESIGN—HORIZ: 30 k. Graph showing outlines of human faces.

286 "Justice" **287** Agah Efendi and Front Page of Newspaper "Turcamani Ahval"

1960. Trial of Ex-Government Officials.
1920 – 40 k. bistre and violet . 15 10
1921 – 105 k. red and green . . 15 10
1922 **286** 195 k. red and green . . 20 10
DESIGNS—HORIZ: 40 k. Badge of Turkish Army; 105 k. Trial scene.

1960. Turkish Press Centenary.
1923 **287** 40 k. purple and blue . 15 10
1924 60 k. purple and ochre . 20 10

288 U.N. Headquarters and Emblem

1960. 15th Anniv of U.N.O.
1925 – 90 k. ultramarine and blue 20 10
1926 **288** 105 k. brown and green 25 10
DESIGN—VERT: 90 k. U.N. emblem, "XV" and hand holding torch.

289 Revolutionaries

1960. Revolution of 27th May, 1960.
1927 **289** 10 k. grey and black . . 10 10
1928 – 30 k. violet 10 10
1929 – 40 k. red and black . . 10 10
1930 – 105 k. multicoloured . . 25 25
DESIGNS—HORIZ: 30 k. Kemal Ataturk and hand with torch; 105 k. Soldiers and wounded youth. VERT: 40 k. Prancing horse breaking chain.

290 Faculty Building

1960. 25th Anniv of History and Geography Faculty.
1931 **290** 30 k. black and green . 10 10
1932 – 40 k. black and buff . . 15 10
1933 – 60 k. olive, buff & green 20 10
DESIGNS—HORIZ: 40 k. Sun disc, cuneiform writing and map of Turkey. VERT: 60 k. Ataturk's statue.

291 "Communications and Transport" **292**

1961. 9th Central Treaty Organization Ministers' Meeting, Ankara.
1934 **291** 30 k. black and violet . 30 15
1935 – 40 k. black and green . 60 20
1936 – 75 k. black and blue . . 25 10
DESIGNS: 40 k. Road and rail construction, telephone and telegraph; 75 k. Parliament building, Ankara.

1961. 1st Anniv of 27th May Revolution.
1937 **292** 30 k. multicoloured . . 10 10
1938 – 40 k. green, cream & blk 15 10
1939 – 60 k. red, green and deep green 25 10
DESIGNS—HORIZ: 40 k. Boz Kurt and warriors. VERT: 60 k. "Progress".

293 North American F100 Jet and Rocket

1961. 50th Anniv of Turkish Air Force.
1940 – 38 k. orange, lake & blk . 20 10
1941 **293** 40 k. violet and red . . . 20 10
1942 – 75 k. buff, grey & black . 50 15
DESIGNS—HORIZ: 30 k. Rockets. VERT: 75 k. Ataturk, eagle and North American Super Sabre jets.

294 Old Observatory

1961. 50th Anniv of Kandilli Observatory, Istanbul.
1943 10 k. + 5 k. turq & green . . 10 10
1944 30 k. + 5 k. voilet & black . 20 10
1945 40 k. + 5 k. brown & sepia . 20 10
1946 75 k. + 5 k. olive and green . 40 15
DESIGNS—HORIZ: 10 k. Type **294**; 30 k. Observatory emblem; 75 k. Observatory building. VERT: 40 k. F. Gokmen.

295 Kemal Ataturk **295a**

1961.
1947 **295a** 1 k. brown 10 10
1948 5 k. blue 20 10
1949 **295** 10 k. mauve 25 10
1950 **295a** 10 k. sepia 50 10
1951 30 k. green . . . . . . 2·25 10
1952 10 l. vio (22 × 32 mm) . 5·50 15

296 Doves

1961. Europa.
1960 **296** 30 k. blue 60 50
1961 40 k. grey 60 50
1962 75 k. red . . . . 1·00 50

297 Tulip and Cogwheel **298** "The Constitution"

1961. Centenary of Professional and Technical Schools.
1963 **297** 30 k. pink, silver and slate 10 10
1964 – 75 k. red, black & blue . 20 10
DESIGN—HORIZ: 75 k. Inscr "100 Yili 1861–1961" and tulip and cogwheel emblem.

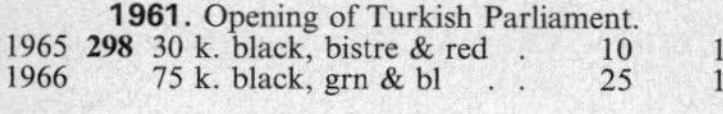

1961. Opening of Turkish Parliament.
1965 **298** 30 k. black, bistre & red . 10 10
1966 75 k. black, grn & bl . . 25 10

299 Insecticide-sprayers ("Malaria Eradication") **300** N.A.T.O. and Anniversary Emblem

1961. 15th Anniv of U.N.I.C.E.F.
1967 **299** 10 k. + 5 k. turquoise . . 10 10
1968 – 30 k. + 5 k. violet . . 20 10
1969 – 75 k. + 5 k. brown . . . 25 10
DESIGNS—HORIZ: 30 k. Mother and child ("Child Welfare"). VERT: 75 k. Mother giving pasteurized milk to children ("Education on Nourishment")

1962. 10th Anniv of Turkish Admission to N.A.T.O.
1970 – 75 k. black, silver & blue 30 10
1971 **300** 105 k. black, silver & red 40 15
DESIGN—VERT: 75 k. Peace dove over N.A.T.O. and Anniv emblems.

301 Mosquito on Map of Turkey **302** "Strelitzia reginae"

1962. Malaria Eradication.
1972 **301** 30 k. + 5 k. brown . . 15 10
1973 75 k. + 5 k. mve & blk . 25 10

1962. Flowers. Multicoloured.
1974 30 k. + 10 k. "Poinsettia pulcherrima" 35 15
1975 40 k. + 10 k. Type **302** . . . 40 20
1976 75 k. + 10 k. "Nymphea alba" 75 25

303 Scouts in Camp **304** Soldier (Victory Monument, Ankara)

1962. 50th Anniv of Turkish Scout Movement.
1977 **303** 30 k. red, black & green 25 10
1978 – 60 k. red, black & lilac . 35 10
1979 – 105 k. red, black & brn . 35 10
DESIGNS: 60 k. Two scouts with flag; 105 k. Wolf Cub and Brownie.

1962. 40th Anniv of Battle of Dumlupinar.
1980 **304** 30 k. green 15 10
1981 – 40 k. brown and black . 20 10
1982 – 75 k. grey 35 10
DESIGNS—HORIZ: 40 k. Ox-cart carrying ammunition. (Victory Monument, Ankara). VERT: 75 k. Kemal Ataturk.

305 Europa "Tree" **306** Shrine of the Virgin Mary

1962. Europa.
1983 **305** 75 k. sepia and green . . 30 20
1984 105 k. sepia and red . . 35 30
1985 195 k. sepia and blue . . 75 60

1962. Tourist Issue. Multicoloured.
1986 30 k. Type **306** 20 10
1987 40 k. Interior 25 15
1988 75 k. Exterior 30 10
1989 105 k. Statue of the Virgin . 25 15
DESIGNS: The 40 and 75 k. show horiz views of the Virgin Mary's house at Ephesus.

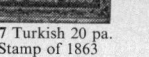

307 Turkish 20 pa. Stamp of 1863 **308** Julian's Column, Ankara

1963. Stamp Centenary.
1990 **307** 10 k. black, yell & brn . 10 10
1991 – 30 k. black, pink & vio . 20 10
1992 – 40 k. black, blue & turq 20 10
1993 – 75 k. black, pink & brn . 35 15
DESIGNS—Turkish stamps of 1863: 30 k. (1 pi.); 40 k. (2 pi.); 75 k. (5 pi.).

1963.
1994 **308** 1 k. green and olive . . 10 10
1995 1 k. violet 10 10
1996 – 5 k. sepia and brown . . 10 10
1997 – 10 k. mauve and green . 15 10
1998 – 30 k. black and violet . . 75 10
1999 – 50 k. green, brn & yell . 60 10
2000 – 60 k. grey . . . . . . 1·10 10
2001 – 100 k. brown 65 10
2002 – 150 k. green . . . . . 4·25 25
DESIGNS—HORIZ: 5 k. Ethnographic Museum; 10 k. Citadel; 30 k. Educational Establishment, Gazi; 50 k. Ataturk's Mausoleum; 60 k. Presidential Palace, Ankara; 100 k. Ataturk's house; 150 k. National Museum, Ankara.

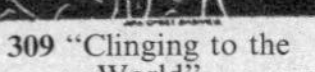

309 "Clinging to the World" **310** Wheat and Census Graph

1963. Freedom from Hunger.
2010 **309** 30 k. deep blue and blue . . . 10 10
2011 – 40 k. dp brown & brown . . . 15 15
2012 – 75 k. dp green & green . . . 25 20
DESIGNS: 40 k. Sowers; 75 k. Emblem and Globe within hands.

1963. Agricultural Census. Unissued stamps with "KASIM 1960" obliterated with bars. Inscr "UMUMI ZIRAAT SAYIMI".
2013 **310** 40 k. + 5 k. multicoloured . . . 20 20
2014 – 60 k. + 5 k. multicoloured . . . 25 25
DESIGN—HORIZ: 60 k. Wheat and chart.

311 Atomic Symbol on Map **312** Ucserefili Mosque

1963. 1st Anniv of Opening of Turkish Nuclear Research Centre.
2015 **311** 50 k. brown & dp brown . . . 20 10
2016 – 60 k. multicoloured . . . 25 15
2017 – 100 k. blue & ultram . . . 60 25
DESIGNS: 60 k. Various symbols; 100 k. Emblem of Turkish Atomic Energy Commission.

1963. 600th Anniv of Conquest of Edirne.
2018 **312** 10 k. green, ultramarine and blue . . . 10 10
2019 – 30 k. blue and red . . . 15 10
2020 – 60 k. multicoloured . . . 20 10
2021 – 100 k. multicoloured . . . 55 20
DESIGNS—HORIZ: 30 k. Meric Bridge; 60 k. Kum Kasri (building). VERT: 100 k. Sultan Amurat I.

313 Soldier and Sun

1963. 600th Anniv of Turkish Army.
2022 **313** 50 k. black, red & blue . . . 20 10
2023 100 k. black, red & bistre . . . 35 25

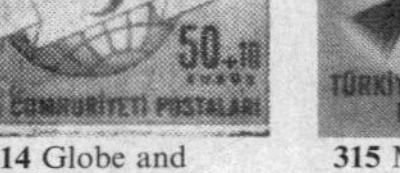

314 Globe and Emblems **315** Mithat Pasha (founder)

1963. Red Cross Centenary. Multicoloured.
2024 50 k. + 10 k. Type **314** . . . 25 25
2025 60 k. + 10 k. "Flowers" emblem (vert) . . . 35 30
2026 100 k. + 10 k. Three emblems on flags . . . 45 40

1963. Centenary of Turkish Agricultural Bank.
2027 – 30 k. brown, green and yellow . . . 10 10
2028 – 50 k. blue and lilac . . . 20 10
2029 **315** 60 k. green and black . . . 25 20
DESIGNS—HORIZ: 30 k. Ploughing and irrigation; 50 k. Agricultural Bank, Ankara.

316 Exhibition Hall, Istanbul, and 5 pi. stamp of 1863

1963. "Istanbul '63" International Stamp Exn.
2030 **316** 10 k. salmon, black and yellow . . . 10 10
2031 – 50 k. green, red and black . . . 15 10
2032 – 60 k. sepia, black & blue . . . 20 10
2033 – 100 k. violet and purple . . . 40 30
2034 – 130 k. brown, orge & yell . . . 60 40
DESIGNS: 50 k. Sultan Ahmed's Mosque, Obelisk and 3 pi. on 2 pa. Nationalist Government (Angora) stamp of 1920; 60 k. Istanbul skyline and 10 pi. (Angora) stamp of 1922; 100 k. Rumeli Fort and 6 k. stamp of 1929/30; 130 k. Ankara Fort and 12½ k. air stamp of 1934.

317 "Co-operation"

1963. Europa.
2035 **317** 50 k. orange, blk & red . . . 25 10
2036 130 k. blue, black & grn . . . 45 25

318 Ataturk and Old Parliament House **319** Kemal Ataturk

1963. 40th Anniv of Turkish Republic. Multicoloured.
2037 30 k. Type **318** . . . 20 10
2038 50 k. Ataturk and flag . . . 25 15
2039 60 k. Ataturk and new Parliament House . . . 35 20

1963. 25th Death Anniv of Kemal Ataturk.
2040 **319** 50 k. multicoloured . . . 20 15
2041 60 k. multicoloured . . . 30 20

320 R.S. Dag (painter) **321** N.A.T.O. Emblem and "XV"

1964. Cultural Celebrities.
2042 – 1 k. black and red . . . 10 10
2043 – 5 k. black and green . . . 10 10
2044 **320** 10 k. black and brown . . . 10 10
2045 – 50 k. black and blue . . . 45 10
2046 – 60 k. black and grey . . . 95 15
2047 – 100 k. ultram & blue . . . 1·00 10
2048 – 130 k. black and green . . . 2·75 20
PORTRAITS: 1 k. H. R. Gurpinar (romanticist, birth centenary); 5 k. J. H. Izmirli (savant, 20th death anniv); 10 k. Type **320** (20th death anniv); 50 k. R. Z. M. Ekrem (writer, 50th death anniv); 60 k. A. M. Pasa (commander, 125th birth anniv); 100 k. A. Rasim (writer, birth centenary); 130 k. S. Zeki (mathematician, birth centenary).

1964. 15th Anniv of N.A.T.O.
2049 **321** 50 k. red, violet & turq . . . 25 10
2050 – 130 k. black and red . . . 50 15
DESIGN: 130 k. N.A.T.O. emblem and laurel sprig.

322 "Europa" holding Torch

1964. 15th Anniv of Council of Europe.
2051 **332** 50 k. blue, brown & yell . . . 35 10
2052 – 130 k. orange, ultramarine and blue . . . 50 25
DESIGN: 130 k. Torch and circlet of stars.

323 Haga Mosque, Istanbul **324** Kars Castle

1964. Tourist Issue.
2053 **323** 50 k. green and olive . . . 25 15
2054 – 50 k. red and purple . . . 25 15
2055 – 50 k. violet and blue . . . 25 15
2056 – 60 k. green, black & pur . . . 35 20
2057 – 60 k. brown and sepia . . . 35 20
DESIGNS—HORIZ: No. 2054 Temple of Zeus, Silifke; 2055 Amasra.VERT: No. 2056 Mersin; 2057 Augustus' Temple, Ankara.

1964. 900th Anniv of Conquest of Kars.
2058 **324** 50 k. black and lilac . . . 20 15
2059 – 130 k. multicoloured . . . 45 25
DESIGN: 130 k. Alpaslan warrior.

325 Europa "Flower" **326** Grazing Cattle

1964. Europa.
2060 **325** 50 k. blue, grey & orge . . . 50 20
2061 130 k. purple, green & bl . . . 1·00 60

1964. Animal Protection Fund. Multicoloured.
2062 10 k. + 5 k. Type **326** . . . 10 10
2063 30 k. + 5 k. Horned sheep . . . 20 10
2064 50 k. + 5 k. Horses . . . 30 10
2065 60 k. + 5 k. Three horned sheep . . . 40 10
2066 100 k. + 5 k. Dairy cows . . . 60 25
The 30 k. and 60 k. are vert.

327 Running **328** Mustafa Resit

1964. Olympic Games, Tokyo.
2067 **327** 10 k. + 5 k. black, red and brown . . . 15 10
2068 – 50 k. + 5 k. black, red and olive . . . 25 10
2069 – 60 k. + 5 k. black, red and blue . . . 25 10
2070 – 100 k. + 5 k. black, red and violet . . . 50 25
DESIGNS—VERT: 50 k. Torch-bearer; 60 k. Wrestling; 100 k. Throwing the discus.

1964. 125th Anniv of Reformation Decrees. Multicoloured.
2071 50 k. Mustafa Resit and the pashas (horiz 48 × 32 mm) . . . 25 10
2072 60 k. Type **328** . . . 25 10
2073 100 k. As 50 k. . . . 40 15

329 Kemal Ataturk **330** Glider

1964.
2074 **329** 1 k. green . . . 10 10
2075 5 k. blue . . . 10 10
2076 10 k. blue . . . 20 10
2077 25 k. green . . . 50 10
2078 30 k. purple . . . 55 10
2079 50 k. brown . . . 1·40 10
2080 150 k. orange . . . 2·75 10

1965. 40th Anniv of Turkish Civil Aviation League. Multicoloured.
2081 60 k. Parachutist . . . 25 10
2082 90 k. Type **330** . . . 35 10
2083 130 k. Ataturk and squadron of aircraft . . . 80 10
The 60 k. and 130 k. are vert.

331 CENTO Emblem

1965. Completion of CENTO Telecommunications Projects. Multicoloured.
2084 30 k. Type **331** . . . 10 10
2085 50 k. Aerial mast (vert) . . . 15 10
2086 75 k. Hand pressing button (inaugural ceremony) . . . 25 10

332 Monument and Soldiers

1965. 50th Anniv of Battle of the Dardanelles. Multicoloured.
2087 50 k. + 10 k. Wreath and map . . . 20 20
2088 90 k. + 10 k. Type **332** . . . 25 20
2089 130 k. + 10 k. Dardanelles Monument and flag (vert) . . . 50 35

333 Beach at Ordu

1965. Tourism. Multicoloured.
2090 30 k. Type **333** . . . 20 15
2091 50 k. Manavgat Falls . . . 25 10
2092 60 k. Istanbul . . . 25 10
2093 100 k. Urfa . . . 40 20
2094 130 k. Alanya . . . 70 25

334 I.T.U. Emblem and Symbols

1965. I.T.U. Centenary.
2095 **334** 50 k. multicoloured . . . 25 20
2096 130 k. multicoloured . . . 55 30

335 I.C.Y. Emblem

1965. International Co-operation Year.
2097 **335** 100 k. red, green and salmon . . . 35 10
2098 130 k. violet, green and grey . . . 50 25

336 "Co-operation" **337** R. N. Guntekin

1965. 1st Anniv of Regional Development Co-operation Pact. Multicoloured.
2099 50 k. Type **336** . . . 25 10
2100 75 k. Globe and flags of Turkey, Iran and Pakistan . . . 30 15

1965. Cultural Celebrities.
2101 **337** 1 k. black and red . . . 10 10
2102 – 5 k. black and blue . . . 10 10
2103 – 10 k. black and ochre . . . 15 10
2104 – 25 k. black and brown . . . 30 10
2105 – 30 k. black and grey . . . 30 10
2106 – 50 k. black and yellow . . . 65 10
2107 – 60 k. black and purple . . . 65 10
2108 – 150 k. black and green . . . 1·10 10
2109 – 220 k. black and brown . . . 90 35
PORTRAITS: 5 k. Dr. B. O Akalin; 10 k. T. Fikret; 25 k. T. Cemil; 30 k. Ahmet Vefik Pasa; 50 k. O. Seyfettin; 60 k. K. Mimaroglu; 150 k. H. Z. Usakligil; 220 k. Y. K. Beyatli.

338 Kemal Ataturk and Signature **339** Tobacco Plant

1965.
2110 **338** 1 k. black and mauve . . . 10 10
2111 5 k. black and green . . . 15 10
2112 10 k. black and blue . . . 15 10
2113 50 k. black and gold . . . 40 10
2114 150 k. black and silver . . . 85 10
See also Nos. 2170/4.

1965. 2nd International Tobacco Congress. Mult.
2115 30 k. + 5 k. Type **339** . . . 25 20
2116 50 k. + 5 k. Leander's Tower and tobacco leaves (horiz) . . . 25 20
2117 100 k. + 5 k. Tobacco leaf . . . 60 40

340 Europa "Sprig"

341 Civilians supporting Map

1965. Europa.

2118 340 50 k. green, blue & grey . 50 35
2119 130 k. grn, blk & ochre . 1·25 1·00

1965. National Census. Inscr "GENEL NUFUS SAYIMI".

2120 341 10 k. multicoloured . . . 10 10
2121 – 50 k. light green, green and black 20 10
2122 – 100 k. black, bl & orge . 25 15

DESIGNS—HORIZ: 50 k. Year "1965". VERT: 100 k. Human eye and figure.

342 Ankara Castle and Airliner

1965. "Ankara '65" National Stamp Exn. Inscr "I. MILLI PUL SERGISI".

2123 342 10 k. red, yellow & violet 10 10
2124 – 30 k. multicoloured . . . 15 10
2125 – 50 k. blue, red & olive . 20 10
2126 – 100 k. multicoloured . 40 15

DESIGNS: 30 k. Archer; 50 k. Horseman; 100 k. Three thematic "stamps" and medal.

343 Training-ship "Savarona"

344 Halide E. Adivar

1965. Turkish Naval Society Congress.

2128 343 50 k. brown and blue . . 35 20
2129 – 60 k. indigo and blue . . 45 20
2130 – 100 k. brown and blue . 65 30
2131 – 130 k. purple and blue . 1·10 60
2132 – 220 k. black and blue . 1·90 90

DESIGNS: 60 k. Submarine "Piri Reis"; 100 k. Destroyer "Alpaslan"; 130 k. Destroyer "Gelibolu"; 220 k. Destroyer "Gemlik".

1966. Cultural Celebrities.

2133 – 25 k. brown and grey . . 50 10
2134 – 30 k. brown and mauve . 25 10
2135 344 50 k. black and blue . . 25 10
2136 – 60 k. brown and green . 60 10
2137 – 130 k. black and blue . 1·50 15

PORTRAITS: 25 k. H. S. Arel; 30 k. K. Akdik; 60 k. Abdurrahman Seref; 130 k. Naima.

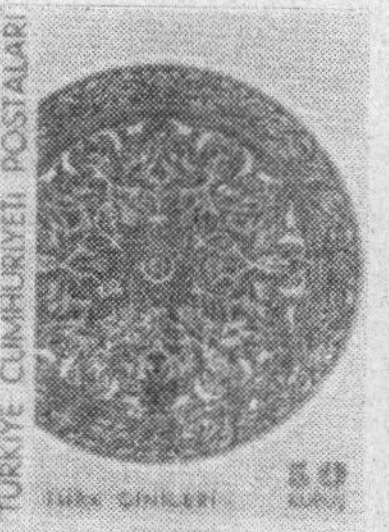
345 Roof Panel, Green Mausoleum, Burs

346 Volleyball

1966. Turkish Faience. Multicoloured.

2138 50 k. Type 345 . . . . . . 35 20
2139 60 k. "Spring Flowers", Sultan Mausoleum, Istanbul . . . 1·10 75
2140 130 k. 16th-cent tile, Iznik . . 75 40

1966. Int Military Volleyball Championships.

2141 346 50 k. multicoloured . . . 35 20

347 Bodrum

348 Golden Pitcher

1966. Tourism. Multicoloured.

2142 10 k. Type 347 . . . . . . 10 10
2143 30 k. Kusadasi 55 40
2144 50 k. Anadoluhisari 15 10
2145 90 k. Marmaris 30 20
2146 100 k. Izmir 35 25

The 50 k. and 100 k. are horiz.

1966. Ancient Works of Art. Multicoloured.

2147 30 k. + 5 k. Ivory eagle and rabbit 35 20
2148 50 k. + 5 k. Deity in basalt . 45 25
2149 60 k. + 5 k. Bronze bull . . 65 35
2150 90 k. + 5 k. Type 348 . . . 80 40

The 30 k. is horiz.

349 View of Dam

1966. Inaug of Keban Dam. Multicoloured.

2151 50 k. Type 349 . . . . . . 15 10
2152 60 k. Keban valley and bridge 45 10

350 King Faisal

1966. Visit of King of Saudi Arabia.

2153 350 100 k. deep red and red 55 30

351 "Stamp" and "Postmark"

1966. "Balkanfila" Stamp Exhibition, Istanbul. Multicoloured.

2154 50 k. Type 351 . . . . . 15 10
2155 60 k. Stamp "flower" . . . 20 15
2156 75 k. "Stamps" in form of display frames 25 20

353 Sultan Suleiman on Horseback

354 Europa "Ship"

1966. 400th Death Anniv of Sultan Suleiman. Multicoloured.

2158 60 k. Type 353 . . . . . . 25 20
2159 90 k. Mausoleum, Istanbul . . 55 25
2160 130 k. Sultan Suleiman (profile) 1·25 65

1966. Europa.

2161 354 50 k. ultram, bl & blk . 75 25
2162 130 k. purple, lilac & blk 75 55

355 Grand Hotel Ephesus, Izmir

1966. 33rd International Fairs Union Congress, Izmir. Multicoloured.

2163 50 k. + 5 k. Type 355 . . . 20 10
2164 60 k. + 5 k. Konak Square, Izmir (vert) 25 15
2165 130 k. + 5 k. Izmir Fair . . 35 20

356 "Education, Science and Culture"

1966. 20th Anniv of U.N.E.S.C.O.

2166 356 130 k. chestnut, yellow and brown 45 20

357 University of Technology

358 Ataturk (equestrian statue)

1966. 10th Anniv of Middle East University of Technology. Multicoloured.

2167 50 k. Type 357 . . . . . . 15 10
2168 100 k. Atomic symbol 25 10
2169 130 k. Symbols of the sciences 35 15

1966. As Nos. 2110/14.

2170 338 25 k. black and green . . 15 10
2171 30 k. black and pink . . 15 10
2172 50 k. black and violet . . 50 10
2173 90 k. black and brown . . 75 10
2174 100 k. black and drab . . 80 10

1966. Greetings Card Stamp.

2175 358 10 k. black and yellow . . 15 10

See also Nos. 2218/9, 2257/8, 2303 and 2418.

359 De Havilland Dragon Rapide

360 A. Mithat (author)

1967. Air. Aircraft.

2176 359 10 k. black and pink . . 25 10
2177 – 60 k. red, black & grn . . 25 10
2178 – 130 k. red, black & blue . 65 20
2179 – 220 k. red, sepia and ochre 1·10 35
2180 – 270 k. red, blue and salmon 1·75 50

DESIGNS: 60 k. Fokker F27 Friendship; 130 k. Douglas DC-9-30; 220 k. Douglas DC-3; 270 k. Vickers Viscount 700.

1967. Cultural Celebrities.

2181 360 1 k. black and green . . . 10 10
2182 – 5 k. black and ochre . . 10 10
2183 – 50 k. black and violet . . 85 10
2184 – 100 k. black and yellow . 1·50 10
2185 – 150 k. black and yellow . 2·75 10

PORTRAITS: 5 k. T. Reis (naval commander); 50 k. S. Mehmet (statesman); 100 k. Nedim (philosopher); 150 k. O. Hamdi (painter).

361 Karogoz and Hacivat (puppets)

1967. International Tourist Year. Multicoloured.

2186 50 k. Type 361 . . . . . . 40 10
2187 60 k. Sword and shield game . 50 15
2188 90 k. Military Band 80 40
2189 100 k. Karagoz (puppet) (vert) 95 45

362 "Vaccination"

363 Fallow Deer

1967. 250th Anniv of 1st Smallpox Vaccination, Edirne.

2190 362 100 k. multicoloured . . 40 15

1967. Game Animals. Multicoloured.

2191 50 k. Type 363 . . . . . . 45 10
2192 60 k. Wild goat 50 20
2193 100 k. Brown bear 75 25
2194 130 k. Wild boar . . . . . 1·00 35

364 Emblem and Footballers

365 Cogwheels

1967. 20th Int Junior Football Tournament. Mult.

2195 50 k. Type 364 . . . . . . 75 15
2196 130 k. Footballers and emblem 95 35

1967. Europa.

2197 365 100 k. + 10 k. mult . . . 40 15
2198 130 k. + 10 k. mult . . . 65 25

366 Kemal Ataturk

367 Road Junction on Map

1967.

2199 366 10 k. black and green . . 1·00 10
2200 50 k. black and pink . . 1·00 10

1967. Opening of "E 5" Motorway. Mult.

2201 60 k. + 5 k. Type 367 . . . 20 10
2202 130 k. + 5 k. Motorway map and emblem (vert) 40 15

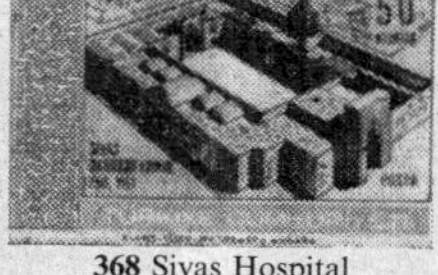
368 Sivas Hospital

1967. 750th Anniv of Sivas Hospital.

2203 368 50 k. multicoloured . . . 25 10

369 Selim Tarcan and Olympic Rings

1967. 1st Turkish Olympic Competitions, Istanbul. Multicoloured.

2204 50 k. Type 369 . . . . . . 35 25
2205 60 k. Pierre de Coubertin and Olympic Rings 35 25

370 St. John's Church, Ephesus

371 Common Kestrel

1967. Pope Paul VI's Visit to Virgin Mary's House, Ephesus. Multicoloured.

2206 130 k. Interior of Virgin Mary's House, Ephesus 35 15
2207 220 k. Type 370 . . . . . . 60 20

1967. Air. Birds.

2208 371 10 k. brown and salmon 85 15
2209 – 60 k. brown and yellow . 55 15
2210 – 130 k. purple and blue . 1·10 30
2211 – 220 k. sepia and green . 1·40 45
2212 – 270 k. brown and lilac . 1·75 55

DESIGNS: 60 k. Imperial eagle; 130 k. Pallid harrier; 220 k. European sparrow hawk; 270 k. Common buzzard.

372 Exhibition Emblem

1967. International Ceramics Exn, Istanbul.

2213 372 50 k. multicoloured . . . 30 15

373 Emblem and Istanbul Skyline

374 "Stamps" and Map

1967. Congress of International Large Dams Commission, Istanbul.

2214 373 130 k. blue and drab . . 30 20

1967. "Izmir '67" Stamp Exhibition. Mult.

2215 50 k. Type 374 . . . . . . 20 12
2216 60 k. "Stamps" and grapes . 25 20

1967. Greetings Card Stamps. As T 358.

2218 10 k. black and green 25 10
2219 10 k. black and red 25 10

DESIGNS: Equestrian statues of Ataturk at: No. 2218 Samsun; No. 2219 Izmir.

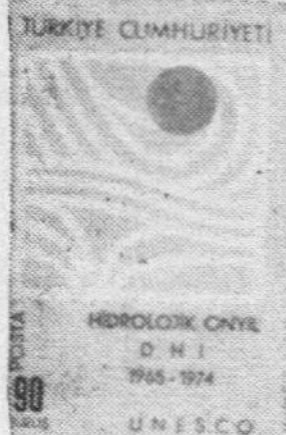

375 Decade Emblem 376 Girl with Angora Cat

1967. International Hydrological Decade.
2220 375 90 k. yellow, blk & grn . 25 10
2221 130 k. yellow, blk & lilac 25 15

1967. 125th Anniv of Turkish Veterinary Medical Service. Multicoloured.
2222 50 k. Type 376 . . . . 50 10
2223 60 k. Horse 60 10

377 Human Rights Emblem 378 Kemal Ataturk

1968. Human Rights Year.
2224 377 50 k. multicoloured . . . 10 10
2225 130 k. multicoloured . . 15 10

1968.
2226 378 1 k. blue and light blue . 10 10
2227 5 k. green and lt green . . 10 10
2228 50 k. brown and yellow . 1·25 10
2229 200 k. brown and pink . 2·50 15

379 "The Investiture"

1968. Turkish Book Miniatures. Multicoloured.
2230 50 k. Type 379 . . . . 25 20
2231 60 k. "Suleiman the Magnificent receiving an ambassador" (vert) 35 20
2232 90 k. "The Sultan's Archery Practice" 45 30
2233 100 k. "The Musicians" . . . 65 35

380 Scales of Justice

1968. Turkish Courts Centenary. Multicoloured. (a) Supreme Court.
2234 50 k. Type 380 . . . . 20 15
2235 60 k. Ahmet Cevdet Pasha (president) and scroll . . . 25 20

(b) Court of Appeal.
2236 50 k. Book 20 15
2237 60 k. Mithat Pasha (first president) and scroll . . . 25 20

381 W.H.O. Emblem 382 Europa "Key"

1968. 20th Anniv of W.H.O.
2238 381 130 k. + 10 k. yellow, black and blue 55 30

1968. Europa.
2239 382 100 k. yellow, red & blue 75 25
2240 130 k. yellow, red & grn . 1·50 85

383 Etem Pasha and Dr. Marko

1968. Turkish Red Crescent Fund. Multicoloured.
2241 50 k. + 10 k. Type 383 . . 35 20
2242 60 k. + 10 k. Omer Pasha and Dr. Abdullah 40 35
2243 100 k. + 10 k. Kemal Ataturk and Dr. Refik Saydam in front of Red Crescent Headquarters (vert) . . . 50 40

384 "Kismet" 385 "Protection against Usury" (after Koseoglu)

1968. Sadun Boro's World Voyage in Ketch "Kismet".
2244 384 50 k. multicoloured . . 45 15

1968. Centenary of Pawnbroking Office, Istanbul.
2245 385 50 k. multicoloured . . 30 20

386 Battle of Sakarya and Obverse of Medal

1968. Independence Medal. Multicoloured.
2246 50 k. Type 386 . . . . . . 20 20
2247 130 k. National Anthem and reverse of medal 45 30

387 Old and New Emblems within "100"

1968. Centenary of Galatasaray High School. Multicoloured.
2248 50 k. Type 387 . . . . . . 20 20
2249 60 k. Gulbaba offering flowers to Bayazet II 30 20
2250 100 k. Kemal Ataturk and School Building 45 35

388 President De Gaulle 389 Kemal Ataturk

1968. President De Gaulle's Visit to Turkey.
2251 388 130 k. multicoloured . . 75 25

1968. 30th Death Anniv of Kemal Ataturk.
2252 389 30 k. black and yellow . 15 10
2253 – 50 k. black and green . 15 10
2254 – 60 k. black and turq . . 50 20
2255 – 100 k. black, green and bistre 40 20
2256 – 250 k. multicoloured . 1·25 40
DESIGNS: 50 k. Ataturk's Cenotaph; 60 k. Ataturk at railway carriage window. ($32\frac{1}{2} \times 43$ mm): 100 k. Ataturk's portrait and "address to youth"; 250 k. Ataturk in military uniform.

1968. Greetings Card Stamps. As T 358 but dated "1968".
2257 10 k. black and mauve . . . 10 10
2258 10 k. black and blue 10 10
DESIGNS: Equestrian statues of Ataturk at: No. 2257 Antakya; No. 2258 Zonguldak.

390 Ince Minara Mosque, Konya 391 Dove and N.A.T.O. Emblem

1968. Historic Buildings.
2259 390 1 k. sepia and brown . . 10 10
2260 – 10 k. maroon and purple 15 10
2261 – 50 k. green and grey . . . 60 10
2262 – 100 k. green & lt green . 1·75 10
2263 – 200 k. blue & light blue . 1·25 10
DESIGNS: 10 k. Doner Kumbet (tomb), Kayseri; 50 k. Karatay University, Konya; 100 k. Ortakoy Mosque, Istanbul; 200 k. Ulu Mosque, Divrigi.

1969. 20th Anniv of N.A.T.O.
2264 391 50 k. + 10 k. black, blue and green 35 15
2265 – 130 k. + 10 k. gold, blue and deep blue 45 40
DESIGN: 130 k. Stars around globe and N.A.T.O. emblem.

392 "Education"

1969. Turkish Economy.
2266 392 1 k. black and red 10 10
2267 1 k. black and green . . . 10 10
2268 1 k. black and violet . . 10 10
2269 1 k. black and brown . . 10 10
2270 1 k. black and grey . . . 10 10
2271 – 50 k. brown and ochre . 40 10
2272 – 90 k. black and olive . 75 10
2273 – 100 k. red and black . . 65 10
2274 – 180 k. violet and orange . 1·75 10
DESIGNS: 50 k. Farm workers and tractor ("Agriculture"); 90 k. Ladle, factory and cogwheel ("Industry"); 100 k. Road sign and graph ("Highways"); 180 k. Derricks ("Oil Industry").

393 I.L.O Emblem

1969. 50th Anniv of I.L.O.
2275 393 130 k. red and black . . 25 10

394 "Hafsa Sultan" (unknown artist) 395 Colonnade

1969. Hafsa Sultan (medical pioneer) Commem.
2276 394 60 k. multicoloured . . . 30 10

1969. Europa.
2277 395 100 k. multicoloured . . 40 25
2278 130 k. multicoloured . . 75 40

396 Kemal Ataturk in 1919 397 Symbolic Map of Istanbul

1969. 50th Anniv of Kemal Ataturk's Landing at Samsun. Multicoloured.
2279 50 k. Type 396 . . . . 20 15
2280 60 k. Cargo liner "Bandirma" (horiz) 50 15

1969. 22nd Int Chambers of Commerce Congress, Istanbul.
2281 397 130 k. multicoloured . . 20 10

398 "Suleiman the Great holding Audience" (16th-cent Turkish miniature) 399 Kemal Ataturk in Civilian Dress

1969. 5th Anniv of Regional Co-operation for Development. Multicoloured.
2282 50 k. Type 398 . . . . 30 15
2283 80 k. "Kneeling Servant" (17th-cent Persian) 45 20
2284 130 k. "Lady on Balcony" (18th-cent Mogul–Pakistan) 65 40

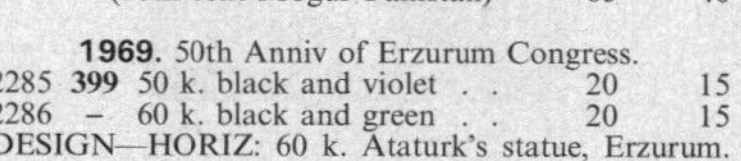

1969. 50th Anniv of Erzurum Congress.
2285 399 50 k. black and violet . . 20 15
2286 – 60 k. black and green . . 20 15
DESIGN—HORIZ: 60 k. Ataturk's statue, Erzurum.

401 Red Cross Societies' Emblems

1969. 21st International Red Cross Conf, Istanbul.
2291 401 100 k. + 10 k. red, blue and ultramarine 35 20
2292 – 130 k. + 10 k. mult . . 40 20
DESIGN: 130 k. Conference emblem and silhouette of Istanbul.

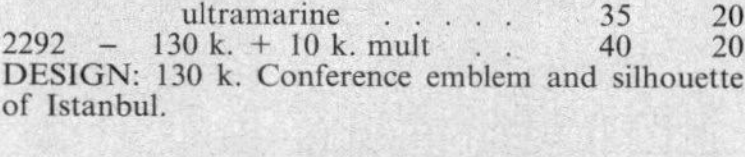

402 Congress Hall

1969. 50th Anniv of Sivas Congress.
2293 402 50 k. purple, blk and red 20 15
2294 – 60 k. olive, black & yell . 25 15
DESIGN: 60 k. Congress delegates.

403 Halay Scarf Dance

1969. Turkish Folk-dances. Multicoloured.
2295 30 k. Bar dancers 15 15
2296 50 k. Caydacira "candle" dance 30 20
2297 60 k. Type 403 . . . . 35 25
2298 100 k. Kilic-Kalkan sword dance 60 25
2299 130 k. Zeybek dance (vert) . 1·25 50

404 Bleriot XI "Prince Celaladdin"

1969. 55th Anniv of First Turkish Airmail Service.
2300 404 60 k. deep blue & blue . 40 10
2301 – 75 k. black and bistre . . 25 15
DESIGN: 75 k. 1914 First Flight cover.

405 "Kutadgu Bilig"

1969. 900th Anniv of "Kutadgu Bilig" (political manual) Compilation.
2302 405 130 k. brown, gold and bistre 25 10

1969. Greetings Card Stamp. As T 358.
2303 10 k. brown and green . . . 10 10
DESIGN: 10 k. Equestrian statue of Ataturk at Bursa.

406 "Ataturk's Arrival" (S. Tuna)

1969. 50th Anniv of Kemal Ataturk's Arrival in Ankara. Multicoloured.

2304 50 k. Type **406** 30 10
2305 60 k. Ataturk's motorcade . . 30 15

407 "Erosion Control"

1970. Nature Conservation Year. Multicoloured.

2306 50 k. + 10 k. Type **407** . . . 25 20
2307 60 k. + 10 k. "Protection of Flora" 40 25
2308 130 k. + 10 k. "Protection of Wildlife" 90 75

408 Bosphorus Bridge (model)
(Illustration reduced. Actual size 79 × 30½ mm)

1970. Commencement of Work on Bosphorus Bridge. Multicoloured.

2309 60 k. Type **408** 50 15
2310 130 k. Symbolic bridge linking Europe and Asia 75 50

409 Ataturk and Signature

410 Education Year Emblem

1970.

2311 **409** 1 k. brown and red . . . 10 10
2312 50 k. green and olive . . 25 10

1970. International Education Year.

2313 **410** 130 k. blue, purple & mve 25 10

411 Turkish Pavilion Emblem

412 Kemal Ataturk

1970. World Fair "Expo '70", Osaka, Japan. Multicoloured.

2314 50 k. Type **411** 15 10
2315 100 k. Turkish pavilion and Expo emblem 30 10

1970.

2316 **412** 5 k. black and silver . . 10 10
2317 30 k. black and bistre . . 25 10
2318 50 k. black and pink . . 35 10
2319 75 k. black and lilac . . 85 10
2320 100 k. black and blue . . 60 10

413 Opening Ceremony

1970. 50th Anniv of Turkish National Assembly. Multicoloured.

2321 50 k. Type **413** 15 10
2322 60 k. First Assembly in session 20 10

414 Emblem of Cartography Directorate

1970. "75 Years of Turkish Cartography". Multicoloured.

2323 50 k. Type **414** 10 10
2324 60 k. Dornier Do-28 airplane and contour map 35 10
2325 100 k. Survey equipment . . 20 10
2326 130 k. Lt.-Gen. Mehmet Sevki Pasha and relief map of Turkey 25 10
Nos. 2324 and 2326 are larger, size 48 × 33 mm.

415 "Flaming Sun"

1970. Europa.

2327 **415** 100 k. red, orange & blk 45 10
2328 130 k. green, orge & blk 75 25

416 New U.P.U. Headquarters Building

417 "Roe-deer" (Seker Ahmet Pasha)

1970. New U.P.U. Headquarters Building, Berne.

2329 **416** 60 k. black, blue & lt bl 15 10
2330 130 k. black, green and light green 25 10

1970. Turkish Paintings. Multicoloured.

2331 250 k. Type **417** 80 50
2332 250 k. "Lady with Mimosa" (Osman Hamdi) 80 50
See also Nos. 2349/50, 2364/5, 2396/7, 2416/17 and 2443/4.

418 "Turkish Folklore"

1970. "Ankara 70" National Stamp Exhibition. Multicoloured.

2333 10 k. "Tree" of stamps and open album (vert) 10 10
2334 50 k. Type **418** 25 10
2335 60 k. Ataturk statue and "stamps" 30 15

419 Fethiye (Turkey)

1970. 6th Anniv of Regional Co-operation for Development. Multicoloured.

2337 60 k. Type **419** 20 10
2338 80 k. Seeyo-Se-Pol Bridge, Isfahan (Iran) 25 10
2339 130 k. Saiful Malook Lake (Pakistan) 35 10
No. 2338 is larger 41 × 26 mm.

420 Tomb of Haci Bektas Veli

421 Symbolic "Fencer" and Globe

1970. 700th Death Anniv of Haci Bektas Veli (mystic). Multicoloured.

2340 30 k. Type **420** 10 10
2341 100 k. Sultan Balim's tomb (vert) 35 10
2342 180 k. Haci Bektas Veli (vert) 40 15
No. 2342 is larger, size 32 × 49 mm.

1970. World Fencing Championships.

2343 **421** 90 k. + 10 k. black, blue and light blue 25 10
2344 – 130 k. + 10 k. orange, green, black and blue . 30 10
DESIGN: 130 k. Modern fencer, folk-dancer and globe.

422 I.S.O. Emblem

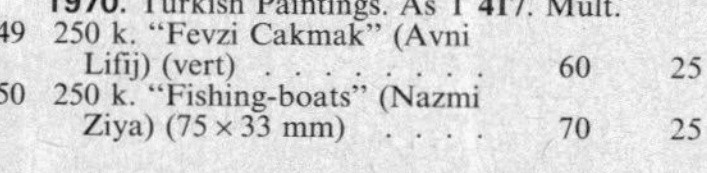

423 U.N. Emblem within Windmill

1970. 8th Int Standardisation Organisation General Assembly, Ankara.

2345 **422** 110 k. red, gold & black . 25 10
2346 150 k. blue, gold & black 30 15

1970. 25th Anniv of United Nations. Mult.

2347 100 k. Type **423** 30 10
2348 220 k. World's people supporting U.N. (vert) . . 40 15

1970. Turkish Paintings. As T **417**. Mult.

2349 250 k. "Fevzi Cakmak" (Avni Lifij) (vert) 60 25
2350 250 k. "Fishing-boats" (Nazmi Ziya) (75 × 33 mm) 70 25

424 Turkish Troops Advancing

1971. 50th Anniv of First Battle of Inonu.

2351 **424** 100 k. multicoloured . . 30 20
See also No. 2368.

425 Kemal Ataturk

429 Hands enclosing "Four Races"

428 "Turkish Village" (A.Sekur)

1971.

2352 **425** 5 k. blue and grey 15 10
2353 25 k. red and grey 40 10
2354 – 25 k. brown and pink . . 15 10
2355 **425** 100 k. violet and grey . . 75 10
2356 – 100 k. green and flesh . . 60 10
2357 – 250 k. blue and drab . . 1·25 10
2358 **425** 400 k. green and bistre . 1·50 10
DESIGNS: Nos. 2354, 2356 and 2357, Portraits similar to Type **425** but larger, 21 × 26 mm, and with face value at bottom right.

1971. Turkish Paintings. Multicoloured.

2364 250 k. Type **428** 65 25
2365 250 k. "Yildiz Palace Garden" (A. R. Bicakcilar) 65 25
See also Nos. 2396/7, 2416/17 and 2443/4.

1971. Racial Equality Year.

2366 **429** 100 k. multicoloured . . 20 10
2367 250 k. multicoloured . . 25 10

1971. 50th Anniv of Second Battle of Inonu. Design similar to T **424**. Multicoloured.

2368 100 k. Turkish machine-gunners 40 10

430 Europa Chain

431 Pres. C. Gursel

1971. Europa.

2369 **430** 100 k. violet, yell & blue 55 25
2370 150 k. green, red & orge 85 40

1971. 11th Anniv of May 27th 1960 Revolution.

2371 **431** 100 k. multicoloured . . 30 10

432 Lockhead Super Starfighter

433 "Care of Children"

1971. Air. "60 Years of Turkish Aviation". Multicoloured.

2372 110 k. Type **432** 60 10
2373 200 k. Victory Monument, Afyon and aircraft 85 10
2374 250 k. Air Force emblem and jet fighters (horiz) 95 10
2375 325 k. Lockheed Super Starfighters and pilot . . . 1·50 10
2376 400 k. Bleriot XI airplane of 1911 (horiz) . . . . . . 1·25 10
2377 475 k. Hezarfen Celebi's "bird flight" from Galata Tower (horiz) . . . . 2·00 15

1971. 50th Anniv of Children's Protection Society.

2378 **433** 50 k. + 10 k. red, pur & blk 20 10
2379 – 100 k. + 15 k. mult . . 25 15
2380 – 110 k. + 15 k. mult . . 35 15
DESIGNS—VERT: 100 k. Child standing on protective hand. HORIZ: 110 k. Mother and child.

434 Selimiye Mosque, Edirne

1971. 7th Anniv of Regional Co-operation for Development Pact. Mosques. Multicoloured.

2381 100 k. Type **434** 20 15
2382 150 k. Chalharbagh Mosque School (Iran) 25 15
2383 200 k. Badshahi Mosque (Pakistan) (horiz) 50 25

435 Alpaslan (Seljuk leader) and Cavalry

1971. 900th Anniv of Battle of Malazgirt.

2384 **435** 100 k. multicoloured . . 25 15
2385 – 250 k. red, yellow & blk 55 25
DESIGN: 250 k. Seljuk mounted archer.

436 Officer and Troop Column

1971. 50th Anniv of Battle of Sakarya.

2386 **436** 100 k. multicoloured . . 40 10

437 Diesel Train and Map (Turkey-Iran route)

1971. International Rail Links.
2387 – 100 k. multicoloured . . 1·75 20
2388 – 110 k. violet and blue . . 1·60 20
2389 437 250 k. multicoloured . . 75 45
DESIGNS: 100 k. Diesel train crossing bridge (Turkey–Bulgaria route); 110 k. Train ferry "Orhan Atliman", Lake Van (Turkey–Iran route).

438 Football

1971. Mediterranean Games, Izmir.
2390 438 100 k. black, violet & bl . 25 10
2391 – 200 k. multicoloured . . 30 15
DESIGN—VERT: 200 k. "Athlete and stadium".

439 Tomb of Cyrus the Great

1971. 2500th Anniv of Persian Empire.
2393 439 25 k. multicoloured . . . 15 10
2394 – 100 k. multicoloured . . 30 15
2395 – 150 k. brown and drab . . 50 15
DESIGNS—VERT: 100 k. Persian mosaic of woman. HORIZ: 150 k. Kemal Ataturk and Riza Shah Pahlavi.

1971. Turkish Paintings. As T **428**. Mult.
2396 250 k. "Sultan Mohammed I and Entourage" 75 25
2397 250 k. "Cinili Kosk Palace" . 75 25

441 U.N.I.C.E.F. Emblem

442 Yunus Emre

1971. 25th Anniv of U.N.I.C.E.F.
2404 441 100 k. + 10 k. mult . . 30 15
2405 250 k. + 15 k. mult . . 30 25

1971. 650th Death Anniv of Yunus Emre (folk-poet).
2406 442 100 k. multicoloured . . 30 20

443 First Turkish Map of the World (1072) and Book Year Emblem

1972. International Book Year.
2407 443 100 k. multicoloured . . 30 15

444 Doves and N.A.T.O. Emblem

445 Human Heart

1972. 20th Anniv of Turkey's Membership of N.A.T.O.
2408 444 100 k. black, grey & grn . 65 20
2409 250 k. black, grey & blue 1·10 45

1972. World Health Day.
2410 445 250 k. + 25 k. red, black and grey 35 15

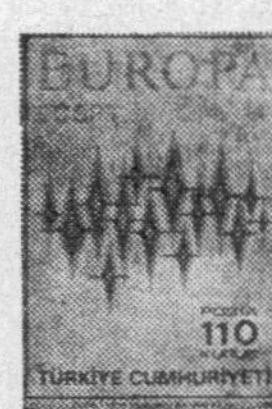

447 "Communications"

448 "Fisherman" (G. Dareli)

1972. Europa.
2414 447 110 k. multicoloured . . 90 55
2415 250 k. multicoloured . . 1·90 1·10

1972. Turkish Paintings. As T **428**. Multicoloured.
2416 250 k. "Gebze" (Osman Hamdi) 75 25
2417 250 k. "Forest" (S. A. Pasa) 75 25

1972. As T **358**.
2418 25 k. black and brown . . . 10 10
DESIGN: 25 k. Equestrian statue of Ataturk at Ankara.

1972. Regional Co-operation for Development. Multicoloured.
2419 100 k. Type **448** 40 20
2420 125 k. "Will and Power" (Chughtai) 40 20
2421 150 k. "Iranian Woman" (Behzad) 65 35

449 Olympic Rings

1972. Olympic Games, Munich.
2422 449 100 k. + 15 k. mult . . 30 20
2423 – 110 k. + 25 k. mult . . 35 20
2424 – 250 k. + 25 k. mult . . 55 40
DESIGNS: 110 k. "Athletes"; 250 k. "Stadium".

450 Ataturk at Observation Post

1972. 50th Anniv of Turkish War of Liberation. Multicoloured. (a) The Great Offensive.
2425 100 k. Type **450** 30 15
2426 110 k. Artillery 40 20

(b) Commander-in-Chief's Offensive.
2427 100 k. Hand-to-hand fighting 30 15

(c) Entry into Izmir.
2428 100 k. Commanders in open car 30 15

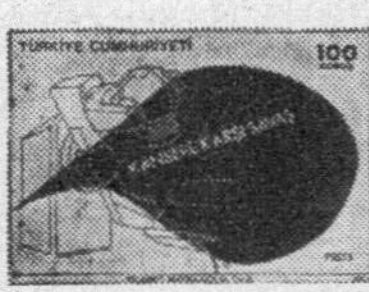

451 "Diagnosis and Cure"

452 Kemal Ataturk

1972. Fight against Cancer.
2429 451 100 k. red, black & blue 25 10

1972. Various sizes.
2430 452 5 k. lt blue on blue . . 10 10
2430a 25 k. orange on orange 10 10
2431 100 k. lake on buff . . 60 10
2431a 100 k. lt grey on grey 10 10
2431b 100 k. olive on green . 20 10
2432 110 k. blue on blue . . 80 10
2432a 125 k. green and grey . 65 10
2433 150 k. brown on buff . 60 10
2433a 150 k. green on green . 10 10
2434 175 k. purple on yellow 80 10
2434a 200 k. red on buff . . 60 10
2434b 200 k. brown on buff . 20 10
2435 250 k. lilac on pink . . 75 10
2435a 400 k. turquoise on blue 25 10
2436 500 k. violet on pink . 1·60 10
2437 500 k. blue on blue . . 40 10
2438 10 l. mauve on pink . . 1·25 10

INDEX

Countries can be quickly located by referring to the index at the end of this volume.

453 U.I.C Emblem

454 University Emblem

1972. 50th Anniv of International Railway Union.
2439 453 100 k. brn, buff and grn . 60 15

1973. Bicent of Technical University, Istanbul.
2440 454 100 k. + 25 k. mult . . . 30 15

455 Europa "Posthorn"

456 Helmet and Sword

1973. Europa.
2441 455 110 k. multicoloured . . 65 20
2442 250 k. multicoloured . . 1·00 35

1973. Turkish Painters. As T **428**. Multicoloured.
2443 250 k. "Old Almshouses, Istanbul" (Ahmet Ziya Akbulut) (horiz) 65 30
2444 250 k. "Flowers in Vase" (Suleyman Seyyit) (vert) . . 65 30

1973. Land Forces' Day.
2445 456 90 k. green, brn & grey . 15 10
2446 – 100 k. green, brown and light green 20 15
DESIGN: 100 k. As Type **456**, but wreath enclosing design.

457 Carved Head, Tomb of Antiochus I (Turkey)

458 Peace Dove and "50"

1973. Regional Co-operation for Development. Multicoloured.
2447 100 k. Type **457** 20 10
2448 150 k. Statue, Lut excavations (Iran) 30 15
2449 200 k. Street in Moenjodaro (Pakistan) 40 20

1973. 50th Anniv of Lausanne Peace Treaty.
2450 458 100 k. + 25 k. mult . . . 25 10

459 Minelayer "Nusret II"

460 "Al-Biruni" (from 16th-century miniature)

1973. Bicentenary of Turkish Navy. Mult.
2451 5 k. Type **459** 10 10
2452 25 k. Destroyer "Istanbul" . 15 10
2453 100 k. Motor torpedo-boat "Simsek" 30 25
2454 250 k. Cadet brig "Nurud-i-Futuh" (48 × 32 mm) . . . 2·25 45

1973. Millenary of Abu Reihan al-Biruni.
2455 460 250 k. multicoloured . . 30 10

461 "Equal Opportunity"

463 "Balkanfila" Emblem

1973. Centenary of Darussafaka High School.
2456 461 100 k. multicoloured . . 25 10

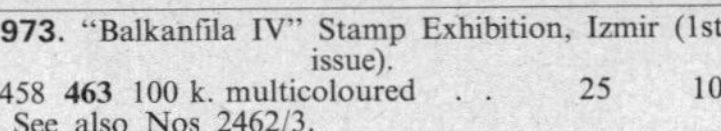
1973. "Balkanfila IV" Stamp Exhibition, Izmir (1st issue).
2458 463 100 k. multicoloured . . 25 10
See also Nos 2462/3.

464 Sivas Sheepdog

465 Kemal Ataturk

1973. Animals.
2459 464 25 k. blue, yellow & blk 10 10
2460 – 100 k. yellow, black & bl 60 10
DESIGN: 100 k. Angora cat.

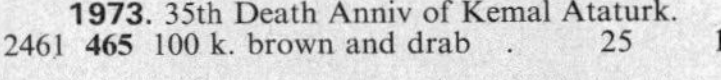
1973. 35th Death Anniv of Kemal Ataturk.
2461 465 100 k. brown and drab . 25 10

466 Bosphorus and "Stamps"

467 "Flower" Emblem

1973. "Balkanfila IV" Stamp Exhibition (2nd issue). Multicoloured.
2462 110 k. Type **466** 20 10
2463 250 k. "Balkanfila" in decorative script 35 15

1973. 50th Anniv of Republic.
2464 467 100 k. red, violet and blue 15 10
2465 – 250 k. multicoloured . . 25 10
2466 – 475 k. yellow and blue . 35 15
DESIGNS: 250 k. "Hands" supporting "50"; 475 k. Cogwheels and ears of corn.

468 Bosphorus Bridge

469 Bosphorus Bridge and U.N.I.C.E.F. Emblem

1973. Opening of Bosphorus Bridge, Istanbul. Multicoloured.
2468 100 k. Type **468** 25 10
2469 150 k. View of Bosphorus and bridge 35 15

1973. U.N.I.C.E.F. Ceremony. Children of Europe and Asia linked by Bosphorus Bridge.
2470 469 200 k. multicoloured . . 40 10

470 Mevlana Celaleddin

471 Cotton

1973. 700th Death Anniv of Mevlana Celaleddin (poet and mystic).
2471 – 100 k. green, blue & blk 20 10
2472 470 250 k. multicoloured . . 35 10
DESIGN: 100 k. Tomb and dancing dervishes.

1973. Export Products.
2473 471 75 k. grey, blue & black 10 10
2474 – 90 k. bistre, blue & blk . 15 10
2475 – 100 k. black, blue & grn 20 10
2476 – 250 k. multicoloured . . 1·25 15
2477 – 325 k. yellow, blue & blk 95 10
2478 – 475 k. black, blue & brn 60 10
DESIGNS: 90 k. Grapes; 100 k. Figs; 250 k. Citrus fruits; 325 k. Tobacco; 475 k. Hazelnuts.

472 Fokker Fellowship

473 President Inonu

1973. Air. Multicoloured.
2479 110 k. Type **472** 55 10
2480 250 k. Douglas DC-10 . . . 85 10

1973. President Inonu's Death.
2481 **472** brown and buff 20 10

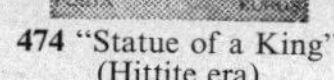

474 "Statue of a King" (Hittite era) **475** Doctor and Patient

1974. Europa. Sculptures. Multicoloured.
2482 110 k. Type **474** . . . . . . 1·25 30
2483 250 k. "Statuette of a Child" (c. 2000 B.C.) . . . . . . 2·25 55

1974. 75th Anniv of Sisli Paediatrics Hospital.
2484 **475** 110 k. black, grey & blue 20 10

476 Silver and Gold Idol **477** Population Year Emblem

1974. Archaeological Treasures. Multicoloured.
2485 125 k. Type **476** 20 10
2486 175 k. Painted jar (horiz) . . 20 10
2487 200 k. Bulls (statuettes) (horiz) 35 10
2488 250 k. Jug 45 25

1974. World Population Year.
2489 **477** 250 k. + 25 k. mult . . 40 15

479 Turkish Carpet

1974. Regional Co-operation for Development. Multicoloured.
2496 100 k. Type **479** 40 10
2497 150 k. Iranian carpet 95 15
2498 200 k. Pakistani carpet . . . 1·25 10

480 Dove and Map of Cyprus

1974. Turkish Intervention in Cyprus.
2499 **480** 250 k. multicoloured . . 50 10

481 "Getting to Grips" **482** Dove with Letter

1974. World Free-style Wrestling Championships, Ankara. Multicoloured.
2500 90 k. Type **481** 25 10
2501 100 k. "Throw" (vert) . . . 30 10
2502 250 k. "Lock" 40 20

1974. Centenary of Universal Postal Union.
2503 **482** 110 k. gold, dp blue & bl 20 10
2504 – 200 k. brown and green . 35 15
2505 – 250 k. multicoloured . . 40 15
DESIGNS: 200 k. Dove; 250 k. Arrows encircling globe.

483 Open Book (Law Reform)

1974. Works and Reforms of Ataturk (1st series).
2506 **453** 50 k. black and blue . . 10 10
2507 – 150 k. multicoloured . . 20 10
2508 – 400 k. multicoloured . . 50 10
DESIGNS—VERT: 150 k. "Tree" ("National Economy"); 400 k. Students facing sun ("Reform of Education").
See also Nos. 2543/5, 2566/8, 2597/9, 2639/41 and 2670/2.

484 Marconi **485** Arrows (3rd Five Year Development Programme)

1974. Birth Centenary of Marconi (radio pioneer).
2509 **484** 250 k. + 25 k. black, brown and red 40 30

1974. "Turkish Development".
2510 **485** 25 k. black and brown . 15 10
2511 – 100 k. grey and brown . 35 10
DESIGNS—HORIZ: 100 k. Map of Turkey within cogwheel (industrialisation).

486 Volleyball **487** Dr. Albert Schweitzer

1974. Ball Games.
2512 **486** 125 k. black and blue . . 25 10
2513 – 175 k. black and orange . 30 10
2514 – 250 k. black and green . 40 10
DESIGNS: 175 k. Basketball; 250 k. Football.

1975. Birth Centenary of Dr. Albert Schweitzer.
2515 **487** 250 k. + 50 k. mult . . 50 25

488 Automatic Telex Network

1975. Posts and Telecommunications.
2516 **488** 5 k. black and yellow . . 10 10
2517 – 50 k. green and orange . 15 10
2518 – 100 k. black and blue . 20 10
DESIGNS: 50 k. Postal cheques; 100 k. Radio link.

489 "Going to the Classroom" (I. Sivga) **490** Karacaoglan Monument (H. Gezer), Mut

1975. Children's Drawings. Multicoloured.
2519 25 k. Type **489** 10 10
2520 50 k. "View from a Village" (H. Dogru) 10 10
2521 100 k. "Folklore" (B. Aktan) 20 10

1975. Karacaoglan (musician) Commem.
2522 **490** 110 k. mauve, grn & brn 40 10

491 "Orange-gathering in Hatay" (C. Tollu)

1975. Europa. Paintings. Multicoloured.
2523 110 k. Type **491** 55 10
2524 250 k. "The Yoruks" (T. Zaim) 90 40

492 Turkish Porcelain Vase **493** Namibia located on Map of Africa

1975. Regional Co-operation for Development. Traditional Crafts. Multicoloured.
2525 110 k. Type **492** 35 15
2526 200 k. Ceramic plate (Iran) (horiz) 55 25
2527 250 k. Camel-skin vase (Pakistan) 75 35

1975. Namibia Day.
2528 **493** 250 k. + 50 k. mult . . . 35 15

494 Horon Folk-dancers

1975. Turkish Folk Dances. Multicoloured.
2529 100 k. Type **494** 25 10
2530 125 k. Kasik 25 10
2531 175 k. Bengi 35 10
2532 250 k. Kasap 45 15
2533 325 k. Kafkas (vert) 65 15

495 "Oguz Khan slaying Dragon" **497** Turbot

1975. Tales of Dede Korkut. Multicoloured.
2534 90 k. Type **495** 20 10
2535 175 k. Tale of Duha Koca Oglu Deli Dumrul Hikayesi (horiz) 25 10
2536 200 k. "Pillaging the Home of Salur Kazan" 30 10

1975. Fishes. Multicoloured.
2538 75 k. Type **497** 25 10
2539 90 k. Common carp 40 10
2540 175 k. Trout 50 10
2541 250 k. Red mullet . . . . . . 1·10 15
2542 475 k. Red bream . . . . . . 1·25 15

498 Two Women and Symbol (Women's Participation in Public Life)

1975. Works and Reforms of Ataturk (2nd series).
2543 **498** 100 k. red, black & stone 15 10
2544 – 110 k. multicoloured . . 15 10
2545 – 250 k. multicoloured . . 25 10
DESIGNS—VERT: 110 k. Symbol and inscription (Nationalisation of Insurance Companies). HORIZ: 250 k. Arrows (Orientation of the Fine Arts).

499 Z. Gokalp **500** Ceramic Plate

1976. Birth Cent of Ziya Gokalp (philosopher).
2546 **499** 200 k. + 25 k. mult . . 25 10

1976. Europa. Multicoloured.
2547 200 k. Type **500** 55 25
2548 400 k. Dessert jug . . . . . 1·25 45

501 Silhouette of Istanbul

1976. 7th Islamic Conference, Istanbul.
2549 **501** 500 k. multicoloured . . 45 10

502 "Lunch in Field" (S. Yucel)

1976. "Samsun '76" Youth Stamp Exn. Mult.
2550 50 k. Type **502** 10 10
2551 200 k. "Boats on the Bosphorus" (E. Kosemen) (vert) 20 10
2552 400 k. "Winter View" (R. Cetinkaya) 35 10

503 Sultan Marshes

1976. European Wetlands Conservation Year. Turkish Landscapes. Multicoloured.
2553 150 k. Type **503** . . . . . . 1·60 50
2554 200 k. Lake Manyas 40 10
2555 250 k. Lake Borabey 60 10
2556 400 k. Manavgat waterfalls . 60 15

504 "Hodja with Liver" **505** Games Emblem and Flame

1976. Nasreddin Hodja (humourist) Commem. "The Liver and the Kite". Multicoloured.
2557 150 k. Type **504** 20 10
2558 250 k. "Friend offers recipe" 25 10
2559 600 k. "Kite takes liver, leaving recipe" 55 15

1976. Olympic Games, Montreal.
2560 **505** 100 k. red and blue . . . 25 10
2561 – 400 k. multicoloured . . 35 10
2562 – 600 k. multicoloured . . 55 15
DESIGNS—HORIZ: 400 k. "Athlete" as "76". VERT: 600 k. Games emblem.

506 Kemal Ataturk (Turkey)

1976. Regional Co-operation for Development. Heads of State. Multicoloured.
2563 100 k. Type **506** 25 10
2564 200 k. Riza Shah Pahlavi (Iran) 25 10
2565 250 k. Mohammed Ali Jinnah (Pakistan) 35 15

507 Peace Dove and Sword (Army Reform)

508 White Spoonbill

1976. Works and Reforms of Ataturk (3rd series).
2566 **507** 100 k. black and red 10 10
2567 – 200 k. multicoloured . . 20 10
2568 – 400 k. multicoloured . . 40 25
DESIGNS: 200 k. Words, books and listeners (Ataturk's speeches); 400 k. Peace doves and globe ("Peace throughout the World").

1976. Turkish Birds. Multicoloured.
2569 100 k. + 25 k. Type **508** . . 35 20
2570 150 k. + 25 k. Common roller 45 30
2571 200 k. + 25 k. Greater flamingo 60 40
2572 400 k. + 25 k. Waldrapp (horiz) 1·25 60

509 "Hora" (oil exploration ship)

510 Musical Symbols

1977.
2573 **509** 400 k. multicoloured . . 85 25

1977. 150th Anniv of Presidential Symphony Orchestra.
2574 **510** 200 k. multicoloured . . 25 10

511 Kemal Ataturk in "100"

1977. Centenary of Parliament.
2575 **511** 200 k. black and red . . 15 10
2576 – 400 k. black and brown . . 25 10
DESIGN: 400 k. Hand placing ballot-paper in box.

512 Pamukkale

1977. Europa. Landscapes. Multicoloured.
2577 200 k. Type **512** 75 20
2578 400 k. Zelve . . . . 1·50 40

513 Edict of Karamanoglu Mehmet Bey and "Ongun" Bird

1977. 700th Anniv of Official Turkish Language.
2579 **513** 200 k. + 25 k. black and green 20 10

514 Head-shaped Vase, Turkey

1977. Regional Co-operation for Development. Pottery. Multicoloured.
2580 100 k. Type **514** 25 10
2581 255 k. Earthenware pot (Iran) 45 10
2582 675 k. Model bullock cart (Pakistan) . . . . 1·10 10

515 Stylized Sailing Yacht

522 "Globe" and Emblem

1977. European Finn Class Sailing Championships.
2584 **515** 150 k. black, blue and light blue 25 10
2585 – 200 k. blue and deep blue 45 15
2586 – 250 k. black and blue . . 65 20
DESIGNS—HORIZ: 200 k. VERT: 250 k. Both showing stylized sailing yachts.

1977. Surch **10 KURUS**.
2592 **409** 10 k. on 1 k. brn & red . 15 10

1977. 10th World Energy Conference.
2593 **522** 100 k. + 25 k. black, brown and pink 15 10
2594 – 600 k. + 50 k. red, black and blue 30 25
DESIGN: 600 k. Similar design showing a "globe" and emblem.

523 Kemal Ataturk

524 "Head and Book" (Rationalism)

1977. Size $20\frac{1}{2} \times 22\frac{1}{2}$ mm.
2595 **523** 200 k. blue on light blue 25 10
2596 250 k. turq on blue . . 30 10
See also Nos. 2619/25.

1977. Works and Reform of Ataturk (4th series). Multicoloured.
2597 100 k. Type **524** 10 10
2598 200 k. Words by Ataturk (National Sovereignty) . . 15 10
2599 400 k. Symbol (Leadership for Liberation of Nations) . . 25 10

525 Allama Muhammad Iqbal

526 Overturned Car

1977. Birth Centenary of Allama Muhammad Iqbal (Pakistani poet).
2600 **525** 400 k. multicoloured . . 25 10

1977. Road Safety.
2601 **526** 50 k. black, blue & red . 10 10
2602 – 150 k. black, grey & red 15 10
2603 – 250 k. black, brn & red . 20 10
2604 – 500 k. black, grey & red 40 10
2605 – 800 k. deep green, green and red 65 10
2606 – 10 l. green, red & blk . 75 10
DESIGNS—VERT: 150 k. Arrow crossing white lines and pool of blood; 500 k. "Children crossing" sign; 800 k. "No overtaking" sign; 10 l. Footprints in road and on pedestrian crossing. HORIZ: 250 k. Tractor pulling trailer loaded with people.

527 Lighted Match and Trees

531 Riza Shah Pahlavi of Iran

530 Ishakpasa Palace, Dogubeyazit

1977. Forest Conservation.
2607 **527** 50 k. black, red & grn . . 15 10
2608 – 250 k. black, grn & grey . 25 10
DESIGN: 250 k. "Tree germination".
See also No. 2699.

1978. Europa. Multicoloured.
2616 $2\frac{1}{2}$ l. Type **530** 45 10
2617 5 l. Anamur Castle 85 25

1978. Birth Centenary of Riza Shah Pahlavi of Iran.
2618 **531** 5 l. multicoloured 30 10

1978. As Type **523** but larger, 19 × 25 mm.
2619 10 k. brown 10 10
2620 50 k. grey 10 10
2621 1 l. red 10 10
2622 $2\frac{1}{2}$ l. lilac 10 10
2623 5 l. blue 20 10
2624 25 l. blue and light blue . . . 85 10
2625 50 l. orange & light orange . 2·00 10

532 Athletics

1978. "Gymnasiade '78" World School Games.
2626 **532** 1 l. + 50 k. deep green and green 10 10
2627 – $2\frac{1}{2}$ l. + 50 k. blue & orge 25 10
2628 – 5 l. + 50 k. blue & pink . 30 15
2629 – 8 l. + 50 k. blue & green 50 20
DESIGNS: $2\frac{1}{2}$ l. Gymnastics; 5 l. Table tennis; 8 l. Swimming.

533 Salmon Rose

1978. Regional Co-operation for Development. Multicoloured.
2630 $2\frac{1}{2}$ l. Type **533** 40 10
2631 $3\frac{1}{2}$ l. Pink roses 60 10
2632 8 l. Red roses 70 10

534 Anti-Apartheid Year Emblem

535 View of Ankara

1978. International Anti-Apartheid Year.
2633 **534** 10 l. multicoloured . . . 45 10

1978. Turkish–Libyan Friendship. Multicoloured.
2634 $2\frac{1}{2}$ l. Type **535** 25 10
2635 5 l. View of Tripoli 35 10

536 Ribbon and Chain

537 Independence Medal

1978. 25th Anniv of European Convention on Human Rights.
2636 **536** $2\frac{1}{2}$ l. + 50 k. blue, green and black 35 20
2637 – 5 l. + 50 k. red, blue and black 65 30
DESIGN: 5 l. Ribbon and flower.

1978. Works and Reforms of Ataturk (5th series).
2639 **538** $2\frac{1}{2}$ l. multicoloured . . . 10 10
2640 – $3\frac{1}{2}$ l. red and black . . . 15 10
2641 – 5 l. multicoloured . . . 30 10
DESIGNS—HORIZ: $3\frac{1}{2}$ l. Talking heads (Language Reform). VERT: 5 l. "ABC" in Arabic and Roman scripts (Adoption of Latin alphabet).

539 Bosphorus Waterside Residence of Koprulu Huseyin Pasa, Istanbul (1699)

1978. Traditional Turkish Houses. Multicoloured.
2642 1 l. Type **539** 10 10
2643 $2\frac{1}{2}$ l. Residence of Saatci Ali Efendi, Izmit, 1774 . . . . 20 10
2644 $3\frac{1}{2}$ l. House of Bey, Kula (vert) 30 10
2645 5 l. House of Bahaeddin Aga, Milas (vert) 35 10
2646 8 l. House of Safranbolu . . 45 15

541 Children with Globe as Balloon

542 Mail Transport

1979. International Year of the Child.
2649 – $2\frac{1}{2}$ l. + 50 k. black, gold and red 10 10
2650 **541** 5 l. + 50 k. multicoloured 30 15
2651 – 8 l. + 50 k. multicoloured 50 25
DESIGNS: $2\frac{1}{2}$ l. Children embracing beneath hearts; 8 l. Adult and child balancing globe.

1979. Europa.
2652 **542** $2\frac{1}{2}$ l. black, green and blue 35 10
2653 – 5 l. orange and black . . 15 10
2654 – $7\frac{1}{2}$ l. black and blue . . 25 10
DESIGNS: 5 l. Telex keyboard, morse key and telegraph poles; $7\frac{1}{2}$ l. Telephone dial and dish aerial.

543 Kemal Ataturk

544 "Turkish Harvest" (Namik Ismail)

1979.
2655 **543** 50 k. green 10 10
2656 1 l. green and lt green . 10 10
2657 $2\frac{1}{2}$ l. lilac 15 10
2657a $2\frac{1}{2}$ l. blue 10 10
2748 $2\frac{1}{2}$ l. orange 15 10
2658 5 l. blue and lt blue . . 15 10
2659 $7\frac{1}{2}$ l. brown 40 10
2659a $7\frac{1}{2}$ l. red 30 10
2660 10 l. mauve 50 10
2661a 10 l. mauve (22 × 22 mm) 40 10
2661 20 l. grey 40 10

1979. Regional Co-operation for Development. Paintings. Multicoloured.
2662 5 l. Type **544** 20 10
2663 $7\frac{1}{2}$ l. "Iranian Goldsmith" (Kamal el Molk) 25 10
2664 10 l. "Pakistan Village Scene" (Ustad Baksh) 35 20

545 Colemanite

546 Highway forming Figure 8

1979. 10th World Mining Congress. Mult.
2665 5 l. Type **545** 40 10
2666 $7\frac{1}{2}$ l. Chromite 50 10
2667 10 l. Antimonite 60 10
2668 15 l. Sulphur 75 10

1979. 8th European Communications Ministers' Symposium.
2669 **546** 5 l. multicoloured . . . 60 25

547 "Confidence in Youth"

548 Poppy ("Papaver somniferum")

1979. Works and Reforms of Ataturk (6th series).
2670 **547** $2\frac{1}{2}$ l. multicoloured . . . 15 10
2671 – $3\frac{1}{2}$ l. multicoloured . . . 20 10
2672 – 5 l. black and orange . . 25 10
DESIGNS—HORIZ: $3\frac{1}{2}$ l. "Secularism". VERT: 5 l. "National Oath".

1979. Flowers (1st series). Multicoloured.
2673 5 l. Type **548** 25 10
2674 $7\frac{1}{2}$ l. Oleander ("Nerium oleander") 30 10

2675 10 l. Late spider orchid ("Ophrys holosericea") . . 1·00 20
2676 15 l. Mandrake ("Mandragora autumnalis") 60 10
See also Nos. 2705/8.

549 Ibrahim Muteferrika (first printer) and Presses

1979. 250th Anniv of Turkish Printing.
2678 549 10 l. multicoloured . . . 35 15

550 Black Partridge

551 Olives, Leaves and Globe in Oil-drop

1979. Wildlife Conservation. Multicoloured.
2679 5 l. + 1 l. Type 550 . . . . 45 15
2680 5 l. + 1 l. Great bustard . . 45 15
2681 5 l. + 1 l. Demoiselle crane . 45 15
2682 5 l. + 1 l. Goitred gazelle . . 45 15
2683 5 l. + 1 l. Mouflon 45 15
Nos. 2679/83 were issued together, se-tenant, forming a composite design.

1979. 2nd World Olive-Oil Year.
2684 551 5 l. multicoloured 20 10
2685 – 10 l. yellow and green . . 35 10
DESIGN: 10 l. Globe in oil drop.

553 Uskudarli Hoca Ali Riza (artist)

1980. Europa. Multicoloured.
2692 7½ l. Type 553 . . . . 20 10
2693 10 l. Ali Sami Boyar (artist) . 35 10
2694 20 l. Dr. Hulusi Behcet (skin specialist) 60 20

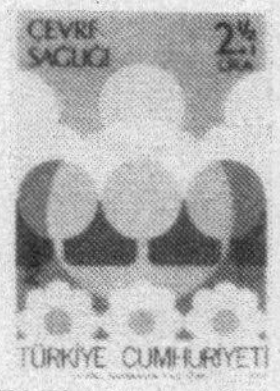

554 Flowers and Trees

555 Lighted Match and Trees

1980. Environmental Protection. Multicoloured.
2695 2½ l. + 1 l. Type 554 . . . . 10 10
2696 7½ l. + 1 l. Sun and water . . 15 10
2697 15 l. + 1 l. Factory polluting atmosphere 25 15
2698 20 l. + 1 l. Flower surrounded by oil 35 25

1980. Forest Conservation.
2699 555 50 k. green, red & brn . 10 10
See also No. 2607.

556 Seismological Graph

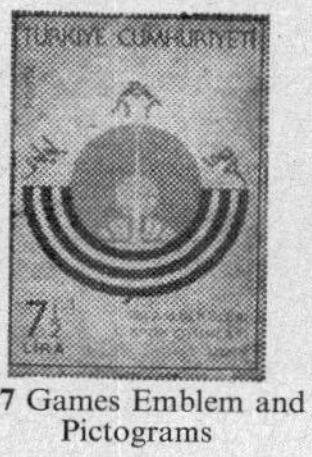

557 Games Emblem and Pictograms

1980. 7th World Conference on Earthquake Engineering.
2700 – 7½ l. brown, blue & orge . 15 10
2701 556 20 l. black, orge & blue . 40 20
DESIGN: 7½ l. Pictorial representation of earthquake within globe.

1980. 1st Islamic Games, Izmir. Multicoloured.
2702 7½ l. Type 557 . . . . 15 10
2703 20 l. As No. 2702 but with different sports around emblem 40 20

558 Ornamental Window

559 "Bracon hebetor" and Larva of Dark Arches Moth

1980. 1400th Anniv of Hegira.
2704 558 20 l. multicoloured . . . 40 15

1980. Flowers (2nd series). As T 548. Mult.
2705 2½ l. Manisa tulip ("Tulipa hayatii") 10 10
2706 7½ l. Ephesian bellflower ("Campanula ephesia") . 15 10
2707 15 l. Crocus ("Crocus ancyrensis") 25 15
2708 20 l. Anatolian orchid ("Orchis anatolica") . . . . 1·40 25

1980. Useful Insects (1st series). Multicoloured.
2709 2½ l. + 1 l. "Rodolia cardinalis" (ladybird) and cottony cushion scale 25 15
2710 7½ l. + 1 l. Type 559 . . . . 25 20
2711 15 l. + 1 l. Caterpillar-hunter and larva of gypsy moth . 35 25
2712 20 l. + 1 l. "Deraeocoris rutilus" (leaf bug) 40 30
See also Nos. 2763/6.

560 Kemal Ataturk

561 Ibn Sina Teaching

1980.
2713 560 7½ l. brown and pink . 20 10
2714 10 l. brown & lt brown 10 10
2719a 15 l. blue 20 10
2715 20 l. violet and mauve . 25 10
2719b 20 l. orange 25 10
2716 30 l. grey and lt grey . 75 10
2717 50 l. red and yellow . . 60 10
2719c 65 l. green 75 10
2718 75 l. green and lt green 1·10 10
2719d 90 l. mauve . . . . . 1·25 10
2719 100 l. blue and lt blue . 1·40 10

1980. Birth Millenary of Ibn Sina (Avicenna) (philosopher and physician). Multicoloured.
2720 7½ l. Type 561 . . . . . . 25 10
2721 20 l. Ibn Sina (vert) 45 15

562 Ataturk and Figures "100"

563 Disabled Person in Wheelchair

1981. "Balkanfila VIII" Stamp Exhibition, Ankara.
2722 562 10 l. red and black . . . 25 10

1981. International Year of Disabled Persons.
2723 563 10 l. + 2½ l. multicoloured 25 20
2724 20 l. + 2½ l. multicoloured 35 30

564 Sultan Mohammed the Conqueror

565 Gaziantep

1981. 500th Death Anniv of Mohammed the Conqueror.
2725 564 10 l. multicoloured . . . 20 10
2726 20 l. multicoloured . . . 35 20

1981. Folk Dances and Europa (35, 70 l.). Multicoloured.
2727 ½ l. Type 565 . . . . 15 10
2728 10 l. Balikesir 15 10
2729 15 l. Kahramanmaras 25 10
2730 35 l. Antalya 60 30
2731 70 l. Burdur . . . . 1·25 55

566 Ataturk in 1919 (S.G. 2279)

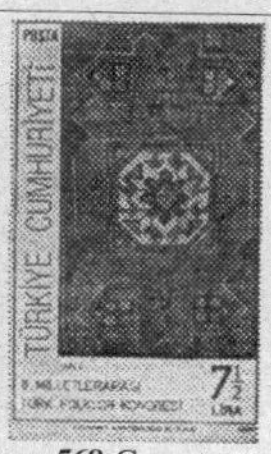

568 Carpet

1981. Birth Centenary of Kemal Ataturk. Previous stamps showing Ataturk. Multicoloured.
2732 566 2½ l. multicoloured . . . 10 10
2733 – 7½ l. black and brown . . 10 10
2734 – 10 l. multicoloured . . . 15 10
2735 – 20 l. blue, red and black . 25 15
2736 – 25 l. black, red & orange . 30 20
2737 – 35 l. multicoloured . . . 45 30
DESIGNS: 7½ l. Ataturk in civilian dress (S.G. No. 2285); 10 l. Ataturk and old Parliament House (S.G. No. 2037); 20 l. Ataturk teaching Latin alphabet (S.G. No. 1222); 25 l. Remilitarization of Dardanelles surcharged stamp (S.G. No. 1188); 35 l. Ataturk in evening dress (from miniature sheet).

1981. Various stamps surch **10 LIRA**.
2739 – 10 l. on 60 k. red, black and green (No. 2177) . . . 25 10
2740 452 10 l. on 110 k. blue on blue 25 10
2741 10 l. on 400 k. turquoise on blue 25 10
2742 – 10 l. on 800 k. green, turq & red (No. 2605) 65 10

1981. 2nd International Congress of Turkish Folklore. Multicoloured.
2743 7½ l. Type 568 . . . . 15 10
2744 10 l. Embroidery 15 10
2745 15 l. Drum and "zurna" . . . 25 15
2746 20 l. Embroidered napkin . . 40 15
2747 30 l. Rug 50 20

570 Ataturk Centenary and E.P.S. Emblem

1981. 5th European Physical Society General Congress.
2750 570 10 l. multicoloured . . . 30 10
2751 30 l. multicoloured . . . 45 20

571 F.A.O. Emblem

1981. World Food Day.
2752 571 10 l. multicoloured . . . 20 10
2753 30 l. multicoloured . . . 50 20

572 Olive Branch and Constitution on Map of Turkey

1981. Inauguration of Constituent Assembly.
2754 572 10 l. multicoloured . . . 25 10
2755 30 l. multicoloured . . . 45 30

574 Kemal Ataturk

575 Green Tiger Beetle

1981.
2762 574 2½ l. red on grey 15 10

1981. Useful Insects (2nd series). Multicoloured.
2763 10 l. + 2½ l. Type 575 . . . . 30 20
2764 20 l. + 2½ l. "Syrphus vitripennis" (hover fly) . . 45 35
2765 30 l. + 2½ l. "Ascalaphus macaronius" (owl-fly) . . . 60 45
2766 40 l. + 2½ l. "Empusa fasciata" 75 55

MINIMUM PRICE

The minimum price quoted is 10p which represents a handling charge rather than a basis for valuing common stamps. For further notes about prices, see introductory pages.

576 Students and Silhouette of Ataturk

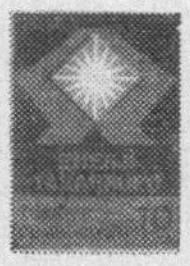

577 Sun

578 Kemal Ataturk

1981. Literacy Campaign
2767 576 2½ l. orange and blue . . 15 10

1982. Energy Conservation.
2768 577 10 l. yellow, blue & green 25 10

1982.
2769 578 1 l. green 10 10
2770 – 2½ l. lilac 10 10
2771 – 5 l. blue 20 10
2772 – 10 l. red 30 10
2773 – 35 l. brown 65 10
DESIGNS: 2½ to 35 l. Different portraits of Ataturk.

579 "Magnolias"

580 Dr. Tevfik Saglam

1982. Birth Centenary of Ibrahim Calli (painter). Multicoloured.
2774 10 l. Type 579 . . . . 20 10
2775 20 l. "Fishermen" (horiz) . . 40 10
2776 30 l. "Sewing Woman" . . . 60 10

1982. Centenary of Discovery of Tubercle Bacillus. Multicoloured.
2777 10 l. + 2½ l. Type 580 . . . 30 15
2778 30 l. + 2½ l. Dr. Robert Koch 60 35

582 Kul Tigin Monument

584 Demirkazik

583 Tanker and Emblem

1982. 1250th Anniv of Kul Tigin Monument. Multicoloured.
2780 10 l. Type 582 . . . . 15 10
2781 30 l. Head of Kul Tigin . . . 35 15

1982. Inauguration of Pendik Shipyard.
2782 583 30 l. multicoloured . . . 35 15

1982. Anatolian Mountains. Multicoloured.
2783 7½ l. Agri Dagi 15 10
2784 10 l. Buzul Dagi (horiz) . . . 20 10
2785 15 l. Type 584 . . . . 25 10
2786 20 l. Erciyes (horiz) 40 10
2787 30 l. Kackar Dagi 55 10
2788 35 l. Uludag (horiz) 75 10

585 Colorado Potato Beetle

1982. Insect Pests (1st series). Multicoloured.
2789 10 l. + 2½ l. "Eurydema spectabile" (shield-bug) . . 30 25
2790 15 l. + 2½ l. Olive fruit-fly . 40 30
2791 20 l. + 2½ l. "Klapperichicen viridissima" (cicada) . . . 45 40
2792 20 l. + 2½ l. Type 585 . . . 60 50
2793 35 l. + 2½ l. "Rhynchites auratus" (weevil) 70 55
See also Nos. 2830/4.

586 Open Book and Figures 587 Drum

1982. Centenary of Beyazit State Library.

2794 **586** 30 l. multicoloured . . . 35 10

1982. Musical Instruments. Multicoloured.

2796 7½ l. Type **587** 20 10
2797 10 l. Lute ("Baglama") . . . 25 10
2798 15 l. Horn ("Zurna") (horiz) 30 10
2799 20 l. Stringed instrument ("Kemence") (horiz) . . . 45 15
2800 30 l. Flute ("Mey") 55 20

588 Temple of Artemis, Sart

1982. Ancient Cities.

2801 **588** 30 l. multicoloured . . . 35 10

589 Family on Map

1983. Family Planning and Mother and Child Health. Multicoloured.

2802 10 l. Type **589** 20 10
2803 35 l. Mother and child . . . 25 10

590 Council Emblem

1983. 30th Anniv of Customs Co-operation Council.

2804 **590** 45 l. multicoloured . . . 65 15

591 People, Ballot Box and Constitution

1983. 1982 Constitution. Multicoloured.

2805 10 l. Type **591** 15 10
2806 30 l. Constitution, scales and olive branch 30 10

592 Richard Wagner

1983. Death Centenary of Richard Wagner (composer).

2807 **592** 30 l. + 5 l. mult 75 15

593 Hamdi Bey

1983. 38th Death Anniv of Hamdi Bey (telegraphist).

2808 **593** 35 l. multicoloured . . . 35 10

INDEX

Countries can be quickly located by referring to the index at the end of this volume.

594 Piri Reis (geographer) and Map

1983. Europa. Multicoloured.

2809 50 l. Type **594** 90 15
2810 100 l. Ulugh Bey (Central Asian ruler) and observatory . . 1·60 25

595 Olive Branch and Athletes

1983. Youth Week.

2811 **595** 15 l. multicoloured . . . 20 10

596 Junkers Ju 52/3m and Boeing 727

1983. 50th Anniv of Turkish State Airline. Multicoloured.

2812 50 l. Type **596** . . . . 1·00 15
2813 70 l. Airport at night . . . . 1·00 15

No. 2812 is wrongly inscribed "F-13".

597 Hellenic Statue of Eros 598 Oludeniz

1983. 18th Council of Europe Art Exhibition, Istanbul. Multicoloured.

2814 15 l. Type **597** 30 10
2815 35 l. Hittite carving of two-headed duck (horiz) . . . 45 10
2816 50 l. Ottoman zinc flask and jug 75 15
2817 70 l. Busts of Marcus Aurelius and his wife Faustina (horiz) 85 15

1983. Coastal Protection. Multicoloured.

2818 10 l. Type **598** 15 10
2819 25 l. Olimpos 50 10
2820 35 l. Kekova 65 15

1983. Nos. 2655 and 2699 surch **5 LIRA**.

2821 **543** 5 l. on 50 k. green . . . 25 10
2822 **555** 5 l. on 50 k. green, red and brown 25 10

600 Dove carrying Letter 601 Kemal Ataturk

1983. World Communications Year. Mult.

2823 15 l. Type **600** 35 10
2824 50 l. Telephone pole and telephone wires (horiz) . . 45 10
2825 70 l. Telephone dial and letter within ornamental design . 80 15

1983.

2826 **601** 15 l. blue and lt blue . . 15 10
2827 50 l. blue and green . . 55 10
2828 100 l. blue and orange . 1·25 10

602 Topkapi Serail, Istanbul

1983. Aga Khan Award for Architecture.

2829 **602** 50 l. yellow, blk & grn . . 65 10

1983. Insect Pests (2nd series). As T **585**. Multicoloured.

2830 15 l. + 5 l. Sun pest 25 35
2831 25 l. + 5 l. "Phyllobius nigrofasciatus" (weevil) . . 45 45
2832 35 l. + 5 l. "Cercopsis intermedia" (froghopper) . 55 55
2833 50 l. + 10 l. Striped bug . . 80 80
2834 75 l. + 10 l. "Capnodis miliaris" . . . . 1·00 1·00

604 Map and Flag of Turkey

1983. 60th Anniv of Republic.

2836 **604** 15 l. multicoloured . . . 25 10
2837 50 l. multicoloured . . . 55 15

605 Temple of Aphrodite, Aphrodisias

1983. Ancient Cities.

2838 **605** 50 l. multicoloured . . . 50 10

607 St. Sophia's from Sultan Ahmed Mosque, Istanbul 608 Police Badge and Ribbon protecting Citizens

1984. U.N.E.S.C.O. International Campaign for Istanbul and Goreme. Multicoloured.

2850 25 l. Type **607** 25 10
2851 35 l. Rock dwellings and chapels, Goreme 40 10
2852 50 l. Suleymaniye district, Istanbul 60 10

1984. Turkish Police Organization.

2853 **608** 15 l. multicoloured . . . 20 10

609 Bridge 610 Kaftan (16th-century)

1984. Europa. 25th Anniv of C.E.P.T.

2854 **609** 50 l. multicoloured . . . 75 15
2855 100 l. multicoloured . . . 1·50 25

1984. Topkapi Museum (1st series). Mult.

2856 20 l. + 5 l. Type **610** 40 15
2857 70 l. + 15 l. Ceremonial ewer 75 15
2858 90 l. + 20 l. Gold inlaid and jewelled swords . . . . 1·25 15
2859 100 l. + 25 l. Kaaba lock . . 1·50 20

See also Nos. 2892/5, 2925/8 and 2967/70.

611 Mete Khan and Flag of Great Hun Empire

1984. Turkic States (1st series). Multicoloured.

2860 10 l. Type **611** 20 10
2861 20 l. Panu and flag of Western Hun Empire 40 10
2862 50 l. Attila and flag of European Hun Empire 75 15
2863 70 l. Aksunvar and flag of Ak Hun Empire . . . . . . 1·00 25

See also Nos. 2896/9, 2930/3 and 2971/4.

612 Peace Dove

1984. 10th Anniv of Turkish Forces in Cyprus.

2864 **612** 70 l. multicoloured . . . 60 10

613 Olympic Colours 614 Marsh Mallow

1984. Olympic Games, Los Angeles. Mult.

2865 20 l. + 5 l. Type **613** 25 10
2866 70 l. + 15 l. Medallion of wrestler (vert) 80 15
2867 100 l. + 20 l. Stylised athlete 1·25 25

1984. Wild Flowers. Multicoloured.

2868 5 l. "Narcissus tazetta" . . 10 10
2868a 10 l. Type **614** 15 10
2869 20 l. Common poppy . . . 15 10
2870 70 l. "Cyclamen pseudoibericum" 80 10
2870a 100 l. False chamomile . . 60 10
2871 200 l. Snowdrops . . . . . 1·50 15
2872 300 l. "Tulipa sintenesii" . 2·25 15

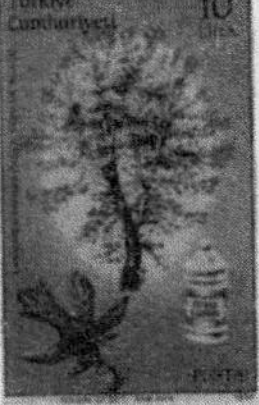

615 Soldier and Flag 616 Liquidamber

1984. Armed Forces Day.

2873 **615** 20 l. multicoloured . . . 15 10
2874 – 50 l. multicoloured . . . 40 10
2875 – 70 l. red, blue and black 65 15
2876 – 90 l. multicoloured . . . 75 15

DESIGNS: 50 l. Olive branch as sword hilt; 70 l. Emblem, soldier and flag; 90 l. Soldier, olive branch and map.

1984. Forest Resources. Multicoloured.

2877 10 l. Type **616** 25 10
2878 20 l. Oriental spruce 35 10
2879 70 l. Oriental beech 85 10
2880 90 l. Cedar of Lebanon . . . 1·00 15

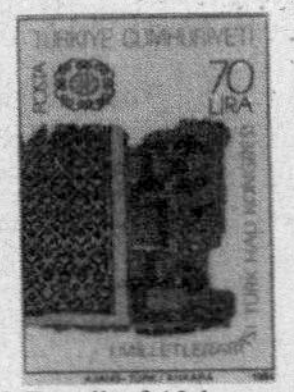

617 Pres. Inonu 618 Detail of 13th-century Seljukian Carpet

1984. Birth Centenary of Ismet Inonu (Prime Minister 1923–37 and 1962–65; President 1938–50).

2881 **617** 20 l. multicoloured . . . 50 10

1984. 1st Int Congress on Turkish Carpets.

2882 **618** 70 l. multicoloured . . . 30 10

619 Great Mosque and University, Harran

1984. Ancient Cities.

2883 **619** 70 l. multicoloured . . . 60 10

620 Women and Ballot Box

1984. 50th Anniv of Turkish Women's Suffrage.
2884 620 20 l. multicoloured . . . 25 10

621 "Icarus" (Hans Herni)

1984. 40th Anniv of I.C.A.O.
2885 621 100 l. multicoloured . . . 75 15

623 Glider and Parachutist

1985. 60th Anniv of Turkish Aviation League. Multicoloured.
2887 10 l. Type 623 . . . 45 15
2888 20 l. Cameron Viva 77 hot-air balloon (vert) . . . 55 15

624 Globe and Satellite
625 Score and Ulvi Cemal Erkin (composer)

1985. 20th Anniv of International Telecommunications Satellite Organization.
2889 624 100 l. multicoloured . . . 65 15

1985. Europa. Music Year. Multicoloured.
2890 100 l. Type 625 . . . 1·00 75
2891 200 l. Score and Mithat Fenmen (composer and pianist) . . 1·75 60

1985. Topkapi Museum (2nd series). As T 610. Multicoloured.
2892 10 l. + 5 l. Plate decorated with peacock . . . 15 10
2893 20 l. + 10 l. Jug and cup . . 25 15
2894 100 l. + 15 l. Porcelain ewer and bowl . . . 75 25
2895 120 l. + 20 l. Chinese porcelain plate . . . 90 30

1985. Turkic States (2nd series). As T 611. Multicoloured.
2896 10 l. Bilge Kagan and flag of Gokturk Empire . . . 10 10
2897 20 l. Bayan Kagan and flag of Avar Empire . . . 20 10
2898 70 l. Hazar Kagan and flag of Hazar Empire . . . 50 15
2899 100 l. Kutlug Kul Bilge Kagan and flag of Uygur Empire . 75 15

626 Louis Pasteur working in Laboratory
627 I.Y.Y. Emblem within Globe and Profiles

1985. Centenary of Discovery of Anti-rabies Vaccine.
2900 626 100 l. + 15 l. mult . . . 75 15

1985. International Youth Year. Multicoloured.
2901 100 l. Type 627 . . . 50 10
2902 120 l. Globe and I.Y.Y. Emblem . 85 10

628 Postman and Couple Dancing
629 Aynalikavak Palace

1985. Introduction of Post Codes.
2903 628 10 l. black, yellow & brn . 10 10
2904 20 l. black, yellow & red . 15 10
2905 20 l. black, yellow & grn . 15 10
2906 20 l. black, yellow & bl . 15 10
2907 70 l. blue, yellow & pur . 45 10
2908 100 l. black, yellow and grey . 65 10

1985. National Palaces Symposium. Multicoloured.
2909 20 l. Type 629 . . . 15 10
2910 100 l. Beylerbeyi Palace . . 60 15

630 U.N. Emblem, Headquarters and Flags in "40"

1985. 40th Anniv of U.N.O.
2911 630 100 l. multicoloured . . 60 20

631 Alanya
632 Satellite and Infra-red Picture of Earth's Surface

1985. Ancient Cities.
2912 631 100 l. multicoloured . . 60 15

1985. 60th Anniv of Meteorological Institute.
2913 632 100 l. multicoloured . . 85 15

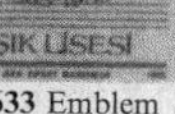

633 Emblem
634 Kemal Ataturk

1985. Centenary of Isik Lyceum, Istanbul.
2914 633 20 l. gold, blue & red . 25 10

1985.
2915 634 10 l. blue and cobalt . . 10 10
2916 20 l. brown and lilac . . 15 10
2917 100 l. purple and lilac . 55 10

635 Girl and Flower

1986. International 23rd April Children's Festival, Ankara. Multicoloured.
2918 20 l. Type 635 . . . 10 10
2919 100 l. Family . . . 35 10
2920 120 l. Balloon seller . . . 55 10

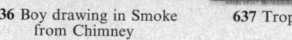

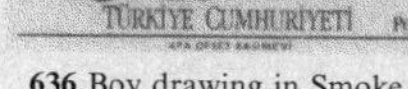
636 Boy drawing in Smoke from Chimney
637 Trophy

1986. Europa. Multicoloured.
2921 100 l. Type 636 . . . 55 10
2922 200 l. Plaster on dead half of leaf (vert) . . . 1·25 50

1986. Ataturk International Peace Prize. Multicoloured.
2923 20 l. Type 637 . . . 10 10
2924 100 l. Front view of trophy . 35 10

1986. Topkapi Museum (3rd series). As T 610. Multicoloured.
2925 20 l. + 5 l. Censer . . . 15 10
2926 100 l. + 10 l. Jade and jewelled tankard . . . 35 15
2927 120 l. + 15 l. Dagger and sheath 55 25
2928 200 l. + 30 l. Willow buckler 95 30

638 "Abdulhamit"
639 Wrestlers oiling Themselves

1986. Centenary of Turkish Submarine Fleet.
2929 638 20 l. multicoloured . . . 15 10

1986. Turkic States (3rd series). As T 611. Multicoloured.
2930 10 l. Bilge Kul Kadir Khan and flag of Kara Khanids Empire 15 10
2931 20 l. Alp Tekin and flag of Ghaznavids Empire . . . 25 10
2932 100 l. Seljuk and flag of Great Seljuk Empire . . . 60 10
2933 120 l. Muhammed Harezmsah and flag of Harezmsah State 85 10

1986. Kirkpinar Wrestling. Multicoloured.
2934 10 l. Type 639 . . . 10 10
2935 20 l. Opening ceremony . . . 15 10
2936 100 l. Wrestlers . . . 55 15

640 Chateau de la Muette, Paris (headquarters)

1986. 25th Anniv of Organization for Economic Co-operation and Development.
2937 640 100 l. multicoloured . . . 55 10

641 Benz "Einspur" Tricar, 1886

1986. Centenary of Motor Car. Multicoloured.
2938 10 l. Type 641 . . . 15 10
2939 20 l. Rolls-Royce "Silver Ghost", 1906 . . . 35 10
2940 100 l. Mercedes touring car, 1928 . . . 60 15
2941 200 l. Impression of speeding car . . . 1·10 20

642 "Arrangement with Tulips" (Feyhaman Duran)
643 Celal Bayar

1986. Artists' Birth Centenaries. Multicoloured.
2942 100 l. Type 642 . . . 35 10
2943 120 l. "Landscape with Fountain" (Huseyin Avni Lifij) (horiz) . . . 55 15

1986. Celal Bayar (Prime Minister 1937–39; President 1950–60) Commemoration.
2944 643 20 l. brown, gold and mauve . . . 10 10
2945 – 100 l. green, gold and mauve . . . 45 10
DESIGN: 100 l. Profile of Celal Bayar.

645 Kubad-Abad

1986. Ancient Cities.
2950 645 100 l. multicoloured . . 45 10

646 N.A.T.O. Emblem and Dove with Olive Branch

1986. 32nd N.A.T.O. Assembly, Istanbul.
2951 646 100 l. + 20 l. mult . . . 55 15

647 Ersoy and National Flag
648 Driver wearing Seat Belt

1986. 50th Death Anniv of Mehmet Akif Ersoy (composer of national anthem).
2952 647 20 l. multicoloured . . . 25 10

1987. Road Safety.
2953 648 10 l. violet, red & blue . 15 10
2954 – 20 l. red, blue & brown . 25 10
2955 – 150 l. brown, red & grn . 85 10
DESIGNS: 20 l. Smashed drinking glass and road; 150 l. Broken speed limit sign and road.

649 Spurge Hawk Moth

1987. Moths and Butterflies. Multicoloured.
2956 10 l. Type 649 . . . 15 10
2957 20 l. Red admiral . . . 20 15
2958 100 l. Jersey tiger moth . . 55 15
2959 120 l. Clouded yellow . . 65 20

650 Modern Housing and Emblem
651 Casting

1987. International Year of Shelter for the Homeless.
2960 650 200 l. multicoloured . . 75 10

1987. 50th Anniv of Turkish Iron and Steel Works. Multicoloured.
2961 50 l. Type 651 . . . 15 10
2962 200 l. Karabuk Works . . . 65 10

652 Map of Turkey and Grand National Assembly Building, Ankara

1987. "Sovereignty belongs to the People".
2963 652 50 l. multicoloured . . . 15 10

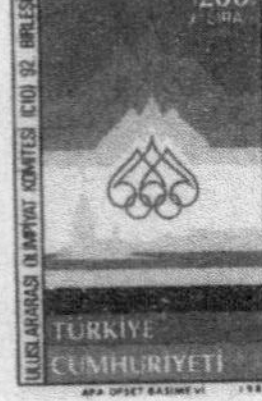

653 Turkish History Institution, Ankara (Turgut Cansever and Ertur Yener)

654 Olympic Rings as Flames

1987. Europa. Architecture. Multicoloured.
2964 50 l. Type **653** 15 10
2965 200 l. Social Insurance Institution, Zeyrek (Sedad Hakki Eldem) 75 10

1987. 92nd Session of International Olympic Committee, Istanbul.
2966 **654** 200 l. multicoloured . . . 75 10

1987. Topkapi Museum (4th series). As T **610**. Multicoloured.
2967 20 l. + 5 l. Crystals and jewelled ewer 20 10
2968 50 l. + 10 l. Emerald, gold and diamond ceiling pendant (horiz) 30 10
2969 200 l. + 15 l. Sherbet jug . . 85 15
2970 250 l. + 30 l. Crystal, gold and jewelled writing drawer (horiz) . . . . 1·10 20

1987. Turkic States (4th series). As T **611**. Multicoloured.
2971 10 l. Batu Khan and flag of Golden Horde State . . . 15 10
2972 20 l. Timur (Tamerlane) and flag of Great Timur Empire 20 10
2973 50 l. Babur Shah and flag of Mughal Empire 25 10
2974 200 l. Osman Bey and flag of Ottoman Empire 65 10

655 Men

1987. Paintings from Mehmet Siyah Kalem's "Album of the Conqueror". Multicoloured.
2975 10 l. Type **655** 10 10
2976 20 l. Donkey rider and attendants (horiz) 10 10
2977 50 l. Man whipping fallen horse (horiz) 20 10
2978 200 l. Demon 35 10

656 Cancer Cells and Pipette holding Drug

1987. 15th International Chemotherapy Congress, Istanbul.
2979 **656** 200 l. + 25 l. mult . . . 75 20

657 Ihlamur Pavilion

1987. Royal Pavilions (1st series). Multicoloured.
2980 50 l. Type **657** 15 10
2981 200 l. Kucuksu Pavilion . . . 60 10
See also Nos. 3019/20.

658 Suleiman receiving Barbarossa (miniature)

1987. Suleiman the Magnificent. Multicoloured.
2982 30 l. Suleiman 10 10
2983 50 l. Suleiman's tougra (horiz) 15 10
2984 200 l. Type **658** 35 10
2985 270 l. Sculpture of Suleiman from U.S. House of Representatives and inscribed scroll 40 10

660 Sinan and Selimiye Mosque, Edirne

661 Means of Transport

1988. 400th Death Anniv of Mimar Sinan (architect). Multicoloured.
2987 50 l. Type **660** 15 10
2988 200 l. Suleiman Mosque . . 55 10

1988. Europa. Transport and Communications. Multicoloured.
2989 200 l. Type **661** 30 10
2990 600 l. Electric impulses forming globe between telephone and computer terminal (horiz) 60 15

662 Syringes between Healthy and Sick Children

1988. Health. Multicoloured.
2991 50 l. Type **662** 10 10
2992 200 l. Capsules forming cross on bottle (vert) 20 10
2993 300 l. Heart in cogwheel and heart-shaped worker . . . 35 10
2994 600 l. Organs for transplant on open hands (vert) 60 10

663 American Standard Steam Locomotive, 1850s

1988. Locomotives. Each agate, light brown and brown.
2995 50 l. Type **663** 15 10
2996 100 l. Steam locomotive, 1913 35 10
2997 200 l. Henschel Krupp steam locomotive, 1926 . . . . 50 20
2998 300 l. Toshiba "E 43001" electric locomotive, 1987 . 70 25
2999 600 l. MTE-Tulomsas diesel-electric locomotive, 1984 . 1·10 25

664 Articulated Lorry

1988. 21st International Road Transport Union World Congress, Istanbul.
3000 **664** 200 l. + 25 l. mult . . . 25 15

665 Scales and Map

1988. 120th Anniv of Court of Cassation (appeal court).
3001 **665** 50 l. multicoloured . . . 10 10

666 Fatih Sultan Mohamed Bridge, Bosphorus

1988. Completion of Bridges. Multicoloured.
3002 200 l. Type **666** 25 10
3003 300 l. Seto Great road and rail Bridge, Japan 35 10

667 Telephone Dial and Wires over Villages

1988. Completion of Telephone Network to Every Village.
3004 **667** 100 l. multicoloured . . . 15 10

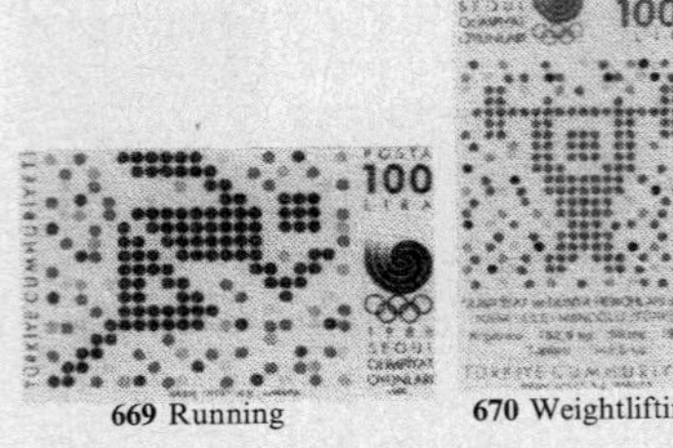

669 Running

670 Weightlifting

1988. Olympic Games, Seoul. Multicoloured.
3005 100 l. Type **669** 15 10
3006 200 l. Archery 20 10
3007 400 l. Weightlifting 30 10
3008 600 l. Football (vert) 55 15

1988. Naim Suleymanoglu, Olympic and World Heavyweight Record Holder for Weightlifting.
3009 **670** 1000 l. multicoloured . . 85 15

671 Lush Scene in Hands surrounded by Barren Earth

672 General Dynamics F-16 Fighters and Cogwheel

1988. European Campaign for Rural Areas. Multicoloured.
3010 100 l. + 25 l. Type **671** . . . 15 10
3011 400 l. + 50 l. Rural scene in eye 60 15

1988. Turkish Aerospace Industries. Mult.
3012 50 l. Type **672** 10 10
3013 200 l. Birds forming jet fighter (horiz) 40 10

673 "Gonepteryx cleopatra"

1988. Butterflies. Multicoloured.
3014 100 l. Type **673** (wrongly inscr "G. rhamni") 10 10
3015 200 l. Hermit 25 15
3016 400 l. Eastern festoon 40 20
3017 600 l. Camberwell beauty . . 75 35

1988. Royal Pavilions (2nd series). As T **657**. Multicoloured.
3019 100 l. Kasr-i Humayun Imperial Lodge, Maslak 15 10
3020 400 l. Sale Pavilion, Yildiz . . 75 10

675 Large-leaved Lime

1988. Medicinal Plants. Multicoloured.
3022 150 l. Type **675** 20 10
3023 300 l. Common mallow . . . 35 10
3024 600 l. Henbane 55 10
3025 900 l. Deadly nightshade . . 95 15

676 Seated Goddess with Child (clay statuette)

1989. Archaeology (1st series). Multicoloured.
3026 150 l. Type **676** 10 10
3027 300 l. Lead figurine of god and goddess 25 10
3028 600 l. Clay human-shaped vase 55 10
3029 1000 l. Hittite ivory figurine of mountain god . . . . . . 1·00 15
See also Nos. 3062/5, 3104/7 and 3134/7.

1989. Nos. 2826, 2915 and 2916 surch.
3030 **601** 50 l. on 15 l. blue and light blue 10 10
3031 **634** 75 l. on 10 l. blue and cobalt 10 10
3032 150 l. on 20 l. brown and lilac 20 10

678 Dove and Emblem

1989. 40th Anniv of N.A.T.O.
3033 **678** 600 l. ultram, blue & red . . 35 10

679 Silkworm Moth Larva on Leaf

680 Leap-frog

1989. Silk Industry. Multicoloured.
3034 150 l. + 50 l. Type **679** . . . 15 15
3035 600 l. + 100 l. Silkworm moth cocoon and lengths of cloth 50 50

1989. Europa. Children's Games. Multicoloured.
3036 600 l. Type **680** 35 10
3037 1000 l. Children going under arch formed by other children ("Open the Door, Head Bezirgan") 55 10

681 Arrow and Anniversary Emblem

1989. 40th Anniv of Council of Europe.
3038 **681** 600 l. + 100 l. mult . . 50 20

683 Paddle-steamer "Sahilbent"

684 Birds

1989. Steamers. Multicoloured.
3045 150 l. Type **683** 40 15
3046 300 l. "Ragbet" (paddle-steamer) 50 15
3047 600 l. "Tari" (freighter) . . . 75 20
3048 1000 l. "Guzelhisar" (ferry) . . 1·40 25

1989. Bicentenary of French Revolution.
3049 **684** 600 l. multicoloured . . 40 10

685 Kemal Ataturk

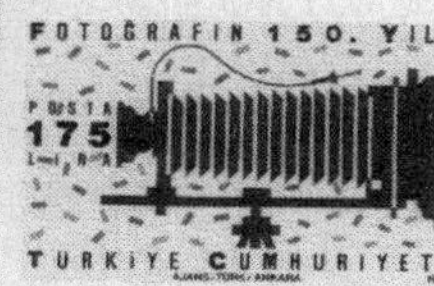
687 Camera

1989.
3050 **685** 2000 l. blue and grey . . 1·00 15
3051 5000 l. brown and grey . 2·50 25
See also Nos. 3093/4, 3144 and 3199/3200.

1989. No. 2916 surch **LIRA 500**.
3052 **634** 500 l. on 20 l. brown and lilac 30 10

1989. 150th Anniv of Photography. Mult.
3053 175 l. Type **687** 10 10
3054 700 l. Coloured lens shutter . 35 10

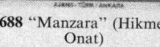

688 "Manzara" (Hikmet Onat)

689 Nehru

1989. State Exhibition of Paintings and Sculpture. Multicoloured.
3055 200 l. Type **688** 10 10
3056 700 l. "Sari Saz" (Bedri Rahmi Eyuboglu) 35 10
3057 1000 l. "Kadin" (sculpture, Zuhtu Muridoglu) 55 10

1989. Birth Centenary of Jawaharlal Nehru (Indian statesman).
3058 **689** 700 l. multicoloured . . . 45 10

690 Loggerhead Turtle

691 Turkish Memorial

1989. Sea Turtles. Multicoloured.
3059 700 l. Type **690** 55 10
3060 1000 l. Common green turtle 75 20

1990. Archaeology (2nd series). As T **676**. Multicoloured.
3062 100 l. Ivory statuette of goddess (vert) 10 10
3063 200 l. Clay ram's head and antelope's head twin ceremonial vessel 10 10
3064 500 l. Gold goddess pendant (vert) 25 10
3065 700 l. Ivory statuette of lion . 30 10

1990. 75th Anniv of Gallipoli Campaign.
3066 **691** 1000 l. multicoloured . . 55 10

692 Turkish Garden (left half)

1990. International Garden and Greenery Exposition, Osaka. Multicoloured.
3067 1000 l. Type **692** 55 10
3068 1000 l. Right half of garden . 55 10
Nos. 3067/8 were issued together, se-tenant, forming a composite design.

1990. Various stamps surch.
3069 – 50 l. on 5 l. mult (No. 2868) 10 10
3070 **648** 100 l. on 10 l. red, violet and blue 10 10
3071 150 l. on 10 l. red, violet and blue 10 10
3072 – 200 l. on 70 l. mult (No. 2870) 10 10
3073 – 300 l. on 20 l. red, blue and brown (No. 2954) . . . 15 10
3074 – 300 l. on 70 l. mult (No. 2870) 15 10
3075 – 1500 l. on 20 l. mult (No. 2869) 15 10

694 "70" and Ataturk

695 Antalya

1990. 70th Anniv of Establishment of Nationalist Provisional Government.
3076 **694** 300 l. multicoloured . . 15 10

1990. European Tourism Year. Multicoloured.
3077 300 l. + 50 l. Type **695** . . 15 10
3078 1000 l. + 100 l. Istanbul . . 55 20

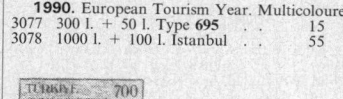

696 Ankara Post Office

697 Map and Dove as Open Book

1990. Europa. Post Office Buildings. Mult.
3079 700 l. Type **696** 30 10
3080 1000 l. Istanbul Post Office (horiz) 55 10

1990. European Supreme Courts' Conference, Ankara.
3081 **697** 1000 l. blue, dp bl & red 55 10

698 Fire Salamander

1990. World Environment Day. Multicoloured.
3082 300 l. Type **698** 15 10
3083 500 l. Banded newt 25 10
3084 1000 l. Fire-bellied toads . . 55 10
3085 1500 l. Common tree frog (vert) 65 10

699 "Ertugrul" (frigate) and Turkish and Japanese Women

701 Smoker's Body shattering

1990. Centenary of First Turkish Envoy to Japan.
3086 **699** 1000 l. multicoloured . . 75 15

1990. Anti-addiction Campaign. Multicoloured.
3087 300 l. on 50 l. Type **701** . . 15 10
3088 1000 l. on 100 l. Addict injecting drug into skeletal arm (horiz) 55 20

702 "Self-portrait"

703 Emblem, Pen, Open Book and Globe

1990. Death Centenary of Vincent van Gogh (painter). Multicoloured.
3089 300 l. Type **702** 15 10
3090 700 l. "Boats in Saintes Maries" (horiz) 30 10
3091 1000 l. "Sunflowers" 50 10
3092 1500 l. "Road with Cypress" 60 10

1990. As T **685** but inscription redrawn and dated "1990".
3093 **685** 500 l. green and grey . . 25 10
3094 1000 l. mauve and grey . 50 10

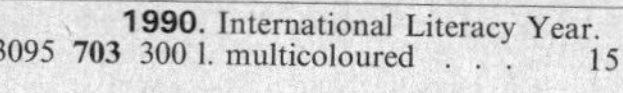

1990. International Literacy Year.
3095 **703** 300 l. multicoloured . . . 15 10

704 "Portrait" (Nurullah Berk)

705 Tatar Courier and Modern Postal Transport

1990. State Exhibition of Painting and Sculpture. Multicoloured.
3096 300 l. Type **704** 15 10
3097 700 l. "Derya Kuzulari" (Cevat Dereli) 30 10
3098 1000 l. "Artist's Mother" (bust) (Nijad Sirel) 50 10

1990. 150th Anniv of Ministry of Posts and Telecommunications. Multicoloured.
3099 200 l. Type **705** 10 10
3100 250 l. Computer terminal and Morse key 10 10
3101 400 l. Manual and digital telephone exchanges 20 10
3102 1500 l. Telegraph wires, dish aerial and satellite 60 10

1991. Archaeology (3rd series). As T **676**. Multicoloured.
3104 300 l. Clay figurine of woman (vert) 10 10
3105 500 l. Bronze sistrum (vert) . 20 10
3106 1000 l. Clay kettle on stand (vert) 40 10
3107 1500 l. Clay ceremonial vessel (vert) 50 10

707 Lake Abant

708 Satellite and Map of Europe

1991. Lakes. Multicoloured.
3110 250 l. Type **707** 10 10
3111 500 l. Lake Egirdir 15 10
3112 1500 l. Lake Van 50 10

1991. Europa. Europe in Space. Multicoloured.
3113 1000 l. Type **708** 40 10
3114 1500 l. Satellite and map of Europe (different) 50 10

709 Graph on Globe

1991. National Statistics Day.
3115 **709** 500 l. multicoloured . . . 15 10

710 Cable Ship, Map, Cable and Telephone Handset

711 Emblem

1991. Eastern Mediterranean Fibre Optic Cable System (EMOS-1).
3116 **710** 500 l. multicoloured . . . 20 10

1991. European Transport Ministers' Conference, Antalya.
3117 **711** 500 l. multicoloured . . . 15 10

MINIMUM PRICE

The minimum price quoted is 10p which represents a handling charge rather than a basis for valuing common stamps. For further notes about prices, see introductory pages.

712 Emre

713 Harpsichord, Score and Mozart

1991. "Yunus Emre (13th-century poet) Year of Love". Multicoloured.
3118 500 l. + 100 l. Type **712** . . 15 10
3119 1500 l. + 100 l. Globe, and Emre as tree 45 20

1991. Death Bicentenary of Wolfgang Amadeus Mozart (composer).
3120 **713** 1500 l. + 100 l. mult . . 45 20

714 "Abdulcanbaz" (Turhan Selcuk)

715 13th-century Seljukian Wall Plaque

1991. Caricature. Multicoloured.
3121 500 l. "Amcabey" (Cemal Nadir Guler) (horiz) 30 10
3122 1000 l. Type **714** 30 10

1991. Turkish Ceramics. Multicoloured.
3123 500 l. Type **715** 15 10
3124 1500 l. Late 16th-century Ottoman wall plaque . . . 45 10

716 Emblem

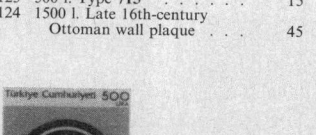

717 Dam, Water and Sun

1991. Turkish Grand National Assembly's Protection of Human Rights International Symposium, Ankara.
3125 **716** 500 l. multicoloured . . 15 10

1991. South-eastern Anatolia Project (hydro-electric power and irrigation development).
3126 **717** 500 l. multicoloured . . 15 10

718 Keloglan and Genie with Tray of Food

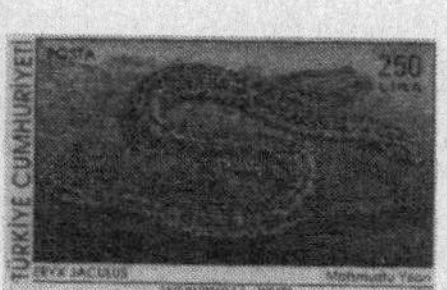
719 Sand Boa

1991. "Keloglan" (fairy tale). Multicoloured.
3127 500 l. Type **718** 10 10
3128 1000 l. Keloglan and dinner guests 25 10
3129 1500 l. Keloglan ploughing . . 35 10

1991. World Environment Day. Snakes. Mult.
3130 250 l. Type **719** 10 10
3131 500 l. Four-lined snake . . . 10 10
3132 1000 l. Ottoman viper . . . 25 10
3133 1500 l. Caucasus viper . . . 35 10

1992. Archaeology (4th series). As T **676**. Multicoloured.
3134 300 l. Clay statuette of Mother Goddess (vert) 10 10
3135 500 l. Bronze statuette (vert) 10 10
3136 1000 l. Hittite clay vase (vert) 20 10
3137 1500 l. Urartian lion (vert) . 25 10

721 Emblem and People 722 Balloons

1992. 30th Anniv of Supreme Court.
3140 **721** 500 l. + 100 l. mult . . 10 10

1992. Europa. 500th Anniv of Discovery of America by Columbus.
3141 – 1500 l. blue and red . . . 20 10
3142 **722** 2000 l. multicoloured . . 30 10
DESIGN—HORIZ: 1500 l. Stylised caravel.

723 Immigrant Ship 724 Kemal Ataturk

1992. 500th Anniv of Jewish Immigration.
3143 **723** 1500 l. multicoloured . . 20 10

1992.
3144 – 250 l. orange, ochre and gold 10 10
3145 **724** 10000 l. bl, grey & gold . 1·50 15
DESIGN: 250 l. Portrait of Ataturk as in Type **685**.

725 Court Emblem 726 Congress Emblem

1992. 130th Anniv of Court of Accounts.
3146 **725** 500 l. multicoloured . . . 10 10

1992. 3rd Turkish Economy Congress, Izmir.
3147 **726** 1500 l. multicoloured . . 20 10

727 Lapwing 728 Ears of Grain, Cogwheel and Hands

1992. World Environment Day. Birds. Mult.
3148 500 l. Type **727** 10 10
3149 1000 l. Golden oriole 15 10
3150 1500 l. Common shelduck . . 20 10
3151 2000 l. White-breasted kingfisher (vert) 30 10

1992. Black Sea Economic Co-operation Conference, Istanbul.
3152 **728** 1500 l. multicoloured . . 20 10

729 Doves forming Olympic Flame 730 Soldiers and Old Woman

1992. Olympic Games, Barcelona. Multicoloured.
3153 500 l. Type **729** 10 10
3154 1000 l. Boxing 15 10
3155 1500 l. Weightlifting 20 10
3156 2000 l. Wrestling 30 10

1992. Legend of Anatolia. Multicoloured.
3157 500 l. Type **730** 10 10
3158 1000 l. Old woman filling trough with buttermilk . . 15 10
3159 1500 l. Soldiers drinking from trough 20 10

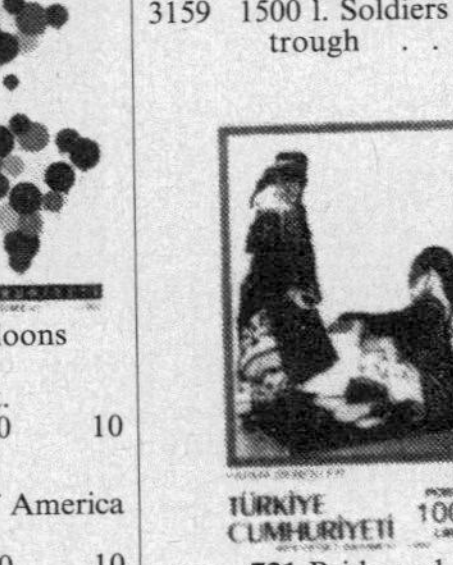

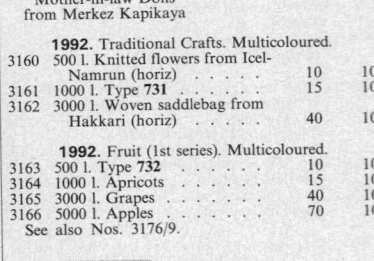

731 Bride and Mother-in-law Dolls from Merkez Kapikaya 732 Cherries

1992. Traditional Crafts. Multicoloured.
3160 500 l. Knitted flowers from Icel-Namrun (horiz) 10 10
3161 1000 l. Type **731** 15 10
3162 3000 l. Woven saddlebag from Hakkari (horiz) 40 10

1992. Fruit (1st series). Multicoloured.
3163 500 l. Type **732** 10 10
3164 1000 l. Apricots 15 10
3165 3000 l. Grapes 40 10
3166 5000 l. Apples 70 10
See also Nos. 3176/9.

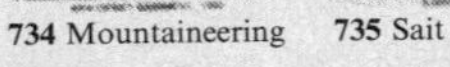

734 Mountaineering 735 Sait Faik Abasiyanik

1992. 26th Anniv of Turkish Mountaineering Federation (3169) and 80th Anniv of Turkish Scout Movement (3170). Multicoloured.
3169 1000 l. + 200 l. Type **734** . 15 10
3170 3000 l. + 200 l. Scouts watering sapling (horiz) 45 20

1992. Anniversaries. No value expressed.
3171 **735** (T) blue, indigo and red 10 10
3172 – (T) blue, orange & violet 10 10
3173 – (M) blue, green & orange 15 10
3174 – (M) blue, red and indigo 15 10
3175 – (M) blue, red and green 15 10
DESIGNS: No. 3171, Type **935** (writer, 86th birth anniv); 3172, Fikret Mualla Saygi (painter, 25th death anniv); 3173, Muhsin Ertugrul (actor and producer, birth centenary); 3174, Cevat Sakir Kabaagaeli (writer, 19th death anniv); 3175, Asik Veysel Satiroglu (poet, 98th birth anniv).
Nos. 3171/2 were intended for greeting cards and Nos. 3173/5 for inland letters.

1993. Fruit (2nd series). As T **732**. Multicoloured.
3176 500 l. Bananas 10 10
3177 1000 l. Oranges 10 10
3178 3000 l. Pears 15 10
3179 5000 l. Pomegranates . . . 20 10

736 Sculpture (Hadi Bara) 737 Terraces

1993. Europa. Contemporary Art. Multicoloured.
3180 1000 l. Type **736** 10 10
3181 3000 l. Carved figure (Zuhtu Muridoglu) 15 10

1993. Campaign for the Preservation of Pamukkale. Multicoloured.
3182 1000 l. + 200 l. Type **737** . 10 10
3183 3000 l. + 500 l. Close-up of terrace 15 10

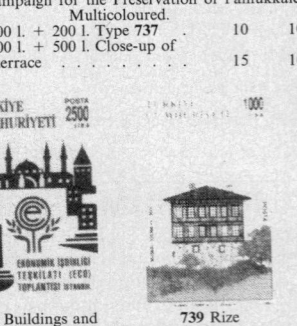

738 Buildings and Emblem 739 Rize

1993. Economic Co-operation Organization Conference, Istanbul.
3184 **738** 2500 l. ultramarine, blue and gold 10 10

1993. Traditional Houses (1st series). Multicoloured.
3185 1000 l. Type **739** 10 10
3186 2500 l. Rize (different) (horiz) 10 10
3187 3000 l. Trabzon 15 10
3188 5000 l. Black Sea houses (horiz) 20 10
See also Nos. 3222/5.

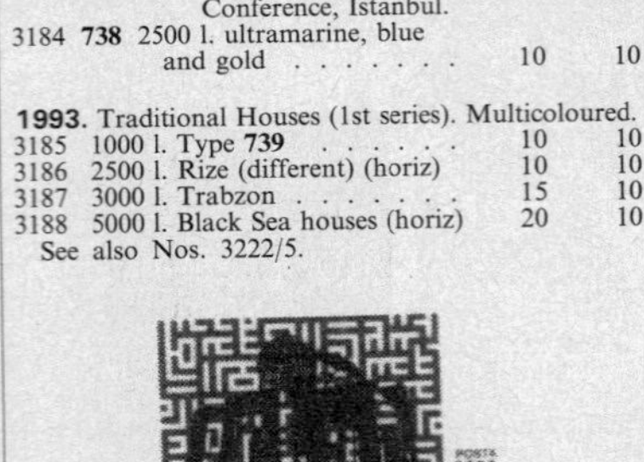

740 Mausoleum

1993. 900th Birth Anniv of Hoca Ahmet Yesevi (philosopher).
3189 **740** 3000 l. gold, blue & lt bl . 15 10

741 Haci Arif Bey

1993. Death Anniversaries. No value expressed. Each brown and red.
3190 (T) Type **741** (composer, 109th) 10 10
3191 (T) Neyzen Tevfik Kolayli (singer, 40th) 10 10
3192 (M) Orhan Veli Kanik (poet, 43rd) 10 10
3193 (M) Cahit Sitki Taranci (poet, 27th) 10 10
3194 (M) Munir Nurettin Seluk (composer, 12th) 10 10
Nos. 3190/1 were intended for greetings cards and Nos. 3192/4 for inland letters.

742 Emblem

1993. Istanbul's Bid to host Summer Olympic Games in Year 2000.
3195 **742** 2500 l. multicoloured . . 10 10

1993. As T **685** but inscription redrawn and dated "1993".
3199 **685** 5000 l. violet and gold . . 20 10
3200 20000 l. mauve & gold . . 85 10

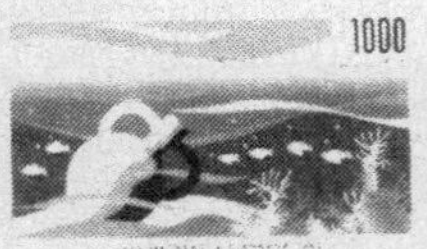

744 Amphora on Sea-bed

1993. Mediterranean Treaty. Multicoloured.
3201 1000 l. Type **744** 10 10
3202 3000 l. Dolphin 15 10

745 Emblem

1993. U.N. Natural Disaster Relief Day.
3203 **745** 3000 l. + 500 l. mult . . 15 10

746 Prayer Mat 747 Laurel Wreath, Torch and Silhouette of Kemal Ataturk

1993. Handicrafts. Multicoloured.
3204 1000 l. Type **746** 10 10
3205 2500 l. Silver earrings . . . 10 10
3206 5000 l. Crocheted purse . . . 20 10

1993. 70th Anniv of Republic.
3207 **747** 1000 l. multicoloured . . 10 10

748 Man in Gas Mask and Fire

1993. Civil Defence.
3208 **748** 1000 l. multicoloured . . 10 10

749 Satellite, Globe and Map 750 Ears of Corn

1994. "Turksat" Communications Satellite. Multicoloured.
3209 1500 l. Type **749** 10 10
3210 5000 l. Satellite and map showing satellite's "foot-print" 20 10

1994. 40th Anniv of Water Supply Company.
3211 **750** 1500 l. multicoloured . . 10 10

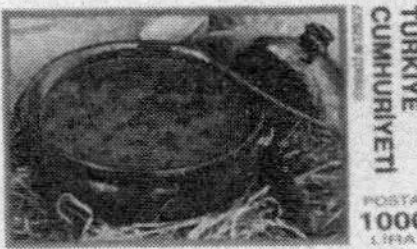

751 Ezogelin Corbasi

1994. Traditional Dishes. Multicoloured.
3212 1000 l. Type **751** 10 10
3213 1500 l. Karisik dolma . . . 10 10
3214 3500 l. Shish kebabs 10 10
3215 5000 l. Baklava 15 10

752 Marie Curie

1994. Europa. Discoveries. Multicoloured.
3216 1500 l. Type **752** (discoverer of radium) 10 10
3217 5000 l. Albert Einstein and equation (formulator of Theory of Relativity) (horiz) 15 10

754 Faselis, Antalya

1994. Environment Day. Multicoloured.
3220 6000 l. Type **754** 15 10
3221 8500 l. Gocek, Mugla (vert) . 25 10

755 Bursa

1994. Traditional Houses (2nd series). Multicoloured.
3222 2500 l. Type **755** 10 10
3223 3500 l. Uskudar 10 10
3224 6000 l. Anadolu Hisari . . . 15 10
3225 8500 l. Edirne 25 10

756 Trekking in Mountains 757 Centenary Emblem over City

1994. Tourism. Multicoloured.

3226		5000 l. Type **756**	15	10
3227		10000 l. White-water rafting (horiz)	30	10

1994. Centenary of International Olympic Committee.

3228	**757**	12500 l. + 500 l. mult	40	15

758 "2001"

1994. Seven Year Plan.

3229	**758**	2500 l. multicoloured	10	10

759 Kusak Design **760** Kemal Ataturk

1994. Embroidery. Multicoloured.

3230		7500 l. Type **759**	20	10
3231		12500 l. Paalik design (horiz)	35	10

1994.

3232	**760**	50000 l. violet, mve & red	1·50	20

761 Common Morel **762** "Platanus orientalis"

1994. Fungi. Multicoloured.

3233		2500 l. Type **761**	10	10
3234		5000 l. "Agaricus bernardii"	15	10
3235		7500 l. Saffron milk cap	20	10
3236		12500 l. Parasol mushroom	35	10

1994. Trees. Multicoloured.

3237		7500 l. + 500 l. Type **762**	25	10
3238		12500 l. + 1000 l. "Cupressus sempervirens" (vert)	40	15

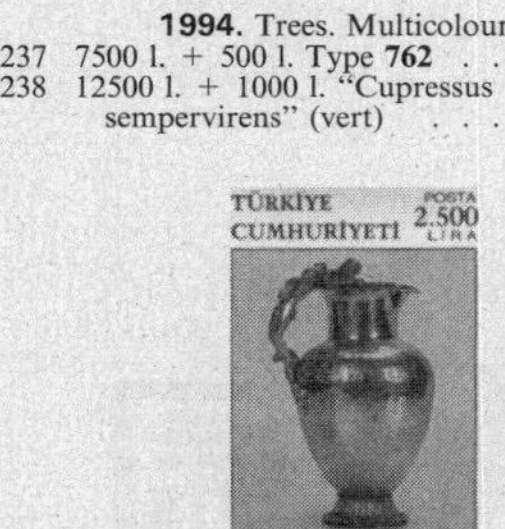

763 Silver Jug

1994. Traditional Crafts. Multicoloured.

3239		2500 l. Type **763**	10	10
3240		5000 l. Silver censer	15	10
3241		7500 l. Necklace (horiz)	20	10
3242		12500 l. Gold brooch (half horse and half fish) (horiz)	35	10

OBLIGATORY TAX STAMPS

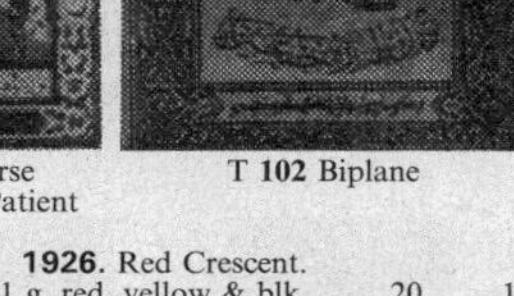

T 101 Nurse bandaging Patient **T 102** Biplane

1926. Red Crescent.

T1035	–	1 g. red, yellow & blk	20	10
T1036	**T 101**	2½ g. multicoloured	25	10
T1037	–	5 g. multicoloured	35	15
T1038	–	10 g. multicoloured	70	45

DESIGNS—VERT: 1 g. Red crescent and decorative archway; 5 g. Refugees. HORIZ: 10 g. Stretcher bearers.

1926. Aviation Fund.

T1039	**T 102**	20 pa. brown & grn	65	15
T1040		1 g. green & stone	65	15
T1041		5 g. violet & green	1·50	25
T1042		5 g. red and green	19·00	2·10

The 5 g. stamps are 40×29 mm.

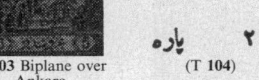

T 103 Biplane over Ankara

۲۰ پاره

(**T 104**)

1927. Aviation Fund.

T1043	**T 102**	20 pa. red and green	10	10
T1044		1 g. green and ochre	10	10
T1045	**T 103**	2 g. brown & green	50	40
T1046		2½ g. red and green	2·50	2·00
T1047		5 g. blue and buff	35	35
T1048		10 g. blue and pink	3·00	2·00
T1049		15 g. green & yellow	2·25	2·50
T1050		20 g. brown & ochre	3·00	2·00
T1051		50 g. blue & lt blue	5·50	4·00
T1052		100 g. red and blue	35·00	23·00

The 20 pa. and 1 g. are 25×15 mm.

1927. Red Crescent No. T1035 and charity labels surch with Type **T 104** or similar types.

T1053		20 pa. on 1 g. red, yellow and black	75	25
T1054		20 pa. on 1 g. brown	2·00	45
T1055		20 pa. on 2½ g. lilac	80	50

DESIGNS: 26×21 mm. No. T1054 Hospital ship. No. T1055 Nurse tending patient.

No. T1053 has an extra line of Turkish characters in the surcharge.

T 105 Red Crescent on Map of Turkey **T 106** Cherubs holding Star

1928. Red Crescent. Various frames. Crescent in red.

T1067	**T 105**	½ pi. brown	10	10
T1068		1 pi. purple	10	10
T1069		2½ pi. orange	10	10
T1070		5 pi. brown	10	10
T1071		10 pi. green	40	30
T1072		20 pi. blue	85	30
T1073		50 pi. purple	2·25	1·60

See also Nos. T1171/4 and T1198/1212.

1928. Child Welfare.

T1074	**T 106**	1 g. olive and red	10	10
T1075		2½ g. brown and red	20	10
T1076		5 g. green and red	25	20
T1077		25 g. black and red	2·00	1·10

See also Nos. T1160/1 and T1165/6.

1930. Aviation Fund. Nos. T1039, T1043, T1045 and T1049 surch.

T1099	**T 102**	Bir (1) k. on 20 pa. brown & green	32·00	22·00
T1100		Bir (1) k. on 20 pa. red and green	10	10
T1101	**T 103**	Yuz (100) pa. on 2 g. brown & green	10	15
T1102	**T 102**	5 k. on 20 pa. red and green	15	15
T1103		Bes (5) k. on 20 pa. red and green	90	15
T1104	**T 103**	On (10) k. on 2 g. brown and green	35	25
T1105		Elli (50) k. on 2 g. brown and green	3·25	1·25
T1106		Bir (1) l. on 2 g. brown and green	7·50	2·00
T1107		Bes (5) l. on 15 g. green and yellow	£180	£120

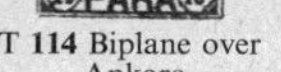

T 114 Biplane over Ankara **T 118** Biplane

1931. Aviation Fund.

T1141	**T 114**	20 pa. black	30	10

See also Nos. T1154/6.

1932. Child Welfare. No. T1074 surch.

T1150	**T 106**	20 pa. on 1 g. olive and red	30	10
T1153		3 k. on 1 g. olive and red	70	10

1932. Aviation Fund. As Type **T 114** but larger, 22×30 mm., and with sky shaded.

T1154		1 k. purple	10	10
T1155		5 k. red	45	20
T1156		10 k. green	80	25

1932. Red Crescent. Nos. T1067, T1069 and T1071 surch.

T1157	**T 105**	1 k. on 2½ pi. orange	25	15
T1158		5 k. on ½ pi. brown	50	20
T1159		5 k. on 10 pi. green	60	30

1933. Child Welfare. As Type **T 106** but inscr "IZMIR HIMAYEI ETFAL CEMIYETI".

T1160		1 k. violet and red	30	10
T1161		5 k. brown and red	75	35

1933. Aviation Fund.

T1162	**T 118**	On (10) pa. green	30	10
T1163		Bir (1) k. red	50	15
T1164		Bes (5) k. lilac	60	40

1934. Child Welfare. As Type **T 106** but inscr "Turkiye Himayeietfal Cemiyeti".

T1165		20 pa. purple and red	20	10
T1166		15 k. green and red	1·25	45

T 119 Red Crescent and Map of Turkey

1934. Inscr "TURKIYE HILALIAHMER CEMIYETI" (different frame on 5 k.).

T1171	**T 119**	½ k. blue and red	10	10
T1172		1 k. brown and red	10	10
T1173		2½ k. brown and red	10	10
T1174		5 k. green and red	40	30

See also Nos. T1198/1212.

1936. Child Welfare. Nos. T1074/5 and T1165 optd **P.Y.S.** or surch also.

T1186	**T 106**	20 pa. purple & red	75	25
T1187		1 g. olive and red	55	15
T1188		3 k. on 2½ g. brn & red	75	35

1937. Red Crescent. As Types **T 105** and **T 119** but inscr "TURKIYE KIZILAY CEMIYETI". Various frames.

T1204		½ k. blue and red	10	10
T1199		1 k. mauve and red	10	10
T1200		2½ k. orange and red	10	10
T1201		5 k. green and red	25	10
T1209		5 k. brown and red	60	15
T1202		10 k. green and red	75	25
T1203		20 k. black and red	1·25	60
T1211		50 k. purple and red	3·75	75
T1212		1 l. blue and red	12·00	2·25

1938. Child Welfare. No. T1075 surch. (a) Value in figures and words above **P. Y. S.**

T1213	**T 106**	20 pa. on 2½ g. brown and red	45	20
T1214		1 k. on 2½ g. brown and red	45	20

(b) **P. Y. S.** above value in figures and words.

T1215	**T 106**	20 pa. on 2½ g. brown and red	55	30
T1216		1 k. on 2½ g. brown and red	55	25

(c) **1 kurus**

T1217	**T 106**	1 k. on 2½ g. brown and red	65	20

T 138 Laughing Child **T 139** Nurse and Baby

1940. Child Welfare. Star in red.

T1259	**T 138**	20 pa. green	10	10
T1260		1 k. lilac	10	10
T1261	**T 139**	1 k. blue	10	10
T1262		2½ k. mauve	10	10
T1263	**T 138**	3 k. black	10	10
T1264	**T 139**	5 k. lilac	15	10
T1265		10 k. green	60	20
T1266	**T 138**	15 k. blue	30	15
T1267	**T 139**	25 k. olive	1·25	40
T1268		50 k. olive	2·75	70

T 145 Soldier and Map of Turkey **T 151** Child eating

1941. National Defence.

T1289	**T 145**	1 k. violet	25	10
T1290		2 k. blue	1·50	10
T1291		3 k. brown	1·50	20
T1292		4 k. mauve	1·25	10
T1293		5 k. pink	5·50	40
T1294		10 k. blue	10·00	60

1943. Child Welfare. Inscr "SEFKAT PULLARI 1943".

T1330	**T 151**	0.50 k. violet and red	10	10
T1331		0.50 k. green and red	10	10
T1332	–	1 k. blue and red	10	10
T1333	–	3 k. red and orange	25	10
T1334	–	15 k. black, buff and red	40	20
T1335	–	100 k. blue and red	1·25	60

DESIGNS—VERT: 1 k. Nurse with baby; 15 k. Baby and emblem; 100 k. President Inonu and child. HORIZ: 3 k. Nurse and child.

T 152 Child Welfare Emblem **T 155** Pres. Inonu and Victim

1943. Child Welfare. Star in red.

T1337	**T 152**	20 pa. blue	10	10
T1338	–	1 k. green	10	10
T1339	–	3 k. brown	10	10
T1340	–	5 k. orange	85	20
T1341	–	5 k. brown	20	15
T1342	–	10 k. red	25	15
T1343	–	15 k. lilac	45	15
T1344	–	25 k. violet	95	15
T1345	–	50 k. blue	1·60	20
T1346	–	100 k. green	3·00	40

DESIGNS—VERT: 1 k. Hospital; 3 k. Nurse and children; 5 k. Baby in cot; 10 k. Nurse bathing baby; 15 k. Nurse helping child to drink; 50 k. Child. HORIZ: 25 k. Baby with bottle; 100 k. Hospital.

1944. Red Crescent. Inscr "TURKIYE KIZILAY CEMIYETI".

T1347	–	20 pa. brown, flesh, red and blue	15	10
T1348	**T 155**	1 k. olive, yellow, green and red	15	10
T1349	–	2½ k. blue and red	25	10
T1350	–	5 k. blue and red	70	10
T1351	–	10 k. blue, green and red	80	25
T1352	–	50 k. green, black and red	2·25	60
T1353	–	1 l. yellow, black and red	4·50	85

DESIGNS—VERT: 20 pa. Nurse tending dreaming patient; 5 k. Soldier and nurse; 10 k. Feeding victims; 50 k. Wounded soldiers on raft; 1 l. Nurse within red crescent. HORIZ: 2½ k. Stretcher bearers and hospital ship.

T 156 Nurse helping Child to Drink **T 159** Nurse tucking baby in Cot

1945. Child Welfare. Star in red.

T1354	–	1 k. lilac	10	10
T1355	–	2½ k. blue	20	15
T1356	**T 156**	5 k. green	20	15
T1357	–	10 k. brown	75	25
T1358	–	250 k. black	7·50	2·75
T1359	–	500 k. violet	15·00	5·00

DESIGNS—VERT (21×20 mm): 1 k. Nurse carrying baby; 2½ k. Nurse holding child; 10 k. Child sucking thumb. HORIZ (28×22 mm): 250, 500 k. Emblem.

1946. 25th Anniv of Child Welfare Organization.

T1360	**T 159**	20 pa. brown & red	10	10
T1361	–	1 k. blue and red	10	10
T1362	–	2½ k. red	10	10
T1363	–	5 k. brown and red	10	10
T1364	–	15 k. purple & red	20	10
T1365	–	25 k. green and red	50	30

T1366	–	50 k. green and red .	85	40
T1367	–	150 k. brown and red	2·50	60

DESIGNS: 1 k. Mother and baby; 2½ k. Nurse holding child above head; 5 k. Doctor examining baby; 15 k. Nurse feeding baby; 25 k. Nurse bathing baby; 50 k. Nurse weighing baby; 150 k. Nurse, and child in cot.

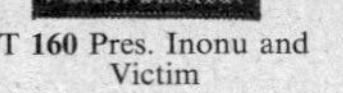

T 160 Pres. Inonu and Victim — T 169 Nurse and Children playing

1946. Red Crescent. As Nos. T1347/8, T1350 and T1353 and new design inscr "TURKIYE KIZILAY DERNEGI".

T1369	–	20 pa. yellow, grey, blue and red	10	10
T1532	–	20 pa. brown, yellow, violet and red . .	10	10
T1370	T 155	1 k. multicoloured . .	1·00	10
T1371	T 160	1 k. brown, blue and red	20	10
T1533	–	1 k. grn, blk & red . .	10	10
T1372	–	5 k. blue and red . .	40	10
T1373	–	20 k. red, bl & pur . .	75	20
T1374	–	1 l. blk, yell & red . .	2·25	75
T1375	–	250 k. black, green and red	5·50	75
T1376	–	5 l. black, pink and red	7·50	75
T1377	–	10 l. blue and red . .	20·00	10·00

DESIGNS—VERT: 20 pa. As No. T1347; 1 k. (T1533), As No. T1352; 5 k. As No. T1350; 1 l. As No. T1353; 5 l. Nurse tending patient; 10 l. Soldier, red crescent and figure symbolising Victory. HORIZ: 20 k. Ankara Hospital; 250 k. Nurse helping injured soldier.

1948. Child Welfare. Star in red.

T1399	T 169	20 pa. blue	10	10
T1400	–	20 pa. mauve	10	10
T1401	–	1 k. green	10	10
T1402	–	3 k. purple	25	25
T1403	–	15 k. grey	1·40	50
T1404	–	30 k. orange	2·25	1·25
T1405	–	150 k. green	4·50	2·25
T1406	–	300 k. red	5·50	4·00

DESIGNS—VERT: 20 pa. (No. 1400) Nurse and children walking; 1 k. Nurse feeding two children; 3 k. Nurse with three children; 15 k. Parents and two children; 150 k. Nurse holding baby; 300 k. Heads of nurse and child. HORIZ: 30 k. Father handing baby to nurse.

T 177 Ruins and Tent — T 179 "Grief"

1949. Red Crescent.

T1422	T 177	5 k. black, red & pur	25	10
T1423		10 k. purple, red and flesh	25	10

1950. Red Crescent. Crescent in red.

T1425	T 179	½ k. blue	55	25
T1426		1 k. blue	10	10
T1427		2 k. mauve	15	10
T1428		2½ k. orange	15	10
T1429		3 k. green	15	10
T1430		4 k. drab	25	20
T1431		5 k. blue	50	10
T1432		10 k. pink	90	15
T1433		25 k. brown	1·25	35
T1434	–	50 k. blue	2·00	60
T1435	–	100 k. green	3·50	75

DESIGN: 50, 100 k. Plant with broken stem.

1952. (a) Red Crescent. Nos. T1427 and T1429/30 surch.

T1489	T 179	20 pa. on 2 k. mauve and red	25	10
T1490		20 pa. on 3 k. green and red	25	10
T1491		20 pa. on 4 k. drab and red	25	10

(b) Child Welfare. Nos. T1355, T1362 and T1339 surch.

T1492	–	1 k. on 2½ k. blue and red	20	10
T1493	–	1 k. on 2½ k. red . .	20	10
T1494	–	1 k. on 3 k. brown and red	20	10

T 208 Nurse and Baby — T 211 Globe and Flag

1954. Child Welfare. Inscr "SEFKAT PULLARI 1954".

T1534	–	20 pa. yellow & orge	10	10
T1535	–	20 pa. green and red	10	10
T1536	T 208	1 k. blue and red . .	10	10

DESIGN: Nos. 1534/5, Nurse with two children. See also Nos. T1569 and T1573/4.

1954. Red Crescent.

T1545	T 211	1 k. multicoloured . .	10	10
T1546	–	5 k. red, grey and green	10	10
T1547	–	10 k. grey, green and red	15	10

DESIGNS: 5 k. Nurse with wings on cloud; 10 k. Arm and hand.
See also Nos. T1652, T1656/8, T1838 and T1840/3.

T 212 Florence Nightingale — T 215 Children Kissing

1954. Red Crescent. Centenary of Florence Nightingale's Arrival at Scutari.

T1551	T 212	20 k. green, brown and red	40	20
T1552	–	30 k. brown, black and red	40	25
T1553	–	50 k. stone, black and red	1·10	75

DESIGNS: 30 k. Florence Nightingale (three-quarter face); 50 k. Selimiye Barracks.

1955. Child Welfare. Inscr "SEFKAT PULLARI 1955". Star in red.

T1564	T 215	20 pa. blue	10	10
T1565		20 pa. brown . . .	10	10
T1566		1 k. purple	10	10
T1567		3 k. bistre	10	10
T1568		5 k. orange	10	10
T1569	T 208	10 k. green	1·10	60
T1570	–	15 k. blue	10	10
T1571	–	25 k. lake	75	25
T1572	–	50 k. green	1·25	75
T1573	T 208	2½ l. brown	40·00	25·00
T1574		10 l. violet	95·00	50·00

DESIGN: 15 to 50 k. Nurse carrying baby.

1955. Red Crescent. Nos. T1373 and T1435 surch.

T1575	20 pa. on 20 k. red, blue and purple	10	10
T1576	20 pa. on 100 k. green and red	20	10

T 219 Nurse — T 227 Woman and Children

1955. Red Crescent. Congress of International Council of Nurses.

T1578	T 219	10 k. brown, red and black	75	25
T1579	–	15 k. green, red and black	75	25
T1580	–	100 k. blue and red .	1·75	1·00

DESIGNS—HORIZ: 15 k. Nurses marching. VERT: 100 k. Emblem, Red Cross and Red Crescent flags and nurses.

1956. Child Welfare. Star in red.

T1614	T 227	20 pa. salmon . . .	10	10
T1615		20 pa. olive	10	10
T1616		1 k. blue	15	10
T1617		1 k. violet	15	10
T1618		3 k. brown	30	10
T1619	–	10 k. red	1·50	10
T1620	–	25 k. green	3·25	1·25
T1621	–	50 k. blue	4·50	1·50
T1622	–	2½ l. lilac	8·00	4·00
T1623	–	5 l. brown	12·00	5·00
T1624	–	10 l. green	22·00	10·00

DESIGNS: 10 k. to 50 k. Flag and building; 2½ l. to 10 l. Mother and baby.

1956. Red Crescent. No. T1545 surch.

T1625	T 211	20 pa. on 1 k. mult .	15	10
T1626		2.5 k. on 1 k. mult .	10	10

1956. Child Welfare. Nos. 1399/1406 optd **IV. DUNYA Cocuk Gunu 1 Ekim 1956**. Nos. 1644/6 surch. also.

T1639	T 169	20 pa. red and blue .	3·75	3·75
T1640	–	20 pa. mauve & red	3·75	3·75
T1641	–	1 k. green and red .	3·75	3·75
T1642	–	3 k. purple and red .	3·75	3·75
T1643	–	15 k. grey and red .	4·75	4·75
T1644	–	25 k. on 30 k. orange and red	4·75	4·75
T1645	–	100 k. on 150 k. green and red	5·75	5·75
T1646	–	250 k. on 300 k. deep red and red . . .	7·50	7·50

1957. Red Crescent. As No. T1373 but inscr "TURKIYE KIZILAY CEMIYETI", new design and as Nos. T1545/6. Crescent in red.

T1651	–	½ k. drab & brown . .	10	10
T1652	T 211	1 k. black, bis & grn	10	10
T1653	–	2½ k. green & dp grn .	10	10
T1655	–	20 k. red, brown and blue	25	15
T1656	T 211	25 k. grey, black and green	55	45
T1657		50 k. blue and green .	65	50
T1658		100 k. violet, black and green	1·50	75

DESIGNS—VERT: ½, 2½ k. Flower being watered. HORIZ: 20 k. Ankara hospital.

T 239 Two Babies — T 246 Nurse and Child

1957. Child Welfare.

T1659	T 239	20 pa. green and red .	10	10
T1660		20 pa. pink and red .	10	10
T1661		1 k. blue and red . .	10	10
T1662		3 k. orange and red .	40	15
T1683	T 246	100 k. brown & red .	75	25
T1684		150 k. green and red .	75	25
T1685		250 k. violet and red .	1·00	75

T 254 Florence Nightingale — T 225 Child's Head and Butterfly

1958. Florence Nightingale Foundation. Crescent in red.

T1829	T 254	1 l. green	40	25
T1830		1½ l. grey	65	40
T1831		2½ l. blue	90	40

1958. Child Welfare. Butterflies. Multicoloured.

T1832	20 k. Type **255**	25	15
T1833	25 k. Brimstone	25	15
T1834	50 k. Little tiger blue (horiz)	30	25
T1835	75 k. Green-veined white (horiz)	85	70
T1836	150 k. Peacock	2·00	1·50

1958. Red Crescent. As Nos. T1651/3, T1546 and T1656/8 but colours changed. Crescent in red.

T1837	–	½ k. lilac	15	10
T1838	T 211	1 k. black, brown and green	15	10
T1839	–	2½ k. grey and red . .	25	10
T1840	–	5 k. red, brown and green	35	10
T1841	T 211	25 k. black, green and brown	55	20
T1842		50 k. purple, black and green	1·75	25
T1843		100 k. drab, black and green	2·75	75

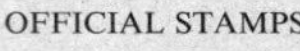

OFFICIAL STAMPS

O 160 — O 241 — O 284

1947.

O1360	O 160	10 pa. brown	10	10
O1361		1 k. green	10	10
O1362		2 k. purple	15	10
O1363		3 k. orange	15	10
O1364		5 k. turquoise	6·50	10
O1365		10 k. brown	1·50	10
O1366		15 k. violet	80	10
O1367		20 k. blue	85	10
O1368		30 k. olive	90	10
O1369		50 k. blue	90	10
O1370		1 l. green	1·00	10
O1371		2 l. red	1·25	10

1951. Postage stamps optd **RESMI** between bars with star and crescent above.

O1458	165	0.25 k. red	10	10
O1454		5 k. blue	20	10
O1461		10 k. brown	20	10
O1462		15 k. violet	40	10
O1456		20 k. blue	50	10
O1469		30 k. brown	35	10
O1470		60 k. black	1·00	10

1955. Postage stamps optd **RESMI** between wavy bars with star and crescent above or surch also.

O1568	165	0.25 k. red	10	10
O1587		½ k. on 1 k. black . . .	10	10
O1569		1 k. black	10	10
O1570		2 k. purple	10	10
O1593	165	2 k. on 4 k. green . .	10	10
O1571		3 k. orange	10	10
O1594		3 k. on 4 k. green . .	10	10
O1572		4 k. green	10	10
O1573		5 k. on 15 k. violet . .	10	10
O1581		5 k. blue	35	10
O1595		10 k. on 12 k. red . .	10	10
O1574		10 k. on 15 k. violet . .	10	10
O1575		15 k. violet	10	10
O1576		20 k. blue	15	10
O1585		30 k. brown	60	10
O1577		40 k. on 1 l. olive . .	25	10
O1590		75 k. on 1 l. olive . .	60	10
O1578		75 k. on 2 l. brown . .	60	15
O1579		75 k. on 5 l. purple . .	6·00	2·75

1957.

O1655	O 241	5 k. blue	10	10
O1843		5 k. red	10	10
O1656		10 k. brown	10	10
O1844		10 k. olive	10	10
O1657		15 k. violet	10	10
O1845		15 k. red	10	10
O1658		20 k. red	10	10
O1846		20 k. violet	10	10
O1659		30 k. olive	10	10
O1660		40 k. purple	15	10
O1847		40 k. blue	10	10
O1661		50 k. grey	15	10
O1662		60 k. green	20	10
O1848		60 k. orange	30	10
O1663		75 k. orange	30	10
O1849		75 k. grey	30	10
O1664		100 k. green	35	10
O1850		100 k. violet	35	10
O1665		200 k. lake	70	25
O1851		200 k. brown	85	15

1960.

O1916	O 284	1 k. orange	10	10
O1917		5 k. red	10	10
O1918		10 k. green	60	10
O1919		30 k. brown	10	10
O1920		60 k. green	20	10
O1921		1 l. purple	40	10
O1922		1½ l. blue	25	10
O1923		2½ l. violet	75	10
O1924		5 l. blue	4·50	20

O 303 — O 320

1962.

O1977	O 303	1 k. brown	10	10
O1978		5 k. green	10	10
O1979		10 k. brown	10	10
O1980		15 k. blue	10	10
O1981		25 k. red	10	10
O1982		30 k. blue	15	10

1963. Surch.

O2003	O 303	50 k. on 30 k. blue .	25	10
O2004	O 284	100 k. on 60 k. green	45	10

1963.

O2042	O 320	1 k. green	10	10
O2043		5 k. brown	10	10
O2044		10 k. green	10	10
O2045		50 k. red	15	10
O2046		100 k. blue	30	10

O 329 — O 344

1964.

O2074	O 329	1 k. grey	10	10
O2075		5 k. blue	15	10
O2076		10 k. yellow	15	10
O2077		30 k. red	40	10
O2078		50 k. green	40	10
O2079		60 k. brown	85	10
O2080		80 k. turquoise . . .	2·25	10
O2081		130 k. blue	2·00	10
O2082		200 k. purple	3·25	10

1965.

O2133	O 344	1 k. green	10	10
O2134		10 k. blue	10	10
O2135		50 k. orange	20	10

O 358 Usak Carpet — O 372 Doves Emblem — O 383

1966. Turkish Carpets.

O2175	O 358	1 k. orange	10	10
O2176	–	50 k. green	10	10
O2177	–	100 k. red	30	10
O2178	–	150 k. blue	40	10
O2179	–	200 k. bistre	40	10
O2180	–	500 k. lilac	1·00	10

DESIGNS (Carpets of): 50 k. Bergama; 100 k. Ladik; 150 k. Selcuk; 200 k. Nomad; 500 k. Anatolia.

1967.
O2213 O 372 1 k. blue & lt blue . 10 10
O2214 50 k. blue & orange 15 10
O2215 100 k. blue & mauve 25 10

1968.
O2241 O 383 50 k. brown & green 10 10
O2242 150 k. black & orge 25 10
O2243 500 k. brown & blue 60 10

O 400 O 427 O 440

1969.
O2287 O 400 1 k. red and green . 10 10
O2288 10 k. blue & green 10 10
O2289 50 k. brown & green 10 10
O2290 100 k. mauve & grn 35 10

1971.
O2359 O 427 5 k. blue & brown . 10 10
O2360 10 k. red and blue 10 10
O2361 30 k. violet & orge 15 10
O2362 50 k. brown & blue 20 10
O2363 75 k. green & buff 35 10

1971. Face-value and border colour given first.
O2398 O 440 5 k. blue and grey . 10 10
O2399 25 k. green & brown 10 10
O2400 100 k. brown & grn 25 10
O2401 200 k. brn & ochre 20 10
O2402 250 k. purple & vio 25 10
O2403 500 k. blue & light blue 65 10

O 446 O 462 O 478 Trellis Motif

1972.
O2411 O 446 5 k. blue & brown . 10 10
O2412 100 k. green & brn 25 10
O2413 200 k. red & brown . 40 20

1973.
O2457 O 462 100 k. blue & cream 20 10

1974.
O2490 O 478 10 k. brown on pink 10 10
O2491 25 k. purple on blue 10 10
O2492 50 k. red on mauve 10 10
O2493 150 k. brown on grn 20 10
O2494 250 k. red on pink 30 10
O2495 500 k. brown on yell 65 10

O 496 O 528 O 529

1975.
O2537 O 496 100 k. red and blue . 15 10

1977. Surch.
O2587 O 320 5 k. on 1 k. green 10 10
O2588 O 329 5 k. on 1 k. grey 10 10
O2589 O 344 5 k. on 1 k. green 10 10
O2590 O 358 5 k. on 1 k. orange 10 10
O2591 O 372 5 k. on 1 k. blue and light blue 10 10

1977.
O2609 O 528 250 k. green & blue . 25 10

1978.
O2610 O 529 50 k. pink and red 10 10
O2611 2½ l. buff and brown 10 10
O2612 4½ l. lilac and green 15 10
O2613 5 l. blue and violet 20 10
O2614 10 l. light green and green 25 10
O2615 25 l. yellow and red 65 10

O 540 O 552 O 573

1979.
O2647 O 540 50 k. deep orange and orange 10 10
O2648 2½ l. blue & lt blue 15 10

1979.
O2686 O 552 50 k. violet & pink 10 10
O2687 1 l. red and green 10 10
O2688 2½ l. mauve and light mauve 10 10
O2689 O 552 5 l. purple & blue . 15 10
O2690 7½ l. blue and lilac 20 10
O2691 10 l. blue and buff . 60 10
O2692 35 l. purple & silver 45 10
O2693 50 l. blue and pink 65 10

1981.
O2756 O 573 5 l. red and yellow . 10 10
O2757 10 l. red and pink 15 10
O2758 35 l. mauve & grey 40 10
O2759 50 l. blue and pink 60 10
O2760 75 l. emerald & green 85 10
O2761 100 l. blue & lt blue 1·10 10

O 606 O 644 O 720

1983.
O2839 O 606 5 l. blue & yellow 10 10
O2840 15 l. blue & yellow . 15 10
O2841 20 l. blue and grey . 15 10
O2842 50 l. blue and lt blue 40 10
O2843 65 l. blue & mauve . 70 10
O2844 70 l. blue and pink . 25 10
O2845 90 l. blue & brown . 95 10
O2846 90 l. blue & lt blue . 45 10
O2847 100 l. blue & green . 60 10
O2848 125 l. blue & green . 1·25 10
O2849 230 l. blue & orange 1·10 10

1986.
O2946 O 644 5 l. blue and yellow 10 10
O2947 10 l. blue and pink . 10 10
O2948 20 l. blue and grey 10 10
O2949 50 l. blue & lt blue . 15 10
O2950 100 l. blue & green . 40 10
O2951 300 l. blue and lilac 65 10

1989. Various stamps surch.
O3039 O 644 500 l. on 10 l. blue and pink 25 10
O3040 O 606 500 l. on 15 l. blue and yellow 25 10
O3041 O 644 500 l. on 20 l. blue and grey 25 10
O3042 O 606 1000 l. on 70 l. blue and pink 50 10
O3043 1000 l. on 90 l. blue and brown 50 10
O3044 1250 l. on 230 l. blue and orange 50 10

1991. Nos. O2843 and O2846 surch.
O3108 O 606 100 l. on 65 l. blue and mauve 10 10
O3109 250 l. on 90 l. blue and light blue 10 10

1992.
O3138 O 720 3000 l. deep brown and brown 45 15
O3139 5000 l. grn & lt grn 75 25

O 733 O 743

1992.
O3167 O 733 1000 l. blue & green 15 10
O3168 10000 l. green & blue 1·40 45

1993.
O3196 O 743 1000 l. green & brn 10 10
O3197 1500 l. green & brn 10 10
O3198 5000 l. brn & green 20 10

O 753

1994.
O3218 O 753 2500 l. dp mve & mve 10 10
O3219 25000 l. brn & stone 75 25

POSTAGE DUE STAMPS

D 2 D 4

1863. Imperf.
D 7 D 2 20 pa. black on brown 55·00 22·00
D 8 1 pi. black on brown . 66·00 24·00
D 9 2 pi. black on brown . £225 65·00
D10 5 pi. black on brown . £100 55·00

1865.
D18 D 4 20 pa. brown 15 1·00
D19 1 pi. brown 15 90
D74 2 pi. brown 30 1·00
D70 5 pi. brown 25 2·50
D76 25 pi. brown 5·00 12·00

1888. As T 9.
D117 9 20 pa. black 1·50 45
D118 1 pi. black 25 75
D119 2 pi. black 25 1·00

1892. As T 15.
D146 15 20 pa. black 1·50 45
D147 20 pa. black on red 20 50
D148 1 pi. black 2·75 95
D149 2 pi. black 1·25 60

1901. As T 21.
D195 21 10 pa. black on red 55 30
D196 20 pa. black on red 60 50
D197 1 pi. black on red 50 45
D198 2 pi. black on red 75 45

1905. As T 23.
D228 23 1 pi. black on red 85 75
D229 2 pi. black on red 1·75 1·75

1908. As T 25.
D250 25 1 pi. black on red 15·00 1·50
D251 2 pi. black on red 2·00 4·75

1909. As T 28.
D288 28 1 pi. black on red 2·50 7·50
D287 2 pi. black on red 18·00 20·00

1913. As T 30.
D347 30 2 pa. black on red 10 40
D348 5 pa. black on red 10 40
D349 10 pa. black on red 10 40
D350 20 pa. black on red 10 40
D351 1 pi. black on red 85 75
D352 2 pi. black on red 1·75 3·25

1913. Adrianople Issue surch.
D356 31 2 pa. on 10 pa. green 30 15
D357 5 pa. on 20 pa. red 40 30
D358 10 pa. on 40 pa. blue 1·25 60
D359 20 pa. on 40 pa. blue 3·50 1·75

D 49 D 50

D 51 D 52

1914.
D516 D 49 5 pa. brown 40 1·25
D517 D 50 20 pa. red 40 1·00
D518 D 51 1 pi. blue 75 1·25
D519 D 52 2 pi. blue 1·50 1·75

AD 26 D 101 Bridge over Kizil Irmak

1921.
AD91 AD 26 20 pa. green 20 45
AD92 1 pi. green 30 50
AD93 2 pi. brown 1·10 1·10
AD94 3 pi. red 1·75 2·25
AD95 5 pi. blue 2·25 2·75

1926.
D1035 D 101 20 pa. orange 35 20
D1036 1 gr. red 1·00 25
D1037 2 gr. green 1·10 45
D1038 3 gr. purple 1·60 50
D1039 5 gr. violet 3·75 1·45

D 121

1936.
D1186 D 121 20 pa. brown 10 10
D1187 2 k. blue 10 10
D1188 3 k. violet 10 10
D1189 5 k. green 10 10
D1190 12 k. red 10 10

PRINTED MATTER STAMPS

1879. Optd **IMPRIMES** in scroll.
N88 9 10 pa. black and mauve . . 65·00 45·00

(N 14)

1891. Stamps of 1876 optd with Type N 14.
N132 9 10 pa. green 4·75 2·50
N134 20 pa. pink 6·50 2·00
N136 1 pi. blue 28·00 10·00
N138 2 pi. yellow £170 35·00
N139 5 pi. brown £225 £130

1892. Stamps of 1892 optd with Type N 14.
N150 15 10 pa. green 35·00 5·00
N151 20 pa. red 60·00 24·00
N152 1 pi. blue 15·00 8·00
N153 2 pi. brown 24·00 12·00
N154 5 pi. purple £350 £350

مطبوعه

(N 16) (N 23) (N 27)

1894. Stamps of 1892 optd with Type N 16.
N161 15 5 pa. on 10 pa. grn (160) 40 20
N155 10 pa. green 20 15
N156a 20 pa. red 20 15
N157 1 pi. blue 20 15
N158 2 pi. brown 4·50 1·50
N159 5 pi. purple 25·00 7·50

1901. Stamps of 1901 optd with Type N 23.
N183 21 5 pa. violet 25 15
N184 10 pa. green 2·75 50
N185 20 pa. red 15 10
N186 1 pi. blue 1·50 20
N187 2 pi. orange 7·50 1·10
N188 5 pi. mauve 15·00 6·50

1901. Stamps of 1901 optd with Type N 23.
N189 22 5 pa. brown 20 20
N190 10 pa. green 65 35
N191 20 pa. mauve 2·40 1·40
N192 1 pi. blue 3·75 1·90
N193 2 pi. blue 20·00 9·00
N194 5 pi. brown 30·00 16·00

1905. Stamps of 1905 optd with Type N 23.
N222 23 5 pa. brown 20 10
N223 10 pa. green 2·75 80
N224 20 pa. pink 40 10
N225 1 pi. blue 40 10
N226 2 pi. blue 9·00 3·00
N227 5 pi. brown 15·00 5·00

1908. Stamps of 1908 optd with Type N 27.
N244 25 5 pa. brown 2·00 15
N245 10 pa. green 2·00 25
N246 20 pa. red 2·10 55
N247 1 pi. blue 5·50 75
N248 2 pi. black 14·00 2·25
N249 5 pi. purple 22·00 4·00

1909. Stamps of 1909 optd with Type N 27.
N276 28 5 pa. brown 45 15
N277 10 pa. green 70 15
N278 20 pa. red 5·50 75
N279 1 pi. blue 12·00 2·25
N280 2 pi. black 25·00 12·00
N281 5 pi. purple 28·00 12·00

1911. New value of 1909 issue.
N332 28 2 pa. olive 10 10

1920. No. 500 surch.
N961 – 5 on 4 pa. brown 10 45

TUSCANY Pt. 8

Formerly an independent duchy in C. Italy, now part of Italy.

1851. 60 quattrini = 20 soldi = 12 crazie = 1 Tuscan lira
1859. 1 Tuscan lira = 1 Italian lira

1 Arms of Tuscany

5 Arms of Savoy

1851. Imperf.

No.	Type	Description	Unused	Used
24	**1**	1 q. black	£500	£650
5		1 s. orange	£5500	£1400
6		2 s. red	£22000	£4500
9		1 c. red	£2750	35·00
29		2 c. blue	£900	35·00
15		4 c. green	£2750	50·00
19		6 c. blue	£2750	55·00
21		9 c. purple	£7000	90·00
23		60 c. red	£48000	£15000

1860. Imperf.

No.	Type	Description	Unused	Used
36	**5**	1 c. purple	£800	£450
40		5 c. green	£4500	£110
43		10 c. brown	£650	13·00
45		20 c. blue	£3000	65·00
48		40 c. red	£4500	£120
50		80 c. red	£11000	£500
51		3 l. yellow	£110000	£48000

NEWSPAPER STAMP TAX

N 3

1854.

No.	Type	Description	Unused	Used
N1	N 3	2 s. black	13·00	

TUVA Pt. 10

A province lying between the Sajan and Tannu Ola range. Formerly known as North Mongolia and Tannu, Tuva was incorporated into the U.S.S.R. on 11th October 1944.

PRICES. The prices quoted in the used column are for stamps cancelled to order where these occur. Postally used copies are worth considerably more.

1926. 100 kopeks = 1 rouble
1934. 100 kopeks = 1 tugrik
1936. 100 kopeks = 1 aksha

1 Wheel of Eternity

1926.

No.	Type	Description	Unused	Used
1	**1**	1 k. red	1·00	1·10
2		2 k. blue	1·00	1·10
3		5 k. orange	1·10	1·10
4		8 k. green	1·25	1·25
5		10 k. violet	1·25	1·25
6		30 k. brown	1·50	1·25
7		50 k. black	1·50	1·25
8		1 r. turquoise	2·25	2·25
9		3 r. red	4·00	4·50
10		5 r. blue	7·00	6·00

The rouble values are larger $22\frac{1}{2} \times 30$ mm.

1927. Surch **TOUVA POSTAGE** and value.

No.	Type	Description	Unused	Used
11	**1**	8 k. on 50 k. black	4·75	5·50
12		14 k. on 1 r. turquoise	5·00	5·50
13		18 k. on 3 r. red	7·50	9·00
14		28 k. on 5 r. blue	8·00	9·50

4 Tuvan Woman

5 Map of Tuva

6 Mongolian Sheep and Tents

7 Fording a River

8 Reindeer

1927.

No.	Type	Description	Unused	Used
15	**4**	1 k. brown, red and black	40	35
16	–	2 k. brown, green & violet	80	45
17	–	3 k. green, yellow & black	1·25	50
18	–	4 k. brown and blue	45	35
19	–	5 k. blue, black and orange	45	35
20	**5**	8 k. sepia, blue and red	55	55
21	–	10 k. red, black and green	3·50	75
22	–	14 k. orange and blue	6·50	3·25
23	**6**	18 k. brown and blue	7·00	3·50
24	–	28 k. sepia and green	4·50	2·25
25	**7**	40 k. green and red	3·25	2·00
26	–	50 k. brown, black and green	2·50	1·75
27	–	70 k. bistre and red	4·00	2·75
28	**8**	1 r. violet and brown	7·50	5·50

DESIGNS—As Type **4**: 2 k. Red deer; 3 k. Common goral; 4 k. Mongolian tent; 5 k. Tuvan man. As Type **5**: 10 k. Archers; 14 k. Camel caravan. As Type **6**: 28 k. Landscape. As Type **7**: 50 k. Girl carpet-weaver; 70 k. Horseman.

1932. Stamps of 1927 surch **TbBA POSTA** and value (10 k. optd only).

No.	Type	Description	Unused	Used
29	**7**	1 k. on 40 k. green and red	4·75	6·50
30	–	2 k. on 50 k. brown, black and green	5·00	5·50
31	–	3 k. on 70 k. bistre and red	5·50	5·50
32	**5**	5 k. on 8 k. sep, blue & red	5·50	5·50
33	–	10 k. red, black and green	6·00	7·50
34	–	15 k. on 14 k. orange & blue	6·50	7·00

1932. Stamps of 1927 surch.

No.	Type	Description	Unused	Used
35	**5**	10 k. on 8 k. brown	£120	
36	–	15 k. on 14 k. orange & blue	£120	
37	**6**	35 k. on 18 k. brown & blue	48·00	60·00
38	–	35 k. on 28 k. sepia and green	55·00	70·00

1933. Fiscal stamps (20 × 39 mm) surch **Posta** and value. (a) Numerals $6\frac{3}{4}$ mm tall.

No.	Description	Unused	Used
39	15 k. on 6 k. yellow	55·00	70·00
40	35 k. on 15 k. brown	£190	£275

(b) Numerals $5\frac{1}{4}$ mm tall.

No.	Description	Unused	Used
41	15 k. on 6 k. yellow	70·00	90·00
42	35 k. on 15 k. brown	£225	£350

12 Mounted Hunter

13 Interior of Tent

14 Yak

1934. Perf or imperf.

No.	Type	Description	Unused	Used
43	**12**	1 k. orange	75	40
44	–	2 k. green	90	75
45	**13**	3 k. red	90	75
46	–	4 k. purple	1·50	1·50
47	**14**	5 k. blue	1·50	1·50
48	–	10 k. brown	1·50	1·50
49	–	15 k. lake	1·50	1·50
50	–	20 k. black	2·25	2·00

DESIGNS—As Type **12**: 2 k. Hunter. As Type **13**: 4 k. Tractor. As Type **14**: 10 k. Camel caravan; 15 k. Lassoing reindeer; 20 k. Corsac fox-hunting.

15 Yaks

16 Capercaillie

1934 Air.

No.	Type	Description	Unused	Used
51	**15**	1 k. red	85	75
52	–	5 k. green	85	75
53	**16**	10 k. brown	2·75	2·25
54	–	15 k. red	1·60	75
55	–	25 k. purple	1·60	75
56	**15**	50 k. green	1·60	75
57	–	75 k. red	1·60	75
58	**15**	1 t. blue	1·60	1·25
59	–	2 t. blue (55 × 28 mm)	2·10	2·25

DESIGNS (embodying monoplane) As Type **15**: 5, 15 k. Camels. As Type **16**: 25 k. Argali; 75 k. Ox-cart; 2 t. Roe deer.

The 2 t. also comes larger, 61 × 31 mm.

1935. No. 49 surch.

No.	Description	Unused	Used
60	20 k. on 15 k. lake	85·00	

18 Map of Tuva

19 Rocky Outcrop

1935. Landscapes.

No.	Type	Description	Unused	Used
61	**18**	1 k. orange	75	75
62	–	3 k. green	75	75
63	–	5 k. red	90	75
64	–	10 k. violet	90	75
65	**19**	15 k. green	90	95
66	–	25 k. blue	90	95
67	–	50 k. sepia	90	1·00

DESIGNS—As Type **18**: 3, 5, 10 k. Views of River Yenisei. As Type **19**: 25 k. Bei-kem rapids; 50 k. Mounted hunter.

20 Eurasian Badger

21 Corsac Fox

22 Elk

1935. Animals.

No.	Type	Description	Unused	Used
68	**20**	1 k. orange	90	85
69	–	3 k. green	90	85
70	–	5 k. mauve	90	90
71	**21**	10 k. red	90	90
72	–	25 k. red	1·00	1·00
73	–	50 k. blue	1·00	1·00
74	**22**	1 t. violet	1·00	1·00
75	–	2 t. blue	1·00	1·00
76	–	3 t. brown	1·10	1·10
77	–	5 t. blue	1·25	1·25

DESIGNS—As Type **20**—VERT: 3 k. Eurasian red squirrel. HORIZ: 5 k. Sable. As Type **21**: 25 k. European Otter; 50 k. Lynx. LARGER (61 × 31 mm): 2 t. Yak; 3 k. Bactrian camel. As Type **22**: 5 t. Brown bear.

See also No. 115.

23 Arms of Republic

24 Wrestlers

25 Herdsman

26 Sports Meeting

27 Partisans

1936. 15th Anniv of Independence. (a) Postage.

78 **23** 1 k. green . . . . 1·10 55
79 – 2 k. sepia . . . . 1·10 55
80 – 3 k. blue . . . . 1·25 60
81 **24** 4 k. red . . . . 1·50 60
82 – 5 k. purple . . . . 2·50 50
83 **24** 6 k. green . . . . 2·50 50
84 – 8 k. purple . . . . 2·25 55
85 – 10 k. red . . . . 2·50 50
86 – 12 k. agate . . . . 3·25 75
87 – 15 k. green . . . . 3·50 55
88 – 20 k. blue . . . . 3·50 75
89 **25** 25 k. red . . . . 3·00 55
90 – 30 k. purple . . . . 6·00 1·00
91 **25** 35 k. red . . . . 2·50 55
92 – 40 k. sepia . . . . 2·50 55
93 – 50 k. blue . . . . 2·50 55
94 **26** 70 k. plum . . . . 3·50 1·10
95 – 80 k. green . . . . 3·00 1·10
96 **27** 1 a. red . . . . 3·00 1·10
97 2 a. red . . . . 3·00 1·10
98 – 3 a. blue . . . . 3·25 1·10
99 – 5 a. agate . . . . 3·25 1·40

DESIGNS—As Type **23**: 2 k. President Gyrmittazi; 3 k. Camel and driver. As Type **24**: 5, 8 k. Archers; 10, 15 k. Fishermen; 12, 20 k. Brown bear hunt. As Type **25**: 30 k. Bactrian camel and steam train; 40, 50 k. Horse-racing. As Type **26**: 8 k., 5 a. 1921 war scene; 3 a. Confiscation of cattle.

See also Nos. 116 and 118/19.

28 Yak Transport

29 Horseman and Airship

30 Seaplane over Waves

(b) Air.

100 **28** 5 k. blue and flesh . . . . 2·25 75
101 – 10 k. purple and brown . . 2·50 80
102 **28** 15 k. agate and grey . . . 2·50 80
103 **29** 25 k. purple and cream . . 3·50 90
104 – 50 k. red and cream . . . 3·00 1·10
105 **29** 75 k. green and yellow . . 3·00 1·10
106 **30** 1 a. green and turquoise . . 3·00 1·25
107 2 a. red and cream . . . . 3·50 1·25
108 3 a. sepia and flesh . . . . 3·50 2·00

DESIGNS—As Type **28**: 10 k. Horse-drawn reaper. As Type **29**: 50 k. Feast of the women.

See also No. 117.

1938. Various stamps surch with large numerals and old values obliterated.

109 5 k. on 2 a. red (No. 97) . . .
110 5 k. on 2 a. red and cream (No. 107) . . . .
111 10 k. on 1 t. blue (No. 58) . . .
112 20 k. on 50 k. sepia (No. 67) . .
113 30 k. on 2 a. red and cream (No. 107) . . . .
114 30 k. on 3 a. sepia & flesh (No. 108) . . . .

See also Nos. 120/1.

1938. Previous types with designs modified and colours changed.

115 5 k. green (No. 70) . . . . . 85·00
116 10 k. blue (No. 85) . . . . . 90·00
117 15 k. brown (No. 102) . . . . 85·00
118 20 k. red (No. 88) £225
119 30 k. purple (as No. 95) . . . £100

In Nos. 116/19 the dates have been removed and in No. 117 "AIR MAIL" also.

1939. Nos. 58 and 67 surch with small thick numerals and old values obliterated.

120 1 k. on 1 t. blue . . . . . .
121 20 k. on 50 k. sepia . . . . .

See also Nos. 122/3.

1940. Various stamps surch.

122 10 k. on 1 t. blue (No. 58) . .
123 20 k. on 50 k. sepia (No. 67) .
124 20 k. on 50 k. blue (No. 73) .
125 20 k. on 50 k. blue (No. 93) .
126 20 k. on 50 k. red on cream (No. 104) . . . .
127 20 k. on 75 k. green and yellow (No. 105) . . . .
128 20 k. on 80 k. green (No. 95)

1942. Nos. 98/9 surch.

129 25 k. on 3 a. blue . . . . . .
130 25 k. on 5 a. agate . . . . .

34 Tuvan Woman

1942. 21st Anniv of Independence. Imperf.

131 **34** 25 k. blue £225
132 – 25 k. blue £225
133 – 25 k. blue £225

DESIGNS: No. 132 Agricultural Exhibition building; No. 133 Government building.

35 Coat of Arms

36 Government Building

1943. 22nd Anniv of Independence. With or without gum.

134 **35** 25 k. blue . . . . 20·00
135 25 k. black . . . . 30·00
136 25 k. green . . . . 60·00
137 **36** 50 k. green . . . . 60·00

UBANGI-SHARI Pt. 6

Formerly part of the French Congo. Ubangi-Shari became a separate colony in 1904 (although stamps of the French Congo continued to be used until 1915). From 1915 to 1922 it shared a postal administration with Chad.

From 1936 to 1958 Ubangi-Shari was part of French Equatorial Africa. In December 1958 it became the autonomous state of the Central African Republic.

100 centimes = 1 franc

A. UBANGI-SHARI-CHAD

1915. Stamps of Middle Congo optd **OUBANGUI-CHARI-TCHAD**.

1 **1** 1 c. green and brown . . . 25 40
2 2 c. violet and brown . . . 20 45
3 4 c. blue and brown 40 65
4 5 c. green and blue 30 50
19 5 c. yellow and blue 65 70
5 10 c. red and blue 70 80
20 10 c. green and turquoise . . 55 65
5a 15 c. purple and pink . . . 1·40 1·40
6 20 c. brown and blue . . . 2·25 2·50
7 **2** 25 c. blue and green 75 85
21 25 c. green and black 55 60
8 30 c. red and green 65 70
22 30 c. red 55 65
9 35 c. brown and blue . . . 3·75 4·50
10 40 c. green and brown . . . 3·75 5·50
11 45 c. violet and orange . . . 3·50 5·50
12 50 c. green and orange . . . 4·25 6·75
23 50 c. blue and green 55 70
13 75 c. brown and blue . . . 9·00 11·00
14 **3** 1 f. green and violet . . . . 9·75 11·00
15 2 f. violet and green . . . . 10·00 11·00
16 5 f. blue and pink . . . . 35·00 38·00

1916. No. 5 surch **5c** and cross.

18 10 c. + 5 c. red and blue . . . 55 80

B. UBANGI-SHARI

1922. Stamps of Middle Congo, new colours, optd **OUBANGUI-CHARI**.

24 **1** 1 c. violet and green 35 55
25 2 c. green and pink 50 65
26 4 c. brown and purple 60 80
27 5 c. blue and pink 75 95
28 10 c. green and turquoise . . 1·40 1·40
29 15 c. pink and blue . . . . 1·50 1·90
30 20 c. brown and pink . . . . 4·00 5·75
31 **2** 25 c. violet and pink . . . . 3·00 5·00
32 30 c. red . . . . 2·00 3·00
33 35 c. violet and green . . . . 3·75 5·50
34 40 c. blue and mauve . . . . 3·25 5·00
35 45 c. brown and mauve . . . 3·25 5·00
36 50 c. blue and light blue . . . 2·00 3·00
37 60 on 75 c. violet on pink . . 2·50 3·25
38 75 c. brown and pink . . . . 3·50 5·75
39 **3** 1 f. green and blue . . . . . 4·25 5·75
40 2 f. green and pink . . . . . 5·25 8·00
41 5 f. green and brown . . . . 12·50 16·00

1924. Stamps of 1922 and similar stamps additionally overprinted **AFRIQUE EQUATORIALE FRANCAISE**.

42 **1** 1 c. violet and green 10 45
43 2 c. green and pink 10 45
44 4 c. brown and chocolate . . 10 45
44c 4 c. brown . . . . 1·10 1·10
45 5 c. blue and pink 15 45
46 10 c. green and turquoise . . 40 55
47 10 c. red and blue 30 45
48 15 c. pink and blue 45 75
49 20 c. brown and pink 40 65
50 **2** 25 c. violet and pink 45 30
51 30 c. red 35 45
52 30 c. brown and pink 45 45
53 30 c. olive and green 75 90
54 35 c. violet and green 20 45
55 40 c. blue and mauve 50 60
56 45 c. brown and mauve . . . 55 70
57 50 c. blue and light blue . . . 55 55
58 50 c. grey and blue . . . . . 1·00 80
59 60 on 75 c. violet on pink . . 50 55
60 65 c. brown and blue . . . . 1·75 1·90
61 75 c. brown and pink 75 80
62 75 c. blue and light blue . . . 50 60
63 75 c. purple and brown . . . 1·60 1·90
64 90 c. pink and red . . . . . 4·25 5·75
65a **3** 1 f. green and blue 50 60
66 1 f. 10 brown and blue . . . 2·00 2·25
67 1 f. 25 mauve and green . . 4·25 5·25
68 1 f. 50 ultramarine & blue . . 5·75 6·75
69 1 f. 75 brown and orange . . 7·50 7·50
70 2 f. green and pink 80 80
71 3 f. mauve on pink . . . . . 5·25 5·50
72 5 f. green and brown . . . . 3·50 3·50

1925. As last but new colours and surch.

73 **3** 65 on 1 f. violet and brown . 50 1·40
74 85 on 1 f. violet and brown . 1·00 1·40
75 **2** 90 on 75 c. pink and red . . 95 1·40
76 **3** 1 f. 25 on 1 f. blue & ultram . 70 80
77 1 f. 50 on 1 f. ultram & blue . 1·00 85
78 3 f. on 5 f. brown and red . . 1·90 2·25
79 10 f. on 5 f. red and mauve . 12·00 16·00
80 20 f. on 5 f. mauve and grey . 20·00 23·00

1931. "International Colonial Exhibition" key-types inscr "OUBANGUI-CHARI".

103 E 40 c. green . . . . 3·00 4·50
104 F 50 c. mauve . . . . 3·00 3·75
105 G 90 c. red . . . . 3·00 4·50
106 H 1 f. 50 blue . . . . 3·50 3·75

POSTAGE DUE STAMPS

1928. Postage Due type of France optd **OUBANGUI-CHARI A. E. F.**

D81 D **11** 5 c. blue . . . . 85 1·90
D82 10 c. brown . . . . . . 1·00 1·90
D83 20 c. olive . . . . . . 1·40 1·90
D84 25 c. red . . . . 1·40 1·90
D85 30 c. red . . . . 1·40 1·90
D86 45 c. green . . . . . . 1·40 1·90
D87 50 c. purple . . . . . . 1·60 2·25
D88 60 c. brown on cream . . 1·90 2·75
D89 1 f. red on cream . . . 2·25 3·50
D90 2 f. red . . . . 2·50 4·50
D91 3 f. violet . . . . . . 2·50 4·50

D **12** Mobaye D **13** E. Gentil

1930.

D 92 D **12** 5 c. olive and blue . . 40 80
D 93 10 c. brown and red . . 50 1·10
D 94 20 c. brown and green . 80 1·40
D 95 25 c. brown and blue . 1·10 1·40
D 96 30 c. green and brown . 1·60 2·25
D 97 45 c. olive and green . 2·50 3·50
D 98 50 c. brown and mauve . 4·25 6·25
D 99 60 c. black and violet . 5·00 6·75
D100 D **13** 1 f. black and brown . 1·75 2·50
D101 2 f. brown and mauve . 2·00 4·00
D102 3 f. brown and red . . 2·50 6·00

UKRAINE Pt. 10

A district of S.W. Russia, which issued stamps during its temporary independence after the Russian Revolution. In 1923 it became a constituent republic of the U.S.S.R.

In 1991 it became an independent republic.

1918. 100 shagiv = 1 grivna or hriven
2 grivni or hriven = 1 rouble
100 kopeks = 1 rouble
1992 (Nov). Karbovanets (coupon currency)

(6)

(8)

1918. Arms types of Russia optd with Trident device in various types according to the district. Imperf or perf.

L 51 **22** 1 k. orange 10 10
L 52 2 k. green 10 10
L 53 3 k. red 10 10
L 54 **23** 4 k. red 10 10
L 55 **22** 5 k. red 10 10
L138 7 k. blue 10 10
L 57 **23** 10 k. blue 10 10
L 58 **22** 10 k. on 7 k. blue 15 10
L159 **9** 14 k. red and blue . . . 15 20
L 60 15 k. blue and purple . . 10 10
L 61 **14** 20 k. red and blue . . . 10 10
L 62 **9** 20 k. on 14 k. red & blue . 10 10
L145 25 k. mauve and green . 10 25
L 64 35 k. green and purple . . 10 10
L 65 **14** 50 k. green and purple . . 10 10
L 66 **9** 70 k. orange and brown . 10 70
L 47 **15** 1 r. orange and brown . . 15 15
L 72 **11** 3 r. 50 grey and black . . 10·00 16·00
L212 3 r. 50 green and brown . 20 20
L 49 **20** 5 r. blue and green . . . 40 60
L 73 **11** 7 r. yellow and black . . 7·00 10·00
L 14 7 r. pink and green . . . 90 2·00
L 36 **20** 10 r. grey, red and yellow . 5·50 6·50

1 Trident (from Arms of Grand Duke Vladimir the Great)

2 Peasant

3 Ceres

4 Trident

5

1918. Without inscription on back. Imperf.

1 **1** 10 s. brown on buff 20 50
2 **2** 20 s. brown 20 50
3 **3** 30 s. blue 20 50
4 **4** 40 s. green 20 50
5 **5** 50 s. red 20 50

1918. With trident and four lines of inscription on back.

6 **1** 10 s. brown . . . . 2·50 5·00
7 **2** 20 s. brown . . . . 2·50 5·00
8 **3** 30 s. blue . . . . 2·50 5·00
9 **4** 40 d. green . . . . 2·50 5·00
10 **5** 50 s. red . . . . 2·50 5·00

6a Trident **6b** Parliament Building

Stamps of the above and similar designs were prepared for use but never used.

7 Spectre of Famine

8 T. G. Shevchenko (Ukrainian poet)

1923. Charity.

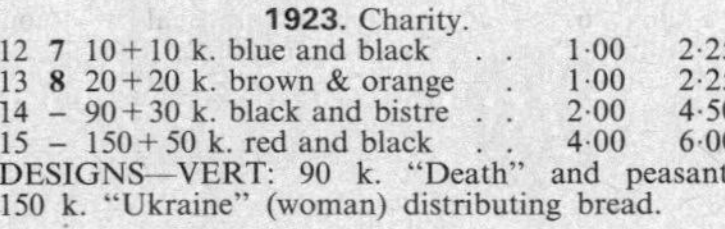

12 7 10+10 k. blue and black . . 1·00 2·25
13 8 20+20 k. brown & orange . 1·00 2·25
14 – 90+30 k. black and bistre . . 2·00 4·50
15 – 150+50 k. red and black . . 4·00 6·00
DESIGNS—VERT: 90 k. "Death" and peasant; 150 k. "Ukraine" (woman) distributing bread.

11 Cossack Chief with Musician and Standard Bearer

12 Ukrainian Emigrant Couple

1992. 500th Anniv (1990) of Ukraine Cossacks.
20 11 15 k. multicoloured 40 40

1992. Centenary (1991) of Ukrainian Emigration to Canada.
21 12 15 k. multicoloured 40 40

13 Mykola Lysenko and Score from "Taras Bulba"

1992. 150th Birth Anniv of Mykola Lysenko (composer).
22 13 1 r. brown, red and bistre . 1·10 1·10

14 Mykola Kostamarov, Quill, Pen and Scroll

15 Ceres

1992. 175th Birth Anniv of Mykola Kostamarov (historian).
23 14 20 k. brown and light brown 35 35

1992.
24 15 50 k. blue 10 10
25 70 k. brown 10 10
26 1 r. green 10 20
27 2 r. violet 15 15
28 5 r. blue 30 30
29 10 r. red 40 40
30 20 r. green 80 80
31 50 r. brown . . . . 2·00 2·00

16 Gymnastics

17 Ukraine Flag and Trident Symbol

1992. Olympic Games, Barcelona. Multicoloured.
32 3 r. Type **16** 25 25
33 4 r. Pole vaulting 45 45
34 5 r. Type **16** 50 50

1992. 1st Anniv of Regained Independence.
35 17 2 r. multicoloured 35 35

18 Three Cranes on Globe

1992. World Congress of Ukrainians, Kiev.
36 18 2 r. multicoloured 35 35

20 U.P.U. Symbol and Hand writing

1992. Correspondence Week.
38 20 5 r. multicoloured 50 50

21 Congress Emblem

1992. World Congress of Ukranian Jurists, Kiev.
39 21 15 r. multicoloured . . . . 1·25 1·25

22 Embroidery

1992. Ukraine Folk Art.
40 22 0.50 k. black and orange . 10 10

23 Arms of Austria and Ukraine with Traditional Costumes of Galicia and Bukovina

1992. Ukrainians in Austria.
41 23 5 k. multicoloured . . . . 1·25 1·25

24 Laying Foundation Stone, 1632

1992. 360th Anniv of Mogilyanska's Academy, Kiev.
42 24 1 k. 50 black, blue & brown 35 35

26 Lvov Arms

27 Cardinal Slipij

1993. Regional Arms.
44 26 3 k. blue, dp blue & gold . 95 95
45 – 5 k. lake, gold and red . . 1·25 1·25
DESIGN: 5 k. Kiev.

1993. Birth Centenary (1992) of Cardinal Joseph Slipij.
68 27 15 k. multicoloured . . . . 1·75 1·75

28 Hansa Brandenburg C-I

1993. 75th Anniv of First Vienna–Cracow–Lvov–Kiev Flight.
69 28 35 k. black, blue & mauve . 65 65
70 – 50 k. multicoloured 80 80
DESIGN: 50 k. Airbus Industrie A300.

29 Candles and Traditional Foods

1993. Easter.
71 29 15 k. multicoloured . . . . 1·25 1·25

30 "Country Wedding in Lower Austria" (Ferdinand Georg Waldmuller)

31 Cross and Figures

1993. 45th Anniv of Declaration of Human Rights.
72 30 5 k. multicoloured . . . . . 1·25 1·25

1993. 60th Anniv of Famine Deaths.
73 31 75 k. brown 80 80

32 1918 10 sh. Stamp

1993. Stamp Day. 75th Anniv of First Ukrainian Postage Stamps.
74 32 100 k. blue and brown . . . 1·00 1·00

33 Kiev

34 Mowing

1993. 50th Anniv of Liberation of Kiev.
75 33 75 k. multicoloured 90 90

1993. Agricultural Scenes.
76 34 50 k. green 10 10
77 – 100 k. blue 15 15
78 – 150 k. red 25 25
79 – 200 k. orange 30 30
80 – 300 k. purple 55 55
81 – 500 k. brown 85 85
DESIGNS: 100 k. Laden bullock carts; 150, 300 k. Shepherd and flock; 200, 500 k. Women cutting corn.

35 Madonna and Child

36 Agapit

1994. Ukrainian Health Fund.
82 35 150 k. + 20 k. black, gold and red . . . . 1·40 1·40

1994. Agapit (medieval doctor).
83 36 200 k. black and red . . . . 1·75 1·75

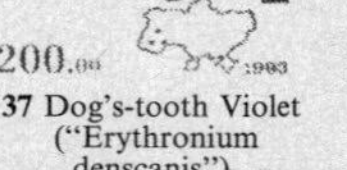
37 Dog's-tooth Violet ("Erythronium denscanis")

38 Laden Bullock Carts

1994. Red Book of Ukraine. Multicoloured.
84 200 k. Type **37** 70 70
85 200 k. Lady's slipper ("Cypripedium calceolus") . 70 70

1994. Agricultural Scenes. Value expressed by Cyrillic letter.
86 – A (5000 k.) red 60 60
87 38 V (10000 k.) blue . . . . . 1·25 1·25
DESIGN: A, Shepherd and flock.
The Cyrillic "V" on No. 87 resembles a "B".

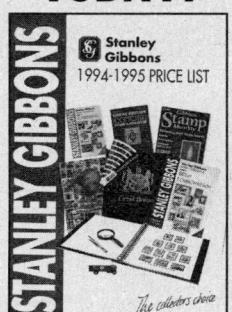

UMM AL QIWAIN Pt. 19

One of the Trucial States in the Persian Gulf. In July 1971 formed the United Arab Emirates with five other Gulf Shaikdoms.

1964. 100 naye paise = 1 rupee
1967. 100 dirhams = 1 riyal

1 Shaikh Ahmed bin Rashid al Moalla and Mountain Gazelles

1964. Multicoloured. (a) Size as T **1**.

1 1 n.p. Type **1** 10 10
2 2 n.p. Snake 10 10
3 3 n.p. Striped hyena 10 10
4 4 n.p. Fish 10 10
5 5 n.p. Fish (different) 10 10
6 10 n.p. Fish (different) 10 10
7 15 n.p. Palace 10 10
8 20 n.p. Town buildings 15 10
9 30 n.p. Tower 20 10

(b) Size $42\frac{1}{2} \times 27$ mm.

10 40 n.p. Type **1** 40 10
11 50 n.p. Snake 70 10
12 50 n.p. Striped hyena 80 10
13 1 r. Fish . . . . 1·00 10
14 1 r. 50 Fish (different) . . . . 1·40 25
15 2 r. Fish (different) . . . . . 1·75 35

(c) Size $53\frac{1}{2} \times 33\frac{1}{2}$ mm.

16 3 r. Palace . . . . 2·25 55
17 5 r. Town buildings . . . . . . 3·50 90
18 10 r. Tower . . . . 5·00 1·50

2 Discus Thrower and Stadium

1964. Olympic Games, Tokyo. Multicoloured.

19 50 n.p. Type **2** 20 10
20 1 r. Main stadium 45 15
21 1 r. 50 Swimming pool 65 20
22 2 r. Main stadium 90 30
23 3 r. Komazawa gymnasium . . 1·25 40
24 4 r. Stadium entrance . . . . . 1·75 50
25 5 r. Type **2** . . . . 2·00 70

3 Cortege leaving White House

1965. Pres. Kennedy Commem. Each black and gold on coloured paper as given below.

26 **3** 10 n.p. pale blue 10 10
27 – 15 n.p. pale stone 10 10
28 – 50 n.p. pale stone 10 10
29 – 1 r. pale pink 20 10
30 – 2 r. pale stone 35 15
31 – 3 r. pale lavender 65 35
32 – 5 r. pale blue 95 45
33 – 7 r. 50 pale buff . . . . . . 2·25 75

DESIGNS (Funeral scenes): 15 n.p. Coffin-bearers; 50 n.p. Hearse; 1 r. Presidents Eisenhower and Truman; 2 r. Foreign dignitaries (33×51 mm); 3 r. Mrs. Kennedy and family at grave; 5 r. Last salute; 7 r. 50, Pres. Kennedy.

1965. Air. Designs similar to Nos. 1/9 but inscr "AIR MAIL". Multicoloured. (a) Size $43 \times 26\frac{1}{2}$ mm.

34 15 n.p. Type **1** 20 10
35 25 n.p. Snake 25 10
36 35 n.p. Striped hyena 35 10
37 50 n.p. Fish 55 10
38 75 n.p. Fish (different) 75 10
39 1 r. Fish (different) 90 15

(b) Size 53×34 mm.

40 2 r. Palace . . . . 1·25 30
41 3 r. Town buildings . . . . . . 1·75 50
42 5 r. Tower . . . . 2·50 90

MINIMUM PRICE

The minimum price quoted is 10p which represents a handling charge rather than a basis for valuing common stamps. For further notes about prices, see introductory pages.

4 Tribute to Ruler (reverse of 10 n.p. piece)

1965. Arabian Gulf Area Monetary Conf. Circular designs on silver foil, backed with paper inscr overall "Walsall Security Paper" in English and Arabic. Imperf. (a) Diameter $1\frac{11}{16}$ in.

43 **4** 10 n.p. purple and black . . 10 10
44 – 25 n.p. blue and green . . . 15 15

(b) Diameter $2\frac{3}{16}$ in.

45 **4** 1 r. red and violet 45 45
46 – 2 r. green and orange . . . 90 90

(c) Diameter $2\frac{1}{2}$ in.

47 **4** 3 r. blue and mauve . . . . 1·25 1·25
48 – 5 r. purple and blue . . . . 1·90 1·90

SILVER PIECES: Nos. 44, 46, 48 each show the obverse side (Shaikh Ahmed).

5 "Penny Black" and Egyptian 5 p. Stamp of 1866

1966. Centenary Stamp Exhibition, Cairo.

49 **5** 3 n.p. multicoloured 10 10
50 – 5 n.p. multicoloured 10 10
51 – 7 n.p. multicoloured 10 10
52 – 10 n.p. multicoloured . . . 10 10
53 – 15 n.p. multicoloured . . . 10 10
54 – 25 n.p. multicoloured . . . 10 10
55 – 50 n.p. multicoloured . . . 25 10
56 – 75 n.p. multicoloured . . . 35 10
57 – 1 r. multicoloured 45 15
58 – 2 r. multicoloured 90 35

DESIGNS: As Type **5** with Egyptian 5 p. stamp: 7 n.p. Brazil; 30 r. "Bull's-eye" of 1843; 15 n.p. Mauritius "Post Office" One Penny of 1847; 50 n.p. Belgium; 10 c. "Epaulettes" of 1849; 1 r. New South Wales One Penny and Victoria One Penny of 1850. As Type **5**, but with Egyptian "Pyramid and Star" watermark of 1866: 5 n.p. Basle; $2\frac{1}{2}$ r. "Dove" of 1845, Geneva 5 c.+5 c. "Double Eagle" and Zurich; 4 r. "Numeral" of 1843; 10 n.p. U.S. St. Louis "Bears" 5 c., Baltimore 5 c. and New York 5 c. "Postmasters" stamps of 1845; 25 n.p. France 20 c. "Ceres" of 1849; 75 n.p. Bavaria 1 k. of 1850; 2 r. Spain 6 c. of 1850.

6 Sir Winston Churchill with Lord Alanbrooke and Field Marshal Montgomery

1966. Churchill Commem. Multicoloured designs each including Churchill.

59 3 n.p. Type **6** 10 10
60 4 n.p. With Roosevelt and Stalin at Yalta 10 10
61 5 n.p. In garden at No. 10 Downing Street London . . 10 10
62 10 n.p. With Eisenhower . . . 10 10
63 15 n.p. With Lady Churchill in car 10 10
64 50 n.p. Painting in Morocco . 30 10
65 75 n.p. Walking — on holiday 35 10
66 1 r. Funeral cortege 50 15
67 3 r. Lying-in-state, Westminster Hall . . . . 1·25 50
68 5 r. Churchill giving "Victory" sign . . . . 2·25 75

7 Communications Satellite

1966. Centenary of I.T.U. (in 1965). Designs showing communications satellites.

70 **7** 5 n.p. multicoloured 10 10
71 – 10 n.p. multicoloured 15 10
72 – 25 n.p. multicoloured 20 10
73 – 50 n.p. multicoloured 40 15
74 – 75 n.p. multicoloured 60 20
75 – 1 r. multicoloured 80 20
76 – 2 r. multicoloured . . . . . . 1·40 35
77 – 3 r. multicoloured . . . . . . 1·75 45
78 – 5 r. multicoloured . . . . . . 2·50 85

NEW CURRENCY SURCHARGES. In 1967 various issues appeared surcharged in dirhams and riyals. The 1964 definitives, 1965 air stamps and officials with this surcharge are listed as there is evidence of their postal use. Nos. 19/33 and 49/68 also exist with these surcharges.

1967. Various issues with currency names changed by overprinting. (i) Nos. 1/18 (1964 Definitives).

80 1 d. on 1 n.p. 10 10
81 2 d. on 2 n.p. 10 10
82 3 d. on 3 n.p. 10 10
83 4 d. on 4 n.p. 10 10
84 5 d. on 5 n.p. 10 10
85 10 d. on 10 n.p. 10 10
86 15 d. on 15 n.p. . . . . . . 2·50 1·00
87 20 d. on 20 n.p. . . . . . . 2·50 1·00
88 30 d. on 30 n.p. . . . . . . 2·50 1·00
89 40 d. on 40 n.p. 40 20
90 50 d. on 50 n.p. 50 30
91 70 d. on 70 n.p. 60 35
92 1 r. on 1 r. 75 40
93 1 r. 50 on 1 r. 50 . . . . . 1·25 70
94 2 r. on 2 r. . . . . 1·50 85
95 3 r. on 3 r. . . . . 6·50 2·50
96 5 r. on 5 r. . . . . 8·50 3·75
97 10 r. on 10 r. . . . . 13·00 6·00

(ii) Nos. 34/42 (Airmails).

98 15 d. on 15 n.p. 15 10
99 25 d. on 25 n.p. 20 10
100 35 d. on 35 n.p. 25 20
101 50 d. on 50 n.p. 45 25
102 75 d. on 75 n.p. 55 30
103 1 r. on 1 r. 70 40
104 2 r. on 2 r. . . . . 2·50 90
105 3 r. on 3 r. . . . . 2·50 1·25
106 5 r. on 5 r. . . . . 3·50 2·50

9 Box Fish

1967. Fish of the Arabian Gulf. Multicoloured.

(a) Postage. (i) Size 46×21 mm.

116 1 d. Type **9** 10 10
117 2 d. Parrot fish 10 10
118 3 d. Sweet lips 10 10
119 4 d. Butterfly fish 10 10
120 5 d. Soldier fish 10 10
121 10 d. Damsel fish 15 10
122 15 d. Picasso triggerfish . . . 15 10
123 20 d. Striped triggerfish . . . 25 10
124 30 d. Israeli puffer 35 10

(ii) Size 56×26 mm.

125 40 d. Type **9** 40 10
126 50 d. As 2 d. 50 10
127 70 d. As 3 d. 70 10
128 1 r. As 4 d. 80 15
129 1 r. 50 As 5 d. . . . . . . 1·25 25
130 2 r. As 10 d. . . . . 1·40 35
131 3 r. As 15 d. (No. 122) . . . 2·00 45
132 5 r. As 20 d. . . . . 3·25 75
133 10 r. As 30 d. . . . . 5·00 1·50

(b) Air. Size 70×35 mm.

134 15 d. Type **9** 15 10
135 25 d. As 2 d. 25 10
136 35 d. As 3 d. 35 10
137 50 d. As 4 d. 50 10
138 75 d. As 5 d. 70 10
139 1 r. As 10 d. 80 15
140 2 r. As 15 d. (No. 122) . . . . 1·40 35
141 3 r. As 20 d. . . . . 2·00 45
142 5 r. As 30 d. . . . . 3·25 75

OFFICIAL STAMPS

1965. Designs similar to Nos. 1/9, additionally inscr "ON STATE'S SERVICE". Multicoloured.

(a) Postage. Size $42\frac{1}{2} \times 26\frac{1}{2}$ mm.

O49 25 n.p. Type **1** 15 10
O50 40 n.p. Snake 20 10
O51 50 n.p. Striped hyena 30 10
O52 75 n.p. Fish 40 15
O53 1 r. Fish (different) 55 20

(b) Air. (i) Size $42\frac{1}{2} \times 26\frac{1}{2}$ mm.

O54 75 n.p. Fish (different) 40 15

(ii) Size $53 \times 33\frac{1}{2}$ mm.

O55 2 r. Palace 90 40
O56 3 r. Town buildings . . . . . 1·25 60
O57 5 r. Tower . . . . 1·90 90

1967. Nos. O1/9 with currency names changed by overprinting.

O107 25 d. on 25 n.p.(postage) . . 30 15
O108 40 d. on 40 n.p. 35 15
O109 50 d. on 50 n.p. 45 25
O110 75 d. on 75 n.p. 60 35
O111 1 r. on 1 r. 75 45
O112 75 d. on 75 d. (air) 60 35
O113 2 r. on 2 r. . . . . 1·75 90
O114 3 r. on 3 r. . . . . 2·25 1·25
O115 5 r. on 5 r. . . . . 3·25 1·90

For later issues see **UNITED ARAB EMIRATES**.

APPENDIX

The following stamps have either been issued in excess of postal needs or have not been available to the public in reasonable quantities at face value. Such stamps may later be given full listing if there is evidence of regular postal use.

1967.

Self-portraits of Famous Painters. Postage 10, 15, 25, 50, 75 d., 1, 1 r. 50; Air 1 r. 25, 2, 2 r. 50, 3, 5 r.

Dogs. Postage 15, 25, 50, 75 d., 1 r.; Air 1 r. 25, 2 r. 50, 4 r.

"Expo '67" World Fair, Montreal. Famous Paintings. 25, 50, 75 d., 1, 1 r. 50, 2, 3 r.

1968.

Falcons. Postage 15, 25, 50, 75 d., 1 r.; Air 1 r. 50, 3, 5 r.

Winter Olympic Games, Grenoble. Postage 10, 25, 75 d., 1 r.; Air 1 r. 50, 2, 3, 5 r.

Famous Paintings. Postage 25, 50, 75 d., 1, 1 r. 50, 2 r. 50; Air 1, 2, 3, 4, 5 r.

Olympic Games, Mexico (1st issue). Optd on (a) 1964 Tokyo Olympic Games Issue. Postage 1 r. 50, 2, 4, 5 r. (b) 1968 Winter Olympic Games issue. Air 1 r. 50, 2, 5 r.

Robert Kennedy Memorial. Optd on 1965 Pres. Kennedy issue. Postage 3, 5, 7 r. 50.

Olympic Games, Mexico (2nd issue). Postage 10, 25, 50 d., 1, 2 r.; Air 2 r. 50, 3, 4, 5 r.

Still Life Paintings. Postage 25, 50 d., 1, 1 r. 50, 2 r.; Air 1 r. 25, 2 r. 50, 3, 3 r. 50, 5 r.

Mexico Olympic Medal Winners. Optd on Olympic Games, Mexico issue. Postage 10, 25, 50 d., 1, 2 r.; Air 2 r. 50, 3, 4, 5 r.

Aviation History. Aircraft. Postage 25, 50 d., 1, 1 r. 50, 2 r.; Air 1 r. 25, 2 r. 50, 3, 5 r.

1969.

"Apollo 8" Moon Orbit. Optd on 1968 Aviation History issue. Postage 25, 50 d., 1, 1 r. 50, 2 r.; Air 1 r. 25, 2 r. 50, 3, 5 r.

Horses (1st series). Postage 25, 50, 75 d., 1, 2 r.; Air 1 r. 50, 2 r. 50, 4, 5 r.

Olympic Games, Munich, 1972 (1st issue). Optd on 1968 Olympic Games, Mexico issue. Postage 10, 25, 50 d., 1, 2 r.; Air 2 r. 50, 3, 4, 5 r.

Winter Olympic Games, Sapporo 1972 (1st issue). Optd on 1968 Winter Olympics Grenoble issue. Postage 10, 25, 75 d., 1 r.; Air 1 r. 50, 2, 3, 5 r.

Veteran and Vintage Cars. Postage 15 d.×8, 25 d.×8, 50 d.×8, 75 d.×8; Air 1 r.×8, 2 r.×8.

Famous Films. Postage 10, 15, 25, 50, 75 d., 1 r.; Air 1 r. 50, 2 r. 50, 3, 4, 5 r.

"Apollo 12" Moon Landing. 10, 20, 30, 50, 75 d., 1 r.

1970.

"Apollo 13" Astronauts. 10, 30, 50 d.

"Expo '70" World Fair, Osaka, Japan. 5, 10, 20, 40 d., 1, 1 r. 25.

150th Anniv of British Landing on Trucial Coast. Uniforms. 10, 20, 30, 50, 75 d., 1 r.

1971.

Animals. Postage 10, 15, 20, 25 d.; Air 5 r.

Winter Olympic Games, Saporro, 1972 (2nd issue). Postage 5, 10, 15, 20, 25 d.; Air 50, 75 d., 1, 3, 5 r.

Olympic Games, Munich, 1972 (2nd issue). Postage 5, 10, 15, 20, 25 d.; Air 50, 75 d., 1, 3, 5 r.

1972.

Durer's Religious Paintings. Postage 5, 10, 15, 20, 25 d.; Air 3 r.

Horses (2nd series). Postage 10, 15, 20, 25 d.; Air 50 d., 3 r.

Locomotives (plastic surfaced). Postage 5, 10, 20, 40, 50 d.; Air 6 r.

Winter Olympic Games, Sapporo, 1972 (3rd issue) (plastic surfaced). Postage 5, 10, 20, 40, 50 d.; Air 6 r.

Easter, Religious Paintings. Postage 5, 10, 20, 50 d.; Air 1, 3 r.

Kennedy Brothers Memorial. Postage 5, 10, 15, 20 d.; Air 1, 3 r.

Winston Churchill Memorial. Postage 5, 10, 15, 20 d.; Air 3 r.

Arab Rulers. Postage 5 d.×6, 10 d.×6, 15 d.×6, 20 d.×6; Air 3 r.×6.

13th World Jamboree, 1971 (plastic surfaced). Postage 5, 10, 20, 40, 50 d.; Air 6 r.

Fish. Postage 5, 10, 20, 40, 50 d.; Air 6 r.

International Airlines. Postage 5, 10, 15, 20, 25 d.; Air 50 d.

"Apollo 15" Moon Mission. Postage 5, 10, 15, 20, 25 d.; Air 50, 75 d., 1, 3, 5 r.

Olympic Games, Munich, 1972 (3rd issue) (plastic surfaced). Postage 5, 10, 20, 40, 50 d.; Air 6 r.

2500th Anniv of Founding of Persian Empire. Postage 10, 20, 30, 40, 50, 60 d.; Air 1 r.

Portraits of Charles de Gaulle. 5, 10, 15, 20, 25 d.

Paintings of Napoleon. Postage 5, 10, 15, 20, 25 d.; Air 5 r.

Butterflies. Postage 5, 10, 15, 20, 25 d.; Air 3 r.

Penguins. Postage 5, 10, 15, 20 d.; Air 50 d., 4 r.

Cars. Postage 5, 10, 15, 20, 25 d.; Air 3 r.

Masks (1st series). Postage 5, 10, 15, 20, 25 d.; Air 50 d., 1, 3 r.

Dogs and Cats. Postage 5, 5, 10, 10, 15, 15, 20, 20, 25, 25 d.; Air 5, 5 r.

Roses. Postage 10, 15, 20, 25 d.; Air 50 d., 5 r.

Marine Fauna. Postage 5, 10, 15, 20, 25, 50 d.; Air 1, 3 r.

Masks (2nd series). Postage 5, 10, 15, 20, 25 d.; Air 50 d., 1, 3 r.

Navigators. Postage 5, 10, 15, 20, 25, 50 d.; Air 1, 3 r.

Exotic Birds (1st series). Horiz and vert designs. Air 1 r. × 16.

Exotic Birds (2nd series). Horiz designs. Air 1 r. × 16.

In common with the other states of the United Arab Emirates the Umm al Qiwain stamp contract was terminated on 1 August 1972 and any further new issues released after that date were unauthorised.

UNITED ARAB EMIRATES Pt. 19

Following the withdrawal of British forces from the Gulf and the ending of the Anglo-Trucial States treaties six of the states, Abu Dhabi, Ajman, Dubai, Fujeira, Sharjah and Umm al Qiwain, formed an independent union on 2nd December 1971. The seventh state, Ras al Khaima, joined during February 1972. Each emirate continued to use its own stamps, pending the introduction of a unified currency. A Union Postal administration came into being on 1st August 1972 and the first stamps appeared on 1st January 1973. (For Abu Dhabi stamps optd U.A.E., etc., see under that heading).

100 fils = 1 dirham

1 U.A.E. Flag and Map of Gulf

1973. Multicoloured. (a) Size 42 × 25 mm.

No.	Type	Description	Mint	Used
1		5 f. Type **1**	15	10
2		10 f. Type **1**	20	10
3		15 f. Eagle emblem	35	10
4		35 f. As 15 f.	65	10

(b) Size 46 × 30 mm.

No.	Type	Description	Mint	Used
5		65 f. Almaqta Bridge, Abu Dhabi	1·75	25
6		75 f. Khor Fakkan, Sharjah	1·75	25
7		1 d. Clock Tower, Dubai	1·75	25
8		1¼ d. Buthnah Fort, Fujeira	1·75	55
9		2 d. Alfalaj Fort, Umm al Qiwain	15·00	1·75
10		3 d. Khor Khwair, Ras al Khaima	5·00	1·75
11		5 d. Ruler's Palace, Ajman	6·00	3·00
12		10 d. President Shaikh Zaid	9·50	7·50

2 Youth and Girl within Shield

1973. National Youth Festival. Multicoloured.

No.	Type	Description	Mint	Used
13		10 f. Type **2**	1·50	15
14		1 d. 25 Allegory of Youth	4·00	2·25

3 Traffic Lights and Road Sign

1973. Traffic Week. Multicoloured.

No.	Type	Description	Mint	Used
15		35 f. Type **3**	1·25	20
16		75 f. Pedestrian-crossing (horiz)	2·25	90
17		1 d. 25 Traffic policeman	3·75	1·50

4 "Three Races of the World"

1973. 25th Anniv of Declaration of Human Rights.

No.	Type	Description	Mint	Used
18	4	35 f. black, yellow and blue	80	20
19		65 f. black, yellow and red	1·25	65
20		1¼ d. black, yellow & green	2·40	1·25

5 U.P.U. Emblem

1974. Centenary of Universal Postal Union.

No.	Type	Description	Mint	Used
21	5	25 f. multicoloured	55	20
22		60 f. multicoloured	1·25	75
23		1¼ d. multicoloured	2·40	2·00

6 Medical Equipment (Health Service)

1974. Third National Day.

No.	Type	Description	Mint	Used
24	6	10 f. red, brown and lilac	45	15
25	–	35 f. gold, green and blue	85	20
26	–	65 f. brown, sepia and blue	1·40	70
27	–	1¼ d. multicoloured	2·50	1·50

DESIGNS—HORIZ: (49 × 30 mm): 35 f. Children reading (Education); 65 f. Tools and buildings (Construction); 1¼ d. U.A.E. flag with emblems of U.N. and Arab League.

7 Arab Couple with Candle and Book

1974. International Literacy Day.

No.	Type	Description	Mint	Used
28	7	35 f. multicoloured	1·00	20
29	–	65 f. black, blue and brown	1·60	70
30	–	1 d. 25 black, blue & brown	2·00	1·25

DESIGN—VERT: 65 f., 1 f. 25, Arab couple with book.

8 Oil De-gassing Installation

1975. 9th Arab Oil Conference. Multicoloured.

No.	Type	Description	Mint	Used
31		25 f. Type **8**	60	20
32		50 f. "Al Ittiad" (offshore oil drilling platform)	1·40	35
33		100 f. Underwater storage tank	2·25	1·00
34		125 f. Marine oil production platform	3·00	1·75

9 Station and Dish Aerial

1975. Opening of Jabal Ali Satellite Earth Station. Multicoloured.

No.	Type	Description	Mint	Used
36		15 f. Type **9**	50	15
37		35 f. Satellite beaming information to Earth	1·25	25
38		65 f. As 35 f.	2·00	40
39		2 d. Type **9**	4·75	2·50

10 "Snapshots" within Eagle Emblem

11 Symbols of Learning

1975. Fourth National Day. Multicoloured.

No.	Type	Description	Mint	Used
40		10 f. Type **10**	25	15
41		35 f. Shaikh Mohamed bin Hamad al Sharqi of Fujeira	85	35
42		60 f. Shaikh Rashid bin Humaid al Naimi of Ajman	1·25	40
43		80 f. Shaikh Ahmed bin Rashid al Moalla of Umm al Qiwain	1·75	80
44		90 f. Shaikh Sultan bin Mohammed al Qasimi of Sharjah	2·00	1·25
45		1 d. Shaikh Saqr bin Mohammed al Qasimi of Ras al Khaima	2·00	1·25
46		1 d. 40 Shaikh Rashid bin Said of Dubai	3·00	2·25
47		5 d. Shaikh Zaid bin Sultan al Nahayyan of Abu Dhabi, President of U.A.E.	12·00	8·50

1976. Arab Literacy Day. Multicoloured.

No.	Type	Description	Mint	Used
48		15 f. Type **11**	35	10
49		50 f. Arabs seeking enlightenment	1·25	35
50		3 d. As 50 f.	5·00	3·00

1976. No. 6 surch in English and Arabic.

No.	Type	Description	Mint	Used
50a		50 f. on 75 f. multicoloured	20·00	15·00

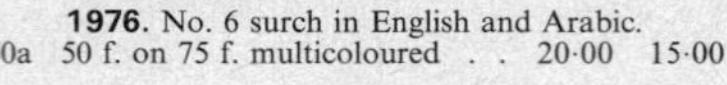

12 Man and Road Signs

13 Headphones

1976. Traffic Week. Multicoloured.

No.	Type	Description	Mint	Used
51		15 f. Type **12**	55	10
52		80 f. Example of dangerous driving and road signals (horiz)	2·50	1·75
53		140 f. Children on road crossing (horiz)	4·75	3·25

1976. International Telecommunications Day.

No.	Type	Description	Mint	Used
54	13	50 f. multicoloured	55	25
55		80 f. multicoloured	7·25	55
56		2 d. multicoloured	3·50	2·00

14 U.A.E. Crest

15 President Shaikh Zaid

1976.

No.	Type	Description	Mint	Used
57	14	5 f. red	10	30
58		10 f. brown	15	20
59		15 f. pink	20	20
60		35 f. brown	35	10
61		50 f. violet	60	15
62		60 f. bistre	90	15
63		80 f. green	1·25	25
64		90 f. blue	1·50	10
65		1 d. blue	1·75	30
66		140 f. green	2·25	70
67		250 f. violet	2·75	95
68		2 d. grey	3·25	80
69		5 d. blue	7·00	3·50
70		10 d. mauve	12·00	8·00

1976. Fifth National Day.

No.	Type	Description	Mint	Used
71	15	15 f. multicoloured	50	10
72		140 f. multicoloured	1·40	1·10

MINIMUM PRICE

The minimum price quoted is 10p which represents a handling charge rather than a basis for valuing common stamps. For further notes about prices, see introductory pages.

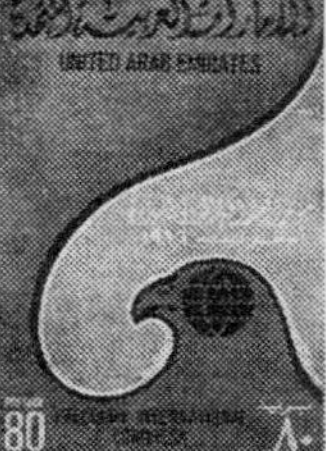

16 Falcon's Head and Gulf

17 Mohammed Ali Jinnah (Quaid-i-Azam)

1976. International Falconry Congress, Abu Dhabi.

No.	Type	Description	Mint	Used
73	16	80 f. multicoloured	1·25	65
74		2 d. multicoloured	2·75	1·75

1976. Birth Centenary of Mohammed Ali Jinnah.

No.	Type	Description	Mint	Used
75	17	50 f. multicoloured	1·25	45
76		80 f. multicoloured	2·00	1·40

19 A.P.U. Emblem

20 U.A.E. Crest

1977. 25th Anniv of Arab Postal Union.

No.	Type	Description	Mint	Used
78	19	50 f. multicoloured	1·25	40
79		80 f. multicoloured	2·00	1·25

1977.

No.	Type	Description	Mint	Used
80	20	5 f. red and black	10	30
81		10 f. brown and black	15	20
82		15 f. pink and black	20	20
83		35 f. brown and black	40	10
84		50 f. mauve and black	65	15
85		60 f. bistre and black	1·00	30
86		80 f. green and black	1·00	20
87		90 f. blue and black	1·00	10
88		1 d. blue and black	1·40	25
89		1 d. 40 green and black	2·00	60
90		1 d. 50 violet and black	2·25	75
91		2 d. grey and black	2·75	95
92		5 d. turquoise and black	6·00	2·75
93		10 d. mauve and black	10·00	5·50

21 Arab Scholar and Emblems

1977. International Literacy Day.

No.	Type	Description	Mint	Used
94	21	50 f. multicoloured	75	25
95		3 d. multicoloured	2·75	1·75

22 Armoured Cars

1977. Sixth National Day. Multicoloured.

No.	Type	Description	Mint	Used
96		15 f. Type **22**		
97		50 f. Anti-aircraft missiles		
98		150 f. Soldiers marching		
		Set of 3	£250	

Nos. 96/8 were withdrawn from sale on day of issue as the date in Arabic was wrongly inscribed backwards.

23 Posthorn Dhow

24 Koran on Map of World

1979. Second Gulf Postal Organization Conf, Dubai.

No.	Type	Description	Mint	Used
99	23	50 f. multicoloured	45	20
100		5 d. multicoloured	3·00	2·50

1980. The Arabs.

No.	Type	Description	Mint	Used
101	24	50 f. multicoloured	45	20
102		1 d. 40 multicoloured	95	60
103		3 d. multicoloured	2·00	1·50

25 Dassault Mirage III Jet Fighters and Sud Aviation Alouette III Helicopter

1980. Ninth National Day.

104 **25** 15 f. multicoloured 20 10
105 50 f. multicoloured 65 20
106 80 f. multicoloured 90 60
107 150 f. multicoloured . . . 1·60 1·25

26 Family on Graph

27 Mosque and Kaaba, Mecca

1980. Population Census.

109 **26** 15 f. blue and pink 20 10
110 – 80 f. brown and grey . . . 80 35
111 – 90 f. brown and buff . . . 1·00 50
112 **26** 2 d. deep blue and blue . . 2·50 2·00
DESIGN: 80, 90 f. Figure standing in doorway.

1980. 1400th Anniv of Hejira.

113 **27** 15 f. multicoloured 25 10
114 80 f. multicoloured 80 35
115 90 f. multicoloured . . . . 1·00 45
116 140 f. multicoloured . . . 2·25 1·50

28 Figures supporting O.P.E.C. Emblem

29 Policeman helping Child across Road

1980. 20th Anniv of Organization of Petroleum Exporting Countries. Multicoloured.

118 50 f. Type **28** 55 30
119 80 f. Type **28** 90 45
120 90 f. O.P.E.C. emblem and globe 1·10 50
121 140 f. As No. 120 . . . . . . 2·00 1·50

1981. Traffic Week. Multicoloured.

123 15 f. Type **29** 45 15
124 50 f. Policeman and traffic signs (21 × 31 mm) . . . . 1·00 40
125 80 f. Type **29** . . . . 1·50 70
126 5 d. As No. 124 . . . . 4·75 4·25

30 Symbols of Industry

1981. Tenth National Day.

127 **30** 25 f. blue and black 35 15
128 – 150 f. multicoloured . . . 1·50 1·00
129 – 2 r. red, green and black . . 2·25 1·75
DESIGNS: 150 f. Soldiers; 2 r. Flag, U.N. and U.A.E emblems.

31 Helping the Disabled (pictogram) and I.Y.D.P. Emblem

32 U.A.E. Crest

1981. International Year of Disabled Persons. Multicoloured.

130 25 f. Type **31** 40 15
131 45 f. Disabled person in wheelchair (pictogram) (vert) 70 30
132 150 f. As No. 131 . . . . . . 1·50 1·25
133 2 d. Type **31** . . . . 2·50 2·00

1982. Multicoloured. Background colour given.

(a) Size 17 × 21 mm.

134 **32** 5 f. pink 10 10
135 10 f. green 10 10
136 15 f. violet 10 10
137 25 f. brown 15 10
138 35 f. brown 15 10
139 50 f. blue 20 10
140 75 f. yellow 35 25
141 100 f. grey 45 35
142 110 f. green 45 35
143 125 f. mauve 55 40
144 150 f. blue 70 50
145 175 f. blue 80 60

(b) Size 23 × 27 mm.

146 **32** 2 d. green 90 40
147 250 f. pink . . . . 1·00 80
148 3 d. blue . . . . 1·25 90
149 5 d. yellow . . . . 1·60 1·10
150 10 d. brown . . . . 3·25 2·00
151 20 d. silver . . . . 6·00 4·00
151c 50 d. red . . . . 18·00 13·00

33 Flags of Competing Countries and Emblem

1982. 6th Arab Gulf Football Championships. Multicoloured.

152 25 f. Type **33** 35 15
153 75 f. American bald eagle holding ball over stadium (vert) . . 80 45
154 125 f. Footballers (vert) . . . 1·25 80
155 3 d. As No. 153 . . . . . . 2·75 2·50

34 Figure breaking Gun

1982. 2nd U.N. Disarmament Conference.

156 **34** 25 f. multicoloured 40 15
157 75 f. multicoloured 90 50
158 125 f. multicoloured . . . 1·50 1·00
159 150 f. multicoloured . . . 2·00 1·50

35 National Emblems

1982. 11th National Day. Multicoloured.

160 25 f. Type **35** 40 15
161 75 f. Dove and flag (vert) . . 90 50
162 125 f. As 75 f. . . . . 1·50 1·00
163 150 f. Type **35** . . . . 2·00 1·50

36 Arab writing

37 W.C.Y. Emblem

1983. Arab Literacy Day.

164 – 25 f. multicoloured . . . . 10·00
165 **36** 35 f. brown, violet & black 40 20
166 – 75 f. yellow, black & purple 12·00
167 **36** 3 d. brown, yellow & black 2·50 2·25
DESIGN: 25, 75 f. Koran and lamp.

1983. World Communications Year.

168 **37** 25 f. multicoloured 35 10
169 150 f. multicoloured . . . 1·50 1·00
170 2 d. multicoloured . . . . 1·75 1·40
171 3 d. multicoloured . . . . 2·50 2·25

38 Satellite Orbit within "20"

1984. 20th Anniv of International Telecommunications Satellite Consortium.

172 **38** 2 d. blue, purple & dp blue 2·25 1·75
173 2½ d. blue, purple & green . 2·75 2·25

39 Shaikh Hamad bin Mohamed al Sharqi and Buthnah Fort, Fujeira

1984. 13th National Day. Multicoloured.

174 1 d. Type **39** . . . . 1·10 95
175 1 d. Shaikh Rashid bin Ahmed al Moalla and Alfalaj Fort, Umm al Qiwain . . . . 1·10 95
176 1 d. Shaikh Humaid bin Rashid al Naimi and Palace, Ajman 1·10 95
177 1 d. Shaikh Saqr bin Mohammed al-Qasimi and harbour, Ras al Khaima . . . . 1·10 95
178 1 d. Shaikh Zaid bin Sultan al Nahayyan and refinery, Abu Dhabi . . . . 1·10 95
179 1 d. Shaikh Sultan bin Mohammed al Qasimi, oil well and mosque, Sharjah . . . . 1·10 95
180 1 d. Shaikh Rashid bin Said and building, Dubai . . . . . . 1·10 95

40 Pictograms of Refuse Collection

41 Globe and Knights

1985. Tidy Week.

181 **40** 5 d. orange and black . . . 5·50 4·25

1985. World Junior Chess Championship, Sharjah.

182 **41** 2 d. multicoloured . . . . 2·75 1·75
183 250 f. multicoloured . . . . 3·75 2·50

42 Map and Hand holding Flag

43 Stylised People and Map

1985. 14th National Day.

184 **42** 50 f. multicoloured 40 20
185 3 d. multicoloured . . . . 2·75 1·50

1985. Population Census.

186 **43** 50 f. multicoloured 40 20
187 1 d. multicoloured . . . . 1·50 1·00
188 3 d. multicoloured . . . . 1·75 1·25

44 Profiles looking at Sapling

45 Emblem

1985. International Youth Year. Multicoloured.

189 50 f. Type **44** 40 20
190 175 f. Open book, flame and people between hemispheres (horiz) . . . . 1·50 1·00
191 2 d. Youth carrying globe on back . . . . 1·75 1·25

1986. Arabic Woman and Family Day.

192 **45** 1 d. multicoloured 85 45
193 3 d. multicoloured . . . . 2·25 1·50

46 Globe, Map and Posthorn

47 Sakar Falcon

1986. 1st Anniv of General Postal Authority. Multicoloured.

194 50 f. Type **46** 40 20
195 1 d. Banner around globe (vert) 85 50
196 2 d. As No. 195 . . . . 1·60 1·40
197 250 f. Type **46** . . . . 1·90 1·75

1986.

198 **47** 50 f. gold, blue and green . 35 35
199 75 f. gold, blue and mauve 60 60
200 125 f. gold, blue and grey . 90 90

48 Container Ship in Dock

49 Dawn, Satellite, Telephone Dial and Dish Aerials

1986. 10th Anniv of United Arab Shipping Company. Multicoloured.

201 2 d. Type **48** . . . . 1·75 1·25
202 3 d. Container ship at sea (vert) 2·25 1·50

1986. 10th Anniv of Emirate Telecommunications Corporation.

203 250 f. Type **49** . . . . 2·00 1·50
204 3 d. As Type **49** but with sun behind emblem . . . . . . 2·25 1·75

50 Emblem, Boeing 737 and Camel Rider

51 Emblem and Member States' Crests

1986. 1st Anniv of Emirates Airlines. Multicoloured.

205 50 f. Type **50** 50 40
206 175 f. Boeing 737, emblem and national colours . . . . . . 2·50 2·10

1986. 7th Supreme Council Session of Gulf Co-operation Council, Abu Dhabi.

207 50 f. Type **51** 40 30
208 1 d. 75 Emblem beneath tree . 1·50 1·50
209 3 d. As No. 208 . . . . 2·50 2·50

52 Dubai Trade Centre

1986. 27th Chess Olympiad, Dubai. Mult.

210 50 f. Type **52** 60 40
211 2 d. Chess players (miniature from King Alfonso X's "Book of Chess, Dice and Tablings") (horiz) . . . . 2·50 2·00
212 250 f. Chess players (miniature) (different) (horiz) . . . . . . 3·00 2·50

53 Dhow, Oil Rig, Tower Block and Sun's Rays

1986. 15th National Day. Multicoloured.

214		50 f. Type **53**	40	20
215		1 d. Type **53**	85	50
216		175 f. Flag and hands holding Arabic "15" (vert)	1·50	1·25
217		2 d. As No. 216	1·90	1·75

54 Emblem

1986. Arab Police Day.

218	**54**	50 f. multicoloured	60	45
219		1 d. multicoloured	1·25	1·00

55 Emblem on Landscape **56** Boeing 737 and Map

1987. Municipalities and Environment Week.

220	**55**	50 f. multicoloured	40	35
221		1 d. multicoloured	80	75

1987. 1st Anniv of United Arab Emirates Flight Information Region.

222	**56**	200 f. multicoloured	2·00	1·90
223		250 f. multicoloured	2·25	2·10

57 Flower in Droplet **58** University Emblem

1987. "Save Energy". Multicoloured.

224		50 f. Type **57**	40	40
225		2 d. Globe as sun over oil derrick	1·50	1·50

1987. 10th Anniv of U.A.E. University.

226	**58**	1 d. multicoloured	80	80
227		3 d. multicoloured	2·25	2·25

59 Drilling Platform

1987. 25th Anniv of First Crude Oil Shipment from Abu Dhabi.

228	**59**	50 f. multicoloured	40	30
229	–	1 d. blue, black and light blue	80	70
230	–	175 f. grey, black and blue	1·40	1·40
231	–	2 d. multicoloured	1·90	1·90

DESIGNS—VERT: 1 d. Aerial view of drilling platform; 175 f. Rig workers with drill head. HORIZ: 2 d. Oil tanker at sea.

60 Trees and Dates in Arched Window **61** Graph and Woman holding Baby

1987. Arab Palm Tree and Dates Day. Multicoloured.

232		50 f. Type **60**	40	40
233		1 d. Trees and fruit	80	80

1987. U.N.I.C.E.F Child Survival Campaign.

234	**61**	50 f. multicoloured	30	30
235	–	1 d. blue, black and flesh	60	60
236	–	175 f. black, green and deep green	1·00	1·00
237	–	2 d. multicoloured	1·40	1·40

DESIGNS—VERT: 1 d. Vaccinating baby; 175 f. Oral rehydration therapy. HORIZ: 2 d. Mother breastfeeding.

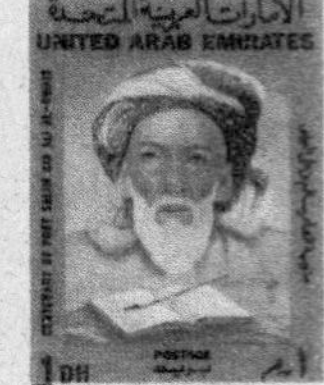

62 Emblem on Man's Head and Globe **63** Salim bin Ali al-Owais

1987. International Year of Shelter for the Homeless.

238	**62**	2 d. multicoloured	1·50	1·50
239		250 f. multicoloured	1·75	1·75

1987. Birth Centenary of Salim bin Ali al-Owais (poet).

240	**63**	1 d. multicoloured	75	75
241		2 d. multicoloured	1·50	1·50

64 Lockheed TriStar 500 and Terminal Building

1987. 6th Anniv of Abu Dhabi International Airport. Multicoloured.

242		50 f. Type **64**	55	50
243		50 f. Reception area	55	50
244		100 f. Lockheed TriStar 500 over air traffic control centre	1·10	1·00
245		100 f. Lockheed TriStar 500 and Boeing 737 at gangways	1·10	1·00

65 Writing in Sand, Oyster and Pearls

1988. National Arts Festival.

246	**65**	50 f. multicoloured	40	40
247		250 f. multicoloured	1·90	1·90

66 Fisherman on Shore (Layla Mohammed Khalfan)

1988. Children's Paintings. Multicoloured.

248		50 f. Type **66**	30	25
249		1 d. Woman and flowers (Zeinab Nasir Mohammed) (vert)	60	60
250		1 d. 75 Flowers with girls' faces (Fatma Ali Abdullah) (vert)	1·00	1·00
251		2 d. Teddy bear, cat and girls playing (Saaly Mohammed Jowda)	1·40	1·40

67 Masked Youth **68** Emblem and Urban and Desert Scenes

1988. Palestinian "Intifida" Movement.

252	**67**	2 d. multicoloured	1·40	1·40
253		250 f. multicoloured	1·60	1·60

1988. National Banking Anniversaries. Mult.

254		50 f. Type **68** (20th anniv of National Bank of Abu Dhabi)	30	30
255		50 f. Emblem (25th anniv of National Bank of Dubai Ltd)	30	30

69 Map, Fork-lift Truck and Container Lorry **70** Swimming

1988. 16th Anniv of Port Rashid. Multicoloured.

256		50 f. Type **69**	30	30
257		1 d. Container ship and view of port	60	60
258		175 f. Ro-ro ferry and small boats at anchorages	1·00	1·00
259		2 d. Container ship at dockside	1·40	1·40

1988. Olympic Games, Seoul. Multicoloured.

260		2 d. Type **70**	1·25	1·25
261		250 f. Cycling	1·40	1·40

71 Vase

1988. 1st Anniv of Ras al Khaimah National Museum. Multicoloured.

262		50 f. Type **71**	25	25
263		3 d. Gold ornament (horiz)	1·50	1·50

72 Emblem

1988. 18th Arab Scouts Conference, Abu Dhabi.

264	**72**	1 d. multicoloured	50	50

73 Dahlia

1989. 10th Tree Day. Multicoloured.

265		50 f. Ghaf tree	25	25
266		100 f. Palm tree	50	50
267		250 f. Type **73**	1·25	1·25

74 Airport

1989. 10th Anniv of Sharjah International Airport.

268	**74**	50 f. multicoloured	40	35
269		100 f. multicoloured	85	65

75 Short S.23 Flying Boat **76** Newspaper

1989. 80th Anniv of Gulf Postal Services. Multicoloured.

270		50 f. Type **75**	35	25
271		3 d. "Bombala" (freighter)	1·25	1·25

1989. 20th Anniv of "Al-Ittihad" (newspaper). Multicoloured.

272		50 f. Type **76**	20	20
273		1 d. Newspaper offices	40	40

77 Emblem and Map

1989. 5th Anniv of Gulf Investment Corporation.

274	**77**	50 f. multicoloured	20	20
275		2 d. multicoloured	80	80

78 Offering Leaf to Child

1989. International Volunteer Day. U.A.E. Red Crescent Society. Multicoloured.

276		2 d. type 78	40	40
277		250 f. Crippled child in open hands (vert)	1·00	1·00

79 Bank Emblem and Buildings **80** Compass and Dhow

1989. 20th Anniv of Dubai Commercial Bank. Multicoloured.

278		50 f. Type **79**	20	20
279		1 d. Bank building	40	40

80 Compass and Dhow

1989. Bin Majid (navigator) Commemoration. Multicoloured.

280		1 d. Type **80**	35	35
281		3 d. Dhow (vert)	1·40	1·40

81 Festival Sites **82** Saker Falcon

1990. 3rd Al Ain Festival.

282	**81**	50 f. multicoloured	20	20
283		1 d. multicoloured	40	40

1990. Multicoloured, background colour given.

(a) Size 17 × 22 mm.

284	**82**	5 f. blue	10	10
285		20 f. mauve	10	10
286		25 f. pink	10	10
287		50 f. brown	15	15
288		100 f. bistre	30	30
289		150 f. green	50	50
290		175 f. green	55	55

(b) Size 21 × 26 mm.

291	**82**	2 d. lilac	65	65
292		250 f. blue	80	80
293		3 d. pink	95	95
294		5 d. orange	1·60	1·60
295		10 d. yellow	3·25	3·25
296		20 d. green	6·25	6·25
297		50 d. green	16·00	16·00

83 Children and Leaves **84** Leaning Tower of Pisa, Flag and U.A.E. Mascot

1990. Children's Culture Festival.

301	**83**	50 f. multicoloured	15	15
302		250 f. multicoloured	80	80

1990. World Cup Football Championship, Italy. Multicoloured.
303 50 f. Type **84** 15 15
304 1 d. Desert, flag and mascot (vert) 30 30
305 2 d. Mascot on ball (vert) 60 60
306 250 f. Flags around mascot 80 80

85 Projects and Buildings

1990. 25th Anniv of Dubai Chamber of Commerce and Industry. Multicoloured.
308 **85** 50 f. multicoloured 25 25
309 1 d. multicoloured 45 45

86 Weeping Eyes and Child on Globe
87 "Catharanthus roseus"

1990. Child Survival Programme. Multicoloured.
310 175 f. Type **86** 55 55
311 2 d. Emaciated child and newspapers 65 65

1990. Flowers. Multicoloured.
312 50 f. "Centavrea pseudo sinaica" 15 15
313 50 f. "Calotropis procera" 15 15
314 50 f. "Argyrolobeum roseum" 15 15
315 50 f. "Lamranthus roseus" 15 15
316 50 f. "Hibiscus rosa sinensis" 15 15
317 50 f. "Nerium oleander" 15 15
318 50 f. Type **87** 15 15
319 50 f. "Bougainvillaea glabra" 15 15

88 O.P.E.C. Emblem and Flame
89 Industrial Pollution and Dead Fish

1990. 30th Anniv of Organization of Petroleum Exporting Countries. Multicoloured.
321 50 f. Emblem, flames, hands and oil rigs 20 15
322 1 d. Type **88** 30 30
323 175 f. Emblem and droplet 55 55

1990. "Our Planet Our Health". Multicoloured.
324 50 f. Type **89** 15 15
325 3 d. Industrial and vehicle pollution covering globe 95 95

90 Grand Mosque, Abu Dhabi
91 U.A.E. Crest and Graph

1990. Mosques. Multicoloured.
326 1 d. type 90 30 30
327 2 d. Al-Jumeirah Mosque, Dubai (vert) 65 65

1990. 10th Anniv of Central Bank. Mult.
328 50 f. Type **91** 15 15
329 175 f. Banknotes and building (horiz) 55 55

92 Tree
93 Globes and Buildings

1990. International Conference on High Salinity Tolerant Plants, Al-Ain. Multicoloured.
330 50 f. Type **92** 15 15
331 250 f. Trees along shoreline 80 80

1991. Abu Dhabi International Fair.
332 **93** 50 f. multicoloured 20 20
333 2 d. multicoloured 70 70

94 Emblem

1991. World Telecommunications Day "Telecommunications and Safety of Human Life".
334 **94** 2 d. multicoloured 70 70
335 3 d. multicoloured 1·10 1·10

95 Shaikh Saqr Mosque, Ras al Khaimah

1991. Mosques. Multicoloured.
336 1 d. Type **95** 35 35
337 2 d. King Faisal Mosque, Sharjah 70 70
See also Nos. 371/2 and 411/2.

96 "Native Games" (Robba Mohamed Sofian)

1991. Children's Paintings. Multicoloured.
338 50 f. Type **96** 20 20
339 1 d. "National Day" (Yasmin Mohamed al-Rahim) 35 35
340 175 f. "Blind Man's Buff" (Amal Ibrahim Mohamed) 65 65
341 250 f. "Native Dance" (Amina Ali Hassan) 90 90

97 Yellow-marked Butterfly Fish

1991. Fishes. Multicoloured.
342 50 f. Type **97** 20 20
343 50 f. Red snapper 20 20
344 50 f. Golden trevally 20 20
345 50 f. Two-banded porgy 20 20
346 1 d. Black bream 35 35
347 1 d. Three-banded grunt 35 35
348 1 d. Greasy grouper 35 35
349 1 d. Rabbit fish 35 35

98 Shaikh Rashid and Abu Dhabi International Airport
99 Fire Fighting

1991. 1st Death Anniv of Shaikh Rashid bin Said al-Maktoum (ruler of Dubai). Multicoloured.
351 50 f. Type **98** 30 20
352 1 d. Shaikh Rashid and modern and old buildings (horiz) 35 35
353 175 f. Shaikh Rashid and seafront hotels 65 65
354 2 d. Jebel Ali container port, Shaikh Rashid and dish aerial (horiz) 70 70

1991. Civil Defence Day.
355 **99** 50 f. multicoloured 20 20
356 1 d. multicoloured 35 35

100 Panavia Tornado over Dubai Airport
101 Flags and Emblem

1991. International Aerospace Exhibition, Dubai. Multicoloured.
357 175 f. Type **100** 75 75
358 2 d. View of under-side of Panavia Tornado over Dubai airport 85 85

1991. 10th Anniv of Gulf Co-operation Council.
359 **101** 50 f. multicoloured 20 20
360 3 d. multicoloured 1·10 1·10

102 Shaikh Zaid bin Sultan al Nahayyan of Abu Dhabi (President of U.A.E.)

1991. 20th National Day. Multicoloured.
361 75 f. Type **102** 25 25
362 75 f. Shaikh Humaid bin Rashid al Naimi of Ajman and fort (to right of stamp) with cannon 25 25
363 75 f. Shaikh Maktoum bin Rashid al-Maktoum of Dubai and fort (to left of stamp) with cannon 25 25
364 75 f. Shaikh Hamad bin Mohamed al Sharqi of Fujeira and fort on hillock 25 25
365 75 f. Shaikh Saqr bin Mohamed al-Qasimi of Ras al Khaima and fort (tower and tree in foreground) 25 25
366 75 f. Shaikh Sultan bin Mohamed al Qasimi of Sharjah and fort (to left of stamp with Arabs in doorway) 25 25
367 75 f. Shaikh Rashid bin Ahmed al Moalla of Umm al Qiwain and fort (to right of stamp with trees growing over walls) 25 25

103 Derrick
104 Fort Jahili, Al Ain

1992. 20th Anniv of Abu Dhabi National Oil Company.
369 **103** 175 f. multicoloured 65 65
370 250 f. multicoloured 90 90

1992. Mosques. As T **95**. Multicoloured.
371 50 f. Shaikh Rashid bin Humaid al Naimi Mosque, Ajman 20 20
372 1 d. Shaikh Ahmed bin Rashid al Moalla Mosque, Umm al Qiwain 35 35

1992. "Expo '92" World's Fair, Seville.
373 **104** 2 d. multicoloured 70 70
374 250 f. multicoloured 90 90

105 Emblem and Family

1992. Deaf Child Week. Multicoloured.
375 1 d. Type **105** 35 35
376 3 d. Hearing aid in ear 1·10 1·10

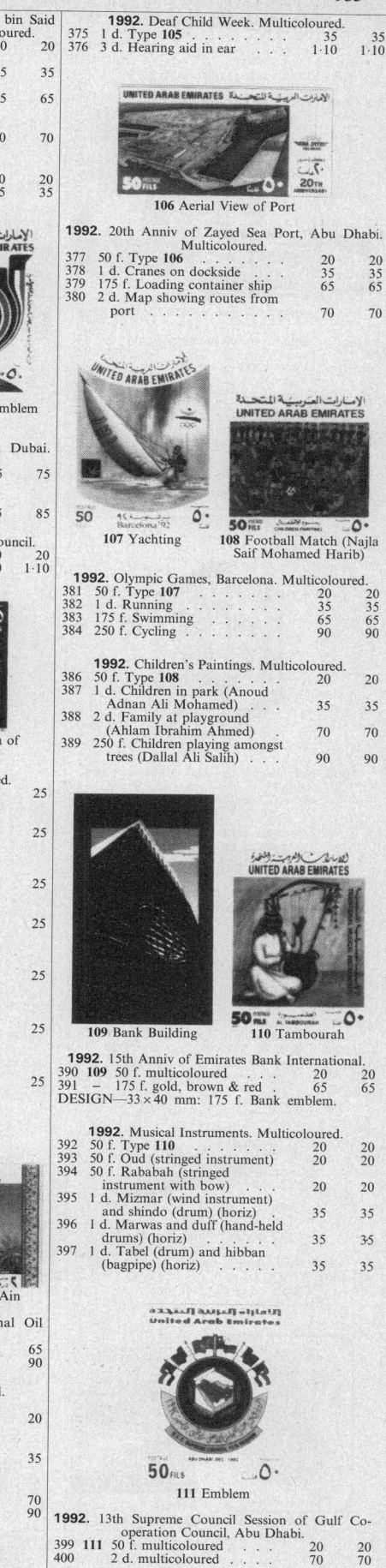

106 Aerial View of Port

1992. 20th Anniv of Zayed Sea Port, Abu Dhabi. Multicoloured.
377 50 f. Type **106** 20 20
378 1 d. Cranes on dockside 35 35
379 175 f. Loading container ship 65 65
380 2 d. Map showing routes from port 70 70

107 Yachting
108 Football Match (Najla Saif Mohamed Harib)

1992. Olympic Games, Barcelona. Multicoloured.
381 50 f. Type **107** 20 20
382 1 d. Running 35 35
383 175 f. Swimming 65 65
384 250 f. Cycling 90 90

1992. Children's Paintings. Multicoloured.
386 50 f. Type **108** 20 20
387 1 d. Children in park (Anoud Adnan Ali Mohamed) 35 35
388 2 d. Family at playground (Ahlam Ibrahim Ahmed) 70 70
389 250 f. Children playing amongst trees (Dallal Ali Salih) 90 90

109 Bank Building
110 Tambourah

1992. 15th Anniv of Emirates Bank International.
390 **109** 50 f. multicoloured 20 20
391 – 175 f. gold, brown & red 65 65
DESIGN—33 × 40 mm: 175 f. Bank emblem.

1992. Musical Instruments. Multicoloured.
392 50 f. Type **110** 20 20
393 50 f. Oud (stringed instrument) 20 20
394 50 f. Rababah (stringed instrument with bow) 20 20
395 1 d. Mizmar (wind instrument) and shindo (drum) (horiz) 35 35
396 1 d. Marwas and duff (hand-held drums) (horiz) 35 35
397 1 d. Tabel (drum) and hibban (bagpipe) (horiz) 35 35

111 Emblem

1992. 13th Supreme Council Session of Gulf Co-operation Council, Abu Dhabi.
399 **111** 50 f. multicoloured 20 20
400 2 d. multicoloured 70 70

112 Camel Race

1992. The Dromedary. Multicoloured.
401 50 f. Type **112** 20 20
402 1 d. Camel riders and mother with young (vert) 35 35
403 175 f. Camels at well and mother with young 65 65
404 2 d. Camels (vert) 70 70

113 Golf
114 Club Building 

1993. Tourism. Multicoloured.
405 50 f. Type **113** 20 20
406 1 d. Fishing (vert) 35 35
407 2 d. Sailing 70 70
408 250 f. Sight-seeing by car 90 90

1993. Dubai Creek Golf and Yacht Club. Mult.
409 2 d. Type **114** 70 70
410 250 f. Club building and sea shore 90 90

1993. Mosques. As T **95**. Multicoloured.
411 50 f. Thabit bin Khalid Mosque, Fujeira 20 20
412 1 d. Sharq al Morabbah Mosque, Al Ain 35 35

115 National Crest and Sports

1993. National Youth Festival. Multicoloured.
413 50 f. Type **115** 20 20
414 3 d. National crest and sciences 1·10 1·10

116 "Conus textile"

1993. Sea Shells. Multicoloured.
415 25 f. Type **116** 15 15
416 50 f. "Pinctada radiata" 25 25
417 100 f. "Murex scolopax" 45 45
418 150 f. "Natica pulicaris" 75 75
419 175 f. "Lambis truncata sebae" 85 85
420 200 f. "Cardita bicolor" 1·00 1·00
421 250 f. "Cypraea grayana" 1·25 1·25
422 300 f. "Cymatium trilineatum" 1·40 1·40

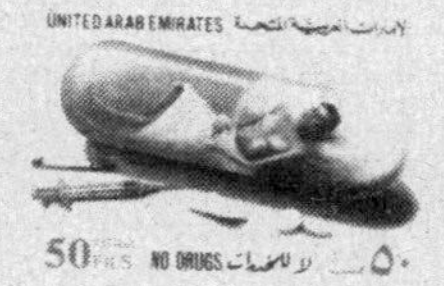

117 Addict within Capsule

1993. Anti-drugs Campaign. Multicoloured.
423 50 f. Type **117** 20 20
424 1 d. Family on skull, globe and drugs (vert) 35 35

118 Commercial Buildings
119 Aerial View of Port 

1993. 25th Anniv of Abu Dhabi National Bank. Multicoloured.
425 50 f. Type **118** 20 20
426 1 d. Bank emblem 35 35
427 175 f. Bank building and emblem 65 65
428 2 d. Commercial buildings within shield 75 75

1993. Dubai Ports Authority. Multicoloured.
429 50 f. Type **119** 20 20
430 1 d. Cranes loading containers 35 35
431 2 d. Aerial view of port (different) 75 75
432 250 f. Arrowed routes on globe 90 90

120 Soldiers on Parade (Mouza Musabah al-Mazroui)

1993. National Day. Children's Paintings. Multicoloured.
433 50 f. Type **120** 20 20
434 1 d. Woman and children (Shreen Naeem Hassan Radwan) (vert) 35 35
435 175 f. Flag and dhow (Samiha Mohamad Sultan) 65 65
436 2 d. Decorations and fireworks (Omer Abdulla Rabia Thani) 75 75

121 Hili Tomb

1993. Archaeological Finds from Al-Ain. Multicoloured.
437 50 f. Type **121** 20 20
438 1 d. Hili decorative tile 35 35
439 175 f. Qattarah figure 65 65
440 250 f. Hili bow 90 90

122 Horse rearing

1994. Arabian Horses. Multicoloured.
441 50 f. Type **122** 15 15
442 1 d. Grey (horiz) 35 35
443 175 f. Bay with white blaze 60 60
444 250 f. Piebald (horiz) 85 85

123 Children with Flags and Balloons

1994. 10th Children's Festival, Sharjah. Children's Paintings. Multicoloured.
445 50 f. Type **123** 15 15
446 1 d. Children in forest 35 35
447 175 f. Children with balloons and child painting 60 60
448 2 d. Children in garden 70 70

124 Dubai, Map and Emblems
125 Holy Kaaba and Globe 

1994. 10th Arab Towns Organization Congress, Dubai. Multicoloured.
449 50 f. Type **124** 15 15
450 1 d. Different view of Dubai, map and emblems (horiz) 35 35

1994. Pilgrimage to Mecca. Multicoloured.
451 50 f. Type **125** 15 15
452 2 d. Crowds around Holy Kaaba 70 70

126 Homes (Arab Housing Day)
127 Covered Vessel 

1994. Anniversaries and Events. Multicoloured.
453 1 d. Type **126** 35 35
454 1 d. Children playing and couple (International Year of the Family) (horiz) 35 35
455 1 d. National Olympic Committee emblem, rings and sports (centenary of International Olympic Committee) (horiz) 35 35
456 1 d. Paper, pen-nib and dove (10th anniv of Emirates Writers' Association) 35 35

1994. Archaeological Finds from Al Qusais, Dubai. Multicoloured.
457 50 f. Type **127** 15 15
458 1 d. Jug (horiz) 35 35
459 175 f. Jug (different) (horiz) 60 60
460 250 f. Bowl (horiz) 85 85

128 Arabian Leopard

1994. Environmental Protection. The Cat Family. Multicoloured.
461 50 f. Type **128** 15 15
462 1 d. Gordon's wildcat 35 35
463 2 d. Caracal 70 70
464 250 f. Sandcat 85 85

129 Little Green Bee Eaters

1994. Birds. Multicoloured.
465 50 f. Type **129** 15 15
466 175 f. White-collared kingfishers 60 60
467 2 d. Crab plovers 70 70
468 250 f. Indian rollers 85 85

130 Championship Emblem

1994. 12th Arab Gulf Football Championship, Abu Dhabi. Multicoloured.
470 50 f. Type **130** 15 15
471 3 d. Match scene (horiz) 1·00 1·00

UNITED NATIONS Pt. 22; Pt. 8; Pt. 2

A. NEW YORK HEADQUARTERS

For use on mail posted at the Post Office at U.N. Headquarters, New York.

NOTE: Similar designs, but in different colours and values in Swiss Francs (F.S.) are issues of the Geneva office. Those with face values in Austrian Schillings are issues of the Vienna office. These are listed after the New York issues.

100 cents = 1 dollar

1 "Peoples of the World"
2 U.N. Emblem 

1951.
1 **1** 1 c. mauve 10 10
2 – $1\frac{1}{2}$ c. green 10 10
3 **3** 2 c. violet 10 10
4 – 3 c. blue and purple 10 10
5 – 5 c. blue 15 10
6 **1** 10 c. brown 15 10
7 – 15 c. blue and violet 20 15
8 – 20 c. brown 50 30
9 – 25 c. blue and black 45 30
10 – 50 c. blue 5·00 1·75
11 **3** $1 red 2·00 85
DESIGNS—VERT: $1\frac{1}{2}$, 50 c. U.N. Headquarters, New York; 5 c. Clasped hands. HORIZ: 3, 15, 25 c. U.N. flag; 20 c. Hemispheres and U.N. emblem.

A 7 Seagull and Airplane

1951. Air.
A12 A **3** 6 c. red 15 15
A13 10 c. green 15 15
A14 – 15 c. blue 25 15
A15 – 25 c. black 90 40
DESIGN: 15, 25 c. Swallows and U.N. emblem.

7 Veterans' War Memorial Building, San Francisco

1952. 7th Anniv of Signing of U.N. Charter.
12 **7** 5 c. blue 25 15

8 "Flame of Freedom"

1952. Human Rights Day.
13 **8** 3 c. green 15 15
14 5 c. blue 40 15

9 Homeless Family

1953. Protection for Refugees.
15 **9** 3 c. brown 15 15
16 5 c. blue 70 30

10 "Universal Postal Union"

1953. Universal Postal Union.
17 **10** 3 c. sepia 20 15
18 5 c. blue 90 25

11 Gearwheels and U.N. Emblem

12 "Flame of Freedom"

1953. Technical Assistance for Underdeveloped Areas.
19 **11** 3 c. grey 15 15
20 5 c. green 75 30

1953. Human Rights Day.
21 **12** 3 c. blue 20 15
22 5 c. red . . . . 1·40 25

13 F.A.O. Symbol

14 U.N. Emblem and Anvil

1954. Food and Agriculture Organization.
23 **13** 3 c. yellow and green . . . 40 15
24 8 c. yellow and blue . . . 85 40

NOTE. In the following issues the majority of the values unillustrated have the commemorative inscription or initials in another language.

1954. International Labour Organization.
25 **14** 3 c. brown 20 15
26 8 c. mauve . . . . 1·50 40

15 U.N. European Office, Geneva

16 Mother and Child

1954. United Nations Day.
27 **15** 3 c. violet . . . . 2·75 60
28 8 c. red 25 15

1954. Human Rights Day.
29 **16** 3 c. orange . . . . 6·50 1·25
30 8 c. green 25 15

17 "Flight"

1955. International Civil Aviation Organization.
31 **17** 3 c. blue . . . . 2·50 40
32 8 c. red 80 60

18 U.N.E.S.C.O. Symbol

1955. U.N. Educational, Scientific and Cultural Organization.
33 **18** 3 c. mauve 40 15
34 8 c. blue 15 15

19 U.N. Charter

20 "Flame of Freedom"

1955. 10th Anniv of U.N.
35 **19** 3 c. red . . . . 2·50 35
36 4 c. green 20 10
37 8 c. black 20 15

1955. Human Rights Day.
39 **20** 3 c. blue 15 15
40 8 c. green 50 20

21 "Telecommunication"

22 Staff of Aesculapius

1956. International Telecommunication Union.
41 **21** 3 c. blue 40 15
42 8 c. red . . . . 1·10 40

1956. World Health Organization.
43 **22** 3 c. blue 15 15
44 8 c. brown 85 45

23 General Assembly

1956. United Nations Day.
45 **23** 3 c. slate 10 10
46 8 c. olive 15 15

24 "Flame of Freedom"

25 Weather Balloon

1956. Human Rights Day.
47 **24** 3 c. purple 10 10
48 8 c. blue 15 10

1957. World Meteorological Organization.
49 **25** 3 c. blue 10 10
50 8 c. red 20 10

26 U.N.E.F. Badge

A **26** "Flight"

1957. United Nations Emergency Force.
51 **26** 3 c. blue 10 10
52 8 c. red 15 10

1957. Air.
A51 A **26** 4 c. brown 10 10
A52 5 c. red 10 10
A53 – 7 c. blue 20 15
DESIGNS—HORIZ: 7 c. U.N. flag and Douglas DC-8-60 airplane.
On the 5 c. value inscriptions are redrawn larger than those on Type A **26**.

27 U.N. Emblem over Globe

28 "Flames of Freedom"

1957. U.N. Security Council.
55 **27** 3 c. brown 10 10
56 8 c. green 15 10

1957. Human Rights Day.
57 **28** 3 c. brown 10 10
58 8 c. black 10 10

29 Atomic Symbol

30 Central Hall, Westminster (site of first General Assembly)

1958. International Atomic Energy Agency.
59 **29** 3 c. olive 10 10
60 8 c. blue 15 10

1958. U.N. General Assembly Buildings.
61 **30** 3 c. blue 10 10
62 8 c. purple 10 10
See also Nos. 69/70, 77/8 and 123/4.

31 U.N. Seal

32 Cogwheels

1958.
63 **31** 4 c. orange 10 10
64 8 c. blue 15 10

1958. Economic and Social Council.
65 **32** 4 c. turquoise 10 10
66 8 c. red 15 10

33 Hands holding Globe

1958. Human Rights Day.
67 **33** 4 c. green 10 10
68 8 c. brown 15 10

34 New York City Building, Flushing Meadows (1946–50)

35 Emblems of U.N. Industry and Agriculture

1959. U.N. General Assembly Buildings.
69 **34** 4 c. mauve 10 10
70 8 c. turquoise 15 10

1959. U.N. Economic Commission for Europe.
71 **35** 4 c. blue 10 10
72 8 c. red 20 15

36 "The Age of Bronze" (Rodin)

37 "Protection for Refugees"

1959. U.N. Trusteeship Council.
73 **36** 4 c. red 10 10
74 8 c. green 15 10

1959. World Refugee Year.
75 **37** 4 c. red and bistre 10 10
76 8 c. blue and bistre 10 10

38 Palais de Chaillot, Paris (1948, 1951)

1960. U.N. General Assembly Buildings.
77 **38** 4 c. blue and purple 10 10
78 8 c. brown and green 10 10

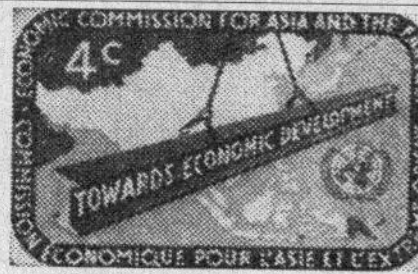

79 Steel Girder and Map

1960. U.N. Economic Commission for Asia and the Far East ("ECAFE").
79 **39** 4 c. purple, buff and turq . 10 10
80 8 c. green, pink and blue . . 15 15

40 Tree and Emblems

41 U.N. Headquarters and Emblem

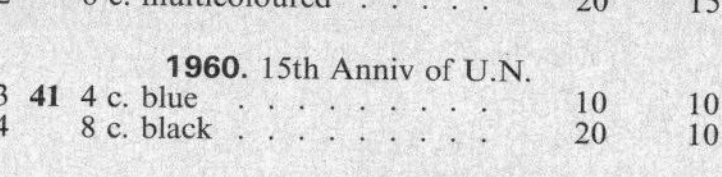

1960. 5th World Forestry Congress, Seattle.
81 **40** 4 c. multicoloured 10 10
82 8 c. multicoloured 20 15

1960. 15th Anniv of U.N.
83 **41** 4 c. blue 10 10
84 8 c. black 20 10

42 Double Block and Hook

43 Scales of Justice

1960. International Bank for Reconstruction and Development ("World Bank").
86 **42** 4 c. multicoloured 10 10
87 8 c. multicoloured 20 10

1961. International Court of Justice.
88 **43** 4 c. black, brown & yellow . 10 10
89 8 c. black, green & yellow . 20 15

44 I.M.F. Emblem

1961. International Monetary Fund.
90 **44** 4 c. blue 10 10
91 7 c. brown and yellow . . . 20 15

45 "Peace"

53 Globe and Weather Vane

52 Flags

1961.
92 **45** 1 c. multicoloured 10 10
93 – 2 c. multicoloured 10 10
94 – 3 c. multicoloured 10 10
95 – 5 c. red 15 10
96 – 7 c. brown, black & blue . 15 10
97 – 10 c. black, green & blue . 15 10
98 – 11 c. gold, light blue and blue 15 10
99 **52** 30 c. multicoloured 35 15
100 **53** 50 c. multicoloured 75 25
DESIGNS—HORIZ: 32×23 mm: 2 c. Map of the World; 10 c. Three figures on globe ("Races United"). 30½×23½ mm: 3 c. U.N. Flag. 36½×23½ mm: 5 c. Hands supporting "UN" and globe. 37½×22½ mm: 11 c. U.N. emblem across globe. VERT—21×26 mm: 7 c. U.N. emblem as flowering plant.
For 1 c. in same design, but smaller, see No. 146 and for 5 c. multicoloured see No. 165.

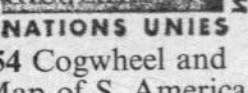

54 Cogwheel and Map of S. America **55** Africa Hall, Addis Ababa

1961. Economic Commission for Latin America.
101 **54** 4 c. red, olive and blue . . 15 10
102 11 c. purple, red and green 25 15

1961. Economic Commission for Africa.
103 **55** 4 c. multicoloured 10 10
104 11 c. multicoloured 20 15

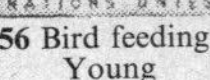

56 Bird feeding Young **57** "Housing and Community Facilities"

1961. 15th Anniv of U.N.I.C.E.F.
105 **56** 3 c. multicoloured 10 10
106 4 c. multicoloured 10 10
107 13 c. multicoloured 20 15

1962. U.N. Housing and Related Community Facilities Programme.
108 **57** 4 c. multicoloured 10 10
109 7 c. multicoloured 15 10

58 Mosquito and W.H.O. Emblem **59** U.N. Flag at Half-mast

1962. Malaria Eradication.
110 **58** 4 c. multicoloured 10 10
111 11 c. multicoloured 15 10

1962. Dag Hammarskjold (U.N. Secretary-General, 1953–61) Memorial Issue.
112 **59** 5 c. indigo, blue and black . 10 10
113 15 c. blue, grey and black . 40 15

60 Congo on World Map **61** "Peace in Space"

1962. U.N. Congo Operation.
114 **60** 4 c. multicoloured 15 10
115 11 c. multicoloured 30 15

1962. U.N. Committee on Peaceful Uses of Outer Space.
116 **61** 4 c. blue 10 10
117 11 c. mauve 15 10

62 Conference Emblem **63** Wheat

1963. Science and Technology Conf, Geneva.
118 **62** 5 c. multicoloured 10 10
119 11 c. multicoloured 20 15

1963. Freedom from Hunger.
120 **63** 5 c. yellow, green & orange 15 10
121 11 c. yellow, red & orange . 20 15

A **65** "Flight" **64** "Bridge" over Map of West New Guinea

1963. Air. Multicoloured.
A122 6 c. "Space" 10 10
A123 8 c. Type **A65** 15 10
A124 13 c. "Bird" 20 15
A125 15 c. "Birds in Flight" . . 25 15
A126 25 c. Douglas DC-8 and airmail envelope 50 20
SIZES—HORIZ: 6 c. As Type **A 65**: 13, 25 c. $30\frac{1}{2}\times23$ mm. VERT: 15 c. $23\times30\frac{1}{2}$ mm.

1963. United Nations Temporary Executive Authority (UNTEA) in West New Guinea.
122 **64** 25 c. green, blue & drab . 40 15

65 General Assembly Building and Flags **66** "Flame of Freedom"

1963. U.N. General Assembly Buildings.
123 **65** 5 c. multicoloured 10 10
124 11 c. multicoloured . . . 20 15

1963. 15th Anniv of Declaration of Human Rights.
125 **66** 5 c. multicoloured 10 10
126 11 c. multicoloured . . . 20 15

67 Ships at Sea

1964. Inter-Governmental Maritime Consultative Organization (I.M.C.O.).
127 **67** 5 c. multicoloured 15 10
128 11 c. multicoloured . . . 35 30

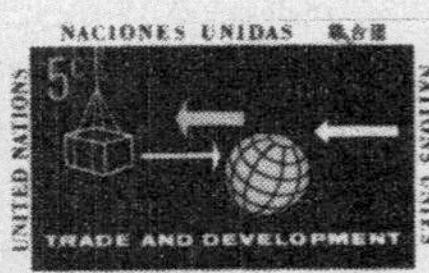

68 "Trade and Development"

1964. U.N. Trade and Development Conf, Geneva.
129 **68** 5 c. yellow, black & red . 10 10
130 11 c. yellow, black & bistre 20 15

69 Opium Poppy and Reaching Hands **70** Atomic Explosion and Padlock

1964. Narcotics Control.
131 **69** 5 c. red and black 15 10
132 11 c. green and black . . . 40 20

1964. Cessation of Nuclear Testing.
133 **70** 5 c. sepia and brown . . . 10 10

71 "Teaching" **72** Key, Globe and "Graph"

1964. "Education for Progress".
134 **71** 4 c. multicoloured 10 10
135 5 c. multicoloured 10 10
136 11 c. multicoloured 15 15

1965. U.N. Special Fund.
137 **72** 5 c. multicoloured 10 10
138 11 c. multicoloured . . . 20 15

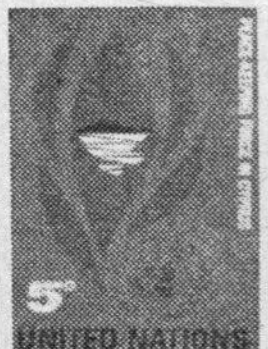

73 Cyprus "Leaves" and U.N. Emblem **74** "From Semaphore to Satellite"

1965. Peace-keeping Force in Cyprus.
139 **73** 5 c. olive, black & orange . 10 10
140 11 c. green, black & lt grn . 20 15

1965. I.T.U. Centenary.
141 **74** 5 c. multicoloured 10 10
142 11 c. multicoloured 25 20

75 I.C.Y. Emblem **76** "Peace"

1965. 20th Anniv of United Nations and International Co-operation Year.
143 **75** 5 c. blue 15 10
144 15 c. mauve 30 20

1965.
146 **76** 1 c. multicoloured 10 10
147 – 15 c. multicoloured 20 10
148 – 20 c. multicoloured 25 15
149 – 25 c. ultramarine and blue . 40 15
150 – $1 blue and turquoise . . . 1·25 60
DESIGNS—$24\frac{1}{2}\times30$ mm: 15 c. Opening words, U.N. Charter. 22×32 mm: 20 c. U.N. emblem and Headquarters. 24×24 mm: 25 c. U.N. emblem. 33×23 mm: $1 U.N. emblem encircled.

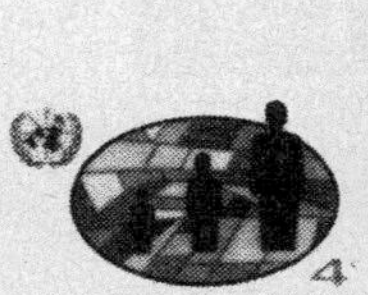
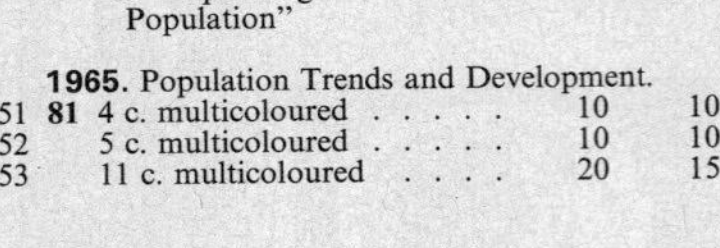

81 "Expanding Population" **82** Globe and Flags

1965. Population Trends and Development.
151 **81** 4 c. multicoloured 10 10
152 5 c. multicoloured 10 10
153 11 c. multicoloured 20 15

1966. World Federation of United Nations Assns. (W.F.U.N.A.).
154 **82** 5 c. multicoloured 10 10
155 15 c. multicoloured 20 20

83 W.H.O. Building

1966. Inaug of W.H.O. Headquarters, Geneva.
156 **83** 5 c. multicoloured 10 10
157 11 c. multicoloured 20 20

84 Coffee

1966. International Coffee Agreement of 1962.
158 **84** 5 c. multicoloured 10 10
159 11 c. multicoloured 20 15

85 Military Observer **86** Children in Closed Rail Wagon

1966. U.N. Military Observers.
160 **85** 15 c. multicoloured 25 20

1966. 20th Anniv of U.N.I.C.E.F. Multicoloured.
161 4 c. Type **86** 10 10
162 5 c. Children in locomotive and tender 15 10
163 11 c. Children in open rail wagon 30 20

89 U.N. Headquarters and World Map **91** "UN" and Emblem

1967.
164 **89** $1\frac{1}{2}$ c. multicoloured 10 10
165 – 5 c. multicoloured 15 10
166 – 6 c. multicoloured 15 10
167 **91** 13 c. blue, gold & black . . 30 20
DESIGNS—HORIZ: 5 c. As No. 95, 23×34 mm: 6 c. Aerial view of U.N. Headquarters.

92 "Progress through Development" **93** U.N. Emblem and Fireworks

1967. U.N. Development Programme.
168 **92** 5 c. multicoloured 10 10
169 11 c. multicoloured 20 15

1967. New Independent Nations Commem.
170 **93** 5 c. multicoloured 10 10
171 11 c. multicoloured 20 15

94 "Peace" **99** Baggage Labels

1967. "Expo 67", World Fair, Montreal.
172 **94** 4 c. brown and red 10 10
173 – 5 c. brown and blue . . . 10 10
174 – 8 c. multicoloured 15 10
175 – 10 c. brown and green . . 20 15
176 – 15 c. chestnut and brown . 30 30
DESIGNS—VERT: 5 c. "Justice"; 10 c. "Fraternity"; 15 c. "Truth". HORIZ ($32\times23\frac{1}{2}$ mm): 8 c. Facade of U.N. Pavilion.
The above stamps are expressed in Canadian currency and were valid for postage only from the U.N. Pavilion at the World Fair.

1967. International Tourist Year.
177 **99** 5 c. multicoloured 15 10
178 15 c. multicoloured 35 20

100 "Towards Disarmament" **101** "The Kiss of Peace" (part of Chagall's stained glass window)

1967. Disarmament Campaign.
179 **100** 6 c. multicoloured 10 10
180 13 c. multicoloured . . . 25 15

1967. United Nations Art (1st issue). Chagall's Memorial Window in U.N. Secretariat Building.
181 **101** 6 c. multicoloured 10 10
See also Nos. 185/6, 201/2, 203/4, 236/7 and 251/2.

103 Globe and Diagram of U.N. Organs **104** Starcke's Statue

1968. U.N. Secretariat.
183 **103** 6 c. multicoloured 10 10
184 13 c. multicoloured . . . 20 15

1968. United Nations Art (2nd issue). Henrik Starcke's Statue in U.N. Trusteeship Council Chamber.
185 **104** 6 c. multicoloured 15 10
186 75 c. multicoloured . . . 1·00 70

105 Industrial Skyline

1968. U.N. Industrial Development Organization (U.N.I.D.O.).
187 **105** 6 c. multicoloured 10 10
188 13 c. multicoloured . . . 20 15

A **106** "Winged Envelopes"

A **107** Aircraft and U.N. Emblem

1968. Air.
A189 A **106** 10 c. multicoloured . 25 15
A190 A **107** 20 c. multicoloured . 30 25

106 Radar Scanner

1968. World Weather Watch.
189 **106** 6 c. multicoloured 15 10
190 20 c. multicoloured . . . 40 30

107 Human Rights Emblem **108** Textbooks

1968. Human Rights Year.
191 **107** 6 c. gold, ultramarine & bl 15 10
192 13 c. gold, red and pink . 20 15

1969. United Nations Institute for Training and Research (U.N.I.T.A.R.).
193 **108** 6 c. multicoloured 10 10
194 13 c. multicoloured . . . 20 15
In the 13 c. the name and value panel is at foot of stamp.

109 U.N. Building, Santiago

1969. U.N. Building, Santiago, Chile.
195 **109** 6 c. blue, lt blue & green . 10 10
196 15 c. purple, red & buff . 25 20

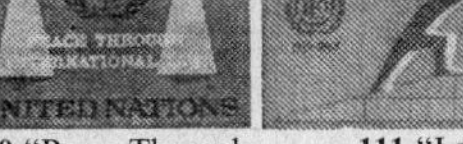
110 "Peace Through International Law" **111** "Labour and Development"

1969. 20th Anniv of Session of U.N. Int Law Commission.
197 **110** 6 c. multicoloured 10 10
198 13 c. multicoloured . . . 20 15

1969. 50th Anniv of I.L.O.
199 **111** 6 c. multicoloured 10 10
200 20 c. multicoloured . . . 30 20

112 "Ostrich" **114** Peace Bell

1969. United Nations Art (3rd issue). 3rd-century A.D. Tunisian Mosaic, Delegates' North Lounge. Multicoloured.
201 6 c. Type **112** 10 10
202 13 c. "Ring-necked Pheasant" 20 15

1970. United Nations Art (4th issue). Japanese Peace Bell.
203 **114** 6 c. multicoloured 10 10
204 25 c. multicoloured . . . 35 30

115 River, Power Lines and Map

1970. Lower Mekong Basin Development Project.
205 **115** 6 c. multicoloured 10 10
206 13 c. multicoloured . . . 20 15

116 "Fight Cancer"

1970. 10th Int Cancer Congress, Houston, Texas.
207 **116** 6 c. black and blue . . . 10 10
208 13 c. black and olive . . 35 15

117 Laurel Branch **120** Scales and Olive-branch

1970. 25th Anniv of United Nations.
209 **117** 6 c. multicoloured 15 15
210 13 c. multicoloured . . . 20 20
211 – 25 c. gold, lt blue & blue 40 40
DESIGN—VERT: 25 c. U.N. emblem.
On No. 210 the inscription is in French.

1970. "Peace, Justice and Progress" (Aims of the United Nations).
213 **120** 6 c. multicoloured 10 10
214 13 c. multicoloured . . . 20 15

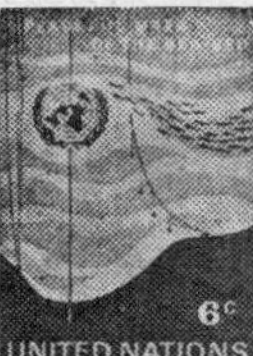

121 U.N. Emblem on Sea-bed **122** "Refugees" (sculpture, Kaare Nygaard)

1971. Peaceful Uses of the Sea-bed.
215 **121** 6 c. multicoloured 15 10

1971. U.N. Work with Refugees.
216 **122** 6 c. black, yellow & brown 10 10
217 13 c. black, turq & blue . 20 15

123 Wheatsheaf on Globe **124** New U.P.U. H.Q. Building

1971. World Food Programme.
218 **123** 13 c. multicoloured . . . 30 20

1971. Opening of New U.P.U. Headquarters Building, Berne.
219 **124** 20 c. multicoloured . . . 30 25

125 Four-leafed Clover **127** U.N. H.Q., New York

1971. Racial Equality Year. Multicoloured.
220 8 c. Type **125** 15 10
221 13 c. Linked globes (horiz) . . 15 15

1971. Multicoloured.
222 8 c. Type **127** 15 10
223 60 c. U.N. emblem and flags . 60 45
224 95 c. "Letter changing Hands" 1·00 45

130 "Maia" (Picasso) **131** "X" over Atomic Explosion

1971. U.N. International Schools.
225 **130** 8 c. multicoloured 15 10
226 21 c. multicoloured 35 30

1972. Non-proliferation of Nuclear Weapons.
227 **131** 8 c. blue, black and pink . 30 15

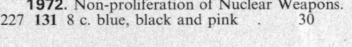

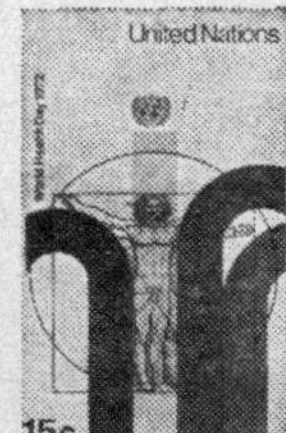

132 "Proportions of Man" (Leonardo da Vinci) A **134** Birds in Flight

1972. World Health Day.
228 **132** 15 c. multicoloured 30 15

1972. Air.
A229 – 9 c. multicoloured . . 15 10
A230 A **134** 11 c. multicoloured . . 15 10
A231 – 17 c. orange, yellow and red 25 15
A232 – 21 c. multicoloured . . 30 20
DESIGNS—23 × 31 mm: 9 c. "Contemporary Flight". 38 × 23 mm: 17 c. Clouds. 33 × 23 mm: 21 c. "U.N." jetstream.

137 Environmental Emblem **138** Europe "Flower"

1972. U.N. Environmental Conservation Conf, Stockholm.
233 **137** 8 c. multicoloured 15 10
234 15 c. multicoloured 25 20

1972. Economic Commission for Europe (E.C.E.).
235 **138** 21 c. multicoloured 35 30

139 "World United" (detail, Sert mural, Geneva) **140** Laurel and Broken Sword

1972. United Nations Art (5th issue).
236 **139** 8 c. brown, gold & lt brn . 15 10
237 15 c. brown, gold & green 40 25

1973. Disarmament Decade.
238 **140** 8 c. multicoloured 15 10
239 15 c. multicoloured 25 20

141 Skull on Poppy **142** Emblems within Honeycomb

1973. "Stop Drug Abuse" Campaign.
240 **141** 8 c. multicoloured 25 15
241 15 c. multicoloured . . . 45 25

1973. U.N. Volunteers Programme.
242 **142** 8 c. multicoloured 15 10
243 21 c. multicoloured . . . 35 30

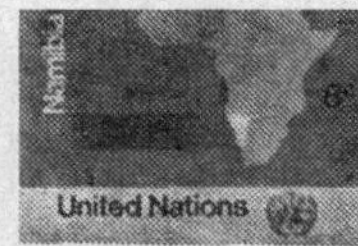

143 Namibia on Map of Africa

1973. U.N. Resolution on Namibia (South West Africa).
244 **143** 8 c. multicoloured 15 10
245 15 c. multicoloured . . . 35 30

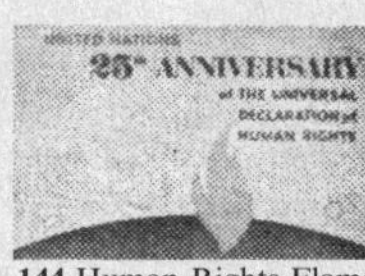

144 Human Rights Flame

1973. 25th Anniv of Declaration of Human Rights.
246 **144** 8 c. multicoloured 20 10
247 21 c. multicoloured . . . 35 20

145 H.Q. Building

1973. Inauguration of New I.L.O. Headquarters Building, Geneva.
248 **145** 10 c. multicoloured . . . 20 10
249 21 c. multicoloured . . . 35 30

146 Globe within Posthorn

1974. Centenary of U.P.U.
250 **148** 10 c. multicoloured . . . 15 10

147 "Children's Choir" (mural detail, C. Portinari) **148** Peace Dove

1974. United Nations Art (6th issue). Brazilian Peace Mural, Delegates' Lobby.
251 **147** 10 c. multicoloured . . . 15 15
252 18 c. multicoloured . . . 25 25

1974.
253 **148** 2 c. blue and ultramarine 10 10
254 – 10 c. multicoloured . . . 15 10
255 – 18 c. multicoloured . . . 25 15
DESIGNS—VERT: 10 c. U.N. Headquarters, New York; 18 c. Globe over U.N. emblem and flags.

A **151** Globe and Jet Aircraft **154** Young Children with Globe

1974. Air. Multicoloured.

A256 13 c. Type **A151** 20 15
A257 18 c. "Channels of Communication" (38 × 23 mm) 25 15
A258 26 c. Dove in flight and U.N. Headquarters 35 30

1974. World Population Year.

259 **154** 10 c. multicoloured . . . 20 10
260 18 c. multicoloured . . . 35 30

155 Ship and Fish

156 Satellite, Globe and Symbols

1974. U.N. Conference on "Law of the Sea".

261 **155** 10 c. multicoloured . . . 25 15
262 26 c. multicoloured . . . 60 35

1975. Peaceful Uses of Outer Space.

263 **156** 10 c. multicoloured . . . 20 10
264 26 c. multicoloured . . . 45 40

157 "Sex Equality"

158 "The Hope of Mankind"

1975. International Women's Year.

265 **157** 10 c. multicoloured . . . 15 10
266 18 c. multicoloured . . . 30 25

1975. 30th Anniv of U.N.O.

267 **158** 10 c. multicoloured . . . 15 10
268 26 c. multicoloured . . . 35 30

160 Cupped Hand

161 Wild Rose and Barbed Wire

1975. "Namibia—United Nations Direct Responsibility".

270 **160** 10 c. multicoloured . . . 20 10
271 18 c. multicoloured . . . 25 25

1975. U.N. Peace-keeping Operations.

272 **161** 13 c. blue 20 15
273 26 c. mauve 40 35

162 "Bird of Peace"

166 Linked Ribbons

1976. Multicoloured.

274 3 c. Type **162** 10 10
275 4 c. "Gathering of Peoples" (39 × 23 mm) 10 10
276 30 c. U.N. flag (23 × 39 mm) . 50 30
277 50 c. "Universal Peace" (Dove and rainbow) (23 × 39 mm) . 95 50

1976. World Federation of U.N. Associations.

278 **166** 13 c. multicoloured . . . 15 10
279 26 c. multicoloured . . . 40 35

167 Globe and Crate

168 Houses bordering Globe

1976. U.N. Conf on Trade and Development.

280 **167** 13 c. multicoloured . . . 25 15
281 31 c. multicoloured . . . 50 45

1976. U.N. Conf on Human Settlements.

282 **168** 13 c. multicoloured . . . 25 15
283 25 c. multicoloured . . . 50 45

169 Magnifying Glass and Emblem

170 Stylised Ear of Wheat

1976. 25th Anniv of U.N. Postal Administration.

284 **169** 13 c. multicoloured . . . 40 15
285 31 c. multicoloured . . . 2·75 1·10

1976. World Food Council.

286 **170** 13 c. multicoloured . . . 30 25

171 U.N. Emblem

173 Rain Drops and Funnel

172 W.I.P.O. Headquarters Building

1976.

287 **171** 9 c. multicoloured 20 10

1977. World Intellectual Property Organization Headquarters.

288 **172** 13 c. multicoloured . . . 25 15
289 31 c. multicoloured . . . 45 35

1977. United Nations Water Conference.

290 **173** 13 c. multicoloured . . . 25 15
291 25 c. multicoloured . . . 45 35

174 Severed Fuse

175 Winged Airmail Letter

1977. Security Council.

292 **174** 13 c. multicoloured . . . 15 15
293 31 c. multicoloured . . . 35 35

1977. Air. Multicoloured.

A294 25 c. Type **175** 35 30
A295 31 c. Globe and airplane (horiz) 40 40

177 "Combat Racism"

178 Atomic Symbol and Produce

1977. Campaign Against Racial Discrimination.

296 **177** 13 c. black and yellow . . 25 15
297 25 c. black and red . . . 40 30

1977. Peaceful Uses of Atomic Energy.

298 **178** 13 c. multicoloured . . . 25 15
299 18 c. multicoloured . . . 35 25

179 U.N. Charter

1978. Multicoloured.

300 1 c. Type **179** 10 10
301 25 c. Knotted flags 30 20
302 $1 Multi-racial group . . . . 1·40 80

182 Smallpox Bacilli

1978. Global Eradication of Smallpox.

303 **182** 13 c. black and red 30 15
304 31 c. black and blue . . . 65 45

183 Broken Manacle

184 Clouds within Ribbon

1978. "Namibia: Liberation, Justice, Co-operation".

305 **183** 13 c. multicoloured 25 15
306 18 c. multicoloured 35 30

1978. International Civil Aviation Organization—Safety in the Air.

307 **184** 13 c. multicoloured 25 15
308 25 c. multicoloured 40 35

185 General Assembly

1978. General Assembly.

309 **185** 13 c. multicoloured 20 15
310 18 c. multicoloured 30 30

186 Hemispheres within Cogwheels

187 Hand holding Olive Branch

1978. Technical Co-operation among Developing Countries.

311 **186** 13 c. multicoloured 25 15
312 31 c. multicoloured 50 40

1979. Multicoloured.

313 5 c. Type **187** 10 10
314 14 c. Multiple "tree" 20 10
315 15 c. Globe and peace dove . . 25 15
316 20 c. Doves crossing globe . . 30 15

191 Fire and Flood

1979. U.N. Disaster Relief Co-ordinator.

317 **191** 15 c. multicoloured 25 20
318 20 c. multicoloured 35 25

192 Child's Drawing

193 Olive Branch and Map of Namibia

1979. International Year of the Child.

319 **192** 15 c. multicoloured 30 15
320 31 c. multicoloured 60 60

1979. "For a Free and Independent Namibia".

321 **193** 15 c. multicoloured 20 15
322 31 c. multicoloured 50 40

194 Sword and Scales of Justice

195 Graph

1979. International Court of Justice.

323 **194** 15 c. olive, green & black 20 15
324 20 c. blue, lt blue & black 30 30

1980. New International Economic Order. Multicoloured.

325 15 c. Type **195** 25 15
326 31 c. Key 50 50

197 Doves

1980. U.N. Decade for Women.

327 **197** 15 c. multicoloured . . . 30 20
328 20 c. multicoloured . . . 35 30

198 Helmet

1980. Peace-keeping Operations.

329 **198** 15 c. blue and black . . . 30 20
330 – 31 c. multicoloured . . . 55 45

DESIGN: 31 c. "Peace-keeping".

200 "35" composed of Flags

203 Flag of Bangladesh

1980. 35th Anniv of United Nations. Mult.

331 15 c. Type **200** 25 20
332 31 c. Stylized flower 50 45

1980. Flags of Member Nations (1st series). Multicoloured.

334 15 c. Type **203** 30 30
335 15 c. Guinea 30 30
336 15 c. Mali 30 30
337 15 c. Surinam 30 30
338 15 c. Cameroun 30 30
339 15 c. Hungary 30 30
340 15 c. Madagascar 30 30
341 15 c. Rwanda 30 30
342 15 c. El Salvador 30 30
343 15 c. France 30 30
344 15 c. Venezuela 30 30
345 15 c. Yugoslavia 30 30
346 15 c. Fiji 30 30
347 15 c. Luxembourg 30 30
348 15 c. Turkey 30 30
349 15 c. Vietnam 30 30

See also Nos. 359/74, 383/98, 408/23, 434/9, 458/74, 486/501, 508/23, 537/52 and 563/78.

204 Various Emblems forming Bunch of Flowers

1980. Economic and Social Council. Mult.

350 15 c. Type **204** 30 20
351 20 c. Economic and social emblems 40 30

206 Text and U.N. Emblem

207 Jigsaw

1981. Inalienable Rights of the Palestinian People.
352 **206** 15 c. multicoloured . . . 30 20

1981. International Year of Disabled Persons.
353 **207** 20 c. multicoloured . . . 35 30
354 – 35 c. black and orange . . 55 30
DESIGN: 35 c. Disabled person.

209 "Sebastocrator Kaloyan and his Wife Desislava" (13th-century Bulgarian fresco)

210 Sun and Sea

1981. Art.
355 **209** 20 c. multicoloured . . . 35 35
356 31 c. multicoloured . . . 55 60

1981. New and Renewable Sources of Energy.
357 **210** 20 c. multicoloured . . . 30 30
358 – 40 c. gold and blue . . . 65 70
DESIGN: 40 c. U.N. energy conference emblem.

1981. Flags of Member Nations (2nd series). As T **203**. Multicoloured.
359 20 c. Djibouti 30 30
360 20 c. Sri Lanka 30 30
361 20 c. Bolivia 30 30
362 20 c. Equatorial Guinea . . . 30 30
363 20 c. Malta 30 30
364 20 c. Czechoslovakia 30 30
365 20 c. Thailand 30 30
366 20 c. Trinidad and Tobago . . 30 30
367 20 c. Ukrainian S.S.R. 30 30
368 20 c. Kuwait 30 30
369 20 c. Sudan 30 30
370 20 c. Egypt 30 30
371 20 c. United States 30 30
372 20 c. Singapore 30 30
373 20 c. Panama 30 30
374 20 c. Costa Rica 30 30

212 Grafted Plant

214 "Respect for Human Rights"

1981. 10th Anniv of U.N. Volunteers Programme. Multicoloured.
375 18 c. Type **212** 30 25
376 28 c. "10" enclosing symbols of services 45 50

1982. Multicoloured.
377 17 c. Type **214** 25 10
378 28 c. "Granting of Independence to Colonial Countries and Peoples" 40 20
379 40 c. "Second Disarmament Decade" 60 30

217 Hand holding Seedling

219 Olive Branch and U.N. Emblem

1982. Human Environment. Multicoloured.
380 20 c. Type **217** 30 30
381 40 c. Symbols of the environment 65 70

1982. Second United Nations Conference on Exploration and Peaceful Uses of Outer Space.
382 **219** 20 c. ultramarine, blue and green 45 30

1982. Flags of Member Nations (3rd series). As T **203**. Multicoloured.
383 20 c. Austria 30 30
384 20 c. Malaysia 30 30
385 20 c. Seychelles 30 30
386 20 c. Ireland 30 30
387 20 c. Mozambique 30 30
388 20 c. Albania 30 30
389 20 c. Dominica 30 30
390 20 c. Solomon Islands 30 30
391 20 c. Philippines 30 30
392 20 c. Swaziland 30 30
393 20 c. Nicaragua 30 30
394 20 c. Burma 30 30
395 20 c. Cape Verde 30 30
396 20 c. Guyana 30 30
397 20 c. Belgium 30 30
398 20 c. Nigeria 30 30

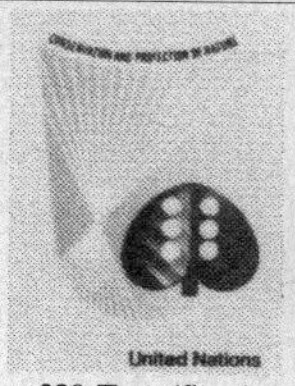

220 Tree (flora)

222 Interlocking Arrows

1982. Conservation and Protection of Nature. Multicoloured.
399 20 c. Type **220** 30 30
400 28 c. Butterfly (insects) . . . 50 60

1983. World Communications Year. Mult.
401 20 c. Type **222** 50 35
402 40 c. Cable network 90 75

224 Ship and Buoy

226 Giving Food

1983. Safety at Sea: International Maritime Organization. Multicoloured.
403 20 c. Type **224** 60 35
404 37 c. Stylized liner . . . . . 1·00 90

1983. World Food Programme.
405 **226** 20 c. red 55 35

227 Coins and Cogwheels

229 "Window Right"

1983. Trade and Development. Multicoloured.
406 20 c. Type **227** 50 35
407 28 c. Emblems of trade . . . 75 55

1983. Flags of Member Nations (4th series). As T **203**. Multicoloured.
408 20 c. United Kingdom . . . 35 30
409 20 c. Barbados 35 30
410 20 c. Nepal 35 30
411 20 c. Israel 35 30
412 20 c. Malawi 35 30
413 20 c. Byelorussian S.S.R. . . . 35 30
414 20 c. Jamaica 35 30
415 20 c. Kenya 35 30
416 20 c. China 35 30
417 20 c. Peru 35 30
418 20 c. Bulgaria 35 30
419 20 c. Canada 35 30
420 20 c. Somalia 35 30
421 20 c. Senegal 35 30
422 20 c. Brazil 35 30
423 20 c. Sweden 35 30

1983. 35th Anniv of Declaration of Human Rights. Multicoloured.
424 20 c. Type **229** 40 25
425 40 c. "Treaty with Nature" . 1·00 70

231 World Population

1984. International Conference on Population, Mexico.
426 **231** 20 c. multicoloured . . . 50 20
427 40 c. multicoloured . . . 1·10 65

232 Fertilizing Crops

1984. World Food Day. Multicoloured.
428 20 c. Type **232** 40 20
429 40 c. Planting rice 85 45

234 Grand Canyon, U.S.A

236 Mother with Baby

1984. World Heritage—U.N. Educational, Scientific and Cultural Organization. Multicoloured.
430 20 c. Type **234** 40 20
431 50 c. Polonnaruwa, Sri Lanka . 1·25 65

1984. Future for Refugees.
432 **236** 20 c. brown and black . . 40 20
433 – 50 c. black and blue . . . 1·00 70
DESIGN: 50 c. Mother with child.

1984. Flags of Member Nations (5th series). As T **203**. Multicoloured.
434 20 c. Burundi 50 40
435 20 c. Pakistan 50 40
436 20 c. Benin 50 40
437 20 c. Italy 50 40
438 20 c. Poland 50 40
439 20 c. Papua New Guinea . . . 50 40
440 20 c. Uruguay 50 40
441 20 c. Chile 50 40
442 20 c. Paraguay 50 40
443 20 c. Bhutan 50 40
444 20 c. Central African Republic 50 40
445 20 c. Australia 50 40
446 20 c. Tanzania 50 40
447 20 c. United Arab Emirates . . 50 40
448 20 c. Ecuador 50 40
449 20 c. Bahamas 50 40

238 Emblem and Figures linking Arms

239 Turin Centre Emblem

1984. International Youth Year.
450 **238** 20 c. multicoloured 50 15
451 35 c. multicoloured 90 40

1985. 20th Anniv of Turin Centre of International Labour Organization.
452 **239** 23 c. blue 60 35

240 Farming and Mediums of Communication

1985. 10th Anniv of United Nations University, Tokyo.
453 **240** 50 c. multicoloured . . . . 1·25 75

241 People of Various Nations

1985. Multicoloured.
454 22 c. Type **241** 30 15
455 $3 Paintbrush and emblem . . 4·50 2·75

243 "Snow Scene" (Andrew Wyeth)

1985. 40th Anniv of U.N.O. Multicoloured.
456 22 c. Type **243** 45 20
457 45 c. "Harvest Scene" (Andrew Wyeth) 95 65

1985. Flags of Member Nations (6th series). As T **203**. Multicoloured.
459 22 c. Grenada 50 40
460 22 c. Federal Republic of Germany 50 40
461 22 c. Saudi Arabia 50 40
462 22 c. Mexico 50 40
463 22 c. Liberia 50 40
464 22 c. Mauritius 50 40
465 22 c. Chad 50 40
466 22 c. Dominican Republic . . . 50 40
467 22 c. Oman 50 40
468 22 c. Ghana 50 40
469 22 c. Sierra Leone 50 40
470 22 c. Finland 50 40
471 22 c. Uganda 50 40
472 22 c. St. Thomas and Prince Islands 50 40
473 22 c. U.S.S.R. 50 40
474 22 c. India 50 40

246 Woman feeding Child

248 "Africa in Crisis"

1985. U.N.I.C.E.F. Child Survival Campaign. Multicoloured.
475 32 c. Type **246** 45 25
476 33 c. Mother breast-feeding child 85 55

1986. Africa in Crisis.
477 **248** 22 c. multicoloured . . . 45 25

249 Dam

1986. Development Programme. Water Resources. Multicoloured.
478 22 c. Type **249** . . . . 1·00 70
479 22 c. Working in the fields . . 1·00 70
480 22 c. Girls at waterhole . . . 1·00 70
481 22 c. Women at well . . . . 1·00 70
Nos. 478/81 were printed together, se-tenant, forming a composite design.

253 Magnifying Glass and Stamp

1986. Philately: the International Hobby.
482 **253** 22 c. lilac and blue . . . 50 20
483 – 44 c. brown and green . . 90 55
DESIGN: 44 c. Engraver.

255 Peace Doves

1986. International Peace Year.
484 **255** 22 c. multicoloured . . . 60 20
485 – 33 c. multicoloured . . . 80 50
DESIGN: 33 c. Words for "Peace" around U.N. emblem.

1986. Flags of Member Nations (7th series). As T **203**. Multicoloured.
486 22 c. New Zealand 45 35
487 22 c. Laos 45 35
488 22 c. Burkina Faso 45 35
489 22 c. Gambia 45 35
490 22 c. Maldives 45 35
491 22 c. Ethiopia 45 35
492 22 c. Jordan 45 35
493 22 c. Zambia 45 35
494 22 c. Iceland 45 35
495 22 c. Antigua and Barbuda . . 45 35
496 22 c. Angola 45 35
497 22 c. Botswana 45 35
498 22 c. Rumania 45 35
499 22 c. Togo 45 35
500 22 c. Mauritania 45 35
501 22 c. Colombia 45 35

258 Trygve Lie (after Harald Dal)

259 Men with Surveying Equipment and Blueprints

1987. 9th Death Anniv of Trygve Lie (first U.N. Secretary-General).
503 **258** 22 c. multicoloured . . . 45 20

1987. International Year of Shelter for the Homeless.
504 **259** 22 c. deep brown, brown and black 40 20
505 – 44 c. multicoloured . . . 85 65
DESIGN: 44 c. Cutting bamboo.

261 Construction Workers

1987. Anti-Drugs Campaign. Multicoloured.

506 22 c. Type **261** 45 20
507 33 c. University graduates . . 80 55

1987. Flags of Member Nations (8th series). As T **203**. Multicoloured.

508 22 c. Comoros 40 30
509 22 c. People's Democratic Republic of Yemen 40 30
510 22 c. Mongolia 40 30
511 22 c. Vanuatu 40 30
512 22 c. Japan 40 30
513 22 c. Gabon 40 30
514 22 c. Zimbabwe 40 30
515 22 c. Iraq 40 30
516 22 c. Argentina 40 30
517 22 c. Congo 40 30
518 22 c. Niger 40 30
519 22 c. St. Lucia 40 30
520 22 c. Bahrain 40 30
521 22 c. Haiti 40 30
522 22 c. Afghanistan 40 30
523 22 c. Greece 40 30

263 Family and U.N. Building, New York **265** Measles

1987. United Nations Day. Multicoloured.

524 22 c. Type **263** 35 15
525 39 c. Dancers 75 65

1987. "Immunize Every Child". Multicoloured.

526 22 c. Type **265** 40 15
527 44 c. Tetanus 85 75

267 Wheat as U.N. Emblem

1988. "For a Better World".

528 **267** 3 c. yellow, brown and black 15 10

268 Fisherman

1988. International Fund for Agricultural Development "For a World Without Hunger" Campaign. Multicoloured.

529 2 c. Type **268** 40 15
530 33 c. Farmers ploughing with oxen 55 50

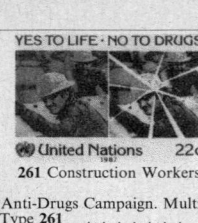

270 Tropical Rain Forest Canopy **271** Teacher at Blackboard

1988. "Survival of the Forests". Multicoloured.

531 25 c. Type **270** . . . . 1·75 70
532 44 c. Tropical rain forest floor 4·00 2·10

Nos. 531/2 were printed together, se-tenant, forming a composite design.

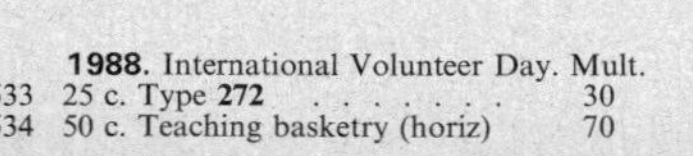

1988. International Volunteer Day. Mult.

533 25 c. Type **272** 30 15
534 50 c. Teaching basketry (horiz) 70 65

274 Cycling **276** Flame

1988. "Health in Sports". Multicoloured.

535 25 c. Type **274** 45 20
536 38 c. Marathon (horiz) 65 55

1988. Flags of Member Nations (9th series). As T **203**. Multicoloured.

537 25 c. Spain 40 30
538 25 c. St. Vincent and Grenadines 40 30
539 25 c. Ivory Coast 40 30
540 25 c. Lebanon 40 30
541 25 c. Yemen 40 30
542 25 c. Cuba 40 30
543 25 c. Denmark 40 30
544 25 c. Libya 40 30
545 25 c. Qatar 40 30
546 25 c. Zaire 40 30
547 25 c. Norway 40 30
548 25 c. German Democratic Republic 40 30
549 25 c. Iran 40 30
550 25 c. Tunisia 40 30
551 25 c. Samoa 40 30
552 25 c. Belize 40 30

1989. 40th Anniv of Declaration of Human Rights.

553 **276** 25 c. multicoloured 40 25

278 Electricity Production **280** "Blue Helmet" Soldier

1989. World Bank. Multicoloured.

555 25 c. Type **278** 40 15
556 45 c. Planting rice 70 50

1989. Award of Nobel Peace Prize to United Nations Peace-keeping Forces.

557 **280** 25 c. multicoloured 40 15

281 U.N. Headquarters, New York

1989.

558 **281** 45 c. multicoloured 70 40

282 Satellite Image of Storm over Chesapeake Bay Area **284** Band

1989. 25th Anniv of World Weather Watch. Multicoloured.

559 25 c. Type **282** 45 20
560 36 c. Typhoon Abby approaching China 65 40

1989. 10th Anniv of United Nations Vienna International Centre. Multicoloured.

561 25 c. Type **284** 45 15
562 90 c. Mountain and butterfly as tree . . . . 1·40 1·10

1989. Flags of Member Nations (10th series). As T **203**. Multicoloured.

563 25 c. Indonesia 35 30
564 25 c. Lesotho 35 30
565 25 c. Guatemala 35 30
566 25 c. Netherlands 35 30
567 25 c. Algeria 35 30
568 25 c. Brunei 35 30
569 25 c. St. Kitts and Nevis . . 35 30
570 25 c. United Nations 35 30
571 25 c. Honduras 35 30
572 25 c. Kampuchea 35 30
573 25 c. Guinea-Bissau 35 30
574 25 c. Cyprus 35 30
575 25 c. South Africa 35 30
576 25 c. Portugal 35 30
577 25 c. Morocco 35 30
578 25 c. Syria 35 30

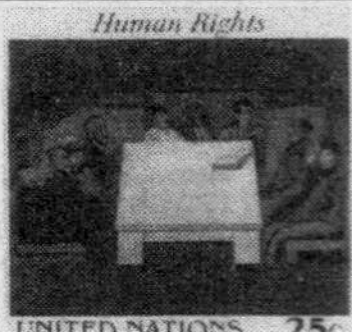

286 "Table of Universal Brotherhood" (Jose Clemente Orozco) (Article 1)

1989. Declaration of Human Rights (1st series). Multicoloured.

579 25 c. Type **286** 40 15
580 45 c. "Composition II" (V. Kandinsky) (Article 2) . 70 40

See also Nos. 592/3, 609/10, 626/7 and 637/8.

288 Port Activities

1990. International Trade Centre.

581 **288** 25 c. multicoloured 60 20

289 "AIDS" **290** Madagascar Periwinkle

1990. Anti-AIDS Campaign. Multicoloured.

582 25 c. Type **289** 50 20
583 40 c. Group at risk . . . . . . 1·00 45

1990. Medicinal Plants. Multicoloured.

584 25 c. Type **291** 45 15
585 90 c. American ginseng . . . . 1·40 1·10

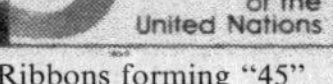

293 Ribbons forming "45" **296** Youth waylaying Elderly Man

1990. 45th Anniv of U.N.O. Multicoloured.

586 25 c. Type **293** 50 20
587 45 c. "45" and U.N. Emblem . 1·40 80

1990. Crime Prevention. Multicoloured.

590 25 c. Type **296** 70 25
591 36 c. Burglars leaving burning building . . . . 1·40 80

1990. Universal Declaration of Human Rights (2nd series). As T **286**. Multicoloured.

592 25 c. Sarcophagus of Plotinus (detail) (Article 7) 35 20
593 45 c. "Combined Chambers of High Court of Appeal" (Charles Paul Renouard), from "The Dreyfus Case" (Article 8) 60 35

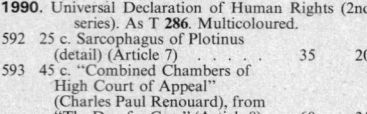

300/303 Alpine Lake and Wildlife

1991. Economic Commission for Europe. "For a Better Environment".

594 **300** 30 c. multicoloured 50 30
595 **301** 30 c. multicoloured 50 30
596 **302** 30 c. multicoloured 50 30
597 **303** 30 c. multicoloured 50 30

Nos. 594/7 were printed together, se-tenant, forming the composite design illustrated.

304 Desert **306** U.N. Building

1991. 1st Anniv of Namibian Independence. Multicoloured.

598 30 c. Type **304** 45 20
599 50 c. Open grassland 75 45

1991.

600 **306** $2 blue . . . . 2·50 1·50

307 Children around Globe (Nicole Delia Legnani)

1991. 30th Anniv (1989) of U.N. Declaration on the Rights of the Child and 1990 World Summit on Children, New York. Children's Drawings. Multicoloured.

601 30 c. Type **307** 40 20
602 70 c. Dove, rainbow and houses (Alissa Duffy) 95 55

309 Bubbles of Toxin approaching City

1991. Banning of Chemical Weapons. Mult.

603 30 c. Type **309** 40 20
604 90 c. Hand pushing back barrels of toxins 95 55

311 U.N. Flag

1991. Multicoloured.

605 30 c. Type **311** 40 15
606 50 c. "The Golden Rule" (mosaic, Norman Rockwell) (vert) 65 35

313 1951 1 c. Stamp

1991. 40th Anniv of United Nations Postal Administration.

607 **313** 30 c. red on cream . . . 40 20
608 – 40 c. purple on cream . . . 55 30

DESIGN: 40 c. 1951 2 c. stamp.

1991. Declaration of Human Rights (3rd series). As T **286**. Multicoloured.

609 30 c. "The Last of England" (Ford Maddox Brown) (Article 13) 40 20
610 50 c. "The Emigration to the East" (Tito Salas) (Article 14) 65 35

317 Uluru National Park, Australia **319/20** Sea Life ($\frac{1}{2}$-size illustration)

1992. 20th Anniv of U.N.E.S.C.O. World Heritage Convention. Multicoloured.
611 30 c. Type **317** 40 20
612 50 c. Great Wall of China . . 65 25

1992. "Clean Oceans".
613 **319** 29 c. multicoloured . . . 40 15
614 **320** 29 c. multicoloured . . . 40 15
Nos. 613/14 were issued together, se-tenant, forming the composite design illustrated.

321/324 Planet Earth

1992. 2nd U.N. Conference on Environment and Development, Rio de Janeiro.
615 **321** 29 c. multicoloured . . . 40 15
616 **322** 29 c. multicoloured . . . 40 15
617 **323** 29 c. multicoloured . . . 40 15
618 **324** 29 c. multicoloured . . . 40 15
Nos. 615/18 were issued together, se-tenant, forming the composite design illustrated.

325/326 "Mission Planet Earth"

1992. International Space Year. Roul.
619 **325** 29 c. multicoloured . . . 40 20
620 **326** 29 c. multicoloured . . . 40 20
Nos. 619/20 were issued together, se-tenant, forming the composite design illustrated.

327 Winged Man with V.D.U

1992. Commission on Science and Technology for Development. Multicoloured.
621 29 c. Type **327** 40 15
622 50 c. Man sitting in crocodile's mouth 65 35

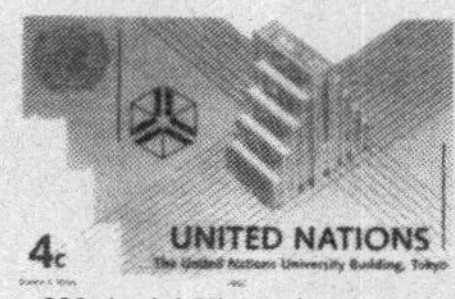

329 Aerial View of Building

1992. United Nations University, Tokyo. Mult.
623 4 c. Type **329** 10 10
624 40 c. Front elevation of building 55 30

331 U.N. Headquarters, New York **334** Family Life

1992.
625 **331** 29 c. multicoloured . . . 40 15

1992. Universal Declaration of Human Rights (4th series). As T **286**. Multicoloured.
626 29 c. "Lady writing a letter with her Maid" (Johannes Vermeer) (Article 19) 40 15
627 50 c. "The Meeting"(Ester Almqvist) (Article 20) . . . 65 35

1993. "Ageing: Dignity and Participation". 10th Anniv (1992) of International Plan of Action on Ageing. Multicoloured.
628 29 c. Type **334** 40 15
629 52 c. Health and nutrition . . 70 40

336 Queensland Hairy-nosed Wombat

1993. Endangered Species (1st series). Multicoloured.
630 29 c. Type **336** 40 15
631 29 c. Whooping crane 40 15
632 29 c. Giant clams 40 15
633 29 c. Sable antelope 40 15
See also Nos. 649/52.

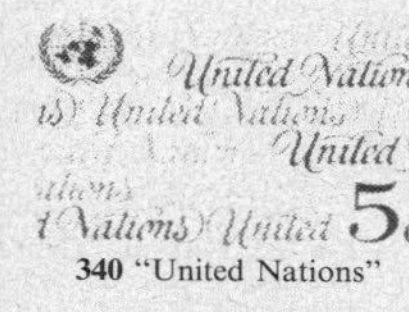

340 "United Nations"

1993.
634 **340** 5 c. multicoloured 10 10

341 Personal Environment

1993. 45th Anniv of W.H.O. Multicoloured.
635 29 c. Type **341** 40 15
636 50 c. Family environment . . 65 35

1993. Declaration of Human Rights (5th series). As T **286**. Multicoloured.
637 29 c. "Shocking Corn" (Thomas Hart Benton) (Article 25) . 40 15
638 35 c. "The Library" (Jacob Lawrence) (Article 26) . . 45 25

345/348 Peace

1993. International Peace Day. Roul.
639 **345** 29 c. multicoloured . . . 40 15
640 **346** 29 c. multicoloured . . . 40 15
641 **347** 29 c. multicoloured . . . 40 15
642 **348** 29 c. multicoloured . . . 40 15
Nos. 639/42 were issued together, se-tenant, forming the composite design illustrated.

349 Chameleon

1993. The Environment—Climate. Mult.
643 29 c. Type **349** 40 15
644 29 c. Storm 40 15
645 29 c. Antelopes fleeing from flood 40 15
646 29 c. Bird of paradise 40 15
Nos. 643/6 were issued together, se-tenant, forming a composite design.

353 Equality across Generations

1994. International Year of the Family. Multicoloured.
647 29 c. Type **353** 35 10
648 45 c. Poor family 55 30

355 Chimpanzees

1994. Endangered Species (2nd series). Multicoloured.
649 29 c. Type **355** 35 10
650 29 c. St. Lucia amazon . . . 35 10
651 29 c. American crocodile . . . 35 10
652 29 c. Addra gazelles 35 10

359 "Dove of Peace" (mosaic) **362** Refugee crossing Bridge of Hands

1994.
653 **359** 10 c. multicoloured 10 10
654 – 19 c. multicoloured 25 10
655 – $1 brown . . . . 1·25 75
DESIGNS: 19 c. "Sleeping Child" (stained-glass window after drawing by Stanislaw Wyspianski); $1 "Mourning Owl" (Vanessa Isitt).

1994. United Nations High Commissioner for Refugees.
656 **362** 50 c. multicoloured 60 35

363/366 Shattered Globe and "Warning" (⅔-size illustration)

1994. International Decade for Natural Disaster Reduction.
657 **363** 29 c. multicoloured 35 10
658 **364** 29 c. multicoloured 35 10
659 **365** 29 c. multicoloured 35 10
660 **366** 29 c. multicoloured 35 10
Nos. 657/60 were issued together, se-tenant, forming the composite design illustrated.

367 Children playing (health and family planning)

1994. International Population and Development Conference, Cairo. Multicoloured.
661 29 c. Type **367** 35 10
662 52 c. Family unit (demographic changes) 65 35

369 Map and Looped Ribbon **371** Anniversary Emblem

1994. 30th Anniv of United Nations Conference on Trade and Development. Multicoloured.
663 29 c. Type **369** 35 10
664 50 c. Map and coiled ribbon . 60 35

1995. 50th Anniv of U.N.O.
665 **371** 32 c. multicoloured 40 15

B. GENEVA HEADQUARTERS

For use on mail posted at the United Nations Geneva Headquarters. Before 1969 the Swiss PTT issued stamps for use at the Palais des Nations; these are listed at the end of Switzerland.

NOTE: References to numbers and types in this section. other than to those with a "G" prefix are to the United Nations (New York Office) listing. Designs adapted for the Geneva issue are inscribed in French and have face values in francs.

G **4** Palais des Nations, Geneva

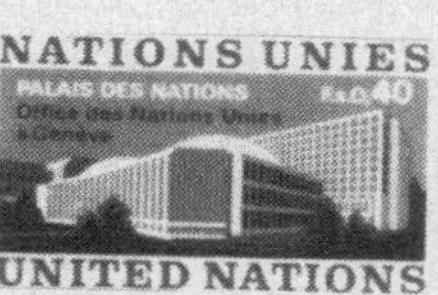

G **5** Palais des Nations, Geneva

1969. Existing United Nations (New York) designs adapted with new colours and values in Swiss francs (F.S.). 30 and 40 c. new designs. Multicoloured unless otherwise stated.
G 1 – 5 c. (As No. 164) . . . 10 10
G 2 – 10 c. (As No. 94) . . . 10 10
G 3 – 20 c. (As No. 97) . . . 15 15
G 4 **G 4** 30 c. multicoloured . . 25 20
G 5 **G 5** 40 c. multicoloured . . 30 30
G 6 – 50 c. (As No. 147, but scroll inscr in French) 40 40
G 7 – 60 c. gold, red and brown (As No. 98) 45 45
G 8 – 70 c. red, gold and black (As No. 167) 50 50
G 9 – 75 c. (As No. A125) . . 55 55
G10 – 80 c. (As No. 148) . . 60 60
G11 **52** 90 c. (Inscr in French) . . 80 80
G12 – 1 f. deep green and green (As No. 149) 85 85
G13 **53** 2 f. multicoloured . . . 1·50 1·50
G14 **104** 3 f. multicoloured . . . 2·40 1·40
G15 **3** 10 f. blue . . . . . . 7·50 7·50

1971. Peaceful Uses of the Sea-bed.
G16 **121** 30 c. multicoloured . . . 40 40

1971. United Nations Work with Refugees.
G17 **122** 50 c. black, orge & red . 1·00 1·00

1971. World Food Programme.
G18 **123** 50 c. multicoloured . . . 1·00 1·00

1971. Opening of new U.P.U. Headquarters Building, Berne.
G19 **124** 75 c. multicoloured . . . 1·50 1·50

1971. Racial Equality Year. Designs as Nos. 220/1, with background colours changed.
G20 30 c. Type **125** 75 75
G21 50 c. Linked globes (horiz) . 75 75

1971. U.N. International Schools.
G22 **130** 1 f. 10 multicoloured . . 1·50 1·50

1972. Non-proliferation of Nuclear Weapons.
G23 **131** 40 c. multicoloured . . . 1·10 1·10

1972. World Health Day.
G24 **132** 80 c. multicoloured . . . 1·00 1·00

1972. U.N. Environmental Conservation Conf, Stockholm.
G25 **137** 40 c. multicoloured . . . 70 70
G26 80 c. multicoloured . . . 1·10 1·10

1972. Economic Commission for Europe. (ECE).
G27 **138** 1 f. 10 multicoloured . . 1·90 1·90

1972. United Nations Art.
G28 **139** 40 c. multicoloured . . . 75 75
G29 80 c. multicoloured . . . 1·25 1·25

1973. Disarmament Decade.
G30 **140** 60 c. multicoloured . . . 60 60
G31 1 f. 10 multicoloured . . 1·00 1·00

1973. "No Drugs" Campaign.
G32 **141** 60 c. multicoloured . . . 1·25 1·25

1973. U.N. Volunteers Programme.
G33 **142** 80 c. multicoloured . . . 85 85

1973. "Namibia" (South West Africa).
G34 **143** 60 c. multicoloured . . . 85 85

1973. 25th Anniv of Declaration of Human Rights.
G35 **144** 40 c. multicoloured . . . 55 55
G36 80 c. multicoloured . . . 1·10 1·10

1973. Inauguration of New I.L.O. Headquarters, Geneva.
G37 **145** 60 c. multicoloured . . . 60 60
G38 80 c. multicoloured . . . 1·00 1·00

1973. Centenary of Universal Postal Union.
G39 **146** 30 c. multicoloured . . . 35 35
G40 60 c. multicoloured . . . 55 55

1974. Brazilian Peace Mural.
G41 **147** 60 c. multicoloured . . . 70 70
G42 1 f. multicoloured . . . 1·10 1·10

1974. World Population Year.
G43 **154** 60 c. multicoloured . . . 60 60
G44 80 c. multicoloured . . . 80 80

1974. U.N. Conference on "Law of the Sea".
G45 **155** 1 f. 30 multicoloured . . 1·50 1·50

1975. Peaceful Uses of Outer Space.
G46 **156** 60 c. multicoloured . . . 70 70
G47 90 c. multicoloured . . . 90 90

1975. International Women's Year.
G48 **157** 60 c. multicoloured . . . 65 65
G49 90 c. multicoloured . . . 85 85

1975. 30th Anniv of U.N.O.
G50 **158** 60 c. multicoloured . . . 55 55
G51 90 c. multicoloured . . . 70 70

1975. "Namibia—U.N. Direct Responsibility".
G53 **160** 50 c. multicoloured . . . 55 55
G54 1 f. 30 multicoloured . . 1·25 1·25

1975. U.N. Peace Keeping Operations.
G55 **161** 60 c. turquoise 55 55
G56 70 c. violet 70 70

1976. World Federation of U.N. Associations.
G57 **166** 90 c. multicoloured . . . 1·10 1·10

1976. U.N. Conf on Trade and Development.
G58 **167** 1 f. 10 multicoloured . . 1·25 1·25

1976. U.N. Conf on Human Settlements.
G59 **168** 40 c. multicoloured . . . 30 30
G60 1 f. 50 multicoloured . . 1·25 1·25

G **46** U.N. Emblem within Posthorn

G **49** Rain Drop and Globe

1976. 25th Anniv of U.N. Postal Administration.
G61 G **46** 80 c. multicoloured . . 3·00 3·00
G62 1 f. 10 multicoloured . . 3·00 3·00

1976. World Food Council Publicity.
G63 **170** 70 c. multicoloured . . . 90 90

1977. World Intellectual Property Organization Publicity.
G64 **172** 80 c. multicoloured . . . 90 90

1977. U.N. Water Conference.
G65 G **49** 80 c. multicoloured . . 80 80
G66 1 f. 10 multicoloured . 1·10 1·10

G **50** Protective Hands

1977. Security Council Commemoration.
G67 G **50** 80 c. multicoloured . . 60 60
G68 1 f. 10 multicoloured . 90 90

G **51** "Intertwining of Races"

1977. "Combat Racism".
G69 G **51** 40 c. multicoloured . . 40 40
G70 1 f. 10 multicoloured . 1·00 1·00

G **52** Atoms and Laurel Leaf

G **53** Tree and Birds

1977. "Peaceful Uses for Atomic Energy".
G71 G **52** 80 c. multicoloured . . 70 70
G72 1 f. 10 multicoloured . 1·10 1·10

1978.
G73 G **53** 35 c. multicoloured . . 30 30

G **54** Smallpox Bacilli and Globe

G **56** Aircraft Flightpaths

1978. Global Eradication of Smallpox.
G74 G **54** 80 c. multicoloured . . 70 70
G75 1 f. 10 multicoloured . 1·10 1·10

1978. "Namibia: Liberation, Justice, Co-operation".
G76 **183** 80 c. multicoloured . . . 80 80

1978. Int Civil Aviation Organization—Safety in the Air.
G77 G **56** 70 c. multicoloured . . 60 60
G78 80 c. multicoloured . . 80 80

G57 Globe, Flags and General Assembly Interior

1978. General Assembly.
G79 G **57** 70 c. multicoloured . . 60 60
G80 1 f. 10 multicoloured . 1·10 1·10

1978. Technical Co-operation among Developing Countries.
G81 **186** 80 c. multicoloured . . . 70 70

G **59** "Disaster"

1979. United Nations Disaster Relief Co-ordinator.
G82 G **59** 80 c. multicoloured . . 65 65
G83 1 f. 50 multicoloured . 1·40 1·40

G **60** Children and Rainbow

G **62** Int Court of Justice and Scales

1979. International Year of the Child.
G84 G **60** 80 c. multicoloured . . 2·00 2·00
G85 1 f. 10 multicoloured . 2·00 2·00

1979. "For a Free and Independent Namibia".
G86 **198** 1 f. 10 multicoloured . . 1·00 1·00

1979. International Court of Justice.
G87 G **62** 80 c. multicoloured . . 65 65
G88 1 f. 10 multicoloured . 1·10 1·10

G **63** Key symbolizing Unity of Action

G **64** Emblem

1980. New International Economic Order.
G89 G **63** 80 c. multicoloured . . 70 70

1980. U.N. Decade for Women.
G90 G **64** 40 c. multicoloured . . 45 45
G91 70 c. multicoloured . . 65 65

1980. Peace Keeping Operations.
G92 **198** 1 f. 10 blue and green . 90 90

1980. 35th Anniv of United Nations.
G93 – 40 c. blk and turquoise . 40 40
G94 **200** 70 c. multicoloured . . . 70 70
DESIGN: 40 c. Dove and "35".

1980. Economic and Social Council.
G96 **204** 40 c. multicoloured . . . 35 35
G97 – 70 c. blue, red and black 65 65
DESIGN: 70 c. Human figures ascending graph.

1981. Inalienable Rights of the Palestinian People.
G98 **206** 80 c. multicoloured . . . 65 65

G **71** Disabled Person

G **77** "Anti-apartheid"

1981. International Year of Disabled Persons.
G 99 G **71** 40 c. black and blue . 30 30
G100 – 1 f. 50 black and red . 1·25 1·25
DESIGN: 1 f. 50, Knot pattern.

1981. Art.
G101 **209** 80 c. multicoloured . . . 65 65

1981. New and Renewable Sources of Energy.
G102 **210** 1 f. 10 multicoloured . . 85 85

1981. 10th Anniv of U.N. Volunteers Programme. Multicoloured.
G103 40 c. Type **212** 30 30
G104 70 c. Emblems of science, agriculture and industry . 55 55

1982. Multicoloured.
G105 30 c. Type G **77** 20 20
G106 1 f. Flags 70 50

1982. Human Environment. Multicoloured.
G107 40 c. Leaves 30 30
G108 1 f. 20 Type **217** 90 90

1982. Second United Nations Conference on Exploration and Peaceful Uses of Outer Space.
G109 **219** 80 c. violet, pink & grn . 60 60
G110 – 1 f. multicoloured . . . 75 75
DESIGN: 1 f. Satellite and emblems.

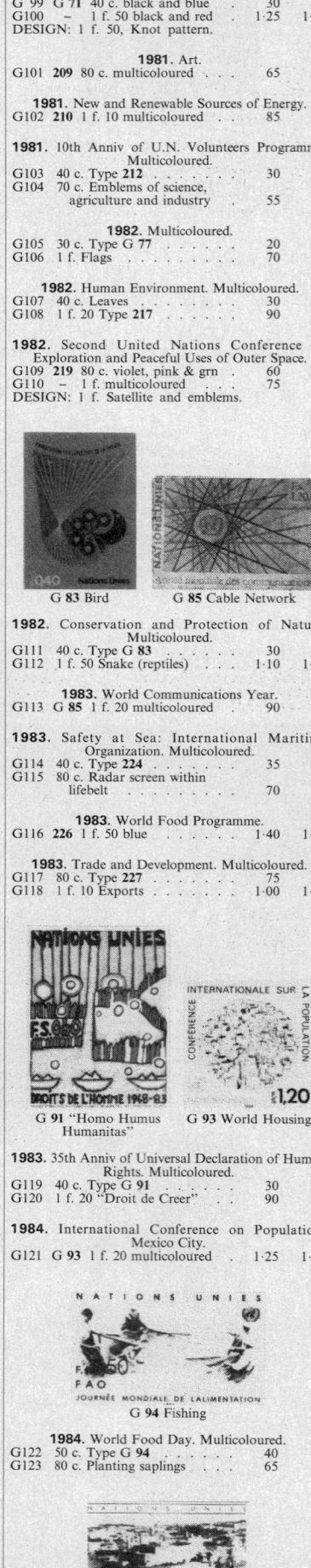

G **83** Bird

G **85** Cable Network

1982. Conservation and Protection of Nature. Multicoloured.
G111 40 c. Type G **83** 30 30
G112 1 f. 50 Snake (reptiles) . . . 1·10 1·10

1983. World Communications Year.
G113 G **85** 1 f. 20 multicoloured . 90 90

1983. Safety at Sea: International Maritime Organization. Multicoloured.
G114 40 c. Type **224** 35 35
G115 80 c. Radar screen within lifebelt 70 70

1983. World Food Programme.
G116 **226** 1 f. 50 blue . . . . . 1·40 1·40

1983. Trade and Development. Multicoloured.
G117 80 c. Type **227** 75 75
G118 1 f. 10 Exports . . . . . . 1·00 1·00

G **91** "Homo Humus Humanitas"

G **93** World Housing

1983. 35th Anniv of Universal Declaration of Human Rights. Multicoloured.
G119 40 c. Type G **91** 30 30
G120 1 f. 20 "Droit de Creer" . . 90 90

1984. International Conference on Population, Mexico City.
G121 G **93** 1 f. 20 multicoloured . 1·25 1·25

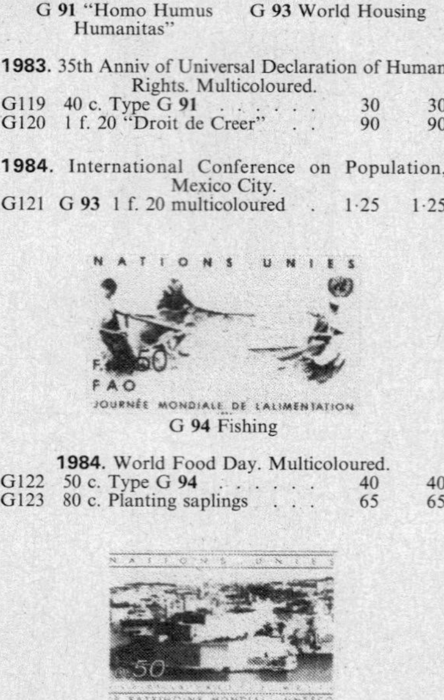

G **94** Fishing

1984. World Food Day. Multicoloured.
G122 50 c. Type G **94** 40 40
G123 80 c. Planting saplings . . . 65 65

G **96** Fort St. Angelo, Malta (wrongly inscr "Valetta")

1984. World Heritage—U.N.E.S.C.O. Mult.
G124 50 c. Type G **96** 40 40
G125 70 c. Los Glaciares, Argentina 60 60

G **98** Man and Woman

G **100** Heads

1984. Future for Refugees.
G126 G **98** 35 c. black and green . 25 25
G127 – 1 f. 50 black & brown 1·10 1·10
DESIGN: 1 f. 50, Head of woman.

1984. International Youth Year.
G128 G **100** 1 f. 20 multicoloured 90 90

1985. 20th Anniv of Turin Centre of International Labour Organization.
G129 **239** 80 c. red 60 60
G130 V **43** 1 f. 20 green 90 90

G **103** Ploughing and Group of People

1985. 10th Anniv of United Nations University, Tokyo. Multicoloured.
G131 G **103** 50 c. multicoloured . 35 35
G132 80 c. multicoloured . 55 55

G **104** Postman

G **108** Children

1985.
G133 G **104** 20 c. multicoloured . 10 10
G134 – 1 f. 20 blue and black 80 80
DESIGN: 1 f. 20, Doves.

1985. 40th Anniv of United Nations Organization. Multicoloured.
G135 50 c. Type G **108** 40 40
G136 70 c. "Harvest Scene" (Andrew Wyeth) 60 60

1985. U.N.I.C.E.F. Child Survival Campaign. Multicoloured.
G138 50 c. Type G **108** 40 40
G139 1 f. 20 Child drinking . . . 1·10 1·10

G **110** Children raising Empty Bowls to weeping Mother

G **111** Herring Gulls

1986. Africa in Crisis.
G140 G **110** 1 f. 40 multicoloured 1·25 1·25

1986.
G141 G **111** 5 c. multicoloured . . 10 10

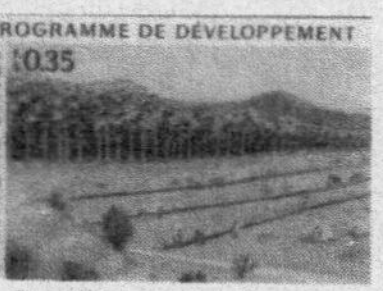

G **112** Tents in Clearing

1986. Development Programme. Timber Production. Multicoloured.
G142 35 c. Type G **112** 85 85
G143 35 c. Felling tree 85 85
G144 35 c. Logs on lorries 85 85
G145 35 c. Girls with sapling . . . 85 85
Nos. G142/5 were printed together, se-tenant, forming a composite design.

1986. Philately: International Hobby.
G146 **253** 50 c. green and red . . 45 45
G147 – 80 c. black and orange . 80 80
DESIGN: 80 c. United Nations stamps.

G 118 Ribbon forming Dove

1986. International Peace Year. Multicoloured.
G148 45 c. Type **G 118** 35 35
G149 1 f. 40 "Peace" and olive branch . . . . 1·25 1·25

1987. 9th Death Anniv of Trygve Lie (first U.N. Secretary-General).
G151 **258** 1 f. 40 multicoloured . . 1·25 1·25

G 122 Abstract

G 124 Mixing Cement and Carrying Bricks

1987. Multicoloured.
G152 90 c. Type **G 122** 65 65
G153 1 f. 40 Armillary Sphere, Geneva Centre 95 95

1987. International Year of Shelter for the Homeless.
G154 **G 124** 50 c. green and black 50 50
G155 – 90 c. blue, turquoise and black 80 80
DESIGN: 90 c. Fitting windows and painting.

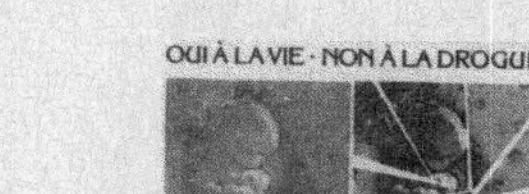
G 126 Mother and Baby

1987. Anti-Drugs Campaign. Multicoloured.
G156 80 c. Type **G 126** 75 75
G157 1 f. 20 Workers in paddy field 1·25 1·25

G 128 People in Boat and Palais des Nations, Geneva

G 130 Whooping Cough

1987. United Nations Day. Multicoloured.
G158 35 c. Type **G 128** 35 35
G159 50 c. Dancers 50 50

1987. "Immunize Every Child". Multicoloured.
G160 90 c. Type **G 130** 85 85
G161 1 f. 70 Tuberculosis . . . . 1·75 1·75

G 132 Goatherd

G 134 People

1988. International Fund for Agricultural Development "For a World Without Hunger" Campaign. Multicoloured.
G162 35 c. Type **G 132** 30 30
G163 1 f. 40 Women and baskets of fruit . . . . 1·25 1·25

1988.
G164 **G 134** 50 c. multicoloured . 40 40

G 135 Mountains and Pine Forest

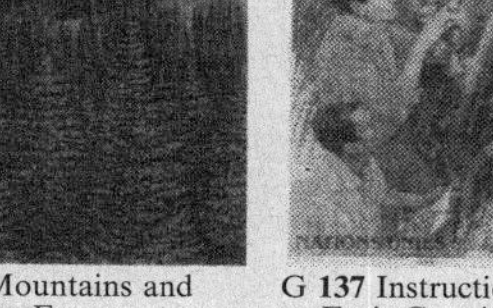
G 137 Instruction in Fruit Growing

1988. "Survival of the Forests". Multicoloured.
G165 50 c. Type **G 135** . . . . . 3·25 3·25
G166 1 f. 10 Pine forest and lake shore . . . . 3·25 3·25
Nos. G165/6 were printed together, se-tenant, forming a composite design.

1988. International Volunteer Day. Mult.
G167 80 c. Type **G 137** 70 70
G168 90 c. Teaching animal husbandary 80 80

G 139 Football

G 142 Communications

1988. "Health in Sports". Multicoloured.
G169 50 f. Type **G 139** 45 45
G170 1 f. 40 Swimming . . . . . 1·25 1·25

1988. 40th Anniv of Declaration of Human Rights.
G171 **276** 90 c. multicoloured . . 80 80

1989. World Bank. Multicoloured.
G173 80 c. Type **G 142** 70 70
G174 1 f. 40 Industry . . . . . . 1·25 1·25

1989. Award of Nobel Peace Prize to United Nations Peace-keeping Forces.
G175 **280** 90 c. multicoloured . . 80 80

G 145 Cold Arctic Air over Europe

G 147 Tree and Birds

1989. 25th Anniv of World Weather Watch.
G176 90 c. Type **G 145** 80 80
G177 1 f. 10 Surface temperatures of Kattegat 95 95

1989. 10th Anniv of United Nations Vienna International Centre.
G178 50 c. Type **G 147** 45 45
G179 2 f. Woman and flower . . 1·75 1·75

G 149 "Young Mother sewing" (Mary Cassatt) (Article 3)

1989. Universal Declaration of Human Rights (1st series). Multicoloured.
G180 35 f. Type **G 149** 25 25
G181 80 f. "Runaway Slave" (Albert Mangones) (Article 4) . . 60 60
See also Nos. G193/4, G209/10, G224/5 and G234/5.

1990. International Trade Centre.
G182 **287** 1 f. 50 multicoloured . 1·25 1·25

G 152 Palais des Nations **G 155** Frangipani

1990.
G183 **G 152** 5 f. multicoloured . 3·75 3·75

1990. Anti-AIDS Campaign. Multicoloured.
G184 50 c. Type **289** 45 45
G185 80 c. "Man" (Leonardo da Vinci) 70 70

1990. Medicinal Plants. Multicoloured.
G186 90 c. Type **G 155** 70 70
G187 1 f. 40 "Cinchona officinalis" 1·10 1·10

G 157 Projects forming "45"

1990. 45th Anniv of U.N.O. Multicoloured.
G188 90 c. Type **G 157** 70 70
G189 1 f. 10 Dove and "45" . . . 85 85

G 159 Men making Deal over Painting

1990. Crime Prevention. Multicoloured.
G191 50 c. Type **G 159** 45 45
G192 2 f. Man spilling waste from cart . . . . 1·50 1·50

1990. Universal Declaration of Human Rights (2nd series). As Type **G 149**.
G193 35 c. multicoloured 30 30
G194 90 c. black and flesh 75 75
DESIGNS: 35 c. "Prison Courtyard" (Vincent van Gogh) (Article 9); 90 c. "Katho's Son Redeems the Evil Doer from Execution" (Albrecht Durer) (Article 10).

G 163/166 Lake

1991. Economic Commission for Europe. "For a Better Environment".
G195 **G 163** 90 c. multicoloured . 80 80
G196 **G 164** 90 c. multicoloured . 80 80
G197 **G 165** 90 c. multicoloured . 80 80
G198 **G 166** 90 c. multicoloured . 80 80
Nos. G195/8 were issued together, se-tenant, forming the composite design illustrated.

G 167 Mountains **G 169** Papers and Ballot Box

1991. 1st Anniv of Namibian Independence. Multicoloured.
G199 70 c. Type **G 167** 65 65
G200 90 c. Baobab 80 80

1991. Multicoloured.
G201 80 c. Type **G 169** 75 75
G202 1 f. 50 U.N. emblem . . . . 1·40 1·40

G 171 Baby in Open Hands (Ryuta Nakajima)

1991. 30th Anniv (1989) of U.N. Declaration of the Rights of the Child and 1990 World Summit on Children, New York. Children's Drawings. Multicoloured.
G203 80 c. Type **G 171** 75 75
G204 1 f. 10 Children playing amongst flowers (David Popper) . . . . 1·00 1·00

G 173 Bubble of Toxin, City and Drums

1991. Banning of Chemical Weapons. Mult.
G205 80 c. Type **G 173** 75 75
G206 1 f. 40 Hand pushing back gas mask . . . . 1·25 1·25

G 175 U.N. (New York) 1951 15 c. Stamp

1991. 40th Anniv of United Nations Postal Administration.
G207 **G 175** 50 c. blue and lilac on cream 45 45
G208 – 1 f. 60 bl on cream . 1·50 1·50
DESIGN: 1 f. 60, U.N. (New York) 1951 50 c. stamp.

1991. Declaration of Human Rights (3rd series). As Type **G 149**. Multicoloured.
G209 50 c. "Early Morning in Ro, 1925" (Paul Klee) (Article 15) 45 45
G210 90 c. "The Marriage of Arnolfini" (Jan van Eyck) (Article 16) 80 80

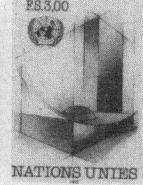

G 179 Sagarmatha National Park, Nepal **G 181** U.N. Headquarters, New York

1992. 20th Anniv of U.N.E.S.C.O. World Heritage Convention. Multicoloured.
G211 50 c. Type **G 179** 45 45
G212 1 f. 10 Stonehenge, United Kingdom . . . . 1·00 1·00

1992.
G213 **G 181** 3 f. multicoloured . . 2·75 2·75

G 182/183 Sea Life (½-size illustration)

1992. "Clean Oceans"
G214 **G 182** 80 c. multicoloured . 75 75
G215 **G 183** 80 c. multicoloured . 75 75
Nos. G214/15 were issued together, se-tenant, forming the composite design illustrated.

G 184/187 Planet Earth

1992. 2nd U.N. Conference on Environment and Development, Rio de Janeiro.
G216 **G 184** 75 c. multicoloured . 70 70
G217 **G 185** 75 c. multicoloured . 70 70
G218 **G 186** 75 c. multicoloured . 70 70
G219 **G 187** 75 c. multicoloured . 70 70
Nos. G216/19 were issued together, se-tenant, forming the composite design illustrated.

G 188/189 "Mission Planet Earth"

1992. International Space Year. Roul.

G220 G **188** 1 f. 10 multicoloured 1·00 1·00
G221 G **189** 1 f. 10 multicoloured 1·00 1·00

Nos. G220/1 were issued together, se-tenant, forming the composite design illustrated.

G **190** Women in Science and Technology — G **194** Voluntary Work

1992. Commission on Science and Technology for Development. Multicoloured.

G222 90 c. Type G **190** 80 80
G223 1 f. 60 Graduate using V.D.U. 1·50 1·50

1992. Universal Declaration of Human Rights (4th series). As Type G **149**. Multicoloured.

G224 50 c. "The Oath of the Tennis Court" (Jacques Louis David) (Article 21) 45 45
G225 90 c. "Rocking Chair I" (Henry Moore) (Article 22) 80 80

1993. "Ageing: Dignity and Participation". 10th Anniv (1992) of International Plan of Action on Ageing. Multicoloured.

G226 50 c. Type G **194** 45 45
G227 1 f. 60 Security of employment 1·50 1·50

G **196** Gorilla

1993. Endangered Species (1st series.) Multicoloured.

G228 80 c. Type G **196** 70 70
G229 80 c. Peregrine falcon . . . 70 70
G230 80 c. Amazon manatee . . . 70 70
G231 80 c. Snow leopard 70 70

See also Nos. G246/9.

G **200** Neighbourhood and Community Environment

1993. 45th Anniv of W.H.O. Multicoloured.

G232 60 c. Type G **200** 55 55
G233 1 f. Urban environment . . 90 90

1993. Declaration of Human Rights (5th series). As Type G **149**. Multicoloured.

G234 50 c. "Three Musicians" (Pablo Picasso) (Article 27) . . . 45 45
G235 90 c. "Voice of Space" (Rene Magritte) (Article 28) . . 80 80

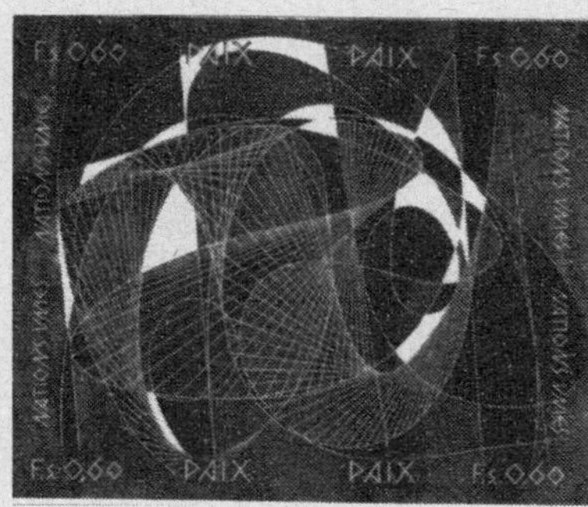

G **204/207** Peace

1993. International Peace Day. Roul.

G236 G **204** 60 c. multicoloured . 55 55
G237 G **205** 60 c. multicoloured . 55 55
G238 G **206** 60 c. multicoloured . 55 55
G239 G **207** 60 c. multicoloured . 55 55

Nos. G236/9 were issued together, se-tenant, forming the composite design illustrated.

G **208** Polar Bears

1993. The Environment—Climate. Multicoloured.

G240 1 f. 10 Type G **208** . . . . 1·00 1·00
G241 1 f. 10 Whale in melting ice 1·00 1·00
G242 1 f. 10 Elephant seal . . . 1·00 1·00
G243 1 f. 10 Penguins . . . . . 1·00 1·00

Nos. G240/3 were issued together, se-tenant, forming a composite design.

G **212** Father calling Child — G **218** Hand delivering Refugee to New Country

G **214** Mexican Prairie Dogs

1994. International Year of the Family. Multicoloured.

G244 80 c. Type **G 212** 85 85
G245 1 f. Three generations . . . 1·10 1·10

1994. Endangered Species (2nd series). Multicoloured.

G246 80 c. Type **G 214** 85 85
G247 80 c. Jabiru 85 85
G248 80 c. Blue whale 85 85
G249 80 c. Golden lion tamarin . 85 85

1994. United Nations High Commissioner for Refugees.

G250 G **218** 1 f. 20 multicoloured 1·25 1·25

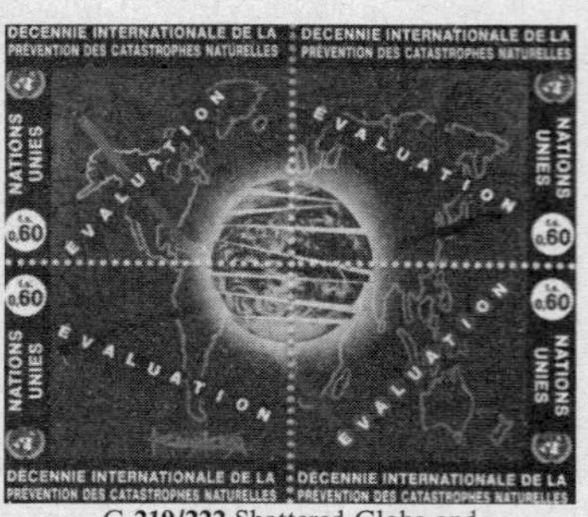

G **219/222** Shattered Globe and "Evaluation" (⅔-size illustration)

1994. International Decade for Natural Disaster Reduction.

G251 G **219** 60 c. multicoloured . 65 65
G252 G **220** 60 c. multicoloured . 65 65
G253 G **221** 60 c. multicoloured . 65 65
G254 G **222** 60 c. multicoloured . 65 65

Nos. G251/4 were issued together, se-tenant, forming the composite design illustrated.

G **223** Mobilization of Resources in Developing Countries

1994. International Population and Development Conference, Cairo. Multicoloured.

G255 60 c. Type **G 223** 65 65
G256 80 c. Internal migration of population 85 85

G **225** Palais des Nations

1994. Multicoloured.

G257 60 c. Type G **225** 65 65
G258 80 c. "Creation of the World" (detail of tapestry, Oili Maki) 85 85
G259 1 f. 80 Palais des Nations . . 2·00 2·00

G **228** Map and Linked Ribbons

1994. 30th Anniv of United Nations Conference on Trade and Development.

G260 80 c. Type G **228** 85 85
G261 1 f. Map and ribbons . . . . 1·10 1·10

1995. 50th Anniv of U.N.O

G262 **371** 80 c. multicoloured . . . 85 85

C. VIENNA HEADQUARTERS.

For use on mail posted at the United Nations Vienna International Centre and by the International Atomic Energy Agency.

NOTE. Reference to numbers and types in this section, other than those with a "V" prefix, are to the United Nations (New York or Geneva) Headquarters listing. Designs adapted for the Vienna issues are inscribed in Austrian and have face values in schillings.

V **4** Donaupark Complex

1979. Some designs adapted from issues of New York or Geneva Headquarters. Multicoloured.

V1 50 g. Type G **53** 10 10
V2 1 s. As No. 94 . . . . 10 10
V3 2 s. 50 Type **162** 30 30
V3a 3 s. "...for a better world" . . 35 35
V4 4 s. Type V **4** 45 45
V5 5 s. Type A **134** 55 55
V6 6 s. Aerial view of Donaupark (vert) 65 65
V7 10 s. As Type **52**, but without frame . . . . 1·10 1·10

1980. New International Economic Order.

V8 **195** 4 s. multicoloured . . . . 1·00 90

V **9** Dove and World Map

1980. U.N. Decade for Women.

V 9 V **9** 4 s. multicoloured . . . 40 30
V10 6 s. multicoloured . . . 85 65

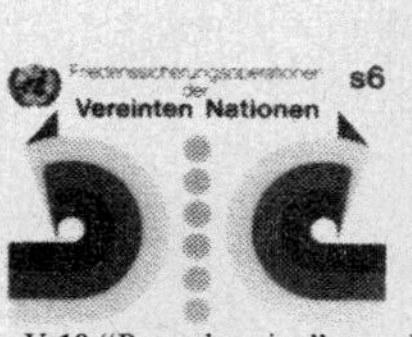

V **10** "Peace-keeping" — V **11** Dove and "35"

1980. Peace-keeping Operations.

V11 V **10** 6 s. multicoloured . . . 65 65

1980. 35th Anniv of U.N.O.

V12 V **11** 4 s. black and red . . . 35 30
V13 – 6 s. multicoloured . . . 75 70

DESIGN: 6 s. Stylized flower.

V **13** Economic and Social Emblems

1980. Economic and Social Council. Multicoloured.

V15 V **13** 4 s. multicoloured . . . 45 40
V16 – 6 s. green, red & black . 65 55

DESIGN: 6 s. Figures ascending graph.

1981. Inalienable Rights of the Palestinian People.

V17 **206** 4 s. multicoloured . . . 65 50

1981. International Year of Disabled Persons.

V18 **207** 4 s. multicoloured . . . 45 35
V19 – 6 s. orange and black . . 65 55

DESIGN: 6 s. Knot pattern.

1981. Art.

V20 **209** 6 s. multicoloured . . . 60 60

V **19** U.N. Energy Conference Emblem

1981. New and Renewable Sources of Energy.

V21 V **19** 7 s. 50 gold and mauve 70 70

V **20** Symbols of Services

1981. 10th Anniv of U.N. Volunteers Programme. Multicoloured.
V22 5 s. Type V **20** 45 40
V23 7 s. Emblems of science, agriculture and industry . . 65 60

V **22** Symbols of the Environment
V **24** Satellite and Emblems

1982. Human Environment. Multicoloured.
V24 5 s. Type V **22** 45 45
V25 7 s. Leaves 65 65

1982. Second United Nations Conference on Exploration and Peaceful Uses of Outer Space.
V26 V **24** 5 s. multicoloured . . . 70 60

V **25** Fish
V **28** Radar Screen within Lifebelt

1982. Conservation and Protection of Nature. Multicoloured.
V27 5 s. Type V **10** 60 60
V28 7 s. Elephant (mammals) . . 1·00 80

1983. World Communications Year.
V29 **222** 4 s. multicoloured 60 50

1983. Safety at Sea: International Maritime Organization. Multicoloured.
V30 4 s. Type V **28** 50 50
V31 6 s. Stylized liner 75 75

1983. World Food Programme.
V32 **226** 5 s. green 60 50
V33 7 s. brown 65 60

V **31** Exports
V **33** "Die Zweite Haut"

1983. Trade and Development. Multicoloured.
V34 5 s. Type V **31** 50 40
V35 8 s. 50 Emblems of trade . . 90 85

1983. 35th Anniv of Declaration of Human Rights. Multicoloured.
V36 5 s. Type V **33** 50 40
V37 7 s. "Recht auf Traume" . . 75 60

V **35** World Agriculture

1984. International Conference on Population, Mexico City.
V38 V **35** 7 s. multicoloured . . . 95 95

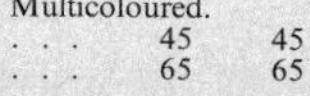

V **36** Irrigation

1984. World Food Day. Multicoloured.
V39 4 s. 50 Type V **36** 45 45
V40 6 s. Combine harvesters . . . 65 65

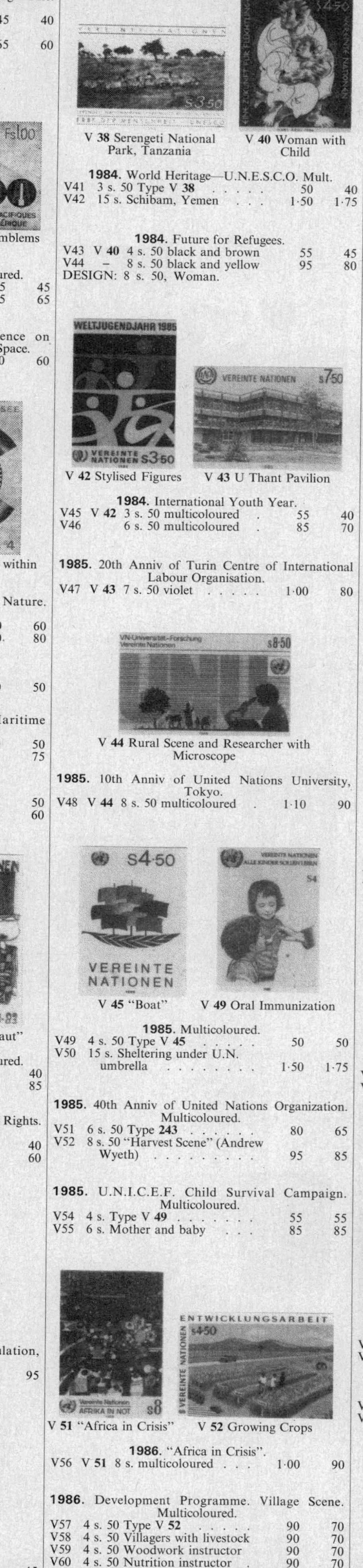

V **38** Serengeti National Park, Tanzania
V **40** Woman with Child

1984. World Heritage—U.N.E.S.C.O. Mult.
V41 3 s. 50 Type V **38** 50 40
V42 15 s. Schibam, Yemen . . . 1·50 1·75

1984. Future for Refugees.
V43 V **40** 4 s. 50 black and brown 55 45
V44 – 8 s. 50 black and yellow 95 80
DESIGN: 8 s. 50, Woman.

V **42** Stylised Figures
V **43** U Thant Pavilion

1984. International Youth Year.
V45 V **42** 3 s. 50 multicoloured . 55 40
V46 6 s. 50 multicoloured . 85 70

1985. 20th Anniv of Turin Centre of International Labour Organisation.
V47 V **43** 7 s. 50 violet . . . . . 1·00 80

V **44** Rural Scene and Researcher with Microscope

1985. 10th Anniv of United Nations University, Tokyo.
V48 V **44** 8 s. 50 multicoloured . 1·10 90

V **45** "Boat"
V **49** Oral Immunization

1985. Multicoloured.
V49 4 s. 50 Type V **45** 50 50
V50 15 s. Sheltering under U.N. umbrella . . . . 1·50 1·75

1985. 40th Anniv of United Nations Organization. Multicoloured.
V51 6 s. 50 Type **243** 80 65
V52 8 s. 50 "Harvest Scene" (Andrew Wyeth) 95 85

1985. U.N.I.C.E.F. Child Survival Campaign. Multicoloured.
V54 4 s. Type V **49** 55 55
V55 6 s. Mother and baby . . . 85 85

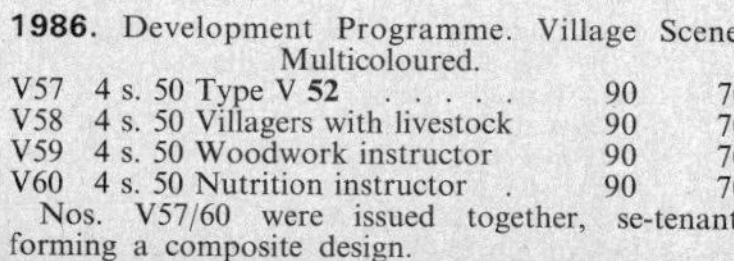

V **51** "Africa in Crisis"
V **52** Growing Crops

1986. "Africa in Crisis".
V56 V **51** 8 s. multicoloured . . . 1·00 90

1986. Development Programme. Village Scene. Multicoloured.
V57 4 s. 50 Type V **52** 90 70
V58 4 s. 50 Villagers with livestock 90 70
V59 4 s. 50 Woodwork instructor 90 70
V60 4 s. 50 Nutrition instructor . 90 70
Nos. V57/60 were issued together, se-tenant, forming a composite design.

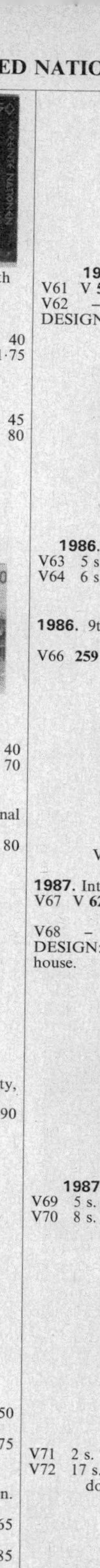

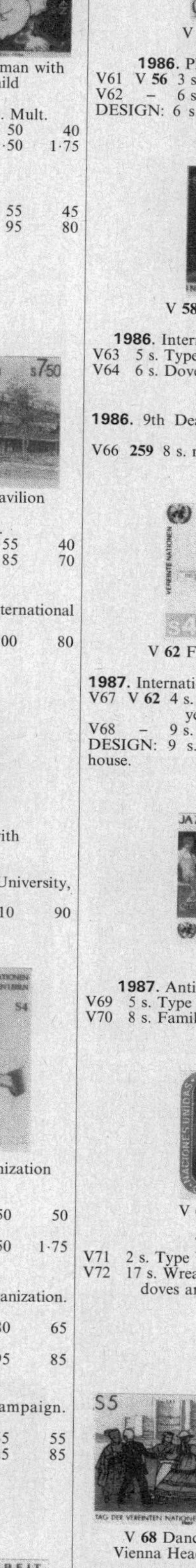

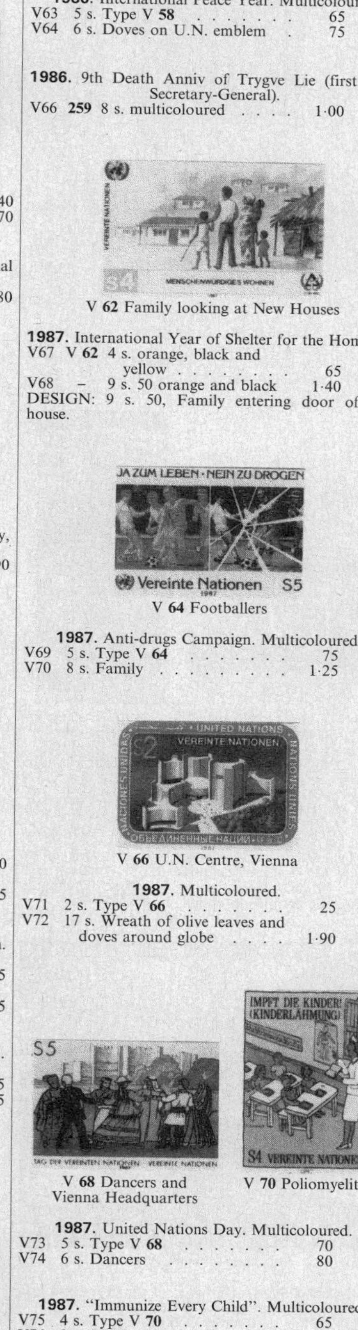

V **56** United Nations Stamps

1986. Philately: An International Hobby.
V61 V **56** 3 s. 50 blue and brown . 50 40
V62 – 6 s. 50 blue and red . . 75 70
DESIGN: 6 s. 50, Engraver.

V **58** Olive Branch and Rainbow

1986. International Peace Year. Multicoloured.
V63 5 s. Type V **58** 65 55
V64 6 s. Doves on U.N. emblem . 75 65

1986. 9th Death Anniv of Trygve Lie (first U.N. Secretary-General).
V66 **259** 8 s. multicoloured . . . . 1·00 90

V **62** Family looking at New Houses

1987. International Year of Shelter for the Homeless.
V67 V **62** 4 s. orange, black and yellow 65 50
V68 – 9 s. 50 orange and black 1·40 1·10
DESIGN: 9 s. 50, Family entering door of new house.

V **64** Footballers

1987. Anti-drugs Campaign. Multicoloured.
V69 5 s. Type V **64** 75 60
V70 8 s. Family . . . . 1·25 90

V **66** U.N. Centre, Vienna

1987. Multicoloured.
V71 2 s. Type V **66** 25 25
V72 17 s. Wreath of olive leaves and doves around globe . . . . 1·90 1·90

V **68** Dancers and Vienna Headquarters
V **70** Poliomyelitis

1987. United Nations Day. Multicoloured.
V73 5 s. Type V **68** 70 60
V74 6 s. Dancers 80 70

1987. "Immunize Every Child". Multicoloured.
V75 4 s. Type V **70** 65 50
V76 9 s. 50 Diphtheria . . . . . 1·25 1·10

V **72** Woman planting

1987. International Fund for Agricultural Development "For a World without Hunger" Campaign. Multicoloured.
V77 4 s. Type V **72** 55 55
V78 6 s. Women and foodstuffs . 70 70

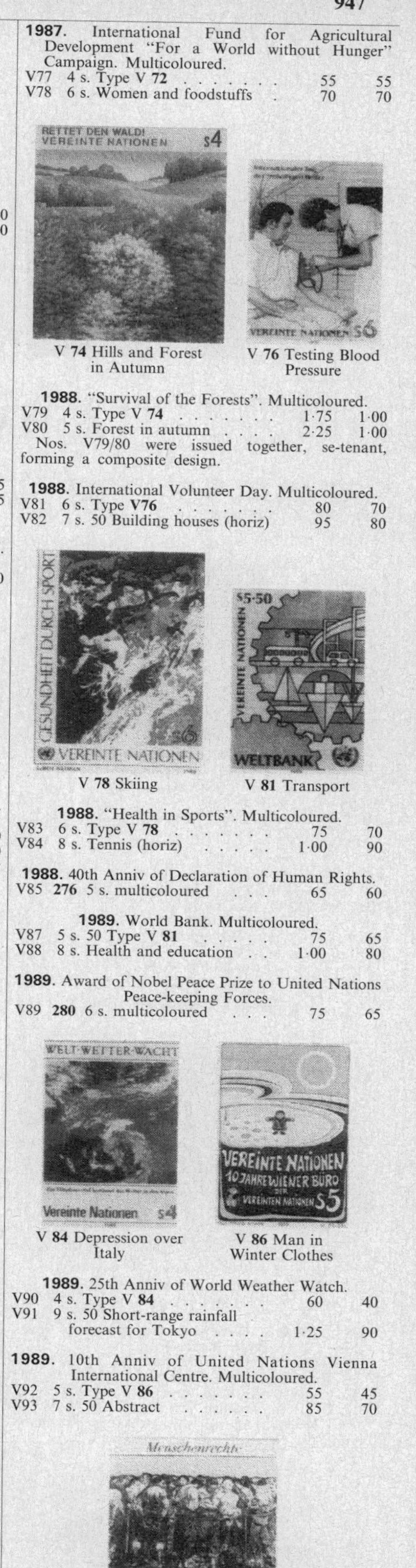

V **74** Hills and Forest in Autumn
V **76** Testing Blood Pressure

1988. "Survival of the Forests". Multicoloured.
V79 4 s. Type V **74** . . . . 1·75 1·00
V80 5 s. Forest in autumn . . . . 2·25 1·00
Nos. V79/80 were issued together, se-tenant, forming a composite design.

1988. International Volunteer Day. Multicoloured.
V81 6 s. Type **V76** 80 70
V82 7 s. 50 Building houses (horiz) 95 80

V **78** Skiing
V **81** Transport

1988. "Health in Sports". Multicoloured.
V83 6 s. Type V **78** 75 70
V84 8 s. Tennis (horiz) . . . . . 1·00 90

1988. 40th Anniv of Declaration of Human Rights.
V85 **276** 5 s. multicoloured . . . 65 60

1989. World Bank. Multicoloured.
V87 5 s. 50 Type V **81** 75 65
V88 8 s. Health and education . . 1·00 80

1989. Award of Nobel Peace Prize to United Nations Peace-keeping Forces.
V89 **280** 6 s. multicoloured . . . 75 65

V **84** Depression over Italy
V **86** Man in Winter Clothes

1989. 25th Anniv of World Weather Watch.
V90 4 s. Type V **84** 60 40
V91 9 s. 50 Short-range rainfall forecast for Tokyo . . . . 1·25 90

1989. 10th Anniv of United Nations Vienna International Centre. Multicoloured.
V92 5 s. Type V **86** 55 45
V93 7 s. 50 Abstract 85 70

V **88** "Prisoners" (Kathe Kollwitz) (Article 5)

1989. Universal Declaration of Human Rights (1st series).
V94 V **88** 4 s. black 40 35
V95 – 6 s. multicoloured . . . 70 65
DESIGN: 6 s. "Jurisprudence" (Raphael) (Article 6).
See also Nos. V107/8, V122/3, V138/9 and V149/150.

1990. International Trade Centre.
V96 **287** 12 s. multicoloured . . . 1·75 1·75

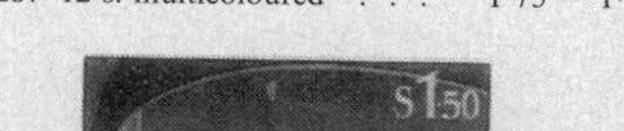

V **91** "Earth" (painting by Kurt Regschek in I.A.E.A. Building)

1990.
V97 V **91** 1 s. 50 multicoloured . . 20 15

1990. Anti-AIDS Campaign. Multicoloured.
V98 5 s. Type **289** 75 45
V99 11 s. Attacking infected blood 1·50 1·00

V **94** Annatto · V **96** "45"

1990. Medicinal Plants. Multicoloured.
V100 4 s. 50 Type V **94** 60 40
V101 9 s. 50 Cundeamor . . . . . 1·40 90

1990. 45th Anniv of U.N.O. Multicoloured.
V102 7 s. Type V **96** . . . . 1·00 80
V103 9 s. "45" (different) . . . . 1·40 1·10

V **98** Men fighting

1990. Crime Prevention. Multicoloured.
V105 6 s. Type V **98** 85 70
V106 8 s. Masked man damaging painting . . . . 1·10 90

1990. Universal Declaration of Human Rights (2nd series). As Type V **88**. Multicoloured.
V107 4 s. 50 "Before the Judge" (Sandor Bihari) (Article 11) 60 50
V108 7 s. "Young Man greeted by Woman writing Poem" (Suzuki Harunobu) (Article 12) 80 65

V **102/105** Mediterranean Coastline and Wildlife

1991. Economic Commission for Europe. "For a Better Environment".
V109 V **102** 5 s. multicoloured . . 55 45
V110 V **103** 5 s. multicoloured . . 55 45
V111 V **104** 5 s. multicoloured . . 55 45
V112 V **105** 5 s. multicoloured . . 55 45
Nos. V109/12 were issued together, se-tenant, forming the composite design illustrated.

V **106** Scrubland V **108** Different Races

1991. 1st Anniv of Namibian Independence. Multicoloured.
V113 6 s. Type V **106** 70 60
V114 9 s. 50 Sand dune . . . . . 1·10 90

1991.
V115 V **108** 20 s. multicoloured . 2·25 1·90

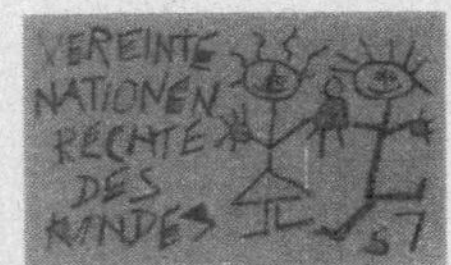

V **109** Boy and Girl (Anna Harmer)

1991. 30th Anniv (1989) of U.N. Declaration of the Rights of the Child and 1990 World Summit on Children, New York. Children's Drawings. Multicoloured.
V116 7 s. Type V **109** 80 65
V117 9 s. Child's world (Emiko Takegawa) . . . . 1·00 80

V **111** City, Bubbles of Toxin and Gas Mask

1991. Banning of Chemical Weapons. Mult.
V118 5 s. Type V **111** 55 45
V119 10 s. Hand pushing back cloud of toxin sprayed from airplane . . . . 1·10 90

V **113** U.N. (New York) 1951 20 c. Stamp

1991. 40th Anniv of United Nations Postal Administration.
V120 V **113** 5 s. brown on cream 55 45
V121 – 8 s. blue on cream . 90 75
DESIGN: 8 s. U.N. (New York) 1951 5 c. stamp.

1991. Declaration of Human Rights (3rd series). As Type V **88**. Multicoloured.
V122 4 s. 50 Ancient Mexican pottery (Article 17) 50 40
V123 7 s. "Windows, 1912" (Robert Delaunay) (Article 18) . . 80 65

V **117** Iguacu National Park, Brazil V **119/120** Sea Life (½-size illustration)

1992. 20th Anniv of U.N.E.S.C.O. World Heritage Convention. Multicoloured.
V124 5 s. Type V **117** 55 45
V125 9 s. Abu Simbel, Egypt . . 1·00 80

1992. "Clean Oceans".
V126 V **119** 7 s. multicoloured . . 80 65
V127 V **120** 7 s. multicoloured . . 80 65
Nos. V126/7 were issued together, se-tenant, forming the composite design illustrated.

V **121/124** Planet Earth

1992. 2nd U.N. Conference on Environment and Development, Rio de Janeiro.
V128 V **121** 5 s. 50 multicoloured 60 50
V129 V **122** 5 s. 50 multicoloured 60 50
V130 V **123** 5 s. 50 multicoloured 60 50
V131 V **124** 5 s. 50 multicoloured 60 50
Nos. V128/131 were issued together, se-tenant, forming the composite design illustrated.

V **125/126** "Mission Planet Earth"

1992. International Space Year. Roul.
V132 V **125** 10 s. multicoloured . . 1·10 90
V133 V **126** 10 s. multicoloured . . 1·10 90
Nos. V132/3 were printed together, se-tenant, forming the composite design illustrated.

V **127** Woman with Book emerging from V.D.U. V **129** Woman's Profile, Birds, Butterfly and Rose

1992. Commission on Science and Technology for Development. Multicoloured.
V134 5 s. 50 Type V **127** 60 50
V135 7 s. Flowers growing from thumb 80 65

1992. Multicoloured.
V136 5 s. 50 Type V **129** 60 50
V137 7 s. Vienna International Centre (horiz) 80 65

1992. Universal Declaration of Human Rights (4th series). As Type V **88**. Multicoloured.
V138 6 s. "The Builders" (Fernand Leger) (Article 23) 70 60
V139 10 s. "Sunday Afternoon on the Island of La Grande Jatte" (Georges Seurat) (Article 24) 1·10 90

V **133** Housing and Environment V **135** Grevy's Zebra

1993. "Ageing: Dignity and Participation". 10th Anniv (1992) of International Plan of Action on Ageing. Multicoloured.
V140 5 s. 50 Type V **133** 60 50
V141 7 s. Education 80 65

1993. Endangered Species (1st series). Multicoloured.
V142 7 s. Type V **135** 80 65
V143 7 s. Humboldt penguin . . . 80 65
V144 7 s. Desert monitor 80 65
V145 7 s. Wolf 80 65
See also Nos. V161/4.

V **139** Globe, Doves and U.N. Emblem V **140** Regional and National Environment

1993.
V146 V **139** 13 s. multicoloured . . 1·50 1·25

1993. 45th Anniv of W.H.O. Multicoloured.
V147 6 s. Type V **140** 70 60
V148 10 s. Continental and global environment . . . . 1·10 90

1993. Declaration of Human Rights (5th series). As Type V **88**. Multicoloured.
V149 5 s. "Lower Austrian Peasants' Wedding" (Ferdinand Waldmuller) (Article 29) 55 45
V150 6 s. "Outback" (Sally Morgan) (Article 30) . . . 70 60

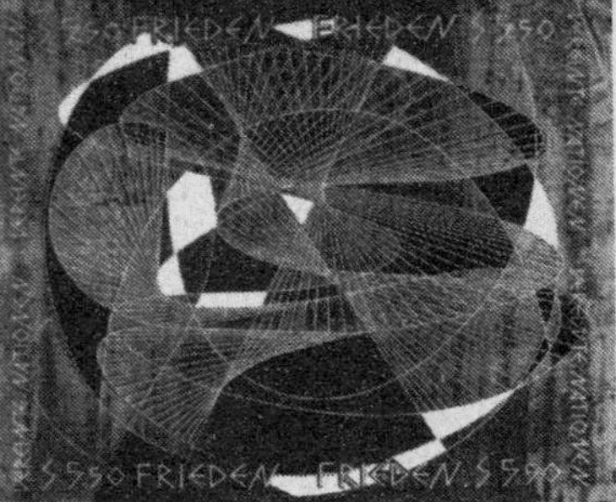
V **144/147** Peace

1993. International Peace Day. Roul.
V151 V **144** 5 s. 50 multicoloured 60 50
V152 V **145** 5 s. 50 multicoloured 60 50
V153 V **146** 5 s. 50 multicoloured 60 50
V154 V **147** 5 s. 50 multicoloured 60 50
Nos. V151/4 were issued together, se-tenant, forming the composite design illustrated.

V **148** Monkeys

1993. The Environment—Climate. Multicoloured.
V155 7 s. Type V **148** 80 65
V156 7 s. Bluebird and factory chimneys 80 65
V157 7 s. Volcano, smokestacks and tree stumps 80 65
V158 7 s. Owl in desert 80 65
Nos. V155/8 were issued together, se-tenant, forming a composite design.

V **152** Family holding Hands

1994. International Year of the Family. Mult.
V159 5 s. 50 Type V **152** 70 60
V160 8 s. Family at work . . . . 1·00 80

V **154** Ocelot

1994. Endangered Species (2nd series). Multicoloured.
V161 7 s. Type V **154** 90 75
V162 7 s. White-crested white eye 90 75
V163 7 s. Mediterranean monk seals 90 75
V164 7 s. Indian elephant 90 75

V **158** Tree and Doves V **161** Hands ready to help Refugees

1994. Multicoloured.
V165 50 g. Type V **158** 10 10
V166 4 s. Herring gulls 50 40
V167 30 s. Globe and dove . . . 3·75 3·00

1994. United Nations High Commissioner for Refugees.
V168 V **161** 12 s. multicoloured . 1·50 1·25

V **162/165** Shattered Globe and "Preparation" (⅔-size illustration)

1994. International Decade for Natural Disaster Reduction.

V169	V **162**	6 s. multicoloured . .	75	60
V170	V **163**	6 s. multicoloured . .	75	60
V171	V **164**	6 s. multicoloured . .	75	60
V172	V **165**	6 s. multicoloured . .	75	60

Nos. V169/72 were issued together, se-tenant, forming the composite design illustrated.

V **166** Enhancing Role of Women

1994. International Population and Development Conference, Cairo. Multicoloured.

V173	5 s. 50 Type V **166**	70	60
V174	7 s. Relationship of population and environment	90	75

V **168** Map and Crossed Ribbons

1994. 30th Anniv of United Nations Conference on Trade and Development. Multicoloured.

V175	6 s. Type V **168**	75	60
V176	7 s. Map and ribbons forming star	90	75

1995. 50th Anniv of U.N.O.

V177	**371**	7 s. multicoloured . . .	90	75

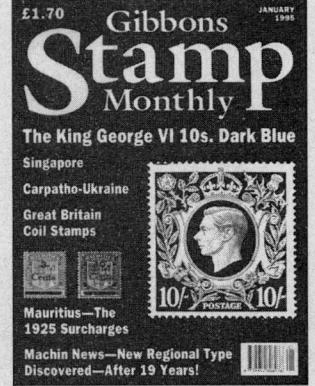

UNITED STATES OF AMERICA

Pt. 22

A Federal Republic in N. America, consisting of 50 states and one federal district.

100 cents = 1 dollar

PRICES. On the issues before 1890 the gum is rarely complete and the unused prices quoted are for stamps with part original gum.

1 Franklin (after drawings by James B. Longacre)

2 Washington (after painting by Stuart)

1847. Imperf.

1	1	5 c. brown	£3750	£350
2	2	10 c. black	£14000	£1100

The 5 c. blue and 10 c. orange both imperf come from miniature sheets isssued in 1947 to commemorate the Centenary Philatelic Exhibition, New York.

3 Franklin (after bust by Caffieri)

4 Washington (after bust by Houdon)

5 Jefferson (after painting by Stuart)

6 Washington

7 Washington

8 Washington

(after paintings by Stuart)

9 Franklin (after bust by Caffieri)

10 Washington (after Trumbull painting)

1851. Imperf.

11	3	1 c. blue	£250	55·00
13a	4	3 c. red	90·00	4·25
14	5	5 c. brown	£6500	£650
16	6	10 c. green	£1300	£150
19	7	12 c. black	£1700	£170

1857. Perf.

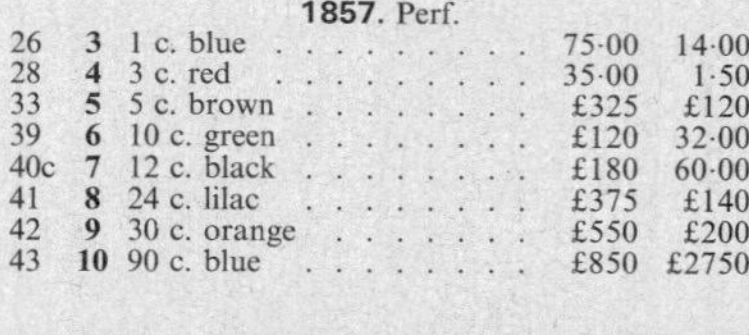

26	3	1 c. blue	75·00	14·00
28	4	3 c. red	35·00	1·50
33	5	5 c. brown	£325	£120
39	6	10 c. green	£120	32·00
40c	7	12 c. black	£180	60·00
41	8	24 c. lilac	£375	£140
42	9	30 c. orange	£550	£200
43	10	90 c. blue	£850	£2750

11 Franklin

12 Washington

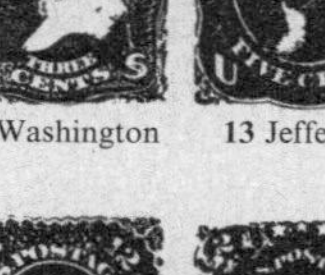

13 Jefferson

14 Washington

15 Washington

16 Washington

17 Franklin

18 Washington

19 Andrew Jackson (after miniature by J. W. Dodge)

20 Lincoln (from a photograph)

1861.

60b	11	1 c. blue	90·00	11·00
69	19	2 c. black	£110	16·00
62	12	3 c. red	45·00	60
63b	13	5 c. yellow	£3750	£275
72		5 c. brown	£250	38·00
64a	14	10 c. green	£190	18·00
65	15	12 c. black	£375	38·00
73	20	15 c. black	£375	50·00
66c	16	24 c. blue	£2750	£200
74		24 c. lilac	£200	32·00
74b		24 c. grey	£200	32·00
67	17	30 c. orange	£375	48·00
68a	18	90 c. blue	£1000	£170

21 Franklin (after Houdon bust)

22 Post Rider

23 Steam Locomotive

24 Washington (after Stuart)

25 Shield and Eagle

26 Paddle-steamer "Adriatic" (after C. Parsons)

27 Landing of Columbus (after Vanderlyn)

28 Declaration of Independence (after Trumbull)

30 Lincoln (from a photograph)

1869.

114	21	1 c. brown	£160	45·00
115	22	2 c. brown	£130	18·00
116	23	3 c. blue	£140	4·25
117	24	6 c. blue	£550	60·00
118	25	10 c. orange	£650	60·00
119	26	12 c. green	£550	65·00
121	27	15 c. blue and brown	£700	95·00
122	28	24 c. purple and green	£1700	£325
123	25	30 c. red and blue	£1800	£150
124	30	90 c. black and red	£5500	£900

31 Franklin

32 Jackson

33 Washington

34 Lincoln

35 Stanton

36 Jefferson

37 Henry Clay

38 Daniel Webster

39 General Winfield Scott

40 Alexander Hamilton

41 Commodore Perry

42 General Zachary Taylor (from a daguerreotype)

1870.

207	31	1 c. blue	26·00	30
148	32	2 c. brown	50·00	2·50
185		2 c. red	45·00	70
208	33	3 c. green	32·00	10
219		3 c. red	32·00	27·00
161	34	6 c. red	£150	50
151	35	7 c. red	£250	35·00
210	36	10 c. brown	60·00	1·50
153	37	12 c. purple	£400	42·00
191	38	15 c. orange	£120	11·00
155	39	24 c. violet	£450	55·00
192	40	30 c. black	£350	21·00
222		30 c. brown	£275	55·00
193	41	90 c. red	£800	£110
223		90 c. violet	£600	£110

1875.

181	42	5 c. blue	£140	4·75

43 Garfield (from a photograph)

44 Washington (after bust by Houdon)

45 Jackson (after bust by Powers)

46 Franklin

47 Franklin

1882.

217	46	1 c. blue	45·00	40
213	44	2 c. brown	23·00	10
218		2 c. green	17·00	10
214	45	4 c. green	£120	4·50
220		4 c. red	£120	7·50
211	43	5 c. brown	90·00	2·50
221		5 c. blue	£110	3·50

1890. No triangles in upper corners.

224	47	1 c. blue (Franklin)	14·00	10
225a	–	2 c. red (Washington)	12·00	10
226	–	3 c. violet (Jackson)	40·00	3·00
227	–	4 c. sepia (Lincoln)	38·00	1·00
228	–	5 c. brown (Grant)	40·00	1·00
229	–	6 c. red (Garfield)	42·00	11·00
230	–	8 c. purple (Sherman)	26·00	5·50
231	–	10 c. green (Webster)	70·00	1·00
232	–	15 c. blue (Clay)	£120	10·00
233	–	30 c. black (Jefferson)	£180	14·00
234	–	90 c. orange (Perry)	£300	70·00

58 Columbus in sight of Land

83 Jefferson

1893. Columbian Exposition, Chicago.

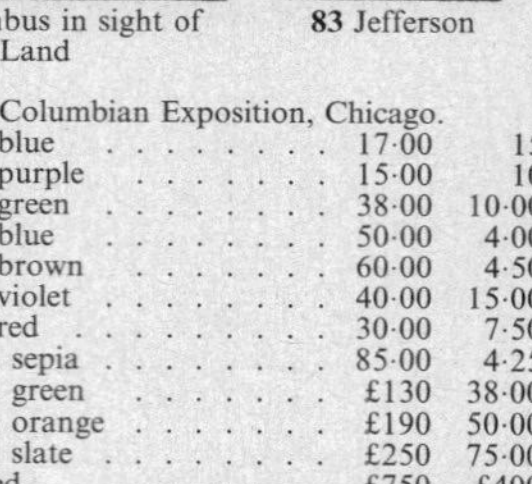

235	58	1 c. blue	17·00	15
236	–	2 c. purple	15·00	10
237	–	3 c. green	38·00	10·00
238	–	4 c. blue	50·00	4·00
239	–	5 c. brown	60·00	4·50
240	–	6 c. violet	40·00	15·00
241	–	8 c. red	30·00	7·50
242	–	10 c. sepia	85·00	4·25
243	–	15 c. green	£130	38·00
244	–	30 c. orange	£190	50·00
245	–	50 c. slate	£250	75·00
246	–	$1 red	£750	£400
247	–	$2 lake	£900	£325
248	–	$3 green	£1900	£700
249a	–	$4 red	£2750	£1000
250	–	$5 black	£2750	£1100

DESIGNS: 2 c. Landing of Columbus; 3 c. "Santa Maria", flagship of Columbus; 4 c. Fleet of Columbus; 5 c. Columbus soliciting aid of Isabella; 6 c. Columbus welcomed at Barcelona, Ferdinand (left) and Balboa (right); 8 c. Columbus restored to favour; 10 c. Columbus presenting natives; 15 c. Columbus announcing his discovery; 30 c. Columbus at La Rabida; 50 c. Recall of Columbus; $1 Isabella pledging her jewels; $2 Columbus in chains; $3 Columbus describing his third voyage; $4 Isabella and Columbus; $5 Columbus, America and Liberty.

1894. Triangles in upper corners as T 83. Same portraits as issue of 1890 except dollar values.

267	–	1 c. blue	3·50	10
283	–	1 c. green	6·00	10
270	–	2 c. red	2·75	10
271	–	3 c. violet	22·00	60
285	–	4 c. brown	20·00	40
273	–	5 c. brown	22·00	90
286	–	5 c. blue	22·00	30
274	–	6 c. brown	48·00	2·00
287a	–	6 c. purple	28·00	1·00
275	–	8 c. brown	25·00	60
276	–	10 c. green	35·00	60
289	–	10 c. brown	70·00	1·00
277	–	15 c. blue	£120	4·50
290	–	15 c. green	85·00	3·50
278	83	50 c. orange	£160	12·00
279	–	$1 black (Perry)	£350	40·00
281a	–	$2 blue (Madison)	£650	£190
282	–	$5 green (Marshall)	£1400	£300

88 Father Marquette on the Mississippi

97 "City of Alpena" (Great Lakes steamer)

1898. Trans-Mississippi Exposition, Omaha.

291	88	1 c. green	18·00	2·75
292	–	2 c. red	17·00	70
293	–	4 c. orange	90·00	13·00
294	–	5 c. blue	75·00	10·00
295	–	8 c. purple	£120	21·00
296	–	10 c. violet	£140	12·00
297	–	50 c. green	£550	60·00
298	–	$1 black	£1400	£375
299	–	$2 brown	£2000	£700

DESIGNS: 2 c. Farming in the West; 4 c. Indian hunting American bison; 5 c. Fremont on Rocky Mountains; 8 c. Troops guarding emigrant train; 10 c. Hardships of emigration; 50 c. Western mining prospector; $1 Western cattle in storm; $2 Bridge over Mississippi at St. Louis and paddle-steamer "Grey Eagle".

1901. Pan-American Exhibition, Buffalo. Inscr "COMMEMORATIVE SERIES, 1901."

300	97	1 c. black and green	15·00	2·75
301	–	2 c. black and red	15·00	75
302	–	4 c. black and brown	65·00	10·00
303	–	5 c. black and blue	85·00	13·00
304	–	8 c. black and brown	£100	50·00
305	–	10 c. black and brown	£160	20·00

DESIGNS: 2 c. "Empire State Express"; 4 c. Automobile; 5 c. Railway bridge below Niagara Falls; 8 c. Canal locks at Sault Sainte Marie; 10 c. "Saint Paul" (liner).

103 Franklin

104 Washington

105 Jackson

106 Grant

107 Lincoln

108 Garfield

109 Martha Washington

110 Webster

111 Harrison

112 Clay

113 Jefferson

114 Farragut

115 Madison

116 Marshall

1902. Inscr "SERIES 1902". 1, 4 and 5 c. perf or imperf.

306	103	1 c. green	6·00	10
307	104	2 c. red	7·00	10
308	105	3 c. violet	35·00	1·75
309	106	4 c. brown	35·00	70
310	107	5 c. blue	40·00	45
311	108	6 c. lake	42·00	1·40
312	109	8 c. violet	24·00	5·00
313	110	10 c. brown	50·00	70
314	111	13 c. purple	24·00	5·00
315	112	15 c. olive	95·00	3·25
316	113	50 c. orange	£250	14·00
317	114	$1 black	£550	32·00
485	115	$2 blue	£375	32·00
486	116	$5 green	£300	35·00

117 Washington (after Stuart)

118 Robert R. Livingston (after Stuart)

1903. Perf or imperf.
326 **117** 2 c. red 3·50 10

1904. International Exposition, St. Louis, and Louisiana Purchase. Inscr "COMMEMORATIVE SERIES OF 1904".
330 **118** 1 c. green 20·00 2·75
331 – 2 c. red 18·00 80
332 – 2 c. violet 65·00 22·00
333 – 5 c. blue 75·00 12·00
334 – 10 c. brown £130 18·00
DESIGNS: 2 c. Thomas Jefferson; 3 c. James Monroe (after Vanderlyn); 5 c. William McKinley; 10 c. Map of Louisiana Purchase.

123 Capt. John Smith, Pocahontas and Powhatan (after painting)

1907. Jamestown Exposition.
335 **123** 1 c. green 12·00 2·75
336 – 2 c. red 15·00 1·75
337 – 5 c. blue 65·00 17·00
DESIGN: 2 c. Founding of Jamestown, 1607; 5 c. Princess Pocahontas.

126 Franklin **127** **128**
Washington (after Houdon bust)

1908. 1 to 5 c. perf or imperf.
338 **126** 1 c. green 4·00 10
505 **128** 1 c. green 25 10
339 **127** 2 c. red 3·75 10
506 **128** 2 c. red 20 10
537 3 c. violet 65 10
510 4 c. brown 10·00 10
503 5 c. blue 3·50 70
513 6 c. orange 11·00 15
514 7 c. black 22·00 85
344 8 c. green 23·00 1·75
345 10 c. yellow 45·00 1·00
346 13 c. green 25·00 16·00
347 15 c. blue 40·00 3·50
348 50 c. violet £200 9·50
349 $1 black £325 48·00

129 Lincoln (detail of statue by Saint Gaudens in Grant Park, Chicago)

1909. Birth Centenary of Abraham Lincoln. Perf or imperf.
374 **129** 2 c. red 3·75 1·50

130 Wm. H. Seward **131** "Clermont" and "Half Moon" on Hudson River

1909. Alaska–Yukon–Pacific Exposition. Perf or imperf.
377 **130** 2 c. red 6·50 1·00

1909. Hudson–Fulton Celebration. Perf or imperf.
379**131** 2 c. red 11·00 3·25

133 Franklin (after Caffieri bust) **138**

1912.
515 **133** 8 c. olive 11·00 55
516 9 c. pink 13·00 1·50
517 10 c. yellow 15·00 10
518 11 c. green 8·00 2·50
519 12 c. brown 8·00 30
520 13 c. green 10·00 5·50
521 15 c. grey 3·00 70
522 20 c. blue 40·00 15
523 30 c. orange 30·00 55
524 50 c. lilac 70·00 40
525 $1 black 65·00 1·00
526 **138** $2 black and orange £650 £170
527 $2 black and red £275 23·00
528 $5 black and green £300 22·00

134 Balboa **135** Panama Canal (after model of Pedro Miguel Locks)

1913. Panama–Pacific Exposition. Inscr "SAN FRANCISCO 1915".
423 **134** 1 c. green 11·00 1·00
424 **135** 2 c. red 12·00 30
425 – 5 c. blue 60·00 6·00
426 – 10 c. yellow £170 10·00
DESIGNS: 5 c. Golden Gate, San Francisco; 10 c. Discovery of San Francisco Bay (after painting by Mathew).

A **139** Curtiss JN-4 "Jenny" **139** Liberty and Allies' Flags

1918. Air.
A546 A **139** 6 c. orange 70·00 26·00
A547 16 c. green £100 32·00
A548 24 c. blue and red £100 35·00

1919. Victory
546 **139** 3 c. violet 6·00 2·50

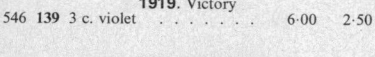

140 The "Mayflower"

1920. Tercentenary of Landing of Pilgrim Fathers. Inscr as in T **140**.
556 **140** 1 c. green 3·75 2·00
557 – 2 c. red 6·50 1·25
558 – 5 c. blue 32·00 10·00
DESIGNS: 2 c. Landing of the Pilgrims (after drawing by White); 5 c. Signing the Compact.

144 Franklin **157** Indian Chief **158** Statue of Liberty

159 Golden Gate **165** America

1922. Perf or imperf (1 c., 1½ c. 2 c).
559 – ½ c. brown (Hale) 15 10
632 **144** 1 c. green 15 10
603 – 1½ c. brown (Harding) 50 10
634 – 2 c. red (Washington) 15 10
636a – 3 c. violet (Lincoln) 20 10
637 – 4 c. brown (Martha Washington) 2·75 10
608 – 5 c. bl (T. Roosevelt) 1·00 10
639 – 6 c. orange (Garfield) 2·25 10
640 – 7 c. black (McKinley) 2·25 10
641 – 8 c. green (Grant) 2·25 10
642 – 9 c. pink (Jefferson) 2·25 10
610 – 10 c. orange (Monroe) 3·00 10
571a – 11 c. blue (Hayes) 1·50 15
571b – 11 c. green (Hayes) 1·40 35
693 – 12 c. violet (Cleveland) 5·00 10
694 – 13 c. green (B. Harrison) 1·75 15
695 **157** 14 c. blue 3·00 40
696 **158** 15 c. grey 8·00 10
698 **159** 20 c. red 9·00 10
699 – 25 c. green (Niagara) 8·50 10
700 – 30 c. brown (American bison) 13·00 10
701 – 50 c. lilac (Arlington Amphitheatre and Unknown Soldier's Tomb) 38·00 10
579 – $1 brown (Lincoln Memorial) 45·00 20
580 – $2 blue (Capitol, Washington) £100 5·50
581 **165** $5 blue and red £225 8·00
The 25 c. to $2 are horiz designs as T **159**, the remainder vert as T **144**

A **166** Aeroplane Radiator and Propeller A **168** De Havilland D.H.4M "Liberty"

1923. Air.
A614 A **166** 8 c. green 30·00 14·00
A615 – 16 c. blue 95·00 32·00
A616 A **168** 24 c. red £110 28·00
DESIGN: 16 c. Air mail service insignia.

168 Harding **167** "Nieu Nederland" (emigrant ship.)

1923. President Harding Memorial.
614 **166** 2 c. black 70 10

1924. Huguenot–Walloon Tercentenary.
618 **167** 1 c. green 3·25 3·00
619 – 2 c. red 7·00 2·00
620 – 5 c. blue 24·00 14·00
DESIGNS: 2 c. Landing at Fort Orange; 5 c. Ribault Memorial, Mayport, Florida.

170 Washington at Cambridge **173** Sloop "Restaurationen"

1925. 150th Anniv of Battle of Lexington and Concord.
621 **170** 1 c. green 3·00 3·00
622 – 2 c. red 5·50 3·75
623 – 5 c. blue 22·00 13·00
DESIGNS: 2 c. Battle of Lexington-Concord; 5 c. Statue of "Minute Man".

1925. Norse-American Centennial. Dated "1825 1925".
624 **173** 2 c. black and red 4·00 2·50
625 – 5 c. black and blue 18·00 16·00
DESIGN: 5 c. "Raven" (replica Viking longship).

176 Wilson

1925.
679 **176** 17 c. black 4·00 25

A **177** Relief Map of U.S.A.

1926. Air.
A628 A **177** 10 c. blue 3·00 20
A629 15 c. brown 3·25 2·00
A630 20 c. green 9·00 1·25

177 Liberty Bell

1926. 150th Anniv of Independence and Sesquicentennial Exhibition.
628 **177** 2 c. red 2·75 45

178 Ericsson Memorial (after statue by J. E. Fraser in Washington, D.C.) **179** Alexander Hamilton's Battery (after painting by E. F. Ward)

1926. John Ericsson Commemoration.
629 **178** 5 c. violet 5·00 2·50

1926. 150th Anniv of Battle of White Plains.
644 **179** 2 c. red 1·50 1·25

A **180** "Spirit of St. Louis"

1927. Air. Lindbergh's Transatlantic Flight.
A646 A **180** 10 c. blue 8·50 1·25

181 Green Mountain Boy **182** Surrender of Gen. Burgoyne (after painting by Trumbull)

1927. 150th Anniv of Independence of Vermont and Battle of Bennington.
646 **181** 2 c. red 1·25 80

1927. 150th Anniv of Burgoyne Campaign.
647 **182** 2 c. red 3·00 2·00

183 Washington at Valley Forge (after engraving by J. C. McRae) A **184** Air Beacon, Sherman Hill, Rocky Mountains

1928. 150th Anniv of Valley Forge.
648 **183** 2 c. red 70 35

1928. Air.
A649 A **184** 5 c. blue and red 4·00 30

1928. 150th Anniv of Discovery of Hawaii. Optd **HAWAII 1778-1928**.
649 2 c. red (No. 634) 3·25 4·00
650 5 c. blue (No. 608) 12·00 15·00

1928. 150th Anniv of Battle of Monmouth. Optd **MOLLY PITCHER**.
651 2 c. red (No. 634) 1·00 1·00

186 Wright Flyer I

1928. Civil Aeronautics Conference and 25th Anniv of Wright Bros. First Flight.
652 **186** 2 c. red 1·25 90
653 – 5 c. blue 6·00 2·75
DESIGN: 5 c. Globe and Ryan B-5 Brougham airplane.

188 George Rogers Clark at Vincennes (from painting by F. C. Yohn)

1929. 150th Anniv of Surrender of Fort Sackville.
654 **188** 2 c. black and red 75 60

1929. Stamps of 1922 optd. (a) **Kans.**
655 **144** 1 c. green 1·75 2·00
656 **166** 1½ c. brown 2·50 3·25
657 – 2 c. red 3·00 65
658 – 3 c. violet 13·00 12·00
659 – 4 c. brown 15·00 7·00
660 – 5 c. blue 11·00 8·50
661 – 6 c. orange 24·00 17·00
662 – 7 c. black 22·00 25·00
663 – 8 c. olive 65·00 60·00
664 – 9 c. red 11·00 10·00
665 – 10 c. yellow 19·00 10·00

(b) **Nebr.**
666 **144** 1 c. green 2·00 1·75
667 **166** 1½ c. brown 2·25 2·75
668 – 2 c. red 1·60 70
669 – 3 c. violet 11·00 9·00
670 – 4 c. brown 17·00 14·00
671 – 5 c. blue 15·00 13·00
672 – 6 c. orange 35·00 25·00
673 – 7 c. black 19·00 16·00
674 – 8 c. olive 25·00 22·00
675 – 9 c. red 30·00 24·00
676 – 10 c. yellow 90·00 16·00

191 Edison's Original Lamp **192** Maj.-Gen. Sullivan

1929. 50th Anniv of Edison's First Electric Lamp.
678 **191** 2 c. red 60 20

1929. 150th Anniv of Maj.-Gen. Sullivan's Western Campaign.
680 **192** 2 c. red 55 50

193 Gen. Wayne Memorial in Fallen Timbers Park, by E.W. Laville
194 Ohio River Lock No. 5, Monongahela R.

1929. 135th Anniv of Battle of Fallen Timbers.
681 **193** 2 c. red 75 75

1929. Completion of Ohio River Canalisation.
682 **194** 2 c. red 55 55

A **195** Air Mail Pilot's Badge

1930. Air.
A684 A **195** 5 c. violet . . . . . . 5·50 25
A685 6 c. orange . . . . . 2·25 10
A686 8 c. green . . . . . . 2·25 15

195 Seal of the Colony
196 Governor and Indian

1930. Massachusetts Bay Colony Tercentenary.
683 **195** 2 c. red 50 40

1930. 250th Anniv of Original Settlement near Charleston.
684 **196** 2 c. red . . . . 1·00 1·10

A **197** Over the Atlantic

1930. Air. "Graf Zeppelin" Europe–Pan-American Flight.
A687 A **197** 65 c. green £300 £225
A688 – $1.30 brown £650 £425
A689 – $2.60 blue £1000 £650
DESIGNS: $1.30, Between continents; $2.60, Over the globe.

197 Harding
199 George Washington (after statue by F. Vittor in Braddock, Pa.)

1930.
685 **197** $1\frac{1}{2}$ c. brown 30 10
686 – 4 c. brown 80 10
DESIGN: 4 c. Taft.

1930. 175th Anniv of Battle of Braddock's Field.
689 **199** 2 c. red 80 90

200 Gen. Wilhelm von Steuben (from medallion by Karl Dautert)
201 Gen. Casimir Pulaski (from etching by H. B. Hall)

1930. Birth Bicentenary of Gen. von Steuben.
690 **200** 2 c. red 50 50

1931. 150th Death Anniv of Gen. Pulaski.
691 **201** 2 c. red 30 15

202 Red Cross Nurse (from poster "The World's Greatest Mother")
203 Rochambeau, Washington, De Grasse (Washington after painting by Trumbull, others from old engravings)

1931. 50th Anniv of American Red Cross Society.
702 **202** 2 c. black and red 15 10

1931. 150th Anniv of Surrender of Cornwallis at Yorktown.
703 **203** 2 c. black and red 30 25

204 George Washington **205**

1932. Birth Bicentenary of George Washington. Portraits dated "1732 1932".
704 **204** $\frac{1}{2}$ c. sepia 10 10
705 **205** 1 c. green 10 10
706 – $1\frac{1}{2}$ c. brown 50 10
707 – 2 c. red 10 10
708 – 3 c. violet 70 10
709 – 4 c. brown 40 10
710 – 5 c. blue . . . . 1·75 10
711 – 6 c. orange . . . . 3·25 10
712 – 7 c. black 50 15
713 – 8 c. olive . . . . 3·25 70
714 – 9 c. red . . . . 3·00 10
715 – 10 c. yellow . . . . . . 11·00 10
For 3 c. as No. 707, see No. 720.

216 Skiing
217 Tree-planting

1932. Winter Olympic Games, Lake Placid.
716 **216** 2 c. red 60 20

1932. 60th Anniv of Establishment of Arbor Day.
717 **217** 2 c. red 15 10

218 Sprinter
219 Discus Thrower
221 Wm. Penn

1932. Summer Olympic Games, Los Angeles.
718 **218** 3 c. violet . . . . 1·25 10
719 **219** 5 c. blue . . . . 2·25 30

1932. As No. 707, but without date.
720 3 c. violet 20 10

1932. 250th Anniv of Penn's Arrival in America.
723 **221** 3 c. violet 30 20

222 Webster
223 Gen. Oglethorpe
224 Washington's H.Q

1932. 150th Birth Anniv of Daniel Webster.
724 **222** 3 c. violet 35 30

1933. Bicentenary of Founding of Georgia.
725 **223** 3 c. violet 30 15

1933. 150th Anniv of Proclamation of Peace after War of Independence.
726 **224** 3 c. violet 15 10

225 Fort Dearbon (after painting by Dwight Benton)
226 Federal Building

1933. "Centenary of Progress" International Exhibition, Chicago.
727 **225** 1 c. green 15 10
728 **226** 3 c. violet 15 10

227 Agriculture, Commerce and Industry

1933. National Recovery Act.
729 **227** 3 c. violet 10 10

A **230** Chicago Federal Building, "Graf Zeppelin" and Friedrichshafen Hanger

1933. Air. "Graf Zeppelin" Chicago Flight.
A732 A **230** 50 c. green . . . . . £100 75·00

230 Routes of various Admiral Byrd Flights

1933. Byrd Antarctic Expedition.
752 **230** 3 c. blue 45 50

231 Gen. Kosciuszko (from statue in Lafayette Park, Washington)
233 The "Ark" and the "Dove" (from drawing by E. Tunis)

1933. 150th Anniv of Naturalization of Kosciuszko.
733 **231** 5 c. blue 50 25

1934. Maryland Tercentenary.
735 **233** 3 c. red 20 15

234 "Portrait of my Mother" by Whistler

1934. Mothers' Day. Perf or imperf.
736 **234** 3 c. violet 10 10

235 Nicolet's Landing at Green Bay (after painting by E. W. Deming)

1934. Tercentenary of Wisconsin.
738 **235** 3 c. violet 15 10

236 "El Capitan", Yosemite
237 Grand Canyon

1934. National Parks. Perf or imperf.
739 **236** 1 c. green 15 10
740 **237** 2 c. red 20 10
741 – 3 c. violet 25 10
742 – 4 c. brown 50 40
743 – 5 c. blue . . . . 1·00 70
744 – 6 c. blue . . . . 1·50 1·10
745 – 7 c. black 75 85
762 – 8 c. green . . . . 1·75 2·25
747 – 9 c. red . . . . 1·75 60
748 – 10 c. grey . . . . 3·50 90
DESIGNS—VERT: 5 c. "Old Faithful" geyser, Yellowstone; 8 c. Great White Throne, Zion; 10 c. Mount le Conte, Smoky Mountain. HORIZ: 3 c. Mirror Lake, Mt Rainier; 4 c. Cliff dwellings, Mesa Verde; 6 c. Crater Lake and Wizard Is; 7 c. Great Head, Acadia; 9 c. Mt Rockwell and Two Medicine Lake Glacier.

248 The Charter Oak

1935. Connecticut Tercentenary.
771 **248** 3 c. purple 10 10

249 Exhibition Grounds, Point Loma and San Diego Bay

1935. California Pacific Int Exn, San Diego.
772 **249** 3 c. violet 10 10

250 Boulder Dam, Nevada
251 Seal of Michigan

1935. Dedication of Boulder Dam.
773 **250** 3 c. violet 15 10

1935. Michigan Centenary.
774 **251** 3 c. violet 10 10

A **253** Martin M-130 Flying Boat

1935. Air Trans-Pacific Air Mail.
A775 – 20 c. green . . . . . 11·00 1·50
A776 A **253** 25 c. blue . . . . . 2·00 75
A777 – 50 c. red . . . . . 12·00 2·25
Nos. A775 and A777 are as Type A **253** but without the date.

252 S. Houston, S. F. Austin, and the Alamo
253 Roger Williams (from statue in Roger Williams Park, Providence, R. I.)

1936. Centenary of Declaration of Texan Independence.
775 **252** 3 c. violet 10 10

1936. Rhode Island Tercentenary.
776 **253** 3 c. violet 10 10

255 First Settlement, Old State House and Capitol

1936. Centenary of Arkansas.
778 **255** 3 c. violet 10 10

256 Map of Old Oregon Territory
257 Susan B. Anthony (detail from statue by Adelaide Johnson in Capitol)

1936. Centenary of Oregon.
779 **256** 3 c. violet 15 10

1936. 16th Anniv of Women's Suffrage.
780 **257** 3 c. purple 10 10

258 Washington and Greene, Mt.Vernon in background

263 Jones, Barry and Battle of Flamborough Head

1936. Army and Navy Heroes. (a) Army.

781	**258**	1 c. green	10	10
782	–	2 c. red	10	10
783	–	3 c. purple	20	10
784	–	4 c. blue	40	15
785	–	5 c. blue	70	15

DESIGNS: 2 c. Jackson, Scott and the Hermitage; 3 c. Sherman, Grant and Sheridan; 4 c. Lee, Jackson and Stratford Hall; 5 c. West Point Military Acadamy.

(b) Navy.

786	**263**	1 c. green	15	10
787	–	2 c. red	15	10
788	–	3 c. purple	25	10
789	–	4 c. blue	40	15
790	–	5 c. blue	70	15

DESIGNS: 2 c. Decatur, MacDonough and U.S.S. "United States"; 3 c. Farragut, Porter and U.S.S. "Hartford"; 4 c. Sampson, Dewey and Schley; 5 c. Seal of Naval Academy and cadets.

268 Cutler, Putnam and Map of N. W. Territory

269 Virginia Dare

1937. 150th Anniv of Enactment of North West Territory Ordinance.

791	**268**	3 c. violet	15	10

1937. 350th Birth Anniv of Virginia Dare.

792	**269**	5 c. blue	15	15

271 Signing the Constitution (after painting by J. B. Stearns)

1937. 150th Anniv of U.S. Constitution.

794	**271**	3 c. mauve	10	10

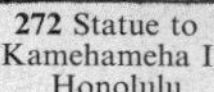
272 Statue to Kamehameha I, Honolulu

273 Mt McKinley, Alaska

274 Fortaleza Castle, Puerto Rico

275 Charlotte Amalie (St. Thomas), Virgin Islands

1937. Territorial Issue.

795	**272**	3 c. violet	10	10
796	**273**	3 c. violet	10	10
797	**274**	3 c. violet	10	10
798	**275**	3 c. mauve	10	10

276 Benjamin Franklin

A 308 American Bald Eagle and Shield

1938. Presidential Series.

799	**276**	$\frac{1}{2}$ c. orange	10	10
800	–	1 c. green	10	10
801	–	1$\frac{1}{2}$ c. brown	10	10
802	–	2 c. red	10	10
803	–	3 c. violet	10	10
804	–	4 c. purple	50	10
805	–	4$\frac{1}{2}$ c. grey	15	10
806	–	5 c. blue	20	10
807	–	6 c. red	30	10
808	–	7 c. brown	35	10
809	–	8 c. green	50	10
810	–	9 c. pink	50	10
811	–	10 c. red	35	10
812	–	11 c. blue	60	10
813	–	12 c. mauve	1·10	10
814	–	13 c. green	1·50	10
815	–	14 c. blue	80	10
816	–	15 c. slate	55	10
817	–	16 c. black	1·00	35
818	–	17 c. red	1·00	15
819	–	18 c. purple	1·60	10
820	–	19 c. mauve	1·25	50
821	–	20 c. green	70	10
822	–	21 c. blue	1·75	15
823	–	22 c. red	1·00	50
824	–	24 c. black	3·00	15
825	–	25 c. mauve	70	10
826	–	30 c. blue	4·25	10
827	–	50 c. lilac	6·50	10
828	–	$1 black and purple	7·50	10
830	–	$2 black and green	20·00	3·50
831	–	$5 black and red	90·00	3·00

DESIGNS: 1 c. Washington; 1$\frac{1}{2}$ c. Martha Washington; 2 c. John Adams; 3 c. Jefferson; 4 c. Madison; 4$\frac{1}{2}$ c. White House; 5 c. James Monroe; 6 c. John Quincy Adams; 7 c. Jackson; 8 c. Martin van Buren; 9 c. Wm. Henry Harrison; 10 c. John Tyler; 11 c. James K. Polk; 12 c. Zachary Taylor; 13 c. Millard Fillmore; 14 c. Franklin Pierce; 15 c. James Buchanan; 16 c. Lincoln; 17 c. Johnson; 18 c. Grant; 19 c. Rutherford B. Hayes; 20 c. James A. Garfield; 21 c. Chester A. Arthur; 22 c. Grover Cleveland; 24 c. Benjamin Harrison; 25 c. William McKinley; 30 c. Theodore Roosevelt; 50 c. Taft; $1 Woodrow Wilson; $2 Harding; $5 Coolidge.

1938. Air.

A845	A **308**	6 c. red and blue	60	10

308 Colonial Court House

1938. 150th Anniv of Ratification of U.S. Constitution.

845	**308**	3 c. violet	15	10

309 Landing of the Swedes and Finns from "Calmare Nyckel" (after S. Arthurs)

310 Colonization of the West (from statue by G. Borglum at Marietta, Ohio)

1938. Tercentenary of Scandinavian Settlement in America.

846	**309**	3 c. mauve	15	10

1938. Northwest Territory Sesquicentennial.

847	**310**	3 c. violet	15	10

311 Old Capitol Building, Iowa

312 Tower of the Sun

1938. Iowa Territory Centennial.

848	**311**	3 c. violet	15	10

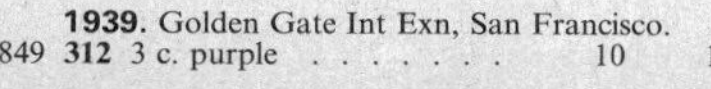
1939. Golden Gate Int Exn, San Francisco.

849	**312**	3 c. purple	10	10

313 Trylon and Perisphere

314 Inauguration of Washington

1939. New York World's Fair.

850	**313**	3 c. violet	10	10

1939. 150th Anniv of Election of Washington as First President.

851	**314**	3 c. purple	20	10

A 315 Winged Globe

1939. Air.

A852	A **315**	30 c. blue	10·00	70

315 Baseball

1939. Baseball Centenary.

852	**315**	3 c. violet	45	10

316 T. Roosevelt Goethals and "Andrea F. Luckenbach" in Gaillard Cut

317 Stephen Daye Press (from sketch by G. F. Trenholm)

1939. 25th Anniv of Opening of Panama Canal.

853	**316**	3 c. purple	25	10

1939. Tercent of Printing in Colonial America.

854	**317**	3 c. violet	10	10

318 Washington, Montana, N. and S. Dakota

319 Washington Irving

324 Henry W. Longfellow

329 Horace Mann

334 John James Audubon

339 Stephen Collins Foster

344 Gilbert Charles Stuart

349 Eli Whitney

1939. 50th Anniv of Statehood of Washington, Montana and N. and S. Dakota.

855	**318**	3 c. mauve	15	10

1940. Famous Americans. (a) Authors.

856	**319**	1 c. green	10	10
857	–	2 c. red	10	10
858	–	3 c. purple	10	10
859	–	5 c. blue	35	25
860	–	10 c. brown	1·90	1·40

PORTRAITS: 2 c. J. Fenimore Cooper; 3 c. Ralph Waldo Emerson; 5 c. Louisa May Alcott; 10 c. Samuel L. Clemens ("Mark Twain).

(b) Poets.

861	**324**	1 c. green	10	10
862	–	2 c. red	10	10
863	–	3 c. purple	10	10
864	–	5 c. blue	35	25
865	–	10 c. brown	2·00	1·75

PORTRAITS: 2 c. John Greenleaf Whittier; 3 c. James Russell Lowell; 5 c. Walt Whitman; 10 c. James Whitcomb Riley.

(c) Educationlists.

866	**329**	1 c. green	10	10
867	–	2 c. red	10	10
868	–	3 c. purple	20	10
869	–	5 c. blue	45	25
870	–	10 c. brown	1·75	1·40

PORTRAITS: 2 c. Mark Hopkins; 3 c. Charles W. Eliot; 5 c. Frances E. Willard; 10 c. Booker T. Washington.

(d) Scientists.

871	**334**	1 c. green	10	10
872	–	2 c. red	10	10
873	–	3 c. purple	10	10
874	–	5 c. blue	30	25
875	–	10 c. brown	1·10	1·00

PORTRAITS: 2 c. Dr. Crawford W. Long; 3 c. Luther Burbank; 5 c. Dr. Walter Reed; 10 c. Jane Addams.

(e) Composers.

876	**339**	1 c. green	10	10
877	–	2 c. red	15	10
878	–	3 c. purple	15	10
879	–	5 c. blue	50	25
880	–	10 c. brown	4·50	1·25

PORTRAITS: 2 c. John Philip Sousa; 3 c. Victor Herbert; 5 c. Edward A. MacDowell; 10 c. Ethelbert Nevin.

(f) Artists.

881	**344**	1 c. green	10	10
882	–	2 c. red	10	10
883	–	3 c. purple	10	10
884	–	5 c. blue	50	25
885	–	10 c. brown	1·75	1·40

PORTRAITS: 2 c. James A. McNeill Whistler; 3 c. Augustus Saint-Gaudens; 5 c. Daniel Chester French; 10 c. Frederic Remington.

(g) Inventors.

886	**349**	1 c. green	10	10
887	–	2 c. red	10	10
888	–	3 c. purple	15	10
889	–	5 c. blue	85	30
890	–	10 c. brown	11·00	2·00

PORTRAITS: 2 c. Samuel F. B. Morse; 3 c. Cyrus Hall McCormick; 5 c. Elias Howe; 10 c. Alexander Graham Bell.

354 "Pony Express"

355 "The Three Graces" (after Botticelli's "Spring")

1940. 80th Anniv of Inauguration of Pony Express.

891	**354**	3 c. red	30	10

1940. 50th Anniv of Pan-American Union.

892	**355**	3 c. mauve	20	10

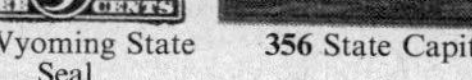
357 Wyoming State Seal

356 State Capitol, Boise

1940. 50th Anniv of Idaho.

893	**358**	3 c. violet	20	10

1940. 50th Anniv of Wyoming.

894	**357**	3 c. purple	20	10

358 Coronado and His Captains (after painting by Gerald Cassidy)

360 Anti-aircraft Gun

1940. 400th Anniv of Coronado Expedition.
895 **358** 3 c. violet 20 10

1940. National Defence.
896 – 1 c. green 10 10
897 **360** 2 c. red 10 10
898 – 3 c. violet 10 10
DESIGNS: 1 c. Statue of Liberty; 3 c. Hand holding torch.

362 Emancipation Monument (from statue by Thomas Ball, Lincoln Park, Washington)

363 State Capitol Building, Montpelier

1940. 75th Anniv of Abolition of Slavery.
899 **362** 3 c. violet 20 10

1941. 150th Anniv of Vermont.
900 **363** 3 c. violet 20 10

A **364** Mail Plane

1941. Air.
A901 A **364** 6 c. red 15 10
A902 8 c. green 30 10
A903 10 c. violet 1·25 15
A904 15 c. red 3·00 10
A905 20 c. green 2·00 20
A906 30 c. blue 2·25 15
A907 50 c. orange 10·00 3·00

364 Daniel Boone and Companions viewing Kentucky (from mural by Gilbert White in State Capitol, Frankfort)

365 Symbolical of Victory

1942. 150th Anniv of Kentucky.
901 **364** 3 c. violet 15 10

1942. Independence Day.
902 **365** 3 c. violet 10 10

366 Lincoln and Sun Yat-sen

367 Allegory of Victory

1942. Chinese War Effort.
903 **366** 5 c. blue 30 20

1943. Allied Nations.
904 **367** 2 c. red 10 10

368 Liberty holding Torch of Freedom and Enlightenment

369 Flag of Poland

1943. Four Freedoms.
905 **368** 1 c. green 10 10

1943. Flags of Oppressed Nations. Frames in violet, flags in national colours.
906 5 c. Type **369** 20 10
907 5 c. Czechoslovakia 25 10
908 5 c. Norway 15 10
909 5 c. Luxembourg 15 10
910 5 c. Netherlands 15 10
911 5 c. Belgium 15 10
912 5 c. France 20 10
913 5 c. Greece 60 25
914 5 c. Yugoslavia 45 15
915 5 c. Albania 35 15
916 5 c. Austria 30 15
917 5 c. Denmark 40 15
918 5 c. Korea 25 15

382 "Golden Spike Ceremony" (painting, John McQuarrie)

1944. 75th Anniv of First Transcontinental Railway.
919 **382** 3 c. violet 35 10

383 Paddle-steamer "Savannah"

1944. 125th Anniv of Transatlantic Crossing of "Savannah."
920 **383** 3 c. violet 10 10

384 "What Hath God Wrought"

1944. Centenary of First Telegraph Message.
921 **384** 3 c. mauve 10 10

385 View of Corregidor

1944. Defence of Corregidor.
922 **385** 3 c. violet 15 10

386 Open-air Cinema

1944. 50th Anniv of Motion Pictures.
923 **386** 3 c. violet 10 10

387 Gates of St. Augustine, State Seal and Capitol

1945. Centenary of Statehood of Florida.
924 **387** 3 c. purple 10 10

388 "Toward United Nations"

1945. San Francisco Conference.
925 **388** 5 c. blue 10 10

389 Franklin D. Roosevelt and Hyde Park

393 Raising U.S.A. Flag at Iwo Jima

1945. Pres. Roosevelt Commemoration-Inscr "1882 1945".
926 **389** 1 c. green 10 10
927 – 2 c. red 10 10
928 – 3 c. violet 15 10
929 – 5 c. blue 15 10
DESIGNS: 2 c. "Little White House", Warm Springs, Georgia; 3 c. "White House", Washington; 5 c. Western Hemisphere and Four Freedoms.

1945. U.S. Marines.
930 **393** 3 c. green 10 10

394 U.S. Troops marching through Paris

1945. U.S. Army.
931 **394** 3 c. olive 10 10

395 U.S. Sailors

1945. U.S. Navy.
932 **395** 3 c. blue 10 10

396 "Arthur Middleton" (supply ship) and Coastguard Landing Craft)

397 Alfred E. Smith

1945. U.S. Coastguard.
933 **396** 3 c. green 10 10

1945. Alfred E. Smith (Governor of New York) Commemoration.
934 **397** 3 c. violet 10 10

398 Flags of U.S.A. and Texas

1945. Centenary of Texas Statehood.
935 **398** 3 c. blue 10 10

399 "Liberty" type Freighter unloading Cargo

400 Honourable Discharge Emblem

1946. U.S. Mercantile Marine.
936 **399** 3 c. green 10 10

1946. Honourable Discharged Veterans of Second World War.
937 **400** 3 c. violet 10 10

401 Andrew Jackson, John Sevier and Tennessee State Capitol

1946. 150th Anniv of Tennessee Statehood.
938 **401** 3 c. violet 10 10

402 Iowa State Flag and Map

1946. Centenary of Iowa Statehood.
939 **402** 3 c. blue 10 10

403 Smithsonian Institution

1946. Centenary of Smithsonian Institution.
940 **403** 3 c. purple 10 10

404 Douglas DC-4

1946. Air.
A941 A **404** 5 c. red 15 10

404 Entry into Santa Fe (after painting by Kenneth M. Chapman)

405 Thomas A. Edison

1946. Centenary of Entry of Stephen Watts Kearny Expedition into Santa Fe.
941 **404** 3 c. purple 10 10

1947. Birth Cent of Thomas Edison (scientist).
942 **405** 3 c. violet 10 10

A **406** Douglas DC-4

406 Joseph Pulitzer (from portrait by J. S. Sargent)

1947. Air.
A943 A **406** 5 c. red 10 10
A944 6 c. red 15 10

1947. Birth Centenary of Joseph Pulitzer (journalist and newspaper publisher).
943 **406** 3 c. violet 10 10

407 Washington, Franklin and Evolution of Postal Transport

1947. U.S. Postage Stamp Centenary.
944 **407** 3 c. blue 15 10

409 "The Doctor" (after painting by Sir Luke Fildes)

1947. Medical Profession.
946 **409** 3 c. purple 10 10

410 Pioneer Caravan

1947. Centenary of Utah.
947 **410** 3 c. violet 10 10

A **411** Pan-American Union Building, Washington

1947. Air.
A948 A **411** 10 c. black 25 10
A949 – 15 c. green 30 10
A950 – 25 c. blue 75 10
DESIGNS: 15 c. Statue of Liberty and New York City; 25 c. San Fransisco–Oakland Bay Suspension Bridge.

411 U.S.S. "Constitution"

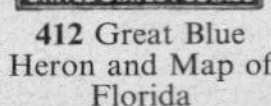

412 Great Blue Heron and Map of Florida

1947. 150th Anniv of Launching of Frigate U.S.S. "Constitution" ("Old Ironsides").
948 **411** 3 c. green 15 10

1947. Dedication of Everglades National Park Florida.
949 **412** 3 c. green 30 10

413 George Washington Carver **414** Sutter's Mill, Coloma

1948. 5th Death Anniv of George Washington Carver (scientist).
950 **413** 3 c. violet 10 10

1948. Cent of Discovery of Gold in California.
951 **414** 3 c. violet 10 10

415 Gov. Winthrop Sargent, Map and Seal of Mississippi Territory (from portrait by Gilbert Stuart)

1948. 150th Anniv of Mississippi Territory.
952 **415** 3 c. purple 10 10

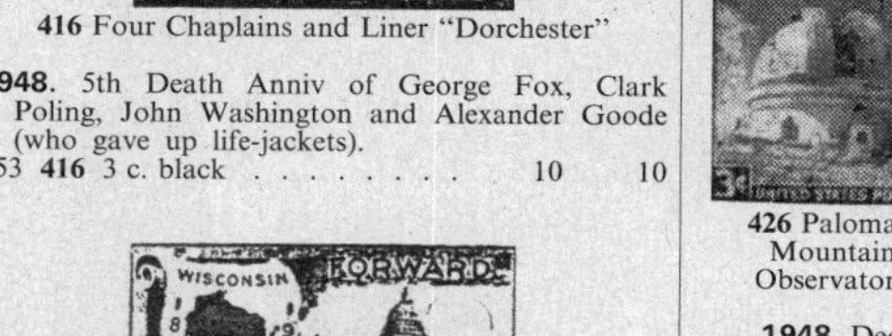

416 Four Chaplains and Liner "Dorchester"

1948. 5th Death Anniv of George Fox, Clark Poling, John Washington and Alexander Goode (who gave up life-jackets).
953 **416** 3 c. black 10 10

417 Scroll and State Capitol, Madison

1948. Centenary of Statehood of Wisconsin.
954 **417** 3 c. violet 10 10

418 Pioneer and Covered Wagon

1948. Centenary of Swedish Pioneers in Middle West.
955 **418** 5 c. blue 15 10

419 Elizabeth Stanton, Carrie C. Catt, and Lucretia Mott

A **420** Map of New York, Ring and Planes (from Poster by G. A. Lorimer)

1948. Progress of American Women.
956 **419** 3 c. violet 10 10

1948. Air. Golden Anniv of New York City Council.
A957 **420** 5 c. red 15 10

420 William Allen White

421 Niagara Railway Suspension Bridge (from print by H. Peters)

1948. Honouring W. A. White (editor and author).
957 **420** 3 c. purple 10 10

1948. Centenary of Friendship between United States and Canada.
958 **421** 3 c. blue 15 10

422 Francis Scott Key

1948. Honouring F. S. Key (author of "Star Spangled Banner").
959 **422** 3 c. red 10 10

423 Boy and Girl Students

1948. Salute to Youth.
960 **423** 3 c. blue 10 10

424 John McLoughlin, Jason Lee and Covered Wagon **425** Harlan Fiske Stone

1948. Oregon Territory Centennial.
961 **424** 3 c. red 10 10

1948. Honouring Chief Justice H. F. Stone.
962 **425** 3 c. purple 10 10

426 Palomar Mountain Observatory **427** Clara Barton and Cross

1948. Dedication of Palomar Observatory.
963 **426** 3 c. blue 15 10

1948. Honouring Clara Barton (founder of American Red Cross).
964 **427** 3 c. red 10 10

428 Light Brahma Rooster

1948. Centenary of American Poultry Industry.
965 **428** 3 c. brown 10 10

429 Star and Palm Branch

430 Fort Kearny and Pioneers. (Pioneer group from sculpture on Nebraska State Capitol)

1948. Honouring Bereaved Mothers.
966 **429** 3 c. yellow 10 10

1948. Centenary of Fort Kearny, Nebraska.
967 **430** 3 c. violet 10 10

431 Peter Stuyvesant and Fire Engines (from painting in Library of Congress)

1948. Tercentenary of Volunteer Firemen.
968 **431** 3 c. red 10 10

432 Indian Seals and Map of Oklahoma

1948. Centenary of Five Civilized Indian Tribes of Oklahoma.
969 **432** 3 c. brown 10 10

433 Statue of Capt. William Owen "Bucky" O'Neill, Prescott, Arizona (S. H. Borglum)

1948. 50th Anniv of Organization of Rough Riders.
970 **433** 3 c. purple 10 10

434 Juliette Gordon Low **435** Will Rogers

1948. Honouring Juliette Gordon Low (founder of U.S.A. Girl Scouts).
971 **434** 3 c. green 15 10

1948. Honouring Will Rogers (political commentator).
972 **435** 3 c. purple 10 10

436 Rocket Testing **437** Moina Michael and Poppies

1948. Centenary of Fort Bliss.
973 **436** 3 c. red 10 10

1948. Honouring Moina Michael (founder of Memorial Poppy).
974 **437** 3 c. red 10 10

438 Abraham Lincoln (from statue by D. C. French at Lincoln, Neb.) **439** Torch and Emblem

1948. 85th Anniv of Gettysburg Address.
975 **438** 3 c. blue 10 10

1948. Centenary of American Turners' Society.
976 **439** 3 c. red 10 10

440 Joel Chandler Harris **441** Pioneer and Red River Ox Cart

1948. Birth Centenary of J. C. Harris (author).
977 **440** 3c. purple 10 10

1949. Cent of Territorial Status of Minnesota.
978 **441** 3 c. green 10 10

442 Washington, Lee and University Building

1949. Bicentenary of Washington and Lee University, Lexington, Virginia.
979 **442** 3 c. blue 10 10

443 Puerto Rican, Cogwheel and Ballot Box

1949. 1st Gubernatorial Election in Puerto Rico.
980 **443** 3 c. green 10 10

A **444** Wings, Seal, Carlyle House and Gadsby's Tavern

1949. Air. Bicentenary of Alexandria, Virginia.
A981 A **444** 6 c. red 15 10

444 Map, "Het Vergulde Vsanker" and Shield

1949. Tercentenary of Annapolis, Maryland.
981 **444** 3 c. green 10 10

445 Young and Old Soldiers **446** Edgar Allan Poe

1949. Final National Encampment of the Grand Army of the Republic.
982 **445** 3 c. red 10 10
For similar stamp see No. 995.

1949. Death Centenary of Edgar Allan Poe (poet and author).
983 **446** 3 c. purple 10 10

A **447** U.P.U Monument, Berne and P.O. Department, Washington

1949. Air. 75th Anniv of U.P.U.

A984	A **447**	10 c. violet	20	25
A985	–	15 c. blue	30	35
A986	–	25 c. red	40	45

DESIGNS: 15 c. Globe and birds; 25 c. Globe and Boeing 377 Stratocruiser.

A **450** Wright Brothers and Flyer I

1949. Air. 46th Anniv of Wright Brothers' First Flight.
A987 A **450** 6 c. purple 20 10

447 Symbolic of Investments **448** Samuel Gompers

1950. 75th Anniv of American Bankers' Assn.
984 **447** 3 c. green 10 10

1950. Birth Centenary of Samuel Gompers (labour leader).
985 **448** 3 c. purple 10 10

449 Statue of Freedom (by Crawford) on Capitol Dome

450 The White House

1950. National Capital Sesquicentennial.

986 **449** 3 c. blue 10 10
987 **450** 3 c. green 10 10
988 – 3 c. violet 10 10
989 – 3 c. purple 10 10

DESIGNS—HORIZ: No. 988 U.S. Supreme Court building; No. 989 Capitol, Washington.

453 "Casey" Jones and Railway Locomotives

1950. Honouring Railway Engineers.

990 **453** 3 c. purple 10 10

454 Kansas City in 1850 and 1950

1950. Centenary of Kansas City.

991 **454** 3 c. violet 10 10

455 Scouts and Badge

1950. American Boy Scouts.

992 **455** 3 c. brown 15 10

456 First Capitol and W. H. Harrison

1950. Sesquicentennial of Indiana.

993 **456** 3 c. blue 10 10

457 Pioneers

1950. Centenary of California.

994 **457** 3 c. yellow 10 10

1951. Final Reunion of United Confederate Veterans. As T **445**, but initials at left and in hat badge changed to "UCV".

995 **445** 3 c. grey 10 10

458 Log Cabin

1951. Centenary of Nevada.

996 **458** 3 c. olive 10 10

459 Cadillac Disembarking

1951. 250th Anniv of Landing of Cadillac at Detroit.

997 **459** 3 c. blue 10 10

460 Mount of the Holy Cross, State Seal and Capitol

1951. 75th Anniv of Colorado.

998 **460** 3 c. violet 10 10

461 Emblem and Chemical Plant

1951. 75th Anniv of American Chemical Society.

999 **461** 3 c. purple 10 10

462 Washington at Brooklyn

1951. 175th Anniv of Battle of Brooklyn.

1000 **462** 3 c. violet 10 10

463 Betsy Ross and Flag

1952. Birth Bicentenary of Betsy Ross (maker of First American flag).

1001 **463** 3 c. red 10 10

464 Emblem and Young Club Members

1952. 50th Anniv of 4-H Clubs.

1002 **464** 3 c. green 10 10

465 Rail Transport

1952. 125th Anniv of Baltimore and Ohio Railway.

1003 **465** 3 c. blue 15 10

466 Cars of 1902 and 1952

467 "Torch of Freedom"

1952. 50th Anniv of American Automobile Assn.

1004 **466** 3 c. blue 10 10

1952. 3rd Anniv of N.A.T.O.

1005 **467** 3 c. violet 10 10

A 467 Diamond Head, Oahu, Honolulu

1952. Air.

A1005 A **467** 80 c. purple . . . . 7·50 1·00

468 Grand Coulee Dam

1952. 50th Anniv of Columbia Basin Reclamation.

1006 **468** 3 c. green 15 10

469 Lafayette and Flags

1952. 175th Anniv of Lafayette's Arrival in America.

1007 **469** 3 c. blue 10 10

470 Mt Rushmore National Memorial

471 Bridges in 1852 and 1952

1952. 25th Anniv of Mt Rushmore National Memorial.

1008 **470** 3 c. green 15 10

1952. Centenary of American Society of Civil Engineers.

1009 **471** 3 c. blue 15 10

472 Women in Uniform

1952. Women's Services Commemoration.

1010 **472** 3 c. blue 10 10

473 Gutenberg and Elector of Mainz (after Edward Laning)

1952. 500th Anniv of Printing of First Book from Movable Type.

1011 **473** 3 c. violet 10 10

474 Newspaperboy and Torch of Free Enterprise

1952. Newspaperboys Commemoration.

1012 **474** 3 c. violet 10 10

475 Red Cross and Globe

1952. International Red Cross.

1013 **475** 3 c. blue and red 10 10

476 Guardsman and amphibious Landing

477 Map and Seal of Ohio

1953. National Guard.

1014 **476** 3 c. blue 10 10

1953. 150th Anniv of Ohio.

1015 **477** 3 c. sepia 10 10

478 Seal of Washington Territory and Settlers

1953. Centenary of Washington Territory.

1016 **478** 3 c. green 10 10

479 Monroe, Livingston and Marbois signing Transfer (from sculpture plaque by Karl Bitter)

1953. 150th Anniv of Louisiana Purchase.

1017 **479** 3 c. purple 10 10

A 480 Wright Flyer I and Boeing 377 Stratocruiser

1953. Air. 50th Anniv of Aviation.

A1018 A **480** 6 c. red 15 15

480 Commodore Perry and U.S.S. "Susquehanna" and "Mississippi" in Tokyo Bay

1953. Centenary of Opening of Japan to Foreign Trade.

1018 **480** 5 c. turquoise 15 15

481 "Wisdom","Justice and Divine Inspiration" and "Truth"

1953. 75th Anniv of American Bar Association.

1019 **481** 3 c. violet 10 10

482 "Sagamore Hill"

1953. Opening of Theodore Roosevelt's Home.

1020 **482** 3 c. green 10 10

483 Young Farmer and Landscape

1953. 25th Anniv of "Future Farmers of America".

1021 **483** 3 c. blue 10 10

484 Truck and Distant City

1953. 50th Anniv of Trucking Industry.

1022 **484** 3 c. violet 10 10

485 Gen. Patton and Tanks in Action

1953. Gen. George Patton and U.S. Armoured Forces.

1023 **485** 3 c. violet 15 10

486 New York in 1653 and 1953

1953. Tercent of Foundation of New York City.

1024 **486** 3 c. purple 10 10

487 Pioneer Family

1953. Centenary of Gadsden Purchase.

1025 **487** 3 c. chestnut 10 10

488 Low Memorial Library

1954. Bicentenary of Columbia University.

1026 **488** 3 c. blue 10 10

490 Washington (after Stuart)

492 Mount Vernon

501 Statue of Liberty

1954. Liberty Issue.

1027	–	½ c. red	10	10
1028	**490**	1 c. green	10	10
1029	–	1¼ c. turquoise	10	10
1030	**492**	1½ c. lake	10	10
1031	–	2 c. red	10	10
1032	–	2½ c. blue	10	10
1033	**501**	3 c. violet	10	10
1034	–	4 c. mauve	10	10
1035	–	4½ c. green	20	10
1036	–	5 c. blue	10	10
1037	–	6 c. red	30	10
1038	–	7 c. red	30	10
1039	**501**	8 c. red and blue	30	10
1040	–	8 c. red and blue	30	10
1041	–	8 c. brown	30	10
1042	–	9 c. purple	40	10
1043	–	10 c. red	20	10
1044	–	11 c. blue and red	30	10
1045	–	12 c. red	45	10
1046	–	15 c. red	75	10
1047	–	20 c. blue	50	10
1059	–	25 c. turquoise	40	20
1049	–	30 c. black	1·25	10
1050	–	40 c. lake	1·75	10
1051	–	50 c. violet	1·75	10
1052	–	$1 violet	6·00	10
1053	–	$5 black	70·00	3·50

DESIGNS — As Type **490**: ½ c. Benjamin Franklin; 2 c. Jefferson; 4 c. Lincoln; 5 c. Monroe; 6 c. Theodore Roosevelt; 7 c. Woodrow Wilson; 8 c. (No. 1040), As Type **501** but torch flame below "P"; 8 c. (No. 1041), Gen. John J. Pershing; 11 c. As No. 1040; 12 c. Benjamin Harrison; 15 c. John Jay; 25 c. Paul Revere; 30 c. Robert E. Lee; 40 c. John Marshall; 50 c. Susan B. Anthony; $1 Patrick Henry; $5 Alexander Hamilton. As Type **492** — VERT: 2½ c. Bunker Hill Monument and Massachusetts flag. HORIZ: 1¼ c. Palace of the Governors, Santa Fe; 4½ c. The Hermitage; 9 c. The Alamo; 10 c. Independence Hall; 20 c. Monticello, Thomas Jefferson's home.

516 "The Sower" and Mitchell Pass (from statue on Capitol, Lincoln, Neb)

1954. Centenary of Nebraska Territory.

1062 **516** 3 c. violet 10 10

517 Pioneers and Cornfield

518 George Eastman

1954. Centenary of Kansas Territory.

1063 **517** 3 c. salmon 10 10

1954. Birth Centenary of Eastman (inventor).

1064 **518** 3 c. purple 10 10

519 Landing on Riverbank, Missouri

A **520** American Bald Eagle in Flight

1954. 150th Anniv of Lewis and Clark Expedition.

1065 **519** 3 c. purple 10 10

1954. Air.

A1066 A **520** 4 c. blue 15 10
A1067 5 c. red 15 10

520 "Peale in his Museum" (self-portrait)

521 Open Book and Symbols of Subjects taught

1955. 150th Anniv of Pennsylvania Academy of Fine Arts.

1066 **520** 3 c. purple 10 10

1955. Centenary of First Land-Grant Colleges.

1067 **521** 3 c. green 10 10

522 Torch, Globe and Rotary Emblem

1955. 50th Anniv of Rotary International.

1068 **522** 8 c. blue 15 10

523 Marine, Coastguard, Soldier, Sailor, Airman

1955. Armed Forces Reserve.

1069 **523** 3 c. purple 10 10

524 "The Old Man of the Mountains"

525 The Great Lakes and "Altadoc" (freighter)

1955. 150th Anniv of Discovery of "The Old Man of the Mountains" (New Hampshire landmark).

1070 **524** 3 c. turquoise 15 10

1955. Soo Locks Centenary.

1071 **525** 3 c. blue 15 10

526

1955. "Atoms for Peace".

1072 **526** 3 c. blue 10 10

527 Plan of Fort, Ethan Allen and Artillery

528 Mellon (after Edward Birley)

1955. Bicentenary of Fort Ticonderoga.

1073 **527** 3 c. brown 10 10

1955. Birth Centenary of Andrew W. Mellon (philanthropist).

1074 **528** 3 c. red 10 10

529 Benjamin Franklin (after painting by Benjamin West)

530 Log Cabin

1956. 250th Birth Anniv of Franklin.

1075 **529** 3 c. red 10 10

1956. Birth Centenary of Booker T. Washington.

1076 **530** 3 c. blue 10 10

532 New York Coliseum and Columbus Monument

1956. 5th International Philatelic Exn, New York.

1078 **532** 3 c. violet 10 10

533 Common Turkey

536 H. W. Wiley

1956. Wild Life Conservation.

1079 **533** 3 c. purple 30 10
1080 – 3 c. sepia 25 10
1081 – 3 c. green 20 10

DESIGNS: No. 1080, Pronghorns; No. 1081, King salmon.

1956. 50th Anniv of Pure Food and Drug Laws.

1082 **536** 3 c. green 10 10

537 Wheatland

538 Mosaic by L. M. Winter, A.F.L-C.I.O. Headquarters

1956. Home of James Buchanan.

1083 **537** 3 c. sepia 10 10

1956. Labour Day.

1084 **538** 3 c. blue 10 10

539 Nassau Hall (contemporary engraving by Dawkins)

540 Devils Tower

1956. Bicentenary of Nassau Hall.

1085 **539** 3 c. black on orange . . . 10 10

1956. 50th Anniv of Devils Tower National Monument.

1086 **540** 3 c. violet 10 10

541 "The Key to World Peace"

1956. Children's Friendship.

1087 **541** 3 c. blue 10 10

542 Alexander Hamilton and Federal Hall, New York

543 Women, Children and Shield

1957. Birth Bicentenary of Alexander Hamilton.

1088 **542** 3 c. red 10 10

1957. Infantile Paralysis Relief Campaign.

1089 **543** 3 c. mauve 10 10

544 Survey Flag and Coastguard Vessels "Pathfinder", "Explorer" and "Surveyor"

1957. 150th Anniv of Coast and Geodetic Survey.

1090 **544** 3 c. blue 10 10

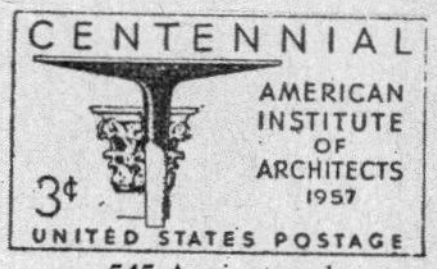

545 Ancient and Modern Capitals

546 Eagle and Ladle

1957. Cent of American Institute of Architects.

1091 **545** 3 c. mauve 10 10

1957. Centenary of American Steel Industry.

1092 **546** 3 c. blue 10 10

547 Festival Emblem and Aircraft Carrier U.S.S. "Forrestal"

1957. Jamestown Festival and Int Naval Review.

1093 **547** 3 c. green 15 10

548 Arrow piercing Atomic Symbol

1957. 50th Anniv of Oklahoma Statehood.

1094 **548** 3 c. blue 10 10

549 Teacher with Pupils

1957. Teachers of America Commemoration.

1095 **549** 3 c. red 10 10

550 U.S. Flag

1957. Flag Issue.

1096 **550** 4 c. red and blue 10 10

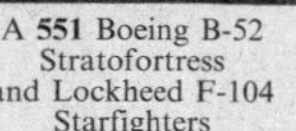

A **551** Boeing B-52 Stratofortress and Lockheed F-104 Starfighters

551 "Virginia of Sagadahock" and Arms of Maine

1957. Air. 50th Anniv of U.S. Air Force.
A1097 A **551** 6 c. blue 15 10

1957. 350th Anniv of American Shipbuilding.
1097 **553** 3 c. violet 10 10

552 Pres. Magsaysay of the Philippines (medallion)

553 Marquis de Lafayette (portrait by Court in Versailles Museum)

1953. Pres. Magsaysay Commemoration.
1098 **552** 8 c. ochre, blue and red . 15 10

1957. Birth Bicentenary of Marquis de Lafayette.
1099 **553** 3 c. red 10 10

554 Whooping Cranes

555 "Religious Freedom"

1957. Wild Life Conservation.
1100 **554** 3 c. blue, orange & green 30 10

1957. Tercentenary of Flushing Remonstrance.
1101 **555** 3 c. black 10 10

556 "Abundance"

557 U.S. Pavilion

1958. Gardening and Horticulture Commem.
1102 **556** 3 c. green 10 10

1958. Brussels International Exhibition.
1103 **557** 3 c. purple 10 10

558 James Monroe (portrait by Stuart)

559 Lake in Minnesota

1958. Birth Bicentenary of Pres. James Monroe.
1104 **558** 3 c. violet 10 10

1958. Centenary of Minnesota Statehood.
1105 **559** 3 c. green 10 10

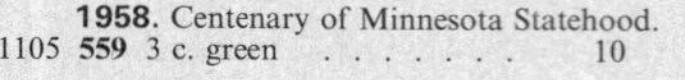

560 Sun's Surface and Hands (after Michelangelo's "The Creation of Adam")

1958. I.G.Y.
1106 **560** 3 c. red and black . . . 15 10

561 Gunston Hall (after drawing by Rene Clarke)

562 Mackinac Bridge

1958. Bicentenary of Gunston Hall, Virginia (home of George Mason, patriot).
1107 **561** 3 c. green 10 10

1958. Mackinac Bridge Commemoration.
1108 **562** 3 c. turquoise 10 10

563 Simon Bolivar (after painting by Ricardo Arcevedo-Bernal)

A **564** Silhouette of Jet Airliner

1958. Bolivar Commemoration.
1109 **563** 4 c. ochre 10 10
1110 8 c. brown, blue & red . 15 10
See also Nos. 1116/17, 1124/5, 1135/6, 1146/7. 1158/9, 1164/5, 1167/8 and 1173/4.

1958. Air.
A1111 A **564** 7 c. blue 15 10
A1112 7 c. red 15 10

564 Globe, Neptune and Mermaid

1958. Centenary of Inaug of Atlantic Cable.
1111 **564** 4 c. purple 10 10

565 Abraham Lincoln (from painting by G. Healy)

570 Hand with Quill Pen and Printing Press

1958. 150th Birth Anniv of Lincoln.
1112 **565** 1 c. green 10 10
1113 – 3 c. red 15 10
1114 – 4 c. brown 15 10
1115 – 4 c. blue 15 10
DESIGNS: No. 1113, Bust of Lincoln; No. 1114, Addressing Electorate; No. 1115, Lincoln Statue, Washington.

1958. Kossuth Commemoration. Medallion portrait as T **563**.
1116 4 c. green 10 10
1117 8 c. brown, blue and red . . 15 10

1958. Freedom of the Press.
1118 **570** 4 c. black 10 10

571 Mail Coach under Attack

572 Noah Webster (engraving by G. Parker after painting by James Herring)

1958. Overland Mail Centenary.
1119 **571** 4 c. red 10 10

1958. Birth Bicentenary of Noah Webster (lexicographer).
1120 **572** 4 c. red 10 10

573 Forest Pines

574 British Forces occupying Fort Duquesne (from etching by T.B. Smith)

1958. Forest Conservation.
1121 **573** 4 c. yellow, green & brn . 10 10

1958. Bicentenary of Fort Duquesne.
1122 **574** 4 c. blue 10 10

A **575** Stars on Alaskan Map

1959. Air. Alaska Statehood.
A1123 A **575** 7 c. blue 25 10

575 Covered Wagon and Mt Hood

577 N.A.T.O. Emblem

1959. Centenary of Oregon Statehood.
1123 **575** 4 c. green 10 10

1959. San Martin Commem. Medallion portrait as T **563**.
1124 4 c. blue 10 10
1125 8 c. ochre, red and blue . . . 15 10

1959. 10th Anniv of N.A.T.O.
1126 **577** 4 c. blue 10 10

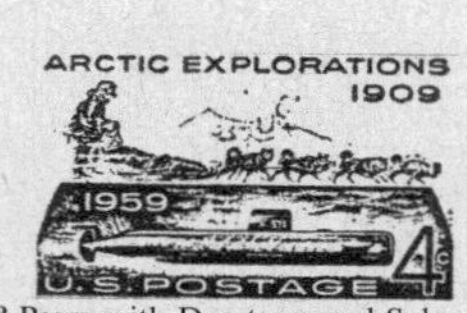

578 Peary with Dog-team and Submarine U.S.S. "Nautilus"

1959. Arctic Explorations by Robert Peary (50th anniv of reaching North Pole) and U.S.S. "Nautilus".
1127 **578** 4 c. blue 10 10

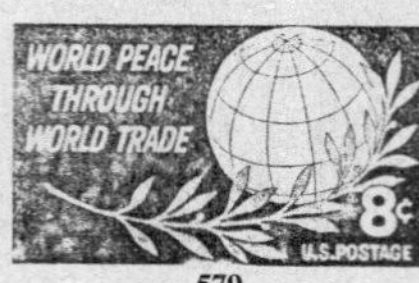

579

1959. World Peace through World Trade.
1128 **579** 8 c. red 15 10

580 Discovery of Silver at Mt Davidson, Nevada (from a print)

1959. Cent of Discovery of Silver in Nevada.
1129 **580** 4 c. black 10 10

581 Maple Leaf linked with American Eagle

1959. Opening of St. Lawrence Seaway.
1130 **581** 4 c. blue and red 10 10

582 New U.S. Flag (with 49 stars)

1959. Inauguration of New United States Flag.
1131 **582** 4 c. red, blue & orange . 15 10

A **583** Balloon "Jupiter"

A **584** Hawaiian Warrior, Map and Star

1959. Air. Centenary of Balloon "Jupiter's" Mail-carrying Flight.
A1132 A **583** 7 c. red and blue . . 20 10

1959. Air. Hawaii Statehood.
A1133 A **584** 7 c. red 20 10

583 "The Good Earth"

584 Oil Derrick

1959. Soil Conservation.
1132 **583** 4 c. green, brown and blue 10 10

1959. Centenary of First Oil-well at Titusville, Pennsylvania.
1133 **584** 4 c. brown 10 10

A **585** Runner with Olympic Torch

585 "Happy Children with Healthy Teeth"

1959. Air. 3rd Pan-American Games, Chicago.
A1134 A **585** 10 c. red and blue . 30 30

1959. Dental Health. Cent of American Dental Assn.
1134 **585** 4 c. green 10 10

1959. Ernst Reuter Commem. Medallion portrait as T **563**.
1135 4 c. grey 10 10
1136 8 c. ochre, red and blue . . . 20 10

A **588** Statue of Liberty

587 Dr. E. McDowell (from painting)

1959. Air.
A1137 – 10 c. black & green . 1·75 70
A1138 – 13 c. black and red . 40 10
A1139 A **588** 15 c. blk & orge (A) 35 10
A1140 15 c. blk & orge (B) 30 10
A1141 – 25 c. black & brown 50 10
DESIGNS: 10 c., 13 c. Liberty Bell; 15 c. Statue has double frame-line (A) or single frame-line (B); 25 c. Abraham Lincoln.

1959. 150th Anniv of First Recorded Successful Abdominal Operation.
1137 **587** 4 c. purple 10 10

588

1960. "American Credo" series.
1138 **588** 4 c. red and blue 15 10
1139 – 4 c. green and bistre . . 15 10
1140 – 4 c. red and grey 15 10
1141 – 4 c. blue and red 15 10
1142 – 4 c. green and purple . . 20 10
1143 – 4 c. brown and green . . 20 10
INSCRIPTIONS: No. 1139, "Fear to do ill, and you need fear Nought else" (Franklin); No. 1140, "I have sworn . . . Hostility against every form of TYRANNY over the mind of man" (Jefferson); No. 1141, "And this be our Motto in GOD is our TRUST" (Francis Scott Key); No. 1142, "Those who Deny freedom to others Deserve it not for Themselves" (Lincoln); No. 1143, "Give me LIBERTY or give me DEATH" (P. Henry).

594 Scout Saluting

595 Olympic Rings and Snow Crystal

1960. 50th Anniv of American Boy Scout Movement.
1144 **594** 4 c. ochre, red & blue . . 10 10

1960. Winter Olympic Games.
1145 **595** 4 c. blue 10 10

1960. Thomas Masaryk Commem. Medallion portrait as T **563**.
1146 4 c. blue 10 10
1147 8 c. ochre, red and blue . . . 20 10

597 "Towards the Light"

1960. World Refuge Year.
1148 **597** 4 c. black 10 10

598 "Irrigation"

599 S.E.A.T.O. Emblem

1960. Water Conservation Campaign.
1149 **598** 4 c. green, brown & blue 10 10

1960. S.E.A.T.O. Conference.
1150 **599** 4 c. blue 10 10

600 Mother and Child

601 New U.S. Flag (with 50 stars)

1960. American Womanhood Commemoration.
1151 **600** 4 c. violet 10 10

1960. New United States Flag (50 stars).
1152 **601** 4 c. red and blue 10 10

602 Pony Express

1960. Centenary of Pony Express.
1153 **602** 4 c. brown 10 10

603 Cripple operating Press

604 Congress Seal

1960. Employment of the Handicapped Campaign.
1154 **603** 4 c. blue 10 10

1960. 5th World Forestry Congress, Seattle.
1155 **604** 4 c. green 10 10

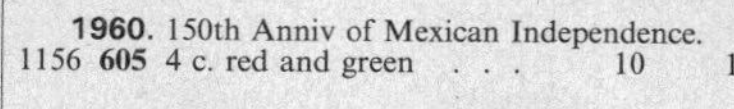
605 Dolores Bell (Mexico)
606 Washington Monument and Cherry Blossom

1960. 150th Anniv of Mexican Independence.
1156 **605** 4 c. red and green . . . 10 10

1960. Centenary of U.S.–Japan Treaty.
1157 **606** 4 c. red and turquoise . 10 10

1960. Jan Paderewski Commem. Medallion portrait as T **563**.
1158 4 c. blue 10 10
1159 8 c. ochre, red and blue . . 20 10

608 Robert A. Taft

609 Steering Wheel, Motor Transport and Globes

1960. Robert A. Taft Memorial Issue.
1160 **608** 4 c. violet 10 10

1960. "Wheels of Freedom" (Motor Industry).
1161 **609** 4 c. blue 10 10

610 Boy

611 New P.O. Building

1960. Cent of Boys' Clubs of America Movement.
1162 **610** 4 c. red, black & indigo 10 10

1960. Inauguration of 1st U.S. Automated P.O., Providence, Rhode Island.
1163 **611** 4 c. blue and red 15 10

1960. Marshal Mannerheim Commem. Medallion portrait as T **563**.
1164 4 c. blue 10 10
1165 8 c. ochre, red and blue . . 20 10

613 Camp Fire Girls Emblem

615 George

1960. 50th Anniv of Camp Fire Girls Movement.
1166 **613** 4 c. rd and blue 10 10

1960. Garibaldi Commem. Medallion portrait as T **563**.
1167 4 c. green 10 10
1168 8 c. ochre, red and blue . . 15 10

1960. Senator Walter F. George Memorial Issue.
1169 **615** 4 c. violet 10 10

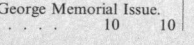

616 Andrew Carnegie

617 Dulles

1960. Andrew Carnegie.
1170 **616** 4 c. red 10 10

1960. John Foster Dulles Memorial Issue.
1171 **617** 4 c. violet 10 10

618 "Echo I" Communications Satellite

1960. "Communications for Peace".
1172 **618** 4 c. violet 20 10

1961. Mahatma Gandhi Commem. Medallion portrait as T **563**.
1173 4 c. red on orange 20 10
1174 8 c. ochre, red and blue . . 35 10

620 Trail Boss and Prairie

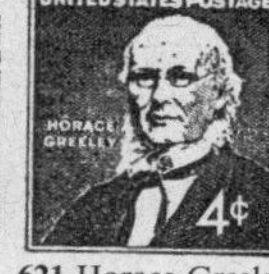

621 Horace Greeley (from steel engraving by A. H. Ritchie)

1961. Range Conservation.
1175 **620** 4 c. black, orange & bl . . 15 10

1961. Horace Greeley (editor).
1176 **621** 4 c. violet 10 10

622 Sea Coast Gun

1961. Civil War Centennial. Battles.
1177 **622** 4 c. green 20 10
1178 – 4 c. black on pink . . . 20 10
1179 – 5 c. indigo and blue . . . 20 10
1180 – 5 c. black and red . . . 20 10
1181 – 5 c. black and blue . . . 30 10
DESIGNS—HORIZ: No. 1178, Rifleman (Shiloh); No. 1179, Armed combat (Gettysburg); No. 1180, Artillery crew (Wilderness). VERT: No. 1181, Soldier and rifles (Appomattox).

627 Sunflower and Pioneers

1961. Centenary of Kansas Statehood.
1182 **627** 4 c. red, green and brown on yellow 10 10

628 Senator G. W. Norris

1961. Birth Centenary of George W. Norris.
1183 **628** 4 c. green 10 10

629 Curtiss A-1 Seaplane, 1911 (Navy's first Plane)

1961. 50th Anniv of U.S. Naval Aviation.
1184 **629** 4 c. blue 10 10

630 "Balanced Judgement"
631 "The Smoke Signal" (after Remington)

1961. 150th Anniv of Workmen's Compensation Law.
1185 **630** 4 c. blue 10 10

1961. Birth Centenary of Frederic Remington (painter).
1186 **631** 4 c. multicoloured . . . 10 10

632 Dr. Sun Yat-sen
633 Basketball

1961. 50th Anniv of Republic of China.
1187 **632** 4 c. blue 10 10

1961. Birth Centenary of Dr. James A. Naismith (inventor of basketball).
1188 **633** 4 c. brown 15 10

634 Nurse lighting Candle of Dedication

635 Ship Rock. New Mexico

1961. Nursing.
1189 **634** 4 c. multicoloured . . . 10 10

1962. 50th Anniv of Statehood of New Mexico.
1190 **635** 4 c. lake, ochre & turq . 10 10

636 Saguaro Cactus and Flowers

637 "U.S. Man in Space"

1962. 50th Anniv of Arizona Statehood.
1191 **636** 4 c. blue, green and red . 10 10

1962. Project Mercury. Colonel John Glenn's Space Flight.
1192 **637** 4 c. blue and yellow . . 10 10

638 U.S. and Campaign Emblems

1962. Malaria Eradication.
1193 **638** 4 c. ochre and blue . . . 10 10

639 C. E. Hughes

640 Space Needle and Monorail

1962. Birth Centenary of Chief Justice Hughes.
1194 **639** 4 c. black on buff . . . 10 10

1962. "Century 21" Exn ("World's Fair"), Seattle.
1195 **640** 4 c. blue and red 10 10

641 Mississippi Sternwheel Steamer

1962. 150th Anniv of Lousiana Statehood.
1196 **641** 4 c. myrtle, red & blue . 10 10

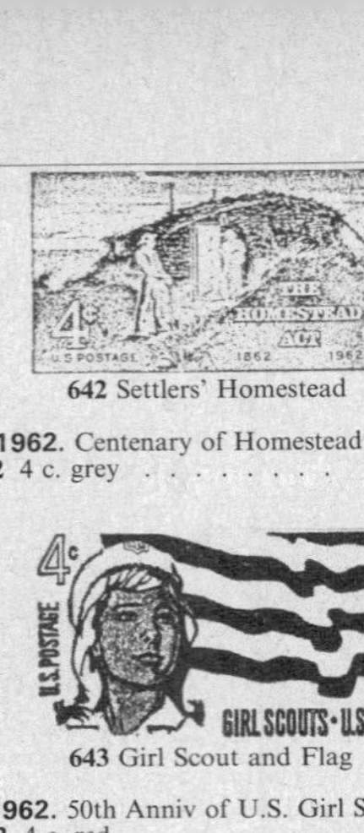

642 Settlers' Homestead

1962. Centenary of Homestead Act.
1197 **642** 4 c. grey 10 10

643 Girl Scout and Flag

1962. 50th Anniv of U.S. Girl Scouts.
1198 **643** 4 c. red 10 10

644 Senator McMahon and Atomic Symbol

1962. Brien McMahon.
1199 **644** 4 c. violet 10 10

645 "Transfer of Skill" 646 Sam Rayburn

1962. 25th Anniv of National Apprenticeship Act.
1200 **645** 4 c. black on olive . . . 10 10

1962. Sam Rayburn (Speaker of House of Representatives) Commemoration.
1201 **646** 4 c. brown and blue . . . 10 10

647 Dag Hammarskjold and U.N. Headquarters 648 Christmas Laurel Wreath

1962. Hammarskjold.
1202 **647** 4 c. brown, yell & black . 10 10
1203 4 c. brown, yellow & blk 10 10
No. 1203 has the yellow colour inverted and comes from a special printing made after a few examples had been discovered.

1962. Christmas.
1204 **648** 4 c. green and red . . . 10 10

649 "Lamp of Learning" and Map

1962. Higher Education.
1205 **649** 4 c. black and green . . 10 10

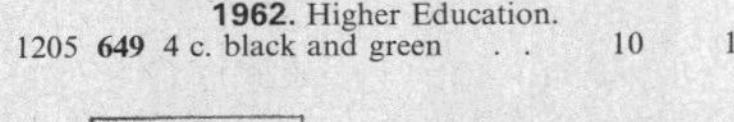

651 Washington (after Houdon) A 652 Capitol, Washington and Douglas DC-8

1962.
1206 – 1 c. green 10 10
1207 **651** 5 c. blue 10 10
DESIGN: 1 c. Andrew Jackson.

1962. Air.
A1210 A **652** 8 c. red 30 10

652 "Breezing Up" (after Winslow Homer) 653 U.S. Flag and White House

1962. Winslow Homer.
1210 **652** 4 c. multicoloured . . . 10 10

1963.
1211 **653** 5 c. red and blue 15 10

654 Charter and Quill

1963. 300th Anniv of Carolina Charter.
1212 **654** 5 c. sepia and red . . . 10 10

A **655** P.M.G. Montgomery Blair, Letters and Globe (after portrait by Thomas Sully) 655 "Food for Peace"

1963. Air. Centenary of Paris Postal Conferences.
A1213 A **655** 15 c. pur, bl & red . 60 40

1963. Freedom from Hunger.
1213 **655** 5 c. brown, green & red 10 10

656 Map and State Capitol, Charleston A 657 American Bald Eagle

1963. Centenary of West Virginia Statehood.
1214 **656** 5 c. red, black & green . 10 10

1963. Air.
A1215 A **657** 6 c. red 30 10

657 Broken Link A 658 Amelia Earhart and Lockheed "Electra"

1963. Centenary of Emancipation Proclamation.
1215 **657** 5 c. black, blue & red . 20 10

1963. Air. Amelia Earhart Commemoration.
A1216 A **658** 8 c. purple and red . 25 10

658 Torch of Progress 659 Cordell Hull

1963. "Alliance for Progress".
1216 **658** 5 c. green and blue . . . 10 10

1963. Cordell Hull Commemoration.
1217 **659** 5 c. turquoise 10 10

660 Eleanor Roosevelt

1963. Eleanor Roosevelt Commemoration.
1218 **660** 5 c. violet 10 10

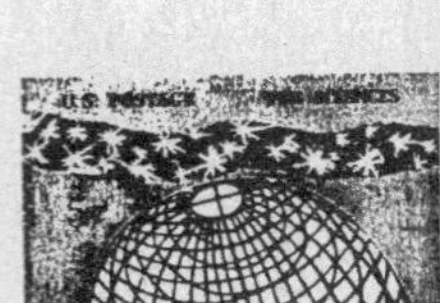

661 "The Sciences" 662 City Mail Postman

1963. Centenary of National Academy of Science.
1219 **661** 5 c. black, red & blue . . 10 10

1963. Cent of City Mail Delivery.
1220 **662** 5 c. black and turquoise . 10 10

663 Red Cross Flag and S.S."Morning Light" 664 Christmas Tree

1963. Red Cross Centenary.
1221 **663** 5 c. black and red 10 10

1963. Christmas.
1222 **664** 5 c. black, blue and red . 10 10

665 "Columbia Jays" (print) (Actually Collie's Magpie-jays) 666 Sam Houston (from lithograph by F. Davignon)

1963. John James Audubon Commemoration.
1223 **665** 5 c. multicoloured 30 10
See also No. A1304.

1964. Sam Houston Commemoration.
1224 **666** 5 c. black 20 10

667 "Jerked Down"

1964. Birth Centenary of C. M. Russell (artist).
1225 **667** 5 c. multicoloured . . . 20 10

668 Mall with Unisphere and "The Rocket Thrower" (after De Lue) 669 John Muir (naturalist) and Forest

1964. New York World's Fair.
1226 **668** 5 c. turquoise 10 10

1964. John Muir Commemoration.
1227 **669** 5 c. brown, emer & grn . 10 10

670 Pres. Kennedy and "Eternal Flame" 671 Philip Carteret at Elizabethtown (1664) (after painting in Union County Courthouse)

1964. President Kennedy Memorial Issue.
1228 **670** 5 c. blue on grey 10 10

1964. Tercentenary of New Jersey.
1229 **671** 5 c. blue 10 10

672 Virginia City in 19th Century 673 U.S. Flag

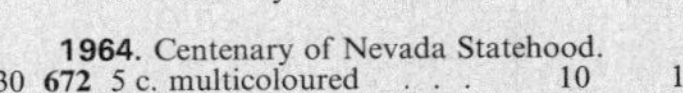

1964. Centenary of Nevada Statehood.
1230 **672** 5 c. multicoloured . . . 10 10

1964. "Register and Vote" Campaign.
1231 **673** 5 c. red and blue 10 10

674 Shakespeare 675 Drs. William and Charles Mayo (after J. E. Fraser)

1964. 400th Birth Anniv of William Shakespeare.
1232 **674** 5 c. sepia on buff 10 10

1964. Mayo Brothers (founders of Mayo Clinic) Commemoration.
1233 **675** 5 c. green 10 10

A **676** R.H. Goddard, "Atlas" Rocket and Launching Tower

1964. Air. Robert H. Goddard Commem.
A1234 A **676** 8 c. blue, red & yell 60 10

676 Lute, Horn and Music Score

1964. American Music.
1234 **676** 5 c. black, red and blue on light blue 10 10

677 Sampler

1964. "Homemakers" Commemoration.
1235 **677** 5 c. multicoloured . . . 10 10

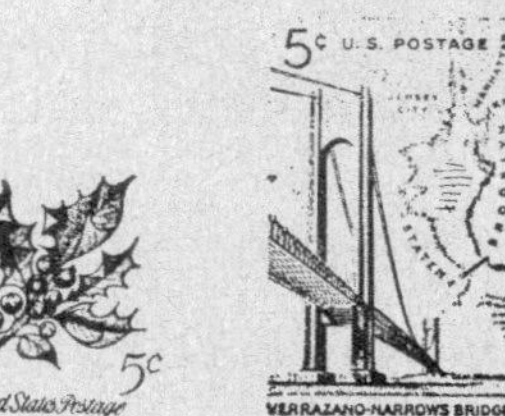

678 Holly 682 Verrazano-Narrows Bridge

1964. Christmas. Each red, green and black.
1236 5 c. Type **678** 30 10
1237 5 c. Mistletoe 30 10
1238 5 c. Poinsettia 30 10
1239 5 c. Pine cone 30 10

1964. Opening of Verrazano-Narrows Bridge, New York.
1240 **682** 5 c. green 10 10

683 "Abstract Art" (from lithograph by S. Davis)

1964. "To the Fine Arts".
1241 **683** 5 c. red, black and blue . 15 10

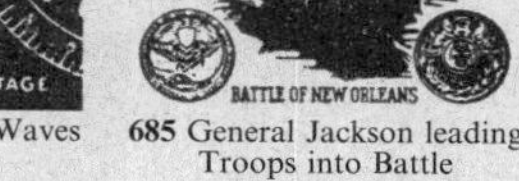

684 Radio Waves 685 General Jackson leading Troops into Battle

1964. Amateur Radio.
1242 **684** 5 c. purple 10 10

1965. 150th Anniv of Battle of New Orleans.
1243 **685** 5 c. red, blue and black . 15 10

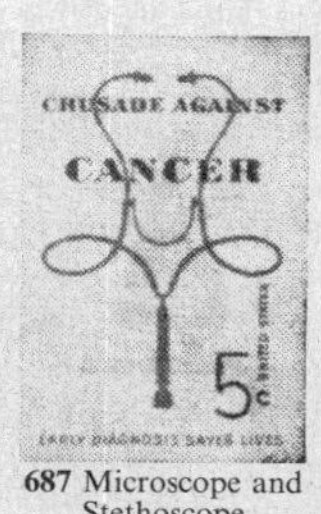

686 Discus-thrower (Washington statue) 687 Microscope and Stethoscope

1965. Centenary of Sokol Physical Fitness Organization in the U.S.A.
1244 **686** 5 c. blue and lake 10 10

1965. Crusade Against Cancer.
1245 **687** 5 c. black, violet & red 10 10

CHURCHILL

U.S. 5 CENTS

688 Sir Winston Churchill (from photo by Karsh)

1965. Churchill Commemoration.
1246 **688** 5 c. black 10 10

689 Procession of Barons, and King John's Crown

1965. 750th Anniv of Magna Carta.
1247 **689** 5 c. black, yell & violet . 10 10

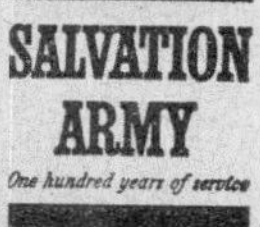

690 I.C.Y. Emblem 691 "One hundred years of service"

1965. International Co-operation Year.
1248 **690** 5 c. black and blue . . . 10 10

1965. Centenary of Salvation Army.
1249 **691** 5 c. black, red and blue . 15 10

692 Dante 693 Herbert Hoover

1965. 700th Anniv of Dante's Birth.
1250 **692** 5 c. red on flesh 10 10

1965. Hoover Commemoration.
1251 **693** 5 c. red 10 10

694 Robert Fulton (after Houdon) and "Clermont" 695 Spanish Knight and Banners

1965. Birth Bicent of Robert Fulton (inventor).
1252 **694** 5 c. black and blue . . . 10 10

1965. 400th Anniv of Florida Settlement.
1253 **695** 5 c. black, red & yellow 10 10

696 Traffic Signal 697 Elizabeth Clarke Copley (from "The Copley Family" by John S. Copley)

1965. Traffic Safety.
1254 **696** 5 c. red, black & green . 10 10

1965. John Singleton Copley.
1255 **697** 5 c. brown, drab & black 10 10

STEVENSON

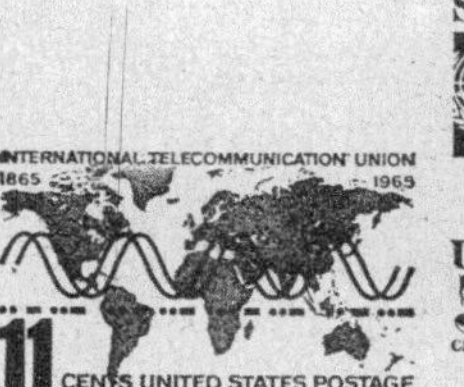

698 Radio "Waves" on World Map (based on Galt projection) 699 Adlai Stevenson (from photo by P. Halsman)

1965. Centenary of I.T.U.
1256 **698** 11 c. red, black & brown 35 15

1965. Stevenson Commemoration.
1257 **699** 5 c. multicoloured . . . 10 10

700 Archangel Gabriel (weathervane) (after painting by L. Chabot) 705 Lincoln (after photo by M. Brady)

1965. Christmas.
1258 **700** 5 c. green, ochre & red . . 10 10

1965. Prominent Americans (1st series).

1259	–	1 c. green	10	10
1260	–	$1\frac{1}{4}$ c. green	10	15
1261	–	2 c. blue	10	10
1262	–	3 c. violet	10	10
1263	**705**	4 c. black	15	10
1265	–	5 c. blue	10	10
1266	–	6 c. brown	15	10
1282	–	6 c. brown	30	10
1267	–	8 c. violet	20	10
1268	–	10 c. purple	20	10
1269	–	12 c. black	20	10
1270	–	13 c. brown	20	10
1271	–	15 c. red	25	10
1272	–	20 c. green	30	10
1273	–	25 c. red	40	10
1274	–	30 c. purple	60	10
1275	–	40 c. blue	75	10
1276	–	50 c. purple	1·25	10
1283	–	$1 purple	1·50	60
1278	–	$5 black	8·50	1·25

DESIGNS—VERT: 1 c. Thomas Jefferson (after Rembrandt Peale); $1\frac{1}{4}$ c. Albert Gallatin; 2 c. Frank Lloyd Wright and Guggenheim Museum, New York; 5 c. Washington (after Rembrandt Peale); 6 c. (1282) Franklin D. Roosevelt; 8 c. Albert Einstein; 10 c. Andrew Jackson (after T. Sully); 13 c. John F. Kennedy; 15 c. Justice Wendell Holmes; 20 c. George C. Marshall; 25 c. Frederick Douglass; 40 c. Tom Paine (after John W. Jarvis); 50 c. Lucy Stone; $1 Eugene O'Neill; $5 John Bassett Moore. HORIZ: 3 c. Francis Parkman; 6 c. (No. 1266) Franklin D. Roosevelt; 12 c. Henry Ford and Model "T" car; 30 c. John Dewey.
See also Nos. 1383/9.

719 "Migratory Birds"

1966. 50th Anniv of Migratory Bird Treaty.
1286 **719** 5 c. red, blue and black . 10 10

720 Dog 721 Seal, Emblem and Map

1966. Humane Treatment of Animals.
1287 **720** 5 c. black and brown . . 10 10

1966. 150th Anniv of Indiana Statehood.
1288 **721** 5 c. blue, brown and yell . 10 10

722 Lou Jacobs (clown) 723 SIPEX "Letter"

1966. The American Circus.
1289 **722** 5 c. Multicoloured . . . 10 10

1966. 6th Int Philatelic Exn, Washington. (SIPEX).
1290 **723** 5 c. multicoloured 10 10

725 "Freedom" opposing "Tyranny" 726 Polish Eagle

1966. 175th Anniv of Bill of Rights.
1292 **725** 5 c. red, indigo and blue . 10 10

1966. Polish Millennium.
1293 **726** 5 c. red 10 10

727 N.P.S. Emblem 728 Marines Past and Present

1966. 50th Anniv of National Park Service.
1294 **727** 5 c. black, green & yell . 10 10

1966. 50th Anniv of Marine Corps Reserve.
1295 **728** 5 c. multicoloured 10 10

729 Women of 1891 and 1966 730 Johnny Appleseed and Apple

1966. 75th Anniv of General Federation of Women's Clubs.
1296 **729** 5 c. black, pink & blue . 10 10

1966. Johnny Appleseed.
1297 **730** 5 c. black, red & green . 10 10

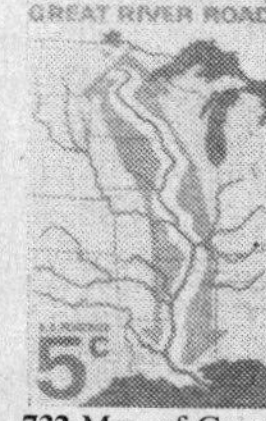

731 Jefferson Memorial, Washington 732 Map of Great River Road

1966. "Beautification of America" Campaign.
1298 **731** 5 c. black, green & pink 10 10

1966. Opening of Great River Road.
1299 **732** 5 c. red, yellow and blue 10 10

733 Statue of Liberty and U.S. Flag (after photo by B. Noble) 734 "Madonna and Child" (after Memling)

1966. 25th Anniv of U.S. Savings Bond Programme and Tribute to U.S. Servicemen.
1300 **733** 5 c. multicoloured . . . 10 10

1966. Christmas.
1301 **734** 5 c. multicoloured . . . 10 10

735 "The Boating Party" (after Mary Cassatt) A 736 Tlingit Totem, Southern Alaska

1966. Mary Cassatt.
1302 **735** 5 c. multicoloured . . . 10 10

1967. Air. Centenary of Alaska Purchase.
A1303 A **736** 8 c. brown 30 15

736 Recruiting Poster A 737 "Columbia Jays" by Audubon

1967. Centenary of National Grange (farmers' organization).
1303 **736** 5 c. multicoloured . . . 10 10

1967. Air.
A1304 A **737** 20 c. multicoloured . 1·60 10
See also No. 1223.

737 Canadian Landscape

1967. Canadian Centennial.
1304 **737** 5 c. multicoloured . . . 10 10

738 Canal Barge

1967. 150th Anniv of Erie Canal.
1305 **738** 5 c. multicoloured . . . 10 10

739 Peace Dove Emblem

1967. "Search for Peace" (Lions Int essay theme).
1306 **739** 5 c. black, red and blue . 10 10

740 H. D. Thoreau **742** Radio Tower and "Waves"

741 Hereford Bull

1967. 150th Birth Anniv of Henry Thoreau (writer).
1307 **740** 5 c. black, red & green . 15 10

1967. Centenary of Nebraska Statehood.
1308 **741** 5 c. multicoloured . . . 10 10

1967. "Voice of America". 25th Anniv of Radio Branch of United States Information Agency.
1309 **742** 5 c. black, red and blue . 15 10

743 Davy Crockett and Pine

1967. Davy Crockett Commemoration.
1310 **743** 5 c. black, green & yell . 10 10

744 Astronaut in Space **746** "Planned City"

1967. U.S. Space Achievements. Multicoloured.
1311 5 c. Type **744** 40 15
1312 5 c. "Gemini 4" over Earth . 40 15
Nos. 1311/2 were issued together se-tenant, forming a composite design.

1967. Urban Planning.
1313 **746** 5 c. ultramarine, blk & bl 10 10

747 Arms of Finland **748** "The Biglin Brothers racing" (Eakins)

1967. 50th Anniv of Finnish Independence.
1314 **747** 5 c. blue 10 10

1967. Thomas Eakins.
1315 **748** 5 c. multicoloured . . . 15 10

749 "Madonna and Child with Angels" (Memling) **750** Magnolia

1967. Christmas.
1316 **749** 5 c. multicoloured . . . 10 10

1967. 150th Anniv of Mississippi Statehood.
1317 **750** 5 c. brown, green and turquoise 10 10

A **751** "Fifty Stars" **751** U.S. Flag and The White House

1968. Air.
A1318 A **751** 10 c. red 25 5

1968. Flag Issue.
1318 **751** 6 c. multicoloured . . . 20 10
1320 8 c. multicoloured . . . 25 10

752 Homestead and Cornfield **753** Map of the Americas

1968. 150th Anniv of Illinois Statehood.
1323 **752** 6 c. multicoloured . . . 15 10

1968. "HemisFair'68" Exn, San Antonio.
1324 **753** 6 c. blue, pink & white . 15 10

754 Eagle with Pennant (after late 19th-century wood carving)

1968. "Airlift".
1325 **754** $1 brown, blue & buff . 2·75 1·25
No. 1325 was issued primarily for a special reduced-rate parcels service to forces personnel overseas and in Alaska, Hawaii and Puerto Rico.

755 Boys and Girls **756** Policeman with Small Boy

A **756** Curtiss JN-4 "Jenny"

1968. Youth Programme of Elks Benevolent Society.
1326 **755** 6 c. blue and red 15 10

1968. Air. 50th Anniv of Scheduled Airmail Services.
A1327 A **756** 10 c. blk, red & bl . 30 10

1968. "Law and Order".
1328 **756** 6 c. blue, red & black . . 15 10

757 Eagle Weathervane **758** Fort Moultrie, 1776

1968. "Register and Vote".
1329 **757** 6 c. yellow, orge & blk . 15 10

1968. Historic Flags.
1330 **758** 6 c. blue 45 20
1331 – 6 c. red and blue 45 20
1332 – 6 c. green and blue . . . 45 20
1333 – 6 c. red and blue 45 20
1334 – 6 c. blue, yellow & red . . 45 20
1335 – 6 c. red and blue 45 20
1336 – 6 c. blue, red & green . . 45 20
1337 – 6 c. red and blue 45 20
1338 – 6 c. blue, red & yellow . . 45 20
1339 – 6 c. red, yellow & blue . . 45 20
FLAGS: No. 1331, U.S. (Fort McHenry), 1795–1818; 1332, Washington's Cruisers, 1775; 1333, Bennington, 1777; 1334, Rhode Island, 1775; 1335, First Stars and Stripes, 1777; 1336, Bunker Hill, 1775; 1337, Grand Union, 1776; 1338, Philadelphia Light Horse, 1775; 1339, First Navy Jack, 1775.

768 Walt Disney (after portrait by P. E. Wenzel) **769** Father Jacques Marquette (explorer) with Jolliet and Indians Canoeing

1968. Walt Disney Commemoration.
1340 **768** 6 c. multicoloured 25 10

1968. Marquette Commemoration.
1341 **769** 6 c. multicoloured 15 10

770 Rifle, Tomahawk, Powder-horn and Knife

1968. Daniel Boone Commemoration.
1342 **770** 6 c. multicoloured 15 10

771 Ship's Wheel and River Tanker

1968. Arkansas River Navigation Project.
1343 **771** 6 c. black, blue & lt blue . 15 10

772 "Leif Erikson" (statue by Stirling Calder, Reykjavik, Iceland) **773** Pioneers racing to Cherokee Strip

1968. Leif Erikson Commemoration.
1344 **772** 6 c. sepia and brown . . 15 10

1968. 75th Anniv of Opening of Cherokee Strip to Settlers.
1345 **773** 6 c. brown 15 10

774 "Battle of Bunker's Hill (detail) (after John Trumbull) **775** Wood Ducks

1968. John Trumbull.
1346 **774** 6 c. multicoloured . . . 20 10

1968. Waterfowl Conservation.
1347 **775** 6 c. multicoloured . . . 30 10

776 "The Annunciation" (Jan van Eyck) **777** "Chief Joseph" (after C. Hall)

1968. Christmas.
1348 **776** 6 c. multicoloured . . . 15 10

1968. "The American Indian".
1349 **777** 6 c. multicoloured . . . 30 10

A **778** "U.S.A." and Jet Aircraft

1968. Air.
A1350 A **778** 20 c. red, blue & blk 60 10
A1351 21 c. blue, red & blk 55 10

778 Capitol and Flowers ("Cities")

1969. "Beautification of America" Campaign.
1352 **778** 6 c. multicoloured . . . 40 10
1353 – 6 c. multicoloured . . . 40 10
1354 – 6 c. multicoloured . . . 40 10
1355 – 6 c. multicoloured . . . 40 10
DESIGNS: No. 1353, Potomac River and flowers ("Parks"); 1354, Motorway and flowers ("Highways"); 1355, Road and trees ("Streets").

782 "Eagle" (U.S. Seal) **783** "July Fourth"

1969. 50th Anniv of American Legion.
1356 **782** 6 c. black, blue and red . 15 10

1969. Grandma Moses (Mrs. A. M. R. Moses).
1357 **783** 6 c. multicoloured . . . 15 10

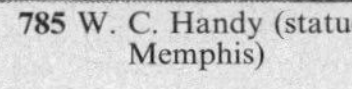

784 Earth and Moon's Surface (from an astronaut's photograph) **785** W. C. Handy (statue, Memphis)

1969. Moon Flight of "Apollo 8".
1358 **784** 6 c. ochre, blue and black 20 10

1969. Handy (composer) Commemoration.
1359 **785** 6 c. mauve, blue and violet 20 10

786 Belfry, Carmel Mission

787 Powell exploring Colorado River

1969. Bicentenary of California.
1360 **786** 6 c. multicoloured . . . 15 10

1969. John Wesley Powell (geologist). Centenary of Colorado River Exploration.
1361 **787** 6 c. multicoloured . . . 15 10

788 Camellia and Common Flicker

1969. 150th Anniv of Alabama Statehood.
1362 **788** 6 c. multicoloured . . . 30 10

791 Ocotillo

1969. 11th International Botanical Congress, Seattle. Multicoloured.
1363 6 c. Douglas Fir 50 10
1364 6 c. Lady's slipper 50 10
1365 6 c. Type **791** 50 10
1366 6 c. Franklinia 50 10

A **793** Astronaut setting foot on Moon

1969. Air. 1st Man on the Moon.
A1367 A **793** 10 c. multicoloured . 15 10

793 Daniel Webster and Dartmouth Hall

794 Striker

1969. 150th Anniv of Dartmouth College Legal Case.
1368 **793** 6 c. green 15 10

1969. Centenary of Professional Baseball.
1369 **794** 6 c. multicoloured . . . 45 10

795 Footballer and Coach

1969. Centenary of Intercollegiate Football.
1370 **795** 6 c. green and red . . . 25 10

796 Dwight D. Eisenhower (from photograph by B. Noble)

1969. Eisenhower Commemoration.
1371 **796** 6 c. black, blue & lake . 20 10

797 "Winter Sunday in Norway, Maine" (unknown artist)

1969. Christmas.
1372 **797** 6 c. multicoloured . . . 15 10

798 Rehabilitated Child

800 "Old Models" (William Harnett)

1969. Rehabilitation of the Handicapped.
1373 **798** 6 c. multicoloured . . . 15 10
No. 1373 also commemorates the 50th anniv of the National Society for Crippled Children and Adults.

1969. William M. Harnett.
1376 **800** 6 c. multicoloured . . . 10 10

804 Prehistoric Creatures (from mural by R. Zallinger in Yale's Peabody Museum)

1970. Natural History. Centenary of American Natural History Museum. Multicoloured.
1377 6 c. American bald eagle . . 30 10
1378 6 c. African elephant herd . 30 10
1379 6 c. Haida ceremonial canoe 20 10
1380 6 c. Type **804** 20 10

805 "The Lighthouse at Two Lights" (painting by Edward Hopper in Metropolitan Museum of Art, New York

1970. Maine Statehood Sesquicentennial.
1381 **805** 6 c. multicoloured . . . 30 10

806 American Bison

1970. Wildlife Conservation.
1382 **806** 6 c. black on brown . . 15 10

807 Dwight D. Eisenhower

809 Benjamin Franklin

1970. Prominent Americans (2nd series).
1383 **807** 6 c. blue 10 10
1384 **809** 7 c. blue 10 10
1392 **807** 8 c. maroon 30 10
1390 8 c. black, blue & red . 10 10
1386 – 14 c. black 30 10
1387 – 16 c. brown 30 10
1388 – 18 c. violet 45 10
1389 – 21 c. green 50 10
DESIGNS: VERT: 14 c. F. H. La Guardia; 16 c. Ernest T. Pyle; 18 c. Dr. Elizabeth Blackwell; 21 c. Amadeo P. Giannini (after painting by J. Kozlowski).

822 Edgar Lee Masters

823 Suffragettes, 1920, and Woman operating Voting Machine

1970. Edgar Lee Masters (poet) Commem.
1401 **822** 6 c. black and bistre . . . 15 10

1970. 50th Anniv of Women's Suffrage.
1402 **823** 6 c. blue 15 10

824 Symbols of South Carolina

1970. 300th Anniv of South Carolina.
1403 **824** 6 c. multicoloured 15 10

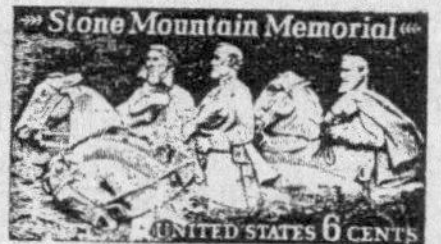

825 Stone Mountain Memorial

1970. Dedication of Stone Mountain Confederate Memorial.
1404 **825** 6 c. black 15 10

826 Fort Snelling and Keel Boat

1970. 150th Anniv of Fort Snelling, Minnesota.
1405 **826** 6 c. multicoloured 15 10

828 City Park

1970. Prevention of Pollution.
1406 6 c. Wheat 45 10
1407 6 c. Type **828** 45 10
1408 6 c. Blue-gill 45 10
1409 6 c. Western gull 45 10

832 Toy Locomotive (after drawing by C. Hemming)

1970. Christmas. Multicoloured.
1410 6 c. "The Nativity" (L. Lotto) (vert) 15 10
1411 6 c. Type **832** 65 10
1412 6 c. Toy horse on wheels . . 40 10
1413 6 c. Mechanised tricycle . . 40 10
1414 6 c. Doll's pram 40 10
Nos. 1412/14 are taken from "Golden Age of Toys" by Fondin and Remise.

836 "U.N." and Emblem

1970. 25th Anniv of U.N.O.
1415 **836** 6 c. red, blue and black . 15 10

837 "Mayflower" and Pilgrims

838 Disabled American Veterans Emblem

1970. 350th Anniv of Landing of the Pilgrim Fathers in America.
1416 **837** 6 c. multicoloured . . . 20 10

1970. 50th Anniv of Disabled American Veterans Organization, and Armed Forces Commemoration.
1417 **838** 6 c. multicoloured . . . 20 10
1418 – 6 c. black, blue and red . 20 10
DESIGN: No. 1418, Inscriptions—"Prisoners of War", "Missing and Killed in Action".

840 Ewe and Lamb

841 General Douglas MacArthur

1970. 450th Anniv of Introduction of Sheep into North America.
1419 **840** 6 c. multicoloured . . . 15 10

1971. 91st Birth Anniv of General Douglas MacArthur.
1420 **841** 6 c. black, blue and red . 15 10

842 "Giving Blood Saves Lives"

1971. Salute to Blood Donors
1421 **842** 6 c. deep blue, red & blue 15 10

A **844** Jet Aircraft

A **845** Winged Letter

1971. Air.
A1422 – 9 c. red 25 25
A1423 A **844** 11 c. red 35 10
A1424 A **845** 13 c. red 30 10
DESIGN—HORIZ: 9 c. Delta-wing plane.

846 "Settlers and Indians" (after mural "Independence and the Opening of the West" by Thomas H. Benton)

1971. 150th Anniv of Missouri Statehood.
1427 **846** 8 c. multicoloured . . . 25 10

847 Trout

1971. Wildlife Conservation. Multicoloured.
1428 8 c. Type **847** 30 10
1429 8 c. Alligator 30 10
1430 8 c. Polar bear and cubs . . 30 15
1431 8 c. Californian condor . . . 30 10

851 Antarctic Map Emblem

852 Postal Service Emblem

1971. 10th Anniv of Antarctic Treaty.
1432 **851** 8 c. blue and red 20 10

1971. Reorganization of U.S. Post Office as U.S. Postal Service.
1433 **852** 8 c. multicoloured . . . 15 10

853 Bicentennial Emblem

A 854 Head of Statue of Liberty

1971. American Revolution Bicentennial. Bicentennial Commisssion Emblem.
1434 **853** 8 c. multicoloured . . . 25 10

1971. Air.
A1435 A **854** 17 c. blue, red & grn 55 10

855 "The Wake of the Ferry" (John Sloan)

1971. Birth Centenary of John Sloan (artist).
1436 **855** 8 c. multicoloured . . . 15 10

856 Landing Module on Moon

858 Emily Dickinson

1971. Decade of U.S. Space Achievements. Multicoloured.
1437 8 c. Type **856** 15 10
1438 8 c. Astronauts in lunar rover 15 10
Nos. 1437/8 were issued together se-tenant, forming a composite design.

1971. 85th Death Anniv of Emily Dickinson (poet).
1439 **858** 8 c. mult on green . . . 15 10

859 Watch-tower, El Morro, San Juan

860 Drug Victim

1971. 450th Anniv of San Juan, Puerto Rico.
1440 **859** 8 c. multicoloured . . . 15 10

1971. Drug Abuse Prevention Week.
1441 **860** 8 c. black, lt blue & bl . 25 10

861 Hands reaching to "CARE"

866 "Adoration of the Shepherds" (Giorgione)

862 Decatur House, Washington D.C.

1971. 25th Anniv of "CARE" (Co-operative for American Relief Everywhere).
1442 **861** 8 c. multicoloured . . . 20 10

1971. Historic Preservation.
1443 **862** 8 c. blk & flesh on cream 20 10
1444 – 8 c. blk & flesh on cream 20 10
1445 – 8 c. blk & flesh on cream 25 10
1446 – 8 c. blk & flesh on cream 20 10
DESIGNS: No. 1444, Whaling ship, "Charles W. Morgan", Mystic, Conn; No. 1445, San Francisco cable-car; No. 1446, San Xavier del Bac Mission, Tucson, Arizona.

1971. Christmas. Multicoloured.
1447 8 c. Type **866** 25 10
1448 8 c. "Partridge in a Pear Tree" 30 10

868 Sidney Lanier

869 Peace Corps Poster (D. Battle)

1972. 90th Death Anniv (1971) of Sidney Lanier (poet).
1449 **868** 8 c. black, brown & bl . 20 10

1972. Peace Corps.
1450 **869** 8 c. red, lt blue & blue . 15 10

870/873 Cape Hatteras National Seashore

875 "Old Faithful", Yellowstone Park

A 877 Statue and Temple, City of Refuge, Hawaii

1972. Centenary of National Parks.
1451 **870** 2 c. multicoloured (postage) 15 10
1452 **871** 2 c. multicoloured . 15 10
1453 **872** 2 c. multicoloured . 20 10
1454 **873** 2 c. multicoloured . 20 10
1455 – 6 c. multicoloured . 20 10
1456 **875** 8 c. multicoloured . 30 10
1457 – 15 c. multicoloured . 50 45
A1458 A **877** 11 c. mult (air) . . . 35 10
DESIGNS—HORIZ: (As Type A **877**). 6 c. Theatre at night, Wolf Trap Farm, Virginia; 15 c. Mt. McKinley, Alaska.

878 American Family

879 Glassblower

1972. Family Planning.
1459 **878** 8 c. multicoloured . . . 20 10

1972. Bicentenary of American Revolution. American Colonial Craftsmen.
1460 **879** 8 c. brown on yellow . . 20 10
1461 – 8 c. brown on yellow . . 20 10
1462 – 8 c. brown on yellow . . 20 10
1463 – 8 c. brown on yellow . . 20 10
DESIGNS: No. 1461, Silversmith; No. 1462, Wigmaker; No. 1463, Hatter.

883 Cycling

1972. Olympic Games, Munich and Sapporo, Japan. Multicoloured.
1464 6 c. Type **883** (postage) . . . 20 15
1465 8 c. Bobsleighing 25 10
1466 15 c. Running 40 40
A1467 11 c. Skiing (air) 35 15

887 Classroom Blackboard

1972. 75th Anniv of Parent Teacher Association.
1468 **887** 8 c. black and yellow . . 15 10

888 Northern Fur Seals

1972. Wildlife Conservation. Multicoloured.
1469 8 c. Type **888** 20 10
1470 8 c. Common cardinal (bird) 30 10
1471 8 c. Brown pelicans 30 10
1472 8 c. American bighorn 20 10

892 19th-century Country Post Office and Store

1972. Centenary of Mail Order Business.
1473 **892** 8 c. multicoloured 15 10

893 "Quest for Health"

894 "Tom Sawyer" (N. Rockwell)

1972. 75th Anniv of American Osteopaths.
1474 **893** 8 c. multicoloured 15 10

1972. "The Adventures of Tom Sawyer" by Mark Twain.
1475 **894** 8 c. multicoloured 25 10

895 "Angels" (detail, "Mary, Queen of Heaven" by Master of the St. Lucy Legend)

897 Pharmaceutical Equipment

1972. Christmas. Multicoloured.
1476 8 c. Type **895** 20 10
1477 8 c. Santa Claus 20 10

1972. 120th Anniv of American Pharmaceutical Association.
1478 **897** 8 c. multicoloured 25 10

898 Five Cent Stamp of 1847 under Magnifier

1972. 125th Anniv of 1st U.S. Stamp, and Stamp Collecting Promotion.
1479 **898** 8 c. brown, black & grn . 15 10

899 "LOVE"

1973. Greetings Stamp.
1480 **899** 8 c. red, green and blue . 15 10

900 Pamphleteers with Press

1973. American Revolution Bicentennial. Colonial Communications.
1481 **900** 8 c. green, blue and red . 25 10
1482 – 8 c. black, red and blue . 25 10
1483 – 8 c. multicoloured . . 25 10
1484 – 8 c. multicoloured . . . 25 10
DESIGNS: No. 1482, Posting a broadside; 1483, Post-rider; 1484, Drummer.

904 George Gershwin (composer) and Scene from "Porgy and Bess"

908 Nicolas Copernicus (after 18th-cent engraving)

1973. American Arts Commemoration. Mult.
1485 8 c. Type **904** 25 10
1486 8 c. Robinson Jeffers (poet) and people of Carmel 25 10
1487 8 c. Henry Tanner (painter) and palette 25 10
1488 8c. Willa Cather (novelist) and pioneer family 25 10

1973. 500th Birth Anniv of Copernicus (astronomer).
1489 **908** 8 c. black and yellow . . 15 10

909 Counter Clerk

919 Harry S. Truman

1973. Postal Service Employees. Multicoloured.
1490 8 c. Type **909** 15 10
1491 8 c. Collecting mail 15 10
1492 8 c. Sorting on conveyor belt 15 10
1493 8 c. Sorting parcels 15 10
1494 8 c. Cancelling letters 15 10
1495 8 c. Sorting letters by hand . 15 10
1496 8 c. Coding desks 15 10
1497 8 c. Loading mail-van . . . 15 10
1498 8 c. City postman 15 10
1499 8 c. Rural postman 15 10

1973. Pres. Harry Truman Commemoration.
1500 **919** 8 c. black, red and blue . 15 10

920/23 Boston Tea Party. (Illustration reduced. Actual size 77 × 47 mm)

1973. American Revolution Bicentennial. The Boston Tea Party.
1501 **920** 8 c. multicoloured . . . 15 10
1502 **921** 8 c. multicoloured . . . 15 10
1503 **922** 8 c. multicoloured . . . 15 10
1504 **923** 8 c. multicoloured . . . 15 10

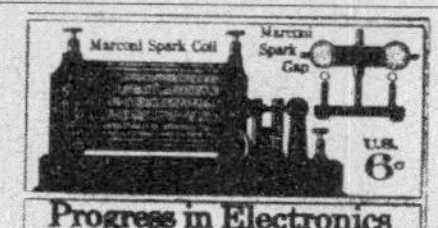

924 Marconi's Spark Coil and Gap (1901)

1973. Progress in Electronics. Multicoloured.
1505 6 c. Type **924** (postage) . . 20 15
1506 8 c. Modern transistor circuit 25 10
1507 15 c. Early microphone and radio speaker, radio and T.V. camera tubes 45 40
A1508 11 c. DeForest audions (1915) (air) 35 15

928 Lyndon B. Johnson (from painting by Elizabeth Shoumatoff)
929 Angus and Longhorn Cattle (painting by F. C. Murphy)

1973. Pres. Lyndon B. Johnson Commem.
1509 **928** 8 c. multicoloured . . . 20 10

1973. "Rural America" Centenaries.
1510 8 c. Type **929** 20 10
1511 10 c. Institute marquee . . . 40 10
1512 10 c. Steam train crossing wheatfield 40 10
CENTENARIES: No. 1510, Introduction of Aberdeen Angus cattle into United States; 1511, Foundation of Chautauqua Institution (adult education organization); 1512, Introduction of hard winter wheat into Kansas.

932 "Small Cowper Madonna" (Raphael)
933 Christmas Tree in Needlepoint

1973. Christmas.
1513 **932** 8 c. multicoloured . . . 20 10
1514 **933** 8 c. multicoloured . . . 20 10

934 U.S. Flags of 1777 and 1973
935 Jefferson Memorial

936 "Mail Transport" (from poster by R. McDougall)
937 Liberty Bell

1973.
1519 **937** 6.3 c. red 20 20
1515 **934** 10 c. red and blue . . . 30 10
1516 **935** 10 c. blue 30 10
1517 **936** 10 c. multicoloured . . . 20 10

A **938** Statue of Liberty

1974. Air.
A1521 A **938** 18 c. blk, red & bl . 70 40
A1522 – 26 c. blk, bl & red . 80 10
DESIGN: 26 c. Mt. Rushmore National Memorial.

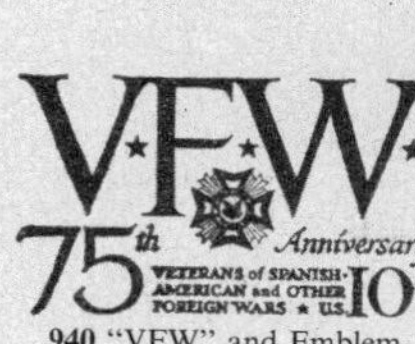

940 "VFW" and Emblem
941 Robert Frost

1974. 75th Anniv of Veterans of Foreign Wars Organization.
1523 **940** 10 c. red and blue . . . 20 10

1974. Birth Centenary of Robert Frost (poet).
1524 **941** 10 c. black 15 10

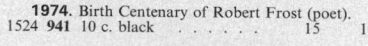

942 "Cosmic Jumper" and "Smiling Sage" ("Preserve the Environment" theme)

1974. "Expo 74" World Fair, Spokane.
1525 **942** 10 c. multicoloured . . 15 10

943 Horse-racing

1974. Centenary of Kentucky Derby.
1526 **943** 10 c. multicoloured . . 20 10

944 "Skylab" in Orbit

1974. "Skylab" Space Project.
1527 **944** 10 c. multicoloured . . 25 10

945 "Michelangelo" (detail from "School of Athens" by Raphael)

1974. Centenary of U.P.U. Multicoloured.
1528 10 c. Type **945** 15 10
1529 10 c. "Five Feminine Virtues" (Hokusai) 15 10
1530 10 c. "Old Scraps" (J. F. Peto) 15 10
1531 10 c. "The Lovely Reader" (J. Liotard) 15 10
1532 10 c. "The Lady Writing Letter" (G. Terborch) 15 10
1533 10 c. "Inkwell and Quill" (detail from "Young Boy with Top" by J. Chardin) 15 10
1534 10 c. "Mrs. John Douglas" (T. Gainsborough) 15 10
1535 10 c. "Don Antonio Noriega" (F. Goya) 15 10

955 Amethyst
957 Covered Wagon at Fort Harrod

1974. Mineral Heritage. Multicoloured.
1536 10 c. Petrified wood 25 10
1537 10 c. Tourmaline 25 10
1538 10 c. Type **955** 25 10
1539 10 c. Rhodochrosite 25 10

1974. Bicentenary of Fort Harrod, First Settlement in Kentucky.
1540 **957** 10 c. multicoloured . . . 25 10

959 "We ask but for peace..." (First Continental Congress)
962 Slogan, Molecules and Petrol Drops

1974. American Revolution Bicentennial. First Continental Congress.
1541 – 10 c. blue and red 25 10
1542 **959** 10 c. grey, blue and red . 25 10
1543 – 10 c. grey, red and blue . 25 10
1544 – 10 c. red and blue 25 10
DESIGNS: No. 1541, Carpenters' Hall, Philadelphia; 1543, "Deriving their just powers . . ." (Declaration of Independence); 1544, Independence Hall, Philadelphia.

1974. Energy Conservation.
1545 **962** 10 c. multicoloured . . . 20 10

963 "The Headless Horseman"
964 Child clasping Hand

1974. Washington Irving's "Legend of Sleepy Hollow".
1546 **963** 10 c. multicoloured . . . 20 10

1974. Help for Retarded Children.
1547 **964** 10 c. lake and brown . . 25 10

966 "The Road — Winter" (from a Currier and Ives print, drawn by O. Knirsch)

1974. Christmas. Multicoloured.
1548 10 c. "Angel" (detail, Perussis altarpiece) (vert) 20 10
1549 10 c. Type **966** 20 10
1550 10 c. Dove weathervane, Mount Vernon 20 10
No. 1550 has self-adhesive gum.

968 "Benjamin West" (self-portrait)
969 "Pioneer" Spacecraft passing Jupiter

1975. Benjamin West (painter) Commem.
1551 **968** 10 c. multicoloured . . . 15 10

1975. U.S. Unmanned Space Missions. Mult.
1552 10 c. Type **969** 30 10
1553 10 c. "Mariner 10", Venus and Mercury 30 10

971 Overlapping Circles

1975. Collective Bargaining in Labour Relations.
1554 **971** 10 c. multicoloured . . . 15 10

972 Sybil Ludington on Horseback

1975. American Revolution Bicentennial. Contributors to the Cause.
1555 **972** 8 c. multicoloured . . . 20 20
1556 – 10 c. multicoloured . . . 25 10
1557 – 10 c. multicoloured . . . 25 10
1558 – 18 c. multicoloured . . . 50 60
DESIGNS: No. 1556, Salem Poor loading musket; 1557, Haym Salomon writing in ledger; 1558, Peter Francisco carrying cannon.

976 "Lexington" (from painting "Birth of Liberty" by H. Sandham)
977 Paul Laurence Dunbar (poet)

1975. American Revolution Bicentennial. Battles of Lexington and Concord.
1559 **976** 10 c. multicoloured . . . 25 10

1975. Dunbar Commemoration.
1560 **977** 10 c. multicoloured . . . 20 10

978 D. W. Griffith (film producer)

1975. Griffith Commemoration.
1561 **978** 10 c. multicoloured . . . 25 10

979 "Bunker Hill, 1775", (John Trumbull)
980 Marine with Musket

1975. Bicentenary of American Revolution. Battle of Bunker Hill.
1562 **979** 10 c. multicoloured . . . 25 10

1975. American Revolution Bicentennial. U.S. Military Services. Multicoloured.
1563 10 c. Type **980** 25 10
1564 10 c. Militiaman with musket 25 10
1565 10 c. Soldier with flintlock . 25 10
1566 10 c. Sailor with grappling-iron 25 10

984 Docking Manoeuvre

1975. "Apollo-Soyuz" Space Test Project. Mult.
1567 10 c. Type **984** 20 10
1568 10 c. Spacecraft docked . . . 20 10

986 "Worldwide Equality"

1975. International Women's Year.
1569 **986** 10 c. multicoloured . . . 20 10

987 Stagecoach and Modern Lorry

1975. Bicentenary of Postal Services. Mult.
1571 10 c. Type **987** 20 10
1572 10 c. Early steam and modern diesel locomotives 20 10
1573 10 c. Curtiss JN-4 "Jenny" and Boeing 747-100 aircraft . . 20 10
1574 10 c. Telecommunications satellite 20 10

991 Law Book, Gavel and Globe

1975. "World Peace through Law".
1575 **991** 10 c. brown, blue & grn . 20 10

992 Coins and Engine-turned Motif

1975. "Banking and Commerce".
1576 **992** 10 c. multicoloured . . . 20 10
1577 – 10 c. multicoloured . . . 20 10
DESIGN: No. 1577, As Type **992**, but design reversed with different coins.

994 "Madonna and Child" (Ghirlandaio) **995** "Christmas Card" (from early design by Louis Prang)

1975. Christmas.
1578 **994** (10 c.) multicoloured . . 20 10
1579 **995** (10 c.) multicoloured . . 20 10
Nos. 1578/9 were each sold at 10 c. Because of an imminent increase in the postage rates the two designs were issued without face values.

1002 Early Printing Press **1020** Flag over Independence Hall

1975.

1580	–	1 c. deep blue on grey .	10	10
1581	–	2 c. red on cream . . .	10	10
1582	–	3 c. olive on green . .	10	10
1597b	–	3.1 c. lake on yellow .	15	10
1598	–	3.5 c. lilac on yellow .	15	10
1582a	–	4 c. red on cream . . .	10	10
1599	–	7.7 c. brown on yellow	30	15
1600	–	7.9 c. red on yellow . .	30	15
1601	–	8.4 c. blue on yellow .	30	15
1583	–	9 c. green on grey . .	25	10
1584	–	9 c. green	30	10
1585	–	10 c. purple on grey . .	15	10
1585a	**1002**	11 c. orange on grey .	20	10
1585b	–	12 c. brown on cream .	20	10
1586	–	13 c. brown on cream .	20	10
1595	–	13 c. multicoloured . .	40	10
1596	–	15 c. blue, red & blk .	45	10
1605	–	16 c. blue	50	15
1589	–	24 c. red on blue . . .	70	10
1589a	–	28 c. brown on blue . .	75	10
1590	–	29 c. blue on light bl .	90	30
1591	–	30 c. green on turq . .	55	10
1592	–	50 c. black, red & brn .	70	10
1593	–	$1 multicoloured . . .	1·50	10
1594	–	$2 multicoloured . . .	3·00	20
1594a	–	$5 multicoloured . . .	8·00	1·25

DESIGNS: 1 c. Inkwell and quill; 2 c. Speaker's stand; 3 c. Ballot box; 3.1 c. Guitar; 3.5 c. Weaver violins; 4 c. Books, spectacles and bookmark; 7.7 c. Saxhorns; 7.9 c. Drum; 8.4 c. Grand piano; 9 c. (both) Dome of Capitol; 10 c. "Contemplation of Justice" (statue, J. E. Fraser); 12 c. Statue of Liberty torch; 13 c. (No. 1586) Liberty Bell; 13 c. (No. 1595) Eagle and shield; 15 c. Fort McHenry flag; 16 c. Statue of Liberty; 24 c. Old North Church, Boston; 28 c. Fort Nisqually, Washington; 29 c. Sandy Hook Lighthouse, N.J; 30 c. Morris Township School; 50 c. Iron "Betty" lamp; $1 Rush lamp and candle holder; $2 Kerosene lamp; $5 Railway conductor's lantern.

1975.
1606 **1020** 13 c. red and blue . . 40 10
1606c – 13 c. red and blue . . 35 10
DESIGN: No. 1606c, Flag over Capitol, Washington.

MORE DETAILED LISTS
are given in the Stanley Gibbons Catalogues referred to in the country headings. For lists of current volumes see introduction

1021 Drummer Boy (after A. M. Willard) **1024**

1976. American Revolution Bicentennial. "The Spirit of '76". Multicoloured.
1607 13 c. Type **1021** 20 10
1608 13 c. Old drummer 20 10
1609 13 c. Fifer 20 10
Nos. 1607/9 were issued together, se-tenant, forming a composite design.

1976. Air.
A1610 **1024** 25 c. black, bl & red . 50 10
A1611 – 31 c. black, bl & red . 55 10
DESIGN: 31 c. As 25 c. but with background of U.S. flag.

1026 "Interphil 76"

1976. "Interphil 76" International Stamp Exhibition, Philadelphia.
1612 **1026** 13 c. red and blue . . . 35 10

1027 Delaware Flag

1976. Bicentenary of American Revolution. State Flags. Multicoloured.

1613	13 c. Type **1027**	30	20
1614	13 c. Pennsylvania	30	20
1615	13 c. New Jersey	30	20
1616	13 c. Georgia	30	20
1617	13 c. Connecticut	30	20
1618	13 c. Massachusetts	30	20
1619	13 c. Maryland	30	20
1620	13 c. South Carolina	30	20
1621	13 c. New Hampshire . . .	30	20
1622	13 c. Virginia	30	20
1623	13 c. New York	30	20
1624	13 c. North Carolina	30	20
1625	13 c. Rhode Island	30	20
1626	13 c. Vermont	30	20
1627	13 c. Kentucky	30	20
1628	13 c. Tennessee	30	20
1629	13 c. Ohio	30	20
1630	13 c. Louisiana	30	20
1631	13 c. Indiana	30	20
1632	13 c. Mississippi	30	20
1633	13 c. Illinois	30	20
1634	13 c. Alabama	30	20
1635	13 c. Maine	30	20
1636	13 c. Missouri	30	20
1637	13 c. Arkansas	30	20
1638	13 c. Michigan	30	20
1639	13 c. Florida	30	20
1640	13 c. Texas	30	20
1641	13 c. Iowa	30	20
1642	13 c. Wisconsin	30	20
1643	13 c. California	30	20
1644	13 c. Minnesota	30	20
1645	13 c. Oregon	30	20
1646	13 c. Kansas	30	20
1647	13 c. West Virginia	30	20
1648	13 c. Nevada	30	20
1649	13 c. Nebraska	35	20
1650	13 c. Colorado	30	20
1651	13 c. North Dakota	30	20
1652	13 c. South Dakota	30	20
1653	13 c. Montana	30	20
1654	13 c. Washington	30	20
1655	13 c. Idaho	30	20
1656	13 c. Wyoming	30	20
1657	13 c. Utah	30	20
1658	13 c. Oklahoma	30	20
1659	13 c. New Mexico	30	20
1660	13 c. Arizona	30	20
1661	13 c. Alaska	30	20
1662	13 c. Hawaii	30	20

1028 Bell's Telephone

1976. Telephone Centenary.
1663 **1028** 13 c. violet, black and red on brown 25 10

1029 Stout Air Pullman and Laird Swallow Biplane

1976. Commercial Aviation.
1664 **1029** 13 c. multicoloured . . . 20 10

1030 Laboratory Equipment

1976. Centenary of American Chemical Society.
1665 **1030** 13 c. multicoloured . . . 20 10

1035 Benjamin Franklin and 1776 Map of North America

1076. American Revolution Bicentennial.
1667 **1035** 13 c. multicoloured . . . 20 10

1036 Part of Assembly **1040** Diving

1976. American Revolution Bicentennial.
1668 **1036** 13 c. multicoloured . . . 30 10
1669 – 13 c. multicoloured . . . 30 10
1670 – 13 c. multicoloured . . . 30 10
1671 – 13 c. multicoloured . . . 30 10
DESIGNS: Nos. 1668/71 as T **1036** form the complete painting "Signing of Declaration of Independence" (John Trumbull).

1976. Olympic Games, Innsbruck and Montreal. Multicoloured.
1672 13 c. Type **1040** 25 10
1673 13 c. Skiing 25 10
1674 13 c. Running 25 10
1675 13 c. Skating 25 10

1044 Clara Maass **1045** A. S. Ochs

1976. Birth Centenary of Clara Maass (martyr to yellow fever).
1676 **1044** 13 c. multicoloured . . . 20 10

1976. Adolph S. Ochs (publisher of "New York Times") Commemoration.
1677 **1045** 13 c. black 20 10

1046 "Winter Pastime" (N. Currier)

1976. Christmas.
1678 13 c. Type **1046** 20 10
1679 13 c. "Nativity" (John S. Copley) 20 10

1048 "Washington at Princeton" (Peale) **1050** Zia Pot

1049 Early Gramophone

1977. American Revolution Bicentennial.
1680 **1048** 13 c. multicoloured . . 20 10

1977. Centenary of Sound Recording.
1681 **1049** 13 c. multicoloured . . 20 10

1977. American Folk Art, Pueblo Art.
1682 13 c. Type **1050** 20 10
1683 13 c. San Ildefonso pot . . . 20 10
1684 13 c. Hopi pot 20 10
1685 13 c. Acoma pot 20 10

1054 "Spirit of St. Louis"

1977. 50th Anniv of Lindbergh's Transatlantic Flight.
1686 **1054** 13 c. multicoloured . . 20 10

1055 Columbine and Rocky Mountains **1056** American Swallowtail

1977. Centenary (1976) of Colorado Statehood.
1687 **1055** 13 c. multicoloured . . 20 10

1977. Butterflies. Multicoloured.
1688 13 c. Type **1056** 20 10
1689 13 c. Checkerspot 20 10
1690 13 c. Dogface 20 10
1691 13 c. Falcate orange-tip . . . 20 10

US Bicentennial 13c
1060 Marquis de Lafayette

1977. American Revolution Bicentennial. Bicentenary of Lafayette's Landing on Coast of South Carolina.
1692 **1060** 13 c. black, blue & red . 20 10

1061 Seamstress

1977. American Revolution Bicentenary. "Skilled Hands for Independence". Multicoloured.
1693 13 c. Type **1061** 20 10
1694 13 c. Blacksmith 20 10
1695 13 c. Wheelwright 20 10
1696 13 c. Leatherworker 20 10

1065 Peace Bridge and Dove

1977. 50th Anniv of Opening of Peace Bridge.
1697 **1065** 13 c. blue 20 10

1066 "Herkimer at Oriskany" (F. Yohn)

1977. American Revolution Bicentennial. Bicentenary of Battle of Oriskany.
1698 **1066** 13 c. multicoloured . . 20 10

1067 Farmhouses, El Pueblo

1977. Bicentenary of First Civil Settlement in Alta California.
1699 **1067** 13 c. multicoloured . . 20 10

1068 Members of the Continental Congress

1977. Bicentenary of Drafting of the Articles of Constitution.
1700 **1068** 13 c. brown and red . . 20 10

1069 "Vitaphone" Projector and Sound Equipment

1977. 50th Anniv of Talking Pictures.
1701 **1069** 13 c. multicoloured . . 30 10

1070 "Surrender of Burgoyne at Saratoga" (J. Trumbull)

1977. American Revolution Bicentennial. Surrender of General Burgoyne.
1702 **1070** 13 c. multicoloured . . 20 10

1071 "Conservation" **1073** Washington at Valley Forge (after Leyendecker)

1977. Energy Conservation and Development.
1703 **1071** 13 c. multicoloured . . 20 10
1704 – 13 c. multicoloured . . 20 10
DESIGN: No. 1704, "Development".

1977. Christmas.
1705 **1073** 13 c. multicoloured . . 20 10
1706 – 13 c. multicoloured . . 20 10
DESIGN: No. 1706, Rural mailbox.

1075 Carl Sandburg **1076** Indian Head Penny

1978. Birth Centenary of Carl Sandburg (poet and biographer).
1707 **1075** 13 c. black and brown . 20 10

1978.
1708 **1076** 13 c. brown & bl on buff 20 10

1077 Captain James Cook (after Nathaniel Dance) **1079** Harriet Tubman and Slaves

1978. Bicentenary of Capt. Cook's Visits to Hawaii and Alaska.
1709 **1077** 13 c. blue 40 10
1710 – 13 c. green 40 10
DESIGNS—HORIZ: No. 1710, H.M.S. "Resolution" and H.M.S. "Discovery" at Hawaii (after John Webber).

1978. Black Heritage. Harriet Tubman (organizer of slave "underground railway").
1711 **1079** 13 c. multicoloured . . 20 10

1082 Quilt Design

1978. American Folk Art. Quilts.
1712 – 13 c. brown and grey . 20 10
1713 – 13 c. red and grey . . . 20 10
1714 **1082** 13 c. multicoloured . . 20 10
1715 – 13 c. multicoloured . . 20 10
DESIGNS: No. 1712, Chequered; 1713, Dotted; 1715, Striped.

1084 Ballet

1978. American Dance.
1716 **1084** 13 c. blue, mve & blk . 20 10
1717 – 13 c. orange, red & blk 20 10
1718 – 13 c. green, yell & blk . 20 10
1719 – 13 c. blue, ultram & blk 20 10
DESIGNS: No. 1717, Theatre; 1718, Folk dance; 1719, Modern.

1088 "Louis XVI and Benjamin Franklin" (statuette, C.G. Sauvage) **1089** Dr. Papanicolaou

1978. Bicentenary of French Alliance.
1720 **1088** 13 c. black, blue & red 25 10

1978. Dr. George Papanicolaou (developer of Pap (cancer detection) test) Commemoration.
1721 **1089** 13 c. brown 20 10

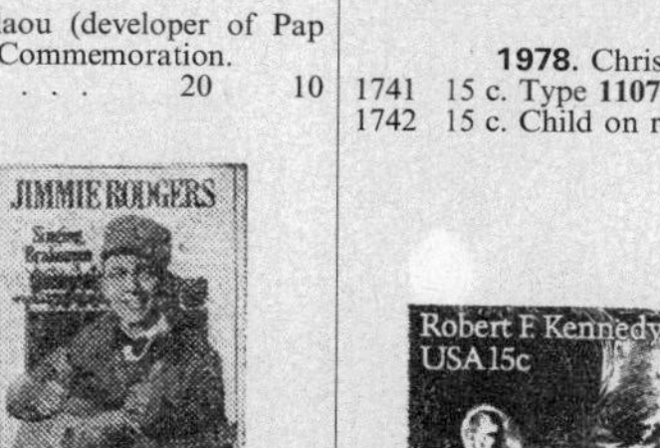

1090 American Eagle **1091** Jimmie Rodgers

1978. No value expressed.
1722 **1090** (15 c.) orange 20 10
For "B" stamp see No. 1843, for "C" stamp Nos 1909/10 and for "D" stamp Nos. 2137/8.

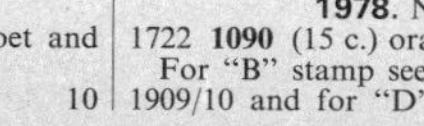

1978. Performing Arts and Artists. Jimmie Rodgers, "Father of Country Music".
1725 **1091** 13 c. multicoloured . . . 30 10

1093 Camera and Accessories **1094** George M. Cohan

1978. Photography.
1727 **1093** 15 c. multicoloured . . . 20 10

1978. Performing Arts. Birth Centenary of George M. Cohan (actor and playwright).
1728 **1094** 15 c. multicoloured . . . 20 10

1095 "Red Masterpiece" and "Medallion" Roses **1096** "Viking 1" Lander scooping Soil from Mars

1978. Roses.
1729 **1095** 15 c. red, orange & grn . 50 10

1978. 2nd Anniv of "Viking 1" Landing on Mars.
1730 **1096** 15 c. multicoloured . . . 20 10

1097 Great Grey Owl **1101** Wright Brothers and Flyer I

1978. Wildlife Conservation. American Owls. Multicoloured.
1731 15 c. Type **1097** 40 10
1732 15 c. Saw-whet owl 40 10
1733 15 c. Barred owl 40 10
1734 15 c. Great horned owl . . . 40 10

1978. Air. 75th Anniv of First Powered Flight. Multicoloured.
A1735 31 c. Type **1101** 75 10
A1736 31 c. Flyer I and Wright Brothers (in bowler hats) 75 10

1103 White Pine **1107** "Madonna and Child with Cherubim" (Andrea della Robbia)

1978. American Trees. Multicoloured.
1737 15 c. Type **1103** 30 10
1738 15 c. Giant sequoia 30 10
1739 15 c. Grey birch 30 10
1740 15 c. White oak 30 10

1978. Christmas. Multicoloured.
1741 15 c. Type **1107** 20 10
1742 15 c. Child on rocking horse . 20 10

1109 Robert F. Kennedy **1110** Martin Luther King

1979. Robert F. Kennedy Commemoration.
1743 **1109** 15 c. blue 20 10

1979. Black Heritage. Martin Luther King (Civil Rights leader).
1744 **1110** 15 c. multicoloured . . 20 10

1111 Children of Different Races **1112** John Steinbeck

1979. International Year of the Child.
1745 **1111** 15 c. red 20 10

1979. Literary Arts. John Steinbeck (novelist).
1746 **1112** 15 c. blue 20 10

1113 Einstein **1114** Chanute and Glider

1979. Birth Cent of Albert Einstein (physicist).
1747 **1113** 15 c. brown 20 10

1979. Air. Aviation Pioneers. Octave Chanute. Multicoloured.
A1748 21 c. Type **1114** 75 10
A1749 21 c. Chanute and glider (different) 75 10

1116 Coffee Pot **1120** Virginia Rotunda (Thomas Jefferson)

1979. American Folk Art. Pennsylvania Toleware. Multicoloured.
1750 15 c. Type **1116** 20 10
1751 15 c. Tea caddy 20 10
1752 15 c. Sugar bowl with lid . . 20 10
1753 15 c. Coffee pot with gooseneck spout 20 10

1979. American Architecture. Each black and red.
1754 15 c. Type **1120** 20 10
1755 15 c. Baltimore Cathedral (Benjamin Latrobe) . . . 20 10
1756 15 c. Boston State House (Charles Bulfinch) 20 10
1757 15 c. Philadelphia Exchange (William Strickland) . . . 20 10

1124 Persistent Trillium **1128** Guide Dog

1979. Endangered Flora. Multicoloured.
1758 15 c. Type **1124** 20 10
1759 15 c. Hawaiian wild broadbean 20 10
1760 15 c. Contra costa wallflower 20 10
1761 15 c. Antioch dunes evening primrose 20 10

1979. 50th Anniv of First U.S. Guide Dog Programme.
1762 **1128** 15 c. multicoloured . . 30 10

1129 Child with Medal **1130** Throwing the Javelin (Decathlon)

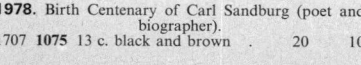

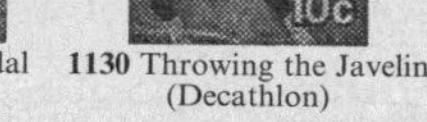

1979. Special Olympic Games for the Handicapped.
1763 **1129** 15 c. multicoloured . . 20 10

1979. Olympic Games, Moscow (1980). Multicoloured.
1764 10 c. Type **1130** (postage) . 15 10
1765 15 c. Running (horiz) . . . 20 10
1766 15 c. Swimming (horiz) . . 20 10
1767 15 c. Rowing (horiz) 20 10
1768 15 c. Show jumping (horiz) . 20 10
A1769 31 c. High jumping (horiz) (air) 50 55

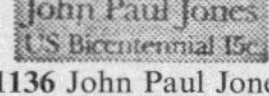

1136 John Paul Jones (after Peale) **1137** "Rest on the Flight to Egypt" (G. David)

1979. American Revolution Bicentennial. John Paul Jones (naval commander).
1770 **1136** 15 c. multicoloured . . 20 10

1979. Christmas. Multicoloured.
1771 15 c. Type **1137** 20 10
1772 15 c. Santa Claus tree ornament 20 10

1139 Will Rogers **1140** Vietnam Service Medal Ribbon

1979. Performing Arts and Artists. Will Rogers (cowboy philosopher).
1773 **1139** 15 c. multicoloured . . 20 10

1979. Vietnam Veterans.
1774 **1140** 15 c. multicoloured . . 20 10

1141 Wiley Post **1143** W. C. Fields

1979. Air. Aviation Pioneers. Wiley Post. Mult.
A1775 25 c. Type **1141** . . . . . 1·50 40
A1776 25 c. Wiley Post and airplane "Winnie Mae" . . . . . 1·50 40

1980. Performing Arts and Artists. W. C. Fields (comedian).
1777 **1143** 15 c. multicoloured . . 20 10

1144 Speed Skating **1148** Robertson Windmill, Williamsburg, Va

1980. Winter Olympic Games, Lake Placid. Mult.
1778 15 c. Type **1144** 20 10
1779 15 c. Downhill skiing 20 10
1780 15 c. Ski jumping 20 10
1781 15 c. Ice hockey 20 10

1980. Windmills.
1782 **1148** 15 c. brown on yellow . 45 10
1783 – 15 c. brown on yellow . 45 10
1784 – 15 c. brown on yellow . 45 10
1785 – 15 c. brown on yellow . 45 10
1786 – 15 c. brown on yellow . 45 10
DESIGNS: No. 1783, Replica of old windmill, Portsmouth, R.I; 1784, Cape Cod windmill, Eastham, Mass; 1785, Dutch mill, Fabyan Park Forest Preserve, Ill; 1786, Southwestern windmill, Texas.

1153 Benjamin Banneker

1980. Black Heritage. Benjamin Banneker (astronomer and mathematician).
1787 **1153** 15 c. multicoloured . . 20 10

1154 Photograph and Envelope **1157** "P.S. Write Soon"

1980. National Letter Writing Week.
1788 **1154** 15 c. multicoloured . . 20 10
1789 **1157** 15 c. multicoloured (purple background) 20 10
1790 – 15 c. multicoloured . . 20 10
1791 **1157** 15 c. multicoloured (green background) 20 10
1792 – 15 c. multicoloured . . 20 10
1793 **1157** 15 c. blue, blk & red . . 20 10
DESIGNS—As T **1154**: No. 1790, Flowers and envelope; 1792, Capitol and envelope.

1158 Frances Perkins **1159** Dolley Madison (after Stuart)

1980. Frances Perkins (first woman Cabinet member) Commemoration.
1794 **1158** 15 c. blue 20 10

1980.
1795 **1159** 15 c. dp brown & brn . 20 10

1160 Emily Bissell **1161** Helen Keller and Anne Sullivan

1980. Emily Bissell (crusader against tuberculosis) Commemoration.
1796 **1160** 15 c. black and red . . 25 10

1980. Birth Centenary of Helen Keller.
1797 **1161** 15 c. multicoloured . . 20 10

1162 Veterans Administration Emblem **1163** Statue of Gen. Galvez, Mobile

1980. 50th Anniv of Veterans Administration.
1798 **1162** 15 c. red and blue . . . 20 10

1980. General Bernardo de Galvez (leader of Spanish forces in Louisiana during American Revolution) Commemoration.
1799 **1163** 15 c. multicoloured . . 20 10

1164 Brain Corals **1168** American Bald Eagle

1980. Coral Reefs. Multicoloured.
1800 15 c. Type **1164** 20 10
1801 15 c. Elkhorn coral 20 10
1802 15 c. Chalice coral 20 10
1803 15 c. Finger coral 20 10

1980. Organized Labour.
1804 **1168** 15 c. multicoloured . . . 30 10

1169 Edith Wharton **1170** "Homage to the Square: Glow" (J. Albers)

1980. Literary Arts. Edith Wharton (novelist).
1805 **1169** 15 c. violet 20 10

1980. American Education.
1806 **1170** 15 c. multicoloured . . . 20 10

1171 Heiltsuk, Bella Bella

1980. American Folk Art, Indian Masks. Mult.
1807 15 c. Type **1171** 20 10
1808 15 c. Chilkat Tlingit 20 10
1809 15 c. Tlingit 20 10
1810 15 c. Bella Coola 20 10

1175 Smithsonian Institution, Washington (James Renwick) **1179** Philip Mazzei

1980. American Architecture.
1811 **1175** 15 c. black and red . . . 20 10
1812 – 15 c. black and red . . . 20 10
1813 – 15 c. black and red . . . 20 10
1814 – 15 c. black and red . . . 20 10
DESIGNS: No. 1812, Trinity Church, Boston (Henry Hobson Richardson); 1813, Penn Academy, Philadelphia, (Frank Furness); 1814, Lyndhurst, Tarrytown, New York (Alexander Jackson Davis).

1980. Air. Philip Mazzei (patriot) Commem.
A1815 **1179** 40 c. multicoloured . . 50 15

1180 "Madonna and Child" (Epiphany Window, Washington Cathedral) **1181** Antique Toys

1980. Christmas.
1816 **1180** 15 c. multicoloured . . . 20 10
1817 **1181** 15 c. multicoloured . . . 20 10

1191 Sequoyah (Cherokee scholar) (after C. B. Wilson) **1203** Blanche Stuart Scott

1980. Great Americans. With "c" after face value.
1818 – 1 c. black 10 10
1819 – 2 c. black 10 10
1820 – 3 c. green 10 10
1821 – 4 c. violet 10 10
1822 – 5 c. red 10 10
1823 – 10 c. blue 25 10
1824 – 13 c. red 30 10
1825 – 17 c. green 30 10
1826 – 18 c. blue 40 10
1827 **1191** 19 c. brown 40 10
1828 – 20 c. purple 30 10
1829 – 20 c. green 45 10
1830 – 20 c. black 45 10
1831 – 30 c. green 40 10
1832 – 35 c. black 60 10
1833 – 37 c. blue 50 10
1834 – 40 c. green 70 10
DESIGNS: 1 c. Dorothea Dix (social pioneer); 2 c. Igor Stravinsky (composer); 3 c. Henry Clay (politician); 4 c. Carl Schurz (reformer); 5 c. Pearl Buck (author) (after F. Elliot); 10 c. Richard Russell (politician); 13 c. Crazy Horse (Sioux chief) (after K. Ziolkowski); 17 c. Rachel Carson (scientist); 18 c. George Mason (patriot); 20 c. (1828), Ralph Bunche (U.N. Secretariat member); 20 c. (1829), Thomas H. Gallaudet (educator of the deaf); 20 c. (1830), Pres. Harry S. Truman; 30 c. Frank C. Laubach (literacy educator); 35 c. Charles R. Drew (surgeon); 37 c. Robert Millikan (physicist); 40 c. Lillian M. Gilbreth (engineer).
For similar designs without "c", see Nos. 2108/42.

1980. Air. Aviation Pioneers. Multicoloured.
A1839 28 c. Type **1203** 55 15
A1839 35 c. Glenn Curtiss 60 15

1205 Everett Dirksen **1206** Whitney Moore Young

1981. Senator Everett Dirksen Commemoration.
1841 **1205** 15 c. grey 20 10

1981. Black Heritage. Whitney Moore Young (civil rights leader).
1842 **1206** 15 c. multicoloured . . 20 10

1981. Non-denominational "B" stamp. As T **1090**.
1843 (18 c.) lilac 50 10

1207 Rose

1981. Flowers. Multicoloured.
1846 18 c. Type **1207** 25 10
1847 18 c. Camellia 25 10
1848 18 c. Dahlia 25 10
1849 18 c. Lily 25 10

1211 ". . . for amber waves of grain" **1212** Stars

1981.
1851 **1212** 6 c. blue and red . . . 90 15
1850 **1211** 18 c. brown, red and bl 30 10
1852 – 18 c. lilac, red and blue 35 10
1853 – 18 c. brown, blue & red 55 10
DESIGNS—As T **1211**: No. 1852, ". . . for purple mountain majesties"; 1853, ". . . from sea to shining sea".

1215 Nurse and Child **1216** Money Box

1981. Centenary of American Red Cross.
1854 **1215** 18 c. multicoloured . . 25 10

1981. 150th Anniv of First Savings and Loans Association.
1855 **1216** 18 c. multicoloured . . 25 10

1217 American Bighorn **1238** Detroit Electric Auto, 1917

1981. Wildlife.
1856 **1217** 18 c. brown 60 10
1857 – 18 c. brown 60 10
1858 – 18 c. brown 60 10
1859 – 18 c. brown 60 10
1860 – 18 c. brown 60 10
1861 – 18 c. brown 60 10
1862 – 18 c. brown 60 10
1863 – 18 c. brown 60 10
1864 – 18 c. brown 60 10
1865 – 18 c. brown 60 10
DESIGNS: No. 1857, Puma; 1858, Common seal; 1859, American bison; 1860, Brown bear; 1861, Polar bear; 1862, Red deer; 1863, Elk; 1864, White-tailed deer; 1865, Pronghorn.

1981. Transport. With "c" after face value.
1866 – 1 c. violet 10 10
1867 – 2 c. black 10 10
1868 – 3 c. green 10 10
1869 – 4 c. brown 10 10
1870 – 5 c. green 10 10
1871 – 5.2 c. red 15 10
1872 – 5.9 c. blue 10 10
1873 – 7.4 c. brown 25 10
1874 – 9.3 c. red 30 10
1875 – 10.9 c. mauve 50 10
1876a – 11 c. red 15 10
1877 **1238** 17 c. blue 20 10
1878 – 18 c. brown 40 10
1879 – 20 c. red 45 10
DESIGNS: 1 c. Omnibus, 1880s; 2 c. Locomotive, 1870s; 3 c. Handcar, 1880s; 4 c. Concord stage-coach, 1890s; 5 c. Pope motor-cycle, 1913; 5.2 c. Sleigh, 1880s; 5.9 c. Bicycle, 1870s; 7.4 c. Baby buggy, 1880s; 9.3 c. Mail wagon, 1880s; 10.9 c. Hansom cab, 1890s; 11 c. Railway caboose, 1890s; 18 c. Surrey, 1890s; 20 c. Amoskeag fire pumper, 1860s.
For similar designs without "c", see Nos. 2150/74 and 2480/96.

1247 Exploring the Moon ("Apollo" mission) **1255** Joseph Wharton (founder of Wharton School)

1981. Space Achievements.
1886 **1247** 18 c. multicoloured . . 30 10
1887 – 18 c. multicoloured . . 30 10
1888 – 18 c. multicoloured . . 30 10
1889 – 18 c. multicoloured . . 30 10
1890 – 18 c. multicoloured . . 30 10
1891 – 18 c. multicoloured . . 30 10
1892 – 18 c. multicoloured . . 30 10
1893 – 18 c. multicoloured . . 30 10
DESIGNS: No. 1887, Space Shuttle loosing boosters; 1888, Space Shuttle performing experiment; 1889, Understanding the Sun ("Skylab"); 1890, Probing the Planets ("Pioneer II"); 1891, Space Shuttle launch; 1892, Space Shuttle landing; 1893, Comprehending the Universe (space telescope).
Nos. 1886/93 were issued together in se-tenant blocks of eight, each block forming a composite design.

1981. Cent of Professional Management Education.
1894 **1255** 18 c. blue and black . . 25 10

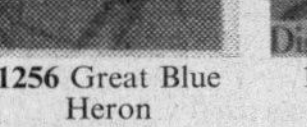
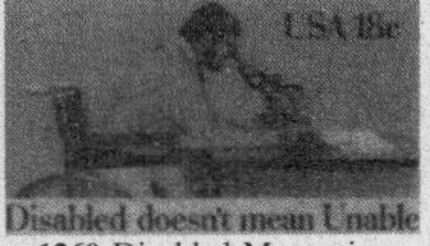

1256 Great Blue Heron **1260** Disabled Man using Microscope

1981. Wildlife Habitats.
1895 **1256** 18 c. multicoloured . . 50 20
1896 – 18 c. multicoloured . . 50 20
1897 – 18 c. multicoloured . . 50 20
1898 – 18 c. multicoloured . . 50 20
DESIGNS: No. 1896, American badger; 1897, Brown bear; 1898, Ruffed grouse.

1981. International Year of Disabled Persons.
1899 **1260** 18 c. multicoloured . . 25 10

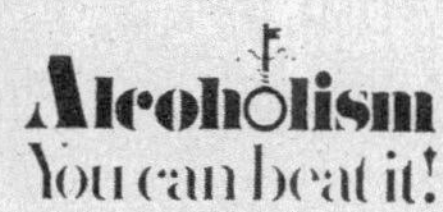

1261 Edna St. Vincent Millay **1262** "Alcoholism. You can beat it"

1981. Edna St. Vincent Millay (poet) Commem.
1900 **1261** 18 c. multicoloured . . 25 10

1981. Anti-alcoholism Campaign.
1901 **1262** 18 c. blue and black . . 25 10

1263 New York University Library (Stanford White) **1267** Bobby Jones (golfer)

1981. American Architecture (3rd series).
1902 **1263** 18 c. black & brown . 25 10
1903 – 18 c. black & brown . 25 10
1904 – 18 c. black & brown . 25 10
1905 – 18 c. black & brown . 25 10
DESIGNS: No. 1903, Biltmore House, Asheville, North Carolina (Richard Morris Hunt); 1904, Palace of Arts, San Francisco (Bernard Maybeck); 1905, Bank, Owatonna, Minnesota (Louis Sullivan).

1981. American Sports Personalities.
1906 **1267** 18 c. green 50 10
1907 – 18 c. red 50 10
DESIGN: No. 1907, Babe Zaharias (golfer and athlete).

1269 "Coming through the Rye"

1981. Frederic Remington (sculptor) Commemoration.
1908 **1269** 18 c. brown, green and light brown 40 10

1981. Non-denominational "C" stamp. As T **1090** but inscribed "Domestic Mail".
1909 (20 c.) brown (19 × 22 mm) . 40 10
1910 (20 c.) brown (15 × $18\frac{1}{2}$ mm) 45 10

1271 James Hoban and White House

1981. 150th Death Anniv of James Hoban (architect).
1912 **1271** 18 c. multicoloured . . 40 20
1913 20 c. multicoloured . . 40 10

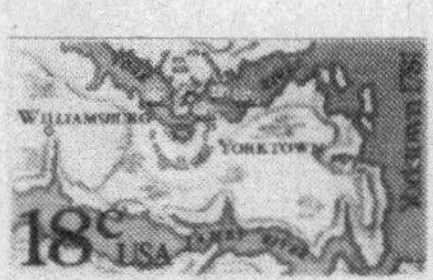

1272 Map of Yorktown Peninsula **1274** "Madonna and Child" (Botticelli)

1981. Bicentenary of Battles of Yorktown and Virginia Capes. Multicoloured.
1914 18 c. Type **1272** 35 10
1915 18 c. French ships blocking Chesapeake Bay 35 10

1981. Christmas. No value expressed. Mult.
1916 (20 c.) Type **1274** 25 10
1917 (20 c.) Teddy bear on sleigh 25 10

1276 John Hanson **1277** Barrel Cactus

1981. John Hanson (American revolutionary leader) Commemoration.
1918 **1276** 20 c. multicoloured . . . 35 10

1981. Desert Plants. Multicoloured.
1919 20 c. Type **1277** 50 10
1920 20 c. Agave (horiz) 50 10
1921 20 c. Saguaro 50 10
1922 20 c. Beavertail cactus (horiz) 50 10

1281 Flag over Supreme Court **1282** American Bighorn

1981.
1923 **1281** 20 c. black, red & blue . 35 10

1982.
1926 **1282** 20 c. blue 40 10

1283 Franklin D. Roosevelt

1982. Birth Centenary of President Franklin D. Roosevelt.
1927 **1283** 20 c. blue 30 10

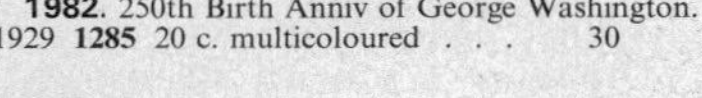

1284 Flowers spelling "Love" **1285** George Washington

1982. Greetings Stamp.
1928 **1284** 20 c. multicoloured . . . 30 10

1982. 250th Birth Anniv of George Washington.
1929 **1285** 20 c. multicoloured . . . 30 10

1286 Common Flicker (inscr "Yellow-hammer") and Camellia (Alabama) **1287** Stripes in National Colours

1982. State Birds and Flowers. Multicoloured.
1930 20 c. Type **1286** 55 20
1931 20 c. Willow grouse (inscr "Ptarmigan") and forget-me-not (Alaska) 55 20
1932 20 c. Cactus wren and saguaro cactus blossom (Arizona) . 55 20
1933 20 c. Northern mockingbird and apple blossom (Arkansas) . 55 20
1934 20 c. California quail and California poppy (California) 55 20
1935 20 c. Lark bunting and Rocky Mountain columbine (Colorado) 55 20
1936 20 c. American robin and mountain laurel (Connecticut) 55 20
1937 20 c. Blue hen chicken and peach blossom (Delaware) . 55 20
1938 20 c. Northern mockingbird and orange blossom (Florida) 55 20
1939 20 c. Brown thrasher and Cherokee rose (Georgia) . . 55 20

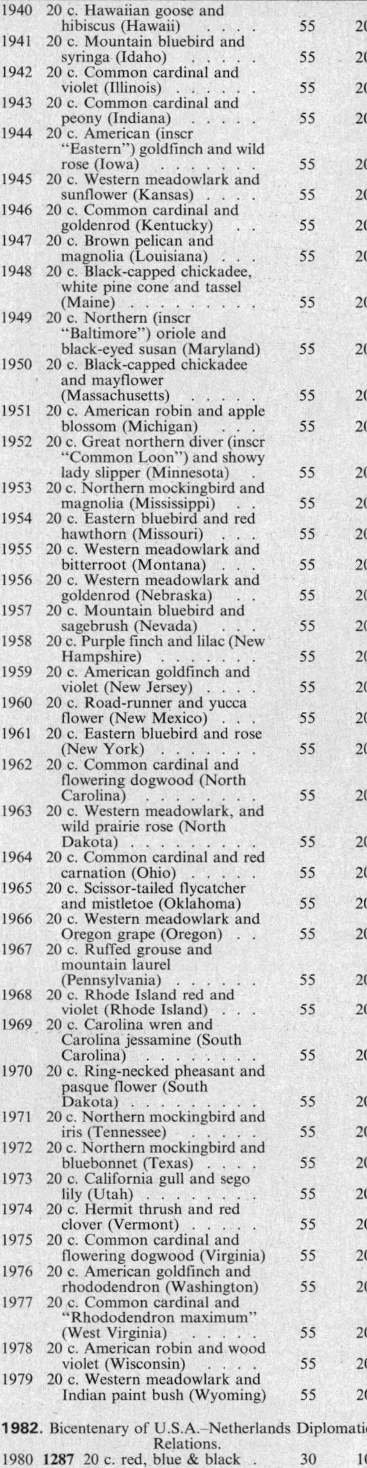
1940 20 c. Hawaiian goose and hibiscus (Hawaii) 55 20
1941 20 c. Mountain bluebird and syringa (Idaho) 55 20
1942 20 c. Common cardinal and violet (Illinois) 55 20
1943 20 c. Common cardinal and peony (Indiana) 55 20
1944 20 c. American (inscr "Eastern") goldfinch and wild rose (Iowa) 55 20
1945 20 c. Western meadowlark and sunflower (Kansas) 55 20
1946 20 c. Common cardinal and goldenrod (Kentucky) . . 55 20
1947 20 c. Brown pelican and magnolia (Louisiana) . . . 55 20
1948 20 c. Black-capped chickadee, white pine cone and tassel (Maine) 55 20
1949 20 c. Northern (inscr "Baltimore") oriole and black-eyed susan (Maryland) 55 20
1950 20 c. Black-capped chickadee and mayflower (Massachusetts) 55 20
1951 20 c. American robin and apple blossom (Michigan) . . . 55 20
1952 20 c. Great northern diver (inscr "Common Loon") and showy lady slipper (Minnesota) . 55 20
1953 20 c. Northern mockingbird and magnolia (Mississippi) . . 55 20
1954 20 c. Eastern bluebird and red hawthorn (Missouri) . . . 55 20
1955 20 c. Western meadowlark and bitterroot (Montana) . . . 55 20
1956 20 c. Western meadowlark and goldenrod (Nebraska) . . 55 20
1957 20 c. Mountain bluebird and sagebrush (Nevada) . . . 55 20
1958 20 c. Purple finch and lilac (New Hampshire) 55 20
1959 20 c. American goldfinch and violet (New Jersey) 55 20
1960 20 c. Road-runner and yucca flower (New Mexico) . . . 55 20
1961 20 c. Eastern bluebird and rose (New York) 55 20
1962 20 c. Common cardinal and flowering dogwood (North Carolina) 55 20
1963 20 c. Western meadowlark, and wild prairie rose (North Dakota) 55 20
1964 20 c. Common cardinal and red carnation (Ohio) 55 20
1965 20 c. Scissor-tailed flycatcher and mistletoe (Oklahoma) 55 20
1966 20 c. Western meadowlark and Oregon grape (Oregon) . . 55 20
1967 20 c. Ruffed grouse and mountain laurel (Pennsylvania) 55 20
1968 20 c. Rhode Island red and violet (Rhode Island) . . . 55 20
1969 20 c. Carolina wren and Carolina jessamine (South Carolina) 55 20
1970 20 c. Ring-necked pheasant and pasque flower (South Dakota) 55 20
1971 20 c. Northern mockingbird and iris (Tennessee) 55 20
1972 20 c. Northern mockingbird and bluebonnet (Texas) 55 20
1973 20 c. California gull and sego lily (Utah) 55 20
1974 20 c. Hermit thrush and red clover (Vermont) 55 20
1975 20 c. Common cardinal and flowering dogwood (Virginia) 55 20
1976 20 c. American goldfinch and rhododendron (Washington) 55 20
1977 20 c. Common cardinal and "Rhododendron maximum" (West Virginia) 55 20
1978 20 c. American robin and wood violet (Wisconsin) 55 20
1979 20 c. Western meadowlark and Indian paint bush (Wyoming) 55 20

1982. Bicentenary of U.S.A.–Netherlands Diplomatic Relations.
1980 **1287** 20 c. red, blue & black . 30 10

1288 Library of Congress **1289** Garment Tag

1982. Library of Congress.
1981 **1288** 20 c. black and red . . 30 10

1982. Consumer Education.
1982 **1289** 20 c. blue 30 10

1290 Solar Energy **1294** Frontispiece from "Ragged Dick"

1982. Knoxville World's Fair.

1983	**1290**	20 c. multicoloured	40	10
1984	–	20 c. multicoloured	40	10
1985	–	20 c. blue, light blue and black	40	10
1986	–	20 c. blue, black and brown	40	10

DESIGNS: No. 1984, Synthetic fuels; 1985, Breeder reactor; 1986, Fossil fuels.

1982. 150th Birth Anniv of Horatio Alger (novelist).
1987 **1294** 20 c. black and red on buff 30 10

1295 Family Group **1296** John, Ethel and Lionel Barrymore

1982. Ageing Together.
1988 **1295** 20 c. red 30 10

1982. Performing Arts and Artists. The Barrymores (theatrical family).
1989 **1296** 20 c. multicoloured 30 10

1297 Dr. Mary Walker **1298** Maple Leaf and Rose

1982. Dr. Mary Walker (army surgeon) Commemoration.
1990 **1297** 20 c. multicoloured 30 10

1982. 50th Anniv of International Peace Garden (on U.S.A.–Canada border).
1991 **1298** 20 c. multicoloured 30 10

1299 Typographic Design **1300** Jackie Robinson

1982. America's Libraries.
1992 **1299** 20 c. red and black 30 10

1982. Black Heritage, Jackie Robinson (baseball player).
1993 **1300** 20 c. multicoloured 95 10

1301 Touro Synagogue

1982. Touro Synagogue, Newport, Rhode Island.
1994 **1301** 20 c. multicoloured 40 10

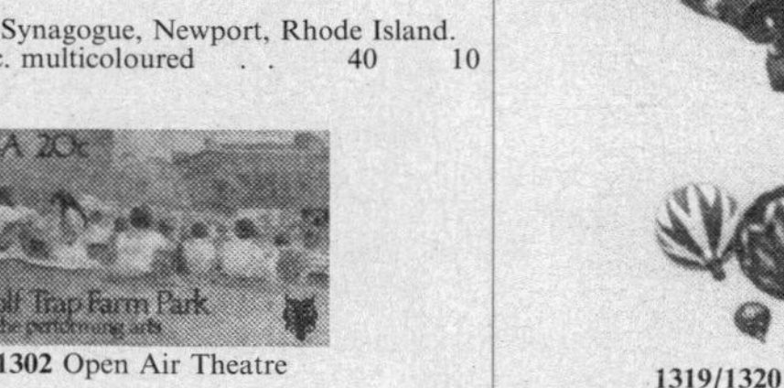

1302 Open Air Theatre

1982. Wolf Trap Farm Park, Vienna, Virginia.
1995 **1302** 20 c. multicoloured 35 10

1303 Fallingwater, Mill Run, Philadelphia (Frank Lloyd Wright)

1982. American Architecture.

1996	**1303**	20 c. black & brown	50	10
1997	–	20 c. black & brown	50	10
1998	–	20 c. black & brown	50	10
1999	–	20 c. black & brown	50	10

DESIGNS: No. 1997, Illinois Institute of Technology, Chicago (Mies van der Rohe); 1998, Gropius House, Lincoln, Massachusetts (Walter Gropius); 1999, Dulles Airport, Washington D.C. (Eero Saarinen).

1307 St. Francis and Doves

1982. 800th Birth Anniv of St. Francis of Assisi.
2000 **1307** 20 c. multicoloured 30 10

1308 Ponce de Leon and Map of Florida **1309** "Madonna and Child" (Tiepolo)

1982. Ponce de Leon (explorer) Commemoration.
2001 **1308** 20 c. multicoloured 30 10

1982. Christmas. Multicoloured.

2002	20 c. Type **1309**	25	10
2003	20 c. Building a snowman (horiz)	35	10
2004	20 c. Sledging (horiz)	35	10
2005	20 c. Decorating a Christmas tree (horiz)	35	10
2006	20 c. Skating (horiz)	35	10

1314 Puppy and Kitten **1316** Industrial Complex

1982.
2007 **1314** 13 c. multicoloured 20 10

1983. Science and Industry.
2015 **1316** 20 c. multicoloured 30 10

1317 Benjamin Franklin and Great Seal of Sweden

1983. Bicentenary of Sweden–U.S.A. Treaty of Amity and Commerce.
2016 **1317** 20 c. indigo, brown and black 30 10

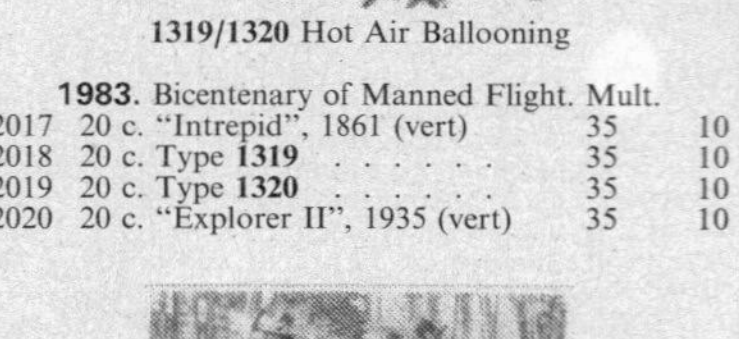

1319/1320 Hot Air Ballooning

1983. Bicentenary of Manned Flight. Mult.

2017	20 c. "Intrepid", 1861 (vert)	35	10
2018	20 c. Type **1319**	35	10
2019	20 c. Type **1320**	35	10
2020	20 c. "Explorer II", 1935 (vert)	35	10

1322 C.C.C. Workers repairing Trail

1983. 50th Anniv of Civilian Conservation Corps.
2021 **1322** 20 c. multicoloured 30 10

1323 Shot Putting **1327** Joseph Priestley (after G. Stuart)

1983. Air. Olympic Games, Los Angeles (1984) (1st issue). Multicoloured.

A2022	40 c. Type **1323**	60	25
A2023	40 c. Gymnastics	60	25
A2024	40 c. Swimming	60	25
A2025	40 c. Weightlifting	60	25

See also Nos. A2034/7, 2040/3, A2058/61 and 2079/82.

1983. 250th Birth Anniv of Joseph Priestley (discoverer of oxygen).
2026 **1327** 20 c. multicoloured 30 10

1328 Reaching Hands

1983. Voluntary Work.
2027 **1328** 20 c. black and red 30 10

1329 "Concord"

1983. 300th Anniv of First German Settlers in America.
2028 **1329** 20 c. brown 40 10

1330 Joggers and Electrocardiograph Trace

1983. Physical Fitness.
2029 **1330** 20 c. multicoloured 30 10

1331 Brooklyn Bridge

1983. Centenary of Brooklyn Bridge.
2030 **1331** 20 c. blue 40 10

1332 Norris Hydro-electric Dam

1983. 50th Anniv of Tennessee Valley Authority.
2031 **1332** 20 c. multicoloured 30 10

1333 Army, Air Force and Navy Medals of Honour **1334** Scott Joplin

1983. Medal of Honour.
2032 **1333** 20 c. multicoloured 30 10

1983. Black Heritage. Scott Joplin (ragtime composer).
2033 **1334** 20 c. multicoloured 35 10

1335 Gymnastics **1339** Babe Ruth

1983. Air. Olympic Games, Los Angeles (1984) (2nd issue). Multicoloured.

A2034	28 c. Type **1335**	60	15
A2035	28 c. Hurdling	60	15
A2036	28 c. Basketball	60	15
A2037	28 c. Football	60	15

1983. American Sports Personalities. Babe Ruth (baseball player).
2038 **1339** 20 c. blue 1·00 10

1340 Hawthorne (after C. G. Thompson) **1341** Discus

1983. Literary Arts. Nathaniel Hawthorne (writer).
2039 **1340** 20 c. multicoloured 30 10

1983. Olympic Games, Los Angeles (1984) (3rd issue). Multicoloured.

2040	13 c. Type **1341**	25	10
2041	13 c. High jump	25	10
2042	13 c. Archery	25	10
2043	13 c. Boxing	25	10

1345 American Bald Eagle and Moon

1983.
2044 **1345** $9.35 multicoloured 17·00 7·00

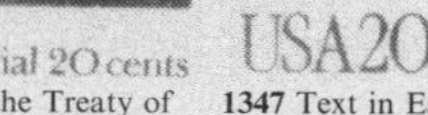

1346 Signing the Treaty of Paris (after Benjamin West) **1347** Text in Early and Modern Type

1983. Bicentenary of Treaty of Paris.
2045 **1346** 20 c. multicoloured 35 10

1983. Centenary of Civil Service.
2046 **1347** 20 c. stone, red & black 30 10

1348 Part of Proscenium and Modern Facade

1983. Centenary of Metropolitan Opera, New York.
2047 **1348** 20 c. yellow & purple 40 10

1349 Charles Steinmetz and Graph

1983. American Inventors.

2048 **1349** 20 c. pink and black . . 35 10
2049 – 20 c. pink and black . . 35 10
2050 – 20 c. pink and black . . 35 10
2051 – 20 c. pink and black . . 35 10

DESIGNS: No. 2049, Edwin Armstrong and frequency modulator; 2050, Nikola Tesla and induction motor; 2051, Philo T. Farnsworth and television camera.

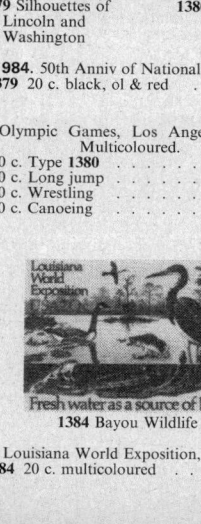

1353 "John Mason" Streetcar, New York, 1832

1983. Streetcars. Multicoloured.

2052 20 c. Type **1353** 45 15
2053 20 c. Early electric streetcar, Montgomery, 1886 . . . . 45 15
2054 20 c. "Bobtail" horsecar, Sulphur Rock, 1926 . . . . 45 15
2055 20 c. St. Charles Streetcar, New Orleans, 1923 . . . . . . 45 15

1357 "Madonna and Child" (Raphael)

1358 Santa Claus

1983. Christmas.

2056 **1357** 20 c. multicoloured . . 25 10
2057 **1358** 20 c. multicoloured . . 25 10

1359 Fencing

1983. Air. Olympic Games, Los Angeles (1984) (4th issue). Multicoloured.

A2058 35 c. Type **1359** 60 20
A2059 35 c. Cycling 60 20
A2060 35 c. Volleyball 60 20
A2061 35 c. Pole vault 60 20

1363 Martin Luther

1364 Reindeer and Pipeline

1983. 500th Birth Anniv of Martin Luther.

2062 **1363** 20 c. multicoloured . . 30 10

1984. 25th Anniv of Alaska Statehood.

2063 **1364** 20 c. multicoloured . . 30 10

1365 Ice Dancing

1369 Column and "$" Sign

1984. Winter Olympic Games, Sarajevo. Mult.

2064 20 c. Type **1365** 50 10
2065 20 c. Downhill skiing 50 10
2066 20 c. Cross-country skiing . . 50 10
2067 20 c. Ice hockey 50 10

1984. 50th Anniv of Federal Deposit Insurance Corporation.

2068 **1369** 20 c. multicoloured . . 30 10

1370 "Love"

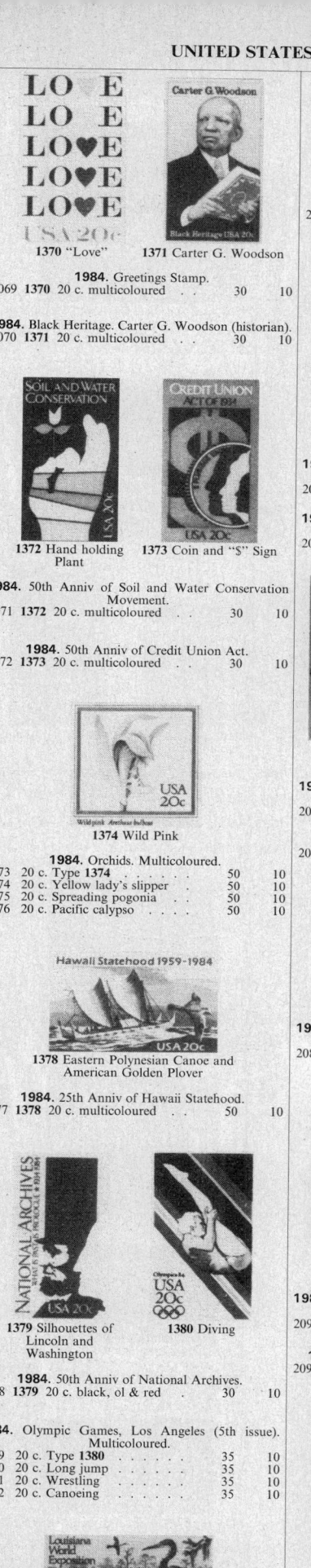

1371 Carter G. Woodson

1984. Greetings Stamp.

2069 **1370** 20 c. multicoloured . . 30 10

1984. Black Heritage. Carter G. Woodson (historian).

2070 **1371** 20 c. multicoloured . . 30 10

1372 Hand holding Plant

1373 Coin and "$" Sign

1984. 50th Anniv of Soil and Water Conservation Movement.

2071 **1372** 20 c. multicoloured . . 30 10

1984. 50th Anniv of Credit Union Act.

2072 **1373** 20 c. multicoloured . . 30 10

1374 Wild Pink

1984. Orchids. Multicoloured.

2073 20 c. Type **1374** 50 10
2074 20 c. Yellow lady's slipper . . 50 10
2075 20 c. Spreading pogonia . . 50 10
2076 20 c. Pacific calypso 50 10

1378 Eastern Polynesian Canoe and American Golden Plover

1984. 25th Anniv of Hawaii Statehood.

2077 **1378** 20 c. multicoloured . . 50 10

1379 Silhouettes of Lincoln and Washington

1380 Diving

1984. 50th Anniv of National Archives.

2078 **1379** 20 c. black, ol & red . 30 10

1984. Olympic Games, Los Angeles (5th issue). Multicoloured.

2079 20 c. Type **1380** 35 10
2080 20 c. Long jump 35 10
2081 20 c. Wrestling 35 10
2082 20 c. Canoeing 35 10

1384 Bayou Wildlife

1984. Louisiana World Exposition, New Orleans.

2083 **1384** 20 c. multicoloured . . 40 10

1385 Laboratory Equipment

1984. Health Research.

2084 **1385** 20 c. multicoloured . . . 30 10

1386 Fairbanks in Film Roles

1387 Jim Thorpe

1984. Performing Arts and Artists. Douglas Fairbanks (film actor).

2085 **1386** 20 c. multicoloured . . . 40 10

1984. American Sports Personalities. Jim Thorpe (athlete, footballer and baseball player).

2086 **1387** 20 c. brown 40 10

1388 John McCormack

1389 St. Lawrence Seaway

1984. Performing Arts and Artists. John McCormack (singer).

2087 **1388** 20 c. multicoloured . . . 50 10

1984. 25th Anniv of St. Lawrence Seaway.

2088 **1389** 20 c. multicoloured . . . 30 10

1390 "Mallards dropping In" (Jay Norwood Darling)

1984. 50th Anniv of Migratory Bird Hunting and Conservation Stamp Act.

2089 **1390** 20 c. blue 50 10

1391 "Elizabeth"

1392 Melville (after J. O. Eaton)

1984. Explorers. 400th Anniv of First Raleigh Expedition to Roanoke Island, North Carolina.

2090 **1391** 20 c. multicoloured . . . 40 10

1984. Literary Arts. Herman Melville (novelist).

2091 **1392** 20 c. green 30 10

1393 Horace Moses

1394 Smokey Bear and American Black Bear Cub clinging to burnt Tree

1984. Horace Moses (founder of Junior Achievement (training organization) Commemoration.

2092 **1393** 20 c. orange & black . . 30 10

1984. Smokey Bear (symbol of forest fire prevention campaign).

2093 **1394** 20 c. multicoloured . . . 30 10

1395 Clemente and Flag of Puerto Rico

1396 Beagle and Boston Terrier

1984. American Sports Personalities. Roberto Clemente (baseball player).

2094 **1395** 20 c. multicoloured . . 75 10

1984. Centenary of American Kennel Club. Multicoloured.

2095 20 c. Type **1396** 50 10
2096 20 c. Chesapeake Bay retriever and cocker spaniel 50 10
2097 20 c. Alaskan malamute and collie 50 10
2098 20 c. Black and Tan coonhound and American foxhound . . . 50 10

1400 McGruff (campaign character)

1401 "Family Unity"

1984. National Crime Prevention Month.

2099 **1400** 20 c. multicoloured . . 30 10

1984. National Stamp Collecting Month.

2100 **1401** 20 c. black, red and blue 30 10

1402 Eleanor Roosevelt

1403 Abraham Lincoln reading to his Son, Tad

1984. Eleanor Roosevelt Commemoration.

2101 **1402** 20 c. blue 30 10

1984. "Nation of Readers"

2102 **1403** 20 c. brown and red . . 30 10

1404 "Madonna and Child (Fra Filippo Lippi)

1406 Uniformed Group and Flag

1984. Christmas.

2103 20 c. Type **1404** 25 10
2104 20 c. Santa Claus 25 10

1984. Hispanic Americans.

2105 **1406** 20 c. multicoloured . . 30 10

1407 Memorial (Maya Ying Lin)

1984. Vietnam Veterans Memorial, Washington, D.C.

2106 **1407** 20 c. black, green and deep green 30 10

1408 Kern 1409 Margaret Mitchell (writer)

1985. Performing Arts and Artists. Birth Centenary of Jerome Kern (composer).

2107	**1408**	22 c. multicoloured . .	30	10

1985. Great Americans. Without "c" after face value.

2108	**1409**	1 c. brown	10	10
2109	–	2 c. blue	10	10
2110	–	3 c. blue	10	10
2111	–	4 c. blue	10	10
2112	–	5 c. green	10	10
2113	–	6 c. red	10	10
2114	–	7 c. red	10	10
2115	–	8 c. brown	10	10
2116	–	9 c. green	10	10
2117	–	10 c. red	15	10
2118	–	11 c. blue	15	10
2119	–	14 c. green	20	10
2120	–	14 c. red	20	10
2121	–	15 c. purple	25	10
2122	–	17 c. green	25	10
2123	–	21 c. purple	30	10
2124	–	22 c. blue	30	10
2125	–	23 c. violet	30	10
2126	–	25 c. blue	30	10
2127	–	28 c. green	40	10
2128	–	39 c. mauve	45	10
2129	–	45 c. blue	70	10
2130ab	–	50 c. brown	65	10
2131	–	56 c red	80	10
2132	–	65 c. blue	85	10
2133	–	$1 green	1·40	10
2134	–	$1 blue	1·25	10
2135	–	$2 violet	2·50	10
2136	–	$5 brown	7·25	1·50

DESIGNS: 2 c. Mary Lyon (educator); 3 c. Paul Dudley White (cardiologist); 4 c. Father Flanagan (founder of Boys Town); 5 c. Hugo L. Black (Supreme Court Justice); 6 c. Walter Lippmann (journalist); 7 c. Abraham Baldwin (politician); 8 c. General Henry Knox; 9 c. Sylvanus Thayer (military educator) (after R. Weir); 10 c. Red Cloud (Oglala Sioux chief); 11 c. Alden Partridge (educationist); 14 c. (2119) Sinclair Lewis (writer) (after S. Melik); 14 c. (2120) Julia Ward Howe (author of "Battle Hymn of the Republic") (after J. Elliott); 15 c. Buffalo Bill Cody (showman); 17 c. Belva Ann Lockwood (women's rights campaigner); 21 c. Chester Carlson (inventor of photocopying); 22 c. J. J. Audubon (ornithologist); 23 c. Mary Cassatt (artist); 25 c. Jack London (writer); 28 c. Sitting Bull (Hunkpapa Sioux chief); 39 c. Grenville Clark (peace activist); 45 c. Dr. Harvey Cushing (neurosurgeon); 50 c. Admiral Chester W. Nimitz; 56 c. John Harvard (philanthropist) (after D. C. French); 65 c. Gen. Henry Harley "Hap" Arnold; $1 (2133) Bernard Revel (scholar); $1 (2134) Johns Hopkins (medical pioneer); $2 William Jennings Bryan (politician); $5 Bret Harte (writer).

1985. Non-denominational "D" stamp. As T **1090** but inscribed "Domestic Mail".

2137	(22 c.) green (18×21 mm) . .	30	10
2138	(22 c.) green (15×18 mm) . .	60	10

1438 Alfred V. Verville

1985. Air. Aviation Pioneers.

A2142	33 c. Type **1438**		45	15
A2143	39 c. Lawrence and Elmer Sperry		50	15

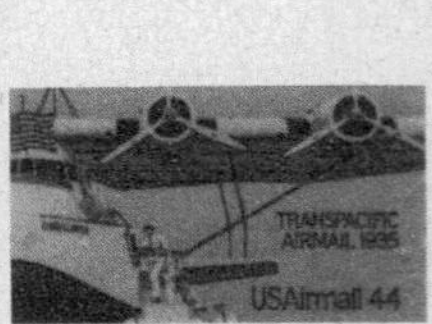

1440 Loading Mail into Martin M-130 Flying Boat 1441 Mary McLeod Bethune

1985. Air. 50th Anniv of First Transpacific Airmail Flight.

A2144	**1440**	44 c. multicoloured . .	55	15

1985. Black Heritage. Mary McLeod Bethune (social activist).

2145	**1441**	22 c. multicoloured	40	10

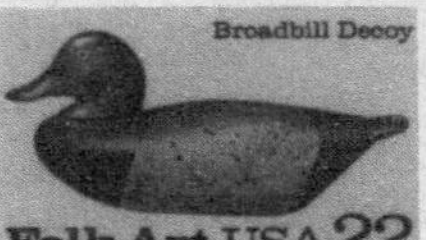

1442 Broadbill Decoy, 1890 (Ben Holmes) 1446 Omnibus, 1880s

1985. American Folk Art. Duck Decoys. Multicoloured.

2146	22 c. Type **1442**	45	10
2147	22 c. Mallard decoy, 1900 (Percy Grant)	45	10
2148	22 c. Canvasback decoy, 1929 (Bob McGraw)	45	10
2149	22 c. Redhead decoy, 1925 (Keyes Chadwick)	45	10

1985. Transport. Without "c" after face value.

2150	**1446**	1 c. violet	10	10
2151	–	2 c. black	10	10
2152	–	3 c. purple	10	10
2153	–	3.4 c. green	10	10
2154	–	4.9 c. black	10	10
2155	–	5 c. black	10	10
2156	–	5.3 black	10	10
2157	–	5.5 c. red	10	10
2158	–	6 c. brown	10	10
2159	–	7.1 c. red	10	10
2160	–	7.6 c. brown	10	10
2161	–	8.3 c. green	10	10
2162	–	8.4 c. purple	10	10
2163	–	8.5 c. green	10	10
2163a	–	10 c. blue	15	10
2164	–	10.1 c. grey	20	10
2165	–	11 c. black	15	10
2166	–	12 c. blue	15	10
2167	–	12.5 c. green	15	10
2167b	–	13 c. black	15	10
2168	–	13.2 c. green	20	10
2169	–	14 c. blue	20	10
2170	–	15 c. violet	25	10
2170b	–	16.7 c. red	25	10
2171	–	17 c. blue	25	10
2172	–	17.5 c. violet	25	10
2172b	–	20 c. purple	25	10
2172c	–	20.5 c. red	25	10
2172d	–	21 c. green	25	10
2173	–	24.1 c. blue	35	10
2174	–	25 c. brown	35	10

DESIGNS: 2 c. Locomotive, 1870s; 3 c. Conestoga wagon, 1800s; 3.4 c. School bus, 1920s; 4.9 c. Buckboard, 1880s; 5 c. Milk wagon, 1900s; 5.3 c. Lift, 1900s; 5.5 c. Star Route truck, 1910s; 6 c. Tricycle, 1880s; 7.1 c. Tractor, 1920s; 7.6 c. Carreta, 1770s; 8.3 c. "McKean" ambulance, 1860s; 8.4 c. Wheelchair, 1920s; 8.5 c. Tow truck, 1920s; 10 c. Canal barge, 1880s; 10.1 c. Oil wagon, 1890s; 11 c. Stutz "Bearcat", 1933; 12 c. Stanley "Steamer", 1909; 12.5 c. Pushcart, 1880s; 13 c. Police patrol wagon, 1880s; 13.2 c. Coal wagon, 1870s; 14 c. Iceboat, 1880s; 15 c. Tug, 1900s; 16.7 c. Popcorn wagon, 1902; 17 c. Dog sledge, 1920s; 17.5 c. Marmon "Wasp", 1911; 20 c. Cable car, 1880s; 20.5 c. Ahrens-Fox fire engine, 1900s; 21 c. Railway mail van, 1920s; 24.1 c. Pope tandem, 1890s; 25 c. Bread wagon, 1880s.

The 5.3, 7.6, 8.4, 13, 13.2, 16.7, 21 and 24.1 c. were only issued with precancelled inscription of the type of service in red and the 20.5 c. in black. Prices in the unused column are for stamps with full gum.

1471 Ice Skating, Skiing and Emblem 1472 Flag over Capitol, Washington

1985. Winter Special Olympic Games, Park City, Utah.

2175	**1471**	22 c. multicoloured . .	40	10

1985.

2176	**1472**	22 c. black, red and blue	30	10
2178	–	22 c. black, red and blue	40	10

DESIGNS—40×22 mm: No. 2178, Flag over Capitol, Washington, and inscription "Of the People By the People For the People".

1474 Frilled Dogwinkle 1479 Coloured Lines and "Love"

1985. Sea Shells.

2179	**1474**	22 c. red and black . .	55	10
2180	–	22 c. red, purple and black	55	10
2181	–	22 c. red and black . .	55	10
2182	–	22 c. purple and black . .	55	10
2183	–	22 c. red, purple and black	55	10

DESIGNS: No. 2180, Reticulated helmet; 2181, New England neptune; 2182, Calico scallop; 2183, Lightning whelk.

1985. Greetings Stamp.

2184	**1479**	22 c. multicoloured . . .	35	10

1480 American Bald Eagle and Moon

1985.

2185	**1480**	$10.75 multicoloured . .	13·00	12·00

1481 Electricity Pole and Rural Landscape

1985. 50th Anniv of Rural Electrification Administration.

2186	**1481**	22 c. multicoloured . . .	40	10

1482 1 c. Franklin Stamp, 1870 1483 Abigail Adams

1985. "Ameripex 86" International Stamp Exhibition, Chicago.

2187	**1482**	22 c. multicoloured . . .	40	10

1985. Abigail Adams (wife of Pres. John Adams and writer) Commemoration.

2188	**1483**	22 c. multicoloured . . .	35	10

1484 Bartholdi (after J. Frappa) and Statue of Liberty)

1985. Frederic Auguste Bartholdi (sculptor of Statue of Liberty) Commemoration.

2189	**1484**	22 c. multicoloured . . .	35	10

1485 Troops in Mountain Pass

1985. Korean War Veterans.

2190	**1485**	22 c. green and red . . .	55	10

1486 Disabled and Needy People

1985. 50th Anniv of Social Security Act.

2191	**1486**	22 c. blue and deep blue	55	10

1487 Junipero Serra and Mission San Gabriel

1985. Air. Death Bicentenary (1984) of Father Junipero Serra (missionary).

A2192	**1487**	44 c. multicoloured . .	75	20

1488 "Battle of the Marne" (Harvey Dunn)

1985. World War I Veterans.

2193	**1488**	22 c. green and red . .	50	10

1489 Quarter Horse 1493 Alphabet, Spectacles, Quill and Apple

1985. Horses. Multicoloured.

2194	22 c. Type **1489**	70	10
2195	22 c. Morgan horse	70	10
2196	22 c. Saddlebred horse . . .	70	10
2197	22 c. Appaloosa	70	10

1985. Public Education.

2198	**1493**	22 c. multicoloured . .	35	10

1494 Y.M.C.A. Youth Camping (centenary)

1985. International Youth Year. Multicoloured.

2199	22 c. Type **1494**	40	10
2200	22 c. Boy Scouts of America (75th anniv)	40	10
2201	22 c. Big Brothers and Big Sisters	40	10
2202	22 c. Camp Fire Inc. (75th anniv)	40	10

1498 Hungry Faces 1499 Envelopes

1985. "Help End Hunger".

2203	**1498**	22 c. multicoloured . .	35	10

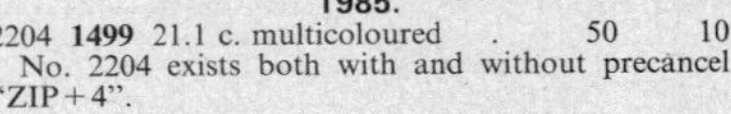

1985.

2204	**1499**	21.1 c. multicoloured .	50	10

No. 2204 exists both with and without precancel "ZIP+4".

1500 "Genoa Madonna" (Luca della Robbia) 1502 George Washington (after Stuart) and Washington Monument

1985. Christmas.

2205	**1500**	22 c. multicoloured . .	35	10
2206	–	22 c. red, green and black	35	10

DESIGN—HORIZ: No. 2206, Poinsettias.

1985.

2207	**1502**	18 c. multicoloured . .	35	10

No. 2207 exist both with and without precancel "PRESORTED FIRST-CLASS".

1503 Old State House, Little Rock

1986. 150th Anniv of Arkansas State.

2208	**1503**	22 c. multicoloured . .	40	10

1504 Sheet of Stamps, Handstamp and Magnifying Glass 1508 Puppy

1986. "Ameripex 86" International Stamp Exhibition, Chicago. Stamp Collecting. Multicoloured.

2209 22 c. Type **1504** 55 10
2210 22 c. Boy holding stamp in tweezers 55 10
2211 22 c. Mounted stamps and 3 c. U.S. stamp under glass . . 55 10
2212 22 c. "Ameripex" miniature sheet on cover and handstamp 55 10

1986. Greetings Stamp.

2213 **1508** 22 c. multicoloured . . 40 10

1509 Sojourner Truth

1510 Texan Flag and Santa Anna's Spur

1986. Black Heritage. Sojourner Truth (human rights activist).

2214 **1509** 22 c. multicoloured . . 40 10

1986. 150th Anniv of Battle of San Jacinto.

2215 **1510** 22 c. red, blue & black . 40 10

1511 Muskellunge

1986. Fishes. Multicoloured.

2216 22 c. Type **1511** 60 10
2217 22 c. Atlantic cod 60 10
2218 22 c. Largemouth bass . . . 60 10
2219 22 c. Bluefin tuna 60 10
2220 22 c. Catfish 60 10

1516 Modern Hospital

1517 Ellington

1986. Public Hospitals. 250th Anniv of Bellevue Hospital Centre, New York.

2221 **1516** 22 c. multicoloured . . 40 10

1986. Performing Arts and Artists. Duke Ellington (jazz musician).

2222 **1517** 22 c. multicoloured . . 40 10

1519 Elisha Kent Kane and Polar Brig "Advance"

1523 Head of Statue

1986. Polar Explorers. Multicoloured.

2224 22 c. Type **1519** 60 10
2225 22 c. Adolphus W. Greely . . 60 10
2226 22 c. Vilhjalmur Stefansson . 60 10
2227 22 c. Robert E. Peary and Matthew Henson 60 10

1986. Centenary of Statue of Liberty.

2228 **1523** 22 c. blue and red . . . 40 10

1524 Blanket Designs **1525**

1526 Blanket Designs **1527**

1986. American Folk Art. Navajo Blankets.

2229 **1524** 22 c. multicoloured . . 40 10
2230 **1525** 22 c. multicoloured . . 40 10
2231 **1526** 22 c. multicoloured . . 40 10
2232 **1527** 22 c. multicoloured . . 40 10

1528 T. S. Eliot

1529 Highlander Figure (tobacconist)

1986. Literary Arts. Thomas Stearns Eliot (poet).

2233 **1528** 22 c. red 35 10

1986. American Folk Art. Carved Wooden Figures. Multicoloured.

2234 22 c. Type **1529** 45 10
2235 22 c. Ship's figurehead . . . 45 10
2236 22 c. Nautical figure (nautical instrument maker) 45 10
2237 22 c. Indian (cigar store) . . 45 10

1533 "Madonna" (Il Perugino)

1535 White Pine and Lake Huron

1986. Christmas. Multicoloured.

2238 22 c. Type **1533** 35 10
2239 22 c. Winter village 35 10

1987. 150th Anniv of Michigan Statehood.

2240 **1535** 22 c. multicoloured . . 35 10

1536 Stylized Runner

1537 Heart

1986. 10th Pan-American Games, Indianapolis.

2241 **1536** 22 c. multicoloured . . 35 10

1987. Greetings Stamp.

2242 **1537** 22 c. multicoloured . . 30 10

1538 Du Sable

1539 Caruso as Duke of Mantua in "Rigoletto"

1987. Black Heritage. Jean Baptiste Pointe du Sable (founder of Chicago).

2243 **1538** 22 c. multicoloured . . 30 10

1987. Performing Arts and Artists. Enrico Caruso (operatic tenor).

2244 **1539** 22 c. multicoloured . . 40 10

1540 Badges

1987 75th Anniv of Girl Scouts of America.

2245 **1540** 22 c. multicoloured . . . 30 10

1541 "Congratulations!"

1987. Greetings Stamps. Multicoloured.

2246 22 c. Type **1541** 50 10
2247 22 c. "Get Well!" (18 × 33 mm) 50 10
2248 22 c. "Thank You!" (18 × 33 mm) 50 10
2249 22 c. "Love You, Dad!" . . . 50 10
2250 22 c. "Best Wishes!" (18 × 21 mm) 50 10
2251 22 c. "Happy Birthday!" (18 × 21 mm) 50 10
2252 22 c. "Love You, Mother!" . 50 10
2253 22 c. "Keep in Touch!" (18 × 21 mm) 50 10

1549 Ethnic Faces

1550 Flag and Fireworks

1987. Centenary of United Way Volunteer Organization.

2254 **1549** 22 c. multicoloured . . . 30 10

1987.

2255 **1550** 22 c. multicoloured . . . 30 10

1551 Barn Swallows

1552 State Seal

1987. "Capex '87" International Stamp Exhibition, Toronto. North American Wildlife. Multicoloured.

2256 22 c. Type **1551** 45 10
2257 22 c. Monarch butterflies on field thistle 45 10
2258 22 c. Bighorn sheep 45 10
2259 22 c. Broad-tailed hummingbird on Colorado columbine . . 45 10
2260 22 c. Rabbit and red clover . 45 10
2261 22 c. Osprey 45 10
2262 22 c. Mountain lion 45 10
2263 22 c. Luna moth on trumpet honeysuckle 45 10
2264 22 c. Mule deer 45 10
2265 22 c. Grey squirrel on red oak 45 10
2266 22 c. Armadillo and Texas prickly pear 45 10
2267 22 c. Eastern chipmunk and European white birch . . . 45 10
2268 22 c. Moose 45 10
2269 22 c. Black bear 45 10
2270 22 c. Tiger swallowtail butterflies on orange milkweed 45 10
2271 22 c. Bobwhite and purple coneflower 45 10
2272 22 c. Ringtail and Cape marigold 45 10
2273 22 c. Red-winged blackbird on common cattail 45 10
2274 22 c. American lobster 45 10
2275 22 c. Black-tailed hare and beavertail 45 10
2276 22 c. Scarlet tanager and American basswood 45 10
2277 22 c. Woodchuck and dandelion 45 10
2278 22 c. Roseate spoonbill and red mangrove 45 10
2279 22 c. American bald eagle . . 45 10
2280 22 c. Alaskan brown bear . . 45 10
2281 22 c. Iiwi on "Ohia lehua" . . 45 10
2282 22 c. Badger 45 10
2283 22 c. Pronghorns 45 10
2284 22 c. River otter 45 10
2285 22 c. Ladybird on rose 45 10
2286 22 c. Beaver, maple and quaking aspen 45 10
2287 22 c. White-tailed deer . . . 45 10
2288 22 c. Blue jays on Table Mountain pine 45 10
2289 22 c. Pikas 45 10
2290 22 c. Bison 45 10
2291 22 c. Snowy egret 45 10
2292 22 c. Grey wolf 45 10
2293 22 c. Mountain goat 45 10
2294 22 c. Deer mouse 45 10
2295 22 c. Black-tailed prairie dog 45 10
2296 22 c. Box turtle and Virginia creeper 45 10
2297 22 c. Wolverine 45 10
2298 22 c. American elk 45 10
2299 22 c. California sea-lion . . . 45 10
2300 22 c. Northern mockingbird on royal poinciana 45 10
2301 22 c. Racoon 45 10
2302 22 c. Bobcat 45 10
2303 22 c. Black-footed ferret . . 45 10
2304 22 c. Canada goose 45 10
2305 22 c. Red fox and red maple . 45 10

1987. Bicentenary of Delaware Statehood.

2306 **1552** 22 c. multicoloured . . 30 10

1553 Arabesque from Door, Dar Batha Palace, Fez

1554 Faulkner (after M. L. Goldsborough)

1987. Bicentenary of Diplomatic Relations with Morocco.

2307 **1553** 22 c. red and black . . 30 10

1987. Literary Arts. 25th Death Anniv of William Faulkner (novelist).

2308 **1554** 22 c. green 30 10

1555 Squash Blossoms (Ruth Maxwell)

1556 Floral Design (Mary McPeek)

1557 Floral Design (Leslie Saari)

1558 Dogwood Blossoms (Trenna Ruffner)

1987. American Folk Art. Lacemaking.

2309 **1555** 22 c. white, blue and ultramarine 40 10
2310 **1556** 22 c. white, blue and ultramarine 40 10
2311 **1557** 22 c. white, blue and ultramarine 40 10
2312 **1558** 22 c. white, blue and ultramarine 40 10

1559 Independence Hall

1987. Bicentenary of Pennsylvania Statehood.

2313 **1559** 22 c. multicoloured . . 30 10

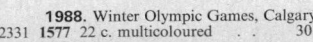

1560 "The Bicentennial. . ."

1987. Bicentenary of United States Constitution (1st issue). Multicoloured.

2314 22 c. Type **1560** 45 10
2315 22 c. "We the people. . ." . . 45 10
2316 22 c. "Establish justice. . ." . 45 10
2317 22 c. "And secure. . ." . . . 45 10
2318 22 c. "Do ordain. . ." 45 10
See also No. 2320.

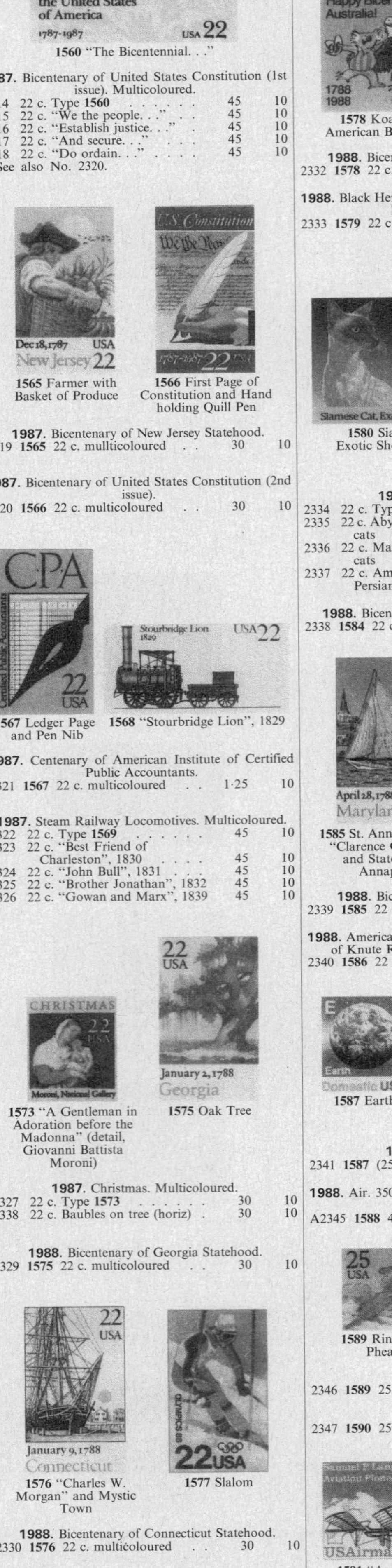

1565 Farmer with Basket of Produce

1566 First Page of Constitution and Hand holding Quill Pen

1987. Bicentenary of New Jersey Statehood.
2319 **1565** 22 c. mullticoloured . . 30 10

1987. Bicentenary of United States Constitution (2nd issue).
2320 **1566** 22 c. multicoloured . . 30 10

1567 Ledger Page and Pen Nib

1568 "Stourbridge Lion", 1829

1987. Centenary of American Institute of Certified Public Accountants.
2321 **1567** 22 c. multicoloured . . 1·25 10

1987. Steam Railway Locomotives. Multicoloured.
2322 22 c. Type **1569** 45 10
2323 22 c. "Best Friend of Charleston", 1830 . . . . 45 10
2324 22 c. "John Bull", 1831 . . . 45 10
2325 22 c. "Brother Jonathan", 1832 45 10
2326 22 c. "Gowan and Marx", 1839 45 10

1573 "A Gentleman in Adoration before the Madonna" (detail, Giovanni Battista Moroni)

1575 Oak Tree

1987. Christmas. Multicoloured.
2327 22 c. Type **1573** 30 10
2338 22 c. Baubles on tree (horiz) . 30 10

1988. Bicentenary of Georgia Statehood.
2329 **1575** 22 c. multicoloured . . 30 10

1576 "Charles W. Morgan" and Mystic Town

1577 Slalom

1988. Bicentenary of Connecticut Statehood.
2330 **1576** 22 c. multicoloured . . 30 10

1988. Winter Olympic Games, Calgary.
2331 **1577** 22 c. multicoloured . . 30 10

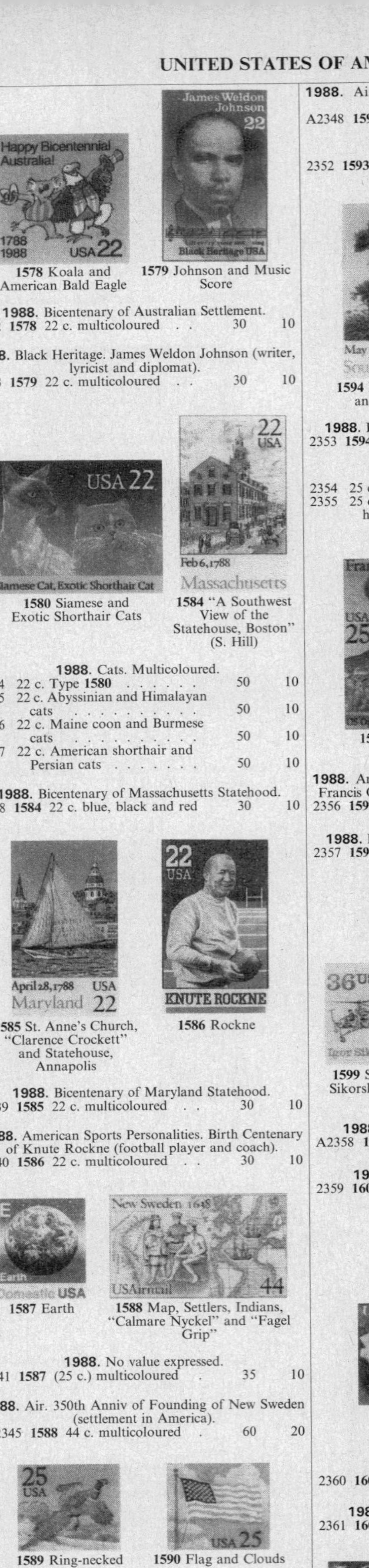

1578 Koala and American Bald Eagle

1579 Johnson and Music Score

1988. Bicentenary of Australian Settlement.
2332 **1578** 22 c. multicoloured . . 30 10

1988. Black Heritage. James Weldon Johnson (writer, lyricist and diplomat).
2333 **1579** 22 c. multicoloured . . 30 10

1580 Siamese and Exotic Shorthair Cats

1584 "A Southwest View of the Statehouse, Boston" (S. Hill)

1988. Cats. Multicoloured.
2334 22 c. Type **1580** 50 10
2335 22 c. Abyssinian and Himalayan cats 50 10
2336 22 c. Maine coon and Burmese cats 50 10
2337 22 c. American shorthair and Persian cats 50 10

1988. Bicentenary of Massachusetts Statehood.
2338 **1584** 22 c. blue, black and red 30 10

1585 St. Anne's Church, "Clarence Crockett" and Statehouse, Annapolis

1586 Rockne

1988. Bicentenary of Maryland Statehood.
2339 **1585** 22 c. multicoloured . . 30 10

1988. American Sports Personalities. Birth Centenary of Knute Rockne (football player and coach).
2340 **1586** 22 c. multicoloured . . 30 10

1587 Earth

1588 Map, Settlers, Indians, "Calmare Nyckel" and "Fagel Grip"

1988. No value expressed.
2341 **1587** (25 c.) multicoloured . . 35 10

1988. Air. 350th Anniv of Founding of New Sweden (settlement in America).
A2345 **1588** 44 c. multicoloured . 60 20

1589 Ring-necked Pheasant

1590 Flag and Clouds

1988.
2346 **1589** 25 c. multicoloured . . 35 10

1988.
2347 **1590** 25 c. multicoloured . . 35 10

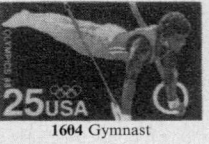

1591 "Aerodrome No.5" and Langley

1593 Flag over Half Dome, Yosemite National Park

1988. Air. Aviation Pioneers. Samuel Pierpont Langley.
A2348 **1591** 45 c. multicoloured . . 60 20

1988.
2352 **1593** 25 c. blue, red & green . 35 10

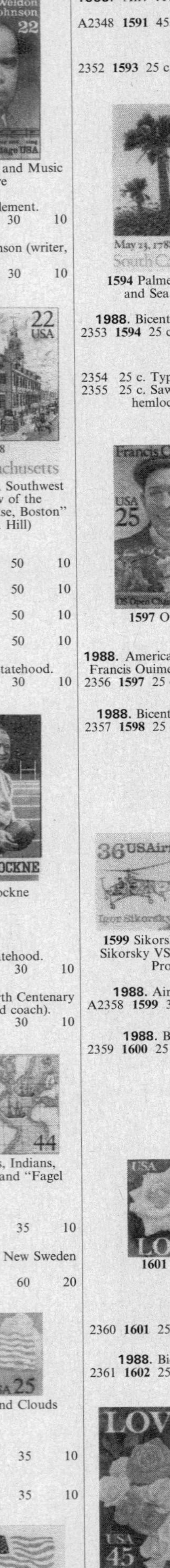

1594 Palmetto Trees and Sea Grass

1595 Rose-breasted Grosbeak on Dogwood

1988. Bicentenary of South Carolina Statehood.
2353 **1594** 25 c. multicoloured . . . 35 10

1988. Multicoloured.
2354 25 c. Type **1595** 35 10
2355 25 c. Saw-whet owl on Eastern hemlock 35 10

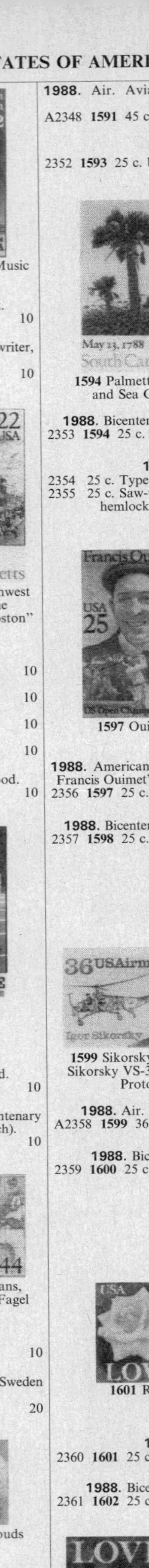

1597 Ouimet

1598 Old Man of the Mountain

1988. American Sports Personalities. 75th Anniv of Francis Ouimet's Open Golf Championship Victory.
2356 **1597** 25 c. multicoloured . . . 35 10

1988. Bicentenary of New Hampshire Statehood.
2357 **1598** 25 c. multicoloured . . . 35 10

1599 Sikorsky and Vought Sikorsky VS-300 Helicopter Prototype

1600 Carriage and Capitol Building, Williamsburg

1988. Air. Aviation Pioneers. Igor Sikorsky.
A2358 **1599** 36 c. multicoloured . . 50 20

1988. Bicentenary of Virginia Statehood.
2359 **1600** 25 c. multicoloured . . . 35 10

1601 Rose

1602 Trinity Church, Wall Street and Federal Hall, New York City

1988. Greetings Stamp.
2360 **1601** 25 c. multicoloured . . . 35 10

1988. Bicentenary of New York Statehood.
2361 **1602** 25 c. multicoloured . . . 35 10

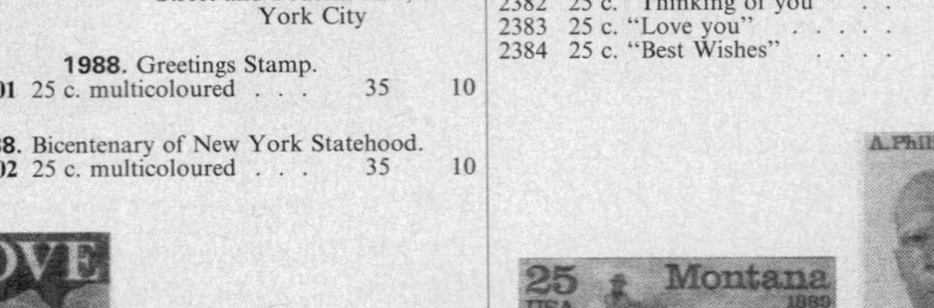

1603 Roses

1604 Gymnast

1988. Greetings Stamp.
2362 **1603** 45 c. multicoloured . . . 60 20

1988. Olympic Games, Seoul.
2363 **1604** 25 c. multicoloured . . . 35 10

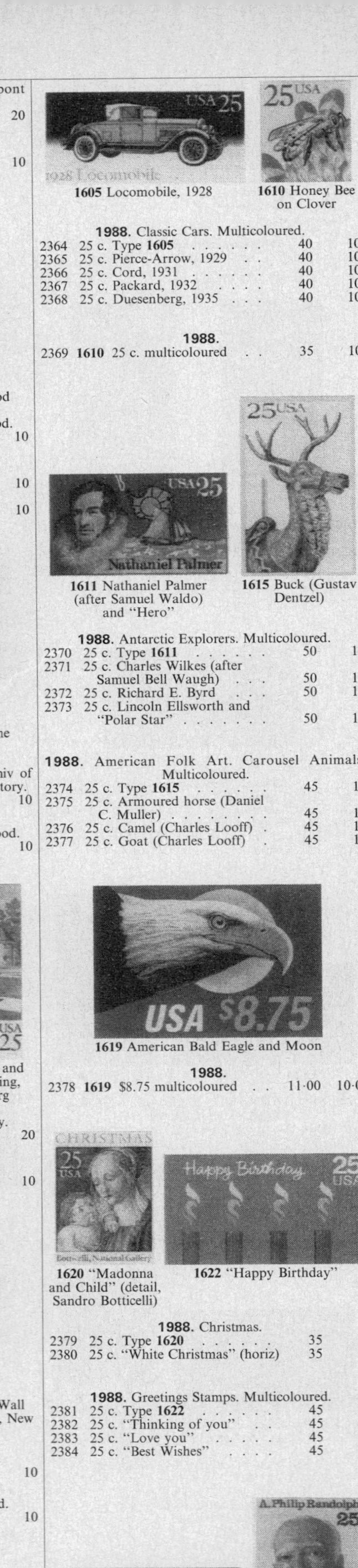

1605 Locomobile, 1928

1610 Honey Bee on Clover

1988. Classic Cars. Multicoloured.
2364 25 c. Type **1605** 40 10
2365 25 c. Pierce-Arrow, 1929 . . 40 10
2366 25 c. Cord, 1931 . . . . . . 40 10
2367 25 c. Packard, 1932 . . . . 40 10
2368 25 c. Duesenberg, 1935 . . . 40 10

1988.
2369 **1610** 25 c. multicoloured . . 35 10

1611 Nathaniel Palmer (after Samuel Waldo) and "Hero"

1615 Buck (Gustav Dentzel)

1988. Antarctic Explorers. Multicoloured.
2370 25 c. Type **1611** 50 10
2371 25 c. Charles Wilkes (after Samuel Bell Waugh) . . . 50 10
2372 25 c. Richard E. Byrd . . . 50 10
2373 25 c. Lincoln Ellsworth and "Polar Star" 50 10

1988. American Folk Art. Carousel Animals. Multicoloured.
2374 25 c. Type **1615** 45 10
2375 25 c. Armoured horse (Daniel C. Muller) 45 10
2376 25 c. Camel (Charles Looff) . 45 10
2377 25 c. Goat (Charles Looff) . 45 10

1619 American Bald Eagle and Moon

1988.
2378 **1619** $8.75 multicoloured . . 11·00 10·00

1620 "Madonna and Child" (detail, Sandro Botticelli)

1622 "Happy Birthday"

1988. Christmas.
2379 25 c. Type **1620** 35 10
2380 25 c. "White Christmas" (horiz) 35 10

1988. Greetings Stamps. Multicoloured.
2381 25 c. Type **1622** 45 10
2382 25 c. "Thinking of you" . . 45 10
2383 25 c. "Love you" 45 10
2384 25 c. "Best Wishes" 45 10

1626 "C.M. Russell and Friends" (Charles M. Russell)

1627 A. Philip Randolph

1989. Centenary of Montana Statehood.
2385 **1626** 25 c. multicoloured . . 40 10

1989. Black Heritage. A. Philip Randolph (trade union activist).
2386 **1627** 25 c. multicoloured . . 30 10

1628 Grain Elevator and Buckboard

1629 Mt. Rainer and Canoe on Reflection Lake

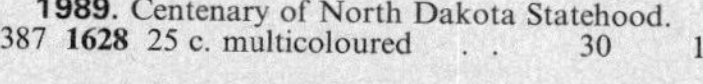

1989. Centenary of North Dakota Statehood.

2387 **1628** 25 c. multicoloured . . 30 10

1989. Centenary of Washington Statehood.

2388 **1629** 25 c. multicoloured . . 30 10

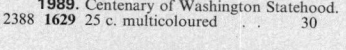

1630 "Experiment", 1788–90

1989. Paddle-steamers. Multicoloured.

2389 25 c. Type **1630** 45 10
2390 25 c. "Phoenix", 1809 . . . . 45 10
2391 25 c. "New Orleans", 1812 . 45 10
2392 25 c. "Washington", 1816 . . 45 10
2393 25 c. "Walk in the Water", 1818 45 10

1635 Cancelled 1869 90 c. Lincoln Stamp

1636 Toscanini

1989. "World Stamp Expo'89" International Stamp Exhibition, Washington D.C.

2394 **1635** 25 c. red, black & brown 30 10

1989. Performing Arts and Artists. Arturo Toscanini (conductor).

2395 **1636** 25 c. multicoloured . . 40 10

1637 "Car of History" Clock (Carlo Franzoni)

1638 Eagle and Shield over Vice-President's Chair

1989. Bicentenary of House of Representatives.

2396 **1637** 25 c. multicoloured . . 30 10

1989. Bicentenary of Senate.

2397 **1638** 25 c. multicoloured . . 30 10

1639 George Washington (statue, J. Q. A. Ward)

1640 Pasque Flowers, Pioneer Woman and House

1989. Bicentenary of Executive Branch.

2398 **1639** 25 c. multicoloured . . 30 10

1989. Centenary of South Dakota Statehood.

2399 **1640** 25 c. multicoloured . . 30 10

1641 Gehrig

1643 Hemingway

1642 Liberty, Equality and Fraternity

1989. American Sports Personalities. Lou Gehrig (baseball player).

2400 **1641** 25 c. multicoloured . . 45 10

1989. Air. Bicentenary of French Revolution.

A2401 **1642** 45 c. multicoloured . 60 20

1989. Literary Arts. Ernest Hemingway (novelist).

2402 **1643** 25 c. multicoloured . . 30 10

1644 Astronauts planting Flag on Moon

1645 Dogwood Blossoms

1989. 20th Anniv of First Manned Moon Landing

2403 **1644** $2.40 multicoloured . . 3·00 2·00

1989. Bicentenary of North Carolina Statehood.

2404 **1645** 25 c. multicoloured . . 30 10

1646 Letter Carriers

1647 Eagle and Flag as Shield

1989. Centenary of National Association of Letter Carriers.

2405 **1646** 25 c. multicoloured . . 30 10

1989. Bicentenary of Bill of Rights.

2406 **1647** 25 c. black, red & blue 30 10

1648 Tyrannosaurus Rex

1652 Mimbres Ritual Figure

1989. Prehistoric Animals. Multicoloured.

2407 25 c. Type **1648** 60 10
2408 25 c. Pteranodon 60 10
2409 25 c. Stegosaurus 60 10
2410 25 c. Brontosaurus 60 10

1989. America. Pre-Columbian Carvings. Mult.

2411 25 c. Type **1652** (postage) . 30 10
A2412 45 c. Calusa "Key Marco cat" (air) 55 20

1654 "Dream of St. Catherine of Alexandria" (detail, Ludovico Carracci)

1656 Eagle and Shield

1989. Christmas. Multicoloured.

2413 25 c. Type **1654** 40 10
2415 25 c. Gifts on sleigh (horiz) . 30 10

1989. Self-adhesive. Imperf.

2416 **1656** 25 c. multicoloured . . . 30 10

1658 Western Stagecoach

1663 Hypersonic Airliner

1989. 20th U.P.U. Congress, Washington D.C. (1st issue). Classic Mail Transport. Multicoloured.

2418 25 c. Type **1658** 45 10
2419 25 c. "Chesapeake" (Mississippi river steamer) 45 10
2420 25 c. Curtiss JN-4 "Jenny" biplane 45 10
2421 25 c. Motor car 45 10
See also Nos. A2423/6.

1989. Air. 20th Universal Postal Union Congress, Washington D.C. (2nd issue). Mail Transport of the Future. Multicoloured.

A2423 45 c. Type **1663** 80 20
A2424 45 c. Hovercar 80 20
A2425 45 c. Rover vehicle delivering mail to space colony . . . 80 20
A2426 45 c. Space shuttle delivering mail to space station . . 80 20

1668 Mountain Bluebird

1669 Lovebirds

1990. Centenary of Idaho Statehood.

2428 **1668** 25 c. multicoloured . . . 40 10

1990. Greetings Stamp.

2429 **1669** 25 c. multicoloured . . . 40 10

1670 Ida Wells

1671 John Marshall

1990. Black Heritage. Ida B. Wells (civil rights activist).

2431 **1670** 25 c. multicoloured . . . 30 10

1990. Bicentenary of Supreme Court.

2432 **1671** 25 c. multicoloured . . . 30 10

1672 Beach Umbrella

1677 Luis Munoz Marin

1990.

2433 **1672** 15 c. multicoloured . . . 25 10

1990. Great Americans.

2438 **1677** 5 c. red 10 10
2445 – 20 c. red 25 10
2448 – 29 c. blue 40 10
2449 – 29 c. black 40 10
2452 – 35 c. black 45 10
2454 – 40 c. blue 55 10
2457 – 52 c. lilac 70 10
2462 – 75 c. red . . . . 1·00 15

DESIGNS: 20 c. Virginia Agpar; 29 c. (2448) Earl Warren; 29 c. (2449) Thomas Jefferson (President, 1801–09); 35 c. Dennis Chavez; 40 c. Lt-Gen. Claire Chennault; 52 c. Hubert Humphrey (Vice-president, 1965–69); 75 c. Wendell Wilkie.

1710 "High Mountain Meadows" (Conrad Schwiering)

1990. Centenary of Wyoming Statehood.

2471 **1710** 25 c. multicoloured . . 40 10

1711 Judy Garland ("The Wizard of Oz")

1715 Marianne Moore

1990. Classic Films. Multicoloured.

2472 25 c. Type **1711** 50 10
2473 25 c. Clark Gable and Vivien Leigh ("Gone with the Wind") 50 10
2474 25 c. Gary Cooper ("Beau Geste") 50 10
2475 25 c. John Wayne ("Stagecoach") 50 10

1990. Literary Arts. Marianne Moore (poet).

2476 **1715** 25 c. multicoloured . . 40 10

1720 Circus Wagon, 1900s

1755 Admiralty Head, Nugent Sound

1990. Transport.

2480 – 4 c. purple 10 10
2481 **1720** 5 c. red 10 10
2504 – 5 c. brown 10 10
2643 – 5 c. red 10 10
2507 – 10 c. green 15 15
2489 – 23 c. blue 30 10
2496 – $1 blue and red . . . . 1·25 35

DESIGNS; 4 c. Richard Dudgeon steam carriage, 1866; 5 c. (Noss. 2504, 2643) Birch bark canoe, 1800s; 10 c. Tractor trailer, 1930s; 23 c. Lunch wagon, 1890s; $1 Benoist Type XIV flying boat.

1990. Lighthouses. Multicoloured.

2516 25 c. Type **1755** 50 10
2517 25 c. Cape Hatteras 50 10
2518 25 c. West Quoddy Head . . 50 10
2519 25 c. American Shoals . . . 50 10
2520 25 c. Sandy Hook, New York Harbour 50 10

1760 Stars and Stripes

1761 Slater Mill

1990. Self-adhesive. Imperf.

2521 **1760** 25 c. red and blue . . . 35 10

1990. Bicentenary of Rhode Island Statehood.

2522 **1761** 25 c. multicoloured . . 35 10

1763 Bobcat

1990. Wildlife.

2524 **1763** $2 multicoloured . . . 2·75 85

1769 Jesse Owens

1990. American Olympic Medal Winners. Multicoloured.
2530 25 c. Type **1769** 35 10
2531 25 c. Ray Ewry 35 10
2532 25 c. Hazel Wightman . . . 35 10
2533 25 c. Eddie Eagan 35 10
2534 25 c. Helene Madison 35 10

1774 Assiniboine

1990. American Folk Art. Indian Headdresses. Multicoloured.
2535 25 c. Type **1774** 35 10
2536 25 c. Cheyenne 35 10
2537 25 c. Comanche 35 10
2538 25 c. Flathead 35 10
2539 25 c. Shoshone 35 10

1779 Micronesian Outrigger Canoe and Flag

1990. 4th Anniv of Ratification of Marshall Islands and Micronesia Compacts of Free Association. Multicoloured.
2540 25 c. Type **1779** 35 10
2541 25 c. Marshallese stick chart, outrigger canoe and flag . 35 10

1781 Killer Whales

1990. Marine Mammals. Multicoloured.
2542 25 c. Type **1781** 35 10
2543 25 c. Northern sea lions . . . 35 10
2544 25 c. Sea otter 35 10
2545 25 c. Common dolphin . . . 35 10

1785 Grand Canyon

1990. America. Natural World. Multicoloured.
2546 25 c. Type **1785** (postage) . 35 10
A2547 45 c. Tropical island coastline (air) 60 15

1787 Eisenhower and Soldiers

1788 "Madonna and Child" (Antonello da Messina)

1990. Birth Centenary of Dwight David Eisenhower (President, 1953–61).
2548 **1787** 25 c. multicoloured . . 35 10

1990. Christmas. Multicoloured.
2549 25 c. Type **1788** 35 10
2551 25 c. Christmas tree 35 10

1790 Tulip

1791

1991. No value expressed.
2552 **1790** (29 c.) multicoloured . . 40 10

1991. No value expressed. Make-up Rate stamp.
2556 **1791** (4 c.) red and brown . . 10 10

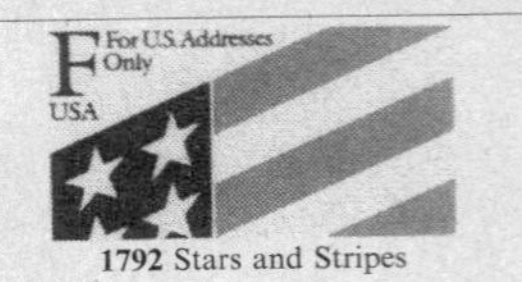

1792 Stars and Stripes

1991. No value expressed. Self-adhesive. Imperf.
2557 **1792** (29 c.) red, blue & black 40 15

1794 Federal Palace, Berne, and Capitol, Washington

1795 Farm

1991. 700th Anniv of Swiss Confederation.
2559 **1794** 50 c. multicoloured . . 65 15

1991. Bicentenary of Vermont Statehood.
2560 **1795** 29 c. multicoloured . . 40 10

1796 Fawn

1797 Flag over Mt. Rushmore

1991.
2561 **1796** 19 c. multicoloured . . 25 10

1991.
2562 **1797** 29 c. red, brown & blk 40 10

1798 Tulip

1799 Wood Duck

1991.
2563 **1798** 29 c. multicoloured . . 40 10

1991. (a) Inscriptions in black.
2565 **1799** 29 c. multicoloured . . 40 15

(b) Inscriptions in red.
2566 **1799** 29 c. multicoloured . . 40 15

1800 Flag and Olympic Rings

1801 Quimby and Bleriot XI

1991.
2567 **1800** 29 c. multicoloured . . 40 10

1991. Air. Aviation Pioneers. Harriet Quimby (first American woman pilot).
A2568 **1801** 50 c. multicoloured . . 65 15

1802 American Bald Eagle

1803 Heart-shaped Globe

1991. 50th Anniv of "E Series" Defence Bonds.
2569 **1802** 29 c. multicoloured . . 40 15

1991. Greetings Stamps. Multicoloured.
2570 29 c. Type **1803** 40 10
2572 52 c. Fischer's lovebirds (21 × 35 mm) 70 20

1805 Hot-air Balloon

1806 Piper and Piper J-3 Cub

1991.
2573 **1805** 19 c. multicoloured . . 25 10

1991. Air. Aviation Pioneers. William Piper.
A2574 **1806** 40 c. multicoloured . . 55 15

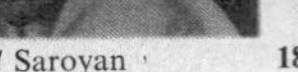

1807 Saroyan

1808 Flags on Parade

1991. Literary Arts. 10th Death Anniv of William Saroyan (dramatist and novelist).
2575 **1807** 29 c. multicoloured . . . 40 10

1991. 125th Anniv of Memorial Day.
2576 **1808** 29 c. multicoloured . . . 40 10

1809 Royal Wulff

1814 Porter and Score

1991. Fishing Flies. Multicoloured.
2577 29 c. Type **1809** 40 10
2578 29 c. Jock Scott 40 10
2579 29 c. Apte tarpon fly 40 10
2580 29 c. Lefty's deceiver 40 10
2581 29 c. Muddler minnow . . . 40 10

1991. Performing Arts and Artists. Birth Centenary of Cole Porter (composer).
2582 **1814** 29 c. multicoloured . . . 40 10

1815 American Bald Eagle

1991. U.S. Olympic Festival.
2583 **1815** $9.95 multicoloured . . 11·50 4·00

1816 U.S.S. "Glacier" (ice-breaker) near Palmer Station

1817 American Kestrel

1991. Air. 30th Anniv of Antarctic Treaty.
A2584 **1816** 50 c. multicoloured . . 65 20

1991. Birds. Multicoloured.
2585 1 c. Type **1817** 10 10
2586 3 c. Eastern bluebird 10 10
2590 30 c. Common cardinal . . . 40 10

1823 Liberty Torch

1824 South-West Asia Service Medal

1991. Self-adhesive. Imperf.
2591 **1823** 29 c. green, gold & blk . 40 10

1991. Operations Desert Shield and Desert Storm (liberation of Kuwait).
2592 **1824** 29 c. multicoloured . . . 40 10

1825 American Bald Eagle

1991.
2595 **1825** $2.90 multicoloured . . 3·75 1·90

1826 Pole Vaulting

1831 Rowing Boat

1991. Olympic Games, Barcelona (1992). Mult.
2596 29 c. Type **1826** 40 10
2597 29 c. Throwing the discus . . 40 10
2598 29 c. Running 40 10
2599 29 c. Throwing the javelin . 40 10
2600 29 c. Hurdling 40 10

1991.
2601 **1831** 19 c. multicoloured . . 25 10

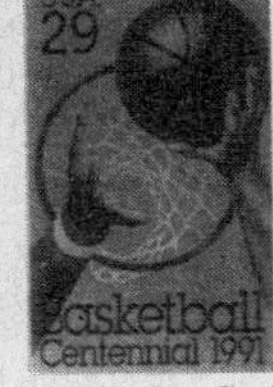

1832 Coins and Banknotes

1833 Shot at Goal

1991. Centenary Convention of American Numismatic Association.
2602 **1832** 29 c. multicoloured . . 40 10

1991. Centenary of Basketball.
2604 **1833** 29 c. multicoloured . . 40 10

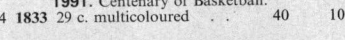

1834 Stan Laurel and Oliver Hardy

1991.
2605 **1834** 29 c. black, violet & red 40 10
2606 – 29 c. black, red & violet 40 10
2607 – 29 c. black, violet & red 40 10
2608 – 29 c. black, violet & red 40 10
2609 – 29 c. black, red & violet 40 10

DESIGNS: No. 2606, Edgar Bergen and Charlie McCarthy; 2607, Jack Benny; 2608, Fanny Brice; 2609, Bud Abbott and Lou Costello.

1839 American Bald Eagle

1991.
2610 **1839** $14 multicoloured . . . 18·00 5·50

1840 Burma Road Convoy

1991. 50th Anniv of America's Entry into Second World War. Multicoloured.
2611 29 c. Type **1840** 40 15
2612 29 c. America's first peacetime draft 40 15
2613 29 c. Lend-Lease Act 40 15
2614 29 c. Roosevelt and Churchill (Atlantic Charter) 40 15
2615 29 c. Munitions factory . . . 40 15
2616 29 c. Sinking of "Reuben James" (destroyer) 40 15
2617 29 c. Gas mask (Civil Defence) 40 15
2618 29 c. Delivery of "Patrick Henry" (first "Liberty" freighter) 40 15
2619 29 c. U.S.S. "West Virginia" and U.S.S. "Tennessee" ablaze, Pearl Harbor . . . 40 15
2620 29 c. U.S. Declaration of War on Japan 40 15

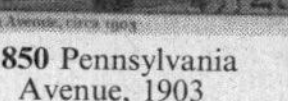

1850 Pennsylvania Avenue, 1903 — **1851** Matzeliger

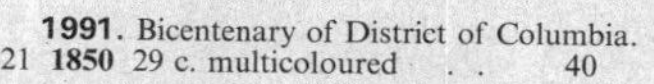

1991. Bicentenary of District of Columbia.

2621 **1850** 29 c. multicoloured . . 40 10

1991. Black Heritage. Jan Ernst Matzeliger (inventor of shoe lasting machine).

2622 **1851** 29 c. multicoloured . . 40 10

1852 Flag — **1853** Postal Service Emblem and Olympic Rings

1991.

2623 **1852** 23 c. blue, red & black . 30 30

1991.

2624 **1853** $1 multicoloured . . . 1·25 35

1854 "Mariner 10" and Mercury

1991. Space Exploration. Multicoloured.

2625 29 c. Type **1854** 40 10
2626 29 c. Venus and "Mariner 2" 40 10
2627 29 c. Earth and "Landsat" 40 10
2628 29 c. Moon and Lunar Orbiter 40 10
2629 29 c. "Viking" Orbiter and Mars 40 10
2630 29 c. Jupiter and "Pioneer 11" 40 10
2631 29 c. "Voyager 2" and Saturn 40 10
2632 29 c. Uranus and "Voyager 2" 40 10
2633 29 c. Neptune and "Voyager 2" 40 10
2634 29 c. Pluto 40 10

1864 Early Explorers from Asia — **1865** "Madonna and Child with Donor" (detail, Antoniazzo Romano)

1991. Air. America. Voyages of Discovery.

A2635 **1864** 50 c. multicoloured . . 65 15

1991. Christmas. No value expressed. Mult.

2636 (29 c.) Type **1865** 40 10
2637 (29 c.) Santa Claus in chimney (horiz) 40 10
2639 (29 c.) Santa Claus checking list (horiz) 40 10
2640 (29 c.) Santa Clause leaving by chimney (horiz) 40 10
2642 (29 c.) Santa Claus on sleigh (horiz) 40 10

1871 Eagle and Shield — **1872** Ice Hockey

1991. Inscr "Bulk Rate USA".

2644 **1871** (10 c.) multicoloured . . 15 15

For design T **1871** but inscribed "USA Bulk Rate" see Nos. 2801/2.

1992. Winter Olympic Games, Albertville. Multicoloured.

2645 29 c. Type **1872** 40 10
2646 29 c. Figure skating 40 10
2647 29 c. Speed skating 40 10
2648 29 c. Skiing 40 10
2649 29 c. Two-man bobsleigh . . 40 10

1877 1869 15 c. Columbus Stamp — **1878** Du Bois

1992. "World Columbian Stamp Expo'92", Chicago.

2650 **1877** 29 c. multicoloured . . 40 10

1992. Black Heritage. William Edward Burghardt Du Bois (founder of Niagara Movement (precursor of National Association for Advancement of Coloured People).

2651 **1878** 29 c. multicoloured . . 40 10

1879 Heart in Envelope — **1880** Catcher and Baserunner

1992. Greetings Stamp.

2652 **1879** 29 c. multicoloured . . 40 10

1992. Addition of Baseball to Olympic Games.

2654 **1880** 29 c. multicoloured . . 40 10

1881 Flag over White House — **1882** Seeking Queen Isabella's Support

1992. Bicentenary of White House.

2655 **1881** 29 c. red and blue . . . 40 10

1992. 500th Anniv of Discovery of America by Columbus. Multicoloured.

2656 29 c. Type **1882** 40 15
2657 29 c. Crossing the Atlantic . 40 15
2658 29 c. Approaching land . . 40 15
2659 29 c. Coming ashore 40 15

1886 Exchange Facade and Trading Floor — **1893** Russian Cosmonaut and Space Shuttle

1992. Bicentenary of New York Stock Exchange.

2660 **1886** 29 c. green, black & red 40 10

1992. International Space Year. Multicoloured.

2662 29 c. Type **1893** 40 10
2663 29 c. American astronaut and "Mir" space station . . . 40 10
2664 29 c. "Apollo" and "Vostok" spacecraft and Sputnik . . 40 10
2665 29 c. "Soyuz", "Mercury" and "Gemini" spacecraft . . . 40 10

1897 Army Lorry using New Highway — **1898** My Old Kentucky Home State Park, Bardstown

1992. 50th Anniv of Alaska Highway.

2666 **1897** 29 c. multicoloured . . 40 10

1992. Bicentenary of Kentucky Statehood.

2667 **1898** 29 c. multicoloured . . 40 10

1899 Football — **1904** Ruby-throated Hummingbird

1992. Olympic Games, Barcelona. Multicoloured.

2668 29 c. Type **1899** 40 10
2669 29 c. Gymnastics 40 10
2670 29 c. Volleyball 40 10
2671 29 c. Boxing 40 10
2672 29 c. Swimming 40 10

1992. Hummingbirds. Multicoloured.

2673 29 c. Type **1904** 40 10
2674 29 c. Broad-billed hummingbird 40 10
2675 29 c. Costa's hummingbird . 40 10
2676 29 c. Rufous hummingbird . 40 10
2677 29 c. Calliope hummingbird . 40 10

1909 Flag in "USA" — **1910** Indian Paintbrush

1992. Presorted First Class stamp.

2678 **1909** 23 c. multicoloured . . . 30 30

1992. Wild Flowers. Multicoloured.

2680 29 c. Type **1910** 40 10
2681 29 c. Fragrant water lily . . . 40 10
2682 29 c. Meadow beauty 40 10
2683 29 c. Jack-in-the-pulpit . . . 40 10
2684 29 c. California poppy . . . 40 10
2685 29 c. Large-flowered trillium . 40 10
2686 29 c. Tickseed 40 10
2687 29 c. Shooting star 40 10
2688 29 c. Stream violet 40 10
2689 29 c. Bluets 40 10
2690 29 c. Herb Robert 40 10
2691 29 c. Marsh marigold 40 10
2692 29 c. Sweet white violet . . . 40 10
2693 29 c. Claret cup cactus . . . 40 10
2694 29 c. White mountain avens . 40 10
2695 29 c. Sessile bellwort 40 10
2696 29 c. Blue flag 40 10
2697 29 c. Harlequin lupine . . . 40 10
2698 29 c. Twinflower 40 10
2699 29 c. Common sunflower . . . 40 10
2700 29 c. Sego lily 40 10
2701 29 c. Virginia bluebells . . . 40 10
2702 29 c. Ohi'a lehua 40 10
2703 29 c. Rosebud orchid 40 10
2704 29 c. Showy evening primrose 40 10
2705 29 c. Fringed gentian 40 10
2706 29 c. Yellow lady's slipper . . 40 10
2707 29 c. Passionflower 40 10
2708 29 c. Bunchberry 40 10
2709 29 c. Pasqueflower 40 10
2710 29 c. Round-lobed hepatica . . 40 10
2711 29 c. Wild columbine 40 10
2712 29 c. Fireweed 40 10
2713 29 c. Indian pond lily 40 10
2714 29 c. Turk's cap lily 40 10
2715 29 c. Dutchman's breeches . . 40 10
2716 29 c. Trumpet honeysuckle . . 40 10
2717 29 c. Jacob's ladder 40 10
2718 29 c. Plains prickly pear . . . 40 10
2719 29 c. Moss campion 40 10
2720 29 c. Bearberry 40 10
2721 29 c. Mexican hat 40 10
2722 29 c. Harebell 40 10
2723 29 c. Desert five spot 40 10
2724 29 c. Smooth Solomon's seal . 40 10
2725 29 c. Red maids 40 10
2726 29 c. Yellow skunk cabbage . 40 10
2727 29 c. Rue anemone 40 10
2728 29 c. Standing cypress 40 10
2729 29 c. Wild flax 40 10

1911 Doolittle Raid on Tokyo — **1921** Dorothy Parker

1992. United States Participation in Second World War. Multicoloured.

2730 29 c. Type **1911** 40 15
2731 29 c. Ration stamps 40 15
2732 29 c. Douglas SBD-3 Dauntless on aircraft carrier (Battle of Coral Sea) 40 15
2733 29 c. Japanese occupation of Corregidor 40 15
2734 29 c. Japanese invasion of Aleutian Islands 40 15
2735 29 c. Allies decipher enemy codes 40 15
2736 29 c. U.S.S. "Yorktown" ablaze (Battle of Midway) 40 15
2737 29 c. Woman engaged in war effort 40 15
2738 29 c. Marines landing at Guadalcanal 40 15
2739 29 c. Allied tanks in North Africa 40 15

1992. Literary Arts. Dorothy Parker (short story writer, poet and critic).

2740 **1921** 29 c. multicoloured . . 40 10

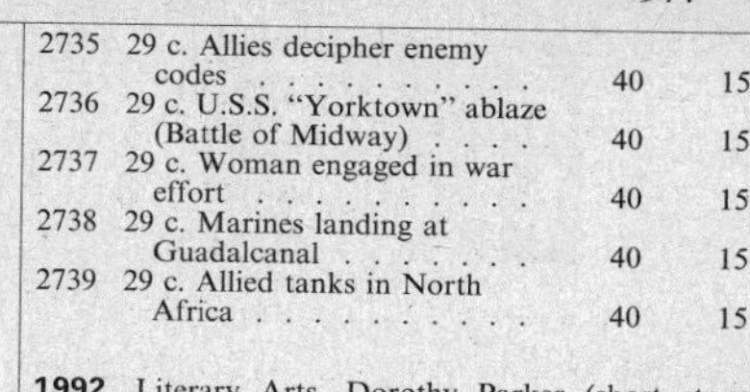

1922 Von Karman and Rocket — **1923** Flag and "I pledge allegiance..."

1992. Theodore von Karman (space pioneer).

2741 **1922** 29 c. multicoloured . . 40 10

1992. Centenary of Pledge of Allegiance.

2742 **1923** 29 c. multicoloured (value in black) 40 10
2788 29 c. multicoloured (value in red) 40 10

1924 Azurite — **1928** Eagle and Shield

1992. Minerals. Multicoloured.

2743 29 c. Type **1924** 40 10
2744 29 c. Copper 40 10
2745 29 c. Variscite 40 10
2746 29 c. Wulfenite 40 10

1992. Self-adhesive. Imperf.

2747 **1928** 29 c. multicoloured (inscr in red) 40 15
2748 29 c. multicoloured (inscr in green) 40 15
2749 29 c. multicoloured (inscr in brown) 40 15

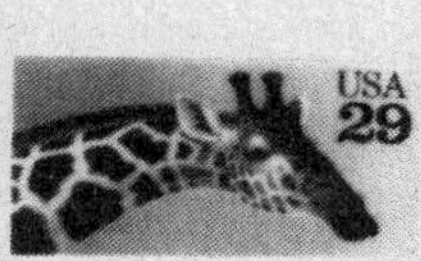

1929 Spanish Galleon, Map and Cabrillo — **1930** Giraffe

1992. 450th Anniv of Discovery of California by Juan Rodriguez Cabrillo.

2750 **1929** 29 c. multicoloured . . 40 15

1992. Wild Animals. Multicoloured.

2751 29 c. Type **1930** 40 10
2752 29 c. Giant panda 40 10
2753 29 c. Flamingo 40 10
2754 29 c. King penguins 40 10
2755 29 c. White Bengal tiger . . 40 10

1935 "Madonna and Child with Saints" (Giovanni Bellini) — **1940** Pumpkinseed Sunfish

1992. Christmas. Multicoloured.

2756 29 c. Type **1935** 40 10
2757 29 c. Wheeled racing horse (horiz) 40 10
2758 29 c. Locomotive (horiz) . . 40 10
2759 29 c. Steam engine (horiz) . 40 10
2760 29 c. Steamer (horiz) 40 10

No. 2758 also comes imperf and self-adhesive.

1992.

2766 **1940** 45 c. multicoloured . . 60 10

1941 Rooster

1992. New Year.
2768 **1941** 29 c. multicoloured . . 40 10

1942 Elvis Presley **1943** Spacecraft and Ringed-planet

1993. Elvis Presley (rock singer and actor).
2769 **1942** 29 c. multicoloured . . 40 10
For similar design but inscr "ELVIS PRESLEY" see Type **1987**.

1993. Space Fantasy. Multicoloured.
2770 29 c. Type **1943** 40 10
2771 29 c. Space capsules 40 10
2772 29 c. Astronauts 40 10
2773 29 c. Spaceship 40 10
2774 29 c. Spacecraft and planet . 40 10

1948 Julian **1949** Route Map

1993. Black Heritage. Percy Lavon Julian (research chemist).
2775 **1948** 29 c. multicoloured . . 40 10

1993. 150th Anniv of Oregon Trail.
2776 **1949** 29 c. multicoloured . . 40 10

1950 Athletes **1951** Princess Grace

1993. World University Games, Buffalo.
2777 **1950** 29 c. multicoloured . . 40 10

1993. 10th Death Anniv of Princess Grace of Monaco (former Grace Kelly).
2778 **1951** 29 c. blue 40 10

1952 "Oklahoma"

1993. Broadway Musicals. Multicoloured. (a) No frame. Size 36 × 28 mm.
2779 29 c. Type **1952** 40 10

(b) With frame. Size 35 × 27 mm.
2780 29 c. "Show Boat" 40 10
2781 29 c. "Porgy and Bess" . . . 40 10
2782 29 c. Type **1952** 40 10
2783 29 c. "My Fair Lady" . . . 40 10

1956 Clown

1993. Bicentenary of First Circus Performance in America. Multicoloured.
2784 29 c. Type **1956** 40 10
2785 29 c. Ringmaster 40 10
2786 29 c. Trapeze artiste 40 10
2787 29 c. Elephant 40 10

1960 Pioneers racing to Cherokee Strip **1961** Acheson

1993. Centenary of Cherokee Strip Land Run.
2789 **1960** 29 c. multicoloured . . 40 10

1993. Birth Centenary of Dean Acheson (Secretary of State, 1949–53).
2790 **1961** 29 c. green 40 10

1962 Steeplechase **1966** Hyacinths

1993. Equestrian Sports. Multicoloured.
2791 29 c. Type **1962** 40 10
2792 29 c. Thoroughbred racing . 40 10
2793 29 c. Harness racing 40 10
2794 29 c. Polo 40 10

1993. Garden Flowers. Multicoloured.
2796 29 c. Type **1966** 40 10
2797 29 c. Daffodils 40 10
2798 29 c. Tulips 40 10
2799 29 c. Irises 40 10
2800 29 c. Lilac 40 10

USA Bulk Rate
1971 Eagle and Shield **1972** Atlantic Convoy

1993. Coil stamps. Inscr "USA Bulk Rate". Multicoloured, colours of eagle given.
2801 **1971** (10 c.) yellow & brown 10 10
2802 (10 c.) gold & brown . 10 10
For design as Type **1971** but inscr "Bulk Rate USA" see No. 2644.

1993. United States Participation in Second World War. Multicoloured.
2803 29 c. Type **1972** 40 10
2804 29 c. Treating the wounded . 40 10
2805 29 c. Allied attack on Sicily . 40 10
2806 29 c. Consolidated B-24 Liberators bombing Ploesti refineries 40 10
2807 29 c. G.I.s with mail from home 40 10
2808 29 c. Allied invasion of Italy 40 10
2809 29 c. War Savings stamps and bonds 40 10
2810 29 c. Willie and Joe (cartoon characters) 40 10
2811 29 c. Gold Star emblem . . 40 10
2812 29 c. Marine assault on Tarawa, Gilbert Islands 40 10

1982 Futuristic Space Shuttle

1993.
2813 **1982** $2.90 multicoloured . . 3·75 1·50

1983 Hank Williams

1993. Country Music. Multicoloured. (a) No frame.
2815 29 c. Type **1982** 40 10
2816 29 c. Patsy Cline 40 10
2817 29 c. Carter Family 40 10
2818 29 c. Bob Wills 40 10

(b) With frame.
2819 29 c. Type **1983** 40 10
2820 29 c. Carter Family 40 10
2821 29 c. Patsy Cline 40 10
2822 29 c. Bob Wills 40 10

1987 Elvis Presley **1994** Louis

1993. Rock and Rhythm and Blues Music. Multicoloured. (a) No frame.
2823 29 c. Type **1987** 40 10
2824 29 c. Buddy Holly 40 10
2825 29 c. Ritchie Valens 40 10
2826 29 c. Bill Haley 40 10
2827 29 c. Dinah Washington . . . 40 10
2828 29 c. Otis Redding 40 10
2829 29 c. Clyde McPhatter . . . 40 10

(b) With frame.
2830 29 c. Type **1987** 40 10
2831 29 c. Bill Haley 40 10
2832 29 c. Clyde McPhatter . . . 40 10
2833 29 c. Ritchie Valens 40 10
2834 29 c. Otis Redding 40 10
2835 29 c. Buddy Holly 40 10
2836 29 c. Dinah Washington . . . 40 10

1993. Joe Louis (boxer).
2837 **1994** 29 c. multicoloured . . . 40 10

1995 Red Squirrel **1996** Benjamin Franklin, Liberty Hall, Philadelphia, Post Rider and Printing Press

1993. Self-adhesive. Imperf.
2838 **1995** 29 c. multicoloured . . . 40 10

1993. Inauguration of National Postal Museum, Washington. Multicoloured.
2840 29 c. Type **1996** 40 10
2841 29 c. Pony Express rider, Civil War soldier and stagecoach 40 10
2842 29 c. Curtiss JN-4 "Jenny" biplane, pilot, railway mail carriage and mail truck . . 40 10
2843 29 c. Gold rush miner's letter and stamps 40 10

2000 Rose **2001** Mother signing "I Love You"

1993. Self-adhesive. Imperf.
2844 **2000** 29 c. multicoloured . . . 40 10

1993. Deaf Communication. Multicoloured.
2845 29 c. Type **2001** 40 10
2846 29 c. "I Love You" in sign language 40 10

2003 African Violet

1993.
2847 **2003** 29 c. multicoloured . . . 40 10

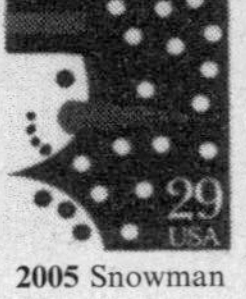

2004 "Madonna and Child in a Landscape" (Giovanni Battista Cima de Conegliano) **2005** Snowman

1993. Christmas. (a) Type **2004**.
2848 29 c. multicoloured 40 10

(b) As T **2005**. Multicoloured. Perf or imperf (self-adhesive).
2849 29 c. Type **2005** 40 10
2850 29 c. Toy soldier 40 10
2851 29 c. Jack-in-the-box . . . 40 10
2852 29 c. Reindeer 40 10
All designs come in more than one version which differ slightly in size.

2009 "Rebecca of Sunnybrook Farm" (Kate Douglas Wiggin)

1993. Classic Children's Books. Multicoloured.
2863 29 c. Type **2009** 40 10
2864 29 c. "Little House on the Prairie" (Laura Ingalls Wilder) 40 10
2865 29 c. "The Adventures of Huckleberry Finn" (Mark Twain) 40 10
2866 29 c. "Little Women" (Louisa May Alcott) 40 10

2013 Latte Stones and Flag **2014** Pine Cone

1993. 15th Anniv of Commonwealth of Northern Mariana Islands.
2867 **2013** 29 c. multicoloured . . 40 10

1993. Self-adhesive. Imperf.
2868 **2014** 29 c. red, green & black 40 10

2015 Caravels off Puerto Rico **2016** Emblem

1993. 500th Anniv of Columbus's Landing at Puerto Rico.
2869 **2015** 29 c. multicoloured . . 40 10

1993. World AIDS Day.
2870 **2016** 29 c. red and black . . 40 10

2017 Skiing **2022** Murrow

1994. Winter Olympic Games. Lillehammer. Multicoloured.
2872 29 c. Type **2017** 40 10
2873 29 c. Luge 40 10
2874 29 c. Ice dancing 40 10
2875 29 c. Cross-country skiing . 40 10
2876 29 c. Ice hockey 40 10

1994. 29th Death Anniv of Edward Murrow (radio and television journalist).
2877 **2022** 29 c. brown 40 10

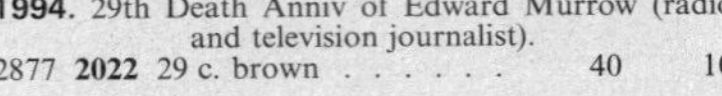

2023 Heart-shaped Sun **2024** Davis

1994. Greetings Stamp. Self-adhesive. Imperf.

2878	**2023**	29 c. multicoloured	40	10

1994. Black Heritage. Dr. Allison Davis (educationist).

2879	**2024**	29 c. sepia and brown	40	10

2025 Eagle **2026** Pekingese

1994. Self-adhesive. Imperf.

2880	**2025**	29 c. multicoloured	40	10

1994. New Year.

2881	**2026**	29 c. multicoloured	40	10

2027 Dove on Heart-shaped Bouquet of Roses **2029** Troopers on Western Frontier

1994. Greetings Stamps. Multicoloured.

2882	29 c. Type **2027**	40	10
2883	52 c. Doves on flower arrangement	70	25

1994. "Buffalo Soldiers" (U.S. Army black regiments).

2884	**2029**	29 c. multicoloured	40	10

2030 Rudolph Valentino

2040 Lilies

1994. Silent Screen Stars.

2885	**2030**	29 c. black, vio & red	40	10
2886	–	29 c. black, vio & red	40	10
2887	–	29 c. black, red & vio	40	10
2888	–	29 c. black, red & vio	40	10
2889	–	29 c. black, vio & red	40	10
2890	–	29 c. black, red & vio	40	10
2891	–	29 c. black, vio & red	40	10
2892	–	29 c. black, vio & red	40	10
2893	–	29 c. black, red & vio	40	10
2894	–	29 c. black, red & vio	40	10

DESIGNS: No. 2886, Clara Bow; 2887, Charlie Chaplin; 2888, Lon Chaney; 2889, John Gilbert; 2890, Zasu Pitts; 2891, Harold Lloyd; 2892, Keystone Cops; 2893, Theda Bara; 2894, Buster Keaton.

1994. Garden Flowers. Multicoloured.

2895	29 c. Type **2040**	40	10
2896	29 c. Zinnias	40	10
2897	29 c. Gladioli	40	10
2898	29 c. Marigolds	40	10
2899	29 c. Roses	40	10

2045 Surrender at Saratoga (after John Trumbull)

2046 U.S.A. Player kicking Ball

1994.

2900	**2045**	$1 blue	1·25	45

1994. World Cup Football Championship, U.S.A. Multicoloured.

2902	29 c. Type **2046**	35	10
2903	40 c. Controlling the ball	50	20
2904	50 c. Heading the ball	60	20

2050 Liberating New Guinea

2060 Statue of Liberty

1994. United States Participation in Second World War. Multicoloured.

2906	29 c. Type **2050**	35	10
2907	29 c. P-51 escorting B-17 bombers	35	10
2908	29 c. Normandy Landings	35	10
2909	29 c. Glider and paratroops	35	10
2910	29 c. Submarine crew	35	10
2911	29 c. Liberating Rome	35	10
2912	29 c. Troops clearing Saipan bunkers	35	10
2913	29 c. Red Ball Express truck	35	10
2914	29 c. Battleship (Battle of Leyte Gulf)	35	10
2915	29 c. Battle of the Bulge	35	10

1994. Self-adhesive. Imperf.

2917	**2060**	29 c. multicoloured	35	10

2061 "Triple Self-Portrait"

1994. Birth Centenary of Norman Rockwell (illustrator).

2919	**2061**	29 c. multicoloured	35	10

2063 Astronauts planting Flag on Moon

1994. 25th Anniv of First Manned Moon Landing.

2921	**2063**	$9.95 multicoloured	12·50	4·25

2065 Hudson's "General", 1855

1994. Locomotives. Multicoloured.

2923	29 c. Type **2065**	35	10
2924	29 c. McQueen's "Jupiter", 1868	35	10
2925	29 c. Eddy's No. 242, 1874	35	10
2926	29 c. Ely's No. 10, 1881	35	10
2927	29 c. Buchanan's No. 999, 1893	35	10

2070 Meany

2072 Al Jolson

2071 Presidents Washington and Jackson

1994. Birth Centenary of George Meany (trades unionist).

2928	**2070**	29 c. blue	35	10

1994.

2929	**2071**	$5 green	6·25	2·10

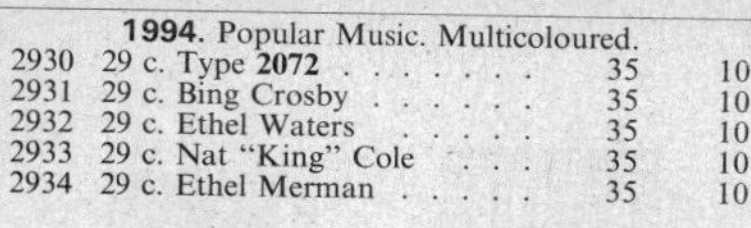

1994. Popular Music. Multicoloured.

2930	29 c. Type **2072**	35	10
2931	29 c. Bing Crosby	35	10
2932	29 c. Ethel Waters	35	10
2933	29 c. Nat "King" Cole	35	10
2934	29 c. Ethel Merman	35	10

2077 "Male Type (eastern seaboard)"

2078 Bessie Smith

1994. Literary Arts. Birth Centenary of James Thurber (writer and cartoonist).

2935	**2077**	29 c. multicoloured	35	10

1994. Jazz and Blues Music. Multicoloured.

2936	29 c. Type **2078**	35	10
2937	29 c. Muddy Waters	35	10
2938	29 c. Billie Holiday	35	10
2939	29 c. Robert Johnson	35	10
2940	29 c. Jimmy Rushing	35	10
2941	29 c. "Ma" Rainey	35	10
2942	29 c. Mildred Bailey	35	10
2943	29 c. Howlin' Wolf	35	10

2086/9 Sea Life (½-size illustration)

1994. Wonders of the Seas.

2944	**2086**	29 c. multicoloured	35	10
2945	**2087**	29 c. multicoloured	35	10
2946	**2088**	29 c. multicoloured	35	10
2947	**2089**	29 c. multicoloured	35	10

Nos. 2944/7 were issued together, se-tenant, forming the composite design illustrated.

2090 Black-necked Crane

2092 Home on the Range

1994. Cranes. Multicoloured.

2948	29 c. Type **2090**	35	10
2949	29 c. Whooping crane	35	10

1994. Legends of the West. Multicoloured.

2950	29 c. Type **2092**	35	10
2951	29 c. Buffalo Bill	35	10
2952	29 c. Jim Bridger	35	10
2953	29 c. Annie Oakley	35	10
2954	29 c. Native American culture	35	10
2955	29 c. Chief Joseph	35	10
2956	29 c. Bill Pickett	35	10
2957	29 c. Bat Masterson	35	10
2958	29 c. John Fremont	35	10
2959	29 c. Wyatt Earp	35	10
2960	29 c. Nellie Cashman	35	10
2961	29 c. Charles Goodnight	35	10
2962	29 c. Geronimo	35	10
2963	29 c. Kit Carson	35	10
2964	29 c. Wild Bill Hickok	35	10
2965	29 c. Western wildlife	35	10
2966	29 c. Jim Beckwourth	35	10
2967	29 c. Bill Tilghman	35	10
2968	29 c. Sacagawea	35	10
2969	29 c. Overland mail	35	10

Each stamp is inscribed on the back, under the gum, with a brief history of the subject depicted.

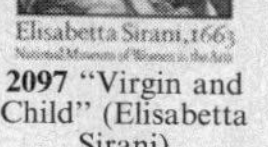

2097 "Virgin and Child" (Elisabetta Sirani)

2100 Cardinal

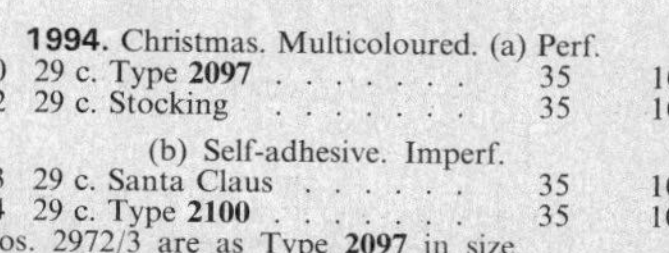

1994. Christmas. Multicoloured. (a) Perf.

2970	29 c. Type **2097**	35	10
2972	29 c. Stocking	35	10

(b) Self-adhesive. Imperf.

2973	29 c. Santa Claus	35	10
2974	29 c. Type **2100**	35	10

Nos. 2972/3 are as Type **2097** in size.

CERTIFIED MAIL

C **524** Postman

1955.

C1070	C **524**	15 c. red	35	25

NEWSPAPER STAMPS

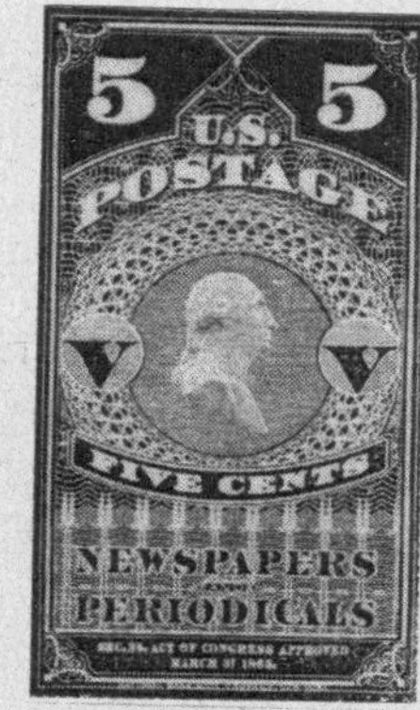

N **21** Washington (½-size illustration)

1865. 5 c. with coloured or white border.

N78a	N **21**	5 c. blue	22·00	18·00
N80	–	10 c. green	25·00	
N81	–	25 c. red	48·00	

DESIGNS: 10 c. Franklin; 20 c. Lincoln.

N **42** "Freedom"

N **87** "Freedom"

1875. Different Frames.

N252	N **42**	1 c. black	5·50	3·00
N291	N **87**	1 c. black	2·25	1·75
N228	N **42**	2 c. black	4·00	3·00
N292	N **87**	2 c. black	2·50	1·25
N229	N **42**	3 c. black	5·00	3·25
N230		4 c. black	5·50	3·25
N293	N **87**	5 c. black	4·00	3·00
N231	N **42**	6 c. black	10·00	7·00
N232		8 c. black	10·00	7·00
N185		9 c. black	42·00	38·00
N233		10 c. black	10·00	6·00
N294	N **87**	10 c. black	2·50	1·75
N253	A	12 c. red	19·00	8·50
N254		24 c. red	22·00	10·00
N295		25 c. red	5·50	5·50
N255		36 c. red	30·00	12·00
N256		48 c. red	42·00	20·00
N296		50 c. red	6·50	8·00
N191		60 c. red	55·00	30·00
N258		72 c. red	70·00	32·00
N240		84 c. red	£120	60·00
N241		96 c. red	75·00	42·00
N242	–	$1.92 brown	60·00	38·00
N297	–	$2 red	7·50	11·00
N243	–	$3 red	60·00	38·00
N298	–	$5 blue	13·00	18·00
N244	–	$6 blue	£110	65·00
N245	–	$9 orange	75·00	42·00
N299	–	$10 green	12·00	18·00
N246	–	$12 green	£110	55·00
N300	–	$20 black	13·00	19·00
N247	–	$24 purple	£140	75·00
N248	–	$36 red	£180	90·00
N249	–	$48 brown	£225	£120
N301	–	$50 red	16·00	22·00
N250	–	$60 violet	£225	£120
N302	–	$100 violet	18·00	27·00

DESIGNS: A, Astraea or "Justice"; $1.92, Ceres; $2, $3 "Victory"; $5, $6 Clio; $9 Minerva; $10, $12 Vesta; $20, $24 "Peace"; $36, $50 "Commerce"; $48 Hebe; $60, $100 Minnehaha.

OFFICIAL STAMPS

For list of stamps used on correspondence from individual Government Departments, between 1873 and 1879, see the Stanley Gibbons Part 22 (U.S.A.) Catalogue.

O **1315** Eagle

O **1438**

O **1588**

1983.

O2008	O **1315**	1 c. blue, red and black	10	10
O2009		4 c. blue, red and black	10	15
O2010		13 c. blue, red and black	15	45
O2011		14 c. blue, red and black	25	50
O2012		17 c. blue, red and black	25	30
O2015		20 c. blue, red and black	1·75	65
O2016		22 c. blue, red and black	55	50
O2013		$1 blue, red and black	1·50	70
O2014		$5 blue, red and black	6·00	4·00

1985. No value expressed. (a) Inscr "Postal Card Rate D".

O2140	O **1438**	(14 c.) blue, red and black	3·00	70

(b) Inscr "Domestic Letter Rate D".

O2141	–	(22 c.) blue, red and black	3·00	70

1988. No value expressed.

O2344	O **1588**	(25 c.) blue, black and red	35	15

O 1592 O 1793

1988.

O2348	O **1592**	1 c. blue, blk & red	10	10
O2349		4 c. blue, blk & red	10	10
O2350		10 c. blue, black and red	10	10
O2354		15 c. blue, black and red	25	10
O2351		19 c. blue, black and red	25	35
O2355		20 c. blue, black and red	30	10
O2352		23 c. blue, black and red	30	15
O2356		25 c. blue, black and red	35	10
O2357		29 c. blue, black and red	40	15
O2353		$1 blue, blk & red	1·25	25

The 10 c. and $1 have an additional inscription ("USA1993" repeated several times) above the face value.

1991. No value expressed.

O2558	O **1793**	(29 c.) blue, black and red	40	15

PARCEL POST STAMPS

P 134 Post Office Clerk

1912.

P423	P **134**	1 c. red	2·75	80
P424	–	2 c. red	2·75	50
P425	–	3 c. red	11·00	4·50
P426	–	4 c. red	20·00	1·50
P427	–	5 c. red	35·00	1·25
P428	–	10 c. red	40·00	1·50
P429	–	15 c. red	50·00	7·00
P430	–	20 c. red	85·00	13·00
P431	–	25 c. red	75·00	4·25
P432	–	50 c. red	£180	28·00
P433	–	75 c. red	50·00	20·00
P434	–	$1 red	£250	16·00

DESIGNS: 2 c. City carrier; 3 c. Railway postal clerk; 4 c. Rural carrier; 5 c. Steam mail train; 10 c. "Kronprinz Wilhelm" (liner) and mail tender; 15 c. Automobile service; 20c. Wright Type A biplane carrying mail; 25 c. Manufacturing (Pullman works); 50 c. Dairying; 75 c. Harvesting; $1 Fruit growing.

PARCEL POST POSTAGE DUE STAMPS

PD 134

1912.

PD423	PD **134**	1 c. green	6·50	2·50
PD424		2 c. green	50·00	12·00
PD425		5 c. green	8·00	2·50
PD426		10 c. green	£120	28·00
PD427		25 c. green	55·00	2·75

POSTAGE DUE STAMPS

D 43 D 87

1879.

D207	D **43**	1 c. brown	18·00	3·50
D222		2 c. brown	28·00	1·50
D209		3 c. brown	16·00	1·75
D224		5 c. brown	£180	7·50
D225		10 c. brown	£160	4·50
D226		30 c. brown	75·00	16·00
D213		50 c. brown	£170	26·00

1891.

D235	D **43**	1 c. red	8·50	35
D236		2 c. red	11·00	30
D237		3 c. red	24·00	2·50
D238		5 c. red	26·00	2·50
D239		10 c. red	48·00	6·50
D240		30 c. red	£180	60·00
D241		50 c. red	£200	65·00

1894.

D529	D **87**	½ c. red	40	10
D530		1 c. red	1·25	10
D531		2 c. red	1·00	10
D532		3 c. red	6·00	10
D533		5 c. red	6·00	10
D534a		10 c. red	9·00	10
D535a		30 c. red	38·00	30
D536		50 c. red	60·00	10

D 201 D 202 D 581

1931.

D702	D **201**	½ c. red	75	10
D703		1 c. red	15	10
D704		2 c. red	20	10
D705		3 c. red	25	10
D706		5 c. red	35	10
D707		10 c. red	1·10	10
D708		30 c. red	8·00	10
D709		50 c. red	8·50	10
D699a	D **202**	$1 red	22·00	10
D700a		$5 red	32·00	15

1959. Centres in black.

D1130	D **581**	½ c. red	1·25	1·25
D1131		1 c. red	15	10
D1132		2 c. red	15	10
D1133		3 c. red	15	10
D1134		4 c. red	15	10
D1135		5 c. red	15	10
D1136		6 c. red	15	10
D1137		7 c. red	15	10
D1138		8 c. red	15	10
D1139		10 c. red	15	10
D1140		11 c. red	25	15
D1141		13 c. red	30	25
D1142		17 c. red	30	25
D1143		30 c. red	50	10
D1144		50 c. red	75	10
D1145		$1 red	1·60	10
D1146		$5 red	7·50	15

In the dollar values the numerals are double-lined and vertical.

REGISTERED LETTER STAMP

R 133 American Bald Eagle

1911.

R404	R **133**	10 c. blue	75·00	3·00

SPECIAL DELIVERY AIR STAMPS

AE 247 Great Seal of U.S.A.

1934.

AE750	AE **247**	16 c. blue	60	70
AE751		16 c. blue and red	40	15

SPECIAL DELIVERY STAMPS

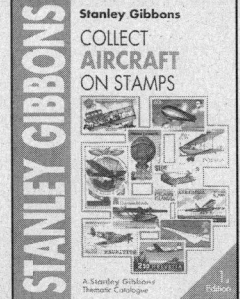

E 46 Messenger Running

1885. Inscr "AT A SPECIAL DELIVERY OFFICE".

E217	E **46**	10 c. blue	£160	20·00

1888. As Type E **46**, but inscr "AT ANY POST OFFICE".

E283	E **46**	10 c. blue	90·00	1·75
E251		10 c. orange	£110	8·50

E 117 Messenger on Bicycle

1917.

E529	E **117**	10 c. blue	11·00	15

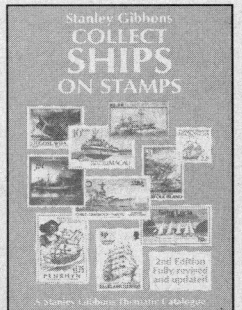

E 129 Hat of Mercury and Olive-branch E 143 Delivery by Motor Cycle

1908.

E374	E **129**	10 c. green	48·00	20·00

1922.

E648	E **143**	10 c. blue	60	10
E648a		10 c. violet	60	10
E649		13 c. blue	45	10
E650		15 c. orange	65	10
E651		17 c. yellow	3·00	2·75

E 144 Delivery by Van

1925.

E652	E **144**	20 c. black	1·50	10

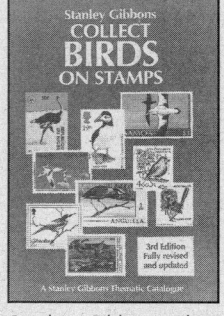

E 520 Delivery by Hand

1954.

E1066	E **520**	20 c. blue	60	10
E1067		30 c. lake	70	10

E 799 Arrows

1969.

E1374	E **799**	45 c. red and blue	1·40	15
E1375		60 c. blue and red	1·40	10

SPECIAL HANDLING STAMPS

SH 173

1925.

SH624	SH **173**	10 c. green	1·00	80
SH625		15 c. green	1·10	80
SH626		20 c. green	1·50	25
SH628		25 c. green	16·00	6·00

UNITED STATES POSTAL AGENCY IN SHANGHAI Pt. 17

These stamps were valid for use on mail despatched from the U.S. Postal Agency in Shanghai to addresses in the United States. This agency was closed 31st December 1922.

100 cents = 1 dollar (Chinese)

1919. United States stamps of 1908–12 surch **SHANGHAI CHINA** and new value.

1 **128** 2 c. on 1 c. green . . . . 14·00 16·00
17 2 Cts. on 1 c. green . . . 75·00 80·00
2 4 c. on 2 c. pink . . . . 14·00 17·00
18 4 Cts. on 2 c. red . . . 75·00 75·00
3 6 c. on 3 c. violet . . . 28·00 40·00
4 8 c. on 4 c. brown . . . 32·00 42·00
5 10 c. on 5 c. blue . . . 38·00 45·00
6 12 c. on 6 c. orange . . . 48·00 60·00
7 14 c. on 7 c. black . . . 50·00 65·00
8 **133** 16 c. on 8 c. olive . . . 40·00 45·00
9 18 c. on 9 c. orange . . . 40·00 45·00
10 20 c. on 10 c. yellow . . . 38·00 40·00
11a 24 c. on 12 c. red . . . 40·00 50·00
12 30 c. on 15 c. grey . . . 55·00 60·00
13 40 c. on 20 c. blue . . . 85·00 95·00
14 60 c. on 30 c. red . . . 80·00 95·00
15 $1 on 50 c. lilac £500 £400
16 $2 on $1 black £325 £325

UPPER SENEGAL AND NIGER Pt. 6

A French Colony in W. Africa, E. of Senegal, formerly called Senegambia and Niger, and became part of French Sudan in 1920.

1906. "Faidherbe", "Palms" and "Balay" key-types inscr "HT-SENEGAL-NIGER" in blue (10, 40 c., 5 f.) or red (others).

35 I 1 c. grey 50 60
36 2 c. brown 50 65
37 4 c. brown on blue 70 70
38 5 c. green . . . . 2·50 1·25
39 10 c. red . . . . 2·50 95
40 15 c. violet . . . . . . 3·25 2·25
41 J 20 c. black on blue . . . . 1·00 2·25
42 25 c. blue . . . . 6·50 4·50
43 30 c. brown on pink . . . . 2·75 4·00
44 35 c. black on yellow . . . 2·50 1·75
45 40 c. red on blue . . . . 4·00 4·00
46 45 c. brown on green . . . 4·75 5·25
47 50 c. violet . . . . . . 4·50 4·00
48 75 c. green on orange . . . 5·00 5·50
49 K 1 f. black on blue . . . . 10·00 10·00
50 2 f. blue on red . . . . 30·00 30·00
51 5 f. red on yellow . . . . 50·00 60·00

7 Touareg

1914.

59 **7** 1 c. violet and purple . . . 10 25
60 2 c. purple and grey . . . 10 25
61 4 c. blue and black 10 25
62 5 c. green and light green . . 10 25
63 10 c. carmine and red . . . 10 90
64 15 c. yellow and brown . . . 25 60
65 20 c. black and purple . . . 30 70
66 25 c. blue and ultramarine . . 40 80
67 30 c. chocolate and brown . . 40 80
68 35 c. violet and red . . . . 30 1·00
69 40 c. red and grey 80 85
70 45 c. brown and blue . . . 30 65
71 50 c. green and black . . . 50 75
72 75 c. brown and yellow . . . 40 85
73 1 f. purple and brown . . . 1·40 1·75
74 2 f. blue and green . . . . 60 1·40
75 5 f. black and violet . . . 6·75 4·75

1915. Red Cross. Surch **5c** and red cross.

76 **7** 10 c. + 5 c. carmine and red . . 50 55

POSTAGE DUE STAMPS

1906. "Natives" key-type inscr "HT-SENEGAL-NIGER".

D52 L 5 c. green and red . . . . 1·25 1·25
D53 10 c. purple and blue . . . 3·75 3·00
D54 15 c. blue & red on blue . . 5·50 4·75
D55 20 c. black & red on yell . . 6·00 3·25
D56 50 c. violet and red . . . 15·00 11·00
D57 60 c. black & red on buff . . 9·75 9·00
D58 1 f. black & red on flesh . . 25·00 18·00

1915. "Figures" key-type inscr "HT. SENEGAL-NIGER".

D77 M 5 c. green 60 70
D78 10 c. red 60 70
D79 15 c. grey 65 70
D80 20 c. brown 65 70
D81 30 c. blue . . . . 1·25 1·50
D82 50 c. black . . . . . . 1·00 1·25
D83 60 c. orange . . . . . . 3·00 3·25
D84 1 f. violet . . . . . . 2·25 3·00

For later issues see **FRENCH SUDAN**.

UPPER SILESIA Pt. 7

Stamps issued during a Plebiscite held in 1921 to decide the future of the district.

100 pfenning = 1 mark

1

9 Coal-mine in Silesia

1920.

1 **1** 2½ pf. grey 35 50
3 3 pf. brown 30 65
3 5 pf. green 15 25
4 10 pf. brown 15 30
5 15 pf. violet 15 25
6 20 pf. blue 15 25
7 50 pf. brown . . . . . . 3·50 4·75
8 1 m. red . . . . 3·50 6·50
9 5 m. orange . . . . . . 3·50 6·50

1920. Surch.

10 **1** 5 pf. on 15 pf. violet . . . . 6·50 18·00
12 5 pf. on 20 pf. blue 10 15
14 10 pf. on 20 pf. blue . . . 10 10
17 50 pf. on 5 m. orange . . . 10·00 22·00

1920.

19 **9** 2½ pf. grey 15 10
20 3 pf. red 20 10
21 5 pf. green 10 10
22 10 pf. red 10 10
23 15 pf. violet 10 10
24 20 pf. blue 10 10
25 25 pf. brown 15 10
26 30 pf. yellow 10 10
27 40 pf. olive 10 10

Same design, but larger.

28 **9** 50 pf. grey 10 10
29 60 pf. blue 20 15
30 75 pf. green 60 40
31 80 pf. red 50 40
32 1 m. purple 30 15
33 2 m. brown 30 30
34 3 m. violet 50 30
35 5 m. orange . . . . . . 1·10 85

1921. Optd **Plebiscite 20 mars 1921.**

36 **9** 10 pf. red . . . . 1·50 5·50
37 15 pf. violet . . . . . . 1·50 5·50
38 20 pf. blue . . . . 1·50 7·00
39 25 pf. brown . . . . . . 4·25 12·00
40 30 pf. yellow . . . . . . 4·25 12·00
41 40 pf. olive . . . . . . 4·25 14·00
42 50 pf. grey . . . . 4·00 16·00
43 60 pf. blue . . . . 5·50 14·00
44 75 pf. green . . . . . . 5·50 17·00
45 80 pf. red . . . . 6·00 22·00
46 1 m. purple . . . . . . 10·00 38·00

1922. As last, new colours. surch.

47 **9** 4 m. on 60 pf. green 45 85
48 10 m. on 75 pf. red . . . . 70 1·50
49 20 m. on 80 pf. orange . . . 3·50 9·00

OFFICIAL STAMPS

1920. Official stamps of Germany (Types as O **31** and O **32** with figures "21" in corners) optd **C.G.H.S.**

O25 5 pf. green 15 25
O26 10 pf. red 15 25
O27 15 pf. brown 15 25
O28 20 pf. blue 15 25
O29 30 pf. orange on buff 15 25
O30 50 pf. violet on buff 30 50
O31 1 m. red on buff . . . . . 4·25 7·00

1920. Official stamps of Germany, without figs. "21" in corners, optd **C.G.H.S.**

O32 5 pf. green . . . . 55 1·75
O33 10 pf red 10 10
O34 15 pf. purple 10 10
O35 20 pf. blue 10 10
O36 30 pf. orange on buff 10 10
O37 40 pf. red 10 10
O38 50 pf. violet on buff 10 10
O39 60 pf. brown 10 10
O40 1 m. red on buff 10 10
O41 1 m. 25 blue on yellow . . . 10 10
O43 2 m. blue 10 20
O44 5 m. brown on yellow . . . 10 20

UPPER VOLTA Pt. 6; Pt 14

Formerly part of Upper Senegal and Niger, Upper Volta was created a separate colony in 1919. In 1932 it was divided among French Sudan, Ivory Coast and Niger but was reconstituted as a separate territory in 1947 from when it used the stamps of French West Africa.

In 1958 it became an autonomous republic within the French Community and attained full independence in 1960.

In 1984 the name of the state was changed to Burkina Faso.

100 centimes = 1 franc

1920. Stamps of Upper Senegal and Niger optd **HAUTE-VOLTA.**

1 **7** 1 c. violet and purple . . . 10 30
2 2 c. purple and grey 10 30
3 4 c. blue and black 10 30
4 5 c. green and light green . . 30 65
18 5 c. chocolate and brown . . 10 30
5 10 c. carmine and red . . . 35 65
19 **7** 10 c. green and light green . . 15 30
20 10 c. blue and mauve 25 55
6 15 c. yellow and brown . . . 35 65
7 20 c. black and purple . . . 50 1·00
8 25 c. blue and ultramarine . . 60 1·00
21 25 c. green and black . . . 45 75
9 30 c. chocolate and brown . . 1·10 1·50
22 30 c. carmine and red . . . 40 80
23 30 c. red and violet 40 80
23a 30 c. turquoise and green . . 40 80
10 35 c. violet and red 45 95
11 40 c. red and grey . . . . 45 1·00
12 45 c. brown and blue . . . 35 85
13 50 c. green and black . . . 1·50 3·00
24 50 c. blue & ultramarine . . . 20 45
25 50 c. blue and orange . . . 35 80
26 60 c. red 20 40
26a 65 c. blue and brown . . . 65 1·25
14 75 c. brown and yellow . . . 70 1·50
15 1 f. purple and brown . . . 70 1·25
16 2 f. blue and green . . . . 90 1·75
17 5 f. black and violet . . . 2·00 3·00

1922. Surch in figures and bars.

27 **7** 0,01 on 15 c. yellow & brn . . 45 1·00
28 0,20 on 15 c. yellow & brn . . 45 1·00
29 0,05 on 15 c. yellow & brn . . 45 1·00
30 25 c. on 2 f. blue and green . . 50 1·00
31 25 c. on 5 f. black and vio . . 50 1·00
32 60 on 75 c. violet on pink . . 35 75
33 65 on 45 c. brown and blue . . 50 1·00
34 85 on 45 c. brown and yellow . 70 1·40
35 90 c. on 75 c. pink and red . . 90 1·75
36 1 f. 25 on 1 f. lt blue & blue . 45 1·00
37 1 f. 50 on 1 f. ultram & bl . . 1·25 2·00
37a 3 f. on 5 f. brown and pink . . 1·75 2·75
38 10 f. on 5 f. pink and green . . 7·75 10·00
39 20 f. on 5 f. violet & brown . . 10·00 15·00

3 Hausa Man

5 Hausa Warrior

1928.

40 **3** 1 c. blue and green 10 35
41 2 c. brown and mauve . . . 10 35
42 4 c. black and yellow . . . 15 35
43 5 c. indigo and blue 20 40
44 10 c. blue and pink . . . . 50 1·00
45 15 c. brown and blue . . . 95 1·50
46 20 c. brown and green . . . 95 1·50
47 – 25 c. brown and yellow . . . 1·00 1·40
48 – 30 c. deep green and green . . 1·00 1·60
49 – 40 c. black and pink . . . 1·00 1·90
50 – 45 c. brown and blue . . . 1·25 2·00
51 – 50 c. black and green . . . 1·25 1·40
52 – 65 c. indigo and blue . . . 1·50 2·00
53 – 75 c. black and mauve . . . 1·25 2·00
54 – 90 c. red and mauve . . . 1·25 2·00
55 **5** 1 f. brown and green . . . 1·10 1·90
56 1 f. 10 blue and mauve . . . 1·25 1·90
57 1 f. 50 blue . . . . . . 1·90 3·00
58 2 f. black and blue . . . . 2·00 3·00
59 3 f. brown and yellow . . . 2·25 3·50
60 5 f. brown and mauve . . . 2·25 3·50
61 10 f. black and green . . . 8·25 12·00
62 20 f. black and pink . . . . 14·00 18·00

DESIGN—VERT: 25 c. to 90 c. Hausa woman.

1931. "Colonial Exhibition" key-types inscr "HAUTE-VOLTA".

63 E 40 c. green and black . . . 1·75 3·00
64 F 50 c. mauve and black . . . 1·75 3·00
65 G 90 c. red and black . . . . 1·75 3·00
66 B 1 f. 50 blue and black . . . 2·75 4·25

6 President Coulibaly

7 Antelope Mask

1959. 1st Anniv of Republic.

67 **6** 25 f. purple and black 30 20

1960. Animal Masks.

68 **7** 30 c. violet and red 10 10
69 40 c. purple and ochre . . . 10 10
70 50 c. olive and turquoise . . . 10 10
71 – 1 f. black, brown and red . . 10 10
72 – 2 f. multicoloured 10 10
73 – 4 f. black, violet and blue . . 10 10
74 – 5 f. red, brown and bistre . . 15 10
75 – 6 f. purple and turquoise . . 15 10
76 – 8 f. brown and red 20 15
77 – 10 f. purple and green . . . 25 20
78 – 15 f. blue, brown and red . . 35 25
79 – 20 f. green and blue . . . 40 30
80 – 25 f. purple, green and blue . 50 30
81 – 30 f. black, brown & turq . . 65 30
82 – 40 f. black, red and blue . . 90 40
83 – 50 f. brown, green & mauve . 1·10 45
84 – 60 f. blue and brown . . . 1·25 45
85 – 85 f. blue and turquoise . . 2·00 60

MASKS: 1 f. to 4 f. Wart-hog; 5 f. to 8 f. Monkey; 10 f. to 20 f. Buffalo; 25 f. Antelope; 30 f. to 50 f. Elephant; 60 f., 85 f. Secretary bird.

8 President Yameogo

1960.

86 **8** 25 f. purple and grey 50 25

1960. 10th Anniv of African Technical Co-operation Commission. As T **4** of Malagasy Republic.

87 25 f. indigo and blue 50 40

1960. 1st Anniv of Conseil de l'Entente. As T **9** of Niger.

88 25 f. multicoloured 65 40

9

1960. Proclamation of Independence.

89 **9** 25 f. brown, red and black . . 55 40

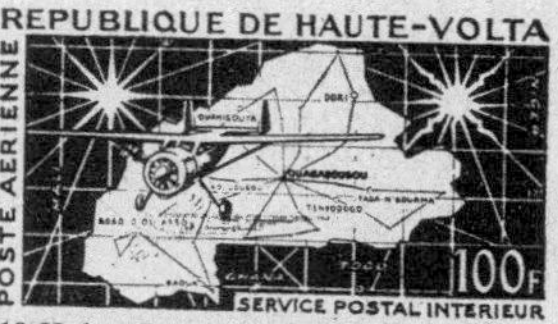

10 Holste Broussard Airplane and Map

1961. Air.

90 **10** 100 f. blue, green and red . . 1·90 80
91 – 200 f. brown, red and green . 4·75 1·40
92 – 500 f. multicoloured . . . 11·00 5·00

DESIGNS: 200 f. Scene at Ouagadougou Airport; 500 f. Aerial view of Champs Elysees, Ouagadougou.

11 W.M.O. Emblem, Sun and Meteorological Instruments

1961. 1st World Meteorological Day.

93 **11** 25 f. red, blue and black . . 55 35

12 Arms of Republic

1961. Independence Festival.

94 **12** 25 f. multicoloured 45 30

1962. Air. "Air Afrique" Airline. As T **42** of Mauritania.

95 25 f. mauve, green and purple . . 55 30

13 W.M.O. Emblem, Weather Station and Crops

1962. World Meteorological Day.

96 **13** 25 f. blue, green and black . . 55 40

1962. Malaria Eradication. As T **43** of Mauritania.

97 25 f. + 5 f. red 70 70

14 Nurse and Hospital

1962. Establishment of Red Cross in Upper Volta.

98	14	25 f. brown, blue and red	60	40

15 African Buffalo at Water-hole

1962. Hunting and Tourism.

99	15	5 f. green, blue and sepia	35	20
100	–	10 f. green, yellow & brn	45	35
101	–	15 f. green, yellow & brn	1·10	60
102	–	25 f. green, blue & mauve	1·10	60
103	–	50 f. green, blue & mauve	1·60	1·40
104	–	85 f. green, blue & brown	3·75	2·40

DESIGNS—VERT: 15 f. Waterbuck; 85 f. Kob. HORIZ: 10 f. Lion and lioness; 25 f. Arly Camp; 50 f. Diapaga Camp.

1962. Abidjan Games, 1961. As T **13** of Niger Republic. Multicoloured.

105		20 f. Football	45	30
106		25 f. Cycling	65	35
107		85 f. Boating	1·40	70

1962. 1st Anniv of Union of African and Malagasy States. As T **45** of Mauritania.

108		30 f. multicoloured	1·10	75

16 Flag and U.N. Emblem

1962. Air. 2nd Anniv of Admission to U.N.

109	16	50 f. multicoloured	65	35
110		100 f. multicoloured	1·40	65

17 G.P.O., Ouagadougou

1962. Air. Opening of Ouagadougou P.O.

111	17	100 f. multicoloured	1·40	60

1963. Freedom from Hunger. As T **51** of Mauritania.

112		25 f. +5 f. blue, brn & myrtle	70	70

18 Rainfall Map

19 Basketball

1963. World Meteorological Day.

113	18	70 c. multicoloured	85	55

1963. Dakar Games. Centres in black and red.

114	19	20 f. violet	35	20
115	–	25 f. ochre (Discus)	45	20
116	–	50 f. blue (Judo)	90	40

20 "Argyreia nervosa"

1963. Flowers. Multicoloured.

117	50 c. "Hibiscus rosa sinensis"	10	10
118	1 f. "Oldenlandia grandiflora"	10	10
119	1 f. 50 "Portulaca grandiflora"	10	10
120	2 f. "Nicotiana tabacum"	10	10
121	4 f. "Ipomaea stolonifera"	15	10
122	5 f. "Striga senegalensis"	15	10
123	6 f. "Vigna"	20	10
124	8 f. "Lepidagathis heudelotiana"	30	20
125	10 f. "Euphorbia splendens"	30	15
126	15 f. "Hippeastrum equestre"	40	30
127	25 f. Type **20**	55	30
128	30 f. "Quisqualis indica"	70	35
129	40 f. "Nymphea lotus"	1·25	50
130	50 f. "Plumeria alba"	1·40	55
131	60 f. "Crotalaria retusa"	1·75	80
132	85 f. "Hibiscus esculentus"	2·40	1·10

The 50 c. to 10 f. are vert.

21 Douglas DC-8 in Flight

1963. Air. 1st Jet-flight, Ouagadougou–Paris.

133	21	200 f. multicoloured	4·25	1·25

1963. Air. African and Malagasy Posts and Telecommunications Union. As T **56** of Mauritania.

134		85 f. multicoloured	1·25	60

22 Centenary Emblem and Globe

24 "Declaration universelle. . ."

1963. Red Cross Centenary.

135	22	25 f. multicoloured	90	65

1963. Air. 1st Anniv of "Air Afrique". Surch **AIR AFRIQUE 19-11-63 50F**.

136	21	50 f. on 200 f. multicoloured	1·10	65

1963. 15th Anniv of Declaration of Human Rights.

137	24	25 f. multicoloured	60	40

25 "Europafrique"

26 "Telecommunications"

1964. Air. "Europafrique".

138	25	50 f. multicoloured	1·25	70

1964. Admission of Upper Volta to I.T.U.

139	26	25 f. multicoloured	45	30

27 Rameses II, Abu Simbel

28 Barograph, Landscape and W.M.O. Emblem

1964. Air. Nubian Monuments Preservation.

140	27	25 f. purple and green	65	45
141		100 f. brown and blue	2·25	1·75

1964. World Meteorological Day.

142	28	50 f. mauve, blue & green	85	55

29 Dove and Letters

1964. 1st Anniv of Admission to U.P.U.

143	29	25 f. sepia and blue	45	30
144	–	60 f. sepia and orange	90	65

DESIGN: 60 f. Jet airliner and letters.

30 Head of Athlete (bronze)

31 Symbols of Solar Research

1964. Air. Olympic Games, Tokyo.

145	30	15 f. green, red and sepia	35	15
146	–	25 f. green, red and sepia	50	20
147	–	85 f. green, red and brown	1·10	70
148	–	100 f. chocolate, red & brn	1·60	85

DESIGNS: 25 f. Seated athlete (bronze); 85 f. "Victorious athlete" (bronze); 100 f. Venus de Milo.

1964. International Quiet Sun Years.

149	31	30 f. red, ochre and green	60	40

32 Grey Woodpecker

33 President Kennedy

1964. Air.

150	32	250 f. multicoloured	7·25	4·00

1964. French, African and Malagasy Co-operation. As T **68** of Mauritania.

151		70 f. brown, red and blue	1·00	55

1964. Air. Pres. Kennedy Commemoration.

152	33	100 f. multicoloured	1·60	1·10

34 Independence Hotel

35 Pygmy Sunbird

1964. Opening of Independence Hotel, Ouagadougou.

153	34	25 f. multicoloured	1·75	65

1965. Birds. Multicoloured.

154	10 f. Type **35** (postage)	1·60	55
155	15 f. Olive-bellied sunbird	1·75	75
156	20 f. Splendid sunbird	3·00	1·10
157	500 f. Abyssinian roller (27 × 48 mm) (air)	35·00	11·00

36 Sun and Emblems

1965. Air. World Meterological Day.

158	36	50 f. multicoloured	85	35

37 Grand Cascade, Banfora

1965. Banfora Waterfalls.

159	–	5 f. brown, blue and green	15	10
160	37	25 f. blue, green and red	55	20

DESIGN—VERT: 5 f. Comoe Cascade.

38 Hughes Telegraph and Modern Telephone

1965. Air. I.T.U. Centenary.

161	38	100 f. red, green & turq	1·90	85

39 I.C.Y. Emblem

1965. Air. International Co-operation Year.

162	39	25 f. multicoloured	45	20
163		100 f. multicoloured	1·25	50

40 Football, Boots and Net

42 "Early Bird" Satellite in Orbit

41 Sacred Alligator of Sabou

1965. 1st African Games, Brazzaville.

164	40	15 f. green, red and purple	30	20
165	–	25 f. purple, orange & blue	40	25
166	–	70 f. red and green	1·00	55

DESIGNS: 25 f. Boxing-gloves and ring; 70 f. Tennis-racquets, ball and net.

1965. Air. Fauna.

167	41	60 f. green, turq & brown	2·25	65
168	–	85 f. brown, bistre & green	2·75	85

DESIGN—VERT: 85 f. Lion.

1965. Air. Space Telecommuncations.

169	42	30 f. red, brown and blue	55	30

43 Lincoln

45 Dromedary

44 President Yameogo

1965. Death Centenary of Abraham Lincoln.

170	43	50 f. multicoloured	65	40

1965. Pres. Yameogo.

171	44	25 f. multicoloured	45	20

1966. Insects and Fauna. Multicoloured.

172 1 f. "Nemopistha imperatrix" (vert) 10 10
173 2 f. Python (vert) 10 10
174 3 f. "Sphodromantis lineola" . 10 10
175 4 f. "Staurocleis magnifica occidentalis" 15 10
176 5 f. Warthog (vert) 20 10
177 6 f. "Pandinus imperator" . . 20 10
178 8 f. Savanna monkey (vert) . . 35 15
179 10 f. Type **45** 35 20
180 15 f. Leopard (vert) 65 25
181 20 f. African buffalo 90 30
182 25 f. Pygmy hippopotamus (vert) 1·00 35
183 30 f. Agama (lizard) 70 35
184 45 f. Viper (vert) . . . . . . 1·40 40
185 50 f. Chameleon (vert) . . . . 1·75 55
186 60 f. "Ugada limbata" (vert) . 2·25 80
187 85 f. African elephant . . . . 2·40 1·00

The 1, 3, 4, 6 and 60 f. are insects, the remainder are fauna.

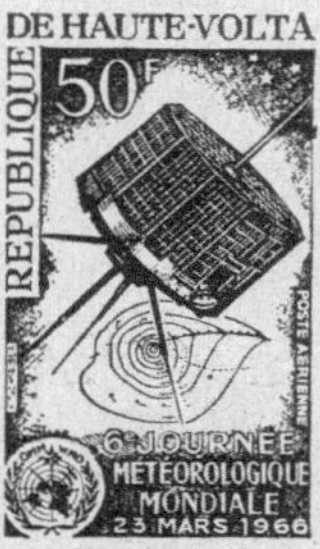

46 Communications Satellite **47** Ritual Mask

1966. Air. World Meteorological Day.

188 **46** 50 f. black, lake and blue . 55 30

1966. World Festival of Negro Arts, Dakar. Multicoloured.

189 20 f. Type **47** 40 15
190 25 f. Plumed head-dress . . . 45 20
191 60 f. Dancer . . . . 1·10 40

48 Bobo-Dioulasso Mosque

1966. Religious Buildings. Multicoloured.

192 25 f. Type **48** 45 30
193 25 f. Po Church 45 30

49 Satellite "FR 1" and Ouagadougou Tracking Station

1966. Air. Inauguration of Ouagadougou Tracking Station.

194 **49** 250 f. lake, brown and blue 4·00 1·90

50 W.H.O. Building

1966. Air. Inauguration of W.H.O. Headquarters, Geneva.

195 **50** 100 f. black, blue & yellow 1·60 70

51 Nurse and Red Cross on Globe **52** Scouts by Camp Fire

1966. Red Cross.

196 **51** 25 f. multicoloured 55 30

1966. Scouting.

197 **52** 10 f. multicoloured 35 15
198 – 15 f. black, brown & buff . 35 15

DESIGN: 15 f. Scouts on cliff.

53 Inoculating Cattle

1966. Prevention of Cattle Plague Campaign.

199 **53** 25 f. black, yellow & blue . 85 45

1966. Air. Inaug of DC-8F Air Services. As T **87** of Mauritania.

200 25 f. olive, black and brown . 55 35

54 Ploughing with Donkey

1966. Rural Education (25 f.) and 3rd Anniv of Kamboince Centre (30 f.). Multicoloured.

201 25 f. Type **54** 40 20
202 30 f. "Rotation of crops", Kamboince Centre 45 20

55 Sir Winston Churchill

1966. Air. Churchill Commemoration.

203 **55** 100 f. green and red . . . 1·60 65

56 Pope Paul and Dove over U.N. General Assembly Building

1966. Air. Pope Paul's Peace Appeal before U.N.

204 **56** 100 f. violet and blue . . . 1·60 65

57 U.N.E.S.C.O. Emblem

1966. 20th Anniv of U.N.E.S.C.O. and U.N.I.C.E.F.

205 **57** 50 f. red, blue and black . 65 40
206 – 50 f. violet, purple and red 65 40

DESIGN: No. 206, U.N.I.C.E.F. emblem and child-care theme.

58 Arms of Upper Volta **59** Man and Woman holding Emblems

1967.

207 **58** 30 f. multicoloured 55 15

1967. Europafrique.

208 **59** 60 f. multicoloured 90 40

60 Acclaiming Lions Emblem

1967. Air. 50th Anniv of Lions International.

209 **60** 100 f. ultram, bl & brn . . 1·60 65

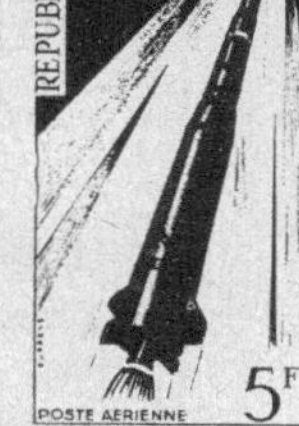

61 W.M.O. Emblem and Landscape **62** "Diamant" Rocket

1967. Air. World Meteorological Day.

210 **61** 50 f. green, turq & blue . . 85 40

1967. Air. French Space Achievements.

211 **62** 5 f. green, orange and blue . 15 10
212 – 20 f. lilac, purple and blue . 40 15
213 – 30 f. green, blue and red . . 55 20
214 – 100 f. green, violet & pur . 1·40 60

DESIGNS—HORIZ: 20 f. "FR-1" satellite; 100 f. "D1-D" satellite. VERT: 30 f. "D1-C" satellite.

63 Dr. Schweitzer and Organ Pipes **64** Scout waving Hat

1967. Air. 2nd Death Anniv of Dr Albert Schweitzer.

215 **63** 250 f. black and purple . . 4·00 1·90

1967. World Scout Jamboree, Idaho. Mult.

216 5 f. Type **64** (postage) 35 10
217 20 f. Scouts' handclasp 80 45
218 100 f. Jamboree emblem and world map (48 × 27 mm) (air) 1·40 65

65 "Virgin and Child" (by 15th-century master) **67** Postman on Cycle

66 Bank Book and Coins

1967. Air. Religious Paintings. Multicoloured.

219 30 f. Type **65** 50 30
220 50 f. "The Deposition of Christ" (Dirk Bouts) 85 40
221 100 f. "Christ giving Blessing" (Bellini) . . . . 1·40 80
222 250 f. "The Evangelists" (Jordaens) . . . . 4·00 1·90

See also Nos. 237/40.

1967. National Savings Bank.

223 **66** 30 f. green, brown & orge . 45 20

1967. Air. 5th Anniv of U.A.M.P.T. As T **101** of Mauritania.

224 100 f. green, lake and blue . . 1·40 55

1967. Stamp Day.

225 **67** 30 f. brown, green & blue . 65 45

1967. 5th Anniv of West African Monetary Union. As T **103** of Mauritania.

226 30 f. violet and blue 30 15

68 "The Two Alps" **69** Human Rights Emblem

1967. Winter Olympic Games, Grenoble (1968).

227 – 15 f. green, blue & brown . 40 30
228 **68** 50 f. blue and green . . . 70 40
229 – 100 f. green, blue and red . 1·60 1·00

DESIGNS—HORIZ: 15 f. St. Nizier-du-Moucherotte; 100 f. Cable-car, Villard-de-Lans.

1968. Human Rights Year.

230 **69** 20 f. red, gold and blue . . 40 15
231 30 f. red, gold and green . 45 20

70 Student and School

1968. National School of Administration.

232 **70** 30 f. blue, turquoise & brn 45 20

71 Sud Aviation Caravelle "Ouagadougou"

1968. Air.

233 **71** 500 f. black, blue & purple 9·00 4·50

72 W.M.O. Emblem, Sun and Cloud-burst

1968. Air. World Meteorological Day.

234 **72** 50 f. blue, red and green . 85 35

73 Human Figures and W.H.O. Emblem

1968. 20th Anniv of W.H.O.

235 **73** 30 f. indigo, red and blue . 45 20
236 50 f. blue, brown & green . 65 35

1968. Air. Paintings. Old Masters in the Louvre. Multicoloured. As T **65**.

237 20 f. "Still Life" (Gauguin) (36 × 50 mm) 35 30
238 60 f. "Anne of Cleves" (Holbein the Younger) (36 × 50 mm) . 65 50
239 90 f. "The Pawnbroker and His Wife" (Quentin Metsys) (38 × 40 mm) . . . . 1·00 70
240 200 f. "The Cart" (Le Nain) (50 × 37 mm) . . . . 2·40 1·60

74 "Europafrique"

1968. Air. "Europafrique".

241 **74** 50 f. red, black and ochre . 70 35

75 Telephone Exchange

1968. Inauguration of Automatic Telephone Exchange, Bobo-Dioulasso.

242 **75** 30 f. multicoloured 55 30

76 Colima Acrobat with Bells

1968. Air. Olympic Games, Mexico.
243 **76** 10 f. brown, yellow & red . . 35 20
244 – 30 f. blue, red and green . . 50 30
245 – 60 f. lake, brown and blue . 1·10 45
246 – 100 f. lake, blue and green . 1·40 70
DESIGNS—VERT: 30 f. Pelota-player (Veracruz); 60 f. Javelin-thrower (Colima). HORIZ: 100 f. Athlete with cape (Jalisco).
The designs represent early Mexican statuary.

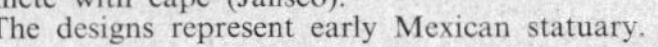

77 Weaving

1968. Handicrafts.
247 – 5 f. black, purple and brown (postage) 20 10
248 **77** 30 f. brown, orange and mauve 50 20
249 – 100 f. purple, red and yellow (air) . . . . 1·40 65
250 – 150 f. black, blue & brown 2·25 1·00
DESIGNS—As Type **77**: 5 f. Metal-work; 48 × 27 mm: 100 f. Pottery; 150 f. Basket-making.

1968. Air. "Philexafrique" Stamp Exn, Abidjan (Ivory Coast, 1969) (1st issue). As T **113a** of Mauritania. Multicoloured.
251 100 f. "Too Late" or "The Letter" (A. Cambon) . . . 2·50 2·25
See also No. 256.

78 Mahatma Gandhi **79** "Grain for the World"

1968. Air. "Workers for Peace".
252 **78** 100 f. black, yellow & grn . 1·40 80
253 – 100 f. black, light green and green . . . . 1·40 80
DESIGNS: No. 253, Albert Luthuli.

1969. World Food Programme.
255 **79** 30 f. purple, slate and blue 45 20

1969. Air. "Philexafrique" Stamp Exn, Abidjan (Ivory Coast) (2nd issue). As T **114a** of Mauritania. Multicoloured.
256 50 f. Dancers of Tengrela and stamp of 1928. . . . . . . 2·50 2·25

80 Loom and I.L.O. Emblem

1969. 50th Anniv of I.L.O.
257 **80** 30 f. blue, lake and green . 50 30

81 Cattle and Labourer

1969. Air. World Meteorological Day.
258 **81** 100 f. brown, blue & grn . 2·50 1·40

82 "Lions" Emblem within Eye

1969. Air. 12th Congress of 403 District, Lions International, Ouagadougou.
259 **82** 250 f. multicoloured . . . 2·75 1·40

83 Blood Donor

1969. 50th Anniv of League of Red Cross Societies.
260 **83** 30 f. black, red and blue . 60 40

84 "Mormyrops curviceps"

1969. Fishes.
261 – 20 f. buff, brown and blue (postage) 80 35
262 – 25 f. purple, brown and bl 80 35
263 **84** 30 f. black and olive . . . 1·10 50
264 – 55 f. olive, yellow & green 1·40 65
265 – 85 f. blue, mauve & brown 2·50 1·40
266 – 100 f. blue, yellow and purple (air) . . . . 1·60 85
267 – 150 f. blue, black and red . 2·50 1·10
DESIGNS: 20 f. "Nannocharax gobioides"; 25 f. "Hemigrammocharax polli"; 55 f. "Alestes luteus"; 85 f. "Micralestes voltae". LARGER 48 × 27 mm: 100 f. "Phenacogrammus pabrensis"; 150 f. "Synodontis arnoulti".

85 Astronaut and Moon

1969. Air. Moon Flight of "Apollo 8". Embossed on gold foil.
268 **85** 1,000 f. gold . . . . 18·00

1969. Air. 1st Man on the Moon. No. 214 optd **L'HOMME SUR LA LUNE JUILLET 1969** and "Apollo 11".
269 100 f. green, violet and purple 3·25 3·25

1969. Air. Birth Bicent of Napoleon Bonaparte. As T **114b** of Mauritania. Multicoloured.
270 50 f. "Bonaparte crossing the Great St. Bernard" (J. L. David) . . . . 1·60 80
271 150 f. "First Presentation of the Legion of Honour" (Debret) 5·00 2·00
272 250 f. "Napoleon before Madrid" (C. Vernet) . . . 6·75 3·25

1969. 5th Anniv of African Development Bank.
273 30 f. brown, emerald and green 35 15

88 Millet **89** Stylised Tree

1969. Agricultural Produce.
274 **88** 15 f. brown, green and yellow (postage) 45 20
275 – 30 f. blue and mauve . . . 55 35
276 – 100 f. brown & violet (air) 1·40 40
277 – 200 f. green and red . . . 2·50 80
DESIGNS: 30 f. Cotton; LARGER 48 × 27mm: 100 f. Ground-nuts; 200 f. Rice.

1969. Air. Europafrique.
278 **89** 100 f. multicoloured . . . 90 55

1969. 10th Anniv of Aerial Navigation Security Agency for Africa and Madagascar (A.S.E.C.N.A.). As T **94a** of Niger.
279 100 f. brown . . . . 1·25 75

INDEX

Countries can be quickly located by referring to the index at the end of this volume.

90 "Niadale" **91** Lenin

1970. Figurines and Masks in National Museum.
280 **90** 10 f. brown, orge and red . 20 10
281 – 30 f. brown, blue and violet 40 20
282 – 45 f. brown, blue & green . 70 30
283 – 80 f. brown, pur, & violet . 1·25 60
DESIGNS: 30 f. "Niaga"; 45 f. "Iliu bara"; 80 f. "Karan Weeba".

1970. Air. Birth Centenary of Lenin.
284 **91** 20 f. brown and ochre . . . 35 20
285 – 100 f. red, blue and green . 1·25 80
DESIGN—HORIZ: 100 f. "Lenin addressing workers" (A. Serov).

92 African Huts and City Buildings **93** Cauris Dancers

1970. Linked Cities' Day.
286 **92** 30 f. brown, blue and red . 50 30

1970. Upper Volta Dances. Multicoloured.
287 5 f. Mask of Nebwa Gnomo dance (horiz) 20 15
288 8 f. Type **93** 30 15
289 20 f. Gourmantches dancers . 40 15
290 30 f. Larlle dancers (horiz) . . 50 20

94 "Pupils", Sun and Emblem of Education Year

1970. Int Education Year. Multicoloured.
291 40 f. Type **94** 40 20
292 90 f. Visual aids and emblem . 95 45

95 New U.P.U. Headquarters Building, U.P.U. Monument and Abraham Lincoln

1970. New U.P.U. Headquarters Building.
293 **95** 30 f. grey, red and brown . 50 20
294 60 f. purple, green & brn . 85 35

96 Footballers and Cup

1970. Air. World Cup Football Championships, Mexico.
295 **96** 40 f. lake, green & brown . 45 30
296 – 100 f. brown, purple & grn . 1·10 55
DESIGN: 100 f. Goalkeeper saving ball, Globe and footballers.

97 Franklin D. Roosevelt **98** Naval Construction

1970. Air. 25th Anniv of Roosevelt's Death.
297 **97** 10 f. brown, black & grn . 20 20
298 – 200 f. red, violet and grey . 1·60 80
DESIGN—HORIZ: 200 f. Roosevelt with his stamp collection.

1970. Hanover Fair.
299 **98** 15 f. multicoloured 50 35
300 – 45 f. green, blue and black 60 35
301 – 80 f. purple, brown & blk . 1·40 50
DESIGNS: 45 f. Test-tubes and retorts ("Chemistry"); 80 f. Power transmission lines and pylons ("Electro-techniques").

99 Inoculating Cattle

1970. National Veterinary School.
302 **99** 30 f. multicoloured 55 35

100 "Manchurian Cranes and Seashore" and Expo Monorail Coach **101** Nurse attending Patient

1970. Air. World Fair "EXPO 70" Osaka, Japan.
303 50 f. Type **100** 55 35
304 150 f. "Geisha", rocket and satellite . . . . 1·40 80

1970. Upper Volta Red Cross.
305 **101** 30 f. brown, red & green . 60 35

102 "Nurse and Child" (F. Hals) **103** U.N. Emblem and Dove

1970. "Europafrique". Multicoloured.
306 25 f. Type **102** 50 20
307 30 f. "Courtyard in Delft" (Hoogh) 60 35
308 150 f. "Christina of Denmark" (Holbein) . . . . 2·25 90
309 250 f. "Hofburg Courtyard, Innsbruck" (Durer) . . . . 4·00 1·40

1970. Air. 25th Anniv of U.N.O.
310 **103** 60 f. ultram, blue & grn . 65 30
311 – 250 f. violet, brn & grn . 2·75 1·10
DESIGNS—HORIZ: 250 f. U.N. emblem and two doves.

104 Front of Car

1970. Paris Motor Show.
312 **104** 25 f. green, lake & brown 90 35
313 – 40 f. blue, purple & green 1·10 55
DESIGN: 40 f. Old and new cars.

105 "Holy Family"

1970. Christmas.
314 **105** 300 f. silver . . . . 6·75
315 1000 f. gold . . . . 18·00

106 Centre Buildings

1970. Inauguration of Austro-Voltaic Centre.
316 **106** 50 f. orange, green & red . 55 30

107 Arms and Stork

1970. 10th Anniv of Independence.
317 **107** 30 f. multicoloured (postage) 45 20
318 – 500 f. blk, red and gold (air) 5·50
DESIGN—VERT: (27×37 mm): 500 f. Family and flag.
No. 318 is embossed on gold foil.

108 U.N. "Key" and Split Globe

1970. 10th Anniv of U.N. Declaration on Colonies.
319 **108** 40 f. red, blue and brown . . 60 35
320 – 50 f. multicoloured . . . 55 30
DESIGN: 50 f. Two maps of Africa showing former colonies.

109 Pres. Nasser

111 Heads of Different Races

110 Beingolo Hunting Horn

1971. Air. Pres. Nasser Commemoration.
321 **109** 100 f. multicoloured . . . 90 40

1971. Musical Instruments.
322 **110** 5 f. brown, red and blue . 20 15
323 – 15 f. brown, red & green . 35 20
324 – 20 f. red, grey and blue . 65 20
325 – 25 f. drab, green and red . 80 40
INSTRUMENTS—VERT: 15 f. Mossi "guitar"; 20 f. Gurunssi "flutes". HORIZ: 25 f. Lunga "drum".

1971. Racial Equality Year.
326 **111** 50 f. brown, red & turq . 55 30

112 "The Purple Herons" (Egypt, 1354)

1971. Air. Muslim Miniatures. Multicoloured.
327 100 f. Type **112** . . . . 1·10 55
328 250 f. Page from the Koran (Egypt c. 1368–88) (vert) . . 2·75 1·25

113 Telephone and Hemispheres

1971. World Telecommunications Day.
329 **113** 50 f. violet, grey & brown 60 30

114 Olympic Rings and Events

1971. Air. "Pre-Olympic Year".
330 **114** 150 f. red, violet and bl . 2·25 1·10

115 Cutting Cane and Sugar Factory, Banfora

117 Scout and Pagodas

116 "Gonimbrasia hecate"

1971. Local Industries. Multicoloured.
331 10 f. Type **115** 20 10
332 35 f. Cotton-plant and textiles ("Voltex" project) 35 20

1971. Butterflies. Multicoloured.
333 1 f. Type **116** 10 10
334 2 f. "Hamanumida daedalus" . . 10 10
335 3 f. "Ophideres materna" . . 20 10
336 5 f. "Danaus chrysippus" . . 45 20
337 40 f. "Hypolimnas misippus" . 2·25 1·10
338 45 f. "Danaus petiverana" . . 3·25 1·40

1971. Air. 13th World Scout Jamboree, Asagari (Japan).
339 **117** 45 f. multicoloured . . . 65 35

118 Actor with Fan

119 African with Seed-packet

1971. "Philatokyo" Stamp Exn, Tokyo. Mult.
340 25 f. Type **118** 35 20
341 40 f. Actor within mask . . . 50 25

1971. National Seed-protection Campaign. Multicoloured.
342 35 f. Grading seeds (horiz) . 40 20
343 75 f. Type **119** 60 30
344 100 f. Harvesting crops (horiz) 60 35

1971. 10th Anniv of Volta Red Cross. Surch **Xe ANNIVERSAIRE** and new value.
345 **101** 100 f. on 30 f. brown, red and purple . . . . . . 1·25 65

121 Teacher and Class

122 Soldier and Tractors

1971. "Women's Access to Education". Multicoloured.
346 35 f. Type **121** 45 20
347 50 f. Family learning alphabet 60 35

1971. Dakiri Project. Military Aid for Agriculture. Multicoloured.
348 15 f. Type **122** 45 15
349 40 f. Soldiers harvesting (horiz) 65 40

123 General De Gaulle and Map

1971. Air. De Gaulle Commemoration.
350 **123** 40 f. multicoloured 55 55
351 – 500 f. gold and green . . . 10·50 9·50
DESIGN—VERT (30×40 mm): 500 f. De Gaulle.
No. 351 is embossed on gold foil.

1971. Air. 10th Anniv of African and Malagasy Posts and Telecommunications Union. As T **139a** of Mauritania. Multicoloured.
352 100 f. U.A.M.P.T.H.Q. and Mossi dancer . . . . 1·10 50

124 "Simulium damnosum" and Preventive Measures

1971. Regional Anti-Onchocerciasis Campaign.
353 **124** 40 f. multicoloured 55 35

125 Pres. Lamizana

126 Children acclaiming Emblem

1971.
354 **125** 35 f. multicoloured 30 20

1971. 25th Anniv of U.N.I.C.E.F.
355 **126** 45 f. multicoloured 50 35

127 Peulh Straw Hut

1971. Traditional Housing (1st series). Mult.
356 10 f. Type **127** 15 10
357 20 f. Gourounsi house 30 15
358 35 f. Mossi huts 45 30
See also Nos. 370/2.

128 Town Halls of Bobo-Dioulasso and Chalons-sur-Marne, France

1971. "Twin Cities" Co-operation.
359 **128** 40 f. multicoloured 65 40

129 Ice-hockey

130 Running

1972. Air. Winter Olympic Games, Sapporo, Japan.
360 **129** 150 f. purple, blue and red 1·90 1·00

1972. Air. U.N.E.S.C.O. "Save Venice" Campaign. As T **145** of Senegal. Multicoloured.
361 100 f. "La Musica" (P. Longhi) (vert) . . . . 1·90 1·00
362 150 f. "Panorama da Ponte della Marina" (detail-Caffi) (horiz) 2·75 1·25

1972. Air. Olympic Games, Munich.
363 **130** 65 f. brown, blue and green 60 45
364 – 200 f. brown and blue . . 1·90 1·25
DESIGN: 200 f. Throwing the discus.

131 Louis Armstrong

1972. Famous Negro Musicians. Multicoloured.
366 45 f. Type **131** (postage) . . . 1·25 65
367 500 f. Jimmy Smith (air) . . . 6·75 4·50

132 Globe and Emblems

1972. World Red Cross Day.
368 **132** 40 f. multicoloured (postage) 55 40
369 100 f. multicoloured (air) . 1·10 45

133 Bobo House

134 Hair Style

1972. Traditional Housing (2nd series). Mult.
370 45 f. Type **133** 55 30
371 50 f. Dagari house 65 35
372 90 f. Interior of Bango house (horiz) . . . . 1·25 50

1972. Upper Volta Hair Styles.
373 **134** 25 f. multicoloured . . . 35 15
374 – 35 f. multicoloured . . . 50 20
375 – 75 f. multicoloured . . . 1·10 45
DESIGNS: 35, 75 f. Similar hair styles.

135 "Teaching"

1972. 2nd National Development Plan.
376 **135** 10 f. mauve, green and turquoise (postage) . . 10 10
377 – 15 f. brown, orge & grn . 20 15
378 – 20 f. brown, grn & blue . 30 15
379 – 35 f. brown, blue & grn . 50 20
380 – 40 f. brown, green & pur . 55 30
381 – 85 f. black, red & bl (air) 70 50
DESIGNS: 15 f. Doctor and patient ("Health"); 20 f. Factory and silos ("Industry"); 35 f. Cattle ("Cattle-raising"); 40 f. Rice-planting ("Agriculture"); 85 f. Road-making machine ("Infrastructure").

1972. 10th Anniv of West African Monetary Union. As T **149** of Mauritania.
382 40 f. grey, blue and mauve . . 45 20

136 Lottery Building

1972. 5th Anniv of National Lottery.
383 **136** 35 f. multicoloured . . . 50 20

137 Presidents Pompidou and Lamizana

1972. Air. Visit of Pres. Pompidou to Upper Volta.
384 **137** 40 f. multicoloured . . . 1·60 1·60
385 – 250 f. multicoloured . . 6·00 6·00
DESIGN: 250 f. As T **137** but frame differs and portraits are embossed on gold.

138 Mary Peters (pentathlon)

1972. Air. Gold Medal-winners, Olympic Games, Munich. Multicoloured.

386 40 f. Type **138** 35 15
387 65 f. Ragno-Lonzi (fencing) . . 55 20
388 85 f. Touritcheva (gymnastics) . 80 30
389 200 f. Maury (sailing) . . . . 1·60 65
390 300 f. Meyfarth (high-jumping) . 2·75 1·10

139 Donkeys

1972. Animals. Multicoloured.

392 5 f. Type **139** 10 10
393 10 f. Spur-winged geese . . . 10 10
394 30 f. Goat 55 20
395 50 f. Bull 80 30
396 65 f. Dromedaries . . . . . . 1·10 40

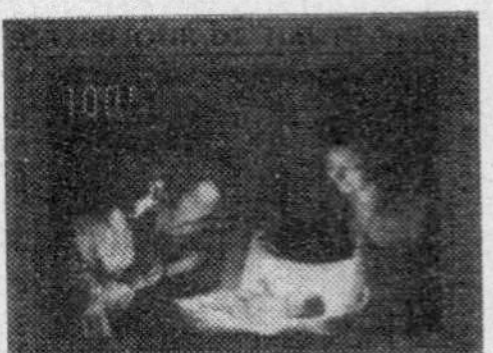
140 "The Nativity" (Della Notte)

1972. Air. Christmas. Religious Paintings. Multicoloured.

397 100 f. Type **140** . . . . . 1·10 65
398 200 f. "The Adoration of the Magi" (Durer) . . . . . . 2·25 1·60

141 Mossi Hair-style and Village

1973. Air.

399 **141** 5 f. multicoloured 10 10
400 40 f. multicoloured . . . 55 20

1973. 25th Anniv of W.H.O. No. 353 surch **O.M.S. 25 Anniversaire** and value.

401 **124** 45 f. on 40 f. multicoloured 50 30

1973. African and Malagasy Posts and Telecommunications Union. As T **155** of Mauritania

402 100 f. purple, red and yellow . 1·00 55

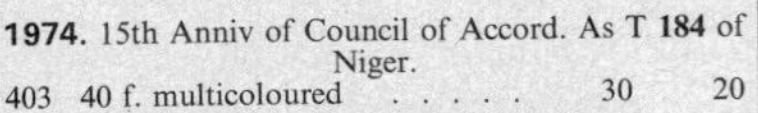

1974. 15th Anniv of Council of Accord. As T **184** of Niger.

403 40 f. multicoloured 30 20

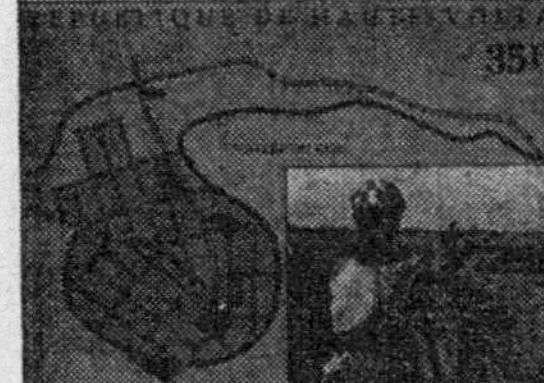

143 Map and Harvester

1974. Kou Valley Project.

404 **143** 35 f. multicoloured . . . 55 35

144 Woman, Globe and I.W.Y. Emblem

1975. International Women's Year.

405 **144** 65 f. multicoloured . . . 65 45

145 Mgr. Joanny Thevenoud and Cathedral

1975. 75th Anniv of Evangelization of Upper Volta.

406 **145** 55 f. black, brn and grn . 65 35
407 – 65 f. black, brn and red . 80 45

DESIGN: 65 f. Father Guillaume Templier and Cathedral.

146 Farmer's Hat, Hoe and Emblem 147 Diseased People

1975. Development of the Volta Valleys.

408 **146** 15 f. multicoloured . . . 15 10
409 50 f. multicoloured . . . 50 25

1976. Campaign against Onchocerciasis (roundworm).

410 **147** 75 f. mauve, orge & grn . . 85 35
411 250 f. sepia, orge and brown 2·50 1·10

148 Globe and Emblem

1976. Non-aligned Countries' Summit Conference, Colombo, Sri Lanka. Multicoloured.

412 55 f. Type **148** 45 20
413 100 f. Globe, dove and emblem 90 50

149 Washington at Trenton

1976. "Interphil '76" International Stamp Exhibition, Philadelphia. Multicoloured.

414 60 f. Type **149** (postage) . . . 55 15
415 90 f. Seat of Government, Pennsylvania 80 20
416 100 f. Siege of Yorktown (air) 80 30
417 200 f. Battle of Cape St. Vincent 1·60 60
418 300 f. Peter Francisco's act of bravery . . . . 2·40 80

150 U.P.U. and U.N. Emblems

1976. 25th Anniv of U.N. Postal Administration.

420 **150** 200 f. blue, bronze & red 1·60 90

151 Tenkodogo Commune 152 Bronze Statuette

1977. Arms. Multicoloured.

421 10 f. Type **151** 15 10
422 20 f. Ouagadougou 20 10
423 55 f. Type **151** 55 20
424 100 f. As 20 f. 70 35

1977.

425 **152** 55 f. multicoloured 45 20
426 – 65 f. multicoloured 45 20

DESIGN: 65 f. Bronze statuette of woman with bowl.

153 Samo Granary 154 Gouin Basket

1977. Millet Granaries. Multicoloured.

427 5 f. Type **153** 10 10
428 35 f. Boromo 30 20
429 45 f. Banfora 45 20
430 55 f. Mossi 55 30

1977. Local Handicrafts. Baskets and Bags. Multicoloured.

431 30 f. Type **154** 20 15
432 40 f. Bissa 40 20
433 60 f. Lobi 60 25
434 70 f. Mossi 65 30

155 "Crinum ornatum" 156 General De Gaulle

1977. Fruits and Flowers. Multicoloured.

435 2 f. "Cordia myxa" 10 10
436 3 f. "Opilia celtidifolia" . . . 15 10
437 15 f. Type **155** 20 10
438 25 f. "Haemanthus multiflorus" 20 10
439 50 f. "Hannoa undulata" . . . 10 10
440 90 f. "Cochlospermum planchonii" . . . . 1·00 40
441 125 f. "Clitoria ternatea" . . . 1·10 50
442 150 f. "Cassia alata" . . . . 1·40 90
443 175 f. "Nauclea latifolia" (horiz) 1·60 1·00
444 300 f. "Bombax costatum" (horiz) . . . . 2·50 1·40
445 400 f. "Eulophia cucullata" . . 4·25 1·40

1977. Personalities. Multicoloured.

446 100 f. Type **156** . . . . . . 1·60 50
447 200 f. King Baudouin . . . . 1·60 50

157 Queen Elizabeth II

1977. Silver Jubilee of Queen Elizabeth II. Multicoloured.

448 200 f. Type **157** . . . . . . 1·60 50
449 300 f. Queen Elizabeth II taking salute at Trooping the Colour 2·25 60

158 Cars on "Road" of Banknotes

1977. 10th Anniv of National Lottery.

451 **158** 55 f. multicoloured . . . 55 40

159 Selma Lagerlof and Bean Geese

1977. Nobel Prize Winners. Multicoloured.

452 55 f. Type **159** (Literature, 1909) 65 20
453 65 f. Guglielmo Marconi and early transmitter (Physics, 1909) 45 20
454 125 f. Bertrand Russell, laurel, book and dove (Literature, 1950) 95 30
455 200 f. L. C. Pauling, formula and atomic explosion (Chemistry, 1954) . . . . 1·40 50
456 300 f. Robert Koch, slide and X-ray plate (Medicine, 1905) 2·40 70

160 "The Three Graces"

1977. 400th Birth Anniv of Rubens.

458 55 f. "Heads of Four Negroes" (horiz) 40 10
459 65 f. Type **160** 50 15
460 85 f. "Bathsheba at the Fountain" 50 20
461 150 f. "The Drunken Silenus" 12·5 45
462 200 f. "The Story of Maria de Medici" (detail) . . . . . 1·60 55
463 300 f. "The Story of Maria de Medici" (different detail) . 2·50 70

161 Lenin

1977. 60th Anniv of Russian Revolution. Multicoloured.

465 10 f. Type **161** 15 10
466 85 f. Lenin Monument and Kremlin 65 40
467 200 f. Lenin with children (horiz) 1·90 1·10
468 500 f. Lenin and Pres. Brezhnev (horiz) . . . . 4·50 2·25

162 Stadium and Brazil 5 cr. 80 Stamp of 1950

1978. World Cup Football Championship, Argentina. Multicoloured.
469 55 f. Type **162** 35 10
470 65 f. Brazil 1969 Pele stamp . . 45 15
471 125 f. G.B. 1966 England winners stamp 90 30
472 200 f. Chile 1962 World Cup stamp . . . . 1·40 45
473 300 f. Switzerland 1954 World Cup stamp . . . . 2·00 65

163 Jean Mermoz

1978. Aviation History. Multicoloured.
475 65 f. Type **163** 60 20
476 75 f. Anthony Fokker 65 30
477 85 f. Wiley Post 75 35
478 90 f. Otto Lilienthal (vert) . . 85 35
479 100 f. Concorde . . . . 1·10 40

164 "Crateva religiosa" **165** Microwave Antennae

1978. Trees of Upper Volta. Multicoloured.
481 55 f. Type **164** 55 35
482 75 f. "Ficus sp" 65 45

1978. World Telecommunications Day.
483 **165** 65 f. multicoloured . . . 55 40

166 Bobo Fetish Portals

1978. Sacred Objects. Multicoloured.
484 55 f. Type **166** 55 30
485 65 f. Mossi fetish 65 40

167 U.P.U. Emblem over Globe

1978. Air. Centenary of Paris Postal Congress.
486 **167** 350 f. multicoloured . . . 2·75 1·60

168 Capt. Cook and H.M.S. "Endeavour"

1978. 250th Birth Anniv of Captain James Cook. Multicoloured.
487 65 f. Type **168** . . . . 1·00 40
488 85 f. Death of Captain Cook . 55 15
489 250 f. Cook and navigation instruments . . . . 1·60 55
490 350 f. Cook and H.M.S. "Resolution" . . . . 3·50 2·25

169 Yuri Gagarin and Spacecraft

1978. "Conquest of Space". Multicoloured.
491 50 f. Type **169** 40 20
492 60 f. Jules Verne, "Apollo 11" badge and Neil Armstrong in space-suit 45 20
493 100 f. Montgolfier medallion and balloon, Bleriot XI and Concorde 85 40

170 I.A.Y. Emblem

1978. Air. Anti-Apartheid Year.
494 **170** 100 f. multicoloured . . . 80 45

1978. 25th Anniv of Coronation of Queen Elizabeth II. Nos. 448/9 optd **ANNIVERSAIRE DU COURONNEMENT 1953-1978**.
495 **157** 200 f. multicoloured . . . 1·40 90
496 – 300 f. multicoloured . . . 2·25 1·40

1978. Air. "Philexafrique" Stamp Exhibition, Libreville (Gabon), and Int Stamp Fair, Essen, West Germany (1st series). As T **262** of Niger. Multicoloured.
498 100 f. Common kingfisher and Hanover 1850 1 ggr. stamp . . 1·50 1·25
499 100 f. Hippopotamus and 1964 250 f. Grey woodpecker stamp 1·50 1·25
See also Nos. 518/9.

172 "Trent Castle"

1978. 450th Death Anniv of Albrecht Durer. Multicoloured.
500 65 f. Type **172** 55 15
501 150 f. "Virgin and Child" (vert) 1·10 35
502 250 f. "Saints George and Eustace" (vert) . . . . . . 1·90 60
503 350 f. "H. Holzschuher" (vert) 2·75 90

173 Horus **174** Jules Verne

1978. Air. U.N.E.S.C.O. Campaign: "Save the Philae Temples". Multicoloured.
504 200 f. Type **173** . . . . . . 1·40 65
505 300 f. Stylised falcon . . . . 2·00 1·00

1978. 150th Birth Anniv of Jules Verne (author).
506 **174** 20 f. purple, blue & green 1·60 90

175 Human Rights Flame

1978. 30th Anniv of Declaration of Human Rights.
507 **175** 55 f. multicoloured . . . 50 30

1979. World Cup Football Championship Winners. Nos. 469/73 optd.
508 **162** 55 f. multicoloured . . . 45 25
509 – 65 f. multicoloured . . . 50 30
510 – 125 f. multicoloured . . . 95 55
511 – 200 f. multicoloured . . . 1·40 85
512 – 300 f. multicoloured . . . 2·10 1·10

OPTS.: 55 f. **VAINQUEURS 1950 URUGUAY 1978 ARGENTINE**; 65 f. **VAINQUEURS 1970; BRESIL 1978 ARGENTINE**; 125 f. **VAINQUEURS 1966 GRANDE BRETAGNE 1978 ARGENTINE**; 200 f. **VAINQUEURS 1962 BRESIL 1978 ARGENTINE**; 300 f. **VAINQUEURS 1954 ALLEMAGNE (RFA) 1978 ARGENTINE**.

177 Radio Station **179** Wave Pattern and Human Figures

178 Children listening to Story

1979. 10th Anniv of Posts and Telecommunications Organization. Multicoloured.
514 55 f. Type **177** 40 20
515 65 f. Loading mail aboard Beech A100 King Air monoplane . 50 30

1979. International Year of the Child.
516 **178** 75 f. multicoloured 85 45

1979. World Telecommunications Day.
517 **179** 70 f. multicoloured 55 35

180 Basket Weaving and Upper Volta 50 c. Stamp of 1963

1979. "Philexafrique" Exhibition, Libreville, Gabon (2nd series). Multicoloured.
518 100 f. Type **180** . . . . 1·60 1·40
519 100 f. Concorde, van, shouting man and U.P.U. emblem . . 1·60 1·40

181 "Synodontis voltae" **183** Kob

182 Steam Train

1979. Freshwater Fish. Multicoloured.
520 20 f. Type **181** 35 20
521 50 f. "Micralestes comoensis" 1·00 45
522 85 f. "Silurus" . . . . 1·40 70

1979. Death Centenary of Sir Rowland Hill. Multicoloured.
523 65 f. Type **182** 55 15
524 165 f. Diesel train . . . . . . 1·40 40
525 200 f. Diesel train (different) . 1·60 50
526 300 f. French high-speed train . 2·75 60

1979. Endangered Animals. Multicoloured.
528 30 f. Type **183** 20 10
529 40 f. Roan antelope 35 10
530 60 f. Caracal 65 10
531 100 f. African elephant . . . . 1·00 35
532 175 f. Hartebeest . . . . . . 1·60 45
533 250 f. Leopard . . . . 2·50 55

184 Teacher and Class

1979. World Literacy Day. Multicoloured.
534 55 f. Farmer reading book (vert) 45 35
535 250 f. Type **184** . . . . . . 2·00 1·25

185 Telecommunications

1979. 3rd World Telecommunications Exhibition, Geneva.
536 **185** 200 f. multicoloured . . . 1·40 70

186 King Vulture **187** Airport

1979. Protected Birds. Multicoloured.
537 5 f. Type **186** 20 10
538 10 f. Hoopoe 20 10
539 15 f. Ruppell's griffon 25 15
540 25 f. Intermediate egret . . . 40 15
541 35 f. Ostrich 60 20
542 45 f. Crowned crane 70 25
543 125 f. Cassin's hawk eagle . . 1·60 1·00

1979. 20th Anniv of A.S.E.C.N.A. (Air Navigation Security Agency).
544 **187** 65 f. multicoloured . . . 60 40

188 Headquarters Building

1979. Opening of West African Savings Bank Building, Dakar, Senegal.
545 **188** 55 f. multicoloured . . . 50 30

189 Jamot, Map and Tsetse Fly

1979. Birth Centenary of Eugene Jamot (discoverer of cure for sleeping sickness).
546 **189** 55 f. multicoloured . . . 85 45

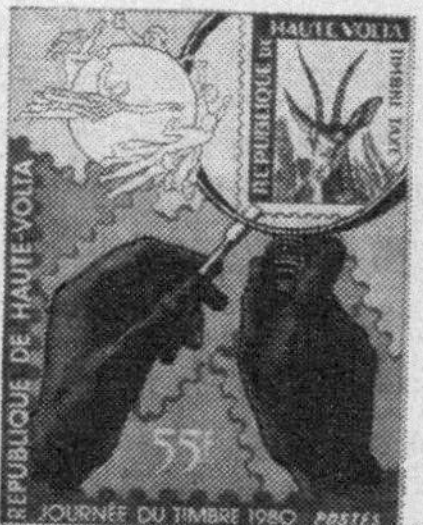

190 Stamp under Magnifying Glass

1980. Stamp Day.

547 **190** 55 f. multicoloured . . . 50 25

191 Electric Locomotives

192 Pope John Paul II

1980. 25th Anniv of World Locomotive Speed Record.

548 **191** 75 f. multicoloured . . . 1·00 45

549 100 f. multicoloured . . . 1·50 65

1980. Papal Visit. Multicoloured.

550 55 f. Pres. Lamizana, Pope and Cardinal Pau Zoungrana (horiz) . . . 85 35

551 100 f. Type **192** . . . 1·40 85

193 Telephone

194 Mountains and Statue

1980. World Telecommunications Day.

552 **193** 50 f. multicoloured . . . 40 20

1980. Solar Energy. Multicoloured.

553 65 f. Sun and Earth . . . 50 20

554 100 f. Type **194** . . . 80 40

195 Downhill Skiing (L. Stock)

1980. Winter Olympic Games Winners. Mult.

555 65 f. Type **195** . . . 45 15

556 100 f. Women's downhill skiing (A. Moser-Proell) . . . 65 20

557 200 f. Figure skating (A. Poetzsch) . . . 1·40 35

558 350 f. Slalom (I. Stenmark) (vert) 2·25 60

196 Map of Europe and Africa

197 Hand pushing back Sand Dune

1980. Europafrique.

560 **196** 100 f. red, black & green . 90 45

1980. Operation "Green Sahara". Multicoloured.

561 50 f. Type **197** . . . 50 20

562 55 f. Hands planting saplings . 60 35

198 Cyclists

1980. Air. Olympic Games, Moscow. Cycling.

563 **198** 65 f. multicoloured . . . 55 15

564 – 150 f. multicoloured (vert) 1·10 40

565 – 250 f. multicoloured . . . 1·90 55

566 – 350 f. multicoloured . . . 2·75 90

DESIGNS: 150 f. to 350 f. Different cyclists.

199 Installation of Chief

1980. National History. Multicoloured.

568 30 f. Type **199** . . . 35 15

569 55 f. Moro Naba, Emperor of Mossis . . . 55 30

570 65 f. Princess Guimbe Ouattara (vert) . . . 60 30

200 Gourounsi Mask

201 Tractor, Cattle and Grain (Agriculture)

1980. World Tourism Conference, Manila.

571 **200** f. 65 f. multicoloured . . 55 30

1980. 5th Anniv of West African Economic Council. Multicoloured.

572 55 f. Type **201** . . . 35 15

573 65 f. "Communications" . . 40 30

574 75 f. Dam and highway . . . 45 30

575 100 f. "Industry" . . . 80 40

1980. Air. Olympic Winners. Nos. 563/6 optd.

576 **198** 65 f. multicoloured . . . 30 25

577 – 150 f. multicoloured . . . 75 50

578 – 250 f. multicoloured . . . 1·25 90

579 – 350 f. multicoloured . . . 1·60 1·00

OVERPRINTS: 65 f. **SOUKHOROUCHENKOV (URSS)**; 150 f. **"HESSLICH (RDA)"**; 250 f. **"LANG (POL)"**; 350 f. **"DILL-BUNDI (SUISSE)"**.

203 Coat of Arms and Map

1980. 20th Anniv of Independence.

581 **203** 500 f. multicoloured . . . 4·25 2·50

204 "Sistine Madonna" (detail)

205 "Scarabaeus sacer"

1980. Christmas. Multicoloured.

582 60 f. Type **204** . . . 45 15

583 150 f. "Virgin de l'Impannata" 1·10 40

584 250 f. "Alba Madonna" . . . 1·75 55

1980. 5th Anniv of African Post and Telecommunications. As T **292** of Niger.

585 55 f. multicoloured. . . . 50 30

1981. Insects. Multicoloured.

586 5 f. Type **205** . . . 10 10

587 10 f. "Gryllus campestris" . . 10 10

588 15 f. "Termites" . . . 15 10

589 20 f. "Mantis religiosa" (vert) 25 10

590 55 f. "Nyctaon pyri" . . . 75 25

591 65 f. "Locusta migratorius" (vert) . . . 85 35

MINIMUM PRICE

The minimum price quoted is 10p which represents a handling charge rather than a basis for valuing common stamps. For further notes about prices, see introductory pages.

206 Bobo Mask, Hounde

207 College Emblem

1981. Masks. Multicoloured.

592 45 f. Type **206** . . . 40 15

593 55 f. Bwa mask . . . 45 20

594 85 f. Kouroumba mask . . . 60 35

595 105 f. Gourounsi mask . . . 80 40

1981. 25th Anniv of Notre-Dame College, Kologh'naba.

596 **207** 55 f. multicoloured . . . 45 20

208 Von Stephan and U.P.U. Emblem

1981. 150th Birth Anniv of Heinrich von Stephan (founder of U.P.U.).

597 **208** 65 f. multicoloured . . . 60 35

209 Ribbons forming Caduceus, I.T.U. and W.H.O. Emblems

210 Diesel Railcar

1981. World Telecommunications Day.

598 **209** 90 f. multicoloured . . . 60 35

1981. Abidjan–Niger Railway. Multicoloured.

599 25 f. Type **210** . . . 30 15

600 30 f. Diesel train "La Gazelle" 45 20

601 40 f. Diesel locomotive "Le Belier" . . . 55 35

211 Group of Trees

1981. Tree Month.

602 **211** 70 f. multicoloured . . . 70 40

212 Nurse and Doctor with Medical Equipment

213 Handicapped Sculptor

1981. 25th Anniv of Upper Volta Red Cross.

603 **212** 70 f. multicoloured . . . 60 40

1981. International Year of Disabled People.

604 **213** 70 f. multicoloured . . . 60 35

214 Koudougou

1981. Landscapes. Multicoloured.

605 35 f. Type **214** . . . 30 15

606 45 f. Toma . . . 40 20

607 85 f. Volta Noire . . . 65 30

215 Agricultural Scenes within Map

1981. World Food Day.

608 **215** 90 f. multicoloured . . . 70 45

216 Topi

1981. Wildlife Protection. Multicoloured.

609 5 f. Type **216** . . . 10 10

610 15 f. Waterbuck . . . 15 15

611 40 f. Roan antelopes . . . 35 20

612 60 f. Dorcas gazelle . . . 60 35

613 70 f. African elephant . . . 1·00 55

217 Campaign Emblem

219 Donkey

218 Papaya

1981. Anti-Apartheid Campaign.

614 **217** 90 f. red . . . 60 35

1981. Fruit and Vegetables. Multicoloured.

615 20 f. Type **218** . . . 15 10

616 35 f. Fruit and vegetables . . 30 15

617 75 f. Mangoes (vert) . . . 50 30

618 90 f. Melons . . . 60 35

1981. Stock Breeding. Multicoloured.

619 10 f. Type **219** . . . 10 10

620 25 f. Pig . . . 20 10

621 70 f. Cow . . . 55 20

622 90 f. Helmet guineafowl (vert) 1·25 55

623 250 f. Rabbit . . . 1·75 90

220 Women carrying Rice

221 Father and Son

1981. 10th Anniv of West African Rice Development Association.

625 **220** 90 f. multicoloured . . . 90 45

1982. 20th Anniv of World Food Programme.

626 **221** 50 f. multicoloured . . . 40 15

222 Morhonaba Palace, Ouagadougou

1982. Traditional Houses. Multicoloured.

627 30 f. Type **222** . . . 20 10

628 70 f. Bobo . . . 50 20

629 100 f. Gourounsi . . . 70 30

630 200 f. Peulh . . . 1·40 60

631 250 f. Dagari . . . 1·60 65

223 Hexagonal Pattern

1982. World Telecommunications Day.
632 **223** 90 f. multicoloured . . . 85 40

224 Symbols of National Life **225** Passing Ball

1982. National Life.
633 **224** 90 f. multicoloured . . . 60 30

1982. Air. World Cup Football Championship, Spain. Multicoloured.
634 70 f. Type **225** 50 15
635 90 f. Tackle 60 30
636 150 f. Running with ball . . . 1·10 40
637 300 f. Receiving ball . . . . . 2·00 85

226 Water Lily **227** Symbols of Communication on Map of Africa

1982. Flowers. Multicoloured.
639 25 f. Type **226** 15 10
640 40 f. Kapoka 35 10
641 70 f. Frangipani 60 35
642 90 f. "Cochlospermum planchonii" 80 45
643 100 f. Cotton 90 45

1982. African Post and Telecommunications Union.
644 **227** 70 f. multicoloured . . . 45 15
645 90 f. multicoloured . . . 65 35

228 Children holding Torch

1982. 25th Anniv of Cultural Aid Fund.
646 **228** 70 f. multicoloured . . . 50 30

229 Hairstyle

1983.
647 **229** 90 f. multicoloured . . . 65 30
648 120 f. multicoloured . . . 90 35
649 170 f. multicoloured . . . 1·25 50

230 Audience watching Film

1983. 8th Film Festival, Ouagadougou. Mult.
650 90 f. Type **230** 85 55
651 500 f. Dumarou Ganda . . . 4·25 2·50

231 Joseph Montgolfier and First Demonstration of Hot-air Balloon, 1783

1983. Bicentenary of Manned Flight. Mult.
652 15 f. Type **231** (postage) . . . 10 10
653 25 f. Jean-Francois Pilatre de Rozier and first manned flight, 1783 . . . . 15 10
654 70 f. Jacques Charles and hydrogen balloon "The Globe", 1783 . . . . . . 50 10
655 90 f. John Jeffries and first Channel crossing, 1785 . . 65 20
656 100 f. Wilhelmine Reichardt and ascent on a horse, 1798 (air) 85 30
657 250 f. Salomon Andree and Spitzbergen–Expedition, 1897 1·60 55

232 Campaign Emblem and River **233** Man reading Letter

1983. International Drinking Water Decade. Mult.
659 60 f. Type **232** 45 20
660 70 f. Woman carrying water . 55 35

1983. World Communications Year. Multicoloured.
661 30 f. Type **233** 20 15
662 35 f. Type **233** 30 15
663 90 f. Canoe and Boeing 727 airliner 40 20
664 90 f. Woman on telephone . 65 35

234 Space Shuttle "Challenger"

1983. Air. World Events. Multicoloured.
665 90 f. Type **234** 60 20
666 120 f. World Cup football final 85 30
667 300 f. World Cup football final (different) . . . . 1·90 60
668 450 f. Royal wedding . . . . 2·50 85

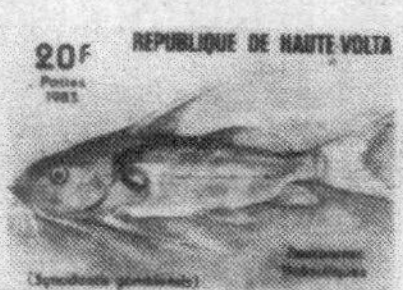

235 "Synodontis gambiensis"

1983. Fishery Resources. Multicoloured.
670 20 f. Type **235** 15 15
671 30 f. "Palmatochromis guntheri" 35 15
672 40 f. Line fishing (vert) . . . 35 15
673 50 f. Net fishing 40 15
674 75 f. Trap fishing 55 20

236 Soling Class Yacht

1983. Air. Pre-Olympic Year. Multicoloured.
675 90 f. Type **236** 65 20
676 120 f. Type 470 yacht . . . . 1·00 30
677 300 f. Windsurfing . . . . . 2·25 60
678 400 f. Windsurfing (different) . 2·75 85

237 Planting a Sapling

1983. Campaign for Control of the Desert. Multicoloured.
680 10 f. Type **237** 15 10
681 50 f. Plantation 40 10
682 100 f. Control of forest fires . 90 35
683 150 f. Woman cooking . . . . 1·40 60
684 200 f. Control of timber trade (vert) . . . . 1·60 90

238 Arms of Upper Volta

1983. 25th Anniv of Republic. Multicoloured.
685 90 f. Type **238** 55 30
686 500 f. Family with flag . . . . 3·25 1·40

239 "Self-portrait" (Picasso)

1983. Celebrities' Anniversaries. Multicoloured.
687 120 f. Type **239** . . . . 1·40 35
688 185 f. "Self-portrait with a Palette" (Manet (1832–1883)) 1·40 45
689 300 f. Fresco detail (Raphael (1483–1520)) (horiz) . . . . 2·25 60
690 350 f. Fresco detail (Raphael) (different) (horiz) . . . . 2·50 85
691 500 f. J. W. Goethe (1749–1832) (portrait by Georg Oswald) . 3·50 1·10

240 "Adoration of the Shepherds" **242** Handball

1983. Air. Christmas. Multicoloured.
692 120 f. Type **240** 85 30
693 350 f. "Virgin of the Garland" 2·40 65
694 500 f. "Adoration of the Magi" 3·00 1·00

1984. Air. Olympic Games, Los Angeles. Multicoloured.
695 90 f. Type **242** 55 20
696 120 f. Volleyball 80 30
697 150 f. Handball (horiz) . . . . 1·10 35
698 250 f. Basketball (horiz) . . . 1·60 50
699 300 f. Football (horiz) . . . . 2·00 65

243 Greater Flamingo

1984. Air. Birds. Multicoloured.
701 90 f. Type **243** . . . . 1·00 40
702 185 f. Kori bustard (vert) . . 1·75 1·00
703 200 f. Red-billed oxpecker (vert) 1·90 1·10
704 300 f. Southern ground hornbill 2·50 1·75

244 Pres. Houari Boumedienne of Algeria

1984. Air. Celebrities. Multicoloured.
705 5 f. Type **244** 10 10
706 125 f. Gottlieb Daimler (automobile designer) and car 90 30
707 250 f. Louis Bleriot (aviator) and Bleriot XI airplane . . . . 1·60 50
708 300 f. Pres. Abraham Lincoln of U.S.A. and White House . 2·25 55
709 400 f. Henry Dunant (founder of Red Cross), red cross and battle of Solferino . . . . 2·75 70
710 450 f. Auguste Piccard and bathyscape "Trieste" . . . 3·00 1·40
711 500 f. Robert Baden-Powell (founder of Boy Scout movement) and scouts . . . 3·25 95
712 600 f. Anatole Karpov, 1978 world chess champion . . . 3·75 1·10

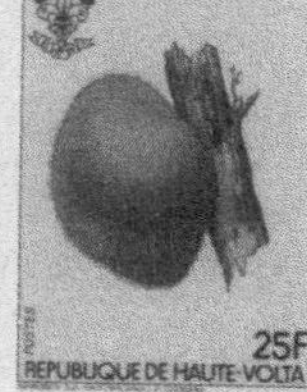

245 Seedling and Clasped Hands within Circle of Flags **246** "Polystictus leoninus"

1984. 25th Anniv of Council of Unity.
714 **245** 90 f. multicoloured . . . 65 30
715 100 f. multicoloured . . . 80 35

1984. Fungi and Flowers. Multicoloured.
716 25 f. Type **246** (postage) . . . 20 10
717 185 f. "Pterocarpus lucens" . 1·60 60
718 200 f. "Phlebopus colossus sudanicus" . . . . 1·90 65
719 250 f. "Cosmos suplhureus" . 2·25 85
720 300 f. "Trametes versicolour" (air) . . . . 2·50 95
721 400 f. "Ganoderma lucidum" . 3·50 1·25

247 Cheetah with Cubs

1984. Protected Animals. Multicoloured.
723 15 f. Type **247** (postage) . . . 10 10
724 35 f. Two cheetahs 30 10
725 90 f. Cheetah 65 20
726 120 f. Cheetah with cubs (different) 90 35
727 300 f. Baboons (air) . . . . . 2·25 55
728 400 f. Marabou stork and African white-backed vulture 2·75 65

248 "CC2400 ch"

1984. Transport. Multicoloured. (a) Locomotives.

730		40 f. Type **248**	30	10
731		100 f. Steam locomotive No. 1806	75	30
732		145 f. "Livingstone"	1·25	50
733		450 f. Pacific class "C51" steam locomotive	3·25	1·60

(b) Ships.

734		20 f. "Maiden Queen"	15	10
735		60 ff. "Scawfell"	45	15
736		120 f. "Harbinger"	90	35
737		400 f. "True Briton"	3·00	1·25

For later issues see **BURKINA FASO**.

OFFICIAL STAMPS

O 18 African Elephant

1963.

O112	O 18	1 f. sepia and brown	10	10
O113		5 f. sepia and green	15	15
O114		10 f. sepia and violet	20	20
O115		15 f. sepia & orange	25	25
O116		25 f. sepia and purple	35	35
O117		50 f. sepia and green	65	65
O118		60 f. sepia and red	75	75
O119		85 f. sepia and myrtle	1·25	1·25
O120		100 f. sepia and blue	1·50	1·50
O121		200 f. sepia and mve	2·75	2·75

POSTAGE DUE STAMPS

1920. Postage Due stamps of Upper Senegal and Niger, "Figures" Key-type, optd **HAUTE-VOLTA**.

D18	M	5 c. green	25	50
D19		10 c. red	25	50
D20		15 c. grey	25	50
D21		20 c. brown	30	60
D22		30 c. blue	45	90
D23		50 c. black	70	1·40
D24		60 c. orange	65	1·40
D25		1 f. violet	90	1·90

1927. Surch.

D40	M	2 f. on 1 f. mauve	2·25	3·50
D41		3 f. on 1 f. brown	2·50	3·75

1928. "Figures" key-type inscr "HAUTE-VOLTA".

D63	M	5 c. green	35	75
D64		10 c. red	35	75
D65		15 c. grey	50	95
D66		20 c. brown	50	95
D67		30 c. blue	65	1·25
D68		50 c. black	1·75	3·00
D69		60 c. orange	2·25	4·00
D70		1 f. violet	3·50	6·50
D71		2 f. purple	6·75	10·00
D72		3 f, brown	7·50	11·00

D 13 Red-fronted Gazelle

1962. Figures of value in black.

D 95	D 13	1 f. blue	10	10
D 96		2 f. orange	10	10
D 97		5 f. blue	15	15
D 98		10 f. purple	30	30
D 99		20 f. green	55	55
D100		50 f. red	1·40	1·40

APPENDIX

The following stamps have either been issued in excess of postal needs or have not been available to the public in reasonable quantities at face value. Such stamps may later be given full listing if there is evidence of regular postal use.

1973.

Gold Medal Winners, Munich Olympic Games (2nd series). Air 50, 60, 90, 150, 350 f.

Christmas 1972. Paintings of the Madonna and Child. Air 50, 75, 100, 125, 150 f.

Moon Mission of "Apollo 17". Air 50, 65, 100, 150, 200 f.

Gold Medal Winners, Munich Olympic Games (3rd series). Air 35, 45, 75, 250, 400 f.

Exploration of the Moon. Air 50, 65, 100, 150, 200 f.

Wild Animals. Air 100, 150, 200, 250, 500 f.

10th Anniv of Organization of African Unity. Air 45 f.

Europafrique. European Paintings. Air 50, 65, 100, 150, 200 f.

Historic Railway Locomotives, French Railway Museum, Mulhouse. Air 10, 40, 50, 150, 250 f.

Upper Volta Boy Scouts. Postage 20 f.; Air 40, 75, 150, 200 f.

Pan-African Drought Relief. Surch on values of 1973 Europafrique issue. Air 100 f. on 65 f., 200 f. on 150 f.

10th Death Anniv of President John Kennedy. Rockets. Postage 5, 10, 30 f.; Air 200, 300 f.

50th Anniv of International Police Organization (Interpol). 50, 65, 70, 150 f.

Tourism. Postage 35, 40 f.; Air 100 f.

Religious Buildings. Postage 35, 40 f.; Air 200 f.

Folk-dancers. Postage 35, 40 f.; Air 100, 225 f.

Famous Men. 5, 10, 20, 25, 30, 50, 60, 75, 100, 175, 200, 250 f.

1974.

World Cup Football Championship, Munich (1st issue). Postage 5, 40 f.; Air 75, 100, 250 f.

Pres. De Gaulle Commemoration. Postage 35, 40, 60 f.; Air 300 f.

World Cup Football Championship (2nd issue). Postage 10, 20, 50 f.; Air 150, 300 f.

Centenary of Universal Postal Union. Postage 35, 40, 85 f.; Air 100, 200, 300 f.

World Cup Football Championship (3rd issue). Previous Finals. Postage 10, 25, 50 f.; Air 150, 200, 250 f.

Centenary of Berne Convention. 1974 U.P.U. issue optd. Postage 35, 40, 85 f., Air 100, 200, 300 f.

Bouquets of Flowers. Postage 5, 10, 30, 50 f.; Air 300 f.

1975.

Birth Centenary of Sir Winston Churchill. 50, 75, 100, 125, 300 f.

Bicentenary of American Revolution (1st issue). 35, 40, 75, 100, 200, 300 f.

Railway Locomotives. Postage 15, 25, 50 f.; Air 100, 200 f.

Vintage and Veteran Cars. Postage 10, 30, 35 f.; Air 150, 200 f.

Bicent of American Revolution (2nd issue). Postage 30, 40, 50 f.; Air 200, 300 f.

Birth Cent of Dr Albert Schweitzer. Postage 5, 15 f.; Air 150, 175, 200 f.

"Apollo–Soyuz" Joint Space Test Project. Postage 40, 50 f.; Air 100, 200, 300 f.

Paintings by Picasso. Postage 50, 60, 90 f.; Air 150, 350 f.

"Expo '75" Exhibition, Okinawa, Japan. Postage 15, 25, 45, 50, 60 f.; Air 150 f.

Winter Olympic Games, Innsbruck. Postage 35, 45, 85 f.; Air 100, 200 f.

1976.

Olympic Games, Montreal (1st issue). "Pre-Olympic Year" (1975). Postage 40, 50, 100 f.; Air 125, 150 f.

Olympic Games, Montreal (2nd issue). Postage 30, 55, 75 f.; Air 150, 200 f.

Zeppelin Airships. Postage 10, 40, 50 f.; Air 100, 200, 300 f.

"Viking" Space Flight. Postage 30, 55, 75 f.; Air 200, 300 f.

1977.

Olympic Games Medal Winners, 1976 Olympic Games issue optd. Postage 30, 55, 75 f.; Air 150, 200 f.

1983.

Bicentenary of Manned Flight. Air 1500 f.

UPPER YAFA — Pt. 19

A Sultanate of South Arabia, formerly part of the Western Aden Protectorate. Independent from September to December 1967 and then part of the People's Democratic Republic of Yemen.

1000 fils = 1 dinar

1 Flag and Map

1967.

UY 1	1	5 f. multicoloured (post)	15	15
UY 2		10 f. multicoloured	15	15
UY 3		20 f. multicoloured	20	20
UY 4		25 f. multicoloured	25	20
UY 5		40 f. multicoloured	40	25
UY 6		50 f. multicoloured	50	30
UY 7	–	75 f. multicoloured (air)	65	50
UY 8	–	100 f. multicoloured	85	60
UY 9	–	250 f. multicoloured	2·00	2·00
UY10	–	500 f. multicoloured	3·50	3·50

DESIGNS: UY 7/10, Arms of Sultanate.

APPENDIX

The following stamps have either been issued in excess of postal needs or have not been available to the public in reasonable quantities at face value. Such stamps may later be given full listing if there is evidence of regular postal use.

1967.

Olympic Games, Mexico (1968). Postage 15, 25, 50, 75 f.; Air 150 f.

Sculptures. Postage 10, 30, 60, 75 f.; Air 150 f.

Paintings from the Louvre. Postage 50 f.; Air 100, 150, 200, 250 f.

World Cup Football Championships, England (1966). Postage 5, 10, 50 f.; Air 100 f.

Paintings by Old Masters. Postage 10, 15, 20, 25, 30, 40, 50, 60, 75 f.; Air 150 f.

Human Rights Year and 5th Death Anniv of J. F. Kennedy. Postage 5, 10, 50, 75 f.; Air 125 f.

Persian Miniatures. 10, 20, 30, 40, 50 f.

Ballet Paintings. 20, 30, 40, 50, 60 f.

Portraits by Old Masters. Postage 25, 50, 75 f.; Air 100, 125, 150, 175, 200, 225, 250 f.

Winter Olympic Games, Grenoble (1968). 1967 World Cup issue optd. Postage 5 f. × 2, 10 f. × 2, 50 f. × 2; Air 100 f. × 2.

20th Anniv of UNICEF. Paintings. Postage 50, 75 f.; Air 100, 125, 250 f.

Flower Paintings. Postage 5, 10, 50 f.; Air 100, 150 f.

URUGUAY — Pt. 20

A republic in S. America, bordering on the Atlantic Ocean, independent since 1828.

1856. 120 centavos = 1 real
1859. 1000 milesimos = 100 centesimos = 1 peso

1

1856. Imperf.

1	1	60 c. blue	£190	
2		80 c. green	£170	
3		1 r. red	£150	

3 4

1858. Imperf.

5	3	120 c. blue	£130	£120
6		180 c. green	38·00	55·00
7		240 c. red	38·00	£225

1859. Imperf.

15	4	60 c. purple	15·00	13·50
16		80 c. yellow	£130	25·00
17		100 c. red	38·00	29·00
18		120 c. blue	25·00	9·50
12		180 c. green	9·50	11·50
13		240 c. red	35·00	35·00

6 8 9

1864. Imperf.

20a	6	6 c. red	5·75	3·75
21		8 c. green	9·75	9·75
22		10 c. yellow	13·50	9·25
23		12 c. blue	5·75	4·50

1866. Surch in figures. Imperf.

24	6	5 c. on 12 c. blue	9·50	19·00
25		10 c. on 8 c. green	9·50	25·00
26		15 c. on 10 c. yellow	11·50	29·00
27a		20 c. on 6 c. red	13·50	29·00

1866. Imperf.

28	8	1 c. black	95	1·50
29	9	5 c. blue	1·50	85
30		10 c. green	5·50	2·25
31		15 c. yellow	9·25	3·75
32		20 c. red	11·00	3·75

1866. Perf.

37	8	1 c. black	2·25	2·25
33	9	5 c. blue	2·00	35
34		10 c. green	3·75	35
35		15 c. yellow	2·00	1·40
36		20 c. red	4·50	1·10

10  11

1877. Roul. Various frames.

42	10	1 c. brown	25	20
43	11	5 c. green	30	15
44	10	10 c. red	40	15
45		20 c. bistre	60	25
46		50 c. black	3·00	1·10
47		1 p. blue	17·00	5·50

15 J. Suarez

16

1881. Perf.

60a	15	7 c. blue	75	90

1882.

62	16	1 c. green	40	40
63	–	2 c. red	35	35

The central device on the 2 c. is a mountain.

18 Arms

20 Gen. Maximo Santos

21 General Artigas

26

1883.

66	18	1 c. green	50	30
67		2 c. red	60	40
68	20	5 c. blue	75	60
69	21	10 c. brown	1·10	75

1883. Optd **1883 Provisorio**. Roul.

75	11	5 c. green	50	40

1884. Optd **PROVISORIO 1884** or surch **1 CENTESIMO** also.

76	10	1 c. on 10 c. red	15	15
77	–	2 c. red (No. 63)	50	50

1884.

79	26	5 c. blue	1·00	50

28

29

31 Gen. Artigas

32 M. Santos

33

34

1884. Roul.

100	28	1 c. green	20	20
83a		1 c. grey	40	30
101	29	2 c. red	20	25
85a	28	5 c. blue	1·00	15
86		5 c. lilac	25	10
87	31	7 c. brown	95	60
103		7 c. orange	60	40
88	32	10 c. brown	20	20
89	33	20 c. mauve	75	30
105		20 c. brown	75	40
90	34	25 c. lilac	1·40	50
106		25 c. red	1·10	60

35

36

1887. Roul.
99 **35** 10 c. mauve 70 40

1888. Roul.
104 **36** 10 c. violet 25 25

1889. Optd **Provisorio**. Roul.
114 **28** 5 c. lilac 15 15

38 39 40

41 42 43

44 Figure of Justice 45 Mercury 46

1889. Perf.
115 **38** 1 c. green 40 20
116 **39** 2 c. red 20 25
117 **40** 5 c. blue 20 15
118 **41** 7 c. brown 60 25
119 **42** 10 c. green . . . . 1·50 25
120 **43** 20 c. orange . . . . 1·10 30
121 **44** 20 c. brown . . . . 2·00 40
122 **45** 50 c. blue . . . . 3·50 1·10
123 **46** 1 p. violet . . . . 8·50 2·00
See also Nos. 142/52, 220, 222 224 and 236/7.

1891. Optd **Provisorio 1891**. Roul.
133 **28** 5 c. lilac 10 10

1892. Optd **Provisorio 1892** or surch also in words.
135 **28** 1 c. green 40 40
137 **43** 1 c. on 20 c. orange 15 10
136 **41** 5 c. on 7 c. brown 15 30

50 51 52

53 54 55

1892. Perf.
138 **50** 1 c. green 20 15
139 **51** 2 c. red 25 20
140 **52** 5 c. blue 20 15
141 **53** 10 c. orange 90 40

1894.
142 **38** 1 c. blue 20 25
143 **39** 2 c. brown 25 25
144 **40** 5 c. red 50 20
145 **41** 7 c. green . . . . 2·75 1·10
146 **42** 10 c. orange . . . . 1·50 30
147 **43** 20 c. brown . . . . 2·75 75
148 **44** 25 c. red . . . . 3·50 1·50
149 **45** 50 c. purple . . . . 6·25 2·25
150 **46** 1 p. blue . . . . 11·00 3·00
151 **54** 2 p. red . . . . 11·50 7·00
152 **55** 3 p.purple . . . . 11·50 7·00

56 Gaucho 57 Solis Theatre 58 Steam Locomotive

59 Bull's Head  60 Ceres  61 Steamer "Elbe"

62 Amazon  63 Mercury

64  65 Montevideo Fortress

66 Montevideo Cathedral

1895.
153 **56** 1 c. bistre 20 20
154 **57** 2 c. blue 20 20
155 **58** 5 c. red 20 20
156 **59** 7 c. green . . . . 3·75 1·00
157 **60** 10 c. brown 85 30
158 **61** 20 c. black and green . . . 6·00 55
159 **62** 25 c. black and brown . . 2·75 60
160 **63** 50 c. black and blue . . . 3·50 1·50
161 **64** 1 p. black and brown . . 5·50 2·00
162 **65** 2 p. green and violet . . . 11·50 7·75
163 **66** 3 p. blue and red . . . . 11·50 6·25
For further stamps in these types, see Nos. 183/93 and 221.

67 J. Suarez  68 J. Suarez Monument  72

1896. Unveiling of President Joaquin Suarez Monument.
177 **67** 1 c. black and red 20 15
178 **68** 5 c. black and blue 25 20
179 – 10 c. black and lake . . . 45 25
DESIGN: 10 c. Larger stamp showing whole Suarez Monument.

1897. Optd **PROVISORIO 1897**.
180 **67** 1 c. black and red 30 30
181 **68** 5 c. black and blue 40 30
182 – 10 c. black and lake . . . 50 50

1897.
183 **56** 1 c. blue 20 15
184 **57** 2 c. purple 30 20
185 **58** 5 c. green 30 15
186 **59** 7 c. orange . . . . 1·75 60
187 **72** 10 c. red 85 35
188 **61** 20 c. black and mauve . . 5·50 40
189 **62** 25 c. blue and red . . . . 1·50 35
190 **63** 50 c. brown and green . . 2·75 70
191 **64** 1 p. blue and brown . . . 4·50 1·40
192 **65** 2 p. red and yellow . . . 4·50 65
193 **66** 3 p. red and lilac . . . . 4·25 1·10
See also No. 223.

1897. End of Civil War. Optd with palm leaf and **PAZ 1897**.
197 **56** 1 c. blue 40 30
198 **57** 2 c. purple 55 55
199 **58** 5 c. green 85 75
200 **72** 10 c. red . . . . 1·40 1·40

1898. Surch **PROVISIONAL $\frac{1}{2}$ CENTESIMO**.
209 **38** $\frac{1}{2}$ c. on 1 c. blue 15 15
210 **56** $\frac{1}{2}$ c. on 1 c. bistre 15 15
211 **67** $\frac{1}{2}$ c. on 1 c. black and red . 15 15
212 **57** $\frac{1}{2}$ c. on 2 c. blue 15 15
213 **68** $\frac{1}{2}$ c. on 5 c. black & blue . . 20 15
214 **59** $\frac{1}{2}$ c. on 7 c. green 20 15

75 Liberty  76 Monument to Gen. Artigas

1898.
215 **75** 5 m. red 20 20
216 5 m. violet 25 25

1899.
217 **76** 5 m. blue 25 15
218 5 m. orange 25 15
220 **39** 2 c. orange 20 20
221a **58** 5 c. blue . . . . 1·50 15
222 **41** 7 c. red . . . . 2·25 1·10
223 **72** 10 c. purple 30 25
224 **43** 20 c. blue . . . . 1·10 20

1900. No. 182 surch **1900 5 CENTESIMOS** and bar.
229 5 c. on 10 c. black and lake . . 25 15

78  79  80

81  82

1900.
230 **78** 1 c. green 30 15
231a **79** 2 c. red 10 15
232b **80** 5 c. blue 60 15
233 **81** 7 c. brown 85 30
234 **82** 10 c. lilac 45 20
236 **45** 50 c. red . . . . 3·50 35
237 **46** 1 p. green . . . . 11·00 75

85 General Artigas  86

87  88

89  90

91

1904.
251 **85** 5 m. yellow 30 15
252 **86** 1 c. green 50 15
253a **87** 2 c. orange 20 15
254b **88** 5 c. blue 40 10
255 **89** 10 c. lilac 40 20
256 **90** 20 c. green . . . . 1·40 40
257 **91** 25 c. bistre . . . . 1·50 40

1904. End of the Civil War. Optd **Paz-1904**.
258 **86** 1 c. green 35 30
259 **87** 2 c. orange 40 35
260 **88** 5 c. blue . . . . 1·00 50

95  96

1906.
268 **95** 5 c. blue 50 15

1906.
269 **96** 5 c. blue 20 10
270 7 c. brown 40 25
271 50 c. red . . . . 2·25 40

98 Cruiser "Montevideo" and Cadet Ship "Diez-y-Ocho de Julio"

1908. 83rd Anniv of Revolt of the "Immortal 33" under Levalleja. Roul.
279 **98** 1 c. green and red . . . . 1·10 85
280 2 c. green . . . . 1·10 85
281 5 c. green and orange . . . 1·10 85

99 Montevideo Port

1909. Opening of the Port of Montevideo.
282 **99** 2 c. black and brown . . . 1·50 80
283 5 c. black and red . . . . 1·50 80

1909. Surch **Provisorio** and value.
284 **82** 8 c. on 10 c. violet 40 30
285 **44** 23 c. on 25 c. brown . . . 75 30

103 Centaur

1910. Centenary of 1810 Argentine Revolution.
286 **103** 2 c. red 30 20
287 5 c. blue 30 20

1910. Surch **PROVISORIO 5 MILESIMOS** (or **CENTESIMOS**) **1910**.
294 **78** 5 m. on 1 c. green 10 20
295 **45** 5 c. on 50 c. red 15 30
296 **96** 5 c. on 50 c. red 40 30

107 Artigas  108

1910.
297 **107** 5 m. purple 15 10
298 1 c. green 15 10
299 2 c. red 20 10
324 2 c. pink 25 10
319 4 c. yellow 30 10
300 5 c. blue 20 10
301 8 c. black 40 15
327 8 c. blue 25 10
302 20 c. brown 70 20
303 **108** 23 c. blue . . . . 1·10 25
330 50 c. orange . . . . 1·50 60
331 1 p. red . . . . 4·50 40

109  114 Liberty offering Peace to Uruguay

1911. 1st Pan-American Postal Congress.
306 **109** 5 c. black and red 35 25

1911. Centenary of Battle of Las Piedras. Surch **ARTIGAS**, value and **1811-1911**.
314 **81** 2 c. on 7 c. brown 35 25
315 5 c. on 7 c. brown 35 20

1913. Centenary of 1813 Conference. Optd **CENTENARIO DE LAS INSTRUCCIONES DEL ANO XIII.**
332 **107** 2 c. brown 30 40
333 4 c. yellow 30 40
334 5 c. blue 30 40

1918. Promulgation of New Constitution.
347 **114** 2 c. brown and green . . 35 25
348 5 c. blue and brown . . . 35 25

115 Montevideo Harbour
116 Statue of Liberty, New York
118 J. E. Rodo

1919.
349 **115** 5 m. grey and violet . . . 15 10
350 1 c. grey and green . . . 20 10
351 2 c. grey and red . . . 20 10
352 4 c. grey and orange . . . 50 10
353 5 c. grey and blue . . . 60 10
354 8 c. brown and blue . . . 70 20
355 20 c. grey and brown . . 2·50 35
356 23 c. brown and green . . 3·50 70
357 50 c. blue and brown . . 4·00 3·25
358 1 p. blue and red . . . . 9·50 2·75

1919. Peace Commemoration.
359 **116** 2 c. brown and red . . . 20 10
360 4 c. brown and orange . . 30 10
361 5 c. brown and blue . . . 35 10
362 8 c. blue and brown . . . 50 20
363 20 c. black and bistre . . 1·40 40
364 23 c. black and green . . 2·00 70

1920. Honouring J. E. Rodo (writer).
372 **118** 2 c. black and lake 35 45
373 4 c. blue and orange . . . 40 30
374 5 c. brown and blue . . . 50 35

1921. Air. Optd with airplane and **CORREO AEREO.**
377 **44** 25 c. brown . . . . 2·10 1·50

120 Mercury

122 Damaso A. Larranaga

1921.
378 **120** 5 m. mauve 30 10
410 5 m. black 20 10
380 1 c. green 30 10
411a 1 c. violet 25 10
411 1 c. mauve 25 10
412 2 c. orange 35 10
412a 2 c. red 40 10
384 3 c. green 40 20
385 4 c. yellow 25 10
386 5 c. blue 25 10
413 5 c. brown 40 10
414 8 c. red 55 50
388 12 c. blue . . . . 1·10 50
389 36 c. olive . . . . 4·50 1·50

1921. 150th Birth Anniv of D. A. Larranaga.
390 **122** 5 c. slate 75 55

127 Artigas Monument

128 Chilian Lapwing

1923. Unveiling of Monument to Artigas.
418 **127** 2 c. brown and red . . . 30 10
419 5 c. brown and violet . . . 30 10
420 12 c. brown and blue . . 40 20

1923. Various sizes.
450 **128** 5 m. grey 15 10
422 1 c. yellow 10 15
451 1 c. pink 25 15
477 1 c. purple 50 20
528 1 c. violet 10 20
423 2 c. mauve 10 15
529 2 c. red 10 20
453 3 c. green 35 15
454 5 c. blue 25 10
455 8 c. red 35 15
456 10 c. green 25 10
457 12 c. blue 40 15
458 15 c. mauve 30 15
459 20 c. brown 70 15
429 36 c. green . . . . 1·50 65
460 36 c. red . . . . 2·25 55
430 50 c. orange . . . . 3·00 1·00
461 50 c. olive . . . . 3·00 75
431 1 p. red . . . . 12·50 7·75
462 1 p. buff . . . . 4·75 1·75
432 2 p. green . . . . 12·50 7·75
463 2 p. lilac . . . . 9·50 5·00

130

131 Biplane

1923. Centenary of Battle of Sarandi.
433 **130** 2 c. green 35 25
434 5 c. red 35 25
435 12 c. blue 35 25

1924. Air.
436 **131** 6 c. blue 75 85
437 10 c. red . . . . 1·10 1·25
438 20 c. green . . . . 2·00 2·00

134 "Victory" of Samothrace

1924. Uruguayan Football Victory in Olympic Games.
464 **134** 2 c. red . . . . 8·50 6·25
465 5 c. purple . . . . 8·50 6·25
466 12 c. blue . . . . 8·50 6·25

135 Landing of Lavalleja

1925. Centenary of Rising against Brazilian Rule.
467 **135** 2 c. grey and red 60 70
468 5 c. grey and mauve . . . 60 70
469 12 c. grey and blue . . . 60 70

136 Parliament House

137 White-necked Heron

1925. Inauguration of Parliament House.
470 **136** 5 c. black and violet . . . 60 40
471 12 c. black and blue . . . 60 40

1925. Air. Centenary of Assembly of Florida. (a) Inscr "MONTEVIDEO".
472 **137** 14 c. black and blue . . . 15·00 7·75

(b) Inscr "FLORIDA".
473 **137** 14 c. black and blue . . . 15·00 7·75

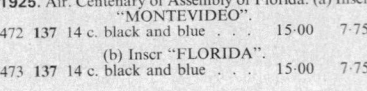

138 Gen. F. Rivera

139 Gaucho Cavalryman at Rincon

1925. Centenary of Battle of Rincon.
474 **138** 5 c. pink (postage) . . . 40 30
475 **139** 45 c. green (air) . . . . . — 4·50

140 Battle of Sarandi

1925. Centenary of Battle of Sarandi.
482 **140** 2 c. green 60 55
483 5 c. mauve 60 55
484 12 c. blue 75 60

141 Albatross

145 New G.P.O., Montevideo

1926. Air. Imperf.
495 **141** 6 c. blue 70 70
496 10 c. red 95 95
497 20 c. green . . . . 1·40 1·40
498 25 c. violet . . . . 1·40 1·40
See also Nos. 569/80.

1927. Philatelic Exhibition, Montevideo. Imperf.
534 **145** 2 c. green . . . . 2·00 2·00
535 5 c. red . . . . 2·00 2·00
536 8 c. blue . . . . 2·00 2·00

1928. Opening of San Carlos–Rocha Railway. Surch **Inauguracion Ferrocarril SAN CARLOS a ROCHA 14/1/928** and value.
537 **128** 2 c. on 12 c. blue 85 85
538 5 c. on 12 c. blue 85 85
539 10 c. on 12 c. blue 85 85
540 15 c. on 12 c. blue 85 85

147 Gen. F. Rivera (after M. Bucasso)

1928. Centenary of Conquest of Las Misiones.
541 **147** 5 c. red 30 15

148 Artigas

149 Artigas Statue, Paysandu

1928.
542 **148** 5 m. black 10 10
762 5 m. brown 10 10
868 5 m. orange 10 10
543 1 c. violet 10 10
544 1 c. purple 10 10
869 1 c. blue 10 10
687 15 m. black 25 15
545 2 c. green 10 10
764 2 c. brown 10 10
870 2 c. red 10 10
546 3 c. bistre 20 10
871 3 c. green 10 10
548 5 c. red 15 10
549 5 c. olive 15 10
766 5 c. blue 15 10
767 5 c. turquoise 30 10
872 5 c. violet 10 10
550 7 c. red 15 10
551 8 c. blue 20 10
552 8 c. brown 20 10
553 10 c. orange 30 15
768 12 c. blue 30 10
556 15 c. blue 45 10
557 17 c. violet 40 15
558 20 c. brown 55 15
757 20 c. buff 70 35
770 20 c. red 40 30
771 20 c. violet 35 10
560 24 c. red 70 40
561 24 c. yellow 40 35
562 36 c. olive 70 40
563 50 c. grey . . . . 1·75 95
564 50 c. black . . . . 2·25 85
772 50 c. sepia . . . . 1·10 45
566 1 p. green . . . . 4·00 1·50
567 **149** 2 p. brown and blue . . . 5·00 2·75
568 3 p. black and red . . . 6·25 6·25

1928. Air. Re-issue of T **141**. Perf.
634 **141** 4 c. brown . . . . 1·50 1·50
569 10 c. green 75 70
570 20 c. orange . . . . 1·10 85
571 30 c. blue . . . . 1·10 85
572 38 c. green . . . . 1·75 1·50
573 40 c. yellow . . . . 2·10 2·00
574 50 c. violet . . . . 2·25 2·25
575 76 c. orange . . . . 4·25 4·25
576 1 p. red . . . . 3·50 3·50
577 1 p. 14 blue . . . . 10·00 8·75
578 1 p. 52 yellow . . . . 15·00 15·00
579 1 p. 90 violet . . . . 18·00 17·00
580 3 p. 80 red . . . . 50·00 45·00

150 Goal Posts

151 General Garzon

1928. Uruguayan Football Victories in 1924 and 1928 Olympic Games.
581 **150** 2 c. purple . . . . 4·50 3·75
582 5 c. red . . . . 4·50 3·75
583 8 c. blue . . . . 4·50 3·75

1928. Unveiling of Monument to Gen. Garzon. Imperf.
584 **151** 2 c. red 75 75
585 5 c. green 75 75
586 8 c. blue 75 75

154 Artigas

156 Pegasus

1929.
759 **154** 1 p. brown . . . . 3·00 1·40
596 2 p. green . . . . 5·00 2·75
597 2 p. red . . . . 11·00 7·75
760 2 p. blue . . . . 5·75 5·50
598 3 p. blue . . . . 7·00 5·00
761 3 p. black . . . . 8·75 7·00
600 4 p. violet . . . . 11·00 8·50
601 4 p. green . . . . 11·00 7·75
602 5 p. red . . . . 13·50 11·00
603 5 p. orange . . . . 11·00 7·75
604 10 p. blue . . . . 38·00 35·00
605 10 p. red . . . . 38·00 35·00

1929. Air. Size $34\frac{1}{2} \times 23\frac{1}{2}$ mm.
617 **156** 1 c. mauve 25 25
659 1 c. blue 25 25
618 2 c. yellow 25 25
660 2 c. olive 25 25
619 4 c. blue 45 40
661 4 c. lake 45 40
620 6 c. violet 25 40
662 6 c. brown 25 40
621 8 c. orange . . . . 1·10 1·10
663 8 c. grey . . . . 1·25 1·10
664 8 c. green 35 30
622 16 c. blue . . . . 1·10 75
665 16 c. red . . . . 1·10 1·10
623 24 c. purple 95 95
666 24 c. violet . . . . 1·25 1·10
624 30 c. brown . . . . 1·10 1·10
667 30 c. green 60 30
625 40 c. brown . . . . 2·00 2·00
668 40 c. orange . . . . 2·00 1·75
626 60 c. blue . . . . 1·75 1·25
669 60 c. green . . . . 3·00 2·25
670 60 c. red 95 60
627 80 c. blue . . . . 3·00 3·00
671 80 c. green . . . . 5·00 4·00
628 90 c. blue . . . . 3·00 2·10
672 90 c. olive . . . . 5·00 4·00
629 1 p. red . . . . 2·25 2·00
630 1 p. 20 olive . . . . 7·00 7·00
673 1 p. 20 red . . . . 11·00 9·25
631 1 p. 50 purple . . . . 7·00 5·50
674 1 p. 50 sepia . . . . 3·75 3·50
632 3 p. red . . . . 11·50 11·00
675 3 p. blue . . . . 7·75 7·75
633 4 p. 50 black . . . . 20·00 18·00
676 4 p. 50 lilac . . . . 14·00 12·50
677 10 p. blue . . . . 7·00 5·50
For stamps as Type **156**, but smaller, see Nos. 725/44.

157 Rio Negro Bridge

159 "Peace"

1930. Independence Centenary.
639 **157** 5 m. black 20 15
640 – 1 c. sepia 20 15
641 **159** 2 c. lake 20 15
642 – 3 c. green 25 20
643 – 5 c. blue 25 20
644 – 8 c. red 35 20
645 – 10 c. violet 25 35
646 – 15 c. green 30 25
647 – 20 c. blue . . . . 1·40 70
648 – 24 c. lake 60 30
649 – 50 c. red . . . . 3·25 1·75
650 – 1 p. black . . . . 3·00 1·50
651 – 2 p. blue . . . . 7·00 4·50
652 – 3 p. red . . . . 10·00 7·00
653 – 4 p. orange . . . . 11·50 8·50
654 – 5 p. lilac . . . . 17·00 10·00
DESIGNS—HORIZ: 1 c. Gaucho horse-breaker; 5 c. Head of Liberty and Uruguayan flag; 10 c. "Artigas", from picture by Blanes; 15 c. Seascape; 20 c. Montevideo harbour, 1830; 24 c. Head of Liberty and Arms of Uruguay; 50 c. Montevideo Harbour, 1930. VERT: 3 c. Montevideo; 8 c. Allegorical figure with torch; 1 p. to 5 p. Artigas Monument.

161

163 J. Zorrilla de San Martin

1930. Fund for Old People.

No.	Type	Description	Unused	Used
655	161	1 c.+1 c. violet	20	15
656		2 c.+2 c. green	25	25
657		5 c.+5 c. red	30	30
658		8 c.+8 c. blue	30	30

1932.

No.	Type	Description	Unused	Used
679	163	1½ c. purple	20	10
680		3 c. green	30	10
681		7 c. blue	35	10
682		12 c. blue	30	35
683		1 p. brown	9·25	6·25

1932. Surch.

No.	Type	Description	Unused	Used
684	161	1½ c. on 2 c.+2 c. green	25	15

167 J. Zorrilla de San Martin

168 Flag of the Race

1933. Various portraits.

No.	Type	Description	Unused	Used
689	–	15 m. red (Lavalleja)	15	10
690	–	3 c. green (Rivera)	10	10
691	167	7 c. grey	15	10

1933. 441st Anniv of Columbus' Departure from Palos.

No.	Type	Description	Unused	Used
692	168	3 c. green	15	20
693		5 c. pink	20	25
694		7 c. blue	20	20
695		8 c. red	60	30
696		12 c. blue	25	25
697		17 c. violet	75	40
698		20 c. brown	1·50	95
699		24 c. bistre	2·00	95
700		36 c. red	2·25	1·10
701		50 c. brown	2·75	1·40
702		1 p. brown	7·75	3·50

169 Sower

170 Map and Albatross

1933. Opening of the 3rd National Assembly.

No.	Type	Description	Unused	Used
703	169	3 c. green	20	15
704		5 c. violet	35	25
705		7 c. blue	30	20
706		8 c. red	40	40
707		12 c. blue	75	45

1933. 7th Pan-American Conference, Montevideo.

No.	Type	Description	Unused	Used
708	170	3 c. green, brown & blk	1·10	1·10
709		7 c. blue, black & brown	60	45
710		12 c. blue, red and grey	95	75
711		17 c. red, blue and grey	2·10	2·10
712		20 c. yellow, green & blue	2·25	2·25
713		36 c. red, yellow & black	3·00	3·00

1934. Air. Closure of the 7th Pan-American Conference. Optd **SERVICIO POSTAL AEREO 1-1-34** in circle.

No.	Type	Description	Unused	Used
714	170	17 c. red, blue and grey	7·75	6·25
715		36 c. red, yellow & black	7·25	6·25

172

1934. 1st Anniv of Third Republic.

No.	Type	Description	Unused	Used
716	172	3 c. green	25	35
717		7 c. red	25	35
718		12 c. blue	60	30
719		17 c. brown and pink	75	70
720		20 c. yellow and grey	95	75
721		36 c. violet and green	95	95
722		50 c. grey and blue	2·50	2·00
723		1 p. red and mauve	6·25	4·00

1935. Air. As T **156**, but size 31½×21½ mm.

No.	Type	Description	Unused	Used
725		15 c. yellow	95	75
726		22 c. red	60	50
727		30 c. purple	95	75
728		37 c. purple	50	40
729		40 c. red	75	50
730		47 c. red	1·50	1·40
731		50 c. blue	50	50
732		52 c. blue	1·50	1·40
733		57 c. blue	75	70
734		62 c. green	70	50
735		87 c. green	2·10	1·75
736		1 p. olive	1·40	85
737		1 p. 12 brown	1·40	85
738		1 p. 20 brown	4·50	3·75
739		1 p. 27 brown	4·50	3·75
740		1 p. 62 red	3·00	3·00
741		2 p. lake	5·00	4·50
742		2 p. 12 grey	5·00	4·50
743		3 p. blue	4·50	4·50
744		5 p. orange	16·00	16·00

173 Friendship of Uruguay and Brazil

174 Florencio Sanchez

1935. Visit of President Vargas of Brazil.

No.	Type	Description	Unused	Used
747	173	5 m. brown	50	30
748		15 m. black	25	25
749		3 c. green	30	25
750		7 c. orange	35	20
751		12 c. blue	50	50
752		50 c. brown	2·00	1·50

1935. 25th Death Anniv of F. Sanchez (dramatist).

No.	Type	Description	Unused	Used
753	174	3 c. green	15	10
754		7 c. brown	20	10
755		12 c. blue	55	35

176 Rio Negro Dam

178 Artigas

1937.

No.	Type	Description	Unused	Used
780	176	1 c. violet (postage)	30	10
781		10 c. blue	20	10
782		15 c. red	75	50
783		1 p. brown	3·00	1·10
793		8 c. green (air)	35	35
794		20 c. green	75	50
785		35 c. brown	2·10	2·00
786		62 c. green	25	20
787		68 c. orange	60	40
788		68 c. brown	50	20
789		75 c. violet	2·10	60
790		1 p. red	75	55
791		1 p. 38 red	7·00	6·25
792		3 p. blue	3·75	75

1939. (a) Plain background.

No.	Type	Description	Unused	Used
806	178	5 m. orange	10	10
807		1 c. blue	10	10
808		2 c. violet	10	10
809		5 c. brown	15	10
810		8 c. red	20	10
811		10 c. green	35	10
812		15 c. blue	40	30
813		1 p. brown	1·25	30
1008		1 p. purple	1·25	30
814		2 p. lilac	3·00	1·25
815		4 p. orange	3·75	1·50
816		5 p. red	5·25	2·50

Nos. 806/12 are size 16×19 mm. No. 1008 is 18×22 mm. and Nos. 813/6 are 24×29½ mm.

(b) Lined background. (i) Size 17×22 mm.

No.	Type	Description	Unused	Used
835	178	5 m. orange	10	10
848		5 m. black	10	10
849		5 m. blue	10	10
836		1 c. blue	10	10
837		1 c. purple	10	10
838		2 c. violet	10	10
839		2 c. orange	15	10
840a		2 c. brown	10	10
1152		2 c. grey	10	10
841		3 c. green	15	10
842		5 c. brown	15	10
843b		7 c. blue	10	10
844		8 c. red	25	10
845		10 c. green	15	10
851		10 c. brown	25	10
852		12 c. blue	25	10
853		20 c. mauve	70	15
846		50 c. bistre	3·00	60
847		50 c. green	2·10	75
1153		50 c. brown	10	10

(ii) Size 23½×29½ mm.

No.	Type	Description	Unused	Used
1024	178	2 p. brown	3·50	1·50

180 Airplane over "La Carreta" (sculpture, Jose Bellini)

1939. Air.

No.	Type	Description	Unused	Used
817	180	20 c. blue	30	25
818		20 c. violet	20	25
820		35 c. red	25	20
821		50 c. orange	25	20
822		75 c. pink	30	15
823		1 p. blue	85	10
824		1 p. 38 violet	1·50	60
825		1 p. 38 orange	1·40	1·25
826a		2 p. blue	2·25	45
827		5 p. lilac	3·00	60
828		5 p. green	3·75	1·50
829		10 p. red	23·00	15·00

181 Congress of Montevideo

1939. 50th Anniv of 1st International Juridical Congress, Montevideo.

No.	Type	Description	Unused	Used
830	181	1 c. red	20	10
831		2 c. green	25	20
832		5 c. red	25	20
833		12 c. blue	30	35
834		50 c. violet	1·10	75

183 Juan Manuel Blanes (artist)

185 Francisco Acuna de Figueroa

1941. 40th Death Anniv of Blanes.

No.	Type	Description	Unused	Used
855	183	5 m. brown	20	10
856		1 c. brown	20	10
857		2 c. green	20	10
858		5 c. red	50	10
859		12 c. blue	60	45
860		50 c. violet	2·75	2·10

1942. 80th Death Anniv of Figueroa (author of words of National Anthem).

No.	Type	Description	Unused	Used
863	185	1 c. brown	15	15
864		2 c. green	15	15
865		5 c. red	30	15
866		12 c. blue	60	40
867		50 c. violet	1·75	1·50

1943. Surch **Valor $ 0.005**.

No.	Type	Description	Unused	Used
873	178	5 m. on 1 c. blue		

187

189 Clio

1943.

No.	Type	Description	Unused	Used
874	187	1 c. on 2 c. brown	10	10
875		2 c. on 2 c. brown	15	10

1943. Centenary of Historical and Geographical Institute. Montevideo.

No.	Type	Description	Unused	Used
878	189	5 m. violet	20	10
879		1 c. blue	20	10
880		2 c. red	35	15
881		5 c. brown	35	20

191

192 Emblems of Y.M.C.A.

1944. 75th Anniv of Founding of Swiss Colony.

No.	Type	Description	Unused	Used
889	191	1 c. on 3 c. green	10	10
890		5 c. on 7 c. brown	20	10
891		10 c. on 12 c. blue	40	25

1944. Centenary of Young Men's Christian Assn.

No.	Type	Description	Unused	Used
892	192	5 c. blue	10	10

1944. Air. Air stamps of 1935, Nos. 730, etc, surch.

No.	Type	Description	Unused	Used
893		40 c. on 47 c. red	25	40
894		40 c. on 57 c. blue	30	25
895		74 c. on 1 p. 12 brown	30	25
896		79 c. on 87 c. green	1·10	75
897		79 c. on 1 p. 27 brown	1·50	1·25
898		1 p. 20 on 1 p. 62 red	85	60
899		1 p. 43 on 2 p. 12 grey	1·10	75

194 Legislative Palace

1945. Air.

No.	Type	Description	Unused	Used
900	194	2 p. blue	1·75	70

195 Book

198 Statue

1945. Birth Centenary of Jose Pedro Varela (writer).

No.	Type	Description	Unused	Used
901	195	5 m. green	15	10
902	–	1 c. brown (Varela)	15	10
903	–	2 c. red (Statue)	15	10
904a	198	5 c. blue	15	10

Nos. 902/3 are vert.

205 Eduardo Acevedo (statesman)

200 Jose Pedro Varela (writer)

1945.

No.	Type	Description	Unused	Used
905	–	5 m. violet	10	10
911	–	1 c. brown	10	10
912	205	2 c. purple	10	10
945	–	3 c. green	10	10
906	200	5 c. red	15	10
907	–	10 c. blue	25	15
946	–	20 c. brown and green	55	30

PORTRAITS: 5 m. Santiago Vazquez (statesman); 1 c. Sylvestre Blanco (statesman); 3 c. Bruno Mauricio de Zabala (founder of Montevideo); 10 c. Jose Ellauri (President, 1873–75); 20 c. Col. Luis de Larrobla (first Postmaster).

206 Full-rigged Ship "La Eolo"

1945. Air.

No.	Type	Description	Unused	Used
913	206	8 c. green	1·75	35

1945. Air. Victory. Surch figure as "Victory of Samothrace", **1945** and new value. No. 908 optd **VICTORIA** also.

No.	Type	Description	Unused	Used
914	180	14 c. on 50 c. orange	35	30
915		23 c. on 50 c. orange	40	35
916		23 c. on 1 p. 38 orange	50	40
908	156	44 c. on 75 c. brown	70	40
917	180	1 p. on 1 p. 38 orange	2·00	1·10

1946. Inaug of Rio Negro Hydro-electric Power Plant. Optd **INAUGURACION DICIEMBRE, 1945.** No. 918 also surch **CORREO 20 CENTS.**

No.	Type	Description	Unused	Used
918	176	20 c. on 68 c. brown (postage)	80	35
919		62 c. green (air)	50	45

1946. As T **187**. (a) Postage. Optd **CORREOS** and Caduceus.

No.	Type	Description	Unused	Used
920	187	5 m. orange	10	10
921		2 c. brown	10	10
922		3 c. green	10	10
923		5 c. blue	10	10
924		10 c. brown	15	10
925		20 c. green	50	15
926		50 c. brown	1·10	60
927		3 p. red	4·25	2·25

(b) Air. Optd **SERVICIO AEREO** and an airplane.

No.	Type	Description	Unused	Used
928	187	8 c. red	10	10
929		50 c. brown	40	25
930		1 p. blue	50	30
931		2 p. olive	2·25	1·10
932		3 p. red	2·25	1·10
933		5 p. red	4·50	3·00

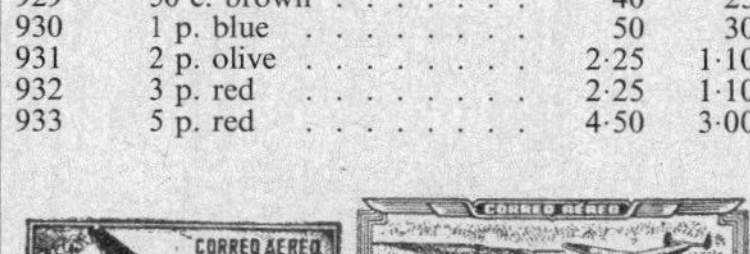

217 Douglas DC-4

215 National Airport

1947. Air.

No.	Type	Description	Unused	Used
947	217	3 c. brown	10	10
948		8 c. red	15	10
949		10 c. black	10	10
950		10 c. red	10	10
951		14 c. blue	25	15
952		15 c. brown	15	10
953		20 c. purple	15	15
954		21 c. lilac	20	15
955		23 c. green	25	20
956		27 c. green	20	10
957		31 c. brown	30	15
958		36 c. blue	20	10
959		36 c. black	20	15
960		50 c. turquoise	35	25
961		50 c. blue	25	10
962		62 c. blue	40	25
963		65 c. red	40	25
964		84 c. orange	55	40
941	215	1 p. brown and red	95	80
965	217	1 p. 08 plum	65	45
966		2 p. blue	1·10	40

942 **215** 3 p. brown and blue . . . 1·75 95
967 **217** 3 p. orange . . . . 1·25 50
943 **215** 5 p. brown and green . . 3·75 2·00
968 **217** 5 p. green . . . . 2·50 1·10
969 5 p. grey . . . . 1·50 75
944 **215** 10 p. brown and purple . 4·00 3·00
970 **217** 10 p. green . . . . 6·25 3·50

1947. As T **187** but surch in figures above shield and wavy lines.
976 2 c. on 5 c. blue 10 10
977 3 c. on 5 c. blue 10 10

219 "Ariel" **221** Bas-reliefs

1948. Unveiling of Monument to J. E. Rodo (writer).
978 **219** 1 c. brown and olive . . . 10 10
979 – 2 c. brown and violet . . 10 10
980 **221** 3 c. brown and green . . 15 10
981 5 c. brown and mauve . . 20 10
982 10 c. brown and red . . . 20 10
983 12 c. brown and blue . . 25 15
984 **219** 20 c. brown and purple . . 55 35
985 – 50 c. brown and red . . . 1·50 70
DESIGN: 2, 50 c. Bust of J. E. Rodo.
The 5 c. and 12 c. are as Type **221** but inscr "UN GRAN AMOR ES EL ALMA MISMA DE QUIEN AMA".

1948. Air. As T **187**, optd **AVIACION** and airplane.
986 12 c. blue 20 10
987 24 c. green 35 15
988 36 c. grey 50 25

223 Paysandu **225** River Santa Lucia Bridge

1948. Industrial and Agricultural Exhibitions, Paysandu.
989 **223** 3 c. green 15 10
990 – 7 c. blue 20 10
DESIGN—HORIZ: 7 c. Livestock, sower and arms of Paysandu.

1948. Uruguayan–Brazilian Friendship.
991 **225** 10 c. blue 30 15
992 50 c. green . . . . 1·25 50

226 Ploughing

1949. 4th American Labour Conference.
993 **226** 3 c. green 15 10
994 – 7 c. blue 20 10
DESIGN—HORIZ: 7 c. Horseman herding cattle.

227 Medical Faculty

1949. Air. Centenary of Montevideo University.
995 – 15 c. red 10 10
996 **227** 27 c. brown 15 10
997 – 31 c. blue 25 10
998 – 36 c. green 30 10
DESIGNS: 15 c. Architectural faculty; 31 c. Engineering faculty; 36 c. View of University.

228 Cannon and Buildings **229** Kicking Football

1950. Bicentenary of Cordon (district of Montevideo).
1003 **228** 1 c. mauve 10 10
1004 3 c. green 10 10
1005 7 c. blue 15 10

1951. 4th World Football Championship.
1006 **229** 3 c. green 50 15
1007 7 c. blue 75 35

230 Gen. Artigas

231 Emigration from Eastern Provinces

1952. Death Cent of Artigas. Dated "1950".
1009 **230** 5 m. blue 10 10
1010 – 1 c. black and blue . . . 10 10
1011 – 2 c. brown and violet . . 10 10
1012 **231** 3 c. sepia and green . . 10 10
1013 – 5 c. black and orange . . 15 10
1014 **231** 7 c. black and olive . . 15 10
1015 – 8 c. black and red . . . 25 10
1016 – 10 c. red, blue & brown 25 10
1017 – 14 c. blue 30 10
1018 – 20 c. red, blue & yellow 45 20
1019 – 50 c. olive and brown . . 80 35
1020 – 1 p. olive and blue . . 1·75 70
DESIGNS (all show Artigas except 10 c. and 20 c.)—As Type **230**: 1 c. at Las Huerfanas; 2 c. at Battle of Las Piedras; 5 c. in Cerrito; 14 c. at Ciudadela; 20 c. Arms; 50 c. in Paraguay; 1 p. Bust. As Type **231**: 7 c. Dictating instructions; 8 c. in Congress; 10 c. Flag.

232 Boeing 377 Stratocruiser over Mail Coach **234** Franklin D. Roosevelt

1952. 75th Anniv of U.P.U. (1949).
1021 **232** 3 c. green 10 10
1022 7 c. black 15 10
1023 12 c. blue 20 10

1953. 5th Postal Congress of the Americas and Spain.
1025 **234** 3 c. green 10 10
1026 7 c. blue 15 10
1027 12 c. brown 25 15

235 Ceibo (National Flower) **236** Ombu Tree

237 Parliament House **239** Exhibition Entrance

1954.
1028 **235** 5 m. multicoloured . . . 10 10
1029 – 1 c. black and red . . . 10 10
1030 **236** 2 c. green and brown . . 10 10
1031 – 3 c. multicoloured . . . 10 10
1032 **237** 5 c. brown and lilac . . 10 10
1033 – 7 c. green and brown . . 10 10
1034 – 8 c. blue and red . . . 20 10
1035 **236** 10 c. green and orange . 20 10
1036 – 12 c. sepia and blue . . 15 10
1037 – 14 c. black and purple . 20 10
1038 **235** 20 c. multicoloured . . 25 10
1039 – 50 c. multicoloured . . 55 20
1040 **237** 1 p. brown and red . . 95 30
1041 – 2 p. sepia and red . . 2·00 80
1042 – 3 p. green and lilac . . 2·10 60
1043 – 4 p. blue and brown . . 5·50 2·50
1044 **236** 5 p. green and blue . . 5·00 2·00
DESIGNS—As T **235**: 3 c., 50 c. Passion flower. As T **236**—HORIZ: 1 c., 14 c. Gaucho breaking-in horse. VERT: 7 c., 3 p. Montevideo Citadel. As T **237**—VERT: 8 c., 4 p. Isla de Lobos lighthouse and southern sealions. HORIZ: 12 c., 2 p. Outer Gateway of Montevideo, 1836.

1956. 1st National Production Exhibition.
1050 **239** 3 c. green (postage) . . . 10 10
1051 7 c. blue 10 10
1052 – 20 c. blue (air) 30 20
1053 – 31 c. green 35 30
1054 – 36 c. red 60 35
DESIGN—HORIZ: Nos. 1052/4, Exhibition symbol and two airliners.

241 Uruguay's First Stamp and "Diligencia"

1956. Air. Centenary of First Uruguay Stamps. Stamp in blue.
1055 **241** 20 c. green and yellow . . 35 20
1056 31 c. brown and blue . . 40 25
1057 36 c. red and pink . . . 50 35

242 Pres. Jose Batlle y Ordonez **248** High Diver

1956. Birth Centenary of Jose Batlle y Ordonez (President, 1903–07 and 1911–15).
1058 **242** 3 c. red (postage) 10 10
1059 – 7 c. sepia 10 10
1060 – 10 c. mauve (air) 10 10
1061 **242** 20 c. slate 15 10
1062 – 31 c. brown 20 15
1063 – 36 c. green 30 20
PORTRAIT OF PRESIDENT—VERT: 7 c. Wearing overcoat; 10 c. Similar to Type **242**; 36 c. Profile, facing right. HORIZ: 31 c. Seated at desk.

1957. Surch **5** or **10 Cts.**
1071 **242** 5 c. on 3 c. red 10 10
1072 – 10 c. on 7 c. sepia (No. 1059) 10 10

1958. 14th S. American Swimming Championships, Montevideo. Inscr as in T **248**.
1073 **248** 5 c. green 15 10
1074 – 10 c. blue 35 15
DESIGN—HORIZ: 10 c. Diving.

249 Dr. E. Acevedo **250** Flags

1958. Birth Centenary of Dr. Eduardo Acevedo (lawyer).
1075 **249** 5 c. black and green . . . 10 10
1076 10 c. black and blue . . . 15 10

1958. Air. Day of the Americas.
1077 **250** 23 c. black and blue . . . 15 15
1078 34 c. black and green . . 20 15
1079 44 c. black and mauve . . 35 20

251 Baygorria Dam **252** "Flame of Freedom"

1958. Inauguration of Baygorria Hydro-Electric Power Station.
1080 **251** 5 c. black and green . . . 10 10
1081 10 c. black and brown . . 10 10
1082 – 1 p. black and blue . . 40 15
1083 – 2 p. black and mauve . . 60 35
DESIGN: 1, 2 p. Aerial view of dam.

1958. Air. 10th Anniv of Declaration of Human Rights.
1084 **252** 23 c. black and blue . . 15 10
1085 34 c. black and green . . 20 15
1086 44 c. black and red . . 35 25

1958. Nos. 1028, 1031 and 1033 surch with Caduceus and value.
1087 5 c. on 3 c. multicoloured . . 10 10
1088 10 c. on 7 c. green and brn . 10 10
1089 20 c. on 5 m. multicoloured . 15 10

254 Statue on Capt. Boiso Lanza Monument

1959. Air. Centres in black.
1090 **254** 3 c. brown 10 10
1091 8 c. mauve 10 10
1092 38 c. black 10 10
1093 50 c. yellow 15 10
1094 60 c. violet 15 10
1095 90 c. olive 20 15
1096 1 p. blue 30 15
1097 2 p. orange 70 50
1098 3 p. green 85 50
1099 5 p. purple . . . . . . 1·10 85
1100 10 p. red . . . . 3·75 2·50
See also Type **266**.

255 Santos-Dumont and his Biplane "14 bis"

1959. Air. Santos-Dumont Commemoration.
1101 **255** 31 c. multicoloured . . . 15 15
1102 36 c. multicoloured . . . 15 15

257 "Tourism in Uruguay" **258** Gabriela Mistral (poet)

1959. Air. Tourist Publicity and 50th Anniv of Punta del Este.
1103 **257** 10 c. blue and ochre . . 10 10
1104 – 38 c. buff and green . . 15 10
1105 – 60 c. buff and violet . . 25 15
1106 **257** 90 c. green and red . . . 30 20
1107 – 1 p. 05 buff and blue . . 35 25
DESIGN: 38, 60 c., 1 p. 05, Beach and compass.

1959. 2nd Death Anniv of Gabriela Mistral.
1108 **258** 5 c. green 10 10
1109 10 c. blue 10 10
1110 20 c. red 15 10

259 Dr. Vaz Ferreira **260** Emblem of Y.M.C.A.

1959. Honouring Dr. Carlos Vaz Ferreira (philosopher).
1111 **259** 5 c. black and blue . . . 10 10
1112 10 c. black and ochre . . 10 10
1113 20 c. black and red . . 10 10
1114 50 c. black and violet . . 25 10
1115 1 p. black and green . . 40 20

1959. Air. 50th Anniv of Y.M.C.A. in Uruguay.
1116 **260** 38 c. blk, grey and green 25 25
1117 50 c. blk, grey and blue . 30 20
1118 60 c. black, grey and red 35 35

261 Boy and Dam **262** Artigas and Washington

1959. National Recovery.
1119 **261** 5 c.+10 c. green and orange (postage) 10 10
1120 10 c.+10 c. blue & orge . 10 10
1121 1 p.+10 c. violet & orge 40 30
1122 38 c.+10 c. brown and orange (air) 20 20
1123 60 c.+10 c. green & orge 30 30

1960. Air. Visit of President Eisenhower.
1124 **262** 38 c. black and red . . . 15 15
1125 50 c. black and blue . . 20 15
1126 60 c. black and green . . 25 15

1960. Air. Surch with Caduceus and **20 c.**
1128 **217** 20 c. on 27 c. green . . . 10 10

265 Dr. M. C. Martinez  **266** Statue on Lanza Monument

1960. Birth Centenary of Dr. Martin C. Martinez.
1129 **265** 3 c. black and purple . . 10 10
1130 5 c. black and violet . . 10 10
1131 10 c. black and blue . . 10 10
1132 20 c. black and brown . . 10 10
1133 1 p. black and grey . . 25 10
1134 2 p. black and orange . . 55 15
1135 3 p. black and olive . . 85 30
1136 4 p. black and brown . . 1·10 65
1137 5 p. black and red . . 1·25 70

1960. Air.
1138 **266** 3 c. black and lilac . . . 10 10
1139 20 c. black and red . . . 10 10
1140 38 c. black and blue . . . 10 10
1141 50 c. black and buff . . . 10 10
1142 60 c. black and green . . 15 10
1143 90 c. black and red . . 25 15
1144 1 p. black and grey . . 30 15
1145 2 p. black and green . . 45 25
1146 3 p. black and purple . . 40 20
1147 5 p. black and salmon . . 60 40
1148 10 p. black and yellow . 1·10 65
1149 20 p. black and blue . . 2·50 1·25

267 Refugees  **268** Scene of Revolution

1960. World Refugee Year.
1150 – 10 c. blk & bl (postage) . 10 10
1151 **267** 60 c. black & mve (air) . 20 20
DESIGN: 10 c. "Uprooted tree".

1960. 150th Anniv of Argentine May Revolution.
1154 **268** 5 c. black & bl (postage) 10 10
1155 10 c. brown and blue . . 10 10
1156 38 c. olive & blue (air) . 15 10
1157 59 c. red and blue . . . 15 15
1158 60 c. violet and blue . . 25 15

269 Pres. M. Oribe  **270** Pres. Gronchi

1961. 104th Death Anniv of Manuel Oribe (President, 1835–38).
1159 **269** 10 c. black and blue . . 10 10
1160 20 c. black and brown . . 10 10
1161 40 c. black and green . . 15 10

1961. Air. Visit of President of Italy.
1162 **270** 90 c. multicoloured . . . 25 20
1163 1 p. 20 multicoloured . . 30 25
1164 1 p. 40 multicoloured . . 35 30

271 Carrasco Airport Building

1961. Air. Carrasco National Airport.
1165 **271** 1 p. grey and violet . . 20 20
1166 2 p. grey and olive . . 45 10
1167 3 p. grey and yellow . . 35 35
1168 4 p. grey and purple . . 55 20
1169 5 p. grey and turquoise . 60 30
1170 10 p. grey and blue . . 1·10 45
1171 20 p. grey and red . . . 2·00 1·25

272 "Charging Horsmen" (by C. M. Herrera)  **273** Welfare, Justice and Education

1961. 150th Anniv of February 28th Revolution.
1172 **272** 20 c. black and blue . . 15 10
1173 40 c. black and green . . 25 10

1961. Latin-American Economic Commission Conference, Punta del Este. (a) Postage. Centres in bistre.
1174 **273** 2 c. violet 10 10
1175 5 c. orange 10 10
1176 10 c. red 10 10
1177 20 c. green 10 10
1178 50 c. lilac 10 10
1179 1 p. blue 25 15
1180 2 p. yellow 55 35
1181 3 p. grey 55 35
1182 4 p. blue 85 45
1183 5 p. brown 95 60

(b) Air. Centres in black.
1184 **273** 20 c. orange 10 10
1185 45 c. green 15 10
1186 50 c. purple 15 10
1187 90 c. violet 20 15
1188 1 p. red 25 20
1189 1 p. 40 lilac 35 25
1190 2 p. ochre 20 25
1191 3 p. blue 30 35
1192 4 p. yellow 40 50
1193 5 p. blue 55 40
1194 10 p. green . . . . . . 1·10 70
1195 20 p. mauve . . . . . . 2·00 1·50

274 Gen. Rivera  **275** Symbols of Swiss Settlers

1962. Honouring Gen. Fructuoso Rivera (1st President, 1830–35).
1196 **274** 10 c. black and red . . 10 10
1197 20 c. black and ochre . . 10 10
1198 40 c. black and green . . 15 10

1962. Centenary of First Swiss Settlers.
1199 **275** 10 c. red, black and blue (postage) 10 10
1200 20 c. red, black & green 10 10
1201 – 90 c. black, red and orange (air) 20 20
1202 – 1 p. 40 black, red & bl 30 30
DESIGN—HORIZ: 90 c., 1 p. 40, Wheatsheaf, harvester and Swiss flag.

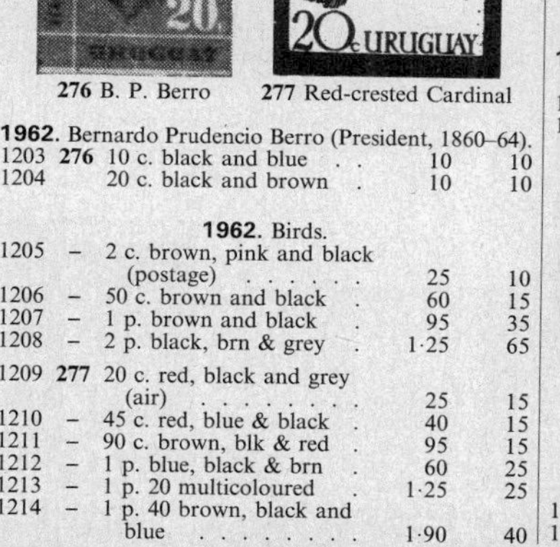

276 B. P. Berro  **277** Red-crested Cardinal

1962. Bernardo Prudencio Berro (President, 1860–64).
1203 **276** 10 c. black and blue . . 10 10
1204 20 c. black and brown . . 10 10

1962. Birds.
1205 – 2 c. brown, pink and black (postage) 25 10
1206 – 50 c. brown and black . 60 15
1207 – 1 p. brown and black . 95 35
1208 – 2 p. black, brn & grey . 1·25 65
1209 **277** 20 c. red, black and grey (air) 25 15
1210 – 45 c. red, blue & black . 40 15
1211 – 90 c. brown, blk & red . 95 15
1212 – 1 p. blue, black & brn . 60 25
1213 – 1 p. 20 multicoloured . 1·25 25
1214 – 1 p. 40 brown, black and blue . . . . 1·90 40
1215 – 2 p. yellow, black & brn . 1·25 40
1216 – 3 p. black, yellow & brn . 1·90 60
1217 – 5 p. black, blue & grn . 3·00 85
1218 – 10 p. multicoloured . . . 5·00 1·75
1219 – 20 p. orange, black and grey 11·00 6·00
BIRDS—HORIZ: 2 c. Rufous-bellied thrush 45 c. Diademed tanager; 50 c. Rufous hornero; 1 p. (1207), Chalk-browed mockingbird; 1 p. (1212), Common cowbird; 1 p. 20, Great kiskadee; 2 p. (1208), Rufous-collared sparrow; 2 p. (1215), Yellow cardinal; 3 p. Hooded siskin; 5 p. Sayaca tanager; 10 p. Blue and yellow tanager; 20 p. Scarlet-headed blackbird. VERT: 90 c. Vermilion flycatcher; 1 p. 40, Fork-tailed flycatcher.
Nos. 1208, 1210, 1212 and 1215 have no frame; Nos. 1206 and 1214 have a thin frame line; the others are as Type **277**.

278 D. A. Larranaga

1963. 85th Death Anniv of Damaso Antonio Larranaga (founder of National Library).
1220 **278** 20 c. sepia and turquoise . 10 10
1221 40 c. sepia and drab . . . 10 10

279 U.P.A.E. Emblem

1963. 50th Anniv of Postal Union of the Americas and Spain.
1222 **279** 20 c. blue & black (postage) 10 10
1223 45 c. green & black (air) . 10 10
1224 90 c. red and black . . . 20 15

280 Campaign Emblem  **281** Anchors

1963. Freedom from Hunger.
1225 **280** 10 c. yell & grn (postage) 10 10
1226 20 c. yellow and brown . 10 10
1227 90 c. yellow & red (air) . 20 15
1228 1 p. 40 yellow & violet . 25 20

1963. World Voyage of "Alferez Campora".
1229 **281** 10 c. vio & orge (postage) 10 10
1230 20 c. grey and red 10 10
1231 – 90 c. green & orge (air) . 20 10
1232 – 1 p. 40 blue and yellow . 30 25
DESIGN: 90 c., 1 p. 40, Sailing ship "Alferez Campora".

282 Large Intestine Congress Emblem

1963. 1st Uruguayan Proctological Congress, Punta del Este.
1233 **282** 10 c. red, black & green . 10 10
1234 20 c. red, black & ochre . 10 10

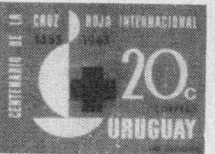

283 Centenary Emblem

1964. Red Cross Centenary.
1235 **283** 20 c. red and blue 10 10
1236 40 c. red and grey 15 10

284 L. A. de Herrera

1964. 5th Death Anniv of Luis A. de Herrera (statesman).
1237 **284** 20 c. black, green & blue 10 10
1238 40 c. black, lt blue and blue 10 10
1239 80 c. black, yell & blue . 15 10
1240 1 p. black, lilac & blue . 15 10
1241 2 p. black, slate & blue . 25 20

285 Pres. De Gaulle

1964. Air. Visit of President of France. Multicoloured.
1242 1 p. 50 Type **285** 40 15
1243 2 p. 40 Flags of France and Uruguay 50 40

286 Reliefs from Abu Simbel

1964. Nubian Monuments Preservation. Multicoloured.
1244 20 c. Type **286** (postage) . . 10 10
1245 1 p. 30 Sphinx, Sebua (air) . 30 15
1246 2 p. Rameses II, Abu Simbel 65 30
Nos. 1245/6 are vert.

292 Arms **288** Pres. Kennedy

1965. Air.
1261 **292** 20 p. multicoloured . . . 1·25 70
1248 – 50 p. blue, yell & grey . 3·75 3·00
DESIGN—HORIZ (38×27 mm) 50 p. National flag.

1965. Pres. Kennedy Commemoration. Frame and laurel in gold.
1249 **288** 20 c. blk & grn (postage) 10 10
1250 40 c. black and brown . 10 10
1251 1 p. 50 blk & lilac (air) . 20 10
1252 2 p. 40 black and blue . 30 15

289 "Tete-beche" Pair of Uruguayan 8 c. Stamps of 1864

290 6 c. "Arms-type" of 1964

1965. 1st River Plate Stamp Exn, Montevideo. (a) Postage. T **289**.
1253 40 c. green and black 10 10

(b) Air. As T **290** showing Arms-type stamps of 1864 (values in brackets).
1254 1 p. black and blue (12 c.) . 10 10
1255 1 p. black & orange (T **290**) . 10 10
1256 1 p. black and green (8 c.) . 10 10
1257 1 p. black and bistre (10 c.) . 10 10
1258 1 p. black and red (6 c.) . . 10 10
Nos. 1254/8 were issued together in sheets of 10 (5×2), each design arranged in a vertical pair with "URUGUAY" either at top or bottom.

291 B. Nardone

1965. 1st Death Anniv of Benito Nardone (statesman).
1259 **291** 20 c. black and green . . 10 10
1260 – 40 c. black and green . . 10 10
DESIGN—VERT: 40 c. Portrait as Type **291**, but Nardone with microphone.

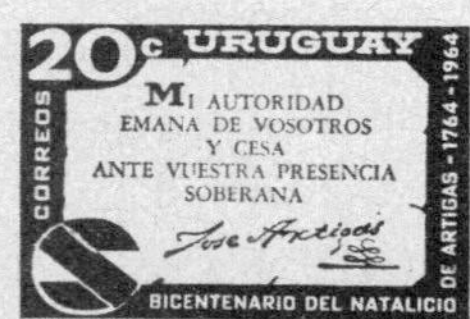

293 Part of Artigas' Speech before the 1813 Congress

1965. Birth Bicent (1964) of Gen. Jose Artigas.
1262 **293** 20 c. red, blue and yellow (postage) 10 10
1263 – 40 c. olive, black & blue . 10 10
1264 – 80 c. multicoloured . . . 10 10
1265 – 1 p. multicoloured (air) . 10 10
1266 – 1 p. 50 multicoloured . . 15 15
1267 **293** 2 p. 40 multicoloured . . 25 20
DESIGNS—HORIZ: 40 c. Bust of Artigas; 80 c. Artigas and his army flag; 1 p. 50, Bust, flag and exodus of his followers to Argentina. VERT: 1 p. Artigas' statue.

295 Football

1965. Olympic Games, Tokyo (1964).
1269 **295** 20 c. orange, black and green (postage) 10 10
1270 – 40 c. olive, black & brown 10 10
1271 – 80 c. red, black & drab . 10 10
1272 – 1 p. green, black & blue . 10 10
1273 – 1 p. grey, blk & red (air) 10 10
1274 – 1 p. 50 blue, black & grn 15 15
1275 – 2 p. blue, black and red . 15 15
1276 – 2 p. 40 orange, blk & bl . 20 15
1277 – 3 p. yellow, black & lilac 25 20
1278 – 20 p. pink, blue & indigo 70 50
DESIGNS: 40 c. Basketball; 80 c. Cycling; 1 p. (No. 1272) Swimming; 1 p. (No. 1273) Boxing; 1 p. 50, Running; 2 p. Fencing; 2 p. 40, Sculling; 3 p. Pistol-shooting; 20 p. Olympic "Rings".

1965. Surch with Caduceus and value.
1280 **178** 10 c. on 7 c. blue 10 10

1966. 50th Anniv of Uruguay Architects' Assn. Surch **CINCUENTENARIO Sociedad Arquitectos del Uruguay** and value.
1281 **261** 4 c. on 5 c. + 10 c. green and orange 10 10

298 I.T.U. Emblem and Satellite

1966. Air. Centenary of I.T.U.
1282 **298** 1 p. deep bl, red & blue . 15 10

299 Sir Winston Churchill

1966. Churchill Commemoration.
1283 **299** 40 c. brown, red and blue (postage) 10 10
1284 – 2 p. brn, red & gold (air) 20 10
DESIGN—VERT: 2 p. Churchill—full-face portrait and signed quotation.

300 Arms and View of Rio de Janeiro

1966. 400th Anniv. of Rio de Janeiro.
1285 **300** 40 c. grn & brn (postage) 10 10
1286 80 c. red & brown (air) . 10 10

301 I.C.Y. Emblem

1966. Air. I.C.Y.
1287 **301** 1 p. black and green . . 15 10

302 Army Engineer

304 Pres. Shazar

1966. 50th Anniv of Army Engineers.
1288 **302** 20 c. multicoloured . . 15 10

1966. Air. Visit of President of Israel.
1291 **304** 7 p. multicoloured . . . 40 30

305 Crested Screamer
306 Jules Rimet Cup, Ball and Globe

1966. Air.
1292 **305** 100 p. multicoloured . . 4·50 2·50

1966. Air. World Cup Football Championships.
1293 **306** 10 p. yellow and violet . 50 30

307 Hereford Bull
308 L. Batlle Berres (1947–51 and 1955–56)

1966. Air. Cattle-breeding.
1294 **307** 4 p. brown, chest & sepia 15 10
1295 – 6 p. black, grn & turq . 25 10
1296 – 10 p. mauve, grn & turq 35 20
1297 – 15 p. black, red & orge . 30 30
1298 – 20 p. brown, yell & grey 50 40
1299 – 30 p. brown & yellow . 75 55
1300 – 50 p. brown, grey & grn 1·25 85
DESIGNS (Cattle breeds): 6 p. Dutch; 10 p. Shorthorn; 15 p. Aberdeen Angus; 20 p. Norman; 30 p. Jersey; 50 p. Charolais.

1966. Former Uruguayan Presidents.
1301 **308** 20 c. black and red . . . 10 10
1302 – 20 c. black and blue . . 10 10
1303 – 20 c. brown and blue . . 10 10
PRESIDENTS: No. 1302, Daniel Fernandez Crespo (1963–64); 1303, Dr. Washington Beltran (1965–66).

309 Gutenberg Press

310 Capt. Boiso Lanza

1966. 50th Anniv of State Printing Works.
1304 **309** 20 c. sepia, green & brn 10 10

1966. Air. Honouring Boiso Lanza (pioneer military aviator).
1305 **310** 25 c. black, bl & ultram 75 55

311 Fireman
313 General J. A. Lavalleja

1966. 50th Anniv of Firemen's Corps.
1306 **311** 20 c. black and red . . . 25 15

1966. 2nd River Plate Stamp Exn, Montevideo. (a) Postage. No. 1253 optd **Segunda Muestra y Jornadas Rioplatenses**, etc.
1307 **187** 40 c. green and black . . 10 10

(b) Air. Nos. 1254/8 optd **CENTENARIO DEL SELLO ESCUDITO RESELLADO**, etc.
1308 1 p. blue 10 10
1309 1 p. orange 10 10
1310 1 p. green 10 10
1311 1 p. bistre 10 10
1312 1 p. red 10 10
Nos. 1308/12 commemorate the centenary of Uruguay's first surcharged stamps.

1966. Heroes of War of Independence.
1313 **313** 20 c. brown, red & blue . 10 10
1314 – 20 c. blue, black & grey . 10 10
1315 – 20 c. black and blue . . . 10 10
DESIGNS—VERT: No. 1314, Gen. L. Gomez. HORIZ: 1315, Gen. A. Saravia on horseback.

1966. Air. 40th Anniv of Uruguayan Philatelic Club. No. 1036 surch **40 ANIVERSARIO Club Filatelico del Uruguay $ 1.00 aereo.**
1316 1 p. on 12 p. sepia and blue . 10 10

315 Dante

316 Sunflower

1966. Air. 700th Birth Anniv (1965) of Dante (writer).
1317 **315** 50 c. blown and sepia . . 10 10

1967. 20th Anniv of Young Farmers' Movement.
1318 **316** 40 c. sepia, yellow & brn . 10 10

317 Planetarium

1967. 10th Anniv of Montevideo Planetarium.
1319 **317** 40 c. blk & mve (postage) 15 10
1320 – 5 p. black and blue (air) . 35 15
DESIGN: 5 p. Planetarium projector.

318 Pres. Makarios
319 Dr. Schweitzer

1967. Air. Visit of President of Cyprus.
1321 **318** 6 p. 60 black & mauve . 20 15

1967. Air. Schweitzer Commemoration.
1322 **319** 6 p. multicoloured . . . 20 15

320 Corriedale Ram

322 Church, San Carlos

321 Uruguayan Flag and Globe

1967. Air. Uruguayan Sheep-breeding.
1323 **320** 3 p. black, bistre & red . 10 10
1324 – 4 p. black, bistre & grn . 15 10
1325 – 5 p. black, bistre & blue 20 10
1326 – 10 p. black, bis & yell . 35 30
DESIGNS (sheep breeds): 4 p. "Ideal"; 5 p. Romney Marsh; 10 p. Australian merino.

1967. Air. Heads of State Meeting, Punta del Este.
1327 **321** 10 p. gold, blue & black 25 20

1967. Bicentenary of San Carlos.
1328 **322** 40 c. black, red & blue . 10 10

323 E. Acevedo (lawyer and statesman)

325 Ansina

324 "Numeral" Stamps of 1866

1967. Eduardo Acevedo Commemoration.
1329 **323** 20 c. brown and green . 10 10
1330 40 c. green and orange . 10 10

1967. Air. Centenary of "Numeral" Stamps of 1866.
1331 **324** 3 p. blue, green & blk . 20 10
1332 – 6 p. ochre, red & black . 35 15
DESIGN: 6 p. As T **324**, but depicting 15 c. and 20 c. stamps of 1866.

1967. Air. Honouring Ansina (servant of Gen. Artigas).
1334 **325** 2 p. red, blue and black . 10 10

326 Douglas DC-4 over Runway
327 Making Basket

1967. Air. 30th Anniv of PLUNA Airline.
1335 **326** 10 p. multicoloured . . . 35 25

1967. Air. World Basketball Championships, Montevideo. Multicoloured.
1336 5 p. Type **327** 20 10
1337 5 p. Running 20 10
1338 5 p. Holding 20 10
1339 5 p. Pivot 20 10
1340 5 p. Dribbling 20 10

1967. Air. Nos. 1210 and 1223 surch with new value in figures only.
1343 – 5 p. 90 on 45 c. red, blue and black 45 15
1344 **279** 5 p. 90 on 45 c. green and black 20 15

330 "Don Quixote and Sancho Panza" (after Denry Torres)

1967. Air. 420th Birth Anniv of Cervantes (writer).
1345 **330** 8 p. brown and bistre . . 25 15

331 Arms of Carmelo

332 J. E. Rodo

1967. 150th Anniv of Founding of Carmelo.
1346 **331** 40 c. deep blue, ochre and blue 10 10

1967. 50th Death Anniv of Jose E. Rodo (writer). Multicoloured.
1347 1 p. Type **332** 10 10
1348 2 p. Portrait and sculpture . 10 10
The 2 p. is horiz.

333 S. Rodriguez (founder), Steam Locomotive and Diesel Railcar

334 Child and Map of Americas

1967. Centenary of 1st National Railway in Uruguay.
1349 **333** 2 p. brown and ochre . . 30 10

1967. 40th Anniv of Inter-American Children's Institute.
1350 **334** 1 p. red and violet . . . 15 10

1967. No. 1033 surch **1.00 PESO** and Caduceus.
1351 1 p. on 7 c. green & brown . 10 10

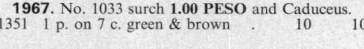

336 Primitive Club

337 Level Crossing and Traffic Sign

1967. Air. Archaeological Discoveries. Each black and grey.
1352 15 p. Type **336** 10 10
1353 20 p. Lance-head 20 10
1354 30 p. Axe-head 45 15
1355 50 p. Sculptured "bird of El Polonio" 60 25
1356 75 p. Cooking pot 60 40
1357 100 p. Sculptured "bird" of Balizas (horiz) 85 35
1358 150 p. Bolas . . . . 1·10 40
1359 200 p. Arrow-heads . . . . . 1·50 85

1967. Air. Pan American Highways Congress.
1360 **337** 4 p. black, yellow & red . 10 10

338 Lions Emblem and Map

339 Boy Scout

1967. Air. 50th Anniv of Lions International.
1361 **338** 5 p. violet, yellow & grn . 15 10

1968. Air. Lord Baden-Powell Commemoration.
1362 **339** 9 p. brown & orange . . 15 10

340 Cocoi Heron

341 Sun, Transport and U.N. Emblem

1968. Birds.
1363 – 1 p. brown and buff . . 20 10
1364 **340** 2 p. black and green . . 20 10
1365 – 3 p. purple, blk & orge . 25 10
1366 – 4 p. black and brown . 50 20
1367 – 4 p. black and orange . 50 20
1368 – 5 p. black, yell & brn . 60 30
1369 – 10 p. violet and black . 1·10 30
BIRDS—VERT: 1 p. Great horned owl; 4 p. (No. 1367), Black-tailed stilt. HORIZ: 3 p. Brown-hooded gull; 4 p. (No. 1366), White-faced whistling duck; 5 p. Wattled jacana; 10 p. Snowy egret.

1968. Air. International Tourist Year (1967).
1370 **341** 10 p. multicoloured . . 40 15

342 Presidents of Uruguay and Brazil, and Concord Bridge

343 Footballer

1968. Opening of Concord Bridge between Uruguay and Brazil.
1371 **342** 6 p. brown 15 10

1968. Penarol Club's Victory in Intercontinental Soccer Championships.
1372 **343** 1 p. black and lemon . . 15 10

344 St. John Bosco

1968. 75th Anniv of "Don Bosco Workshops".
1373 **344** 2 p. black and brown . 10 10

345 Octopus

1968. Air. Uruguayan Marine Fauna.
1374 **345** 15 p. black, blue and turquoise 30 15
1375 – 20 p. brown, blue & grn 25 15
1376 – 25 p. multicoloured . . 30 20
1377 – 30 p. black, green & blue 35 25
1378 – 50 p. salmon, blue and green 95 40
DESIGNS—HORIZ: 20 p. Mackerel; 25 p. "Dorado". VERT: 30 p. "Surubi"; 50 p. Squid.

346 Sailors' Monument, Montevideo

1968. 150th Anniv of Uruguayan Navy.
1379 **346** 2 p. black and green (postage) 10 10
1380 – 6 p. black and green . . 10 10
1381 – 12 p. black and blue . . 35 15
1382 – 4 p. blk, red & bl (air) . 10 10
1383 – 6 p. multicoloured . . . 10 10
1384 – 10 p. red, yellow & blue 15 10
1385 – 20 p. black and blue . . 65 15
DESIGNS—HORIZ: 4 p. Tailplane (Naval Air Force); 6 p. (No. 1383), Naval Arms; 12 p. Screw gunboat "Suarez"; 20 p. Artigas's privateer "Isabel". VERT: 6 p. (No. 1380), Buoy and lighthouse; 10 p. Mast-head and signal flags.

347 President Gestido

1968. 1st Death Anniv of President Oscar D. Gestido.
1386 **347** 6 p. brown, red & blue . 10 10

348 Sculling

1969. Air. Olympic Games, Mexico.
1387 **348** 30 p. black, brown & bl 30 20
1388 – 50 p. black, brown & yell 45 30
1389 – 100 p. black, brn & grn . 75 50
DESIGNS: 50 p. Running; 100 p. Football.

349 Cogwheel, Ear of Wheat and Two Heads

1969. 25th Anniv of Uruguay Trades University.
1390 **349** 2 p. black and red 10 10

350 Cycling

1969. World Cycling Championships, Montevideo (1968).
1391 **350** 6 p. blue, orange and green (postage) 20 10
1392 – 20 p. multicoloured (air) . 30 15
DESIGN—VERT: 20 p. Cyclist and globe.

351 EFIMEX "Stamp" on Easel

1969. Air. "EFIMEX" Stamp Exhibition, Mexico City (1968).
1393 **351** 20 p. red, green & blue . 20 15

353 Gymnasts and Emblem

354 Presi. Baltasar Brum

1969. 75th Anniv of "L'Avenir" Gymnastics Club.
1395 **353** 6 p. black and red 15 10

1969. 36th Death Anniv of Baltasar Brum (President, 1919–23).
1396 **354** 6 p. black and red 15 10

356 Sun and Fair Emblem (Actual size 72 × 23 mm)

1969. 2nd World Industrial Fair, Montevideo.
1399 **356** 2 p. multicoloured . . . 15 10

357 Emblem, Quill and Book

358 Modern Diesel Locomotive

1969. Air. 10th Latin-American Notaries' Congress, Montevideo.
1400 **357** 30 p. black, orge & grn . 35 25

1969. Centenary of Uruguayan Railways.
1401 **358** 6 p. black, red & blue . . 30 25
1402 – 6 p. black, red & blue . . 30 25
DESIGN: No. 1402 Early locomotive and diesel train.

360 Automobile Club Badge

362 I.L.O. Emblem

361 Belloni and "Combat" (monument). (Actual size 72 × 23 mm)

1969. Air. 50th Anniv of Uruguay Automobile Club.
1404 **360** 10 p. blue and red . . . 15 10

1969. 4th Death Anniv of Jose Belloni (sculptor).
1405 **361** 6 p. grn, black & gold . . 10 10

1969. Air. 50th Anniv of I.L.O.
1406 **362** 30 p. turquoise & black . 30 20

363 Training Centre Emblem

364 Exhibition Emblem

1969. 25th Anniv (1967) of Reserve Officers' Training Centre.
1407 **363** 1 p. lemon and blue . . 10 10
1408 – 2 p. brown and blue . . 15 10
DESIGN: 2 p. Reservist in uniform and civilian dress.

1969. Air. "ABUEXPO 69" Philatelic Exhibition, Sao Paulo, Brazil.
1409 **364** 20 p. yellow, blue & grn 25 10

365 Rotary Emblem and Hemispheres

366 Dr. Morquio and Child

1969. Air. South American Regional Rotary Conference, and 50th Anniv of Rotary Club, Montevideo.
1410 **365** 20 p. gold, ultram & blue 40 10

1969. Air. Birth Cent (1967) of Dr. Luis Morquio (pediatrician).
1411 **366** 20 p. brown and red . . 20 10

1969. Air. New Year. No. 1345 surch **FELIZ ANO 1970** and value.
1412 **330** 6 p. on 8 p. brown & bis 10 10

368 Pres. Tomas Berreta

369 Mahatma Gandhi

1969. 22nd Death Anniv of Dr. Tomas Berreta (President, 1947).
1413 **368** 6 p. red and black . . . 15 10

1970. Air. Birth Cent (1969) of Mahatma Gandhi.
1414 **369** 100 p. brown, ochre & blue 85 85

370 Teju Lizard

371 Dr. E. C. Ciganda

1970. Air. Fauna.
1415 – 20 p. black, grn & pur . 45 15
1416 **370** 30 p. black, grn & yell . 40 20
1417 – 50 p. black, brn & yell . 40 35
1418 – 100 p. brown, bistre and orange 60 55
1419 – 150 p. brown & green . 95 80
1420 – 200 p. black, brn & red . 1·25 1·25
1421 – 250 p. black, bl & grey . 1·50 1·50
DESIGNS—VERT: 20 p. Greater rhea. HORIZ: 50 p. Capybara; 100 p. Mulita armadillo; 150 p. Puma; 200 p. Coypu; 250 p. South American fur seal.

1970. Air. Birth Centenary of Evaristo C. Ciganda (pioneer of teachers' pensions law).
1422 **371** 6 p. brown and green . . 10 10

372 Garibaldi **373** Bank Emblem

1970. Air. Centenary of Garibaldi's Participation in Defence of Uruguay against Brazil and Argentina.
1423 **372** 20 p. mauve and pink . . 15 10

1970. 11th Inter-American Development Bank Governors' Meeting, Punta del Este.
1424 **373** 10 p. blue and gold . . . 15 10

374 Stylised Tree **375** Footballer and Emblem

1970. 2nd National Forestry Exhibition.
1425 **374** 2 p. black, green & red . 10 10

1970. Air. World Cup Football Championships, Mexico.
1426 **375** 50 p. multicoloured . . . 55 30

376 Artigas' House, Sauce **377** "U.N."

1970. 120th Death Anniv of Artigas.
1427 **376** 15 p. black, blue & red . 15 10

1970. Air. 25th Anniv of United Nations.
1428 **377** 32 p. blue, gold and light blue 25 15

378 Sun, Sea and Map

1970. Tourist Publicity.
1429 **378** 5 p. blue 10 10

379 Eisenhower and U.S. Flag

1970. Air. 1st Death Anniv of Dwight D. Eisenhower (American soldier and statesman).
1430 **379** 30 p. blue, red and grey . 30 15

380 First Man on the Moon

1970. Air. 1st Anniv of Moon Landing from "Apollo 11".
1431 **380** 200 p. multicoloured . . 1·50 1·50

381 Mt. Fuji

1970. "EXPO 70" World Fair, Osaka, Japan. Each with EXPO emblem and arms of Uruguay.
1432 **381** 25 p. blue, green & yell . 25 15
1433 – 25 p. blue, orange & grn 25 15
1434 – 25 p. blue, yellow & vio 25 15
1435 – 25 p. blue, violet & orge 25 15
DESIGNS: No. 1433, Geishas; 1434, Tower of the Sun; 1435, Youth totem.

382 Flag of 1825

1970. Air. 145th Anniv of Revolt of the "Immortal 33" under Levalleja.
1436 **382** 500 p. black, red & blue 3·50 3·50

383 Rheumatology Congress Emblem **384** Street Scene

1970. Air. 5th Pan-American Rheumatology Congress, Punta del Este.
1437 **383** 30 p. deep blue, blue and yellow 30 15

1970. 290th Anniv of Colonia del Sacramento (1st European settlement in Uruguay).
1439 **384** 5 p. multicoloured . . . 10 10

385 "Mother and Son" (statue, E. Prati) **386** Flags of Member Countries

1970. "Homage to Mothers".
1440 **385** 10 p. black and green . 15 10

1970. Air. 10th Anniv of Founding of Latin-American Association for Free Trade by the Montevideo Treaty.
1441 **386** 22 p. multicoloured . . 30 15

387 "Stamp" Emblem **389** Dr. Alfonso Espinola

388 "Playing Ring-o-Roses" (Ana Gaye)

1970. "URUEXPO 70" Stamp Exn, Montevideo.
1442 **387** 15 p. violet, blue & brn . 15 10

1970. International Education Year. Children's Drawings. Multicoloured.
1443 10 p. Type **388** 20 15
1444 10 p. "Two Girls" (Andrea Burcatovsky) (vert) 20 15
1445 10 p. "Boy at Desk" (Humberto Abel Garcia) (vert) . . . 20 15
1446 10 p. "Spaceman" (Aquiles Vaxelaire) 20 15

1971. 125th Birth Anniv (1970) of Dr. Alfonso Espinola (physician and philanthropist).
1447 **389** 5 p. black and orange . . 15 10

391 "Stamps" and Poster (Actual size 71 × 23 mm)

1971. "EFU 71" Stamp Exn, Montevideo.
1449 **391** 15 p. multicoloured . . . 20 10

392 5 c. Coin of 1840 (obverse) **393** Dr. Domingo Arena (from caricature by A. Sifredi)

1971. Numismatics Day.
1450 **392** 25 p. black, brown & bl . 40 30
1451 – 25 p. black, brown & bl . 40 30
DESIGN: No. 1451, Reverse of coin showing "Sun" emblem.

1971. Birth Centenary (1970) of Arena (lawyer and statesman).
1452 **393** 5 p. lake 10 10

394 Opening Bars of Anthem **395** Dr. Jose Arias

1971. National Anthem Commemoration.
1453 **394** 15 p. black, blue & gold . 40 25

1971. 1st Death Anniv of Dr Jose Arias (statesman).
1454 **395** 5 p. brown 15 10

396 "Yellow Fever" (J. M. Blanes)

1971. Air. 70th Death Anniv of Juan Blanes (artist).
1455 **396** 50 p. multicoloured . . . 30 30

397 Eduardo Fabini

1971. 21st Death Anniv of Eduardo Fabini (composer).
1456 **397** 5 p. black and red 40 10

398 "Two Races"

1971. Air. Racial Equality Year.
1457 **398** 27 p. black, pink & gold 30 15

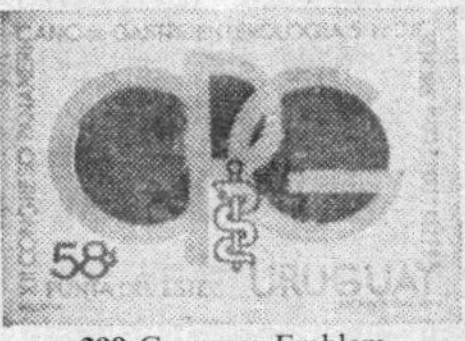

399 Congress Emblem

1971. Air. 12th Pan-American Gastro-enterological Congress, Punta del Este.
1458 **399** 58 p. orange, blk & grn . 55 35

400 J. E. Rodo and U.P.A.E. Emblem

1971. Birth Centenary of Jose E. Rodo (writer and first delegate to U.P.A.E).
1459 **400** 15 p. black and blue . . 20 15

401 Old Water-cart and Tap

1971. Centenary of Montevideo's Water Supply.
1460 **401** 5 p. multicoloured . . . 15 10

402 Sheep and Roll of Cloth

1971. Wool Production.
1461 **402** 5 p. green, grey & lt grn 10 10
1462 – 15 p. grey, violet & blue 20 10
DESIGN: 15 p. Sheep, and loading bales of cloth.

403 Dr. Jose Elorza and Sheep

1971. 12th Death Anniv of Dr. Jose Elorza (sheep-breeder).
1463 **403** 5 p. black, green & bl . . 15 10

404 Creole Horse

1971. Uruguayan Horse-breeding.
1464 **404** 5 p. black, blue and orge 20 10

405 Bull, Sheep and Ears of Corn

1971. Cent of Uruguayan Rural Association.
1465 **405** 20 p. multicoloured . . . 30 15

406 Police Emblem

1971. Honouring Police Heroes.
1466 **406** 10 p. blue, black & grey . 25 10
1467 – 20 p. multicoloured . . . 45 15
DESIGN: 20 p. Policeman and flag.

407 1896 10 Peso Banknote (obverse)

1971. 75th Anniv of Uruguayan State Bank.
1468 **407** 25 p. green, blk & gold . 30 25
1469 – 25 p. green, blk & gold . 30 25
DESIGN: No. 1469 Reverse of banknote showing rural scene.

408 Labourer and Arms

1971. 150th Anniv of Town of Durazno.
1470 **408** 20 p. multicoloured . . . 25 10

409 Shield and Laurel
(Actual size 72 × 24½ mm)

1971. Uruguay's Victory in Liberators' Cup Football Championships.
1471 **409** 10 p. gold, red and blue . 20 10

411 Voter and Ballot-box

1971. General Election.
1473 **411** 10 p. black and blue . . 10 10
1474 – 20 p. black and blue . . 25 15
DESIGN—HORIZ: 20 p. Voters in line.

412 C.I.M.E. Emblem and Globe

1971. Air. 20th Anniv of Inter-Governmental Committee for European Migration (C.I.M.E.).
1475 **412** 30 p. multicoloured . . . 35 25

413 Exhibition Emblem and Map of Uruguay
414 Juan Lindolfo Cuestas (1897–1903)

1971. "EXPO LITORAL" Industrial Exhibition, Paysandu.
1476 **413** 20 p. purple and blue . 35 15

1971. Uruguayan Presidents. Each brown and blue.
1477 10 p. Type **414** 10 10
1478 10 p. J. Herrara y Obes (1890–94) 10 10
1479 10 p. Claudio Williman (1907–11) 10 10
1480 10 p. Jose Serrato (1923–27) 10 10
1481 10 p. Andres Martinez Trueba (1951–55) 10 10

415 Llama Emblem
417 Olympic Symbols

1971. Air. "EXFILIMA" Stamp Exn, Lima, Peru.
1482 **415** 37 p. multicoloured . . 35 30

1972. Air. Olympic Games, Munich (1st issue).
1484 **417** 50 p. black, red & yellow 20 10
1485 – 100 p. multicoloured . . 40 30
1486 – 500 p. grey, red & blue . 1·10 1·10
DESIGNS: 100 p. Athlete and torch; 500 p. Discus-thrower.
See also Nos. 1493/4.

418 Chemical Jar
419 Bartolome Hidalgo

1972. Air. 50th Anniv of Discovery of Insulin.
1487 **418** 27 p. multicoloured . . 20 10

1972. 150th Death Anniv (1973) of Bartolome Hidalgo (Gaucho poet).
1488 **419** 5 p. black, red & brown 20 10

420 "Flagship"
421 "Face" on Beethoven Score

1972. Air. American Stamp Day.
1489 **420** 37 p. multicoloured . . 25 15

1972. 12th Eastern Uruguay Choral Festival.
1491 **421** 20 p. black, green & pur 25 10

422 Dove supporting Wounded Bird (after Maria Mullin)
424 Columbus Monument, Colon

423 Footballer and 1928 Gold Medal

1972. Dionisio Diaz (9 year-old hero) Commemoration.
1492 **422** 10 p. multicoloured . . . 15 10

1972. Air. Olympic Games, Munich. Mult.
1493 100 p. Type **423** 40 30
1494 300 p. Olympic flag (vert) . . 70 75

1972. Cent of Colon (suburb of Montevideo).
1495 **424** 20 p. black, blue & red . 10 10

1972. Uruguay's Victory in Intercontinental Football Cup Championships. No. 1471 surch **COPA INTER CONTINENTAL 1971**, football cup and **50**.
1496 **409** 50 p. on 10 p. gold, red and blue 35 30

426 Sapling and Spade
428 U.N.C.T.A.D. Emblem

427 Cross of Remembrance

1972. Tree Planting Campaign.
1497 **426** 20 p. black, myrtle & grn 15 10

1972. Air. 2nd Death Anniv of Dan Mitrione (U.S. police instructor assassinated by terrorists in Uruguay).
1498 **427** 37 p. violet and gold . . 15 10

1972. Air. 3rd United Nations Conference on Trade and Development (U.N.C.T.A.D.), Santiago, Chile.
1499 **428** 30 p. multicoloured . . . 15 10

429 Brazilian "Bull's-Eye" Stamp of 1843

1972. Air. "EXFILBRA 72" Stamp Exhibition, Rio de Janeiro.
1500 **429** 50 p. multicoloured . . . 20 10

430 Compass Rose and Map of South America
431 "Birds' Nests in Tree"

1972. Air. Campaign for Extension of Territorial Waters to 200 Mile Limit.
1501 **430** 37 p. multicoloured . . . 15 10

1972. National Building Project for Communal Dwellings.
1502 **431** 10 p. multicoloured . . . 10 10

432 Amethyst

1972. Uruguayan Mineralogy. Rocks and Gems.
1503 **432** 5 p. multicoloured . . . 15 10
1504 – 9 p. multicoloured . . . 20 10
1505 – 15 p. green, brown & blk 35 15
DESIGNS: 9 p. Agate; 15 p. Chalcedony.

433 "The Three Holy Kings" (R. Barradas)

1972 Air. Christmas.
1506 **433** 20 p. multicoloured . . . 20 15

435 Infantry Uniform of 1830
436 Red Cross over Map

1972. Military Uniforms. Multicoloured.
1509 10 p. Type **435** 15 10
1510 20 p. Artigas cavalry regiment uniform 30 15

1972. 75th Anniv of Uruguayan Red Cross.
1511 **436** 30 p. multicoloured . . . 30 10

438 Open Book
439 General Jose Artigas

1972. 25th Anniv of Full Civil Rights for Uruguayan Women.
1513 **438** 10 p. gold, blue & lt blue 10 10

1972.
1514 **439** 5 p. yellow 10 10
1515 10 p. brown 10 10
1516 15 p. green 10 10
1517 20 p. lilac 10 10
1518 30 p. blue 20 10
1519 40 p. orange 20 10
1520 50 p. red 15 10
1521 75 p. green 25 15
1522 100 p. green 30 15
1523 150 p. brown 15 25
1524 200 p. blue 25 30
1525 250 p. violet 30 35
1526 500 p. grey 60 75
1527 1000 p. blue . . . . . . 1·10 1·10

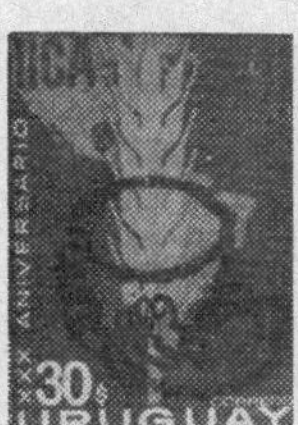

440 Cup and Ear of Wheat on Map
441 E. Fernandez and J. P. Varela (founders)

1973. 30th Anniv of Inter-american Institute for Agricultural Sciences.
1531 **440** 30 p. black, yell & red . 15 10

1973. Centenary (1968) of Friends of Popular Education Society.
1532 **441** 10 p. black, green & brn 10 10

442 Columbus and Map

1973. American Tourist Year.
1533 **442** 50 p. purple 20 15

443 Carlos Ramirez

1973. Eminent Uruguayan Jurists. Each black, brown and bistre.
1534 10 p. Type **443** 10 10
1535 10 p. Justino Jimenez de Arechaga 10 10
1536 10 p. Juan Ramirez 10 10
1537 10 p. Justino E. Jimenez de Arechaga 10 10

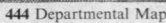

444 Departmental Map

447 Priest, Indians and Soriano Church

446 Francisco de los Santos and Artigas

1973. Uruguayan Departments.
1538 **444** 20 p. multicoloured . . . 30 15
See also No. 1844.

1973. Francisco de los Santos (courier) Commem.
1540 **446** 20 p. emerald, black and green 20 10

1973. Villa Santo Domingo Soriano (first Spanish Settlement in Uruguay) Commemoration.
1541 **447** 20 p. black, violet & blue 15 10

448 "SOYP" and Fish

1973. Inauguration of 1st Fishery Station of Oceanographic and Fishery Service (S.O.Y.P.).
1542 **448** 100 p. multicoloured . . 35 15

449 Flower and Sun

451 Luis A. de Herrera

1973. Italian Chamber of Commerce in Uruguay.
1543 **449** 100 p. multicoloured . . 25 15

1973. Birth Centenary of Luis A. de Herrera (conservative leader).
1545 **451** 50 p. brown, sepia & grey 20 10

452 Festival Emblem

1973. "Festival of Nations", Montevideo.
1546 **452** 50 p. multicoloured . . . 20 10

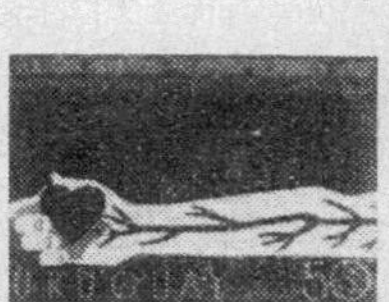

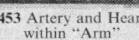

453 Artery and Heart within "Arm"

454 "Madonna (R. Barradas)

1973. 3rd Pan-American Voluntary Blood Donors' Congress.
1547 **453** 50 p. black, red & pink . 20 10

1973. Christmas.
1548 **454** 50 p. black, yell & grn . 15 10

455 Copernicus
(actual size 72 x 23 mm)

1973. 500th Birth Anniv of Nicholas Copernicus (astronomer).
1549 **455** 50 p. multicoloured . . 15 10

456 Hands in Prayer, and Andes

457 O.E.A. Emblem and Map

1973. Rescue of Survivors from Andes Air-crash.
1550 **456** 50 p. green, blue & blk . 15 10
1551 – 75 p. multicoloured . . 20 15
DESIGN: 75 p. Flower with broken stem, and Christ of the Andes statue.

1974. 25th Anniv of Organization of American States (O.E.A.).
1552 **457** 250 p. multicoloured . . 40 50

458 Games' Emblem

1974. 1st International Scout Games, Montevideo.
1553 **458** 250 p. multicoloured . . 40 50

459 Hector Sedes and Motor-car

462 "The Three Gauchos"

1974. Hector Sedes (motor-racing driver) Commemoration.
1554 **459** 50 p. brown, black & grn 15 10

1974. Centenary of Antonio Lussich's Poem "Los Tres Gauchos".
1560 **462** 50 p. multicoloured . . 15 10

463 Rifle, Target and Swiss Flag

1974. Centenary of Swiss Rifle Club, Nueva Helvecia.
1561 **463** 100 p. multicoloured . . 30 15

464 Compass Rose on Map

465 Emblem and Stadium

1974. Military Geographical Service.
1562 **464** 50 p. black, emerald & grn 15 10

1974. World Cup Football Championships, Munich. Multicoloured.
1563 50 p. Type **465** 15 10
1564 75 p. Emblem and footballer (horiz) 20 15
1565 1000 p. Emblem and footballer (different) (horiz) . . . . . 11·00 7·50

466 Old and New School Buildings, and Founders

1974. Centenary of Osimani-Llerena Technical School, Salto.
1566 **466** 75 p. black and brown . . 20 15

467 Carlos Gardel

468 "Ball and Net"

1974. 39th Death Anniv of Carlos Gardel (singer).
1567 **467** 100 p. multicoloured . . 35 15

1974. 1st Women's World Cup Volleyball Championships.
1568 **468** 200 p. purple, yell & blk . 45 25

469 "Protect Your Heart"

470 Vidal and Statue

1974. Uruguayan "Pro Cardias" Heart Foundation.
1569 **469** 75 p. red, yellow & green 20 15

1974. Bicentenary (1973) of Founding of San Jose by Eusebio Vidal.
1570 **470** 75 p. blue and light blue . 15 10
No. 1570 is incorrectly inscr "1873–1973".

471 Artigas Monument

472 W.P.Y. Emblem

1974. Dedication of Artigas Monument, Buenos Aires, Argentine Republic.
1571 **471** 75 p. multicoloured . . . 15 10

1974. Air. World Population Year.
1572 **472** 500 p. red, black and grey 55 70

473 Montevideo Citadel Gateway and Emblem

474 Mast and Radio Waves

1974. Air. Events of 1974.
1573 **473** 200 p. multicoloured . . 55 40
1574 300 p. multicoloured . . 70 60

1974. 50th Anniv of Broadcasting in Uruguay.
1575 **474** 100 p. multicoloured . . 20 10

475 "Sheet of Stamps" and "URUEXPO 74" Emblem

1974. 10th Anniv of "Circulo Filatelico" Journal of Montevideo Stamp Club.
1576 **475** 100 p. blue, red & blk . 20 10

476 Envelopes and Emblem

1974. Centenary of Universal Postal Union.
1577 **476** 100 p. multicoloured . . 10 10
1578 – 200 p. black, gold & lilac 20 10
DESIGN—VERT: 200 p. U.P.U. emblem on envelope, laurel and globe.

477 Mexican Official Stamp of 1884 and Arms

1974. Air. "EXFILMEX" Interamerican Philatelic Exhibition, Mexico City.
1579 **477** 200 p. multicoloured . . 20 10

478 Artigas Monument

1974. Dedication of Artigas Monument, Ventura Hill, Minas.
1580 **478** 100 p. multicoloured . . 10 10

479 Early Map of Montevideo

1974. 250th Anniv of Montevideo's Fortifications.
1581 **479** 300 p. brown, red & grn 50 20

480 Naval Vessel in Dry-dock and Badge

1974. Centenary of Montevideo Naval Arsenal.
1582 **480** 200 p. multicoloured . . 40 30

481 Balloon

1974. History of Aviation. Multicoloured.

1583 100 p. Type **481** 25 15
1584 100 p. Farman H.F.III biplanes 25 15
1585 100 p. Castaibert's Morane Saulnier Type I 25 15
1586 100 p. Bleriot XI 25 15
1587 150 p. Military and civil pilots' "wings" 35 20
1588 150 p. Nieuport 17 biplane . 35 20
1589 150 p. Breguet Bidon biplane 35 20
1590 150 p. Caproni Ca 5 biplane . 35 20

482 Pan de Azucar Mountain and Cross

1974. Centenary of Pan de Azucar (town).

1591 **356** 150 p. multicoloured . . 25 20

483 Adoration of the Kings

1974. Christmas. Multicoloured.

1592 100 p. Type **483** (postage) . . 10 10
1593 150 p. Kings with Gifts . . . 15 10
1594 240 p. Kings following the Star (air) 20 15

484 Rowers, Fireworks and Nike of Samothrace Statue

1975. Centenary of Montevideo Rowing Club.

1596 **484** 150 p. multicoloured . . 15 10

485 "Treaty of Purificacion, 1817" (J. Zorrilla de San Martin)

1975. Recognition of Artigas Government by Great Britain in Treaty of Purificacion, 1817.

1597 **485** 100 p. multicoloured . . 10 10

486 Spanish 6 c. Stamp of 1850, and National Colours

1975. Air. "ESPANA 75" Stamp Exhibition, Madrid.

1598 **486** 400 p. multicoloured . . 35 20

487 Rose

1975. Bicentenary of Rosario.

1600 **487** 150 p. multicoloured . . 20 10

488 "The Oath of the Thirty-three" (J. M. Blanes)

1975. 150th Anniv of 1825 Liberation Movement.

1601 **488** 150 p. multicoloured . . 20 10

489 Michelangelo's Motif for Floor of Capitol, Rome

1975. Air. 500th Birth Anniv of Michelangelo.

1602 **489** 1 p. multicoloured . . . 60 50

490 Columbus and Caravel

492 Emblem of Montreal Olympics (1976) and World Cup Football Championship Finals (Argentina, 1978)

491 Sun and 4 p. 50 Air Stamp of 1929

1975. Spanish–American Stamp Day.

1603 **490** 1 p. multicoloured . . . 1·00 60

1975. Air. Uruguayan Stamp Day.

1604 **491** 1 p. blk, yell and grey . 2·00 70

1975. Air. "Exfilmo-Espamer 75" Stamp Exhibition, Montevideo. Multicoloured.

1605 1 p. Type **492** 40 60
1606 1 p. "Independence" (U.S. and Uruguayan flags) 40 60
1607 1 p. Emblems of U.P.U. and Spanish–American Postal Union 40 60

493 Jose Artigas and J. Francisco de Larrobla

1975. 150th Anniv of Independence.

1608 **493** 50 c. multicoloured . . 40 35

494 Col. L. Oliveira and Fortress

1975. 150th Anniv of Capture of Santa Teresa Fortress.

1609 **494** 10 c. multicoloured . . . 20 10

495 Battle Scene from Painting by D. Hequet

1975. 150th Anniv of Battle of Rincon.

1610 **495** 15 c. black and gold . . . 20 10

See also Nos. 1620/1.

496 Florencio Sanchez

1975. Birth Cent of Florencio Sanchez (dramatist). Multicoloured.

1611 20 c. Type **496** 30 10
1612 20 c. "En Familia" 30 10
1613 20 c. "Barranca Abajo" . . . 30 10
1614 20 c. "Mi Hijo el Doctor" . . 30 10
1615 20 c. "Camilita" 30 10

Nos. 1612/15 show scenes from plays and are horiz 38 × 26 mm.

1975. Surch in revalued currency.

1616 **439** 10 c. on 20 p. lilac . . . 10 10
1617 15 c. on 40 p. orange . . 10 10
1618 50 c. on 50 p. red 35 20
1619 1 p. on 1000 p. blue . . . 40 40

1975. 150th Anniv of Artigas' Exile and Battle of Sarandi. As T **495**. Multicoloured.

1620 15 c. Artigas' house, Ibiray (Paraguay) 20 10
1621 25 c. Battle scene 40 20

498 Maria E. Vaz Ferreira (poetess)

1975. Birth Centenaries.

1622 **498** 15 c. black, yellow & pur 20 10
1623 – 15 c. black, orge & pur . 20 10

DESIGN: No. 1623, Julio Herrera y Reissig (poet).

499 "Virgin and Child" (stained-glass window)

500 Colonel L. Latorre

1975. Christmas. Multicoloured.

1624 20 c. Type **499** 35 15
1625 30 c. "Virgin and Child" (different) 50 30
1626 60 c. "Fireworks" (horiz) . . 40 40

1975. 59th Death Anniv of Col. Lorenzo Latorre (President, 1876–80).

1627 **500** 15 c. multicoloured . . . 15 10

501 "Ariel", Stars and Book

1976. 75th Anniv of Publication of "Ariel" by Jose Rodo.

1628 **501** 15 c. multicoloured . . . 15 10

502 "Oncidium bifolium" (orchid)

1976. Air. Multicoloured.

1629 50 c. Type **502** 45 20
1630 50 c. Geoffroy's cat 45 20

503 "Water Sports" **504** Telephone Receiver

1976. 23rd South American Swimming, Diving and Water-polo Championships, Maldonado.

1631 **503** 30 c. multicoloured . . . 20 15

1976. Telephone Centenary.

1632 **504** 83 c. multicoloured . . . 30 25

505 Dornier Wal Flying Boat "Plus Ultra"

506 Dornier Wal Flying Boat and Airliner rising around Hour-glass

1976. 50th Anniv of "Plus Ultra" Spain–South America Flight.

1633 **505** 63 c. multicoloured . . . 60 25

1976. 50th Anniv of Lufthansa Airline.

1634 **506** 83 c. multicoloured . . . 55 35

507 Louis Braille and word "Braille"

1976. 150th Anniv of Braille System for the Blind.

1635 **507** 60 c. black and brown . 40 25

508 Signing of Declaration of Independence

1976. Bicentenary of American Revolution.

1636 **508** 1 p. 50 multicoloured . . 1·25 95

509 "Candombe" (Pedro Figari)

1976. 150th Anniv of Abolition of Slavery.

1637 **509** 30 c. multicoloured . . . 15 10

510 Rivera Monument **511** Chilian Lapwing

1976. Dedication of General Rivera Monument.

1638 **510** 5 p. on 10 p. mult . . . 2·00 95

1976.

1639 **511** 1 c. violet 30 10

1640 – 5 c. green 10 10

1641 – 15 c. red 15 10

1642 – 20 c. black 10 10

1643 – 30 c. grey 15 10

1644 – 45 c. blue 10 10

1645 – 50 c. green 25 10

1646 – 1 p. brown 45 10

1646b – 1 p. yellow 25 10

1647 – 1 p. 75 green 35 10

1648 – 1 p. 95 grey 40 10

1649 – 2 p. green 90 70

1649a – 2 p. mauve 35 10

1650 – 2 p. 65 violet 45 15

1651 – 5 p. blue . . . . 2·00 2·00

1651a – 10 p. brown . . . . . . 3·25 2·00

DESIGNS—VERT: 5 c. Passion flower; 15 c. National flower; 20 c. Indian lance-head; 30 c. Indian statue; 45 c., 1 p. (No. 1646b), 1 p. 75, 1 p. 95, 2 p. (both), 2 p. 65, 5, 10 p., Artigas; 1 p. (No. 1646), "At Dawn" (J. M. Blanes). HORIZ: 50 c. "Branding Cattle" (J. M. Blanes).

513 Office Building and Reverse of First Uruguayan Coin of 1840

1976. 150th Anniv of State Accounting Office.

1652 **513** 30 c. black, brown & bl . 25 15

514 Hand-pump within Flames **516** Championship Emblem

515 Uruguay 60 c. Stamp of 1856 and "Commemorative Postmark"

1976. Centenary of Fire Service.

1653 **514** 20 c. black and red . . . 15 10

1976. 50th Anniv of Uruguay Philatelic Club.

1654 **515** 30 c. red, blue & bistre . 15 10

1976. 5th World Universities' Football Championships, Montevideo.

1655 **516** 83 c. multicoloured . . . 40 20

517 Human Eye and Spectrum

1976. Prevention of Blindness.

1656 **517** 20 c. multicoloured . . 25 10

518 Map of Montevideo

1976. 250th Anniv of Montevideo. Multicoloured.

1657 30 c. Type **518** 15 10

1658 45 c. Montevideo panorama. 1842 . . . . 20 10

1659 70 c. First settlers, 1726 . . 35 15

1660 80 c. Montevideo coin (vert) 40 20

1661 1 p. 15 Montevideo's first arms (vert) 55 30

519 "VARIG" Emblem

1977. 50th Anniv of VARIG Airline.

1662 **519** 80 c. multicoloured . . 50 40

520 Artigas Mausoleum

1977. Mausoleum of General Jose Artigas.

1663 **520** 45 c. multicoloured . . 30 10

521 Arch on Map

1977. Cent of Salesian Education in Uruguay.

1664 **521** 45 c. multicoloured . . 30 10

522 Globe and Emblems **523** Children

1977. Air. 150th Anniv of Uruguayan Postal Services.

1665 **522** 8 p. multicoloured . . . 2·75 2·50

1977. 50th Anniv of Inter-American Children's Institute.

1667 **523** 45 c. multicoloured . . 30 10

524 "Windmills" **525** Sun on "Stamp" and Stripes of Uruguayan Flag

1977. Hispanidad Day.

1668 **524** 70 c. red, yellow & blk . 35 15

1977. Stamp Day.

1669 **525** 45 c. multicoloured . . 20 10

527 Globe and Aircraft

1977. 30th Anniv of International Civil Aviation Organization.

1670 **527** 45 c. mutlicoloured . . . 15 10

528 "The Holy Family"

1977. Christmas.

1671 **528** 45 c. multicoloured . . . 15 10

1672 – 70 c. red, yellow & blk . 20 10

DESIGN—HORIZ: (45 × 26 mm): 70 c. "Santa Claus".

529 Arms, Map and Products **530** Postman clearing Mail-box

1977. Rio Negro Department.

1673 **529** 45 c. multicoloured . . . 15 10

1977. 150th Anniv of National Mail Service. Multicoloured.

1674 50 c. Type **530** 15 10

1675 50 c. Loading mail-van . . . 15 10

1676 50 c. Post Office counter, Montevideo G.P.O. 15 10

1677 50 c. Post-boxes area 15 10

1678 50 c. Sorting mail 15 10

1679 50 c. Postal sorters 15 10

1680 50 c. Postmen sorting "walks" 15 10

1681 50 c. Postman on rounds . . 15 10

1682 50 c. Postmen on motor-scooters 15 10

1683 50 c. Postal counter, Carrasco Airport 15 10

531 Edison's First "Phonograph"

1977. Centenary of Sound Recording.

1684 **531** 50 c. purple and yellow . 15 10

532 "R" and Spectrum

1977. World Rheumatism Year.

1685 **532** 50 c. multicoloured . . . 15 10

533 Emblem, Diploma, Sword and Flag

1978. 50th Anniv of Military College.

1686 **533** 50 c. multicoloured . . . 15 10

534 Arms and Map **537** "Wandering Angels" (detail)

1978. Department of Artigas.

1687 **534** 45 c. multicoloured . . . 30 10

1978. Air. "Riccione" and "Europhil 78" Stamp Exhibitions, Italy and Urphila Stamp Exhibition, Uruguay. Optd **EUROPA 1978 ITALIA Riccione 78 urphila 78**.

1689 **522** 8 p. multicoloured . . . 3·00 2·50

1978. National Artists. Luis A. Solari. Multicoloured.

1690 1 p. 50 Type **537** 30 20

1691 1 p. 50 "Wandering Angels" (horiz 38 × 30 mm) 30 20

1692 1 p. 50 "Wandering Angels" (detail) 30 20

538 Bernardo O'Higgins

1978. Birth Bicentenary of Bernardo O'Higgins (national hero of Chile).

1693 **538** 1 p. multicoloured . . . 25 10

539 Telephone Dials and "Antel" Emblem

1978. Telephone Automatisation.

1694 **539** 50 c. multicoloured . . . 10 10

540 San Martin and Army of the Andes Monument (J. M. Ferrari) **541** Spanish Tiles

1978. Birth Bicentenary of General Jose de San Martin.

1695 **540** 1 p. multicoloured . . . 25 10

1978. Hispanidad.

1696 **541** 1 p. blue, yellow & blk . 25 10

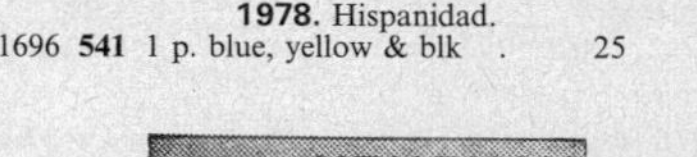

542 Corners of "Stamps"

1978. Stamp Day.

1697 **542** 50 c. multicoloured . . . 10 10

543 Boeing 727 in Flight **545** Flag Monument, Montevideo

544 Angel blowing Trumpet

1978. PLUNA Airline Inaugural Boeing 727 Flight.

1698 **543** 50 c. multicoloured . . . 15 10

1978. Christmas.

1699 **544** 50 c. green, orge & blk . 10 10

1700 1 p. blue, red and black . 20 10

1978. Homage to the National Flag.

1701 **545** 1 p. multicoloured . . . 25 10

546 Horacio Quiroga **547** Arms and Map of Paysandu

1978. Birth Centenary of Horacio Quiroga (playwright).

1702 **546** 1 p. black, yellow & red . 25 10

1979. Department of Paysandu.

1703 **547** 45 c. multicoloured . . . 10 10

548 Olympic Rings and Ciudadela

1979. Olympic Games, Moscow (1980) and Winter Olympics, Lake Placid (1980). Multicoloured.

1704 5 p. Type **548** 90 85

1705 7 p. Lake Placid emblem . . 1·10 1·25

See also Nos. 1728/9.

549 Arms and Map of Salto **550** Artilleryman, 1830

1979. Department of Salto.

1706 **549** 45 c. multicoloured . . . 10 10

1979. Uruguayan Military Uniforms. Mult.

1707 5 p. Type **550** 85 85

1708 5 p. Sapper, 1837 . . . . . . 85 85

551 Arms and Map of Maldonado **553** Centenary Symbol and Branch

552 Salto Grande Dam

1979. Department of Maldonado.

1709 **551** 45 c. multicoloured . . . 10 10

1979. Salto Grande Dam.

1710 **552** 2 p. multicoloured . . . 50 15

1979. Centenary of Crandon Uruguayan–American High School.

1711 **553** 1 p. blue and violet . . 20 10

554 Kites

1979. International Year of the Child (1st issue).

1712 **554** 2 p. multicoloured . . . 35 15

See also Nos. 1715, 1718 amd 1720.

555 Arms and Map of Cerro Largo

1979. Department of Cerro Largo.

1713 **555** 45 c. multicoloured . . 10 10

556 Arms and Map of Trienta y Tres **557** Cinderella

1979. Department of Trienta y Tres.

1714 **556** 50 c. multicoloured . . 10 10

1979. International Year of the Child (2nd issue).

1715 **557** 2 p. multicoloured . . . 35 20

558 National Coat of Arms

1979. 150th Anniv of First National Coat of Arms.

1716 **558** 8 p. multicoloured . . . 1·10 1·10

559 U.P.U. Emblem and Arrow

1979. 18th U.P.U. Congress, Rio de Janeiro.

1717 **559** 5 p. multicoloured . . . 85 50

560 "Chico Carlo" (Juana de Ibarbourou) **561** Drawing by J. M. Torres-Garcia

1979. International Year of the Child (3rd issue).

1718 **560** 1 p. multicoloured . . . 20 10

1979. 31st Death Anniv of Joaquin Torres-Garcia (artist).

1719 **561** 10 p. yellow and black . 1·40 1·25

562 Madonna and Child

1979. Christmas and International Year of the Child (4th issue).

1720 **562** 10 p. multicoloured . . . 1·40 1·25

563 Arms and Map of Durazno

1979. Department of Durazno.

1721 **563** 50 c. multicoloured . . . 15 10

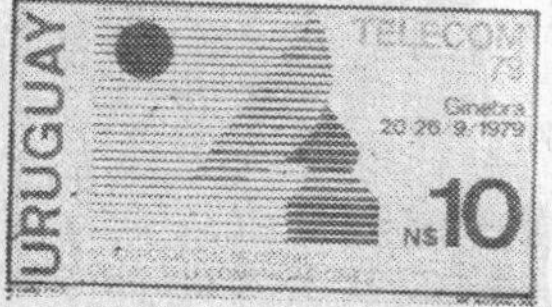

564 Dish Aerial and Sun

1979. 3rd World Telecommunications Exposition, Geneva.

1722 **564** 10 p. black, yell & lavender 95 80

565 Caravel

1979. Hispanidad Day.

1723 **565** 10 p. multicoloured . . . 1·75 85

566 10 c. Coin of 1877

1979. Centenary of 1st Silver Coinage. Multicoloured.

1724 **566** 10 c. silver, black & green 10 10

1725 – 20 c. silver, black & green 10 10

1726 – 50 c. silver, black & blue . 10 10

1727 – 1 p. silver, black & blue . 20 10

DESIGNS: 20 c. 1877 20 c. coin; 50 c. 1877 50 c. coin; 1 p. 1877 1 p. coin.

1980. Events. Multicoloured.

1728 3 p. Type **548** 60 25

1729 3 p. As No. 1705 . . . . . . 60 25

1730 5 p. Olympic rings 90 40

1731 5 p. "Uruguay 79" stamp exhibition emblem 90 40

1732 7 p. Chessboard and rook (23rd Chess Olympiad, Buenos Aires, 1978) . . . . . . 1·25 55

1733 7 p. Detail from Greek vase (Olympic Games) . . . . . 1·25 55

1734 10 p. Detail from Greek vase (different) . . . . 1·75 80

568 Thomas Edison and Lamp

1980. Centenary of Electric Light.

1736 **568** 2 p. multicoloured . . . 40 20

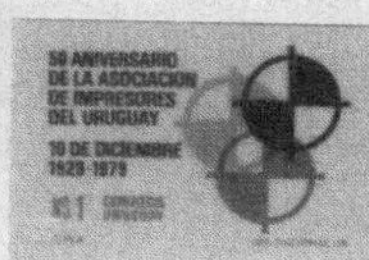

569 Arms of Colonia **571** Association Emblem

1980. Colonia.

1737 **569** 50 c. multicoloured . . . 15 10

1980. 50th Anniv of Uruguayan Printers' Association.

1739 **571** 1 p. yellow, mauve & bl . ·20 15

572 Geometric Design **573** Zorilla de San Martin and Page of "La Leyenda Patria"

1980. Stamp Day.

1740 **572** 1 p. multicoloured . . . 20 10

1980. "La Leyenda Patria".

1741 **573** 1 p. multicoloured . . . 20 10

574 Boeing 747-200C Cargo Airplane

1980. Inauguration of Lufthansa Cargo Container Service.

1742 **574** 2 p. multicoloured . . . 40 20

575 Conference Emblem and Flags

1980. 8th World Hereford Conference, Punta del Este, and Livestock Exhibition, Prado, Montevideo.

1743 **575** 2 p. multicoloured . . . 40 20

576 Lions Emblem and Map of South America

1980. 9th Latin-American Lions Forum.

1744 **576** 1 p. multicoloured . . . 20 10

579 Rotary Emblem and Globe **580** Hand stubbing out Cigarette

1980. 75th Anniv of Rotary International.

1747 **579** 5 p. multicoloured . . . 85 70

1980. World Health Day. Anti-smoking Campaign.

1748 **580** 1 p. pink, black and grn 20 10

581 Jose Artigas

582 Angel blowing Trumpet

1980.

1749 **581** 10 c. blue 10 10
1750 20 c. orange 10 10
1751 50 c. red 10 10
1752 60 c. yellow 10 10
1753 1 p. grey 15 15
1754 2 p. brown 35 15
1755 3 p. green 55 30
1756 4 p. blue 65 40
1757 5 p. green 30 10
1757a 6 p. orange 10 10
1758 7 p. purple 95 70
1759 10 p. blue 50 25
1760 12 p. black 20 10
1761 15 p. 50 green 25 15
1762 20 p. purple . . . . . . 1·00 85
1763 30 p. brown . . . . . . 1·25 1·25
1764 50 p. blue . . . . 2·00 2·00

1980. Christmas.
1765 **582** 2 p. multicoloured . . . 30 15

583 Title Page of Constitution

1980. 150th Anniv of Constitution.
1766 **583** 4 p. blue and gold . . . 70 35

584 Montevideo Football Stadium
585 Conquistador

1980. Gold Cup Football Championship, Montevideo.
1767 **584** 5 p. multicoloured . . . 50 35
1768 – 5 p. yellow, black & red . 50 35
1769 – 10 p. multicoloured . . 1·10 1·10
DESIGNS—As T **584**. No. 1768, Gold cup. 25 × 79 mm: No. 1769, Mascot and flags of participating countries.

1981. Hispanidad Day.
1771 **585** 2 p. multicoloured . . . 35 15

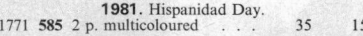

586 U.P.U. Emblem
587 Alexander von Humboldt

1981. Centenary of U.P.U. Membership.
1772 **586** 2 p. multicoloured . . . 35 15

1981. 122nd Death Anniv of Alexander von Humboldt (naturalist).
1773 **587** 2 p. multicoloured . . . 40 15

588 Trophy and Open Book

1981. International Education Exhibition and Congress, Montevideo.
1774 **588** 2 p. green, blk & lilac . 35 15

589 Flags and Trophy

590 Musical Notes over Map of the Americas

1981. Uruguayan Victory in Gold Cup Football Championship.
1775 **589** 2 p. multicoloured . . . 40 15
1776 5 p. multicoloured . . . 60 35

1981. 40th Anniv of Inter-american Institute of Musicology.
1777 **590** 2 p. multicoloured . . . 40 15

591 Boeing 707

1981. Inaugural Flight to Madrid of Pluna Airline.
1778 **591** 2 p. multicoloured . . . 40 15
1779 5 p. multicoloured . . . 60 40
1780 10 p. multicoloured . . 1·25 70
Nos 1778/80 are inscribed "BOEING 737".

592 Cavalryman of Gen. Manuel Oribe, 1843

1981. Army Day. Multicoloured.
1781 2 p. Type **592** 40 15
1782 2 p. Infantry of Montevideo, 1843 . . . . 40 15

593 Conference Emblem on Suitcase

1981. World Tourism Conference, Manila (1980).
1783 **593** 2 p. multicoloured . . . 35 15

594 Peace Dove and Atomic Emblem
595 Footballer

1981. 25th Anniv of National Atomic Energy Commission.
1784 **594** 2 p. multicoloured . . . 35 15

1981. Europe–South America Football Cup.
1785 **595** 2 p. multicoloured . . . 40 15

596 Arms and Map of Rocha
597 Carved Stone Tablets

1981. Department of Rocha.
1786 **596** 2 p. multicoloured . . . 40 15

1981. Salto Grande Archaeological Rescue Excavations.
1787 **597** 2 p. multicoloured . . . 40 15

598 Artigas Monument, Minas
599 A.N.C.A.P. Anniversary Emblem

1981. 10th Lavalleja Week.
1788 **598** 4 p. multicoloured . . . 70 35

1981. 50th Anniv of National Administration for Combustible Fuels, Alcohol and Portland Cement.
1789 **599** 2 p. multicoloured . . . 35 15

600 I.Y.D.P. Emblem

1981. International Year of Disabled Persons.
1790 **600** 2 p. deep blue, red and blue 35 15

601 Sun Disc

1981. Senior Level Meeting on Environmental Law, Montevideo.
1791 **601** 5 p. multicoloured . . . 60 35

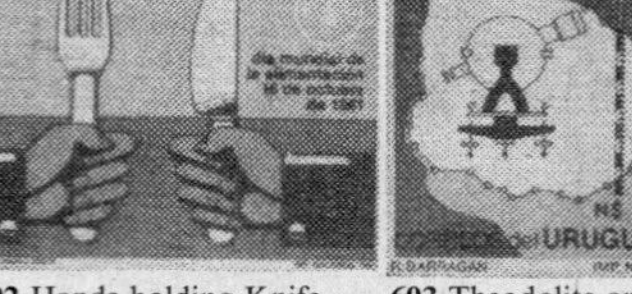

602 Hands holding Knife and Fork
603 Theodolite and Measuring Rod on Map of Uruguay

1981. World Food Day.
1792 **602** 2 p. multicoloured . . . 40 15

1981. 150th Anniv of Topographic Survey.
1793 **603** 2 p. multicoloured . . . 40 15

604 Bank of Uruguay

1981. 85th Anniv of Bank of Uruguay.
1794 **604** 2 p. multicoloured . . . 40 15

605 Palmar Dam

1981. Palmar Central Hydro-electric Project.
1795 **605** 2 p. multicoloured . . . 40 15

606 Father Christmas
607 Joaquin Suarez

1981. Christmas.
1796 **606** 2 p. multicoloured . . . 40 15

1982. Birth Bicentenary of Joaquin Suarez.
1797 **607** 5 p. multicoloured . . . 60 35

608 Lockheed Super Constellation and Route Map

1982. 25th Anniv of 1st Germany–Uruguay Lufthansa Flight. Multicoloured.
1798 3 p. Type **608** 50 30
1799 7 p. Boeing 747-200 and route map 90 70

609 American Air Forces Co-operation Emblem
610 Private, Florida Battalion, 1865

1982. 22nd American Air Forces' Commanders Conference.
1800 **609** 10 p. multicoloured . . . 1·25 80

1982. Army Day. Multicoloured.
1801 3 p. Type **610** 55 20
1802 3 p. Captain of Artillery, 1872 55 20

611 Face and Satellite in Outer Space
612 Pinocchio

1982. Peaceful Uses of Outer Space Conference, Vienna.
1803 **611** 3 p. multicoloured . . . 75 40

1982. Centenary of Publication of Carlo Collodi's "Pinocchio".
1804 **612** 2 p. multicoloured . . . 40 15

613 Arms of Flores

1982. Department of Flores.
1805 **613** 2 p. multicoloured . . . 40 15

614 Zorrilla de San Martin

1982. 50th Death Anniv of Juan Zorrilla de San Martin (writer).
1806 **614** 3 p. multicoloured . . . 60 35

615 Cadet Schooner "Capitan Miranda" (after J. Rivera)

1982. 165th Anniv of Navy.
1807 **615** 3 p. multicoloured . . . 75 20

616 Figures reading Book **617** Scales of Justice

1982. National Literacy Campaign.
1808 **616** 3 p. blue, deep blue and yellow 25 10

1982. Stamp Day.
1809 **617** 3 p. green 30 15
1810 – 3 p. red 30 15
DESIGN: No. 1810, Volcano.

618 Star, Family and Symbols of Economic Progress

1982. Christmas.
1811 **618** 3 p. multicoloured . . . 30 15

619 Fabini

1983. Birth Centenary of Edouardo Fabini (composer).
1812 **619** 3 p. deep brown & brown 30 15

620 2nd Cavalry Regiment, 1885 **621** "Santa Maria" on Globe

1983. Army Day. Multicoloured.
1813 3 p. Type **620** 40 15
1814 3 p. Military College, 1885 . 40 15

1983. Visit of King and Queen of Spain. Multicoloured.
1815 3 p. Type **621** . . . . 1·50 30
1816 7 p. Royal couple and Uruguayan and Spanish flags (44 × 31 mm) 80 40

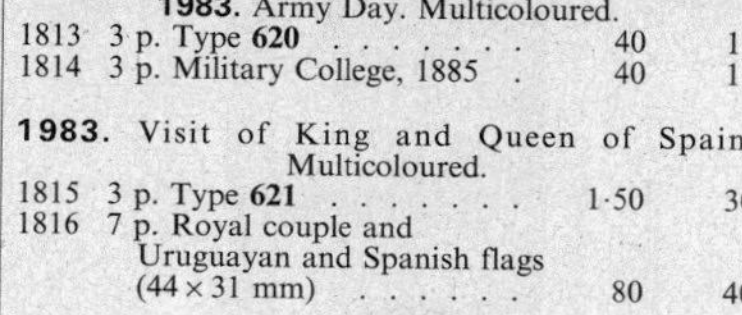

622 Headquarters Building **623** Exhibition Emblem

1983. Inauguration of Postal Union of the Americas and Spain H.Q., Montevideo.
1817 **622** 3 p. black, blue & brn . 30 15

1983. "Brasiliana 83" International Stamp Exhibition, Rio de Janeiro.
1818 **623** 3 p. multicoloured . . . 30 15

624 Space Shuttle "Columbia"

1983. 1st Flight of Space Shuttle "Columbia".
1819 **624** 7 p. multicoloured . . . 65 30

625 "Delin 1900" Car

1983. 1st Imported Car.
1820 **625** 3 p. blue and black . . 30 15

626 Goethe and Scene from "Faust"

1983. 150th Death Anniv (1982) of Johann Wolfgang von Goethe (writer).
1821 **626** 7 p. blue and black . . 65 30

627 "Moonlit Landscape" **628** Statue of Lavelleja

1983. 6th Death Anniv of Jose Cuneo (artist).
1822 **627** 3 p. multicoloured . . . 30 15

1983. Bicentenary of Minas City.
1823 **628** 3 p. multicoloured . . . 30 15

629 W.C.Y. Emblem

1983. World Communications Year.
1824 **629** 3 p. multicoloured . . . 20 10

630 Garibaldi

1983. Death Centenary (1982) of Guiseppe Garibaldi (Italian revolutionary).
1825 **630** 7 p. multicoloured . . . 50 30

631 "Graf Zeppelin"

1983. Zeppelin Flight over Montevideo (1934).
1826 **631** 7 p. black, blue & mauve 90 35

632 Footballers, World Cup and Italian Team Badge

1983. Italy's Victory in World Cup Football Championship (1982).
1827 **632** 7 p. multicoloured . . . 65 30

633 Virgin, Child and Star

1983. Christmas.
1828 **633** 4 p. 50 multicoloured . . 25 10

634 "50" on Telephone Dial

1984. 50th Anniv of Automatic Telephone Dialling.
1829 **634** 4 p. 50 multicoloured . . 25 10

635 Leandro Gomez **636** Emblem, Map, Flag and Tanker

1984. General Leandro Gomez Commemoration.
1830 **635** 4 p. 50 blue, light blue and black 25 10

1984. 25th Anniv (1983) of International Maritime Organization.
1831 **636** 4 p. 50 multicoloured . . 50 15

637 Flags and Emblem **638** Map of Uruguay and Bank Emblem

1984. American Women's Day.
1832 **637** 4 p. 50 multicoloured . . 25 10

1984. 25th Annual Meeting of Governors of International Development Bank, Punta del Este.
1833 **638** 10 p. blue, gold & black 55 20

639 Simon Bolivar

1984. Birth Bicentenary (1983) of Simon Bolivar.
1834 **639** 4 p. 50 lt brown & brown 25 10

640 Club Emblem and Radio Waves **641** Monument

1984. 50th Anniv (1983) of Uruguay Radio Club.
1835 **640** 7 p. multicoloured . . . 40 20

1984. 1930 World Cup Football Championship Monument.
1836 **641** 4 p. 50 multicoloured . . 25 10

642 National Emblem within "200"

1984. Bicentenary (1983) of San Jose de Mayo.
1837 **642** 4 p. 50 multicoloured . . 25 10

643 Emblem

1984. 50th Anniv of Tourist Organization.
1838 **643** 4 p. 50 gold, violet and blue 25 10

644 Artillery Uniform, 1895 **645** Artigas on Horseback

1984. Army Day. Multicoloured.
1839 4 p. 50 Type **644** 25 15
1840 4 p. 50 2nd Battalion Cazadores uniform, 1894 . . . . . . 25 15

1984.
1841 **645** 4 p. 50 black and blue . 25 15
1842 8 p. 50 brown and blue . 45 25

646 Trophy

1984. Penarol Athletic Club. Winners of European–South American Football Cup, 1982.
1843 **646** 4 p. 50 black, yellow and deep yellow 25 10

1984. Uruguayan Departments.
1844 **444** 4 p. 50 multicoloured 25 10

647 Child holding Flower and "50 ANOS"

1984. 50th Anniv of Children's Council.
1845 **647** 4 p. 50 multicoloured 25 10

648 Christmas Tree with Candles

649 Pelota Player and Flags

1984. Christmas.
1846 **648** 6 p. multicoloured 30 10

1985. 1st Junior Pelota World Championship.
1847 **649** 4 p. 50 multicoloured 25 10

650 Bruno Mauricio de Zabala

652 Carlos Gardel

651 Emblems of Los Angeles and Sarajevo Games and Olympic Rings

1985. 300th Birth Anniv (1983) of Don Bruno Mauricio de Zabala (Governor of Buenos Aires and founder of Montevideo).
1848 **650** 4 p. 50 multicoloured 25 10

1985. 90th Anniv of International Olympic Committee.
1849 **651** 12 p. multicoloured 45 25

1985. 50th Death Anniv of Carlos Gardel (entertainer).
1850 **652** 6 p. grey, blue and brown 25 10

653 Emblem and Flags of Member States

1985. 25th Anniv of American Air Forces' Co-operation System.
1851 **653** 12 p. multicoloured 20 10

654 Icarus

1985. 40th Anniv of I.C.A.O.
1852 **654** 4 p. 50 deep blue, green and blue 10 10

655 Stylised Factory and "50"

656 Cross and Clasped Hands

1985. 50th Anniv of FUNSA Tyre Factory.
1853 **655** 6 p. multicoloured 10 10

1985. Centenary of Catholic Workers Circle.
1854 **656** 6 p. multicoloured 10 10

657 I.Y.Y. Emblem

659 Books forming "8"

658 Peace Dove and Sun

1985. International Youth Year.
1855 **657** 12 p. red and black 20 10

1985. "Return to Democracy".
1856 **658** 20 p. blue, yellow and violet 30 15

1985. 8th International Book Exhibition.
1857 **659** 20 p. multicoloured 30 15

660 Emblem

661 Map and Arms

1985. Centenary of Military School.
1858 **660** 10 p. multicoloured 20 10

1985. Centenary of Flores Department.
1859 **661** 6 p. multicoloured 10 10

662 Father Christmas

1985. Christmas.
1860 **662** 10 p. multicoloured 20 10
1861 22 p. multicoloured 35 20

663 Monument to Isabel the Catholic

1985. Hispanidad Day.
1862 **663** 12 p. black, red and brown 15 10

664 Emblem and Meeting Logo

1986. 3rd Inter-American Agriculture Co-operation Institute Meeting.
1863 **664** 12 p. yellow, red & black 20 10

665 Emblem and Flag

1986. World Post Day.
1864 **665** 15 p 50 multicoloured 25 10

666 Map and Symbolic House

1986. 6th Population and 4th Housing Census (1985).
1865 **666** 10 p. black, blue and yellow 20 10

667 Emblem

1986. 50th Anniv (1985) of Conaprole Milk and Cattle Co-operative.
1866 **667** 10 p. gold, blue and light blue 20 10

668 U.N. Emblem and Population Diagram

1986. 40th Anniv (1985) of U.N.O.
1867 **668** 20 p. multicoloured 30 15

669 Emblem **670** Manuel Oribe

1986. 50th Anniv (1985) of National Brokers and Auctioneers Association.
1868 **669** 10 p. black, deep blue and blue 15 10

1986. Liberation Heroes.
1869 **670** 1 p. green (postage) 10 10
1870 2 p. red 10 10
1871 A 3 p. blue 10 10
1872 5 p. blue 10 10
1872a **670** 5 p. blue 10 10
1873 7 p. brown 10 10
1874 B 10 p. mauve 10 10
1875 C 10 p. green 10 10
1875a **670** 10 p. green 10 10
1876 15 p. blue 10 10
1877 B 17 p. blue 15 10
1877a **670** 20 p. brown 15 10
1877b A 25 p. orange 10 10
1878 B 26 p. brown 10 10
1879 C 30 p. orange 20 15
1879a A 30 p. blue 10 10
1879b B 45 p. red 25 20
1880 C 50 p. ochre 30 20
1880a A 50 p. mauve 30 20
1881 C 60 p. grey 40 40
1881a A 60 p. orange 10 20
1881b B 60 p. mauve 10 10
1881c 75 p. red 10 10
1881d 90 p. red 10 10
1882 C 100 p. red 60 75
1882a 100 p. brown 30 30
1882b 150 p. green 35 35
1883 200 p. green 1·25 1·10
1883a 300 p. blue 60 60
1883b 500 p. red 1·25 1·25
1883c 1000 p. red 2·00 2·00

1884 B 22 p. violet (air) 15 10

DESIGNS: A, Lavalleja; B, Jose Fructuoso Rivera; C, Jose Gervasio Artigas.

671 Mosaic in National Colours

1986. Italian Chamber of Commerce in Uruguay.
1885 **671** 20 p. multicoloured 20 10

672 Armenian Flag and Monument

673 Emblem and Footballer

1986. 71st Anniv of Armenian Genocide.
1886 **672** 10 p. black, red & blue 10 10

1986. World Cup Football Championship, Mexico.
1887 **673** 20 p. multicoloured 20 15

674 Newspaper Page

675 Alan Garcia

1986. Centenary of "El Dia".
1888 **674** 10 p. gold, black & red 10 10

1986. Visit of President of Peru.
1889 **675** 20 p. brown, red & blue 15 15

676 Map, Gen. Sucre and Simon Bolivar

677 Jose Sarney

1986. Visit of Pres. Jaime Lusinchi of Venezuela.
1890 **676** 20 p. multicoloured 15 15

1986. Visit of President of Brazil.
1891 **677** 20 p. multicoloured 15 15

678 Michelini

679 Menorah and "50"

1986. 10th Death Anniv of Zelmar Michelini (senator).
1892 **678** 10 p. blue and red . . . 10 10

1986. 50th Anniv of B'nai B'rith in Uruguay.
1893 **679** 10 p. brown, gold & red . 10 10

680 Handshake across "GATT"

681 Dr. Raul Alfonsin

1986. General Agreement on Tariffs and Trade Assembly, Punta del Este.
1894 **680** 10 p. multicoloured . . . 10 10

1986. Visit of President of Argentina.
1895 **681** 20 p. orange, black & bl . 15 15

682 Fishes in Sea

1986. Quality Exports. Multicoloured.
1896 20 p. Type **682** 15 15
1897 20 p. Lambs 15 15

683 Flags and Dr. Blanco

684 Dr. Pertini

1986. Visit of Dr. Salvador Jorge Blanco, President of Dominican Republic.
1898 **683** 20 p. multicoloured . . . 15 15

1986. Visit of Dr. Sandro Pertini, President of Italy.
1899 **684** 20 p. yellow and green . 15 15

685 Douglas DC-10 and Douglas DC-3 Aircraft and Flags

1986. 40th Anniv of First Scheduled Spain–Uruguay Flight.
1900 **685** 20 p. multicoloured . . . 45 15

686 Statue of Sts. Philip and John and Montevideo Cathedral

1987. Hispanidad Day.
1901 **686** 10 p. red and black . . . 10 10

687 Emblem

688 Ruiz

1987. 50th Anniv (1986) of Juventus Catholic Cultural Organization.
1902 **687** 10 p. yellow, black and blue 10 10

1987. 10th Death Anniv (1986) of Hector Gutierrez Ruiz (Chamber of Deputies member).
1903 **688** 10 p. brown and red . . 10 10

689 Emblem

690 "Arrowhead" of Flying Doves

1987. International Science and Technology Symposium, Montevideo and Punta del Este (1986).
1904 **689** 20 p. multicoloured . . 15 15

1987. Visit of Pope John Paul II.
1905 **690** 50 p. orange and grey . 35 45

691 Dr. Arias and Emblem

692 "70" and Menorah

1987. Birth Centenary of Dr. Jose F. Arias (founder of Uruguay Trades University).
1906 **691** 10 p. multicoloured . . 10 10

1987. 70th Anniv of Uruguayan Jewish Community.
1907 **692** 10 p. blue, orange & blk 10 10

693 De Havilland Dragon Fly

1987. 50th Anniv (1986) of Pluna National Airline. Multicoloured.
1908 10 p. Type **693** 10 10
1909 20 p. Douglas DC-3 . . . . 15 10
1910 25 p. Vickers Viscount 810 . 15 15
1911 30 p. Boeing 707 . . . . . 20 15

694 Artigas Antarctic Base

1987.
1912 **694** 20 p. multicoloured . . 15 15

695 Sun, Symbolic House and "75"

1987. 75th Anniv of Uruguayan Mortgage Bank.
1913 **695** 26 p. multicoloured . . 20 15

696 Dairy Products

697 "Holy Family"

1987. Uruguayan Quality Exports. Multicoloured.
1914 51 p. Type **696** 35 20
1915 51 p. Map and cattle 35 20

1987. Christmas. Stained Glass Windows. Multicoloured.
1916 17 p. Type **697** 15 10
1917 66 p. "Angels" 45 55

698 Pres. Duarte

699 Airplane and Globe forming "60"

1988. Visit of Pres. Jose Napoleon Duarte of El Salvador.
1918 **698** 20 p. blue and yellow . . 15 15

1988. 60th Anniv (1987) of VARIG (airline).
1919 **699** 66 p. blue, yellow & blk . 45 50

700 Emblem and Globe

1988. International Peace Year (1986).
1920 **700** 10 p. multicoloured . . . 10 10

701 Flags and Beret

702 Farman "Shorthorn" within Airplane Wing

1988. 75th Anniv (1987) of Basque Immigration.
1921 **701** 66 p. multicoloured . . . 45 45

1988. 75th Anniv of Air Force.
1922 **702** 17 p. multicoloured . . . 20 10

703 Lantern and "75"

1988. 75th Anniv (1987) of UTE (hydro-electric dam programme).
1923 **703** 17 p. multicoloured . . . 15 10
1924 – 17 p. black, blue & grn . 15 10
1925 – 51 p. black and blue . . . 35 20
1926 – 51 p. black, blue & red . 35 20
1927 – 66 p. blue, black & yell . 45 25
DESIGNS: No. 1924, Baygorria Dam; 1925, Dr. Gabriel Terra Dam; 1926, Constitucion Dam; 1927, Map showing dam sites on River Negro.

704 Flag and Globe

1988. 75th Anniv (1986) of Postal Union of the Americas and Spain.
1928 **704** 66 p. multicoloured . . . 45 45

705 Menorah in "40"

1988. 40th Anniv of Israel.
1929 **705** 66 p. blue and black . . 45 45

706 Airmail Envelope and Postman

1988. "Post, Messenger of Peace".
1930 **706** 66 p. multicoloured . . . 45 45

707 Emblem on Map

1988. 60th Anniv of Inter-american Institute for the Child.
1931 **707** 30 p. lt green, grn & blk 20 15

708 Matos Rodriguez

1988. Gerardo H. Matos Rodriguez (composer) Commemoration.
1932 **708** 17 p. black and violet . . 15 10
1933 – 51 p. brown on lt brown 35 20
DESIGN: 51 p. Matos Rodriguez and score of "La Cumparsita".

709 Col. Pablo Banales (founder)

711 Citrus Fruits

710 Route Map and u Capitan Miranda"

1988. Centenary (1987) of Fire Service. Mult.
1934 17 p. Type **709** 15 10
1935 26 p. Fireman, 1900 . . . . 20 15
1936 34 p. Emblem (horiz) 20 15
1937 51 p. Merryweather fire engine, 1907 (horiz) 35 20
1938 66 p. 8-man hand pump, 1888 (horiz) 45 25
1939 100 p. Magirus mechanical ladder, 1921 (44 × 25 mm) . 70 40

1988. 1st World Voyage of "Capitan Miranda".
1940 **710** 30 p. multicoloured . . . 50 20

1988. Exports. Multicoloured.
1941 30 p. Type **711** 20 15
1942 45 p. Rice 35 20
1943 55 p. Shoes 40 20
1944 55 p. Clothes 40 20

712 "Toxodon platensis" (mammal bone) 713 Bird posting Letter

1988. 150th Anniv of National Natural History Museum, Montevideo.
1945 – 30 p. brown, yell & blk . . . 20 15
1946 712 90 p. brown, blue & blk . . 65 60
DESIGN: 30 p. "Usnea densirostra" (moss).

1988. Postal Officers' Day. Unissued stamp surch.
1947 713 30 p. on 10 p. + 5 p. yellow, black and blue 10 10

714 Abstract

1988. 150th Anniv (1986) of Battle of Carpinteria.
1948 714 30 p. multicoloured . . . 10 10

715 Virgin and Child 716 "Self-portrait" (Joaquin Torres Garcia)

1988. Christmas.
1949 715 115 p. multicoloured . . 55 55

1988. Uruguayan Painters. Multicoloured.
1950 115 p. Type 716 . . . . . . 50 50
1951 115 p. Poster for Pedro Figari exhibition, Montevideo . . 50 50
1952 115 p. "Squares and Rectangles LXXVIII" (Jose P. Costigliolo) 50 50
1953 115 p. "Manolita Pina, 1920" (Joaquin Torres Garcia) . . 50 50

717 "Santa Maria"

1989. Hispanidad Day.
1954 717 90 p. multicoloured . . . 40 40
1955 115 p. multicoloured . . . 50 50

718 Emblem

1989. Cent of Armenian Organization Hnchakian.
1956 718 210 p. blue, yellow & red . . 40 35

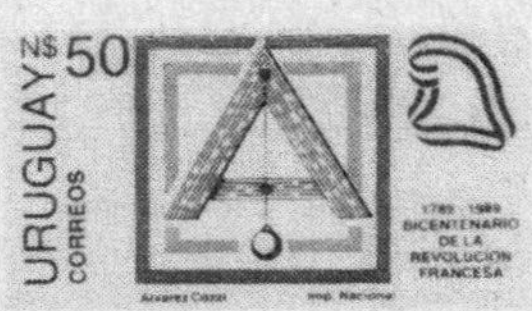

719 Plumb Line suspended on Frame

1989. Bicentenary of French Revolution. Each black, red and blue.
1957 50 p. Type 719 . . . . . . 10 10
1958 50 p. Tree of Liberty 10 10
1959 210 p. Eye in centre of sunburst . 40 35
1960 210 p. "Liberty", "Equality", "Fraternity" around phrygian cap 40 35

720 Map

1989. "Use the Post Code". Each black and red.
1961 50 p. Type 720 . . . . . . 10 10
1962 210 p. Map showing numbered zones (vert) 40 35

721 Map, Cow, Factory and Baby 722 "Tiradentes"

1989. 3rd Pan-American Milk Congress.
1963 721 170 p. dp blue & blue . . 30 25

1989. Birth Bicentenary of Joaquin Jose da Silver Xavier.
1964 722 170 p. multicoloured . . 30 25

723 Emblem and Flag

1989. Interparliamentary Union Centenary Conference, London.
1965 723 210 p. red, blue & black . . 40 35

724 F.A.O. Emblem, Map and Fruit Slices

1989. 8th Intergovernmental Group on Citrus Fruits Meeting.
1966 724 180 p. multicoloured . . 30 25

725 Flower, Hand and Emblem

1989. U.N. Decade for Disabled People. Mult.
1967 50 p. Type 725 . . . . . . 10 10
1968 210 p. Disabled people and emblem 40 35

726 Nacurutu Artefact 727 Virgin of the Thirty Three

1989. America. Pre-Columbian Culture.
1969 726 60 p. multicoloured . . . 10 10
1970 180 p. multicoloured . . . 30 25

1989. Christmas. Multicoloured.
1971 70 p. Type 727 . . . . 10 10
1972 210 p. "Adoration of the Animals" (Barradas) (horiz) . . 15 15

728 Old and Modern Buildings

1989. Bicentenary of Pando.
1973 728 60 p. multicoloured . . . 10 10

729 Hospital Building

1990. Bicentenary of Charity Hospital.
1974 729 60 p. flesh, black & brown . 10 10

730 Map and Arms of Soriano 731 Luisa Luisi

1990. Departments. Multicoloured.
1975 70 p. Type 730 . . . . 10 10
1976 70 p. Florida (vert) 10 10
1977 90 p. San Jose (vert) 10 10
1978 90 p. Canelones 10 10
1979 90 p. Lavalleja (vert) 10 10
1980 90 p. Rivera 10 10

1990. Writers. Multicoloured.
1981 60 p. Type 731 . . . . 10 10
1982 60 p. Javier de Viana 10 10
1983 75 p. J. Zorilla de San Martin . 10 10
1984 75 p. Dekmira Agustini . . . 10 10
1985 170 p. Julio Casal 45 45
1986 170 p. Alfonsina Storni . . . 45 45
1987 210 p. Juana de Ibarbourou . . 55 55
1988 210 p. Carlos Roxlo 55 55

732 Mercedes Church 733 Ear of Wheat and Tractor

1990. Bicentenary of Mercedes.
1989 732 70 p. multicoloured . . . 10 10

1990. 10th Anniv of International Agricultural Fund.
1990 733 210 p. multicoloured . . 55 55

734 Glass and Smashed Car

1990. Road Safety. Multicoloured.
1991 70 p. Type 734 . . . . 70 70
1992 70 p. Traffic waiting at red light 70 70
1993 70 p. Road signs 70 70
1994 70 p. Children crossing road at green light 70 70

735 Sculpture of Artigas 736 Woman

1990. Artigas Day.
1995 735 60 p. blue and red . . . 10 10

1990. International Women's Day.
1996 736 70 p. multicoloured . . . 10 10

737 Gonzalo Ramirez 738 Microphone and Radio Mast

1990. Centenary of 1st International Juridical Congress, Montevideo.
1997 737 60 p. black, yell & mve . 55 55
1998 – 60 p. black, blue & mve . 55 55
1999 – 60 p. multicoloured . . . 55 55
2000 – 60 p. multicoloured . . . 55 55
DESIGNS: No. 1998, Ildefonso Garcia; 1999, Flags and left half of 50th anniversary memorial; 2000, Flags and right half of memorial.

1990. The Media. Multicoloured.
2001 70 p. Type 738 . . . . 70 70
2002 70 p. Newpaper vendor . . . 70 70
2003 70 p. Television screen, camera and aerial 70 70
2004 70 p. Books and type 70 70

739 Burning Trees 741 "Nativity" (Juan B. Maino)

740 American Deer

1990. Fire Prevention.
2005 739 70 p. black, yell & red . 70 70

1990. America. The Natural World. Mult.
2006 120 p. Type 740 . . . . . . 10 10
2007 360 p. "Peltophorum dubium" (vert) 85 85

1990. Christmas.
2008 741 170 p. multicoloured . . 40 40
2009 830 p. multicoloured . . 2·00 2·00

742 Carlos Federico Saez

1990. Artists. Multicoloured.
2010 90 p. Type **742** 10 10
2011 90 p. Pedro Blanes Viale . . 10 10
2012 210 p. Edmundo Prati . . . 55 55
2013 210 p. Jose L. Zorrilla de San Martin 55 55

743 Mechanical Digger

1991. 75th Anniv of Army Engineers Division.
2014 **743** 170 p. multicoloured . . 40 40

744 Drum and Masks

1991. Carnival.
2015 **744** 170 p. multicoloured . . 40 40

745 Campaign Emblem

1991. Campaign against Aids.
2016 **745** 170 p. multicoloured . . 40 40
2017 830 p. multicoloured . . 2·00 2·00

746 Anniversary Emblem

1991. Centenary of Organization of American States.
2018 **746** 830 p. yellow, blue & blk 2·00 2·00

747 Textiles

1991. Uruguayan Quality Exports. Multicoloured.
2019 120 p. Type **747** 10 10
2020 120 p. Clothes (vert) . . . 10 10
2021 400 p. Semi-precious stones and granite 55 60

748 Flint Axe and Stone Monument

1991. Education. Multicoloured.
2022 120 p. Type **748** 10 10
2023 120 p. Wheel and pyramids . 10 10
2024 330 p. Printing press and diagram of planetary orbits 45 45
2025 330 p. Space probe and computer diagram 45 45

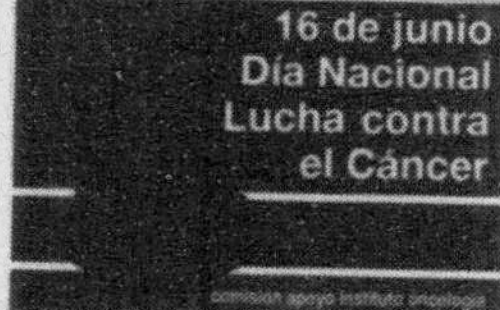

749 Sword piercing Crab

1991. Anti-Cancer Day.
2026 **749** 360 p. red and black . . 45 45

750 College Arms **751** College Building

1991. Centenary of Holy Family College.
2027 **750** 360 p. multicoloured . . 45 45

1991. Centenary of Immaculate Heart of Mary College.
2028 **751** 1370 p. multicoloured . 1·60 1·60

752 Emblem

1991. 7th Pan-American Maccabiah Games.
2029 **752** 1490 p. multicoloured . 1·75 1·75

753 World Map and Dornier Wal Flying Boat "Plus Ultra"

1991. "Espamer '91" Spain–Latin America Stamp Exhibition, Buenos Aires.
2030 **753** 1510 p. multicoloured . 2·00 2·00

754 "Oath of the Constitution" (P. Blanes Viale)

1991. 1830 Constitution.
2031 **754** 360 p. multicoloured . . 45 45

755 Gateway, Sacramento

756 "William Tell" (statue) and Flags

1991.
2032 **755** 360 p. brown & yellow . 45 45
2033 – 540 p. grey and blue . . 65 65
2034 **755** 600 p. brown, yell & blk 55 55
2035 – 825 p. grey, blue & blk . 75 75
2036 – 1510 p. brown & green . 2·00 2·00
2037 – 2500 p. brn, grn & blk . 2·00 2·00
DESIGNS: 540, 825 p. First locomotive, 1869; 1510, 2500 p. Horse-drawn tram.
For 800 p. as Type **755** see No. 2103.

1991. 700th Anniv of Swiss Confederation.
2038 **756** 1510 p. multicoloured . 2·50 2·50

757 Yacht

758 Emblem

1991. Whitbread Regatta.
2040 **757** 1510 p. multicoloured . . 1·75 1·75

1991. 50th Anniv of Uruguayan Society of Actors.
2041 **758** 450 p. black and red . . 50 50

759 Camera and Photograph

1991. 150th Anniv of First Photograph in Rio de la Plata.
2042 **759** 1370 p. multicoloured . . 1·50 1·50

760 Anniversary Emblem

1991. 25th Anniv of CREA (livestock organization).
2043 **760** 450 p. multicoloured . . 50 50

761 Margarita Xirgu

1991. 22nd Death Anniv of Margarita Xirgu (actress).
2044 **761** 360 p. brown, light brown and yellow 40 40

762 "General Rivera" (gunboat)

1991. Centre for Study of Naval and Maritime History. Multicoloured.
2045 450 p. Type **762** 45 45
2046 450 p. "Salto" (coastguard patrol boat) 45 45
2047 1570 p. "Uruguay" (cruiser) . 1·60 1·60
2048 1570 p. "Pte. Oribe" (tanker) 1·60 1·60

763 "Rio de la Plata, 1602" (woodcut)

1991. America. Voyages of Discovery.
2049 **763** 450 p. brown and yellow . 50 50
2050 – 1740 p. green and brown 1·90 1·90
DESIGN—HORIZ: 1740 p. Amerigo Vespucci.

764 "The Tree is the Fountain of Life"

1991. World Food Day.
2051 **764** 1740 p. multicoloured . . 1·75 1·75

765 "The Table" (Zoma Baitler)

1991.
2052 **765** 360 p. multicoloured . . 40 40

766 Gladiator, 1902

1991. Old Cars. Multicoloured.
2053 360 p. Type **766** 40 40
2054 1370 p. E.M.F., 1909 . . . . 1·50 1·50
2055 1490 p. Renault, 1912 . . . 1·50 1·50
2056 1510 p. Clement-Bayard, 1903 (vert) . . . . 1·75 1·75

767 Emblem

768 Club Badge and Trophy

1991. 60th General Assembly of Interpol, Punta del Este.
2057 **767** 1740 p. multicoloured . . 1·75 1·75

1991. National Football Club, Winners of World Cup Football Cup, 1988, and the Toyota Cup. Multicoloured.
2058 450 p. Type **768** 50 50
2059 450 p. Trophies on football pitch (horiz) 50 50

769 School and Pupils

1991. Centenary of Maria Auxiliadora Institute.
2060 **769** 450 p. blue, black & red 50 50

770 "LATU"

1991. 25th Anniv of Uruguay Technological Laboratory.
2061 **770** 1570 p. blue & deep blue 1·50 1·50

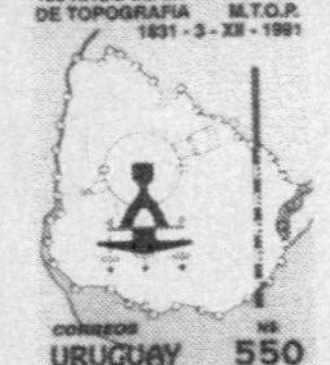

771 Emblem and Couple **772** Theodolite and Measuring Rod on Map of Uruguay

1991. World AIDS Day.

2062 **771** 550 p. black, yellow & bl . . 55 55
2063 2040 p. black, lilac & grn . . 2·00 2·00

1991. 160th Anniv of Topographic Survey.

2064 **772** 550 p. multicoloured . . 55 55

773 Angel

1991. Christmas. Multicoloured.

2065 550 p. Type **773** 55 55
2066 2040 p. "Adoration of the Angels" . . . . 1·90 1·90

774 Anibal Troilo

1992. Musicians.

2067 **774** 450 p. black, mauve & bl . . 40 40
2068 – 450 p. black, orge & red . . 40 40
2069 – 450 p. black, light green and green 40 40
2070 – 450 p. black, blue & mve . . 40 40

DESIGNS: No. 2068, Francisco Canaro; 2069, Pintin Castellanos; 2070, Juan de Dios Filiberto.

775 Worker and Factory Building

1992. Quality Exports.

2071 **775** 120 p. multicoloured . . 15 15

776 Pres. Aylwin **777** Trophy

1992. Visit of President Patricio Aylwin of Chile.

2072 **776** 550 p. multicoloured . . 50 50

1992. Penarol F.C., Three-times World Club Football Champions.

2073 **777** 600 p. black and yellow . . 55 55

778 Hands holding Hammer and Chisel **779** No Smoking Emblem

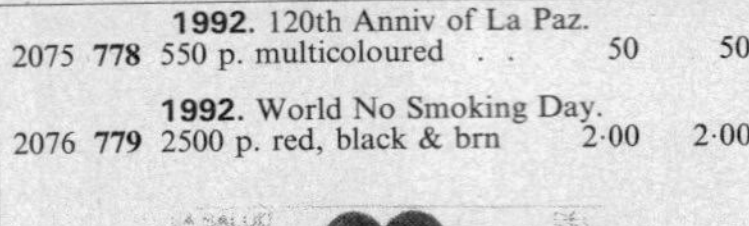

1992. 120th Anniv of La Paz.

2075 **778** 550 p. multicoloured . . 50 50

1992. World No Smoking Day.

2076 **779** 2500 p. red, black & brn . . 2·00 2·00

780 Heart and Emblems

1992. World Health Day. "Health in Rhythm with the Heart".

2077 **780** 2500 p. ultramarine, blue and red . . . . 2·10 2·10

781 Map of South America and Food Products

1992. Mercosur (South American economic organization).

2078 **781** 2500 p. multicoloured . . 2·10 2·10

782 Stamp

1992. "Olymphilex 92" International Olympic Stamps Exhibition, Barcelona.

2079 **782** 2900 p. multicoloured . . 2·25 2·25

783 Emblems

1992. 22nd Latin American–Caribbean Regional Conference of Food and Agricultural Organization.

2080 **783** 2500 p. multicoloured . . 1·75 1·75

784 Children with Basket of Food

1992. International Nutrition Conference, Rome.

2081 **784** 2900 p. multicoloured . . 2·10 2·10

785 Vallejo

1992. Birth Centenary of Cesar Vallejo (painter and poet).

2082 **785** 2500 p. brown & lt brown . . 1·75 1·75

786 Monument and Route Map **787** Ruins of Sacramento and Lighthouse

1992. Centenary of Christopher Columbus Monument, Durazno.

2083 **786** 700 p. black, blue & grn . . 50 50

1992. 500th Anniv of Discovery of America by Columbus.

2084 **787** 700 p. multicoloured . . 50 50

788 Caravel **789** Emblem

1992. America. 500th Anniv of Discovery of America by Columbus. Multicoloured.

2085 700 p. Type **788** 50 50
2086 2900 p. Globe showing Americas and old map (horiz) . . 2·10 2·10

1992. Centenary of Christopher Columbus Philanthropic Society.

2087 **789** 700 p. black, mauve and magenta 50 50

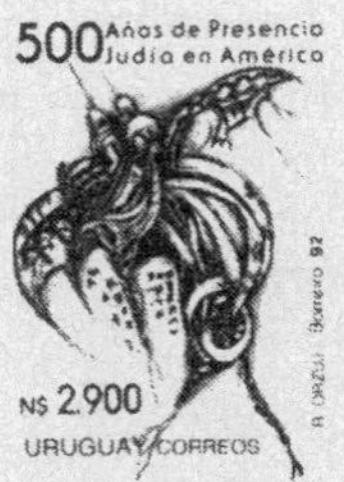

790 Emblem

1992. 500th Anniv of Presence of Jews in America.

2088 **790** 2900 p. multicoloured . . 2·10 2·10

791 Arms

1992. 50th Anniv of Jose Pedro Varela Teachers' College.

2089 **791** 700 p. multicoloured . . 50 50

792 Cambadu Building **793** Emblem

1992. Centenary of Chamber of Wholesale and Retail Traders.

2090 **792** 700 p. grey, black & red . . 50 50

1992. 50th Anniv of Lebanon Club of Uruguay.

2091 **793** 2900 p. multicoloured . . 2·10 2·10

794 Nativity **796** Immigrant

795 Map and Emblem

1992. Christmas. Multicoloured.

2092 800 p. Type **794** 55 55
2093 3200 p. Star . . . . 2·10 2·10

1992. 22nd Latin American and Carribean Lions Clubs Forum.

2094 **795** 2700 p. multicoloured . . 1·75 1·75

1992. Immigrants Day.

2095 **796** 800 p. green and black . . 55 55

797 Oribe **799** Anniversary Emblem

798 Anniversary Emblem

1992. Birth Bicentenary of Manuel Oribe (Liberation hero). Multicoloured.

2096 800 p. Type **797** 55 55
2097 800 p. Oribe (founder) and Eastern University (horiz) . . 55 55

1992. 90th Anniv of Pan-American Health Organization.

2098 **798** 3200 p. multicoloured . . 2·10 2·10

1992. 50th Anniv of Jose H. Molaguero S.A.

2099 **799** 800 p. brown and stone . . 55 55

800 Satellite and Map

1992. 70th Anniv of ANDEBU (association of broadcasting stations).

2100 **800** 2700 p. multicoloured . . 1·75 1·75

801 Emblem and Shanty Town

1992. 30th Anniv of Caritas Uruguaya.

2101 **801** 3200 p. multicoloured . . 2·00 2·00

802 Gonzalez Pecotche (founder) and Emblem

1992. 60th Anniv of Logosofia.

2102 **802** 800 p. yellow and blue . . 55 55

1993. Size 35 × 24 mm.

2103 **755** 800 p. olive and green . . 30 15

Currency Reform
1 (new) peso = 1000 (old) pesos

803 Wilson Ferreira Aldunate

804 Post Car

1993.
2104 **803** 80 c. red, black and grey . . 30 15

1993.
2105 **804** 1 p. blue and yellow . . 40 20

805 Graph and Personal Computer

1993. Centenary of Economic Sciences and Accountancy College.
2106 **805** 1 p. multicoloured . . . 40 20

807 Magirus Deutz Fire Engine, 1958

808 Earth

1993. 50th Anniv of National Fire Service.
2108 **807** 1 p. multicoloured . . . 40 20

1993. 15th Congress of Postal Union of the Americas, Spain and Portugal.
2109 **808** 3 p. 50 multicoloured . . 1·25 60

LATE FEE STAMPS

L 175

1936.
L774 **L 175** 3 c. green 10 10
L775 5 c. violet 15 10
L776 6 c. green 15 10
L777 7 c. brown 20 10
L778 8 c. red 40 25
L779 12 c. blue 60 50

NEWSPAPER STAMPS

1922. Optd **PRENSA** (= Printed Matter) or surch also.
N519 **128** 3 c. olive (imperf) . . . 40 25
N447 **118** 3 c. on 2 c. black and lake (perf) 40 35
N403 **120** 3 c. on 4 c. yellow (perf) 20 30
N448 **118** 6 c. on 4 c. blue and orange (perf) 40 35
N449 9 c. on 5 c. brown and blue (perf) 40 35
N520 **128** 9 c. on 10 c. green (imperf) 45 35
N521 15 c. mauve (imperf) . . 60 40

OFFICIAL STAMPS

1880. Optd **OFICIAL**. Perf.
O51 **9** 15 c. yellow . . . . 2·00 2·00

1880. Optd **OFICIAL**. Roul.
O48 **10** 1 c. brown . . . . 1·10 1·10
O49 **11** 5 c. green 45 45
O61 **15** 7 c. blue (perf) . . . . . 1·50 1·50
O50 **10** 10 c. red 70 70
O52 20 c. bistre 95 95
O53 50 c. black . . . . 6·25 6·25
O55 1 p. blue . . . . 6·25 6·25

1883. Optd **OFICIAL**.
O64 **16** 1 c. green . . . . 2·00 2·00
O65 – 2 c. red (No. 63) . . . . 3·75 3·00

1883. Optd **OFICIAL**.
O70 **18** 1 c. green . . . . 11·50 11·50
O71 2 c. red . . . . 3·70 3·75
O72 **20** 5 c. blue . . . . 1·10 85
O73 **21** 10 c. brown . . . . . . 2·75 1·40

1884. Optd **FRANCO** in frame.
O74 **18** 1 c. green . . . . 13·50 11·50

1884. Optd **OFICIAL**.
O80 **10** 1 c. on 10 c. (No. 76) . . 80 80
O81 – 2 c. red (No. 77) . . . . 2·25 2·25
O82 **26** 5 c. blue 95 70

1884. Optd **OFICIAL**. Roul.
O 91a **28** 1 c. grey . . . . 3·75 2·00
O 91 1 c. green 75 45
O 92 **29** 2 c. red 45 30
O 93a **28** 5 c. blue . . . . 1·25 1·40
O 94 5 c. lilac . . . . 1·50 1·25
O 95 **31** 7 c. brown . . . . . . 1·10 65
O110 7 c. orange . . . . . . 1·10 75
O 96 **32** 10 c. brown 60 35
O111 **36** 10 c. violet . . . . . . 5·75 3·00
O 97 **33** 20 c. mauve . . . . . . 1·10 65
O112 20 c. brown . . . . . . 5·75 2·25
O 98 **34** 25 c. lilac . . . . . . 1·10 75
O113 25 c. red . . . . 5·75 2·25

1890. Optd **OFICIAL**. Perf.
O124 **38** 1 c. green 40 20
O125 **39** 2 c. red 40 20
O126 **40** 5 c. blue 75 80
O127 **41** 7 c. brown 60 60
O128 **42** 10 c. green 60 50
O129 **43** 20 c. orange 60 50
O130 **44** 25 c. brown 60 50
O131 **45** 50 c. blue . . . . . . 2·75 2·75
O132 **46** 1 p. violet . . . . . . 3·00 2·75

1891. Optd **OFICIAL**.
O134 **28** 5 c. lilac (No. 133) . . . 75 75

1895. Optd **OFICIAL**.
O164 **38** 1 c. blue 85 85
O165 **39** 2 c. brown . . . . . . 1·10 1·10
O166 **40** 5 c. red . . . . 1·50 1·50
O167 **45** 50 c. purple . . . . . . 3·00 3·00

1895. Optd **OFICIAL**.
O168 **56** 1 c. bistre 20 20
O169 **57** 2 c. blue 20 20
O170 **58** 5 c. red 40 25
O171 **59** 7 c. green 40 40
O172 **60** 10 c. brown 40 40
O173 **61** 20 c. black and green . . 1·25 60
O174 **62** 25 c. black and brown . . 60 60
O175 **63** 50 c. black and blue . . 55 55
O176 **64** 1 p. black and brown . . 2·75 2·75

1897. Nos. 180/2 optd **OFICIAL**.
O194 **67** 1 c. black and red . . . 60 60
O195 **68** 5 c. black and blue . . . 70 60
O196 – 10 c. black and lake . . 95 75

1897. Optd **OFICIAL**.
O201 **56** 1 c. blue 35 30
O202 **57** 2 c. purple 60 55
O203 **58** 5 c. green 60 35
O204 **72** 10 c. red . . . . 2·00 1·10
O205 **61** 20 c. black and mauve . . 5·50 2·00
O206 **62** 25 c. blue and red . . . 2·25 1·10
O207 **63** 50 c. brown and green . . 3·00 1·10
O208 **64** 1 p. blue and brown . . 4·50 3·00

1899. Optd **OFICIAL**.
O226 **39** 2 c. orange 50 25
O227a **58** 5 c. blue 60 50
O228 **72** 10 c. purple 95 95
O243 **43** 20 c. blue . . . . 3·00 2·25

1901. Optd **OFICIAL**.
O238 **78** 1 c. green 20 25
O239 **79** 2 c. red 25 25
O240 **80** 5 c. blue 25 30
O241 **81** 7 c. brown 30 30
O242 **82** 10 c. lilac 35 35
O245 **46** 1 p. green . . . . . . 3·75 3·00

1904. Optd **OFICIAL**.
O272 **86** 1 c. green 20 15
O262 **87** 2 c. orange 20 20
O263 **88** 5 c. blue 20 20
O275 **89** 10 c. lilac 20 15
O276 **90** 20 c. green . . . . . . 1·10 70
O277 **91** 25 c. bistre 75 35

1907. Optd **OFICIAL**.
O273 **96** 5 c. blue 20 15
O274 7 c. brown 20 15
O278 50 c. red 45 40

1910. Optd **OFICIAL 1910**.
O288 **79** 2 c. red . . . . 3·75 2·25
O289 **80** 5 c. blue . . . . 2·25 2·00
O290 **82** 10 c. lilac . . . . . . 1·10 70
O291 **43** 20 c. green . . . . . . 1·10 70
O292 **44** 25 c. brown . . . . . . 2·00 1·40
O293 **96** 50 c. red . . . . 2·50 1·40

O 110

1911.
O307 **O 110** 2 c. brown 25 25
O308 5 c. blue 25 20
O309 8 c. slate 25 20
O310 20 c. brown 40 30
O311 23 c. red 60 40
O312 50 c. orange 75 45
O313 1 p. red . . . . . . 2·00 70

1915. Optd **Oficial**.
O340 **107** 2 c. pink 40 45
O341 5 c. blue 40 45
O342 8 c. blue 40 45
O343 20 c. brown 85 35
O344 **108** 23 c. blue . . . . . . 2·25 2·00
O345 50 c. orange . . . . . . 3·75 2·00
O346 1 p. red . . . . 4·50 2·00

1919. Optd **Oficial**.
O365 **115** 2 c. grey and red . . . 60 30
O366 5 c. grey and blue . . . 70 25
O367 8 c. brown and blue . . 70 25
O368 20 c. grey and brown . . 1·40 45
O369 23 c. brown & green . . 1·40 45
O370 50 c. blue and brown . . 2·00 95
O371 1 p. blue and red . . . 5·00 1·50

1924. Optd **OFICIAL** in frame. (a) Perf.
O439 **128** 2 c. mauve 40 15
O440 5 c. blue 40 15
O593 8 c. red 95 25
O594 10 c. green . . . . . . 1·40 25
O441 12 c. blue 25 15
O442 20 c. brown 25 25
O443 36 c. green 95 70
O444 50 c. orange . . . . . . 2·10 1·50
O445 1 p. red . . . . 3·50 2·75
O446 2 p. green . . . . . . 6·25 5·00

(b) Imperf.
O499 **128** 2 c. mauve 45 10
O500 5 c. blue 40 15
O501 8 c. red 45 20
O502 12 c. blue 60 20
O503 20 c. brown 95 40
O504 36 c. pink . . . . 2·00 60

PARCEL POST STAMPS

P 123

P 144

1922. (a) Inscr "EXTERIOR".
P391 **P 123** 5 c. green on buff . . . 20 10
P516 5 c. black on yellow . . 30 10
P392 10 c. green on blue . . 35 10
P517 10 c. black on blue . . 40 10
P393 20 c. green on rose . . 1·10 50
P518 20 c. black on pink . . 85 15
P394 30 c. green on green . . 1·10 20
P395 50 c. green on blue . . 2·00 30
P396 1 p. green on orange . . 2·75 70

(b) Inscr "INTERIOR".
P397 **P 123** 5 c. green on buff . . . 25 10
P512 5 c. black on yellow . . 30 10
P398 10 c. green on blue . . 25 10
P513 10 c. black on blue . . 35 10
P399 20 c. green on pink . . 50 25
P514 20 c. black on pink . . 45 15
P400 30 c. green on green . . 85 25
P515 30 c. black on green . . 85 25
P401 50 c. green on blue . . 1·10 30
P402 1 p. green on orange . . 3·00 60

1927.
P522 **P 144** 1 c. blue 10 10
P606 1 c. violet 10 10
P523 2 c. green 10 10
P524 4 c. violet 15 10
P609a 5 c. red 15 10
P526 10 c. brown 30 10
P527 20 c. orange 40 20

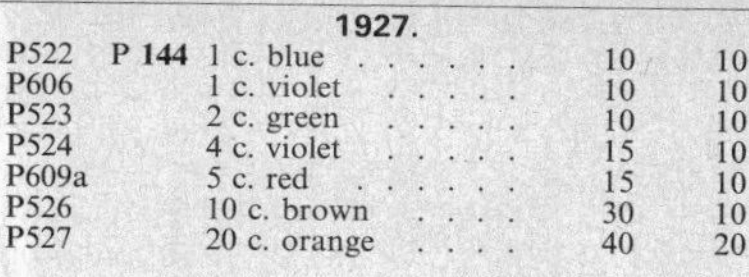

P 152

P 155

P 177 Sea and Rail Transport

1928.
P587 **P 152** 5 c. black on yellow . . 10 10
P588 10 c. black on blue . . 15 10
P589 20 c. black on red . . 35 10
P590 30 c. black on green . . 55 10

1929. Agricultural parcels.
P610 **P 155** 10 c. orange 30 20
P611 15 c. blue 30 20
P612 20 c. brown 45 30
P613 25 c. red 50 35
P614 50 c. grey 95 45
P615 75 c. violet . . . . . 3·75 3·75
P616 1 p. olive . . . . . . 2·75 1·40

1938.
P 971 **P 177** 5 c. orange 10 35
P 801 10 c. red 40 25
P 972 10 c. purple 15 10
P1066 10 c. green 20 40
P 973 20 c. red 35 35
P1067 20 c. blue 25 30
P 974 30 c. blue 40 10
P1068 30 c. purple 55 20
P1069 50 c. green 85 30
P 805 1 p. red . . . . . . 1·40 10
P 975 1 p. blue 20 20
P1070 1 p. green 70 90

P 188

P 204 University

1943.
P876 **P 188** 1 c. red 10 10
P877 2 c. green 10 10

1944. Optd **ANO 1943**.
P882 **P 155** 10 c. orange 20 10
P883 15 c. blue 20 20
P884 20 c. brown 30 20
P885 25 c. red 50 30
P886 50 c. grey 70 50
P887 75 c. violet . . . . . 1·40 95
P888 1 p. olive . . . . . . 1·75 1·40

1945.
P 909 A 1 c. green 10 10
P 999 **P 204** 1 c. red 10 10
P 910 2 c. violet 10 10
P1000 A 2 c. blue 10 10
P1047 B 5 c. grey 35 10
P1045 5 c. brown 10 10
P1001 A 10 c. turqoise 10 10
P1002 10 c. olive 10 10
P1048 C 20 c. yellow 10 10
P1049 20 c. brown 15 10
P1046 D 1 p. blue . . . . 1·50 1·10
P1290 1 p. brown 10 10

DESIGNS—HORIZ: A, Bank. VERT: B, Custom House; C. Solis Theatre; D. Montevideo Railway Station.

P 211 Custom House

P 212 Mail Coach (Guillermo Rodriguez)

1946.
P934 **P 211** 5 c. blue & brown . . 15 10

1946.
P935 **P 212** 5 p. brown & red . . 7·00 2·25

1946. Armorial type as T **187** obliterated by arrow-head device. (a) Optd **IMPUESTO** and **ENCOMIENDAS**.
P936 1 c. mauve 10 10
P937 2 c. brown 10 10
P938 5 c. blue 10 10

(b) Optd **ENCOMIENDAS** only.
P939 1 p. blue 75 20
P940 5 p. red . . . . 2·50 95

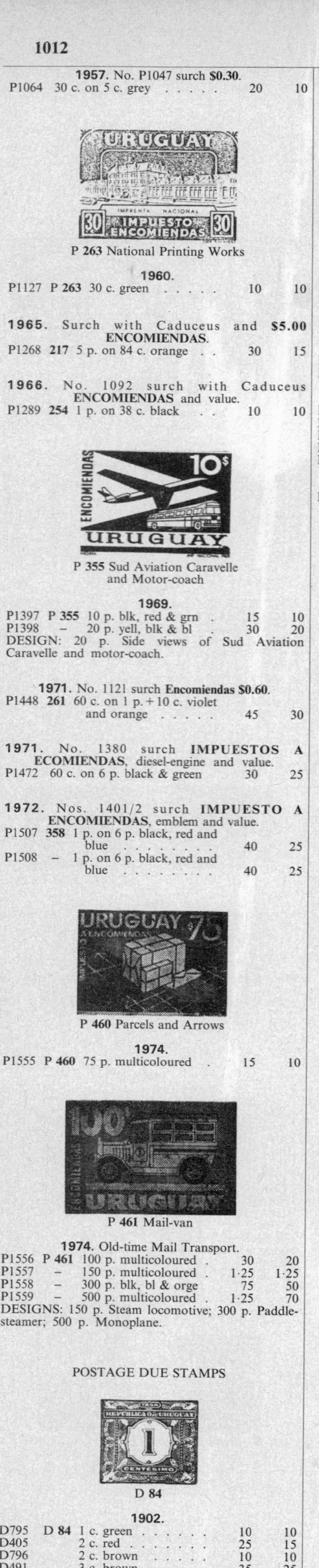

1957. No. P1047 surch **$0.30.**
P1064 30 c. on 5 c. grey 20 10

P **263** National Printing Works

1960.
P1127 P **263** 30 c. green 10 10

1965. Surch with Caduceus and **$5.00 ENCOMIENDAS.**
P1268 **217** 5 p. on 84 c. orange . . 30 15

1966. No. 1092 surch with Caduceus **ENCOMIENDAS** and value.
P1289 **254** 1 p. on 38 c. black . . 10 10

P **355** Sud Aviation Caravelle and Motor-coach

1969.
P1397 P **355** 10 p. blk, red & grn . 15 10
P1398 – 20 p. yell, blk & bl . 30 20
DESIGN: 20 p. Side views of Sud Aviation Caravelle and motor-coach.

1971. No. 1121 surch **Encomiendas $0.60.**
P1448 **261** 60 c. on 1 p. + 10 c. violet and orange 45 30

1971. No. 1380 surch **IMPUESTOS A ECOMIENDAS**, diesel-engine and value.
P1472 60 c. on 6 p. black & green 30 25

1972. Nos. 1401/2 surch **IMPUESTO A ENCOMIENDAS**, emblem and value.
P1507 **358** 1 p. on 6 p. black, red and blue 40 25
P1508 – 1 p. on 6 p. black, red and blue 40 25

P **460** Parcels and Arrows

1974.
P1555 P **460** 75 p. multicoloured . 15 10

P **461** Mail-van

1974. Old-time Mail Transport.
P1556 P **461** 100 p. multicoloured . 30 20
P1557 – 150 p. multicoloured . 1·25 1·25
P1558 – 300 p. blk, bl & orge 75 50
P1559 – 500 p. multicoloured . 1·25 70
DESIGNS: 150 p. Steam locomotive; 300 p. Paddle-steamer; 500 p. Monoplane.

POSTAGE DUE STAMPS

D **84**

1902.
D795 D **84** 1 c. green 10 10
D405 2 c. red 25 15
D796 2 c. brown 10 10
D491 3 c. brown 35 25
D797 3 c. red 10 10
D798 4 c. violet 10 10
D799 5 c. blue 10 10
D746 5 c. red 35 20
D494 6 c. brown 40 30
D800 8 c. red 15 10
D249 10 c. blue 45 35
D409a 10 c. green 30 15
D250 20 c. orange 85 45

1904. Surch **PROVISORIO UN cent'mo.**
D267 D **84** 1 c. on 10 c. blue . . 45 45

SPECIAL DELIVERY STAMPS

1921. Overprinted **MENSAJERIAS.**
E389 **120** 2 c. orange 50 20

E **126** Caduceus E **153**

1923.
E415 E **126** 2 c. red 30 10
E416 2 c. blue 30 10

1928.
E591 E **153** 2 c. black on green . 15 10
E635a 2 c. green 15 10
E636 2 c. blue 15 10
E637 2 c. pink 15 10
E638 2 c. brown 10 10

1957. Surch **$0.05.**
E1065 E **153** 5 c. on 2 c. brown . 15 10

VATHY Pt. 6

A town on the island of Samos, where there was a French Post Office which closed in 1914.

25 centimes = 1 piastre

1893. Stamps of France optd **Vathy** or surch also.
82 **10** 5 c. green . . . . 3·25 4·25
84 10 c. black and lilac . . . 6·75 6·75
86 15 c. blue . . . . 6·75 6·75
87 1 pi. on 25 c. black on pink . 5·50 6·25
88 2 pi. on 50 c. pink . . . . 16·00 17·00
89 4 pi. on 1 f. green . . . . 18·00 11·50
90 8 pi. on 2 f. brown on blue . 50·00 45·00
91 20 pi. on 5 f. mauve . . . 70·00 65·00

VATICAN CITY Pt. 8

A small area in Rome under the independent sovereignty of the Pope since 1929.

100 centesimi = 1 lira

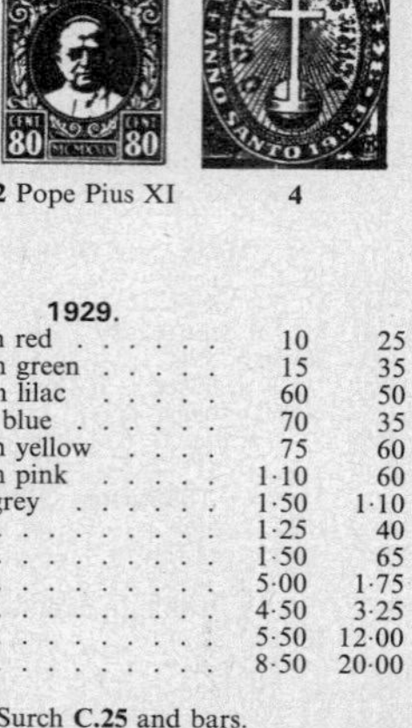

1 Papal Tiara and St. Peter's Keys **2** Pope Pius XI **4**

1929.
1 **1** 5 c. brown on red 10 25
2 10 c. green on green 15 35
3 20 c. violet on lilac 60 50
4 25 c. blue on blue 70 35
5 30 c. black on yellow . . . 75 60
6 50 c. black on pink . . . . 1·10 60
7 75 c. red on grey . . . . . 1·50 1·10
8 **2** 80 c. red . . . . 1·25 40
9 1 l. 25 blue . . . . 1·50 65
10 2 l. brown . . . . 5·00 1·75
11 2 l. 50 red . . . . 4·50 3·25
12 5 l. green . . . . 5·50 12·00
13 10 l. black . . . . 8·50 20·00

1931. Surch **C.25** and bars.
14 **1** 25 c. on 30 c. black on yell . . 1·25 70

1933. "Holy Year".
15 **4** 25 c.+ 10 c. green . . . . 4·50 5·50
16 75 c.+ 15 c. red . . . . . 7·00 13·00
17 80 c.+ 20 c. brown . . . . 26·00 20·00
18 1 l. 25 + 25 c. blue . . . . 7·00 16·00
The 80 c. and 1 l. 25 have inscriptions and frame differently arranged.

6 Arms of Pope Pius XI **9** Pope Pius XI

1933.
19 **6** 5 c. red 10 10
20 – 10 c. black and brown . . . 10 10
21 – 12½ c. black and green . . . 10 10
22 – 20 c. black and orange . . . 10 10
23 – 25 c. black and olive . . . 10 10
24 – 30 c. brown and black . . . 10 10
25 – 50 c. brown and purple . . . 10 10
26 – 75 c. brown and red 10 10
27 – 80 c. brown and red 10 10
28 **9** 1 l. black and violet . . . 4·00 75
29 1 l. 25 black and blue . . . 13·00 4·00
30 2 l. black and brown . . . 22·00 14·00
31 2 l. 75 black and purple . . 24·00 24·00
32 – 5 l. green and brown . . . 20 35
33 – 10 l. green and blue . . . 25 45
34 – 20 l. green and black . . . 30 60
DESIGNS—As Type **6**: 10 c. to 25 c. Wing of Vatican Palace; 30 c. to 80 c. Vatican Gardens and Dome of St. Peter's. As Type **9**: 5 l. to 20 l. St. Peter's Basilica.

1934. Surch.
35 **2** 40 c. on 80 c. red . . . . . 2·00 1·50
36 1 l. 30 on 1 l. 25 blue . . . 80·00 25·00
37 2 l. 05 on 2 l. brown . . . £150 5·50
38 2 l. 55 on 2 l. 50 red . . . 80·00 £140
39 3 l. 05 on 5 l. green . . . £300 £300
40 3 l. 70 on 10 l. black . . . £275 £350

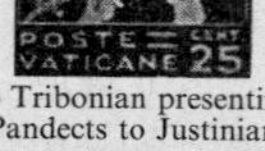

13 Tribonian presenting Pandects to Justinian **15** Doves and Bell

1935. International Juridical Congress, Rome. Frescoes by Raphael.
41 **13** 5 c. orange 20 40
42 10 c. violet 20 40
43 25 c. green . . . . 2·00 3·50
44 – 75 c. red . . . . 28·00 18·00
45 – 80 c. brown . . . . . . 20·00 17·00
46 – 1 l. 25 blue . . . . . . 24·00 12·00
DESIGN: 75 c. to 1 l. 25, Pope Julius II (wrongly inscr as representing Pope Gregory IX).

1936. Catholic Press Exhibition, Rome.
47 **15** 5 c. green 25 60
48 – 10 c. black 25 60
49 – 25 c. green . . . . 13·00 4·00
50 **15** 50 c. purple 25 60
51 – 75 c. red . . . . 30·00 22·00
52 – 80 c. brown . . . . 50 1·75
53 – 1 l. 25 blue . . . . 60 1·75
54 – 5 l. brown . . . . 60 6·00
DESIGNS: 10, 75 c. Church and Bible; 25, 80 c. St. John Bosco; 1 l. 25, 5 l. St. Francis of Sales.

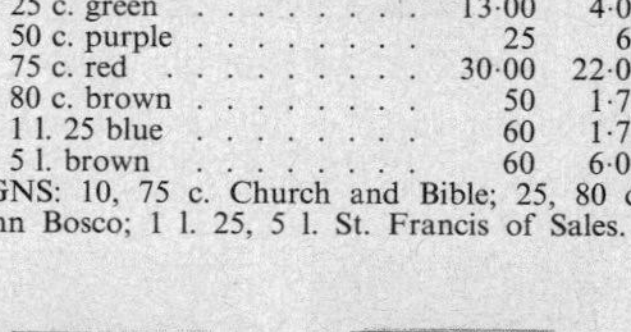

16 Statue of St. Peter **17** Ascension of Elijah

1938. Air.
55 **16** 25 c. brown 10 15
56 – 50 c. green 10 15
57 **17** 75 c. red 15 20
58 – 80 c. blue 25 40
59 **16** 1 l. violet 35 45
60 – 2 l. blue 55 65
61 **17** 5 l. black . . . . 1·25 1·90
62 – 10 l. purple . . . . . . 1·25 1·90
DESIGNS: 50 c., 2 l. Dove with olive branch and St. Peter's Square; 80 c., 10 l. Transportation of the Holy House.

18 Crypt of Basilica of St. Cecilia **20** Coronation

1938. International Christian Archaeological Congress. Inscr "CONGRESSVS INTERNAT. ARCHAEOLOGIAE CHRIST".
63 **18** 5 c. brown 20 20
64 10 c. orange 20 20
65 25 c. green 20 20
66 – 75 c. red . . . . 6·00 6·00
67 – 80 c. violet . . . . . . 14·00 16·00
68 – 1 l. 25 blue . . . . . . 17·00 13·00
DESIGN: 75, 80 c. and 1 l. 25, Basilica of Saints Nereus and Achilles in the Catacombs of Domitilla.

1939. Death of Pope Pius XI. Optd **SEDE VACANTE MCMXXXIX.**
69 **1** 5 c. brown on red . . . . 25·00 3·50
70 10 c. green on green 20 20
71 20 c. violet on lilac 20 20
72 25 c. blue on blue . . . . . 40 3·50
73 30 c. black on yellow . . . 40 20
74 50 c. black on pink 40 20
75 75 c. red on grey 40 20

1939. Coronation of Pope Pius XII.
76 **20** 25 c. green 85 20
77 75 c. red 15 30
78 80 c. violet . . . . 1·90 2·10
79 1 l. 25 blue 15 30

21 Arms of Pope Pius XII **22** Pope Pius XII

1940. 1st Anniv of Coronation of Pope Pius XII.
80 **21** 5 c. red 10 10
99 5 c. grey 10 10
100 30 c. brown 10 10
101 50 c. green 10 10
81 **22** 1 l. black and violet . . . 15 10
102 – 1 l. black and brown . . . 10 10
82 – 1 l. 25 black and blue . . . 15 10
103 – 1 l. 50 black and red . . . 15 15
83 **22** 2 l. black and brown . . . 60 1·00
104 – 2 l. 50 black and blue . . . 15 15
84 – 2 l. 75 black and purple . . 60 1·50
105 **22** 5 l. black and lilac . . . 20 20
106 20 l. black and green . . . 35 45
DESIGN: 1 l. (No. 102); 1 l. 25, 1 l. 50, 2 l. 50, and 2 l. 75, as Type **22** but with portrait of Pope facing left.

23

24 Consecration of Archbishop Pacelli

1942. Prisoners of War Relief Fund. 1st series. Inscr "MCMXLII".
85 **23** 25 c. green 10 15
86 80 c. brown 10 15
87 1 l. 25 blue 10 15
See also Nos. 92/4 and 107/9.

1943. Pope's Episcopal Silver Jubilee.
88 **24** 25 c. turquoise and green . . 10 10
89 80 c. chocolate and brown . . 10 20
90 1 l. 25 blue & ultramarine . 10 20
91 5 l. blue and black 15 45

1944. Prisoners of War Relief Fund. 2nd series. Inscr "MCMXLIII".
92 **23** 25 c. green 10 10
93 80 c. brown 10 15
94 1 l. 25 blue 15 25

25 Raphael

27 St. Ignatius of Loyola

1944. 4th Centenary of Pontifical Academy of the Virtuosi of the Pantheon.
95 **25** 25 c. olive and green 10 10
96 – 80 c. violet and lilac 20 20
97 – 1 l. 25 blue and violet . . . 20 20
98 – 10 l. bistre and yellow . . . 40 1·75
PORTRAITS: 80 c. Antonio da Sangallo (architect); 1 l. 25, Carlo Maratti (painter) (after Francesco Maratta); 10 l. Antonio Canova (sculptor, self-portrait).

1945. Prisoners of War Relief Fund. 3rd series. Inscr "MCMXLIV".
107 **23** 1 l. green 10 15
108 3 l. red 10 15
109 5 l. blue 10 15

1946. Surch in figures between bars.
110 **21** 20 c. on 5 c. grey 10 10
111 25 c. on 30 c. brown . . . 10 10
112 1 l. on 50 c. green 10 10
113 – 1 l. 50 on 1 l. black and brown (No. 102) 10 10
114 – 3 l. on 1 l. 50 black and red (No. 103) 15 15
115 – 5 l. on 2 l. 50 black and blue (No. 104) 20 20
116 **22** 10 l. on 5 l. black & lilac . 1·25 55
117 30 l. on 20 l. black & green 3·50 1·40

1946. 400th Anniv of Inauguration of Council of Trent.
118 – 5 c. brown and bistre . . . 15 15
119 – 25 c. brown and violet . . . 15 15
120 – 50 c. sepia and brown . . . 15 15
121 **27** 75 c. brown and black . . . 15 15
122 – 1 l. brown and purple . . . 15 15
123 – 1 l. 50 brown and red . . . 15 15
124 – 2 l. brown and green . . . 15 15
125 – 2 l. 50 brown and blue . . 15 15
126 – 3 l. brown and red 15 15
127 – 4 l. brown and bistre . . . 15 15
128 – 5 l. brown and blue 15 15
129 – 10 l. brown and red 15 15
DESIGNS: 5 c. Trent Cathedral; 25 c. St. Angela Merici; 50 c. St. Anthony Maria Zaccaria; 1 l. St. Cajetan of Thiene; 1 l. 50, St. John Fisher, Bishop of Rochester; 2 l. Cristoforo Madrussi, Bishop of Trent; 2 l. 50, Reginald Pole, Archbishop of Canterbury; 3 l. Marcello Cervini; 4 l. Giovanni Maria Del Monte; 5 l. Emperor Charles V; 10 l. Pope Paul III Farnese.

28 Dove with Olive Branch over St. Peter's Forecourt

29 Barn Swallows circling Spire of St. Peter's Basilica

30 "Raphael accompanying Tobias" (after Botticelli)

1947. Air.
130 **28** 1 l. red 10 10
131 – 4 l. brown 10 10
132 **28** 5 l. blue 10 10
133 **29** 15 l. violet 90 75
134 – 25 l. green . . . . 3·50 1·40
135 **29** 50 l. black . . . . 5·00 2·25
136 100 l. orange . . . . . . 18·00 4·25
137 **30** 250 l. black . . . . . . 11·00 2·00
138 500 l. blue £375 £250
DESIGN—VERT: As Type **28**: 4 l., 25 l. Transportation of the Holy House.

31 St. Agnes's Basilica

32 Pope Pius XII

1949.
139 **31** 1 l. brown 10 10
140 – 3 l. violet 10 10
141 – 5 l. orange 10 10
142 – 8 l. green 15 15
143 – 13 l. green . . . . 2·25 2·25
144 – 16 l. grey 25 25
145 – 25 l. red . . . . 4·50 55
146 – 35 l. mauve . . . . 22·00 9·50
147 – 40 l. blue 25 15
148 **32** 100 l. black . . . . 3·50 3·50
DESIGNS (Basilicas)—VERT: 3 l. St. Clement; 5 l. St. Praxedes; 8 l. St. Mary in Cosmedin. HORIZ: 13 l. Holy Cross; 16 l. St. Sebastian; 25 l. St. Laurence's; 35 l. St. Paul's; 40 l. Sta. Maria Maggiore.

33 Angels over Globe

1949. Air. 75th Anniv of U.P.U.
149 **33** 300 l. blue . . . . 20·00 10·00
150 1000 l. green . . . . 90·00 55·00

34 "I Will Give You the Keys of the Kingdom"

35 Guards Marching

1949. "Holy Year".
151 **34** 5 l. brown and lt brown . . 10 10
152 – 6 l. brown and black . . . 10 10
153 – 8 l. green and blue 60 60
154 – 10 l. blue and green . . . 10 10
155 **34** 20 l. brown and green . . . 90 40
156 – 25 l. blue and brown . . . 60 30
157 – 30 l. purple and green . . 1·60 1·25
158 – 60 l. red and brown . . . 1·40 1·25
DESIGNS: 6, 25 l. Four Basilicas; 8, 30 l. Pope Boniface VIII; 10, 60 l. Pope Pius XII opening the Holy Door.

1950. Centenary of Papal Guard.
159 **35** 25 l. sepia . . . . 7·00 4·50
160 35 l. green . . . . 3·75 4·50
161 55 l. brown . . . . 2·25 4·50

36 Pope Proclaiming Dogma

37 Pope Pius X

1951. Proclamation of Dogma of the Assumption.
162 **36** 25 l. purple . . . . 7·00 80
163 – 55 l. blue . . . . 4·50 10·00
DESIGN: 55 l. Angels over St. Peter's.

1951. Beatification of Pope Pius X.
164 **37** 6 l. gold and violet 10 15
165 10 l. gold and green 15 15
166 – 60 l. gold and blue . . . . 5·00 5·00
167 – 115 l. gold and brown . . . 12·00 12·00
DESIGN: 60, 115 l. Pope looking left.

38 Final Session of Council (fresco)

1951. 1500th Anniv of Council of Chalcedon.
168 **38** 5 l. grey 15 15
169 – 25 l. red . . . . 2·25 1·40
170 **38** 35 l. red . . . . 3·25 3·00
171 – 60 l. blue . . . . 12·00 11·00
172 **38** 100 l. brown . . . . 30·00 22·00
DESIGN: 25, 60 l. "Pope Leo I meeting Attila" (Raphael).

39 Gratian

41 Mail Coach and First Stamp

1951. Air. 800th Anniv of Decree of Gratian.
173 **39** 300 l. purple £160 £130
174 500 l. blue . . . . 30·00 13·00

1952. No. 143 surch **L. 12** and bars.
175 – 12 l. on 13 l. green . . . . . 1·90 1·25

1952. Centenary of First Papal States' Stamp.
176 **41** 50 l. black and blue . . . . 5·00 5·00

42 St. Maria Goretti

43 St. Peter and Inscription

1953. 50th Anniv of Martyrdom of St. Maria Goretti.
177 **42** 15 l. violet and brown . . . 4·25 2·75
178 25 l. brown and red . . . . 2·75 2·75

1953. St. Peter's Basilica. Medallions in black.
179 **43** 3 l. red 10 10
180 – 5 l. grey 10 10
181 – 10 l. green 10 10
182 – 12 l. brown 10 10
183 – 20 l. violet 25 15
184 – 25 l. brown 10 10
185 – 35 l. red 10 10
186 – 45 l. brown 25 20
187 – 60 l. blue 10 10
188 – 65 l. red 35 25
189 – 100 l. purple 10 10
DESIGNS—VERT: 5 l. Pius XII and Roman sepulchre; 10 l. St. Peter's tomb; 12 l. St. Sylvester I and Constantine's basilica (previous building); 20 l. Julius II and Bramante's design; 25 l. Paul III and apse; 35 l. Sixtus V and cupola; 45 l. Paul V and facade; 60 l. Urban VIII and baldaquin; 65 l. Alexander VII and colonnade; 100 l. Pius VI and sacristy.

44 Dome of St. Peter's

45 St. Clare of Assisi (after Giotto)

1953. Air.
190 **44** 500 l. brown & dp brown . 20·00 6·00
190a 500 l. green & turquoise . 10·00 4·50
191 1000 l. blue and dp blue . 55·00 11·00
191a 1000 l. red and lake . . . 85 85

1953. 700th Death Anniv of St. Clare (founder of Poor Clares Order).
192 **45** 25 l. dp brown, brown & bl 1·75 75
193 35 l. brown, lt brown & red 12·00 12·00

46 "St. Bernard" (after Lippi)

47 Lombard's Episcopal Seal

1953. 800th Death Anniv of St. Bernard of Clairvaux.
194 **46** 20 l. mauve and olive . . . 75 75
195 60 l. myrtle and blue . . . 7·50 6·00

1953. 800th Anniv of "Libri Sententiarum" (theological treatise by Peter Lombard, Bishop of Paris).
196 **47** 100 l. yellow, blue and red 23·00 17·00

48 Pope Pius XI and Vatican City

1954. 25th Anniv of Lateran Treaty.
197 **48** 25 l. red, brown and blue . 1·40 90
198 60 l. blue, grey and brown 2·75 2·25

49 Pope Pius XII

1954. Marian Year and Centenary of Dogma of the Immaculate Conception.
199 – 3 l. violet 10 10
200 **49** 4 l. red 10 10
201 – 6 l. red 10 10
202 **49** 12 l. turquoise . . . . . . 1·50 1·25
203 – 20 l. brown . . . . 1·00 1·00
204 **49** 35 l. blue . . . . 1·75 1·50
DESIGN: 3, 6, 20 l. Pope Pius IX facing right with different inscr and dates "1854–1954".

50 St. Pius X

51 Basilica of St. Francis of Assisi

1954. Canonization of Pope Pius X.
205 **50** 10 l. yellow, red & brown . 20 20
206 25 l. yellow, red and violet 2·75 2·25
207 35 l. yellow, red and black 4·00 3·50

1954. Bicentenary of Elevation of Basilica of St. Francis of Assisi to Papal Chapel.
208 **51** 20 l. black and cream . . . 2·25 1·25
209 35 l. brown and cream . . 1·90 2·25

52 "St. Augustine" (after Botticelli)

53 Madonna of Ostra Brama, Vilna

1954. 1600th Birth Anniv of St. Augustine.
210 **52** 35 l. green . . . . 1·25 75
211 50 l. brown . . . . 2·25 1·75

1954. Termination of Marian Year.
212 **53** 20 l. multicoloured 75 75
213 35 l. multicoloured . . . . 6·00 5·00
214 60 l. multicoloured . . . . 10·00 8·00

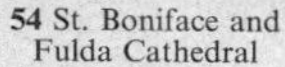

54 St. Boniface and Fulda Cathedral

55 "Pope Sixtus II and St. Lawrence" (fresco, Nicolina Chapel)

1955. 1200th Anniv of Martyrdom of St. Boniface.
215 **54** 10 l. black 10 10
216 35 l. violet 65 55
217 60 l. turquoise 90 70

1955. 500th Death Anniv of Fra Giovanni da Fiesole, "Fra Angelico" (painter).
218 **55** 50 l. red and blue 4·75 2·75
219 100 l. blue and flesh 2·75 2·75

56 Pope Nicholas V

57 St. Bartholomew

1955. 5th Death Centenary of Pope Nicholas V.
220 **56** 20 l. brown and blue 35 20
221 35 l. brown and red 45 35
222 60 l. brown and green 90 90

1955. 900th Death Anniv of St. Bartholomew the Young.
223 **57** 10 l. black and brown 10 10
224 25 l. black and red 60 40
225 100 l. black and green 2·75 2·00

58 "Annunciation" (Melozzo da Forli)

59 Corporal of the Guard

1956. Air.
226 **58** 5 l. black 10 10
227 A 10 l. green 10 10
228 B 15 l. orange 10 10
229 **58** 25 l. red 10 10
230 A 35 l. red 35 35
231 B 50 l. sepia 10 10
232 **58** 60 l. blue 3·00 3·00
233 A 100 l. brown 10 10
234 B 300 l. violet 70 70
PAINTINGS: A, "Annunciation" (P. Cavallini); B, "Annunciation" (Leonardo da Vinci).

1956. 450th Anniv of Swiss Guard.
235 – 4 l. red 10 10
236 **59** 6 l. orange 10 10
237 – 10 l. blue 10 10
238 – 35 l. brown 65 65
239 **59** 50 l. violet 90 90
240 – 60 l. green 95 95
DESIGNS: 4, 35 l. Captain Roust; 10, 60 l. Two drummers.

60 St. Rita

61 St. Ignatius presenting Jesuit Constitution to Pope Paul III

1956. 5th Death Centenary of St. Rita at Cascia.
241 **60** 10 l. grey 10 10
242 25 l. brown 70 70
243 35 l. blue 50 50

1956. 4th Death Cent of St. Ignatius of Loyola.
244 **61** 35 l. brown 65 65
245 60 l. slate 1·10 1·10

62 St. John of Capistrano

63 Madonna and Child

1956. 5th Death Centenary of St. John of Capistrano.
246 **62** 25 l. green and black 2·50 2·50
247 35 l. brown and purple 90 90

1956. "Black Madonna" of Czestochowa Commemoration.
248 **63** 35 l. black and blue 50 50
249 60 l. blue and green 60 60
250 100 l. lake and sepia 85 85

64 St. Domenico Savio

65 Cardinal D. Capranica (founder) and Capranica College

1957. Death Centenary of St. Domenico Savio.
251 **64** 4 l. brown 10 10
252 – 6 l. red 10 10
253 **64** 25 l. green 10 10
254 – 60 l. blue 1·40 1·40
DESIGN: 6, 60 l. St. Domenico Savio and St. John Bosco.

1957. 5th Centenary of Capranica College.
255 **65** 5 l. lake 10 10
256 – 10 l. brown 10 10
257 **65** 35 l. slate 20 20
258 – 100 l. blue 90 90
DESIGNS—HORIZ: 10, 100 l. Pope Pius XII and plaque.

66 Pontifical Academy of Science

1957. 20th Anniv of the Pontifical Academy of Science.
259 **66** 35 l. green and blue 75 75
260 60 l. blue and brown 75 75

67 Mariazell Basilica

68 Apparition of the Virgin Mary

1957. 8th Centenary of Mariazell Basilica.
261 **67** 5 l. green 10 10
262 – 15 l. slate 10 10
263 **67** 60 l. blue 85 85
264 – 100 l. violet 1·10 1·10
DESIGN: 15, 100 l. Statue of the Virgin of Mariazell within Sanctuary.

1958. Centenary of Apparition of the Virgin Mary at Lourdes.
265 **68** 5 l. blue 10 10
266 – 10 l. green 10 10
267 – 15 l. brown 10 10
268 **68** 25 l. red 10 10
269 – 35 l. sepia 10 10
270 – 100 l. violet 10 10
DESIGNS—VERT: 10, 35 l. Invalid at Lourdes; 15, 100 l. St. Bernadette.

69 "Civitas Dei" ("City of God" at Exhibition)

70 Pope Clement XIII (from sculpture by A. Canova)

1958. Brussels International Exhibition.
271 – 35 l. purple 25 25
272 **69** 60 l. red 55 55
273 100 l. violet 2·00 2·00
274 – 300 l. blue 1·10 1·75
DESIGN: 35, 300 l. Pope Pius XII.

1958. Birth Bicentenary of Antonio Canova (sculptor).
275 **70** 5 l. brown 10 10
276 – 10 l. red 10 10
277 – 35 l. green 35 25
278 – 100 l. blue 1·25 1·25
SCULPTURES: 10 l. Pope Clement XIV; 35 l. Pope Pius VI; 100 l. Pope Pius VII.

71 St. Peter's Keys

1958. "Vacant See".
279 **71** 15 l. sepia on yellow 1·40 1·40
280 25 l. sepia 10 10
281 60 l. sepia on lavender 10 10

72 Pope John XXIII

1959. Coronation of Pope John XXIII. Inscr "IV-XI MCMLVIII".
282 **72** 25 l. multicoloured 10 10
283 – 35 l. multicoloured 10 10
284 **72** 60 l. multicoloured 10 10
285 – 100 l. multicoloured 10 10
DESIGN: 35, 100 l. Arms of Pope John XXIII.

73 St. Lawrence

74 Pope Pius XI

1959. 1700th Death Annivs (15 to 100 l in 1958) of Martyrs under Valerian.
286 **73** 15 l. brown, yellow & red 10 10
287 – 25 l. brown, yellow & lilac 20 20
288 – 50 l. multicoloured 35 35
289 – 60 l. brown, yellow & grn 25 25
290 – 100 l. brown, yell & pur 35 35
291 – 300 l. sepia and buff 40 40
PORTRAITS: 25 l. Pope Sixtus II; 50 l. St. Agapitus; 60 l. St. Filisissimus; 100 l. St. Cyprian; 300 l. St. Fructuosus.

1959. 30th Anniv of Lateran Treaty.
292 **74** 30 l. brown 10 10
293 100 l. blue 20 15

75 Radio Mast

76 Obelisk and St. John Lateran Basilica

1959. 2nd Anniv of St. Maria di Galeria Radio Station Vatican City.
294 **75** 25 l. red, yellow & black 10 10
295 60 l. yellow, red and blue 25 25

1959. Air. Roman Obelisks.
296 **76** 5 l. violet 10 10
297 – 10 l. green 10 10
298 – 15 l. sepia 10 10
299 – 25 l. green 10 10
300 – 35 l. blue 10 10
301 **76** 50 l. green 15 15
302 – 60 l. red 15 15
303 – 100 l. blue 20 20
304 – 200 l. brown 25 25
305 – 500 l. brown 50 50
DESIGNS: 10, 60 l. Obelisk and Church of Sta. Maria Maggiore; 15, 100 l. Vatican Obelisk and Apostolic Palace; 25, 200 l. Obelisk and Churches of St. Mary in Montesanto and St. Mary of the Miracles, Piazza del Popolo; 35, 500 l. Sallustian Obelisk and Trinita dei Monti Church.

77 St. Casimir, Vilna Palace and Cathedral

1959. 500th Birth Anniv of St. Casimir (patron saint of Lithuania).
306 **77** 50 l. brown 15 15
307 100 l. green 15 15

78 "Christ Adored by the Magi" (after Raphael)

1959. Christmas.
308 **78** 15 l. black 10 10
309 25 l. red 10 10
310 60 l. blue 20 20

79 "St. Antoninus" (after Dupre)

80 Transept of St. John Lateran Basilica

1960. 500th Death Anniv of St. Antoninus of Florence.
311 **79** 15 l. blue 10 10
312 – 25 l. turquoise 10 10
313 **79** 60 l. brown 25 25
314 – 110 l. red 40 40
DESIGN: 25, 110 l. "St. Antoninus preaching sermon" (after Portigiani).

1960. Roman Diocesan Synod.
315 **80** 15 l. brown 10 10
316 60 l. black 20 20

81 "The Flight into Egypt" (after Beato Angelico)

82 Cardinal Sarto (Pius X) leaving Venice for Conclave in Rome

1960. World Refugee Year.
317 **81** 5 l. green 10 10
318 – 10 l. sepia 10 10
319 – 25 l. red 15 15
320 **81** 60 l. violet 25 25
321 – 100 l. blue 1·25 1·50
322 – 300 l. turquoise 70 75
DESIGNS: 10, 100 l. "St. Peter giving Alms" (Masaccio); 25, 300 l. "Madonna of Mercy" (Piero della Francesca).

1960. 1st Anniv of Transfer of Relics of Pope Pius X from Rome to Venice.
323 **82** 15 l. brown 10 10
324 – 35 l. red 65 65
325 – 60 l. turquoise 1·40 1·40
DESIGNS: 35 l. Pope John XXIII kneeling before relics of Pope Pius X; 60 l. Relics in procession across St. Mark's Square, Venice.

83 "Feeding the Hungry"

1960. "Corporal Works of Mercy". Della Robbia paintings. Centres in sepia.
326 **83** 5 l. brown 10 10
327 – 10 l. green 10 10
328 – 15 l. black 10 10
329 – 20 l. red 10 10

330	–	30 l. violet	10	10
331	–	35 l. brown	10	10
332	–	40 l. orange	10	10
333	–	70 l. ochre	10	10

DESIGNS: 10 l. "Giving drinks to the thirsty"; 15 l. "Clothing the naked"; 20 l. "Sheltering the homeless"; 30 l. "Visiting the sick"; 35 l. "Visiting the imprisoned"; 40 l. "Burying the dead"; 70 l. Pope John XXIII between "Faith" and "Charity".

84 "The Nativity" after Gerard Honthorst (Gherardo delle Notte)

85 St. Vincent de Paul

1960. Christmas.

334	84	10 l. black and green	10	10
335		15 l. dp brown & brown	10	10
336		70 l. blue and turqoise	15	15

1960. Death Tercentenary of St. Vincent de Paul and St. Louise de Marillac.

337	85	40 l. violet	15	15
338	–	70 l. black	25	25
339	–	100 l. brown	35	35

DESIGNS: 70 l. St. Louise de Marillac; 100 l. St. Vincent giving child to care of St. Louise.

86 St. Meinrad

87 "Pope Leo I meeting Attila" (Algardi)

1961. 11th Death Centenary of St. Meinrad.

340	86	30 l. black	35	35
341	–	40 l. lilac	70	80
342	–	100 l. brown	1·25	1·50

DESIGNS—VERT: 40 l. The "Black Madonna", Einsiedeln Abbey. HORIZ: 100 l. Einsiedeln Abbey, Switzerland.

1961. 15th Death Centenary of Pope Leo I.

343	87	15 l. lake	10	10
344		70 l. green	40	40
345		300 l. sepia	1·00	1·25

88 Route of St. Paul's Journey to Rome

1961. 1900th Anniv of St. Paul's Arrival in Rome.

346	88	10 l. green	10	10
347	–	15 l. black and brown	10	10
348	–	20 l. black and red	15	15
349	88	30 l. blue	20	20
350	–	75 l. black and brown	45	45
351	–	200 l. black and blue	95	1·10

DESIGNS: 15, 75 l. St. Paul's arrival in Rome (after sculpture by Maraini); 20, 200 l. Basilica of St. Paul-outside-the-Walls, Rome.

89 "L'Osservatore Romano", 1861 and 1961

1961. Centenary of "L'Osservatore Romano" (Vatican newspaper).

352	89	40 l. black and brown	20	20
353	–	70 l. black and blue	50	50
354	–	250 l. black and yellow	1·10	1·10

DESIGNS: 70 l. "L'Osservatore Romano" offices; 250 l. Printing machine.

90 St. Patrick (ancient sculpture)

1961. 15th Death Centenary of St. Patrick.

355	90	10 l. green and buff	10	10
356	–	15 l. sepia and blue	10	10
357	90	40 l. green and yellow	20	20
358	–	150 l. brown & turquoise	50	65

DESIGN: 15, 150 l. St. Patrick's Sanctuary, Lough Derg.

91 Arms of Roncalli Family

92 "The Nativity"

1961. Pope John XXIII's 80th Birthday.

359	91	10 l. brown and black	10	10
360	–	25 l. green and bistre	10	10
361	–	30 l. violet and blue	10	10
362	–	40 l. blue and violet	15	15
363	–	70 l. brown and grey	20	20
364	–	115 l. black and brown	30	30

DESIGNS: 25 l. Church of St. Mary, Sotto il Monte; 30 l. Church of St. Mary, Monte Santo; 40 l. Church of Saints Ambrose and Charles, Rome; 70 l. St. Peter's Chair, Vatican Basilica; 115 l. Pope John XXIII.

1961. Christmas. Centres multicoloured.

365	92	15 l. turquoise	10	10
366		40 l. black	10	10
367		70 l. purple	15	15

93 "Annunciation" (after F. Valle)

94 "Land Reclamation" Medal of 1588

1962. Air.

368	93	1000 l. brown	1·25	1·25
369		1500 l. blue	1·75	1·75

1962. Malaria Eradication.

370	94	15 l. violet	10	10
371	–	40 l. red	10	10
372	94	70 l. brown	20	20
373	–	300 l. green	40	45

DESIGN: 40, 300 l. Map of Pontine Marshes reclamation project (at time of Pope Pius VI).

95 "The Good Shepherd" (statue, Lateran Museum)

96 St. Catherine (after Il Sodoma (Bazzi))

1962. Religious Vocations.

374	95	10 l. black and violet	10	10
375	–	15 l. brown and blue	10	10
376	95	70 l. black and green	30	30
377	–	115 l. brown and red	1·10	1·10
378	95	200 l. black and brown	1·10	1·10

DESIGN: 15, 115 l. Wheatfield ready for harvest.

1962. 5th Centenary of St. Catherine of Siena's Canonization.

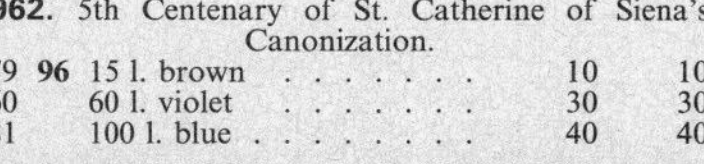

379	96	15 l. brown	10	10
360		60 l. violet	30	30
381		100 l. blue	40	40

97 Paulina M. Jaricot

98 St. Peter and St. Paul (from graffito on child's tomb)

1962. Death Centenary of Paulina M. Jaricot (founder of Society for the Propagation of the Faith). Multicoloured centres.

382	97	10 l. lilac	10	10
383		50 l. turquoise	25	20
384		150 l. grey	50	60

1962. 6th International Christian Archaeology Congress, Ravenna.

385	98	20 l. sepia and violet	10	10
386	–	40 l. green and brown	10	10
387	98	70 l. sepia and turquoise	10	10
388	–	100 l. green and red	15	15

DESIGN: 40, 100 l. "The Passion" (from bas relief on tomb in Domitilla cemetery, near Rome).

99 "Faith" (after Raphael)

100 "The Nativity"

1962. Ecumenical Council.

389	99	5 l. sepia and blue	10	10
390	–	10 l. sepia amd green	10	10
391	–	15 l. sepia and red	10	10
392	–	25 l. grey and red	10	10
393	–	30 l. black and mauve	10	10
394	–	40 l. sepia and red	10	10
395	–	60 l. brown and green	10	10
396	–	115 l. red	10	10

DESIGNS—Divine Virtues: 10 l. "Hope"; 15 l. "Charity" (both after Raphael); 25 l. Arms of Pope John XXIII and symbols of Evangelists (frontispiece of "Humanae Salutis" by Arrigo Bravi); 30 l. Central Nave, St. Peter's (council venue); 40 l. Pope John XXIII; 60 l. "St. Peter" (bronze in Vatican Basilica); 115 l. The Holy Ghost in form of dove.

1962. Christmas. Centres multicoloured.

397	100	10 l. grey	10	10
398		15 l. drab	10	10
399		90 l. green	15	15

101 "Miracle of the Loaves and Fishes" (after Murillo)

102 Pope John XXIII

1963. Freedom from Hunger.

400	101	15 l. sepia and brown	10	10
401	–	40 l. green and red	10	10
402	101	100 l. sepia and blue	10	10
403	–	200 l. green and turquoise	10	10

DESIGN: 40, 200 l. "Miracle of the Fishes" (after Raphael).

1963. Award of Balzan Peace Prize to Pope John XXIII.

404	102	15 l. brown	10	10
405		160 l. black	20	20

103 St. Peter's Keys

104 Pope Paul VI

1963. "Vacant See".

406	103	10 l. sepia	10	10
407		40 l. sepia on yellow	10	10
408		100 l. sepia on violet	10	10

1963. Coronation of Pope Paul VI.

409	104	15 l. black	10	10
410	–	40 l. red	10	10
411	104	115 l. brown	15	15
412	–	200 l. grey	15	15

DESIGN: 40, 200 l. Arms of Pope Paul VI.

105 "The Nativity" (African terracotta statuette)

106 St. Cyril

1963. Christmas.

413	105	10 l. brown and bistre	10	10
414		40 l. brown and blue	10	10
415		100 l. brown and olive	10	10

1963. 1100th Anniv of Conversion of Slavs by Saints Cyril and Methodius.

416	106	30 l. purple	10	10
417	–	70 l. brown	15	15
418	–	150 l. red	20	20

DESIGNS: 70 l. Map of Moravia; 150 l. St. Methodius.

107 Pope Paul VI

108 St. Peter, Pharoah's Tomb, Wadi-es-Sebua

1964. Pope Paul's Visit to the Holy Land.

419	107	15 l. black	10	10
420	–	25 l. red	10	10
421	–	70 l. sepia	10	10
422	–	160 l. blue	15	15

DESIGNS: 25 l. Church of the Nativity, Bethlehem; 70 l. Church of the Holy Sepulchre, Jerusalem; 160 l. Well of the Virgin Mary, Nazareth.

1964. Nubian Monuments Preservation.

423	108	10 l. brown and blue	10	10
424	–	20 l. multicoloured	10	10
425	108	70 l. brown and olive	10	10
426	–	200 l. multicoloured	20	20

DESIGN: 20, 200 l. Philae Temple.

109 Pope Paul VI

110 Michelangelo

1964. Vatican City's Participation in New York World's Fair.

427	109	15 l. blue	10	10
428	–	50 l. sepia	10	10
429	109	100 l. blue	10	10
430	–	250 l. brown	25	25

DESIGNS: 50 l. Michelangelo's "Pieta"; 250 l. Detail of Madonna's head from "Pieta".

1964. 400th Death Anniv of Michelangelo. Paintings in the Sistine Chapel.

431	110	10 l. black	10	10
432	–	25 l. red	10	10
433	–	30 l. olive	10	10
434	–	40 l. violet	10	10
435	–	150 l. green	10	10

PAINTINGS: 25 l. Prophet Isaiah; 30 l. Delphic Sibyl; 40 l. Prophet Jeremiah; 150 l. Prophet Joel.

111 "The Good Samaritan" (after Emilio Greco)

1964. Red Cross Centenary (1963). Cross in red.

436	111	10 l. brown	10	10
437		30 l. blue	10	10
438		300 l. sepia	30	30

112 "Christmas Scene" (after Kimiko Koseki) 114 Pope Paul at prayer

113 Cues's Birthplace

1964. Christmas.

439	**112**	10 l. multicoloured	10	10
440		15 l. multicoloured	10	10
441		135 l. multicoloured	10	10

1964. 500th Death Anniv of Nicholas Cues (Cardinal Cusanus).

442	**113**	40 l. green	10	10
443	–	200 l. red	20	20

DESIGN: 200 l. Cardinal Cusanus's sepulchre, St. Peter's (relief by A. Bregno).

1964. Pope Paul's Visit to India.

444	**114**	15 l. purple	10	10
445	–	25 l. green	10	10
446	–	60 l. sepia	10	10
447	–	200 l. purple	20	20

DESIGN—HORIZ: 25 l. Public altar, "The Oval", Bombay; 60 l. "Gateway to India", Bombay. VERT: 200 l. Pope Paul walking across map of India.

115 Sts. Mbaga Tuzinde, Carolus Lwanga and Kizito 116 Dante (after Raphael)

1965. Ugandan Martyrs. T **115** and similar portrait designs.

448	–	15 l. turquoise	10	10
449	**115**	20 l. brown	10	10
450	–	30 l. blue	10	10
451	–	75 l. black	10	10
452	–	100 l. red	10	10
453	–	160 l. violet	15	15

DESIGNS: 15 l. St. Joseph Mukasa and six other martyrs; 30 l. Sts. Matthias Mulumba, Noe Mawagalli and Lucas Banabakintu; 75 l. Sts. Gonzaga Gonza, Athanasius Bazzekuketta, Pontianus Ngondwe and Bruno Serunkuma; 100 l. Sts. Anatolius Kiriggwajjo, Andreas Kaggwa and Adulphus Mukasa; 160 l. Sts. Mukasa Kiriwananvu and Gyavira.

1965. 700th Anniv of Dante's Birth.

454	**116**	10 l. brown & light brown	10	10
455	–	40 l. brown and red	10	10
456	–	70 l. brown and green	15	15
457	–	200 l. brown and blue	20	20

DESIGNS—After drawings by Botticelli. 40 l. "Inferno"; 70 l. "Purgatory"; 200 l. "Paradise".

117 St. Benedict (after Perugino) 118 Pope Paul

1965. Declaration of St. Benedict as Patron Saint of Europe.

458	**117**	40 l. brown	10	10
459	–	300 l. green	25	25

DESIGN: 300 l. Monte Cassino Abbey.

1965. Pope Paul's Visit to the U.N., New York.

460	**118**	20 l. brown	10	10
461	–	30 l. blue	10	10
462	–	150 l. green	10	10
463	**118**	300 l. purple	25	25

DESIGN: 30, 150 l. U.N.O. Headquarters, New York.

119 "The Nativity" (Peruvian setting) 120 Pope Paul

1965. Christmas.

464	**119**	20 l. lake	10	10
465		40 l. brown	10	10
466		200 l. green	15	15

1966.

467	**120**	5 l. brown	10	10
468	–	10 l. violet	10	10
469	–	15 l. brown	10	10
470	–	20 l. green	10	10
471	–	30 l. brown	10	10
472	–	40 l. turquoise	10	10
473	–	55 l. blue	10	10
474	–	75 l. purple	10	10
475	–	90 l. mauve	10	10
476	–	130 l. green	10	10

DESIGNS (SCULPTURES): 10 l. "Music"; 15 l. "Science"; 20 l. "Painting"; 30 l. "Sculpture"; 40 l. "Building"; 55 l. "Carpentry"; 75 l. "Agriculture"; 90 l. "Metallurgy"; 130 l. "Learning".

121 Queen Dabrowka and King Mieszko I

1966. Poland's Christian Millennium.

477	**121**	15 l. black	10	10
478	–	25 l. violet	10	10
479	–	40 l. red	10	10
480	–	50 l. red	10	10
481	–	150 l. slate	10	10
482	–	220 l. brown	15	15

DESIGNS: 25 l. St. Adalbert (Wojciech) and Wrocław and Gniezno Cathedrals; 40 l. St. Stanislas, Skalka Cathedral and Wawel Royal Palace, Cracow; 50 l. Queen Jadwiga (Hedwig), Ostra Brama Gate with Mater Misericordiae, Wilno and Jagellon University Library, Cracow; 150 l. "Black Madonna", Jasna Gora Monastery (Czestochowa) and St. John's Cathedral, Warsaw; 220 l. Pope Paul VI greeting Poles.

122 Pope John XXIII and St. Peter's, Rome

1966. 4th Anniv of Opening of Ecumenical Council.

483	**122**	10 l. black and red	10	10
484	–	15 l. green and brown	10	10
485	–	55 l. mauve and sepia	10	10
486	–	90 l. black and green	10	10
487	–	100 l. yellow and green	10	10
488	–	130 l. sepia and brown	10	10

DESIGNS: 15 l. Book of Prayer, St. Peter's; 55 l. Mass; 90 l. Pope Paul with Patriarch Athenagoras; 100 l. Episcopal ring; 130 l. Pope Paul at closing ceremony (12.10.65).

123 "The Nativity" (after sculpture by Scorzelli) 124 Jet Airliner over St. Peter's

1966. Christmas.

489	**123**	20 l. purple	10	10
490		55 l. green	10	10
491		225 l. brown	15	15

1967. Air.

492	**124**	20 l. violet	10	10
493	–	40 l. lilac and pink	10	10
494	–	90 l. blue and grey	10	10
495	**124**	100 l. black and red	10	10
496	–	200 l. lilac and grey	15	10
497	–	500 l. brown & light brown	45	35

DESIGNS: 40, 200 l. Radio mast and St. Gabriel's statue; 90, 500 l. Aerial view of St. Peter's.

125 St. Peter 126 "The Three Shepherd Children" (sculpture)

1967. 1900th Anniv of Martyrdom of Saints Peter and Paul. Multicoloured.

498	15 l. Type **125**	10	10
499	20 l. St. Paul	10	10
500	55 l. The two Saints	10	10
501	90 l. Bernini's baldachin, St. Peter's	10	10
502	220 l. Arnolfo di Cambio's tabernacle, St. Paul's Basilica	20	20

1967. 50th Anniv of Fatima Apparitions. Multicoloured.

503	30 l. Type **126**	10	10
504	50 l. Basilica of Fatima	10	10
505	200 l. Pope Paul VI praying before Virgin's statue at Fatima	20	20

127 Congress Emblem 128 "The Nativity" (Byzantine carving)

1967. 3rd World Apostolic Laity Congress, Rome.

506	**127**	40 l. red	15	15
507		130 l. blue	15	15

1967. Christmas.

508	**128**	25 l. multicoloured	10	10
509		55 l. multicoloured	10	10
510		180 l. multicoloured	15	15

129 "Angel Gabriel" (detail from "The Annunciation" by Fra Angelico) 130 Pope Paul VI

1968. Air.

511	**129**	1000 l. red on cream	70	80
512		1500 l. black on cream	90	1·10

1968. Pope Paul's Visit to Colombia.

513	**130**	25 l. brown and black	10	10
514	–	55 l. ochre, grey & black	10	10
515	–	220 l. sepia, blue & black	20	20

DESIGNS: 55 l. Monstrance (Raphael's "Disputa"); 220 l. Map of South America.

131 "The Holy Child of Prague" 132 "The Resurrection" (Fra Angelico)

1968. Christmas.

516	**131**	20 l. purple and red	10	10
517		50 l. violet and lilac	10	10
518		250 l. blue and light blue	20	20

1969. Easter.

519	**132**	20 l. red and buff	10	10
520		90 l. green and buff	10	10
521		180 l. blue and buff	15	15

133 Colonnade 134 Pope with Young Africans

1969. Europa.

522	**133**	50 l. brown and slate	10	10
523		90 l. brown and red	15	15
524		130 l. brown and green	15	15

1969. Pope Paul's Visit to Uganda.

525	**134**	25 l. brown and ochre	10	10
526	–	55 l. brown and red	10	10
527	–	250 l. multicoloured	20	20

DESIGNS: 55 l. Pope with African bishops; 250 l. Map of Africa and olive branch.

EXPO 70
POSTE VATICANE L.25

135 Pope Pius IX 136 "Expo 70" Emblem

1969. Centenary of St. Peter's Circle Society.

528	**135**	30 l. brown	10	10
529	–	50 l. slate	10	10
530	–	220 l. purple	20	20

DESIGNS: 50 l. Monogram of Society; 220 l. Pope Paul VI.

1970. "Expo 70" World's Fair, Osaka. Mult.

531	25 l. Type **136**	10	10
532	40 l. Osaka Castle	10	10
533	55 l. "Madonna and Child" (Domoto)	10	10
534	90 l. Vatican pavilion	10	10
535	110 l. Mt. Fuji	10	10

137 Commemorative Medal of Pius IX

1970. Centenary of 1st Vatican Council.

536	**137**	20 l. brown and orange	10	10
537	–	50 l. multicoloured	10	10
538	–	180 l. purple and red	15	15

DESIGNS: 50 l. Arms of Pius IX; 180 l. Council souvenir medal.

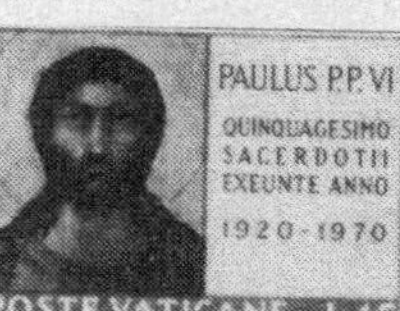

138 "Christ" (Simone Martini)

1970. 50th Anniv of Pope Paul's Ordination as Priest. Multicoloured.

539	15 l. Type **138**	10	10
540	25 l. "Christ" (R. v. d. Weyden)	10	10
541	50 l. "Christ" (Durer)	10	10
542	90 l. "Christ" (El Greco)	10	10
543	180 l. Pope Paul VI	15	15

139 "Adam" (Michelangelo) 140 Pope Paul VI

1970. 25th Anniv of United Nations.
544 20 l. Type **139** 10 10
545 90 l. "Eve" (Michelangelo) . . 10 10
546 220 l. Olive branch 20 20

1970. Pope Paul's Visit to Asia and Oceania. Multicoloured.
547 25 l. Type **140** 10 10
548 55 l. "Holy Child of Cebu" (Philippines) 10 10
549 100 l. "Madonna and Child", Darwin Cathedral (G. Hamori) 10 10
550 130 l. Manila Cathedral . . . 10 10
551 220 l. Sydney Cathedral . . . 15 15

141 "Angel with Lectern" **142** "Madonna and Child" (F. Gnissi)

1971. Racial Equality Year. Multicoloured.
552 20 l. Type **141** 10 10
553 40 l. "Christ Crucified, and Doves" 10 10
554 50 l. Type **141** 10 10
555 130 l. As 40 l. 10 10

1971. Easter. Religious Paintings. Multicoloured.
556 25 l. Type **142** 10 10
557 40 l. "Madonna and Child" (Sassetta—S. di Giovanni) . 10 10
558 55 l. "Madonna and Child" (C. Crivelli) 10 10
559 90 l. "Madonna and Child" (C. Maratta) 10 10
560 180 l. "The Holy Family" (G. Ceracchini) 15 15

143 "St. Dominic Guzman" (Sienese School)

1971. 800th Birth Anniv of St. Dominic Guzman (founder of Preaching Friars Order). Multicoloured.
561 25 l. Type **143** 10 10
562 55 l. Portrait by Fra Angelico 10 10
563 90 l. Portrait by Titian 10 10
564 180 l. Portrait by El Greco . . 15 15

144 "St. Matthew"

1971. Air.
565 **144** 200 l. black and green . . 25 25
566 – 300 l. black and brown . . 35 35
567 – 500 l. black and pink . . 80 65
568 – 1000 l. black and mauve . . 90 75
DESIGNS: "The Four Evangelists" (ceiling frescoes by Fra Angelico in the Niccolina Chapel, Vatican City)—300 l. "St. Mark"; 500 l. "St. Luke"; 1000 l. "St. John".

145 "St. Stephen" (from chasuble, Szekesfehervar Church, Hungary) **146** Bramante's Design for Cupola, St. Peter's

1971. Millennium of St. Stephen, King of Hungary.
569 **145** 50 l. multicoloured 10 10
570 – 180 l. black and yellow . . 20 20
DESIGN: 180 l. "Madonna, Patroness of Hungary", (sculpture, circa 1511).

1972. Bramante Celebrations.
571 **146** 25 l. black and yellow . . 10 10
572 – 90 l. black and yellow . . 10 10
573 – 130 l. black and yellow . . 15 15
DESIGNS: 90 l. Donato Bramante (architect) from medal; 130 l. Spiral staircase, Innocent VIII's Belvedere, Vatican.

147 "St. Mark at Sea" (mosaic)

1972. U.N.E.S.C.O. "Save Venice" Campaign. Multicoloured.
574 25 l. Type **147** 25 25
575 50 l. Venice (top left-hand section) 15 15
576 50 l. Venice (top right-hand section) 15 15
577 50 l. Venice (bottom left-hand section) 15 15
578 50 l. Venice (bottom right-hand section) 15 15
579 180 l. St. Mark's Basilica . . 1·00 1·00
Nos. 575/8 are smaller 39 × 28 mm and were issued together, se-tenant, forming a composite design.

148 Gospel of St. Mark (from codex "Biblia dell'Aracoeli")

1972. International Book Year. Illuminated Manuscripts. Multicoloured.
581 30 l. Type **148** 10 10
582 50 l. Gospel of St. Luke ("Biblia dell'Aracoeli") 10 10
583 90 l. 2nd Epistle of St. John (Bologna codex) 10 10
584 100 l. Revelation of St. John (Bologna codex) 10 10
585 130 l. Epistle of St. Paul to the Romans (Italian codex) . . 20 20

149 Luigi Orione (founder of "Caritas")

1972. Birth Centenaries. Multicoloured.
586 50 l. Type **149** 10 10
587 180 l. Lorenzo Perosi (composer) 25 30

150 Cardinal Bassarione (Roselli fresco, Sistine Chapel) **151** Congress Emblem

1972. 500th Death Anniv of Cardinal Bassarione.
588 – 40 l. green 10 10
589 **150** 90 l. red 10 10
590 – 130 l. black 15 15
DESIGNS: 40 l. "Reading of Bull of Union" (relief); 130 l. Arms of Cardinal Bassarione.

1973. International Eucharistic Congress. Melbourne. Multicoloured.
591 25 l. Type **151** 10 10
592 75 l. Michelangelo's "Pieta" . 10 10
593 300 l. Melbourne Cathedral . 30 30

152 St. Theresa's Birthplace **153** Torun (birthplace)

1973. Birth Centenary of St. Theresa of Lisieux.
594 **152** 25 l. black and red . . . 10 10
595 – 55 l. black and yellow . . 10 10
596 – 220 l. black and blue . . 25 25
DESIGNS: 55 l. St. Theresa; 220 l. Basilica of Lisieux.

1973. 500th Birth Anniv of Copernicus.
597 **153** 20 l. green 10 10
598 – 50 l. brown 10 10
599 **153** 100 l. purple 15 15
600 – 130 l. blue 15 20
DESIGN: 50, 130 l. Copernicus.

154 "St. Wenceslas"

1973. Millenary of Prague Diocese. Mult.
601 20 l. Type **154** 10 10
602 90 l. Arms of Prague Diocese . 10 10
603 150 l. Tower of Prague Cathedral 15 15
604 220 l. "St. Adalbert" 25 25

155 Church of St. Hripsime **156** "Angel" (porch of St. Mark's, Venice)

1973. 800th Death Anniv of St. Narsete Shnorali (Armenian patriarch).
605 **155** 25 l. brown and ochre . . 10 10
606 – 90 l. black and lilac . . . 10 10
607 – 180 l. purple and green . . 20 20
DESIGNS: 90 l. Armenian "khatchkar" (stone stele) inscribed "Victory"; 180 l. St. Narsete Shnorali.

1974. Air.
608 **156** 2500 l. multicoloured . . . 1·75 2·00

157 "And there was Light" **159** Pupils

158 Noah's Ark and Dove

1974. International Book Year (1973). "The Bible". Biblical Texts. Multicoloured.
609 15 l. Type **157** 10 10
610 25 l. "Noah entrusts himself to God" (horiz) 10 10
611 50 l. "The Annunciation" . . . 10 10
612 90 l. "The Nativity" 10 10
613 180 l. "The Lord feeds His People" (horiz) 20 20

1974. Centenary of Universal Postal Union. Mosaics. Multicoloured.
614 50 l. Type **158** 15 15
615 90 l. Sheep in landscape . . . 15 15

1974. 700th Death Anniv of St. Thomas Aquinas (founder of Fra Angelico School). "The School of St. Thomas" (painting, St. Mark's Convent, Florence). Each brown and gold.
616 50 l. Type **159** 10 10
617 90 l. St. Thomas and pupils (24 × 40 mm) 15 15
618 220 l. Pupils (different) 20 20
Nos. 616/18 were issued together, se-tenant, forming a composite design.

160 "Civita" (medieval quarter), Bagnoregio **161** Christus Victor

1974. 700th Death Anniv of St. Bonaventura of Bagnoregio. Wood-carvings. Multicoloured.
619 40 l. Type **160** 10 10
620 90 l. "Tree of Life" (13th-century motif) 15 15
621 220 l. "St. Bonaventura (B. Gozzoli) 20 20

1974. Holy Year (1975). Multicoloured.
622 10 l. Type **161** 10 10
623 25 l. Christ 10 10
624 30 l. Christ (different) 10 10
625 40 l. Cross and dove 10 10
626 50 l. Christ enthroned 10 10
627 55 l. St. Peter 10 10
628 90 l. St. Paul 10 10
629 100 l. St. Peter 10 10
630 130 l. St. Paul 10 10
631 220 l. Arms of Pope Paul VI . 20 20
632 250 l. Pope Paul VI giving blessing 20 20

162 Fountain, St. Peter's Square

1975. European Architectural Heritage Year. Vatican Fountains.
633 **162** 20 l. black and brown . . 10 10
634 – 40 l. black and lilac . . . 10 10
635 – 50 l. black and pink . . . 10 10
636 – 90 l. black and green . . 10 10
637 – 100 l. black and green . . 10 10
638 – 200 l. black and blue . . 15 15
FOUNTAINS: 40 l. Piazza St. Martha; 50 l. Del Forno; 90 l. Belvedere courtyard; 100 l. Academy of Sciences; 200 l. Galley fountain.

163 "Pentecost" (El Greco) **164** "Miracle of Loaves and Fishes" (gilt glass)

1975. Pentecost.
639 **163** 300 l. orange and red . . 30 30

1975. 9th International Christian Archaeological Congress. 4th-century Art. Multicoloured.
640 30 l. Type **164** 10 10
641 150 l. Christ (painting) . . . 10 10
642 200 l. Raising of Lazarus (gilt glass) 20 20

165 Pope Sixtus IV investing Bartolomeo Sacchi as First Librarian (fresco)

1975. 500th Anniv of Apostolic Library.
643 **165** 70 l. red and violet . . . 10 10
644 – 100 l. green & light green 10 10
645 – 250 l. red and blue . . . 25 25
DESIGNS—VERT: 100 l. Pope Sixtus IV (codex). HORIZ: 250 l. Pope Sixtus IV visiting library (fresco).

166 Passionists' House, Argentario **167** Detail from Painting

1975. Death Bicentenary of St. Paul of the Cross (founder of Passionist religious order). Multicoloured.
646 50 l. Type **166** 10 10
647 150 l. "St. Paul" (D. della Porta) (26 × 31 mm) 15 15
648 300 l. Basilica of Saints John and Paul 30 30

1975. International Women's Year. Painting by Fra Angelico. Multicoloured.
649 100 l. Type **167** 15 15
650 200 l. Detail from painting (different) 25 25

168 "The Last Judgement" (detail) **170** Eucharist and Ear of Wheat and Globe

169 "Madonna in Glory with the Child Jesus and Six Saints" (detail)

1976. Air.
651 **168** 500 l. brown and blue . . 1·25 1·00
652 – 1000 l. brown and blue . . 1·40 1·00
653 – 2500 l. brown and blue . . 1·90 1·50
DESIGNS: 1000 l. and 2500 l. show different motifs from Michelangelo's "The Last Judgement".

1976. 400th Death Anniv of Titian. Details from "The Madonna in Glory with the Child Jesus and Six Saints".
654 **169** 100 l. red 20 20
655 – 300 l. red 30 30

1976. 41st Int Eucharist Congress, Philadelphia.
656 **170** 150 l. multicoloured . . . 15 15
657 – 200 l. gold and blue . . . 20 20
658 – 400 l. gold and green . . . 40 40
DESIGNS: 200 l. Eucharist within protective hands; 400 l. Adoration of the Eucharist.

171 "Transfiguration" (detail)

1976. Details of Raphael's "Transfiguration". Multicoloured.
659 30 l. Type **171** ("Moses") . . 10 10
660 40 l. "Christ Transfigured" . . 10 10
661 50 l. "Prophet Elijah" 10 10
662 100 l. "Two Apostles" 10 10
663 150 l. "The Relatives" 15 15
664 200 l. "Landscape" 20 20

172 St. John's Tower and Fountain

1976. Architecture.
665 **172** 50 l. brown and lilac . . 10 10
666 – 100 l. brown & lt brown . . 10 10
667 – 120 l. black and green . . 10 10
668 – 180 l. black and grey . . 20 20
669 – 250 l. brown and ochre . . 25 25
670 – 300 l. purple 30 30
DESIGNS: 100 l. Fountain of the Sacrament; 120 l. Fountain at entrance to Gardens; 180 l. Cupola of St. Peter's and Sacristy Basilica; 250 l. Borgia Tower, Sistine Chapel and Via della Fondamenta; 300 l. Apostolic Palace, Courtyard of St. Damasius.

173 "Canticles of Brother Sun" (detail)

1977. 750th Death Anniv of St. Francis of Assisi. Details from "Canticles of Brother Sun" by D. Cambellotti. Multicoloured.
671 50 l. Type **173** ("The Lord's Creatures") 10 10
672 70 l. "Brother Sun" 10 10
673 100 l. "Sister Moon and Stars" . . 10 10
674 130 l. "Sister Water" 15 15
675 170 l. "Praise in Infirmities and Tribulations" 20 25
676 200 l. "Praise for Bodily Death" . . 20 25

174 Detail from Fresco **175** "Death of the Virgin"

1977. 600th Anniv of Return of Pope Gregory from Avignon. Fresco by G. Vasari. Multicoloured.
677 170 l. Type **174** 30 35
678 350 l. Detail from fresco (different) 40 40

1977. Festival of Assumption. Miniatures from Apostolic Library. Multicoloured.
679 200 l. Type **175** 25 25
680 400 l. "Assumption of Virgin into Heaven" 45 45

176 "God of the Nile"

1977. Classical Sculpture in Vatican Museums (1st series). Statues. Multicoloured.
681 50 l. Type **176** 10 10
682 120 l. "Pericles" 15 15
683 130 l. "Husband and Wife with joined Hands" 15 15
684 150 l. "Belvedere Apollo" . . 15 15
685 170 l. "Laocoon" 15 15
686 350 l. "Belvedere Torso" . . 30 40
See also Nos. 687/92.

177 "Creation of the Human Race"

1977. Classical Sculpture in Vatican Museums (2nd series). Paleo-Christian Sarcophagi Carvings. Multicoloured.
687 50 l. Type **177** 10 10
688 70 l. "Three Youths in the Fiery Furnace" 10 10
689 100 l. "Adoration of the Magi" . . 10 10
690 130 l. "Christ raising Lazarus from the Dead" 15 15
691 200 l. "The Good Shepherd" . . 25 25
692 400 l. "Resurrection" 40 40

178 "Madonna with the Parrot" (detail) **180** Arms of Pope Pius IX

179 "The Face of Christ"

1977. 400th Birth Anniv of Rubens.
693 **178** 350 l. multicoloured . . . 45 40

1978. 80th Birthday of Pope Paul VI. Mult.
694 350 l. Type **179** 35 35
695 400 l. "Pope Paul VI" (drawing by L. B. Barriviera) 40 40

1978. Death Cent of Pope Pius IX. Multicoloured.
696 130 l. Type **180** 15 15
697 170 l. Seal of Pius IX 20 20
698 200 l. Portrait of Pius IX . . . 25 25

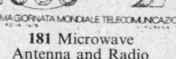

181 Microwave Antenna and Radio Vatican Emblem **182** St. Peter's Keys

1978. Air. Tenth World Telecommunications Day.
699 **181** 1000 l. multicoloured . . . 90 75
700 2000 l. multicoloured . . . 2·25 2·00
701 3000 l. multicoloured . . . 3·25 2·50

1978. "Vacant See".
702 **182** 120 l. blue and violet . . . 15 15
703 150 l. pink and violet . . . 15 15
704 250 l. yellow and violet . . 20 20

183 St. Peter's Keys **184** Pope John Paul I on Throne

1978. "Vacant See".
705 **183** 120 l. yellow, blue & blk . 15 20
706 200 l. yellow, red & blk . . 15 20
707 250 l. multicoloured . . . 20 30

1978. Pope John Paul I Commemoration. Multicoloured.
708 70 l. Type **184** 10 10
709 120 l. The Pope smiling . . . 15 15
710 250 l. The Pope in Vatican Gardens 20 20
711 350 l. The Pope giving blessing (horiz) 30 30

185 Arms of Pope John Paul II **186** The Martyrdom (14th-century Latin codex)

1979. Inauguration of Pontificate of Pope John Paul II. Multicoloured.
712 170 l. Type **185** 20 20
713 250 l. The Pope giving his blessing 25 25
714 400 l. "Christ handing the keys to St. Peter" (relief, A. Buonvicino) 45 45

1979. 900th Death Anniv of St. Stanislaus. Multicoloured.
715 120 l. Type **186** 15 15
716 150 l. St. Stanislaus appears to the people (14th century Latin codex) 15 15
717 250 l. Gold reliquary 25 25
718 500 l. Cracow Cathedral . . . 40 40

187 Meteorograph

1979. Death Centenary of Angelo Secchi (astronomer). Multicoloured.
719 180 l. Type **187** 20 20
720 220 l. Spectroscope 25 25
721 300 l. Telescope 30 30

188 St. Basil and Vignette "Handing Monastic Laws to a Hermit" **189** Aerial View of Vatican City

1979. 160th Death Anniv of St. Basil the Great. Multicoloured.
722 150 l. Type **188** 15 15
723 520 l. St. Basil and vignette "Caring for the Sick" . . . 45 55

1979. 50th Anniv of Vatican City State.
724 **189** 50 l. brown, black & red . 15 15
725 – 70 l. multicoloured . . . 15 15
726 – 120 l. multicoloured . . . 15 15
727 – 150 l. multicoloured . . . 15 15
728 – 170 l. multicoloured . . . 20 20
729 – 250 l. multicoloured . . . 30 30
730 – 450 l. multicoloured . . . 55 65
DESIGNS—POPES AND ARMS: 70 l. Pius XI; 120 l. Pius XII; 150 l. John XXIII; 170 l. Paul VI; 250 l. John Paul I; 450 l. John Paul II.

190 Child in Swaddling Clothes (relief, Foundling Hospital, Florence)

1979. International Year of the Child. Sculptures by Della Robbia.
731 **190** 50 l. multicoloured . . . 10 10
732 – 120 l. multicoloured . . . 20 20
733 – 200 l. multicoloured . . . 25 25
734 – 350 l. multicoloured . . . 40 45
DESIGNS: 120 l. to 350 l. Similar sculptures.

191 Abbot Desiderius offering Codices to St. Benedict

1980. 1500th Birth Anniv of St. Benedict of Nursia (founder of Benedictine Order). Multicoloured.
735 80 l. Type **191** 10 10
736 100 l. St. Benedict composing rules of the Order 10 10
737 150 l. Page of St. Benedict's Rules 15 15
738 220 l. Death of St. Benedict . . 20 20
739 450 l. Montecassino Abbey (after Paul Bril) 50 50

192 Hands reaching out to Pope and Arms of Santo Domingo

1980. Air. Pope John Paul II's Journeys (1st series). Different coats of arms.

740 **192** 200 l. multicoloured . . . 25 25
741 – 300 l. multicoloured . . . 35 35
742 – 500 l. violet, red & black . 60 60
743 – 1000 l. multicoloured . . . 1·25 90
744 – 1500 l. multicoloured . . . 1·75 1·40
745 – 2000 l. red, blue & black . 2·25 2·00
746 – 3000 l. black, red & blue . 3·50 3·00

COATS OF ARMS: 300 l. Mexico; 500 l. Poland; 1000 l. Ireland; 1500 l. United States; 2000 l. United Nations; 3000 l. Pope John Paul II and Archbishop Dimitrios of Turkey.

See also Nos. 768/78, 814/25, 862/9, 886/93, 912/16, 940/4, 963/6, 992/6, 1019/22 and 1076/80.

193 Bernini (self-portrait) and Medallion showing Baldacchino, St. Peter's

194 St. Albertus on Mission of Peace

1980. 300th Death Anniv of Gian Lorenzo Bernini (artist and architect). Multicoloured.

747 80 l. Type **193** 10 10
748 170 l. Bernini and medallion showing his plan for St. Peter's . 20 15
749 250 l. Bernini, medallion of bronze chair and group "Doctors of the Church", St. Peter's 25 25
750 350 l. Bernini and medallion of Apostolic Palace stairway . 35 35

1980. 700th Death Anniv of St. Albertus Magnus. Multicoloured.

751 300 l. Type **194** 35 35
752 400 l. St. Albertus as Bishop . 45 45

195 Communion of the Saints

1980. Feast of All Saints. Multicoloured.

753 250 l. Type **195** 30 30
754 500 l. Christ and saints . . . 55 55

196 Marconi, Pope Pius XI and Radio Emblem

1981. 50th Anniv of Vatican Radio. Mult.

755 100 l. Type **196** 10 10
756 150 l. Microphone 15 15
757 200 l. Antenna of Santa Maria di Galeria Radio Centre and statue of Archangel Gabriel 20 20
758 600 l. Pope John Paul II . . . 65 65

197 Virgil and his Writing-desk

1981. Death Bimillenary of Virgil (Roman poet). Multicoloured.

759 350 l. Type **197** 40 50
760 600 l. As Type **197** but inscr "P. VERGILI MARONIS AENEIDOS LIBRI" . . . 50 65

198 Congress Emblem and Apparition of Virgin to St. Bernadette

199 Jan van Ruusbroec writing Treatise

1981. 42nd International Eucharistic Congress, Lourdes. Multicoloured.

761 80 l. Congress emblem . . . 10 10
762 150 l. Type **198** 20 20
763 200 l. Emblem and pilgrims going to Lourdes 25 25
764 500 l. Emblem and Bishop with faithful venerating Virgin . 60 40

1981. 600th Death Anniv of Jan van Ruusbroec (Flemish mystic). Multicoloured.

765 200 l. Type **199** 30 30
766 300 l. Ruusbroec 35 35

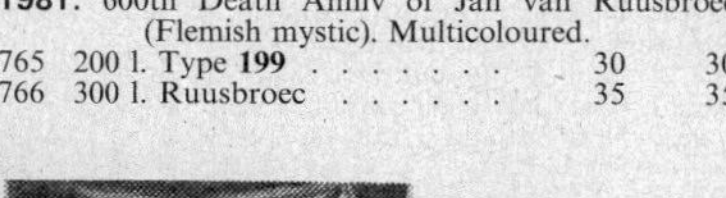

200 Turin Shroud and I.Y.D.P. Emblem

201 Arms of John Paul II

1981. International Year of Disabled Persons.

767 **200** 600 l. multicoloured . . . 70 70

1981. Pope John Paul II's Journeys (2nd series). Multicoloured.

768 50 l. Type **201** 10 10
769 100 l. Crucifix and map of Africa 10 10
770 120 l. Hands holding crucifix 15 15
771 150 l. Pope performing baptism 20 20
772 200 l. Pope embracing African bishop 25 25
773 250 l. Pope blessing sick man 30 30
774 300 l. Notre-Dame Cathedral, Paris 40 40
775 400 l. Pope addressing U.N.E.S.C.O., Paris . . . 60 60
776 600 l. "Christ of the Andes", Rio de Janeiro 90 90
777 700 l. Cologne Cathedral . . 1·00 1·00
778 900 l. Pope giving blessing . . 1·25 1·25

202 Agnes handing Church to Grand Master of the Crosiers of the Red Star

203 "Pueri Cantores" (left panel)

1982. 700th Death Anniv of Blessed Agnes of Prague. Multicoloured.

779 700 l. Type **202** 90 90
780 900 l. Agnes receiving letter from St. Clare . . . . 1·00 1·00

1982. 500th Death Anniv of Luca della Robbia (sculptor).

781 **203** 1000 l. green and blue . . 1·10 1·10
782 – 1000 l. multicoloured . . 1·10 1·10
783 – 1000 l. green and blue . . 1·10 1·10

DESIGNS—As T **203**: No. 783, "Pueri Cantores" (right panel). 44 × 36 mm: No. 782, "Virgin Mary in Prayer".

204 Virgin Mary and St. Joseph clothe St. Theresa

205 Examining Globe

1982. 400th Death Anniv of St. Theresa of Avila.

784 **204** 200 l. orange, grey and red 25 25
785 – 600 l. grey, orange and blue 75 75
786 – 1000 l. grey, orange and mauve . . . . 1·25 1·25

DESIGNS: 600 l. Ecstasy of St. Theresa; 1000 l. St. Theresa writing "The Interior Castle".

1982. 400th Anniv of Gregorian Calendar. Details from Pope Gregory XIII's tomb.

787 **205** 200 l. green 20 20
788 – 300 l. black 35 35
789 – 700 l. purple . . . . 1·00 1·00

DESIGNS: 300 l. Presenting proposals to Pope Gregory XIII; 700 l. Kneeling figures.

206 "Nativity" (Veit Stoss)

1982. Christmas.

791 **206** 300 l. stone, brn & gold . 40 40
792 – 450 l. lilac, purple & sil . . 60 60

DESIGN: 450 l. "Nativity with Pope John Paul II" (Enrico Manfrini).

207 Crucifixion

209 "Theology"

1983. Holy Year. Multicoloured.

793 300 l. Type **207** 40 40
794 350 l. Christ the Redeemer . . 45 45
795 400 l. Pope bringing message of redemption to world 55 55
796 2000 l. Dove of the Holy Spirit passing through Holy Door . 2·50 2·50

1983. 500th Birth Anniv of Raphael (artist).

798 **209** 50 l. blue & ultramarine . 10 10
799 – 400 l. purple and mauve . 50 50
800 – 500 l. brown & chestnut . 65 65
801 – 1200 l. green & turquoise . 1·50 1·50

DESIGNS—Allegories on the Segnatura Room ceiling: 400 l. "Poetry"; 500 l. "Justice"; 1200 l. "Philosophy".

210 "Moses explaining the Law to the People" (Luca Signorelli)

1983. Air. World Communications Year. Multicoloured.

804 2000 l. Type **210** . . . . . . 2·50 2·00
805 5000 l. "St. Paul preaching in Athens" (Raphael) . . . . . 5·50 4·75

211 Mendel and Hybrid Experiment

212 St. Casimir and Vilna Cathedral and Castle

1984. Death Centenary of Gregor Johan Mendel (geneticist).

806 **211** 450 l. multicoloured . . . 75 75
807 1500 l. multicoloured . . . 2·00 2·00

1984. 500th Death Anniv of St. Casimir (patron saint of Lithuania).

808 **212** 550 l. multicoloured . . . 75 75
809 1200 l. multicoloured . . . 1·75 1·75

213 Pontifical Academy of Sciences

1984. Cultural and Scientific Institutions.

810 **213** 150 l. yellow and brown . 25 25
811 – 450 l. multicoloured . . . 65 65
812 – 550 l. yellow and violet . 80 80
813 – 1500 l. yellow and blue . 1·90 1·90

DESIGNS: 450 l. Seals and document from Vatican Secret Archives; 550 l. Entrance to Vatican Apostolic Library; 1500 l. Vatican Observatory, Castelgandolfo.

214 Pope in Karachi

215 Damascus and Sepulchre of Sts. Marcellinus and Peter

1984. Pope John Paul II's Journeys (3rd series). Multicoloured.

814 50 l. Type **214** 10 10
815 100 l. Pope and image of Our Lady of Penafrancia, Philippines 10 10
816 150 l. Pope with crucifix (Guam) 20 20
817 250 l. Pope and Tokyo Cathedral 50 50
818 300 l. Pope at Anchorage, Alaska 30 30
819 400 l. Crucifix, crowd and map of Africa 40 40
820 450 l. Pope and image of Our Lady of Fatima (Portugal) . 45 45
821 550 l. Pope, Archbishop of Westminster and Canterbury Cathedral . . . . 1·25 1·25
822 1000 l. Pope and image of Our Lady of Lujan (Argentina) . 2·00 2·00
823 1500 l. Pope, Lake Leman and Geneva . . . . 3·00 3·00
824 2500 l. Pope and Mount Titano (San Marino) . . . . 5·00 5·00
825 4000 l. Pope and Santiago de Compostela Cathedral (Spain) 8·00 8·00

1984. 1600th Death Anniv of Pope St. Damasus. Multicoloured.

826 200 l. Type **215** 30 30
827 500 l. Damasus and epigraph from St. Januarius's tomb . 90 90
828 2000 l. Damasus and basilica ruins . . . . 4·00 4·00

216 More (after Holbein) and Map

217 St. Methodius holding Religious Paintings

1985. 450th Death Anniv of Saint Thomas More. Multicoloured.

829 250 l. Type **216** 45 45
830 400 l. St. Thomas More and title page of "Utopia" 85 85
831 2000 l. St. Thomas More and title page of "Life of Thomas More" by Domenico Regi . 3·50 3·50

1985. 1100th Death Anniv of Saint Methodius. Multicoloured.

832 500 l. Type **217** 90 90
833 600 l. Saints Cyril and Methodius with Pope Clement I's body 1·25 1·25
834 1700 l. Saints Benedict, Cyril and Methodius . . . . 2·75 2·75

218 Cross on Map of Africa

219 Eagle (from Door, St. Paul's Basilica, Rome)

1985. 43rd International Eucharistic Congress, Nairobi. Multicoloured.
835 100 l. Type **218** 20 20
836 400 l. Assembly of bishops . . 60 60
837 600 l. Chalice 90 90
838 2300 l. Family gazing at cross 3·50 3·50

1985. 900th Death Anniv of Pope Gregory VII. Multicoloured.
839 150 l. Type **219** 25 25
840 450 l. Pope Gregory VII . . . 75 75
841 2500 l. Pope Gregory's former sarcophagus (horiz) . . . . 4·00 4·00

220 Mosaic Map of Italy and Symbol of Holy See

1985. Ratification of Modification of 1929 Lateran Concordat.
842 **220** 400 l. multicoloured . . . 60 60

221 Carriage

222 "Nation shall not Lift up Sword against Nation. . ."

1985. "Italia '85" International Stamp Exhibition, Rome.
843 **221** 450 l. red and blue 65 65
844 – 1500 l. blue and mauve . . 2·10 2·10
DESIGN: 1500 l. Carriage (different).

1986. International Peace Year. Multicoloured.
846 50 l. Type **222** 10 10
847 350 l. Messenger's feet ("How beautiful. . .are the feet. . .") 50 50
848 450 l. Profiles and olive branch ("Blessed are the peacemakers. . .") 80 80
849 650 l. Dove and sun ("Glory to God in the highest. . .") . . 1·00 1·00
850 2000 l. Pope's hand releasing dove over rainbow ("Peace is a value with no frontiers. . .") 3·00 3·00

223/228 Vatican City (actual size 89 × 80 mm)

1986. World Heritage. Vatican City. Mult.
851 **223** 550 l. multicoloured . . . 1·00 1·00
852 **224** 550 l. multicoloured . . . 1·00 1·00
853 **225** 550 l. multicoloured . . . 1·00 1·00
854 **226** 550 l. multicoloured . . . 1·00 1·00
855 **227** 550 l. multicoloured . . . 1·00 1·00
856 **228** 550 l. multicoloured . . . 1·00 1·00
Nos. 851/6 were printed together, se-tenant, forming the composite design illustrated.

229 St. Camillus saving Invalid from Flood (after Pierre Subleyras)

230 "The Philosophers"

1986. Centenary of Proclamation of St. Camillus de Lellis and St. John of God as Patron Saints of Hospitals and the Sick.
857 **229** 700 l. green, violet & red . 1·25 1·25
858 – 700 l. blue, green & red . 1·25 1·25
859 – 2000 l. multicoloured . . . 3·75 3·75
DESIGNS: No. 858, St. John supporting the sick (after Gomez Moreno); 859, Emblems of Ministers of the Sick and Brothers Hospitallers, and Pope John Paul II talking to patient.

1986. 50th Anniv of Pontifical Academy of Sciences. Details from fresco "School of Athens" by Raphael. Multicoloured.
860 1500 l. Type **230** . . . . . . 2·25 2·25
861 2500 l. "The Scientists" . . . 3·25 3·25

231 Pope and Young People (Central America)

232 "St. Augustine reading St. Paul's Epistles" (fresco, Benozzo Gozzoli)

1986. Air. Pope John Paul II's Journeys (4th series). Multicoloured.
862 350 l. Type **231** 55 55
863 450 l. Pope in prayer, Warsaw Cathedral and Our Lady of Czestochowa (Poland) . . . 70 70
864 700 l. Pope kneeling and crowd at Lourdes (France) . . . . 1·00 90
865 1000 l. Sanctuary of Mariazell and St. Stephen's Cathedral, Vienna (Austria) . . . . . 1·50 1·25
866 1500 l. Pope and representatives of nations visited (Alaska, Asia and Pacific Islands) . . . . 2·25 1·75
867 2000 l. Image of St. Nicholas of Flue, Basilica of Einsiedeln and Pope (Switzerland) . . 3·00 2·25
868 2500 l. Crosses, Notre Dame Cathedral, Quebec and Pope (Canada) . . . . 3·50 2·75
869 5000 l. Pope, bishop and young people with cross (Spain, Dominican Republic and Puerto Rico) . . . . 7·00 5·50

1987. 1600th Anniv of Conversion and Baptism of St. Augustine. Multicoloured.
870 300 l. Type **232** 50 50
871 400 l. "Baptism of St. Augustine" (Bartolomeo di Gentile) . . 60 60
872 500 l. "Ecstasy of St. Augustine" (fresco, Benozzo Gozzoli) . 70 70
873 2200 l. "Dispute of the Sacrament" (detail of fresco, Raphael) . . . . 3·50 3·50

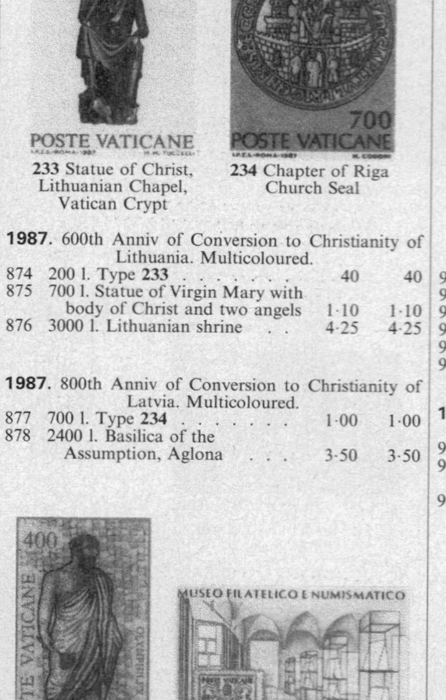

233 Statue of Christ, Lithuanian Chapel, Vatican Crypt

234 Chapter of Riga Church Seal

1987. 600th Anniv of Conversion to Christianity of Lithuania. Multicoloured.
874 200 l. Type **233** 40 40
875 700 l. Statue of Virgin Mary with body of Christ and two angels 1·10 1·10
876 3000 l. Lithuanian shrine . . 4·25 4·25

1987. 800th Anniv of Conversion to Christianity of Latvia. Multicoloured.
877 700 l. Type **234** . . . . 1·00 1·00
878 2400 l. Basilica of the Assumption, Aglona . . . 3·50 3·50

235 Judge

236 Stamp Room and 1929 5 c. Stamp

1987. "Olymphilex '87" Olympic Stamps Exhibition, Rome. Figures from Caracalla Baths floor mosaic. Multicoloured.
879 400 l. Type **235** 60 60
880 500 l. Runner 80 80
881 600 l. Discus-thrower 90 90
882 2000 l. Athlete . . . . . . 3·00 3·00

1987. Inauguration of Philatelic and Numismatic Museum. Multicoloured.
884 400 l. Type **236** 60 60
885 3500 l. Coin room and reverse of 1000 l. 1986 coin . . . . . . 4·75 4·75

1987. Pope John Paul II's Journeys (5th series). As T **231**. Multicoloured.
886 50 l. Youths, Pope and Machu Picchu (Venezuela, Ecuador, Peru, Trinidad and Tobago) 20 20
887 250 l. Antwerp Cathedral, smoke stacks and Pope (Netherlands, Luxembourg and Belgium) . 50 50
888 400 l. People, buildings and Pope (Togo, Ivory Coast, Cameroun, Central African Republic, Zaire, Kenya and Morocco) 85 85
889 500 l. Pope holding Cross and youths (Liechtenstein) . . . 1·00 1·00
890 600 l. Pope, Indians and Delhi Mosque (India) . . . . . . 1·40 1·40
891 700 l. Pope, people, ceramic and Bogota Cathedral (Colombia and St. Lucia) . . . . 1·50 1·50
892 2500 l. Pope, Cure d'Ars and Lyon Cathedral (France) . . 5·00 5·00
893 4000 l. Hands releasing dove and symbols of countries visited (Bangladesh, Singapore, Fiji, New Zealand, Australia and Seychelles) . . . . 8·00 8·00

237 Arrival of Relics

238 Children and Sister of Institute of the Daughters of Mary Help of Christians

1987. 900th Anniv of Transfer of St. Nicholas's Relics from Myra to Bari. Multicoloured.
894 500 l. Type **237** 90 90
895 700 l. St. Nicholas giving purses of gold to save from dishonour the three daughters of a poor man . . . . 1·40 1·40
896 3000 l. St. Nicholas saving a ship 8·50 8·50

1988. Death Centenary of St. John Bosco (founder of Salesian Brothers). Multicoloured.
897 500 l. Type **238** 75 75
898 1000 l. Bosco and children . . 1·25 1·25
899 2000 l. Children and Salesian lay brother . . . . 2·50 2·50
Nos. 897/9 were printed together, se-tenant, forming a composite design.

239 The Annunciation

240 Prince Vladimir the Great (15th-century icon)

1988. Marian Year. Multicoloured.
900 50 l. Type **239** 10 10
901 300 l. Nativity 40 40
902 500 l. Pentecost 65 65
903 750 l. The Assumption . . . 85 85
904 1000 l. Mother of the Church . 1·25 1·25
905 2400 l. Refuge of Sinners . . . 3·00 3·00

1988. Millenary of Conversion to Christianity of Rus of Kiev. Multicoloured.
906 450 l. Type **240** 60 60
907 650 l. St. Sophia's Cathedral, Kiev 90 90
908 2500 l. "Mother of God in Prayer" (mosaic, St. Sophia's Cathedral) . . . . 3·25 3·25

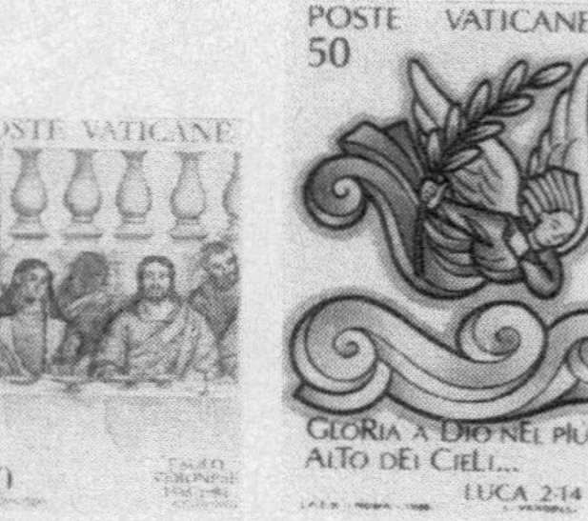

241 "Marriage of Cana" (detail)

242 Angel with Olive Branch

1988. 400th Death Anniv of Paolo Veronese (painter).
909 **241** 550 l. blue and red . . . 80 80
910 – 650 l. multicoloured . . . 1·25 1·25
911 – 3000 l. red and brown . . 3·25 3·25
DESIGNS—HORIZ: 650 l. "Self-portrait". VERT: 3000 l. "Marriage of Cana" (different detail).

1988. Air. Pope John Paul II's Journeys (6th series). As T **231**. Multicoloured.
912 450 l. Hands releasing dove, St. Peter's, Rome, Santiago Cathedral and Sanctuary of Our Lady, Lujan (Uruguay, Chile and Argentina) . . . 75 75
913 650 l. Pope in act of blessing, Speyer Cathedral and youths (German Federal Republic) 90 90
914 1000 l. Hands releasing dove, Gdansk altar and intertwined flowers and thorns (Poland) 1·25 1·25
915 2500 l. Skyscrapers and Pope blessing youths (U.S.A.) . . 3·25 3·25
916 5000 l. Hands releasing dove, tepee at Fort Simpson and American Indians (Canada) 6·00 6·00

1988. Christmas. Multicoloured.
917 50 l. Type **242** 10 10
918 400 l. Angel holding olive branch in both hands 50 50
919 500 l. Angel with olive branch (flying from right) 70 70
920 550 l. Shepherds 75 75
921 850 l. Nativity . . . . 1·00 1·00
922 1500 l. Wise Men . . . . . . 1·75 1·75

244 The Annunciation

245 Yellow-bibbed Lory

1989. 600th Anniv of Feast of Visitation of Virgin Mary. Illuminated initials. Multicoloured.
925 550 l. Type **244** 75 75
926 750 l. Virgin Mary and St. Elizabeth 85 85
927 2500 l. Virgin Mary and St. Elizabeth with Jesus and John the Baptist as babies . . . 3·00 3·00

1989. Birds featured in "Histoire Naturelle des Oiseaux" by Eleazar Albin. Multicoloured.
928 100 l. Type **245** 15 15
929 150 l. Green woodpecker . . . 20 20
930 200 l. Goldcrest ("Crested wren") and common wren 30 30
931 350 l. Common kingfisher . . 45 45
932 500 l. Common cardinal ("red Gros beak of Virginia") . . . 65 65
933 700 l. Bullfinch 90 90
934 1500 l. Lapwing ("Lapwing plover") . . . . 2·25 2·25
935 3000 l. Green-winged teal ("French teal") . . . . . . 4·50 4·50

246 Broken Bread (Congress emblem)

247 Pope's Arms, Map of South America and Pope

1989. 44th International Eucharistic Congress, Seoul.
936 **246** 550 l. red and green . . . 65 65
937 – 850 l. multicoloured . . . 1·10 1·10
938 – 1000 l. multicoloured . . 1·25 1·25
939 – 2500 l. green, pink and violet 3·00 3·00
DESIGNS: 850 l. Cross; 1000 l. Cross and fishes; 2500 l. Small cross on wafer.

1989. Pope John Paul II's Journeys (7th series). Multicoloured.
940 50 l. Type **247** 15 15
941 550 l. Austria 75 75
942 800 l. Southern Africa . . . . 1·25 1·25
943 1000 l. France . . . . 1·50 1·50
944 4000 l. Italy . . . . 4·75 4·75

248 Basilica of the Assumption, Baltimore

249 Vision of Ursulines on Mystical Stair

1989. Bicentenary of 1st Catholic Diocese in U.S.A. Each deep brown and brown.

945 450 l. Type **248** 55 55
946 1350 l. John Carroll (first Archbishop of Baltimore) . 1·75 1·75
947 2400 l. Cathedral of Mary Our Queen, Baltimore (after Martin Barry) . . . . 3·25 3·25

1990. 450th Death Anniv of St. Angela Merici (founder of Company of St. Ursula). Multicoloured.

948 700 l. Type **249** 80 80
949 800 l. St. Angela teaching Ursulines . . . . 1·10 1·10
950 2800 l. Ursulines . . . . . . 3·75 3·75

250 Ordination and Arrival in Frisia   **251** Abraham

1990. 1300th Anniv of Beginning of St. Willibrord's Missions. Multicoloured.

951 300 l. Type **250** 35 35
952 700 l. St. Willibrord in Antwerp, creation as bishop by Pope Sergius I and gift of part of Echternach by Abbess of Euren 85 85
953 3000 l. Gift of Echternach by King Pepin and St. Willibrord's death . . . . . 3·75 3·75

1990. 40th Anniv of Caritas Internationalis. Details of mosaic from Basilica of Sta. Maria Maggiore, Rome. Multicoloured.

954 450 l. Type **251** 50 50
955 650 l. Three visitors 75 75
956 800 l. Sarah making bread . . 90 90
957 2000 l. Visitors seated at Abraham's table . . . . . . 2·25 2·25

252 Fishermen on Lake Peking   **253** Pope and African Landscape

1990. 300th Anniv of Peking–Nanking Diocese. Details of two enamelled bronze vases given by Peking Apostolic Delegate to Pope Pius IX. Multicoloured.

959 500 l. Type **252** 60 60
960 750 l. Church of the Immaculate Conception (first Peking church, 1650) 90 90
961 1500 l. Lake Peking . . . . . . 1·75 1·75
962 2000 l. Church of the Redeemer, Peking, 1703 . . . . 2·50 2·50

1990. Air. Pope John Paul II's Journeys (8th series). Multicoloured.

963 500 l. Type **253** 60 60
964 1000 l. Northern European landscape (Scandinavia) . . 1·10 1·10
965 3000 l. Cathedral (Santiago de Compostela, Spain) . . . . 3·25 3·25
966 5000 l. Oriental landscape (Korea, Indonesia and Mauritius) . . . . 5·50 5·50

254 Choir of Angels

1990. Christmas. Details of painting by Sebastiano Mainardi. Multicoloured.

967 50 l. Type **254** 15 15
968 200 l. St. Joseph 25 25
969 650 l. Holy Child 70 70
970 750 l. Virgin Mary 85 85
971 2500 l. "Nativity" (complete picture) (vert) . . . . 3·00 3·00

255 "Eleazar" (left half)

1991. Restoration of Sistine Chapel. Details of "Lunettes of the Ancestors of Christ" by Michelangelo. Multicoloured.

972 50 l. Type **255** 15 15
973 100 l. "Eleazar" (right half) . 15 15
974 150 l. "Jacob" (left half) . . 15 15
975 250 l. "Jacob" (right half) . . 30 30
976 350 l. "Josiah" (left half) . . 45 45
977 400 l. "Josiah" (right half) . . 55 55
978 500 l. "Asa" (left half) . . . 60 60
979 650 l. "Asa" (right half) . . . 80 80
980 800 l. "Zerubbabel" (left half) 1·00 1·00
981 1000 l. "Zerubbabel" (right half) 1·40 1·40
982 2000 l. "Azor" (left half) . . 2·50 2·50
983 3000 l. "Azor" (right half) . . 3·75 3·75

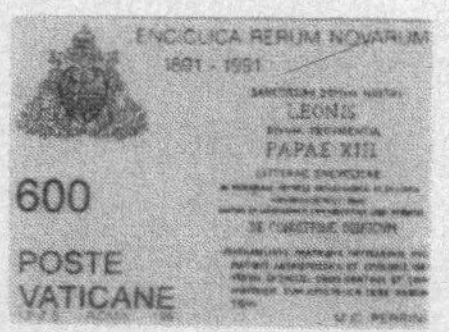

256 Title Page and Pope Leo XIII's Arms

1991. Centenary of "Rerum Novarum" (encyclical on workers' rights).

984 **256** 600 l. black and green . . 75 75
985 – 750 l. green and brown . 90 90
986 – 3500 l. purple and black . 4·50 4·50

DESIGNS: 750 l. Allegory of Church, workers and employers (from Leo XIII's 15th Anniv medal, 1892); 3500 l. Profile of Pope Leo XIII (from same medal).

257 Astrograph (astronomical camera)   **258** "Apparition of Virgin Mary" (Biagio Puccini)

1991. Centenary of Vatican Observatory. Mult.

987 750 l. Type **257** 90 90
988 1000 l. Castelgandolfo observatory (horiz) . . . . 1·40 1·40
989 3000 l. Vatican Observatory telescope, Mount Graham, Tucson, U.S.A. . . . . . . 4·25 4·25

1991. 600th Anniv of Canonisation of St. Bridget (founder of Order of the Holy Saviour). Multicoloured.

990 1500 l. Type **258** . . . . . . 2·00 2·00
991 2000 l. "Revelation of Christ" (Biagio Puccini) . . . . . 2·50 2·50

259 Cathedral of the Immaculate Conception, Ouagadougou   **260** Colonnade of St. Peter's Cathedral, Rome

1991. Pope John Paul II's Journeys (9th series). Multicoloured.

992 200 l. Type **259** (Cape Verde, Guinea-Bissau, Mali, Burkina Faso and Chad) 30 30
993 550 l. St. Vitus's Cathedral, Prague (Czechoslovakia) . 70 70
994 750 l. Basilica of Our Lady of Guadaloupe (Mexico and Curacao) 95 95
995 1500 l. Ta'Pinu Sanctuary, Gozo (Malta) . . . . 2·00 2·00
996 3500 l. Cathedral of Christ the King, Giteca (Tanzania, Burundi, Rwanda and Ivory Coast) . . . . 5·00 5·00

1991. Synod of Bishops' Special Assembly for Europe. Each black and blue.

997 300 l. Type **260** 45 45
998 500 l. St. Peter's Cathedral and square 70 70
999 4000 l. Apostolic Palace and colonnade . . . . 6·00 6·00

Nos. 997/9 were issued together, se-tenant, forming a composite design.

261 Christopher Columbus   **262** "Our Lady of Childbirth"

1992. 500th Anniv of Discovery of America by Columbus. Multicoloured.

1000 500 l. Type **261** 65 65
1001 600 l. St. Pedro Claver . . . 75 75
1002 850 l. "Virgin of the Catholic Kings" . . . . 1·10 1·10
1003 1000 l. Bortolome de las Casas 1·40 1·40
1004 2000 l. Junipero Serra . . . . 2·75 2·75

1992. 500th Death Anniv of Piero della Francesca (painter). Multicoloured.

1006 300 l. Type **262** 35 35
1007 750 l. "Our Lady of Childbirth" (detail) 80 80
1008 1000 l. "The Resurrection" . 1·25 1·25
1009 3000 l. "The Resurrection" (detail) . . . . 3·25 3·25

263 St. Giuseppe comforting the Sick   **264** Maize

1992. 150th Death Anniv of St. Giuseppe Benedetto Cottolengo. Multicoloured.

1010 650 l. Type **263** 70 70
1011 850 l. St. Giuseppe holding Piccolo Casa della Divina Provvidenza (infirmary), Turin 90 90

1992. Plants of the New World. Illustrations from the 18th-century "Phytanthoza Iconographia". Multicoloured.

1012 850 l. Type **264** 85 85
1013 850 l. Tomatoes 85 85
1014 850 l. Cactus 85 85
1015 850 l. Cacao 85 85
1016 850 l. Peppers 85 85
1017 850 l. Pineapple 85 85

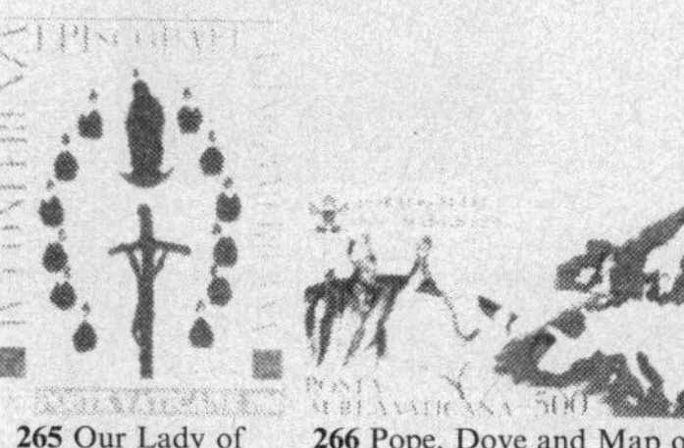

265 Our Lady of Guadalupe, Crucifix and Mitres   **266** Pope, Dove and Map of Europe

1992. 4th Latin American Episcopal Conference, Santo Domingo.

1018 **265** 700 l. gold, emerald and green . . . . 2·50 2·50

1992. Air. Pope John Paul II's Journeys (10th series). Multicoloured.

1019 500 l. Type **266** (Portugal) . . 50 50
1020 1000 l. Map of Europe highlighting Poland . . . . 1·00 1·00
1021 4000 l. Our Lady of Czestochowa and map highlighting Poland and Hungary . . . . 4·00 4·00
1022 6000 l. Map of South America highlighting Brazil . . . . 6·00 6·00

267 "The Annunciation"   **268** "St. Francis healing the Man from Ilerda" (fresco by Giotto in Upper Church, Assisi)

1992. Christmas. Mosaics in Church of Sta. Maria Maggiore, Rome. Multicoloured.

1023 600 l. Type **267** 60 60
1024 700 l. "Nativity" 70 70
1025 1000 l. "Adoration of the Kings" . . . . 1·00 1·00
1026 1500 l. "Presentation in the Temple" . . . . 1·50 1·50

1993. "Peace in Europe" Prayer Meeting, Assisi.

1027 **268** 1000 l. multicoloured . . 1·00 1·00

269 Dome of St. Peter's Basilica   **270** "The Sacrifice of Isaac"

1993. Architectural Treasures. Multicoloured.

1028 200 l. Type **269** 15 15
1029 300 l. St. John Lateran Basilica 25 25
1030 350 l. Sta. Maria Maggiore Basilica 30 30
1031 500 l. St. Paul's Basilica . . 40 40
1032 600 l. Apostolic Palace, Vatican 50 50
1033 700 l. Apostolic Palace, Lateran (Rome) 60 60
1034 850 l. Papal Palace, Castelgandolfo 70 70
1035 1000 l. Chancery Palace, Rome 85 85
1036 2000 l. Palace of Propagation of the Faith, Rome . . . . . 1·60 1·60
1037 3000 l. San Calisto Palace . . 2·50 2·50

1993. Ascension Day. Multicoloured.

1038 200 l. Type **270** 15 15
1039 750 l. Jesus handing New Law to St. Peter 60 60
1040 3000 l. Christ watching servant washing Pilate's hands . . 2·50 2·50

Nos. 1038/40 were issued together, se-tenant, forming a composite design of the bas-relief "Traditio Legis" from 4th-century sarcophagus.

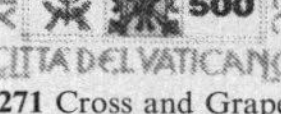

271 Cross and Grape Vines   **273** St. John, Cross, Fish and Moldava River

272 "Crucifixion" (Felice Casorati)

1993. 45th International Eucharistic Congress, Seville. Multicoloured.

1041 500 l. Type **271** 40 40
1042 700 l. Cross and hands offering broken bread 60 60
1043 1500 l. Hands holding chalice 1·25 1·25
1044 2500 l. Cross, banner and ears of wheat . . . . 2·10 2·10

1993. Europa. Contemporary Art. Multicoloured.

1045 750 l. Type **272** 60 60
1046 850 l. "Rouen Cathedral" (Maurice Utrillo) . . . 70 70

1993. 600th Death Anniv of St. John of Nepomuk (patron saint of Bohemia). Multicoloured.

1047 1000 l. Type **273** 85 85
1048 2000 l. Charles Bridge, Prague 1·60 1·60

274 Pope praying

1993. Pope John Paul II's Journeys (11th series). Multicoloured.

1049 600 l. Type **274** (Senegal, Gambia and Guinea) 50 50
1050 1000 l. Pope with Pastoral Staff (Angola and St. Thomas and Prince Islands) 85 85
1051 5000 l. Pope with hands clasped in prayer (Dominican Republic) . . . . 4·25 4·25

275 "Madonna of Solothurn" (detail)

1993. 450th Death Anniv of Hans Holbein the Younger (artist). Multicoloured.

1052 700 l. Type **275** 60 60
1053 1000 l. "Madonna of Solothurn" 85 85
1054 1500 l. "Self-portrait" . . . . 1·25 1·25

276 "Creation of the Planets" (left detail) **277** Crosier and Dome

1994. Completion of Restoration of Sistine Chapel. Multicoloured.

1055 350 l. Type **276** 25 25
1056 350 l. God creating planets (right detail) 25 25
1057 500 l. Adam (left detail, "The Creation of Adam") . . . 35 35
1058 500 l. God (right detail) . . . 35 35
1059 1000 l. Adam and Eve taking forbidden fruit (left detail, "The Original Sin") . . . 75 75
1060 1000 l. Angel casting out Adam and Eve from the Garden (right detail) 75 75
1061 2000 l. People climbing from swollen river onto riverbank (left detail, "The Flood") . 1·50 1·50
1062 2000 l. Floodwaters surrounding temporary shelter (right detail) . . . . 1·50 1·50

Stamps of the same value were issued together, se-tenant, each pair forming a composite design.

1994. Special Assembly for Africa of Synod of Bishops. Multicoloured.

1064 850 l. Type **277** 60 60
1065 1000 l. Crucifix, dome of St. Peter's and African scene . 75 75

278 God creating Man and Woman **280** Bishop Euphrasius and Archdeacon Claudius

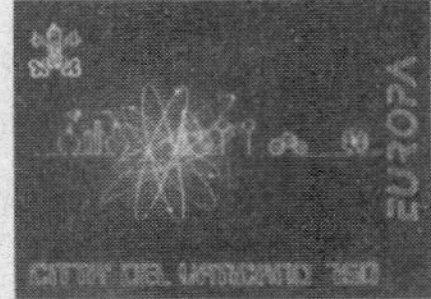

279 Timeline of Progress from Wheel to Atom

1994. International Year of the Family. Multicoloured.

1066 400 l. Type **278** 30 30
1067 750 l. Family 55 55
1068 1000 l. Parents teaching son . 75 75
1069 2000 l. Youth helping elderly couple . . . . 1·50 1·50

1994. Europa. Discoveries. Multicoloured.

1070 750 l. Type **279** 55 55
1071 850 l. Galileo, solar system and scientific apparatus 60 60

1994. 13th International Convention on Christian Archaeology, Split and Porec, Croatia. Mosaics from Euphrasian Basilica, Porec. Multicoloured.

1072 700 l. Type **280** 50 50
1073 1500 l. Madonna and Child with two angels . . . . 1·10 1·10
1074 3000 l. Jesus Christ between Apostles St. Peter and St. Paul . . . . 2·25 2·25

281 Route Map, Mongolian Village and Giovanni da Montecorvino

1994. 700th Anniv of Evangelization of China.

1075 **281** 1000 l. multicoloured . . 75 75

282 Houses, Mahdi's Mausoleum, Omdurman, and St. Mary's Basilica, Lodonga (Benin, Uganda and Sudan)

1994. Pope John Paul II's Journeys (12th series).

1076 **282** 600 l. brown, green and red 45 45
1077 – 700 l. violet, brown and green 50 50
1078 – 1000 l. brown, blue and violet 75 75
1079 – 2000 l. black, blue and orange . . . . 1·50 1·50
1080 – 3000 l. blue, violet and brown . . . . . . 2·25 2·25

DESIGNS: 700 l. St. Mary's Church, Apollonia, Mosque and statue of Skanderbeg, Tirana (Albania); 1000 l. Church of the Saint, Huelva Region, and The Giralda, Real Maestranza and Golden Tower, Seville (Spain); 2000 l. Skyscrapers and St. Thomas's Theological Seminary, Denver, "El Castillo" (pyramid), Kulkulkan, Jamaican girl and Mexican boy (Jamaica, Mexico and United States); 3000 l. Tallin, "Hymn to Liberty" (monument), Riga, and Tower, Cathedral Square, Vilnius (Lithuania, Latvia and Estonia).

283 Holy Family

1994. Christmas. Details of "Nativity" by Tintoretto. Multicoloured.

1081 700 l. Type **283** 50 50
1082 1000 l. As Type **283** but 45 × 28 mm 75 75
1083 1000 l. Shepherds and animals in the stable (45 × 28 mm) 75 75

Nos. 1082/3 were issued together, se-tenant, forming a composite design of the complete painting.

EXPRESS LETTER STAMPS

E 3

1929.

E14 E **3** 2 l. red . . . . 11·00 11·00
E15 2 l. 50 blue . . . . . . 8·00 12·00

E **12** Vatican City

1933.

E 35 E **12** 2 l. brown and red . . 30 35
E 36 2 l. 50 brown and blue 30 35
E107 3 l. 50 blue and red . 35 35
E108 5 l. green and blue . . 40 85

1945. Surch in figures over bars.

E118 E **12** 6 l. on 3 l. 50 blue & red 2·50 1·25
E119 12 l. on 5 l. grn & blue 2·50 1·25

E **28** Matthew Giberti, Bishop of Verona

1946. 400th Anniv of Council of Trent.

E130 E **28** 6 l. brown and green . . 15 15
E131 – 12 l. sepia & brown . . 25 25

DESIGN: 12 l. Cardinal Gaspare Contarini, Bishop of Belluno.

1949. As Nos. 139/48 (Basilicas), but inscr "ESPRESSO".

E149 40 l. grey . . . . 9·00 3·50
E150 80 l. brown . . . . 26·00 15·00

DESIGNS—HORIZ: 40 l. St. Peter's; 80 l. St. John's.

1953. Designs as Nos. 179/89, but inscr "ESPRESSO".

E190 50 l. brown and turquoise . . 20 15
E191 85 l. brown and orange . . . 45 35

DESIGNS: 50 l. St. Peter and tomb; 85 l. Pius XII and sepulchre.

1960. Designs as Nos. 326/33 (Works of Mercy), but inscr "ESPRESSO". Centres in sepia.

E334 75 l. red 10 10
E335 100 l. blue 10 10

DESIGN: 75, 100 l. Arms of Pope John XXIII between "Justice" and "Hope".

1966. Designs as Nos. 467/76, but inscr "ESPRESSO".

E477 – 150 l. sepia 10 10
E478 **120** 180 l. brown 15 15

DESIGN: 150 l. Arms of Pope Paul VI.

PARCEL POST STAMPS

1931. Optd **PER PACCHI**.

P15 **1** 5 c. brown on red 20 40
P16 10 c. green on green 20 40
P17 20 c. violet on lilac . . . . 1·00 1·25
P18 25 c. blue on blue . . . . . 4·50 4·75
P19 30 c. black on yellow . . . 5·50 4·75
P20 50 c. black on pink . . . . 7·00 4·75
P21 75 c. red on grey . . . . . 85 4·75
P22 **2** 80 c. red . . . . 55 4·75
P23 1 l. 25 blue . . . . 70 4·75
P24 2 l. brown . . . . 55 4·75
P25 2 l. 50 red . . . . 55 4·75
P26 5 l. green . . . . 55 4·75
P27 10 l. black . . . . 55 4·75

PARCEL POST EXPRESS STAMPS

1931. Optd **PER PACCHI**.

PE15 E **3** 2 l. red . . . . 80 4·75
PE16 2 l. 50 blue . . . . 80 4·75

POSTAGE DUE STAMPS

1931. Optd **SEGNATASSE** and cross or surch also.

D15 **1** 5 c. brown on red 20 60
D16 10 c. green on green 20 60
D17 20 c. violet on lilac . . . . 1·25 2·25
D18 40 c. on 30 c. blk on yell . . 1·40 5·50
D19 **2** 60 c. on 2 l. brown . . . . 32·00 24·00
D20 1 l. 10 on 2 l. 50 red . . . . 4·75 18·00

D 26 D **49** State Arms

1945. Coloured network shown in brackets.

D107 D **26** 5 c. black (yellow) . . 10 10
D108 20 c. black (violet) . . 10 10
D109 80 c. black (red) . . . 10 10
D110 1 l. black (green) . . . 10 10
D111 2 l. black (blue) . . . 10 15
D112 5 l. black (grey) . . . 10 15

1954. Coloured network shown in brackets.

D199 D **49** 4 l. black (red) 10 10
D200 6 l. black (green) 20 20
D201 10 l. black (yellow) . . . 10 10
D202 20 l. black (blue) 40 40
D203 50 l. black (sepia) . . . 10 10
D204 70 l. black (brown) . . . 10 10

D **130**

1968.

D513 D **130** 10 l. black on grey . . 10 10
D514 20 l. black on blue . . 10 10
D515 50 l. black on pink . . 10 10
D516 60 l. black on grn . . 10 10
D517 100 l. black on buff . . 10 10
D518 180 black on mauve . . 10 10

VEGLIA Pt. 8

During the period of D'Annunzio's Italian Regency of Carnaro (Fiume), separate issues were made for the island of Veglia (now Krk).

100 centesimi = 1 lira

1920. Nos. 146, etc, of Fiume optd **VEGLIA**.
1 5 c. green 2·50 2·50
2 10 c. red 4·50 4·50
3 20 c. brown 7·50 7·50
4 25 c. blue 7·50 7·50
5 50 on 20 c. brown 7·50 7·50
6 55 on 5 c. green 7·50 7·50

EXPRESS LETTER STAMPS

1920. Nos. E163/4 of Fiume optd **VEGLIA**.
E7 30 c. on 20 c. brown 42·00 35·00
E8 50 on 5 c. green 32·00 35·00

VENEZIA GIULIA AND ISTRIA Pt. 3

Formerly part of Italy. Stamps issued during Allied occupation, 1945-47. The Peace Treaty of 1947 established the Free Territory of Trieste (q.v.) and gave the rest of the territory to Yugoslavia.

For stamps of Austria overprinted Venezia Giulia see under Italian Austria.

100 centesimi = 1 lira

A. YUGOSLAV OCCUPATION PROVISIONAL ISSUES

Issue for Trieste.

1945. Stamps of Italian Social Republic 1944, surch **1.V.1945 TRIESTE TRST**, five-pointed star and value.
4 – 20 c.+ 1 l. on 5 c. brown (No. 106) 10 30
5 **13** + 1 l. on 25 c. green 10 30
6 – + 1 l. on 30 c. brown (No. 110) 10 30
7 – + 1 l. on 50 c. violet (No. 111) 10 30
8 – + 1 l. on 1 l. violet (No. 113) 10 30
9 – + 2 l. on 1 l. 25 blue (No. 114) 10 30
2 **12** 2 + 2 l. on 25 c. green 10 15
10 – + 2 l. on 3 l. green (No. 115) 10 30
11 – 5 + 5 l. on 1 l. violet (No. 113) 10 30
12 – 10 + 10 l. on 30 c. brown (No. 110) 70 1·10
13 – 20 + 20 l. on 5 c. brown (No. 106) 1·50 2·25

Issue for Istria.

In 1945 various stamps of Italy were overprinted "ISTRA" and further surcharged for use in Istria and Pola but they were not issued. However, four of these were further surcharged and issued later.

1945. Stamps of Italy (No. 14) or Italian Social Republic (others) surch **ISTRA** with new value and bars obliterating old surch.
14 **99** 4 l. on 2 l. on 1 l. (No. 249) violet 15 30
15 – 6 l. on 1.50 l. on 75 c. (No. 112) red 2·00 2·75
16 – 10 l. on 0.10 l. on 5 c. (No. 106) brown 8·00 10·00
17 **103** 20 l. on 1 l. on 50 c. (No. 59) violet 3·00 3·50

Issue for Fiume.

1945. Stamps of Italian Social Republic 1944, surch **3-V-1945 FIUME RIJEKA**, five-pointed star over rising sun and new value.
18 **12** 2 l. on 25 c. green 10 30
20 – 4 l. on 1 l. vio (No. 113) 10 30
21 – 5 l. on 10 c. brn (No. 107) 10 30
22 – 6 l. on 10 c. brn (No. 107) 10 30
23 **13** 10 l. on 25 c. green 10 30
19 – 16 l. on 75 c. red (No. 112) 2·75 3·50
25 **E 16** 20 l. on 1 l. 25 c. green 40 75

B. ALLIED MILITARY GOVERNMENT

1945. Stamps of Italy optd **A.M.G. V.G.** in two lines.

(a) Imperial Series.
26 – 10 c. brown (No. 241) 15 15
27 – 10 c. brown (No. 633) 15 15
28 **99** 20 c. red (No. 243) 15 30
29 20 c. red (No. 640) 15 15
31 – 60 c. orange (No. 636) 15 15
32 **103** 60 c. green (No. 641) 15 15
33 **99** 1 l. violet (No. 642) 20 15
34 – 2 l. red (No. 644) 20 15
35 **98** 5 l. red (No. 645) 40 25
36 – 10 l. violet (No. 646) 50 70
37 **99** 20 l. green (No. 257) 1·25 1·90

(b) Stamps of 1945–48.
38 – 25 c. turquoise (No. 649) 15 20
39 – 2 l. brown (No. 656) 35 40
40 – 3 l. red (No. 657) 25 15
41 – 4 l. red (No. 658) 40 20
42 **195** 6 l. violet (No. 660) 1·10 1·40
43 – 20 l. purple (No. 665) 20·00 1·00
44 **196** 25 l. green (No. 666) 2·50 3·50
45 50 l. purple (No. 668) 3·00 4·25
46 **197** 100 l. red (No. 669) 10·00 14·00

1945. Air stamps of Italy, optd as above.
47 **110** 50 c. brown (No. 271) 15 25
48 **198** 1 l. slate (No. 670) 20 25
49 – 2 l. blue (No. 671) 15 25
50 – 5 l. green (No. 673) 1·10 1·40
51 **198** 10 l. red (No. 674) 1·10 1·40
52 – 25 l. blue (No. 675) 1·10 1·40
53 – 25 l. brown (No. 676) 10·00 12·00
54 **198** 50 l. green (No. 677) 2·00 3·00

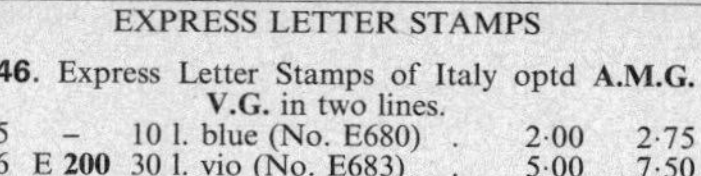

EXPRESS LETTER STAMPS

1946. Express Letter Stamps of Italy optd **A.M.G. V.G.** in two lines.
E55 – 10 l. blue (No. E680) 2·00 2·75
E56 **E 200** 30 l. vio (No. E683) 5·00 7·50

C. YUGOSLAV MILITARY GOVERNMENT

6 Grapes

7 Roman Amphitheatre, Pula

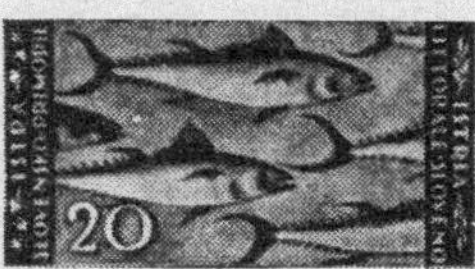

8 Tunny

1945. Inscr "ISTRA SLOVENSKO PRIMORJE — ISTRIA LITTORALE SLOVENO".
74 **6** 0.25 l. green 10 10
58 – 0.50 l. brown 10 10
59 – 1 l. red 10 10
76 – 1 l. green 10 10
77 – 1.50 l. olive 10 10
61 – 2 l. green 10 10
100 – 3 l. red 15 10
62 **7** 4 l. blue 10 10
79 4 l. red 10 10
80 – 5 l. black 10 10
101 **7** 6 l. blue 20 15
81 – 10 l. brown 10 10
65 **8** 20 l. purple 2·25 2·25
82 20 l. blue 1·00 30
66 – 30 l. mauve 1·50 1·50

DESIGNS—As Type **6**: 0.50 l. Donkey and view; 1 l. Rebuilding damaged homes; 1.50 l. Olive branch; 2, 3 l. Duino Castle near Trieste. As Type **7**: 5 l. Birthplace of Vladimir Gortan, Piran; 10 l. Ploughing. As Type **8**: 30 l. Viaduct over the Solkan.

1946. Nos. 82 and 66 surch.
96 **8** 1 on 20 l. blue 30 15
97 – 2 on 30 l. mauve 2·75 2·25

1947. As Nos. 514 and O540 of Yugoslavia with colours changed, surch **VOJNA UPRAVA JUGOSLAVENSKE ARMIJE** and new value.
102 1 l. on 9 d. pink 10 10
103 1.50 l. on 50 p. blue 10 10
104 2 l. on 9 d. pink 10 10
105 3 l. on 50 p. blue 10 10
106 5 l. on 9 d. pink 10 10
107 6 l. on 50 p. blue 10 10
108 10 l. on 9 d. pink 10 10
109 15 l. on 50 p. blue 10 10
110 35 l. on 9 d. pink 10 10
111 50 l. on 50 p. blue 10 10

POSTAGE DUE STAMPS

1945. Stamps of 1945 surch **PORTO** and value in "Lit".
D72 **8** 0.50 on 20 l. purple 20 20
D67 **6** 1 l. on 0.25 l. green 1·00 40
D73 – 2 l. on 30 l. mauve 50 50
D68 – 4 l. on 0.50 l. brown 30 15
D69 – 8 l. on 0.50 l. brown 30 15
D70 – 10 l. on 0.50 l. brown 1·00 40
D71 – 20 l. on 0.50 l. brown 1·25 60

1946. Stamps of 1945 surch **PORTO** and value expressed in "Lira".
D90 **6** 1 l. on 0.25 l. green 10 10
D84 – 1 l. on 1 l. green (No. 76) 10 10
D91 **6** 2 l. on 0.25 l. green 10 10
D85 – 2 l. on 1 l. green (No. 76) 10 10
D92 **6** 4 l. on 0.25 l. green 10 10
D86 – 4 l. on 1 l. green (No. 76) 10 15
D93 **8** 10 l. on 20 l. blue 30 15
D87 – 10 l. on 30 l. mauve (No. 66) 2·00 1·50
D94 **8** 20 l. on 20 l. blue 1·50 55
D88 – 20 l. on 30 l. mauve (No. 66) 3·25 2·75
D95 **8** 30 l. on 20 l. blue 1·50 55
D89 – 30 l. on 30 l. mauve (No. 66) 3·25 2·75

1947. No. D528 of Yugoslavia with colour changed and surch **Vojna Uprava Jugoslavenske Armije** and value.
D112 1 l. on 1 d. green 10 10
D113 2 l. on 1 d. green 10 10
D114 6 l. on 1 d. green 10 10
D115 10 l. on 1 d. green 10 10
D116 30 l. on 1 d. green 10 10

VENEZUELA Pt. 20

A republic in the N. of S. America, independent since 1811.

1859. 100 centavos = 8 reales = 1 peso
1879. 100 centesimos = 1 venezolano
1880. 100 centimos = 1 bolivar

1

2

3

1859. Imperf.
7 **1** ½ r. orange 6·75 2·50
8 1 r. blue 11·50 7·25
3 2 r. red 27·00 9·25

1862. Imperf.
13 **2** ¼ c. green 11·50 65·00
14 ½ c. lilac 19·00 £120
15 1 c. brown 27·00 £140

1863. Imperf.
16 **3** ½ c. red 32·00 55·00
17a 1 c. grey 38·00 60·00
21 ½ r. yellow 2·50 1·50
19 1 r. blue 11·00 5·00
20 2 r. green 15·00 13·50

4

5 Bolivar

1866. Imperf.
22 **4** ½ c. green £140 £200
23 1 c. green £140 £170
24 ½ r. red 5·50 1·60
26 1 r. red 27·00 10·00
27a 2 r. yellow 90·00 50·00

1871. Optd with inscription in very small letters. Imperf.
58 **5** 1 c. yellow 65 30
59d 2 c. yellow 1·00 35
60 3 c. yellow 1·60 40
61 4 c. yellow 2·00 40
62b 5 c. yellow 2·00 40
63b 1 r. red 2·00 30
64a 2 r. red 3·25 75
65a 3 r. red 3·75 75
66a 5 r. red 3·75 85
52a 7 r. red 4·50 1·60
53a 9 r. green 11·50 3·00
54 15 r. green 23·00 6·25
68 20 r. green 55·00 10·50
56 30 r. green £250 85·00
70 50 r. green £850 £225

1873. Optd with inscription in very small letters. Imperf.
74a **4** 1 c. lilac 4·50 12·50
75a 2 c. green 27·00 35·00
76a ½ r. pink 19·00 2·50
77a 1 r. red 23·00 6·25
78a 2 r. yellow 80·00 32·00

7 Bolivar

8 Bolivar

1879. New Currency. Optd with inscription in small letters. Imperf.
83 **7** 1 c. yellow 2·00 15
84 5 c. yellow 3·00 30
85 10 c. blue 4·25 40
86 30 c. blue 5·25 1·00
87 50 c. blue 6·25 1·00
88 90 c. blue 25·00 5·25
89 1 v. red 55·00 7·25
90 3 v. red 90·00 29·00
91 5 v. red £160 55·00

1880. New Currency. Without opt. Perf.
92 **7** 5 c. yellow 1·00 15
93 10 c. yellow 1·60 15
94 25 c. yellow 1·50 20
95 50 c. yellow 3·00 25
96 1 b. blue 7·25 60
97 2 b. blue 11·50 70
98 5 b. blue 27·00 60
99 10 b. red £140 45·00
100 20 b. red £850 £140
101 25 b. red £3500 £425

1880.
107 **8** 5 c. blue 6·25 3·25
108 10 c. red 10·50 6·25
109 25 c. yellow 6·25 3·25
110 50 c. brown 32·00 17·00
106 1 b. green 50·00 25·00

9 Bolivar

10 Bolivar

1882. Various frames. Perf or roul.
111 **9** 5 c. green 10 10
112 10 c. brown 10 10
113 25 c. orange 10 10
114 50 c. blue 15 10
115 1 b. red 20 10
116 3 b. violet 20 10
117 10 b. brown 40 50
118 20 b. purple 55 55

1882. Various frames. Perf or roul.
119 **10** 5 c. blue 20 10
120 10 c. brown 20 10
121 25 c. brown 40 20
122 50 c. green 1·25 25
123 1 b. violet 2·10 70

1892. Surch **RESOLUCION DE 10 DE OCTUBRE DE 1892** and value in circle.
134 **9** 25 c. on 5 c. green 8·25 5·00
138 **10** 25 c. on 5 c. blue 25·00 25·00
135 **9** 25 c. on 10 c. brown 8·25 5·00
139 **10** 25 c. on 10 c. brown 10·00 10·00
136 **9** 1 b. on 25 c. orange 10·50 5·75
140 **10** 1 b. on 25 c. brown 10·00 10·00
137 **9** 1 b. on 50 c. blue 14·50 5·75
141 **10** 1 b. on 50 c. green 11·00 11·00

1893. Optd with coat of arms and diagonal shading.
142 **9** 5 c. green 10 10
150 **10** 5 c. blue 20 10
143 **9** 10 c. brown 10 10
151 **10** 10 c. brown 55 65
144 **9** 25 c. orange 10 10
152 **10** 25 c. brown 35 25
145 **9** 50 c. blue 10 10
153 **10** 50 c. green 50 20
146 **9** 1 b. red 55 20
154 **10** 1 b. violet 1·25 50
147 **9** 3 b. violet 50 35
148 10 b. brown 1·50 1·25
149 20 b. purple 1·25 1·25

13 Bolivar

14 Bolivar

1893. Schools Tax stamps.
155 **13** 5 c. grey 10 10
156 10 c. green 10 10
157 25 c. blue 10 10
158 50 c. orange 10 10
159 1 b. purple 30 10
160 3 b. red 45 20
161 10 b. violet 55 60
162 20 b. brown 1·60 1·50
See also Nos. 227/35.

1893.
163 **14** 5 c. brown 60 10
164 10 c. blue 2·10 65
165 25 c. mauve 10·00 20
166 50 c. purple 2·10 20
167 1 b. green 2·75 65

15 Landing of Columbus

1893. Columbian Exposition, Chicago, and 400th Anniv of Discovery of America by Columbus.
168 **15** 25 c. purple 6·75 40

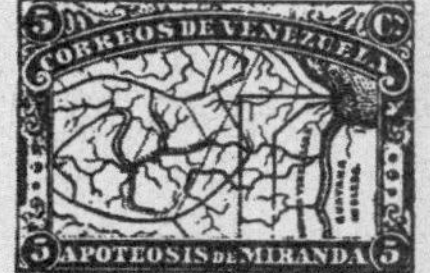

16 Map of Venezuela

18 Bolivar

1896. 80th Death Anniv of Gen. Miranda.
169 **16** 5 c. green 2·10 1·60
170 10 c. blue 2·10 1·60
171 25 c. yellow 2·50 3·25
172 50 c. red 32·00 17·00
173 1 b. mauve 25·00 17·00

1899.
179 **18** 5 c. green 65 15
180 10 c. red 85 15
181 25 c. blue 1·00 50
182 50 c. black 1·25 60
183 50 c. orange 1·00 30
184 1 b. green 21·00 10·50
185 2 b. yellow £250 £160

(21) "R.T.M." = Ramon Tellos Mendoza, Minister of Interior

(23)

1900. Stamps of 1893 optd with T **21**.
191 **13** 5 c. grey 10 10
192 10 c. green 10 10
193 25 c. blue 10 10
194 50 c. orange 10 10
195 1 b. purple 20 10
196 3 b. red 30 10
197 10 b. violet 65 40
198 20 b. brown 4·25 4·25

1900. Stamps of 1899 optd with T **21**.
199 **18** 5 c. green 60 30
200 10 c. red 60 35
201 25 c. blue 4·25 60
202 50 c. black 2·10 50
203 1 b. green 85 40
204 2 b. yellow 1·50 1·00

1900. Stamps of 1893 optd **1900**. Colours changed.
206 **13** 5 c. orange 10 10
207 10 c. blue 10 10
208 25 c. purple 10 10
209 50 c. green 60 10
210 1 b. black 4·75 55
211 3 b. brown 1·25 60
212 10 b. red 5·00 1·40
213 20 b. violet 10·00 2·75

1900. Stamps of 1899 optd **1900**.
214 **18** 5 c. green £120 £120
215 10 c. red £120 £120
216 25 c. blue £250 £120
217 50 c. orange 15·00 85
218 1 b. black 85 60

1900. Stamps of 1899 optd with T **23**.
219 **18** 5 c. green 4·25 50
220 10 c. red 3·25 55
221 25 c. blue 4·25 50

1901. Re-issue of T **13** in new colours.
227 **13** 5 c. orange 10 10
228 10 c. red 10 10
229 10 c. blue 10 10
231 50 c. green 15 15
232 1 b. black 2·25 55
233 3 b. brown 20 10
234 10 b. red 35 25
235 20 b. violet 80 50

1902. Stamp of 1901 optd **1901**.
236 **13** 1 b. black 45 30

1904. No. 231 surch **CORREOS Vale B 0,05 1904**.
310 **13** 5 c. on 50 c. green 40 55

38 General Sucre **39** Bolivar

1904.
311 **38** 5 c. green 40 15
312 10 c. red 25 15
313 15 c. violet 45 30
314 25 c. blue 3·25 30
315 50 c. red 45 40
316 1 b. red 50 40

1904.
317 **39** 5 c. green 10 10
318 10 c. grey 10 10
319 25 c. red 10 10
320 50 c. yellow 10 10
321 1 b. red 1·90 25
322 3 b. blue 35 15
323 10 b. violet 45 25
324 20 b. red 1·10 35

41 President Castro **42** Liberty

1905. 6th Anniv of General Castro's Revolt.
330 **41** 5 c. red 2·10 2·10
331a 10 c. blue 3·25 2·75
332a 25 c. yellow 1·00 1·00

1910. Independence Centenary.
333 **42** 25 c. blue 8·25 45

43 F. de Miranda **44**

1911. Portraits as T **43**.
340 **43** 5 c. green 25 15
341 10 c. red 35 10
342 – 15 c. grey (Urdaneta) 3·25 20
343 – 25 c. blue (Urdaneta) 1·60 25
344 – 50 c. violet (Bolivar) 2·10 25
339 – 1 b. orange (Bolivar) 2·10 1·00

1911. Portraits as T **44**.
345 – 5 c. blue (Vargas) 10 10
346 – 10 c. yellow (Avila) 10 10
347 – 25 c. grey (Sanz) 10 10
348 **44** 50 c. red (Blanco) 10 10
349 – 1 b. green (Bello) 10 10
350 – 2 b. brown (Sanabria) 55 35
351 – 3 b. violet (Paez) 55 25
352 – 10 b. purple (Sucre) 1·10 50
353 – 20 b. blue (Bolivar) 1·10 70

46 Bolivar **47** Bolivar

1914.
359 **46** 5 c. green 20·00 25
360 10 c. red 17·00 40
361 25 c. blue 3·25 20

1915. Various Frames.
362a **47** 5 c. green 2·75 25
379 5 c. brown 55 10
570 7½ c. green 60 35
571 10 c. red 2·10 30
380 10 c. green 20 10
381 15 c. olive 1·25 50
382 15 c. brown 30 10
383 25 c. blue 1·25 10
384 25 c. red 20 10
368 40 c. green 14·50 6·25
385 40 c. blue 55 20
369 50 c. violet 3·75 40
386 50 c. blue 55 20
371 75 c. turquoise 38·00 12·50
387 1 b. black 55 25
388 3 b. orange 8·25 2·75
389 5 b. violet 10·00 5·50
See also Nos. 414/5.

48 Bolivar and Sucre

1924. Centenary of Battle of Ayacucho.
390 **48** 25 c. blue 1·90 35

1926. Fiscal stamps surch **CORREOS VALE 1926** and value.
392 0,05 b. on 1 b. olive 40 35
393 0,25 b. on 5 c. brown 40 40
DESIGNS: No. 392, Portrait of Sucre; No. 393, Numeral.

50 General J. V. Gomez and Ciudad Bolivar **51** Biplane and Venezuela

1928. 25th Anniv of Capture of Ciudad Bolivar and Peace in Venezuela.
394 **50** 10 c. green 1·10 55

1930. Air.
395 **51** 5 c. brown 15 10
575 5 c. green 30 10
396 10 c. yellow 15 10
576 10 c. ornge 1·10 55
577 12½ c. purple 50 30
397 15 c. grey 15 10
578 15 c. blue 70 15
398 25 c. violet 15 10
579 25 c. brown 2·40 65
399 40 c. green 15 10
581 70 c. red 17·00 5·25
400 75 c. red 45 15
401 1 b. blue 55 15
402 1 b. 20 green 50 35
403 1 b. 70 blue 70 40
404 1 b. 90 green 75 50
405 2 b. 10 blue 1·25 60
406 2 b. 30 red 1·25 50
407 2 b. 50 blue 1·25 50
408 3 b. 70 green 1·25 45
409 10 b. purple 3·25 1·10
410 20 b. green 5·50 2·50
See also Nos. 426/49.

52 Simon Bolivar **53**

1930. Death Centenary of Bolivar.
411 **52** 5 c. yellow 60 40
412 10 c. blue 60 30
413 25 c. red 60 30

1932. Stamps of 1915 on paper printed with pattern as T **53**.
414 **47** 5 c. violet 40 10
415 7½ c. green 50 40
416 10 c. green 25 10
417 15 c. yellow 65 25
418 22½ c. red 1·60 35
419 25 c. red 55 10
420 37½ c. blue 2·10 1·00
421 40 c. blue 2·10 30
422 50 c. olive 2·10 40
423 1 b. blue 2·75 45
424 3 b. brown 21·00 8·25
425 5 b. brown 27·00 11·00

1932. Air. Air stamps as 1930 on paper printed with pattern as T **53**.
426 **51** 5 c. brown 40 10
427 10 c. yellow 40 10
428 15 c. grey 40 10
429 25 c. blue 55 10
430 40 c. green 50 10
431 70 c. red 65 10
432 75 c. orange 70 25
433 1 b. slate 85 10
434 1 b. 20 green 1·50 60
435 1 b. 70 brown 3·00 40
436 1 b. 80 blue 1·50 30
437 1 b. 90 green 3·50 2·50
438 1 b. 95 blue 4·25 2·10
439 2 b. brown 3·00 1·75
440 2 b. 10 blue 6·25 4·25
441 2 b. 30 red 3·00 1·60
442 2 b. 50 blue 3·50 1·00
443 3 b. violet 3·50 60
444 3 b. 70 green 5·00 4·25
445 4 b. orange 3·50 1·00
446 5 b. black 5·00 1·60
447 8 b. red 9·75 3·25
448 10 b. violet 20·00 5·25
449 20 b. green 42·00 15·00

54 Arms of Bolivar

1933. 150th Birth Anniv of Bolivar.
450 **54** 25 c. red 1·60 1·25

1934. Surch **1933** and figures of value and old value blocked out.
451 **47** 7½ on 10 c. green (380) 55 30
453 22½ on 25 c. red (384) 1·10 60
452 22½ on 25 c. red (419) 1·00 1·00
454 37½ on 40 c. blue (385) 1·25 60

1937. Air. Air stamps of 1932 surch **1937 VALE POR** and new value.
455 **51** 5 c. on 1 b. 70 brown 8·00 4·50
456 10 c. on 3 b. 70 green 8·00 4·50
457 15 c. on 4 b. orange 3·50 2·25
458 25 c. on 5 b. black 3·50 2·25
459 1 b. on 8 b. red 2·75 2·25
460 2 b. on 2 b. 10 blue 21·00 15·00

1937. Surch **1937 VALE POR** and value.
461 **47** 25 c. on 40 c. (No. 421) 4·25 55

59 Nurse and Child **60** Ploughing

61 "Flight" **64** Caribbean Coast

1937. (a) Postage.
463 **59** 5 c. violet 35 25
464 – 10 c. green 80 25
465 – 15 c. brown 65 35
466 **59** 25 c. red 65 40
467 – 50 c. green 4·25 2·75
468 **60** 3 b. red 7·25 5·00
469 **59** 5 b. brown 15·00 10·00
DESIGNS—VERT: 10 c. Sailing barges on Orinoco; 15 c. Women gathering cocoa-beans. HORIZ: 50 c. Rounding up cattle.

(b) Air.
470 **61** 5 c. brown 35 35
471 – 10 c. orange 20 10
472 – 15 c. black 40 35
473 **64** 25 c. violet 50 35
474 – 40 c. green 70 40
475 **61** 70 c. red 70 35
476 – 75 c. bistre 1·60 65
477 **61** 1 b. grey 1·00 45
478 – 1 b. 20 green 4·25 1·90
479 **61** 1 b. 80 blue 2·10 90
480 – 1 b. 95 blue 6·25 3·75
481 **64** 2 b. brown 2·50 1·50
482 2 b. 50 blue 7·50 4·75
483 – 3 b. lilac 4·25 2·25
484 **64** 3 b. 70 red 6·00 5·00
485 – 10 b. purple 16·00 6·50
486 **61** 20 b. black 17·00 11·50
DESIGNS—HORIZ: 10, 40 c., 1 b. 20, 3 b. Puerto Cabello; 15, 75 c., 1 b. 95, 10 b. Caracas.

65 "Venezuela" welcoming La Guaira **67** Bolivar

1937. Acquisition of La Guaira Harbour.
487 **65** 25 c. blue (postage) 85 55
488 – 70 c. green (air) 2·25 80
489 – 1 b. 80 blue 4·00 1·50
DESIGN: 70 c., 1 b. 80, Statue of Bolivar and La Guaira Harbour.

1937. Red Cross Fund.
490 **67** 5 c. green 75 50

1937. Stamps of 1937 optd **RESELLADO 1937-1938**.
491 **59** 5 c. violet (postage) 3·00 1·60
492 – 10 c. green 1·40 65
493 **59** 25 c. red 60 55
494 **60** 3 b. red £120 60·00
495 – 10 c. orange (air) 85 55
496 **64** 25 c. violet 1·60 75
497 – 40 c. green 1·60 1·10
498 **61** 70 c. red 1·25 75
499 1 b. grey 1·60 1·10
500 – 1 b. 20 green 25·00 15·00
501 **61** 1 b. 80 blue 4·25 1·90
502 – 1 b. 95 blue 6·50 3·75
503 **64** 2 b. brown 42·00 19·00
504 2 b. 50 blue 42·00 15·00
505 – 3 b. lilac 25·00 9·50
506 – 10 b. purple 60·00 32·00
507 **61** 20 b. black 65·00 38·00

69 Gathering Coffee Beans **72** La Guaira

1938. (a) Postage. As T **69**.
508 **69** 5 c. green 40 15
509 A 10 c. red 40 15
510 B 15 c. violet 85 25
544 15 c. green 55 30
511 A 25 c. blue 40 15
546 37½ c. blue 1·60 55
513 B 40 c. sepia 12·50 3·25
547 40 c. black 10·50 3·25
514 **69** 50 c. olive 17·00 3·25
548 50 c. violet 5·75 55
515 A 1 b. brown 6·75 3·25
516 **69** 3 b. orange 60·00 22·00
517 B 5 b. black 7·25 3·25
750 5 b. orange 27·00 13·50
751 5 b. brown 9·25 3·50
DESIGNS: A, Bolivar; B, G.P.O., Caracas.

(b) Air. As T **72**.
550 **72** 5 c. gren 65 40
551 C 10 c. red 20 10
552 **72** 12½ c. violet 35 30
520 D 15 c. violet 2·00 75
553 15 c. blue 60 10
521 **72** 25 c. blue 2·00 75
554 25 c. brown 25 10
555 D 30 c. violet 1·40 20
522 C 40 c. violet 2·25 85
556 40 c. brown 1·60 20
557 **72** 45 c. green 65 20
558 C 50 c. blue 75 10
523 D 70 c. red 60 40
524 **72** 75 c. brown 4·50 1·25
559 75 c. green 90 25
560 D 90 c. red 65 20
525 C 1 b. green 4·50 1·75
561 1 b. violet 75 20
526 D 1 b. 20 orange 13·00 4·25
562 1 b. 20 green 1·40 60

527 **72** 1 b. 80 blue . . . . 1·40 35
528 C 1 b. 90 black . . . . 3·25 2·10
529 D 1 b. 95 blue . . . . 2·75 1·90
530 **72** 2 b. green . . . . 29·00 10·00
563 2 b. red . . . . 1·10 50
531 C 2 b. 50 brown . . . . 29·00 12·00
564 2 b. 50 orange . . . . 7·25 2·10
565 D 3 b. green . . . . 3·25 1·25
533 **72** 3 b. 70 black . . . . 4·75 3·50
566 D 5 b. red . . . . 4·75 1·25
771 5 b. green . . . . 3·50 1·60
534 C 10 b. purple . . . . 14·50 1·75
773 10 b. yellow . . . . 4·50 1·75
535 D 20 b. orange . . . . 40·00 19·00
DESIGNS: C, National Pantheon; D, Oil Wells.

1938. Surch **VALE BS. 0,40 1938.**
536 **59** 40 c. on 5 b. brown . . . . 5·75 2·50

1938. Air. Postage stamps surch **1938 VALE CINCO** (or other value) **CENTIMOS.**
537 **61** 5 c. on 1 b. 80 blue 70 50
538 **64** 10 c. on 2 b. 50 blue . . . 2·10 60
539 15 c. on 2 b. brown . . . . 1·00 60
540 – 25 c. on 40 c. green (No. 474) 1·10 70
541 **64** 40 c. on 3 b. 70 red . . . . 2·25 1·25

77 Teresa Carreno **78** Allegory of Labour and Statue of Bolivar

1938. Repatriation of Ashes of Teresa Carreno (concert pianist).
567 **77** 25 c. blue . . . . 3·25 55

1938. Labour Day.
568 **78** 25 c. blue . . . . 3·75 55

80 Monuments at Carabobo **81** **82** Gen. J. I. Paz Castillo

1938. Air. Independence Issue.
583 – 20 c. brown 25 35
584 **80** 30 c. violet 35 35
585 **81** 45 c. blue 55 25
586 – 50 c. blue 45 25
587 **81** 70 c. red . . . . 8·25 4·50
588 **80** 90 c. orange 75 30
589 **81** 1 b. 35 black 90 45
590 – 1 b. 40 slate . . . . 3·75 1·50
591 **80** 2 b. 25 green . . . . 1·90 1·00
DESIGN: 20, 50 c., 1 b. 40, Airplane over Sucre Monument.

1939. 80th Anniv of Venezuelan Posts.
592 **82** 10 c. red . . . . 1·50 55

83 View of Ojeda **84** Dr. Cristobal Mendoza

1939. Founding of Ojeda.
593 **83** 25 c. blue . . . . 5·50 40

1939. Centenary of Death of Dr. Mendoza.
594 **84** 5 c. green 25 30
595 10 c. red 25 30
596 15 c. violet 65 40
597 25 c. blue 55 30
598 $37\frac{1}{2}$ c. blue . . . . 10·00 5·00
599 50 c. olive . . . . 10·00 3·25
600 1 b. brown . . . . 4·25 2·75

85 Diego B. Urbaneja **86** Bolivar and Carabobo Monument

1940. Independence Issue.
601 **85** 5 c. green (postage) . . . 50 15
602 $7\frac{1}{2}$ c. green 40 25
603 15 c. olive 55 25
604 $37\frac{1}{2}$ c. blue 85 40
605 40 c. blue 60 30
745 40 c. mauve 30 25
746 40 c. orange 30 25
606 50 c. violet . . . . 3·25 85
607 1 b. brown . . . . 1·60 55
748 1 b. blue . . . . 1·00 25
608 3 b. red . . . . 5·00 2·00
749 3 b. grey . . . . 2·10 55
609 **86** 15 c. blue (air) 25 15
610 20 c. olive 20 10
611 25 c. brown . . . . 1·40 35
612 40 c. brown . . . . 1·00 15
613 1 b. lilac . . . . 2·25 25
614 2 b. red . . . . 4·25 35

87 Foundation of Greater Colombia

1940. Air. 50th Anniv of Pan-American Union.
615 **87** 15 c. brown 60 30

88 Battle of Carabobo **89** "The Crossing of the Andes" (after Salas)

1940. 150th Birth Anniv of Gen. Paez.
616 **88** 25 c. blue . . . . 3·75 55

1940. Death Centenary of Gen. Santander.
617 **89** 25 c. blue . . . . 3·75 55

90 Monument and Urn **91** Statue of Bolivar at Caracas

1940. 110th Anniv of Death of Simon Bolivar. (a) Postage.
738 **90** 5 c. green 10 10
739 5 c. blue 15 10
619 – 10 c. pink 30 10
620 – 15 c. green 40 15
741 – 15 c. red 30 10
621 – 20 c. blue 70 10
622 – 25 c. blue 40 10
742 – 25 c. violet 25 10
623 – 30 c. mauve . . . . 1·00 25
743 – 30 c. black 50 35
744 – 30 c. purple . . . . 1·00 15
624 – $37\frac{1}{2}$ c. blue . . . . 2·10 70
625 – 50 c. violet . . . . 1·25 50
747 – 50 c. green 55 25
DESIGNS—VERT: 15 c. Bolivar's baptism; 25 c. Simon Bolivar on horseback. HORIZ: 10 c. Bolivar's bed; 20 c. House where Bolivar was born; 30 c. Courtyard and Bolivar's baptismal font; $37\frac{1}{2}$ c. Courtyard of house where Bolivar was born; 50 c. "Rebellion of 1812".

(b). Air.
626 **91** 5 c. green 10 10
752 5 c. orange 35 10
627 10 c. red 10 10
753 10 c. green 10 10
628 $12\frac{1}{2}$ c. violet 45 35
754 $12\frac{1}{2}$ c. brown 25 45
629 15 c. blue 25 10
755 15 c. grey 25 10
630 20 c. brown 35 10
756 20 c. violet 20 10
631 25 c. brown 35 10
757 25 c. green 15 10
632 30 c. violet 25 10
758 30 c. blue 20 10
633 40 c. brown 35 10
759 40 c. green 35 10
634 45 c. green 35 10
760 45 c. red 30 15
635 50 c. blue 35 10
761 50 c. claret 30 15
636 70 c. pink . . . . 1·00 35
762 70 c. red 55 30
637 75 c. olive . . . . 4·25 75
763 75 c. orange . . . . 2·75 1·60
764 75 c. violet 30 15
638 90 c. orange 65 35
765 90 c. black 45 40
639 1 b. mauve 35 10
766 1 b. blue 35 20
640 1 b. 20 green . . . . 1·40 35
767 1 b. 20 brown 65 45
641 1 b. 35 black . . . . 5·50 2·50
642 2 b. red . . . . 1·10 20
643 3 b. black . . . . 1·60 35
768 3 b. brown . . . . 6·75 2·50
769 3 b. blue . . . . 1·00 35
644 4 b. black . . . . 1·40 35
645 5 b. brown . . . . 11·00 4·00

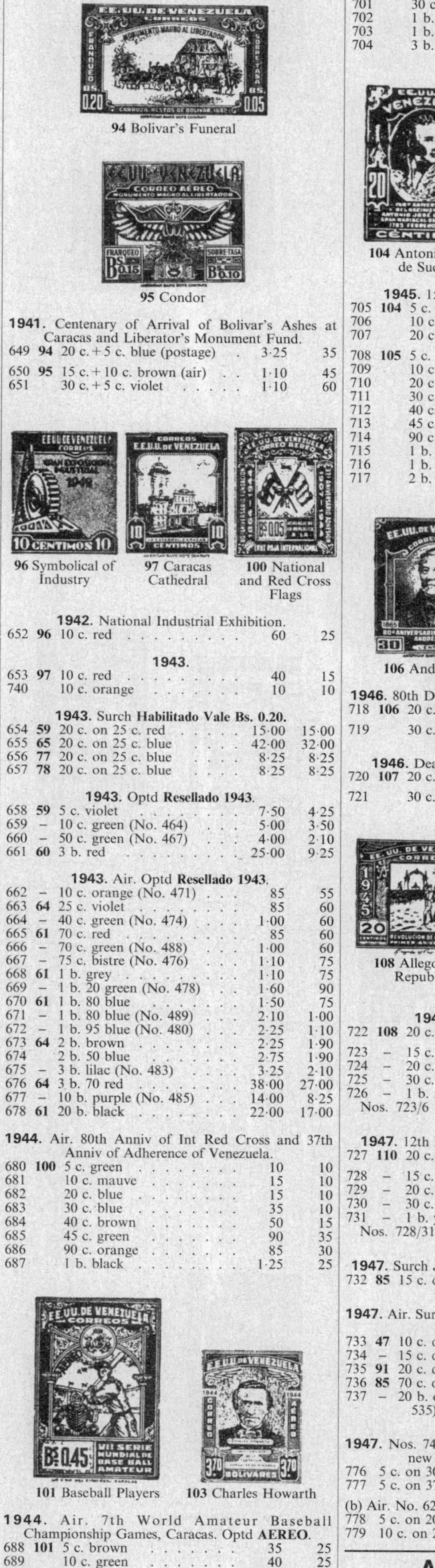

1941. No. 622 surch **HABILITADO 1941 VALE BS.0.20.**
646 20 c. on 25 c. blue 40 15

1941. Optd **HABILITADO 1940.**
647 **59** 5 c. violet . . . . 1·25 50
648 – 10 c. green (No. 464) . . . 1·25 35

94 Bolivar's Funeral

95 Condor

1941. Centenary of Arrival of Bolivar's Ashes at Caracas and Liberator's Monument Fund.
649 **94** 20 c. + 5 c. blue (postage) . 3·25 35
650 **95** 15 c. + 10 c. brown (air) . . 1·10 45
651 30 c. + 5 c. violet . . . . 1·10 60

96 Symbolical of Industry **97** Caracas Cathedral **100** National and Red Cross Flags

1942. National Industrial Exhibition.
652 **96** 10 c. red 60 25

1943.
653 **97** 10 c. red 40 15
740 10 c. orange 10 10

1943. Surch **Habilitado Vale Bs. 0.20.**
654 **59** 20 c. on 25 c. red . . . . 15·00 15·00
655 **65** 20 c. on 25 c. blue . . . . 42·00 32·00
656 **77** 20 c. on 25 c. blue . . . 8·25 8·25
657 **78** 20 c. on 25 c. blue . . . 8·25 8·25

1943. Optd **Resellado 1943.**
658 **59** 5 c. violet . . . . 7·50 4·25
659 – 10 c. green (No. 464) . . . 5·00 3·50
660 – 50 c. green (No. 467) . . . 4·00 2·10
661 **60** 3 b. red . . . . 25·00 9·25

1943. Air. Optd **Resellado 1943.**
662 – 10 c. orange (No. 471) . . . 85 55
663 **64** 25 c. violet 85 60
664 – 40 c. green (No. 474) . . . 1·00 60
665 **61** 70 c. red 85 60
666 – 70 c. green (No. 488) . . . 1·00 60
667 – 75 c. bistre (No. 476) . . . 1·10 75
668 **61** 1 b. grey . . . . 1·10 75
669 – 1 b. 20 green (No. 478) . . . 1·60 90
670 **61** 1 b. 80 blue . . . . 1·50 75
671 – 1 b. 80 blue (No. 489) . . . 2·10 1·00
672 – 1 b. 95 blue (No. 480) . . . 2·25 1·10
673 **64** 2 b. brown . . . . 2·25 1·90
674 2 b. 50 blue . . . . 2·75 1·90
675 – 3 b. lilac (No. 483) . . . 3·25 2·10
676 **64** 3 b. 70 red . . . . 38·00 27·00
677 – 10 b. purple (No. 485) . . . 14·00 8·25
678 **61** 20 b. black . . . . 22·00 17·00

1944. Air. 80th Anniv of Int Red Cross and 37th Anniv of Adherence of Venezuela.
680 **100** 5 c. green 10 10
681 10 c. mauve 15 10
682 20 c. blue 15 10
683 30 c. blue 35 10
684 40 c. brown 50 15
685 45 c. green 90 35
686 90 c. orange 85 30
687 1 b. black . . . . 1·25 25

101 Baseball Players **103** Charles Howarth

1944. Air. 7th World Amateur Baseball Championship Games, Caracas. Optd **AEREO.**
688 **101** 5 c. brown 35 25
689 10 c. green 40 25
690 20 c. blue 50 35
691 30 c. red 40 50
692 45 c. purple . . . . 1·00 45
693 90 c. orange . . . . 1·90 90
694 1 b. grey . . . . 2·10 90
695 1 b. 20 green . . . . 6·25 4·75
696 1 b. 80 yellow . . . . 8·25 6·50

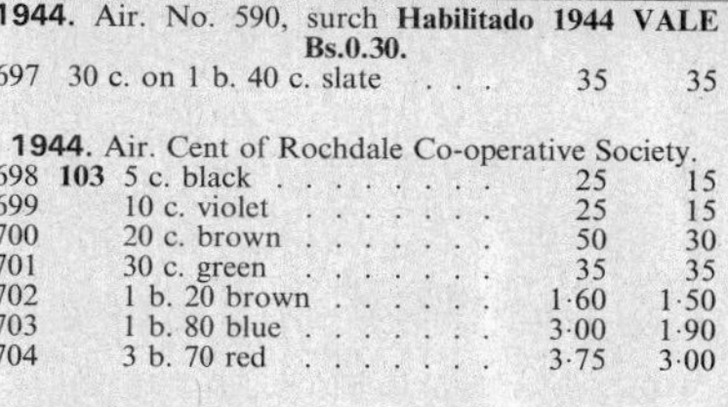

1944. Air. No. 590, surch **Habilitado 1944 VALE Bs.0.30.**
697 30 c. on 1 b. 40 c. slate . . . 35 35

1944. Air. Cent of Rochdale Co-operative Society.
698 **103** 5 c. black 25 15
699 10 c. violet 25 15
700 20 c. brown 50 30
701 30 c. green 35 35
702 1 b. 20 brown . . . . 1·60 1·50
703 1 b. 80 blue . . . . 3·00 1·90
704 3 b. 70 red . . . . 3·75 3·00

104 Antonio Jose de Sucre **105** Antonio Jose de Sucre and Douglas DC-4

1945. 150th Anniv of Birth of Gen. Sucre.
705 **104** 5 c. yellow (postage) . . . 75 35
706 10 c. blue . . . . 1·00 70
707 20 c. red . . . . 1·25 70
708 **105** 5 c. orange (air) 20 15
709 10 c. purple 25 20
710 20 c. black 35 25
711 30 c. green 55 40
712 40 c. olive 55 35
713 45 c. brown 70 35
714 90 c. brown . . . . 1·25 45
715 1 b. mauve 90 35
716 1 b. 20 black . . . . 2·10 1·90
717 2 b. yellow . . . . 3·00 1·50

106 Andres Bello **107** Gen. Rafael Urdaneta

1946. 80th Death Anniv of A. Bello (educationalist).
718 **106** 20 c. blue (postage) . . . 55 35
719 30 c. green (air) 40 30

1946. Death Centenary of Gen. R. Urdaneta.
720 **107** 20 c. blue (postage) . . . 55 35
721 30 c. green (air) 40 30

108 Allegory of Republic **110** Western Hemisphere and Anti-tuberculosis Inst, Maracaibo

1946. 1st Anniv of Revolution.
722 **108** 20 c. blue (postage) . . . 55 35
723 – 15 c. blue (air) 20 30
724 – 20 c. bistre 25 30
725 – 30 c. violet 30 25
726 – 1 b. red . . . . 2·10 1·50
Nos. 723/6 are as Type **108**, but vert.

1947. 12th Pan-American Health Conf, Caracas.
727 **110** 20 c. yell & blue (postage) . 50 35
728 – 15 c. yellow & blue (air) . 35 25
729 – 20 c. yellow and brown . . 35 40
730 – 30 c. yellow and violet . . 35 25
731 – 1 b. yellow and red . . . 2·50 2·10
Nos. 728/31 are as Type **110** but vert.

1947. Surch **J.R.G. CORREOS Vale Bs. 0.15 1946.**
732 **85** 15 c. on 1 b. brown . . . 55 35

1947. Air. Surch **J.R.G. AEREO Vale Bs.**, new value, and **1946.**
733 **47** 10 c. on $22\frac{1}{2}$ c. red (No. 418) 20 10
734 – 15 c. on 25 c. blue (No. 622) 45 15
735 **91** 20 c. on 50 c. blue 40 25
736 **85** 70 c. on 1 b. brown . . . 50 35
737 – 20 b. on 20 b. orange (No. 535) . . . . 17·00 9·50

1947. Nos. 743 and 624 surch **CORREOS Vale Bs.**, new value, and **1947.** (a) Postage.
776 5 c. on 30 c. black 25 10
777 5 c. on $37\frac{1}{2}$ c. blue 30 10

(b) Air. No. 621 with **AEREO** instead of **CORREOS.**
778 5 c. on 20 c. blue 40 10
779 10 c. on 20 c. blue 40 10

116 117
Freighter "Republica de Venezuela" and Ship's Wheel

1948. 1st Anniv of Greater Colombia Merchant Marine. Frame size 37½×22½ mm or 22½×37½ mm. Inscr "AMERICAN BANK NOTE COMPANY" at foot.

780 116 5 c. blue (postage) 20 10
781 7½ c. red 70 35
782 10 c. red 55 10
783 15 c. grey 75 15
784 20 c. sepia 40 10
785 25 c. violet 75 20
786 30 c. yellow . . . . 4·75 1·90
787 37½ c. brown . . . . 2·00 1·40
788 40 c. olive . . . . 3·00 1·75
789 50 c. mauve 85 25
790 1 b. green . . . . 2·00 50

791 117 5 c. brown (air) 10 10
792 10 c. green 10 10
793 15 c. buff 15 10
794 20 c. purple 20 10
794 25 c. grey 25 10
796 30 c. olive 35 15
797 45 c. blue 60 25
798 50 c. black 80 35
799 70 c. orange . . . . 1·75 35
800 75 c. blue . . . . 3·00 45
801 90 c. red . . . . 1·75 1·00
802 1 b. violet . . . . 2·00 70
803 2 b. slate . . . . 2·25 1·00
804 3 b. green . . . . 8·50 3·25
805 4 b. blue . . . . 4·00 3·25
806 5 b. red . . . . 17·00 5·50

For stamps as T **116/17** in larger size and inscribed "COURVOISIER S.A." at foot, see Nos. 1012/7.

118 Arms of Venezuela

1948. New Constitution Promulgation.

807 118 5 c. blue . . . . 1·00 55
808 10 c. red . . . . 1·25 60

120 Santos Michelena **121**

1949. 110th Anniv of 1st International Postal Convention, Bogota.

810 120 5 c. blue (postage) 25 15
811 10 c. red 25 15
812 20 c. sepia . . . . 1·00 35
813 1 b. green . . . . 3·25 1·60

814 121 5 c. brown (air) 20 15
815 10 c. grey 25 15
816 15 c. orange 30 15
817 25 c. green 60 30
818 30 c. purple 60 30
819 1 b. violet . . . . 3·00 1·25

122 **123**
Columbus, Indian, "Santa Maria" and Map

1949. 450th Anniv of Columbus's Discovery of America.

820 122 5 c. blue (postage) 75 15
821 10 c. red . . . . 3·50 60
822 20 c. sepia . . . . 4·75 90
823 1 b. green . . . . 10·00 3·25

824 123 5 c. brown (air) 70 10
825 10 c. grey 75 25
826 15 c. orange . . . . 1·40 30
827 25 c. green . . . . 2·50 65
828 30 c. mauve . . . . 3·50 90
829 1 b. violet . . . . 14·00 2·75

124 Hand, Bird, Airplane and Globe **125** Francisco de Miranda

126 Declaration of Independence

1950. Air. 75th Anniv of U.P.U.

830 124 5 c. lake 20 10
831 10 c. green 10 10
832 15 c. brown 20 10
833 25 c. grey 25 40
834 30 c. olive 35 20
835 50 c. black 25 25
836 60 c. blue 75 35
837 90 c. red . . . . 1·00 45
838 1 b. violet . . . . 1·10 30

1950. Birth Bicentenary of Miranda.

839 125 5 c. blue (postage) 25 10
840 10 c. green 30 10
841 20 c. brown 60 25
842 1 b. red . . . . 2·75 1·25

843 126 5 c. red (air) 35 15
844 10 c. brown 35 15
845 15 c. violet 30 35
846 30 c. blue 45 25
847 1 b. green . . . . 2·50 1·10

127 Tabebuia (National Tree) **128** Map and Statistics

1950. Air. Protection of Flora. Centres in yellow.

848 127 5 c. brown 35 20
849 10 c. green 25 10
850 15 c. mauve 35 15
851 25 c. green . . . . 2·50 1·00
852 30 c. orange . . . . 2·75 1·40
853 50 c. grey . . . . 1·50 35
854 60 c. blue . . . . 2·50 65
855 90 c. red . . . . 4·50 1·40
856 1 b. violet . . . . 5·50 1·60

1950. Census of the Americas.

857 128 5 c. blue (postage) 20 10
858 10 c. grey 20 10
859 15 c. sepia 30 10
860 25 c. green 25 15
861 30 c. red 35 25
862 50 c. violet 65 25
863 1 b. brown . . . . 1·60 85

864 128 5 c. grey (air) 15 10
865 10 c. green 10 10
866 15 c. olive 30 15
867 25 c. black 25 25
868 30 c. orange 35 20
869 50 c. brown 25 25
870 60 c. blue 25 35
871 90 c. red 90 35
872 1 b. violet . . . . 1·50 1·10

129 Alonso de Ojeda **131**

1950. 450th Anniv of Discovery of Lake Maracaibo.

873 129 5 c. blue (postage) 25 15
874 10 c. red 35 15
875 15 c. grey 40 20
876 20 c. blue . . . . 1·00 40
877 1 b. green . . . . 4·25 2·10

878 5 c. brown (air) 25 10
879 10 c. red 35 15
880 15 c. sepia 45 20
881 25 c. purple 45 40
882 30 c. orange 90 35
883 1 b. green . . . . 3·75 1·90

1951. Surch **RESELLADO** and new value.

884 116 5 c. on 7½ c. red 35 15
885 10 c. on 37½ c. brown 35 15

1951. Telegraph stamps surch as in T **131**.

886 5 c. on 5 c. brown 15 10
887 10 c. on 10 c. green 35 10
888 20 c. on 1 b. black 40 15
889 25 c. on 25 c. red 55 30
890 30 c. on 2 b. olive 70 55

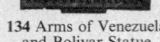

132 Arms of Caracas and View **133** Statue of Bolivar, New York

1951. Arms issue. Federal District of Caracas.

891 132 5 c. green (postage) 30 10
892 10 c. red 40 10
893 15 c. brown . . . . 1·00 25
894 20 c. blue . . . . 2·10 25
895 25 c. brown . . . . 3·00 55
896 30 c. blue . . . . 2·75 60
897 35 c. violet . . . . 27·00 16·00

898 5 c. turquoise (air) 40 15
899 7½ c. green . . . . 1·60 60
900 10 c. red 25 25
901 15 c. brown . . . . 3·75 40
902 20 c. blue . . . . 2·50 40
903 30 c. blue . . . . 4·25 85
904 45 c. purple . . . . 2·50 55
905 60 c. green . . . . 8·25 1·00
906 90 c. red . . . . 5·00 4·25

See also Nos. 922/37, 938/53, 954/69, 970/85, 991/1006, 1018/33, 1034/49, 1050/65, 1066/81, 1082/97, 1098/113, 1137/52, 1153/68, 1169/84, 1185/1200, 1201/16, 1217/32, 1258/73, 1274/89, 1290/1305, 1306/21, 1322/37, and 1338/53.

1951. Transfer of Statue of Bolivar to Central Park, New York.

907 133 5 c. green (postage) 35 10
908 10 c. red 35 25
909 20 c. blue 35 25
910 30 c. grey 45 40
911 40 c. green 60 40
912 50 c. brown . . . . 1·25 45
913 1 b. black . . . . 4·00 2·10

914 5 c. violet (air) 40 15
915 10 c. green 25 15
916 20 c. grey 25 15
917 25 c. olive 30 20
918 30 c. red 35 25
919 40 c. brown 35 25
920 50 c. slate . . . . 1·10 45
921 70 c. orange . . . . 1·90 1·10

134 Arms of Venezuela and Bolivar Statue **138** Isabella the Catholic

1951. Arms issue. National Arms of Venezuela.

922 134 5 c. green (postage) 25 10
923 10 c. red 35 10
924 15 c. brown . . . . 1·90 35
925 20 c. blue . . . . 1·90 45
926 25 c. brown . . . . 3·00 70
927 30 c. blue . . . . 3·00 70
928 35 c. violet . . . . 17·00 12·50

929 5 c. turquoise (air) 25 10
930 7½ c. green 70 55
931 10 c. red 35 15
932 15 c. brown . . . . 1·60 55
933 20 c. blue . . . . 2·25 40
934 30 c. blue . . . . 4·25 90
935 45 c. purple . . . . 1·90 35
936 60 c. green . . . . 9·25 1·90
937 90 c. red . . . . 5·75 4·25

1951. Arms issue. State of Tachira. As T **132** showing Arms of Tachira and agricultural products.

938 5 c. green (postage) 25 10
939 10 c. red 30 25
940 15 c. brown 60 20
941 20 c. blue . . . . 1·50 35
942 50 c. orange . . . . 90·00 11·50
943 1 b. green . . . . 1·50 55
944 5 b. purple . . . . 3·75 2·10

945 5 c. turquoise (air) 15 15
946 10 c. red 25 10
947 15 c. brown 55 25
948 30 c. blue . . . . 7·50 90
949 60 c. green . . . . 5·75 90
950 1 b. 20 lake . . . . 5·75 4·25
951 3 b. green . . . . 1·50 75
952 5 b. purple . . . . 3·25 1·60
953 10 b. violet . . . . 4·75 3·25

1951. Arms issue. State of Zulia. As T **132** showing Arms of Zulia and Oil Well.

954 5 c. green (postage) 25 10
955 10 c. red 25 10
956 15 c. brown 55 25
957 20 c. blue 70 35
958 50 c. orange . . . . 4·25 3·00
959 1 b. green . . . . 1·50 55
960 5 b. purple . . . . 3·00 2·10

961 5 c. turquoise (air) 30 15
962 10 c. red 15 10
963 15 c. brown 35 35
964 30 c. blue . . . . 2·50 1·00
965 60 c. green . . . . 1·40 35
966 1 b. 20 lake . . . . 5·75 4·25
967 3 b. green . . . . 1·50 65
968 5 b. purple . . . . 2·50 1·60
969 10 b. violet . . . . 4·25 3·25

1951. Arms issue. State of Carabobo. As T **132** showing Arms of Carabobo and agricultural produce.

970 5 c. green (postage) 15 10
971 10 c. red 15 10
972 15 c. brown 20 20
973 20 c. blue 30 30
974 25 c. brown 35 35
975 30 c. blue 70 30
976 35 c. violet . . . . 2·75 2·25

977 5 c. turquoise (air) 10 10
978 7½ c. green 25 25
979 10 c. red 15 10
980 15 c. brown 20 20
981 20 c. blue 30 30
982 30 c. blue . . . . 1·00 35
983 45 c. purple 45 40
984 60 c. green 90 45
985 90 c. red . . . . 2·50 1·50

1951. Air. 500th Birth Anniv of Isabella the Catholic.

986 138 5 c. green and light green 25 15
987 10 c. red and yellow 25 15
988 20 c. blue and grey 45 25
989 30 c. blue and grey 45 20

1951. Arms issue. State of Anzoategui. As T **132** showing Arms of Anzoategui and globe.

991 5 c. green (postage) 15 10
992 10 c. red 20 10
993 15 c. brown 55 25
994 20 c. blue 90 30
995 40 c. orange . . . . 1·90 90
996 45 c. purple . . . . 5·50 3·00
997 3 b. blue . . . . 2·10 1·00

998 5 c. turquoise (air) 25 10
999 10 c. red 20 10
1000 15 c. brown 25 25
1001 25 c. black 35 15
1002 30 c. blue 90 65
1003 50 c. orange 90 35
1004 60 c. green . . . . 1·40 20
1005 1 b. violet . . . . 1·60 65
1006 2 b. violet . . . . 3·00 1·50

140 National Stadium **147** Juan de Villegas

1951. Air. 3rd Bolivarian Games, Caracas.

1007 140 5 c. green 55 25
1008 10 c. red 60 25
1009 20 c. brown 70 35
1010 30 c. blue 90 45

1951. As Nos. 780/806 but frame size 38×23½ mm or 23½×38 mm. Inscr "COURVOISIER S.A." at foot.

1012 116 5 c. green (postage) 55 10
1013 10 c. red 90 10
1014 15 c. slate . . . . 3·00 10

1015 117 5 c. brown (air) 75 10
1016 10 c. brown . . . . 1·10 10
1017 15 c. olive . . . . 1·50 10

1952. Arms issue. State of Aragua. As T **132** showing Arms of Aragua and Stylised Farm.

1018 5 c. green (postage) 20 10
1019 10 c. red 15 10
1020 15 c. brown 35 10
1021 20 c. blue 30 30
1022 25 c. brown 75 40
1023 30 c. blue 75 35
1024 35 c. violet . . . . 4·25 3·00

1025 5 c. turquoise (air) 35 15
1026 7½ c. green 25 60
1027 10 c. red 15 10
1028 15 c. brown 85 40
1029 20 c. blue 45 40
1030 30 c. blue . . . . 1·40 25
1031 45 c. purple . . . . 1·10 40
1032 60 c. green . . . . 2·25 35
1033 90 c. red . . . . 11·50 6·75

1952. Arms issue. State of Bolivar. As T **132** showing Arms of Bolivar and Iron Foundry.

1034 5 c. green (postage) 15 10
1035 10 c. red 25 10
1036 15 c. brown 25 20
1037 20 c. blue 55 30
1038 40 c. orange . . . . 2·10 70
1039 45 c. purple . . . . 5·50 3·75
1040 3 b. blue . . . . 2·50 1·60

1041 5 c. turquoise (air) . . . . . 2·50 25
1042 10 c. red 15 10
1043 15 c. brown 30 15
1044 25 c. black 25 10
1045 30 c. blue . . . . 1·50 75
1046 50 c. red . . . . 1·00 35
1047 60 c. green . . . . 1·90 45
1048 1 b. violet . . . . 1·50 35
1049 2 b. violet . . . . 3·00 1·50

1952. Arms issue. State of Lara. As T **132** showing Arms of Lara and Sisal Industry.
1050 5 c. green (postage) 25 10
1051 10 c. red 25 10
1052 15 c. brown 20 30
1053 20 c. blue 50 35
1054 25 c. brown 60 45
1055 30 c. blue . . . . 1·00 35
1056 35 c. violet . . . . 4·25 3·00

1057 5 c. turquoise (air) 35 15
1058 7½ c. green 25 25
1059 10 c. red 15 10
1060 15 c. brown 55 20
1061 20 c. blue 75 30
1062 30 c. blue . . . . 1·90 35
1063 45 c. purple 75 30
1064 60 c. green . . . . 1·90 55
1065 90 c. red . . . . 11·00 8·25

1952. Arms issue. State of Miranda. As T **132** showing Arms of Miranda and Agricultural Products.
1066 5 c. green (postage) 20 10
1067 10 c. red 25 10
1068 15 c. brown 35 20
1069 20 c. blue 40 30
1070 25 c. brown 55 40
1071 30 c. blue 90 40
1072 35 c. violet . . . . 5·50 3·75

1073 5 c. turquoise (air) 35 10
1074 7½ c. green 45 25
1075 10 c. red 15 10
1076 15 c. brown 35 30
1077 20 c. blue 55 40
1078 30 c. blue 90 35
1079 45 c. purple 75 30
1080 60 c. green . . . . 1·90 55
1081 90 c. red . . . . 10·00 6·75

1952. Arms issue. State of Sucre. As T **132** showing Arms of Sucre, Palms and Seascape
1082 5 c. green (postage) 25 10
1083 10 c. red 25 10
1084 15 c. brown 60 20
1085 20 c. blue 60 15
1086 40 c. orange . . . . 2·10 55
1087 45 c. purple . . . . 7·50 4·50
1088 3 b. blue . . . . 1·90 1·25

1089 5 c. turquoise (air) 25 15
1090 10 c. red 25 10
1091 15 c. brown 30 20
1092 25 c. black . . . . 7·00 25
1093 30 c. blue . . . . 2·25 70
1094 50 c. red . . . . 1·00 35
1095 60 c. green . . . . 1·40 55
1096 1 b. violet . . . . 1·60 40
1097 2 b. violet . . . . 3·75 1·90

1952. Arms issue. State of Trujillo. As T **132** showing Arms of Trujillo and Stylised Coffee Plant.
1098 5 c. green (postage) 15 10
1099 10 c. red 25 10
1100 15 c. brown 75 25
1101 20 c. blue 75 35
1102 50 c. orange . . . . 4·25 2·50
1103 1 b. green . . . . 1·00 45
1104 5 b. purple . . . . 2·50 1·60

1105 5 c. turquoise (air) . . . . . 3·75 30
1106 10 c. red 15 10
1107 15 c. brown 90 15
1108 30 c. blue . . . . 4·25 90
1109 60 c. green . . . . 3·25 85
1110 1 b. 20 lake . . . . 3·00 2·00
1111 3 b. green . . . . 1·40 85
1112 5 b. purple . . . . 3·00 1·50
1113 10 b. violet . . . . 5·00 3·25

1952. 4th Centenary of Barquisimeto.
1114 **147** 5 c. green (postage) . . . 35 10
1115 10 c. red 35 10
1116 20 c. slate 55 35
1117 40 c. orange . . . . . . 2·50 1·25
1118 50 c. brown . . . . 1·40 65
1119 1 b. violet . . . . 2·50 85

1120 5 c. turquoise (air) 30 10
1121 10 c. red 15 10
1122 20 c. blue 25 10
1123 25 c. black 35 25
1124 30 c. blue 45 20
1125 40 c. orange . . . . . . 2·50 1·25
1126 50 c. bronze 85 35
1127 1 b. purple . . . . 3·25 1·60

148 Our Lady of Coromoto

157 G.P.O., Caracas

1952. 300th Anniv of Apparition of Our Lady of Coromoto.
1128 **148** 1 b. red (17×26½ mm) . 4·25 65
1129 1 b. red (26½×41 mm) . 3·00 65
1130 1 b. red (36×65 mm) . . 1·40 55

1952. National Objective Exn. Telegraph stamps as T **131** surch **Correos Exposicion Objetiva Nacional 1948-1952** and new value.
1131 5 c. on 25 c. red 35 10
1132 10 c. on 1 b. black 35 10

1952. Telegraph stamps as T **131** surch **CORREOS HABILITADO 1952** and new value.
1133 20 c. on 25 c. red 45 15
1134 30 c. on 2 b. olive . . . . . 1·60 1·00
1135 40 c. on 1 b. black 60 50
1136 50 c. on 3 b. orange . . . . 2·10 1·25

1953. Arms issue. State of Merida. As T **132** showing Arms of Merida and Church.
1137 5 c. green (postage) 15 10
1138 10 c. red 15 10
1139 15 c. brown 20 25
1140 20 c. blue 55 25
1141 50 c. orange . . . . 2·50 1·00
1142 1 b. green 65 45
1143 5 b. purple . . . . 2·50 1·40

1144 5 c. turquoise (air) 20 15
1145 10 c. red 20 10
1146 15 c. brown 35 15
1147 30 c. blue . . . . 3·00 65
1148 60 c. green . . . . 1·40 35
1149 1 b. 20 lake . . . . 2·50 1·60
1150 3 b. green . . . . 1·40 65
1151 5 b. purple . . . . 3·00 1·60
1152 10 b. violet . . . . 4·25 2·75

1953. Arms issue. State of Monagas. As T **132** showing Arms of Monagas and Horses.
1153 5 c. green (postage) 15 10
1154 10 c. red 20 10
1155 15 c. brown 25 25
1156 20 c. blue 35 35
1157 40 c. orange . . . . 1·60 60
1158 45 c. purple . . . . 5·25 3·00
1159 3 b. blue . . . . 2·10 1·60

1160 5 c. turquoise (air) 20 15
1161 10 c. red 15 10
1162 15 c. brown 35 20
1163 25 c. black 25 15
1164 30 c. blue . . . . 2·50 75
1165 50 c. red 90 35
1166 60 c. green . . . . 1·10 35
1167 1 b. violet . . . . 1·60 45
1168 2 b. violet . . . . 2·25 1·40

1953. Arms issue. State of Portuguesa. As T **132** showing Arms of Portuguesa and Woodland.
1169 5 c. green (postage) 15 10
1170 10 c. red 15 10
1171 15 c. brown 20 20
1172 20 c. blue 45 20
1173 50 c. orange . . . . 2·25 1·50
1174 1 b. green 60 25
1175 5 b. purple . . . . 2·50 1·60

1176 5 c. turquoise (air) 90 40
1177 10 c. red 35 10
1178 15 c. brown 40 25
1179 30 c. blue . . . . 3·00 1·25
1180 60 c. green . . . . 2·10 40
1181 1 b. 20 lake . . . . 5·25 3·00
1182 3 b. green . . . . 1·60 85
1183 5 b. purple . . . . 3·00 1·60
1184 10 b. violet . . . . 4·50 3·75

1953. Arms issue. Federal Territory of Delta Amacuro. As T **132** showing Arms of Delta Amacuro and map.
1185 5 c. green (postage) 15 10
1186 10 c. red 20 10
1187 15 c. brown 25 15
1188 20 c. blue 40 25
1189 40 c. orange . . . . 1·40 85
1190 45 c. purple . . . . 6·25 3·75
1191 3 b. blue . . . . 1·60 1·25

1192 5 c. turquoise (air) 25 10
1193 10 c. red 15 10
1194 15 c. brown 35 25
1195 25 c. black 55 40
1196 30 c. blue . . . . 1·90 55
1197 50 c. red 90 40
1198 60 c. green . . . . 1·50 40
1199 1 b. violet . . . . 1·90 60
1200 2 b. violet . . . . 3·00 2·25

1953. Arms issue. State of Falcon. As T **132** showing Arms of Falcon and Stylised Oil Refinery.
1201 5 c. green (postage) 15 10
1202 10 c. red 20 10
1203 15 c. brown 35 15
1204 20 c. blue 35 20
1205 50 c. orange . . . . 1·60 85
1206 1 b. green . . . . 1·00 65
1207 5 b. purple . . . . 3·00 1·60

1208 5 c. turquoise (air) 40 30
1209 10 c. red 15 10
1210 15 c. brown 35 25
1211 30 c. blue . . . . 3·00 75
1212 60 c. green . . . . 2·25 75
1213 1 b. 20 lake . . . . 3·00 2·50
1214 3 b. green . . . . 3·00 1·60
1215 5 b. purple . . . . 5·00 3·25
1216 10 b. violet . . . . 5·00 3·75

1953. Arms issue. State of Guarico. As T **132** showing Arms of Guarico and Factory.
1217 5 c. green (postage) 15 10
1218 10 c. red 15 10
1219 15 c. brown 30 25
1220 20 c. blue 35 30
1221 40 c. orange . . . . 1·60 1·10
1222 45 c. purple . . . . 3·75 2·25
1223 3 b. blue . . . . 1·60 1·00

1224 5 c. turquoise (air) 25 10
1225 10 c. red 35 10
1226 15 c. brown 35 20
1227 25 c. black 55 25
1228 30 c. blue . . . . 2·10 85
1229 50 c. red . . . . 1·00 50
1230 60 c. green . . . . 1·25 55
1231 1 b. violet . . . . 2·10 55
1232 2 b. violet . . . . 3·00 1·60

1953. Inscr "EE. UU. DE VENEZUELA".
1233 **157** 5 c. green (postage) . . . 15 10
1234 7½ c. green 30 20
1235 10 c. red 35 10
1236 15 c. black 30 10
1237 20 c. blue 40 15
1238 25 c. mauve 30 10
1239 30 c. blue . . . . 1·60 25
1240 35 c. mauve 70 25
1241 40 c. orange . . . . . . 1·00 35
1242 45 c. violet . . . . 1·60 55
1243 50 c. orange . . . . . . 1·00 35

1244 5 c. orange (air) 10 10
1245 7½ c. green 20 20
1246 15 c. purple 15 10
1247 20 c. slate 20 10
1248 25 c. sepia 60 10
1249 30 c. brown . . . . 3·50 1·50
1250 40 c. red 60 15
1251 45 c. purple 60 15
1252 50 c. red 85 10
1253 60 c. red . . . . 3·50 1·75
1254 70 c. myrtle . . . . 2·00 85
1255 75 c. blue . . . . 3·00 1·25
1256 90 c. brown . . . . 1·60 70
1257 1 b. violet . . . . 1·60 60

See also Nos. 1365/82.

1953. Arms issue. State of Cojedes. As T **132** showing Arms of Cojedes and Cattle.
1258 5 c. green (postage) 15 10
1259 10 c. red 25 10
1260 15 c. brown 25 10
1261 20 c. blue 30 15
1262 25 c. brown 75 35
1263 30 c. blue . . . . 1·10 35
1264 35 c. violet . . . . 1·50 90

1265 5 c. turquoise (air) . . . . . 2·10 45
1266 7½ c. green 55 50
1267 10 c. red 20 10
1268 15 c. brown 35 15
1269 20 c. blue 40 20
1270 30 c. blue . . . . 2·75 40
1271 45 c. purple . . . . 1·00 35
1272 60 c. green . . . . 2·10 35
1273 90 c. red . . . . 2·50 1·50

1954. Arms issue. Federal Territory of Amazonas. As T **132** showing Arms of Amazonas and Orchid.
1274 5 c. green (postage) 40 10
1275 10 c. red 40 10
1276 15 c. brown 90 20
1277 20 c. blue . . . . 2·50 40
1278 40 c. orange . . . . 3·00 90
1279 45 c. purple . . . . 4·50 2·25
1280 3 b. blue . . . . 6·75 2·50

1281 5 c. turquoise (air) 70 10
1282 10 c. red 40 10
1283 15 c. brown 70 25
1284 25 c. black . . . . 1·50 25
1285 30 c. blue . . . . 3·75 35
1286 50 c. red . . . . 3·00 60
1287 60 c. green . . . . 3·75 60
1288 1 b. violet . . . . 14·50 2·10
1289 2 b. violet . . . . 5·75 2·50

1954. Arms issue. State of Apure. As T **132** showing Arms of Apure, Horse and Bird.
1290 5 c. green (postage) 15 10
1291 10 c. red 15 10
1292 15 c. brown 25 20
1293 20 c. blue . . . . 1·50 25
1294 50 c. orange . . . . 1·90 1·50
1295 1 b. green 60 55
1296 5 b. purple . . . . 3·75 2·10

1297 5 c. turquoise (air) 35 15
1298 10 c. red 15 10
1299 15 c. brown 35 20
1300 30 c. blue . . . . 1·60 65
1301 60 c. green . . . . 1·60 35
1302 1 b. 20 lake . . . . 2·50 1·60
1303 3 b. green . . . . 1·60 65
1304 5 b. purple . . . . 3·00 1·40
1305 10 b. violet . . . . 4·25 3·00

1954. Arms issue. State of Barinas. As T **132** showing Arms of Barinas, Cow and Horse.
1306 5 c. green (postage) 15 10
1307 10 c. red 15 10
1308 15 c. brown 20 20
1309 20 c. blue . . . . 1·50 35
1310 50 c. orange . . . . 1·60 1·00
1311 1 b. green 45 35
1312 5 b. purple . . . . 3·75 1·90

1313 5 c. turquoise (air) 35 15
1314 10 c. red 15 10
1315 15 c. brown 60 25
1316 30 c. blue . . . . 2·10 85
1317 60 c. green . . . . 2·10 40
1318 1 b. 20 lake . . . . 3·00 1·60
1319 3 b. green . . . . 1·90 85
1320 5 b. purple . . . . 3·00 1·00
1321 10 b. violet . . . . 4·50 3·25

1954. Arms issue. State of Nueva Esparta. As T **132** showing Arms of Nueva Esparta and Fishes.
1322 5 c. green (postage) 15 10
1323 10 c. red 15 10
1324 15 c. brown 35 25
1325 20 c. blue 40 15
1326 40 c. orange . . . . 1·90 70
1327 45 c. purple . . . . 4·50 2·75
1328 3 b. blue . . . . 2·10 1·50

1329 5 c. turquoise (air) 30 15
1330 10 c. red 20 10
1331 15 c. brown 55 20
1332 25 c. black 90 35
1333 30 c. blue . . . . 1·90 40
1334 50 c. red . . . . 1·90 40
1335 60 c. green . . . . 1·90 40
1336 1 b. violet . . . . 2·75 60
1337 2 b. violet . . . . 3·75 1·90

1954. Arms issue. State of Yaracuy. As T **132** showing Arms of Yaracuy and Tropical Foliage.
1338 5 c. green (postage) 30 10
1339 10 c. red 15 10
1340 15 c. brown 25 20
1341 20 c. blue 35 30
1342 25 c. brown 55 40
1343 30 c. blue 60 30
1344 35 c. violet . . . . 1·50 90

1345 5 c. turquoise (air) 35 20
1346 7½ c. green . . . . 5·00 5·00
1347 10 c. red 20 10
1348 15 c. brown 55 15
1349 20 c. blue 70 15
1350 30 c. blue . . . . 1·50 40
1351 45 c. purple . . . . 1·00 40
1352 60 c. green . . . . 1·00 40
1353 90 c. red . . . . 3·00 2·10

164 Simon Rodriguez

165 Bolivar and 1824 Edict

1954. Air. Death Cent of Rodriguez (Bolivar's tutor).
1354 **164** 5 c. turquoise 35 10
1355 10 c. red 50 10
1356 20 c. blue 35 10
1357 45 c. purple 55 35
1358 65 c. green . . . . 1·90 85

1954. Air. 10th Pan-American Conf, Caracas.
1359 **165** 15 c. black and brown . . . 15 10
1360 25 c. brown and grey . . 45 15
1361 40 c. brown and orange . . 35 15
1362 65 c. black and blue . . 90 45
1363 80 c. brown and red . . 75 35
1364 1 b. violet and mauve . . 1·50 30

1954. As T **157** but inscr "REPUBLICA DE VENEZUELA".
1365 5 c. green (postage) 15 10
1366 10 c. red 15 10
1367 15 c. black 30 10
1368 20 c. blue 35 10
1369 30 c. blue 55 50
1370 35 c. mauve 55 20
1371 40 c. orange 85 30
1372 45 c. violet . . . . 1·00 40

1373 5 c. yellow (air) 15 10
1374 10 c. bistre 15 10
1375 15 c. purple 20 10
1376 20 c. slate 35 10
1377 30 c. brown 35 10
1378 40 c. red 60 30
1379 45 c. purple 60 40
1380 70 c. green . . . . 1·60 70
1381 75 c. blue . . . . 1·00 40
1382 90 c. brown 55 30

166

167

1955. 400th Anniv of Valencia Del Rey.
1383 **166** 5 c. green (postage) . . . 25 10
1384 20 c. blue 50 10
1385 25 c. brown 55 10
1386 50 c. orange 85 35

1387 5 c. turquoise (air) . . . 10 10
1388 10 c. red 15 10
1389 20 c. blue 25 10
1390 25 c. black 25 10
1391 40 c. violet 35 35
1392 50 c. red 35 10
1393 60 c. olive 75 35

1955. 1st Postal Convention, Caracas.
1394 **167** 5 c. green (postage) . . . 25 10
1395 20 c. blue 80 10
1396 25 c. lake 65 10
1397 50 c. orange 85 10

1398 5 c. yellow (air) 15 10
1399 15 c. brown 35 10
1400 25 c. black 35 10
1401 40 c. red 35 20
1402 50 c. orange 35 25
1403 60 c. red 75 50

168 O'Leary College, Barinas

1956. Air. Public Works.
1404 **168** 5 c. yellow 15 10
1405 10 c. sepia 15 10
1406 15 c. brown 20 10
1407 A 20 c. blue 20 10
1408 25 c. black 25 10
1409 30 c. brown 25 15

1410	B	40 c. red	30	20
1411		45 c. brown	20	15
1412		50 c. orange	35	15
1413	C	60 c. olive	35	25
1414		65 c. blue	60	35
1415	168	70 c. green	60	25
1416	C	75 c. blue	65	30
1417	A	80 c. red	75	35
1418	B	1 b. purple	45	20
1419	C	2 b. red	90	60

DESIGNS—HORIZ: A, University Hospital, Caracas; B, Caracas–La Guaira Highway; C, Simon Bolivar Centre.

169

170

1956. 1st American Book Festival, Caracas.

1420	169	5 c. turquoise and green (postage)	10	10
1421		10 c. purple and red	10	10
1422		20 c. blue and ultram	25	10
1423		25 c. grey and green	35	15
1424		30 c. blue & light blue	35	15
1425		40 c. sepia and brown	50	25
1426		50 c. brown and red	55	35
1427		1 b. slate and violet	85	40
1428	170	5 c. brown & orge (air)	10	10
1429		10 c. sepia and brown	15	10
1430		20 c. blue and turquoise	15	10
1431		25 c. slate and violet	35	10
1432		40 c. purple and red	50	15
1433		45 c. brn and chocolate	35	15
1434		60 c. grey and olive	75	35

171 Tamanaco Hotel, Caracas

172 Simon Bolivar

1957. Tamanaco Hotel, Caracas Commem.

1435	171	5 c. green (postage)	10	10
1436		10 c. red	10	10
1437		15 c. black	40	10
1438		20 c. blue	25	10
1439		25 c. purple	25	10
1440		30 c. blue	45	35
1441		35 c. lilac	25	15
1442		40 c. orange	35	25
1443		45 c. purple	45	35
1444		50 c. yellow	60	25
1445		1 b. myrtle	85	35
1446		5 c. yellow (air)	10	10
1447		10 c. brown	10	10
1448		15 c. brown	15	10
1449		20 c. slate	30	10
1450		25 c. brown	25	10
1451		30 c. blue	15	20
1452		40 c. red	20	15
1453		45 c. brown	25	15
1454		50 c. orange	25	20
1455		60 c. green	45	25
1456		65 c. orange	1·25	60
1457		70 c. black	65	30
1458		75 c. turquoise	75	35
1459		1 b. purple	75	35
1460		2 b. black	1·25	45

1957. 150th Anniv of Oath of Monte Sacro and 125th Anniv of Death of Bolivar.

1461	172	5 c. green (postage)	10	10
1462		10 c. red	15	10
1463		20 c. blue	50	15
1464		25 c. red	50	15
1465		30 c. blue	40	15
1466		40 c. orange	60	25
1467		50 c. yellow	85	40
1468		5 c. orange (air)	15	10
1469		10 c. brown	20	10
1470		20 c. blue	45	20
1471		25 c. purple	50	25
1472		40 c. red	45	20
1473		45 c. purple	55	35
1474		65 c. brown	90	35

173 G.P.O., Caracas

174 Arms of Santiago de Merida

1958.

1475	173	5 c. green (postage)	10	10
1476		10 c. red	10	10
1477		15 c. grey	10	10
1478		20 c. blue	20	10
1479		25 c. yellow	20	10
1480	173	30 c. grey	25	10
1481		35 c. purple	30	10
1482		40 c. red	50	15
1483		45 c. violet	1·00	70
1484		50 c. yellow	45	15
1485		1 b. olive	60	50
1486		5 c. yellow (air)	10	10
1487		10 c. brown	10	10
1488		15 c. brown	10	10
1489		20 c. blue	10	10
1490		25 c. grey	20	10
1491		30 c. blue	20	10
1492		35 c. olive	30	10
1493		40 c. green	30	10
1494		50 c. red	30	10
1495		55 c. olive	45	20
1496		60 c. mauve	15	20
1497		65 c. red	20	20
1498		70 c. green	55	25
1499		75 c. brown	80	20
1500		80 c. brown	80	35
1501		85 c. red	1·00	50
1502		90 c. violet	30	35
1503		95 c. purple	90	50
1504		1 b. mauve	35	35
1505		1 b. 20 brown	4·50	3·60

1958. 400th Anniv of Santiago de Merida de los Caballeros.

1506	174	5 c. green (postage)	10	10
1507		10 c. red	10	10
1508		15 c. grey	10	10
1509		20 c. blue	20	10
1510		25 c. purple	35	10
1511		30 c. violet	35	15
1512		35 c. violet	40	15
1513		40 c. orange	50	35
1514		45 c. purple	25	15
1515		50 c. yellow	45	35
1516		1 b. grey	1·25	45
1517		5 c. ochre (air)	10	10
1518		10 c. brown	10	10
1519		15 c. brown	15	10
1520		20 c. blue	15	10
1521		25 c. olive	40	15
1522		30 c. blue	35	10
1523		40 c. red	50	15
1524		45 c. purple	50	20
1525		50 c. orange	35	35
1526		60 c. olive	50	25
1527		65 c. brown	90	35
1528		70 c. black	55	50
1529		75 c. blue	1·00	55
1530		80 c. violet	65	50
1531		90 c. green	65	30
1532		1 b. lilac	75	35

175 G.P.O., Caracas

176 Arms of Trujillo and Bolivar Monument

1958.

1533	175	5 c. green (postage)	35	10
1534		10 c. red	50	10
1535		15 c. black	40	10
1536		5 c. yellow (air)	35	10
1537		10 c. brown	50	10
1538		15 c. brown	40	10

1958. 400th Anniv of Trujillo.

1539	176	5 c. green (postage)	10	10
1540		10 c. red	10	10
1541		15 c. grey	10	10
1542		20 c. blue	15	10
1543		25 c. mauve	35	10
1544		30 c. blue	50	15
1545		35 c. lilac	55	25
1546		45 c. purple	40	35
1547		50 c. yellow	40	25
1548		1 b. olive	1·00	55
1549		5 c. buff (air)	10	10
1550		10 c. brown	20	10
1551		15 c. brown	25	10
1552		20 c. blue	30	15
1553		25 c. grey	40	20
1554		30 c. blue	40	20
1555		40 c. green	25	25
1556		50 c. orange	25	30
1557		60 c. mauve	35	40
1558		65 c. red	1·10	55
1559		1 b. violet	75	25

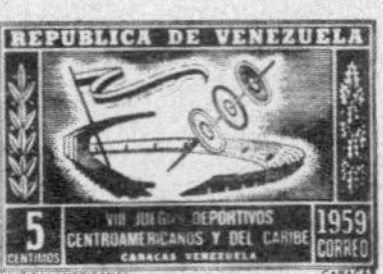

177 Caracas Stadium

178 "Eternal Flame"

1959. 8th Central American and Caribbean Games.

1560	177	5 c. green (postage)	25	10
1561		10 c. mauve	25	10
1562		20 c. blue	35	35
1563		30 c. blue	45	40
1564		50 c. lilac	65	35
1565	178	5 c. yellow (air)	15	10
1566		10 c. brown	35	15
1567		15 c. orange	40	20
1568		30 c. slate	35	40
1569		50 c. green	45	50

179 Venezuelan ½ Real Stamp of 1859, Gen. J. I. Paz Castillo and Postman

180 Alexander von Humboldt

1959. Cent of First Venezuelan Postage Stamps.

1570	179	25 c. ochre (postage)	25	15
1571	–	50 c. blue	45	35
1572	–	1 b. red	85	35
1573	179	25 c. ochre (air)	25	15
1574	–	50 c. blue	35	35
1575	–	1 b. red	75	35

DESIGNS: 50 c. (2), 1 real stamp of 1859, Don Jacinto Gutierrez and postman on mule; 1 b. (2), 2 reales stamp of 1859, Don Miguel Herrera, and steam mail train and Douglas DC-6 airliner.

1960. Death Centenary of Von Humboldt (naturalist).

1576	180	5 c. olive & grn (postage)	35	10
1577		30 c. violet and blue	85	20
1578		40 c. brown and orange	1·00	50
1579		5 c. brown & bistre (air)	35	10
1580		20 c. turquoise and blue	85	20
1581		40 c. bronze and olive	1·10	50

181 Bolivar Peak, Merida

1960. Tourist issue.

1582	181	5 c. green & emerald (postage)	85	85
1583	–	15 c. grey and purple	2·25	2·25
1584	–	35 c. purple & light purple	1·90	1·90
1585	181	30 c. blue and deep blue (air)	1·75	1·60
1586	–	50 c. brown and orange	1·75	1·60
1587	–	65 c. brown and orange	1·75	1·60

DESIGNS: 15, 50 c. Caroni Falls, Bolivar; 35, 65 c. Cuacharo Caves, Monagas.

182 National Pantheon, Caracas

183 A. Eloy Blanco

1960. Pantheon in olive.

1588	182	5 c. green (postage)	10	10
1589		20 c. blue	50	15
1590		25 c. olive	70	20
1591		30 c. grey	85	25
1592		40 c. brown	1·25	50
1593		45 c. violet	1·25	50
1594		5 c. bistre (air)	10	10
1595		10 c. brown	25	10
1596		15 c. brown	35	10
1597		20 c. blue	50	15
1598		25 c. grey	1·10	35
1599		30 c. violet	1·25	55
1600		40 c. green	50	15
1601		45 c. violet	75	20
1602		60 c. mauve	75	40
1603		65 c. red	75	40
1604		70 c. grey	90	35
1605		75 c. blue	1·90	60
1606		80 c. blue	1·60	50
1607		1 b. 20 yellow	1·90	70

1960. 5th Death Anniv of Blanco (poet). Portrait in black.

1608	183	5 c. green (postage)	15	10
1609		30 c. grey	35	15
1610		50 c. yellow	60	30
1611		20 c. blue (air)	35	15
1612		75 c. turquoise	1·00	40
1613		90 c. violet	1·00	40

184 1808 Newspaper and Caracas, 1958

185 A. Codazzi

1960. 150th Anniv of "Gazeta de Caracas". Centres in black.

1614	184	10 c. red (postage)	35	15
1615		20 c. blue	45	20
1616		35 c. violet	85	70
1617		5 c. yellow (air)	1·50	65
1618		15 c. brown	1·00	35
1619		65 c. orange	1·25	60

1960. Death Centenary of Codazzi (geographer).

1620	185	5 c. deep green and light green (postage)	10	10
1621		15 c. black and grey	45	15
1622		20 c. blue & light blue	40	15
1623		45 c. purple and lilac	45	30
1624		5 c. brown & orge (air)	10	10
1625		10 c. sepia and brown	15	10
1626		25 c. black and grey	35	10
1627		30 c. deep blue & blue	45	15
1628		50 c. brown and lt brown	70	30
1629		70 c. black and brown	1·25	45

186 Declaration of Independence

1960. 150th Anniv of Independence. Centres multicoloured.

1630	186	5 c. green (postage)	50	10
1631		20 c. blue	1·00	30
1632		30 c. blue	1·00	40
1633		50 c. orange (air)	80	30
1634		75 c. turquoise	1·00	35
1635		90 c. violet	1·25	40

187 Drilling for Oil

188 L. Caceres de Arismendi

1960. Oil Industry.

1636	187	5 c. myrtle & turquoise (postage)	1·40	70
1637		10 c. brown and red	70	25
1638		15 c. mauve and purple	85	30
1639	–	30 c. indigo & blue (air)	50	20
1640	–	40 c. olive and green	85	35
1641	–	50 c. brown & orange	1·00	40

DESIGN: Nos. 1639/41, Oil refinery.

1960. 94th Death Anniv of Luisa Caceres de Arismendi. Centres multicoloured.

1642	188	20 c. blue (postage)	1·00	30
1643		25 c. yellow	85	30
1644		30 c. blue	1·10	40
1645		5 c. bistre (air)	80	30
1646		10 c. brown	1·00	45
1647		60 c. red	1·90	55

189 Gen. J. A. Anzoategui

190 Gen. A. J. de Sucre

1960. 140th Death Anniv of Gen. Anzoategui.

1648	189	5 c. olive & grn (postage)	20	10
1649		15 c. purple and brown	40	10
1650		20 c. deep blue & blue	45	15
1651		25 c. brown & grey (air)	40	20
1652		40 c. olive and yellow	40	30
1653		45 c. purple and mauve	60	30

1960. 130th Death Anniv of Gen. A. J. de Sucre.

1654	190	10 c. mult (postage)	35	15
1655		15 c. multicoloured	40	20
1656		20 c. multicoloured	60	30
1657		25 c. multicoloured (air)	60	30
1658		30 c. multicoloured	85	40
1659		50 c. multicoloured	1·25	60

191 Skyscraper   192 "Population and Farming"

1961. National Census. Skyscraper in orange.

1660 **191** 5 c. green 10 10
1661 10 c. red 10 10
1662 15 c. grey 10 10
1663 20 c. blue 15 10
1664 25 c. brown 25 15
1665 30 c. blue 25 10
1666 35 c. purple 35 15
1667 40 c. brown 50 25
1668 45 c. violet 70 35
1669 50 c. yellow 50 20

1961. Air. 9th Population Census and 3rd Farming Census. Animal's head and inscr in black.

1670 **192** 5 c. yellow 10 10
1671 10 c. brown 10 10
1672 15 c. orange 10 10
1673 20 c. blue 15 10
1674 25 c. grey 20 10
1675 30 c. blue 25 10
1676 40 c. green 35 15
1677 45 c. violet 35 20
1678 50 c. orange 40 25
1679 60 c. mauve 50 25
1680 65 c. red 45 35
1681 70 c. grey 65 25
1682 75 c. turquoise 60 40
1683 80 c. violet 60 35
1684 90 c. violet 90 35

193 R. M. Baralt   195 Arms of San Cristobal

1961. Death Centenary of R. M. Baralt (writer).

1685 **193** 5 c. turq & grn (postage) 10 10
1686 15 c. brown and grey . . 25 10
1687 35 c. violet and mauve . 40 15
1688 25 c. sepia & grey (air) . 45 30
1689 30 c. violet and blue . . 55 35
1690 40 c. bronze and green . 65 35

1961. Air. 4th Centenary of San Cristobal. Arms in red, yellow and blue.

1692 **195** 5 c. sepia and orange . . 10 10
1693 55 c. black and green . . 45 25

196 Yellow-crowned Amazon   197 J. J. Aguerrevere (first College President)

1961. Birds. Multicoloured.

1694 30 c. Type **196** (postage) . . 90 40
1695 40 c. Snowy egret . . . . 1·10 40
1696 50 c. Scarlet ibis . . . . 2·40 80
1697 5 c. Troupial (air) . . . . . 1·75 1·10
1698 10 c. Guianan cock of the rock 90 60
1699 15 c. Tropical mockingbird . 1·10 65

1961. Engineering College Centenary.

1700 **197** 25 c. blue 15 10

198 Battle Scene

1961. 140th Anniv of Battle of Carabobo. Centres multicoloured.

1702 **198** 5 c. green (postage) . . . 10 10
1703 40 c. brown 70 30
1704 – 50 c. blue (air) 70 15
1705 – 1 b. 05 orange . . . . . 1·10 60
1706 – 1 b. 50 mauve . . . . . 1·60 60
1707 – 1 b. 90 violet . . . . . 1·90 85
1708 – 2 b. sepia . . . . . . 2·10 85
1709 – 3 b. blue . . . . . . 2·75 1·00

DESIGN: 50 c. to 3 b. Cavalry charge.

199 Cardinal's Arms   200 Archbishop Blanco

1962. Air. Elevation to Cardinal of Jose Humberto Quintero.

1710 **199** 5 c. mauve 10 10

1962. Air. 4th Anniv of Archbishop Blanco's Pastoral Letter.

1712 **200** 75 c. mauve 70 30

201 "Oncidium papilio Lindl"

1962. Orchids. Multicoloured.

1713 5 c. Type **201** (postage) . . . 10 10
1714 10 c. "Caularthron bilamellatum (Rchb. f.) R.E. Schultes" 15 10
1715 20 c. "Stanhopea Wardii Lodd. ex Lindl" 40 10
1716 25 c. "Catasetum pileatum Rchb. f." 35 10
1717 30 c. "Masdevallia tovarensis Rchb. f." 40 15
1718 35 c. "Epidendrum Stamfordianum Batem" (horiz) 45 25
1719 50 c. "Epidendrum atropurpureum Willd" . . . 55 35
1720 3 b. "Oncidium falcipetalum Lindl." . . . . . . 3·00 1·60
1721 5 c. "Oncidium volvox Rchb. f." (air) 10 10
1722 20 c. "Cycnoches chlorochilon Kl." 20 10
1723 25 c. "Cattleya Gaskelliana Rchb. f. var. alba" 30 15
1724 30 c. "Epidendrum difforme Jacq." (horiz) 20 15
1725 40 c. "Catasetum callosum Lindl" (horiz) 30 20
1726 50 c. "Oncidium bicolor Lindl" 35 30
1727 1 b. "Brassavola nodosa Lindl" (horiz) 60 25
1728 1 b. 05 "Epidendrum lividum Lindl" . . . . . . 1·60 85
1729 1 b. 50 "Schomburgkia undulata Lindl" . . . . 1·90 90
1730 2 b. "Oncidium zebrinum Rchb. f." . . . . 2·25 1·40

202 Signing of Independence

1962. 150th Anniv of Declaration of Independence. Multicoloured centres; frame colours given.

1731 **202** 5 c. green (postage) . . 15 10
1732 20 c. blue 35 15
1733 25 c. orange 55 30
1734 55 c. green (air) 45 20
1735 1 b. 05 mauve . . . . . 1·50 60
1736 1 b. 50 violet . . . . . 1·25 55

1962. Air. Bicentenary of Upata. Surch **BICENTENARIO DE UPATA 1762–1962 RESELLADO AEREO VALOR Bs 2,00.**

1739 **173** 2 b. on 1 b. olive . . . 1·60 75

204 Putting the Shot

1962. 1st National Games, Caracas, 1961.

1740 **204** 5 c. green (postage) . . 10 10
1741 – 10 c. mauve 15 10
1742 – 25 c. blue 30 15
1744 – 40 c. grey (air) 40 25
1745 – 75 c. brown 60 35
1746 – 85 c. red . . . . 1·40 55

SPORTS: 10 c. Football; 25 c. Swimming; 40 c. Cycling; 75 c. Baseball; 85 c. Gymnastics.

Each value is arranged in blocks of 4 within the sheet, with the top corners of each stamp converging to the centre of the block.

205 Vermilion Cardinal   206 Campaign Emblem and Map

1962. Birds. Multicoloured.

1748 5 c. Type **205** (postage) . . . 20 10
1749 10 c. Great kiskadee 40 10
1750 20 c. Glossy-black thrush . . 95 20
1751 25 c. Collared trogons . . . 1·10 30
1752 30 c. Swallow tanager . . . 1·50 35
1753 40 c. Long-tailed sylph . . . 1·90 50
1754 3 b. Black-necked stilts . . . 10·50 5·00
1755 5 c. American kestrel (air) . . 40 15
1756 20 c. Red-billed whistling duck (horiz) 95 20
1757 25 c. Amazon kingfisher . . . 1·10 30
1758 30 c. Rufous-vented chachalaca 1·40 35
1759 50 c. Oriole blackbird . . . . 2·10 55
1760 55 c. Pauraque . . . . . . 3·75 1·00
1761 2 b. 30 Red-crowned woodpecker . . . . . . 10·50 4·25
1762 2 b. 50 White-faced quail dove 10·50 4·00

1962. Malaria Eradication.

1763 **206** 50 c. brn & blk (postage) 40 20
1764 – 30 c. green & black (air) . 35 20

DESIGN: As T **206** but size 26×36 mm.

207 Collared Peccary   208 Fisherman

1963. Venezuelan Wild Life. Multicoloured.

1766 5 c. White-tailed deer (postage) 10 10
1767 10 c. Type **207** 10 10
1768 35 c. Widow monkey 25 10
1769 50 c. Giant otter 35 25
1770 1 b. Puma . . . . 1·60 85
1771 3 b. Capybara . . . . . . 3·25 1·60
1772 5 c. Spectacled bear (vert) (air) 20 10
1773 40 c. Paca 60 25
1774 50 c. Pale-throated sloth . . . 80 35
1775 55 c. Giant anteater . . . . 1·00 40
1776 1 b. 50 Brazilian tapir . . . 2·75 1·60
1777 2 b. Jaguar . . . . 4·25 2·10

1963. Freedom from Hunger.

1778 **208** 25 c. bl on pink (postage) 20 15
1779 – 40 c. red on green (air) . 50 25
1780 – 75 c. sepia on yellow . . 30 40

DESIGNS: 40 c. Farmer with lambs; 75 c. Harvester.

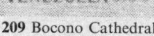

209 Bocono Cathedral   211 Flag

210 St. Peter's Basilica, Vatican City

1963. 400th Anniv of Bocono.

1781 **209** 50 c. mult on buff (postage) 45 20
1782 – 1 b. mult on buff (air) . . 1·25 40

DESIGNS: 1 b. Bocono Arms.

1963. Ecumenical Council, Vatican City.

1783 **210** 35 c. brn & bl (postage) . 35 15
1784 45 c. brown and green . . 35 20
1785 – 80 c. multicoloured (air) . 85 35
1786 – 90 c. multicoloured . . . 85 40

DESIGN: 80, 90 c. Arms of Vatican City and Venezuela.

1963. National Flag and Arms Centenary. Mult.

1787 30 c. Type **211** (postage) . . 20 15
1788 70 c. Venezuela Arms (vert) (air) 85 50

212 Maracaibo Bridge   213 Arms, Map and Guardsman

1963. Opening of Higher Bridge, Lake Maracaibo.

1789 **212** 30 c. brn & bl (postage) . 55 10
1790 35 c. brown and green . 65 20
1791 80 c. brown and green . 1·25 40
1792 – 90 c. ochre, brown and green (air) . . . . . . 1·00 50
1793 – 95 c. ochre, brown & bl . 1·00 55
1794 – 1 b. ochre, brown & blue 95 50

DESIGN—HORIZ: 90 c. to 1 b. Aerial view of bridge and mainland.

1963. 25th Anniv of National Guard.

1795 **213** 50 c. green, red & blue on cream (postage) . . . 40 20
1796 1 b. blue and red on cream (air) . . . . 1·25 70

214 Dag Hammarskjold and Atlantic Map

1963. 1st Death Anniv (1962) of Dag Hammarskjold (U.N. Secretary-General, 1953–61).

1797 **214** 25 c. indigo & bl (postage) 20 15
1798 55 c. green & turquoise . 75 35
1799 80 c. blue and dp blue (air) 75 45
1800 90 c. violet and blue . . 1·00 60

215 Dr. L. Razetti (medallion)   216 Dr. F. A. Risquez (Venezuelan Red Cross President, 1922–23)

1963. Birth Centenary (1962) of Dr. Luis Razetti (founder of University School of Medicine and of Vargas Hospital).

1802 **215** 35 c. brown, ochre and blue (postage) 35 20
1803 45 c. brn, ochre & mve . 50 20
1804 – 95 c. blue & mauve (air) 90 60
1805 – 1 b. 05 sepia and green . 1·25 70

DESIGN: 95 c., 1 b. 05, Portrait of Dr. Razetti.

1963. Red Cross Centenary. Multicoloured.

1806 15 c. Type **216** (postage) . . 15 10
1807 20 c. Dr. Carlos J. Bello (President of Venezuelan Red Cross, 1928–31) 20 10
1808 40 c. Sir Vincent K. Barrington (first President of Venezuelan Red Cross) (air) 40 35
1809 75 c. Nurse and child 70 50

All designs show centenary emblem.

217 Labourer   218 Pedro Gual

1964. Centenary of Venezuelan Ministry of Works and National Industries Exhibition, Caracas. Multicoloured.

1810 5 c. Type **217** (postage) 10 10
1811 10 c. Petrol industry 20 10
1812 15 c. Building construction 25 10
1813 30 c. Road and rail transport 25 35
1814 40 c. Agricultural machine 60 25

1815 5 c. Loading ship (air) 10 10
1816 10 c. Tractor and maize 10 10
1817 15 c. Type **217** 15 10
1818 20 c. Petrol industry 20 10
1819 50 c. Building construction 60 30

1964. Death Cent (1962) of Pedro Gual (statesman).

1820 **218** 40 c. olive (postage) 40 20
1821 50 c. brown 45 25

1822 75 c. turquoise (air) 60 25
1823 1 b. mauve 70 30

219 Dr. C. Arvelo

1964. Death Cent (1962) of Carlos Arvelo (physician).

1824 **219** 1 b. black and blue 1·00 40

220 Blast Furnace

1964. Inaug of Orinoco Steel Works. Mult.

1825 20 c. Type **220** (postage) 25 10
1826 50 c. Type **220** 50 20

1827 80 c. Cauldron and map (air) 85 35
1828 1 b. As 80 c. 1·10 40

The 80 c. and 1 b. are vert.

221 Arms of Ciudad Bolivar

222 R. Gallegos

1964. Air. Bicentenary of Ciudad Bolivar.

1829 **221** 1 b. multicoloured 1·10 70

1964. 80th Birth Anniv of Romulo Gallegos (novelist).

1830 **222** 5 c. green and yellow (postage) 10 10
1831 10 c. blue & light blue 15 10
1832 15 c. purple and mauve 25 15

1833 – 30 c. brown & yell (air) 30 15
1834 – 40 c. purple and pink 40 20
1835 – 50 c. brown and orange 55 30

DESIGN: Nos. 1833/5, Gallegos and book.

223 Angel Falls (Bolivar State)

224 Eleanor Roosevelt

1964. Tourist Publicity. Inscr "Conozca a Venezuela Primera" ("See Venezuela First"). Multicoloured.

1836 5 c. Type **223** 10 10
1837 10 c. Tropical landscape (Sucre) 15 10
1838 15 c. Rocks, San Juan (Guarico) 20 10
1839 30 c. Fishermen casting nets (Anzoategui) 40 15
1840 40 c. Mountaineering (Merida) 60 15

1964. Air. 15th Anniv (1963) of Declaration of Human Rights.

1841 **224** 1 b. orange and violet 70 40

1965. Various stamps surch **RESELLADO VALOR** and new value. (a) Postage.

1842 5 c. on 1 b. (No. 1485) 50 10
1843 10 c. on 45 c. (1668) 15 10
1844 15 c. on 55 c. (1798) 15 10
1845 20 c. on 3 b. (1754) 80 15
1846 25 c. on 45 c. (1623) 20 15
1847 25 c. on 3 b. (1720) 25 15
1848 25 c. on 1 b. (1770) 35 15
1849 25 c. on 3 b. (1771) 20 15
1850 30 c. on 1 b. (1516) 25 15
1851 40 c. on 1 b. (1824) 70 20
1852 60 c. on 80 c. (1791) 85 35

(b) Air.

1853 5 c. on 55 c. (1495) 10 10
1854 5 c. on 70 c. (1498) 10 10
1855 5 c. on 80 c. (1500) 15 10
1856 5 c. on 85 c. (1501) 10 10
1857 5 c. on 90 c. (1502) 10 10
1858 5 c. on 95 c. (1503) 10 10
1859 5 c. on 1 b. (1796) 50 35
1860 10 c. on 3 b. (804) 15 10
1861 10 c. on 4 b. (805) 70 35
1862 10 c. on 70 c. (1681) 35 15
1863 10 c. on 90 c. (1684) 25 10
1864 10 c. on 1 b. 05 (1705) 50 25
1865 10 c. on 1 b. 90 (1707) 25 15
1866 10 c. on 2 b. (1708) 35 15
1867 10 c. on 3 b. (1709) 35 15
1868 10 c. on 80 c. (1785) 15 10
1869 10 c. on 90 c. (1786) 15 10
1870 15 c. on 3 b. (769) 35 15
1871 15 c. on 90 c. (1613) 25 10
1872 15 c. on 80 c. (1799) 25 10
1873 15 c. on 90 c. (1800) 25 10
1874 15 c. on 1 b. (1829) 35 15
1875 20 c. on 2 b. (1460) 40 15
1876 20 c. on 55 c. (1693) 30 10
1877 20 c. on 55 c. (1760) 1·25 25
1878 20 c. on 2 b. 30 (1761) 80 15
1879 20 c. on 2 b. 50 (1762) 1·25 25
1880 20 c. on 70 c. (1788) 50 35
1881 25 c. on 70 c. (1629) 55 30
1882 25 c. on 1 b. 05 (1728) 35 15
1883 25 c. on 1 b. 50 (1729) 35 15
1884 25 c. on 2 b. (1730) 50 25
1885 25 c. on 1 b. 50 (1776) 50 15
1886 25 c. on 2 b. (1777) 50 25
1887 25 c. on 95 c. (1804) 45 25
1888 25 c. on 1 b. 05 (1805) 50 25
1889 30 c. on 1 b. (1782) 70 35
1890 40 c. on 1 b. 05 (1736) 50 25
1891 50 c. on 65 c. (1603) 25 15
1892 50 c. on 1 b. 20 (1607) 70 35
1893 50 c. on 1 b. (1841) 35 15
1894 60 c. on 90 c. (1792) 1·00 50
1895 60 c. on 95 c. (1793) 75 35
1896 75 c. on 85 c. (1746) 75 40

(c) Revenue stamps additionally optd **CORREOS**.

1897 5 c. on 5 c. green 10 10
1898 5 c. on 20 c. brown 10 10
1899 10 c. on 10 c. bistre 10 10
1900 15 c. on 40 c. green 10 10
1901 20 c. on 3 b. blue 35 15
1902 25 c. on 5 b. blue 70 35
1903 25 c. on 5 b. blue 35 15
1904 60 c. on 3 b. blue 60 40

226 Pres. Kennedy and Alliance Emblem

227 Federation Emblem

1965. "Alliance for Progress".

1905 **226** 20 c. black (postage) 35 15
1906 40 c. violet 50 20

1907 60 c. turquoise (air) 70 30
1908 80 c. brown 85 35

1965. Air. 20th Anniv of Venezuelan Medical Federation.

1909 **227** 65 c. red and black 1·00 45

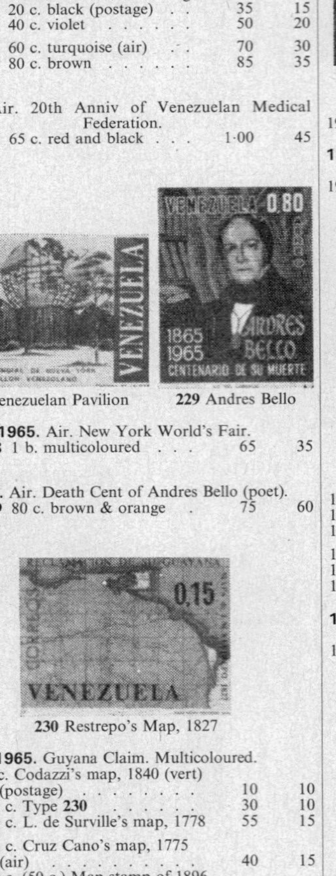

228 Venezuelan Pavilion

229 Andres Bello

1965. Air. New York World's Fair.

1910 **228** 1 b. multicoloured 65 35

1965. Air. Death Cent of Andres Bello (poet).

1911 **229** 80 c. brown & orange 75 60

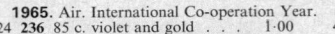

230 Restrepo's Map, 1827

1965. Guyana Claim. Multicoloured.

1912 5 c. Codazzi's map, 1840 (vert) (postage) 10 10
1913 15 c. Type **230** 30 10
1914 40 c. L. de Surville's map, 1778 55 15

1915 25 c. Cruz Cano's map, 1775 (air) 40 15
1916 40 c. (50 c.) Map stamp of 1896 (vert) 55 15
1917 75 c. Foreign Relations Ministry map 75 35

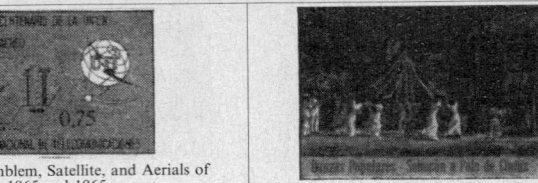

231 I.T.U. Emblem, Satellite, and Aerials of 1865 and 1965

1965. Air. I.T.U. Centenary.

1919 **231** 75 c. black and green 70 30

232 Bolivar and Part of Letter

233 Children on "Magic Carpet" and "Three Kings"

1965. Air. 150th Anniv of Bolivar's Letter from Jamaica.

1920 **232** 75 c. black and blue 60 30

1965. Air. Children's (Christmas) Festival.

1921 **233** 70 c. blue and yellow 80 55

234 Father F. Toro

235 Sir Winston Churchill

1965. Air. Death Cent of Father Fermin Toro.

1922 **234** 1 b. black and orange 60 30

1965. Air. Churchill Commemoration.

1923 **235** 1 b. black and lilac 90 40

236 I.C.Y. Emblem

237 Emblem and Map

1965. Air. International Co-operation Year.

1924 **236** 85 c. violet and gold 1·00 40

1965. Air. 75th Anniv of Organization of American States.

1925 **237** 50 c. gold, black & blue 85 35

238 "Eurytides protesilaus"

239 Farms of 1936 and 1966

1966. Butterflies. Multicoloured.

1926 20 c. Type **238** (postage) 40 15
1927 30 c. "Morpho peleides" 55 20
1928 50 c. "Papilio zagreus" 80 30

1929 65 c. "Anaea marthesia" (air) 1·00 40
1930 85 c. "Anaea clytemnestra" 1·60 55
1931 1 b. "Caligo atreus" 2·10 60

1966. Air. 30th Anniv of Ministry of Agriculture and Husbandry.

1932 **239** 55 c. black, green & yell 60 25

240 19th-century Sailing Packet crossing Atlantic

1966. Bicentenary of Maritime Mail.

1933 **240** 60 c. black, blue & brown 1·50 50

241 Sebucan Dance

1966. "Popular Dances". Multicoloured.

1934 5 c. Type **241** (postage) 10 10
1935 10 c. Candlemas 20 10
1936 15 c. Chichamaya 30 10
1937 20 c. Carite 40 15
1938 25 c. "Round Drum" 60 25
1939 35 c. Devil Dance, Feast of Corpus Christi 65 35

1940 40 c. Tamunanque (air) 50 35
1941 50 c. Parranda de San Pedro 60 40
1942 60 c. Las Turas 35 25
1943 70 c. Joropo 85 55
1944 80 c. Chimbanguele 90 35
1945 90 c. "The Shepherds" 1·10 50

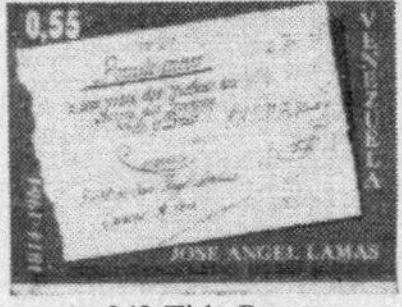

242 Title Page

1966. Air. 150th Death Anniv (1964) of Jose Lamas (composer).

1946 **242** 55 c. black, bistre & grn 60 30
1947 95 c. black, bistre & mve 60 40

243 A. Michelena (self-portrait)

244 Lincoln

1966. Birth Centenary (1963) of Arturo Michelena (painter). Multicoloured.

1948 95 c. sepia and cream (Type **243**) (postage) 85 35
1949 1 b. "Pentesilea" (battle scene) 75 35
1950 1 b. 05 "La Vara Rota" ("The Red Cloak") 85 35

1951 95 c. "Escena de Circo" ("Circus Scene") (air) 60 35
1952 1 b. "Miranda in La Carraca" 75 35
1953 1 b. 05 "Carlota Corday" 85 35

Nos. 1949/53 are horiz.

1966. Air. Death Cent (1965) of Abraham Lincoln.

1954 **244** 1 b. black and drab 70 55

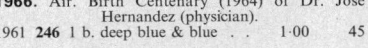

245 Construction Worker

246 Dr. Hernandez

1966. 2nd O.E.A. Labour Ministers Conference.

1955 **245** 10 c. black and yellow 10 10
1956 20 c. black and turquoise 20 10
1957 – 30 c. violet and blue 15 15
1958 – 35 c. olive and yellow 25 15
1959 – 50 c. purple and pink 40 20
1960 – 65 c. purple and red 60 30

DESIGNS: 30, 65 c. Labour Monument; 35 c. Machinist; 50 c. Car assembly line.

1966. Air. Birth Centenary (1964) of Dr. Jose Hernandez (physician).

1961 **246** 1 b. deep blue & blue 1·00 45

247 Dr. M. Dagnino (founder) and Hospital

1966. Air. Centenary of Chiquinquira Hospital, Maracaibo.

1962 **247** 1 b. deep green & green 1·00 40

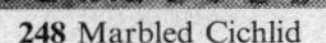

248 Marbled Cichlid   249 R. Arevalo Gonzalez

1966. Fishes. Multicoloured.

1963 15 c. Type **248** (postage) . . 15 10
1964 25 c. Eye spot cichlid 25 15
1965 45 c. Piranha 70 30
1966 75 c. Head-standing fish (vert) (air) 90 50
1967 90 c. Swordtail characin . . . 90 50
1968 1 b. Butterfly dwarf cichlid . 90 50

1966. Air. Birth Centenary of Rafael Arevalo Gonzalez.

1969 **249** 75 c. black and yellow . 65 35

250 Simon Bolivar, 1816 (after anonymous artist)   251 "Justice"

1966. Air. Bolivar Commemoration.

1970 **250** 5 c. multicoloured . . . 10 10
1971 10 c. multicoloured . . . 10 10
1972 20 c. multicoloured . . . 10 10
1973 – 25 c. multicoloured . . . 15 10
1974 – 30 c. multicoloured . . . 20 10
1975 – 35 c. multicoloured . . . 15 10
1976 – 40 c. multicoloured . . . 30 15
1977 – 50 c. multicoloured . . . 30 15
1978 – 60 c. multicoloured . . . 30 15
1979 – 80 c. multicoloured . . . 60 30
1980 – 1 b. 20 multicoloured . . 80 60
1981 – 4 b. multicoloured . . . 3·00 1·90

BOLIVAR PORTRAITS: 25, 30, 35 c. After paintings by Jose Gil de Castro, 1825; 40, 50, 60 c. Anonymous artist, 1825; 80 c., 1 b. 20., 4 b. Anonymous artist, circa 1829.

1966. Air. 50th Anniv of Political and Social Sciences Academy.

1982 **251** 50 c. purple and lilac . . 55 25

252 The Nativity   253 Globe and Communications Emblems

1966. Christmas.

1983 **252** 65 c. black and violet . . 50 25

1966. 30th Anniv of Venezuelan Communications Ministry.

1984 **253** 45 c. multicoloured . . . 40 20

254 Angostura Bridge

1967. Air. Opening of Angostura Bridge, Orinoco River.

1985 **254** 40 c. multicoloured . . . 35 20

255 Ruben Dario (poet)   256 University Building and Arms

1967. Birth Centenary of Ruben Dario.

1986 **255** 70 c. indigo and blue . . 85 35

1967. 75th Anniv of Zulia University.

1987 **256** 80 c. black, red & gold . 85 35

257 Venzuelan Pavilion

1967. Air. World Fair, Montreal.

1988 **257** 1 b. multicoloured . . . 60 30

258 Cacique Guaicaipuro (statue)   259 Francisco Esteban Gomez

1967. Air. 400th Anniv of Caracas. Multicoloured.

1989 10 c. Palace of the Academies (horiz) 10 10
1990 15 c. Type **258** 10 10
1991 45 c. Capt. F. Fajardo . . . 35 15
1992 50 c. St. Teresa's Church . . 35 15
1993 55 c. Diego de Losada (founder) 45 20
1994 60 c. Constellations over Caracas (horiz) 50 25
1995 65 c. Arms of Caracas . . . 55 30
1996 70 c. Federal Legislative Building (horiz) 55 25
1997 75 c. University City (horiz) 70 30
1998 85 c. El Pulpo road junction (horiz) 70 35
1999 90 c. Map of Caracas (horiz) 75 35
2000 1 b. Plaza Mayor, Caracas c. 1800 (horiz) 85 45
2001 2 b. Avenida Libertador (horiz) 2·00 65

1967. Air. 150th Anniv of Battle of Matasiete.

2003 **259** 90 c. multicoloured . . 70 35

260 J. V. Gonzalez   261 Child with Toy Windmill

1967. Air. Death Centenary of Juan Gonzalez (journalist).

2016 **260** 80 c. black and yellow . 55 30

1967. Air. Children's Festival.

2017 **261** 45 c. multicoloured . . 40 20
2018 75 c. multicoloured . . 60 25
2019 90 c. multicoloured . . 70 35

262 "The Madonna of the Rosary" (Lochner)   263 Dr. J. M. Nunez Ponte (educator)

1967. Air. Christmas.

2020 **262** 1 b. multicoloured . . . 80 40

1968. Air. 3rd Death Anniv of Dr. Jose Manuel Nunez Ponte.

2021 **263** 65 c. multicoloured . . 35 25

264 General Miranda and Printing Press

1968. Air. 150th Death Anniv of General Francisco de Miranda. Multicoloured.

2022 20 c. Type **264** 20 10
2023 35 c. Portrait and Houses of Parliament, London 35 15
2024 45 c. Portrait and Arc de Triomphe, Paris 55 30
2025 70 c. Portrait (vert) 65 25
2026 80 c. Bust and Venezuelan flags (vert) 80 45

265 Title Page and Printing Press

1968. 150th Anniv of Newspaper "Correo del Orinoco".

2027 **265** 1 b. 50 multicoloured . . 1·25 50

266 "Spodoptera frugiperda"   267 Keys

1968. Insects. Multicoloured.

2028 20 c. Type **266** (postage) . . . 50 20
2029 75 c. "Anthonomus grandis" . 60 30
2030 90 c. "Manduca sexta" . . . 80 40
2031 5 c. "Atta sextens" (air) . . . 15 10
2032 15 c. "Aeneolamia varia" . . 35 15
2033 20 c. "Systena sp." 50 20

The 20 (air), 75 and 90 c. are horiz.

1968. Air. 30th Anniv of Office of Controller-General.

2034 **267** 95 c. multicoloured . . . 65 30

268 Pistol-shooting   269 Guayana Sub-station

1968. Air. Olympic Games, Mexico. Mult.

2035 5 c. Type **268** 10 10
2036 15 c. Running (horiz) 25 10
2037 30 c. Fencing (horiz) 35 20
2038 75 c. Boxing (horiz) 75 35
2039 5 b. Sailing . . . . 3·75 1·40

1968. Rural Electrification. Multicoloured.

2040 15 c. Type **269** 15 10
2041 45 c. Encantado Dam 40 20
2042 50 c. Macagua Dam 55 20
2043 80 c. Guri Dam 85 40

The 45 and 50 c. are horiz.

270 "The Holy Family" (F. J. de Lerma)   271 House and Savings Bank

1968. Air. Christmas.

2044 **270** 40 c. multicoloured . . . 35 15

1968. National Savings System.

2045 **271** 45 c. multicoloured . . . 30 20

272 Children and Star   273 Planting a Tree

1968. Air. Children's Festival.

2046 **272** 80 c. orange and violet . 55 25

1968. Conservation of Natural Resources. Multicoloured designs each incorporating central motif as in T **273**.

2047 15 c. Type **273** (postage) . . 10 10
2048 20 c. Plantation 15 10
2049 30 c. Waterfall 30 15
2050 45 c. Logs 35 15
2051 55 c. Cultivated land 70 35
2052 75 c. Bonito (fish) 50 25
2053 15 c. Marbled wood quails (air) 50 15
2054 20 c. Scarlet ibis, jabiru, great blue heron and red-billed whistling duck 60 15
2055 30 c. Wood-carving 25 10
2056 90 c. Brown trout 75 35
2057 95 c. Mountain highway . . 1·25 55
2058 1 b. Red-eyed vireo and common cowbird (young) . 1·25 50

The 15 c. (both), 20 c. (air), 30 c. (both) and 55 c. are vert the remainder are horiz.

274 Colorada Beach, Sucre   276 Dr. Martin Luther King

275 Bolivar addressing Congress

1969. Tourism. Multicoloured.

2059 15 c. Type **274** (postage) . . 15 10
2060 45 c. San Francisco de Yare Church, Miranda 50 15
2061 90 c. Houses on stilts, Zulia . 75 55
2062 15 c. Desert landscape, Falcon (air) 20 10
2063 30 c. Humboldt Hotel, Caracas 25 15
2064 40 c. Mountain cable-car, Merida 45 25

1969. 150th Anniv of Angostura Congress.

2066 **275** 45 c. multicoloured . . . 40 20

1969. 1st Death Anniv of Martin Luther King (American Civil Rights leader).

2067 **276** 1 b. multicoloured . . . 50 25

277 "Tabebuia pentaphylla"   278 "On the Balcony" (C. Rojas)

1969. Nature Conservation. Trees. Multicoloured.

2068 50 c. Type **277** (postage) . . 50 20
2069 65 c. "Erythrina poeppigiana" 70 30
2070 90 c. "Platymiscium sp." . . 1·00 50
2071 5 c. "Cassia grandis" (air) . 10 10
2072 20 c. "Triplaris caracasana" . 25 10
2073 25 c. "Samanea saman" . . 35 15

1969. Paintings by Cristobal Rojas. Multicoloured.

2074 25 c. Type **278** 20 15
2075 35 c. "The Pheasant" 35 20
2076 45 c. "The Christening" . . 55 30
2077 50 c. "The Empty Place" . . 70 35
2078 60 c. "The Tavern" 85 40
2079 1 b. "The Arm" (27 × 55 mm) 1·25 70

Nos. 2075/2078 are horiz.

279 I.L.O. Emblem

1969. 50th Anniv of I.L.O.

2080 279 2 b. 50 black and brown 1·40 1·10

280 Charter and Arms of Guayana

1969. Industrial Development. Multicoloured.

2081 45 c. Type 280 45 20
2082 1 b. SIDOR steel-works 65 30

281 Arcade, Casa del Balcon

1969. 400th Anniv of Carora. Multicoloured.

2083 20 c. Type 281 15 10
2084 25 c. Ruins of La Pastora Church 25 15
2085 55 c. Chapel of the Cross 60 30
2086 65 c. Museum and library building 70 35

282 Alexander von Humboldt" (J. Stieler)
283 A. Alfinger, A. Pacheco and P. Maldonado (founders)

1969. Air. Birth Bicent of Alexander von Humboldt (German naturalist).

2087 282 50 c. multicoloured 50 20

1969. Air. 400th Anniv of Maracaibo. Mult.

2088 20 c. Type 283 20 15
2089 25 c. Map of Maracaibo, 1562 25 15
2090 40 c. City coat-of-arms 30 20
2091 70 c. University Hospital 60 35
2092 75 c. Cacique Mara Monument 70 40
2093 1 b. Baralt Plaza 80 50
Nos. 2089/92 are vert.

284 "Bolivar's Wedding" (T. Salas)

1969. "Bolivar in Spain".

2094 284 10 c. multicoloured 10 10
2095 – 15 c. black and red 20 10
2096 – 35 c. multicoloured 35 15
DESIGNS—VERT: 15 c. "Bolivar as a Student" (artist unknown); 35 c. Bolivar's statue, Madrid.

285 Astronauts and Moon Landing

1969. Air. 1st Man on the Moon.

2098 285 90 c. multicoloured 1·00 45

286 "Virgin of the Rosary" (17th-cent Venetian School)

1969. Air. Christmas. Multicoloured.

2100 75 c. Type 286 60 25
2101 80 c. "The Holy Family" (Landaeta School, Caracas, 18th cent) 65 30

287 "Children and Birds"

1969. Children's Day. Multicoloured.

2102 5 c. Type 287 10 10
2103 45 c. "Children's Camp" 55 30

288 Map of Greater Colombia

1969. 150th Anniv of Greater Colombia Federation.

2104 288 45 c. multicoloured 50 20

289 San Antonio Church, Clarines

1970. Architecture of the Colonial Era. Mult.

2105 10 c. Type 289 10 10
2106 30 c. Church of the Conception, Caroni 25 15
2107 40 c. San Miguel Church, Burbusay 50 25
2108 45 c. San Antonio Church, Maturin 70 35
2109 75 c. San Nicolas Church, Moruy 85 40
2110 1 b. Coro Cathedral 1·00 50

290 Seven Hills of Valera
291 "Simon Bolivar" (M. N. Bate)

1970. 150th Anniv of Valera.

2112 290 95 c. multicoloured 65 30

1970. Air. Portraits of Bolivar. Stamps in brown on buff; inscriptions in green; colours of country name and value given below.

2113 291 15 c. brown 15 10
2114 45 c. blue 35 15
2115 55 c. orange 50 25
2116 – 65 c. brown 50 25
2117 – 70 c. blue 55 35
2118 – 75 c. orange 70 40
2119 – 85 c. brown 60 45
2120 – 90 c. blue 65 25
2121 – 95 c. orange 75 25
2122 – 1 b. brown 75 25
2123 – 1 b. 50 blue 90 55
2124 – 2 b. orange 1·90 90
PORTRAITS BY: 65, 70, 75 c. F. Roulin; 85, 90, 95 c. J. M. Espinoza (1828); 1, 1 b. 50, 2 b. J. M. Espinoza (1830).

292 Gen. A. Guzman Blanco and Dr. M. J. Sanabria

1970. Air. Centenary of Free Compulsory Education in Venezuela.

2125 292 75 c. black, green & brn 50 30

293 Map of Venezuela

1970. States of Venezuela. Maps and Arms of the various States. Multicoloured.

2126 5 c. Federal District (postage) 10 10
2127 15 c. Monagas 15 10
2128 20 c. Nueva Esparta 20 10
2129 25 c. Portuguesa (vert) 25 10
2130 45 c. Sucre 35 15
2131 55 c. Tachira (vert) 20 20
2132 65 c. Trujillo 30 25
2133 75 c. Yaracuy 45 35
2134 85 c. Zulia (vert) 60 35
2135 90 c. Amazonas Federal Territory (vert) 90 40
2136 1 b. Federal Island Dependencies 1·10 45
2137 5 c. Type 293 (air) 10 10
2138 15 c. Apure 20 10
2139 20 c. Aragua 25 10
2140 20 c. Anzoategui 25 10
2141 25 c. Barinas 25 10
2142 25 c. Bolivar 25 10
2143 45 c. Carabobo 55 20
2144 55 c. Cojedes (vert) 60 25
2145 65 c. Falcon 65 25
2146 75 c. Guarico 60 30
2147 85 c. Lara 95 35
2148 90 c. Merida (vert) 95 40
2149 1 b. Miranda 95 50
2150 2 b. Delta Amacuro Federal Territory 2·00 80

294 "Monochaetum humboldtianum"
295 "The Battle of Boyaca" (M. Tovar y Tovar)

1970. Flowers of Venezuela. Multicoloured.

2151 20 c. Type 294 (postage) 30 10
2152 25 c. "Symbolanthus vasculosus" 60 15
2153 45 c. "Cavendishia splendens" 80 35
2154 1 b. "Befaria glauca" 1·10 50
2155 20 c. "Epidendrum secundum (air) 25 10
2156 25 c. "Oyedaea verbesinoides" 35 15
2157 45 c. "Heliconia villosa" 80 35
2158 1 b. "Macleania nitida" 1·10 50

1970. 150th Anniv (1969) of Battle of Boyaca.

2159 295 30 c. multicoloured 35 15

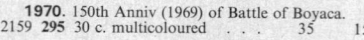

296 Archiepiscopal Cross
297 "Caracciolo Parra Olmedo" (T. Salas)

1970. Religious Art. Multicoloured.

2160 35 c. Type 296 35 15
2161 40 c. "Our Lady of the Valley" 45 25
2162 60 c. "Our Lady of Belen de San Mateo" 65 35
2163 90 c. "The Virgin of Chiquinquira" 75 50
2164 1 b. "Our Lady of Socorro de Valencia" 1·00 55

1970. Air. 150th Birth Anniv of Caracciola Parra Olmedo (lawyer).

2166 297 20 c. multicoloured 25 10

298 National Flags and Exhibition Emblem
299 "Guardian Angel" (J. P. Lopez)

1970. "EXFILCA 70" Philatelic Exhibition, Caracas. Multicoloured.

2167 20 c. Type 298 20 10
2168 25 c. 1871 1 c. stamp and emblem (horiz) 30 15
2169 70 c. 1930 2 b. 50 air stamp and emblem 50 30

1970. Christmas.

2171 299 45 c. multicoloured 35 15

300 Caudron G-3 Biplane and Dassault Mirage III

1970. 50th Anniv of Venezuelan Air Force.

2172 300 5 c. multicoloured 20 10

301 People in Question Mark

1971. National Census.

2173 301 30 c. black, green and red (postage) 60 30
2174 – 70 c. multicoloured (air) 65 45
DESIGN: 70 c. National flag and "pin-men".

302 Battle Scene

1971. 150th Anniv of Battle of Carabobo.

2175 302 2 b. multicoloured 1·10 80

303 "Cattleya percivaliana"
304 Adoration of the Child

1971. Air. Venezuelan Orchids. Multicoloured.

2176 20 c. Type 303 25 15
2177 25 c. Cattleya gaskelliana (horiz) 30 20
2178 75 c. "Cattleya mossiae" 60 40
2179 90 c. "Cattleya violacea o superba" (horiz) 65 35
2180 1 b. "Cattleya lawrenceana" (horiz) 80 40

1971. Christmas. Multicoloured.

2181 25 c. Type 304 25 15
2182 25 c. Madonna and Child 25 15

305 Dr. Luis D. Beauperthuy   306 Constitution and Government Building

1971. Death Centenary of Luis P. Beauperthuy (scientist).
2183 **305** 1 b. multicoloured . . . 70 30

1971. Air. 10th Anniv of 1961 Constitution.
2184 **306** 90 c. multicoloured . . . 80 35

307 Heart-shaped Globe

308 Arms of Venezuela and National Flags

1972. World Heart Month.
2185 **307** 1 b. black, red and blue . 60 40

1972. "Venezuela in the Americas". Mult.
2186 3 b. Type **308** . . . . 1·40 85
2187 4 b. Venezuelan flag . . . . 1·60 1·40
2188 5 b. National anthem . . . . 2·10 1·60
2189 10 b. "Araguaney" (national tree) . . . . 4·25 2·50
2190 15 b. Map of the Americas . 6·25 3·50

309 Tower Blocks

1972. Central Park Housing Project. Mult.
2191 30 c. Type **309** 25 15
2192 30 c. View from ground level 25 15
2193 30 c. Aerial view 25 15

310 Mahatma Gandhi

1972. Birth Centenary (1969) of Mahatma Gandhi.
2194 **310** 60 c. multicoloured . . . 50 35

311 Children making Music

1972. Christmas. Multicoloured.
2195 30 c. Type **311** 25 15
2196 30 c. Children roller-skating . 25 15
Nos. 2195/6 were issued together, se-tenant, forming a composite design.

312 Head of "Drymarchon corais"

313 Planetary System

1972. Snakes. Multicoloured.
2197 10 c. Type **312** 10 10
2198 15 c. "Spilotes pullatus" . . . 15 10
2199 25 c. "Bothrops venezuelensis" 40 15
2200 30 c. "Micrurus dumerili carinicaudus" 50 20
2201 60 c. "Crotalus vegrandis" . 50 35
2202 1 b. Boa constrictor 75 50

1973. 500th Birth Anniv of Copernicus (astronomer). Multicoloured.
2203 5 c. Type **313** 10 10
2204 10 c. Copernicus 20 10
2205 15 c. Book—"De Revolutionibus rbium Coelestium" 25 10

314 The Sun   315 Part of Solar System (left-hand)

1973. 10th Anniv of Humboldt Planetarium. Multicoloured. (a) As Type **314**.
2206 5 c. Type **314** 10 10
2207 5 c. Earth 10 10
2208 20 c. Mars 35 10
2209 20 c. Saturn 25 10
2210 30 c. Asteroids 30 15
2211 40 c. Neptune 35 20
2212 50 c. Venus 50 35
2213 60 c. Jupiter 60 40
2214 75 c. Uranus 75 50
2215 90 c. Pluto 90 40
2216 90 c. Moon . . . . 1·00 70
2217 1 b. Mercury . . . . 1·25 60

(b) As Type **315**.
2218 10 c. Type **315** 30 10
2219 15 c. Solar System (centre) . 40 10
2220 15 c. Solar System (right-hand) 40 10
Nos. 2218/20 form a composite design of the Solar System.

316 O.A.S. Emblem and Map

1973. 25th Anniv of Organization of American States.
2221 **316** 60 c. multicoloured . . 50 20

317 General Paez in Uniform

319 Bishop Ramos de Lora

318 Admiral Padilla, Gen. Montilla and Gen. Manrique

1973. Death Centenary of General Jose A. Paez.
2222 **317** 10 c. multicoloured . . 10 10
2223 – 30 c. gold, black & red . 25 15
2224 – 50 c. black, ultramarine and blue 50 25
2225 – 1 b. multicoloured . . . 75 50
2226 – 2 b. multicoloured . . . 1·25 75
DESIGNS—VERT: 30 c. Paez and horse (old engraving); 50 c. Gen. Paez in civilian dress; 1 b. Street of the Lancers, Puerto Cabello. HORIZ: 2 b. "The Charge at Centauro".

1973. 150th Anniv of Naval Battle of Maracaibo. Multicoloured.
2227 50 c. Type **318** 40 20
2228 1 b. "Battle of Maracaibo" (M. F. Rincon) 60 40
2229 2 b. Plan of opposing fleets . 1·10 60

1973. 250th Birth Anniv (1972) of Bishop Ramos de Lora.
2230 **319** 75 c. gold and brown . . 45 20

320 Ship, Jet Airliner and Map   322 General Paez Dam

321 Waterfall and Map

1973. Margarita Island Free Zone.
2231 **320** 5 c. multicoloured 15 10

1973. Completion of Golden Highway. Multicoloured.
2232 5 c. Type **321** 10 10
2233 10 c. Map and scarlet macaw 65 10
2234 20 c. Map and Santa Elena Church, Uairen 25 10
2235 50 c. Map and ancient mountain sanctuary 65 25
2236 60 c. As 50 c. 65 25
2237 90 c. Map and Santa Teresita church, Cabanayen 85 35
2238 1 b. Map and flags of Venezuela and Brazil 90 40

1973. Completion of General Paez Dam, Merida.
2239 **322** 30 c. multicoloured . . . 30 10

323 Child on Slide

1973. Children's Festival. Multicoloured.
2240 10 c. Type **323** 25 15
2241 10 c. Fairy tale animals . . . 25 15
2242 10 c. "Paginas Para Imaginar" (children's book) 25 15
2243 10 c. Holidaymakers leaving airliner 25 15

324 King on White Horse

326 Vase and Lace ("Handicrafts")

325 Regional Map

1973. Christmas. Multicoloured.
2244 30 c. Type **324** 25 10
2245 30 c. Two Kings 25 10

1973. Regional Development.
2246 **325** 25 c. multicoloured . . . 30 10

1973. Venezuelan Industrial Development Commission. Multicoloured.
2247 15 c. Type **326** 15 10
2248 35 c. Industrial estate ("Construction") 35 10
2249 45 c. Cogwheels and chimney ("Small and medium industries") 50 20

327 Map and Revellers

1974. 10th Anniv of Carupano Carnival.
2250 **327** 5 c. multicoloured . . . 10 10

328 Congress Emblem

1974. 9th Venezuelan Engineering Congress, Maracaibo.
2251 **328** 50 c. multicoloured . . . 50 15

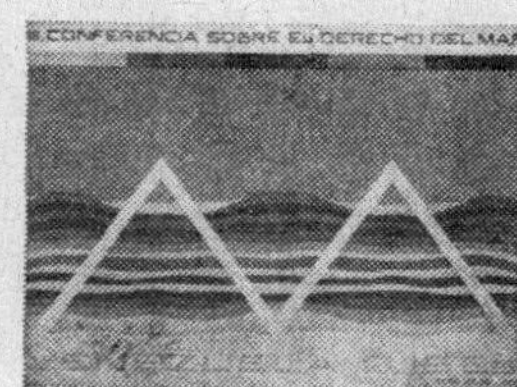

329 "Law of the Sea" Emblem

1974. 3rd Law of the Sea Conference, Caracas. Multicoloured.
2252 15 c. Type **329** 10 10
2253 35 c. Fish in sea-weed . . . 20 10
2254 75 c. Sea-bed scene 50 25
2255 80 c. Underwater grotto . . 55 35

330 Pupil and New School

1974. "Pay Your Taxes" Campaign.
2256 **330** 5 c. multicoloured . . . 10 10
2257 10 c. multicoloured . . . 10 10
2258 15 c. multicoloured . . . 10 10
2259 20 c. multicoloured . . . 10 10
2260 A 25 c. multicoloured . . . 15 10
2261 30 c. multicoloured . . . 40 20
2262 35 c. multicoloured . . . 20 10
2263 40 c. multicoloured . . . 35 15
2264 B 45 c. multicoloured . . . 35 15
2265 50 c. multicoloured . . . 35 15
2266 55 c. multicoloured . . . 55 30
2267 60 c. multicoloured . . . 45 20
2268 C 65 c. multicoloured . . . 1·00 50
2269 70 c. multicoloured . . . 50 20
2270 75 c. multicoloured . . . 50 25
2271 80 c. multicoloured . . . 50 25
2272 D 85 c. multicoloured . . . 50 25
2273 90 c. multicoloured . . . 70 25
2274 95 c. multicoloured . . . 1·00 70
2275 1 b. multicoloured . . . 70 35
DESIGNS: A, Suburban housing project; B, City centre motorway; C, Sports stadium; D, Surgical team in operating theatre.

331 "Bolivar at Junin" (A. H. Tovar)

1974. 150th Anniv of Battle of Junin.
2276 **331** 2 b. multicoloured . . . 1·25 70

332 World Map

1974. Centenary of U.P.U. Multicoloured.
2277 45 c. Type **332** 35 15
2278 50 c. Mounted courier, sailing packet, modern liner and jet airliner 40 20

333 Rufino Blanco-Fombona and Books

334 Children on Paper Dart

1974. Birth Centenary of Rufino Blanco-Fombona (writer).

2279 **333** 10 c. multicoloured . . . 10 10
2280 – 30 c. multicoloured . . . 20 10
2281 – 45 c. multicoloured . . . 30 15
2282 – 90 c. multicoloured . . . 50 25

DESIGNS: Nos. 2280/2, Portraits of Rufino Blanco-Fombona against a background of books similar to Type **333**.

1974. Children's Festival.

2283 **334** 70 c. multicoloured . . . 40 20

335 Marshal Sucre

336 "Shepherd"

1974. 150th Anniv of Battle of Ayacucho. Multicoloured.

2284 30 c. Type **335** 20 10
2285 50 c. South American flags on globe 30 25
2286 1 b. Map showing battle sites 55 35
2287 2 b. "Battle of Ayacucho" (43½ × 22 mm) . . . . . . 1·00 70

1974. Christmas. Details from "The Adoration of the Shepherds" (J. B. Mayno). Multicoloured.

2288 30 c. Type **336** 25 15
2289 30 c. "Holy Family" 25 15

Nos. 2288/9 were issued se-tenant, forming a composite design.

337 Road Construction, 1905, and El Ciempies Junction, 1972

1974. Centenary of Ministry of Public Works. Multicoloured.

2290 5 c. Type **337** 10 10
2291 20 c. J. Munoz Tebar (first Minister of Public Works) . 25 10
2292 25 c. Bridges on Caracas–La Guaira Road, 1912 and 1953 30 10
2293 40 c. Views of Caracas, 1874 and 1974 . . . . 30 15
2294 70 c. Tucacas Railway Station, 1911, and projected Caracas terminal 70 20
2295 80 c. Anatomical Institute, 1911, and Social Security Hospital, 1969 . . . . . . 85 30
2296 85 c. Quininari River bridge, 1904, and Orinoco River bridge, 1967 . . . . 1·00 35
2297 1 b. As 20 c. . . . . 1·40 50

338 Women in Profile

340 The Nativity

339 Emblem and "Tents"

1975. International Women's Year.

2298 **338** 90 c. multicoloured . . 50 30

1975. 14th World Scout Jamboree.

2299 **339** 20 c. multicoloured . . 15 10
2300 80 c. multicoloured . . 55 25

1975. Christmas. Multicoloured.

2301 30 c. Type **340** 20 10
2302 30 c. "The Shepherds" . . . 20 10

Nos. 2301/2 were issued se-tenant, forming a composite design.

341 Red Cross Nurse

342 Altar

1975. Venezuelan Red Cross.

2303 **341** 30 c. + 15 c. multicoloured 35 20
2304 50 c. + 25 c. multicoloured 50 30

1976. Centenary of National Pantheon.

2305 **342** 30 c. grey and blue . . . 15 10
2306 – 1 b. 05 brown and red . . 50 25

DESIGN: 1 b. 05, Pantheon building.

343 Coloured Panels

344 "Charting from Aircraft"

1976. 150th Anniv of Bolivian Independence (1975).

2307 **343** 60 c. multicoloured . . 25 15

1976. 40th Anniv of National Cartographic Institute (1975).

2308 **344** 1 b. black and blue . . 50 20

345 Signature of General Jose Felix Ribas

1976. Birth Bicentenary of General Jose Ribas. Multicoloured.

2309 **345** 40 c. green and red . . . 25 10
2310 – 55 c. multicoloured . . . 35 15

DESIGN—HORIZ: (40 × 30 mm): 55 c. General Jose Felix Ribas.

346 "Musicians of Chacao School" (A. Barrios)

1976. Birth Bicentenary (1975) of Jose Angel Lamas (composer).

2311 **346** 75 c. multicoloured . . 45 25
2312 – 1 b. 25 red, grey and buff 65 35

DESIGN—40 × 28 mm: 1 b. 25, Lamas' colophon.

347 "Bolivar" (J. M. Espinoza)

348 Maze symbolising Opportunity

1976.

2313	**347**	5 c. turquoise	10	10
2314		10 c. red	10	10
2315		15 c. brown	10	10
2316		20 c. black	10	10
2317		25 c. orange	10	10
2613		25 c. red	10	10
2318		30 c. blue	10	10
2319		45 c. lilac	15	10
2320		50 c. orange	20	10
2614		50 c. blue	10	10
2321		65 c. blue	25	10
2615		75 c. mauve	10	10
2322		1 b. red	35	15
2616		1 b. orange	10	10
2323		2 b. grey	70	35
2617		2 b. yellow	15	10
2324		3 b. blue	65	50
2618		3 b. green	10	10
2325		4 b. orange	85	45
2619		4 b. brown	15	10
2620		5 b. red	15	10
2327		10 b. lilac	2·25	1·10
2621		10 b. yellow	65	15
2328		15 b. blue	3·50	1·60
2622		15 b. purple	1·00	15
2329		20 b. red	4·50	2·25
2623		20 b. blue	1·40	65
2329a		25 b. blue	4·25	2·25
2623a		25 b. bistre	1·60	85
2329b		30 b. blue	5·50	2·75
2623b		30 b. lilac	2·00	1·00
2329c		50 b. purple	8·75	4·25
2623c		50 b. red	3·25	1·60

Nos. 2323/9 are larger, 27 × 33 mm.

1976. 250th Anniv of Central University.

2330 **348** 30 c. multicoloured . . . 15 10
2331 – 50 c. black, orge & yell . 25 15
2332 – 90 c. yellow and black . . 50 30

DESIGNS: 50 c. University building; 90 c. Faculty symbols.

349 C. A. Fernadez de Leoni (founder)

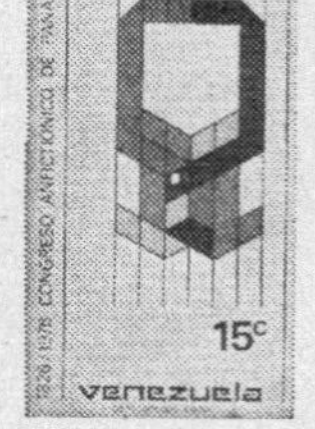

350 "Unity" Emblem

1976. Children's Foundation. Multicoloured.

2333 30 c. + 15 c. Type **349** 25 20
2334 50 c. + 25 c. Children in "home" (31 × 44 mm) 45 30

1976. 150th Anniv of Panama Amphictyonic Congress.

2335 **350** 15 c. multicoloured . . . 10 10
2336 – 45 c. multicoloured . . . 25 10
2337 – 1 b. 25 multicoloured . . 55 30

DESIGN: 45 c., 1 b. 25, As Type **275**, but with different "Unity" emblems.

351 George Washington

1976. Bicentenary of American Revolution.

2338 **351** 1 b. black and brown . . 55 35
2339 – 1 b. black and green . . . 55 55
2340 – 1 b. black and purple . . 55 35
2341 – 1 b. black and blue . . . 55 35
2342 – 1 b. black and brown . . 55 35

DESIGNS: No. 2339, Thomas Jefferson; No. 2340, Abraham Lincoln; No. 2341, Franklin D. Roosevelt; No. 2342, John F. Kennedy.

352 Valve in Oil Pipeline

353 "The Nativity" (B. Rivas)

1976. Oil Nationalization.

2343 **352** 10 c. multicoloured . . . 10 10
2344 – 30 c. multicoloured . . . 15 10
2345 – 35 c. multicoloured . . . 20 10
2346 – 40 c. multicoloured . . . 20 10
2347 – 55 c. multicoloured . . . 30 15
2348 – 90 c. multicoloured . . . 55 25

DESIGNS: 30 c. to 90 c. Various computer drawings of valves and pipelines.

1976. Christmas.

2349 **353** 30 c. multicoloured . . . 25 10

354 Patient

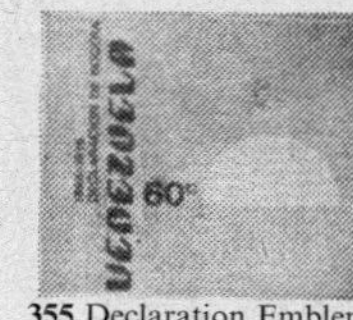

355 Declaration Emblem

1976. Anti-tuberculosis Society Fund.

2350 **354** 10 c. + 5 c. multicoloured 15 15
2351 30 c. + 10 c. multicoloured 20 20

1976. 10th Anniv of Bogota Declaration.

2352 **355** 60 c. black and yellow . 30 15

356 Arms of Barinas

1977. 400th Anniv of Barinas.

2353 **356** 50 c. multicoloured . . . 30 15

357 "Christ Crucified"

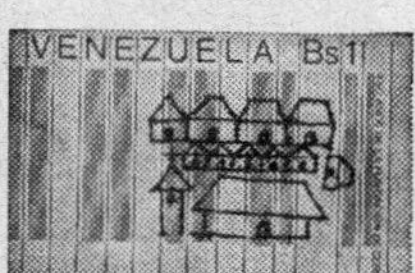

358 Coro Settlement

1977. 400th Anniv (1976) of La Grita.

2354 **357** 30 c. multicoloured . . . 15 10

1977. 450th Anniv of Coro.

2355 **358** 1 b. multicoloured . . . 35 15

359 I.P.C.T.T. Emblem and Stylised Dove

1977. 9th Inter-American Postal and Telecommunications Staff Congress, Caracas.

2356 **359** 85 c. multicoloured . . . 35 15

360 Cable Links to Domestic Equipment

361 "VENEZUELA" and Value as Rolled Steel

1977. Inauguration of "Columbus" Submarine Cable.

2357 **360** 95 c. grey, blue & green . 35 15

1977. 1st Anniv of Nationalization and Exploitation of Steel.

2358 **361** 30 c. black and yellow . 15 10
2359 – 50 c. black and orange . 25 10
2360 – 80 c. black and grey . . 35 15
2361 – 1 b. 05 black and red . . 40 20
2362 – 1 b. 25 black & yellow . 45 20
2363 – 1 b. 50 black and grey . 65 25

DESIGNS: 50 c. to 1 b. 50, Similar to Type **361** but each differently arranged.

362 J. P. Duarte

363 "The Holy Family"

1977. Death Cent (1976) of Juan Pablo Duarte.

2364 **362** 75 c. black and mauve . 30 15

1977. Christmas.

2365 **363** 30 c. multicoloured . . . 15 10

364 O.P.E.C. Emblem

1977. 50th O.P.E.C. Conference, Caracas.

2366	**364**	1 b. 05 black and blue .	50	15

365 Cyclists Racing

1978. World Cycling Championships, San Cristobal, Tachira. Multicoloured.

2367		5 v. Type **365**	10	10
2368		1 b. 25 Cyclist racing	65	20

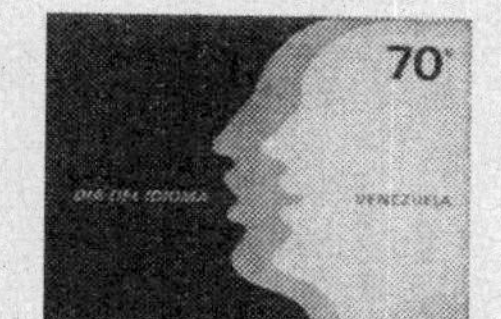

366 Heads in Profile

1978. Language Day.

2369	**366**	70 c. black, grey & mve .	25	15

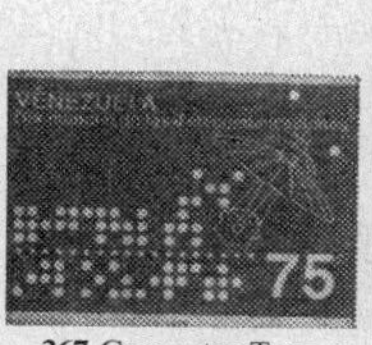

367 Computer Tape and Satellite — 368 "1777–1977"

1978. 10th World Telecommunications Day.

2370	**367**	75 c. blue	30	20

1978. Bicentenary of Venezuelan Unification. Multicoloured.

2381		30 c. Type **368**	10	10
2382		1 b. Computer print of Goya's "Carlos III"	40	15

369 Bolivar in Nurse Hipolita's Arms

1978. Birth Bicent (1983) of Simon Bolivar (1st issue).

2383	**369**	30 c. black, brown & grn	15	10
2384	–	1 b. black, brown & bl .	40	25

DESIGN: 1 b. Juan Vicente Bolivar (father).

See also Nos. 2399/40, 2408/9, 2422/3, 2431/2, 2467/8, 2480/1, 2483/4, 2494/5, 2498/9, 2518/19 and 2521/2.

370 "T" ("Traba3jadors") — 371 Medical Abstract

1978. Workers' Day.

2385	**370**	30 c. red and black . . .	10	10
2386	–	30 c. blue and black . . .	10	10
2387	–	30 c. yellow, blue & blk .	10	10
2388	–	30 c. red, blue & black .	10	10
2389	–	30 c. red and black . . .	10	10
2390	–	95 c. black and red . . .	30	15
2391	–	95 c. grey and blue . . .	30	15
2392	–	95 c. black and red . . .	30	15
2393	–	95 c. blue and black . . .	30	15
2394	–	95 c. multicoloured . . .	30	15

DESIGNS: Nos. 2386/94 based on the letter "T", also inscribed "CTV".

1978. Birth Centenary (1977) of Rafael Rangel (physician and scientist).

2395	**371**	50 c. brown	40	20

372 Drill Head and Map of Tachira Oilfield

1978. Centenary of Venezuelan Oil Industry. Multicoloured.

2396		30 c. Type **372**	15	10
2397		1 b. 05 Letter "P" as pipeline	50	20

373 Christmas Star — 375 Dam holding back Water

374 "P T"

1978. Christmas.

2398	**373**	30 c. multicoloured . .	15	10

1978. Birth Bicentenary (1983) of Simon Bolivar (2nd issue). As T **369**.

2399		30 c. black, brown & pur . .	10	10
2400		1 b. black, grey and red . .	30	15

DESIGNS: 30 c. Bolivar at 25 (after M. N. Bate); 1 b. Simon Rodriguez (Bolivar's tutor).

1979. Creation of Postal and Telegraph Institute.

2402	**374**	75 c. blk, & red on cream	25	15

1979. 10th Anniv of Guri Dam.

2403	**375**	2 b. silver, grey & black	70	30

376 "General San Martin" (E. J. Maury)

1979. Birth Bicentenary of General Jose de San Martin. Multicoloured.

2404		40 c. Type **376**	15	10
2405		60 c. Portrait by Mercedes San Martin	25	10
2406		70 c. San Martin Monument, Guayaquil	30	15
2407		75 c. San Martin's signature	35	20

1979. Birth Bicentenary (1983) of Simon Bolivar (3rd series). As T **369**.

2408		30 c. black, violet and red .	10	10
2409		1 b. black, orange and red .	30	15

DESIGNS: 30 c. Alexandre Sabes Petion (President of Haiti); 1 b. Bolivar's signature.

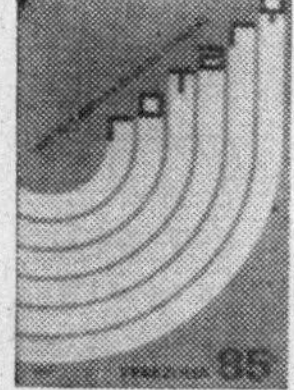

377 "Rotary" and Curves — 378 Statue of Virgin working Miracles, 1654

1979. 50th Anniv of Rotary Club of Caracas.

2411	**377**	85 c. black and gold . .	25	15

1979. 25th Anniv of Canonization of Virgin of Coromoto.

2412	**378**	55 c. black and red . . .	20	10

379 Miranda, London Residence and Arms

1979. Acquisition by Venezuela of Francisco de Miranda's House in London.

2413	**379**	50 c. multicoloured . . .	20	10

380 O'Leary and Maps

1979. 125th Death Anniv of Daniel O'Leary (publisher of Bolivar's memoirs).

2414	**380**	30 c. multicoloured . . .	10	10

381 Boy with Nest — 382 Candle

2979. International Year of the Child.

2415	**381**	70 c. black and blue . . .	25	15
2416	–	80 c. multicoloured . . .	30	15

DESIGN: 80 c. Boys playing in sea.

1979. Christmas.

2417	**382**	30 c. multicoloured . . .	10	10

383 Caudron G-3 Biplane

1979. "Exfilve 79" National Stamp Exhibition and 59th Anniv of Air Force. Multicoloured.

2418		75 c. Type **383**	35	20
2419		75 c. Stearman Kaydett biplane	35	20
2420		75 c. Bell Iroquois helicopter .	35	20
2421		75 c. Dassault Mirage IIIC jet fighter	55	20

1979. Birth Bicentenary (1983) of Simon Bolivar (4th series). As T **369**.

2422		30 c. black, red and turq . .	10	10
2423		1 b. black, blue and red . . .	30	15

DESIGNS: 30 c. Bolivar; 1 b. Slave.

384 Emblem and World Map

1979. Introduction of New Emblem for Postal and Telegraph Institute.

2425	**384**	75 c. multicoloured . . .	25	15

385 Queen Victoria and Hill

1980. Death Centenary of Sir Rowland Hill (1979).

2426	**385**	55 c. multicoloured . . .	20	10

386 Augusto Pi Suner

1980. Birth Centenary (1979) of Dr. Augusto Pi Suner (physiologist).

2427	**386**	80 c. multicoloured . . .	30	15

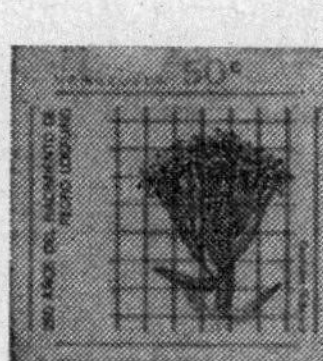

387 "Cotyledon hispanica" — 388 Lovera (self-portrait)

1980. 250th Birth Anniv of Pedro Loefling (Swedish botanist).

2428	**387**	50 c. multicoloured . . .	20	10

1980. Birth Bicentenary (1978) of Juan Lovera (artist).

2429	**388**	60 c. blue and red . . .	20	10
2430		75 c. violet and orange .	25	15

1980. Birth Bicentenary (1983) of Simon Bolivar (5th issue). As T **369**.

2431		30 c. black, green & purple .	10	10
2432		1 b. black, dp brown & brown	30	15

DESIGNS: 30 c. Signing document; 1 b. Congress House, Angostura.

389 "Self-portrait with Children" (detail) — 390 Bernardo O'Higgins

1980. 25th Death Anniv (1979) of Armando Reveron (artist). Multicoloured.

2434		50 c. Type **389**	20	10
2435		65 c. "Self-portrait" (26 × 41 mm)	35	20

1980. 204th Birth Anniv of Bernardo O'Higgins.

2436	**390**	85 c. black, red & blue .	50	25

391 Frigate "Mariscal Sucre"

1980. Venezuelan Navy. Multicoloured.

2437		1 b. 50 Type **391**	1·00	40
2438		1 b. 50 Submarine "Picua" .	1·00	40
2439		1 b. 50 Naval School	1·00	40
2440		1 b. 50 Cadet barque "Simon Bolivar" (33 × 52 mm) . .	1·00	40

392 Figures supporting O.P.E.C. Emblem

1980. 20th Anniv of Organization of Petroleum Exporting Countries. Multicoloured.

2441		1 b. 50 Type **392**	50	25
2442		1 b. 50 O.P.E.C. emblem and globe	50	25

393 "The Death of Bolivar" (Antonio Herrera Toro)

1980. 150th Death Anniv of Simon Bolivar.

2443	**393**	2 b. multicoloured . . .	70	30

394 Antonio Jose de Sucre — 395 "The Adoration of the Shepherds" (Rubens)

1980. 150th Death Anniv of Marshal Antonio Jose de Sucre.

2444	**394**	2 b. multicoloured . . .	70	30

1980. Christmas.

2445	**395**	1 b. multicoloured . . .	20	10

396 Helen Keller's Initials in Braille and Print

1981. Birth Centenary (1980) of Helen Keller.
2446 **396** 1 b. 50 grey, orge & blk . 40 15

397 Gateway, San Felipe
398 Jean Baptiste de la Salle (founder)

1981. 250th Anniv of San Felipe.
2447 **397** 3 b. blue, grey and red . 70 35

1981. 300th Anniv (1980) of Brothers of Christian Schools.
2448 **398** 1 b. 25 silver, red & black 30 15

399 Municipal Theatre

1981. Centenary of Caracas Municipal Theatre.
2449 **399** 1 b. 25, pink, blk & lilac 30 15

400 U.P.U. Emblem, Map of Venezuela and Envelope
401 People on Map

1981. Centenary of Admission to Universal Postal Union.
2450 **400** 2 b. multicoloured . . . 50 20

1981. 11th National Population and Housing Census.
2451 **401** 1 b. lilac, violet, and blk . 30 15

402 Games Emblem
404 Musicians

403 "Penny-farthing" Bicycle

1981. 9th Bolivarian Games, Barquismeto.
2452 **402** 95 c. multicoloured . . . 30 15

1981. Transport History (1st series). Mult.
2453 1 b. Type **403** 35 20
2454 1 b. 05 Steam locomotive, 1926 90 60
2455 1 b. 25 Buick car, 1937 . . . 40 25
2456 1 b. 50 Horse-drawn cab . . 50 25
See also Nos. 2490/3 and 2514/7.

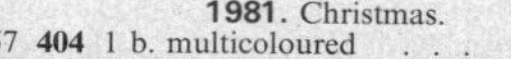

1981. Christmas.
2457 **404** 1 b. multicoloured . . . 25 10

405 Mt. Autana
407 "Landscape"

406 Calligraphic Script and Arms

1982. 50th Anniv of Venezuelan Natural Sciences Society. Multicoloured.
2458 1 b. Type **405** 30 20
2459 1 b. 50 Sarisarinama 50 20
2460 2 b. Guacharo Cave 40 35

1982. 20th Anniv of Constitution.
2461 **406** 1 b. 85 gold and black . 40 25

1982. 20th Anniv of Agricultural Reform.
2462 **407** 3 b. multicoloured . . . 70 40

408 Jules Verne
410 Rose

409 Bars of National Anthem

1982. Jules Verne (writer) Commemoration.
2463 **408** 1 b. deep blue and blue . 30 15

1982. Centenary of National Anthem (1981).
2464 **409** 1 b. multicoloured . . . 30 15

1982. 1300th Anniv of Bulgarian State.
2465 **410** 65 c. multicoloured . . 20 10

411 Flags
412 Cecilio Acosta

1982. 6th National Plan.
2466 **411** 2 b. multicoloured . . . 35 15

1982. Birth Bicentenary (1983) of Simon Bolivar (6th issue). As T **369**.
2467 30 c. black, brown and orange 10 10
2468 1 b. black, brown and green 25 15
DESIGNS: 30 c. Col. Rondon; 1 b. General Anzoategui.

1982. Death Centenary (1981) of Cecilio Acosta (statesman).
2469 **412** 3 b. black, blue and violet 35 25

413 "Fourcroya humboldtiana"

1982. Flora and Fauna. Multicoloured.
2471 1 b. 05 Type **413** 35 15
2472 2 b. 55 Turtle ("Podocnemis expansa") 85 30
2473 2 b. 75 "Oyedaea verbesinoides" 90 35
2474 3 b. Oilbird . . . . 2·75 85

414 Andres Bello and Initials

1982. Birth Bicentenary of Andres Bello (1981).
2475 **414** 1 b. 05 light blue, blue and black 25 15
2476 2 b. 55 yellow, violet and black 45 30
2477 2 b. 75 blue, deep blue and black 50 35
2478 3 b. olive, deep olive and black 55 40

415 "Nativity"
416 Bermudez

1982. Christmas.
2479 **415** 1 b. multicoloured . . . 20 10

1982. Birth Bicentenary (1983) of Simon Bolivar (7th issue). As T **369**.
2480 30 c. black, grey and red . . 10 10
2481 1 b. black, grey and red . . 25 15
DESIGNS: 30 c. Carabobo Monument; 1 b. Gen. Jose Antonio Paez.

1982. Birth Bicentenary (1983) of Simon Bolivar (8th issue). As T **369**.
2483 30 c. black, blue & dp blue . 10 10
2484 1 b. black, violet and red . . 25 15
DESIGNS: 30 c. Commemorative plaque to the meeting at Guayaquil; 1 b. Bolivar and San Martin (detail of monument).

1982. Birth Bicentenary of General Jose Francisco Bermudez (statesman).
2486 **416** 3 b. multicoloured . . . 35 30

417 Briceno

1982. Birth Bicentenary of Antonio Nicolas Briceno (liberation hero).
2487 **417** 3 b. multicoloured . . . 35 30

418 Rejoicing Crowd and Flag

1983. 25th Anniv of 1958 Reforms.
2488 **418** 3 b. multicoloured . . . 35 30

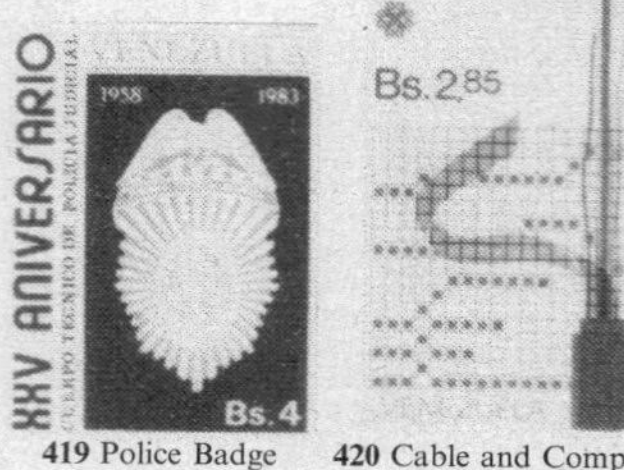

419 Police Badge
420 Cable and Computer Circuitboard

1983. 25th Anniv of Judicial Police Technical Department.
2489 **419** 4 b. red and green 40 30

1983. Transport History (2nd series). As T **403**. Multicoloured.
2490 75 c. Lincoln touring car, 1923 20 10
2491 80 c. Steam locomotive No. 129, 1889 . . . . 1·50 90
2492 85 c. Willys truck, 1927 . . . 25 10
2493 95 c. Cleveland motorcycle, 1920 . . . . 25 10

1983. Birth Bicentenary of Simon Bolivar (9th issue). As T **369**.
2494 30 c. black, red and blue . . 10 10
2495 1 b. black, gold and blue . . 25 15
DESIGNS: 30 c. Gen. Antonio Sucre; 1 b. Sword hilt.

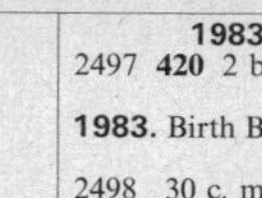

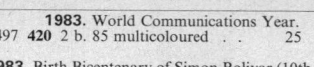

1983. World Communications Year.
2497 **420** 2 b. 85 multicoloured . . 25 30

1983. Birth Bicentenary of Simon Bolivar (10th issue). As T **369**.
2498 30 c. multicoloured 10 10
2499 1 b. black, yellow and blue . 25 15
DESIGNS: 30 c. Flags; 1 b. "Ascent of Potosi".

421 Map of the Americas
422 Power Pylon

1983. 9th Pan-American Games, Caracas. Multicoloured.
2501 2 b. Type **421** 30 20
2502 2 b. Swimming 30 20
2503 2 b. 70 Cycling 15 30
2504 2 b. 70 Fencing 15 30
2505 2 b. 85 Weightlifting 20 15
2506 2 b. 85 Running 20 15

1983. 25th Anniv of State Electricity Authority.
2508 **422** 3 b. blue, silver and red . 70 30

423 Nativity

1983. Christmas.
2509 **423** 1 b. multicoloured . . . 10 10

424 Erecting a Tent

1983. 75th Anniv (1982) of Scout Movement. Multicoloured.
2510 2 b. 25 Type **424** 30 15
2511 2 b. 55 Nature watch 30 15
2512 2 b. 75 Mountaineering . . . 35 15
2513 3 b. Camp at night 35 15

1983. Transport History (3rd series). Caracas Underground Railway. As T **403**. Multicoloured.
2514 55 c. black, orange & silver . 30 10
2515 75 c. black, yellow & silver . 45 15
2516 95 c. black, green and silver . 55 20
2517 2 b. black, blue and silver . . 1·25 45
DESIGNS: 55 c. Central computer building; 75 c. Maintenance bay; 95 c. Train on elevated section; 2 b. Train at Cano Amarillo station.

1984. Birth Bicentenary of Simon Bolivar (11th issue). As T **369**.
2518 30 c. black, red and brown . 10 10
2519 1 b. black, green and blue . 10 10
DESIGNS: 30 c. Open volume of "Opere de Raimondo Montecuccoli"; 1 b. Dr. Jose Maria Vargas (President, 1835–36).

1984. Birth Bicentenary of Simon Bolivar (12th issue). As T **369**.
2521 30 c. black, red and lilac . . 10 10
2522 1 b. black, green & orange . 10 10
DESIGNS: 30 c. Pedro Gual (President, 1859 and 1861); 1 b. Jose Faustino Sanchez Carrion.

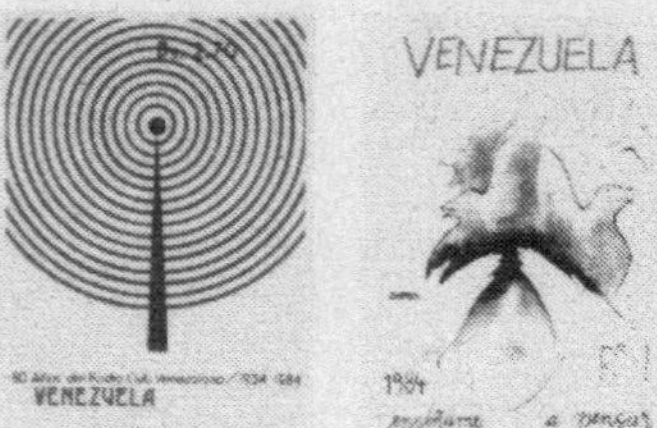

425 Radio Mast and Waves
426 Doves and Hands covering Eyes

1984. 50th Anniv of Venezuela Radio Club.
2524 **425** 2 b. 70 multicoloured . . 35 15

1984. "Intelligentsia for Peace". Multicoloured.
2525 1 b. Type **426** 10 10
2526 2 b. 70 Profile head 30 15
2527 2 b. 85 Profile head, flower and hexagonal nut 35 15

427 Romulo Gallegos

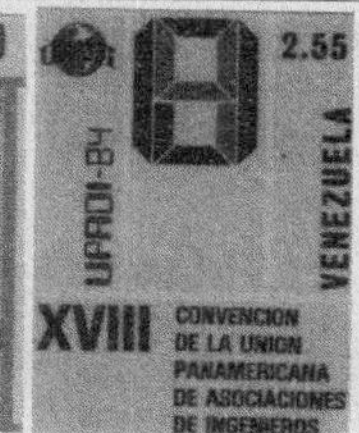

428 Emblem and Digital Eight

1984. Birth Centenary of Romulo Gallegos (writer and President, 1948). Multicoloured.

2528 **427** 1 b. 70 multicoloured . . 25 15
2529 – 1 b. 70 multicoloured . . 25 15
2530 – 1 b. 70 green, grey and black 25 15
2531 – 1 b. 70 deep green, green and black 25 15

DESIGNS: Nos. 2529/31, Different portraits of Gallegos.

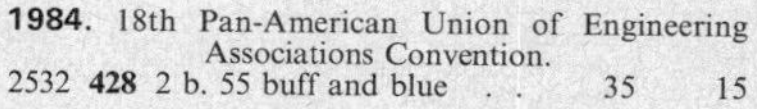

1984. 18th Pan-American Union of Engineering Associations Convention.

2532 **428** 2 b. 55 buff and blue . . 35 15

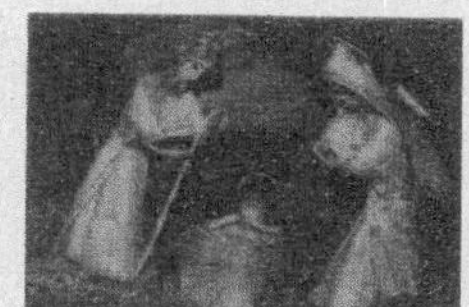
429 "Nativity" (Maria Candelaria de Ramirez)

1984. Christmas.

2533 **429** 1 b. multicoloured . . . 10 10

430 Pope and "Virgin of Coromoto"

1985. Visit of Pope John Paul II (1st issue).

2534 **430** 1 b. multicoloured . . . 20 10

See also Nos. 2628/33.

431 Cross, Hand holding Candle and Agricultural Scene

1985. Bicentenary of Valle de la Pascua City.

2535 **431** 1 b. 50 multicoloured . . 20 10

432 St. Vincent de Paul

1985. Centenary of Venezuelan Society of St. Vincent de Paul.

2536 **432** 1 b. brown, yellow & red 15 10

433 Text and "SELA"

1985. 10th Anniv of Latin American Economic System.

2537 **433** 4 b. black and red . . . 70 35

434 "Divine Shepherdess"

435 Map and Emblem

1985. 2000th Birth Anniv of Virgin Mary. Multicoloured.

2538 1 b. Type **434** 20 15
2539 1 b. "Virgin of Chiquinquira" 20 15
2540 1 b. "Virgin of Coromoto" . 20 15
2541 1 b. "Virgin of the Valley" 20 15
2542 1 b. "Virgin of Perpetual Succour" 20 15
2543 1 b. "Virgin of Peace" . . . 20 15
2544 1 b. "Virgin of the Immaculate Conception" 20 15
2545 1 b. "Virgin of Solitude" . . 20 15
2546 1 b. "Virgin of Consolation" 20 15
2547 1 b. "Virgin of the Snow" . 20 15

1985. 25th Anniv of Organization of Petroleum Exporting Countries.

2548 **435** 6 b. black, blue and light blue 70 35

436 Dr Briceno-Iragorry

1985. 27th Death Anniv of Dr. Mario Briceno-Iragorry (politician).

2549 **436** 1 b. 25 silver and red . . 15 10

437 Museum

1985. 10th Anniv (1983) of Museum of Modern Art, Caracas.

2550 **437** 3 b. multicoloured . . . 35 20

438 Emblem and Dove as Hand

1985. 40th Anniv of U.N.O.

2551 **438** 10 b. blue and red . . . 1·10 60

439 Rainbow and Emblem

1985. International Youth Year.

2552 **439** 1 b. 50 multicoloured . 20 10

440 Shepherds and Camels

1985. Christmas. Multicoloured.

2553 2 b. Type **440** 25 10
2554 2 b. Holy Family and the Three Kings 25 10

Nos. 2553/4 were printed together, se-tenant, forming a composite design of the Nativity.

441 Petroleos de Venezuela Emblem

1985. 10th Anniv of National Petrochemical Industry.

2555 **441** 1 b. blue and black . . . 15 10
2556 – 1 b. multicoloured . . . 15 10
2557 – 2 b. multicoloured . . . 25 15
2558 – 2 b. multicoloured . . . 25 15
2559 – 3 b. multicoloured . . . 35 20
2560 – 3 b. multicoloured . . . 80 30
2561 – 4 b. multicoloured . . . 50 25
2562 – 4 b. multicoloured . . . 50 25
2563 – 5 b. multicoloured . . . 60 30
2564 – 5 b. multicoloured . . . 60 30

DESIGNS: No. 2556, Refinery and Isla S. A. emblem; 2557, Bariven oil terminal; 2558, Pequiven storage tank; 2559, Corpoven drilling site; 2560, Support vessel, oil rig and Maraven emblem; 2561, Meneven refinery; 2562, Intervep scientist; 2563, "Nodding Donkey"; 2564, Lagoven refinery.

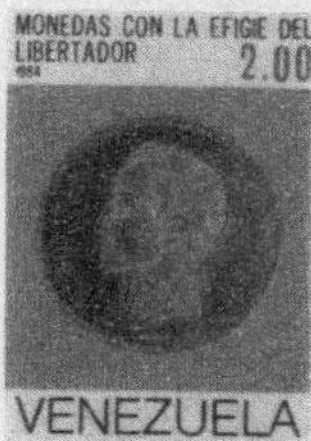

442 Five Reales Silver Coin, 1873

443 Drago

1985. Coins with Portrait of Simon Bolivar. Multicoloured.

2565 2 b. Type **442** 25 15
2566 2 b. 70 Five bolivares gold coin, 1886 . . . . 30 15
2567 3 b. Birth bicentenary gold proof coin, 1983 . . . . . 35 20

1985. 125th Birth Anniv (1984) of Dr. Luis Maria Drago (Argentine politician).

2568 **443** 2 b. 70 black, orge & red 30 15

444 Guayana City

1985. 25th Anniv of Guayana Development Corporation. Multicoloured.

2569 2 b. Type **444** 25 15
2570 3 b. Orinoco steel mill 35 20
2571 5 b. Raul Leoni-Guri dam . . 60 35

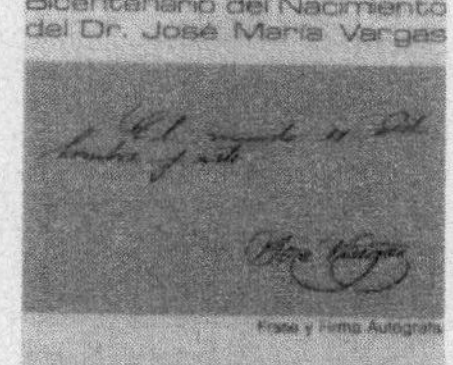

445 Signature

1985. Birth Bicentenary of Dr. Jose Maria Vargas (President, 1835–36). Multicoloured.

2572 3 b. Type **445** 30 15
2573 3 b. "Vargas" (Martin Tovar y Tovar) (vert) 30 15
2574 3 b. Statue at Palace of Academies (vert) 30 15
2575 3 b. "Exfilbo '86" National Stamp Exhibition emblem and flags 30 15
2576 3 b. Facade of Vargas Hospital, Caracas 30 15
2577 3 b. Title page of Vargas's "Manual and Compendium of Surgery" (vert) 30 15
2578 3 b. "Vargas" (Alirio Palacios) (vert) 30 15
2579 3 b. "Gesneria vargasii" (flower) 30 15
2580 3 b. Portraits of Vargas and Bolivar on Sixth Venezuelan Congress of Medical Sciences medal 30 15
2581 3 b. "Vargas" (anonymous) (vert) 30 15

446 Francisco Miranda

1986. Bicentenary (1981) of Francisco Miranda's Work for Latin American Liberation.

2583 **446** 1 b. 05 multicoloured . . 10 10

447 Children painting Wall

448 Lorries and Processing Plant

1986. Foundation for Educational Buildings and Equipment. Multicoloured.

2584 3 b. Type **447** 25 15
2585 5 b. Boys at woodwork class 35 15

1986. 45th Anniv of Venezuelan Dairy Industry Corporation. Multicoloured.

2586 2 b. 55 Type **448** 20 15
2587 2 b. 70 Map and milk containers 25 15
2588 3 b. 70 Processing plant Machiques, Edo Zulia (horiz) 35 15

449 Emblem

1986. 25th Anniv of VIASA (airline). Mult.

2589 3 b. Type **449** 35 20
2590 3 b. Douglas DC-8 in flight . 35 20
2591 3 b. Douglas DC-8 on ground 35 20
2592 3 b. Boeing 747 flying out to sea 35 20
2593 3 b. Tail fins of Douglas DC-10s 35 20
2594 3 b. 25 Hemispheres 35 20
2595 3 b. 25 Douglas DC-10 flying through cloud 35 20
2596 3 b. 25 Douglas DC-8 and DC-10 on ground 35 20
2507 3 b. 25 Douglas DC-9 flying over mountains 35 20
2598 3 b. 25 Manned flight deck . 35 20

450 Giant Armadillo

1986. Flora and Fauna. Dated "1983". Mult.

2599 70 c. Type **450** 10 10
2600 85 c. "Espeletia angustifolia" 10 10
2601 2 b. 70 Orinoco crocodile . . 20 10
2602 3 b. Mountain rose 20 10

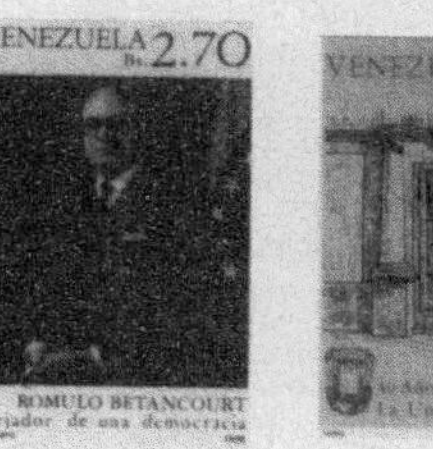

451 Romulo Betancourt

452 Library Entrance

1986. 5th Death Anniv of Romulo Betancourt (President, 1959–64). Each black, deep brown and brown.

2603 2 b. Type **451** 20 10
2604 2 b. 70 Betancourt in armchair 20 10
2605 2 b. 70 Betancourt and inscription 20 10
2606 2 b. 70 Betancourt wearing sash 20 10
2607 2 b. 70 Betancourt working . 20 10
2608 3 b. As No. 2606 . . . . . . 25 15
2609 3 b. As No. 2607 . . . . . . 25 15
2610 3 b. As No. 2605 . . . . . . 25 15
2611 3 b. Type **451** 25 15
2612 3 b. As No. 2604 . . . . . . 25 15

1986. 40th Anniv of Re-opening of Zulia University. Each grey, black and blue.

2624 2 b. 70 Type **452** 20 10
2625 2 b. 70 University building . 20 10

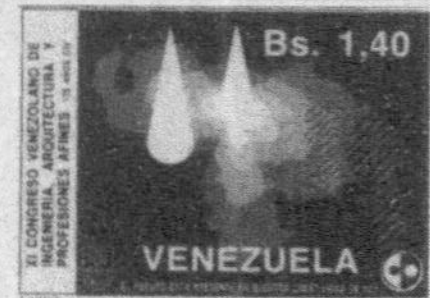

453 Map and Droplets

1986. 11th Venezuelan Engineers, Architects and Affiliated Professions Congress.

2626 453 1 b. 40 blue, blk & yell . 25 15
2627 1 b. 55 multicoloured . . 25 15

454 Pope and Andes 455 "United Families" (Vianny Hernandez)

1986. Visit of Pope John Paul II (1985) (2nd issue). Multicoloured.

2628 1 b. Type **454** 10 10
2629 1 b. Pope and Maracaibo bridge 15 10
2630 3 b. Pope kissing ground . . 25 15
2631 3 b. Pope and "Virgin of Coromoto" 25 15
2632 4 b. Pope holding crucifix, Caracas 35 15
2633 5 b. 25 Pope and waterfall . 40 20

1986. 20th Anniv of Childrens' Paintings. Multicoloured.

2634 2 b. 55 Type **455** 20 10
2635 2 b. 55 "Love and Peace" (Yuraima L. Jimenez) . . . 20 10
2636 2 b. 55 "Woodland Animals" (Maria Valentina Arias) . . 20 10
2637 2 b. 55 "Noah's Ark" (Andreina Acero) 20 10
2638 2 b. 55 "House on Hillside" (Yenelsa) 20 10
2639 2 b. 70 "Flowers on Table" (Yenny Jimenez) 20 10
2640 2 b. 70 "Peace Lover" (Ramon Briceno) 20 10
2641 2 b. 70 "Children for World Peace" (Blanca Yesenia Hernandez) 20 10
2642 2 b. 70 "Lighthouse and Cable Railway" (Julio V. Hernandez) 20 10
2643 2 b. 70 "Flowers of a Thousand Colours" (with butterfly) (Maryolin Rodriguez Ortega) 20 10

456 Three Kings

1986. Christmas. Crib figures modelled by Eliecer Alvarez. Multicoloured.

2644 2 b. Type **456** 15 10
2645 2 b. Nativity 15 10

Nos. 2644/5 were printed together, se-tenant, forming a composite design.

457 Treating Accident Victim

1986. 17th Anniv of Caracas City Police. Multicoloured.

2646 2 b. 70 Type **457** 20 10
2647 2 b. 70 On duty at sporting event 20 10
2648 2 b. 70 Computer identification bar code 20 10
2649 2 b. 70 Cadets on parade . . 20 10
2650 2 b. 70 Motor cycle police . . 20 10

458 Prehispanic Musical Instrument

1987. Native Art. Multicoloured.

2651 2 b. Type **458** 15 10
2652 2 b. Woven fabric 15 10
2653 3 b. Prehispanic ceramic bottle 25 15
2654 3 b. Basket design 25 15

459 Robert Koch (discoverer) and Bacillus Symbol

1987. Centenary (1982) of Discovery of Tubercle Bacillus.

2655 459 2 b. 55 multicoloured . 20 10

460 "Entry of Jesus into Jerusalem" (Antonio Herrera Toro)

1987. Holy Week. Multicoloured.

2656 2 b. Type **460** 15 10
2657 2 b. "Christ at the Pillar" (statue, Jose Francisco Rodriguez) 15 10
2658 2 b. "Jesus of Nazareth" (wood carving, School of Seville) 15 10
2659 2 b. "Descent from the Cross" (Jose Rivadefrecha, El Campeche) 15 10
2660 2 b. "Virgin of Solitude" (sculpture) 15 10
2661 2 b. 25 "The Last Supper" (Arturo Michelena) . . . 15 10
2662 2 b. 25 "Ecce Homo" (sculpture) 15 10
2663 2 b. 25 "The Crucifixion" (sculpture, Gregorio de Leon Quintana) 15 10
2664 2 b. 25 "Holy Sepulchre" (sculpture, Sebastian de Ochoa Montes) 15 10
2665 2 b. 25 "The Resurrection" (attr. Peter Paul Rubens) . 15 10

461 "Bolivar and Bello" (Marisol Escobar) 462 Barquisimeto Hilton Hotel

1987. World Neurochemical Congress. Mult.

2666 3 b. Type **461** 25 15
2667 4 b. 25 Retinal cells 30 15

1987. Tourism Development. Multicoloured.

2668 6 b. Type **462** 35 15
2669 6 b. Lake Hotel Intercontinental, Maracaibo 35 15
2670 6 b. Macuto Sheraton Hotel, Caraballeda 35 15
2671 6 b. Melia Caribe Hotel, Caraballeda 35 15
2672 6 b. Melia Hotel, Puerto la Cruz 55 20
2673 6 b. 50 Pool, Barquisimeto Hilton Hotel 35 15
2674 6 b. 50 Lake Hotel Intercontinental, Maracaibo, at night 35 15
2675 6 b. 50 Macuto Sheraton Hotel, Caraballeda, and marina . 55 20
2676 6 b. 50 Melia Caribe Hotel, Caraballeda (different) . . 35 15
2677 6 b. 50 Melia Hotel, Puerto la Cruz (different) 55 20

463 Amazon Federal Terrritory Map and Ship's Bow

1987. 35th Anniv of National Canals Institute. Multicoloured.

2678 2 b. Type **463** 10 10
2679 4 b. 25 Map of River Orinoco and buoy 25 15

464 Music School, Caracas

1987. Birth Centenary of Vicente Emilio Sojo (composer). Each deep brown and brown.

2680 2 b. Type **464** 15 10
2681 4 b. Conducting choir 25 15
2682 5 b. Score of "Hymn to Bolivar" 30 15
2683 6 b. Standing beside blackboard 40 20
2684 7 b. Sojo and signature . . . 50 25

465 "Simon Bolivar, Academician" (Roca Rey)

1987. 20th Anniv of Simon Bolivar University. Multicoloured.

2685 2 b. Type **465** 10 10
2686 3 b. "Solar Delta" (sculpture, Alejandro Otero) 15 10
2687 4 b. Rector's residence . . . 20 10
2688 5 b. Laser beam 25 15
2689 6 b. Owl sculpture 30 15

466 Motor Vehicles

1987. 10th Anniv of Ministry of Transport and Communications. Multicoloured.

2690 2 b. Type **466** 10 10
2691 2 b. Bulk carrier and crane . 20 10
2692 2 b. Electric local train . . . 10 10
2693 2 b. Envelopes and telegraph key 10 10
2694 2 b. Transmission masts and globe 10 10
2695 2 b. 25 Motorway interchange system 10 10
2696 2 b. 25 Boeing 737 airliner . . 30 15
2697 2 b. 25 Electric mainline train 10 10
2698 2 b. 25 Dish aerial 10 10
2699 2 b. 25 Globe and communications satellite . . 10 10

Nos. 2690/9 were printed together, se-tenant, each horizontal pair forming a composite design.

467 Administration Building, Caracas

1987. 70th Anniv of Venezuelan Navigation Company. Multicoloured.

2700 2 b. Type **467** 10 10
2701 2 b. Containers being loaded . 10 10
2702 3 b. Company emblem on ship's funnel 15 10
2703 3 b. Ship's engine-room . . . 15 10
2704 4 b. "Zulia" (freighter) at sea 40 20
2705 4 b. "Guarico" (freighter) off Venezuelan coast 50 20
2706 5 b. "Cerro Bolivar" (bulk carrier) 55 20
2707 5 b. Ship's bridge 25 15
2708 6 b. Map 30 15
2709 6 b. Containers being loaded onto Ro-Ro ferry 30 15

468 Air-sea Rescue

1987. 50th Anniv of National Guard. Mult.

2710 2 b. Type **468** 35 10
2711 2 b. Traffic patrol 10 10
2712 2 b. Guard on horseback . . 10 10
2713 2 b. Guard with children . . 10 10
2714 2 b. Armed guard on industrial site 10 10
2715 4 b. As No. 2714 . . . . . . 20 10
2716 4 b. As No. 2713 . . . . . . 20 10
2717 4 b. As No. 2712 . . . . . . 20 10
2718 4 b. As No. 2711 . . . . . . 20 10
2719 4 b. Type **468** 60 20

469 "Departure from Puerto Palos" (detail, Jacobo Borges)

1987. 500th Anniv (1992) of Discovery of America by Columbus. Multicoloured.

2720 2 b. Type **469** 10 10
2721 7 b. "Discovery of America" (Tito Salas) 30 15
2722 11 b. 50 "Fr. de las Casas, Protector of the Indians" (detail, Tito Salas) 50 25
2723 12 b. "Trade in Venezuela during the Time of the Conquest" (detail, Tito Salas) 70 25
2724 12 b. 50 "Rout of Guaicaipuro" (Jacobo Borges) 55 25

470 "Annunciation" (Juan Pedro Lopez)

1987. Christmas. Multicoloured.

2725 2 b. Type **470** 10 10
2726 3 b. "Nativity" (Jose Francisco Rodriguez) 15 10
2727 5 b. 50 "Adoration of the Kings" (anon) 30 15
2728 6 b. "Flight into Egypt" (Juan Pedro Lopez) 30 15

471 Steel Plant Building

1987. 25th Anniv of Steel Production by National SIDOR Mills.

2729 471 2 b. multicoloured . . . 10 10
2730 – 2 b. multicoloured . . . 10 10
2731 – 6 b. multicoloured . . . 30 15
2732 – 6 b. multicoloured . . . 30 15
2733 – 7 b. multicoloured . . . 30 15
2734 – 7 b. multicoloured . . . 30 15
2735 – 11 b. 50 multicoloured . 75 25
2736 – 11 b. 50 multicoloured . 75 25
2737 – 12 b. black 80 25
2738 – 12 b. multicoloured . . . 80 25

DESIGNS: No. 2730, Rolling strip; No. 2731, Walkways and towers of plant; No. 2732, Drawing steel bars; No. 2733, Walkway, towers and buildings; No. 2734, Slab mill; No. 2735, Building and towers; No. 2736, Steel bar production; No. 2737, Company emblem; No. 2738, Anniversary emblem.

Nos. 2729/38 were printed together, se-tenant, Nos. 2729, 2731, 2733 and 2735 forming a composite design of the SIDOR steel plant.

472 Flags

1987. 1st Meeting of Eight Latin-American Presidents of Contadora and Lima Groups, Acapulco.

2739 472 6 b. multicoloured . . . 30 15

473 Plastics

1987. 10th Anniv of Petro-Chemical Company of Venezuela. Multicoloured.
2740 2 b. Type **473** 10 10
2741 6 b. Formulae (oil refining) . 30 15
2742 7 b. Leaves (fertilizers) . . . 30 15
2743 11 b. 50 Pipes (installations) . 75 25
2744 12 b. Expansion 80 25

474 St. John Bosco and People on Map

1987. Birth Centenary of St. John Bosco (founder of Salesian Brothers). Multicoloured.
2745 2 b. Type **474** 10 10
2746 3 b. National Temple, Caracas 15 10
2747 4 b. Vocational training . . . 15 10
2748 5 b. Church of Maria Auxiliadora 20 10
2749 6 b. Missionary work 25 15

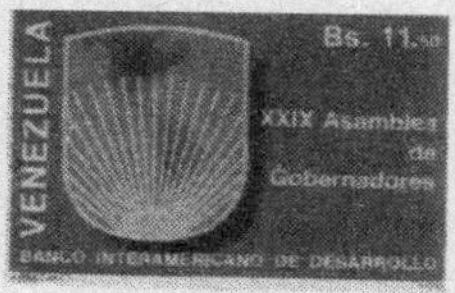

475 Emblem

1988. 29th Governors' Meeting of Inter-American Development Bank.
2750 **475** 11 b. 50 multicoloured . 60 30

476 Bank Branch

1988. 30th Anniv of Banco Republica. Mult.
2751 2 b. Type **476** 10 10
2752 2 b. Pottery (small business finance) 10 10
2753 2 b. Factory and security guards (industrial finance) 10 10
2754 2 b. Laboratory workers (technology finance) . . . 10 10
2755 2 b. Quay-side scene (exports and imports) 10 10
2756 6 b. Farm workers (agricultural finance) 35 15
2757 6 b. Fishing boat (fisheries finance) 35 15
2758 6 b. Milk production (livestock development) 35 15
2759 6 b. Building site (construction finance) 35 15
2760 6 b. Tourist bus (tourism development) 35 15

477 "Mother and Children" and Emblems

1988. Rotary International Anti-polio Campaign Victory Day.
2761 **477** 11 b. 50 multicoloured . 65 35

478 Carlos Eduardo Frias (publicist)

1989. 50th Anniv of Publicity Industry. Mult.
2762 4 b. Three profiles of Frias . 30 15
2763 10 b. Type **478** 60 30

479 Smelter 481 Bolivar in Dress Uniform, 1828

480 Red Siskins

1988. 10th Anniv of Venalum (aluminium company).
2764 **479** 2 b. multicoloured . . . 10 10
2765 – 6 b. black 30 15
2766 – 7 b. multicoloured . . . 30 15
2767 – 11 b. 50 multicoloured . 65 35
2768 – 12 b. multicoloured . . 65 35
DESIGNS: 6 b. Plan of electrolytic cell; 7 b. Aluminium pipes; 11 b. 50, Loading ship with aluminium for export; 12 b. Workers playing football.

1988. Endangered Birds. Multicoloured.
2769 2 b. Type **480** 15 10
2770 6 b. Scarlet ibis 45 25
2771 11 b. 50 Harpy eagle 95 45
2772 12 b. Greater flamingoes . . 95 45
2773 12 b. 50 Northern helmeted curassow . . . . 1·00 55

1988. Army Day. Multicoloured.
2774 2 b. Type **481** 10 10
2775 2 b. Lieutenant in ceremonial uniform, 1988 . . . . . . 10 10
2776 6 b. Gen. Jose Antonio Paez in dress uniform, 1821 . . . 30 15
2777 6 b. Major-General in No. 1 dress, 1988 . . . . . . 30 15
2778 7 b. Major-General, 1820 . . 30 15
2779 7 b. Line infantryman, 1820 30 15
2780 11 b. 50 Brigadier-General, 1820 60 30
2781 11 b. 50 Garrison infantryman, 1820 . . . . 60 30
2782 12 b. Artilleryman, 1836 . . 60 30
2783 12 b. Light cavalryman, 1820 60 30

482 Urdaneta (after Salas)

1988. Birth Bicentenary of General Rafael Urdaneta. Multicoloured.
2784 2 b. Sword and scabbard . . 10 10
2785 4 b. 75 "Wedding of the General" (Tito Salas) . . 20 10
2786 6 b. Type **482** 30 15
2787 7 b. "Siege of Valencia" (Tito Salas) 30 15
2788 12 b. "Retreat from San Carlos" (Tito Salas) . . . 65 35

483 Marino (after Martin Tovar y Tovar) 484 Games Emblem

1988. Birth Bicentenary of General Santiago Marino.
2789 **483** 4 b. 75 multicoloured . . 20 10

1988. Olympic Games, Seoul.
2790 **484** 12 b. multicoloured . . 60 30

485 "Virgin of Copacabana" (Bolivia)

1988. Marian Year. Multicoloured.
2791 4 b. 75 Type **485** 25 15
2792 4 b. 75 "Virgin of Chiquinquira" (Colombia) . 25 15
2793 4 b. 75 "Virgin of Coromoto" (Venezuela) 25 15
2794 4 b. 75 "Virgin of the Cloud" (Ecuador) 25 15
2795 4 b. 75 "Virgin of Antigua" (Panama) 25 15
2796 6 b. "Virgin of Evangelisation" (Peru) 30 15
2797 6 b. "Virgin of Lujan" (Argentina) 30 15
2798 6 b. "Virgin of Altagracia" (Dominican Republic) . . . 30 15
2799 6 b. "Virgin of Aparecida" (Brazil) 30 15
2800 6 b. "Virgin of Guadelupe" (Mexico) 30 15

486 Bardou Refracting Telescope 487 Keys

1988. Centenary of Juan Manuel Cagigal Observatory. Multicoloured.
2801 2 b. Type **486** 20 10
2802 4 b. 75 Universal "AUZ-27" theodolite 25 15
2803 6 b. Bust of Cagigal 30 15
2804 11 b. 50 Boulton Cupola and night sky over Caracas in September 60 30
2805 12 b. Satellite photographing Hurricane Allen 65 35

1988. 50th Anniv of Controller-General's Office.
2806 **487** 10 b. multicoloured . . . 45 25

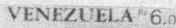

488 Commemorative Medal

1988. Cent of National Historical Museum. Mult.
2807 6 b. Type **488** 30 15
2808 6 b. 50 Juan Pablo Rojas Paul (founder) (after Cristobal Rojas) 30 15

489 First Headquarters

1988. Centenary of Electricity Industry. Mult.
2809 2 b. Type **489** 10 10
2810 4 b. 75 "Electrical Plant, 1888" (Jaime Carrillo) 20 15
2811 10 b. Plaza Bolivar, 1888 . . 45 25
2812 11 b. 50 Baralt Theatre, 1888 60 30
2813 12 b. 50 Ramon Laguna Central Thermo-electricity Station . 60 30

490 "Nativity" (Tito Salas, left-hand detail)

1988. Christmas. Multicoloured.
2814 4 b. Type **490** 20 10
2815 6 b. "Christ Child" (anonymous) 30 15
2816 15 b. "Nativity" (Salas, right-hand detail) 65 35
Nos. 2814 and 2816 form a composite design.

491 "Bolivar and Ricardo" (John de Pool)

1989. "The Liberator at Curacao". Multicoloured.
2817 10 b. Type **491** 60 15
2818 10 b. "The Octagon" (John de Pool) 60 15
2819 11 b. "Doctor Mordechay Ricardo" 75 20

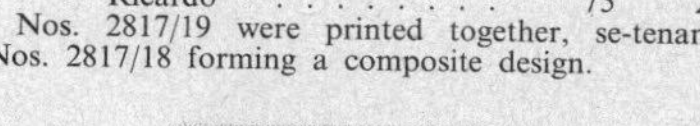
Nos. 2817/19 were printed together, se-tenant, Nos. 2817/18 forming a composite design.

492 Cardinal Quintero (Archbishop of Caracas, 1960–80)

1989. 25th Anniv of Convention with Holy See. Multicoloured.
2820 4 b. Type **492** 15 10
2821 4 b. Dr. Raul Leoni (President, 1964–69) 15 10
2822 12 b. Arms of Luciano Storero (Papal Nuncio) 70 20
2823 12 b. Arms of Cardinal Lebrun (Archbishop of Caracas) . 70 20
2824 16 b. Pope Paul VI 90 25

493 "Cacao Harvest" (Tito Salas)

1989. Centenary of Bank of Venezuela. Mult.
2825 4 b. Type **493** 15 10
2826 4 b. "Teaching Sowing Time of Coffee" (Tito Salas) . . . 15 10
2827 4 b. Head Office, Caracas . . 15 10
2828 4 b. Archive of the Liberator, Caracas 15 10
2829 4 b. Tree-planting programme 15 10
2830 4 b. Family planting tree . . 15 10
2831 8 b. Left-hand side of 50 b. banknote 25 15
2832 8 b. Right-hand side of 50 b. bank-note 25 15
2833 8 b. Portrait of Bolivar on left-hand side of 500 b. banknote 25 15
2834 8 b. Right-hand side of 500 b. banknote 25 15
Nos. 2825/34 were printed together, se-tenant, Nos. 2831/2 and 2833/4 forming composite designs.

494 Dish

1989. America. Pre-Columbian Artefacts. Multicoloured.
2835 6 b. Type **494** 20 10
2836 24 b. Figure . . . . 2·00 1·00

495 Shepherds and Sheep

1989. Christmas. Multicoloured.
2837 5 b. As Type **495** but inscr at top 10 10
2838 5 b. Type **495** 10 10
2839 6 b. Angel and shepherds (inscr at top) 15 10

No.	Description	Mint	Used
2840	6 b. As No. 2839 but inscr at bottom	15	10
2841	6 b. Nativity (inscr at top)	15	10
2842	6 b. As No. 2841 but inscr at bottom	15	10
2843	12 b. Shepherds (inscr at top)	70	15
2844	12 b. As No. 2843 but inscr at bottom	70	15
2845	15 b. Adoration of the Magi (inscr at top)	85	15
2846	15 b. As No. 2845 but inscr at bottom	85	45

Nos. 2837/46 were printed together, each horizontal strip forming a composite design.

496 Araguaney Tree and State Arms

1990. 20th Anniv of Bank of Venezuela Foundation. Multicoloured.

No.	Description	Mint	Used
2847	10 b. Type **496**	20	10
2848	10 b. Silk-cotton tree and Federal District arms	20	10
2849	10 b. "Myrospermum frutescens" and Anzoategui State arms	20	10
2850	10 b. "Pithecellobium saman" and Aragua State arms	20	10
2851	10 b. West Indian cedar and Barinas State arms	20	10
2852	10 b. "Dipteryx punctata" and Bolivar State arms	20	10
2853	10 b. Pink trumpet tree and Cojedes State arms	20	10
2854	10 b. "Prosopis juliflora" and Falcon State arms	20	10
2855	10 b. "Copernicia tectorum" and Guarico State arms	20	10
2856	10 b. Mountain immortelle and Merida State arms	20	10
2857	10 b. "Brawnea leucantha" and Miranda State arms	20	10
2858	10 b. "Mauritia flexuosa" and Monagas State arms	20	10
2859	10 b. Mahogany and Portuguesa State arms	20	10
2860	10 b. "Platymiscium diadelphum" and Sucre State arms	20	10
2861	10 b. "Prumnopitys montana de Laub" and Tachira State arms	20	10
2862	10 b. "Roystonea venezuelana" and Yaracuy State arms	20	10
2863	10 b. Coconut palm and Zulia State arms	20	10
2864	10 b. "Hevea benthamiana" and Amazonas Federal Territory arms	20	10
2865	40 b. "Licania pyrofolia" and Apure State arms	1·60	85
2866	40 b. "Malpighia glabra" and Lara State arms	1·60	85
2867	40 b. "Erythrina fusca" and Trujillo State arms	1·60	85
2868	50 b. "Sterculia apetala" and Carabobo State arms	2·10	1·00
2869	50 b. "Lignum vitae" and Nueva Esparta State arms	2·10	1·00
2870	50 b. Mangrove and Amacuro Federal Territory arms	2·10	1·00

497 Dr. Francisco Ochoa (founder)

1990. Centenary of Zulia University.

No.	Type	Description	Mint	Used
2871	497	10 b. black and blue	20	10
2872	–	10 b. black and blue	20	10
2873	–	15 b. multicoloured	60	15
2874	–	15 b. multicoloured	60	15
2875	–	20 b. multicoloured	85	25

DESIGNS: No. 2872, Dr. Jesus E. Lossada (Rector, 1946–47); 2873, Research into acid soils; 2874, Petroleum research; 2875, Transplant surgery.

498 Santa Capilla, 1943

1990. 50th Anniv of Central Bank. Multicoloured.

No.	Description	Mint	Used
2876	10 b. Type **498**	20	10
2877	10 b. Headquarters, 1967	20	10
2878	10 b. Left half of 1940 500 b. note	20	10
2879	10 b. Right half of 1940 500 b. note	20	10
2880	10 b. "Sun of Peru" decoration, 1825	20	10
2881	10 b. Medals	20	10
2882	15 b. Peruvian sword, 1825	60	15
2883	15 b. Cross, Bucaramanga, 1830	60	15
2884	40 b. Medallion of George Washington, 1826	1·60	85
2885	50 b. Gen. O'Leary (enamel portrait)	2·10	1·00

Nos. 2876/85 were printed together, se-tenant, Nos. 2878/9 forming a composite design.

500 "St. Joseph and the Child" (Juan Pedro Lopez)

501 Lake House, Maracaibo

1990. Christmas. Multicoloured.

No.	Description	Mint	Used
2887	10 b. Type **500**	20	10
2888	10 b. "Nativity" (Juan Pedro Lopez)	20	10
2889	10 b. "Return from Egypt" (Matheo Moreno)	20	10
2890	20 b. "Holy Family" (anon)	85	25
2891	20 b. "Nativity" (Juan Pedro Lopez) (different)	85	25

1990. America. The Natural World. Mult.

No.	Description	Mint	Used
2892	10 b. Type **501**	20	10
2893	40 b. East Venezuelan shore	1·60	80

502 Globe and "30"

503 Death Mask

1990. 30th Anniv of O.P.E.C. Multicoloured.

No.	Description	Mint	Used
2894	10 b. Type **502**	20	10
2895	10 b. O.P.E.C. emblem	20	10
2896	20 b. Anniversary emblem	85	25
2897	30 b. O.P.E.C. emblem and dates	1·25	60
2898	40 b. Members' flags around O.P.E.C. emblem	1·60	85

1991. 500th Birth Anniv of St. Ignatius de Loyola (founder of Society of Jesus). Multicoloured

No.	Description	Mint	Used
2899	12 b. Type **503**	25	15
2900	12 b. St. Ignatius de Loyola College, Caracas	25	15
2901	40 b. Silver statue of Loyola by Francisco de Vergara	1·50	75
2902	50 b. "Our Lady of Montserrat" (wooden statue)	1·90	95

504 Elisa Elvira Zuloaga (painter and engraver)

1991. 50th Anniv of American–Venezuelan Cultural Centre. Designs showing Centre directors.

No.	Type	Description	Mint	Used
2903	504	12 b. green and black	25	15
2904	–	12 b. violet and black	25	15
2905	–	12 b. red and black	25	15
2906	–	40 b. blue and black	1·50	80
2907	–	50 b. brown and black	1·50	80

DESIGNS: No. 2904, Gloria Stolk (writer); 2905, Caroline Lloyd (composer); 2906, Jules Waldman (linguist and journalist); 2907, William Coles (entrepreneur).

505 "Acineta alticola"

1991. Orchids. Multicoloured.

No.	Description	Mint	Used
2908	12 b. Type **505**	25	15
2909	12 b. "Brassavola nodosa"	25	15
2910	12 b. "Brachionidium brevicaudatum"	25	15
2911	12 b. "Bifrenaria maguirei"	25	15
2912	12 b. "Odontoglossum spectatissimum"	25	15
2913	12 b. "Catasetum macrocarpum"	25	15
2914	40 b. "Mendocella jorisiana"	80	40
2915	40 b. "Cochleanthes discolor"	80	40
2916	50 b. "Maxillaria splendens"	1·00	50
2917	50 b. "Pleurothallis dunstervillei"	1·00	50

506 Voters at Ballot Box

1991. 50th Anniv of Democratic Action Party.

No.	Type	Description	Mint	Used
2919	506	12 b. multicoloured	25	15
2920	–	12 b. multicoloured	25	15
2921	–	12 b. multicoloured	25	15
2922	–	12 b. black and blue	25	10

DESIGNS: No. 2920, Agrarian reform; 2921, Education; 2922, Nationalization of petroleum industry.

507 Rodrigues Suarez and Terepaima Chieftain

1991. America. Voyages of Discovery. Showing paintings by Pedro Centeno. Multicoloured.

No.	Description	Mint	Used
2923	12 b. Type **507**	25	15
2924	40 b. Paramaconi chieftain and Garcia Gonzalez	1·60	80

508 Family in House

1991. 25th Anniv of Children's Foundation. Multicoloured.

No.	Description	Mint	Used
2925	12 b. Type **508**	20	10
2926	12 b. Children's playground	20	10
2927	12 b. Fairground	20	10
2928	12 b. Mother and daughter	20	10
2929	12 b. Boy in hospital	20	10
2930	12 b. Children and tree	20	10
2931	40 b. Girls at home	65	35
2932	40 b. Children in classroom	65	35
2933	50 b. Children acting in play	80	40
2934	50 b. Children playing ring-a-ring of roses	80	40

509 "Stable" (Barbaro Rivas)

1991. Christmas. Multicoloured.

No.	Description	Mint	Used
2935	10 b. Type **509**	15	10
2936	12 b. "Nativity" (Elsa Morales)	20	10
2937	20 b. "Nativity" (model, Glenda Mendoza)	30	15
2938	25 b. "Shepherds watching flock (Maritza Marin)	40	20
2939	30 b. "Nativity" (Antonia Azuaje)	50	25

1991. Nos. 2613/15 surch **RESELLADO** and value.

No.	Type	Description	Mint	Used
2940	347	5 b. on 25 c. red	10	10
2941		5 b. on 75 c. mauve	10	10
2942		10 b. on 25 c. red	15	10
2943		10 b. on 75 c. mauve	15	10
2944		12 b. on 50 c. blue	20	10
2945		12 b. on 75 c. mauve	20	10
2946		20 b. on 50 c. blue	30	15
2947		20 b. on 75 c. mauve	30	10
2948		40 b. on 50 c. blue	65	35
2949		40 b. on 75 c. mauve	65	35
2950	347	50 b. on 50 c. blue	80	40
2951		50 b. on 75 c. mauve	80	40

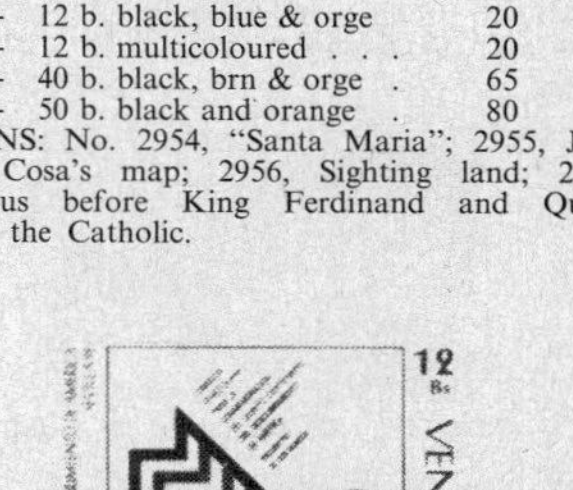

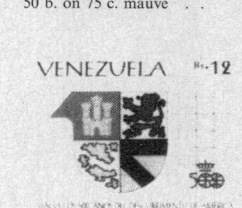

512 Columbus's Arms

1991. 500th Anniv (1992) of Discovery of America by Columbus.

No.	Type	Description	Mint	Used
2953	512	12 b. multicoloured	20	10
2954	–	12 b. black, blue & orge	20	10
2955	–	12 b. multicoloured	20	10
2956	–	40 b. black, brn & orge	65	35
2957	–	50 b. black and orange	80	40

DESIGNS: No. 2954, "Santa Maria"; 2955, Juan de la Cosa's map; 2956, Sighting land; 2957, Columbus before King Ferdinand and Queen Isabella the Catholic.

513 Anniversary Emblem

1992. "Expo 92" World's Fair, Seville. 500th Anniv of Discovery of America by Columbus.

No.	Type	Description	Mint	Used
2958	513	12 b. black, red & blue	20	10
2959	–	12 b. multicoloured	20	10
2960	–	12 b. multicoloured	20	10
2961	–	12 b. multicoloured	20	10
2962	–	12 b. multicoloured	20	10
2963	–	12 b. multicoloured	20	10
2964	–	40 b. multicoloured	65	35
2965	–	40 b. multicoloured	65	35
2966	–	50 b. multicoloured	80	40
2967	–	50 b. black and brown	80	40

DESIGNS: No. 2959, Venezuelan pavilion at "Expo 92"; 2960, Landmarks and map of southern Spain; 2961, Columbus; 2962, "Encounters"; 2963, "0x500 America"; 2964, "Imago-Mundi"; 2965, "The Grand Voyage"; 2966, "Golden Beach"; 2967, Idols.

514 Red-footed Tortoise

1992. Tortoises. Multicoloured.

No.	Description	Mint	Used
2969	12 b. Type **514**	20	10
2970	12 b. "Red-footed tortoise ("Geochelone carbonaria") (different)	20	10
2971	12 b. South American river turtle ("Podocnemis expansa") (on land)	20	10
2972	12 b. South American river turtle (swimming)	20	10

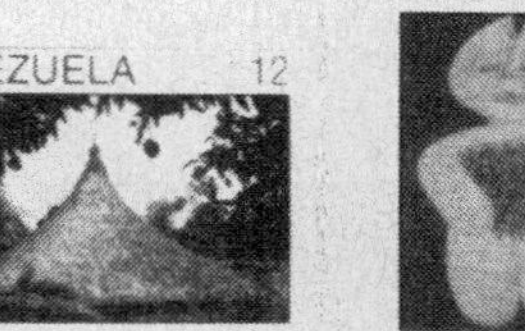

515 Native Hut

516 Figure holding Sheaf of Wheat

1992. Electricity Distribution in the South.

No.	Type	Description	Mint	Used
2973	515	12 b. multicoloured	20	10
2974	–	12 b. black and blue	20	10
2975	–	12 b. multicoloured	20	10
2976	–	40 b. multicoloured	65	35
2977	–	50 b. multicoloured	80	40

DESIGNS: No. 2974, Pylons; 2975, Horses galloping through water; 2976, Engineers working on pylon; 2977, Traditional baskets beside lake.

1992. "Offering to My Race" (Mateo Manaure). Designs showing various "mother" figures. Multicoloured.

No.	Description	Mint	Used
2978	12 b. Type **516**	20	10
2979	12 b. Orange figure	20	10
2980	12 b. Yellow figure	20	10
2981	12 b. Pink figure	20	10
2982	40 b. Brown figure	65	35
2983	40 b. Purple and orange figures	65	35
2984	50 b. Three-quarter length figure	80	40
2985	50 b. Head and shoulders	80	40

517 Catechism in Venezuela, 1975

518 "And on the Third Voyage" (Elio Caldera)

1992. Beatification of Josemaria Escriva (founder of Opus Dei).

2986 **517** 18 b. multicoloured . . . 20 10
2987 – 18 b. multicoloured . . . 20 10
2988 – 18 b. multicoloired . . . 20 10
2989 – 18 b. black and yellow . 20 10
2990 – 18 b. multicoloured . . . 20 10
2991 – 18 b. multicoloured . . . 20 10
2992 – 60 b. multicoloured . . . 70 35
2993 – 60 b. multicoloured . . . 70 35
2994 – 75 b. multicoloured . . . 85 45
2995 – 75 b. multicoloured . . . 85 45

DESIGNS: No. 2987, Celebrating mass; 2988, Jose Escriva and Dolores Albas (parents); 2989, Text and autograph; 2990, With statuette of Madonna and Child; 2991, Commemorative medal; 2992, With Pope Paul VI, 1964; 2993, Writing at desk; Portrait; 2995, Portrait in St. Peter's Square, 17 May 1992.

1992. America. 500th Anniv of Discovery of America by Columbus. Multicoloured.

2996 18 b. Type **518** 20 10
2997 60 b. "Descontextura" (Juan Pablo Nascimiento) 70 35

519 "Adoration of the Shepherds"

520 Simon Bolivar

1992. Christmas. Paintings by Lucio Rivas. Multicoloured.

2998 18 b. Type **519** 20 10
2999 75 b. "Adoration of the Magi" 85 45

1993. Portraits and Monuments.

3001 **520** 1 b. silver 10 10
3002 – 2 b. blue 10 10
3005 – 5 b. red 10 10
3007 – 10 b. purple 10 10
3009 – 20 b. green 25 15
3011 – 50 b. orange 60 30
3013 – 100 b. brown . . . . . . 1·10 55

DESIGNS: 5 b. National Pantheon, Caracas; 10 b. War of Independence Memorial, Carabobo; 20 b. General Jose Antonio de Paez (President, 1830–35, 1837–43 and 1861–63); 50 b. National Library; 100 b. Bolivar (different).

521 "Cattleya percivaliana"

1993. Orchids. Multicoloured.

3016 20 b. Type **521** 25 15
3017 20 b. "Anguloa ruckeri" . . 25 15
3018 20 b. "Chondrorhyncha flaveola" 25 15
3019 20 b. "Stenia pallida" 25 15
3020 20 b. "Zygosepalum lindeniae" 25 15
3021 20 b. "Maxillaria triloris" . . 25 15
3022 80 b. "Stanhopea wardii" . . 90 45
3023 80 b. "Oncidium papilio" . . 90 45
3024 100 b. "Oncidium hastilabium" 1·10 55
3025 100 b. "Sobralia cattleya" . . 1·10 55

522 Woman

1993. 150th Anniv of Tovar Colony, Aragua State. Multicoloured.

3027 24 b. Type **522** 30 15
3028 24 b. Children 30 15
3029 24 b. Catholic church . . . 30 15
3030 24 b. St. Martin of Tours (patron saint) 30 15
3031 24 b. Vegetables and fruit . . 30 15
3032 24 b. School 30 15
3033 80 b. House of Augustin Codazzi (founder) 90 45
3034 80 b. House of Alexander Benitz 90 45
3035 100 b. Breidenbach mill . . 1·10 55
3036 100 b. Procession of Jokili (carnival group) . . . . . 1·10 55

523 Tucacas Steam Locomotive, 1813

524 Smoker and Non-Smoker

1993. 19th Pan-American Railways Congress. Multicoloured.

3037 24 b. Type **523** 30 15
3038 24 b. Halcon steam locomotive, 1894, on Las Mostazas bridge 30 15
3039 24 b. Maracaibo steam locomotive 30 15
3040 24 b. Tender and carriages in Palo Grande station . . . 30 15
3041 24 b. Fiat diesel locomotive, 1957 . . . . 30 15
3042 24 b. "GP-9-L" diesel locomotive, 1957 . . . . 30 15
3043 80 b. "GP-15-L" diesel locomotive, 1982 . . . . 90 45
3044 80 b. Underground train, Caracas 90 45
3045 100 b. Electric locomotive . 1·10 55
3046 100 b. Carriages . . . . . . 1·10 55

Nos. 3037/46 were issued together, se-tenant, Nos. 3039/40 and 3043/4 forming composite designs.

1993. World No Smoking Day. Each black, blue and red.

3047 24 b. Type **524** 30 15
3048 80 b. No smoking sign . . . 90 45

525 Yellow-shouldered Amazon

526 Yanomami Boys

1993. America. Endangered Animals. Mult.

3049 24 b. Type **525** 30 15
3050 80 b. Scarlet macaw 90 45

1993. Amerindians. Multicoloured.

3051 1 b. Type **526** 10 10
3052 1 b. Yanomami woman preparing casabe 10 10
3053 40 b. Panare children in Katyayinto ceremony . . . 50 25
3054 40 b. Taurepan man paddling canoe 50 25
3055 40 b. Piaroa mother holding child 50 25
3056 40 b. Panare man playing nose flute 50 25
3057 40 b. Taurepan woman weaving 50 25
3058 40 b. Masked Piaroa dancers in Warime ceremony 50 25
3059 100 b. Hoti man with blowpipe 1·25 65
3060 100 b. Hoti woman carrying child and fruit . . . . . . 1·25 65

527 Joseph

1993. Christmas. (a) Each cream, brown and black

3062 24 b. Type **527** 30 15
3063 24 b. Madonna and Child . . 30 15
3064 24 b. Shepherd girl, wise man and sheep 30 15
3065 80 b. Wise man and shepherd girl . . . . 1·10 55
3066 100 b. Wise man and shepherd girl . . . . 1·25 65

(b) Each cream, purple and black

3067 24 b. Type **527** 30 15
3068 24 b. As No. 3063 . . . . . 30 15
3069 24 b. As No. 3064 . . . . . 30 15
3070 80 b. As No. 3065 . . . . . 1·10 55
3071 100 b. As No. 3066 . . . . . 1·25 65

Nos. 3062/71 were issued together, se-tenant, each horizontal strip forming a composite design of the Nativity.

528 "Chrysocycnis schlimii"

1994. Orchids. Multicoloured.

3072 35 b. Type **528** 35 20
3073 35 b. "Galeandra minax" . . 35 20
3074 35 b. "Oncidium falcipetalum" 35 20
3075 35 b. "Oncidium lanceanum" 35 20
3076 40 b. "Sobralia violacea" . . 40 20
3077 40 b. "Sobralia infundibuligera" 40 20
3078 80 b. "Mendoncella burkei" . 75 40
3079 80 b. "Phragmipedium caudatum" 75 40
3080 100 b. "Phragmipedium kaieteurum" 95 50
3081 200 b. "Stanhopea grandiflora" 1·90 95

529 Federation Emblem

1994. 50th Anniv of Federation of Chambers of Industry and Commerce.

3083 – 35 b. blue, gold and black 25 15
3084 – 35 b. black and brown . . 25 15
3085 **529** 35 b. blue and black . . . 25 15
3086 80 b. blue and black . . . 60 30
3087 – 80 b. black, brown and blue 60 30
3088 – 80 b. blue, gold and black 60 30

DESIGNS: Nos. 3083, 3088, "50" on text; 3084, 3087, Luis Gonzalo Marturet (first Federation President).

EXPRESS LETTER STAMPS

E 119

E 194

1949.

E809 E **119** 30 c. lake 30 25

1961.

E1691 E **194** 30 c. orange 50 25

OFFICIAL STAMPS

O 17

1898.

O174 O **17** 5 c. black and green . . 30 50
O175 10 c. black and red . . 60 65
O176 25 c. black and blue . . 85 90
O177 50 c. black and yellow . 1·60 1·60
O178 1 b. black and mauve . 1·60 1·50

1899. Surch **1899** and new value.

O187 O **17** 5 c. on 50 c. black and yellow . . . . 3·00 2·75
O188 5 c. on 1 b. black and mauve . . . . 11·50 10·50
O189 25 c. on 50 c. black and yellow . . . . 11·50 10·50
O190 25 c. on 1 b. black and mauve . . . . 6·75 6·25

1900. Optd **1900** in upper corners.

O222 O **17** 5 c. black and green . . 35 35
O223 10 c. black and red . . 45 45
O224 25 c. black and blue . . 45 45
O225 50 c. black and yellow . 50 50
O226 1 b. black and mauve . 55 55

O 40 With Stars   O 41 Without Stars

1904.

O325 O **40** 5 c. black and green . 25 25
O326 10 c. black and red . . 50 50
O327 25 c. black and blue . . 50 50
O328 50 c. black and red . . 2·10 1·90
O329 1 b. black and lake . . 1·00 90

1912.

O354 O **41** 5 c. black and green . 15 25
O355 10 c. black and red . . 15 25
O356 25 c. black and blue . 15 25
O357 50 c. black and violet . 20 35
O358 1 b. black and yellow . 40 35

REGISTRATION STAMPS

R 19 Bolivar

1899.

R186 R **19** 25 c. brown . . . . . 2·10 1·60

1899. Optd with T **21**.

R205 R **19** 25 c. brown . . . . . 1·25 1·25

VIETNAM Pt. 21

A. DEMOCRATIC REPUBLIC

The Democratic Republic was proclaimed by the Viet Minh Nationalists on 2 September 1945 and recognised by France on 6 March, 1946, as a free state within the Indo-China Federation. It consisted of Tongking, Annam and Cochin-China.

1945. 100 cents = 1 piastre
1945. 100 xu = 10 hao = 1 dong

Stamps of Indo-China overprinted.

VIET-NAM
DAN-CHU CONG-HOA
DOC-LAP
TU-DO HANH-PHUC
BUU-CHINH III
(1)

("DAN-CHU CONG-HOA" = Democratic Republic; "DOC-LAP TU-DO HANH-PHUC = Independence, Freedom, Happiness; "BUU-CHINH" = Postage.)

1945. Independence. Variously optd as T **1** (all with **DOC-LAP TU-DO HANH-PHUC** in opt).

No.	Type	Description	Unused	Used
1	53	1 c. brown	40	40
2	–	2 c. mauve (No. 315)	25	25
3	–	3 c. brown (Courbet)	25	25
4	–	4 c. brown (No. 316)	25	25
5	–	5 c. sepia (De Genouilly)	35	35
6	–	6 c. red (No. 304)	35	35
7	–	6 c. red (No. 305)	60	60
8	–	10 c. green (No. 307)	60	60
9	–	10 c. green (No. 322)	40	40
10	–	20 c. red (No. 309)	75	75
11	64	40 c. blue	35	35
12	–	$1 green (No. 311)	75	75

Nos. 3 and 5 were not issued without opt and are as Nos. 304 and 305 of Indo-China respectively.

1945. Variously optd as follows:—(a) **VIET-NAM DAN-CHU CONG-HOA**.

No.	Type	Description	Unused	Used
13	69	10 c. purple and yellow	1·50	1·25
14	–	15 c. purple (No. 292)	25	25
15	–	30 c. brown (No. 294)	40	40
16	69	50 c. red	3·75	3·75
17	–	$1 green (No. 295)	25	25

(b) **VIET-NAM DAN-CHU CONG-HOA BUU-CHINH**.

No.	Type	Description	Unused	Used
18	53	3 c. brown	40	40
19	–	4 c. yellow (No. 317)	40	40
20	53	6 c. red	40	40
21		10 c. green	75	75
22	–	10 c. green (No. 320)	70	70
23	–	20 c. red (Pavie)	35	35
24	53	40 c. blue	50	50
25		40 c. grey	1·25	1·25

No. 23 was not issued without opt and is as No. 320 of Indo-China.

VIET-NAM
3$00 DAN-CHU CONG-HOA
CUU-DOI
(2)

("CUU-DOI" = Famine Relief.)

1945. Famine Relief. Surch as T **2**.

No.	Type	Description	Unused	Used
26	70	"2 $00" on 15 c. + 60 c. purple	5·00	5·00
27		"3 $00" on 40 c. + $1.10 c. blue	5·00	5·00

1945. War Wounded. Surch as T **2** but with **Binh-si Bi-nan** (= Fund for War Wounded).

No.	Type	Description	Unused	Used
28	70	"5 $00" on 15 c. + 60 c. purple	7·00	7·00

1945. Surch in new currency and variously optd as before (except Nos. 43/7). (a) **VIET-NAM DAN-CHU CONG-HOA BUU-CHINH**.

No.	Type	Description	Unused	Used
29	64	30 x. on 1 c. brown	40	40
30	–	30 x. on 15 c. purple (Garnier)	35	35
31	67	50 x. on 1 c. brown	75	75
32	–	60 x. on 1 c. brown (313)	70	70
33	–	1 d. on 5 c. brown (303)	1·50	1·50
34	–	1 d. 60 x. on 10 c. green (319)	40	40
35	64	3 d. on 15 c. purple	75	75
36	67	3 d. on 15 c. purple	1·00	1·00
37	–	4 d. on 1 c. brown (302)	50	50
38	–	5 d. on 1 c. brown (301)	90	90

(b) **VIET-NAM DAN-CHU CONG-HOA**.

No.	Type	Description	Unused	Used
39	–	1 d. on 5 c. purple (318)	50	50
40	49	2 d. on 3 c. brown	7·50	7·50
41	–	2 d. on 10 c. green (321)	75	75
42	49	4 d. on 6 c. red	7·50	7·50

(c) Surch only.

No.	Type	Description	Unused	Used
43	56	50 x. on 1 c. brown	60	60
44		2 d. on 6 c. red	5·00	5·00
45	48	5 d. on 1 c. orange	7·50	7·50
46		10 d. on 6 c. violet	8·75	8·75
47		15 d. on 25 c. blue	8·75	8·75

No. 30 was not issued without opt and is as No. 301 of Indo-China.

OVERPRINT. Nos. 48/55 are all optd **VIET-NAM DAN-CHU CONG-HOA** with varying additional words as noted in headings.

1945. National Defence (**Quoc-Phong**).

No.	Type	Description	Unused	Used
48	49	"+ 5 d." on 3 c. brown	1·25	1·50
49		"+ 10 d." on 6 c. red	1·25	1·50

1946. People's Livelihood. (**DAN SINH**).

No.	Type	Description	Unused	Used
50	57	"30 xu. + 3 d." on 6 c. red	65	65
51	55	"30 xu. + 3 d." on 6 c. red	65	65

1946. Campaign against Illiteracy (**Chong nan mu chu**).

No.	Type	Description	Unused	Used
52	59	"+ 4 dong" on 6 c. red	75	75

1946. New Life Movement (**Doi song moi**).

No.	Type	Description	Unused	Used
53	66	"+ 4 dong" on 6 c. red	1·50	1·50

1946. Child Welfare (**Bao-Anh**).

No.	Type	Description	Unused	Used
54	–	"+ 2 dong" on 6 c. red (290)	75	75

1946. War Wounded (**Binh si bi nan**).

No.	Type	Description	Unused	Used
55	–	"+ 3 dong" on 20 c. red (293)	1·50	1·25

Definitive issues.

3 Ho Chi Minh

1946.

No.	Type	Description	Unused	Used
56	3	1 h. green	40	40
57		3 h. red	40	40
58		9 h. yellow	40	40

1946. National Defence.

No.	Type	Description	Unused	Used
59	3	4 + 6 h. blue	75	75
60		6 + 9 h. brown	75	75

The Viet-Minh Government was at war with the French from 19 December 1946, until July 1954, and the stamps issued by the Democratic Republic in this period are listed as North Viet-Nam Nos. N1/13, NO 1/9 and ND 1/4.

B. INDEPENDENT STATE

On 14 June 1949, Vietnam, comprising Tongking, Annam and Cochin-China, became an independent state within the French Union under Emperor Bao-Dai. Until the 1951 issue Indo-Chinese stamps continued in use.

By the Geneva Declaration of 21 July 1954, Vietnam was partitioned near the 17th Parallel, and all authority of Bao-Dai's Government north of that line ended. Later issues are therefore those of SOUTH VIETNAM and NORTH VIETNAM.

100 cents = 1 piastre

4 Bongour Falls, Dalat

1951.

No.	Type	Description	Unused	Used
61	4	10 c. bronze	10	10
62	–	20 c. purple	20	10
63	–	30 c. blue	25	10
64	–	50 c. red	50	20
65	4	60 c. sepia	25	10
66	–	1 p. brown	25	10
67	–	1 p. 20 brown	1·90	1·25
68	–	2 p. violet	60	20
69	–	3 p. blue	1·90	25
70	4	5 p. green	1·40	35
71	–	10 p. red	3·50	65
72	–	15 p. brown	11·50	3·25
73	–	30 p. green	25·00	4·50

DESIGNS—HORIZ: 20 c., 2 p., 10 p. Imperial Palace, Hue; 30 c., 15 p. Small Lake, Hanoi; 50 c., 1 p. Temple of Remembrance, Saigon. VERT: 1 p. 20, 3 p., 30 p. Emperor Bao Dai.

9

1952. Air.

No.	Type	Description	Unused	Used
74	9	3 p. 30 green and lake	45	35
75		4 p. yellow and brown	70	25
76		5 p. 10 pink and blue	60	55
77	–	6 p. 30 red and yellow (symbolic of airlines)	75	65

10 Empress Nam Phuong

11 Globe and Lightning

1952.

No.	Type	Description	Unused	Used
78	10	30 c. brown, yellow & purple	30	40
79		50 c. brown, yellow & blue	60	40
80		1 p. 50 brown, yell & olive	1·25	40

1952. 1st Anniv of Admission of Vietnam into I.T.U.

No.	Type	Description	Unused	Used
81	11	1 p. blue	3·75	1·90

12 Dragon

1952. Air. Day of Wandering Souls.

No.	Type	Description	Unused	Used
82	12	40 c. red	1·00	65
83		70 c. green	1·00	65
84		80 c. blue	1·00	65
85		90 c. brown	1·00	80
86	–	3 p. 70 purple	1·40	90

DESIGN—VERT: 3 p. 70, Dragon.

13 U.P.U. Monument, Berne, and Coastline

1952. 1st Anniv of Admission of Vietnam into U.P.U.

No.	Type	Description	Unused	Used
87	13	5 p. brown	4·75	1·25

1952. Red Cross. T **10** surch, with red cross and **+50 c.**

No.	Type	Description	Unused	Used
88	10	1 p. 50 + 50 c. brown, yellow and blue	4·50	4·50

15 Emperor Bao Dai and Gateway

1952. 40th Birthday of Emperor.

No.	Type	Description	Unused	Used
89	15	1 p. 50 purple	2·25	95

16 Sabres and Flag

17 Crown Prince Bao Long

1952. Wounded Soldiers' Relief Fund.

No.	Type	Description	Unused	Used
90	16	3 p. 30 + 1 p. 70 lake	1·60	1·60

1959.

No.	Type	Description	Unused	Used
91	17	40 c. turquoise	50	50
92		70 c. lake	60	60
93		80 c. sepia	75	75
94	–	90 c. green	1·75	1·75
95	–	20 p. red	3·75	3·75
96	–	50 p. violet	8·00	8·00
97	17	100 p. blue	17·00	17·00

PORTRAIT: 90 c. to 50 p. Crown Prince in uniform.

POSTAGE DUE STAMPS

D 10 Dragon

1952.

No.	Type	Description	Unused	Used
D78	D 10	10 c. green and red	20	10
D79		20 c. yellow and green	35	10
D80		30 c. orange and violet	35	10
D81		40 c. pink and green	40	15
D82		50 c. grey and lake	70	25
D83		1 p. silver and blue	1·00	35

C. SOUTH VIETNAM

100 cents = 1 piastre

INDEPENDENT STATE
(Within the French Union)

1 Turtle

1955. 1st Anniv of Govt of Ngo Dinh Diem.

No.	Type	Description	Unused	Used
S1	1	30 c. purple	75	25
S2		50 c. green	2·75	90
S3		1 p. 50 blue	1·25	40

2 Phoenix

1955. Air.

No.	Type	Description	Unused	Used
S4	2	4 p. mauve and violet	1·00	25

0$70
BƯU-CHÍNH
VIỆT-NAM

3 Refugees

1955. 1st Anniv of Arrival of Refugees from North Vietnam.

No.	Type	Description	Unused	Used
S 5	3	70 c. red	65	40
S 6		80 c. purple	1·50	85
S 7		10 p. blue	2·75	1·60
S 8		20 p. brown, orange & vio	5·50	2·25
S 9		35 p. sepia, yellow & blue	11·00	8·75
S10		100 p. purple, orge & grn	25·00	14·50

No. S9 is inscribed "CHIEN-DICH-HUYNE-DE" in margin at foot. See also No. S26.

REPUBLIC
(from 26th October, 1955)

4 G.P.O., Saigon

5 Pres. Ngo Dinh Diem

1956. 5th Anniv of Entry of Vietnam into U.P.U.

No.	Type	Description	Unused	Used
S11	4	60 c. green	55	40
S12		90 c. violet	1·75	65
S13		3 p. brown	3·00	90

1956.

No.	Type	Description	Unused	Used
S14	5	20 c. brown	10	10
S15		30 c. purple	20	20
S16		50 c. red	10	10
S17		1 p. violet	30	15
S18		1 p. 50 violet	50	15
S19		3 p. sepia	50	15
S20		4 p. blue	70	20
S21		5 p. brown	95	20
S22		10 p. blue	1·25	40
S23		20 p. black	3·25	70
S24		35 p. green	8·50	1·60
S25		100 p. brown	18·00	6·25

1956. No. S9 with bottom marginal inscription obliterated by bar.

No.	Type	Description	Unused	Used
S26	3	35 p. sepia, yellow & blue	4·75	3·25

1956. Optd **Cong-thu Buu-dien** (= "Government Postal Building").

No.	Type	Description	Unused	Used
S27	4	60 c. green	85	50
S28		90 c. violet	1·50	50
S29		3 p. brown	2·25	75

7 Bamboo

2đ
BƯU-CHÍNH
VIỆT-NAM CỘNG-HÒA

8 Refugee Children

1956. 1st Anniv of Republic.

No.	Type	Description	Unused	Used
S30	7	50 c. red	30	10
S31		1 p. 50 purple	65	10
S32		2 p. green	85	10
S33		4 p. blue	2·10	20

1956. United Nations "Operation Brotherhood".

No.	Type	Description	Unused	Used
S34	8	1 p. mauve	30	10
S35		2 p. turquoise	40	15
S36		6 p. violet	75	15
S37		35 p. blue	4·25	1·00

9 Hunters on Elephants

10 Ship's Cargo being offloaded at Saigon

1957. 3rd Anniv of Govt of Ngo Dinh Diem.

S38	9	20 c. purple and green	30	10
S39		30 c. red and bistre	40	10
S40	–	90 c. sepia and green	50	20
S41	–	2 p. blue and green	85	25
S42	–	3 p. brown and violet	1·25	40

DESIGN—VERT: 90 c. to 3 p. Mountain hut.

1957. 9th Colombo Plan Conference, Saigon.

S43	10	20 c. purple	15	10
S44		40 c. olive	20	15
S45		50 c. red	35	15
S46		2 p. blue	60	25
S47		3 p. green	90	30

11 Torch and Constitution

12 Youth felling Tree

1957. Inauguration of National Assembly.

S48	11	50 c. salmon, green & blk	10	10
S49		80 c. purple, blue & black	20	10
S50		1 p. red, green and black	25	15
S51		4 p. brown, myrtle & blk	45	20
S52		5 p. olive, turq and black	60	30
S53		10 p. brown, blue and black	1·00	60

1958. Better Living Standards.

S54	12	50 c. green	25	20
S55		1 p. violet	35	20
S56		2 p. blue	45	20
S57		10 p. red	1·10	50

13 Young Girl with Chinese Lantern

14

1958. Children's Festival.

S58	13	30 c. lemon	20	20
S59		50 c. red	20	20
S60		2 p. red	20	20
S61		3 p. green	50	25
S62		4 p. olive	60	25

1958. United Nations Day.

S63	14	1 p. light brown	25	20
S64		2 p. turquoise	35	20
S65		4 p. red	40	20
S66		5 p. purple	90	40

15 U.N.E.S.C.O. Emblem and Building

16 U.N. Emblem and "Torch of Freedom"

1958. Inauguration of U.N.E.S.C.O. Headquarters Building, Paris.

S67	15	50 c. blue	20	20
S68		2 p. red	25	20
S69		3 p. purple	40	20
S70		6 p. violet	70	40

1958. 10th Anniv of Declaration of Human Rights.

S71	16	50 c. blue	30	15
S72		1 p. lake	40	20
S73		2 p. green	60	20
S74		6 p. purple	95	45

MINIMUM PRICE

The minimum price quoted is 10p which represents a handling charge rather than a basis for valuing common stamps. For further notes about prices, see introductory pages.

17 PhuCam Cathedral

18 Saigon Museum

1958.

S75	17	10 c. slate	20	10
S76	–	30 c. green	30	20
S77	18	40 c. green	15	15
S78	–	50 c. green	25	15
S79	–	2 p. blue	40	20
S80	–	4 p. lilac	40	25
S81	18	5 p. red	55	25
S82	17	6 p. brown	65	25

DESIGNS—HORIZ: 30 c., 4 p. Thien Mu Pagoda; 50 c., 2 p. Palace of Independence, Saigon.

19 Trung Sisters (national heroines) on Elephants

1959. Trung Sisters Commemoration.

S83	19	50 c. multicoloured	80	55
S84		2 p. multicoloured	1·25	75
S85		3 p. multicoloured	2·40	1·10
S86		6 p. multicoloured	3·00	1·60

20

21 Diesel Train

1959. Agricultural Reform.

S87	20	70 c. purple	15	10
S88		2 p. green and blue	15	10
S89		3 p. olive	30	10
S90		6 p. red and deep red	65	40

1959. Re-opening of Trans-Vietnam Railway. Centres in green.

S91	21	1 p. violet	50	20
S92		2 p. grey	70	40
S93		3 p. blue	80	30
S94		4 p. lake	1·60	50

22 Tilling the Land

25 Scout climbing Mountain

1959. 4th Anniv of Republic.

S95	22	1 p. brown, green & blue	30	20
S96		2 p. violet, green & orge	30	20
S97		4 p. indigo, blue & bistre	75	35
S98		5 p. brown, olive and light brown	95	50

1959. 1st National Scout Jamboree, Trang Bom.

S 99	25	3 p. green	45	20
S100		4 p. mauve	60	25
S101		8 p. mauve and purple	1·40	50
S102		20 p. dp turq & turq	3·00	1·25

26 "Family Code"

1960. 1st Anniv of Family Code.

S103	26	20 c. green	15	10
S104		30 c. blue	25	15
S105		2 p. red and orange	25	15
S106		6 p. violet and red	60	30

27 Refugee Family in Flight

28 Henri Dunant

1960. World Refugee Year.

S107	27	50 c. mauve	35	10
S108		3 p. green	30	15
S109		4 p. red	70	30
S110		5 p. violet	80	40

1960. Red Cross Day. Cross in red.

S111	28	1 p. blue	45	20
S112		3 p. green	55	25
S113		4 p. red	85	35
S114		6 p. mauve	1·00	55

29 Co-operative Farm

1960. Establishment of Co-operative Rice Farming.

S115	29	50 c. blue	20	15
S116		1 p. green	20	15
S117		3 p. orange	50	25
S118		7 p. mauve	90	25

30 X-ray Camera and Patient

31 Flag and Map

1960. National T.B. Relief Campaign Day.

S119	30	3 p. + 50 c. green & red	60	60

1960. 5th Anniv of Republic. Flag and map in red and yellow.

S120	31	50 c. turquoise	15	10
S121		1 p. blue	20	10
S122		3 p. violet	35	10
S123		7 p. green	55	25

32 Woman with Rice

1960. F.A.O. Regional Conference, Saigon.

S124	32	2 p. turquoise and green	45	25
S125		4 p. ultramarine and blue	65	40

33 Crane carrying Letter

1960. Air.

S126	33	1 p. green	50	20
S127		4 p. blue and turquoise	75	40
S128		5 p. violet and brown	1·25	65
S129		10 p. mauve	2·25	1·00

34 Farm Tractor

35 Child and Plant

1961. Agricultural Development and Pres. Diem's 60th Birthday.

S130	34	50 c. brown	20	10
S131		70 c. mauve	25	10
S132		80 c. red	25	20
S133		10 p. mauve	80	35

1961. Child Welfare.

S134	35	70 c. blue	20	10
S135		80 c. blue	20	10
S136		4 p. bistre	35	20
S137		7 p. green and turquoise	75	40

36 Pres. Ngo Dinh Diem

37 Young People and Torch

1961. 2nd Term of President.

S138	36	50 c. blue	25	20
S139		1 p. red	40	20
S140		2 p. purple	50	20
S141		4 p. violet	95	35

1961. Sports and Youth.

S142	37	50 c. red	15	10
S143		70 c. mauve	25	10
S144		80 c. mauve and red	35	20
S145		8 p. purple and red	75	35

38 Bridge over Mekong

1961. Inaug of Saigon–Bien Hoa Motor Highway.

S146	38	50 c. green	25	15
S147		1 p. brown	25	15
S148		2 p. blue	35	20
S149		5 p. purple	60	25

39 Alexander of Rhodes

40 Vietnamese with Torch

1961. Death Tercent of Alexander of Rhodes.

S150	39	50 c. red	20	10
S151		1 p. purple	20	10
S152		3 p. bistre	30	10
S153		6 p. green	70	25

1961. Youth Moral Rearmament.

S154	40	50 c. red	15	10
S155		1 p. green	20	10
S156		3 p. red	35	20
S157		8 p. brown and purple	70	25

41 Gateway of Van Mieu Temple, Hanoi

42 Tractor and Cottages

1961. 15th Anniv of U.N.E.S.C.O.

S158	41	1 p. green	25	10
S159		2 p. red	25	20
S160		5 p. olive	50	25

1961. Rural Reform.

S161	42	50 c. green	20	10
S162		1 p. lake and blue	20	20
S163		2 p. brown and green	25	20
S164		10 p. turquoise	70	45

43 Attack on Mosquito

44 Postal Cheque Building, Saigon

1962. Malaria Eradication.

S165	43	50 c. mauve	25	10
S166		1 p. orange	25	15
S167		2 p. green	35	20
S168		6 p. blue	75	25

1962. Inauguration of Postal Cheques Service.

S169	44	70 c. green	25	20
S170		80 c. brown	25	20
S171		4 p. purple	50	20
S172		7 p. red	60	40

45 St. Mary of La Vang **46** Armed Guards and Fortified Village

1962. St. Mary of La Vang Commemoration.

S173 **45** 50 c. red and violet . . . 20 10
S174 1 p. blue and brown . . . 25 15
S175 2 p. lake and brown . . . 40 15
S176 8 p. blue and turquoise . . 90 35

1962. Strategic Villages.

S177 **46** 50 c. red 20 10
S178 1 p. bronze 20 15
S179 1 p. 50 purple 35 15
S180 7 p. blue 60 30

47 Gougah Waterfalls, Dalat **48** Trung Sisters Monument

1963. Pres. Ngo Dinh Diem's 62nd Birthday and Spring Festival.

S181 **47** 60 c. red 20 15
S182 1 p. blue 35 15

1963. Women's Day.

S183 **48** 50 c. green 20 10
S184 1 p. red 25 15
S185 3 p. purple 30 20
S186 8 p. blue 60 40

49 Harvester

1963. Freedom from Hunger.

S187 **49** 50 c. red 20 10
S188 1 p. red 25 15
S189 3 p. purple 35 20
S190 5 p. violet 60 35

50 Sword and Fortress **51** Soldier and Emblem

1963. Communal Defence and 9th Anniv of Inaug of Pres. Diem.

S191 **50** 30 c. bistre 20 10
S192 50 c. mauve 25 15
S193 3 p. green 45 20
S194 8 p. red 70 35

1963. Republican Combatants.

S195 **51** 50 c. red 15 10
S196 1 p. green 20 15
S197 4 p. violet 40 20
S198 5 p. orange 65 45

52 Centenary Emblem and Globe **53** Scales of Justice and Book

1963. Red Cross Centenary. Cross in red.

S199 **52** 50 c. blue 25 10
S200 1 p. red 35 20
S201 3 p. orange 45 20
S202 6 p. brown 80 45

1963. 15th Anniv of Declaration of Human Rights.

S203 **53** 70 c. orange 20 10
S204 1 p. mauve 25 15
S205 3 p. green 35 15
S206 8 p. ochre 75 35

54 Danhim Hydro-Electric Station

1964. Inauguration of Danhim Hydro-Electric Station.

S207 **54** 40 c. red 15 10
S208 1 p. brown 25 15
S209 3 p. violet 35 20
S210 8 p. green 65 35

55 Atomic Reactor

1964. Peaceful Uses of Atomic Energy.

S211 **55** 80 c. olive 20 10
S212 1 p. 50 brown 25 20
S213 3 p. brown 45 20
S214 7 p. blue 70 40

56 "Meteorology" **57** "Unification"

1964. World Meteorological Day.

S215 **56** 50 c. ochre 20 10
S216 1 p. red 25 20
S217 1 p. 50 lake 35 20
S218 10 p. green 65 40

1964. 10th Anniv of Partition of Vietnam.

S219 **57** 30 c. blue and green . . 15 15
S220 50 c. blue, red & yellow . 20 15
S221 1 p. 50 indigo, bl & orge 25 15

58 Hatien Beach

1964.

S222 **58** 20 c. blue 20 10
S223 3 p. green 40 15

59 "Support of the People"

1964. 1st Anniv of Revolution of 1 November 1963.

S224 **59** 50 c. blue and purple . . 25 10
S225 – 80 c. brown and lilac . . 30 20
S226 – 3 p. brown and blue . . 50 20

DESIGNS—HORIZ: 80 c. Soldier breaking chain. VERT: 3 p. Allegory of Revolution.

60 Temple and Monument, Botanic Gardens, Saigon

1964. Monuments and Views.

S227 **60** 50 c. brown, green & bl . 20 15
S228 – 1 p. slate and bistre . . . 25 15
S229 – 1 p. 50 green and drab . 40 20
S230 – 3 p. red, green & violet . 75 25

DESIGNS: 1 p. Tomb of Minh Mang, Hue; 1 p. 50, Phan Thiet waterfront; 3 p. General Le Van Duyet Temple, Gia Dinh.

For 1 p. in smaller size, see No. S352.

61 Face of Bronze Drum

1965. Hung Vuong (legendary founder of Vietnam, 2000 B.C.).

S231 **61** 3 p. orange and lake . . . 1·90 65
S232 100 p. violet and purple . 12·00 6·50

62 Dharmachakra and "Fire of Clemency" **63** I.T.U. Emblem and Symbols

1965. Buddhism.

S233 **62** 50 c. red 20 15
S234 – 1 p. 50 orange, blue & deep blue 20 15
S235 – 3 p. deep brown, sepia and brown 40 20

DESIGNS—HORIZ: 1 p. 50, Dharmachakra, lotus and globe. VERT: 3 p. Dharmachakra and flag.

1965. I.T.U. Centenary.

S236 **63** 1 p. red and bistre 25 20
S237 3 p. red, mauve & brown . 40 20

64 "World Solidarity" **65** Ixora

1965. International Co-operation Year.

S238 **64** 50 c. blue and brown . . . 20 15
S239 1 p. sepia and brown . . 25 15
S240 1 p. 50 red and grey . . . 35 15

1965. Mid-Autumn Festival.

S241 **65** 70 c. red, green & dp green 20 15
S242 – 80 c. purple, grn & mve . 30 20
S243 – 1 p. yellow, blue and deep blue 50 25
S244 – 1 p. 50 green and olive . . 60 25
S245 – 3 p. orange and green . . 80 40

FLOWERS—VERT: 80 c. Orchid; 1 p. Chrysanthemum; 3 p. "Ochna harmandii". HORIZ: 1 p. 50, Nenuphar.

66 Student and University Building

1965. Re-opening of Vietnam University.

S246 **66** 50 c. brown 20 15
S247 1 p. green 25 20
S248 3 p. red 40 20
S249 7 p. violet 45 25

67 Young Farmers

1965. 10th Anniv of "4-T" Rural Youth Clubs.

S250 **67** 3 p. red and green 50 25
S251 – 4 p. violet, blue & purple . 50 25

DESIGN: 4 p. Young farmer and club banner.

68 Basketball **69** Aerial Mast and Equipment

1965. 3rd S.E. Asia Peninsular Games, Kuala Lumpur (Malaysia).

S252 **68** 50 c. bistre, brown and red 35 10
S253 – 1 p. red and brown . . . 40 20
S254 – 1 p. 50 green 55 25
S255 – 10 p. lake and purple . . 1·50 60

DESIGNS: 1 p. Throwing the javelin; 1 p. 50, "Physical Culture" (gymnasts and Olympic Games' symbols); 10 p. Pole-vaulting.

1966. 1st Anniv of Saigon Microwave Station.

S256 **69** 3 p. sepia, blue & brown . 25 15
S257 – 4 p. purple, red & green . 40 20

DESIGN: 4 p. Aerial mast, telephone dial and map.

70 Hook and Hemispheres **71** Help for Refugees

1966. "Free World's Aid to Vietnam".

S258 **70** 3 p. red and grey 20 10
S259 4 p. violet and brown . . 25 15
S260 6 p. blue and green . . . 35 20

1966. Refugee Aid.

S261 **71** 3 p. olive, mauve & brn . 25 15
S262 7 p. vio, brown & mve . 40 20

72 Paper "Soldiers"

1966. Wandering Souls' Festival.

S263 **72** 50 c. bistre, brown & red 20 10
S264 – 1 p. 50 red, green & brn . 30 15
S265 – 3 p. vermilion, crim & red 50 20
S266 – 5 p. brown, ochre and deep brown 65 25

DESIGNS: 1 p. 50, Obeisance; 3 p. Pool of candles; 5 p. Votive offering.

73 "Violinist"

1966. Ancient Musical Instruments.

S267 **73** 1 p. deep brown, mauve and brown 20 10
S268 – 3 p. violet and purple . . 25 15
S269 – 4 p. brown and red . . . 40 20
S270 – 7 p. deep blue and blue . 75 30

DESIGNS; 3 p. "Harpist"; 4 p. Small band; 7 p. "Flautists".

For 3 p. in smaller size, see No. S302.

74 W.H.O. Building

1966. Inaug of W.H.O. Headquarters, Geneva.

S271 **74** 50 c. pur, violet & red . . 20 10
S272 – 1 p. 50 black, blue & lake 25 15
S273 – 8 p. blue, sepia & turq . . 40 20

DESIGNS—VERT: 1 p. 50, W.H.O. Building and flag; 8 p. U.N. flag and W.H.O. Building.

75 Spade in Hand, and Soldiers

1966. 3rd Anniv of Overthrow of Diem Government.

S274 **75** 80 c. brown and bistre . . 20 10
S275 – 1 p. 50 purple, red & yell 20 15
S276 – 3 p. grn, brown & chest . 25 20
S277 – 4 p. lake, black & purple 65 35

DESIGNS—HORIZ: 1 p. 50, Agricultural workers, soldier and flag. VERT: 3 p. Soldier, tractor and labourers; 4 p. Soldier and horseman.

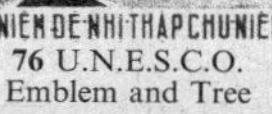

76 U.N.E.S.C.O. Emblem and Tree **77** Cashew Apples

1966. 20th Anniv of U.N.E.S.C.O.

S278	**76**	1 p. brown and lake	20	10
S279	–	3 p. brown, turq & blue	25	20
S280	–	7 p. blue, turquoise & red	65	30

DESIGNS—VERT: 3 p. Globe and laurel sprigs. HORIZ: 7 p. Pagoda.

1967. Exotic Fruits.

S281	**77**	50 c. red, green & blue	30	10
S282	–	1 p. 50 orange, grn & brn	30	15
S283	–	3 p. brown, green & choc	45	20
S284	–	20 p. olive, green & lake	1·50	65

FRUITS—HORIZ: 1 p. 50, Bitter "cucumbers"; 3 p. Cinnamon apples; 20 p. Areca-nuts.

78 Phan Boi Chau

1967. Vietnamese Patriots.

S285	**78**	1 p. purple, brown & red	25	10
S286	–	20 p. black, violet & grn	90	50

DESIGN: 20 p. Phan Chau-Trinh (portrait and making speech).

79 Horse-cab

1967. Life of the People.

S287	–	50 c. ultram, bl & grn	20	10
S288	–	1 p. violet, grn & myrtle	25	10
S289	**79**	3 p. lake and red	30	15
S290	–	8 p. violet and red	50	20

DESIGNS: 50 c. Itinerant merchant; 1 p. Market-place; 8 p. Pastoral activities.

80 Pottery-making

1967. Arts and Crafts. Multicoloured.

S291	50 c. Type **80**	20	10
S292	1 p. 50 Wicker basket and vase	25	20
S293	3 p. Weavers and potters	40	25
S294	35 p. Baskets and pottery	1·75	90

The 3 p. is a horiz design.

81 Wedding Procession

1967. Vietnamese Wedding.

S295	**81**	3 p. red, violet & purple	50	25

82 "Culture"

1967. Foundation of Vietnamese Cultural Institute.

S296	**82**	10 p. multicoloured	50	25

83 "Freedom and Justice"

1967. Democratic Elections. Multicoloured.

S297	4 p. Type **83**	30	20
S298	5 p. Vietnamese and hands casting votes	45	25
S299	30 p. Two Vietnamese with Constitution and flaming torch	1·25	65

84 Lions Emblem and Pagoda

1967. 50th Anniv of Lions International.

S300	**84**	3 p. multicoloured	75	40

85 Class on Globe

1967. World Literacy Day (8 Sept).

S301	**85**	3 p. multicoloured	55	15

1967. Mobile Post Office Inaug. As No. S268 but smaller size 23 × 17 mm.

S302	3 p. violet and purple	12·00	10·00

87 Tractor

1968. Rural Development. Multicoloured.

S303	1 p. Type **87**	30	20
S304	9 p. Bulldozer	35	20
S305	10 p. Workers with wheel-barrow and tractor	50	20
S306	20 p. Building construction	1·00	40

88 W.H.O. Emblem

1968. 20th Anniv of W.H.O.

S307	**88**	10 p. yellow, blk & grn	50	25

89 Flags of Allied Nations

1968. Thanks for International Aid. Mult.

S308	1 p. Handclasp, flags and soldiers	45	10
S309	1 p. 50 S.E.A.T.O. emblem and flags	50	20
S310	3 p. Handclasp and flags	70	25
S311	50 p. Type **89**	3·25	90

92 Farmers, Farm, Factory and Transport

93 Human Rights Emblem

1968. Development of Private Ownership. Multicoloured.

S318	80 c. Type **92**	20	10
S319	2 p. Motor vehicles and labourers	20	10
S320	10 p. Tractor and tri-car	40	20
S321	30 p. Motor vehicles and labourers	1·40	60

1968. Human Rights Year. Multicoloured.

S322	10 p. Type **93**	40	15
S323	16 p. Men of all races acclaiming Human Rights Emblem	55	25

94 Children with U.N.I.C.E.F. "Kite"

1968. U.N.I.C.E.F. Day. Multicoloured.

S324	6 p. Type **94**	45	20
S325	16 p. Mother and child	70	25

95 Diesel Train, Map and Mechanical Loader

97 Peasant Woman

1968. Re-opening of Trans-Vietnam Railway. Multicoloured.

S326	1 p. 50 Type **95**	40	20
S327	3 p. Type **95**	55	20
S328	9 p. Diesel train and permanent-way workers	1·00	30
S329	20 p. As No. S328	2·50	95

1969. Vietnamese Women.

S331	**97**	50 c. violet, ochre & blue	20	10
S332	–	1 p. brown and green	20	15
S333	–	3 p. black, blue & sepia	35	15
S334	–	20 p. multicoloured	70	40

DESIGNS—VERT: 1 p. Tradeswoman; 20 p. "Ladies of fashion". HORIZ: 3 p. Nurse.

98 Soldier and Militiaman

1969. "Open-arms" National Unity Campaign. Multicoloured.

S335	2 p. Type **98**	30	20
S336	50 p. Family welcoming soldier	1·25	50

99 Vietnamese and Scales of Justice

1969. 1st Anniv of New Constitution. Mult.

S337	1 p. Type **99**	25	10
S338	20 p. Voters at polling station	50	35

100 Mobile Post Office Van in Street

1969. Vietnamese Mobile Post Offices System. Multicoloured.

S339	1 p. Type **100**	25	10
S340	3 p. Clerk serving customers	25	15
S341	4 p. Child with letter, and mobile post office	35	20
S342	20 p. Queue at mobile post office, and postmark	60	40

101 Djarai Woman

1969. 2nd Anniv of Ethnic Minorities Statute. Multicoloured.

S343	1 p. Type **101**	45	25
S344	6 p. Mnong-gar woman	1·00	40
S345	50 p. Bahnar man	5·00	1·75

102 "Civilians to Soldiers"

1969. General Mobilisation.

S346	**102**	1 p. 50 multicoloured	15	10
S347	–	3 p. multicoloured	20	10
S348	–	5 p. brown, red & yellow	35	20
S349	–	10 p. multicoloured	40	25

DESIGNS: 3 p. Bayonet practice; 5 p. Recruits arriving at depot; 10 p. Happy conscripts.

103 I.L.O. Emblem and Globe

104 Imperial Palace, Hue

1969. 50th Anniv of I.L.O.

S350	**103**	6 p. black, grey & green	25	10
S351		20 p. black, grey & red	65	25

1970. Reconstruction of Hue.

S352	**104**	1 p. blue and brown	6·50	6·50

105 Asian Golden Weaver and Baya Weaver

1970. Birds of Vietnam. Multicoloured.

S353	2 p. Type **105**	40	20
S354	6 p. Chestnut mannikin	75	40
S355	7 p. Great Indian hornbill	1·10	65
S356	30 p. Tree sparrow	5·00	1·60

106 Ruined House and Family

1970. Aid for Victims of Communist Tet Offensive. Multicoloured.

S357	10 p. Type **106**	40	20
S358	20 p. Refugee family, and First Aid	55	30

107 Man, Woman and Priest in Traditional Costume

1970. Vietnamese Traditional Costumes. Multicoloured.

S359	1 p. Type **107**	25	10
S360	2 p. Seated woman (horiz)	25	10
S361	3 p. Three women with carved lion (horiz)	35	20
S362	100 p. Man and woman (horiz)	3·00	1·75

108 Builders and Pagoda

1970. Reconstruction of Hue. Multicoloured.

S363	6 p. Type **108**	45	25
S364	20 p. Mixing cement	85	40

109 Ploughing Paddyfield

1970. "Land to the Tiller" Agrarian Reform Law.

S365	**109**	6 p. black, green & brn	45	25

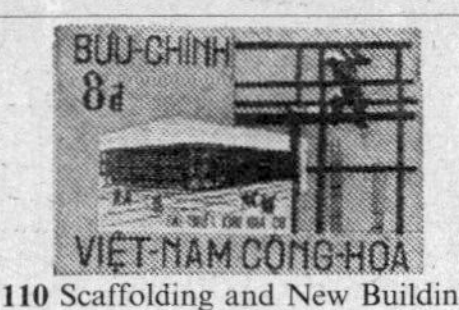

110 Scaffolding and New Building

1970. Reconstruction after Tet Offensive. Multicoloured.
S366 8 p. Type **110** 40 20
S367 16 p. Construction workers 55 25

111 A.P.Y. Symbol

1970. Asian Productivity Year.
S368 **111** 10 p. multicoloured 50 25

112 Nguyen Dinh Chieu and Poems **113** I.E.Y. Emblem

1970. Nguyen Dinh Chieu (poet) Commem.
S369 **112** 6 p. brown, red & violet 25 20
S370 10 p. brown, red & grn 50 25

1970. International Education Year.
S371 **113** 10 p. black, yell & brn 50 20

114 Senate House **115** Two Dancers

1970. 9th Council Meeting and 6th General Assembly of Asian Interparliamentary Union, Saigon. Multicoloured.
S372 6 p. Type **114** 25 20
S373 10 p. House of Representatives 50 20

1971. Vietnamese Traditional Dances.
S374 **115** 2 p. multicoloured 30 10
S375 – 6 p. brown, blue & grn 45 20
S376 – 7 p. red, blue & brown 65 25
S377 – 10 p. multicoloured 80 35
DESIGNS—HORIZ: 6 p. Drum dance; 7 p. Drum dancers in various positions. VERT: 10 p. Flower dance.

116 Paddyfield, Peasants and Agrarian Law

1971. 1st Anniv of "Land to the Tiller" Agrarian Reform Law. Multicoloured.
S378 2 p. Type **116** 30 20
S379 3 p. Tractor and Law 30 20
S380 16 p. Peasants ringing Law 45 25

117 Postal Courier **119** Hog-deer

118 Armed Forces on Map of Vietnam

1971. History of Vietnam Postal Service. Multicoloured.
S381 2 p. Type **117** 35 20
S382 6 p. Mounted courier with banner 75 30

1971. Armed Forces Day.
S383 **118** 3 p. multicoloured 35 25
S384 40 p. multicoloured 1·60 70

1971. Vietnamese Fauna. Multicoloured.
S385 9p. Type **119** 50 20
S386 30 p. Tiger 1·00 50

120 Rice Harvesters

1971. "The Rice Harvest".
S387 **120** 1 p. multicoloured 25 10
S388 – 30 p. lilac, black & red 75 25
S389 – 40 p. brown, yell & blue 1·00 45
DESIGNS: 30 p. Threshing and winnowing rice; 40 p. Harvesters in paddyfield.

121 New H.Q. Building

1971. New U.P.U. Headquarters Building, Berne.
S390 **121** 20 p. multicoloured 80 40

122 Ca Bong **123** "Local Delivery"

1971. Vietnam Fishes. Multicoloured.
S391 2 p. Type **122** 30 10
S392 10 p. Ca Nau (horiz) 95 20
S393 100 p. Ca Ong Tien (horiz) 6·75 2·75

1971. Development of Rural Post System. Multicoloured.
S394 5 p. Type **123** 30 15
S395 10 p. Symbolic crane 60 25
S396 20 p. Cycle postman delivering letter 70 25

124 Fishermen in Boat, and Modern Trawler

1972. Vietnamese Fishing Industry. Multicoloured.
S397 4 p. Type **124** 35 25
S398 7 p. Fishermen hauling net 35 25
S399 50 p. Trawl net 2·00 1·00

125 Emperor Quang Trung **126** Community Workers

1972. Emperor Quang Trung (victor of Dong Da) Commemoration.
S400 **125** 6 p. multicoloured 25 10
S401 20 p. multicoloured 65 30

1972. Community Development Projects.
S403 **126** 3 p. multicoloured 15 10
S404 8 p. multicoloured 25 10

127 Harvesting Rice

1972. Farmers' Day. Multicoloured.
S405 1 p. Type **127** 20 10
S406 10 p. Sowing rice 30 15

128 Boeing 727 over Dalat

1972. 20th Anniv of Viet-Nam Airlines. Mult.
S407 10 p. Type **128** 65 30
S408 10 p. Boeing 727 over Ha Tien 65 30
S409 10 p. Boeing 727 over Hue 65 30
S410 10 p. Boeing 727 over Saigon 65 30
S411 25 p. Type **128** 95 65
S412 25 p. As No. S408 95 65
S413 25 p. As No. S409 95 65
S414 25 p. As No. S410 95 65

129 Vietnamese Scholar **130** Sentry

1972. Vietnamese Scholars. Multicoloured.
S415 5 p. Type **129** 20 10
S416 20 p. Scholar with pupils 45 25
S417 50 p. Scholar with scroll 1·50 50

1972. Civilian Self-defence Force. Multicoloured.
S418 2 p. Type **130** 20 10
S419 6 p. Young volunteer and badge (horiz) 25 20
S420 20 p. Volunteers at rifle practice 50 35

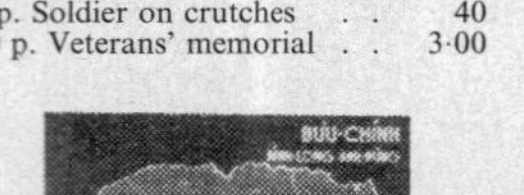

131 Hands supporting Savings Bank

1972. Treasury Bonds Savings Scheme.
S421 **131** 10 p. multicoloured 25 10
S422 25 p. multicoloured 50 20

132 Three Guards with Horse **133** Wounded Soldier

1972. Traditional Vietnamese Frontier Guards. Multicoloured.
S423 10 p. Type **132** 35 20
S424 30 p. Pikeman (vert) 65 35
S425 40 p. Guards on parade 95 50

1972. Vietnamese War Veterans. Multicoloured.
S426 9 p. Type **133** 15 10
S427 16 p. Soldier on crutches 40 20
S428 100 p. Veterans' memorial 3·00 1·10

134 Soldiers on Tank, and Memorial

1972. Victory at Binh Long. Mulicoloured.
S429 5 p. Type **134** 20 10
S430 10 p. Soldiers on map of An Loc (vert) 90 15

135 "Books for Everyone" **136** "200,000th Returnees"

1972. International Book Year. Multicoloured.
S431 2 p. Type **135** 15 10
S432 4 p. Book Year emblems encircling globe 20 10
S433 5 p. Emblem, books and globe 50 20

1973. 200,000th Returnees under "Open Arms" National Unity Campaign.
S434 **136** 10 p. multicoloured 50 25

137 Soldiers raising Flag **138** Satellite and Globe

1973. Victory at Quang Tri. Multicoloured.
S435 3 p. Type **137** 65 10
S436 10 p. Map and defenders 95 20

1973. World Meteorological Day.
S437 **138** 1 p. multicoloured 60 15

139 Programme Emblem and Farm-workers

1973. Five-Year Agricultural Development Programme. Multicoloured.
S438 2 p. Type **139** 1·50 15
S439 5 p. Ploughing in paddy-field 1·50 15

140 Emblem and H.Q. Paris

1973. 50th Anniv of International Criminal Police Organization (Interpol). Multicoloured.
S440 1 p. Type **140** 10 10
S441 2 p. "INTERPOL 1923 1973" 20 15
S442 25 p. Emblem and view of headquarters (different) 1·40 25

141 I.T.U. Emblem **142** Lamp in Hand

1973. World Telecommunications Day.
S443 **141** 1 p. multicoloured 15 15
S444 – 2 p. black and blue 35 15
S445 – 3 p. multicoloured 60 15
DESIGNS: 2 p. Globe; 3 p. I.T.U. emblem in frame.

1973. National Development.
S446 **142** 8 p. multicoloured 30 15
S447 – 10 p. blue, black & brn 45 15
S448 – 15 p. multicoloured 70 15
DESIGNS: 10 p. "Agriculture, Industry and Fisheries"; 15 p. Workers on power pylon.

143 Water Buffaloes

1973. "Year of the Buffalo". Multicoloured.
S449 5 p. Type **143** 50 15
S450 10 p. Water buffalo 75 20

144 Flame Emblem and "Races of the World"

1973. 25th Anniv of Declaration of Human Rights. Multicoloured.
S451 15 p. Type **144** 45 15
S452 100 p. Flame emblem and scales of justice (vert) 1·50 30

145 Emblem within "25"

1973. 25th Anniv of W.H.O.
S453 **145** 8 p. multicoloured 40 15
S454 – 15 p. blue, red & brown 60 15
DESIGN: 15 p. W.H.O. emblem and inscription.

146 Sampan crossing River

1974. Vietnamese Sampan Women. Multicoloured.
S455 5 p. Type **146** 60 25
S456 10 p. Sampan and passengers 95 25

147 Flags and Soldiers of Allies
148 Trung Sisters on Elephant

1974. Allies Day. Multicoloured.
S457 8 p. Type **147** 25 15
S458 15 p. Soldiers and flags . . . 60 15
S459 15 p. Allied Nations Monument 60 15
S460 60 p. Raising South Vietnamese flag, and map (vert) . . . 1·75 30

1974. Trung Sisters' Festival.
S461 **148** 8 p. green, yellow & blk . 30 25
S462 15 p. red, yellow & blk . 45 25
S463 80 p. blue, pink & blk . 95 40

149 Pres. Thieu holding Agrarian Reform Law

1974. Farmers' Day. Multicoloured.
S464 10 p. Type **149** 60 15
S465 20 p. Farm-workers (32 × 22 mm) 35 15
S466 70 p. Girl harvesting rice (22 × 32 mm) 60 35

150 King Hung Vuong

1974. King Hung Vuong (first Vietnamese monarch) Commemoration. Multicoloured.
S467 20 p. Type **150** 40 25
S468 100 p. Banner inscribed "Hung Vuong, National Founder" 1·50 60

151 National Library
152 Allied Nations Memorial, Saigon

1974. New National Library Building. Mult.
S469 10 p. Type **151** 35 20
S470 15 p. Library and Phoenix bas-relief 50 25

1974. Surch.
S470a **142** 10 p. on 8 p. mult . . .
S470b **145** 10 p. on 8 p. mult . . .
S470c **120** 25 p. on 1 p. mult . . .
S470d **140** 25 p. on 1 p. mult . . .
S470e **138** 25 p. on 1 p. mult . . .
S470f **141** 25 p. on 1 p. mult . . .
S470g – 25 p. on 7 p. red, blue and brown (No. S376) . .
S470h **147** 25 p. on 8 p. mult . . .
S470i – 25 p. on 16 p. mult (No. S427) . . . .
S470j – 25 p. on 16 p. mult (No. S380) . . . .

1974. International Aid Day. Multicoloured.
S471 10 p. Type **152** 35 10
S472 20 p. Flags on crane (horiz) . 75 15
S473 60 p. Crate on hoist . . . . 2·50 35

153 "Tourist Attractions"

1974. Tourism. Multicoloured.
S474 5 p. Type **153** 45 15
S475 10 p. Xom Bong Bridge Nhatrang 45 15
S476 15 p. Thien Mu Pagoda, Hue (vert) 80 15

154 "Rhynchostylis gigantea"

1974. Orchids. Multicoloured.
S477 10 p. Type **154** 20 15
S478 20 p. "Cypripedium callosum" (vert) 30 15
S479 200 p. "Dendrobium nobile" 3·25 1·00

155 "International Exchange of Mail"

1974. Centenary of U.P.U. Multicoloured.
S480 20 p. Type **155** 50 20
S481 30 p. "U.P.U. letter" and Hemispheres 90 20
S482 300 p. U.P.U. emblem and Vietnamese girl (vert) . . 3·00 1·25

156 Hien Lam Pavilion, Hue
157 Conference Emblem

1975. Historical Sites. Multicoloured.
S483 25 p. Type **156** 50 10
S484 30 p. Throne Room, Imperial Palace, Hue 60 20
S485 60 p. Tu Duc's Pavilion, Hue 1·10 25

1975. International Conference on Children and National Development, Saigon. Multicoloured.
S486 20 p. Type **157** 35 20
S487 70 p. Vietnamese family (32 × 22 mm) . . . . . . 1·25 25

158 Unicorn Dance

1975. Vietnamese New Year Festival. Mult.
S488 20 p. Type **158** 40 20
S489 30 p. Letting-off fire-crackers (vert) 55 30
S490 100 p. New Year greeting custom (vert) . . . . . . 1·25 60

159 Military Mandarin ("San Hau" play)

1975. "Hat Bo" Vietnamese Traditional Theatre. Multicoloured.
S491 25 p. Type **159** 50 20
S492 40 p. Two characters from "Tam Ha Nam Duong" (vert) 75 35
S493 100 p. Heroine, "Luu Kim Giai Gia Tho Chau" (vert) . . 2·50 1·10

160 Produce for Export and Map

1975. Farmers' Day. Multicoloured.
S494 10 p. Type **160** 25 15
S495 50 p. Ancient and modern irrigation 75 30

MILITARY FRANK STAMPS

MF **29** Soldier and Barracks

1961. No value indicated. Roul.
SMF115 MF **29** (–) yellow, brown, green & black . 5·00 5·00
SMF116 (–) yellow, brown and green . . . 6·00 6·00

POSTAGE DUE STAMPS

D **1** Dragon

1955.
SD 1 D **1** 2 p. yellow and mauve . 40 40
SD 2 3 p. turquoise & violet . 45 45
SD 3 5 p. yellow and violet . 75 60
SD 4 10 p. red and green . . 95 70
SD14 – 20 p. green and red . . 2·50 1·60
SD15 – 30 p. yellow and green . 3·75 2·50
SD16 – 50 p. yellow & brown . 8·00 5·75
SD17 – 100 p. yellow & violet . 12·50 10·00
The 20 p. to 100 p. are inscribed "BUU-CHINH" instead of "TIMBRE TAXE".

D **90** Butterfly
D **91** Butterflies

1968.
SD312 D **90** 50 c. multicoloured . 55 50
SD313 1 p. multicoloured . . 55 50
SD314 2 p. multicoloured . . 1·00 95
SD315 D **91** 3 p. multicoloured . . 1·40 1·25
SD316 5 p. multicoloured . . 2·50 2·40
SD317 10 p. multicoloured . . 4·00 3·50

1974. Surch.
SD470k D **91** 5 p. on 3 p. mult . . 5·00
SD470l D **90** 10 p. on 50 c. mult . 5·00
SD470m 40 p. on 1 p. mult . 5·00
SD470n 60 p. on 2 p. mult . 5·00

D. NATIONAL FRONT FOR THE LIBERATION OF SOUTH VIETNAM

The National Front for the Liberation of South Vietnam was formed by the Communists, known as the Vietcong, in December 1960. With the support of troops from North Vietnam the Vietcong gradually gained control of more and more territory within South Vietnam until the surrender of the last South Vietnamese Republican forces in May 1975 enabled them to take control of the entire country. The following stamps were used in those areas controlled by the National Liberation Front.

1963. 100 xu = 1 dong

The value of the N.L.F. dong fluctuated considerably and was not on parity with the North Vietnamese currency.

1 Vietcong Flag

1963. 3rd Anniv of National Liberation Front.
NLF1 **1** 20 x. multicoloured (English inscr) . . . . 3·25 2·75
NLF2 20 x. multicoloured (French inscr) . . . . 3·25 2·75
NLF3 20 x. multicoloured (Spanish inscr) . . . . 3·25 2·75

2 Attack on Village

1963. 3rd Anniv of Revolutionary Struggle in South Vietnam. Multicoloured.
NLF4 10 x. Type **2** . . . . 2·50 1·50
NLF5 10 x. Attack on U.S. helicopter . . . . 2·50 1·50

3 Demonstrators with Banner

1964. 4th Anniv of National Liberation Front.
NLF6 10 x. Type **3** . . . . 1·00 1·00
NLF7 20 x. multicoloured . . . . 1·40 1·40
NLF8 30 x. green and blue . . . 3·00 2·25
DESIGNS: 20 x. Harvesting rice; 30 x. Sinking of U.S.S. "Card" (destroyer).

4 Attack on Bien Hoa Airfield

1965. 5th Anniv of National Liberation Front.
NLF 9 **4** 10 x. multicoloured . . 75 75
NLF10 – 20 x. black, grey & red . 1·10 1·10
NLF11 – 40 x. multicoloured . . 5·25 5·25
DESIGNS: 20 x. Nguyen Van Troi facing firing squad; 40 x. Vietcong flags.

5 Vietcong Soldiers on U.S. Tanks
6 "Guerrilla"

1967. 7th Anniv of National Liberation Front. Multicoloured.
NLF12 20 x. Type **5** 70 60
NLF13 20 x. Vietcong guerrillas (horiz) 70 60
NLF14 30 x. Crowd with banners 1·50 1·50

1968. "The Struggle For Freedom". Paintings. Multicoloured.
NLF15 10 x. Type **6** 70 70
NLF16 20 x. "Jungle Patrol" (horiz) 90 90
NLF17 30 x. "Woman Soldier" . 1·50 1·50
NLF18 40 x. "Towards the Future" (horiz) . . . . 2·25 2·25

7 Casting Votes

1968. 8th Anniv of National Liberation Front. Multicoloured.
NLF19 20 x. Type **7** 35 35
NLF20 20 x. Bazooka crew and burning airplane . . . 35 35
NLF21 30 x. Vietcong flag and crowd (French inscr) . 70 70
NLF22 30 x. Vietcong flag and crowd (English inscr) 70 70

8 Lenin and Vietcong Flag

1970. Birth Centenary of Lenin.
NLF23 **8** 20 x. multicoloured . . 30 20
NLF24 30 x. multicoloured . . 35 30
NLF25 50 x. multicoloured . . 50 35
NLF26 2 d. multicoloured . . . 1·90 1·40

9 Ho Chi Minh watering Kainito Plant

10 Vietcong "Lightning Flash"

1970. 80th Birth Anniv of Ho Chi Minh.
NLF27 **9** 20 x. multicoloured . . 30 20
NLF28 30 x. multicoloured . . 35 30
NLF29 50 x. multicoloured . . 50 35
NLF30 2 d. multicoloured . . . 1·60 1·40

1970. 10th Anniv of National Liberation Front.
NLF31 **10** 20 x. multicoloured . . 30 20
NLF32 30 x. multicoloured . . 35 30
NLF33 50 x. multicoloured . . 55 50
NLF34 3 d. multicoloured . . 3·00 2·25

11 Home Guards defending Village

1971. 10th Anniv of People's Liberation Armed Forces. Multicoloured.
NLF35 20 x. Type **11** 65 65
NLF36 30 x. Surrender of U.S. tank 1·00 1·00
NLF37 50 x. Agricultural workers 1·40 1·40
NLF38 1 d. Vietcong ambush . . 2·25 2·25

12 Children in School

13 Harvesting Rice

14 Ho Chi Minh with Vietcong Soldiers

1971. 2nd Anniv of Provisional Government. Life in Liberated Areas. Multicoloured.
NLF39 20 x. Type **12** 20 20
NLF40 30 x. Women sewing Vietcong flag 35 35
NLF41 40 x. Fortifying village . . 1·10 1·10
NLF42 50 x. Medical clinic . . . 1·50 1·50
NLF43 1 d. Harvesting . . . . . 2·25 2·25

1974. 5th Anniv of Provisional Government. Multicoloured.
NLF44 10 d. Type **13** 20 20
NLF45 10 d. Demonstrators with banner 20 20
NLF46 10 d. Schoolchildren . . . 20 20
NLF47 10 d. Women home guards 20 20
NLF48 10 d. Vietcong conference delegate 20 20
NLF49 10 d. Soldiers and tanks . 20 20
NLF50 10 d. Type **14** 30 30
NLF51 20 d. Type **14** 80 80
For other values as Type **14**, see Nos. NLF57/60.

15 Ho Chi Minh watering Kainito Plant

1975. 85th Birth Anniv of Ho Chi Minh (1st issue).
NLF52 **15** 5 d. multicoloured . . 20 20
NLF53 10 d. multicoloured . 25 25
NLF54 30 d. mult (mauve frame) . . . . . . 1·50 1·50
NLF54a 30 d. mult (green frame) 1·50 1·50

1975. 15th Anniv of National Front for Liberation of South Vietnam. As T **14** but 35½ × 26 mm.
NLF55 **14** 15 d. black and green . 50 50
NLF56 30 d. black and red . 1·00 1·00
NLF57 60 d. black and blue . 1·50 1·50
NLF58 300 d. black & yellow . 4·50 4·50

1975. 85th Birth Anniv of Ho Chi Minh (2nd issue). As T **284** of North Vietnam, but inscr "MIEN NAM VIET NAM".
NLF59 30 d. multicoloured . . . 60 60
NLF60 60 d. multicoloured . . . 1·10 1·10

1976. Various stamps surch in South Vietnamese currency.
NLF61 – 10 p. on 1 d. multicoloured (NLF38)
NLF62 – 20 p. on 6 x. yellow and red (NLF75) . . . .
NLF63 – 20 p. on 20 x. multicoloured (NLF27)
NLF64 – 20 p. on 40 x. multicoloured (NLF11)
NLF65 **9** 20 p. on 2 d. multicoloured (NLF30)
NLF66 **15** 20 p. on 5 d. multicoloured (NLF52)
NLF67 **14** 20 p. on 10 d. multicoloured (NLF50)
NLF68 **15** 20 p. on 10 d. multicoloured (NLF53)
NLF69 20 p. on 30 d. multicoloured (NLF54)
NLF70 20 p. on 30 d. mult (NLF54a) . . . . .

17 "Cocos nucifera"

1976. Fruits. Multicoloured.
NLF71 20 d. Type **17** 80 80
NLF72 30 d. "Garcinia mangostana" . . . . 1·25 1·25
NLF73 60 d. "Nargifera indica" . 2·50 2·50

1976. First Elections to Unified National Assembly. As Nos. N858/60 of North Vietnam, but inscr "MIEN NAM VIET NAM".
NLF74 6 x. red and blue (as N858) 20 20
NLF75 6 x. yellow and red (as N859) 20 20
NLF76 12 x. red and green (as N860) 50 50

18 Flag of Provisional Revolutionary Government

1976. 1st Anniv of Liberation of South Vietnam.
NLF77 **18** 30 d. multicoloured . 60 50

1976. 1st Session of Unified National Assembly. As Nos. N861/2 of North Vietnam, but inscr "MIEN NAM VIET NAM".
NLF78 6 x. brown, red & yellow 20 20
NLF79 12 x. turquoise, red & yell 40 40

The unified National Assembly proclaimed the reunification of Vietnam on 2 July 1976 and the united country was then known as the Socialist Republic of Vietnam.

E. NORTH VIETNAM

(Vietnam Democratic Republic)

Issues before April 1954 were made in Tongking and Central Annam, in areas under Viet Minh control. From 21 July 1954 French troops withdrew from north of the 17th Parallel and the Ho Chi Minh Government assumed complete control.

1946. 100 cents = 1 dong
1959. 100 xu = 1 dong

GUM. All stamps were issued without gum unless otherwise stated.

I. TONGKING

1946. No. 190 of Indo-China optd **V VIET-NAM N DAN-CHU CONG-HOA BUU CHINH**.
N1 25 c. blue . . . . 60·00 60·00

2 Ho Chi Minh

3 Ho Chi Minh and Vietnam Map

1948.
N2a **2** 2 d. brown . . . . 10·00
N3a 5 d. red . . . . 10·00

1951. Imperf or perf.
N4 **3** 100 d. green . . . . 3·00 3·00
N5 100 d. brown . . . . 3·00 3·00
N6 200 d. red . . . . 3·00 3·00

5 Blacksmith

7 Malenkov, Ho Chi Minh, Mao Tse-tung and Flags

1953. Production Campaign.
N11 **5** 100 d. violet . . . . 4·25 1·25
N12 500 d. brown . . . . 8·00 3·75

1954. Friendship Month.
N13 **7** 100 d. red . . . . 18·00 18·00

II. CENTRAL ANNAM

NA 1 Ho Chi Minh

1950. Figures in white. Imperf.
NA1 NA **1** 1 d. violet . . . . . .
NA2 1 d. green . . . . . .
NA3 5 d. green . . . . . .
NA4 15 d. brown . . . . . .

1952. Nos. NA3 and NA1 surch in figures. Imperf.
NA5 NA **1** 30 d. on 5 d. green . . £200 £170
NA6 60 d. on 1 d. violet . . £250 £225

1952. Figures of values coloured. Imperf.
NA7 NA **1** 300 d. blue £325 £325
NA8 500 d. red £700 £700

III. GENERAL ISSUES

8 Malenkov, Ho Chi Minh & Mao Tse-tung

1954.
N14 **8** 50 d. brown and red . . . . 18·00 18·00
N15 100 d. red and yellow . . . 20·00 20·00

9 Battlefield

1954. Dien Bien Phu Victory. Imperf or perf.
N16a **9** 10 d. bistre and red . . . . 10·00 2·50
N17a 50 d. ochre and red . . . . 10·00 2·75
N18d 150 d. blue and brown . . 10·00 4·50
See also No. NO24.

1954. (a) Handstamped thus: **10 dNH**.
N19 **3** 10 d. on 100 d. green . . . 5·00 5·00
N20 10 d. on 100 d. brown . . . 7·00 7·00
N21 20 d. on 200 d. red . . . . 5·00 5·00

(b) Handstamped thus: **10 d.**
N22 **3** 10 d. on 100 d. green . . . 6·00 6·00
N25 10 d. on 100 d. brown . . . 10·00 10·00
N28 20 d. on 200 d. red . . . . 10·00 10·00
See also Nos. N46/9.

12 Lake of the Returned Sword; Hanoi

1954. Proclamation of Hanoi as Capital.
N30 **12** 10 d. blue . . . . 3·75 3·75
N31 50 d. green . . . . 3·75 3·75
N32 150 d. red . . . . 7·50 7·50

13 Distribution of Title Deeds

1955. Land Reform.
N33 **13** 5 d. green . . . . 6·00 6·00
N34 10 d. grey . . . . 6·00 6·00
N35 20 d. orange . . . . . . 7·50 7·50
N36 50 d. mauve . . . . . . 18·00 18·00
N37 100 d. brown . . . . . . 28·00 28·00

14 Crowd welcoming Steam Train

1956. Hanoi-China Railway Re-opening.
N38 **14** 100 d. blue . . . . 18·00 18·00
N39 200 d. turquoise . . . . . 18·00 18·00
N40 300 d. violet . . . . . . 32·00 32·00
N41 500 d. brown . . . . . . 40·00 40·00

15 Parade, Ba Dinh Square, Hanoi

1956. Return of Govt to Hanoi.
N42 **15** 1000 d. violet . . . . . . 50·00 38·00
N43 1500 d. blue . . . . . . 75·00 55·00
N44 2000 d. turquoise . . . . 75·00 55·00
N45 3000 d. turquoise . . . . 85·00 80·00

1956. Surch thus: **10 d** in frame.
N46 **3** 10 d. on 100 d. green . . . 14·00 14·00
N48 10 d. on 100 d. brown . . 16·00 16·00
N49 20 d. on 200 d. red . . . . 12·00 12·00

17 Tran Dang Ninh

1956. 1st Death Anniv of Tran Dang Ninh (patriot).
N50 **17** 5 d. green . . . . 4·00 1·75
N51 10 d. red . . . . 4·00 1·75
N52 20 d. brown . . . . 5·00 2·40
N53 100 d. blue . . . . 5·50 3·00

18 Mac Thi Buoi

1956. 5th Death Anniv of Mac Thi Buoi (guerilla heroine).
N54 **18** 1000 d. red . . . . 12·00 8·00
N55 2000 d. brown . . . . . . 19·00 9·25
N56 4000 d. green . . . . . . 30·00 23·00
N57 5000 d. blue . . . . . . 50·00 28·00

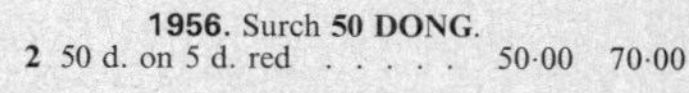

19 Bai Thuong Dam

1956. Reconstruction of Bai Thuong Dam.
N58 **19** 100 d. violet and brown . 6·75 6·00
N59 200 d. red and black . . 10·00 6·00
N60a 300 d. red and lake . . . 13·50 11·50

1956. Surch **50 DONG**.
N61 **2** 50 d. on 5 d. red . . . . . 50·00 70·00

21 Cotton Mill

1957. 1st Anniv of Opening of Nam Dinh Mill.
N62 **21** 100 d. brown and red . . 5·00 5·00
N63 200 d. grey and blue . . . 5·75 5·75
N64 300 d. lt green & green . . 7·50 7·50

22 Pres. Ho Chi Minh 23 Arms of Republic

1957. President's 67th Birthday.
N65 **22** 20 d. green . . . . 2·50 1·75
N66 60 d. bistre . . . . 2·50 1·75
N67 100 d. blue . . . . 3·00 2·75
N68 300 d. brown . . . . 5·00 4·00

1957. 12th Anniv of Democratic Republic.
N69 **23** 20 d. green . . . . 2·75 2·25
N70 100 d. red . . . . 5·75 3·75

24 Congress Emblem

1957. 4th World T.U. Congress, Leipzig.
N71 **24** 300 d. purple . . . . . . 7·50 5·00
See also Nos. NO69/72.

25 Presidents Voroshilov and Ho Chi Minh

1957. 40th Anniv of Russian Revolution.
N72 **25** 100 d. red . . . . 6·25 5·00
N73 500 d. brown . . . . 8·25 5·50
N74 1000 d. orange . . . . . 17·00 16·00

26 Open-air Class 27 Girl Gymnast

1958. Education Campaign.
N75 **26** 50 d. blue . . . . 4·75 3·75
N76 150 d. red . . . . 7·00 5·50
N77 1000 d. brown . . . . . . 16·00 9·00

1958. Physical Education.
N78 **27** 150 d. brown and blue . . 11·00 9·00
N79 500 d. brown and rose . . 18·00 14·00

28 29 Congress Emblem

1958. Labour Day.
N80 **28** 50 d. yellow and red . . . 3·25 2·10
N81 150 d. red and yellow . . 5·00 3·75

1958. 4th International Congress of Democratic Women, Vienna.
N82 **29** 150 d. blue . . . . 7·00 5·75

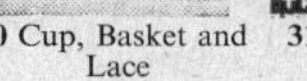

30 Cup, Basket and Lace 31 Hanoi–Saigon Railway Reconstruction

1958. Arts and Crafts Fair, Hanoi.
N83 **30** 150 d. sepia and turq . . . 2·75 1·60
N84 2000 d. black and lilac . . 9·00 5·25

1958. Re-unification of Vietnam Propaganda.
N85 **31** 50 d. blue . . . . 1·40 85
N86 150 d. brown . . . . 1·60 1·50

32 Revolution in Hanoi

1958. 13th Anniv of Vietnamese Revolution.
N87 **32** 150 d. red . . . . 1·90 1·10
N88 500 d. blue . . . . 3·75 1·90

33 Woman Potter

1958. Handicrafts Exhibition.
N89 **33** 150 d. lake and red . . . 1·90 1·60
N90 1000 d. brown & ochre . . 9·00 3·50

34 Vo Thi Sau and Crowd 35 Tran Hung Dao

1958. 13th Anniv of South Vietnam Resistance Movement.
N91 **34** 50 d. green and buff . . . 2·75 1·40
N92 150 d. red and orange . . 5·50 1·60

1958. 658th Death Anniv of Tran Hung Dao.
N93 **35** 150 d. grey and blue . . 1·75 80

36 Hanoi Factories 37 Harvesting Rice

1958. Hanoi Mechanical Engineering Plant.
N94 **36** 150 d. sepia . . . . . . 2·25 95

1958. Mutual Aid Teams.
N95 **37** 150 d. lake . . . . 5·25 1·60
N96 500 d. brown . . . . . . 6·50 3·25

38 Temple of Jade, Hanoi 39 Furniture-makers

1958.
N 97 **38** 150 d. green . . . . . . 3·75 1·75
N 98 – 150 d. blue . . . . . . 2·25 55
N 99 – 350 d. brown . . . . . 3·75 95
N100 **38** 2000 d. green . . . . . 32·00 9·00
DESIGNS—HORIZ: 150 d. blue, 350 d. Bay of Halong.

1958. Furniture Co-operatives.
N101 **39** 150 d. blue . . . . . . 2·25 60

40 Cam Pha Coal Mines 41 The Trung Sisters

1959.
N102 **40** 150 d. blue . . . . . . 2·00 80

1959. Trung Sisters Commemoration.
N103 **41** 5 x. red and yellow . . . 1·10 50
N104 8 x. deep brown and brown 1·75 65

42 Mother and Child

1959. 10th Anniv of World Peace Movement.
N105 **42** 12 x. violet . . . . 1·10 55

43 Xuan Quan Dam

1959. Bac Hung Hai Irrigation Project.
N106 **43** 6 x. yellow, green & vio . 3·25 80
N107 12 x. ochre, blue & grey . 6·25 1·10

44 Victims in Phu Loi Concentration Camp 45 Radio Mast

1959. The Phu Loi Massacre on 1 December 1958.
N108 **44** 12 x. salmon, olive & blk 1·90 45
N109 20 x. ochre, grey & black 4·00 90

1959. Me Tri Radio Station.
N110 **45** 3 x. green and orange . . 1·40 35
N111 12 x. sepia and blue . . . 2·25 55

46 Hien Luong Railway Bridge

1959. Vietnam Day.
N112 **46** 12 x. red and black . . . 1·40 65

47 Rifle-shooting

1959. Sports.
N113 **47** 1 x. deep blue and blue . 1·60 55
N114 – 6 x. olive and red . . . 2·25 90
N115 – 12 x. red and rose . . . 3·25 1·40
DESIGNS: 6 x. Swimming; 12 x. Wrestling.

48 Balloons 49 Coconuts

1959. 10th Anniv of Chinese People's Republic.
N116 **48** 12 x. red, yellow & grn . 95 45

1959. Fruits. Multicoloured.
N117 3 x. Type **49** . . . . 1·10 45
N118 12 x. Bananas . . . . . . 2·10 85
N119 30 x. Pineapple . . . . . . 6·00 1·90

50 Convair CV 340

1959. Air.
N120 **50** 20 x. black and blue . . . 10·00 6·25

51 Soldiers 52 Sailing Ship

1959. 15th Anniv of N. Vietnam People's Army.
N121 **51** 12 x. yellow, brown & bl 1·50 75

1959. 30th Anniv of N. Vietnam Workers' Party.
N122 **52** 2 x. multicoloured . . . 1·10 65
N123 12 x. multicoloured . . . 2·25 1·25

53 Girl in "E-De" Costume 54 Women of Vietnam

1960. National Costumes.
N124 **53** 2 x. red, blue & purple . 80 35
N125 – 10 x. blue, orange & grn 1·25 45
N126 – 12 x. blue and brown . . 1·90 70
N127 – 12 x. blue and buff . . 1·90 70
COSTUMES: No. N125, "Meo"; N126, "Thai"; N127, "Tay".

1960. National Census.
N128 **54** 1 x. green 40 20
N129 – 12 x. brown and red . . 55 25
DESIGN: 12 x. Workers and factories.

55 Emblem and Women 56 Hung Vuong Temple

1960. 50th Anniv of International Women's Day.
N130 **55** 12 x. multicoloured . . . 75 35

1960. Hung Vuong Anniversary Day.
N131 **56** 12 x. green and buff . . 6·50 3·75
N132 4 d. brown and blue . . 65·00 28·00

57 Lenin 58 Ballot Box

1960. 90th Birth Anniv of Lenin.
N133 **57** 5 x. red and blue 55 30
N134 12 x. blue and buff . . . 80 50

1960. 2nd Election of Parliamentary Deputies.
N135 **58** 12 x. multicoloured . . . 65 35

59 Red Cross Nurse 60 Pres. Ho Chi Minh

1960. International Red Cross Commem.
N136 **59** 8 x. blue, red and bistre . 65 35
N137 12 x. green, red & grey . 1·00 50

1960. President Ho Chi Minh's 70th Birthday.
N138 **60** 4 x. lilac and green . . . 45 30
N139 12 x. purple and rose . . 85 40
N140 – 12 x. multicoloured . . . 85 40
DESIGN—24½ × 39 mm: No. N140, Ho Chi Minh and children.

61 "New Constitution"

1960. Opening of 2nd National Assembly.
N141 **61** 12 x. sepia and ochre . . 1·50 75

62 Pres. Ho Chi Minh at Microphone

1960. 15th Anniv of Vietnam Democratic Republic.
N142 **62** 4 x. multicoloured . . . 2·50 1·00
N143 12 x. multicoloured . . . 3·75 1·10
N144 – 12 x. deep blue & blue . 3·75 1·10
N145 – 12 x. green and yellow . 3·75 1·10
N146 – 12 x. blue and brown . . 3·75 1·10
DESIGNS: No. N144, Ploughing; N145, Electricity Works, Vietri; N146, Classroom.

63 Workers and Flags

1960. 3rd Vietnam Workers' Party Congress.
N147 **63** 1 x. multicoloured . . . 1·75 70
N148 12 x. multicoloured . . . 2·25 90

64 Handclasp of Three Races

1960. 15th Anniv of W.F.T.U.
N149 **64** 12 x. black and red . . . 5·75 4·00

65 Dragon

1960. 950th Anniv of Hanoi.
N150 **65** 8 x. yellow, brn & turq . 1·75 95
N151 12 x. yellow, brown & bl . 3·75 1·40

66 Exhibition Entrance

1960. "Fifteen Years of Republic" Exhibition.
N152 **66** 2 x. grey and red . . . 90 60
N153 12 x. green and red . . 1·75 85

67 Badge, Dove and Flag

1960. 15th Anniv of World Federation of Democratic Youth.
N154 **67** 12 x. multicoloured . . . 2·50 1·50

68 Emblem of Vietnamese Trade Unions
69 Woman, Globe and Dove

1961. 2nd National Congress of Trade Unions.
N155 **68** 12 x. red, blue & yellow 1·75 70

1961. 3rd National Congress of Women.
N156 **69** 6 x. green and blue . . . 2·40 50
N157 12 x. green & salmon . . 2·40 75

IMPERF STAMPS. Many issues from here onwards also exist imperf.

70 Sambar
71 Ly Tu Trong (revolutionary)

1961. Vietnamese Fauna.
N158 **70** 12 x. buff, black & olive 3·00 1·25
N159 – 20 x. multicoloured . . 4·25 2·50
N160 – 50 x. grey, black & grn 7·50 3·75
N161 – 1 d. black, grey & green 10·00 5·00
DESIGNS: 20 x. Sun bear; 50 x. Indian elephant; 1 d. Crested gibbon.

1961. 3rd Congress of Vietnam Labour Youth Union.
N162 **71** 2 x. olive and blue . . . 90 45
N163 12 x. olive and salmon . . 2·10 1·00

72 Bugler and Drummer
73 Disabled Soldier learning to use Crutches

1961. 20th Anniv of Vietnam Youth Pioneers.
N164 **72** 1 x. multicoloured . . . 1·50 75
N165 12 x. multicoloured . . . 2·75 1·40

1961. 101st Anniv of Proposal for Int Red Cross.
N166 **73** 6 x. multicoloured . . . 1·90 75
N167 12 x. multicoloured . . 3·50 1·40

74 Nurse weighing Baby

1961. International Children's Day.
N168 **74** 4 x. green, black & red . 1·25 65
N169 12 x. yellow, blk & red . 2·75 1·40

75 Major Yuri Gagarin

1961. World's First Manned Space Flight.
N170 **75** 6 x. red and violet . . . 12·50 5·00
N171 12 x. red and green . . . 12·50 5·00

76

77 Women

1961. Vietnam Reunification Campaign.
N172 **76** 12 x. multicoloured . . . 50 50
N173 2 d. multicoloured . . . . 8·50 4·00

1961. Tripling of Hanoi, Hue and Saigon.
N174 **77** 12 x. multicoloured . . . 2·50 1·60
N175 3 d. brown, myrtle and green . . . . 20·00 11·00

78 Mother and Child
79 Prospecting Team

1961. National Savings Campaign.
N176 **78** 3 x. multicoloured 85 40
N177 12 x. multicoloured . . . 1·50 85

1961. Geological Research.
N178 **79** 2 x. green, blue & purple . 1·50 40
N179 12 x. brown, blk & turq . 3·00 85

80 Thien Mu Tower, Hue
81 Workers and Rocket

1961. Ancient Towers.
N180 **80** 6 x. brown and chestnut . 75 40
N181 – 10 x. olive and buff . . . 1·50 55
N182 – 12 x. olive and green . . 2·10 65
N183 – 12 x. brown and blue . . 2·10 65
TOWERS: No. N181, Pen Brush, Bac Ninh; N182, Binh Son, Vinh Phuc; N183, Cham, Phan Rang.

1961. 22nd Communist Party Congress, Moscow.
N184 **81** 12 x. red and black . . . 2·00 1·25

82 Major Titov and Rocket

1961. 2nd Manned Space Flight.
N185 **82** 6 x. multicoloured . . . . 2·00 90
N186 12 x. multicoloured . . . 3·50 1·75

83 Freighter at Haiphong

1961. Haiphong Port Commemoration.
N187 **83** 5 x. grey, grn & myrtle . 1·25 60
N188 12 x. brown, light brown and sepia . . . . 3·00 1·25

84 Cymbalist
85 Congress Emblem

1961. 3rd Writers and Artists Congress. Mult.
N189 12 x. Type **84** . . . . 1·25 60
N190 12 x. Flautist . . . . 1·25 90
N191 30 x. Fan dancer . . . . . . 3·50 1·25
N192 50 x. Guitarist . . . . 5·00 2·40

1961. 5th W.F.T.U. Congress, Moscow.
N193 **85** 12 x. mauve and drab . . 60 40

86 Resistance Fighters
87 "Pigs"

1961. 15th Anniv of National Resistance.
N194 **86** 4 x. multicoloured . . . 35 20
N195 12 x. multicoloured . . . 65 35

1962. New Year.
N196 **87** 6 x. multicoloured . . . 1·00 50
N197 – 12 x. multicoloured . . . 2·00 1·00
DESIGN: 12 x. "Poultry".

88 Watering Tree
89 Tea Plant

1962. Tree-planting Festival.
N198 **88** 12 x. multicoloured . . . 1·60 85
N199 40 x. multicoloured . . . 2·50 1·50

1962. Multicoloured.
N200 2 x. Type **89** 75 40
N201 6 x. Aniseed 75 40
N202 12 x. Coffee . . . . 2·75 1·10
N203 12 x. Castor-oil . . . . . . 2·75 1·10
N204 30 x. Lacquer-tree . . . . . 5·75 2·50

90 Gong Dance
91 Hibiscus

1962. Folk-dancing. Multicoloured.
N205 12 x. Type **90** . . . . . . 2·00 60
N206 12 x. Bamboo dance . . . . 2·00 60
N207 30 x. Hat dance . . . . . . 5·00 60
N208 50 x. Parasol dance . . . . 10·00 2·00

1962. Flowers. Multicoloured.
N209 12 x. Type **91** . . . . . . 2·00 75
N210 12 x. Frangipani . . . . . 2·00 75
N211 20 x. Chrysanthemum . . . 3·75 2·10
N212 30 x. Lotus . . . . 6·00 2·75
N213 50 x. Ipomoea . . . . 9·00 3·50

92 Kim Lien Flats, Hanoi
93 Workers and Rose

1962. 1st Five-Year Plan (1st issue).
N214 **92** 1 x. blue, black & grey . 40 20
N215 – 3 x. multicoloured . . . 70 30
N216 – 8 x. violet, blk & stone . 1·25 50
DESIGNS: 3 x. State agricultural farm; 8 x. Institute of Hydraulic and Electro-Dynamic Studies.
See also Nos. N245/8, N251/2, N270/1 and N294/6.

1962. 3rd National "Heroes of Labour" Congress.
N217 **93** 12 x. orange, olive & red 1·75 40

94 Dai Lai Lake

1962.
N218 **94** 12 x. turq and brown . . 2·25 85

95 "Plough of Perfection"

1962.
N219 95 6 x. black & turquoise . . 1·10 40

96 Titov greeting Children

1962. Visit of Major Titov.
N220 96 12 x. sepia and blue . . . 85 50
N221 – 20 x. sepia and salmon . 1·75 55
N222 – 30 x. sepia and green . . 3·25 1·10
DESIGNS: 20 x. Pres. Ho Chi Minh pinning medal on Titov; 30 x. Titov in space-suit.

97 Mosquito and Red Cross

1962. Malaria Eradication.
N223 97 8 x. red, black & blue . . 1·25 55
N224 12 x. red, black & violet . 1·50 80
N225 20 x. red, black & purple 2·75 1·10

98 Factory and Soldiers 99 Ban Gioc Falls

1962. 8th Anniv of Geneva Vietnamese Agreements.
N226 98 12 x. multicoloured . . . 70 35

1962. Vietnamese Scenery.
N227 – 12 x. purple and blue . 1·10 35
N228 99 12 x. sepia & turquoise . 1·10 35
DESIGN—HORIZ: ($32\frac{1}{2}\times23$ mm): No. N227, Ba Be Lake.

99a Weightlifting

1962. Int Military Sports Festival of Socialist States, Prague.
N228a 99a 12 x. multicoloured . . 60·00 95·00

100 Quang Trung 101 Groundnuts

1962. National Heroes.
N229 100 3 x. yellow, brn & grey . 60 25
N230 – 3 x. orange, blk & ochre 50 25
N231 100 12 x. yellow, grn & grey 85 35
N232 – 12 x. orge, blk & grey 85 35
PORTRAIT: Nos. N230, N232, Nguyen Trai.

1962. Multicoloured.
N233 1 x. Type **101** 40 25
N234 4 x. Haricot beans 70 30
N235 6 x. Sweet potatoes . . . 90 35
N236 12 x. Maize . . . . 2·25 80
N237 30 x. Manioc . . . . 5·00 2·00

102 Girl feeding Poultry

1962. Farm Stock-breeding.
N238 102 2 x. red, grey & blue . 60 30
N239 – 12 x. ochre, turquoise and blue . . . . 1·75 40
N240 – 12 x. brown, green and deep green . . . . . 1·75 40
N241 – 12 x. buff, mauve and sepia 1·75 40
DESIGNS: No. N239, Woman tending pigs; N240, Herdgirl with oxen; N241, Boy feeding buffalo.

103 Popovich in "Vostok 4"

1962. First "Team" Manned Space Flights.
N242 103 12 x. multicoloured . . . 1·00 60
N243 – 20 x. ochre, blue & blk 1·75 60
N244 – 30 x. red, blue & black 2·75 1·25
DESIGNS—HORIZ: 20 x. Nikolaev in "Vostok 3". VERT: 30 x. "Vostoks 3 and 4".

104 Teacher and Students

1962. 1st Five-Year Plan (2nd issue). Higher Education and Land Cultivation.
N245 104 12 x. black & yellow . 1·00 35
N246 – 12 x. black, brn & buff 2·10 90
DESIGN: No. N246, Tree felling.

105 Guerrilla Fighter 106 Hoang Hoa Tham

1963. 1st Five-Year Plan (3rd issue). National Defence.
N247 105 5 x. green and grey . . 75 25
N248 12 x. brown and buff . 1·10 40

1963. 50th Death Anniv of Hoang Hoa Tham (freedom fghter).
N249 106 6 x. myrtle and blue . . 60 40
N250 12 x. black and brown . 85 50

107 Workers in Field 108 Karl Marx

1963. 1st Five-Year Plan (4th issue). Agricultural and Chemical Manufacture.
N251 107 12 x. multicoloured . . 1·00 60
N252 – 12 x. red, mauve and black 75 40
DESIGN: No. N252, Lam Thao Fertiliser Factory.

1963. 80th Death Anniv of Karl Marx.
N253 108 3 x. black and green . . 50 30
N254 12 x. black and drab on pink 75 35

109 Castro and Vietnamese Soldiers 111 Nurse tending Child

110 Doves and Labour Emblem

1963. Vietnamese–Cuban Friendship.
N255 109 12 x. multicoloured . . . 75 45

1963. Labour Day.
N256 110 12 x. orange, blk & bl . 75 40

1963. Red Cross Centenary.
N257 111 12 x. red, black & blue . 1·25 55
N258 – 12 x. red, grey & turq . 1·25 55
N259 – 20 x. red, grey and yellow 2·10 75
DESIGNS: No. N258, Child and syringe inscr "BCG". 25×42 mm: 20 x. Centenary emblem.

112 "Mars 1" Interplanetary Station

1963. Launching of Soviet Rocket "Mars 1". Multicoloured.
N260 6 x. Type **112** 60 35
N261 12 x. Type **112** 80 45
N262 12 x. "Mars 1" in space (vert) 80 45
N263 20 x. "Mars 1" in space (vert) 2·00 80

113 Carp

1963. Fishing Industry. Multicoloured.
N264 12 x. Type **113** . . . . 4·50 1·60
N265 12 x. Fishes and trawler . . 4·50 1·60

114 Pres. Ho Chi Minh embracing Prof. Nguyen Van Hien of South Vietnam

1963. Campaign for Reunification of Vietnam.
N266 114 12 x. black, blue & turq 70 35

115 Globe and "Vostoks 3 and 4"

1963. 1st Anniv of "Team" Manned Space Flights.
N267 115 12 x. black, brn & yell . 70 35
N268 – 20 x. black, blue & grn . 1·00 60
N269 – 30 x. black, violet & bl . 1·75 95
DESIGNS: 20 x. Nikolaev and "eagle" motif; 30 x. Popovich and "phoenix" motif.

116 Viet Tri Insecticide Factory

1963. 1st Five-Year Plan (5th issue).
N270 116 3 x. buff, brown & blue . 30 25
N271 – 12 x. pink, brown and bistre 65 40
DESIGN: 12 x. Viet Tri chemical factory.

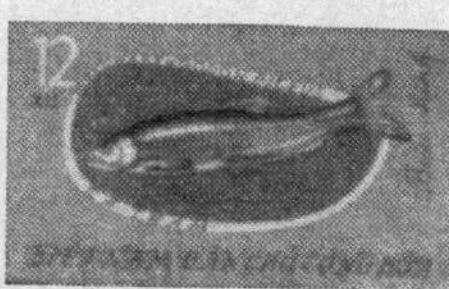

117 Black Amur

1963. Freshwater Fish Culture. Multicoloured.
N272 12 x. Type **117** . . . . . . 1·25 60
N273 12 x. Carp . . . . 1·25 60
N274 12 x. Silver carp . . . . . 1·25 60
N275 20 x. Snakehead . . . . . 3·00 1·25
N276 30 x. Mozambique mouth-breeder . . . . 4·50 2·75

118 Chinese Francolin 119 Broken Chain and Map

1963. Birds. Multicoloured.
N277 12 x. Type **118** . . . . . . 2·25 1·00
N278 12 x. Chinese jungle mynah 2·25 1·00
N279 12 x. White-breasted kingfisher 2·25 1·00
N280 20 x. Siamese fireback pheasant (horiz) . . . . . 5·50 2·10
N281 30 x. Eastern reef heron . . 9·00 3·25
N282 40 x. Slaty-headed parakeet 12·00 5·00

1963. W.F.T.U. Assembly, Hanoi.
N283 119 12 x. multicoloured . . 50 40

120 Football 121 "Rauwolfia verticillata"

1963. "GANEFO" Athletic Games, Jakarta.
N284 120 12 x. black, grey & ochre 80 35
N285 – 12 x. black, grey & orge 80 35
N286 – 12 x. black, grey & blue 80 35
N287 – 30 x. black, grey & mag 1·60 75
DESIGNS—VERT: No. N285, Volleyball. HORIZ: No. N286, Swimming; N287, High-jumping.

1963. Medicinal Plants. Multicoloured.
N288 6 x. Type **121** 80 35
N289 12 x. "Chenopodium ambrosioides" 95 35
N290 12 x. "Sophora japonica" . 95 65
N291 12 x. "Fibraurea tinctoria" . 95 65
N292 20 x. "Momordica cochinchinensis" . . . . 4·50 1·10

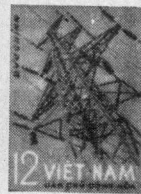

122 "Solidarity" 123 Pylon

1963. 3rd Anniv of South Vietnam National Liberation Front.
N293 122 12 x. blk, brn & ochre . 55 35

1964. 1st Five-Year Plan (6th issue).
N294 – 6 x. black, red & pur . 50 30
N295 – 12 x. multicoloured . . 1·60 50
N296 123 12 x. black, grey & orge . 1·60 50
DESIGNS—HORIZ: ($40\times22\frac{1}{2}$ mm): 6 x. Tapping cast-iron; No. N295, Thai Ngyuen Iron and Steel Works.

124 Sun, Globe and Dragon

1964. International Quiet Sun Years.
N297 124 12 x. orange, blk & grn 40 25
N298 50 x. drab, black & pur 1·50 85

125 Twin Space Flights

1964. Space Flights of Bykovsky and Tereshkova. Multicoloured.

N299 12 x. Type **125** . . . . . . 1·25 35
N300 12 x. Bykovsky and "Vostok 5" . . . . 1·25 35
N301 30 x. Tereshkova and "Vostok 6" . . . . 3·00 1·10

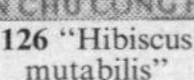

126 "Hibiscus mutabilis"   127 Rural Costume

1964. Flowers. Multicoloured.

N302 12 x. Type **126** . . . . . . 1·50 40
N303 12 x. "Persica vulgaris" . . 1·50 40
N304 12 x. "Saraca dives" . . . 1·50 40
N305 12 x. "Passiflora hispida" . . 1·50 40
N306 20 x. "Michelia champaca" . 3·75 1·25
N307 30 x. "Camellia amplexicaulis" 5·50 1·75

1964. National Costumes. Multicoloured.

N308 6 x. Type **127** 50 25
N309 12 x. "Ceremonial" . . . . 1·00 35
N310 12 x. "Everyday" . . . . . 1·00 35

128 Artillery

1964. 10th Anniv of Battle of Dien Bien Phu.

N311 **128** 3 x. black and red . . . 40 25
N312 – 6 x. black and blue . . 50 35
N313 – 12 x. black and yellow . 95 40
N314 – 12 x. black and purple . 95 40

DESIGNS: 6 x. Machine-gun post; No. N313, Bomb-disposal; N314, Dien Bien Phu and tractor.

129 Ham Rong Railway Bridge

1964. Inaug of Reconstructed Ham Rong Bridge.

N315 **129** 12 x. multicoloured . . 1·25 50

130 Spotted Deer   131 Women Fighters, Map, Industrial Scene and Watch-towers

1964. Wild Animals. Multicoloured.

N316 12 x. Type **130** . . . . . . 1·90 60
N317 12 x. Malayan tapir (horiz) . 1·90 60
N318 12 x. Tiger . . . . 1·90 60
N319 20 x. Water buffalo (horiz) . 3·75 1·25
N320 30 x. Sumatran rhinoceros (horiz) . . . . 4·25 1·90
N321 40 x. Banteng (horiz) . . . 5·00 2·50

1964. 10th Anniv of Geneva Agreements on Vietnam.

N322 **131** 12 x. multicoloured . . 65 35
N323 – 12 x. multicoloured . . 65 35

DESIGN—VERT: (23 × 45 mm): No. N323, Map of Vietnam, T.U. emblem and flag, inscr ("NHAN DAN MIEN NAM") etc.

132 Nhu Quynh Pumping Station

1964. Irrigation for Agriculture.

N324 **132** 12 x. slate and black . 75 35

133 Populace Greeting Soldiers

1964. 10th Anniv of Liberation of Hanoi. Multicoloured.

N325 6 x. Type **133** 35 25
N326 12 x. Building construction 70 50

134 Naval Longboat

1964. "National Defence" Games.

N327 **134** 5 x. black, grey & blue 90 35
N328 – 12 x. black, grey & yell 1·90 50
N329 – 12 x. black, brn & bl . 1·90 50
N330 – 12 x. multicoloured . . 1·90 50

DESIGNS—HORIZ: No. N328, Pistol-shooting. VERT: No. N329, Gliding; N330, Parachuting.

135 "Guarcinia mangostana"

1964. Tropical Fruits. Multicoloured.

N331 12 x. Type **135** . . . . . . 1·60 45
N332 12 x. "Mangifera indica" . 1·60 45
N333 12 x. "Nephelium litchi" . 1·60 45
N334 20 x. "Anona squamosa" . 2·75 85
N335 50 x. "Citrus medica" . . . 7·50 1·90

136 Conference Building

1964. World Solidarity Conf, Hanoi. Mult.

N336 12 x. Type **136** 75 35
N337 12 x. Soldier greeting workers 75 35
N338 12 x. Clenched fist, ships and Boeing B-52 Stratofortress 75 35

137 Soldiers with Standard

1964. 20th Anniv of Vietnamese People's Army. Multicoloured.

N339 12 x. Type **137** . . . . . . 1·00 30
N340 12 x. Coastguards . . . . . 1·00 30
N341 12 x. Frontier guards (vert) 1·00 30

138 Cuban Revolutionaries   139 Le Hong Phong

140 Party Flag

1965. 6th Anniv of Cuban Republic.

N342 **138** 12 x. black, red & blue 75 35
N343 – 12 x. multicoloured . . 75 35

DESIGN: No. N343, Flags of Cuba and North Vietnam.

1965. 35th Anniv of Vietnamese Workers' Party.

(a) As T **139**. Portraits and inscr purple-brown; background colours given.

N344 **139** 6 x. grey 40 20
N345 – 6 x. bistre 40 20
N346 – 6 x. drab 40 20
N347 – 6 x. brown 40 20
N348 – 6 x. lilac 40 20

DESIGNS: No. N345, Tran Phu; N346, Hoang Van Thu; N347 Hgo Gia Tu; N348 Nguyen van Cu (Party leaders).

(b) As T **140**.

N349 **140** 12 x. yellow, red and mauve 60 30
N350 – 12 x. mauve, yellow and red 60 30

DESIGN: No. N350, Foundryman and guerilla fighter.

141 Women tending Maize   142 Locomotive and Nguyen Van Troi (patriot)

1965. Populating Mountain Settlements.

N351 **141** 2 x. multicoloured . . . 25 20
N352 3 x. multicoloured . . . 35 25
N353 – 12 x. indigo, orange and blue 60 35

DESIGN: 12 x. Young girls going to school.

1965. Transport Ministers' Congress, Hanoi.

N354 **142** 12 x. blue and red . . . 1·60 50
N355 – 30 x. black and green . . 3·00 1·10

DESIGN: 30 x. As Type **142** but position of locomotive, portrait and value transposed.

143 Cosmonauts Komarov, Feoktistov, Yegorov, and "Voskhod I"

1965. Three-manned Space Flight.

N356 **143** 20 x. violet, green & bl . 1·50 40
N357 – 1 d. violet, red & mauve 5·25 1·50

DESIGN: 1 d. "Voskhod I" and cosmonauts.

144 Lenin with Red Guards   145 Pres. Ho Chi Minh

1965. Lenin's 95th Birth Anniv.

N358 **144** 8 x. purple and buff . . 50 25
N359 12 x. purple and grey . . 75 30

1965. Pres. Ho Chi Minh's 75th Birthday.

N360 **145** 6 x. violet, yell & grn . . 50 20
N361 12 x. violet, yell & buff . 1·00 25

146 Hands clasping Serpent   147 Two Soldiers advancing

1965. 10th Anniv of Afro-Asian Conf, Bandung.

N362 **146** 12 x. multicoloured . . . 60 30

1965. Trade Union Conference, Hanoi.

N363 **147** 12 x. blue and purple . . 60 25
N364 – 12 x. multicoloured . . . 60 25
N365 – 12 x. red, black & grn . 60 25

DESIGNS—HORIZ: No. N364, Sea battle; N365, "Peoples of the World" on Globe, and soldiers.

148 Yellow-throated Marten

1965. Fauna Protection. Multicoloured.

N366 12 x. Type **148** 80 45
N367 12 x. Owston's palm civet . 1·25 45
N368 12 x. Chinese pangolin . . . 1·25 45
N369 12 x. Francois' monkey (vert) 1·25 45
N370 20 x. Red giant flying squirrel 3·75 1·25
N371 50 x. Lesser slow loris (vert) 6·25 2·25

149 Marx and Lenin   150 Nguyen Van Troi (patriot)

1965. Postal Ministers Congress, Peking.

N372 **149** 12 x. multicoloured . . 1·00 35

1965. Nguyen Van Troi Commemoration.

N373 **150** 12 x. sepia, brn & grn . 60 25
N374 50 x. sepia, brn & ochre 1·25 70
N375 4 d. sepia and red . . . 8·00 3·75

151 "Rhynchocoris humeralis"   152 Revolutionaries

1965. Noxious Insects. Multicoloured.

N376 12 x. Type **151** . . . . . . 1·00 45
N377 12 x. "Tessaratoma papillosa" 1·00 45
N378 12 x. "Poeciliocoris latus" . 1·00 45
N379 12 x. "Tosena melanoptera" 1·00 45
N380 20 x. "Cicada sp." . . . . 3·50 1·60
N381 30 x. "Fulgora candelaria" . 5·00 2·00

Nos. N379/81 are vert $20\frac{1}{2} \times 38$ mm.

1965. 20th Anniv of August Revolution.

N382 **152** 6 x. sep, black & blue . 30 20
N383 12 x. black and red . . 65 25

153 Prawn

1965. Marine Life. Multicoloured.

N384 12 x. Type **153** . . . . . . 2·25 60
N385 12 x. Shrimp . . . . 2·25 60
N386 12 x. Swimming crab . . . 2·25 60
N387 12 x. Serrate swimming crab 2·25 60
N388 20 x. Spiny lobster . . . . 4·25 1·90
N389 50 x. Fiddler crab . . . . . 8·75 3·25

154 Air Battle   155 Foundryman ("Heavy Industries")

1965. "500th U.S. Aircraft Brought Down over North Vietnam".

N390 **154** 12 x. green and lilac . . 5·50 3·75

1965. 20th Anniv of Republic and Completion of 1st Five-Year Plan.

N391 **155** 12 x. black and orange . 50 20
N392 – 12 x. black and green . 50 15
N393 – 12 x. black and purple . 50 15

DESIGNS: No. N392, Irrigation, pylon and power station ("Hydro-electric Power"); N393, Nurse examining child ("Social Medicine").

See also Nos. N417/19.

156 Drummer and Peasants

1965. 35th Anniv of Movement of Nghe An and Ha Tinh Soviet Peasants.
N394 **156** 10 x. multicoloured . . 35 20
N395 12 x. multicoloured . . 65 25

157 Girls and Flags

1965. 16th Anniv of Friendship between China and Vietnam. Multicoloured.
N396 12 x. Type **157** 50 25
N397 12 x. Vietnamese and Chinese girls with flags (vert) . . . 50 25

158 Tsiolkovsky and "Sputnik 1"

1965. Space Flight of "Voskhod 2".
N398 **158** 12 x. blue and purple . . 90 30
N399 – 12 x. ochre and blue . . 90 30
N400 – 50 x. blue and green . . 2·10 90
N401 – 50 x. blue & turquoise . . 2·10 90
DESIGNS: No. N399, Leonov, Belyaev and "Voskhod 2"; N400, Gagarin; N401, Leonov in space.

159 Red Lacewing

1965. Butterflies. Multicoloured.
N402 12 x. Type **159** . . . . . . 2·50 50
N403 12 x. Leopard lacewing . . . 2·50 50
N404 12 x. Blue triangle . . . . 2·50 50
N405 12 x. Indian purple emperor 2·50 50
N406 20 x. Paris peacock . . . . 7·50 1·75
N407 30 x. Common rose . . . . 10·50 3·00

160 Norman R. Morrison and Demonstrators

161 Birthplace of Nguyen Du (poet)

1965. Homage to Norman R. Morrison (American Quaker who immolated himself).
N408 **160** 12 x. black and red . . 60 30

1965. Nguyen Du Commem. Multicoloured.
N409 12 x. Type **161** 50 25
N410 12 x. Nguyen Du Museum . 50 25
N411 20 x. "Kieu" (volume of poems) . . . . 1·00 35
N412 1 d. Scene from "Kieu" . . 2·10 1·00

162 Pres. Ho Chi Minh

163 Rice-field and Insecticide-sprayer ("Agriculture")

1965. Engels' 145th Birth Anniv. Multicoloured.
N413 12 x. Type **162** 60 25
N414 12 x. Marx 60 25
N415 12 x. Lenin 60 25
N416 50 x. Engels . . . . 1·90 90

1965. Completion of First Five-Year Plan (2nd issue).
N417 **163** 12 x. orange and green 60 25
N418 – 12 x. blue and red . . . 60 25
N419 – 12 x. orange and blue . . 60 25
DESIGNS: No. N418, Factory-worker ("Light Industries"); N419, Children at play and students ("Social Education").

164 Soldier and Demonstrators

1965. 5th Anniv of South Vietnam National Liberation Front.
N420 **164** 12 x. violet and lilac . . 60 25

165 Casting Votes

166 "Dendrobium moschatum"

1966. 20th Anniv of 1st Vietnamese General Elections.
N421 **165** 12 x. black and red . . 45 20

1966. Orchids. Multicoloured.
N422 12 x. Type **166** . . . . . 1·25 40
N423 12 x. "Vanda teres" . . . . 1·25 40
N424 12 x. "Dendrobium crystallinum" . . . . . . 1·25 40
N425 12 x. "Dendrobium nobile" 1·25 40
N426 20 x. "Vandopsis gigantea" 3·00 1·00
N427 30 x. "Dendrobium" . . . 5·75 1·90

167 Child on Rocking-horse

168 "Physignathus cocincinus"

1966. New Year.
N428 **167** 12 x. multicoloured . . 50 20

1966. Protection of Nature—Reptiles. Multicoloured.
N429 12 x. Type **168** . . . . . 1·00 40
N430 12 x. "Trionyx sinensis" . . 1·00 40
N431 12 x. Gecko (inscr "GEKKO GECKO") . . . . 1·00 40
M432 12 x. "Testudo elongata" . 1·00 40
M433 20 x. "Varanus salvator" . 2·75 1·60
M434 40 x. "Eretmochelys imbricata" . . . . 4·50 1·60

169 Wrestling

170 Ly Tu Trong (revolutionary), Badge and Banner

1966. National Games.
N435 **169** 12 x. multicoloured . . 60 30
N436 – 12 x. multicoloured . . 60 30
N437 – 12 x. multicoloured . . 60 30
GAMES: No. N436, Archery (with crossbow); N437, "Fencing".

1966. 35th Anniv of Labour Youth Union.
N438 **170** 12 x. multicoloured . . 45 20

171 Republic Thunderchief in Flames

1966. "1,000th U.S. Aircraft Brought Down over North Vietnam".
N439 **171** 12 x. multicoloured . . . 4·25 1·90

172 Worker and Rifle **174** Children and Banners

173 Battle Scene on Con Co Island

1966. Labour Day.
N440 **172** 6 x. black, red and salmon 50 25

1966. Defence of Con Co ("Steel Island").
N441 **173** 12 x. multicoloured . . . 50 20

1966. 25th Anniv of Vietnam Youth Pioneers.
N442 **174** 12 x. black and red . . . 50 25

175 View of Dien An (Yenan)

176 "Luna 9" in Space

1966. 45th Anniv of Chinese Communist Party. Multicoloured.
N443 3 x. Type **175** 35 20
N444 12 x. Ho Chi Minh and Mao Tse-tung 60 40

1966. "Luna 9". Space Flight. Multicoloured. Inscr "MAT TRANG 9".
N445 12 x. Type **176** 50 25
N446 50 x. "Luna 9" on Moon . . 2·00 1·00

177 Airplane in Flames

1966. "1,500th U.S. Aircraft Brought Down over North Vietnam".
N447 **177** 12 x. multicoloured . . . 4·50 2·50
N448 12 x. mult (optd **NGAY 14.10.1966**) . . . . . 5·00 3·25

178 Liberation Fighter

1966. Victories of Liberation Army. Inscr "1965–1966".
N449 **178** 1 x. purple 25 15
N450 12 x. multicoloured . . . 50 25
N451 – 12 x. multicoloured . . . 50 25
DESIGN: No. N451, Soldier escorting prisoners-of-war.
See also No. 646.

179 Women from different Regions, and Child

1966. 20th Anniv of Vietnamese Women's Union.
N452 **179** 12 x. black & salmon . 50 25

180 Moluccan Pittas

1966. Birds. Multicoloured.
N453 12 x. Type **180** . . . . . . 1·60 40
N454 12 x. Black-naped orioles . 1·60 40
N455 12 x. Common kingfisher . 1·60 40
N456 12 x. Long-tailed broadbill . 1·60 40
N457 20 x. Hoopoe . . . . 3·50 1·50
N458 30 x. Maroon orioles . . . 6·50 1·90
Nos. N454/5 and N457 are vert.

181 Football

1966. Ganefo Games. Multicoloured.
N459 12 x. Type **181** 50 25
N460 12 x. Rifle-shooting 50 25
N461 30 x. Swimming . . . . . . 1·25 50
N462 30 x. Running . . . . 1·25 50

182 Harvesting Rice

1967. Agricultural Production.
N463 **182** 12 x. multicoloured . . 60 25

183 Ho Chi Minh Text and Fighters

1967. Ho Chi Minh's Appeal.
N464 **183** 12 x. purple and red . . 30 20
N465 – 12 x. purple and red . . 45 20
DESIGNS: No. N465, Ho-Chi-Minh text and marchers with banners.
See also Nos. 519/22.

184 Bamboo ("Arundinaria rolleana")

1967. Bamboo. Multicoloured.
N466 12 x. Type **184** 75 25
N467 12 x. "Arundinaria racemosa" 75 25
N468 12 x. "Bambusa bingami" . 75 25
N469 12 x. "Bambusa arundinaceu" 75 25
N470 30 x. "Bambusa nutans" . 2·00 1·00
N471 50 x. "Dendrocalamus patellaris" . . . . 3·75 1·75

185 Dhole

1967. Wild Animals. Multicoloured.

N472 12 x. Type **185** . . . . . . 1·00 40
N473 12 x. Binturong . . . . . . 1·00 40
N474 12 x. Hog-badger . . . . . 1·00 40
N475 20 x. Large Indian civet . . 2·00 75
N476 40 x. Bear macaque . . . . 3·25 1·25
N477 50 x. Clouded leopard . . . 5·00 1·90

186 Captured Pilot

187 Rocket Launching and Agricultural Scene

1967. "2,000th U.S. Aircraft Brought Down over North Vietnam".

N478 **186** 6 x. blk & red on pink . 1·90 80
N479 12 x. blk & red on grn . 1·90 80

1967. Launching of First Chinese Rocket. Multicoloured.

N480 12 x. Type **187** 60 25
N481 30 x. Rocket launching, and Gate of Heavenly Peace, Peking . . . . 1·25 50

188 Siamese Tiger Fish

1967. Vietnamese Fishes. Multicoloured.

N482 12 x. Type **188** 65 20
N483 12 x. Spanish mackerel . . . 65 20
N484 12 x. Lizard fish 65 25
N485 20 x. Spangled emperor . . 1·25 50
N486 30 x. German fish . . . . . 2·50 75
N487 50 x. Golden-striped snapper 3·75 95

189 Lenin and Revolutionary Soldiers

1967. 50th Anniv of October Revolution. Multicoloured.

N488 6 x. Type **189** 25 15
N489 12 x. Lenin and revolutionaries 45 20
N490 12 x. Lenin, Marx and Vietnamese soldiers . . . 45 20
N491 20 x. Cruiser "Aurora" . . 75 40

190 Air Battle

1967. "2,500th U.S. Aircraft Brought Down over North Vietnam".

N492 **190** 12 x. black, red & grn . 4·25 1·25
N493 – 12 x. black, red & blue . 4·25 1·25

DESIGN—VERT: No. N493, Boeing B-52 Stratofortress falling in flames.

191 Atomic Symbol and Gate of Heavenly Peace, Peking

1967. 1st Chinese "H"-Bomb Test. Multicoloured.

N494 12 x. Type **191** 75 30
N495 20 x. Chinese lantern, atomic symbol & dove (30 × 35 mm) 1·10 45

192 Factory Anti-aircraft Unit

1967. Anti-aircraft Defences. Multicoloured.

N496 12 x. Type **192** 50 25
N497 12 x. Rifle-fire from trenches 50 25
N498 12 x. Seaborne gun-crew . . 50 25
N499 12 x. Militiawoman with captured U.S. pilot . . . 50 25
N500 20 x. Air battle 95 40
N501 30 x. Military anti-aircraft post 1·75 75

193 Chickens

1968. Domestic Fowl. Multicoloured designs showing cocks and hens.

N502 12 x. Type **193** 85 40
N503 12 x. Inscr "Ga ri" 85 40
N504 12 x. Inscr "Ga trong thien ri" 85 40
N505 12 x. Inscr "Ga den chanchi" 85 40
N506 20 x. Junglefowl . . . . . 1·90 60
N507 30 x. Hen . . . . 2·25 1·00
N508 40 x. Hen and chicks . . . 2·75 1·25
N509 50 x. Two hens . . . . . 3·25 1·60

194 Gorky

1968. Birth Centenary of Maxim Gorky.

N510 **194** 12 x. black & brown . 60 30

195 Burning Village

1968. Victories of 1966–67.

N511 **195** 12 x. brown and red . . 50 25
N512 – 12 x. brown and red . . 50 25
N513 – 12 x. brown and red . . 50 25
N514 – 12 x. brown and red . . 50 25
N515 – 12 x. black and violet . 50 25
N516 – 12 x. black and violet . 50 25
N517 – 12 x. black and violet . 50 25
N518 – 12 x. black and violet . 50 25

DESIGNS: No. N512, Firing mortars; N513, Attacking tanks with rocket-gun; N514, Sniping; N515, Attacking gun-site; N516, Escorting prisoners; N517, Interrogating refugees; N518, Civilians demonstating.

197 Ho Chi Minh Text and Fighters

198 Hong boch Rose

1968. Intensification of Production.

N519 **197** 6 x. blue on yellow . . 30 15
N520 12 x. blue 40 20
N521 12 x. purple 40 20
N522 12 x. red 40 20

1968. Roses. Multicoloured.

N523 12 x. Type **198** 60 25
N524 12 x. Hong canh sap . . . 60 25
N525 12 x. Hong leo 60 25
N526 20 x. Hong vang . . . . . 1·90 65
N527 30 x. Hong nhung . . . . 2·50 80
N528 40 x. Hong canh tim . . . 3·75 1·25

199 Ho Chi Minh and Flag

200 Karl Marx

1968. Ho Chi Minh's New Year Message.

N529 **199** 12 x. brown and violet . 40 20

1968. 150th Birth Anniv of Karl Marx.

N530 **200** 12 x. black and green . . 50 25

201 Anti-aircraft Machine-gun Crew

1968. "3,000th U.S. Aircraft Brought Down over North Vietnam". Multicoloured.

N531 12 x. Type **201** . . . . . . 1·50 65
N532 12 x. Women manning anti-aircraft gun . . . . . . 1·50 65
N533 40 x. Aerial dogfight . . . 3·50 1·40
N534 40 x. Anti-aircraft missile . . 3·50 1·40

202 Rattan-cane Work

1968. Arts and Crafts. Multicoloured.

N535 6 x. Type **202** 35 15
N536 12 x. Bamboo work 40 25
N537 12 x. Pottery 40 25
N538 20 x. Ivory carving 80 35
N539 30 x. Lacquer work . . . . 1·25 45
N540 40 x. Silverware . . . . . 1·60 75

203 Quarter-staff Contest

1968. Traditional Sports. Multicoloured.

N541 12 x. Type **203** 50 20
N542 12 x. Dagger fighting . . . 50 20
N543 12 x. Duel with sabres . . 50 20
N544 30 x. Unarmed combat . . . 1·25 55
N545 40 x. Scimitar fighting . . . 2·00 70
N546 50 x. Sword and buckler . . 2·25 95

205 Temple, Khue

1968. Vietnamese Architecture. Multicoloured.

N548 12 x. Type **205** 50 25
N549 12 x. Bell tower, Keo Pagoda 50 25
N550 20 x. Bridge, Bonze Pagoda (horiz) 70 30
N551 30 x. Mot Cot Pagoda, Hanoi 70 35
N552 40 x. Gateway, Ninh Phuc Pagoda (horiz) . . . . . . 1·25 55
N553 50 x. Tay Phuong Pagoda (horiz) . . . . 1·75 60

206 Vietnamese Militia

1968. Cuban–North Vietnamese Friendship. Multicoloured. With gum.

N554 12 x. Type **206** 35 20
N555 12 x. Cuban revolutionary (vert) 35 20
N556 20 x. "Revolutionary Solidarity" (vert) 80 25

207 "Ploughman with Rifle"

1968. "The War Effort". Paintings. With gum.

N557 **207** 12 x. black, bl & yell . . 25 15
N558 – 12 x. multicoloured . . 25 15
N559 – 30 x. brown, blue and turquoise 85 30
N560 – 40 x. multicoloured . . 95 35

DESIGNS—HORIZ: No. N558, "Defending the Mines"; N559, "Repairing Railway Track"; N560, "Crashed Aircraft".

208 Nam Ngai shooting down Aircraft

1969. Lunar New Year. Victories of the National Liberation Front. Multicoloured.

N561 12 x. Type **208** 40 20
N562 12 x. Tay Nguyen throwing grenade 40 20
N563 12 x. Gun crews, Tri Thien 40 20
N564 40 x. Insurgents, Tay Ninh . 1·00 40
N565 50 x. Home Guards . . . . 1·60 80

209 Loading Timber Lorries

1969. North Vietnamese Timber Industry. Multicoloured.

N566 6 x. Type **209** 25 15
N567 12 x. Log raft on river . . . 35 20
N568 12 x. Tug towing "log train" 35 20
N569 12 x. Elephant hauling logs 60 20
N570 12 x. Insecticide spraying . 35 20
N571 20 x. Buffalo hauling log . . 1·25 40
N572 30 x. Logs on overhead cable 1·90 75

210 "Young Guerrilla" (Co Tan Long Chau)

1969. "South Vietnam—Land and People". Paintings. Multicoloured.

N573 12 x. Type **210** 45 30
N574 12 x. "Scout on Patrol" (Co Tan Long Chau) 45 30
N575 20 x. "Woman Guerrilla" (Le Van Chuong) (vert) . . 70 45
N576 30 x. "Halt at a Relay Station" (Co Tan Long Chau) . . 70 45
N577 40 x. "After a Skirmish" (Co Tan Long Chau) . . . . 1·50 1·10
N578 50 x. "Liberated Hamlet" (Huynh Phuong Dong) . 1·90 1·25

211 Woman Soldier, Ben Tre

1969. Victories in Tet Offensive (1968).

N579 **211** 8 x. black, grn & pink . . 45 20
N580 12 x. black, emer & green 45 20
N581 – 12 x. multicoloured . . 45 20
N582 – 12 x. multicoloured . . 45 20
N583 – 12 x. multicoloured . . 45 20

DESIGNS—VERT: No. N581, Urban guerilla and attack on U.S. Embassy, Saigon; N582, Two soldiers with flag, Hue; N583, Mortar crew, Khe Sanh.

212 Soldier with Flame-thrower

1969. 15th Anniv of Liberation of Hanoi.
N584 **212** 12 x. black and red . . 1·10 50
N585 – 12 x. multicoloured . . 1·10 50
DESIGN: No. N585, Children with construction toy.

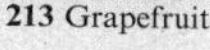
213 Grapefruit 214 Tribunal Emblem and Falling Airplane

1969. Fruits. Multicoloured.
N586 12 x. Type **213** 35 15
N587 12 x. Pawpaw 35 15
N588 20 x. Tangerines 50 20
N589 30 x. Oranges 85 35
N590 40 x. Lychees . . . . 1·40 70
N591 50 x. Persimmons . . . . . . 1·90 1·00
See also Nos. N617/21 and N633/6.

1969. Int. War Crimes Tribunal, Stockholm and Roskilde.
N592 **214** 12 x. black, red & brown 45 20

215 Ho Chi Minh in 1924

1970. 40th Anniv of Vietnamese Workers' Party. Multicoloured.
N593 12 x. Type **215** 40 20
N594 12 x. Ho Chi Minh in 1969 . 40 20
N595 12 x. Le Hong Phong . . . 40 20
N596 12 x. Tran Phu 40 20
N597 12 x. Nguyne Van Cu . . . 40 20
Nos. N595/7 are smaller than Type **215**, size 40 × 24 mm.

216 Playtime in Nursery School

1970. Children's Activities. Multicoloured.
N598 12 x. Type **216** 30 20
N599 12 x. Playing with toys . . . 30 20
N600 20 x. Watering plants . . . 45 25
N601 20 x. Pasturing buffalo . . . 45 25
N602 30 x. Feeding chickens . . . 60 40
N603 40 x. Making music 80 50
N604 50 x. Flying model airplane . 1·25 75
N605 60 x. Going to school . . . 2·10 95

217 Lenin and Red Flag

1970. Birth Centenary of Lenin.
N606 **217** 12 x. multicoloured . . 30 15
N607 – 1 d. purple, red & yell . 1·90 50
DESIGN: 1 d. Portrait of Lenin.

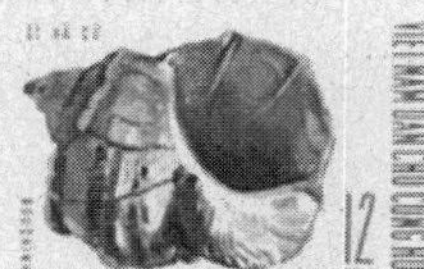
218 Oc Xa Cu Sea-shell

1970. Sea-shells. Multicoloured.
N608 12 x. Type **218** . . . . . 1·25 25
N609 12 x. Oc Con Lon shell . . 1·25 25
N610 20 x. Oc Tien shell . . . . 1·60 35
N611 1 d. Oc Tu Va shell . . . . 4·75 1·00

219 Ho Chi Minh in 1930

1970. Ho Chi Minh's 80th Birth Anniv.
N612 **219** 12 x. black, brn & flesh 30 15
N613 – 12 x. black, bl & grn . 30 15
N614 – 2 d. black, ochre & yell 1·90 1·10
PORTRAITS: No. N613, In 1945 with microphone; N614, In 1969.

220 Vietcong Flag

1970. 1st Anniv of National Liberation Front Provisional Government in South Vietnam.
N616 **220** 12 x. multicoloured . . 40 20

221 Water-melon 222 Power Linesman

1970. Fruits. Multicoloured.
N617 12 x. Type **221** 30 20
N618 12 x. Pumpkin 30 20
N619 20 x. Cucumber 45 25
N620 50 x. Courgette . . . . . 1·00 45
N621 1 d. Charantais melon . . . 2·00 85

1970. North Vietnamese Industries.
N622 **222** 12 x. blue and red . . . 50 15
N623 – 12 x. red, yellow & bl . 50 15
N624 – 12 x. black, orge & bl . 50 25
N625 – 12 x. yellow, pur & grn 50 25
DESIGNS—VERT: No. N623, Hands winding thread on bobbin ("Textiles"); N624, Stoker and power station ("Electric Power"); N625, Workers and lorry ("More coal for the Fatherland").

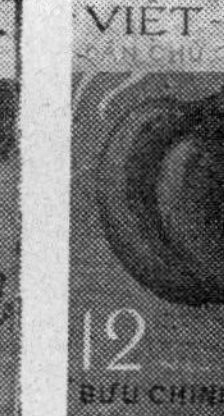
223 Peasant Girl with Pigs 225 Chuoi Tieu Bananas

224 Ho Chi Minh proclaiming Republic, 1945

1970. North Vietnamese Agriculture.
N626 **223** 12 x. multicoloured . . 60 25

1970. 25th Anniv of Democratic Republic of Vietnam.
N627 **224** 12 x. black, brn & red . 25 10
N628 – 12 x. deep brown, brown and green 25 10
N629 – 12 x. brn, grey and red 25 10
N630 – 12 x. deep brown, brown and green 25 10
N631 – 20 x. brn, red & bistre . 40 15
N632 – 1 d. brown, drab and chestnut . . . . . 1·40 60
DESIGNS: No. N628, Vo Thi Sau facing firing-squad; N629, Nguyen Van Troi and captors; N630, Phan Dinh Giot attacking pill-box; N631, Nguyen Viet Xuan encouraging troops; N632, Nguyen Van Be attacking tank.

1970. Bananas. Multicoloured.
N633 12 x. Type **225** 35 20
N634 12 x. Chuoi Tay 35 20
N635 50 x. Chuoi Ngu 95 35
N636 1 d. Chuoi Mat . . . . . 1·90 75

226 Flags, and Bayonets in Helmet

1970. Indo-Chinese People's Summit Conference.
N637 **226** 12 x. multicoloured . . . 35 15

227 Engels and Signature

1970. 150th Birth Anniv of Friedrich Engels.
N638 **227** 12 x. black, brn & red . 35 15
N639 1 d. black, brown & grn 1·10 60

228 "Akistrodon ciatus" 229 Mother and Child with Flag

1970. Snakes. Multicoloured.
N640 12 x. Type **228** 60 20
N641 20 x. "Calliophis macclellandii" 95 40
N642 50 x. "Bungarus faciatus" . . 1·60 55
N643 1 d. "Trimeresurus gramineus" 2·50 95

1970. 10th Anniv of National Front for Liberation of South Vietnam. Multicoloured.
N644 6 x. Type **229** 20 15
N645 12 x. Vietcong flag and torch (horiz) 25 15

1971. Victories of Liberation Army. As No. N449, but value and colours changed.
N646 **178** 2 x. black and orange . . 30 20

232 Satellite in Earth Orbit

1971. 1st Anniv of Launching of Chinese Satellite.
N649 **232** 12 x. multicoloured . . . 50 20
N650 50 x. multicoloured . . 1·10 30

234 Ho Chi Minh Medal

1971. 81st Birth Anniv of Pres. Ho Chi Minh.
N652 **234** 1 x. multicoloured . . . 10 10
N653 3 x. multicoloured . . . 20 10
N654 10 x. multicoloured . . . 25 10
N655 12 x. multicoloured . . . 35 20

235 Emperor Quang Trung liberating Hanoi

1971. Bicentenary of Tay Son Rising.
N657 **235** 6 x. multicoloured . . . 35 20
N658 12 x. multicoloured . . . 50 25

236 Karl Marx and Music of the "Internationale"

1971. Centenary of Paris Commune.
N659 **236** 12 x. black, red & pink 50 25

237 Hai Thuong Lan Ong

1971. 250th Birth Anniv of Hai Thuong Lan Ong (physician).
N660 **237** 12 x. black, grn & brn . 25 10
N661 50 x. multicoloured . . 50 25

238 "Kapimala" 239 Ho Chi Minh, Banner and Young Workers

1971. Folk Sculptures in Tay Phuong Pagoda. Multicoloured.
N662 12 x. Type **238** 45 20
N663 12 x. "Sangkayasheta" . . . 45 20
N664 12 x. "Vasumitri" 45 20
N665 12 x. "Dhikaca" 45 20
N666 30 x. "Bouddha Nandi" . . 1·50 35
N667 40 x. "Rahulata" . . . . 1·60 50
N668 50 x. "Sangha Nandi" . . 1·75 55
N669 1 d. "Cakyamuni" . . . . 2·10 70

1971. 40th Anniv of Ho Chi Minh Working Youth Union.
N670 **239** 12 x. multicoloured . . 30 15

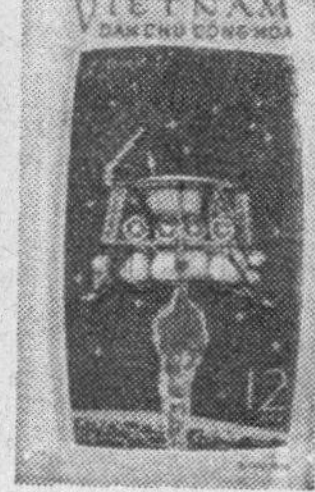
240 "Luna 16" on Moon 241 "Luna 17" landing on Moon

1971. Moon Flight of "Luna 16".
N671 – 12 x. multicoloured . . 40 20
N672 – 12 x. multicoloured . . 40 20
N673 **240** 1 d. brown, bl & turq . 1·75 60
DESIGNS: No. N671, Flight to Moon; N672, Return to Earth.
Nos. N671/2 were issued together horizontally se-tenant, each pair forming a composite design.

1971. Moon Flight of "Luna 17".
N674 **241** 12 x. red, blue & grn . . 40 20
N675 – 12 x. pink, green & myrtle 40 20
N676 – 1 d. pink, brown & grn 1·10 50
DESIGNS—HORIZ: No. N675, "Luna 17" on Moon; N676, "Lunokhod 1" crossing Moon crevasse.

243 "White Tiger"

1971. "The Five Tigers" (folk-art paintings). Multicoloured.

N679 12 x. Type **243** 40 25
N680 12 x. "Yellow Tiger" 40 25
N681 12 x. "Red Tiger" 40 25
N682 40 x. "Green Tiger" . . . . 1·10 35
N683 50 x. "Grey Tiger" . . . . 1·50 50
N684 1 d. "Five Tigers" . . . . . 2·50 95

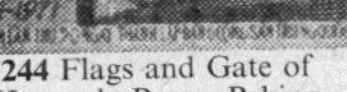

244 Flags and Gate of Heavenly Peace, Peking

245 Mongolian Emblem

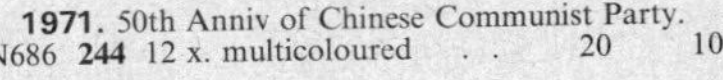

1971. 50th Anniv of Chinese Communist Party.

N686 **244** 12 x. multicoloured . . 20 10

1971. 50th Anniv of Mongolian People's Republic.

N687 **245** 12 x. multicoloured . . 30 15

246 Drum Procession

1972. Dong Ho Folk Engravings.

N688 **246** 12 x. pink, brown & blk 40 25
N689 – 12 x. pink and black . . 40 25
N690 – 12 x. multicoloured . . 40 25
N691 – 12 x. multicoloured . . 40 25
N692 – 40 x. multicoloured . . 1·75 40
N693 – 50 x. multicoloured . . 2·10 75

DESIGNS—HORIZ: No. N689, "Traditional Wrestling"; N692, "Wedding of Mice"; N693, "The Toads' School". VERT: No. N690, "Jealous Attack"; N691, "Gathering Coconuts".

247 Workers

248 Planting Rice

1972. 3rd Vietnamese Trade Unions Congress.

N694 **247** 1 x. black and blue . . 25 10
N695 – 12 x. black and orange . 35 20

DESIGN: 12 x. As Type **247**, but design reversed.

1972. 25th Anniv of National Resistance.

N696 **248** 12 x. multicoloured . . 25 15
N697 – 12 x. multicoloured . . 25 15
N698 – 12 x. multicoloured . . 25 15
N699 – 12 x. turq, red & pink . 25 15

DESIGNS: No. N697, Munitions worker; N698, Soldier with flame-thrower; N699, Text of Ho Chi Minh's Appeal.

249 Ho Chi Minh's Birthplace

1972. 82nd Birth Anniv of Ho Chi Minh.

N700 **249** 12 x. black, drab & ochre 25 15
N701 – 12 x. black, grn & pink . 25 15

DESIGN: No. N701, Ho Chi Minh's house, Hanoi.

250 Captured Pilot and Falling Airplane

251 Georgi Dimitrov

1972. "3,500th U.S. Aircraft Brought Down over North Vietnam".

N702 **250** 12 x. green and red . . 95 60
N703 12 x. black and red . . 95 60

No. N703 has the inscription, amended to record the actual date on which the 3,500th aircraft was brought down–20.4.1972.

1972. 90th Birth Anniv of Georgi Dimitrov (Bulgarian statesman).

N704 **251** 12 x. brown and green . 25 15
N705 – 12 x. black and pink . . 25 15

DESIGN: No. N705, Dimitrov at Leipzig Court, 1933.

252 Falcated Teal

253 Anti-aircraft Gunner

1972. Vietnamese Birds. Multicoloured.

N706 12 x. Type **252** 55 25
N707 12 x. Red-wattled lapwing . . 55 25
N708 30 x. Cattle egret 85 30
N709 40 x. Water cock . . . . . 1·10 45
N710 50 x. Purple swamphen . . 1·75 75
N711 1 d. Greater adjutant stork 3·50 1·10

1972. "4,000th U.S. Aircraft Brought Down over North Vietnam".

N712 **253** 12 x. black, mauve and pink 65 25
N713 – 12 x. green, black and red 65 25

DESIGN: No. N713, Anti-aircraft gunner with shell.

254 Umbrella Dance

1972. Tay Nguyen Folk Dances. Multicoloured.

N714 12 x. Type **254** 25 15
N715 12 x. Drum dance 25 15
N716 12 x. Shield dance 25 15
N717 20 x. Horse dance 45 20
N718 30 x. Ka-Dong dance . . . 50 20
N719 40 x. Grinding-rice dance . . 70 25
N720 50 x. Gong dance 90 50
N721 1 d. Cham Rong dance . . 1·75 70

255 "Soyuz 11" Spacecraft and "Salyut" Space Laboratory

1972. Space Flight of "Soyuz 11".

N722 **255** 12 x. blue and lilac . . 25 15
N723 – 1 d. brown and flesh . 1·00 45

DESIGN: 1 d. "Soyuz 11" astronauts.

256 Dhole

1973. Wild Animals (1st series). Multicoloured.

N724 12 x. Type **256** 40 20
N725 30 x. Leopard 60 20
N726 50 x. Leopard cat . . . . 1·10 40
N727 1 d. European otter . . . . 2·00 50

See also Nos. N736/9.

257 Copernicus and Globe

1973. 500th Birth Anniv of Copernicus (astronomer).

N728 **257** 12 x. black, red & brn . 30 20
N729 – 12 x. black, red & brn . 30 20
N730 – 30 x. black & brown . . 65 25

DESIGNS—HORIZ: 12 x. (No. N729), Copernicus and sun. VERT: 30 x. Copernicus and facsimile signature.

258 "Drummers"

1973. Engravings from Ngoc Lu Bronze Drums. Each yellow and green.

N731 12 x. Type **258** 50 25
N732 12 x. "Pounding rice" . . . 50 25
N733 12 x. "Folk-dancing" . . . 50 25
N734 12 x. "War canoe" 50 25
N735 12 x. "Birds and beasts" . . 50 25

259 Lesser Malay Chevrotain

260 Striated Canegrass Warblers

1973. Wild Animals (2nd series). Multicoloured.

N736 12 x, Type **259** 35 20
N737 30 x. Mainland serow . . . 60 20
N738 50 x. Wild boar . . . . . 1·10 35
N739 1 d. Siberian musk deer . . . 2·00 50

1973. Birds useful to Agriculture. Multicoloured.

N740 12 x. Type **260** 50 30
N741 12 x. Red-whiskered bulbuls . 50 30
N742 20 x. Magpie robin 65 35
N743 40 x. White-browed fantails . 1·10 40
N744 50 x. Great tits . . . . . 1·90 70
N745 1 d. Japanese white eyes . . 3·75 1·00

262 "Ready to Learn"

1973. "Three Readies" Youth Movement.

N748 **262** 12 x. brown and green . 20 10
N749 – 12 x. violet and blue . 20 10
N750 – 12 x. green and mauve . 20 10

DESIGNS: No. N749, Soldiers on the march ("Ready to Fight"); N750, Road construction ("Ready to Work").

263 Flags of North Vietnam and North Korea

1973. 25th Anniv of People's Republic of Korea.

N751 **263** 12 x. multicoloured . . . 25 10

264 Dogfight over Hanoi

1973. Victory over U.S. Air Force.

N752 **264** 12 x. multicoloured . . . 25 15
N753 – 12 x. multicoloured . . . 25 15
N754 – 12 x. multicoloured . . . 25 15
N755 – 1 d. black and red . . 1·25 55

DESIGNS: No. N753, Boeing B-52 Stratofortress exploding over Haiphong; N754, Anti-aircraft gun; N755, Aircraft wreckage in China Sea.

266 Elephant hauling Logs

267 Dahlia

1974. Vietnamese Elephants. Multicoloured.

N758 12 x. Type **266** 50 20
N759 12 x. War elephant 50 20
N760 40 x. Elephant rolling logs . 1·25 35
N761 50 x. Circus elephant . . . 1·50 45
N762 1 d. Elephant carrying war supplies . . . . 3·25 95

1974. Flowers.

N763 **267** 12 x. red, lake & green . 45 20
N764 – 12 x. red, lake & green . 45 20
N765 – 12 x. yellow, grn & bl . 45 20
N766 – 12 x. multicoloured . . 75 30
N767 – 12 x. multicoloured . . 75 30

FLOWERS: No. N764, Rose; N765, Chrysanthemum; N766, Bach Mi; N767, Dai Doa.

268 Soldier planting Flag

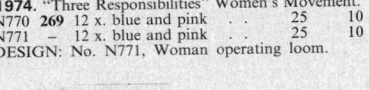

269 Armed Worker and Peasant

1974. 20th Anniv of Victory at Dien Bien Phu.

N768 12 x. Type **268** 20 10
N769 12 x. Victory badge 20 10

1974. "Three Responsibilities" Women's Movement.

N770 **269** 12 x. blue and pink . . 25 10
N771 – 12 x. blue and pink . . 25 10

DESIGN: No. N771, Woman operating loom.

270 Cuc Nau Chrysanthemum

271 "Corchorus capsularis"

1974. Vietnamese Chrysanthemums. Mult.

N772 12 x. Type **270** 30 20
N773 12 x. Cuc Vang 30 20
N774 20 x. Cuc Ngoc Khong Tuoc 55 25
N775 30 x. Cuc Trang 60 30
N776 40 x. Kim Cuc 75 45
N777 50 x. Cuc Hong Mi . . . . 1·10 50
N778 60 x. Cuc Gam . . . . . 1·40 55
N779 1 d. Cuc Tim . . . . . 2·50 1·00

1974. Textile Plants.

N780 **271** 12 x. brown, green and olive 50 15
N781 – 12 x. brown, grn & pink . 50 15
N782 – 30 x. brown, grn & yell 1·00 35

DESIGNS: No. N781, "Cyperus tojet jormis"; N782, "Morus alba".

272 Nike Statue, Warsaw

1974. 30th Anniv of People's Republic of Poland.

N783 **272** 1 x. pur, pink and red . 25 15
N784 2 x. red, pink and red . 25 15
N785 3 x. brn, pink and red . 25 15
N786 12 x. lt red, pink & red 65 25

273 Flags of China and Vietnam

1974. 25th Anniv of People's Republic of China.

N787 **273** 12 x. multicoloured . . 35 15

274 Handclasp with Vietnamese and East German Flags

1974. 25th Anniv of German Democratic Republic.
N788 **274** 12 x. multicoloured . . 35 15

275 Woman Bricklayer

276 Pres. Allende with Chilean Flag

1974. 20th Anniv of Liberation of Hanoi. Multicoloured.
N789 12 x. Type **275** 20 10
N790 12 x. Soldier with child . . . 20 10

1974. 1st Death Annivs of Salvador Allende (President of Chile) and Pablo Neruda (Chilean poet).
N791 **276** 12 x. blue and red . . . 20 10
N792 – 12 x. blue (Pablo Neruda) 20 10

277 "Rhizostoma"

1974. Marine Life. Multicoloured.
N793 12 x. Type **277** 50 15
N794 12 x. "Loligo" 50 15
N795 30 x. "Haleotis" 75 20
N796 40 x. "Pteria martensii" . . 1·00 25
N797 50 x. "Sepia officinalis" . . 1·60 50
N798 1 d. "Palinurus japonicus" . 3·25 1·00

278 Flags of Algeria and Vietnam

279 Albanian Emblem

1974. 20th Anniv of Algerian War of Liberation.
N799 **278** 12 x. multicoloured . . 40 15

1974. 30th Anniv of People's Republic of Albania. Multicoloured.
N800 12 x. Type **279** 20 10
N801 12 x. Girls from Albania and North Vietnam 20 10

280 Signing of Paris Agreement

1975. 2nd Anniv of Paris Agreement on Vietnam.
N802 **280** 12 x. blk, grn and emerald 25 20
N803 – 12 x. blk, blue and grey 25 20
DESIGN: No. N803, International Conference in session.

281 Tran Phu

1975. 45th Anniv of Vietnamese Workers' Party.
N804 **281** 12 x. brown, red & pink 20 10
N805 – 12 x. brown, red & pink 20 10
N806 – 12 x. brown, red & pink 20 10
N807 – 12 x. brown, red & pink 20 10
N808 – 60 x. brown, chestnut and pink 75 35
PORTRAITS—HORIZ: No. N805, Nguyen Van Cu; N806, Le Hong Phong; N807, Ngo Gia Tu. VERT: No. N808, Ho Chi Minh in 1924.

282 "Costus speciosus" 283 "Achras sapota"

1975. Medicinal Plants. Multicoloured.
N809 12 x. Type **282** 30 15
N810 12 x. "Rosa laevigata" . . 30 15
N811 12 x. "Curcuma zedoaria" . . 30 15
N812 30 x. "Erythrina indica" . . 55 20
N813 40 x. "Lilium brownii" . . 70 25
N814 50 x. "Hibiscus sagittifolius" 75 35
N815 60 x. "Papaver somniferum" 1·10 40
N816 1 d. "Belamcanda chinensis" 2·25 70

1975. Fruits. Multicoloured.
N817 12 x. Type **283** 20 10
N818 12 x. "Persica vulgaris" . . 20 10
N819 20 x. "Eugenia jambos" . . 25 15
N820 30 x. "Chrysophyllum cainito" 35 20
N821 40 x. "Lucuma mamosa" . 40 20
N822 50 x. "Prunica granitum" . 55 20
N823 60 x. "Durio ziberthinus" . 75 35
N824 1 d. "Prunus salicina" . . . 1·40 65

284 Ho Chi Minh 285 Ho Chi Minh proclaiming Independence, 1945

1975. 85th Birth Anniv of Ho Chi Minh.
N825 **284** 12 x. multicoloured . . 20 15
N826 60 x. multicoloured . . 45 20

1975. 30th Anniv of Democratic Republic of Vietnam. Multicoloured.
N827 12 x. Type **285** 20 10
N828 12 x. Democratic Republic emblem 20 10
N829 12 x. Democratic Republic flag 20 15

286 "Dermochelys coriacea" 287 Arms of Hungary

1975. Reptiles. Multicoloured.
N831 12 x. Type **286** 35 15
N832 12 x. "Physignathus cocincinus" 35 15
N833 20 x. "Hydrophis brookii" . . 50 15
N834 30 x. "Platysternum megacephalum" 60 20
N835 40 x. "Leiolepis belliana" . 90 20
N836 50 x. "Python molurus" . 1·00 35
N837 60 x. "Naja hannah" . . . 1·25 45
N838 1 d. "Draco maculatus" . . 2·50 55

1975. 30th Anniv of Liberation of Hungary.
N839 **287** 12 x. multicoloured . . 35 15

288 "Pathysa antiphates"

1976. Butterflies. Multicoloured.
N840 12 x. Type **288** 50 10
N841 12 x. "Danaus genutia" . . 50 10
N842 20 x. "Gynautocera papilionaria" 65 15
N843 30 x. "Maenas salaminia" . 75 20
N844 40 x. "Papilio machaon" . 1·00 20
N845 50 x. "Ixias pyrene" . . . 1·10 30
N846 60 x. "Eusemia vetula" . . 1·50 50
N847 1 d. "Eriboea hbri" . . . 2·75 65

289 Hoang Thao Orchid 290 Masked Palm Civet

1976. Lunar New Year.
N848 **289** 6 x. yellow, grn & blue . 60 25
N849 12 x. yellow, grn & red . 95 25

1976. Wild Animals. Multicoloured.
N850 12 x. Type **290** 25 10
N851 12 x. Belly-banded squirrel . 25 10
N852 20 x. Rhesus macaque . . . 30 10
N853 30 x. Chinese porcupine . . 50 15
N854 40 x. Racoon-dog 60 20
N855 50 x. Asiatic black bear . . 75 30
N856 60 x. Leopard . . . . 1·10 45
N857 1 d. Malayan flying lemur . 1·90 65

291 Voters and Map

1976. 1st Elections Unified National Assembly.
N858 **291** 6 x. red and sepia . . . 25 10
N859 – 6 x. yellow and red . . . 25 10
N860 **291** 12 x. red and blue . . . 75 20
DESIGN:—35 × 24 mm: No. N859, Map and ballot box.
See also Nos. NLF64/6 of National Front for the Liberation of South Vietnam.

292 Map and Text

1976. 1st Session of Unified National Assembly.
N861 **292** 6 x. purple, red & yell . 25 10
N862 12 x. turquoise, red & yell 60 20
N863 – 12 x. bistre, red & yellow 60 20
DESIGN—VERT (27 × 42 mm): No. N863, Vietnam map and design from Ngoc Lu Drum. No. N862 shows different text from Type **292**.
See also Nos. NLF68/9 of National Front for the Liberation of South Vietnam.

293 "Dendrobium devonianum"

1976. Orchids. Multicoloured.
N864 12 x. Type **293** 25 10
N865 12 x. "Habenaria rhodocheila" 25 10
N866 20 x. "Dendrobium tortile" . 40 10
N867 30 x. "Doritis pulcherima" . 50 10
N868 40 x. "Dendrobium farmeri" 70 15
N869 50 x. "Dendrobium aggregatum" 80 25
N870 60 x. "Eria pannae" . . . 1·10 45
N871 1 d. "Paphiopedilum concolor" 1·40 55

FRANK STAMPS

F 29 F 42 Invalids in Rice-field

1958. No value indicated.
NF82 F **29** (–) red, yellow and green 10·00 4·50
Issued to war-disabled persons for private correspondence.

1959. No value indicated.
NF105 F **42** (–) brown . . . . . . 3·00 90
NF106 (–) olive and blue . . 4·50 1·40
Issued to invalids in agriculture for private correspondence

F **230** Invalid's Badge

1971. No value indicated.
NF647 F **230** (–) brown and red . 60 25
Issued to disabled ex-servicemen for private correspondence.

F **233** Disabled Soldier with Baby F **261** "Returning Home"

1971. No value indicated.
NF651 F **233** (–) brown, red and yellow 45 20

1973.
NF746 F **261** 12 x. black and red 30 10
NF747 – 12 x. black & blue . 30 10
DESIGN—22 × 33 mm: No. NF747, Disabled soldier with drill.
Issued to disabled veterans for private correspondence.

MILITARY FRANK STAMPS

MF **46** Soldier and Steam Train

1959. No value indicated.
NMF112 MF **46** (–) black & grn . 6·50 2·25

MF **68** Mounted Frontier Guard MF **118** Military Medal and Invalid's Badge

1961. No value indicated.
NMF154 MF **68** (–) multicoloured 11·00 5·50

1963.
NMF277 MF **118** 12 x. mult . . . 3·50 2·50
For use on disabled soldier's mail.

MF **133** Soldier and Army Badge MF **150** Soldier in Action

1964. No value indicated.
NMF325 MF **133** (–) green, black and orange . 1·90 60

1965. No value indicated.
NMF373 MF **150** (–) black & red 1·75 45
NMF374 (–) black & grn 1·75 45

MF **177** Soldiers and Weapons

1966. No value indicated.
NMF447 MF **177** (–) violet & black 6·50 6·50

MF 189 "Star" Badge of People's Army **MF 204** Soldiers attacking

1967. No value indicated.
NMF488 **MF 189** (–) mult 60 30

1968. No value indicated.
NMF519 (–) brown and green . .
No. NMF519 is similar in design to No. NMF447, but shows more modern equipment and is dated "1967".

1968. No value indicated.
NMF547 **MF 204** (–) lilac 65 30

1969. Type **MF 177**, but undated. No value indicated.
NMF579 **MF 177** (–) brown & grn

MF 231 Nguyen Van Be attacking Tank

1971. No value indicated.
NMF648 **MF 231** (–) black, red & drab 50 25

MF 242 Nguyen Viet Yuan and Anti-aircraft Gun

1971. No value indicated.
NMF677 **MF 242** (–) black, pink and buff . . . 40 20
NMF678 (–) brown & grn 40 20

MF 265 Soldier with Bayonet advancing

1974. No value indicated.
NMF756 **MF 265** (–) black, yell and blue 25 10
NMF757 – (–) black, red and brown 25 10
NMF758 **MF 265** (–) black, flesh and red . . . 50 20
DESIGN: No. NMF757 Soldier with sub-machine gun, and tanks. No. NMF757 is 40×24 mm; No. NMF758 31×21 mm.

OFFICIAL STAMPS

The values on Official stamps issued 1952 to 1954 are in kilogrammes of rice, the basis of the State's economy.

A. Tongking.

O 6 Rice-harvester

1953. Production and Economy Campaign.
NO17 **O 6** 0.600 k. red . . . . 4·50 1·90
NO18 1.000 k. brown . . . . 4·50 3·25
NO19 2.000 k. orange . . . . 7·00 3·75
NO20 5.000 k. slate . . . . 9·00 7·00

B. Central Annam.

NAO 3 "Family Left Behind"

1952. Issue for Central Annam. Imperf.
NAO 9 **NAO 3** 0.050 k. red . . . — £150
NAO10 0.300 k. red . . . — £150
NAO11 0.300 k. violet . . — £150
NAO12 0.600 k. green . . — £150
NAO13 0.600 k. blue . . — £150
NAO14 1000 k. green . . — £250

1954. No. NA5 surch **TEMSU VU 0. k 300 THOC.**
NAO15 **NA 1** 0.300 k. on 30 d. on 5 d. green . . . £325 £225

1954. Nos. 56/7 of Vietnam Democratic Republic surch, No. NAO17 also optd **"LKV"** at top and **"THOC"** below value.
NAO16 **3** 0 kg 05 on 1 h. green . £170
NAO17 0 kg 050 on 3 h. red . £170

C. General issues.

1954. Dien-Bien-Phu Victory. As T **9** but value in "KILO". Imperf.
NO24 0.600 k. ochre and sepia . 12·50 7·50

1955. Surch **0 k, 100 THOC.**
NO33 **2** 0.100 k. on 2 d. brown . £150 £120
NO34 0.100 k. on 5 d. red . . £150 £120

1955. Land Reform. As T **13** but inscr "SU VU".
NO38 40 d. blue . . . . 10·00 5·00
NO39 80 d. red . . . . 15·00 6·25

O 17 Cu Chinh Lan (Tank Destroyer)

1956. Cu Chinh Lan Commemoration.
NO50 **O 17** 20 d. green & turq . 2·75 2·75
NO51 80 d. mauve and red 3·50 3·50
NO52 100 d. sepia & drab . 4·00 4·00
NO53 500 d. blue & lt bl 11·50 11·50
NO54 1000 d. brown & orge 26·00 26·00
NO55 2000 d. purple & grn 40·00 40·00
NO56 3000 d. lake & lilac 75·00 75·00

1957. 4th World T.U. Conference, Leipzig. As T **24** but inscr "SU VU".
NO69 20 d. green . . . . 2·10 1·25
NO70 40 d. blue . . . . 2·50 1·25
NO71 80 d. lake . . . . 3·75 2·25
NO72 100 d. brown . . . . . . 4·00 2·75

O 26 Mot Cot Pagoda, Hanoi **O 30** Lathe

1957.
NO75 **O 26** 150 d. brown & green 5·50 2·75
NO76 150 d. black & yellow 8·50 4·75

1958. Arts and Crafts Fair, Hanoi.
NO83 **O 30** 150 d. black & pink . 1·90 1·40
NO84 200 d. blue & orange 2·75 1·90

O 31 Congress Symbol

1958. 1st World Congress of Young Workers, Prague.
NO85 **O 31** 150 d. red and green 2·25 90

O 34 Soldier, Factory and Crops

1958. Military Service.
NO91 **O 34** 50 d. blue and purple 1·40 60
NO92 150 d. brown & green 2·25 75
NO93 200 d. red and yellow 2·75 90

O 40 Footballer and Hanoi Stadium

1958. Opening of New Hanoi Stadium.
NO102 **O 40** 10 d. lilac and blue . 65 30
NO103 20 d. olive & salmon 1·00 50
NO104 80 d. brown & ochre 1·75 45
NO105 150 d. brown & turq 2·75 85

O 97 Armed Forces on Boat **O 100** Woman with Rice-planter

1962. Miltiary Service.
NO223 **O 97** 12 x. multicoloured . 4·25 1·75

1962. Rural Service.
NO229 **O 100** 3 x. red 50 20
NO230 6 x. turquoise . . . 75 25
NO231 12 x. olive 95 35

O 176 Postman delivering Letter

1966. Rural Service.
NO445 **O 176** 3 x. purple, bistre and lilac 40 25
NO446 – 6 x. purple, bistre and turquoise 65 25
DESIGN: 6 x. As Type **O 176** but design reversed.

POSTAGE DUE STAMPS

1952. Handstamped **TT** in diamond frame.
ND33 **3** 100 d. green . . . . . . 40·00 40·00
ND34 100 d. brown . . . . . . 40·00 40·00
ND35 **5** 100 d. violet . . . . . . 50·00 50·00
ND36 **3** 200 d. red . . . . 50·00 50·00

D 13 Letter Scales **D 39**

1955.
ND40 **D 13** 50 d. brown & lemon 11·00 8·75

1958.
ND101 **D 39** 10 d. red and violet . 70 60
ND102 20 d. green & orange 1·50 90
ND103 100 d. red and slate . 3·00 2·40
ND104 300 d. red and olive . 4·50 3·25

F. SOCIALIST REPUBLIC OF VIETNAM

Following elections in April 1976 a National Assembly representing the whole of Vietnam met in Hanoi on 24 June 1976 and on 2 July proclaimed the reunification of the country as the Socialist Republic of Vietnam, with Hanoi as capital.

100 xu = 1 dong

18 Red Cross and Vietnam Map on Globe

1976. 30th Anniv of Vietnamese Red Cross.
99 **18** 12 x. red, blue and green . . 50 25

20 "Lutjanus sebae"

1976. Marine Fishes. Multicoloured.
102 12 x. Type **20** 25 10
103 12 x. "Dampieria melanotaenia" 25 10
104 20 x. "Therapon theraps" . . 35 10
105 30 x. "Amphiprion bifasciatus" 50 15
106 40 x. "Abudefduf sexfasciatus" 65 15
107 50 x. "Heniochus acuminatus" 75 20
108 60 x. "Amphiprion macrostoma" 95 35
109 1 d. "Symphorus spilurus" . . 1·60 50

22 Party Flag and Map **23** Workers and Flag

1976. 4th Congress of Vietnam Workers' Party (1st issue). Flag in yellow and red, background colours given below.
111 **22** 2 x. turquoise 10 10
112 3 x. purple 10 10
113 5 x. turquoise 20 10
114 10 x. green 25 10
115 12 x. myrtle 30 10
116 20 x. green 50 20

1976. 4th Congress of Vietnam Workers' Party (2nd issue).
117 **23** 12 x. black, red & yellow . 30 10
118 12 x. red, orange & black . 30 10

24 Ho Chi Minh and Map of Vietnam

1976. "Unification of Vietnam".
119 **24** 6 x. multicoloured 20 15
120 12 x. multicoloured 25 15

25 Soldiers seizing Buon Me Thuot

1976. Liberation of South Vietnam. Mult.
121 2 x. Type **25** 20 10
122 3 x. Soldiers on Son Tra peninsula, Da Nang 20 10
123 6 x. Soldiers attacking Presidential Palace, Saigon . 20 10
124 50 x. Type **25** 55 20
125 1 d. As 3 x. 95 45
126 2 d. As 6 x. . . . . 1·75 90

1976. As Nos. N848/9 but inscr "VIET NAM 1976" at foot and background colours changed.
126a **289** 6 x. yellow, grn & orge . 1·60 50
126b 12 x. yellow, light green and green . . . . 1·60 50

26 "Crocothemis servilia" (Ho)

1977. Dragonflies. Multicoloured.
127 12 x. Type **26** 20 10
128 12 x. "Ictinogomphus clavatus" (Bao) 20 10
129 20 x. "Rhinocypha fenestrella" 30 10
130 30 x. "Neurothemis tullia" . . 35 15
131 40 x. "Neurobavis chinensis" . 50 15
132 50 x. "Neurothemis fulvia" . 75 15
133 60 x. "Rhyothemis variegata" 1·00 35
134 1 d. "Rhyothemis fuliginosa" 1·75 45

27 Great Indian Hornbill and Emblem of Protection **28** Thang Long Tower and Bronze Drum

1977. Protection of Rare Birds. Multicoloured.

135 12 x. Type **27** 20 10
136 12 x. Tickell's hornbill 20 10
137 20 x. Long-crested hornbill 35 15
138 30 x. Wreathed hornbill 45 20
139 40 x. Indian pied hornbill 55 30
140 50 x. Black hornbill 75 30
141 60 x. Great Indian hornbill 90 45
142 1 d. Rufous-necked hornbill 1·60 60

1977. 1st Anniv of National Assembly General Election. Multicoloured.

143 4 x. Type **28** 15 10
144 5 x. Map of Vietnam 15 10
145 12 x. Lotus flower 15 10
146 50 x. Vietnamese flag 40 20

Each design shows a bronze drum in the background.

29 "Anoplophora bowringii" **30** "Thevetia peruviana"

1977. Beetles. Multicoloured.

147 12 x. Type **29** 15 10
148 12 x. "Anoplophora horsfieldi" 15 10
149 20 x. "Aphrodisium griffithi" 25 10
150 30 x. "Aromia moschata" 35 15
151 40 x. "Calloplophora tonkinea" 50 20
152 50 x. "Thysia wallacei" 60 25
153 60 x. "Aristobia approximator" 1·00 40
154 1 d. "Batocera rubus" 1·60 60

1977. Wild Flowers. Multicoloured.

155 12 x. Type **30** 20 10
156 12 x. "Broussonetia papyrifera" 20 10
157 20 x. "Aleurites montana" 25 15
158 30 x. "Cerbera manghes" 35 15
159 40 x. "Cassia multijuga" 50 20
160 50 x. "Cassia nodosa" 60 20
161 60 x. "Hibiscus schizopetalus" 85 35
162 1 d. "Lagerstroesnia speciosa" 1·40 55

31 Pink Dahlias (Hoa Dong Tien) **32** Children drawing Map of Vietnam

1977. Flowers. Multicoloured.

163 6 x. Type **31** 15 10
164 6 x. Orange cactus dahlias (Bong tien kep) 15 10
165 12 x. Type **31** 25 10
166 12 x. As No. 164 25 10

1977. Unification of Vietnam.

167 **32** 4 x. multicoloured 20 15
168 5 x. multicoloured 20 15
169 10 x. multicoloured 30 15
170 12 x. multicoloured 30 15
171 30 x. multicoloured 50 20

33 Goldfish (Dong Nai Hoa)

1977. Goldfish. Multicoloured.

172 12 x. Type **33** 20 15
173 12 x. Hoa nhung 20 15
174 20 x. Tau xanh 35 15
175 30 x. Mat rong 35 15
176 40 x. Cam trang 45 20
177 50 x. Ngu sac 75 25
178 60 x. Dong nai 1·00 30
179 1 d. Thap cam 1·75 50

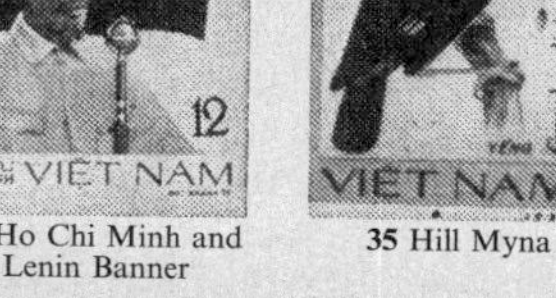

34 Ho Chi Minh and Lenin Banner **35** Hill Myna

1977 60th Anniv of Russian Revolution. Mult.

180 12 x. Type **34** (blue background) 25 10
181 12 x. Type **34** (brown background) 25 10
182 50 x. Mother holding child with flag 45 20
183 1 d. Workers and banner 95 40

1978. Vietnamese Songbirds. Multicoloured.

184 12 x. Type **35** 30 25
185 20 x. Spotted dove 35 30
186 20 x. Hwamei 35 30
187 30 x. Black-headed shrike 75 35
188 40 x. Crimson-winged laughing thrush 1·00 45
189 50 x. Black-throated laughing thrush 1·60 50
190 60 x. Chinese jungle mynah 2·10 75
191 1 d. Yersin's laughing thrush 3·00 1·25

1978. Flowers. As T **31**. Multicoloured.

192 5 x. Sunflower 15 10
193 6 x. Marguerites 15 10
194 10 x. As 5 x. 25 10
195 12 x. As 6 x. 25 10

36 Vietnamese Children **37** Throwing the Discus

1978. International Children's Day.

196 **36** 12 x. multicoloured 35 20

1978. Athletics. Multicoloured.

197 12 x. Type **37** 20 10
198 12 x. Long jumping 20 10
199 20 x. Hurdling 25 10
200 30 x. Throwing the hammer 45 15
201 40 x. Putting the shot 55 20
202 50 x. Throwing the javelin 75 25
203 60 x. Sprinting 1·10 40
204 1 d. High jumping 1·60 55

38 Ho Chi Minh and Workers **39** Ho Chi Minh

1978. 4th Vietnamese Trade Union Congress. Multicoloured.

205 10 x. Trade Union Emblem 25 10
206 10 x. Type **38** 25 10

1978. 88th Birth Anniv of Ho Chi Minh. Multicoloured.

207 10 x. Type **39** 35 20
208 12 x. Ho Chi Minh Monument (38 × 22 mm) 35 20

40 Young Pioneers' Cultural House, Hanoi

1978. International Children's Day.

209 **40** 10 x. black, flesh and salmon 35 20

41 Sanakavasa

1978. Sculptures from Tay Phoung Pagoda. Multicoloured.

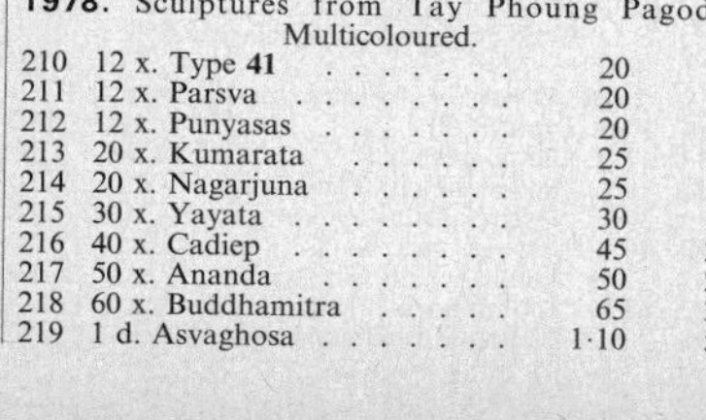

210 12 x. Type **41** 20 10
211 12 x. Parsva 20 10
212 12 x. Punyasas 20 10
213 20 x. Kumarata 25 10
214 20 x. Nagarjuna 25 10
215 30 x. Yayata 30 15
216 40 x. Cadiep 45 20
217 50 x. Ananda 50 25
218 60 x. Buddhamitra 65 30
219 1 d. Asvaghosa 1·10 50

42 Cuban Flag **43** Worker, Peasant, Soldier and Intellectual

1978. 25th Anniv of Cuban Revolution.

220 **42** 6 x. red, black and blue 25 10
221 12 x. red, black and blue 30 10

1978. 33rd Anniv of Proclamation of Vietnam Democratic Republic.

222 **43** 6 x. red, mauve & yellow 15 10
223 – 6 x. turquoise and lt green 15 10
224 **43** 12 x. red, mauve & yellow 25 15
225 – 12 x. red and pink 25 15

DESIGN: Nos. 223 and 225, Symbols of agriculture and industry.

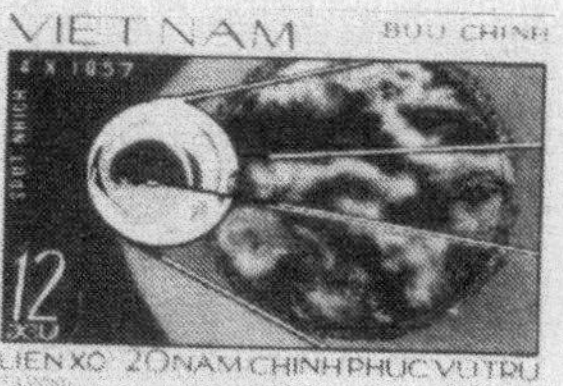

44 "Sputnik"

1978. Space Research. Multicoloured.

226 12 x. Type **44** 20 10
227 12 x. "Venus 1" 20 10
228 30 x. Space capsules docking 20 15
229 40 x. "Molniya 1" 30 20
230 60 x. "Soyuz" 50 25
231 2 d. A. Gubarev and G. Grechko 1·75 75

45 Printed Circuit **47** Chrysanthemum "Cu Tim"

46 Telephone Dial and Letter

1978. World Telecommunications Day.

232 **45** 12 x. orange and brown 25 10
233 – 12 x. brown and orange 25 10

DESIGN: No. 233, I.T.U. emblem.

1978. 20th Congress Socialist Countries' Postal Ministers.

234 **46** 12 x. multicoloured 35 10

1978. Chrysanthemums. Multicoloured.

235 12 x. Type **47** 20 10
236 12 x. "Cuc Kim Tien" 20 10
237 20 x. "Cuc Hong" 25 15
238 30 x. "Cuc Van Tho" 35 15
239 40 x. "Cuc Vang" 35 15
240 50 x. "Cuc Thuy Tim" 55 25
241 60 x. "Cuc Vang Mo" 90 35
242 1 d. "Cuc Nau Do" 1·60 50

48 Plesiosaurus **49** Cuban and Vietnamese Flags and Militiawomen

1979. Prehistoric Animals. Multicoloured.

243 12 x. Type **48** 20 10
244 12 x. Brontosaurus 20 10
245 20 x. Iguanodon 25 10
246 30 x. Tyrannosaurus 30 15
247 40 x. Stegosaurus 35 15
248 50 x. Mozasaurus 45 20
249 60 x. Triceratop 1·10 25
250 1 d. Pteranodon 1·60 45

1979. 20th Anniv of Cuban Republic.

251 **49** 12 x. multicoloured 30 10

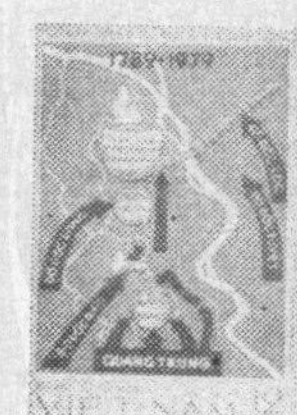

50 Battle Plan **51** Einstein

1979. 190th Anniv of Quang Trung's Victory over the Thanh.

252 **50** 12 x. green, red and blue 25 10
253 – 12 x. multicoloured 25 10

DESIGN: No. 253, Quang Trung.

1979. Birth Centenary of Albert Einstein (physicist).

254 **51** 12 x. black, brown & blue 25 10
255 – 60 x. multicoloured 80 30

DESIGN: 60 x. Equation, sun and planets.

52 Ram **53** Emblem

1979. Domestic Animals. Multicoloured.

256 10 x. Type **52** 20 10
257 12 x. Ox 20 10
258 20 x. Ewe and lamb 35 15
259 30 x. White buffalo (vert) 45 15
260 40 x. Cow 50 15
261 50 x. Goat 60 20
262 60 x. Buffalo and calf 1·00 30
263 1 d. Young goat (vert) 1·75 55

1979. Five Year Plan.

264 **53** 6 x. purple and pink 10 10
265 – 6 x. green and buff 10 10
266 – 6 x. green and lilac 10 10
267 – 6 x. orange and blue 10 10
268 – 6 x. blue and yellow 10 10
269 **53** 12 x. red and pink 20 10
270 – 12 x. brown and pink 20 10
271 – 12 x. green and yellow 20 10
272 – 12 x. blue and brown 20 10
273 – 12 x. red and blue 20 10

DESIGNS: Nos. 265, 270, Worker; 266, 271, Peasant; 267, 272, Soldier; 268, 273, Intellectual.

54 "Philaserdica '79" Emblem **55** Ho Chi Minh and Children

1979. "Philaserdica '79" International Stamp Exhibition, Sofia, Bulgaria.

274 **54** 12 x. blue, brown & orange 25 10
275 30 x. blue, brown and pink 35 10

1979. International Year of the Child. Mult.

276 12 x. Type **55** 15 10
277 20 x. Nurse, mother and child 30 10
278 50 x. Children with model glider 45 15
279 1 d. Children of different races 95 35

56 Silver Pheasant **58** Cat (Meo Muop)

57 "Dendrobium heterocacpum"

1979. Ornamental Birds. Multicoloured.

280 12 x. Siamese fireback pheasant (horiz) 20 10
281 12 x. Temminck's tragopan (horiz) 20 10
282 20 x. Ring-necked pheasant (horiz) 30 15
283 30 x. Edward's pheasant (horiz) 40 20
284 40 x. Type **56** 45 25
285 50 x. Germain's peacock-pheasant 60 35
286 60 x. Rheinhard's pheasant 95 40
287 1 d. Green peafowl 1·40 60

1979. Orchids. Multicoloured.

288 12 x. Type **57** 20 10
289 12 x. "Cymbidium hybridum" 20 10
290 20 x. "Rhynchostylis gigantea" 25 10
291 30 x. "Dendrobium nobile" 30 15
292 40 x. "Aerides falcatum" 35 15
293 50 x. "Paphiopedilum callosum" 60 25
294 60 x. "Vanda teres" 95 25
295 1 d. "Dendrobium phalaenopsis" 1·50 45

1979. Cats. Multicoloured.

296 12 x. Type **58** 20 10
297 12 x. Meo Tam The (horiz) 20 10
298 20 x. Meo Khoang 25 10
299 30 x. Meo Dom Van (horiz) 35 15
300 40 x. Meo Muop Dom 40 15
301 50 x. Meo Vang 70 30
302 60 x. Meo Xiem (horiz) 1·00 40
303 1 d. Meo Van Am (horiz) 1·90 55

60 Citizens greeting Soldiers

1979. 35th Anniv of Vietnam People's Army.

306 **60** 12 x. brown and green 30 20
307 – 12 x. brown and green 30 20
DESIGN: No. 307, Soldiers in action.

62 Red and Pink Roses **63** "Nelumbium nuciferum"

1980. Roses. Multicoloured.

311 1 x. Type **62** 15 10
312 2 x. Single pink rose 15 10
313 12 x. Type **62** 30 20
314 12 x. As No. 312 30 20

1980. Water Flowers. Multicoloured.

315 12 x. Type **63** 15 10
316 12 x. "Nymphala stellata" 15 10
317 20 x. "Ipomola reptans" 20 10
318 30 x. "Nymphoides indicum" 30 15
319 40 x. "Jussiala repens" 35 15
320 50 x. "Eichhornia crassipes" 70 25
321 60 x. "Monochoria voginalis" 95 25
322 1 d. "Nelumbo nucifera" 1·50 40

64 Peasants with Banner and Implements as Weapons

1980. 50th Anniv of Vietnamese Communist Party. Multicoloured.

323 12 x. Type **64** 10 10
324 12 x. Ho Chi Minh proclaiming independence 10 10
325 20 x. Victory of Dien Bien Phu 25 15
326 20 x. Unification of North and South Vietnam 25 15
327 2 d. Ho Chi Minh and armed Vietnamese 1·60 60

65 Lenin

1980. 110th Birth Anniv of Lenin.

328 **65** 6 x. green and flesh 15 10
329 12 x. red and flesh 25 10
330 1 d. blue and flesh 80 35

66 Running **67** Ho Chi Minh in 1924

1980. Olympic Games, Moscow. Multicoloured.

331 12 x. Type **66** 10 10
332 12 x. Hurdles 10 10
333 20 x. Basketball 20 15
334 30 x. Football 30 15
335 40 x. Wrestling 40 15
336 50 x. Gymnastics (horiz) 45 20
337 60 x. Swimming (horiz) 65 25
338 1 d. Sailing (horiz) 95 45

1980. President Ho Chi Minh's 90th Birthday.

339 12 x. Type **67** 35 15
340 40 x. Ho Chi Minh 50 20

68 Children dancing around Globe **69** Soviet and Vietnamese Cosmonauts

1980. International Children's Day.

341 **68** 5 x. multicoloured 25 15

1980. Soviet–Vietnamese Space Flight. Mult.

342 12 x. Type **69** 10 10
343 12 x. Rocket 10 10
344 20 x. "Soyuz 37" 20 10
345 40 x. "Soyuz-Salyut" space complex 30 15
346 1 d. "Soyuz" returning to Earth 70 25
347 2 d. Capsule landing by parachute 1·40 65

70 "Rhincodon typus"

1980. Fishes. Multicoloured.

349 12 x. Type **70** 15 10
350 12 x. "Galeocerdo cuvier" 15 10
351 20 x. "Orectolobus japonicus" 20 10
352 30 x. "Heterodontus zebra" 30 10
353 40 x. "Dasyatis uarnak" 50 15
354 50 x. "Pristis microdon" 60 20
355 60 x. "Sphyrna lewini" 85 25
356 1 d. "Myliobatis tobijei" 1·25 40

71 Ho Chi Minh telephoning **72** Pink Rose (Hong Bach)

1980. Posts and Telecommunications Day. Multicoloured.

357 12 x. Ho Chi Minh reading newspaper "Nhan Dan" 20 10
358 12 x. Type **71** 25 10
359 50 x. Kim Dong, "the heroic postman", carrying magpie robin in cage 75 30
360 1 d. Dish aerial 1·00 35

1980. Flowers.

361 **72** 12 x. pink and green 35 15
362 – 12 x. red and green 35 15
363 – 12 x. pink, mve and grn 35 15
DESIGNS: No. 362, Red roses (Hong nhung). 15×20 mm: No. 363, Camellia.

73 Telephone Switchboard Operator **74** Ho Chi Minh

1980. National Telecommunications Day.

364 12 x. Type **73** 20 10
365 12 x. Diesel train and railway route map 30 10

1980. 35th Anniv of Republic of Vietnam. Multicoloured.

366 12 x. Type **74** 25 10
367 12 x. Arms of Vietnam (29×40 mm) 25 10
368 40 x. Pac Bo cave (29×40 mm) 40 15
369 1 d. Source of Lenine (40×29 mm) 95 40

75 Vietnamese Arms **76** Nguyen Trai

1980. National Emblems.

370 **75** 6 x. multicoloured 25 10
371 – 12 x. yellow, red and blk 25 10
372 – 12 x. black, yell and orge 25 10
DESIGNS—VERT: No. 372, National Anthem. HORIZ: No. 371, National flag.

1980. 600th Birth Anniv of Nguyen Trai (national hero).

373 **76** 12 x. yellow and black 20 10
374 – 50 x. black and blue 45 20
375 – 1 d. brown and black 95 40
DESIGNS—HORIZ: 50 x. Three books by Nguyen Trai. VERT: 1 d. Ho Chi Minh reading commemorative stele in Con Son Pagoda.

77 Ho Chi Minh with Women **78** "Biguoniaceae venusta"

1980. 50th Anniv of Vietnamese Women's Union.

376 **77** 12 x. green, blue and lilac 25 10
377 – 12 x. blue and lilac 25 10
DESIGN: No. 377, Group of women.

1980. Flowers. Multicoloured.

378 12 x. Type **78** 20 10
379 12 x. "Ipomoea pulchella" 20 10
380 20 x. "Petunia hybrida" 30 10
381 30 x. "Trapaeolum majus" 40 15
382 40 x. "Thunbergia grandiflora" 45 15
383 50 x. "Anlamanda cathartica" 55 20
384 60 x. "Campsis radicans" 80 25
385 1 d. "Bougainvillaea spectabilis" 1·50 45

79 "Symphysodon aequifasciata"

1981. Ornamental Fishes. Multicoloured.

386 12 x. Type **79** 20 10
387 12 x. "Betta splendens" 20 10
388 20 x. "Poecilobrycon eques" 30 10
389 30 x. "Gyrinocheilus aymonieri" 40 15
390 40 x. "Barbus tetrazona" 45 15
391 50 x. "Pterophyllum eimekei" 60 20
392 60 x. "Xiphophorous helleri" 85 25
393 1 d. "Trichopterus sumatranus" 1·50 50

80 Rocket, Flowers and Flag **82** Green Imperial Pigeon

81 Bear Macaque

1981. 26th U.S.S.R. Communist Party Congress. Multicoloured.

394 20 x. Type **80** 25 10
395 50 x. Young citizens with flag 50 20

1981. Animals of Cue Phuong Forest. Mult.

396 12 x. Type **81** 10 10
397 12 x. Crested gibbons 10 10
398 20 x. Asiatic black bears 20 10
399 30 x. Dhole 40 15
400 40 x. Wild boar 50 15
401 50 x. Sambars 65 25
402 60 x. Leopard 75 25
403 1 d. Tiger 1·40 40

1981. Turtle Doves. Multicoloured.

404 12 x. Type **82** 25 20
405 12 x. White-bellied wedge-tailed green pigeon (horiz) 25 20
406 20 x. Red turtle dove 30 25
407 30 x. Bar-tailed cuckoo dove 50 30
408 40 x. Mountain imperial pigeon 70 35
409 50 x. Pin-tailed green pigeon (horiz) 90 40
410 60 x. Emerald dove (horiz) 1·10 45
411 1 d. White-bellied pin-tailed green pigeon (horiz) 2·10 85

83 Yellow-backed Sunbird **85** "Elaeagnus latifolia"

1981. Nectar-sucking Birds. Multicoloured.

412 20 x. Type **83** 30 25
413 20 x. Ruby-cheeked sunbird 30 25
414 20 x. Black-throated sunbird 40 30
415 40 x. Mrs. Gould's sunbird 70 35
416 50 x. Macklot's sunbird 85 40
417 50 x. Blue-naped sunbird 85 40
418 60 x. Van Hasselt's sunbird 1·00 45
419 1 d. Green-tailed sunbird 1·75 70

1981. Fruits. Multicoloured.

422 20 x. Type **85** 20 10
423 20 x. "Fortunella japonica" 20 10
424 30 x. "Nephelium lappaceum" 35 15
425 40 x. "Averrhoa bilimbi" 40 15
426 50 x. "Ziziphus mauritiana" 50 20
427 50 x. "Fragaria vesca" 50 20
428 60 x. "Bouea oppositifolia" 60 25
429 1 d. "Syzygium aqueum" 1·25 40

86 Girl with Rice Sheaf **87** Ho Chi Minh planting Tree

1981. World Food Day.

430 **86** 30 x. green 25 15
431 50 x. green 30 15
432 – 2 d. orange 1·10 40
DESIGN: 2 d. F.A.O. emblem and rice.

1981. Tree Planting Festival.

433 **87** 30 x. orange and blue 55 25
434 – 30 x. red and blue 55 25
DESIGN: No. 434, Family planting tree.

88 European Bison

1981. Animals. Multicoloured.

435 30 x. Type **88** 25 10
436 30 x. Orang-utan 25 10
437 40 x. Hippopotamus 40 20
438 40 x. Red kangaroo 40 20
439 50 x. Giraffe 60 20
440 50 x. Javan rhinoceros 60 20
441 60 x. Common zebra 65 25
442 1 d. Lion . . . . 1·40 45

89 Congress Emblem

1982. 10th World Trade Unions Congress, Havana, Cuba.

443 **89** 50 x. multicoloured 30 15
444 5 d. multicoloured . . . . 3·25 1·10

90 Ho Chi Minh and Party Flag

1982. 5th Communist Party Congress (1st issue). Multicoloured.

445 30 x. Type **90** 50 20
446 30 x. Hammer, sickle and rose 50 20

See also Nos. 455/6.

91 "Thyreus decorus"

1982. Bees. Multicoloured.

447 20 x. Type **91** 20 10
448 20 x. "Vespa affinis" 20 10
449 30 x. "Eumenes esuriens" . . . 30 15
450 40 x. "Polistes sp." 45 20
451 50 x. "Sphex sp." 65 25
452 50 x. "Chlorion lobatum" . . . 65 25
453 60 x. "Xylocopa sp." 75 35
454 1 d. "Apis mellifera" . . . . 1·25 50

92 Electricity Worker and Pylon

1982. 5th Communist Party Congress (2nd issue).

455 **92** 30 x. yellow, black & red . . 60 25
456 – 50 x. multicoloured 70 25

DESIGN: 50 x. Women harvesting rice.

93 Football

1982. Football Training Movement.

457 **90** 30 x. multicoloured 35 15
458 – 30 x. multicoloured 35 15
459 – 40 x. multicoloured 40 20
460 – 40 x. mult (diag striped background) 40 20
461 – 50 x. mult (vert striped background) 45 20
462 – 50 x. mult (horiz striped background) 45 20
463 – 60 x. multicoloured 65 25
464 – 1 d. multicoloured 90 40

DESIGNS: Nos. 458/64, Various football scenes.

94 Militiawoman

1982.

465 **94** 30 x. multicoloured . . . 65 25

See also Nos. MF466/7.

95 Arms of Bulgaria

1982. 1300th Anniv of Bulgarian State.

468 **95** 30 x. pink and red 40 10
469 50 x. brown and red . . . 50 15
470 2 d. orange and red . . . 2·25 75

96 Map of Vietnam and Red Cross **97** Georgi Dimitrov

1982. 35th Anniv of Vietnam Red Cross.

471 **96** 30 x. red, blue and black . 30 15
472 – 1 d. red, green and black . 1·25 50

DESIGN: 1 d. Red Cross.

1982. Birth Centenary of Georgi Dimitrov (Bulgarian statesman).

473 **97** 30 x. orange and black . . 35 15
474 3 d. brown and black . . 2·75 95

98 Rejoicing Women **99** Common Kestrel

1982. 5th National Women's Congress. Mult.

475 12 x. Type **98** 40 15
476 12 x. Congress emblem and three women 40 15

1982. Birds of Prey. Multicoloured.

477 30 x. Type **99** 40 35
478 30 x. Pied falconet 40 35
479 40 x. Black baza 60 40
480 50 x. Black kite 80 45
481 50 x. Lesser fishing eagle . . 80 45
482 60 x. Fieldens falconet (horiz) 90 55
483 1 d. Black-shouldered kite (horiz) 1·90 1·10
484 1 d. Short-toed eagle . . . . 1·90 1·10

100 Red Dahlia **101** Dribble

1982. Dahlias. Multicoloured.

485 30 x. Type **100** 40 15
486 30 x. Orange dahlia 40 15
487 40 x. Rose dahlia 45 15
488 50 x. Red decorative dahlia . 60 20
489 50 x. Yellow dahlia 60 20
490 60 x. Red single dahlia . . . 70 25
491 1 d. White dahlia . . . . . 1·25 50
492 1 d. Pink dahlia . . . . . 1·25 50

1982. World Cup Football Championship, Spain. Multicoloured.

493 50 x. Type **101** 50 20
494 50 x. Tackle 50 20
495 50 x. Passing ball 50 20
496 1 d. Heading ball . . . . . 1·10 40
497 1 d. Goalkeeper saving ball . . 1·10 40
498 2 d. Shooting . . . . 1·90 70

102 Cuban Flag **104** Rabindranath Tagore

103 Ho Chi Minh and Children planting Tree

1982. 20th Anniv of Cuban Victory at Giron.

499 **102** 30 x. multicoloured 45 15

1982. World Environment Day.

500 **103** 30 x. green and black . . . 35 15
501 – 30 x. green and black . . . 35 15

DESIGN: No. 501, U.N. environment emblem and plants.

1982. 120th Birth Anniv (1981) of Rabindranath Tagore (Indian poet).

502 **104** 30 x. orange, brown and black 45 25

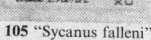

105 "Sycanus falleni" **106** Lenin and Cruiser "Aurora"

1982. Harmful Insects. Multicoloured.

503 30 x. Type **105** 30 10
504 30 x. "Catacanthus incarnatus" 30 10
505 40 x. "Nezara viridula" . . . 40 15
506 50 x. "Helcomeria spinosa" . . 70 20
507 50 c. "Lohita grandis" 70 20
508 60 x. "Chrysocoris stolli" . . . 75 25
509 1 d. "Tiarodes ostentans" . . . 1·25 50
510 1 d. "Pterygamia grayi" . . . 1·25 50

1982. 65th Anniv of Russian Revolution.

511 **106** 30 x. red and black 40 15
512 – 30 x. red and black 40 15

DESIGN: No. 512, Russian man and woman, Lenin and space station.

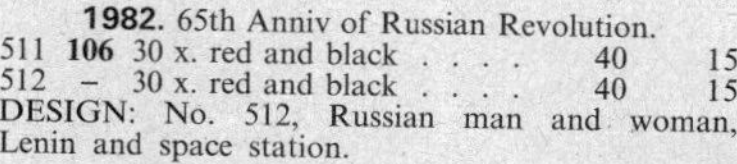

108 Swimming

1982. 9th South East Asian Games, New Delhi.

514 **108** 30 x. blue and lilac 40 15
515 – 30 x. blue and mauve . . . 40 15
516 – 1 d. orange and blue . . . 1·10 40
517 – 2 d. green and brown . . . 1·90 65

DESIGNS: 30 x. (No. 515) Table tennis; 1 d. Wrestling; 2 d. Rifle shooting.

109 "Samaris cristatus"

1982. Fishes. Soles. Multicoloured.

518 30 x. Type **109** 30 10
519 30 x. "Tephrinectes sinensis" . 30 10
520 40 x. "Psettodes erumei" . . . 45 15
521 40 x. "Zebrias zebra" 45 15
522 50 x. "Pardachirus pavoninus" . 65 20
523 50 x. "Cynoglossus puncticeps" . 65 20
524 60 x. "Brachirus orientalis" . . 80 35
525 1 d. "Psettina iijimae" . . . . 1·10 45

110 Foundry and Textile Workers **112** Sampan

111 Lenin on Map

1982. "All for Socialist Fatherland, All for Happiness of People".

526 **110** 30 x. blue and deep blue . 30 10
527 – 30 x. brown and yellow . 30 10
528 – 1 d. brown and green . . 1·10 40
529 – 2 d. pink and purple . . . 2·00 75

DESIGNS: 30 x. Women holding sheaf of wheat and basket of grain; 1 d. Soldiers; 2 d. Nurse with children holding books.

1982. 60th Anniv of U.S.S.R.

530 **111** 30 x. multicolouired . . . 55 20

1983. Boats. Multicoloured.

531 30 x. Type **112** 20 10
532 50 x. Junk with striped sails . 30 10
533 1 d. Houseboats 65 25
534 3 d. Junk 95 30
535 5 d. Sampan with patched sails 1·40 40
536 10 d. Sampan (horiz) . . . . 2·00 95

113 Class "231-300"

1983. Steam Locomotives. Multicoloured.

537 30 x. Type **113** 25 10
538 50 x. Class "230-000" 35 10
539 1 d. Class "140-601" 50 25
540 2 d. Class "241-000" 75 30
541 3 d. Class "141-500" 95 30
542 5 d. Class "150-000" . . . . 1·40 50
543 8 d. Class "40-300" . . . . . 2·25 75

114 Montgolfier Balloon, 1783 **115** Flags and Dove

1983. Bicentenary of Manned Flight. Mult.

544 30 x. Type **114** 25 10
545 50 x. Charles's hydrogen balloon, 1783 . . . . 40 10
546 1 d. Parseval Sigsfeld kite-type observation balloon, 1898 . . 65 25
547 2 d. Eugene Godard's balloon "L'Aigle", 1864 . . . . . . 95 30
548 3 d. Blanchard and Jeffries' balloon, 1785 . . . . . . 1·10 30
549 5 d. Nadar's balloon "Le Geant", 1863 . . . . 1·75 40
550 8 d. Balloon . . . . 2·75 70

1983. Laos–Kampuchea–Vietnam Summit Conference.

552 **115** 50 x. red, yellow & blue . 35 15
553 5 d. red, blue & yellow . 3·50 1·60

116 Robert Koch

1983. Centenary of Discovery of Tubercle Bacillus.
554 116 5 d. black, blue & red . . 3·50 1·60

117 "Teratolepis fasciata"

1983. Reptiles. Multicoloured.
555 30 x. Type 117 . . . . 20 10
556 30 x. Jackson's chameleon . . 20 10
557 50 x. Spiny-tailed agamid . . 25 15
558 80 x. "Heloderma suspectum" 35 15
559 1 d. "Chamaeleo meileri" . . 50 20
560 2 d. "Amphibolurus barbatus" 1·00 25
561 5 d. "Chlamydosaurus kingi" . 2·00 40
562 10 d. "Phrynosoma coronatum" 4·00 90

118 A. Gubarev and V. Remek

1983. Cosmonauts. Multicoloured.
563 30 x. Type 118 . . . . 20 10
564 50 x. P. Klimuk and Miroslaw Hermaszewski 25 10
565 50 x. V. Bykovsky and Sigmund Jahn 25 10
566 1 d. Nikolai Rukavishnikov and Georgi Ivanov 40 15
567 1 d. Bertalan Farkas and V. Kubasov 40 15
568 2 d. V. Gorbatko and Pham Tuan 70 25
569 2 d. Arnaldo Tamayo Mendez and I. Romanenko 70 25
570 5 d. V. Dzhanibekov and Gurragcha . . . . 1·40 40
571 8 d. L. Popov and D. Prunariu 1·75 60

119 "Madonna of the Chair"

121 Burmese King and Rook

1983. 500th Birth Anniv of Raphael (artist). Multicoloured.
573 30 x. Type 119 . . . . 25 10
574 50 x. "Madonna of the Grand Duke" 40 10
575 1 d. "Sistine Madonna" . . . 50 15
576 2 d. "The Marriage of Mary" . 90 30
577 3 d. "The Beautiful Gardener" 1·25 35
578 5 d. "Woman with Veil" . . . 1·75 45
579 8 d. "Self-portrait" . . . . . 2·25 65

1983. Chess Pieces. Multicoloured.
582 30 x. Type 121 . . . . 20 10
583 50 x. 18th-century Delhi king (elephant) 25 10
584 1 d. Lewis knight and bishop . 40 15
585 2 d. 8th/9th-century Arabian king (elephant) 80 30
586 3 d. 12th-century European knight . . . . 1·25 35
587 5 d. 16th-century Russian rook (sailing boat) . . . . 1·75 50
588 8 d. European Chinese-puzzle bishop and rook (fool and elephant) . . . . 2·25 75

123 Long Jumping

125 Common Grass Yellow

1983. Olympic Games, Los Angeles (1984). Multicoloured.
591 30 x. Type 123 . . . . 20 10
592 50 x. Running 25 10
593 1 d. Javelin throwing 40 15
594 2 d. High jumping (horiz) . . 70 30
595 3 d. Hurdling (horiz) . . . . 1·00 35
596 5 d. Putting the shot . . . . 1·40 45
597 8 d. Pole vaulting . . . . . . 1·75 65

1983. Butterflies and Moths. Multicoloured.
600 30 x. Type 125 . . . . 30 10
601 30 x. Green dragontail ("Lamproptera meges") . . 30 10
602 40 x. "Nyctalemon patroclus" 40 15
603 40 x. Tailed jay ("Zetides agamemnon") 40 15
604 50 x. Peacock ("Precis almana") 50 20
605 50 x. "Papilio chaon" 50 20
606 60 x. Tufted jungle king . . . 60 25
607 1 d. Leaf buttefly . . . . . . 1·00 40

128 Karl Marx

1983. Death Centenary of Karl Marx.
617 128 50 x. black and red . . . 45 25
618 10 d. black and red . . . 5·00 2·75

129 Postman

1983. World Communications Year. Mult.
619 50 x. Type 129 . . . . 25 10
620 2 d. Mail sorting office . . . 75 30
621 8 d. Telephonists . . . . . . 2·00 50
622 10 d. Wireless operator and dish aerial . . . . 3·00 75

130 Running, Stadium and Sports Pictograms

1983. National Youth Sports Festival.
624 130 30 x. dp blue and blue . . 65 25
625 1 d. brown and orange . 1·60 70

131 Oyster Fungus ("Pleurotus ostreatus")

132 Child with Fish

1983. Fungi. Multicoloured.
626 50 x. Type 131 . . . . 40 10
627 50 x. Common ink cap ("Coprinus atramentarius") 40 10
628 50 x. Golden mushroom ("Flammulina velutipes") . 40 10
629 50 x. Chanterelle ("Cantharellus cibarius") 40 10
630 1 d. Chinese mushroom . . . 60 20
631 2 d. Red-staining mushroom . 1·25 35
632 5 d. Common morel . . . . 2·25 50
633 10 d. Caesar's mushroom . . 5·00 1·00

1983. World Food Day. Multicoloured.
634 50 x. Type 132 . . . . 25 10
635 4 d. Family . . . . 1·25 45

133 Envelope with I.T.U. Emblem

1983. World Telecommunications Day and Year.
636 133 50 x. + 10 x. blue, green & red 95 65
637 – 50 x. + 10 x. red, light brown and brown 95 65
DESIGN: No. 637, W.C.Y. emblem and dish aerial.

134 Building Dam

1983. 5th Anniv of U.S.S.R.–Vietnam Co-operation Treaty.
640 134 4 d. grey and black . . . . 1·90 65

135 Girl with Flowers

1983. 5th Trade Unions Congress.
642 135 50 x. blue, orange & blk . 20 10
643 – 2 d. black, blue & brown . 50 25
644 – 30 d. black, blue & red . . 7·50 2·25
DESIGNS: 2, 30 d. Worker and industrial complex.

136 Grey Herons

137 Conference Emblem and Hands

1983. Birds. Multicoloured.
645 50 x. Type 136 . . . . 35 25
646 50 x. Painted storks 35 25
647 50 x. Black storks 35 25
648 50 x. Purple herons 35 25
649 1 d. Common cranes 50 30
650 2 d. Black-faced spoonbills . . 1·10 55
651 5 d. Black-crowned night herons 2·25 80
652 10 d. Asian open-bill storks . . 4·75 1·50

1983. World Peace Conference, Prague.
653 – 50 x. blue, red & yellow . 15 10
654 137 3 d. green, red & yellow . 1·10 45
655 5 d. lilac, red & yellow . 1·90 75
655 20 d. blue, red & yellow . 7·50 2·50
DESIGN: 50 x. Conference emblem and woman.

138 Biathlon

1984. Winter Olympic Games, Sarajevo. Multicoloured.
657 50 x. Type 138 . . . . 30 10
658 50 x. Cross-country skiing . . 30 10
659 1 d. Speed skating 45 15
660 2 d. Bobsleighing 75 30
661 3 d. Ice hockey (horiz) . . . . 1·00 35
662 5 d. Ski jumping (horiz) . . . 1·60 45
663 6 d. Slalom (horiz) . . . . . 1·90 65

139 Marbled Cat

1984. Protected Animals. Multicoloured.
665 50 x. Type 139 . . . . 25 10
666 50 x. Leopard 25 10
667 50 x. Tiger 25 10
668 1 d. Common gibbon 50 25
669 1 d. Slow loris 50 25
670 2 d. Indian elephant . . . . 1·00 30
671 2 d. Gaur . . . . 1·00 30

140 "Bauhinia variegata"

141 "Brasse cattleya"

1984. Flowers. Multicoloured.
672 50 x. Type 140 . . . . 15 10
673 50 x. "Caesalpinia pulcherrima" 15 10
674 1 d. "Cassia fistula" 35 15
675 2 d. "Delonix regia" 70 25
676 3 d. "Artabotrys uncinatus" . 1·00 40
677 5 d. "Corchorus olitorius" . . 1·75 65
678 8 d. "Bauhinia grandiflora" . 2·75 1·00

1984. Orchids. Multicoloured.
680 50 x. Type 141 . . . . 25 10
681 50 x. "Cymbidium sp." . . . 25 10
682 1 d. "Cattleya dianx" var. "alba" 40 15
683 2 d. "Cymbidium sp." (different) 70 30
684 3 d. "Cymbidium hybridum" . 1·10 35
685 5 d. Phoenix-winged orchids . 1·75 45
686 8 d. Yellow queen orchids . . 2·25 65

1984. Nos. 362 and 373 surch.
687 – 50 x. on 12 x. red and green 60 15
688 76 50 x. on 12 x. yellow and black 60 15

143 "Cypselurus spilopterus"

1984. Deep Sea Fishes. Multicoloured.
688a 30 x. Type 143 . . . . 10 10
688b 30 x. "Ostracion cornutus" . 10 10
688c 50 x. "Diodon hystrix" . . . 20 10
688d 80 x. "Chelmon rostratus" . 30 10
688e 1 d. "Antennarius bidens" . 40 10
688f 2 d. "Pterois russelli" 75 20
688g 5 d. "Mola mola" . . . . . 1·90 55
688h 10 d. "Minous monodactylus" 3·75 1·00

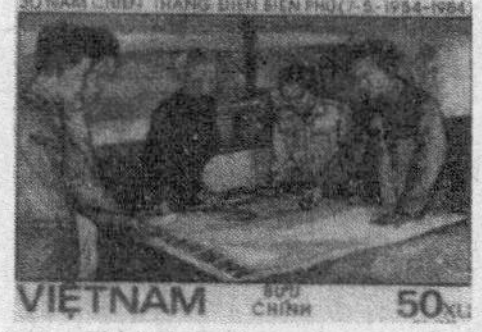

146 Ho Chi Minh discussing Battle Plan

1984. 30th Anniv of Battle of Dien Bien Phu. Multicoloured.
691 50 x. Type 146 . . . . 25 10
692 50 x. Vietnamese soldiers and truck 25 10
693 1 d. Students carrying provisions 50 15
694 2 d. Pulling field gun up hill . 90 30
695 3 d. Anti-aircraft gun and crashed airplane . . . . . 1·10 40
696 5 d. Fighting against tanks . . 1·60 50
697 8 d. Vietnamese soldiers with flag on bunker . . . . 2·00 65

148 "Trichogaster trichopterus"

149 Nguyen Duc Canh

1984. Fishes. Multicoloured.
700 50 x. Type 148 . . . . 20 10
701 50 x. "Brachydanio rerio" . . 20 10
702 1 d. "Macropodus opercularis" 40 15
703 2 d. "Gymnocorymbus ternetzi" 75 25
704 3 d. "Hyphessobrycon serpae" 1·25 35
705 5 d. "Labeo bicolor" . . . . 1·75 45
706 8 d. "Betta splendens" . . . . 2·25 65

1984. 55th Anniv of Vietnamese Trade Union Movement.
707 149 50 x. red and black . . . 15 10
708 – 50 x. red and black . . . 15 10
709 – 1 d. multicoloured 35 15
710 – 2 d. multicoloured 70 25
711 – 3 d. multicoloured . . . . 1·25 40
712 – 5 d. multicoloured . . . . 1·90 90
DESIGNS—VERT: No. 708, Founder's house. HORIZ: No. 709, Workers presenting demands to employer; 710, Ho Chi Minh with workers; 711, Factory; 712, Workers, procession and doves.

150 Hon Dua

1984. Coastal Scenes. Multicoloured.

714	50 x. Type **150**	20	10
715	50 x. Hang Con Gai	20	10
716	50 x. Hang Bo Nau	20	10
717	50 x. Nui Yen Ngua	20	10
718	1 d. Hon Ga Choi	40	15
719	1 d. Hon Coc	40	15
720	2 d. Hon Dinh Huong	75	30
721	3 d. Hon Su Tu	1·10	35
722	5 d. Hon Am	1·75	50
723	8 d. Nui Bai Tho	2·75	80

151 Styracosaurus

1984. Prehistoric Animals. Multicoloured.

724	50 x. Type **151**	20	10
725	50 x. Diplodocus	20	10
726	1 d. Rhamphorhynchus	40	10
727	1 d. Corythosaurus	40	10
728	2 d. Seymouria	85	25
729	3 d. Allosaurus	1·25	35
730	5 d. Dimetrodon	2·10	55
731	8 d. Brachiosaurus	3·25	85

153 Dove and Flags

155 Students and Cultural and Industrial Motifs

1984. Laos–Kampuchea–Vietnam Co-operation.

733	**153**	50 x. red, blue & yellow	25	10
734		10 d. red, blue & yellow	3·75	1·25

1984. 5th Anniv of Kampuchea–Vietnam Friendship Treaty. Multicoloured.

736	50 x. Type **155**	15	15
737	3 d. Type **155**	85	25
738	50 d. Kampuchean and Vietnamese dancers	12·00	2·50

156 Bridge

1984. 30th Anniv of Liberation of Hanoi.

739	**156**	50 x. green and yellow	55	20
740	–	1 d. brown and red	1·00	45
741	–	2 d. brown and pink	2·25	75

DESIGNS: 1 d. Gateway; 2 d. Ho Chi Minh mausoleum.

157 Vis-a-vis

159 "Lenin" (V. A. Serov)

1984. Motor Cars. Multicoloured.

743	50 x. Type **157**	20	10
744	50 x. Two-seater	20	10
745	1 d. Tonneau	40	15
746	2 d. Double phaeton	75	25
747	3 d. Landaulet	1·00	35
748	5 d. Torpedo	1·75	45
749	6 d. Town coupe	1·90	65

1984. 60th Death Anniv of Lenin. Multicoloured.

751	50 x. Type **159**	20	10
752	1 d. Painting by A. Plotnov of Lenin at meeting	40	15
753	3 d. Painting by K. V. Filatov of Lenin at factory	1·25	35
754	5 d. Painting by V. A. Serov of Lenin with three comrades	2·25	65

160 "Madonna and Child"

1984. 450th Death Anniv of Correggio (artist). Multicoloured.

755	50 x. Type **160**	15	10
756	50 x. "Bolognini Madonna"	15	10
757	1 d. "Campori Madonna"	25	15
758	2 d. "Virgin adoring the Child"	55	30
759	3 d. "Madonna della Cesta"	75	35
760	5 d. "Madonna della Scodella"	1·40	45
761	6 d. "Madonna and Child with Angels"	1·90	50

161 "Keep the Peace" (Le Quoc Loc)

1984. United Nations Children's Fund. Paintings. Multicoloured.

763	30 x. Type **161**	15	10
764	50 x. "Sunday" (Nguyen Tien Chung)	20	15
765	1 d. "Baby of the Mining Region" (Tran Van Can)	30	15
766	3 d. "Little Thuy" (Tran Van Can) (vert)	80	25
767	5 d. "Children at Play" (Nguyen Phan Chanh)	1·75	65
768	10 d. "After Guard Duty" (Nguyen Phan Chanh) (vert)	3·75	1·10

162 Mounted Frontier Guards

163 Water Buffalo

1984. 25th Anniv of Frontier Forces.

769	**162**	50 x. black, blue & brn	20	15
770		30 d. black, green & bl	8·00	2·00

1984.

771	**163**	20 x. brown	10	10
772	–	30 x. red	10	10
773	–	50 x. green	15	10
774	–	50 x. pink	15	10
775	–	50 x. mauve	15	10
776	–	50 x. brown	15	10
777	–	1 d. violet	35	15
778	–	1 d. orange	35	15
779	–	1 d. blue	35	15
780	–	1 d. blue	55	15
781	–	2 d. brown	70	25
782	–	2 d. orange	70	25
783	–	2 d. brown	70	25
784	–	5 d. mauve	1·75	65
785	–	10 d. green	3·50	1·40

DESIGNS: No. 772, Marbled cat; 773, Fighting fish; 774, Cabbage rose; 775, Hibiscus; 776, Lesser panda; 777, "Chrysanthemum sinense"; 778, Tiger; 779, Water lily; 780, Eastern white pelican; 781, Slow loris; 782, Dahlia; 783, Crab-eating macaque; 784, Tokay gecko; 785, Great Indian hornbill.

165 Ho Chi Minh and Troops

984. 40th Anniv of Vietnamese People's Army. Multicoloured.

787	50 x. Type **165**	15	10
788	50 x. Oath-taking ceremony	15	10
789	1 d. Soldier with flag and Boeing B-52 Stratofortress on fire	35	15
790	2 d. Civilians building gun emplacement	70	25
791	5 d. Soldiers and tank breaking through gates	1·00	40
792	5 d. Soldier instructing civilians	1·75	45
793	8 d. Map and soldiers	2·75	1·00

166 Boy on Buffalo

167 "Echinocereus knippelianus"

1985. New Year. Year of Buffalo.

795	**166**	3 d. purple and pink	1·10	40
796		5 d. brown and orange	1·75	65

1985. Flowering Cacti. Multicoloured.

797	50 x. Type **167**	20	10
798	50 x. "Lemaireocereus thurberi"	20	10
799	1 d. "Notocactus haselbergii"	40	10
800	2 d. "Parodia chrysacanthion"	75	20
801	3 d. "Pelecyphora pseudopectinata"	1·10	30
802	5 d. "Rebutia frebrighii"	1·90	50
803	8 d. "Lobivia aurea"	2·75	70

168 Nguyen Ai Quoc (Ho Chi Minh)

169 Soldiers with Weapons

1985. 55th Anniv of Vietnam Communist Party.

804	**168**	2 d. grey and red	75	25

1985. 10th Anniv of Reunification of South Vietnam. Multicoloured.

805	1 d. Type **169**	35	10
806	2 d. Soldiers and tank	75	25
807	4 d. Soldier and oil rig	1·50	50
808	5 d. Map, flag and girls	1·75	60

170 Long Chau Lighthouse

1985. 30th Anniv of Liberation of Haiphong.

810	**170**	2 d. multicoloured	70	30
811	–	5 d. multicoloured	1·75	80

DESIGN: 5 d. An Duong bridge.

171 Ho Chi Minh and Soldiers

1985. 95th Birth Anniv of Ho Chi Minh (former President). Multicoloured.

813	1 d. Type **171**	35	15
814	2 d. Ho Chi Minh reading	70	25
815	4 d. Portrait (vert)	1·40	50
816	5 d. Ho Chi Minh writing	1·75	65

172 Soviet Memorial, Berlin-Treptow

173 Globe and People carrying Flags

1985. 40th Anniv, of Victory in Europe Day. Multicoloured.

818	1 d. Type **172**	35	15
819	2 d. Soldier and fist breaking swastika	75	25
820	4 d. Hand releasing dove and eagle falling	1·50	50
821	5 d. Girl releasing doves	1·90	65

1985. 12th World Youth and Students' Festival, Moscow. Multicoloured.

823	2 d. Type **173**	65	25
824	2 d. Workers, pylons and dish aerial	65	25
825	4 d. Sailor, soldier and lighthouse	1·40	50
826	5 d. Youths and balloons	1·75	65

174 Daimler, 1885

1985. Centenary of Motor Cycle. Multicoloured.

828	1 d. Type **174** (wrongly inscr "1895")	30	10
829	1 d. Three-wheeled vehicle, France, 1898	30	10
830	2 d. Harley Davidson, U.S.A., 1913	60	20
831	2 d. Cleveland, U.S.A., 1918	60	20
832	3 d. Simplex, U.S.A., 1935	90	30
833	4 d. Minarelli, Italy, 1984	1·10	40
834	6 d. Honda, Japan, 1984	1·75	1·10

175 King Penguin

176 "Holothuria monacaria"

1985. "Argentina '85". International Stamp Exhibition, Buenos Aires. Multicoloured.

836	1 d. Type **175**	35	10
837	1 d. Patagonian cavy	35	10
838	2 d. Capybara (horiz)	65	20
839	2 d. Leopard (horiz)	65	20
840	3 d. Lesser rhea	95	30
841	4 d. Giant armadillo (horiz)	1·25	45
842	6 d. Andean condor (horiz)	1·90	65

1985. Marine Life. Multicoloured.

844	3 d. Type **176**	1·10	30
845	3 d. "Stichopus chloronotus"	1·10	30
846	3 d. "Luidia maculata"	1·10	30
847	3 d. "Nadoa tuberculata"	1·10	30
848	4 d. "Astropyga radiata"	1·40	35
849	4 d. "Linckia laevigata"	1·40	35
850	4 d. "Astropecten scoparius"	1·40	35

177 Flag and Sickle "40"

178 Globe, Transport and People around Postman

1985. 40th Anniv of Socialist Republic. Mult.

851	2 d. Type **177**	65	20
852	3 d. Doves around globe as heart above handclasp	95	30
853	5 d. Banner	1·60	50
854	10 d. Ho Chi Minh, flag and laurel branch	3·25	1·00

1985. 40th Anniv of Postal and Telecommunications Service. Multicoloured.

856	2 d. Type **178**	45	15
857	2 d. Telephonist and telegraph operator	45	15
858	4 d. Soldiers and postwoman Nguyen Thi Nghia	90	30
859	5 d. Dish aerial	1·10	35

179 Profile of Ho Chi Minh and Policeman

1985. 40th Anniv of People's Police.

860	**179**	10 d. orange and black	4·50	1·25

180 Gymnasts

1985. 1st National Sports and Gymnastics Games. Multicoloured.

862 5 d. Type **180** . . . . 1·60 55
863 10 d. Badminton player, gymnast, athlete and swimmer 3·25 1·10

181 Locomotive "Reuth", 1840

1985. 150th Anniv of German Railways. Multicoloured.

864 1 d. Type **181** 30 10
865 1 d. German tank locomotive, 1990 . . . . 30 10
866 2 d. Locomotive "Der Adler", 1835 . . . . 60 20
867 2 d. German passenger locomotive, 1850 . . . . . 60 20
868 3 d. German steam locomotive No. 2024, 1910 . . . . . 90 30
869 4 d. German steam tank locomotive, 1920 . . . . 1·25 40
870 6 d. Bavarian State steam locomotive No. 659, 1890 . 1·75 60

182 Oil Rig, Derrick and Helicopter

1985. 30th Anniv of Geological Service.

872 **182** 1 d. blue and purple . . . 65 25
873 – 1 d. green and brown . . 65 25

DESIGN: No. 873, Airplane over coastline.

183 Alfa Romeo, 1922

1985. "Italia '85" International Stamp Exhibition, Rome. Motor Cars. Multicoloured.

874 1 d. Type **183** 30 10
875 1 d. Bianchi "Berlina", 1932 . 30 10
876 2 d. Isotta Fraschini, 1928 . . 60 20
877 2 d. Bugatti, 1930 . . . . . . 60 20
878 3 d. Itala, 1912 . . . . 90 30
879 4 d. Lancia "Augusta", 1934 . 1·25 40
880 6 d. Fiat, 1927 . . . . 1·75 60

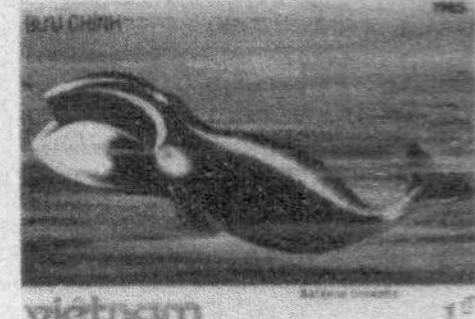

184 Sei Whale

1985. Marine Mammals. Multicoloured.

882 1 d. Type **184** 30 10
883 1 d. Blue whale 30 10
884 2 d. Killer whale 60 20
885 2 d. Common dolphin 60 20
886 3 d. Humpback whale 90 30
887 4 d. Fin whale . . . . 1·25 40
888 6 d. Black right whale . . . 1·75 60

185 Goalkeeper attempting to save Ball

1985. World Cup Football Championship, Mexico (1986) (1st issue). Various footballing scenes. Multicoloured.

889 **185** 1 d. multicoloured 30 10
890 – 1 d. multicoloured 30 10
891 – 2 d. multicoloured 60 20
892 – 2 d. multicoloured (vert) . 60 25
893 – 3 d. multicoloured (vert) . 90 30
894 – 4 d. multicoloured (vert) . 1·25 40
895 – 6 d. multicoloured (vert) . 1·75 60

See also Nos. 920/6.

186 Laotian Girl and Dove

187 Decorated Drum

1985. 10th Anniv of Laos People's Democratic Republic. Multicoloured.

897 1 d. Type **186** 50 20
898 1 d. Laotian girl and arms . . 50 20

1985. Traditional Musical Instruments. Mult.

899 1 d. Type **187** 40 10
900 1 d. Xylophone 40 10
901 2 d. Double-ended drum . . . 80 25
902 2 d. Flutes 80 25
903 3 d. Single-stringed instrument 80 25
904 4 d. Four-stringed instrument 1·25 35
905 4 d. Double-stringed instrument with bow . . . . 1·60 25

188 Agriculture

189 Hands, Emblem and Dove

1985. 40th Anniv of Independence.

906 10 d. Type **188** 80 20
907 10 d. Industry 80 20
908 20 d. Health care . . . . . . 1·60 40
909 30 d. Education . . . . 2·40 60

1986. 40th Anniv of U.N.O.

910 **189** 1 d. multicoloured . . . 55 20

190 Ho Chi Minh, Map Line of Voters and Ballot Box

191 Isaac Newton

1986. 40th Anniv of First Assembly Elections.

911 **190** 50 x. mauve and black . . 35 15
912 1 d. orange and black . . 65 25

1986. Appearance of Halley's Comet.

913 2 d. Type **191** 85 20
914 2 d. Edmond Halley 85 20
915 3 d. Launch of "Vega" space probe and flags . . . . . 1·25 40
916 5 d. Comet and planet . . . 2·10 65

192 Map of U.S.S.R. and Kremlin Buildings

193 Battle Plan of Chi Lang

1986. 27th Communist Party Congress, Moscow. Multicoloured.

917 50 x. Type **192** 30 15
918 1 d. Lenin on flag, transport, industrial and scientific motifs 65 25

1986. 600th Birth Anniv of Le Loi (founder of Le Dynasty).

919 **193** 1 d. multicolourerd 65 25

194 Footballer

1986. World Cup Football Championship, Mexico (2nd issue). Multicoloured.

920 1 d. Type **194** 25 10
921 1 d. Two players 25 10
922 2 d. Player heading ball . . . 50 20
923 3 d. Player tackling 75 30
924 3 d. Two players chasing ball . 75 30
925 5 d. Footballer (different) . . 1·25 40
926 5 d. Two players (different) . . 1·25 40

195 Konstantin Tsiolkovski and "Sputnik 1"

1986. 25th Anniv of 1st Man in Space. Multicoloured.

928 1 d. Type **195** 25 10
929 1 d. Rocket on launch vehicle, Baikanur cosmodrome . . . 25 10
930 2 d. Yuri Gagarin and "Vostok 1" 50 20
931 3 d. Valentina Tereshkova and "Vostok 6" on launch vehicle (vert) 75 30
932 3 d. Cosmonaut Leonov and cosmonaut on space walk . . 70 30
933 5 d. "Soyuz"–"Apollo" link and astronauts . . . . 1·25 40
934 5 d. "Salyut"–"Soyuz" link and cosmonauts . . . . 1·25 40

196 Thalmann and Flag

197 Flag, Hammer and Globe in Sickle

1986. Birth Centenary of Ernst Thalmann (German Communist leader).

936 **196** 2 d. red and brown . . . . 1·10 25

1986. Centenary of May Day.

937 **197** 1 d. red and blue 40 10
938 5 d. red and brown . . . . 2·10 55

198 Hawker Hart

1986. "Expo '86" World's Fair, Vancouver. Historic Aircraft. Multicoloured.

939 1 d. Type **198** 25 10
940 1 d. Curtiss JN-4 "Jenny" . . 25 10
941 2 d. PZL P-23 Karas 55 20
942 3 d. Yakovlev Yak-11 . . . . 80 30
943 3 d. Fokker Dr-1 triplane . . . 80 30
944 5 d. Boeing P12, 1920 . . . . 1·40 55
945 5 d. Nieuport-Delage 29C1, 1929 1·40 55

199 Ho Chi Minh and People working on Barriers

1986. 40th Anniv of Foundation of Committee for Protection of Flood Barriers.

946 **199** 1 d. red and brown 50 20

200 Black and White Cat

1986. Cats. Multicoloured.

947 1 d. Type **200** 30 10
948 1 d. Grey and white cat . . . 30 10
949 2 d. White cat 65 20
950 3 d. Brown-faced cat 95 30
951 3 d. Beige cat 95 30
952 5 d. Black-faced cat (vert) . . 1·60 50
953 5 d. Beige and cream cat . . . 1·60 50

201 Thai Den House

1986. Traditional Architecture. Multicoloured.

954 1 d. Type **201** 35 15
955 1 d. Nung house 35 15
956 2 d. Thai Trang house 70 25
957 3 d. Tay house . . . . 1·00 40
958 3 d. H'mong house . . . . . 1·00 40
959 5 d. Dao house . . . . 1·75 65
960 5 d. Tay Nguyen house (vert) 1·75 65

202 European Bee Eater

203 Plymouth Rock Cock

1986. "Stockholmia 86" International Stamp Exhibition. Birds. Multicoloured.

962 1 d. Type **202** 25 10
963 1 d. Green magpie 25 10
964 2 d. Red-winged shrike babbler 55 20
965 3 d. White-crested laughing thrush 80 30
966 3 d. Long-tailed broadbill (horiz) 80 30
967 5 d. Pied wagtail . . . . . . 1·40 55
968 5 d. Azure-winged magpie (horiz) 1·40 55

1986. Domestic Fowl. Multicoloured.

970 1 d. Type **203** 40 15
971 1 d. Common turkey 40 15
972 2 d. Rhode Island Red cock . . 75 25
973 2 d. White Plymouth Rock cock 75 25
974 3 d. Rhode Island Red hen . 1·10 35
975 3 d. White Leghorn cock . . 1·10 35
976 3 d. Rhode Island Red cock (different) . . . . 1·10 35
977 5 d. Barred Plymouth Rock cock 1·90 65

204 Emblem

1986. 11th World Federation of Trades Union Congress, Berlin.

978 **204** 1 d. blue and red 50 15

206 Woman-shaped Sword Handle

1986. Historic Bronzes Excavated at Mt. Do. Multicoloured.

980 1 d. Type **206** 35 10
981 1 d. Seated figure with man on back 35 10
982 2 d. Saddle pommel (horiz) . . 75 25

983 3 d. Shoe-shaped hoe (horiz) . 1·10 40
984 3 d. Bowl (horiz) . . . . . . 1·10 40
985 5 d. Vase (horiz) . . . . . . 1·75 60
986 5 d. Pot with lid (horiz) . . . 1·75 60

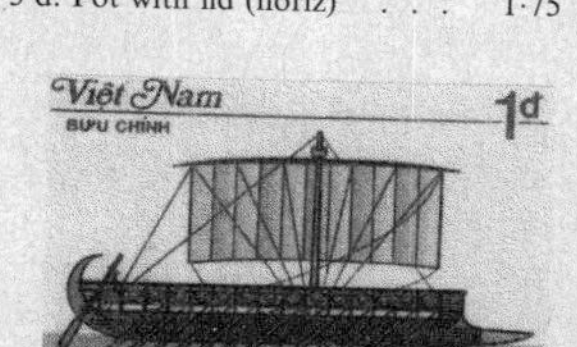

207 Greek Bireme

1986. Sailing Ships. Multicoloured.
988 1 d. Type **207** 25 10
989 1 d. Viking longship 25 10
990 2 d. Medieval kogge (36 × 46 mm) 55 20
991 3 d. Greek cargo galley . . . 80 30
992 3 d. Phoenician war galley with ram 80 30
993 5 d. Ancient Mediterranean cargo ship . . . . 1·40 55
994 5 d. Roman trireme . . . . . 1·40 55

208 Hands cupping Red Cross in Flower

1986. 40th Anniv of Vietnamese Red Cross.
995 **208** 3 d. mauve and blue . . . 1·10 30

209 "Catopsilia scylla"

1986. Butterflies. Multicoloured.
996 1 d. Type **209** 25 10
997 1 d. "Euploea midamus" . . 25 10
998 2 d. Orange albatross ("Appias nero") 55 20
999 3 d. Common mormon ("Papilio polytes stichius") 80 30
1000 3 d. African monarch ("Danaus chrysippus") 80 30
1001 5 d. Tawny rajah ("Charaxes polyxena") . . . . 1·40 55
1002 5 d. Magpie crow ("Euploea diocletianus") . . . . . 1·40 55

210 Red Flag and Symbols of Industry and Agriculture

1986. 6th Vietnamese Communist Party Congress. Multicoloured.
1003 1 d. Type **210** 30 10
1004 2 d. Red flag and weapons . 65 20
1005 4 d. Red flag and Ho Chi Minh 1·25 40
1006 5 d. Red flag and symbols of peace . . . . 1·60 50

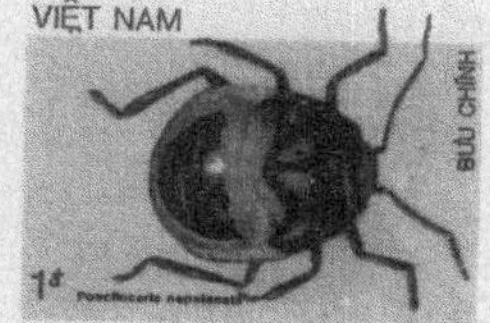

211 "Poecilocoris nepalensis" (shieldbug)

1986. Insects. Multicoloured.
1008 1 d. Type **211** 25 10
1009 1 d. "Bombus americanorum" (bee) 25 10
1010 2 d. "Romalea microptera" (grasshopper) 55 20
1011 3 d. "Chalcocoris rutilans" (shieldbug) 80 30
1012 3 d. "Chrysocoris sellatus" (shieldbug) 80 30
1013 5 d. "Crocisa crucifera" (wasp) 1·40 55
1014 5 d. "Paranthrene palmii" (moth) . . . . 1·40 55

212 Dove and Emblem

213 "Ficus glomerata"

1986. International Peace Year.
1016 **212** 1 d. green and black . . 40 15
1017 3 d. pink and black . . 1·25 40

1986. Bonsai. Multicoloured.
1018 1 d. Type **213** 35 10
1019 1 d. "Ficus benjamina" . . 35 10
1020 2 d. "Ulmus tonkinensis" . . 75 25
1021 3 d. "Persica vulgaris" . . . 1·10 35
1022 3 d. "Strebius asper" . . . . 1·10 35
1023 5 d. "Podocarpus macrophyllus" . . . . . . 1·75 60
1024 5 d. "Pinus khasya" . . . . 1·75 60

214 Basket

1986. Basketry and Wickerwork. Multicoloured.
1026 1 d. Type **214** 35 10
1027 1 d. Tall basket with lid and handles 35 10
1028 2 d. Stool 75 25
1029 3 d. Handbag . . . . 1·10 35
1030 3 d. Dish . . . . 1·10 35
1031 5 d. Tall basket for carrying on back . . . . 1·75 60
1032 5 d. Square basket with star-shaped foot . . . . 1·75 60

215 Soldiers and Women

216 "Fokienia hodginsii"

1986. 40th Anniv of National Resistance.
1034 **215** 2 d. brown and green . 80 20

1986. Fruits of Conifers. Multicoloured.
1035 1 d. Type **216** 35 10
1036 1 d. "Amentotaxus yunnanensis" 35 10
1037 2 d. "Pinus kwangtungensis" . 70 20
1038 3 d. "Cupressus torulosa" . 1·10 35
1039 3 d. "Taxus chinensis" . . . 1·10 35
1040 5 d. "Tsuga yunnanensis" . . 1·75 55
1041 5 d. "Ducampopinus krempfii" 1·75 55

217 Mother and Calf

1986. Elephants.
1043 1 d. Type **217** 30 10
1044 1 d. Two elephants 30 10
1045 3 d. Elephant (vert) 85 30
1046 3 d. Elephant feeding . . . 85 30
1047 5 d. Working elephant (vert) 1·40 50
1048 5 d. Elephants by water (68 × 27 mm) . . . . 1·40 50

218 Girl watering Tree

219 My Chan

1987. New Year. Year of the Cat.
1049 **218** 3 d. brown and mauve . . 50 25

1987. "Son Tinh-Thuy Tinh" (folktale). Multicoloured.
1050 3 d. Type **219** . . . . 1·10 30
1051 3 d. Mountain Genius bearing gift and leading horse . . 1·10 30
1052 3 d. Elephants carrying materials for flood barrier . 1·10 30
1053 3 d. Men working against flood through the night . . . . . 1·10 30
1054 3 d. Men felling trees . . . . 1·10 30
1055 3 d. Pounding rice . . . . . 1·10 30
1056 3 d. Canoes bringing fruit and grain to store . . . . 1·10 30
1057 3 d. Canoe . . . . 1·10 30
Nos. 1050/7 were issued together, se-tenant, forming a composite design.

220 "Nymphaea lotus"

222 Temple, Da Nang

221 Crowd attacking Building (August 1945 Revolution)

1987. Water Lilies. Multicoloured.
1058 5 d. Type **220** 25 10
1059 10 d. "Nymphaea nouchali" . 50 15
1060 10 d. "Nymphaea pubescens" 50 15
1061 20 d. "Nymphaea rubra" . . 1·00 25
1062 20 d. "Nymphaea gigantea" . 1·00 25
1063 30 d. "Nymphaea laydekeri" . 1·60 40
1064 50 d. "Nymphaea capensis" . 2·50 65

1987. 8th National Assembly. Multicoloured.
1065 10 d. Type **221** 60 15
1066 20 d. Proclamation of Democratic Republic (Sept 1945) . . . . 1·25 30
1067 30 d. Fall of Dien Bien Phu (May 1954) . . . . 1·75 45
1068 50 d. Tank entering Saigon (April 1975) . . . . . . 3·00 1·75

1987. Cham Culture. Multicoloured.
1069 3 d. Type **222** 15 10
1070 10 d. Temple, Phu Khanh . . 50 15
1071 15 d. Temple, Da Nang (different) 80 25
1072 20 d. Figure of dancer, Nghia Binh . . . . 1·00 30
1073 25 d. Bust, Da Nang . . . . 1·25 40
1074 30 d. Woman playing flute (statuette), Nghia Binh . . 1·60 50
1075 40 d. Figure of dancer on capital, Da Nang . . . . . 2·10 65

223 Hanoi

1987. Tourism. Multicoloured.
1077 5 d. Type **223** 25 10
1078 10 d. Hai Phong 50 15
1079 15 d. Thien Mu Pagoda, Hue 75 25
1080 20 d. Da Nang . . . . . . 1·00 25
1081 25 d. Nha Trang . . . . . . 1·25 30
1082 30 d. Waterfall, Da Lat . . . 1·50 35
1083 40 d. Ho Chi Minh City . . . 2·00 50

224 Cactus

226 Man from Bana

225 People on Globe

1987. Cacti.
1085 **224** 5 d. multicoloured . . . 15 10
1086 – 10 d. multicoloured . . . 30 15
1087 – 15 d. multicoloured . . . 50 20
1088 – 20 d. multicoloured . . . 65 25
1089 – 25 d. multicoloured . . . 80 30
1090 – 30 d. multicoloured . . . 1·00 35
1091 – 40 d. multicoloured . . . 1·25 40
DESIGNS: 10 to 40 d. Various flowering cacti.

1987. Day of Five Billion Inhabitants of Earth.
1093 **225** 5 d. mauve and blue . . 65 20

1987. Costumes. Multicoloured.
1094 5 d. Type **226** 25 10
1095 20 d. Woman from Bana . . 1·00 25
1096 20 d. Woman from Gia Rai . 1·00 25
1097 30 d. Man from Gia Rai . . 1·60 45
1098 30 d. Man from Ede . . . . 1·60 45
1099 40 d. Woman from Ede . . . 2·10 55

227 Silhouettes of Soldiers and Disabled Soldier

228 Rose

1987. 40th Anniv of Association of Disabled Soldiers.
1100 **227** 5 d. red and violet . . . 65 20

1987. Roses.
1101 **228** 5 d. multicoloured . . . 15 10
1102 – 10 d. multicoloured . . . 35 15
1103 – 15 d. multicoloured . . . 50 20
1104 – 20 d. multicoloured . . . 70 25
1105 – 25 d. multicoloured . . . 85 30
1106 – 30 d. multicoloured . . . 1·00 35
1107 – 40 d. multicoloured . . . 1·40 50
DESIGNS: 10 to 40 d. Various roses.

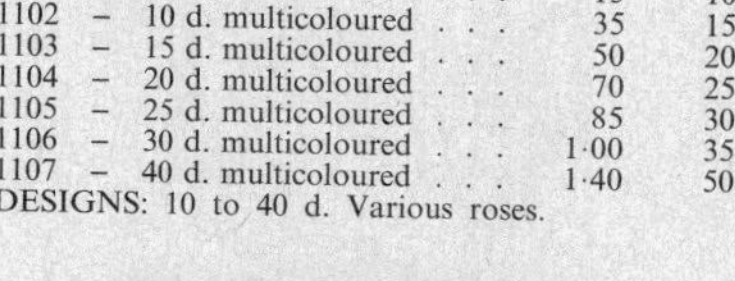

229 Postwoman and Mail Transport

1987. 40th Anniv of Postal Trade Union.
1109 **229** 5 d. black and red . . . 20 10
1110 – 30 d. black and green . . 1·25 40
DESIGN: 30 d. Linesman, dish aerial and telephonist.

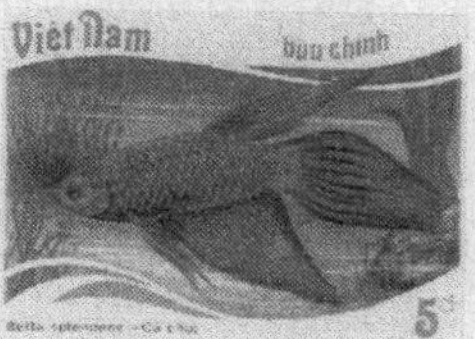

230 Siamese Fighting Fish

1987. Fishes. Multicoloured.
1111 5 d. Type **230** 15 10
1112 10 d. Red-tailed black labeo . 35 10
1113 15 d. "Puntis tetrazona" . . 50 15
1114 20 d. Pearl danio 70 20
1115 25 d. "Puntis conchonius" . . 85 25
1116 30 d. Siamese fighting fish (different) . . . . 1·00 30
1117 40 d. "Botia lecontei" . . . 1·40 45

231 Emblem

1987. International Year of Shelter for the Homeless.

1118	**231**	5 d. black and blue	65	25

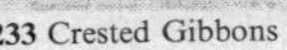

233 Crested Gibbons — 235 Industrial and Agricultural Symbols

234 "Musicians"

1987. Monkeys. Multicoloured.

1120	5 d. Type **233**	15	10
1121	5 d. Variegated langurs	15	10
1122	15 d. Crested gibbon (different)	50	20
1123	40 d. Variegated langur (different)	1·40	50

1987. Paintings by Picasso. Multicoloured.

1124	3 d. Type **234**	10	10
1125	20 d. Horse-drawn wagon	70	20
1126	20 d. Winged horse on shore	70	20
1127	30 d. "Child with Dove" (vert)	1·00	30
1128	30 d. "Gertrude Stein" (vert)	1·00	30
1129	40 d. "Guernica" (44 × 27 mm)	1·40	45

1987. 70th Anniv of Russian Revolution. Mult.

1131	5 d. Type **235**	20	10
1132	20 d. Soviet Memorial, Berlin-Treptow, cruiser "Aurora" and Lenin	70	25
1133	30 d. "70" and symbols of progress	1·10	35
1134	50 d. Ho Chi Minh and historical scenes	1·75	60

236 Consolidated PBY-5 Catalina Flying Boat

1987. "Hafnia 87" International Stamp Exhibition, Copenhagen. Flying Boats. Multicoloured.

1136	5 d. Type **236**	15	10
1137	10 d. Liore et Olivier LeO 246	35	10
1138	15 d. Dornier Do-18	50	15
1139	20 d. Short Sunderland	70	20
1140	25 d. Flying boat, 1923	85	25
1141	30 d. Chetverikov ARK-3	1·00	30
1142	40 d. Cant Z.509	1·40	45

237 "Epanouis"

1987. Corals. Multicoloured.

1144	5 d. Type **237**	25	10
1145	10 d. "Acropora"	55	15
1146	15 d. "Rhizopsammia"	80	25
1147	20 d. "Acropora" (different)	1·10	35
1148	25 d. "Alcyone"	1·40	40
1149	30 d. "Corollum"	1·60	50
1150	40 d. "Cristatella"	2·10	65

238 Doves as Clasped Hands forming Heart

1987. 5th Anniv of Vietnam–Czechoslovak Friendship Treaty. Each blue, yellow and red.

1151	10 d. Type **238**	35	10
1152	50 d. Flags and buildings	1·75	50

239 Symbols of Industry and Agriculture

1987. Soviet–Vietnam Friendship Treaty. Each red, brown and yellow.

1153	5 d. Type **239**	15	10
1154	50 d. National emblems and buildings	1·75	55

240 Coloured Circles

1987. Peace.

1155	**240**	10 d. multicoloured	90	30

241 Saddle-back Fungus — 243 Wrecked Boeing B-52 Stratofortress and Girl watering Flowers

242 Dove on Open Hands

1987. Fungi. Multicoloured.

1156	5 d. Type **241**	15	10
1157	10 d. Trumpet agaric	35	10
1158	15 d. "Tricholoma terreum"	50	15
1159	20 d. Golden russula	70	20
1160	25 d. Spindle shank	85	25
1161	30 d. "Cortinarius violaceus"	1·00	30
1162	40 d. Bronze boletus	1·40	45

1987. 30th Anniv of Africa–Asia Co-operation Committee.

1163	**242**	10 d. blue, black & yell	40	15
1164	–	30 d. black, brown & yell	1·25	40

DESIGN—VERT: 30 d. Hands and map.

1987. 15th Anniv of U.S. Air Bombardment of Vietnam.

1165	**243**	10 d. black and yellow	40	15
1166	–	30 d. black and orange	1·10	45

DESIGN: 30 d. Young Pioneers and weapons.

244 Woman carrying Bales of Cloth — 246 Anniversary Emblem and Dove

245 Junk, Man blowing Horn and Map

1987. 6th Party Congress Decisions.

1167	**244**	5 d. green and brown	20	10
1168	–	20 d. orange & brown	80	25
1169	–	30 d. violet and blue	1·25	45

DESIGNS: 20 d. Tractor driver; 30 d. Loading crate on freighter.

1988. Paracel and Spratley Islands.

1170	**245**	10 d. black, red & pink	35	15
1171	–	100 d. light brown, black and brown	3·50	1·75

DESIGN: 100 d. Maps showing Paracel Islands.

1988. 125th Anniv of International Red Cross.

1172	**246**	10 d. red, black & blue	75	25

247 Fleet

1988. 700th Anniv of Battle of Bach Dang River.

1173	**247**	80 d. black, pink & red	1·25	45
1174	–	200 d. multicoloured	3·25	1·10

DESIGN: 200 d. Battle scene.

248 Oil Rig — 249 Blue and Yellow Macaw

1988. Oil Industry.

1175	**248**	1000 d. black, blue & red	10·50	2·50

1988. Parrots. Multicoloured.

1176	10 d. Type **249**	50	20
1177	10 d. Slaty-headed parakeet	50	20
1178	20 d. Red-winged parrot	95	40
1179	20 d. Green-winged macaw	95	40
1180	30 d. Moustached parakeet	1·50	60
1181	30 d. Military macaw	1·50	60
1182	50 d. Vernal hanging parrot	2·40	95

250 Map — 251 Child and Syringe

1988. 33rd Council for Mutual Economic Aid Meeting and 10th Anniv of Vietnam's Membership.

1184	**250**	200 d. multicoloured	1·25	45
1185	–	300 d. blue and bistre	1·90	70

DESIGN: 300 d. Headquarters building, Moscow.

1988. Child Vaccination Campaign.

1186	**251**	60 d. orange, black & bl	90	40

252 Emblem and Building

1988. 30th Anniv of "Peace and Socialism" (magazine).

1187	**252**	20 d. multicoloured	75	30

INDEX

Countries can be quickly located by referring to the index at the end of this volume.

253 Ton Duc Thang — 254 Emblem

1988. Birth Centenary of Pres. Ton Duc Thang.

1188	**253**	150 d. multicoloured	1·75	65

1988. 6th Trade Unions Congress. Multicoloured.

1189	50 d. Type **254**	80	40
1190	100 d. "VI" and couple	1·75	75

255 Pointed-scaled Pit Viper

1988. Snakes. Multicoloured.

1191	10 d. Type **255**	35	10
1192	10 d. Pope's pit viper ("Trimeresurus popeorum")	35	10
1193	20 d. Banded krait ("Bungarus fasciatus")	75	25
1194	20 d. Malayan krait ("Bungarus candidus")	75	25
1195	30 d. Coral snake ("Calliophis maclellandii")	1·10	35
1196	30 d. Striped-beaked snake ("Ancistron acutus")	1·10	35
1197	50 d. King cobra (vert)	1·90	55

256 Family (Trieu Khac Tien)

1988. Children's Drawings. Multicoloured.

1198	10 d. Type **256**	35	10
1199	10 d. Couple and house (Phuong Ti)	35	10
1200	20 d. Fishermen (Lam Hoang Thang)	75	25
1201	20 d. Children flying kite (Nguyen Xuan Anh)	75	25
1202	30 d. Couple (Hong Hanh) (vert)	1·10	35
1203	30 d. Animals and girl playing guitar (Quynh May)	1·10	35
1204	50 d. Woman holding dove (Ta Phuong Tra) (vert)	1·90	55

257 Tri An

1988. U.S.S.R.–Vietnam Co-operation. Hydro-electric Power Stations.

1206	**257**	2000 d. blk, orge & red	6·00	4·25
1207	–	3000 d. black, bistre and red	9·00	3·50

DESIGN: 3000 d. Hoa Binh.

258 Kamov Ka-26

1988. Helicopters. Multicoloured.

1208	10 d. Type **258**	35	10
1209	10 d. Boeing-Vertol 234 Commercial Chinook	35	10
1210	20 d. MBB-Bolkow Bo 105	75	25
1211	20 d. Mil Mi-10K	75	25
1212	30 d. Kawasaki-Hughes 369HS	1·10	35
1213	30 d. Bell JetRanger	1·10	35
1214	50 d. Mil Mi-8	1·90	55

259 Gaur

260 Flower and Banners

1988. Mammals. Multicoloured.

1216	10 d. Type **259**	30	10
1217	10 d. Banteng	30	10
1218	20 d. Malayan tapir	60	20
1219	20 d. Hog deer	60	20
1220	30 d. Mainland serow	85	30
1221	30 d. Wild boar	85	30
1222	50 d. Water buffalo	1·50	50

1988. 10th Anniv of U.S.S.R.–Vietnam Friendship.

1224 **260**	50 d. multicoloured	55	25

261 Indian Star Tortoise ("Testudo elegans")

262 Skaters

1988. Turtles and Tortoises.

1225	10 d. Type **261**	35	10
1226	10 d. Three-banded box turtle ("Cuora trifasciata")	35	10
1227	20 d. Big-headed turtle ("Platysternon megacephalum")	75	25
1228	20 d. Hawksbill turtle ("Eretmochelys imbricata")	75	25
1229	30 d. Indian Ocean green turtle ("Chelonia mydas")	1·10	35
1230	30 d. Leatherback turtle ("Dermochelys coriacea")	1·10	35
1231	50 d. Loggerhead turtle ("Caretta caretta")	1·90	55

1988. Ice Skating. Multicoloured.

1233 **262**	10 d. multicoloured	30	10
1234 –	10 d. multicoloured	30	10
1235 –	20 d. multicoloured	60	20
1236 –	20 d. mult (horiz)	60	20
1237 –	30 d. multicoloured	85	30
1238 –	30 d. mult (horiz)	85	30
1239 –	50 d. mult (horiz)	1·50	50

DESIGNS: Nos. 1234/9 Different skating scenes.

263 Bowden "Spacelander"

264 Fidel Castro

1988. Bicycles. Multicoloured.

1241	10 d. Type **263**	35	10
1242	10 d. Rabasa Derbi with red tyres	35	10
1243	20 d. Huffy	70	25
1244	20 d. Rabasa Derbi with black tyres	70	25
1245	30 d. VMX-PL	1·00	35
1246	30 d. Premier	1·00	35
1247	50 d. Columbia RX5	1·75	55

1988. 30th Anniv of Cuban Revolution. Mult.

1248	100 d. Type **264**	40	15
1249	300 d. National flags and Cuban and Vietnamese workers	1·10	45

265 Cosmonauts on Spacecraft Wing

1988. Cosmonauts Day. Multicoloured.

1250	10 d. Type **265**	30	10
1251	10 d. Spacecraft moving across surface of planet	30	10
1252	20 d. Space rocket heading for planet	60	20
1253	20 d. Spacecraft and cosmonauts on planet with Earth in sky	60	20
1254	30 d. Spacecraft hovering over surface	85	30
1255	30 d. "Soyuz"–"Salyut" complex	85	30
1256	50 d. Space "bubble" and rocket	1·50	50

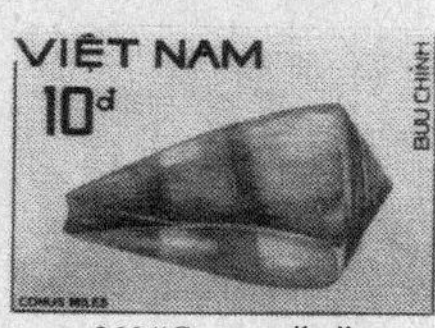

266 "Conus miles"

1988. Sea Shells. Multicoloured.

1258	10 d. Type **266**	35	10
1259	10 d. "Strombus lentiginosus"	35	10
1260	20 d. "Bursa rana"	70	25
1261	20 d. Turban shell ("Turbo petholatus")	70	25
1262	30 d. "Oliva erythrostoma"	1·00	35
1263	30 d. "Nautilus"	1·00	35
1264	50 d. "Mitra episcopalis" (wrongly inscr "eriscopalis")	1·75	55

The inscriptions on Nos. 1261 and 1263 have been transposed.

267 Class "VL85" Locomotive, U.S.S.R

1988. Electric Locomotives. Multicoloured.

1266	20 d. Type **267**	60	20
1267	20 d. LRC, Canada	60	20
1268	20 d. Monorail, Japan	60	20
1269	20 d. KIHA 80, Japan	60	20
1270	30 d. Class "DR 1A", U.S.S.R.	90	30
1271	30 d. Class "RC 1"	90	30
1272	50 d. Class "TE-136", U.S.S.R.	1·50	50

268 Gourd

1988. Fruits. Multicoloured.

1274	10 d. Type **268**	35	10
1275	10 d. "Momordica charantia"	35	10
1276	20 d. Pumpkin	70	25
1277	20 d. Eggplant	70	25
1278	30 d. "Benincasa hispida"	1·00	35
1279	30 d. Luffa gourd	1·00	35
1280	50 d. Tomatoes	1·75	55

269 Soldiers and Field Workers

1989. 10th Anniv of People's Republic of Kampuchea. Multicoloured.

1281	100 d. Type **269**	40	15
1282	500 d. Crowd greeting soldier and mother with child	1·90	70

270 Junk from Quang-Nam

1989. Regional Fishing Junks. Multicoloured.

1283	10 d. Type **270**	35	10
1284	10 d. Quang-Tri	35	10
1285	20 d. Thua-Thien	75	20
1286	20 d. Da-Nang	75	20
1287	30 d. Quang-Tri (different)	1·10	30
1288	30 d. Da-Nang (different)	1·10	30
1289	50 d. Hue	1·90	55

271 Caribbean Buckeye ("Junonia evarete")

1989. "India '89" International Stamp Exhibition, New Delhi (1st issue). Butterflies. Multicoloured.

1290	50 d. Type **271**	30	15
1291	50 d. "Anaea echemus"	30	15
1292	50 d. Great southern white ("Ascia monuste")	30	15
1293	100 d. Red-splashed sulphur ("Phoebis avellaneda")	60	25
1294	100 d. Jamaican orange ("Eurema proterpia")	60	25
1295	200 d. "Papilio palamedes"	1·25	55
1296	300 d. Monarch ("Danaus plexippus")	1·90	80

272 Flag and Telecommunications

274 Emblems on Banner

273 Festival

1989. "India '89" International Stamp Exhibition, New Delhi (2nd issue).

1298 **272**	100 d. multicoloured	40	15
1299 –	100 d. multicoloured	40	15
1300 –	300 d. multicoloured	1·10	35
1301 –	600 d. brown, orge & grn	2·25	75

DESIGNS: 100 d. (No. 1299), Oil and electricity industries; 300 d. Government Secretariat and Asokan capital; 600 d. Jawaharlal Nehru (Indian statesman, birth centenary).

1989. Bicentenary of Battle of Dongda.

1302 **273**	100 d. violet and green	40	15
1303 –	1000 d. mauve and red	4·00	1·40

DESIGN: 1000 d. Battle scene.

1989. Centenary of Interparliamentary Union.

1304 **274**	100 d. multicoloured	50	20
1305 –	200 d. gold, ultramarine and blue	1·00	40

DESIGN: 200 d. "100" on banner.

275 Dachshunds

1989. Dogs. Multicoloured.

1306	50 d. Type **275**	30	10
1307	50 d. Basset hounds	30	10
1308	50 d. Setter (vert)	30	10
1309	100 d. Hunting dog (vert)	65	20
1310	100 d. Basset hounds (66 × 25 mm)	65	20
1311	200 d. Hound (vert)	1·25	40
1312	300 d. Basset hound puppy	1·90	65

276 Footballers

277 Jug

1989. World Cup Football Championship, Italy (1st issue). Multicoloured.

1313	50 d. Type **276**	30	10
1314	50 d. Striker and goalkeeper	30	10
1315	50 d. Goalkeeper	30	10
1316	100 d. Player No. 5 tackling	65	20
1317	100 d. Tackling (vert)	65	20
1318	200 d. Player No. 3 (vert)	1·25	40
1319	300 d. Players heading ball (vert)	1·90	65

See also Nos. 1382/8.

1989. Pottery. Multicoloured.

1321	50 d. Type **277**	30	10
1322	100 d. Bowl with geometric pattern	65	20
1323	100 d. Round pot with flower decoration	65	20
1324	200 d. Tall pot with animal decoration	1·25	40
1325	300 d. Vase	1·90	65

278 Baby Thanh Giong with Mother

1989. Legend of Thanh Giong. Multicoloured.

1326	50 d. Type **278**	30	10
1327	100 d. Thanh Giong with King's messenger	65	20
1328	100 d. Thanh Giong at head of army	65	20
1329	200 d. Thanh Giong beating out flames	1·25	40
1330	300 d. Thanh Giong riding to heaven	1·90	65

279 "Fuchsia fulgens"

280 Bird carrying Envelope above Dish Aerial

1989. Flowers. Multicoloured.

1331	50 d. Type **279**	35	10
1332	50 d. Bird-of-paradise flower ("Strelitzia reginae")	35	10
1333	100 d. Glory lily ("Gloriosa superba")	70	25
1334	100 d. Orange day lily ("Hemerocallis fulva")	70	25
1335	200 d. "Paphiopedilum siamense"	1·40	45
1336	300 d. "Iris sp."	2·10	70

On Nos. 1332 and 1335 the inscriptions have been transposed.

1989. Communications.

1337 **280**	100 d. brown	65	25

281 Birds

283 Man and Ox

282 "Return from Varennes"

1989. Bicentenary of French Revolution. (a) As T **281**. Multicoloured.

1338	100 d. Type **281**	55	20
1339	500 d. "Liberty guiding the People" (detail, Eugene Delacroix)	2·75	90

(b) As T **282**.

1340	50 d. Type **282**	25	10
1341	50 d. "Revolutionary Court"	25	10
1342	50 d. "Oath of the Tennis Court" (Jacques-Louis David) (vert)	25	10
1343	100 d. "Assassination of Marat" (David) (vert)	55	20
1344	100 d. "Storming the Bastille" (vert)	55	20
1345	200 d. Two children (Pierre-Paul Prud'hon) (vert)	1·10	35
1346	300 d. "Slave Trade" (Jean-Leon Gerome)	1·60	55

1989. Rice Cultivation. Multicoloured.

1348 50 d. Type **283** 30 10
1349 100 d. Ploughing with ox . . 65 20
1350 100 d. Flooding fields 65 20
1351 200 d. Fertilizing . . . . . . 1·25 40
1352 300 d. Harvesting crop . . . 1·90 65

284 Appaloosa

1989. Horses. Multicoloured.

1353 50 d. Type **284** 35 10
1354 50 d. Tennessee walking horse 35 10
1355 50 d. Tersky 35 10
1356 100 d. Kladruber 70 25
1357 100 d. Welsh cob 70 25
1358 200 d. Pinto . . . . 1·40 40
1359 300 d. Pony and bridle (68 × 27 mm) . . . . 2·10 70

285 Brandenburg Gate, Flag and Emblem

1989. 40th Anniv of German Democratic Republic.

1360 **285** 200 d. yellow, blk & mve 65 25

286 Polio Oral Vaccination

1989. Immunization Campaign.

1361 **286** 100 d. brown, blk & red . 30 20
1362 – 100 d. pink, blk & grn . 30 20
1363 – 100 d. green, blk & red . 30 20

DESIGNS: No. 1362, Vaccinating pregnant woman; 1363, Health clinic.

287 Horse

1989. Paintings of Horses by Hsu Pei-Hung. Multicoloured.

1364 100 d. Type **287** 10 10
1365 200 d. Two horses galloping . 15 10
1366 300 d. Three horses grazing . 25 10
1367 500 d. Horse galloping (horiz) 45 15
1368 800 d. Galloping horse . . . 70 25
1369 1000 d. Two horses under tree 85 30
1370 1500 d. Galloping horse (different) . . . . 1·25 40

288 "Nina", "Pinta" and "Santa Maria" and Mochica Ceramic Figure

1989. 500th Anniv of Discovery of America by Columbus (1st issue). Multicoloured.

1372 50 d. Type **288** 20 10
1373 100 d. Columbus and King Ferdinand the Catholic and Peruvian ceramic bottle . . 35 10
1374 100 d. Columbus's arrival at Rabida and Mexican decorated vessel 35 10
1375 100 d. Columbus offering gifts (18th-century engraving) and human-shaped jug 35 10
1376 200 d. Early map and Peruvian ceramic 70 25
1377 200 d. Portrait and arms of Columbus and Nazca ceramic 70 25
1378 300 d. Chart by Toscanelli and Chimu vessel 70 25

See also Nos. 1545/51 and 1664/8.

289 Storming of Presidential Palace, Saigon and Ho Chi Minh

1990. 60th Anniv of Vietnamese Communist Party. Multicoloured.

1380 100 d. Type **289** 10 10
1381 500 d. Industry, workers, hammer and sickle and flag 30 10

290 Players

1990. World Cup Football Championship, Italy (2nd issue). Multicoloured.

1382 100 d. Type **290** 10 10
1383 200 d. Argentina player with possession 10 10
1384 300 d. Netherlands and Scotland players 15 10
1385 500 d. Soviet Union player tackling 25 10
1386 1000 d. Scotland and West Germany player 55 20
1387 2000 d. Soviet Union player losing possession . . . . 1·10 35
1388 3000 d. Goalkeeper . . . . 1·60 55

291 Hybrids of Mallard and Local Species

1990. Ducks. Multicoloured.

1390 100 d. Type **291** 25 10
1391 300 d. European mallard . . 25 10
1392 500 d. Mallards 40 15
1393 1000 d. Red-billed pintails . 65 20
1394 2000 d. White duck preening 1·10 35
1395 3000 d. African yellow-bills . 1·60 55

292 Mack Truck and Trailer

1990. Trucks. Multicoloured.

1396 100 d. Type **292** 10 10
1397 200 d. Volvo "F89" tipper . 10 10
1398 300 d. Tatra "915 S1" tipper 15 10
1399 500 d. Hino "KZ30000" lorry 25 10
1400 1000 d. Italia Iveco 55 20
1401 2000 d. Leyland-Daf "Super Comet" tipper . . . . . 1·10 35
1402 3000 d. Kamaz "53212" lorry 1·60 55

293 8th–9th Century Viking Longship

1990. Sailing Ships. Multicoloured.

1403 100 d. Type **293** 10 10
1404 500 d. 15th-century caravel . 25 10
1405 1000 d. 15th-century carrack (vert) 50 15
1406 1000 d. 14th-15th-century carrack 50 15
1407 1000 d. 17th-century frigate . 50 15
1408 2000 d. 16th-century galleons and pinnace (vert) . . . . 1·00 35
1409 3000 d. 16th-century galleon 1·50 50

294 Red-bodied Goldfish

1990. Goldfish.

1411 **294** 100 d. multicoloured . . 10 10
1412 – 300 d. multicoloured . . 15 10
1413 – 500 d. multicoloured . . 25 10
1414 – 1000 d. mult (vert) . . . 45 15
1415 – 2000 d. mult (vert) . . . 95 30
1416 – 3000 d. mult (vert) . . . 1·40 45

DESIGNS: 300 d. to 3000 d. Different goldfish.

295 Gate of Noble Mankind

1990. Hue Temples. Multicoloured.

1417 100 d. Type **295** 35 10
1418 100 d. Lotus pool at tomb of Emperor Tu Duc 35 10
1419 200 d. Southern Gate 70 25
1420 300 d. Thien Pagoda . . . . 1·10 35

296 "Antonia Zarate" (Francisco de Goya)

1990. "Stamp World London 90" International Stamp Exhibition. Portraits of women by painters named. Multicoloured.

1422 100 d. Type **296** 10 10
1423 200 d. "Girl with Paper Fan", (Auguste Renoir) 10 10
1424 300 d. "Janet Grizel" (John Russell) 15 10
1425 500 d. "Love unfasten's Beauty's Girdle" (Joshua Reynolds) 25 10
1426 1000 d. "Portrait of a Lady" (George Romney) (wrongly inscr "Omney") 55 20
1427 2000 d. "Mme. Ginoux" (Vincent van Gogh) . . . . 1·10 35
1428 3000 d. "Lady in Green" (Thomas Gainsborough) 1·60 55

297 Henry Giffard's Steam-powered Dirigible Airship, 1851

1990. "Helvetia 90" International Stamp Exhibition, Geneva. Airships. Multicoloured. With or without gum.

1430 100 d. Type **297** 10 10
1431 200 d. Lebaudy-Juillot airship No. 1 "La Jaune", 1910 10 10
1432 300 d. "Graf Zeppelin", 1924 15 10
1433 500 d. R-101, 1930 . . . . . 25 15
1434 1000 d. "Osoaviachim", 1936 55 20
1435 2000 d. Tissandier Brothers' airship, 1883 . . . . 1·10 40
1436 3000 d. U.S. Navy "N" Class airship . . . . 1·60 60

No. 1431 is wrongly inscr "Lebandy".

298 Silver Tabby and White Cat

1990. Cats. Multicoloured.

1438 100 d. Type **298** 10 10
1439 200 d. Black cat (vert) 10 10
1440 300 d. Black and white cat . . 15 10
1441 500 d. Brown tabby and white (vert) 30 10
1442 1000 d. Silver tabby 55 20
1443 2000 d. Tortoiseshell and white (vert) . . . . 1·10 35
1444 3000 d. Tortoiseshell tabby and white (vert) . . . . 1·75 60

INDEX

Countries can be quickly located by referring to the index at the end of this volume.

299 Ho Chi Minh, 1923 **300** King Charles Spaniel

1990. Birth Centenary of Ho Chi Minh. Mult.

1446 100 d. Type **299** 10 10
1447 300 d. Ho Chi Minh, 1945 . 15 10
1448 500 d. Dove, hand holding rifle, and Ho Chi Minh 25 10
1449 1000 d. Ho Chi Minh conducting 50 15
1450 2000 d. Ho Chi Minh embracing child . . . . 1·00 35
1451 3000 d. Globe and Ho Chi Minh 1·50 50

1990. "New Zealand 90" International Stamp Exhibition, Auckland. Dogs. Multicoloured.

1453 100 d. Type **300** 10 10
1454 200 d. Spaniel 10 10
1455 300 d. Saluki 15 10
1456 500 d. Dachshund 30 10
1457 1000 d. Dalmatian 55 20
1458 2000 d. Highland terrier . . 1·10 35
1459 3000 d. Boxer . . . . 1·75 60

301 Gorgosaurus

1990. Prehistoric Animals. Multicoloured.

1461 100 d. Type **301** 10 10
1462 500 d. Ceratosaurus 30 10
1463 1000 d. Ankylosaurus . . . 60 20
1464 2000 d. Ankylosaurus (different) . . . . 1·25 40
1465 3000 d. Edaphosaurus . . . 1·90 65

302 High Jumping

1990. 11th Asian Games, Peking. Multicoloured.

1466 100 d. Type **302** 10 10
1467 200 d. Basketball 10 10
1468 300 d. Table tennis 15 10
1469 500 d. Volleyball 25 10
1470 1000 d. Gymnastics 55 20
1471 2000 d. Tennis . . . . 1·10 35
1472 3000 d. Judo . . . . 1·60 55

1990. Tourism. Nos. 626/33 optd **DULICH '90** and emblem.

1474 50 x. Type **131** 10 10
1475 50 x. Common ink cap ("Coprinus atramentarius") 10 10
1476 50 x. Golden mushroom ("Flammulina velutipes") . 10 10
1477 50 x. Chanterelle ("Cantharellus cibarius") 10 10
1478 1 d. Chinese mushroom . . . 15 10
1479 2 d. Red-staining mushroom 35 10
1480 5 d. Common morel 85 30
1481 10 d. Caesar's mushroom . . 1·75 60

1990. World Cup Football Championship, Italy (3rd series). Nos. 457/64 optd **ITALIA '90** and ball.

1482 **90** 30 x. multicoloured . . . 20 10
1483 – 30 x. multicoloured . . . 20 10
1484 – 40 x. multicoloured . . . 25 10
1485 – 40 x. multicoloured . . . 25 10
1486 – 50 x. multicoloured . . . 45 15
1487 – 50 x. multicoloured . . . 45 15
1488 – 60 x. multicoloured . . . 55 20
1489 – 1 d. multicoloured . . . 1·25 40

305 "Pyotr Yemtsov" (container ship)

1990. Ships. Multicoloured.

1490 100 d. Type **305** 10 10
1491 300 d. Mexican Lines container ship 15 10
1492 500 d. Liner 25 10
1493 1000 d. "Ben Nevis" (tanker) 55 20
1494 2000 d. "RoRo" ferry . . . 1·10 35
1495 3000 d. Sealink train ferry . . 1·75 60

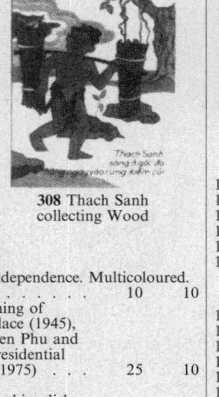

306 Emblem, Globe and Dove

1990. 45th Anniv of Postal Service. Mult.

1496 100 d. Type **306** 10 10
1497 1000 d. Emblem, dish aerial and globe 55 20

307 Red Flags and Symbols of Construction and Agriculture

308 Thach Sanh collecting Wood

1990. 45th Anniv of Independence. Multicoloured.

1498 100 d. Type **307** 10 10
1499 500 d. Map, storming of Government Palace (1945), siege of Dien Bien Phu and tank entering Presidential Palace, Saigon (1975) . . . 25 10
1500 1000 d. Satellite communications ship, dish aerial and "VI" 50 15
1501 3000 d. Hammer and sickle, industrial symbols and couple 1·50 50

1990. Legend of Thach Sanh. Multicoloured.

1503 100 d. Type **308** 10 10
1504 300 d. Ly Thong 15 10
1505 500 d. Thach Sanh fighting fire-breathing snake 25 10
1506 1000 d. Thach Sanh shooting down bird 55 20
1507 2000 d. Thach Sanh in prison 1·10 35
1508 3000 d. Thach Sanh and wife 1·75 60

1990 World Cup Football Championship Results. Nos. 1382/1388 optd **1. GERMANY 2. ARGENTINA 3. ITALY.**

1509 **290** 100 d. multicoloured . . 10 10
1510 – 200 d. multicoloured . . 10 10
1511 – 300 d. multicoloured . . 15 10
1512 – 500 d. multicoloured . . 25 10
1513 – 1000 d. multicoloured . . 55 20
1514 – 2000 d. multicoloured . . 1·10 35
1515 – 3000 d. multicoloured . . 1·60 55

1990. Red Cross. Child Welfare. Nos. N598/605 optd, with red cross and **FOR THE FUTURE GENERATION** in various languages (given in brackets).

1517 12 x. mult (Italian) 20 10
1518 12 x. mult (Chinese) 20 10
1519 20 x. mult (German) 30 10
1520 20 x. mult (Vietnamese) . . . 30 10
1521 30 x. mult (English) 45 15
1522 40 x. mult (Russian) 60 20
1523 50 x. mult (French) 75 25
1524 60 x. mult (Spanish) 90 30

311 Soldier

1990. 60th Anniv of Vietnamese Women's Union. Multicoloured.

1525 100 d. Type **311** 10 10
1526 500 d. Women in various occupations 30 10

312 Emblems

1990. 20th Anniv of Asian–Pacific Postal Training Centre, Bangkok.

1527 **312** 150 d. multicoloured . . . 20 10

313 Hands holding Forest and City

1990. Preservation of Forests. Multicoloured.

1528 200 d. Type **313** 10 10
1529 1000 d. Forest fire, "S.O.S." and river 55 20

314 Panther Cap **315** Yachting

1991. Poisonous Fungi. Multicoloured.

1530 200 d. Type **314** 10 10
1531 300 d. Death cap 15 10
1532 1000 d. Destroying angel . . 50 15
1533 1500 d. Fly agaric 75 25
1534 2000 d. "Russula emetica" . 1·00 35
1535 3000 d. Satan's mushroom . . 1·60 55

1991. Olympic Games, Barcelona (1992). Mult.

1536 200 d. Type **315** 10 10
1537 300 d. Boxing 15 10
1538 400 d. Cycling 20 10
1539 1000 d. High jumping . . . 45 15
1540 2000 d. Show jumping . . . 95 30
1541 3000 d. Judo . . . . 1·40 45
1542 3000 d. Wrestling (horiz) . . 1·40 45

316 Nguyen Binh Khiem

1991. 500th Birth Anniv of Nguyen Binh Khiem (poet).

1544 **316** 200 d. black, brown and ochre 40 25

317 "Marisiliana" **318** Woman in Blue Tunic

1991. 500th Anniv (1992) of Discovery of America by Columbus (2nd issue). Multicoloured.

1545 200 d. Type **317** 10 10
1546 400 d. "Venitien" 15 10
1547 400 d. "Cromster" (vert) . . 15 10
1548 2000 d. "Pinta" 75 25
1549 2000 d. "Nina" 75 25
1550 3000 d. "Howker" (vert) . . 1·10 35
1551 5000 d. "Santa Maria" . . . 1·90 65

1991. Golden Heart Charity.

1553 **318** 200 d. multicoloured . . 10 10
1554 – 500 d. multicoloured . . 10 10
1555 – 1000 d. multicoloured . 45 15
1556 – 5000 d. multicoloured . 2·10 70

DESIGNS: 500 d. to 5000 d. Traditional women's costumes.

319 Japanese White-necked Crane

1991. Birds. Multicoloured.

1557 200 d. Type **319** 10 10
1558 300 d. Sarus crane chick (vert) 10 10
1559 400 d. Manchurian crane (vert) 15 10
1560 1000 d. Sarus cranes (adults) (vert) 40 15
1561 2000 d. Black-necked crane (vert) 80 25
1562 3000 d. South African crowned cranes (vert) . . . . 1·25 40
1563 3000 d. Great white crane . . 1·25 40

320 Blacktip Reef Shark

1991. Sharks. Multicoloured.

1564 200 d. Type **320** 10 10
1565 300 d. Grey reef shark . . . 10 10
1566 400 d. Leopard shark 15 10
1567 1000 d. Great hammerhead . 40 15
1568 2000 d. Whitetip reef shark . 80 25
1569 3000 d. Great white shark . . 1·25 40
1570 3000 d. Bull shark . . . . . 1·25 40

321 Lobster

1991. Shellfish. Multicoloured.

1571 200 d. Type **321** 10 10
1572 300 d. "Alpheus bellulus" . . 10 10
1573 400 d. "Periclemenes brevicarpalis" 15 10
1574 1000 d. Lobster (different) . . 40 15
1575 2000 d. Lobster (different) . . 80 25
1576 3000 d. Lobster (different) . . 1·25 40
1577 3000 d. "Astacus sp." . . . . 1·25 40

322 "Fusee", 1829 **323** Ho Chi Minh, "VII" and Buildings

1991. Early Locomotives. Multicoloured.

1578 400 d. Type **322** 15 10
1579 400 d. Hedley's "Puffing Billy", 1811 . . . . 15 10
1580 500 d. John Stevens locomotive, 1825 (horiz) 20 10
1581 1000 d. Crampton No. 80 locomotive, 1852 (horiz) . . 40 15
1582 2000 d. "Locomotion", 1825 (horiz) 80 25
1583 3000 d. "Saint-Lo", 1843 (horiz) 1·25 40
1584 3000 d. "Coutances", 1855 (horiz) . . . . 1·25 40

1991. 7th Vietnamese Communist Party Congress. Multicoloured.

1586 200 d. Type **323** 25 10
1587 300 d. Workers 35 10
1588 400 d. Mother and children . 45 10

324 Pioneers **326** Yellow-banded Poison-arrow Frog

325 Lada

1991. 50th Anniv of Vietnam Youth Pioneers (200 d.) and United Nations Convention on Children's Rights (400 d.). Multicoloured.

1589 200 d. Type **324** 30 10
1590 400 d. Child's face and U.N. emblem 65 20

1991. Rally Cars. Multicoloured.

1591 400 d. Type **325** 15 10
1592 400 d. Nissan 15 10
1593 500 d. Ford Sierra RS Cosworth 20 10
1594 1000 d. Suzuki 40 15
1595 2000 d. Mazda "323" 80 25
1596 3000 d. Peugeot . . . . . . 1·25 40
1597 3000 d. Lancia . . . . 1·25 40

1991. Frogs. Multicoloured.

1599 200 d. Type **326** 10 10
1600 400 d. Edible frog 15 10
1601 500 d. Golden mantella . . . 25 10
1602 1000 d. Dyeing poison-arrow frog 40 15
1603 2000 d. Tree frog 80 25
1604 3000 d. Red-eyed tree frog . 1·25 40
1605 3000 d. Golden tree frog . . 1·25 40

327 Ho Chi Minh and Party Emblem **328** Speed Skating

1991. 60th Anniv (1990) of Vietnamese Communist Party.

1606 **327** 100 d. red 10 10

1991. Winter Olympic Games, Albertville (1992) (1st issue). Multicoloured.

1607 200 d. Type **328** 10 10
1608 300 d. Freestyle skiing . . . 10 10
1609 400 d. Four-man bobsleighing (horiz) 15 10
1610 1000 d. Biathlon (rifle shooting) (horiz) 40 15
1611 2000 d. Skiing (horiz) 80 25
1612 3000 d. Cross-country skiing 1·25 40
1613 3000 d. Ice skating . . . . . 1·25 40

See also Nos. 1659/63.

329 "Arsinoitherium zitteli"

1991. Prehistoric Animals. Multicoloured.

1615 200 d. Type **329** 10 10
1616 500 d. "Elephas primigenius" 25 10
1617 1000 d. "Baluchitherium" . . 45 15
1618 2000 d. "Deinotherium giganteum" 90 30
1619 3000 d. "Brontops" . . . . 1·40 45
1620 3000 d. "Uintatherium" . . 1·40 45

330 Pawn

1991. Chess. Staunton Pieces.

1621 200 d. Type **330** 10 10
1622 300 d. Knight 15 10
1623 1000 d. Rook 45 15
1624 2000 d. Queen 85 30
1625 3000 d. Bishop . . . . . . 1·40 40
1626 3000 d. King . . . . 1·40 40

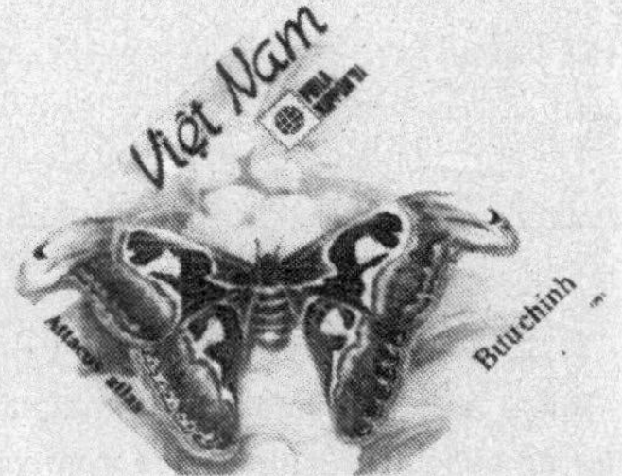

331 Atlas Moth

1991. "Phila Nippon '91" Int Stamp Exn, Tokyo. Moths and Butterflies. Multicoloured.

1628 200 d. Type **331** 10 10
1629 400 d. Blue morpho 15 10
1630 500 d. Birdwing 20 10
1631 1000 d. Red admiral 40 15
1632 1000 d. "Papilio demetrius" . 40 15
1633 3000 d. "Papilio weiskei" . . 1·25 40
1634 5000 d. Lesser purple emperor 2·00 65

332 Means of Communication

333 Eye and Clasped Hands

1991. 25th Anniv of Posts and Telecommunications Research Institute.

1636 **332** 200 d. multicoloured . . 40 20

1991. Golden Heart Charity for Disabled People.

1638 **333** 200 d. blue, lilac & orge . 10 10
1639 – 3000 d. ultramarine, blue and light blue . . . . 1·25 40

DESIGN: 3000 d. Tennis player in wheelchair.

334 Gymnastics

1992. Olympic Games, Los Angeles (1984). Mult.

1640 50 x. Type **334** 15 10
1641 50 x. Football (vert) 15 10
1642 1 d. Wrestling 25 10
1643 2 d. Volleyball (vert) . . . 50 15
1644 3 d. Hurdling 75 25
1645 5 d. Basketball (vert) . . . 1·25 40
1646 8 d. Weightlifting . . . . . 2·00 65

1992. "Expo '92" World's Fair, Seville. Nos. 1372/8 optd **SEVILLA '92** and emblem.

1648 **288** 50 d. multicoloured . . . 25 10
1649 – 100 d. mult (No. 1373) . 50 15
1650 – 100 d. mult (No. 1374) . 50 15
1651 – 100 d. mult (No. 1375) . 50 15
1652 – 200 d. mult (No. 1376) . 95 30
1653 – 200 d. mult (No. 1377) . 95 30
1654 – 300 d. multicoloured . . 1·40 45

336 Chu Van An teaching

1992. 700th Death Anniv of Chu Van An.

1656 **336** 200 d. multicoloured . . 25 15

337 Atomic Symbol, Communications, Industry and Agriculture

1992. Resolutions of 7th Communist Party Congress. Multicoloured.

1657 200 d. Type **337** 10 10
1658 2000 d. Hands clasped and map of Asia 55 20

338 Biathlon

1992. Winter Olympic Games, Albertville (2nd issue). Multicoloured.

1659 200 d. Type **338** 10 10
1660 2000 d. Ice hockey 45 15
1661 4000 d. Skiing (slalom) . . . 85 30
1662 5000 d. Ice skating . . . . 1·10 35
1663 6000 d. Skiing (downhill) . . 1·25 40

339 Columbus's Fleet

1992. 500th Anniv of Discovery of America by Columbus (3rd issue). Multicoloured.

1664 400 d. Type **339** 10 10
1665 3000 d. "Santa Maria" . . . 60 20
1666 4000 d. Columbus and flag on land 80 25
1667 6000 d. Columbus offering gifts to Amerindians . . . . 1·25 40
1668 8000 d. Ship returning home 1·60 55

340 Tupolev Tu-154M

1992. Aircraft. Multicoloured.

1670 400 d. Type **340** 10 10
1671 500 d. Concorde 10 10
1672 1000 d. Airbus Industrie A320 20 10
1673 3000 d. Airbus Industrie A340-300 . . . . 65 20
1674 4000 d. De Havilland D.H.C.8 Dash Eight-400 . . . . . 90 30
1675 5000 d. Boeing 747-200 . . 1·10 35
1676 6000 d. McDonnell Douglas MD-11CF . . . . 1·25 40

341 Weather System and Forecasting Equipment

342 Archery

1992. International Decade for Natural Disaster Reduction. Multicoloured.

1677 400 d. Type **341** 10 10
1678 4000 d. Man taking flood depth readings 90 30

1992. Olympic Games, Barcelona (2nd issue). Multicoloured.

1679 400 d. Type **342** 10 10
1680 600 d. Volleyball 15 10
1681 1000 d. Wrestling 20 10
1682 3000 d. Fencing 65 20
1683 4000 d. Running 90 30
1684 5000 d. Weightlifting . . . . 1·10 35
1685 6000 d. Hockey . . . . . . 1·25 40

343 Suzuki "500 F"

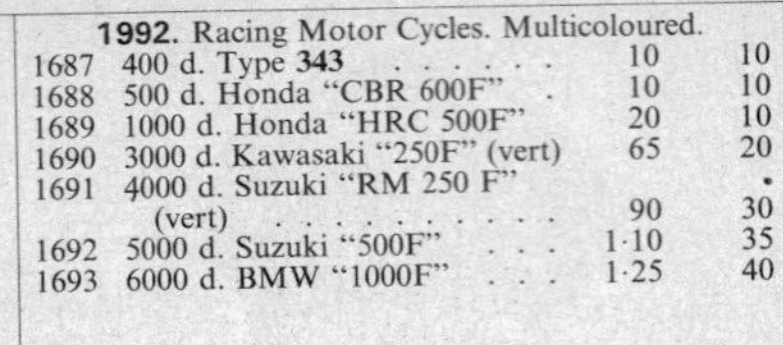
1992. Racing Motor Cycles. Multicoloured.

1687 400 d. Type **343** 10 10
1688 500 d. Honda "CBR 600F" . 10 10
1689 1000 d. Honda "HRC 500F" . 20 10
1690 3000 d. Kawasaki "250F" (vert) 65 20
1691 4000 d. Suzuki "RM 250 F" (vert) 90 30
1692 5000 d. Suzuki "500F" . . . 1·10 35
1693 6000 d. BMW "1000F" . . . 1·25 40

344 Shuttle Launch

346 Footballer

345 Main Entrance

1992. International Space Year. Multicoloured.

1695 400 d. Type **344** 10 10
1696 500 d. Launch of space shuttle "Columbia" 10 10
1697 3000 d. "Columbia" in space (horiz) 65 20
1698 4000 d. Projected shuttle "Hermes" docked at space station (horiz) 85 30
1699 5000 d. "Hermes" in space with solar panel (horiz) . . . 1·10 35
1700 6000 d. Astronauts repairing Hubble space telescope . . 1·25 40

1992. Centenary of Saigon Post Office.

1701 **345** 200 d. multicoloured . . 40 15

1992. European Cup Football Championship. Multicoloured.

1703 200 d. Type **346** 10 10
1704 2000 d. Goalkeeper 45 15
1705 4000 d. Two players with ball on ground 85 30
1706 5000 d. Two players with ball in air . . . . 1·10 35
1707 6000 d. Three players . . . . 1·25 40

347 "Portrait of a Girl" (Francisco de Zurbaran)

1992. "Expo '92" World's Fair, Seville. Paintings by Spanish Artists. Multicoloured.

1709 400 d. Type **347** 10 10
1710 500 d. "Woman with a Jug" (Bartolome Esteban Murillo) 10 10
1711 1000 d. "Maria Aptrickaia" (Diego Velazquez) 20 10
1712 3000 d. "Holy Family with St. Katharine" (Jose de Ribera) 60 20
1713 4000 d. "Madonna and Child with Sts. Agnes and Thekla" (El Greco) 80 25
1714 5000 d. "Woman with Jug" (Francisco Goya) . . . . 1·00 35
1715 6000 d. "The Naked Maja" (Francisco Goya) (horiz) . 1·25 40

348 Clean Water sustaining Life and Polluted Water

1992. 20th Anniv of United Nations Conference on Environmental Protection. Multicoloured.

1717 200 d. Type **348** 10 10
1718 4000 d. Graph comparing current world development and environmentally sound development 95 30

349 Cu Lao Xanh Lighthouse

350 "Citrus maxima"

1992. "Genova '92" International Thematic Stamp Exhibition. Lighthouses. Multicoloured.

1719 200 d. Type **349** 10 10
1720 3000 d. Can Gio 60 20
1721 5000 d. Vung Tau . . . . 1·00 35
1722 6000 d. Long Chau . . . . 1·40 45

1992. Flowers. Multicoloured.

1723 200 d. Type **350** 10 10
1724 2000 d. "Nerium indicum" . 40 15
1725 4000 d. "Ixora coccinea" . . 80 25
1726 5000 d. "Cananga oborata" . 1·00 35
1727 6000 d. "Cassia surattensis" . 1·25 40

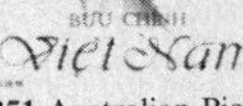
351 Australian Pied Imperial Pigeons

353 Memorials and "45"

200đ VIỆT NAM
Bưu chính

352 Guinea Pig

1992. Pigeons and Doves. Multicoloured.

1728 200 d. Type **351** 10 10
1729 2000 d. Red-plumed pigeon . 40 15
1730 4000 d. Rock dove 80 25
1731 5000 d. Top-knot pigeon . . 1·00 35
1732 6000 d. Laughing doves (horiz) 1·25 40

1992. Rodents. Multicoloured.

1733 200 d. Type **352** 10 10
1734 500 d. Guinea pigs 10 10
1735 3000 d. Indian crested porcupine 60 20
1736 4000 d. Lesser Egyptian gerbil 80 25
1737 5000 d. Red giant flying squirrel (vert) . . . . 1·00 35
1738 6000 d. Common rabbit (vert) 1·25 40

1992. 45th Anniv of Disabled Soldiers' Day.

1739 **353** 200 d. multicoloured . . 40 15

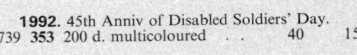

354 Stylized Sportsmen

1992. 3rd Phu Dong Games.

1740 **354** 200 d. light blue, ultramarine and blue . 40 15

355 Siamese Fighting Fish

1992. Siamese Fighting Fishes.

1741 **355** 200 d. multicoloured . . 10 10
1742 – 500 d. multicoloured . . 10 10
1743 – 3000 d. multicoloured . . 60 20
1744 – 4000 d. multicoloured . . 80 25
1745 – 5000 d. multicoloured . . 1·00 35
1746 – 6000 d. multicoloured . . 1·25 40

DESIGNS: 500 d. to 6000 d. Different Siamese fighting fishes.

356 Members' Locations on Map

358 Adult protecting Child

357 Trainee Doctors

1992. 40th Anniv of International Planned Parenthood Federation. Multicoloured.

1747 200 d. Type **356** 10 10
1748 4000 d. Emblem on world map (horiz) 95 30

1992. 90th Anniv of Hanoi Medical School. Multicoloured.

1749 200 d. Type **357** 10 10
1750 5000 d. Alexandre Yersin (bacteriologist) and school . 1·10 35

1992. SOS Children's Villages. Multicoloured.

1751 200 d. Type **358** 10 10
1752 5000 d. Houses and woman with children . . . . 1·10 35

359 Kick Boxing

1993. 17th South-East Asian Games, Singapore.

1753 **359** 200 d. multicoloured . . 40 15

360 Giant Bee

1993. Bees. Multicoloured.

1754 200 d. Type **360** 10 10
1755 800 d. "Apis koschevnikovi" . . 15 10
1756 1000 d. "Apis laboriosa" . . . 20 10
1757 2000 d. "Apis cerana japonica" . . 40 15
1758 5000 d. "Apis cerana cerana" 1·00 35
1759 10000 d. Honey bee (vert) . . 2·00 65

361 Tam-Cam returning from the River 362 Rooster with Family

1993. Legend of Tam-Cam. Multicoloured.

1760 200 d. Type **361** 10 10
1761 800 d. Apparition of old man by goldfish basin 15 10
1762 1000 d. Tam-Cam with unsold rice at the market 20 10
1763 3000 d. Tam-Cam trying on slipper for Prince 60 20
1764 4000 d. Tam-Cam rising from lotus 80 25
1765 10000 d. The royal couple . . 2·00 65

1993. New Year. Year of the Cock. Multicoloured.

1766 200 d. Type **362** 10 10
1767 5000 d. Rooster with family (different) . . . . 1·10 35

MINIMUM PRICE

The minimum price quoted is 10p which represents a handling charge rather than a basis for valuing common stamps. For further notes about prices, see introductory pages.

363 "Atractylodes macrocephala" 364 Communications Equipment

1993. Medicinal Plants. Multicoloured.

1768 200 d. Type **363** 10 10
1769 1000 d. Rangoon creeper ("Quisqualis indica") . . . 20 10
1770 1000 d. Japanese honeysuckle ("Lonicera japonica") . . 20 10
1771 3000 d. "Rehmannia glutinosa" 65 20
1772 12000 d. "Gardenia jasminoides" . . . . . 2·50 85

1993. "Communication in Service of Life". Multicoloured.

1773 200 d. Type **364** 10 10
1774 2500 d. Fibre-optic cable and map of Hong Kong–Sri Racha submarine cable route 60 20

365 Giant Panda

1993. Mammals. Multicoloured.

1775 200 d. Type **365** 10 10
1776 800 d. Tiger 15 10
1777 1000 d. Indian elephant . . 20 10
1778 3000 d. Indian rhinoceros . 55 20
1779 4000 d. Family of gibbons . 75 25
1780 10000 d. Clouded leopard . 1·90 65

366 Players, Statue of Liberty and Emblem

1993. World Cup Football Championship, U.S.A. (1994) (1st issue).

1782 **366** 200 d. multicoloured . . 10 10
1783 – 1500 d. multicoloured . . 20 10
1784 – 7000 d. multicoloured . 1·10 35

DESIGNS: 1500, 7000 d. Different match scenes.

See also Nos. 1865/70.

367 Wheelbarrow

1993. Traditional Transport. Multicoloured.

1785 200 d. Type **367** 10 10
1786 800 d. Buffalo cart 15 10
1787 1000 d. Rickshaw 20 10
1788 2000 d. Rickshaw with passenger 40 15
1789 5000 d. Rickshaw (different) . 1·00 35
1790 10000 d. Horse-drawn carriage 2·00 65

368 Pylon and Lightbulb 369 "Sunflowers" (Vincent van Gogh)

1993. 500kv Electricity Lines.

1791 **368** 300 d. black, orange and red 20 10
1792 400 d. black, blue and orange 25 10

1993. "Polska'93" International Stamp Exhibition, Poznan. Paintings. Multicoloured.

1793 200 d. Type **369** 10 10
1794 1000 d. "Young Woman" (Amedeo Modigliani) . . . 20 10
1795 1000 d. "Couple in Forest" (Henri Rousseau) 20 10
1796 5000 d. "Harlequin with Family" (Pablo Picasso) . . 90 30
1797 10000 d. "Female Model" (Henri Matisse) (horiz) . . 1·75 60

370 "Paphiopedilum hirsutissimum"

1993. Centenary of Da Lat. Orchids. Multicoloured.

1799 400 d. Type **370** 10 10
1800 1000 d. "Paphiopedilum gratrixianum" 20 10
1801 1000 d. "Paphiopedilum malipoense" 20 10
1802 12000 d. "Paphiopedilum hennisianum" . . . . 2·10 70

371 Wat Phra Sri Rattana Satsadaram, Thailand

1993. Historic Asian Architecture. Multicoloured.

1803 400 d. Type **371** 10 10
1804 800 d. Prambanan Temple, Indonesia 15 10
1805 1000 d. City Hall, Singapore . 15 10
1806 2000 d. Angkor Vat, Cambodia (horiz) 30 10
1807 2000 d. Ubudiah Mosque, Kuala Kangsar, Malaysia (horiz) 30 10
1808 6000 d. That Luang, Laos (horiz) 95 30
1809 8000 d. Omar Ali Saifuddin Mosque, Brunei (horiz) . . 1·25 40

372 Industry and Communications

1993. 7th Trade Union Congress. Multicoloured.

1811 400 d. Type **372** 10 10
1812 5000 d. Doves, atomic symbol, hammer in hand and flowers 90 30

373 "Scylla serrata"

1993. Salt-water Crabs. Multicoloured.

1813 400 d. Type **373** 10 10
1814 800 d. "Portunus sanguinolentus" 15 10
1815 1000 d. "Charybdis bimaculata" 15 10
1816 2000 d. "Paralithodes brevipes" 30 10
1817 5000 d. "Portunus pelagicus" 75 25
1818 10000 d. "Lithodes turritus" . 1·50 50

374 Stamps and Globe

1993. Stamp Day. Multicoloured.

1819 400 d. Type **374** 10 10
1820 5000 d. Airmail letter 90 30

375 Player 376 Lo Lo Costume

1994. Tennis.

1821 **375** 400 d. multicoloured . . 10 10
1822 – 1000 d. multicoloured (male player) 15 10
1823 – 1000 d. multicoloured (female player) 15 10
1824 – 12000 d. multicoloured . 2·10 70

DESIGNS: Nos. 1822/4, Different players.

1994. "Bangkok 1993" International Stamp Exhibition.

1825 400 d. Type **376** 10 10
1826 800 d. Thai costume 15 10
1827 1000 d. Dao Do costume . . 15 10
1828 2000 d. H'mong costume . . 30 10
1829 5000 d. Kho Mu costume . . 70 25
1830 10000 d. Kinh costume . . . 1·40 45

377 Dog with Puppies

1994. New Year. Year of the Dog. Multicoloured.

1832 400 d. Type **377** 10 10
1833 6000 d. Dog . . . . 1·10 35

378 Peach 380 Hoi Lim

379 Anatoly Karpov

1994. Flowers of the Four Seasons. Multicoloured.

1834 400 d. Type **378** (spring) . . 15 10
1835 400 d. "Chrysanthemum morifolium" (autumn) . . 15 10
1836 400 d. "Rosa chinensis" (winter) 15 10
1837 15000 d. "Delonix regia" (summer) . . . . 2·10 70

1994. Chess. Multicoloured.

1838 400 d. Type **379** 10 10
1839 1000 d. Gary Kasparov . . . 15 10
1840 2000 d. Robert Fischer . . . 35 10
1841 4000 d. Emanuel Lasker . . . 70 25
1842 10000 d. Jose Raul Capablanca 1·75 60

No. 1840 is wrongly inscribed "Robers".

1994. "Hong Kong '94" Stamp Exhibition. Traditional Festivals. Multicoloured.

1844 400 d. Type **380** 10 10
1845 800 d. Cham 15 10
1846 1000 d. Tay Nguyen 20 10
1847 12000 d. Nam Bo . . . . . 2·10 70

381 Loi Nhuoc 382 Red Gladioli

1994. Operatic Masks. Multicoloured.

1848 400 d. Type **381** 10 10
1849 500 d. Dao Tax Xuan 10 10
1850 2000 d. Ta Ngoc Lan 35 10
1851 3000 d. Ly Khac Minh . . . 55 20
1852 4000 d. Ta On Dinh 75 25
1853 7000 d. Khuong Linh Ta . . 1·25 40

1994. Gladioli. Multicoloured.
1854 400 d. Type **382** 10 10
1855 2000 d. Salmon gladioli . . . 35 10
1856 5000 d. White gladioli . . . 80 25
1857 8000 d. Magenta gladioli . . 1·25 40

383 Painting by Utamaro Kitagawa

1994. Paintings by Japanese Artists. Multicoloured.
1858 400 d. Type **383** (wrongly inscr "Kigatawa") . . . 10 10
1859 500 d. Harunobu Suzuki . . 10 10
1860 1000 d. Hokusai Katsushika . 15 10
1861 2000 d. Hiroshige 35 10
1862 3000 d. Hokusai Katsushika (different) 50 15
1863 4000 d. Utamaro Kitagawa (different) 65 20
1864 9000 d. Choki Eishosai . . . 1·50 50

384 Footballers

386 Pioneers reading Newspaper

385 Hauling Piece of Equipment

1994. World Cup Football Championship, U.S.A. (2nd issue). Multicoloured.
1865 400 d. Type **384** 10 10
1866 600 d. Running with ball . . 10 10
1867 1000 d. Heading ball 15 10
1868 2000 d. Goalkeeper 35 10
1869 3000 d. Two players chasing ball 50 15
1870 11000 d. Tackling . . . . . . 1·90 65

1994. 40th Anniv of Victory at Dien Bien Phu.
1872 **385** 400 d. brown, cinnamon and black 10 10
1873 – 3000 d. ultramarine, blue and black 50 15
DESIGN: 3000 d. Entertaining the troops.

1994. 40th Anniv of "Young Pioneer" (newspaper).
1874 **386** 400 d. red and black . . 30 10

387 Estuarine Crocodile

1994. Reptiles. Multicoloured.
1875 400 d. Type **387** 10 10
1876 600 d. Mississippi alligator . 10 10
1877 2000 d. Nile crocodile 35 10
1878 3000 d. Chinese alligator . . 50 15
1879 4000 d. Paraguay caiman . . 65 20
1880 9000 d. Australian crocodile . 1·50 50

388 Alexandre Yersin

389 Pierre de Coubertin (founder)

1994. Centenary of Discovery of Plague Bacillus.
1882 **388** 400 d. multicoloured . . 30 10

1994. Centenary of International Olympic Committee. Multicoloured.
1883 400 d. Anniversary and National Committee emblems and sports pictograms . . 10 10
1884 6000 d. Type **389** . . . . . . 1·10 35

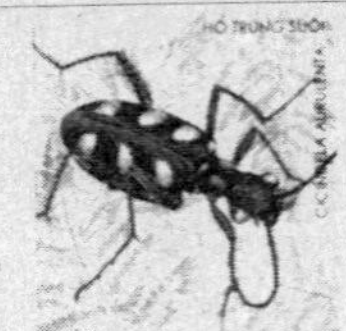

390 "Cicindela aurulenta"

1994. Beetles. Multicoloured.
1885 400 d. Type **390** 10 10
1886 1000 d. "Harmonia octomaculata" 15 10
1887 6000 d. "Cicindela tennipes" 1·00 35
1888 7000 d. "Collyris sp." . . . 1·25 40

391 Anniversary Emblem

1994. 120th Anniv of U.P.U. Multicoloured.
1889 400 d. Type **391** 10 10
1890 5000 d. Envelopes forming world map 75 25

392 Curlew

393 "Bambusa blumeana"

1994. "Philakorea 1994" International Stamp Exhibition, Seoul. Sea Birds. Multicoloured.
1892 400 d. Type **392** 10 10
1893 600 d. Wilson's petrel . . . 10 10
1894 1000 d. Great frigate bird . 15 10
1895 2000 d. Cape gannet 30 10
1896 3000 d. Tufted puffins . . . 50 15
1897 11000 d. Band-tailed gulls . 1·75 60

1994. "Singpex '94" Stamp Exhibition, Singapore. Bamboos. Multicoloured.
1899 400 d. Type **393** 10 10
1900 1000 d. "Phyllostachys aurea" 15 10
1901 2000 d. "Bambusa vulgaris" 30 10
1902 4000 d. "Tetragonocalamus quadrangularis" 65 20
1903 10000 d. "Bambusa venticosa" 1·60 55

394 Log Bridge with Handrail

1994. Rudimentary Bridges. Multicoloured.
1904 400 d. Type **394** 10 10
1905 900 d. Interwoven bridge . . 15 10
1906 8000 d. Log bridge on stilts . 1·10 35

395 Girl in Wheelchair and Boy playing

1994. "For Our Children's Future". Multicoloured.
1907 400 d. + 100 d. Type **395** . 10 10
1908 2000 d. Children dancing around emblem (vert) . . 40 15

396 Tram with Overhead Conductor

1994. Trams. Multicoloured.
1909 400 d. Type **396** 10 10
1910 900 d. Paris tram 15 10
1911 8000 d. Philadelphia mail tram 1·10 35

397 Civilians greeting Soldiers

1994. 40th Anniv of Liberation of Hanoi. Multicoloured.
1912 400 d. Type **397** 10 10
1913 2000 d. Workers and students and symbols of development 35 10

398 Airplane in Air

1994. 50th Anniv of I.C.A.O. Multicoloured.
1914 400 d. Type **398** 10 10
1915 3000 d. Airplane on ground . 50 15

399 Parade

1994. 50th Anniv of Vietnamese People's Army. Multicoloured.
1916 400 d. Type **399** 10 10
1917 1000 d. Plan of attacks on Saigon 15 10
1918 2000 d. Veteran recounting the past to young girl 35 10
1919 4000 d. Naval anti-aircraft gun crew 70 25

400 Sow with Piglets

401 Osprey ("Pandion haliaetus")

1995. New Year. Year of the Pig. Multicoloured.
1920 400 d. Type **400** 10 10
1921 8000 d. Pig . . . . 1·00 35

1995. Birds.
1922 **401** 400 d. blue 10 10
1923 – 400 d. green 10 10
1924 – 400 d. purple 10 10
1925 – 400 d. orange 10 10
1926 – 5000 d. red 75 25
DESIGNS—HORIZ: No. 1923, Sociable weaver ("Philetarius socius"); 1924, Sharpbill ("Oxyruncus cristatus"); 1925, Golden plover ("Pluvialis apricaria"). VERT: No. 1926, Red-legged seriema ("Cariama cristata").

402 Girls with Bicycle

1995. Women's Costumes. Multicoloured.
1927 400 d. Type **402** 10 10
1928 3000 d. Girl with sheaf of flowers 40 15
1929 5000 d. Girl with traditional hat 65 20

FRANK STAMPS

F 19 Invalid's Badge

F 158 Children and Disabled Teacher

1976. For use by disabled veterans. Dated "27.7.75". No value indicated.
F100 F **19** (–) red and blue . . . 50 25
F101 – (–) green, light green and brown 50 25
DESIGN: No. F101, Disabled veteran in factory.

1984. Disabled and Invalids. No value indicated.
F750 F **158** (–) brown & ochre . . 50 25

No value indicated. As T **179**.
F861 (–) Policeman and militia members 50 25

MILITARY FRANK STAMPS

MF 21 Soldier and Map of Vietnam

1976. No value indicated.
MF110 MF **21** (–) black and red . 60 25

MF 59 Pilot

1979. 35th Anniv of Vietnam People's Army. No value indicated.
MF304 MF **59** (–) red and pink . 35 10
MF305 – (–) red and pink . 35 10
DESIGN: No. MF305, Badge of People's Army.

MF 61 Tank Driver and Tanks

MF 84 Ho Chi Minh in Naval Uniform

1979. No value indicated.
MF308 MF **61** (–) black and mauve 30 15
MF309 – (–) black and red . 30 15
MF310 – (–) black and red . 30 15
DESIGNS: No. MF309, Sailor and ship; MF310, Pilot and jet fighters.

1981. No value indicated.
MF420 MF **84** (–) pink and blue . 25 20
MF421 – (–) multicoloured . 25 20
DESIGN—VERT (13×17 mm): No. MF421, Factory militiawomen.

1982. Multicoloured. No value indicated.
MF466 (–) Soldier and militiawoman 25 10
MF467 (–) Type **94** 25 10

MF 107 Disabled Soldier

1982. 35th Anniv of Disabled Soldiers' Day. No value indicated.
MF513 MF **107** (–) purple and green 50 20

MF 120 Militia

1983. No value indicated.
MF581 MF **120** (–) multicoloured . 60 25

MF **145** Star and Soldiers on Bunker
MF **152** Coastal Militia

1984. 30th Anniv of Battle of Dien Bien Phu.
MF690 MF **145** (–) yellow, orange and brown . . 25 20

1984. No value indicated.
MF732 MF **152** (–) brown, orange and yellow . . 25 20

MF **164** Soldiers and Emblem
MF **205** Soldier and Woman holding Sheaf of Rice

1984. No value indicated.
MF786 MF **164** (–) orange, red and black 50 25

1986.
MF979 MF **205** 1 d. brown and black 65 30

MF **232** Armed Forces Personnel and Flag

1987.
MF1119 MF **232** 5 d. red and brown 90 40

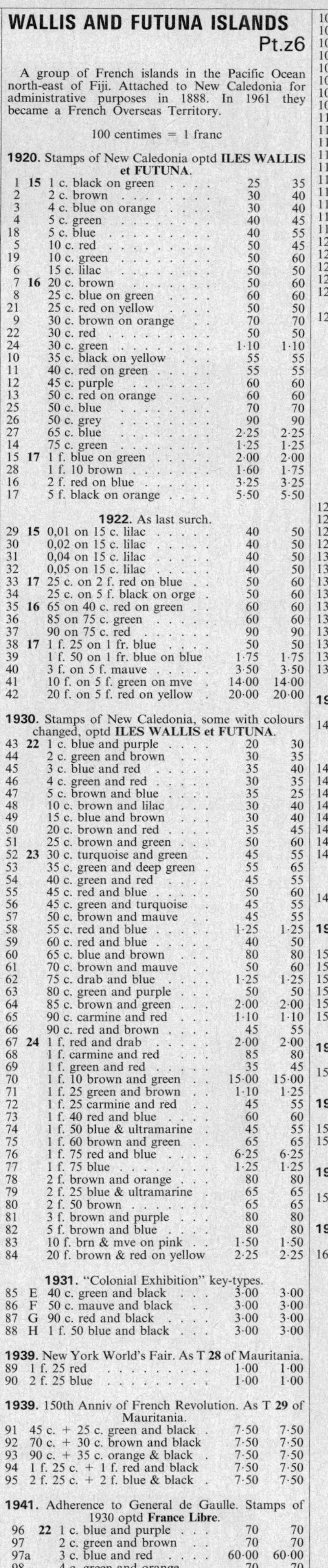

WALLIS AND FUTUNA ISLANDS
Pt.z6

A group of French islands in the Pacific Ocean north-east of Fiji. Attached to New Caledonia for administrative purposes in 1888. In 1961 they became a French Overseas Territory.

100 centimes = 1 franc

1920. Stamps of New Caledonia optd **ILES WALLIS et FUTUNA.**
1 **15** 1 c. black on green 25 35
2 2 c. brown 30 40
3 4 c. blue on orange 30 40
4 5 c. green 40 45
18 5 c. blue 40 55
5 10 c. red 50 45
19 10 c. green 50 60
6 15 c. lilac 50 50
7 **16** 20 c. brown 50 60
8 25 c. blue on green 60 60
21 25 c. red on yellow 50 50
9 30 c. brown on orange . . . 70 70
22 30 c. red 50 50
24 30 c. green . . . . 1·10 1·10
10 35 c. black on yellow . . . 55 55
11 40 c. red on green 55 55
12 45 c. purple 60 60
13 50 c. red on orange 60 60
25 50 c. blue 70 70
26 50 c. grey 90 90
27 65 c. blue . . . . 2·25 2·25
14 75 c. green . . . . 1·25 1·25
15 **17** 1 f. blue on green . . . . . 2·00 2·00
28 1 f. 10 brown . . . . 1·60 1·75
16 2 f. red on blue . . . . . 3·25 3·25
17 5 f. black on orange . . . . 5·50 5·50

1922. As last surch.
29 **15** 0,01 on 15 c. lilac 40 50
30 0,02 on 15 c. lilac 40 50
31 0,04 on 15 c. lilac 40 50
32 0,05 on 15 c. lilac 40 50
33 **17** 25 c. on 2 f. red on blue . . 50 60
34 25 c. on 5 f. black on orge . . 50 60
35 **16** 65 on 40 c. red on green . . 60 60
36 85 on 75 c. green 60 60
37 90 on 75 c. red 90 90
38 **17** 1 f. 25 on 1 fr. blue 50 50
39 1 f. 50 on 1 fr. blue on blue 1·75 1·75
40 3 f. on 5 f. mauve . . . . . 3·50 3·50
41 10 f. on 5 f. green on mve . 14·00 14·00
42 20 f. on 5 f. red on yellow 20·00 20·00

1930. Stamps of New Caledonia, some with colours changed, optd **ILES WALLIS et FUTUNA**.
43 **22** 1 c. blue and purple 20 30
44 2 c. green and brown 30 35
45 3 c. blue and red 35 40
46 4 c. green and red 30 35
47 5 c. brown and blue 35 25
48 10 c. brown and lilac 30 40
49 15 c. blue and brown 30 40
50 20 c. brown and red 35 45
51 25 c. brown and green . . . 50 60
52 **23** 30 c. turquoise and green . . 45 55
53 35 c. green and deep green . 55 65
54 40 c. green and red 45 55
55 45 c. red and blue 50 60
56 45 c. green and turquoise . . 45 55
57 50 c. brown and mauve . . . 45 55
58 55 c. red and blue . . . . . 1·25 1·25
59 60 c. red and blue 40 50
60 65 c. blue and brown 80 80
61 70 c. brown and mauve . . . 50 60
62 75 c. drab and blue . . . . 1·25 1·25
63 80 c. green and purple . . . 50 50
64 85 c. brown and green . . . 2·00 2·00
65 90 c. carmine and red . . . 1·10 1·10
66 90 c. red and brown 45 55
67 **24** 1 f. red and drab . . . . . 2·00 2·00
68 1 f. carmine and red 85 80
69 1 f. green and red 35 45
70 1 f. 10 brown and green . . 15·00 15·00
71 1 f. 25 green and brown . . 1·10 1·25
72 1 f. 25 carmine and red . . . 45 55
73 1 f. 40 red and blue 60 60
74 1 f. 50 blue & ultramarine . . 45 55
75 1 f. 60 brown and green . . 65 65
76 1 f. 75 red and blue . . . . 6·25 6·25
77 1 f. 75 blue . . . . 1·25 1·25
78 2 f. brown and orange . . . 80 80
79 2 f. 25 blue & ultramarine . 65 65
80 2 f. 50 brown 65 65
81 3 f. brown and purple . . . 80 80
82 5 f. brown and blue 80 80
83 10 f. brn & mve on pink . . 1·50 1·50
84 20 f. brown & red on yellow 2·25 2·25

1931. "Colonial Exhibition" key-types.
85 E 40 c. green and black . . . 3·00 3·00
86 F 50 c. mauve and black . . . 3·00 3·00
87 G 90 c. red and black . . . . 3·00 3·00
88 H 1 f. 50 blue and black . . . 3·00 3·00

1939. New York World's Fair. As T **28** of Mauritania.
89 1 f. 25 red . . . . 1·00 1·00
90 2 f. 25 blue . . . . 1·00 1·00

1939. 150th Anniv of French Revolution. As T **29** of Mauritania.
91 45 c. + 25 c. green and black . 7·50 7·50
92 70 c. + 30 c. brown and black 7·50 7·50
93 90 c. + 35 c. orange & black . 7·50 7·50
94 1 f. 25 c. + 1 f. red and black 7·50 7·50
95 2 f. 25 c. + 2 f. blue & black . 7·50 7·50

1941. Adherence to General de Gaulle. Stamps of 1930 optd **France Libre**.
96 **22** 1 c. blue and purple . . . 70 70
97 2 c. green and brown . . 70 70
97a 3 c. blue and red . . . . 60·00 60·00
98 4 c. green and orange . . 70 70
99 5 c. brown and blue . . . 70 70
100 10 c. brown and lilac . . 70 70
101 15 c. blue and brown . . 70 70
102 20 c. brown and red . . . 1·40 1·40
103 25 c. brown and green . . 1·40 1·40
104 **23** 30 c. green . . . . 1·40 1·40
105 35 c. green 70 70
106 40 c. green and red . . . . 1·40 1·40
107 45 c. red and blue . . . . 1·40 1·40
107a 45 c. green & turquoise . . 60·00 60·00
108 50 c. brown and mauve . . 70 70
109 55 c. red and blue 70 70
109a 60 c. red and blue . . . . 60·00 60·00
110 65 c. blue and brown . . . 70 70
111 70 c. brown and mauve . . 70 70
112 75 c. drab and blue . . . 1·40 1·40
113 80 c. green and purple . . 70 70
114 85 c. brown and green . . 1·40 1·40
115 90 c. carmine and red . . 70 70
116 **24** 1 f. carmine and red . . . 1·40 1·40
117 1 f. green and brown . . . 1·40 1·40
118 1 f. blue and deep blue . . 70 70
119 1 f. blue 70 70
120 2 f. brown and orange . . 1·40 1·40
121 2 f. 50 brown £110 £110
122 3 f. brown and purple . . 70 70
123 3 f. brown and blue . . . 2·75 2·75
124 10 f. brown and mauve on pink . . . . 35·00 35·00
125 20 f. brown & red on yell 55·00 55·00

5 Native Ivory Head

1944. Free French Administration.
126 **5** 5 c. brown 15 30
127 10 c. blue 15 30
128 25 c. green 15 20
129 30 c. orange 15 30
130 40 c. green 30 45
131 80 c. purple 35 45
132 1 f. purple 30 40
133 1 f. 50 red 20 30
134 2 f. black 25 35
135 2 f. 50 blue 45 60
136 4 f. violet 40 50
137 5 f. yellow 40 50
138 10 f. brown 85 90
139 20 f. green . . . . 1·10 1·25

1944. Mutual Aid and Red Cross Funds. As T **31** of New Caledonia.
140 5 f. + 20 f. orange . . . . . . 1·10 1·10

1945. Surch.
141 **5** 50 c. on 5 c. brown 50 60
142 60 c. on 5 c. brown 50 60
143 70 c. on 5 c. brown 45 55
144 1 f. 20 on 5 c. brown . . . 40 50
145 2 f. 40 on 35 c. green . . . 40 50
146 3 f. on 25 c. green 60 70
147 4 f. 50 on 25 c. green . . . 1·10 1·25
148 15 f. on 2 f. 50 blue . . . 1·10 1·25

1946. Air. Victory. As T **34** of New Caledonia.
149 8 f. violet 50 75

1946. Air. From Chad to the Rhine. As Nos. 300/305 of New Caledonia.
150 5 f. violet 80 90
151 10 f. green 80 90
152 15 f. brown 80 90
153 20 f. blue . . . . 1·00 1·25
154 25 f. orange . . . . 1·25 1·50
155 50 f. red . . . . 1·75 2·00

1949. Air. 75th Anniv of Universal Postal Union. As T **38** of New Caledonia.
156 10 f. multicoloured . . . . . . 4·25 5·00

1949. Air. Nos. 325/6 of New Caledonia, with colours changed, optd **WALLIS ET FUTUNA.**
157 **37** 50 f. red and yellow . . . . 4·75 4·75
158 – 100 f. brown and yellow . . 6·75 7·00

1952. Centenary of Military Medal. As T **40** of New Caledonia.
159 2 f. turquoise, yellow & green . 1·90 1·75

1954. Air. 10th Anniv of Liberation. As T **42** of New Caledonia.
160 3 f. brown and deep brown . . 4·25 4·50

7 Making Tapa (cloth)
9 "Charonia tritonis"

8 Father Chanel

1955. (a) Postage, as T **7**.
161 – 3 f. purple, mauve & lilac . 75 80
162 **7** 5 f. chocolate, brn & grn . 75 80
163 – 7 f. brown and turquoise . 1·10 1·10
164 – 9 f. deep purple, purple and blue . . . . 1·50 1·50
165 – 17 f. multicoloured . . . . 1·90 1·90
166 – 19 f. green and red . . . . 2·00 2·00

(b) Air, as T **8**.
167 **8** 14 f. blue, green & ind . . 2·00 1·40
168 – 21 f. green, brown & bl . 3·50 2·75
168a – 27 f. green, blue & brn . . 3·50 2·00
169 – 33 f. brown, blue & turq . 5·50 5·00
DESIGNS—HORIZ: 9 f. Wallisian and island view; 7 f. Preparing kava; 17 f. Dancers; 21 f. View of Mata-Utu, Queen Amelia and Mgr. Bataillon; 27 f. Wharf, Mata-Utu; 33 f. Map of Wallis and Futuna Islands and "Stella Matutina" (full-rigged ship). VERT: 19 f. Paddle dance.

1958. Tropical Flora As T **47** of New Caledonia.
170 5 f. multicoloured . . . . . . 2·75 2·00
DESIGN—HORIZ: 5 f. "Montrouziera".

1958. 10th Anniv of Declaration of Human Rights. As T **48** of New Caledonia.
171 17 f. blue and ultramarine . . 3·50 3·50

1962. 5th South Pacific Conference. Pago Pago As T **49d** of New Caledonia.
172 16 f. multicoloured . . . . . 2·75 2·25

1962. Marine Fauna.
173 **9** 25 c. brown and green (postage) 55 55
174 – 1 f. red and green 55 55
175 – 2 f. brown and blue . . . 1·10 1·10
176 – 4 f. brown and blue . . . 1·60 1·60
177 – 10 f. multicoloured . . . . 3·50 3·50
178 – 20 f. brown and blue . . . 6·50 6·50
179 – 50 f. brown, bl & pur (air) 7·75 5·00
180 – 100 f. black, green & pur . 15·00 11·00
DESIGNS—As T **9**: 1 f. "Mitra episcopalis"; 2 f. "Cypraecassis rufa"; 4 f. "Murex tenuispina"; 10 f. "Oliva erythrostoma"; 20 f. "Cypraea tigris". 26½ × 48 mm: 50 f. "Harpa ventricosa". 48 × 26½ mm: 100 f. Fishing under water for trochus shells.

1962. Air. 1st Trans-Atlantic TV Satellite Link. As T **50** of New Caledonia.
181 12 f. blue, purple and violet . 2·50 2·50

1963. Red Cross Cent. As T **53** of New Caledonia.
182 12 f. red, grey and purple . . 2·50 1·60

1963. 15th Anniv of Declaration of Human Rights. As T **54** of New Caledonia.
183 29 f. ochre and red . . . . . 5·50 4·50

1964. "PHILATEC 1964" Int Stamp Exn, Paris. As T **54c** of New Caledonia.
184 9 f. red, green and deep green 2·50 1·75

10 Throwing the Javelin

11 Inter-island Ferry "Reine Amelia"

1964. Air. Olympic Games. Tokyo.
185 **10** 31 f. purple, red & green . 15·00 10·00

1965.
186 **11** 11 f. multicoloured . . . . 5·00 4·00

1965. Air. Centenary of I.T.U. As T **56** of New Caledonia
187 50 f. brown, purple and red . 16·00 12·00

1966. Air. Launching of 1st French Satellite. As Nos. 398/9 of New Caledonia
188 7 f. red, claret & vermilion . . 2·75 2·75
189 10 f. red, claret & vermilion . 3·50 3·50

1966. Air. Launching of Satellite "D1" As T **56e** of New Caledonia.
190 10 f. red, lake and green . . . 2·50 2·50

12 W.H.O. Building

1966. Air. Inauguration of W.H.O. Headquarters, Geneva.
191 **12** 30 f. red, yellow and blue . 3·00 3·00

13 Art Students

1966. Air. 20th Anniv of U.N.E.S.C.O.
192 **13** 50 f. brown, green & orange . . 4·50 3·50

14 Athlete and Decorative Pattern

1966. Air. South Pacific Games, Noumea.
193 **14** 32 f. multicoloured . . . . 3·50 2·50
194 – 38 f. green and mauve . . . 4·00 3·00
DESIGN: 38 f. Woman with ball, and decorative pattern.

15 Samuel Wallis's Frigate H.M.S. "Dolphin" at Uvea

1967. Air. Bicentenary of Discovery of Wallis Island.
195 **15** 12 f. multicoloured . . . . 5·00 3·50

1968. 20th Anniv of W.H.O. As T **68** of New Caledonia.
196 17 f. purple, orange & green . . 4·00 3·50

1968. Human Rights Year As T **69** of New Caledonia.
197 19 f. brown, mauve & purple . 2·50 2·50

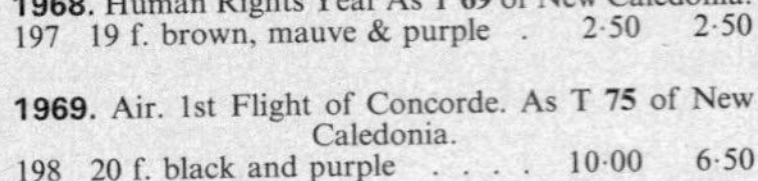

1969. Air. 1st Flight of Concorde. As T **75** of New Caledonia.
198 20 f. black and purple . . . . 10·00 6·50

16 Gathering Coconuts

1969. Scenes of Everyday Life. Multicoloured.
199 1 f. Launching outrigger canoe (35 × 22 mm) (postage) . . . 80 80
200 20 f. Type **16** (air) . . . . . . 1·75 1·00
201 32 f. Horse-riding . . . . . . 3·00 1·50
202 38 f. Wood-carving . . . . . 3·50 1·90
203 50 f. Fishing . . . . 5·00 3·50
204 100 f. Marketing fruit . . . . 10·00 5·50

1969. 50th Anniv of Int Labour Organization. As T **79** of New Caledonia.
205 9 f. blue, brown and salmon . 2·00 2·00

1970. Inauguration of New U.P.U. Headquarters Building, Berne As T **81** of New Caledonia.
206 21 f. brown, blue and purple . 2·50 2·50

1971. Surch.
207 12 f. on 19 f. (No. 166) (postage) 1·10 1·10
208 21 f. on 33 f. (No. 169) (air) . 3·50 2·75

18 Weightlifting 20 Pacific Island Dwelling

1971. 4th South Pacific Games, Papeete, Tahiti.
209 **18** 24 f. brown, blue and green (postage) . . . . 3·00 2·25
210 – 36 f. blue, olive and red . 3·75 2·75
211 – 48 f. brown, green and lilac (air) . . . . 4·25 2·25
212 – 54 f. red, purple and blue . 4·50 3·50
DESIGNS—As T **18**: 36 f. Basketball. 47 × 27 mm: 48 f. Pole-vaulting; 54 f. Archery.

1971. 1st Death Anniv of General Charles de Gaulle. As Nos. 493/4 of New Caledonia.
213 30 f. black and blue . . . . . 5·00 2·75
214 70 f. black and blue . . . . . 9·00 5·50

1972. Air. 25th Anniv of South Pacific Commission. As T **96** of New Caledonia.
215 44 f. multicoloured . . . . . 4·50 2·75

1972. Air. South Pacific Arts Festival, Fiji.
216 **20** 60 f. violet, green & red . 5·50 3·50

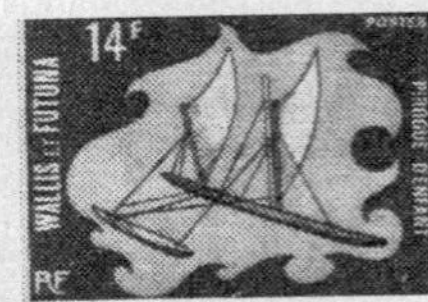

21 Model Pirogue

1972. Sailing Pirogues. Multicoloured.
217 14 f. Type **21** (postage) . . . 4·00 2·25
218 16 f. Children with model pirogues . . . . 4·00 2·25
219 18 f. Racing pirogue . . . . 4·50 3·50
220 200 f. Pirogue race (47 × 27 mm) (air) . . . . 25·00 14·00

22 La Perouse and "La Boussole"

1973. Air. Explorers of the Pacific.
221 **22** 22 f. brown, grey and red . 2·40 1·60
222 – 28 f. green, red and blue . 3·00 2·25
223 – 40 f. brown, blue & lt bl . 5·00 3·50
224 – 72 f. brown, blue & violet . 7·50 4·50
DESIGNS: 28 f. Samuel Wallis and H.M.S. "Dolphin"; 40 f. Dumont d'Urville and "L'Astrolabe"; 72 f. Bougainville and "La Boudeuse.".

23 General De Gaulle

1973. Air. 3rd Death Anniv of General Charles de Gaulle.
225 **23** 107 f. purple and brown . 9·50 6·00

24 "Plumeria rubra"

1973. Air. Flora of Wallis Islands. Multicoloured.
226 12 f. Type **24** . . . . 1·10 75
227 17 f. "Hibiscus tiliaceus" . . 1·40 90
228 19 f. "Phaeomeria magnifica" 1·60 1·00
229 21 f. "Hibiscus rosa sinensis" 1·60 1·00
230 23 f. "Allamanda cathartica" . 2·00 1·50
231 27 f. "Barringtonia asiatica" . 2·00 2·00
232 39 f. Bouquet in vase . . . . 5·50 3·50

25 Rhinoceros Beetle

1974. Insects Multicoloured.
233 15 f. Type **25** . . . . 1·40 90
234 25 f. "Cosmopolites sordidus" (weevil) . . . . 2·00 1·40
235 35 f. Tropical fruit-piercer . . 2·75 1·60
236 45f "Pantala flavescens" (darter) 4·50 2·75

26 "Flower Hand" holding Letter 27 "Holy Family" (Kamalielf-Filimoehala)

1974. Air. Centenary of Universal Postal Union.
237 **26** 51 f. purple, brown & grn . 4·50 2·75

1974. Air. Christmas.
238 **27** 150 f. multicoloured . . . . 8·50 5·50

28 Tapa Pattern

1975. Air. Tapa Mats. Each brown, gold and yellow.
239 3 f. Type **28** 55 45
240 24 f. "Villagers" . . . . . . 1·60 1·10
241 36 f. "Fishes" . . . . 2·75 1·75
242 80 f. "Fishes and Dancers" . . 5·50 4·00

29 Boeing 707 in Flight 30 Volleyball

1975. Air. 1st Regular Air Service to New Caledonia.
243 **29** 100 f. multicoloured . . . . 5·00 4·00

1975. Air. 5th South Pacific Games, Guam. Multicoloured.
244 26 f. Type **30** . . . . 1·50 85
245 44 f. Football . . . . 1·75 1·25
246 56 f. Throwing the javelin . . 3·00 2·00
247 105 f. Aqua-diving . . . . . 6·00 4·50

1976. Pres. Pompidou Commemoration. As T **125** of New Caledonia.
248 50 f. grey and blue . . . . . 4·00 2·50

31 Lalolalo Lake, Wallis

1976. Landscapes. Multicoloured.
249 10 f. Type **31** (postage) . . . 80 40
250 29 f. Vasavasa, Futuna (air) . 2·00 1·10
251 41 f. Sigave Bay, Futuna . . . 2·75 1·50
252 68 f. Gahi Bay, Wallis . . . . 4·00 2·50

32 Concorde

1976. Air. 1st Commercial Flight of Concorde.
253 **32** 250 f. multicoloured . . . . 18·00 11·00

33 Washington and Battle of Yorktown

1976. Bicentenary of American Revolution.
254 **33** 19 f. green, blue and red . 1·40 90
255 – 47 f. purple, red and blue . 3·00 2·25
DESIGN: 47 f. Lafayette and sea-battle of the Virginia Capes.

34 Throwing the Hammer

1976. Air. Olympic Games, Montreal.
256 **34** 31 f. purple, blue and red . 2·00 1·50
257 – 39 f. mauve, red & purple . 3·00 2·00
DESIGN: 39 f. High-diving.

35 "Conus ammiralis"

1976. Sea Shells. Multicoloured.
258 20 f. Type **35** . . . . 1·40 1·25
259 23 f. "Cyprae assellus" . . . 1·40 1·25
260 43 f. "Turbo petholatus" . . . 3·00 2·50
261 61 f. "Mitra papalis" . . . . 4·50 4·00

36 Father Chanel and Sanctuary Church, Poi

1977. Father Chanel Memorial. Multicoloured.
262 22 f. Type **36** . . . . 1·25 85
263 32 f. Father Chanel and map . 1·60 1·00

36a De Gaulle Memorial

1977. 5th Anniv of General de Gaulle Memorial.
264 **36a** 100 f. multicoloured . . . 6·00 4·50

37 Tanoa (bowl), Lali (mortar trough) and Ipu (coconut shell)

1977. Handicrafts. Multicoloured.
265 12 f. Type **37** 65 30
266 25 f. Wallis and Futuna kumetes (bowls) and tuluma (box) . 1·25 60
267 33 f. Milamila (comb), ike (club) and tutua (model outrigger) 1·50 80
268 45 f. Kolo (Futuna clubs) . . 1·60 1·25
269 69 f. Kailao (Wallis and Futuna lances) . . . . 2·75 2·00

1977. Air. 1st Commercial Flight of Concorde. Paris–New York. Optd **PARIS NEW-YORK 22.11.77 1er VOL COMMERCIAL**.
270 **32** 250 f. multicoloured . . . 13·50 10·00

39 Post Office, Mata-Utu

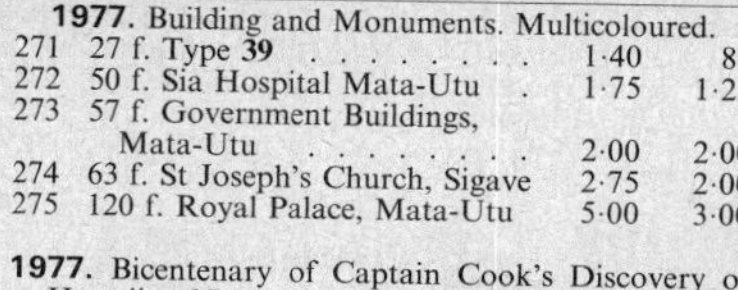

1977. Building and Monuments. Multicoloured.
271 27 f. Type **39** . . . . 1·40 80
272 50 f. Sia Hospital Mata-Utu . . 1·75 1·25
273 57 f. Government Buildings, Mata-Utu . . . . 2·00 2·00
274 63 f. St Joseph's Church, Sigave 2·75 2·00
275 120 f. Royal Palace, Mata-Utu 5·00 3·00

1977. Bicentenary of Captain Cook's Discovery of Hawaii. Nos. 254/5 optd **JAMES COOK Bicentenaire de la decouverte des Iles Hawaii 1778–1978.**
276 **33** 19 f. green, blue and red . 2·50 1·60
277 – 47 f. purple, red & blue . . 4·50 2·75

41 "Balistes niger"

1977. Air. Fishes. Multicoloured.
278 26 f. Type **41** . . . . 1·00 55
279 35 f. Anemone fish . . . . . 1·40 1·75
280 49 f. Emperor angelfish . . . 2·00 1·75
281 51 f. Moorish idol . . . . . . 2·75 2·00

42 Map of Futuna and Alofi

1978. Maps of Wallis and Futuna Islands.
282 **42** 300 f. turquoise, blue and ultramarine . . . . . . 12·00 9·50
283 – 500 f. brown, blue and ultramarine . . . . . . 16·00 12·75
DESIGN—VERT: 500 f. Map of Wallis Island.

43 Father Bataillon and Churches

1978. Air. Arrival of 1st French Missionaries. Multicoloured.
284 60 f. Type **43** . . . . 2·00 1·50
285 72 f. Monsgr. Pompallier and map . . . . 2·50 2·00

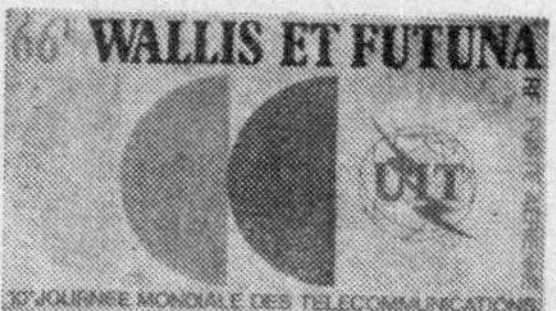

44 I.T.U. Emblem and Antennae

1978. Air. World Telecommunications Day.
286 **44** 66 f. multicoloured . . . . 2·50 1·60

45 "Triomphant" (destroyer)

1978. Free French Pacific Naval Force. 1940–1944. Multicoloured.
287 150 f. Type **45** . . . . 7·25 5·00
288 200 f. "Cap des Palmes" and "Chevreuil" (patrol boats) . 10·00 6·50
289 280 f. "Savorgnan de Brazza" (destroyer) . . . . 14·00 10·00

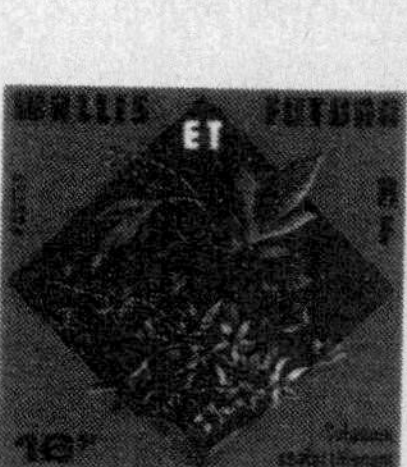

46 "Solanum seaforthianum" **47** Eastern Reef Heron

1978. Tropical Flowers. Multicoloured.
290 16 f. Type **46** 80 40
291 24 f. "Cassia alata" 90 55
292 29 f. "Gloriosa superba" . . 1·50 80
293 36 f. "Hymenocallis littoralis" 2·00 1·10

1978. Ocean Birds. Multicoloured.
294 17 f. Type **47** 65 40
295 18 f. Red-footed booby . . . 65 40
296 28 f. Brown booby . . . . . 1·40 80
297 35 f. White tern . . . . . . 1·90 1·25

48 Costumed Carpet-sellers

1978. Costumes and Traditions. Multicoloured.
298 53 f. Type **48** . . . . 1·75 1·10
299 55 f. "Festival of God" procession . . . . 2·25 1·50
300 59 f. Guards of honour . . . 2·75 1·50

49 Nativity Scene

1978. Air. Christmas.
301 **49** 160 f. multicoloured . . . 5·50 3·50

50 Human Rights Emblem

1978. 30th Anniv of Declaration of Human Rights.
302 **50** 44 f. multicoloured . . . . 1·50 1·00
303 56 f. multicoloured . . . . 2·00 1·50

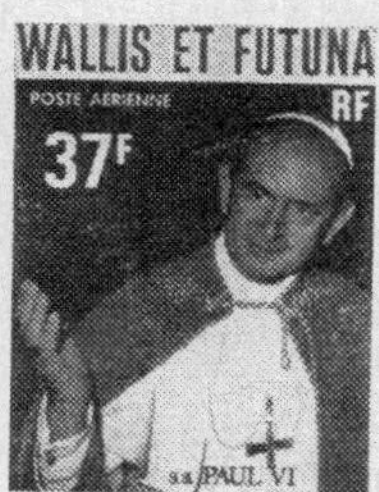

51 Pope Paul VI

1979. Air. Popes. Multicoloured.
304 37 f. Type **51** . . . . 1·40 1·00
305 41 f. Pope John-Paul I . . . 1·60 1·40
306 105 f. St Peter's, Rome, and Popes Paul VI and John-Paul I (horiz) . . . . 4·00 2·50

52 Britten Norman Islander

1979. Air. Inter-Island Communications (1st series). Multicoloured.
307 46 f. Type **52** . . . . 1·40 90
308 68 f. Freighter "Moana II" . 1·75 1·40
309 80 f. Hihifo Airport . . . . . 2·50 1·60
See also Nos. 349/51.

53 Fishing Boat

1979. Tagging Bonito Fish. Multicoloured.
310 10 f. Type **53** 40 30
311 30 f. Weighing bonito 90 55
312 34 f. Young fishes . . . . . . 1·00 75
313 38 f. Tagging bonito . . . . . 1·40 85
314 40 f. Angling for bonito . . . 1·50 1·10
315 48 f. Bonito fish . . . . 2·00 1·60

54 Boy with Model Outrigger Canoe

1979. International Year of the Child. Multicoloured.
317 52 f. Type **54** . . . . 1·50 95
318 58 f. Girl on horseback . . . . 1·75 1·00

55 "Bombax ellipticum"

1979. Flowering and Fruiting Trees. Mult.
319 50 f. Type **55** . . . . 1·25 90
320 64 f. "Callophyllum inophyllum" 2·10 1·00
321 76 f. "Pandanus odoratissimus" 2·75 1·75

56 French 1876 5 c Stamp and "Eole" Meteorological Satellite

1979. Air. Death Centenary of Sir Rowland Hill.
322 **56** 5 f. multicoloured 55 30
323 – 70 f. multicoloured . . . . 1·75 1·10
324 – 90 f. black and red . . . . 2·50 1·50
325 – 100 f. brown, yellow & bl . 2·75 2·00
DESIGNS—VERT: 70 f. Hibiscus and Wallis and Futuna 1920 1 f. stamp. HORIZ: 90 f. Sir Rowland Hill and Great Britain Penny Black; 100 f. "Birds" (Kano School) and Japan 1872 ½ stamp.

57 Normal and Distorted Landscapes

1979. Anti-alcoholism Campaign.
326 **57** 22 f. multicoloured . . . . 1·10 90

58 Heads looking at Cross of Lorraine

1979. Air. 39th Anniv of 18 June Appeal by General de Gaulle.
327 **58** 33 f. red, blue and grey . . 1·40 1·00

59 "Crinum moorei" **60** Map of Islands and French Arms

1979. Flowers (1st series) Multicoloured.
328 20 f. Type **59** 50 30
329 42 f. Passion flower . . . . . 1·50 90
330 62 f. "Canna indica" . . . . 2·00 1·40
See also Nos. 392/4.

1979. Air. Presidential Visit.
331 **60** 47 f. multicoloured . . . . 1·90 1·10

61 Cook and Death Scene, Hawaii

1979. Air. Death Bicentenary of Captain Cook.
332 **61** 130 f. grey, blue & brown . 4·00 2·75

62 Swimmers

1979. Sixth South Pacific Games, Fiji.
333 **62** 31 f. olive, red and green . 1·50 80
334 – 39 f. brown, turq & grn . . 2·00 1·00
DESIGN: 39 f. High-jumper.

63 Garlands

1979. Necklaces. Multicoloured.
335 110 f. Type **63** . . . . 2·50 2·00
336 140 f. Coral necklaces . . . . 4·50 2·50

64 Satellite and Dish Aerial

1979. Air. 3rd World Telecommunications Exhibition, Geneva.
337 **64** 120 f. multicoloured . . . 3·50 2·50

65 Detail of Painting by Mme. Sutita

1979. Works of Local Artists. Multicoloured.
338 27 f. Painting by Mme Sutita (detail) (different) . . . . . 1·00 90
339 65 f. Painting by M. A. Pilioko (detail) (vert) . . . . 1·75 1·40
340 78 f. Type **65** . . . . 2·50 1·75

66 Squilla

1979. South Pacific Fauna. Multicoloured.
341 15 f. Type **66** 50 30
342 23 f. "Hexabranchus sanguineus" 60 50
343 25 f. "Spondylus barbatus" . . 1·00 65
344 43 f. Sea fan . . . . 1·25 65
345 45 f. Starfish . . . . 1·40 8

67 "Virgin of the Crescent Moon" (detail, Durer)

1979. Air. Christmas.
347 **67** 180 f. black and red . . . 5·50 4·00
See also No. 554.

68 Concorde, Map and Rotary Emblem

1980. Air. 75th Anniv of Rotary International.
348 **68** 86 f. multicoloured . . . . 3·50 2·50

1980. Inter-Island Communications (2nd series). As Nos. 307/9.
349 1 f. Type **52** 15 15
350 3 f. As No. 308 . . . . 15 15
351 5 f. As No. 309 . . . . 25 15

69 Radio Station

71 "Rochambeau and Soldiers"

70 "Jesus laid in the Tomb" (Maurice Denis)

1980. 1st Anniv of Radio Station FR3.
352 **69** 47 f. multicoloured . . . . 1·50 1·00

1980. Easter.
353 **70** 25 f. multicoloured . . . . 1·10 65

1980. Air. Bicentenary of Rochambeau's Landing at Newport, Rhode Island.
354 **71** 102 f. sepia, blue & brown . 3·50 2·75

72 Flags and Island

1980. Air. National Day.
355 **72** 71 f. multicoloured . . . . 1·75 1·00

73 "Gnathodentex mossambicus"

1980. Fishes. Multicoloured.
356 23 f. Type **73** 70 40
357 27 f. Blue-spotted snapper . . 85 55
358 32 f. Ruby snapper . . . . . 1·25 90
359 51 f. Rock cod . . . . 1·75 1·25
360 59 f. Flame snapper . . . . . 2·50 2·00

74 Mermoz and "Arc en Ciel"

1980. Air. 50th Anniv of 1st South Atlantic Airmail Flight.
361 **74** 122 f. blue, dp blue & red 3·50 2·50

1980. "Sydpex 80" International Stamp Exhibition, Sydney. No. 315 surch **50F SYDPEX 80 29 Septembre**.
362 50 f. on 48 f. multicoloured . 2·00 2·10

76 Fleming and Penicillin Slide

1980. Air. 25th Death Anniv of Alexander Fleming (discoverer of penicillin).
363 **76** 101 f. blue, brown & red . 2·50 1·75

77 Charles de Gaulle

1980. Air. 10th Death Anniv of Charles de Gaulle (French statesman).
364 **77** 200 f. green and brown . . 5·50 4·00

78 "The Virgin, Child and St. Catherine" (Lorenzo Lotto)

1980. Air. Christmas.
365 **78** 150 f. multicoloured . . . 3·50 2·50

79 Alan Shepard and "Freedom 7"

1981. Air. 20th Anniv of First Men in Space. Multicoloured.
366 37 f. Type **79** . . . . 1·00 65
367 44 f. Yury Gagarin and "Vostok 1" . . . . 1·25 90

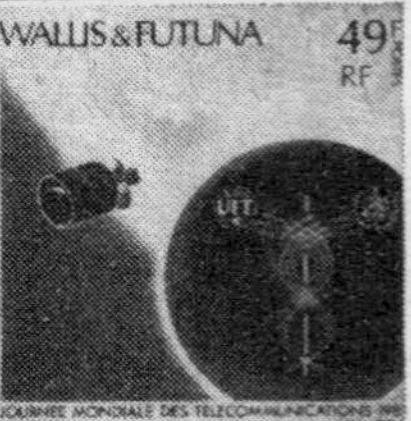

80 Ribbons and I.T.U. and W.H.O. Emblems forming Caduceus and Satellite

1981. World Telecommunications Day.
368 **80** 49 f. multicoloured . . . . 1·25 90

81 Curie and Laboratory Equipment

1981. 75th Death Anniv of Pierre Curie (physicist and discoverer of radium).
369 **81** 56 f. multicoloured . . . . 1·40 1·00

82 Coral

83 Doctor inoculating Child

84 Section of Globe

1981. Undersea Fauna. Multicoloured.
370 28 f. Type **82** 85 60
371 30 f. Blue-green algae 85 60
372 31 f. "Ceratium vultur" (dinoflagellate) . . . . . . 1·00 65
373 35 f. "Amphiprion frenatus" (fish) . . . . 1·10 65
374 40 f. "Conus textile" (mollusc) 1·25 90
375 55 f. Feather-star (echinoderm) 1·75 1·00

1981. 60th Anniv of 1st B.C.G. Anti-tuberculosis Inoculation.
376 **83** 27 f. multicoloured 75 50

1981. International Year of Disabled Persons.
377 **84** 42 f. multicoloured . . . . 1·40 75

85 Edison and Phonograph

1981. 50th Death Anniv of Thomas Edison (inventor).
378 **85** 59 f. black, blue and red . . 1·40 1·00

1981. No. 341 surch **5F.**
379 5 f. on 15 f. multicoloured . . 30 20

87 Battle Scene

88 "Vase of Flowers" (Cezanne)

1981. Bicentenary of Battle of Virginia Capes.
380 – 66 f. purple, blue and slate . 1·40 1·10
381 **87** 74 f. green, violet and light green . . . . 2·00 1·10
DESIGN: 66 f. Admiral Francois de Grasse and battle scene.

1981. Air. 75th Death Anniv of Paul Cezanne and Birth Centenary of Pablo Picasso (artists).
382 53 f. Type **88** . . . . 1·50 1·00
383 135 f. "Harlequin leaning" (Picasso) . . . . 3·50 2·25

89 Football

1981. Air. World Cup Football Championship, Spain (1982).
384 **89** 120 f. brown, black & green 2·50 2·00
385 120 f. brown, mauve and green . . . . 2·50 2·00

90 Patrol Boat "La Dieppoise"

1981. Surveillance of 200-mile zone. Mult.
386 60 f. Type **90** . . . . 1·40 1·00
387 85 f. Frigate "Protet" . . . . 2·00 1·50

91 Crib

1981. Air. Christmas.
388 **91** 180 f. multicoloured . . . 4·00 2·75

92 "Pilioko Aloi" (tapestry)

93 Dr Robert Koch at Microscope

1982. Air.
389 **92** 100 f. multicoloured . . . 2·25 1·75

1982. Centenary of Discovery of Tubercle Bacillus.
390 **93** 45 f. multicoloured . . . . 1·10 90

94 "Fishing Boats at Collioure"

1982. Air. Death Centenary of Georges Braque (painter).
391 **94** 300 f. multicoloured . . . 6·50 4·50

1982. Flowers (2nd series). Multicoloured.
392 1 f. As Type **59** 10 10
393 2 f. As No. 329 . . . . 15 10
394 3 f. As No. 330 . . . . 15 10

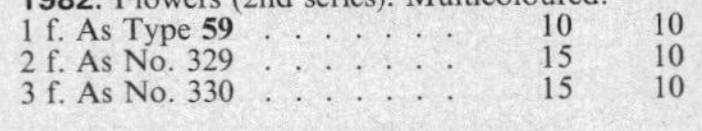

95 1930 Stamp

1982. "Philexfrance" International Stamp Exhibition, Paris.
395 **95** 140 f. violet, blue and red . 2·50 1·75

96 "Acanthe phippium"

1982. Orchids. Multicoloured.
396 34 f. Type **96** 80 55
397 68 f. "Acanthe phippium" (different) . . . . 1·75 1·25
398 70 f. "Spathoglottis pacifica" . 2·00 1·25
399 83 f. "Mussaenda raiateensis" 2·50 1·75

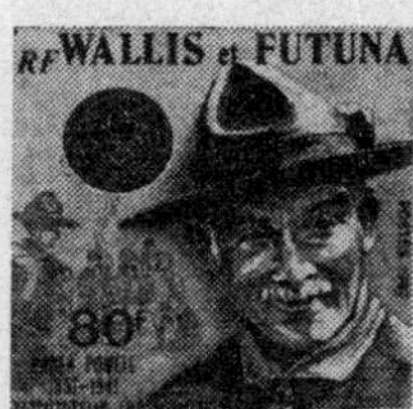

97 Lord Baden-Powell

1982. 125th Birth Anniv of Lord Baden-Powell (founder of Boy Scout Movement).
400 **97** 80 f. multicoloured . . . . 2·00 1·25

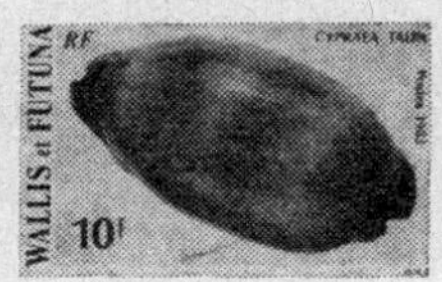

98 "Cypraea talpa"

1982. Sea Shells (1st series). Multicoloured.
401 10 f. Type **98** 20 15
402 15 f. "Cypraea vitellus" . . . 30 15
403 25 f. "Cypraea argus" 40 30
404 27 f. "Cypraea carneola" . . . 55 40
405 40 f. "Cypraea mappa" . . . 80 55
406 50 f. "Cypraea tigris" . . . . 1·10 80
See also Nos. 428/33, 440/5, 459/64, 481/6 and 510/15.

99 Santos-Dumont, Airship "Ballon No. 14" and Biplane "14 bis"

1982. Air. 50th Death Anniv of Alberto Santos-Dumont (aviation pioneer).
407 **99** 95 f. brown, green and blue 2·25 1·40

1982. Air. World Cup Football Championship Result. No. 384 optd **ITALIE VAINQUEUR 1982**.
408 **89** 120 f. brown, black and green 2·75 2·00

101 Beach

1982. Air. Overseas Week.
409 **101** 105 f. multicoloured . . . 2·25 1·75

102 Coral

1982. Marine Life. Multicoloured.
410 32 f. Type **102** 65 45
411 35 f. Starfish 75 45
412 46 f. "Hexabranchus sanguineus" . . . . 1·00 75
413 63 f. "Spondylus barbatus" . . 1·40 1·10

103 Hands reaching towards Eye
104 St Theresa of Avila

1982. Air. Blind Day.
414 **103** 130 f. blue, scarlet & red 2·25 2·00

1982. 400th Death Anniv of St. Theresa of Avila.
415 **104** 31 f. brown, green and deep brown 80 55
See also No. 447.

105 "Adoration of the Virgin" (Correggio)

1982. Air. Christmas.
416 **105** 170 f. multicoloured . . . 3·50 2·50

106 Wallis Meeting House

1983.
417 **106** 19 f. multicoloured . . . 55 30

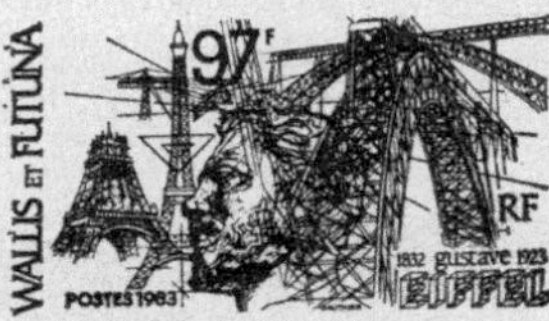

107 Eiffel and Eiffel Tower under Construction

1983. 60th Death Anniv of Gustave Eiffel (engineer).
418 **107** 97 f. purple, red and green 2·00 1·60

108 Windsurfing
110 Vincenzo Lunardi's Balloon, 1784

109 Island Scene and U.P.U. Emblem

1983. Air.
419 **108** 270 f. multicoloured . . . 5·50 3·25

1983. Air. World U.P.U. Day.
420 **109** 100 f. multicoloured . . . 2·25 1·40

1983. Air. Bicentenary of Manned Flight.
421 **110** 205 f. multicoloured . . . 4·25 2·75

111 "Cat"

1983. Air. 15th Death Anniv of Foujita (painter).
422 **111** 102 f. multicoloured . . . 2·25 1·40

112 Thai Goddess
113 Javelin-thrower

1983. "Bangkok 1983" International Stamp Exn.
423 **112** 92 f. red, black and blue . 1·75 1·10

1983. Air. Olympic Games, Los Angeles (1984) (1st issue).
424 **113** 250 f. brown, grn & yell . 4·50 3·50
See also No. 438.

114 Nobel

1983. Air. 150th Birth Anniv of Alfred Nobel (inventor of dynamite and founder of Nobel Prizes).
425 **114** 150 f. red and green . . . 3·00 2·00

115 Satellite, Dish Aerial and W.C.Y. Emblem
117 "Conus tulipa"

116 Niepce and Early Photograph

1983. World Communications Year.
426 **115** 20 f. multicoloured 45 35

1983. Air. Death Centenary of Nicephore Niepce (pioneer of photography).
427 **116** 75 f. purple and green . . 1·90 1·10

1983. Sea Shells (2nd series). Multicoloured.
428 10 f. Type **117** 40 15
429 17 f. "Conus capitaneus" . . . 45 20
430 21 f. "Conus virgo" 45 20
431 39 f. "Conus vitulinus" 75 20
432 52 f. "Conus marmoreus" . . 1·00 80
433 65 f. "Conus leopardus" . . . 1·40 1·00

118 "Triumph of Galatea"

1983. Air. 500th Birth Anniv of Raphael (artist).
434 **118** 167 f. multicoloured . . . 3·25 2·50

119 Pandanus Tree

1983. Air.
435 **119** 137 f. multicoloured . . . 2·75 1·75

120 "Madonna and Pope Sixtus" (Raphael)

1983. Air. Christmas.
436 **120** 200 f. multicoloured . . . 4·25 2·75

121 Frigate "Commandant Bory"

1984. Air.
437 **121** 67 f. multicoloured . . . 1·50 1·00

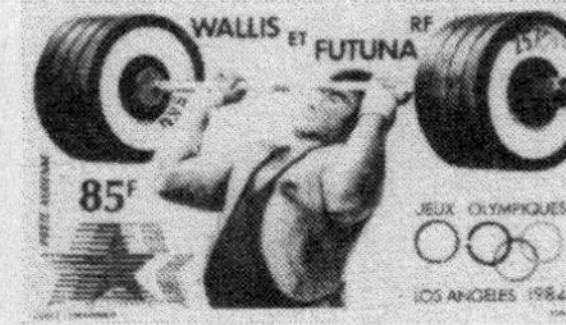

122 Weightlifting

1984. Air. Olympic Games, Los Angeles (2nd issue).
438 **122** 85 f. multicoloured . . . 2·00 1·40

123 Frangipani

1984. Air.
439 **123** 130 f. multicoloured . . . 2·75 1·75

1984. Sea Shells (3rd series). As T **117**. Mult.
440 22 f. "Strombus lentiginosus" 40 30
441 25 f. "Lambis chiragra" . . . 40 30
442 35 f. "Strombus dentatus" . . 75 40
443 43 f. "Lambis scorpius" . . . 1·10 65
444 49 f. "Strombus aurisdianae" 1·40 90
445 76 f. "Lambis crocata" . . . 1·90 1·40

124 "Deposition of Christ" (Alele Chapel)

1984. Air. Easter.
446 **124** 190 f. multicoloured . . . 3·50 2·50

1984. "Espana 84" International Stamp Exhibition, Madrid. As T **104** but with "Espana 84" emblem.
447 70 f. sepia, green and brown . 1·50 1·10

125 Diderot and Title Page of Encyclopedia

126 Killer Whale

1984. Death Bicent of Denis Diderot (encyclopedist).
448 **125** 100 f. brown and blue . . 2·00 1·40

1984. Nature Protection.
449 **126** 90 f. multicoloured . . . 2·00 1·40

127 Painting

128 Tiki

1984. Air. 95th Birth Anniv of Jean Cocteau (artist).
450 **127** 150 f. multicoloured . . . 3·00 2·25

1984. Air. Soane Hoatau Sculpture.
451 **128** 175 f. multicoloured . . . 3·25 2·50

"**129** Alice"

"**130** Pilioko Aloi" (tapestry)

1984. Air. Birth Centenary of Amedeo Modigliani (painter).
452 **129** 140 f. multicoloured . . . 3·00 2·00

1984. Air. "Ausipex 84" International Stamp Exhibition, Melbourne.
453 **130** 180 f. multicoloured . . . 3·50 2·25

131 "Local Dances" (Jean Michon)

1984. Air.
454 **131** 110 f. multicoloured . . . 2·50 1·75

132 Altar, Mount Lulu Chapel

1984. Air.
455 **132** 52 f. multicoloured . . . 1·10 75

133 Islanders wearing Leis

1985. 4th Pacific Arts Festival.
456 **133** 160 f. multicoloured . . . 3·00 2·25

134 Conch Shell and Virgin and Child

1984. Air. Christmas.
457 **134** 260 f. multicoloured . . . 5·00 2·75

135 Lapita Pottery

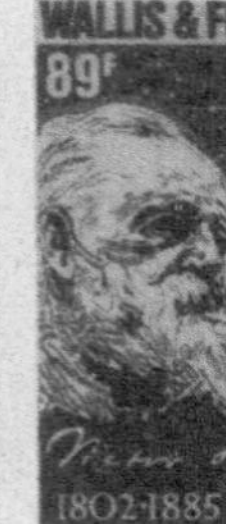

136 Victor Hugo

1985. Archaeological Expedition, 1983
458 **135** 53 f. multicoloured . . . 1·00 55

1985. Sea Shells (4th series). As T **117**. Multicoloured.
459 2 f. "Nautilus pompilius" . . 10 10
460 3 f. "Murex bruneus" . . . 10 10
461 41 f. "Casmaria erinaceus" . . 75 45
462 47 f. "Conus vexillum" . . . 1·00 65
463 56 f. "Harpa harpa" . . . 1·10 75
464 71 f. "Murex ramosus" . . . 1·60 1·00

1985. Death Centenary of Victor Hugo (writer).
465 **136** 89 f. deep blue, blue and red 2·00 1·25

137 "Pilioko Aloi" (tapestry)

1985. Air.
466 **137** 500 f. multicoloured . . . 8·50 5·50

138 Flying Fox

139 Children

1985.
467 **138** 38 f. multicoloured . . . 1·00 55

1985. International Youth Year.
468 **139** 64 f. multicoloured . . . 1·25 80

140 "The Post Office"

1985. Air. 30th Death Anniv of Maurice Utrillo (artist).
469 **140** 200 f. multicoloured . . . 3·50 2·25

141 Hands and U.N. Emblem

1985. 40th Anniv of U.N.O.
470 **141** 49 f. green, blue & red . . 1·00 65

142 Sailing Canoe

1985. Air.
471 **142** 350 f. multicoloured . . . 6·00 3·25

143 Ronsard, Organist and Muse of Poetry

1985. 400th Death Anniv of Pierre de Ronsard (poet).
472 **143** 170 f. brown, deep brown and blue . . . . 3·50 2·25

144 Landing Ship "Jacques Cartier"

145 "Portrait of Young Woman" (Patrice Nielly)

1985. Air.
473 **144** 51 f. deep blue, blue and turquoise . . . . 1·00 65

1985. Air.
474 **145** 245 f. multicoloured . . . 4·25 2·25

146 Schweitzer, African Boy and Cathedral Organ

1985. 20th Death Anniv of Dr. Albert Schweitzer (missionary).
475 **146** 50 f. black, purple & brown 1·00 65

INDEX

Countries can be quickly located by referring to the index at the end of this volume.

147 "Virgin and Child" (Jean Michon)

1985. Air. Christmas.
476 **147** 330 f. multicoloured . . . 6·00 4·00

148 Bread-fruit

1986. Food and Agriculture Organization.
477 **148** 39 f. multicoloured . . . 90 55

149 Flamboyant Flower

1986.
478 **149** 38 f. multicoloured . . . 90 55

150 Comet and "Giotto" Space Probe

1986. Air. Appearance of Halley's Comet.
479 **150** 100 f. multicoloured . . . 2·00 1·40

151 Vianney praying

1986. Air. Birth Bicentenary of Cure d'Ars.
480 **151** 200 f. light brown, brown and black . . . . . . 4·00 2·50

1986. Sea Shells (5th series). As T **117**. Mult.
481 4 f. "Lambis truncata" . . . 10 10
482 5 f. "Charonia tritonis" . . . 10 10
483 10 f. "Oliva miniacea" . . . 20 15
484 18 f. "Distorsio anus" . . . 30 20
485 25 f. "Mitra mitra" 55 35
486 107 f. "Conus distans" . . . 2·00 1·40

152 Players and Boy with Football

1986. World Cup Football Championship, Mexico.
487 **152** 95 f. multicoloured . . . 2·00 1·25

153 Willem Schouten and "Eendracht"

1986. 370th Anniv of Discovery of Horn Islands. Each purple, green and blue.

488	8 f. Type **153**	20	15
489	9 f. Jacob le Maire and "Hoorn"	20	15
490	155 f. Map of Futuna and Alofi Islands	3·00	2·50

154 Watt and Steam Engine

1986. 250th Birth Anniv of James Watt (inventor).

491	**154**	74 f. red and black	1·50	1·10

155 Queen Amelia

1986. Air. Centenary of Request for Protectorate and 25th Anniv of French Overseas Territory Status. Each purple, red and blue.

492	90 f. Type **155**	1·75	1·75
493	137 f. Law of 1961 bestowing Overseas Territory status	2·50	2·50

156 Patrol Boat "La Lorientaise"

1986. Naval Ships.

494	**156**	6 f. red, purple and blue	15	10
495	–	7 f. violet, orange & red	15	10
496	–	120 f. turquoise, red & bl	2·25	1·60

DESIGNS: 7 f. Frigate "Commandant Blaison"; 120 f. Frigate "Balny".

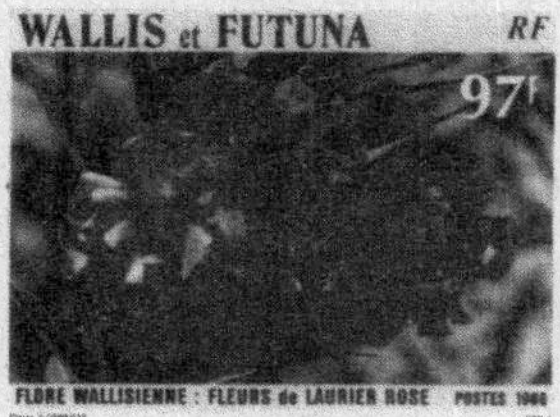
157 Oleander

1986.

497	**157**	97 f. multicoloured	2·00	1·40

158 U.P.U. Emblem and Dove carrying Envelope

1986. Air. World Post Day.

498	**158**	270 f. multicoloured	5·00	3·50

159 New York, Statue and Paris

1986. Air. Centenary of Statue of Liberty.

499	**159**	205 f. multicoloured	4·00	2·50

160 "Virgin and Child" (Botticelli)

1986. Christmas.

500	**160**	250 f. multicoloured	4·50	3·00

161 "Papilio montrouzieri"

162 Father Chanel and Basilica

1987. Butterflies. Multicoloured.

501	2 f. Type **161**	30	20
502	42 f. Caper white	75	45
503	46 f. "Delias ellipsis"	90	55
504	50 f. "Danaus pumila"	1·00	65
505	52 f. "Lutbrodes cleotas"	1·00	65
506	59 f. Meadow argus	1·40	90

1987. Air. 1st Anniv of Poi Basilica.

507	**162**	230 f. multicoloured	4·50	2·50

163 "Telstar", Globe and Pleumeur-Bodou

1987. Air. World Communications Day. 25th Anniv of Launch of "Telstar" Communications Satellite.

508	**163**	200 f. blue, black and red	3·50	2·00

164 Wrestlers

1987. World Wrestling Championships, Clermont-Ferrand.

509	**164**	97 f. multicoloured	1·90	1·25

1987. Sea Shells (6th series). As T **117**. Mult.

510	3 f. "Cymatium pileare"	15	10
511	4 f. "Conus textile"	15	10
512	28 f. "Cypraea mauritiana"	55	35
513	44 f. "Bursa bubo"	90	55
514	48 f. "Cypraea testudinaria"	1·00	65
515	78 f. "Cypraecassis rufa"	1·60	1·10

165 Piccard, Stratosphere Balloon "F.N.R.S." and Bathyscaphe

167 Bust of Girl

1987. Air. 25th Death Anniv of Auguste Piccard (physicist).

516	**165**	135 f. deep blue, blue and green	2·50	1·60

1987. "Olymphilex 87" Olympic Stamps Exhibition, Rome. No 509 optd **OLYMPHILEX '87 ROME** and Olympic rings.

517	**164**	97 f. multicoloured	1·90	1·25

1987. 70th Death Anniv of Auguste Rodin (sculptor).

518	**167**	150 f. purple	2·75	1·75

See also No. 557.

168 Letters between Globes and Postbird

1987. World Post Day.

519	**168**	116 f. blue, deep blue and yellow	2·25	1·40

169 Spotbill Duck

1987. Birds. Multicoloured.

520	6 f. Type **169**	10	10
521	19 f. American golden plover	35	20
522	47 f. Friendly quail dove	90	55
523	56 f. Turnstone	1·00	65
524	64 f. Banded rail	1·25	65
525	68 f. Bar-tailed godwit	1·40	90

170 Mgr. Bataillon, French Frigate and Islands

1987. Air. 150th Anniv of Arrival of First Missionaries.

526	**170**	260 f. turquoise, blue and brown	4·75	3·00

171 Nativity Scene

1987. Air. Christmas.

527	**171**	300 f. multicoloured	5·50	3·50

172 Carco and Parisian Scenes

1988. 30th Death Anniv of Francis Carco (writer).

528	**172**	40 f. multicoloured	80	45

173 Morane Saulnier Type I and Garros

1988. Air. 70th Death Anniv of Roland Garros (aviator).

529	**173**	600 f. deep blue, brown and blue	10·50	6·75

174 La Perouse, "L'Astrolabe" and "La Boussole"

1988. Bicentenary of Disappearance of La Perouse's Expedition.

530	**174**	70 f. green, blue & brown	1·50	90

175 "Self-portrait wearing Lace Jabot"

1988. Air. Death Bicentenary of Maurice Quentin de la Tour (painter).

531	**175**	500 f. multicoloured	9·00	6·00

176 Arrows and Dish Aerial

1988. Air. World Telecommunications Day.

532	**176**	100 f. multicoloured	1·75	1·25

177 Map and Bishop with Crosier

1988. Air. South Pacific Episcopal Conference.

533	**177**	90 f. multicoloured	1·75	1·10

178 Nurse, Child and Anniversary Emblem

1988. 125th Anniv of International Red Cross.

534	**178**	30 f. black, green & red	60	45

179 Throwing the Javelin

1988. Olympic Games, Seoul. Each brown, red and blue.

535	11 f. Type **179**	35	20
536	20 f. Volleyball	45	35
537	60 f. Windsurfing	1·25	1·00
538	80 f. Yachting	1·60	1·40

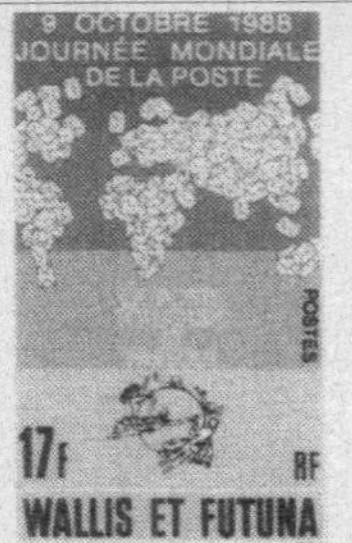

180 Envelopes forming Map

1988. World Post Day.
539 **180** 17 f. yellow, blue & black . . . 40 20

181 Becquerel

1988. Birth Bicentenary of Antoine Becquerel (physicist).
540 **181** 18 f. black and blue . . . 40 20

182 Nativity Scene

1988. Air. Christmas.
541 **182** 400 f. multicoloured . . . 7·25 4·50

183 "Amiral Charner" (frigate)

1989. International Maritime Organization.
542 **183** 26 f. multicoloured . . . 75 45

184 Renior and Scene from "The Great Illusion"

1989. 10th Death Anniv of Jean Renoir (film director).
543 **184** 24 f. brown, mauve & orge 50 35

185 Royal Throne (Aselo Kulimoetoke)

186 Map

1989. Air.
544 **185** 700 f. multicoloured . . . 12·00 7·25

1989. Futuna Hydro-electric Power Station.
545 **186** 25 f. multicoloured . . . 50 35

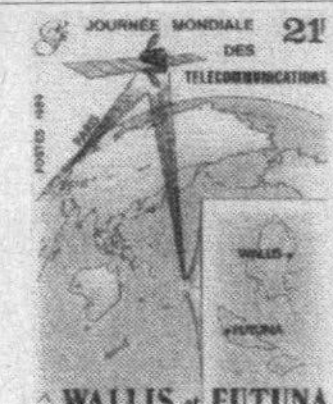

188 Satellite above Earth

1989. International Telecommunications Day.
546 **188** 21 f. multicoloured . . . 45 35

189 Mural (H. Tailhade)

1989.
547 **189** 22 f. multicoloured . . . 45 35

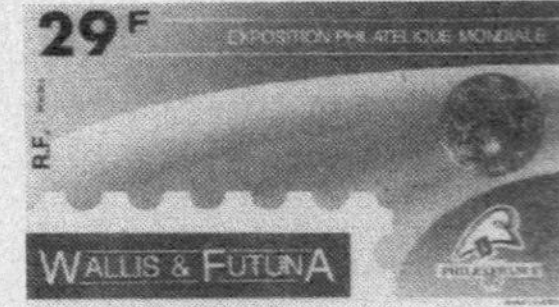

190 Globe and Emblem

1989. "Philexfrance '89" International Stamp Exhibition Paris (548) and Bicentenary of Declaration of Rights of Man and South Pacific Youth Meeting (549). Multicoloured.
548 29 f. Type **190** (postage) . . . 50 35
549 900 f. Sportsmen (air) . . . . 14·50 11·50

191 Cyclists

1989. World Cycling Championships, France.
551 **191** 10 f. black, brown & grn 30 15

192 Envelopes around Globe of Flags

1989. World Post Day.
552 **192** 27 f. multicoloured . . . 50 35

193 Landscape

1989.
553 **193** 23 f. multicoloured . . . 75 60

1989. Air. Christmas. As No. 347 but date, value and colour changed.
554 **67** 800 f. mauve . . . . . . 14·00 9·00

194 "Star of Bethlehem"

1990.
555 **194** 44 f. multicoloured . . . 80 55

195 Tortoise Fossil

1990.
556 **195** 48 f. multicoloured 80 55

1990. 150th Birth Anniv of Auguste Rodin (sculptor). As No. 518 but value and colour changed.
557 **167** 200 f. blue . . . . 4·00 2·25

197 Footballers

1990. World Cup Football Championship, Italy.
558 **197** 59 f. multicoloured . . . . 1·10 80

198 Orchids

1990. Mothers' Day.
559 **198** 78 f. multicoloured . . . . 1·60 1·10

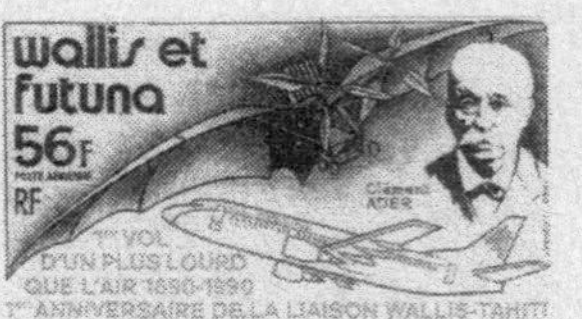

199 "Avion III", Airbus Industrie A310 and Clement Ader

1990. Air. Cent of First Heavier-than-Air Flight and 1st Anniv of Wallis–Tahiti Air Link.
560 **199** 56 f. brown, mauve & red . 1·10 65

200 Red-tailed Tropic Bird

1990. Multicoloured.
561 300 f. Type **200** . . . . 5·50 3·25
562 600 f. South Pacific islet . . . 11·50 6·75

201 "Moana II" (inter-island freighter)

1990. Ships.
563 **201** 40 f. brown, green & blue . 90 60
654 – 50 f. brown, blue & green . 1·10 80
DESIGN: 50 f. "Moana III" (container ship) at jetty.

202 Traditional Dwellings

1990.
565 **202** 28 f. multicoloured 55 35

203 Doves and Globe

204 Outrigger Canoe

1990. Stamp Day.
566 **203** 97 f. multicoloured . . . 1·90 1·40

1990.
567 **204** 46 f. multicoloured . . . 1·25 65

205 De Gaulle

1990. Air. Birth Centenary of Charles de Gaulle (French statesman).
568 **205** 1000 f. multicoloured . . 17·00 10·00

206 Palm Trees

1990. "Best Wishes".
569 **206** 100 f. multicoloured . . . 1·90 1·40

207 Patrol Boat "La Glorieuse"

1991.
570 **207** 52 f. blue, green and red . 1·50 85
See also No. 578.

208 Warrior

1991.
571 7 f. Breadfruit gatherer Tradition 10 10
572 54 f. Taro planter . . . . . . 1·00 55
573 63 f. Spear fisherman . . . . 1·10 65
574 72 f. Type **208** . . . . 1·25 65
575 90 f. Kailao dancer . . . . . 1·60 80

209 Aspects of Health Care

1991. 20th Anniv of Medecins sans Frontieres (medical charity).
577 **209** 55 f. multicoloured . . . 1·00 65

1991. Patrol Boat "La Moqueuse". As T **207**.
578 42 f. black, blue and red . . . 1·25 65

210 Chanel and Reliquary

1991. Air. 150th Death Anniv of Father Chanel (missionary).
579 **210** 235 f. multicoloured . . . 4·50 2·75

211 Players through the Ages (½-size illustration)

1991. Air. Centenary of French Open Tennis Championships.
580 **211** 250 f. black, orange & grn 4·75 2·75

212 Map and Microlight

1991. Microlight Aircraft Flying in Wallis and Futuna.
581 **212** 85 f. multicoloured . . . 1·75 1·10

213 "Portrait of Jean"

1991. 150th Birth Anniv of Pierre Auguste Renior (painter). Perf or imperf (self-adhesive).
582 **213** 400 f. multicoloured . . . 7·25 4·00

214 Map

1991. 30th Anniv of French Overseas Territory Status.
584 **214** 102 f. multicoloured . . . 1·60 1·10

215 Islanders in Festive Dress and Angel

1991. Feast of the Assumption.
585 **215** 30 f. multicoloured . . . 55 35

216 Mozart and Scene from "The Marriage of Figaro"

1991. Air. Death Bicentenary of Wolfgang Amadeus Mozart (composer).
586 **216** 500 f. blue, lilac and red . 8·25 4·50

217 Imprisoned Figure

1991. 30th Anniv of Amnesty International.
587 **217** 140 f. yellow, violet & blue 2·75 1·40

218 House and Generator

1991. 50th Anniv of Central Economic Co-operation Bank.
588 **218** 10 f. multicoloured . . . 15 10

219 "Allamanda cathartica"

1991. Flowers. Multicoloured.
589 1 f. Type **219** 10 10
590 4 f. "Hibiscus rosa sinensis" (vert) 10 10
591 80 f. Water lily . . . . 1·40 90

220 Santa Claus on Beach

1991. Christmas.
592 **220** 60 f. multicoloured . . . . 1·00 55

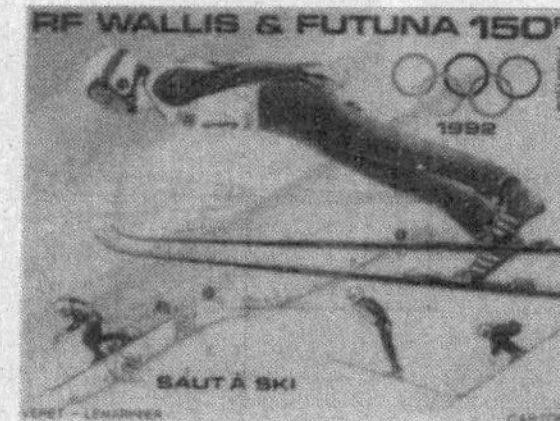
221 Ski Jumping

1992. Winter Olympic Games, Albertville.
593 **221** 150 f. multicoloured . . . 2·75 1·60

222 Map, Plants and Dassault Breguet Mystere Falcon 20

1992. "Escadrille 9S' Maritime Surveillance Service.
594 **222** 48 f. multicoloured . . . 90 45

223 Canadian 1938 $1 and Wallis & Futuna 1920 2 f. Stamps (½ size illustration)

1992. "Canada 92" International Youth Philatelic Exhibition, Montreal.
595 **223** 35 f. black, red and violet 45 30

224 Throwing the Javelin

1992. Olympic Games, Barcelona.
596 **224** 106 f. indigo, blue & grn . 1·60 95

225 Spanish 1975 4 p. Stamp and Wallis Post Office

1992. "Granada 92" International Stamp Exhibition.
597 **225** 100 f. black, blue & purple 1·40 85

226 Columbus's Fleet, Pavilion and Seville

1992. "Expo 92" World's Fair, Seville.
598 **226** 200 f. green, blue & orange 2·75 2·10

227 Saddleback Butterfly Fish

1992. Butterfly and Angel Fishes, Multicoloured.
599 21 f. Type **227** 25 20
600 22 f. Threadfin butterfly fish . 30 20
601 23 f. Horned coachman . . . 30 20
602 24 f. Royal angelfish 30 20
603 25 f. Spectacled angelfish . . . 30 20
604 26 f. One spot butterfly fish . . 35 25

228 Columbus and Map

1992. Air. "World Columbian Stamp Expo 92", Chicago.
605 **228** 100 f. multicoloured . . . 1·25 80
See also No. 612.

229 Three Spearmen

1992. Wallis Islands. Multicoloured.
606 70 f. Type **229** 90 55
607 70 f. Two spearmen and palm trees 90 55
608 70 f. Pirogues 90 55
609 70 f. Two fishermen and palm trees 90 55
610 70 f. Three fishermen and palm trees 90 55
Nos. 606/10 were issued together, se-tenant, forming a composite design.

1992. Air. "Genova '92" International Thematic Stamp Exhibition. As T **228** but with different Exhibition emblem.
612 800 f. multicoloured . . . . 10·00 6·25

230 Victorious Marianne

1992. Air. Bicentenary of Year One of First French Republic.
613 **230** 350 f. black, blue and red 4·50 2·75

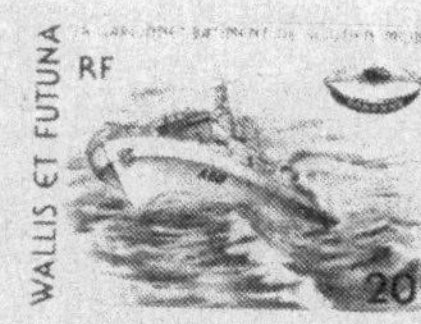
231 "La Garonne" (supply vessel)

1992.
614 **231** 20 f. multicoloured . . . 25 15

232 "L'Idylle d'Ixelles"

1992. 75th Death Anniv of Auguste Rodin (sculptor).
615 **232** 300 f. black and mauve . 3·75 2·40

233 "Mirabilis jalapa"

1992.
616 **233** 200 f. multicoloured . . . 2·50 1·60

234 Dassault Breguet Gardian, Frigate and Native Canoes

1993. French Naval Forces in the Pacific.
617 **234** 130 f. multicoloured . . . 1·75 1·25

235 Abstract (J. E. Korda)

1993. School Art.
618 **235** 56 f. multicoloured . . . 1·60 1·00
See also Nos. 635/6.

236 Banded Rail

1993. Birds. Multicoloured.
619 50 f. Type **236** 65 40
620 60 f. Purple swamphen . . . 75 50
621 110 f. Grey's fruit dove . . . 1·40 85

237 Building Facade

1993. Air. Bicentenary of the Louvre, Paris.
622 **237** 315 f. ultramarine, red and blue . . . . 4·00 2·50

238 Copernicus and Planetary Model

1993. Air. "Polska 93" International Stamp Exhibition, Poznan. 450th Death Anniv of Nicolas Copernicus (astronomer).
623 **238** 600 f. red, brown and crimson . . . . 7·75 4·75

239 Hibiscus

1993. Mothers' Day. Multicoloured.
624 95 f. Type **239** . . . . 1·25 75
625 120 f. Bouquet of stephanotis . 1·50 95

240 Sailfin Surgeon Fish

1993. Fishes. Multicoloured.
626 27 f. Spinefoot 35 25
627 35 f. Type **240** 45 30
628 45 f. Flag-tailed surgeon fish . 60 40
629 53 f. Fox-face 70 45

241 D'Entrecasteaux and Flagship

1993. Death Bicentenary of Bruni d'Entrecasteaux (explorer).
630 **241** 170 f. red, blue & black . 2·25 1·40

242 Symbols of Taiwan

1993. "Taipei '93" International Stamp Exhibition.
631 **242** 435 f. multicoloured . . . 5·50 3·25

243 Tepa Church, Wallis Island

1993. Churches. Multicoloured.
632 30 f. Type **243** 40 25
633 30 f. Vilamalia Church, Futuna Island 40 25

244 "La Marseillaise"

1993. Air. Bicentenary of Year Two of First French Republic.
634 **244** 400 f. red, blue & black . 5·00 3·00

1993. School Art. As T **235**.
635 28 f. blue, black and grey . . 35 25
636 52 f. multicoloured 65 40
DESIGNS—HORIZ: 28 f. Palm trees (T. Tuhimutu). VERT: 52 f. People (M. Hakula).

245 Nativity

1993. Christmas.
637 **245** 80 f. multicoloured . . . 1·00 60

246 "Wallis Landscape" (P. Legris)

1994. Air.
638 **246** 400 f. multicoloured . . . 5·00 3·00

247 Landscape and Emblem

1994. Air. "Hong Kong '94" International Stamp Exhibition.
639 **247** 700 f. multicoloured . . . 9·00 5·50

248 Emblem

1994. Traditional Crafts Show, Wallis and Futuna.
640 **248** 80 f. multicoloured . . . 1·10 70

249 Manning the Barricades

1994. 50th Anniv of Liberation of Paris.
641 **249** 110 f. black, red and blue 1·60 1·00

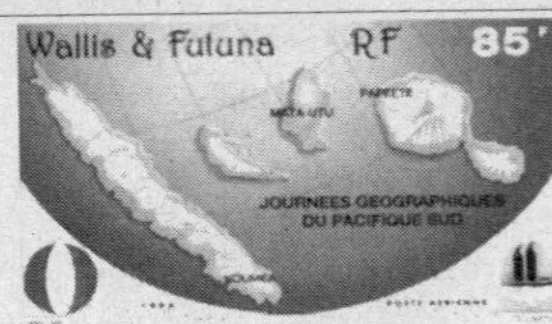

250 Pacific Islands on Globe

1994. Air. South Pacific Geographical Days.
642 **250** 85 f. multicoloured . . . . 1·25 75

251 Earth Station

1994. Satellite Communications.
643 **251** 10 f. multicoloured 15 10

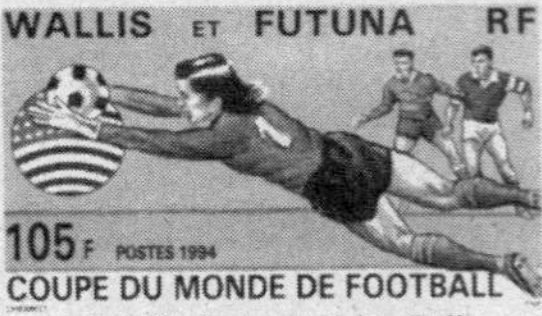

252 Goalkeeper saving Ball

1994. World Cup Football Championship, U.S.A.
644 **252** 105 f. multicoloured . . . 1·50 90

253 Uvean Princesses, 1903

1994.
645 **253** 90 f. black, red and blue . 1·25 75

254 Seaplane

1994. Microlight Aircraft.
646 **254** 5 f. multicoloured 10 10

255 Four Suits

1994. Bridge.
647 **255** 40 f. multicoloured 55 35

256 Dahlia 257 Trees and Coconuts

1994. Air. 1st European Stamp Salon, Flower Gardens, Paris.
648 **256** 300 f. multicoloured . . . 4·25 2·75

1994. The Coconut.
649 **257** 36 f. multicoloured 50 30

POSTAGE DUE STAMPS

1920. Postage Due Stamps of New Caledonia optd **ILES WALLIS et FUTUNA.**
D18 **D 18** 5 c. blue 60 70
D19 10 c. brown on buff . . 60 70
D20 15 c. green 60 70
D21 20 c. black on yellow . 70 80
D22 30 c. red 70 80
D23 50 c. blue on cream . . 1·00 1·25
D24 60 c. green on blue . . 1·40 1·50
D25 1 f. green on cream . . 1·75 1·75

1927. As Postage Due stamp of New Caledonia, but colour changed, surch.
D43 **D 18** 2 f. on 1 f. mauve . . . 6·50 7·00
D44 3 f. on 1 f. brown . . . 6·50 7·00

1930. Postage Due stamps of New Caledonia optd **ILES WALLIS et FUTUNA.**
D85 **D 25** 2 c. brown and blue . . 20 30
D86 4 c. green and red . . 25 35
D87 5 c. blue and red . . . 25 35
D88 10 c. blue and purple . 25 35
D89 15 c. red and green . . 30 40
D90 20 c. brown & purple . 30 45
D91 25 c. blue and brown . 30 45
D92 30 c. brown & green . 60 75
D93 50 c. red and brown . . 40 50
D94 60 c. red and mauve . . 1·00 1·25
D95 1 f. green and blue . . 75 85
D96 2 f. brown and red . . 75 90
D97 3 f. brown and mauve . 75 90

1943. Nos. D85/97 optd **FRANCE LIBRE.**
D126 **D 25** 2 c. brown and blue . 18·00 25·00
D127 4 c. green and red . . 18·00 25·00
D128 5 c. blue and red . . . 18·00 25·00
D129 10 c. blue & purple . 18·00 25·00
D130 15 c. red and green . . 18·00 25·00
D131 20 c. brown & purple . 18·00 25·00
D132 25 c. blue and brown . 18·00 25·00
D133 30 c. brown & green . 18·00 25·00
D134 50 c. red and brown . 18·00 25·00
D135 60 c. red and mauve . 18·00 25·00
D136 1 f. green and blue . 20·00 27·00
D137 2 f. brown and red . . 20·00 27·00
D138 3 f. brown and mauve 20·00 27·00

D 18 Moorish Idol

1963. Fishes.
D182 **D 18** 1 f. black, yellow & bl 65 65
D183 – 3 f. red, green & blue . 1·00 1·00
D184 – 5 f. orange, blk & bl . 1·60 1·60
DESIGNS—HORIZ: 3 f. Green wrasse; 5 f. Orange anemone fish.

WENDEN Pt.10

Formerly part of W. Russia but later became part of Latvia. Issued stamps for use within the district until 1903.

100 kopeks = 1 rouble

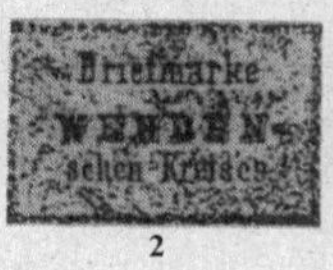

2

3

1863. Inscr "Briefmarke des WENDEN-schen Kreises". Imperf.
1 **2** 2 k. black and red £180 £225

1863. Inscr "Packenmarke des WENDEN-schen Kreises". Imperf.
2 **3** 4 k. black and green £120 £200

6

7

8

1863. Imperf.
6 **6** 2 k. green and red . . . . . . 20·00 24·00

1864. As T **6**, but with horse in central oval. Imperf.
5 2 k. green and red . . . . . . 60·00 £120

1871. Imperf.
7 **7** 2 k. green and red . . . . . . 15·00 18·00

1872. Perf.
8 **8** 2 k. red and green . . . . . . 20·00 27·00

9 Arms of Wenden 10

1875.
9 **9** 2 k. green and red . . . . . . 5·00 7·00

1878.
10 **10** 2 k. green and red . . . . . 5·00 9·00
11 2 k. red, brown and green . . . . 5·00 9·00
13 2 k. green, black and red . . 6·00 15·00

11 Castle of Wenden

1901.
14 **11** 2 k. brown and green . . . 4·00 10·00
15 2 k. red and green . . . . . 4·00 10·00
16 2 k. purple and green . . . 4·00 10·00

WEST IRIAN Pt.21

The following stamps superseded Nos. 1/19 of West New Guinea, after the former Dutch territory became part of Indonesia. From 1971 Indonesian stamps have been used.

100 cents or sen = 1 rupiah

1963. Stamps of Indonesia optd **IRIAN BARAT**, or surch also.
1 – 1 s. on 70 s. red (No. 724) . 10 15
2 – 2 s. on 90 s. grn (No. 727) . 10 15
3 – 5 s. grey (No. 830) 10 15
4 – 6 s. on 20 s. bistre (No. 833) 10 15
5 – 7 s. on 50 s. blue (No. 835) 10 15
6 – 10 s. brown (No. 831) . . . 10 15
7 – 15 s. purple (No. 832) . . . 10 15
8 **134** 25 s. green 10 20
9 – 30 s. on 75 s. red (No. 836) 10 20
10 – 40 s. on 1 r. 15 red (No. 837) 10 20
11 **99** 1 r. mauve 20 35
12 2 r. green 25 45
13 3 r. blue 50 65
14 5 r. brown . . . . 80 1·10

1a Indonesia, from Atjeh to Merauke

1963. Acquisition of West Irian.
21 **1a** 12 s. orange, red and blk . 10 15
22 17 s. orange, red and blk . 10 15
23 – 20 s. blue, green & purple . 10 15
24 – 50 s. blue, green & purple . 10 15
25 – 60 s. brown, yellow & grn . 75 35
26 – 75 s. brown, yellow & grn . 95 40
DESIGNS: 20, 50 s. Parachutist; 60, 75 s. Greater bird of paradise.

2 "Maniltoa gemmipara"

4 Mother and Child Figurine

3 Map of Indonesia

1968. Flora and Fauna.
27 **2** 5 s. purple and green . . . 25 25
28 – 15 s. violet and green . . . 25 25
29 – 30 s. green and orange . . . 25 25
30 – 40 s. violet and yellow . . . 35 35
31 – 50 s. black and purple . . . 85 50
32 – 75 s. black and blue . . . . 1·40 65
33 – 1 r. black and brown . . . 1·10 80
34 – 3 r. black and green . . . . 2·40 1·60
35 – 5 r. multicoloured . . . . 1·10 1·25
36 – 10 r. multicoloured . . . . 2·25 1·90
DESIGNS: 15 s. "Dendrobium lancifolium"; 30 s. "Gardenia gjellerupii"; 40 s. "Maniltoa gemmipara" (blossom); 50 s. Common phalanger; 75 s. One-wattled cassowary; 1 r. Common forest wallaby 3 r. Blue crowned pigeons; 5 r. Black-capped lory; 10 r. Greater bird of paradise.

1968. West Irian People's Pledge of 9 May 1964.
43 **3** 10 s. gold and blue 65 25
44 25 s. gold and red 95 40

1970. West Irian Woodcarvings. Multicoloured.
45 5 s. Type **4** 10 15
46 6 s. Carved shield 10 15
47 7 s. Man and serpents 10 15
48 10 s. Drum 10 15
49 25 s. Seated warrior 15 20
50 30 s. "Female" drum 20 20
51 50 s. Bamboo vessel 20 20
52 75 s. Seated man and tree . . 20 20
53 1 r. Decorated shield 25 35
54 2 r. Seated figure 25 35
Nos. 45/54 are inscr "I.B." ("Irian Barat").

POSTAGE DUE STAMPS

1963. Postage Due Stamps as Type D **100** of Indonesia optd **IRIAN BARAT**.
D15 1 s. slate 10 25
D16 5 s. olive 10 25
D17 10 s. turquoise 10 25
D18 25 s. slate 10 25
D19 40 s. orange 10 50
D20 100 s. brown 15 95

1968. As Type D **100** of Indonesia, but with coloured network background incorporating "1968" optd **IRIAN BARAT**.
D37 1 s. blue and green 10 25
D38 5 s. green and pink 10 25
D39 10 s. red and grey 10 25
D40 25 s. green and yellow 10 25
D41 40 s. purple and green . . . 20 50
D42 100 s. red and olive 35 95

WEST NEW GUINEA Pt.4

U.N. Administration of former Netherlands New Guinea from 1 Oct 1962 to 30 April 1963, when it became known as West Irian and became part of Indonesia.

100 cents = 1 gulden

1962. "United Nations Temporary Executive Authority". Stamps of Netherlands New Guinea optd **UNTEA**.
1 **5** 1 c. yellow and red . . . . 1·10 1·25
21 – 2 c. orange . . . . 1·10 1·40
3 **5** 5 c. yellow and brown . . . 1·10 1·40
4 – 7 c. pur, bl & brn (No. 60) 1·50 1·60
5 – 10 c. brown & bl (No. 27) . 1·10 1·40
6 – 12 c. pur, bl & grn (No. 61) 1·60 1·90
7 – 15 c. brown & yell (No. 28) 1·60 1·90
8 – 17 c. pur, bl & blk (No. 62) 1·60 1·60
9 – 20 c. brown & grn (No. 29) 1·60 1·60
10 **6** 25 c. red . . . . 2·75 2·75
11 30 c. blue . . . . 2·75 2·75
12 40 c. orange . . . . 2·75 2·75
13 45 c. green . . . . 3·25 4·00
14 55 c. turquoise . . . . . . 3·25 4·00
34 80 c. grey . . . . 21·00 18·00
16 85 c. brown . . . . 8·50 8·00
17 1 g. purple . . . . 8·50 7·50
18 – 2 g. brown (No. 20) . . . 25·00 20·00
19 – 5 g. green (No. 21) . . . 20·00 17·00
For later issues see **WEST IRIAN**.

WEST UKRAINE Pt.10

Before the 1914/18 War this district, known as E. Galicia was part of Austria. It achieved temporary independence after the war when stamps were issued. In June 1919 it became part of Poland but was transferred to the Ukraine in 1945.

100 heller = 1 krone

(5)

1919. Stamps of Austria 1916 optd with T **5**.
70 **49** 3 h. violet 30
71 5 h. green 30
72 6 h. orange 30
73 10 h. red 30
74 12 h. blue 30
75 **60** 15 h. red 30
76 20 h. green 30
77 25 h. blue 30
78 30 h. violet 30
79 **51** 40 h. olive 40
80 50 h. green 40
81 60 h. blue 40
82 80 h. brown 50
83 90 h. purple 50
84 1 k. red on yellow 55
85 **52** 2 k. blue 65
86 3 k. red 90
87 4 k. green . . . . 5·00
88 10 k. violet . . . . 6·50
For other issues which were mainly of a local character, see Part 10 (Russia) of the standard catalogue.

WURTTEMBERG Pt.7

Formerly an independent kingdom, Wurttemberg became part of the German Empire in 1902.

1851 60 kreuzer = 1 gulden
1875 100 pfennige = 1 mark

1

2

1851. Imperf.
1 **1** 1 k. black on buff . . . . . £600 80·00
3 3 k. black on yellow . . . . . £170 3·00
5 6 k. black on green . . . . . £800 26·00
7 9 k. black on red . . . . . . £4000 24·00
9 18 k. black on lilac £950 £600

1857. Imperf.
10 **2** 1 k. brown . . . . £375 55·00
24 3 k. orange . . . . £200 3·25
15 6 k. green . . . . £450 45·00
17 9 k. red . . . . £750 38·00
19 18 k. blue £1400 £950
85 70 k. purple £1400 £3000

1859. Perf.
37 **2** 1 k. brown £475 £130
40 3 k. yellow . . . . 55·00 19·00
41 6 k. green . . . . £225 45·00
42 9 k. red £650 £140
43 9 k. purple £750 £190
44 18 k. blue £900 £900

1863. Perf or roul.
60 **2** 1 k. green . . . . 32·00 5·50
63 3 k. red . . . . 25·00 1·40
54 6 k. blue . . . . £110 35·00
66 7 k. blue £800 £130
57 9 k. brown . . . . £190 42·00
59 18 k. orange £900 £325

3

4

1869. Roul or perf (1 k).
72 **3** 1 k. green . . . . 20·00 1·40
74 2 k. orange . . . . £120 85·00
77 3 k. red . . . . 10·00 70
78 7 k. blue . . . . 55·00 15·00
80 9 k. bistre . . . . 70·00 35·00
82 14 k. yellow . . . . 70·00 35·00

1875. Perf.
123 **4** 2 pf. grey . . . . 1·75 80
89 3 pf. green . . . . 10·00 1·50
124 3 pf. brown 60 10
91 5 pf. mauve . . . . 6·50 30
127 5 pf. green . . . . 1·75 10
93 10 pf. red . . . . 1·00 10
95 20 pf. blue . . . . 1·00 10
97 25 pf. brown . . . . 70·00 8·50
130 25 pf. orange . . . . 3·00 70
151 30 pf. black and orange . . 4·00 3·25
152 40 pf. black and red . . . . 4·25 7·00
99 50 pf. grey . . . . £500 27·00
101 50 pf. green . . . . 45·00 3·75
132 50 pf. brown . . . . 3·00 60
102 2 m. yellow £650 £225
103 2 m. red on orange £1500 £110
121 2 m. black and orange . . . 7·50 10·00
122 5 m. black and blue . . . . 55·00 £130
For issues of 1947–49 see Germany (French Zone).

MUNICIPAL SERVICE STAMPS

M 5

1875.
M168 **M 5** 2 pf. grey . . . . . . 40 1·00
M169 2½ pf. grey 40 65
M170 3 pf. brown 40 40
M104 5 pf. mauve . . . . . . 19·00 1·00
M171 5 pf. green 40 40
M172 7½ pf. orange 40 65
M173 10 pf. red 40 40
M261 10 pf. orange 15 85
M174 15 pf. brown . . . . . . 1·25 75
M262 15 pf. violet 15 90
M176 20 pf. blue 40 70
M263 20 pf. green 15 85
M177 25 pf. orange 40 70
M178 25 pf. black & brown . . . 60 65
M179 35 pf. brown . . . . . . 3·50 17·00
M264 40 pf. red 15 15
M265 50 pf. purple 30 85
M266 60 pf. green . . . . . . 50 1·00
M267 1 m. 25 green 30 90
M268 2 m. grey 35 85
M269 3 m. brown 35 85

1906. Cent of Wurttemberg becoming a Kingdom. Optd **1806–1906** under crown.
M153 **M 5** 2 pf. grey . . . . . . 40·00 85·00
M154 3 pf. brown . . . . . . 14·00 10·00
M155 5 pf. green . . . . . . 3·75 1·25
M156 10 pf. red . . . . . . 3·75 1·25
M157 25 pf. orange . . . . . 48·00 80·00

1916. Surch **25 Pf.**
M199 **M 5** 25 pf. on 25 pf. orange . . 3·00 3·50

M 9

M 14

1916. Jubilee of King William.
M202 **M 9** 2½ pf. grey . . . . . . 3·75 12·00
M203 7½ pf. red . . . . . . 3·00 60
M204 10 pf. red . . . . . . 3·00 7·50
M205 15 pf. bistre . . . . . 3·00 1·40
M206 20 pf. blue . . . . . . 3·00 6·50
M207 25 pf. grey . . . . . . 8·00 15·00
M208 50 pf. brown . . . . . 14·00 80·00

1919. Surch with large figure **2**.
M219 **M 5** 2 on 2½ pf. grey . . . 1·10 1·50

1919. Optd **Volksstaat Wurttemberg**.
M222 **M 5** 2½ pf. grey . . . . . 20 1·25
M223 3 pf. brown . . . . . . 12·00 14·00
M224 5 pf. green 20 30
M225 7½ pf. orange . . . . . 50 3·25
M226 10 pf. red 20 30
M227 15 pf. violet 20 30
M228 20 pf. blue 20 30
M229 25 pf. black & brown . . . 20 1·40
M230 35 pf. brown . . . . . . 4·50 14·00
M231 50 pf. purple . . . . . . 5·50 5·50

1920.
M245 **M 14** 10 pf. red . . . . . . 2·00 7·50
M246 15 pf. brown . . . . . 2·00 3·25
M247 20 pf. blue . . . . . . 2·00 1·25
M248 30 pf. green . . . . . 3·00 17·00
M249 50 pf. yellow . . . . . 3·00 38·00
M250 75 pf. bistre . . . . . 6·50 85·00

1922. Surch.
M270 **M 5** 5 m. on 10 pf. orange . 10 65
M271 10 m. on 15 pf. mauve 10 65
M272 12 m. on 40 pf. red . . 20 1·40
M273 20 m. on 10 pf. orange 20 5·50
M274 25 m. on 20 pf. green . 10 60
M275 40 m. on 20 pf. green . 30 5·00
M276 50 m. on 60 pf. olive . 10 60
M277 60 m. on 1 m. 25 grn . 10 90
M278 100 m. on 40 pf. red . 10 85
M279 200 m. on 2 m. grey . 10 85
M280 300 m. on 50 pf. pur . 15 85
M281 400 m. on 3 m. brown . 20 1·75
M282 1000 m. on 60 pf. olive 20 1·75
M283 2000 m. on 1 m. 25 grn 20 60

1923. Surch with new value (T = Tausend (thousand); M = Million; Md = Milliard).

M284 M 5 5 T. on 10 pf. orange . . 20 6·50
M285 20 T. on 40 pf. red . . 20 3·50
M286 50 T. on 15 pf. mauve 1·25 15·00
M287 75 T. on 2 m. grey . . 5·00 65
M288 100 T. on 20 pf. green 20 6·50
M289 250 T. on 3 m. brown . 20 85
M290 1 M. on 60 pf. olive . 2·50 20·00
M291 2 M. on 50 pf. purple . 20 65
M292 5 M. on 1 m. 25 green 30 4·50
M293 4 Md. on 50 pf. purple 7·00 £100
M294 10 Md. on 3 m. brown 1·00 12·00

1923. Surch in figures representing gold pfennige.

M295 M 5 3 pf. on 25 pf. orange . 2·00 8·00
M296 5 pf. on 25 pf. orange . 30 85
M297 10 pf. on 25 pf. orange 30 85
M298 20 pf. on 25 pf. orange 60 2·50
M299 50 pf. on 25 pf. orange 3·00 £950

OFFICIAL STAMPS

O 5

O 10 King Wilhelm II

1881.

O181 O 5 2 pf. grey 40 15
O182 2½ pf. grey 45 40
O108 3 pf. green . . . . . 5·00 2·75
O183 3 pf. brown 40 15
O112 5 pf. mauve . . . . . 3·25 60
O184 5 pf. green 40 15
O185 7½ pf. orange 45 40
O186 10 pf. red 40 15
O187 15 pf. brown 45 40
O188 15 pf. purple 90 20
O189 20 pf. blue 40 15
O117 25 pf. brown . . . . . 12·00 3·75
O191 25 pf. orange 40 15
O192 25 pf. black & brown . . 35 15
O193 30 pf. black & orange . . 40 15
O194 35 pf. brown . . . . . 1·60 22·00
O195 40 pf. black and red . . 40 15
O119 50 pf. green . . . . . 22·00 4·50
O141 50 pf. brown £180 £1200
O196 50 pf. purple 40 20
O120 1 m. yellow . . . . . 90·00 £190
O197 1 m. violet . . . . . 3·00 4·50
O198 1 m. black and grey . . 5·50 17·00

1906. Optd **1806–1906** under crown.

O158 O 5 2 pf. grey . . . . . 32·00 60·00
O159 3 pf. brown . . . . . 6·00 3·25
O160 5 pf. green . . . . . 4·50 60
O161 10 pf. red . . . . . 4·50 75
O162 20 pf. blue . . . . . 4·50 2·00
O163 25 pf. orange . . . . 12·00 11·00
O164 30 pf. black & orange . 12·00 11·00
O165 40 pf. black and red . . 35·00 45·00
O166 50 pf. purple . . . . 35·00 45·00
O167 1 m. violet . . . . . 75·00 85·00

1916. Surch.

O200 O 5 25 pf. on 25 pf. orange . 3·50 3·25
O201 50 pf. on 50 pf. purple . 3·50 15·00

1916. 25th Year of Reign.

O209 O 10 2½ pf. grey . . . . . 3·75 11·00
O210 7½ pf. red . . . . . 2·50 75
O211 10 pf. red . . . . . 2·50 2·25
O212 15 pf. bistre . . . . . 2·50 75
O213 20 pf. blue . . . . . 2·50 3·00
O214 25 pf. grey . . . . . 3·75 10·00
O215 30 pf. green . . . . . 3·75 17·00
O216 40 pf. red . . . . . 5·50 17·00
O217 50 pf. brown . . . . . 7·50 30·00
O218 1 m. mauve . . . . . 7·50 55·00

1919. Surch in large figures.

O220 O 5 2 on 2½ pf. grey . . . 1·10 5·50
O221 75 on 3 pf. brn (O183) . 2·25 35·00

1919. Optd **Volksstaat Wurttemberg**.

O232 O 5 2½ pf. grey . . . . . 35 1·25
O233 3 pf. brown . . . . . 10·00 13·00
O234 5 pf. green 20 30
O235 7½ pf. orange . . . . 35 2·25
O236 10 pf. red 20 30
O237 15 pf. purple 20 30
O238 20 pf. blue 35 30
O239 25 pf. black & brown . . 35 85
O240 30 pf. black & orange . . 75 1·50
O241 35 pf. brown . . . . . 35 7·00
O242 40 pf. black and red . . 60 3·00
O243 50 pf. purple . . . . 70 3·00
O244 1m. black and grey . . 1·00 6·50

O 16 Ulm

1920.

O251 – 10 pf. red . . . . . 1·50 5·50
O252 O 16 15 pf. brown . . . . 1·50 7·50
O253 – 20 pf. blue . . . . . 1·50 1·75
O254 – 30 pf. green . . . . . 1·50 17·00
O255 – 50 pf. yellow . . . . 1·50 32·00
O256 O 16 75 pf. bistre . . . . 2·25 27·00
O257 – 1 m. red . . . . . 2·25 27·00
O258 – 1 m. 25 violet . . . . 2·25 40·00
O259 – 2 m. 50 blue . . . . 3·75 42·00
O260 – 3 m. green . . . . . 3·75 60·00

VIEWS: 10, 50 pf., 2 m. 50, 3 m. Stuttgart; 20 pf., 1 m. Tubingen; 30 pf., 1 m. 25, Ellwangen.

YEMEN Pt.19

A Republic in S.W. Arabia, ruled as a kingdom and imamate until 1962. From 1962 stamps were issued concurrently by the Republican Government and the Royalists. The latter are listed after the Republican issues.

In 1990 the Yemen Arab Republic and Yemen People's Democratic Republic united (see YEMEN REPUBLIC (combined)).

1926. 40 bogaches = 1 imadi
1964. 40 bogaches = 1 rial
1975. 100 fils = 1 riyal

KINGDOM

1 (2½ b.)

2

1926. Imperf or perf.

1 1 2½ b. black on white . . . . . 35·00 45·00
2 2½ b. black on orange . . . . 35·00 45·00
3 5 b. black on white . . . . . 35·00 45·00

1930. The 6 b. to 1 im. values are larger.

10 2 ½ b. orange 20 20
11 1 b. green 25 25
5 2 b. green 50 40
12 2 b. brown 40 40
13 3 b. lilac 50 50
14 4 b. red 65 65
15 5 b. grey 45 45
16 6 b. blue . . . . 1·00 65
17 8 b. purple . . . . 1·50 1·00
18 10 b. brown . . . . 1·50 1·00
19 20 b. green . . . . 6·00 5·00
9 1 im. blue and brown . . . 12·00 9·50
20 1 im. green and purple . . . 12·00 9·00

4 Flags of Saudi Arabia, Yemen and Iraq

7

6 8

1939. 2nd Anniv of Arab Alliance.

21 4 4 b. blue and red . . . . . 1·00 70
22 6 b. blue and slate . . . . 1·00 75
23 10 b. blue and brown . . . 1·50 1·00
24 14 b. blue and olive . . . . 2·25 1·75
25 20 b. blue and green . . . 2·75 2·50
26 1 im. blue and purple . . . 6·00 4·50

1939. Surch with T 6.

27 2 4 b. on ½ b. orange . . . . 7·50 2·00
65 4 b. on 1 b. olive . . . . . 2·00 1·00
66 4 b. on 2 b. brown . . . . 8·00 3·25
67 4 b. on 3 b. lilac . . . . . 2·00 1·00
68 4 b. on 5 b. grey . . . . . 2·00 1·00

1940.

28 7 ½ b. blue and orange 40 20
29 1 b. red and green 40 20
30 2 b. violet and bistre 40 20
31 3 b. blue and mauve 40 20
32 4 b. green and red 40 20
33 5 b. bistre and green 60 30
34 8 6 b. orange and blue 60 30
35 8 b. blue and purple . . . . 1·00 50
36 10 b. olive and orange . . . 1·00 50
37 14 b. violet and olive . . . . 1·50 75
38 18 b. black and green . . . 1·75 90
39 20 b. red and green . . . . 3·00 1·50
40 1 im. red, olive and purple . . 7·00 3·00

The 5 b. (for which there had originally been no postal use) was released in 1957 to serve as 4 b., without surcharge).

9

10

1942.

41 9 1 b. olive and orange 20 15
42 2 b. olive and orange 25 15
43 4 b. olive and orange 35 25
44 6 b. blue and orange 45 30
45 8 b. blue and orange 75 45
46 10 b. blue and orange . . . . 1·00 60
47 12 b. blue and orange . . . . 1·25 90
48 20 b. blue and orange . . . . 2·50 1·50

These stamps, formerly listed under Nos. D1/8, although inscribed "TAXE A PERCEVOIR" were only used for ordinary postage purposes as there is no postage due system in Yemen.

1945. Surch with T 6.

49a 7 4 b. on ½ b. blue & orange . 2·00 80
50 4 b. on 1 b. red and green . 2·00 1·00
51a 4 b. on 2 b. violet & bistre 1·25 90
52a 4 b. on 3 b. blue & mauve . 1·50 1·00
53 4 b. on 5 b. bistre and green 2·00 1·00

1949. Inauguration of Yemeni Hospital.

54 10 4 b. black and green 75 75
55 6 b. red and green . . . . 1·00 1·00
56 10 b. blue and green . . . . 1·90 1·90
57 14 b. olive and green . . . . 2·25 2·25

11 Coffee Plant

13 View of Sana'a Parade Ground

12 Douglas DC-4 over Sana'a

1947.

58 11 ½ b. brown (postage) 65 65
59 1 b. purple . . . . 1·50 1·50
60 2 b. violet . . . . 3·00 3·00
61 – 4 b. red . . . . 3·00 3·00
62 – 5 b. blue . . . . 3·00 3·00
62a 11 6 b. green . . . . 3·00 3·00
63 12 10 b. blue (air) . . . . . 5·50 5·50
64 20 b. green . . . . 7·50 7·50

DESIGN—VERT: 4 b., 5 b. Palace, Sana'a.

The 5 b. was put on sale in 1957 to serve as 4 b., without surcharge.

1949. Surch as T 6.

68a 11 4 b. on ½ b. brown . . . 1·75 1·10
69a 4 b. on 1 b. purple . . . 1·60 1·10
70b 4 b. on 2 b. violet . . . 2·00 50

1951. (a) Postage.

71 13 1 b. brown 35 20
72 2 b. brown 75 45
73 3 b. purple . . . . 1·00 60
74 – 5 b. red and blue . . . . 1·50 1·10
75 – 6 b. red and purple . . . . 1·50 1·25
76 – 8 b. green and blue . . . . 1·75 1·40
77 – 10 b. purple . . . . . . 1·75 1·50
78 – 14 b. turquoise . . . . . 3·00 2·25
79 – 20 b. red . . . . 4·00 3·00
80 – 1 im. violet . . . . . . 10·00 5·50

DESIGNS—HORIZ: 5 b. Yemeni flag; 10 b. Mosque, Sana'a; 14 b. Walled city of Sana'a; 20 b., 1 im. Taiz and citadel. VERT: 6 b. Eagle and Yemeni flag; 8 b. Coffee plant.

(b) Air. With airplane.

81 6 b. blue . . . . 1·75 1·40
82 8 b. sepia . . . . 2·50 1·75
83 10 b. green . . . . 5·00 3·75
84 12 b. blue . . . . 3·25 2·50
85 16 b. purple . . . . 3·25 2·50
86 20 b. orange . . . . 5·00 3·75
87 1 im. red . . . . 13·00 8·00

DESIGNS—HORIZ: 6 b., 8 b. Sana'a; 10 b. Trees; 16 b. Taiz Palace. VERT: 12 b. Palace of the Rock, Wadi Dhahr; 20 b. Crowd of people; 1 im. Landscape.

The 5 b. postage stamp was released in 1956 to serve as 4 b. without surcharge and it was again put on sale as 8 b. in 1957. The 6 b. and 8 b. air stamps were released in 1957 to serve as ordinary postage stamps.

14 Flag and View of Sana'a and Hodeida

1952. 4th Anniv of Accession of King Ahmed. Flag in red. Perf or imperf.

88 14 1 im. blk & lake (postage) . 12·00 12·00
89 1 im. blue & brown (air) . . 9·00 9·00

1952. 4th Anniv of Victory. As T **14** but inscr "COMMEMORATION OF VICTORY". Flag in red. Perf or imperf.

90 30 b. green and red (postage) . 7·50 8·50
91 30b. blue and green (air) . . . 7·50 10·00

1952. Surch as T 6.

91a 13 4 b. on 1 b. brown . . . . 3·00 2·75
92 4 b. on 2 b. brown . . . . 2·50 2·50
93 4 b. on 3 b. purple . . . . 3·25 2·50

15 Palace of the Rock, Wadi Dhahr

1952. Sky in blue. Perf or imperf.

94 15 12 b. grn & sepia (postage) . 7·50 7·50
95 – 20 b. brown and red . . . . 8·50 10·00
96 15 12 b. brown & green (air) . 9·00 9·00
97 – 20 b. brown and blue . . . 7·50 7·50

DESIGN: 20 b. (2), Walls of Ibb.

1953. Surch as T 6.

98 9 4 b. on 1 b. green & orange . 7·70 5·00
99 4 b. on 2 b. green & orange . 7·50 4·00

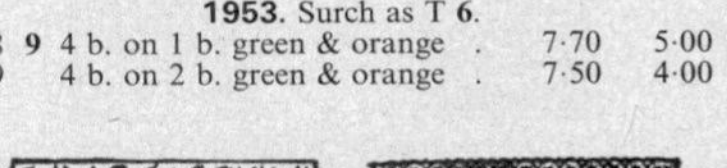

16

16a Bab al-Yemen Gate, Sana'a

1953.

100 16 4 b. orange (postage) . . . 1·75 1·75
101 6 b. blue . . . . 2·25 2·25
102 8 b. turquoise . . . . . 2·75 2·75
103 10 b. red (air) . . . . . 3·00 3·00
104 12 b. blue . . . . 3·50 3·50
105 20 b. bistre . . . . . . 6·50 6·50

1956. Unissued official stamps issued for ordinary postal use without surch.

105a 16a 1 b. brown . . . . . . 85 3·50
105b 5 b. turquoise . . . . . 95 2·75
105c 10 b. blue . . . . . . 1·25 2·75

The 1 and 5 b. were each sold for use as 4 b. and the 10 b. as 10 b. for inland registered post.

1957. Arab Postal Union. As T **96a** of Syria but inscr "YEMEN" at top and inscriptions in English.

106 4 b. brown . . . . 1·75 1·75
107 6 b. green . . . . 2·00 2·00
108 16 b. violet . . . . 4·00 4·00

1959. 1st Anniv of Proclamation of United Arab States (U.A.R. and Yemen). As T **139a** of Syria.

109 1 b. black and lake (postage) . 30 25
110 2 b. black and green 45 35
111 4 b. red and green 55 45
112 6 b. black and orange (air) . 1·25 85
113 10 b. black and red . . . . 1·75 1·50
114 16 b. red and violet . . . . 2·00 1·75

1959. Arab Telecommunications Union Commem. As T **138a** of Syria.

115 4 b. red . . . . 1·75 90

1959. Inaug. of Automatic Telephone, Sana'a. Optd **AUTOMATIC TELEPHONE INAUGURATION SANAA MARCH 1959** in English and Arabic.

116 2 6 b. blue . . . . 2·00 2·00
117 8 b. red . . . . 2·50 2·50
118 10 b. orange . . . . 3·25 3·25
119 20 b. olive . . . . 6·50 6·50
120 1 im. olive and red . . . . 9·00 9·00

1960. Air. Optd with Douglas DC-4 airliner and **AIR MAIL 1959** in English and Arabic.

121 2 6 b. blue . . . . 2·00 2·00
122 10 b. brown . . . . 3·50 3·50

1960. Inaug of Arab League Centre, Cairo. As T **154a** of Syria but with different arms.
123 4 b. black and green 75 60

IMPERF STAMPS. From this point many issues also exist imperf. This applies also to Republican and Royalist issues.

1960. World Refugee Year. As T **155a** of Syria.
124 4 b. brown 1·00 1·25
125 6 b. green 1·25 1·75

19 Olympic Torch

1960. Olympic Games, Rome.
126 **19** 2 b. red and black 1·25 1·25
127 4 b. yellow and black 1·40 1·40
128 6 b. orange and black 2·00 2·00
129 8 b. turquoise and black 2·50 2·50
130 20 b. orange and violet 5·00 5·00

20 U.N. Emblem

1961. 15th Anniv of U.N.
131 **20** 1 b. violet 30 30
132 2 b. green 35 35
133 3 b. turquoise 40 40
134 4 b. blue 45 45
135 6 b. purple 55 55
136 14 b. red 1·25 1·25
137 20 b. sepia 1·75 1·75

21 Hodeida Port and Freighter

1961. Hodeida Port Inaug.
138 **21** 4 b. multicoloured 75 60
139 6 b. multicoloured 75 60
140 16 b. multicoloured 2·00 2·00

22 Alabaster Death-mask

23 Imam's Palace, Sana'a

1961. Statues of Marib.
141 1 b. black & orange (postage) 30 20
142 2 b. black and violet 45 25
143 4 b. black and brown 60 35
144 8 b. black and purple 75 50
145 10 b. black and yellow 1·25 80
146 12 b. black and violet 1·50 1·00
147 20 b. black and grey 1·75 1·25
148 1 im. black and green 3·75 2·50

149 6 b. black & turquoise (air) 75 45
150 16 b. black and blue 2·50 1·50

DESIGNS: 1 b. Type **22**; 2 b. Horned head (8th-century B.C. frieze, Temple of the Moon God); 4 b. Bronze head of Himyaritic emperor of 1st or 2nd-century; 6 b. "Throne of Bilqis" (8th century B.C. limestone columns, Moon God Temple); 8 b. Bronze figure of Himyaritic Emperor Dhamar Ali, 2nd or 3rd century; 10 b. Alabaster statuette of 2nd or 3rd-century child; 12 b. Entrance to Moon God Temple; 16 b. Control tower and spillway, Marib dam; 20 b. 1st century alabaster relief of boy with dagger riding legendary monster, Moon God Temple; 1 im. 1st-century alabaster relief of woman with grapes, Moon God Temple.

1961. Yemeni Buildings.
151 4 b. blk, grn & turq (postage) 30 30
152 8 b. black, green and red 50 50
153 10 b. black, green and orange 80 80

154 6 b. black, grn & blue (air) 55 55
155 16 b. black, green and red 1·75 2·00

DESIGNS—VERT: 4 b. Type **23**; 10 b. Palace of the Rock, Wadi Dhahr; 16 b. Palace of the Rock (different view). HORIZ: 6 b. Bab al-Yemen Gate, Sana'a; 8 b. Imam's Palace, Sana'a (different view).

24 Hodeida–Sana'a Highway

1961. Inaug of Hodeida–Sana'a Highway
156 **24** 4 b. multicoloured 60 45
157 6 b. multicoloured 75 70
158 10 b. multicoloured 1·25 85

25 Nubian Temple

1962. U.N.E.S.C.O. Campaign for Preservation of Nubian Monuments.
159 **25** 4 b. brown 2·50 1·75
160 6 b. green 4·50 2·50

1962. Arab League Week. As T **76** of Libya.
161 4 b. green 55 55
162 6 b. blue 65 65

26 Nurse weighing Child

26a Campaign Emblem

1962. Maternity and Child Centre. Multicoloured.
163 2 b. Putting child to bed 60 40
164 4 b. Type **26** 80 50
165 6 b. Taking child's temperature 90 65
166 10 b. Weighing baby 1·60 80

1962. Malaria Eradication.
167 **26a** 4 b. orange and black 60 45
168 – 6 b. green and brown 90 65

DESIGN: 6 b. As T **26a** but with laurel and inscription around emblem.

1962. 17th Anniv of U.N. Nos. 131/7 optd **1945–1962** in English and Arabic with bars over old dates.
169 **20** 1 b. violet 1·75 1·75
170 2 b. green 1·75 1·75
171 3 b. turquoise 1·75 1·75
172 4 b. blue 1·75 1·75
173 6 b. purple 1·75 1·75
174 14 b. red 1·75 1·75
175 20 b. sepia 1·75 1·75

REPUBLIC

الجمهورية العربية اليمنية
١٩٦٢/٩/٢٧-١٣٨٢/٤/٢٨
Y.A.R. 27.9.1962

(28)

1963. Various issues optd as T **28**. (a) Nos. 141/50.
176 1 b. black & orange (postage) 15 15
177 2 b. black and violet 15 15
178 4 b. black and brown 45 45
179 8 b. black and mauve 90 90
180 10 b. black and yellow 1·25 1·25
181 12 b. black and violet 1·25 1·25
182 20 b. black and grey 1·40 1·40
183 1 im. black and grey 3·75 3·75

184 6 b. black & turquoise (air) 90 90
185 16 b. black and blue 1·40 1·40

(b) Nos. 151/5.
186 4 b. black, grn & turq (post) 35 35
187 8 b. black, green and red 90 90
188 10 b. black, green & orange 1·50 1·50

189 6 b. blk, green & blue (air) 70 70
190 16 b. black, green and red 1·75 1·75

(c) Nos. 163/6.
191 2 b. multicoloured 35 35
192 4 b. multicoloured 40 40
193 6 b. multicoloured 60 60
194 10 b. multicoloured 1·40 1·40

29 "Torch of Freedom"

1963. "Proclamation of Republic".
195 – 4 b. brown & pur (postage) 70 70
196 – 6 b. red and blue 70 70

197 – 8 b. black & purple (air) 1·00 1·00
198 **29** 10 b. red and violet 1·00 1·00
199 – 16 b. red and green 1·75 1·75

DESIGNS—VERT: 4 b. Soldier with flag; 6 b. Tank and flag; 8 b. Bayonet and torch. HORIZ: 16 b. Flag and torch.

29a Cow and Emblem

1963. Freedom from Hunger.
200 **29a** 4 b. brown and red 40 25
201 – 6 b. yellow and violet 60 40

DESIGN: 6 b. Corn-cob and ear of wheat.

الجمهورية العربية اليمنية
Y.A.R.
١٩٦٢/٩/٢٧-١٣٨٢/٤/٢٨
27-9-1962

(30)

الجمهورية
العربية اليمنية
١٣٨٢/٤/٢٨
١٩٦٢/٩/٢٧
Y. A. R.
27. 9. 1962
بريد اليمن

(31)

1963. Various issues optd. (a) With T **30**. On Nos. 161/2.
202 4 b. green 2·50 2·50
203 6 b. blue 4·75 4·75

(b) With T **31**.
207 **2** 5 b. grey 1·25 1·25
204 6 b. blue 1·75 1·75
208 8 b. red 1·50 1·50
205 10 b. brown 2·25 2·25
209 10 b. orange 1·75 1·75
210 20 b. olive 2·50 2·50
206 1 im. blue and brown 6·00 6·00
211 1 im. olive and red 4·25 4·25

(c) As T **31** but with lowest line of inscription at top.
212 **7** 6 b. red and green 1·00 1·90
213 10 b. blue and green 3·25 3·25
214 14 b. olive and green 5·50 5·50

(d) As T **31** but with lowest line of inscription omitted and bar at top. On Nos. 167/8.
215 4 b. orange and black 2·75 2·75
216 6 b. green and sepia 3·50 3·50

الجمهورية العربية اليمنية
٢٨-٤-١٣٨٢ — ٢٧-٩-١٩٦٢
Y. A. R 27. 9. 1962

(32)

(e) With T **32**. (i) On Nos. 139/40.
217 **21** 6 b. multicoloured 1·25 1·25
218 16 b. multicoloured 2·00 2·00

(ii) On Nos. 157/8.
219 **24** 6 b. multicoloured 1·25 1·25
220 10 b. multicoloured 1·75 1·75

(f) As T **32** but with only one bar over old inscription.
(i) Nos. 126/8.
221 **19** 2 b. red and black 5·50 5·50
222 4 b. yellow and black 5·50 5·50
223 6 b. orange and black 5·50 5·50

(ii) Nos. 159/60.
224 **25** 4 b. brown 8·50 8·50
225 6 b. green 9·00 9·00

(34)

35 Flag and Laurel Sprig

(g) Air. With T **34**.
226 **4** 6 b. blue and slate 1·00 1·00
227 10 b. blue and brown 1·25 1·25
228 14 b. blue and olive 1·60 1·60
229 20 b. blue and green 2·25 2·25
230 1 im. blue and purple 4·25 4·25

1963. 1st Anniv of Revolution.
231 – 2 b. red, green and black 30 15
232 – 4 b. red, black and green 45 25
233 **35** 6 b. red, black and green 95 55

DESIGNS—HORIZ: 4 b. Flag, torch and broken chain. VERT: 2 b. Flag, torch and candle.

36 Hands reaching for Centenary Emblem

38 Globe and Scales of Justice

37

1963. Red Cross Centenary. Crescent red; inscription black.
234 **36** $\frac{1}{4}$ b. blue 90 30
235 $\frac{1}{3}$ b. brown 90 40
236 $\frac{1}{2}$ b. grey 90 45
237 – 4 b. lilac 1·25 65
238 – 8 b. ochre 1·50 80
239 – 20 b. green 4·00 1·75

DESIGN: 4 b. to 20 b. Centenary emblem.

1963. Air. "Honouring Astronauts". T **37** and similar designs showing rockets, etc.
240 **37** $\frac{1}{4}$ b. multicoloured 75 50
241 – $\frac{1}{3}$ b. multicoloured 75 50
242 – $\frac{1}{2}$ b. multicoloured 75 50
243 – 4 b. multicoloured 1·25 90
244 – 20 b. multicoloured 6·00 3·75

1963. 15th Anniv of Declaration of Human Rights.
245 – 4 b. black, orange & lilac 25 15
246 **38** 6 b. black and green 35 25

DESIGN: 4 b. As Type **38** but differently arranged.

39 Darts

1964. Olympic Games, Tokyo (1st issue).
247 $\frac{1}{4}$ b. bronze, brown and orange (postage) 20 15
248 $\frac{1}{3}$ b. brown, blue and violet 20 15
249 $\frac{1}{2}$ b. brown, blue and mauve 20 15
250 1 b. brown, green and blue 35 15
251 $1\frac{1}{2}$ b. red, brown and grey 50 15

252 4 b. brown, black & bl (air) 50 25
253 20 b. blue, indigo & brown 1·50 1·00
254 1 r. red, brown & turquoise 3·25 2·25

DESIGNS—HORIZ: $\frac{1}{4}$ b. Type **39**; $\frac{1}{3}$ b. Table tennis; 4 b. Horse-racing; 20 b. Pole vaulting. VERT: $\frac{1}{2}$ b. Running; 1 b. Volleyball; $1\frac{1}{2}$ b. Football; 1 r. Basketball. All designs include the Olympic "Rings" symbol.

See also Nos. 272/80.

40 Factory, Bobbins and Cloth

42 Boeing 707 on Runway

1964. Inauguration of Bagel Spinning and Weaving Factory.
255 – 2 b. blue & yellow (postage) 20 10
256 – 4 b. blue and yellow 30 15
257 **40** 6 b. green and brown 40 25

258 – 16 b. orange , blue and grey (air) 90 65

DESIGNS—VERT: 2 b. Factory, bobbins and cloth (different); 4 b. Loom. HORIZ: 16 b. Factory and lengths of cloth.

1964. Air. President Kennedy Memorial Issue. Nos. 240/2 optd **JOHN F. KENNEDY 1917 1963** in English and Arabic and with portrait and laurel.
259 **37** ¼ b. multicoloured 75 75
260 – ⅓ b. multicoloured 75 75
261 – ½ b. multicoloured 75 75

1964. Inauguration of Hodeida Airport.
262 **42** 4 b. yellow and blue . . . 35 20
263 – 6 b. green and blue 45 30
264 – 10 b. blue, yellow and indigo 60 40
DESIGNS: 6 b. Control tower and Boeing 707 on runway; 10 b. Control tower, Boeing 707 and ship.

43 New York, Boeing 707 and Sana'a

1964. New York World's Fair.
265 **43** ¼ b. brn, bl & grn (postage) 15 10
266 – ⅓ b. black, red & green . . 20 15
267 – ½ b. turquoise, red & blue . 25 20
268 **43** 1 b. indigo, blue & green . 35 25
269 – 4 b. blue, red & green . . . 50 35
270 – 16 b. brn, red & blue (air) . 1·75 1·25
271 **43** 20 b. purple, blue & green . 2·25 1·40
DESIGNS: ⅓ b., 4 b. Flag, Empire State Building, New York and Mosque, Sana'a; ½ b., 16 b. Liner, freighter, Statue of Liberty, New York and Harbour, Hodeida.

44 Globe and Flags **45** Scout hoisting Flag

1964. Olympic Games, Tokyo (2nd issue). Multicoloured.
272 ¼ b. Type **44** (postage) 15 10
273 ⅓ b. Olympic Torch 20 10
274 ½ b. Discus-thrower 25 15
275 1 b. Yemeni flag 35 20
276 1½ b. Swimming (horiz) . . . 40 25
277 4 b. Swimming (horiz) (air) . . 55 40
278 6 b. Olympic Torch 60 45
279 12 b. Type **44** . . . . 1·50 1·00
280 20 b. Discus-thrower . . . . . 2·75 1·50

1964. Yemeni Scouts. Multicoloured.
281 ¼ b. Type **45** (postage) 20 10
282 ⅓ b. Scout badge and scouts guarding camp 25 15
283 ½ b. Bugler 25 20
284 1 b. As No. 282 . . . . 30 20
285 1½ b. Scouts by camp-fire . . . 40 25
286 4 b. Type **45** (air) 40 25
287 6 b. As No. 282 . . . . 45 25
288 16 b. Bugler . . . . 1·25 75
289 20 b. Scouts by camp-fire . . 1·75 1·25

46 Hamadryas Baboons **47** Gentian

1964. Animals.
290 **46** ¼ b. brn & lilac (postage) . 20 10
291 – ⅓ b. brown and blue 25 15
292 – ½ b. sepia and orange . . . 25 15
293 – 1 b. brown and blue . . . 40 15
294 – 1½ b. brown and blue . . . 45 15
295 – 4 b. red and green (air) . . 70 30
296 – 12 b. drab and buff . . . . 2·25 95
297 – 20 b. brown and blue . . . 3·50 1·50
ANIMALS: ½ Arab horses; ½, 12 b. Bullock; 1, 20 b. Lion and lioness; 1½, 4 b. Mountain gazelles.

1964. Flowers. Multicoloured.
298 ¼ b. Type **47** (postage) 20 10
299 ⅓ b. Lily 25 10
300 ½ b. Poinsettia 30 15
301 1 b. Rose 40 15
302 1½ b. Viburnum 45 20
303 4 b. Rose (air) 70 30
304 12 b. Poinsettia . . . . 2·25 90
305 20 b. Viburnum . . . . 3·50 1·75

48 Boeing 707 and Hawker Siddeley Comet 4 over Mountains **49** A.P.U. Emblem

1964. Inauguration of Sana'a Int Airport.
306 **48** 1 b. brn & blue (postage) . 10 10
307 – 2 b. brown and blue . . . 15 10
308 – 4 b. brown and blue . . . 35 20
309 **48** 8 b. brown and blue . . . 55 45
310 – 6 b. brown & blue (air) . . 40 30
DESIGNS: 2 b., 4 b. Boeing 707 and Vickers Viscount 800 airliners over runway; 6 b. Hawker Siddeley Comet 4 airliners in flight and on ground.

1964. 10th Anniv of Arab Postal Union.
311 **49** 4 b. black, red and orange (postage) 45 40
312 6 b. black, green and turquoise (air) 65 50

50 Flags and Dove **51** Flaming Torch

1964. 2nd Arab Summit Conference.
313 **50** 4 b. green 45 40
314 – 6 b. brown 65 50
DESIGN: 6 b. Arms within conference emblem and map.

1964. 2nd Anniv of Revolution.
315 **51** 2 b. ochre and blue . . . 25 20
316 – 4 b. green and yellow . . 50 40
317 – 6 b. rose, red and green . 50 40
DESIGNS: 4 b. Yemeni soldier; 6 b. Candles on map.

52 Western Reef Herons **53** Dagger on Deir Yassin, Palestine

1965. Birds. Multicoloured.
318 ¼ b. Type **52** (postage) 55 25
319 ½ b. Arabian chukar 55 25
320 ¾ b. Eagle owl (vert) 75 25
321 1 b. Hammerkop 55 25
322 1½ b. Yemeni linnets 60 35
323 4 b. Hoopoes 95 45
324 6 b. Violet starlings (air) . . 1·10 55
325 8 b. Waldrapp (vert) . . . . 1·90 1·00
326 12 b. Arabian woodpecker (vert) 3·25 1·60
327 20 b. Bateleur (vert) . . . . 4·25 2·25
328 1 r. Yellow-bellied green pigeon 5·50 3·00

1965. Deir Yassin Massacre.
329 **52a** 4 b. purple and blue (postage) 70 30
330 6 b. red and orange (air) . 80 45

53 I.T.U. Emblem and Symbols

1965. I.T.U. Centenary.
331 – 4 b. red and blue 75 35
332 **53** 6 b. green and red 85 45
DESIGN—VERT: 4 b. As Type **53** but rearranged.

53a Lamp and Burning Library

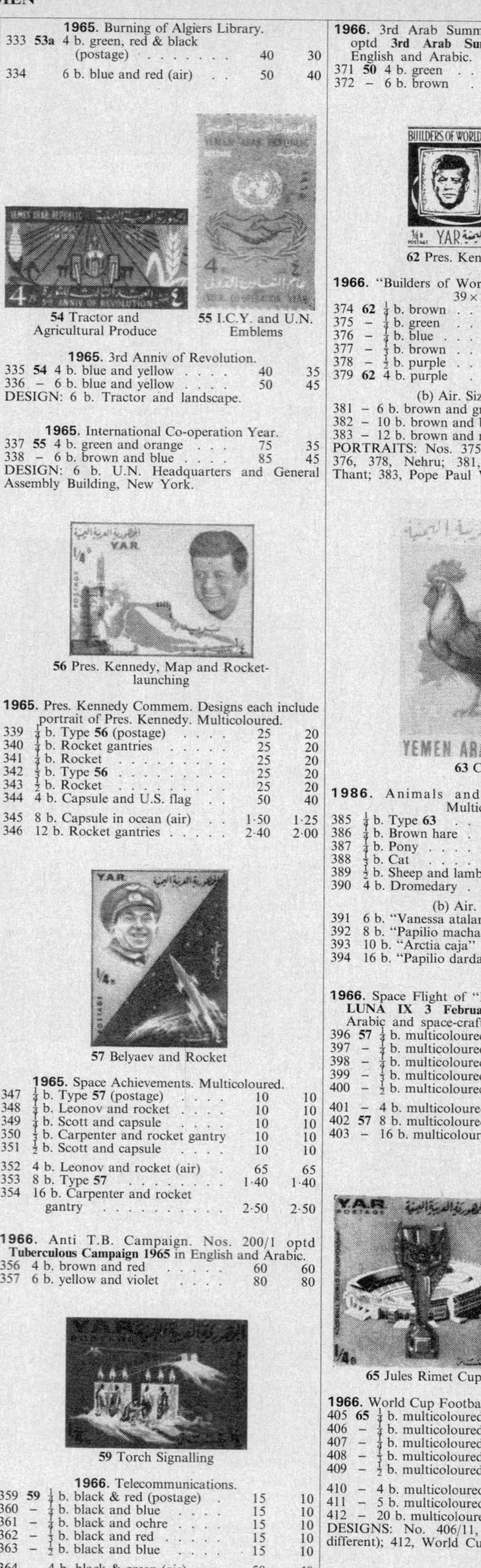

1965. Burning of Algiers Library.
333 **53a** 4 b. green, red & black (postage) 40 30
334 6 b. blue and red (air) . . 50 40

54 Tractor and Agricultural Produce **55** I.C.Y. and U.N. Emblems

1965. 3rd Anniv of Revolution.
335 **54** 4 b. blue and yellow 40 35
336 – 6 b. blue and yellow 50 45
DESIGN: 6 b. Tractor and landscape.

1965. International Co-operation Year.
337 **55** 4 b. green and orange . . . 75 35
338 – 6 b. brown and blue 85 45
DESIGN: 6 b. U.N. Headquarters and General Assembly Building, New York.

56 Pres. Kennedy, Map and Rocket-launching

1965. Pres. Kennedy Commem. Designs each include portrait of Pres. Kennedy. Multicoloured.
339 ¼ b. Type **56** (postage) 25 20
340 ¼ b. Rocket gantries 25 20
341 ¼ b. Rocket 25 20
342 ⅓ b. Type **56** 25 20
343 ½ b. Rocket 25 20
344 4 b. Capsule and U.S. flag . . 50 40
345 8 b. Capsule in ocean (air) . . 1·50 1·25
346 12 b. Rocket gantries . . . . . 2·40 2·00

57 Belyaev and Rocket

1965. Space Achievements. Multicoloured.
347 ¼ b. Type **57** (postage) 10 10
348 ¼ b. Leonov and rocket 10 10
349 ¼ b. Scott and capsule 10 10
350 ⅓ b. Carpenter and rocket gantry 10 10
351 ½ b. Scott and capsule 10 10
352 4 b. Leonov and rocket (air) . 65 65
353 8 b. Type **57** . . . . 1·40 1·40
354 16 b. Carpenter and rocket gantry . . . . 2·50 2·50

1966. Anti T.B. Campaign. Nos. 200/1 optd **Tuberculous Campaign 1965** in English and Arabic.
356 4 b. brown and red 60 60
357 6 b. yellow and violet 80 80

59 Torch Signalling

1966. Telecommunications.
359 **59** ¼ b. black & red (postage) . 15 10
360 – ¼ b. black and blue 15 10
361 – ¼ b. black and ochre 15 10
362 – ⅓ b. black and red 15 10
363 – ½ b. black and blue 15 10
364 – 4 b. black & green (air) . . 50 40
365 – 6 b. black and brown . . . 1·00 90
366 – 20 b. black and blue . . . . 2·25 2·00
DESIGNS: No. 360, Morse telegraphy; 361, Early telephone; 362, Wireless telegraphy; 363, Television; 364, Radar; 365, Telex; 366, "Early Bird" Satellite.

1966. Prevention of Cruelty to Animals. Nos. 318/20 optd **Prevention of Cruelty to Animals** in English and Arabic.
368 **52** ¼ b. multicoloured 50 25
369 – ½ b. multicoloured 50 25
370 – ¾ b. multicoloured 90 55

1966. 3rd Arab Summit Conference Nos. 313/14 optd **3rd Arab Summit Conference 1965** in English and Arabic.
371 **50** 4 b. green 65 65
372 – 6 b. brown . . . . 1·25 1·25

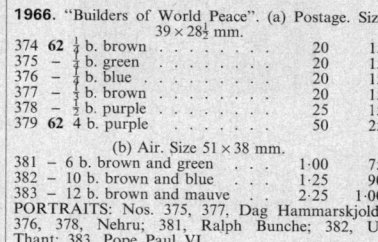

62 Pres. Kennedy and Globe

1966. "Builders of World Peace". (a) Postage. Size 39 × 28½ mm.
374 **62** ¼ b. brown 20 15
375 – ¼ b. green 20 15
376 – ¼ b. blue 20 15
377 – ⅓ b. brown 20 15
378 – ½ b. purple 25 15
379 **62** 4 b. purple 50 25

(b) Air. Size 51 × 38 mm.
381 – 6 b. brown and green . . . 1·00 75
382 – 10 b. brown and blue . . . 1·25 90
383 – 12 b. brown and mauve . . 2·25 1·00
PORTRAITS: Nos. 375, 377, Dag Hammarskjold; 376, 378, Nehru; 381, Ralph Bunche; 382, U. Thant; 383, Pope Paul VI.

63 Cockerel

1986. Animals and Insects. (a) Postage. Multicoloured.
385 ¼ b. Type **63** 30 20
386 ¼ b. Brown hare 30 20
387 ¼ b. Pony 30 20
388 ⅓ b. Cat 30 20
389 ½ b. Sheep and lamb 30 20
390 4 b. Dromedary 75 40

(b) Air. Butterflies.
391 6 b. "Vanessa atalanta" . . . 3·00 90
392 8 b. "Papilio machaon" . . . 3·50 1·10
393 10 b. "Arctia caja" . . . . . 4·00 1·25
394 16 b. "Papilio dardanus" . . 5·50 1·75

1966. Space Flight of "Luna 9". Nos. 347/54 optd **LUNA IX 3 February 1966** in English and Arabic and space-craft.
396 **57** ¼ b. multicoloured (postage) 25 20
397 – ¼ b. multicoloured 25 20
398 – ¼ b. multicoloured 25 20
399 – ⅓ b. multicoloured 25 20
400 – ½ b. multicoloured 25 20
401 – 4 b. multicoloured (air) . . 50 40
402 **57** 8 b. multicoloured . . . . 1·00 75
403 – 16 b. multicoloured . . . . 1·75 1·40

65 Jules Rimet Cup **66** Traffic Signals

1966. World Cup Football Championships, England.
405 **65** ¼ b. multicoloured (postage) 25 20
406 – ¼ b. multicoloured 25 20
407 – ¼ b. multicoloured 25 20
408 – ⅓ b. multicoloured 25 20
409 – ½ b. multicoloured 25 20
410 – 4 b. multicoloured (air) . . 65 50
411 – 5 b. multicoloured . . . . 1·00 90
412 – 20 b. multicoloured . . . . 2·25 2·00
DESIGNS: No. 406/11, Footballers in play (all different); 412, World Cup emblems.

1966. Traffic Day.
414 **66** 4 b. red, deep green & grn 85 40
415 6 b. red, deep green & grn 1·25 60

1966. Space Flight of "Surveyor 1". Nos. 347/51 surch **SURVEYOR 1 2 June 1966** space-craft and new value in English and Arabic.
417 **57** 1 b. on ¼ b. multicoloured . 65 65
418 – 1 b. on ¼ b. multicoloured . 65 65
419 – 1 b. on ¼ b. multicoloured . 65 65
420 – 3 b. on ⅓ b. multicoloured . 1·90 1·90
421 – 4 b. on ½ b. multicoloured . 2·25 2·25

68 Yemeni Flag

1966. 4th Anniv of Revolution.

422 **68** 2 b. black, red and green . 20 15
423 – 4 b. multicoloured 40 25
424 – 6 b. multicoloured 60 40
DESIGNS—VERT (25×42 mm): 4 b. Automatic weapon; 6 b. "Agriculture and Industry".

1966. "World Fair, Sana'a, 1965". Nos. 265/71 optd **1965 SANA'A** in English and Arabic.

425 **43** ¼ b. brn, bl & grn (postage) 20 15
426 – ⅓ b. black, red and green . 20 15
427 – ½ b. green, red and blue . . 20 15
428 **43** 1 b. indigo, blue & green . 35 25
429 – 4 b. blue, red and green . . 50 30
430 – 16 b. brown, red & bl (air) 2·50 2·00
431 **43** 20 b. purple, blue & green . 3·25 2·75

70 Galen, Helianthus and W.H.O. Building

1966. Inauguration of W.H.O. Headquarters, Geneva. Multicoloured. Designs incorporating W.H.O. Building.

433 ¼ b. Type **70** (postage) 30 20
434 ¼ b. Hippocrates and ipomoeas 30 20
435 ¼ b. Ibn Sina (Avicenna) and peonies 30 20
436 4 b. Type **70** (air) 85 45
437 8 b. As No. 434 . . . . 1·25 75
438 16 b. As No. 435 . . . . . . 2·75 2·00

71 Space-craft Launching

1966. Space Flight of "Gemini 6 and 7". Multicoloured.

440 ¼ b. Type **71** (postage) 15 15
441 ¼ b. Astronauts 15 15
442 ¼ b. "Gemini" space-craft (horiz) 15 15
443 ⅓ b. "Gemini 6 and 7" (horiz) 15 15
444 ½ b. Recovery operations at sea 15 15
445 2 b. As ⅓ b. 40 25
446 8 b. As ½ b. (air) 95 75
447 12 b. "Gemini 6 and 7" link (horiz) . . . . 1·40 95

1966. Space Flight of "Gemini 9". Nos. 440/7 optd **GEMINI IX CERNAN–STAFFORD JUNE 3-1966** in English and Arabic.

449 **71** ¼ b. multicoloured (postage) 15 15
450 – ¼ b. multicoloured 15 15
451 – ¼ b. multicoloured 15 15
452 – ⅓ b. multicoloured 15 15
453 – ½ b. multicoloured 15 15
454 – 2 b. multicoloured 40 25
455 – 8 b. multicoloured (air) . . 1·40 1·00
456 – 12 b. multicoloured . . . . 1·75 1·40

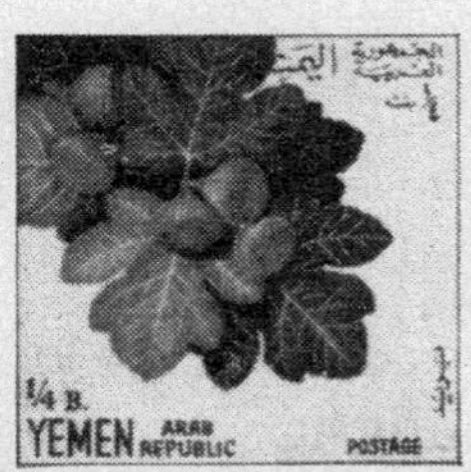

73 Figs

1967. Fruits. Multicoloured.

458 ¼ b. Type **73** (postage) 20 10
459 ⅓ b. Quinces 20 10
460 ¼ b. Grapes 20 10
461 ⅓ b. Dates 20 10
462 ½ b. Apricots 20 15
463 2 b. Quinces 60 25
464 4 b. Oranges . . . . 1·25 60
465 6 b. Bananas (air) . . . . . 1·50 75
466 8 b. Type **73** . . . . 1·75 90
467 10 b. Grapes . . . . 2·00 95

1967. Arab League Day. As T **328** of Egypt.

471 4 b. brown and violet 50 50
472 6 b. brown and violet . . . . 1·00 1·00
473 8 b. brown and violet . . . . 1·40 1·40
474 20 b. brown and green . . . 2·00 1·75
475 40 b. black and green . . . . 5·00 4·50

73a Women in Factory

1967. Labour Day.

475a **73a** 2 b. blue and violet . . 45 40
475b 4 b. green and red . . . 90 75
475c 6 b. red and green . . . 1·50 1·00
475d 8 b. olive and blue . . . 1·75 1·00

74 Ploughing and Sunset

1967.

476 **74** 1 b. multicoloured 15 15
477 2 b. multicoloured 20 15
478 4 b. multicoloured 35 15
479 6 b. multicoloured 45 15
480 8 b. multicoloured 75 15
481 10 b. multicoloured . . . 1·25 30
482 12 b. multicoloured . . . 1·50 50
483 16 b. multicoloured . . . 1·75 60
484 20 b. multicoloured . . . 2·50 90
485 40 b. multicoloured . . . 4·75 2·25

75 Pres. Al-Salal and Soldiers

1968. 6th Anniv of Revolution. Multicoloured.

486 2 b. Type **75** 12 12
487 4 b. Yemen Arab Republic flag 30 30
488 6 b. Pres. Abdullah al-Salal (vert) 50 50

76 Map of Yemen and Dove

1969. 7th Anniv of Revolution. Multicoloured.

490 2 b. Type **76** 10 10
491 4 b. Government building (horiz) 20 20
492 6 b. Yemeni workers (horiz) . 50 50

77 "Lenin addressing Crowd"

1970. Air. Birth Centenary of Lenin. Mult.

494 6 b. Type **77** . . . . 1·25 80
495 10 b. "Lenin with Arab Delegates" . . . . 2·50 2·00

78 Arab League Flag, Arms and Map

1970. 25th Anniv of Arab League.

496 **78** 5 b. purple, green & pink . 25 25
497 7 b. brown, green & blue . 30 30
498 16 b. blue, green and olive . 90 90

1971. Various 1968 issues listed in Appendix surch.

499a 40 b. on 10 b. black, red and green on gold foil (Yemen Red Crescent issue) . . . . 4·50 4·50
499b 60 b. on 15 b. multicoloured on gold foil (Olympics— Chariot Racing issue) . . . . 6·00 6·00
499c 80 b. on 10 b. multicoloured on gold foil (Int. Human Rights and U Thant issue) . . . . 8·00 8·00

79 Yemeni Castle

1971. 8th Anniv (1970) of Revolution. Mult.

500 5 b. Type **79** (postage) 90 50
501 7 b. Yemeni workers and soldier (air) . . . . 1·10 65
502 16 b. Clasped hands, flag and torch . . . . 1·50 90

1971. Air. Proclamation of first Permanent Constitution. No. 502 optd **PROCLAMATION OF THE INSTITUTION 1/11/1390 H. 28/12/1970 C.** in English and Arabic.

504 16 b. multicoloured . . . . . 4·00 3·25

81 U.N. Emblem and Globe

1971. 25th Anniv (1970) of U.N.O.

505 **81** 5 b. purple, green and olive 40 25
506 7 b. deep blue, green and blue 50 35

82 View of Sana'a

1972. 9th Anniv (1971) of Revolution.

508 7 b. Type **82** 60 60
509 18 b. Military parade . . . . . 2·00 2·00
510 24 b. Mosque, Sana'a . . . . 2·50 2·50

83 A.P.U. Emblem and Flags

1972. 25th Anniv (1971) of Founding of Arab Postal Union at Sofar Conference.

512 **83** 3 b. multicoloured 40 25
513 7 b. multicoloured 60 45
514 10 b. multicoloured . . . 80 70

84 Arms and Flags

85 Skeleton and Emblem

1972. 10th Anniv of Revolution.

516 **84** 7 b. mult (postage) 60 40
517 10 b. multicoloured 90 65
518 21 b. multicoloured (air) . 2·50 2·00

1972. 25th Anniv of W.H.O.

519 **85** 2 b. multicoloured 50 30
520 21 b. multicoloured . . . . 2·00 1·50
521 37 b. multicoloured . . . . 3·00 2·50

86 Dome of the Rock, Jerusalem

1973. 2nd Anniv of Burning of Al-Aqsa Mosque, Jerusalem.

522 **86** 7 b. multicoloured (postage) 85 55
523 18 b. multicoloured . . . . 2·50 1·50
524 24 b. multicoloured (air) . 3·00 2·25

87 Arab Child with Book

1973. 25th Anniv (1971) of U.N.I.C.E.F.

526 **87** 7 b. multicoloured (postage) 70 50
527 10 b. multicoloured 90 65
528 18 b. multicoloured (air) . 1·40 90

88 Modern Office Building

1973. Air. 11th Anniv of Revolution.

530 **88** 7 b. red and green 45 30
531 – 10 b. pink and green . . . 90 75
532 – 18 b. violet and green . . 1·25 90
DESIGNS: 10 b. Factory; 18 b. Flats.

89 U.P.U. Emblem

90 Yemeni Town and Emblem

1974. Centenary of U.P.U.

533 **89** 10 b. red, black and blue . 35 25
534 30 b. red, black & green . 85 85
535 40 b. red, black & yellow . 1·00 1·10

1975. 10th Anniv of F.A.O. World Food Programme.

536 **90** 10 b. multicoloured 45 30
537 30 b. multicoloured . . . . 1·50 1·00
538 63 b. multicoloured . . . . 2·75 2·25

91 Janad Mosque

1975. 12th Anniv (1974) of Revolution. Mult.

539 25 f. Type **91** 50 30
540 75 f. Althawra Hospital . . . 1·75 1·25

1975. Various stamps surch.

541 **84** 75 f. on 7 b. mult (postage) 1·40 1·40
542 **86** 75 f. on 7 b. multicoloured 1·25 70
542a **85** 75 f. on 21 b. multicoloured 1·40 1·40
542b **89** 160 f. on 40 b. red, black and yellow . . . . 2·50 2·50
543 **86** 278 f. on 7 b. multicoloured 4·75 4·75
544 **87** 75 f. on 18 b. mult (air) . 1·50 1·50
544a **84** 75 f. on 21 b. multicoloured 1·50 1·50
545 **88** 90 f. on 7 b. red and grn . 1·50 1·50
546 – 120 f. on 18 b. violet and green (No. 532) . . . . 2·25 2·25

93 Early and Modern Telephones

94 Coffee Beans

1976. Telephone Centenary.

547 **93** 25 f. black and purple 40 25
548 75 f. black and green 1·25 80
549 160 f. black and brown 2·00 1·60

1976.

551 **94** 1 f. multicoloured 10 15
552 3 f. multicoloured 10 15
553 5 f. multicoloured 10 10
554 10 f. multicoloured 15 10
555 25 f. multicoloured 40 25
556 50 f. multicoloured 75 45
557 75 f. multicoloured 1·25 70
558 1 r. multicoloured 1·50 90
559 1 r. 50 multicoloured 2·25 1·75
560 2 r. multicoloured 2·75 2·50
561 5 r. multicoloured 6·50 6·00

Nos. 558/61 are larger 22 × 30 mm.

95 Industrial Scaffolding

96 Emblem of National Institute of Public Administration

1976. 2nd Anniv of Reformation Movement. Multicoloured.

562 75 f. Type **95** 1·00 80
563 135 f. Hand holding pick 1·75 1·50

1976. 14th Anniv of Revolution. Mult.

565 25 f. Type **96** 35 30
566 75 f. Yemeni family (Housing and population census) 1·00 80
567 160 f. Shield emblem (Sana'a University) 2·00 1·75

97 President Ibrahim M. al-Hamdi

1977. 1st Anniv of Assassination of Pres. Ibrahim al-Hamdi.

569 **97** 25 f. green and black 35 30
570 75 f. brown and black 80 70
571 160 f. blue and black 1·50 1·40

98 Sa'ada and Sana'a

1978. 15th Anniv (1977) of Revolution. Mult.

573 25 f. Type **98** 35 25
574 75 f. Television and transmitter 75 60
575 160 f. Type **98** 1·40 1·25

99 A.P.U. Emblem

100 Dish Aerial

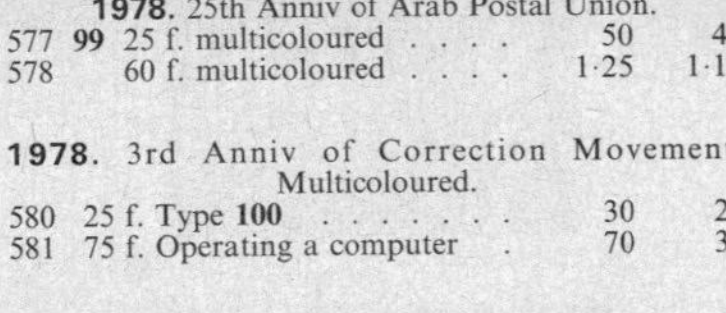

1978. 25th Anniv of Arab Postal Union.

577 **99** 25 f. multicoloured 50 45
578 60 f. multicoloured 1·25 1·10

1978. 3rd Anniv of Correction Movement. Multicoloured.

580 25 f. Type **100** 30 20
581 75 f. Operating a computer 70 35

101 View of Sana'a

1979. 30th Anniv of I.C.A.O.

583 **101** 75 f. multicoloured 90 45
584 135 f. multicoloured 1·60 1·00

102 Koran on Map of World

1979. The Arabs.

586 **102** 25 f. multicoloured 30 20
587 75 f. multicoloured 85 55

103 Viewers and Video-screen

104 Dome of the Rock, Jerusalem

1980. World Telecommunications Day (1979). Multicoloured.

589 75 f. Type **103** 90 45
590 135 f. As No. 589 but horiz 1·60 1·00

1980. Palestinian Welfare.

592 **104** 5 f. multicoloured 35 10
593 10 f. multicoloured 45 10

105 Girl and Chaffinch

1980. International Year of the Child (1979). Multicoloured.

594 25 f. Type **105** (postage) 1·10 30
595 50 f. Girl and great tit 1·60 65
596 75 f. Child and butterfly 1·60 90

597 80 f. Girl and bullfinch (air) 2·25 1·10
598 100 f. Child and butterfly 1·75 90
599 150 f. Child and butterfly 2·75 1·25

Each stamp shows a different variety of bird or butterfly.

106 Scoring a Goal (Austria v. Spain)

1980. World Cup Football Championship, Argentina (1978). Multicoloured.

601 25 f. Type **106** (postage) 35 35
602 30 f. Tunisia v. Mexico 40 35
603 35 f. Netherlands v. Iran 55 35
604 50 f. Brazil v. Sweden 80 50

605 60 f. Peru v. Scotland (air) 85 65
606 75 f. Italy v. France 1·00 80
607 80 f. Argentina v. Hungary 1·25 95
608 100 f. West Germany v. Poland 1·60 1·00

107 Scout Fishing

1980. World Scout Jamboree. Multicoloured.

610 25 f. Type **107** (postage) 50 25
611 35 f. Scouts and Concorde 1·10 45
612 40 f. Parade and scout on horseback 80 35
613 50 f. Scouts with telescope 1·00 50

614 60 f. Parade and cyclist (air) 1·25 55
615 75 f. Poppy and fencer 1·75 75
616 120 f. Scouts catching butterflies 2·25 1·00

108 Match Scene and Flag of Poland

1980. World Cup Football Championship Quarter Finalists. Match scenes and Flags. Multicoloured.

617 25 f. Type **108** (postage) 45 25
618 30 f. Peru 55 30
619 35 f. Brazil 65 35
620 50 f. Austria 95 60

621 60 f. Italy (air) 1·00 60
622 75 f. Netherlands 1·40 70
623 80 f. West Germany 1·50 80
624 100 f. Argentina (winners) 1·90 1·00

109 Kaaba, Mecca

1980. Pilgrimage to Mecca. Multicoloured.

625 25 f. Type **109** 30 20
626 75 f. Type **109** 80 55
627 160 f. Pilgrims around the Kaaba 1·90 70

110 Government Buildings, Sana'a

1980. 18th Anniv of Revolution. Multicoloured.

629 25 f. Arm and cogwheel encircling flower and factories (vert) 45 30
630 75 f. Type **110** 1·25 70

111 Al-Rawdha Mosque

1980. 1400th Anniv of Hegira. Multicoloured.

632 25 f. Type **111** 30 20
633 75 f. Al-Aqsa Mosque 85 55
634 100 f. Al-Nabawi Mosque 1·90 75
635 160 f. Al-Haram Mosque 2·25 1·25

112 Figure clothed in Palestinian Flag

1980. International Day of Solidarity with Palestinian People.

637 **112** 25 f. multicoloured 75 35
638 75 f. multicoloured 2·25 1·25

113 Al-Aamiriya Mosque

1981. 9th Arab Archaeological Conference. Multicoloured.

639 75 f. Type **113** 1·50 75
640 125 f. Al-Hadi Mosque 2·00 1·40

114 Tower and Ramparts

1981. World Tourism Conference, Manila. Multicoloured.

642 25 f. Type **114** 35 15
643 75 f. Mosque and houses 1·00 45
644 100 f. Columns (horiz) 1·25 60
645 135 f. Bridge 1·75 85
646 160 f. View of Sana'a (horiz) 1·90 1·00

115 Hill and U.P.U. Emblem

1981. Sir Roland Hill Commem. Multi.

648 25 f. Type **115** (postage) 85 45
649 30 f. U.P.U. and A.P.U. emblems and Y.A.R. 4 b. stamp of 1963 90 55
650 50 f. Hill, magnifying glass and stamps 1·40 85
651 75 f. Hill and jet airliner circling globe (air) 2·25 1·40
652 100 f. Hill, album and hand holding stamp with tweezers 3·00 1·75
653 150 f. Air letter, jet airliner and Y.A.R. 160 f. stamp of 1976 4·50 2·75

1981. Nos. 551/5 surch.

654 **94** 125 f. on 1 f. multicoloured 1·50 80
655 150 f. on 3 f. multicoloured 1·75 1·00
656 325 f. on 5 f. multicoloured 4·00 2·25
657 350 f. on 10 f. multicoloured 4·50 2·50
658 375 f. on 25 f. multicoloured 4·75 2·75

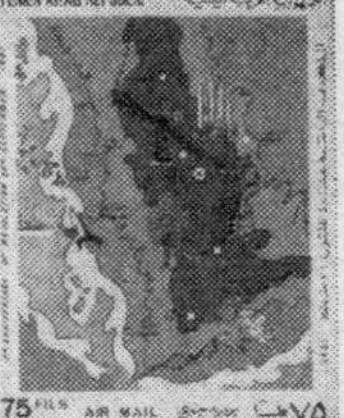
117 Map of Yemen

1982. Air. 19th Anniv (1981) of Revolution. Multicoloured.

No.	Description	Mint	Used
659	75 f. Type **117**	70	40
660	125 f. Yemenis looking towards map within sun	1·00	55
661	325 f. Sun, fist, dove with flags for wings and industrial scene	2·50	1·75
662	400 f. Air display	3·50	2·25

118 Al-Hasan ibn Ahmed al-Hamadani

1982. Air. Birth Millenary of Al-Hasan ibn Ahmed al-Hamadani (philosopher).

No.	Type	Description	Mint	Used
664	**118**	125 f. multicoloured	1·00	55
665		325 f. multicoloured	2·25	1·50

119 Common Rabbits

1982. World Food Day. Multicoloured.

No.	Description	Mint	Used
667	25 f. Type **119**	70	30
668	50 f. Cock and hens	1·50	60
669	60 f. Turkeys	1·75	75
670	75 f. Sheep	1·90	90
671	100 f. Cow and calf	2·00	1·25
672	125 f. Red deer	2·50	1·50

120 Gymnast

1982. Air. Olympic Games, Moscow (1980). Multicoloured.

No.	Description	Mint	Used
674	25 f. Type **120**	50	20
675	50 f. Pole vault	1·00	40
676	60 f. Throwing the javelin	1·25	55
677	75 f. Runner	1·40	70
678	100 f. Basketball	1·60	80
679	125 f. Football	1·90	1·00

121 Otto Lilienthal's Monoplane Glider and Satellite

1982. Air. Progress in Air Transport. Multicoloured.

No.	Description	Mint	Used
681	25 f. Type **121**	40	20
682	50 f. Alberto Santos-Dumont's biplane "14 bis"	60	35
683	60 f. Biplane and satellite	70	45
684	75 f. Early airplane and satellite	80	50
685	100 f. De Havilland Gipsy Moth and satellite	1·00	65
686	125 f. Fokker F.VIIa/3m and satellite	1·40	85

122 Crocuses and Nurse pushing Wheelchair

1982. Air. International Year of Disabled People (1981). Each shows nurse with wheelchair and different flowers.

No.	Description	Mint	Used
688	25 f. Type **122**	50	25
689	50 f. Roses	80	45
690	60 f. Pasque flowers	90	55
691	75 f. Mixed arrangement	1·25	70
692	100 f. Lilies	1·50	80
693	125 f. Gladioli	1·75	1·25

123 Aerials and Satellite circling Globe

1982. Air. Telecommunications Progress. Multicoloured.

No.	Description	Mint	Used
695	25 f. Modern radio communications	35	20
696	50 f. Type **123**	55	35
697	60 f. Radio masts, watch and dish aerials	65	45
698	75 f. Dish aerials and landscape	85	60
699	100 f. Dish aerials, satellites and morse transmitter	1·00	65
700	125 f. Aerials, jet airliner and globe	1·75	1·25

124 Oranges, "TB" and Cross of Lorraine

1982. Air. Centenary of Discovery of Tubercle Bacillus. Multicoloured.

No.	Description	Mint	Used
702	25 f. Type **124**	40	20
703	50 f. Blossom, pears, cross of Lorraine and Robert Koch	65	35
704	60 f. Pomegranates, flowers and cross of Lorraine	80	50
705	75 f. Roses, grapes and bacillus	95	65
706	100 f. Cherries, blossom and microscope	1·25	70
707	125 f. Lemons, cross of Lorraine and microscope	1·50	1·00

125 Tackling

1982. Air. World Cup Football Championship, Spain. Multicoloured.

No.	Description	Mint	Used
709	25 f. Type **125**	30	15
710	50 f. Marking the opposition	50	25
711	60 f. Players with ball	70	35
712	75 f. Scoring a goal	85	45
713	100 f. Dribbling	1·00	55
714	125 f. Intercepting the ball	1·25	70

126 Map, Boy with Flag, Tents and Dome of the Rock

1982. Air. Palestinian Children's Day. Multicoloured.

No.	Description	Mint	Used
716	75 f. Type **126**	1·25	60
717	125 f. As Type **126** but girl with flag	2·00	1·25
718	325 f. As Type **126** but boy and girl	4·50	2·50

127 Map under Grid and Airplane

1982. Air. 30th Anniv of Arab Postal Union. Multicoloured.

No.	Description	Mint	Used
720	75 f. Type **127**	85	45
721	125 f. Map under grid and ship	1·40	70
722	325 f. Map under grid and emblem	3·75	1·50

128 Passengers and Aircraft

1983. 20th Anniv of Yemen Airways.

No.	Type	Description	Mint	Used
724	**128**	75 f. multicoloured	1·00	60
725		125 f. multicoloured	1·75	90
726		325 f. multicoloured	3·75	2·00

129 Man with Donkey and Foal

1983. Traditional Costumes. Multicoloured.

No.	Description	Mint	Used
727	50 f. Type **129** (postage)	1·75	90
728	50 f. Woman in embroidered veil carrying jug on head	1·75	90
729	50 f. Shepherds in country	1·75	90
730	50 f. Man walking through city and shepherds	1·75	90
731	75 f. Women at well (horiz) (air)	2·50	1·40
732	75 f. Woman sitting by shore (horiz)	2·50	1·40
733	75 f. Man ploughing with camel (horiz)	2·50	1·40
734	75 f. Man reading (horiz)	2·50	1·40

130 Map of Yemen

1983. 20th Anniv (1982) of Revolution. Mult.

No.	Description	Mint	Used
736	100 f. Houses, airliner, telephones and dish aerial	1·25	70
737	150 f. Literacy campaign emblem	1·75	1·00
738	325 f. Tree and houses	4·00	2·25
739	400 f. Type **130**	6·00	2·75

131 Emblem, Satellite, Dish Aerial and Telephone on Flag

1983. World Communications Year.

No.	Type	Description	Mint	Used
741	**131**	150 f. multicoloured	2·00	1·25
742		325 f. multicoloured	4·50	2·50

132 Man at Window and Men planting Tree

1984. 21st Anniv (1983) of Revolution. Mult.

No.	Description	Mint	Used
744	100 f. Type **132**	1·50	70
745	150 f. Fist and bust	1·75	95
746	325 f. Sun, tank and open gates	4·00	2·00

133 Woman in Bombed Street

134 Profiles and Clasped Hands as Doves

1984. "Israeli Aggression against Lebanon".

No.	Type	Description	Mint	Used
748	**133**	150 f. multicoloured	2·00	1·00
749		325 f. multicoloured	4·50	2·50

1985. International Anti-apartheid Year (1978).

No.	Type	Description	Mint	Used
751	**134**	150 f. multicoloured	1·75	1·00
752		325 f. multicoloured	4·25	2·25

135 Winged Figure and Globe

1985. 40th Anniv of I.C.A.O.

No.	Type	Description	Mint	Used
754	**135**	25 f. multicoloured	40	20
755		50 f. multicoloured	70	30
756		150 f. multicoloured	1·75	1·00
757		325 f. multicoloured	3·75	2·00

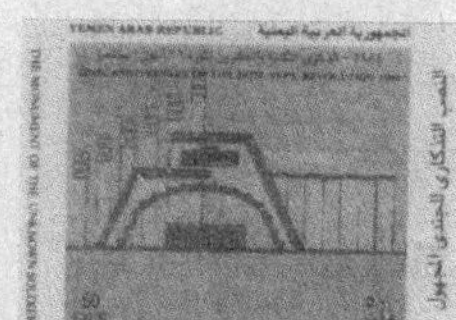

136 Monument of Unknown Soldier

1985. 22nd Anniv (1984) of Revolution. Mult.

No.	Description	Mint	Used
759	50 f. Type **136**	70	30
760	150 f. Reconstruction of Marem Dam	2·00	1·25
761	325 f. Althawrah Sports Stadium	4·00	2·25

137 Wrestling

1985. Air. Olympic Games, Los Angeles (1984). Multicoloured.

No.	Description	Mint	Used
763	20 f. Type **137**	25	15
764	30 f. Boxing	35	20
765	40 f. Running	45	30
766	60 f. Hurdling	55	40
767	150 f. Pole vaulting	1·10	70
768	325 f. Javelin throwing	2·75	1·50

138 Emblem and Satellite over Globe

1986. 1st Anniv of "Arabsat" Satellite.

No.	Type	Description	Mint	Used
770	**138**	150 f. multicoloured	2·00	1·25
771		325 f. multicoloured	4·50	2·50

139 Dish Aerial and Cables

1986. 120th Anniv of World Telecommunications.

No.	Type	Description	Mint	Used
773	**139**	150 f. multicoloured	2·00	1·25
774		325 f. multicoloured	4·50	2·50

140 Emblem

1986. 2nd Anniv of General People's Conference.

No.	Type	Description	Mint	Used
776	**140**	150 f. multicoloured	1·75	1·25
777		325 f. multicoloured	3·50	2·50

141 Emblem and Sana'a **142** Emblem and Dove

1986. 15th Islamic Foreign Ministers Conference, Sana'a (1984).
779 **141** 150 f. multicoloured . . . 1·75 1·25
780 325 f. multicoloured . . . 3·50 2·50

1986. 40th Anniv of U.N.O.
782 **142** 150 f. multicoloured . . . 1·75 1·25
783 325 f. multicoloured . . . 3·50 2·50

143 Members' Flags, Map and Emblem

1986. 39th Anniv (1984) of Arab League.
785 **143** 150 f. multicoloured . . . 1·75 1·25
786 325 f. multicoloured . . . 3·50 2·50

144 Anniversary Emblem

1987. 25th Anniv of Revolution.
787 **144** 100 f. multicoloured . . . 55 30
788 150 f. multicoloured . . . 80 55
789 425 f. multicoloured . . . 2·25 1·75
790 450 f. multicoloured . . . 2·50 2·00

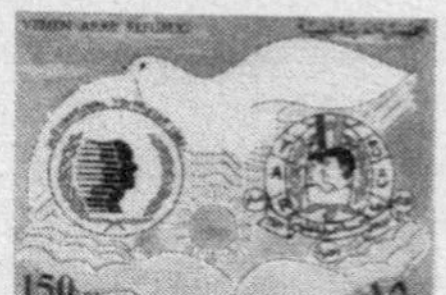

145 Dove, Emblems and Open Hands

1987. International Youth Year (1985).
792 **145** 150 f. multicoloured . . . 70 45
793 425 f. multicoloured . . . 2·00 1·50

146 Burning Oil

1987. 3rd Anniv of Discovery of Oil in Yemen Arab Republic. Multicoloured.
795 150 f. Type **146** 70 45
796 425 f. Oil derrick and refinery 2·00 1·50

147 Numbers and Emblem

1987. General Population and Housing Census (1986).
798 **147** 150 f. multicoloured . . . 70 45
799 425 f. multicoloured . . . 2·00 1·50

148 Footballers and Pique (mascot) **149** Skin Diving

1988. World Cup Football Championship, Mexico (1986). Multicoloured.
801 100 f. Type **148** 40 25
802 150 f. Goalkeeper saving ball 65 45
803 425 f. Players and Pique (horiz) 1·75 1·25

1988. 17th Scout Conference, Sana'a. Scout Activities. Multicoloured.
805 25 f. Type **149** 20 10
806 30 f. Table tennis 20 10
807 40 f. Tennis 20 15
808 50 f. Game with flag 20 15
809 60 f. Volleyball 25 20
810 100 f. Tug-of-war 40 30
811 150 f. Basketball 65 50
812 425 f. Archery . . . . . . 1·75 1·50

150 Old City

1988. International Campaign for Preservation of Old Sana'a.
814 **150** 25 f. multicoloured . . . 15 10
815 50 f. multicoloured . . . 20 15
816 100 f. multicoloured . . . 40 30
817 150 f. multicoloured . . . 65 50
818 425 f. multicoloured . . . 1·75 1·50

151 Horseman

1988. 800th Anniv (1987) of Battle of Hattin.
820 **151** 150 f. multicoloured . . . 2·25 1·10
821 425 f. multicoloured . . . 5·50 2·25

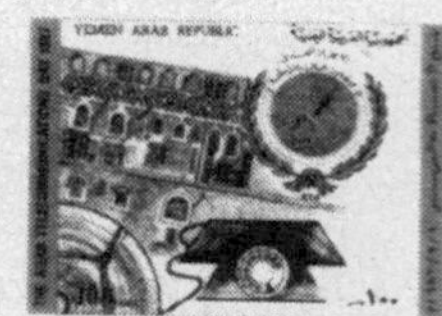

152 Building, Dish Aerial, Telephone and Emblem

1988. Arab Telecommunications Day (1987).
823 **152** 100 f. multicoloured . . . 1·50 75
824 150 f. multicoloured . . . 2·25 1·10
825 425 f. multicoloured . . . 3·50 1·75

153 Torch and Symbols of Development

1989. 26th Anniv (1988) of Revolution. Mult.
827 300 f. Type **153** . . . . . . 1·10 45
828 375 f. Type **153** . . . . . . 1·40 55
829 850 f. Flag, Koran and symbols of agriculture and industry (vert) . . . . . 3·00 1·10
830 900 f. As No. 829 . . . . . 3·50 1·40

154 Old and New Cities and Crowd

1989. 25th Anniv of 14th October Revolution. Multicoloured.
831 300 f. Type **154** . . . . . . 1·10 45
832 375 f. Type **154** . . . . . . 1·40 55
833 850 f. City street and crowd (vert) 3·00 1·10
834 900 f. As No. 833 (vert) . . . 3·50 1·40

155 Sports

1989. Olympic Games, Seoul (1988). Mult.
835 300 f. Type **155** . . . . . . 1·25 45
836 375 f. Football . . . . . . 1·50 55
837 850 f. Football and judo (vert) 3·00 1·10
838 900 f. Emblem and torch bearer 4·25 1·40

156 Flag, Couple and Fist

1989. Palestinian "Intifida" Movement. Multicoloured.
840 300 f. Type **156** . . . . . . 1·10 45
841 375 f. Soldier raising flag (vert) 1·40 55
842 850 f. Dome of the Rock, youths and burning tyres . . . . . 3·00 1·10
843 900 f. Crowd of youths (vert) . 3·50 1·40

157 Emblem

1990. 1st Anniv of Arab Co-operation Council.
845 **157** 300 f. multicoloured . . . 1·10 45
846 375 f. multicoloured . . . 1·40 55
847 850 f. multicoloured . . . 3·00 1·10
848 900 f. multicoloured . . . 3·50 1·40

158 Loading Tanker **159** Emblem

1990. 1st Shipment of Oil. Multicoloured.
850 300 f. Type **158** . . . . . . 1·10 45
851 375 f. Type **158** . . . . . . 1·40 1·10
852 850 f. Pipeline around globe and tanker . . . . 3·00 1·10
853 900 f. As No. 852 . . . . . 3·50 1·40

1990. 10th Anniv (1989) of Arab Board for Medical Specializations.
855 **159** 300 f. multicoloured . . . 75 30
856 375 f. multicoloured . . . 90 40
857 850 f. multicoloured . . . 2·10 1·00
858 900 f. multicoloured . . . 2·75 1·25

160 Woman feeding Baby

1990. Immunization Campaign. Multicoloured.
860 300 f. Type **160** . . . . . . 1·10 45
861 375 f. Type **160** . . . . . . 1·25 55
862 850 f. Nurse weighing baby (horiz) . . . . 3·00 1·10
863 900 f. As No. 862 . . . . . 3·50 1·40

For further issues see **YEMEN REPUBLIC (combined).**

POSTAGE DUE STAMPS

1964. Designs as Nos. 291, 295/6 (Animals), but inscr "POSTAGE DUE".
D298 4 b. brown and green . . . . 2·00 70
D299 12 b. brown and orange . . 3·75 2·50
D300 20 b. black and violet . . . 6·00 3·25
DESIGNS: 4 b. Mountain gazelles; 12 b. Bullock; 20 b. Arab horses.

1964. Designs as Nos. 303/5, but inscr "POSTAGE DUE". Multicoloured.
D306 4 b. Roses . . . . . . 1·75 60
D307 12 b. Poinsettia . . . . . 4·25 1·75
D308 20 b. Viburnum . . . . . 6·00 5·50

1966. Nos. 324/8 optd **POSTAGE DUE** in English and Arabic.
D371 6 b. multicoloured . . . . . 2·25 1·50
D372 8 b. multicoloured . . . . . 2·50 1·90
D373 12 b. multicoloured . . . . . 3·25 2·40
D374 20 b. multicoloured . . . . . 5·50 4·25
D375 1 r. multicoloured . . . . . 11·50 8·50

1966. Designs as Nos. 410/12 (Football), but inscr "POSTAGE DUE".
D414 4 b. multicoloured . . . . . 1·60 1·00
D415 5 b. multicoloured . . . . . 4·00 2·00
D416 20 b. multicoloured . . . . . 9·00 4·00

1967. Designs as Nos. 465/7, but inscr "POSTAGE DUE" instead of "AIR MAIL". Multicoloured.
D468 – 6 b. Bananas . . . . . . 2·50 1·25
D469 **73** 8 b. Figs . . . . . . 3·25 1·75
D470 – 10 b. Grapes . . . . . . 4·25 2·25

ROYALIST ISSUES

Fighting continued between the Royalists and Republicans until 1970. In 1970 Saudi Arabia recognised the Republican government as the rulers of Yemen, and the royalist position crumbled.

1962. Various issues optd (i) Optd **FREE YEMEN FIGHTS FOR GOD, IMAM, COUNTRY** in English and Arabic.
R1 **19** 2 b. red and black . . . . 2·25 4·00
R3 4 b. yellow and black . . . 2·25 4·00

(ii) Optd **FREE YEMEN FIGHTS FOR GOD, IMAM & COUNTRY** in English and Arabic.

(a) Nos. 156/8.
R5 **24** 4 b. multicoloured . . . . 3·00 4·50
R6 6 b. multicoloured . . . . 3·00 4·50
R7 10 b. multicoloured . . . . 5·00 6·00

(b) Nos. 159/60.
R8 **25** 4 b. brown . . . . 18·00 18·00
R9 6 b. green . . . . 18·00 18·00

(c) Nos. 161/2.
R10 4 b. green . . . . 2·50 3·50
R11 6 b. blue . . . . 2·50 3·50

(d) Nos. 167/8.
R12 4 b. orange and black . . . 2·25 3·50
R13 6 b. green and sepia . . . 2·25 3·50

(e) Nos. 126/30.
R14 **19** 2 b. red and black . . .
R15 4 b. yellow and black . .
R16 6 b. orange and black . .
R17 8 b. turquoise and black . .
R18 20 b. orange and violet
Set of 5 . . . . 90·00 90·00

(f) Nos. 169/75.
R19 **20** 1 b. violet . . . . 1·50 1·50
R20 2 b. green . . . . 1·50 1·50
R21 3 b. turquoise . . . . . . 1·60 1·60
R22 4 b. blue . . . . 3·00 3·00
R23 6 b. purple . . . . 3·75 3·75
R24 14 b. red . . . . 5·00 5·00
R25 20 b. sepia . . . . 6·50 6·50

R **6** Five Ears of Wheat

1963. Air. Freedom from Hunger.
R26 R **6** 4 b. red, green & ochre . . 2·25 2·75
R27 6 b. red, green & blue . 2·25 2·75

(R 7) (R 8)

1963. Nos. 195/6 variously optd. (a) No. 195 optd with Type R **7**.
R28 4 b. brown and mauve . . . 40·00 45·00

(b) No. 196 optd with Type R **7** with first line of Arabic inscr repeated at foot.
R29 6 b. red and blue . . . . . . 40·00 45·00

(c) No. 196 optd with Types R **7** and R **8**.
R30 6 b. red and blue . . . . . . 50·00 60·00

1963. Surch in figures with stars over old value, for use on circulars.
R31 R **6** 1 b. on 4 b. red, green and ochre . . . . 1·50 1·75
R32 2 b. on 6 b. red, green and blue . . . . 1·50 2·25

R **10** Red Cross Field Post

1963. Red Cross Cent. Flags in red; inscr in black.
R33 R **10** ⅛ b. violet (postage) . . 60 65
R34 ¼ b. mauve 60 65
R35 ½ b. brown 60 65
R36 4 b. turquoise . . . . . 85 1·50
R37 6 b. blue (air) . . . . . 2·25 2·50

R 11

1963. Consular Fee stamp optd **YEMEN** in English and "POSTAGE 1383" (Moslem Year) in Arabic with bar over old inscr, as in Type R **11**.
R38 R **11** 10 b. black and red . . 65·00 65·00

R **12** Troops in Action

1964. Air. "The Patriotic War". Flags and emblem in red.
R39 R **12** ½ b. green 50 75
R40 1 b. black 50 75
R41 2 b. slate 50 75
R42 4 b. turquoise . . . . . 75 1·00
R43 6 b. blue . . . . 1·25 1·75

1964. Air. Surch **AIR MAIL**, red cross. **1963–64 HONOURING BRITISH RED CROSS SURGICAL TEAM** and value and Arabic equivalent.
R44 R **12** 10 b. on 4 b. turquoise . 3·75 3·75
R45 18 b. on ½ b. green . . . 5·00 5·00

1964. Air. Surch **AIR MAIL** and value in English and Arabic airplane motif.
R46 R **10** 10 b. on ⅛ b. violet . . 3·25 3·75
R47 18 b. on ¼ b. purple . . 5·00 6·00
R48 28 b. on ½ b. brown . . 7·50 7·50

1964. Air. Surch **4 REVALUED** in English and Arabic with dotted frameline around stamp.
R49 R **12** 4 b. on ½ b. green . . . 7·50 7·50
R50 4 b. on 1 b. black . . . 7·50 7·50
R51 4 b. on 2 b. slate . . . 7·50 7·50

R **16** Olympic Flame and "Rings"

1964. Olympic Games, Tokyo.
R52 R **16** 2 b. blue (postage) . . . 1·50 1·50
R53 4 b. violet . . . . 2·50 2·50
R54 6 b. brown (air) . . . . 3·75 3·75

R **17** Rocket

1964. Astronauts.
R55 R **17** 2 b. brown, violet and black (postage) . . . 1·50 1·50
R56 4 b. brown, blue and black 3·25 3·25
R57 6 b. yellow & blk (air) . 5·00 5·00

R **18** (Actual size 80 × 26 mm)

1964. Consular Fee stamps optd across a pair as in Type R **18**.
R58 R **18** 10 b. (5 b. + 5 b.) purple

Owing to a shortage of 10 b. postage stamps, 5 b. Consular Fee stamps were optd across pairs with **YEMEN** in English and "POSTAGE 1383" (Moslem Year) in Arabic, in frame, together with the Ministry of Communications' Royal Arms seal and a bar over old inscription at foot. Price is for horiz or vert pair.

1965. Air. British Yemen Relief Committee. Nos. R 46/8 additionally optd **HONOURING BRITISH YEMEN RELIEF COMMITTEE 1963 1965**, in English and Arabic.
R59 R **10** 10 b. on ⅛ b. violet . . . 2·50 2·50
R60 18 b. on ¼ b. magenta . 5·00 5·00
R61 28 b. on ½ b. brown . . 6·50 6·50

R **20** Seif-al-Islam Ali

1965. Prince Seif-al-Islam Ali Commemoration.
R62 R **20** 4 b. grey and red . . . 1·75 1·75

R **21** Kennedy as Young Man

1965. Pres. Kennedy Commemoration.
R63 R **21** ⅛ b. black, mauve and gold (postage) 40 40
R64 – ¼ b. vio, turq & gold . 40 40
R65 – ½ b. brn, blue & gold . 50 50
R66 – 4 b. sep, yell & gold . 3·25 3·25
R67 – 6 b. black, green and gold (air) . . . . 5·00 5·00
DESIGNS (Kennedy): ¼ b. As naval officer; ½ b. Sailing with Mrs. Kennedy; 4 b. In rocking chair; 6 b. Full face portrait.

1965. Churchill Commem (1st issue). No. R62, with colours changed, optd **IN MEMORY OF SIR WINSTON CHURCHILL 1874–1965** in English and Arabic.
R68 R **20** 4 b. blue and red . . . 8·00 8·00

R **23** Satellite and Emblems

1965. I.T.U. Centenary.
R69 R **23** 2 b. yellow, violet and black (postage) . . . 3·00 2·25
R70 4 b. red, blue and blk . 3·75 2·50
R71 6 b. green, violet and black (air) . . . . 5·50 5·00

R **24** Hammerkop

1965. Birds. Multicoloured.
R72 ⅛ b. Type R **24** (postage) . . 90 30
R73 ¼ b. Golden winged grosbeak 90 30
R74 ½ b. Hoopoe 90 30
R75 4 b. Arabian woodpecker . . 2·75 1·10
R76 6 b. Violet starling (air) . . . 4·75 1·75

R **25** Sir Winston Churchill and St. Paul's Cathedral

1965. Churchill Commemoration (2nd issue). Multicoloured.
R77 ⅛ b. Type R **25** 50 25
R78 ¼ b. Churchill and Houses of Pariament 50 25
R79 ½ b. Full-face portrait 60 30
R80 1 b. Type R **25** 80 40
R81 2 b. Churchill and Houses of Parliament . . . . 1·50 70
R82 4 b. Full-face portrait . . . 3·25 1·25

R **26** Iman Al-Badr

1965.
R83 R **26** 1 b. blk & bl (postage) 45 35
R83a 1½ b. black and green . 20 25
R84 – 2 b. red and green . . 1·00 75
R85 R **26** 4 b. black and purple . 1·50 1·00
R86 – 6 b. red & violet (air) . 1·75 1·40
R87 – 18 b. red and brown . 4·50 3·75
R88 – 24 b. red and blue . 7·50 6·50
DESIGNS—VERT: 2 b., 18 b. Royal arms. HORIZ: 6 b., 24 b. Flag.

1965. Space Flight of "Mariner 4". Nos. R 55/7 optd **MARINER 4** in English and Arabic.
R89 R **17** 2 b. brown, violet and black (postage) . . . 1·90 1·90
R90 4 b. brown, blue & blk . 4·50 4·50
R91 6 b. yell and black (air) . 7·00 7·00

R **28** I.C.Y. Emblem, King Faisal of Saudi Arabia and Iman Al-Badr

1965. International Co-operation Year.
R92 R **28** 2 b. blue and brown (postage) . . . . . . 1·75 1·50
R93 4 b. red and green . . . 3·00 2·50
R94 6 b. sepia & blue (air) . 4·50 4·25

1965. Space Flight of "Gemini 5". Nos. R 69/71 optd **'GEMINI-V' GORDON COOPER & CHARLES CONRAD AUGUST 21-29, 1965** and space capsule.
R95 R **23** 2 b. yellow, violet and black (postage) . . . 1·50 1·50
R96 4 b. red, blue and black 3·00 3·00
R97 6 b. green, violet and black (air) . . . . 5·50 5·50

R **30** Black Persian

1965. Cats. Multicoloured.
R 99 ⅛ b. Type R **30** 50 25
R100 ¼ b. Tortoise-shell 50 25
R101 ½ b. Seal point Siamese . . . 70 40
R102 1 b. Silver tabby Persian . . 80 50
R103 2 b. Cream Persian . . . . . 1·75 75
R104 4 b. Red tabby . . . . 3·00 1·50
Nos. R 102/4 are vert.

R **31** Red Saxifrage

1965. Flowers. Multicoloured.
R106 ⅛ b. Verbena 45 25
R107 ¼ b. Dianthus 45 25
R108 ½ b. Dahlia 65 40
R109 1 b. Nasturtium 75 50
R110 2 b. Type R **31** . . . . . . 1·50 65
R111 4 b. Wild rose . . . . 2·75 1·25
Nos. R106/8 are vert.

R **32** Flag and Globe

1965. Pope Paul's Visit to U.N. Organization.
R113 R **32** 2 b. red, black & grn . 2·00 1·25
R114 4 b. red, black & vio . 3·50 2·50
R115 6 b. red, black & blue . 4·25 3·75

R **33** Moon Landing

1965. Space Achievements. Multicoloured. (a) Postage. (i) Size as Type R **33**.
R117 ⅛ b. Type R **33** 25 25
R118 ¼ b. Astronauts on Moon . 25 25
R119 ½ b. Pres. Kennedy and Cape Kennedy (vert) 40 40

(ii) Size 48 × 28 mm.
R120 4 b. Belyaev and Leonov in space . . . . 2·50 1·25

(b) Air. Size 48 × 28 mm.
R121 6 b. White and Mcdivitt in space . . . . 3·75 1·75

R **34** Football and Gold Medal

1965. Winners of Olympic Games, Tokyo (1964). Each design showing a sport with a gold medal. Multicoloured.
R123 ⅛ b. Type **R 34** (postage) . . 25 25
R124 ¼ b. Running 25 25
R125 ½ b. Throwing the discuss . 40 40
R126 2 b. Judo . . . . 1·00 70
R127 4 b. Wrestling . . . . . . 2·50 1·25
R128 6 b. Horse-jumping (air) . . 3·75 1·75

R **35** Arms R **36** Nehru

1966. Air. Imperf.
R130 R **35** 10 b. red on white . .
R131 10 b. violet on white . .
R132 10 b. red on yellow . .
R133 10 b. violet on orange
R134 10 b. violet on mag . .
These handstamps were also applied directly to envelopes and aerogrammes.

1966. Builders of World Peace (1st series). Portraits in gold and black; inscr in black.
R136 R **36** ⅛ b. green 25 25
R137 – ¼ b. brown 25 25
R138 – ½ b. grey 75 40
R139 – 1 b. blue . . . . . . 1·25 50
R140 – 4 b. green . . . . . . 2·50 1·00
DESIGNS: ¼ b. Dag Hammarskjold; ½ b. Pope John XXIII; 1 b. Sir Winston Churchill; 4 b. Pres. Kennedy.
See also Nos. R146/51.

1966. Nos. R63/5 and R67 surch with new values in English and Arabic.
R142 R **21** 4 b. on ⅛ b. black, mauve and gold (postage) . 1·00 75
R143 – 8 b. on ¼ b. violet, blue and gold . . . . . 2·00 1·50
R144 – 10 b. on ½ b. brown, blue and gold . . . . . 2·50 2·00
R145 – 1 r. on 6 b. black, green and gold (air) . . . 7·00 6·00

1966. Builders of World Peace (2nd series). As Type R **36**. Portraits in black and gold; inscr in black.
R146 ⅛ b. yellow 25 25
R147 ¼ b. flesh 25 25
R148 ½ b. mauve 75 40
R149 1 b. blue 60 50
R150 1 b. turquoise 60 45
R151 4 b. green . . . . 2·50 1·00
PORTRAITS: ⅛ b. Pres. Lubke; ¼ b. Pres. De Gaulle; ½ b. Pope Paul VI; 1 b. (R149) Pres. Johnson; 1 b. (R150) King Faisal of Saudi Arabia; 4 b. U. Thant.

1966. Newspaper Stamps. Optd **PERIODICALS** in English and Arabic in frame.

(a) Similar to Nos. R26/7, but imperf.

R153	R **6**	4 b. red, grn & ochre	10·00	
R154		6 b. red, green & blue	10·00	

(b) Unissued 1963 Red Cross Centenary issue (Nos. R 26/7 surch).

R155	R **6**	1 b. on 4 b. red, green and ochre	10·00	
R156		2 b. on 6 b. red, green and blue	18·00	

1966. Air. Olympic Games Preparation, Mexico (1968). Nos. R 123/5 in new colours surch **AIR MAIL OLYMPIC GAMES PREPARATION MEXICO 1968** and new value in English and Arabic with aircraft and flag.

R158	R **34**	12 b. on $\frac{1}{8}$ b. mult	1·90	1·90
R159	–	28 b. on $\frac{1}{4}$ b. mult	3·75	3·75
R160	–	34 b. on $\frac{1}{2}$ b. mult	5·00	5·00

R **40** Yemeni Cannon

1966. Shaharah Fortress. Frame and stars in red.

R162	R **40**	$\frac{1}{2}$ b. bistre (postage)	25	15
R163	–	1 b. grey	35	25
R164	–	$1\frac{1}{2}$ b. blue	55	40
R165	–	2 b. brown	70	50
R166	–	4 b. green	1·25	1·00
R167	–	6 b. violet (air)	1·75	1·50
R168	–	10 b. black	2·25	2·00

DESIGNS—VERT: 1 b. Bombed Mosque; 2 b. Victory Gate; 4 b. Yemeni cannon (different); 10 b. Bombed houses. HORIZ: $1\frac{1}{2}$ b. Shaharah Fortress; 6 b. Yemeni cannon (different).

1966. Nos. R33/5 surch **4 B REVALUED** in English and Arabic within border of stars. Flags red; inscr in black.

R170	R **10**	4 b. on $\frac{1}{8}$ b. violet	25·00	25·00
R171		4 b. on $\frac{1}{4}$ b. mauve	25·00	25·00
R172		4 b. on $\frac{1}{2}$ b. brown	25·00	25·00

R **42** President Kennedy

1967. 3rd Anniv of Pres. Kennedy's Death and Inaug of Arlington Grave.

R173	R **42**	12 b. multicoloured	1·90	1·90
E174		28 b. multicoloured	3·75	3·75
E175		34 b. multicoloured	5·00	5·00

1967. England's Victory in World Cup Football Championships (1966). Nos. R123/8 optd **WORLD CHAMPIONSHIP CUP ENGLAND 1966** in English and Arabic, **ENGLAND WINNER** in English only and World Cup emblem.

R177	R **34**	$\frac{1}{8}$ b. mult (postage)	25	25
R178	–	$\frac{1}{4}$ b. multicoloured	25	25
R179	–	$\frac{1}{2}$ b. multicoloured	25	25
R180	–	2 b. multicoloured	2·00	2·00
R181	–	4 b. multicoloured	3·50	3·50
R182	–	6 b. multicoloured (air)	4·00	4·00

1967. Surch **4 B REVALUED** in English and Arabic within border of stars. (a) Nos. R123/5.

R183	R **34**	4 b. on $\frac{1}{8}$ b. mult		
R184	–	4 b. on $\frac{1}{4}$ b. mult		
R185	–	4 b. on $\frac{1}{2}$ b. mult		

(b) Nos. R177/9.

R186	R **34**	4 b. on $\frac{1}{8}$ b. mult		
R187	–	4 b. on $\frac{1}{4}$ b. mult		
R188	–	4 b. on $\frac{1}{2}$ b. mult		

R **44** Bazooka

1967. Freedom Fighters. Designs showing Freedom Fighters with various weapons. Multicoloured.

R189	4 b. Type R **44**	75	30
R190	4 b. Fighter in fez with rifle	75	30
R191	4 b. Bare-headed man with rifle	75	30
R192	4 b. Fighters holding bazooka and round	75	30
R193	4 b. Anti-aircraft gun	75	30
R194	4 b. Heavy machine-gun	75	30
R195	4 b. Light machine-gun	75	30
R196	4 b. Fighter with bazooka on mount and rifle	75	30

R **45** Rembrandt — Self-portrait

1967. "AMPHILEX" Stamp Exn, Amsterdam. Rembrandt Paintings. Multicoloured. (a) Borders in gold.

R198	2 b. "An Elderly Man as St. Paul"	15	15
R199	4 b. Type R **45**	25	25
R200	6 b. "Portrait of Jacob Trip"	30	25
R201	10 b. "An Old Man in an Armchair"	50	40
R202	12 b. Self-portrait (different)	75	45
R203	20 b. "A Woman Bathing"	1·00	1·75

(b) Borders in silver.

R205	2 b. As No. R198	20	20
R206	4 b. Type R **45**	35	35
R207	6 b. As No. R200	40	40
R208	10 b. As No. R201	60	50
R209	12 b. As No. R202	90	55
R210	20 b. As No. R203	1·50	65

1967. Pres. Kennedy's 50th Birth Anniv Nos. R173/5 optd **50th. ann. 29 MAY** in English only.

R212	R **42**	12 b. multicoloured	1·10	1·10
R213		28 b. multicoloured	2·50	2·50
R214		34 b. multicoloured	3·00	3·00

R **47** Trigger Fish

1967. Red Sea Fish. Multicoloured.

R216	$\frac{1}{8}$ b. Type R **47** (postage)	40	10
R217	$\frac{1}{4}$ b. Rudder fish	40	10
R218	$\frac{1}{2}$ b. Butterfly fish	40	10
R219	1 b. Grouper	45	10
R220	4 b. Dragon fish	60	10
R221	6 b. Dark clown fish	75	10
R222	10 b. Violet-hued berycid	1·25	10
R224	12 b. As No. R222 (air)	1·00	10
R225	14 b. Cuckoo wrasse	1·25	10
R226	16 b. Deepwater squirrel fish	1·50	10
R227	18 b. As No. R221	1·75	15
R228	24 b. As No. R220	2·00	25
R229	34 b. As No. R219	2·50	35

Nos. R216/22 are Type R **47**; Nos. R224/9 are larger, size 58 × 42 mm.

R **48** "The Gipsy Girl" (Frans Hals)

1967. Air. Famous Paintings. Multicoloured.

R230	8 b. Type R **48**	35	15
R231	10 b. "The Zouave" (Van Gogh)	40	15
R232	12 b. Self-portrait (Rubens)	50	15
R233	14 b. "Boys Eating Melon" (Murillo)	75	20
R234	16 b. "The Knight's Dream" (Raphael)	1·00	20
R235	20 b. "St. George and the Dragon" (Ucello) (horiz)	1·25	25

1967. "For Poison Gas Victims". Surch **FOR POISON GAS VICTIMS** and surcharge in English and Arabic, with skull and Crossbones within frame.

R236	R **40**	$\frac{1}{2}$ b. + 1 b. (No. R162) (postage)		
R237	–	1 b. + 1 b. (R163)		
R238	–	$1\frac{1}{2}$ b. + 1 b. (R164)		
R239	–	2 b. + 1 b. (R84)		
R240	–	2 b. + 1 b. (R126)		
R241	–	2 b. + 1 b. (R165)		
R242	R **20**	4 b. + 2 b. (R62)		
R243	–	4 b. + 2 b. (R66)		
R244	R **20**	4 b. + 2 b. (R68)		
R245	R **26**	4 b. + 2 b. (R85)		
R246	R **34**	4 b. + 2 b. (R93)		
R247	–	4 b. + 2 b. (R127)		
R248	–	4 b. + 2 b. (R167)		
R249	–	6 b. + 3 b. (R86) (air)		
R250	–	6 b. + 3 b. (R128)		
R251	–	6 b. + 3 b. (R167)		
R252	R **35**	10 b. + 5 b. (R130)		
R253	–	10 b. + 5 b. (R168)		
R254	R **32**	12 b. + 6 b. (R158)		
R255	–	18 b. + 9 b. (R87)		
R256	R **12**	24 b. + 12 b. red and blue (imperf size 57 × 36 mm)		
R257	–	24 b. + 12 b. (R88)		
R258	–	28 b. + 14 b. (R159)		
R259	–	34 b. + 17 b. (R160)		

The amount of surcharge was 50 per cent of the face value of each stamp (except Nos. R236/8 where the surcharge was 1 b. each). Some higher values have two handstamps, which, when added together make up the 50 per cent.

1967. Jordan Relief Fund. Surch **JORDAN RELIEF FUND** and value in English and Arabic with Crown. (a) No. R66 (Kennedy).

R261	–	4 b. + 2 b. sepia, yellow and gold	5·00	5·00

(b) Nos. R75/6 (Birds).

R262	–	4 b. + 2 b. mult (postage)	1·50	1·00
R263	–	6 b. + 3 b. mult (air)	2·25	1·75

(c) Nos. R92/4 (I.C.Y).

R265	R **34**	2 b. + 1 b. blue and brown (postage)	1·00	1·00
R266		4 b. + 2 b. lake and green	1·00	1·00
R267		6 b. + 3 b. sepia and blue (air)	1·00	1·00

(d) Nos. R102/4 (Cats).

R269	–	1 b. + 1 b. multicoloured	1·00	1·00
R270	–	2 b. + 1 b. multicoloured	1·00	1·00
R271	–	4 b. + 2 b. multicoloured	1·00	1·00

(e) R109/11 (Flowers).

R273	–	1 b. + 1 b. multicoloured	1·00	1·00
R274	R **30**	2 b. + 1 b. multicoloured	1·00	1·00
R275	–	4 b. + 2 b. multicoloured	1·00	1·00

(f) Nos. R136/40 ("Builders").

R277	R **36**	$\frac{1}{8}$ b. + 1 b. gold, black and green	70	70
R278	–	$\frac{1}{4}$ b. + 1 b. gold, black and brown	70	70
R279	–	$\frac{1}{2}$ b. + 1 b. gold, black and grey	70	70
R280	–	1 b. + 1 b. gold, black and blue	1·00	1·00
R281	–	4 b. + 2 b. gold, black and green	3·00	3·00

(g) Nos. R146/51 ("Builders").

R283	–	$\frac{1}{8}$ b. + 1 b. gold, black and yellow	30	30
R284	–	$\frac{1}{4}$ b. + 1 b. gold, black and flesh	30	30
R285	–	$\frac{1}{2}$ b. + 1 b. gold, black and mauve	30	30
R286	–	1 b. + 1 b. gold, black and blue	50	50
R287	–	1 b. + 1 b. gold, black and turquoise	50	50
R288	–	4 b. + 2 b. gold, black and green	75	75

R **51** "The Pharmacy"

1967. Air. Paintings. Multicoloured. (a) Asiatic Paintings.

R290	$\frac{1}{8}$ b. "Mountains and Forests" (Wang Hwei)	10	10
R291	$\frac{1}{4}$ b. "Tiger" (Sim Sajoug)	10	10
R292	$\frac{1}{2}$ b. "Mountain Views" (Tong K'itch'ang)	10	10
R293	$\frac{3}{4}$ b. "Rama Lakshama and Shiva" (Indian 16th century)	15	10
R294	1 b. "Ladies" (T. Kiyomitsu)	15	10

(b) Arab Paintings.

R295	$1\frac{1}{2}$ b. "Bayad plays the Oud and sings"	20	10
R296	2 b. Type R **51**	25	10
R297	3 b. "Dioscorides and a Student"	30	10
R298	4 b. "The Scribe"	50	20
R299	6 b. "Abu Zayd asks to be taken over by boat"	90	25

The $\frac{1}{8}$ b., $1\frac{1}{2}$ b. and 6 b. are horiz and the remainder vert.

R **52** Bugler

1967. World Scout Jamboree, Idaho. Mult.

R301	$\frac{1}{4}$ b. Type R **52** (postage)	15	10
R302	$\frac{1}{2}$ b. Campfire	15	10
R303	4 b. Type R **52**	55	10
R304	6 b. As $\frac{1}{2}$ b.	75	15
R305	$\frac{1}{8}$ b. Scout badge and Yemeni flag (air)	15	10
R306	10 b. As $\frac{1}{8}$ b.	75	15
R307	20 b. Scout and satellite	2·00	20

1967. Jordan Refugees Relief Fund. Surch **JORDAN REFUGEES RELIEF FUND** and value in English and Arabic, and Refugee Emblem. (a) Nos. R52/4 (Olympic Games).

R309	R **16**	2 b. + 2 b. bl (postage)	50	50
R310		4 b. + 4 b. violet	70	70
R311		6 d. + 6 d. brown (air)	1·25	1·25

(b) Nos. R55/7 (Astronauts).

R313	R **17**	2 b. + 2 b. brown, violet & black (postage)	50	50
R314		4 b. + 4 b. brown, blue and black	70	70
R315		6 b. + 6 b. yellow and black (air)	1·25	1·25

(c) Nos. R63/7 (Kennedy).

R317	R **21**	$\frac{1}{8}$ b. + $\frac{1}{8}$ b. black, mauve and gold (postage)	20	20
R318	–	$\frac{1}{4}$ b. + $\frac{1}{4}$ b. violet, turquoise & gold	20	20
R319	–	$\frac{1}{2}$ b. + $\frac{1}{2}$ b. brown, blue & gold	20	20
R320	–	4 b. + 4 b. sepia, yellow and gold	2·00	2·00
R321	–	6 b. + 6 b. black, green and gold (air)	3·00	3·00

(d) No. R68 (Churchill opt).

R323	R **20**	4 b. + 4 b. bl & red	12·00	12·00

(e) R69/71 (I.T.U.).

R324	R **23**	2 b. + 2 b. yell, violet and black (postage)	40	40
R325		4 b. + 4 b. red, blue and black	70	70
R326		6 b. + 6 b. grn, violet and black (air)	2·50	2·50

(f) R77/82 (Churchill).

R328	R **25**	$\frac{1}{8}$ b. + $\frac{1}{8}$ b. multicoloured	25	25
R329	–	$\frac{1}{4}$ b. + $\frac{1}{4}$ b. multicoloured	25	25
R330	–	$\frac{1}{2}$ b. + $\frac{1}{2}$ b. multicoloured	30	30
R331	R **25**	1 b. + 1 b. multicoloured	40	40
R332	–	2 b. + 2 b. multicoloured	70	70
R333	–	4 b. + 4 b. multicoloured	1·00	1·00

R **54** Gaucho

1967. Olympic Games, Mexico (1968). Multicoloured.

R335	$\frac{1}{8}$ b. Type R **54** (postage)	10	10
R336	$\frac{1}{4}$ b. Fishermen on Lake Patzcuaro	10	10
R337	$\frac{1}{2}$ b. Football	10	10
R338	4 b. Avenida de la Reforma, Mexico City	30	10
R339	8 b. Fine Arts Theatre, Mexico City	60	10
R340	12 b. Mayan ruins (air)	80	10
R341	16 b. Type R **54**	1·10	15
R342	20 b. As $\frac{1}{4}$ b.	2·00	60

The $\frac{1}{2}$ b. is vert.

R **55** Battle Scene

1967. Moorish Art in Spain. Multicoloured.

R344	2 b. Moor slaying knight (horiz) (postage)	10	10
R345	4 b. Arab kings of Granada (horiz)	15	10
R346	6 b. Diagram of chess game (from King Alfonso X's "Book of Chess, Dice and Tablings") (horiz)	50	10
R347	10 b. Type R **55**	50	10
R348	12 b. Moors with prisoners	70	10
R349	20 b. Meeting of Moor and Christian (air)	1·75	10
R350	22 b. Bullfight	1·75	10
R351	24 b. Lute players	2·00	15

APPENDIX

The following stamps have either been issued in excess of postal needs or have not been available to the public in reasonable quantities at face value. Such stamps may later be given full listing if there is evidence of regular postal use.

REPUBLIC

1967.

5th Anniv of Revolution Nos. 476/81 optd in Arabic 1, 2, 4, 6, 8, 10 b.

Paintings by Flemish Masters. Postage ¼, ⅓, ½ b.; Air 3, 6 b.

Paintings by Florentine Masters. Postage ¼, ⅓, ½ b.; Air 3, 6 b.

Paintings by Spanish Masters. Postage ¼, ⅓, ½ b.; Air 3, 6 b.

Winter Olympic Games, Grenoble (1968) (1st issue). Embossed on gold foil. Air 5, 10, 15, 50 b.

Winter Olympic Games, Grenoble (1968) (2nd issue). Sports ¼, ⅓, ½, 3, 6 b.

Chancellor Adenauter Commemoration (1st issue). Embossed on gold foil. Air 50 b.

1968.

Yemen Red Crescent. Embossed on gold foil. Air 5, 10, 15, 50 b.

Paintings by Gauguin. Postage ¼, ¼, ⅓, ½, ½ b.; Air 3, 3, 6, 6 b.

Paintings by Van Gogh. Postage ¼, ¼, ⅓, ⅓, ½, ½ b.; Air 3, 3, 6, 6 b.

Paintings by Rubens. Postage ¼, ¼, ⅓, ⅓, ½, ½ b.; Air 3, 3, 6, 6 b.

Provisionals. Various 1930/31 values optd "Y.A.R." and date in English and Arabic. ½, 1, 1, 2, 2, 3, 4, 4, 5, 6, 6, 10, 10, 20 b., 1, 1 l.

Gold Medal Winners. Winter Olympic Games, Grenoble (1st issue). 1967 Winter Olympic Games (1st issue) optd with names of various winners. Air 50 b. × 4.

1st Death Anniv of Vladimir Komarov (Russian cosmonaut). Air 5, 10, 15, 50 b.

International Human Rights Year and U Thant Commemoration. Embossed on gold foil. Air 5, 10, 15, 50 b.

Chancellor Adenauer Commemoration (2nd issue). Air 5, 10, 15 b.

Refugee Relief. Adenauer (2nd issue) optd in Arabic only. Air 5, 10, 15, 50 b.

Olympic Games, Mexico (1st issue). Chariot-racing. Embossed on gold foil. Air 5, 10, 15, 50 b.

Paintings of Horses. Postage ¼, ⅓, ½ b.; Air 3, 6 b.

Paintings by Raphael. Postage ¼, ⅓, ½ b.; Air 3, 6 b.

Paintings by Rembrandt. Postage ¼, ⅓, ½ b.; Air 3, 6 b.

Dr. Martin Luther King Commemoration (1st issue). Human Rights issue optd. Air 50 b.

Gold Medal Winners. Winter Olympic Games, Grenoble (2nd issue). Postage ¼, ⅓, ½ b.; Air 3, 6 b.

Olympic Games, Mexico (2nd issue). Greek and Mexican Folklore. Postage ¼, ⅓, ½, 2 b.; Air 3, 4 b.

Gold Medal Winners, Olympic Games, Mexico (1st issue). Mexico Olympics (1st issue) optd with names of various winners. Air 50 b. × 4.

Gold Medal Winners Olympic Games, Mexico (2nd issue). Postage ¼, ⅓, ½, 2 b.; Air 3, 4 b.

Dr. Martin Luther King Commemoration (2nd issue). Embossed on gold foil. 16 b.

Emblems of Winter Olympic Games. Postage ¼, ⅓, ½, 2 b.; Air 3, 4 b.

Emblems of Olympic Games. Postage ¼, ⅓, ½, 2 b.; Air 3, 4 b.

Dag Hammarskjold and Kennedy Brothers Commemoration. ½, 2, 6, 14 b.

Dr. Christian Barnard's Heart Transplant Operations. ¼, ¾, 8, 10 b.

Dr. Martin Luther King Commemoration (3rd issue). 1, 4, 12, 16 b.

John and Robert Kennedy Commemoration. Embossed on gold foil. 10 b.

1969.

Paintings from the Louvre, Paris. Postage ¼, ⅓, ½, 2 b.; Air 3, 4 b.

1st Death Anniv of Yury Gagarin (Russian cosmonaut). Optd on 1968 Komarov issue. Air 50 b.

Paintings from the Uffizi Gallery, Florence. Postage ¼, ⅓, ½, 2 b.; Air 3, 4 b.

Paintings from the Prado, Madrid. Postage ¼, ⅓, ½, 2 b.; Air 3, 4 b.

Birth Bicentenary of Napoleon (1st issue). Embossed on gold foil. Air 4 b.

Space Exploration (1st series). Inscr "DISCOVERIES OF UNIVERSE". Postage ¼, ¼, ⅓, ⅓ b.; Air 3, 6, 10 b.

Space Exploration (2nd series). Inscr "FLIGHTS TO THE PLANETS". Postage ¼, ¼, ⅓, ⅓ b.; Air 2, 4, 22 b.

First Man on the Moon. Embossed on gold foil. Air 10 b.

50th Anniv of International Labour Organization. Postage 1, 2, 3, 4 b.; Air 6, 8, 10 b.

Space Exploration (3rd series). Inscr "MAN IN SPACE". Postage ¼, ¼, ⅓, ⅓ b.; Air 3, 6, 10 b.

Birth Bicentenary of Napoleon (2nd issue). Postage ¼, ⅓, ½, ¾ b.; Air 4, 8, 10 b.

Space Exploration (4th series). "Apollo" Moon Flights. Postage ¼, ¼, ⅓, ⅓ b.; Air 2, 4, 22 b.

Winter Olympic Games, Sapporo (1972) Preparation. Optd on 1967 Grenoble Winter Olympics issue. Air 50 b.

Olympic Games, Munich (1972) Preparation. Optd on 1968 Mexico Olympics issue. Air 50 b.

Paintings from the National Gallery, Washington. Postage ¼, ⅓, ½, 2 b.: Air 3, 4 b.

Paintings from the National Gallery, London. Postage ¼, ⅓, ½, 2 b.: Air 3, 4 b.

French Monarchs and Statesmen. Postage 1¾, 2, 2¼, 2½ b.: Air 3½, 5, 6 b.

1970.

Tutankhamun Exhibition, Paris. Postage ¼, ⅓, ½, 2 b.; Air 3, 4 b.

Siamese Sculptures. Postage ¼, ⅓, ½, 2 b.; Air 3, 4 b.

"EXPO 70" World Fair, Osaka, Japan (1st issue). Japanese Paintings. Postage ¼, ⅓, ½, 2 b.; Air 3, 4 b.

EXPO 70" World Fair, Osaka, Japan (2nd issue). Japanese Puppets. Postage ¼, ⅓, ½, 2 b.; Air 3, 4 b.

World Cup Football Championships, Mexico (1st issue). Views and Maps. Postage 1½, 2, 2¼, 2½ b.; Air 3½, 5, 6, 7, 8 b.

World Cup Football Championships, Mexico (2nd issue). Jules Rimet. Embossed on gold foil. Air 10 b.

"United Europe". Postage 1⅓, 1¾, 2¼, 2½, 5 b.; Air 7, 8, 10 b.

25th Anniv of Victory in Second World War. Gen. De Gaulle. Embossed on gold foil. Air 6 b.

Moon Mission of "Apollo 12". Postage 1, 1¼, 1⅓, 1½ b.; Air 4, 4½, 7 b.

World Cup Football Championships, Mexico (3rd issue). Teams. Postage ¼, ⅓, ½, ¾ b.; Air 4, 4½ b.

World Cup Football Championship, Mexico (4th issue). Beckenbauer and Pele. Embossed on gold foil. Air 10 b.

World Cup Football Championship, Mexico (5th issue). Footballers and Mexican Antiquities. Postage 1, 1¼, 1⅓, 1½ b.; Air 3, 10 b.

Interplanetary Space Travel. Postage 1¾, 2, 2¼, 2½ b.; Air 5, 8, 10, 22 b.

Inauguration of New U.P.U. Headquarters Building, Berne. Postage ⅓, 1¼, 1½, 2 b.; Air 3½, 4½, 6 b.

"Philympia 70" Stamp Exhibition, London. Postage ¼, ½, ¾, 1, 3 b.; Air 4 b.

8th Anniv of Revolution. Flowers. ¼ b. × 5.

Olympic Games, Munich (1972) (1st issue). Buildings. Postage 1, 1¾, 2½, 3, 3½ b.; Air 8, 10 b.

Olympic Games, Munich (2nd issue). Statue. Embossed on gold foil. Air 6 b.

25th Anniv of United Nations. Human Rights Year issue of 1968 optd. Air 50 b.

Winter Olympic Games, Sapporo (1st issue). Buildings and Emblem. Postage 1½, 2½, 4½, 5, 7 b.; Air 8, 10 b.

Winter Olympic Games, Sapporo (2nd issue). Snow Sculpture. Embossed on gold foil. Air 40 b.

General Charles de Gaulle Commemoration. 1970 25th Anniv of Victory issue optd. Air 6 b.

German Gold Medal Winners in Olympic Games. Postage ¼, ⅓, ⅓, ¾ b. Air 6 b.

1971.

Pres. Gamal Nasser of Egypt Commemoration, Postage ¼ b. × 4½ b. × 2; Air 1, 2, 5, 7, 10, 16 b.

International Sporting Events. Postage ¼, ⅓, ½, 2 b.; Air 3, 4 b.

Olympic Games, Munich (3rd issue). Theatre Productions. Postage ½, 1¼, 1¾, 2¼, 4½ b.; Air 5, 6 b.

Moon Mission of "Apollo 14" 1969 Moon Landing issue optd. Air 10 b.

Olympic Games, Munich (4th issue). Paintings from the Pinakothek. Postage ¼, ⅓, ¾, 1½, 2 b.; Air 4, 7 b.

Chinese Paintings. Postage ¼, ⅓, ½, 2 b.; Air 3, 4 b.

Winter Olympic Games, Sapporo (3rd issue). Winter Sports and Japanese Works of Art. Postage ¼, ½, 1, 1⅓, 2 b.; Air 3, 4 b.

Winter Olympic Games, Sapporo (4th issue). Japanese Skier. Embossed on gold foil. Air 8 b.

Launching of Soviet "Salyut" Space Station. Interplanetary issue of 1970 optd. Air 22 b.

Olympic Games, Munich (5th issue). Sports and Sculptures. Postage ⅓, 1, 1⅓, 1¾, 2¼ b.; Air 4½, 7, 10 b.

Olympic Games, Munich (6th issue). Gold Medals. Embossed on gold foil. Air 8 b.

Exploration of Outer Space. Postage ¼, ⅓, ½, ¾ b.; Air 3, 3½, 6 b.

Birth Bicentenary of Beethoven. Postage ¼ × 4, ½ b. × 2; Air 1, 2, 5, 7, 10 b.

Indian Paintings. Postage ¼, ⅓, ½, 2 b.; Air 3, 4 b.

Olympic Games, Munich (7th issue). Sailing Events at Kiel. Postage ¼, ½, 1¼, 2, 3 b.; Air 4 b.

Winter Olympic Games, Sapporo (5th issue). Sports. Postage ⅓, ¾, 1¼, 1¾, 2¼ b.; Air 3½, 6 b.

Winter Olympic Games, Sapporo (6th issue). Slalom Skier. Embossed on gold foil. Air 10 b.

Persian Miniatures. Postage ¼, ⅓, ½, 2 b.; Air 3, 4 b.

Olympic Games, Munich (8th issue). Sports. Postage ¾, 1½, 2½, 3½, 5 b.; Air 6, 8 b.

Olympic Games, Munich (9th issue). Discus thrower. Embossed on gold foil. Air 10 b.

Italian Gold Medal Winners in Olympic Games. Postage ¼ b. × 2, ⅓ b. × 2; Air 22 b.

1972.

French Gold Medal Winners in Olympic Games. Postage 2, 3 b.; Air 4, 10 b.

Works of Art. Postage 1, 1¼, 1⅓, 1½ b.; Air 3, 4½, 7 b.

ROYALIST ISSUES

1967.

Visit of Queen of Sheba to Solomon. ⅛, ¼, ½, 4, 6, 20, 24 b.

Arab Horses. ⅛, ¼, ½, 4, 10 b.

1968.

Winter Olympic Games, Grenoble (1st issue). Nos. R216/29 optd. Postage ⅛, ¼, ½, 1, 4, 6, 10 b.; Air 12, 14, 16, 24, 34 b.

Butterflies. Air 16, 20, 40 b.

Postage Due. Butterflies and Horse. 4, 16, 20 b.

Winter Olympic Games, Grenoble (2nd issue). Sports. Postage 1, 2, 3, 4, 6 b.; Air 10, 12, 18, 24, 28 b.

Gold Medal Winners, Grenoble Winter Olympics. Winter Olympic Games, Grenoble (2nd issue). Optd with names of various medal winners. Postage 1, 2, 3, 4, 6 b.; Air 10, 12, 18, 24, 28 b.

20th Anniv of UNESCO. ½, 1, 1½, 2, 3, 4, 6, 10 b.

Mothers' Day. Paintings. Postage 2, 4, 6 b.; Air 24, 28, 34 b.

Olympic Games, Mexico (1st issue). Sports. Postage 1, 2, 3, 4, 6 b.; Air 10, 12, 18, 24, 28 b.

UNESCO. "Save Florence" Campaign. Paintings. Postage 2, 4, 6 b.; Air 10, 12, 18 b.

UNESCO. "Save Venice" Campaign. Paintings. ½, 1, 1½, 24 b.; Air 28, 34 b.

Olympic Games, Mexico (2nd issue). Athletes and Flags. 4 b. × 11.

Winter Olympic Games since 1924. Competitors and Flags. Postage. 1, 2, 3, 4, 6 b.; Air 10, 12, 18, 24, 28 b.

International Human Rights Year. 2 b. × 4, 4 b. × 4, 6 b. × 4.

Paintings by European and American Artists. Postage 1, 2, 3, 4, 6, 10 b.; Air 12, 18, 24, 28 b.

Coronation of Shah of Iran. Postage 1, 2, 3, 4 b.; Air 24, 28 b.

International Philately. Postage 1, 2, 3, 4, 6 b.; Air 10, 12, 18, 24, 28 b.

World Racial Peace. Postage 4, 6, 18 b.; Air 10 b.

Children's Day. Paintings. Postage 1, 2, 3, 4 b.; Air 6, 10, 12, 18, 24, 28 b.

Gold Medal Winners, Mexico Olympic Games (1st issue). Mexico Olympics (1st issue) optd with names of various medal winners. Postage 1, 2, 3, 4, 6 b.; Air 10, 12, 18, 24, 28 b.

Gold Medal Winners, Mexico Olympics (2nd issue). Athletes and Medals. Air 12, 18, 24, 28, 34 b.

Gold Medal Winners, Mexico Olympics (3rd issue). Embossed on gold foil. 28 b.

"EFIMEX 68" Stamp Exhibition, Mexico City. Air 12, 18, 24, 28, 34 b.

1969.

Motor-racing Drivers. Postage 1, 2, 3, 4, 6 b.; Air 10, 12, 18, 24, 28 b.

Space Flight of "Apollo 7". 4, 8, 12, 24, 28 b.

Space Flight of "Apollo 8" (1st issue). 4, 6, 10, 18, 34 b.

Space Flight of "Apollo 8" (2nd issue). Embossed on gold foil. 28 b.

5th Anniv of Imam's Meeting with Pope Paul VI at Jerusalem (1st issue). Scenes from Pope's Visit. ⅛, ¼, ¼, 1, 1½, 2, 3, 4, 5, 6 b.

5th Anniv of Imam's Meeting with Pope Paul VI at Jerusalem (2nd issue). Paintings of the Life of Christ. Postage 1, 2, 3, 4, 5, 6, 7, 8, 9, 10 b.; Air 11, 12, 13, 14, 15, 16, 17, 18, 19, 20, 21, 22, 23, 24, 25, 26, 27, 28, 29, 30 b.

5th Anniv of Imam's Meeting with Pope Paul VI at Jerusalem (3rd issue). Abraham's Tomb, Hebron. 4 b.

Paintings by Rembrandt (1st series). Postage 1, 2, 4 b.; Air 6, 12 b., 1 i.

Paintings by Rembrandt (2nd series). Embossed on gold foil. 20 b.

Paintings by European Artists. Postage 1, 2, 3, 4, 5 b.; Air 6, 7, 8, 9, 10, 11, 12, 13, 14, 15 b.

Moon Flight of "Apollo 10". Postage 2, 4, 6 b.; Air 8, 10, 12, 18, 24, 28, 34 b.

Olympic Games, Munich (1972). Athletes and Olympic Rings. Postage 1, 2, 4, 5, 6 b.; Air 10, 12, 18, 24, 34 b.

World Wildlife Conservation. Postage ½ b. × 2 1 b. × 2, 2 b. × 2, 4 b. × 2, 6 b. × 2; Air 8 b. × 2, 10 b. × 2, 18 b. × 2.

First Man on the Moon (1st issue). Air 6, 10, 12, 18 b.

First Man on the Moon (2nd issue). Air 6, 10, 12, 18, 24 b.

First Man on the Moon (3rd issue). Embossed on gold foil. 24 b. × 2.

First Man on the Moon (4th issue). Embossed on gold foil. 28 b.

First Man on the Moon (5th issue). Air 10, 12 18, 24 b.

Palestine Holy Places. Postage 4 b. × 4, 6 b. × 10; Air 12 b. × 2.

Famous Men. Postage 4 b. × 4, 6 b. × 10, Air 12 b. × 2.

History of Space Exploration. Air 6 b. × 27.

Olympic Sports. Postage 1, 2, 4, 5, 6 b.; Air 10, 12, 18, 24, 34 b.

World Cup Football Championships, Mexico. Air 12 b. × 8.

Christmas. Ikons. Postage ½, 1, 1½, 2, 4, 5, 6 b.; Air 10, 12, 18, 24, 28, 34 b.

Burning of Al-Aqsa Mosque, Jerusalem. Postage 4 b. × 2 b., 6 b. + 3 b.; Air 10 b. + 5 b.

1970.

Brazil's Victory in World Cup Football Championships, Mexico. 1969 World Cup issue optd. Air 12 b. × 3.

Dogs. Postage 2, 4, 6 b.; Air 8, 12 b.

Paintings of Horses. Postage 2, 4, 6 b.; Air 8, 12 b.

We close the Appendix with stamps believed to have been issued prior to July 1970, when first Saudi Arabia and then the United Kingdom recognised the Republican government in Yemen.

YEMEN PEOPLE'S DEMOCRATIC REPUBLIC Pt. 19

The former People's Republic of Southern Yemen was known by the above title from 30 November 1970.

In 1990 it united with Yemen Arab Republic (see YEMEN REPUBLIC (combined)).

1000 fils = 1 dinar

22 Temple of Isis, Philae, Egypt

1971. Preservation of Philae Temples Campaign.

65	**22**	5 f. multicoloured	10	10
66		35 f. multicoloured	45	25
67		65 f. multicoloured	90	55

23 Symbols of Constitution

1971. Introduction of First Constitution.

68	**23**	10 f. multicoloured	10	10
69		15 f. multicoloured	15	15
70		35 f. multicoloured	30	30
71		50 f. multicoloured	40	40

24 Heads of Three Races and Flame

1971. Racial Equality Year.

72	**24**	20 f. multicoloured	15	15
73		35 f. multicoloured	30	30
74		75 f. multicoloured	55	55

25 Map, Flag and Products　**26** Hand holding Sub-machine Gun, and Map

1971.

75 25 5 f. multicoloured 10 10
76 10 f. multicoloured 10 10
77 15 f. multicoloured 15 10
78 20 f. multicoloured 15 10
79 25 f. multicoloured 20 10
80 35 f. multicoloured 25 15
81 40 f. multicoloured 35 15
82 50 f. multicoloured 55 20
82a 60 f. multicoloured 60 20
83 65 f. multicoloured 75 25
84 80 f. multicoloured 85 30
84a 90 f. multicoloured 85 30
84b – 110 f. multicoloured . . . 90 35
85 – 125 f. multicoloured . . . 1·00 60
86 – 250 f. multicoloured . . . 2·00 1·40
87 – 500 f. multicoloured . . . 3·75 3·00
88 – 1 d. multicoloured . . . 7·00 6·00

DESIGN—HORIZ (42×25 mm): Nos. 84b/8, "Dam-al-Khawain" tree, Socotra.

1971. 6th Anniv of Revolutionary Activity in Arabian Gulf Area. Multicoloured.

89 15 f. Type **26** 20 15
90 45 f. Girl guerrilla and emblem (horiz) 55 35
91 50 f. Guerrilla on the march . . 75 50

27 Hands supporting Cogwheel

29 Gamal Nasser

28 Eagle and Flags

1971. 2nd Anniv of "Corrective Move" in Revolutionary Government. Multicoloured.

92 15 f. Type **27** 15 10
93 25 f. Torch and revolutionary emblems 25 20
94 65 f. Salt-works and windmill . 60 45

1971. 9th Anniv of 26th September Revolution. Multicoloured.

95 10 f. Type **28** 10 10
96 40 f. Flag on "United Jemen" . 35 30

1971. 1st Death Anniv of Gamal Nasser (Egyptian statesman).

97 29 65 f. multicoloured 50 35

30 "Children of the World"

31 Domestic Pigeons

1971. 25th Anniv of U.N.I.C.E.F.

98 30 15 f. black, red & orange . 10 10
99 40 f. black, purple & blue . 20 15
100 50 f. black, red and green . 35 30

1971. Birds.

101 31 5 f. black, purple & blue . 30 20
102 – 40 f. multicoloured . . . 85 40
103 – 65 f. black, red and green . 1·25 75
104 – 100 f. multicoloured . . . 2·40 1·10

DESIGNS: 40 f. Arabian chukar; 65 f. Helmet guineafowl and Arabian chukar; 100 f. Black kite.

32 Dhow-building

1972. Dhow-building in Aden. Multicoloured.

105 25 f. Type **32** 50 20
106 80 f. Dhow at sea (vert) . . . 1·50 90

33 Singer with Oud (lute), and Band

1972. Folk Dances. Multicoloured.

107 10 f. Type **33** 20 10
108 25 f. Yemeni girls dancing . . 35 15
109 40 f. Dancing teams 70 30
110 80 f. Festival dance . . . . . 1·50 90

34 Palestinian Guerrilla and Barbed-wire

1972. Palestine Day.

111 34 5 f. multicoloured 20 15
112 20 f. multicoloured 45 15
113 65 f. multicoloured . . . . 1·50 90

35 Police Colour Party

1972. Police Day. Multicoloured.

114 25 f. Type **35** 50 20
115 80 f. Girls of People's Militia on parade . . . . 2·00 1·00

36 Start of Cycle Race

1972. Arab Youth Week. Multicoloured.

117 10 f. Type **36** 15 10
118 15 f. Girls on parade 20 10
119 40 f. Guides and scouts . . . 65 35
120 80 f. Acrobatic team (vert) . 1·25 80

37 Turtle

1972. Marine Life. Multicoloured.

121 15 f. Type **37** 55 20
122 40 f. Sailfish 75 45
123 65 f. Kingfish . . . . 1·00 75
124 125 f. Lobster . . . . 2·25 1·40

38 Book Year Emblem

1972. International Book Year.

125 38 40 f. multicoloured 50 35
126 65 f. multicoloured 75 55

39 Farmworkers and Field

1972. Agriculture Day.

127 39 10 f. multicoloured 15 15
128 25 f. multicoloured 25 15
129 40 f. multicoloured 60 45

40 Soldiers advancing

1972. 5th Anniv of Independence. Multicoloured.

130 5 f. Type **40** 15 15
131 20 f. Soldier and town 35 15
132 65 f. Vignettes of Yemeni life (vert) 80 50

41 Population Graph

1973. Population Census.

134 41 25 f. dp green, red & grn . 25 15
135 40 f. lt blue, red and blue . 45 30

42 W.H.O. Emblem within "25"

43 Taweela Tanks, Aden

1973. 25th Anniv of W.H.O. Multicoloured.

136 5 f. Type **42** 15 15
137 25 f. W.H.O. emblem on globe (horiz) 25 15
138 125 f. "25" and W.H.O. emblem (horiz) . . . . 1·25 1·00

1973. Tourism. Multicoloured.

139 20 f. Type **43** 20 15
140 25 f. Shibam Town (horiz) . . 25 15
141 40 f. Elephant Bay, Aden (horiz) 55 35
142 100 f. Al-Mohdar Mosque, Tarim (horiz) . . . . 1·25 90

44 Modern Apartments and Slum Clearance

1973. Nationalization of Buildings (1972). Multicoloured.

143 20 f. Type **44** 20 15
144 80 f. Street scene (vert) 70 60

45 Women's Corps on Parade

1973. People's Army. Multicoloured.

145 10 f. Type **45** 20 20
146 20 f. Soldiers marching 35 20
147 40 f. Naval contingent 90 50
148 80 f. Column of tanks . . . . 1·75 1·00

46 Quayside Crane

1973. 10th Anniv of World Food Programme. Multicoloured.

149 20 f. Type **46** 25 10
150 80 f. Granary workers . . . . 1·25 75

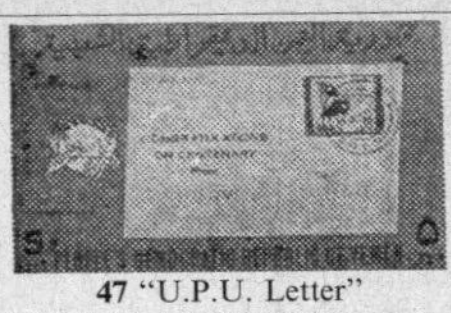

47 "U.P.U. Letter"

1974. Centenary of U.P.U. Multicoloured.

151 5 f. Type **47** 10 10
152 20 f. "100" formed of people and U.P.U. emblems 15 15
153 40 f. U.P.U. emblem and Yemeni flag (vert) 30 30
154 125 f. Map of People's Republic (vert) 65 65

48 Irrigation Canal

1974. Agricultural Progress. Multicoloured.

155 10 f. Type **48** 15 15
156 20 f. Bulldozers clearing land . 25 15
157 100 f. Tractors with harrows . 85 55

49 Lathe Operator

50

1975. Industrial Progress. Multicoloured.

158 10 f. Type **49** 15 15
159 40 f. Workers in clothing factory 40 25
160 80 f. Women textile workers (horiz) 75 35

1975. Women's Costumes.

161 50 5 f. brown and black . . . 15 15
162 – 10 f. violet and black . . . 15 15
163 – 15 f. yellow and black . . . 20 15
164 – 25 f. purple and black . . 40 25
165 – 40 f. blue and black . . . 65 40
166 – 50 f. brown and black . . 75 55

DESIGNS: Nos. 162/6 show different costumes.

51 Women in Factory

1975. International Women's Year.

167 51 40 f. brown and black . . 40 25
168 50 f. green and black . . . 50 35

52

53 Lunar Launch

1976. Yemeni Football.

169 52 5 f. multicoloured 10 10
170 – 40 f. multicoloured 40 25
171 – 80 f. multicoloured 70 40

DESIGNS: Nos. 170/1 show footballers in different positions.

1976. Russian Space Exploration. Multicoloured.

172 10 f. Type **53** 10 10
173 15 f. V. A. Shatalov (cosmonaut) 15 10
174 40 f. Luna vehicle (horiz) . . . 45 25
175 65 f. Valentina Tereshkova and rocket 75 45

54 Members of Presidential Council

1977. 1st Anniv of Unification Congress. Multicoloured.

176 25 f. Type **54** 15 15
177 35 f. Text of document 25 25
178 65 f. Girls of People's Militia 35 35
179 95 f. Aerial view of textile factory 45 45

55 Traffic Policeman and Woman Trainee

1977. Traffic Change to Right.

180 **55** 25 f. black and red 40 20
181 60 f. black and yellow 1·00 70
182 75 f. black and green 1·50 90
183 110 f. black and blue 2·25 1·75

56 A.P.U. Emblem within Flags of Member States

1977. 25th Anniv of Arab Postal Union.

184 **56** 20 f. multicoloured 15 15
185 60 f. multicoloured 45 35
186 70 f. multicoloured 50 40
187 90 f. multicoloured 55 50

57 "Festilyria-duponti" **58** Dove of Peace and Flag

1977. Cowries. Multicoloured.

188 60 f. Type **57** 60 35
189 90 f. "Afrivoluta pringlei" (horiz) 80 50
190 110 f. "Conus splendidulus" (horiz) 1·25 65
191 180 f. "Cypraea broderipii" (horiz) 1·90 1·25

1977. 10th Anniv of Independence. Multicoloured.

192 5 f. Type **58** 10 10
193 20 f. Man with broken manacle 15 10
194 90 f. Oil pipeline 45 45
195 110 f. "Pillar of Freedom" 60 60

59 Dome of the Rock, Jerusalem

1978. Palestinian Welfare.

196 **59** 5 f. multicoloured 30 10

For smaller design with value at top right, see No. 264.

60 Almarfaa (drum)

1978. Musical Instruments. Multicoloured.

197 35 f. Type **60** 20 15
198 60 f. Almizmar (pipes) 40 35
199 90 f. Alqnboos (fiddle) 55 45
200 110 f. Simsimiya (lyre) 80 70

61 Almotl (armbands)

1978. Silver Ornaments. Multicoloured.

201 10 f. Type **61** 10 10
202 15 f. Aloodhad (ring) 15 15
203 20 f. Al Hizam (necklace) 20 15
204 60 f. Alhoogaalah (bangle) 35 30
205 90 f. Al Muk-Hala (perfume flask) 50 45
206 110 f. Al Janbiya (dagger) 70 60

62 Palm Tree Emblem **63** "V" for Vanguard and Cogwheel

1978. 11th World Youth Festival, Cuba. Multicoloured.

207 5 f. Type **62** 10 10
208 60 f. Global emblem 30 30
209 90 f. Flower emblem 40 40
210 110 f. Girl, youth and emblems 50 50

1978. 1st Conference of Vanguard Party.

211 **63** 5 f. multicoloured 10 10
212 20 f. multicoloured 15 10
213 60 f. multicoloured 25 25
214 180 f. multicoloured 65 65

64 Calligraphic Emblem, Symbols of Peace and Freedom

1978. 15th Anniv of 14 October Revolution. Mult.

215 10 f. Type **64** 10 10
216 35 f. Emblems of growth (vert) 15 15
217 60 f. Candle and figure "15" (vert) 20 20
218 110 f. Revolutionaries and figure "15" (vert) 40 40

65 Map of Yemen, Child with Olive-branch and Dove **66** "Agricultural Progress"

1979. International Year of the Child.

219 **65** 15 f. multicoloured 15 15
220 20 f. multicoloured 15 15
221 60 f. multicoloured 25 25
222 90 f. multicoloured 35 35

1979. 10th Anniv of "Corrective Move" in Revolutionary Government. Multicoloured.

223 20 f. Type **66** 10 10
224 35 f. "Industrial Progress" 15 15
225 60 f. Students 25 20
226 90 f. Woman with star and doves 35 30

67 Sir Rowland Hill and Yemeni Costume Stamp of 1970

1979. Death Cent of Sir Rowland Hill. Mult.

227 90 f. Type **67** 35 30
228 110 f. Yemeni camel stamp of 1970 40 30

68 World Map, Koran and Symbols of Arab Achievements

1979. The Arabs.

230 **68** 60 f. multicoloured 30 20

69 Emblem of Yemeni Socialist Party **70** "Cassia adenensis"

1979. 1st Anniv of Yemeni Socialist Party.

231 **69** 60 f. multicoloured 25 20

1979. Flowers (1st series). Multicoloured.

232 20 f. Type **70** 15 15
233 90 f. "Nerium oleander" 55 35
234 110 f. "Calligonum comosum" 60 55
235 180 f. "Adenium obesum" 90 80

See also Nos. 265/8.

71 Ayatollah Khomeini and Crowd **73** Woman Basket-making

72 "Dido"

1980. 1st Anniv of Iranian Revolution.

236 **71** 60 f. multicoloured 75 60

1980. Screw Steamers. Multicoloured.

237 110 f. Type **72** 70 50
238 180 f. "Anglia" 1·00 75
239 250 f. "India" 1·60 1·25

1980. "London 1980". Handicrafts. Mult.

240 60 f. Type **73** 20 20
241 90 f. Making a hubble-bubble pipe 35 25
242 110 f. Man at loom 40 35
243 250 f. Boy making clay pot 80 70

74 Skink

1980. Reptiles. Multicoloured.

244 20 f. Type **74** 20 15
245 35 f. Mole viper 25 15
246 110 f. Gecko 65 50
247 180 f. Cobra 1·10 80

75 Misha the Bear (Olympic Mascot) **77** Lenin

76 Farming

1980. Olympic Games, Moscow.

248 **75** 110 f. multicoloured 45 30

1980. 10th Anniv of Peasants' Uprising. Multicoloured.

249 50 f. Type **76** 20 15
250 90 f. Peasants 35 25
251 110 f. Corn sickle and fist 45 40

1980. 110th Birth Anniv of Lenin.

252 **77** 35 f. multicoloured 30 15

78 Douglas DC-3

1981. Democratic Yemen Airlines. Multicoloured.

253 60 f. Type **78** 50 25
254 90 f. Boeing 707 80 35
255 250 f. De Havilland Dash Seven 2·25 1·50

79 Map, Dish Aerial and Satellite **80** "Conocarpus lancifolius"

1981. Ras Boradli Satellite Station.

256 **79** 60 f. multicoloured 60 30

1981. Trees. Multicoloured.

257 90 f. Type **80** 55 25
258 180 f. "Ficus vasta" 1·25 70
259 250 f. "Maerua crassifolia" 1·75 1·25

81 Council Building, Citizens and Flag

1981. 10th Anniv of Supreme People's Council.

260 **81** 180 f. multicoloured 1·00 75

82 Sand Fox

1981. Wildlife Conservation. Multicoloured.

261 50 f. Type **82** 40 35
262 90 f. Leopard 1·25 85
263 250 f. Ibex 2·50 2·00

1981. Palestinian Welfare. As T **59**, but smaller 25 × 27 mm and value at top right.

264 5 f. multicoloured 25 10

1981. Flowers (2nd series). As T **70**. Mult.

265 50 f. "Tephrosia apollinea" 45 20
266 90 f. "Citrullus colocynthis" 75 50
267 110 f. "Aloe squarrosa" 95 65
268 250 f. "Lawsonia inermis" 2·00 1·50

83 Blind People Basket-weaving and Typing

1982. International Year of Disabled Persons

269 **83** 50 f. multicoloured 30 20
270 100 f. multicoloured 70 35
271 150 f. multicoloured 1·10 80

84 Microscope Slides and Lungs

1982. Centenary of Discovery of Tubercle Bacillus.
272 **84** 50 f. black, orange and red 60 25

85 A.P.U. Emblem and Map within Heart

1982. 30th Anniv of Arab Postal Union.
273 **85** 100 f. red, black and blue . 85 65

86 Footballers

1982. World Cup Football Championship, Spain. Multicoloured.
274 50 f. Type **86** 40 25
275 100 f. Match scene 70 55
276 150 f. Players and shield . . . 1·10 75
277 290 f. Player and flags . . . . 1·40 1·10

87 Emblems and Flags of Russia and Yemen

1982. 60th Anniv of U.S.S.R.
279 **87** 50 f. multicoloured 35 25

1982. World Cup Football Championship Result. Nos. 274/7 optd **WORLD CUP WINNERS 1982 1st ITALY 2nd W-GERMANY 3rd POLAND 4th FRANCE.**
280 50 f. Type **86** 40 30
281 100 f. Match scene 70 60
282 150 f. Players and shield . . . 1·10 85
283 200 f. Player and flags . . . . 1·40 1·25

89 Yasser Arafat

1983. Palestinian Solidarity. Multicoloured.
285 50 f. Type **89** 75 25
286 100 f. Yasser Arafat and Dome of the Rock . . . . 1·25 75

1983. "Tembal 83" Stamp Exhibition, Basel. No. 248 optd **TEMBAL 83 MAY 21st-29th, 1983.**
288 **75** 110 f. multicoloured . . . 2·50 1·75

91 Man with Letter, Postal Barge and Postman

1983. World Communications Year.
289 **91** 50 f. black and blue 50 35
290 – 100 f. black and red . . . 90 55
291 – 150 f. black, light green and green . . . . 1·25 1·00
292 – 200 f. multicoloured . . . 1·50 1·25
DESIGNS: 100 f. Postman, stage coach and morse code equipment; 150 f. Motor coach and telephones; 200 f. Transmitter, airplane, satellite, television, envelope and dish aerial.

92 "The Poor Family"

1983. 10th Death Anniv of Picasso (artist). Multicoloured.
294 50 f. Type **92** 45 25
295 100 f. "Woman with Crow" . 75 50

93 Show Jumping

1983. Olympic Games, Los Angeles (1st issue). Equestrian Events. Multicoloured.
297 25 f. Type **93** 20 15
298 50 f. Show jumping (different) 35 25
299 100 f. Horse crossing water (Three-day event) 65 40
See also Nos. 316/18.

94 "P 8" Steam Engine, 1905

1983. Railway Locomotives. Multicoloured.
301 25 f. Type **94** 70 35
302 50 f. "880" steam engine, 1915 1·25 50
303 100 f. "Gt 2 × 4/4" locomotive, 1923 . . . . 2·25 80

95 "Europa"

1983. Liners. Multicoloured.
305 50 f. Type **85** . . . . 1·00 45
306 100 f. "World Discoverer" . . 1·50 95

96 "20" and Hand holding Sheaf of Corn

1983. 20th Anniv of Revolution. Multicoloured.
308 50 f. Type **96** 45 25
309 100 f. Flag, man with gun and "XX" 80 45

97 Pierre Testu-Brissy's Balloon Ascent on Horseback, 1798

1983. Bicentenary of Manned Flight. Mult.
310 50 f. Type **97** 60 25
311 100 f. Montgolfier Balloon, 1783 . . . . 1·00 50

98 Skiing

1983. Winter Olympic Games, Sarajevo. Multicoloured.
313 50 f. Type **98** 40 25
314 100 f. Bobsleigh 70 40

99 Fencing

1984. Olympic Games, Los Angeles (2nd issue). Multicoloured.
316 25 f. Type **99** 25 20
317 50 f. Fencing (different) . . 45 25
318 100 f. Fencing (different) . . . 75 45

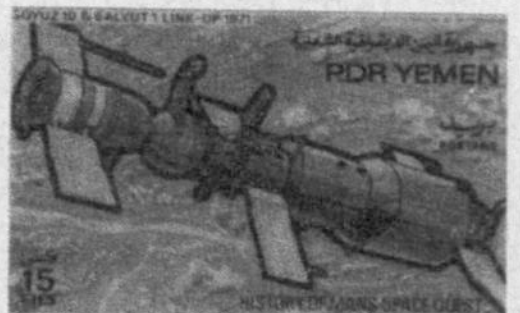

100 "Soyuz 10"-"Salyut 1" Link-up, 1971

1984. Space. Multicoloured.
320 15 f. Type **100** 15 15
321 20 f. "Apollo 8" and Moon, 1968 20 15
322 50 f. "Apollo 11" and first man on Moon, 1969 . . . . . . 50 35
323 100 f. "Soyuz"–"Apollo" link-up, 1975 . . . . 90 55

1984. Nos. 83 and 84b. surch.
325 **25** 50 f. on 65 f. multicoloured 50 40
326 – 100 f. on 110 f. multicoloured 90 70

102 "Abalistes stellaris"

1984. Fishes. Multicoloured.
327 10 f. Type **102** 10 10
328 15 f. "Caranx speciocus" . . . 10 10
329 20 f. "Pomadasys maculatus" . 15 10
330 35 f. "Chaetodon fasciatus" . . 15 10
331 35 f. Imperial angelfish 25 15
332 50 f. "Rastrelliger kanagurta" . 35 20
333 100 f. Wavyback skipjack . . . 70 40
334 150 f. Longfin butterfly fish . 1·10 65
335 200 f. Blue moon angelfish . . 1·40 80
336 250 f. "Pterois russelli" . . . . 1·75 1·00
337 400 f. "Argyrops spinifer" . . 2·75 1·50
338 500 f. "Dasyatis uarnak" . . . 3·50 1·90
339 1 d. "Epinephelus chlorostigma" 7·00 3·75
340 2 d. "Drepane longimana" . . . 14·00 8·00

1984. Olympic Winners, Sarajevo. No. 314 optd **WINNERS. B Lehmann-B. Musiol (DDR).**
341 100 f. multicoloured 90 70

104 Women writing 105 Victory Parade, Red Square

1985. National Literacy Campaign. Mult.
343 50 f. Type **104** 50 35
344 100 f. Pen held in manacled hand 90 60

1985. 40th Anniv of End of Second World War.
345 **105** 100 f. multicoloured . . . . 1·00 55

106 Flag within Emblem 107 Modern Buildings

1985. 12th World Youth and Students' Festival, Moscow. Multicoloured.
346 50 f. Type **106** 50 35
347 100 f. Hand holding emblem as placard 90 60

1985. U.N.E.S.C.O. World Heritage Site. Shibam City. Multicoloured.
348 50 f. Type **107** 50 40
349 50 f. View of city 50 40
350 100 f. Screen 90 70
351 100 f. Gate (vert) 90 70

108 Industrial Symbols 109 Mother feeding Child

1985. Third Yemeni Socialist Party General Congress. Multicoloured.
352 25 f. Type **108** 25 20
353 50 f. Crane loading ship . . . 50 35
354 100 f. Combine harvesters . . 90 65

1985. U.N.I.C.E.F. Child Survival Campaign. Multicoloured.
355 50 f. Type **109** 50 40
356 50 f. Immunization 50 40
357 100 f. Breastfeeding 90 70
358 100 f. Oral rehydration therapy 90 70

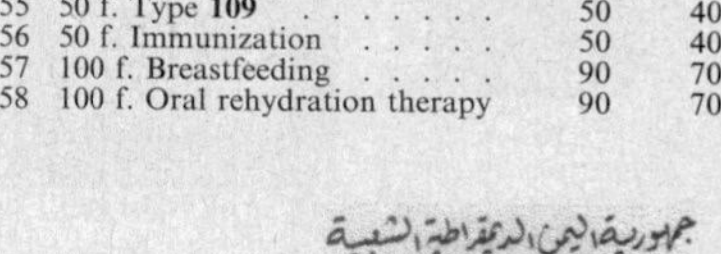

110 Wheat and Al-Mohdar Mosque, Tarim 111 Lenin addressing Crowd in Red Square

1986. World Food Day. 40th Anniv (1985) of F.A.O. Multicoloured.
359 20 f. Type **110** 40 25
360 180 f. Palm trees . . . . . . 2·25 1·50

1986. 27th Russian Communist Party Congress. Multicoloured.
361 **111** 75 f. multicoloured 70 50
362 250 f. multicoloured . . . 2·40 1·75

112 Bride in Yashmak 113 Ali Ahmed N. Antar

1986. Brides and Bridegrooms of Yemen. Mult.
363 50 f. Type **112** 75 45
364 50 f. Bride with striped shawl 70 45
365 50 f. Bride with long dressed hair 70 45
366 100 f. Bridegroom in modern jacket with knife . . . . . . 1·25 70
367 100 f. Bridegroom in traditional clothes with gun . . . . . 1·25 70
368 100 f. Bride in modern dress . 1·25 70

1986. "Party and Homeland Martyrs". Mult.
369 75 f. Type **113** 60 50
370 75 f. Saleh Musleh Kasim . . 60 50
371 75 f. Ali Shayaa Hadi 60 50
372 75 f. Abdul Fattah Ismail . . 60 50

114 Immunizing Pregnant Woman against Tetanus

1987. U.N.I.C.E.F. Immunization Campaign. Multicoloured.
373 20 f. Type **114** 15 15
374 75 f. Immunizing baby 50 35
375 140 f. Nurse giving oral poliomyelitis vaccine to baby 90 60
376 150 f. Pregnant woman and children carrying syringes . 1·00 70

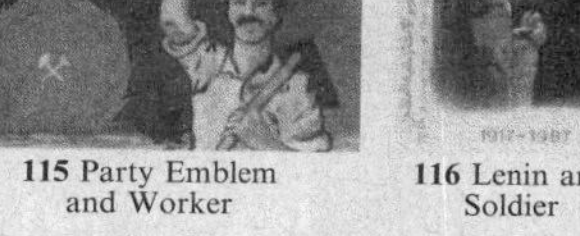

115 Party Emblem and Worker
116 Lenin and Soldier

1987. Yemeni Socialist Party General Conference.
377 **115** 75 f. multicoloured . . . 55 35
378 150 f. multicoloured . . . 1·00 75

1987. 70th Anniv of Russian October Revolution.
379 **116** 250 f. multicoloured . . . 1·60 1·25

117 Steps to King's Court

1987. Shabwa Remains. Multicoloured.
380 25 f. Type **117** 15 15
381 75 f. Royal Palace 45 30
382 140 f. Winged lion, King's Court (vert) 80 60
383 150 f. Inscribed bronze plaque (vert) 90 70

118 Students and College Buildings

1987. 20th Anniv of Independence. Mult.
384 25 f. Type **118** 15 15
385 75 f. Family and housing . . . 45 30
386 140 f. Workers, oil derrick and power station 80 60
387 150 f. Party headquarters and members 90 70

119 Tank and Liberty Monument, Sana'a

1988. 25th Anniv (1987) of 26th September Revolution in Yemen.
388 **119** 75 f. multicoloured . . . 55 30

120 Tap, Boy and Rainbow (safe water)
121 Weightlifting

1988. World Health Day. 40th Anniv of W.H.O. Multicoloured.
389 40 f. Type **120** 25 20
390 75 f. Child with globe as head breaking cigarette (No Smoking day) 45 30
391 140 f. Nurse immunizing baby (immunization campaign) . 80 65
392 250 f. Red Crescent worker instructing group (Health for all) . . . . 1·50 1·25

1988. Olympic Games, Seoul. Multicoloured.
393 40 f. Type **121** 25 20
394 75 f. Running 40 30
395 140 f. Boxing 70 55
396 150 f. Football 75 60

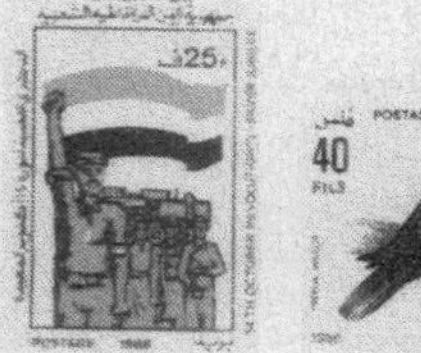

122 Crowd and Flag
123 Yellow-bellied Green Pigeon

1988. 25th Anniv of 14 October Revolution.
397 **122** 25 f. black and red . . . 15 15
398 – 75 f. multicoloured . . . 40 30
399 – 300 f. multicoloured . . . 1·50 1·25
DESIGNS—HORIZ: 75 f. Radfan mountains and revolutionary. VERT: 300 f. Anniversary emblem.

1988. Birds. Multicoloured.
400 40 f. Type **123** 40 25
401 50 f. Lilac-breasted roller (vert) 50 30
402 75 f. Hoopoe (vert) 75 40
403 250 f. Houbara bustard . . . 2·25 1·50

124 Incense Burner
125 Shipping entering Old Harbour

1988. Traditional Crafts. Multicoloured.
404 25 f. Type **124** 15 15
405 70 f. Mashjub (rack used when impregnating dresses with incense) 40 30
406 150 f. Cosmetic basket made of palm fibre with cowrie shell decoration . . . . 1·10 80
407 250 f. Woman making palm fibre basket . . . . 1·25 1·00

1988. Centenary of Port of Aden. Mult.
408 75 f. Type **125** 60 40
409 300 f. Section of new harbour project . . . . 1·90 1·50

126 Old City

1988. International Campaign for Preservation of Old Sana'a. Multicoloured.
410 75 f. Type **126** 40 30
411 250 f. City (different) . . . . 1·25 1·00

127 Sand Cat Kitten

1989. Endangered Animals. Multicoloured.
412 20 f. Type **127** 10 10
413 25 f. Adult sand cat 15 10
414 50 f. Fennec fox cub 30 20
415 75 f. Adult fennec fox 40 30

128 Symbols of War in Star
129 Ismail

1989. 20th Anniv of "Corrective Movement" in Revolutionary Government. Multicoloured.
416 25 f. Type **128** 15 10
417 35 f. Industrial symbols in hook 20 10
418 40 f. Agricultural symbols . . 25 15

1989. 50th Birth Anniv of Adbul Fattah Ismail (founder of People's Socialist Party).
419 **129** 75 f. multicoloured 40 30
420 150 f. multicoloured . . . 75 60

130 "Children at Play" (Abeer Anwer)
131 Sana'a and Fighters

1989. 15th Anniv of Ali Anter Pioneer Organization. Multicoloured.
421 10 f. Type **130** 10 10
422 25 f. Girl pioneer 15 10
423 75 f. Pioneers parading at Khormaksar (horiz) 40 30

1989. 22nd Anniv of Siege of Sana'a.
424 **131** 150 f. multicoloured . . . 50 40

132 Taj Mahal and Nehru
133 Coffee Plant

1989. Birth Centenary of Jawaharal Nehru (Indian statesman).
425 **132** 250 f. black and brown . . . 90 75

1989. Centenary of Interparliamentary Union.
426 **133** 300 f. multicoloured . . . 1·00 80

134 Seera Rock, Aden, Birds and Arc de Triomphe, Paris

1989. Bicentenary of French Revolution.
427 **134** 250 f. multicoloured . . . 90 75

135 U.S.A. v Belgium (Uruguay, 1930)

1990. World Cup Football Championship, Italy. Matches from previous championships. Multicoloured.
428 5 f. Type **135** 10 10
429 10 f. Switzerland v Netherlands (Italy, 1934) 10 10
430 20 f. Italy v France (France, 1938) 10 10
431 35 f. Sweden v Spain (Brazil, 1950) 10 10
432 50 f. West Germany v Austria (Switzerland, 1954) 15 10
433 60 f. Brazil v England (Sweden, 1958) 15 10
434 500 f. U.S.S.R. v Uruguay (Chile, 1962) . . . . 1·10 85

YEMEN REPUBLIC (combined)

Pt. 19

A draft joint constitution was ratified by the parliaments of Yemen Arab Republic and the Yemen People's Democratic Republic on 21 May 1990 and the unification of the two countries was declared the following day.

The currencies of both the previous republics have legal validity throughout Yemen.

100 fils = 1 rial (North Yemen)
1000 fils = 1 dinar (South Yemen)

1 Scouts supporting Globe

1990. 60th Anniv of Arab Scout Movement. Multicoloured.
1 300 f. Type **1** 85 40
2 375 f. Type **1** . . . . 1·10 50
3 850 f. Oil derrick, scouts with flag, anniversary emblem and tower 2·00 95
4 900 f. As No. 3 . . . . 2·40 1·25
Nos. 1/4 are inscribed "YEMEN ARAB REPUBLIC".

2 Pintail
3 City Rooftops

1990. Ducks. Multicoloured.
6 10 f. Type **210** 10 10
7 20 f. Wigeon 10 10
8 25 f. Ruddy shelduck 10 10
9 40 f. Gadwall 15 10
10 75 f. Shelduck 30 10
11 150 f. Shoveler pair 60 20
12 600 f. Teal . . . . 2·40 80

1990. 40th Anniv of U.N. Development Programme.
14 **3** 150 f. multicoloured 60 30

4 "Dirphia multicolor"
5 Protembolotherium

1990. Moths and Butterflies. Multicoloured.
15 5 f. Type **4** 10 10
16 20 f. "Automeris sp." 10 10
17 25 f. Swallowtail 10 10
18 40 f. Bhutan glory 15 10
19 55 f. Silver king shoemaker . . 20 10
20 75 f. Tiger moth 30 15
21 700 f. "Attacus edwardsii" (moth) 2·75 85

1990. Prehistoric Animals. Multicoloured.
23 5 f. Type **5** 10 10
24 10 f. Diatryma 10 10
25 35 f. Mammoth (horiz) 15 10
26 40 f. Edaphosaurus (horiz) . . . 15 10
27 55 f. Dimorphodon (horiz) . . . 20 10
28 75 f. Phororhacos (horiz) . . . 30 10
29 700 f. Ichthyosaurus (wrongly inscr "Ichtyosaurus") . . . . 3·00 90

6 Abyssinian Kitten
7 "Boletus aestivalis"

1990. Cats. Multicoloured.
31 5 f. Type **6** 10 10
32 15 f. Blue longhair 10 10
33 35 f. Siamese 15 15
34 55 f. Burmese 25 10
35 60 f. Sealpoint colourpoint . . . 25 10
36 150 f. Red British shorthair . . 65 10
37 600 f. Leopard cat . . . . . . 2·50 80

1991. Fungi. Multicoloured.
39 50 f. Type **7** 10 10
40 60 f. Butter mushroom 25 10
41 80 f. Beefsteak morel 30 10
42 100 f. Brown birch bolete . . . 40 15
43 130 f. Fly agaric 55 20
44 200 f. Flaky-stemmed witches' mushroom 80 25
45 300 f. Red cap . . . . 1·25 60

8 State Arms
9 Shaking Hands

1991. 1st Anniv of Yemen Republic. Mult.
47 300 f. Type **8** 45 15
48 375 f. Type **8** 70 25
49 850 f. Hand holding flag, map and sun . . . . 1·10 45
50 900 f. As No. 49 . . . . 1·40 60

1991. Signing of Unity Agreement (in November 1989) Commemoration. Multicoloured.

52 225 f. Type **9** 65 20
53 300 f. Hand holding flag over map 85 30
54 375 f. As No. 53 . . . . 1·10 45
55 650 f. Type **9** . . . . 1·50 60
56 850 f. As No. 53 . . . . 2·40 1·10

10 Cigarettes and Skull on Globe

1991. World Anti-smoking Day. Multicoloured.

58 225 f. Type **10** 30 10
59 300 f. Skull smoking and man . 45 15
60 375 f. As No. 59 . . . . 60 20
61 650 f. Type **10** . . . . 1·00 40
62 850 f. As No. 59 . . . . 1·25 50

11 Emblem

1991. 45th Anniv of U.N.O.

64 **11** 5 r. multicoloured . . . . . 1·10 45
65 8 r. multicoloured . . . . . 1·25 50
66 10 r. multicoloured . . . . 1·40 60
67 12 r. multicoloured . . . . 1·75 70

1993. Various stamps surch. (a) Stamps of Yemen Arab Republic. (i) Postage.

69 **94** 5 r. on 75 f. multicoloured 60 25
70 **144** 8 r. on 425 f. multicoloured 1·00 45
71 **150** 8 r. on 425 f. multicoloured 1·00 45
72 – 10 r. on 900 f. mult (No. 830) 1·40 65
73 – 10 r. on 900 f. mult (No. 834) 1·40 65
74 – 10 r. on 900 f. mult (No. 838) 1·40 65
75 – 10 r. on 900 f. mult (No. 843) 1·40 65
76 **157** 10 r. on 900 f. multicoloured 1·40 65
77 – 10 r. on 900 f. mult (No. 853) 1·40 65
78 **159** 10 r. on 900 f. multicoloured 1·40 65
79 – 10 r. on 900 f. mult (No. 863) 1·40 65
80 – 12 r. on 850 f. mult (No. 829) 1·75 80
81 – 12 r. on 850 f. mult (No. 833) 1·75 80
82 – 12 r. on 850 f. mult (No. 837) 1·75 80
83 – 12 r. on 850 f. mult (No. 842) 1·75 80
84 **157** 12 r. on 850 f. multicoloured 1·75 80
85 – 12 r. on 850 f. mult (No. 852) 1·75 80
86 **159** 12 r. on 850 f. multicoloured 1·75 80

(ii) Air. Additionally optd **AIR MAIL** (except for No. 87).

87 **118** 3 r. on 125 f. multicoloured 60 25
88 – 3 r. on 125 f. mult (No. 672) 60 25
89 – 3 r. on 125 f. mult (No. 679) 60 25
90 – 3 r. on 125 f. mult (No. 686) 60 25
91 – 3 r. on 125 f. mult (No. 700) 60 25
92 – 3 r. on 125 f. mult (No. 707) 60 25
93 – 5 r. on 75 f. mult (No. 670) 60 25
94 – 5 r. on 75 f. mult (No. 677) 60 25
95 – 5 r. on 75 f. mult (No. 684) 60 25
96 – 5 r. on 75 f. mult (No. 691) 60 25
97 – 5 r. on 75 f. mult (No. 698) 60 25
98 – 5 r. on 75 f. mult (No. 705) 60 25
99 **145** 8 r. on 425 f. multicoloured 1·00 45
100 – 8 r. on 425 f. mult (No. 796) 1·00 45
101 **147** 8 r. on 425 f. multicoloured 1·00 45
102 – 8 r. on 425 f. mult (No. 803) 1·00 45
103 – 8 r. on 425 f. mult (No. 812) 1·00 45
104 **151** 8 r. on 425 f. multicoloured 1·00 45
105 **152** 8 r. on 425 f. multicoloured 1·00 45
106 – 12 r. on 850 f. mult (No. 862) 1·75 80

(b) Stamps of Yemen Republic (combined).

107 – 10 r. on 900 f. mult (No. 4) 1·40 65
108 – 10 r. on 900 f. mult (No. 50) 1·40 65
109 – 12 r. on 850 f. mult (No. 3) 1·75 80
110 – 12 r. on 850 f. mult (No. 49) 1·75 80
111 – 12 r. on 850 f. mult (No. 56) 1·75 80
112 – 12 r. on 850 f. mult (No. 62) 1·75 80
113 – 50 r. on 50 f. mult (No. 11) 10·50 4·50
114 **3** 50 r. on 150 f. multicoloured 10·50 4·50
115 **8** 50 r. on 375 f. multicoloured 10·50 4·50
116 – 50 r. on 375 f. mult (No. 54) 10·50 4·50
117 – 50 r. on 375 f. mult (No. 60) 10·50 4·50
118 **8** 100 r. on 300 f. mult . . . 21·00 9·25

(c) Stamps of Yemen People's Democratic Republic.

119 – 8 r. on 110 f. mult (No. 84b) 1·25 55
120 – 8 r. on 110 f. mult (No. 200) 1·25 55
121 – 8 r. on 110 f. mult (No. 206) 1·25 55
122 – 8 r. on 110 f. mult (No. 218) 1·25 55
123 – 8 r. on 110 f. mult (No. 234) 1·25 55
124 **72** 8 r. on 110 f. multicoloured 1·25 55
125 – 8 r. on 110 f. mult (No. 246) 1·25 55
126 – 8 r. on 110 f. mult (No. 267) 1·25 55
127 **133** 100 r. on 300 f. mult . . . 21·00 9·00
128 – 100 r. on 2 d. mult (No. 340) 21·00 9·00
129 **25** 200 r. on 5 f. multicoloured 42·00 18·00
130 **127** 200 r. on 20 f. multicoloured 42·00 18·00
131 – 200 r. on 75 f. mult (No. 423) 42·00 18·00
132 **132** 200 r. on 250 f. mult . . . 42·00 18·00
133 **100** 200 r. on 15 f. multicoloured 42·00 18·00
134 – 200 r. on 15 f. mult (No. 328) 42·00 18·00
135 – 200 r. on 20 f. mult (No. 321) 42·00 18·00
136 – 200 r. on 20 f. mult (No. 329) 42·00 18·00

15 Sana'a

16 Player dribbling Ball

1994. 4th Anniv of Yemen Republic.

137 – 3 r. multicoloured 55 25
138 – 5 r. multicoloured 90 40
139 **15** 8 r. multicoloured . . . . 1·60 70
140 – 20 r. multicoloured . . . . 3·25 1·40

DESIGNS: Nos. 137/8, 140, Different views of the principal building in Type **15**.

1994. World Cup Football Championship, U.S.A. Multicoloured.

142 2 r. Type **16** 45 20
143 6 r. Dribbling (different) . . 1·25 55
144 10 r. Goalkeeper catching ball (horiz) . . . . 1·90 85
145 12 r. Player heading ball . . 2·25 1·00

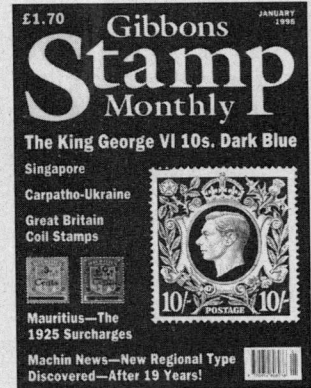

YUGOSLAVIA Pt. 3

The kingdom of the Serbs, Croats and Slovenes, in S.E. Europe, established after the 1914-18 war and comprising Serbia, Montenegro, Bosnia, Herzegovina and parts of pre-war Hungary.

From 1945 it was a Federal Republic comprising six republics. In 1991 four of these republics seceded, leaving Serbia and Montenegro.

A. KINGDOM OF THE SERBS, CROATS AND SLOVENES

I. ISSUES FOR BOSNIA AND HERZEGOVINA

100 heller = 1 kruna

1918. 1910 commem stamps of Bosnia (with date labels) optd **DRZAVA S.H.S. 1918 1918 Bosna i Hercegovina** or the same in Cyrillic characters or surch also.

1		3 h. olive (No. 345)	50	1·00
2		5 h. green	30	45
3		10 h. red	30	45
4		20 h. sepia	30	45
5		25 h. blue	30	45
6		30 h. green	30	45
7		40 h. orange	30	45
8		45 h. red	30	45
9		50 h. purple	20	25
10		60 h. on 50 h. purple	15	25
11		80 h. on 6 h. brown	10	75
12		90 h. on 35 h. green	10	20
13		2 k. green	20	50
14		3 k. on 3 h. olive	1·50	1·00
15		4 k. on 1 k. lake	3·00	3·00
16		10 k. on 2 h. violet	7·50	3·75

1918. Newspaper Express stamps of Bosnia. 5 h. optd as last and **HELERA** and 2 h. the same but in Cyrillic.

17	N 35	2 h. red	2·50	4·00
18		5 h. green	1·75	2·00

These were issued for use as ordinary postage stamps.

1918 Bosnian War Invalids Fund stamps optd **DRAVA S.H.S. Bosna Hercegovina** or the same in Cyrillic characters.

19	31	5 h. (+2 h.) green	£130	£160
20	–	10 h. (+2 h.) red	85·00	£140
21	–	10 h. (+2 h.) blue	75	3·75
22	31	15 h. (+2 h.) brown	1·25	3·25

КРАЉЕВСТВО

6a

(7)

1918. Newspaper stamps of Bosnia of 1913 (as T **6a**) surch. Imperf.

50	6a	2 on 6 h. mauve	£120	£150
51		2 on 10 h. red	60·00	90·00
52		2 on 20 h. green	7·50	15·00
23		3 on 2 h. blue	10	20
24		5 on 6 h. mauve	10	20

Most of these were used for ordinary postage purposes.

1919. Perf.

25	6a	2 h. blue	10	25
26		6 h. mauve	75	1·25
27		10 h. red	25	25
28		20 h. green	20	25

The above were issued for use as ordinary postage stamps.

These stamps imperforate were issued as Newspaper stamps for Bosnia q.v.

1919. Types of Bosnia optd with T **7** or similar type with wording **KRALJEVSTVO S.H.S.**, or surch also.

29	25	3 h. lake	10	1·10
30		5 h. green	10	10
31		10 on 6 h. black	10	10
32	26	20 on 35 h. green	10	15
33	25	25 h. blue	10	15
34		30 h. red	75	25
35	26	45 h. brown	10	25
36	33	45 on 80 h. brown	10	10
37	26	50 h. blue	40·00	50·00
38		50 h. on 72 h. blue	10	10
39		60 h. purple	10	25
40	33	80 h. brown	10	25
41		90 h. purple	10	25
42	–	2 k. green (No. 200)	15	25
43	26	3 k. red on green	25	50
44	34	4 k. red on green	1·00	1·50
45	26	5 k. lilac on grey	2·40	1·75
46	34	10 k. violet on grey	2·40	3·00

1919. War Victims' Fund. Stamps of Bosnia of 1906 surch **KRALJEVSTVO Srba. Hrvata i Slovenaca** or same in Cyrillic characters and new value.

47	–	10 x. + 10 x. on 40 h. orange (No. 196)	1·25	2·25
48	–	20 x. + 10 x. on 20 h. sepia (No. 192)	65	1·50
49	5	45 x. + 15 x. on 1 k. lake	3·75	6·00

II. ISSUES FOR CROATIA

100 filir (heller) = 1 kruna (krone)

The provisional issues on Hungarian stamps were sold in Yugoslavia "heller" and "krone" currency, but as this is not expressed on the stamps (except for Nos. 69/73) we have retained the Hungarian descriptions to facilitate reference to the original stamps.

1918. Various issues of Hungary optd **HRVATSKA SHS** and bar or wheel

"Turul" issue of 1900

53	7	6 f. olive	75	1·25
54		50 f. lake on blue	1·00	1·90

"Harvesters" and "Parliament" issues of 1916.

55	18	2 f. brown	10	15
56		3 f. red	10	10
57		5 f. green	10	10
58		6 f. green	10	10
59		10 f. red	6·00	4·50
60		15 f. violet (No. 244)	45·00	60·00
61		15 f. violet (No. 251)	10	10
62		20 f. brown	10	10
63		25 f. blue	10	20
64		35 f. brown	10	10
65		40 f. olive	15	30
66	19	50 f. purple	10	10
67		75 f. blue	10	10
68		80 f. green	10	20
69		1 k. lake	10	10
70		2 k. brown	10	10
71		3 k. grey and violet	20	30
72		5 k. brown	1·00	1·25
73		10 k. lilac and brown	7·50	9·00

The kroner values are overprinted **KRUNA** or **KRUNE** also.

"Charles" and "Zita" issue of 1918.

74	27	10 f. red	10	15
75		20 f. brown	10	15
76		25 f. blue	10	40
77	28	40 f. olive	10	15

1918. Stamps of Hungary optd **HRVATSKA SHS. ZF. ZA NAROD. VIJECE.**

War Charity issue of 1916.

78	20	10+2 f. red	20	30
79	–	15+2 f. violet	10	25
80	22	40+2 f. lake	10	25

Coronation issue of 1916.

81	23	10 f. mauve	22·00	55·00
82	–	15 f. red	22·00	55·00

20 "Freedom of Croatia"

1918. Freeing of the Yugoslavs.

83	20	10 h. lake	2·40	2·50
84		20 h. violet	2·40	4·25
85		25 h. blue	6·00	7·50
86		45 h. black	35·00	40·00

21 Angel of Peace

22 Sailor with Standard and Falcon

23 Falcon ("Liberty")

1919.

87	21	2 h. brown	10	25
88		3 h. mauve	10	30
89		5 h. green	10	10
90	22	10 h. red	10	10
91		20 h. brown	10	10
92		25 h. blue	10	10
93		45 h. olive	10	10
94	23	1 k. red	15	15
95	–	3 k. purple	75	65
96	–	5 k. brown	75	55

DESIGN: 3, 5 k. as Type **5** but light background behind falcon.

III. ISSUES FOR SLOVENIA

1919. 100 vinar (heller) = 1 kruna (krone)
1920. 100 paras = 1 dinar

25 Chainbreakers 26

27 "Yugoslavia" with Three Falcons

28 Angel of Peace

29 King Peter I

1919. Perf or rouletted.

97a	25	3 v. violet	10	10
127		3 v. purple	10	10
98a		5 v. green	15	10
99b		10 v. red	20	10
100		15 v. blue	10	10
101	26	20 v. brown	30	10
102		25 v. blue	25	10
103		30 v. pink	25	10
111		30 v. red	25	10
104a		40 v. yellow	25	10
122	27	50 v. green	15	10
113b		60 v. violet	60	25
114b	28	1 k. red	35	20
120		2 k. blue	35	15
126	29	5 k. red	35	15
139a		10 k. blue	2·00	55
105		15 k. green	5·25	12·50
106		20 k. purple	1·00	1·40

31 Chainbreaker

32 "Yugoslavia" with Three Falcons

34 King Peter I

1920. Perf (2 d. to 10 d.) or roul.

150	31	5 p. olive	15	10
151		10 p. green	10	10
152		15 p. brown	10	10
153		20 p. red	40	25
154		25 p. brown	40	10
155	32	40 p. violet	10	15
156		45 p. yellow	10	15
157		50 p. blue	10	10
158		60 p. brown	10	10
159	34	1 d. brown	10	10
160	–	2 d. black	10	10
161	34	4 d. slate	20	20
162	–	6 d. olive	10	65
163	–	10 d. brown	20	50

The 2, 6 and 10 d. are as Type **34** but larger.

1920. Carinthian Plebiscite. Newspaper stamps of Yugoslavia of 1919 surch **KGCA** and new value. Imperf.

163a	N 30	5 p. on 4 v. grey	10	15
163b		15 p. on 4 v. grey	10	15
163c		25 p. on 4 v. grey	10	20
163d		45 p. on 2 v. grey	15	40
163e		50 p. on 2 v. grey	10	25
163f		2 d. on 2 v. grey	90	3·50

These stamps were sold at three times face value on aid of the Plebiscite Propaganda Fund.

IV. ISSUES FOR THE WHOLE KINGDOM

100 paras = 1 dinar

35 King Alexander when Prince

37 Kosovo Maiden, 1389

1921. Inscr "KRALJEVSTVO" at foot.

164	35	2 p. brown	10	10
165		5 p. green	10	10
166		10 p. red	10	10
167		15 p. purple	10	10
168		20 p. black	10	10
169		25 p. blue	10	10
170		50 p. olive	10	10
171		60 p. red	20	10
172		75 p. violet	10	10
173	–	1 d. orange	20	10
174	–	2 d. olive	40	10
175	–	4 d. green	90	10
176	–	5 d. red	2·50	15
177	–	10 d. brown	5·50	50

DESIGN: 1 d. to 10 d. as Type **35**, but portrait of King Peter I.

1921. Disabled Soldiers' Fund.

178	37	10+10 p. red	10	10
179	–	15+15 p. brown	10	10
180	–	25+25 p. blue	10	15

DESIGN: 15 p. Albanian retreat, 1915; 25 p. National Unity.

1922. Nos. 178/180 surch.

181		1 d. on 10 p. red	10	10
183		1 d. on 15 p. brown	10	10
182		1 d. on 25 p. blue	20	10
184		3 d. on 15 p. brown	25	10
186		8 d. on 15 p. brown	1·00	25
187		20 d. on 15 p. brown	9·00	75
188		30 d. on 15 p. brown	12·50	2·25

1923. As T **35**, but inscr "KRALJEVINA" at foot.

189	35	1 d. brown	1·25	10
190		5 d. red	6·50	30
191		8 d. purple	7·50	30
192		20 d. green	30·00	75
193		30 d. orange	90·00	2·50

1924. Nos. 171 and 191 surch.

195	35	20 p. on 60 p. red	25	10
196		5 d. on 8 d. purple	8·00	65

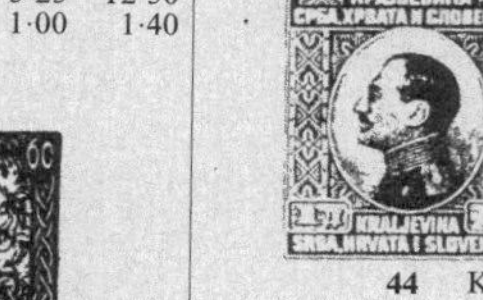

44 King Alexander 46

1924.

197	44	20 p. black	10	10
198		50 p. brown	10	10
199		1 d. red	10	10
200		2 d. green	30	10
201		3 d. blue	30	10
202		5 d. brown	3·00	10
203	–	10 d. violet	15·00	10
204	–	15 d. olive	10·50	20
205	–	20 d. orange	10·50	20
206	–	30 d. green	7·50	1·25

The 10 d. to 30 d. have the head in a square panel.

1925. Surch.

207	44	25 p. on 3 d. blue	15	10
208		50 p. on 3 d. blue	15	10

1926.

209	46	25 p. green	10	10
210		50 p. sepia	10	10
211		1 d. red	20	10
212		2 d. black	20	10
213		3 d. blue	35	10
214		4 d. orange	70	10
215		5 d. violet	1·40	10
216		8 d. brown	4·50	10
217		10 d. olive	2·50	10
218		15 d. brown	12·00	10
219		20 d. purple	15·00	15
220		30 d. yellow	75·00	50

1926. Danube Flood Fund. Surch.

221	46	25 p. + 0.25 green	10	10
222		50 p. + 0.50 sepia	10	10
223		1 d. + 0.50 red	20	10
224		2 d. + 0.50 black	40	10
225		3 d. + 0.50 blue	25	15
226		4 d. + 0.50 orange	40	10
227		5 d. + 0.50 violet	60	10
228		8 d. + 0.50 brown	90	40
229		10 d. + 1.00 olive	3·00	15
230		15 d. + 1.00 brown	6·50	50
231		20 d. + 1.00 purple	5·00	40
232		30 d. + 1.00 yellow	22·00	1·25

1928. Nos. 223/32 optd **XXXX** over previous surch.

233	46	1 d. red	50	10
234		2 d. black	75	10
235		3 d. blue	1·40	25
236		4 d. orange	2·75	30
237		5 d. violet	2·00	15
238		8 d. brown	9·00	50
239	46	10 d. olive	18·00	15
240		15 d. brown	90·00	1·90
241		20 d. purple	55·00	1·90
242		30 d. yellow	£120	11·50

B. KINGDOM OF YUGOSLAVIA

100 paras = 1 dinar

49 Duvno Cathedral

1929. Millenary of Croatian Kingdom (1925).

243	49	50 p. + 50 p. olive	30	25
244	–	1 d. + 50 p. red	70	35
245	–	3 d. + 1 d. blue	1·25	65

DESIGNS—As Type **49**: 3 d. King Tomislav. HORIZ (34×23 mm): 1 d. Kings Tomislav and Alexander I.

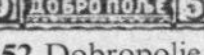

52 Dobropolje

53 Serbian War Memorial, Paris

1931. Serbian War Memorial (Paris) Fund.

246 **52** 50 p. + 50 p. green 10 10
247 **53** 1 d. + 50 p. red 10 15
248 – 3 d. + 1 d. blue 15 25

DESIGN—As Type **52**: 3 d. Kajmaktchalan.

55 King Alexander

57 Rowing "four" on Lake Bled

1931.

249 **55** 25 p. black 15 10
250 50 p. green 15 10
262 75 p. green 25 10
251 1 d. red 15 10
263 1 d. 50 red 50 10
263b 1 d. 75 red 1·00 45
252 3 d. blue 1·00 10
263c 3 d. 50 blue 1·25 15
253 4 d. orange 3·75 10
254 5 d. violet 4·50 10
255 10 d. olive 12·00 10
256 15 d. brown 11·00 10
257 20 d. purple 22·00 15
258 30 d. red 13·50 55

1931. Optd **KRALJEVINA JUGOSLAVIJA** and also in Cyrillic characters.

259 **49** 50 p. + 50 p. olive 10 10
260 – 1 d. + 50 p. red 10 10
261 – 3 d. + 1 d. blue 35 20

1932. European Rowing Championship. Inscr ending "EUROPE 1932".

264 – 75 p. + 50 p. green 65 1·00
265 **57** 1 d. + ½ d. red 1·00 1·25
266 – 1½ d. + ½ d. red 1·00 1·25
267 – 3 d. + 1 d. blue 1·75 2·50
268 – 4 d. + 1 d. blue and orange 5·25 12·00
269 – 5 d. + 1 d. lilac and violet 5·25 10·00

DESIGNS—HORIZ: 75 p. Single sculler on Danube at Smederevo; 1½ d. Rowing "eight" on Danube at Belgrade; 3 d. Rowing "pair" at Split harbour. VERT: 4 d. Rowing "pair" on river and Zagreb Cathedral; 5 d. Prince Peter.

1933. 11th Int Pen Club Congress Dubrovnik. As T **25** with additional value and "XI. int. kongres Pen-Klubova u Dubrovniku 1933" below in Roman or Cyrillic characters.

270 **55** 50 p. + 25 p. black 3·75 7·00
271 75 p. + 25 p. green 3·75 7·00
272 1 d. 50 + 50 p. red 3·75 7·00
273 3 d. + 1 d. blue 3·75 7·00
274 4 d. + 1 d. green 3·75 7·00
275 5 d. + 1 d. yellow 3·75 7·00

60 Crown Prince Peter in "Sokol" Uniform

62

1933. "Sokol" Meeting, Ljubjana.

276 **60** 75 p. + 25 p. green 25 30
277 1½ d. + ½ d. red 25 30

1933. Optd **JUGOSLAVIJA** in Roman and Cyrillic characters. (a) Postage.

278 **46** 25 p. green 15 10
279 50 p. sepia 15 10
280 1 d. red 50 10
281 2 d. black 55 15
282 3 d. blue 1·90 10
283 4 d. orange 1·00 10
284 5 d. violet 1·90 10
285 8 d. brown 4·75 1·25
286 10 d. olive 9·25 10
287 15 d. brown 14·00 1·40
288 20 d. purple 24·00 50
289 30 d. yellow 23·00 50

(b) Charity stamps. Nos. 221/3.

290 **46** 25 p. + 0.25 green 35 25
291 50 p. + 0.50 sepia 35 15
292 1 d. + 0.50 red 1·40 45

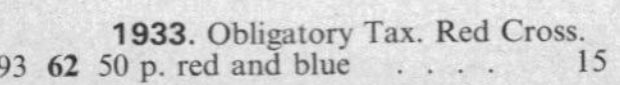

1933. Obligatory Tax. Red Cross.

293 **62** 50 p. red and blue 15 10

63 Osprey over R. Bosna

64 Athlete and Falcon (from sculpture by Krsinic)

1934. 20th Anniv of "Sokol" Games, Sarajevo.

294 **63** 75 p. + 25 p. green 6·25 4·50
295 1 d. 50 + 50 p. red 6·75 5·25
296 1 d. 75 + 25 p. brown 17·00 7·00

1934. 60th Anniv of Croat "Sokol" Games, Zagreb.

297 **64** 75 p. + 25 p. green 2·50 2·50
298 1 d. 50 + 50 p. red 3·75 5·00
299 1 d. 75 + 25 p. brown 10·00 6·00

65 Dubrovnik

69 Mostar Bridge

1934. Air.

300 **65** 50 p. purple 15 20
301 – 1 d. green 15 20
302 – 2 d. red 35 25
303 – 3 d. blue 1·25 40
304 **69** 10 d. orange 2·25 2·00

DESIGNS: 1 d. Lake of Bled; 2 d. Waterfall at Jajce; 3 d. Oplenats.

1934. King Alexander Mourning issue. With black margins.

305 **55** 25 p. black (postage) 10 10
306 50 p. green 10 10
307 75 p. green 10 10
308 1 d. red 10 10
309 1 d. 50 red 10 10
310 1 d. 75 red 10 10
311 3 d. blue 10 10
312 3 d. 50 p. blue 30 10
313 4 d. orange 30 10
314 5 d. violet 40 10
315 10 d. olive 2·10 10
316 15 d. brown 4·00 15
317 20 d. purple 7·00 15
318 30 d. red 4·00 40
319 – 3 d. blue (No. 303) (air) 3·75 2·00

70 King Peter II

71 King Alexander

1935.

320 **70** 25 p. black 10 10
321 50 p. orange 10 10
322 75 p. green 15 10
323 1 d. brown 15 10
324 1 d. 50 red 15 10
325 1 d. 75 red 30 10
325a 2 d. red 15 10
326 3 d. orange 15 10
327 3 d. 50 blue 50 10
328 4 d. green 1·10 10
329 4 d. blue 30 10
330 10 d. violet 90 10
331 15 d. brown 90 10
332 20 d. blue 2·75 25
333 30 d. pink 2·25 25

1935. 1st Anniv of King Alexander's Assassination.

334 **71** 75 p. green 20 25
335 1 d. 50 red 20 25
336 1 d. 75 brown 25 50
337 3 d. 50 blue 1·60 2·10
338 7 d. 50 red 1·00 2·10

72

73 Queen Marie

1935. Winter Relief Fund.

339 **72** 1 d. 50 + 1 d. brown 1·00 1·75
340 3 d. 50 + 1 d. 50 blue 2·10 2·75

1936. Child Welfare.

341 **73** 75 p. + 25 p. green 45 40
342 1 d. 50 + 50 p. red 45 40
343 1 d. 75 + 75 p. brown 1·10 75
344 3 d. 50 + 1 d. blue 1·60 1·10

74 Nicola Tesla

1936. 80th Birthday of Dr. Tesla (physicist).

345 **74** 75 p. brown and green 15 20
346 1 d. 75 black and blue 25 25

75 Prince Paul

76 Dr. V. Georgevitch

1936. Red Cross Fund.

347 **75** 75 p. + 50 p. green 10 30
348 1 d. 50 + 50 p. red 15 40

1936. Obligatory Tax. Jubilee of Serbian Red Cross.

349 **76** 50 p. brown 15 10

77 Princess Tomislav and Andrew

78 Oplenats

1937. Child Welfare. T **77** and similar horiz portrait.

350 – 25 p. + 25 p. brown 15 25
351 – 75 p. + 75 p. orange 35 50
352 **77** 1 d. 50 + 1 d. orange 65 50
353 2 d. + 1 d. purple 75 75

1937. Little Entente.

354 **78** 3 d. green 75 20
355 4 d. blue 75 30

80 St. Naum Convent, Lake Ochrid

83 Arms of Yugoslavia, Greece, Rumania and Turkey

1937. Air.

360 **80** 50 p. brown 15 10
361 – 1 d. green 15 10
362 – 2 d. blue 15 10
363 – 2 d. 50 red 25 15
364 **80** 5 d. violet 30 20
365 – 10 d. red 50 25
366 – 20 d. green 75 65
367 – 30 d. blue 1·40 1·10

DESIGNS—VERT: 1, 10 d. Rab (Arbe) Harbour. HORIZ: 2, 20 d. Sarajevo; 2 d. 50, 30 d. Laibach (Ljubljana).

1937. Balkan Entente.

368 **83** 3 d. green 55 15
369 4 d. blue 80 50

84

85

1938. Child Welfare.

370 **84** 50 p. + 50 p. brown 20 30
371 **85** 1 d. + 1 d. green 20 30
372 **84** 1 d. 50 + 1 d. 50 red 45 60
373 **85** 2 d. + 2 d. mauve 1·00 1·00

86 Searchlight Display and Parachute Tower

87 Entrance to Demir Kapija Cliff

1938. Int Aeronautical Exhibition, Belgrade, and Yugoslav Air Club Fund.

374 **86** 1 d. + 50 p. green 30 60
375 1 d. 50 + 1 d. red 1·00 75
376 2 d. + 1 d. mauve 2·25 1·50
377 3 d. + 1 d. blue 2·75 2·25

1938. Railway Employees' Hospital Fund.

378 **87** 1 d. + 1 d. green 40 45
379 – 1 d. 50 + 1 d. 50 red 1·10 95
380 – 2 d. + 2 d. mauve 2·00 2·10
381 – 3 d. + 3 d. blue 2·40 2·40

DESIGNS—HORIZ: 1 d. 50, Demir Kapija Hospital. VERT: 2 d. Runner carrying torch; 3 d. King Alexander.

90 Hurdling

1938. 9th Balkan Games.

382 – 50 p. + 50 p. orange 75 1·00
383 **90** 1 d. + 1 d. green 1·50 1·50
384 – 1 d. 50 + 1 d. 50 mauve 2·25 2·00
385 – 2 d. + 2 d. blue 3·00 3·00

DESIGNS—HORIZ: 1 d. 50, Pole-vaulting. VERT: 50 p. Runner; 2 d. Putting the shot.

91 Maiden of Kosovo (after P. Jovanovic)

1938. Red Cross.

386 **91** 50 p. multicoloured 15 10
386a 50 p. red and blue 20 10

1938. Child Welfare. Optd **SALVATE PARVULOS.**

387 **84** 50 p. + 50 p. brown 30 30
388 **85** 1 d. + 1 d. green 30 50
389 **84** 1 d. 50 + 1 d. 50 red 60 85
390 **85** 2 d. + 2 d. mauve 1·25 2·00

93 Mail Carrier

1939. Postal Centenary and Railway Benevolent Association Fund.

391 – 50 p. + 50 p. orange and brown 50 75
392 **93** 1 d. + 1 d. green and black 50 75
393 – 1 d. 50 + 1 d. 50 red 2·75 1·25
394 – 2 d. + 2 d. purple & violet 1·40 2·75
395 – 4 d. + 4 d. blue 2·25 4·50

DESIGNS: 50 p. Mounted postmen; 1 d. 50, Mail train; 2 d. Mail coach; 4 d. Lockheed 10 Electra mail plane.

94 Meal-time

95 Milosh Obilich

1939 Child Welfare.

396 **94** 1 d. + 1 d. green 40 75
397 – 1 d. 50 + 1 d. 50 red and brown 2·00 3·50
398 – 2 d. + 2 d. mauve & brown 1·25 2·40
399 – 4 d. + 4 d. blue 2·40 4·75

DESIGNS—HORIZ: 2 d. Young carpenter. VERT: 1 d. 50, Children playing on sands; 4 d. Children whispering.

1939. 550th Anniv of Battle of Kosovo.

400 – 1 d. + 1 d. green 1·00 1·25
401 **95** 1 d. 50 + 1 d. 50 red 1·00 1·25

DESIGN: 1 d. King Lazar.

96 Motor Cycle and Sidecar

97 Cadet Barquentine "Jadran"

1939. Fig 1st International Motor Races, Belgrade. Inscr "I. MEDUNARODNE AUTO I MOTO", etc.
402 **96** 50 p.+50 p. orange and brown . . . 1·10 85
403 – 1 d.+1 d. green and black . 1·40 1·25
404 – 1 d. 50+1 d. 50 red . . . 2·00 2·00
405 – 2 d.+2 d. blue . . . 3·00 3·00
DESIGNS—HORIZ: 1, 2 d. Racing cars. VERT: 1 d. 50, Motor cycle.

1939. King Peter's Birthday and Adriatic Guard Fund. Inscr "ZA JADRANSKU STRAZU".
406 **97** 50 p.+50 p. red . . . 65 60
407 – 1 d.+50 p. green . . . 85 60
408 – 1 d. 50+1 d. red . . . 1·50 1·25
409 – 2 d. +1 d. 50 blue . . . 2·40 2·00
DESIGNS: 1 d. Liner "King Alexander"; 1 d. 50, Freighter "Triglav"; 2 d. Destroyer "Dubrovnik".

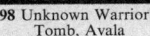

98 Unknown Warrior's Tomb, Avala
99 King Peter II

1939. 5th Death Anniv of King Alexander. War Invalids' Fund.
410 **98** 1 d.+50 p. green . . . 1·10 1·25
411 1 d. 50+1 d. red . . . 1·10 1·25
412 2 d.+1 d. 50 purple . . . 1·60 1·60
413 3 d.+2 d. blue . . . 2·50 2·50

1939.
414 **99** 25 p. black . . . 15 10
415 50 p. orange . . . 15 10
416 1 d. green . . . 15 10
417 1 d. 50 red . . . 15 10
418 2 d. mauve . . . 15 10
419 3 d. brown . . . 20 10
420 4 d. blue . . . 20 10
420a 5 d. blue . . . 20 20
420b 5 d. 50 violet . . . 50 10
421 6 d. blue . . . 90 10
422 8 d. brown . . . 90 10
423 12 d. violet . . . 1·90 10
424 16 d. purple . . . 2·00 20
425 20 d. blue . . . 2·00 20
426 30 d. pink . . . 6·00 35

100 Postman delivering Letters
101 Arrival of Thorval

1940. Belgrade Postal Employees' Fund. Inscr "ZA DOM P.T.T. ZVAN. I SLUZ".
427 **100** 50 p.+50 p. orge & brn . 50 1·10
428 – 1 d.+1 d. green & black . 50 1·10
429 – 1 d. 50+1 d. 50 red & brown 1·00 2·40
430 – 2 d.+2 d. mauve & purple 5·00 3·75
431 – 4 d.+4 d. blue and grey . 3·75 6·00
DESIGNS—VERT: 1 d. Postman collecting letters; 4 d. Telegraph linesman. HORIZ: 1 d. 50, Mail-van; 2 d. Mail-train.

1940. Zagreb Postal Employees' Fund. Inscr "ZA DOM P.T.T. CINOV U ZAGREBU".
432 **101** 50 p.+50 p. orange & brown 50 1·10
433 – 1 d.+1 d. green . . . 35 40
434 – 1 d. 50 +1 d. 50 red . . . 55 75
435 – 2 d.+2 d. red . . . 1·00 1·25
436 – 4 d.+2 d. blue . . . 1·50 1·75
DESIGNS—VERT (25½×37½mm): 1 d. King Tomislav enthroned; 1 d. 50, Death of Matthew Gubac. HORIZ (37×27mm): 2 d. Radich Brothers. (34×25mm): 4 d. Divisional map of Yugoslavia.

102 Winter Games

1940. Child Welfare. Inscr "ZA NASU DECU".
437 **102** 50 p.+50 p. orange and brown . . . 20 25
438 – 1 d.+1 d. green . . . 20 30
439 **102** 1 d. 50+1 d. 50 red and brown . . . 50 60
440 – 2 d.+2 d. mauve . . . 1·25 1·40
DESIGN—VERT: 1, 2 d. Children at seaside (Summer games).

103 Arms of Yugoslavia, Greece, Rumania and Turkey
104 Zagreb Cathedral and Junkers Ju 86

1940. Balkan Entente. Inscr "JUGOSLAVIJA" alternately at top in Cyrillic (I) or Roman (II) throughout the sheet.

			I.		II.	
441	**103**	3 d. blue	90	55	90	55
442		4 d. blue	90	55	90	55

1940 Air.
443 **104** 40 d. green . . . 1·25 2·00
444 – 50 d. blue . . . 1·75 2·50
DESIGN: 50 d. Suspension Bridge at Belgrade and Fokker F.VIIa/3m.

105 Obod, scene of early Press, 1493

1940. 5th Centenary of Invention of Printing Press by Johannes Gutenberg.
445 **105** 5 d. 50 green . . . 1·50 3·50

1940. Anti-T.B. Fund. Nos. 364/7 surch.
446 **80** 50 p.+50 p. on 5 d. violet 20 35
447 – 1 d.+1 d. on 10 d. red . . 20 35
448 – 1 d. 50+1 d. 50 on 20 d. green 80 1·10
449 – 2 d.+2 d. on 30 d. blue . 1·25 2·10

107 St. Peter's Cemetery, Ljubljana
109 Kamenita Gate, Zagreb

1941. Ljubljana War Veterans' Fund.
450 **107** 50 p.+50 p. green . . . 20 25
451 – 1 d.+1 d. red . . . 20 25
452 – 1 d. 50+1 d. 50 green . . 80 75
453 – 2 d.+2 d. lilac and blue . 1·25 2·10
DESIGNS—HORIZ: 2 d. War Memorial, Brezje. VERT: 1 d. National costumes; 1 d. 50, Memorial Chapel, Kajmakcalan.

1941. Philatelic Exhibitions. (a) 2nd Croatian Philatelic Exhibition, Zagreb.
454 **109** 1 d. 50+1 d. 50 brown . 50 1·50
455 – 4 d.+3 d. black . . . 50 1·50

(b) 1st Philatelic Exhibition, Slav Brod.
456 **109** 1 d. 50+1 d. 50 black . 7·50 18
457 – 4 d.+3 d. brown . . . 7·50 18·00
DESIGN: 4 d. (2) Old Cathedral, Zagreb.

NOTE. From 1941 until 1945 Yugoslavia ceased to exist as a stamp-issuing entity, except for the following series, Nos 468/81, which were issued by the exiled government for the use of the Yugoslav Merchant Navy working with the Allies.

110 King Peter II
112 Vodnik

1943. 2nd Anniv of Overthrow of Regency and King Peter's Assumption of Power.
468 **110** 2 d. blue . . . 15 15
469 3 d. grey . . . 15 20
470 5 d. red . . . 20 35
471 10 d. black . . . 30 70

1943. Red Cross Fund. Surch **CRVENI KRST + 12.50.**
472 **110** 2 d.+12 d. 50 blue . . . 70 1·25
473 3 d.+12 d. 50 grey . . . 70 1·25
474 5 d.+12 d. 50 red . . . 70 1·25
475 10 d.+12 d. 50 black . . . 70 1·25

1944. 25th Anniv of Formation of Yugoslavia. 19th-century Patriots and Writers.
476 **112** 1 d. black and red . . . 10
477 – 2 d. black and green . . . 15
478 – 3 d. blue and blue . . . 15
479 – 4 d. black and violet . . . 40
480 – 5 d. brown and purple . . 40
481 – 10 d. deep brown and brown 1·10
PORTRAITS: 2 d. Njegos; 3 d. Gaj; 4 d. Karadzic; 5 d. Strosmajer; 10 k. Karageorge.

C. DEMOCRATIC FEDERATION OF YUGOSLAVIA

I. REGIONAL ISSUES

Bosnia and Herzegovina

Currency: Croatian Kunas

1945: Mostar Issue. Stamps of Croatia surch **Demokratska Federativna Jugoslavija** and value.

(a) Pictorial Stamps of 1941–43.
R 1 10 k. on 25 b. red . . . 35 35
R 2 10 k. on 50 b. green . . . 20 20
R 3 10 k. on 2 k. red . . . 25 25
R 4 10 k. on 3 k. 50 brown . . . 60 60
R 5 40 k. on 1 k. green . . . 20 20
R 6 50 k. on 4 k. blue . . . 3·00 3·00
R 7 50 k. on 5 k. blue . . . 16·00 16·00
R 8 50 k. on 6 k. green . . . 3·00 3·00
R 9 50 k. on 7 k. red . . . 90·00 90·00
R10 50 k. on 8 k. brown . . . £110 £110
R11 50 k. on 10 k. violet . . . 60 60

(b) Famous Croats issue of 1943.
R12 30 k. on 1 k. blue . . . 25 25
R13 30 k. on 12 k. 50 purple . . . 20 20

(c) Boskovic issue of 1943.
R14 **28** 30 k. on 3 k. 50 blue . . . 25 25
R15 30 k. on 12 k. 50 purple . 1·50 1·50

(d) War Victims Charity Tax stamps of 1944.
R16 **34** 20 k. on 1 k. green . . . 15 15
R17 **35** 20 k. on 2 k. red . . . 25 25
R18 20 k. on 5 k. green . . . 25 25
R19 20 k. on 10 k. blue . . . 25 25
R20 20 k. on 20 k. brown . . . 70 70

Croatia

Currency: Kunas

DEMOKRATSKA FEDERATIVNA
★ 20 KUNA
JUGOSLAVIJA
(R 2)

1945. Split issue. Stamps of Croatia 1941–43 surch as Type R **2**.
R21 10 k. on 25 b. red . . . 10 10
R22 10 k. on 50 b. green . . . 10 10
R23 10 k. on 75 b. green . . . 10 10
R24 10 k. on 1 k. green . . . 10 10
R25 20 k. on 2 k. red . . . 10 10
R26 20 k. on 3 k. brown . . . 15 15
R27 20 k. on 3 k. 50 brown . . . 10 10
R28 20 k. on 4 k. blue . . . 10 10
R29 20 k. on 5 k. blue . . . 15 15
R30 20 k. on 6 k. green . . . 8·50 8·50
R31 30 k. on 7 k. red . . . 10 10
R32 30 k. on 8 k. brown . . . 9·25 9·25
R33 30 k. on 10 k. violet . . . 10 10
R34 30 k. on 12 k. 50 black . . . 10 10
R35 40 k. on 20 k. brown . . . 15 15
R36 40 k. on 30 k. brown . . . 20 20
R37 50 k. on 50 k. green . . . 15 15

1945. Zagreb issue. Stamps of Croatia, 1941–43, surch **DEMOKRATISKA FEDERATIVNA JUGOSLAVIJA KN**, value and star.
R38 20 k. on 5 k. blue . . . 15 15
R39 40 k. on 1 k. green . . . 10 10
R40 60 k. on 3 k. 50 brown . . . 10 10
R41 80 k. on 2 k. red . . . 10 10
R42 160 k. on 50 b. green . . . 15 15
R43 200 k. on 12 k. 50 black . . . 25 20
R44 400 k. on 25 b. red . . . 20 20

Montenegro

Currency: Italian Lire.

Демократска ★
Федеративна
Југославија
Лира 3.– Лира 3.–
(R 4)

1945. Cetinje issue. Stamps of Italian Occupation surch with Type R **4**. (a) National Poem Issue of 1943.
R50 1 l. on 10 c. green . . . 65 80
R51 2 l. on 25 c. green . . . 40 50
R52 3 l. on 50 c. mauve . . . 40 50
R53 5 l. on 1 l. 25 blue . . . 40 50
R54 10 l. on 15 c. brown . . . 80 1·00
R55 15 l. on 20 c. orange . . . 80 1·00
R56 20 l. on 2 l. green . . . 80 1·00

(b) Air stamps of 1943, for use as ordinary postage stamps.
R57 3 l. on 50 c. brown . . . 3·00 3·00
R58 6 l. on 1 l. blue . . . 3·00 3·00
R59 10 l. on 2 l. red . . . 3·00 3·00
R60 20 l. on 5 l. green . . . 3·00 3·00

Serbia

Currency: Hungarian Filler

1944. Senta issue. Various stamps of Hungary optd with a large star, **8.X.1944** and "Yugoslavia" in Cyrillic characters.
R63 1 f. grey . . . 6·25 4·75
R64 2 f. red . . . 6·25 4·75
R65 3 f. blue . . . 6·25 4·75
R66 4 f. brown . . . 6·25 4·75
R67 5 f. red . . . 6·25 4·75
R68 8 f. green . . . 6·25 4·75
R69 10 f. brown . . . £120 £120
R70 24 f. brown . . . £150 £150
R71 24 f. purple . . . 9·25 9·25
R72 30 f. red . . . £120 £120

Slovenia

Currencies: Italian (Ljubljana)
German (Maribor)
Hungarian (Murska Sobota)

JUGOSLAVIJA
SLOVENIJA
9*5
1945
JUGOSLAVIJA
(R 5)

1945. Ljubljana issue. Pictorial stamps of German Occupation, 1945, optd as Type R **5**.
R74 5 c. brown . . . 10 10
R75 10 c. orange . . . 10 10
R76 20 c. brown . . . 10 10
R77 25 c. green . . . 10 10
R78 50 c. violet . . . 10 10
R79 75 c. red . . . 40 40
R80 1 l. green . . . 15 10
R81 1 l. 25 blue . . . 25 20
R82 1 l. 50 green . . . 10 10
R83 2 l. blue . . . 20 15
R84 2 l. 50 brown . . . 10 10
R85 3 l. mauve . . . 35 25
R86 5 l. brown . . . 40 35
R87 10 l. green . . . 30 35
R88 20 l. blue . . . 3·00 3·00
R89 30 l. red . . . 20·00 20·00

1945. Maribor issue. Hitler stamps of Germany, 1941–44, optd **SLOVENIJA 9.5.1945 JUGOSLAVIJA** and star.
R 90 **173** 1 pf. grey . . . 2·75 2·75
R 91 3 pf. brown . . . 25 25
R 92 4 pf. grey . . . 2·00 2·00
R 93 5 pf. green . . . 1·75 1·75
R 94 6 pf. violet . . . 25 15
R 95 8 pf. red . . . 50 50
R 96 10 pf. brown (No. 775) . 1·75 1·75
R 97 12 pf. red (No. 776) . . 15 15
R 98 15 pf. brown . . . 3·75 3·75
R 99 20 pf. blue . . . 2·50 2·50
R100 24 pf. brown . . . 2·00 2·00
R101 25 pf. blue . . . 6·00 6·00
R102 30 pf. green . . . 50 50
R103 40 pf. mauve . . . 50 50
R104 **225** 42 pf. green . . . 40 40
R105 **173** 50 pf. green . . . 1·25 1·25
R106 60 pf. brown . . . 50 50
R107 80 pf. blue . . . 1·00 1·00

1945. Murska Sobota issue. Various stamps of Hungary optd as Nos. R90/107.
R108 1 f. grey . . . 5·00 5·00
R109 4 f. brown . . . 35 35
R110 5 f. red . . . 4·50 4·50
R111 10 f. brown . . . 35 35
R112 18 f. black . . . 35 35
R113 20 f. brown . . . 35 35
R114 30 f. red . . . 35 35
R115 30 f. red . . . 35 35
R116 50 f. blue . . . 7·50 7·50
R117 70 f. brown . . . 7·50 7·50
R118 80 f. brown . . . 42·00 42·00
R119 1 p. green . . . 6·25 6·25

II. GENERAL ISSUES

100 paras = 1 dinar

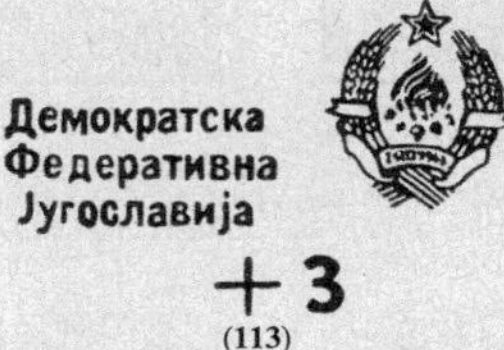
Демократска
Федеративна
Југославија
+3
(113)

1944. Stamps of Serbia, 1942, surch as T **113**.
482 – 3 d.+2 d. pink (No. 64) . . 10 20
485 – 4 d.+21 d. blue (No. 65) . . 10 20
483 – 7 d.+3 d. green (No. 66) . . 10 20

114 Marshal Tito
115 Chapel at Prohor Pcinjski

1945.

491 **114** 25 p. green 35 15
492 50 p. green 35 10
493 1 d. red 4·50 40
494 2 d. red 35 10
495 4 d. blue 75 10
487 5 d. green 10 10
496 6 d. violet 80 10
497 9 d. brown 1·40 20
488 10 d. red 10 10
498 20 d. yellow 5·00 1·40
489 25 d. violet 15 15
490 30 d. blue 25 15

1945. 1st Anniv of Anti-Fascist Chamber of Deputies, Macedonia.

499 **115** 2 d. red 70 25

116 Partisans

1945. Red Cross Fund.

500 **116** 1 d.+4 d. blue 90 80
501 – 2 d.+6 d. red 90 80

DESIGN—VERT: 2 d.+6 d. Child's head.

119 Partisans **120** Marshal Tito

1945. Partisans.

502 **119** 50 p. brown 10 10
503 1 d. green 15 10
504 – 1 d. 50 brown 20 10
505 **120** 2 d. red 15 10
506 – 2 d. 50 red 60 10
507 – 3 d. brown 1·00 10
508 – 3 d. red 60 10
509 **120** 4 d. blue 30 10
510 – 5 d. green 1·00 10
511 – 5 d. blue 1·75 10
512 – 6 d. black 60 10
513 – 8 d. yellow 65 10
514 – 9 d. mauve 55 10
515 – 12 d. blue 1·00 10
516 **119** 16 d. blue 1·00 10
517 – 20 d. red 2·25 20

DESIGNS—As Type **119**: 1 d. 50, 12, 20 d. Riflemen. VERT: 3, 5 d. Town of Jajce inscr "29-XI-1943". HORIZ: 2 d. 50, 6, 8, 9 d. Girl with flag.

122 Russian and Yugoslav Flags

1945. 1st Anniv of Liberation of Belgrade.

518 **122** 2 d. +5 d. multicoloured 70 40

124 "Industry and Agriculture" **126**

1945. Meeting of the Constituent Assembly. Inscr in Cyrillic at top and Roman characters at foot (I) or vice-versa (II).

			I.		II.	
519	**124**	2 d. red	3·00	3·00	3·00	3·00
520		4 d. blue	3·00	3·00	3·00	3·00
521		6 d. green	3·00	3·00	3·00	3·00
522		9 d. orange	3·00	3·00	3·00	3·00
523		16 d. blue	3·00	3·00	3·00	3·00
524		20 d. brown	3·00	3·00	3·00	3·00

D. FEDERAL PEOPLE'S REPUBLIC

100 paras = 1 dinar

1946. Type of 1945 (Girl with flag), surch.

525 2 d. 50 on 6 d. red 60 10
526 8 d. on 9 d. orange 1·00 10

1946 1st Anniv of Victory over Fascism. Star in red.

527 **126** 1 d. 50 orange 40 50
528 2 d. 50 red 60 70
529 5 d. blue 1·75 1·50

127 Symbolic of Communications **128** Railway Construction

1946. Postal Congress.

530 **127** 1 d. 50+1 d. green 4·50 4·50
531 2 d. 50+1 d. 50 red 4·50 4·50
532 5 d.+2 d. blue 4·50 4·50
533 8 d.+3 d. 50 brown 4·50 4·50

1946. Volunteer Workers' Railway Reconstruction Fund.

534 **128** 50 p.+50 p. brown, red and blue 3·50 2·00
535 1 d. 50+1 d. green, blue and red 3·50 1·75
536 2 d. 50+2 d. lilac, red and blue 3·50 1·75
537 5 d.+3 d. grey, red and bl 3·50 2·25

129 Svetozar Markovic **130** Theatre in Sofia

1946. Birth Centenary of S. Markovic (socialist writer).

538 **129** 1 d. 50 green 75 40
539 2 d. 50 purple 75 45

1948. Slav Congress.

540 **130** ½ d. brown 10 10
541 – 1 d. green 10 10
542 – 1½ d. red 15 10
543 – 2½ d. orange 20 10
544 – 5 d. blue 75 60

DESIGNS—HORIZ: 1 d. Charles Bridge and Hradcany, Prague. VERT: 1½ d. Sigismund Monument, Warsaw; 2½ d. Victory Monument, Belgrade; 5 d. Kremlin Tower, Moscow.

131 Roofless Houses **132** Ilyushin Il-4 DB-3 over Kalimegdan Terrace, Belgrade

1947. Obligatory Tax. Red Cross.

545 **131** 50 p. brown 15 10

1947. Air. Inscr in Cyrillic at top and Roman characters at foot (I) or vice versa (II).

			I.		II.	
546	**132**	50 p. olive & lake	15	15	15	15
547	–	1 d. red & olive	25	20	25	20
548	**132**	2 d. blue & blk	40	25	40	25
549	–	5 d. grn & grey	45	30	45	30
550	–	10 d. brn & sep	55	40	55	40
551	**132**	20 d. blue & ol	1·00	65	1·00	65

DESIGN: 1, 5, 20 d. Ilyushin Il-4 DB-3 over Dubrovnik.

133 "Wreath of Mountains" **134** P. P. Njegos

1947. Centenary of Publication of "Wreath of Mountains".

552 **133** 1½ d. black and green 15 10
553 **134** 2 d. 50 red and buff 20 15
554 **133** 5 d. black and blue 35 20

135 Girl Athlete, Star and Flags **137** Gymnast

1947. Federal Sports Meeting.

555 – 1 d. 50 brown 15 10
556 **135** 2 d. 50 red 20 15
557 – 4 d. blue 50 40

DESIGNS—VERT: 1 d. 50, Physical training groups. HORIZ: 4 d. Parade of athletes.

1947. Balkan Games.

558 **137** 1 d. 50+50 p. green 15 10
559 2 d. 50+50 p. red 30 20
560 4 d.+50 p. blue 40 35

138 Star and Map of Julian Province **139** Railway Construction

1947. Annexation of Julian Province to Yugoslavia.

561 **138** 2 d. 50 red and blue 15 10
562 5 d. brown and green 15 10

1947. Juvenile Labour Organizations' Relief Fund.

563 **139** 1 d.+50 p. orange 30 15
564 1 d. 50+1 d. green 35 25
565 2 d. 50+1 d. 50 red 60 30
566 5 d.+2 d. blue 1·25 70

140 Music Book and Fiddle **141** Vuk Karadzic (poet)

1947. Centenary of Serbian Literature.

567 **140** 1 d. 50 green 10 10
568 **141** 2 d. 50 red 15 15
569 **140** 5 d. blue 20 20

142 "B.C.G. Vaccine Defeating Tuberculosis" **143** "Illness and Recovery"

144 "Fight against Tuberculosis" **145** Map of Yugoslavia and Symbols of Industry and Agriculture

1948. Anti-T.B. Fund.

570 **142** 1 d. 50+1 d. green & red 10 10
571 **143** 2 d. 50+2 d. green & red 15 15
572 **144** 5 d.+3 d. blue and red 25 20

1948. International Fair, Zagreb.

573 **145** 1 d. 50 green, blue and red 10 10
574 2 d. 50 purple, blue and red 10 10
575 5 d. indigo, blue and red 15 10

146 Flag-bearers **147** Djura Danicic

1948. 5th Yugoslav Communist Party Congress, Belgrade.

576 **146** 2 d. green 20 15
577b 3 d. red and lake 20 15
578a 10 d. blue 45 45

1948. 80th Anniv of Yugoslav Academy.

579 **147** 1 d. 50+50 p. green 15 15
580 – 2 d. 50+1 d. red 25 15
581 – 4 d.+2 d. blue 35 30

PORTRAITS: 2 d. 50, Franjo Racki; 4 d. Josip J. Strosmajer.

148 Danube Bridge and "Krajina" (former royal yacht)

1948. Danube Conference.

582 **148** 2 d. green 2·50 2·50
583 3 d. red 3·75 3·75
584 5 d. blue 4·50 4·50
585 10 d. brown 8·50 8·50

149 Laurence Kosir **150** Kosir and his Birthplace

1948. 80th Death Anniv of Laurence Kosir ("idealogical creator of first postage stamp").

586 **149** 3 d. purple (postage) 15 10
587 5 d. blue 15 15
588 10 d. orange 20 10
589 12 d. green 35 25
590 **150** 15 d. mauve (air) 90 45

151 Putting the Shot **152** **153** Arms of Montenegro

1948. Projected Balkan Games.

591 **151** 2 d.+1 d. green 30 20
592 – 3 d.+1 d. red 30 20
593 – 5 d.+2 d. blue 50 40

DESIGNS: 3 d. Girl hurdler; 5 d. Pole-vaulting.

1948. Obligatory Tax. Red Cross.

594 **152** 50 p. red and blue 15 10

1948. 5th Anniv of Republic.

595 – 3 d. blue (Serbia) 40 30
596 – 3 d. red (Croatia) 40 30
597 – 3 d. orange (Slovenia) 40 30
598 – 3 d. green (Bosnia and Herzegovina) 40 30
599 – 3 d. mauve (Macedonia) 40 30
600 **153** 3 d. black 40 30
601 – 10 d. red (Yugoslavia) 2·00 2·00

No. 601 is larger 24½×34½ mm.

154 F. Presern **155** Ski-jump, Planica

1949. Death Centenary of Franc Presern (author).

602 **154** 3 d. blue 20 15
603 5 d. orange 25 20
604 10 d. sepia 1·50 35

1949. Ski-jumping Competition, Planica.

605 **154** 3 d. blue 20 12
606 – 12 d. slate (Ski-jumper) 1·25 65

156 Soldiers **158** Globe, Letters and Forms of Transport

1949. 5th Anniv of Liberation of Macedonia.

(a) Postage

607 **156** 3 d. red 50 40
608 – 5 d. blue 1·25 65
608a – 12 d. brown 2·75 2·50

DESIGNS: 5 d. Industrial and agricultural workers; 12 d. Arms and flags of Yugoslavia and Macedonia.

(b) Air. Optd with Lisunov Li-2 airplane and **AVIONSKA POSTA**.

609 **156** 3 d. red 2·50 2·50
610 – 5 d. blue (No. 608) 2·50 2·50
610a – 12 d. brown (No. 608a) 2·50 2·50

1949. 75th Anniv of U.P.U.

611 **158** 3 d. red 2·75 2·75
612 – 5 d. blue 45 45
613 **158** 12 d. brown 45 45

DESIGN—HORIZ: 5 d. Airplane, train and mail coach.

1949. Surch with bold figures and bars.

614 O **130** 3 d. on 8 d. brown 40 10
615 3 d. on 12 d. violet 50 15

160 Nurse and Child

1949. Obligatory Tax. Red Cross.
616 **180** 50 p. brown and red . . . 15 10

ФНР ЈУГОСЛАВИЈА

D3
FNR JUGOSLAVIJA
(161)

F N R
D10
JUGOSLAVIJA
(162)

1949. Surch with T **161** or **162.**
617 – 3 d. on 8 d. yellow (No. 513) 50 10
618 – 10 d. on 20 d. red (No. 517) 65 10

FNR JUGOSLAVIJA
(163)

ФНР

F N R
(164)

F N R JUGOSLAVIJA
(165)

1949. Optd with T **163** on 2 d., **164** on 3 d. and 5 d., or **165** on others.
619 **119** 50 p. olive 10 10
620 1 d. green 10 10
621 1 d. orange 30 10
622 **120** 2 d. red 15 10
623 2 d. green 30 10
624 – 3 d. red (No. 508) . . . 15 10
625 – 3 d. pink 30 10
626 – 5 d. blue (No. 511) . . . 40 20
627 – 5 d. blue 50 10
628 – 12 d. violet (No. 515) . . 35 10
629 **119** 16 d. blue . . . . 1·25 40
630 20 d. red 85 15

166 Steam Locomotive of 1849

167 Surveying

1949. Centenary of National Railways.
631 **166** 2 d. green . . . . 1·25 35
632 – 3 d. red . . . . 1·25 35
633 – 5 d. blue . . . . 5·00 65
633a – 10 d. orange . . . . . 23·00 8·00
DESIGNS: 3 d. Modern steam locomotive; 5 d. Diesel train; 10 d. Electric locomotive.

1950. Completion of Belgrade–Zagreb Road.
634 **167** 2 d. green 40 15
635 – 3 d. pink 25 15
636 – 5 d. blue . . . . 1·00 70
DESIGNS: 3 d. Map, road and car; 5 d. Youth, road and flag.

168 Marshal Tito

169 Child Eating

1950. May Day.
637 **168** 3 d. red . . . . 2·10 40
638 5 d. blue . . . . 2·10 40
639 10 d. brown . . . . . . 35·00 21·00
640 12 d. black . . . . . . 2·10 2·00

1950. Child Welfare.
641 **169** 3 d. red 35 10

170 Launching Model Glider

171 Chessboard and Bishop

1950. 3rd Aeronautical Meeting.
642 **170** 2 d. green 80 90
643 – 3 d. red 85 90
644 – 5 d. violet . . . . 2·10 90
645 – 10 d. brown . . . . . . 2·25 2·10
646 – 20 d. blue . . . . 15·00 15·00
DESIGNS—VERT: 3 d. Glider in flight; 5 d. Parachutists landing; 10 d. Woman pilot; 20 d. Glider on water.

1950. 9th Chess Olympiad, Dubrovnik.
647 **171** 2 d. red 90 40
648 – 3 d. bistre, sepia and drab 90 30
649 – 5 d. multicoloured . . . 1·75 50
650 – 10 d. multicoloured . . . 2·40 1·25
651 – 20 d. yellow and blue . . 30·00 20·00
DESIGNS—VERT: 3 d. Rook and flags; 5 d. Chessboard showing position in 1924 Capablanca v. Lasker game, pieces and globe; 10 d. Chequered globe and map; 20 d. Knights and flags.

172 Girl Harvester

173 Train and Map

1950.
652 – 50 p. brown 10 10
653 – 1 d. green 20 10
705 – 1 d. grey 20 10
654 **172** 2 d. orange 20 10
718 2 d. red . . . . 3·00 15
655 – 3 d. red 20 10
656 – 5 d. blue . . . . 1·25 10
719 – 5 d. orange . . . . . . 1·40 15
657 – 7 d. grey . . . . 1·25 10
720 – 8 d. blue . . . . 4·50 25
658 – 10 d. brown . . . . . . 1·50 10
721 – 10 d. green . . . . . . 7·50 15
722 – 12 d. purple . . . . . . 45·00 25
723 – 15 d. red . . . . 18·00 10
660 – 16 d. blue . . . . . . 3·50 15
723a – 17 d. purple . . . . . . 6·00 20
661 – 20 d. olive . . . . . . 3·50 15
710 – 20 d. purple . . . . . . 7·50 10
711a **172** 25 d. bistre . . . . . . 13·50 10
662 – 30 d. brown . . . . . . 9·00 35
712 – 30 d. blue . . . . 1·75 10
713 – 35 d. brown . . . . . . 2·50 10
662a – 50 d. violet . . . . . . 45·00 16·00
714 – 50 d. green . . . . . . 2·00 10
715 – 75 d. violet . . . . . . 3·00 10
716 – 100 d. sepia . . . . . 10·50 20
DESIGNS—VERT: 50, 100 d. Metallurgy; 1 d. Electrical supply engineer; 3, 35 d. Man and woman with wheelbarrow; 5 d. Fishing; 7, 8 d. Mining; 10 d. Apple-picking; 12, 75 d. Lumbering; 14, 15, 16 d. Picking sunflowers; 17, 20 d. Woman and farm animals; 30 d. Girl printer; 50 d. Dockers unloading cargo.

1950. Zagreb Exhibition.
663 **173** 3 d. red . . . . 1·25 50

174 Girl in National Costume

175 Galleon

1950. Obligatory Tax. Red Cross
664 **174** 50 p. green and red . . . 15 10

1950. Navy Day.
665 **175** 2 d. purple 30 15
666 – 3 d. brown 30 10
667 – 5 d. green . . . . 1·40 10
668 – 10 d. blue 80 15
669 – 12 d. grey . . . . 1·90 50
670 – 20 d. red . . . . 4·25 2·00
DESIGNS: 3 d. Partisan patrol boat; 5 d. Freighter discharging cargo; 10 d. "Zagreb" (freighter) and globe; 12 d. Yachts; 20 d. Sailor, gun and "Golesnica" (torpedo boat).

176 Patriots of 1941

177 Stane-Rozman

1951. 10th Anniv of Revolt against Pact with Axis.
671 **176** 3 d. lake and red . . . . 3·75 2·25

1951. 10th Anniv of Partisan Rising in Slovenia.
672 **177** 3 d. brown 50 25
673 – 5 d. blue (Boy courier) . 75 35

178 Children Painting

1951. International Children's Day.
674 **178** 3 d. red . . . . 1·10 25

179 "Iron Gates", Danube

181 Z. Jovanovic

1951. Air.
675 **179** 1 d. orange 15 10
676 – 2 d. green 25 10
677 – 3 d. red 25 10
677a – 5 d. brown 30 10
678 – 6 d. blue . . . . 4·50 4·50
679 – 10 d. brown 50 10
680 – 20 d. grey 75 10
681 – 30 d. red . . . . 2·50 10
682 – 50 d. violet . . . . . . 3·75 10
683 – 100 d. grey . . . . . . 60·00 5·00
683a – 100 d. green . . . . . . 1·40 15
683b – 200 d. red . . . . 1·75 25
683c – 500 d. blue . . . . . . 7·00 1·25
DESIGNS: (all show airplane)—As T **179**: 2, 5 d. Plitvice Cascades; 3, 100 d. (green) Gozd-Martuljak (mountain village); 6, 200 d. Old Bridge, Mostar; 10 d. Ohrid; 20 d. Kotor Bay; 30 d. Dubrovnik; 50 d. Bled. 40 × 27 mm: 100 d. (grey), 500 d. Belgrade.

1951. Air. Zagreb Philatelic Exn., No. 678 in new colour optd **ZEFIZ 1951.**
684 6 d. green 90 70

1951. 10th Anniv of Serbian Insurrection.
685 **181** 3 d. brown 75 40
686 – 5 d. blue . . . . 1·10 65
DESIGN—HORIZ: 5 d. Armed insurgents.

183 Mt. Kopaonik

184 S. Kovacevic

1951. Air. International Mountaineering Assn Meeting, Bled. Inscr "UIAA-1951".
687 **183** 3 d. mauve . . . . 1·60 1·60
688 – 5 d. blue . . . . 1·60 1·60
689 – 20 d. green . . . . 95·00 65·00
DESIGNS: 5 d. Mt. Triglav; 20 d. Mt. Kalnik.

1951. 10th Anniv of Montenegrin Insurrection.
690 **184** 3 d. red . . . . 1·00 75
691 – 5 d. blue . . . . 1·75 1·00
DESIGN—HORIZ: 5 d. Partisan and mountains.

185 M. Oreskovic Statue

186 S. Solaj

1951. 10th Anniv of Croatian Insurrection.
692 **185** 3 d. red 75 35
693 – 5 d. green . . . . 1·25 65
DESIGN—VERT: 5 d. Statue: "Transport of a Wounded Man".

1951. 10th Anniv of Insurrection of Bosnia and Herzegovina.
694 **186** 3 d. red 90 40
695 – 5 d. blue . . . . 1·25 65
DESIGN—VERT: 5 d. Group of insurgents.

187 Parachutists Landing

189 P. Trubar (author)

1951. Air. 1st World Parachute Jumping Championship, Bled.
696 **187** 6 d. lake . . . . 5·00 2·00

As No. 682 in new colour optd **I SVETSKO TAKMICENJE PADOBRANACA 1951.**
697 50 d. blue . . . . 80·00 45·00

1951. Cultural Anniversaries.
698 **189** 10 d. black 40 25
699 – 12 d. orange 40 25
700 – 20 d. violet . . . . 5·75 4·75
PORTRAITS: 12 d. M Marulic (poet); 20 d. Tsar Stefan Dusan.

190 National Products

191 Hoisting the Flag

1951. Zagreb International Fair.
701 **190** 3 p. yellow, red & blue . 1·10 35

1951. Obligatory Tax. Red Cross.
702 **191** 50 p. blue and red 15 10

192 M. Acev

193 P. P. Njegos

1951. 10th Anniv of Macedonian Insurrection.
703 **192** 3 d. mauve 75 40
704 – 5 d. violet . . . . 1·75 55
DESIGN—HORIZ: 5 d. War Victims' Monument, Skopje.

1951. Death Centenary of Njegos (poet).
724 **193** 15 d. purple . . . . . . 1·75 55

194 Soldier and Badge

195 Marshal Tito

1951. Army Day.
725 **194** 15 d. red (postage) . . . 60 10
726 **195** 150 d. blue (air) . . . . 15·00 9·00

196 Marshal Tito **197**

1952. Marshal Tito's 60th Birthday.
727 **196** 15 d. brown . . . . . . 1·00 1·00
728 **197** 28 d. lake . . . . 1·75 1·75
729 – 50 d. green . . . . 45·00 42·00
DESIGN—As T **196**: 50 d. Statue of Marshal Tito.

198

199 Gymnastics

1952. Children's Week.
730 **198** 15 d. red . . . . 7·50 40

1952 15th Olympic Games, Helsinki. Inscr "XV OLIMPIJADA 1952".
731 **199** 5 d. brown on buff . . . 40 25
732 – 10 d. brown on yellow . . 40 25
733 – 15 d. brown on pink . . . 90 30
734 – 28 d. brown on flesh . . . 1·25 90
735 – 50 d. green on green . . . 6·00 3·00
736 – 100 d. brown on mauve . 60·00 23·00
DESIGNS: 10 d. Running; 15 d. Swimming; 28 d. Boxing; 50 d. Basketball; 100 d. Football.

200 "Fishing Boat" (from relief by Krsinic)

200a Belgrade (XVI Cent)

1952. Navy Day. Views. Inscr "1952".
737 – 15 d. purple . . . . 1·75 60
738 **200** 28 d. brown . . . . 3·25 90
739 – 50 d. black . . . . 23·00 19·00
DESIGNS: 15 d. Split, Dalmatia; 50 d. Sveti Stefan, Montenegro.

1952. Philatelic Exhibition, Belgrade.
739a **200a** 15 d. purple . . . . . . 9·00 9·00
No. 739a was only sold at the Exhibition at 35 d. (20 d. entrance fee).

201

202 Workers in Procession (from fresco by S. Pengov)

1952. Obligatory Tax. Red Cross.
740 **201** 50 p. red, grey & black . . 30 10

1952. 6th Yugoslavia Communist Party Congress.
741 **202** 15 d. brown . . . . 1·50 1·10
742 15 d. turquoise . . . . . 1·50 1·10
743 15 d. brown . . . . 1·50 1·10
744 15 d. blue . . . . 1·50 1·10

203 N. Tesla

204 Fresco, Sopocani Monastery

1953. 10th Death Anniv of Tesla (inventor).
745 **203** 15 d. lake . . . . 1·25 15
746 30 d. blue . . . . 4·00 40

1953. United Nations Commemoration.
747 **203** 15 d. green . . . . 1·50 60
748 – 30 d. blue . . . . 3·00 60
749 – 50 d. lake . . . . 18·00 4·75
DESIGNS—VERT: 30 d. Fresco, St. Panteleimon Church, Nerezim, Skopje; 50 d. Fresco, St. Dimitri Church, Pec.

205

1953. Adriatic Car and Motor-cycle Rally.
750 **205** 15 d. lake and pink . . . 25 10
751 – 30 d. deep blue and blue . . 70 10
752 – 50 d. brown and yellow . . 1·60 10
753 – 70 d. green & turquoise . . 5·00 80
DESIGNS—HORIZ: 30 d. Motor-cyclist and coastline; 50 d. Racing car and flags; 70 d. Saloon car descending mountain roadway.

206 Marshal Tito

207

1953. Marshal Tito Commemoration.
754 **206** 50 d. violet . . . . 9·00 1·25

1953. 38th Esperanto Congress, Zagreb.
755 **207** 15 d. grn & blk (postage) . 4·50 1·50
756 300 d. green & blue (air) . £300 £275

208 "Insurrection" (from painting by B. Lazevski)

209

1953. 50th Anniv of Macedonian Insurrection.
757 **208** 15 d. purple . . . . . . 1·00 75
758 – 30 d. green . . . . 3·25 2·00
DESIGN: 30 d. N. Karev (revolutionary).

1953. 10th Anniv of Liberation of Istria and Slovene Coast.
759 **209** 15 d. green . . . . 12·50 1·75

210 B. Radicevic

211 Blood-transfusion

1953. Death Centenary of Radicevic (poet).
760 **210** 15 d. purple . . . . . . 6·00 1·00

1953. Obligatory Tax. Red Cross.
761 **211** 2 d. red and purple . . . 35 35

212 Jajce

213 European Souslik

1953. 10th Anniv of 1st Republican Legislative Assembly.
762 **212** 15 d. green . . . . 1·50 45
763 – 30 d. red . . . . 2·00 1·00
764 – 50 d. sepia . . . . 11·50 9·00
DESIGNS: 30 d. Assembly Building; 50 d. Marshal Tito addressing assembly.

1954. Animals.
765 **213** 2 d. slate, buff and green 20 10
766 – 5 d. brown and green . . 35 15
767 – 10 d. brown and slate . . 60 25
768 – 15 d. brown and blue . . 80 30
769 – 17 d. sepia and purple . . 1·40 30
770 – 25 d. yellow, blue & vio . 2·50 30
771 – 30 d. sepia and blue . . 4·50 35
772 – 35 d. black and brown . 6·00 90
773 – 50 d. brown and bronze . 15·00 1·75
774 – 65 d. black and lake . . 21·00 12·00
775 – 70 d. brown and turq . . 18·00 12·00
776 – 100 d. black and blue . . 60·00 32·00
DESIGNS—HORIZ: 5 d. Lynx; 10 d. Red deer; 15 d. Brown bear; 17 d. Chamois; 25 d. Eastern white pelican. VERT: 30 d. Lammergeier; 35 d. "Procerus gigas" (black beetle); 50 d. "Callimenius microgaster" (grasshopper); 65 d. Black Dalmatian lizard; 70 d. Blind cave-dwelling salamander; 100 d. Trout.

214 Ljubljana (XVII Cent)

1954. Philatelic Exhibition, Ljubljana.
777 **214** 15 d. brown, grn & blk . 15·00 11·00
No. 777 was only sold at the Exhibition at 35 d. (20 d. entrance fee).

215 Cannon, 1804

1954. 150th Anniv of Serbian Insurrection. Multicoloured.
778 15 d. Serbian flag . . . . . . 1·25 40
779 30 d. Type **215** . . . . . . 2·00 75
780 50 d. Seal of insurgents' council 3·75 90
781 70 d. Karageorge . . . . . 35·00 10·00

215a

216

1954. Children's Week.
781a **215a** 2 d. red 35 60

1954. Obligatory Tax. Red Cross.
782 **216** 2 d. red and green 20 10

217 V. Lisinski (composer)

218 "A Midsummer Night's Dream" (Shakespeare)

1954. Cultural Anniversaries.
783 **217** 15 d. green . . . . 3·00 45
784 – 30 d. brown . . . . 2·25 1·00
785 – 50 d. purple . . . . 2·50 1·60
786 – 70 d. blue . . . . 5·00 3·00
787 – 100 d. violet . . . . . . 22·00 18·00
PORTRAITS—VERT: 30 d. A. Kacic-Miosic (writer); 50 d. J. Vega (mathematician); 70 d. Z. J. Jovanovic (poet); 100 d. F. Visnjic (poet and musician).
See also Nos. 975/80.

1955. Dubrovnik Festival.
788 – 15 d. lake . . . . 1·00 35
789 **218** 30 d. blue . . . . 3·50 1·10
DESIGN—VERT: 15 d. Scene from "Robinja" by Hanibal Lucic.

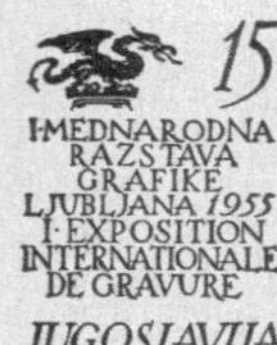

219

220

1955. 1st Int Exn of Engraving, Ljubljana.
790 **219** 15 d. brown and green on grey . . . . 3·75 75

1955. 2nd World Congress of the Deaf and Dumb.
791 **220** 15 d. lake . . . . 1·90 35

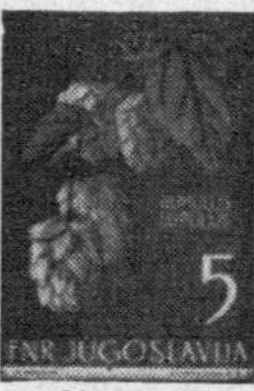

221 Hops

222 Laughing Girl

1955. Vert floral designs as T **221**.
792 5 d. green & brown (T **221**) . . 15 10
793 10 d. purple, green & buff . . 15 10
794 15 d. multicoloured 20 10
795 17 d. buff, green and lake . . 30 15
796 25 d. yellow, green and blue . 30 15
797 30 d. multicoloured 70 45
798 50 d. red, green and brown . 3·75 1·75
799 70 d. orange, green and brown 5·00 3·00
800 100 d. multicoloured . . . . 26·00 15·00
FLOWERS: 10 d. Tobacco; 15 d. Poppy; 17 d. Linden; 25 d. Camomile; 30 d. Sage; 50 d. Wild rose; 70 d. Gentian; 100 d. Adonis.

1955. Obligatory Tax. Children's Week.
801 **222** 2 d. red 15 10

223 Peace Monument, U.N. Building, New York (A. Augustincic)

224 Red Cross Nurse

1955. 10th Anniv of United Nations.
802 **223** 30 d. black and blue . . . 1·40 55

1955. Obligatory Tax. Red Cross.
803 **224** 2 d. grey and red 20 10

225 Woman and Dove

226 St. Donat's Church, Zadar

1955. 10th Anniv of Republic.
804 **225** 15 d. violet 40 20

1956. Yugoslav Art.
805 **226** 5 d. grey 40 10
806 – 10 d. myrtle 40 10
807 – 15 d. brown 45 10
808 – 20 d. lake 45 15
809 – 25 d. sepia 55 15
810 – 30 d. red 55 20
811 – 35 d. olive . . . . 1·10 30
812 – 40 d. lake . . . . 2·00 40
813 – 50 d. brown . . . . 5·00 30
814 – 70 d. green . . . . 12·00 7·50
815 – 100 d. purple . . . . . . 32·00 18·00
816 – 200 d. blue . . . . 48·00 30·00
DESIGNS—VERT: 10 d. Bas-relief of Croat King, Diocletian Palace, Split; 15 d. Church portal, Studenica, Serbia; 20 d. Master Radovan's portal, Trogir Cathedral; 25 d. Fresco, Sopocani, Serbia; 30 d. Monument, Radimije, Herzegovina; 50 d. Detail from Bozidarevic Triptych, Dubrovnik; 70 d. Carved figure, Belec Church, Croatia; 100 d. Self-portrait of R. Jakopic; 200 d. Peace Monument by A. Augustinic, New York. HORIZ: 35 d. Heads from Cathedral cornice, Sibenik, Dalmatia; 40 d. Frieze, Kotor Cathedral, Montenegro.

227 Zagreb through the Centuries

228 Houses ruined by Avalanche

1956. Yugoslav Int Philatelic Exn, Zagreb.
817 **227** 15 d. brown, orange and black (postage) 30 15
818 30 d. blue, red and black (air) 1·50 55

1956. Obligatory Tax. Red Cross.
819 **228** 2 d. sepia and red 15 10

229 "Technical Education"

230 Induction Motor

1956. Air. 10th Anniv of Technical Education.
820 **229** 30 d. red and black . . . 1·25 90

1956. Birth Centenary of Tesla (inventor).
821 **230** 10 d. olive 15 10
822 – 15 d. brown 40 10
823 – 30 d. blue 70 15
824 – 50 d. purple . . . . 2·25 40
DESIGNS: 15 d. Transformer; 30 d. "Telekomanda" (invention); 50 d. Portrait.

231 Sea-horse

232

1956. Adriatic Sea Creatures. Multicoloured.
825 10 d. Type **231** 15 10
826 15 d. Paper nautilus 15 10
827 20 d. Rock lobster 20 10
828 25 d. "Sea prince" 30 10
829 30 d. Perch 40 10
830 35 d. Red mullet 80 15
831 50 d. Scorpion fish . . . . . 3·25 75
832 70 d. Wrasse . . . . 4·75 1·25
833 100 d. Dory . . . . 14·00 3·50

1956. Obligatory Tax. Children's Week.
834 **232** 2 d. green 15 10

233 Running 234

1956. Olympic Games. Figures, values and country name in ochre.

No.	Type	Description	Unused	Used
835	233	10 d. red	10	10
836	–	15 d. blue (Canoeing)	10	10
837	–	20 d. blue (Skiing)	20	10
838	–	30 d. green (Swimming)	30	10
839	–	35 d. sepia (Football)	45	10
840	–	50 d. green (Water-polo)	1·25	15
841	–	70 d. purple (Table-tennis)	3·75	1·25
842	–	100 d. red (Shooting)	6·50	2·50

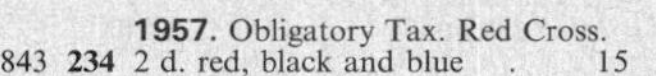

1957. Obligatory Tax. Red Cross.

No.	Type	Description	Unused	Used
843	234	2 d. red, black and blue	15	10

235 Centaury 236 Factory in Worker's Hand

1957. Flowers. Multicoloured.

No.	Description	Unused	Used
844	10 d. Type 235	10	10
845	15 d. Belladonna	15	10
846	20 d. Autumn crocus	15	10
847	25 d. Marsh-mallow	20	10
848	30 d. Valerian	25	15
849	35 d. Woolly foxglove	50	15
850	50 d. Fern	1·50	40
851	70 d. Green-winged orchid	3·00	75
852	100 d. Pyrethrum	16·00	9·00

1957. 1st Congress of Workers' Councils, Belgrade.

No.	Type	Description	Unused	Used
853	236	15 d. lake	40	10
854		30 d. blue	85	25

237 Gymnastics

1957. 2nd Gymnastics Festival, Zagreb. Vert designs as T 237.

No.	Type	Description	Unused	Used
855	237	10 d. olive and black	25	10
856	–	15 d. brown and black	25	10
857	–	30 d. blue and black	65	10
858	–	50 d. brown and black	2·00	1·50

239 Musician and Dancers of Slovenia 240 Children

1957. Yugoslav Costumes (1st series).

No.	Type	Description	Unused	Used
860	–	10 d. multicoloured	20	10
861	–	15 d. multicoloured	30	10
862	–	30 d. multicoloured	30	10
863	–	50 d. green, brn & buff	1·00	2·00
864	–	70 d. black, brn & buff	1·25	35
865	239	100 d. multicoloured	6·00	2·50

DESIGNS—HORIZ: 10 d. Montenegrin musician, man and woman; 15 d. Macedonian dancers; 30 d. Croatian shepherdess and shepherd boys. VERT: 50 d. Serbian peasants; 70 d. Bosnian villagers.
See also Nos. 1020/5.

1957. Obligatory Tax. Children's Week.

No.	Type	Description	Unused	Used
866	240	2 d. slate and red	15	10

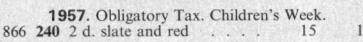

241 Revolutionaries 242 S. Gregorcic (poet)

1957. 40th Anniv of Russian Revolution.

No.	Type	Description	Unused	Used
867	241	15 d. red and ochre	40	20

1957. Cultural Anniversaries.

No.	Type	Description	Unused	Used
868	242	15 d. sepia	30	10
869	–	30 d. blue	40	10
870	–	50 d. brown	90	10
871	–	70 d. violet	8·50	2·25
872	–	100 d. green	14·00	13·00

PORTRAITS—VERT: 30 d. A. Linhart (dramatist); 50 d. O. Kucera (physicist); 70 d. S. Mokranjac (composer); 100 d. J. Popovic (writer).

244 245 Fresco of Sopocani Monastery

1958. 7th Yugoslav Communist Party Congress.

No.	Type	Description	Unused	Used
877	244	15 d. purple	20	10

1958. Obligatory Tax. Red Cross.

No.	Type	Description	Unused	Used
878	245	2 d. multicoloured	20	10

246 Mallard 247 Pigeon

1958. Yugoslav Game Birds. Birds in natural colours. Background colours given below.

No.	Type	Description	Unused	Used
879	246	10 d. brown	10	10
880	–	15 d. mauve (Capercaillie)	15	10
881	–	20 d. blue (Ring-necked pheasant)	30	10
882	–	25 d. green (Common coot)	35	10
883	–	30 d. turquoise (Water rail)	55	15
884	–	35 d. bistre (Great bustard)	65	15
885	–	50 d. purple (Rock partridge)	2·75	65
886	–	70 d. blue (woodcock)	4·75	1·50
887	–	100 d. brown & black (Common crane)	10·50	3·50

The 25, 30, 50 and 100 d. values are vert.

1958. Opening of Postal Museum, Belgrade.

No.	Type	Description	Unused	Used
888	247	15 d. black	20	15

248 Battle Flag 249 Pomet, hero of Drzic's comedy "Dundo Maroje", and ancient fountain at Dubrovnik

1958. 15th Anniv of Battle of Sutjeska River.

No.	Type	Description	Unused	Used
889	248	15 d. lake	25	10

1958. 450th Birth Anniv of Marin Drzic (writer).

No.	Type	Description	Unused	Used
890	249	15 d. brown and black	40	15

243 Steel Plant, Sisak 250 Children at Play

1958.

No.	Type	Description	Unused	Used
891	–	2 d. green	10	10
892	–	5 d. red	15	10
983	–	5 d. orange	30	10
893	–	8 d. purple	25	10
984	–	8 d. violet	30	10
894	243	10 d. green	35	10
985		10 d. brown	30	10
896	–	15 d. red	30	10
986	–	15 d. green	35	10
898	–	17 d. purple	15	10
899	–	20 d. red	75	10
987	–	20 d. blue	45	10
987a	–	20 d. green	45	10
900	–	25 d. grey	35	10
988	–	25 d. red	30	10
901	–	30 d. blue	30	10
989	–	30 d. brown	4·50	10
989a	–	30 d. red	75	10
902	–	35 d. red	30	10
903	–	40 d. red	35	10
904	–	40 d. blue	1·75	10
990	–	40 d. purple	40	10
905	–	50 d. blue	35	10
991	–	50 d. blue	75	10
906	–	55 d. red	3·00	10
992	–	65 d. green	20	10
907	–	70 d. red	1·00	10
908	–	80 d. red	7·00	10
909	–	100 d. green	9·00	10
993	–	100 d. green	3·00	10
994	–	150 d. red	1·00	15
910	–	200 d. brown	3·25	15
995	–	200 d. blue	70	10
996	–	300 d. green	1·75	30
911	–	500 d. blue	6·00	35
997	–	500 d. violet	1·60	10
998	–	1000 d. brown	3·00	15
999	–	2000 d. purple	7·50	40

DESIGNS—VERT: 2, 100 d. (993) Oil derricks, Nafta; 5 d. Shipbuilding; 8, 17 d. Timber industry, cable railway; 15 (896), 20 d. Jablanica Dam; 15 (986), 25 d. (900) Ljubljana–Zagreb motor road; 25 d. (988) Cable industry; 30 d. "Litostroj" turbine factory, Ljubljana; 35, 40 d. (990) Coke plant, Lukavac; 50 d. (991) Iron foundry, Zenica; 65 d. Furnace, Sovojno. HORIZ: 40 (903/4), 150 d. Hotel Titograd; 50 (905), 55, 200 d. (995) Skopje; 70, 80, 300 d. Sarajevo railway station and obelisk; 100 (909), 500 d. (997) Bridge, Ljubljana; 200 (910), 1000 d. Theatre, Zagreb; 500 (911), 2000 d. Parliament House, Belgrade.
See also Nos. 1194/1204.

1958. Obligatory Tax. Children's Week.

No.	Type	Description	Unused	Used
912	250	2 d. black, olive & yellow	15	10

251 Ship with Oceanographic equipment 252 "Human Rights"

1958. I.G.Y.

No.	Type	Description	Unused	Used
913	251	15 d. purple (postage)	55	15
914	–	300 d. blue (air)	7·50	2·25

DESIGN: 300 d. Moon and earth with orbital tracks of artificial satellites.

1958. 10th Anniv of Declaration of Human Rights.

No.	Type	Description	Unused	Used
915	252	30 d. green	65	45

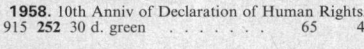

253 Old City, Dubrovnik 254 Communist Party Emblem and Red Flags

1959. Tourist Publicity (1st series). Views.

No.	Type	Description	Unused	Used
916	253	10 d. yellow and red	10	10
917	–	10 d. blue and green	10	10
918	–	15 d. violet and blue	10	10
919	–	15 d. green and blue	10	10
920	–	20 d. green and brown	15	10
921	–	20 d. green and turquoise	15	10
922	–	30 d. violet and buff	1·00	10
923	–	30 d. green and blue	1·00	10
924	–	70 d. black and turquoise	3·00	1·00

DESIGNS: No. 917, Bled; 918, Postojna grottoes; 919, Ohrid; 920, Plitvice Lakes; 921, Opatija; 922, Split; 923, Sveti Stefan; 924, Belgrade.
See also Nos. 1033/41, 1080/5 and 1165/70.

1959. 40th Anniv of Yugoslav Communist Party.

No.	Type	Description	Unused	Used
925	254	20 d. multicoloured	15	10

255 "Family Assistance" 256 Dubrovnik (XV Cent)

1959 Obligatory Tax. Red Cross.

No.	Type	Description	Unused	Used
926	255	2 d. blue and red	15	10

1959. Philatelic Exhibition, Dubrovnik ("JUFIZ IV").

No.	Type	Description	Unused	Used
927	256	20 d. myrtle, green and blue	75	65

257 Lavender 258 Tug-of-War

1959. Medicinal Plants.

No.	Type	Description	Unused	Used
928	257	10 d. violet, green & bl	10	10
929	–	15 d. multicoloured	10	10
930	–	20 d. purple, green & bis	10	10
931	257	25 d. lilac, green & olive	20	10
932	–	30 d. green, blue & pink	25	15
933	–	35 d. blue, green & brn	50	15
934	–	50 d. yellow, grn & brn	2·00	40
935	–	70 d. multicoloured	3·00	75
936	–	100 d. grey, green & brn	5·00	2·00

FLOWERS: 15 d. Black alder; 20 d. Scopolia; 25 d. Monk's-head; 30 d. Bilberry; 35 d. Juniper; 50 d. Cowslip; 70 d. Pomegranate; 100 d. Thorn-apple.

1959. "Partisan" Physical Culture Festival, Belgrade.

No.	Type	Description	Unused	Used
937	258	10 d. black and ochre	10	10
938	–	15 d. blue and sepia	10	10
939	–	20 d. violet and brown	10	10
940	–	35 d. purple and grey	15	10
941	–	40 d. violet and grey	20	10
942	–	55 d. green and brown	35	10
943	–	80 d. olive and slate	75	40
944	–	100 d. violet and ochre	2·25	75

DESIGNS—HORIZ: 15 d. High-vaulting and running; 20 d. Gymnasium exercise; 35 d. Female exercises with hoops; 40 d. Sailors' exercises; 55 d. Handball and basketball; 80 d. Swimming and diving. VERT: 100 d. "Partisan" Association insignia.

259 Fair Emblem 260

1959. Zagreb International Fair.

No.	Type	Description	Unused	Used
945	259	20 d. black and blue	45	15

1959. Obligatory Tax. Children's Tax.

No.	Type	Description	Unused	Used
946	260	2 d. slate and yellow	15	10

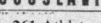

261 Athletes 262 "Reconstruction" (sculpture by L. Dolinar)

1960. Olympic Games.

No.	Type	Description	Unused	Used
947	261	15 d. yellow, buff and violet	10	10
948	–	20 d. drab, lav and blue	10	10
949	–	30 d. bl, stone & ultram	15	10
950	–	35 d. grey, brn & purple	15	10
951	–	40 d. drab, green and bronze	20	10
952	–	55 d. blue, drab & green	35	15
953	–	80 d. ochre, grey & red	50	25
954	–	100 d. ochre, drab and violet	60	30

DESIGNS: 20 d. Swimming; 30 d. Skiing; 35 d. Graeco-Roman wrestling; 40 d. Cycling; 55 d. Yachting; 80 d. Horse-riding; 100 d. Fencing.
Nos. 948, 950, 952 and 954 are inscr in Cyrillic characters.

1960. Obligatory Tax. Red Cross.

No.	Type	Description	Unused	Used
955	262	2 d. blue and red	15	10

1960. Yugoslav Forest Mammals. As T 213. Animals in natural colours. Background colours given.

No.	Description	Unused	Used
956	15 d. blue (West European hedgehog)	10	10
957	20 d. olive (Eurasian red squirrel)	15	10
958	25 d. turq (Pine marten)	15	10
959	30 d. olive (Brown hare)	20	10
960	35 d. brown (Red fox)	25	10
961	40 d. lake (Eurasian badger)	30	10
962	55 d. blue (Wolf)	45	20
963	80 d. violet (Roe deer)	70	20
964	100 d. red (Wild boar)	1·25	90

263 Lenin 264 Accelerator

1960. 90th Birth Anniv of Lenin.

No.	Type	Description	Unused	Used
965	263	20 d. grey and green	15	10

1960. Nuclear Energy Exhibition, Belgrade.

No.	Type	Description	Unused	Used
966	264	15 d. green	10	10
967	–	20 d. red	10	10
968	–	40 d. blue	20	15

DESIGNS: 20 d. Neutron generator; 40 d. Nuclear reactor.

265 Young Girl

266 Serbian National Theatre. Novi Sad (Centenary)

1960. Obligatory Tax. Children's Week.
969 **265** 2 d. red 15 10

1960. Jubilee Anniversaries.
970 **266** 15 d. black 10 10
971 – 20 d. sepia 10 10
972 – 40 d. blue 10 10
973 – 55 d. purple 15 10
974 – 80 d. green 15 10
DESIGNS: 20 d. Part of "Illyrian Renaissance" (allegorical figure), after V. Bukovac (cent of Croat National Theatre, Zagreb); 40 d. Edvard Rusijan and Bleriot XI airplane (50th anniv of 1st flight in Yugoslavia); 55 d. Symbolic hand holding fruit (15th anniv of Republic); 80 d. Symbol of nuclear energy (15th anniv of U.N.O.).

1960. Cultural Annivs. Portraits as T **217**.
975 15 d. green 10 10
976 20 d. brown 10 10
977 40 d. bistre 15 10
978 55 d. red 20 10
979 80 d. blue 40 10
980 100 d. turquoise 40 15
PORTRAITS: 15 d. I. Cankar (writer); 20 d. S. S. Kranjcevic (poet); 40 d. P. Jovanovic (painter); 55 d. D. Jaksic (writer); 80 d. M. Pupin (physician); 100 d. R. Boskovic (astronomer).

268 "Blood Transfusion"

269 "Atomic Energy"

1961. Obligatory Tax. Red Cross. Perf or imperf.
981 **268** 2 d. multicoloured 15 10

1961. Int Nuclear Electronic Conference, Belgrade.
982 **288** 25 d. red and grey 15 10

271 Stevan Filipovic (statue by V. Bakic)

273 St. Clement (14th-century wood-carving)

272

1961. Medicinal Plants. As T **257**. Multicoloured.
1000 10 d. Yellow foxglove 10 10
1001 15 d. Marjoram 10 10
1002 20 d. Hyssop 10 10
1003 25 d. White thorn 10 10
1004 40 d. Rose mallow 15 10
1005 50 d. Soapwort 15 10
1006 60 d. Clary-sage 25 10
1007 80 d. Blackthorn 40 10
1008 100 d. Marigold 90 40
See also Nos. 1074/9.

1961. 20th Anniv of Yugoslav Insurrection. Inscriptions in gold.
1009 **271** 15 d. brown and red . . 10 10
1010 – 20 d. yellow and sepia . . 10 10
1011 – 25 d. green and turq . . 10 10
1012 – 60 d. violet and blue . . 15 10
1013 – 100 d. indigo and blue . 30 20
DESIGNS: 20 d. Insurrection Monument, Bosansko Grahovo (relief by S. Stojanovic); 25 d. Executed Inhabitants Monument, Kragujevac (by A Grzetic); 60 d. Nova Gradiska Victory monument (by A. Augustincic); 100 d. Marshal Tito (Revolution Monument, Titovo Uzice, statue by Krsinic).

1961. Non-Aligned Countries Conf, Belgrade.
1014 **272** 25 d. sepia (postage) . . 10 10
1015 – 50 d. green 20 10

1016 **272** 250 d. purple (air) . . . 1·00 50
1017 – 500 d. blue . . . . 2·50 1·25
DESIGN: 50, 500 d. National Assembly Building, Belgrade.

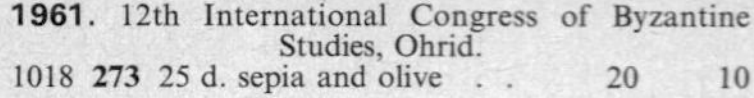

1961. 12th International Congress of Byzantine Studies, Ohrid.
1018 **273** 25 d. sepia and olive . . 20 10

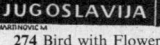

274 Bird with Flower in Beak

275 L. Vukalovic (revolutionary leader)

1961. Obligatory Tax. Children's Week.
1019 **274** 2 d. orange and violet . 15 10

1961. Yugoslav Costumes (2nd series). As T **239**. Inscr "1941–1961".
1020 15 d. multicoloured 15 10
1021 25 d. black, red and brown . 15 10
1022 30 d. sepia, red and brown . 25 10
1023 50 d. multicoloured 35 10
1024 65 d. multicoloured 45 10
1025 100 d. multicoloured . . . . 1·60 50
DESIGNS-HORIZ: Costumes of: 15 d. Serbia; 25 d. Montenegro; 30 d. Bosnia and Herzegovina; 50 d. Macedonia; 65 d. Croatia; 100 d. Slovenia.

1961. Centenary of Herzegovina Insurrection.
1026 **275** 25 d. black 15 10

276 Hands holding Flower and Rifle

277 Miladinovci Brothers

1961. 20th Anniv of Yugoslav Partisan Army.
1027 **276** 25 d. blue and red . . . 20 10

1961. Centenary of Macedonian National Songs by brothers Miladinovci.
1028 **277** 25 d. purple and buff . . 20 10

278 "Mother's Play" (after P. Krsinic)

279 Mosquito

1962. 15th Anniv of U.N.I.C.E.F.
1029 **278** 50 d. black on buff . . 15 10

1962. Malaria Eradication.
1030 **279** 50 d. black on blue . . 15 10

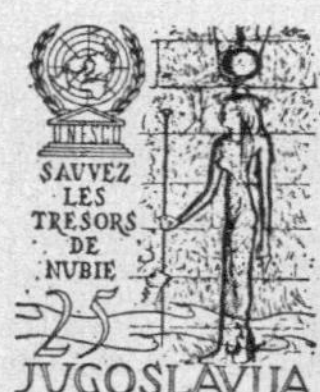

280 Goddess Isis (from temple at Kalabscha)

281 Bandages and Symbols

1962. 15th Anniv of U.N.E.S.C.O.
1031 **280** 25 d. green on cream . . 10 10
1032 – 50 d. brown on buff . . 20 10
DESIGN: 50 d. Rameses II (Nubian monument) and U.N.E.S.C.O. emblem.

1962. Tourist Publicity (2nd series). Views as T **253**. Inscr "1941–1961".
1033 15 d. olive and blue 15 10
1034 15 d. orange and turquoise . 15 10
1035 25 d. brown and blue . . . 20 10
1036 25 d. blue and light blue . . 20 10
1037 30 d. blue and brown . . . 30 10
1038 30 d. blue and purple . . . 50 10
1039 50 d. turq and bistre . . . 1·25 10
1040 50 d. blue and bistre . . . 1·25 10
1041 100 d. grey and green . . . 5·00 60
VIEWS: No. 1033, Portoroz; 1034, Jajce; 1035, Zadar; 1036, Popova Sapka; 1037, Hvar; 1038, Kotor Bay; 1039, Djerdap; 1040, Rab; 1041, Zagreb.

1962. Obligatory Tax. Red Cross.
1042 **281** 5 d. red, brown & grey . 15 10

282 Marshal Tito (after sculpture by A. Augustincic)

283 Pole-vaulting

1962. Marshal Tito's 70th Birthday.
1043 **282** 25 d. turquoise 10 10
1044 – 50 d. brown 20 10
1045 **282** 100 d. blue 65 20
1046 – 200 d. myrtle . . . . . 1·50 75
DESIGN: 50, 200 d. As Type **282** but profile view of bust.

1962. Yugoslav Amphibians and Reptiles. As T **213**. Inscr "1962". Animals in natural colours. Background colours given.
1047 15 d. green (Crested newt) . . 15 10
1048 20 d. violet (Spotted salamander) 15 10
1049 25 d. brown (Yellow-bellied toad) 15 10
1050 30 d. blue (Marsh frog) . . . 15 10
1051 50 d. brown (Pond tortoise) . 20 10
1052 65 d. green (Wall lizard) . . . 25 10
1053 100 d. black (Green lizard) . 40 25
1054 150 d. brn (Leopard snake) . 1·00 50
1055 200 d. red (Common viper) . 2·25 1·10

1962. 7th European Athletic Championships, Belgrade. Sportsmen in black.
1056 **283** 15 d. blue 10 10
1057 – 25 d. purple 10 10
1058 – 30 d. green 10 10
1059 – 50 d. red 10 10
1060 – 65 d. blue 15 10
1061 – 100 d. turquoise 25 15
1062 – 150 d. orange 35 20
1063 – 200 d. brown 65 40
DESIGNS—HORIZ: 25 d. Throwing the discus; 50 d. Throwing the javelin; 100 d. Start of sprint; 200 d. High jumping. VERT: 30 d. Running; 65 d. Putting the shot; 150 d. Hurdling.

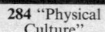

284 "Physical Culture"

285 "Bathing the Newborn Child" (Decani Monastery)

1962. Children's Week.
1064 **284** 25 d. black and red . . . 15 10

1962. Yugoslav Art. Multicoloured.
1065 25 d. Situla of Vace (detail from bronze vessel) (horiz) . . . 10 10
1066 30 d. Golden Mask of Trebiniste (5th-cent burial mask) (horiz) 10 10
1067 50 d. The God Kairos (Trogir Monastery) 15 10
1068 65 d. Pigeons of Nerezi (detail from series of frescoes, "The Visitation", Nerezi Church, Skopje) 25 20
1069 100 d. Type **285** 55 30
1070 150 d. Icon of Ohrid (detail from 14th-cent icon, "The Annunciation") (horiz) . . 1·10 75
See also Nos. 1098/1103.

286 Ear of Wheat and Parched Earth

287 Dr. A. Mohorovicic (meteorologist)

1963. Freedom from Hunger.
1071 **286** 50 d. purple on stone . . 20 10

1963. World Meteorological Day.
1072 **287** 50 d. blue on grey 20 10

288 Centenary Emblem

289 Partisans in File

1963. Obligatory Tax. Red Cross Centenary and Red Cross Week.
1073 **288** 5 d. red, grey and ochre . 20 10

1963. Medicinal Plants. As T **257** but dated "1963". Flowers in natural colours. Colours of backgrounds, panels and inscr given.
1074 15 d. dp green, green & blk . 15 10
1075 25 d. cobalt, blue & violet . 15 10
1076 30 d. grey and blue 15 10
1077 50 d. light brown & brown . 20 10
1078 65 d. light brown & brown . 40 15
1079 100 d. slate and deep slate . 1·40 40
FLOWERS: 15 d. Lily of the valley; 25 d. Iris; 30 d. Bistort; 50 d. Henbane; 65 d. St. John's wort; 100 d. Caraway.

1963. Tourist Publicity (3rd series). Views as T **253**. Inscr "1963". Multicoloured.
1080 15 d. Pula 10 10
1081 25 d. Vrnjacka Banja 10 10
1082 30 d. Crikvenica 10 10
1083 50 d. Korcula 15 10
1084 65 d. Durmitor 15 15
1085 100 d. Ljubljana 90 25

1963. 20th Anniv of Battle of Sutjeska River.
1086 **289** 15 d. green and drab . . 10 10
1087 – 25 d. green 10 10
1088 – 50 d. violet and pale brn 20 10
DESIGNS—VERT: 25 d. Sutjeska Gorge. HORIZ: 50 d. Partisans in battle.
See also No. 1125.

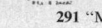

290 Gymnast on "Horse"

291 "Mother"

1963. 5th European Cup Gymnastic Championships.
1089 **290** 25 d. green and black . . 10 10
1090 – 50 d. blue and black . . 15 15
1091 – 100 d. brown and black . 50 45
DESIGNS—Gymnast: 50 d. on parallel bars; 100 d. exercising with rings.

1963. Sculptures by Ivan Mestrovic.
1092 **291** 25 d. bistre on brown . . 10 10
1093 – 50 d. blue on black . . 15 10
1094 – 65 d. green on blue . . . 50 30
1095 – 100 d. black on grey . . 65 50
SCULPTURES: 50 d. "Reminiscence" (nude female figure); 65 d. "Kraljevic Marko" (head); 100 d. "Indian on horseback".

292 Children with Toys

293 Soldier and Emblem

1963. Children's Week.
1096 **292** 25 d. multicoloured . . . 25 10

1963. 20th Anniv of Yugoslav Democratic Federation.
1097 **293** 25 d. red, green and drab 15 10

1963 Yugoslav Art. Designs as T **285**. Inscr "1963". Multicoloured .
1098 25 d. "Man", relief on Radimlje tombstone (13th-15th cents) 10 10
1099 30 d. Detail of relief on door of Split Cathedral, after A. Buvina (13th-cent) 10 10
1100 50 d. Detail of fresco in Beram Church (15th-cent) 15 10
1101 65 d. Archangel Michael from plaque in Dominican Monastery, Dubrovnik (15th-cent) 20 15
1102 100 d. Figure of man on Baroque fountain, by F. Robba, Ljubljana (18th-cent) 25 15
1103 150 d. Archbishop Eufraise, detail of mosaic in Porec Basilica (6th-cent) 70 70
The 30 and 50 d. are horiz.

294 D. Obradovic (writer)

295 Parachute

1963. Cultural Celebrities.

No.	Type	Description	Unused	Used
1104	294	25 d. black on buff	10	10
1105	–	30 d. black on blue	10	10
1106	–	50 d. black on cream	15	10
1107	–	65 d. black on lilac	25	20
1108	–	100 d. black on pink	40	35

PORTRAITS: 30 d. V. S. Karadzic (language reformer); 50 d. F. Miklosic (philologist); 65 d. L. Gaj (writer); 100 d. P. P. Njegos (poet).

See also Nos. 1174/9.

1964. Obligatory Tax. Red Cross Week and 20th Anniv of Yugoslav Red Cross.

No.	Type	Description	Unused	Used
1109	295	5 d. red, purple & blue	15	10

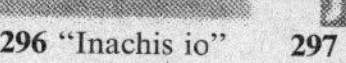

296 "Inachis io"

297 Fireman saving Child

1964. Butterflies. Multicoloured.

No.	Type	Description	Unused	Used
1110		25 d. Type 296	10	10
1111		30 d. "Nymphalis antiopa"	10	10
1112		40 d. "Daphnis nerii"	10	10
1113		50 d. "Parnassius apollo"	15	10
1114		150 d. "Nyctaon pyri"	45	25
1115		200 d. "Papilio machaon"	65	35

1964. Centenary of Voluntary Fire Brigade

No.	Type	Description	Unused	Used
1116	297	25 d. sepia and red	20	10

298 Running

299 "Reconstruction"

1964. Olympic Games, Tokyo.

No.	Type	Description	Unused	Used
1117	298	25 d. yellow, blk & grey	10	10
1118	–	30 d. violet, blk & grey	10	10
1119	–	40 d. green, blk & grey	10	10
1120	–	50 d. multicoloured	15	10
1121	–	150 d. multicoloured	20	15
1122	–	200 d. blue, black & grey	30	25

DESIGNS: 30 d. Boxing; 40 d. Rowing; 50 d. Basketball; 150 d. Football; 200 d. Water-polo.

1964. 1st Anniv of Skopje Earthquake.

No.	Type	Description	Unused	Used
1123	299	25 d. brown	15	10
1124	–	50 d. blue	20	10

DESIGN: 50 d. "International Aid" (U.N. flag over town).

1964. 20th Anniv of Occupation of Vis Island. As T 289 but inscr "VIS 1944–1964" at foot.

No.	Type	Description	Unused	Used
1125		25 d. red and grey	15	10

300 Costumes of Kosovo-Metohija (Serbia)

301 F. Engels

1964. Yugoslav Costumes (3rd series). As T 300. Multicoloured.

No.	Type	Description	Unused	Used
1126		25 d. Type 300	10	10
1127		30 d. Slovenia	15	10
1128		40 d. Bosnia and Herzegovina	15	10
1129		50 d. Hrvatska (Croatia)	15	10
1130		150 d. Macedonia	65	25
1131		200 d. Crna Gora (Montenegro)	85	40

1964. Centenary of "First International".

No.	Type	Description	Unused	Used
1132	301	25 d. black on cream	10	10
1133	–	50 d. black on lilac	15	10

DESIGN: 50 d. Karl Marx.

302 Children on Scooter

303 "Victor" (after Ivan Mestrovic)

1964. Children's Week.

No.	Type	Description	Unused	Used
1134	302	25 d. green, black & red	20	10

1964. 20th Anniv of Liberation of Belgrade.

No.	Type	Description	Unused	Used
1135	303	25 d. black and green on pink	10	10

304 Initial of Hilander's Gospel (13th cent)

305 "Hand of Equality"

1964. Yugoslav Art. Inscr "1964". Multicoloured.

No.	Type	Description	Unused	Used
1136		25 d. Type 304	10	10
1137		30 d. Initial of Miroslav's gospel (12th cent)	10	10
1138		40 d. Detail from Cetinje octateuch (15th cent)	10	10
1139		50 d. Miniature from Trogir's gospel (13th cent)	10	10
1140		150 d. Miniature from Hrvoe's missal (15th cent)	30	10
1141		200 d. Miniature from Herman Priory, Bistrica (14th cent) (horiz)	55	40

1964. 8th Yugoslav Communist League Congress. Multicoloured.

No.	Type	Description	Unused	Used
1142		25 d. Type 305	10	10
1143		50 d. Dove and factory ("Peace and Socialism")	10	10
1144		100 d. Industrial plant ("Socialism")	25	20

306 Table-tennis Player

307 Children around Red Cross

1965. World Table-tennis Championship, Ljubljana.

No.	Type	Description	Unused	Used
1145	306	50 d. multicoloured	15	10
1146	–	150 d. multicoloured	35	20

DESIGN: 150 d. As Type 306 but design arranged in reverse.

1965. Obligatory Tax. Red Cross Week.

No.	Type	Description	Unused	Used
1147	307	5 d. red and brown	10	10

308 Titograd

309 Young Partisan (after D. Andrejevic-Kun)

1965. 20th Anniv of Liberation. Yugoslav Capitals.

No.	Type	Description	Unused	Used
1148	308	25 d. purple	10	10
1149	–	30 d. brown	10	10
1150	–	40 d. violet	10	10
1151	–	50 d. green	10	10
1152	–	150 d. violet	25	20
1153	–	200 d. blue	50	45

CAPITALS: 30 d. Skopje; 40 d. Sarajevo; 50 d. Ljubljana; 150 d. Zagreb; 200 d. Belgrade.

1965. "Twenty Years of Freedom" Pioneer Games.

No.	Type	Description	Unused	Used
1154	309	25 d. blk & brn on buff	15	10

310 T.V. Tower, Avala (Belgrade)

311 Yarrow

1965. Centenary of I.T.U.

No.	Type	Description	Unused	Used
1155	310	50 d. blue	15	10

1965. Inauguration of Djerdap Hydro-Electric Project. As Nos. 3271/2 of Rumania.

No.	Type	Description	Unused	Used
1156	–	25 d. (30 b.) green & grey	15	10
1157	–	50 d. (55 b.) red & grey	30	10

DESIGN: 25 d. Djerdap Gorge; 50 d. Djerdap Dam.

Nos. 1156/7 were issued simultaneously in Rumania.

1965. Medicinal Plants. Multicoloured.

No.	Type	Description	Unused	Used
1158		25 d. Type 311	15	10
1159		30 d. Rosemary	15	10
1160		40 d. Inula	15	10
1161		50 d. Belladonna	20	10
1162		150 d. Mint	35	15
1163		200 d. Digitalis	70	40

312 I.C.Y. Emblem

313 Sibenik

1965. International Co-operation Year.

No.	Type	Description	Unused	Used
1164	312	50 d. violet, indigo and blue	15	10

1965. Tourist Publicity (4th series) Multicoloured.

No.	Type	Description	Unused	Used
1165		25 d. Rogaska Slatina	10	10
1166		30 d. Type 313	10	10
1167		40 d. Prespa Lake	10	10
1168		50 d. Prizren	10	10
1169		150 d. Skadar Lake	25	10
1170		200 d. Sarajevo	40	40

314 Cat

316 Marshal Tito

1965. Children's Week.

No.	Type	Description	Unused	Used
1171	314	30 d. lake and yellow	40	10

1965. Nos. 984 and 988 surch.

No.	Type	Description	Unused	Used
1172		5 d. on 8 d. violet	40	10
1173		50 d. on 25 d. red	40	10

1965. Cultural Celebrities. Portraits as T 294.

No.	Type	Description	Unused	Used
1174		30 d. red on pink	10	10
1175		50 d. slate on blue	10	10
1176		60 d. sepia on brown	10	10
1177		85 d. indigo on blue	15	10
1178		200 d. olive on pale olive	15	15
1179		500 d. mauve on purple	35	30

PORTRAITS: 30 d. B. Nusic (author and dramatist); 50 d. A. G. Matos (poet); 60 d. I. Mazuranic (author); 85 d. F. Levstik; 200 d. J. Pancic (botanist); 500 d. D. Tucovic (politician).

(Currency revalued. 100 paras = 1 dinar = 100 old dinars)

1966.

No.	Type	Description	Unused	Used
1180	316	20 p. green	25	10
1181		30 p. red	45	10

317 Jumping (Balkan Games, Sarajevo)

318 "T", 15th-cent Psalter

1966. Sports Events.

No.	Type	Description	Unused	Used
1182	317	30 p. red	10	10
1183	–	50 p. violet	10	10
1184	–	1 d. green	10	10
1185	–	3 d. brown	20	15
1186	–	5 d. blue	45	35

DESIGNS AND EVENTS: 50 p. Ice-hockey and 3 d. Ice-hockey sticks and puck (World Ice-hockey Championships, Jesenice, Ljubljana and Zagreb); 1 d. Rowing and 5 d. Oars (World Rowing Championships, Bled).

1966. Yugoslav Art. Manuscript initials. Multicoloured.

No.	Type	Description	Unused	Used
1187		30 p. Type 318	10	10
1188		50 p. "V", 14th-cent Divos gospel	10	10
1189		60 p. "R", 12th-cent Libri moralium of Gregory I	10	10
1190		85 p. "P", 12th-cent Miroslav gospel	15	15
1191		2 d. "B", 13th-cent Radomir gospel	25	15
1192		5 d. "F", 11th-cent passional	45	30

319 Red Cross Emblem

320 Beam Aerial on Globe

1966. Obligatory Tax. Red Cross Week.

No.	Type	Description	Unused	Used
1193	319	5 p. multicoloured	10	10

1966. As Nos. 983, etc, but values expressed "0.05" etc, colours changed and new values.

No.	Type	Description	Unused	Used
1194		5 p. orange	10	10
1195		10 p. brown	10	10
1196		15 p. blue	20	10
1197		20 p. green	25	10
1198		30 p. red	75	10
1199		40 p. purple	30	10
1200		50 p. blue	30	10
1201		60 p. brown	30	10
1202		65 p. green	30	10
1203		85 p. purple	40	10
1204		1 d. olive	65	10

NEW VALUES: 60 p. as No. 988, 85 p. as No. 984.

1966. International Amateur Radio Union Regional Conference, Opatija.

No.	Type	Description	Unused	Used
1205	320	85 p. blue	15	10

321 "Lucanus cervus"

322 Serbian 1 para Stamp of 1866

1966. Insects. Multicoloured.

No.	Type	Description	Unused	Used
1206		30 p. Type 321	10	10
1207		50 p. "Cetonia aurata"	10	10
1208		60 p. "Meloe violaceus"	10	10
1209		85 p. "Coccinella septempunctata"	15	10
1210		2 d. "Rosalia alpina"	25	15
1211		5 d. "Dytiscus marginalis"	55	25

1966. Serbian Stamp Centenary.

No.	Type	Description	Unused	Used
1212	322	30 p. green, lake & brn	10	10
1213	–	50 p. lake, bistre & ochre	10	10
1214	–	60 p. orange and green	10	10
1215	–	85 p. red and blue	15	15
1216	–	2 d. bl, bronze & green	45	25

DESIGNS—(Serbian Stamps of 1866): 50 p.—2 p.; 60 p.—10 p.; 85 p.—20 p.; 2 d.—40 p.

323 Rebels on Shield

324 Strossmayer and Racki (founders)

1966. 25th Anniv of Yugoslav Insurrection.

No.	Type	Description	Unused	Used
1218	323	20 p. brown, gold & grn	10	10
1219		30 p. mauve, gold & buff	10	10
1220		85 p. blue, gold and stone	10	10
1221		2 d. violet, gold & blue	15	15

1966. Centenary of Yugoslav Academy.

No.	Type	Description	Unused	Used
1222	324	30 p. black and drab	15	10

325 Old Bridge, Mostar

325a Medieval View of Sibenik

1966. 400th Anniv of Old Bridge, Mostar.

No.	Type	Description	Unused	Used
1223	325	30 p. purple	75	10

1966. 900th Anniv of Sibenik.

No.	Type	Description	Unused	Used
1224	325a	30 p. purple	20	10

326 "The Girl in Pigtails"

327 U.N.E.S.C.O. Emblem

1966. Children's Week.

No.	Type	Description	Unused	Used
1225	326	30 p. multicoloured	50	10

1966. 20th Anniv of U.N.E.S.C.O.

1226	**327**	85 p. blue	20	10

328 Stylised Winter Landscape

329 Dinar of Durad I Balsic

1966. Christmas.

1227	**328**	15 p. yellow and blue	10	10
1228	–	20 p. yellow and blue	10	10
1229	–	30 p. yellow and green	10	10

DESIGNS: 20 p. Father Christmas; 30 p. Stylised Christmas tree.

See also Nos. 1236/8.

1966. Yugoslav Art. Designs showing different coins.

1230	**329**	30 p. multicoloured	10	10
1231	–	50 p. multicoloured	10	10
1232	–	60 p. multicoloured	10	10
1233	–	85 p. multicoloured	10	10
1234	–	2 d. multicoloured	30	15
1235	–	5 d. multicoloured	70	30

MEDIEVAL COINS (Dinars of): 50 p. King Stefan Tomasevic; 60 p. Durad Brankovic; 85 p. Ljubljana; 2 d. Split; 5 d. Emperor Stefan Dusan.

1966. New Year. As Nos. 1227/9 but colours changed.

1236		15 p. gold, blue and indigo	15	15
1237		20 p. gold, red and pink	15	15
1238		30 p. gold, myrtle and green	15	15

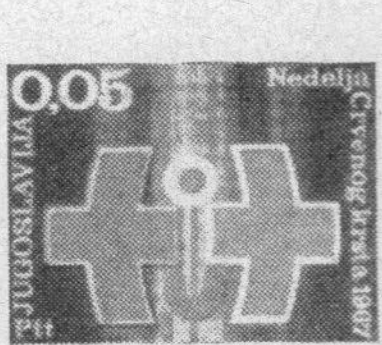

330 Flower between Red Crosses

331 "Arnica montana"

1967. Obligatory Tax. Red Cross Week.

1239	**330**	5 p. red, green and blue	10	10

1967. Medicinal Plants. Multicoloured.

1240		30 p. Type **331**	10	10
1241		50 p. "Linum usitatissimum"	10	10
1242		85 p. "Nerium oleander"	10	10
1243		1 d. 20 "Gentiana cruciata"	15	10
1244		3 d. "Laurus nobil"	30	10
1245		5 d. "Peganum harmais"	65	40

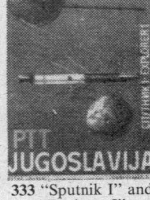

332 President Tito

333 "Sputnik I" and "Explorer I"

1967. Pres. Tito's 75th Birthday. (a) Size as T **332**.

1256	**332**	5 p. orange	15	10
1257		10 p. brown	15	10
1258		15 p. violet	15	10
1259		20 p. green	15	10
1260		20 p. blue	1·50	10
1261		25 p. red	15	10
1262a		30 p. red	1·50	10
1263		30 p. myrtle	30	10
1264		40 p. black	15	10
1265		50 p. turquoise	2·00	10
1266a		50 p. red	30	10
1267		60 p. purple	15	10
1268		70 p. sepia	40	10
1269		75 p. green	50	10
1270		80 p. brown	2·25	10
1270a		80 p. red	45	10
1271		85 p. blue	50	10
1272		90 p. brown	35	10
1273		1 d. lake	25	15
1274		1 d. 20 blue	75	10
1274a		1 d. 20 green	70	10
1275		1 d. 25 blue	55	10
1276		1 d. 50 green	50	10

(b) Size 20 × 30 mm.

1277	**332**	2 d. sepia	1·50	10
1278		2 d. 50 green	1·50	10
1279		5 d. purple	1·25	20
1280		10 d. purple	3·00	35
1281		20 d. green	2·75	40

1967. World Fair, Montreal. Space Achievements. Multicoloured.

1282		30 p. Type **333**	10	10
1283		50 p. "Tiros", "Telstar" and "Molyna"	10	10
1284		85 p. "Luna 9" and lunar orbiter	10	10
1285		1 d. 20 "Mariner 4" and "Venus 3"	15	10
1286		3 d. "Vostok I" and Gemini-Agena space vehicle	15	15
1287		5 d. Leonov in space	50	50

334 St. Tripun's Church, Kotor

1967. International Tourist Year.

1288	**334**	30 p. green and blue	10	10
1289	–	50 p. violet and brown	10	10
1290	–	85 p. purple and blue	10	10
1291	–	1 d. 20 brown & purple	15	10
1292	–	3 d. olive and brown	40	10
1293	–	5 d. brown and olive	60	55

DESIGNS: 50 p. Town Hall, Maribor; 85 p. Trogir Cathedral; 1 d. 20, Fortress gate, Nis; 3 d. Bridge, Visegrad; 5 d. Ancient bath, Skopje.

335 Bobwhite

336 Congress Emblem

1967. International Hunting and Fishing Exhibition and Fair, Novi Sad. Multicoloured.

1294		30 p. Type **335**	40	10
1295		50 p. Pike	15	10
1296		1 d. 20 Red deer	25	10
1297		5 d. Peregrine falcon	2·00	55

1967. International Astronautical Federation Congress, Belgrade.

1298	**336**	85 p. gold light blue and blue	15	10

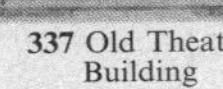

337 Old Theatre Building

338 "Winter Landscape" (A. Becirovic)

1967. Centenary of Slovene National Theatre, Ljubljana.

1299	**337**	30 p. brown and green	15	10

1967. Children's Week.

1300	**338**	30 p. multicoloured	50	10

339 "Lenin" (from bust by Ivan Mestrovic)

340 Four-leaved Clover

1967. 50th Anniv of October Revolution.

1301	**339**	30 p. violet	10	10
1302		85 p. brown	15	10

1967. New Year. Inscr "1968".

1304	**340**	20 p. gold, blue & grn	10	10
1305	–	30 p. gold, violet and yellow	10	10
1306	–	50 p. gold, red and lilac	10	10

DESIGNS: 30 p. Sweep with ladder; 50 p. Horseshoe and flower.

See also Nos. 1347/9.

341 "The Young Sultana" (V. Bukovac)

1967. Yugoslav Paintings (1st series). Multicoloured.

1307		85 p. "The Watchtower" (D. Jaksic)	10	10
1308		1 d. Type **341**	15	10
1309		2 d. "At Home" (J. Petkovsek)	20	15
1310		3 d. "The Cock-fight" (P. Jovanovic)	30	25
1311		5 d. "Summer" (I. Kobilca)	50	40

The 85 p. and 5 d. are vert.

See also Nos. 1337/41, 1399/1404. 1438/43, 1495/1500, 1535/40, 1570/5, 1616/19, 1750/5 and 1793/8.

342 Ski-jumping

1968. Winter Olympic Games, Grenoble.

1312	**342**	50 p. purple and blue	10	10
1313	–	1 d. olive and brown	10	10
1314	–	2 d. lake and black	15	10
1315	–	5 d. blue and olive	50	40

DESIGNS: 1 d. Figure-skating (pairs); 2 d. Downhill skiing; 5 d. Ice-hockey.

343 "The Madonna and Child" (St. George's Church, Prizren)

344 Honeycomb on Red Cross

1968. Medieval Icons. Multicoloured.

1316		50 p. Type **343**	10	10
1317		1 d. "The Annunciation" (Ohrid Museum)	15	10
1318		1 d. 50 "St. Sava and St. Simeon" (Belgrade Museum)	20	10
1319		2 d. "The Descent" (Ohrid Museum)	30	20
1320		3 d. "The Crucifixion" (St. Clement's Church, Ohrid)	35	25
1321		5 d. "The Madonna and Child" (Gospe od zvonika Church, Split)	75	75

1968. Obligatory Tax. Red Cross Week.

1322	**344**	5 p. multicoloured	10	10

345 Bullfinch

346 Running (Women's 800 metres)

1968. Song Birds. Multicoloured.

1323		50 p. Type **345**	15	10
1324		1 d. Goldfinch	15	10
1325		1 d. 50 Chaffinch	30	10
1326		2 d. Greenfinch	35	15
1327		3 d. Red crossbill	75	15
1328		5 d. Hawfinch	1·10	50

1968. Olympic Games, Mexico.

1329	**346**	50 p. pur & brn on cream	10	10
1330	–	1 d. olive & turq on grn	10	10
1331	–	1 d. 50 sep & bl on flesh	15	10
1332	–	2 d. grn & bistre on cream	15	10
1333	–	3 d. indigo & violet on blue	15	10
1334	–	5 d. pur & grn on mauve	35	40

DESIGNS: 1 d. Basketball; 1 d. 50, Gymnastics; 2 d. Sculling; 3 d. Water-polo; 5 d. Wrestling.

347 Rebel Cannon

348 "Mother and Children" (fresco in Hrastovlje Church, Slovenia)

1968. 65th Anniv of Ilinden Uprising.

1335	**347**	50 p. brown and gold	15	10

1968. 25th Anniv of Partisan Occupation of Istria and Slovenian Littoral.

1336	**348**	50 p. multicoloured	10	10

349 "Lake of Klansko" (M. Pernhart)

1968. Yugoslav Paintings (2nd series). 19th-cent Landscapes. Multicoloured.

1337		1 d. Type **349**	10	10
1338		1 d. 50 "Bavarian Landscape" (M. Popovic)	15	10
1339		2 d. "Gateway, Zadar" (F. Quiquerez)	25	10
1340		3 d. "Triglav from Bohinj" (A. Karinger)	35	20
1341		5 d. "Studenica Monastery" (D. Krstic)	85	90

350 A. Santic

351 "Promenade" (Marina Cudov)

1968. Birth Centenary of Aleksa Santic (poet).

1342	**350**	50 p. blue	10	10

1968. Children's Week.

1343	**351**	50 p. multicoloured	15	10

352 Karl Marx (after sculpture by N. Mitric)

353 Aztec Emblem and Olympic Rings

1968. 150th Birth Anniv of Karl Marx.

1344	**352**	50 p. red	10	10

1968. Obligatory Tax. Olympic Games Fund.

1345	**353**	10 p. multicoloured	10	10

354 Old Theatre and View of Kalemegdan

355 Hassan Brkic

1968. Centenary of Serbian National Theatre, Belgrade.

1346	**354**	50 p. bistre and green	10	10

1968. New Year. Designs as Nos. 1304/6 but colours changed and inscr "1969".

1347		20 p. gold, blue and lilac	10	10
1348		30 p. gold, violet and green	10	10
1349		50 p. gold, red and yellow	10	10

1968. Yugoslav National Heroes.

1350	**355**	50 p. violet	10	10
1351	–	75 p. black	15	10
1352	–	1 d. 25 brown	15	10
1353	–	2 d. blue	20	10
1354	–	2 d. 50 green	25	15
1355	–	5 d. lake	60	60

PORTRAITS: 75 p. I. Milutinovic; 1 d. 25, R. Koncar; 2 d. K. Josifovski; 2 d. 50, T. Tomsic; 5 d. M. Pijade.

356 "Family" (sculpture by J. Soldatovic) and Human Rights Emblem

357 I.L.O. Emblem

1968. Human Rights Year.
1357 **357** 1 d. 25 blue 10 10

1969. 50th Anniv of I.L.O.
1358 **357** 1 d. 25 black and red . . 10 10

358 Dove on Hammer and Sickle Emblem
359 "St. Nikita" (Manasija Monastery)

1969. 50th Anniv of Yugoslav Communist Party.
1359 **358** 50 p. red and black . . . 10 10
1360 – 75 p. black and ochre . . 10 10
1361 – 1 d. 25 black and red . . 15 10
DESIGNS: 75 p. "Tito" and star (wall graffiti); 1 d. 25, Five-pointed crystal formation.

1969. Medieval Frescoes in Yugoslav Monasteries. Multicoloured.
1363 50 p. Type **359** 10 10
1364 75 p. "Jesus and the Apostles" (Sopocani) 10 10
1365 1 d. 25 "The Crucifixion" (Studenica) 15 10
1366 2 d. "Cana Wedding Feast" (Kalenic) 20 10
1367 3 d. "Angel guarding Tomb" (Mileseva) 20 10
1368 5 d. "Mourning over Christ" (Nerezi) 90 90

360 Roman Memorial and View of Ptuj
361 Vasil Glavinov

1969. 1900th Anniv of Ptuj (Poetovio) (Slovene town).
1369 **360** 50 p. brown 10 10

1969. Birth Centenary of Vasil Glavinov (Macedonian revolutionary).
1370 **361** 50 p. purple and brown . 10 10

362 Globe between Hands
363 Single Peony

1969. Obligatory Tax. Red Cross Week.
1371 **362** 20 p. black, red and deep red 10 10

1969. Flowers. Multicoloured.
1372 50 p. Type **363** 10 10
1373 75 p. Coltsfoot 15 10
1374 1 d. 25 Primrose 15 10
1375 2 d. Christmas rose 25 10
1376 2 d. 50 Violet 30 10
1377 5 d. Pasque flower 85 75

364 "Eber" (V. Ivankovic)

1969. Dubrovnik Summer Festival. Sailing Ships. Multicoloured.
1378 50 p. Type **364** 10 10
1379 1 d. 25 "Tare in Storm" (Franasovic) 15 10
1380 1 d. 50 "Brig Sela" (Ivankovic) 25 10
1381 2 d. 50 "16th-century Dubrovnik Galleon" . . . 30 20
1382 3 d. 25 "Frigate Madre Mimbelli" (A. Roux) . . . 60 25
1383 5 d. "Shipwreck" (16th-century icon) . . . . 1·40 1·25

365 Games' Emblem
366 Bosnian Mountain Horse

1969. 9th World Deaf and Dumb Games, Belgrade.
1384 **385** 1 d. 25 lilac and red . . 20 10

1969. 50th Anniv of Veterinary Faculty, Zagreb. Multicoloured.
1385 75 p. Type **366** 15 10
1386 1 d. 25 Lipizzaner horse . . 15 10
1387 3 d. 25 Ljutomer trotter . . 40 10
1388 5 d. Yugoslav half-breed . . 85 75

367 Children and Chicks
368 Arms of Belgrade

1969. Children's Week.
1389 **367** 50 p. multicoloured . . 15 10

1969. 25th Anniv of Yugoslav Liberation. Arms of Regional Capitals. Multicoloured.
1390 50 p. Type **368** 15 10
1391 50 p. Skopje 15 10
1392 50 p. Titograd (Podgorica) . 15 10
1393 50 p. Sarajevo 15 10
1394 50 p. Zagreb 15 10
1395 50 p. Ljubljana 15 10

369 Dr. Josip Smodlaka
370 Torch, Globe and Olympic Rings

1969. Birth Centenary of Dr. Josip Smodlaka (politician).
1397 **369** 50 p. blue 10 10

1969. Obligatory Tax. Olympic Games Fund.
1398 **370** 10 p. multicoloured . . 10 10

371 "Gipsy Girl" (N. Martinoski)

1969. Yugoslav Nude Paintings. Mult.
1399 50 p. Type **371** 15 10
1400 1 d. 25 "Girl in Red Armchair" (S. Sumanovic) 20 10
1401 1 d. 50 "Girl Brushing Hair" (M. Tartaglia) 25 10
1402 2 d. 50 "Olympia" (M. Kraljevic) (horiz) . . 40 20
1403 3 d. 25 "The Bather" (J. Bijelic) 70 40
1404 5 d. "Woman on a Couch" (M. Sternen) (horiz) . . . 1·50 1·50

372 University Building

1969. 50th Anniv of Ljubljana University.
1405 **372** 50 p. green 10 10

373 University Seal
374 Colonnade

1969. 300th Anniv of Zagreb University.
1406 **373** 50 p. gold, purple & blue 10 10

1969. Europa.
1407 **374** 1 d. 25 brown & green . . 3·00 3·00
1408 3 d. 25 blue, grey & purple 9·00 9·00

375 Jovan Cvijic (geographer)
376 "Punishment of Dirka" (4th-cent mosaic)

1970. Famous Yugoslavs.
1409 **375** 50 p. purple 10 10
1410 – 1 d. 25 black 15 10
1411 – 1 d. 50 purple 15 10
1412 – 2 d. 50 olive 15 15
1413 – 3 d. 25 brown 25 15
1414 – 5 d. blue 30 40
CELEBRITIES: 1 d. 25, Dr. A. Stampar (hygienist); 1 d. 50, J. Krcovski (author); 2 d. 50, M. Miljanov (soldier); 3 d. 25, V. Pelagic (socialist revolutionary); 5 d. O. Zupancic (poet).

1970. Mosaics. Multicoloured.
1415 50 p. Type **376** 10 10
1416 1 d. 25 "Cerberus" (5th-cent) (horiz) 15 10
1417 1 d. 50 "Angel of Annunciation" (6th-cent) 15 10
1418 2 d. 50 "Hunters" (4th-cent) 25 10
1419 3 d. 25 "Bull beside Cherries" (5th-cent) (horiz) 35 15
1420 5 d. "Virgin and Child Enthroned" (6th-cent) . . . 90 90

377 Lenin (after sculpture by S. Stojanovic)
378 Trying for Goal

1970. Birth Centenary of Lenin.
1421 **377** 50 p. lake 10 10
1422 – 1 d. 25 blue 15 10
DESIGN: 1 d. 25, As Type **377**, but showing left side of Lenin's bust.

1970. 6th World Basketball Championships.
1423 **378** 1 d. 25 red 15 10

379 Red Cross Trefoil

1970. Obligatory Tax. Red Cross Week.
1424 **379** 20 p. multicoloured . . . 10 10

380 "Flaming Sun"

1970. Europa.
1425 **380** 1 d. 25 deep blue, turquoise and blue 15 10
1426 3 d. 25 brown, vio & pur 35 40

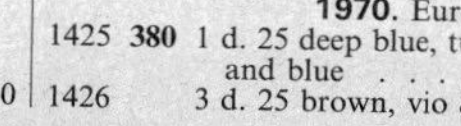

381 Istrian Short-haired Hound
382 Olympic Flag

1970. Yugoslav Dogs. Multicoloured.
1427 50 p. Type **381** 10 10
1428 1 d. 25 Yugoslav tricolour hound 15 10
1429 1 d. 50 Istrian hard-haired hound 15 10
1430 2 d. 50 Balkan hound . . . 25 15
1431 3 d. 25 Dalmatian 40 15
1432 5 d. Shara mountain dog . . 1·00 1·00

1970. Obligatory Tax. Olympic Games Fund.
1433 **382** 10 p. multicoloured . . . 10 10

383 Telegraph Key
384 "Bird in Meadow"

1970. Montenegro Telegraph Centenary.
1434 **383** 50 p. gold, black & brn . . 10 10

1970. Children's Week.
1435 **384** 50 p. multicoloured . . . 15 10

385 "Gymnast"
386 "Hand Holding Dove" (Makoto)

1970. 17th World Gymnastic Championships, Ljubljana.
1436 **385** 1 d. 25 blue and purple . 15 10

1970. 25th Anniv of United Nations.
1437 **386** 1 d. 25 multicoloured . . 15 10

1970. Yugoslav Paintings Baroque Period. Designs as T **341**. Multicoloured.
1438 50 p. "The Ascension" (T. Kracun) 10 10
1439 75 p. "Abraham's Sacrifice" (F. Benkovic) 10 10
1440 1 d. 25 "The Holy Family" (F. Jelovsek) 15 10
1441 2 d. 50 "Jacob's Dream" (H. Zefarovic) 25 15
1442 3 d. 25 "Christ's Baptism" (Serbian village artist) . . 35 15
1443 5 d. 75 "Coronation of the Virgin" (T. Kokolja) . . . 75 75

388 Rusty-leaved Alpenrose

1970. Nature Conservation Year. Multicoloured.

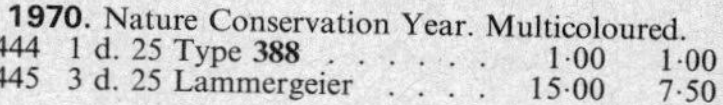

1444 1 d. 25 Type **388** . . . . . 1·00 1·00
1445 3 d. 25 Lammergeier . . . . 15·00 7·50

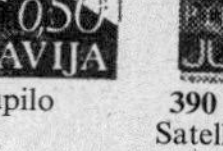

389 F. Supilo

390 Different Nations' Satellites ("International Co-operation")

1971. Birth Cent of Frano Supilo (politician).

1446	**389**	50 p. brown and buff . .	10	10

1971. Space Exploration. Multicoloured.

1447		50 p. Type **390**	15	10
1448		75 p. Telecommunications satellite	15	10
1449		1 d. 25 Unmanned Moon flights	20	10
1450		2 d. 50 Exploration of Mars and Venus (horiz)	35	15
1451		3 d. 25 Space-station (horiz) .	50	30
1452		5 d. 75 Astronauts on the Moon (horiz)	1·75	1·75

391 "Proclamation of the Commune" (A. Daudenarde, after A. Lamy)

1971. Centenary of Paris Commune.

1453	**391**	1 d. 25 brown & orange .	15	10

392 Red Cross Ribbon

1971. Obligatory Tax. Red Cross Week.

1454	**392**	20 p. multicoloured . . .	10	10

393 Europa Chain

1971. Europa.

1455	**393**	1 d. 50 multicoloured . .	15	10
1456		4 d. pink, purple & mve .	55	55

394 Congress Emblem (A. Pajvancic)

1971. 20th Anniv of Yugoslav "Self-Managers" Movement.

1457	**394**	50 p. red, black & gold .	15	10
1458	–	1 d. 25 red, black & gold	60	60

DESIGN: 1 d. 25, "Self-Managers" emblem (designed by M. Miodragovic).

395 Common Mallow

396 Olympic "Spiral" and Rings

1971. Flowers. Multicoloured.

1459		50 p. Type **395**	15	10
1460		1 d. 50 Buckthorn	15	10
1461		2 d. Water-lily	20	10
1462		2 d. 50 Wild poppy	40	10
1463		4 d. Wild chicory	50	15
1464		6 d. Bladder-herb	90	70

1971. Obligatory Tax. Olympic Games Fund.

1465	**396**	10 p. black, purple & blue	10	10

397 Krk, Dalmatia

398 "Prince Lazar Hrebeljanovic" (from fresco, Lazarica Church)

1971. Tourism.

1641	–	5 p. orange	10	10
1642	–	10 p. brown	10	10
1468	–	20 p. lilac	15	10
1644	–	25 p. red	20	10
1469	**397**	30 p. green	55	10
1645		30 p. olive	10	10
1646	–	35 p. red	15	10
1647	–	40 p. olive	10	10
1473	–	50 p. red	1·00	15
1474	–	50 p. green	20	10
1650	–	60 p. purple	10	10
1476	–	75 p. green	50	10
1652	–	75 p. purple	20	10
1477	–	80 p. red	1·10	10
1478	–	1 d. red	2·25	30
1656	–	1 d. lilac	15	10
1657	–	1 d. green	15	10
1479	–	1 d. 20 green	1·40	15
1480	–	1 d. 25 blue	65	15
1481	–	1 d. 50 blue	30	10
1660	–	1 d. 50 red	20	10
1482	–	2 d. turquoise	60	10
1661	–	2 d. 10 green	25	10
1483	–	2 d. 50 violet	60	15
1662a	–	2 d. 50 red	20	10
1663	–	2 d. 50 blue	20	10
1664a	–	3 d. grey	10	10
1665	–	3 d. 20 blue	45	10
1666	–	3 d. 40 green	20	10
1667	–	3 d. 50 red	20	10
1668a	–	4 d. red	10	10
1669	–	4 d. 90 blue	35	10
1670	–	5 d. green	10	10
1671	–	5 d. 60 olive	25	10
1672	–	6 d. brown	10	10
1673a	–	6 d. 10 green	20	10
1674	–	8 d. grey	30	10
1675a	–	8 d. 80 grey	25	10
1676	–	10 d. purple	20	10
1677	–	16 d. 50 blue	25	10
1678	–	26 d. blue	30	10
1679	–	38 d. mauve	50	10
1680	–	70 d. blue	45	10

DESIGNS: 5 p. Krusevo, Macedonia; 10 p. Gradacac; 20 p., 75 p. Bohinj, Slovenia; 25 p. Budva; 35 p. Omis, Dalmatia; 40 p. Pec; 50 p. (1473/4), Krusevac, Serbia; 60 p. Logarska valley; 75 p. (1652), Rijeka; 80 p. Piran; 1 d. (1478), Bitola, Macedonia; 1 d. (1656/7), 16 d. 50, Ohrid; 1 d. 20, 4 d. Pocitelj; 1 d. 25, 1 d. 50 (1481), 8 d. 80, Herceg Novi; 1 d. 50 (1660), Bihac; 2 d. Novi Sad; 2 d. 10, 6 d. 10, Hvar; 2 d. 50 (1483), Rijeka Crnojevica, Montenegro; 2 d. 50 (1662a/3), Kragujevac; 3 d., 3 d. 20, Skofja Loka; 3 d. 40, Vranje; 3 d. 50, Vrsac; 4 d. 90, Perast; 5 d. Osijek; 5 d. 60, Travnik; 6 d. Kikinda; 8 d. Dubrovnik; 10 d. Sarajevo; 26 d. Korcula; 38 d. Maribor; 70 d. Zagreb.

1971. 600th Anniv of City of Krusevac.

1487	**398**	50 p. multicoloured . .	10	10

399 "Satyr"

400 "Children in Balloon"

1971. Bronze Archaeological Discoveries. Multicoloured.

1488		50 p. Head of Emperor Constantine	10	10
1489		1 d. 50 "Boy with Fish" (statuette)	10	10
1490		2 d. "Hercules" (statuette) .	15	10
1491		2 d. 50 Type **399**	30	10
1492		4 d. "Goddess Aphrodite" (head)	40	15
1493		6 d. "Citizen of Emona" (statue)	70	70

1971. Children's Week and 25th Anniv of U.N.I.C.E.F.

1494	**400**	50 p. multicoloured . .	25	10

1971. Yugoslav Portraits. As T **371**. Multicoloured.

1495		50 p. "Girl in Serbian Dress" (K. Ivanovic)	10	10
1496		1 d. 50 "Ivanisevic the Merchant" (A. Bocaric)	15	10
1497		2 d. "Anne Kresic" (V. Karas)	15	10
1498		2 d. 50 "Pavla Jagodica" (K. Danil)	20	10
1499		4 d. "Louise Pasjakova" (M. Stroj)	30	15
1500		6 d. "Old Man at Ljubljana" (M. Langus)	90	75

402 "Postal Codes"

403 Dame Gruev

1971. Introduction of Postal Codes.

1501	**402**	450 p. multicoloured . .	10	10

1971. Birth Centenary of Dame Gruev (Macedonian revolutionary).

1502	**403**	50 p. blue	10	10

404 Speed-skating

1972. Winter Olympic Games, Sapporo, Japan. Multicoloured.

1503		1 d. 25 Type **404**	60	45
1504		6 d. Slalom-skiing	2·00	2·25

405 First Page of Statute

406 Ski-jump, Planica

1972. 700th Anniv of Dubrovnik Law Statutes.

1505	**405**	1 d. 25 multicoloured . .	15	10

1972. 1st World Ski-jumping Championships, Planica.

1506	**406**	1 d. 25 multicoloured . .	20	10

407 Water-polo

408 Red Cross and Hemispheres

1972. Olympic Games, Munich. Multicoloured.

1507		50 p. Type **407**	10	10
1508		1 d. 25 Basketball	10	10
1509		2 d. 50 Swimming	15	10
1510		3 d. 25 Boxing	20	10
1511		5 d. Running	30	15
1512		6 d. 50 Sailing	60	55

1972. Obligatory Tax. Red Cross Week.

1513	**408**	20 p. multicoloured . . .	10	10

409 "Communications"

410 Wallcreeper

1972. Europa.

1514	**409**	1 d. 50 multicoloured . .	25	20
1515		5 d. multicoloured . . .	1·10	1·00

1972. Birds. Multicoloured.

1516		50 p. Type **410**	15	10
1517		1 d. 25 Little bustard	15	10
1518		2 d. 50 Chough	30	15
1519		3 d. 25 White spoonbill . . .	70	20
1520		5 d. Eagle owl	1·25	20
1521		6 d. 50 Rock ptarmigan . . .	3·00	95

411 President Tito

412 Communications Tower, Olympic Rings and 1972 Games' Emblem

1972. President Tito's 80th Birthday.

1522	**411**	50 d. brown and buff . .	15	10
1523		1 d. 25 blue and grey . .	50	25

1972. Obligatory Tax. Olympic Games Fund.

1525	**412**	10 p. multicoloured . . .	10	10

413 Locomotive No. 1 "King of Serbia", 1882

1972. 50th Anniv of International Railway Union. Multicoloured.

1526		1 d. 50 Type **413**	20	10
1527		5 d. Modern "Bo-Bo" electric locomotive	80	40

414 Glider in Flight

415 Pawn

1972. 13th World Gliding Championships, Vrsac.

1528	**414**	2 d. black, blue & gold .	20	15

1972. 20th Chess Olympiad, Skopje.

1529	**415**	1 d. 50 brown, vio & pur	35	15
1530	–	6 d. black, blue & dp bl .	80	75

DESIGN: 6 d. Stylised king and queen on board.

416 "Child on Horse" (B. Zlatec)

417 G. Delcev

1972. Children's Week.

1531	**416**	80 p. multicoloured . . .	15	10

1972. Birth Centenary of Goca Delcev (Macedonian revolutionary).

1532	**417**	80 p. black and green . .	10	10

418 Father Martica

1972. 150th Birth Anniv of Father Grge Martica (politician).

1533	**418**	80 p. black, green and red	10	10

419 National Library

1972. 140th Anniv of and Re-opening of National Library, Belgrade.

1534	**419**	50 p. brown	10	10

420 "Fruit Dish and Broken Majolica Vase" (M. Tenkovic)

1972. Yugoslav Art. Still Life. Mult.

1535		50 p. Type **420**	10	10
1536		1 d. 25 "Mandoline and Book" (J. Petkovsec) (vert) . . .	10	10
1537		2 d. 50 "Basket with Grapes" (K. Jovanovic)	20	10
1538		3 d. 25 "Water-melon" (K. Danil)	35	15
1539		5 d. "In a Stable" (N. Masic) (vert)	45	20
1540		6 d. 50 "Scrap-books" (C. Medovic)	1·00	1·00

421 Battle of Stubica

1973. 500th Anniv of Slovenian Peasant Risings and 400th Anniv of Croatian–Slovenian Rebellion. Multicoloured.

1541 2 d. Type **421** 20 10
1542 6 d. Battle of Krsko . . . . 1·25 75

422 R. Domanovic

424 "Novi Sad" (P. Demetrovic)

423 Skofja Loka

1973. Birth Centenary of Radoje Domanovic (Serbian satirist).

1543 **422** 80 p. brown and drab . . 25 10

1973. Millenary of Skofja Loka.

1544 **423** 80 p. brown 20 10

1973. Old Engravings of Yugoslav Towns. Each black and gold.

1545 50 p. Type **424** 10 10
1546 1 d. 25 "Zagreb" (J. Szeman) 10 10
1547 2 d. 50 "Kotor" (P. Montier) 15 10
1548 3 d. 25 "Belgrade" (Mancini) 20 15
1549 5 d. "Split" (L. F. Cassas) . . 30 15
1550 6 d. 50 "Kranj" (M. Merian) 60 45

425 Table-tennis Bat and Ball

1973. 32nd World Table-tennis Championships, Sarajevo.

1551 **425** 2 d. multicoloured . . . 30 10

426 Red Cross Emblem

427 Europa "Posthorn"

1973. Obligatory Tax. Red Cross Week.

1552 **426** 20 p. multicoloured . . . 10 10

1973. Europa.

1553 **427** 2 d. lilac, green & blue . 15 10
1554 5 d. 50 pink, green & purple 1·40 1·25

428 "Aristolochia clematatis"

429 Globe and Olympic Rings

1973. Flora. Medicinal Plants. Multicoloured.

1555 80 p. Type **428** 15 10
1556 2 d. "Echinops ritro" 20 10
1557 3 d. "Olea europaea" 30 10
1558 4 d. "Corydalis cava" 45 15
1559 5 d. "Viscum album" 65 20
1560 6 d. "Symphytum officinale" 2·00 2·00

1973. Obligatory Tax. Olympic Games Fund.

1561 **429** 10 p. multicoloured . . . 10 10

430 A. Jansa and Bee

431 Aquatic Symbol

1973. Death Bicentenary of Anton Jansa (apiculturist).

1562 **430** 80 p. black 10 10

1973. 1st World Aquatic Championships, Belgrade.

1563 **431** 2 d. multicoloured . . . 20 10

432 "Children on Boat"

433 Posthorn

1973. Children's Week.

1564 **432** 80 p. multicoloured . . 25 10

1973.

1565 **433** 30 p. brown 15 10
1565a 50 p. blue 15 10
1566 80 p. red 15 10
1566a 1 d. green 15 10
1567 1 d. 20 red 15 10
1567a 1 d. 50 red 15 10

434 J. Dalmatinac (from sculpture by I. Mestrovic)

435 "N. Petrovic" (self-portrait)

1973. 500th Death Anniv of Juraj Dalmatinac (sculptor and architect).

1568 **434** 80 p. olive and green . . 10 10

1973. Birth Centenary of Nadezda Petrovic (painter).

1569 **435** 2 d. multicoloured . . . 20 15

436 "The Plaster Head" (M. Celebonovic)

1973. Yugoslav Art. Interiors. Mult.

1570 80 p. Type **436** 10 10
1571 2 d. "St. Duja Church" (E. Vidovic) 10 10
1572 3 d. "Slovenian Housewife" (M. Tartaglia) 15 10
1573 4 d. "Dedicated to Karas"—painter at easel (M. Stancic) 30 15
1574 5 d. "My Studio" (M Konjovic) 50 15
1575 6 d. "Tavern in Stara Loka" (F. Slana) 70 60

437 D. Dudic

438 "M" for "Metrication"

1973. National Heroes. (a) Each black.

1576 80 p. Type **437** 10 10
1577 80 p. S. Pindzur 10 10
1578 80 p. B. Kidric 10 10
1579 80 p. R. Dakic 10 10

(b) Each red.

1580 2 d. J. Mazar-Sosa 15 15
1581 2 d. Z. Zrenjanin 15 15
1582 2 d. E. Duraku 15 15
1583 2 d. I. Lola Ribar 15 15

1974. Centenary of Introduction of Metric System in Yugoslavia.

1584 **438** 80 p. multicoloured . . . 10 10

439 Skater

440 Satjeska Monument

1974. European Figure-skating Championships, Zagreb.

1585 **439** 2 d. multicoloured . . . 40 20

1974. Monuments.

1586 – 3 d. green 75 10
1587 – 4 d. 50 brown . . . . . 1·25 10
1588 – 5 d. violet . . . . 1·25 10
1589 **440** 10 d. green . . . . . . 1·50 20
1590 – 20 d. purple . . . . . . 1·75 20
1591 – 50 d. blue . . . . 4·00 90

DESIGNS—VERT: 3 d. Ljubljana; 4 d. 50, Kozara; 5 d. Belcista. HORIZ: 20 d. Podgaric; 50 d. Kragujevac.

441 Mailcoach

1974. Centenary of Universal Postal Union.

1592 **441** 80 p. black, yellow and buff 10 10
1593 – 2 d. black, red and rose . 10 10
1594 – 8 d. black, blue and pale blue 40 45

DESIGNS: 2 d. U.P.U. H.Q. Building; 8 d. Boeing 707 airliner.

442 Montenegro 25 n. Stamp of 1874

443 President Tito

1974. Montenegro Stamp Centenary. Mult.

1595 80 p. Montenegrin 2 n. stamp of 1874 . . . . 15 10
1596 6 d. Type **442** 35 35

1974.

1597 **443** 50 p. green 15 10
1598 80 p. red 20 10
1599 1 d. 20 green 25 10
1600 2 d. blue 30 10

444 Lenin

445 Red Cross Emblems

1974. 50th Death Anniv of Lenin.

1601 **444** 2 d. black and silver . . . 15 10

1974. Obligatory Tax. Red Cross Week.

1602 **445** 20 p. multicoloured . . . 10 10

446 "Dwarf" (Lepenski settlement, c. 4950 B.C.)

447 Great Tit

1974. Europa. Sculptures. Multicoloured.

1603 2 d. Type **446** 15 15
1604 6 d. "Widow and Child" (I. Mestrovic) . . . . 1·00 1·25

1974. Youth Day. Multicoloured.

1605 80 p. Type **447** 70 15
1606 2 d. Roses 50 15
1607 6 d. "Pieris brassicae" (butterfly) . . . . 2·00 1·10

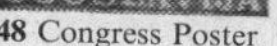

448 Congress Poster

449 Olympic Rings and Stadium

1974. 10th Yugoslav League of Communists' Congress, Belgrade.

1608 **448** 80 p. multicoloured . . . 10 10
1609 2 d. multicoloured . . . 15 10
1610 6 d. multicoloured . . . 35 30

1974. Obligatory Tax. Olympic Games Fund.

1611 **449** 10 p. multicoloured . . . 10 10

450 Dish Aerial, Ivanjica

451 World Cup

1974. Inauguration of Satellite Communications Station, Ivanjica.

1612 **450** 80 p. blue 20 10
1613 – 6 d. lilac . . . . 1·25 70

DESIGN: 6 d. "Intelstat 4" in orbit.

1974. World Cup Football Championships, West Germany.

1614 **451** 4 d. 50 multicoloured . . 70 50

452 Edelweiss and Klek Mountain

1974. Centenary of Croatian Mountaineers' Society.

1615 **452** 2 d. multicoloured . . . 15 10

453 "Children's Dance" (J. Knjazovic)

1974. Paintings. Multicoloured.

1616 80 p. Type **453** 10 10
1617 2 d. "Crucified Rooster" (I. Generalic) (vert) 15 15
1618 5 d. "Laundresses" (I. Lackovic) (vert) 35 20
1619 8 d. "Dance" (J. Brasic) . . 1·10 1·25

454 "Rooster and Flower" (K. Milinojsin)

1974. Children's Week and 6th "Joy of Europe" meeting, Belgrade. Children's Paintings. Mult.

1620 1 d. 20 Type **454** 15 10
1621 3 d. 20 "Girl and Boy" (E. Medrzecka) (vert) . . . 25 10
1622 5 d. "Cat and Kitten" (J. Anastasijevic) 70 40

455 Interior of Library

1974. Bicentenary of National and University Library.

1623 **455** 1 d. 20 black 10 10

456 "White Peonies" (P. Dobrovic) **458** Dove and Map of Europe

457 Title Page of Volume I

1974. Floral Paintings. Multicoloured.
1624 80 p. Type **458** 10 10
1625 2 d. "Carnations" (V. Gecan) 15 15
1626 3 d. "Flowers" (M. Konjovic) 15 15
1627 4 d. "White Vase" (S. Sumanovic) 35 20
1628 5 d. "Branching Larkspurs" (S. Kregar) 40 20
1629 8 d. "Roses" (P. Lubarda) . 70 50

1975. 150th Anniv of "Matica Srpska" Annals.
1630 **457** 1 d. 20 blk, brn and green 10 10

1975. 2nd European Security and Co-operation Conference, Belgrade.
1631 **458** 3 d. 20 multicoloured . . 20 10
1632 8 d. multicoloured . . . 90 65

459 Gold-plated Bronze Ear-ring (14th–15th-century), Alisici, Bosnia **460** "S. Markovic" (sculpture by S. Bodnarov)

1975. Archaeological Discoveries. Multicoloured.
1633 1 d. 20 Type **459** 10 10
1634 2 d. 10 Silver bracelet (19th-century), Kosovo 10 10
1635 3 d. 20 Gold-plated silver buckle (18th-century), Bitola . . . 15 10
1636 5 d. Gold-plated ring (14th-century), Novi Sad 30 10
1637 6 d. Silver necklace (17th-century), Kosovo 45 15
1638 8 d. Gold-plated bronze bracelet (18th-century), Bitola . . . 75 70

1975. Death Centenary of Svetozar Markovic (writer and statesman).
1639 **460** 1 d. 20 blue 10 10

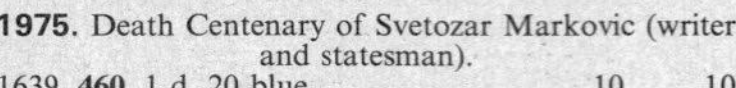

461 "Fettered" (sculpture by F. Krsinic)

1975. International Women's Year.
1640 **461** 3 d. 20 brown and gold . 15 15

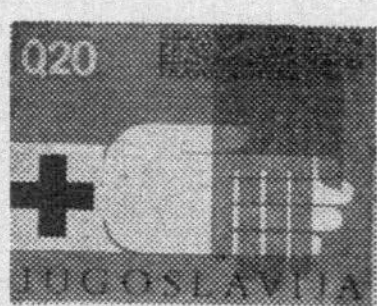

462 Red Cross and Hands

1975. Obligatory Tax. Red Cross Week.
1681 **462** 20 p. multicoloured . . . 10 10

463 "Still Life with Eggs" (M. Pijade)

1975. Europa. Paintings. Multicoloured.
1682 3 d. 20 Type **463** 15 15
1683 8 d. "The Three Graces" (I. Radovic) 50 50

464 "Liberation Monument" (Dzamonja) **465** Garland-flower

1975. 30th Anniv of Liberation.
1684 **464** 3 d. 20 multicoloured . 15 10

1975. National Youth Day. Flowers. Mult.
1685 1 d. 20 Type **465** 15 10
1686 2 d. 10 Touch-me-not . . . 15 10
1687 3 d. 20 Rose-mallow 20 10
1688 5 d. Mourning widow . . . 40 10
1689 6 d. Crocus 50 15
1690 8 d. Rose-bay 75 50

466 Games Emblem **467** Canoeing

1975. Obligatory Tax. Olympic Games Fund.
1691 **466** 10 p. multicoloured . . 10 10

1975. World Canoeing Championships, Macedonia.
1692 **467** 3 d. 20 multicoloured . . 20 10

468 "Herzegovinian Insurgents in Ambush"

1975. Centenary of Bosnian-Herzegovinian Uprising.
1693 **468** 1 d. 20 multicoloured . 15 10

469 "Skopje Earthquake" **470** S. M. Ljubisa

1975. Obligatory Tax. Solidarity Week.
1694 **469** 30 p. black, grey & bl . 10 10
See also Nos. 1885 and 1933.

1975. Writers.
1695 **470** 1 d. 20 black and red . . 10 10
1696 – 2 d. 10 black and grn . 15 10
1697 – 3 d. 20 black and brown 15 10
1698 – 5 d. black and orange . 20 10
1699 – 6 d. black and green . . 20 10
1700 – 8 d. black and blue . . 35 50
PORTRAITS: 2 d. 10, I. Prijatelj; 3 d. 20, J. Ignjatovic; 5 d. D. Jarnevic; 6 d. S. Corivic; 8 d. I. Brlic-Mazuranic.

471 "Young Lion" (A. Savic)

1975. Children's Week and 7th "Joy of Europa" meeting, Belgrade. Children's Paintings. Mult.
1701 3 d. 20 Type **471** 20 10
1702 6 d. "Baby in Pram" 90 50

472 Peace Dove within "EUROPA"

1975. European Security and Co-operation Conference, Helsinki.
1703 **472** 3 d. 20 multicoloured . . 15 10
1704 8 d. multicoloured . . . 50 30

473 Red Cross and Map within "100"

1975. Centenary of Red Cross. Multicoloured.
1705 1 d. 20 Type **473** 15 10
1706 8 d. Red Cross and people . . 50 25

474 "Folk Kitchen" (D. Andrejevic-Kun)

1975. Republic Day. Paintings. Multicoloured.
1707 1 d. 20 Type **474** 10 10
1708 2 d. 10 "On the Doorstep" (V. Grdan) 10 10
1709 3 d. 20 "The Drunken Coach-load" (M. Detoni) (horiz) . 15 10
1710 5 d. "Lunch" (T. Kralj) (horiz) 20 10
1711 6 d. "Waterwheel" (L. Licenoski) 30 15
1712 8 d. "Justice" (K. Hegedusic) 55 60

475 Diocletian's Palace, Split (3rd-century)

1975. European Architectural Heritage Year.
1713 **475** 1 d. 20 brown 15 10
1714 – 3 d. 20 black 15 10
1715 – 8 d. blue 50 50
DESIGNS—VERT: 3 d. 20, House of Ohrid (19th-century). HORIZ: 8 d. Gracanica Monastery, Kosovo (14th-century).

476 Ski-jumping

1976. Winter Olympic Games, Innsbruck.
1716 **476** 3 d. 20 blue 15 10
1717 – 8 d. lake 55 50
DESIGN: 8 d. Figure-skating.

477 Red Flag

1976. Centenary of "Red Flag" Insurrection (workers' demonstration), Kragujevac.
1718 **477** 1 d. 20 multicoloured . . 15 10

478 S. Miletic **479** B. Stankovic

1976. 150th Birth Anniv of Svetozar Miletic (politician).
1719 **478** 1 d. 20 green and grey . . 15 10

1976. Birth Cent of Boran Stankovic (writer).
1720 **479** 1 d. 20 red, brown and yellow 15 10

480 "King Matthias" (sculpture J. Pogorelec)

1976. Europa. Handicrafts. Multicoloured.
1721 3 d. 20 Type **480** 10 10
1722 8 d. Base of beaker 40 40

481 I. Cankar

1976. Birth Centenary of Ivan Cankar (Slovenian writer).
1723 **481** 1 d. 20 purple, brown and pink 10 10

482 Stylized Figure

1976. Obligatory Tax. Red Cross Week.
1724 **482** 20 p. multicoloured . . . 60 60

483 Train crossing Viaduct

1976. Inauguration of Belgrade–Bar Railway.
1725 **483** 3 d. 20 brown 25 15
1726 – 8 d. blue 65 45
DESIGN: 8 d. Train crossing bridge.

484 "Anax Imperator" **485** V. Nazor

1976. Youth Day. Freshwater Fauna. Multicoloured.
1727 1 d. 20 type 484 . . . . . . 10 10
1728 2 d. 10 Snail 10 10
1729 3 d. 20 Rudd 15 10
1730 5 d. Common frog 30 10
1731 6 d. Ferruginous duck . . . 1·25 20
1732 8 d. Muskrat 60 60

1976. Birth Centenary of Vladimir Nazor (writer).
1733 **485** 1 d. 20 blue and lilac . . 10 10

486 "Battle of Vucji Dol" (from "Eagle" journal of 1876)

1976. Centenary of Montenegrin Liberation Wars.
1734 **486** 1 d. 20 multicoloured . . 10 10

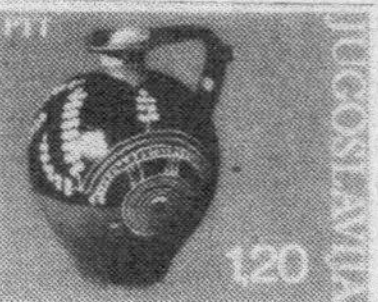

487 Jug, Aleksandrova, Serbia

1976. Ancient Pottery. Multicoloured.
1735 1 d. 20 Type **487** 10 10
1736 2 d. 10 Pitcher, Ptuj, Slovenia 10 10
1737 3 d. 20 Coffee-pot, Visnjica, Sarajevo 15 10

1738 5 d. Pitcher, Backi Breg, Vojvodina 30 15
1739 6 d. Goblet, Vranestice, Macedonia 40 15
1740 8 d. Jug, Prizren, Kosovo 75 50

488 N. Tesla Monument and Niagara Falls

1976. 120th Birth Anniv of Nikola Tesla (scientist).
1741 **488** 5 d. blue and green 25 10

489 Long-jumping

1976. Olympic Games, Montreal.
1742 **489** 1 d. 20 purple 10 10
1743 – 3 d. 20 brown 15 10
1744 – 5 d. brown 20 10
1745 – 8 d. blue 40 35
DESIGNS: 3 d. 20, Handball; 5 d. Shooting; 8 d. Rowing.

490 Stadium and Olympic Rings 491 Globe

1976. Obligatory Tax. Olympic Games Fund.
1746 **490** 10 p. blue 10 10

1976. 5th Non-aligned Nations' Summit Conf, Colombo.
1747 **491** 4 d. 90 multicoloured 20 10

492 "Navy Day" (N. Mitar)

1976. Children's Week. 8th "Joy of Europe" meeting, Belgrade. Children's Paintings. Multicoloured.
1748 4 d. 90 Type **492** 15 10
1749 8 d. "Children's Trains" (W. Gulbrandsen) 50 40

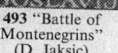

493 "Battle of Montenegrins" (D. Jaksic) 495 "Prota Mateja Nenadovic" (U. Knezevic)

1976. Paintings. Historical events. Mult.
1750 1 d. 20 Type **493** 10 10
1751 2 d. 10 "Nikola Subic Zrinjski at Siget" (O. Ivekovic) 15 10
1752 3 d. 20 "Herzegovinian Fugitives" (U. Predic) (horiz) 20 10
1753 5 d. "The Razlovic Uprising" (B. Lazeski) (horiz) 25 15
1754 6 d. "Enthronement of the Slovenian Duke, Gospsvetsko Field" (A. G. Kos) (horiz) 40 20
1755 8 d. "Breach of the Solun Front" (V. Stanojevic) (horiz) 50 45

1976. No. 1203 surch.
1756 1 d. on 85 p. plum 15 10

1977. Birth Bicentenary of P. M. Nenadovic (soldier and diplomat).
1757 **495** 4 d. 90 multicoloured 25 25

496 R. Zinzifov 497 Phlox

1977. Death Centenary of Rajko Zinzifov (writer).
1758 **496** 1 d. 50 brown & sepia 10 10

1977. Flowers. Multicoloured.
1759 1 d. 50 Type **497** 10 10
1760 3 d. 40 Tiger-lily 20 10
1761 4 d. 90 Dicentra 25 10
1762 6 d. Zinnia 30 15
1763 8 d. Marigold 40 15
1764 10 d. Horseshoe geranium 65 60

498 Institute Building 499 Alojz Kraigher

1977. 150th Anniv of Croatian Music Institute.
1765 **498** 4 d. 90 blue & brown 20 10

1977. Birth Centenary of Alojz Kraigher (author).
1766 **499** 1 d. 50 brown and buff 10 10

500 "Boka Kotorske" (Milo Milunovic)

1977. Europa. Landscapes. Multicoloured.
1767 4 d. 90 Type **500** 15 10
1768 10 d. "Zagorje in November" (Ljubo Babic) 40 40

501 Figure and Emblems

1977. Obligatory Tax. Red Cross Week.
1769 **501** 20 p. red and brown 1·75 70
1770 50 p. red and green 50 20
1771 1 d. red and blue 25 10

502 "President Tito" (O. Mujadzic) 503 Alpine Scene

1977. 85th Birthday of President Tito.
1772 **502** 1 d. 50 brown, olive and gold 10 10
1773 4 d. 90 brown, pink and gold 20 15
1774 8 d. brn, olive and gold 50 45

1977. International Environment Protection Day. Multicoloured.
1775 4 d. 90 Type **503** 20 10
1776 10 d. Plitvice waterfall and red-breasted fly-catcher 2·25 55

504 Petar Kocic

1977. Birth Centenary of Petar Kocic (writer).
1777 **504** 1 d. 50 mauve & green 10 10

505 Dove and Map of Europe

1977. European Security and Co-operation Conference, Belgrade (1st issue).
1778 **505** 4 d. 90 multicoloured 30 15
1779 10 d. multicoloured 1·50 1·50
See also Nos. 1784/5.

506 Tree 507 "Bather" (M. Franci)

1977. Obligatory Tax. Anti-tuberculosis Week.
1780 **506** 50 p. multicoloured 3·00 3·00
1781 1 d. multicoloured 45 45

1977. Children's Week and 9th "Joy of Europe" meeting, Belgrade. Children's Paintings. Mult.
1782 4 d. 90 Type **507** 20 10
1783 10 d. "One Fruit into Pail — the other into Mouth" (T. Ilinskaja) 70 50

508 Congress Building, Belgrade 509 Exhibition Emblem

1977. European Security and Co-operation Conference, Belgrade (2nd issue).
1784 **508** 4 d. 90 grey, blue & gold 25 15
1785 10 d. red, rose and gold 1·50 1·50

1977. "Balkanphila 6" Stamp Exhibition, Belgrade.
1786 **509** 4 d. 90 multicoloured 15 10

510 Double Flute

1977. Musical Instruments in Ethnographical Museum, Belgrade.
1787 **510** 1 d. 50 brown & yellow 10 10
1788 – 3 d. 40 brown & green 20 10
1789 – 4 d. 90 yellow & brown 25 10
1790 – 6 d. brown and blue 30 15
1791 – 8 d. brown and orange 50 25
1792 – 10 d. brown and green 65 55
DESIGN: 3 d. 40, Tamburitza; 4 d. 90, Fiddle; 6 d. Lijerica; 8 d. Bagpipe; 10 d. Pan's flute.

511 Ivan Vavpotic 512 Globe and Olympic Rings

1977. Self-portraits. Multicoloured.
1793 1 d. 50 Type **511** 10 10
1794 3 d. 40 Mihailo Vukotic 15 10
1795 4 d. 90 Kosta Hakman 20 10
1796 6 d. Miroslav Kraljevic 25 15
1797 8 d. Nikola Martinovski 35 20
1798 10 d. Milena Paviovic-Barili 60 65

1977. Obligatory Tax. Olympic Games Fund.
1799 **512** 10 p. yellow, turq and bl 10 10

513 "Ceremony of Testaccio" (miniature from Officum Virginis) 514 Pre-stamp letter (Bavaniste-Kubin)

1978. 400th Death Anniv of Julije Klovic (Croat miniaturist). Multicoloured.
1800 4 d. 90 Type **513** 20 10
1801 10 d. "Portrait of Klovic" (El Greco) 50 35

1978. Post Office Museum Exhibits. Mult.
1802 1 d. 50 Type **514** 10 10
1803 3 d. 40 19th-century mail box 15 10
1804 4 d. 90 Ericsson induction table telephone 20 10
1805 10 d. Morse's first electro-magnetic telegraph set 40 40

515 Battle of Pirot

1978. Centenary of Serbo-Turkish War.
1806 **515** 1 d. 50 multicoloured 90 45

516 S-49A Trainer

1978. Aeronautical Day.
1807 **516** 1 d. 50 pink, brown and orange 10 10
1808 – 3 d. 40 blue, black and slate 15 10
1809 – 4 d. 90 black & brown 30 10
1810 – 10 d. yellow, brn & grn 55 50
DESIGNS: 3 d. 40, SOKO Gabeb 3 jet trainer; 4 d. 90, UTVA 75 elementary trainer; 10 d. Jurom Orao jet fighter.

517 Golubac 518 Boxing Glove on Globe

1978. Europa. Multicoloured.
1811 4 d. 90 Type **517** 20 15
1812 10 d. St. Naum Monastery 1·00 1·00

1978. 2nd World Amateur Boxing Championship, Belgrade.
1813 **518** 4 d. 90 brown, blue and deep blue 20 10

519 Symbols of Red Crescent, Red Cross and Red Lion 520 "Apis mellifera"

1978. Obligatory Tax. Red Cross Week. No. 1814 surch.
1814 **519** 20 p. on 1 d. blue & red 30 10
1815 1 d. blue and red 10 10

1978. Bees. Multicoloured.
1816 1 d. 50 Type **520** 10 10
1817 3 d. 40 "Halictus scabiosae" 25 10
1818 4 d. 90 "Xylocopa violacea" 40 15
1819 10 d. "Bombus terrestris" 85 65

521 Filip Filipovic and Radovan Dragovic

1978. Birth Centenaries of F. Filipovic and R. Dragovic (socialist movement leaders).
1820 **521** 1 d. 50 green and red . . 10 10

522 President Tito (poster) **524** Conference Emblem over Belgrade

1978. 11th Communist League Congress. Mult.
1821 2 d. Type **522** 10 10
1822 4 d. 90 Hammer and sickle (poster) 25 10

1978. Various stamps surch.
1829 – 35 p. on 10 p. brown (No. 1642) 15 10
1830 **332** 60 p. on 85 p. blue (No. 1271) 15 10
1831 **443** 80 p. on 1 d. 20 green (No. 1599) 15 10
1832 – 2 d. on 1 d. green (No. 1657) 15 10
1833 – 3 d. 40 on 2 d. 10 green (No. 1662) 20 10

1978. Conference of Foreign Ministers of Non-aligned Countries.
1834 **524** 4 d. 90 blue and lt blue . 10 10

525 Championship Emblem **526** North Face, Mount Triglav

1978. 14th Kayak and Canoe "Still Water" World Championships, Belgrade.
1835 **525** 4 d. 90 black, blue and light blue 20 10

1978. Bicent of First Ascent of Mount Triglav.
1836 **526** 2 d. multicoloured . . . 15 10

527 Hand holding Flame **528** Black Lake, Durmitor

1978. Obligatory Tax. Anti-tuberculosis Week.
1837 **527** 1 d. multicoloured . . . 20 10

1978. Protection of the Environment. Multicoloured.
1838 4 d. 90 Type **528** 25 10
1839 10 d. River Tara 60 40

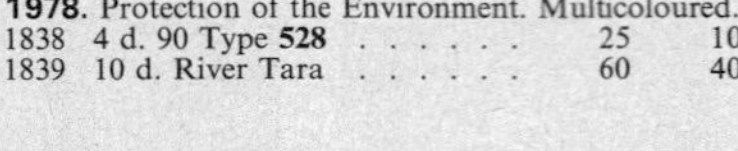

529 Olympic Rings on Map of World

1978. Obligatory Tax. Olympic Games Fund.
1840 **529** 30 p. multicoloured . . . 10 10

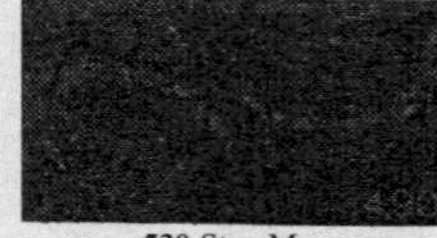

530 Star Map

1978. 29th International Astronautical Federation Congress, Dubrovnik.
1841 **530** 4 d. 90 multicoloured . . 20 10

531 "People in Forest" (I. Balen)

1978. Children's Week and 10th "Joy of Europe" Meeting, Belgrade. Multicoloured.
1842 4 d. 90 Type **531** 20 10
1843 10 d. "Family round a Pond" (V. Christel) 70 40

532 Seal

1978. Centenary of Kresna Uprising.
1844 **532** 2 d. black, brown and gold 15 10

533 Old College Building

1978. Bicentenary of Teachers' Training College, Sombor.
1845 **533** 2 d. brown, yell & gold . 15 10

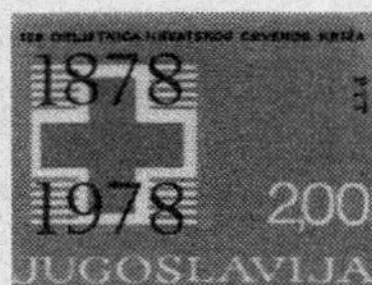

534 Red Cross

1978. Centenary of Croatian Red Cross.
1846 **534** 2 d. red, blue & black . 15 10

535 Metallic Sculpture "XXII" (D. Dzamonja)

1978. Modern Sculpture.
1847 **535** 2 d. blk, brn, and silver . 10 10
1848 – 3 d. 40 blue, grey and silver 15 10
1849 – 4 d. 90 olive, brown and silver 15 10
1850 – 10 d. brown, buff and silver 40 45
DESIGNS—VERT: 3 d. 40, "Circulation in Space I" (V. Bakic); 4 d. 90, "Tectonic Octopod" (O. Jevric). HORIZ: 10 d. "The Tree of Life" (D. Trsar).

536 "Crossing the Neretva" (I. Mujezinovic) **537** "People from the Seine" (Marijan Detoni)

1978. 35th Anniv of Battle of Neretva.
1851 **536** 2 d. multicoloured . . . 15 10

1978. Republic Day. Graphic Art.
1852 **537** 2 d. black, stone and gold 10 10
1853 – 3 d. 40 black, grey and gold 15 10
1854 – 4 d. 90 black, yellow and gold 15 10
1855 – 6 d. black, flesh and gold 20 15
1856 – 10 d. black, flesh and gold 35 40
DESIGNS 3 d. 40, "Labourers" (Maksim Sedej); 4 d. 90, "Felling of Trees" (Daniel Ozmo); 6 d. "At a Meal" (Pivo Karamatijevic); 10 d. "They are not afraid, even at a most loathsome crime" (Djordje Andrejevic Kun).

538 Eurasian Red Squirrel **539** Masthead

1978. New Year. Multicoloured.
1857 1 d. 50 Type **538** 15 10
1858 1 d. 50 Larch 15 10
1859 2 d. Red deer 15 10
1860 2 d. Sycamore 15 10
1861 3 d. 40 Rock partridge (pink background) 75 15
1861a 3 d. 40 Rock partridge (green background) 50 25
1862 3 d. 40 Alder (pink background) 25 10
1862a 3 d. 40 Alder (green background) 40 15
1863 4 d. 90 Capercaillie (green background) 85 15
1863a 4 d. 90 Capercaillie (yellow background) 70 25
1864 4 d. 90 Oak (green background) 30 10
1864a 4 d. 90 Oak (yellow background) 55 25

1979. 75th Anniv of "Politika" Newspaper.
1865 **539** 2 d. black and gold . . . 15 10

540 Flags **541** Games Mascot

1979. 10th Anniv of Self-Managers' Meeting.
1866 **540** 2 d. multicoloured . . . 15 10

1979. Obligatory Tax. Mediterranean Games Fund.
1867 **541** 1 d. blue and deep blue . 15 10
See also No. 1886.

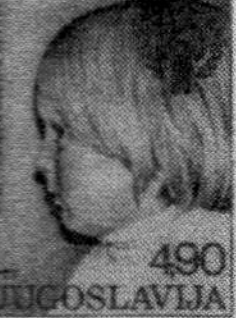

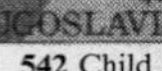

542 Child **543** Sabre, Mace and Enamluk (box holding Koranic texts)

1979. International Year of the Child.
1868 **542** 4 d. 90 blue and gold . . 40 30

1979. Ancient Weapons from Ethnographic Museum, Belgrade. Multicoloured.
1869 2 d. Type **543** 10 10
1870 3 d. 40 Pistol and ammunition stick 15 10
1871 4 d. 90 Carbine and powder-horn 25 10
1872 10 d. Rifle and cartridge-pouch 55 45

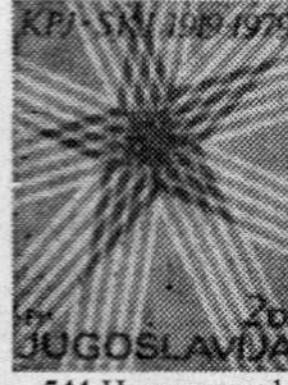

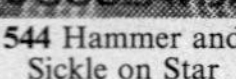

544 Hammer and Sickle on Star **545** Kiril-Meotdij University

1979. 60th Anniv of Yugoslav Communist Party and League for Communist Youth.
1873 **544** 2 d. multicoloured . . . 10 10
1874 4 d. 90 multicoloured . . 25 15

1979. 30th Anniv of Kiril-Metodij University.
1875 **545** 2 d. brown, buff and pink 10 10

546 "Panorama of Belgrade" (C. Goebel)

1979. Europa. Multicoloured.
1876 4 d. 90 Type **548** 15 15
1877 10 d. Postilion and view of Ljubljana (after Jan van der Heyden) 40 40

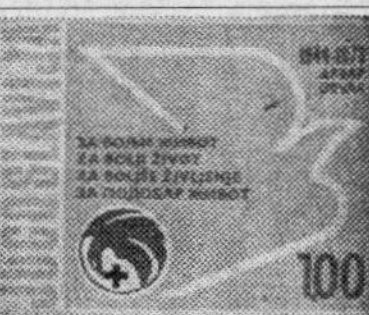

547 Stylized Bird

1979. Obligatory Tax. Red Cross Week.
1878 **547** 1 d. turq, blue and red . 15 10

548 "Cicerbita alpina" **549** Milutin Milankovic (after Paja Jovanovic)

1979. Alpine Flowers. Multicoloured.
1879 2 d. Type **548** 10 10
1880 3 d. 40 "Anemone narcissiflora" 15 10
1881 4 d. 90 "Astragalus sempervirens" 30 15
1882 10 d. "Trifolium alpinum" . 60 40

1979. Birth Centenary of Milutin Milankovic (scientist).
1883 **549** 4 d. 90 multicoloured . . 20 10

550 Kosta Abrasevic **551** Rowing Crew

1979. Birth Centenary of Kosta Abrasevic (poet).
1884 **550** 2 d. grey, pink & black . 10 10

1979. Obligatory Tax. Solidarity Week. As T **469** but inscribed "1.-7.VI".
1885 30 p. black, grey and blue . 15 10

1979. Obligatory Tax. Mediterranean Games Fund. As No. 1867 but colour changed.
1886 **541** 1 d. blue & deep blue . . 10 10

1979. 9th World Rowing Championships. Bled.
1887 **551** 4 d. 90 multicoloured . . 30 10

552 Games Emblem **553** Girl playing Hopscotch

1979. 8th Mediterranean Games. Multicoloured.
1888 2 d. Type **552**. 10 10
1889 4 d. 90 Mascot and emblem . 20 10
1890 10 d. Map and flags of participating countries . . 45 40

1979. Obligatory Tax. Anti-tuberculosis Week.
1891 **553** 1 d. multicoloured . . . 10 10

554 Arms of Zagreb, 1499 **555** Lake Palic

1979. 450th Anniv of Zagreb Postal Service.
1892 **554** 2 d. grey and red 15 10

1979. Environmental Protection. Multicoloured.
1893 4 d. 90 Type **555** 20 10
1894 10 d. Lake in Prokletije range 55 30

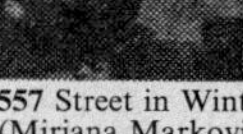

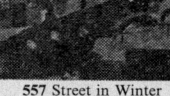

556 Emblems **557** Street in Winter (Mirjana Markovic)

1979. Meeting of International Bank for Reconstruction and Development and of International Monetary Fund.
1895 **556** 4 d. 90 multicoloured . . 20 10
1896 10 d. multicoloured . . . 40 30

1979. 11th "Joy of Europe" Meeting, Belgrade. Children's Paintings. Multicoloured.
1897 4 d. 90 Type **557** 20 10
1898 10 d. House and garden (Jacques An) 65 45

558 Milhailo Pupin

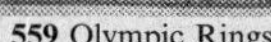
559 Olympic Rings

1979. 125th Birth Anniv of Milhailo Pupin (scientist).
1899 **558** 4 d. 90 brown, light blue and blue 20 10

1979. Obligatory Tax. Olympic Games Fund.
1900 **559** 30 p. red and blue . . . 10 10

560 Marko Cepenkov

561 Pristina University

1979. 150th Anniv of Marko Cepenkov (author and folklorist).
1901 **560** 2 d. brown, green and olive 15 10

1979. 10th Anniv of Pristina University.
1902 **561** 2 d. multicoloured . . . 10 10

562 Lion on Column (Trogir Cathedral)

563 Sarajevo University

1979. Romanesque Sculpture. Multicoloured.
1903 2 d. Type **562** 10 10
1904 3 d. 40 Apostle (detail of choir stall, Split Cathedral) . . . 15 10
1905 4 d. 90 Window (Church of the Ascension, Decani) 20 10
1906 6 d. Detail of Buvina door (Split Cathedral) 30 15
1907 10 d. Virgin and Child (West door, Church of the Virgin, Studenica) 40 40

1979. 30th Anniv of Sarajevo University.
1908 **563** 2 d. black, brown & grey 10 10

564 Djakovic and Hecimovic

1979. 50th Death Anniv of Djuro Djakovic and Nikola Hecimovic (leaders of socialist movement).
1909 **564** 2 d. multicoloured . . . 10 10

565 Paddle Steamer "Serbia"

1979. Danube Conference. Multicoloured.
1910 4 d. 90 Paddle steamer "Deligrad" 75 50
1911 10 d. Type **565** . . . . 1·50 1·00

566 Milton Manaki

567 Edvard Kardelj

1980. Birth Centenary of Milton Manaki (first Balkan film maker).
1912 **566** 2 d. purple and ochre . 15 10

1980. 70th Birth Anniv of Edvard Kardelj (revolutionary).
1913 **567** 2 d. multicoloured . . . 10 10

1980. Renaming of Ploce as Kardeljevo. No. 1913 optd **PLOCE-1980-KARDELJEVO**.
1914 **567** 2 d. multicoloured . . . 15 15

569 Speed Skating

1980. Winter Olympic Games, Lake Placid. Multicoloured.
1915 4 d. 90 Type **569** 15 10
1916 10 d. Skiing 75 70

570 Belgrade University

1980. 75th Anniv of Belgrade University.
1917 **570** 2 d. multicoloured . . . 10 10

571 Fencing

1980. Olympic Games, Moscow. Multicoloured.
1918 2 d. Type **571** 10 10
1919 3 d. 40 Cycling 15 10
1920 4 d. 90 Hockey 20 10
1921 10 d. Archery 40 40

572 President Tito (relief by Antun Augustincic)

573 Pres. Tito

1980. Europa. Multicoloured.
1922 2 d. 50 purple 15 10
1923 13 d. Portrait of Tito by Djordje Prudnikov . . . . 1·75 1·75

1980. Death of President Tito. Portraits by Bozidar Jakac.
1924 **573** 2 d. 50 purple 15 10
1925 – 4 d. 90 black 30 20
DESIGN: 4 d. 90, Different portrait of President Tito.

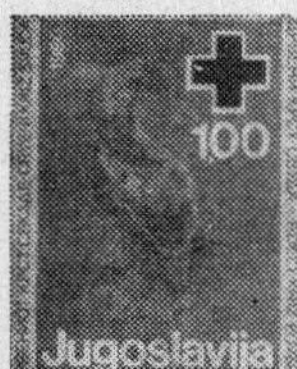
574 Sculpture of S. Kovacevic

575 Sava Kovacevic

1980. Obligatory Tax. Red Cross Week.
1926 **574** 1 d. multicoloured . . . 15 10

1980. 75th Birth Anniv of Sava Kovacevic (partisan).
1927 **575** 2 d. brown, orge & yell . 10 10

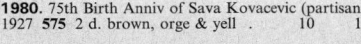

576 Estafette and Letter from Youth of Belgrade, 1945

1980. 35th Anniv of Tito's 1st Estafette (youth celebration of Tito's birthday).
1928 **576** 2 d. multicoloured . . . 15 10

577 Flying Gurnard

578 Decius Trajan (249–51)

1980. Adriatic Sea Fauna, Multicoloured.
1929 2 d. Type **577** 15 10
1930 3 d. 40 Turtle 25 15
1931 4 d. 90 Little tern 80 15
1932 10 d. Common dolphin . . . 45 40

1980. Obligatory Tax. Solidarity Week. As No. 1885.
1933 **469** 1 d. black, grey and blue . 15 10

1980. Roman Emperors on Coins. Multicoloured.
1934 2 d. Type **578** 15 10
1935 3 d. 40 Aurelian (270–75) . . 20 10
1936 4 d. 90 Probus (276–82) . . . 30 15
1937 10 d. Diocletian (284–305) . . 55 40

1980. Nos. 1660 and 1652 surch.
1938 2 d. 50 on 1 d. 50 red 15 10
1939 5 d. on 75 p. purple 40 10

580 Lipica Horses

581 Tito

1980. 400th Anniv of Lipica Stud Farm.
1940 **580** 2 d. 50 black 20 10

1980. 30th Anniv of Self-Management Law.
1941 **581** 2 d. deep red and red . . 10 10

582 Novi Sad University

583 Mljet

1980. 20th Anniv Novi Sad University.
1942 **582** 2 d. 50 green 10 10

1980. Protection of the Environment. Mult.
1943 4 d. 90 Type **583** 25 10
1944 13 d. Galicica, Ohrid 65 50

584 Pyrrhotine

585 Lake

1980. Crystals. Multicoloured.
1945 2 d. 50 Type **584** 10 10
1946 3 d. 40 Dolomite 15 10
1947 4 d. 90 Sphalerite 25 15
1948 13 d. Wulfenite 50 40

1980. Obligatory Tax. Anti-Tuberculosis Week.
1949 **585** 1 d. multicoloured . . . 15 10

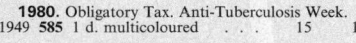

586 Kotor

1980. 21st Session of U.N.E.S.C.O. General Conference, Belgrade.
1950 **586** 4 d. 90 blue, gold, and deep blue 20 10

587 "Children with Balloons" (Gabrijela Radojevic)

588 Olympic Flag and Globe

1980. 12th "Joy of Europe" Meeting, Belgrade. Multicoloured.
1951 4 d. 90 Type **587** 20 10
1952 13 d. "Face" (Renata Pisarcikova) 65 40

1980. Obligatory Tax. Olympic Games Fund.
1953 **588** 50 p. multicoloured . . . 10 10

589 Dove and Madrid

1980. European Security and Co-operation Conference, Madrid.
1954 **589** 4 d. 90 green and deep green 20 15
1955 13 d. bistre and brown . 40 40

590 Flag of Bosnia and Herzegovina Socialist Republic

1980. Flags of Yugoslav Socialist Republics and of Federal Republic.
1956 **590** 2 d. 50 multicoloured . . 10 10
1957 – 2 d. 50 multicoloured . . 10 10
1958 – 2 d. 50 multicoloured . . 10 10
1959 – 2 d. 50 multicoloured . . 10 10
1960 – 2 d. 50 multicoloured . . 10 10
1961 – 2 d. 50 red, gold and grey 10 10
1962 – 2 d. 50 multicoloured . . 10 10
1963 – 2 d. 50 multicoloured . . 10 10
DESIGNS: No. 1957, Montenegro; 1958, Croatia; 1959, Yugoslavia (inscr in Roman alphabet); 1960, Yugoslavia (inscr in Cyrillic alphabet); 1961, Macedonia; 1962, Slovenia; 1963, Serbia.

591 "Complaint" (Milos Vuskovic)

593 Ivan Ribar

592 Sports Complex, Novi Sad

1980. Paintings. Multicoloured.
1964 2 d. 50 "Woman in a Straw Hat" (Stojan Aralica) (horiz) 10 10
1965 3 d. 40 "Atelier No. 1" (Gabrijel Stupica) (horiz) 15 10
1966 4 d. 90 "To the Glory of Sutjeska Fighters" (detail Ismet Mujezinovic) (horiz) 20 10
1967 8 d. "Serenity" (Marino Tartaglia) 35 15
1968 13 d. Type **591** 50 45

1980. Obligatory Tax. World Table Tennis Championships, Novi Sad.
1969 **592** 1 d. green, yellow & bl . 15 10

1981. Birth Centenary of Ivan Ribar (politician).
1970 **593** 2 d. 50 black and red . . 10 10

594 "Cementusa" Hand Bomb

1981. Partisan Arms in Belgrade Military Museum.
1971 **594** 3 d. 50 black and red . . 15 10
1972 – 5 d. 60 black and green . 25 10
1973 – 8 d. black and brown . . 30 10
1974 – 13 d. black and purple . 45 35
DESIGNS: 5 d. 60, "Partizanka" rifle; 8 d. Cannon; 13 d. Tank.

595 Virgin of Eleousa Monastery

1981. 900th Anniv of Virgin of Eleousa Monastery, Veljusa, Macedonia.
1975 **595** 3 d. 50 grey, brown and blue 15 10

596 Table Tennis

1981. "SPENS '81" World Table Tennis Championships, Novi Sad.
1976 **596** 8 d. multicoloured . . . 30 15

597 "Lamp" **598** "Herzegovinian Wedding" (detail)

1981. Obligatory Tax. Red Cross Week.
1977 **597** 1 d. multicoloured . . . 10 10

1981. Europa. Paintings by Nikola Arsenovic. Multicoloured.
1978 8 d. Type **598** 25 10
1979 13 d. "Witnesses at a Wedding" 50 30

599 Tucovic and Dimitrije Tucovic Square **600** Tito (after Milivoje Unkovic)

1981. Birth Centenary of Dimitrije Tucovic (socialist leader).
1980 **599** 3 d. 50 blue and red . . 15 10

1981. 89th Birth Anniv of Tito.
1981 **600** 3 d. 50 multicoloured . . 35 15

601 Sunflower **602** Congress Emblem

1981. Cultivated Plants. Multicoloured.
1982 3 d. 50 Type **601** 15 10
1983 5 d. 60 Hop 20 15
1984 8 d. Corn 30 15
1985 13 d. Wheat 60 35

1981. 3rd Congress of Self-managers.
1986 **602** 3 d. 50 multicoloured . . 15 10

603 Djordje Petrov **604** Star

1981. 60th Death Anniv of Djordje Petrov (politician).
1987 **603** 3 d. 50 yellow and red . . 15 10

1981. 40th Anniv of Yugoslav Insurrection.
1988 **604** 3 d. 50 yellow and red . 15 10
1989 8 d. orange and red . . . 25 15

605 Apple and Target

1981. Obligatory Tax. "Spet 81" European Shooting Championships, Titograd.
1991 **605** 1 d. blue, red & orange . 3·00 3·00

1981. Nos. 1666 and 1669 surch.
1992 3 d. 50 on 3 d. 40 green . . 25 10
1993 5 d. on 4 d. 90 blue 25 10

606 Varazdin (18th-century illustration)

1981. 800th Anniv of Varazdin.
1994 **606** 3 d. 50 yellow and blue . 15 10

607 Parliament Building, Belgrade **608** "Flower"

1981. 20th Anniv of 1st Non-aligned Countries Conference, Belgrade.
1995 **607** 8 d. blue and red . . . 25 10

1981. Obligatory Tax. Anti-tuberculosis Week.
1996 **608** 1 d. red, yellow & blue . 15 10

609 Printing Press and Serbian Newspaper

1981. 150th Anniv of First Serbian Printing House.
1997 **609** 3 d. 50 pink and blue . 15 10

610 Fran Levstik

1981. 150th Birth Anniv of Fran Levstik (writer).
1998 **610** 3 d. 50 grey and red . . 15 10

611 "Village Scene" (Saso Arsovski)

1981. 13th "Joy of Europe" Meeting, Belgrade. Multicoloured.
1999 8 d. Type **611** 20 10
2000 13 d. "Skiers" (Aino Jokinen) 55 45

612 Pusher "Karlovac"

1981. 125th Anniv of European Danube Commission. Multicoloured.
2001 8 d. Type **612** 50 25
2002 13 d. Sip Canal . . . . . . 1·25 70

613 Postal Savings Bank Emblem **614** Emblem

1981. 60th Anniv of Postal Savings Bank.
2003 **613** 3 d. 50 red and yellow . . 15 10

1982. World Intellectual Property Organization Conference.
2004 **614** 8 d. red and gold 25 15

615 Forsythia and Rugovo Ravine **616** August Senoa

1981. Protection of Nature. Multicoloured.
2005 8 d. Type **615** 25 10
2006 13 d. Lynx and Prokletije . . 60 40

1981. Death Centenary of August Senoa (writer).
2007 **616** 3 d. 50 purple and brown 15 10

617 "Still Life with Fish" (Jovan Bijelic)

1981. Paintings of Animals. Multicoloured.
2008 3 d. 50 Type **617** 15 10
2009 5 d. 60 "Raven" (Milo Milunovic) 35 10
2010 8 d. "Bird on Blue Background" (Marko Celebonovic) . . . 45 10
2011 10 d. "Horses" (Peter Lubarda) 40 15
2012 13 d. "Sheep" (Nikola Masic) 40 35

618 Mosa Pijade (politician)

1982. 40th Anniv of Foca Regulations.
2013 **618** 3 d. 50 blue and mauve . 15 10

619 Mastheads **620** Cetinje

1982. 60th Anniv of "Borba" (newspaper).
2014 **619** 3 d. 50 black and red . . 15 10

1982. 500th Anniv of City of Cetinje.
2015 **620** 3 d. 50 brown and black . 15 10

621 Visin's Ship "Splendido"

1982. Europa. Multicoloured.
2016 8 d. Capt. Ivo Visin (first Yugoslav to sail round world) and naval chart 25 15
2017 15 d. Type **621** 80 25

622 Clasped Hands **624** House Sparrow (male)

1982. Obligatory Tax. Red Cross Week.
2018 **622** 1 d. black and red . . . 10 10

1982. Multicoloured.
2020 3 d. 50 Type **624** 30 10
2021 5 d. 60 House sparrow (female) 35 15
2022 8 d. Spanish sparrow (female) 55 25
2023 15 d. Tree sparrow (male) . . 1·40 40

625 "Tito" (after Dragan Dosen) **627** Jaksic (self-portrait)

626 Poster (Dobrilo Nikolic)

1982. 90th Birth Anniv of Tito.
2024 **625** 3 d. 50 multicoloured . . 15 10

1982. 12th Communist League Congress, Belgrade.
2025 **626** 3 d. 50 brn, orge & red . 15 10
2026 8 d. light grey, grey and red 25 15

1982. 150th Birth Anniv of Dura Jaksic (writer and painter).
2028 **627** 3 d. 50 multicoloured . . 15 10

628 Kayaks

1982. Sports Championships.
2029 **628** 8 d. light blue and blue . 25 15
2030 – 8 d. light green and green 25 15
2031 – 8 d. pink and red 25 15
DESIGNS AND EVENTS: No. 2029, Type **628** (World Kayak and Canoe Still Water Championships, Belgrade); 2030, Weightlifting (36th World Weightlifting Championships, Ljubljana); 2031, Gymnastics (6th World Gymnastic Cup, Zagreb).

629 Ivan Zajc **630** Breguet 19 and Potez 25 Biplanes

1982. 150th Birth Anniv of Ivan Zajc (composer)
2032 **629** 4 d. orange & brown 15 10

1982. 40th Anniv of Air Force, Anti-aircraft Defence and Navy.
2033 **630** 4 d. black and blue . . . 20 10
2034 – 6 d. 10 multicoloured . . 30 10
2035 – 8 d. 80 black and green . 50 15
2036 – 15 d. multicoloured . . . 90 30
DESIGNS: 6 d. 10, SOKO G-4 Super Galeb jet trainer; 8 d. 80, National Liberation Army armed tug; 15 d. "Rade Koncar" (missile gunboat).

631 Tara National Park and Pine Cones

1982. Nature Protection. Multicoloured.
2037 8 d. 80 Type **631** 25 15
2038 15 d. Kornati National Park and Mediterranean monk seal 50 40

632 Dr. Robert Koch

1982. Obligatory Tax. Anti-tuberculosis Week.
2039 **632** 1 d. orange, blk & red . 10 10

633 "Traffic" (Tibo Bozo)

1982. 14th "Joy of Europe" Meeting, Belgrade. Children's Drawings. Multicoloured.
2040 8 d. 80 Type **633** 25 15
2041 15 d. "In the Bath" (Heiko Jakel) 50 35

634 Small Onofrio Fountain, Dubrovnik

1982. 16th World Federation of Travel Agents' Associations Congress, Dubrovnik.
2042 **634** 8 d. 80 multicoloured . . 25 15

635 Herceg Novi (from old engraving)

1982. 600th Anniv of Herceg Novi.
2043 **635** 4 d. multicoloured . . . 15 10

636 Bridge, Miljacka

1982. Winter Olympic Games, Sarajevo. Each black, light blue and blue.
2044 4 d. Type **636** 25 15
2045 6 d. 10 Mosque tower and cable cars, Sarajevo 30 20
2046 8 d. 80 Evangelical Church, Sarajevo 40 25
2047 15 d. Old Street, Sarajevo . . 55 40

637 Bihac

1982. 40th Anniv of Avnoj-a (anti-fascist council) Session, Bihac.
2048 **637** 4 d. brown and orange . 15 10

638 "Prophet on Golden Background" (Joze Ciuha)
639 Predic (self-portrait)

1982. Modern Art. Multicoloured.
2049 4 d. Type **638** 15 10
2050 6 d. 10 "Journey to the West" (Andrej Jemec) 20 10
2051 8 d. 80 "Black Comb with Red Band" (Riko Debenjak) . 25 15
2052 10 d. "Manuscript" (Janez Bernik) (horiz) 30 20
2053 15 d. "Display Case" (Adriana Maraz) (horiz) 50 35

1982. 125th Birth Anniv of Uros Predic (painter).
2054 **639** 4 d. orange and brn . . 15 10

641 Pioneer Badge
644 Lead Pitcher (16th century)

1982. 40th Anniv of Pioneer League.
2056 **641** 4 d. brown, silver and red 15 10

1983. Nos. 1663 and 1667 surch.
2057 30 p. on 2 d. 50 blue . . . 10 10
2055a 50 p. on 2 d. 50 blue . . . 10 10
2058 60 p. on 2 d. 50 blue . . . 10 10
2059a 1 d. on 3 d. 50 red 10 10
2060 2 d. on 2 d. 50 red 10 10

1983. Museum Exhibits.
2061 **644** 4 d. black, bistre and silver 10 10
2062 – 6 d. 10 black, brown and silver 15 10
2063 – 8 d. 80 gold, purple and grey 20 15
2064 – 15 d. gold, purple and grey 40 25
DESIGNS: 6 d. 10, Silver-plated tin jar (18th century); 8 d. 80, Silver-gilt dish (16th century); 15 d. Bronze mortar (15th century).

645 Jalovec Mountain Peak and Edelweiss
646 Ericsson Wall Telephone and War Ministry, Belgrade

1983. 90th Anniv of Slovenian Mountaineering Society.
2065 **645** 4 d. blue, light blue and deep blue 10 10

1983. Centenary of Telephone in Serbia.
2066 **646** 3 d. brown and blue . . 10 10

647 I.M.O. Emblem and Freighters

1983. 25th Anniv of International Maritime Organization.
2067 **647** 8 d. 80 multicoloured . 35 15

648 Field Mushroom

1983. Edible Mushrooms. Multicoloured.
2068 4 d. Type **648** 15 10
2069 6 d. 10 Morel 25 10
2070 8 d. 80 Cep 40 15
2071 15 d. Chanterelle 80 30

649 Series "401" Steam Locomotive
650 Monument, Landovica

1983. 110th Anniv of Rijeka Railway.
2072 **649** 4 d. grey and red . . . 20 10
2073 – 23 d. 70 on 8 d. 80 red and grey 60 30
DESIGN: 23 d. 70, Series "442" electric locomotive. No. 2073 was only issued surcharged.

1983. 40th Death Anniv of Boro Vukmorivic and Ramiz Sadiku (revolutionaries).
2074 **650** 4 d. grey and violet . . 10 10

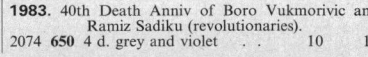

651 Nobel Prize Medal and Manuscript of "Travnik Chronicle" by Andric

1983. Europa. Multicoloured.
2075 8 d. 80 Type **651** 20 15
2076 20 d. Ivo Andric (author and Nobel Prize winner) and bridge over the Drina . . . 50 40

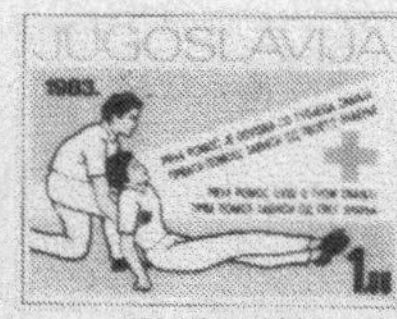

652 First Aid

1983. Obligatory Tax. Red Cross Week.
2077 **652** 1 d. deep brown, brown and red 15 10
2078 2 d. deep brown, brown and red 15 10

653 Combine Harvester
654 "Assault" (Pivo Karamatijevic)

1983. 50th International Agriculture Fair. Novi Sad.
2079 **653** 4 d. green and purple . . 10 10

1983. 40th Anniv of Battle of Sutjeska.
2080 **654** 3 d. pink and brown . . 10 10

655 Tito (after Bozidar Jakac) and Parliament Building
656 Delahaye Postbus, 1903

1983. 30th Anniv of Tito's Election to Presidency.
2081 **655** 4 d. brown and green . . 10 10

1983. 80th Anniv of Postbus Service in Montenegro.
2082 **656** 4 d. black and brown . . 10 10
2083 – 16 d. 50 brown & black . 40 25
DESIGN: 16 d. 50, Road used by first postbus.

657 Statue by V. Bakic, Valjevo
658 Graph

1983. Monuments.
2084 **657** 100 d. orange and blue . 1·25 50
2085 – 200 d. orange and green . 2·50 50
DESIGN—HORIZ: 200 d. Triumphal Arch, Titograd.

1983. 6th U.N. Conference for Trade and Development Session, Belgrade.
2086 **658** 23 d. 70 multicoloured . . 50 30

659 Pazin (after engraving by Valvasor)
660 Skopje

1983. Millenary of Pazin.
2087 **659** 4 d. brown and green . . 10 10

1983. 20th Anniv of Skopje Earthquake.
2088 **660** 23 d. 70 red 50 30

661 "The Victor"
662 Gentian and Kupaonik National Park

1983. Birth Cent of Ivan Mestrovic (sculptor).
2089 **681** 6 d. deep brown, brown and blue 15 10

1983. Nature Protection. Multicoloured.
2090 16 d. 50 Type **662** 40 25
2091 23 d. 70 Chamois and Sutjeska National Park 50 30

663 Apple
664 "Newly Weds" (Vesna Paunkovic)

1983. Obligatory Tax. Anti-tuberculosis Week.
2092 **663** 1 d. red, black & turq . 10 10
2093 2 d. red, black & turq . 15 10

1983. 15th "Joy of Europe" Meeting, Belgrade. Children's Drawings.
2094 **664** 16 d. 50 yellow, black and red 40 25
2095 – 23 d. 70 multicoloured . . 50 30
DESIGN: 23 d. 70, "Andres and his Mother" (Marta Lopez-Ibor).

665 School and Seal
666 Monument by Antun Augustincic

1983. 150th Anniv of Kragujevac Grammar School.
2096 **665** 5 d. brown and blue . . 10 10

1983. Centenary of Timocka Buna Uprising.
2097 **666** 5 d. blue and purple . . 10 10

667 Skier and Games Emblem
668 Zmaj and "Neven" Periodical

1983. Obligatory Tax. Winter Olympic Games, Sarajevo.
2098 **667** 2 d. blue and deep blue . 15 10

1983. 150th Birth Anniv of Jovan Jovanovic Zmaj (poet and editor).
2099 **668** 5 d. red and green . . . 10 10

669 Ski Jump, Malo Polje, Mt. Igman

1983. Winter Olympic Games, Sarajevo (1st issue).
2100 **669** 4 d. black, green & brn . 10 10
2101 – 4 d. dp blue, bl & brn . 10 10
2102 – 16 d. 50 lilac, deep brown and brown 35 20
2103 – 16 d. 50 green, bl & brn . 35 30
2104 – 23 d. 70 deep brown, green and brown 45 30
2105 – 23 d. 70 black, green and brown 45 30
DESIGNS: No. 2101, Women's slalom run, Mt Jahorina; 2102, Bob-sleigh and luge run, Mt. Trebevic; 2103, Men's alpine downhill ski run, Mt. Bjelasnica; 2104, Olympic Hall (for ice hockey and figure skating), Zetra; 2105, Speed skating rink, Zetra.

670 "The Peasant Wedding" (Brueghel the Younger)
671 Jajce

1983. Paintings. Multicoloured.

2107 4 d. Type **670** 10 10
2108 16 d. 50 "Susanna and the Elders" (Master of "The Prodigal Son") 35 20
2109 16 d. 50 "The Allegory of Wisdom and Strength" (Veronese) 35 20
2110 23 d. 70 "The Virgin Mary from Salamanca" (Robert Campin) 45 30
2111 23 d. 70 "St. Anne with the Madonna and Jesus" (Durer) 45 30

1983. 40th Anniv of 2nd Avnoj-a (anti-fascist council) Session, Jajce.

2112 **671** 5 d. red and blue 10 10

672 Drawing by Hasukic Sabina
673 Koco Racin

1983. World Communications Year.

2114 **672** 23 d. 70 multicoloured . 40 25

1983. 75th Birth Anniv of Koco Racin (writer).

2115 **673** 5 d. blue and brown . . 10 10

674 First Issue of "Politika"
675 Veljko Petrovic

1984. 80th Anniv of "Politika" (daily newspaper).

2116 **674** 5 d. black and red . . . 10 10

1984. Birth Centenary of Veljko Petrovic (writer).

2117 **675** 5 d. brown, orange and grey 10 10

676 Giant Slalom

1984. Winter Olympic Games, Sarajevo (2nd issue). Multicoloured.

2118 4 d. Type **676** 10 10
2119 4 d. Biathlon 10 10
2120 5 d. Slalom 10 10
2121 5 d. Bobsleigh 10 10
2122 16 d. 50 Speed skating . . . 25 15
2123 16 d. 50 Ice hockey 25 15
2124 23 d. 70 Ski jumping 35 20
2125 23 d. 70 Downhill skiing . . . 35 20

677 Marija Bursac
678 Bond and Banknote

1984. Women's Day. National Heroines. Each grey, blue and black.

2127 5 d. Type **677** 10 10
2128 5 d. Jelena Cetkovic 10 10
2129 5 d. Nada Dimic 10 10
2130 5 d. Elpida Karamandi . . . 10 10
2131 5 d. Toncka Cec Olga 10 10
2132 5 d. Spasenija Babovic Cana . 10 10
2133 5 d. Jovanka Radivojevic Kica 10 10
2134 5 d. Sonja Marinkovic . . . 10 10

1984. 40th Anniv of Slovenian Monetary Institute.

2135 **678** 5 d. blue and red 10 10

679 Belgrade Central Station and Steam Mail Train, 1884
680 Jure Franko and Silver Medal

1984. Centenary of Serbian Railway.

2136 **679** 5 d. brown and deep brown 10 10

1984. 1st Yugoslav Winter Olympics Medal.

2137 **680** 23 d. 70 multicoloured . 35 20

681 Bridge
682 Globe as Jigsaw Pieces

1984. Europa. 25th Anniv of European Post and Telecommunications Conference.

2138 **681** 23 d. 70 multicoloured . . 35 20
2139 50 d. multicoloured . . 75 40

1984. Obligatory Tax. Red Cross Week.

2140 **682** 1 d. multicoloured . . . 10 10
2141 2 d. multicoloured . . . 15 10
2142 4 d. multicoloured . . . 30 15
2143 5 d. multicoloured . . . 35 25

683 Basketball

1984. Olympic Games, Los Angeles. Multicoloured.

2144 5 d. Type **683** 10 10
2145 16 d. 50 Diving 25 15
2146 23 d. 70 Equestrian 35 20
2147 50 d. Running 70 40

684 Tito (after Bozidar Jakac)
685 "Skopje Earthquake"

1984. 40th Anniv of Failure of German Attack on National Liberation Movement's Headquarters at Drvar.

2148 **684** 5 d. brown and light brown 10 10

1984. Obligatory Tax. Solidarity Week.

2149 **685** 1 d. 50 blue and red . .

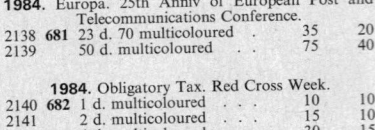

686 Mt. Biokovo Natural Park and "Centaurea gloriosa"

1984. Nature Protection. Multicoloured.

2150 26 d. Type **686** 40 25
2151 40 d. Pekel Cave and "Anophthalmus schmidti" 60 35

687 Great Black-backed Gull

1984. Birds. Multicoloured.

2152 4 d. Type **687** 15 10
2153 5 d. Black-headed gull . . . 15 10
2154 16 d. 50 Herring gull . . . 40 20
2155 40 d. Common tern 90 45

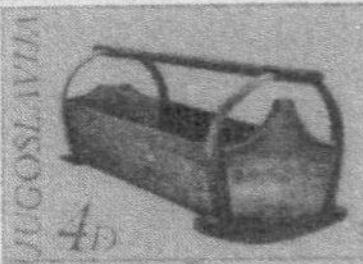

688 Cradle from Bihac, Bosnia and Herzegovina

1984. Museum Exhibits. Cradles.

2156 **688** 4 d. green 10 10
2157 – 5 d. purple and red . . . 10 10
2158 – 26 d. light brown and brown 35 20
2159 – 40 d. ochre and orange . 60 40

DESIGNS: Cradles from—5 d. Montenegro; 26 d. Macedonia; 40 d. Rasina, Serbia.

689 Red Cross and Leaves
691 "National Costume" (Erika Sarcevic)

690 Olive Trees, Mirovica

1984. Obligatory Tax. Anti-tuberculosis Week.

2160 **689** 1 d. multicoloured . . . 10 10
2161 2 d. multicoloured . . . 10 10
2162 2 d. 50 multicoloured . . . 10 10
2163 4 d. multicoloured . . . 20 10
2164 5 d. multicoloured . . . 25 15

1984.

2165 **690** 5 d. multicoloured . . . 10 10

1984. 16th "Joy of Europe" Meeting, Belgrade. Children's Paintings. Multicoloured.

2166 26 d. Type **691** 35 20
2167 40 d. "Girl pushing bear in buggy" (Eva Gug) 60 40

692 Virovitica (17th-century engraving)

1984. 750th Anniv of Virovitica.

2168 **692** 5 d. orange and black . . 10 10

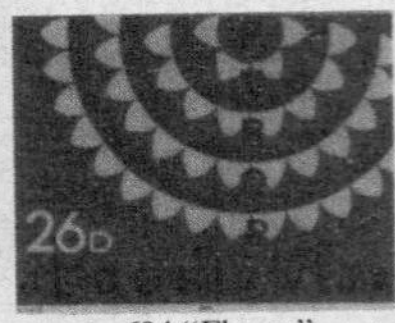

693 Map and Radio Waves
694 "Flower"

1984. 80th Anniv of Radio-Telegraphic Service in Montenegro.

2169 **693** 6 d. blue and green . . . 15 10

1984. Veterans' Conference on Security, Disarmament and Co-operation in Europe, Belgrade.

2170 **694** 26 d. pink, black and violet 90 90
2171 40 d. green, black and blue 90 90

695 City Arms and "40"
696 Milojevic and Music Score

1984. 40th Anniv of Liberation of Belgrade.

2172 **695** 6 d. red, silver and blue . 15 10

1984. Birth Centenary of Miloje Milojevic (composer).

2173 **696** 6 d. lilac and green . . . 15 10

697 Issues of 1944 and 1984

1984. 40th Anniv of "Nova Makedoniya" (newspaper).

2174 **697** 6 d. blue and red 15 10

698 Boxing

1984. Yugoslav Olympic Games Medal Winners. Each blue and red.

2175 26 d. Type **698** 35 20
2176 26 d. Wrestling 35 20
2177 26 d. Canoeing 35 20
2178 26 d. Handball 35 20
2179 26 d. Football 35 20
2180 26 d. Basketball 35 20
2181 26 d. Water polo 35 20
2182 26 d. Rowing 35 20

699 "Madame Tatichek" (Ferdinand Waldmuller)

1984. Paintings. Multicoloured.

2183 6 d. Type **699** 15 10
2184 26 d. "The Bathers" (Pierre-Auguste Renoir) 35 20
2185 26 d. "At the Window" (Henri Matisse) 35 20
2186 38 d. "The Tahitians" (Paul Gauguin) (horiz) 40 25
2187 40 d. "The Ballerinas" (Edgar Degas) (horiz) 60 40

1984. Nos. 1675a, 1668a and 2088 surch.

2188a 2 d. on 8 d. 80 grey 10 10
2189 6 d. on 4 d. red 10 10
2190 20 d. on 23 d. 70 red . . . 25 10

701 "Aturia aturi" (cephalopod)

1985. Museum Exhibits. Fossils.

2191 **701** 5 d. purple and blue . . 10 10
2192 – 6 d. brown and light brown 10 10
2193 – 33 d. brown and yellow . 40 25
2194 – 60 d. brown & orange . 65 45

DESIGNS: 6 d. "Pachyophis woodwardil" (snake); 33 d. "Chaetodon hoeferi" (fish); 60 d. Skull of Neanderthal man.

702 Hopovo Church
703 Three Herons in Flight

1985. 40th Anniv of Organized Protection of Yugoslav Cultural Monuments.

2195 **702** 6 d. red, yellow & grn . . 10 10

1985. 50th Anniv of Planica Ski-jump.

2196 **703** 6 d. multicoloured . . . 90 30

704 Lammergeier and Douglas DC-10 over Mountains
705 Osprey

1985. Air. Multicoloured.
2197 500 d. Type **704** . . . . . . 5·00 2·00
2199 1000 d. Swallow and airplane at airport . . . . 10·00 4·50

1985. Nature Protection. Birds. Multicoloured.
2202 42 d. Type **705** . . . . 1·25 55
2203 60 d. Hoopoe . . . . 1·60 80

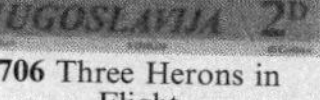

706 Three Herons in Flight

707 "St. Methodius" (detail "Seven Slav Saints", St. Naum's Church Ohrid)

1985. Obligatory Tax. 50th Anniv of Planica Ski-jump.
2204 **706** 2 d. blue and green . . . 10 10

1985. 1100th Death Anniv of Saint Methodius, Archbishop of Moravia.
2205 **707** 10 d. multicoloured . . . 1·10 60

708 Handshake

1985. Tenth Anniv of Osimo Agreements between Yugoslavia and Italy.
2206 **708** 6 d. blue and deep blue . 10 10

709 Flute, Darabukka and Josip Slavenski (composer)

1985. Europa. Multicoloured.
2207 60 d. Type **709** 60 60
2208 80 d. Score of "Balkanophonia" (Slavenski) 60 60

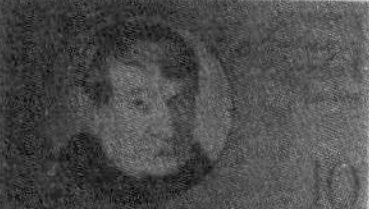

710 Red Cross and Faces

711 Vujic (after Dimitrije Auramovic)

1985. Obligatory Tax. Red Cross Week.
2209 **710** 1 d. violet and red . . . 10 10
2210 2 d. violet and red . . . 10 10
2211 3 d. violet and red . . . 10 10
2212 4 d. violet and red . . . 15 10

1985. 150th Anniv of Joakim Vujic Theatre, Kragujevac.
2213 **711** 10 d. multicoloured . . . 15 10

712 Order of Liberty

1985. 40th Anniv of V.E. (Victory in Europe) Day. Multicoloured.
2214 10 d. Type **712** 15 10
2215 10 d. Order of National Liberation 15 10

713 Franjo Kluz and Rudi Cajavec (pilots) and Potez 25 Biplane

714 Tito (after Bozidar Jakac)

1985. Air Force Day.
2216 **713** 10 d. blue, purple & brn 30 10

1985. 93rd Birth Anniv of Tito.
2217 **714** 10 d. multicoloured . . 45 10

715 Red Cross and "Skopje Earthquake"

716 Villa, Map of Islands and Arms

1985. Obligatory Tax. Solidarity Week. (a) As Nos. 1885 and 1933.
2218 2 d. 50 black, grey and bl . 10 10
2219 3 d. black, grey and blue . . 10 10

(b) Type **715**.
2220 **715** 3 d. blue and red . . . 60 60
See also Nos. 2315/16, 2460 and 2532.

1985. Centenary of Tourism in Cres-Losinj Region.
2221 **716** 10 d. multicoloured . . 15 10

717 U.N. Emblem and Rainbow

718 Regatta Emblem

1985. 40th Anniv of U.N.O.
2222 **717** 70 d. multicoloured . . 35 35

1985. 30th Anniv of International European Danubian Regatta.
2223 **718** 70 d. multicoloured . . 35 35

719 Aerial View of Yacht

720 Model Airplane

1985. Nautical Tourism. Multicoloured.
2225 8 d. Type **719** 10 10
2226 10 d. Windsurfing 15 10
2227 50 d. Yacht in sunset . . . 55 30
2228 70 d. Yacht by coastline . . 75 45

1985. World Free Flight Aeromodels Championships, Livno.
2229 **720** 70 d. multicoloured . . 80 35

721 Emblem and Text

722 Boy with Football

1985. Obligatory Tax. 20th European Shooting Championships, Osijek.
2230 **721** 3 d. blue 10 10

1985. Obligatory Tax. Anti-tuberculosis Week.
2231 **722** 2 d. black, orge & red . 10 10
2232 3 d. black, orge & red . 10 10
2233 4 d. black, orge & red . 10 10
2234 5 d. black, orge & red . 15 10

723 "Corallina officinalis" and Seahorses

725 Selling Vegetables from Cart (Branka Lukic)

724 Federation Emblem

1985. Marine Flora. Multicoloured.
2235 8 d. Type **723** 10 10
2236 10 d. "Desmarestia viridis" . 10 10
2237 50 d. Bladder wrack seaweed . 45 25
2238 70 d. "Padina pavonia" . . . 1·00 75

1985. 73rd International Stomatologists Federation Congress, Belgrade.
2239 **724** 70 d. multicoloured . . . 60 35

1985. 17th "Joy of Europe" Meeting, Belgrade. Children's Paintings. Multicoloured.
2240 50 d. Type **725** 40 20
2241 70 d. "Children playing" (Suzanne Straathof) 90 90

726 Detail of Theatre Facade

1985. 125th Anniv of Croatian National Theatre, Zagreb.
2242 **726** 10 d. multicoloured . . . 10 10

727 Miladin Popovic

728 State Arms

1985. 75th Birth Anniv and 40th Death Anniv of Miladin Popovic (Communist Party worker).
2243 **727** 10 d. brown & orange . . 10 10

1985. 40th Anniv of Federal Republic.
2244 **728** 10 d. multicoloured . . . 10 10

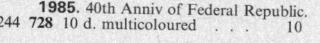

729 "Royal Procession" (Iromie Wijewardena)

1985. Paintings. Multicoloured.
2246 8 d. Type **729** 10 10
2247 10 d. "Return from Hunting" (Mama Cangare) 10 10
2248 50 d. "Drum of Coca" (Agnes Ovando Sanz de Franck) . 35 20
2249 50 d. "The Cock" (Mariano Rodriguez) (vert) 35 20
2250 70 d. "Three Women" (Quamrul Hassan) (vert) . . 80 80

1985. Nos. 1641, 1644, 1646, 1671, 1672 and 1677/9 surch.
2251 1 d. on 25 p. red 60 10
2252 2 d. on 5 p. orange 35 10
2253 3 d. on 35 p. red 10 10
2254 4 d. on 5 d. 60 olive 10 10
2255 8 d. on 6 d. brown 10 10
2256 20 d. on 26 d. blue 15 10
2257 50 d. on 16 d. 50 blue . . . 60 15
2258 70 d. on 38 d. mauve 90 20

731 Zagreb Exhibition Hall

1986.
2259 **731** 100 d. violet and yellow . 40 40

732 Patrol Car

1986. 40th Anniv of Yugoslav Automobile Association. Multicoloured.
2260 10 d. Type **732** 10 10
2261 70 d. Emergency first aid helicopter . . . . 1·25 75

733 Wildlife on River Bank

734 Church of the Virgin

1986. Nature Protection. River Tara. Mult.
2262 100 d. Type **733** . . . . . 2·50 60
2263 150 d. Bridge over river . . . 90 90

1986. 800th Anniv of Studenica Monastery.
2264 **734** 10 d. red, green & blue . 60 30

735 Postman on Motor Cycle

736 Player and Ball in Goal

1986. Postal Services.
2265 **735** 20 d. purple 10 10
2266 – 30 d. brown 10 10
2267 – 40 d. red 10 10
2268 – 50 d. violet 10 10
2269 – 60 d. green 10 10
2273 – 93 d. blue 10 10
2275 – 100 d. purple 10 10
2276 – 106 d. red 10 10
2277 – 106 d. brown 10 10
2277a – 120 d. green 10 10
2277b – 140 d. red 10 10
2277c – 170 d. green 10 10
2278 – 200 d. blue 10 10
2278c – 220 d. brown 10 10
2278d – 300 d. red 10 10
2280 – 500 d. blue and brown . 15 10
2281 – 500 d. blue and yellow . 15 10
2282 **735** 800 d. blue 10 10
2284 – 1000 d. violet & green . 30 10
2284b – 2000 d. green & orange . 10 10
2285 – 5000 d. blue and red . . 1·50 40
2285b – 10000 d. violet & orange 30 20
2285c – 20000 d. brown & green 65 35

DESIGNS—VERT: 30, 10000 d. Postman giving letters to man; 60 d. Posting letters; 93 d. Envelope and leaflet; 106 d. (No. 2276) Woman working at computer and woman filling envelope; 106 d. (No. 2277) Woman working at computer; 120 d. Woman with Valentine card; 140 d. Woman working at computer; 170, 300 d. Flower and postbox; 220 d. Mail coach and cover; 500 d. Postal sorter; 1000 d. Woman using public telephone; 5000 d. Posthorn, globe and bird with stamp. HORIZ: 40 d. Forklift truck; 50, 20000 d. Train; 200 d. Freighter; 2000 d. Telephone card, tokens and handset. 20 × 18 mm: 100 d. Postman and van.
See also Nos. 2586/99.

1986. World Cup Football Championships, Mexico. Multicoloured.
2286 70 d. Type **736** 60 60
2287 150 d. Players and ball in goal 60 60

737 St. Clement and Model of Ohrid (fresco, Church of St. Spas)

1986. 1100th Anniv of Arrival of St. Clement of Ohrid in Macedonia.
2288 **737** 10 d. multicoloured . . . 1·00 60

1986. No. 1674 surch.
2289 5 d. on 8 d. grey 10 10

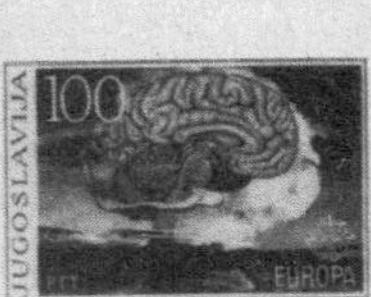

739 Human Brain as Nuclear Cloud

740 Judo

1986. Europa. Multicoloured.

2290 100 d. Type **739** 50 30
2291 200 d. Injured deer on road . 90 50

1988. European Men's Judo Championships, Belgrade.

2292 **740** 70 d. brown, pink & bl . 30 20

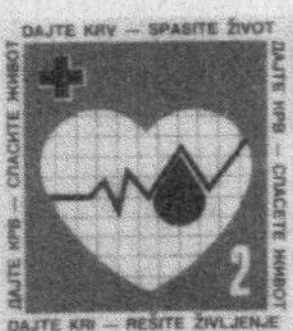

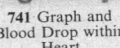

741 Graph and Blood Drop within Heart

742 Costume of Slovenia

1986. Obligatory Tax. Red Cross Week.

2293 **741** 2 d. black, blue and red . 10 10
2294 3 d. black, blue and red . 10 10
2295 4 d. black, blue and red . 10 10
2296 5 d. black, blue and red . 10 10
2297 11 d. black, bl and red . 10 10
2298 20 d. black, bl and red . 15 10

1986. Yugoslav Costumes. Multicoloured.

2299 50 d. Type **742** 25 15
2300 50 d. Vojvodina (woman with red apron) 25 15
2301 50 d. Croatia (man in embroidered trousers) . . . 25 15
2302 50 d. Macedonia (woman hand spinning) 25 15
2303 50 d. Serbia (woman in bolero) 25 15
2304 50 d. Montenegro (man with rifle) 25 15
2305 50 d. Kosovo (woman carrying basket) 25 15
2306 50 d. Bosnia and Herzegovina (man carrying bag on back) 25 15

743 Sailing Boats

744 Tito (after Safet Zec)

1986. "Flying Dutchman" Class European Sailing Championships, Moscenicka Draga. Multicoloured.

2307 50 d. Type **743** 25 15
2308 80 d. Sailing boats (different) 35 25

1986. 94th Birth Anniv of Tito.

2310 **744** 10 d. multicoloured . . . 10 10

745 "Eudia pavonia"

746 "Skopje Earthquake"

1986. Butterflies and Moths. Multicoloured.

2311 10 d. Type **745** 10 10
2312 20 d. "Inachis io" 15 10
2313 50 d. "Parnassius apollo" . . 20 20
2314 100 d. "Apatura iris" 25 35

1986. Obligatory Tax. Solidarity Week. (a) As No. 2200.

2315 **715** 10 d. blue and red . . . 10 10

(b) As Type **715** but inscr "Solidarity Week" in four languages.

2316 10 d. blue and red 10 10

(c) Type **746**.

2317 **746** 10 d. lilac and red . . . 10 10

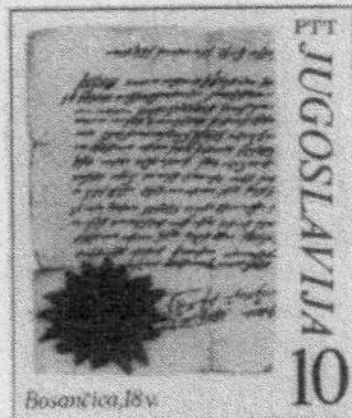

747 Bosancica Manuscript

1986. Museum Exhibits. Ancient Manuscripts. Multicoloured.

2319 10 d. Type **747** 10 10
2320 20 d. Leontije's Gospel . . . 10 10
2321 50 d. Astrological writing, Mesopotamia 25 15
2322 100 d. Hagada (ritual book), Spain 50 30

748 Congress Poster (B. Dobanovacki)

1986. 13th Communist League Conference, Belgrade.

2323 **748** 10 d. black and red . . 10 10
2324 – 20 d. black and red . . 10 10

DESIGN: 20 d. Another part of the Congress poster.

749 Trubar and Title Page of "Abecedari"

1986. 400th Death Anniv of Primoz Trubar (founder of Slovenian literary language and religious reformer).

2326 **749** 20 d. multicoloured . . 45 25

750 Emblem

751 Dancers

1986. 125th Anniv of Serbian National Theatre, Novi Sad.

2327 **750** 40 d. multicoloured . . 20 10

1986. Rugovo Dance.

2328 **751** 40 d. multicoloured . . 20 10

753 Crosses forming Earth and Sky

1986. Obligatory Tax. Anti-tuberculosis Week.

2330 **753** 2 d. multicoloured . . . 10 10
2331 5 d. multicoloured . . . 10 10
2332 6 d. multicoloured . . . 10 10
2333 7 d. multicoloured . . . 15 10
2334 8 d. multicoloured . . . 15 10
2335 10 d. multicoloured . . 15 10
2336 11 d. multicoloured . . 20 15
2337 14 d. multicoloured . . 20 15
2338 20 d. multicoloured . . 20 15

754 Volleyball

755 "Bird and Child running on Globe" (Tanja Faletic)

1986. "Universiade '87" University Games, Zagreb. Multicoloured.

2339 30 d. Type **754** 10 10
2340 40 d. Canoeing 15 10
2341 100 d. Gymnastics 40 25
2342 150 d. Fencing 60 35

1986. 18th "Joy of Europe" Meeting, Belgrade. Children's Paintings. Multicoloured.

2343 100 d. Type **755** 40 25
2344 150 d. "City of the Future" (Johanna Kraus) 60 35

756 Diagram of Rotary Selector and Bled

1986. 50th Anniv of Automatic Telephone Exchange Network.

2345 **756** 40 d. multicoloured . . . 15 10

757 Criminal in Stocking Mask

758 Brigade Member addressing Crowd (after D. Andrejevic-Kun)

1986. 55th Interpol General Assembly Session, Belgrade.

2346 **757** 150 d. multicoloured . . 60 35

1986. 50th Anniv of Formation of International Brigades in Spain.

2347 **758** 40 d. brown, gold and orange 15 10

759 Academy

1986. Centenary of Serbian Academy of Arts and Sciences.

2348 **759** 40 d. multicoloured . . . 15 10

760 People riding on Doves (Branislav Barnak)

1986. International Peace Year.

2349 **760** 150 d. multicoloured . . 65 35

761 "Portrait" (Bernard Buffet)

762 European Otter

1986. Paintings in Museum of Contemporary Arts, Skopje. Multicoloured.

2350 30 d. "Still Life" (Frantisek Muzika) 10 10
2351 40 d. "Disturbance" (detail, Rafael Canogar)(horiz) . . 15 10
2352 100 d. Type **761** 40 25
2353 100 d. "IOL" (Victor Vasarely) 40 25
2354 150 d. "Woman's Head" (Pablo Picasso) 60 35

1987. Protected Animals. Multicoloured.

2355 30 d. Type **762** 10 10
2356 40 d. Goat 15 10
2357 100 d. Red deer 40 25
2358 150 d. Brown bear 60 35

763 Boskovic, Brera Observatory and Solar Eclipse

764 Mountains, Woodlands and Animal Feeder

1987. Death Bicentenary of Ruder Boskovic (astronomer).

2359 **763** 150 d. multicoloured . . 60 35

1987. Nature Protection. Triglav National Park. Multicoloured.

2360 150 d. Type **764** 90 90
2361 400 d. Mountains, woodland and glacial lake 90 90

765 Potez 29-4 Biplane

1987. 60th Anniv of Civil Aviation in Yugoslavia. Multicoloured.

2362 150 d. Type **765** 75 40
2363 400 d. Douglas DC-10 . . . 1·75 1·00

766 Mateja Svet

1987. Yugoslav Medals at World Alpine Skiing Championships, Crans Montana.

2364 **768** 200 d. multicoloured . . 50 50

767 Kole Nedelkovski

1987. 75th Birth Anniv of Kole Nedelkovski (poet and revolutionary).

2365 **767** 40 d. multicoloured . . . 15 10

768 Battle Flags and Gusle

1987. 125th Anniv of Liberation Wars of Montenegro.

2366 **768** 40 d. multicoloured . . . 15 10

769 "Founding the Party at Cebine, 1937" (Anton Gojmir Kos)

1987. 50th Anniv of Slovenian Communist Party.

2367 **769** 40 d. multicoloured . . . 15 10

770 Tito Bridge (Ilija Stojadinovic)

771 Children of Different Races in Flower

1987. Europa. Architecture. Multicoloured.
2368 200 d. Type **770** . . . . . . 1·50 60
2369 400 d. Bridges over River Ljubljanica (Joze Plecnik) . 85 75

1987. Obligatory Tax. Red Cross Week.
2370 **771** 2 d. multicoloured . . . 10 10
2371 4 d. multicoloured . . . 10 10
2372 5 d. multicoloured . . . 10 10
2373 6 d. multicoloured . . . 10 10
2374 7 d. multicoloured . . . 10 10
2375 8 d. multicoloured . . . 10 10
2376 10 d. multicoloured . . . 10 10
2377 11 d. multicoloured . . . 10 10
2378 12 d. multicoloured . . . 10 10
2379 14 d. multicoloured . . . 10 10
2380 17 d. multicoloured . . . 10 10
2381 20 d. multicoloured . . . 10 10

772 Almonds

773 "Josip Broz Tito" (Mosa Pijade)

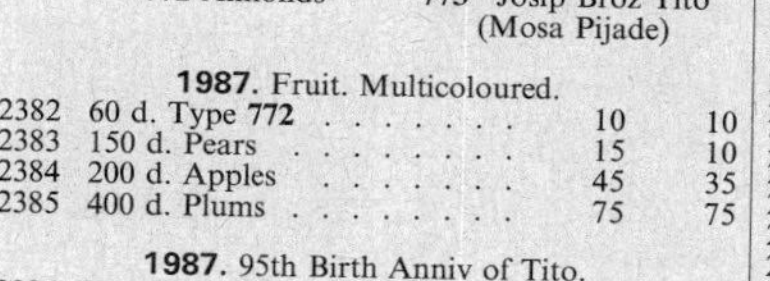

1987. Fruit. Multicoloured.
2382 60 d. Type **772** 10 10
2383 150 d. Pears 15 10
2384 200 d. Apples 45 35
2385 400 d. Plums 75 75

1987. 95th Birth Anniv of Tito.
2386 **773** 60 d. multicoloured . . . 10 10

774 "Skopje Earthquake"

776 Mail Coach in Zrenjanin

775 Bust of Karadzic (Petar Ubavkic), Trsic (birthplace) and Vienna

1987. Obligatory Tax. Solidarity Week.
2387 **774** 30 d. multicoloured . . . 10 10

1987. Birth Bicentenary of Vuk Stefanovic Karadzic (linguist and historian). Multicoloured.
2388 60 d. Type **775** 10 10
2389 200 d. Serbian alphabet and Karadzic (portrait by Uros Knezevic) 20 10

1987. 250th Anniv of Postal Services in Zrenjanin.
2390 **776** 60 d. multicoloured . . . 10 10

777 Emblem and Mascot

778 Hurdling

1987. Obligatory Tax. "Universiade '87" University Games, Zagreb.
2391 **777** 20 d. blue and green . . 10 10

1987. "Universiade '87" University Games, Zagreb. Multicoloured.
2392 60 d. Type **778** 10 10
2393 150 d. Basketball 15 10
2394 200 d. Gymnastics 20 10
2395 400 d. Swimming 75 75

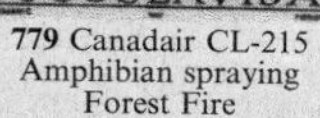

779 Canadair CL-215 Amphibian spraying Forest Fire

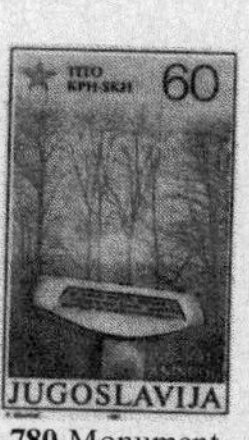

780 Monument, Anindol Park

1987. Fire Fighting. Multicoloured.
2396 60 d. Type **779** 20 10
2397 200 d. Fire-fighting tug . . . 20 10

1987. 50th Anniv of Croatian Communist Party.
2398 **780** 60 d. multicoloured . . 10 10

781 School and Foundation Document

782 Crosses and Children's Head

1987. 150th Anniv of Sabac High School.
2399 **781** 80 d. brown, orange and blue 10 10

1987. Obligatory Tax. Anti-tuberculosis Week.
2400 **782** 2 d. multicoloured . . . 10 10
2401 4 d. multicoloured . . . 10 10
2402 6 d. multicoloured . . . 10 10
2403 8 d. multicoloured . . . 10 10
2404 10 d. multicoloured . . 10 10
2405 12 d. multicoloured . . 10 10
2406 14 d. multicoloured . . 10 10
2407 20 d. multicoloured . . 10 10
2408 25 d. multicoloured . . 10 10
2409 40 d. multicoloured . . 10 10

783 Emblem, Map and Flowers

785 "Children playing amongst Trees" (Bedic Aranka)

1987. "Balkanphila XI" International Stamp Exhibition, Novi Sad.
2410 **783** 250 d. multicoloured . . 20 10

1987. No. 2269 surch **80**.
2412 80 d. on 60 d. green 10 10

1987. 19th "Joy of Europe" Meeting. Mult.
2413 250 d. Type **785** 60 60
2414 400 d. "Child and scarecrow in orchard" (Ingeborg Schaffer) 60 60

786 Arslanagica Bridge, Trebinje

1987. Bridges. Multicoloured.
2415 80 d. Type **786** 10 10
2416 250 d. Terzija Bridge, Djakovica 20 10

787 Tug in Canal

788 SPRAM Emblem

1987. 600th Anniv of Titov Vrbas.
2417 **787** 80 d. multicoloured . . 15 10

1987. Obligatory Tax.
2418 **788** 20 d. blue 10 10

789 Eclipse, Telescope and Old Observatory Building

1987. Centenary of Astronomocal and Meteorological Observatory, Belgrade.
2419 **789** 80 d. multicoloured . . 10 10

790 "St. Luke the Evangelist (Raffaello Santi)

1987. Paintings in Mimara Museum, Zagreb. Multicoloured.
2420 80 d. Type **790** 10 10
2421 200 d. "Infanta Maria Theresa" (Diego Velazquez) 20 10
2422 250 d. "Nicolaes Rubens" (Peter Paul Rubens) 20 10
2423 400 d. "Louise Laure Sennegon" (Camille Corot) 35 20

791 Bull Fighting (Grmec)

1987. Museum Exhibits. Folk Games. Multicoloured.
2424 80 d. Type **791** 10 10
2425 200 d. Sword used in Ljuvicevo Horse Games 20 10
2426 250 d. Crown worn at Moresca Games (Korcula) 20 10
2427 400 d. Sinj Iron Ring 60 60

792 Foundation Document, View of Town and Arms

1988. 700th Anniv of Vinodolski.
2428 **792** 100 d. multicoloured . . 10 10

793 Skier

794 Cub

1988. 25th Anniv of Golden Fox Skiing Competition, Maribor.
2429 **793** 350 d. multicoloured . . 30 15

1988. Protected Wildlife. Brown Bear. Multicoloured.
2430 70 d. Type **794** 10 10
2431 80 d. Bears among branches . 10 10
2432 200 d. Adult bear 20 10
2433 350 d. Adult stalking prey . . 30 15

795 Slalom Skier

797 Basketball

1988. Winter Olympic Games, Calgary. Multicoloured.
2434 350 d. Type **795** 60 55
2435 1200 d. Ice hockey 60 55

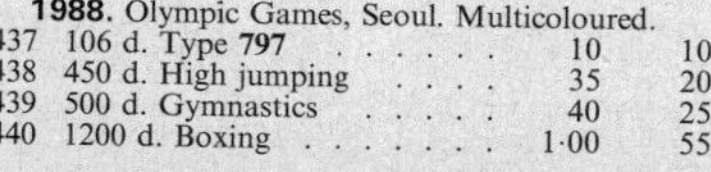

1988. Olympic Games, Seoul. Multicoloured.
2437 106 d. Type **797** 10 10
2438 450 d. High jumping 35 20
2439 500 d. Gymnastics 40 25
2440 1200 d. Boxing . . . . . . 1·00 55

798 White Carnations

799 "INTELSAT V-A", Globe and Dish Aerials, Ivanjica

1988. Obligatory Tax. Anti-cancer Campaign. Multicoloured.
2442 4 d. Type **798** 10 10
2443 8 d. Red flowers 10 10
2444 12 d. Red roses 10 10

1988. Europa. Transport and Communications. Multicoloured.
2445 450 d. Type **799** 15 10
2446 1200 d. Woman using mobile telephone and methods of transport 40 25

800 "Gibbula magus"

801 Anniversary Emblem

1988. Molluscs. Multicoloured.
2447 106 d. Type **800** 50 50
2448 550 d. "Pecten jacobaeus" . 50 50
2449 600 d. "Tonna galea" . . . 55 50
2450 1000 d. "Argonauta argo" . 65 50

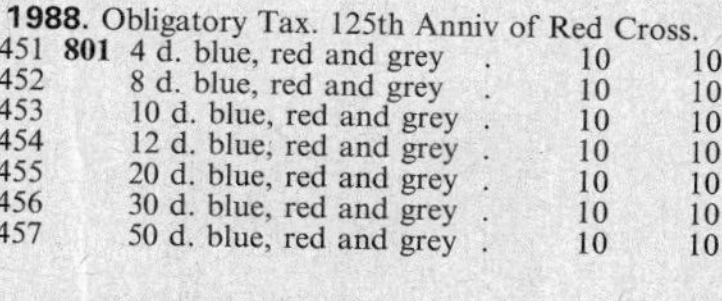

1988. Obligatory Tax. 125th Anniv of Red Cross.
2451 **801** 4 d. blue, red and grey . 10 10
2452 8 d. blue, red and grey . 10 10
2453 10 d. blue, red and grey . 10 10
2454 12 d. blue, red and grey . 10 10
2455 20 d. blue, red and grey . 10 10
2456 30 d. blue, red and grey . 10 10
2457 50 d. blue, red and grey . 10 10

802 Josip Broz Tito

803 "Skopje Earthquake"

1988. 60th Anniv of Trial of Tito.
2458 **802** 106 d. brown and black . 10 10

1988. Obligatory Tax. Solidarity Week. (a) Type **803**.
2459 **803** 50 d. grey, brown & red 10 10

(b) As No. 2220 but value changed.
2460 **715** 50 d. blue and red . . . 10 10

(c) No. 2387 surch.
2461 **774** 50 d. on 30 d. mult . . . 10 10

1988. Nos. 2273 and 2277 surch.
2462 120 d. on 93 d. blue 10 10
2463 140 d. on 106 d. brown . . . 10 10

806 First Lyceum Building

807 Krleza

1988. 150th Anniv of Belgrade University.
2464 **806** 106 d. multicoloured . . 10 10

1988. Obligatory Tax. Culture Fund. 95th Birth Anniv of M. Krleza (writer).
2465 **807** 30 d. brown & orange . 10 10

808 "Phelypaea boissieri"

809 Globe and Flags

1988. Nature Protection Macedonian Plants. Multicoloured.

2466 600 d. Type **808** 60 60
2467 1000 d. "Campanula formanekiana" 60 60

1988. Centenary of Esperanto (invented language).

2468 **809** 600 d. blue and green . . 20 10

810 Shipping on the Danube

811 Globe as Ball in Basket

1988. 40th Anniv of Danube Conference.

2469 **810** 1000 d. multicoloured . . 30 15

1988. 13th European Junior Basketball Championships, Tito Vrbas and Srbobran.

2471 **811** 600 d. multicoloured . . 20 10

812 Horse Racing

1988. 125th Anniv of Belgrade Horse Races. Multicoloured.

2472 140 d. Type **812** 10 10
2473 600 d. Show-jumping event . . 20 10
2474 1000 d. Trotting race 30 15

813 Douglas DC-10 and Globe

1988. Air.

2475 **813** 2000 d. multicoloured . . 80 30

814 Museum and Bosnian Bellflower

815 Flame and Hand

1988. Centenary of Bosnia amd Herzegovina Museum, Sarajevo.

2476 **814** 140 d. multicoloured . . 10 10

1988. Obligatory Tax. Anti-tuberculosis Week.

2477 **815** 4 d. multicoloured . . . 10 10
2478 8 d. multicoloured . . . 10 10
2479 12 d. multicoloured . . . 10 10
2480 20 d. multicoloured . . . 10 10
2481 50 d. multicoloured . . . 10 10
2482 70 d. multicoloured . . . 10 10

1988. Obligatory Tax. No. 2039 surch **1988 12**.

2483 **632** 12 d. on 1 d. orange, black and red 10 10

817 Arm and Crab's Claw (Anti-cancer)

818 "Daughter of the Artist" (Peter Ranosovic)

1988. Health Campaigns. Multicoloured.

2484 140 d. Type **817** 10 10
2485 1000 d. Screaming mouth in splash of blood (Anti-AIDS) 30 15

1988. 20th "Joy of Europe" Meeting. Mult.

2486 1000 d. Type **818** 60 60
2487 1100 d. "Girl wuth Straw Hat" (Pierre-Auguste Renoir) . . 60 60

819 1701 Arms and Present Emblem

1988. 50th Anniv of Slovenian Academy of Arts and Sciences.

2488 **819** 200 d. multicoloured . . 10 10

820 Galicnik Wedding

1988. Museum Exhibits. Traditional Crafts and Customs. Multicoloured.

2489 200 d. Type **820** 10 10
2490 1000 d. Weapons from Bokelji 30 15
2491 1000 d. Vojvodina embroidery (horiz) 30 15
2492 1100 d. People wearing masks, Kurenti (horiz) 35 20

821 Title Page of "Gorski Vijenac" and Njegos (after J. Boss)

1988. 175th Birth Anniv of Prince-Bishop Petar II of Montenegro. Multicoloured.

2493 200 d. Type **821** 10 10
2494 1000 d. Njegos Mausoleum, Lovcen and Njegos in bishop's robes (after Josip Tominc) 30 15

822 "Girl with Lyre"

1988. Greek Terracotta Figures from Josip Broz Tito Memorial Centre Collection. Multicoloured.

2495 200 d. Type **822** 10 10
2496 1000 d. "Girl on a stone" . 30 15
2497 1000 d. "Eros and Psyche" . 30 15
2498 1100 d. "Girl by the Stele" . 35 20

823 Krsmanovic House, Belgrade

1988. 70th Anniv of Yugoslavian State.

2499 **823** 200 d. multicoloured . . 10 10

1988. Nos. 2277a and 2277b surch.

2500 170 d. on 120 d. green . . . 10 10
2501 220 d. on 140 d. red 10 10

825 Pistol shooting

826 Gundulic and Dubrovnik

1988. Yugoslavian Medals at Olympic Games. Multicoloured.

2502 500 d. Type **825** (2 gold, 1 bronze) 15 10
2503 500 d. Handball (bronze) . . 15 10
2504 500 d. Table tennis (silver and bronze) 15 10
2505 500 d. Wrestling (silver) . . . 15 10
2506 500 d. Rowing (bronze) . . . 15 10
2507 500 d. Basketball (2 silver) . . 15 10
2508 500 d. Waterpolo (gold) . . . 15 10
2509 500 d. Boxing (bronze) . . . 15 10

1989. 400th Birth Anniv of Ivan Gundulic (poet).

2510 **826** 220 d. multicoloured . . 10 10

827 Mallard

828 Valvasor and Wagensperg Castle

1989. Wild Ducks. Multicoloured.

2511 300 d. Type **827** 15 10
2512 2100 d. Green-winged teal . . 85 40
2513 2200 d. Pintail 90 45
2514 2200 d. Common shoveller . . 90 45

1989. 300th Anniv of Publishing of "The Glory of the Duchy of Kranjska" by Johann Weickhard Valvasor.

2515 **828** 300 d. multicoloured . . 10 10

829 "Bulbocodium vernum"

832 Competitor

830 Envelopes and Dish Aerial

1989. Flowers. Multicoloured.

2516 300 d. Type **829** 10 10
2517 2100 d. White water-lily . . . 65 35
2518 2200 d. "Fritillaria degeniana" (vert) 70 40
2519 3000 d. "Orchis simia" (vert) . 90 45

1989. Air.

2520 **830** 10000 d. blue, mauve and yellow . . . . 1·50 90
2521 – 20000 d. orange, violet and red . . . . 1·40 1·40

DESIGN: 20000 d. Map and satellite.

1989. No. 1657 surch **100 d**.

2522 100 d. on 1 d. green 10 10

1989. 6th World Air Gun Championships, Sarajevo.

2523 **832** 3000 d. multicoloured . . 40 40

833 Girl looking through Magic Cube

834 Anniversary Emblem

1989. Europa. Children's Games and Toys. Multicoloured.

2524 3000 d. Type **833** 90 75
2525 6000 d. Boy playing with marbles and paper boats . . 90 90

1989. Obligatory Tax. 125th Anniv of Red Cross Movement (1988).

2526 **834** 20 d. blue, silver and red . 10 10
2527 80 d. blue, silver and red . . 10 10
2528 150 d. bl, silver and red . . 10 10
2529 160 d. bl, silver and red . . 10 10

835 Tito

836 "Skopje Earthquake"

1989. 70th Anniv of Yugoslavian Communist Party.

2530 **835** 300 d. multicoloured . . 10 10

1989. Obligatory Tax. Solidarity Week. (a) Type **836**.

2531 **836** 250 d. silver and red . . 10 10

(b) As T **715**.

2532 **715** 400 d. blue and red . . . 10 10

837 Pole Vaulting

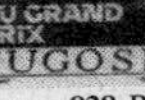

838 Racers

1989. 15th European Trophy Athletic Clubs Championship, Belgrade.

2533 **837** 4000 d. multicoloured . . 15 10

1989. Motor Cycle Grand Prix, Rijeka. Mult.

2534 500 d. Type **838** 10 10
2535 4000 d. Racers (different) . . 15 10

839 Flags of Netherlands, Italy, USSR and Spain and Ball

1989. 26th European Men's Basketball Championship, Zagreb. Multicoloured.

2537 2000 d. Type **839** 10 10
2538 2000 d. Flags of France, Yugoslavia, Greece and Bulgaria and ball 10 10

840 Ancient Greek Galleys

1989. Sailing Ships. Multicoloured.

2539 1000 d. Type **840** 15 10
2540 1000 d. Roman warships . . 15 10
2541 1000 d. 13th-century Crusader nefs 15 10
2542 1000 d. 16th-century Dubrovnik navas 15 10
2543 1000 d. 17th-century French warships 15 10
2544 1000 d. 18th-century ships of the line 15 10

841 "Battle of Kosovo" (lithograph, Adam Stefanovic)

1989. 600th Anniv of Battle of Kosovo.

2546 **841** 500 d. multicoloured . . 10 10

842 Danilovgrad

1989. Centenary of First Reading Room at Danilovgrad.

2547 **842** 500 d. multicoloured . . 10 10

1989. No. 2278c surch **700**.
2548 700 d. on 220 d. brown . . . 10 10

1989. Nos. 2266 and 2277c surch.
2549 400 d. on 30 d. brown . . . 10 10
2550 700 d. on 170 d. green . . . 10 10

845 Stone Tablet, Detail of Charter and Mule Train

1989. 800th Anniv of Kulin Ban Charter (granting free trade to Dubrovnik).
2551 **845** 500 d. multicoloured . . 10 10

846 Rowers **847** Houses of Parliament, London

1989. World Rowing Championship, Bled.
2552 **846** 10000 d. multicoloured . 30 15

1989. Centenary of Interparliamentary Union.
2553 10000 d. Type **847** 30 15
2554 10000 d. Notre Dame Cathedral, Paris 30 15

848 Belgrade and Cairo **849** Emblem

1989. 9th Non-aligned Conference, Belgrade. Multicoloured.
2555 10000 d. Type **848** 30 15
2556 10000 d. Lusaka and Algiers 30 15
2557 10000 d. Colombo and Havana 30 15
2558 10000 d. New Delhi and Harare 30 15

1989. Obligatory Tax. USAOJ-A Conference, Bihac.
2560 **849** 400 d. blue and red . . . 10 10

850 Brezovica-Jazinac Lake, Kosovo **851** Crosses as Basket of Flowers

1989. Nature Protection. Multicoloured.
2561 8000 d. Type **850** 25 15
2562 10000 d. Mirusa Canyon, Kosovo 30 15

1989. Obligatory Tax. Anti-tuberculosis Week.
2563 **851** 20 d. red and black . . . 10 10
2564 200 d. red and black . . 10 10
2565 250 d. red and black . . 10 10
2566 400 d. red and black . . 10 10
2567 650 d. red and black . . 10 10

852 "Child with Lamb" (Jovan Popovic) **853** Men Fighting

1989. 21st "Joy of Europe" Meeting. Mult.
2568 10000 d. Type **852** 30 15
2569 10000 d. "Girl feeding Dog" (Aelbert Cuyp) 30 15

1989. 300th Anniv of Karpos Insurrection.
2570 **853** 1200 d. multicoloured . 10 10

854 Cancelled 100 d. Stamp, Quill and Seal

1989. Stamp Day.
2571 **854** 1200 d. multicoloured . 10 10

855 Packsaddle Maker

1989. Museum Exhibits. Traditional Crafts. Multicoloured.
2572 1200 d. Type **855** 10 10
2573 14000 d. Cooper 45 25
2574 15000 d. Wine maker . . . 50 25
2575 30000 d. Weaver 95 50

856 Aerospatiale/Aeritalia ATR 42, Arrows and Map **857** "Apostle Mathias"

1989. Air.
2576 **856** 50000 d. blue & orange . 1·60 80

1989. Frescoes by Iohannes de Kastua from Holy Trinity Church, Hrastovlje, Slovenia. Multicoloured.
2577 2100 d. Type **857** 10 10
2578 21000 d. "St. Barbara" . . . 35 35
2579 30000 d. "Creation of the Universe, the Fourth Day" (horiz) 60 50
2580 50000 d. "Creation of the Universe, the Fifth Day" (horiz) 90 80

858 Barn Swallow, Envelope and Flower **860** Colour Spectrum entering Star

1989.
2581 **858** 100000 d. green & orge . 1·75 1·50

1989. No. 1680 surch.
2582 700 d. on 70 d. blue 10 10

1990. 14th Extraordinary Congress of League of Communists of Yugoslavia.
2583 **860** 10000 d. multicoloured . 30 15
2584 – 50000 d. multicoloured . 40 40
DESIGN: 50000 d. Hammer and sickle on V.D.U. screen.

1990. Postal Services. As T **735** but in revised currency.
2586 10 p. violet and green . . . 10 10
2587 20 p. red and yellow . . . 10 10
2588 30 p. green and orange . . . 10 10
2589 40 p. green and purple . . . 10 10
2590 50 p. green and violet . . . 10 10
2591 60 p. mauve and red . . . 10 10
2595 1 d. blue and purple . . . 10 10
2596 2 d. blue and red 20 10
2597 3 d. blue and red 30 15
2599 5 d. ultramarine and blue . . 50 25
2603 10 d. blue and red . . . . 1·50 60
2605 20 d. red and orange . . . . 1·10 55
DESIGNS—VERT: 10 p. Man posting letters; 20 p. Postal sorter; 30 p. Postman giving letters to man; 40 p., 20 d. Woman telephoning; 50 p. Posthorn, globe and bird; 60 p. Telephone card, tokens and handset; 3 d. Post-box; 5 d. Aerospatiale/Aeritalia ATR 42 airplane, letters and map; 10 d. Barn Swallow, flower and envelope. HORIZ: 1 d. Train; 2 d. Freighter.

861 Gloved Hand holding Lighted Cigarette

1990. Anti-smoking Campaign.
2610 **861** 10 d. multicoloured . . . 1·00 85

862 Northern Pike

1990. Endangered Fishes. Multicoloured.
2611 1 d. Type **862** 10 10
2612 5 d. European catfish 50 25
2613 10 d. Burbot . . . . 1·00 85
2614 15 d. River perch . . . . . . 1·50 1·25

863 Zabljak Fortress, Printed Page and Arms

1990. 500th Anniv of Enthronement of Djuradj Crnojevic.
2615 **863** 50 p. multicoloured . . . 10 10

864 Telegraphist and V.D.U. Screen

1990. 125th Anniv of I.T.U.
2616 **864** 6 d. 50 multicoloured . . 65 35

865 Footballers **866** Skopje Posts and Telecommunications Centre

1990. World Cup Football Championship, Italy.
2617 – 6 d. 50 multicoloured . . 65 30
2618 **865** 10 d. multicoloured . . 1·00 50
DESIGN: 6 d. 50, Footballers (different).

1990. Europa. Post Office Buildings. Mult.
2619 6 d. 50 Type **866** 65 30
2620 10 d. Belgrade Telephone Exchange . . . . 1·00 50

867 Chicago Water Tower and Carnation **868** Record, Notes and Pen

1990. Centenary of Labour Day.
2621 **867** 6 d. 50 multicoloured . . 65 30

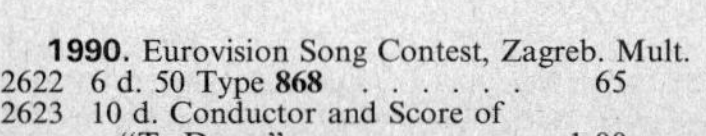

1990. Eurovision Song Contest, Zagreb. Mult.
2622 6 d. 50 Type **868** 65 30
2623 10 d. Conductor and Score of "Te Deum" . . . . 1·00 50

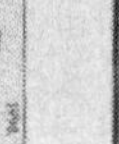

869 Cross and Leaves **870** Large Yellow Flowers

1990. Obligatory Tax. Red Cross Week.
2624 **869** 10 p. red and green . . . 10 10
2625 20 p. red and green . . . 10 10
2626 30 p. red and green . . . 10 10
(b) 45th Anniv of Macedonian Red Cross. Flower Paintings by Zivko A. Popovski. Multicoloured.
2627 20 p. Type **870** 10 10
2628 20 p. Arrangement of small yellow flowers 10 10
2629 20 p. Anniversary emblem . 10 10
See also Nos. 2636/7.

871 Server **873 Tito (bronze Antun Augustincic)**

1990. Yugoslav Open Tennis Championship, Umag. Multicoloured.
2630 6 d. 50 Type **871** 65 30
2631 10 d. Receiver . . . . 1·00 50

1990. No. 2282 surch **0,50**.
2632 **735** 50 p. on 800 d. blue . . 10 10

1990. 98th Birth Anniv of Tito.
2633 **873** 50 p. multicoloured . . . 10 10

874 "Tartar Post Riders" (Carl Goebel)

1990. 150th Anniv of Public Postal Service in Serbia.
2634 **874** 50 p. multicoloured . . . 10 10

875 "Skopje Earthquake" **876**

1990. Obligatory Tax. Solidarity Week.
2635 **875** 20 p. brown, red & silver 10 10
2636 – 20 p. multicoloured . . . 10 10
2637 – 20 p. multicoloured . . . 10 10
2638 **876** 20 p. blue and red . . . 10 10
2639 **715** 30 p. blue and red . . . 10 10
DESIGNS—As T **870**: No. 2636, Mauve flowers; 2637, Red and yellow flowers.

877 Fantail **878** Idrija Town

1990. Pigeons. Multicoloured.
2640 50 p. Type **877** 10 10
2641 5 d. Serbian high flier . . . 50 25
2642 6 d. 50 Carrier pigeon (vert) 65 30
2643 10 d. Pouter (vert) . . . . . 1·00 50

1990. 500th Anniversaries of Idrija Town (2644) and Mercury Mine (2645). Multicoloured.
2644 50 p. Type **878** 10 10
2645 6 d. 50 Mine 65 30

879 Newspaper Offices, Museum and Mastheads

881 Runners leaving Blocks

1990. 50th Anniv of "Vjesnik" (newspaper).

2646 **879** 60 p. multicoloured . . . 10 10

1990. Nos. 2587 and 2588 surch.

2647 50 p. on 20 p. red & yellow . 10 10
2648 1 d. on 30 p. green & orange 10 10

1990. European Athletics Championships, Split. Multicoloured.

2649 1 d. Type **881** 10 10
2650 6 d. 50 Runners' feet 65 30

882 Nurse and Sun

883 Flowers in Vase and Birds

1990. Obligatory Tax. Anti-tuberculosis Week.

2652 **882** 20 p. yellow, blue & red . 10 10
2653 25 p. yellow, blue & red . 10 10
2654 50 p. yellow, blue & red . 10 10
2655 **883** 50 p. brown, red & grey . 10 10

884 "Pec Patriachate" (D. Cudov)

1990. 300th Anniv of Great Migration of Serbs. Multicoloured.

2656 1 d. Type **884** 10 10
2657 6 d. 50 "Migration of Serbs" (Paja Jovanovic) 65 30

1990. No. 2589 surch **2**.

2658 2 d. on 40 p. green & pur . . 20 10

887 "Little Sisters" (Ivana Kobilca)

888 Chess Pieces

1990. 22nd "Joy of Europe" Meeting. Mult.

2660 6 d. 50 Type **887** 65 30
2661 10 d. "Willem III of Orange as a child" (Adriaen Hanneman) (vert) . . . . 1·00 50

1990. 29th Chess Olympiad, Novi Sad. Mult.

2662 1 d. Type **888** 10 10
2663 5 d. Rook, bishop, knight and chessboard 50 25
2664 6 d. 50 Knights, queen, king, pawn and chessboard . . . 65 30
2665 10 d. Chess pieces and symbols 1·00 50

889 "St. Vlaho and Ragusa" (detail of triptych, Nikola Bozidarevic) and Penny Black

1990. Stamp Day.

2667 **889** 2 d. multicoloured . . . 20 10

890 Vransko Lake

1990. Nature Protection. Multicoloured.

2668 6 d. 50 Type **890** 65 30
2669 10 d. Griffon vulture . . . . 1·50 60

891 "King Milutin" and Notre Dame Monastery, Ljeviska

1990. Monastery Frescoes. Multicoloured.

2670 2 d. Type **891** 20 10
2671 5 d. "St. Sava" and Mileseva Monastery 50 25
2672 6 d. 50 "St. Elias" and Moraca Monastery 65 30
2673 10 d. "Jesus Christ" and Sopocani Monastery . . . 1·00 50

892 Milanovic and Kringa (birthplace)

1990. Birth Centenary of Dr. Bozo Milanovic (politician).

2674 **892** 2 d. multicoloured . . . 20 10

893 Bringing Mary into the Temple

894 Lapwing

1990. Iconostasis of St. Jovan Bigorski Monastery. Multicoloured.

2675 2 d. Type **893** 20 10
2676 5 d. Nativity 50 25
2677 6 d. Flight into Egypt (horiz) 65 30
2678 10 d. Entry into Jerusalem (horiz) . . . . 1·00 50

1991. Protected Birds. Multicoloured.

2679 2 d. Type **894** 20 10
2680 5 d. Woodchat shrike . . . 50 25
2681 6 d. 50 Common crane . . . 65 30
2682 10 d. Goosander . . . . . . 1·00 50

895 "Crocus kosaninii"

896 Bishop Josip Juraj Strossmayer (founder) (after Vlaho Bukovac)

1991. Crocuses. Multicoloured.

2683 2 d. Type **895** 20 10
2684 6 d. "Crocus scardicus" . . . 60 30
2685 7 d. 50 "Crocus rujanensis" . 75 35
2686 15 d. "Crocus adamii" . . . 1·50 75

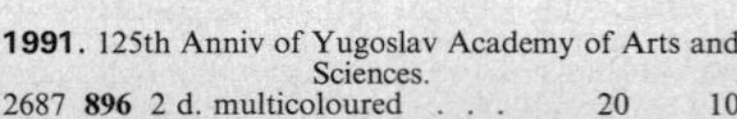

1991. 125th Anniv of Yugoslav Academy of Arts and Sciences.

2687 **896** 2 d. multicoloured . . . 20 10

897 Mozart (after P. A. Lorenzoni)

898 Edvard Rusijan (Slovenian pioneer)

1991. Death Bicentenary of Wolfgang Amadeus Mozart (composer).

2688 **897** 7 d. 50 multicoloured . . 75 35

1991. Centenary of First Heavier-than-Air Flight by Lilienthal. Multicoloured.

2689 7 d. 50 Type **898** 75 35
2690 15 d. Otto Lilienthal . . . . 1·50 75

899 Route of Climb and Cesen

1991. 1st Anniv of Tomo Cesen's Ascent of South Face of Lhotse Peak.

2691 **899** 7 d. 50 multicoloured . . 75 35

900 Satellite and Earth

1991. Europa. Europe in Space. Multicoloured.

2692 7 d. 50 Type **900** 75 35
2693 15 d. Telecommunications . . 1·50 75

901 Figures

902 Red Cross and Rays

1991. Obligatory Tax. Red Cross Week.

2694 **901** 60 p. multicoloured . . . 10 10
2695 1 d. 20 multicoloured . . 10 10
2696 1 d. 50 multicoloured . . 15 10
2697 – 1 d. 70 multicoloured . . 10 10
2698 **902** 1 d. 70 multicoloured . . 10 10
2699 – 1 d. 70 multicoloured . . 10 10
2700 – 1 d. 70 multicoloured . . 10 10
2701 – 1 d. 70 multicoloured . . 10 10

DESIGNS—29 × 24mm: No. 2697, similar to T **901** but differently inscribed. As T **902**: No. 2699, Pink flowers; 2700, Children on globe; 2701, Yellow flowers.

903 Miraculous Icon of St. Mary of Trsat (14th-century)

904 River Steamer

1991. 700th Anniv of Franciscan Monastery, Rijeka.

2702 **903** 3 d. 50 multicoloured . . 20 10

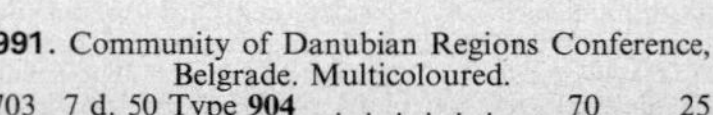

1991. Community of Danubian Regions Conference, Belgrade. Multicoloured.

2703 7 d. 50 Type **904** 70 25
2704 15 d. River at sunset . . . . 1·40 50

905 Woman with Horse

1991. Obligatory Tax. Solidarity Week.

2706 **876** 2 d. green and orange . 10 10
2707 – 2 d. brown, red & gold . 10 10
2708 **905** 2 d. brown, red & gold . 10 10
2709 – 2 d. brown, red & gold . 10 10
2710 – 2 d. brown, red & gold . 10 10
2711 **715** 2 d. 20 blue and red . . 10 10

DESIGNS—As T **905**: No. 2707, "Skopje Earthquake"; 2709, Woman and tree; 2710, Woman holding cockerel.

906 "Karawanke Pass" (17th-century engraving, J. Valvasor)

1991. Karawanke Road Tunnel. Multicoloured.

2712 4 d. 50 Type **906** 25 15
2713 11 d. Tunnel entrance . . . 60 35

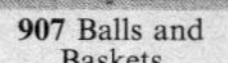

907 Balls and Baskets

908 Order of the Partisan Star

1991. Centenary of Basketball. Multicoloured.

2714 11 d. Type **907** 60 35
2715 15 d. Aerial view of baskets . 80 50

1991. 50th Anniversaries of Yugoslav Insurrection and National Army. Multicoloured.

2716 4 d. 50 Type **908** 25 15
2717 11 d. Order for Bravery . . . 60 35

909 Ujevic

910 Score and Gallus

1991. Birth Centenary of Tin Ujevic (writer).

2718 **909** 4 d. 50 multicoloured . . 25 15

1991. 400th Death Anniv of Jacobus Gallus (composer).

2719 **910** 11 d. multicoloured . . . 60 35

911 Savudrija, 1818

1991. Lighthouses of the Adriatic and the Danube. Multicoloured.

2720 10 d. Type **911** 50 30
2721 10 d. Sveti Ivan na Pucini, 1853 50 30
2722 10 d. Porer, 1833 . . . . . . 50 30
2723 10 d. Stoncica, 1865 . . . . 50 30
2724 10 d. Olipa, 1842 . . . . . . 50 30
2725 10 d. Glavat, 1884 . . . . . 50 30
2726 10 d. Veli Rat, 1849 . . . . 50 30
2727 10 d. Vir, 1881 . . . . 50 30
2728 10 d. Tajerske Sestrice, 1876 50 30
2729 10 d. Razanj, 1875 . . . . . 50 30
2730 10 d. Derdap, Danube . . . 50 30
2731 10 d. Tamis, Danube 50 30

912 "Sremski Karlovci School" (Ljubica Sokic)

1991. Bicent of Sremski Karlovci High School.
2732 **912** 4 d. 50 multicoloured . . 25 15

913 Girl

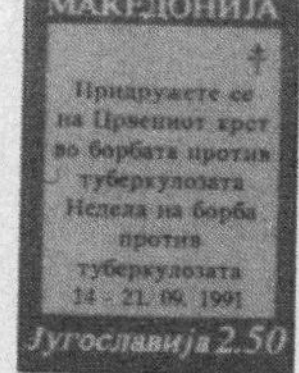

914 Inscription

1991. Obligatory Tax. Anti-tuberculosis Week.
2733 **913** 1 d. 20 blue, red & yellow 10 10
2734 2 d. 50 blue, red & yellow 15 10
2735 **914** 2 d. 50 black, yell & mve 15 10
2736 – 2 d. 50 multicoloured . . 15 10
2737 – 2 d. 50 multicoloured . . 15 10
2738 – 2 d. 50 blk, yell & mve . . 15 10
DESIGNS—As T **914**: No. 2736, Doctor; 2737, Children; 2738, Girls with birds and flowers.

915 Mayfly

916 Town Hall (stained glass)

1991. Nature Protection. Multicoloured.
2739 11 d. Type **915** 60 35
2740 15 d. Pygmy cormorants . . 80 40

1991. 600th Anniv of Subotica.
2741 **916** 4 d. 50 multicoloured . . 25 15

917 Honey Bees and Congress Emblem

918 "Little Dubravka" (Jovan Bijelic)

1991. "Apimondia" 33rd International Bee Keeping Congress, Split.
2742 **917** 11 d. multicoloured . . . 60 35

1991. 23rd "Joy of Europe" Meeting. Mult.
2743 5 d. Type **918** 25 15
2744 30 d. "Little Girl with a Cat" (Mary Cassatt) . . . . . . 1·60 95

919 Statue of Prince Michael Obrenovich and Serbian 1866 1 p. Newspaper Stamp

1991. Stamp Day.
2745 **919** 4 d. 50 multicoloured . . 25 15

920 Battle of Vucji. Flag and Medal for Military Valour

921 Angel carrying Sun (Andrija Raicevic) (17th century)

1991. Cetinje Museum Exhibits, Montenegrin Flags and Medals. Multicoloured.
2746 20 d. Type **920** . . . . . . 1·10 65
2747 30 d. Battle of Grahovo flag and medal . . . . 1·60 95
2748 40 d. State flag and Medal for bravery . . . . 2·10 1·25
2749 50 d. Court flag and Petrovic dynasty commemorative medal . . . . 2·60 1·60

1991. Illustrations from Ancient Manuscripts. Multicoloured.
2750 20 d. Type **921** . . . . . 1·10 65
2751 30 d. "April" (Celnica Gospel) (14th century) . . . . . . 1·60 95
2752 40 d. "Annunciation" (Trogir Evangeliarum) (13th century) 2·10 1·25
2753 50 d. Mary Magdalene in initial V (Miroslav Gospel) (12th century) . . . . 2·60 1·60

1991. Nos. 2591 and 2586 surch.
2754 5 d. on 60 p. mauve and red 25 15
2755 10 d. on 10 p. violet & grn . 50 30

923 Delcev

924 Trophies and Club Emblem

1992. 120th Birth Anniv of Goce Delcev (revolutionary).
2756 **923** 5 d. multicoloured . . . 25 15

1992. Victories of Red Star Club, Belgrade, in European and World Football Championships.
2757 **924** 17 d. multicoloured . . 90 55

925 Luge

1992. Winter Olympic Games, Albertville. Multicoloured.
2758 80 d. Type **925** . . . . . 4·00 2·40
2759 100 d. Acrobatic skiing . . . 5·25 3·25

926 European Hare

927 "Mary feeding Jesus" (fresco, Pec Patriarchate)

1992. Protected Animals. Multicoloured.
2760 50 d. Type **926** . . . . . 2·50 1·50
2761 60 d. Siberian flying squirrels 3·00 1·75
2762 80 d. Forest dormouse . . . 4·00 2·50
2763 100 d. Common hamsters . 5·25 3·25

1992. United Nations Children's Fund Breastfeeding Campaign.
2764 **927** 80 d. multicoloured . . 4·00 2·50

928 Skier

1992. Centenary of Skiing in Montenegro.
2765 **928** 8 d. multicoloured . . . 40 25

929 Fountain, Belgrade

930 "Titanic"

1992.
2766 **929** 50 d. violet . . . . 2·50 1·50

1992. 80th Anniv of Sinking of "Titanic".
2785 **930** 150 d. multicoloured . . 8·00 4·75

931 La Barqueta Bridge and Seville (engraving)

1992. "Expo '92" World's Fair, Seville.
2786 **931** 150 d. multicoloured . . 8·00 4·75

EXPRESS LETTER STAMP

CROATIA

1918. Express Letter stamp of Hungary optd **HRVATSKA SHS ZURNO.**
E84 E **18** 2 f. olive and red . . . 10 15

NEWSPAPER STAMPS

CROATIA

1918. Newspaper stamp of Hungary optd **HRVATSKA SHS.**
N83 N **9** 2 f. orange 10 15

N 25

1919. Imperf.
N97 N **25** 2 h. yellow 10 75

SLOVENIA

N 30 Cherub with Newspapers

1919. Imperf.
N150 N **30** 2 v. grey 10 15
N155 2 v. blue 10 10
N151 4 v. grey 10 25
N156 4 v. blue 10 15
N152 6 v. grey . . . . . . 3·00 3·75
N157 6 v. blue . . . . . . 2·50 3·00
N153 10 v. grey 10 15
N158 10 v. blue 10 10
N154 30 v. grey 10 25

(N 35)

(N 36)

1920. Surch as Type N **35** (2 to 6 p.) or Type N **36** (10 p. and 30 p.).
N164 N **30** 2 p. on 2 v. grey . . . 30 65
N169 2 p. on 2 v. blue . . . 10 10
N165 4 p. on 2 v. grey . . . 30 65
N170 4 p. on 2 v. blue . . . 10 10
N166 6 p. on 2 v. grey . . . 45 65
N171 6 p. on 2 v. blue . . . 10 10
N167 10 p. on 2 v. grey . . 65 75
N172 10 p. on 2 v. blue . . 15 40
N168 30 p. on 2 v. grey . . 65 1·00
N173 30 p. on 2 v. blue . . 20 50

OFFICIAL STAMPS

O 130

1946.
O540 O **130** 50 p. orange 15 10
O541 1 d. green 15 10
O542 1 d. 50 olive 30 10
O543 2 d. 50 red 30 10
O544 4 d. brown 60 10
O545 5 d. blue 80 10
O546 8 d. brown . . . . . 1·10 15
O547 12 d. violet . . . . . 1·40 30

POSTAGE DUE STAMPS

BOSNIA AND HERZEGOVINA

ДРЖАВА С.Х.С.
БОСНА И
ХЕРЦЕГОВИНА

хелера
(D 5)

КРАЉЕВСТВО
СРВА. ХРВАТА
И СЛОВЕНАЦА

ПОРТО

(D 13)

1918. Postage Due Stamps of Bosnia optd as Type D 5 or **DRZAVA S.H.S. BOSNA I HERCEGOVINA HELERA.**

D19 **D 35** 2 h. red 10 10
D20 4 h. red 30 50
D21 5 h. red 10 10
D22 6 h. red 50 35
D23 10 h. red 10 10
D24 15 h. red . . . . 5·25 5·25
D25 20 h. red 10 10
D26 25 h. red 35 35
D27 30 h. red 35 35
D28 40 h. red 15 15
D29 50 h. red 70 70
D30 1 k. blue 35 35
D31 3 k. blue 25 25

1919. "Eagle" type of Bosnia surch as Type D 13 or **KRALJEVSTVO SRBA, HRVATA I SLOVENACA PORTO** and value.

D50 **2** 2 h. on 35 h. blue 25 15
D51 5 h. on 45 h. blue 45 75
D52 10 h. on 10 h. red 10 10
D53 15 h. on 40 h. orange 25 30
D54 20 h. on 5 h. green 10 10
D55 25 h. on 20 h. pink 20 25
D56 30 h. on 30 h. brown 20 25
D57 1 k. on 50 h. purple 10 35
D58 3 k. on 25 h. blue 25 35

КРАЉЕВСТВО
СРБА, ХРВАТА
И СЛОБЕНАЦА
40

40 хелера 40
(D 14)

1919. Postage Due stamps of Bosnia with surch or optd as Type D 14 or **KRALJEVSTVO SRBA HRVATA SLOVENACA** and value.

D59 **D 4** 40 h. on 6 h. black, red and yellow 10 10
D60 50 h. on 8 h. black, red and yellow 10 10
D61 200 h. black, red & grn . 6·25 5·25
D62 4 k. on 7 h. black, red and yellow 20 35

CROATIA

1919. Postage Due stamps of Hungary, with figures in red (except 50 f. in black), optd **HRVATSKA SHS.**

D85 **D 9** 1 f. green (No. D190) . . 22·00 28·00
D86 2 f. green 90 90
D87 10 f. green 65 65
D88 12 f. green . . . . . . 85·00 95·00
D89 15 f. green 50 50
D90 20 f. green 50 50
D91 30 f. green . . . . . . 1·60 1·60
D92 50 f. green (No. D177) . 25·00 30·00

SLOVENIA

D 30

1919.

D150 **D 30** 5 v. red 10 10
D151 10 v. red 10 10
D152 20 v. red 10 10
D153 50 v. red 10 10
D154 1 k. blue 25 25
D155 5 k. blue 45 25
D156 10 k. blue 80 65

(D 35)

(D 36)

1920. Stamps of 1919 issue surch as Types D 35 or D 36.

D164 **25** 5 p. on 15 v. blue 10 10
D165 10 p. on 15 v. blue . . . 50 40
D166 20 p. on 15 v. blue . . . 15 10
D167 50 p. on 15 v. blue . . . 10 10
D168 **26** 1 d. on 30 v. pink (or red) 15 15
D169 3 d. on 30 v. pink (or red) 30 15
D170 8 d. on 30 v. pink (or red) 75 45

GENERAL ISSUES

D 39 King Alexander I when Prince

D 40

1921.

D182 **D 39** 10 on 5 p. green . . . 15 10
D183 30 on 5 p. green . . . 20 10

1921.

D184 **D 40** 10 p. red 10 10
D185 30 p. green 15 10
D197 50 p. violet 10 10
D187 1 d. brown 10 10
D188 2 d. blue 20 10
D189 5 d. orange . . . . . 1·60 10
D190 10 d. brown . . . . . 7·50 25
D191 25 d. pink . . . . . 30·00 1·00
D192 50 d. green . . . . . 30·00 1·50

There are two issues in this type, differing in the lettering, etc.

1928. Surcharged **10.**

D233 **D 40** 10 on 25 d. pink . . . 3·75 25
D234 10 on 50 d. green . . 3·75 25

D 56

(D 62)

1931.

D259 **D 56** 50 p. violet 10 10
D260 1 d. red 10 10
D261 2 d. blue 10 10
D262 5 d. orange 10 10
D263 10 d. brown 20 10

1933. Optd with Type D **62.**

D293a **D 40** 50 p. violet 15 10
D294a 1 d. brown 15 10
D295b 2 d. blue 30 10
D296 5 d. orange 90 35
D297a 10 d. brown . . . . 3·50 10

1933. Red Cross. As T **62** but inscr "PORTO" in Latin and Cyrillic characters.

D298 **62** 50 p. red and green . . 25 10

DEMOCRATIC FEDERATION OF YUGOSLAVIA

(a) REGIONAL ISSUES

CROATIA

1945. Zagreb issue. Croatian Postage Due stamps of 1942 surch **DEMOKRATSKA FEDERATIVNA JUGOSLAVIJA**, value and star.

RD45 **D 15** 40 k. on 50 b. brown and blue 10 10
RD46 60 k. on 1 k. brown and blue 10 10
RD47 80 k. on 2 k. brown and blue 10 10
RD48 100 k. on 5 k. brown and blue 15 15
RD49 200 k. on 6 k. brown and blue 20 20

MONTENEGRO

1945. Cetinje issue. National Poem issue of Italian Occupation surch as Type R **4**, with "PORTO" in addition.

RD61 10 l. on 5 c. violet . . . . 62·00 £225
RD62 20 l. on 5 l. red on brown . 90·00 85·00

SERBIA

1944. Senta issue. No. D684 of Hungary optd with a large star, **8.X.1944** and "Yugoslavia" in Cyrillic characters and surch in addition.

RD73 **D 115** 10 (f.) on 2 f. brn . 45·00 45·00

(b) GENERAL ISSUES

D 114

D 115

D 126

1944. Postage Due stamps of Serbia optd in Cyrillic characters, as Type D **114.**

D487 10 d. red 30 50
D488 20 d. blue 30 50

1945. (a) Value in black.

D489 **D 115** 2 d. brown 10 10
D490 3 d. violet 10 10
D491 5 d. green 10 10
D492 7 d. brown 10 10
D493 10 d. lilac 15 10
D494 20 d. blue 20 10
D495 30 d. green 35 15
D496 40 d. red 40 20

(b) Value in colour.

D497 **D 115** 1 d. green 10 10
D498 1 d. 50 blue 10 10
D499 2 d. red 15 10
D500 3 d. brown 30 10
D501 4 d. violet 40 20

1946.

D 527 **D 126** 50 p. orange 10 10
D 528 1 d. orange 10 10
D 724 1 d. brown 25 10
D 529 2 d. blue 10 10
D 725 2 d. green 25 10
D 530 3 d. green 15 10
D 531 5 d. violet 15 10
D 726 5 d. blue 40 10
D 532 7 d. red 65 10
D 533 10 d. pink . . . . . 1·00 20
D 727 10 d. red . . . . . . 1·60 10
D 534 20 d. lake . . . . . 2·25 45
D1030 20 d. violet . . . . . 2·40 10
D1031 30 d. orange . . . . 5·25 10
D1032 50 d. blue . . . . . 26·00 40
D1033 100 d. purple . . . . 10·50 95

1947. Red Cross. As No. 545, but with "PORTO" added. Colour changed.

D546 **131** 50 p. green and red . . . 30 10

1948. Red Cross. As No. 594, but inscr "PORTO".

D595 **152** 50 p. red and green . . . 25 10

1949. Red Cross. As T **160** but inscr "PORTO".

D617 **160** 50 p. purple and red . . 40 10

ФНРЈУГОСЛАВИЈА

FNR JUGOSLAVIJA
(D 168)

D **175** Map

1950. Optd with Type D **168.**

D637 **D 115** 1 d. 50 blue 10 10
D638 3 d. brown 10 10
D639 4 d. violet 20 15

1950. Red Cross.

D665 **D 175** 50 p. brown & red . . . 30 10

1951. Red Cross. Inscr "PORTO".

D703 **191** 50 p. green and red . . . 30 10

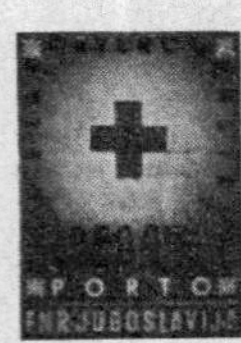
D 202

D **251** Child with Toy

1952. Red Cross.

D741 **D 202** 50 p. red and grey . . 30 10

1953. Red Cross. Inscr "PORTO".

D762 **211** 2 d. red and brown . . . 50 10

1954. Red Cross. Inscr "PORTO".

D783 **216** 2 d. red and lilac 45 10

1955. Children's Week. Inscr "PORTO".

D802 **222** 2 d. green 35 10

1955. Red Cross. Inscr "PORTO".

D804 **224** 2 d. brown, deep red & red 50 10

1956. Red Cross. Inscr "PORTO".

D820 **228** 2 d. green and red . . . 35 10

1956. Children's Week. Inscr "PORTO".

D835 **232** 2 d. green and red . . . 30 10

1957. Red Cross. Inscr "PORTO".

D844 **234** 2 d. red, black and grey . 35 10

1957. Children's Week. Inscr "PORTO".

D867 **240** 2 d. brown and blue . . 30 10

1958. Red Cross. Inscr "PORTO".

D879 **245** 2 d. multicoloured . . . 50 10

1958. Children's Week.

D913 **D 251** 2 d. black and blue . 40 10

1959. Red Cross. Inscr "PORTO".

D927 **255** 2 d. orange and red . . 30 10

1959. Children's Week. As T **260.** Inscr "PORTO".

D947 2 d. purple and yellow . . . 25 10

DESIGN: Tree, cockerel and ears of wheat.

1960. Red Cross. Inscr "PORTO".

D956 **262** 2 d. purple and red . . . 25 10

1960. Children's Week. As T **265.** Inscr "PORTO".

D970 2 d. blue (Young boy) . . 20 10

1961. Red Cross. Inscr "PORTO". Perf or imperf.

D982 **268** 2 d. multicoloured . . . 25 10

1961. Children's Week. Inscr "PORTO".

D1020 **274** 2 d. green and sepia . . 20 10

1962. Red Cross. Inscr "PORTO".

D1043 **281** 5 d. red, brown and blue 20 10

1963. Red Cross Cent. and Week. Inscr "PORTO".

D1074 **288** 5 d. red, purple and orange 30 10

YUNNANFU Pt.17

Yunnanfu (formerly Yunnansen), the chief city of the Chinese province of Yunnan, had an Indo-Chinese Post Office from 1900 to 1922.

1901. 100 centimes = 1 franc
1918. 100 cents = 1 piastre

Stamps of Indo-China surcharged.

1903. "Tablet" key-type surch with value in Chinese and **YUNNANSEN.**

1 **D** 1 c. black and red on blue . 3·75 3·00
2 2 c. brown and blue on buff 3·00 3·00
3 4 c. brown and blue on grey 3·00 3·00
4 5 c. green and red . . . . 3·00 2·75
5 10 c. red and blue . . . . 3·00 2·75
6 15 c. grey and red . . . . 3·75 2·00
7 20 c. red and blue on green 4·50 3·50
8 25 c. blue and red . . . . 3·00 3·25
9 30 c. brown and blue on drab 4·75 3·50
10 40 c. red and blue on yellow 45·00 27·00
11 50 c. red and blue on pink . £200 £200
12 50 c. brown and red on blue £100 £100
13 75 c. brown and red on orange 30·00 27·00
14 1 f. green and red . . . . . 32·00 30·00
15 5 f. mauve and blue on lilac 70·00 65·00

1906. Surch **Yunnan-Fou** and value in Chinese.

16 **8** 1 c. green . . . . 1·40 1·40
17 2 c. purple on yellow . . . 1·40 1·40
18 4 c. mauve on blue . . . . 1·75 1·60
19 5 c. green . . . . 1·90 1·90
20 10 c. pink . . . . 1·90 1·90
21 15 c. brown on blue . . . . 3·75 3·75
22 20 c. red on green . . . . 2·25 2·25
23 25 c. blue . . . . 2·75 2·50
24 30 c. brown on cream . . . 2·25 2·25
25 35 c. black on yellow . . . 3·75 3·75
26 40 c. black on grey . . . . 2·75 2·75
27 50 c. brown on cream . . . 3·75 3·75
28 **D** 75 c. brown on orange . . . 27·00 27·00
29 **8** 1 f. green . . . . 12·50 12·50
30 2 f. brown on yellow . . . 12·50 12·50
31 **D** 5 f. mauve on lilac . . . . 45·00 45·00
32 **8** 10 f. red on green . . . . 50·00 50·00

1908. Native types surch **YUNNANFOU** and value in Chinese.

33 **10** 1 c. black and brown . . . 45 50
34 2 c. black and brown . . . 45 55
35 4 c. black and blue 45 55
36 5 c. black and green . . . 60 60
37 10 c. black and red 45 50
38 15 c. black and violet . . . 2·50 1·75
39 **11** 20 c. black and violet . . . 2·75 2·25
40 25 c. black and blue . . . 2·75 2·25
41 30 c. black and brown . . . 2·50 2·75
42 35 c. black and green . . . 3·75 3·00
43 40 c. black and brown . . . 4·00 4·00
44 50 c. black and red . . . . 4·00 4·00
45 **12** 75 c. black and orange . . . 4·75 4·00
46 1 f. black and red . . . . . 7·50 6·25
47 2 f. black and green . . . . 13·50 12·00
48 5 f. black and blue . . . . 32·00 27·00
49 10 f. black and violet . . . 60·00 60·00

1919. As last, surch in addition with value in figures and words.

50 **10** ⅖ c. on 1 c. black & brown . 45 40
51 ⅘ c. on 2 c. black & brown . 55 55
52 1⅗ c. on 4 c. black and blue 65 60
53 2 c. on 5 c. black and green 55 55
54 4 c. on 10 c. black and red . 60 50
55 6 c. on 15 c. black and violet 60 45
56 **11** 8 c. on 20 c. black & violet . 85 70
57 10 c. on 25 c. black & blue . 1·10 95
58 12 c. on 30 c. black & brown 95 85
59 14 c. on 35 c. black & grn . 1·90 1·60
60 16 c. on 40 c. black & brn . 2·00 1·60
61 20 c. on 50 c. black & red . 1·10 1·10
62 **12** 30 c. on 75 c. black & orge . 2·00 2·00
63 40 c. on 1 f. black and red . 2·50 2·25
64 80 c. on 2 f. black & green . 3·25 3·25
65 2 p. on 5 f. black and blue . 23·00 23·00
66 4 p. on 10 f. black & violet . 8·00 7·50

ZAIRE Pt.14

In 1971 the Congo Republic (Kinshasa), formerly Belgian Congo, changed its name to Zaire.

100 sengi = 1(li) kuta. 100 (ma) kuta = 1 zaire

176 Nurse tending Child

177 Pres. Mobutu, Memorial and Emblem

1971. 25th Anniv of U.N.I.C.E.F. Multicoloured.

788 4 k. Type **176** 30 20
789 14 k. Zaire Republic on map of Africa 85 55
790 17 k. Child in African village . 1·10 90

1972. 5th Anniv of Revolution.
791 177 4 k. multicoloured . . . . 3·25 2·75
792 14 k. multicoloured . . . 3·25 2·75
793 22 k. multicoloured . . . 4·50 3·25

177a Arms

177b Pres. Mobutu

1972.
794 177a 10 s. orange and black . 10 10
795 40 s. blue and black . . . 10 10
796 50 s. yellow and black . . 10 10
797 177b 1 k. multicoloured . . . 10 10
798 2 k. multicoloured . . . 10 10
799 3 k. multicoloured . . . 10 10
800 4 k. multicoloured . . . 10 10
801 5 k. multicoloured . . . 15 10
802 6 k. multicoloured . . . 15 10
803 8 k. multicoloured . . . 20 15
804 9 k. multicoloured . . . 30 15
805 10 k. multicoloured . . . 35 15
806 14 k. multicoloured . . . 45 20
807 17 k. multicoloured . . . 50 35
808 20 k. multicoloured . . . 65 40
809 50 k. multicoloured . . . 1·75 85
810 100 k. multicoloured . . 3·50 2·00

178 Inga Dam

1973. Inga Dam. Completion of 1st Stage.
811 178 0.04 z. multicoloured . . . 10 10
812 0.14 z. multicoloured . . . 45 35
813 0.18 z. multicoloured . . . 80 45

1973. As T **177b**, but face values in Zaires.
814 0.01 z. multicoloured 10 10
815 0.02 z. multicoloured 10 10
816 0.03 z. multicoloured 10 10
817 0.04 z. multicoloured 10 10
818 0.10 z. multicoloured 45 20
819 0.14 z. multicoloured 80 35

179 Africa on World Map

1973. 3rd International Fair, Kinshasa.
820 179 0.04 z. multicoloured . . . 15 10
821 0.07 z. multicoloured . . . 30 15
822 0.18 z. multicoloured . . . 80 45

180 Emblem on Hand

1973. 50th Anniv of Criminal Police Organisation (Interpol).
823 180 0.06 z. multicoloured . . . 35 20
824 0.14 z. multicoloured . . . 80 35

181 Leopard with Football on Globe

1974. World Cup Football Championships, Munich.
825 181 1 k. multicoloured 10 10
826 2 k. multicoloured 10 10
827 3 k. multicoloured 15 10
828 4 k. multicoloured 20 10
829 5 k. multicoloured 30 10
830 14 k. multicoloured . . . 1·40 55

182 Muhamed Ali and George Foreman

185 Waterfall

1974. World Heavyweight Boxing Title Fight, Kinshasa.
831 182 1 k. multicoloured . . . 10 10
832 4 k. multicoloured . . . 15 10
833 6 k. multicoloured . . . 20 10
834 14 k. multicoloured . . . 55 30
835 20 k. multicoloured . . . 90 40

1975. World Heavyweight Boxing Title Fight, Kinshasa. As T **182** optd with amended date **25-9-74**.
836 182 0.01 z. multicoloured . . 10 10
837 0.04 z. multicoloured . . 10 10
838 0.06 z. multicoloured . . 20 10
839 0.14 z. multicoloured . . 45 15
840 0.20 z. multicoloured . . 80 30

Nos. 836/40 differ from Type **182** by having the face values expressed as decimals of the zaire. Both dates are in fact incorrect as the fight was held on 30 October, 1974.

1975. 12th U.I.C.N. General Assembly, Kinshasa.
858 185 1 k. multicoloured . . . 10 10
859 2 k. multicoloured . . . 10 10
860 3 k. multicoloured . . . 20 10
861 4 k. multicoloured . . . 30 10
862 5 k. multicoloured . . . 40 10

186 Okapis

1975. 50th Anniv of Virunga National Park.
863 186 1 k. multicoloured . . . 10 10
864 2 k. multicoloured . . . 20 10
865 3 k. multicoloured . . . 35 10
866 4 k. multicoloured . . . 45 10
867 5 k. multicoloured . . . 55 10

187 Woman Judge with Barristers

1975. International Women's Year.
868 187 1 k. multicoloured . . . 10 10
869 2 k. multicoloured . . . 10 10
870 4 k. multicoloured . . . 20 10
871 14 k. multicoloured . . . 65 20

188 Sozacom Building **189** Pende Statuette

1976. 10th Anniv of "New Regime". Mult.
872 1 k. Type **188** 10 10
873 2 k. Siderna Maluku Industrial Complex (horiz) 10 10
874 3 k. Flour mill, Matadi . . . 10 10
875 4 k. Women parachutists (horiz) 20 10
876 8 k. Pres. Mobutu with Mao Tse-Tung 35 10
877 10 k. Soldiers clearing vegetation along the Salongo (horiz) . 45 20
878 14 k. Pres. Mobutu addressing U.N. General Assembly, 4 October 1973 (horiz) . . . 65 30
879 15 k. Rejoicing crowd (horiz) 80 20

1977. Masks and Statuettes. Multicoloured.
880 2 z. Type **189** 10 10
881 4 z. Type **189** 10 10
882 5 z. Tshokwe mask 10 10
883 7 z. As 5 k. 15 10
884 10 z. Suku mask 20 10
885 14 z. As 10 k. 35 15
886 15 z. Kongo statuette 40 15
887 18 z. As 15 k. 45 30
888 20 z. Kuba mask 65 35
889 25 z. As 20 k. 80 45

190 U.P.U. Emblem on Map

192 "Pantodon buchholzi"

1977. Centenary of Universal Postal Union.
890 190 1 k. multicoloured 10 10
891 4 k. multicoloured 20 10
892 7 k. multicoloured 50 35
893 50 k. multicoloured . . . 4·25 2·25

1977. Various stamps of Congo (Kinshasa) and Zaire, surch **REPUBLIQUE DU ZAIRE** or with new value only (No. 904).
894 158 1 k. on 10 s. red & black . 10 10
895 152 2 k. on 9.6 k. blk on red . 10 10
896 158 5 k. on 30 s. grn & blk . 10 10
897 173 10 k. on 10 s. mult . . . 35 10
898 158 10 k. on 15 s. blue & blk . 15 10
899 – 20 k. on 9.6 k. mult (No. 673) 35 15
900 167 25 k. on 10 s. mult . . . 65 30
901 174 30 k. on 12 s. mult . . . 65 35
902 159 40 k. on 9.6 k. mult . . 1·00 50
903 168 48 k. on 10 s. mult . . . 1·10 55
904 158 100 k. on 40 s. blue & blk 2·40 95

1978. Fishes. Multicoloured.
905 30 s. Type **192** 10 10
906 70 s. "Aphyosemion striatum" 10 10
907 5 k. "Ctenopoma fasciolatum" 10 10
908 8 k. "Malapterurus" 20 10
909 10 k. "Hemichromis bimaculatus" 35 10
910 30 k. "Marcusenius isidori" . . 55 40
911 40 k. "Synodontis nigriventris" 90 50
912 48 k. "Julidochromis ornatus" 1·10 65
913 100 k. "Nothobranchius brieni" 2·75 1·25

193 Argentina v. France

194 Mama Mobutu

1978. World Cup Football Championship, Argentina. Multicoloured.
915 1 k. Type **193** 10 10
916 3 k. Austria v Brazil 10 10
917 7 k. Scotland v Iran 10 10
918 9 k. Netherlands v Peru . . . 10 10
919 10 k. Hungary v Italy 15 10
920 20 k. West Germany v Mexico 35 20
921 50 k. Tunisia v Poland 85 45
922 100 k. Spain v Sweden . . . . 1·90 1·00

1978. 1st Death Anniv of Mama Mobutu Sese Seko (wife of President).
924 194 8 k. multicoloured 20 10

197 Da Vinci, Lilienthal and Flying Machines

1978. History of Aviation. Multicoloured.
927 30 s. Type **197** 10 10
928 70 s. Wright Type A and Santos-Dumont's "14 bis" 10 10
929 1 k. Farman F 60 Goliath and Bleriot XI 10 10
930 5 k. Junkers G.38ce "Deutschland" and "Spirit of St. Louis" 10 10
931 8 k. Macchi Castoldi MC-72 seaplane and Sikorsky S-42B flying boat 15 15
932 10 k. Boeing 707 and Fokker F.VIIb/3m 30 20
933 50 k. "Apollo XI" space capsule and Concorde . . . . . 1·10 55
934 75 k. Sikorsky S-61N helicopter and Douglas DC 10 . . . . 1·40 90

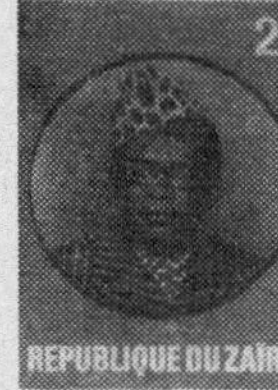
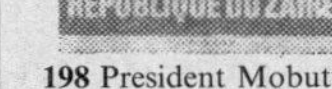

198 President Mobutu

199 "Phylloporus ampliporus"

1978.
936 198 2 k. multicoloured . . . 10 10
937 5 k. multicoloured . . . 10 10
938 6 k. multicoloured . . . 10 10
939 8 k. multicoloured . . . 10 10
940 10 k. multicoloured . . . 10 10
941 25 k. multicoloured . . . 10 10
942 48 k. multicoloured . . . 35 15
942a 50 k. multicoloured . . . 20 10
943 1 z. multicoloured . . . 80 30
943a 2 z. multicoloured . . . 65 35
943b 5 z. multicoloured . . . 1·50 85

1979. Mushrooms. Multicoloured.
944 30 s. Type **199** 10 10
945 5 k. "Engleromyces goetzei" . 10 10
946 8 k. "Scutellinia virungae" . . 10 10
947 10 k. "Pycnoporus sanguineus" 20 10
948 30 k. "Cantharellus miniatescens" 55 20
949 40 k. "Lactarius phlebonemus" 90 20
950 48 k. "Phallus indusiatus" . . 1·40 35
951 100 k. "Ramaria moelleriana" 2·25 70

200 Ntore Dancer

1979. Zaire River Expedition. Multicoloured.
952 1 k. Type **200** 10 10
953 3 k. Regal sunbird 10 10
954 4 k. African elephant 10 10
955 10 k. Diamond, cotton boll and tobacco 10 10
956 14 k. Hand holding flaming torch 15 10
957 17 k. Lion and water lily . . . 20 15
958 25 k. Inzia Falls 30 15
959 50 k. Wagenia fisherman . . . 55 35

201 President Mobutu and Flag

1979. 5th Anniv (1970) of 2nd Republic.
961 201 3 z. gold, red and blue . . 22·00

203 Globe and Drummer

204 Boy with Drum

1979. 6th International Fair, Kinshasa.
963 203 1 k. multicoloured 10 10
964 9 k. multicoloured 10 10
965 90 k. multicoloured . . . 65 30
966 100 k. multicoloured . . . 80 35

1979. International Year of the Child. Mult.
968 5 k. Type **204** 10 10
969 10 k. Girl 10 10
970 20 k. Boy 20 10
971 50 k. Laughing boy 40 20
972 100 k. Two children 85 35
973 300 k. Mother and child . . . 3·00 1·60

205 Desk standing on Globe

1979. 50th Anniv of International Bureau of Education.
975 205 10 k. multicoloured . . . 15 10

207 "Puffing Billy", England

1980. Locomotives. Multicoloured.

977 50 s. Type **207** 15 15
978 1 k. 50 Buddicom No. 33, France 15 15
979 5 k. "Elephant", Belgium 25 25
980 8 k. No. 601, Zaire 25 25
981 50 k. "Slieve Gullion", Ireland 50 50
982 75 k. "Black Elephant", Germany 95 95
983 2 z. Type "1-15", Zaire 2·75 2·75
984 5 z. "Golden State", U.S.A. 6·75 6·75

208 Sir Rowland Hill and Congo 5 f. Stamp, 1886

1980. Death Cent of Sir Rowland Hill. Mult.

986 2 k. Type **208** 10 10
987 4 k. Congo 10 f. stamp, 1887 10 10
988 10 k. Congo 1 f. African elephant stamp, 1884 10 10
989 20 k. Belgian Congo overprinted 3 f. 50 stamp, 1909 15 10
990 40 k. Belgian Congo 10 f. African Elephant stamp, 1925 20 10
991 150 k. Belgian Congo 1 f. 50+ 1 f. 50 Chimpanzees stamp, 1939 85 40
992 200 k. Belgian Congo 1 f. 75 Leopard stamp, 1942 1·25 60
993 250 k. Belgian Congo 2 f. 50 Railway stamp, 1948 2·50 2·50

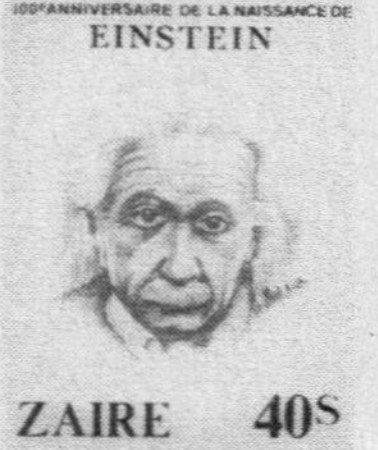

209 Einstein

1980. Birth Centenary of Albert Einstein (physicist).

995 **209** 40 s. brown, black & mve 10 10
996 2 k. brown, blk & grn 10 10
997 4 k. brown, blk & yell 10 10
998 15 k. brown, blk, & bl 15 10
999 50 k. brown, blk & red 35 20
1000 300 k. brown, blk & lilac 2·00 1·00

210 Booth Memorial Medical Centre, Flushing, New York

1980. Centenary of Salvation Army in the United States. Multicoloured.

1002 50 s. Type **210** 10 10
1003 4 k. 50 Arrival of Railton in America 10 10
1004 10 k. Mobile dispensary, Musina, Zaire 10 10
1005 20 k. General Evangeline Booth and salvationist holding child (vert) 10 10
1006 40 k. Army band 20 15
1007 75 k. Mobile clinic in bush, Zaire 45 20
1008 1 z. 50 Canteen serving firefighters 90 40
1009 2 z. American unit marching with flags (vert) 1·40 55

212 Musical Instrument

1980. 75th Anniv of Rotary International. Mult.

1013 50 k. Drawing of mother and child (Kamba) 30 15
1014 100 k. Type **212** 55 30
1015 500 k. Statuette (Liyolo) (vert) 2·00 1·40

213 "Chaetodon collaris"

1980. Tropical Fishes Multicoloured.

1017 1 k. Type **213** 10 10
1018 5 k. "Zebrasoma veliferum" 10 10
1019 10 k. "Euxiphipops xanthometapon" 10 10
1020 20 k. "Pomacanthus annularis" 10 10
1021 50 k. "Centropyge loriculus" 15 10
1022 150 k. "Oxymonacanthus longirostris" 50 30
1023 200 k. "Balistoides niger" 1·40 65
1024 250 k. "Rhinecanthus aculeatus" 1·25 60

214 Belgium 40 c. Congo Independence Stamp, 1960 and "Phibelza"

1980. "Phibelza" Belgian-Zaire Stamp Exhibition, Kinshasa. Multicoloured.

1026 1 z. Type **214** 40 30
1027 1 z. Congo 20 f. Independence stamp, 1960 40 30
1028 2 z. Belgium 10 f. + 5 f. Zoo stamp, 1968 85 55
1029 2 z. Congo 40 c. Birds stamp, 1963 85 40
1030 3 z. Belgium 10 f. + 5 f. Brussels stamp, 1971 1·25 85
1031 3 z. Zaire 22 k. stamp, 1972 1·25 85
1032 4 z. Belgium 25 f. + 10 f. stamp, 1980 1·60 1·10
1033 4 z. Congo 24 f. stamp, 1966 1·60 1·10

Nos. 1026/33 exist in two versions with the exhibition logo either at the right or the left of the design. Prices are the same for either version.

1980. 20th Anniv of Independence. Various stamps optd **20e Anniversaire - Independance - 1960–1980.**

1034 **207** 50 s. "Puffing Billy" 10 10
1035 – 1 k. 50 Locomotive "Buddicom" No. 33 (No. 978) 25 25
1036 – 10 k. Boeing 707 and Fokker F.VIIb/3m (No. 932) 10 10
1037 – 50 k. "Slieve Gullion" (No. 981) 25 25
1038 – 75 k. Sikorsky S-61N helicopter and Douglas DC-10 (No. 934) 35 15
1039 **203** 100 k. Globe and drummer 45 25
1040 – 1 z. on 5 z. on 100 k. Two children (No. 972) 45 25
1041 – 250 k. Rowland Hill and railway stamp of 1948 (No. 993) 2·25 2·25
1042 – 5 z. on 100 k. Two children (No. 972) 2·75 1·25

216 Leopold I and 1851 Map of Africa

1980. 150th Anniv of Belgian Independence.

1043 **216** 10 k. green and blue 10 10
1044 – 75 k. brown and blue 45 20
1045 – 100 k. violet and blue 45 20
1046 – 145 k. blue & deep blue 1·00 35
1047 – 270 k. red and blue 1·60 85

DESIGNS: 75 k. Leopold II and Stanley's expedition; 100 k. Albert I and colonial troops of 1914–18 war; 145 k. Leopold III and African animals; 270 k. Baudouin I and visit to Zaire of King Baudouin and Queen Fabiola.

217 Angels appearing to Shepherds

1980. Christmas. Multicoloured.

1048 10 k. Type **217** 10 10
1049 75 k. Flight into Egypt 35 20
1050 80 k. Three Kings 45 20
1051 145 k. In the stable 80 45

218 Girl dancing to Cello

1981. Norman Rockwell Paintings. Multicoloured.

1053 10 k. Type **218** 10 10
1054 20 k. Couple with saluting boy scout 10 10
1055 50 k. Sorter reading mail 20 10
1056 80 k. Cupid whispering in youth's ear 35 15
1057 100 k. Signing Declaration of Independence 50 20
1058 125 k. Boy looking through telescope held by sailor 80 25
1059 175 k. Boy in armchair playing trumpet 1·00 40
1060 200 k. Weakling exercising with dumb bells 1·10 50

219 Pope John-Paul II and Pres. Mobutu

220 Footballers

1981. Papal Visit. Multicoloured.

1061 5 k. Pope kneeling at shrine (horiz) 10 10
1062 10 k. Pres. Mobutu greeting Pope (horiz) 10 10
1063 50 k. Type **219** 20 10
1064 100 k. Pope talking to child (horiz) 65 35
1065 500 k. Pope leading prayers 2·75 1·25
1066 800 k. Pope making speech (horiz) 4·00 2·00

1981. World Cup Football Championship, Spain (1982).

1067 **220** 2 k. multicoloured 10 10
1068 – 10 k. multicoloured 10 10
1069 – 25 k. multicoloured 10 10
1070 – 90 k. multicoloured 35 15
1071 – 2 z. multicoloured 65 35
1072 – 3 z. multicoloured 1·25 55
1073 – 6 z. multicoloured 2·40 1·10
1074 – 8 z. multicoloured 3·25 1·60

DESIGN: Nos. 1068/74, Similar football scenes.

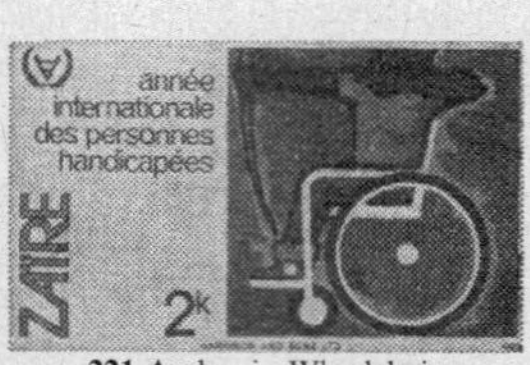

221 Archer in Wheelchair

1981. International Year of Disabled People. Multicoloured.

1076 2 k. Type **221** 10 10
1077 5 k. Ear and sound wave 10 10
1078 10 k. One-legged person with crutch 10 10
1079 18 k. Glasses, Braille and white cane 10 10
1080 50 k. Crippled legs 20 10
1081 150 k. Sign language 45 20
1082 500 k. Hand and model showing joints 1·60 90
1083 800 k. Dove shedding feathers 2·50 1·60

222 Children performing Carols

224 Red Cross Helicopters

1981. Christmas. Multicoloured.

1084 25 k. Type **224** 10 10
1085 1 z. Boy lighting candle 35 15
1086 1 z. 50 Boy praying 45 20
1087 3 z. Girl with presents 95 45
1088 5 z. Children admiring baby 1·75 85

1982. Telecommunications and Health. Mult.

1091 1 k. Type **224** 10 10
1092 25 k. Doctor and telephone 10 10
1093 90 k. Antenna and map 20 15
1094 1 z. Patient 35 15
1095 1 z. 70 Teleprinter 45 20
1096 3 z. Nurse and television 90 35
1097 4 z. 50 Tape recorder 1·60 85
1098 5 z. Babies and walkie-talkie 1·75 85

225 U.P.U. Emblem

1982. 20th Anniv (1981) of African Postal Union.

1099 **225** 1 z. green and gold 45 20

226 El Salvador v Hungary

1982. World Cup Championship, Spain. Multicoloured.

1100 2 k. Type **226** 10 10
1101 8 k. Cameroun v Peru 10 10
1102 25 k. Brazil v Russia 10 10
1103 50 k. Kuwait v Czechoslovakia 10 10
1104 90 k. Yugoslavia v Northern Ireland 30 15
1105 1 z. Austria v Chile 35 15
1106 1 z. 45 France v England 45 15
1107 1 z. 70 West Germany v Algeria 55 35
1108 3 z. Spain v Honduras 1·00 50
1109 3 z. 50 Belgium v Argentina 1·10 60
1110 5 z. Scotland v New Zealand 1·60 85
1111 6 z. Italy v Poland 2·00 95

228 Hands reaching towards Zaire

1982. Ninth French and African Heads of State Conference, Kinshasa.

1113 **228** 75 k. multicoloured 20 10
1114 90 k. multicoloured 30 15
1115 1 z. multicoloured 35 15
1116 1 z. 50 multicoloured 45 20
1117 3 z. multicoloured 95 50
1118 5 z. multicoloured 1·60 85
1119 8 z. multicoloured 2·50 1·10

229 Lions

1982. Virunga National Park. Multicoloured.

1120 1 z. Type **229** 35 20
1121 1 z. 70 African buffalo 55 35
1122 3 z. 50 African elephant 1·10 65
1123 6 z. 50 Topi 2·00 1·00
1124 8 z. Hippopotamus 2·75 1·40
1125 10 z. Savanna monkey 4·00 1·60
1126 10 z. Leopard 4·00 1·60

230 Scout Camp

233 Malachite

231 Red-billed Quelea

1982. 75th Anniv of Boy Scout Movement. Multicoloured.

1127	90 k. Type **230**	30	15
1128	1 z. 70 Camp-fire	55	25
1129	3 z. Scout	95	45
1130	5 z. Scout carrying injured person	1·75	85
1131	8 z. Scout signalling with flags	2·75	1·10

1982. Birds. Multicoloured.

1133	25 k. Type **231**	20	15
1134	50 k. African pygmy kingfisher	30	20
1135	90 k. Kynsna turaco	50	25
1136	1 z. 50 Three-banded plover	80	45
1137	1 z. 70 Temminck's courser	90	50
1138	2 z. Bennett's woodpecker	1·10	65
1139	3 z. Little grebe	1·40	75
1140	3 z. 50 Lizard buzzard (vert)	1·75	1·00
1141	5 z. Black crake	2·50	1·40
1142	8 z. White-headed vulture (vert)	4·00	2·40

1983. Malachite. Multicoloured.

1144	2 k. Type **233**	10	10
1145	45 k. Quartz (horiz)	20	10
1146	75 k. Gold (horiz)	35	10
1144	1 z. Uranium and pitch-blende (horiz)	45	15
1148	1 z. 50 Bournonite	55	30
1149	3 z. Cassiterite (horiz)	1·10	50
1150	6 z. Dioptase	2·25	95
1151	8 z. Cuprite	3·25	1·40

234 Dr. Koch and Microscope

1983. Centenary (1982) of Discovery of Tubercle Bacillus.

1153	**234** 80 k. multicoloured	20	15
1154	1 z. 20 multicoloured	35	20
1155	3 z. 60 multicoloured	1·10	55
1156	9 z. 60 multicoloured	2·75	1·40

235 "Zaire Diplomat" (Lufwa Mawidi)

1983. Kinshasa Monuments. Multicoloured.

1157	50 k. Type **235**	15	10
1158	1 z. "Echo of Zaire" (Lufwa Mawidi) (horiz)	25	15
1159	1 z. 50 "Messengers" (Liyolo Limbe Mpuanga)	40	20
1160	3 z. "Shield of Revolution" (Liyolo Limbe Mpuanga)	85	20
1161	5 z. "Weeping Woman" (Wuma Mbambila) (horiz)	1·40	85
1162	10 z. "The Militant" (Liyolo Limbe Mpuanaga)	2·50	1·25

236 Satellite over Globe

1983. I.T.U. Delegates' Conference, Nairobi. Multicoloured.

1163	2 k. Type **236**	10	10
1164	4 k. Dish aerial	10	10
1165	25 k. Dish aerial (different)	10	10
1166	1 z. 20 Satellite and microwave antenna	45	15
1167	2 z. 05 Satellite	65	30
1168	3 z. 60 Satellite and microwave antenna (different)	1·10	45
1169	6 z. Map of Zaire	1·60	70
1170	8 z. Satellite (different)	2·40	1·40

238 Giant Eland

1984. Garamba National Park. Multicoloured.

1172	10 k. Type **238**	10	10
1173	15 k. Tawny eagles	40	15
1174	3 z. Servals	20	10
1175	10 z. White rhinoceros	80	35
1176	15 z. Lions	1·00	55
1177	37 z. 50 Warthogs	2·75	1·10
1178	40 z. Kori bustards	3·50	2·00
1179	40 z. South African crowned-cranes and game lodge	3·50	2·00

239 Visual Display Unit and Ferry

1984. World Communications Year. Multicoloured.

1180	10 k. Type **239**	10	10
1181	15 k. Communications satellite	10	10
1182	8 z. 50 Radio telephone	45	30
1183	10 z. Satellite and aerial	55	35
1184	15 z. Video camera	1·00	55
1185	37 z. 50 Satellite and dish antenna	2·75	1·25
1186	80 z. Switchboard operator	5·50	2·75

240 "Hypericum revolutum"

241 Basketball

1984. Flowers. Multicoloured.

1187	10 k. Type **240**	10	10
1188	15 k. "Borreria dibrachiata"	10	10
1189	3 z. "Disa erubescens"	20	10
1190	8 z. 50 "Scaevola plumieri"	55	35
1191	10 z. "Clerodendron thompsonii"	80	35
1192	15 z. "Thumbergia erecta"	1·10	65
1193	37 z. 50 "Impatiens niamniamesis"	2·75	1·60
1194	100 z. "Canarina eminii"	7·75	3·25

1984. Olympic Games, Los Angeles. Multicoloured.

1195	2 z. Type **241**	15	10
1196	3 z. Equestrian	20	10
1197	10 z. Running	70	35
1198	15 z. Long jump	1·10	55
1199	20 z. Football	1·60	80

242 Montgolfier Balloon, 1783

243 Okapi feeding

1984. Bicentenary of Manned Flight. Mult.

1201	10 k. Type **242**	10	10
1202	15 k. Charles's hydrogen balloon, 1783	10	10
1203	3 z. Montgolfier balloon "Le Gustave", 1784	15	10
1204	5 z. Santos-Dumont's airship "Ballon No. 3", 1899	30	15
1205	10 z. Piccard's stratosphere balloon "F.N.R.S.", 1931	70	40
1206	15 z. Airship "Hindenburg"	1·10	60
1207	37 z. 50 Balloon "Double Eagle II", 1978	2·50	1·40
1208	80 z. Hot-air balloons	6·00	3·00

1984. Wildlife Protection. Okapi. Multicoloured.

1209	2 z. Type **243**	15	10
1210	3 z. Okapi resting	30	10
1211	8 z. Okapi and foal	65	35
1212	10 z. Okapi crossing stream	85	35

1985. 50th Anniv of SABENA Brussels–Kinshasa Air Service. Nos. 927/34 surch **SABENA/1935-1985** and new value.

1214	2 z. 50 on 30 s. multicoloured	15	10
1215	5 z. on 5 k. multicoloured	40	20
1216	6 z. on 70 s. multicoloured	45	30
1217	7 z. 50 on 1 k. multicoloured	55	35
1218	8 z. 50 on 1 k. multicoloured	65	40
1219	10 z. on 8 k. multicoloured	80	45
1220	12 z. 50 on 75 k. multicoloured	90	60
1221	30 z. on 50 k. multicoloured	2·25	1·25

245 Swimming

1985. "Olymphilex '85" Olympic Stamps Exhibition, Lausanne. Multicoloured.

1223	1 z. Type **245**	10	10
1224	2 z. Football (vert)	15	10
1225	3 z. Boxing	20	10
1226	4 z. Basketball (vert)	30	15
1227	5 z. Show jumping	35	20
1228	10 z. Volleyball (vert)	70	45
1229	15 z. Running	1·00	65
1230	30 z. Cycling (vert)	2·25	1·25

1985. Second Papal Visit. Nos. 1061/5 surch **AOUT 1985.**

1231	2 z. on 5 k. multicoloured	15	10
1232	3 z. on 10 k. mult	20	15
1233	5 z. 50 multicoloured	45	20
1234	10 z. on 100 k. mult	90	50
1235	15 z. on 500 k. mult	1·40	65
1236	40 z. on 800 k. mult	3·00	1·40

247 Great Egrets

1985. Birth Bicentenary of John J. Audubon (ornithologist). Multicoloured.

1238	5 z. Type **247**	45	25
1239	10 z. Common scoter	90	50
1240	15 z. Black-crowned night heron	1·50	75
1241	25 z. Surf scoter	3·00	1·60

248 National Flag and "25" on Flag

249 U.N. and Zaire Flags

1985. 25th Anniv of Independence.

1242	**248** 5 z. multicoloured	20	10
1243	10 z. multicoloured	45	20
1244	15 z. multicoloured	65	35
1245	20 z. multicoloured	90	40

1985. 40th Anniv of U.N.O. and 25th Anniv of Zaire Membership. Multicoloured.

1247	10 z. Type **249**	45	30
1248	50 z. U.N. building and emblem	2·25	1·10

1985. International Youth Year. Nos. 1127/31 optd **1985** and I.Y.Y. emblem and surch also.

1249	3 z. on 3 z. multicoloured	10	10
1250	5 z. on 5 z. multicoloured	20	10
1251	7 z. on 90 k. multicoloured	35	15
1252	10 z. on 90 k. multicoloured	45	15
1253	15 z. on 1 z. 70 multicoloured	55	25
1254	20 z. on 8 z. multicoloured	1·10	45
1255	50 z. on 90 k. multicoloured	2·75	1·00

252 "Kokolo" (pusher tug)

1985. 50th Anniv of National Transport Office.

1258	7 z. Type **252**	30	10
1259	10 z. Early steam locomotive	45	20
1260	15 z. "Luebo" (pusher tug)	55	35
1261	50 z. Modern diesel locomotive	1·75	85

253 Pope John Paul II

1985. Beatification of Sister Anuarite Nengapeta. Multicoloured.

1262	10 z. Type **253**	45	20
1263	15 z. Sister Anuarite	65	35
1264	25 z. Pope and Sister Anuarite (horiz)	1·10	55

254 Map and 1886 25 c. Stamp

1988. Centenary of 1st Congo Free State Stamp.

1266	**254** 25 z. blue, grey and deep blue	1·10	55

255 Congo Free State 1898 10 f. stamp

1988. "Cenzapost" Stamp Centenary Exhibition. Multicoloured.

1267	7 z. Type **255**	30	10
1268	15 z. Belgian Congo 1939 1 f. 25 + 1 f. 25 stamp	55	30
1269	20 z. Belgian Congo 1942 50 f. stamp (vert)	65	30
1270	25 z. Zaire 1982 8 k. stamp	80	35
1271	40 z. Zaire 1984 37 z. 50 stamp (vert)	1·40	65

256 African Egg Eater

1987. Reptiles. Multicoloured.

1273	2 z. Type **256**	10	10
1274	5 z. Rainbow lizard	10	10
1275	10 z. Royal python	20	10
1276	15 z. Cape chameleon	45	15
1277	25 z. Green mamba	65	30
1278	50 z. Black-necked cobra	1·25	55

257 "Virgin and Child with Angels" (from Cortone triptych)

1987. Christmas. Paintings by Fr. Angelico. Multicoloured.
1279 50 z. Type **257** 65 35
1280 100 z. "St. Catherine and St. Peter adoring the Child" . 1·40 65
1281 120 z. "Virgin and Child of the Angels and Four Saints" (detail, Fiesole Retable) . . 1·60 80
1282 180 z. "Virgin and Child and Six Saints" (detail, Annalena Retable) . . . . 2·50 1·10

1990. Various stamps surch.
1283 – 20 z. on 20 k. mult (No. 920) 20 10
1284 **236** 40 z. on 2 k. mult . . . 45 30
1285 – 40 z. on 4 k. mult (1164) 45 30
1286 **218** 40 z. on 10 k. mult . . . 45 30
1287 **231** 40 z. on 25 k. mult . . . 45 30
1288 – 40 z. on 25 k. mult (1165) 45 30
1289 – 40 z. on 50 k. mult (1055) 45 30
1290 – 40 z. on 50 k. mult (1134) 45 30
1291 **235** 40 z. on 50 k. mult . . . 45 30
1292 **228** 40 z. on 75 k. mult . . . 45 30
1293 – 40 z. on 80 k. mult (1056) 45 30
1294 – 40 z. on 90 k. mult (1093) 45 30
1295 **228** 40 z. on 90 k. mult . . . 45 30
1296 – 40 z. on 90 k. mult (1135) 45 30
1297 **236** 80 z. on 2 k. mult . . . 90 35
1298 – 80 z. on 4 k. mult (1164) 95 55
1299 **218** 80 z. on 10 k. mult . . . 95 55
1300 **231** 80 z. on 25 k. mult . . . 90 35
1301 – 80 z. on 25 k. mult (1165) 95 55
1302 – 80 z. on 50 k. mult (1134) 95 55
1303 **235** 80 z. on 50 k. mult . . . 90 35
1304 **228** 80 z. on 75 k. mult . . . 90 35
1305 – 80 z. on 80 k. mult (1056) 95 55
1306 – 80 z. on 90 k. mult (1093) 90 35
1307 **228** 80 z. on 90 k. mult . . . 95 55
1308 – 80 z. on 90 k. mult (1135) 95 55
1309 **209** 100 z. on 40 s. brown, black and mauve . . . . . . 1·10 45
1311 **220** 100 z. on 2 k. mult . . . 1·10 45
1312 **221** 100 z. on 2 k. mult . . . 1·10 45
1313 **226** 100 z. on 2 k. mult . . . 1·10 45
1314 **209** 100 z. on 4 k. brown, black and yellow . . . . . . 1·10 55
1315 – 100 z. on 5 k. mult (930) 1·10 45
1316 – 100 z. on 5 k. mult (1061) 1·10 45
1317 – 100 z. on 5 k. mult (1077) 1·10 55
1318 – 100 z. on 8 k. mult (908) 1·10 45
1319 – 100 z. on 8 k. mult (931) 1·10 55
1320 – 100 z. on 8 k. mult (946) 1·10 45
1322 – 100 z. on 10 k. mult (947) 1·10 55
1323 – 100 z. on 10 k. mult (969) 1·10 45
1324 – 100 z. on 10 k. mult (1036) 1·10 55
1325 **217** 100 z. on 10 k. mult . . 1·10 55
1326 – 100 z. on 10 k. mult (1062) 1·10 55
1327 – 100 z. on 10 k. mult (1068) 1·10 55
1328 **209** 100 z. on 15 k. brown, black and blue . . . . . . 1·10 55
1329 – 100 z. on 18 k. mult (1079) 1·10 55
1330 – 100 z. on 20 k. mult (970) 1·10 55
1331 – 100 z. on 20 k. mult (1020) 1·10 45
1332 **177** 100 z. on 22 k. mult . . 1·10 45
1333 – 100 z. on 25 k. mult (1069) 1·10 55
1335 – 100 z. on 48 k. mult (912) 1·10 55
1336 – 100 z. on 48 k. mult (950) 1·10 55
1337 – 100 z. on 50 k. mult (1013) 1·10 45
1338 – 100 z. on 50 k. mult (1080) 1·10 55
1339 – 100 z. on 50 k. mult (1103) 1·10 55
1340 – 100 z. on 75 k. mult (1038) 1·10 45
1341 – 100 z. on 75 k. mult (1049) 1·10 45
1342 **203** 100 z. on 90 k. mult . . 1·10 45
1343 – 100 z. on 80 k. mult (1050) 1·10 55
1344 **234** 100 z. on 80 k. mult . . 1·10 45
1345 – 100 z. on 90 k. mult (1070) 1·10 55
1346 – 100 z. on 90 k. mult (1104) 1·10 55
1348 **233** 300 z. on 2 k. mult . . . 3·50 1·60
1349 – 300 z. on 8 k. mult (980) 3·50 1·60
1350 **216** 300 z. on 10 k. green and blue . . . . 3·50 1·60
1351 – 300 z. on 14 k. mult (789) 3·50 1·60
1352 **159** 300 z. on 17 k. mult (807) 3·50 1·60
1353 – 300 z. on 20 k. mult (989) 3·50 1·60
1354 – 300 z. on 45 k. mult (1145) 3·50 1·60
1355 – 300 z. on 75 k. brown and blue (1044) . . . . . . 3·50 1·60
1356 – 300 z. on 75 k. mult (1146) 3·50 2·00
1357 **198** 500 z. on 8 k. multicoloured 6·00 3·25
1358 500 z. on 10 k. mult . . 6·00 2·75
1359 500 z. on 25 k. mult . . 6·00 2·75
1360 500 z. on 48 k. mult . . 6·25 2·75

259 "Sida" forming Owl's Face

1990. Anti-AIDS Campaign. Multicoloured.
1361 30 z. Type **259** 50 20
1362 40 z. Skeleton firing arrow through "SIDA" 60 35
1363 80 z. Leopard . . . . 1·10 80

260 Administration Building

1990. 50th Anniv of Regideso (development organization). Multicoloured.
1365 40 z. Type **260** 55 35
1366 50 z. Modern factory . . . 65 45
1367 75 z. Old water treatment plant 1·00 65
1368 120 z. Communal water tap 1·40 80

261 Maps of France and Zaire and Birds

1990. Bicentenary of French Revolution. Mult.
1369 40 z. Type **261** 55 35
1370 50 z. Article 1 of Declaration of Rights of Man and the Citizen within outline of person 65 45
1371 100 z. Crowd . . . . 1·25 65
1372 120 z. Globe . . . . 1·40 80

262 Stairs of Venus, Mount Hoyo

1990. Tourist Sites. Multicoloured.
1373 40 z. Type **262** 45 20
1374 60 z. Scenic road to village . 65 35
1375 100 z. Lake Kivu . . . . . 1·25 55
1376 120 z. Niyara Gongo volcano 1·60 25

1991. Various stamps surch.
1379 – 1000 z. on 100 k. mult (1064) 15 15
1380 – 1000 z. on 1 z. mult (1105) 15 15
1381 **214** 1000 z. on 1 z. mult (1026) 15 15
1383 – 1000 z. on 1 z. mult (1027) 15 15
1385 – 2000 z. on 100 k. violet and blue (1045) 30 30
1386 – 2000 z. on 1 z. mult (1147) 30 30
1387 **228** 2500 z. on 1 z. mult . . 40 40
1388 **225** 3000 z. on 1 z. green and gold 45 45
1389 – 4000 z. on 1 z. mult (1158) 60 60
1390 – 5000 z. on 1 z. mult (1158) 75 75
1391 **228** 10000 z. on 1 z. mult . . 1·50 1·50
1392 **225** 15000 z. on 1 z. green and gold . . . . 2·25 2·25

Nos. 1381 and 1383 exist in two versions with the exhibition logo either at the right or left of the design.

1992. Various stamps surch.
1393 – 50,000 z. on 125 k. multicoloured (1058) . 10 10
1394 – 100,000 z. on 1 z. 20 multicoloured (1166) . 10 10
1395 **234** 150,000 z. on 1 z. 20 multicoloured 10 10
1396 – 200,000 z. on 145 k. blue and indigo (1046) . . 15 10
1397 **234** 250,000 z. on 1 z. 20 multicoloured 20 15
1398 – 300,000 z. on 1 z. 20 multicoloured (1166) . 25 20
1399 **234** 500,000 z. on 1 z. 20 multicoloured 35 25

1993. Various stamps surch. (a) Nos. 944/51
1400 **199** 500,000 z. on 30 s. multicoloured 10 10
1401 – 500,000 z. on 5 k. multicoloured 10 10
1402 – 750,000 z. on 8 k. multicoloured 15 10
1403 – 750,000 z. on 10 k. multicoloured 15 10
1404 – 1,000,000 z. on 30 k. multicoloured 20 15
1405 – 1,000,000 z. on 40 k. multicoloured 20 15
1406 – 5,000,000 z. on 48 k. multicoloured 95 60
1407 – 10,000,000 z. on 400 k. multicoloured . . . . 1·90 1·10

(b) Nos. 1262/4
1408 **253** 3,000,000 z. on 10 z. multicoloured 55 35
1409 – 5,000,000 z. on 15 z. multicoloured 95 60
1410 – 10,000,000 z. on 25 z. multicoloured . . . . 1·90 1·10

BOGUS SURCHARGES. Surcharges with commemorative inscriptions on Nos. 1365/8 for the inauguration of a pumping station and on Nos. 1373/6 for the sixth anniversary of the National Tourism Office are bogus.

OFFICIAL STAMPS

1975. Optd **SP**.
O841 **172** 10 s. orange & black . 10 10
O842 40 s. blue and black . 10 10
O843 50 s. yellow and black 10 10
O844 **177b** 1 k. multicoloured . . 10 10
O845 **177b** 2 k. multicoloured . . . 10 10
O846 3 k. multicoloured . . . 10 10
O847 4 k. multicoloured . . . 15 10
O848 5 k. multicoloured . . . 20 10
O849 6 k. multicoloured . . . 20 10
O850 8 k. multicoloured . . . 35 15
O851 9 k. multicoloured . . . 35 20
O852 10 k. multicoloured . . 45 20
O853 14 k. multicoloured . . 55 25
O854 17 k. multicoloured . . 80 45
O855 20 k. multicoloured . . 1·00 50
O856 50 k. multicoloured . . 2·50 1·00
O857 100 k. multicoloured . . 6·75 2·75

ZAMBEZIA Pt.9

Formerly administered by the Zambezia Co. This district of Portuguese E. Africa was later known as Quelimane and is now part of Mozambique.

1000 reis = 1 milreis

1894. "Figures" key-type inscr "ZAMBEZIA"
1 R 5 r. orange 15 15
2 10 r. mauve 20 20
3 15 r. brown 25 25
4 20 r. lilac 25 25
12 25 r. green 40 30
13 50 r. blue 40 30
14 75 r. red 90 90
15 80 r. green 75 60
8 100 r. brown on buff 70 60
16 150 r. red on rose 90 75
17 200 r. blue on blue 90 80
18 300 r. blue on brown . . . . 1·75 1·50

1898. "King Carlos" key-type inscr "ZAMBEZIA". Name and value in red (500 r.) or black (others).
20 S 2½ r. grey 20 15
21 5 r. orange 20 15
22 10 r. green 20 15
55 15 r. brown 45 40
24 20 r. lilac 40 35
25 25 r. green 40 35
56 25 r. red 40 30
26 50 r. blue 50 40
57 50 r. brown . . . . 1·00 90
58 65 r. blue . . . . 2·50 2·00
27 75 r. red . . . . 2·75 1·90
59 75 r. purple . . . . 1·25 95
28 80 r. mauve . . . . 1·75 1·50
29 100 r. blue on blue 80 75
60 115 r. brown on pink . . . 3·25 2·50
61 130 r. brown on yellow . . . 3·25 2·50
30 150 r. brown on yellow . . . 1·75 1·40
31 200 r. purple on pink . . . 1·75 1·40
32 300 r. blue on pink . . . . 2·00 1·50
62 400 r. blue on yellow . . . 3·50 3·00
33 500 r. black on blue . . . 3·00 2·50
34 700 r. mauve on yellow . . . 3·50 3·00

1902. Surch.
63 S 50 r. on 65 r. blue . . . . 2·00 1·25
35 R 65 r. on 10 r. mauve . . . 2·00 1·75
36 65 r. on 15 r. brown . . . 2·00 1·75
37 65 r. on 20 r. lilac . . . . 2·00 1·75
38 65 r. on 300 r. blue on brn 2·00 1·75
40 115 r. on 5 r. orange . . . 2·00 1·75
41 115 r. on 25 r. green . . . 2·00 1·75
42 115 r. on 80 r. green . . . 2·00 1·75
46 V 130 r. on 2½ r. brown . . . 2·00 1·75
43 R 130 r. on 75 r. red . . . 2·00 1·75
45 130 r. on 150 r. red on rose 1·75 1·40
47 400 r. on 50 r. blue 80 70
49 400 r. on 100 r. brn on buff 80 70
50 400 r. on 200 r. blue on bl 80 70

1902. 1898 issue optd **PROVISORIO**.
51 S 15 r. brown 65 50
52 25 r. blue 65 50
53 50 r. blue 65 50
54 75 r. red . . . . 2·00 1·40

1911. 1898 issue optd **REPUBLICA**.
64 S 2½ r. grey 10 10
65 5 r. orange 10 10
66 10 r. green 15 15
67 15 r. green 15 10
68 20 r. lilac 20 10
69 25 r. red 45 20
108 25 r. green . . . . 4·00 3·00
70 50 r. brown 15 15
71 75 r. purple 35 25
72 100 r. blue on blue 35 25
73 115 r. brown on pink . . . 40 30
74 130 r. brown on yellow . . . 40 30
75 200 r. purple on pink . . . 40 30
76 400 r. blue on cream . . . 70 55
77 500 r. black on blue . . . 70 55
78 700 r. mauve on yellow . . . 70 55

1914. 1902 **PROVISORIO** issue optd **REPUBLICA**.
94 S 50 r. blue 25 20
81 75 r. red 50 40

1914. Provisionals of 1902 optd **REPUBLICA**.
95 S 50 r. on 65 r. blue . . . . 1·00 80
96 R 115 r. on 5 r. orange . . . 25 20
97 115 r. on 25 r. green . . . 25 20
98 115 r. on 80 r. green . . . 25 20
99 V 130 r. on 2½ r. brown . . . 25 20
100 R 130 r. on 75 r. red 25 20
102 130 r. on 150 r. red on rose 20 20
90 400 r. on 50 r. blue 70 60
92 400 r. on 100 r. brn on buff 80 60
93 400 r. on 200 r. bl on blue 80 70

NEWSPAPER STAMP

1893. "Newspaper" key-type inscr "ZAMBEZIA".
N1 V 2½ r. brown 20 15

ADDENDA AND CORRIGENDA

KOREA

SOUTH KOREA

1286 "600" and Map

1287 Pigs travelling in Snow

1994. 600th Anniv of Seoul as Capital (2nd issue).
2139 **1286** 130 w. multicoloured . . 20 10

1994. Lunar New Year ("Year of the Pig"). Multicoloured.
2140 130 w. Type **1287** 20 10
2141 130 w. Family in Forest . . . 20 10

KUWAIT

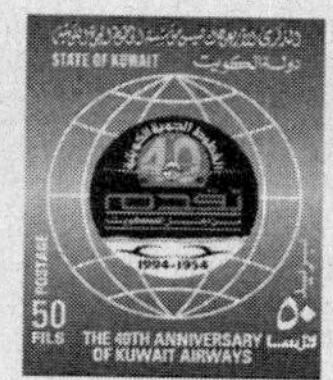

375 Anniversary Emblem

1994. 40th Anniv of Kuwait Airways.
1403 **375** 50 f. multicoloured . . . 20 10
1404 100 f. multicoloured . . 45 25
1405 150 f. multicoloured . . 65 35

LATVIA

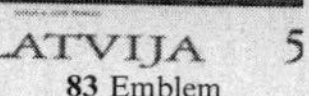

83 Emblem

84 Coins in Scales

1994. 75th Anniv of Latvia University.
405 **83** 5 s. gold, blue and green . . 10 10

1994. Europa. Multicoloured.
406 10 s. Type **84** 20 20
407 50 s. Money chest and notes in scales . . . . 1·10 1·10

85 Eating Cherries

86 Angel

1994. The Fat Dormouse. Multicoloured.
408 5 s. Type **85** 10 10
409 10 s. Eating strawberries . . . 20 20
410 10 s. On leafy branch 20 20
411 15 s. On branch of apple tree . 35 35

1994. Christmas. Multicoloured.
412 3 s. Type **86** 10 10
413 8 s. Angels playing violin and flute 20 20
414 13 s. Angels singing 30 30
415 100 s. Wreath of candles . . . 2·25 2·25

LIECHTENSTEIN

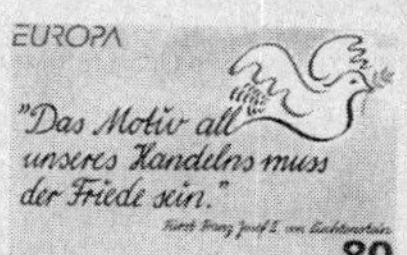

350 "The Theme of all our Affairs must be Peace"

1995. Europa. Peace and Freedom. Quotations of Franz Josef II. Multicoloured.
1094 80 r. Type **350** 80 80
1095 1 f. "Through Unity comes Strength and the Bearing of Sorrows" . . . . 1·00 1·00

351 Princess Marie with Children

1995. Anniversaries and Event. Multicoloured.
1096 60 r. Type **351** (50th anniv of Liechtenstein Red Cross) . 60 60
1097 1 f. 80 Flag and bouquet of flowers (50th anniv of U.N.O. (vert) . . . . 1·75 1·75
1098 3 f. 50 Alps (European Nature Conservation Year) (vert) 3·50 3·50

MACAO

200 "Lou Lim Iok Garden"

1995. Paintings of Macao by Lio Man Cheong. Multicoloured.
871 50 a. Type **200** 10 10
872 1 p. "Guia Fortress and Lighthouse" 15 10
873 1 p. 50 "Barra Temple" . . . 25 15
874 2 p. "Avenida da Praia, Taipa" . 30 20
875 2 p. 50 "Kun Iam Temple" . 40 30
876 3 p. "St. Paul's Seminary" . . 50 35
877 3 p. 50 "Penha Hill" 55 40
878 4 p. "Gates of Understanding Monument" 65 45

201 Magnifying Glass over Goods

1995. World Consumer Day.
879 **201** 1 p. multicoloured . . . 15 10

MEXICO

904 Mother and Baby

905 Foot and Heart

1994. Friendship Hospital. Mother and Child Health Month.
2180 **904** 1 p. 30 multicoloured . . 30 20

1994. Prevention of Mental Retardation.
2181 **905** 1 p. 30 multicoloured . . 30 20

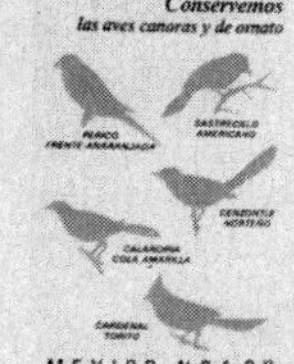

906 Song and Ornamental Birds

907 Player

1994. Nature Conservation. Multicoloured.
2182 1 p. 30 Type **906** 30 20
2183 1 p. 30 Game birds (silhouettes) 30 20
2184 1 p. 30 Threatened animals (silhouettes) 30 20
2185 1 p. 30 Animals in danger of extinction (silhouettes) . . 30 20
2186 1 p. 30 Yellow-crowned amazons 30 20
2187 1 p. 30 Wood lark 30 20
2188 1 p. 30 Common cardinals . . 30 20
2189 1 p. 30 Great grey shrike . . 30 20
2190 1 p. 30 Northern mocking-bird 30 20
2191 1 p. 30 Common turkey . . . 30 20
2192 1 p. 30 White-winged collared dove 30 20
2193 1 p. 30 White-winged wood duck 30 20
2194 1 p. 30 Snow goose 30 20
2195 1 p. 30 Californian quail . . . 30 20
2196 1 p. 30 Peregrine falcon . . . 30 20
2197 1 p. 30 Jaguar 30 20
2198 1 p. 30 Jaguarundi 30 20
2199 1 p. 30 Mantled howler monkey 30 20
2200 1 p. 30 Californian sealions . 30 20
2201 1 p. 30 Pronghorn 30 20
2202 1 p. 30 Scarlet macaw 30 20
2203 1 p. 30 Mexican prairie dogs . 30 20
2204 1 p. 30 Wolf 30 20
2205 1 p. 30 American manatee . . 30 20

1994. World Cup Football Championship, U.S.A. Multicoloured.
2206 2 p. Type **907** 45 30
2207 2 p. Goalkeeper 45 30
Nos. 2206/7 were issued together, se-tenant, forming a composite design.

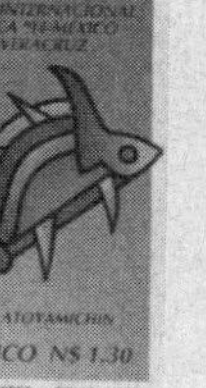

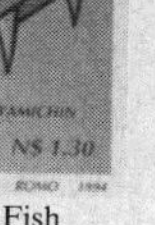

908 Fish

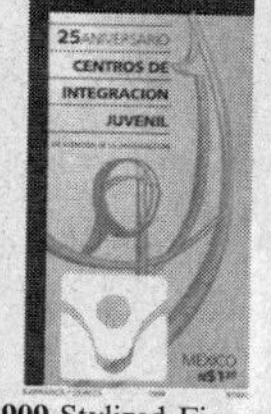

909 Stylized Figure and Emblem

1994. International Fishing Festival, Veracruz.
2208 **908** 1 p. 30 multicoloured . . 30 20

1994. 25th Anniv of Juvenile Integration Centres.
2209 **909** 1 p. 30 multicoloured . . 30 20

910 "Butterflies" (Carmen Parra)

1994. 50th Aniv of Diplomatic Relations with Canada.
2210 **910** 2 p. multicoloured . . . 45 30

911 Emblems

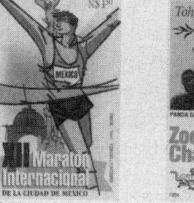

912 Emblem and Family

1994. 20th Anniv of National Population Council.
2211 **911** 1 p. 30 multicoloured . . 30 20

1994. International Year of the Family.
2212 **912** 2 p. multicoloured . . . 45 30

913 Runner breasting Tape

914 Giant Panda

1994. 12th Mexico City International Marathon.
2213 **913** 1 p. 30 multicoloured . . 30 20

1994. Chapultepec Zoo.
2214 **914** 1 p. 30 multicoloured . . 30 20

915 Tree

916 Anniversary Emblem

1994. Tree Day.
2215 **915** 1 p. 30 brown and green 30 20

1994. 60th Anniv of Economic Culture Fund.
2216 **916** 1 p. 30 multicoloured . . 30 20

917 Statue and Underground Train

918 Cathedral and Gardens

1994. 25th Anniv of Mexico City Transport System.
2217 **917** 1 p. 30 multicoloured . . 30 20

1994. 350th Anniv of Salvatierra City, Guanajuato.
2218 **918** 1 p. 30 purple, grey and black 30 20

919 State Flag and National Anthem

1994. National Symbols Week.
2219 **919** 1 p. 30 multicoloured . . 30 20

920 Building and Anniversary Emblem

921 Figures with Flags

1994. 40th Anniv of University City.
2220 **920** 1 p. 30 multicoloured . . 30 20

1994. 5th Solidarity Week.
2221 **921** 1 p. 30 black, red and green 30 20

922 Lopez Mateos

923 Palace Facade

1994. 25th Death Anniv of Adolfo Lopez Mateos (President, 1958–64).
2222 **922** 1 p. 30 multicoloured . . 30 20

1994. 60th Anniv of Palace of Fine Arts.
2223 **923** 1 p. 30 black and grey . 30 20

924 Rings and "100"

1994. Centenary of International Olympic Committee.
2224 **924** 2 p. multicoloured . . . 45 30

925 Quarter Horse (Juan Rayas)

1994. Horses. Paintings by artists named. Multicoloured.

2225 1 p. 30 Aztec horse (Heladio Velarde) 30 20
2226 1 p. 30 Type **925** 30 20
2227 1 p. 30 Quarter horse (Rayas) (different) 30 20
2228 1 p. 30 Vaquero on horseback (Velarde) 30 20
2229 1 p. 30 Aztec horse (Velarde) 30 20
2230 1 p. 30 Rider with lance (Velarde) 30 20

926 Emblem

927 Saint-Exupery and The Little Prince (book character)

1994. Inauguration of 20th November National Medical Centre.

2231 **926** 1 p. 30 multicoloured . . 30 20

1994. 50th Death Anniv of Antoine de Saint-Exupery (pilot and writer).

2232 **927** 2 p. multicoloured . . . 45 30

MONACO

689 Clown playing Trombone

690 Crown Prince Albert

1995. 19th Int Circus Festival, Monte Carlo.

2207 **689** 2 f. 80 multicoloured . . 70 45

1995. 35th Television Festival, Monte Carlo.

2208 **690** 8 f. brown . . . . 2·00 1·25

691 Fontvieille

1995. European Nature Conservation Year.

2209 **691** 2 f. 40 multicoloured . . 60 40

692 American Cocker Spaniel

1995. International Dog Show, Monte Carlo.

2210 **692** 4 f. multicoloured . . . . 1·00 60

693 Parrot Tulips

1995. Monte Carlo Flower Show.

2211 **693** 5 f. multicoloured . . . . 1·25 75

694 "Acer palmatum"

1995. European Bonsai Congress.

2212 **694** 6 f. multicoloured . . . . 1·50 90

NEPAL

285 Pasang Sherpa

1994. 1st Death Anniv of Pasang Sherpa (mountaineer).

570 **285** 10 r. multicoloured . . . 30 20

286 Cigarette, Lungs and Crab's Claws

287 Postal Delivery

1994. Anti-smoking Campaign.

571 **286** 1 r. multicoloured 10 10

1994.

572 **287** 1 r. 50 multicoloured . . 10 10

288 Khuda

1994. Weapons. Multicoloured.

573 5 r. Kukris (three swords and two scabbards) 15 10
574 5 r. Type **288** 15 10
575 5 r. Dhaal (swords and shield) 15 10
576 5 r. Katari (two daggers) . . 15 10

289 Workers and Emblem

1994. 75th Anniv of I.L.O.

577 **289** 15 r. gold, blue and ultramarine 40 20

290 Landscape

1994. World Food Day.

578 **290** 25 r. multicoloured . . . 65 40

291 "Dendrobium densiflorum"

292 Family

1994. Orchids. Multicoloured.

579 10 r. Type **291** 25 15
580 10 r. "Coelogyne flaccida" . . 25 15
581 10 r. "Cymbidium devonianum" 25 15
582 10 r. "Coelogyne corymbosa" 25 15

1994. International Year of the Family.

583 **292** 9 r. emerald, green and red 25 15

293 Emblem and Airplane

294 "Russula nepalensis"

1994. 50th Anniv of I.C.A.O.

584 **293** 11 r. blue, gold and deep blue 30 20

1994. Fungi. Multicoloured.

585 7 r. Type **294** 20 10
586 7 r. Morels ("Morchella conica") 20 10
587 7 r. Caesar's mushroom ("Amanita caesarea") . . . 20 10
588 7 r. "Cordyceps sinensis" . . . 20 10

295 Dharanidhar Koirala (poet)

1994. Celebrities. Multicoloured.

589 1 r. Type **295** 10 10
590 2 r. Narayan Gopal Guruwacharya (singer) . . . 10 10
591 6 r. Bahadur Shah (vert) . . . 15 10
592 7 r. Balaguru Shadananda . . 20 10

296 King Birendra, Flag, Map and Crown

1994. King Birendra's 50th Birthday.

593 **296** 9 r. multicoloured 25 15

297 Lake Tilicho, Manang

298 Health Care

1994. Tourism. Multicoloured.

594 9 r. Type **297** 25 15
595 11 r. Taleju Temple, Katmandu (vert) 30 20

1994. Children's Activities. Multicoloured.

596 1 r. Type **298** 10 10
597 1 r. Classroom 10 10
598 1 r. Playground equipment . . 10 10
599 1 r. Stamp collecting 10 10

NETHERLANDS

479 Star and Christmas Tree

481 "Prayer" (detail)

480 Flying Cow

1994. Christmas. Multicoloured.

1748 55 c. Type **479** 45 15
1749 55 c. Candle and star 45 15

1995.

1750 **480** 100 c. multicoloured . . . 80 25

1995. Anniversary and Events.

1751 **481** 80 c. multicoloured . . . 65 10
1752 – 80 c. multicoloured . . . 65 10
1753 – 80 c. black and red . . . 65 10

DESIGNS—VERT: No. 1751, Type **481** (50th death anniv of Hendrik Werkman (graphic designer); 1752, "Mesdag Panorama" (detail) (re-opening of Mesdag Museum). HORIZ: No. 1753, Mauritius 1847 2d. "POST OFFICE" stamp (purchase by PTT Museum of remaining mint example in private hands).

482 Joriz Ivens (documentary maker)

1995. Year of the Film (centenary of motion pictures). Multicoloured.

1754 70 c. Type **482** 55 15
1755 80 c. Scene from "Turkish Delight" 65 10

NETHERLANDS ANTILLES

302 Dove in Hands

1994. Christmas. Multicoloured.

1144 30 c. Type **302** 20 15
1145 115 c. Globe and planets in hands 80 65

303 Carnival and Houses

304 Handicapped and Able-bodied Children

1995. Carnival. Multicoloured.

1146 125 c. Type **303** 90 75
1147 175 c. Carnival and harbour 1·25 1·00
1148 250 c. Carnival and rural house 1·75 1·40

1995. 50th Anniv of Mgr. Verriet Institute (for the physically handicapped). Multicoloured.

1149 65 c. Type **304** 45 35
1150 90 c. Cedric Virginie (wheelchair-bound bookbinder) 65 55

NORWAY

383 Cowberry

384 Swan Pharmacy, Bergen ("Vaccinium vitis-idaea")

1995. Wild Berries. Multicoloured.

1197 3 k. 50 Type **383** 70 10
1198 3 k. 50 Bilberry ("Vaccinium myrtillus") 70 10

1995. 400th Anniv of Norwegian Pharmacies.

1199 **384** 3 k. 50 green and brown 70 10
1200 – 25 k. multicoloured . . . 5·00 2·00

DESIGN: 25 k. Scales, pestle and mortar and ingredients.

385 German Commander saluting Terje Rollem (Home Guard commander)

1995. 50th Anniv of Liberation of Norway.

1201 **385** 3 k. 50 silver, green and black 70 10
1202 – 4 k. 50 silver, blue and black 90 35
1203 – 5 k. 50 silver, red and black 1·10 45

DESIGNS: 4 k. 50, King Haakon VII and family returning to Norway; 5 k. 50, Children waving Norwegian flags.

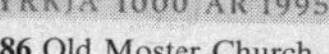

386 Old Moster Church

387 Skudeneshavn

1995. Millenary of Christianity in Norway. Multicoloured.

1204 3 k. 50 Type **386** 70 10

1205 15 k. Slettebakken Church, Bergen . . . . 3·00 1·25

1995. Nordic Countries' Postal Co-operation. Tourism. Multicoloured.

1206 4 k. Type **387** 80 20

1207 4 k. 50 Hole in the Hat (coastal rock formation) 90 35

PARAGUAY

337 Nicolas Copernicus and Eclipse

339 Mother and Child

338 Steam Locomotive

1994. Total Eclipse of the Sun, November 1994. Astronomers. Multicoloured.

1452 50 g. Type **337** 10 10

1453 200 g. Johannes Kepler and sun dial, St. Cosmas and Damian Jesuit settlement 15 10

1994. America. Postal Transport. Multicoloured.

1454 100 g. Type **338** 10 10

1455 1000 g. Express mail motor cycle 65 50

1994. International Year of the Family. Details of paintings by Olga Blinder. Multicoloured.

1456 50 g. Type **339** 10 10

1457 250 g. Mother and children . 15 10

340 Holy Family and Angels

1994. Christmas. Ceramic Figures. Multicoloured.

1458 150 g. Type **340** 10 10

1459 700 g. Holy Family (vert) . . 45 20

341 Red Cross Workers and Dr. Andres Barbero (founder)

1994. 75th Anniv of Paraguay Red Cross. Multicoloured.

1460 150 g. Scouts, anniversary emblem and Henri Dunant (founder of International Red Cross) 10 10

1461 700 g. Type **341** 45 20

342 Sculpture by Herman Guggiari and Pope John Paul II

1994. 90th Anniv of San Jose College. Multicoloured.

1462 200 g. Type **342** 15 10

1463 250 g. College entrance and Pope John Paul II 15 10

PHILIPPINES

1994. As T **793**.

2646 6 p. Leaf 30 15

2647 7 p. Costume 35 20

819 Gloria Diaz (Miss Universe 1969)

820 Antonio Molina (composer)

1994. Miss Universe Beauty Contest. Multicoloured.

2653 2 p. Type **819** 10 10

2654 2 p. Margie Moran (Miss Universe 1973) 10 10

2655 6 p. Crown 30 15

2656 7 p. Contestant 35 20

1994. Birth Centenaries. Multicoloured.

2658 2 p. Type **820** 10 10

2659 2 p. Jose Yulo (Secretary of Justice) 10 10

2660 2 p. Josefa Jara-Martinez (social worker) 10 10

2661 2 p. Nicanor Reyes (accountant) 10 10

2662 2 p. Sabino Padilla (judge) . 10 10

POLAND

1068 Musicians playing Carols

1994. Christmas.

3543 **1068** 2500 z. multicoloured . 15 10

1069 Landscape and E.U. Flag

1994. Application by Poland for Membership of European Union.

3544 **1069** 6000 z. multicoloured . 35 15

Currency reform. 10000 (old) zlotys = 1 (new) zloty

1070 "I Love You" on Pierced Heart

1995. Greetings Stamp.

3545 **1070** 35 g. red and blue . . 20 10

1071 Rain, Sun and Water

1995. 75th Anniv of Hydrological-Meteorological Service.

3546 **1071** 60 g. multicoloured . . . 30 10

1072 Flag and Sea

1073 St. John

1995. 75th Anniv of Poland's "Marriage to the Sea" (symbolic ceremony commemorating renewal of access to sea).

3547 **1072** 45 g. multicoloured . . . 25 10

1995. Polish Rulers (10th series). As T **893** showing drawings by Jan Matejko.

3548 35 g. deep brown, brown and light brown 20 10

3549 45 g. olive, deep green and green 25 10

3550 60 g. brown and ochre . . . 30 10

3551 80 g. black and blue . . . 45 15

DESIGNS: 35 g. Waclaw II; 45 g. Wladyslaw I; 60 g. Kazimierz III, the Great; 80 g. Ludwik Wegierski.

1995. 500th Birth Anniv of St. John of God (founder of Order of Hospitallers).

3552 **1073** 60 g. multicoloured . . . 30 10

1074 Eggs

1995. Easter. Decorated Easter eggs. Multicoloured, background colours given.

3553 **1074** 35 g. red 20 10

3554 – 35 g. lilac 20 10

3555 – 45 g. blue 25 10

3556 – 45 g. green 25 10

1995. Cones. As T **974**. Multicoloured.

3557 45 g. European larch 25 10

3558 80 g. Mountain pine 45 15

PORTUGAL

521 Great Bustard

1995. European Nature Conservation Year. Multicoloured.

2418 42 e. Type **521** 35 15

2419 90 e. Osprey 75 35

2420 130 e. Schreiber's green lizard 1·10 55

522 St. John and Sick Man

1995. 500th Birth Anniv of St. John of God (founder of Order of Hospitallers).

2422 **522** 45 e. multicoloured . . . 40 20

523 Electrico No. 22, 1895

1995. Centenaries of Trams and Motor Cars in Portugal. Multicoloured.

2423 90 e. Type **523** 75 35

2424 130 e. Panhard and Levassor motor car . . . . 1·10 55

RUSSIA

2595 Horses and Father Christmas

1994. New Year.

6506 **2595** 125 r. blue, red and black 15 10

2596 Griboedov (after Utkin)

1995. Birth Bicentenary of Aleksandr Sergeevich Griboedov (dramatist and diplomat).

6507 **2596** 250 r. brown, light brown and black 25 10

THAILAND

594 Water Polo

1994. 18th South-East Asian Games, Chiang Mai. Multicoloured.

1759 2 b. + 1 b. Type **594** 15 10

1760 2 b. + 1 b. Tennis 15 10

1761 2 b. + 1 b. Hurdling 15 10

1762 2 b. + 1 b. Gymnastics . . . 15 10

595 First Bar Building and Kings Vajiravudh and Bhumibol

1995. 80th Anniv of the Bar.

1764 **595** 2 b. multicoloured . . . 10 10

URUGUAY

809 Schooner and Pedro Campbell (first Navy General)

1993. 175th Anniv (1992) of Uruguayan Navy.

2110 **809** 1 p. multicoloured . . . 20 10

810 Emblem

1993. 25th Anniv of International University Circles.

2111 **810** 1 p. multicoloured . . . 20 10

811 Hupmobile, 1910

1993. 75th Anniv of Uruguay Automobile Club.
2112 **811** 3 p. 50 multicoloured . . 70 35

813 Bird 814 Armadillo

1993. No value expressed.
2114 **813** (1 p. 20) blue and azure . 25 15
2115 (1 p. 40) emerald and green 30 15
Nos. 2114/15 were sold at the current inland letter rate.
See also No. 2147.

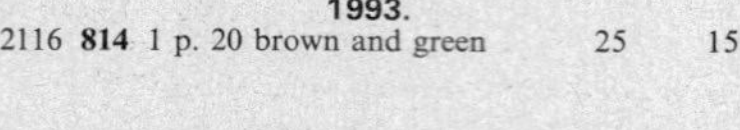

1993.
2116 **814** 1 p. 20 brown and green 25 15

815 Village and Soldier

1993. Uruguayan Battalion of Peace-keeping Force in Cambodia.
2117 **815** 1 p. multicoloured . . . 20 10

816 Dish Aerials and Studio

1993. 30th Anniv of National Television Channel 5.
2118 **816** 1 p. 20 multicoloured . . 25 15

817 "The Tree of Life" (detail, Pablo Serrano)

1993. 60th Anniv of Anda.
2119 **817** 1 p. 20 multicoloured . . 25 15

818 Arms and Officers

1993. 50th Anniv of Juan Carlos Gomez Folle National Police School.
2120 **818** 1 p. 20 multicoloured . . 25 15

819 Graphics

1993. 75th Anniv of "Diario El Pais" (newspaper).
2121 **819** 1 p. 20 multicoloured . . 25 15

820 Broad-nosed Caiman

1993. America. Endangered Animals. Multicoloured.
2122 1 p. 20 Type **820** 25 15
2123 3 p. 50 Burrowing owl (vert) 70 35

821 Power Lines supplying Illuminated Building

1993. 14th Latin-American Conference on Rural Electrification.
2124 **821** 3 p. 50 multicoloured . 70 35

822 Emblem

823 Red-legged Seriema

1993. 150th Anniv of B'nai B'rith (Jewish cultural and social organization).
2125 **822** 3 p. 70 multicoloured . 75 40

1993. Natural World.
2126 **823** 20 c. brown and pink . 10 10
2127 – 30 c. yellow and violet . 10 10
2128 – 50 c. brown and pink . 10 10
DESIGNS—VERT: 30 c. Brown-yellow marshbird. HORIZ: 50 c. Two-toed anteater.

825 Crucifix, Mother Francisca and Nuns with Sick People

826 Amerindian

1993. Beatification of Mother Francisca Rubatto.
2130 **825** 1 p. 20 multicoloured . 25 15

1993. International Year of Indigenous Peoples.
2131 **826** 3 p. 50 multicoloured . 70 35

827 Emblem on Map

1993. 75th Anniv of Montevideo Rotary Club.
2132 **827** 3 p. 50 blue and gold . . 70 35

829 Phoenician Cargo Ship (carving)

1993. 50th Anniv of Independence of Lebanon.
2134 **829** 3 p. 70 brown, deep brown and green 75 40

830 Haedo 831 Ribbon

1993. Eduardo Victor Haedo.
2135 **830** 1 p. 20 multicoloured . . 25 15

1993. Anti-AIDS Campaign.
2136 **831** 1 p. 40 multicoloured . . 30 15

832 Adoration of the Wise Men 833 Adult with Chick and Eggs

1993. Christmas. Multicoloured.
2137 1 p. 40 Type **832** 30 15
2138 4 p. Adoration of the Shepherds 80 40

1993. The Greater Rhea. Multicoloured.
2139 20 c. Type **833** 10 10
2140 20 c. Adults sitting and standing 10 10
2141 50 c. Close-up of head . . . 10 10
2142 50 c. Adults feeding 10 10

834 Child's view of life (Alejandro Cuende) 835 Emblem

1994. Children's Rights Day.
2143 **834** 1 p. 40 multicoloured . . 30 15

1994. National Postal Directorate.
2144 **835** 1 p. 40 blue and yellow . . 30 15

836 Torch Carrier

1994. 5th World Sports Congress, Punta del Este.
2145 **836** 4 p. multicoloured . . . 80 40

837 Frigate

1994. 17th Inter-American Naval Conference.
2146 **837** 3 p. 70 multicoloured . . 75 40

1994. No value expressed.
2147 813 (1 p. 60) red and pink . . 35 20
See note below No. 2115.

NOTE. The first supplement containing new issues not in this catalogue or the Addenda appeared in the September 1995 number of *Gibbons Stamp Monthly*.

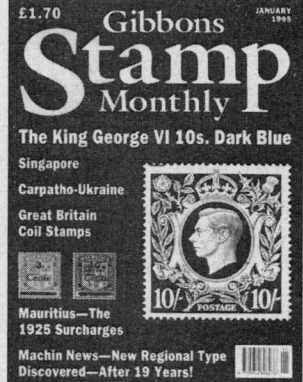

INDEX